Stanley Gibbons Simplified Catalogue

Western Europe

2nd Edition

Stanley Gibbons Ltd
London and Ringwood

By Appointment to
Her Majesty The Queen
Stanley Gibbons Limited
London
Philatelists

2nd Edition
Published in Great Britain by
Stanley Gibbons Ltd
Publications Editorial, Sales Offices and Distribution Centre
7, Parkside, Christchurch Road,
Ringwood, Hampshire BH24 3SH
Telephone +44 (0) 1425 472363

British Library Cataloguing in
Publication Data.
A catalogue record for this book is available
from the British Library.

ISBN 10: 0-85259-842-4
ISBN 13: 978-0-85259-842-9

Item No. R2818-12

Printed and bound in Wales by Stephens & George

Contents

The Stanley Gibbons Group plc - About us

Our History

Edward Stanley Gibbons started trading postage stamps in his father's chemist shop in Plymouth in 1856; we have been at the forefront of stamp collecting for more than 150 years, making us the world's oldest philatelic company.

As Royal Warrant holders since 1914 we offer unsurpassed expertise and provide collectors worldwide with peace of mind that all stamps purchased from us come with our certified lifetime guarantee of authenticity*.

If you think of stamp collecting, you think of Stanley Gibbons and we are proud to uphold that tradition for you.

399 Strand

Our world famous stamp shop is a collector's paradise, with all of our latest catalogues, albums and accessories and of course, our unrivalled stockholding of postage stamps.

www.stanleygibbons.com
shop@stanleygibbons.co.uk
+44 (0)20 7836 8444

Specialist Stamp Sales

For the collector that appreciates the value of collecting the highest quality examples, Stanley Gibbons is the only choice. Our extensive range is unrivalled in terms of quality and quantity, with specialist stamps available from all over the world.

www.stanleygibbons.com/stamps
shop@stanleygibbons.co.uk
+44 (0)20 7836 8444

Mail order

Stamp collecting made easy! Order anything you need to enhance your collection, from our world famous catalogues to brand new supplements, from our long-running range of albums to cutting edge accessories, all available via telephone, email or post.

orders@stanleygibbons.com
FREEPHONE (UK only) 0800 611 622
+44 (0) 1425 472363

Stanley Gibbons Auctions and Valuations

Sell your collection or individual rare items through our prestigious public auctions and regular postal auctions. You too can benefit from the excellent prices being realised at auction currently.

We also provide an unparalleled valuation service-drop your collection or rare items into us at 399 Strand, call us about our collection service or make an appointment at one of our valuation days held at venues across the UK.

www.stanleygibbons.com/auctions
auctions@stanleygibbons.co.uk
+44 (0)20 7836 8444

Stanley Gibbons Investments

The Stanley Gibbons Investment Department offers a unique range of investment propositions that have consistently outperformed more traditional forms of investment, from guaranteed minimum return products with unlimited upside to portfolios made up of the world's rarest stamps and autographs.

www.stanleygibbons.com/investment
investment@stanleygibbons.co.uk
+44 (0)1481 708 270

Stanley Gibbons Publications

Stanley Gibbons' first stamp catalogue was published in 1865 and we haven't looked back since! Our catalogues are trusted worldwide as the industry standard and we print countless titles each year. We also publish the consumer and trade magazines, *Gibbons Stamp Monthly* and *Philatelic Exporter*, bringing you news, views and insights into all things philatelic. For more information see 'Stanley Gibbons Publications Information.'

www.stanleygibbons.com/shop
orders@stanleygibbons.co.uk
+44 (0)1425 472 363

stanleygibbons.com

Our website offers the complete philatelic service. Whether you are looking to buy stamps, invest, read news articles, browse our online stamp catalogue or find new issues, you are just one click away from anything you desire in the world of stamp collecting at stanleygibbons.com. Happy browsing!

www.stanleygibbons.com

Fraser's Autographs

Autographs, manuscripts and memorabilia from Henry VIII to current day. We have over 60,000 items in stock, including movie stars, musicians, sport stars, historical figures and royalty. Fraser's is the UK's market leading autograph dealer and has been dealing in high quality autographed material since 1978.

www.frasersautographs.com
sales@frasersautographs.co.uk
+44 (0)20 7557 4404

The Stanley Gibbons Lifetime Guarantee of Authenticity

Stanley Gibbons sells stamps and philatelic items on the basis that they are genuine originals; if they are proved not to fit the description as represented by us, you may return them at any time and we will refund you the original purchase price.

All stamps supplied by Stanley Gibbons are guaranteed originals under the following terms:

If not as described, and returned by the purchaser, we undertake to refund the price paid in the original transaction.

If any stamp is certified as genuine by the Expert Committee of the Royal Philatelic Society, London, or by B.P.A. Expertising Ltd., the purchaser shall not be entitled to make any claim against us for any error, omission or mistake in such certificate.

Consumers' statutory rights are not affected by the above guarantee.

Stanley Gibbons Auctions

399 Strand, London WC2R OLX
Telephone + 44 (0)20 7836 8444
Fax + 44 (0) 20 7836 7342
enquires@stanleygibbons.co.uk
www.stanleygibbons.com for all departments

Auction and Specialist Stamp Departments

Open Monday–Friday 9.30am to 5pm
Shop open Monday–Friday 9am to 5.30pm and Saturday 9.30am to 5.30pm

Fraser's

(a division of Stanley Gibbons Group plc)
399 Strand, London WC2R OLX
Autographs, photographs, letters and documents
Telephone + 44 (0) 20 7836 8444
Fax +44 (0) 20 7836 7342,
info@frasersautographs.co.uk
www.frasersautographs.com
Monday–Friday 9am to 5.30pm
and Saturday 10am to 4pm

Stanley Gibbons Publications

7 Parkside, Christchurch Road, Ringwood,
Hampshire BH24 3SH.
Telephone + 44 (0)1425 472363
(24 hour answer phone service)
UK FREEPHONE 0800611 622
Fax +44 (0) 1425 470247
info@stanleygibbons.co.uk

Publications Mail Order

FREEPHONE 0800 611622
Monday–Friday 8.30 am to 5pm

Stanley Gibbons (Guernsey) Limited Investments

18-20 Le Bordage, St Peter Port,
Guernsey, Channel Islands, GY1 1DE
+44 (0) 1481 708 270
Toll free from USA +1 866 644 6146
investment@stanleygibbons.co.uk
www.stanleygibbons.com/investment

Stanley Gibbons (Jersey) Limited

6 Vine Street, St Helier, Jersey,
Channel Islands JE2 4WB.
Telephone +44 (0)1534 766711
Fax +44 (0)1534 766177
investment@stanleygibbons.com

Benham Collectibles Limited

Unit K, Concept Court, Shearway Business Park
Folkestone Kent CT19 4RG
benham@benham.com

Gibbons Stamp Monthly and Philatelic Exporter

7 Parkside, Christchurch Road, Ringwood,
Hampshire BH24 3SH.
Subscriptions. 01425 472363
Fax 01425 470247
gsm@stanleygibbons.co.uk

Introduction

This is the second edition of the Stanley Gibbons Western Europe Simplified Catalogue. It is based on our *Stamps of the World* Catalogue and brings together the key issuing countries of Western Europe, including Austria, France, Germany, Gibraltar, Ireland, Netherlands, Portugal and Spain.

The Stanley Gibbons catalogue provides an illustrated, priced guide to postage stamps, and is the standard reference tool for every collector. It will help you to identify your stamps, to value your collection, and to learn more about the background issues.

This catalogue follows the style of the newly redesigned *Stamps of the World* and provides collectors with a wealth of information to enhance your enjoyment of stamp collecting.

Features:

- Ireland prices have been updated in-line with the new Ireland One-Country Catalogue
- Current prices for every stamp
- Easy-to-use simplified listings
- World-recognised Stanley Gibbons catalogue numbers
- A wealth of historical, geographical and currency information

The first *Gibbons Stamp Monthly* Catalogue Supplement to this edition is January 2012.

Some of the countries have been updated since *Stamps of the World 2012*, these include:

- Aland Islands
- Austria
- Denmark
- Faroe Islands
- Finland
- France
- Germany
- Gibraltar
- Iceland
- Ireland
- Italy
- Malta
- Norway
- Spain
- Sweden
- Vatican City

Information for users

Scope of the Catalogue

Western Europe Simplified contains listings of postage stamps only. Apart from the ordinary definitive, commemorative and airmail stamps of each country there are sections for the following, where appropriate. Noted below are the Prefixes used for each section (see Guide to Entries for further information):

- postage due stamps – Prefix in listing D
- parcel post or postcard stamps – Prefix P
- official stamps – Prefix O
- express and special delivery stamps - Prefix E
- frank stamps – Prefix F
- charity tax stamps – Prefix J
- newspaper and journal stamps – Prefix N
- printed matter stamps – Prefix
- registration stamps - Prefix R
- acknowledgement of receipt stamps – Prefix AR
- late fee and too late stamps – Prefix L
- military post stamps- Prefix M
- recorded message stamps – Prefix RM
- personal delivery stamps – Prefix P
- concessional letter post – Prefix CL
- concessional parcel post – Prefix CP
- pneumatic post stamps – Prefix PE
- publicity envelope stamps – Prefix B
- bulk mail stamps – Prefix BP
- telegraph used for postage – Prefix PT
- telegraph (Commonwealth Countries) – Prefix T
- obligatory tax – Prefix T

As this is a simplified listing, the following are NOT included:
Fiscal or revenue stamps: stamps used solely in collecting taxes or fees for non-postal purposes. For example, stamps which pay a tax on a receipt, represent the stamp duty on a contract, or frank a customs document. Common inscriptions found include: Documentary, Proprietary, Inter. Revenue and Contract Note.
Local stamps: postage stamps whose validity and use are limited in area to a prescribed district, town or country, or on certain routes where there is no government postal service. They may be issued by private carriers and freight companies, municipal authorities or private individuals.
Local carriage labels and Private local issues: many labels exist ostensibly to cover the cost of ferrying mail from offshore islands to the nearest mainland post office. They are not recognised as valid for national or international mail.
Telegraph stamps: stamps intended solely for the prepayment of telegraphic communication.
Bogus or "phantom" stamps: labels from mythical places or non-existent administrations. Examples in the classical period were Sedang, Counani, Clipperton Island and in modern times Thomond and Monte Bello Islands. Numerous labels have also appeared since the War from dissident groups as propaganda for their claims and without authority from the home governments.
Railway letter fee stamps: special stamps issued by railway companies for the conveyance of letters by rail. Similar services are now offered by some bus companies and the labels they issue likewise do not qualify for inclusion in the catalogue.
Perfins ("perforated initials"): stamps perforated with the initials or emblems of firms as a security measure to prevent pilferage by office staff.
Labels: Slips of paper with an adhesive backing. Collectors tend to make a distinction between stamps, which have postal validity and anything else, which has not.
Cut-outs: Embossed or impressed stamps found on postal stationery, which are cut out if the stationery has been ruined and re-used as adhesives.

Further information on a wealth of terms is in *Philatelic Terms Illustrated*, published by Stanley Gibbons, details are listed under Stanley Gibbons Publications.

Organisation of the Catalogue

The catalogue lists countries in alphabetical order with country headers on each page and extra introductory information such as philatelic historical background at the beginning of each section.

Each country lists postage stamps in order of date of issue, from earliest to most recent, followed by separate sections for categories such as postage due stamps, express stamps, official stamps, and so on (see above for a complete listing).

"Appendix" Countries

Since 1968 Stanley Gibbons has listed in an appendix stamps which are judged to be in excess of true postal needs. The appendix also contains stamps which have not fulfilled all the normal conditions for full catalogue listing. Full catalogue listing requires a stamp to be:

- issued by a legitimate postal authority
- recognised by the government concerned
- adhesive

- valid for proper postal use in the class of service for which they are inscribed
- available to the general public at face value with no artificial restrictions being imposed on their distribution (with the exception of categories as postage dues and officials)

Only stamps issued from component parts of otherwise united territories which represent a genuine political, historical or postal division within the country concerned have a full catalogue listing. Any such issues which do not fulfil this stipulation will be recorded in the Catalogue Appendix only.

Stamps listed in the Appendix are constantly under review in light of newly acquired information about them. If we are satisfied that a stamp qualifies for proper listing in the body of the catalogue it will be moved in the next edition.

"Undesirable Issues"

The rules governing many competitive exhibitions are set by the Federation Internationale de Philatelie and stipulate a downgrading of marks for stamps classed as "undesirable issues".

This catalogue can be taken as a guide to status. All stamps in the main listings are acceptable. Stamps in the Appendix are considered, "undesirable issues" and should not be entered for competition.

Correspondence

We welcome information and suggestions but we must ask correspondents to include the cost of postage for the return of any materials, plus registration where appropriate. Letters and emails should be addressed to Michelle Briggs, 7 Parkside, Christchurch Road, Ringwood, Hampshire BH24 3SH, UK. mrbriggs@stanleygibbons.co.uk. Where information is solicited purely for the benefit of the enquirer we regret we are seldom able to reply.

Identification of Stamps

We regret we do not give opinion on the a[illegible] stamps, nor do we identify stamps or numb[illegible] Catalogue.

Thematic Collectors

Stanley Gibbons publishes a range of thematic catalogues (see page xii for details) and *Stamps of the World* is ideal to use with these titles, as it supplements those listings with extra information.

Type numbers

Type numbers (in bold) refer to illustrations, and are not the Stanley Gibbons Catalogue numbers.

A brief description of the stamp design subject is given below or beside the illustrations, or close by in the entry, where needed. Where a design is not illustrated, it is usually the same shape and size as a related design, unless otherwise indicated.

Watermarks

Watermarks are not covered in this catalogue. Stamps of the same issue with differing watermarks are not listed separately.

Perforations

Perforations – all stamps are perforated unless otherwise stated. No distinction is made between the various gauges of perforation but early stamp issues which exist both imperforate and perforated are usually listed separately. Where a heading states, "Imperf or perf" or "Perf. or rouletted" this does not necessarily mean that all values of the issue are found in both conditions

Se-tenant Pairs

Se-tenant Pairs – Many modern issues are printed in sheets containing different designs or face values. Such pairs, blocks, strips or sheets are described as being "*se-tenant*" and they are outside the scope of this catalogue, although reference to them may occur in instances where they form a composite design.

Miniature Sheets are now fully listed.

Guide to Entries

Ⓐ Country of Issue

Ⓑ Part Number – shows where to find more detailed listings in the Stanley Gibbons Comprehensive Catalogue. Part 6 refers to France and so on – see p. xli for further information on the breakdown of the Catalogue.

Ⓒ Country Information – Brief geographical and historical details for the issuing country.

Ⓓ Currency – Details of the currency, and dates of earliest use where applicable, on the face value of the stamps. Where a Colony has the same currency as the Mother Country, see the details given in that country.

Ⓔ Year Date – When a set of definitive stamps has been issued over several years the Year Date given is for the earliest issue, commeorative sets are listed in chronological order. As stamps of the same design or issue are usually grouped together a list of King George VI stamps, for example, headed "1938" may include stamps issued from 1938 to the end of the reign.

Ⓕ Stanley Gibbons Catalogue number – This is a unique number for each stamp to help the collector identify stamps in the listing. The Stanley Gibbons numbering system is universally recognized as definitive. The majority of listings are in chronological order, but where a definitive set of stamps has been re-issued with a new watermark, perforation change or imprint date, the cheapest example is given; in such cases catalogue numbers may not be in numerical order.

Where insufficient numbers have been left to provide for additional stamps to a listing, some stamps will have a suffix letter after the catalogue number. If numbers have been left for additions to a set and not used they will be left vacant.

The separate type numbers (in bold) refer to illustrations (see **M**).

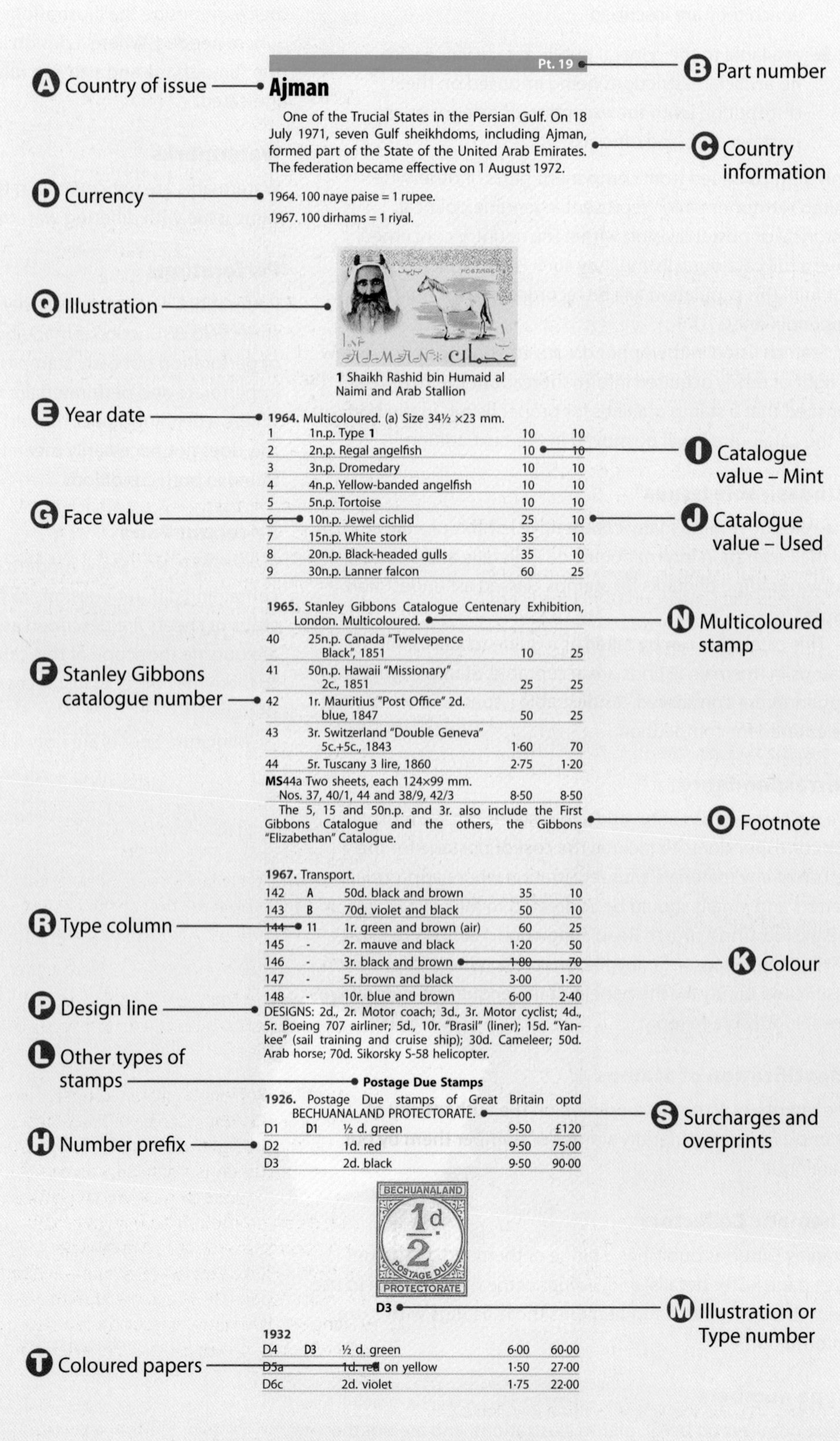

462 Canadian Maple Leaf Emblem

1981

1030a	**462**	A (30c.) red	20	40

No. 1030a was printed before a new first class domestic letter rate had been agreed, "A" representing the face value of the stamp, later decided to be 30c.

Ⓖ **Face value** – This refers to the value of each stamp and is the price it was sold for at the Post Office when issued. Some modern stamps do not have their values in figures but instead shown as a letter, see for example the entry above for Canada 1030a/Illustration **462**.

Ⓗ **Number Prefix** – Stamps other than definitives and commemoratives have a prefix letter before the catalogue number. Such stamps may be found at the end of the normal listing for each country. (See Scope of the Catalogue p.viii for a list of other types of stamps covered, together with the list of the main abbreviations used in the Catalogue).

Other prefixes are also used in the Catalogue. Their use is explained in the text: some examples are A for airmail, E for East Germany or Express Delivery stamps.

Ⓘ **Catalogue Value** – Mint/Unused. Prices quoted for pre-1945 stamps are for lightly hinged examples. Prices quoted of unused stamps from 1945 onwards are for unmounted mint.

Ⓙ **Catalogue Value** – Used. Prices generally refer to fine postally used examples. For certain issues they are for cancelled-to-order.

Prices

Prices are given in pence and pounds. Stamps worth £100 and over are shown in whole pounds:

Shown in Catalogue as	Explanation
10	10 pence
1.75	£1.75
15.00	£15
£150	£150
£2300	£2300

Prices assume stamps are in 'fine condition'; we may ask more for superb and less for those of lower quality. The minimum catalogue price quoted is 10p and is intended as a guide for catalogue users. The lowest price for individual stamps purchased from Stanley Gibbons is £1.

Prices quoted are for the cheapest variety of that particular stamp. Differences of watermark, perforation, or other details, outside the scope of this catalogue, often increase the value. Prices quoted for mint issues are for single examples. Those in *se-tenant* pairs, strips, blocks or sheets may be worth more. Where no prices are listed it is either because the stamps are not known to exist in that particular condition, or, more usually, because there is no reliable information on which to base their value.

All prices are subject to change without prior notice and we cannot guarantee to supply all stamps as priced. Prices quoted in advertisements are also subject to change without prior notice. Due to differing production schedules it is possible that new editions of Parts 2 to 22 will show revised prices which are not included in that year's Stamps of the World.

Ⓚ **Colour** – Colour of stamp (if fewer than four colours, otherwise noted as "multicoloured"– see N below). Colour descriptions are simple in this catalogue, and only expanded to aid identification – see other more comprehensive Stanley Gibbons catalogues for more detailed colour descriptions (see p.xii).

Where stamps are printed in two or more colours, the central portion of the design is the first colour given, unless otherwise stated.

Ⓛ **Other Types of Stamps** – See Scope of the Catalogue p.viii for a list of the types of stamps included.

Ⓜ **Illustration or Type Number** – These numbers are used to help identify stamps, either in the listing, type column, design line or footnote, usually the first value in a set. These type numbers are in a bold type face – **123**; when bracketed (**123**) an overprint or a surcharge is indicated. Some type numbers include a lower-case letter – **123a**, this indicates they have been added to an existing set. New cross references are also normally shown in bold, as in the example below.

1990. Small Craft of Canada (2nd series). Early Work Boats. As T **563**. Multicoloured.

Ⓝ **Multicoloured** – Nearly all modern stamps are multicoloured; this is indicated in the heading, with a description of the stamp given in the listing.

Ⓞ **Footnote** – further information on background or key facts on issues

Ⓟ **Design line** – Further details on design variations

Ⓠ **Illustration** – Generally, the first stamp in the set. Stamp illustrations are reduced to 75%, with overprints and surcharges shown actual size.

Ⓡ **Key Type** – indicates a design type on which the stamp is based. These are the bold figures found below each illustration. The type numbers are also given in bold in the second column of figures alongside the stamp description to indicate the design of each stamp. Where an issue comprises stamps of similar design, the corresponding type number should be taken as indicating the general design. Where there are blanks in the type number column it means that the type of the corresponding stamp is that shown by the number in the type column of the same issue. A dash (–) in the type column means that the stamp is not illustrated. Where type numbers refer to stamps of another country, e.g. where stamps of one country are overprinted for use in another, this is always made clear in the text.

Ⓢ **Surcharges and Overprints** – usually described in the headings. Any actual wordings are shown in bold type. Descriptions clarify words and figures used in the overprint. Stamps with the same overprints in different colours are not listed separately. Numbers in brackets after the descriptions are the catalogue numbers of the non-overprinted stamps. The words "inscribed" or "inscription" refer to the wording incorporated in the design of a stamp and not surcharges or overprints.

Ⓣ **Coloured Papers** – stamps printed on coloured paper are shown – e.g. "brn on yell" indicates brown printed on yellow paper. No information on the texture of paper, e.g. laid or wove, is provided in this catalogue.

Stanley Gibbons Stamp Catalogue Complete list of parts

1 Commonwealth & British Empire Stamps 1840–1970
(114th edition, 2012)

Commonwealth Country Catalogues

Australia and Dependencies (6th edition, 2010)
Bangladesh, Pakistan & Sri Lanka (2nd edition, 2011)
Belize, Guyana, Trinidad & Tobago (1st edition, 2009)
Brunei, Malaysia & Singapore (3rd edition, 2009)
Canada (4th edition, 2011)
Central Africa (2nd edition, 2008)
Cyprus, Gibraltar & Malta (3rd edition, 2011)
East Africa with Egypt and Sudan (2nd edition, 2010)
Eastern Pacific (2nd edition, 2011)
Falkland Islands (4th edition, 2010)
Hong Kong (3rd edition, 2010)
India (including Convention and Feudatory States) (3rd edition, 2009)
Indian Ocean (1st edition, 2006)
Ireland (5th edition, 2011)
Leeward Islands (1st edition, 2007)
New Zealand (4th edition, 2010)
Northern Caribbean, Bahamas & Bermuda (2nd edition, 2009)
St. Helena & Dependencies (4th edition, 2011)
Southern Africa (2nd edition, 2007)
West Africa (1st edition, 2009)
Western Pacific (2nd edition, 2009)
Windward Islands and Barbados (1st edition, 2007)

Stamps of the World 2012

Volume 1 ***Abu Dhabi – Charkhari***
Volume 2 ***Chile – Georgia***
Volume 3 ***German Commands – Jasdan***
Volume 4 ***Jersey – New Republic***
Volume 5 ***New South Wales – Singapore***
Volume 6 ***Sirmoor – Zululand***

Foreign Countries

2 ***Austria & Hungary*** (7th edition, 2009)
3 ***Balkans*** (5th edition, 2009)
4 ***Benelux*** (6th edition, 2010)
5 ***Czechoslovakia & Poland*** (6th edition, 2002)
6 ***France*** (7th edition, 2010)
7 ***Germany*** (9th edition, 2011)
8 ***Italy & Switzerland*** (7th edition, 2010)
9 ***Portugal & Spain*** (6th edition, 2011)
10 ***Russia*** (6th edition, 2008)
11 ***Scandinavia*** (6th edition, 2008)
12 ***Africa since Independence A-E*** (2nd edition, 1983)
13 ***Africa since Independence F-M*** (1st edition, 1981)
14 ***Africa since Independence N-Z*** (1st edition, 1981)
15 ***Central America*** (3rd edition, 2007)
16 ***Central Asia*** (4th edition, 2006)
17 ***China*** (8th edition, 2011)
18 ***Japan & Korea*** (5th edition, 2008)
19 ***Middle East*** (7th edition, 2009)
20 ***South America*** (4th edition, 2008)
21 ***South-East Asia*** (4th edition, 2004)
22 ***United States of America*** (7th edition, 2010)

Great Britain Catalogues

Collect British Stamps (62nd edition, 2011)
Great Britain Concise Stamp Catalogue (26th edition, 2011)
Volume 1 ***Queen Victoria*** (16th edition, 2012)
Volume 2 ***King Edward VII to King George VI*** (13th edition, 2009)
Volume 3 ***Queen Elizabeth II Pre-decimal issues*** (12th edition, 2011)
Volume 4 ***Queen Elizabeth II Decimal Definitive Issues – Part 1*** (10th edition, 2008)
Queen Elizabeth II Decimal Definitive Issues – Part 2 (10th edition, 2010)
Volume 5 ***Queen Elizabeth II Decimal Special Issues*** (3rd edition, 1998 with 1998-99 and 2000/1 Supplements)

Thematic Catalogues

Stanley Gibbons Catalogues for use with ***Stamps of the World.***
Collect Aircraft on Stamps (2nd edition, 2009)
Collect Birds on Stamps (5th edition, 2003)
Collect Chess on Stamps (2nd edition, 1999)
Collect Fish on Stamps (1st edition, 1999)
Collect Motor Vehicles on Stamps (1st edition 2004)

Other publications

Africa Simplified (1st edition, 2011)
Asia Simplified (1st edition, 2010)
Antarctica (including Australian and British Antarctic Territories, French Southern and Antarctic Territories and Ross Dependency) (1st edition, 2010)
Collect Channel Islands and Isle of Man Stamps (27th edition, 2012)
Commonwealth Simplified (4th edition, 2010)
Enjoy Stamp Collecting (7th edition, 2006)
Great Britain Numbers Issued (3rd edition, 2008)
How to Identify Stamps (4th edition, 2007)
North America Combined (1st edition, 2010)
Philatelic Terms Illustrated (4th edition, 2003)
United Nations (also including International Organizations based in Switzerland and UNESCO) (1st edition, 2010)

For other titles, and further details on the above, please see *www.stanleygibbons.com*

Glossary of terms

English	*French*	*German*	*Spanish*	*Italian*
Agate	Agate	Achat	Agata	Agata
Air stamp	Timbre de la poste aérienne	Flugpostmarke	Sello de correo aéreo	Francobollo per posta aerea
Apple Green	Vert-pomme	Apfelgrün	Verde manzana	Verde mela
Barred	Annulé par barres	Balkenentwertung	Anulado con barras	Sbarrato
Bisected	Timbre coupé	Halbiert	Partido en dos	Frazionato
Bistre	Bistre	Bister	Bistre	Bistro
Bistre-brown	Brun-bistre	Bisterbraun	Castaño bistre	Bruno-bistro
Black	Noir	Schwarz	Negro	Nero
Blackish Brown	Brun-noir	Schwärzlichbraun	Castaño negruzco	Bruno nerastro
Blackish Green	Vert foncé	Schwärzlichgrün	Verde negruzco	Verde nerastro
Blackish Olive	Olive foncé	Schwärzlicholiv	Oliva negruzco	Oliva nerastro
Block of four	Bloc de quatre	Viererblock	Bloque de cuatro	Bloco di quattro
Blue	Bleu	Blau	Azul	Azzurro
Blue-green	Vert-bleu	Blaugrün	Verde azul	Verde azzuro
Bluish Violet	Violet bleuâtre	Bläulichviolett	Violeta azulado	Violtto azzurrastro
Booklet	Carnet	Heft	Cuadernillo	Libretto
Bright Blue	Bleu vif	Lebhaftblau	Azul vivo	Azzurro vivo
Bright Green	Vert vif	Lebhaftgrün	Verde vivo	Verde vivo
Bright Purple	Mauve vif	Lebhaftpurpur	Púrpura vivo	Porpora vivo
Bronze Green	Vert-bronze	Bronzegrün	Verde bronce	Verde bronzo
Brown	Brun	Braun	Castaño	Bruno
Brown-lake	Carmin-brun	Braunlack	Laca castaño	Lacca bruno
Brown-purple	Pourpre-brun	Braunpurpur	Púrpura castaño	Porpora bruno
Brown-red	Rouge-brun	Braunrot	Rojo castaño	Rosso bruno
Buff	Chamois	Sämisch	Anteado	Camoscio
Cancellation	Oblitération	Entwertung	Cancelación	Annullamento
Cancelled	Annulé	Gestempelt	Cancelado	Annullato
Carmine	Carmin	Karmin	Carmín	Carminio
Carmine-red	Rouge-carmin	Karminrot	Rojo carmín	Rosso carminio
Centred	Centré	Zentriert	Centrado	Centrato
Cerise	Rouge-cerise	Kirschrot	Color de ceresa	Color Ciliegia
Chalk-surfaced paper	Papier couché	Kreidepapier	Papel estucado	Carta gessata
Chalky Blue	Bleu terne	Kreideblau	Azul turbio	Azzurro smorto
Charity stamp	Timbre de bienfaisance	Wohltätigkeitsmarke	Sello de beneficenza	Francobollo di beneficenza
Chestnut	Marron	Kastanienbraun	Castaño rojo	Marrone
Chocolate	Chocolat	Schokolade	Chocolate	Cioccolato
Cinnamon	Cannelle	Zimtbraun	Canela	Cannella
Claret	Grenat	Weinrot	Rojo vinoso	Vinaccia
Cobalt	Cobalt	Kobalt	Cobalto	Cobalto
Colour	Couleur	Farbe	Color	Colore
Comb-perforation	Dentelure en peigne	Kammzähnung, Reihenzähnung	Dentado de peine	Dentellatura e pettine
Commemorative stamp	Timbre commémoratif	Gedenkmarke	Sello conmemorativo	Francobollo commemorativo
Crimson	Cramoisi	Karmesin	Carmesí	Cremisi

English	*French*	*German*	*Spanish*	*Italian*
Deep Blue	Blue foncé	Dunkelblau	Azul oscuro	Azzurro scuro
Deep bluish Green	Vert-bleu foncé	Dunkelbläulichgrün	Verde azulado oscuro	Verde azzurro scuro
Design	Dessin	Markenbild	Diseño	Disegno
Die	Matrice	Urstempel. Type Platte,	Cuño	Conio, Matrice
Double	Double	Doppelt	Doble	Doppio
Drab	Olive terne	Trüboliv	Oliva turbio	Oliva smorto
Dull Green	Vert terne	Trübgrün	Verde turbio	Verde smorto
Dull purple	Mauve terne	Trübpurpur	Púrpura turbio	Porpora smorto
Embossing	Impression en relief	Prägedruck	Impresión en relieve	Impressione a relievo
Emerald	Vert-eméraude	Smaragdgrün	Esmeralda	Smeraldo
Engraved	Gravé	Graviert	Grabado	Inciso
Error	Erreur	Fehler, Fehldruck	Error	Errore
Essay	Essai	Probedruck	Ensayo	Saggio
Express letter stamp	Timbre pour lettres par exprès	Eilmarke	Sello de urgencia	Francobollo per espresso
Fiscal stamp	Timbre fiscal	Stempelmarke	Sello fiscal	Francobollo fiscale
Flesh	Chair	Fleischfarben	Carne	Carnicino
Forgery	Faux, Falsification	Fälschung	Falsificación	Falso, Falsificazione
Frame	Cadre	Rahmen	Marco	Cornice
Granite paper	Papier avec fragments de fils de soie	Faserpapier	Papel con filamentos	Carto con fili di seta
Green	Vert	Grün	Verde	Verde
Greenish Blue	Bleu verdâtre	Grünlichblau	Azul verdoso	Azzurro verdastro
Greenish Yellow	Jaune-vert	Grünlichgelb	Amarillo verdoso	Giallo verdastro
Grey	Gris	Grau	Gris	Grigio
Grey-blue	Bleu-gris	Graublau	Azul gris	Azzurro grigio
Grey-green	Vert gris	Graugrün	Verde gris	Verde grigio
Gum	Gomme	Gummi	Goma	Gomma
Gutter	Interpanneau	Zwischensteg	Espacio blanco entre dos grupos	Ponte
Imperforate	Non-dentelé	Geschnitten	Sin dentar	Non dentellato
Indigo	Indigo	Indigo	Azul indigo	Indaco
Inscription	Inscription	Inschrift	Inscripción	Dicitura
Inverted	Renversé	Kopfstehend	Invertido	Capovolto
Issue	Émission	Ausgabe	Emisión	Emissione
Laid	Vergé	Gestreift	Listado	Vergato
Lake	Lie de vin	Lackfarbe	Laca	Lacca
Lake-brown	Brun-carmin	Lackbraun	Castaño laca	Bruno lacca
Lavender	Bleu-lavande	Lavendel	Color de alhucema	Lavanda
Lemon	Jaune-citron	Zitrongelb	Limón	Limone
Light Blue	Bleu clair	Hellblau	Azul claro	Azzurro chiaro
Lilac	Lilas	Lila	Lila	Lilla
Line perforation	Dentelure en lignes	Linienzähnung	Dentado en linea	Dentellatura lineare
Lithography	Lithographie	Steindruck	Litografía	Litografia
Local	Timbre de poste locale	Lokalpostmarke	Emisión local	Emissione locale
Lozenge roulette	Percé en losanges	Rautenförmiger Durchstich	Picadura en rombos	Perforazione a losanghe
Magenta	Magenta	Magentarot	Magenta	Magenta
Margin	Marge	Rand	Borde	Margine
Maroon	Marron pourpré	Dunkelrotpurpur	Púrpura rojo oscuro	Marrone rossastro
Mauve	Mauve	Malvenfarbe	Malva	Malva
Multicoloured	Polychrome	Mehrfarbig	Multicolores	Policromo
Myrtle Green	Vert myrte	Myrtengrün	Verde mirto	Verde mirto

English	French	German	Spanish	Italian
New Blue	Bleu ciel vif	Neublau	Azul nuevo	Azzurro nuovo
Newspaper stamp	Timbre pour journaux	Zeitungsmarke	Sello para periódicos	Francobollo per giornali
Obliteration	Oblitération	Abstempelung	Matasello	Annullamento
Obsolete	Hors (de) cours	Ausser Kurs	Fuera de curso	Fuori corso
Ochre	Ocre	Ocker	Ocre	Ocra
Official stamp	Timbre de service	Dienstmarke	Sello de servicio	Francobollo di
Olive-brown	Brun-olive	Olivbraun	Castaño oliva	Bruno oliva
Olive-green	Vert-olive	Olivgrün	Verde oliva	Verde oliva
Olive-grey	Gris-olive	Olivgrau	Gris oliva	Grigio oliva
Olive-yellow	Jaune-olive	Olivgelb	Amarillo oliva	Giallo oliva
Orange	Orange	Orange	Naranja	Arancio
Orange-brown	Brun-orange	Orangebraun	Castaño naranja	Bruno arancio
Orange-red	Rouge-orange	Orangerot	Rojo naranja	Rosso arancio
Orange-yellow	Jaune-orange	Orangegelb	Amarillo naranja	Giallo arancio
Overprint	Surcharge	Aufdruck	Sobrecarga	Soprastampa
Pair	Paire	Paar	Pareja	Coppia
Pale	Pâle	Blass	Pálido	Pallido
Pane	Panneau	Gruppe	Grupo	Gruppo
Paper	Papier	Papier	Papel	Carta
Parcel post stamp	Timbre pour colis postaux	Paketmarke	Sello para paquete postal	Francobollo per pacchi postali
Pen-cancelled	Oblitéré à plume	Federzugentwertung	Cancelado a pluma	Annullato a penna
Percé en arc	Percé en arc	Bogenförmiger Durchstich	Picadura en forma de arco	Perforazione ad arco
Percé en scie	Percé en scie	Bogenförmiger Durchstich	Picado en sierra	Foratura a sega
Perforated	Dentelé	Gezähnt	Dentado	Dentellato
Perforation	Dentelure	Zähnung	Dentar	Dentellatura
Photogravure	Photogravure, Heliogravure	Rastertiefdruck	Fotograbado	Rotocalco
Pin perforation	Percé en points	In Punkten durchstochen	Horadado con alfileres	Perforato a punti
Plate	Planche	Platte	Plancha	Lastra, Tavola
Plum	Prune	Pflaumenfarbe	Color de ciruela	Prugna
Postage Due stamp	Timbre-taxe	Portomarke	Sello de tasa	Segnatasse
Postage stamp	Timbre-poste	Briefmarke, Freimarke, Postmarke	Sello de correos	Francobollo postale
Postal fiscal stamp	Timbre fiscal-postal	Stempelmarke als Postmarke verwendet	Sello fiscal-postal	Fiscale postale
Postmark	Oblitération postale	Poststempel	Matasello	Bollo
Printing	Impression, Tirage	Druck	Impresión	Stampa, Tiratura
Proof	Épreuve	Druckprobe	Prueba de impresión	Prova
Provisionals	Timbres provisoires	Provisorische Marken. Provisorien	Provisionales	Provvisori
Prussian Blue	Bleu de Prusse	Preussischblau	Azul de Prusia	Azzurro di Prussia
Purple	Pourpre	Purpur	Púrpura	Porpora
Purple-brown	Brun-pourpre	Purpurbraun	Castaño púrpura	Bruno porpora
Recess-printing	Impression en taille douce	Tiefdruck	Grabado	Incisione
Red	Rouge	Rot	Rojo	Rosso
Red-brown	Brun-rouge	Rotbraun	Castaño rojizo	Bruno rosso
Reddish Lilac	Lilas rougeâtre	Rötlichlila	Lila rojizo	Lilla rossastro
Reddish Purple	Poupre-rouge	Rötlichpurpur	Púrpura rojizo	Porpora rossastro
Reddish Violet	Violet rougeâtre	Rötlichviolett	Violeta rojizo	Violetto rossastro
Red-orange	Orange rougeâtre	Rotorange	Naranja rojizo	Arancio rosso
Registration stamp	Timbre pour lettre chargée (recommandée)	Einschreibemarke	Sello de certificado lettere	Francobollo per raccomandate
Reprint	Réimpression	Neudruck	Reimpresión	Ristampa
Reversed	Retourné	Umgekehrt	Invertido	Rovesciato

English	French	German	Spanish	Italian
Rose	Rose	Rosa	Rosa	Rosa
Rose-red	Rouge rosé	Rosarot	Rojo rosado	Rosso rosa
Rosine	Rose vif	Lebhaftrosa	Rosa vivo	Rosa vivo
Roulette	Percage	Durchstich	Picadura	Foratura
Rouletted	Percé	Durchstochen	Picado	Forato
Royal Blue	Bleu-roi	Königblau	Azul real	Azzurro reale
Sage green	Vert-sauge	Salbeigrün	Verde salvia	Verde salvia
Salmon	Saumon	Lachs	Salmón	Salmone
Scarlet	Écarlate	Scharlach	Escarlata	Scarlatto
Sepia	Sépia	Sepia	Sepia	Seppia
Serpentine roulette	Percé en serpentin	Schlangenliniger Durchstich	Picado a serpentina	Perforazione a serpentina
Shade	Nuance	Tönung	Tono	Gradazione de colore
Sheet	Feuille	Bogen	Hoja	Foglio
Slate	Ardoise	Schiefer	Pizarra	Ardesia
Slate-blue	Bleu-ardoise	Schieferblau	Azul pizarra	Azzurro ardesia
Slate-green	Vert-ardoise	Schiefergrün	Verde pizarra	Verde ardesia
Slate-lilac	Lilas-gris	Schierferlila	Lila pizarra	Lilla ardesia
Slate-purple	Mauve-gris	Schieferpurpur	Púrpura pizarra	Porpora ardesia
Slate-violet	Violet-gris	Schieferviolett	Violeta pizarra	Violetto ardesia
Special delivery stamp	Timbre pour exprès	Eilmarke	Sello de urgencia	Francobollo per espressi
Specimen	Spécimen	Muster	Muestra	Saggio
Steel Blue	Bleu acier	Stahlblau	Azul acero	Azzurro acciaio
Strip	Bande	Streifen	Tira	Striscia
Surcharge	Surcharge	Aufdruck	Sobrecarga	Soprastampa
Tête-bêche	Tête-bêche	Kehrdruck	Tête-bêche	Tête-bêche
Tinted paper	Papier teinté	Getöntes Papier	Papel coloreado	Carta tinta
Too-late stamp	Timbre pour lettres en retard	Verspätungsmarke	Sello para cartas retardadas	Francobollo per le lettere in ritardo
Turquoise-blue	Bleu-turquoise	Türkisblau	Azul turquesa	Azzurro turchese
Turquoise-green	Vert-turquoise	Türkisgrün	Verde turquesa	Verde turchese
Typography	Typographie	Buchdruck	Tipografia	Tipografia
Ultramarine	Outremer	Ultramarin	Ultramar	Oltremare
Unused	Neuf	Ungebraucht	Nuevo	Nuovo
Used	Oblitéré, Usé	Gebraucht	Usado	Usato
Venetian Red	Rouge-brun terne	Venezianischrot	Rojo veneciano	Rosso veneziano
Vermilion	Vermillon	Zinnober	Cinabrio	Vermiglione
Violet	Violet	Violett	Violeta	Violetto
Violet-blue	Bleu-violet	Violettblau	Azul violeta	Azzurro violetto
Watermark	Filigrane	Wasserzeichen	Filigrana	Filigrana
Watermark sideways	Filigrane couché liegend	Wasserzeichen	Filigrana acostado	Filigrana coricata
Wove paper	Papier ordinaire, Papier uni	Einfaches Papier	Papel avitelado	Carta unita
Yellow	Jaune	Gelb	Amarillo	Giallo
Yellow-brown	Brun-jaune	Gelbbraun	Castaño amarillo	Bruno giallo
Yellow-green	Vert-jaune	Gelbgrün	Verde amarillo	Verde giallo
Yellow-olive	Olive-jaunâtre	Gelboliv	Oliva amarillo	Oliva giallastro
Yellow-orange	Orange jaunâtre	Gelborange	Naranja amarillo	Arancio giallastro
Zig-zag roulette	Percé en zigzag	Sägezahnartiger Durchstich	Picado en zigzag	Perforazione a zigzag

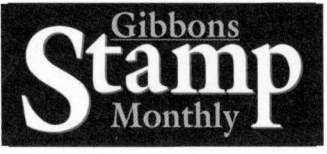

Abbreviations

Printers

A.B.N. Co.	American Bank Note Co, New York.
B.A.B.N.	British American Bank Note Co. Ottawa
B.W.	Bradbury Wilkinson & Co, Ltd.
C.B.N.	Canadian Bank Note Co, Ottawa.
Continental B.N. Co.	Continental Bank Note Co.
Courvoisier	Imprimerie Courvoisier S.A., La-Chaux-de-Fonds, Switzerland.
D.L.R.	De La Rue & Co, Ltd, London.
Enschedé	Joh. Enschedé en Zonen, Haarlem, Netherlands.
Harrison	Harrison & Sons, Ltd. London
P.B.	Perkins Bacon Ltd, London.
Waterlow	Waterlow & Sons, Ltd, London.

General Abbreviations

Alph	Alphabet
Anniv	Anniversary
Comp	Compound (perforation)
Des	Designer; designed
Diag	Diagonal; diagonally
Eng	Engraver; engraved
F.C.	Fiscal Cancellation
H/S	Handstamped
Horiz	Horizontal; horizontally
Imp, Imperf	Imperforate
Inscr	Inscribed
L	Left
Litho	Lithographed
mm	Millimetres
MS	Miniature sheet
N.Y.	New York
Opt(d)	Overprint(ed)
P or P-c	Pen-cancelled
P, Pf or Perf	Perforated
Photo	Photogravure
Pl	Plate
Pr	Pair
Ptd	Printed
Ptg	Printing
R	Right
R.	Row
Recess	Recess-printed
Roto	Rotogravure
Roul	Rouletted
S	Specimen (overprint)
Surch	Surcharge(d)
T.C.	Telegraph Cancellation
T	Type
Typo	Typographed
Un	Unused
Us	Used
Vert	Vertical; vertically
W or wmk	Watermark
Wmk s	Watermark sideways

(†) = Does not exist

(–) (or blank price column) = Exists, or may exist, but no market price is known.

/ between colours means "on" and the colour following is that of the paper on which the stamp is printed.

Colours of Stamps

Bl	(blue)
blk	(black)
brn	(brown)
car, carm	(carmine)
choc	(chocolate)
clar	(claret);
emer	(emerald)
grn	(green)
ind	(indigo)
mag	(magenta)
mar	(maroon)
mult	(multicoloured)
mve	(mauve)
ol	(olive)
orge	(orange)
pk	(pink)
pur	(purple)
scar	(scarlet)
sep	(sepia)
turq	(turquoise)
ultram	(ultramarine)
verm	(vermilion)
vio	(violet)
yell	(yellow).

Colour of Overprints and Surcharges

(B.) = blue
(Blk.) = black
(Br.) = brown,
(C.) = carmine
(G.) = green
(Mag.) = magenta
(Mve.) = mauve
(Ol.) = olive
(O.) = orange,
(P.) = purple
(Pk.) = pink,
(R.) = red,
(Sil.) = silver
(V.) = violet
(Vm.) or (Verm.) = vermilion,
(W.) = white
(Y.) = yellow.

Arabic Numerals

As in the case of European figures, the details of the Arabic numerals vary in different stamp designs, but they should be readily recognised wit-h the aid of this illustration:

٠	١	٢	٣	٤	٥	٦	٧	٨	٩
0	1	2	3	4	5	6	7	8	9

Pt. 11

ALAND ISLANDS

Aland is an autonomous province of Finland. From 1984 separate stamps were issued for the area although stamps of Finland could also still be used there. On 1 January 1993 Aland assumed control of its own postal service and Finnish stamps ceased to be valid there.

1984. 100 pennia = 1 markka.
2002. 100 cents = 1 euro.

1 Fishing Boat

1984

1	**1**	10p. mauve	15	20
2	**1**	20p. green	25	20
3	**1**	50p. green	25	20
4	-	1m. green	55	45
5	**1**	1m.10 blue	55	45
6	**1**	1m.20 black	55	55
7	**1**	1m.30 green	65	65
8	-	1m.40 multicoloured	1·20	80
9a	-	1m.50 multicoloured	1·00	55
10	-	1m.90 multicoloured	1·00	95
12	-	3m. blue, green and black	1·50	1·10
14	-	10m. black, chestnut & brn	4·25	2·75
15	-	13m. multicoloured	6·00	5·00

DESIGNS—20×29 mm: 1m.50, Midsummer pole, Storby village. 21×31 mm: 13m. Rug, 1793. 26×32 mm: 3m. Map of Aland Islands. 30×20 mm: 1m. Farjsund Bridge. 31×21 mm: 1m.40, Aland flag; 1m.90, Mariehamn Town Hall. 32×26 mm: 10m. Seal of Aland showing St. Olaf (patron saint).

2 "Pommern" (barque) and Car Ferries, Mariehamn West Harbour

1984. 50th Anniv of Society of Shipowners.

16	**2**	2m. multicoloured	4·75	2·30

3 Grove of Ashes and Hazels

1985. Aland Scenes. Multicoloured.

17	2m. Type **3**	1·90	1·00
18	5m. Kokar Church and shore (horiz)	1·90	1·70
19	8m. Windmill and farm (horiz)	3·25	2·75

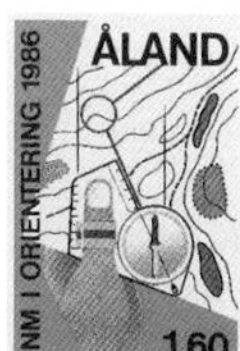

4 Map, Compass and Measuring Instrument

1986. Nordic Orienteering Championships, Aland.

20	**4**	1m.60 multicoloured	3·00	1·70

5 Clay Hands and Burial Mounds, Skamkulla

1986. Archaeology. Multicoloured.

21	1m.60 Type **5**	1·90	80
22	2m.20 Bronze staff from Finby and Apostles	1·00	90
23	20m. Monument at ancient court site, Saltvik, and court in session (horiz)	7·75	7·50

6 "Onnigeby" (drawing, Victor Westerholm)

1986. Centenary of Onnigeby Artists' Colony.

24	**6**	3m.70 multicoloured	4·00	2·10

7 Eiders

1987. Birds. Multicoloured.

25	1m.70 Type **7**	7·75	7·25
26	2m.30 Tufted ducks	3·75	2·75
27	12m. Velvet scoters	5·00	4·75

8 Firemen in Horse-drawn Cart

1987. Centenary of Mariehamn Fire Brigade.

28	**8**	7m. multicoloured	7·00	7·75

9 Meeting and Item 3 of Report

1987. 70th Anniv of Aland Municipalities Meeting, Finstrom.

29	**9**	1m.70 multicoloured	1·70	1·20

10 Loading Mail Barrels at Eckero

1988. 350th Anniv of Postal Service in Aland.

30	**10**	1m.80 multicoloured	2·40	1·70

11 Ploughing with Horses

1988. Centenary of Agricultural Education in Aland.

31	**11**	2m.20 multicoloured	2·10	2·10

12 Baltic Galleass "Albanus"

1988. Sailing Ships. Multicoloured.

32	1m.80 Type **12**	2·50	1·50
33	2m.40 Schooner "Ingrid" (horiz)	3·75	3·25
34	11m. Barque "Pamir" (horiz)	10·00	8·50

13 St. Olaf's Church, Jomala

1988

35	**13**	1m.40 multicoloured	1·90	1·50

14 Elder-flowered Orchid

1989. Orchids. Multicoloured.

36	1m.50 Type **14**	2·50	1·60
37	2m.50 Narrow-leaved helleborine	3·25	2·20
38	14m. Lady's slipper	11·50	10·00

15 Teacher and Pupils

1989. 350th Anniv of First Aland School, Saltvik.

39	**15**	1m.90 multicoloured	1·50	1·30

16 St. Michael's Church, Finstrom

1989

40		[illegible]50 multicoloured	1·50	1·40

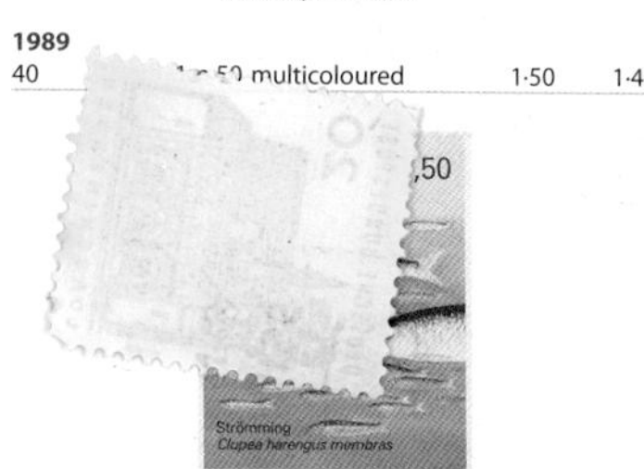

17 Baltic Herring

1990. Fishes. Multicoloured.

41	1m.50 Type **17**	1·30	1·00
42	2m. Northern pike	1·30	1·00
43	2m.70 European flounder	1·30	1·40

18 St. Andrew's Church, Lumparland

1990

44	**18**	1m.70 multicoloured	1·50	1·30

19 "St. Catherine" (fresco, St. Anna's Church, Kumlinge)

1990

45	**19**	2m. multicoloured	90	85

20 West European Hedgehog

1991. Mammals. Multicoloured.

46	1m.60 Type **20**	1·30	85
47	2m.10 Eurasian red squirrel	1·30	1·00
48	2m.90 Roe deer	1·50	1·60

21 Volleyball

1991. Small Island Games, Mariehamn. Sheet 117×81 mm containing T **21** and similar vert designs. Multicoloured.

MS49	2m.10; Type **21**; 2m.10; Shooting; 2m.10; Football; 2m.10, Running	5·00	4·75

22 Canoeing

1991. Nordic Countries' Postal Co-operation. Tourism. Multicoloured.

50	2m.10 Type **22**	90	90
51	2m.90 Cycling	1·50	1·50

23 "League of Nations Meeting, Geneva, 1921" (print by F. Rackwitz)

1991. 70th Anniv of Aland Autonomy.

52	**23**	16m. multicoloured	9·00	7·00

24 St. Mathias's Church, Vardo

1991

53	**24**	1m.80 multicoloured	1·50	1·00

25 Von Knorring (after Karl Jansson)

1992. Birth Bicentenary of Rev. Frans Peter von Knorring (social reformer).

54	**25**	2 klass (1m.60) mult	1·30	90

26 Barque "Herzogen Cecilie" and Wheat Transport Route Map

1992. 48th International Association of Cape Horners Congress, Mariehamn.

55	**26**	1 klass (2m.10) mult	2·00	1·50

27 Ranno Lighthouse

1992. Lighthouses. Multicoloured.

56	2m.10 Type **27**	5·75	2·50
57	2m.10 Salskar	5·75	2·50
58	2m.10 Lagskar	5·75	2·50
59	2m.10 Market	5·75	2·50

28 "Lemland Landscape"

1992. Birth Cent of Joel Pettersson (painter). Multicoloured

60	2m.90 Type **28**	1·30	1·10
61	16m. "Self-portrait"	6·50	6·25

29 Delegates processing to Church Service

1992. 70th Anniv of First Aland Provincial Parliament.

62	**29**	3m.40 multicoloured	1·90	1·50

30 St. Catherine's Church, Hammarland

1992

63	**30**	1m.80 multicoloured	1·50	90

31 Arms

1993. Postal Autonomy. Multicoloured.

64	1m.60 Type **31**	1·20	85
MS65	129×80 mm. 1m.90 Cover with Kastelholm single-line postmark (26×35 mm); 1m.90 Mareinhamm Post Office; 1m.90 Post van leaving *Alfågeln* (ferry); 1m.90 Postal emblem (26×31 mm)	4·25	3·00

32 Fiddler

1993. Nordic Countries' Postal Co-operation. Tourism. Exhibits from Jan Karlsgarden Open-air Museum.

66	**32**	2m. red, pink and black	1·00	85
67	-	2m.30 blue, black and azure	1·00	1·00

DESIGN—HORIZ: 2m.30, Boat-house.

33 Saltvik Woman

1993. Costumes. Multicoloured.

68	1m.90 Type **33**	1·30	85
69	3m.50 Eckero and Brando women and Mariehamn couple	1·50	1·50
70	17m. Finstrom couple	8·25	7·25

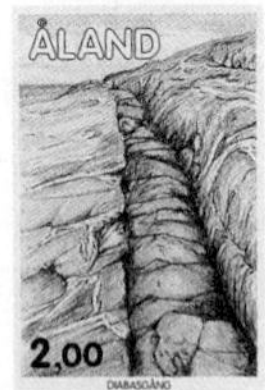

34 Diabase Dyke, Sottunga

1993. Aland Geology. Multicoloured.

71	10p. Boulder field, Dano Gamlan	25	20
72	1m.60 Drumlin (hillock), Markusbole	75	75
73	2m. Type **34**	90	70
74	2m.30 Pitcher of Kallskar	90	75
75	2m.70 Pillow lava, Kumlinge	1·20	90
76	2m.90 Red Cow (islet), Lumpurn	1·30	1·30
77	3m.40 Erratic boulder, Torsskar, Kokar Osterbygge (horiz)	1·40	1·40
78	6m. Folded gneiss	2·50	2·30
79	7m. Pothole, Bano Foglo (horiz)	2·75	2·50

35 Mary Magdalene Church, Sottunga

1993

80	**35**	1m.80 multicoloured	1·30	1·20

37 Glanville's Fritillary ("Melitaea cinxia")

1994. Butterflies. Multicoloured.

81	2m.30 Type **37**	1·30	1·20
82	2m.30 "Quercusia querqus"	1·30	1·10
83	2m.30 Clouded apollo ("Parnassius mnemosyne")	1·30	1·20
84	2m.30 "Hesperia comma"	1·30	1·10

38 Genetic Diagram

1994. Europa. Medical Discoveries. Multicoloured.

85	2m.30 Type **38** (discovery of Von Willebrand's disease (hereditary blood disorder))	2·50	2·00
86	2m.90 Molecular diagram (purification of heparin by Erik Jorpes)	2·50	2·00

39 Comb Ceramic and Pitted Ware Pottery

1994. The Stone Age.

87	**39**	2m.40 brown	1·00	1·20
88	-	2m.80 blue	1·20	1·30
89	-	18m. green	7·75	7·75

DESIGNS—VERT: 2m.80, Stone tools. HORIZ: 18m. Canoe and tent by river (reconstruction of Stone-age village, Langbergsoda).

40 St. John the Baptist's Church, Sund

1994

90	**40**	2m. multicoloured	1·50	1·10

42 "Skuta" (Cargo Sailing Boat)

1995. Cargo Sailing Ships. Multicoloured.

91	2m.30 Type **42**	1·00	1·20
92	2m.30 "Sump" (well-boat)	1·00	1·20
93	2m.30 "Storbat" (farm boat)	1·00	1·20
94	2m.30 "Jakt"	1·00	1·20

43 National Colours and E.U. Emblem

1995. Admission of Aland Islands to European Union.

95	**43**	2m.90 multicoloured	1·70	1·30

44 Doves and Cliffs

1995. Europa. Peace and Freedom. Multicoloured.

96	2m.80 Type **44**	1·30	1·30
97	2m.90 Dove, night sky and island	1·30	1·40

45 Golf

1995. Nordic Countries' Postal Co-operation. Tourism. With service indicator. Multicoloured.

98	2 klass (2m.) Type **45**	1·30	1·20
99	1 klass (2m.30) Sport fishing	1·50	1·20

46 Racing Dinghies

1995. Optimist World Dinghy Championships, Mariehamn.

100	**46**	3m.40 multicoloured	2·00	1·40

47 St. George's Church, Geta

1995

101	**47**	2m. multicoloured	1·30	90

48 "St. Olaf" (Wooden Carving from Sund Church)

1995. Birth Millenary of St. Olaf.

102	**48**	4m.30 multicoloured	1·90	2·00

49 Fish holding Flag in Mouth ("Greetings from Aland")

1996. Greetings Stamps. With service indicator. Multicoloured.

103	1 klass Type **49**	1·50	1·20
104	1 klass Bird holding flower in beak ("Congratulations")	1·50	1·20

50 Landing on Branch

1996. Endangered Species. The Eagle Owl. Multicoloured.

105	2m.40 Type **50**	1·00	1·20
106	2m.40 Perched on branch	1·00	1·10
107	2m.40 Adult owl	1·00	1·20
108	2m.40 Juvenile owl	1·00	1·10

Nos. 105/6 form a composite design.

51 Sally Salminen (novelist)

1996. Europa. Famous Women. Multicoloured.

109	2m.80 Type **51**	1·20	1·10
110	2m.90 Fanny Sundstrom (politician)	1·20	1·40

52 Choir

1996. Aland '96 Song and Music Festival, Mariehamn.

111	**52**	2m.40 multicoloured	1·30	1·10

53 "Haircut"

1996. 150th Birth Anniv of Karl Jansson (painter).

112	**53**	18m. multicoloured	8·50	8·25

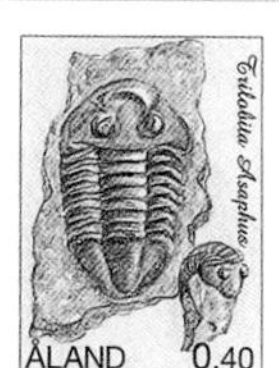

54 "Trilobita asaphus"

1996. Fossils. Multicoloured.

113	40p. Type **54**	25	35
114	9m. "Gastropoda euomophalus"	3·50	3·25

55 Brando Church

1996

115	**55**	2m. multicoloured	1·30	1·00

56 Giant Isopod ("Saduria entomon") and Opossum Shrimp ("Mysis relicta")

1997. Marine Survivors from the Ice Age. Multicoloured.

116	30p. Type **56**	25	25
117	2m.40 Four-horned sculpin ("Myotocephalus quadricornis")	1·30	1·00
118	4m.30 Ringed seal ("Phoca hispida botrica")	1·70	1·70

57 Coltsfoot ("Tussilago farfara")

1997. Spring Flowers. Multicoloured.

119	2m.40 Type **57**	1·00	1·20
120	2m.40 Blue anemone (*Hepatica nobilis*)	1·00	1·20
121	2m.40 Wood anemone (*Anemone nemorosa*)	1·00	1·20
122	2m.40 Yellow anemone (*Anemone ranunculoides*)	1·00	1·20

58 Floorball

1997. First Women's Floorball World Championship, Mariehamn and Godby.

123	**58**	3m.40 multicoloured	2·00	1·30

59 The Devil's Dance

1997. Europa. Tales and Legends.

124	**59**	2m.90 multicoloured	2·50	2·30

60 Kastelholm Castle and Arms

1997. 600th Anniv of Kalmar Union between Sweden, Denmark and Norway.

125	**60**	2m.40 multicoloured	1·20	1·30

61 Hologram of Schooner "Linden" and "75 Years"

1997. 75th Anniv of Aland Autonomy. Sheet 128×80 mm.

MS126 **61**	20m. multicoloured	10·00	9·00

62 "Thornbury" (freighter)

1997. Steam Freighters. Multicoloured.

127	2m.80 Type **62**	1·20	1·20
128	3m.50 *Osmo* (freighter)	1·40	1·30

63 St George's Church, Mariehamn

1997. 70th Anniv of Mariehamn Church.

129	**63**	1m.90 multicoloured	1·30	1·00

64 Man harvesting Apples

1998. Horticulture. Multicoloured.

130	2m. Type **64**	75	85
131	2m.40 Woman harvesting cucumbers	1·30	85

65 Boy on Moped

1998. Youth Activities. Multicoloured.

132	2m.40 Type **65**	1·00	1·20
133	2m.40 Laptop computer	1·00	1·20
134	2m.40 CD disk and headphones	1·00	1·20
135	2m.40 Step aerobics	1·00	1·20

66 Midsummer Celebrations

1998. Europa. National Festivals.

136	**66**	4m.20 multicoloured	2·75	1·80

67 "Isabella" (car ferry)

1998. Nordic Countries' Postal Co-operation. Shipping.

137	**67**	2m.40 multicoloured	1·30	1·00

68 Waves breaking

1998. International Year of the Ocean.

138	**68**	6m.30 multicoloured	3·00	2·40

69 Players

1998. Association of Tennis Professionals Senior Tour, Mariehamn. Self-adhesive.

139	**69**	2m.40 multicoloured	1·30	1·00

70 Schooner, Compass Rose and Knots

1998. Ninth International Sea Scout Camp, Bomarsund Fortress, Aland.

140	**70**	2m.80 multicoloured	1·40	1·10

71 Seffers Homestead, Onningeby

1998. Traditional Porches. Multicoloured.

141	1m.60 Type **71**	65	65
142	2m. Labbas homestead, Storby	75	85
143	2m.90 Abras homestead, Bjorko	1·20	1·20

72 Eckero Church

1998

144	**72**	1m.90 multicoloured	1·30	85

73 Sword and Dagger

1999. Bronze Age Relics. Multicoloured.

145	2m. Type **73**	75	85
146	2m.20 "Ship" tumulus (vert)	90	1·00

74 Wardrobe

1999. Folk Art. Decorated Furniture. Multicoloured

147	2m.40 Type **74**	1·00	1·00
148	2m.40 Distaff	1·00	1·00
149	2m.40 Chest	1·00	1·00
150	2m.40 Spinning wheel	1·00	1·00

75 "'Pamir' and 'Passat' (barques) off Port Victoria" (R. Castor)

1999. 50th Anniv of Rounding of Cape Horn by *Pamir* on Last Wheat-carrying Voyage.

151	**75**	3m.40 multicoloured	1·70	1·40

76 Cowslip

1999. Provincial Plant of Aland. Self-adhesive.

152	**76**	2m.40 multicoloured	1·20	1·00

77 Ido Island, Kokar

1999. Europa. Parks and Gardens.

153	**77**	2m.90 multicoloured	2·20	1·20

No. 153 is denominated both in markkas and in euros.

78 Racing Yachts

1999. Sailing.

154	**78**	2m.70 multicoloured	1·40	1·10

79 Puffed Shield Lichen ("Hypogymnia physodes")

1999. Lichens. With service indicator. Multicoloured

155	2 klass (2m.) Type **79**	1·30	90
156	1 klass (2m.40) Common orange lichen ("Xanthoria parietina")	1·50	1·00

80 Loading Avions de Transport Regional ATR72

1999. 125th Anniv of Universal Postal Union.

157	**80**	2m.90 multicoloured	1·20	1·30

81 St. Bridget's Church, Lemland

1999

158	**81**	1m.90 multicoloured	1·20	1·00

82 Runners

1999. Finnish Cross-country Championships, Mariehamn.
159 **82** 3m.50 multicoloured 1·50 1·30

DENOMINATION. From No. 162 to 207 Aland Islands stamps are denominated both in markkas and in euros. As no cash for the latter is in circulation, the catalogue continues to use the markka value.

83 Arctic Tern (*Sterna paradisaea*)

2000. Sea Birds. Multicoloured.
162 1m.80 Type **83** 75 70
164 2m.20 Mew gull (*Larus canus*) (vert) 90 85
166 2m.60 Great black-backed gull (*Larus marinus*) 1·00 95

84 International Peace Symbol and State Flag

2000. New Millennium Sheet. 100×80 mm. Multicoloured.
MS171 **84** 3m.40, yellow; 3m.40, red; 3m.40, blue; 3m.40, white 8·00 5·25

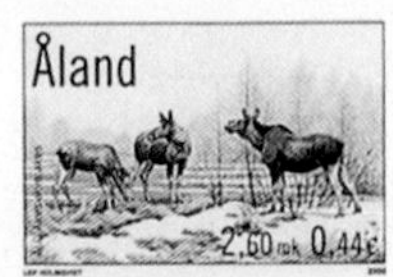

85 Elk

2000. The Elk (*Alces alces*). Multicoloured.
172 2m.60 Type **85** 1·00 1·00
173 2m.60 With young 1·00 1·00
174 2m.60 Beside lake 1·00 1·00
175 2m.60 In snow 1·00 1·00

86 "Building Europe"

2000. Europa.
176 **86** 3m. multicoloured 2·20 1·60

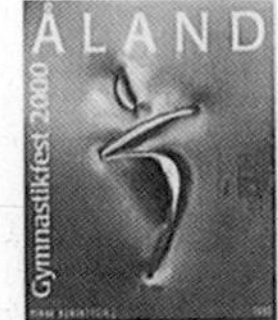

87 Gymnast

2000. Finno-Swedish Gymnastics Association Exhibition, Mariehamn. Self-adhesive.
177 **87** 2m.60 multicoloured 1·30 1·00

88 Crew and *Linden* (schooner)

2000. Visit by Cutty Sark Tall Ships' Race Competitors to Mariehamn.
178 **88** 3m.40 multicoloured 1·60 1·20

89 Lange on prow of Longship

2000. Death Millenary of Hlodver Lange the Viking.
179 **89** 4m.50 multicoloured 2·40 1·90

90 Wooden Ornamented Swiss-style House, Mariehamn

2000. 48th Death Anniv of Hilda Hongell (architect). Multicoloured.
180 3m.80 Type **90** 1·50 1·30
181 10m. House with central front entrance, Mariehamn 3·75 3·50

91 The Nativity

2000. 2000 Years of Christianity.
182 **91** 3m. multicoloured 1·50 1·20

92 Kokar Church

2000
183 **92** 2m. multicoloured 1·20 95

93 Steller's Eider in Flight

2001. Endangered Species. The Steller's Eider (*Polysticta stelleri*). Multicoloured.
184 2m.70 Type **93** 1·00 1·20
185 2m.70 Duck and drake 1·00 1·20
186 2m.70 Duck and drake swimming 1·00 1·20
187 2m.70 Drake swimming 1·00 1·20

94 Swamp Horsetail (*Equisetum fluviatile*)

2001. Plants. Multicoloured.
188 1m.90 Type **94** 90 85
189 2m.80 Stiff clubmoss (*Lycopodium annotinum*) 1·20 1·20
190 3m.50 Polypody (*Polybodium vulgare*) 1·40 1·30

95 Heart and Graffiti on Brick Wall

2001. St. Valentine's Day.
200 **95** 3m.20 multicoloured 1·40 1·30

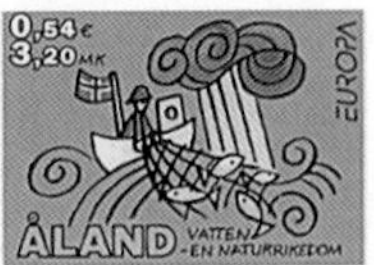

96 Fisherman and Fish

2001. Europa. Water Resources.
201 **96** 3m.20 multicoloured 2·10 1·90

97 Archipelago Windmill

2001. Windmills. Multicoloured.
202 3m. Type **97** 1·20 1·20
203 7m. Timbered windmill (horiz) 2·75 2·50
204 20m. Nest windmill (horiz) 8·00 7·50

98 Golden Retriever

2001. Puppies. Multicoloured.
205 2 klass (2m.30) Type **98** 1·20 90
206 1 klass (2m.70) Wire-haired dachshund 1·40 1·00

99 Foglo Church

2001
207 **99** 2m. multicoloured 90 75

100 Smooth Snake (*Coronella Austriaca*)

2002. Endangered Animals. Multicoloured.
208 5c. Type **100** 25 20
209 70c. Great crested newt (*Triturus cristatus*) 1·40 1·50

101 Woman pushing Shopping Trolley

2002. Euro Currency.
210 **101** 60c. multicoloured 1·50 1·30

102 Tidying up Christmas

2002. St. Canute's Day.
211 **102** €2 multicoloured 4·75 4·50

103 Spiced Salmon and New Potatoes

2002. Traditional Dishes. Multicoloured.
212 1 klass (55c.) Type **103** 1·40 1·20
213 1 klass (55c.) Fried herring, mashed potatoes and beetroot 1·40 1·20
214 1 klass (55c.) Black bread and butter 1·40 1·20
215 1 klass (55c.) Aland pancake with stewed prune sauce and whipped cream 1·40 1·20

104 Building

2002. Inauguration of New Post Terminal, Sviby.
216 **104** €1 multicoloured 2·50 2·20

105 Circus Elephant and Rider

2002. Europa. Circus.
217 **105** 40c. multicoloured 1·50 1·20

106 "Radar II" (sculpture, Stefan Lindfors)

2002. Nordic Countries' Postal Co-operation. Modern Art.
218 **106** €3 multicoloured 7·00 6·25

107 Kayaking

2002
219 **107** 90c. multicoloured 2·30 2·50

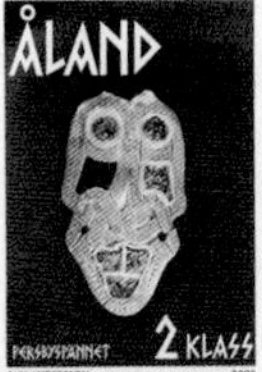

108 8th-century Buckle, Persby, Sud

2002. Iron Age Jewellery found on Aland. Multicoloured.
220 2 klass. (45c.) Type **108** 1·20 1·00
221 1 klass. (55c.) 8th-century pin, Sylloda, Saltvik 1·40 1·20

109 Saltvik Church

2002

222	**109**	35c. multicoloured	1·00	85

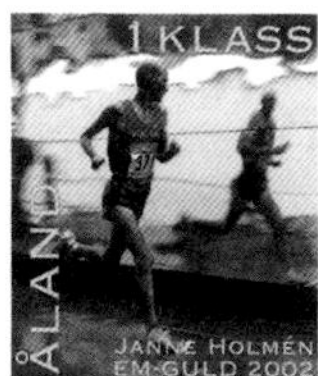

110 Holmen

2002. Janne Holmen (Olympic gold medallist, men's marathon).

223	**110**	1 klass. (55c.) mult	1·40	1·20

111 *Cantharellus cibarius*

2003. Fungi. Multicoloured.

224	10c. Type **111**	25	30
225	50c. *Boletus edulis*	1·30	95
226	€2.50 *Macrolepiota procera*	6·50	5·75

112 Tovis (kitten)

2003. Cat Photograph Competition Winners. Multicoloured.

227	2 klass (45c.) Type **112**	1·20	1·10
228	1 klass (55c.) Randi (cat) (horiz)	1·40	1·30

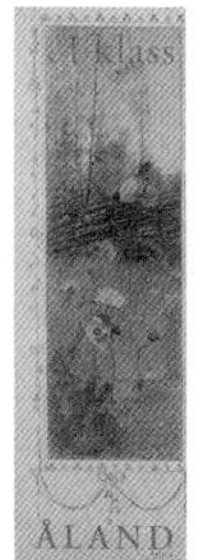

113 "Landscape in Summer" (detail) (Elin Danielson-Gambogi)

2003. Designs showing details of the painting. Multicoloured.

229	1 klass (55c.) Type **113**	1·40	1·30
230	1 klass (55c.) Trees and flowers	1·40	1·30
231	1 klass (55c.) Sunset over sea	1·40	1·30
232	1 klass (55c.) Shoreline and boats	1·40	1·30

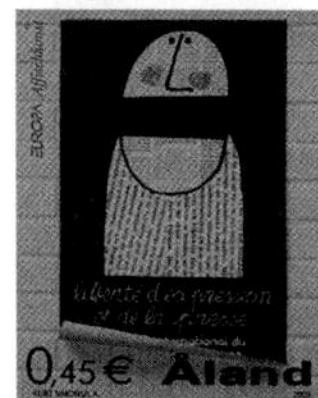

114 "Freedom of Speech and Press" (Kurt Simons)

2003. Europa. Poster Art.

233	**114**	45c. multicoloured	1·70	1·30

115 "Pommern" (Arthur Victor Gregory)

2003. Centenary of Pommern (four mast steel barque, now museum). Self-adhesive.

234	**115**	55c. multicoloured	2·10	1·40

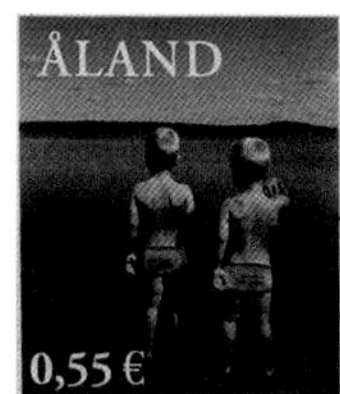

116 Two Boys

2003. 'My Aland'. Mark Levengood.

235	**116**	55c. multicoloured	1·40	1·30

117 Fiddle Player

2003. 50th Anniv of Aland Folk Music Association.

236	**117**	€1.10 multicoloured	2·50	2·10

118 Kumlinge Church

2003

237	**118**	40c. multicoloured	1·00	90

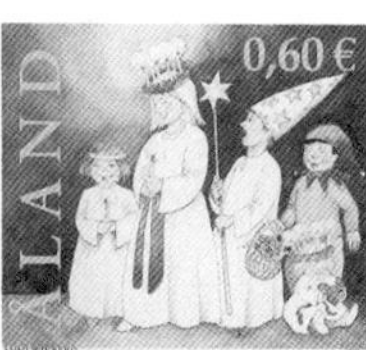

119 Children dressed as St. Lucia and her Attendants

2003. St. Lucia Celebrations.

238	**119**	60c. multicoloured	1·50	1·20

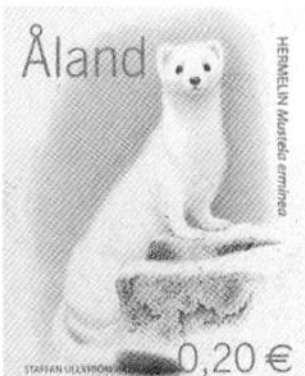

120 Ermine (*Mustela erminea*)

2004. Predators. Multicoloured.

239	20c. Type **120**	65	50
240	60c. Fox (*Vulpes vulpes*)	1·50	1·50
241	€3 Pine martin (*Martes martes*)	7·75	6·75

121 Fenja and Menja (giantesses)

2004. Nordic Mythology. Sheet 105×70 mm.

MS250	**121** 55c. multicoloured	1·40	1·30

Stamps of a similar theme were issued by Denmark, Faroe Islands, Finland, Greenland, Iceland, Norway and Sweden.

122 Flag

2004. 50th Anniv of Aland Flag. Self-adhesive.

251	**122**	1klass (60c.) multicoloured	1·40	1·30

123 *Cajsa* (longboat) and Passengers, 1986

2004. 'My Aland'. Mauno Koivisto (Finnish president 1982–94).

252	**123**	90c. multicoloured	2·20	2·00

124 Yacht moored in Inlet

2004. Europa. Holidays.

253	**124**	75c. multicoloured	1·80	1·60

125 Bomarsund Fortress

2004. 150th Anniv of Fall of Bomarsund Fortress. Sheet 170×95 mm containing T **125** and similar vert designs.

MS254	75c.×4, Type **125**; Bomarsund (different); Three soldiers; Six soldiers	7·25	6·75

The stamps and margin of No. **MS**254 form a composite design of painting by A. Lourde-Laplace.

126 Storklyndan, Brando

2004. Landscapes. Multicoloured.

255	2 klass (50c.) Type **126**	1·00	1·10
256	1 klass (60c.) Prästgardsnaset, Findstrom	1·70	1·30

127 Panathenaic Stadium, Athens

2004. Olympic Games, Athens.

257	**127**	80c. multicoloured	1·80	1·70

128 Father Christmas delivering Mail

2004. Christmas.

258	**128**	45c. multicoloured	1·20	1·10

129 Great Cormorant (*Phalacrocorax carbo sinensis*)

2005. Birds. Multicoloured.

259	15c. Type **129**	50	45
260	65c. Whooper swan (*Cygnus Cygnus*)	1·90	1·70
261	€4 Grey heron (*Ardea cinerea*)	9·50	8·25

130 Oakland Sport Chevrolet (1928) (⅔-size illustration)

2005. Vintage Cars. Multicoloured.

262	(60c.) Type **130**	1·70	1·30
263	(60c.) Ford V8 (1939)	1·70	1·30
264	(60c.) Buick Super 4D HT (1957)	1·70	1·30
265	(60c.) Volkswagen 1200 (1964)	1·70	1·30

131 Family and Bonfire

2005. Walpurgis Night. Self-adhesive.

266	**131**	(50c.) multicoloured	1·50	1·20

132 Fish

2005. Europa. Gastronomy.

267	**132**	90c. multicoloured	1·90	1·70

133 Bjorn Borg

2005. 'My Aland'. Bjorn Borg (tennis player).

268	**133**	55c. multicoloured	1·30	1·20

134 "A Visit to Bomarsund Fortress" (Fritz von Dardel)

2005. 150th Anniv of Fall of Bomarsund Fortress (2004) (2nd series).

269	**134**	€1.30 multicoloured	3·25	2·75

135 *Linden* (schooner)

2005

270	**135**	60c. multicoloured	1·70	1·40

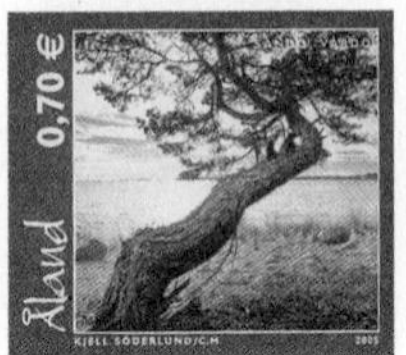
136 Sando, Vardo

2005. Landscapes. Multicoloured.

271	70c. Type **136**	1·90	1·40
272	80c. Grondal, Geta	2·20	2·00

137 Boy and Girl Brownies

2005. Christmas.

273	**137**	45c. multicoloured	90	75

138 *Potosia cuprea*

2006. Beetles.

274	40c. Type **138**	75	35
275	65c. *Coccinella septempunctata*	1·30	85
276	€2 *Oryctes nasicornis*	4·50	3·00

139 Face

2006. Centenary of Women's Suffrage.

277	**139**	85c. multicoloured	2·40	2·00

140 Letesgubbe

2006. Nordic Mythology. Sheet 105×70 mm.

MS278 **140**	85c. multicoloured	2·40	2·40

Stamps of a similar theme were issued by Denmark, Greenland, Faroe Islands, Finland, Iceland, Norway and Sweden.

141 Bomarsund Fortress

2006. 150th Anniv of Demilitarization.

279	**141**	€1.50 multicoloured	4·25	4·00

142 Boy as King

2006. Europa. Integration.

280	**142**	€1.30 multicoloured	3·75	3·50

143 Girl posting Letter

2006. My Stamp. Self-adhesive.

281	**143**	1 klass multicoloured	1·75	1·50

144 Sail Boat

2006. 'My Aland'. Ake Lindman (actor and filmmaker).

282	**144**	75c. multicoloured	2·10	2·00

145 Soderby, Lemland

2006. Landscapes. Multicoloured.

283	55c. Type **145**	1·50	1·50
284	€1.20 Norra Essvik, Sottunga	3·50	3·25

146 Tribal-style Tattoo (Thomas Dahlgren)

2006. Tattoos. Multicoloured.

285	65c. Type **146**	2·10	2·00
286	65c. Seaman style (Mikael Sandholm)	2·10	2·00
287	65c. Floral (in memory of Tsunami disaster) (Linda Aberg)	2·10	2·00

147 Horse-drawn Sleigh

2006. Christmas. Inscribed 'JULPOST 06.

288	**147**	(50c.) multicoloured	1·40	1·40

148 *Tripolium vulgare*

2007. Waterside Plants. Multicoloured.

289	80c. Type **148**	2·20	2·00
290	90c. *Lythrum salicaria*	2·60	2·50
291	€5 *Angelica archangelica*	12·50	12·00

149 Junkers F13 flying boat

2007. Postal Transport. Multicoloured.

292	2klass Type **149**	1·60	1·50
293	1klass SAAB 340	2·00	1·80

150 Skaftö, Kumlinge

2007. Landscape.

294	**150**	2klass multicoloured	1·60	1·50

151 *Fillyjonks, Sea Monster and Cliffs* (painting by Tove Janson)

2007. Art.

295	**151**	85c. multicoloured	2·50	2·40

152 Scout Emblem and Window

2007. Europa. Centenary of Scouting.

296	**152**	70c. multicoloured	2·20	2·10

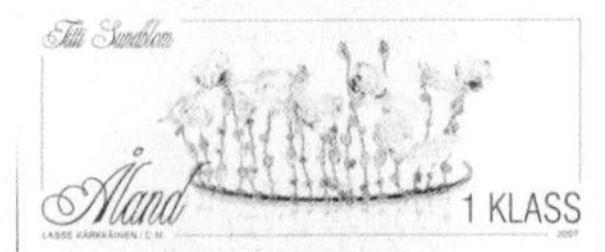
153 Bridal Crown (Titti Sundblom)

2007. Arts and Crafts. Multicoloured.

297	1klass Type **153**	2·20	2·00
298	1klass Flower print (Maria Korpi-Gordon and Adam Gordon)	2·20	2·00
299	1klass Ceramics (Judy Kuitunen)	2·20	2·00

154 Two Players

2007. My Stamp. Girls' Football in Aland. Self-adhesive.

300	**154**	1klass multicoloured	2·00	1·90

155 *Windmills* (Ture Bengtz)

2007. Birth Centenary of Ture Bengtz (artist and emigrant to USA). Emigration.

301	**155**	75c. multicoloured	2·10	2·00

156 Landscape, Kjusan, Hammarland

2007. SEPAC (Ssmall European Postal Administration Co-operation).

302	**156**	1klass multicoloured	2·00	1·90

157 Santa Claus (poster by Haddon Sundblom)

2007. Christmas. Inscr 'Julpost 07'.

303	**157**	(50c.) multicoloured	1·40	1·30

158 *Perca fluviatilis*

2008. Fish. Paintings by Gosta Sundman. Multicoloured.

304	45c. Type **158**	1·30	1·30
305	€4.50 *Zander lucioperca*	11·50	11·50

159 Signhild at Drottningkleven

2008. Nordic Mythology. Mythical Places. Sheet 105×70 mm. Inscr 'VARLDEN'.

MS306 **159**	multicoloured	2·75	2·75

Stamps of a similar theme were issued by Denmark, Faroe Islands, Finland, Greenland, Iceland, Norway and Sweden.

The stamp and margin of No. **MS**306 form a composite design.

MS306 was for use on international mail and was originally on sale for 85c.

160 Langvikshagen, Lumparland

2008. Landscapes. Inscr 'INRIKES'. Multicoloured.

307	(70c.) Type **160**	2·50	2·50
308	(70c.) Badhusberget, Marie-hamn	2·50	2·50

Nos. 307/8 were for use on domestic mail and were originally on sale for 70c.

161 Emblem

2008. Olympic Games, Beijing. Inscr 'VARLDEN'.

309	**161**	(90c.) multicoloured	2·50	2·50

No. 309 was for use on international mail and was originally on sale for 90c.

162 Letter, Ship and Sailor's Wife

2008. Europa. The Letter.

310	**162**	€1 multicoloured	2·75	2·75

163 Marhallan

2008. Lighthouses. Inscr 'EUROPA'. Multicoloured.

311	(75c.) Type **163**	2·20	2·20
312	(75c.) Gustaf Dalen	2·20	2·20
313	(75c.) Bogskar	2·20	2·20
314	(75c.) Kokarsoren	2·20	2·20

Nos. 311/14 were for use on mail within Europe and were originally on sale for 75c.

164 Gravel Road and Profiles of Marcus Gronholm and Christoph Treier (trainer)

2008. My Aland. Marcus Gronholm (rally driver). Inscr 'VARLDEN'.

315	**164**	(90c.) multicoloured	2·75	2·75

No. 315 was for use on international mail and was originally on sale for 90c.

165 *Aland Peasant Bride* (Karl Emanuel Jansson)

2008. Art.

316	**165**	€1.50 multicoloured	4·50	4·50

166 Angel

2008. Christmas. Inscr 'JULPOST'.

317	**166**	(55c.) multicoloured	1·50	1·50

No. 317 was on sale for 55c.

167 Horse Rider

2008. My Stamp. Inscr 'EUROPA'. Self-adhesive.

318	**167**	(75c.) multicoloured	2·25	2·25

No. 318 was for use on mail within Europe and was originally on sale for 75c.

168 Boundary Post, Flojtan

2009. New Borders (bicentenary of Aland's integration into Russia). Inscr 'EUROPA'.

319	**168**	(80c.) multicoloured	3·00	3·00

No. 319 was for use on mail within Europe and was originally on sale for 80c.

169 Wind Turbine

2009. Preserve Polar Regions and Glaciers. Centenary of Electricity Supply. Sheet 120×80 mm.

MS320	multicoloured	7·25	7·25

170 Ulla-Lena Lundberg

2009. Authors. Inscr 'EUROPA'. Multicoloured.

321	(80c.) Type **170**	3·00	3·00
322	(80c.) Anni Blomqvist	3·00	3·00
323	(80c.) Valdemar Nyman	3·00	3·00

Nos. 321/3, were issued for use on mail within Europe and were originally on sale for 80c.

171 May Irwin and John Rice

2009. Centenary of Cinema in Aland.

324	**171**	€1.60 multicoloured	6·00	6·00

172 Divers and *Plus* (wreck)

2009. Diving. Inscr 'INRIKES'.

325	**172**	(75c.) multicoloured	2·75	2·75

No. 325 was for use on mail within Aland and Finland and was originally on sale for 75c.

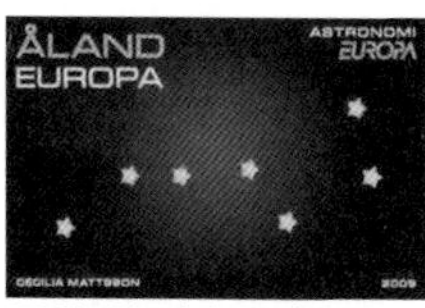

173 The Plough (constellation)

2009. Europa. Astronomy. Inscr 'EUROPA'.

326	**173**	(80c.) multicoloured	3·00	3·00

No. 326 was for use on mail within Europe and was originally on sale for 80c.

174 *Viking*

2009. Ferries. Inscr 'INRIKES' (327)or 'EUROPA' (328). Multicoloured.

327	(75c.) Type **174**	2·50	2·50
328	(80c.) *Newbuilding*	3·25	3·25

No. 327 was for use on mail within Aland and Finland and was originally on sale for 75c.

No. 328 was for use on mail within Europe and was originally on sale for 80c.

175 Athlete

2009. My Stamp. Island Games XIII, Aland. Inscr 'VARLDEN'. Self-adhesive.

329	**175**	(90c.) multicoloured	3·25	3·25

No. 329 was for use on international mail and was originally on sale for 90c.

2009. Aland Flag. Multicoloured.

329a	(65c.) As Type **122**	3·25	3·25

176 Algerso, Foglo

2009. Landscapes. SEPAC (small european mail services) (331). Inscr 'INRIKES' (330) or 'EUROPA' (331). Multicoloured.

330	(75c.) Type **176**	2·50	2·50
331	(80c.) Orrdalsklint, Saltvik	3·25	3·25

No. 330 was for use on mail within Aland and Finland and was originally on sale for 75c.

No. 331 was for use on mail within Europe and was originally on sale for 80c.

177 Cabin by Water

2009. My Aland. Martti Ahtisaari (President of Finland 1994–2000). Inscr 'VARLDEN'.

332	**177**	(90c.) multicoloured	3·25	3·25

No. 332 was for use on international mail and was originally on sale for 90c.

178 Santa's Helpers

2009. Christmas. Inscr 'JULPOST' (333) or 'VARLDEN' (334). Multicoloured.

333	(60c.) Type **178**	2·20	2·20
334	(90c.) Girl	3·25	3·25

No. 333 was for use on Christmas mail within Aland and Finland and was originally on sale for 60c.

No. 334 was for use on international mail and was originally on sale for 90c.

179 *Mail Jetty at Eckero*

2010. 150th Birth Anniv of Victor Westerholm (artist). Inscr 'EUROPA'.

335	**179**	(80c.) multicoloured	3·00	3·00

No. 335 was for use on mail within Europe and was originally on sale for 80c.

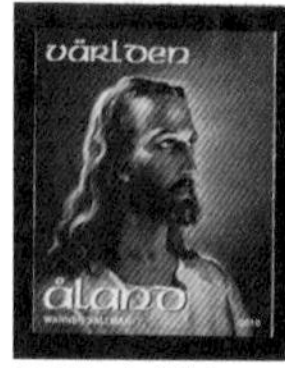

180 *Head of Christ* (Walter Sallman)

2010. Religious Art. Inscr 'VARLDEN'.

336	**180**	(90c.) multicoloured	3·00	3·00

No. 336 was for use on international mail and was originally on sale for 90c.

181 Boats and Kobba Klintar (image scaled to 68% of original size)

2010. Life at the Coast. Kobba Klintar (heritage pilot station). Inscr 'VARLDEN'. Sheet 105×70 mm.

MS337	**181** multicoloured	3·00	3·00

No. 336 was for use on international mail and was originally on sale for 90c.

Stamps of a similar theme were issued by Denmark, Greenland, Faroe Islands, Finland, Iceland, Norway and Sweden.

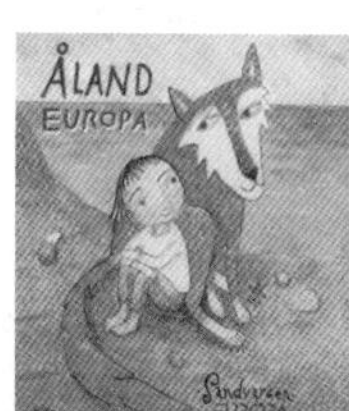

182 Sandwolf and Zackarina (*Sandvargen* by Åsa Lind)

2010. Europa. Children's Books. Inscr 'EUROPA'

338	**182**	(85c.) multicoloured	3·25	3·25

No. 338 was for use on European mail and was originally on sale for 85c.

183 *Skandia*

2010. Ferries. Multicoloured.

339	75c. Type **183**	4·25	4·25
340	€3.50 *Prinsessan*	12·00	12·00

184 Moon Creature, c. 1960

2010. Plastic Toys by Plasto. Booklet stamps. Inscr 'EUROPA'. Multicoloured.

341	(85c.) Type **184**	3·25	3·25
342	(85c.) Tipper lorry	3·25	3·25
343	(85c.) Ducks	3·25	3·25

No. 341/3 were for use on European mail and were originally on sale for 85c.

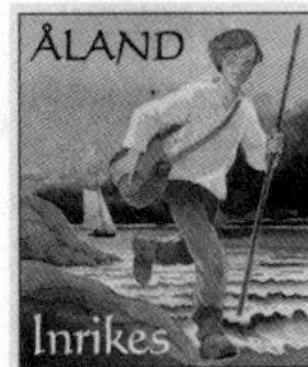

185 Farm Hand delivering Mail

2010. Early Mail Delivery. Inscr 'INRIKES'

344	**185**	(75c.) multicoloured	4·25	4·25

186 Boy sailing Laser Radial

2010. My Stamp. Inscr 'EUROPA'

345	**186**	(85c.) multicoloured	3·00	3·00

No. 345 was for use on mail within Europe and was originally on sale for 85c.

187 Stained Glass Window (detail) (Ture Bengtz), Jomala Church

2010. Church Interiors. Multicoloured.

346		80c. Type **187**	3·00	3·00
MS347		105×70 mm. €1.60 Stained glass window (horiz)	6·25	6·25

Stamps of a similar design were issued by Macau.

No. **MS**347 also contains a representation of the stamp issued by Macau.

188 Degersand Beach, Eckerö

2010. Aland Scenery. Multicoloured.

348		80c. Type **188**	3·00	3·00
349		(85c.) Lillnäsberget, Sund	3·25	3·25

189 Grannies bring Home the Christmas Tree

2010. Christmas. Inscr 'JULPOST'

350	**189**	(60c.) multicoloured	3·25	3·25

Pt. 7

ALLENSTEIN

A district of E. Prussia retained by Germany as the result of a plebiscite in 1920. Stamps issued during the plebiscite period.

100 pfennig = 1 mark.

1920. Stamps of Germany inscr "DEUTSCHES REICH" optd **PLEBISCITE OLSZTYN ALLENSTEIN.**

1	**17**	5pf. green	55	1·10
2	**17**	10pf. red	55	1·10
3	**24**	15pf. violet	55	1·10
4	**24**	15pf. purple	7·50	12·50
5	**17**	20pf. blue	55	1·40
6	**17**	30pf. black & orge on buff	55	1·40
7	**17**	40pf. black and red	55	1·10
8	**17**	50pf. black & pur on buff	55	1·10
9	**17**	75pf. black and green	55	1·10
10	**18**	1m. red	2·10	4·25
11	**18**	1m.25 green	2·10	4·25
12	**18**	1m.50 brown	1·30	4·25
13b	**20**	2m.50 red	3·25	12·50
14	**21**	3m. black	3·25	4·75

1920. Stamps of Germany inscr "DEUTSCHES REICH" optd **TRAITE DE VERSAILLES** etc. in oval.

15	**17**	5pf. green	55	1·10
16	**17**	10pf. red	55	1·10
17	**24**	15pf. violet	55	1·10
18	**24**	15pf. purple	27·00	55·00
19	**17**	20pf. blue	85	1·70
20	**17**	30pf. black & orge on buff	55	1·10
21	**17**	40pf. black and red	55	1·10
22	**17**	50pf. black & pur on buff	55	1·10
23	**17**	75pf. black and green	85	1·70
24	**18**	1m. red	2·10	3·25
25	**18**	1m.25 green	2·10	3·25
26	**18**	1m.50 brown	1·60	3·25
27	**20**	2m.50 red	3·75	8·50
28	**21**	3m. black	2·30	3·25

Pt. 6

ALSACE AND LORRAINE

Stamps used in parts of France occupied by the German army in the war of 1870 -71, and afterwards temporarily in the annexed provinces of Alsace and Lorraine

100 pfennig = 1 mark

1

1870

1	**1**	1c. green	75·00	£130
3	**1**	2c. brown	95·00	£170
5	**1**	4c. grey	95·00	95·00
8	**1**	5c. green	65·00	12·50
10	**1**	10c. brown	85·00	18·00
14	**1**	20c. blue	85·00	15·00
16	**1**	25c. brown	£140	95·00

For 1940 issues see separate lists for Alsace and Lorraine under German Occupations.

Pt. 6, Pt. 9

ANDORRA

An independent state in the Pyrenees under the joint suzerainty of France and Spain.

French Post Office
1931. 100 centimes = 1 franc.
2002. 100 cents = 1 euro.

Spanish Post Office
1928. 100 centimos = 1 peseta.
2002. 100 cents = 1 euro.

FRENCH POST OFFICES

1931. Stamps of France optd ANDORRE.

F1	**11**	½c. on 1c. grey	1·10	6·50
F2	**11**	1c. grey	1·20	1·70
F3	**11**	2c. red	1·60	8·00
F4	**11**	3c. orange	2·10	4·25
F5	**11**	5c. green	3·25	8·25
F6	**11**	10c. lilac	5·25	10·00
F7	**18**	15c. brown	9·00	9·75
F8	**18**	20c. mauve	14·50	15·00
F9	**18**	25c. brown	12·50	17·00
F10	**18**	30c. green	12·50	15·00
F11	**18**	40c. blue	13·50	23·00
F12	**15**	45c. violet	26·00	31·00
F13	**15**	50c. red	18·00	20·00
F14	**15**	65c. green	37·00	41·00
F15	**15**	75c. mauve	42·00	46·00
F16	**18**	90c. red	55·00	70·00
F17	**15**	1f. blue	60·00	70·00
F18	**18**	1f.50 blue	65·00	80·00
F19	**13**	2f. red and green	60·00	90·00
F20	**13**	3f. mauve and red	£110	£150
F21	**13**	5f. blue and buff	£150	£250
F22	**13**	10f. green and red	£325	£450
F23	**13**	20f. mauve and green	£425	£500

F3 Our Lady's Chapel, Meritxell

F5 St. Michael's Church, Engolasters

1932

F24	**F3**	1c. slate	75	2·75
F25	**F3**	2c. violet	1·10	2·30
F26	**F3**	3c. brown	1·20	2·50
F27	**F3**	5c. green	95	2·75
F28	**A**	10c. lilac	1·80	3·25
F29	**F3**	15c. red	2·75	3·50
F30	**A**	20c. mauve	13·50	17·00
F31	**F5**	25c. brown	5·75	7·50
F32	**A**	25c. brown	13·50	34·00
F33	**A**	30c. green	3·75	4·50
F34	**A**	40c. blue	10·50	9·25
F35	**A**	40c. brown	1·60	4·00
F36	**A**	45c. red	15·00	29·00
F37	**A**	45c. green	7·50	22·00
F38	**F5**	50c. mauve	16·00	17·00
F39	**A**	50c. violet	7·50	20·00
F40	**A**	50c. green	2·10	10·50
F41	**A**	55c. violet	32·00	70·00
F42	**A**	60c. brown	2·10	7·50
F43	**F5**	65c. green	70·00	75·00
F44	**A**	65c. blue	19·00	33·00
F45	**A**	70c. red	2·40	5·75
F46	**F5**	75c. violet	11·50	12·50
F47	**A**	75c. blue	5·25	17·00
F48	**A**	80c. green	28·00	70·00
F49	**B**	80c. green	1·70	6·25
F50	**B**	90c. red	9·50	9·25
F51	**B**	90c. green	7·50	15·00
F52	**B**	1f. green	34·00	23·00
F53	**B**	1f. red	32·00	34·00
F54	**B**	1f. blue	1·40	3·50
F55	**B**	1f. 20 violet	1·30	6·50
F56	**F3**	1f. 25 mauve	65·00	80·00
F57	**F3**	1f.25 red	8·00	20·00
F58	**B**	1f.30 brown	1·70	6·50
F59	**C**	1f.50 blue	26·00	37·00
F60	**B**	1f.50 red	1·10	6·50
F61	**B**	1f.75 violet	£110	£140
F62	**B**	1f.75 blue	60·00	75·00
F63	**B**	2f. mauve	10·50	23·00
F64	**F 3**	2f. red	2·10	8·50
F65	**F 3**	2f. green	1·20	8·50
F66	**F 3**	2f.15 violet	60·00	90·00
F67	**F 3**	2f.25 blue	10·50	30·00
F68	**F 3**	2f.40 red	1·40	6·50
F69	**F 3**	2f.50 black	12·50	36·00
F70	**F 3**	2f.50 blue	2·75	10·50
F71	**B**	3f. brown	25·00	41·00
F72	**F 3**	3f. brown	2·20	7·00
F73	**F 3**	4f. blue	1·60	6·25
F74	**F 3**	4f.50 violet	2·10	8·25
F75	**C**	5f. brown	1·80	7·00
F76	**C**	10f. violet	2·40	7·00
F78	**C**	15f. blue	1·60	4·00
F79	**C**	20f. red	2·10	3·75
F81	**A**	50f. blue	3·00	9·25

DESIGNS—HORIZ: A, St. Anthony's Bridge; C, Andorra la Vella. VERT: B, Valley of Sant Julia.

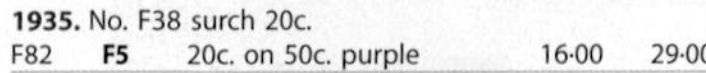

1935. No. F38 surch 20c.

F82	**F5**	20c. on 50c. purple	16·00	29·00

F9

1936

F83	**F9**	1c. black	55	3·25
F84	**F9**	2c. blue	55	3·25
F85	**F9**	3c. brown	55	3·25
F86	**F9**	5c. red	40	3·25
F87	**F9**	10c. blue	40	3·25
F88	**F9**	15c. mauve	3·25	5·25
F89	**F9**	20c. green	40	3·25
F90	**F9**	30c. red	75	7·00
F91	**F9**	30c. black	1·50	6·50
F92	**F9**	35c. green	60·00	90·00
F93	**F9**	40c. brown	1·10	6·25
F94	**F9**	50c. green	1·20	6·50
F95	**F9**	60c. blue	1·60	6·50
F96	**F9**	70c. violet	1·60	6·50

F13 Andorra la Vella **F10**

F14 Councillor Jaume Bonell

1944

F97	**F10**	10c. violet	20	4·00
F98	**F10**	30c. red	20	4·00
F99	**F10**	40c. blue	40	4·00
F100	**F10**	50c. red	20	4·50
F101	**F10**	60c. black	40	4·00
F102	**F10**	70c. mauve	30	5·75
F103	**F10**	80c. green	20	5·75
F104	**F10**	1f. blue	1·10	2·40
F105	**D**	1f. purple	20	6·25
F106	**D**	1f.20 blue	20	6·25
F107	**D**	1f.50 red	20	6·25
F108	**D**	2f. green	20	4·00
F109	**E**	2f.40 red	20	4·00
F110	**E**	2f.50 red	4·25	7·00
F111	**E**	3f. brown	60	2·75
F112	**D**	3f. red	4·25	5·75
F113	**E**	4f. blue	55	6·25
F114	**E**	4f. green	1·10	7·50
F115	**D**	4f. brown	2·30	10·50
F116	**E**	4f.50 brown	60	5·75
F117	**F 13**	4f.50 blue	5·25	20·00
F118	**F 13**	5f. blue	55	6·25
F119	**F 13**	5f. green	1·40	6·50
F120	**E**	5f. green	3·25	11·50
F121	**E**	5f. violet	4·25	8·00
F122	**F 13**	6f. red	55	3·75
F123	**F 13**	6f. purple	55	5·75
F124	**E**	6f. green	3·25	7·50
F125	**F 13**	8f. blue	1·60	8·00
F126	**E**	8f. brown	1·10	3·50
F127	**F 13**	10f. green	40	5·75
F128	**F 13**	10f. blue	1·60	1·80
F129	**F 13**	12f. red	1·40	7·50
F130	**F 13**	12f. green	1·60	5·75
F131	**F 14**	15f. purple	65	6·50
F132	**F 13**	15f. red	85	3·50
F133	**F 13**	15f. brown	7·50	4·50
F134	**F 14**	18f. blue	3·25	12·00
F135	**F 13**	18f. red	12·50	26·00
F136	**F 14**	20f. blue	1·10	6·50
F137	**F 14**	20f. violet	3·25	10·00
F138	**F 14**	25f. red	3·75	10·50
F139	**F 14**	25f. blue	2·10	8·50
F140	**F 14**	30f. blue	21·00	29·00
F141	**F 14**	40f. green	3·25	9·25
F142	**F 14**	50f. brown	1·80	4·25

DESIGNS—HORIZ: D, Church of St. John of Caselles; E, House of the Valleys.

F15 Chamois and Pyrenees

1950. Air.

F143	**F15**	100f. blue	£110	£110

F16 Les Escaldes

1955

F144	**F16**	1f. blue (postage)	20	2·75
F145	**F16**	2f. green	55	2·10
F146	**F16**	3f. red	65	2·10
F147	**F16**	5f. brown	65	2·10
F148	-	6f. green	2·20	2·75
F149	-	8f. red	2·40	3·25
F150	-	10f. violet	4·25	2·75
F151	-	12f. blue	2·30	2·10
F152	-	15f. red	3·00	2·30

F153	-	18f. blue	2·75	3·75
F154	-	20f. violet	3·25	2·30
F155	-	25f. brown	3·50	4·00
F156	-	30f. blue	26·00	34·00
F157	-	35f. blue	13·50	14·50
F158	-	40f. green	35·00	55·00
F159	-	50f. red	4·25	4·50
F160	-	65f. violet	9·50	29·00
F161	-	70f. brown	9·25	22·00
F162	-	75f. blue	45·00	90·00
F163	-	100f. green (air)	10·50	15·00
F164	-	200f. red	21·00	23·00
F165	-	500f. blue	85·00	90·00

DESIGNS—VERT: 15f. to 25f. Gothic cross, Andorra la Vella; 100f. to 500f. East Valira River. HORIZ: 6f. to 12f. Santa Coloma Church; 30f. to 75f. Les Bons village.

F21

F22 Gothic Cross, Meritxell

1961

F166	**F21**	1c. grey, blue and slate (postage)	65	1·60
F167	**F21**	2c. lt orge, blk & orge	65	1·60
F168	**F21**	5c. lt grn, blk & grn	40	1·60
F169	**F21**	10c. pink, blk & red	45	45
F170a	**F21**	12c. yell, pur & grn	2·20	4·50
F171	**F21**	15c. lt bl, blk & bl	75	1·60
F172	**F21**	18c. pink, blk & mve	1·40	3·25
F173	**F21**	20c. lt yell, brn & yell	80	55
F174	**F22**	25c. blue, vio & grn	1·10	1·10
F175	**F22**	30c. pur, red & grn	1·10	80
F175a	**F22**	40c. green and brown	1·30	2·00
F176	**F22**	45c. blue, ind & grn	21·00	34·00
F176a	**F22**	45c. brown, bl & vio	1·30	2·75
F177	**F22**	50c. multicoloured	2·75	2·75
F177a	**F22**	60c. brown & chestnut	1·60	2·10
F178	**F22**	65c. olive, bl & brn	23·00	55·00
F179	**F22**	85c. multicoloured	23·00	40·00
F179a	**F22**	90c. green, bl & brn	1·60	3·50
F180	**F22**	1f. blue, brn & turq	2·75	2·75
F181	-	2f. green, red and purple (air)	2·20	2·30
F182	-	3f. purple, bl & grn	2·40	2·50
F183	-	5f. orange, pur & red	4·00	4·00
F184	-	10f. green and blue	6·00	5·50

DESIGNS—As Type F **22**: 60c. to 1f. Engolasters Lake; 2f. to 10f. Incles Valley.

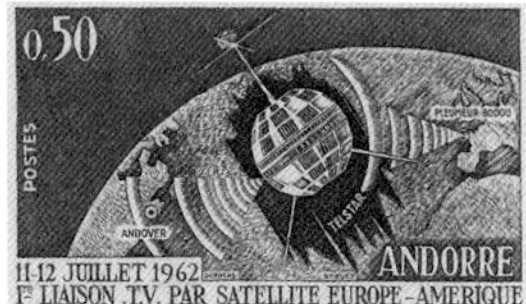

F23 "Telstar" Satellite and part of Globe

1962. 1st Trans-Atlantic TV Satellite Link.

F185	**F23**	50c. violet and blue	1·60	2·75

F24 "La Sardane" (dance)

1963. Andorran History (1st issue).

F186	**F24**	20c. purple, mve & grn	3·75	6·50
F187	-	50c. red and green	6·75	12·50
F188	-	1f. green, blue & brn	9·50	21·00

DESIGNS—LARGER (48½×27 mm): 50c. Charlemagne crossing Andorra. (48×27 mm): 1f. Foundation of Andorra by Louis le Debonnaire.

See also Nos. F190/1.

F25 Santa Coloma Church and Grand Palais, Paris

1964. "PHILATEC 1964" International Stamp Exhibition, Paris.

F189	**F25**	25c. green, pur & brn	1·60	3·25

1964. Andorran History (2nd issue). As Nos. F187/8, inscribed "1964".

F190	60c. green, chestnut and brown	11·50	32·00
F191	1f. blue, sepia and brown	16·00	32·00

DESIGNS (48½×27 mm): 60c. "Napoleon re-establishes the Andorran Statute, 1806"; 1f. "Confirmation of the Co-government, 1288".

F26 Virgin of Santa Coloma

1964. Red Cross Fund.

F192	**F26**	25c.+10c. red, green and blue	21·00	38·00

F27 "Syncom", Morse Key and Pleumeur-Bodou centre

1965. Centenary of I.T.U.

F193	**F27**	60c. violet, blue and red	4·75	8·00

F28 Andorra House, Paris

1965. Opening of Andorra House, Paris.

F194	**F28**	25c. brown, olive & bl	1·10	2·30

F29 Chair-lift

1966. Winter Sports.

F195	**F29**	25c. green, purple & bl	1·30	3·25
F196	-	40c. brown, blue & red	2·10	4·00

DESIGN—HORIZ: 40c. Ski-lift.

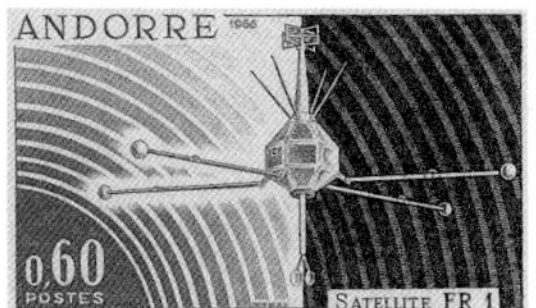

F30 Satellite "FR 1"

1966. Launching of Satellite "FR 1".

F197	**F30**	60c. blue, emer & grn	2·10	4·25

F31 Europa "Ship"

1966. Europa.

F198	**F31**	60c. brown	3·50	6·25

F32 Cogwheels

1967. Europa.

F199	**F32**	30c. indigo and blue	4·25	5·75
F200	**F32**	60c. red and purple	5·50	10·50

F33 "Folk Dancers" (statue)

1967. Centenary (1966) of New Reform.

F201	**F33**	30c. green, olive & slate	1·50	3·50

F34 Telephone and Dial

1967. Inaug of Automatic Telephone Service.

F202	**F34**	60c. black, violet & red	1·60	3·75

F35 Andorran Family

1967. Institution of Social Security.

F203	**F35**	2f.30 brown & purple	8·50	18·00

F36 "The Temptation"

1967. 16th-century Frescoes in House of the Valleys (1st series).

F204	**F36**	25c. red and black	1·10	2·75
F205	-	30c. purple and violet	1·20	3·50
F206	-	60c. blue and indigo	1·60	4·50

FRESCOES: 30c. "The Kiss of Judas"; 60c. "The Descent from the Cross".

See also Nos. F210/12.

F37 Downhill Skiing

1968. Winter Olympic Games, Grenoble.

F207	**F37**	40c. purple, orge & red	1·40	3·75

F38 Europa "Key"

1968. Europa.

F208	**F38**	30c. blue and slate	5·25	8·50
F209	**F38**	60c. violet & brown	8·50	14·00

1968. 16th-century Frescoes in House of the Valleys (2nd series). Designs as Type F 36.

F210	25c. deep green and green	95	3·25
F211	30c. purple and brown	1·20	4·75
F212	60c. brown and red	2·10	6·50

FRESCOES: 25c. "The Beating of Christ"; 30c. "Christ Helped by the Cyrenians"; 60c. "The Death of Christ".

F39 High Jumping

1968. Olympic Games, Mexico.

F213	**F39**	40c. brown and blue	2·10	3·75

F40 Colonnade

1969. Europa.

F214	**F40**	40c. grey, blue and red	9·50	11·50
F215	**F40**	70c. red, green and blue	13·00	22·00

F41 Canoeing

1969. World Kayak-Canoeing Championships, Bourg-St. Maurice.

F216	**F41**	70c. dp blue, bl & grn	2·10	5·25

F41a "Diamond Crystal" in Rain Drop

1969. European Water Charter.

F217	**F41a**	70c. black, blue and ultramarine	5·25	9·75

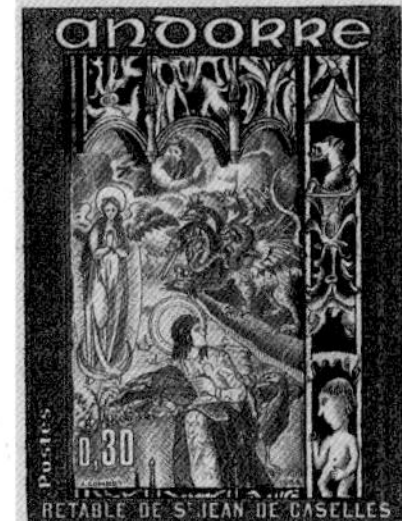

F42 "The Apocalypse"

1969. Altar-screen, Church of St. John of Caselles (1st series). "The Revelation of St. John".

F218	**F42**	30c. red, violet & brn	1·10	2·10
F219	-	40c. bistre, brn & grey	1·60	2·75
F220	-	70c. purple, lake & red	2·10	3·50

DESIGNS: 40c. Angel "clothed with cloud with face as the sun, and feet as pillars of fire" (Rev. 10); 70c. Christ with sword and stars, and seven candlesticks.

See also Nos. F225/7, F233/5 and F240/2.

F43 Handball Player

1970. 7th World Handball Championships, France.

F221	**F43**	80c. blue, brn & dp bl	2·75	5·25

F44 "Flaming Sun"

1970. Europa.

F222	**F44**	40c. orange	9·50	8·00
F223	**F44**	80c. violet	12·00	13·00

F45 Putting the Shot

1970. 1st European Junior Athletic Championships, Paris.

F224	**F45**	80c. purple and blue	2·75	5·50

1970. Altar-screen, Church of St. John of Caselles (2nd series). Designs as Type F 42.

F225	30c. violet, brown and red	1·50	2·50
F226	40c. green and violet	1·60	2·75
F227	80c. red, blue and green	3·25	4·00

DESIGNS: 30c. Angel with keys and padlock; 40c. Angel with pillar; 80c. St. John being boiled in cauldron of oil.

F46 Ice Skaters

1971. World Ice Skating Championships, Lyon.

F228	**F46**	80c. violet, pur & red	3·00	4·75

F47 Western Capercaillie

1971. Nature Protection.

F229	**F47**	80c. multicoloured	4·75	6·25
F230	-	80c. brown, green & bl	4·75	6·25

DESIGN: No. F230, Brown bear.

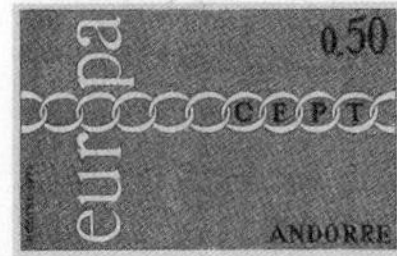

F48 Europa Chain

1971. Europa.

F231	**F48**	50c. red	10·50	12·50
F232	**F48**	80c. green	16·00	20·00

1971. Altar-screen, Church of St. John of Caselles (3rd series). As Type F 42.

F233	30c. green, brown and myrtle	1·80	4·50
F234	50c. brown, orange and lake	2·40	5·25
F235	90c. blue, purple and brown	3·75	7·00

DESIGNS: 30c. St. John in temple at Ephesus; 50c. St. John with cup of poison; 90c. St. John disputing with pagan philosophers.

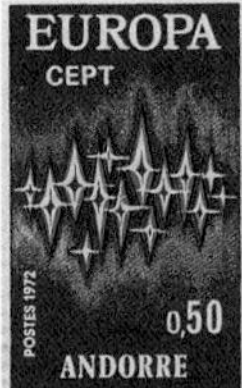

F49 "Communications"

1972. Europa.

F236	**F49**	50c. multicoloured	10·00	10·50
F237	**F49**	90c. multicoloured	15·00	18·00

F50 Golden Eagle

1972. Nature Protection.

F238	**F50**	60c. olive, green & pur	4·75	6·25

F51 Rifle-shooting

1972. Olympic Games, Munich.

F239	**F51**	1f. purple	3·25	4·50

1972. Altar-screen, Church of St. John of Caselles (4th series). As Type F 42.

F240	30c. purple, grey and green	1·40	2·30
F241	50c. grey and blue	1·70	2·75
F242	90c. green and blue	2·75	4·00

DESIGNS: 30c. St. John in discussion with bishop; 50c. St. John healing a cripple; 90c. Angel with spear.

F52 General De Gaulle

1972. 5th Anniv of Gen. De Gaulle's Visit to Andorra.

F243	**F52**	50c. blue	3·50	5·75
F244	-	90c. red	4·75	7·75

DESIGN: 90c. Gen. De Gaulle in Andorra la Vella, 1967.

See also Nos. F434/5.

F53 Europa "Posthorn"

1973. Europa.

F245	**F53**	50c. multicoloured	10·00	10·50
F246	**F53**	90c. multicoloured	10·50	21·00

F54 "Virgin of Canolich" (wood carving)

1973. Andorran Art.

F247	**F54**	1f. lilac, blue and drab	3·00	4·25

F55 Lily

1973. Pyrenean Flowers (1st series). Multicoloured.

F248	30c. Type F **55**	1·10	3·25
F249	50c. Columbine	2·10	4·50
F250	90c. Wild pinks	1·60	3·50

See also Nos. F253/5 and F264/6.

F56 Blue Tit ("Mesange Bleue")

1973. Nature Protection. Birds. Multicoloured.

F251	90c. Type F **56**	2·75	5·25
F252	1f. Lesser spotted woodpecker ("Pic Epeichette")	3·00	5·75

See also Nos. F259/60.

1974. Pyrenean Wild Flowers (2nd series). As Type F 55. Multicoloured.

F253	45c. Iris	55	4·00
F254	65c. Tobacco Plant	65	4·50
F255	90c. Narcissus	1·40	4·75

F57 "The Virgin of Pal"

1974. Europa. Church Sculptures. Mult.

F256	50c. Type F **57**	17·00	11·50
F257	90c. "The Virgin of Santa Coloma"	23·00	18·00

F58 Arms of Andorra

1974. Meeting of Co-Princes, Cahors.

F258	**F58**	1f. blue, violet & orge	1·40	5·75

1974. Nature Protection. Birds. As Type F 56. Multicoloured.

F259	60c. Citril finch ("Venturon Montagnard")	4·25	7·00
F260	80c. Northern bullfinch ("Boureuil")	4·25	7·00

F59 Letters crossing Globe

1974. Centenary of U.P.U.

F261	**F59**	1f.20 red, grey & brn	2·30	4·25

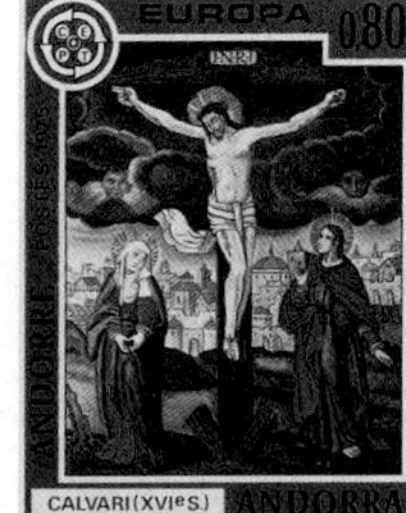

F60 "Calvary"

1975. Europa. Paintings from La Cortinada Church. Multicoloured.

F262	80c. Type F **60**	8·50	15·00
F263	1f.20 "Coronation of St. Martin" (horiz)	10·50	23·00

1975. Pyrenean Flowers (3rd series). As Type F 55.

F264	60c. multicoloured	65	3·25
F265	80c. multicoloured	1·80	4·00
F266	1f.20 yellow, red and green	1·30	3·50

DESIGNS: 60c. Gentian; 80c. Anemone; 1f.20, Colchicum.

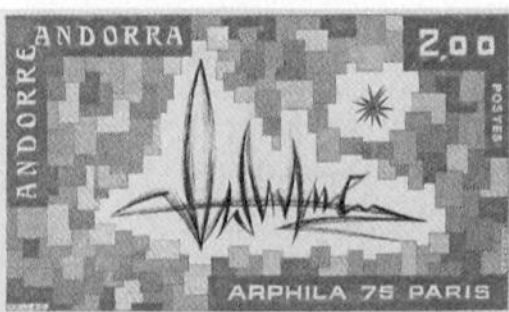

F61 "Arphila" Motif

1975. "Arphila 75" International Stamp Exhibition, Paris.

F267	**F61**	2f. red, green and blue	2·00	4·50

F62 Pres. Pompidou (Co-prince of Andorra)

1976. President Pompidou of France Commem.

F268	**F62**	80c. black and violet	1·10	3·25

F63 "La Pubilla" and Emblem

1976. International Women's Year.

F269	**F63**	1f.20 black, pur & bl	2·10	3·75

F64 Skier

1976. Winter Olympic Games, Innsbruck.

F270	**F64**	1f.20 black, green & bl	1·60	3·50

F65 Telephone and Satellite

1976. Telephone Centenary.

F271	**F65**	1f. green, black and red	1·60	3·75

F66 Catalan Forge

1976. Europa.
F272 **F66** 80c. brown, blue & grn 4·25 4·50
F273 - 1f.20 red, green & blk 5·25 5·75
DESIGN: 1f.20, Andorran folk-weaving.

F67 Thomas Jefferson

1976. Bicentenary of American Revolution.
F274 **F67** 1f.20 dp grn, brn & grn 1·40 3·50

F68 Ball-trap (clay pigeon) Shooting

1976. Olympic Games, Montreal.
F275 **F68** 2f. brown, violet & grn 2·10 4·00

F69 New Chapel

1976. New Chapel of Our Lady, Meritxell.
F276 **F69** 1f. green, purple & brn 1·20 3·25

F70 Apollo

1976. Nature Protection. Butterflies. Mult.
F277 80c. Type F **70** 3·25 6·50
F278 1f.40 Camberwell beauty 4·00 7·00

F71 Stoat

1977. Nature Protection.
F279 **F71** 1f. grey, black & blue 2·40 3·75

F72 Church of St. John of Caselles

1977. Europa.
F280 **F72** 1f. purple, green & bl 6·75 5·75
F281 - 1f.40 indigo, grn & bl 11·00 7·00
DESIGN: 1f.40, St. Vicens Chateau.

F73 Book and Flowers

1977. 1st Anniv of Institute of Andorran Studies.
F282 **F73** 80c. brown, green & bl 1·20 2·75

F74 St. Roma

1977. Reredos, St. Roma's Chapel, Les Bons.
F283 **F74** 2f. multicoloured 2·75 3·50

F75 General Council Assembly Hall

1977. Andorran Institutions.
F284 **F75** 1f.10 red, blue & brn 2·75 4·00
F285 - 2f. brown and red 2·75 4·00
DESIGN—VERT. 2f. Don Guillem d'Areny Plandolit.

F76 Eurasian Red Squirrel

1978. Nature Protection.
F286 **F76** 1f. brown, grn & olive 1·30 2·75

F77 Escalls Bridge

1978. 700th Anniv of Parity Treaties (1st issue).
F287 **F77** 80c. green, brown & bl 85 2·75
See also No. F292.

F78 Church at Pal

1978. Europa.
F288 **F78** 1f. brown, green & red 7·00 5·75
F289 - 1f.40 brown, bl & red 11·50 7·50
DESIGN: 1f.40, Charlemagne's House.

F79 "Virgin of Sispony"

1978. Andorran Art.
F290 **F79** 2f. multicoloured 2·10 3·50

F80 Tribunal Meeting

1978. Tribunal of Visura.
F291 **F80** 1f.20 multicoloured 1·80 2·75

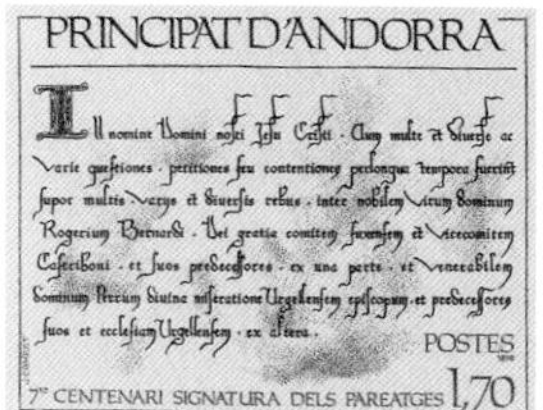

F81 Treaty Text

1978. 700th Anniv of Parity Treaties (2nd issue).
F292 **F81** 1f.50 brown, grn & red 1·30 2·75

F82 Chamois

1978. Nature Protection.
F293 **F82** 1f. brown, lt brn & bl 85 2·40

F83 Rock Ptarmigans ("Perdiu Blanca")

1979. Nature Protection.
F294 **F83** 1f.20 multicoloured 1·70 3·25

F84 Early 20th Century Postman and Church of St. John of Caselles

1979. Europa.
F295 **F84** 1f.20 black, brn & grn 3·25 4·75
F296 - 1f.70 brown, grn & mve 5·25 5·75
DESIGN: 1f.70, Old French Post Office, Andorra.

F85 Wall painting, Church of St. Cerni, Nagol

1979. Pre-Romanesque Art.
F297 **F85** 2f. green, pink and brown 1·60 2·75
See also No. F309.

F86 Boy with Sheep

1979. International Year of the Child.
F298 **F86** 1f.70 multicoloured 1·30 2·75

F87 Co-princes Monument (Luigiteruggi)

1979. Co-princes Monument.
F299 **F87** 2f. dp green, grn & red 1·60 3·25

F88 Judo

1979. World Judo Championships, Paris.
F300 **F88** 1f.30 black, dp bl & bl 1·10 2·75

F89 Cal Pal, La Cortinada

1980
F301 **F89** 1f.10 brown, bl & grn 85 2·40

F90 Cross-country Skiing

1980. Winter Olympics, Lake Placid.
F302 **F90** 1f.80 ultram, bl & red 1·50 3·25

F91 Charlemagne

1980. Europa.

F303	**F91**	1f.30 brn, chest & red	2·10	3·50
F304	-	1f.80 green and brown	2·75	4·00

DESIGN: 1f.80, Napoleon I.

F93 Dog's-tooth Violet

1980. Nature Protection. Multicoloured.

F306	1f.10 Type F **93**	95	2·50
F305	1f.30 Pyrenean lily	85	2·40

F94 Cyclists

1980. World Cycling Championships.

F307	**F94**	1f.20 violet, mve & brn	1·20	2·50

F95 House of the Valleys

1980. 400th Anniv of Restoration of House of the Valleys (meeting place of Andorran General Council).

F308	**F95**	1f.40 brown, vio & grn	1·20	2·50

1980. Pre-Romanesque Art. As Type F 85. Mult.

F309	2f. Angel (wall painting, Church of St. Cerni, Nagol) (horiz)	1·70	3·25

F97 Shepherds' Huts, Mereig

1981. Architecture.

F310	**F97**	1f.40 brown and blue	1·10	1·70

F98 Bear Dance (Emcamp Carnival)

1981. Europa.

F311	**F98**	1f.40 black, green & bl	1·60	2·30
F312	-	2f. black, blue and red	2·10	3·50

DESIGN: 2f. El Contrapas (dance).

F99 Bonelli's Warbler

1981. Nature Protection. Birds. Multicoloured.

F313	1f.20 Type F **99**	1·10	2·75
F314	1f.40 Wallcreeper	1·30	2·75

F100 Fencing

1981. World Fencing Championships, Clermont-Ferrand.

F315	**F100**	2f. blue and black	1·30	2·75

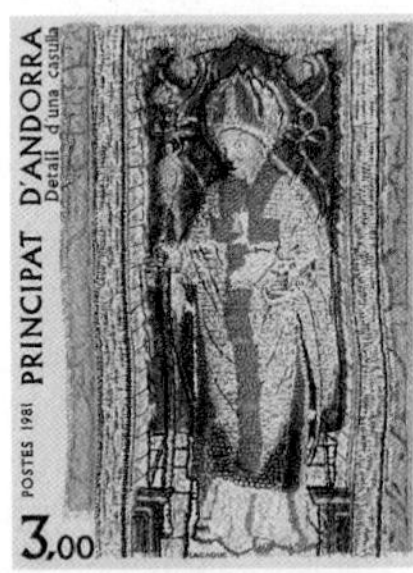

F101 Chasuble of St. Martin (miniature)

1981. Art.

F316	**F101**	3f. multicoloured	1·80	2·75

F102 Fountain, Sant Julia de Loria

1981. International Decade of Drinking Water.

F317	**F102**	1f.60 blue and brown	1·10	2·50

F103 Symbolic Disabled

1981. International Year of Disabled Persons.

F318	**F103**	2f.30 blue, red & grn	1·50	2·75

F104 Scroll and Badge (creation of Andorran Executive Council, 1981)

1982. Europa.

F319	**F104**	1f.60 blue, brn & orge	2·10	2·75
F320	-	2f.30 blue, blk & orge	2·75	3·25

DESIGN: 2f.30, Hat and cloak (creation of Land Council, 1419).

F105 Footballer running to right

1982. World Cup Football Championship, Spain.

F321	**F105**	1f.60 brown and red	1·30	2·40
F322	-	2f.60 brown and red	1·90	2·75

DESIGN: 2f.60, Footballer running to left.

F 106 1933 1f.25 Stamp

1982. 1st Official Exhibition of Andorran Postage Stamps.

MSF323	F **106**	5f. black and red	2·75	4·00

F107 Wall Painting, La Cortinada Church

1982. Romanesque Art.

F324	**F107**	3f. multicoloured	1·60	4·75

F108 Wild Cat

1982. Nature Protection.

F325	**F108**	1f.80 blk, grn & grey	1·60	3·75
F326	-	2f.60 brown & green	1·40	4·00

DESIGN: 2f.60, Scots Pine.

F109 Dr. Robert Koch

1982. Centenary of Discovery of Tubercle Bacillus.

F327	**F109**	2f.10 lilac	1·40	2·75

F110 St. Thomas Aquinas

1982. St. Thomas Aquinas Commemoration.

F328	**F110**	2f. deep brown, brown and grey	1·30	2·75

F111 Montgolfier and Charles Balloon over Tuileries, Paris

1983. Bicentenary of Manned Flight.

F329	**F111**	2f. green, red and brown	1·30	2·75

F112 Silver Birch

1983. Nature Protection.

F330	**F112**	1f. red, brown and green	1·50	3·75
F331	-	1f.50 green, bl & brn	1·60	4·00

DESIGN: 1f.50, Brown trout.

F113 Mountain Cheesery

1983. Europa.

F332	**F113**	1f. purple and violet	2·40	3·75
F333	-	2f.60 red, mve & pur	2·75	4·00

DESIGN: 2f.60, Catalan forge.

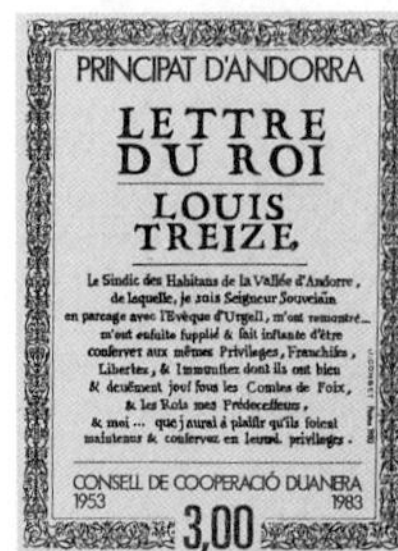

F114 Royal Edict of Louis XIII

1983. 30th Anniv of Customs Co-operation Council.

F334	**F114**	3f. black and slate	2·00	5·50

F115 Early Coat of Arms

1983. Inscr "POSTES".

F335	**F115**	5c. green and red	1·10	2·30
F336	**F115**	10c. dp green & green	1·10	2·30
F337	**F115**	20c. violet and mauve	1·10	2·30
F338	**F115**	30c. purple and violet	1·10	2·30
F339	**F115**	40c. blue & ultram	1·10	2·30
F340	**F115**	50c. black and red	1·10	2·30
F341	**F115**	1f. lake and red	1·10	2·30
F342	**F115**	1f.90 green	3·75	4·75
F343	**F115**	2f. red and brown	1·50	1·60
F344	**F115**	2f.10 green	1·50	2·75
F345	**F115**	2f.20 red	1·10	3·75
F346	**F115**	2f.30 red	1·40	3·75
F347	**F115**	3f. green and mauve	1·60	4·00
F348	**F115**	4f. orange and brown	3·25	6·25
F349	**F115**	5f. brown and red	2·10	5·75
F350	**F115**	10f. red and brown	4·25	6·25
F351	**F115**	15f. green & dp green	6·25	9·00
F352	**F115**	20f. blue and brown	8·00	9·25

For design as Type F **115** but inscribed "LA POSTE" see Nos. F446/9.

F116 Wall Painting, La Cortinada Church

1983. Romanesque Art.

F354	**F116**	4f. multicoloured	2·10	4·00

F117 Plandolit House

1983

F355	**F117**	1f.60 brown & green	1·10	1·70

F118 Snowflakes and Olympic Torch

1984. Winter Olympic Games, Sarajevo.
F356 **F118** 2f.80 red, blue & grn 1·70 2·75

F119 Pyrenees and Council of Europe Emblem

1984. Work Community of Pyrenees Region.
F357 **F119** 3f. blue and brown 1·80 3·25

F120 Bridge

1984. Europa.
F358 **F120** 2f. green 3·75 4·00
F359 **F120** 2f.80 red 4·75 5·25

F121 Sweet Chestnut

1984. Nature Protection.
F360 **F121** 1f.70 grn, brn & pur 1·30 3·75
F361 - 2f.10 green & brown 1·60 4·00
DESIGN: 2f.10, Walnut.

F122 Centre Members

1984. Pyrenean Cultures Centre, Andorra.
F362 **F122** 3f. blue, orange & red 1·80 3·50

F123 "St. George" (detail of fresco, Church of St. Cerni, Nagol)

1984. Pre-Romanesque Art.
F363 **F123** 5f. multicoloured 2·75 4·00

F124 Sant Julia Valley

1985
F364 **F124** 2f. green, olive & brn 1·50 2·75

F125 Title Page of "Le Val d'Andorre" (comic opera)

1985. Europa.
F365 **F125** 2f.10 green 3·75 4·00
F366 - 3f. brown & dp brown 4·75 5·25
DESIGN: 3f. Musical instruments within frame.

F126 Teenagers holding up ball

1985. International Youth Year.
F367 **F126** 3f. red and brown 1·60 3·25

F127 Mallard

1985. Nature Protection. Multicoloured.
F368 1f.80 Type F **127** 1·40 3·50
F369 2f.20 Eurasian goldfinch 1·70 4·00

F128 St. Cerni and Angel (fresco, Church of St. Cerni, Nagol)

1985. Pre-Romanesque Art.
F370 **F128** 5f. multicoloured 2·30 4·00

F130 1979 Europa Stamp

1986. Inauguration of Postal Museum.
F381 **F130** 2f.20 brown & green 1·40 3·25

F131 Ansalonga

1986. Europa.
F382 **F131** 2f.20 black and blue 4·25 4·50
F383 - 3f.20 black and green 5·25 5·50
DESIGN: 3f.20, Pyrenean chamois.

F132 Players

1986. World Cup Football Championship, Mexico.
F384 **F132** 3f. grn, blk & dp grn 2·10 3·50

F133 Angonella Lakes

1986
F385 **F133** 2f.20 multicoloured 1·40 2·75

F134 Title Page of "Manual Digest", 1748

1986. "Manual Digest".
F386 **F134** 5f. black, grn & brn 2·75 4·00

F135 Dove with Twig

1986. International Peace Year.
F387 **F135** 1f.90 blue and indigo 1·30 2·75

F136 St. Vincent's Chapel, Enclar

1986
F388 **F136** 1f.90 brn, blk & grn 1·30 2·75

F137 Arms

1987. Visit of French Co-prince (French president).
F389 **F137** 2f.20 multicoloured 2·00 4·00

F138 Meritxell Chapel

1987. Europa.
F390 **F138** 2f.20 purple and red 5·25 4·50
F391 - 3f.40 violet and blue 7·50 6·25
DESIGN: 3f.40, Ordino.

F139 Ransol

1987
F392 **F139** 1f.90 multicoloured 1·50 3·50

F140 Horse

1987. Nature Protection. Multicoloured.
F393 1f.90 Type F **140** 1·70 4·25
F394 2f.20 Isabel (moth) 2·00 4·50

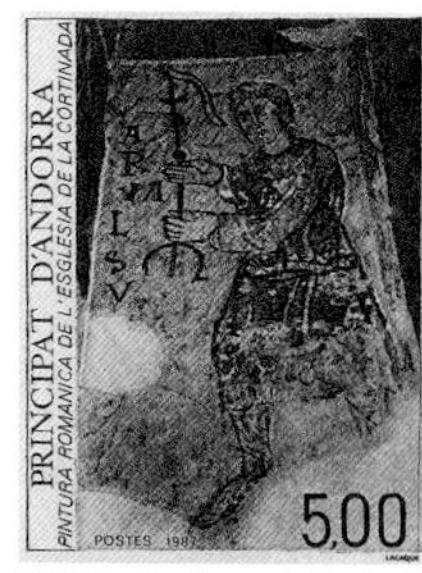

F141 Arualsu (fresco, La Cortinada Church)

1987. Romanesque Art.
F395 **F141** 5f. multicoloured 3·00 4·25

F142 Walker with Map by Signpost

1987. Walking.
F396 **F142** 2f. pur, grn & dp grn 1·40 2·75

F143 Key

1987. La Cortinada Church Key.
F397 **F143** 3f. multicoloured 1·70 3·50

F144 Arms

1988
F398 **F144** 2f.20 red 1·40 2·75
F399 **F144** 2f.30 red 1·60 4·50
F400 **F144** 2f.50 red 1·70 4·50
F401 **F144** 2f.80 red 1·80 4·25
Nos. F400/1 are inscribed "LA POSTE".

F145 Bronze Boot and Mountains

1988. Archaeology.
F407 **F145** 3f. multicoloured 1·70 3·75

F146 Players

1988. Rugby.

F408	F146	2f.20 blk, yell & grn	1·40	4·50

F147 Enclar Aerial

1988. Europa. Transport and Communications. Each green, brown and blue.

F409	2f.20 Type F 147	3·75	4·00
F410	3f.60 Hand pointing to map on screen (tourist information)	4·75	5·75

F148 Les Escaldes Hot Spring

1988

F411	F148	2f.20 blue, brn & grn	1·40	2·75

F149 Ansalonga Pass

1988

F412	F149	2f. blue, green & olive	1·20	2·75

F150 Pyrenean Shepherd Dog

1988. Nature Protection. Multicoloured.

F413	2f. Type F 150	1·90	4·50
F414	2f.20 Hare	2·00	4·50

F151 Fresco, Andorra La Vella Church

1988. Romanesque Art.

F415	F151	5f. multicoloured	3·00	4·00

F152 Birds

1989. Bicentenary of French Revolution.

F416	F152	2f.20 violet, blk & red	1·50	2·75

F153 Pal

1989

F417	F153	2f.20 violet and blue	1·50	2·75

F154 The Strong Horse

1989. Europa. Children's Games. Each brown and cream.

F418	2f.20 Type F 154	3·25	3·50
F419	3f.60 The Handkerchief	4·25	4·75

F155 Wounded Soldiers

1989. 125th Anniv of International Red Cross.

F420	F155	3f.60 brn, blk & red	2·10	3·50

F156 Archaeological Find and St. Vincent's Chapel, Enclar

1989. Archaeology.

F421	F156	3f. multicoloured	1·60	3·50

F157 Wild Boar

1989. Nature Protection.

F422	F157	2f.20 blk, grn & brn	1·60	3·50
F423	-	3f.60 black, green and deep green	2·10	4·50

DESIGN: 3f.60, Palmate newt.

F158 Retable of St. Michael de la Mosquera, Encamp

1989

F424	F158	5f. multicoloured	3·25	5·50

F159 La Margineda Bridge

1990

F425	F159	2f.30 blue, brn & turq	1·60	2·75

F160 Llorts Iron Ore Mines

1990

F426	F160	3f.20 multicoloured	2·10	3·25

F161 Exterior of Old Post Office, Andorra La Vella

1990. Europa. Post Office Buildings.

F427	F161	2f.30 red and black	4·25	5·25
F428	-	3f.20 violet and red	6·25	7·00

DESIGN: 3f.20, Interior of modern post office.

F162 Censer, St. Roma's Chapel, Les Bons

1990

F429	F162	3f. multicoloured	2·10	3·25

F163 Wild Roses

1990. Nature Protection. Multicoloured.

F430	2f.30 Type F 163	1·60	3·25
F431	3f.20 Otter (horiz)	2·10	3·50

F164 Tobacco-drying Sheds, Les Bons

1990

F432	F164	2f.30 yell, blk & red	1·60	2·75

F165 Part of Mural from Santa Coloma Church

1990

F433	F165	5f. multicoloured	2·75	3·75

1990. Birth Centenary of Charles de Gaulle (French statesman). As Nos. F243/4 but values and inscriptions changed.

F434	F52	2f.30 blue	2·10	3·25
F435	F52	3f.20 red	2·50	3·50

F166 Coin from St. Eulalia's Church, Encamp

1990

F436	F166	3f.20 multicoloured	2·10	3·25

F167 Chapel of Sant Roma Dels Vilars

1991

F437	F167	2f.50 blue, blk & grn	1·60	2·75

F168 Emblem and Track

1991. 4th European Small States Games.

F438	F168	2f.50 multicoloured	1·50	2·75

F169 Television Satellite

1991. Europa. Europe in Space. Multicoloured.

F439	2f.50 Type F 169	4·25	4·50
F440	3f.50 Globe, telescope and eye (horiz)	7·50	8·00

F170 Bottles

1991. Artefacts from Tomb of St. Vincent of Enclar.

F441	F170	3f.20 multicoloured	1·80	2·75

F171 Sheep

1991. Nature Protection.

F442	F171	2f.50 brown, bl & blk	2·10	4·50
F443	-	3f.50 brn, mve & blk	2·20	4·75

DESIGN: 3f.50, Pyrenean cow.

F172 Players

1991. World Petanque Championship, Engordany.

F444	F172	2f.50 blk, bistre & red	1·80	2·75

F173 Mozart, Quartet and Organ Pipes

1991. Death Bicentenary of Wolfgang Amadeus Mozart (composer).

F445	F173	3f.40 blue, blk & turq	2·20	3·25

1991. As Type F 115 but inscr "LA POSTE".

F446	F115	2f.20 green	1·40	4·00
F447	F115	2f.40 green	3·00	4·50
F448	F115	2f.50 red	1·60	4·00
F449	F115	2f.70 green	2·75	4·00
F450	F115	2f.80 red	2·75	4·00
F451	F115	3f. red	2·75	4·00

F174 "Virgin of the Remedy of Sant Julia and Sant Germa"

1991

F455	**F174**	5f. multicoloured	3·25	3·75

F175 Slalom

1992. Winter Olympic Games, Albertville. Mult.

F456	2f.50 Type F **175**	2·40	2·75
F457	3f.40 Figure skating	2·75	3·25

F176 St. Andrew's Church, Arinsal

1992

F458	**F176**	2f.50 black and buff	1·80	2·20

F177 Navigation Instrument and Columbus's Fleet

1992. Europa. 500th Anniv of Discovery of America by Columbus. Multicoloured.

F459	2f.50 Type F **177**	4·75	4·50
F460	3f.40 Fleet, Columbus and Amerindians	7·50	5·75

F178 Canoeing

1992. Olympic Games, Barcelona. Multicoloured.

F461	2f.50 Type F **178**	1·90	2·30
F462	3f.40 Shooting	2·20	2·50

F179 Globe Flowers

1992. Nature Protection. Multicoloured.

F463	2f.50 Type F **179**	1·70	2·40
F464	3f.40 Griffon vulture ("El Voltor") (horiz)	2·30	2·75

F180 "Martyrdom of St. Eulalia" (altarpiece, St. Eulalia's Church, Encamp)

1992

F465	**F180**	4f. multicoloured	2·40	2·75

F181 "Ordino Arcalis 91" (Mauro Staccioli)

1992. Modern Sculpture. Multicoloured.

F466	5f. Type F **181**	3·25	3·50
F467	5f. "Storm in a Teacup" (Dennis Oppenheim) (horiz)	3·25	3·50

F182 Grau Roig

1993. Ski Resorts. Multicoloured.

F468	2f.50 Type F **182**	1·60	2·30
F469	2f.50 Ordino	1·60	2·30
F470	2f.50 Soldeu el Tarter	1·60	2·30
F471	3f.40 Pal	2·30	2·75
F472	3f.40 Arinsal	2·30	2·75

F183 "Estructures Autogeneradores" (Jorge du Bon)

1993. Europa. Contemporary Art.

F473	**F183**	2f.50 dp bl, bl & vio	2·20	3·25
F474	-	3f.40 multicoloured	2·40	3·50

DESIGN—HORIZ: 3f.40, "Fisicromia per Andorra" (Carlos Cruz-Diez).

F184 Common Blue

1993. Nature Protection. Butterflies. Multicoloured.

F475	2f.50 Type F **184**	2·10	3·25
F476	4f.20 "Nymphalidae"	3·00	4·00

F185 Cyclist

1993. Tour de France Cycling Road Race.

F477	**F185**	2f.50 multicoloured	2·20	3·50

F186 Smiling Hands

1993. 10th Anniv of Andorran School.

F478	**F186**	2f.80 multicoloured	2·50	3·50

F187 "A Pagan Place" (Michael Warren)

1993. Modern Sculpture.

F479	**F187**	5f. black and blue	3·50	3·00
F480	-	5f. multicoloured	3·50	3·00

DESIGN: No. F480, "Pep, Lu, Canolic, Ton, Meritxell, Roma, Anna, Pau, Carles, Eugenia... and Others" (Erik Dietman).

F188 Cross-country Skiing

1994. Winter Olympic Games, Lillehammer, Norway.

F481	**F188**	3f.70 multicoloured	2·20	2·50

F189 Constitution Monument

1994. 1st Anniv of New Constitution.

F482	**F189**	2f.80 multicoloured	1·90	2·00
F483	-	3f.70 blk, yell & mve	2·40	3·50

DESIGN: 3f.70, Stone tablet.

F190 AIDS Virus

1994. Europa. Discoveries and Inventions. Mult.

F484	2f.80 Type F **190**	2·50	2·50
F485	3f.70 Radio mast	3·00	3·00

F191 Competitors' Flags and Football

1994. World Cup Football Championship, U.S.A.

F486	**F191**	3f.70 multicoloured	2·50	2·75

F192 Horse Riding

1994. Tourist Activities. Multicoloured.

F487	2f.80 Type F **192**	1·90	1·90
F488	2f.80 Mountain biking	1·90	1·90
F489	2f.80 Climbing	1·90	1·90
F490	2f.80 Fishing	1·90	1·90

F193 Scarce Swallowtail

1994. Nature Protection. Butterflies. Multicoloured.

F491	2f.80 Type F **193**	2·50	2·75
F492	4f.40 Small tortoiseshell	3·75	4·00

F194 "26 10 93"

1994. Meeting of Co-princes.

F493	**F194**	2f.80 multicoloured	1·70	2·00

F195 Emblem

1995. European Nature Conservation Year.

F494	**F195**	2f.80 multicoloured	1·90	2·10

F196 Globe, Goal and Player

1995. 3rd World Cup Rugby Championship, South Africa.

F495	**F196**	2f.80 multicoloured	1·90	2·10

F197 Dove and Olive Twig ("Peace")

1995. Europa. Peace and Freedom. Multicoloured.

F496	2f.80 Type F **197**	2·50	2·75
F497	3f.70 Flock of doves ("Free-dom")	2·75	3·00

F198 Emblem

1995. 15th Anniv of Caritas Andorrana (welfare organization).

F498	**F198**	2f.80 multicoloured	1·90	2·30

F199 Caldea Thermal Baths, Les Escaldes-Engordany

1995

F499	**F199**	2f.80 multicoloured	1·90	2·30

F200 National Auditorium, Ordino

1995
F500 **F200** 3f.70 black and buff 2·50 2·75

F201 "Virgin of Meritxell"

1995
F501 **F201** 4f.40 multicoloured 2·75 3·00

F202 Brimstone

1995. Nature Protection. Butterflies. Multicoloured.
F502 2f.80 Type F **202** 2·50 2·75
F503 3f.70 Marbled white (horiz) 3·00 3·25

F203 National Flag over U.N. Emblem

1995. 50th Anniv of U.N.O. Multicoloured.
F504 2f.80 Type F **203** 2·50 2·75
F505 3f.70 Anniversary emblem over flag 2·75 3·00

F204 National Flag and Palace of Europe, Strasbourg

1995. Admission of Andorra to Council of Europe.
F506 **F204** 2f.80 multicoloured 1·90 2·00

F205 Emblem

1996. 4th Borrufa Trophy Skiing Competition.
F507 **F205** 2f.80 multicoloured 1·90 2·00

F206 Basketball

1996
F508 **F206** 3f.70 red, blk & yell 3·00 3·75

F207 Children

1996. 25th Anniv of Our Lady of Meritxell Special School.
F509 **F207** 2f.80 multicoloured 1·90 2·10

F208 European Robin

1996. Nature Protection. Multicoloured.
F510 3f. Type F **208** 2·50 3·00
F511 3f.80 Great tit 3·00 3·25

F209 Cross, St. James's Church, Engordany

1996. Religious Objects. Multicoloured.
F512 3f. Type F **209** 2·50 2·75
F513 3f.80 Censer, St. Eulalia's Church, Encamp (horiz) 2·75 3·00

F210 Ermessenda de Castellbo

1996. Europa. Famous Women.
F514 **F210** 3f. multicoloured 2·50 2·75

F211 Chessmen

1996. Chess.
F515 **F211** 4f.50 red, black & bl 2·50 2·75

F212 Canillo

1996. No value expressed. Self-adhesive.
F516 **F212** (3f.) multicoloured 3·00 3·25

F213 Cycling, Running and Throwing the Javelin

1996. Olympic Games, Atlanta.
F517 **F213** 3f. multicoloured 1·90 2·00

F214 Singers

1996. 5th Anniv of National Youth Choir.
F518 **F214** 3f. multicoloured 1·90 2·00

F215 Man and Boy with Animals

1996. Livestock Fair.
F519 **F215** 3f. yellow, red and black 1·90 2·00

F216 St. Roma's Chapel, Les Bons

1996. Churches. Multicoloured.
F520 6f.70 Type F **216** 4·00 4·25
F521 6f.70 Santa Coloma 4·00 4·25

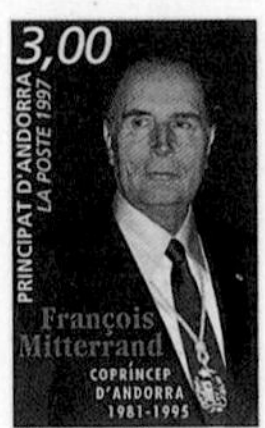

F217 Mitterrand

1997. Francois Mitterrand (President of France and Co-prince of Andorra, 1981–95) Commemoration.
F522 **F217** 3f. multicoloured 1·90 2·00

F218 Parish Emblem

1997. Parish of Encamp. No value expressed. Self-adhesive.
F523 **F218** (3f.) blue 1·90 2·00

F219 Volleyball

1997
F524 **F219** 3f. multicoloured 1·90 2·00

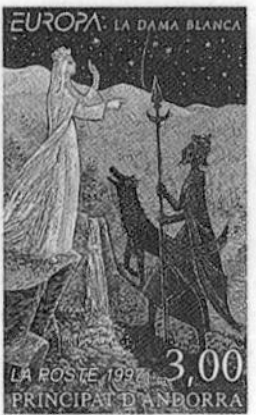

F220 The White Lady

1997. Europa. Tales and Legends.
F525 **F220** 3f. multicoloured 2·50 2·75

F221 House Martin approaching Nest

1997. Nature Protection.
F526 **F221** 3f.80 multicoloured 1·90 2·00

F222 Mill and Saw-mill, Cal Pal

1997. Tourism. Paintings by Francesc Galobardes. Multicoloured.
F527 3f. Type F **222** 2·50 2·75
F528 4f.50 Mill and farmhouse, Sole (horiz) 3·00 3·25

F223 Monstrance, St. Iscle and St. Victoria's Church

1997. Religious Silver Work. Multicoloured.
F529 3f. Type F **223** 2·50 2·75
F530 15f.50 Pax, St. Peter's Church, Aixirivall 7·50 8·00

F224 The Legend of Meritxell

1997. Legends. Multicoloured.
F531 3f. Type F **224** 1·90 2·10
F532 3f. The Seven-armed Cross 1·90 2·10
F533 3f.80 Wrestlers (The Fountain of Esmelicat) 3·00 3·25

F225 St. Michael's Chapel, Engolasters

1997. International Stamp Exn, Monaco.
F534 **F225** 3f. multicoloured 1·90 2·10

F226 Harlequin juggling Candles

1998. Birthday Greetings Stamp.
F535 **F226** 3f. multicoloured 1·90 2·10

F227 Super Giant Slalom

1997. Winter Olympic Games, Nagano, Japan.
F536 **F227** 4f.40 multicoloured 3·25 3·50

F228 Arms of Ordino

1998. No value expressed. Self-adhesive.
F537 **F228** (3f.) multicoloured 1·90 2·10

F229 Altarpiece and Vila Church

1998
F538 **F229** 4f.50 multicoloured 3·25 3·50

F230 Emblem and Cogwheels

1998. 20th Anniv of Rotary Int in Andorra.
F539 **F230** 3f. multicoloured 1·90 2·10

F231 Chaffinch and Berries

1998. Nature Protection.
F540 **F231** 3f.80 multicoloured 3·00 3·25

F232 Players

1998. World Cup Football Championship, France.
F541 **F232** 3f. multicoloured 1·90 2·10

F233 Treble Score and Stylized Orchestra

1998. Europa. National Festivals. Music Festival.
F542 **F233** 3f. multicoloured 1·90 2·10

F234 River

1998. "Expo '98" World's Fair, Lisbon, Portugal.
F543 **F234** 5f. multicoloured 3·75 4·25

F235 Chalice

1998. Chalice from the House of the Valleys.
F544 **F235** 4f.50 multicoloured 3·25 3·75

1998. French Victory in World Cup Football Championship. No. F541 optd FINAL FRANCA/BRASIL 3-0.
F545 **F232** 3f. multicoloured 3·75 4·25

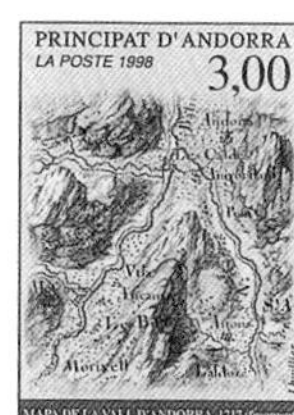

F237 Andorra, 1717

1998. Relief Maps. Multicoloured.
F546 3f. Type F **237** 1·90 2·10
F547 15f.50 Andorra, 1777 (horiz) 9·75 10·50

F238 Museum

1998. Inauguration of Postal Museum.
F548 **F238** 3f. multicoloured 1·90 2·10

F239 Front Page of First Edition

1998. 250th Anniv of "Manual Digest".
F549 **F239** 3f.80 multicoloured 3·00 3·25

F240 Arms of La Massana

1999. No value expressed. Self-adhesive.
F550 **F240** (3f.) multicoloured 1·90 2·10

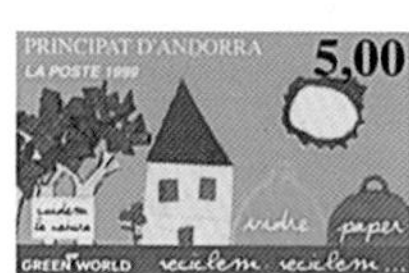

F241 House and Recycling Bins

1999. "Green World". Recycling of Waste.
F551 **F241** 5f. multicoloured 3·75 4·25

F242 Vall de Sorteny (image scaled to 63% of original size)

1999. Europa. Parks and Gardens.
F552 **F242** 3f. multicoloured 1·90 2·10

F243 Council Emblem and Seat, Strasbourg

1999. 50th Anniv of Council of Europe.
F553 **F243** 3f.80 multicoloured 3·00 3·25

F244 "The First Mail Coach"

1999
F554 **F244** 2f.70 multicoloured 1·70 1·90

F245 Footballer and Flags

1999. Andorra–France Qualifying Match for European Nations Football Championship.
F555 **F245** 4f.50 multicoloured 3·50 4·00

F246 St. Michael's Church, Engolasters, and Emblem

1999. "Philexfrance 99" International Stamp Exhibition, Paris, France.
F556 **F246** 3f. multicoloured 1·80 2·00

F247 Winter Scene

1999. Paintings of Pal by Francesc Galobardes. Multicoloured.
F557 3f. Type F **247** 1·80 2·00
F558 3f. Summer scene (horiz) 1·80 2·00

F248 Emblem and "50"

1999. 50th Anniv of International Photographic Art Federation.
F559 **F248** 4f.40 multicoloured 2·75 3·00

F249 Rull House, Sispony

1999
F560 **F249** 15f.50 multicoloured 7·25 8·00

F250 Chest with Six Locks

1999
F561 **F250** 6f.70 multicoloured 3·25 3·50

F251 Angels

1999. Christmas.
F562 **F251** 3f. multicoloured 1·80 2·00

F252 Revellers

2000. New Millennium.
F563 **F252** 3f. multicoloured 1·80 2·00

F253 Arms of La Vella

2000. No value expressed. Self-adhesive.
F564 **F253** (3f.) multicoloured 1·80 2·00

F254 Snow Boarder

2000
F565 **F254** 4f.50 blue, brown and black 2·75 3·00

F255 Emblem

2000. Montserrat Caballe International Opera Competition, Saint Julia de Loria.
F566 **F255** 3f.80 yellow and blue 2·30 2·50

F256 *Campanula cochlearifolia*

2000
F567 **F256** 2f.70 multicoloured 1·80 2·00

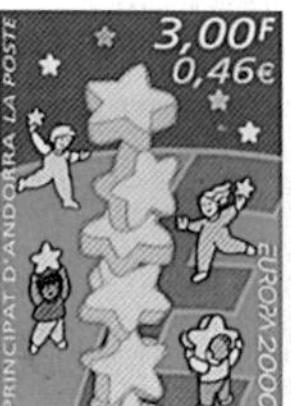

F257 "Building Europe"

2000. Europa.
F568 **F257** 3f. multicoloured 2·50 2·75

F258 Church (Canolich Festival)

2000. Festivals. Multicoloured.

F569	3f. Type F **258**	1·80	2·00
F570	3f. People at Our Lady's Chapel, Meritxell (Meritxell Festival)	1·80	2·00

F259 Sparrow

2000

F571	**F259**	4f.40 multicoloured	2·75	3·00

F260 Hurdling

2000. Olympic Games, Sydney.

F572	**F260**	5f. multicoloured	3·00	3·50

F261 Goat, Skier and Walker

2000. Tourism Day.

F573	**F261**	3f. multicoloured	1·80	2·00

F262 Flower, Text, Circuit Board and Emblems

2000. "EXPO 2000" World's Fair, Hanover.

F574	**F262**	3f. multicoloured	1·80	2·00

F263 Stone Arch and Flag

2000. European Community.

F575	**F263**	3f.80 multicoloured	2·30	2·50

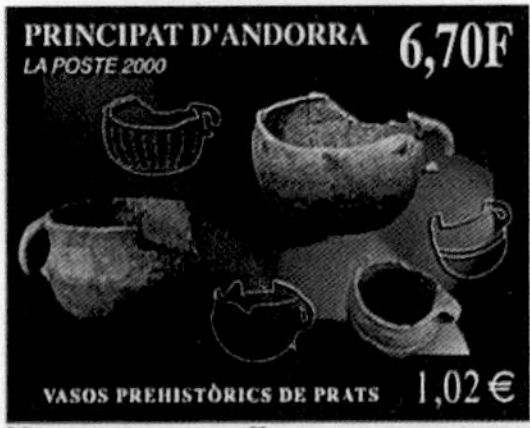
F264 Pottery

2000. Prehistoric Pottery.

F576	**F264**	6f.70 multicoloured	3·25	3·50

F265 Drawing

2000. 25th Anniv of National Archives.

F577	**F265**	15f.50 multicoloured	7·25	8·00

F266 Arms of Saint Julia de Loria

2001. No value expressed. Self-adhesive.

F578	**F266**	(3f.) multicoloured	1·80	2·00

F267 Ski Lift

2001. Canillo Aliga Club.

F579	**F267**	4f.50 multicoloured	2·75	3·00

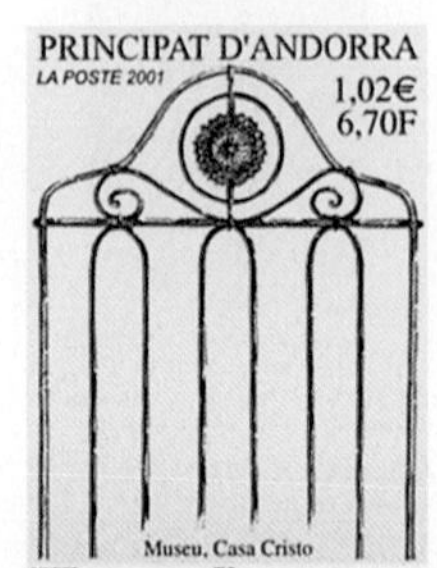
F268 Decorative Metalwork

2001. Casa Cristo Museum.

F580	**F268**	6f.70 multicoloured	3·25	3·50

F269 Legend of Lake Engolasters

2001. Legends. Multicoloured.

F581	3f. Type F **269**	1·80	2·00
F582	3f. Lords before King (foundation of Andorra)	1·80	2·00

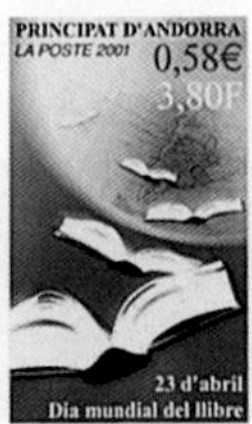
F270 Globe and Books

2001. World Book Day.

F583	**F270**	3f.80 multicoloured	2·30	2·50

F271 Water Splash

2001. Europa. Water Resources.

F584	**F271**	3f. multicoloured	2·50	2·75

F272 Raspberry

2001. Multicoloured.. Multicoloured..

F585	3f. Type F **272**	2·30	2·50
F586	4f.40 Jay (horiz)	3·00	3·50

F273 Profiles talking

2001. European Year of Languages.

F587	**F273**	3f.80 multicoloured	2·75	3·25

F274 Trumpeter

2001. Jazz Festival, Escaldes-Engordany.

F588	**F274**	3f. multicoloured	2·30	2·50

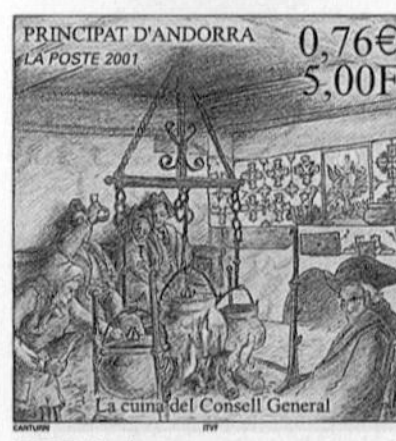
F275 Kitchen

2001

F589	**F275**	5f. multicoloured	3·00	3·50

F276 Chapel

2001. 25th Anniv of Chapel of Our Lady, Meritxell.

F590	**F276**	3f. multicoloured	2·30	2·50

F277 Hotel Pla

2001

F591	**F277**	15f.50 black, violet and green	7·75	8·75

F278 Cross

2001. Grossa Cross (boundary cross at the crossroads between Avinguda Meritxell and Carrer Bisbe Iglesias).

F592	**F278**	2f.70 multicoloured	1·60	1·70

F279 State Arms

2002. (a) With Face Value. Ordinary gum.

F593	**F279**	1c. multicoloured	30	35
F594	**F279**	2c. multicoloured	30	35
F595	**F279**	5c. multicoloured	30	35
F596	**F279**	60c. multicoloured	1·90	2·10

(b) No value expressed.

F598	(46c.) multicoloured	2·30	2·50
F599	(46c.) multicoloured	2·30	2·50

(ii) Size 17×23 mm. Self-adhesive gum.

F599a	(52c.) multicoloured	1·70	1·90

Nos. F598/9 were sold at the rate for inland letters up to 20 grammes.

F280 The Legend of Meritxell

2002. Legends. Designs as Nos. F525, F531/3 and F581/2 but with values in new currency as Type F 280. Multicoloured.

F600	10c. Type F **280**	55	60
F601	20c. Wrestlers (The Fountain of Esmelicat)	55	60
F602	41c. The Piper (La joueurde cornemuse)	1·40	1·60
F603	45c. Legend of Saint Vincent Castle	1·40	1·60
F604	48c. Port Rat (horiz)	2·10	2·30
F604a	48c. The Cave of Ourses	1·40	1·60
F604b	49c. The Testament of llop	1·40	1·60
F604c	50c. El tresor de la font del Manego	1·40	1·60
F605	50c. The Seven-armed Cross	1·40	1·60
F606	51c. The Devils of Aiscirivall Ches Diables d'Aixirivall	2·10	2·30
F606a	75c. 'Le joueur de cornemuse'	2·75	3·00
F606b	90c. Legende du pin de la "Margin eda"	1·20	1·80
F610	€1 Lords before King (foundation of Andorra)	2·75	3·00
F611	€2 Legend of Lake Engolasters	5·50	6·25
F612	€5 The White Lady	12·50	14·00

F281 Pedestrians on Crossing

2002. Schools' Road Safety Campaign.

F615	**F281**	69c. multicoloured	2·50	2·75

F282 Skier

2002. Winter Olympic Games, Salt Lake City, U.S.A.
F616 **F282** 58c. multicoloured 1·90 2·10

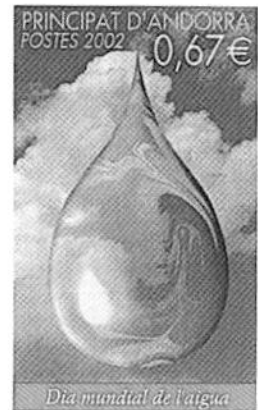

F283 Hotel Rosaleda

2002
F617 **F283** 46c. multicoloured 1·70 1·80

F284 Water Droplet and Clouds

2002. World Water Day.
F618 **F284** 67c. multicoloured 2·10 2·30

F285 Clown

2002. Europa. Circus.
F619 **F285** 46c. multicoloured 2·50 2·75

F286 Myrtle

2002
F620 **F286** 46c. multicoloured 1·70 1·80

F287 Seated Nude (Josep Viladomat)

2002
F621 **F287** €2.26 multicoloured 6·50 7·00

F288 Mountains from Tunnel Entrance

2002. Completion of the Envalira Road Tunnel between Andorra and France.
F622 **F288** 46c. multicoloured 1·70 1·80

F289 Mural (detail) (Santa Coloma Church, Andorra la Vella)

2002
F623 **F289** €1.02 multicoloured 3·25 3·50

F 290 Arms of Escaldes – Engordany

2003. Arms. No value expressed. Self-adhesive.
F624 **F 290** (46c.) multicoloured 1·90 2·10

No. F624 was sold at the rate for inland letters up to 20 grammes.

2003. Legends. 'Legende du pinde la Margineda'. As T F 280.
F625 69c. multicoloured 1·90 2·10

F 291 State Arms

2003. 10th Anniv of Constitution.
F626 **F 291** €2.36 multicoloured 6·50 7·00

F 292 Les Bons

2003. Architecture.
F627 **F 292** 67c. multicoloured 2·50 2·10

F 293 Hotel Mirador

2003
F628 **F 293** €1.02 multicoloured 3·25 3·50

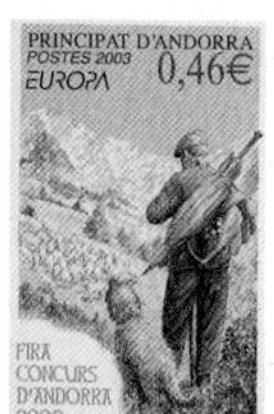

F 294 Man, Dog and Sheep

2003. Europa. Poster Art.
F629 **F 294** 46c. multicoloured 2·50 2·75

F 295 Dancers and Fire

2003. Fires of St. John the Baptist Festival.
F630 **F 295** 50c. multicoloured 1·90 2·10

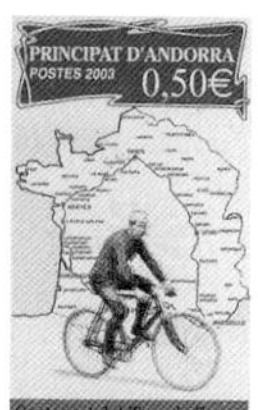

F 296 Cyclist and Map

2003. Centenary of Tour de France (cycle race).
F631 **F 296** 50c. multicoloured 1·90 2·10

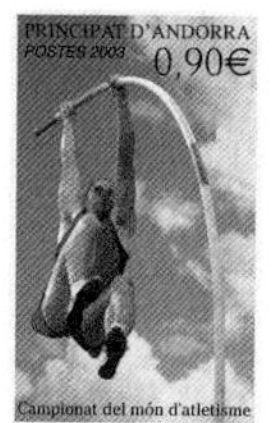

F 297 Pole Vault

2003. World Athletics Championship, Paris.
F632 **F 297** 90c. multicoloured 2·75 3·25

F 298 *Greixa sparassis crispa*

2003
F633 **F 298** 45c. multicoloured 1·30 1·40

F 299 Red Currant

2003
F634 **F 299** 75c. multicoloured 2·50 2·75

F 300 Telephone, Satellite and Globe

2003. Centenary of First Telephone in Andorra.
F635 **F 300** 50c. multicoloured 1·90 2·10

F301 "Maternity" (Paul Gauguin)

2003
F636 **F 301** 75c. multicoloured 2·75 3·00

F302 St. Anthony's Market

2004
F637 **F 302** 50c. multicoloured 1·90 2·10

F303 Children

2004
F638 **F 303** 50c. multicoloured 1·90 2·10

F304 Hotel Valira

2004
F639 **F 304** €1.11 multicoloured 3·50 3·75

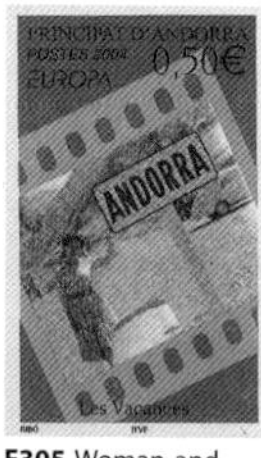

F305 Woman and Andorra Sign

2004. Europa. Holidays.
F640 **F 305** 50c. orange, red and black 2·10 2·30

F306 Madriu-Perafita-Claror Valley

2004. UNESCO World Heritage Site.
F641 **F 306** 75c. multicoloured 2·50 2·75

F307 Poblet de Fontaneda

2004
F642 **F 307** 50c. multicoloured 1·90 2·10

F308 Runner and Swimmer

2004. Olympic Games, Athens 2004.
F643 **F 308** 90c. multicoloured 3·00 3·25

F309 "Pont de la Margineda"(sketch)

2004. Arts. Margineda Bridge by Joaquim Mir (Spanish artist). Multicoloured.
F644 €1 Type F **309** 3·00 3·25

F645 €2 "Pont de la Margineda" (painting) 5·75 6·25

F310 Town Names and Post Codes

2004. Introduction of Postal Codes.
F646 **F310** 50c. vermilion, black and lemon 1·90 2·10

F311 Emblem

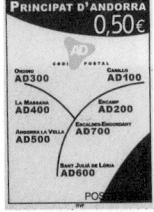

2004. 10th Anniv of Entry into Council of Europe.
F647 **F311** €2.50 multicoloured 7·75 8·50

F312 Children's Nativity

2004. Christmas.
F648 **F312** 50c. black, brown and bistre 1·90 2·10

F313 Three Kings visiting Child

2005
F649 **F313** 50c. multicoloured 1·90 2·10

F314 Mountains and Lake

2005. World Heritage Site. Madriu-Claror-Perafita Valley.
F650 **F314** 50c. multicoloured 1·90 2·10

F 315 Tengmalm's Owl (*Aegolius funereus*)

2005
F651 **F315** 90c. multicoloured 2·75 3·25

F 316 Bottle, Glass, Jug and Fruit

2005. Europa. Gastronomy.
F652 **F316** 55c. multicoloured 2·00 2·20

F 317 Marksman

2005. Small States of Europe Games. Sheet 151×70 mm containing Type F 317 and similar vert designs. Each black and magenta.
MSF653 53c. Type F **317**; 55c. Runner; 82c. Swimmer; €1 Diver 9·00 9·50

F 318 Mountain Hut, Bordes d'Ensegur

2005
F654 **F318** €2.50 multicoloured 8·00 8·75

F319 Motorcycle

2005
F655 **F319** 53c. sepia, brown and black 1·60 1·70

F320 "Prats de Santa Coloma" (Joaquim Mir)

2005. Art.
F656 **F320** 82c. multicoloured 2·75 2·75

F321 Hostel Calones

2005
F657 **F321** €1.98 multicoloured 6·25 6·50

F322 Lorry in Snow (Josep Alsina)

2005. Photography.
F658 **F322** 53c. multicoloured 1·70 1·80

F323 Emblem

2005. Centenary of Rotary International.
F659 **F323** 55c. multicoloured 1·90 2·00

F324 "Adoration of the Shepherds" (A. Viladomat)

2005. Christmas.
F660 **F324** €1.22 multicoloured 4·00 4·25

F325 *Ursus arctos*

2006. Fauna. Multicoloured.
F661 53c. Type F **325** 1·70 1·80
F662 53c. *Rupicapra pyrenaica* (vert) 1·70 1·80

F326 Alpine Skier

2006. Winter Olympic Games, Turin. Multicoloured.
F663 55c. Type F **326** 1·70 1·80
F664 75c. Cross country skier 2·30 2·50

F326a Tobacco Leaves

2006. Tobacco Museum, Sant Julia de Loria.
F665 **F326a** 82c. multicoloured 2·75 2·75

F327 Napoleon (image scaled to 63% of original size)

2006. Bicentenary of Napoleon's Decree restoring Statute of Co-Principality.
F666 **F327** 53c. blue, azure and black 1·70 1·80

F328 Coloured blocks

2006. Europa. Integration.
F667 **F328** 53c. multicoloured 2·00 2·10

F329 Sorteny Valley Nature Reserve

2006
F668 **F329** 55c. multicoloured 1·90 2·00

F330 Pablo Casals

2006. 130th Birth Anniv of Pablo Casals (cellist).
F669 **F330** 90c. multicoloured 3·00 3·25

F331 Model T Ford

2006
F670 **F331** 85c. multicoloured 2·75 3·00

F332 "Montserrat Procession" (Josep Borrell)

2006
F671 **F332** €1.30 multicoloured 4·25 4·50

F333 Reredos (retable), Sant Marti de la Cortinada, Ordino

2006
F672 **F333** 54c. multicoloured 1·90 2·00

F334 Marmot (*Marmota marmota*)

2007. Funa. Multicoloured.
F673 54c. Type F**334** 1·90 2·00
F674 60c. Eurasian red squirrel (*Sciurus vulgaris*) (horiz) 2·00 2·10

F335 "Predel-la de Prats" (Master of Canillo)

2007

F675 **F335** €1.30 multicoloured 4·25 4·50

F336 Heart enclosing Rose

2007. Saint George.

F676 **F336** 86c. multicoloured 3·00 3·25

F337 Salute

2007. Europa. Centenary of Scouting.

F677 **F337** 54c. multicoloured 1·90 2·00

F338 Virgin, Meritxell

2007. Twinning of Meritxell and Sabart. Multicoloured.

F678 54c. Type F **338** 1·90 2·00

F679 54c. Virgin, Sabart 1·90 2·00

F339 'Pinette'

2007

F680 **F339** 60c. multicoloured 2·00 2·10

F340 Players

2007. Rugby World Cup, France.

F681 **F340** 85c. multicoloured 2·75 3·00

F341 Vall del Comapedrosa

2007

F682 **F341** €3.04 multicoloured 10·00 10·50

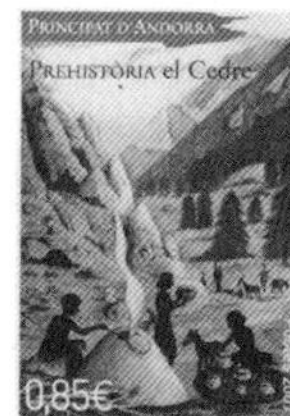

F 341a Prehistoric Family

2007. Pre-Historic Sites. El Cedre.

F683 **F 341a** 85c. multicoloured 3·00 3·25

F 342 Cave Dwellers

2007. Pre-Historic Sites. La Barma de la Marginada.

F684 **F 342** 60c. multicoloured 2·00 2·10

F343 Altarpiece, Sant Marti de la Cortinada

2007. Christmas.

F685 **F343** 54c. multicoloured 1·90 2·00

F344 *Vulpes vulpes* (red fox)

2008. Fauna. Multicoloured.

F686 54c. Type F **344** 2·00 2·10

F687 60c. *Sus scrofa* (wild boar) (vert) 2·20 2·30

F345 Predella's Altar of St. Michaels d'Pratts church

2008. Easter.

F688 **F 345** €1.33 multicoloured 5·00 5·25

F 346 Cartercar, 1906

2008

F689 **F 346** 65c. multicoloured 2·75 2·75

F 347 Symbols of Writing

2008. Europa. The Letter.

F690 **F 347** 55c. multicoloured 2·30 2·40

F 348 Rowing

2008. Olympic Games, Beijing. Sheet 210×60 mm containing T F 348 and similar horiz designs. Multicoloured.

MSF691 55c.×4, Type F **348**; Running; Swimming; Judo 8·25 8·50

The stamps of **MS**F691 were not for sale separately.

F 349 *Narcissus poeticus*

2008

F692 **F 349** 55c. multicoloured 2·30 2·40

F 350 Vall d'Incles (Incles valley)

2008

F693 **F 350** €2.80 multicoloured 10·50 11·00

F 351 Men

2008. 75th Anniv of Male Suffrage.

F694 **F 351** 55c. multicoloured 2·30 2·40

F 352 Valley

2008. Sustainable Development.

F695 **F 352** 88c. multicoloured 3·75 4·00

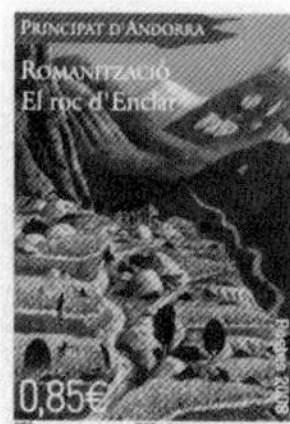

F 353 El roc d'Enclar

2008

F696 **F 353** 85c. multicoloured 3·50 3·75

F 354 St. Mark and St. Mary (alterpiece (reredos))

2008

F697 **F 354** 55c. multicoloured 2·75 2·75

F 355 Louis Braille

2009. Birth Bicentenary of Louis Braille (inventor of Braille writing for the blind).

F698 **F 355** 88c. blue and brown 4·00 4·00

F 356 *Equus mulus* (mule)

2009. Domestic Animals. Multicoloured.

F699 55c. Type **F356** 2·30 2·40

F700 65c. *Bos taurus* (cow) (horiz) 2·50 2·50

F 357 Penguins

2009. Preserve Polar Regions and Glaciers. Sheet 143×120 mm containing Type F 357 and similar multicoloured design.

MSF701 56c. Type F **357**; 85c. Polar ice 6·25 6·50

F 358 *Pradel la des Prats* (detail)

2009

F702 **F 358** €1.35 multicoloured 6·00 6·25

F 359 Nebula

2009. Europa. Astronomy.

F703 **F 359** 56c. multicoloured 2·50 2·50

F 360 Renault Voiturette, 1898

2009. First Car manufactured by Renault.

F704	**F 360**	70c. multicoloured	3·00	3·25

F 361 *Sant Joan de Caselles* (Maurice Utrillo)

2009. Art.

F705	**F 361**	90c. multicoloured	4·00	4·00

F 362 Cercle dels Pessons

2009

F706	**F 362**	€2.80 multicoloured	11·50	12·00

F 363 Cyclist

2009. Tour de France (cycle race).

F707	**F 363**	56c. multicoloured	2·50	2·50

F 364 Allegory

2009. 40th Anniv of Circle of Arts and Letters.

F708	**F 364**	51c. multicoloured	2·40	2·40

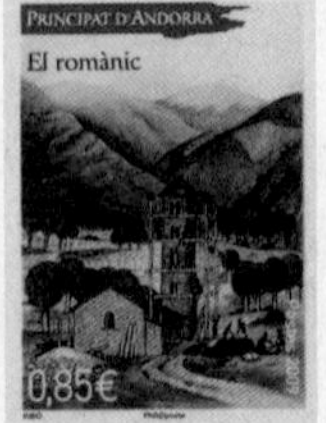

F 365 Santa Coloma Church

2009. Romanesque Art in Andorra.

F709	**F 365**	85c. multicoloured	3·75	3·75

F 366 The Nativity

2009. Christmas.

F710	**F 366**	56c. multicoloured	2·50	2·50

F 366a Arms

2010. State Arms. Background colour given. (a) With face value.

F710a	**366A**	1c. multicoloured (pale lemon)	20	25
F711		5c. multicoloured (cobalt)	25	30
F712		10c. multicoloured (bright yellow-orange)	55	60
F713		20c. multicoloured (lavender)	55	60
F714		50c. multicoloured (olive-bistre)	1·40	1·60

(b) No value expressed.

F715		(60c.) multicoloured (aqua-marine)	2·40	2·50

Nos. F710a/F715 are as No. F **279** but with different inscriptions.

F 367 Athlete

2010. Winter Olympic Games, Vancouver.

F716	**F 367**	85c. multicoloured	3·75	3·75

F 368 Casamanya Peak

2010. Mountains.

F717	**F 368**	€2.80 multicoloured	11·50	12·00

F 369 Anniversary Emblem

2010. 20th Anniv of Convention on Rights of the Child. UNICEF

F718	**F 369**	56c. multicoloured	2·50	2·50

No. F719 and Type F **370** are left for Le Mouton issued on 8 March 2010, not yet received.

No. F720 and Type F **371** are left for Le Vautour issued on 8 March 2010, not yet received.

No. F721 and Type F **372** are left for Ambassador to Brussles issued on 12 April 2010, not yet received.

No. F722 and Type F **373** are left for Legends issued on 26 April 2010, not yet received.

F374 Mirror and 'Mirror, Magic Mirror, tell me which is' (from Snow White)

2010. Europa. Children's Books

F723	**F 374**	56c. silver and bright rose-red	2·50	2·50

No. F724 and Type F **375** are left for Radio Andorra issued on 24 May 2010, not yet received. Type F **376** is vacant.

F377 Ferrari 328 GTS

2010. Classic Cars

F725	**F 377**	70c. multicoloured	3·00	3·00

F378 Still Life (Carme Massana)

2010. Art

F726	**F 378**	95c. multicoloured	3·75	3·75

F379 The Crucifixion of Christ, Predella of the Altar of Saint-Michel De Prats Church (detail)

2010. Religious Art

F727	**F 379**	€1.40 multicoloured	2·50	2·50

See also No. F702.

POSTAGE DUE STAMPS

1931. Postage Due stamps of France optd ANDORRE.

FD24	**D11**	5c. blue	2·10	5·75
FD25	**D11**	10c. brown	2·10	4·50
FD26	**D11**	30c. red	1·10	5·25
FD27	**D11**	50c. purple	2·10	5·75
FD28	**D11**	60c. green	26·00	55·00
FD29	**D11**	1f. brown on yellow	2·10	7·00
FD30	**D11**	2f. mauve	17·00	41·00
FD31	**D11**	3f. mauve	4·25	9·75

1931. Postage Due stamps of France optd ANDORRE.

FD32	**D43**	1c. green	3·25	5·75
FD33	**D43**	10c. red	6·25	14·00
FD34	**D43**	60c. red	31·00	48·00
FD35	**D43**	1f. green	95·00	£140
FD36	**D43**	1f.20 on 2f. blue	90·00	£160
FD37	**D43**	2f. brown	£180	£275
FD38	**D43**	5f. on 1f. purple	95·00	£130

FD7

1935

FD82	**FD7**	1c. green	4·25	9·25

FD10

1937

FD97	**FD10**	5c. blue	7·50	16·00
FD98	**FD10**	10c. brown	5·25	30·00
FD99	**FD10**	2f. mauve	11·50	16·00
FD100	**FD10**	5f. orange	25·00	40·00

FD11 Wheat Sheaves

1943

FD101a	**FD 11**	10c. brown	65	2·10
FD102	**FD 11**	30c. mauve	1·90	2·75
FD103	**FD 11**	50c. green	1·40	3·25
FD104	**FD 11**	1f. blue	2·10	4·75
FD105	**FD 11**	1f.50 red	5·75	14·50
FD106	**FD 11**	2f. blue	2·10	5·25
FD107	**FD 11**	3f. red	2·50	9·75
FD108	**FD 11**	4f. violet	5·25	15·00
FD109	**FD 11**	5f. mauve	4·25	14·50
FD110	**FD 11**	10f. orange	5·75	15·00
FD111	**FD 11**	20f. brown	8·00	22·00

1946. As Type FD 11, but inscr "TIMBRE-TAXE".

FD143	10c. brown	1·10	7·25
FD144	1f. blue	1·30	4·00
FD145	2f. blue	1·40	4·00
FD146	3f. brown	2·75	6·00
FD147	4f. violet	3·75	7·25
FD148	5f. red	2·10	5·75
FD149	10f. orange	3·75	7·50
FD150	20f. brown	7·50	13·00
FD151	50f. green	60·00	55·00
FD152	100f. green	£110	£160

1961. As Nos. FD143/52 but new values and colours.

FD185	5c. red	4·25	8·25
FD186	10c. orange	9·50	17·00
FD187	20c. brown	13·50	29·00
FD188	50c. green	26·00	47·00

1964. Designs as Nos. D1650/6 of France, but inscr "ANDORRE".

FD192	5c. red, green and purple	55	4·25
FD193	10c. blue, grn & pur	85	4·25
FD194	15c. red, green and brown	95	4·25
FD195	20c. purple, green & turq	1·10	4·25
FD196	30c. blue, grn & brn	85	2·50
FD197	40c. yellow, red and green	2·10	2·75
FD198	50c. red, green and blue	1·70	1·70

FD129 Holly Berries

1985. Fruits.

FD371	**FD129**	10c. red and green	1·70	2·75
FD372	-	20c. brown & blue	1·70	2·75
FD373	-	30c. green and red	1·70	2·75
FD374	-	40c. brown & blk	1·70	2·75
FD375	-	50c. olive & violet	1·70	2·75
FD376	-	1f. green and blue	1·70	2·75
FD377	-	2f. red and brown	1·80	3·00
FD378	-	3f. purple & green	2·10	3·50
FD379	-	4f. olive and blue	2·75	3·75
FD380	-	5f. olive and red	3·25	4·25

DESIGNS: 20c. Wild plum; 30c. Raspberry; 40c. Dogberry; 50c. Blackberry; 1f. Juniper; 2f. Rose hip; 3f. Elder; 4f. Bilberry; 5f. Strawberry.

SPANISH POST OFFICES

1928. Stamps of Spain optd CORREOS ANDORRA.

1B	**68**	2c. green	1·70	2·30
2B	**68**	5c. red	2·30	2·75
3B	**68**	10c. green	3·50	4·00
5B	**68**	15c. blue	3·50	4·00
6B	**68**	20c. violet	3·75	4·25
7A	**68**	25c. red	8·50	8·50
8A	**68**	30c. brown	29·00	29·00
9A	**68**	40c. blue	34·00	34·00
10A	**68**	50c. orange	37·00	37·00
11B	**69**	1p. grey	34·00	36·00
12A	**69**	4p. red	£180	£180
13A	**69**	10p. brown	£250	£250

2 House of the Valleys　**3** General Council of Andorra

1929

14A	**2**	2c. green	2·00	2·30
26	**2**	2c. brown	1·40	2·30
15A	-	5c. purple	3·75	4·00
27	-	5c. brown	2·10	2·75
16A	-	10c. green	3·75	4·00
17A	-	15c. blue	5·50	5·75
30	-	15c. green	5·75	7·00
18A	-	20c. violet	5·50	6·25
33	-	25c. red	2·75	3·50
20A	**2**	30c. brown	£150	£160
34	**2**	30c. red	2·75	4·00
21A	-	40c. blue	11·50	8·00
36	**2**	45c. red	2·30	2·75
22A	-	50c. orange	11·50	7·00
38	**2**	60c. blue	4·50	5·75
23A	**3**	1p. slate	23·00	29·00
39	**3**	4p. purple	46·00	50·00
40	**3**	10p. brown	70·00	75·00

DESIGNS: 5, 40c. Church of St. John of Caselles; 10, 20, 50c. Sant Julia de Loria; 15, 25c. Santa Coloma Church.

7 Councillor Manuel Areny Bons

11 Map

1948

41	**F**	2c. olive	1·10	1·70
42	**F**	5c. orange	1·10	1·70
43	**F**	10c. blue	1·10	1·70
44	**7**	20c. purple	10·50	7·00
45	**7**	25c. orange	7·00	3·50
46	**G**	30c. green	23·00	11·50
47	**H**	50c. green	34·00	15·00
48	**I**	75c. blue	33·00	16·00
49	**H**	90c. purple	17·00	11·50
50	**I**	1p. red	29·00	15·00
51	**G**	1p.35 violet	11·50	11·50
52	**11**	4p. blue	34·00	29·00
53	**11**	10p. brown	65·00	34·00

DESIGNS—VERT: F. Edelweiss; G. Arms; H. Market Place, Ordino; I. Shrine near Meritxell Chapel.

12 Andorra La Vella

1951. Air.

54	**12**	1p. brown	40·00	26·00

13 St. Anthony's Bridge

1963

55	**13**	25c. brown and black	25	30
56	-	70c. black and green	35	55
57	-	1p. lilac and grey	90	1·50
58	-	2p. violet and lilac	1·10	1·70
59	-	2p.50 deep red and purple	90	1·40
60	-	3p. slate and black	1·10	1·60
61	-	5p. purple and brown	3·50	3·75
62	-	6p. red and brown	4·50	4·00

DESIGNS—VERT: 70c. Anyos meadows (wrongly inscr "AYNOS"); 1p. Canillo; 2p. Santa Coloma Church; 2p.50, Arms; 6p. Virgin of Meritxell. HORIZ: 3p. Andorra la Vella; 5p. Ordino.

14 Daffodills

1966. Pyrenean Flowers.

63	**14**	50c. blue and slate	55	1·10
64	-	1p. purple and brown	1·10	1·30
65	-	5p. blue and green	3·25	3·50
66	-	10p. slate and violet	1·70	2·75

DESIGNS: 1p. Carnation; 5p. Narcissus; 10p. Anemone (wrongly inscr "HELEBORUS CONI").

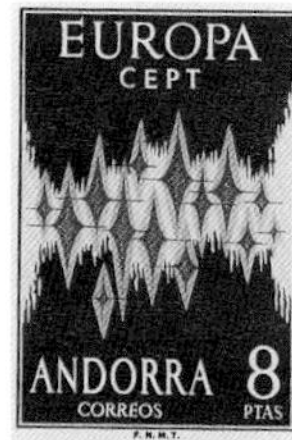

15 "Communications"

1972. Europa.

67	**15**	8p. multicoloured	£150	£140

16 Encamp Valley

1972. Tourist Views. Multicoloured.

68	1p. Type **16**	1·00	1·20
69	1p.50 La Massana	1·10	1·20
70	2p. Skis and snowscape, Pas de la Casa	2·10	2·40
71	5p. Lake Pessons (horiz)	2·30	2·40

17 Volleyball

1972. Olympic Games, Munich. Multicoloured.

72	2p. Type **17**	50	55
73	5p. Swimming (horiz)	70	75

18 St. Anthony's Auction

1972. Andorran Customs. Multicoloured.

74	1p. Type **18**	35	35
75	1p.50 "Les Caramelles" (choir)	35	35
76	2p. Nativity play (Christmas)	55	60
77	5p. Giant cigar (vert)	90	1·00
78	8p. Carved shrine, Meritxell (vert)	1·10	1·20
79	15p. "La Marratxa" (dance)	3·00	3·25

19 "Peoples of Europe"

1973. Europa.

80	**19**	2p. black, red and blue	55	60
81	-	8p. red, brown and black	1·70	1·90

DESIGN: 8p. Europa "Posthorn".

20 "The Nativity"

1973. Christmas. Frescoes from Meritxell Chapel. Multicoloured.

82	2p. Type **20**	55	60
83	5p. "Adoration of the Kings"	1·70	1·90

21 "Virgin of Ordino"

1974. Europa. Sculptures. Multicoloured.

84	2p. Type **21**	2·75	3·00
85	8p. Cross	4·00	4·25

22 Oak Cupboard and Shelves

1974. Arts and Crafts. Multicoloured.

86	10p. Type **22**	2·75	3·00
87	25p. Crown of the Virgin of the Roses	6·25	6·75

23 U.P.U. Monument, Berne

1974. Centenary of Universal Postal Union.

88	**23**	15p. multicoloured	3·50	3·75

24 "The Nativity"

1974. Christmas. Carvings from Meritxell Chapel. Multicoloured.

89	2p. Type **24**	1·10	1·20
90	5p. "Adoration of the Kings"	3·50	3·75

25 19th-century Postman and Church of St. John of Caselles

1975. "Espana 75" Int Stamp Exhibition, Madrid.

91	**25**	3p. multicoloured	55	60

26 "Peasant with Knife"

1975. Europa. 12th-century Romanesque Paintings from La Cortinada Church. Multicoloured.

92	3p. Type **26**	2·75	3·00
93	12p. "Christ"	5·75	6·25

27 Cathedral and Consecration Text

1975. 1100th Anniv of Consecration of Urgel Cathedral.

94	**27**	7p. multicoloured	3·50	3·75

28 "The Nativity"

1975. Christmas. Paintings from La Cortinada Church. Multicoloured.

95	3p. Type **28**	55	60
96	7p. "Adoration of The Kings"	1·10	1·20

29 Copper Cauldron

1976. Europa. Multicoloured.

97	3p. Type **29**	70	75
98	12p. Wooden marriage chest (horiz)	2·10	2·30

30 Slalom Skiing

1976. Olympic Games, Montreal. Multicoloured.

99	7p. Type **30**	70	75
100	15p. Canoeing (horiz)	2·10	2·30

31 "The Nativity"

1976. Christmas. Carvings from La Massana Church. Multicoloured.

101	3p. Type **31**	40	45
102	25p. "Adoration of the Kings"	2·50	2·75

32 Ansalonga

1977. Europa. Multicoloured.

103	3p. Type **32**	70	75
104	12p. Xuclar	2·10	2·30

33 Boundary Cross

1977. Christmas. Multicoloured.

105	5p. Type **33**	55	60
106	12p. St. Michael's Church, Engolasters	2·50	2·75

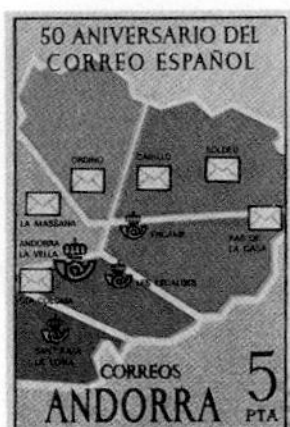

34 Map of Andorran Post Offices

1978. 50th Anniv of Spanish Post Offices. Sheet 105×149 mm containing T 34 and similar vert designs. Multicoloured.
MS107 5p. Type **34**; 10p. Postman delivering letter, 1923; 20p. Spanish Post Office, Andorra la Vella, 1928; 25p. Andorran arms 2·75 3·00

35 House of the Valleys

1978. Europa. Multicoloured.
108 5p. Type **35** 55 75
109 12p. Church of St. John of Caselles 1·40 2·30

36 Crown, Mitre and Crook

1978. 700th Anniv of Parity Treaties.
110 **36** 5p. multicoloured 85 1·50

37 "Holy Family"

1978. Christmas. Frescoes in St. Mary's Church, Encamp. Multicoloured.
111 5p. Type **37** 40 45
112 25p. "Adoration of the Kings" 95 1·10

38 Young Woman's Costume

1979. Local Costumes. Multicoloured.
113 3p. Type **38** 30 30
114 5p. Young man's costume 40 45
115 12p. Newly-weds 70 75

39 Old Mail Bus

1979. Europa.
116 **39** 5p. green & blue on yellow 70 75
117 - 12p. lilac and red on yellow 1·40 1·50
DESIGN: 12p. Pre-stamp letters.

40 Drawing of Boy and Girl

1979. International Year of the Child.
118 **40** 19p. blue, red and black 1·40 1·50

41 Agnus Dei, Santa Coloma Church

1979. Christmas. Multicoloured.
119 **41** 8p. Santa Coloma Church 40 45
120 **41** 25p. Type **41** 95 1·10

42 Pere d'Urg

1979. Bishops of Urgel, Co-princes of Andorra (1st series).
121 **42** 1p. blue and brown 30 30
122 - 5p. red and violet 40 45
123 - 13p. brown and green 85 90
DESIGNS: 5p. Joseph Caixal; 13p. Joan Benlloch.
See also Nos. 137/8, 171, 182 and 189.

43 Antoni Fiter i Rosell

1980. Europa.
124 **43** 8p. brown, ochre and green 40 45
125 - 19p. black, green & dp grn 1·70 1·80
DESIGN: 19p. Francesc Cairat i Freixes.

44 Skiing

1980. Olympic Games, Moscow.
126 **44** 5p. turquoise, red and blk 30 30
127 - 8p. multicoloured 40 45
128 - 50p. multicoloured 1·50 1·70
DESIGNS: 8p. Boxing; 50p. Shooting.

45 Nativity

1980. Christmas. Multicoloured.
129 10p. Type **45** 40 45
130 22p. Epiphany 95 1·10

46 Santa Anna Dance

1981. Europa. Multicoloured.
131 12p. Type **46** 70 75
132 30p. Festival of the Virgin of Canolich 1·40 1·50

47 Militia Members

1981. 50th Anniv of People's Militia.
133 **47** 30p. green, grey and black 1·40 1·50

48 Handicapped Child learning to Write

1981. International Year of Disabled Persons.
134 **48** 50p. multicoloured 2·10 2·30

49 "The Nativity"

1981. Christmas. Carvings from Encamp Church. Multicoloured.
135 12p. Type **49** 70 75
136 30p. "The Adoration" 1·40 1·50

1981. Bishops of Urgel, Co-princes of Andorra (2nd series). As T 42.
137 7p. purple and blue 40 45
138 20p. brown and green 95 1·10
DESIGNS: 7p. Salvador Casanas; 20p. Josep de Boltas.

50 Arms of Andorra

1982. With "PTA" under figure of value.
139 **50** 1p. mauve 30 30
140 **50** 3p. brown 30 30
141 **50** 7p. red 30 30
142 **50** 12p. red 30 30
143 **50** 15p. blue 40 45
144 **50** 20p. green 70 75
145 **50** 30p. red 70 75
146 **50** 50p. green (25×31 mm) 1·70 1·90
147 **50** 100p. blue (25×31 mm) 3·00 3·50
See also Nos. 203/6.

51 The New Reforms, 1866

1982. Europa. Multicoloured.
154 14p. Type **51** 95 1·10
155 33p. Reform of the Institutions, 1981 1·80 2·00

52 Footballers

1982. World Cup Football Championship, Spain. Multicoloured.
156 14p. Type **52** 1·40 1·50
157 33p. Tackle 2·75 3·00

53 Arms and 1929 1p. stamp

1982. National Stamp Exhibition.
158 **53** 14p. black and green 1·40 1·50

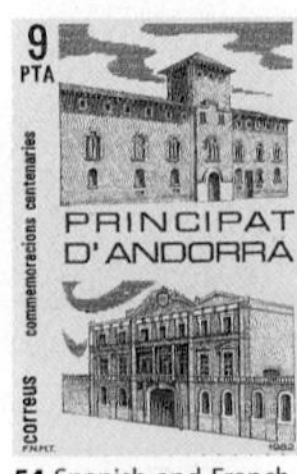

54 Spanish and French Permanent Delegations Buildings

1982. Anniversaries.
159 **54** 9p. brown and blue 40 45
160 - 23p. blue and brown 70 75
161 - 33p. black and green 1·10 1·20
DESIGNS—VERT: 9p. Type **54** (centenary of Permanent Delegations); 23p. "St. Francis feeding the Birds" (after Ciambue) (800th birth anniv of St. Francis of Assisi); 33p. Title page of "Relacio sobre la Vall de Andorra" (birth centenary of Tomas Junoy (writer)).

55 "Virgin and Child" (statue from Andorra la Vella Parish Church)

1982. Christmas. Multicoloured.
162 14p. Type **55** 70 75
163 33p. Children beating log with sticks 2·10 2·30

56 Building Romanesque Church

1983. Europa.
164 **56** 16p. green, purple & black 70 75
165 - 38p. brown, blue and black 2·10 2·30
DESIGN: 38p. 16th-century water mill.

57 "Lactarius sanguifluus"

1983. Nature Protection.
166 **57** 16p. multicoloured 70 75

58 Ballot Box on Map and Government Building

1983. 50th Anniv of Universal Suffrage in Andorra.

167 **58** 10p. multicoloured 70 75

59 Mgr. Cinto Verdaguer

1983. Centenary of Mgr. Cinto Verdaguer's Visit.

168 **59** 50p. multicoloured 2·10 2·30

60 Jaume Sansa Nequi

1983. Air. Jaume Sansa Nequi (Verger-Episcopal) Commemoration.

169 **60** 20p. deep brown & brown 70 75

61 Wall Painting, Church of San Cerni, Nagol

1983. Christmas.

170 **61** 16p. multicoloured 70 75

1983. Bishops of Urgel, Co-princes of Andorra (3rd series). As T 42.

171 26p. brown and red 1·40 1·50

DESIGN: 26p. Joan Laguarda.

62 Ski Jumping

1984. Winter Olympic Games, Sarajevo.

172 **62** 16p. multicoloured 95 1·10

63 Exhibition and F.I.P. Emblems

1984. "Espana 84" Int Stamp Exhibition, Madrid.

173 **63** 26p. multicoloured 1·40 1·50

64 Bridge

1984. Europa.

174 **64** 16p. brown 70 75

175 **64** 38p. blue 2·10 2·30

65 Hurdling

1984. Olympic Games, Los Angeles.

176 **65** 40p. multicoloured 2·10 2·30

66 Common Morel

1984. Nature Protection.

177 **66** 11p. multicoloured 4·25 7·50

67 Pencil, Brush and Pen

1984. Pyrenean Cultures Centre, Andorra.

178 **67** 20p. multicoloured 85 90

68 The Holy Family (wood carvings)

1984. Christmas.

179 **68** 17p. multicoloured 70 75

69 Mossen Enric Marfany and Score

1985. Europa.

180 **69** 18p. green, purple & brown 95 1·10

181 - 45p. brown and green 1·80 2·00

DESIGN: 45p. Musician with viola (fresco detail, La Cortinada Church).

1985. Air. Bishops of Urgel, Co-princes of Andorra (4th series). As T 42.

182 20p. brown and ochre 70 75

DESIGN: 20p. Ramon Iglesias.

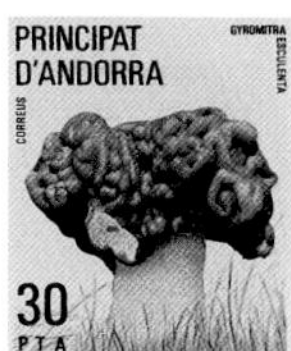

70 Beefsteak Morel

1985. Nature Protection.

183 **70** 30p. multicoloured 1·40 1·50

71 Pal

1985

184 **71** 17p. deep blue and blue 70 75

72 Angels (St. Bartholomew's Chapel)

1985. Christmas.

185 **72** 17p. multicoloured 70 75

73 Scotch Bonnet

1986. Nature Protection.

186 **73** 30p. multicoloured 1·40 1·50

74 Sun, Rainbow, Lighthouse and Fish

1986. Europa. Each blue, red and green.

187 17p. Type **74** 1·40 1·50

188 45p. Sun and trees on rocks 2·10 2·30

1986. Bishops of Urgel, Co-princes of Andorra (5th series). As T 42.

189 35p. blue and brown 1·40 1·50

DESIGN: 35p. Justi Guitart.

75 Bell of St. Roma's Chapel, Les Bons

1986. Christmas.

190 **75** 19p. multicoloured 70 75

76 Arms

1987. Meeting of Co-princes.

191 **76** 48p. multicoloured 1·40 1·50

77 Interior of Chapel

1987. Europa. Meritxell Chapel.

192 **77** 19p. brown and blue 70 75

193 - 48p. blue and brown 1·40 1·50

DESIGN: 48p. Exterior of Chapel.

78 Emblem and House of Valleys

1987. Olympic Games, Barcelona (1992). Sheet 122×86 mm containing T 78 and similar horiz designs. Multicoloured.

MS194 20p. Type **78**; 50p. Torch carrier and St. Michael's Chapel, Fontaneda, bell tower 5·50 6·00

79 Cep

1987. Nature Protection.

195 **79** 100p. multicoloured 3·50 3·75

80 Extract from "Doctrina Pueril" by Ramon Llull

1987. Christmas.

196 **80** 20p. multicoloured 70 75

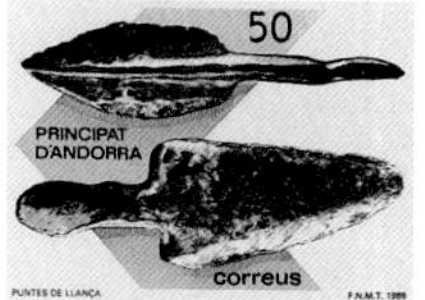

81 Copper Lance Heads

1988. Archaeology.

197 **81** 50p. multicoloured 1·70 1·80

82 Early 20th-century Trader and Pack Mules

1988. Europa. Communications. Each blue and red.

198 20p. Ancient road, Les Bons 70 75

199 45p. Type **82** 2·10 2·30

83 Pyrenean Mountain Dog

1988. Nature Protection.

200 **83** 20p. multicoloured 1·40 1·50

84 Commemorative Coin

1988. 700th Anniv of Second Parity Treaty.

201 **84** 20p. black, grey and brown 70 75

85 Church of St. John of Caselles

1988. Christmas.

202	**85**	20p. multicoloured	70	75

1988. As T 50 but without "PTA" under figure of value.

203	20p. green	70	75
204	50p. green (25×31 mm)	2·10	2·30
205	100p. blue (25×31 mm)	3·75	4·25
206	500p. brown (25×31 mm)	12·50	13·50

86 Leap-frog

1989. Europa. Children's Games. Multicoloured.

210	20p. Type **86**	1·40	1·50
211	45p. Girl trying to pull child from grip of other children (horiz)	2·10	2·30

87 St. Roma's Chapel, Les Bons

1989

212	**87**	50p. black, green and blue	2·10	2·30

88 Anniversary Emblem

1989. 125th Anniv of International Red Cross.

213	**88**	20p. multicoloured	70	75

89 "Virgin Mary" (detail of altarpiece, Les Escaldes Church)

1989. Christmas.

214	**89**	20p. multicoloured	70	75

90 Old French and Spanish Post Offices, Andorra La Vella

1990. Europa. Post Office Buildings. Multicoloured.

215	20p. Type **90**	70	75
216	50p. Modern Spanish post office, Andorra La Vella (vert)	2·10	2·30

91 "Gomphidius rutilus"

1990. Nature Protection.

217	**91**	45p. multicoloured	2·10	2·30

92 Plandolit House

1990

218	**92**	20p. brown and yellow	70	75

93 Angel, La Massana Church

1990. Christmas.

219	**93**	25p. brown, stone and red	85	90

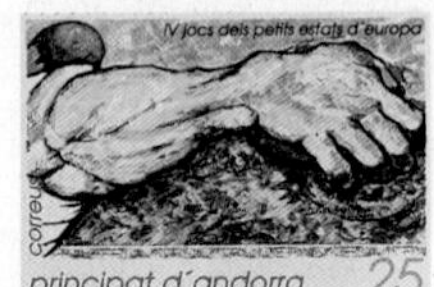

94 Throwing the Discus

1991. European Small States' Games. Multicoloured.

220	25p. Type **94**	95	1·10
221	45p. High jumping and running	1·80	2·00

95 "Olympus 1" Satellite

1991. Europa. Europe in Space. Multicoloured.

222	25p. Type **95**	2·10	2·30
223	55p. Close-up of "Olympus I" telecommunications satellite (horiz)	3·50	3·75

96 Parasol Mushroom

1991. Nature Protection.

224	**96**	45p. multicoloured	2·10	2·30

97 "Virgin of the Three Hands" (detail of triptych in Meritxell Chapel by Maria Assumpta Ortado i Maimo)

1991. Christmas.

225	**97**	25p. multicoloured	1·40	1·50

98 Woman fetching Water from Public Tap

1992

226	**98**	25p. multicoloured	1·40	1·50

99 "Santa Maria"

1992. Europa. 500th Anniv of Discovery of America by Columbus.

227	**99**	27p. multicoloured	2·10	2·30
228	-	45p. brown, red and orange	2·75	3·00

DESIGN—HORIZ: 45p. Engraving of King Ferdinand from map sent by Columbus to Ferdinand and Queen Isabella the Catholic.

100 White-water Canoeing

1992. Olympic Games, Barcelona.

229	**100**	27p. multicoloured	1·40	1·50

101 Benz Velo, 1894 and Sedanca de ville, 1920s

1992. National Motor Car Museum, Encamp.

230	**101**	27p. multicoloured	1·40	1·50

102 "Nativity" (Fra Angelico)

1992. Christmas.

231	**102**	27p. multicoloured	1·40	1·50

103 Chanterelle

1993. Nature Protection.

232	**103**	28p. multicoloured	1·40	1·50

104 "Upstream" (J. A. Morrison)

1993. Europa. Contemporary Art. Multicoloured.

233	28p. Type **104**	1·40	1·50
234	45p. "Ritme" (Angel Calvente) (vert)	2·10	2·30

105 Society Emblem on National Colours

1993. 25th Anniv of Andorran Arts and Letters Circle.

235	**105**	28p. multicoloured	1·40	1·50

106 Illuminated "P" (Galceran de Vilanova Missal)

1993. Christmas.

236	**106**	28p. multicoloured	1·40	1·50

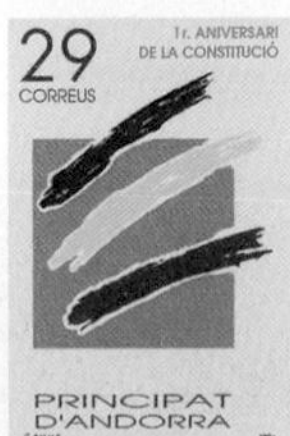

107 National Colours

1994. 1st Anniv of New Constitution. Sheet 105×78 mm.

MS237	**107**	29p. multicoloured	2·10	2·30

108 Sir Alexander Fleming and Penicillin

1994. Europa. Discoveries.

238	**108**	29p. multicoloured	1·40	1·50
239	-	55p. blue and black	2·75	3·00

DESIGN: 55p. Test tube and AIDS virus.

109 "Hygrophorus gliocyclus"

1994. Nature Protection.

240	**109**	29p. multicoloured	1·40	1·50

110 "Madonna and Child" (anon)

1994. Christmas.
241 **110** 29p. multicoloured 1·40 1·50

111 Madriu Valley (south)

1995. European Nature Conservation Year. Mult.
242 30p. Type **111** 85 90
243 60p. Madriu Valley (north) 1·90 2·10

112 Sun, Dove and Barbed Wire

1995. Europa. Peace and Freedom.
244 **112** 60p. green, orange & blk 2·10 2·30

113 "Flight into Egypt" (altarpiece, St. Mark and St. Mary Church, Encamp)

1995. Christmas.
245 **113** 30p. multicoloured 1·40 1·50

114 Palace of Europe, Strasbourg

1995. Admission of Andorra to Council of Europe.
246 **114** 30p. multicoloured 1·40 1·50

115 "Ramaria aurea"

1996. Nature Protection. Multicoloured.
247 30p. Type **115** 1·40 1·50
248 60p. Black truffles 2·30 2·50

116 Isabelle Sandy (writer)

1996. Europa. Famous Women.
249 **116** 60p. multicoloured 2·75 3·00

117 Old Iron

1996. International Museums Day.
250 **117** 60p. multicoloured 2·10 2·30

118 "The Annunciation" (altarpiece, St. Eulalia's Church, Encamp)

1996. Christmas.
251 **118** 30p. multicoloured 1·40 1·50

119 Drais Velocipede, 1818

1997. Bicycle Museum (1st series). Multicoloured.
252 32p. Type **119** 95 1·10
253 65p. Michaux velocipede, 1861 1·90 2·10
See also Nos. 258/9 and 264/5.

120 The Bear and The Smugglers

1997. Europa. Tales and Legends.
254 **120** 65p. multicoloured 2·75 3·00

121 Dove and Cultural Symbols

1997. National UNESCO Commission.
255 **121** 32p. multicoloured 70 75

122 Catalan Crib Figure

1997. Christmas.
256 **122** 32p. multicoloured 70 75

123 Giant Slalom

1998. Winter Olympic Games, Nagano, Japan.
257 **123** 35p. multicoloured 70 75

1998. Bicycle Museum (2nd series). As T 119. Multicoloured.
258 35p. Kangaroo bicycle, Great Britain, 1878 95 1·10
259 70p. The Swallow, France, 1889 1·90 2·10

124 Harlequins of Canillo

1998. Europa. National Festivals.
260 **124** 70p. multicoloured 2·10 2·30

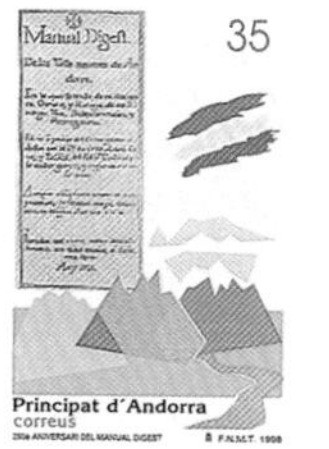

125 Front Page of First Edition and Landscape

1998. 250th Anniv of "Manual Digest".
261 **125** 35p. multicoloured 70 75

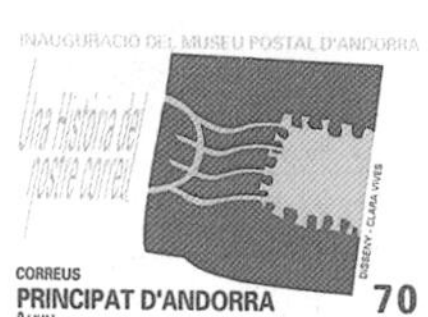

126 Emblem

1998. Inauguration of Postal Museum.
262 **126** 70p. violet and yellow 2·10 2·30

127 St. Lucia Fair

1998. Christmas.
263 **127** 35p. multicoloured 1·40 1·50

1999. Bicycle Museum (3rd series). As T 119. Multicoloured.
264 35p. Salvo tricycle, 1878 (vert) 95 1·10
265 70p. Rudge tricycle, Coventry, England 1·90 2·10

128 Mules

1999. Postal History.
266 **128** 35p. black and brown 1·40 1·50

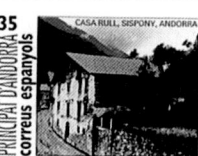

129 Palace of Human Rights, Strasbourg

1999. 50th Anniv of Council of Europe.
267 **129** 35p. multicoloured 1·40 1·50

130 Vall d'Incles National Park, Canillo

1999. Europa. Parks and Gardens.
268 **130** 70p. multicoloured 2·10 2·30

131 Rull House, Sispony

1999
269 **131** 35p. multicoloured 1·40 1·50

132 Angel (detail of altarpiece, St. Serni's Church, Canillo)

1999. Christmas.
270 **132** 35p. brown and light brown 1·40 1·50

133 Santa Coloma Church

1999. European Heritage.
271 **133** 35p. multicoloured 1·40 1·50

134 "Building Europe"

2000. Europa.
272 **134** 70p. multicoloured 2·75 3·00

135 Angonella Lakes, Ordino

2000
273 **135** 35p. multicoloured 1·40 1·50

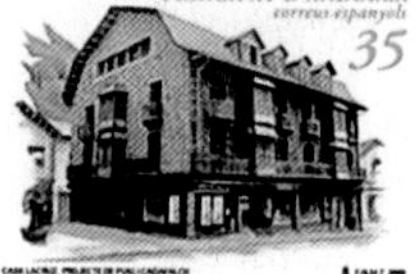

136 Casa Lacruz

2000. 131st Birth Anniv of Josep Cadafalch (architect).
274 **136** 35p. multicoloured 1·40 1·50

137 Dinner Service

2000. D'Areny-Plandolit Museum.
275 **137** 70p. multicoloured 2·10 2·30

138 Hurdling

2000. Olympic Games, Sydney.
276 **138** 70p. multicoloured 2·10 2·30

139 United Nations Headquarters, Strasbourg

2000. 50th Anniv of United Nations Declaration of Human Rights.
277 **139** 70p. multicoloured 2·10 2·30

140 Gradual, St. Roma, Les Bons

2000. 25th Anniv of the National Archives.
278 **140** 35p. multicoloured 70 75

141 "Quadre de les Animes" (Joan Casanovas)

2000. Christmas.
279 **141** 35p. multicoloured 70 75

142 Rec del Sola

2001. Natural Heritage.
280 **142** 40p. multicoloured 1·20 1·40

143 Roc del Metge (thermal spring), Escaldes-Engordany

2001. Europa. Water Resources.
281 **143** 75p. multicoloured 2·10 2·30

144 Casa Palau, Sant

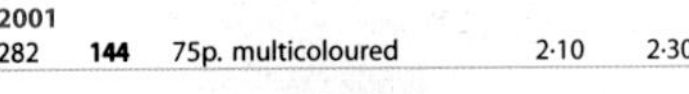
2001
282 **144** 75p. multicoloured 2·10 2·30

145 Part of Sanctuary, Julia de Loria Meritxell

2001. 25th Anniv of Chapel of Our Lady, Meritxell.
283 **145** 40p. multicoloured 1·40 1·50

146 Building

2001. 10th Anniv of National Auditorium, Ordino.
284 **146** 75p. multicoloured 2·10 2·30

147 Angel (detail of altarpiece, Church of St. John of Caselles)

2001. Christmas.
285 **147** 40p. multicoloured 1·40 1·50

148 State Arms

2002

286	**148**	25c. orange	70	75
286a	**148**	27c. blue	70	75
286b	**148**	28c. blue	85	90
286c	**148**	29c. sepia	85	90
286d	**148**	30c. carmine	85	90
287	**148**	50c. red	1·40	1·50
288	**148**	52c. yellow	1·50	1·70
289	**148**	53c. green	1·50	1·70
289a	**148**	57c. blue	1·70	1·80
289b	**148**	58c. black	1·70	1·80
290	**148**	77c. orange	2·20	2·40
291	**148**	78c. magenta	2·20	2·40

149 Alpine Accentor (*Prunella collaris*)

2002. Native Birds. Multicoloured.
300 25c. Type **149** 95 1·10
301 50c. Snow finch (*Montifringilla nivalis*) 1·90 2·10

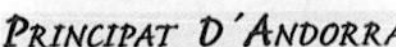

150 Emblem

2002. International Year of the Mountain.
302 **150** 50c. multicoloured 2·10 2·30

151 Tightrope Walker

2002. Europa. Circus.
303 **151** 50c. multicoloured 14·00 15·00

152 Casa Fusile, Escaldes-Engordany

2002. Architectural Heritage. Multicoloured.
304 €1.80 Type **152** 5·50 6·00
305 €2.10 Farga Rossell Iron Museum, La Massana 6·25 6·75

153 Pinette Minim

2002. History of the Motor Car (1st series). Multicoloured.
306 25c. Type **153** 95 1·10
307 50c. Rolls Royce Silver Wraith 1·90 2·10

See also Nos. 317/18 and 324/5.

154 Placa Benlloch, Areny-Plandolit

2002. Christmas.
308 **154** 25c. multicoloured 1·40 1·50

155 Painted Medallion

2002. Cultural Heritage. Romanesque Murals from Santa Coloma Church, Andorra la Vella.
309 25c. Type **155** 70 75
310 50c. Part of damaged fresco showing seated figure 1·40 1·50
311 75c. Frieze 2·10 2·30

156 Sassanat Bridge

2003
312 **156** 26c. multicoloured 1·40 1·50

157 State Arms

2003. 10th Anniv of Constitution.
313 **157** 76c. multicoloured 2·75 3·00

158 Man drinking, Donkey and Market Stalls

2003. Europa. Poster Art.
314 **158** 76c. multicoloured 2·75 3·00

159 Northern Wheatear (*Oenanthe oenanthe*)

2003. Native Birds.
315 **159** 50c. multicoloured 1·40 1·50

160 Multicoloured Stripes

2003. 10th Anniv of Andorras' Membership of United Nations.
316 **160** 76c. multicoloured 2·75 3·00

161 Carter (1908)

2003. History of the Motor Car (2nd series). Multicoloured.
317 51c. Type **161** 1·70 1·80
318 76c. Peugeot (1928) (horiz) 2·50 2·75

162 Roadside Cross, Andorra la Vella

2003. Christmas.
319 **162** 26c. multicoloured 1·40 1·50

163 "Fira del Bestiar" (Joaquim Mir)

2004
320 **163** 27c. multicoloured 1·10 1·20

164 "L'Escorxador" (Joaquim Mir)

2004
321 **164** 52c. multicoloured 1·90 2·10

165 Coaches and Skiers in Snow

2004. Europa. Holidays.
322 **165** 77c. black 2·75 3·00

166 Chaffinch (*Fringilla coelebs*)

2004. Native Birds.
323 **166** 27c. multicoloured 1·10 1·20

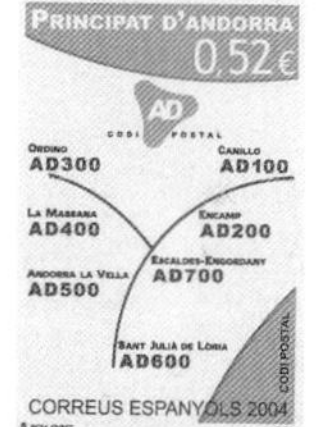

167 Simca 508 C (1939)

2004. History of the Motor Car (3rd series).
324 €1.90 Type **167** 6·50 7·25
325 €2.19 Messerschmitt KR 1 (1955) 7·25 8·00

168 Map showing Postal Districts

2004. Introduction of Postal Codes.
326 **168** 52c. orange, magenta and black 2·10 2·30

169 Stars and Flag as Jigsaw Pieces

2004. 10th Anniv of Entry into Council of Europe.
327 **169** 52c. multicoloured 2·10 2·30

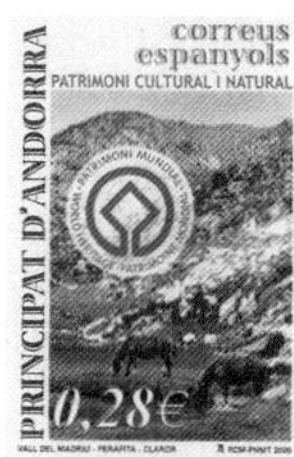

170 Nativity

2004. Christmas.
328 **170** 27c. multicoloured 1·10 1·20

171 Madriu-Perafita-Claror Valley

2005. UNESCO World Heritage Site.
329 **171** 28c. multicoloured 1·10 1·20

172 "Endless" (Mark Brusse)

2005
330 **172** 53c. multicoloured 2·20 2·40

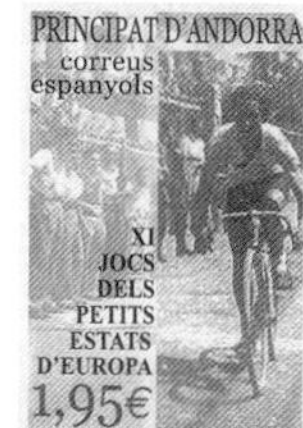

174 Cyclist

2005. Europa. Gastronomy.
331 **173** 78c. multicoloured 3·00 3·50

174 Cyclist

2005. Small States of Europe Games.
332 **174** €1.95 brown and black 5·50 6·00

175 Shrine

2005. 25th Anniv of Caritas Andorra (humanitarian organization).
333 **175** 28c. multicoloured 1·10 1·20

176 Dipper (*Cinclus cinclus*)

2005. Native Birds.
334 **176** €2.21 multicoloured 6·25 6·75

177 The Nativity (Sergei Mas)

2005. Christmas.
335 **177** 28c. multicoloured 1·10 1·20

178 Skiers

2006. Winter Olympic Games, Turin.
336 **178** 29c. multicoloured 1·40 1·50

179 "Ruta del Hierro" (sculpture) (Satora Sato)

2006. Cultural Heritage.
337 **179** 78c. multicoloured 2·50 2·75

180 Stylized People of Many Colours and Abilities

2006. Europa. Integration.
338 **180** 57c. multicoloured 2·20 2·40

181 Grey Partridge (*Perdix perdix*)

2006. Natural Heritage.
339 **181** €2.39 multicoloured 8·25 9·00

182 Scrabble Letters

2006. Fulbright Scholarships.
340 **182** 57c. multicoloured 2·20 2·40

183 Head Containing World Map

2006. 60th Anniv of UNESCO and 10th Anniv of CNAU.
341 **183** €2.33 multicoloured 8·00 8·75

184 Nativity

2006. Christmas.
342 **184** 29c. multicoloured 1·20 1·20

185 "Encamp 1994" (F. Galobardes)

2007. Cultural Heritage.
343 **185** 30c. multicoloured 1·20 1·20

186 Doves and Emblem

2007. Europa. Centenary of Scouting.
344 **186** 58c. multicoloured 2·30 2·50

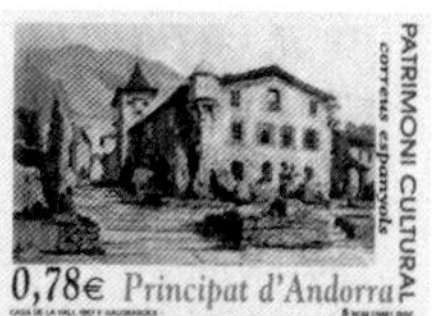

187 'La Familia Jordino' (sculpture by Rachid Khimoune)

2007. Cultural Heritage. The Iron Route (historical trail).
345 **187** €2.43 multicoloured 8·50 9·00

188 Capercaillie (*Tetrao urogallus*)

2007. Natural Heritage.
346 **188** €2.49 multicoloured 8·75 9·25

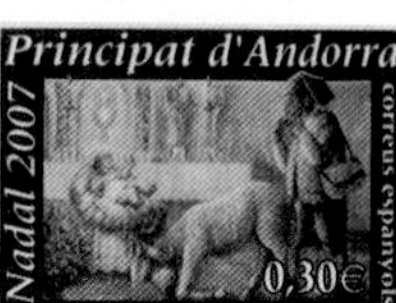

189 *Casa de la Vall* (Francesc Galobardes)

2007. Cultural Heritage.
347 **189** 78c. multicoloured 3·00 3·25

190 Stylized Figures

2007. 25th Anniv of Andorra Red Cross.
348 **190** 30c. carmine and black 1·20 1·20

191 "Lamb kneeling before Infant Jesus" (painting by Sergi Mas)

2007. Christmas.
349 **191** 30c. multicoloured 1·20 1·20

192 *Gypaetus barbatus* (Lammergeier or bearded vulture)

2008. Natural Heritage.
350 **192** 31c. multicoloured 1·40 1·50

193 *Carro Vortiu* (sculpture by Jordi Casamajor)

2008. Cultural Heritage.
351 **193** 60c. multicoloured 2·50 2·75

194 Flag and Ballot Box

2008. 15th Anniv of Constitution.
352 **194** 31c. multicoloured 1·80 2·10

195 Envelope

2008. Europa. The Letter.
353 **195** 60c. blue and black 2·75 3·00

196 Adam, Eve and Graph

2008. 25th Anniv of National Science Society.
354 **196** 78c. blue and black 3·75 4·00

197 Fluvi (exhibition mascot)

2008. Zaragoza 2008 International Water and Sustainable Development Exhibition. Sheet 105×79 mm.
MS355 multicoloured 10·50 11·50

198 Games Emblem

2008. Olympic Games, Beijing.
356 **198** 60c. multicoloured 2·75 3·00

199 Vall del Comapedrosa

2008. Natural Heritage.
357 **199** €2.44 multicoloured 9·25 10·00

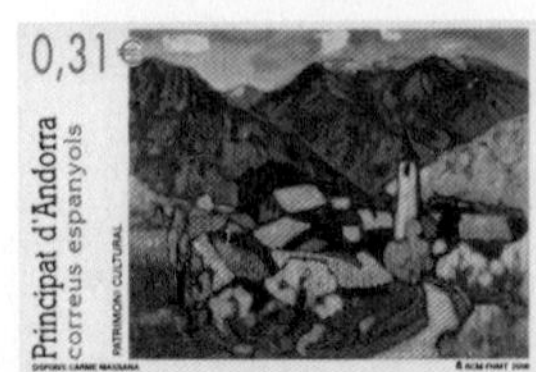
200 *Sispony* (Carme Massana)

2008. Cultural Heritage.
358 **200** 31c. multicoloured 1·60 1·80

201 Midnight Mass

2008. Christmas.
359 **201** 31c. multicoloured 1·60 1·80

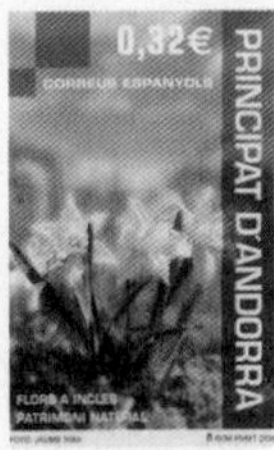
202 Narcissus

2009. Natural Heritage. Flora. Self adhesive.
360 **202** 32c. multicoloured 1·60 1·80

203 '25'

2009. 25th Anniv of Escola Andorrana.
361 **203** 62c. multicoloured 2·75 3·00

204 Merce Rodoreda

2009. Merce Rodoreda (Catalan writer) Commemoration.
362 **204** 78c. black 3·50 3·75

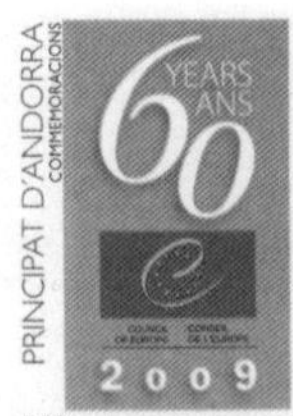
205 Emblem

2009. 60th Anniv of Council of Europe.
363 **205** 32c. multicoloured 1·60 1·80

206 Figures and Stars

2009. Europa. Astronomy.
364 **206** 62c. multicoloured 2·75 3·00

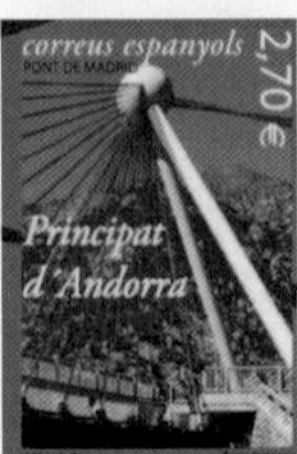
207 Bridge Strut

2009. Pont de Madrid (bridge designed by Carlos Fernandez Casado). Sheet 106×80 mm.
MS365 multicoloured 12·00 13·00

208 Eurasian Sparrowhawk

2009. Natural Heritage. Accipiter nisus.
366 **208** €2.47 multicoloured 9·25 10·00

209 *El Tarter* (Francesc Galobardes)

2009. Cultural Heritage. Multicoloured.
367 62c. Type **209** 2·75 3·00
368 78c. *Contrallum a Canillo* (Carme Massana) 3·50 3·75

210 Three Wise Men as Musicians (homage to National Classical Orchestra of Andorra by Sergei Mas)

2009. Christmas
369 **210** 32c. multicoloured 1·30 1·50

211 *Iris*

2010. Flora. Self-adhesive.
370 **211** 34c. multicoloured 1·70 1·90

212 Jacint Verdaguer

2010. 165th Birth Anniv of Jacint Verdaguer i Santaló (Catalan poet).
371 **212** 64c. black 2·75 3·00

213 Central Section

2010. Pont de Paris (bridge designed by Carlos Fernandez Casado).
372 **213** €2.75 multicoloured 12·00 13·00

214 Boy, Book and Fairy

2010. Europa
373 **214** 64c. multicoloured 2·75 3·00

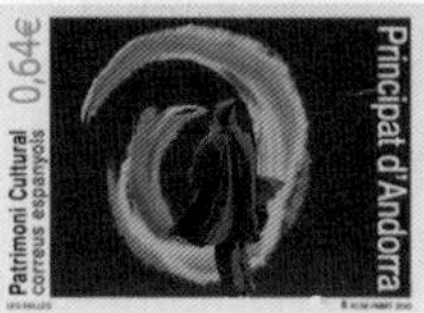
215 Circle of Flame

2010. Cultural Heritage
374 **215** 64c. multicoloured 3·25 3·50

216 Emblem and Globe

2010. World Cup Football Championships, South Africa
375 **216** 78c. multicoloured 4·00 4·25

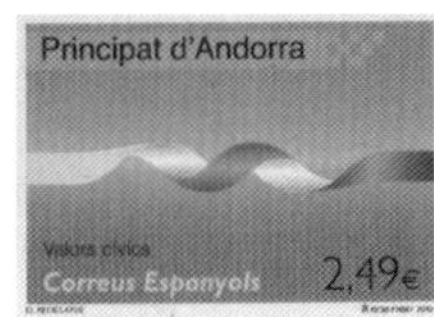

217 Multicoloured Ribbon

2010. Civic Values

376	**217**	€2.49 multicoloured	11·50	12·00

218 Mural (by Josep Oromí), Sant Joan de Sispony Church

2010. Christmas

377	**218**	34c. multicoloured	1·90	2·10

EXPRESS LETTER STAMPS

1928. Express Letter stamp of Spain optd CORREOS ANDORRA.

E15	**E53**	20c. red	70·00	90·00

E4 Lammergeier over Pyrenees

1929

E41	**E4**	20c. red	8·00	10·50

E12 Eurasian Red Squirrel (after Durer) and Arms

1949

E54	**E12**	25c. red	7·00	8·00

Pt. 2

AUSTRIA

A state of central Europe, part of the Austro-Hungarian Monarchy and Empire until 1918. At the end of the First World War the Empire was dismembered and German-spealing Austria became a Republic.

Austria was absorbed into the German Reich in 1938 and remained part of Germany until 1945. Following occupation of the four Allied Powers the Austrian Republic was re-establihed on 14 May 1945.

1850. 60 kreuzer = 1 gulden.
1858. 100 kreuzer = 1 gulden.
1899. 100 heller = 1 krone.
1925. 100 groschen = 1 schilling.
1938. 100 pfennig = 1 German reichsmark.
1945. 100 groschen = 1 schilling.
2002. 100 cents = 1 euro.

1 Arms of Austria

1850. Imperf.

6a	**1**	1k. yellow	£1800	£110
7	**1**	2k. black	£2250	£100
8a	**1**	3k. red	£600	4·75
9	**1**	6k. brown	£1300	8·50
10	**1**	9k. blue	£1300	3·75

For stamps in Type **1** with values in "CENTES", see Lombardy and Venetia.

4

5

1858

22a	**5**	2k. yellow	£1500	70·00
23	**4**	3k. black	£2250	£375
24	**4**	3k. green	£1900	£225
25a	**5**	5k. red	£500	2·75
26a	**5**	10k. brown	£1200	4·25
27a	**5**	15k. blue	£1100	2·75

For stamps in Types **4** and **5** with values in "SOLDI", see Lombardy and Venetia.

The portraits on Austrian stamps to 1906 are of the Emperor Francis Joseph I.

10

1860

33	**10**	2k. yellow	£550	43·00
34	**10**	3k. green	£475	38·00
35	**10**	5k. red	£350	1·10
36	**10**	10k. brown	£450	2·75
37	**10**	15k. blue	£600	1·90

12 Arms of Austria

1863

45	**12**	2k. yellow	£250	17·00
46	**12**	3k. green	£250	17·00
47	**12**	5k. red	70·00	55
48	**12**	10k. blue	£300	4·25
49	**12**	15k. brown	£300	2·40

A H14

A H16

1867

59	**AH14**	2k. yellow	19·00	1·10
60	**AH14**	3k. green	95·00	1·10
62	**AH14**	5k. red	3·00	20
63	**AH14**	10k. blue	£225	1·10
64	**AH14**	15k. brown	21·00	17·00
AH56a	**AH14**	25k. grey	65·00	24·00
66	**AH16**	50k. brown	19·00	£250

20

1883

70c	**20**	2k. brown	8·25	45
71c	**20**	3k. green	8·25	30
72c	**20**	5k. red	£150	20
73c	**20**	10k. blue	21·00	45
74c	**20**	20k. grey	£200	4·25
75a	**20**	50k. mauve	£475	£160

23

24

1890

79	**23**	1k. grey	2·10	55
80	**23**	2k. brown	50	20
81	**23**	3k. green	60	20
82	**23**	5k. red	60	20
83	**23**	10k. blue	1·50	20
84	**23**	12k. purple	3·50	55
85	**23**	15k. purple	3·50	55
86	**23**	20k. green	55·00	3·25
87	**23**	24k. blue	3·00	1·90
88	**23**	30k. brown	3·00	1·30
89	**23**	50k. mauve	8·25	15·00
90	**24**	1g. blue	6·25	4·25
105	**24**	1g. lilac	£100	6·50
91	**24**	2g. red	10·50	38·00
106	**24**	2g. green	41·00	65·00

25

1891. Figures in black.

92	**25**	20k. green	5·25	20
93	**25**	24k. blue	7·25	1·30
94	**25**	30k. brown	5·25	20
95	**25**	50k. mauve	6·25	55

27

28

29

30

1899. Corner numerals in black on heller values.

107	**27**	1h. mauve	1·00	20
108	**27**	2h. grey	4·25	85
140	**27**	3h. brown	1·00	20
141b	**27**	5h. green	1·00	20
142b	**27**	6h. orange	1·00	20
143b	**28**	10h. red	1·00	20
144b	**28**	20h. brown	1·00	20
145b	**28**	25h. blue	1·00	20
146b	**28**	30h. mauve	2·10	1·10
147b	**29**	35h. green	1·50	30
148b	**29**	40h. green	2·10	5·25
149b	**29**	50h. blue	5·25	13·00
150b	**29**	60h. brown	2·10	1·10
119a	**30**	1k. red	11·50	20
120	**30**	2k. lilac	£150	65
121	**30**	4k. green	26·00	32·00

33

35

1904. Types as before, but with corners containing figures altered as T 33 and 35. Figures in black on white on 10h. to 30h. only.

169	**33**	1h. purple	20	65
170	**33**	2h. black	20	45
171	**33**	3h. brown	40	10
173	**33**	6h. orange	60	10
160a	**28**	10h. red	2·30	10
a161	**28**	20h. brown	37·00	1·30
162a	**28**	25h. blue	37·00	1·10
a163	**28**	30h. mauve	55·00	2·10
178	**35**	35h. green	5·25	55
179	**35**	40h. purple	5·25	1·40
180	**35**	50h. blue	5·25	4·75
181	**35**	60h. brown	5·25	1·30
168	**35**	72h. red	6·25	2·10

1906. Figures on plain white ground and stamps printed in one colour.

183	**28**	5h. yellow-green	40	10
184	**28**	10h. red	50	20
185	**28**	12h. violet	1·50	1·10
186	**28**	20h. brown	5·00	30
187	**28**	25h. blue	5·00	75
188	**28**	30h. red	12·50	55

37 Francis Joseph I **38** Francis Joseph I

41 Schonbrunn

42 Francis Joseph I

1908. 60th Anniv of Emperor's Accession.

189A	-	1h. black	40	20
190A	-	2h. violet	40	20
191B	-	3h. purple	30	10
192B	**37**	5h. green	20	10
193A	-	6h. brown	95	1·10
194B	**37**	10h. red	20	10
195A	-	12h. red	2·10	1·60
196B	-	20h. brown	2·75	50
197B	**37**	25h. blue	2·50	45
198B	-	30h. green	6·25	65
199A	-	35h. grey	6·00	40
200	**38**	50h. green	2·00	55
201	-	60h. red	40	20
202	**38**	72h. brown	5·00	55
203	-	1k. violet	21·00	55
204	**41**	2k. green and red	36·00	1·10
205	-	5k. purple and brown	65·00	8·50
206	**42**	10k. brown, blue & ochre	£300	£110

DESIGNS—As Type **37**: 1h. Charles VI; 2h. Maria Theresa; 3h. Joseph II; 6h. Leopold II; 12h. Francis I; 20h. Ferdinand; 30h. Francis Joseph I in 1848; 35h. Same in 1878. As Type **38**: 60h. Francis Joseph I on horseback; 1k. Same in ceremonial robes. As Type **41**: 5k. Hofburg.

45

1910. 80th Birthday of Francis Joseph I. As issue of 1908 but with dates added as T 45.

223		1h. black	6·25	10·50
224		2h. violet	8·25	21·00
225		3h. purple	7·25	18·00
226		5h. green	20	45
227		6h. brown	4·25	16·00
228		10h. red	20	45
229		12h. red	5·25	18·00
230		20h. brown	13·50	20·00
231		25h. blue	3·75	4·25
232		30h. green	5·25	16·00
233		35h. grey	5·25	17·00
234		50h. green	7·25	20·00
235		60h. red	7·25	20·00
236		1k. violet	5·75	9·50
237		2k. green and red	£200	£325
238		5k. purple and brown	£150	£300
239		10k. brown, blue and ochre	£275	£475

47

1914. War Charity Funds.

240	**47**	5h.+(2h.) green	30	45
241	**47**	10h.+(2h.) red	40	75

48 Cavalry

1915. War Charity Funds.

242	-	3h.+1h. brown	10	55
243	**48**	5h.+2h. green	10	10
244	-	10h.+2h. red	10	10
245	-	20h.+3h. green	60	3·25
246	-	35h.+3h. blue	3·00	7·50

DESIGNS: 3h. Infantry; 10h. Artillery; 20h. Battleship "Viribus Unitas" (Navy); 35h. Lohner Pfeilflieger B-1 biplane (Air Force).

49 Imperial Austrian Crown

50 Francis Joseph I

51 Arms of Austria **52**

1916

247	**49**	3h. violet	10	10
248	**49**	5h. green	10	10
249	**49**	6h. orange	40	1·60
250	**49**	10h. red	10	10
251	**49**	12h. blue	40	2·75
252	**50**	15h. red	60	20
253	**50**	20h. brown	3·75	40
254	**50**	25h. blue	8·25	75
255	**50**	30h. slate	7·50	1·30
256	**51**	40h. olive	20	10
257	**51**	50h. green	20	10
258	**51**	60h. blue	20	10
259	**51**	80h. brown	20	10
260	**51**	90h. purple	20	10
261	**51**	1k. red on yellow	40	15
262aa	**52**	2k. blue	10	20
263aa	**52**	3k. red	30	1·10
264a	**52**	4k. green	4·25	1·60
265aa	**52**	10k. violet	10·50	43·00

On Nos. 254/5 the portrait is full face. The 1k. has floral sprays each side of the coat-of-arms.

60 Charles I

1917

290	**60**	15h. red	20	30
291a	**60**	20h. green	20	30
292	**60**	25h. blue	1·00	30
293	**60**	30h. violet	1·00	30

1918. Air. Optd FLUGPOST or surch also.

296A	**52**	1k.50 on 2k. mauve	2·10	9·75
297B	**52**	2k.50 on 3k. brown	10·50	32·00
298A	**52**	4k. grey	7·25	23·00

1918. Optd Deutschosterreich.

299	**49**	3h. violet	10	10
300	**49**	5h. green	10	10
301	**49**	6h. orange	30	2·75
302	**49**	10h. red	10	10
303	**49**	12h. blue	30	2·75
304	**60**	15h. red	30	1·60
305	**60**	20h. green	10	10
306	**60**	25h. blue	10	30
307	**60**	30h. violet	10	10
308	**51**	40h. olive	10	10
309	**51**	50h. green	60	2·10
310	**51**	60h. blue	55	2·00
311	**51**	80h. brown	20	20
312	**51**	90h. red	20	65
313	**51**	1k. red on yellow	20	30
314	**52**	2k. blue	10	10
315	**52**	3k. red	40	1·10
316	**52**	4k. green	2·10	4·25
317	**52**	10k. violet	10·50	27·00

64 Posthorn **65** Republican Arms **66** "New Republic"

1919. Imperf or perf.

336	**64**	3h. grey	10	10
337	**65**	5h. green	10	10
338	**65**	5h. grey	10	10
339	**64**	6h. orange	10	65
340	**65**	10h. red	10	10
342	**64**	12h. blue	10	1·30
343a	**64**	15h. brown	10	10
344	**66**	20h. green	10	10
346	**65**	25h. blue	10	10
347	**64**	25h. violet	10	10
348	**66**	30h. brown	10	10
349	**66**	40h. violet	10	10
350	**66**	40h. red	10	10
351	**65**	45h. green	20	1·10
352	**66**	50h. blue	10	10
353	**64**	60h. green	10	10
354	**65**	1k. red on yellow	10	10
355	**65**	1k. blue	40	1·10

67 Parliament Building

1919

356	**67**	2k. black and red	30	1·10
357	**67**	2½k. bistre	20	55
358	**67**	3k. brown and blue	10	10
359	**67**	4k. black and red	10	10
360	**67**	5k. black	10	30
361	**67**	7½k. purple	30	55
362	**67**	10k. brown and green	25	55
363	**67**	20k. brown and violet	10	55
364	**67**	50k. violet on yellow	70	1·60

71 Republican Arms

1920

402	**71**	80h. red	10	20
403	**71**	1k. brown	10	20
404	**71**	1½k. green	30	20
405	**71**	2k. blue	10	20
406	**71**	3k. black and green	10	30
407	**71**	4k. claret and red	10	20
408	**71**	5k. red and lilac	10	20
409	**71**	7½k. brown and orange	10	30
410	**71**	10k. blue and violet	10	20

The frames of the 3 to 10k. differ.

1920. Issues for Carinthian Plebiscite. Optd Karnten Abstimmung (T 65/7 in new colours). (a) Perf.

411	**65**	5h. (+10h.) grey on yell	70	2·10
412	**65**	10h. (+20h.) red on pink	70	1·60
413	**64**	15h. (+30h.) brn on yell	30	1·10
414	**66**	20h. (+40h.) green on bl	30	85
415	**64**	25h. (+50h.) pur on pink	30	90
416	**66**	30h. (+60h.) brn on buff	1·80	3·75
417	**66**	40h. (+80h.) red on yell	30	1·10
418	**66**	50h. (+100h.) indigo on blue	30	85
419	**64**	60h. (+120h.) green on bl	1·80	3·75
420	**71**	80h. (+160h.) red	45	95
421	**71**	1k. (+2k.) brown	45	1·10
422	**71**	2k. (+4k.) blue	45	1·10

(b) Imperf.

423	**67**	2½k. (+5k.) brown	50	1·40
424	**67**	3k. (+6k.) green & blue	60	1·70
425	**67**	4k. (+8k.) violet & red	85	2·00
426	**67**	5k. (+10k.) blue	75	1·70
427	**67**	7½k. (+15k.) green	75	1·70
428	**67**	10k. (+20k.) red & green	85	1·90
429	**67**	20k. (+40k.) brn & lilac	95	2·40

The plebiscite was to decide whether Carinthia should be part of Austria or Yugoslavia, and the premium was for a fund to promote a vote in favour of remaining in Austria. The result was a vote for Austria.

1921. Flood Relief Fund. Optd Hochwasser 1920 (colours changed).

430	**65**	5h. (+10h.) grey on yell	30	1·10
431	**65**	10h. (+20h.) brown	30	1·10
432	**64**	15h. (+30h.) grey	30	1·10
433	**66**	20h. (+40h.) green on yell	30	1·10
434	**64**	25h. (+50h.) blue on yell	30	1·10
435	**66**	30h. (+60h.) purple on bl	65	2·10
436	**66**	40h. (+80h.) brn on red	75	2·75
437	**66**	50h. (+100h.) green on bl	1·70	4·75
438	**64**	60h. (+120h.) pur on yell	50	2·10
439	**71**	80h. (+160h.) blue	50	2·10
440	**71**	1k. (+2k.) orange on blue	45	2·10
441	**71**	1½k. (+3k.) green on yell	25	1·10
442	**71**	2k. (+4k.) brown	25	1·10
443	**67**	2½k. (+5k.) blue	30	1·10
444	**67**	3k. (+6k.) red & green	30	1·10
445	**67**	4k. (+8k.) brown & lilac	1·00	3·75
446	**67**	5k. (+10k.) green	30	2·10
447	**67**	7½k. (+15k.) red	30	2·10
448	**67**	10k. (+20k.) green & blue	30	2·10
449	**67**	20k. (+40k.) pur & red	60	3·25

80 Pincers and Hammer **81** Ear of Corn

1922

461	**81**	½k. brown	10	85
462	**80**	1k. brown	10	10
463	**80**	2k. blue	10	10
464	**81**	2½k. brown	10	10
465	**80**	4k. purple	10	1·40
466	**80**	5k. green	10	10
467	**81**	7½k. violet	10	10
468	**80**	10k. red	10	10
469	**81**	12½k. green	10	10
470	**81**	15k. turquoise	10	10
471	**81**	20k. blue	10	10
472	**81**	25k. red	10	10
473	**80**	30k. grey	10	10
474	**80**	45k. red	10	10
475	**80**	50k. brown	10	10
476	**80**	60k. green	10	10
477	**80**	75k. blue	10	10
478	**80**	80k. yellow	10	10
479	**81**	100k. grey	10	10
480	**81**	120k. brown	10	10
481	**81**	150k. orange	10	10
482	**81**	160k. green	10	10
483	**81**	180k. red	10	10
484	**81**	200k. pink	10	10
485	**81**	240k. violet	10	10
486	**81**	300k. blue	10	10
487	**81**	400k. green	1·50	55
488	**81**	500k. yellow	10	10
489	**81**	600k. slate	10	10
490	**81**	700k. brown	2·50	20
491	**81**	800k. violet	1·00	2·75
492	**80**	1000k. mauve	1·30	20
493	**80**	1200k. red	85	65
494	**80**	1500k. orange	85	20
495	**80**	1600k. slate	4·25	4·25
496	**80**	2000k. blue	5·25	3·75
497	**80**	3000k. blue	15·00	2·75
498	**80**	4000k. blue on blue	7·75	3·75

82

1922

499	**82**	20k. sepia	10	20
500	**82**	25k. blue	10	20
501	**82**	50k. red	10	20
502	**82**	100k. green	10	20
503	**82**	200k. purple	10	20
504	**82**	500k. orange	40	2·10
505	**82**	1000k. violet on yellow	10	20
506	**82**	2000k. green on yellow	10	20
507	**82**	3000k. red	13·00	1·10
508	**82**	5000k. black	2·40	2·10
509	**82**	10,000k. brown	5·75	7·50

85 Mozart

1922. Musicians' Fund.

519b	-	2½k. brown	9·25	13·00
520	**85**	5k. blue	1·50	2·75
521	-	7½k. black	2·50	4·25
522	-	10k. purple	3·00	5·25
523	-	25k. green	5·75	10·50
524	-	50k. red	3·00	5·25
525	-	100k. green	9·25	21·00

COMPOSERS: 2½k. Haydn; 7½k. Beethoven; 10k. Schubert; 25k. Bruckner; 50k. J. Strauss; 100k. Wolf.

87 Hawk **88** W. Kress

1922. Air.

546	**87**	300k. red	40	2·40
547	**87**	400k. green	6·25	21·00
548	**87**	600k. olive	40	2·10
549	**87**	900k. red	40	2·10
550	**88**	1200k. purple	40	2·10
551	**88**	2400k. slate	40	2·10
552	**88**	3000k. brown	4·25	13·00
553	**88**	4800k. blue	4·25	13·00

89 Bregenz

1923. Artists' Charity Fund.

554	**89**	100k. green	5·25	10·50
555	-	120k. blue	5·25	10·50
556	-	160k. purple	5·25	10·50
557	-	180k. purple	5·25	10·50
558	-	200k. red	5·25	10·50
559	-	240k. brown	5·25	10·50
560	-	400k. brown	5·25	10·50
561	-	600k. green	6·25	10·50
562	-	1000k. black	9·25	17·00

DESIGNS: 120k. Salzburg; 160k. Eisenstadt; 180k. Klagenfurt; 200k. Innsbruck; 240k. Linz; 400k. Graz; 600k. Melk; 1000k. Vienna.

90 "Art the Comforter"

1924. Artists' Charity Fund.

563	**90**	100k.+300k. green	5·25	13·00
564	-	300k.+900k. brown	5·25	13·00
565	-	500k.+1500k. purple	5·25	14·00
566	-	600k.+1800k. turquoise	10·50	25·00
567	-	1000k.+3000k. brown	15·00	31·00

DESIGNS: 300k. "Agriculture and Handicraft"; 500k. "Mother Love"; 600k. "Charity"; 1000k. "Fruitfulness".

91 **92** Plains

93 Minorite Church, Vienna

1925

568	**91**	1g. grey	25	20
569	**91**	2g. red	50	20
570	**91**	3g. red	50	20
571	**91**	4g. blue	1·50	20
572	**91**	5g. brown	2·10	20
573	**91**	6g. blue	1·50	20
574	**91**	7g. brown	2·10	20
575	**91**	8g. green	5·25	20
576	**92**	10g. brown	1·00	20
577	**92**	15g. red	1·00	20
578	**92**	16g. blue	1·00	20
579	**92**	18g. green	1·50	1·10
580	-	20g. violet	1·00	20
581	-	24g. red	1·20	55
582	-	30g. brown	1·50	20
583	-	40g. blue	1·90	20
584	-	45g. brown	2·10	20
585	-	50g. grey	2·10	30
586	-	80g. blue	4·75	6·00
587	**93**	1s. green	23·00	2·10
588	-	2s. red	8·75	14·00

DESIGN—As T **92**—20g. to 80g. Golden eagle on mountains.

96 Pilot and Hansa Brandenburg C-1

97 de Havilland D.H.34 and Common Crane

1925. Air.

616	**96**	2g. brown	50	1·30
617	**96**	5g. red	30	45
618	**96**	6g. blue	1·00	2·10
619	**96**	8g. green	1·00	2·40
620	**97**	10g. red	1·30	3·75
621	**96**	10g. orange	1·30	2·75
622	**97**	15g. red	1·00	2·10
623	**96**	15g. mauve	50	1·10
624	**96**	20g. brown	14·00	16·00
625	**96**	25g. violet	6·25	12·00
626	**97**	30g. purple	1·20	3·75
627	**96**	30g. bistre	10·50	13·00
628	**97**	50g. grey	1·20	3·75
629	**96**	50g. blue	18·00	19·00
630	**96**	80g. green	3·00	5·25
631	**97**	1s. blue	10·50	14·00
632	**97**	2s. green	2·10	5·25
633	**97**	3s. brown	65·00	85·00
634	**97**	5s. blue	18·00	38·00
635	**97**	10s. brown on grey (25×32 mm)	10·50	32·00

98 Siegfried and Dragon

1926. Child Welfare. Scenes from the Nibelung Legend.

636	**98**	3g.+2g. brown	1·20	1·20
637	-	8g.+2g. blue	20	55
638	-	15g.+5g. red	40	55
639	-	20g.+5g. green	60	1·10
640	-	24g.+6g. violet	60	1·10
641	-	40g.+10g. brown	4·25	7·00

DESIGNS: 8g. Gunther's voyage; 15g. Kriemhild and Brunhild; 20g. Hagen and the Rhine maidens; 24g. Rudiger and the Nibelungs; 40g. Dietrich's fight with Hagen.

99 Dr. Michael Hainisch

1928. 10th Anniv of Republic and War Orphans and Invalid Children's Fund.

642	**99**	10g. (+10g.) brown	6·25	16·00
643	**99**	15g. (+15g.) red	6·25	16·00
644	**99**	30g. (+30g.) black	6·25	16·00
645	**99**	40g. (+40g.) blue	6·25	16·00

100 Gussing

101 National Library, Vienna

1929. Views. Size 25½×21½ mm.

646	**100**	10g. orange	1·00	10
647	**100**	10g. brown	1·00	10
648	-	15g. purple	1·00	1·80
649	-	16g. black	20	10
650	-	18g. green	50	65
651	-	20g. black	50	10
653	-	24g. purple	7·25	75
654	-	30g. violet	8·25	10
655	-	40g. blue	10·50	30
656	-	50g. violet	39·00	30
657	-	60g. green	31·00	55
658	**101**	1s. brown	8·25	55
659	-	2s. green	19·00	17·00

VIEWS—As T **100**: 15g. Hochosterwitz; 16, 20g. Durnstein; 18g. Traunsee; 24g. Salzburg; 30g. Seewiesen; 40g. Innsbruck; 50g. Wortherse; 60g. Hohenems. As T **101**: 2s. St. Stephen's Cathedral, Vienna.

See also Nos. 678/91.

102 Pres. Wilhelm Miklas

1930. Anti-tuberculosis Fund.

660	**102**	10g. (+10g.) brown	10·50	30·00
661	**102**	20g. (+20g.) red	10·50	30·00
662	**102**	30g. (+30g.) purple	10·50	30·00
663	**102**	40g. (+40g.) blue	10·50	30·00
664	**102**	50g. (+50g.) green	10·50	30·00
665	**102**	1s. (+1s.) brown	10·50	30·00

1930. Rotarian Congress. Optd with Rotary Int emblem and CONVENTION WIEN 1931.

666	**100**	10g. (+10g.) brown	50·00	85·00
667	-	20g. (+20g.) grey (No. 651)	50·00	85·00
668	-	30g. (+30g.) vio (No. 654)	50·00	85·00
669	-	40g. (+40g.) bl (No. 655)	50·00	85·00
670	-	50g. (+50g.) vio (No. 656)	50·00	85·00
671	**101**	1s. (+1s.) brown	50·00	85·00

104 Johann Nestroy

1931. Austrian Writers and Youth Unemployment Fund.

672	-	10g. (+10g.) purple	21·00	45·00
673	-	20g. (+20g.) grey	21·00	45·00
674	**104**	30g. (+30g.) red	21·00	45·00
675	-	40g. (+40g.) blue	21·00	45·00
676	-	50g. (+50g.) green	21·00	45·00
677	-	1s. (+1s.) brown	21·00	45·00

DESIGNS: 10g. F. Raimund; 20g. E. Grillparzer; 40g. A Stifter; 50g. L. Anzengruber; 1s. P. Rosegger.

105

1932. Designs as No. 646 etc, but size reduced to 20½×16 mm as T 105.

678	**105**	10g. brown	1·00	20
679	-	12g. green	2·10	20
680	-	18g. green	2·10	3·50
681	-	20g. black	1·00	20
682	-	24g. red	6·75	20
683	-	24g. violet	4·25	20
684	-	30g. violet	23·00	20
685	-	30g. red	8·25	30
686	-	40g. blue	27·00	2·10
687	-	40g. violet	10·50	55
688	-	50g. violet	31·00	55
689	-	50g. blue	10·50	55
690	-	60g. green	70·00	5·25
691	-	64g. green	23·00	55

DESIGNS (new values): 12g. Traunsee; 64g. Hohenems.

106 Dr. Ignaz Seipel

1932. Death of Dr. Seipel (Chancellor), and Ex-servicemen's Fund.

692	**106**	50g. (+50g.) blue	19·00	38·00

107 Hans Makart

1932. Austrian Painters.

693	-	12g. (+12g.) green	31·00	65·00
694	-	24g. (+24g.) purple	31·00	65·00
695	-	30g. (+30g.) red	31·00	65·00
696	**107**	40g. (+40g.) grey	31·00	65·00
697	-	64g. (+64g.) brown	31·00	65·00
698	-	1s. (+1s.) red	31·00	65·00

DESIGNS: 12g. F. G. Waldmuller; 24g. Von Schwind; 30g. Alt; 64g. Klimt; 1s. A. Egger-Lienz.

108 The Climb

1933. International Ski Championship Fund.

699	**108**	12g. (+12g.) green	10·50	27·00
700	-	24g. (+24g.) violet	£140	£190
701	-	30g. (+30g.) red	21·00	38·00
702	-	50g. (+50g.) blue	£140	£190

DESIGNS: 24g. Start; 30g. Race; 50g. Ski jump.

109 "The Honeymoon" (M. von Schwind)

1933. International Philatelic Exn, Vienna (WIPA).

703	**109**	50g. (+50g.) blue	£200	£350
MS705		127×105 mm. As No. 703 (+1s.60 admission) in block of four	£3500	£5000

111 John Sobieski

1933. 250th Anniv of Relief of Vienna and Pan-German Catholic Congress.

706	-	12g. (+12g.) green	33·00	55·00
707	-	24g. (+24g.) violet	31·00	48·00
708	-	30g. (+30g.) red	31·00	48·00
709	**111**	40g. (+40g.) grey	44·00	85·00
710	-	50g. (+50g.) blue	31·00	48·00
711	-	64g. (+64g.) brown	36·00	75·00

DESIGNS—VERT: 12g. Vienna in 1683; 24g. Marco d'Aviano; 30g. Count von Starhemberg; 50g. Charles of Lorraine; 64g. Burgomaster Liebenberg.

1933. Winter Relief Fund. Surch with premium and Winterhilfe (5g.) or WINTERHILFE (others).

712	**91**	5g.+2g. green	20	75
713	-	12g.+3g. blue (as 679)	30	1·10
714	-	24g.+6g. brn (as 682)	20	75
715	**101**	1s.+50g. red	41·00	95·00

114

115

1934

716	**114**	1g. violet	10	10
717	**114**	3g. red	10	10
718	-	4g. green	10	10
719	-	5g. purple	10	10
721	-	6g. blue	20	10
722	-	8g. green	10	10
723	-	12g. brown	10	10
724	-	20g. brown	20	10
725	-	24g. turquoise	10	10
726	-	25g. violet	20	25
727	-	30g. red	20	10
728	-	35g. red	40	50
729	**115**	40g. grey	50	30
730	**115**	45g. brown	45	20
731	-	60g. blue	70	55
732	-	64g. brown	1·00	20
733	-	1s. purple	1·50	85
735	-	2s. green	4·75	8·50
736	-	3s. orange	18·00	32·00
737	-	5s. black	41·00	70·00

DESIGNS (Austrian costumes of the districts named)—As Type **114**: 1, 3g. Burgenland; 4, 5g. Carinthia; 6, 8g. Lower Austria; 12, 20g. Upper Austria; 24, 25g. Salzburg; 30, 35g. Styria (Steiermark). As Type **115**: 40, 45g. Tyrol; 60, 64g. Vorarlberg; 1s. Vienna; 2s. Army officer and soldiers. 30×31 mm: 3s. Harvesters; 5s. Builders.

117 Chancellor Dollfuss

1934. Dollfuss Mourning Stamp.

738	**117**	24g. black	60	1·10

See also No. 762.

118 Anton Pilgram

1934. Welfare Funds. Austrian Architects.

739	**118**	12g. (+12g.) black	14·50	32·00
740	-	24g. (+24g.) violet	14·50	32·00
741	-	30g. (+30g.) red	14·50	32·00
742	-	40g. (+40g.) brown	14·50	32·00
743	-	60g. (+60g.) blue	14·50	32·00
744	-	64g. (+64g.) green	14·50	32·00

DESIGNS: 24g. Fischer von Erlach; 30g. J. Prandtauer; 40g. A. von Siccardsburg and E. van der Null; 60g. H. von Ferstel; 64g. Otto Wagner.

119 "Mother and Child" (J. Danhauser)

1935. Mothers Day.

745	**119**	24g. blue	70	55

1935. 1st Anniv of Assassination of Dr. Dollfuss.

762	**117**	24g. blue	1·50	1·40

121 Maria Worth Castle, Carinthia

122 Zugspitze Aerial Railway

1935. Air. Designs showing Junkers airplane (except 10s.) and landscape.

763	-	5g. purple	30	85
764	**121**	10g. orange	10	55
765	-	15g. green	1·00	2·75
766	-	20g. blue	10	55
767	-	25g. purple	10	55
768	-	30g. red	10	55
769	-	40g. green	10	55
770	-	50g. blue	20	95
771	-	60g. sepia	40	1·40
772	-	80g. brown	50	1·80
773	-	1s. red	40	1·60
774	-	2s. green	3·00	8·50
775	-	3s. brown	9·25	32·00
776	**122**	5s. green	5·25	23·00
777	-	10s. blue	85·00	£170

DESIGNS—As T **121**: 5g. Gussing Castle; 15g. Durnstein; 20g. Hallstatt; 25g. Salzburg; 30g. Dachstein Mts.; 40g. Wettersee; 50g. Stuben am Arlberg; 60g. St. Stephen's Cathedral, Vienna; 80g. Minorite Church, Vienna. As T **122**: 1s. River Danube; 2s. Tauern railway viaduct; 3s. Grossglockner mountain roadway; 10s. Glider and yachts on the Attersee.

1935. Winter Relief Fund. As Nos. 719, 723, 725 and 733, but colours changed, surch Winterhilfe (778/80) or WINTERHILFE (781) and premium.

778		5g.+2g. green	70	1·60
779		12g.+3g. blue	1·20	2·10
780		24g.+6g. brown	70	1·60
781		1s.+50g. red	41·00	90·00

123 Prince Eugene of Savoy (born 1663, not 1667 as given)

1935. Welfare Funds. Austrian Heroes.

782	**123**	12g. (+12g.) brown	15·00	32·00
783	-	24g. (+24g.) green	15·00	32·00
784	-	30g. (+30g.) purple	15·00	32·00
785	-	40g. (+40g.) blue	15·00	32·00
786	-	60g. (+60g.) blue	15·00	32·00
787	-	64g. (+64g.) violet	15·00	32·00

PORTRAITS: 24g. Baron von Laudon; 30g. Archduke Charles; 40g. Field-Marshal Radetzky; 60g. Vice-Admiral von Tegetthoff; 64g. Field-Marshal Conrad von Hotzendorff.

124 Slalom Course Skier

1936. International Ski Championship Fund. Inscr "WETTKAMPFE 1936".

788	**124**	12g. (+12g.) green	3·00	6·50
789	-	24g. (+24g.) violet	5·25	8·50
790	-	35g. (+35g.) red	31·00	75·00
791	-	60g. (+60g.) blue	31·00	75·00

DESIGNS: 24g. Skier on mountain slope; 35g. Woman slalom course skier; 60g. View of Maria Theresienstrasse, Innsbruck.

125 Madonna and Child

1936. Mothers' Day.

792	**125**	24g. blue	40	1·30

126 Chancellor Dollfuss

1936. 2nd Anniv of Assassination of Dr. Dollfuss.

793	**126**	10s. blue	£950	£1500

127 "St. Martin sharing Cloak"

1936. Winter Relief Fund. Inscr "WINTERHILFE 1936/37".

794	**127**	5g.+2g. green	35	1·10
795	-	12g.+3g. violet	35	1·10
796	-	24g.+6g. blue	35	1·10
797	-	1s.+1s. red	9·25	25·00

DESIGNS: 12g. "Healing the sick"; 24g. "St. Elizabeth feeding the hungry"; 1s. "Warming the poor".

128 J. Ressel

1936. Welfare Funds. Austrian Inventors.

798	**128**	12g. (+12g.) brown	3·50	10·00
799	-	24g. (+24g.) violet	3·50	10·00
800	-	30g. (+30g.) red	3·50	10·00
801	-	40g. (+40g.) black	3·50	10·00
802	-	60g. (+60g.) blue	3·50	10·00
803	-	64g. (+64g.) green	3·50	10·00

PORTRAITS: 24g. Karl Ritter von Ghega; 30g. J. Werndl; 40g. Carl Freih. Auer von Welsbach; 60g. R. von Lieben; 64g. V. Kaplan.

129 Mother and Child

1937. Mothers' Day.

804	**129**	24g. red	30	55

130 "Maria Anna"

1937. Centenary of Regular Danube Services of Danube Steam Navigation Co. Paddle-steamers.

805	**130**	12g. red	85	1·10
806	-	24g. blue	85	1·10
807	-	64g. green	85	2·10

DESIGNS: 24g. "Helios"; 64g. "Oesterreich".

131 "Child Welfare"

1937. Winter Relief Fund. Inscr "WINTERHILFE 1937 1938".

808	**131**	5g.+2g. green	20	65
809	-	12g.+3g. brown	20	65
810	-	24g.+6g. blue	20	65
811	-	1s.+1s. red	4·75	18·00

DESIGNS: 12g. "Feeding the Children"; 24g. "Protecting the Aged"; 1s. "Nursing the Sick".

132 Steam Locomotive "Austria", 1837

1937. Railway Centenary.

812	**132**	12g. brown	20	40
813	-	25g. violet	85	1·60
814	-	35g. red	2·50	3·75

DESIGNS: 25g. Steam locomotive, 1936; 35g. Electric locomotive.

133 Dr. G. Van Swieten

1937. Welfare Funds. Austrian Doctors.

815	**133**	5g. (+5g.) brown	2·75	7·50
816	-	8g. (+8g.) red	2·75	7·50
817	-	12g. (+12g.) brown	2·75	7·50
818	-	20g. (+20g.) green	2·75	7·50
819	-	24g. (+24g.) violet	2·75	7·50
820	-	30g. (+30g.) red	2·75	7·50
821	-	40g. (+40g.) olive	2·75	7·50
822	-	60g. (+60g.) blue	2·75	7·50
823	-	64g. (+64g.) purple	2·75	7·50

DESIGNS: 8g. L. A. von Auenbrugg; 12g. K. von Rokitansky; 20g. J. Skoda; 25g. F. von Hebra; 30g. F. von Arlt; 40g. J. Hyrtl; 60g. T. Billroth; 64g. T. Meynert.

134 Nosegay and Signs of the Zodiac

1937. Christmas Greetings.

824		12g. green	10	30
825	**134**	24g. red	10	30

ALLIED OCCUPATION. Nos. 826/905 were issued in the Russian Zone of occupation and Nos. 906/22 were a joint issue for use in the British, French and American zones.

1945. Hitler portrait stamps of Germany optd. (a) Optd Osterreich only.

826	**173**	5pf. green	30	1·40
827	**173**	8pf. red	40	1·10

(b) Optd Osterreich and bar.

828	6pf. violet	60	1·60
829	12pf. red	60	1·60

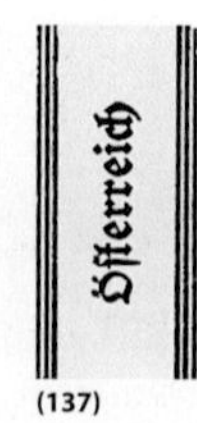

(137)

1945. 1941 and 1944 Hitler stamps of Germany optd as T 137.

830	**137**	1pf. grey	6·25	13·00
831	**137**	3pf. brown	3·25	11·00
832	**137**	4pf. grey	17·00	38·00
833	**137**	5pf. green	4·25	11·00
834	**137**	6pf. violet	1·60	2·20
835	**137**	8pf. red	1·30	3·25
836	**137**	10pf. brown	4·25	11·00
837	**137**	12pf. red	60	1·10
838	**137**	15pf. red	1·60	5·50
839	**137**	16pf. green	40·00	85·00
840	**137**	20pf. blue	4·25	8·50
841	**137**	24pf. brown	37·00	85·00
842	**173**	25pf. blue	5·25	11·00
843	**173**	30pf. green	5·25	11·00
844	**173**	40pf. mauve	5·75	11·50
845	**225**	42pf. green	8·25	19·00
846	**173**	50pf. green	6·75	13·00
847	**173**	60pf. brown	7·25	16·00
848	**173**	80pf. blue	6·25	15·00
853	**182**	1rm. green	34·00	70·00
850	**182**	2rm. violet	29·00	60·00
855	**182**	3rm. red	60·00	£130
856	**182**	5rm. blue	£425	£900

1945. Stamps of Germany surch OSTERREICH and new value.

857	**186**	5pf. on 12+88pf. green	85	2·75
858	-	6pf. on 6+14pf. brown and blue (No. 811)	10·50	24·00
859	**220**	8pf. on 42+108pf. brn	1·40	4·75
860	-	12pf. on 3+7pf. blue (No. 810)	85	2·75

(140)

1945. 1941 and 1944 Hitler stamps of Germany optd as T 140.

862	**173**	5pf. green	1·60	5·50
863	**173**	6pf. violet	1·00	4·25
864	**173**	8pf. red	85	4·50
865	**173**	12pf. red	1·00	5·50
866	**173**	30pf. green	10·50	27·00
867a	**225**	42pf. green	23·00	44·00

141 New National Arms

142 New National Arms

1945

868	**141**	3pf. brown	20	20
869	**141**	4pf. blue	20	45
870	**141**	5pf. green	20	25
871	**141**	6pf. purple	20	25
872	**141**	8pf. orange	20	25
873	**141**	10pf. brown	20	25
874	**141**	12pf. red	20	25
875	**141**	15pf. orange	20	30
876	**141**	16pf. green	25	65
877	**141**	20pf. blue	20	30
878	**141**	24pf. orange	20	45
879	**141**	25pf. blue	20	35
880	**141**	30pf. green	20	25
881	**141**	38pf. blue	20	35
882	**141**	40pf. purple	20	40
883	**141**	42pf. grey	30	45
884	**141**	50pf. green	20	55
885	**141**	60pf. red	20	55
886	**141**	80pf. violet	20	45
887	**142**	1rm. green	40	1·10
888	**142**	2rm. violet	45	1·20
889	**142**	3rm. purple	50	1·70
890	**142**	5rm. brown	70	2·30

Nos. 877/86 are 24×28 mm.

144 Allegorical of the Home Land

1945. Austrian Welfare Charities.

905	**144**	1s.+10s. green	1·80	3·50

145 Posthorn

1945

906	**145**	1g. blue	20	85
907	**145**	3g. orange	20	30
908	**145**	4g. brown	20	30
909	**145**	5g. green	20	25
910	**145**	6g. purple	20	25
911	**145**	8g. red	20	25
912	**145**	10g. grey	20	25
913	**145**	12g. brown	20	25
914	**145**	15g. red	20	30
915	**145**	20g. brown	20	30
916	**145**	25g. blue	20	30
917	**145**	30g. mauve	20	30
918	**145**	40g. blue	20	30
919	**145**	60g. olive	20	45
920	**145**	1s. violet	40	85
921	**145**	2s. yellow	50	1·70
922	**145**	5s. blue	55	1·80

146 Salzburg

148 Durnstein

1945. Views as T 146/8.

923	-	3g. blue	20	20
924	-	4g. red	20	20
925	-	5g. red	20	20
926	**146**	6g. green	20	20
927	-	8g. brown	20	20
928	-	8g. purple	20	20
929	-	8g. green	20	20
930	-	10g. green	20	20
931	-	10g. purple	20	20
932	-	12g. brown	20	20
933	-	15g. blue	20	20
934	-	16g. brown	20	20
935	-	20g. blue	20	20
936	-	24g. green	20	20
937	-	25g. grey	20	20
938	-	30g. red	20	20
939	-	30g. blue	50	55
940	-	35g. red	20	20
941	-	38g. green	20	20
942	-	40g. grey	20	20
943	-	42g. red	20	20
944	-	45g. blue	30	55
945	-	50g. blue	20	20

946	-	50g. purple	85	85
947	-	60g. blue	30	30
948	-	60g. violet	3·00	3·75
949	-	70g. blue	35	55
950	-	80g. brown	40	75
951	-	90g. green	1·70	3·25
952A	**148**	1s. brown	1·00	1·60
953A	-	2s. grey	3·50	5·50
954A	-	3s. green	1·20	2·75
955A	-	5s. red	2·10	3·75

DESIGNS—As Type **146**: 3g. Lermoos; 4g. Iron-ore mine, Erzberg; 5g. Leopoldsberg, Vienna; 8g. (927), Prater Woods, Vienna; 8g. (928/9), Town Hall Park, Vienna; 10g. (930/1), Hochosterwitz; 12g. Schafberg; 15g. Forchtenstein; 16g. Gesauseeingang. 23½×29 mm: 20g. Gebhartsberg; 24g. Holdrichsmuhle, near Modling; 25g. Vent im Otztal; 30g. (938/9), Neusiedler Lake; 35g. Belvedere Palace, Vienna; 38g. Langbath Lake; 40g. Mariazell; 42g. Traunstein; 45g. Burg Hartenstein; 50g. (945/6), Silvretta Peaks, Vorarlberg; 60g. (947/8), Semmering; 70g. Badgastein; 80g. Kaisergebirge; 90g. Wayside shrine near Tragoss. As T **148**: 2s. St. Christof; 3s. Heiligenblut; 5s. Schonbrunn Palace, Vienna.

See also Nos. 1072/86a.

1946. 1st Anniv of U.N.O. No. 938 surch 26. JUNI 1945+20 g 26. JUNI 1946 and globe.

971	30g.+20g. red	3·00	6·50

151 Dr. Karl Renner

1946. 1st Anniv of Establishment of Renner Government.

972	**151**	1s.+1s. green	6·25	11·00
973	**151**	2s.+2s. violet	6·25	11·00
974	**151**	3s.+3s. purple	6·25	11·00
975	**151**	5s.+5s. brown	6·25	11·00

MS976 Four sheets, each 180×155 mm, each with block of 8 of one value (972/5) and Arms in centre. Imperf Set 4 sheets £2500 £17000

152 Dagger and Map

1946. "Anti-Fascist" Exhibition.

977	**152**	5g.+3g. sepia	60	1·30
978	-	6g.+4g. green	40	95
979	-	8g.+6g. orange	40	95
980	-	12g.+12g. blue	40	95
981	-	30g.+30g. violet	40	1·10
982	-	42g.+42g. brown	60	1·10
983	-	1s.+1s. red	50	1·60
984	-	2s.+2s. red	1·20	2·75

DESIGNS: 6g. Broom sweeping Nazi and Fascist emblems; 8g. St. Stephen's Cathedral in flames; 12g. Hand and barbed wire; 30g. Hand strangling snake; 42g. Hammer and broken column; 1s. Hand and Austrian flag; 2s. Eagle and smoking Nazi emblem.

(153)

1946. Congress of Society for Promotion of Cultural and Economic Relations with the Soviet Union. No. 932 optd with T 153.

985	12g. brown	20	55

154 Mare and Foal

1946. Austria Prize Race Fund.

986	**154**	16g.+16g. red	2·50	5·50
987	-	24g.+24g. violet	2·10	4·25
988	-	60g.+60g. green	2·10	4·25
989	-	1s.+1s. blue	2·10	4·25
990	-	2s.+2s. brown	7·25	11·00

DESIGNS: 24g. Two horses' heads; 60g. Racehorse clearing hurdle; 1s. Three racehorses; 2s. Three horses' heads.

155 Ruprecht's Church, Vienna

1946. 950th Anniv of First recorded use of name "Osterreich".

991	**155**	30g.+70g. red	50	1·10

156 Statue of Duke Rudolf

1946. St. Stephen's Cathedral Reconstruction Fund. Architectural and Sculptural designs.

992	**156**	3g.+12g. brown	20	1·10
993	-	5g.+20g. purple	20	1·10
994	-	6g.+24g. blue	20	1·10
995	-	8g.+32g. green	20	1·10
996	-	10g.+40g. blue	20	1·10
997	-	12g.+48g. violet	50	2·20
998	-	30g.+1s.20 red	1·80	2·20
999	-	50g.+1s.80 blue	2·30	6·50
1000	-	1s.+5s. purple	3·00	8·50
1001	-	2s.+10s. brown	6·25	11·00

DESIGNS: 5g. Tomb of Frederick III; 6g. Pulpit; 8g. Statue of St. Stephen; 10g. Statue of Madonna and Child; 12g. Altar; 30g. Organ; 50g. Anton Pilgram; 1s. N.E. Tower; 2s. S.W. Spire.

157 Franz Grillparzer (dramatic poet)

1947. Famous Austrians.

1002		12g. green	30	55
1003	**157**	18g. purple	30	30
1004	-	20g. green	50	30
1005	-	40g. brown	10·50	6·00
1006	-	40g. green	10·50	11·00
1007	-	60g. lake	50	45

PORTRAITS: 12g. Franz Schubert (composer); 20g. Carl Michael Ziehrer (composer); 40g. (No. 1005), Adalbert Stifter (poet); 40g. (No. 1006), Anton Bruckner (composer); 60g. Friedrich Amerling (painter).

158 Harvesting

1947. Vienna Fair Fund.

1009	**158**	3g.+2g. brown	50	1·10
1010	-	8g.+2g. green	50	1·10
1011	-	10g.+5g. slate	50	1·10
1012	-	12g.+8g. violet	50	1·10
1013	-	18g.+12g. olive	50	1·10
1014	-	30g.+10g. purple	50	1·10
1015	-	35g.+15g. red	50	1·60
1016	-	60g.+20g. blue	50	1·70

DESIGNS: 8g. Logging; 10g. Factory; 12g. Pithead; 18g. Oil wells; 30g. Textile machinery; 35g. Foundry; 60g. Electric cables.

159 Airplane over Hinterstoder

1947. Air.

1017		50g. brown	50	1·10
1018		1s. purple	50	1·10
1019		2s. green	50	2·20
1020	**159**	3s. brown	3·50	7·50
1021	-	4s. green	2·50	7·50
1022	-	5s. blue	2·50	7·50
1023	-	10s. blue	1·30	13·00

DESIGNS—Airplane over: 50g. Windmill at St. Andra; 1s. Heidentor; 2s. Gmund; 4s. Pragraten; 5s. Torsaule; 10s. St. Charles's Church, Vienna.

160 Beaker (15th century)

1947. National Art Exhibition Fund.

1024	**160**	3g.+2g. brown	50	85
1025	-	8g.+2g. green	50	85
1026	-	10g.+5g. red	50	85
1027	-	12g.+8g. violet	50	85
1028	-	18g.+12g. brown	50	85
1029	-	20g.+10g. violet	50	1·10
1030	-	30g.+10g. green	50	1·10
1031	-	35g.+15g. red	50	1·10
1032	-	48g.+12g. purple	1·60	1·40
1033	-	60g.+20g. blue	1·60	1·40

DESIGNS: 8g. Statue of "Providence" (Donner); 10g. Benedictine Monastery, Melk; 12g. "Wife of Dr. Brante of Vienna"; 18g. "Children in a Window" (Waldmuller); 20g. Belvedere Palace Gateway; 30g. Figure of "Egeria" on fountain at Schonbrunn; 35g. National Library, Vienna; 48g. "Copper Printer's (Ernst Rohm) Workshop" (Ferdinand Schmutzer); 60g. "Girl in Straw Hat" (Amerling).

161 Racehorse

1947. Vienna Prize Race Fund.

1034	**161**	60+20g. blue on pink	30	1·40

163 Prisoner-of-war

1947. Prisoners-of-war Relief Fund.

1063	**163**	8g.+2g. green	30	85
1064	-	12g.+8g. brown	30	85
1065	-	18g.+12g. black	30	85
1066	-	35g.+15g. purple	30	85
1067	-	60g.+20g. blue	30	85
1068	-	1s.+40g. brown	30	1·60

DESIGNS: 12g. Letter from home; 18g. Gruesome camp visitor; 35g. Soldier and family reunited; 60g. Industry beckons returned soldier; 1s. Soldier sowing.

1947. Nos. 934 and 941 surch.

1069	75g. on 38g. green	50	1·60
1070	1s.40 on 16g. brown	30	55

165 Globe and Tape Machine

1947. Telegraph Centenary.

1071	**165**	40g. violet	40	65

1947. Currency Revaluation. (a) As T 146.

1072	3g. red (Lermoos)	40	20
1073	5g. red (Leopoldsberg)	40	20
1074	10g. red (Hochosterwitz)	40	20
1075	15g. red (Forchtenstein)	2·50	2·40

(b) As T 146 but larger (23½×29 mm).

1076	20g. red (Gebhartsberg)	50	20
1077	30g. red (Neusiedler Lake)	60	30
1078	40g. red (Mariazell)	1·00	20
1079	50g. red (Silvretta Peaks)	1·00	20
1080	60g. red (Semmering)	12·50	2·75
1081	70g. red (Badgastein)	5·25	20
1082	80g. red (Kaisergebirge)	5·25	55
1083	90g. red (Wayside shrine, Tragoss)	6·25	1·40

(c) As T 148.

1084	1s. violet (Durnstein)	1·30	30
1085	2s. violet (St. Christof)	1·60	55
1086	3s. violet (Heiligenblut)	31·00	2·20
1086a	5s. violet (Schonbrunn)	31·00	2·75

Nos. 1072/86a in new currency replaced previous issue at rate of 3s. (old) = 1s. (new).

166 Sacred Olympic Flame

1948. Fund for Entries to 5th Winter Olympic Games, St. Moritz.

1087	**166**	1s.+50g. blue	50	85

167 Laabenbach Viaduct, Neulenbach

1948. Reconstruction Fund.

1088	**167**	10g.+5g. grey	20	30
1089	-	20g.+10g. violet	20	30
1090	-	30g.+10g. green	50	65
1091	-	40g.+20g. green	20	30
1092	-	45g.+20g. blue	20	30
1093	-	60g.+30g. red	20	30
1094	-	75g.+35g. purple	30	45
1095	-	80g.+40g. purple	30	45
1096	-	1s.+50g. blue	30	45
1097	-	1s.40+70g. lake	60	75

DESIGNS (showing reconstruction): 20g. Vermunt Lake Dam; 30g. Danube Port, Vienna; 40g. Erzberg open-cast mine; 45g. Southern Railway Station, Vienna; 60g. Flats; 75g. Vienna Gas Works; 80g. Oil refinery; 1s. Mountain roadway; 1s.40, Parliament Building.

169 Violets

1948. Anti-tuberculosis Fund.

1098	**169**	10g.+5g. violet, mauve and green	35	35
1099	-	20g.+10g. green, light green and yellow	35	35

1100	-	30g.+10g. brown, yellow and green	4·50	4·50
1101	-	40g.+20g. green, yellow and orange	85	85
1102	-	45g.+20g. purple, mauve and yellow	30	30
1103	-	60g.+30g. red, mauve and green	30	30
1104	-	75g.+35g. green, pink and yellow	30	30
1105	-	80g.+40g. blue, pink and green	40	40
1106	-	1s.+50g. blue, ultramarine and green	40	40
1107	-	1s.40+70g. green, blue and yellow	2·75	2·75

FLOWERS: 20g. Anemone; 30g. Crocus; 40g. Primrose; 45g. Pasque flower; 60g. Rhododendron; 75g. Wild rose; 80g. Cyclamen; 1s. Gentian; 1s.40, Edelweiss.

170 Vorarlberg Montafon

1948. Provincial Costumes.

1108		3g. grey	85	1·10
1109		5g. green	30	20
1110		10g. blue	30	20
1111		15g. brown	50	20
1112	**170**	20g. green	30	20
1113	-	25g. brown	30	20
1114	-	30g. red	3·50	20
1115	-	30g. violet	1·00	20
1116	-	40g. violet	4·25	20
1117	-	40g. green	85	20
1118	-	45g. blue	4·25	75
1119	-	50g. brown	1·20	20
1120	-	60g. red	85	20
1121	-	70g. green	85	20
1122	-	75g. blue	7·25	75
1123	-	80g. rose	1·00	20
1124	-	90g. purple	55·00	55
1125	-	1s. blue	16·00	20
1126	-	1s. red	£130	20
1127	-	1s. green	70	20
1128	-	1s.20 violet	1·00	20
1129	-	1s.40 brown	3·00	30
1130	-	1s.45 red	2·50	20
1131	-	1s.50 blue	2·10	20
1132	-	1s.60 red	85	20
1133	-	1s.70 blue	4·25	1·30
1134	-	2s. green	1·60	20
1135	-	2s.20 slate	8·25	30
1136	-	2s.40 blue	2·10	25
1137	-	2s.50 brown	5·75	2·20
1138	-	2s.70 brown	1·00	1·40
1139	-	3s. lake	4·25	20
1140	-	3s.50 green	34·00	30
1141	-	4s.50 purple	1·00	1·30
1142	-	5s. purple	1·60	20
1143	-	7s. olive	6·25	2·20
1144	-	10s. grey	50·00	7·50

DESIGNS—As T **170**: 3g. "Tirol Inntal"; 5g. "Salzburg Pinzgau"; 10, 75g. "Steiermark Salzkammergut" (different designs); 15g. "Burgenland Lutzmannsburg"; 25g., 1s.60, "Wien 1850" (two different designs); 30g. (2) "Salzburg Pongau"; 40g. (2) "Wien 1840"; 45g. "Karnten Lesachtal"; 50g. "Vorarlberg Bregenzerwald"; 60g. "Karnten Lavanttal"; 70g. "Niederosterreich Wachau"; 80g. "Steiermark Ennstal"; 90g. "Steiermark Mittelsteier"; 1s. (3) "Tirol Pustertal"; 1s.20, "Niederosterreich Wienerwald"; 1s.40, "Oberosterreich Innviertel"; 1s.45, "Wilter bei Innsbruck"; 1s.50, "Wien 1853"; 1s.70, "Ost Tirol Kals"; 2s. "Oberosterreich"; 2s.20, "Ischl 1820"; 2s.40, "Kitzbuhel"; 2s.50, "Obersteiermark 1850"; 2s.70, "Kleines Walsertal"; 3s. "Burgenland"; 3s.50, "Niederosterreich 1850"; 4s.50, "Gailtal"; 5s. "Zillertal"; 7s. "Steiermark Sulmtal". 25×35 mm: 10s. "Wien 1850".

172 Kunstlerhaus

173 Hans Makart

1948. 80th Anniv of Creative Artists' Association.

1145	**172**	20g.+10g. green	10·50	8·50
1146	**173**	30g.+15g. brown	3·50	4·25
1147	-	40g.+20g. blue	3·50	4·25
1148	-	50g.+25g. violet	6·25	7·50
1149	-	60g.+30g. red	7·25	6·50
1150	-	1s.+50g. blue	7·25	8·50
1151	-	1s.40+70g. brown	21·00	26·00

PORTRAITS: 40g. K. Kundmann; 50g. A. von Siccardsburg; 60g. H. Canon; 1s. W. Unger; 1s.40, Friedr. Schmidt.

174 St. Rupert

1948. Salzburg Cathedral Reconstruction Fund.

1152	**174**	20g.+10g. green	10·50	11·00
1153	-	30g.+15g. brown	3·00	4·25
1154	-	40g.+20g. green	3·50	4·25
1155	-	50g.+25g. brown	1·00	1·10
1156	-	60g.+30g. red	1·00	1·10
1157	-	80g.+40g. purple	1·00	1·10
1158	-	1s.+50g. blue	1·00	1·60
1159	-	1s.40+70g. green	3·00	4·25

DESIGNS: 30, 40, 50, 80g. Views of Salzburg Cathedral; 60g. St. Peter's; 1s. Cathedral and Fortress; 1s.40, Madonna.

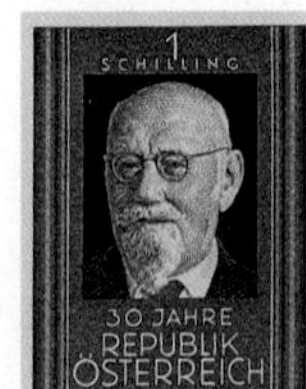

175 Pres. Renner

1948. 30th Anniv of Republic.

1160	**175**	1s. blue	3·00	2·75

See also Nos. 1224 and 1333.

176 F. Gruber and J. Mohr

1948. 130th Anniv of Composition of Carol "Silent Night, Holy Night".

1161	**176**	60g. brown	8·50	8·50

177 Boy and Hare

1949. Child Welfare Fund.

1162	**177**	40g.+10g. purple	22·00	24·00
1163	-	60g.+20g. red	22·00	24·00
1164	-	1s.+25g. blue	22·00	24·00
1165	-	1s.40+35g. green	25·00	27·00

DESIGNS: 60g. Two girls and apples in boot; 1s. Boy and birthday cake; 1s.40, Girl praying before candle.

178 Boy and Dove

1949. U.N. Int. Children's Emergency Fund.

1166	**178**	1s. blue	16·00	4·25

179 Johann Strauss

1949. 50th Death Anniv of Johann Strauss the Younger (composer).

1167	**179**	1s. blue	4·25	3·00

See also Nos. 1174, 1207 and 1229.

180 Esperanto Star

1949. Esperanto Congress, Vienna.

1168	**180**	20g. green	1·40	1·40

181 St. Gebhard

1949. Birth Millenary of St. Gebhard (Bishop of Vorarlberg).

1169	**181**	30g. violet	2·50	2·50

182 Seal of Duke Friedrich II, 1230

1949. Prisoners-of-war Relief Fund. Arms.

1170	**182**	40g.+10g. yell & brn	14·00	13·00
1171	-	60g.+15g. pink & pur	12·00	11·00
1172	-	1s.+25g. red & blue	12·00	11·00
1173	-	1s.60+40g. pink and green	16·00	16·00

ARMS: 60g. Princes of Austria, 1450; 1s. Austria, 1600; 1s.60, Austria, 1945.

1949. Death Centenary of Johann Strauss the Elder (composer). Portrait as T 179.

1174	30g. purple	2·20	2·75

183 Allegory of U.P.U.

1949. 75th Anniv of U.P.U.

1175	**183**	40g. green	5·50	5·50
1176	-	60g. red	6·50	5·50
1177	-	1s. blue	11·00	9·75

DESIGNS: 60g. Children holding "75"; 1s. Woman's head.

185 Magnifying Glass and Covers

1949. Stamp Day.

1206	**185**	60g.+15g. brown	4·25	3·75

1949. 50th Death Anniv of Karl Millocker (composer). Portrait as T 179.

1207	1s. blue	22·00	17·00

186 M. M. Daffinger

1950. 160th Birth Anniv of Moritz Michael Daffinger (painter).

1208	**186**	60g. brown	11·00	8·50

187 A. Hofer

1950. 140th Death Anniv of Andreas Hofer (patriot).

1209	**187**	60g. violet	17·00	13·00

See also Nos. 1211, 1223, 1232, 1234, 1243, 1253, 1288 and 1386.

188 Stamp of 1850

1950. Austrian Stamp Centenary.

1210	**188**	1s. black on yellow	2·75	2·20

1950. Death Centenary of Josef Madersperger (sewing machine inventor). Portrait as T 187.

1211	60g. violet	9·75	5·50

189 Arms of Austria and Carinthia

1950. 30th Anniv of Carinthian Plebiscite.

1212	**189**	60g.+15g. grn & brn	43·00	38·00
1213	-	1s.+25g. red & orange	55·00	43·00
1214	-	1s.70+40g. blue and turquoise	55·00	49·00

DESIGNS: 1s. Carinthian waving Austrian flag; 1s.70, Hand and ballot box.

190 Rooks

1950. Air.

1215	**190**	60g. violet	6·50	5·50
1216	-	1s. violet (Barn swallows)	32·00	30·00
1217	-	2s. blue (Black-headed gulls)	22·00	11·00
1218	-	3s. turquoise (Great cormorants)	£190	£160
1219	-	5s. brown (Common buzzard)	£190	£160
1220	-	10s. purple (Grey heron)	85·00	75·00
1221	-	20s. sepia (Golden eagle)	16·00	4·25

191 Philatelist

1950. Stamp Day.

1222	**191**	60g.+15g. green	13·00	11·00

1950. Birth Centenary of Alexander Girardi (actor). Portrait as T 187.

1223	30g. blue	2·40	1·90

192 Dr. Renner

1951. Death of Pres. Karl Renner.

1224	**192**	1s. black on lemon	1·90	85

193 Miner

1951. Reconstruction Fund.

1225	**193**	40g.+10g. purple	22·00	24·00
1226	-	60g.+15g. green	22·00	24·00
1227	-	1s.+25g. brown	22·00	24·00
1228	-	1s.70+40g. blue	22·00	24·00

DESIGNS: 60g. Bricklayer; 1s. Bridge-builder; 1s.70, Telegraph engineer.

1951. 150th Birth Anniv of Joseph Lanner (composer). Portrait as T 179.

1229	60g. green	7·00	3·75

194 Martin Johann Schmidt

1951. 150th Death Anniv of Schmidt (painter).

1230	**194**	1s. red	10·00	4·75

195 Scout Badge

1951. Boy Scout Jamboree.

1231	**195**	1s. red, yellow & green	7·00	6·50

1951. 10th Death Anniv of Wilhelm Kienzl (composer). Portrait as T 187.

1232	1s.50 blue	4·75	3·25

196 Laurel Branch and Olympic Emblem

1952. 6th Winter Olympic Games, Oslo.

1233	**196**	2s.40+60g. green	32·00	30·00

1952. 150th Birth Anniv of Karl Ritter von Ghega (railway engineer). Portrait as T 187.

1234	1s. green	11·00	3·25

197 Schrammel

1952. Birth Cent of Josef Schrammel (composer).

1235	**197**	1s.50 blue	11·00	3·25

See also No. 1239.

198 Cupid and Letter

1952. Stamp Day.

1236	**198**	1s.50+35g. purple	32·00	31·00

199 Breakfast Pavilion

1952. Bicentenary of Schonbrunn Menagerie.

1237	**199**	1s.50 green	9·75	3·25

200

1952. Int Union of Socialist Youth Camp, Vienna.

1238	**200**	1s.50 blue	11·00	2·20

1952. 150th Birth Anniv of Nikolaus Lenau (writer). Portrait as T 197.

1239	1s. green	11·00	3·25

202

1952. International Children's Correspondence.

1240	**202**	2s.40 blue	18·00	4·25

203 "Christus Pantocrator" (sculpture)

1952. Austrian Catholics' Day.

1241	**203**	1s.+25g. olive	16·00	15·00

204 Hugo Wolf

1953. 50th Death Anniv of Wolf (composer).

1242	**204**	1s.50 blue	12·00	3·25

1953. President Korner's 80th Birthday. As T 187 but portrait of Korner.

1243	1s.50 blue	12·00	3·25

For 1s.50 black, see No. 1288.

1953. 60th Anniv of Austrian Trade Union Movement. As No. 955 (colour changed) surch GEWERKSCHAFTS BEWEGUNG 60 JAHRE 1s+25g.

1244	1s.+25g. on 5s. blue	4·75	4·25

206 Linz National Theatre

1953. 150th Anniv of Linz National Theatre.

1245	**206**	1s.50 turquoise	27·00	4·25

207 Meeting-house, Steyr

1953. Vienna Evangelical School Rebuilding Fund.

1246	**207**	70g.+15g. purple	45	45
1247	-	1s.+25g. blue	45	45
1248	-	1s.50+40g. brown	1·10	1·10
1249	-	2s.40+60g. green	4·75	4·75
1250	-	3s.+75g. lilac	12·00	12·00

DESIGNS: 1s. J. Kepler (astronomer); 1s.50, Lutheran Bible, 1534; 2s.40, T. von Hansen (architect); 3s. School after reconstruction.

208 Child and Christmas Tree

1953. Christmas.

1251	**208**	1s. green	1·80	1·10

See also No. 1266.

209

1953. Stamp Day.

1252	**209**	1s.+25g. brown	12·00	11·00

1954. 150th Birth Anniv of M. Von Schwind (painter). As T 187 but portrait of Von Schwind.

1253	1s.50 lilac	23·00	4·25

210 Baron K. von Rokitansky

1954. 150th Birth Anniv of Von Rokitansky (anatomist).

1254	**210**	1s.50 violet	26·00	4·25

See also No. 1264.

1954. Avalanche Fund. As No. 953 (colour changed) surch LAWINENOPFER 1954 1s+20g.

1255	1s.+20g. blue	55	55

212 Surgeon with Microscope

1954. Health Service Fund.

1256	-	30g.+10g. violet	1·60	1·60
1257	**212**	70g.+15g. brown	55	55
1258	-	1s.+25g. blue	55	55
1259	-	1s.45+35g. green	85	1·10
1260	-	1s.50+35g. red	7·75	11·00
1261	-	2s.40+60g. purple	9·25	12·00

DESIGNS: 30g. Boy patient and sun-ray lamp; 1s. Mother and children; 1s.45, Operating theatre; 1s.50, Baby on scales; 2s.40, Red Cross nurse and ambulance.

213 Esperanto Star

1954. 50th Anniv of Esperanto in Austria.

1262	**213**	1s. green and brown	7·50	75

214 J. M. Rottmayr von Rosenbrunn

1954. Birth Tercentenary of Rottmayr von Rosenbrunn (painter).

1263	**214**	1s. green	19·00	4·75

1954. 25th Death Anniv of Dr. Auer von Welsbach (inventor). Portrait as T 210.

1264	1s.50 blue	55·00	4·25

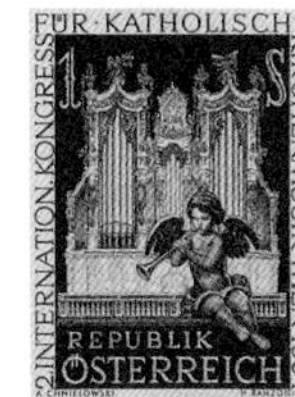

216 Great Organ, Church of St. Florian

1954. 2nd International Congress of Catholic Church Music, Vienna.

1265	**216**	1s. brown	3·50	65

1954. Christmas. As No. 1251, but colour changed.

1266	**208**	1s. blue	6·00	1·10

217 18th-century River Boat

1954. Stamp Day.

1267	**217**	1s.+25g. green	11·00	9·75

218 Arms of Austria and Newspapers

1954. 150th Anniv of State Printing Works and 250th Anniv of "Wiener-Zeitung" (newspaper).

1268	**218**	1s. black and red	4·25	85

219 "Freedom"

1955. 10th Anniv of Re-establishment of Austrian Republic.

1269	-	70g. purple	3·25	55
1270	-	1s. blue	8·50	55
1271	**219**	1s.45 red	14·00	7·00
1272	-	1s.50 brown	36·00	60
1273	-	2s.40 green	14·00	9·75

DESIGNS: 70g. Parliament Buildings; 1s. Western Railway terminus, Vienna; 1s.50, Modern houses; 2s.40, Limberg Dam.

1955. Austrian State Treaty. As No. 888, but colour changed, optd STAATSVERTRAG 1955.

1274	**142**	2s. grey	4·25	1·10

221 "Strength through Unity"

1955. 4th World Trade Unions Congress, Vienna.

1275	**221**	1s. blue	4·25	3·75

222 "Return to Work"

1955. Returned Prisoners-of-war Relief Fund.

1276	**222**	1s.+25g. brown	3·75	3·25

223 Burgtheater, Vienna

1955. Re-opening of Burgtheater and State Opera House, Vienna.

1277	**223**	1s.50 brown	6·00	85
1278	-	2s.40 blue (Opera House)	8·00	4·50

224 Globe and Flags

1955. 10th Anniv of U.N.O.

1279	**224**	2s.40 green	24·00	5·50

225 Stamp Collector

1955. Stamp Day.

1280	**225**	1s.+25g. brown	6·50	6·00

226 Mozart

1956. Birth Bicentenary of Mozart (composer).

1281	**226**	2s.40 blue	9·75	2·75

227

1956. Admission of Austria into U.N.

1282	**227**	2s.40 brown	19·00	3·75

228

1956. 5th World Power Conference, Vienna.

1283	**228**	2s.40 blue	17·00	4·25

229 Vienna and Five New Towns

1956. 23rd International Town Planning Congress.

1284	**229**	1s.45 red, black & green	5·50	1·70

230 J. B. Fischer von Erlach

1956. Birth Tercentenary of Fischer von Erlach (architect).

1285	**230**	1s.50 brown	1·80	1·80

231 "Stamp Day"

1956. Stamp Day.

1286	**231**	1s.+25g. red	5·50	5·50

1956. Hungarian Relief Fund. As No. 1173, but colours changed, surch 1956 1.50 +50 UNGARNHILFE.

1287		1s.50+50g. on 1s.60+40g. red and grey	1·10	1·10

1957. Death of Pres. Korner. As No. 1243, but colour changed.

1288	1s.50 black	3·25	2·75

233 J. Wagner von Jauregg

1957. Birth Centenary of Wagner von Jauregg (psychiatrist).

1289	**233**	2s.40 brown	6·50	4·25

234 Anton Wildgans

1957. 25th Death Anniv of Anton Wildgans (poet).

1290	**234**	1s. blue	85	75

235 Daimber (1907), Graf and Stift (1957) Post Buses

1957. 50th Anniv of Postal Coach Service.

1291	**235**	1s. black on yellow	85	75

237 Mt. Gasherbrum II

1957. Austrian Himalaya–Karakorum Expedition, 1956.

1293	**237**	1s.50 blue	75	75

236 Mariazell Basilica

1957. Buildings. (a) Size 20½×24½ mm.

1295	-	20g. purple	55	20
1296	-	30g. green	65	20
1297	-	40g. red	45	20
1298	-	50g. grey	45	20
1299	-	60g. brown	45	20
1300	-	70g. blue	90	20
1301	-	80g. brown	70	20
1302	**236**	1s. brown	1·90	30
1303	-	1s. brown	1·20	20
1304	-	1s.20 purple	1·30	45
1305	-	1s.30 green	30	20
1306	-	1s.40 blue	1·10	30
1307	-	1s.50 red	1·30	20
1308	-	1s.80 blue	1·40	20
1309	-	2s. blue	6·50	30
1310	-	2s. blue	2·20	60
1311	-	2s.20 green	1·40	20
1312	-	2s.50 violet	3·00	1·10
1313	-	3s. blue	1·60	20
1314	-	3s.40 green	2·30	1·10
1315	-	3s.50 mauve	2·40	65
1316	-	4s. violet	2·50	55
1317	-	4s.50 green	3·25	85
1318	-	5s.50 green	2·40	1·20
1319	-	6s. violet	2·50	50
1320	-	6s.40 blue	4·00	1·10
1321	-	8s. purple	5·50	1·10

(b) Larger.

1322	10s. green	5·50	55
1323	20s. purple	6·50	1·70

(c) Smaller, size 17½×21 mm.

1324	-	50g. grey	45	30
1325	**236**	1s. brown	45	30
1326	-	1s.50 purple	55	30

DESIGNS: 20g. Old Courtyard, Morbisch; 30g. Vienna Town Hall; 40g. Porcia Castle, Spittal; 50g. Heiligenstadt flats; 60g. Lederer Tower, Wells; 70g. Archbishop's Palace, Salzburg; 80g. Old farmhouse, Pinzgau; 1s. (1303) Millstatt; 1s.20, Corn Measurer's House, Bruck-on-the-Mur; 1s.30, Schattenburg Castle; 1s.40, Klagenfurt Town Hall; 1s.50, "Rabenhof" Flats, Erdberg, Vienna; 1s.80, Mint Tower, Hall-in-Tyrol; 2s. (1309) Christkindl Church; 2s. (1310) Dragon Fountain, Klagenfurt; 2s.20, Beethoven's House, Heiligenstadt, Vienna; 2s.50, Danube Bridge, Linz; 3s. "Swiss Portal", Imperial Palace, Vienna; 3s.40, Stein Gate, Krems-on-the-Danube; 3s.50, Esterhazy Palace, Eisenstadt; 4s. Vienna Gate, Hainburg; 4s.50, Schwechat Airport; 5s.50, Chur Gate, Feldkirch; 6s. Graz Town Hall; 6s.40, "Golden Roof", Innsbruck; 8s. Steyr Town Hall. 22×28½ mm: 10s. Heidenreichstein Castle. 28½×37½ mm: 20s. Melk Abbey.

238 Post Office, Linz

1957. Stamp Day.

1327	**238**	1s.+25g. green	4·75	4·25

239 Badgastein

1958. International Alpine Ski Championships, Badgastein.

1328	**239**	1s.50 blue	65	55

240 Vickers Viscount 800 OE-LAB

1958. Austrian Airlines Inaugural Flight, Vienna–London.

1329	**240**	4s. red	1·60	85

241 Mother and Child

1958. Mothers' Day.

1330	**241**	1s.50 blue	65	55

242 Walther von der Vogelweide (after 12th-century manuscript)

1958. 3rd Austrian Choir Festival, Vienna.

1331	**242**	1s.50 multicoloured	65	55

243 Dr. O. Redlich

1958. Birth Cent of Dr. Oswald Redlich (historian).

1332	**243**	2s.40 blue	95	65

1958. 40th Anniv of Republic. As T 175 but inscr "40 JAHRE".

1333	**175**	1s.50 green	1·10	95

244 Post Office, Kitzbuhel

1958. Stamp Day.

1334	**244**	2s.40+60g. blue	1·60	1·40

245 "E" building on Map of Europe

1959. Europa.

1335	**245**	2s.40 green	3·75	75

246 Monopoly Emblem and Cigars

1959. 175th Anniv of Austrian Tobacco Monopoly.

1336	**246**	2s.40 brown	95	55

247 Archduke Johann

1959. Death Cent of Archduke Johann of Austria.

1337	**247**	1s.50 green	65	45

248 Western Capercailie

1959. International Hunting Congress, Vienna.

1338	**248**	1s. purple	55	30
1339	-	1s.50 blue (Roebuck)	85	20
1340	-	2s.40 grn (Wild boar)	1·40	1·50
1341	-	3s.50 brown (Red deer family)	95	65

249 Haydn

1959. 150th Death Anniv of Haydn.

1342	**249**	1s.50 purple	85	55

250 Tyrolean Eagle

1959. 150th Anniv of Tyrolese Rising.

1343	**250**	1s.50 red	65	40

251 Microwave Transmitting Aerial, Zugspitze

1959. Inaug of Austrian Microwave Network.

1344	**251**	2s.40 blue	85	55

252 Handball Player

1959. Sports.

1345	-	1s. violet	65	30
1346	**252**	1s.50 green	95	65
1347	-	1s.80 red	65	55
1348	-	2s. purple	55	45
1349	-	2s.20 blue	65	55

DESIGNS: 1s. Runner; 1s.80, Gymnast; 2s. Hurdling; 2s.20, Hammer thrower.

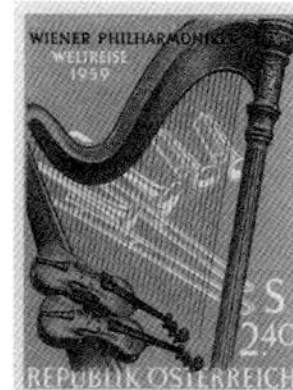
253 Orchestral Instruments

1959. Vienna Philharmonic Orchestra's World Tour.

1350	**253**	2s.40 black and blue	85	60

254 Roman Coach

1959. Stamp Day.

1351	**254**	2s.40+60g. blk & mve	1·30	1·20

255 Refugees

1960. World Refugee Year.

1352	**255**	3s. turquoise	95	70

256 Pres. Adolf Scharf

1960. President's 70th Birthday.

1353	**256**	1s.50 green	95	50

257 Youth Hostellers

1960. Youth Hostels Movement.

1354	**257**	1s. red	55	50

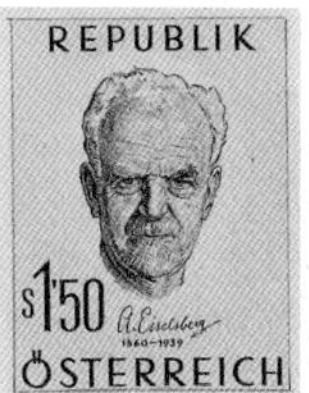
258 Dr. Eiselsberg

1960. Birth Cent of Dr. Anton Eiselsberg (surgeon).

1355	**258**	1s.50 sepia and cream	1·10	50

259 Gustav Mahler

1960. Birth Centenary of Gustav Mahler (composer).

1356	**259**	1s.50 brown	1·10	50

260 Jakob Prandtauer

1960. 300th Birth Anniv of Jakob Prandtauer (architect).

1357	**260**	1s.50 brown	1·10	50

261 Grossglockner Highway

1960. 25th Anniv of Grossglockner Alpine Highway.

1358	**261**	1s.80 blue	2·20	90

262 Ionic Capital

1960. Europa.

1359	**262**	3s. black	2·75	2·30

263 Griffen, Carinthia

1960. 40th Anniv of Carinthian Plebiscite.

1360	**263**	1s.50 green	85	50

264 Examining Proof of Engraved Stamp

1960. Stamp Day.

1361	**264**	3s.+70g. brown	2·20	2·00

265 "Freedom"

1961. Austrian Freedom Martyrs' Commem.

1362	**265**	1s.50 red	95	60

266 Hansa Brandenburg C-1

1961. "LUPOSTA" Exhibition, Vienna, and 1st Austrian Airmail Service Commemoration.

1363	**266**	5s. blue	1·60	1·50

267 Transport and Multi-unit Electric Train

1961. European Transport Ministers' Meeting.

1364	**267**	3s. olive and red	1·10	1·00

268 "Mower in the Alps" (Detail, A. Egger-Lienz)

1961. Centenary of Kunstlerhaus, Vienna. Inscr as in T 268.

1365	**268**	1s. purple and brown	55	30
1366	-	1s.50 lilac and brown	55	30
1367	-	3s. green and brown	1·60	1·20
1368	-	5s. violet and brown	1·60	1·20

PAINTINGS: 1s.50, "The Kiss" (after A. von Pettenkofen). 3s. "Portrait of a Girl" (after A. Romako). 5s. "The Triumph of Ariadne" (detail of Ariadne, after Hans Makart).

269 Observatory on Sonnblick Mountain

1961. 75th Anniv of Sonnblick Meteorological Observatory.

1369	**269**	1s.80 blue	85	60

270 Lavanttaler Colliery

1961. 15th Anniv of Nationalized Industries. Inscr "JAHRE VERSTAATLICHTE UNTERNEHMUNGEN".

1370	**270**	1s. black	30	25
1371	-	1s.50 green	30	25
1372	-	1s.80 red	95	90
1373	-	3s. mauve	1·30	1·20
1374	-	5s. blue	1·60	1·40

DESIGNS: 1s.50, Turbine; 1s.80, Industrial plant; 3s. Steelworks, Linz; 5s. Oil refinery, Schwechat.

271 Mercury

1961. World Bank Congress, Vienna.

1375	**271**	3s. black	95	90

272 Arms of Burgenland

1961. 40th Anniv of Burgenland.

1376	**272**	1s.50 red, yellow & sepia	65	60

273 Liszt

1961. 150th Birth Anniv of Franz Liszt (composer).

1377	**273**	3s. brown	85	60

274 Rust Post Office

1961. Stamp Day.

1378	**274**	3s.+70g. green	2·00	2·00

275 Court of Accounts

1961. Bicentenary of Court of Accounts.

1379	**275**	1s. sepia	55	50

276 Glockner-Kaprun Power Station

1962. 15th Anniv of Electric Power Nationalization. Inscr as in T 276.

1380	**276**	1s. blue	20	25
1381	-	1s.50 purple	45	40
1382	-	1s.80 green	1·20	1·10
1383	-	3s. brown	85	80
1384	-	4s. red	95	90
1385	-	6s.40 black	2·75	2·50

DESIGNS: 1s.50, Ybbs-Persenbeug (Danube); 1s.80, Luner See; 3s. Grossraming (Enns River); 4s. Bisamberg Transformer Station; 6s.40, St. Andra Power Stations.

1962. Death Cent of Johann Nestroy (playwright). Portrait as T 187.

1386	1s. violet	65	60

277 F. Gauermann

1962. Death Cent of Friedrich Gauermann (painter).

1387	**277**	1s.50 blue	65	60

278 Scout Badge and Handclasp

1962. 50th Anniv of Austrian Scout Movement.

1388	**278**	1s.50 green	85	80

279 Forest and Lake

1962. "The Austrian Forest".

1389	**279**	1s. grey	75	70
1390	-	1s.50 brown	85	80
1391	-	3s. myrtle	2·75	2·50

DESIGNS: 1s.50, Deciduous forest; 3s. Fir and larch forest.

280 Electric Locomotive and Steam Locomotive "Austria" (1837)

1962. 125th Anniv of Austrian Railways.

1392	**280**	3s. black and buff	2·20	1·50

281 Engraving Die

1962. Stamp Day.

1393	**281**	3s.+70g. violet	2·75	2·50

282 Postal Officials of 1863

1963. Centenary of Paris Postal Conference.

1394	**282**	3s. sepia and yellow	1·30	90

283 Hermann Bahr

1963. Birth Centenary of Hermann Bahr (writer).

1395	**283**	1s.50 sepia and blue	85	40

284 St. Florian (statue)

1963. Cent of Austrian Voluntary Fire Brigade.

1396	**284**	1s.50 black and pink	85	50

285 Flag and Emblem

1963. 5th Austrian Trade Unions Federation Congress.

1397	**285**	1s.50 red, sepia & grey	65	40

286 Crests of Tyrol and Austria

1963. 600th Anniv of Tyrol as an Austrian Province.

1398	**286**	1s.50 multicoloured	65	40

287 Prince Eugene of Savoy

1963. Birth Tercent of Prince Eugene of Savoy.

1399	**287**	1s.50 violet	65	40

288 Centenary Emblem

1963. Centenary of Red Cross.

1400	**288**	3s. silver, red and black	95	80

289 Skiing (slalom)

1963. Winter Olympic Games, Innsbruck, 1964. Centres black; inscr gold; background colours given.

1401	**289**	1s. grey	30	20
1402	-	1s.20 blue	45	30
1403	-	1s.50 grey	55	40
1404	-	1s.80 purple	65	60
1405	-	2s.20 green	1·10	1·00
1406	-	3s. slate	75	60
1407	-	4s. blue	1·30	1·20

DESIGNS: 1s.20, Skiing (biathlon); 1s.50, Ski jumping; 1s.80, Figure skating; 2s.20, Ice hockey; 3s. Tobogganing; 4s. Bobsleighing.

290 Vienna "101" P.O. and Railway Shed

1963. Stamp Day.

1408	**290**	3s.+70g. black & drab	1·10	1·00

291 "The Holy Family" (Josef Stammel)

1963. Christmas.

1409	**291**	2s. green	65	40

292 Nasturtium

1964. Int Horticultural Exn, Vienna. Multicoloured.

1410	1s. Type **292**	30	20
1411	1s.50 Peony	40	25
1412	1s.80 Clematis	45	40
1413	2s.20 Dahlia	95	90
1414	3s. Convolvulus	1·10	1·00
1415	4s. Mallow	1·60	1·50

293 Gothic Statue and Stained-glass Window

1964. Romanesque Art Exhibition, Vienna.

1416	**293**	1s.50 blue and black	65	60

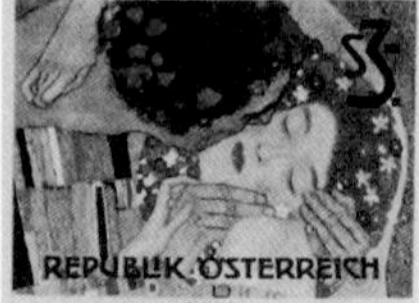

294 Pallas Athene and Interior of Assembly Hall, Parliament Building

1964. 2nd Parliamentary and Scientific Conference, Vienna.

1417	**294**	1s.80 black and green	55	50

295 "The Kiss" (Gustav Klimt)

1964. Re-opening of "Viennese Secession" Exn Hall.

1418	**295**	3s. multicoloured	95	90

296 "Comforting the Sick"

1964. 350th Anniv of Order of Brothers of Mercy in Austria.

1419	**296**	1s.50 blue	75	70

297 "Bringing News of the Victory at Kunersdorf" (Bellotto)

1964. 15th U.P.U. Congress, Vienna. Paintings.

1420	**297**	1s. purple	20	15
1421	-	1s.20 brown	45	30
1422	-	1s.50 blue	30	25
1423	-	1s.80 violet	65	60
1424	-	2s.20 black	85	80

1425	-	3s. purple	55	50
1426	-	4s. green	1·10	1·00
1427	-	6s.40 purple	3·50	3·25

PAINTINGS: 1s.20, "Changing Horses" (Hormann); 1s.50, "The Wedding Trip" (Schwind); 1s.80, "Postboys returning Home" (Raffalt); 2s.20, "The Vienna Mail Coach" (Klein); 3s. "Changing Horses" (Gauermann); 4s. "Postal Tracked-vehicle in Mountain Village" (Pilch); 6s.40, "Saalbach Post Office and Post-bus" (Pilch).

298 Vienna, from the Hochhaus (N.)

1964. "WIPA" Stamp Exhibition, Vienna (1965) (1st issue). Multicoloured.

1428	1s.50+30g. Type **298**	65	65
1429	1s.50+30g. N.E.	65	65
1430	1s.50+30g. E.	65	65
1431	1s.50+30g. S.E.	65	65
1432	1s.50+30g. S.	65	65
1433	1s.50+30g. S.W.	65	65
1434	1s.50+30g. W.	65	65
1435	1s.50+30g. N.W.	65	65

The designs show a panoramic view of Vienna, looking to different points of compass (indicated on stamps). The inscription reads "Vienna welcomes you to WIPA 1965".

See also Nos. 1447/52.

299 "Workers"

1964. Centenary of Austrian Workers' Movement.

1436	**299**	1s. black	55	45

300 Europa "Flower"

1964. Europa.

1437	**300**	3s. blue	2·40	85

301 Radio Receiver Dial

1964. 40th Anniv of Austrian Broadcasting Service.

1438	**301**	1s. sepia and red	55	45

302 Old Printing Press

1964. 6th International Graphical Federation Congress, Vienna.

1439	**302**	1s.50 black and drab	55	45

303 Post-bus Station, St. Gilgen

1964. Stamp Day.

1440	**303**	3s.+70g. multicoloured	1·60	1·30

304 Dr. Adolf Scharf

1965. Pres. Scharf Commemoration.

1441	**304**	1s.50 blue and black	85	45

305 "Reconstruction"

1965. "20 Years of Reconstruction".

1442	**305**	1s.80 lake	65	50

306 University Seal, 1365

1965. 600th Anniv of Vienna University.

1443	**306**	3s. red and gold	95	80

307 "St. George" (after engraving by Altdorfer)

1965. Danubian Art.

1444	**307**	1s.80 blue	65	50

308 I.T.U. Emblem, Morse Key and T.V. Aerial

1965. Centenary of I.T.U.

1445	**308**	3s. violet	95	50

309 F. Raimund

1965. 175th Birth Anniv of Ferdinand Raimund (actor and playwright).

1446	**309**	3s. purple	85	45

310 Egyptian Hieroglyphs on Papyrus

1965. "WIPA" Stamp Exhibition, Vienna (2nd issue). "Development of the Letter".

1447	**310**	1s.50+40g. black and pink	55	45
1448	-	1s.80+50g. black and yellow	65	50
1449	-	2s.20+60g. black and lilac	1·20	95
1450	-	3s.+80g. black & yell	95	80
1451	-	4s.+1s. black & blue	1·50	1·20
1452	-	5s.+1s.20 black & grn	2·20	1·70

DESIGNS: 1s.80, Cuneiform writing; 2s.20, Latin; 3c. Ancient letter and seal; 4s.19th-century letter; 5s. Typewriter.

311 Gymnasts with Wands

1965. 4th Gymnaestrada, Vienna.

1453	**311**	1s.50 black and blue	55	25
1454	-	3s. black and brown	85	45

DESIGNS: 3s. Girls exercising with tambourines.

312 Dr. I. Semmelweis

1965. Death Cent of Ignaz Semmelweis (physician).

1455	**312**	1s.50 lilac	55	25

313 F. G. Waldmuller (self-portrait)

1965. Death Cent of F. G. Waldmuller (painter).

1456	**313**	3s. black	95	50

314 Red Cross and Gauze

1965. Red Cross Conference, Vienna.

1457	**314**	3s. red and black	95	45

315 Flag and Crowned Eagle

1965. 50th Anniv of Austrian Towns Union.

1458	**315**	1s.50 multicoloured	85	50

316 Austrian Flag, U. N. Emblem and Headquarters

1965. 10th Anniv of Austria's Membership of U.N.O.

1459	**316**	3s. sepia, red and blue	95	50

317 University Building

1965. 150th Anniv of University of Technology, Vienna.

1460	**317**	1s.50 violet	65	35

318 Bertha von Suttner

1965. 60th Anniv of Nobel Peace Prize Award to Bertha von Suttner (writer).

1461	**318**	1s.50 black	65	35

319 Postman delivering Mail

1965. Stamp Day.

1462	**319**	3s.+70g. green	1·60	1·30

320 Postal Code Map

1966. Introduction of Postal Code System.

1463	**320**	1s.50 black, red & yell	65	35

321 P.T.T. Headquarters

1966. Centenary of Austrian Posts and Telegraphs Administration.

1464	**321**	1s.50 black on cream	65	35

322 M. Ebner-Eschenbach

1966. 50th Death Anniv of Maria Ebner-Eschenbach (writer).

1465	**322**	3s. purple	95	45

323 Big Wheel

1966. Bicentenary of Vienna Prater.

1466	**323**	1s.50 green	65	25

324 Josef Hoffmann

1966. 10th Death Anniv of Josef Hoffmann (architect).

1467	**324**	3s. brown	95	50

325 Bank Emblem

1966. 150th Anniv of Austrian National Bank.

1468	**325**	3s. brown, grn & drab	95	50

326 Arms of Wiener Neustadt

1966. "Wiener Neustadt 1440–93" Art Exhibition.

1469	**326**	1s.50 multicoloured	65	35

327 Puppy

1966. 120th Anniv of Vienna Animal Protection Society.

1470	**327**	1s.80 black and yellow	65	50

328 Columbine

1966. Alpine Flora. Multicoloured.

1471		1s.50 Type **328**	50	25
1472		1s.80 Turk's cap	55	25
1473		2s.20 Wulfenia	65	40
1474		3s. Globe flower	75	45
1475		4s. Orange lily	85	60
1476		5s. Alpine anemone	1·90	85

329 Fair Building

1966. Wels International Fair.

1477	**329**	3s. blue	95	45

330 Peter Anich

1966. Death Bicent of Peter Anich (cartographer).

1478	**330**	1s.80 black	65	35

331 "Suffering"

1966. 15th International Occupational Health Congress, Vienna.

1479	**331**	3s. black and red	95	50

332 "Eunuchus" by Terence (engraving, Johann Gruninger)

1966. Austrian National Library, Vienna. Mult.

1480		1s.50 Type **332** (Theatre collection)	45	20
1481		1s.80 Detail of title page of Willem Blaeu's atlas (Cartography collection)	50	25
1482		2s.20 "Herrengasse, Vienna" (Anton Stutzinger (Pictures and portraits collection))	55	35
1483		3s. Illustration from Rene of Anjou's "Livre du Cuer d'Amours Espris" (Manuscripts collection)	1·10	50

333 Young Girl

1966. Austrian "Save the Children" Fund.

1484	**333**	3s. black and blue	85	45

334 Strawberries

1966. Fruits. Multicoloured.

1485		50g. Type **334**	55	25
1486		1s. Grapes	55	20
1487		1s.50 Apple	55	25
1488		1s.80 Blackberries	85	70
1489		2s.20 Apricots	85	70
1490		3s. Cherries	95	80

335 16th-century Postman

1966. Stamp Day.

1491	**335**	3s.+70g. multicoloured	1·10	85

336 Arms of Linz University

1966. Inauguration of Linz University.

1492	**336**	3s. multicoloured	95	50

337 Skater of 1867

1967. Centenary of Vienna Skating Assn.

1493	**337**	3s. indigo and blue	95	50

338 Dancer with Violin

1967. Centenary of "Blue Danube" Waltz.

1494	**338**	3s. purple	95	45

339 Dr. Schonherr

1967. Birth Cent of Dr. Karl Schonherr (poet).

1495	**339**	3s. brown	95	50

340 Ice Hockey Goalkeeper

1967. World Ice Hockey Championships, Vienna.

1496	**340**	3s. blue and green	95	80

341 Violin and Organ

1967. 125th Anniv of Vienna Philharmonic Orchestra.

1497	**341**	3s.50 blue	95	45

342 "Mother and Children" (aquarelle, Peter Fendi)

1967. Mother's Day.

1498	**342**	2s. multicoloured	65	50

343 "Madonna" (Gothic wood-carving)

1967. "Gothic Art in Austria" Exhibition, Krems.

1499	**343**	3s. green	95	35

344 Jewelled Cross

1967. "Salzburg Treasures" Exhibition, Salzburg Cathedral.

1500	**344**	3s.50 multicoloured	95	50

345 "The White Swan" (from Kokoschkas tapestry "Cupid and Psyche")

1967. "Art of the Nibelungen District" Exhibition, Pochlarn.

1501	**345**	2s. multicoloured	65	35

346 Vienna

1967. 10th European Talks, Vienna.

1502	**346**	3s. black and red	85	45

347 Champion Bull

1967. Centenary of Ried Fair.

1503	**347**	2s. purple	65	35

348 Colorado Potato Beetle

1967. 6th Int Plant Protection Congress, Vienna.

1504	**348**	3s. multicoloured	95	50

349 Locomotive No. 671

1967. Centenary of Brenner Railway.

1505	**349**	3s.50 green and brown	95	50

350 "Christ" (fresco detail)

1967. Lambach Frescoes.
1506 **350** 2s. multicoloured 65 45

351 Prater Hall, Vienna

1967. International Trade Fairs Congress, Vienna.
1507 **351** 2s. purple and cream 85 45

352 Rector's Medallion and Chain

1967. 275th Anniv of Fine Arts Academy, Vienna.
1508 **352** 2s. brown, yellow & blue 85 45

353 Bible on Rock (from commemorative coin of 1717)

1967. 450th Anniv of the Reformation.
1509 **353** 3s.50 blue 85 45

354 Forest Trees

1967. 100 Years of Austrian University Forestry Studies.
1510 **354** 3s.50 green 1·30 70

355 Memorial, Vienna

1967. 150th Anniv of Land Registry.
1511 **355** 2s. green 55 25

356 "St. Leopold" (stained-glass window, Heiligenkreuz Monastery)

1967. Margrave Leopold the Holy.
1512 **356** 1s.80 multicoloured 55 25

357 "Music and Art"

1967. 150th Anniv of Academy of Music and Dramatic Art, Vienna.
1513 **357** 3s.50 black and violet 95 50

358 St. Mary's Altar, Nonnberg Convent, Salzburg

1967. Christmas.
1514 **358** 2s. green 65 35

359 "The Letter- carrier" (from playing-card)

1967. Stamp Day.
1515 **359** 3s.50+80g. mult 1·60 85

360 Ski Jump, Stadium and Mountains

1968. Winter University Games, Innsbruck.
1516 **360** 2s. blue 65 35

361 C. Sitte

1968. 125th Birth Anniv of Camillo Sitte (architect).
1517 **361** 2s. brown 55 45

362 Mother and Child

1968. Mothers' Day.
1518 **362** 2s. olive 55 45

363 "Veterinary Medicine"

1968. Bicentenary of Vienna Veterinary College.
1519 **363** 3s.50 gold, pur & drab 85 70

364 Bride with Lace Veil

1968. Centenary of Vorarlberg Lace.
1520 **364** 3s.50 blue 85 70

365 Etrich Limousine

1968. "IFA Wien 1968" Airmail Stamp Exhibition, Vienna.
1521 **365** 2s. brown 55 45
1522 - 3s.50 green 95 80
1523 - 5s. blue 1·70 1·40

DESIGNS: 3s.50, Sud Aviation SE 210 Caravelle; 5s. Douglas DC-8 A-8021.

366 Horse-racing

1968. Centenary of Freudenau Gallop Races.
1524 **366** 3s.50 brown 95 50

367 Landsteiner

1968. Birth Centenary of Dr. Karl Landsteiner (physician and pathologist).
1525 **367** 3s.50 blue 95 50

368 P. Rosegger

1968. 50th Death Anniv of Peter Rosegger (writer).
1526 **368** 2s. green 65 35

369 A. Kauffmann (self-portrait)

1968. Exhibition of Angelica Kauffmann's Paintings, Bregenz.
1527 **369** 2s. violet 65 45

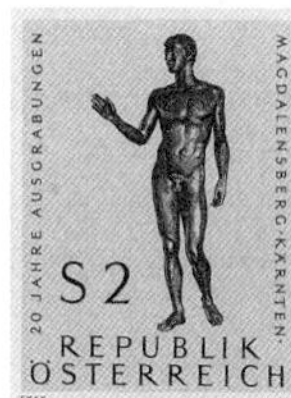

370 Statue of Young Man (Helenenberg site)

1968. Magdalensberg Excavations, Carinthia.
1528 **370** 2s. black and green 55 35

371 "The Bishop" (Romanesque carving)

1968. 750th Anniv of Graz-Seckau Diocese.
1529 **371** 2s. grey 55 35

372 K. Moser

1968. 50th Death Anniv of Koloman Moser (graphic artist).
1530 **372** 2s. brown and red 55 35

373 Human Rights Emblem

1968. Human Rights Year.
1531 **373** 1s.50 red, green & grey 95 50

374 Arms and Provincial Shields

1968. 50th Anniv of Republic. Multicoloured.
1532 2s. Type **374** 55 35
1533 2s. Karl Renner (first President of Second Republic) 55 35
1534 2s. First Article of Constitution 55 35

375 Crib, Oberndorf, Salzburg

1968. 150th Anniv of "Silent Night, Holy Night" (carol).
1535 **375** 2s. green 65 35

376 Mercury

1968. Stamp Day.
1536 **376** 3s.50+80g. green 1·10 1·10

377 Fresco (Troger), Melk Monastery

1968. Baroque Frescoes. Designs showing frescoes in locations given. Multicoloured.

1537	2s. Type **377**	65	60
1538	2s. Altenburg Monastery	65	60
1539	2s. Rohrenbach-Greillenstein	65	60
1540	2s. Ebenfurth Castle	65	60
1541	2s. Halbthurn Castle	65	60
1542	2s. Maria Treu Church, Vienna	65	60

Nos. 1537/9 are the work of Anton Troger and Nos. 1540/2 that of Franz Maulbertsch.

378 "Madonna and Child"

1969. 500th Anniv of Vienna Diocese. Statues in St. Stephen's Cathedral, Vienna.

1543	**378**	2s. blue	65	60
1544	-	2s. grey	65	60
1545	-	2s. green	65	60
1546	-	2s. purple	65	60
1547	-	2s. black	65	60
1548	-	2s. brown	65	60

DESIGNS: No. 1544, "St. Christopher"; No. 1545, "St. George"; No. 1546, "St. Paul"; No. 1547, "St. Sebastian"; No. 1548, "St. Stephen".

379 Parliament Building, Vienna

1969. Interparliamentary Union Meeting, Vienna.
1549 **379** 2s. green 55 35

380 Colonnade

1969. Europa.
1550 **380** 2s. multicoloured 1·60 45

381 "Council Members"

1969. 20th Anniv of Council of Europe.
1551 **381** 3s.50 multicoloured 95 60

382 Soldiers

1969. Austrian Armed Forces.
1552 **382** 2s. brown and red 65 35

383 "Don Giovanni"

1969. Centenary of State Opera, Vienna. Sheet 182×212 mm. T 383 and similar scenes.
MS1553 2s.×8 each brown, red and gold 6·50 6·50
DESIGNS—Scenes from Opera and Ballet: "Don Giovanni" (Mozart), "The Magic Flute" (Mozart), "Fidelio" (Beethoven), "Lohengrin" (Wagner), "Don Carlos" (Verdi), "Carmen" (Bizet), "Der Rosenkavlier" (R. Strauss) and "Swan Lake" (Tchaikovsky).

384 Maximilian's Armour

1969. "Maximilian I" Exhibition, Innsbruck.
1554 **384** 2s. black 65 35

385 Viennese "Privilege" Seal

1969. 19th International Union of Local Authorities Congress, Vienna.
1555 **385** 2s. red, brown & ochre 65 35

386 Young Girl

1969. 20th Anniv of "SOS" Children's Villages Movement.
1556 **386** 2s. brown and green 65 35

387 Hands clasping Spanner

1969. 50th Anniv of Int Labour Organization.
1557 **387** 2s. green 65 35

388 Austrian "Flag" encircling Globe

1969. "Austrians Living Abroad" Year.
1558 **388** 3s.50 red and green 95 50

389 "El Cid killing a Bull" (Goya)

1969. Bicentenary of Albertina Art Collection, Vienna. Multicoloured.

1559	2s. Type **389**	55	55
1560	2s. "Young Hare" (Durer)	55	55
1561	2s. "Madonna with Pomegranate" (Raphael)	55	55
1562	2s. "The Painter and the Amateur" (Bruegel)	55	55
1563	2s. "Rubens's Son, Nicholas" (Rubens)	55	55
1564	2s. "Self-portrait" (Rembrandt)	55	55
1565	2s. "Madame de Pompadour" (detail, Guerin)	55	55
1566	2s. "The Artist's Wife" (Schiele)	55	55

390 Pres. Jonas

1969. Pres. Franz Jonas's 70th Birthday.
1567 **390** 2s. blue and grey 55 45

391 Posthorn and Lightning over Globe

1969. 50th Anniv of Post and Telegraph Employees Union.
1568 **391** 2s. multicoloured 55 45

392 Savings Bank (c. 1450)

1969. 150th Anniv of Austrian Savings Bank.
1569 **392** 2s. green and silver 55 45

393 "The Madonna" (Egger-Lienz)

1969. Christmas.
1570 **393** 2s. purple and yellow 55 45

394 Unken, Salzburg, Post-house Sign (after F. Zeller)

1969. Stamp Day.
1571 **394** 3s.50+80g. black, red and stone 95 85

395 J. Schoffel

1970. 60th Death Anniv of Josef Schoffel ("Saviour of the Vienna Woods").
1572 **395** 2s. purple 45 35

396 St. Clement Hofbauer

1970. 150th Death Anniv of St. Clement Hofbauer (theologian).
1573 **396** 2s. brown and green 45 35

397 Chancellor Leopold Figl

1970. 25th Anniv of Austrian Republic.
1574 **397** 2s. olive 65 35
1575 - 2s. brown 65 35
DESIGN: No. 1575, Belvedere Castle.

398 Krimml Waterfalls

1970. Nature Conservation Year.
1576 **398** 2s. green 1·10 70

399 Oldest University Seal

1970. 300th Anniv of Leopold Franz University, Innsbruck.

1577	**399**	2s. black and red	55	45

400 "Musikverein" Organ

1970. Centenary of "Musikverein" Building.

1578	**400**	2s. purple and gold	55	45

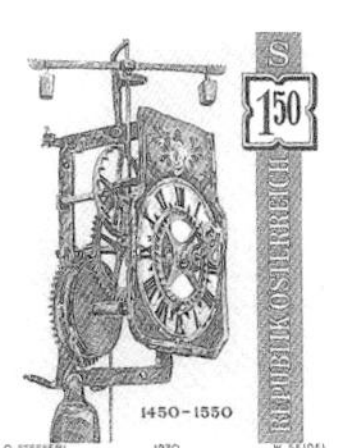
401 Tower Clock, 1450–1550

1970. Antique Clocks.

1579	**401**	1s.50 brown and cream	55	45
1580	-	1s.50 green & lt green	55	45
1581	-	2s. blue and pale blue	65	50
1582	-	2s. red and purple	65	50
1583	-	3s.50 brown and buff	1·10	85
1584	-	3s.50 purple and lilac	1·10	85

DESIGNS: No. 1580, Empire "lyre" clock, 1790–1815; No. 1581, Pendant ball clock, 1600–50; No. 1582, Pocket-watch and signet, 1800–30; No. 1583, Bracket clock, 1720–60; No. 1584, "Biedermeier" pendulum clock and musical-box, 1820–50.

402 "The Beggar Student" (Millocker)

1970. Famous Operettas.

1585	**402**	1s.50 turquoise & green	55	45
1586	-	1s.50 blue and yellow	55	45
1587	-	2s. purple and pink	65	50
1588	-	2s. brown and green	65	50
1589	-	3s.50 blue and light blue	1·10	85
1590	-	3s.50 blue and buff	1·10	85

OPERETTAS: No. 1586, "Die Fledermaus" (Johann Strauss the younger); 1587, "A Waltz Dream" (O. Straus); 1588, "The Birdseller" (C. Zeller); 1589, "The Merry Widow" (F. Lehar); 1590, "Two Hearts in Waltz-time" (R. Stoiz).

403 Scene from "The Gipsy Baron" (J. Strauss)

1970. 25th Anniv of Bregenz Festival.

1591	**403**	3s.50 blue, buff & ult	95	50

404 Festival Emblem

1970. 50th Anniv of Salzburg Festival.

1592	**404**	3s.50 multicoloured	95	50

405 T. Koschat

1970. 125th Birth Anniv of Thomas Koschat (composer and poet).

1593	**405**	2s. brown	55	45

406 "Head of St. John", from sculpture "Mount of Olives", Ried Church (attributed to T. Schwanthaler)

1970. 13th World Veterans Federation General Assembly.

1594	**406**	3s.50 sepia	95	50

407 Climbers and Mountains

1970. "Walking and Mountaineering".

1595	**407**	2s. blue and mauve	55	35

408 A. Cossmann

1970. Birth Cent of Alfred Cossmann (engraver).

1596	**408**	2s. brown	55	35

409 Arms of Carinthia

1970. 50th Anniv of Carinthian Plebiscite.

1597	**409**	2s. multicoloured	55	35

410 U.N. Emblem

1970. 25th Anniv of United Nations.

1598	**410**	3s.50 blue and black	95	50

411 "Adoration of the Shepherds" (carving, Garsten Monastery)

1970. Christmas.

1599	**411**	2s. blue	45	35

412 Saddle, Harness and Posthorn

1970. Stamp Day.

1600	**412**	3s.50+80g. black, yellow and grey	1·10	1·10

413 Pres. K. Renner

1970. Birth Centenary of Pres. Renner.

1601	**413**	2s. purple	55	35

414 Beethoven (after painting by Waldmuller)

1970. Birth Bicentenary of Beethoven.

1602	**414**	3s.50 black and stone	95	60

415 E. Handel-Mazzetti

1971. Birth Centenary of Enrica Handel-Mazzetti (novelist).

1603	**415**	2s. brown	45	25

416 "Safety for Children"

1971. Road Safety.

1604	**416**	2s. multicoloured	65	35

417 Florentine Bowl, c. 1580

1971. Austrian Art Treasures (1st series). Sculpture and Applied Art.

1605	**417**	1s.50 green and grey	55	45
1606	-	2s. purple and grey	85	70
1607	-	3s.50 yellow, brn & grey	1·30	1·00

DESIGNS: 2s. Ivory equestrian statuette of Joseph I, 1693 (Matthias Steinle); 3s.50, Salt-cellar, c. 1570 (Cellini).

See also Nos. 1609/11, 1632/4 and 1651/3.

418 Shield of Trade Association

1971. 23rd International Chamber of Commerce Congress, Vienna.

1608	**418**	3s.50 multicoloured	85	50

419 "Jacopo de Strada" (Titian)

1971. Austrian Art Treasures (2nd series).

1609	**419**	1s.50 purple	55	45
1610	-	2s. black	85	70
1611	-	3s.50 brown	1·30	1·00

PAINTINGS: 2s. "The Village Feast" (Brueghel); 3s.50, "Young Venetian Woman" (Durer).

420 Notary's Seal

1971. Austrian Notarial Statute Cent Congress.

1612	**420**	3s.50 purple and brown	85	45

421 "St. Matthew" (altar sculpture)

1971. "Krems Millennium of Art" Exhibition.

1613	**421**	2s. brown and purple	45	25

422 Dr. A. Neilreich

1971. Death Cent of Dr. August Neilreich (botanist).

1614	**422**	2s. brown	45	25

423 Singer with Lyre

1971. International Choir Festival, Vienna.
1615 **423** 4s. blue, gold & lt blue 95 80

424 Arms of Kitzbuhel

1971. 700th Anniv of Kitzbuhel.
1616 **424** 2s.50 multicoloured 55 45

425 Stock Exchange Building

1971. Bicentenary of Vienna Stock Exchange.
1617 **425** 4s. brown 85 50

426 Old and New Fair Halls

1971. "50 Years of Vienna International Fairs".
1618 **426** 2s.50 purple 55 45

427 O.G.B. Emblem

1971. 25th Anniv of Austrian Trade Unions Federation.
1619 **427** 2s. multicoloured 45 35

428 Arms and Insignia

1971. 50th Anniv of Burgenland Province.
1620 **428** 4s. multicoloured 45 35

429 "Marcus" Veteran Car

1971. 75th Anniv of Austrian Automobile, Motor Cycle and Touring Club.
1621 **429** 4s. black and green 85 60

430 Europa Bridge, Brenner Highway

1971. Inauguration of Brenner Highway.
1622 **430** 4s. blue 85 60

431 Iron-ore Workings, Erzberg

1971. 25 Years of Nationalized Industries.
1623 **431** 1s.50 brown 55 45
1624 - 2s. blue 55 45
1625 - 4s. green 1·10 85
DESIGNS: 2s. Nitrogen Works, Linz; 4s. Iron and Steel works, Linz.

432 Electric Train on the Semmering Line

1971. Railway Anniversaries.
1626 **432** 2s. purple 55 45

433 E. Tschermak-Seysenegg

1971. Birth Centenary of Dr. E. Tshermak-Seysenegg (biologist).
1627 **433** 2s. purple and grey 45 35

434 Angling

1971. Sports.
1628 **434** 2s. brown 45 35

435 "The Infant Jesus as Saviour" (from miniature by Durer)

1971. Christmas.
1629 **435** 2s. multicoloured 55 45

436 "50 Years"

1971. 50th Anniv of Austrian Philatelic Clubs Association.
1630 **436** 4s.+1s.50 pur & gold 1·30 1·00

437 Franz Grillparzer (from miniature by Daffinger)

1972. Death Centenary of Grillparzer (dramatist).
1631 **437** 2s. black, brown & stone 65 35

438 Roman Fountain, Friesach

1972. Austrian Art Treasures (3rd series). Fountains.
1632 **438** 1s.50 purple 55 45
1633 - 2s. brown 85 70
1634 - 2s.50 green 1·30 1·00
DESIGNS: 2s. Lead Fountain, Heiligenkreuz Abbey; 2s.50. Leopold Fountain, Innsbruck.

439 Hofburg Palace

1972. 4th European Postal Ministers' Conf, Vienna.
1635 **439** 4s. violet 95 80

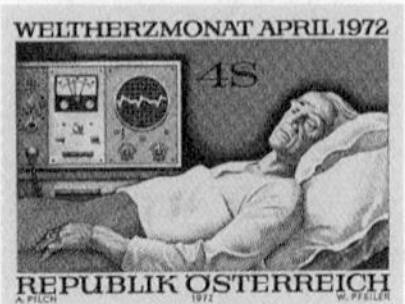

440 Heart Patient

1972. World Heart Month.
1636 **440** 4s. brown 95 80

441 "Woman's Head" (sculpture, Gurk Cathedral)

1972. 900th Anniv of Gurk Diocese.
1637 **441** 2s. purple and gold 65 50

442 Vienna Town Hall and Congress Emblem

1972. 9th International Public and Co-operative Economy Congress, Vienna.
1638 **442** 4s. black, red and yellow 1·10 70

443 Lienz-Pelos Pylon Line

1972. 25th Anniv of Electric Power Nationalization.
1639 **443** 70g. violet and grey 45 35
1640 - 2s.50 brown and grey 65 50
1641 - 4s. blue and grey 1·10 85
DESIGNS: 2s.50, Vienna-Semmering Power Station; 4s. Zemm Dam and lake.

444 Runner with Torch

1972. Passage of the Olympic Torch through Austria.
1642 **444** 2s. brown and red 55 45

445 "Hermes" (C. Laib)

1972. "Late Gothic Art" Exhibition, Salzburg.
1643 **445** 2s. purple 55 45

446 Pears

1972. Amateur Gardeners' Congress, Vienna.
1644 **446** 2s.50 multicoloured 75 60

447 "Spanish Walk"

1972. 400th Anniv of the Spanish Riding School, Vienna. Sheet 136×181 mm containing T 447 and similar square designs each in purple, red and gold.
MS1645 2s. Type **447**; 2s. "Piaffe"; 2s.50 "Levade"; 2s.50 "On the long rein"; 4s. "Capriole"; 4s. "Courbette" 5·50 5·50

448 University Arms

1972. Cent of University of Agriculture, Vienna.
1646 **448** 2s. multicoloured 55 45

449 Old University Buildings (after F. Danreiter)

1972. 350th Anniv of Paris Lodron University, Salzburg.
1647 **449** 4s. brown 95 80

450 C. M. Ziehrer

1972. 50th Death Anniv of Carl M. Ziehrer (composer and conductor).
1648 **450** 2s. red 55 45

451 "Virgin and Child", Inzersdorf Church

1972. Christmas.
1649 **451** 2s. purple and green 65 50

452 18th-century Viennese Postman

1972. Stamp Day.
1650 **452** 4s.+1s. green 1·30 1·00

453 State Sledge of Maria Theresa

1972. Austrian Art Treasures (4th series). Carriages from the Imperial Coach House.
1651 **453** 1s.50 brown and bistre 55 45
1652 - 2s. green and bistre 85 70
1653 - 2s.50 purple and bistre 1·30 1·00
DESIGNS: 2s. Coronation landau; 2s.50, Hapsburg State Coach.

454 Telephone Network

1972. Completion of Austrian Telephone System Automation.
1654 **454** 2s. black and yellow 55 45

455 "Drug Addict"

1973. Campaign against Drug Abuse.
1655 **455** 2s. multicoloured 75 45

456 A. Petzold

1973. 50th Death Anniv of Alfons Petzold (writer).
1656 **456** 2s. purple 55 45

457 Korner

1973. Birth Centenary of Pres. Theodor Korner (President, 1951–57).
1657 **457** 2s. purple and grey 55 45

458 McDonell DC-9 OE-LDA

1973. Austrian Aviation Anniversaries.
1658 **458** 2s. blue and red 55 45

459 Otto Loewi

1973. Birth Cent of Otto Loewi (pharmacologist).
1659 **459** 4s. violet 95 70

460 "Succour"

1973. 25th Anniv of National Federation of Austrian Social Insurance Institutes.
1660 **460** 2s. blue 55 45

461 Telephone Dial within Posthorn

1973. Europa.
1661 **461** 2s.50 black, yell & orge 2·20 70

462 Fair Emblem

1973. 25th Dornbirn Fair.
1662 **462** 2s. multicoloured 65 35

463 Military Pentathlon

1973. 25th Anniv of International Military Sports Council and 23rd Military Pentathlon Championships, Wiener Neustadt.
1663 **463** 4s. green 1·00 55

464 Leo Slezak

1973. Birth Centenary of Leo Slezak (operatic tenor).
1664 **464** 4s. brown 1·00 55

465 Main Entrance, Hofburg Palace

1973. 39th International Statistical Institute's Congress, Vienna.
1665 **465** 2s. brown, red and grey 55 30

466 "Admiral Tegetthof Icebound" (J. Payer)

1973. Centenary of Discovery of Franz Josef Land.
1666 **466** 2s.50 green 80 45

467 I.U.L.C.S. Arms

1973. 13th International Union of Leather Chemists' Societies Congress, Vienna.
1667 **467** 4s. multicoloured 1·00 65

468 "Academy of Sciences, Vienna" (B. Bellotto)

1973. Cent of Int Meteorological Organization.
1668 **468** 2s.50 violet 80 45

469 Max Reinhardt

1973. Birth Centenary of Max Reinhardt (theatrical director).
1669 **469** 2s. purple 55 45

470 F. Hanusch

1973. 50th Death Anniv of Ferdinand Hanusch (politician).
1670 **470** 2s. purple 55 30

471 Light Harness Racing

1973. Centenary of Vienna Trotting Assn.
1671 **471** 2s. green 65 55

472 Radio Operator

1973. 50th Anniv of International Criminal Police Organization (Interpol).
1672 **472** 4s. violet 90 65

473 Petzval Camera Lens

1973. "Europhot" (professional photographers) Congress, Vienna.
1673 **473** 2s.50 multicoloured 90 55

474 Aqueduct, Hollen Valley

1973. Centenary of Vienna's 1st Mountain-spring Aqueduct.
1674 **474** 2s. brown, red & blue 55 30

475 Almsee

1973. Views. (a) Size 23×29 mm.

1674a	-	20g. blue and light blue	90	45
1675	-	50g. green & lt green	45	25
1676	-	1s. sepia and brown	45	25
1677	-	1s.50 purple and pink	65	30
1678	-	2s. indigo and blue	80	30
1679	-	2s.50 deep lilac & lilac	90	30
1680	-	3s. ultramarine & blue	1·10	30
1680a	-	3s.50 brown & orange	1·10	45
1681	**475**	4s. violet and lilac	1·10	30
1681a	-	4s.20 black and grey	1·70	95
1682	-	4s.50 dp green & green	1·50	45
1683	-	5s. violet and lilac	1·50	45
1683a	-	5s.50 blue and violet	2·50	1·90
1683b	-	5s.60 olive and green	3·25	2·75
1684	-	6s. lilac and pink	2·10	30
1684a	-	6s.50 blue & turquoise	2·00	45
1685	-	7s. deep green & green	2·75	45
1685a	-	7s.50 purple & mauve	3·25	45
1686	-	8s. brown and pink	2·75	65
1686a	-	9s. red and pink	3·25	65
1687	-	10s. myrtle and green	3·25	45
1688	-	11s. red and orange	4·00	45
1688a	-	12s. sepia and brown	4·00	95
1688b	-	14s. myrtle and green	5·00	95
1688c	-	16s. brown and orange	5·50	95
1688d	-	20s. green and bistre	6·75	95

(b) Size 28×37 mm.
1689 50s. violet and grey 20·00 2·40

(c) Size 17×20 mm.
1690 3s. ultramarine and blue 80 65

DESIGNS: 20g. Friedstadt Keep, Muhlviertel; 50g. Zillertal; 1s. Kahlenbergerdorf, Vienna; 1s.50, Bludenz; 2s. Old bridge, Finstermunz; 2s.50, Murau, Styria; 3s. Bischofsmutze and Alpine farm; 3s.50, Osterkirche, Oberwart; 4s.20, Hirschegg, Kleinwalsertal; 4s.50, Windmill, Retz; 5s. Ruins of Aggstein Castle; 5s.50, Peace Chapel, Stoderzinken; 5s.60, Riezlern, Kleinwalsertal; 6s. Lindauer Hut, Ratikon Massif; 6s.50, Villach, Carinthia; 7s. Falkenstein Castle; 7s.50, Hohensalzburg Fortress; 8s. Votive column, Reiteregg, Styria; 9s. Asten valley; 10s. Neusiedlersee; 11s. Enns; 12s. Kufstein Fortress; 14s. Weiszsee, Salzburg; 16s. Bad Tatzmannsdorf open-air museum; 20s. Myra Falls, Muggendorf; 50s. Hofburg, Vienna.

476 "The Nativity" (stained-glass window, St. Erhard Church, Bretenau)

1973. Christmas.
1691 **476** 2s. multicoloured 55 30

477 "Archangel Gabriel" (carving by Lorenz Luchsperger)

1973. Stamp Day.
1692 **477** 4s.+1s. purple 1·20 1·20

478 Dr. Fritz Pregl

1973. 50th Anniv of Award of Nobel Prize for Chemistry to Fritz Pregl.
1693 **478** 4s. blue 1·00 65

479 Telex Machine and Globe

1974. 50th Anniv of Radio Austria.
1694 **479** 2s.50 blue & ultramarine 80 45

480 Hugo Hofmannsthal

1974. Birth Cent of Hugo Hofmannsthal (writer).
1695 **480** 4s. blue 1·00 65

481 Anton Bruckner (composer)

1974. Inaug of Bruckner Memorial Centre, Linz.
1696 **481** 4s. brown 1·10 65

482 Vegetables

1974. 2nd Int Horticultural Show, Vienna. Mult.
1697 2s. Type **482** 55 45
1698 2s.50 Fruit 90 75
1699 4s. Flowers 1·10 95

483 Head from Ancient Seal

1974. 750th Anniv of Judenburg.
1700 **483** 2s. multicoloured 65 40

484 Karl Kraus

1974. Birth Centenary of Karl Kraus (poet).
1701 **484** 4s. red 1·00 65

485 "St. Michael" (wood-carving, Thomas Schwanthaler)

1974. "Sculptures by the Schwanthaler Family" Exhibition, Reichersberg.
1702 **485** 2s.50 green 90 45

486 "King Arthur" (statue, Innsbruck)

1974. Europa.
1703 **486** 2s.50 blue and brown 2·20 95

487 Early De Dion-Bouton Motor-tricycle

1974. 75th Anniv of Austrian Association of Motoring, Motor Cycling and Cycling.
1704 **487** 2s. brown and grey 55 45

488 Mask of Satyr's Head

1974. "Renaissance in Austria" Exhibition, Schallaburg Castle.
1705 **488** 2s. black, brown & gold 55 45

489 I.R.U. Emblem

1974. 14th International Road Haulage Union Congress, Innsbruck.
1706 **489** 4s. black and orange 1·10 65

490 F. A. Maulbertsch

1974. 205th Birth Anniv of Franz Maulbertsch (painter).
1707 **490** 2s. brown 65 30

491 Gendarmes of 1849 and 1974

1974. 125th Anniv of Austrian Gendarmerie.
1708 **491** 2s. multicoloured 65 30

492 Fencing

1974. Sports.
1709 **492** 2s.50 black and orange 80 45

493 Transport Emblems

1974. European Transport Ministers' Conference, Vienna.
1710 **493** 4s. multicoloured 1·00 65

494 "St. Virgilius" (wood-carving)

1974. 1200 Years of Christianity in Salzburg.
1711 **494** 2s. blue 65 30

495 Pres. F. Jonas

1974. Pres. Franz Jonas Commemoration.
1712 **495** 2s. black 65 30

496 F. Stelzhamer

1974. Death Cent of Franz Stelzhamer (poet).
1713 **496** 2s. blue 65 30

497 Diving

1974. 13th European Swimming, Diving and Water-polo Championships.
1714 **497** 4s. brown and blue 1·10 65

498 F. R. von Hebra (founder of German scientific dermatology)

1974. 30th Meeting of German-speaking Dermatologists Association, Graz.
1715 **498** 4s. brown 1·00 65

499 A. Schonberg

1974. Birth Cent of Arnold Schonberg (composer).
1716 **499** 2s.50 purple 90 45

500 Broadcasting Studios, Salzburg

1974. 50th Anniv of Austrian Broadcasting.
1717 **500** 2s. multicoloured 65 30

501 E. Eysler

1974. 25th Death Anniv of Edmund Eysler (composer).
1718 **501** 2s. green 55 45

502 19th-century Postman and Mail Transport

1974. Centenary of U.P.U.
1719 **502** 2s. brown and mauve 65 55
1720 - 4s. blue and grey 1·00 85
DESIGN: 4s. Modern postman and mail transport.

503 Sports Emblem

1974. 25th Anniv of Football Pools in Austria.
1721 **503** 70g. red, black and green 55 30

504 Steel Gauntlet grasping Rose

1974. Nature Protection.
1722 **504** 2s. multicoloured 90 55

505 C. D. von Dittersdorf

1974. 175th Death Anniv of Carl Ditters von Dittersdorf (composer).
1723 **505** 2s. green 65 30

506 Mail Coach and P.O., 1905

1974. Stamp Day.
1724 **506** 4s.+2s. blue 1·50 95

507 "Virgin Mary and Child" (wood-carving)

1974. Christmas.
1725 **507** 2s. brown and gold 55 40

508 F. Schmidt

1974. Birth Centenary of Franz Schmidt (composer).
1726 **508** 4s. black and stone 1·00 65

509 "St. Christopher and Child" (altarpiece)

1975. European Architectural Heritage Year and 125th Anniv of Austrian Commission for Preservation of Monuments.
1727 **509** 2s.50 brown and grey 80 40

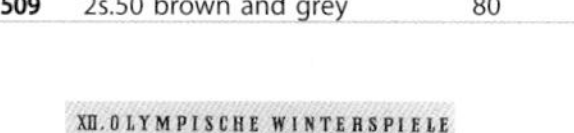

510 Slalom

1975. Winter Olympics, Innsbruck (1976) (1st issue). Multicoloured.
1728 1s.+50g. Type **510** 35 30
1729 1s.50+70g. Ice hockey 45 40
1730 2s.+90g. Ski-jumping 65 55
1731 4s.+1s.90 Bobsleighing 1·30 1·10
See also Nos. 1747/50.

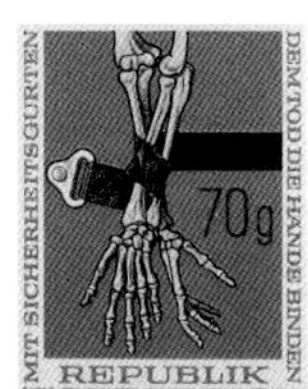

511 Seat-belt around Skeletal Limbs

1975. Car Safety-belts Campaign.
1732 **511** 70g. multicoloured 45 40

512 Stained-glass Window, Vienna Town Hall

1975. 11th European Communities' Day.
1733 **512** 2s.50 multicoloured 65 45

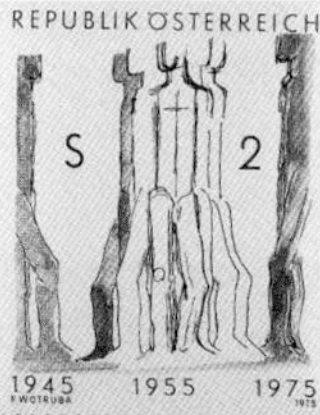

513 "The Buffer State"

1975. 30th Anniv of Foundation of Austrian Second Republic.
1734 **513** 2s. black and brown 55 30

514 Forest Scene

1975. 50th Anniv of Foundation of Austrian Forests Administration.
1735 **514** 2s. green 80 40

515 "The High Priest" (M. Pacher)

1975. Europa.
1736 **515** 2s.50 multicoloured 2·20 45

516 Gosaukamm Cable-way

1975. 4th International Ropeways Congress, Vienna.
1737 **516** 2s. blue and red 65 30

517 J. Misson

1975. Death Centenary of Josef Misson (poet).
1738 **517** 2s. brown and red 55 30

518 "Setting Sun"

1975. Nat Pensioners' Assn Meeting, Vienna.
1739 **518** 1s.50 multicoloured 55 30

519 F. Porsche

1975. Birth Centenary of Prof. Ferdinand Porsche (motor engineer).
1740 **519** 1s.50 purple & green 55 30

520 L. Fall

1975. 50th Death Anniv of Leo Fall (composer).
1741 **520** 2s. violet 55 30

521 Judo "Shoulder Throw"

1975. World Judo Championships, Vienna.
1742 **521** 2s.50 multicoloured 80 45

522 Heinrich Angeli

1975. 50th Death Anniv of Heinrich Angeli (court painter).
1743 **522** 2s. purple 65 30

523 J. Strauss

1975. 150th Birth Anniv of Johann Strauss the Younger (composer).
1744 **523** 4s. brown and ochre 1·10 65

524 "The Cellist"

1975. 75th Anniv of Vienna Symphony Orchestra.
1745 **524** 2s.50 blue and silver 65 40

525 "One's Own House"

1975. 50th Anniv of Austrian Building Societies.
1746 **525** 2s. multicoloured 55 30

1975. Winter Olympic Games, Innsbruck (1976) (2nd issue). As T **510**. Multicoloured.
1747 70g.+30g. Figure-skating (pairs) 45 40
1748 2s.+1s. Cross-country skiing 55 45
1749 2s.50+1s. Tobogganing 90 75
1750 4s.+2s. Rifle-shooting (biathlon) 1·30 1·10

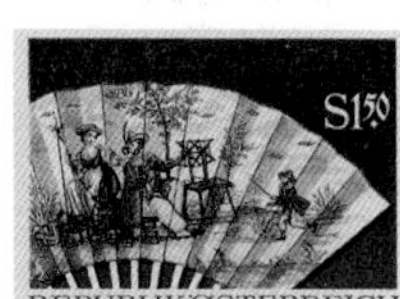

526 Scene on Folding Fan

1975. Bicentenary of Salzburg State Theatre.
1751 **526** 1s.50 multicoloured 55 30

527 Austrian Stamps of 1850, 1922 and 1945

1975. Stamp Day. 125th Anniv of Austrian Postage Stamps.
1752 **527** 4s.+2s. multicoloured 1·30 1·10

528 "Virgin and Child" (Schottenaltar, Vienna)

1975. Christmas.
1753 **528** 2s. lilac and gold 65 40

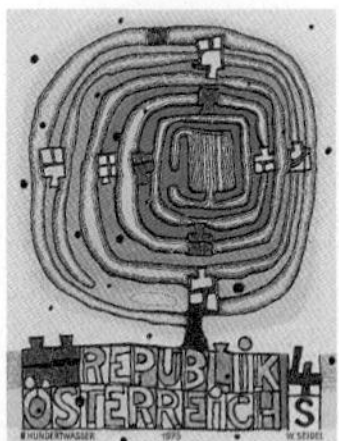
529 "Spiralbaum" (F. Hundertwasser)

1975. Modern Austrian Art.
1754 **529** 4s. multicoloured 1·70 1·20

530 Old Theatre Building

1976. Bicentenary of the Burgtheatre, Vienna. Sheet 130×60 mm containing T 530 and similar horiz design.
MS1755 3s. blue (Type **530**); 3s. brown (Interior of the modern theatre) 2·00 2·00

531 Dr. R. Barany

1976. Birth Centenary of Dr. Robert Barany (Nobel prizewinner for Medicine, 1915).
1756 **531** 3s. brown and blue 1·00 45

532 Ammonite Fossil

1976. Cent Exn, Vienna Natural History Museum.
1757 **532** 3s. multicoloured 1·00 45

533 9th-century Coronation Throne

1976. Millenary of Carinthia.
1758 **533** 3s. black and yellow 1·00 45

534 Stained-glass Window, Klosterneuburg

1976. Babenberg Exhibition, Lilienfeld.
1759 **534** 3s. multicoloured 1·00 45

535 "The Siege of Linz" (contemporary engraving)

1976. 350th Anniv of the Peasants' War in Upper Austria.
1760 **535** 4s. black and green 1·00 55

536 Bowler delivering Ball

1976. 11th World Skittles Championships, Vienna.
1761 **536** 4s. black and orange 1·00 55

537 "St. Wolfgang" (altar painting by Michael Pacher)

1976. International Art Exhibition, St. Wolfgang.
1762 **537** 6s. purple 1·70 95

538 Tassilo Cup, Kremsmunster

1976. Europa.
1763 **538** 4s. multicoloured 2·75 95

539 Fair Emblem

1976. 25th Austrian Timber Fair, Klagenfurt.
1764 **539** 3s. multicoloured 1·00 45

540 Constantin Economo

1976. Birth Centenary of Constantin Economo (brain specialist).
1765 **540** 3s. brown 1·00 45

541 Bohemian Court Chancellery, Vienna

1976. Centenary of Administrative Court.
1766 **541** 6s. brown 1·70 95

542 Arms of Lower Austria

1976. Millenary of Austria. Sheet 135×180 mm containing T 542 and similar vert designs showing provincial arms.
MS1767 2s.×9 multicoloured 5·00 5·00
DESIGNS: Arms of Lower Austria, Upper Austria, Styria, Carinthia, Vorarlberg, Salzberg, Burgenland and Vienna.

543 Cancer the Crab

1976. Fight against Cancer.
1768 **543** 2s.50 multicoloured 80 45

544 U.N. Emblem and Bridge

1976. 10th Anniv of U.N. Industrial Development Organization.
1769 **544** 3s. blue and gold 1·00 55

545 Punched Tapes and Map of Europe

1976. 30th Anniv of Austrian Press Agency.
1770 **545** 1s.50 multicoloured 45 30

546 V. Kaplan

1976. Birth Centenary of Viktor Kaplan (inventor of turbine).
1771 **546** 2s.50 multicoloured 65 55

547 "The Birth of Christ" (Konrad von Friesach)

1976. Christmas.
1772 **547** 3s. multicoloured 90 45

548 Postilion's Hat and Posthorn

1976. Stamp Day.
1773 **548** 6s.+2s. black & lilac 1·80 1·50

549 R. M. Rilke

1976. 50th Death Anniv of Rainer Maria Rilke (poet).
1774 **549** 3s. violet 90 45

550 "Augustin the Piper" (Arik Brauer)

1976. Austrian Modern Art.
1775 **550** 6s. multicoloured 1·70 95

551 City Synagogue

1976. 150th Anniv of Vienna City Synagogue.
1776 **551** 1s.50 multicoloured 45 30

552 N. J. von Jacquin

1977. 250th Birth Anniv of Nikolaus Joseph Freiherrn von Jacquin (botanist).
1777 **552** 4s. brown 1·00 65

553 Oswald von Wolkenstein

1977. 600th Birth Anniv of Oswald von Wolkenstein (poet).
1778 **553** 3s. multicoloured 90 45

554 Handball

1977. World Indoor Handball Championships, Group B, Austria.
1779 **554** 1s.50 multicoloured 45 30

555 A. Kubin

1977. Birth Centenary of Alfred Kubin (writer and illustrator).
1780 **555** 6s. blue 1·70 95

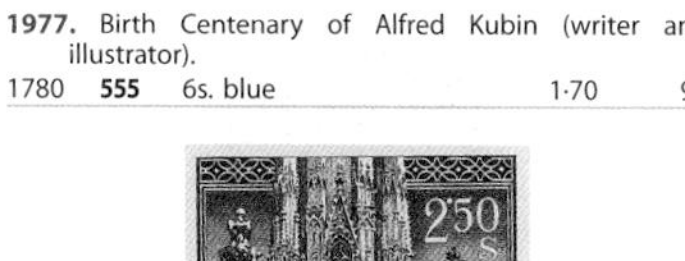

556 Cathedral Spire

1977. 25th Anniv of Re-opening of St. Stephen's Cathedral, Vienna.
1781 **556** 2s.50 brown 90 75
1782 - 3s. blue 1·00 85
1783 - 4s. purple 1·50 1·20
DESIGNS: 3s. West front; 4s. Interior.

557 F. Herzmanovsky-Orlando

1977. Birth Centenary of Fritz Herzmanovsky-Orlando (writer).
1784 **557** 6s. green and gold 1·70 95

558 I.A.E.A. Emblem

1977. 20th Anniv of Int Atomic Energy Agency.
1785 **558** 3s. lt blue, gold & blue 90 45

559 Arms of Schwanenstadt

1977. 350th Anniv of Schwanenstadt.
1786 **559** 3s. multicoloured 90 45

560 Attersee

1977. Europa.
1787 **560** 6s. green 4·00 1·40

561 Globe (Vincenzo Coronelli)

1977. 5th International Symposium and 25th Anniv of Coronelli World Federation of Globe Friends.
1788 **561** 3s. black and stone 90 45

562 Canoeist

1977. World "White Water" Canoe Championships.
1789 **562** 4s. multicoloured 1·00 55

563 "The Samaritan" (Francesco Bassano)

1977. 50th Anniv of Austrian Workers' Samaritan Federation.
1790 **563** 1s.50 multicoloured 55 30

564 Papermakers' Arms

1977. 17th Conference of European Committee of Pulp and Paper Technology.
1791 **564** 3s. multicoloured 90 45

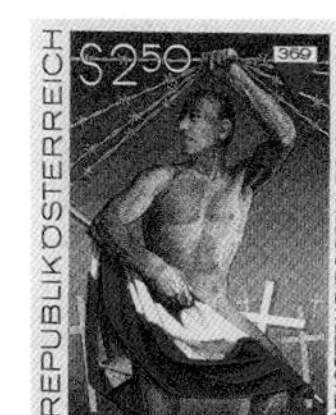

565 "Freedom"

1977. Martyrs for Austrian Freedom.
1792 **565** 2s.50 blue and red 80 45

566 Steam Locomotive, "Austria", 1837

1977. 140th Anniv of Austrian Railways. Mult.
1793 1s.50 Type **566** 65 55
1794 2s.50 Type 214 steam locomotive, 1928 1·00 85
1795 3s. Type 1044 electric locomotive, 1974 1·70 1·40

567 "Madonna and Child" (wood carving, Mariastein Pilgrimage Church)

1977. Christmas.
1796 **567** 3s. multicoloured 90 45

568 "Danube Maiden" (Wolfgang Hutter)

1977. Austrian Modern Art.
1797 **568** 6s. multicoloured 1·70 95

569 Emanuel Herrmann (inventor of postcard)

1977. Stamp Day.
1798 **569** 6s.+2s. brown and cinnamon 2·00 1·40

570 Egon Friedell

1978. Birth Centenary of Egon Friedell (writer).
1799 **570** 3s. black and blue 90 45

571 Underground Train

1978. Opening of Vienna Underground Railway.
1800 **571** 3s. multicoloured 1·10 55

572 Rifleman and Skier

1978. Biathlon World Championships, Hochfilzen.
1801 **572** 4s. multicoloured 1·10 65

573 Aztec Feather Shield

1978. 30th Anniv of Museum of Ethnology, Vienna.
1802 **573** 3s. multicoloured 1·00 45

574 Leopold Kunschak

1978. 25th Death Anniv of Leopold Kunschak (politician).
1803 **574** 3s. blue 1·00 45

575 "Mountain Peasants"

1978. Birth Centenary of Suitbert Lobisser (wood engraver).
1804 **575** 3s. brown and stone 1·00 45

576 Black Grouse, Hunting Satchel and Fowling Piece

1978. International Hunting Exn, Marchegg.
1805 **576** 6s. blue, brown & turq 1·70 95

577 Map of Europe and Austrian Parliament Building

1978. 3rd Interparliamentary European Security Conference, Vienna.
1806 **577** 4s. multicoloured 1·00 65

578 Riegersburg Castle, Styria

1978. Europa.
1807 **578** 6s. purple 4·00 95

579 "Admont Pieta" (Salzburg Circle Master)

1978. "Gothic Art in Styria" Exhibition.
1808 **579** 2s.50 black and ochre 65 55

580 Ort Castle

1978. 700th Anniv of Gmunden Town Charter.
1809 **580** 3s. multicoloured 1·10 45

581 Face surrounded by Fruit and Flowers

1978. 25th Anniv of Austrian Association for Social Tourism.
1810 **581** 6s. multicoloured 1·70 95

582 Franz Lehar and Villa at Bad Ischl

1978. International Lehar Congress.
1811 582 6s. blue 1·70 95

583 Tools and Globe

1978. 15th Congress of International Federation of Building and Wood Workers.
1812 583 1s.50 black, yellow & red 55 45

584 Knights Jousting

1978. 700th Anniv of Battle of Durnkrut and Jedenspeigen.
1813 584 3s. multicoloured 1·10 65

585 Bridge over River Drau

1978. 1100th Anniv of Villach.
1814 585 3s. multicoloured 1·10 65

586 City Seal, 1440

1978. 850th Anniv of Graz.
1815 586 4s. brown, green & grey 1·30 75

587 Angler

1978. 25th Sport Fishing Championships, Vienna.
1816 587 4s. multicoloured 1·30 75

588 Distorted Pattern

1978. Handicapped People.
1817 588 6s. black and brown 1·70 95

589 Concrete Chain

1978. 9th International Concrete and Prefabrication Industry Congress, Vienna.
1818 589 2s.50 multicoloured 65 55

590 "Grace" (Albin Egger-Lienz)

1978. European Family Congress.
1819 590 6s. multicoloured 1·70 95

591 Lise Meitner

1978. Birth Centenary of Lise Meitner (physicist).
1820 591 6s. violet 1·70 95

592 Victor Adler (bust, Anton Hamek)

1978. 60th Death Anniv of Victor Adler (statesman).
1821 592 3s. black and red 1·10 45

593 Franz Schubert (after Josef Kriehuber)

1978. 150th Death Anniv of Franz Schubert (composer).
1822 593 6s. brown 2·00 95

594 "Madonna and Child" (Martino Altomonte, Wilhering Collegiate Church)

1978. Christmas.
1823 594 3s. multicoloured 1·00 45

595 Postbus, 1913

1978. Stamp Day.
1824 595 10s.+5s. multicoloured 3·00 2·50

596 "Archduke Johann Hut, Grossglockner" (E. T. Compton)

1978. Centenary of Austrian Alpine Club.
1825 596 1s.50 violet and gold 55 45

597 "Adam" (Rudolf Hausner)

1978. Austrian Modern Art.
1826 597 6s. multicoloured 1·70 95

598 Bound Hands

1978. 30th Anniv of Declaration of Human Rights.
1827 598 6s. purple 1·70 95

599 "CCIR"

1979. 50th Anniv of International Radio Consultative Committee.
1828 599 6s. multicoloured 1·50 75

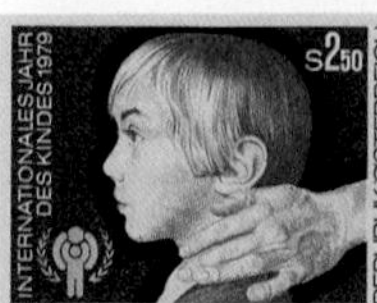
600 Adult protecting Child

1979. International Year of the Child.
1829 600 2s.50 multicoloured 65 55

601 Air Rifle, Pistol and Target

1979. Centenary of Austrian Shooting Club, and European Air Rifle and Air Pistol Shooting Championships.
1830 601 6s. multicoloured 1·70 75

602 "Franz I" (paddle-steamer)

1979. 150th Anniv of Danube Steam Navigation Company.
1831 602 1s.50 blue 55 45
1832 - 2s.50 brown 80 65
1833 - 3s. red 1·50 1·20
DESIGNS: 2s.50, Pusher tug "Linz"; 3s. "Theodor Korner" (passenger vessel).

603 Skater

1979. World Ice Skating and Dancing Championships. Vienna.
1834 603 4s. multicoloured 1·10 75

604 Fashion Drawing by Theo Zache, 1900

1979. 50th Viennese Int Ladies' Fashion Week.
1835 604 2s.50 multicoloured 65 55

605 Wiener Neustadt Cathedral

1979. 700th Anniv of Wiener Neustadt Cathedral.
1836 605 4s. blue and grey 1·10 65

606 Relief from Emperor Joseph II Monument, Vienna

1979. Bicentenary of Education for the Deaf.
1837 606 2s.50 green, black & gold 80 45

607 Population Graph

1979. 150th Anniv of Austrian Central Statistical Office.
1838 607 2s.50 multicoloured 90 45

608 Laurenz Koschier (postal reformer)

1979. Europa.
1839 608 6s. brown and ochre 3·75 95

609 Section through Diesel Engine

1979. 13th Congress of International Combustion Engine Council.
1840 **609** 4s. multicoloured 1·10 65

610 Town Arms of Ried, Braunau and Scharding

1979. Bicentenary of Innviertel District.
1841 **610** 3s. multicoloured 1·10 45

611 Water Pollution

1979. Prevention of Water Pollution.
1842 **611** 2s.50 green and grey 90 45

612 Arms of Rottenmann

1979. 700th Anniv of Rottenmann.
1843 **612** 3s. multicoloured 1·70 45

613 Jodok Fink

1979. 50th Death Anniv of Jodok Fink (politician).
1844 **613** 3s. brown 1·10 45

614 Arms of Wels and Returned Soldiers League Badge

1979. 5th European Meeting of Returned Soldiers.
1845 **614** 4s. green and black 1·10 65

615 Flower

1979. U.N. Conference on Science and Technology for Development, Vienna.
1846 **615** 4s. blue 1·10 65

616 Vienna International Centre

1979. Opening of U.N.O. Vienna Int Centre.
1847 **616** 6s. slate 1·70 95

617 Eye and Blood Vessels of Diabetic

1979. 10th World Congress of International Diabetes Federation, Vienna.
1848 **617** 2s.50 multicoloured 80 45

618 Stanzer Valley seen from Arlberg Road Tunnel

1979. 16th World Road Congress, Vienna.
1849 **618** 4s. multicoloured 1·10 65

619 Steam-driven Printing Press

1979. 175th Anniv of State Printing Works.
1850 **619** 3s. black and stone 90 55

620 Richard Zsigmondy

1979. 50th Death Anniv of Dr. Richard Zsigmondy (Nobel Prize winner for Chemistry).
1851 **620** 6s. brown 1·70 95

621 Bregenz Festival and Congress Hall

1979. Bregenz Festival and Congress Hall.
1852 **621** 2s.50 lilac 90 45

622 Burning Match

1979. "Save Energy".
1853 **622** 2s.50 multicoloured 90 45

623 Lions Emblem

1979. 25th European Lions Forum, Vienna.
1854 **623** 4s. yellow, gold and lilac 1·10 65

624 Wilhelm Exner (founder)

1979. Centenary of Industrial Museum and Technical School, Vienna.
1855 **624** 2s.50 dp purple & purple 80 45

625 "The Suffering Christ" (Hans Fronius)

1979. Austrian Modern Art.
1856 **625** 4s. black and stone 1·10 75

626 Series 52 Goods Locomotive

1979. Centenary of Raab (Gyor)–Odenburg (Sopron)-Ebenfurt Railway.
1857 **626** 2s.50 multicoloured 1·10 75

627 August Musger

1979. 50th Death Anniv of August Musger (pioneer of slow-motion photography).
1858 **627** 2s.50 black and grey 80 45

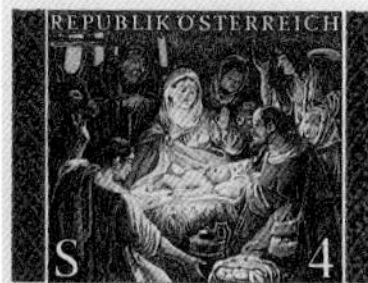

628 "Nativity" (detail of icon by Moses Subotic, St. Barbara Church, Vienna)

1979. Christmas.
1859 **628** 4s. multicoloured 1·10 65

629 Neue Hofburg, Vienna

1979. "WIPA 1981" International Stamp Exhibition, Vienna (1st issue). Inscr "1. Phase".
1860 **629** 16s.+8s. multicoloured 4·75 4·50
See also No. 1890.

630 Arms of Baden

1980. 500th Anniv of Baden.
1861 **630** 4s. multicoloured 1·10 65

631 Loading Exports

1980. Austrian Exports.
1862 **631** 4s. blue, red and black 1·10 65

632 Rheumatic Hand holding Stick

1980. Fight against Rheumatism.
1863 **632** 2s.50 red and blue 80 45

633 Emblems of 1880 and 1980

1980. Centenary of Austrian Red Cross.
1864 **633** 2s.50 multicoloured 80 45

634 Kirchschlager

1980. Pres. Rudolf Kirchschlager's 65th Birthday.
1865 **634** 4s. brown and red 1·10 65

635 Robert Hamerling

1980. 150th Birth Anniv of Robert Hamerling (writer).
1866 **635** 2s.50 green 80 45

636 Town Seal

1980. 750th Anniv of Hallein.
1867 **636** 4s. black and red 1·10 65

637 "Maria Theresa as a Young Woman" (Andreas Moller)

1980. Death Bicentenary of Empress Maria Theresa.

1868	**637**	2s.50 purple	1·10	95
1869	-	4s. blue	1·50	1·20
1870	-	6s. brown	2·50	2·10

DESIGNS: 4s. "Maria Theresa with St. Stephen's Crown" (Martin van Meytens); 6s. "Maria Theresa as Widow" (Joseph Ducreux).

638 Flags of Treaty Signatories

1980. 25th Anniv of Austrian State Treaty.
1871 **638** 4s. multicoloured 1·10 65

639 St. Benedict (statue, Meinrad Guggenbichler)

1980. Congress of Austrian Benedictine Orders, Mariazell.
1872 **639** 2s.50 green 80 45

640 "Hygieia" (Gustav Klimt)

1980. 175th Anniv of Hygiene Education.
1873 **640** 4s. multicoloured 1·10 65

641 Dish Aerial, Aflenz

1980. Inauguration of Aflenz Satellite Communications Earth Station.
1874 **641** 6s. multicoloured 1·70 95

642 Steyr (copperplate engraving, 1693)

1980. Millenary of Steyr.
1875 **642** 4s. brown, black & gold 1·10 65

643 Oil Driller

1980. 50th Anniv of Oil Production in Austria.
1876 **643** 2s.50 multicoloured 80 45

644 Town Seal of 1267

1980. 800th Anniv of Innsbruck.
1877 **644** 2s.50 yellow, blk & red 80 45

645 Ducal Crown

1980. 800th Anniv of Elevation of Styria to Dukedom.
1878 **645** 4s. multicoloured 1·10 65

646 Leo Ascher

1980. Birth Cent of Leo Ascher (composer).
1879 **646** 3s. violet 80 45

647 "Abraham" (illustration from "Viennese Genesis")

1980. 10th Congress of International Organization for Study of the Old Testament.
1880 **647** 4s. multicoloured 1·10 65

648 Robert Stolz

1980. Europa and Birth Centenary of Robert Stolz (composer).
1881 **648** 6s. red 3·25 95

649 Falkenstein Railway Bridge

1980. 11th International Association of Bridge and Structural Engineering Congress, Vienna.
1882 **649** 4s. multicoloured 1·10 65

650 "Moon Figure" (Karl Brandstatter)

1980. Austrian Modern Art.
1883 **650** 4s. multicoloured 1·10 65

651 Customs Officer

1980. 150th Anniv of Customs Service.
1884 **651** 2s.50 brown and red 80 45

652 Masthead of 1810

1980. 350th Anniv of "Linzer Zeitung" (Linz newspaper).
1885 **652** 2s.50 black, red & gold 80 45

653 Frontispiece of Waidhofen Municipal Book

1980. 750th Anniv of Waidhofen.
1886 **653** 2s.50 multicoloured 80 45

654 Heads

1980. 25th Anniv of Federal Army.
1887 **654** 2s.50 green and red 80 45

655 Alfred Wegener

1980. Birth Centenary of Alfred Wegener (explorer and geophysicist).
1888 **655** 4s. blue 1·10 65

656 Robert Musil

1980. Birth Centenary of Robert Musil (writer).
1889 **656** 4s. brown 1·10 65

1980. "WIPA 1981" International Stamp Exhibition, Vienna (2nd issue). Inscr "2. Phase".
1890 **629** 16s.+8s. mult 4·75 4·50

657 "Adoration of the Kings" (stained-glass window, Viktring Collegiate Church)

1980. Christmas.
1891 **657** 4s. multicoloured 1·10 65

658 Ribbon in National Colours

1981. 25th Anniv of General Social Insurance Act.
1892 **658** 2s.50 red, green & black 55 45

1981. WIPA. 1981 International Stamp Exhibtion, Vienna (3rd issue). Sheet 90×71 mm. containing horiz designs as T 629 but in finished state.
MS1893 16s. + 8s. multicoloured 5·50 5·50

659 Unissued Design for 1926 Child Welfare Stamps

1981. Birth Centenary of Wilhelm Dachauer (artist).
1894 **659** 3s. brown 80 45

660 Disabled Person operating Machine Tool

1981. 3rd European Regional Conference of Rehabilitation International.
1895 **660** 6s. brown, blue and red 1·30 85

661 Sigmund Freud

1981. 125th Birth Anniv of Sigmund Freud (psychoanalyst).
1896 **661** 3s. purple 80 45

662 Long-distance Heating System

1981. 20th International Union of Long-distance Heat Distributors Congress, Vienna.
1897 **662** 4s. multicoloured 1·10 65

663 "Azzo and his Vassals" (cover of Monastery's "bearskin" Manuscript)

1981. Kuenring Exhibition, Zwettl Monastery.
1898 **663** 3s. multicoloured 80 45

664 Maypole

1981. Europa.
1899 **664** 6s. multicoloured 4·50 1·40

665 Early Telephone

1981. Centenary of Austrian Telephone System.
1900 **665** 4s. multicoloured 1·10 65

666 "The Frog King"

1981. Art Education in Schools.
1901 **666** 3s. multicoloured 80 45

667 Research Centre

1981. 25th Anniv of Seibersdorf Research Centre.
1902 **667** 4s. blue, dp blue & orge 1·10 65

668 Town Hall and Seal

1981. 850th Anniv of St. Veit-on-Glan.
1903 **668** 4s. yellow, brown & red 1·10 65

669 Johann Florian Heller (chemist)

1981. 11th Int Clinical Chemistry Congress, Vienna.
1904 **669** 6s. brown 1·30 95

670 Boltzmann

1981. 75th Death Anniv of Ludwig Boltzmann (physicist).
1905 **670** 3s. green 80 45

671 Otto Bauer

1981. Birth Centenary of Otto Bauer (writer and politician).
1906 **671** 4s. multicoloured 1·10 65

672 Chemical Balance

1981. International Pharmaceutical Federation Congress, Vienna.
1907 **672** 6s. black, brown and red 1·20 75

673 Impossible Construction (M. C. Escher)

1981. 10th International Austrian Mathematicians' Congress, Innsbruck.
1908 **673** 4s. lt blue, blue & dp blue 1·10 65

674 "Coronation of Virgin Mary" (detail)

1981. 500th Anniv of Michael Pacher's Altarpiece at St. Wolfgang, Abersee.
1909 **674** 3s. blue 80 45

675 Compass Rose

1981. 75th Anniv of Graz S.E. Exhibition.
1910 **675** 4s. multicoloured 1·10 65

676 "Holy Trinity" (illuminated MS, 12th century)

1981. 16th International Congress of Byzantine Scholars, Vienna.
1911 **676** 6s. multicoloured 1·20 75

677 Josef II

1981. Bicentenary of Toleration Act (giving freedom of worship to Protestants).
1912 **677** 4s. black, blue & bistre 1·10 65

678 Hans Kelsen

1981. Bicentenary of Hans Kelsen (law lecturer and contributor to shaping of Austrian Constitution).
1913 **678** 3s. red 80 45

679 Full and Empty Bowls and F.A.O. Emblem

1981. World Food Day.
1914 **679** 6s. multicoloured 1·20 75

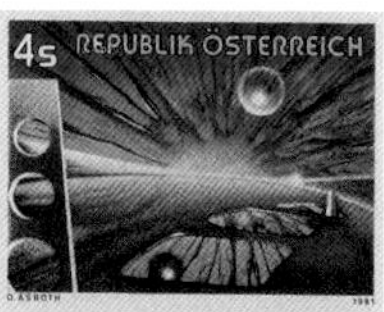

680 "Between the Times" (Oscar Asboth)

1981. Austrian Modern Art.
1915 **680** 4s. multicoloured 1·10 65

681 Workers and Emblem

1981. 7th International Catholic Employees' Meeting, Vienna-Lainz.
1916 **681** 3s. multicoloured 80 45

682 Hammer-Purgstall

1981. 125th Death Anniv of Josef Hammer-Purgstall (orientalist).
1917 **682** 3s. multicoloured 80 45

683 Julius Raab

1981. 90th Birth Anniv of Julius Raab (politician).
1918 **683** 6s. purple 1·10 95

684 Stefan Zweig

1981. Birth Centenary of Stefan Zweig (writer).
1919 **684** 4s. lilac 90 75

685 Christmas Crib, Burgenland

1981. Christmas.
1920 **685** 4s. multicoloured 90 75

686 Arms of St. Nikola

1981. 800th Anniv of St. Nikola-on-Danube.
1921 **686** 4s. multicoloured 90 75

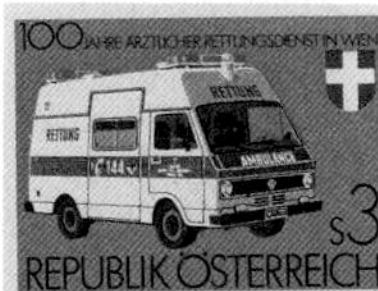

687 Volkswagen Transporter Ambulance

1981. Cent of Vienna's Emergency Medical Service.
1922 **687** 3s. multicoloured 80 45

688 Skier

1982. Alpine Skiing World Championship, Schladming-Haus.
1923 **688** 4s. multicoloured 80 45

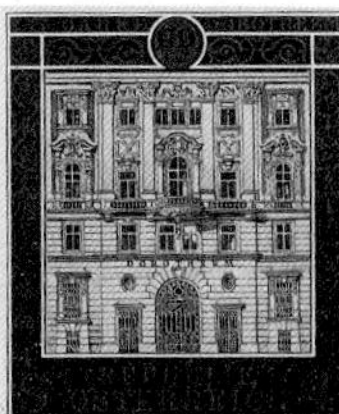

689 Dorotheum Building

1982. 275th Anniv of Dorotheum Auction, Pawn and Banking Society.
1924 **689** 4s. multicoloured 80 45

690 Lifesaving

1982. 25th Anniv of Austrian Water Lifesaving Service.

1925	**690**	5s. blue, red & light blue	1·00	85

691 St. Severin

1982. "St. Severin and the End of the Roman Period" Exhibition, Enns.

1926	**691**	3s. multicoloured	80	45

692 Sebastian Kneipp (pioneer of holistic medicine)

1982. International Kneipp Congress, Vienna.

1927	**692**	4s. multicoloured	80	65

693 Printers' Coat-of-arms

1982. 500th Anniv of Printing in Austria.

1928	**693**	4s. multicoloured	80	65

694 Urine Analysis from "Canon Medicinae" by Avicenna

1982. 5th European Union for Urology Congress, Vienna.

1929	**694**	6s. multicoloured	1·10	95

695 St. Francis preaching to Animals (miniature)

1982. "Franciscan Art and Culture in the Middle Ages" Exhibition, Krems-Stein.

1930	**695**	3s. multicoloured	80	45

696 Haydn and Birthplace, Rohrau

1982. "Joseph Haydn and His Time" Exhibition, Eisenstadt.

1931	**696**	3s. green	1·10	95

697 Globe within Milk Churn

1982. World Dairying Day.

1932	**697**	7s. multicoloured	1·70	95

698 Town Arms (1804 flag)

1982. 800th Anniv of Gfohl.

1933	**698**	4s. multicoloured	80	65

699 Tennis Player

1982. 80th Anniv of Austrian Lawn Tennis Assn.

1934	**699**	3s. multicoloured	80	45

700 Main Square, Langenlois

1982. 900th Anniv of Langenlois.

1935	**700**	4s. multicoloured	90	45

701 Town Arms

1982. 800th Anniv of Weiz.

1936	**701**	4s. multicoloured	1·70	75

702 Linz–Freistadt–Budweis Horse-drawn Railway

1982. Europa.

1937	**702**	6s. brown	5·00	1·00

703 Ignaz Seipel

1982. 50th Death Anniv of Ignaz Seipel (Federal Chancellor).

1938	**703**	3s. purple	80	50

704 Postbus

1982. 75th Anniv of Post-bus Service.

1939	**704**	4s. multicoloured	90	80

705 Rocket Launch

1982. Second U.N. Conference on the Exploration and Peaceful Uses of Outer Space, Vienna.

1940	**705**	4s. multicoloured	1·10	1·00

706 Globe (Federal Office for Standardization and Surveying, Vienna)

1982. Geodesists' Day.

1941	**706**	3s. multicoloured	80	50

707 Great Bustard ("Grosstrappe")

1982. Endangered Animals. Multicoloured.

1942		3s. Type **707**	80	70
1943		4s. Eurasian beaver	1·00	90
1944		6s. Western capercaillie ("Auerhahn")	1·60	1·40

708 Institute Building, Laxenburg

1982. 10th Anniv of International Institute for Applied Systems Analysis.

1945	**708**	3s. black and brown	65	60

709 St. Apollonia (patron saint of dentists)

1982. 70th International Dentists Federation Congress, Vienna.

1946	**709**	4s. multicoloured	90	80

710 Emmerich Kalman

1982. Birth Cent of Emmerich Kalman (composer).

1947	**710**	3s. blue	80	50

711 Max Mell

1982. Birth Centenary of Max Mell (writer).

1948	**711**	3s. multicoloured	80	50

712 Christmas Crib, Damuls Church

1982. Christmas.

1949	**712**	4s. multicoloured	90	80

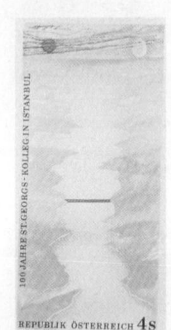

713 Aerial View of Bosphorus

1982. Centenary of St. George's Austrian College, Istanbul.

1950	**713**	4s. multicoloured	90	80

714 "Mainz-Weber" Mailbox, 1870

1982. Stamp Day.

1951	**714**	6s.+3s. multicoloured	2·20	2·00

715 "Muse of the Republic" (Ernst Fuchs)

1982. Austrian Modern Art.

1952	**715**	4s. red and violet	1·10	1·00

716 Bank, Vienna

1983. Centenary of Postal Savings Bank.
1953 **716** 4s. yellow, black and blue 90 80

717 Hildegard Burjan

1983. Birth Centenary of Hildegard Burjan (founder of Caritas Socialis (religious sisterhood)).
1954 **717** 4s. red 90 80

718 Linked Arms

1983. World Communications Year.
1955 **718** 7s. multicoloured 1·50 1·00

719 Young Girl

1983. 75th Anniv of Children's Friends Organization.
1956 **719** 4s. black, blue and red 90 80

720 Josef Matthias Hauer

1983. Birth Centenary of Josef Matthias Hauer (composer).
1957 **720** 3s. purple 65 60

721 Douglas DC-9-80 Super Eighty

1983. 25th Anniv of Austrian Airlines.
1958 **721** 6s. multicoloured 1·30 1·20

722 Hands protecting Workers

1983. Cent of Government Work Inspection Law.
1959 **722** 4s. grn, dp grn & brn 90 80

723 Wels (engraving, Matthaeus Merian)

1983. "Millenary of Upper Austria" Exn, Wels.
1960 **723** 3s. multicoloured 65 60

724 Human Figure, Heart and Electrocardiogram

1983. 7th World Symposium on Pacemakers.
1961 **724** 4s. red, mauve and blue 90 80

725 Monastery Arms

1983. 900th Anniv of Gottweig Monastery.
1962 **725** 3s. multicoloured 65 60

726 Weitra

1983. 800th Anniv of Weitra.
1963 **726** 4s. black, red and gold 90 80

727 Cap, Stick, Ribbon and Emblems

1983. 50th Anniv of MKV and CCV Catholic Students' Organizations.
1964 **727** 4s. multicoloured 90 80

728 Glopper Castle and Town Arms

1983. 650th Anniv of Hohenems Town Charter.
1965 **728** 4s. multicoloured 90 80

729 Hess

1983. Europa. Birth Centenary of Viktor Franz Hess (physicist and Nobel Prize winner).
1966 **729** 6s. green 5·00 1·00

730 Vienna City Hall

1983. 25th Anniv of Vienna City Hall.
1967 **730** 4s. multicoloured 90 80

731 Kiwanis Emblem and View of Vienna

1983. Kiwanis International, World and European Conference, Vienna.
1968 **731** 5s. multicoloured 1·10 1·00

732 Congress Emblem

1983. 7th World Psychiatry Congress, Vienna.
1969 **732** 4s. multicoloured 90 60

733 Hasenauer and Natural History Museum, Vienna

1983. 150th Birth Anniv of Carl Freiherr von Hasenauer (architect).
1970 **733** 3s. brown 90 50

734 Institute for Promotion of Trade and Industry, Linz

1983. 27th International Professional Competition for Young Skilled Workers, Linz.
1971 **734** 4s. multicoloured 1·10 70

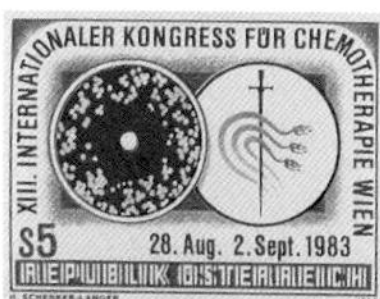

735 Symbols of Penicillin V Efficacy and Cancer

1983. 13th Int Chemotherapy Congress, Vienna.
1972 **735** 5s. red and green 1·10 80

736 Pope John Paul II

1983. Papal Visit.
1973 **736** 6s. black, red and gold 1·70 1·00

737 "Relief of Vienna, 1683" (Franz Geffels)

1983. 300th Anniv of Relief of Vienna. Sheet 90×70 mm.
MS1974 **737** 6s. multicoloured 2·20 2·00

738 Spectrum around Cross

1983. Austrian Catholics' Day.
1975 **738** 3s. multicoloured 80 50

739 Vienna Town Hall

1983. Centenary of Vienna Town Hall.
1976 **739** 4s. multicoloured 1·10 60

740 Karl von Terzaghi

1983. Birth Centenary of Karl von Terzaghi (soil mechanics and foundations engineer).
1977 **740** 3s. blue 90 50

741 Initials of Federation

1983. 10th Austrian Trade Unions Federation Congress.
1978 **741** 3s. red and black 80 50

742 "Evening Sun in Burgenland" (Gottfried Kumpf)

1983. Austrian Modern Art.
1979 **742** 4s. multicoloured 1·10 80

743 Tram No. 5, 1883

1983. Centenary of Modling–Hinterbruhl Electric Railway.
1980 **743** 3s. multicoloured 1·10 50

744 Boy looking at Stamped Envelope

1983. Stamp Day.
1981 **744** 6s.+3s. multicoloured 2·00 1·60

745 Francisco Carolinum Museum, Linz

1983. 150th Anniv of Upper Austrian Provincial Museum.
1982 **745** 4s. multicoloured 1·10 70

746 Crib by Johann Giner the Elder, Kitzbuhel Church

1983. Christmas.
1983 **746** 4s. multicoloured 90 80

747 Parliament Building

1983. Centenary of Parliament Building, Vienna.
1984 **747** 4s. blue 1·10 70

748 "St. Nicholas" (Maria Freund)

1983. Youth Stamp.
1985 **748** 3s. multicoloured 80 50

749 Wolfgang Pauli

1983. 25th Death Anniv of Wolfgang Pauli (Nobel Prize winner for Physics).
1986 **749** 6s. brown 1·30 1·00

750 Gregor Mendel

1984. Death Cent of Gregor Mendel (geneticist).
1987 **750** 4s. ochre and brown 90 80

751 Hanak at Work

1984. 50th Death Anniv of Anton Hanak (sculptor).
1988 **751** 3s. brown and black 80 50

752 Disabled Skier

1984. 3rd World Winter Games for the Disabled, Innsbruck.
1989 **752** 4s.+2s. multicoloured 1·30 1·20

753 Memorial, Wollersdorf

1984. 50th Anniv of 1934 Insurrections.
1990 **753** 4s.50 red and black 90 60

754 Founders' Stone

1984. 900th Anniv of Reichersberg Monastery.
1991 **754** 3s.50 stone, brown & bl 80 50

755 Geras Monastery

1984. Monasteries and Abbeys.

1992	-	50g. yellow, black & grey	20	20
1993	-	1s. yellow, black & mve	45	20
1994	-	1s.50 yellow, red & blue	45	25
1995	-	2s. yellow, green & black	80	30
1996	**755**	3s.50 yellow, sep & brn	1·30	40
1997	-	4s. yellow, purple & red	1·30	30
1998	-	4s.50 yellow, lilac & blue	1·50	50
1999	-	5s. yellow, purple & orge	1·50	50
2000	-	5s.50 yell, dp vio & vio	1·80	50
2001	-	6s. yellow, green & emer	1·80	30
2002	-	7s. yellow, green & blue	2·75	40
2003	-	7s.50 yell, dp brn & brn	2·50	50
2004	-	8s. yellow, blue and red	2·50	50
2005	-	10s. yellow, red & grey	3·00	50
2006	-	11s. yellow, black & brn	3·25	80
2007	-	12s. yellow, brn & orge	5·00	1·20
2008	-	17s. yellow, ultram & bl	5·50	1·30
2009	-	20s. yellow, brown & red	6·75	1·50

DESIGNS: 50g. Vorau Monastery; 1s. Wettingen Abbey, Mehrerau; 1s.50, Monastery of Teutonic Order, Vienna; 2s. Michaelbeuern Benedictine Monastery, Salzburg; 4s. Stams Monastery; 4s.50, Schlagl Monastery; 5s. St. Paul's Monastery, Lavanttal; 5s.50, St. Gerold's Priory, Vorarlberg; 6s. Rein Monastery; 7s. Loretto Monastery; 7s.50, Dominican Monastery, Vienna; 8s. Cistercian Monastery, Zwettl; 10s. Premonstratensian Monastery, Wilten; 11s. Trappist Monastery, Engelszell; 12s. Monastery of the Hospitallers, Eisenstadt; 17s. St. Peter's Abbey, Salzburg; 20s. Wernberg Convent, Carinthia.

756 Cigar Band showing Tobacco Plant

1984. Bicentenary of Tobacco Monopoly.
2012 **756** 4s.50 multicoloured 90 60

757 Kostendorf

1984. 1200th Anniv of Kostendorf.
2013 **757** 4s.50 multicoloured 90 60

758 Wheel Bearing

1984. 20th International Federation of Automobile Engineers' Associations World Congress, Vienna.
2014 **758** 5s. multicoloured 1·10 80

759 Bridge

1984. Europa. 25th Anniv of E.P.T. Conference.
2015 **759** 6s. blue and ultramarine 4·50 1·00

760 Archduke Johann (after Schnorr von Carolsfeld)

1984. 125th Death Anniv of Archduke Johann.
2016 **760** 4s.50 multicoloured 90 60

761 Aragonite

1984. "Ore and Iron in the Green Mark" Exhibition, Eisenerz.
2017 **761** 3s.50 multicoloured 65 50

762 Binding of "Das Buch vom Kaiser", by Max Herzig

1984. Lower Austrian "Era of Emperor Franz Joseph: From Revolution to Grunderzeit" Exhibition, Grafenegg Castle.
2018 **762** 3s.50 red and gold 90 50

763 Upper City Tower and Arms

1984. 850th Anniv of Vocklabruch.
2019 **763** 4s.50 multicoloured 1·10 80

764 Dionysus (Virunum mosaic)

1984. Centenary of Carinthia Provincial Museum, Klagenfurt.
2020 **764** 3s.50 stone, brn & grey 80 50

765 "Meeting of Austrian Army with South Tyrolean Reserves" (detail, Schnorr von Carolsfeld)

1984. "Jubilee of Tyrol Province" Exhibition.
2021 **765** 3s.50 multicoloured 80 50

766 Ralph Benatzky

1984. Birth Cent of Ralph Benatzky (composer).
2022 **766** 4s. brown 90 60

767 Flood Control Barriers

1984. Centenary of Flood Control Systems.
2023 **767** 4s.50 green 1·10 70

768 Christian von Ehrenfels

1984. 125th Death Anniv of Christian von Ehrenfels (philosopher).
2024 **768** 3s.50 multicoloured 80 50

769 Models of European Monuments

1984. 25th Anniv of Minimundus (model world), Worthersee.
2025 **769** 4s. yellow and black 90 80

770 Blockheide Eibenstein National Park

1984. Natural Beauty Spots.
2026 **770** 4s. pink and olive 90 80

771 Electric Train on Schanatobel Bridge (Arlberg Railway Centenary)

1984. Railway Anniversaries.
2027 **771** 3s.50 brown, gold & red 1·10 1·00
2028 - 4s.50 blue, silver and red 1·30 1·20
DESIGN: 4s.50, Electric train on Falkenstein Bridge (75th anniv of Tauern Railway).

772 Johann Georg Stuwer's Flight in Montgolfier Balloon

1984. Bicentenary of First Manned Balloon Flight in Austria.
2029 **772** 6s. multicoloured 1·50 90

773 Lake Neusiedl

1984. Natural Beauty Spots.
2030 **773** 4s. purple and blue 90 80

774 Palace of Justice, Vienna

1984. 20th Int Bar Assn Congress, Vienna.
2031 **774** 7s. multicoloured 1·50 1·30

775 "Joseph Hyrtl" (window, Innsbruck Anatomy Institute)

1984. 7th European Anatomists' Congress, Innsbruck.
2032 **775** 6s. multicoloured 1·30 80

776 "Window" (Karl Korab)

1984. Austrian Modern Art.
2033 **776** 4s. multicoloured 1·10 80

777 Clock of Imms (astrolabe)

1984. 600th Birth Anniv of Johannes von Gmunden (astronomer and mathematician).
2034 **777** 3s.50 multicoloured 80 50

778 Quill

1984. 125th Anniv of Concordia Press Club.
2035 **778** 4s.50 black, gold & red 90 60

779 Fanny Elssler

1984. Death Centenary of Fanny Elssler (dancer).
2036 **779** 4s. multicoloured 1·00 60

780 "Holy Family" (detail, Aggsbach Old High Altar)

1984. Christmas.
2037 **780** 4s.50 multicoloured 1·00 90

781 Detail from Burial Chamber Wall of Seschemnofer III

1984. Stamp Day.
2038 **781** 6s.+3s. multicoloured 2·00 1·60

782 Coat of Arms

1985. 400th Anniv of Graz University.
2039 **782** 3s.50 multicoloured 80 70

783 Dr. Lorenz Bohler

1985. Birth Centenary of Prof. Dr. Lorenz Bohler (surgeon).
2040 **783** 4s.50 purple 90 60

784 Ski Jumping, Skiing and Emblem

1985. World Nordic Skiing Championship, Seefeld.
2041 **784** 4s. multicoloured 1·00 90

785 Linz Cathedral

1985. Bicentenary of Linz Diocese.
2042 **785** 4s.50 multicoloured 90 60

786 Alban Berg

1985. Birth Centenary of Alban Berg (composer).
2043 **786** 6s. blue 1·30 1·00

787 Institute Emblem

1985. 25th Anniv of Institute for Vocational Advancement.
2044 **787** 4s.50 multicoloured 90 60

788 Stylized "B" and Clouds

1985. 2000th Anniv of Bregenz.
2045 **788** 4s. black, ultram & blue 80 50

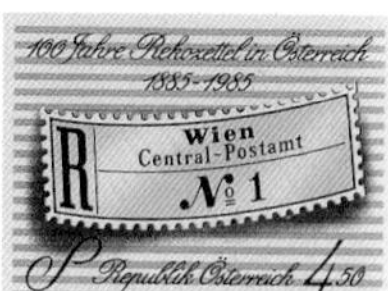

789 1885 Registration Label

1985. Centenary of Registration Labels in Austria.
2046 **789** 4s.50 black, yell & grey 90 60

790 Josef Stefan

1985. 150th Birth Anniv of Josef Stefan (physicist).
2047 **790** 6s. brown, stone and red 1·30 90

791 St. Leopold (Margrave and patron saint)

1985. Lower Austrian Provincial Exhibition, Klosterneuburg Monastery.
2048 **791** 3s.50 multicoloured 80 50

792 "The Story-teller"

1985. 150th Birth Anniv of Franz Defregger (artist).
2049 **792** 3s.50 multicoloured 80 70

793 Barbed Wire, Broken Tree and New Shoot

1985. 40th Anniv of Liberation.
2050 **793** 4s.50 multicoloured 90 60

794 Johann Joseph Fux (composer)

1985. Europa. Music Year.
2051 **794** 6s. brown and grey 4·25 1·00

795 Flags and Caduceus

1985. 25th Anniv of European Free Trade Association.
2052 **795** 4s. multicoloured 1·00 70

796 Town and Arms

1985. Millenary of Boheimkirchen.
2053 **796** 4s.50 multicoloured 1·00 70

797 Bishop's Gate, St. Polten

1985. Bicentenary of St. Polten Diocese.
2054 **797** 4s.50 multicoloured 1·00 70

798 Johannes von Nepomuk Church, Innsbruck

1985. Gumpp Family (architects) Exn, Innsbruck.
2055 **798** 3s.50 multicoloured 80 60

799 Garsten (copperplate, George Matthaus Fischer)

1985. Millenary of Garsten.
2056 **799** 4s.50 multicoloured 1·10 80

800 U.N. Emblem and Austrian Arms

1985. 40th Anniv of U.N.O. and 30th Anniv of Austrian Membership.
2057 **800** 4s. multicoloured 1·00 70

801 Association Headquarters, Vienna

1985. 13th International Suicide Prevention Association Congress, Vienna.
2058 **801** 5s. brown, lt yell & yell 1·10 80

802 Woodland

1985. Forestry Year. Sheet 90×70 mm.
MS2059 **802** 6s. multicoloured 2·20 2·20

803 Operetta Emblem and Spa Building

1985. 25th Bad Ischl Operetta Week.
2060 **803** 3s.50 multicoloured 1·00 70

804 Fireman and Emblem

1985. 8th International Fire Brigades Competition, Vocklabruck.
2061 **804** 4s.50 black, green & red 1·30 80

805 Grossglockner Mountain Road

1985. 50th Anniv of Grossglockner Mountain Road.
2062 **805** 4s. multicoloured 1·00 70

806 Chessboard as Globe

1985. World Chess Association Congress, Graz.
2063 **806** 4s. multicoloured 90 80

807 "Founding of Konigstetten" (August Stephan)

1985. Millenary of Konigstetten.
2064 **807** 4s.50 multicoloured 1·00 70

808 Webern Church and Arms of Hofkirchen and Taufkircher

1985. 1200th Anniversaries of Hofkirchen, Weibern and Taufkirchen.
2065 **808** 4s.50 multicoloured 1·00 70

809 Dr. Adam Politzer

1985. 150th Birth Anniv of Dr. Adam Politzer (otologist).
2066 **809** 3s.50 violet 90 60

810 Emblem and View of Vienna

1985. International Association of Forwarding Agents World Congress, Vienna.
2067 **810** 6s. multicoloured 1·30 90

811 "Clowns Riding High Bicycles" (Paul Flora)

1985. Austrian Modern Art.
2068 **811** 4s. multicoloured 1·10 1·00

812 St. Martin, Patron Saint of Burgenland

1985. 25th Anniv of Eisenstadt Diocese.
2069 **812** 4s.50 black, bistre & red 1·10 80

813 Roman Mounted Courier

1985. 50th Anniv of Stamp Day.
2070 **813** 6s.+3s. multicoloured 2·00 1·80

814 Hanns Horbiger

1985. 125th Birth Anniv of Hanns Horbiger (design engineer).
2071 **814** 3s.50 purple and gold 90 80

815 "Adoration of the Christ Child" (marble relief)

1985. Christmas.
2072 **815** 4s.50 multicoloured 80 50

816 Aqueduct

1985. 75th Anniv of Second Vienna Waterline.
2073 **816** 3s.50 black, red & blue 80 50

818 Chateau de la Muette (headquarters)

1985. 25th Anniv of Organization of Economic Co-operation and Development.
2080 **818** 4s. black, gold & mauve 95 85

819 Johann Bohm

1986. Birth Centenary of Johann Bohm (founder of Austrian Trade Unions Federation).
2081 **819** 4s.50 black and red 1·00 70

820 Dove and Globe

1986. International Peace Year.
2082 **820** 6s. multicoloured 1·30 85

821 Push-button Dialling

1986. Introduction of Digital Preselection Telephone System.
2083 **821** 5s. multicoloured 1·00 60

822 Albrechtsberger and Organ

1986. 250th Birth Anniv of Johann Georg Albrechtsberger (composer).
2084 **822** 3s.50 multicoloured 80 70

823 Main Square and Arms

1986. 850th Anniv of Korneuburg.
2085 **823** 5s. multicoloured 1·20 70

824 Kokoschka (self-portrait)

1986. Birth Centenary of Oskar Kokoschka (artist).
2086 **824** 4s. black and pink 1·00 60

825 Council Flag

1986. 30th Anniv of Membership of Council of Europe.
2087 **825** 6s. black, red and blue 1·30 85

826 Holzmeister and Salzburg Festival Hall

1986. Birth Centenary of Professor Clemens Holzmeister (architect).
2088 **826** 4s. grey, brown & lt brn 80 70

827 Road, Roll of Material, and Congress Emblem

1986. 3rd International Geotextile Congress, Vienna.
2089 **827** 5s. multicoloured 1·00 60

828 Schlosshof Palace (after Bernardo Bellotto) and Prince Eugene

1986. "Prince Eugene and the Baroque Era" Exhibition, Schlosshof and Niederweiden.
2090 **828** 4s. multicoloured 95 70

829 St. Florian Monastery

1986. Upper Austrian "World of Baroque" Exhibition, St. Florian Monastery.
2091 **829** 4s. multicoloured 1·00 70

830 Herberstein Castle and Styrian Arms

1986. "Styria – Bridge and Bulwark" Exhibition, Herberstein Castle, near Stubenberg.
2092 **830** 4s. multicoloured 1·00 70

831 Large Pasque Flower

1986. Europa.
2093 **831** 6s. multicoloured 3·50 1·00

832 Wagner and Scene from Opera "Lohengrin"

1986. International Richard Wagner (composer) Congress, Vienna.
2094 **832** 4s. multicoloured 95 85

833 Antimonite Crystal

1986. Burgenland "Mineral and Fossils" Exhibition, Oberpullendorf.
2095 **833** 4s. multicoloured 95 85

834 Martinswall, Zirl

1986. Natural Beauty Spots.
2096 **834** 5s. brown and blue 1·20 85

835 Waidhofen

1986. 800th Anniv of Waidhofen on Ybbs.
2097 **835** 4s. multicoloured 1·20 85

836 Tschauko Falls, Ferlach

1986. Natural Beauty Spots.
2098 **836** 5s. green and brown 1·20 85

837 19th-century Steam and Modern Articulated Trams

1986. Cent of Salzburg Local Transport System.
2099 **837** 4s. multicoloured 1·20 1·00

838 Enns and Seals of Signatories

1986. 800th Anniv of Georgenberg Treaty (between Duke Leopold V of Austria and Duke Otakar IV of Styria).
2100 **838** 5s. multicoloured 1·20 85

839 Tandler

1986. 50th Death Anniv of Julius Tandler (social reformer).
2101 **839** 4s. multicoloured 95 85

840 "Observatory, 1886" (A. Heilmann)

1986. Centenary of Sonnblick Observatory.
2102 **840** 4s. black, blue and gold 95 85

841 Man collecting Mandragora (from "Codex Tacuinum Sanitatis")

1986. 7th European Anaesthesia Congress, Vienna.
2103 **841** 5s. multicoloured 1·20 85

842 Fire Assistant

1986. 300th Anniv of Vienna Fire Brigade.
2104 **842** 4s. multicoloured 1·70 1·00

843 Stoessl

1986. 50th Death Anniv of Otto Stoessl (writer).
2105 **843** 4s. multicoloured 95 85

844 Viennese Hunting Tapestry (detail)

1986. 5th International Oriental Carpets and Tapestry Conference, Vienna and Budapest.
2106 **844** 5s. multicoloured 1·20 85

845 Minister in Pulpit

1986. 125th Anniv of Protestants Act and 25th Anniv of Protestants Law.
2107 **845** 5s. black and violet 1·20 85

846 "Decomposition" (Walter Schmogner)

1986. Austrian Modern Art.
2108 **846** 4s. multicoloured 1·20 85

847 Liszt, Birthplace and Score

1986. 175th Birth Anniv of Franz Liszt (composer).
2109 **847** 5s. green and brown 1·20 85

848 Aerial View of Vienna (image scaled to 60% of original size)

1986. European Security and Co-operation Conference Review Meeting, Vienna. Sheet 90×70 mm.
MS2110 **848** 6s. multicoloured 1·70 1·60

849 Strettweg Religious Carriage

1986. 175th Anniv of Styrian Joanneum Museum.
2111 **849** 4s. multicoloured 95 85

850 "Nuremberg Letter Messenger" (16th century woodcut)

1986. Stamp Day.
2112 **850** 6s.+3s. multicoloured 2·20 1·70

851 "Adoration of the Shepherds" (woodcut, Johann Georg Schwanthaler)

1986. Christmas.
2113 **851** 5s. brown and gold 1·20 85

852 Headquarters

1986. 40th Anniv of Federal Chamber of Trade and Industry.
2114 **852** 5s. multicoloured 1·20 85

853 Foundry Worker

1986. Austrian World of Work (1st series).
2115 **853** 4s. multicoloured 95 85

See also Nos. 2144, 2178, 2211, 2277, 2386, 2414, 2428, 2486, 2520, 2572 and 2605.

854 "The Educated Eye"

1987. Centenary of Adult Education in Vienna.
2116 **854** 5s. multicoloured 1·20 85

855 "Large Blue Madonna" (Anton Faistauer)

1987. Painters' Birth Centenaries. Multicoloured.
2117 4s. Type **855** 95 85
2118 6s. "Self-portrait" (Albert Paris Gutersloh) 1·40 1·20

856 Hundertwasser House, Vienna

1987. Europa and "Europalia 1987 Austria" Festival, Belgium.
2119 **856** 6s. multicoloured 6·50 2·10

857 Ice Hockey Players

1987. World Ice Hockey Championships, Vienna, and 75th Anniv of Austrian Ice Hockey Association.
2120 **857** 5s. multicoloured 1·50 1·00

858 Austria Centre

1987. Inaug of Austria Conference Centre, Vienna.
2121 **858** 5s. multicoloured 1·50 1·00

859 Salzburg

1987. 700th Anniv of Salzburg Town Charter.
2122 **859** 5s. multicoloured 1·50 1·00

860 Machine Shop, 1920

1987. Upper Austrian "Work–Men–Machines, the Route to Industrialized Society" Exhibition, Steyr.
2123 **860** 4s. black and red 1·20 70

861 Man and Woman

1987. Equal Rights for Men and Women.
2124 **861** 5s. multicoloured 1·20 85

862 "Adele Bloch-Bauer I" (detail, Gustav Klimt)

1987. Lower Austrian "Era of Emperor Franz Joseph: Splendour and Misery" Exhibition, Grafenegg Castle.
2125 **862** 4s. multicoloured 1·20 70

863 Archbishop and Salzburg

1987. 400th Anniv of Election of Prince Wolf Dietrich von Raitenau as Archbishop of Salzburg.
2126 **863** 4s. multicoloured 95 85

864 Schnitzler

1987. 125th Birth Anniv of Arthur Schnitzler (dramatist).
2127 **864** 6s. multicoloured 1·30 95

865 Lace and Arms

1987. 1100th Anniv of Lustenau.
2128 **865** 5s. multicoloured 1·20 85

866 Anniversary Emblem (William Slattery)

1987. 150th Anniv of Austrian Railways. Sheet 90×70 mm.
MS2129 **866** 6s. silver, red and black 2·30 2·10

867 Dachstein Giant Ice Cave

1987. Natural Beauty Spots.
2130 **867** 5s. green and black 1·20 85

868 Engraver at Work

1987. 8th European Association of Engravers and Flexographers International Congress, Vienna.
2131 **868** 5s. brown, pink and grey 1·20 60

869 Dr. Karl Josef Bayer (chemist)

1987. 8th International Light Metal Meeting, Leoben and Vienna.
2132 **869** 5s. multicoloured 1·20 60

870 Passenger Ferry

1987. Centenary of 1st Achensee Steam Service.
2133 **870** 4s. multicoloured 1·20 1·00

871 Office Building, Vienna

1987. 10th Anniv of Office of Ombudsmen.
2134 **871** 5s. black, yellow and red 1·20 85

872 Schrodinger

1987. Birth Cent of Erwin Schrodinger (physicist).
2135 **872** 5s. brown, cream and bistre 1·20 85

873 Freistadt Town Square

1987. 125th Anniv of Freistadt Exhibitions.
2136 **873** 5s. multicoloured 1·20 60

874 Arbing Church

1987. 850th Anniv of Arbing.
2137 **874** 5s. multicoloured 1·20 60

875 Gauertal and Montafon Valleys, Voralberg

1987. Natural Beauty Spots.
2138 **875** 5s. brown and yellow 1·20 85

876 Cyclist

1987. World Cycling Championship, Vienna and Villach.
2139 **876** 5s. multicoloured 1·20 1·00

877 Emblem

1987. World Congress of International Institute of Savings Banks, Vienna.
2140 **877** 5s. multicoloured 1·20 85

878 Hofhaymer at Organ

1987. 450th Death Anniv of Paul Hofhaymer (composer and organist).
2141 **878** 4s. blue, black and gold 95 85

879 Haydn and Salzburg

1987. 250th Birth Anniv of Michael Haydn (composer).
2142 **879** 4s. lilac 95 85

880 Lammergeier ("Bartgeier")

1987. 25th Anniv of Alpine Zoo, Innsbruck.
2143 **880** 4s. multicoloured 95 85

881 Woman using Word Processor

1987. Austrian World of Work (2nd series).
2144 **881** 4s. multicoloured 1·00 70

882 "Tree Goddesses" (Arnulf Neuwirth)

1987. Austrian Modern Art.
2145 **882** 5s. multicoloured 1·20 85

883 Lottery Wheel

1987. Bicentenary of Gambling Monopoly.
2146 **883** 5s. multicoloured 1·20 85

884 Helmer

1987. Birth Centenary of Oskar Helmer (politician).
2147 **884** 4s. multicoloured 95 85

885 Gluck

1987. Death Bicentenary of Christoph Willibald Gluck (composer).
2148 **885** 5s. brown and ochre 1·20 85

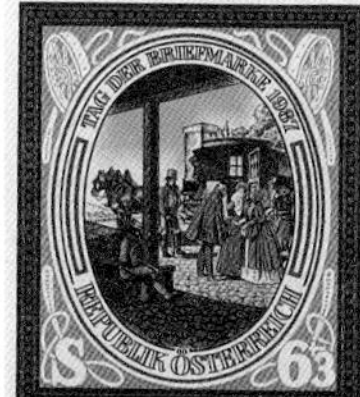

886 Stagecoach and Passengers (lithograph, Carl Schuster)

1987. Stamp Day.
2149 **886** 6s.+3s. multicoloured 2·20 1·80

887 Josef Mohr and Franz Xaver Gruber (composers of "Silent Night")

1987. Christmas.
2150 **887** 5s. multicoloured 1·70 1·00

888 Bosco and Boys

1988. International Educational Congress of St. John Bosco's Salesian Brothers, Vienna.
2151 **888** 5s. purple and orange 1·20 85

889 Cross-country Sledging

1988. 4th World Winter Games for the Disabled, Innsbruck.
2152 **889** 5s.+2s.50 multicoloured 2·00 1·30

890 Mach

1988. 150th Birth Anniv of Ernst Mach (physicist and philosopher).
2153 **890** 6s. multicoloured 1·40 95

891 "Village with Bridge"

1988. 25th Death Anniv of Franz von Zulow (artist).
2154 **891** 4s. multicoloured 1·20 85

892 "The Confiscation" (Ferdinand Georg Waldmuller)

1988. "Patriotism and Protest: Viennese Biedermeier and Revolution" Exhibition, Vienna.
2155 **892** 4s. multicoloured 1·20 85

893 Barbed Wire, Flag and Crosses

1988. 50th Anniv of Annexation of Austria by Germany.
2156 **893** 5s. green, brown and red 1·40 90

894 Steam Locomotive "Aigen", Muhlkreis Railway, 1887

1988. Railway Centenaries. Multicoloured.
2157 4s. Type **894** 1·20 1·00
2158 5s. Modern electric tram and Josefsplatz stop (Viennese Local Railways Stock Corporation) 1·50 1·30

895 European Bee Eater

1988. 25th Anniv of World Wildlife Fund, Austria.
2159 **895** 5s. multicoloured 1·40 1·00

896 Decanter and Beaker

1988. Styrian "Glass and Coal" Exn, Barnbach.
2160 **896** 4s. multicoloured 95 85

897 Late Gothic Silver Censer

1988. Lower Austrian "Art and Monastic Life at the Birth of Austria" Exhibition, Seitenstetten Benedictine Monastery.
2161 **897** 4s. multicoloured 95 85

898 Taking Casualty to Volkswagen Transporter Ambulance and Red Cross

1988. 125th Anniv of Red Cross.
2162 **898** 12s. black, red and green 2·50 1·90

899 Dish Aerials, Aflenz

1988. Europa. Telecommunications.
2163 **899** 6s. multicoloured 4·75 1·60

900 Mattsee Monastery

1988. Salzburg "Bajuvars from Severin to Tassilo" Exhibition, Mattsee Monastery.
2164 **900** 4s. multicoloured 95 85

901 Weinberg Castle

1988. Upper Austrian "Muhlviertel: Nature, Culture, Life" Exhibition, Weinberg Castle, near Kefermarkt.
2165 **901** 4s. multicoloured 95 85

902 Horvath

1988. 50th Death Anniv of Odon von Horvath (writer).
2166 **902** 6s. black and bistre 1·40 95

903 Stockerau Town Hall

1988. 25th Anniv of Stockerau Festival.
2167 **903** 5s. multicoloured 1·20 85

904 Motorway

1988. Completion of Tauern Motorway.
2168 **904** 4s. multicoloured 95 85

905 Brixlegg

1988. 1200th Anniv of Brixlegg.
2169 **905** 5s. multicoloured 1·20 85

906 Klagenfurt (after Matthaus Merian)

1988. 400th Anniv of Regular Postal Services in Carinthia.
2170 **906** 5s. multicoloured 1·20 85

907 Parish Church and Dean's House

1988. 1200th Anniv of Brixen im Thale, Tyrol.
2171 **907** 5s. multicoloured 1·20 85

908 Krimml Waterfalls, Upper Tauern National Park

1988. Natural Beauty Spots.
2172 **908** 5s. black and blue 1·20 85

909 Town Arms

1988. 1100th Anniv of Feldkirchen, Carinthia.
2173 **909** 5s. multicoloured 1·20 85

910 Feldbach

1988. 800th Anniv of Feldbach.
2174 **910** 5s. multicoloured 1·20 85

911 Ansfelden

1988. 1200th Anniv of Ansfelden.
2175 **911** 5s. multicoloured 1·20 85

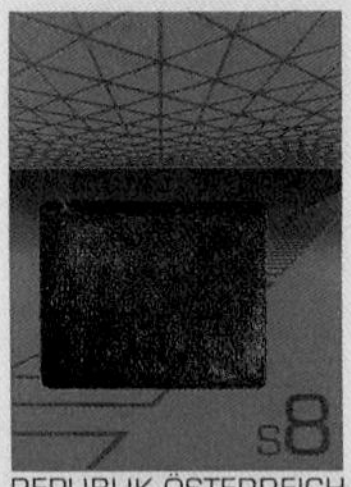

912 Hologram of Export Emblem

1988. Federal Economic Chamber Export Congress.
2176 **912** 8s. multicoloured 3·00 2·30

913 Concert Hall

1988. 75th Anniv of Vienna Concert Hall.
2177 **913** 5s. multicoloured 1·20 85

914 Laboratory Assistant

1988. Austrian World of Work (3rd series).
2178 **914** 4s. multicoloured 1·00 70

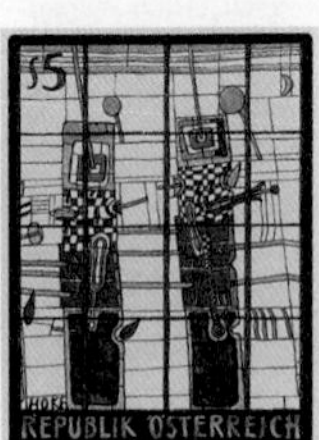

915 "Guards" (Giselbert Hoke)

1988. Austrian Modern Art.
2179 **915** 5s. multicoloured 1·20 85

916 Schonbauer

1988. Birth Centenary of Dr. Leopold Schonbauer (neurosurgeon and politician).
2180 **916** 4s. multicoloured 1·00 70

917 Carnation

1988. Cent of Austrian Social Democratic Party.
2181 **917** 4s. multicoloured 95 85

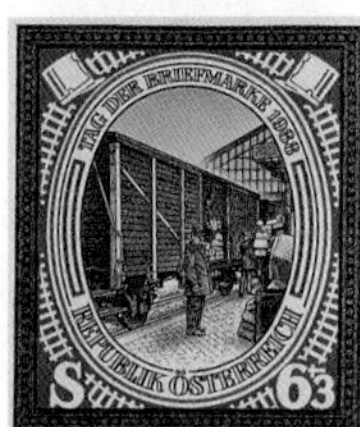

918 Loading Railway Mail Van at Pardubitz Station, 1914

1988. Stamp Day.
2182 **918** 6s.+3s. multicoloured 2·30 1·70

919 "Nativity" (St. Barbara's Church, Vienna)

1988. Christmas.
2183 **919** 5s. multicoloured 1·20 85

920 "Madonna" (Lucas Cranach)

1989. 25th Anniv of Diocese of Innsbruck.
2184 **920** 4s. multicoloured 95 60

921 Margrave Leopold II leading Abbot Sigibold and Monks to Melk (detail of fresco, Paul Troger)

1989. 900th Anniv of Melk Benedictine Monastery.
2185 **921** 5s. multicoloured 1·20 85

922 Marianne Hainisch

1989. 150th Birth Anniv of Marianne Hainisch (women's rights activist).
2186 **922** 6s. multicoloured 1·40 1·00

923 Glider and Paraskier

1989. World Gliding Championships, Wiener Neustadt, and World Paraskiing Championships, Damuls.
2187 **923** 6s. multicoloured 1·40 1·00

924 "The Painting"

1989. 50th Death Anniv of Rudolf Jettmar (painter).
2188 **924** 5s. multicoloured 1·20 85

925 "Bruck an der Leitha" (17th-century engraving, Georg Vischer)

1989. 750th Anniv of Bruck an der Leitha.
2189 **925** 5s. multicoloured 1·20 85

926 Wittgenstein

1989. Birth Centenary of Ludwig Wittgenstein (philosopher).
2190 **926** 5s. multicoloured 1·20 70

927 Holy Trinity Church, Stadl-Paura

1989. 250th Death Anniv of Johann Michael Prunner (architect).
2191 **927** 5s. multicoloured 1·20 70

928 Suess (after Josef Kriehuber) and Map

1989. 75th Death Anniv of Eduard Suess (geologist and politician).
2192 **928** 6s. multicoloured 1·30 85

929 "Judenburg" (17th-century engraving, Georg Vischer)

1989. Upper Styrian "People, Coins, Markets" Exhibition, Judenburg.
2193 **929** 4s. multicoloured 1·00 70

930 Steam Engine (Vinzenz Prick)

1989. Lower Austrian "Magic of Industry" Exhibition, Pottenstein.
2194 **930** 4s. blue and gold 1·00 70

931 Radstadt

1989. 700th Anniv of Radstadt.
2195 **931** 5s. multicoloured 1·20 85

932 Wooden Salt Barge from Viechtau

1989. Europa. Children's Toys.
2196 **932** 6s. multicoloured 4·00 1·00

933 "St. Adalbero and Family before Madonna and Child" (Monastery Itinerary Book)

1989. Upper Austrian "Graphic Art" Exhibition and 900th Anniv of Lambach Monastery Church.
2197 **933** 4s. multicoloured 1·00 70

934 "Gisela" (paddle-steamer)

1989. 150th Anniv of Passenger Shipping on Traunsee.
2198 **934** 5s. multicoloured 1·70 1·00

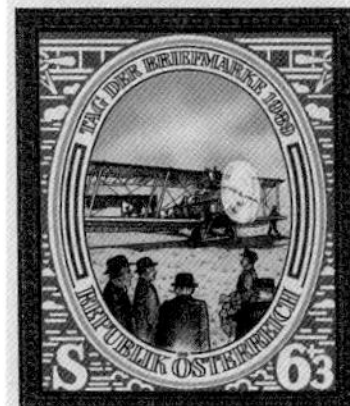

935 Hansa Brandenburg C-1 Mail Biplane at Vienna, 1918

1989. Stamp Day.
2199 **935** 6s.+3s. multicoloured 2·00 1·70

936 St. Andra (after Matthaus Merian)

1989. 650th Anniv of St. Andra.
2200 **936** 5s. multicoloured 1·20 85

937 Strauss

1989. 125th Birth Anniv of Richard Strauss (composer).
2201 **937** 6s. red, brown and gold 1·40 1·00

938 Locomotive

1989. Centenary of Achensee Steam Rack Railway.
2202 **938** 5s. multicoloured 1·50 85

939 Parliament Building, Vienna

1989. Centenary of Interparliamentary Union.
2203 **939** 6s. multicoloured 1·40 95

940 Anniversary Emblem

1989. Centenary of National Insurance in Austria.
2204 **940** 5s. multicoloured 1·20 70

941 U.N. Building, Vienna

1989. 10th Anniv of U.N. Vienna Centre.
2205 **941** 8s. multicoloured 2·00 1·00

942 Lusthaus Water, Prater Woods, Vienna

1989. Natural Beauty Spots.
2206 **942** 5s. black and buff 1·20 1·00

943 Wildalpen and Hammerworks

1989. 850th Anniv of Wildalpen.
2207 **943** 5s. multicoloured 1·20 85

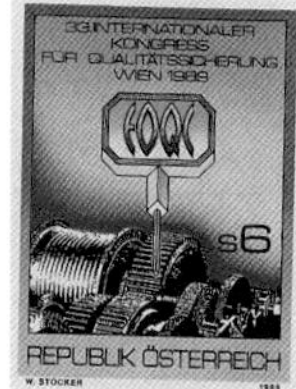

944 Emblem

1989. 33rd Congress of European Organization for Quality Control, Vienna.
2208 **944** 6s. multicoloured 1·40 95

945 Palace of Justice, Vienna

1989. 14th Congress of Int Assn of Criminal Law.
2209 **945** 6s. multicoloured 1·30 90

946 "Tree of Life" (Ernst Steiner)

1989. Austrian Modern Art.
2210 **946** 5s. multicoloured 1·40 95

947 Bricklayer

1989. Austrian World of Work (4th series).
2211 **947** 5s. multicoloured 1·40 95

948 Ludwig Anzengruber (150th birth anniv)

1989. Writers' Anniversaries. Multicoloured.
2212 4s. Type **948** 1·20 85
2213 4s. Georg Trakl (75th death anniv) 1·20 85

949 Fried

1989. 125th Birth Anniv of Alfred Fried (Peace Movement worker).
2214 **949** 6s. multicoloured 1·50 1·00

950 "Adoration of the Shepherds" (detail, Johann Carl von Reslfeld)

1989. Christmas.
2215 **950** 5s. multicoloured 1·20 85

951 "Courier" (Albrecht Durer)

1990. 500th Anniv of Regular European Postal Services.
2216 **951** 5s. chocolate, cinnamon and brown 1·30 85

952 Streif Downhill and Ganslern Slalom Runs

1990. 50th Hahnenkamm Ski Championships, Kitzbuhel.
2217 **952** 5s. multicoloured 1·20 85

953 Sulzer

1990. Death Centenary of Salomon Sulzer (creator of modern Synagogue songs).
2218 **953** 4s.50 multicoloured 1·00 60

954 Emich

1990. 50th Death Anniv of Friedrich Emich (microchemist).
2219 **954** 6s. purple and green 1·20 85

955 Emperor Friedrich III (miniature by Ulrich Schreier)

1990. 500th Anniv of Linz as Capital of Upper Austria.
2220 **955** 5s. multicoloured 1·20 85

956 University Seals

1990. 625th Anniv of Vienna University and 175th Anniv of Vienna University of Technology.
2221 **956** 5s. red, gold and lilac 1·20 85

957 South Styrian Vineyards

1990. Natural Beauty Spots.
2222 **957** 5s. black and yellow 1·20 85

958 Parish Church

1990. 1200th Anniv of Anthering.
2223 **958** 7s. multicoloured 1·90 95

959 1897 May Day Emblem

1990. Centenary of Labour Day.
2224 **959** 4s.50 multicoloured 1·00 95

960 "Our Dear Housewife of Seckau" (relief)

1990. 850th Anniv of Seckau Abbey.
2225 **960** 4s.50 blue 1·00 70

961 Ebene Reichenau Post Office

1990. Europa. Post Office Buildings.
2226 **961** 7s. multicoloured 5·25 1·20

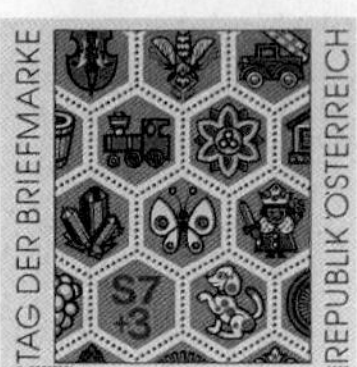
962 Thematic Stamp Motifs

1990. Stamp Day.
2227 **962** 7s.+3s. multicoloured 2·30 1·90

963 Makart (self-portrait)

1990. 150th Birth Anniv of Hans Makart (painter).
2228 **963** 4s.50 multicoloured 1·20 1·00

964 Schiele (self-portrait)

1990. Birth Centenary of Egon Schiele (painter).
2229 **964** 5s. multicoloured 1·20 1·00

965 Raimund

1990. Birth Bicentenary of Ferdinand Raimund (actor and playwright).
2230 **965** 4s.50 multicoloured 1·20 1·00

966 "The Hundred Guilden Note" (Rembrandt)

1990. 2nd Int Christus Medicus Congress, Bad Ischl.
2231 **966** 7s. multicoloured 1·90 95

967 Hardegg

1990. 700th Anniv of Hardegg's Elevation to Status of Town.
2232 **967** 4s.50 multicoloured 1·20 85

968 Oberdrauburg (copperplate engraving, Freiherr von Valvasor)

1990. 750th Anniv of Oberdrauburg.
2233 **968** 5s. multicoloured 1·30 60

969 Church and Town Hall

1990. 850th Anniv of Gumpoldskirchen.
2234 **969** 5s. multicoloured 1·30 60

970 Zdarsky skiing

1990. 50th Death Anniv of Mathias Zdarsky (developer of alpine skiing).
2235 **970** 5s. multicoloured 1·30 60

971 "Telegraph", 1880, and "Anton Chekhov", 1978

1990. 150th Anniv of Modern (metal) Shipbuilding in Austria.
2236 **971** 9s. multicoloured 2·10 1·20

972 Perkonig

1990. Birth Centenary of Josef Friedrich Perkonig (writer).
2237 **972** 5s. sepia, brown & gold 1·20 85

973 "Man of Rainbows" (Robert Zeppel-Sperl)

1990. Austrian Modern Art.
2238 **973** 5s. multicoloured 1·20 85

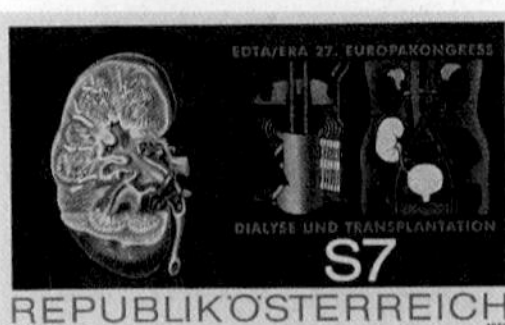
974 Kidney, Dialysis Machine and Anatomical Diagram

1990. 27th European Dialysis and Transplantation Federation Congress, Vienna.
2239 **974** 7s. multicoloured 1·90 95

975 Werfel

1990. Birth Centenary of Franz Werfel (writer).
2240 **975** 5s. multicoloured 1·20 85

976 U.N. and Austrian Flags

1990. 30th Anniv of Austrian Participation in U.N. Peace-keeping Forces.
2241 **976** 7s. multicoloured 1·90 95

977 Arms of Provinces

1990. 45th Anniv of First Provinces Conference (established Second Republic as Federal State).
2242 **977** 5s. multicoloured 1·20 60

978 University Seal

1990. 150th Anniv of Mining University, Leoben.
2243 **978** 4s.50 black, red & green 1·00 60

979 Vogelsang

1990. Death Centenary of Karl von Vogelsang (Christian social reformer).
2244 **979** 4s.50 multicoloured 1·00 60

980 Metal Workers

1990. Centenary of Metal, Mining and Energy Trade Union.
2245 **980** 5s. multicoloured 1·20 60

981 Player

1990. 3rd World Ice Curling Championships, Vienna.
2246 **981** 7s. multicoloured 1·90 95

982 Greenhouse

1990. Re-opening of Schonbrunn Greenhouse.
2247 **982** 5s. multicoloured 1·20 60

983 "Birth of Christ"

1990. Christmas. Detail of Altarpiece by Master Nikolaus of Verdun, Klosterneuburg Monastery.
2248 **983** 5s. multicoloured 1·20 60

984 Grillparzer

1991. Birth Bicent of Franz Grillparzer (dramatist).
2249 **984** 4s.50 multicoloured 1·20 60

985 Skier

1991. World Alpine Skiing Championships, Saalbach-Hinterglemm.
2250 **985** 5s. multicoloured 1·20 85

986 Kreisky

1991. 80th Birth Anniv of Bruno Kreisky (Chancellor, 1970–82).
2251 **986** 5s. multicoloured 1·20 85

987 Schmidt and Vienna Town Hall

1991. Death Centenary of Friedrich von Schmidt (architect).
2252 **987** 7s. multicoloured 1·90 1·20

988 Fountain, Vienna

1991. Anniversaries. Multicoloured.
2253 4s.50 Type **988** (250th death anniv of Georg Raphael Donner (sculptor)) 1·00 95
2254 5s. "Kitzbuhel in Winter" (birth centenary of Alfons Walde (artist and architect)) 1·20 1·00
2255 7s. Vienna Stock Exchange (death centenary of Theophil von Hansen (architect)) 1·70 1·60
See also No. 2269.

989 M. von Ebner-Eschenbach

1991. 75th Death Anniv of Marie von Ebner-Eschenbach (writer).
2256 **989** 4s.50 purple 1·20 85

990 Mozart

1991. Death Bicentenary of Wolfgang Amadeus Mozart (composer). Sheet 115×69 mm containing T 990 and similar vert design, each purple, mauve and gold.
MS2257 5s. Type **990**; 5s. "The Magic Flute" (statue, Vienna) 3·50 3·00

991 Obir Stalactite Caverns, Eisenkappel

1991. Natural Beauty Spots.
2258 **991** 5s. multicoloured 1·30 90

992 Spittal an der Drau (after Matthaus Merian)

1991. 800th Anniv of Spittal an der Drau.
2259 **992** 4s.50 multicoloured 1·30 90

993 "ERS-1" European Remote Sensing Satellite

1991. Europa. Europe in Space.
2260 **993** 7s. multicoloured 6·00 1·30

994 "Garden Party" (Anthoni Bays)

1991. Vorarlberg "Clothing and People" Exhibition, Hohenems.
2261 **994** 5s. multicoloured 1·30 90

995 Grein

1991. 500th Anniv of Grein Town Charter.
2262 **995** 4s.50 multicoloured 1·30 90

996 Bedding Plants forming Arms

1991. 1200th Anniv of Tulln.
2263 **996** 5s. multicoloured 1·30 90

997 Military History Museum

1991. Vienna Museum Centenaries. Multicoloured.
2264 5s. Type **997** 1·30 1·10
2265 7s. Museum of Art History 1·60 1·50

998 "B" and "P"

1991. Stamp Day.
2266 **998** 7s.+3s. brown, sepia and black 2·30 2·00
This is the first of a series of ten annual stamps, each of which will illustrate two letters. The complete series will spell out the words "Briefmarke" and "Philatelie".

999 Tunnel Entrance

1991. Opening of Karawanken Road Tunnel between Carinthia and Slovenia.
2267 **999** 7s. multicoloured 1·60 1·20

1000 Town Hall

1991. 5th Anniv of St. Polten as Capital of Lower Austria.
2268 **1000** 5s. multicoloured 1·40 90

1991. 150th Birth Anniv of Otto Wagner (architect). As T 988. Multicoloured.
2269 4s.50 Karlsplatz Station, Vienna City Railway 1·30 1·10

1001 Rowing

1991. Junior World Canoeing Championships and World Rowing Championships, Vienna.
2270 **1001** 5s. multicoloured 1·30 90

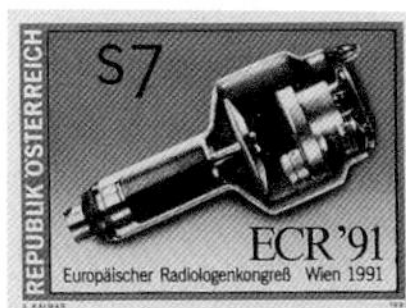

1002 X-ray Tube

1991. European Radiology Congress, Vienna.
2271 **1002** 7s. multicoloured 1·60 1·10

1003 Paracelsus

1991. 450th Death Anniv of Theophrastus Bombastus von Hohenheim (Paracelsus) (physician and scientist).
2272 **1003** 4s. black, red & brown 1·30 90

1004 "Mir" Space Station

1991. "Austro Mir 91" Soviet–Austrian Space Flight.
2273 **1004** 9s. multicoloured 2·10 1·50

1005 Almabtrieb (driving cattle from mountain pastures) (Zell, Tyrol)

1991. Folk Customs and Art (1st series). Multicoloured.
2274 4s.50 Type **1005** 1·00 90
2275 5s. Vintage Crown (Neustift, Vienna) 1·10 1·00
2276 7s. Harvest monstrance (Nestelbach, Styria) 1·60 1·50
See also Nos. 2305/7, 2349/51, 2363/5, 2393/5, 2418, 2432/3, 2450, 2482, 2491, 2500/1, 2508, 2524, 2546, 2547, 2550, 2552, 2569, 2581, 2587, 2595, 2718, 2776 and 2815.

1006 Weaver

1991. Austrian World of Work (5th series).
2277 **1006** 4s.50 multicoloured 1·10 80

1007 "The General" (Rudolf Pointner)

1991. Austrian Modern Art.
2278 **1007** 5s. multicoloured 1·30 90

1008 Raab

1991. Birth Centenary of Julius Raab (Chancellor, 1953–61).
2279 **1008** 4s.50 brown & chestnut 1·30 90

1009 "Birth of Christ" (detail of fresco, Baumgartenberg Church)

1991. Christmas.
2280 **1009** 5s. multicoloured 1·30 1·10

1010 Clerks

1992. Centenary of Trade Union of Clerks in Private Enterprise.
2281 **1010** 5s.50 multicoloured 1·40 1·00

1011 Emblems of Games and Olympic Rings

1992. Winter Olympic Games, Albertville, and Summer Games, Barcelona.
2282 **1011** 7s. multicoloured 2·00 1·10

1012 Competitor

1992. 8th World Toboggan Championships on Natural Runs, Bad Goisern.
2283 **1012** 5s. multicoloured 1·30 90

1013 Hollow Stone, Klostertal

1992. Natural Beauty Spots.
2284 **1013** 5s. multicoloured 1·30 90

1014 Saiko

1992. Birth Centenary of George Saiko (writer).
2285 **1014** 5s.50 brown 1·40 1·00

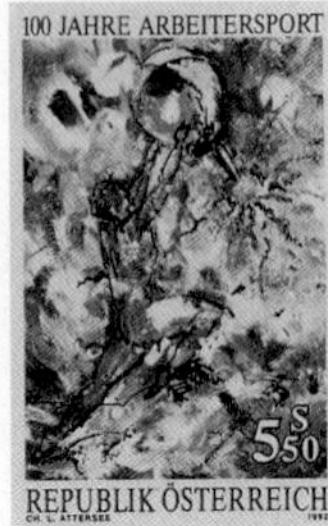

1015 "Athlete with Ball" (Christian Attersee)

1992. Centenary of Workers' Sport Movement.
2286 **1015** 5s.50 multicoloured 1·40 1·00

1016 Franz Joseph Muller (chemist and mineralogist)

1992. Scientific Anniversaries. Multicoloured.
2287 5s. Type **1016** (250th birth anniv) 1·30 1·10
2288 5s.50 Paul Kitaibel (botanist, 175th death anniv) 1·40 1·20
2289 6s. Christian Doppler (physicist) (150th anniv of observation of Doppler Effect) 1·50 1·30
2290 7s. Richard Kuhn (chemist, 25th death anniv) 1·60 1·50

1017 Angels playing Instruments

1992. 150th Anniv of Vienna Philharmonic Orchestra. Sheet 90×70 mm.
MS2291 **1017** 5s.50 black, brown and gold 2·30 2·00

1018 First and Present Emblems

1992. Centenary of Railway Workers' Trade Union.
2292 **1018** 5s.50 red and black 1·30 80

1019 Hanrieder

1992. 150th Birth Anniv of Norbert Hanrieder (writer).
2293 **1019** 5s.50 lilac & brown 1·40 90

1020 Scenes from "The Birdseller" (Zeller) and "The Beggar Student" (Millocker)

1992. 150th Birth Anniversaries of Carl Zeller and Karl Millocker (composers).
2294 **1020** 6s. multicoloured 1·50 1·10

1021 Foundry and Process

1992. Ironworks Day. 40th Anniv of First LD-Process Steel Works, Linz.
2295 **1021** 5s. multicoloured 1·30 90

1022 Woodcut of the Americas by Sebastian Munster (from "Geographia Universalis" by Claudius Ptolomaus)

1992. Europa. 500th Anniv of Discovery of America by Columbus.
2296 **1022** 7s. multicoloured 6·00 1·70

1023 Dredger

1992. Centenary of Treaty for International Regulation of the Rhine.
2297 **1023** 7s. multicoloured 2·00 1·30

1024 Rieger

1992. Centenary of Adoption of Pseudonym Reimmichl by Sebastian Rieger (writer).
2298 **1024** 5s. brown 1·30 90

1025 Flags and Alps

1992. Alpine Protection Convention.
2299 **1025** 5s.50 multicoloured 1·40 1·00

1026 Dr. Anna Dengel

1992. Birth Centenary of Dr. Anna Dengel (founder of Medical Missionary Sisters).
2300 **1026** 5s.50 multicoloured 1·50 90

1027 "R" and "H"

1992. Stamp Day.
2301 **1027** 7s.+3s. multicoloured 2·30 2·00
See note below No. 2266.

1028 Town Hall

1992. 750th Anniv of First Documentation of Lienz as a Town.
2302 **1028** 5s. multicoloured 1·30 90

1029 "Billroth in Lecture Room" (A. F. Seligmann)

1992. Austrian Surgery Society International Congress, Eisenstadt.
2303 **1029** 6s. multicoloured 1·40 1·00

1030 Waldheim

1992. Presidency of Dr. Kurt Waldheim.
2304 **1030** 5s.50 black, red & grey 1·30 90

1992. Folk Customs and Art (2nd series). As T 1005. Multicoloured.
2305 5s. Target with figure of Zieler, Lower Austria, 1732 1·30 1·10
2306 5s.50 Chest, Carinthia 1·50 1·30
2307 7s. Votive tablet from Venser Chapel, Vorarlberg 1·60 1·50

1031 Bridge over Canal

1992. Completion of Marchfeld Canal System.
2308 **1031** 5s. multicoloured 1·30 90

1032 "The Purification of Sea Water" (Peter Pongratz)

1992. Austrian Modern Art.
2309 **1032** 5s.50 multicoloured 1·50 1·10

1033 Gateway, Hofburg Palace (venue)

1992. 5th Int Ombudsmen's Conference, Vienna.
2310 **1033** 5s.50 multicoloured 1·30 90

1034 Academy Seal

1992. 300th Anniv of Academy of Fine Arts, Vienna.
2311 **1034** 5s. blue and red 1·30 90

1035 "The Annunciation"

1992. Death Bicentenary of Veit Koniger (sculptor).
2312 **1035** 5s. multicoloured 1·30 1·10

1036 "Birth of Christ" (Johann Georg Schmidt)

1992. Christmas.
2313 **1036** 5s.50 multicoloured 1·40 90

1037 Earth and Satellite

1992. Birth Centenary of Hermann Potocnik (alias Noordung) (space travel pioneer).
2314 **1037** 10s. multicoloured 2·30 1·70

1038 Dome of Michael Wing, Hofburg Palace, Vienna

1993. Architects' Anniversaries. Multicoloured.
2315 5s. Type **1038** (Joseph Emanuel Fischer von Erlach, 300th birth) 1·10 1·00
2316 5s.50 Kinsky Palace, Vienna (Johann Lukas von Hildebrandt, 325th birth) 1·20 1·10
2317 7s. State Opera House, Vienna (Eduard van der Null and August Siccard von Siccardsburg, 125th death annivs) 1·80 1·70

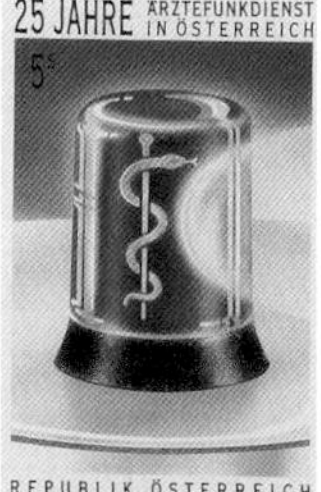

1039 Emergency Vehicle's Flashing Lantern

1993. 25th Anniv of Radio-controlled Emergency Medical Service.
2318 **1039** 5s. multicoloured 1·20 90

1040 Wilder Kaiser Massif, Tyrol

1993. Natural Beauty Spots.
2319 **1040** 6s. multicoloured 1·40 1·00

1041 Mitterhofer Typewriter

1993. Death Centenary of Peter Mitterhofer (typewriter pioneer).
2320 **1041** 17s. multicoloured 4·25 2·75

1042 "Strada del Sole" (record sleeve)

1993. "Austro Pop" (1st series). Rainhard Fendrich (singer).
2321 **1042** 5s.50 multicoloured 1·40 1·10
See also Nos. 2356 and 2368.

1043 Games Emblem

1993. Winter Special Olympics, Salzburg and Schladming.
2322 **1043** 6s.+3s. multicoloured 3·50 2·00

1044 Sealsfield

1993. Birth Bicent of Charles Sealsfield (novelist).
2323 **1044** 10s. red, blue and gold 3·50 1·50

1045 Girl realizing her Rights

1993. Ratification of U.N. Convention on Children's Rights.
2324 **1045** 7s. multicoloured 1·80 1·10

1046 "Death" (detail of sculpture, Josef Stammel), Admont Monastery, Styria

1993. Monasteries and Abbeys.

2325	-	1s. brown, black & grn	35	35
2326	**1046**	5s.50 black, yell & grn	2·40	55
2327	-	6s. black, mauve & yell	1·40	35
2328	-	7s. brown, black & grey	2·40	1·50
2329	-	7s.50 brown, bl & blk	2·40	55
2330	-	8s. orange, black & bl	3·00	90
2331	-	10s. black, blue & orge	3·25	1·30
2332	-	20s. black, blue & yell	7·25	1·10
2333	-	26s. orange, black & bis	7·75	1·10
2334	-	30s. red, yellow & black	10·50	1·80

DESIGNS: 1s. The Annunciation (detail of crosier of Abbess), St. Gabriel Benedictine Abbey, Bertholdstein; 6s. St. Benedict of Nursia (glass painting), Mariastern Abbey, Gwiggen; 7s. Marble lion, Franciscan Monastery, Salzburg; 7s.50, Virgin Mary (detail of cupola painting by Paul Troger), Altenburg Monastery; 8s. Early Gothic doorway, Wilhering Monastery; 10s. "The Healing of St. Peregrinus" (altarpiece), Maria Luggau Monastery; 20s. Hartmann Crosier, St. Georgenberg Abbey, Fiecht; 26s. "Master Dolorosa" (sculpture), Franciscan Monastery, Schwaz; 30s. Madonna and Child, Monastery of the Scottish Order, Vienna.

1047 "Flying Harlequin" (Paul Flora)

1993. Europa. Contemporary Art.
2345 **1047** 7s. multicoloured 4·50 1·10

1048 Silhouette, Script and Signature

1993. 150th Birth Anniv of Peter Rosegger (writer and newspaper publisher).
2346 **1048** 5s.50 black and green 1·20 1·10

1049 "Hohentwiel" (lake steamer) and Flags

1993. Lake Constance European Region.
2347 **1049** 6s. multicoloured 1·80 1·10

1050 Knights in Battle and "I"s

1993. Stamp Day.
2348 **1050** 7s.+3s. gold, black and blue 2·20 2·00
See note below No. 2266.

1005 Almabtrieb (driving cattle from mountain pastures) (Zell, Tyrol)

1993. Folk Customs and Art (3rd series). As T 1005. Multicoloured.
2349 5s. Corpus Christi Day procession, Hallstatt, Upper Austria 1·10 1·00
2350 5s.50 Drawing the block (log), Burgenland 1·20 1·10
2351 7s. Aperschnalzen (whipping the snow away), Salzburg 1·60 1·50

1051 Human Rights Emblem melting Bars

1993. U.N. World Conf on Human Rights, Vienna.
2352 **1051** 10s. multicoloured 2·20 1·50

1052 Jagerstatter

1993. 50th Death Anniv of Franz Jagerstatter (conscientious objector).
2353 **1052** 5s.50 multicoloured 1·20 1·10

1053 Train approaching Wolfgangsee

1993. Centenary of Schafberg Cog Railway.
2354 **1053** 6s. multicoloured 1·60 1·10

1054 "Self-portrait with Doll"

1993. Birth Centenary of Rudolf Wacker (artist).
2355 **1054** 6s. multicoloured 1·20 1·10

1993. "Austro Pop" (2nd series). Ludwig Hirsch (singer and actor). As T 1042. Multicoloured.
2356 5s.50 "Die Omama" (record sleeve) 1·40 1·10

1055 "Concert in Dornbacher Park" (Balthasar Wigand)

1993. 150th Anniv of Vienna Male Choral Society.
2357 **1055** 5s. multicoloured 1·20 90

1056 "Easter" (Max Weiler)

1993. Austrian Modern Art.
2358 **1056** 5s.50 multicoloured 1·20 90

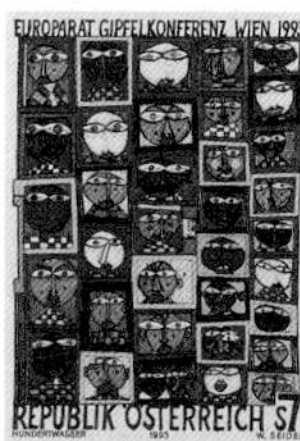

1057 "99 Heads" (detail, Friedensreich Hundertwasser)

1993. Council of Europe Heads of State Conference, Vienna.
2359 **1057** 7s. multicoloured 3·00 2·00

1058 Statue of Athene, Parliament Building

1993. 75th Anniv of Austrian Republic.
2360 **1058** 5s. multicoloured 1·20 90

1059 Workers

1993. Cent of 1st Austrian Trade Unions Congress.
2361 **1059** 5s.50 multicoloured 1·20 90

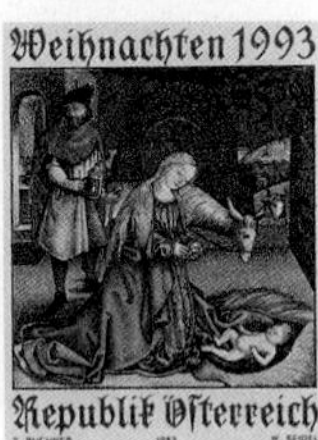

1060 "Birth of Christ" (Krainburg Altar, Styria)

1993. Christmas.
2362 **1060** 5s.50 multicoloured 1·20 90

1994. Folk Customs and Art (4th series). As T 1005. Multicoloured.
2363 5s.50 Rocking cradle, Vorarlberg 1·20 1·10
2364 6s. Carved sleigh, Styria 1·40 1·30
2365 7s. Godparent's bowl and lid, Upper Austria 1·60 1·50

1061 Winter Sports

1994. Winter Olympic Games, Lillehammer, Norway.
2366 **1061** 7s. multicoloured 1·40 1·30

1062 Early Production of Coins

1994. 800th Anniv of Vienna Mint.
2367 **1062** 6s. multicoloured 1·20 1·10

1994. "Austro Pop" (3rd series). Falco (Johann Holzel) (singer). As T 1042. Multicoloured.
2368 6s. "Rock Me Amadeus" (record sleeve) 1·40 1·10

1063 "Reclining Lady" (detail, Herbert Boeckl)

1994. Birth Centenary of Herbert Boeckl (painter).
2369 **1063** 5s.50 multicoloured 1·20 1·10

1064 N.W. Tower of City Wall

1994. 800th Anniv of Wiener Neustadt.
2370 **1064** 6s. multicoloured 1·20 1·10

1065 Lurgrotte (caves), Styria

1994. Natural Beauty Spots.
2371 **1065** 6s. multicoloured 1·20 1·10

1066 Lake Rudolf (Teleki–Hohnel expedition to Africa, 1887)

1994. Europa. Discoveries.
2372 **1066** 7s. multicoloured 3·75 1·80

1067 "E" and "L" as Ruins in Landscape

1994. Stamp Day.
2373 **1067** 7s.+3s. multicoloured 2·20 2·00
See note below No. 2266.

1068 "Allegory of Theology, Justice, Philosophy and Medicine" (detail of fresco, National Library)

1994. 300th Birth Anniv of Daniel Gran (artist).
2374 **1068** 20s. multicoloured 4·75 3·25

1069 Scene from "The Prodigal Son" (opera, Benjamin Britten)

1994. 25th Anniv of Carinthian Summer Festival, Ossiach and Villach.
2375 **1069** 5s.50 gold and red 1·20 1·10

1070 Steam Locomotive and Diesel Railcar (Gailtal)

1994. Railway Centenaries. Multicoloured.
2376 5s.50 Type **1070** 1·40 1·30
2377 6s. Steam locomotive and diesel railcar (Murtal) 1·60 1·50

1071 Gmeiner and Children

1994. 75th Birth Anniv of Hermann Gmeiner (founder of S.O.S. children's villages).
2378 **1071** 7s. multicoloured 1·40 1·30

1072 Seitz (bust, G. Ambrosi)

1994. 125th Birth Anniv of Karl Seitz (acting President, 1920).
2379 **1072** 5s.50 multicoloured 1·20 90

1073 Bohm

1994. Birth Centenary of Karl Bohm (conductor).
2380 **1073** 7s. blue and gold 1·40 1·30

1074 Ethnic Minorities on Map

1994. Legal and Cultural Protection of Ethnic Minorities.
2381 **1074** 5s.50 multicoloured 1·20 1·00

1075 Franz Theodor Csokor (dramatist and poet)

1994. Writers' Anniversaries. Multicoloured.
2382 6s. Type **1075** (25th death anniv) 1·20 1·10
2383 7s. Joseph Roth (novelist, birth cent) 1·40 1·30

1076 "Head" (Franz Ringel)

1994. Austrian Modern Art.
2384 **1076** 6s. multicoloured 1·40 1·10

1077 Money Box

1994. 175th Anniv of Savings Banks in Austria.
2385 **1077** 7s. multicoloured 1·40 1·00

1078 Air Hostess and Child

1994. Austrian World of Work (6th series).
2386 **1078** 6s. multicoloured 1·20 90

1079 Coudenhove-Kalergi and Map of Europe

1994. Birth Cent of Richard Coudenhove-Kalergi (founder of Paneuropa Union).
2387 **1079** 10s. multicoloured 2·10 1·20

1080 "Birth of Christ" (Anton Wollenek)

1994. Christmas.
2388 **1080** 6s. multicoloured 1·20 90

1081 Map and Austrian and E.U. Flags

1995. Austria's Entry into E.U.
2389 **1081** 7s. multicoloured 1·40 90

1082 Loos House, Michaelerplatz, Vienna

1995. 125th Birth Anniv of Adolf Loos (architect).
2390 **1082** 10s. multicoloured 1·90 1·50

1083 Sporting Activities

1995. 50th Anniv of Austrian Gymnastics and Sports Association.
2391 **1083** 6s. multicoloured 1·20 90

1084 Workers

1995. 75th Anniv of Workers' and Employees' Chambers (advisory body).
2392 **1084** 6s. multicoloured 1·20 80

1995. Folk Costumes and Art (5th series). As T 1005. Multicoloured.

2393	5s.50 Belt, Carinthia	1·20	1·10
2394	6s. Costume of Hiata (vineyard guard), Vienna	1·40	1·30
2395	7s. Gold bonnet, Wachau	1·60	1·50

1085 State Seal

1995. 50th Anniv of Second Republic.

2396	**1085**	6s. multicoloured	1·20	90

1086 Heft Ironworks

1995. Carinthian "History of Mining and Industry" Exhibition, Heft, Huttenberg.

2397	**1086**	5s.50 multicoloured	1·20	90

1087 Hiker in Mountains

1995. Centenary of Friends of Nature.

2398	**1087**	5s.50 multicoloured	1·20	90

1088 Heidenreichstein National Park

1995. Natural Beauty Spots.

2399	**1088**	6s. multicoloured	1·30	1·00

1089 Woman and Barbed Wire around Skull

1995. Europa. Peace and Freedom.

2400	**1089**	7s. multicoloured	4·50	1·90

1090 Map, Woman and Child and Transport

1995. Meeting of European Ministers of Transport Conference, Vienna.

2401	**1090**	7s. multicoloured	1·40	90

1091 "F" and "A" on Vase of Flowers

1995. Stamp Day.

2402	**1091**	10s.+5s. mult	3·00	2·75

See note below No. 2266.

1092 Set for "The Flying Dutchman"

1995. 50th Bregenz Festival.

2403	**1092**	6s. multicoloured	1·20	80

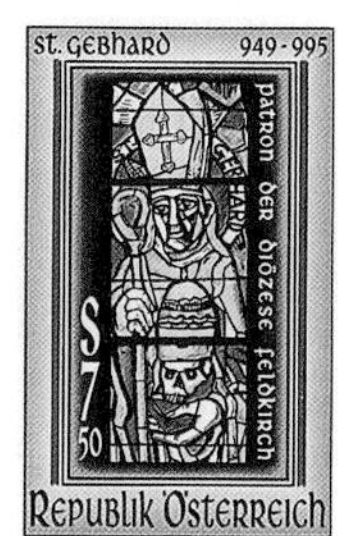

1093 St. Gebhard (stained-glass window, Martin Hausle)

1995. Death Millenary of St. Gebhard, Bishop of Konstanz (patron saint of Vorarlberg chuches).

2404	**1093**	7s.50 multicoloured	1·40	90

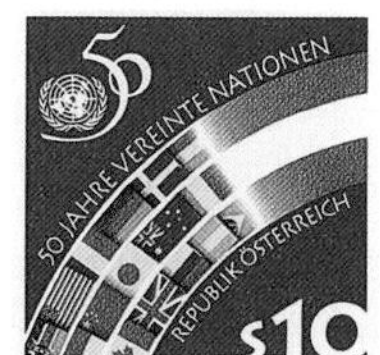

1094 Members' Flags

1995. 50th Anniv of U.N.O.

2405	**1094**	10s. multicoloured	2·10	1·20

1095 Loschmidt

1995. Death Centenary of Josef Loschmidt (physical chemist).

2406	**1095**	20s. black, stone & brn	5·75	3·00

1096 K. Leichter

1995. Birth Cent of Kathe Leichter (sociologist).

2407	**1096**	6s. cream, black & red	1·20	90

1097 Scene from "Jedermann" (Hugo von Hofmannsthal)

1995. 75th Anniv of Salzburg Festival.

2408	**1097**	6s. multicoloured	1·20	90

1098 "European Scene" (Adolf Frohner)

1995. Austrian Modern Art.

2409	**1098**	6s. multicoloured	1·20	90

1099 Franz von Suppe and "The Beautiful Galatea"

1995. Composers' Anniversaries. Scenes from operettas. Multicoloured.

2410	6s. Type **1099** (death cent)	1·20	1·10
2411	7s. Nico Dostal and "The Hungarian Wedding" (birth centenary)	1·40	1·30

1100 University Building

1995. 25th Anniv of Klagenfurt University.

2412	**1100**	5s.50 multicoloured	1·20	80

1101 Hollenburg Castle

1995. 75th Anniv of Carinthian Referendum.

2413	**1101**	6s. multicoloured	1·20	80

1102 Postman

1995. Austrian World of Work (7th series).

2414	**1102**	6s. multicoloured	1·20	80

1103 Anton von Webern (50th death)

1995. Composers' Anniversaries.

2415	**1103**	6s. blue and orange	1·20	1·10
2416	-	7s. red and orange	1·40	1·30

DESIGN: 7s. Ludwig van Beethoven (225th birth).

1104 Christ Child

1995. Christmas. 300th Anniv of Christkindl Church.

2417	**1104**	6s. multicoloured	1·20	80

1996. Folk Customs and Art (6th series). As T 1005.

2418	6s. multicoloured	1·30	1·20

DESIGN: 6s. Masked figures Roller and Scheller (Imst masquerades, Tyrol).

1105 Empress Maria Theresia and Academy Building

1996. 250th Anniv of Theresian Academy, Vienna.

2419	**1105**	6s. multicoloured	1·30	1·20

1106 Ski Jumping

1996. World Ski Jumping Championships, Tauplitz and Bad Mitterndorf.

2420	**1106**	7s. multicoloured	1·60	90

1107 Terminal

1996. Completion of West Terminal, Vienna International Airport.

2421	**1107**	7s. multicoloured	1·60	90

1108 Hohe Tauern National Park

1996. Natural Beauty Spots.

2422	**1108**	6s. multicoloured	1·40	80

1109 "Mother and Child" (Peter Fendi)

1996. Artists' Birth Bicentenaries. Multicoloured.

2423	6s. Type **1109**	1·30	1·20
2424	7s. "Self-portrait" (Leopold Kupelwieser)	1·70	1·60

1110 Organ and Music

1996. Death Cent of Anton Bruckner (composer).
2425 **1110** 5s.50 multicoloured 1·30 80

1111 Kollmitz Castle (from copper engraving)

1996. 300th Death Anniv of Georg Vischer (cartographer and engraver).
2426 **1111** 10s. black and stone 2·20 1·30

1112 Old Market Square

1996. 800th Anniv of Klagenfurt.
2427 **1112** 6s. multicoloured 1·60 90

1113 Hotel Chef and Waitress

1996. Austrian World of Work (8th series).
2428 **1113** 6s. multicoloured 1·20 90

1114 Paula von Preradovic (writer)

1996. Europa. Famous Women.
2429 **1114** 7s. stone, brown & grey 1·60 1·10

1115 "M" and "T" and Bluebirds (mosaic)

1996. Stamp Day.
2430 **1115** 10s.+5s. mult 3·50 2·50
See note below No. 2266.

1116 Mascot with Olympic Flag

1996. Olympic Games, Atlanta.
2431 **1116** 10s. multicoloured 2·20 1·50

1996. Folk Customs and Art (7th series). As T 1005.
2432 5s.50 Flower-bedecked poles, Salzburg 1·40 1·30
2433 7s. Tyrol militia 1·60 1·50

1117 Landscape

1996. 75th Anniv of Burgenland.
2434 **1117** 6s. multicoloured 1·20 80

1118 Mountaineers

1996. Cent of Austrian Mountain Rescue Service.
2435 **1118** 6s. multicoloured 1·20 80

1119 Deed of Otto III, 996

1996. Millenary of Austria. Multicoloured.

2436	6s. Type **1119**	1·20	90
2437	6s. Archduke Joseph II (after Georg Weikert) and Archduchess Maria Theresia (after Martin van Meytens)	1·20	90
2438	7s. "Duke Heinrich II" (stained-glass window, Monastery of the Holy Cross)	1·30	1·10
2439	7s. Arms in flames (1848 Revolution)	1·30	1·10
2440	7s. Rudolf IV, the Founder	1·30	1·10
2441	7s. Karl Renner (first Federal Republic president)	1·30	1·10
2442	10s. Archduke Maximilian I (Holy Roman Emperor) (miniature from Statute Book of Order of the Golden Fleece)	2·20	1·60
2443	10s. Seal and signature of Leopold Figl (State Treaty of 1955)	2·20	1·60
2444	20s. Imperial crown of Rudolf II	4·25	3·25
2445	20s. State arms, stars of Europe and "The Horsebreaker" (bronze by Josef Lax) (Austria and Europe)	4·25	3·25

1120 "Power Station" (Reinhard Artberg)

1996. Austrian Modern Art.
2446 **1120** 7s. multicoloured 1·60 1·10

1121 Children of Different Nations

1996. 50th Anniv of UNICEF.
2447 **1121** 10s. multicoloured 2·20 1·30

1122 Nativity and Vienna Town Hall

1996. Christmas.
2448 **1122** 6s. multicoloured 1·20 90

1123 Kramer

1997. Birth Centenary of Theodor Kramer (poet).
2449 **1123** 5s.50 blue 1·20 80

1997. Folk Customs and Art (8th series). As T 1005. Multicoloured.
2450 7s. Epiphany carol singers, Eisenstadt Burgenland 1·60 1·50

1124 Vineyards on the Nussberg, Vienna

1997. Natural Beauty Spots.
2451 **1124** 6s. multicoloured 1·30 90

1125 Academy and Light

1997. 150th Anniv of Austrian Academy of Sciences, Vienna.
2452 **1125** 10s. multicoloured 2·30 1·30

1126 Emblem

1997. 50th Anniv of Verbund Electricity Company.
2453 **1126** 6s. multicoloured 1·20 90

1127 The Cruel Rosalia of Forchtenstein

1997. Myths and Legends.

2454	-	6s.50 grn, pink & blk	2·20	90
2455	**1127**	7s. black, stone & brn	2·40	65
2456	-	8s. orange, blk & lilac	2·20	1·10
2457	-	9s. black, stone & pur	3·00	1·70
2458	-	10s. black, grey & red	3·50	2·00
2459	-	13s. black, brn & pur	4·25	2·20
2460	-	14s. black, lt blue & bl	4·25	1·90
2461	-	20s. green, blk & stone	6·00	2·75
2462	-	22s. black, bl & stone	5·50	4·50
2463	-	23s. black, ochre and green	7·75	5·00
2464	-	25s. stone, black and yellow	7·25	3·25
2465	-	32s. black, brn & pink	11·00	5·50

DESIGNS: 6s.50, Lindworm of Klagenfurt; 8s. The Black Lady of Hardegg; 9s. Charming Augustin; 10s. Basilisk of Vienna; 13s. The Pied Piper of Korneuburg; 14s. The Strudengau Water-nymph; 20s. St. Notburga; 22s. Witches Whirl; 23s. Loaf Agony; 25s. St. Konrad and Altems Castle; 32s. The Discovery of Erzberg (Mountain of Ore).

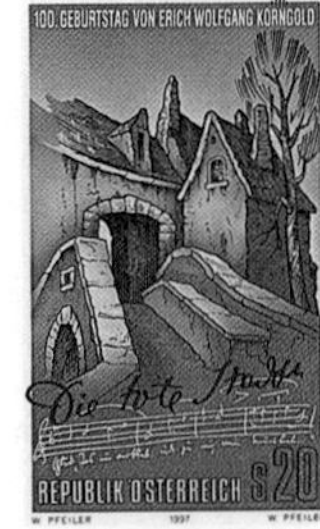

1128 Stage Set for "Die tote Stadt"

1997. Birth Cent of Erich Korngold (composer).
2470 **1128** 20s. black, blue & gold 5·75 2·75

1129 Stadium, Badge and Players

1997. Rapid Vienna, National Football Champions, 1995–96.
2471 **1129** 7s. multicoloured 1·80 90

1130 Red Deer

1997. Hunting and the Environment. Deer Feeding in Winter.
2472 **1130** 7s. multicoloured 1·60 90

1131 Canisius and Children (altar by Josef Bachlechner in Innsbruck Seminary)

1997. 400th Death Anniv of St. Petrus Canisius (patron saint of Innsbruck).
2473 **1131** 7s.50 multicoloured 1·60 90

1132 Johannes Brahms (after L. Michalek)

1997. Composers' Anniversaries.
2474 **1132** 6s. violet and gold 1·30 1·20
2475 - 10s. purple and gold 2·30 2·10
DESIGNS: 6s. Type **1132** (death centenary); 10s. Franz Schubert (birth bicentenary).

1133 "A" and "E"

1997. Stamp Day.
2476 **1133** 7s. multicoloured 1·80 1·10
See note below No. 2266.

1134 The Four Friends

1997. Europa. Tales and Legends. "The Town Band of Bremen" by the Brothers Grimm.
2477 **1134** 7s. multicoloured 4·25 1·10

1135 1850 9k. Stamp and Postman

1997. "WIPA 2000" International Stamp Exhibition, Vienna (1st issue).
2478 **1135** 27s.+13s. mult 9·00 6·75
See also Nos. 2521, 2543, **MS**2551 and **MS**2564.

1136 Train on Hochschneeberg Line

1997. Railway Anniversaries. Multicoloured.
2479 6s. Type **1136** (centenary of Hochschneeberg rack-railway) 1·40 1·30
2480 7s.50 Steam locomotive "Licaon" and viaduct near Mattersburg (150th anniv of Odenburg–Wiener Neustadt line) 1·90 1·80

1137 Cogwheels

1997. 125th Anniv of Austrian Technical Supervisory Association.
2481 **1137** 7s. multicoloured 1·70 90

1997. Folk Customs and Art (9th series). As T 1005. Multicoloured.
2482 6s.50 Tyrolean brass band 1·60 1·10

1138 Waggerl (self-portrait)

1997. Birth Centenary of Karl Waggerl (writer).
2483 **1138** 7s. green, yellow & blue 1·70 90

1139 Adolf Lorenz (founder of German Society of Orthopaedia)

1997. Orthopaedics Congress, Vienna.
2484 **1139** 8s. multicoloured 1·80 1·10

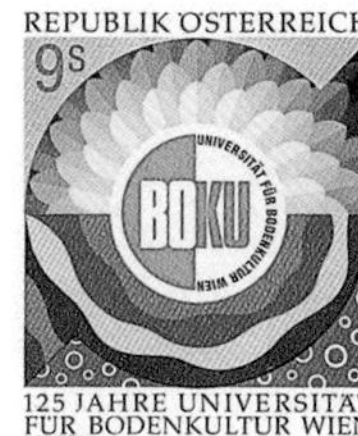

1140 Emblem

1997. 125th Anniv of College of Agricultural Sciences, Vienna.
2485 **1140** 9s. multicoloured 2·10 1·30

1141 Patient, Nurse and Doctor

1997. Austrian World of Work (9th series).
2486 **1141** 6s.50 multicoloured 1·40 90

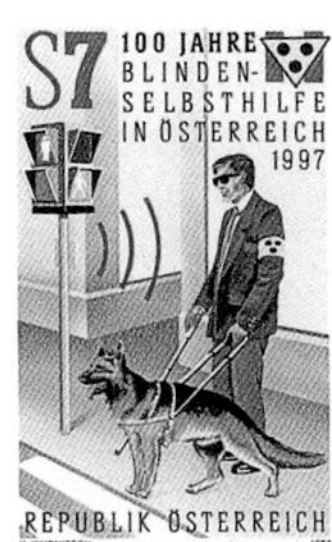

1142 Blind Man with Guide Dog

1997. Cent of Austrian Association for the Blind.
2487 **1142** 7s. multicoloured 1·60 90

1143 "House in Wind" (Helmut Schickhofer)

1997. Austrian Modern Art.
2488 **1143** 7s. multicoloured 1·80 1·10

1144 Klestil

1997. 65th Birthday of Pres. Thomas Klestil.
2489 **1144** 7s. multicoloured 1·80 90

1145 Werner

1997. 75th Birth Anniv of Oskar Werner (actor).
2490 **1145** 7s. black, orge & grey 1·80 90

1997. Folk Customs and Art (10th series). As T 1005. Multicoloured.
2491 6s.50 Tower wind-band, Upper Austria 1·40 1·10

1146 Glowing Light

1997. 25th Anniv of Light in Darkness (umbrella organization of children's charities).
2492 **1146** 7s. blue 1·60 90

1147 "Mariazell Madonna"

1997. Christmas.
2493 **1147** 7s. multicoloured 1·60 90

1148 Kalkalpen National Park

1998. Natural Beauty Spots.
2494 **1148** 7s. multicoloured 1·40 90

1149 Courting Pair

1998. Hunting and the Environment. Preservation of Breeding Habitat of the Black Grouse.
2495 **1149** 9s. multicoloured 1·80 1·30

1150 Ice Skaters

1998. Winter Olympic Games, Nagano, Japan.
2496 **1150** 14s. multicoloured 2·75 2·00

1151 Austrian Poster Exposition Advertising Poster, 1928

1998. Birth Cent of Joseph Binder (designer).
2497 **1151** 7s. multicoloured 1·60 1·10

1152 Alois Senefelder (inventor) on Lithographic Stone

1998. Bicentenary of Invention of Lithography (printing process).
2498 **1152** 7s. blue, yellow & black 1·40 90

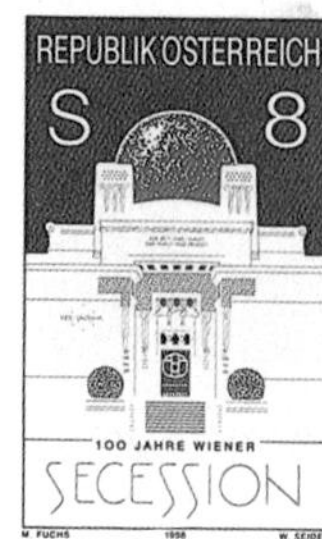

1153 Facade

1998. Centenary of Vienna Secession (exn hall).
2499 **1153** 8s. brown, gold & blue 1·80 1·10

1998. Folk Customs and Art (11th series). As T 1005. Multicoloured.
2500 6s.50 Fiacre, Vienna 1·40 1·30
2501 7s. Palm Sunday procession, Thaur, Tyrol 1·60 1·50

1154 Player and Team Emblem

1998. Austria Memphis Football Club.
2502 **1154** 7s. multicoloured 1·80 1·00

1155 "St. Florian" (glass painting)

1998. St. Florian, Patron Saint of Firemen.
2503 **1155** 7s. multicoloured 1·80 1·00

1156 Rupertus Cross

1998. 1200th Anniv of Salzburg Archdiocese.
2504 **1156** 7s. multicoloured 1·80 1·00

1157 Series Yv Locomotive No. 2, 1895

1998. Centenary of Completion of Ybbs Valley Railway.
2505 **1157** 6s.50 multicoloured 1·80 1·10

1158 "Tyrolia" (Ferdinand Cosandier)

1998. 175th Anniv of Tyrol Ferdinandeum (state museum), Innsbruck.
2506 **1158** 7s. multicoloured 1·60 1·00

1159 Vienna Town Hall (Viennese festive weeks)

1998. Europa. National Festivals.
2507 **1159** 7s. multicoloured 4·00 1·10

1998. Folk Customs and Art (12th series). As T 1005. Multicoloured.
2508 6s.50 Samson and the dwarves, Salzburg 1·80 1·10

1160 Christine Lavant

1998. 25th Death Anniv of Christine Lavant (poet).
2509 **1160** 7s. multicoloured 1·80 1·10

1161 Electric Railcar No. 1

1998. Centenary of Postlingberg Railway.
2510 **1161** 6s.50 multicoloured 1·80 1·10

1162 "R" and "L"

1998. Stamp Day.
2511 **1162** 7s. multicoloured 1·80 1·10
See note below No. 2266.

1163 Presidency Emblem

1998. Austrian Presidency of E.U.
2512 **1163** 7s. multicoloured 1·80 1·10

1164 Railcar No. 5090

1998. Centenary of Pinzgau Railway.
2513 **1164** 6s.50 multicoloured 1·80 1·10

1165 Volksoper, Vienna

1998. Centenary of Volksoper (theatre) and 50th Death Anniv of Franz Lehar (composer).
2514 **1165** 6s.50 multicoloured 1·60 1·10

1166 Empress Elisabeth (after Franz Winterhalter)

1998. Death Centenary of Empress Elisabeth.
2515 **1166** 7s. multicoloured 1·80 1·50

1167 School Building

1998. Centenary of Vienna Business School.
2516 **1167** 7s. multicoloured 1·80 1·50

1168 Kudlich and Farmers

1998. 175th Birth Anniv of Hans Kudlich (promoter of 1848 "Peasants' Liberation" Law).
2517 **1168** 6s.50 multicoloured 1·60 1·00

1169 "My Garden" (Hans Staudacher)

1998. Austrian Modern Art.
2518 **1169** 7s. multicoloured 1·80 1·10

1170 Town Hall and Arms

1998. 350th Anniv of Declaration of Eisenstadt as a Free Town.
2519 **1170** 7s. multicoloured 1·60 1·10

1171 Photographer and Reporter

1998. Austrian World of Work (10th series). Art, Media and Freelances.
2520 **1171** 6s.50 multicoloured 1·40 1·00

1172 1929 2s. Stamp and Post Van

1998. "WIPA 2000" International Stamp Exhibition, Vienna (2nd issue).
2521 **1172** 32s.+13s. mult 9·75 7·75

1173 "Nativity" (fresco, Tainach Church)

1998. Christmas.
2522 **1173** 7s. multicoloured 1·40 1·00

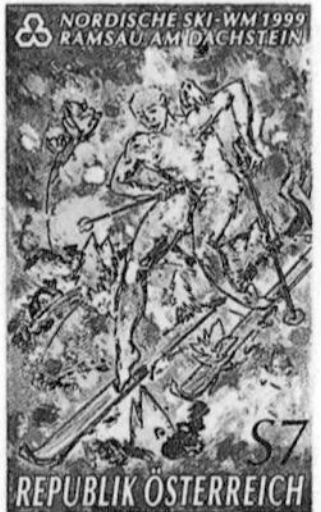
1174 Cross-country Skiing

1999. World Nordic Skiing Championships, Ramsau.
2523 **1174** 7s. multicoloured 1·80 1·20

1999. Folk Customs and Art (13th series). As T 1005. Multicoloured.
2524 6s.50 Walking pilgrimage to Mariazell 1·40 1·10

1175 Stingl Rock, Bohemian Forest

1999. Natural Beauty Spots.
2525 **1175** 7s. multicoloured 1·40 1·10

1176 Books and Compact Disc

1999. Centenary of Austrian Patent Office.
2526 **1176** 7s. multicoloured 1·40 1·10

1177 Player and Club Emblem

1999. SK Puntigamer Sturm Graz Football Club.
2527 **1177** 7s. multicoloured 1·80 1·10

1178 Palace Facade

1999. World Heritage Site. Schonbrunn Palace, Vienna.
2528 **1178** 13s. multicoloured 2·75 2·20

1179 Partridges

1999. Hunting and the Environment. Living Space for Grey Partridges.
2529 **1179** 6s.50 multicoloured 1·40 1·10

1180 Snowboarder

1999. 50th Anniv of Austrian General Sport Federation.
2530 **1180** 7s. multicoloured 1·60 1·10

1181 Council Building, Strasbourg

1999. 50th Anniv of Council of Europe.
2531 **1181** 14s. multicoloured 3·00 2·20

No. 2531 is denominated both in Austrian schillings and in euros.

1182 Steyr Type 50 Baby Saloon

1999. Birth Centenary of Karl Jenschke (engineer and car manufacturer).
2532 **1182** 7s. multicoloured 1·60 1·20

1183 "St. Martin" (marble relief, Peuerbach Church)

1999. Ancient Arts and Crafts (1st series).
2533 **1183** 8s. brown, blue & orange 1·80 1·30

See also Nos. 2542, 2575, 2600 and 2602.

1184 Symbols of Aid and Emblem

1999. 125th Anniv of Diakonie (professional charitable services).
2534 **1184** 7s. multicoloured 1·40 1·10

1185 Johann Strauss, the Younger

1999. Composers' Death Anniversaries. Mult.
2535 7s. Type **1185** (centenary) 1·70 1·60
2536 8s. Johann Strauss, the Elder (150th anniv) 1·80 1·70

1186 Rural Gendarmes

1999. 150th Anniv of National Gendarmerie.
2537 **1186** 7s. multicoloured 1·60 1·10

1187 Donau-auen National Park

1999. Europa. Parks and Gardens.
2538 **1187** 7s. multicoloured 1·80 1·10

1188 "K" and "I"

1999. Stamp Day.
2539 **1188** 7s. multicoloured 1·80 1·10
See note below No. 2266.

1189 Iron Stage Curtain

1999. Centenary of Graz Opera.
2540 **1189** 6s.50 multicoloured 1·80 1·10

1190 Couple on Bench

1999. International Year of the Elderly.
2541 **1190** 7s. multicoloured 1·40 1·10

1191 "St. Anne with Mary and Child Jesus" (wood-carving, St. George's Church, Purgg)

1999. Ancient Arts and Crafts (2nd series).
2542 **1191** 9s. multicoloured 2·20 2·00

1192 1949 25g. Stamp and Vienna Airport

1999. "WIPA 2000" International Stamp Exhibition, Vienna (3rd issue).
2543 **1192** 32s.+16s. mult 11·50 8·50

1193 "Security throughout Life"

1999. 14th Congress of Federation of Austrian Trade Unions.
2544 **1193** 6s.50 multicoloured 1·40 1·10

1194 "Cafe Girardi" (Wolfgang Herzig)

1999. Austrian Modern Art.
2545 **1194** 7s. multicoloured 1·80 1·10

1999. Folk Customs and Art (14th series). As T 1005. Multicoloured.
2546 8s. Pumpkin Festival, Lower Austria 1·80 1·10

1999. Folk Customs and Art (15th series). As T 1005. Multicoloured.
2547 7s. The Pummerin (great bell of St. Stephen's Cathedral) ringing in the New Year 1·80 1·10

1195 Institute and Fossils

1999. 150th Anniv of National Institute of Geology.
2548 **1195** 7s. multicoloured 1·80 1·10

1196 "Nativity" (altar painting, Pinkafeld Church)

1999. Christmas.
2549 **1196** 7s. multicoloured 1·40 1·10

2000. Folk Customs and Art (16th series). As T 1005. Multicoloured.
2550 7s. Chapel procession, Carinthia 1·40 1·30

2000. "WIPA 2000" International Stamp Exhibition, Vienna (4th issue). Sheet 150×95 mm.
MS2551 27s.+13s. No. 2478; 32s.+13s. No. 2521; 32s.+16s. No. 2543 36·00 39·00

2000. Folk Customs and Art (17th series). As T 1005. Multicoloured.
2552 6s.50 Three men wearing masks (Cavalcade of Beautiful Masks, Telfs) 1·40 1·10

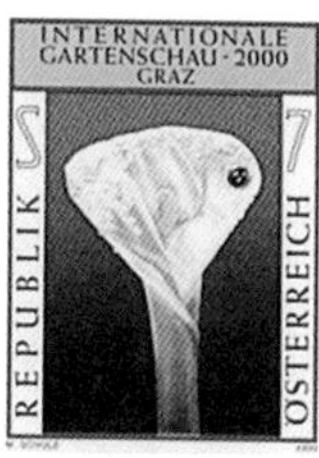

1197 *Zantadeschica aethiopica*

2000. International Garden Show, Graz.
2553 **1197** 7s. multicoloured 1·80 1·10

1198 Ibex

2000. Hunting and the Environment. Return of Ibex to Austrian Mountains.
2554 **1198** 7s. multicoloured 1·60 1·10

1199 Players

2000. F.C. Tirol Innsbruck, National Football Champion 2000.
2555 **1199** 7s. multicoloured 1·60 1·10

1200 Mt. Grossglockner and Viewing Point

2000. Bicentenary of First Ascent of Mt. Grossglockner.
2556 **1200** 7s. multicoloured 1·60 1·10

1201 Weisssee Lake

2000. Natural Beauty Spots.
2557 **1201** 7s. multicoloured 1·40 1·20

1202 "Building Europe"

2000. Europa.
2558 **1202** 7s. multicoloured 1·80 1·70

1203 Junkers F13 Airplane and Air Traffic Control Tower

2000. 75th Anniv of Civil Aviation at Klagenfurt Airport.
2559 **1203** 7s. multicoloured 1·40 1·30

1204 Madonna of Altenmarkt (statue) and Glass Roof, Palm House, Burggarten, Vienna

2000. 150th Anniv of Protection of Historic Monuments.
2560 **1204** 8s. multicoloured 1·80 1·50

1205 Illuminated Letter and Text

2000. Life of St. Malachy (treatise) by St. Bernard of Clairvaux.
2561 **1205** 9s. multicoloured 2·40 2·20

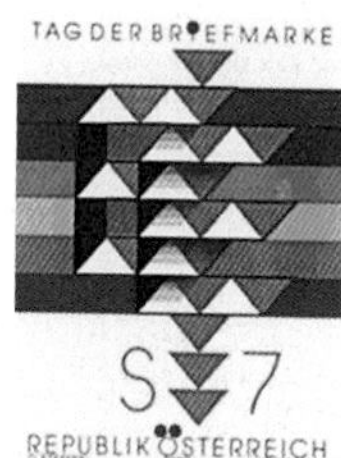

1206 "E" and "E"

2000. Stamp Day.
2562 **1206** 7s. multicoloured 1·80 1·30
See note below No. 2266.

1207 1850 9 Kreuzer and 2000 Stamp Day Stamps

2000. 150th Anniv of Austrian Stamps.
2563 **1207** 7s. multicoloured 1·80 1·30

2000. "WIPA 2000" International Stamp Exhibition, Vienna (5th series). Sheet 65×90 mm.
MS2564 10s. As No. 2458 36·00 34·00

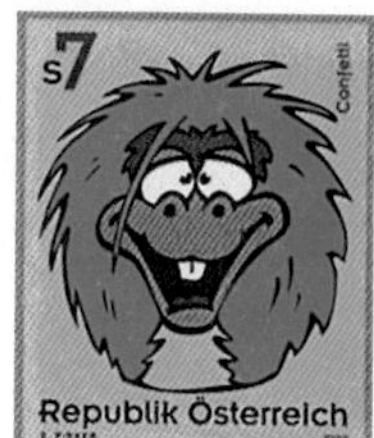

1208 "Confetti"

2000. Confetti (children's television programme).
2565 **1208** 7s. multicoloured 1·60 1·30

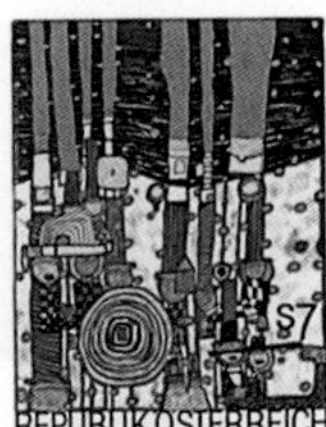

1209 "Blue Blues"

2000. Death Commemoration of Friedensreich Hundertwasser (artist). Sheet 129×126 mm, containing four versions of T 1209 identified by the colours of the vertical strips at the top of the design.

MS2566 7s. silver; 7s. red; 7s. mauve; 7s. black 9·75 9·00

1210 Blood Droplets

2000. Centenary of Discovery of Blood Groups by Karl Landsteiner (pathologist).

2567 **1210** 8s. pink, silver & black 1·60 1·50

1211 Daimler Cannstatter Bus

2000. Centenary of First Regular Bus Route between Purkersdorf and Gablitz.

2568 **1211** 9s. black, blue and light blue 2·40 2·00

2000. Folk Customs and Art (18th series). As T 1005. Multicoloured.

2569 7s. Men on raft (International Rafting Meeting, Carinthia) 1·40 1·30

1212 Dachstein River and Hallstatt

2000. Natural Beauty Spots.

2570 **1212** 7s. multicoloured 1·40 1·30

1213 String Instrument and Emblem

2000. Centenary of Vienna Symphony Orchestra.

2571 **1213** 7s. multicoloured 1·40 1·30

1214 Dinghies

2000. Olympic Games, Sydney.

2572 **1214** 9s. multicoloured 2·20 1·80

1215 Old and Modern Paper Production Methods

2000. Austrian World of Work (11th series). Printing and Paper.

2573 **1215** 6s.50 multicoloured 1·40 1·30

1216 "Turf Turkey" (Ida Szigethy)

2000. Austrian Modern Art.

2574 **1216** 7s. multicoloured 1·40 1·30

1217 Codex 965 (National Library)

2000. Ancient Arts and Crafts (3rd series).

2575 **1217** 8s. multicoloured 1·80 1·70

See also Nos. 2600 and 2602.

1218 Child receiving Vaccination

2000. Bicentenary of Vaccination in Austria.

2576 **1218** 7s. black and cinnamon 1·40 1·30

1219 Urania Building, Vienna

2000. 50th Anniv of Adult Education Association.

2577 **1219** 7s. brown, grey & gold 1·40 1·30

1220 The Nativity (altar piece, Ludesch Church)

2000. Christmas.

2578 **1220** 7s. multicoloured 1·40 1·30

1221 Downhill Skier

2000. World Skiing Championship (2001), St. Anton am Arlberg.

2579 **1221** 7s. multicoloured 1·60 1·50

1222 Pair of Mallards

2001. Hunting and the Environment. Protection of Wetlands.

2580 **1222** 7s. multicoloured 1·60 1·50

2001. Folk Customs and Art (19th series). As T 1005. Multicoloured.

2581 8s. Boat mill, Mureck, Styria 1·80 1·50

1223 Steam Locomotive No. 3

2001. Centenary of Zillertal Railway.

2582 **1223** 7s. multicoloured 1·60 1·50

1224 Players and Club Emblem

2001. SV Casino Salzburg, National Football Champion.

2583 **1224** 7s. multicoloured 1·80 1·30

1225 Rolf Rudiger

2001. Confetti (children's television programme).

2584 **1225** 7s. multicoloured 1·80 1·30

1226 Fieseler Fi-156 Storch and Airport

2001. 75th Anniv of Salzburg Airport.

2585 **1226** 14s. multicoloured 3·25 2·75

1227 Baerenschuetz Gorge

2001. Natural Beauty Spots.

2586 **1227** 7s. multicoloured 1·60 1·50

2001. Folk Customs and Art (20th series). As T 1005. Multicoloured.

2587 7s. Lent season cloth from Eastern Tyrol 1·60 1·50

1228 Water Droplet

2001. Europa. Water Resources.

2588 **1228** 15s. multicoloured 4·75 3·25

1229 Post Office Railway Car

2001. Stamp Day.

2589 **1229** 20s.+10s. mult 11·00 10·00

1230 Air Balloon

2001. Centenary of Austrian Flying Club.

2590 **1230** 7s. multicoloured 1·80 1·50

1231 Refugee

2001. 50th Anniv of United Nations High Commissioner for Refugees.

2591 **1231** 21s. multicoloured 4·75 4·50

1232 Kalte Rinne Viaduct

2001. UNESCO World Heritage Site. The Semmering Railway.

2592 **1232** 35s. multicoloured 11·00 10·00

1233 "Seppl" (mascot) (Michelle Schneeweiss)

2001. 7th International Hiking Olympics, Seefeld.

2593 **1233** 7s. multicoloured 1·60 1·50

1234 Field Post Office at Famagusta

2001. Army Postal Services Abroad.

2594 **1234** 7s. multicoloured 1·60 1·50

2001. Folk Customs and Art (21st series). As T 1005. Multicoloured.

2595 7s. Rifle and Clubhouse, Preberschiessen, Salzburg (Rifleman's gathering) 1·60 1·50

1235 "Taurus" (Railway Engine)

2001. Conversion of East–West Railway to Four-tracked Railway.

2596	**1235**	7s. multicoloured	1·80	1·70

1236 19th-century Theatrical Scene

2001. Birth Bicentenary of Johann Nestroy (playwright and actor).

2597	**1236**	7s. multicoloured	1·60	1·50

1237 "The Continents" (detail Helmut Leherb)

2001. Austrian Modern Art.

2598	**1237**	7s. multicoloured	1·60	1·50

1238 "False Friends" (Von Fuehrich)

2001. 125th Death Anniv of Joseph Ritter von Fuehrich (artist and engraver).

2599	**1238**	8s. deep green & green	1·70	1·60

1239 Pluviale (embroidered religious robe)

2001. Ancient Arts and Crafts (4th series).

2600	**1239**	10s. multicoloured	2·40	2·20

1240 Dobler

2001. Birth Bicentenary of Leopold Ludwig Dobler (magician and inventor).

2601	**1240**	7s. multicoloured	1·60	1·50

1241 Dalmatik (religious vestment) (Carmelite Monastery, Silbergrasse, Vienna)

2001. Ancient Arts and Crafts (5th series).

2602	**1241**	7s. multicoloured	1·60	1·50

1242 Building and Scientific Equipment

2001. 150th Anniv of the Central Institute for Meteorology and Geodynamics, Vienna.

2603	**1242**	12s. multicoloured	3·00	2·20

1243 Cat

2001

2604	**1243**	19s. multicoloured	6·00	5·50

1244 Civil Servants

2001. Austrian World of Work (12th series). Civil Service.

2605	**1244**	7s. multicoloured	1·60	1·50

1245 Figure of Infant Jesus

2001. Christmas. Glass Shrine, Fitzmoos Church.

2606	**1245**	7s. multicoloured	1·40	1·30

New Currency

1246 House of the Basilisk, Vienna

2002. Tourism.

2607	-	4c. multicoloured	25	10
2608	-	7c. blue and black	35	20
2609	-	13c. multicoloured	50	35
2610	-	17c. violet and black	60	45
2611	-	20c. multicoloured	70	65
2612	-	25c. multicoloured	85	80
2613	-	27c. blue and black	95	90
2614	-	45c. multicoloured	1·20	1·10
2615	**1246**	51c. multicoloured	1·40	1·30
2616	-	55c. multicoloured	1·40	1·20
2617	-	58c. multicoloured	1·60	1·50
2618	-	73c. multicoloured	1·80	1·70
2619	-	75c. multicoloured	2·10	1·80
2620	-	87c. multicoloured	2·40	2·20
2621	-	€1 multicoloured	2·75	2·20
2622	-	€1.25 multicoloured	3·25	2·50
2623	-	€2.03 multicoloured	6·00	5·50
2626	-	€3.75 multicoloured	9·25	8·50

DESIGNS: 4c. As No. 2615; 7c. As No. 2623; 13c. As No. 2620; 17c. As No. 2617; 20c. Yachts, Worthersee, Carintha; 25c. Crucifixes on rock, Mondsee, Upper Austria; 27c. As No. 2618; 45c. Snow covered chalet, Jungholz, Kleinwasler; 55c. Gothic houses, Steyr, Upper Austria; 58c. Wine cellars, Hadres, Lower Austria; 73c. Alpine chalet, Salzburg; 75c. Boat on Bodensee, Voralberg; 87c. Alpach Valley, Tyrol; €1 Farmhouse, Rossegg, Styria; €1.25 Wine press building, Eisenburg, Burgenland; €2.03 Heligenkreuz, Lower Austria; €3.75 Gothic shrine, Hochhosterwitz, Carinthia.

1247 Stars, Map of Europe and €1 Coin

2002. Euro Currency.

2630	**1247**	€3.27 multicoloured	9·75	9·00

No. 2630 is printed on the back under the gum with examples of Austrian schilling coins.

1248 Skiers and Olympic Rings

2002. Winter Olympic Games, Salt Lake City, U.S.A.

2631	**1248**	73c. multicoloured	2·20	2·00

1249 Bouquet of Flowers

2002

2632	**1249**	87c. multicoloured	2·30	2·10

1250 Woman and Skyline

2002. Women's Day.

2633	**1250**	51c. multicoloured	3·50	3·25

1251 Mel and Lucy

2002. "Philis" (children's stamp awareness programme) (1st issue).

2634	**1251**	58c. multicoloured	2·20	2·00

See also Nos. 2639 and 2662.

1252 Red Roses

2002. Greetings Stamp.

2635	**1252**	58c. multicoloured	1·80	1·70

1253 Kubin

2002. 125th Birth Anniv of Alfred Kubin (artist).

2636	**1253**	87c. black and buff	2·30	2·10

1254 St. Elizabeth of Thuringia and Sick Man

2002. Caritas (Catholic charity organization).

2637	**1254**	51c. multicoloured	1·90	1·80

1255 Tiger, Clown and Circus Tent

2002. Europa. The Circus.

2638	**1255**	87c. multicoloured	3·50	3·25

1256 Sisko and Mauritius

2002. "Philis" (children's stamp awareness programme) (2nd issue).

2639	**1256**	58c. multicoloured	1·90	1·80

1257 The Nativity

2002. 800th Anniv of Lilienfeld Abbey.

2640	**1257**	€2.03 multicoloured	5·75	5·50

1258 Mimi

2002. Confetti (children's television programme).

2641	**1258**	51c. multicoloured	1·80	1·70

1259 Railway Carriage, 1919

2002. Stamp Day.

2642	**1259**	€1.60+80c. multicoloured	8·50	7·75

1260 Cheetah, Zebra and Orang-utan

2002. 250th Anniv of Schonbrunn Zoo. Mult.

2643	51c. Type **1260**	1·70	1·60
2644	58c. Gulls, flamingos and pelicans	1·80	1·70
2645	87c. Lion, turtle and crocodile	2·40	2·20
2646	€1.38 Elephant, birds and fish	3·50	3·25

Nos. 2643/6 were issued together, se-tenant, forming a composite design.

1261 Teddy Bears

2002. Centenary of the Teddy Bear.

2647	**1261**	51c. multicoloured	1·90	1·80

1262 Chair No. 14 (Michael Thonet)

2002. 75th Anniv of "Design Austria" (design group) (1st issue).

2648	**1262**	€1.38 multicoloured	3·50	3·25

See also Nos. 2661 and 2670.

1263 Crystal Cup

2002. Ancient Arts and Crafts.

2649	**1263**	€1.60 multicoloured	4·25	4·00

1264 Museum Buildings

2002. Museumsquartier (MQ), Messepalast, Vienna.

2650	**1264**	58c. multicoloured	2·20	2·00

1265 Figures supporting Emblem

2002. 50th Anniv of Union of Austrians Abroad.

2651	**1265**	€2.47 multicoloured	6·75	6·25

1266 Clown Doctor

2002. "Rote Nasen" (Red Noses (charity)).

2652	**1266**	51c. multicoloured	1·80	1·70

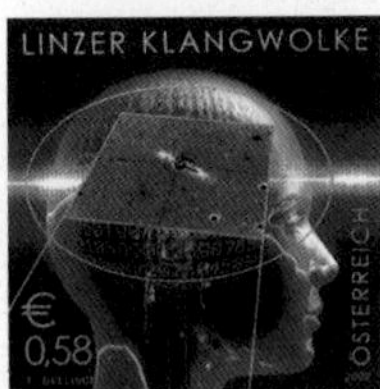

1267 Head

2002. Linzer Klangwolke (sound and light performance), Linz.

2653	**1267**	58c. multicoloured	1·90	1·80

1268 Graf & Stift Type 40/45

2002

2654	**1268**	51c. multicoloured	1·60	1·50

1269 Dog

2002

2655	**1269**	51c. multicoloured	1·60	1·50

1270 Steam Locomotive 109

2002

2656	**1270**	51c. multicoloured	1·80	1·70

1271 "Schutzenhaus" (Karl Goldammer)

2002. Austrian Modern Art.

2657	**1271**	51c. multicoloured	1·80	1·70

1272 Lottery Ball

2002. 250th Anniv of Austrian Lottery. Sheet 72×90 mm.

MS2658	**1272**	87c. multicoloured	3·00	2·75

1273 Thayatal National Park

2002

2659	**1273**	58c. multicoloured	1·80	1·70

1274 Puch 175 SV

2002

2660	**1274**	58c. multicoloured	1·90	1·80

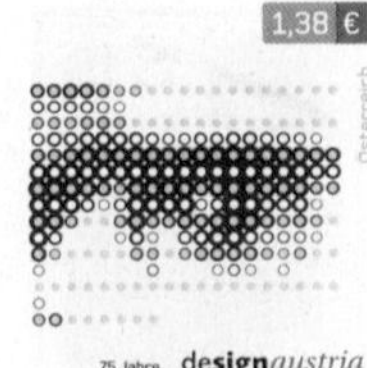

1275 "Eye"

2002. 75th Anniv of "Design Austria" (design group) (2nd issue). Winning Entry in Design Competition.

2661	**1275**	€1.38 multicoloured	4·25	4·00

1276 Edison and Gogo

2002. "Philis" (children's stamp awareness programme) (3rd issue).

2662	**1276**	58c. multicoloured	2·20	2·00

1277 Crib Aureola, Thaur, Tyrol

2002. Christmas.

2663	**1277**	51c. multicoloured	1·60	1·50

1278 Emblem

2003. Make-up Rate Stamp.

2664	**1278**	45c. yellow, silver and black	6·75	4·50

1279 Amphitheatre on River Mur

2003. Graz, Cultural Capital of Europe, 2003.

2665	**1279**	58c. multicoloured	1·80	1·70

1280 Billy Wilder

2003. 1st Death Anniv of Billy Wilder (film director).

2666	**1280**	58c. multicoloured	1·90	1·80

1281 Heart, Linked Rings and Doves

2003. Greetings Stamp. Wedding.

2667	**1281**	58c. multicoloured	1·90	1·80

1282 Kasperl

2003. Confetti (children's television programme). 45th Anniv of Kasperl (puppet).

2668	**1282**	51c. multicoloured	1·60	1·50

1283 Emblem

2003. 10th Anniv of Recycling Enterprise.

2669	**1283**	55c. multicoloured	1·40	1·30

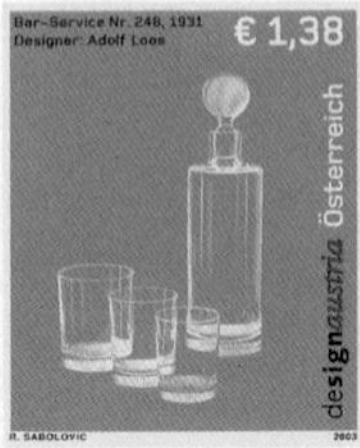

1284 Carafe and Glasses (Adolf Loos)

2003. 75th Anniv of "Design Austria" (design group) (3rd issue).

2670	**1284**	€1.38 blue, black and orange	3·50	3·25

1285 Seated Pandas

2003. Schönbrunn Zoo's Acquisition of Pandas from People's Republic of China. Sheet 110×76 mm containing T 1285 and similar multicoloured design.

MS2671	75c. Pandas nuzzling (40×34 mm) (horiz); €1 Type **1285**	8·50	6·75

1286 St. George's Monastery

2003. Millenary of St. George's Monastery, Carintha.
2672 **1286** 87c. multicoloured 2·20 2·00

1287 Marcel Prawy

2003. Marcel Prawy Commemoration (musician). Sheet 100×100 mm.
MS2673 **1287** €1.75 multicoloured 6·75 6·75

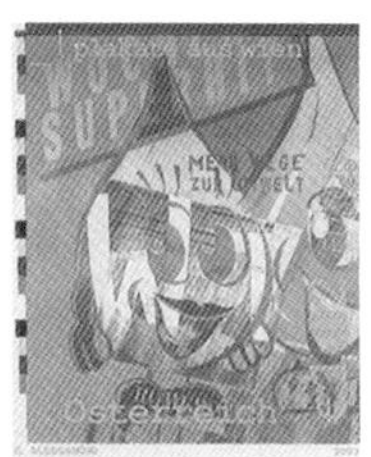
1288 Face

2003. Europa. Poster Art.
2674 **1288** €1.02 multicoloured 3·00 2·75

1289 Siemmens M 320 Postal Wagon

2003. Stamp Day.
2675 **1289** €2.54+€1.26 multicoloured 11·00 10·00

1290 Series 5045 Locomotive "Blue Flash"

2003
2676 **1290** 75c. multicoloured 2·30 2·10

1291 Bridge over Salzach River

2003. Centenary of Oberndorf–Laufen Bridge.
2677 **1291** 55c. multicoloured 2·40 2·20

A stamp of the same design was issued by Germany.

1292 Ford Model T

2003. Centenary of Ford Motor Company. Sheet 150×81 mm containing T 1292 and similar horiz designs. Multicoloured.
MS2678 Type **1292**; 55c. Henry Ford; 55c. Ford Streetka 6·75 6·25

1293 Keith Richards

2003. Rolling Stones. Sheet 101×101 mm containing T 1291 and similar vert designs. Multicoloured.
MS2679 Type **1293**; 55c. Mick Jagger; 55c. Charlie Watts; 55c. Ronnie Woods 9·00 8·50

1294 Panther Airport Fire Appliance

2003
2688 **1294** 55c. multicoloured 1·80 1·70

1295 Apostle and Scribe

2003. Year of the Bible.
2689 **1295** 55c. multicoloured 1·40 1·30

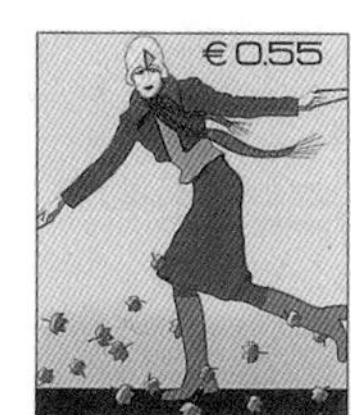
1296 "Prenez le temps d'aimer" (Take time to enjoy) (Kiki Kogelnik)

2003
2690 **1296** 55c. multicoloured 1·80 1·70

1297 Lake

2003. UNESCO World Heritage Site. Lake Neusiedlersee.
2691 **1297** €1 multicoloured 3·00 2·75

1298 Geisha and Samurai

2003. Japan Exhibition, Leoben.
2692 **1298** 55c. multicoloured 1·80 1·70

1299 Princess Turandot

2003. Performance of Puccini's Opera Turandot, St. Margarethen Roman Quarry.
2693 **1299** 55c. multicoloured 1·80 1·70

1300 Family (Eva Wallner)

2003. Children's Stamp.
2694 **1300** 55c. multicoloured 1·80 1·70

1301 Water Tower

2003. 50th Anniv Local Government Conference, Wiener Neustadt.
2695 **1301** 55c. multicoloured 1·60 1·50

1302 TomTom (cartoon character) and Bouquet

2003. Greetings stamp.
2696 **1302** 55c. multicoloured 2·20 2·00

1303 TomTom throwing Parcel from Hot Air Balloon

2003
2697 **1303** 55c. multicoloured 2·20 2·00

1304 Werner Schlager

2003. Werner Schlager, World Table Tennis Champion, 2003.
2698 **1304** 55c. multicoloured 2·40 2·20

1305 Stylized Head (Cornelia Zell)

2003. Jugend-Phila '03 International Youth Stamp Exhibition, Graz.
2699 **1305** 55c. multicoloured 1·40 1·30

1306 Fan and "Elisabeth"

2003. Elisabeth, the Musical (musical based on life of Empress Elisabeth).
2700 **1306** 55c. multicoloured 1·90 1·80

1307 "Judith"

2003. 185th Death Anniv of Gustav Klimt (artist). Sheet 80×100 mm.
MS2701 **1307** €2.10 multicoloured 7·75 7·25

1308 Hands enclosing Light

2003. 30th Anniv of "Licht ins Dunkel" (Bringing light into darkness) (fund raising campaign).
2702 **1308** 55c. multicoloured 1·40 1·30

1309 Grand Piano

2003. 175th Anniv of Bosendorfer (piano manufacturer).
2703 **1309** 75c. multicoloured 2·20 2·00

1310 Oscar Peterson

2003. 78th Birth Anniv of Oscar Peterson (pianist).
2704 **1310** €1.25 multicoloured 3·50 3·25

1311 Stained Glass Window

2003. Christmas.
2705 **1311** 55c. multicoloured 1·90 1·80

1312 Postal Emblem

2003. Greeting Stamps. T 1312 and similar design. Each yellow, black and gold.

2706		55c. Type **1312**	1·40	1·30
2707		55c. Postal emblem (horiz)	1·40	1·30

Nos. 2706/7 could be personalised by the addition of photograph or logo, replacing the design shown on the stamp.

1313 Ricardo Muti

2004. Vienna Philharmonic Orchestra's New Year Concert conducted by Ricardo Muti (principal conductor, La Scala Milan).

2708	**1313**	€1 multicoloured	3·50	3·25

1314 Seiji Ozawa

2004. 2nd Anniv of Seija Ozawa's Appointment as Musical Director of Vienna State Opera House.

2709	**1314**	€1 multicoloured	3·50	3·25

1315 Jose Carreras

2004. 30th Anniv of Jose Carreras Association with Vienna State Opera House.

2710	**1315**	€1 multicoloured	3·50	3·25

1316 Gerard Hanappi

2004. Centenary of Austrian Football. Sheet 196×113 mm containing T 1316 and similar vert designs. Multicoloured.

MS2711 55c.×10, Type **1316**; Mathias Sindelar; Football and anniversary emblem; Bruno Pezzey; Ernst Ocwirk; Walter Zeman; Herbert Prohaska; Hans Krankl; Andreas Herzog; Anton Polster		16·00	16·00

1317 Crucifixion (Werner Berg)

2004. Easter.

2712	**1317**	55c. multicoloured	1·40	1·30

1318 Dancers

2004. Life Ball (AIDS charity).

2713	**1318**	55c. multicoloured	1·60	1·30

1319 Cardinal Franz Konig

2004. Cardinal Franz Konig Commemoration.

2714	**1319**	€1 multicoloured	3·00	2·75

1320 Emperor Franz Joseph and Empress Elisabeth

2004. 150th Anniv of the Marriage of Emperor Franz Joseph and Empress Elisabeth. Sheet 157×109 mm containing T 1320 and similar vert designs. Multicoloured.

MS2715 €1.25 Type **1320**; €1.50 Wedding procession; €1.75 Emperor Franz Joseph and Empress Elisabeth (35×42 mm)		13·50	13·50

1321 Catholics' Day Emblem

2004. Catholics' Day. Sheet 110×160 mm containing T 1321 and similar vert designs. Multicoloured.

MS2716 55c. Type **1321**; €1.25 Pope John Paul II; €1.25 Magna Mater Austriae (Romanesque statue) (Chapel of Grace, Basilica, Mariazell); €1.25 Mother of God on Column of the Blessed Virgin (Basilica, Mariazell); €1.25 Virgin Mary (Treasury Altar, Basilica, Mariazell); €1.25 Crucifix (High Altar, Basilica, Mariazell)		19·00	19·00

1322 Oeffag C.11 Mail Plane

2004. Stamp Day.

2717	**1322**	€2.65+€1.30 multicoloured	11·50	10·50

2004. Folk Customs and Art (22nd series). As T 1005. Multicoloured.

2718		55c. Barrel sliding, Kosterneuburgs	1·80	1·70

1323 Joe Zawinul (musician)

2004

2719	**1323**	55c. multicoloured	1·80	1·70

1324 Sun and Flowers

2004. Europa. Holidays.

2720	**1324**	75c. multicoloured	2·10	1·90

1325 Holy Sepulchre, Jerusalem

2004. Papal Order of the Holy Sepulchre.

2721	**1325**	125c. multicoloured	3·25	3·00

1326 Imperial and Royal Southern State Railway Locomotive *Engerth*

2004

2722	**1326**	55c. multicoloured	1·70	1·60

1327 Fireworks and Bubbles

2004. Danube Island Festival, Vienna.

2723	**1327**	55c. multicoloured	1·40	1·30

1328 Theodor Herzl

2004. Death Centenary of Theodor Herzl (writer and Zionist pioneer).

2724	**1328**	55c. multicoloured	2·30	2·10

A stamp of the same design was issued by Israel and Hungary.

1329 Arnold Schwarzenegger (governor of California)

2004

2725	**1329**	100c. multicoloured	5·50	5·00

1330 Ernst Happel

2004. 12th Death Anniv of Ernst Happel (football trainer).

2726	**1330**	100c. black and scarlet	5·50	5·00

1331 Tom Turbo (bicycle) (Andreas Wolkerstorfer)

2004. Tom Turbo (character from children's television series). Winning Entry in Children's Drawing Competition.

2727	**1331**	55c. multicoloured	1·70	1·60

1332 TomTom (cartoon character) greeting Snail

2004. Greetings Stamp.

2728	**1332**	55c. multicoloured	1·90	1·80

1333 Town Hall and Steam Tram

2004. Incorporation of Floridsdorf into Vienna.

2729	**1333**	55c. multicoloured	1·90	1·80

1334 Crystal

2004. Crystal Worlds (tourist attraction), Wattens. Sheet 147×85 mm containing T 1334 and similar horiz design. Multicoloured.

MS2730 375c.×2, Type **1334**; Swan		21·00	21·00

The stamps of **MS**2730 have crystals applied to the surface.

1335 Hermann Maier

2004. Hermann Maier—World Champion Giant Slalom Skier.

2731	**1335**	55c. multicoloured	2·40	2·20

1336 "Kaspar Winterbild" (Josef Bramer)

2004

2732	**1336**	55c. multicoloured	1·60	1·50

2004. No. 2607 surch BASILISK.

2733		55c. on 51c. multicoloured	1·80	1·70

1338 "Die Wartende" (Sylvia Gredenberg)

2004
2734 **1338** 55c. multicoloured 1·40 1·30

1339 "Junge Sonnenblume" (Max Weiler)

2004. Sheet 80×100 mm.
MS2735 **1339** multicoloured 6·75 6·75

1340 Campaign Poster (Friednsreich Hundertwasser)

2004. 20th Anniv of Campaign to save Danube Meadows (now National Park).
2736 **1340** 55c. multicoloured 3·50 3·25

1341 Soldier and National Arms

2004. 50th Anniv of Federal Army.
2737 **1341** 55c. multicoloured 1·60 1·50

1342 Nikolaus Harnoncourt

2004. 75th Birthday of Nikolaus Harnoncourt (musician).
2738 **1342** €1 multicoloured 2·75 2·50

1343 Salzburg Christmas Market

2004. Christmas.
2739 **1343** 55c. multicoloured 1·40 1·30

1344 Lorin Maazel

2005. Vienna Philharmonic Orchestra's New Year Concert conducted by Lorin Maazel.
2740 **1344** €1 multicoloured 2·75 2·50

1345 Herbert von Karajan

2005. 10th Anniv of Herbert von Karajan Centre.
2741 **1345** 55c. blue, black and deep blue 1·40 1·30

1346 Stephan Eberharter

2005. Stephan Eberharter—World Champion Skier.
2742 **1346** 55c. multicoloured 1·90 1·80

2005. Nos. 2607, 2609/10, 2613, 2617/18, 2620 and 2623 variously surch.
2743 55c. on 4c. multicoloured 1·40 1·30
2744 55c. on 13c. multicoloured 1·40 1·30
2745 55c. on 17c. multicoloured 1·40 1·30
2746 55c. on 27c. multicoloured 1·40 1·30
2747 55c. on 58c. multicoloured 1·40 1·30
2748 55c. on 73c. multicoloured 1·40 1·30
2749 55c. on 87c. multicoloured 1·40 1·30
2750 55c. on €2.03 multicoloured 1·40 1·30

1355 Globe and Rotary Emblem

2005. Centenary of Rotary International (charitable organization).
2751 **1355** 55c. multicoloured 1·60 1·50

1356 Max Schmeling

2005. Death Centenary of Max Schmeling (boxer).
2752 **1356** 100c. multicoloured 2·75 2·50

1357 "Venus in Front of the Mirror" (Peter Paul Rubens)

2005. Liechtenstein Museum, Garden Palace, Vienna.
2753 **1357** 125c. multicoloured 3·50 3·25

1358 Carl Djerassi

2005. 82nd Birth Anniv of Carl Djerassi (chemist and writer). Sheet 60×80 mm.
MS2754 **1358** multicoloured 3·50 3·50

1359 Pope John Paul II

2005. Pope John Paul II Commemoration.
2755 **1359** €1 multicoloured 2·75 2·50

1360 Taurus

2005. Astrology (1st issue). Multicoloured. Self-adhesive gum.
2756 55c. Type **1360** 1·60 1·50
2757 55c. Gemini 1·60 1·50
2758 55c. Cancer 1·60 1·50
2759 55c. Rooster (Year of the Rooster) (Chinese astrology) (red) 1·60 1·50
See also Nos. 2772/5, 2784/7 and 2799/2802.

1361 Post Office Building and Carriages

2005. Imperial Post Office in Jerusalem (1859–1914).
2760 **1361** 100c. multicoloured 2·75 2·50

1362 Saint Florian

2005. Saints (1st issue). Saint Florian (National Patron Saint).
2761 **1362** 55c. multicoloured 1·60 1·50
See also Nos. 2767, 2829, 2857, 2890, 2932 and 2959.

1363 Tracks

2005. 60th Anniv of Liberation of Mauthausen Concentration Camp.
2762 **1363** 55c. multicoloured 1·60 1·50

1364 State Arms

2005. 60th Anniv of Second Republic and 50th Anniv of State Treaty. Sheet 120×80 mm containing T 1364 and similar multicoloured design.
MS2763 55c.×2, Type **1364**; Seals and signatures on treaty (42×35 mm) 3·50 3·50

1365 Heidi Klum

2005. Life Ball (AIDS charity).
2764 **1365** 75c. multicoloured 2·20 2·00

1366 Junkers F13 Flying Boat

2005. Stamp Day.
2765 **1366** 265c.+130c. mult 11·00 11·00

1367 Waiter in Cup of Coffee

2005. Europa. Gastronomy.
2766 **1367** 75c. multicoloured 2·30 2·10

1368 Saint Joseph

2005. Saints (2nd issue).
2767 **1368** 55c. multicoloured 1·60 1·50

1369 Jochen Rindt

2005. 25th Death Anniv of Karl Jochen Rindt (1970—Formula 1 World Champion).
2768 **1369** 55c. multicoloured 1·80 1·70

1370 Melman, Marty, Alex and Gloria (characters)

2005. Madagascar (animated film).
2769 **1370** 55c. multicoloured 1·60 1·50

1371 Peacock Butterfly (*Inachis io*)

2005
2770 **1371** 55c. multicoloured 1·60 1·50

1372 Edelweiss

2005. Vorarlberg Embroidery.

2771	**1372**	375c. green	9·75	9·50

2005. Astrology (2nd issue). As T 1360. Multicoloured. Self-adhesive.

2772	55c. Leo	1·60	1·50
2773	55c. Virgo	1·60	1·50
2774	55c. Libra	1·60	1·50
2775	55c. As No. 2759 (yellow)	1·60	1·50

2005. Customs and Art (23rd series). As T 1005. Multicoloured.

2776	55c. Game of dice, Frankenburg	1·60	1·50

1373 Nikki Lauda

2005. Nikki Lauda (Formula 1 World Champion—1975, 1977 and 1984).

2777	**1373**	55c. multicoloured	1·70	1·60

1374 Pumpkin

2005. Halloween.

2778	**1374**	55c. multicoloured	1·60	1·50

1375 "Houses" (Egon Schiele)

2005. Art. Sheet 100×80 mm.

MS2779	**1375**	210c. multicoloured	6·75	6·75

1376 ET 10.103 Railcar

2005. Centenary of Montafon Railway.

2780	**1376**	55c. multicoloured	1·60	1·50

1377 Presentation of Deed

2005. Landhaus (provincial government building), Klagenfurt.

2781	**1377**	75c. multicoloured	2·10	1·90

1378 "Master of the Woods" (Karl Hodina)

2005

2782	**1378**	55c. multicoloured	1·60	1·50

1379 Adalbert Stifter

2005. Birth Bicentenary of Adalbert Stifter (writer).

2783	**1379**	55c. multicoloured	2·40	2·20

2005. Astrology (3rd issue). As T 1360. Multicoloured. Self-adhesive.

2784	55c. Scorpio	1·60	1·50
2785	55c. Sagittarius	1·60	1·50
2786	55c. Capricorn	1·60	1·50
2787	55c. As No. 2759 (orange)	1·60	1·50

1380 National Theatre

2005. 50th Anniv of Re-opening of National Theatre and Opera House. Sheet 130×60 mm containing T 1380 and similar horiz design.

MS2788 55c. sepia and agate; 55c. indigo and black	4·75	4·75

DESIGNS: 55c.×2, Type **1380**; State Opera House.

1381 Hills

2005. Restoration of Sattler's Cyclorama of Salzburg. Sheet 155×56 mm containing T 381 and similar horiz design. Multicoloured.

MS2789 125c.×2, Type **1381**; Townscape	7·75	7·75

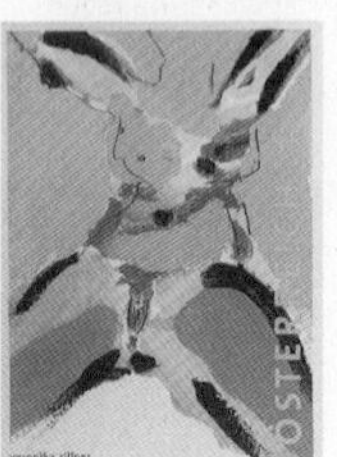
1382 "Nude" (Veronika Zillner)

2005

2790	**1382**	55c. multicoloured	1·60	1·50

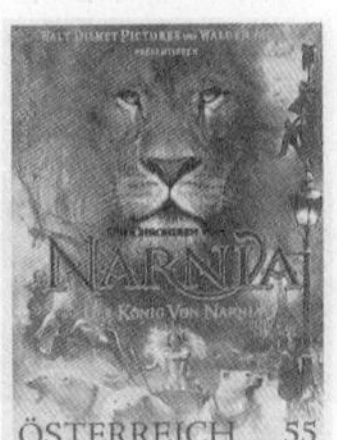
1383 Aslan (character)

2005. The Chronicles of Narnia (film of book by C. S. Lewis).

2791	**1383**	55c. multicoloured	1·60	1·50

1384 "Maria Heimsuchung" (Reinhold Stecher)

2005. Advent.

2792	**1384**	55c. multicoloured	1·40	1·30

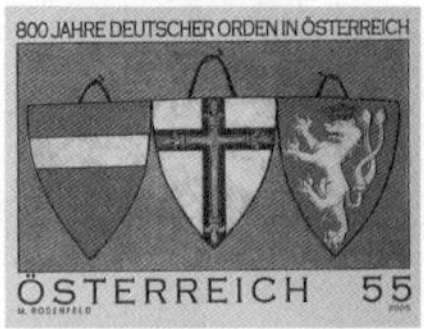
1385 Shields

2005. 800th Anniv of Order of Teutonic Knights.

2793	**1385**	55c. multicoloured	1·40	1·30

1386 Snow-covered Houses

2005. Christmas.

2794	**1386**	55c. multicoloured	1·40	1·30

1387 Mariss Jansons

2006. Vienna Philharmonic Orchestra's New Year Concert conducted by Mariss Jansons.

2795	**1387**	75c. multicoloured	1·90	1·80

1388 Building Facade

2006. Austria's Presidency of European Union.

2796	**1388**	75c. multicoloured	1·90	1·80

1389 "Post" Philatelic Shop

2006. Greeting Stamp.

2797	**1389**	55c. multicoloured	1·40	1·30

1390 Muhammad Ali

2006. Muhammad Ali (boxer).

2798	**1390**	€1.25 multicoloured	3·50	3·25

1391 Dog ("Year of the Dog")

2006. Astrology (4th issue). Multicoloured. Self-adhesive.

2799	55c. Type **1391**	1·60	1·50
2800	55c. Aquarius	1·60	1·50
2801	55c. Pisces	1·60	1·50
2802	55c. Aries	1·60	1·50

1392 Wolfgang Mozart

2006. 250th Birth Anniv of Wolfgang Amadeus Mozart (composer and musician).

2803	**1392**	55c. red and silver	1·60	1·50

1393 Europa (sculpture) (R. Chavanon)

2006. 50th Anniv of Europa Stamps.

2804	**1393**	125c. multicoloured	3·50	3·25

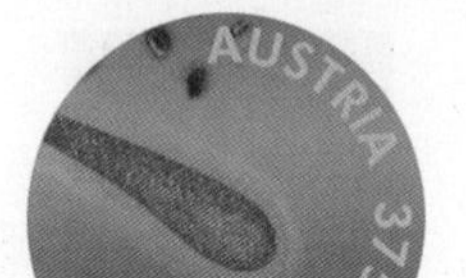
1394 "Lost in her Dreams" (Friedrich von Amerling)

2006. Liechtenstein Museum, Garden Palace, Vienna.

2805	**1394**	125c. multicoloured	3·50	3·25

A stamp of the same design was issued by Liechtenstein.

1395 Meteorite

2006. Post from another World. Meteorite H-chondrite on Stamps. Sheet 81×60 mm.

MS2806	**1395**	375c. multicoloured	11·00	11·00

No. **MS**2806 contains ground meteorite dust and is sold in a folder.

1396 Almaz and Karl Heinz Bohm (founders)

2006. 25th Anniv of Menschen fur Menschen (charity).
2807 **1396** 100c. multicoloured 2·50 2·40

1397 Initiation

2006. Freemasonry in Austria. Sheet 81×61 mm.
MS2808 **1397** 100c. multicoloured 3·50 3·50

1398 Couch

2006. 150th Birth Anniv of Sigmund Freud (psychoanalysis).
2809 **1398** 55c. multicoloured 1·30 1·20

1399 Franz Beckenbauer (Andy Warhol)

2006. Franz Beckenbauer (footballer).
2810 **1399** 75c. multicoloured 1·90 1·80

2006. Flood Relief. No. 2612 surch 75+425 HOCH WASSER HILFE 2006.
2811 75c.+425c. on 25c. multicoloured 9·75 9·50

The surcharge was for the victims of the Marchfeld floods.

2006. No. 2608 surch HEILIGENKREUZ NIEDEROSTERRICH and tree.
2812 55c. on 7c. multicoloured 1·40 1·30

1402 Falco

2006. Hans Holzl (Falco) (rock musician) Commemoration.
2813 **1402** 55c. multicoloured 1·60 1·50

1403 Naomi Campbell

2006. Life Ball (AIDS charity).
2814 **1403** 75c. multicoloured 2·30 2·10

2006. Customs and Art (24th series). As T 1005. Multicoloured.
2815 55c. Weitensfeld Kranzlreiten (race) 1·40 1·30

1404 Emblem

2006. Privatization of Post Office.
2816 **1404** 55c. multicoloured 1·40 1·30

1405 Jim Clark

2006. Formula I Motor Racing Legends. Sheet 140×185 mm containing T 1405 and similar horiz designs. Multicoloured.
MS2817 55c.×4, Type **1405**; Jacky Ickx; Jackie Stewart; Alain Prost; 75c.×2, Stirling Moss; Mario Andretti; 100c. Bruce McLaren; 125c. Jack Brabham 16·00 16·00

See also No. **MS**2868.

1406 Saint Hemma

2006
2818 **1406** 55c. multicoloured 1·40 1·30

1407 Emblem (image scaled to 73% of original size)

2006. 60th Anniv of Federal Chamber of Industry and Commerce.
2819 **1407** 55c. silver, vermilion and black 1·80 1·70

1408 Mozart

2006. 250th Birth Anniv of Wolfgang Amadeus Mozart (composer and musician). Viva Mozart Exhibition, Salzburg.
2820 **1408** 55c. multicoloured 1·40 1·30

1409 Ottfried Fischer

2006. Ottfried Fischer (actor).
2821 **1409** 55c. multicoloured 1·40 1·30

1410 Figures

2006. Europa. Integration.
2822 **1410** 75c. multicoloured 1·90 1·80

1411 Airbus A310-300

2006. Stamp Day.
2823 **1411** 265c.+130c. multicoloured 10·50 10·50

1412 St. Anne's Column, Innsbruck

2006
2824 **1412** 55c. multicoloured 1·40 1·30

1413 K. K. STB Reihe 106 Locomotive

2006. Centenary of Pyhrn Railway.
2825 **1413** 55c. multicoloured 1·40 1·30

1414 Fireworks over Victoria Harbour, Hong Kong

2006. Fireworks. Sheet 146×85 mm containing T 1414 and similar horiz design. Multicoloured.
MS2826 €3.75×2, Type **1414**; Fireworks over Giant Ferris Wheel, Vienna, Austria 21·00 21·00

MS2826 has crystals applied to the surface of the stamps and was sold in a folder.

Stamps of a similar design were issued by Hong Kong.

1415 European Lynx (*Lynx lynx*)

2006. Fauna.
2827 **1415** 55c. multicoloured 1·40 1·30

1416 Emblem

2006. WIPA 2008 International Stamp Exhibition.
2828 **1416** 55c.+20c. multicoloured 2·20 2·00

1417 Saint Gebhard

2006. Saints (3rd issue).
2829 **1417** 55c. multicoloured 1·40 1·30

1418 Steyr 220 Motor Car

2006
2830 **1418** 55c. multicoloured 1·40 1·30

1419 KTM R 125 Tarzan Motorbike

2006
2831 **1419** 55c. multicoloured 1·40 1·30

1420 Benjamin Raich

2006. Benjamin Raich—World Champion Skier.
2832 **1420** 55c. multicoloured 1·40 1·30

1421 Piano

2006. Musical Instruments. Multicoloured.
2833 55c. Type **1421** 1·40 1·30
2834 55c. Guqin 1·40 1·30

Stamps of a similar design were issued by China.

1422 "Young Boy" (Cornelia Schlesinger)

2006
2835 **1422** 55c. multicoloured 1·40 1·30

1423 Alte Saline (salt refinery) and Saint Rupert

2006. German and Austrian Philatelic Exhibition, Bad Reichenhall.
2836 **1423** 55c.+20c. multicoloured 1·90 1·80

1424 "Homo sapiens" (detail) (Valentin Oman)

2006. Modern Art.

2837	**1424**	55c. multicoloured	1·40	1·30

1425 Pond Turtle

2006. Self-adhesive.

2838	**1425**	55c. multicoloured	1·40	1·30

1426 Bald Ibis

2006. Fauna. Multicoloured. Self-adhesive.

2839	55c. Type **1426**	1·40	1·30
2840	55c. Brown bear	1·40	1·30

1427 "The Holy Family at Rest" (Franz Weiss)

2006. Christmas (1st issue).

2841	**1427**	55c. multicoloured	1·40	1·30

1428 "Christkindl Pilgrimage Church" (Reinhold Stecher)

2006. Christmas (2nd issue).

2842	**1428**	55c. multicoloured	1·40	1·30

1429 "Ferdinand Square" (T. Chyshkovskii)

2006. 750th Anniv of Lvov.

2843	**1429**	55c. multicoloured	1·40	1·30

A stamp of a similar design was issued by Ukraine.

1430 Michael Schumacher

1430a Michael Schumacher

2006. Michael Schumacher (Formula 1 World Champion–1994/5 and 2000/4).

2844	**1430**	75c. multicoloured	2·20	2·00
2844a	**1430a**	75c. multicoloured	3·25	3·00

No. 2844a has different (incorrect) championship year dates and includes designer and year of issue at lower margin.

1431 "Zinnoberroten Merkur" (No. N13 "Mercury")

2006. Centenary of National Stamp and Coin Dealers' Association.

2845	**1431**	55c. cerise and gold	1·40	1·30

1432 Zubin Mehta

2007. Vienna Philharmonic Orchestra's New Year Concert conducted by Zubin Mehta.

2846	**1432**	75c. multicoloured	1·90	1·80

1433 Alpine Flowers

2007. Flowers. Multicoloured.

2847	55c. Type **1433**	1·30	1·20
2848	75c. Hellebores	1·80	1·70
2849	€1.25 Spring flowers	3·00	2·75

1434 Symbols of Technology and Figure

2007. Mankind and Technology. Self-adhesive.

2850	**1434**	55c. multicoloured	1·40	1·30

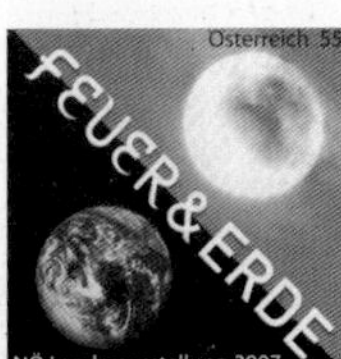
1435 Fire and Earth

2007. Lower Austrian Provincial Exhibition.

2851	**1435**	55c. multicoloured	1·40	1·30

1436 Outline of Robert Baden-Powell

2007. Centenary of Scouting. Sheet 170×130 mm containing T 1436 and similar horiz designs. Multicoloured.

MS2852 55c.×4, Type **1436**; Campfire; Tent; Guitar	6·00	6·00

1437 Roe Deer

2007

2853	**1437**	75c. multicoloured	1·90	1·80

1438 "Portrait of a Lady" (Bernardino Zaganelli da Cottignola)

2007

2854	**1438**	€1.25 multicoloured	3·25	3·00

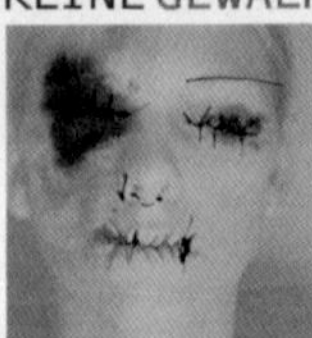

1439 Injured Woman

2007. Stop Violence against Women Campaign.

2855	**1439**	55c. multicoloured	1·40	1·30

1440 Easter Rattles

2007. Traditional Customs.

2856	**1440**	55c. multicoloured	1·40	1·30

1441 Saint Klemens Maria Holbauer

2007. Saints (4th issue).

2857	**1441**	55c. multicoloured	1·40	1·30

1442 Emblem

2007. WIPA 2008 International Stamp Exhibition.

2858	**1442**	55c.+20c. multicoloured	2·20	2·00

1443 Roses

2007. Mourning Stamp. No value expressed.

2859	**1443**	(55c.) multicoloured	1·40	1·30

1444 Flowers

2007. Greetings Stamp. No value expressed.

2860	**1444**	(55c.) multicoloured	1·40	1·30

1445 Salamander (*Salamandra salamandra*)

2007. Fauna. Multicoloured. Self-adhesive.

2861	55c. Type **1445**	1·40	1·30
2862	55c. Crayfish (*Astacus astacus*)	1·40	1·30

1446 Pope Benedict XVI

2007. 80th Birth Anniv of Pope Benedict XVI.

2863	**1446**	100c. multicoloured	2·75	2·50

1447 Inscr "Myotis brandtii"

2007. Whiskered Bat. Self-adhesive.

2864	**1447**	55c. multicoloured	1·40	1·30

No. 2864 is described as "Whiskered Bat", that is Myotis mystacinus but is inscribed "Myotis brandtii", that is Brandt's Bat.

1448 Violet

2007

2865	**1448**	100c. multicoloured	2·40	2·20

1449 'The Good Samaritan' (fresco, Franciscan Monastery, Schwaz)

2007. 80th Anniv of Austrian Workers Samaritan Federation (medical assistance organization).
2866 **1449** 55c. multicoloured 1·40 1·30

1450 'Untitled' (painting by Hermann Nitsch)

2007. Modern Art. Sheet 61×80 mm. Imperf.
MS2867 **1450** scarlet and black 3·00 3·00

2007. Formula I Motor Racing Legends. Sheet 140×185 mm containing horiz designs (size 50×32 mm) as T 1405. Multicoloured.
MS2868 55c.×8, Phil Hill; Clay Regazzoni; Gerhard Berger; Juan Manuel Fangio; John Surtees; Mika Hakkinen; Graham Hill; Emerson Fittipaldi 11·50 11·50

1451 Krause & Comp Electric Locomotive

2007. Centenary of Mariazell Narrow Gauge Railway.
2869 **1451** 55c. multicoloured 1·40 1·30

1452 Church Facade and Tower

2007. 850th Anniv of Mariazell Basilica.
2870 **1452** 55c. multicoloured 1·40 1·30

1453 Trix and Flix

2007. European Football Championships (Euro 2008), Austria and Switzerland. Sheet 100×80 mm containing T 1453 and similar horiz designs. Multicoloured.
MS2871 20c. Type **1453**; 25c. Holding trophy; 30c.Tackling for the ball; 35c. With arms around each other 3·00 3·00

1454 'Self-portrait' (painting by Angelika Kauffmann)

2007. Modern Art. Sheet 81×101 mm.
MS2872 210c. scarlet and black 6·00 6·00

1455 *Wien* (steamer) (painting by Harry Heusser)

2007. Stamp Day.
2873 **1455** 265c.+130c. multicoloured 9·75 9·00

1456 Globe as Scout

2007. Europa. Centenary of Scouting.
2874 **1456** 55c. multicoloured 1·40 1·30

1457 Ignaz Pleyel

2007. 250th Birth Anniv of Ignaz Joseph Pleyel (composer).
2875 **1457** £1 multicoloured 2·40 2·20

1458 Shrek and Fiona

2007. 'Shrek the Third' (animated film).
2876 **1458** 55c. multicoloured 1·40 1·30

1459 Museum Building

2007. Essel Museum. Self-adhesive.
2877 **1459** 55c. multicoloured 1·40 1·30

1460 Wilhelm Kienzl

2007. 150th Birth Anniv of Wilhelm Kienzl (composer).
2878 **1460** 75c. multicoloured 1·80 1·70

1461 U Series Steam Locomotive

2007. Bregenz Forest Railway.
2879 **1461** 75c. multicoloured 1·90 1·80

1462 'Man' (Astrid Bernhart)

2007
2880 **1462** 55c. multicoloured 1·40 1·30

1463 Dandelion

2007. Flora. Multicoloured.

2881	4c. Type **1463**	25	20
2882	10c. Scottish laburnum	35	35
2883	65c. Gelder rose	1·60	1·50
2884	115c. *Gentiana ciliate*	2·75	2·50
2885	140c. Clematis	3·50	3·25

1464 *Haliaeetus albicilla* (white-tailed eagle)

2007
2886 **1464** 55c. multicoloured 1·40 1·30

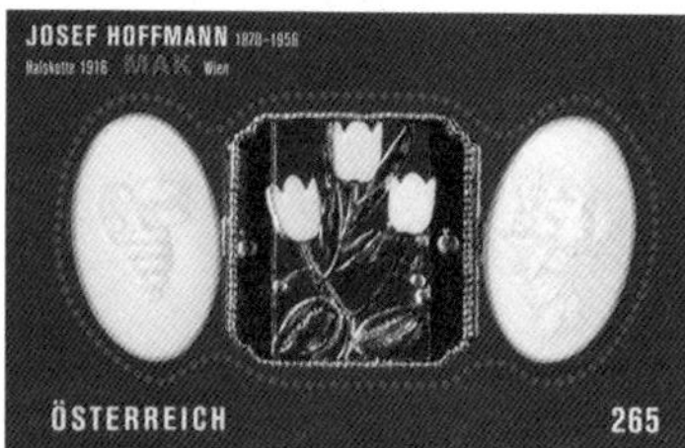
1465 Ivory and Gold Medallions (Necklace, 1916) (image scaled to 60% of original size)

2007. Josef Hoffman (designer and architect) Commemoration. Sheet 81×51 mm. Imperf.
MS2887 **1465** multicoloured 7·75 7·75

1466 Oil Derrick

2007. 75th Anniv of Austrian Oil Production.
2888 **1466** 75c. multicoloured 1·90 1·80

No. 2888 was impregnated with scent of oil which was released by rubbing part of the design.

1467 Stag and Hind

2007. Birth Bicentenary of Friedrich Gauermann (artist).
2889 **1467** 55c. multicoloured 1·40 1·30

1468 Saint Rupert

2007. Saints (5th issue).
2890 **1468** 55c. multicoloured 1·40 1·30

1469 Niki Hosp

2007. Niki Hosp–Women's World Cup Alpine Ski Champion, 2006–2007.
2891 **1469** 55c. multicoloured 1·40 1·30

1470 *Lucanus cervus* (stag beetle)

2007. Self-adhesive.
2892 **1470** 75c. multicoloured 2·10 1·90

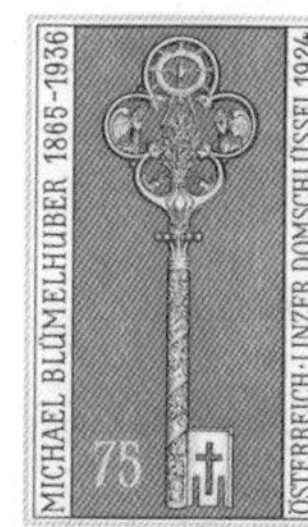
1471 Key

2007. Michel Blumelhuber (iron and steel carver) Commemoration.
2893 **1471** 75c. multicoloured 2·10 1·90

1472 Christiane Horbiger

2007. Christiane Horbiger (actress and recipient of Cross of Honour for Science and Art).
2894 **1472** 55c. multicoloured 1·40 1·30

1473 Scene from 'Queen of Spades' (Peter Illyich Tchaikovsky)

2007. Vienna State Opera Opening Nights (1st issue).
2895 **1473** 55c. multicoloured 1·40 1·30
See also No. 2914.

1474 Nativity (altar painting, Oberwollan)

2007. Christmas. Multicoloured.
2896 55c. Type **1474** 1·40 1·30

2897 65c. Nativity (icon, Church of St. Barbara) 1·60 1·50

1475 Clownfish

2007. 50th Anniv of Haus des Meeres (Aqua Terra Zoo).
2898 **1475** 55c. multicoloured 1·40 1·30

1476 Thomas Gottschalk

2007. Thomas Gottschalk and 'Wetten dass?' (TV presenter and game show).
2899 **1476** 65c. multicoloured 1·70 1·60

1477 *Cypripedium calceolus* (lady's slipper orchid)

2008
2900 **1477** 15c. multicoloured 35 35

1478 Vienna

2008. EURO 2008 Football Championships (1st issue). Venues. Sheet 150×90 mm containing T 1478 and similar square designs. Multicoloured.
MS2901 55c.×4, Type **1478**; Salzburg; Klagenfurt; Innsbruck, 65c.×4, Zurich; Basel; Bern; Geneva 12·00 12·00

The stamps of No. **MS**2901 share a common background design.

See also Nos. 2903/4, 2906/7, 2909, 2910, 2917, 2918, 2919, 2912, 2922, 2926, 2925, **MS**2929, 2930, **MS**2931 and 2951.

1479 Emblem and St Stephen's Cathedral

2008. WIPA 2008 International Stamp Exhibition.
2902 **1479** 55c.+20c. multicoloured 2·20 2·00

See also Nos. 2828 and 2858.

1480 Trix and Flix (mascots)

2008. EURO 2008 Football Championships (2nd issue). Multicoloured. Self-adhesive.
2903 55c. Type **1480** 1·40 1·30
2904 65c. Emblem 1·60 1·50

1481 *Portrait of Martina* (Hans Robert Pippal)

2008. Modern Art.
2905 **1481** 65c. multicoloured 1·60 1·50

1482 Trix and Flix (Alexandra Payer)

2008. EURO 2008 Football Championships (3rd issue). Children's Drawings. Multicoloured.
2906 55c. Type **1482** 1·40 1·30
2907 55c. Footballs as map of Europe (Corina Payr) 1·40 1·30

2008. WIPA 2008 International Stamp Exhibition. Gold. Sheet 126×73 mm containing triangular designs as T 1479. Multicoloured.
MS2908 55c. As No. 2828; 55c. As No. 2858; 65c. As No. 2902 5·75 5·75

1483 Map of Europe, Football and Euro Stars (Saskia Puchegger)

2008. EURO 2008 Football Championships (4th issue). Children's Drawings.
2909 **1483** 65c. multicoloured 1·60 1·50

1484 *Defence* (Maria Lassnig)

2008. EURO 2008 Football Championships (5th issue).
2910 **1484** 55c. multicoloured 1·40 1·30

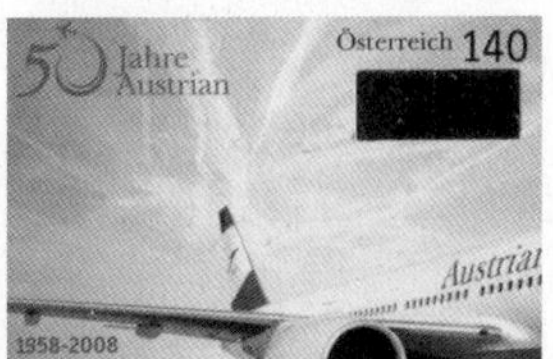
1485 *Hyla arborea* (tree frog)

2008. Fauna. Multicoloured. Self-adhesive.
2911 65c. Type **1485** 1·70 1·60
2912 65c. *Alcedo atthis* (kingfisher) 1·70 1·60

1486 Airbus A320

2008. 50th Anniv of Austrian Airlines.
2913 **1486** 140c. multicoloured 3·50 3·25

No. 2913 includes an area, which when scratched, could win a prize.

1487 Scene from *La Forza del Destino* (Giuseppe Verdi)

2008. Vienna State Opera Opening Nights (2nd issue).
2914 **1487** 55c. multicoloured 1·40 1·30

1488 *Princess Marie Franziska von Liechtenstein* (Friedrich von Amerling)

2008
2915 **1488** 125c. multicoloured 3·50 3·25

A stamp of a similar design was issued by Liechtenstein.

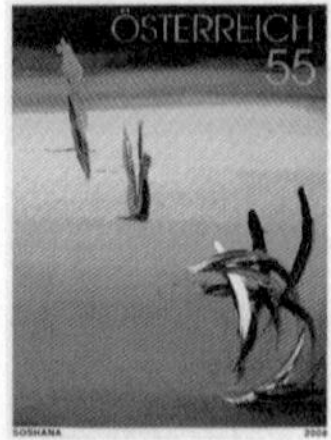
1489 Imaginary Landscape

2008. Modern Art. Sysanne Sculler (Soshana).
2916 **1489** 55c. multicoloured 1·40 1·30

1490 Football

2008. EURO 2008 Football Championships (6th issue). Self-adhesive.
2917 **1490** 375c. multicoloured 9·75 9·25

No. 2917 is made from a synthetic mixture containing polyurethane, as the original ball used for the EURO 2008 (known as the 'Europass').

1491 Football Field, Ball and Player's Legs

2008. EURO 2008 Football Championships (7th issue).
2918 **1491** 55c. multicoloured 1·40 1·30

1492 Lindwurm (symbol of Klagenfurt) on Football and Karawanken Mountains (Bolona Jencic)

2008. EURO 2008 Football Championships (8th issue). Children's Drawings.
2919 **1492** 125c. multicoloured 3·00 2·75

1493 View from River

2008. World Heritage Site. Wachau.
2920 **1493** 100c. multicoloured 2·40 2·20

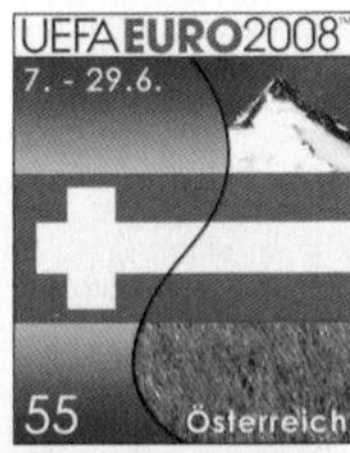
1494 Austrian and Swiss Flags, Alps and Turf (Stefan Gritsch)

2008. EURO 2008 Football Championships (9th issue). Children's Drawings.
2921 **1494** 55c. multicoloured 1·40 1·30

1495 Football wearing Lederhosen (Vanessa Schennach)

2008. EURO 2008 Football Championships (10th issue). Children's Drawings.
2922 **1495** 100c. multicoloured 2·40 2·20

1496 Traditional Clothes

2008. Centenary of Tyrolean Federation of Traditional Provincial Costumes.
2923 **1496** 75c. multicoloured 2·00 1·90

1497 *Erinaceus concolor* (southern white-breasted hedgehog)

2008. Fauna. Multicoloured. Self-adhesive.
2924 55c. Type **1497** 1·40 1·30
2925 55c. *Lepus europaeus* (hare) 1·40 1·30

1498 Preparation and Goal

2008. EURO 2008 Football Championships (11th issue). Andreas Herzog's Winning Goal—World Cup Qualifier, 1997. Self-adhesive.
2926 **1498** 545c. multicoloured 14·00 14·00

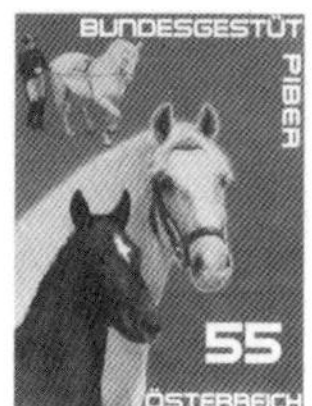

1499 Mare and Foal

2008. Federal Lipizzaner Stud, Piber.
2927 **1499** 55c. multicoloured 1·50 1·40

1500 Turf (Silvia Holemar, Denise Prossegger and Guso Aldijana)

2008. EURO 2008 Football Championships (12th issue). Children's Drawings.
2928 **1500** 75c. multicoloured 2·00 1·90

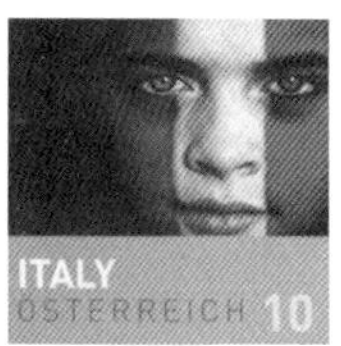

1501 Italy

2008. EURO 2008 Football Championships (13th issue). Participating Teams. Two sheets 150×90 mm containing T 1501 and similar square designs showing faces painted with team flag.
MS2929 (a) 10c. Type **1501**; 10c. Croatia; 15c. Sweden; 15c. Greece; 20c. Austria; 20c. Portugal; 65c. Spain; 65c. Czech Republic. (b) 25c. Switzerland; 25c. Germany; 30c. Romania; 30c. Turkey; 35c. Netherlands; 35c. Poland; 55c. Russia; 55c. France 12·50 12·50

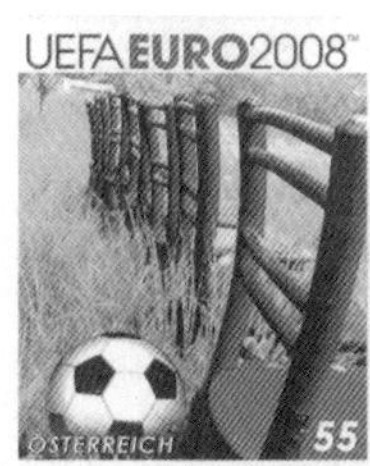

1502 Ball and Chairs (Andrea Kastrun)

2008. EURO 2008 Football Championships (14th issue). Children's Drawings.
2930 **1502** 55c. multicoloured 1·50 1·40

1503 Henri Delaunay Cup (EURO 2008 trophy)

2008. EURO 2008 Football Championships (15th issue). Sheet 65×75 mm.
MS2931 **1503** multicoloured 10·00 10·00

No. **MS**2931 contains four crystals and was issued contained in a folder.

1504 Saint Notburga

2008. Saints (6th issue).
2932 **1504** 55c. multicoloured 1·50 1·40

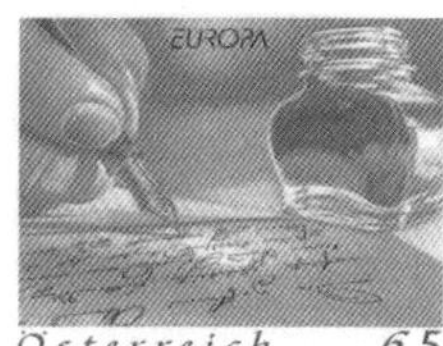

1505 Script, Hand, Pen and Ink

2008. Europa. The Letter.
2933 **1505** 65c. multicoloured 1·80 1·60

1506 *Upupa epops* (hoopoe)

2008. Fauna. Multicoloured. Self-adhesive.
2934 75c. Type **1506** 1·90 1·70
2935 75c. *Hemaris fuciformis* (broad-bordered bee hawk-moth) 1·90 1·70

1507 Steam Locomotive

2008. 110th Anniv of Vienna Urban Railway.
2936 **1507** 75c. multicoloured 2·00 1·90

1508 Letterbox

2008. Death Centenary of Josef Maria Olbrich (artist and architect).
2937 **1508** 65c. multicoloured 1·80 1·60

1509 Statuette

2008. Centenary of Discovery of Willendorf Venus. Self-adhesive.
2938 **1509** 375c. multicoloured 10·00 9·75

1510 Columbine

2008. Flowers.
2939 **1510** 50c. multicoloured 1·40 1·30

1511 Ranunculus

2008. Flowers.
2940 **1511** 55c. multicoloured 1·50 1·40

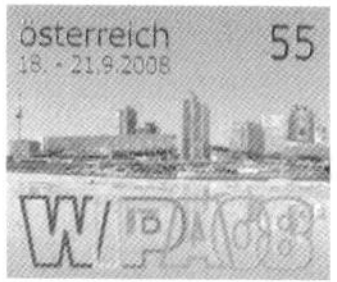

1512 Skyline

2008. WIPA 2008 International Stamp Exhibition. Self-adhesive.
2941 **1512** 55c. multicoloured 1·50 1·40

See also No. 2828, 2858 and 2902.

1513 Series 4130 Rail Car Set

2008. 150th Anniv of Empress Elizabeth Western Railway.
2942 **1513** 100c. multicoloured 2·75 2·50

1514 Express Mail (detail) (painting by K. Schorpfeil)

2008. Praga 2008 and WIPA 2008, International Stamp Exhibitions. Sheet 120×80 mm.
MS2943 multicoloured 7·25 7·00

Stamp of the same design was issued by Czech Republic.

1515 Maze

2008. 80th Birth Anniv of Friedensreich Hundertwasser (artist). Sheet 97×127 mm containing T 1515 and similar vert designs. Multicoloured.
MS2944 55c. Type **1515**; 75c. House; 100c. Stylized lamps; 125c. Maze (different) 10·00 10·00

2008. WIPA 2008 International Stamp Exhibition. Silver. Sheet 126×73 mm containing triangular designs as T 1479. Multicoloured.
MS2945 55c.+20c.×3, As No. 2828; As No. 2902; As No. 2858 6·25 6·25

1516 *Schonbrunn* (paddle steamer)

2008. Stamp Day.
2946 **1516** 265c.+130c. multicoloured 10·50 10·00

1517 Nude (Dina Larot)

2008
2947 **1517** 55c. multicoloured 1·50 1·40

1518 Gentian

2008. Vorarlberg Embroidery. Self-adhesive.
2948 **1518** 375c. blue 10·00 9·75

1519 *Maximilian Schell* ((Arnulf Rainer)

2008. Maximilian Schell (actor).
2949 **1519** 100c. multicoloured 2·75 2·50

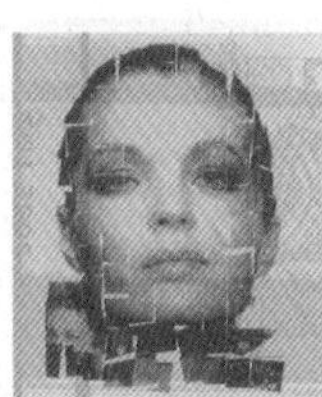

1520 Romy Schneider

2008. 70th Birth Anniv of Romy Schneider (actress).
2950 **1520** 100c. multicoloured 2·75 2·50

1521 Iker Casillas (winning Spanish team captain) holding Trophy

2008. Euro 2008 Football Championships (16th issue).
2951 **1521** 65c. multicoloured 1·80 1·60

1522 Thomas Morgenstern

2008. Thomas Morgenstern—World Champion Ski-jumper, 2007 and Olympic Gold Medallist.
2952 **1522** 100c. multicoloured 2·75 2·50

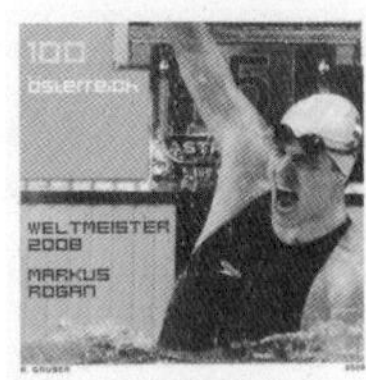
1523 Markus Rogan

2008. Markus Rogan—World Champion Backstroke Swimmer, 2008.
2953 **1523** 100c. multicoloured 2·75 2·50

1524 Heinz Fischer

2008. 70th Birth Anniv of Heinz Fischer (federal president 2004—present).
2954 **1524** 55c. multicoloured 1·50 1·40

1525 Manner Neapolitan Biscuits

2008. Classic Trademarks.
2955 **1525** 55c. multicoloured 1·50 1·40

1526 Koloman Moser

2008. Koloman Moser (artist and stamp designer) Commemoration.
2956 **1526** 130c. multicoloured 3·75 3·50

1527 Trieste Imperial and Royal Post Office Building

2008. Old Austria.
2957 **1527** 65c. multicoloured 2·00 1·90

1528 *First Christmas Tree in Ried* (Felix Ignaz Pollingger)

2008. Art History.
2958 **1528** 65c. multicoloured 2·00 1·90

1529 Saint Martin

2008. Saints (7th issue).
2959 **1529** 55c. multicoloured 1·50 1·40

1530 Karl Schranz

2008. 70th Birth Anniv of Karl Schranz (World Champion skier).
2960 **1530** 65c. multicoloured 2·00 1·90

1531 Adoration of the Magi (ceiling fresco, Collegiate Monastery and Parish Church of St Michael, Flachgau)

2008. Christmas.
2961 **1531** 55c. multicoloured 1·80 1·60

1532 Female Figure

2009. Saliera (salt cellar) by Benvento Cellini. Sheet 110×75 mm containing T 1532 and similar vert design. Multicoloured.
MS2962 210c.×2, Type **1532**; Male figure 14·00 14·00

The stamps of **MS**2962 form a composite design of the salt cellar.

1533 Landskron Castle

2009. Self-adhesive.
2963 **1533** 55c. multicoloured 1·90 1·70

1534 Pez Peppermint Sweets

2009. Classic Trademarks.
2964 **1534** 55c. multicoloured 1·90 1·70

1535 Post Building, Cracow

2009. Old Austria.
2965 **1535** 100c. multicoloured 3·00 2·75

1536 Raimondo Montecuccoli

2009. 400th Birth Anniv of Raimondo Montecuccoli (soldier and writer).
2966 **1536** 130c. multicoloured 4·00 3·75

1537 Girl

2009. 60th Anniv of SOS Children's Villages.
2967 **1537** 55c. multicoloured 1·90 1·70

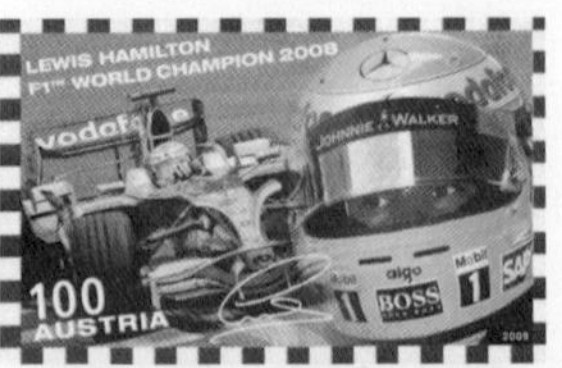
1538 Lewis Hamilton and McLaren Race Car

2009. Lewis Hamilton (Formula I World Champion–2008).
2968 **1538** 100c. multicoloured 3·00 2·75

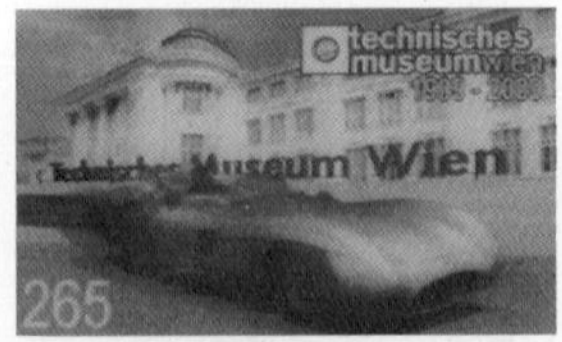
1539 Mercedes W 196 Silver Arrow

2009. Centenary of Technical Museum, Vienna. Self-adhesive.
2969 **1539** 265c. multicoloured 8·00 8·00

1540 Schonbrunn Imperial Palace

2009
2970 **1540** 65c. multicoloured 2·00 1·90

1541 Venediger Glacier

2009. Preserve Polar Regions and Glaciers.
2971 **1541** 65c. multicoloured 2·00 1·90

1542 Haflinger

2009. 50th Anniv of Steyr Daimler Puch Haflinger All Terrain Vehicle.
2972 **1542** 55c. murlticoloured 1·90 1·70

1543 Joseph Haydn

2009. Death Bicentenary of Franz Joseph Haydn (composer).
2973 **1543** 65c. multicoloured 2·00 1·90

1544 *Tyto alba* (barn owl)

2009. Self-adhesive.
2974 **1544** 55c. multicoloured 1·90 1·70

1545 Wrapped Flak Tower

2009. Art. Works by Christo Vladimirov Javashev (Christo, the packaging artist). Sheet 78×80 mm containing T 1545 and similar vert design. Multicoloured.
MS2975 55c.×2, Type **1545**; The 21st Century Collection 3·75 3·75

1546 Fred Zinnemann

2009. Fred Zinnemann (director) Commemoration
2976 **1546** 55c. multicoloured 1·60 1·40

1547 Old Town

2009. 850th Anniv of St Pölten
2977 **1547** 55c. multicoloured 1·60 1·40

1548 Burning Ring

2009. *The Ring of the Nibelungen* (opera) performed at Vienna State Opera House
2978 **1548** 100c. multicoloured 1·60 1·40

1549 *Thalia*

2009. Centenary of *Thalia* (pleasure steamer)
2979 **1549** 55c. multicoloured 1·60 1·60

1550 Baptismal Font, Old Cathedral, Linz

2009. Religious Art
2980 **1550** 55c. multicoloured 6·25 6·00

1551 State Opera House

2009. 140th Anniv of Vienna State Opera House
2981 **1551** 100c. multicoloured 3·00 2·75

1552 Wolfgang Graf Berghe von Trips

2009. Formula I Motor Racing Legends. Multicoloured.
MS2982 55c.×4, Type **1552**; Gilles Villeneuve; James Hunt; Bernie Ecclestone 6·25 6·25

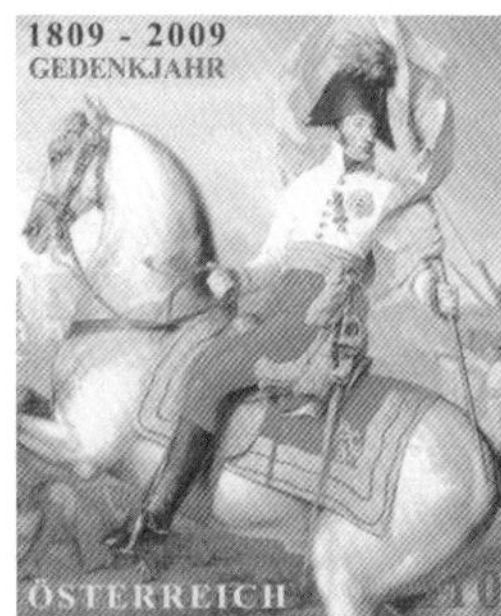

1553 Napoleon

2009. Bicentenary of Battle of Aspern and Essling. Sheet 73×87 mm
MS2983 110c. multicoloured 3·00 3·00

1554 TUGSAT-1 (nano-satellite)

2009
2984 **1554** 65c. multicoloured 2·10 1·90

1555 Graz

2009. Old Town, Graz–World Heritage Site
2985 **1555** 100c. multicoloured 3·00 2·75

1556 Early Aircraft

2009. Centenary of Wiener Neustadt Airfield
2986 **1556** 140c. multicoloured 4·00 3·75

1557 *Rosalia alpina* (longhorn beetle)

2009. Longhorn Beetle
2987 **1557** 75c. multicoloured 2·10 1·90

1558 Steam Locomotive

2009. Centenary of Wachau Railway
2988 **1558** 75c. multicoloured 2·10 1·90

1559 *Apis mellifera* (honeybee)

2009. Fauna. Multicoloured.
2989 55c. Type **1559** 1·60 1·40
2990 55c. *Merops apiaster* (bee-eater) 1·60 1·40
Nos. 2989/90 were issued in *se-tenant* 'hang sell' sheetlets of ten stamps

1560 Anemones

2009. Flowers
2991 **1560** 55c. multicoloured 1·60 1·40

1561 Film Poster

2009. 60th Anniv of *The Third Man* (film by Carol Reed, based on book by Graham Greene)
2992 **1562** 65c. multicoloured 1·90 1·70

1562 '20'

2009. 20th Anniv of Opening of Border between Austria and Hungary
2993 **1562** 65c. multicoloured 1·90 1·70

1563 Gateway and Soldier, Carnuntum

2009. Archaeology. Multicoloured.
MS2994 55c. Type **1563**; 65c. Bas-relief and mounted soldier, Gerulata 5·00 5·00
Stamps of a similar design were issued by Slovakia.

1564 *MS Österreich* (oldest motor powered passenger ship on Lake Constance)

2009. Stamp Day
2995 **1564** 265c.+130c. multicoloured 11·50 10·00

1565 Berta von Suttner

2009. 120th Anniv of *Lay Down Your Arms!* (antiwar novel by Berta von Suttner)
2996 **1565** 55c. multicoloured 1·60 1·40

1566 *The Glorious Rosary*

2009. Tenth Anniv of the Return of Rosary Triptych (painted by Ernst Fuchs), Parish Church of Hetzendorf, Vienna. Multicoloured.
MS2997 55c. Type **1566**; 75c. *The Joyful Rosary*; 100c. *The Sorrowful Rosary* 6·75 6·75

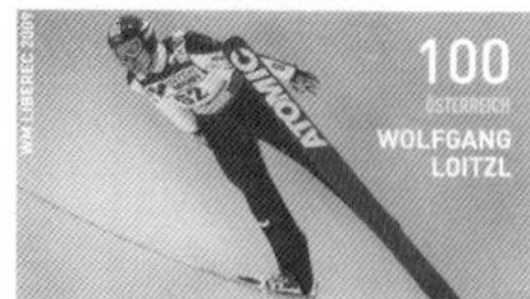

1567 Wolfgang Loitzl (Four Hills Champion)

2009. Champion Ski Jumpers. Multicoloured.
2998 100c. Type **1567** 3·00 2·75
2999 100c. Gregor Schlierenzauer (World Cup winner 2008–9) 3·00 2·75

1568 5042 Series Rail Car in Zistersdorf Station

2009. 120th Anniv of Drösing–Zistersdorf Local Railway
3000 **1568** 100c. multicoloured 3·00 2·75

1569 *Woman rocking on a Chair* (Leander Kaiser)

2009. Modern Art
3001 **1569** 55c. multicoloured 1·90 1·70

1570 *Emilie Flöge* (Gustav Klimt)

2009. Austria–Japan Year. Multicoloured.
MS3002 140c.×2, Type **1570**; *Autumn Clothes* (Shoen Uemura) 8·50 8·50

1571 *Las Meninas (The Royal Family of Felipe IV)*

2009. Diego Rodríguez de Silva y Velázquez (artist) Commemoration. Multicoloured.
MS3003 55c. Type **1571**; 65c.*The Infanta Margarita Teresa in a Blue Dress* 4·25 4·25
Stamps of the same design were issued by Spain

1572 Ranui Church, Vilnös Valley, South Tyrol

2009. Christmas
3004 **1572** 65c. multicoloured 2·00 1·90

1573 Palmers Underwear

2009. Classic Trademarks
3005 **1573** 55c. multicoloured 1·90 1·70

1574 St. Leopold

2009. Patron Saints
3006 **1574** 55c. multicoloured 1·90 1·70

1575 Zum gnadenreichen Christkindl (Blessed Holy Child)

2009. Christmas
3007 **1575** 55c. multicoloured 1·90 1·70

1576 *Tribute to Vedova* (George Baselitz)

2009. Tenth Anniv of Essl Art Museum
3008 **1576** 55c. multicoloured 1·90 1·70

1577 Ape holding Book

2009. Birth Bicentenary of Charles Darwin (naturalist and evolutionary theorist). Multicoloured.
MS3009 55c.×3, Type **1577**; Cherub with head in hands and mirror; Ape holding mirror to cherub 5·75 5·75

The stamps and margins of **MS**3009 form a composite design

1578 *Lutra lutra* (otter)

2010. Fauna (1st issue). Multicoloured.
3010 75c. Type **1578** 2·10 2·00
3011 75c. *Salmo trutta fario* (brown trout) 2·10 2·00

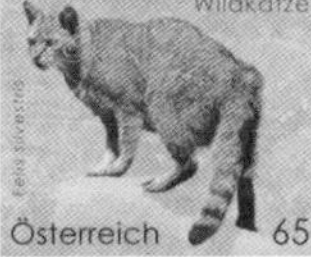

1579 *Felis silvestris* (wild cat)

2010. Fauna (2nd issue)
3012 **1579** 65c. multicoloured 2·00 1·90

1580 View from Salzach River

2010. World Heritage Site
3013 **1580** 100c. multicoloured 3·00 2·75

1581 *Annual Rings of Scent and Bliss* (Helmut Kand)

2010. Modern Art
3014 **1581** 55c. multicoloured 1·90 1·70

1582 *Prince Eugene as Victor over the Turks* (Jacob van Schuppen)

2010. Prince Eugene of Savoy Exhibition, Belvedere, Vienna
3015 **1582** 65c. multicoloured 2·00 1·90

1583 Kleinbahn Model Railways

2010. Classic Trade Marks
3016 **1583** 55c. multicoloured 1·90 1·70

1584 *The Tyrolean Land Army Year Nine* (Joseph Anton Koch)

2010. Death Bicentenary of Andreas Hofer (revolutionary leader)
MS3017 175c. multicoloured 5·75 5·75

1585 Stage Setting for *Medea* (by Marco Auturo Marelli)

2010. Vienna State Opera House
3018 **1585** 100c. multicoloured 3·00 2·75

1586 Otto Preminger

2010. Otto Ludwig Preminger (film director) Commemoration
3019 **1586** 55c. multicoloured 1·90 1·70

1587 Roger Federer

2010. Roger Federer (world champion tennis player)
3020 **1587** 65c. multicoloured 2·00 1·90

1588 *Soon the Sun will rise*

2010. Birth Centenary of Max Weiler (artist)
3021 **1588** 75c. multicoloured 2·10 2·00

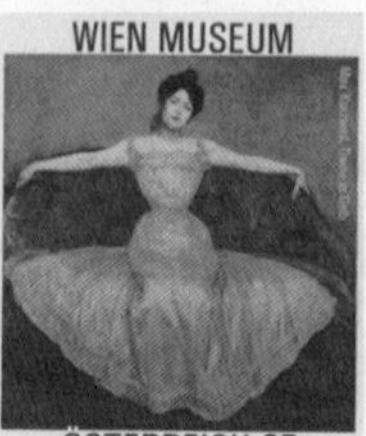

1589 *Lady in Yellow* (Max Kurzwell)

2010. Wien Museum
3022 **1589** 65c. multicoloured 2·00 1·90

1590 Upper Belvedere

2010. Belvedere Palace, Vienna
3023 **1590** 65c. multicoloured 2·00 1·90

1591 671 Steam Locomotive (1860 (oldest operational steam locomotive in the world)

2010. 150th Anniv of Graz Köflach Railway
3024 **1591** 100c. multicoloured 3·00 2·75

1592 Prague Castle and St Vitus Cathedral.

2010. Old Austria
3025 **1592** 65c. multicoloured 2·00 1·90

1593 Empress Elisabeth (Sisi)

2010. Expo 2010, Shanghai
MS3026 55c. multicoloured 1·50 1·50

1594 Railway

2010. Centenary (2003) of Mendel (Mendola) Railway (first electric funicular railway)
3027 **1594** 65c. multicoloured 1·90 1·80

1595 Post Box on Legs

2010. Post–Publicity Campaign 2010
3028 **1595** 55c. multicoloured 1·90 1·80

1596 Palace during Early 19th Century

2010. Imperial Festival Palace Hof
3029 **1596** 55c. multicoloured 1·50 1·40

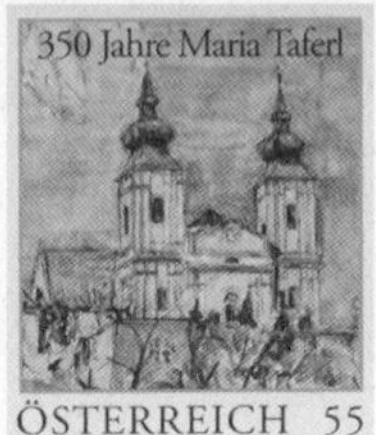

1597 Baroque Church (painting by Franz Knapp

2010. 350th Anniv of Maria Taferl
3030 **1597** 55c. multicoloured 1·50 1·40

1598 Gustav Mahler

2010. 150th Birth Anniv of Gustav Mahler (composer and conductor)
3031 **1598** 100c. multicoloured 3·00 2·75

1599 Festival Poster, 1928 (by Leopoldine (Poldi) Wojtek)

2010. 90th Anniv of Salzburg Festival
3032 **1599** 55c. multicoloured 1·50 1·50

1600 Coracias garrulus (European roller)

2010. Fauna. Multicoloured.
3033 55c. Type **1600** 1·50 1·40
3034 75c. *Aquila chrysaetos* (golden eagle) 2·10 2·00

1601 Crozier

2010. Religious Art
3035 **1601** 75c. multicoloured 2·10 2·00

1602 Fridolin Fuchs (post fox) on Skateboard (illustration by Carola Holland)

2010. Europa
3036 **1602** 65c. multicoloured 1·90 1·80

1603 Self Portrait with Black Vase

2010. 120th Birth Anniv of Egon Schiele (artist)
3037 **1603** 140c. multicoloured 4·00 3·75

1604 Mountain Spring and Fountain in Front of Vienna City Hall

2010. Centenary of Second Pipeline carrying Mountain Spring Water to Vienna
3038 **1604** 55c. multicoloured 2·10 2·00

1605 Simon Wiesenthal in Star of David

2010. Simon Wiesenthal (holocaust survivor and pursuer of war criminals) Commemoration
3039 **1605** 75c. multicoloured 2·10 2·00

1606 Opera House Interior and Ioan Holender

2010. 75th Birth Anniv of Ioan Holender (director of Vienna State Opera)
3040 **1606** 100c. multicoloured 2·75 2·50

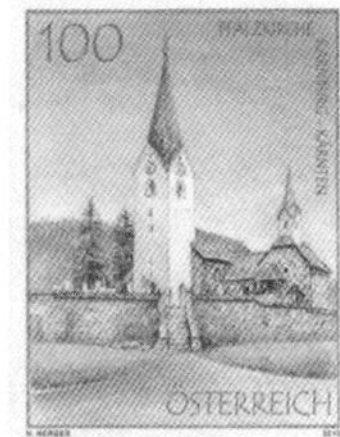

1607 Karnburg Church

2010. Churches
3041 **1607** 100c multicoloured 2·75 2·50

1608 Johann Flux

2010. 350th Birth Anniv of Johann Joseph Fux (composer and musical theorist)
3042 **0608** 100c. multicoloured 3·00 2·75

1609 Grete Rehor and Parliament Building, Vienna

2010. Birth Centenary of Grete Rehor (politician and first female Federal Minister)
3043 **1609** 55c. multicoloured 1·50 1·40

1610 'PARADE'

2010. 15th Anniv of Rainbow Parade
3044 **1610** 55c. multicoloured 3·00 2·75

1611 Steam Locomotive

2010. 125th Anniv of Spielfeld Strass-Bad Radkersburg Railway
3045 **1611** 65c. multicoloured 1·90 1·80

1612 Castle and Grounds

2010. Grafennegg Castle
3046 **1612** 55c. multicoloured 1·50 1·40

1613 Zodiac

2010. 150th Birth Anniv of Alfons Maria Mucha (artist)
3047 **1613** 115c. multicoloured 3·25 3·00

1614 Church

2010. 50th Anniv of Eisenstadt Diocese
3048 **1614** 55c. multicoloured 1·50 1·40

1615 Mother Teresa

2010. Birth Centenary of Agnes Gonxha Bojaxhiu (Mother Teresa) (founder of Missionaries of Charity)
3049 **1615** 130c. multicoloured 3·50 3·25

1616 Railjet Train and Gmunden

2010. Stamp Day
3050 **1616** 265c.+130c. multicoloured 11·00 10·50

1617 Rosa centifolia Bullata

2010. Flowers
3051 **1617** 55c. multicoloured 1·50 1·40

1618 Steam Locomotive, Salzburg, Austria

2010. Orient Express. Multicoloured.
MS3052 65c.×2, Type **1618**; Steam locomotive, Sinaia, Romania 3·50 3·50

1619 Crucifix (Jakob Adhart), ArchAbbey of St. Peter, Salzburg

2010. Sacred Art
3052a **1619** 100c. multicoloured 2·75 2·50

1620 Anniversary Emblem and Members Flags

2010. 50th Anniv of OPEC (Organization of Petroleum Exporting Countries)
3053 **1620** 140c. multicoloured 4·00 4·00

1621 Rose

2010. Petit Point
MS3054 multicoloured 7·25 7·25

1622 Imperial and Royal State Railways Series 199 Locomotive

2010. Centenary of Wechsel Railway
3055 **1622** 100c. multicoloured 2·75 2·50

1623 Andreas and Wolfgang Linger

2010. Andreas and Wolfgang Linger–Winners of Luge Olympic Gold Medal at Winter Olympic Games, Vancouver
3056 **1623** 100c. multicoloured 2·75 2·50

1624 Desk

2010. Austrian Design
3057 **1624** 65c. multicoloured 1·90 1·80

1625 Maria Theresa (Martin van Meytens)

2010. 230th Death Anniv of Archduchess Maria Theresia Walburga Amalia Christina von Österreich (Maria Theresa of Austria) (Archduchess of Austria and Queen of Hungary and Bohemia)
3058 65c. multicoloured 1·90 1·80

1626 Weather Station, City Park, Vienna

2010. Meteorological Architecture. Multicoloured.
MS3059 65c. Type **1626**; 140c. Austria-Hungarian community meteorological station, Botanical Garden, Buenos Aires 5·50 5·50

1627 Ornithopter (first controlled flight, November 1808)

2010. 250th Birth Anniv of Jakob Degen (inventor)
3060 **1627** 125c multicoloured 1·90 1·80

1628 Flag and Soldier

2010. 50th Anniv of Austrian Armed Forces International Assignments
3061 **1628** 65c. multicoloured 1·90 1·80

1629 St Stephen's Cathedral and St Peter's Church, Vienna

Cultural Heritage
3062 **1629** 199c. multicoloured 3·00 2·75

1630 Goldenes Dachl, Innsbruck

2010. Advent
3063 **1630** 65c. multicoloured 2·00 1·90

1631 Three Wise Men (detail from 12th-century missal), St Florian's Monastery

2010. Christmas (1st issue)
3064 **1631** (55c.) multicoloured 1·50 1·40

1632 The Nativity (detail of antiphonal from Cistercian monastery, Rein, Styria)

2010. Christmas (2nd issue)
3065 **1632** 55c. multicoloured 1·50 1·40

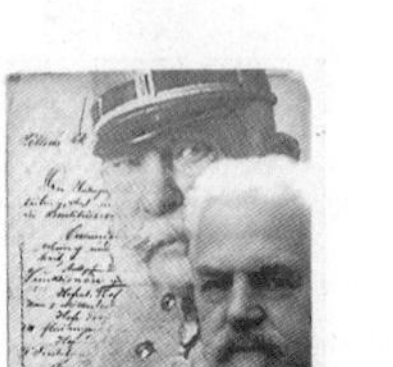

1632a Emperor Franz Joseph and Dr. Anton Freiherr von Eiselsberg

2011. Centenary of Austrian Cancer Aid
3065a **1632a** 55c. multicoloured 1·50 1·40

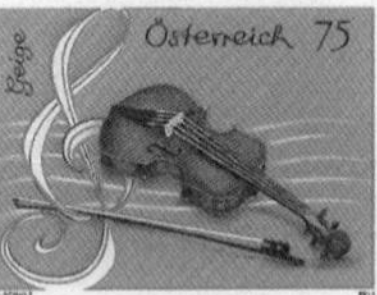

1633 Post Office

2011. Old Austria
3066 **1633** 65c. multicoloured 1·90 1·80

1634 Violin

2011. Musical Instruments
3067 **1634** 75c. multicoloured 2·20 2·10

1635 Bruno Kreisky

2011. Birth Centenary of Bruno Kreisky (politician)
3068 **1635** 55c. multicoloured 1·60 1·50

1636 Stylized Joanneum Graz and Kunsthaus Graz

2011. Bicentenary of Joanneum Graz Museum
3069 **1636** 100c. multicoloured 3·00 2·75

1637 Franz Liszt

2011. Birth Bicentenary of Franz Liszt
3070 **1637** 65c. multicoloured 1·90 1·90

1638 Hedy Lamarr

2011. Hedwig Eva Maria Kiesler (Hedy Lamarr) (film actor) Commemoration
3071 **1638** 55c. multicolured 1·60 1·50

1639 Niemetz Confectioners

2010. Classic Trade Marks
3072 55c. muulticoloured 1·90 1·80

1640 Luigi Hussak, Walter Nausch, Ernst Fiala and Herbert Prohaska (former captains) and Club Emblem

2011. Centenary of FC Austria Vienna
3073 **1640** 65c. multicoloured 2·00 1·90

1641 KTM 125 D.O.H.C. Apfelbeck

2011. Motorbikes
3074 **1641** 75c. multicoloured 2·25 2·10

1642 Puch 500

2011. Cars
3075 **1642** 65c. multicoloured 2·00 1·90

1643 Series 310 Locomotive and Karl Golsdorf

2011. 150th Birth Anniv of Karl Golsdorf (engineer and designer)
3076 **1643** 65c. multicoloured 2·00 1·90

1644 Museum Building

2011. 20th Anniv of Kunst Haus, Vienna
3077 **1644** 175c. multicoloured 5·25 5·00

1645 Cup of Coffee and Café Entrance

2011. Traditional Gastronomy
3078 **1645** 62c. multicoloured 2·00 1·90

1646 Space Walk

2011. 50th Anniv of Manned Space Flight
3079 **1646** 65c. multicoloured 2·00 1·90

1647 Roman Structures

2011. Lower Austrian Regional Exhibition 2011
3080 **1647** 62c. multicoloured 1·90 1·80

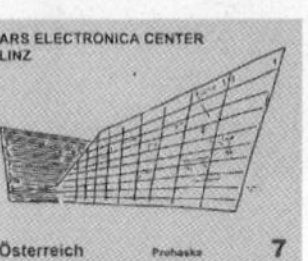

1648 Ars Electronica Centre, Linz

2011. Modern Architecture. All designs black, background colour given.

3081	7c. grey-brown	30	25
3082	62c. azure	1·90	1·80
3083	62c. azure	1·90	1·80
3084	62c. azure (vert)	1·90	1·80
3085	62c. azure (vert)	1·90	1·80
3086	70c. chrome yellow	2·20	2·10
3087	70c. pale yellow	2·20	2·10
3088	90c. pale lilac	2·50	2·40
3089	90c. pale lilac	2·50	2·40
3090	145c. pale turquoise-green	4·75	4·50
3091	170c. pale buff	5·75	5·50
3092	340c. pale greenish yellow (vert)	10·50	10·00

Designs: 7c. Type **1648**; 62c. Kunsthaus Graz Universalmuseum, Joanneum; 62c. Museum of Modern Art Ludwig Foundation, Vienna (Museum Moderner Kunst Stiftung Ludwig, Wien); 62c. Kunsthaus Bregenz; 62c. Kunsthalle Krems; 70c. Museum der Moderne Monchsberg, Salzburg; 70c. Lentos Art Museum, Linz (Lentos Kunstmuseum, Linz); 90c. Forum Stadtpark, Graz; 90c. Essl Museum, Klosterneuburg; 145c. Kunsthalle Wien Project Space Karlsplatz, Vienna; 170c. MAK Centre Schindler Chase House, Los Angeles; 340c. Austrian Cultural Forum, New York.

1649 Horse pulling Railway Wagons

2011. 175 Years of Budweis (Budejowice)-Linz-Gmunden Horse-drawn Railway

3093	**1649**	62c. multicoloured	1·70	1·60

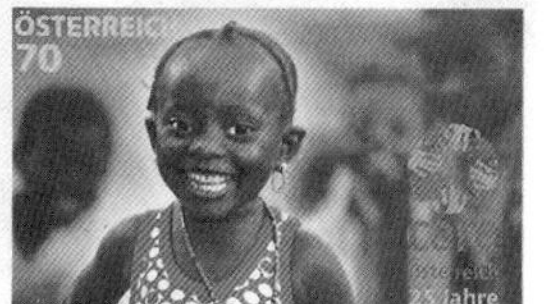

1650 Smiling Child

2011. 25th Anniv of CARE (humanitarian organization) Austria

3094	**1650**	70c. multicoloured	5·25	5·00

1651 Antique Bookcase from Mekhitarist's Library

2011. Bicentenary of Mekhitarists (congregation of Benedictine monks of Armenian Catholic Church founded in 1712 by Mechitar of Sebaste) in Vienna

3095	**1651**	90c. multicoloured	2·75	2·50

1652 Graz

2011. Stamp Day

3096	**1652**	272c.+136c. multicoloured	12·50	12·00

1653 Church

2011. Churches

3097	**1653**	62c. multicoloured	1·70	1·70

1654 *Tower of Babel* (Pieter Bruegel the Elder)

2011. Art

3098	**1654**	145c. multicoloured	4·50	4·25

1655 *Portrait of Dora Fournier-Gabillon*

2011. Art. Works by Hans Makart. Multicoloured.

MS3099	70c. Type **1655**; 170c. *The Triumph of Ariadne*	6·75	6·75

1656 Pheasant, Badger, Deer and Fungi

2011. Country of Forests. International Year of Forests

3100	**1656**	90c. multicoloured	2·50	2·25

2011. Modern Architecture. Horiz design as Type **1648**.

3101	5c. Liaunig Museum	1·00	90

1657 Etrich Taube Aircraft and Black Hawk Helicopter

2011. Centenary of Military Aviation

3102	**1657**	62c. multicoloured	2·00	1·90

1658 Chalice

2011. Religious Art

3103	**1658**	145c. multicoloured	4·50	4·25

1659 St Christoph Hospice

2011. 625th Anniv of St Christopher Brotherhood

3104	**1659**	62c. multicoloured	2·00	1·90

1660 Anniversary Emblem

2011. 50th Anniv of Organisation for Economic Co-operation and Development (OECD) (Organisation de coopération et de développement économiques, OCDE)

3105	**1660**	70c. multicoloured	2·25	2·10

1661 BBÖ 378 series Locomotive and Old Railway Station Building

2011. Centenary of Stammersdorf Railway

3106	**1661**	90c. multicoloured	2·50	2·25

1662 Curing a Woman (Ulrich Henn)

2011. Religious Art. Bronze Relief, Rankwil Basilica

3107	**1662**	90c. multicoloured	2·50	2·25

1663 Girl and Peddler

2011. 175th Death Anniv of Ferdinand Jakob Raimann (Ferdinand Raimund) (dramatist)

3108	**1663**	62c. multicoloured	2·00	1·90

1664 Football Boot

2011. Centenary of Austrian Football Championship

3109	**1664**	62c. multicoloured	2·00	1·90

1665 Vienna Künstlerhaus

2011. Centenary of Vienna Visual Artists Cooperative (Austrian Society of Artists, Künstlerhaus)

3110	**1665**	62c. multicoloured	2·00	1·90

1666 Lotto Ball

2011. 25th Anniv of Lottery. Sheet 70×90 mm

MS3111	**1666**	145c. multicoloured	4·50	4·25

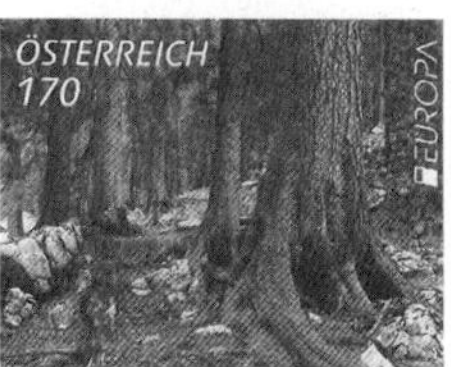

1667 Coniferous Forest

2011. Europa. Forests. Sheet 112×73 mm

MS3112	**1667**	170c. multicoloured	4·25	2·25

IMPERIAL JOURNAL STAMPS

J18

1853. Imperf.

J67		1k. blue	15·00	2·10
J15	**J18**	2k. green	£4250	£120
J68		2k. brown	13·50	3·00
J32		4k. brown	£550	£1600

The 2k. green has different corner ornaments.

For similar values in black or red, see Lombardy and Venetia Imperial Journal stamps, Nos. J22/4.

J21 Arms of Austria

1890. Imperf.

J76	**J21**	1k. brown	15·00	2·10
J77	**J21**	2k. green	13·50	3·00

J22 Arms of Austria

1890. Perf.

J78	**J22**	25k. red	£140	£300

NEWSPAPER STAMPS

N2 Mercury

1851. Imperf.

N11b	**N 2**	(0.6k.) blue	£225	£160
N12	**N 2**	(6k.) yellow	£37000	£12000
N13	**N 2**	(6k.) red	£62000	£108000
N14	**N 2**	(30k.) red	£42000	£17000

N8 Francis Joseph I

1858. Imperf.

N28	**N8**	(1k.05) blue	£800	£900
N29	**N8**	(1k.05) lilac	£1100	£425

N11 Francis Joseph I

1861. Imperf.

N38	**N11**	(1k.05) grey	£250	£225

N13 Arms of Austria

1863. Imperf.

N44	**N13**	(1k.05) lilac	55·00	21·00

AHN17 Mercury

1867. Imperf.

AHN58b	**AHN17**	(1k.) lilac	50	30

N19 Mercury

1880. Imperf.

N69	**N19**	½k. green	11·50	1·60

N31 Mercury

1899. Imperf.

N122	**N31**	2h. blue	30	20
N123	**N31**	6h. orange	3·00	3·00
N124	**N31**	10h. brown	2·10	1·60
N125	**N31**	20h. pink	2·10	3·00

N43 Mercury

1908. Imperf.

N207C	**N43**	2h. blue	1·50	45
N208C	**N43**	6h. orange	6·75	1·10
N209C	**N43**	10h. red	6·75	85
N210C	**N43**	20h. brown	6·75	85

N53 Mercury

1916. Imperf.

N266	**N53**	2h. brown	10	20
N267	**N53**	4h. green	50	1·60
N268	**N53**	6h. blue	40	1·70
N269	**N53**	10h. orange	1·00	2·10
N270	**N53**	30h. red	50	1·90

N54 Mercury

1916. For Express. Perf.

N271	**N54**	2h. red on yellow	1·50	4·25
N272	**N54**	5h. green on yellow	1·50	4·25

N61 Mercury

1917. For Express. Perf.

N294	**N61**	2h. red on yellow	20	55
N295	**N61**	5h. green on yellow	20	55

1919. Optd Deutschosterreich. Imperf.

N318	**N53**	2h. brown	20	1·10
N319	**N53**	4h. green	50	8·50
N320	**N53**	6h. blue	30	10·50
N321	**N53**	10h. orange	1·20	16·00
N322	**N53**	30h. red	60	21·00

1919. For Express. Optd Deutschosterreich. Perf.

N334	**N61**	2h. red on yellow	10	30
N335	**N61**	5h. green on yellow	10	30

N68 Mercury

1920. Imperf.

N365A	**N68**	2h. violet	10	20
N366A	**N68**	4h. brown	10	30
N367A	**N68**	5h. slate	10	20
N368A	**N68**	6h. blue	15	20
N369A	**N68**	8h. green	10	55
N370A	**N68**	9h. bistre	10	20
N371A	**N68**	10h. red	10	20
N372A	**N68**	12h. blue	10	55
N373A	**N68**	15h. mauve	10	25
N374A	**N68**	18h. turquoise	10	30
N375A	**N68**	20h. orange	10	30
N376A	**N68**	30h. brown	10	20
N377A	**N68**	45h. green	10	55
N378A	**N68**	60h. red	10	30
N379A	**N68**	72h. brown	20	55
N380A	**N68**	90h. violet	30	85
N381A	**N68**	1k.20 red	30	1·10
N382A	**N68**	2k.40 green	30	1·10
N383A	**N68**	3k. grey	30	1·10

1921. For Express. No. N334 surch 50 50.

N450	**N 61**	50 on 2h. red on yell	10	45

N78 Mercury

1921. Imperf.

N452	**N78**	45h. grey	20	20
N453	**N78**	75h. red	10	55
N454	**N78**	1k.50 green	10	75
N455	**N78**	1k.80 blue	10	95
N456	**N78**	2k.25 brown	10	1·30
N457	**N78**	3k. green	10	1·10
N458	**N78**	6k. purple	10	1·20
N459	**N78**	7k.50 brown	20	1·60

N79 Posthorn and Arrow

1921. For Express. Perf.

N460	**N79**	50h. lilac on yellow	20	2·10

POSTAGE DUE STAMPS

D26

1894. Perf.

D96	**D26**	1k. brown	6·25	2·10
D97	**D26**	2k. brown	8·25	4·25
D98	**D26**	3k. brown	10·50	2·10
D99	**D26**	5k. brown	10·50	75
D100	**D26**	6k. brown	8·25	9·25
D101	**D26**	7k. brown	4·25	9·25
D102	**D26**	10k. brown	8·25	85
D103	**D26**	20k. brown	4·25	9·25
D104	**D26**	50k. brown	90·00	£120

1899. As Type D 26, but value in heller. Perf or imperf.

D126	1h. brown	75	30
D127	2h. brown	75	20
D128d	3h. brown	75	20
D129	4h. brown	95	20
D130	5h. brown	1·00	20
D131d	6h. brown	75	75
D132	10h. brown	1·20	10
D133	12h. brown	1·50	75
D134	15h. brown	1·20	1·40
D135	20h. brown	1·70	45
D136	40h. brown	3·00	75
D137d	100h. brown	8·25	4·25

D44

1908. Perf.

D210B	**D44**	1h. red	1·00	2·10
D211C	**D44**	2h. red	60	45
D212C	**D44**	4h. red	40	20
D213C	**D44**	6h. red	40	20
D214C	**D44**	10h. red	60	20
D215C	**D44**	14h. red	7·25	3·00
D216C	**D44**	20h. red	15·00	20
D217C	**D44**	25h. red	19·00	6·75
D218C	**D44**	30h. red	10·50	45
D219C	**D44**	50h. red	35·00	55
D220C	**D44**	100h. red	29·00	75
D221C	**D44**	5k. violet	85·00	20·00
D222C	**D44**	10k. violet	£300	5·25

D55 **D56**

1916

D273	**D55**	5h. red	10	20
D274	**D55**	10h. red	10	20
D275	**D55**	15h. red	10	20
D276	**D55**	20h. red	10	20
D277	**D55**	25h. red	25	1·30
D278	**D55**	30h. red	30	55
D279	**D55**	40h. red	20	85
D280	**D55**	50h. red	1·20	3·75
D281	**D 56**	1k. blue	1·00	55
D282	**D 56**	5k. blue	3·00	4·25
D283	**D 56**	10k. blue	4·25	2·30

1916. Nos. 189/90 optd PORTO or surch 15 15 also.

D284	1h. black	10	20
D285	15 on 2h. violet	35	75

1917. Unissued stamps as T 50 surch PORTO and value.

D286	**50**	10 on 24h. blue	2·10	75
D287	**50**	15 on 36h. violet	60	30
D288	**50**	20 on 54h. orange	35	55
D289	**50**	50 on 42h. brown	40	30

The above differ from Type **50** by showing a full-face portrait.

1919. Optd Deutschosterreich.

D323	**D55**	5h. red	10	20
D324	**D55**	10h. red	10	20
D325	**D55**	15h. red	30	55
D326	**D55**	20h. red	30	55
D327	**D55**	25h. red	10·50	32·00
D328	**D55**	30h. red	30	55
D329	**D55**	40h. red	30	1·10
D330	**D55**	50h. red	35	1·60
D331	**D 56**	1k. blue	5·75	19·00
D332	**D 56**	5k. blue	11·50	19·00
D333	**D 56**	10k. blue	13·50	5·25

D69

D70

1920. Imperf or perf (D 69), perf (D 70).

D384A	**D69**	5h. pink	20	45
D385A	**D69**	10h. pink	10	20
D386A	**D69**	15h. pink	10	1·60
D387A	**D69**	20h. pink	10	20
D388A	**D69**	25h. pink	20	1·60
D389A	**D69**	30h. pink	10	45
D390A	**D69**	40h. pink	10	45
D391A	**D69**	50h. pink	10	30
D392A	**D69**	80h. pink	10	55
D393A	**D 70**	1k. blue	10	40
D394A	**D 70**	1½k. blue	10	40
D395A	**D 70**	2k. blue	10	40
D396Aa	**D 70**	3k. blue	10	65
D397Aa	**D 70**	4k. blue	10	85
D398A	**D 70**	5k. blue	10	40
D399A	**D 70**	8k. blue	10	1·10
D400A	**D 70**	10k. blue	10	55
D401A	**D 70**	20k. blue	50	2·75

1921. No. 343a surch Nachmarke 7½ K. Perf.

D451	**64**	7½k. on 15h. brown	10	55

D83

1921

D510	**D83**	1k. brown	20	45
D511	**D83**	2k. brown	20	55
D512	**D83**	4k. brown	20	95
D513	**D83**	5k. brown	20	45
D514	**D83**	7½k. brown	20	1·30
D515	-	10k. blue	20	55
D516	-	15k. blue	20	75
D517	-	20k. blue	20	85
D518	-	50k. blue	20	75

The 10k. to 50k. are larger (22×30 mm).

D86

1922

D526	**D83**	10k. turquoise	10	65
D527	**D83**	15k. turquoise	10	95
D528	**D83**	20k. turquoise	10	75
D529	**D83**	25k. turquoise	10	1·60
D530	**D83**	40k. turquoise	10	55
D531	**D83**	50k. turquoise	10	1·90
D532	**D 86**	100k. purple	10	20
D533	**D 86**	150k. purple	10	20
D534	**D 86**	200k. purple	10	20
D535	**D 86**	400k. purple	10	20
D536	**D 86**	600k. purple	25	65
D537	**D 86**	800k. purple	10	20
D538	**D 86**	1000k. purple	10	20
D539	**D 86**	1200k. purple	1·50	9·25
D540	**D 86**	1500k. purple	10	55
D541	**D 86**	1800k. purple	4·25	18·00
D542	**D 86**	2000k. purple	50	1·30
D543	**D 86**	3000k. purple	9·25	37·00
D544	**D 86**	4000k. purple	6·25	30·00
D545	**D 86**	6000k. purple	10·50	47·00

D94

1925

D589	**D94**	1g. red	10	10
D590	**D94**	2g. red	10	10
D591	**D94**	3g. red	10	10
D592	**D94**	4g. red	10	10
D593	**D94**	5g. red	10	10
D594	**D94**	6g. red	30	45
D595	**D94**	8g. red	20	20
D596	**D94**	10g. blue	30	10
D597	**D94**	12g. blue	10	10
D598	**D94**	14g. blue	10	10
D599	**D94**	15g. blue	10	10
D600	**D94**	16g. blue	30	25
D601	**D94**	18g. blue	2·10	3·75
D602	**D94**	20g. blue	20	10
D603	**D94**	23g. blue	60	20
D604	**D94**	24g. blue	3·00	10
D605	**D94**	28g. blue	2·75	25
D606	**D94**	30g. blue	1·30	10
D607	**D94**	31g. blue	3·00	25
D608	**D94**	35g. blue	3·00	20
D609	**D94**	39g. blue	3·50	10
D610	**D94**	40g. blue	1·50	2·10
D611	**D94**	60g. blue	1·50	1·90
D612	-	1s. green	6·75	95
D613	-	2s. green	36·00	3·75
D614	-	5s. green	£140	60·00
D615	-	10s. green	55·00	5·25

DESIGN: 1 to 10s. Horiz bands of colour.

D120

1935

D746	**D120**	1g. red	10	20
D747	**D120**	2g. red	10	20
D748	**D120**	3g. red	10	20
D749	**D120**	5g. red	10	20
D750	-	10g. blue	10	10
D751	-	12g. blue	10	10
D752	-	15g. blue	30	65
D753	-	20g. blue	30	20
D754	-	24g. blue	35	20
D755	-	30g. blue	35	20
D756	-	39g. blue	40	20
D757	-	60g. blue	85	1·60
D758	-	1s. green	1·00	45
D759	-	2s. green	2·10	1·30
D760	-	5s. green	4·25	4·00
D761	-	10s. green	6·25	85

DESIGNS: 10 to 60g. As Type D **120** but with background of horizontal lines; 1 to 10s. As last, but with positions of figures, arms and inscriptions reversed.

D143

1945

D891	**D143**	1pf. red	20	20
D892	**D143**	2pf. red	20	20
D893	**D143**	3pf. red	20	20
D894	**D143**	5pf. red	20	20
D895	**D143**	10pf. red	20	20
D896	**D143**	12pf. red	20	25
D897	**D143**	20pf. red	20	25
D898	**D143**	24pf. red	20	45
D899	**D143**	30pf. red	20	50
D900	**D143**	60pf. red	20	55
D901	**D143**	1rm. violet	20	60
D902	**D143**	2rm. violet	20	95
D903	**D143**	5rm. violet	30	1·10
D904	**D143**	10rm. violet	30	1·30

1946. Optd PORTO.

D956	**145**	3g. orange	10	10
D957	**145**	5g. green	10	10
D958	**145**	6g. purple	10	10
D959	**145**	8g. red	10	10
D960	**145**	10g. grey	10	20
D961	**145**	12g. brown	10	10
D962	**145**	15g. red	10	20
D963	**145**	20g. brown	10	10
D964	**145**	25g. blue	20	20
D965	**145**	30g. mauve	10	10
D966	**145**	40g. blue	10	10
D967	**145**	60g. green	10	10
D968	**145**	1s. violet	20	20
D969	**145**	2s. yellow	70	1·20
D970	**145**	5s. blue	30	95

D162

1947

D1035	**D162**	1g. brown	10	10
D1036	**D162**	2g. brown	10	10
D1037	**D162**	3g. brown	10	20
D1038	**D162**	5g. brown	10	10
D1039	**D162**	8g. brown	10	10
D1040	**D162**	10g. brown	10	10
D1041	**D162**	12g. brown	10	10
D1042	**D162**	15g. brown	10	10
D1043	**D162**	16g. brown	50	95
D1044	**D162**	17g. brown	40	95
D1045	**D162**	18g. brown	40	95
D1046	**D162**	20g. brown	95	10
D1047	**D162**	24g. brown	40	1·10
D1048	**D162**	30g. brown	20	30
D1049	**D162**	36g. brown	95	1·60
D1050	**D162**	40g. brown	10	10
D1051	**D162**	42g. brown	1·10	1·60
D1052	**D162**	48g. brown	1·10	1·60
D1053	**D162**	50g. brown	95	30
D1054	**D162**	60g. brown	20	30
D1055	**D162**	70g. brown	20	25
D1056	**D162**	80g. brown	6·00	2·75
D1057	**D162**	1s. blue	20	10
D1058	**D162**	1s.15 blue	4·25	55
D1059	**D162**	1s.20 blue	4·50	2·20
D1060	**D162**	2s. blue	40	30
D1061	**D162**	5s. blue	50	40
D1062	**D162**	10s. blue	60	45

D184

1949

D1178	**D184**	1g. red	20	20
D1179	**D184**	2g. red	20	20
D1180	**D184**	4g. red	65	65
D1181	**D184**	5g. red	2·75	75
D1182	**D184**	8g. red	2·75	2·20
D1183	**D184**	10g. red	45	10
D1184	**D184**	20g. red	45	10
D1185	**D184**	30g. red	45	10
D1186	**D184**	40g. red	45	10
D1187	**D184**	50g. red	45	10
D1188	**D184**	60g. red	14·00	75
D1189	**D184**	63g. red	6·75	4·25
D1190	**D184**	70g. red	45	10
D1191	**D184**	80g. red	45	20
D1192	**D184**	90g. red	75	55
D1193	**D184**	1s. violet	75	10
D1194	**D184**	1s.20 violet	75	30
D1195	**D184**	1s.35 violet	45	20
D1196	**D184**	1s.40 violet	75	45
D1197	**D184**	1s.50 violet	75	25
D1198	**D184**	1s.65 violet	65	45
D1199	**D184**	1s.70 violet	65	45
D1200	**D184**	2s. violet	1·10	20
D1201	**D184**	2s.50 violet	75	20
D1202	**D184**	3s. violet	75	30
D1203	**D184**	4s. violet	1·20	1·10
D1204	**D184**	5s. violet	1·60	45
D1205	**D184**	10s. violet	1·80	60

D817

1985

D2074	**D817**	10g. yellow & black	10	10
D2075	**D817**	20g. red and black	10	10
D2076	**D817**	50g. orange & black	10	10
D2077	**D817**	1s. blue and black	20	20
D2078	**D817**	2s. brown & black	40	30
D2079	**D817**	3s. violet and black	50	40
D2080	**D817**	5s. yellow & black	90	60
D2081	**D817**	10s. green & black	1·80	90

Pt. 2

AUSTRIAN TERRITORIES ACQUIRED BY ITALY

Italian territory acquired from Austria at the close of the war of 1914-18, including Trentino and Trieste.

1918. 100 heller = 1 krone.
1918. 100 centesimi = 1 lira.
1919. 100 centesimi = 1 corona.

TRENTINO

1918. Stamps of Austria optd Regno d'Italia Trentino 3 nov 1918.

1	**49**	3h. purple	6·25	12·50
2	**49**	5h. green	4·25	6·25
3	**49**	6h. orange	70·00	£110
4	**49**	10h. red	4·25	9·25
5	**49**	12h. green	£200	£300
6	**60**	15h. brown	6·25	11·50
7	**60**	20h. green	3·00	10·50
8	**60**	25h. blue	55·00	70·00
9	**60**	30h. violet	17·00	26·00
10	**51**	40h. green	60·00	£100
11	**51**	50h. green	36·00	50·00
12	**51**	60h. blue	50·00	90·00
13	**51**	80h. brown	85·00	£130
14	**51**	90h. red	£1700	£3000
15	**51**	1k. red on yellow	85·00	£120
16	**52**	2k. blue	£500	£850
17	**52**	4k. green	£2000	£4000
18	**52**	10k. violet	£94000	

1918. Stamps of Italy optd Venezia Tridentina.

19	**30**	1c. brown	3·00	10·50
20	**31**	2c. brown	3·00	10·50
21	**37**	5c. green	3·00	10·50
22	**37**	10c. red	3·00	10·50
23	**41**	20c. orange	3·00	10·50
24	**39**	40c. brown	65·00	90·00
25	**33**	45c. olive	37·00	90·00
26	**39**	50c. mauve	37·00	90·00
27	**34**	1l. brown and green	37·00	90·00

1919. Stamps of Italy surch Venezia Tridentina and value.

28	**37**	5h. on 5c. green	3·00	5·25
29	**37**	10h. on 10c. red	3·00	5·25
30	**41**	20h. on 20c. orange	3·00	5·25

VENEZIA GIULIA

For use in Trieste and territory, Gorizia and province, and in Istria.

1918. Stamps of Austria optd Regno d'Italia Venezia Giulia 3. XI. 18.

31	**49**	3h. purple	1·60	3·00
32	**49**	5h. green	1·60	3·00
33	**49**	6h. orange	1·80	4·25
34	**49**	10h. red	5·25	5·25
35	**49**	12h. green	2·50	5·25
36	**60**	15h. brown	1·60	3·00
37	**60**	20h. green	1·60	3·00
38	**60**	25h. blue	8·25	13·50
39	**60**	30h. purple	3·00	6·25
40	**51**	40h. green	£100	£300
41	**51**	50h. green	8·25	12·50
42	**51**	60h. blue	29·00	36·00
43	**51**	80h. brown	18·00	23·00
44	**51**	1k. red on yellow	18·00	23·00
45	**52**	2k. blue	£275	£500
46	**52**	3k. red	£350	£600
47	**52**	4k. green	£550	£1200
48	**52**	10k. violet	£65000	£69000

1918. Stamps of Italy optd Venezia Giulia.

49	**30**	1c. brown	3·00	7·25
50	**31**	2c. brown	3·00	7·25
51	**37**	5c. green	2·10	3·00
52	**37**	10c. red	2·10	3·00
53	**41**	20c. orange	2·10	4·25
54	**39**	25c. blue	2·10	5·25
55	**39**	40c. brown	16·00	31·00
56	**33**	45c. green	5·25	11·50
57	**39**	50c. mauve	10·50	14·50
58	**39**	60c. red	90·00	£180
59	**34**	1l. brown and green	41·00	70·00

1919. Stamps of Italy surch Venezia Giulia and value.

60	**37**	5h. on 5c. green	2·10	4·25
61	**41**	20h. on 20c. orange	2·10	4·25

EXPRESS LETTER STAMPS

1919. Express Letter stamp of Italy optd Venezia Giulia.

E60	**E35**	25c. red	70·00	£120

POSTAGE DUE STAMPS

1918. Postage Due Stamps of Italy optd Venezia Giulia.

D60	**D 12**	5c. mauve and orange	1·00	2·10
D61	**D 12**	10c. mauve & orange	1·00	2·10
D62	**D 12**	20c. mauve & orange	1·60	4·25
D63	**D 12**	30c. mauve & orange	4·25	8·25
D64	**D 12**	40c. mauve & orange	36·00	55·00
D65	**D 12**	50c. mauve & orange	60·00	£160
D66	**D 12**	1l. mauve and blue	£200	£500

GENERAL ISSUE

For use throughout the liberated area of Trentino, Venezia Giulia and Dalmatia.

1919. Stamps of Italy surch in new currency.

62	**30**	1ce. di cor on 1c. brown	2·10	3·00
64	**31**	2ce. di cor on 2c. brown	2·10	3·00
65	**37**	5ce. di cor on 5c. green	2·10	2·10
67	**37**	10ce. di cor on 10c. red	2·10	2·10
68	**41**	20ce. di cor on 20c. orange	2·10	2·10
70	**39**	25ce. di cor on 25c. blue	2·10	5·25
71	**39**	40ce. di cor on 40c. brown	2·10	5·25
72	**33**	45ce. di cor on 45c. green	2·10	5·25
73	**39**	50ce. di cor on 50c. mauve	2·10	5·25
74	**39**	60ce. di cor on 60c. red	2·10	9·25
75	**34**	1cor. on 1l. brown & green	4·25	8·25
76	**34**	una corona on 1l. brn & grn	5·25	21·00
82	**34**	5cor. on 5l. blue and red	50·00	£120
83	**34**	10cor. on 10l. green & red	50·00	£120

EXPRESS LETTER STAMPS

1919. Express Letter stamps of Italy surch in new currency.

E76	**E35**	25ce. di cor on 25c. red	2·10	4·25
E77	**E41**	30ce. di cor on 30c. red and blue	3·00	8·25

POSTAGE DUE STAMPS

1919. Postage Due stamps of Italy surch in new currency.

D76	**D12**	5ce. di cor on 5c. mauve and orange	1·00	3·00
D77	**D12**	10ce. di cor. on 10c. mauve and orange	1·00	3·00
D78	**D12**	20ce. di cor on 20c. mauve and orange	2·10	3·00
D79	**D12**	30ce. di cor on 30c. mauve and orange	2·30	5·25
D80	**D12**	40ce. di cor on 40c. mauve and orange	2·30	5·25
D81	**D12**	50ce. di cor on 50c. mauve and orange	5·25	10·50
D82	**D12**	una corona on 1l. mauve and blue	5·25	12·50
D83	**D12**	due corona on 2l. mauve and blue	80·00	£180
D84	**D12**	cinque corona on 5l. mauve and blue	80·00	£180
D86	**D12**	1cor. on 1l. mve & blue	5·25	14·50
D87	**D12**	2cor. on 2l. mve & blue	50·00	£110
D88	**D12**	5cor. on 5l. mve & blue	50·00	£110

Pt. 2

AUSTRO-HUNGARIAN MILITARY POST

A. General Issues.
100 heller = 1 krone.

B. Issues for Italy.
100 centesimi = 1 lira.

C. Issues for Montenegro.
100 heller = 1 krone.

D. Issues for Romania.
100 bani = 1 leu.

E. Issues for Serbia.
100 heller = 1 krone.

A. GENERAL ISSUES

1915. Stamps of Bosnia and Herzegovina optd **K.U.K. FELDPOST.**

1	**25**	1h. olive	50	55
2	**25**	2h. blue	50	55
3	**25**	3h. lake	50	55
4	**25**	5h. green	40	30
5	**25**	6h. black	50	55
6	**25**	10h. red	30	30
7	**25**	12h. olive	50	75
8	**25**	20h. brown	60	1·10
9	**25**	25h. blue	50	75
10	**25**	30h. red	4·25	8·50
11	**26**	35h. green	3·00	7·50
12	**26**	40h. violet	3·00	7·50
13	**26**	45h. brown	3·00	7·50
14	**26**	50h. blue	3·00	7·50
15	**26**	60h. purple	60	1·40
16	**26**	72h. blue	3·00	6·25
17	**25**	1k. brown on cream	3·00	7·00
18	**25**	2k. indigo on blue	3·00	7·00
19	**26**	3k. red on green	31·00	70·00
20	**26**	5k. lilac on grey	28·00	47·00
21	**26**	10k. blue on grey	£200	£375

2

1915

22	**2**	1h. green	10	30
23	**2**	2h. blue	10	45
24	**2**	3h. red	10	30
25	**2**	5h. green	10	30
26	**2**	6h. black	10	45
27	**2**	10h. red	10	30
28	**2**	10h. blue	10	45
29	**2**	12h. green	10	55
30	**2**	15h. red	10	30
31	**2**	20h. brown	40	55
32	**2**	20h. green	40	65
33	**2**	25h. blue	20	45
34	**2**	30h. red	20	65
35	**2**	35h. green	40	95
36	**2**	40h. violet	40	95
37	**2**	45h. brown	40	95
38	**2**	50h. deep green	40	95
39	**2**	60h. purple	40	95
40	**2**	72h. blue	40	95
41	**2**	80h. brown	40	45
42	**2**	90h. red	1·10	1·80
43	-	1k. purple on cream	2·10	3·25
44	-	2k. green on blue	1·20	2·40
45	-	3k. red on green	1·10	7·50
46	-	4k. violet on grey	1·10	12·00
47	-	5k. violet on grey	27·00	49·00
48	-	10k. blue on grey	4·75	22·00

The kronen values are larger, with profile portrait.

1917. As 1917 issue of Bosnia, but inscr "K.u.K. FELDPOST".

49	1h. blue	10	20
50	2h. orange	10	20
51	3h. grey	10	20
52	5h. green	10	20
53	6h. violet	10	20
54	10h. brown	10	20
55	12h. blue	10	20
56	15h. red	10	20
57	20h. brown	10	20
58	25h. blue	40	65
59	30h. grey	10	20
60	40h. bistre	10	20
61	50h. green	10	20
62	60h. red	10	55
63	80h. blue	10	30
64	90h. purple	40	95

65	2k. red on buff	20	55
66	3k. green on blue	1·40	5·50
67	4k. red on green	22·00	38·00
68	10k. violet on grey	2·30	16·00

The kronen values are larger and the border is different.

1918. Imperial and Royal Welfare Fund. As 1918 issue of Bosnia, but inscr "K. UND K. FELDPOST".

69	**40**	10h. (+10h.) green	50	1·10
70	-	20h. (+10h.) red	50	1·10
71	**40**	45h. (+10h.) blue	50	1·10

NEWSPAPER STAMPS

N4 Mercury

1916

N49	**N4**	2h. blue	20	45
N50	**N4**	6h. orange	60	1·60
N51	**N4**	10h. red	60	1·60
N52	**N4**	20h. brown	60	1·60

B. ISSUES FOR ITALY

1918. General Issue stamps of 1917 surch in figs and words.

1	2c. on 1h. blue	10	55
2	3c. on 2h. orange	10	55
3	4c. on 3h. grey	10	55
4	6c. on 5h. green	10	55
5	7c. on 6h. violet	20	55
6	11c. on 10h. brown	10	55
7	13c. on 12h. blue	10	55
8	16c. on 15h. red	10	55
9	22c. on 20h. brown	10	55
10	27c. on 25h. blue	40	1·60
11	32c. on 30h. grey	20	1·50
12	43c. on 40h. bistre	30	1·20
13	53c. on 50h. green	20	1·10
14	64c. on 60h. red	30	1·60
15	85c. on 80h. blue	20	1·10
16	95c. on 90h. purple	20	1·10
17	2l.11 on 2k. red on buff	30	2·20
18	3l.16 on 3k. green on blue	70	3·25
19	4l.22 on 4k. red on green	85	4·25

NEWSPAPER STAMPS

1918. Newspaper stamps of General Issue surch in figs and words.

N20	3c. on 2h. blue	20	45
N21	7c. on 6h. orange	40	1·40
N22	11c. on 10h. red	40	1·40
N23	22c. on 20h. brown	50	1·40

1918. For Express. Newspaper stamps of Bosnia surch in figs and words.

N24	**N 35**	3c. on 2h. red on yell	7·25	26·00
N25	**N 35**	6c. on 5h. green on yell	7·25	26·00

POSTAGE DUE STAMPS

1918. Postage Due stamps of Bosnia surch in figs and words.

D20	**D 35**	6c. on 5h. red	4·25	11·00
D21	**D 35**	11c. on 10h. red	2·50	13·00
D22	**D 35**	16c. on 15h. red	1·00	5·50
D23	**D 35**	27c. on 25h. red	1·00	5·50
D24	**D 35**	32c. on 30h. red	1·00	5·50
D25	**D 35**	43c. on 40h. red	1·00	5·50
D26	**D 35**	53c. on 50h. red	1·00	5·50

C. ISSUES FOR MONTENEGRO

1917. Nos. 28 and 30 of General Issues optd **K.U.K. MILIT. VERWALTUNG MONTENEGRO.**

1	**2**	10h. blue	20·00	16·00
2	**2**	15h. red	20·00	16·00

D. ISSUES FOR ROMANIA

1917. General Issue stamps of 1917 optd **BANI** or **LEI**.

1	3b. grey	3·50	5·75
2	5b. green	3·50	4·00
3	6b. violet	3·50	4·00
4	10b. brown	60	1·20
5	12b. blue	2·30	4·00
6	15b. red	2·30	4·00
7	20b. brown	60	1·20
8	25b. blue	60	1·20
9	30b. grey	1·20	1·70
10	40b. bistre	1·20	1·70
11	50b. green	1·20	1·70
12	60b. red	1·20	1·70
13	80b. blue	60	1·20
14	90b. purple	1·20	2·30
15	2l. red on buff	1·70	3·00
16	3l. green on blue	1·70	3·50
17	4l. red on green	2·30	4·00

3 Charles I

1918

18	**3**	3b. grey	60	1·20
19	**3**	5b. green	60	1·20
20	**3**	6b. violet	60	1·70
21	**3**	10b. brown	60	1·70
22	**3**	12b. blue	60	1·70
23	**3**	15b. red	60	1·20
24	**3**	20b. brown	60	1·20
25	**3**	25b. blue	60	1·20
26	**3**	30b. grey	60	1·20
27	**3**	40b. bistre	60	1·20
28	**3**	50b. green	60	1·20
29	**3**	60b. red	60	1·70
30	**3**	80b. blue	60	1·70
31	**3**	90b. purple	60	1·20
32	**3**	2l. red on buff	60	1·70
33	**3**	3l. green on blue	1·20	4·00
34	**3**	4l. red on green	1·70	4·00

E. ISSUES FOR SERBIA

1916. Stamps of Bosnia optd **SERBIEN**.

22	**25**	1h. olive	2·75	6·50
23	**25**	2h. blue	2·75	6·50
24	**25**	3h. lake	2·75	6·50
25	**25**	5h. green	45	95
26	**25**	6h. black	1·90	4·75
27	**25**	10h. red	45	95
28	**25**	12h. olive	95	2·75
29	**25**	20h. brown	95	95
30	**25**	25h. blue	95	2·75
31	**25**	30h. red	95	1·90
32	**26**	35h. green	95	1·90
33	**26**	40h. violet	95	1·90
34	**26**	45h. brown	95	1·90
35	**26**	50h. blue	95	1·90
36	**26**	60h. brown	95	1·90
37	**26**	72h. blue	95	1·90
38	**25**	1k. brown on cream	1·90	2·75
39	**25**	2k. indigo on blue	1·90	2·75
40	**26**	3k. red on green	1·90	2·75
41	**26**	5k. lilac on grey	1·90	2·75
42	**26**	10k. blue on grey	19·00	37·00

Pt. 7

BADEN

In S.W. Germany. Formerly a Grand Duchy, now part of the German Federal Republic.

60 kreuzer = 1 gulden.

1

1851. Imperf.

1	**1**	1k. black on buff	£650	£350
8	**1**	1k. black on white	£200	34·00
3	**1**	3k. black on yellow	£325	21·00
9	**1**	3k. black on green	£200	10·50
10	**1**	3k. black on blue	£900	42·00
5	**1**	6k. black on green	£1100	65·00
11	**1**	6k. black on orange	£350	34·00
6	**1**	9k. black on red	£275	32·00

2

1860. Shaded background behind Arms. Perf.

13	**2**	1k. black	£110	37·00
16	**2**	3k. blue	£120	26·00
17	**2**	6k. orange	£140	95·00
22	**2**	6k. blue	£200	£140
19	**2**	9k. red	£350	£250
25	**2**	9k. brown	£140	£170

1862. Uncoloured background behind Arms.

27	1k. black	65·00	19·00
28	3k. red	65·00	5·25
30	6k. blue	15·00	34·00
33	9k. brown	21·00	37·00
36	18k. green	£550	£750
38	30k. orange	42·00	£3000

1868. "K. R." instead of "KREUZER".

39	1k. green	5·25	11·50
41	3k. red	3·25	5·25
44	7k. blue	27·00	48·00

RURAL POSTAGE DUE STAMPS

D4

1862

D39	**D4**	1k. black on yellow	6·25	£425
D40	**D4**	3k. black on yellow	3·75	£160
D41	**D4**	12k. black on yellow	48·00	£18000

For later issues of 1947 to 1964 see Germany: Allied Occupation (French Zone).

Pt. 7

BAVARIA

In S. Germany. A kingdom till 1918, then a republic. Incorporated into Germany in 1920.

1849. 60 kreuzer = 1 gulden.
1874. 100 pfennig = 1 mark.

1

1849. Imperf.

1	1k. black	£1200	£1700

2 (Circle cut)

1849. Imperf. Circle cut by labels.

3	**2**	3k. blue	£300	4·75
23	**2**	3k. red	70·00	6·50
7	**2**	6k. brown	£8500	£300

1850. Imperf. As T **2**, but circle not cut.

8a	1k. red	£250	30·00
21	1k. yellow	95·00	25·00
11	6k. brown	60·00	12·00
25	6k. blue	95·00	50·00
16	9k. green	£275	20·00
28	9k. brown	£150	20·00
18	12k. red	£200	£170
31	12k. green	£130	80·00
19	18k. yellow	£180	£250
32	18k. red	£200	£600

3 **6**

1867. Imperf.

34	**3**	1k. green	85·00	15·00
37	**3**	3k. red	90·00	3·00
39	**3**	6k. blue	60·00	24·00
41	**3**	6k. brown	£110	60·00
43	**3**	7k. blue	£550	20·00
46	**3**	9k. brown	60·00	46·00
48	**3**	12k. mauve	£475	£120
50	**3**	18k. red	£180	£225
65	**6**	1m. mauve	£850	£100

1870. Perf.

51A	**3**	1k. green	15·00	2·00
69	**3**	3k. red	1·10	10·00
55A	**3**	6k. brown	42·00	41·00
56A	**3**	7k. blue	4·75	5·50
59A	**3**	9k. brown	5·75	5·00
60A	**3**	10k. yellow	7·50	17·00
61A	**3**	12k. mauve	£1600	£6000
63A	**3**	18k. red	16·00	18·00

8

1876. Perf.

120	**8**	2pf. grey	3·25	70
103	**8**	3pf. green	13·50	2·50
121	**8**	3pf. brown	40	80
107	**8**	5pf. mauve	27·00	10·00
122	**8**	5pf. green	40	80
123	**8**	10pf. red	55	1·00
124	**8**	20pf. blue	55	1·00
114	**8**	25pf. brown	42·00	8·75
125	**8**	25pf. orange	55	1·20
126	**8**	30pf. olive	1·10	1·00
127	**8**	40pf. yellow	1·10	1·40
86	**8**	50pf. red	75·00	9·25
117	**8**	50pf. brown	80·00	5·00
128	**8**	50pf. purple	65	2·00
129	**8**	80pf. mauve	4·25	5·00
100	**6**	1m. mauve	6·25	5·00
101a	**6**	2m. orange	7·50	10·00
136	**6**	3m. brown	11·50	46·00
137	**6**	5m. green	11·50	55·00

11

13 Prince Luitpold

1911. Prince Regent Luitpold's 90th Birthday.

138c	**11**	3pf. brown on drab	40	1·00
139c	**11**	5pf. green on green	40	1·00
140d	**11**	10pf. red on buff	40	1·00
141b	**11**	20pf. blue on blue	2·75	1·60
142a	**11**	25pf. deep brown on buff	4·25	3·00
143a	-	30pf. orange on buff	2·75	2·50
144a	-	40pf. olive on buff	4·25	2·50
145a	-	50pf. red on drab	4·25	13·00
146	-	60pf. green on buff	4·25	4·25
147a	-	80pf. violet on drab	12·50	13·00
148a	**13**	1m. brown on drab	4·25	5·00
149a	**13**	2m. green on green	6·25	15·00
150a	**13**	3m. red on buff	17·00	£100
151	**13**	5m. blue on buff	34·00	60·00
152	**13**	10m. orange on yellow	60·00	95·00
153	**13**	20m. brown on yellow	34·00	50·00

The 30 pf. to 80 pf. values are similar to Type **11**, but larger.

14

1911. 25th Anniv of Regency of Prince Luitpold.

154	**14**	5pf. yellow, green & black	1·10	1·80
155	**14**	10pf. yellow, red & black	1·60	3·00

15 King Ludwig III

16

1914. Imperf or perf.

171A	**15**	2pf. slate	35	2·75
172A	**15**	2½ on 2pf. slate	35	2·75
173A	**15**	3pf. brown	35	2·75
175A	**15**	5pf. green	35	2·75
176A	**15**	7½pf. green	35	2·75
178A	**15**	10pf. red	35	2·75
179A	**15**	15pf. red	35	2·75
182A	**15**	20pf. blue	35	2·75
183A	**15**	25pf. grey	35	2·75
184A	**15**	30pf. orange	1·60	2·75
185A	**15**	40pf. olive	35	2·75
186A	**15**	50pf. brown	35	2·75
187A	**15**	60pf. green	1·60	2·75
188A	**15**	80pf. violet	35	2·75
189A	**16**	1m. brown	35	2·75
190A	**16**	2m. violet	45	3·75
191A	**16**	3m. red	55	7·50
192A	-	5m. blue	75	27·00
193A	-	10m. green	2·40	75·00
194A	-	20m. brown	4·50	£110

The 5, 10 and 20m. are larger.

1919. Peoples' State Issue. Overprinted **Volksstaat Bayern**. Imperf or perf.

195A	**15**	3pf. brown	35	2·75
196A	**15**	5pf. green	35	2·75

197A	15	7½pf. green	35	2·75
198A	15	10pf. lake	35	2·75
199A	15	15pf. red	35	2·75
200A	15	20pf. blue	35	2·75
201A	15	25pf. grey	35	2·75
202A	15	30pf. orange	35	2·75
203A	15	35pf. orange	35	3·25
204A	15	40pf. olive	35	2·75
205A	15	50pf. brown	35	2·75
206A	15	60pf. turquoise	35	2·75
207A	15	75pf. brown	35	2·75
208A	15	80pf. violet	35	2·75
209A	16	1m. brown	35	2·75
210A	16	2m. violet	45	2·75
211A	16	3m. red	65	6·25
212A	-	5m. blue (No. 192)	1·30	16·00
213A	-	10m. green (No. 193)	2·00	75·00
214A	-	20m. brown (No. 194)	3·25	70·00

1919. 1st Free State Issue. Stamps of Germany (inscr "DEUTSCHES REICH") optd **Freistaat Bayern**.

215	24	2½pf. grey	35	2·75
216	10	3pf. brown	35	2·75
217	10	5pf. green	35	2·75
218	24	7½pf. orange	35	2·75
219	10	10pf. red	35	2·75
220	24	15pf. violet	35	2·75
221	10	20pf. blue	35	2·75
222	10	25pf. black & red on yell	35	2·75
223	24	35pf. brown	35	2·75
224	10	40pf. black and red	55	2·75
225	10	75pf. black and green	75	3·25
226	10	80pf. black & red on rose	75	4·25
227	12	1m. red	1·80	6·25
228	13	2m. blue	2·20	15·00
229	14	3m. black	2·20	17·00
230	15	5m. red and black	2·20	17·00

1919. 2nd Free State Issue. Stamps of Bavaria overprinted **Freistaat Bayern**. Imperf or perf.

231A		3pf. brown	35	2·75
232A		5pf. green	35	2·75
233A		7½pf. green	35	21·00
234A		10pf. lake	35	2·75
235A		15pf. red	35	2·75
236A		20pf. blue	35	2·75
237A		25pf. grey	35	2·75
238A		30pf. orange	35	2·75
239A		40pf. olive	35	19·00
240A		50pf. brown	35	2·75
241A		60pf. turquoise	35	19·00
242A		75pf. brown	55	19·00
243A		80pf. violet	35	4·75
244A	16	1m. brown	35	3·75
245A	16	2m. violet	35	7·50
246A	16	3m. red	90	9·50
247A	-	5m. blue (No. 192)	1·50	23·00
248A	-	10m. green (No. 193)	2·75	48·00
249A	-	20m. brown (No. 194)	3·25	80·00

1919. War Wounded. **Surch 5 Pf. fur Kriegs-beschadigte Freistaat Bayern.** Perf.

250	15	10pf.+5pf. lake	55	2·75
251	15	15pf.+5pf. red	55	2·75
252	15	20pf.+5pf. blue	55	3·25

1920. Surch **Freistaat Bayern** and value. Imperf or perf.

253A	16	1m.25pf. on 1m. green	35	3·25
254A	16	1m.50pf. on 1m. orange	35	4·25
255A	16	2m.50pf. on 1m. slate	65	8·50

1920. No. 121 surch **20** in four corners.

256	8	20 on 3pf. brown	35	2·75

26

27

28

29

30

1920

257	26	5pf. green	20	3·25
258	26	10pf. orange	20	3·25
259	26	15pf. red	20	3·25
260	27	20pf. violet	20	3·25
261	27	30pf. blue	20	4·25
262	27	40pf. brown	20	3·25
263	28	50pf. red	20	3·25
264	28	60pf. turquoise	20	3·25
265	28	75pf. red	20	3·25
266	29	1m. red and grey	45	3·25
267	29	1¼m. blue and brown	35	3·25
268	29	1½m. green and grey	35	4·25
269	29	2½m. black and grey	35	42·00
270	30	3m. blue	1·00	19·00
271	30	5m. orange	1·00	19·00
272	30	10m. green	1·60	32·00
273	30	20m. black	2·20	44·00

OFFICIAL STAMPS

O18

1916

O195	O18	3pf. brown	35	1·10
O196	O18	5pf. green	35	1·10
O197	O18	7½pf. green on green	35	65
O198	O18	7½pf. green	35	1·10
O199	O18	10pf. red	35	85
O200	O18	15pf. red on buff	90	95
O201	O18	15pf. red	35	1·10
O202	O18	20pf. blue on blue	2·75	2·75
O203	O18	20pf. blue	35	85
O204	O18	25pf. grey	35	85
O205	O18	30pf. orange	35	85
O206	O18	60pf. turquoise	35	1·60
O207	O18	1m. purple on buff	1·30	3·75
O208	O18	1m. purple	3·75	£650

1919. Optd **Volksstaat Bayern**.

O215	3pf. brown	35	18·00
O216	5pf. green	35	2·75
O217	7½pf. green	35	17·00
O218	10pf. red	35	3·00
O219	15pf. red	35	3·00
O220	20pf. blue	35	3·00
O221	25pf. grey	35	3·00
O222	30pf. orange	35	3·00
O223	35pf. orange	35	3·00
O224	50pf. olive	35	3·25
O225	60pf. turquoise	45	18·00
O226	75pf. brown	45	4·75
O227	1m. purple on buff	1·50	19·00
O228	1m. purple	5·50	£500

O31

O32

O33

1920

O274	O31	5pf. green	35	8·50
O275	O31	10pf. orange	35	8·50
O276	O31	15pf. red	35	8·50
O277	O31	20pf. violet	35	8·50
O278	O31	30pf. blue	35	9·50
O279	O31	40pf. brown	35	9·50
O280	O32	50pf. red	35	30·00
O281	O32	60pf. green	35	12·50
O282	O32	70pf. lilac	35	38·00
O283	O32	75pf. red	35	48·00
O284	O32	80pf. blue	35	48·00
O285	O32	90pf. olive	35	75·00
O286	O33	1m. brown	35	65·00
O287	O33	1¼m. green	35	85·00
O288	O33	1½m. red	35	85·00
O289	O33	2½m. blue	35	95·00
O290	O33	3m. lake	75	£140
O291	O33	5m. green	3·25	£160

POSTAGE DUE STAMPS

D6

1862. Inscr "Bayer. Posttaxe" at top. Imperf.

D34	D6	3k. black	£170	£400

1870. As Type D 6, but inscr "Bayr. Posttaxe" at top. Perf.

D65B	1k. black	16·00	£1100
D66B	3k. black	16·00	£600

1876. Optd **Vom Empfanger zahlbar.**

D130a	8	2pf. grey	1·10	3·00
D131a	8	3pf. grey	1·10	5·00
D132a	8	5pf. grey	1·50	4·50
D133a	8	10pf. grey	1·10	2·50

1895. No. D131a surch 2 in each corner.

D134	2 on 3pf. grey	†	£61000

1908. Stamps of 1876 optd **E.**

R133	3pf. brown	1·10	4·00
R134	5pf. green	30	50
R135	10pf. red	30	50
R136	20pf. blue	65	1·00
R137	50pf. purple	5·75	9·25

Pt. 7

BELGIAN OCCCUPATION OF GERMANY

Stamps used in German territory occupied by Belgian Forces at the end of the War of 1914/18, and including the districts of Eupen and Malmedy, now incorporated in Belgium.

100 centimes = 1 Belgian franc.

1919. Stamps of Belgium optd **ALLEMAGNE DUITSCHLAND.**

1	51	1c. orange	40	85
2	51	2c. brown	40	85
3	51	3c. grey	40	3·25
4	51	5c. green	85	1·60
5	51	10c. red	1·60	3·25
6	51	15c. violet	85	1·60
7	51	20c. purple	1·30	1·60
8	51	25c. blue	1·60	2·75
9	63	25c. blue	5·25	16·00
10	52	35c. black and brown	1·60	1·60
11	-	40c. black and green	1·60	3·25
12	-	50c. black and red	8·00	15·00
13	-	65c. black and red	4·25	16·00
14	55	1f. violet	30·00	26·00
15	-	2f. grey	55·00	65·00
16	-	5f. blue (FRANK, No. 194)	11·50	16·00
17	-	10f. sepia	65·00	85·00

1920. Stamps of Belgium surch **EUPEN & MALMEDY** and value.

18	51	5pf. on 5c. green	40	55
19	51	10pf. on 10c. red	40	55
20	51	15pf. on 15c. violet	75	65
21	51	20pf. on 20c. purple	75	1·50
22	51	30pf. on 25c. blue	1·10	1·50
23	-	75pf. on 50c. black and red	21·00	26·00
24	55	1m.25 on 1f. violet	30·00	27·00

1920. Stamps of Belgium optd **Eupen.**

25	51	1c. orange	55	55
26	51	2c. brown	55	55
27	51	3c. grey	75	2·10
28	51	5c. green	75	1·30
29	51	10c. red	1·30	1·80
30	51	15c. violet	1·80	1·80
31	51	20c. purple	2·10	2·10
32	51	25c. blue	1·80	2·75
33	63	25c. blue	6·25	13·50
34	52	35c. black and brown	2·75	2·75
35	-	40c. black and green	3·25	3·25
36	-	50c. black and red	8·50	10·50
37	-	65c. black and red	4·75	16·00
38	55	1f. violet	34·00	26·00
39	-	2f. grey	60·00	42·00
40	-	5f. blue (FRANK, No. 194)	18·00	16·00
41	-	10f. sepia	75·00	70·00

1920. Stamps of Belgium optd **Malmedy.**

42	51	1c. orange	35	55
43	51	2c. brown	35	55
44	51	3c. grey	55	2·10
45	51	5c. green	85	1·30
46	51	10c. red	1·30	1·80
47	51	15c. violet	2·10	2·10
48	51	20c. purple	2·75	2·75
49	51	25c. blue	2·10	2·75
50	63	25c. blue	6·25	12·50
51	52	35c. black and brown	2·75	3·25
52	-	40c. black and green	2·75	3·25
53	-	50c. black and red	10·50	10·50
54	-	65c. black and red	4·75	16·00
55	55	1f. violet	34·00	23·00
56	-	2f. grey	60·00	42·00
57	-	5f. blue (FRANK, No. 194)	18·00	23·00
58	-	10f. sepia	75·00	80·00

POSTAGE DUE STAMPS

1920. Postage Due stamps of Belgium, 1919. (a) Optd **Eupen.**

D1	5c. green	1·30	1·60
D2	10c. red	2·75	2·75
D3	20c. green	5·25	6·25
D4	30c. blue	5·25	6·25
D5	50c. grey	26·00	21·00

(b) Optd **Malmedy.**

D6	5c. green	2·20	1·30
D7	10c. red	4·50	2·20
D8	20c. green	16·00	13·00
D9	30c. blue	8·75	9·75
D10	50c. grey	18·00	13·00

Pt. 4

BELGIUM

An independent Kingdom of N.W. Europe.

1849. 100 centimes = 1 franc.
2002. 100 cents = 1 euro.

1 "Epaulettes"

1849. Imperf.

1	1	10c. brown	£3500	£100
2a	1	20c. blue	£4000	70·00

3 "Medallions"

1861. Imperf.

12	3	1c. green	£300	£160
13	3	10c. brown	£650	11·50
14	3	20c. blue	£700	11·50
15	3	40c. red	£5500	£100

1863. Perf.

24	1c. green	85·00	35·00
25	10c. brown	£110	4·75
26	20c. blue	£110	4·75
27	40c. red	£600	32·00

5

8

1865. Various frames.

34	5	10c. grey	£250	3·00
35	5	20c. blue	£400	2·50
36	5	30c. brown	£850	13·50
37	8	40c. red	£1100	26·00
38	5	1f. lilac	£2750	£140

10 "Small Lion"

1866

43	10	1c. grey	£140	16·00
44	10	2c. blue	£500	£110
45	10	5c. brown	£600	£100

11

13

14

15

20

1869. Various frames.

46	11	1c. green	11·50	60
59a	11	2c. blue	27·00	4·00
60	11	5c. buff	75·00	1·70
49	11	8c. lilac	£100	70·00
50	13	10c. green	38·00	60
51b	14	20c. blue	£190	1·70
62	15	25c. bistre	£130	4·00

53a	13	30c. buff	£110	4·25
54b	13	40c. red	£190	8·75
55a	15	50c. grey	£375	14·50
56	13	1f. mauve	£550	21·00
57a	20	5f. brown	£2250	£1900

Types **13** to **20** and all later portraits to Type **38** are of Leopold II.

21

1883. Various frames.

63	21	10c. red	35·00	3·50
64	-	20c. grey	£250	14·00
65	-	25c. blue	£500	46·00
66	-	50c. violet	£475	46·00

25

1884. Various frames.

67	11	1c. olive	22·00	85
68	11	1c. grey	5·75	60
69	11	2c. brown	19·00	2·30
70	11	5c. green	50·00	60
71	25	10c. red	17·00	60
72	-	20c. olive	£275	2·30
73	-	25c. blue on red	21·00	3·50
74	-	35c. brown	26·00	3·50
75	-	50c. bistre	17·00	2·50
76	-	1f. brown on green	£1000	21·00
77	-	2f. lilac	80·00	44·00

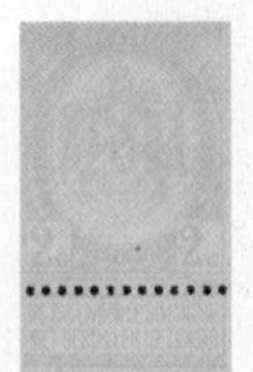

32

33

1893

78a	32	1c. grey	95	35
79	32	2c. yellow	85	1·50
80	32	2c. brown	2·30	60
81	32	5c. green	13·00	60
82	33	10c. brown	3·75	25
83	33	10c. red	3·25	60
84	33	20c. olive	20·00	85
85	33	25c. blue	14·00	60
86a	33	35c. brown	29·00	1·70
87	33	50c. brown	75·00	25·00
88	33	50c. grey	85·00	3·75
89	33	1f. red on green	£110	29·00
90	33	1f. orange	£140	7·50
91	33	2f. mauve	95·00	75·00

The prices for the above and all following issues with the tablet are for stamps with the tablet attached. Without tablet, the prices will be about half those quoted.

See also Nos. 106/8.

34 Arms of Antwerp

1894. Antwerp Exhibition.

93	34	5c. green on red	7·00	4·75
94	34	10c. red on blue	3·50	3·00
95	34	25c. blue on red	1·20	1·20

35 St. Michael encountering Satan

36

1896. Brussels Exhibition of 1897.

96	35	5c. violet	85	85
97	36	10c. red	8·75	5·25
98	36	10c. brown	30	30

37

38

1905. Various frames.

99	37	10c. red	1·70	85
100	37	20c. olive	39·00	1·50
101	37	25c. blue	17·00	1·20
102	37	35c. purple	41·00	3·00
103	38	50c. grey	£140	3·00
104	38	1f. orange	£190	14·00
105	38	2f. mauve	£130	29·00

1907. As T 32 but no scroll pattern between stamps and labels.

106	1c. grey	2·00	30
107	2c. red	23·00	8·75
108	5c. green	20·00	85

40 St. Martin and the Beggar (from altarpiece by Van Dyck)

1910. Brussels Exhibition. A. Unshaded background. B. Shaded background. A.

109	40	1c. (+1c.) grey	1·20	1·20
110	40	2c. (+2c.) purple	13·00	13·00
111	40	5c. (+5c.) green	3·50	3·50
112	40	10c. (+5c.) red	3·50	3·50

B.

113	1c. (+1c.) green	3·50	3·50
114	2c. (+2c.) purple	9·25	9·25
115	5c. (+5c.) green	3·50	3·50
116	10c. (+5c.) red	3·50	3·50

1911. Nos. 109/16 optd 1911. A.

117	1c. (+1c.) grey	42·00	29·00
118	2c. (+2c.) purple	£200	£100
119	5c. (+5c.) green	13·00	11·50
120	10c. (+5c.) red	13·00	11·50

B.

121	1c. (+1c.) green	65·00	41·00
122	2c. (+2c.) purple	£100	46·00
123	5c. (+5c.) green	13·00	11·50
124	10c. (+5c.) red	13·00	11·50

1911. Charleroi Exhibition. Nos. 109/16 optd CHARLEROI–1911. A.

125	1c. (+1c.) grey	8·25	4·25
126	2c. (+2c.) purple	21·00	17·00
127	5c. (+5c.) green	11·50	11·50
128	10c. (+5c.) red	11·50	11·50

B.

129	1c. (+1c.) green	8·25	4·25
130	2c. (+2c.) purple	21·00	17·00
131	5c. (+5c.) green	11·50	11·50
132	10c. (+5c.) red	11·50	11·50

42

43

44

45 Albert I

1912

133	42	1c. orange	25	25
134	43	2c. brown	35	35
135	44	5c. green	25	25
136	45	10c. red	70	60
137	45	20c. olive	22·00	5·75
138	45	35c. brown	1·20	85
139	45	40c. green	23·00	21·00
140	45	50c. grey	1·20	85
141	45	1f. orange	5·00	4·25
142	45	2f. violet	38·00	26·00
143	-	5f. purple	£120	38·00

The 5f. is as Type **45** but larger (23×35 mm).

46 (Larger head)

1912. Large head.

148	46	10c. red	25	25
145	46	20c. olive	35	45
150	46	25c. blue	35	35
147	46	40c. green	75	75

47 Merode Monument

1914. Red Cross.

151	47	5c. (+5c.) red & green	4·75	4·75
152	47	10c. (+10c.) red & pink	7·00	7·00
153	47	20c. (+20c.) red & vio	75·00	75·00

48 Albert I

1914. Red Cross.

154	48	5c. (+5c.) red and green	5·75	5·75
155	48	10c. (+10c.) red	60	60
156	48	20c. (+20c.) red & violet	18·00	18·00

49 Albert I

1915. Red Cross.

157	49	5c. (+5c.) red and green	13·00	3·00
158	49	10c. (+10c.) red and pink	37·00	14·50
159	49	20c. (+20c.) red & violet	65·00	23·00

51 Albert I

52 Cloth Hall, Ypres

55 Freeing of the Scheldt

1915

170	51	1c. orange	25	25
171	51	2c. brown	25	25
179	51	3c. grey	60	45
172	51	5c. green	1·50	25
173	51	10c. red	1·40	25
174	51	15c. violet	2·20	25
187	51	20c. purple	3·50	40
176	51	25c. blue	60	45
188	52	35c. black and brown	60	35
189	-	40c. black and green	60	35
190	-	50c. black and red	6·50	35
191	55	1f. violet	49·00	1·20
192	-	2f. grey	31·00	2·30
193	-	5f. blue (FRANKEN)	£500	£190
194	-	5f. blue (FRANK)	1·70	1·20
195	-	10f. brown	28·00	27·00

DESIGNS: As T **52**: 40c. Dinant; 50c. Louvain. As T **55**: 2f. Annexation of the Congo; 5f. King Albert at Furnes; 10f. The Kings of Belgium.

1918. Red Cross. Surch with new value and cross. Some colours changed.

222	51	1c.+1c. orange	30	30
223	51	2c.+2c. brown	30	30
224	51	5c.+5c. green	1·70	1·50
225	51	10c.+10c. red	3·50	3·25
226	51	15c.+15c. purple	7·00	7·00
227	51	20c.+20c. brown	14·50	13·00
228	51	25c.+25c. blue	29·00	29·00
229	52	35c.+35c. black & violet	14·00	13·50
230	-	40c.+40c. black & brown	14·00	13·50
231	-	50c.+50c. black and blue	14·50	13·50
232	55	1f.+1f. grey	46·00	45·00
233	-	2f.+2f. green	£100	£100
234	-	5f.+5f. brn (FRANKEN)	£250	£250
235	-	10f.+10f. blue	£850	£750

63 "Perron" at Liege

1919

236a	63	25c. blue	3·50	50

64 Albert I

1919

237	64	1c. brown	25	25
238	64	2c. olive	25	25
239	64	5c. green	25	25
240	64	10c. red	35	35
241	64	15c. violet	45	45
242	64	20c. sepia	1·70	1·70
243	64	25c. blue	2·30	2·30
244	64	35c. brown	2·50	2·50
245	64	40c. red	9·25	8·75
246	64	50c. brown	15·00	14·50
247	64	1f. orange	60·00	55·00
248	64	2f. purple	£550	£500
249	64	5f. red	£130	£130
250	64	10f. red	£170	£170

SIZES: 1c., 2c., 18½×21½ mm. 5c. to 2f., 22½×26½ mm. 5f., 10f., 27½×33 mm.

67 Discus thrower

68 Charioteer

1920. Olympic Games, Antwerp.

256	67	5c. (+5c.) green	2·50	2·30
257	68	10c. (+5c.) red	2·00	1·70
258	-	15c. (+5c.) brown	3·00	2·30

DESIGN—VERT: 15c. Runner.

73 Hotel de Ville, Termonde

1920

308b	73	65c. black and purple	85	45

1921. Nos. 256/8 surch 20c. 20c.

309	67	20c. on 5c. green	85	30
310	68	20c. on 10c. red	60	30
311	-	20c. on 15c. brown	85	30

76 Albert I

1921

313	**76**	50c. blue	30	10
314	**76**	75c. red	40	35
315	**76**	75c. blue	50	10
316	**76**	1f. sepia	60	10
317	**76**	1f. blue	50	30
318	**76**	2f. green	1·20	30
319	**76**	5f. purple	19·00	18·00
320	**76**	5f. brown	11·50	11·50
321	**76**	10f. red	13·00	9·25

1921. Surch 55c 55c.

322	**73**	55c. on 65c. black & pur	3·50	45

80

1922. War Invalids Fund.

348	**80**	20c.+20c. brown	1·70	1·70

81 Albert I

1922

349	**81**	1c. orange	10	10
350	**81**	2c. olive	30	30
351	**81**	3c. brown	10	10
352	**81**	5c. slate	10	10
353	**81**	10c. green	25	25
354	**81**	15c. plum	25	25
355	**81**	20c. brown	25	25
356	**81**	25c. purple	30	15
357	**81**	25c. violet	60	15
358	**81**	30c. red	45	25
359	**81**	30c. mauve	35	25
360	**81**	35c. brown	45	45
361	**81**	35c. green	60	30
362	**81**	40c. red	60	25
363	**81**	50c. bistre	65	30
364	**81**	60c. olive	4·25	15
365	**81**	75c. violet	1·30	85
366	**81**	1f. yellow	60	60
367	**81**	1f. red	1·50	30
368	**81**	1f.25 blue	1·70	1·50
369	**81**	1f.50 blue	3·00	60
370	**81**	1f.75 blue	2·00	25
371	**81**	2f. blue	4·25	60
372	**81**	5f. green	60·00	3·00
373	**81**	10f. brown	£100	13·00

83 Wounded Soldier

1923. War Invalids Fund.

374	**83**	20c.+20c. slate	1·70	1·70

87 Leopold I and Albert I

1925. 75th Anniv of 1st Belgian Stamps.

410	**87**	10c. green	11·00	11·00
411	**87**	15c. violet	4·25	4·25
412	**87**	20c. brown	4·25	4·25
413	**87**	25c. slate	4·25	4·25
414	**87**	30c. red	4·25	4·25
415	**87**	35c. blue	4·25	4·25
416	**87**	40c. sepia	4·25	4·25
417	**87**	50c. brown	4·25	4·25
418	**87**	75c. blue	4·25	4·25
419	**87**	1f. purple	9·25	9·25
420	**87**	2f. blue	5·75	5·75
421	**87**	5f. black	4·75	4·75
422	**87**	10f. red	9·75	9·75

88

1925. Anti-T.B. Fund.

423	**88**	15c.+5c. red and mauve	30	30
424	**88**	30c.+5c. red and grey	30	30
425	**88**	1f.+10c. red and blue	1·50	1·50

1926. Flood Relief. Type of 1922 surch Inondations 30 c Watersnood.

426	**81**	30c.+30c. green	1·20	1·20

90

1926. Flood Relief Fund. A. Shaded background. B. Solid background. A.

427	**90**	1f.+1f. blue	7·50	7·50

B.

428		1f.+1f. blue	1·70	1·70

91

92 Queen Elisabeth and King Albert

1926. War Tuberculosis Fund.

429	**91**	5c.+5c. brown	10	10
430	**91**	20c.+5c. brown	60	60
431	**91**	50c.+5c. violet	25	25
432	**92**	1f.50+25c. blue	80	80
433	**92**	5f.+1f. red	7·50	7·50

1927. Stamps of 1922 surch.

434	**81**	3c. on 2c. olive	25	25
435	**81**	10c. on 15c. plum	25	25
436	**81**	35c. on 40c. red	25	10
437	**81**	1f.75 on 1f.50 blue	1·60	1·20

94 Rowing Boat

1927. Anti-T.B. Fund.

438	**94**	25c.+10c. brown	1·20	1·20
439	**94**	35c.+10c. green	1·20	1·20
440	**94**	60c.+10c. violet	30	30
441	**94**	1f.75+25c. blue	1·50	1·50
442	**94**	5f.+1f. purple	5·25	5·25

96 Ogives

97 Ruins of Orval Abbey

1928. Orval Abbey Restoration Fund. Inscr "ORVAL 1928" or "ORVAL".

461	**96**	5c.+5c. red and gold	30	30
462	-	25c.+5c. violet and gold	45	45
463	-	35c.+10c. green	1·30	1·30
464	-	60c.+15c. brown	85	30
465	-	1f.75+25c. blue	3·50	2·30
466	-	2f.+40c. purple	29·00	24·00
467	-	3f.+1f. red	26·00	23·00
468	**97**	5f.+5f. lake	19·00	17·00
469	-	10f.+10f. sepia	19·00	17·00

DESIGNS—VERT: 35c., 2f. Cistercian monk stone-carving; 60c., 1f.75, 3f. Duchess Matilda retrieving her ring.

99 Mons Cathedral

101 Malines Cathedral

1928. Anti-T.B. Fund.

472	**99**	5c.+5c. red	30	30
473	-	25c.+15c. sepia	30	30
474	**101**	35c.+10c. green	1·50	1·50
475	-	60c.+15c. brown	60	60
476	-	1f.75+25c. violet	10·00	10·00
477	-	5f.+5f. purple	23·00	28·00

DESIGNS—As Type **99**: 25c. Tournai Cathedral. As Type **101**: 60c. Ghent Cathedral; 1f.75, St. Gudule Cathedral, Brussels; 5f. Louvain Library.

1929. Surch BRUXELLES 1929 BRUSSEL 5 c in frame.

478	**81**	5c. on 30c. mauve	15	15
479	**81**	5c. on 75c. violet	25	25
480	**81**	5c. on 1f.25c. blue	15	15

The above cancellation, whilst altering the original face value of the stamps, also constitutes a precancel, although stamps also come with additional ordinary postmark. The unused prices are for stamps with full gum and the used prices are for stamps without gum, with or without postmarks. We do not list precancels where there is no change in face value.

104 The Belgian Lion

105 Albert I

1929

487	**104**	1c. orange	25	25
488	**104**	2c. green	60	30
489	**104**	3c. brown	25	10
490	**104**	5c. green	25	10
491	**104**	10c. bistre	25	10
492	**104**	20c. mauve	1·40	40
493	**104**	25c. red	60	10
494	**104**	35c. green	60	10
495	**104**	40c. purple	45	15
496	**104**	50c. blue	45	10
497	**104**	60c. mauve	3·00	30
498	**104**	70c. brown	1·70	25
499	**104**	75c. blue	3·00	25
500	**104**	75c. brown	8·25	30
501	**105**	10f. brown	23·00	5·75
502	**105**	20f. green	£120	35·00
503a	**105**	50f. purple	29·00	29·00
504a	**105**	100f. red	35·00	35·00

1929. Laying of first Stone towards Restoration of Orval Abbey. Nos. 461/9 optd with crown over ornamental letter "L" and 19-8-29.

543		5c.+5c. red and gold	£100	95·00
544		25c.+5c. violet and gold	£100	95·00
545		35c.+10c. green	£100	95·00
546		60c.+15c. brown	£100	95·00
547		1f.75c.+25c. blue	£100	95·00
548		2f.+40c. purple	£120	£100
549		3f.+1f. red	£100	95·00
550		5f.+5f. lake	£100	95·00
551		10f.+10f. sepia	£100	95·00

109 Canal and Belfry, Bruges

1929. Anti-T.B. Fund.

552	-	5c.+5c. brown	30	30
553	-	25c.+15c. grey	2·00	2·00
554	-	35c.+10c. green	1·70	1·70
555	-	60c.+15c. lake	60	60
556	-	1f.75+25c. blue	8·75	8·75
557	**109**	5f.+5f. purple	42·00	42·00

DESIGNS—HORIZ: 5c. Waterfall at Coo; 35c. Menin Gate, Ypres; 60c. Promenade d'Orleans, Spa; 1f.75, "Aquitania" and "Dinteldyk" (liners), Antwerp Harbour. VERT: 25c. Bayard Rock, Dinant.

110 Paul Rubens

111 Zenobe Gramme

1930. Antwerp and Liege Exns.

558	**110**	35c. green	60	30
559	**111**	35c. green	60	30

112 Fokker F. VIIa/m I-BOEO over Ostend

1930. Air.

560	**112**	50c. blue	60	30
561	-	1f.50 brown (St. Hubert)	3·50	3·50
562	-	2f. green (Namur)	2·30	1·20
563	-	5f. red (Brussels)	2·30	1·50
564	-	5f. violet (Brussels)	38·00	38·00

113 "Leopold II" by Jef Lempoels

1930. Centenary of Independence.

565		60c. purple	30	30
566	**113**	1f. red	1·20	85
567	-	1f.75 blue	3·00	1·70

PORTRAITS: 60c. "Leopold I" by Lievin de Winne. 1f.75, King Albert I.

114 Antwerp City Arms

1930. International Philatelic Exhibition, Antwerp. Sheet 138×136 mm.

MS568	**114**	4f. (+6f.) green	£350	£350

1930. I.L.O. Congress. Nos. 565/7 optd B.I.T. OCT. 1930.

569		60c. purple	3·00	3·00
570		1f. red	11·50	11·50
571		1f.75 blue	20·00	20·00

116 Wynendaele

117 Gaesbeek

1930. Anti-T.B. Fund.

572	-	10c.+5c. mauve	45	45
573	**116**	25c.+15c. sepia	1·30	1·30
574	-	40c.+10c. purple	1·20	1·20
575	-	70c.+15c. slate	1·20	1·20
576	-	1f.+25c. red	9·75	9·75
577	-	1f.75+25c. blue	6·50	6·50
578	**117**	5f.+5f. green	49·00	49·00

DESIGNS: 10c. Bornhem; 40c. Beloeil; 70c. Oydonck, 1f. Ghent; 1f.75, Bouillon.

1931. Surch 2c.

579	**104**	2c. on 3c. brown	15	15

1931. Surch BELGIQUE 1931 BELGIE 10c.

580		10c. on 60c. mauve	70	30

See note below No. 480.

121 Albert I

123

1931

582	**121**	75c. brown (18×22 mm)	1·70	10
583	**121**	1f. lake (21×23½ mm)	35	30
584	**123**	1f.25 black	80	60
585	**123**	1f.50 purple	1·70	60
586	**123**	1f.75 blue	60	10
587	**123**	2f. brown	1·20	30
588	**123**	2f.45 violet	3·50	60
589	**123**	2f.50 sepia	13·50	60
590	**123**	5f. green	37·00	1·60
591	**123**	10f. red	70·00	19·00

See also No. 654.

124 Prince Leopold

1931. Disabled Soldiers' Relief Fund. Brussels National Philatelic Exhibition. Sheet 123×161 mm.

MS592 **124**	2f.45+55c. red (sold at 5f.)	£250	£225

125 Queen Elisabeth

1931. Anti-Tuberculosis Fund.

593	**125**	10c.+5c. brown	30	30
594	**125**	25c.+15c. violet	1·50	60
595	**125**	50c.+10c. green	85	60
596	**125**	75c.+15c. sepia	60	30
597	**125**	1f.+25c. lake	11·50	9·75
598	**125**	1f.75+25c. blue	8·50	5·75
599	**125**	5f.+5f. purple	75·00	75·00

1932. Surch BELGIQUE 1932 BELGIE 10c.

600	**104**	10c. on 40c. mauve	4·00	40
601	**104**	10c. on 70c. brown	4·00	15

See Note below No. 480.

126 Reaper

127 Mercury

1932

602	**126**	2c. green	50	50
603	**127**	5c. red	10	10
604	**126**	10c. green	15	10
605	**127**	20c. lilac	1·50	30
606	**126**	25c. red	85	25
607	**127**	35c. green	3·50	10

129 Cardinal Mercier

1932. Cardinal Mercier Memorial Fund.

609	**129**	10c.+10c. purple	60	60
610	**129**	50c.+30c. mauve	3·00	3·00
611	**129**	75c.+25c. brown	3·00	3·00
612	**129**	1f.+2f. red	11·00	11·00
613	-	1f.75+75c. blue	85·00	85·00
614	-	2f.50+2f.50 brown	85·00	85·00
615	-	3f.+4f.50 green	85·00	85·00
616	-	5f.+20f. purple	£120	£120
617	-	10f.+40f. red	£250	£225

DESIGNS: 1f.75, 3f. Mercier protecting refugees at Malines; 2f.50, 5f. Mercier with busts of Aristotle and Thomas Aquinas; 10f. Mercier when Professor at Louvain University.

132

1932. Infantry Memorial.

618	**132**	75c.+3f.25 red	95·00	95·00
619	**132**	1f.75+4f.25 blue	95·00	95·00

133 Prof Piccard's Stratosphere Balloon *F.N.R.S.*, 1931

1932. Scientific Research Fund.

621	**133**	75c. brown	3·50	30
622	**133**	1f.75 blue	20·00	3·25
623	**133**	2f.50 violet	23·00	17·00

134 Hulpe-Waterloo Sanatorium

1932. Anti-T.B. Fund.

624	**134**	10c.+5c. violet	30	30
625	**134**	25c.+15c. mauve	3·25	2·00
626	**134**	50c.+10c. red	3·00	85
627	**134**	75c.+15c. brown	1·70	30
628	**134**	1f.+25c. red	20·00	14·50
629	**134**	1f.75+25c. blue	13·00	11·00
630	**134**	5f.+5f. green	£110	£110

1933. Lion type surch BELGIQUE 1933 BELGIE 10c.

631	**104**	10c. on 40c. mauve	21·00	4·00
632	**104**	10c. on 70c. brown	19·00	1·70

See note below No. 480.

135 The Transept

1933. Orval Abbey Restoration Fund. Inscr "ORVAL".

633	-	5c.+5c. green	75·00	75·00
634	-	10c.+15c. green	75·00	75·00
635	-	25c.+15c. brown	55·00	50·00
636	**135**	50c.+25c. lake	55·00	50·00
637	-	75c.+50c. green	55·00	50·00
638	-	1f.+1f.25 lake	55·00	50·00
639	-	1f.25+1f.75 sepia	55·00	50·00
640	-	1f.75+2f.75 blue	85·00	85·00
641	-	2f.+3f. mauve	85·00	85·00
642	-	2f.50+5f. brown	85·00	85·00
643	-	5f.+20f. purple	85·00	85·00
644	-	10f.+40f. blue	£350	£350

DESIGNS—VERT: 10c. Abbey Ruins; 75c. Belfry, new abbey; 1f. Fountain, new abbey. HORIZ: 5c. The old abbey; 25c. Guests' Courtyard, new abbey; 1f.25, Cloister, new abbey; 1f.75, Foundation of Orval Abbey in 1131; 2f. Restoration of the abbey, XVI and XVII centuries; 2f.50, Orval Abbey, XVIII century; 5f. Prince Leopold laying foundation stone of new abbey; 10f. The Virgin Mary (30×45 mm).

138 Anti-T.B. Symbol

1933. Anti-tuberculosis Fund.

646	**138**	10c.+5c. grey	85	85
647	**138**	25c.+15c. mauve	3·75	3·75
648	**138**	50c.+10c. brown	3·00	3·00
649	**138**	75c.+15c. sepia	60·00	60·00
650	**138**	1f.+25c. red	23·00	21·00
651	**138**	1f.75+25c. blue	36·00	35·00
652	**138**	5f.+5f. purple	£160	£160

1934. Lion type surch BELGIQUE 1934 BELGIE 10c.

653	**104**	10c. on 40c. mauve	19·00	1·70

See note below No. 480.

1934. King Albert's Mourning Stamp.

654	**121**	75c. black	30	10

140 Peter Benoit

1934. Benoit Centenary Memorial Fund.

658	**140**	75c.+25c. brown	7·00	7·00

141 Brussels Palace

1934. International Exhibition, Brussels.

659	-	35c. green	85	45
660	**141**	1f. red	1·50	60
661	-	1f.50 brown	7·00	1·40
662	-	1f.75 blue	7·00	45

DESIGNS: 35c. Congo Palace; 1f.50, Old Brussels; 1f.75, Grand Palace of the Belgian section.

142 King Leopold III

1934. War Invalids' Fund. (a) Size 18×22 mm. (b) Size 21×24 mm. (i) Exhibition Issue.

663	**142**	75c.+25c. green (a)	20·00	20·00
664	**142**	1f.+25c. purple (b)	17·00	17·00

(ii) Ordinary postage stamps.

665	75c.+25c. purple (a)	5·25	5·25
666	1f.+25c. red (b)	8·75	8·75

143 King Leopold III

1934

667		70c. green	45	10
668		75c. brown	70	35
669	**143**	1f. red	3·50	40

144 Health Crusader

1934. Anti-tuberculosis Fund. Cross in red.

670	**144**	10c.+5c. black	25	25
671	**144**	25c.+15c. brown	4·50	4·50
672	**144**	50c.+10c. green	2·30	2·00
673	**144**	75c.+15c. purple	1·50	1·50
674	**144**	1f.+25c. red	14·50	14·50
675	**144**	1f.75+25c. blue	11·50	11·50
676	**144**	5f.+5f. purple	£150	£150

145 The Royal Children

1935. Queen Astrid's Appeal.

680	**145**	35c.+15c. green	1·20	1·20
681	**145**	70c.+30c. purple	1·20	1·20
682	**145**	1f.75+50c. blue	5·75	5·75

146 "Mail-diligence"

1935. Brussels Int Exn.

683	**146**	10c.+10c. olive	60	60
684	**146**	25c.+25c. brown	2·50	2·50
685	**146**	35c.+25c. green	3·75	3·75

1935. Air. Surch with new value twice.

686	**112**	1f. on 1f.50 brown	60	60
687	**112**	4f. on 5f. red	11·00	11·00

148 Francis of Taxis

1935. Brussels Philatelic Exhibition (SITEB). Sheet 93×118 mm.

MS688 **148**	5f.+5f. grey	£170	£170

151 Queen Astrid

1935. Death of Queen Astrid. Mourning Stamp.

713	**151**	70c.+5c. black	25	25

1935. Anti-tuberculosis Fund. Black borders.

714	10c.+5c. olive	25	25
715	25c.+15c. brown	45	45
716	35c.+5c. green	25	25
717	50c.+10c. mauve	60	60
718	1f. +25c. red	1·50	1·50
719	1f.75+25c. blue	2·00	2·00
720	2f.45+55c. violet	4·00	4·00

152 State arms

1936

727	**152**	2c. green	10	10
728	**152**	5c. orange	10	10
729	**152**	10c. olive	10	10
730	**152**	15c. blue	10	10
731	**152**	20c. violet	10	10
732	**152**	25c. red	10	10
733	**152**	25c. yellow	30	10
734	**152**	30c. brown	25	10
735	**152**	35c. green	10	10
736	**152**	40c. lilac	30	30
737	**152**	50c. blue	60	10
738	**152**	60c. grey	15	10
739	**152**	65c. mauve	4·25	45
740	**152**	70c. green	40	30
741	**152**	75c. mauve	1·00	10
742	**152**	80c. green	15·00	35
743	**152**	90c. violet	75	15
744	**152**	1f. brown	70	15

153

1936. Various frames. (a) Size 17½×22 mm.

745	**153**	70c. brown	30	10
746	**153**	75c. olive	30	30
747	**153**	1f. red	35	10

(b) Size 21×24 mm.

748	1f. red	35	10
749	1f.20 brown	2·50	15

750		1f.50 mauve	60	45
751		1f.75 blue	30	30
752		1f.75 red	30	10
753		2f. violet	1·70	1·70
754		2f.25 black	30	30
755		2f.50 red	10·50	40
756		3f.25 brown	30	30
757		5f. green	1·70	70

Nos. 746/7, 751/2, 754/5 and 757 are inscribed "BELGIE BELGIQUE".

155 King Leopold III

1936

760	**155**	1f.50 mauve	85	50
761	**155**	1f.75 blue	30	30
762	**155**	2f. violet	60	35
763	**155**	2f.25 violet	65	65
764	**155**	2f.45 black	60·00	85
765	**155**	2f.50 black	4·75	30
770	**155**	3f. brown	2·00	25
766	**155**	3f.25 brown	40	25
771	**155**	4f. blue	5·00	15
767	**155**	5f. green	3·50	60
772	**155**	6f. red	18·00	45
768	**155**	10f. purple	60	30
769	**155**	20f. red	1·20	60

See also No. 2775.

156 Borgerhout Town Hall

1936. Borgerhout Philatelic Exhibition. Sheet 95×119 mm.
MS775 **156** 70c.+30c. brown £100 95·00

157 Charleroi Town Hall

1936. Charleroi Philatelic Exhibition. Sheet 95×119 mm.
MS776 **157** 2f.45+55c. blue 75·00 75·00

158 Prince Baudouin

1936. Anti-tuberculosis Fund.

777	**158**	10c.+5c. brown	30	30
778	**158**	25c.+5c. violet	30	30
779	**158**	35c.+5c. green	35	35
780	**158**	50c.+5c. brown	60	60
781	**158**	70c.+5c. olive	25	25
782	**158**	1f.+25c. red	1·70	1·70
783	**158**	1f.75+25c. blue	2·30	2·30
784	**158**	2f.45+2f.55 purple	5·75	5·75

1937. Stamp of 1929 surch BELGIQUE 1937 BELGIE 10c.

785	**104**	10c. on 40c. purple	30	30

See note below No. 480.

1937. International Stamp Day.

786	**158**	2f.45c.+2f.55c. slate	3·00	3·00

159 Queen Astrid and Prince Baudouin

1937. Queen Astrid Public Utility Fund.

787	**159**	10c.+5c. purple	30	30
788	**159**	25c.+5c. olive	30	30
789	**159**	35c.+5c. green	30	30
790	**159**	50c.+5c. violet	60	60
791	**159**	70c.+5c. black	30	30
792	**159**	1f.+25c. red	1·70	1·70
793	**159**	1f.75c.+25c. blue	4·00	4·00
794	**159**	2f.45c.+1f.55c. brown	8·75	8·75

160 Queen Elisabeth

1937. Eugene Ysaye Memorial Fund.

795	**160**	70c.+5c. black	35	35
796	**160**	1f.75+25c. blue	80	80

MS797 113×146 mm. **160** 1f.50+2f.50 red (2); 2f.45+3f.55, violet (2) 44·00 20·00

See also **MS**1963.

161 Princess Josephine Charlotte

1937. Anti-tuberculosis Fund.

798	**161**	10c.+5c. green	35	35
799	**161**	25c.+5c. brown	40	40
800	**161**	35c.+5c. green	35	35
801	**161**	50c.+5c. olive	40	40
802	**161**	70c.+5c. purple	30	30
803	**161**	1f.+25c. red	2·00	2·00
804	**161**	1f.75+25c. blue	2·00	2·00
805	**161**	2f.45+2f.55 purple	5·75	5·75

163 King Albert Memorial, Nieuport

1938. King Albert Memorial Fund. Sheet 138×115 mm.
MS809 **163** 2f.45+7f.55 red 23·00 23·00

164 King Leopold

1938. Aeronautical Propaganda.

810	**164**	10c.+5c. purple	35	35
811	**164**	35c.+5c. green	50	50
812	**164**	70c.+5c. black	60	60
813	**164**	1f.75+25c. blue	3·75	3·75
814	**164**	2f.45+2f.55 violet	5·25	5·25

165 Basilica of the Sacred Heart, Koekelberg

1938. Building (Completion) Fund.

815	**165**	10c.+5c. brown	35	35
816	-	35c.+5c. green	35	35
817	**165**	70c.+5c. grey	35	35
818	-	1f.+25c. red	50	50
819	**165**	1f.75+25c. blue	50	50
820	-	2f.45+2f.55 red	5·50	5·50
821	-	5f.+5f. green	11·50	11·50

MS822 95×120 mm. 5f.+5f. violet (as 821) 19·00 17·00

DESIGNS—HORIZ: 35c., 1f., 2f.45, Front view of Basilica. VERT: 5f. Interior view.

1938. Surch 2F50.

823	**155**	2f.50 on 2f.45 black	14·50	30

167 Exhibition Pavilion

1938. International Exhibition, Liege (1939). Inscr "LIEGE 1939 LUIK".

824	-	35c. green	25	25
825	**167**	1f. red	25	35
826	-	1f.50 brown	1·50	60
827	-	1f.75 blue	1·50	30

DESIGNS—VERT: 35c. View of Liege. HORIZ: 1f.50, R. Meuse at Liege; 1f.75, Albert Canal and King Albert.

1938. Koekelberg Basilica Completion Fund. Surch.

828		40c. on 35c.+5c. green (No. 816)	85	85
829	**165**	75c. on 70c.+5c. grey	60	60
830	-	2f.50+2f.50 on 2f.45+2f.55 red (No. 820)	7·75	7·75

170 Prince Albert of Liege

1938. Anti-tuberculosis Fund.

831	**170**	10c.+5c. brown	35	35
832	**170**	30c.+5c. purple	35	35
833	**170**	40c.+5c. olive	35	35
834	**170**	75c.+5c. grey	35	35
835	**170**	1f.+25c. red	1·60	1·60
836	**170**	1f.75+25c. blue	1·40	1·40
837	**170**	2f.50+2f.50 green	7·25	7·25
838	**170**	5f.+5f. purple	16·00	16·00

171 King Leopold and Royal Children

1939. 5th Anniv of Int Red Cross Society.

839	-	10c.+5c. brown	30	30
840	-	30c.+5c. red	35	35
841	-	40c.+5c. olive	35	35
842	**171**	75c.+5c. black	35	35
843	-	1f.+25c. red	2·10	2·10
844	**171**	1f.75+25c. blue	1·50	1·50
845	-	2f.50+2f.50 violet	2·00	2·00
846	-	5f.+5f. green	9·25	9·25

DESIGNS—VERT: 10c. H. Dunant; 30c. Florence Nightingale; 40c. and 1f. Queen Elisabeth and Royal children; 2f.50, Queen Astrid. HORIZ: 5f. Queen Elisabeth and wounded soldier (larger).

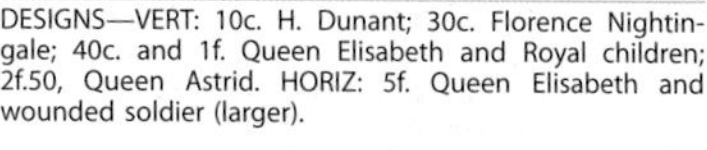

173 Rubens's House (after engraving by Harrewijn)

1939. Rubens's House Restoration Fund.

847	**173**	10c.+5c. brown	35	35
848	-	40c.+5c. purple	35	35
849	-	75c.+5c. green	45	45
850	-	1f.+25c. red	2·30	2·30
851	-	1f.50+25c. brown	3·00	3·00
852	-	1f.75+25c. blue	4·75	4·75
853	-	2f.50+2f.50 purple	18·00	18·00
854	-	5f.+5f. grey	23·00	23·00

DESIGNS—As Type **173**: VERT: 40c. "Rubens's Sons, Albert and Nicholas"; 1f. "Helene Fourment (2nd wife) and Children"; 1f.50, "Rubens and Isabella Brant" (1st wife); 1f.75, Rubens (after engraving by Pontius); 2f.50, "Straw Hat" (Suzanne Fourment). HORIZ: 75c. Arcade of Rubens's house. 35 ×45 mm: 5f. "The Descent from the Cross".

175 Portrait by Memling

1939. Exn of Memling's Paintings, Bruges.

855	**175**	75c.+75c. olive	2·30	2·30

177 Orval Abbey Cloisters and Belfry

1939. Orval Abbey Restoration Fund. Inscr "ORVAL".

861	-	75c.+75c. olive	5·25	5·25
862	**177**	1f.+1f. red	2·50	2·50
863	-	1f.50+1f.50 brown	2·50	2·50
864	-	1f.75+1f.75 blue	3·50	3·50
865	-	2f.50+2f.50 mauve	9·75	9·75
866	-	5f.+5f. purple	11·00	11·00

DESIGNS—As Type **177**: VERT: 75c. Monks in laboratory. HORIZ: 1f.50, Monks harvesting; 1f.75, Aerial view of Orval Abbey; 52½×35½ mm: 2f.50, Cardinal Van Roey, Statue of the Madonna and Abbot of Orval; 5f. Kings Albert and Leopold III and shrine.

180 Thuin

1939. Anti-tuberculosis Fund. Belfries.

868		10c.+5c. olive	35	35
869	**180**	30c.+5c. brown	35	35
870	-	40c.+5c. purple	35	35
871	-	75c.+5c. grey	35	35
872	-	1f.+25c. red	1·50	1·50
873	-	1f.75+25c. blue	1·20	1·20
874	-	2f.50+2f.50 brown	11·00	11·00
875	-	5f.+5f. violet	13·00	13·00

DESIGNS—As Type **180**: 10c. Bruges; 40c. Lier; 75c. Mons. LARGER (21½×34 mm): 1f. Furnes; 1f.75, Namur; 2f.50, Alost; 5f. Tournai.

182 Arms of Mons

1940. Winter Relief Fund.

901	**182**	10c.+5c. black, red and green	35	35
902	-	30c.+5c. multicoloured	35	35
903	-	40c.+10c. multicoloured	35	35
904	-	50c.+10c. multicoloured	35	35
905	-	75c.+15c. multicoloured	35	35
906	-	1f.+25c. multicoloured	45	45
907	-	1f.75c.+50c. mult	70	70
908	-	2f.50c.+2f.50c. olive, red and black	1·30	1·30
909	-	5f.+5f. multicoloured	1·60	1·60

MS910 103×145 mm. Nos. 901/9 each in first colour given, together with red 14·00 14·00

DESIGNS: 30c. to 5f. Arms of Ghent, Arlon, Bruges, Namur, Hasselt, Brussels, Antwerp and Liege, respectively.

183 Painting

184 Monks studying Plans of Orval Abbey

1941. Orval Abbey Restoration Fund.

935	**183**	10c.+15c. brown	50	50
936	-	30c.+30c. grey	50	50
937	-	40c.+60c. brown	50	50
938	-	50c.+65c. violet	50	50
939	-	75c.+1f. mauve	50	50
940	-	1f.+1f.50 red	50	50
941	**183**	1f.25+1f.75 green	50	50
942	-	1f.75+2f.50 blue	50	50
943	-	2f.+3f.50 mauve	50	50
944	-	2f.50+4f.50 brown	50	50
945	-	3f.+5f. green	50	50
946	**184**	5f.+10f. brown	1·80	1·80

MS947 183×165 mm. 5f.+15f. blue (as 946) 10·00 9·25

DESIGNS—As Type **183**. 30c., 1f., 2f.50, Sculpture; 40c., 2f. Goldsmiths (Monks carrying candlesticks and cross); 50c., 1f.75, Stained glass (Monk at prayer); 75c., 3f. Sacred music.

1941. Surch.

955	**152**	10c. on 30c. brown	10	10
956	**152**	10c. on 40c. lilac	10	10
957	**153**	10c. on 70c. brown	10	10
958	**153**	50c. on 75c. olive	30	30
959	**155**	2f.25 on 2f.50 black	65	65

189 Maria Theresa

1941. Soldiers' Families Relief Fund.

960	**189**	10c.+5c. black	25	25
961	-	35c.+5c. green	25	25
962	-	50c.+10c. brown	25	25
963	-	60c.+10c. violet	25	25
964	-	1f.+15c. red	25	25
965	-	1f.50+1f. mauve	25	25
966	-	1f.75+1f.75 blue	25	25
967	-	2f.25+2f.25 brown	30	30
968	-	3f.25+3f.25 brown	50	50
969	-	5f.+5f. green	1·00	1·00

PORTRAITS: 35c. to 5f. Charles of Lorraine, Margaret of Parma, Charles V, Johanna of Castile, Philip the Good, Margaret of Austria, Charles the Bold, Archduke Albert and Archduchess Isabella respectively.

190 St. Martin, Dinant

1941. Winter Relief Fund. Statues.

970	**190**	10c.+5c. brown	30	30
971	-	35c.+5c. green	30	30
972	-	50c.+10c. violet	30	30
973	-	60c.+10c. brown	30	30
974	-	1f.+15c. red	30	30
975	**190**	1f.50+25c. green	30	30
976	-	1f.75+50c. blue	35	35
977	-	2f.25+2f.25 mauve	35	35
978	-	3f.25+3f.25 brown	45	45
979	-	5f.+5f. green	85	85

MS980 105×139 mm. 5f.+20f. purple (as 979) 27·00 27·00

DESIGNS (Statues of St. Martin in churches)—As Type **190**: 35c., 1f. Lennick, St. Quentin; 50c., 3f. Beck, Limberg; 60c., 2f.25, Dave on the Meuse; 1f.75, Hal, Brabant. 35×50 mm: 5f. St. Trond.

192 Concert Hall, Argenteuil

1941. Fund for Queen Elisabeth's Concert Hall. Two sheets, each 103×133 mm.

MS981 **192** 10f.+15f. green 8·25 7·50

MS982 As last with perforated crown and monogram with violet control number on back 8·25 7·50

193 Mercator

1942. Anti-tuberculosis Fund. Portraits.

986	-	10c.+5c. brown	10	10
987	-	35c.+5c. green	10	10
988	-	50c.+10c. brown	10	10
989	-	60c.+10c. green	10	10
990	-	1f.+15c. red	10	10
991	**193**	1f.75+50c. blue	10	10
992	-	3f.25+3f.25 purple	10	10
993	-	5f.+5f. violet	25	25
994	-	10f.+30f. orange	1·70	1·70

MS995 77×59 mm. 3f.25+6f.75 green (as 968); 5f.+10f. red (as 969) 14·00 14·00

SCIENTISTS—As T **193**: 10c. Bolland. 35c. Versale. 50c. S. Stevin. 60c. Van Helmont. 1f. Dodoens. 3f.25, Oertell. 5f. Juste Lipse. 25½×28½ mm: 10f. Plantin.

198 Prisoner writing Letter

1942. Prisoners of War Fund.

1000	**198**	5f.+45f. grey	8·75	8·75

199 St. Martin **200** St. Martin sharing his cloak

1942. Winter Relief Fund.

1001	**199**	10c.+5c. orange	25	25
1002	-	35c.+5c. green	25	25
1003	-	50c.+10c. brown	25	25
1004	-	60c.+10c. black (horiz)	25	25
1005	-	1f.+15c. red	25	25
1006	-	1f.50+25c. green	30	30
1007	-	1f.75+50c. blue	30	35
1008	-	2f.25+2f.25 brn (horiz)	35	35
1009	-	3f.25+3f.25 purple (horiz)	60	60
1010	**200**	5f.+10f. brown	1·60	1·60
1011	**200**	10f.+20f. brown & vio	1·70	1·70
1012	**200**	10f.+20f. red & violet	1·50	1·50

201 Soldiers and Vision of Home

1943. Prisoners of War Relief Fund.

1013	**201**	1f.+30f. red	3·50	3·50
1014	-	1f.+30f. brown	2·30	2·30

DESIGN: No. 1014, Soldiers emptying parcel of books and vision of home.

202 Tiler

1943. Anti-tuberculosis Fund. Trades.

1015	**202**	10c.+5c. brown	25	25
1016	-	35c.+5c. green	25	25
1017	-	50c.+10c. brown	25	25
1018	-	60c.+10c. green	25	25
1019	-	1f.+15c. red	30	25
1020	-	1f.75+75c. blue	25	25
1021	-	3f.25+3f.25 purple	35	35
1022	-	5f.+25f. violet	1·20	1·20

DESIGNS: 35c. Blacksmith; 50c. Coppersmith; 60c. Gunsmith; 1f. Armourer; 1f.75, Goldsmith; 3f.25, Fishmonger; 5f. Clockmaker.

203 Ornamental Letter

204 Ornamental Letter (image scaled to 68% of original size)

1943. Orval Abbey Restoration Fund. Designs showing single letters forming "ORVAL".

1023	**203**	50c.+1f. black	45	45
1024	-	60c.+1f.90 violet	35	35
1025	-	1f.+3f. red	35	35
1026	-	1f.75+5f.25 blue	35	35
1027	-	3f.25+16f.75 green	65	65
1028	**204**	5f.+30f. brown	1·10	1·10

205 St. Leonard's Church, Leon, and St. Martin

206 Church of Notre Dame, Hal, and St. Martin

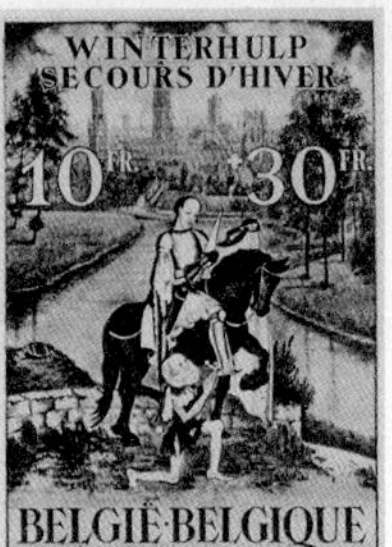

207 St. Martin and River Scheldt

1943. Winter Relief Fund.

1029	**205**	10c.+5c. brown	30	30
1030	-	35c.+5c. green	30	30
1031	-	50c.+15c. green	30	30
1032	-	60c.+20c. purple	30	30
1033	-	1f.+1f. red	35	35
1034	-	1f.75+4f.25 blue	80	80
1035	-	3f.25+11f.75 mauve	1·60	1·60
1036	**206**	5f.+25f. blue	2·40	2·40
1037	**207**	10f.+30f. green	1·90	1·90
1038	-	10f.+30f. brown	1·90	1·90

DESIGNS: (Various churches and statues of St. Martin sharing his cloak). As Type **205**: HORIZ: 35c. Dion-le-Val; 50c. Alost; 60c. Liege; 3f.25, Loppem. VERT: 1f. Courtrai; 1f.75, Angre. As Type **207**: 10f. brown Meuse landscape.

208 "Daedalus and Icarus"

1944. Red Cross.

1039	**208**	35c.+1f.65 green	40	40
1040	-	50c.+2f.50 grey	40	40
1041	-	60c.+3f.40 brown	40	40
1042	-	1f.+5f. red	60	60
1043	-	1f.75+8f.25 blue	60	60
1044	-	5f.+30f. brown	95	95

DESIGNS: 50c. "The Good Samaritan" (Jacob Jordsen); 60c. "Christ healing the Paralytic" (detail); 1f. "Madonna and Child"; 1f.75, "Self-portrait"; 5f. "St. Sebastian".

Nos. 1039 and 1041/4 depict paintings by Anthony van Dyck.

209 Jan van Eyck

1944. Prisoners of War Relief Fund.

1045	**209**	10c.+15c. violet	35	35
1046	-	35c.+15c. green	35	35
1047	-	50c.+25c. brown	35	35
1048	-	60c.+40c. olive	35	35
1049	-	1f.+50c. red	35	35
1050	-	1f.75+4f.25 blue	35	35
1051	-	2f.25+8f.25 slate	80	80
1052	-	3f.25+11f.25 brown	40	40
1053	-	5f.+35f. grey	85	85

PORTRAITS: 35c. "Godefroid de Bouillon". 50c. "Jacob van Maerlant". 60c. "Jean Joses de Dinant". 1f. "Jacob van Artevelde". 1f.75, "Charles Joseph de Ligne". 2f.25, "Andre Gretry". 3f.25, "Jan Moretus-Plantin". 5f. "Ruusbroeck".

210 "Bayard and Four Sons of Aymon", Namur

1944. Anti-tuberculosis Fund. Provincial legendary types.

1054	**210**	10c.+5c. brown	10	10
1055	-	35c.+5c. green	10	10
1056	-	50c.+10c. violet	10	10
1057	-	60c.+10c. brown	10	10
1058	-	1f.+15c. red	10	10
1059	-	1f.75+5f.25 blue	10	10
1060	-	3f.25+11f.75 green	35	35
1061	-	5f.+25f. blue	45	45

DESIGNS—VERT: 35c. "Brabo severing the giant's hand", Antwerp; 60c. "Thyl Ulenspiegel" and "Nele", Flanders; 1f. "St. George and the Dragon", Hainaut; 1f.75, "Genevieve of Brabant, with the Child and the Hind", Brabant. HORIZ: 50c. "St. Hubert encounters the Hind with the Cross", Luxemburg; 3f.25, "Tchantches wrestling with the Saracen", Liege; 5f. "St. Gertrude rescuing the Knight with the cards", Limburg.

211 Lion Rampant

1944. Inscr "BELGIQUE-BELGIE" or "BELGIE-BELGIQUE".

1062A	**211**	5c. brown	10	10
1063A	**211**	10c. green	10	10
1064A	**211**	25c. blue	10	10
1065A	**211**	35c. brown	10	10
1066A	**211**	50c. green	10	10
1067B	**211**	75c. violet	10	10
1068B	**211**	1f. red	10	10

1069B	211	1f.25 brown	25	25
1070B	211	1f.50 orange	40	40
1071A	211	1f.75 blue	10	10
1072B	211	2f. blue	1·70	1·70
1073A	211	2f.75 mauve	10	10
1074B	211	3f. red	25	25
1075B	211	3f.50 grey	15	10
1076B	211	5f. brown	3·50	3·50
1077B	211	10f. black	85	85

1944. Overprinted with large V.

1078	152	2c. green	10	10
1079	152	15c. blue	10	10
1080	152	20c. violet	10	10
1081	152	60c. grey	10	10

213 King Leopold III and "V"

1944

1082	213	1f. red	15	10
1083	213	1f.50 mauve	15	10
1084	213	1f.75 blue	45	45
1085	213	2f. violet	60	35
1086	213	2f.25 green	45	45
1087	213	3f.25 brown	30	15
1088	213	5f. green	1·20	35

214 War Victims

215 Rebuilding Homes

1945. War Victims' Relief Fund.

1114	214	1f.+30f. red	1·90	1·00
1115	215	1¾f.+30f. blue	1·90	1·00

Nos. 1114/15 measure 50×35 mm.

1945. Post Office Employers' Relief Fund.

1119	214	1f.+9f. red	40	25
1120	215	1f.+9f. red	45	25

217 Resister

218 Group of Resisters

1945. Prisoners of War Relief Fund.

1121	217	10c.+15c. orange	25	25
1122	-	20c.+20c. violet	25	25
1123	-	60c.+25c. brown	25	25
1124	-	70c.+30c. green	25	25
1125	217	75c.+50c. brown	25	25
1126	-	1f.+75c. green	30	25
1127	-	1f.50+1f. red	30	25
1128	-	3f.50+3f.50 blue	2·00	1·30
1129	218	5f.+40f. brown	2·50	1·50

DESIGNS—VERT: 20c., 1f. Father and child; 60c., 1f.50, Victim tied to stake. HORIZ: 70c., 3f.50, Rifleman.

219 West Flanders

1945. Anti-tuberculosis Fund.

1130	219	10c.+15c. green	60	30
1131	-	20c.+20c. red	35	30
1132	-	60c.+25c. brown	35	30
1133	-	70c.+30c. green	35	30
1134	-	75c.+50c. brown	35	30
1135	-	1f.+75c. violet	35	30
1136	-	1f.50+1f. red	35	30
1137	-	3f.50+1f.50 blue	75	75
1138	-	5f.+45f. mauve	4·25	2·40

ARMS DESIGNS—VERT: 20c. to 5f. Arms of Luxemburg, East Flanders, Namur, Limburg Hainaut, Antwerp, Liege and Brabant respectively.

222 Douglas DC-400-DAA

1946. Air.

1165	222	6f. blue	40	30
1166	222	8f.50 red	75	60
1167	222	50f. green	7·00	1·20
1168	222	100f. grey	11·50	2·50

1946. Surch -10%, reducing the original value by 10%.

1171	213	"-10%" on 1f.50 mauve	85	30
1172	213	"-10%" on 2f. violet	2·30	85
1173	213	"-10%" on 5f. green	2·00	30

224 "Marie Henriette" (paddle-steamer)

1946. Ostend–Dover Mail-boat Service Centenary.

1174a	-	1f.35 blue	45	25
1175	224	2f.25 green	60	40
1176	-	3f.15 grey	65	30

DESIGNS—21½×18½ or 21×17 mm: 1f.35, "Prince Baudouin" (mail steamer). As T **224**: 3f.15, "Diamant" (paddle-steamer), formerly "Le Chemin de Fer".

225 Paratrooper

1946. Air. Bastogne Monument Fund.

1177	225	17f.50+62f.50 green	1·90	85
1178	225	17f.50+62f.50 purple	1·90	85

226 Father Damien

227 E. Vandervelde

228 Francois Bovesse

1946. Belgian Patriots. (a) Father Damien.

1179	226	65c.+75c. blue	2·30	1·50
1180	-	1f.35+2f. brown	2·30	1·50
1181	-	1f.75+18f. lake	2·30	1·50

DESIGNS—HORIZ: 1f.35, Molokai Leper Colony. VERT: 1f.75, Damien's statue.

(b) Emile Vandervelde.

1182	227	65c.+75c. green	2·30	1·50
1183	-	1f.35+2f. blue	2·30	1·50
1184	-	1f.75+18f. red	2·30	1·50

DESIGNS—HORIZ: 1f.35, Vandervelde, miner, mother and child. VERT: 1f.75, Sower.

(c) Francois Bovesse.

1185		65c.+75c. violet	2·30	1·50
1186	228	1f.35+2f. brown	2·30	1·50
1187	-	1f.75+18f. red	2·30	1·50

DESIGNS—VERT: 65c. Symbols of Patriotism and Learning; 1f.75, Draped memorial figures holding wreath and torch.

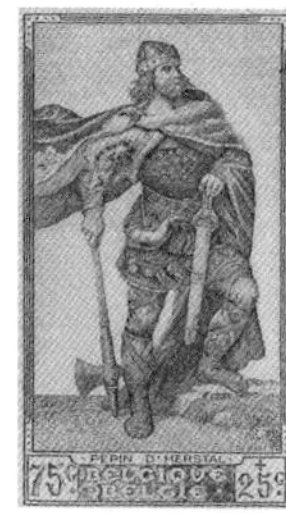

229 Pepin d'Herstal

1946. War Victims' Relief Fund.

1188	229	75c.+25c. green	60	25
1189	-	1f.+50c. violet	85	35
1190	-	1f.50+1f. purple	85	45
1191	-	3f.50+1f.50 blue	1·20	70
1192	-	5f.+45f. mauve	15·00	14·00
1194	-	5f.+45f. orange	13·00	13·00

DESIGNS: 1f. Charlemagne; 1f.50, Godfrey of Bouillon; 3f.50, Robert of Jerusalem; 5f. Baudouin of Constantinople.

See also Nos. 1207/11, 1258/9 and 1302/6.

230 Allegory of "Flight"

1946. Air.

1193	230	2f.+8f. violet	65	60

231 Malines

1946. Anti-tuberculosis Fund. No date.

1195	231	65c.+35c. red	70	25
1196	-	90c.+60c. olive	80	25
1197	-	1f.35+1f.15 green	80	25
1198	-	3f.15+1f.85 blue	1·20	45
1199	-	4f.50+45f.50 brown	19·00	16·00

DESIGNS—(Arms and Industries): 90c. Dinant; 1f.35, Ostend; 3f.15, Verviers; 4f.50, Louvain.

See also Nos. 1212/16.

1947. Air. "Cipex" International Stamp Exhibition, New York. Nos. 1179/87 surch LUCHTPOST POSTE AERIENNE or POSTE AERIENNE LUCHTPOST and new value. (a) Father Damien.

1199a	1f.+2f. on 65c. +75c. blue	95	60
1199b	1f.+50+2f.50 on 1f.35+2f. brown	95	60
1199c	2f.+45f. on 1f.75+18f. red	95	60

(b) Emile Vandervelde.

1199d	1f.+2f. on 65c.+75c. green	95	60
1199e	1f.50+2f.50 on 1f.35+2f. blue	95	60
1199f	2f.+45f. on 1f.75+18f. red	95	60

(c) Francois Bovesse.

1199g	1f.+2f. on 65c.+75c. vio	95	60
1199h	1f.50+2f.50 on 1f.35+2f. brown	95	60
1199i	2f.+45f. on 1f.75+18f. red	95	60

232 Joseph Plateau

1947. Int Film and Belgian Fine Arts Festival.

1200	232	3f.15 blue	1·50	30

233 Adrien de Gerlache

234 Explorers landing from "Belgica"

1947. 50th Anniv of Belgian Antarctic Expedition.

1201	233	1f.35 red	30	10
1202	234	2f.25 grey	4·75	70

1947. War Victims' Relief Fund. Mediaeval Princes as T 229.

1207	65c.+35c. blue	1·30	60
1208	90c.+60c. green	1·90	85
1209	1f.35+1f.15 red	3·75	1·20
1210	3f.15+1f.85 blue	4·75	1·50
1211	20f.+20f. purple	60·00	48·00

DESIGNS: 65c. John II, Duke of Brabant; 90c. Philippe of Alsace; 1f.35, William the Good; 3f.15, Notger, Bishop of Liege; 20f. Philip the Noble.

1947. Anti-Tuberculosis Fund. Arms designs as T 231, but dated "1947".

1212	65c.+35c. orange	70	60
1213	90c.+60c. purple	80	70
1214	1f.35+1f.15 brown	95	75
1215	3f.15+1f.85 blue	3·25	1·50
1216	20f.+20f. green	31·00	20·00

DESIGNS (Arms and Industries): 65c. Nivelles; 90c. St. Truiden; 1f.35, Charleroi; 3f.15, St. Nicholas; 20f. Bouillon.

237 Chemical Industry

240 Textile Machinery

239 Antwerp Docks

1948. National Industries.

1217	237	60c. blue	15	15
1218	237	1f.20 brown	3·00	30
1219	-	1f.35 brown	15	15
1220	-	1f.75 green	70	30
1221	-	1f.75 red	30	25
1222	239	2f.25 grey	85	60
1223	-	2f.50 mauve	9·50	65
1224	239	3f. purple	15·00	60
1225	240	3f.15 blue	1·40	70
1226	240	4f. blue	14·50	45
1227	-	6f. blue	36·00	65
1228	-	6f.30 purple	3·50	2·75

DESIGNS—As Type **237**: 1f.35, 1f.75 green, Woman making lace; 1f.75 red, 2f.50, Agricultural produce. As Type **239**: 6f., 6f.30, Steel works.

242 St. Benedict and King Totila

1948. Achel Abbey Fund. Inscr "ACHEL".

1232	242	65c.+65c. brown	1·20	85
1233	-	1f.35+1f.35 green	1·70	1·20
1234	-	3f.15+2f.85 blue	4·00	1·50
1235	-	10f.+10f. purple	14·00	11·50

DESIGNS—HORIZ: 1f.35, Achel Abbey. VERT: 3f.15, St. Benedict as Law-Giver; 10f. Death of St. Benedict.

243 St. Bega and Chevremont Castle

1948. Chevremont Abbey Fund. Inscr "CHEVREMONT".

1236	**243**	65c.+65c. blue	1·20	85
1237	-	1f.35+1f.35 red	1·70	1·20
1238	-	3f.15+2f.85 blue	3·50	1·50
1239	-	10f.+10f. brown	13·50	10·50

DESIGNS—HORIZ: 1f.35, Chevremont Basilica and Convent. VERT: 3f.15, Madonna of Chevremont and Chapel; 10f. Monk and Madonna of Mt. Carmel.

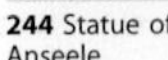

244 Statue of Anseele **245** Ghent and E. Anseele

1948. Inauguration of Edward Anseele (Socialist Leader) Statue.

1245	**244**	65c.+35c. red	3·00	1·70
1246	**245**	90c.+60c. grey	4·00	2·30
1247	-	1f.35+1f.15 brn	3·00	1·70
1248	-	3f.15+1f.85 blue	8·75	5·75
MS1249		82×145 mm. Nos. 1245/8	£250	£110

DESIGNS: 1f.35, Statue and Ed. Anseele; 3f.15, Reverse side of statue.

247 "Liberty" **248** "Resistance"

1948. Antwerp and Liege Monuments Funds.

1253	**247**	10f.+10f. green	60·00	29·00
1254	**248**	10f.+10f. brown	26·00	14·50

249 Cross of Lorraine

1948. Anti-tuberculosis Fund.

1255	**249**	20c.+5c. green	60	30
1256	**249**	1f.20+30c. purple	2·00	60
1257	**249**	1f.75+25c. red	2·30	85
1258	-	4f.+3f.25 blue	9·50	5·75
1259	-	20f.+20f. green	50·00	35·00

DESIGNS—As Type **229**: 4f. Isabel of Austria; 20f. Albert, Archduke of Austria.

250 "Madonna and Child"

1949. Social and Cultural Funds. Sheets 140×90 mm sold at 50f. each incl premium (a) Paintings by R. van der Weyden.

MS1260	90c. brown (T **250** "Madonna and Child"); 1f.75 purple ("Crucifixion"); 4f. blue ("Mary Magdalene")	£225	£200

(b) Paintings by J. Jordaens.

MS1261	90c. violet ("Woman Reading"); 1f.75 red ("Flute-player"); 4f. blue ("Old Woman and Letter")	£225	£200

1949. Surch 1-1-49 at top, 31-XII-49 and value at bottom with posthorn in between. (a) Arms type.

1262	**152**	5c. on 15c. blue	10	10
1263	**152**	5c. on 30c. brown	10	10
1264	**152**	5c. on 40c. lilac	10	10
1265	**152**	20c. on 70c. green	10	10
1266	**152**	20c. on 75c. mauve	10	10

(b) Anseele Statue.

1267	**244**	10c. on 65c.+35c. red	3·00	3·00
1268	**245**	40c. on 90c.+60c. grey	1·70	1·70
1269	-	80c. on 1f.35+1f.15 brown	85	90
1270	-	1f.20 on 3f.15+1f.85 blue	1·50	1·50

251 King Leopold I

252 Forms of Postal Transport

1949. Belgian Stamp Cent.

1271	**251**	90c. green (postage)	75	40
1272	**251**	1f.75 brown	40	30
1273	**251**	3f. red	11·00	3·50
1274	**251**	4f. blue	7·00	1·00
1275	**252**	50f. brown (air)	60·00	23·00

253 St. Madeleine from "The Baptism of Christ"

1949. Exhibition of Paintings by Gerard David, Bruges.

1276	**253**	1f.75 brown	85	30

255 Hemispheres and Allegorical Figure

1949. 75th Anniv of U.P.U.

1295	**255**	4f. blue	5·50	2·50

256 Guido Gezelle

1949. 50th Death Anniv of Gezelle (poet).

1297	**256**	1f.75+75c. green	2·00	1·50

257 Arnica

1949. Anti-tuberculosis and other Funds. (a) Flowers.

1298	**257**	20c.+5c. black, yellow and green	35	30
1299	-	65c.+10c. black, green and buff	1·40	45
1300	-	90c.+10c. black, blue and red	2·00	1·00
1301	-	1f.20+30c. mult	2·50	1·30

FLOWERS: 65c. Thistle. 90c. Periwinkle. 1f.20, Poppy.

(b) Portraits as T 229.

1302	1f.75+25c. orange	1·20	40
1303	3f.+1f.50 red	13·00	8·25
1304	4f.+2f. blue	13·50	8·25
1305	6f.+3f. brown	23·00	11·50
1306	8f.+4f. green	27·00	15·00

PORTRAITS: 1f.75, Philip the Good. 3f. Charles V. 4f. Maria Christina. 6f. Charles of Lorraine. 8f. Maria Theresa.

260 Anglo-Belgian Monument, Hertain

1950. Anglo-Belgian Union and other Funds.

1307	-	80c.+20c. green	1·50	60
1308	-	2f.50+50c. red	6·75	4·00
1309	**260**	4f.+2f. blue	10·50	7·00

DESIGNS—HORIZ: 80c. Arms of Great Britain and Belgium; 2f.50, British tanks at Tournai.

261 Allegory of Saving

1950. National Savings Bank Centenary.

1310	**261**	1f.75 sepia	60	30

262 Hurdling

1950. European Athletic Championships. Inscr "HEYSEL 1950".

1311	**262**	20c.+5c. green	60	30
1312	-	90c.+10c. purple	4·75	2·30
1313	-	1f.75+25c. red	9·25	2·50
1314	-	4f.+2f. blue	44·00	23·00
1315	-	8f.+4f. green	46·00	30·00
MS1316		70×119 mm. 1f.75+25c. (+18f.) (No. 1313)	95·00	60·00

DESIGNS—HORIZ: 1f.75, Relay racing. VERT: 90c. Javelin throwing; 4f. Pole vaulting; 8f. Sprinting.

263 Sikorsky S-51 Helicopter and Douglas DC-4 leaving Melsbroeck Airport

1950. Air. Inauguration of Helicopter Airmail Services and Aeronautical Committee's Fund.

1317	**263**	7f.+3f. blue	9·75	5·75

265 Gentian **266** Sijsele Sanatorium

1950. Anti-tuberculosis and other Funds. Cross in red.

1326	**265**	20c.+5c. blue, green and purple	35	30
1327	-	65c.+10c. green and brown	1·40	45
1328	-	90c.+10c. light green and green	1·70	1·20
1329	-	1f.20+30c. blue, green and ultramarine	2·00	1·30
1330	**266**	1f.75+25c. red	2·50	1·70
1331	-	4f.+2f. blue	23·00	1·70
1332	-	8f.+4f. green	31·00	10·50

DESIGNS—Flowers as Type **265**: 65c. Rushes; 90c. Foxglove; 1f.20, Sea lavender. Sanatoria as Type **266**: HORIZ: 4f. Jauche. VERT: 8f. Tombeek.

267 The Belgian Lion

1951. (a) 17½×20½ mm.

1334	**267**	2c. brown	10	10
1335	**267**	3c. violet	10	10
1336	**267**	5c. lilac	10	10
1336a	**267**	5c. pink	10	10
1337	**267**	10c. orange	10	10
1338	**267**	15c. mauve	10	10
1333	**267**	20c. blue	30	10
1339	**267**	20c. red	10	10
1340	**267**	25c. green	1·70	15
1341	**267**	25c. blue	10	10
1342	**267**	30c. green	10	10
1343	**267**	40c. brown	10	10
1344a	**267**	50c. blue	15	25
1345	**267**	60c. mauve	10	10
1346	**267**	65c. purple	13·50	60
1347	**267**	75c. lilac	10	10
1348	**267**	80c. green	85	35
1349	**267**	90c. blue	1·30	35
1350	**267**	1f. red	10	10
1351	**267**	1f.50 grey	10	10
1353	**267**	2f. green	25	10
1354	**267**	2f.50 brown	25	10
1355	**267**	3f. mauve	25	10
1355a	**267**	4f. purple	35	10
1355b	**267**	4f.50 blue	25	10
1355c	**267**	5f. purple	15	10

(b) 20½×24½ mm.

1356	50c. blue	25	15
1357	60c. purple	80	65
1358a	1f. red	10	10

(c) Size 17½×22 mm.

1359	50c. blue	10	10
1360	1f. pink	1·30	75
1361	2f. green	50	25

268 "Science"

1951. UNESCO Fund. Inscr "UNESCO".

1365	**268**	80c.+20c. green	1·70	60
1366	-	2f.50+50c. brown	12·00	7·00
1367	-	4f.+2f. blue	15·00	8·75

DESIGNS—HORIZ: 2f.50, "Education". VERT: 4f. "Peace".

269 Fairey Tipsy Belfair Trainer I00-TIC

1951. Air. 50th Anniv of National Aero Club.

1368		6f. blue	38·00	20·00
1369	**269**	7f. red	38·00	20·00

DESIGN: 6f. Arsenal Air 100 glider.

1951. Air.

1370	-	6f. brown (glider)	7·25	30
1371	**269**	7f. green	7·25	85

270 Monument

1951. Political Prisoners' National Monument Fund.

1372	**270**	1f.75+25c. brown	3·50	60
1373	-	4f.+2f. blue	37·00	20·00
1374	-	8f.+4f. green	38·00	23·00

DESIGNS—HORIZ: 4f. Breendonk Fort. VERT: 8f. Side view of monument.

272 Queen Elisabeth

1951. Queen Elisabeth Medical Foundation Fund.

1376	**272**	90c.+10c. grey	5·25	1·20
1377	**272**	1f.75+25c. red	11·50	2·50
1378	**272**	3f.+1f. green	38·00	17·00
1379	**272**	4f.+2f. blue	41·00	19·00
1380	**272**	8f.+4f. sepia	49·00	23·00

273 Lorraine Cross and Dragon

274 Beersel Castle

1951. Anti-tuberculosis and other Funds.

1381	**273**	20c.+5c. red	45	30
1382	**273**	65c.+10c. blue	70	35
1383	**273**	90c.+10c. brown	85	40
1384	**273**	1f.20+30c. violet	1·70	60
1385	**274**	1f.75+75c. brown	5·25	1·70
1386	-	3f.+1f. green	16·00	9·50
1387	-	4f.+2f. blue	20·00	11·50
1388	-	8f.+4f. black	30·00	16·00

CASTLES—As Type **274**: VERT: 3f. Horst Castle. 8f. Veves Castle. HORIZ: 4f. Lavaux St. Anne Castle.

For stamps as Type **273** but dated "1952" see Nos. 1416/19 and for those dated "1953" see Nos. 1507/10.

276 Consecration of the Basilica

1952. 25th Anniv of Cardinalate of Primate of Belgium and Koekelberg Basilica Fund.

1389		1f.75+25c. brown	1·70	60
1390		4f.+2f. blue	19·00	9·25
1391	**276**	8f.+4f. purple	28·00	13·50
MS1392 120×72 mm. Nos. 1389/91 (10f.)			£475	£200

DESIGNS—24×35 mm: 1f.75, Interior of Koekelberg Basilica; 4f. Exterior of Koekelberg Basilica.

277 King Baudouin

278 King Baudouin

1952

1393	**277**	1f.50 grey	1·70	25
1394	**277**	2f. red	60	25
1395	**277**	4f. blue	8·75	30
1396a	**278**	50f. purple	4·00	25
1397a	**278**	100f. red	20·00	70

279 Francis of Taxis

1952. 13th U.P.U. Congress, Brussels. Portraits of Members of the House of Thurn and Taxis.

1398	**279**	80c. green	35	30
1399	-	1f.75 orange	35	30
1400	-	2f. brown	70	45
1401	-	2f.50 red	1·40	45
1402	-	3f. olive	1·40	35
1403	-	4f. blue	1·50	30
1404	-	5f. brown	3·75	45
1405	-	5f.75 violet	5·25	1·50
1406	-	8f. black	23·00	4·00
1407	-	10f. purple	29·00	9·25
1408	-	20f. grey	£120	55·00
1409	-	40f.+10f. turquoise	£180	£150

DESIGNS—VERT: 1f.75, John Baptist; 2f. Leonard; 2f.50, Lamoral; 3f. Leonard Francis; 4f. Lamoral Claud; 5f. Eugene Alexander; 5f.75, Anselm Francis; 8f. Alexander Ferdinand; 10f. Charles Anselm; 20f. Charles Alexander; 40f. Beaulieu Chateau.

281 A. Vermeylen

1952. Culture Fund. Writers.

1410	**281**	65c.+30c. lilac	7·25	3·00
1411	-	80c.+40c. green	7·75	3·50
1412	-	90c.+45c. olive	8·25	4·00
1413	-	1f.75+75c. lake	17·00	5·75
1414	-	4f.+2f. blue	46·00	21·00
1415	-	8f.+4f. sepia	49·00	24·00

PORTRAITS: 80c. K. van de Woestijne. 90c. C. de Coster. 1f.75, M. Maeterlinck. 4f. E. Verhaeren. 8f. H. Conscience.

A 4f. blue as No. 1414 and an 8f. lake as No. 1415 each se-tenant with a label showing a laurel wreath and bearing a premium "+ 9 fr." were put on sale by subscription only.

282 Arms, Malmedy

1952. Anti-tuberculosis and other Funds. As T 273 but dated "1952" and designs as T 282.

1416	**273**	20c.+5c. brown	35	30
1417	**273**	80c.+20c. green	80	40
1418	**273**	1f.20+30c. purple	2·00	1·20
1419	**273**	1f.50+50c. olive	2·30	1·30
1420	**282**	2f.+75c. red	3·25	1·50
1421	-	3f.+1f.50 brown	27·00	16·00
1422	-	4f.+2f. blue	25·00	15·00
1423	-	8f.+4f. purple	27·00	17·00

DESIGNS—HORIZ: 3f. Ruins, Burgreuland. VERT: 4f. Dam, Eupen; 8f. Saint and lion, St. Vith.

284 Dewe and Monument at Liege

1953. Walthere Dewe Memorial Fund.

1435	**284**	2f.+1f. lake	3·25	2·00

285 Princess Josephine Charlotte

1953. Red Cross National Disaster Fund. Cross in red.

1436	**285**	80c.+20c. green	4·00	1·70
1437	**285**	1f.20+30c. brown	3·75	1·50
1438	**285**	2f.+50c. lake	3·25	1·50
1439	**285**	2f.50+50c. red	20·00	11·50
1440	**285**	4f.+1f. blue	22·00	10·50
1441	**285**	5f.+2f. black	22·00	10·50

286 Fishing Boats "Marcel", "De Meeuw" and "Jacqueline Denise"

1953. Tourist Propaganda and Cultural Funds.

1442	**286**	80c.+20c. green	2·30	1·20
1443	-	1f.20+30c. brown	7·00	3·25
1444	-	2f.+50c. sepia	8·25	3·25
1445	-	2f.50+50c. mauve	19·00	9·25
1446	-	4f.+2f. blue	30·00	15·00
1447	-	8f.+4f. green	38·00	18·00

DESIGNS—HORIZ: 1f.20, Bridge Bouillon; 2f. Antwerp. VERT: 2f.50, Namur; 4f. Ghent; 8f. Freyr Rocks and River Meuse.

289 King Baudouin

1953. (a) 21×24½ mm.

1453	**289**	1f.50 black	30	10
1454	**289**	2f. red	9·25	30
1455	**289**	2f. green	30	10
2188	**289**	2f.50 brown	25	10
1457	**289**	3f. purple	1·20	10
1458	**289**	3f.50 green	60	10
1459	**289**	4f. blue	4·00	25
2188A	**289**	4f.50 brown	80	50
1462	**289**	5f. violet	1·50	10
1463	**289**	6f. mauve	2·50	10
1464	**289**	6f.50 grey	£120	19·00
2189	**289**	7f. blue	50	25
1466	**289**	7f.50 brown	£110	21·00
1467	**289**	8f. blue	60	15
1468	**289**	8f.50 purple	26·00	60
1469	**289**	9f. olive	£120	2·30
1470	**289**	12f. turquoise	17·00	60
1471	**289**	30f. orange	14·50	35

(b) 17½×22 mm.

1472		1f.50 black	35	35
1473		2f.50 brown	7·50	6·50
1474		3f. mauve	25	10
1475		3f.50 green	35	10
1476		4f.50 brown	1·70	80

290

1953. European Child Welfare Fund.

1482	**290**	80c.+20c. green	5·75	3·50
1483	**290**	2f.50+1f. red	35·00	23·00
1484	**290**	4f.+1f.50 blue	37·00	26·00

293 Ernest Malvoz

1953. Anti-tuberculosis and other Funds. As T 273 but dated "1953" and portraits as T 293.

1507	**273**	20c.+5c. blue	70	35
1508	**273**	80c.+20c. purple	1·90	80
1509	**273**	1f.20+30c. brown	3·00	1·20
1510	**273**	1f.50+50c. slate	3·50	1·50
1511	**293**	2f.+75c. green	4·25	2·00
1512	-	3f.+1f.50 red	20·00	10·50
1513	-	4f.+2f. blue	23·00	13·00
1514	-	8f.+4f. brown	29·00	16·00

PORTRAITS—VERT: 3f. Carlo Forlanini. 4f. Albert Calmette. HORIZ: 8f. Robert Koch.

1954. Surch 20c and I-I-54 at top, 31-XII-54 at bottom and bars in between.

1515	**267**	20c. on 65c. purple	1·70	15
1516	**267**	20c. on 90c. blue	1·70	15

See note below No. 480.

296 King Albert Statue

1954. King Albert Memorial Fund.

1520	**296**	2f.+50c. brown	11·50	4·75
1521	-	4f.+2f. blue	38·00	17·00
1522	-	9f.+4f.50 black	31·00	17·00

DESIGNS—HORIZ: 4f. King Albert Memorial. VERT: 9f. Marche-les-Dames Rocks and medallion portrait.

298 Monument

299 Breendonk Camp and Fort

1954. Political Prisoners' National Monument Fund.

1531	**298**	2f.+1f. red	27·00	24·00
1532	**299**	4f.+2f. brown	55·00	26·00
1533	-	9f.+4f.50 green	65·00	32·00

DESIGN—VERT: 9f. As Type **298** but viewed from different angle.

300 Entrance to Beguinal House

1954. Beguinage of Bruges Restoration Fund.

1534	**300**	80c.+20c. green	1·20	60
1535	-	2f.+1f. red	16·00	8·25
1536	-	4f.+2f. violet	21·00	11·50
1537	-	7f.+3f.50 purple	44·00	24·00
1538	-	8f.+4f. brown	44·00	24·00
1539	-	9f.+4f.50 blue	80·00	38·00

DESIGNS—HORIZ: 2f. River scene. VERT: 4f. Convent Buildings; 7f. Cloisters; 8f. Doorway; 9f. Statue of our Lady of the Vineyard (larger, 35×53 mm).

302 Map of Europe and Rotary Symbol

1954. 50th Anniv of Rotary International and 5th Regional Conference, Ostend.

1540	**302**	20c. red	25	25
1541	-	80c. green	35	25
1542	-	4f. blue	1·70	35

DESIGNS: 80c. Mermaid, "Mercury" and Rotary symbol; 4f. Rotary symbol and hemispheres.

303 Child

304 "The Blind Man and the Paralytic" (after Anto-Carte)

1954. Anti-T.B. and other Funds.

1543	**303**	20c.+5c. green	30	30
1544	**303**	80c.+20c. black	85	35
1545	**303**	1f.20+30c. brown	2·30	1·40
1546	**303**	1f.50+50c. violet	4·75	2·50
1547	**304**	2f.+75c. red	9·25	4·75
1548	**304**	4f.+1f. blue	35·00	15·00

305 Begonia and the Rabot

1955. Ghent Flower Show.

1549	**305**	80c. red	60	60
1550	-	2f.50 sepia	10·50	3·00
1551	-	4f. lake	6·00	80

DESIGNS—VERT: 2f.50, Azaleas and Chateau des Comtes; 4f. Orchid and the "Three Towers".

306 "Homage to Charles V" (A. De Vriendt) **307** "Charles V" (Titian)

1955. Emperor Charles V Exhibition, Ghent.

1552	**306**	20c. red	25	25
1553	**307**	2f. green	95	25
1554	-	4f. blue	5·25	1·50

DESIGN—As Type **306**: 4f. "Abdication of Charles V" (L. Gallait).

308 Emile Verhaeren (after C. Montald)

1955. Birth Centenary of Verhaeren (poet).

1555	**308**	20c. black	25	25

309 "Textile Industry"

1955. 2nd Int Textile Exhibition, Brussels.

1556	**309**	2f. purple	1·30	30

310 "The Foolish Virgin" (R. Wouters)

1955. 3rd Biennial Sculpture Exn, Antwerp.

1557	**310**	1f.20 green	1·20	40
1558	**310**	2f. violet	2·00	30

311 "The Departure of the Liege Volunteers in 1830" (Soubre)

1955. Liege Exn. 125th Anniv of 1830 Revolution.

1559	**311**	20c. green	30	30
1560	**311**	2f. brown	85	30

312 Ernest Solvay

1955. Cultural Fund. Scientists.

1561	**312**	20c.+5c. brown	35	35
1562	-	80c.+20c. violet	1·40	50
1563	-	1f.20+30c. blue	7·50	4·00
1564	-	2f.+50c. red	7·00	3·75
1565	-	3f.+1f. green	16·00	9·75
1566	-	4f.+2f. brown	16·00	9·75

PORTRAITS—VERT: 80c. Jean-Jacques Dony. 2f. Leo H. Baekeland. 3f. Jean-Etienne Lenoir. HORIZ: 1f.20, Egide Walschaerts. 4f. Emile Fourcault and Emile Gobbe.

313 "The Joys of Spring" (E. Canneel) **314** E. Holboll (Danish postal official)

1955. Anti-T.B. and other Funds.

1567	**313**	20c.+5c. mauve	35	35
1568	**313**	80c.+20c. green	70	45
1569	**313**	1f.20+30c. brown	3·25	1·20
1570	**313**	1f.50+50c. violet	3·75	1·50
1571	**314**	2f.+50c. red	12·00	5·75
1572	-	4f.+2f. blue	30·00	14·50
1573	-	8f.+4f. sepia	31·00	18·00

PORTRAITS—As Type **314**: 4f. J. D. Rockefeller (philanthropist). 8f. Sir R. W. Philip (physician).

315 Blood Donors Emblem

1956. Blood Donors.

1574	**315**	2f. red	35	30

316 Mozart when a Child

317 Queen Elisabeth and Mozart Sonata

1956. Birth Bicentenary of Mozart. Inscr as in T 316.

1575	-	80c.+20c. green	60	30
1576	**316**	2f.+1f. purple	4·75	3·00
1577	**317**	4f.+2f. lilac	10·50	5·50

DESIGN—As Type **316**: 80c. Palace of Charles de Lorraine, Brussels.

318

1956. "Scaldis" Exhibitions in Tournai, Ghent and Antwerp.

1578	**318**	2f. blue	30	30

319 Queen Elisabeth Medallion (Courtens)

1956. 80th Birthday of Queen Elisabeth and Foundation Fund.

1579	**319**	80c.+20c. green	60	40
1580	**319**	2f.+1f. lake	4·75	2·40
1581	**319**	4f.+2f. sepia	6·50	3·75

320

1956. Europa.

1582	**320**	2f. green	3·50	25
1583	**320**	4f. violet	13·00	35

321 Electric Train Type 122 and Railway Bridge

1956. Electrification of Brussels–Luxembourg Railway Line.

1584	**321**	2f. blue	30	25

322 E. Anseele

1956. Birth Centenary of Anseele (statesman).

1588	**322**	20c. purple	25	25

323 Medieval Ship **324** Weighing a Baby

1956. Anti-tuberculosis and other Funds.

1589	**323**	20c.+5c. brown	30	30
1590	**323**	80c.+20c. green	60	40
1591	**323**	1f.20+30c. purple	1·20	70
1592	**323**	1f.50+50c. slate	1·50	95
1593	**324**	2f.+50c. green	3·75	2·30
1594	-	4f.+2f. purple	15·00	9·25
1595	-	8f.+4f. red	17·00	11·50

DESIGNS—As Type **324**: HORIZ: 4f. X-ray examination. VERT: 8f. Convalescence and rehabilitation.

325 "Atomium" and Exhibition Emblem

1957. Brussels International Exhibition.

1596	**325**	2f. red	30	30
1597	**325**	2f.50 green	35	30
1598	**325**	4f. violet	70	25
1599	**325**	5f. purple	1·60	70

327 Emperor Maximilian I, with Messenger

1957. Stamp Day.

1603	**327**	2f. red	40	30

328 Charles Plisnier and Albrecht Rodenbach (writers)

1957. Cultural Fund. Belgian Celebrities.

1604	**328**	20c.+5c. violet	30	30
1605	-	80c.+20c. brown	40	30
1606	-	1f.20+30c. sepia	95	70
1607	-	2f.+50c. red	2·40	1·60
1608	-	3f.+1f. green	3·50	2·30
1609	-	4f.+2f. blue	4·00	3·00

DESIGNS: 80c. Professors Emiel Vliebergh and Maurice Wilmotte; 1f.20, Paul Pastur and Julius Hoste; 2f. Lodewijk de Raet and Jules Destree (politicians); 3f. Constantin Meunier and Constant Permeke (artists); 4f. Lieven Gevaert and Edouard Empain (industrialists).

329 Sikorsky S-58 Helicopter

1957. Conveyance of 100,000th Passenger by Belgian Helicopter Service.

1610	**329**	4f. blue, green and grey	95	45

330 Steamer entering Zeebrugge Harbour

1957. 50th Anniv of Completion of Zeebrugge Harbour.

1611	**330**	2f. blue	40	30

331 King Leopold I entering Brussels (after Simonau)

1957. 126th Anniv of Arrival of King Leopold I in Belgium.

1612	**331**	20c. green	30	30
1613	-	2f. mauve	70	30

DESIGN—HORIZ: 2f. King Leopold I at frontier (after Wappers).

332 Scout and Guide Badges

1957. 50th Anniv of Boy Scout Movement and Birth Centenary of Lord Baden-Powell.

1614	**332**	80c. brown	30	30
1615	-	4f. green	1·50	50

DESIGN—VERT: 4f. Lord Baden-Powell.

333 "Kneeling Woman" (after Lehmbruck)

1957. 4th Biennial Sculpture Exn, Antwerp.

1616	**333**	2f.50 green	1·20	60

334 "Agriculture and Industry"

1957. Europa.

1617	**334**	2f. purple	1·20	30
1618	**334**	4f. blue	3·75	45

335 Sledge-dog Team

1957. Belgian Antarctic Expedition, 1957–58.

1619	**335**	5f.+2f.50 orange, brown and grey	4·00	3·00
MS1620 115×83 mm. Block of four of No. 1619 in new colours, brown, red and blue			£200	£160

336 General Patton's Grave at Hamm

1957. General Patton Memorial Issue.

1621	**336**	1f.+50c. black	2·30	1·20
1622	-	2f.50+50c. green	3·50	1·70
1623	-	3f.+1f. brown	4·75	2·30
1624	-	5f.+2f.50 slate	10·50	6·50
1625	-	6f.+3f. red	14·00	9·25

DESIGNS—HORIZ: 2f.50, Patton Memorial project at Bastogne; 3f. Gen. Patton decorating Brig.-General A. MacAuliffe; 6f. (51×35½ mm) Tanks in action. VERT: 5f. General Patton.

337 Adolphe Max

1957. 18th Death Anniv of Burgomaster Adolphe Max (patriot).

1626	**337**	2f.50+1f. blue	1·50	65

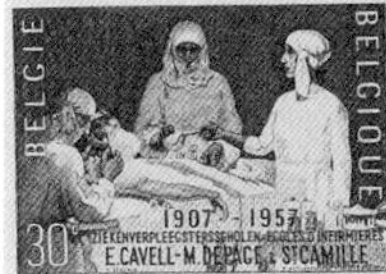

338 Queen Elisabeth with Doctors Depage and Debaisieux at a surgical operation

1957. 50th Anniv of "Edith Cavell-Marie Depage" and "St. Camille" Nursing Schools.

1627	**338**	30c. red	30	30

339 "Carnival Kings of Fosses" (Namur)

340 "Infanta Isabella with Crossbow" (Brussels)

1957. Anti-tuberculosis and other Funds. Provincial Legends.

1628	**339**	30c.+20c. pur & yell	30	30
1629	-	1f.+50c. sepia & blue	35	35
1630	-	1f.50+50c. grey & red	70	40
1631	-	2f.+1f. black & green	1·00	45
1632	**340**	2f.50+1f. grn & mve	2·30	1·70
1633	-	5f.+2f. black & blue	4·75	3·75
1634	-	6f.+2f.50 lake & red	5·75	4·75

DESIGNS: As Type **339**—HORIZ: 1f.50, "St. Remacle and the Wolf" (Liege). VERT: 1f. "Op Signoorken" (Antwerp); 2f. "The Long Man and the Pea Soup" (Limburg). As Type **340**—HORIZ: 6f. "Carnival Kings of Binche" (Hainaut). VERT: 5f. "The Virgin with the Inkwell" (West Flanders).

341 Posthorn and Postilion's Badges

1958. Postal Museum Day.

1635	**341**	2f.50 grey	30	30

342 Benelux Gate

1958. Inauguration of Brussels International Exhibition. Inscr as in T 342.

1636	**342**	30c.+20c. sepia, brown and violet	30	30
1637	-	1f.+50c. purple, slate and green	30	30
1638	-	1f.50+50c. violet, turquoise and green	35	30
1639	-	2f.50+1f. red, blue and vermilion	35	30
1640	-	3f.+1f.50 blue, black and red	85	60
1641	-	5f.+3f. mauve, black and blue	1·90	1·50

DESIGNS—HORIZ: 1f. Civil Engineering Pavilion; 1f.50, Belgian Congo and Ruanda-Urundi Pavilion; 2f.50, "Belgium, 1900"; 3f. Atomium; 5f. (49×33½ mm) Telexpo Pavilion.

343 "Food and Agriculture Organization"

1958. United Nations Commemoration.

1642		50c. grey (postage)	3·00	2·75
1643	**343**	1f. red	35	35
1644	-	1f.50 blue	40	35
1645	-	2f. purple	60	50
1646	-	2f.50 green	40	35
1647	-	3f. turquoise	65	60
1648	-	5f. mauve	40	35
1649	-	8f. brown	75	60
1650	-	11f. lilac	1·60	1·50
1651	-	20f. red	3·25	2·75
1652	-	5f. blue (air)	30	30
1653	-	6f. green	35	30
1654	-	7f.50 violet	45	35
1655	-	8f. sepia	50	40
1656	-	9f. red	60	45
1657	-	10f. brown	70	50

DESIGNS (Emblems and symbols)—HORIZ: 50c. I.L.O. 2f.50, UNESCO 3f. U.N. Pavilion, Brussels Int Exn; 6f. World Meteorological Organization; 8f. (No. 1649), Int Monetary Fund; 8f. (No. 1655), General Agreement on Tariffs and Trade; 10f. Atomic Energy Agency; 11f. W.H.O. 20f. U.P.U. VERT: 1f.50, U.N.O. 2f. World Bank; 5f. (No. 1648), I.T.U. 5f. (No. 1652), I.C.A.O. 7f.50, Protection of Refugees; 9f. UNICEF.

344 Eugene Ysaye

1958. Birth Centenary of Ysaye (violinist).

1658	**344**	30c. blue and red	30	25

345 "Europa"

1958. Europa.

1659	**345**	2f.50 blue and red	3·50	25
1660	**345**	5f. red and blue	7·75	35

346 "Marguerite Van Eyck" (after Jan Van Eyck)

1958. Cultural Relief Funds. Paintings as T 346. Frames in brown and yellow.

1661	**346**	30c.+20c. myrtle	60	30
1662	-	1f.+50c. lake	85	60
1663	-	1f.+50+50c. blue	1·50	85
1664	-	2f.50+1f. sepia	3·00	2·00
1665	-	3f.+1f.50 red	4·00	2·50
1666	-	5f.+3f. blue	6·50	5·25

PAINTINGS—HORIZ: 1f. "Carrying the Cross" (Hieronymus Bosch). 3f. "The Rower" (James Ensor). VERT: 1f.50, "St. Donatien" (Jan Gossaert). 2f.50, Self-portrait (Lambert Lombard). 5f. "Henriette with the Large Hat" (Henri Evenepoel).

347 "Hoogstraten"

348 Pax—"Creche vivante"

1958. Anti-tuberculosis and other Funds. Provincial Legends.

1667	**347**	40c.+10c. blue & grn	30	30
1668	-	1f.+50c. sepia & yell	35	35
1669	-	1f.50+50c. pur & grn	65	35
1670	-	2f.+1f. brown & red	70	45
1671	**348**	2f.50+1f. red and green	2·10	1·20
1672	-	5f.+2f. purple & blue	4·75	3·25
1673	-	6f.+2f. blue & red	5·75	4·75

DESIGNS: As Type **347**—VERT: 1f. "Jean de Nivelles"; 1f.50, "Jeu de Saint Evermare a Russon". HORIZ: 2f. "Les penitents de Furnes". As Type **348**—HORIZ: "Marches de l'Entre Sambre et Meuse". VERT: 6f. "Pax—Vierge".

349 "Human Rights"

1958. 10th Anniv of Human Rights Declaration.

1674	**349**	2f.50 slate	40	25

350 "Europe of the Heart"

1959. "Heart of Europe". Fund for Displaced Persons.

1675	**350**	1f.+50c. purple	45	35
1676	**350**	2f.50+1f. green	1·00	80
1677	**350**	5f.+2f.50 brown	1·70	1·20

351 J. B. de Taxis taking the oath at the hands of Charles V (after J.-E. Van den Bussche)

1959. Stamp Day.

1680	**351**	2f.50 green	50	30

352 N.A.T.O. Emblem

1959. 10th Anniv of N.A.T.O.

1681	**352**	2f.50 blue and red	45	30
1682	**352**	5f. blue and green	1·30	60

On the 5f. value the French and Flemish inscriptions are transposed.

For similar design but inscr "1969", see No. 2112.

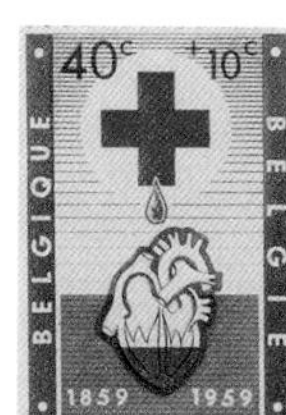

353 "Blood Transfusion"

354 J. H. Dunant and battle scene at Solferino, 1859

1959. Red Cross Commem. Inscr "1859 1959".

1683	**353**	40c.+10c. red & grey	35	35
1684	**353**	1f.+50c. red & sepia	1·30	50
1685	**353**	1f.50+50c. red and lilac	3·75	2·00
1686	-	2f.50+1f. red & grn	4·25	2·30
1687	-	3f.+1f.50 red and blue	7·75	4·75
1688	**354**	5f.+3f. red and sepia	14·50	7·00

DESIGN—As Type **353**—HORIZ: 2f.50, 3f. Red Cross and broken sword ("Aid for the wounded").

355 Philip the Good

356 Arms of Philip the Good

1959. Royal Library of Belgium Fund. Mult.

1689	40c.+10c. Type **355**	30	30
1690	1f.+50c. Charles the Bold	45	45
1691	1f.50+50c. Maximillian of Austria	1·60	1·00
1692	2f.50+1f. Philip the Fair	2·75	2·30
1693	3f.+1f.50 Charles V	5·00	3·50
1694	5f.+3f. Type **356**	6·75	5·00

358 Town Hall, Oudenarde

1959. Oudenarde Town Hall Commem.

1699	**358**	2f.50 purple	40	30

359 Pope Adrian VI

1959. 500th Birth Anniv of Pope Adrian VI.

1700	**359**	2f.50 red	30	30
1701	**359**	5f. blue	40	30

360 "Europa"

1959. Europa.

1702	**360**	2f.50 red	85	30
1703	**360**	5f. turquoise	1·50	40

361 Boeing 707

1959. Inauguration of Boeing 707 Airliners by SABENA.

1704	**361**	6f. blue, grey and red	2·10	75

362 Antwerp fish (float)

363 Stavelot "Blancs Moussis" (carnival figures)

1959. Anti-tuberculosis and other Funds. Carnival scenes.

1705	**362**	40c.+10c. green, red and bistre	30	30
1706	-	1f.+50c. green, violet and olive	40	30
1707	-	2f.+50c. yellow, purple and brown	50	35
1708	**363**	2f.50+1f. blue, violet and grey	85	35
1709	-	3f.+1f. purple, yellow and grey	2·30	1·20
1710	-	6f.+2f. blue, red and olive	5·00	4·50
1711	-	7f.+3f. blk, yell, & bl	6·50	5·25

DESIGNS—As Type **362**—HORIZ: 1f. Mons dragon (float); 2f. Eupen and Malmedy clowns in chariot. As Type **363**—VERT: 3f. Ypres jester. HORIZ: 6f. Holy Family; 7f. Madonna and child.

364 Countess Alexandrine of Taxis (tapestry)

1960. Stamp Day.

1712	**364**	3f. blue	70	30

365 Indian Azalea

1960. Ghent Flower Show. Inscr as in T 365.

1713	**365**	40c. red and purple	30	30
1714	-	3f. yellow, red and green	70	30
1715	-	6f. red, green and blue	1·70	60

FLOWERS: 3f. Begonia. 6f. Anthurium and bromelia.

366 Refugee

1960. World Refugee Year. Inscr as in T 366.

1716		40c.+10c. purple	30	30
1717	**366**	3f.+1f.50 sepia	65	30
1718	-	6f.+3f. blue	1·40	1·20

MS1719 121×93 mm. Nos. 1716/18 in new colours, violet, brown and red respectively £100 85·00

DESIGNS: 40c. Child refugee; 6f. Woman refugee.

367 "Labour" (after Meunier)

1960. 75th Anniv of Belgian Socialist Party. Inscr as in T 367.

1720	**367**	40c. purple and red	30	30
1721	-	3f. brown and red	60	30

DESIGN—HORIZ: 3f. "Workers" (after Meunier).

369 Parachutist on ground

1960. Parachuting. Designs bearing emblem of National Parachuting Club.

1726		40c.+10c. black & blue	35	30
1727		1f.+50c. black & blue	1·90	85
1728		2f.+50c. black, blue and green	4·00	2·30
1729		2f.50+1f. black, turquoise and green	7·00	3·75
1730	**369**	3f.+1f. black, blue and green	7·00	3·75
1731	**369**	6f.+2f. black, blue and green	7·75	4·75

DESIGNS—HORIZ: 40c., 1f., Parachutists dropping from Douglas DC-4 aircraft. VERT: 2f., 2f.50, Parachutists descending.

370 Ship's Officer and Helmsman

1960. Congo Independence.

1732	**370**	10c. red	30	30
1733	-	40c. red	30	30
1734	-	1f. purple	70	25
1735	-	2f. green	70	30
1736	-	2f.50 blue	1·30	30
1737	-	3f. blue	1·30	35
1738	-	6f. violet	3·25	80
1739	-	8f. brown	10·50	6·75

DESIGNS—As Type **370**: 40c. Doctor and nurses with patient; 1f. Tree-planting; 2f. Sculptors; 2f.50, Sport (putting the shot); 3f. Broadcasting from studio. (52×35½ mm): 6f. Children with doll; 8f. Child with globe.

371 Refugee Airlift

1960. Congo Refugees Relief Fund.

1740	**371**	40c.+10c. turquoise	30	30
1741	-	3f.+1f.50 red	3·00	1·70
1742	-	6f.+3f. violet	6·00	4·25

DESIGNS—As Type **371**: 3f. Mother and child. 35×51½ mm: 6f. Boeing 707 airplane spanning map of aircraft route.

1960. Surch.

1743	**267**	15c. on 30c. green	10	10
1744	**267**	15c. on 50c. blue	10	10
1745	**267**	20c. on 30c. green	10	10

373 Conference Emblem

1960. 1st Anniv of E.P.T. Conference.

1746	**373**	3f. lake	1·00	35
1747	**373**	6f. green	1·60	60

374 Young Stamp Collectors

1960. "Philately for the Young" Propaganda.

1748	**374**	40c. black and bistre	30	30

375 Pouring Milk for Child

1960. United Nations Children's Fund.

1749	**375**	40c.+10c. yellow, green and brown	30	30
1750	-	1f.+50c. red, blue and drab	85	60
1751	-	2f.+50c. bistre, green and violet	2·30	1·70
1752	-	2f.50+1f. sepia, blue and red	2·50	1·70
1753	-	3f.+1f. violet, orange and turquoise	3·25	2·00
1754	-	6f.+2f. brown, green and blue	5·25	3·00

DESIGNS: 1f. Nurse embracing children; 2f. Child carrying clothes, and ambulance; 2f.50, Nurse weighing baby; 3f. Children with linked arms; 6f. Refugee worker and child.

376 Frere Orban (founder)

1960. Centenary of Credit Communal (Co-operative Bank).

1755	**376**	10c. brown and yellow	30	30
1756	**376**	40c. brown and green	35	30
1757	**376**	1f.50 brown and violet	1·00	75
1758	**376**	3f. brown and red	1·00	30

377 Tapestry

1960. Anti-T.B. and other Funds. Arts and Crafts.

1759	**377**	40c.+10c. ochre, brown and blue	30	30
1760	-	1f.+50c. blue, brown and indigo	95	85
1761	-	2f.+50c. green, black and brown	1·70	1·20
1762	-	2f.50+1f. yellow and brown	3·75	2·50
1763	-	3f.+1f. black, brown and blue	4·25	3·00
1764	-	6f.+2f. lemon and black	6·25	3·75

DESIGNS—VERT: 1f. Crystalware; 2f. Lace. HORIZ: 2f.50, Brassware; 3f. Diamond-cutting; 6f. Ceramics.

378 King Baudouin and Queen Fabiola

1960. Royal Wedding.

1765	**378**	40c. sepia and green	35	30
1766	**378**	3f. sepia and purple	1·00	30
1767	**378**	6f. sepia and blue	2·75	35

1961. Surch in figs and 1961 at top, 1962 at bottom and bars in between.

1768	**267**	15c. on 30c. green	1·20	25
1769	**267**	20c. on 30c. green	2·40	1·20

See note below No. 480.

379 Nicolaus Rockox (after Van Dyck)

1961. 400th Birth Anniv of Nicolaus Rockox (Burgomaster of Antwerp).

1770	**379**	3f. black, bistre & brn	45	30

380 Seal of Jan Bode

1961. Stamp Day.

1771	**380**	3f. sepia and brown	45	30

381 K. Kats (playwright) and Father N. Pietkin (poet)

1961. Cultural Funds. Portrait in purple.

1772	40c.+10c. lake and pink	60	35
1773	1f.+50c. lake and brown	2·50	1·40
1774	2f.+50c. red and yellow	4·50	3·50
1775	2f.50+1f. myrtle and sage	4·75	3·50
1776	3f.+1f. blue and light blue	5·00	3·50
1777	6f.+2f. blue and lavender	7·00	4·75

PORTRAITS: 40c. Type **381**. 1f. A. Mockel and J. F. Willems (writers). 2f. J. van Rijswijck and X. Neujean (politicians). 2f.50, J. Demarteau (journalist) and A. van de Perre (politician). 3f. J. David (litterateur) and A. du Bois (writer). 6f. H. Vieuxtemps (violinist) and W. de Mol (composer).

382 White Rhinoceros

1961. Philanthropic Funds. Animals of Antwerp Zoo.

1778	40c.+10c. dp brown & brn	35	35
1779	1f.+50c. brown and green	1·30	80
1780	2f.+50c. sepia, red and black	2·00	1·60
1781	2f.50+1f. brown and red	2·20	1·70
1782	3f.+1f. brown and orange	2·50	1·90
1783	6f.+2f. ochre and blue	3·25	2·30

ANIMALS—VERT: 40c. Type **382**; 1f. Wild horse and foal; 2f. Okapi. HORIZ: 2f.50, Giraffe; 3f. Lesser panda; 6f. Elk.

383 Cardinal A.P. de Granville (first Archbishop)

1961. 400th Anniv of Archbishopric of Malines.

1784	**383**	40c.+10c. brown, red and purple	35	35
1785	-	3f.+1f.50 mult	95	80
1786	-	6f.+3f. bistre, violet and purple	1·60	1·50

DESIGNS: 3f. Cardinal's Arms; 6f. Symbols of Archbishopric and Malines.

385 "Interparliamentary Union"

1961. 50th Interparliamentary Union Conference, Brussels.

1791	**385**	3f. brown and turquoise	70	30
1792	**385**	6f. purple and red	1·00	60

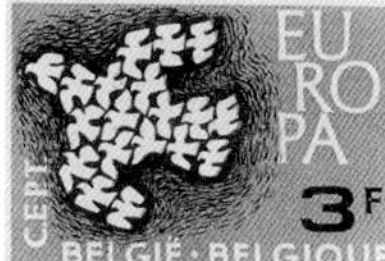

386 Doves

1961. Europa.

1793	**386**	3f. black and olive	45	30
1794	**386**	6f. black and brown	95	45

387 Reactor BR 2, Mol

1961. Euratom Commemoration.

1795	**387**	40c. green	30	30
1796	-	3f. mauve	35	30
1797	-	6f. blue	50	45

DESIGNS—VERT: 3f. Heart of reactor BR 3, Mol. HORIZ: 6f. View of reactor BR 3, Mol.

388 "The Mother and Child" (after Paulus)

1961. Anti-T.B. and other Funds. Belgian paintings of mothers and children. Frames in gold.

1798	**388**	40c.+10c. sepia	30	30
1799	-	1f.+50c. blue	75	70
1800	-	2f.+50c. red	1·30	1·30
1801	-	2f.50+1f. lake	1·40	1·30
1802	-	3f.+1f. violet	1·30	1·20
1803	-	6f.+2f. myrtle	1·90	1·60

PAINTINGS: 1f. "Maternal Love" (Navez). 2f. "Maternity" (Permeke). 2f.50, "The Virgin and the Child" (Van der Weyden). 3f. "The Virgin with the Apple" (Memling), 6f. "The Myosotis Virgin" (Rubens).

389 Horta Museum

1962. Birth Cent of Victor Horta (architect).

1804	**389**	3f. brown	40	30

390 Male Castle

1962. Cultural and Patriotic Funds. Buildings.

1805	**390**	40c.+10c. green	30	30
1806	-	90c.+10c. mauve	35	35
1807	-	1f.+50c. lilac	50	50
1808	-	2f.+50c. violet	1·00	1·00
1809	-	2f.50+1f. brown	1·40	1·40
1810	-	3f.+1f. turquoise	1·50	1·50
1811	-	6f.+2f. red	2·40	2·40

BUILDINGS—HORIZ: 90c. Royal Library, Brussels. 1f. Collegiate Church, Soignies. 6f. Ypres Halls. VERT: 1f. Notre-Dame Basilica, Tongres. 2f.50, Notre-Dame Church, Hanswijk, Malines. 3f. St. Denis-en-Broqueroie Abbey.

391 16th-Century Postilion

1962. Stamp Day.

1812	**391**	3f. brown and green	40	30

See also No. 1997.

392 G. Mercator (after F. Hogenberg)

1962. 450th Birth Anniv of Mercator (geographer).

1813	**392**	3f. sepia	40	30

393 Brother A. M. Gochet (scholar)

1962. Gochet and Triest Commemoration.

1814	**393**	2f. blue	30	30
1815	-	3f. brown	35	30

PORTRAIT: 3f. Canon P.-J. Triest (benefactor of the aged).

394 Guianan Cock of the Rock ("Coq de Roch, Rotshann")

1962. Philanthropic Funds. Birds of Antwerp Zoo. Birds, etc., in natural colours; colours of name panel and inscription given.

1816	**394**	40c.+10c. blue	35	35
1817	-	1f.+50c. blue and red	60	60
1818	-	2f.+50c. mauve & blk	1·00	95
1819	-	2f.50+1f. turq & red	1·30	1·30
1820	-	3f.+1f. brown & grn	1·70	1·60
1821	-	6f.+2f. blue and red	2·00	1·90

BIRDS: 1f. Red lory ("Rode Lori, Lori Rouge"); 2f. Green turaco ("Touracou du Senegal, Senegal Toerakoe"); 2f.50, Keel-billed toucan ("Kortbek Toecan, Toucan a Bec Court"); 3f. Greater bird of paradise ("Grand Paradijsier, Grosse Paradisvogel"); 6f. Congo peafowl ("Kongo Pauw, Paon du Congo").

395 Europa "Tree"

1962. Europa.

1822	**395**	3f. black, yellow & red	75	30
1823	**395**	6f. black, yellow & olive	1·30	45

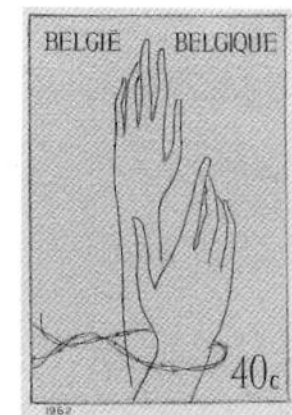

396 "Captive Hands" (after sculpture by Ianchelivici)

1962. Concentration Camp Victims.

1824	**396**	40c. blue and black	30	30

397 Reading Braille

1962. Handicapped Children Relief Funds.

1825	**397**	40c.+10c. brown	35	30
1826	-	1f.+50c. red	60	60
1827	-	2f.+50c. mauve	1·30	1·20
1828	-	2f.50+1f. green	1·30	1·20
1829	-	3f.+1f. blue	1·30	1·20
1830	-	6f.+2f. sepia	1·60	1·50

DESIGNS—VERT: 1f. Girl solving puzzle; 2f.50, Crippled child with ball; 3f. Girl walking with crutches. HORIZ: 2f. Child with earphones; 6f. Crippled boys with football.

398 "Adam" (after Michelangelo)

1962. "The Rights of Man".

1831	**398**	3f. sepia and green	35	30
1832	**398**	6f. sepia and brown	60	40

399 Queen Louise-Marie

1962. Anti-tuberculosis and other Funds. Belgian Queens in green and gold.

1833	40c.+10c. Type **399**	30	30
1834	40c.+10c. As T **399** but inscr "ML"	30	30
1835	1f.+50c. Marie-Henriette	75	65
1836	2f.+1f. Elisabeth	1·50	1·40
1837	3f.+1f.50 Astrid	2·10	1·90
1838	8f.+2f.50 Fabiola	2·30	2·00

400 Menin Gate, Ypres

1962. Ypres Millenary.

1839	**400**	1f.+50c. multicoloured	45	45
MS1840		113×137 mm. Block of eight	7·00	7·00

401 H. Pirenne

1963. Birth Cent of Henri Pirenne (historian).

1841	**401**	3f. blue	40	30

402 "Peace Bell"

1963. Cultural Funds and Installation of "Peace Bell" in Koekelberg Basilica. Bell in yellow; "PAX" in black.

1842	**402**	3f.+1f.50 green & bl	1·90	1·90
1843	**402**	6f.+3f. chestnut & brn	1·00	1·00
MS1844		82×116 mm. No. 1842 (block of four)	9·25	9·25

403 "The Sower" (after Brueghel)

1963. Freedom from Hunger.

1845	**403**	2f.+1f. brown, black and green	35	35
1846	-	3f.+1f. brown, black and purple	40	40
1847	-	6f.+2f. yellow, black and brown	70	70

PAINTINGS—HORIZ: 3f. "The Harvest" (Brueghel). VERT: 6f. "The Loaf" (Anto Carte).

404 17th-century Duel

1963. 350th Anniv of Royal Guild and Knights of St. Michael.

1848	**404**	1f. red and blue	30	30
1849	-	3f. violet and green	35	30
1850	-	6f. multicoloured	80	45

DESIGNS—HORIZ: 3f. Modern fencing. VERT: 6f. Arms of the Guild.

405 19th-century Mail-coach

1963. Stamp Day.

1851	**405**	3f. black and ochre	35	30

See also No. 1998.

406 Hotel des Postes, Paris, and Belgian 1c. Stamp of 1863

1963. Centenary of Paris Postal Conference.

1852	**406**	6f. sepia, mauve & grn	70	40

407 Child in Wheatfield

1963. "8th May" Peace Movement.

1853	**407**	3f. multicoloured	40	30
1854	**407**	6f. multicoloured	1·00	40

408 "Transport"

1963. European Transport Ministers' Conference, Brussels.

1855	**408**	6f. black and blue	70	40

409 Town Seal

1963. Int Union of Towns Congress, Brussels.

1856	**409**	6f. multicoloured	70	40

410 Racing Cyclists

1963. Belgian Cycling Team's Participation in Olympic Games, Tokyo (1964).

1857	**410**	1f.+50c. multicoloured	30	30
1858	-	2f.+1f. multicoloured	35	35
1859	-	3f.+1f.50 mult	40	40
1860	-	6f.+3f. multicoloured	70	70

DESIGNS—HORIZ: 2f. Group of cyclists; 3f. Cyclists rounding bend. VERT: 6f. Cyclists being paced by motorcyclists.

411 Sud Aviation SE 210 Caravelle

1963. 40th Anniv of SABENA Airline.

1861	**411**	3f. black and turquoise	40	30

412 "Co-operation"

1963. Europa.

1862	**412**	3f. black, brown & red	1·30	30
1863	**412**	6f. black, brown & blue	2·40	45

No. 1863 is inscr with "6 F" on the left, "BELGIE" at foot and "BELGIQUE" on right.

413 Princess Paola with Princess Astrid

1963. Centenary of Red Cross and Belgian Red Cross Fund. Cross in red.

1864	-	40c.+10c. red & yell	25	25
1865	**413**	1f.+50c. grey & yellow	30	30
1866	-	2f.+50c. mauve & yell	40	40
1867	-	2f.50+1f. blue & yell	50	50
1868	-	3f.+1f. brown & yell	80	80
1869	-	3f.+1f. bronze & yell	2·50	2·50
1870	-	6f.+2f. green & yellow	2·10	2·10

DESIGNS—As T **413**: 40c. Prince Philippe; 2f. Princess Astrid; 2f.50, Princess Paola; 6f. Prince Albert; 46×35 mm: 3f. (2), Prince Albert and family.

414 J. Destree (writer)

1963. Jules Destree and H. Van de Velde Commems.

1871	**414**	1f. purple	25	25
1872	-	1f. green	25	25

DESIGN: No. 1872, H. Van de Velde (architect).

415 Bas-reliefs from Facade of Postal Cheques Office (after O. Jespars)

1963. 50th Anniv of Belgian Postal Cheques Office.

1873	**415**	50c. black, blue & red	25	25

416 Balthasar Gerbier's Daughter

1963. T.B. Relief and Other Funds. Rubens's Drawings. Background buff; inscr in black: designs colour given.

1874	**416**	50c.+10c. blue	30	30
1875	-	1f.+40c. red	35	35
1876	-	2f.+50c. violet	40	40
1877	-	2f.50+1f. green	80	80
1878	-	3f.+1f. brown	70	70
1879	-	6f.+2f. black	1·20	1·20

DRAWINGS—VERT: Rubens's children—1f. Nicolas (aged 2). 2f. Franz (aged 4). 2f.50, Nicolas (aged 6). 3f. Albert (aged 3). HORIZ: (46½×35½ mm): 6f. Infant Jesus, St. John and two angels.

417 Dr. G. Hansen and Laboratory

1964. Leprosy Relief Campaign.

1880	**417**	1f. black and brown	30	30
1881	-	2f. brown and black	30	30
1882	-	5f. black and brown	60	45
MS1883		135×98 mm. Nos. 1880/2 (+4f.)	3·50	3·50

DESIGNS: 2f. Leprosy hospital; 5f. Father Damien.

418 A. Vesale (anatomist) with Model of Human Arm

1964. Belgian Celebrities.

1884	**418**	50c. black and green	30	30
1885	-	1f. black and green	30	30
1886	-	2f. black and green	30	30

DESIGNS—HORIZ: 1f. J. Boulvin (engineer) and internal combustion engine; 2f. H. Jaspar (statesman) and medallion.

419 Postilion

1964. Stamp Day.

1887	**419**	3f. grey	35	30

420 Admiral Lord Gambier and U.S. Ambassador J. Q. Adams after signing treaty (from painting by Sir A. Forestier)

1964. 150th Anniv of Signing of Treaty of Ghent.

1888	**420**	6f.+3f. blue	70	70

421 Arms of Ostend

1964. Millenary of Ostend.

1889	**421**	3f. multicoloured	35	30

422 Ida of Bure (Calvin's wife)

1964. "Protestantism in Belgium".

1890	-	1f.+50c. blue	30	30
1891	**422**	3f.+1f.50 red	35	35
1892	-	6f.+3f. brown	65	65

PORTRAITS: 1f. P. Marnix of St. Aldegonde (Burgomaster of Antwerp). 6f. J. Jordaens (painter).

423 Globe, Hammer and Flame

1964. Centenary of Socialist International.

1893	**423**	50c. red and blue	30	30
1894	-	1f. red and blue	30	30
1895	-	2f. red and blue	30	30

DESIGNS: 1f. "SI" on Globe; 2f. Flames.

424 Infantryman of 1918

1964. 50th Anniv of German Invasion of Belgium. Multicoloured.

1896	1f.+50c. Type **424**	30	30
1897	2f.+1f. Colour sergeant of the Guides Regt, 1914	30	30
1898	3f.+1f.50 Trumpeter of the Grenadiers & Drummers of the Infantry and Carabiniers, 1914	45	45

425 Soldier at Bastogne

1964. "Liberation–Resistance". Multicoloured.

1899	3f.+1f. Type **425**	35	35
1900	6f.+3f. Soldier at estuary of the Scheldt	70	70

426 Europa "Flower"

1964. Europa.

1901	**426**	3f. grey, red and green	1·70	35
1902	**426**	6f. blue, green and red	4·00	45

427 "Philip the Good"

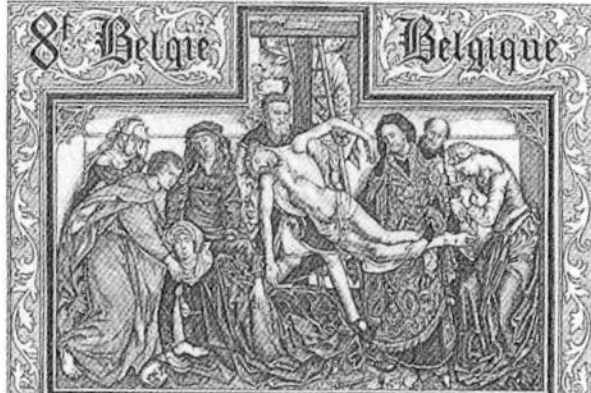

428 "Descent from the Cross"

1964. Cultural Funds. 500th Death Anniv of R. van der Weyden. Two sheets each 153×114 mm showing paintings by Van der Weyden.

MS1903 1f. Type **427**; 2f. "Portrait of a Lady"; 3f. "The Man with the Arrow" (+8f.) 5·00 5·00

MS1904 **428** 8f. (+8f.) brown 4·75 4·75

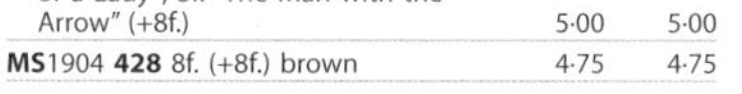

429 Pand Abbey, Ghent

1964. Pand Abbey Restoration Fund.

1905 **429** 2f.+1f. bl, turq & blk 35 30

1906 - 3f.+1f. brown, blue and purple 35 35

DESIGN: 3f. Waterside view of Abbey.

430 King Baudouin, Queen Juliana and Grand Duchess Charlotte

1964. 20th Anniv of "BENELUX".

1907 **430** 3f. purple, blue and olive 50 30

431 "One of Charles I's Children" (Van Dyck)

1964. T.B. Relief and Other Funds. Paintings of Royalty.

1908 **431** 50c.+10c. purple 30 30

1909 - 1f.+40c. red 30 30

1910 - 2f.+1f. purple 30 30

1911 - 3f.+1f. grey 35 35

1912 - 4f.+2f. violet 40 40

1913 - 6f.+3f. violet 50 50

DESIGNS—VERT: 1f. "William of Orange and his fiancee, Marie" (Van Dyck); 2f. "Portrait of a Little Boy" (E. Quellin and Jan Fyt); 3f. "Alexander Farnese at the age of 12 Years" (A. Moro); 4f. "William II, Prince of Orange" (Van Dyck). HORIZ—LARGER (46×35 mm): 6f. "Two Children of Cornelis De Vos" (C. de Vos).

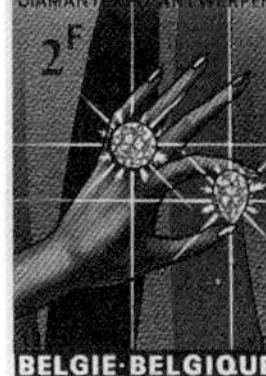

432 "Diamonds"

1965. "Diamantexpo" (Diamonds Exn) Antwerp.

1914 **432** 2f. multicoloured 30 25

433 "Textiles"

1965. "Textirama" (Textile Exn), Ghent.

1915 **433** 1f. black, red and blue 30 25

434 Vriesia

1965. Ghent Flower Show. Inscr "FLORALIES GANTOISES", etc. Multicoloured.

1916 1f. Type **434** 30 30

1917 2f. Echinocactus 30 30

1918 3f. Stapelia 30 30

435 Paul Hymans

1965. Birth Cent of Paul Hymans (statesman).

1919 **435** 1f. violet 30 30

436 Rubens

1965. Centenary of General Savings and Pensions Funds. Painters.

1920 **436** 1f. sepia and mauve 30 30

1921 - 2f. sepia and turquoise 30 30

1922 - 3f. sepia and purple 30 30

1923 - 6f. sepia and red 60 35

1924 - 8f. sepia and blue 75 60

PAINTERS: 2f. Franz Snyders. 3f. Adam van Noort. 6f. Anthony van Dyck. 8f. Jakob Jordaens.

437 "Sir Rowland Hill with Young Collectors" (detail from mural by J. Van den Bussche)

1965. "Philately for the Young".

1925 **437** 50c. green 30 30

438 19th-century Postmaster

1965. Stamp Day.

1926 **438** 3f. green 30 30

1965. U.N.W.R.A. Commemoration. Sheet 123×89 mm. Nos. 1916/18 in new colours.

MS1927 1f., 2f., 3f. (+14f.) 1·70 1·70

439 Globe and Telephone

1965. Centenary of I.T.U.

1928 **439** 2f. black and purple 30 30

440 Handclasp

1965. 20th Anniv of Liberation of Prison Camps.

1929 **440** 50c.+50c. purple, black and bistre 30 30

1930 - 1f.+50c. multicoloured 30 30

1931 - 3f.+1f.50 black, purple and green 40 35

1932 - 8f.+5f. multicoloured 95 95

DESIGNS—VERT: 1f. Hand reaching for barbed wire. HORIZ: 3f. Tank entering prison camp; 8f. Rose within broken wall.

441 Abbey Staircase

1965. Affligem Abbey.

1933 **441** 1f. blue 30 30

442 St. Jean Berchmans, Birthplace and Residence

1965. St. Jean Berchmans.

1934 **442** 2f. brown and purple 30 30

443 Toc H Lamp and Arms of Poperinge

1965. 50th Anniv of Founding of Toc H Movement at Talbot House, Poperinge.

1935 **443** 3f. multicoloured 35 30

444 Maison Stoclet, Brussels

1965. Josef Hoffman (architect) Commemoration.

1936 **444** 3f.+1f. grey and drab 45 45

1937 - 6f.+3f. brown 70 70

1938 - 8f.+4f. purple & drab 1·00 1·00

DESIGNS—Maison Stoclet: VERT: 6f. Entrance hall. HORIZ: 8f. Rear of building.

445 Tractor ploughing

1965. 75th Anniv of Boerenbond (Belgian Farmers' Association). Multicoloured.

1939 50c. Type **445** 30 30

1940 3f. Horse-drawn plough 35 30

446 Europa "Sprig"

1965. Europa.

1941 **446** 1f. black and pink 40 30

1942 **446** 3f. black and green 75 30

447 Jackson's Chameleon

1965. Philanthropic Funds. Reptiles of Antwerp Zoo. Multicoloured.

1943 1f.+50c. Type **447** 30 30

1944 2f.+1f. Iguana 30 30

1945 3f.+1f.50 Nile lizard 40 35

1946 6f.+3f. Komodo lizard 65 60

MS1947 118×98 mm. 8f.+4f. Soft-shelled turtle (larger) 1·20 1·20

448 J. Lebeau (after A. Schollaert)

1965. Death Cent of Joseph Lebeau (statesman).

1948 **448** 1f. multicoloured 30 30

449 Leopold I (after 30c. and 1f. Stamps of 1865)

1965. Death Centenary of King Leopold I.

1949 **449** 3f. sepia 35 30

1950 - 6f. violet 70 45

DESIGN: 6f. As 3f. but with different portrait frame.

450 Huy

1965. Tourist Publicity. Multicoloured.

1951 50c. Type **450** 10 10

1952 50c. Hoeilaart (vert) 10 10

See also Nos. 1995/6, 2025/6, 2083/4, 2102/3, 2123/4, 2159/60, 2240/1 and 2250/1.

451 Guildhouse

1965. T.B. Relief and Other Funds. Public Buildings, Brussels.

1953	**451**	50c.+10c. blue	30	30
1954	-	1f.+40c. turquoise	30	30
1955	-	2f.+1f. purple	30	30
1956	-	3f.+1f.50 violet	35	35
1957	-	10f.+4f.50 sepia and grey	95	95

BUILDINGS—HORIZ: 1f. Brewers' House; 2f. Builders' House; 3f. House of the Dukes of Brabant. VERT: (24½x44½ mm): 10f. Tower of Town Hall.

452 Queen Elisabeth (from medallion by A. Courtens)

1965. Queen Elisabeth Commem.

1958	**452**	3f. black	35	30

453 "Peace on Earth"

1966. 75th Anniv of "Rerum Novarum" (papal encyclical). Multicoloured.

1959	50c. Type **453**	30	30
1960	1f. "Building for Tomorrow" (family and new building)	30	30
1961	3f. Arms of Pope Paul VI (vert 24½x45 mm)	35	30

1966. Queen Elisabeth. Sheets 82x116 mm incorporating old designs, each with se-tenant label showing Crown over "E". (a) In brown, blue, gold and grey.

MS1962 3f. T **125** and 3f. T **317** (sold at 20f.)	1·60	1·60

(b) In brown, myrtle and green.

MS1963 3f. T **160** and 3f. T **172** (sold at 20f.)	1·60	1·60

454 Rural Postman

1966. Stamp Day.

1964	**454**	3f. black, lilac & buff	35	30

455 High Diving

1966. Swimming.

1965	**455**	60c.+40c. brown, green and blue	30	30
1966	-	10f.+4f. brown, purple and green	1·00	1·00

DESIGN: 10f. Diving from block.

456 Iguanodon Fossil (Royal Institute of Natural Sciences)

1966. National Scientific Institutions.

1967	**456**	1f. black and green	30	30
1968	-	2f. black, orge & cream	30	30
1969	-	2f. multicoloured	30	30
1970	-	3f. multicoloured	30	30
1971	-	3f. gold, black and red	30	30
1972	-	6f. multicoloured	40	30
1973	-	8f. multicoloured	65	60

DESIGNS—HORIZ: No. 1968, Kasai head (Royal Central African Museum); No. 1969, Snow crystals (Royal Meteorological Institute). VERT: No. 1970, "Scholar" (Royal Library); No. 1971, Seal (General Archives); No. 1972, Arend-Roland comet and telescope (Royal Observatory); No. 1973, Satellite and rocket (Space Aeronomy Inst.).

457 Eurochemic Symbol

1966. European Chemical Plant, Mol.

1974	**457**	6f. black, red and drab	45	35

458 A. Kekule

1966. Centenary of Professor August Kekule's Benzene Formula.

1975	**458**	3f. brown, black & blue	35	30

1966. 19th World I.P.T.T. Congress, Brussels. Optd XIXe CONGRES IPTT and emblem.

1976	**454**	3f. black, lilac and buff	35	30

460 Rik Wouters (self-portrait)

1966. 50th Death Anniv of Rik Wouters (painter).

1977	**460**	60c. multicoloured	10	10

461 Minorites Convent, Liege

1966. Cultural Series.

1978	**461**	60c.+40c. purple, blue and brown	30	30
1979	-	1f.+50c. blue, purple and turquoise	30	30
1980	-	2f.+1f. red, purple and brown	30	30
1981	-	10f.+4f.50 purple, turquoise and green	85	85

DESIGNS: 1f. Val-Dieu Abbey, Aubel; 2f. Huy and town seal; 10f. Statue of Ambiorix and castle, Tongres.

463 Europa "Ship"

1966. Europa.

1989	**463**	3f. green	45	25
1990	**463**	6f. purple	1·00	40

464 Surveying

1966. Antarctic Expeditions.

1991	**464**	1f.+50c. green	30	30
1992	-	3f.+1f.50 violet	30	30
1993	-	6f.+3f. red	60	60
MS1994		130x95 mm. 10f.+5f. multicoloured	1·20	1·20

DESIGNS: 3f. Commander A. de Gerlache and "Belgica" (polar barque); 6f. "Magga Dan" (Antarctic supply ship) and meteorological operations. 52x35½ mm.—10f. "Magga Dan" and emperor penguins.

1966. Tourist Publicity. As T 450. Multicoloured.

1995	2f. Bouillon	10	10
1996	2f. Lier (vert)	10	10

1966. 75th Anniv of Royal Federation of Belgian Philatelic Circles. Stamps similar to Nos. 1812 and 1851 but incorporating "1890 1996" and F.I.P. emblem.

1997	**391**	60c. purple and green	30	30
1998	**405**	3f. purple and ochre	30	30

466 Children with Hoops

1966. "Solidarity" (Child Welfare).

1999	-	1f.+1f. black & pink	30	30
2000	-	2f.+1f. black & green	30	30
2001	-	3f.+1f.50 black & lav	30	30
2002	**466**	6f.+3f. brown & flesh	60	60
2003	-	8f.+3f.50 brown & grn	70	70

DESIGNS—VERT: 1f. Boy with ball and dog; 2f. Girl with skipping-rope; 3f. Boy and girl blowing bubbles. HORIZ: 8f. Children and cat playing "Follow My Leader".

467 Lions Emblem

1967. Lions International.

2004	**467**	3f. sepia, blue and olive	30	30
2005	**467**	6f. sepia, violet and green	45	40

468 Part of Cleuter Pistol

1967. Arms Museum, Liege.

2006	**468**	2f. black, yellow & red	30	30

469 I.T.Y. Emblem

1967. International Tourist Year.

2007	**469**	6f. blue, red and black	60	35

470 Young Refugee

1967. European Refugee Campaign Fund. Sheet 110x77 mm comprising T 470 and similar vert designs.

MS2008 1f. black and yellow (Type **470**); 2f. black and blue; 3f. black and orange (sold at 20f.)	1·20	1·20

471 Woodland and Trientalis (flowers), Hautes Fagnes

1967. Nature Conservation. Multicoloured.

2009	1f. Type **471**	30	30
2010	1f. Dunes and eryngium (flowers), Westhoek	30	30

472 Paul-Emile Janson (statesman)

1967. Janson Commemoration.

2011	**472**	10f. blue	85	60

473 19th-century Postman

1967. Stamp Day.

2012	**473**	3f. purple and red	30	30

474 Cogwheels

1967. Europa.

2013	**474**	3f. black, red and blue	60	30
2014	**474**	6f. black, yellow & green	1·20	45

475 Flax Plant and Shuttle

1967. Belgian Linen Industry.

2015	**475**	6f. multicoloured	45	35

476 Kursaal in 19th Century

1967. 700th Anniv of Ostend's Rank as Town.

2016	**476**	2f. sepia, buff and blue	30	30

478 With F.I.T.C.E. Emblem

1967. European Telecommunications Day. "Stamp Day" design of 1967 incorporating F.I.T.C.E. emblem as T 478 in green.

2021	**478**	10f. sepia and blue	30	30

"F.I.T.C.E." "Federation des Ingenieurs des Tele-communications de la Communaute Europeenne."

479 Robert Schuman (statesman)

1967. Charity.

2022	**479**	2f.+1f. green	30	30
2023	-	5f.+2f. brown, yellow and black	50	50
2024	-	10f.+5f. multicoloured	1·00	1·00

DESIGNS—HORIZ: 5f. Kongolo Memorial, Gentinnes (Congo Martyrs). VERT: 10f. "Colonial Brotherhood" emblem (Colonial Troops Memorial).

1967. Tourist Publicity. As T 450. Mult.

2025	1f. Ypres	10	10
2026	1f. Spontin	10	10

480 "Caesar Crossing the Rubicon" (Tournai Tapestry)

1967. Charles Plisnier and Lodewijk de Raet Foundations.

2028	**480**	1f. multicoloured	30	30
2029	-	1f. multicoloured	30	30

DESIGN No. 2029, "Maximilian hunting boar" (Brussels tapestry).

481 "Jester in Pulpit" (from Erasmus's "Praise of Folly")

1967. Cultural Series. "Erasmus and His Time".

2030	1f.+50c. multicoloured	30	30
2031	2f.+1f. multicoloured	30	30
2032	3f.+1f.50 multicoloured	35	35
2033	5f.+2f. black, red & carmine	60	60
2034	6f.+3f. multicoloured	70	70

DESIGNS—VERT: 1f. Type **481**. 2f. "Jester declaiming" (from Erasmus' "Praise of Folly"); 3f. Erasmus; 6f. Pierre Gilles ("Aegidius" from painting by Metzijs). HORIZ: 5f. "Sir Thomas More's Family" (Holbein).

482 "Princess Margaret of York" (from miniature)

1967. "British Week".

2035	**482**	6f. multicoloured	55	40

483 Arms of Ghent University

1967. Universities of Ghent and Liege. Mult.

2036	3f. Type **483**	30	30
2037	3f. Liege	30	30

484 Emblem of "Pro-Post" Association

1967. "Postphila" Stamp Exhibition, Brussels. Sheet 110×77 mm.

MS2038 **484**	10f.+5f. black, green, red and brown	1·20	1·20

485 Our Lady of Virga Jesse, Hasselt

1967. Christmas.

2039	**485**	1f. blue	30	30

486 "Children's Games" (section of Brueghel's painting)

1967. "Solidarity".

2040	**486**	1f.+50c. multicoloured	30	30
2041	-	2f.+50c. multicoloured	30	30
2042	-	3f.+1f. multicoloured	40	30
2043	-	6f.+3f. multicoloured	65	60
2044	-	10f.+4f. multicoloured	1·00	90
2045	-	13f.+6f. multicoloured	1·25	1·25

Nos. 2040/5 together form the complete painting.

487 Worker in Protective Hand

1968. Industrial Safety Campaign.

2046	**487**	3f. multicoloured	30	30

489 Army Postman (1916)

1968. Stamp Day.

2068	**489**	3f. purple, brown & blue	30	30

490 Belgian 1c. "Small Lion" Stamp of 1866

1968. Cent of State Printing Works, Malines.

2069	**490**	1f. olive	30	30

491 Grammont and Seal of Baudouin VI

1968. "Historical Series". Multicoloured.

2070	2f. Type **491**	35	30
2071	3f. Theux-Franchimont Castle and battle emblems	35	30
2072	6f. Archaeological discoveries, Spiennes	55	35
2073	10f. Roman oil lamp and town crest, Wervik	85	60

492 Europa "Key"

1968. Europa.

2074	**492**	3f. gold, black & green	90	30
2075	**492**	6f. silver, black and red	1·80	50

493 Queen Elisabeth and Dr. Depage

1968. Belgian Red Cross Fund. Cross in red.

2076	**493**	6f.+3f. sepia, black and green	85	70
2077	-	10f.+5f. sepia, black and green	1·20	1·10

DESIGN: 10f. Queen Fabiola and baby.

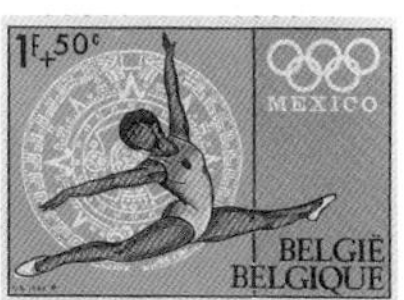
494 Gymnastics

1968. Olympic Games, Mexico. Multicoloured.

2078	1f.+50c. Type **494**	30	30
2079	2f.+1f. Weightlifting	30	30
2080	3f.+1f.50 Hurdling	35	30
2081	6f.+2f. Cycling	70	60
2082	13f.+5f. Sailing (vert 24½×45 mm)	1·30	1·20

Each design includes the Olympic "rings" and a Mexican cultural motif.

1968. Tourist Publicity. As Type 450.

2083	2f. multicoloured	10	10
2084	2f. black, blue and green	10	10

DESIGNS: No. 2083, Farm-house and windmill, Bokrijk; No. 2084, Bath-house and fountain, Spa.

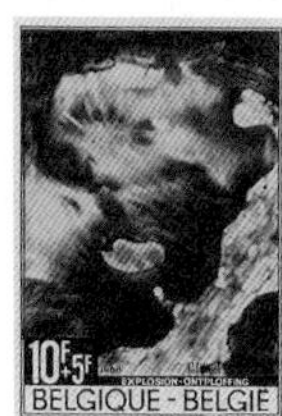
495 "Explosion"

1968. Belgian Disasters. Victims Fund. Mult.

2085	10f.+5f. Type **495**	90	70
2086	12f.+5f. "Fire"	1·20	1·10
2087	13f.+5f. "Typhoon"	1·50	1·20

496 St. Laurent Abbey, Liege

1968. "National Interest".

2088	**496**	2f. black, bistre & blue	30	30
2089	-	3f. brown, grey & lt brn	35	30
2090	-	6f. black, blue & dp bl	70	35
2091	-	10f. multicoloured	95	40

DESIGNS: 3f. Church, Lissewege; 6f. "Mineral Seraing" and "Gand" (ore carriers), canal-lock, Zandvliet; 10f. Canal-lift, Ronquieres.

497 Undulate Triggerfish

1968. "Solidarity" and 125th Anniv of Antwerp Zoo. Designs showing fish. Multicoloured.

2092	1f.+50c. Type **497**	25	25
2093	3f.+1f.50 Ear-spotted angelfish	35	30
2094	6f.+3f. Lionfish	70	55
2095	10f.+5f. Diagonal butterflyfish	1·10	85

498 King Albert in Bruges (October, 1918)

1968. Patriotic Funds.

2096	**498**	1f.+50c. multicoloured	30	30
2097	-	3f.+1f.50 mult	35	30
2098	-	6f.+3f. multicoloured	60	55
2099	-	10f.+5f. multicoloured	90	85

DESIGNS—HORIZ: 3f. King Albert entering Brussels (November, 1918); 6f. King Albert in Liege (November, 1918). LARGER (46×35 mm): 10f. Tomb of the Unknown Soldier, Brussels.

499 Lighted Candle

1968. Christmas.

2100	**499**	1f. multicoloured	30	30

500 "Mineral Seraing" (ore carrier) in Ghent Canal

1968. Ghent Maritime Canal.

2101	**500**	6f. black brown, & blue	55	30

1969. Tourist Publicity. As Type 450.

2102	1f. black, blue & pur (vert)	10	10
2103	1f. black, olive and blue	10	10

DESIGNS. No. 2102, Town Hall, Louvain; No. 2103, Valley of the Ourthe.

501 "Albert Magnis" (detail of wood carving by Quellin, Confessional, St. Paul's Church, Antwerp)

1969. St. Paul's Church, Antwerp, and Aulne Abbey Commemoration.

2104	**501**	2f. sepia	30	30
2105	-	3f. black and mauve	30	30

DESIGN: 3f. Aulne Abbey.

502 "The Travellers" (sculpture, Archaeological Museum, Arlon)

1969. 2,000th Anniv of Arlon.

2106	**502**	2f. purple	30	30

503 Broodjes Chapel, Antwerp

1969. "150 Years of Public Education in Antwerp".

2107	**503**	3f. black and grey	30	30

504 Mail Train

1969. Stamp Day.

2108	**504**	3f. multicoloured	30	30

505 Colonnade

1969. Europa.

2109	**505**	3f. multicoloured	50	30
2110	**505**	6f. multicoloured	85	35

506 "The painter and the Amateur" (detail, Brueghel)

1969. "Postphila 1969" Stamp Exhibition, Brussels. Sheet 91×124 mm.

MS2111	**506**	10f.+5f. brown	1·40	1·20

507 NATO Emblem

1969. 20th Anniv of N.A.T.O.

2112	**507**	6f. blue and brown	55	40

508 "The Builders" (F. Leger)

1969. 50th Anniv of I.L.O.

2113	**508**	3f. multicoloured	35	30

509 "Houses" (I. Dimitrova)

1969. UNICEF "Philanthropy" Funds. Mult.

2114	1f.+50c. Type **509**	30	30
2115	3f.+1f.50 "My Art" (C. Patric)	35	30
2116	6f.+3f. "In the Sun" (H. Rejchlova)	70	60
2117	10f.+5f. "Out for a Walk" (P. Sporn) (horiz)	1·10	85

510 Racing Cyclist

1969. World Championship Cycle Races, Zolder.

2118	**510**	6f. multicoloured	60	30

511 Mgr. V. Scheppers

1969. Monseigneur Victor Scheppers (founder of "Brothers of Mechlin") Commemoration.

2119	**511**	6f.+3f. purple	85	60

512 National Colours

1969. 25th Anniv of BENELUX Customs Union.

2120	**512**	3f. multicoloured	35	30

513 Pascali Rose and Annevoie Gardens

1969. Flowers and Gardens. Multicoloured.

2121	2f. Type **513**	25	30
2122	2f. Begonia and Lochristi Gardens	30	30

1969. Tourist Publicity. As Type 450.

2123	2f. brown, red and blue	25	10
2124	2f. black, green and blue	25	10

DESIGNS: No. 2123, Veurne Furnes; No. 2124, Vielsalm.

514 "Feats of Arms" from "History of Alexander the Great" (Tournai, 15th century)

1969. "Cultural Works" Tapestries. Mult.

2125	1f.+50c. Type **514**	30	30
2126	3f.+1f.50 "The Violinist" from "Festival" (David Teniers II, Oudenarde, c.1700)	50	40
2127	10f.+4f. "The Paralytic", from "The Acts of the Apostles" (Brussels, c.1517)	1·20	1·10

515 Astronauts and Location of Moon Landing

1969. 1st Man on the Moon.

2128	**515**	6f. sepia	50	35
MS2129		95×130 mm. 20f.+10f. blue	3·50	3·00

DESIGN: **MS**2129 is as T **515**, but in vert format.

516 Wounded Soldier

1969. 50th Anniv of National War Invalids Works (O.N.I.G.).

2130	**516**	1f. green	30	30

517 "The Postman" (Daniella Sainteney)

1969. "Philately for the Young".

2131	**517**	1f. multicoloured	30	30

518 John F. Kennedy Motorway Tunnel, Antwerp

1969. Completion of Belgian Road-works. Mult.

2132	3f. Type **518**	35	30
2133	6f. Loncin flyover, Wallonie motorway	55	50

519 Count H. Carton de Wiart (from painting by G. Geleyn)

1969. Birth Centenary of Count Henry Carton de Wiart (statesman).

2134	**519**	6f. sepia	65	50

520 "Barbu d'Anvers" (Cockerel)

1969. "The Poultry-yard" (poultry-breeding).

2135	**520**	10f.+5f. multicoloured	1·30	1·10

521 "Le Denombrement de Bethleem" (detail, Brueghel)

1969. Christmas.

2136	**521**	1f.50 multicoloured	30	30

522 Emblem, "Coin" and Machinery

1969. 50th Anniv of National Credit Society (S.N.C.I.).

2137	**522**	3f.50 brown and blue	35	30

523 Window, St. Waudru Church, Mons

1969. "Solidarity". Musicians in Stained-glass Windows. Multicoloured.

2138	1f.50+50c. Type **523**	30	30
2139	3f.50+1f.50 s-Herenelderen Church	35	30
2140	7f.+3f. St. Jacques Church, Liege	80	70
2141	9f.+4f. Royal Museum of Art and History, Brussels	1·20	1·10

No. 2141 is larger, 36×52 mm.

524 Camellias

1970. Ghent Flower Show. Multicoloured.

2142	1f.50 Type **524**	30	30
2143	2f.50 Water-lily	30	30
2144	3f.50 Azaleas	35	30
MS2145	122×92 mm. Nos. 2142/4 in slightly different shades	2·40	2·20

525 Beech Tree in National Botanical Gardens

1970. Nature Conservation Year. Multicoloured.

2146	3f.50 Type **525**	30	30

2147 7f. Birch 60 35

526 Young "Postman"

1970. "Philately for the Young".
2148 **526** 1f.50 multicoloured 30 30

527 New U.P.U. Headquarters Building

1970. New U.P.U. Headquarters Building.
2149 **527** 3f.50 green 35 30

528 "Flaming Sun"

1970. Europa.
2150 **528** 3f.50 cream, blk & lake 80 30
2151 **528** 7f. flesh, black and blue 1·20 4·75

529 Open-air Museum, Bokrijk

1970. Cultural Works. Multicoloured.
2152 1f.50+50c. Type **529** 30 30
2153 3f.50+1f.50 Relay Post-house, Courcelles 30 30
2154 7f.+3f. "The Reaper of Trevires" (bas-relief, Virton) 65 60
2155 9f.+4f. Open-air Museum, Middelheim, (Antwerp) 90 85

530 Clock-tower, Virton

1970. Historic Towns of Virton and Zelzate.
2156 **530** 2f.50 violet and ochre 30 30
2157 - 2f.50 black and blue 30 30
DESIGN—HORIZ: No. 2157, "Skaustand" (freighter), canal bridge, Zelzate.

531 Co-operative Alliance Emblem

1970. 75th Anniv of Int Co-operative Alliance.
2158 **531** 7f. black and orange 60 30

1970. Tourist Publicity, As Type 450.
2159 1f.50 green, blue and black 20 20
2160 1f.50 buff, blue & deep blue 20 20
DESIGNS—HORIZ: No. 2159, Kasterlee. VERT: No. 2160, Nivelles.

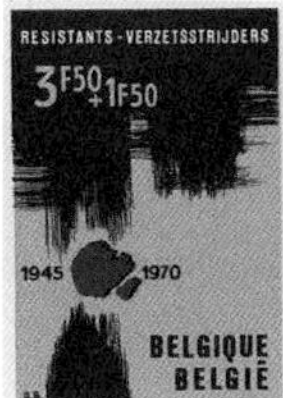

532 Allegory of Resistance Movements

1970. 25th Anniv of Prisoner of War and Concentration Camps Liberation.
2161 **532** 3f.50+1f.50 black, red and green 40 30
2162 - 7f.+3f. black, red and mauve 80 60
DESIGN: 7f. Similar to Type **532**, but inscr "LIBERATION DES CAMPS", etc.

533 King Baudouin

1970. King Baudouin's 40th Birthday.
2163 **533** 3f.50 brown 30 10
See also Nos. 2207/23c and 2335/9b.

534 Fair Emblem

1970. 25th International Ghent Fair.
2164 **534** 1f.50 multicoloured 30 30

535 U.N. Headquarters, New York

1970. 25th Anniv of United Nations.
2165 **535** 7f. blue and black 60 35

536 Queen Fabiola

1970. Queen Fabiola Foundation.
2166 **536** 3f.50 black and blue 30 30

537 Angler's Rod and Reel

1970. Sports. Multicoloured.
2167 3f.50+1f.50 Type **537** 35 35
2168 9f.+4f. Hockey stick and ball (vert) 85 70

538 Belgian 8c. Stamp of 1870

1970. "Belgica 72" Stamp Exhibition, Brussels (1st issue).
MS2169 1f.50+50c. violet and black; 3f.50+1f.50 lilac and black; 9f.+4f. brown and black 4·25 3·50
DESIGNS: 3f.50, Belgian 1f. stamp of 1870; 9f. Belgian 5f. stamp of 1870.

539 "The Mason" (sculpture by G. Minne)

1970. 50th Anniv of National Housing Society.
2170 **539** 3f.50 brown & yell 30 30

540 Man, Woman and Hillside Town

1970. 25th Anniv of Belgian Social Security.
2171 **540** 2f.50 multicoloured 30 30

541 "Madonna and Child" (Jan Gossaert)

1970. Christmas.
2172 **541** 1f.50 brown 30 30

542 C. Huysmans (statesman)

1970. Cultural Works. Famous Belgians.
2173 **542** 1f.50+50c. brown and red 30 30
2174 - 3f.50+1f.50 brown and purple 30 30
2175 - 7f.+3f. brown & green 65 60
2176 - 9f.+4f. brown & blue 1·90 1·80
PORTRAITS: 3f.50, Cardinal J. Cardijn. 7f. Maria Baers (Catholic social worker). 9f. P. Pastur (social reformer).

543 Arms of Eupen, Malmedy and St. Vith

1970. 50th Anniv of Annexation of Eupen, Malmedy and St. Vith.
2177 **543** 7f. brown and sepia 50 35

544 "The Uneasy Town" (detail, Paul Delvaux)

1970. "Solidarity". Paintings. Multicoloured.
2178 3f.50+1f.50 Type **544** 35 35
2179 7f.+3f. "The Memory" (Rene Magritte) 35 60

545 Telephone

1971. Inaug of Automatic Telephone Service.
2183 **545** 1f.50 multicoloured 30 30

546 "Auto" Car

1971. 50th Brussels Motor Show.
2184 **546** 2f.50 black and red 30 30

547 Touring Club Badge

1971. 75th Anniv of Royal Touring Club of Belgium.
2185 **547** 3f.50 gold, red & blue 30 30

548 Tournai Cathedral

1971. 800th Anniv of Tournai Cathedral.
2186 **548** 7f. blue 50 40

549 "The Letter-box" (T. Lobrichon)

1971. "Philately for the Young".
2187 **549** 1f.50 brown 30 30

550 Notre-Dame Abbey, Marche-les-Dames

1971. Cultural Works.

2190	**550**	3f.50+1f.50 black, green and brown	35	30
2191	-	7f.+3f. black, red and yellow	70	65

DESIGN: 7f. Convent, Turnhout.

552 King Albert I, Jules Destree and Academy

1971. 50th Anniv of Royal Academy of French Language and Literature.

2201	**552**	7f. black and grey	30	10

553 Postman of 1855 (from lithograph, J. Thiriar)

1971. Stamp Day.

2202	**553**	3f.50 multicoloured	30	30

554 Europa Chain

1971. Europa.

2203	**554**	3f.50 brown and black	90	30
2204	**554**	7f. green and black	1·50	50

555 Satellite Earth Station

1971. World Telecommunications Day.

2205	**555**	7f. multicoloured	60	50

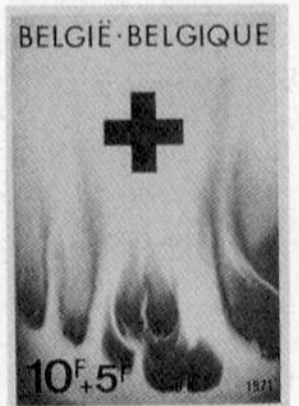

556 Red Cross

1971. Belgian Red Cross.

2206	**556**	10f.+5f. red & black	1·00	70

1971. As T 533, but without dates.

2207	1f.75 green	70	60
2208	2f.25 green	30	10
2208a	2f.50 green	25	10
2209	3f. green	30	10
2209a	3f.25 plum	30	25
2210	3f.50 brown	50	10
2211	4f. blue	40	10
2212	4f.50 purple	95	10
2212a	4f.50 blue	40	10
2213	5f. violet	50	10
2214	6f. red	50	10
2214b	6f.50 violet	50	10
2215	7f. red	65	10
2215ba	7f.50 mauve	40	10
2216a	8f. black	70	10
2217	9f. sepia	95	10
2217a	9f. brown	90	10
2218a	10f. mauve	70	10
2218b	11f. sepia	1·00	10
2219	12f. blue	3·00	30
2219b	13f. blue	1·20	10
2219c	14f. green	1·40	10
2220	15f. violet	1·20	10
2220b	16f. green	2·10	10
2220c	17f. purple	1·40	10
2221	18f. blue	1·40	10
2221a	18f. turquoise	2·10	25
2222	20f. blue	1·60	10
2222b	22f. black	2·10	1·80
2222c	22f. turquoise	1·90	50
2222d	25f. purple	2·10	10
2223a	30f. orange	2·40	10
2223b	35f. turquoise	4·00	30
2223c	40f. blue	4·75	30
2223d	45f. brown	5·75	55

See also Nos. 2335/9.

557 Scientist, Adelie Penguins and "Erika Dan" (polar vessel)

1971. 10th Anniv of Antarctic Treaty.

2230	**557**	10f. multicoloured	80	60

558 "The Discus thrower" and Munich Cathedral

1971. Olympic Games, Munich (1972) Publicity.

2231	**558**	7f.+3f. black & blue	80	70

559 G. Hubin (statesman)

1971. Georges Hubin Commemoration.

2232	**559**	1f.50 violet and black	30	30

560 Notre-Dame Abbey, Orval

1971. 900th Anniv of Notre-Dame Abbey, Orval.

2233	**560**	2f.50 brown	30	30

561 Processional Giants, Ath

1971. Historic Towns.

2234	**561**	2f.50 multicoloured	30	30
2235	-	2f.50 brown	30	30

DESIGN—HORIZ: (46×35 mm): No. 2235, View of Ghent.

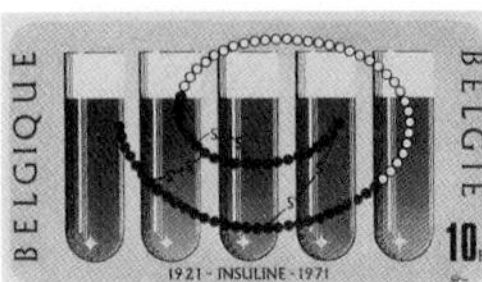

562 Test-tubes and Diagram

1971. 50th Anniv of Discovery of Insulin.

2236	**562**	10f. multicoloured	85	60

563 Flemish Festival Emblem

1971. Cultural Works. Festivals. Multicoloured.

2237	3f.50+1f.50 Type **563**	35	35
2238	7f.+3f. Walloon Festival emblem	85	70

564 Belgian Family and "50"

1971. 50th Anniv of "League of Large Families".

2239	**564**	1f.50 multicoloured	30	30

1971. Tourist Publicity. Designs similar to T 450.

2240	2f.50 black, brown and blue	25	10
2241	2f.50 black, brown and blue	25	10

DESIGNS: No. 2240, St. Martin's Church, Alost; No. 2241, Town Hall and belfry, Mons.

565 Dr. Jules Bordet (medical scientist)

1971. Belgian Celebrities.

2242	**565**	3f.50 green	35	30
2243	-	3f.50 brown	35	30

DESIGN: No. 2242, Type **565** (10th death anniv); No. 2243, "Stijn Streuvels" (Frank Lateur, writer, birth cent.).

566 Achaemenid Tomb, Buzpar

1971. 2500th Anniv of Persian Empire.

2244	**566**	7f. multicoloured	60	50

567 Elewijt Chateau

1971. "Belgica 72" Stamp Exhibition, Brussels (2nd issue).

2245	-	3f.50+1f.50 green	35	35
2246	**567**	7f.+3f. brown	85	85
2247	-	10f.+5f. blue	1·20	1·20

DESIGNS—HORIZ: (52×35½ mm): 3f. Attre Chateau; 10f. Royal Palace, Brussels.

568 F.I.B./V.B.N. Emblem

1971. 25th Anniv of Federation of Belgian Industries.

2248	**568**	3f.50 gold, black & blue	35	30

569 "The Flight into Egypt" (15th-century Dutch School)

1971. Christmas.

2249	**569**	1f.50 multicoloured	30	30

1971. Tourist Publicity. Designs similar to T 450.

2250	1f.50 blue and buff	10	10
2251	2f.50 blue and buff	25	10

DESIGNS—HORIZ: 1f.50, Town Hall, Malines. VERT: 2f.50, Basilica, St. Hubert.

570 "Actias luna"

1971. "Solidarity". Insects in Antwerp Zoo. Multicoloured.

2252	1f.50+50c. Type **570**	30	30
2253	3f.50+1f.50 "Tabanus bromius" (horiz)	35	35
2254	7f.+3f. "Polistes gallicus" (horiz)	85	85
2255	9f.+4f. "Cicindela campestris"	95	95

572 Road Signs and Traffic Signals

1972. 20th Anniv of "Via Secura" Road Safety Organization.

2263	**572**	3f.50 multicoloured	30	30

573 Book Year Emblem

1972. International Book Year.

2264	**573**	7f. blue, brown & black	60	40

574 Coins of Belgium and Luxembourg

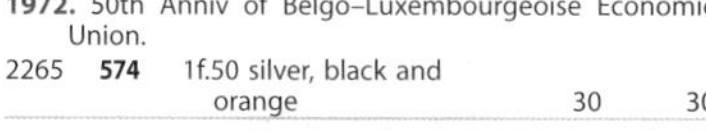

1972. 50th Anniv of Belgo-Luxembourgeoise Economic Union.

2265	**574**	1f.50 silver, black and orange	30	30

576 "Auguste Vermeylen" (I. Opsomer)

1972. Birth Centenary of Auguste Vemeylen (writer).

2267	**576**	2f.50 multicoloured	30	30

577 "Belgica 72" Emblem

1972. "Belgica 72" Stamp Exn., Brussels (3rd Issue).

2268	**577**	3f.50 purple, blue & brn	35	30

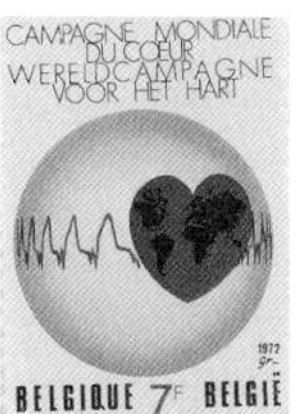

578 Heart Emblem

1972. World Heart Month.

2269	**578**	7f. multicoloured	60	40

579 Astronaut cancelling Letter on Moon

1972. Stamp Day.

2270	**579**	3f.50 multicoloured	35	30

580 "Communications"

1972. Europa.

2271	**580**	3f.50 multicoloured	75	30
2272	**580**	7f. multicoloured	1·20	60

581 Quill Pen and Newspaper

1972. "Liberty of the Press". 50th Anniv of Belga News Agency and 25th Congress of International Federation of Newspaper Editors (F.I.E.J.).

2273	**581**	2f.50 multicoloured	30	30

582 "UIC" on Coupled Wagons

1972. 50th Anniv of Int Railways Union (U.I.C.).

2274	**582**	7f. multicoloured	60	40

See also No. P2266.

583 Couvin

1972. Tourist Publicity.

2275	**583**	2f.50 purple, blue & grn	25	25
2276	-	2f.50 brown and blue	25	25

DESIGN—VERT: No. 2276, Aldeneik Church, Maaseik.

584 Leopold I 10c. "Epaulettes" Stamp of 1849

1972. "Belgica 72" Stamp Exn, Brussels (4th issue).

2277	**584**	1f.50+50c. brown, black and gold	30	30
2278	-	2f.+1f. red, brown and gold	35	35
2279	-	2f.50+1f. red, brown and gold	40	40
2280	-	3f.50+1f.50 lilac, black and gold	45	45
2281	-	6f.+3f. violet, black and gold	60	60
2282	-	7f.+3f. red, black and gold	70	70
2283	-	10f.+5f. blue, black and gold	1·00	1·00
2284	-	15f.+7f.50 green, turquoise and gold	1·60	1·60
2285	-	20f.+10f. chestnut, brown and gold	2·10	2·10

DESIGNS: 2f. Leopold I 40c. "Medallion" of 1849; 2f.50, Leopold II 10c. of 1883. 3f.50, Leopold II 50c. of 1883; 6f. Albert I; 2f. "Tin Hat" of 1919; 7f. Albert I 50f. of 1929; 10f. Albert I 1f.75 of 1931; 15f. Leopold III 5f. of 1936; 20f. Baudouin 3f.50 of 1970.

585 "Beatrice" (G. de Smet)

1972. "Philately for the Young".

2287	**585**	3f. multicoloured	35	30

586 Emblem of Centre

1972. Inauguration of William Lennox Epileptic Centre, Ottignies.

2288	**586**	10f.+5f. multicoloured	1·20	1·20

587 Dish Aerial and "Intelstat 4" Satellite

1972. Inaug of Satellite Earth Station, Lessive.

2289	**587**	3f.50 black, silver & bl	35	30

588 Frans Masereel (wood-carver and painter)

1972. Masereel Commem.

2290	**588**	4f.50 black and green	40	30

589 "Adoration of the Magi" (F. Timmermans)

1972. Christmas.

2291	**589**	3f.50 multicoloured	35	30

590 "Empress Maria Theresa" (unknown artist)

1972. Bicentenary of Belgian Royal Academy of Sciences, Letters and Fine Arts.

2292	**590**	2f. multicoloured	30	30

591 Greylag Goose

1972. "Solidarity". Birds from Zwin Nature Reserve. Multicoloured.

2293	2f.+1f. Type **591**	35	35
2294	4f.50+2f. Northern lapwing	60	60
2295	8f.+4f. White stork	70	95
2296	9f.+4f.50 Common kestrel (horiz)	1·00	1·00

592 "Fire"

1973. Industrial Buildings Fire Protection Campaign.

2297	**592**	2f. multicoloured	30	30

593 W.M.O. Emblem and Meteorological Equipment

1973. Centenary of World Meteorological Organization.

2298	**593**	9f. multicoloured	80	45

594 Bijloke Abbey and Museum, Ghent

1973. Cultural Works. Religious Buildings.

2299	**594**	2f.+1f. green	40	40
2300	-	4f.50+2f. brown	50	50
2301	-	8f.+4f. red	95	95
2302	-	9f.+4f.50 blue	1·20	1·20

DESIGNS: 4f.50, Collegiate Church of St. Ursmer, Lobbes; 8f. Park Abbey, Heverlee; 9f. Floreffe Abbey.

595 W.H.O. Emblem as Man's "Heart"

1973. 25th Anniv of W.H.O.

2303	**595**	8f. black, yellow & red	60	45

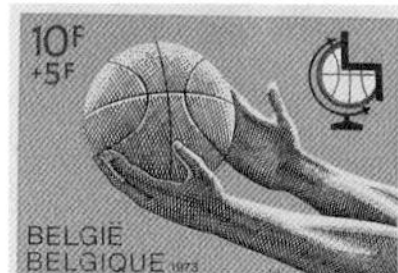

596 Ball in Hands

1973. 1st World Basketball Championships for the Handicapped, Bruges.

2304	**596**	10f.+5f. multicoloured	1·20	1·20

597 Europa "Posthorn"

1973. Europa.

2305	**597**	4f.50 blue, yellow & brn	1·30	35
2306	**597**	8f. blue, yellow & green	2·50	35

598 Thurn and Taxis Courier (17th-cent)

1973. Stamp Day.

2307	**598**	4f.50 brown and red	40	30

599 Fair Emblem

1973. 25th International Fair, Liege.

2308	**599**	4f.50 multicoloured	40	30

600 Arrows encircling Globe

1973. 5th World Telecommunications Day.

2309	**600**	3f.50 multicoloured	35	30

601 "Sport" (poster for Ghent Exhibition, 1913)

1973. 60th Anniv of Workers' International Sports Organization.

2310	**601**	4f.50 multicoloured	40	30

602 Douglas DC-10-30CF and De Havilland D.H.9

1973. 50th Anniv of SABENA.

2311	**602**	8f. black, blue and grey	70	45

603 Ernest Tips's Biplane, 1908

1973. 35th Anniv (1972) of "Les Vieilles Tiges de Belgique" (pioneer aviators' association).

2312	**603**	10f. black, blue & green	85	50

604 15th-Century Printing-press

1973. Historical Events and Anniversaries.

2313	**604**	2f.+1f. blk, brn & red	40	40
2314	-	3f.50+1f.50 mult	40	40
2315	-	4f.50+2f. mult	45	45
2316	-	8f.+4f. multicoloured	85	85
2317	-	9f.+4f.50 mult	1·00	1·00
2318	-	10f.+5f. multicoloured	1·30	1·30

DESIGNS—VERT (As Type **604**): 2f. (500th anniv of first Belgian printed book, produced by Dirk Martens); 3f.50, Head of Amon (Queen Elisabeth Egyptological Foundation. 50th anniv.); 4f.50, "Portrait of a Young Girl" (Petrus Christus, 500th death anniv). HORIZ (36×25 mm): 8f. Gold coins of Hadrian and Marcus Aurelius (Discovery of Roman treasure at Luttre-Liberchies); (52×35 mm); 9f. "Members of the Great Council" (Coessaert) (Great Council of Malines, 500th anniv.). 10f. "Jong Jacob" (East Indiaman) (Ostend Merchant Company, 250th anniv).

605 "Woman Bathing" (fresco by Lemaire)

1973. Thermal Treatment Year.

2319	**605**	4f.50 multicoloured	40	30

606 Adolphe Sax and Tenor Saxophone

1973. Belgian Musical Instrument Industry.

2320	**606**	9f. multicoloured	70	40

607 St. Nicholas Church, Eupen

1973. Tourist Publicity.

2321	**607**	2f. multicoloured	30	30

See also Nos. 2328/9, 2368/70, 2394/5, 2452/5, 2508/11, 2535/8, 2573/6, 2595/6 and 2614.

608 "Little Charles" (Evenepoel)

1973. "Philately for the Young".

2322	**608**	3f. multicoloured	35	30

609 J. B. Moens (philatelist) and Perforations

1973. 50th Anniv of Belgian Stamp Dealers Association.

2323	**609**	10f. multicoloured	80	60

610 "Adoration of the Shepherds" (H. van der Goes)

1973. Christmas.

2324	**610**	4f. blue	40	30

611 Motorway and Emblem

1973. 50th Anniv of "Vlaamse Automobilistenbond" (VAB) (motoring organization).

2325	**611**	5f. multicoloured	45	30

612 L. Pierard (after sculpture by Ianchelevici)

1973. 21st Death Anniv of Louis Pierard (politician and writer).

2326	**612**	4f. red and cream	40	30

613 Early Microphone

1973. 50th Anniv of Belgium Radio.

2327	**613**	4f. black and blue	40	30

1973. Tourist Publicity. As T 607.

2328	3f. grey, brown and blue	30	30
2329	4f. grey and green	40	35

DESIGNS—HORIZ: 3f. Town Hall, Leau; 4f. Chimay Castle.

614 F. Rops (self-portrait)

1973. 75th Death Anniv of Felicien Rops (artist and engraver).

2330	**614**	7f. black and brown	60	35

615 Jack of Diamonds

1973. "Solidarity". Old Playing Cards. Mult.

2331	5f.+2f.50 Type **615**	60	60
2332	5f.+2f.50 Jack of Spades	60	60
2333	5f.+2f.50 Queen of Hearts	60	60
2334	5f.+2f.50 King of Clubs	60	60

1973. As Nos. 2207/23 but smaller, 22×17 mm.

2335	**583**	3f. green	30	10
2336	**583**	4f. blue	35	25
2337	**583**	4f.50 blue	40	10
2338	**583**	5f. mauve	40	25
2338c	**583**	6f. red	50	30
2339	**583**	6f.50 violet	50	30
2339b	**583**	8f. grey	65	30

616 King Albert (Baron Opsomer)

1974. 40th Death Anniv of King Albert I.

2340	**616**	4f. blue and black	35	30

617 "Blood Donation"

1974. Belgian Red Cross. Multicoloured.

2341	4f.+2f. Type **617**	45	45
2342	10f.+5f. "Traffic Lights" (Road Safety)	1·20	1·20

618 "Protection of the Environment"

1974. Robert Schuman Association for the Protection of the Environment.

2343	**618**	3f. multicoloured	35	30

619 "Armand Jamar" (Self-portrait)

1974. Belgian Cultural Celebrities. Multicoloured.

2344	4f.+2f. Type **619**	40	40
2345	5f.+2f.50 Tony Bergmann (author) and view of Lier	45	45
2346	7f.+3f.50 Henri Vieuxtemps (violinist) and view of Verviers	70	70
2347	10f.+5f. "James Ensor" (self-portrait with masks) (35×52 mm)	1·00	1·00

620 N.A.T.O. Emblem

1974. 25th Anniv of North Atlantic Treaty Organization.

2348	**620**	10f. blue and light blue	85	50

621 Hubert Krains (Belgian postal administrator)

1974. Stamp Day.

2349	**621**	5f. black and grey	40	30

622 "Destroyed Town" (O. Zadkine)

1974. Europa. Sculptures.

2350	**622**	5f. black and red	80	30
2351	-	10f. black and blue	1·60	50

DESIGN: 10f. "Solidarity" (G. Minne).

623 Heads of Boy and Girl

1974. 10th Lay Youth Festival.

2352	**623**	4f. multicoloured	40	30

625 New Planetarium, Brussels

1974. Historical Buildings.

2354	**625**	3f. brown and blue	35	30
2355	-	4f. brown and red	45	30
2356	-	5f. brown and green	50	30
2357	-	7f. brown and yellow	65	35
2358	-	10f. brown, orange & bl	80	35

DESIGNS—As T **625**. HORIZ: 4f. Pillory, Braine-le-Chateau. VERT: 10f. Belfry, Bruges. 45×25 mm: 5f. Ruins of Soleilmont Abbey; 7f. "Procession" (fountain sculpture, Ghent).

626 "BENELUX"

1974. 30th Anniv of Benelux Customs Union.

2359	**626**	5f. blue, green & lt blue	40	30

627 "Jan Vekemans at the Age of Five" (Cornelis de Vos)

1974. "Philately for the Young".

2360	**627**	3f. multicoloured	35	30

628 Self-portrait and Van Gogh House, Cuesmes

1974. Opening of Vincent Van Gogh House, Cuesmes.

2361	**628**	10f.+5f. multicoloured	1·20	85

629 Corporal Tresignies and Brule Bridge

1974. 60th Death Anniv of Corporal Leon Tresignies (war hero).

2362	**629**	4f. green and brown	40	30

630 Montgomery Blair and U.P.U. Emblem

1974. Centenary of U.P.U.

2363	**630**	5f. black and green	45	30
2364	-	10f. black and red	80	50

DESIGN: 10f. H. von Stephan and U.P.U. Monument.

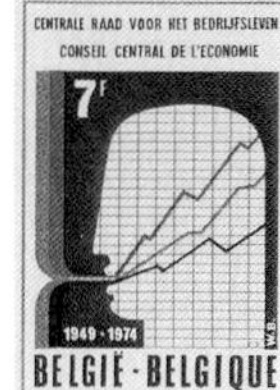

631 Graph within Head

1974. 25th Anniv of Central Economic Council.

2365	**631**	7f. multicoloured	65	40

632 Rotary Emblem on Belgian Flag

1974. 50th Anniv of Rotary Int in Belgium.

2366	**632**	10f. multicoloured	80	45

633 Wild Boar

1974. 40th Anniv of Granting of Colours to Ardennes Regiment of Chasseurs.

2367	**633**	3f. multicoloured	35	30

1974. Tourist Publicity. As T 607.

2368	3f. brown and yellow	40	30
2369	4f. green and blue	40	35
2370	4f. green and blue	40	35

DESIGNS—VERT: No. 2368, Aarschot. HORIZ: No. 2369, Meeting of three frontiers, Gemmenich; 2370, Nassogne.

634 "Angel" (detail, "The Mystic Lamb", Brothers Van Eyck)

1974. Christmas.

2371	**634**	4f. purple	40	30

635 Gentian

1974. "Solidarity". Flora and Fauna. Multicoloured.

2372	4f.+2f. Type **635**	45	45
2373	5f.+2f.50 Eurasian badger (horiz)	65	65
2374	7f.+3f.50 "Carabus auratus" (beetle) (horiz)	75	75
2375	10f.+5f. Spotted cat's-ear	1·20	1·20

636 Adolphe Quetelet (after J. Odevaere)

1974. Death Centenary of Adolphe Quetelet. (scientist).

2376	**636**	10f. black and brown	80	50

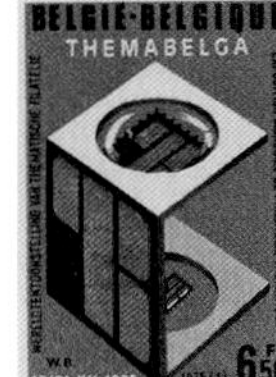

637 Exhibition Emblem

1975. "Themabelga" Stamp Exhibition, Brussels (1st issue).

2377	**637**	6f.50 orange, blk & grn	45	30

See also Nos. 2411/16.

638 "Neoregelia carolinae"

1975. Ghent Flower Show. Multicoloured.

2378	4f.50 Type **638**	40	35
2379	5f. "Tussilago petasites"	45	30
2380	6f.50 "Azalea japonica"	50	30

639 Student and Young Boy

1975. Cent of Charles Buls Normal School.

2381	**639**	4f.50 multicoloured	40	30

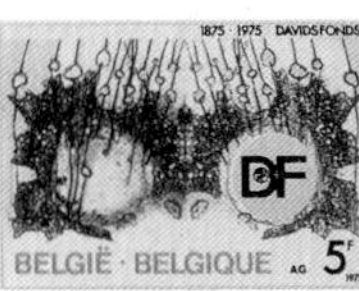

640 Foundation Emblem

1975. Centenary of Davids Foundation (Flemish cultural organisation).

2382	**640**	5f. multicoloured	40	30

641 King Albert I

1975. Birth Centenary of King Albert I.

2383	**641**	10f. black and purple	80	45

642 Pesaro Palace, Venice

1975. Cultural Works.

2384	**642**	6f.50+2f.50 brown	65	65
2385	-	10f.+4f.50 purple	1·00	1·00
2386	-	15f.+6f.50 blue	1·50	1·50

DESIGNS—HORIZ: 10f. Sculpture Museum, St. Bavon Abbey, Ghent. VERT: 15f. "Virgin and Child" (Michelangelo, 500th Birth Anniv.).

643 "Postman of 1840" (J. Thiriar)

1975. Stamp Day.

2387	**643**	6f.50 purple	50	30

644 "An Apostle" (detail, "The Last Supper", Dirk Bouts)

1975. Europa. Paintings.

2388	**644**	6f.50 black, blue & grn	80	30
2389	-	10f. black, red & orange	1·70	60

DESIGN: 10f. "The Suppliant's Widow" (detail, "The Justice of Otho", Dirk Bouts).

645 Prisoners' Identification Emblems

1975. 30th Anniv of Concentration Camps' Liberation.

2390	**645**	4f.50 multicoloured	40	30

646 St John's Hospice, Bruges

1975. European Architectural Heritage Year.

2391	**646**	4f.50 purple	45	30
2392	-	5f. green	50	30
2393	-	10f. blue	1·00	45

DESIGNS—VERT: 5f. St. Loup's Church, Namur. HORIZ: 10f. Martyrs Square, Brussels.

1975. Tourist Publicity. As T 607.

2394	4f.50 brown, buff and red	40	30
2395	5f. multicoloured	50	30

DESIGN—VERT: 4f.50, Church, Dottignies. HORIZ: 5f. Market Square, Saint Truiden.

647 G. Ryckmans and L. Cerfaux (founders), and Louvain University Library

1975. 25th Anniv of Louvain Colloquium Biblicum (Biblical Scholarship Association).

2396	**647**	10f. sepia and blue	85	45

648 "Metamorphosis" (P. Mara)

1975. Queen Fabiola Foundation for the Mentally Ill.

2397	**648**	7f. multicoloured	60	35

649 Marie Popelin (women's rights pioneer) and Palace of Justice

1975. International Women's Year.

2398	**649**	6f.50 purple and green	65	30

650 "Assia" (Charles Despiau)

1975. 25th Anniv of Middelheim Open-air Museum, Antwerp.

2399	**650**	5f. black and green	40	30

651 Dr. Hemerijckx and Leprosy Hospital, Zaire

1975. Dr. Frans Hemerijckx (treatment of leprosy pioneer) Commemoration.

2400	**651**	20f.+10f. mult	2·10	2·10

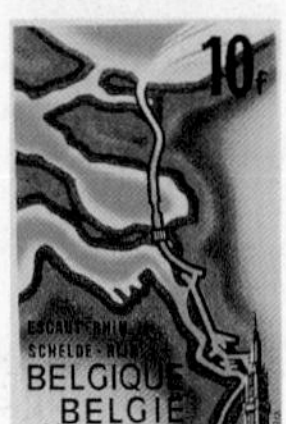

652 Canal Map

1975. Opening of Rhine–Scheldt Canal.

2401	**652**	10f. multicoloured	85	40

653 "Cornelia Vekemans at the Age of Seven" (Cornelis de Vos)

1975. "Philately for the Young".

2402	**653**	4f.50 multicoloured	45	30

654 National Bank and F. Orban (founder)

1975. 125th Anniv of Belgian National Bank.

2403	**654**	25f. multicoloured	2·20	60

655 Edmond Thieffry (pilot) and Hadley Page H.P.26 W.8e Hamilton OË-BAHO "Princess Marie-Jose"

1975. 50th Anniv of First Flight, Brussels–Kinshasa.

2404	**655**	7f. purple and black	60	40

656 University Seal

1975. 550th Anniv of Louvain University.

2405	**656**	6f.50 black, green & bl	60	30

657 "Angels", (detail, "The Nativity", R. de le Pasture)

1975. Christmas.

2406	**657**	5f. multicoloured	40	25

658 Emile Moyson (Flemish Leader)

1975. "Solidarity".

2407	**658**	4f.50+2f. purple	45	45
2408	-	6f.50+3f. green	70	70
2409	-	10f.+5f. vio, blk & bl	1·00	1·00
2410	-	13f.+6f. multicoloured	1·30	1·30

DESIGNS—VERT: 6f.50, Dr. Augustin Snellaert (Flemish literature scholar); 13f. Detail of retable, St. Dymphne Church, Geel. HORIZ: 10f. Eye within hand, and Braille characters (150th anniv of introduction of Braille).

659 Cheese Seller

1975. "Themabelga" International Thematic Stamp Exhibition, Brussels (2nd issue). Traditional Belgian Trades. Multicoloured.

2411	4f.50+1f.50 Type **659**	45	45
2412	6f.50+3f. Potato seller	70	70
2413	6f.50+3f. Basket-carrier	70	70
2414	10f.+5f. Prawn fisherman and pony (horiz)	1·00	1·00
2415	10f.+5f. Knife-grinder and cart (horiz)	1·00	1·00
2416	30f.+15f. Milk-woman with dog-cart (horiz)	2·75	2·75

660 "African" Collector

1976. Centenary of "Conservatoire Africain" (Charity Organization).

2417	**660**	10f.+5f. multicoloured	1·20	1·20

661 Owl Emblem and Flemish Buildings

1976. 125th Anniv of Wilhems Foundation (Flemish cultural organization).

2418	**661**	5f. multicoloured	40	30

662 Bicentennial Symbol

1976. Bicentenary of American Revolution.

2419	**662**	14f. multicoloured	1·20	65

663 Cardinal Mercier

1976. 50th Death Anniv of Cardinal Mercier.

2420	**663**	4f.50 purple	40	30

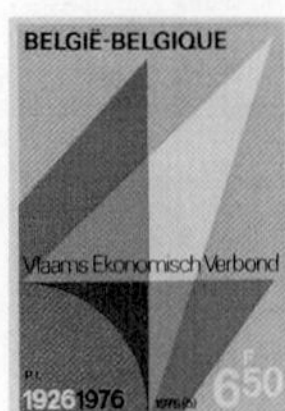

664 "Vlaams Ekonomisch Verbond"

1976. 50th Anniv of Flemish Economic Federation.

2421	**664**	6f.50 multicoloured	50	30

665 Swimming

1976. Olympic Games, Montreal. Multicoloured.

2422	4f.50+1f.50 Type **665**	45	45
2423	5f.+2f. Running (vert)	45	45
2424	6f.50+2f.50 Horse jumping	70	70

666 Money Centre Building, Brussels

1976. Stamp Day.

2425	**666**	6f.50 brown	50	30

667 Queen Elisabeth playing Violin

1976. 25th Anniv of Queen Elisabeth International Music Competitions.

2426	**667**	14f.+6f. red & black	1·40	1·40

668 Basket-making

1976. Europa. Traditional Crafts. Multicoloured.

2427	6f.50 Type **668**	95	25
2428	14f. Pottery (horiz)	2·10	60

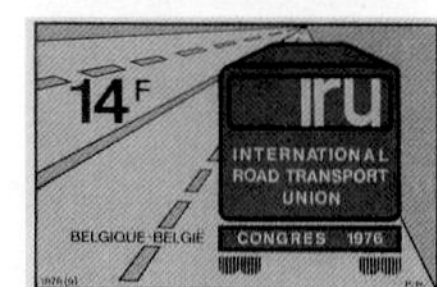

669 Truck on Motorway

1976. 14th Congress of International Road Haulage Union, Brussels.

2429	**669**	14f. black, red & yellow	1·30	50

670 Queen Elisabeth

1976. Birth Centenary of Queen Elisabeth.

2430	**670**	14f. green	1·20	50

672 Jan Olieslagers (aviator), Bleriot XI Monoplane and club Badge

1976. 75th Anniv of Belgian Royal Aero Club. Sheet 82×116 mm.

MS2435	**672**	25f.+10f. black, yellow and blue	2·50	2·50

673 Ardennes Horses

1976. 50th Anniv of Ardennes Draught Horses Society.

2436	**673**	5f. multicoloured	45	35

674 King Baudouin

1976. 25th Anniv of King Baudouin's Accession. Two sheets each 110×62 mm containing stamps as T 674.

MS2437	(a) 4f.50 grey; 6f.50 yellow; 10f. red (sold at 30f.). (b) 20f. green; 30f. blue (sold at 70f.)	7·50	7·50

675 "Madonna and Child" (detail)

1976. 400th Birth Anniv of Peter Paul Rubens (artist) (1st issue). Multicoloured.

2438	4f.50+1f.50 "Descent from the Cross" (detail)	60	60
2439	6f.50+3f. "Adoration of the Shepherds" (detail) (24½x35 mm)	70	60
2440	6f.50+3f. "Virgin of the Parrot" (detail) (24½x35 mm)	70	70
2441	10f.+5f. "Adoration of the Kings" (detail) (24½x35 mm)	1·20	1·20
2442	10f.+5f. "Last Communion of St. Francis" (detail) (24½x35 mm)	1·20	1·20
2443	30f.+15f. Type **675**	3·00	3·00

See also Nos. 2459 and 2497.

676 William the Silent, Prince of Orange

1976. 400th Anniv of Pacification of Ghent.

2444	676	10f. green	85	45

678 Underground Train

1976. Opening of Brussels Metro (Underground) Service.

2446	678	6f.50 multicoloured	65	30

679 "The Young Musician" (W. C. Duyster)

1976. "Philately for the Young" and Young Musicians' Movement.

2447	679	4f.50 multicoloured	40	30

680 Charles Bernard (writer, birth cent)

1976. Cultural Anniversaries.

2448	680	5f. purple	45	30
2449	-	5f. red	45	30
2450	-	6f.50 brown	65	30
2451	-	6f.50 green	65	30

DESIGNS—VERT: No. 2449, Fernand Toussaint van Boelaere (writer, birth cent 1975); No. 2450, "St. Jerome in Mountain Landscape" (J. le Patinier) (25th anniv of Charles Plisnier Foundation). HORIZ: No. 2451, "Story of the Blind" (P. Brueghel) (25th anniv of "Vereniging voor Beschaafde Omgangstaal" (Dutch language organisation)).

1976. Tourist Publicity. As T 607.

2452	4f.50 multicoloured	45	35
2453	4f.50 multicoloured	45	35
2454	5f. brown and blue	45	35
2455	5f. brown and olive	45	35

DESIGNS—HORIZ: No. 2452, Hunnegem Priory, Grammont; No. 2454, River Lys, Sint-Martens-Latem; No. 2455, Chateau. Ham-sur-Heure. VERT: No. 2453, Remouchamps Caves.

681 "Child with Impediment" (Velasquez)

1976. National Association for Aid to the Mentally Handicapped.

2456	681	14f.+6f. multicoloured	1·60	1·60

682 "The Nativity" (detail, Master of Flemalle)

1976. Christmas.

2457	682	5f. violet	45	30

683 Monogram

1977. 400th Birth Anniv of Peter Paul Rubens (2nd issue).

2459	683	6f.50 black and lilac	60	30

684 Belgian Lion

1977. (a) Size 17x20 mm.

2460	684	50c. brown	10	10
2461	684	65c. red	10	10
2462	684	1f. mauve	10	10
2463	684	1f.50 grey	10	10
2464a	684	2f. orange	10	10
2465	684	2f.50 green	35	25
2466	684	2f.75 blue	35	35
2467a	684	3f. violet	25	10
2468	684	4f. brown	25	10
2469	684	4f.50 blue	45	25
2470	684	5f. green	35	10
2471	684	6f. red	45	10
2472	684	7f. red	60	10
2473	684	8f. blue	35	10
2474	684	9f. orange	1·20	10

(b) 17x22 mm.

2475	1f. mauve	25	25
2476	2f. orange	45	35
2477	3f. violet	50	40

685 Dr. Albert Hustin (pioneer of blood transfusion)

1977. Belgian Red Cross.

2478	685	6f.50+2f.50 red and black	75	75
2479	-	14f.+7f. red, blue and black	1·40	1·40

DESIGN: 14f.+7f. Knee joint and red cross (World Rheumatism Year).

686 "50 Years of F.A.B.I."

1977. 50th Anniv of Federation of Belgian Engineers.

2480	686	6f.50 multicoloured	60	30

687 Jules Bordet School, Brussels (bicent)

1977. Cultural Anniversaries.

2481	687	4f.50+1f. mult	40	40
2482	-	4f.50+1f. mult	40	40
2483	-	5f.+2f. multicoloured	50	45
2484	-	6f.50+2f. mult	60	60
2485	-	6f.50+2f. red & black	60	60
2486	-	10f.+5 slate	1·00	1·00

DESIGNS—VERT: 24x37 mm: No. 2482, Marie-Therese College, Herve (bicentenary); 2483, Detail from "La Grande Pyramide Musicale" (E. Tytgat) (50th anniv of Brussels Philharmonic Society). 35x45 mm: No. 2486, Camille Lemonnier (75th anniv of Society of Belgian Authors writing in French). HORIZ: 35x24 mm: No. 2484, Lucien van Obbergh and stage scene (50th anniv of Union of Artists). 37x24 mm: No. 2485, Emblem of Humanist Society (25th anniv).

688 Gulls in Flight

1977. 25th Anniv of District 112 of Lions International.

2487	688	14f. multicoloured	1·20	35

689 Footballers

1977. 30th International Youth Tournament of European Football Association.

2488	689	10f.+5f. multicoloured	1·20	1·20

690 Pillar Box, 1852

1977. Stamp Day.

2489	690	6f.50 olive	65	30

691 Gileppe Dam, Jalhay

1977. Europa. Multicoloured.

2490	6f.50 Type **691**	1·20	30
2491	14f. The Yser, Nieuport	2·00	60

692 "Mars and Mercury Association Emblem"

1977. 50th Anniv of Mars and Mercury Association of Reserve and Retired Officers.

2492	692	5f. green, black & brown	40	30

693 De Hornes Coat of Arms

1977. Historical Anniversaries.

2493	693	4f.50 lilac	40	30
2494	-	5f. red	45	30
2495	-	6f.50 brown	45	30
2496	-	14f. green	1·20	60

DESIGNS AND EVENTS—VERT: 4f.50, Type **693** (300th anniv of creation of principality of Overijse under Eugene-Maximilien de Hornes); 6f.50, Miniature (600th anniv of Froissart's "Chronicles"); 14f. "The Conversion of St. Hubert" (1250th death anniv). HORIZ: (45x24 mm): 5f. Detail from "Oxford Chest" (675th anniv of Battle of Golden Spurs).

694 "Self-Portrait"

1977. 400th Birth Anniv of Peter Paul Rubens (3rd issue).

2497	694	5f. multicoloured	45	30

MS2498 100x152 mm. As No. 2497 but larger (24x37 mm) x3 (sold at 20f.) 1·40 1·40

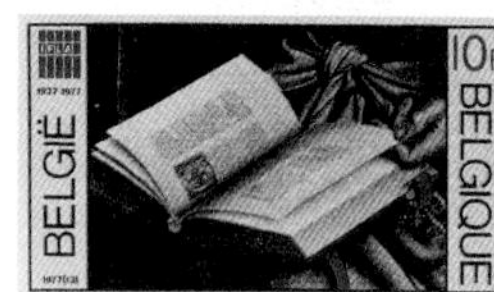

695 "The Mystic Lamb" (detail, Brothers Van Eyck)

1977. 50th Anniv of International Federation of Library Associations and Congress, Brussels.

2499	695	10f. multicoloured	80	45

696 Gymnast and Footballer

1977. Sports Events and Anniversaries.

2500	696	4f.50 red, black & grn	45	30
2501	-	6f.50 black, violet and brown	50	30
2502	-	10f. turquoise, black and salmon	85	45
2503	-	14f. green, blk & ochre	1·30	60

DESIGNS—VERT: 4f.50, Type **696** (50th anniv of Workers' Central Sports Association); 10f. Basketball (20th European Championships); 14f. Hockey (International Hockey Cup competition). HORIZ: 6f.50, Disabled fencers (Rehabilitation through sport).

697 Festival Emblem

1977. "Europalia '77" Festival.

2504	**697**	5f. multicoloured	45	30

699 "The Egg-seller" (Gustave de Smet)

1977. Promoting Belgian Eggs.

2506	**699**	4f.50 black and ochre	40	30

700 "The Stamp Collectors" (detail, Constant Cap)

1977. "Philately for the Young".

2507	**700**	4f.50 sepia	40	30

1977. Tourist Publicity. As T 607.

2508	4f.50 multicoloured	40	30
2509	4f.50 black, blue and green	40	30
2510	5f. multicoloured	40	30
2511	5f. multicoloured	40	30

DESIGNS—VERT: No. 2508, Bailiff's House, Gembloux; No. 2509, St. Aldegone's Church. HORIZ: No. 2510, View of Liege and statue of Mother and Child; No. 2511, View and statue of St. Nicholas.

701 "Nativity" (detail, R. de la Pasture)

1977. Christmas.

2512	**701**	5f. red	40	35

702 Albert-Edouard Janssen (financier)

1977. "Solidarity".

2513	**702**	5f.+2f.50 black	45	45
2514	-	5f.+2f.50 red	45	45
2515	-	10f.+5f. purple	1·00	1·00
2516	-	10f.+5f. grey	1·00	1·00

DESIGNS: No. 2514, Joseph Wauters (politician); No. 2516, Jean Capart (egyptologist); No. 2515, August de Boeck (composer).

703 Distressed Girl (Deserted Children)

1978. Philanthropic Works. Multicoloured.

2517	4f.50+1f.50 Type **703**	40	40
2518	6f.+3f. Blood pressure measurement (World Hypertension Month)	60	60
2519	10f.+5f. De Mick Sanatorium, Brasschaat (Anti-tuberculosis) (horiz)	1·00	1·00

704 Railway Signal as Arrows on Map of Europe

1978. "European Action". Multicoloured.

2520	10f. Type **704** (25th anniv of European Conference of Transport Ministers)	85	35
2521	10f. European Parliament Building, Strasbourg (first direct elections)	85	35
2522	14f. Campidoglio Palace, Rome and map of EEC countries (20th anniv of Treaties of Rome) (horiz)	1·20	50
2523	14f. Paul Henri Spaak (Belgian Prime Minister) (horiz)	1·20	50

705 Grimbergen Abbey

1978. 850th Anniv of Premonstratensian Abbey, Grimbergen.

2524	**705**	4f.50 brown	40	30

706 Emblem

1978. 175th Anniv of Ostend Chamber of Commerce and Industry.

2525	**706**	8f. multicoloured	60	30

707 5f. Stamp of 1878

1978. Stamp Day.

2526	**707**	8f. brown, blk & drab	60	30

708 Antwerp Cathedral

1978. Europa. Multicoloured.

2527	8f. Type **708**	1·20	35
2528	14f. Pont des Trous, Tournai (horiz)	2·30	60

709 Theatre and Characters from "The Brussels Street Singer"

1978. Cultural Anniversaries.

2529	**709**	6f.+3f. multicoloured	60	60
2530	-	6f.+3f. multicoloured	60	60
2531	-	8f.+4f. brown	75	75
2532	-	10f.+5f. brown	1·00	1·00

DESIGNS AND EVENTS: No. 2529, (Type **709**) (Royal Flemish Theatre Cent.); 2530, Arquebusier with standard, arms and Company Gallery, Vise (Royal Company of Crossbowmen of Vise 400th anniv); 2531, Karel van der Woestijne (poet) (birth cent); 2532, Don John of Austria (signing of Perpetual Edict, 400th anniv).

710 "Education"

1978. Teaching. Multicoloured.

2533	6f. Type **710** (Municipal education in Ghent, 150th anniv)	45	35
2534	8f. Paul Pastur Workers' University, Charleroi (75th anniv)	70	30

1978. Tourist Publicity. As T 607.

2535	4f.50 sepia, buff and blue	40	35
2536	4f.50 multicoloured	40	35
2537	6f. multicoloured	50	35
2538	6f. multicoloured	50	35

DESIGNS—VERT: No. 2535, Jonathas House, Enghien. HORIZ: No. 2536, View of Wetteren and couple in local costume; 2537, Brussels tourist hostess; 2538, Carnival Prince and church tower.

711 "K.V.I."

1978. 50th Anniv of Royal Flemish Association of Engineers.

2539	**711**	8f. black and red	60	30

712 Young Stamp Collector

1978. "Philately for the Young".

2540	**712**	4f.50 violet	40	30

713 Mountain Scenery

1978. Olympic Games (1980) Preparation.

2541	**713**	6f.+2f.50 mult	65	65
2542	-	8f.+3f.50 green, brown and black	75	75

MS2543 150×100 mm. 7f. + 3f., 14f.+6f. multicoloured	2·30	2·30

DESIGNS: 7f. Ancient Greek athletes; 8f. Kremlin Towers, Moscow; 14f. Olympic flame.

714 "The Nativity" (detail, Bethlehem Door, Notre Dame, Huy)

1978. Christmas.

2544	**714**	6f. black	50	35

715 Tabernacle, Brussels Synagogue (centenary)

1978. "Solidarity". Anniversaries.

2545	**715**	6f.+2f. brown, grey and black	65	65
2546	-	8f.+3f. multicoloured	80	80
2547	-	14f.+7f. multicoloured	1·50	1·50

DESIGNS—HORIZ: (36×24 mm): 8f. Dancing figures (Catholic Students Action, 50th anniv); 14f. Father Dominique-Georges Pire and African Village (Award of Nobel Peace Prize, 20th anniv).

716 Relief Workers giving First Aid

1978. Belgian Red Cross. Multicoloured.

2548	8f.+3f. Type **716**	85	85
2549	16f.+8f. Skull smoking, bottle and syringe ("Excess kills")	1·70	1·70

717 "Till Eulenspiegel" (legendary character)

1979. 10th Anniv of Lay Action Centres.

2550	**717**	4f.50 multicoloured	40	30

718 "European Dove"

1979. 1st Direct Elections to European Assembly.

2551	**718**	8f. multicoloured	70	30

719 Millenary Emblem

1979. Brussels Millenary (1st issue).

2552	**719**	4f.50 brown, blk & red	35	30
2553	**719**	8f. turquoise, blk & grn	80	30

See also Nos. 2559/62.

720 Sculpture at N.A.T.O. Headquarters and Emblem

1979. 30th Anniv of North Atlantic Treaty Organization.
2554 **720** 30f. blue, gold and light blue 2·30 60

721 Drawing of Monument

1979. 25th Anniv of Breendonk Monument.
2555 **721** 6f. orange and black 45 35

722 Railway Parcels Stamp, 1879

1979. Stamp Day.
2556 **722** 8f. multicoloured 65 30

723 Mail Coach and Renault R4 Post Van

1979. Europa. Multicoloured.
2557 8f. Type **723** 1·70 30
2558 14f. Semaphore posts, satellite and dish aerial 3·00 60

724 "Legend of Our Lady of Sablon" (detail of tapestry, Town Museum of Brussels)

1979. Brussels Millenary (2nd issue). Multicoloured.
2559 6f.+2f. Type **724** 60 60
2560 8f.+3f. Different detail of tapestry 70 70
2561 14f.+7f. "Legend of Our Lady of Sablon" (tapestry) 1·50 1·50
2562 20f.+10f. Different detail of tapestry 2·20 2·20
MS2563 100×150 mm. 20f.+10f. Different detail of Town Museum tapestry (48×37 mm) 2·30 2·30

The tapestry shown on Nos. 2559/60 is from Brussels Town Museum and that on Nos. 2561/2 from the Royal Museum of Art and History.

725 Caduceus and Factory

1979. 175th Anniv of Verviers Chamber of Commerce.
2564 **725** 8f. multicoloured 60 30

726 "50" and Bank Emblem

1979. 50th Anniv of Professional Credit Bank.
2565 **726** 4f.50 blue and gold 40 30

727 Bas-relief

1979. 50th Anniv of Chambers of Trade and Commerce.
2566 **727** 10f. crimson, orange and red 75 40

728 Cambre Abbey

1979. Cultural Anniversaries.
2567 **728** 6f.+2f. multicoloured 60 60
2568 - 8f.+3f. multicoloured 70 75
2569 - 14f.+7f. black, orange and green 1·50 1·50
2570 - 20f.+10f. brown, red and grey 2·20 2·20

DESIGNS: 6f. Type **728** (50th anniv of restoration); 8f. Beauvoorde Chateau; 14f. Barthelemy Dumortier (founder) and newspaper "Courrier de L'Escaut" (150th anniv); 20f. Crypt, shrine and Collegiate Church of St. Hermes, Renaix (850th anniv of consecration).

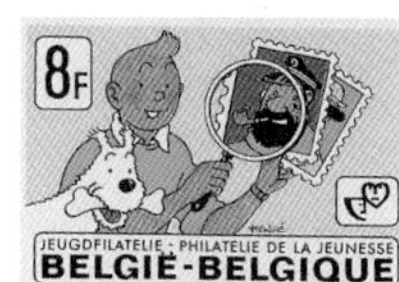

729 "Tintin" with Dog, Stamps and Magnifier

1979. "Philately for the Young".
2571 **729** 8f. multicoloured 2·30 70

730 Le Grand-Hornu

1979. Le Grand-Hornu Industrial Archaeological Site.
2572 **730** 10f.+5f. black & grey 1·00 1·00

1979. Tourist Publicity. As T 607.
2573 5f. multicoloured 45 35
2574 5f. multicoloured 45 35
2575 6f. black, turquoise & green 60 35
2576 6f. multicoloured 60 35

DESIGNS—HORIZ: No. 2573, Royal African Museum, Tervuren, and hunters with hounds; 2575, St. John's Church, Poperinge, and statue of Virgin Mary. VERT: No. 2574, Belfry, Thuin, and men carrying religious image; 2576, St. Nicholas's Church and cattle market, Ciney.

731 Francois Auguste Gevaert

1979. Music. Each brown and ochre.
2577 5f. Type **731** (150th birth anniv) 45 35
2578 6f. Emmanuel Durlet 65 35
2579 14f. Grand piano and string instruments (40th anniv of Queen Elisabeth Musical Chapel) 1·00 60

732 Madonna and Child, Foy-Notre-Dame Church

1979. Christmas.
2580 **732** 6f. black and blue 40 30

733 H. Heyman (politician, birth centenary)

1979. "Solidarity".
2581 **733** 8f.+3f. brown, green and black 60 60
2582 - 10f.+5f. multicoloured 95 95
2583 - 16f.+8f. black, green and yellow 1·60 1·60

DESIGNS—VERT: As Type **733**. 10f. War Invalids Organization medal (50th anniv). HORIZ: (44×24 mm): 16f. Child's head and International Year of the Child emblem.

734 "1830–1980"

1980. 150th Anniv of Independence (1st issue).
2584 **734** 9f. mauve & lt mauve 70 30

See also Nos. 2597/2601.

735 Frans Van Cauwelaert

736 Spring Flowers

1980. Birth Centenary of Frans Van Cauwelaert (politician).
2585 **735** 5f. black 45 30

736 Spring Flowers

1980. Ghent Flower Show. Multicoloured.
2586 5f. Type **736** 45 35
2587 6f.50 Summer flowers 60 35
2588 9f. Autumn flowers 70 35

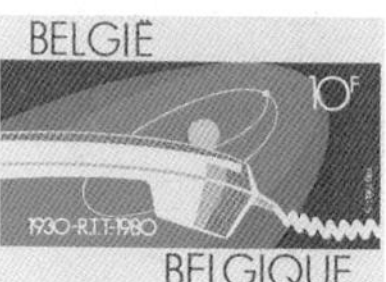

737 Telephone and Diagram of Satellite Orbit

1980. 50th Anniv of Telegraph and Telephone Office.
2589 **737** 10f. multicoloured 80 35

738 5f. Airmail Stamp of 1930

1980. Stamp Day.
2590 **738** 9f. multicoloured 75 30

739 St. Benedict of Nursia

1980. Europa. Multicoloured.
2591 9f. Type **739** 1·40 30
2592 14f. Marguerite of Austria 2·10 70

740 Ivo van Damme

1980. Ivo van Damme (athlete) Commemoration.
2593 **740** 20f.+10f. mult 2·10 2·10

741 Palais de la Nation

1980. 4th Interparliamentary Conference on European Co-operation and Security, Brussels.
2594 **741** 5f. blue, lilac and black 40 35

742 Golden Carriage, Mons

1980. Tourist Publicity. Multicoloured.
2595 6f.50 Type **742** 50 35
2596 6f.50 Damme 50 35

743 King Leopold I and Queen Louise-Marie

1980. 150th Anniv of Belgian Independence (2nd issue).
2597 **743** 6f.50+1f.50 pur & blk 65 65
2598 - 9f.+3f. blue & black 75 75
2599 - 14f.+6f. green & blk 1·40 1·40
2600 - 17f.+8f. orange & blk 1·70 1·70
2601 - 25f.+10f. green & blk 2·40 2·40
MS2602 100×150 mm. 50f. black (sold at 75f.) 5·25 5·25

DESIGNS: 9f. King Leopold II and Queen Marie-Henriette; 14f. King Albert I and Queen Elisabeth; 17f. King Leopold III and Queen Astrid; 25f. King Baudouin and Queen Fabiola; 50f. Royal Mint Theatre, Brussels.

744 King Baudouin

1980. King Baudouin's 50th Birthday.
2603 **744** 9f. red 75 25

745 "Brewer" (detail, Reliquary of St. Lambert)

1980. Millenary of Liege. Multicoloured.
2604 9f.+3f. Type **745** 75 75
2605 17f.+6f. "The Miner" (sculpture by Constantin Meunier) (horiz) 1·70 1·70
2606 25f.+10f. "Seat of Wisdom" (Madonna, Collegiate Church of St. John, Liege) 2·40 2·40
MS2607 150×100 mm. 20f.+10f. Seal of Prince Bishop Notger (43×24 mm) 4·25 4·25

746 Chiny

1980. Tourist Publicity.
2608 **746** 5f. multicoloured 45 30

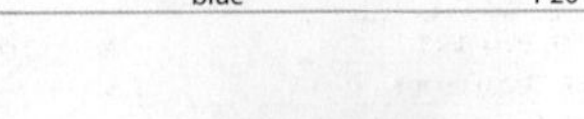
747 Emblem of Cardiological League of Belgium

1980. Heart Week.
2609 **747** 14f. light blue, red and blue 1·20 60

748 Rodenbach (statue at Roulers)

1980. Death Cent of Albrecht Rodenbach (poet).
2610 **748** 9f. brown, blue and deep blue 75 30

749 "Royal Procession" (children of Thyl Uylenspiegel Primary School)

1980. "Philately for the Young".
2611 **749** 5f. multicoloured 40 35

750 Emblem

1980. 50th Anniv of Belgian Broadcasting Corporation.
2612 **750** 10f. black and grey 80 45

751 "Garland of Flowers and Nativity" (attr. D. Seghers)

1980. Christmas.
2613 **751** 6f.50 multicoloured 50 35

752 Gateway, Diest

1980. Tourist Publicity.
2614 **752** 5f. multicoloured 45 35
See also Nos. 2648/51 and 2787/92.

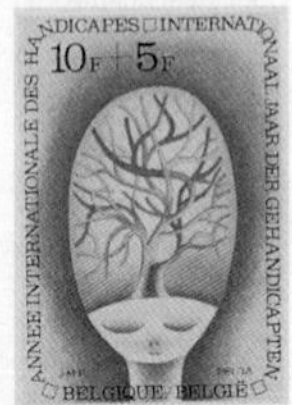

754 Brain

1981. International Year of Disabled Persons. Multicoloured.
2637 10f.+5f. Type **754** 1·20 1·20
2638 25f.+10f. Eye (horiz) 2·50 2·50

755 "Baron de Gerlache" (after F. J. Navez)

1981. Historical Anniversaries.
2639 **755** 6f. multicoloured 45 30
2640 - 9f. multicoloured 70 30
2641 - 50f. brown & yellow 3·75 70

DESIGNS—As T **755**: 6f. Type **755** (1st President of Chamber of Deputies) (150th anniv of Chamber); 9f. Baron de Stassart (1st President of Senate) (after F. J. Navez) (150th anniv of Senate). 35×51 mm: 50f. Statue of King Leopold I by Geefs (150th anniv of royal dynasty).

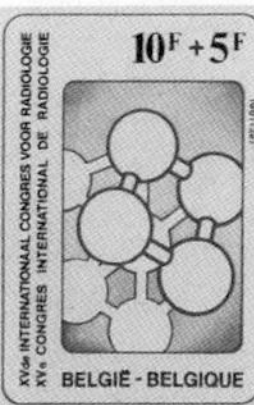

756 Emblem of 15th International Radiology Convention

1981. Belgian Red Cross.
2642 **756** 10f.+5f. bl, blk & red 1·00 1·00
2643 - 25f.+10f. blue, red and black 2·40 2·40

DESIGN: 25f. Dove and globe symbolizing international emergency assistance.

757 Tchantches and Op-Signoorke (puppets)

1981. Europa. Multicoloured.
2644 9f. Type **757** 1·50 30
2645 14f. D'Artagnan and Woltje (puppets) 2·50 85

758 Stamp Transfer-roller depicting A. de Cock (founder of Postal Museum)

1981. Stamp Day.
2646 **758** 9f. multicoloured 75 30

759 Ovide Decroly

1981. 110th Birth Anniv of Dr. Ovide Decroly (educational psychologist).
2647 **759** 35f.+15f. brown & bl 3·50 2·30

1981. Tourist Publicity. As T **752**. Multicoloured.
2648 6f. Statue of our Lady of Tongre 60 35
2649 6f. Egmont Castle, Zottegem 60 35
2650 6f.50 Dams on Eau d'Heure (horiz) 60 35
2651 6f.50 Tongerlo Abbey, Antwerp (horiz) 60 35

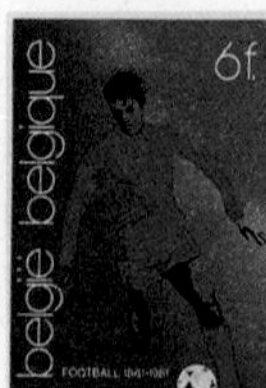

760 Footballer

1981. Cent of Royal Antwerp Football Club.
2652 **760** 6f. red, brown & black 60 30

761 Edouard Remouchamps (Walloon dramatist)

1981. 125th Anniv of Society of Walloon Language and Literature.
2653 **761** 6f.50 brown and stone 50 30

762 French Horn

1981. Centenary of De Vredekring Band, Antwerp.
2654 **762** 6f.50 blue, mve & blk 50 30

763 Audit Office

1981. 150th Anniv of Audit Office.
2655 **763** 10f. purple 80 30

764 Pietà

1981. 25th Anniv of Bois du Cazier Mining Disaster. Sheet 150×100 mm.
MS2656 **764** 20f. multicoloured (sold at 30f.) 2·30 2·30

765 Tombs of Marie of Burgundy and Charles the Bold

1981. Relocation of Tombs of Marie of Burgundy and Charles the Bold in Notre-Dame Church, Bruges.
2657 **765** 50f. multicoloured 3·75 85

766 Boy holding Globe in Tweezers

1981. "Philately for Youth".
2658 **766** 6f. multicoloured 45 30

767 King Baudouin

1981
2659 **767** 50f. light blue and blue 5·50 30
2660 **767** 65f. mauve and black 7·00 95
2661 **767** 100f. brown and blue 11·50 60

768 Max Waller (founder)

1981. Cultural Anniversaries.
2672 **768** 6f. multicoloured 45 30
2673 - 6f.50 multicoloured 50 30
2674 - 9f. multicoloured 70 30
2675 - 10f. multicoloured 80 45
2676 - 14f. lt brn & brn 1·30 60

DESIGNS: 6f. Type **768** (centenary of literary review "La Jeune Belgique"); 6f.50," Liqueur Drinkers" (detail, Gustave van de Woestijne (inscr "Woestyne") (birth centenary); 9f. Fernand Severin (poet, 50th death anniv); 10f. Jan van Ruusbroec (mystic, 600th death anniv); 14f. Owl (La Pensee et les Hommes organization, 25th anniv).

769 Nativity (miniature from "Missale ad usum d. Leodensis")

1981. Christmas.

2677	**769**	6f.50 brown and black	45	30

770 Mounted Gendarme, 1832

1981. "Solidarity". Multicoloured.

2678	9f.+4f. Type **770**	1·00	1·00
2679	20f.+7f. Carabinier	2·00	2·00
2680	40f.+20f. Mounted Guide, 1843	4·00	4·00

771 Cellist and Royal Conservatory of Music, Brussels

1982. 150th Anniversaries. Multicoloured.

2681	6f.50 Type **771**	45	30
2682	9f. Front of former Law Court, Brussels (anniv of judiciary)	70	30

772 Sectional View of Cyclotron

1982. Science. Multicoloured.

2683	6f. Type **772** (Installation of cyclotron at National Radio-elements Institute, Fleurus)	45	35
2684	14f. Telescope and galaxy (Royal Observatory)	1·00	45
2685	50f. Dr. Robert Koch and tubercle bacillus (centenary of discovery)	3·50	80

773 Billiards

1982. Sports. Multicoloured.

2686	6f.+2f. Type **773**	95	95
2687	9f.+4f. Cycling	1·30	1·30
2688	10f.+5f. Football	1·40	1·40
2689	50f.+14f. "Treaty of Rome" (yacht)	4·00	4·00
MS2690	105×100 mm. 25f. multicoloured (Type **773**); 25f. brown, yellow and black (as No. 2687); 25f. red, yellow and black (as No. 2688); 25f. multicoloured (as No. 2689)	8·75	8·25

774 Joseph Lemaire (after Jean Maillard)

1982. Birth Centenary of Joseph Lemaire (Minister of State and social reformer).

2691	**774**	6f.50 multicoloured	50	30

775 Voting (Universal Suffrage)

1982. Europa.

2692	**775**	10f. multicoloured	2·30	35
2693	-	17f. green, black and grey	4·00	60

DESIGN: 17f. Portrait and signature of Emperor Joseph II (Edict of Toleration).

1982. Surch 1 F.

2694	**684**	1f. on 5f. green	10	10

777 17th-century Postal Messenger

1982. Stamp Day.

2695	**777**	10f. multicoloured	75	30

778 "Tower of Babel" (Brueghel the Elder)

1982. World Esperanto Congress, Antwerp.

2696	**778**	12f. multicoloured	95	45

1982. Tourist Publicity. As T 752.

2697	7f. blue and light blue	65	35
2698	7f. black and green	65	35
2699	7f.50 brown and light brown	65	35
2700	7f.50 violet and lilac	65	35
2701	7f.50 black and grey	65	35
2702	7f.50 black and pink	65	35

DESIGNS—VERT: No. 2697, Gosselies Tower; 2698, Zwijveke Abbey, Termonde; 2701, Entrance gate, Grammont Abbey; 2702, Beveren pillory. HORIZ: No. 2699, Stavelot Abbey; 2700, Abbey ruins, Villers-la-Ville.

780 Louis Paul Boon (writer)

1982. Cultural Anniversaries.

2707	**780**	7f. black, red and grey	45	30
2708	-	10f. multicoloured	70	30
2709	-	12f. multicoloured	95	45
2710	-	17f. multicoloured	1·70	45

DESIGNS: 7f. Type **780** (70th birth anniv); 10f. "Adoration of the Shepherds" (detail of Portinari retable) (Hugo van der Goes, 500th death anniv); 12f. Michel de Ghelderode (dramatist, 20th death anniv); 17f. "Motherhood" (Pierre Paulus, birth centenary (1981)).

781 Abraham Hans

1982. Birth Centenary of Abraham Hans (writer).

2711	**781**	17f. black, turquoise and blue	1·10	35

782 Children playing Football

1982. "Philately for the Young". Scout Year.

2712	**782**	7f. multicoloured	65	35

783 Masonic Emblems

1982. 150th Anniv of Belgium Grand Orient (Freemasonry Lodge).

2713	**783**	10f. yellow and black	75	30

784 Star over Village

1982. Christmas.

2714	**784**	10f.+1f. multicoloured	80	30

785 Cardinal Cardijn

1982. Birth Centenary of Cardinal Joseph Cardijn.

2715	**785**	10f. multicoloured	80	10

786 King Baudouin

787 King Baudouin

1982

2716	**786**	10f. blue	95	10
2717	**786**	11f. brown	1·20	10
2718	**786**	12f. green	3·00	60
2719	**786**	13f. red	1·30	10
2720	**786**	14f. black	1·20	10
2721	**786**	15f. red	2·00	35
2722	**786**	20f. blue	2·00	10
2723	**786**	22f. purple	3·00	1·20
2724	**786**	23f. green	3·00	60
2725	**786**	24f. grey	2·30	35
2726	**786**	25f. blue	2·50	30
2727	**786**	30f. brown	2·40	10
2728	**786**	40f. red	4·00	10
2729	**787**	50f. light brown, brown and black	5·75	10
2730	**787**	100f. blue, deep blue and black	16·00	25
2731	**787**	200f. light green, green and deep green	34·00	85

788 St. Francis preaching to the Birds

1982. 800th Birth Anniv of St. Francis of Assisi.

2736	**788**	20f. multicoloured	1·50	60

789 Messenger handing Letter to King in the Field

1982. "Belgica 82" Postal History Exhibition. Multicoloured.

2737	7f.+2f. Type **789**	60	60
2738	7f.50+2f.50 Messenger, Basel (vert)	70	70
2739	10f.+3f. Messenger, Nuremburg (vert)	85	85
2740	17f.+7f. Imperial courier, 1750 (vert)	1·60	1·60
2741	20f.+9f. Imperial courier, 1800	1·90	1·90
2742	25f.+10f. Belgian postman, 1886	2·20	2·20
MS2743	123×89 mm. 50f.+25f. Mail coach (48×37 mm)	5·25	5·25

790 Emblem

1983. 50th Anniv of Caritas Catholica Belgica.

2744	**790**	10f.+2f. red and grey	95	95

791 Horse Tram

1983. Trams. Multicoloured.

2745	7f.50 Type **791**	80	40
2746	10f. Electric tram	1·20	35
2747	50f. Tram with trolley (invented by K. van de Poele)	4·50	70

792 Mountaineer

1983. Belgian Red Cross. Multicoloured.

2748	12f.+3f. Type **792**	1·20	1·20
2749	20f.+5f. Walker	2·00	2·00

793 Brussels Buildings, Open Periodicals and Globe

1983. 24th International Periodical Press Federation World Congress, Brussels.

2750	**793**	20f. multicoloured	1·50	60

794 Woman at Work

1983. Women.

2751	**794**	8f. multicoloured	80	35
2752	-	11f. multicoloured	95	30
2753	-	20f. yellow, brown & bl	1·70	60

DESIGNS: 11f. Woman at home; 20f. Woman manager.

795 Graphic Representation of Midi Railway Station, Brussels

1983. Stamp Day. World Communications Year.

2754	**795**	11f. black, red and blue	95	30

796 Procession of the Holy Blood

1983. Procession of the Holy Blood, Bruges.

2755	**796**	8f. multicoloured	65	35

797 "The Man in the Street"

1983. Europa. Paintings by Paul Delvaux. Mult.

2756	11f. Type **797**	1·70	35
2757	20f. "Night Trains" (horiz)	3·50	70

798 Hot-air Balloon over Town

1983. Bicentenary of Manned Flight. Mult.

2758	11f. Type **798**	80	30
2759	22f. Hot-air balloon over countryside	1·70	70

799 Church of Our Lady, Hastiere

1983. Tourist Publicity. Multicoloured.

2760	8f. Type **799**	75	35
2761	8f. Tumulus, Landen	75	35
2762	8f. Park, Mouscron	75	35
2763	8f. Wijnendale Castle, Torhout	75	35

800 Milkmaid

1983. Tineke Festival, Heule.

2764	**800**	8f. multicoloured	65	35

801 Plaque on Wall

1983. European Small and Medium-sized Industries and Crafts Year.

2765	**801**	11f. yellow, black & red	85	30

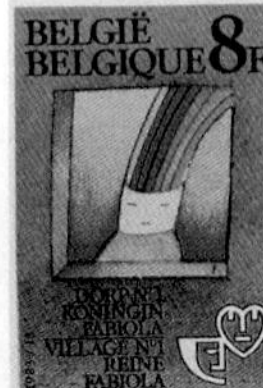
802 Rainbow and Child

1983. "Philately for the Young". 20th Anniv of Queen Fabiola Village No. 1 (for handicapped people).

2766	**802**	8f. multicoloured	65	30

803 Textiles

1983. Belgian Exports (1st series). Multicoloured.

2767	10f. Type **803**	95	35
2768	10f. Steel beams (metallurgy)	95	35
2769	10f. Diamonds	95	35

See also Nos. 2777/80.

804 Conscience (after wood engraving by Nelly Degouy)

1983. Death Centenary of Hendrik Conscience (writer).

2770	**804**	20f. black and green	1·60	45

805 "Madonna" (Jef Wauters)

1983. Christmas.

2771	**805**	11f.+1f. multicoloured	95	95

806 2nd Foot Regiment

1983. "Solidarity". Military Uniforms. Mult.

2772	8f.+2f. Type **806**	85	85
2773	11f.+2f. Lancer	1·50	1·50
2774	50f.+12f. Grenadier	4·25	4·25

1983. King Leopold III Commemoration.

2775	**155**	11f. black	85	30

807 Free University of Brussels

1984. 150th Anniv of Free University of Brussels.

2776	**807**	11f. multicoloured	95	25

1984. Belgian Exports (2nd series). As T 803. Multicoloured.

2777	11f. Retort and test tubes (chemicals)	95	35
2778	11f. Combine harvester (agricultural produce)	95	35
2779	11f. Ship, coach and electric commuter train (transport)	95	35
2780	11f. Atomic emblem and computer terminal (new technology)	95	35

808 Albert I

1984. 50th Death Anniv of King Albert I.

2781	**808**	8f. black and stone	70	35

809 Judo

1984. Olympic Games, Los Angeles. Multicoloured.

2782	8f.+2f. Type **809**	70	70
2783	12f.+3f. Windsurfing (vert)	1·20	1·20
MS2784	125×90 mm. 10f. Archery; 24f. Dressage	2·50	2·50

810 Releasing Doves

1984. 25th Anniv of Movement without a Name.

2785	**810**	12f. multicoloured	95	30

811 Clasped Hands

1984. 50th Anniv of National Lottery.

2786	**811**	12f.+3f. multicoloured	1·20	1·20

812 St. John Bosco with Children

1984. 50th Anniv of Canonization of St. John Bosco (founder of Salesians).

2787	**812**	8f. multicoloured	70	30

813 Bridge

1984. Europa. 25th Anniv of European Posts and Telecommunications Conference.

2788	**813**	12f. red and black	1·50	30
2789	**813**	22f. blue and black	3·25	60

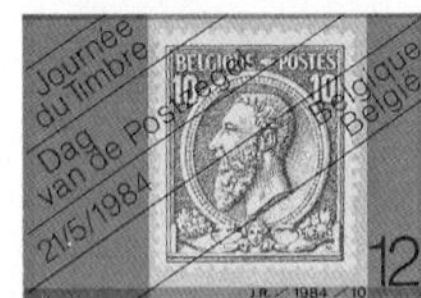
814 Leopold II 1884 10c. Stamp

1984. Stamp Day.

2790	**814**	12f. multicoloured	1·00	30

815 Dove and Pencils

1984. 2nd European Parliament Elections.

2791	**815**	12f. multicoloured	1·00	30

816 Shako

1984. 150th Anniv of Royal Military School.

2792	**816**	22f. multicoloured	1·70	50

817 Church of Our Lady of the Chapel, Brussels

1984. Tourist Publicity. Multicoloured.

2793	10f. Type **817**	85	40
2794	10f. St. Martin's Church and lime tree, Montigny-le-Tilleul	85	40
2795	10f. Belfry and Town Hall, Tielt (vert)	85	40

818 "Curious Masks" (detail, James Ensor)

1984. Inaug of Brussels Modern Art Museum.

2796	**818**	8f.+2f. multicoloured	85	85
2797	-	12f.+3f. multicoloured	1·50	1·50
2798	-	22f.+5f. multicoloured	2·00	2·00
2799	-	50f.+13f. grn, bl & blk	4·75	4·75

DESIGNS: 12f. "The Empire of Lights" (detail, Rene Magritte); 22f. "The End" (detail, Jan Cox); 50f. "Rhythm No. 6" (Jo Delahaut).

819 Symbolic Design

1984. 50th Anniv of Chirojeugd (Christian youth movement).
2800 **819** 10f. yellow, violet & bl 85 40

820 Averbode Abbey

1984. Abbeys.
2801 **820** 8f. green and brown 65 40
2802 - 22f. brown & dp brown 1·70 65
2803 - 24f. green & light green 1·70 65
2804 - 50f. lilac and brown 4·00 85
DESIGNS—VERT: 22f. Chimay; 24f. Rochefort. HORIZ: 50f. Affligem.

821 Smurf as Postman

1984. "Philately for the Young".
2805 **821** 8f. multicoloured 1·50 45

822 Child collecting Flowers

1984. Children.
2806 10f.+2f. Type **822** 95 95
2807 12f.+3f. Children with globe 1·20 1·20
2808 15f.+3f. Child on merry-go-round 1·40 1·40

823 Meulemans

1984. Birth Cent of Arthur Meulemans (composer).
2809 **823** 12f. black and orange 1·00 30

824 Three Kings

1984. Christmas.
2810 **824** 12f.+1f. multicoloured 1·20 1·20

825 St. Norbert

1985. 850th Death Anniv of St. Norbert.
2811 **825** 22f. brown & lt brown 1·80 60

826 "Virgin of Louvain" (attr. Jan Gossaert)

1985. "Europalia 85 Espana" Festival.
2812 **826** 12f. multicoloured 1·00 30

827 Press Card in Hatband

1985. Cent of Professional Journalists Association.
2814 **827** 9f. multicoloured 75 30

828 Blood System as Tree

1985. Belgian Red Cross. Blood Donations.
2815 **828** 9f.+2f. multicoloured 95 95
2816 - 23f.+5f. red, blue and black 2·20 2·20
DESIGN: 23f. Two hearts.

829 "Sophrolaelio cattleya" "Burlingama"

1985. Ghent Flower Festival. Orchids. Mult.
2817 12f. Type **829** 95 30
2818 12f. Phalaenopsis "Malibu" 95 30
2819 12f. Tapeu orchid ("Vanda coerulea") 95 30

830 Pope John Paul II

1985. Visit of Pope John Paul II.
2820 **830** 12f. multicoloured 95 30

831 Rising Sun behind Chained Gates

1985. Centenary of Belgian Workers' Party.
2821 9f. Type **831** 70 40
2822 12f. Broken wall, flag and rising sun 95 30

832 Jean de Bast (engraver)

1985. Stamp Day.
2823 **832** 12f. blue 95 30

834 Class 18 Steam Locomotive, 1896

1985. Public Transport Year. Multicoloured.
2826 9f. Type **834** 80 35
2827 12f. Locomotive "Elephant", 1835 95 30
2828 23f. Class 23 tank engine, 1904 1·90 70
2829 24f. Class I Pacific locomotive, 1935 1·90 70
MS2830 150×100 mm. 50f. Class 27 electric locomotive, 1979 4·75 4·75

835 Cesar Franck and Score

1985. Europa. Music Year. Multicoloured.
2831 12f. Type **835** 2·30 30
2832 23f. Queen and king with viola dressed in music score (Queen Elisabeth International Music Competition) 4·00 70

836 Planned Canal Lock, Strepy-Thieu

1985. Permanent International Navigation Congress Association Centenary Congress, Brussels. Multicoloured.
2833 23f. Type **836** 1·90 70
2834 23f. Aerial view of Zeebrugge harbour 1·90 70

837 Church of Our Lady's Assumption, Avernas-le-Bauduin

1985. Tourist Publicity. Multicoloured.
2835 12f. Type **837** 95 35
2836 12f. Saint Martin's Church, Marcinelle (horiz) 95 35
2837 12f. Roman tower and Church of old beguinage, Tongres 95 35
2838 12f. House, Wachtebeke (horiz) 95 35

838 Queen Astrid

1985. 50th Death Anniv of Queen Astrid.
2839 **838** 12f. lt brown & brown 1·00 30

839 Baking Matton Tart, Grammont

1985. Traditional Customs. Multicoloured.
2840 12f. Type **839** 1·00 30
2841 24f. Young people dancing on trumpet filled with flowers (cent of Red Youths, St. Lambert Cultural Circle, Hermalle-sous-Argenteau) 1·90 60

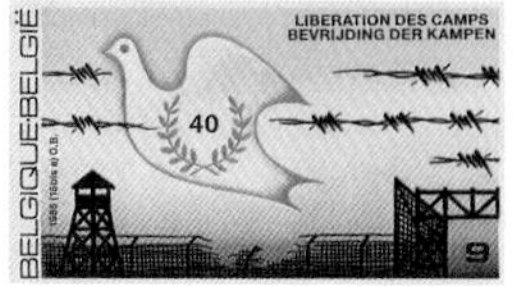

840 Dove and Concentration Camp

1985. 40th Anniv of Liberation. Multicoloured.
2842 9f. Type **840** 80 35
2843 23f. Battle of the Ardennes 1·90 70
2844 24f. Troops landing at Scheldt estuary 1·90 70

841 Hawfinch ("Appelvink – Gros Bec")

1985. Birds (1st series). Multicoloured.
2845 1f. Lesser spotted woodpecker ("Pic epeichette") 35 10
2846 2f. Eurasian tree sparrow ("Moineau friquet") 30 10
2847 3f. Type **841** 60 10
2847a 3f.50 European robin ("Rouge-gorge") 35 10
2848 4f. Bluethroat ("Gorge-bleue") 45 10
2848a 4f.50 Common stonechat ("Traquet patre") 50 25
2849 5f. Eurasian nuthatch ("Sittelle torche-pot") 45 10
2850 6f. Northern bullfinch ("Bouvreuil") 70 10
2851 7f. Blue tit ("Mesange bleue") 70 25
2852 8f. River kingfisher ("Martin-pecheur") 80 10
2853 9f. Eurasian goldfinch ("Chardonneret") 1·20 10
2854 10f. Chaffinch ("Pinson") 85 10
See also Nos. 3073/86 and 3306/23.

842 Claes and Fictional Character

1985. Birth Centenary of Ernest Claes (writer).
2855 **842** 9f. multicoloured 75 30

843 Youth

1985. "Philately for the Young". International Youth Year.
2856 **843** 9f. multicoloured 75 30

844 Trazegnies Castle

1985. "Solidarity". Castles. Multicoloured.
2857 9f.+2f. Type **844** 95 95
2858 12f.+3f. Laarne 1·20 1·20
2859 23f.+5f. Turnhout 2·00 2·00
2860 50f.+12f. Colonster 4·00 4·00

845 Miniature from "Book of Hours of Duc de Berry"

1985. Christmas.

2861	**845**	12f.+1f. multicoloured	1·00	1·00

846 King Baudouin and Queen Fabiola

1985. Royal Silver Wedding.

2862	**846**	12f. grey, blue and deep blue	1·20	30

847 Map and 1886 25c. Stamp

1986. Centenary of First Independent State of Congo Stamp.

2863	**847**	10f. blue, grey & dp blue	1·60	35

848 Giants and Belfry, Alost

1986. Carnivals. Multicoloured.

2864	9f. Type **848**	70	40
2865	12f. Clown, Binche	1·00	30

849 Dove as Hand holding Olive Twig

1986. International Peace Year.

2866	**849**	23f. multicoloured	2·00	60

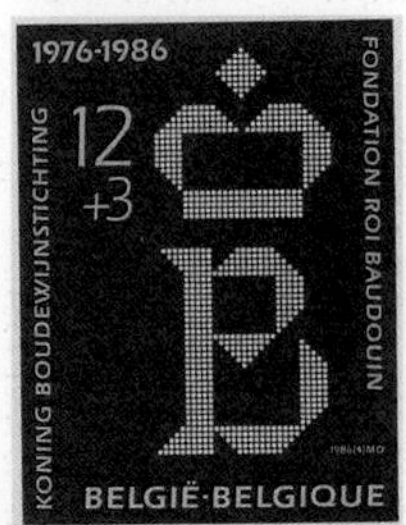

850 Emblem

1986. 10th Anniv of King Baudouin Foundation.

2867	**850**	12f.+3f. blue, light blue and grey	1·50	1·50

851 Virgin Mary

1986. "The Mystic Lamb" (altarpiece, Brothers Van Eyck). Multicoloured.

2868	9f.+2f. Type **851**	90	90
2869	13f.+3f. Christ in Majesty	1·30	1·30
2870	24f.+6f. St. John the Baptist	2·30	2·30
MS2871	92×150 mm. 50f.+12f. The Lamb (central panel) (48×37 mm)	9·00	9·00

852 Exhibits

1986. Stamp Day. 50th Anniv of Postal Museum, Brussels.

2872	**852**	13f. multicoloured	1·10	30

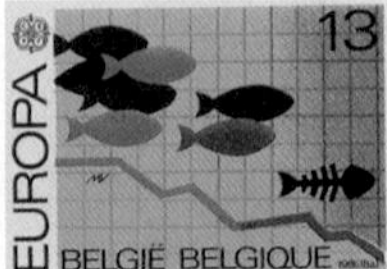

853 Living and Dead Fish and Graph

1986. Europa. Multicoloured.

2873	13f. Type **853**	1·90	30
2874	24f. Living and dead trees and graph	3·75	65

854 Malinois Shepherd Dog

1986. Belgian Dogs. Multicoloured.

2875	9f. Type **854**	85	40
2876	13f. Tervuren shepherd dog	1·30	30
2877	24f. Groenendael cattle dog	2·20	60
2878	26f. Flanders cattle dog	2·30	60

855 St. Ludger Church, Zele

1986. Tourist Publicity.

2879	**855**	9f. brown and flesh	70	35
2880	-	9f. red and pink	70	35
2881	-	13f. green & light green	1·10	35
2882	-	13f. black and green	1·10	35
2883	-	13f. blue and azure	1·10	35
2884	-	13f. brown & lt brown	1·10	35

DESIGNS—VERT: No. 2880, Town Hall, Wavre; 2882, Chapel of Our Lady of the Dunes, Bredene. HORIZ: 2881, Water-mills, Zwalm; 2883, Chateau Licot, Viroinval; 2884, Chateau d'Eynebourg, La Calamine.

856 Boy, Broken Skateboard and Red Triangle

1986. "Philately for the Young". 25th International Festival of Humour, Knokke.

2885	**856**	9f. black, green & red	70	40

857 Constant Permeke (artist)

1986. Celebrities. Multicoloured.

2886	9f. Type **857** (birth centenary)	70	35
2887	13f. Michael Edmond de Selys-Longchamps (naturalist)	1·20	35
2888	24f. Felix Timmermans (writer) (birth cent)	2·10	60
2889	26f. Maurice Careme (poet)	2·20	60

858 Academy Building, Ghent

1986. Centenary of Royal Academy for Dutch Language and Literature.

2890	**858**	9f. blue	70	35

859 Hops, Glass of Beer and Barley

1986. Belgian Beer.

2891	**859**	13f. multicoloured	1·20	30

860 Symbols of Provinces and National Colours

1986. 150th Anniv of Provincial Councils.

2892	**860**	13f. multicoloured	1·10	30

861 Lenoir Hydrocarbon Carriage, 1863

1986. "Solidarity". Cars. Multicoloured.

2893	9f.+2f. Type **861**	90	90
2894	13f.+3f. Pipe de Tourisme saloon, 1911	1·30	1·30
2895	24f.+6f. Minerva 22 h.p. coupe, 1930	2·40	2·40
2896	26f.+6f. FN 8 cylinder saloon, 1931	2·50	2·50

862 Snow Scene

1986. Christmas.

2897	**862**	13f.+1f. multicoloured	1·20	1·20

863 Tree and "100"

1986. Centenaries. Multicoloured.

2898	9f. Type **863** (Textile Workers Christian Union)	70	40
2899	13f. Tree and "100" (Christian Unions)	1·10	30

864 Corneel Heymans

1987. Belgian Red Cross. Nobel Physiology and Medicine Prize Winners. Each black, red and stone.

2900	13f.+3f. Type **864**	1·50	1·50
2901	24f.+6f. Albert Claude	2·75	2·75

865 Emblem

1987. "Flanders Technology International" Fair.

2902	**865**	13f. multicoloured	1·10	30

866 Bee Orchid

1987. European Environment Year. Multicoloured.

2903	9f.+2f. Type **866**	1·10	1·10
2904	24f.+6f. Small horse-shoe bat	2·40	2·40
2905	26f.+6f. Peregrine falcon ("Slechtvalk-Faucan Pelerin")	2·75	2·75

867 "Waiting" (detail of mural, Gustav Klimt)

1987. "Europalia 87 Austria" Festival.

2906	**867**	13f. multicoloured	1·10	30

868 Jakob Wiener (engraver)

1987. Stamp Day.

2907	**868**	13f. deep green and green	1·10	30

869 Penitents' Procession, Furnes

1987. Folklore Festivals. Multicoloured.

2908	9f. Type **869**	70	40
2909	13f. "John and Alice" (play), Wavre	1·10	30

870 Louvain-la-Neuve Church (Jean Cosse)

1987. Europa. Architecture. Multicoloured.

2910 13f. Type **870** 2·40 30

2911 24f. St.-Maartensdal (Regional Housing Association tower block), Louvain (Braem, de Mol and Moerkerke) 4·25 90

871 Statue of Gretry and Stage Set

1987. 20th Anniv of Wallonia Royal Opera.

2912 **871** 24f. multicoloured 2·10 70

872 Virelles Lake

1987. Tourist Publicity. Multicoloured.

2913 13f. St. Christopher's Church, Racour 1·10 30

2914 13f. Type **872** 1·10 30

2915 13f. Heimolen windmill, Keerbergen 1·10 30

2916 13f. Boondael Chapel 1·10 30

2917 13f. Statue of Jan Breydel and Pieter de Coninck, Bruges 1·10 30

873 Rowing

1987. Centenary of Royal Belgian Rowing Association (2918) and European Volleyball Championships (2919). Multicoloured.

2918 9f. Type **873** 70 40

2919 13f. Volleyball (27×37 mm) 1·10 30

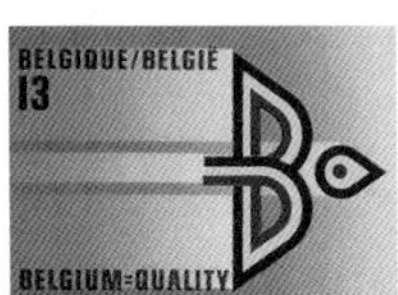

874 Emblem

1987. Foreign Trade Year.

2920 **874** 13f. multicoloured 1·10 30

875 "Leisure Time" (P. Paulus)

1987. Centenary of Belgian Social Law.

2921 **875** 26f. multicoloured 2·10 65

876 Willy and Wanda (comic strip characters)

1987. "Philately for the Young".

2922 **876** 9f. multicoloured 2·10 60

878 Rixensart Castle

1987. "Solidarity". Castles. Multicoloured.

2928 9f.+2f. Type **878** 90 90

2929 13f.+3f. Westerlo 1·20 1·20

2930 26f.+5f. Fallais 2·40 2·40

2931 50f.+12f. Gaasbeek 4·50 4·50

879 "Madonna and Child" (Remi Lens)

1987. Christmas.

2932 **879** 13f.+1f. multicoloured 1·20 1·20

880 Cross and Road

1987. 50th Anniv of Yellow and White Cross (home nursing organization).

2933 **880** 9f.+2f. multicoloured 1·20 1·20

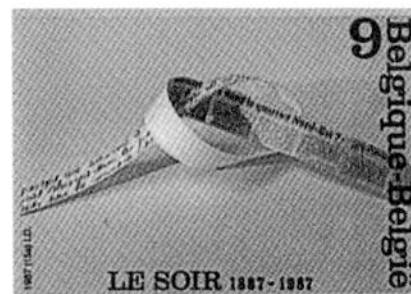

881 Newsprint ("Le Soir")

1987. Newspaper Centenaries.

2934 **881** 9f. multicoloured 85 35

2935 - 9f. black and brown 85 35

DESIGN—VERT: No. 2935, Type characters ("Het Laatste Nieuws" (1988)).

882 Lighthouse, "Snipe" (trawler) and Horse Rider in Sea

1988. The Sea. Multicoloured.

2936 10f. Type **882** 85 70

2937 10f. "Asannot" (trawler) and people playing on beach 85 70

2938 10f. Cross-channel ferry, yacht and bathing huts 85 70

2939 10f. Container ship, spotted redshank and oystercatcher 85 70

Nos. 2936/9 were issued together, *se-tenant*, forming a composite design.

883 "Flanders Alive" (cultural activities campaign)

1988. Regional Innovations.

2940 **883** 13f. multicoloured 1·10 30

2941 - 13f. black, yellow & red 1·10 30

DESIGN: No. 2941, "Operation Athena" emblem (technological advancement in Wallonia).

884 19th-century Postman (after James Thiriar)

1988. Stamp Day.

2942 **884** 13f. brown and cream 1·10 30

885 "Bengale Triomphant"

1988. Philatelic Promotion Fund. Illustrations from "60 Roses for a Queen" by Pierre-Joseph Redoute (1st series). Multicoloured.

2943 13f.+3f. Type **885** 1·50 1·50

2944 24f.+6f. "Centfeuille cristata" 2·40 2·40

MS2945 150×100 mm. 50f.+12f. White tea rose 8·50 8·50

See also Nos. 2979/**MS**2981, 3009/**MS**3011 and **MS**3025.

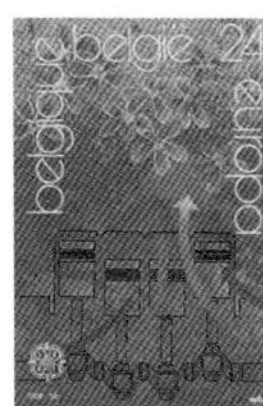

886 Non-polluting Motor

1988. Europa. Transport and Communications. Multicoloured.

2946 13f. Dish aerial 2·40 30

2947 24f. Type **886** 4·75 90

887 Table Tennis

1988. Olympic Games, Seoul. Multicoloured.

2948 9f.+2f. Type **887** 1·30 1·30

2949 13f.+3f. Cycling 1·50 1·50

MS2950 125×85 mm. 50f.+12f. Running 8·50 8·50

888 Amay Tower

1988. Tourist Publicity.

2951 **888** 9f. black and brown 85 35

2952 - 9f. black and blue 85 35

2953 - 9f. black, green and pink 85 35

2954 - 13f. black and pink 1·10 30

2955 - 13f. black and grey 1·10 30

DESIGNS—VERT: No. 2952, Lady of Hanswijk Basilica, Malines; 2954, Old Town Hall and village pump, Peer. HORIZ: No. 2953, St. Sernin's Church, Waimes; 2955, Basilica of Our Lady of Bon Secours, Peruwelz.

889 Monnet

1988. Birth Centenary of Jean Monnet (statesman).

2956 **889** 13f. black and cream 1·10 30

890 Tapestry (detail) and Academy Building

1988. 50th Annivs of Royal Belgian Academy of Medicine (2957) and Royal Belgian Academy of Sciences, Literature and Fine Arts (2958). Multicoloured.

2957 9f. Type **890** 70 35

2958 9f. Symbols of Academy and building 70 35

891 Antwerp Ethnographical Museum Exhibits

1988. Cultural Heritage. Multicoloured.

2959 9f. Type **891** 85 35

2960 13f. Tomb of Lord Gilles Othon and Jacqueline de Lalaing, St. Martin's Church, Trazegnies 1·10 30

2961 24f. Organ, St. Bartholomew's Church, Geraardsbergen 2·10 70

2962 26f. St. Hadelin's reliquary, St. Martin's Church, Vise 2·30 70

892 Spirou (comic strip character) and Stamp

1988. "Philately for the Young". 50th Anniv of "Spirou" (comic).

2963 **892** 9f. multicoloured 1·80 60

893 Jacques Brel (songwriter)

1988. "Solidarity". Death Anniversaries. Mult.

2964 9f.+2f. Type **893** (10th) 1·50 1·50

2965 13f.+3f. Jef Denyn (carilloner) (47th) 1·50 1·50

2966 26f.+6f. Fr. Ferdinand Verbiest (astronomer) (300th) 2·40 2·40

894 "75"

1988. 75th Anniv of Belgian Giro Bank.

2967 **894** 13f. multicoloured 1·20 30

895 Winter Scene

1988. Christmas.

2968	**895**	9f. multicoloured	80	35

896 Standard Bearer and Guards of Royal Mounted Escort

1988. 50th Anniv of Royal Mounted Escort.

2969	**896**	13f. multicoloured	1·10	30

897 Wooden Press, 1600

1988. Printing Presses.

2970	**897**	9f. black, pink and blue	85	30
2971	-	24f. brown, pink and deep brown	1·90	65
2972	-	26f. green, pink and light green	2·10	60

DESIGNS—VERT: 24f. 18th-cent Stanhope metal letter-press. HORIZ: 26f. 19th-cent Krause lithographic press.

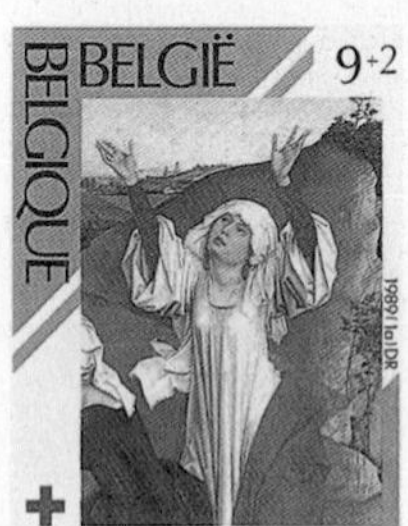

898 "Crucifixion of Christ" (detail, Rogier van der Weyden)

1989. Belgian Red Cross. Paintings. Mult.

2973		9f.+2f. Type **898**	1·20	1·20
2974		13f.+3f. "Virgin and Child" (Gerard David)	1·70	1·70
2975		24f.+6f. "The Good Samaritan" (detail, Denis van Alsloot)	2·50	2·50

899 Marche en Famenne

1989. Lace-making Towns.

2976	**899**	9f. green, black & brown	85	40
2977	-	13f. blue, black & grey	1·10	30
2978	-	13f. red, black & grey	1·10	30

DESIGNS: No. 2977, Bruges; 2978, Brussels.

1989. Philatelic Promotion Fund. "60 Roses for a Queen" by Pierre-Joseph Redoute (2nd series). As T 885. Multicoloured.

2979	13f.+5f. "Centfeuille unique melee de rouge"	1·50	1·50
2980	24f.+6f. "Bengale a grandes feuilles"	2·40	2·40
MS2981	150×100 mm. 50f.+17f. "Aime vibere"	8·50	8·50

900 Post-chaise and Mail Coach

1989. Stamp Day.

2982	**900**	13f. yellow, black & brn	1·00	30

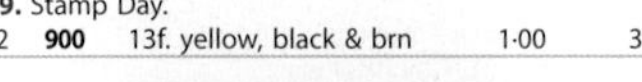

901 Marbles

1989. Europa. Children's Games and Toys. Multicoloured.

2983	13f. Type **901**	2·20	30
2984	24f. Jumping-jack	3·75	70

902 Palette on Column

1989. 325th Anniv of Royal Academy of Fine Arts, Antwerp.

2985	**902**	13f. multicoloured	1·00	30

903 Brussels (image scaled to 63% of original size)

1989. 3rd Direct Elections to European Parliament.

2986	**903**	13f. multicoloured	1·00	30

904 Hand (detail, "Creation of Adam", Michelangelo)

1989. Bicentenary of French Declaration of Rights of Man.

2987	**904**	13f. black, red and blue	1·00	30

905 St. Tillo's Church, Izegem

1989. Tourist Publicity. Multicoloured.

2988	9f. Type **905**	85	35
2989	9f. Logne Castle, Ferrieres (vert)	85	35
2990	13f. Antoing Castle (vert)	1·20	30
2991	13f. St. Laurentius's Church, Lokeren (vert)	1·20	30

906 Mallard

1989. Ducks. Multicoloured.

2992	13f. Type **906**	1·50	60
2993	13f. Green-winged teal ("Sarcelle d'Hiver")	1·50	60
2994	13f. Common shoveler ("Canard Souchet")	1·50	60
2995	13f. Pintail ("Canard Pilet")	1·50	60

907 "Shogun Uesugi Shigefusa" (Kamakura period wood figure)

1989. "Europalia 89 Japan" Festival.

2996	**907**	24f. multicoloured	1·90	70

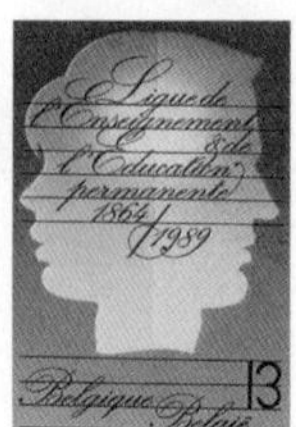

908 Profiles

1989. 125th Anniv of League of Teaching and Permanent Education.

2997	**908**	13f. multicoloured	1·00	30

909 Map

1989. 150th Anniv of Division of Limburg between Netherlands and Belgium.

2998	**909**	13f. multicoloured	1·00	30

910 Nibbs (comic strip character)

1989. "Philately for the Young".

2999	**910**	9f. multicoloured	1·50	50

911 Flower Beds in Greenhouse

1989. "Solidarity". Royal Greenhouses, Laeken. Multicoloured.

3000	9f.+3f. Statue and greenhouses (horiz)	1·20	1·20
3001	13f.+4f. Type **911**	1·60	1·60
3002	24f.+5f. External view of greenhouse	2·30	2·30
3003	26f.+6f. Trees in greenhouse	2·50	2·50

912 Treble Clef

1989. 50th Anniv of Queen Elisabeth Musical Chapel, Waterloo.

3004	**912**	24f.+6f. multicoloured	2·40	2·40

913 Army Musicians

1989. Christmas. Centenary of Salvation Army in Belgium.

3005	**913**	9f. multicoloured	80	30

914 Fr. Damien and Church

1989. Death Cent of Fr. Damien (missionary).

3006	**914**	24f. multicoloured	2·10	65

915 Fr. Daens

1989. 150th Birth Anniv of Fr. Adolf Daens (social reformer).

3007	**915**	9f. turquoise and green	70	30

916 "Courier" (Albrecht Durer)

1990. 500th Anniv of Regular European Postal Services.

3008	**916**	14f. chocolate, buff and brown	1·10	30

1990. Philatelic Promotion Fund. "60 Roses for a Queen" by Pierre-Joseph Redoute (3rd series). As T 885. Multicoloured.

3009	14f.+7f. "Bengale Desprez"	1·80	1·80
3010	25f.+12f. "Bengale Philippe"	3·00	3·00
MS3011	151×100 mm. 50f.+20f. "Maria Leonida"	8·50	8·50

917 "Iris florentina"

1990. Ghent Flower Show. Multicoloured.

3012	10f. Type **917**	85	50
3013	14f. "Cattleya harrisoniana"	1·20	35
3014	14f. "Lilium bulbiferum"	1·20	35

918 Emilienne Brunfaut (women's rights activist)

1990. International Women's Day.

3015	**918**	25f. red and black	2·10	85

919 Special Olympics

1990. Sporting Events. Multicoloured.

3016		10f. Type **919**	80	50
3017		14f. Football (World Cup football championship, Italy)	1·20	35
3018		25f. Disabled pictogram and ball (Gold Cup wheelchair basketball championship, Bruges)	1·90	70

920 Water, Tap and Heart

1990. 75th Anniv of Foundation of National Water Supply Society (predecessor of present water-supply companies).

3019	**920**	14f. multicoloured	1·10	30

921 "Postman Roulin" (Vincent van Gogh)

1990. Stamp Day.

3020	**921**	14f. multicoloured	1·10	30

922 Worker and Crowd

1990. Centenary of Labour Day.

3021	**922**	25f. brown, pink & black	2·10	85

923 Liege I Post Office

1990. Europa. Post Office Buildings.

3022	-	14f. black and blue	2·40	35
3023	**923**	25f. black and red	4·50	85

DESIGN—HORIZ: 14f. Ostend I Post Office.

924 Monument of the Lys, Courtrai

1990. 50th Anniv of the 18 Days Campaign (resistance to German invasion).

3024	**924**	14f. black, yellow & red	1·20	30

1990. "Belgica 90" International Stamp Exhibition, Brussels. "60 Roses for a Queen" by Pierre-Joseph Rerdoute (4th series). Sheet 189×120 mm containing vert designs as T 885. Multicoloured.

MS3025		14f. Tricoloured rose; 14f. "Belle Rubanee"; 14f. "Mycrophylla"; 25f. "Amelie"; 25f. "Adelaide"; 25f. "Helene" (sold at 220f.)	36·00	36·00

925 Battle Scene

1990. 175th Anniv of Battle of Waterloo.

3026	**925**	25f. multicoloured	2·10	1·80

926 Berendrecht Lock, Antwerp

1990. Tourist Publicity. Multicoloured.

3027		10f. Type **926**	95	50
3028		10f. Procession of Bayard Steed, Termonde	95	50
3029		14f. St. Rolende's March, Gerpinnes (vert)	1·10	35
3030		14f. Lommel (1000th anniv)	1·10	35
3031		14f. St. Clement's Church, Watermael	1·10	35

927 King Baudouin

1990

3032	**927**	14f. multicoloured	1·30	25

928 Eurasian Perch

1990. Fishes. Multicoloured.

3033		14f. Type **928**	2·10	70
3034		14f. Eurasian minnow ("Vairon")	2·10	70
3035		14f. European bitterling ("Bouviere")	2·10	70
3036		14f. Three-spined stickle-back ("Epinoche")	2·10	70

929 Orchestra and Children (image scaled to 63% of original size)

1990. "Solidarity". Multicoloured.

3037		10f.+2f. Type **929** (50th anniv of Jeunesses Musicales)	2·20	2·20
3038		14f.+3f. Count of Egmont (16th-century campaigner for religious tolerance) and Beethoven (composer of "Egmont" overture)	2·75	2·75
3039		25f.+6f. Jozef Cantre (sculptor) and sculptures (birth centenary)	3·75	3·75

930 Lucky Luke (comic strip character)

1990. "Philately for the Young".

3040	**930**	10f. multicoloured	1·80	60

931 St. Bernard

1990. 900th Birth Anniv of St. Bernard (Abbot of Clairvaux and Church mediator).

3041	**931**	25f. black and flesh	2·10	70

932 "Pepingen, Winter 1977" (Jozef Lucas)

1990. Christmas.

3042	**932**	10f. multicoloured	85	30

933 "Self-portrait"

1990. 300th Death Anniv of David Teniers, the Younger (painter). Multicoloured.

3043		10f. Type **933**	85	35
3044		14f. "Dancers"	1·20	35
3045		25f. "Peasants playing Bowls outside Village Inn"	2·20	70

934 King Baudouin and Queen Fabiola (photograph by Valeer Vanbeckbergen)

1990. Royal 30th Wedding Anniversary.

3046	**934**	50f.+15f. mult	8·50	8·50

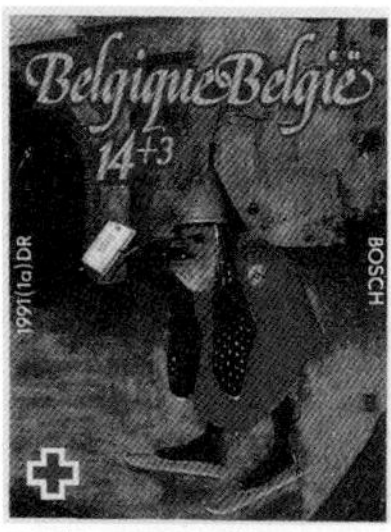

935 "Temptation of St. Anthony" (detail, Hieronymus Bosch)

1991. Belgian Red Cross. Paintings. Mult.

3047		14f.+3f. Type **935**	2·75	2·75
3048		25f.+6f. "The Annunciation" (detail, Dirck Bouts)	4·00	4·00

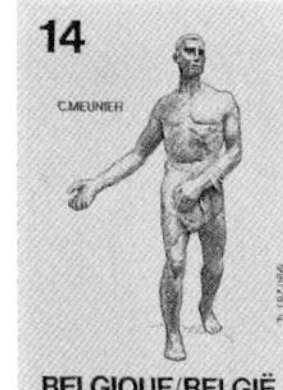

936 "The Sower" (detail of "Monument to Labour", Brussels) (Constantin Meunier)

1991. 19th-Century Sculpture.

3049	**936**	14f. black & cinnamon	1·10	35
3050	-	25f. black and blue	1·80	70

DESIGN: 25f. Detail of Brabo Fountain, Antwerp (Jef Lambeaux).

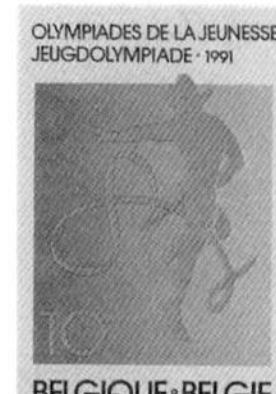

937 Rhythmic Gymnastics (European Youth Olympic Days, Brussels)

1991. Sports Meetings.

3051	**937**	10f. grey, mauve & blk	80	30
3052	-	10f. grey, green & black	80	30

DESIGN: No. 3052, Korfball (Third World Championship, Belgium).

938 New Stamp Printing Office, Malines (Hugo van Hoecke)

1991. Stamp Day.

3053	**938**	14f. multicoloured	1·10	35

939 Cogwheels

1991. Centenary of Liberal Trade Union.

3054	**939**	25f. blue, light blue and deep blue	1·90	70

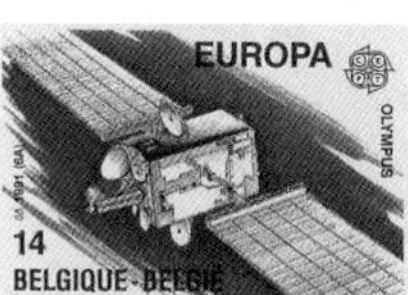

940 "Olympus 1" Communications Satellite

1991. Europa. Europe in Space. Multicoloured.

3055		14f. Type **940**	2·40	30
3056		25f. "Ariane 5" rocket carrying space shuttle "Hermes"	4·00	80

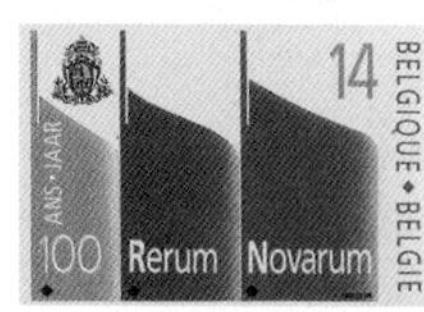

941 Leo XIII's Arms and Standard, and Christian Labour Movement Banners

1991. Centenary of "Rerum Novarum" (encyclical letter from Pope Leo XIII on workers' rights).

3057	**941**	14f. multicoloured	1·10	30

942 "Isabella of Portugal and Philip the Good" (anon)

1991. "Europalia 91 Portugal" Festival.

3058	**942**	14f. multicoloured	1·10	30

943 Neptune Grottoes, Couvin

1991. Tourist Publicity. Multicoloured.

3059	14f. Type **943**	1·10	35
3060	14f. Dieleghem Abbey, Jette	1·10	35
3061	14f. Niel Town Hall (vert)	1·10	35
3062	14f. Hautes Fagnes nature reserve	1·10	35
3063	14f. Giant Rolarius, Roeselare (vert)	1·10	35

944 King Baudouin (photograph by Dimitri Ardelean)

1991. 60th Birthday (1990) and 40th Anniv of Accession to Throne of King Baudouin.

3064	**944**	14f. multicoloured	2·20	30

945 Academy Building, Caduceus and Leopold I

1991. 150th Anniv of Royal Academy of Medicine.

3065	**945**	10f. multicoloured	80	35

946 "The English Coast at Dover"

1991. 61st Death Anniv of Alfred Finch (painter and ceramic artist).

3066	**946**	25f. multicoloured	2·00	70

947 Death Cap

1991. Fungi. Multicoloured.

3067	14f. Type **947**	2·10	85
3068	14f. The Blusher (inscr "Golmotte")	2·10	85
3069	14f. Flaky-stemmed witches' mushroom (inscr "Bolet a pied rouge")	2·10	85
3070	14f. "Hygrocybe persistens" (inscr "Hygrophore jaune conique")	2·10	85

948 Hands reaching through Bars

1991. 30th Anniv of Amnesty International (3071) and 11th Anniv of Belgian Branch of Medecins sans Frontieres (3072). Multicoloured.

3071	25f. Type **948**	2·00	70
3072	25f. Doctor examining baby	2·00	70

1991. Birds (2nd series). As T 841. Mult.

3073	50c. Goldcrest ("Roitelet Huppe")	15	15
3074	1f. Redpoll ("Sizerin Flamme")	25	15
3075	2f. Blackbird ("Merle Noir")	25	15
3076	3f. Reed bunting ("Bruant des Roseaux")	50	15
3077	4f. Pied wagtail ("Bergeronette Grise")	45	15
3078	5f. Barn swallow ("Hirondelle de Cheminee")	45	15
3079	5f.50 Jay ("Geai des Chenes")	65	25
3080	6f. White-throated dipper ("Cincle Plongeur")	65	15
3081	6f.50 Sedge-warbler ("Phragmite des Jones")	65	25
3082	7f. Golden oriole ("Loriot")	75	15
3083	8f. Great tit ("Mesange Charbonniere")	75	15
3084	9f. Song thrush ("Grive Musicienne")	90	25
3085	10f. Western greenfinch ("Verdier")	95	25
3086	11f. Winter wren ("Troglodyte Mignon")	1·00	15
3087	13f. House sparrow ("Moineau Domestique")	1·30	15
3088	14f. Willow warbler ("Pouillot Fitis")	1·30	25
3088a	16f. Bohemian waxwing ("Jaseur Boreal")	1·60	15

949 Exhibition Emblem

1991. "Telecom 91" International Telecommuni- cations Exhibition, Geneva.

3089	**949**	14f. multicoloured	1·10	30

950 Blake and Mortimer in "The Yellow Mark" (Edgar P. Jacobs)

1991. "Philately for the Young". Comic Strips. Multicoloured.

3090	14f. Type **950**	2·00	1·30
3091	14f. Cori the ship boy in "The Ill-fated Voyage" (Bob de Moor)	2·00	1·30
3092	14f. "Cities of the Fantastic" (Francois Schuiten)	2·00	1·30
3093	14f. "Boule and Bill" (Jean Roba)	2·00	1·30

951 Charles Dekeukeleire

1991. "Solidarity". Film Makers.

3094	**951**	10f.+2f. black, brown and green	1·30	1·30
3095	-	14f.+3f. black, orange and brown	1·90	1·90
3096	-	25f.+6f. black, ochre and brown	3·50	3·50

DESIGNS: 14f. Jacques Ledoux; 25f. Jacques Feyder.

952 Printing Press forming "100" ("Gazet van Antwerpen")

1991. Newspaper Centenaries. Multicoloured.

3097	**952**	10f. black, lt grn & grn	80	30
3098	-	10f. yellow, blue & blk	80	30

DESIGN: No. 3098, Cancellation on "stamp" ("Het Volk").

953 "Our Lady rejoicing in the Child" (icon, Chevetogne Abbey)

1991. Christmas.

3099	**953**	10f. multicoloured	75	40

954 Mozart and Score

1991. Death Bicentenary of Wolfgang Amadeus Mozart (composer).

3100	**954**	25f. purple, bl & ultram	2·10	1·00

955 Speed Skating

1992. Olympic Games, Albertville and Barcelona. Multicoloured.

3101	10f.+2f. Type **955**	1·40	1·40
3102	10f.+2f. Baseball	1·40	1·40
3103	14f.+3f. Tennis (horiz)	1·90	1·90
3104	25f.+6f. Clay-pigeon shooting	3·50	3·50

956 Fire Hose and Service Emblem

1992. Fire Service.

3105	**956**	14f. multicoloured	1·10	30

957 Flames and Silhouette of Man

1992. The Resistance.

3106	**957**	14f. yellow, black & red	1·10	30

958 Tapestry and Carpet

1992. Prestige Occupations. Multicoloured.

3107	10f. Type **958**	75	45
3108	14f. Chef's hat and cutlery (10th anniv (1991) of Association of Belgian Master Chefs)	1·10	30
3109	27f. Diamond and "100" (centenary (1993) of Antwerp Diamond Club)	2·20	70

959 Belgian Pavilion and Exhibition Emblem

1992. "Expo '92" World's Fair, Seville.

3110	**959**	14f. multicoloured	1·10	30

960 King Baudouin **961**

1992

3111	**960**	15f. red	1·10	15
3115	**960**	28f. green	2·50	70
3120	**961**	100f. green	9·50	65

962 Van Noten at Work

1992. Stamp Day. 10th Death Anniv of Jean van Noten (stamp designer).

3124	**962**	15f. black and red	1·10	30

963 "White Magic No. VI"

1992. Original Art Designs for Stamps. Mult.

3125	15f. Type **963**	1·10	40
3126	15f. "Colours" (horiz)	1·10	40

964 Compass Rose, Setting Sun and Harbour

1992. Europa. 500th Anniv of Discovery of America. Multicoloured.

3127	15f. Type **964**	2·50	45
3128	28f. Globe and astrolabe forming "500"	5·00	95

965 Faces of Different Colours

1992. Anti-racism.

3129	**965**	15f. grey, black & pink	1·10	30

966 "The Hamlet" (Jacob Smits)

1992. Belgian Paintings in Orsay Museum, Paris. Multicoloured.

3130	11f. Type **966**	80	40
3131	15f. "The Bath" (Alfred Stevens)	1·40	30
3132	30f. "Man at the Helm" (Theo van Rysselberghe)	2·50	90

967 Proud Margaret

1992. Folk Tales. Multicoloured.

3133		11f.+2f. Type **967**	1·60	1·60
3134		15f.+3f. Witches ("Les Macrales")	2·20	2·20
3135		28f.+6f. Reynard the fox	3·75	3·75

968 Mannekin-Pis, Brussels

1992. Tourist Publicity. Multicoloured.

3136		15f. Type **968**	1·10	30
3137		15f. Former Landcommandery of Teutonic Order, Alden Biesen (now Flemish cultural centre) (horiz)	1·10	30
3138		15f. Andenne (1300th anniv)	1·10	30
3139		15f. Carnival revellers on Fools' Monday, Renaix (horiz)	1·10	30
3140		15f. Great Procession (religious festival), Tournai (horiz)	1·10	30

969 European Polecat

1992. Mammals. Multicoloured.

3141		15f. Type **969**	1·90	80
3142		15f. Eurasian red squirrel	1·90	80
3143		15f. Eurasian hedgehog	1·90	80
3144		15f. Common dormouse	1·90	80

970 Henri van der Noot, Jean van der Meersch and Jean Vonck

1992. 203rd Anniv of Brabant Revolution.

3145	**970**	15f. multicoloured	1·10	30

971 Arms of Thurn and Taxis

1992. 500th Anniv of Mention of Thurn and Taxis Postal Services in Lille Account Books.

3146	**971**	15f. multicoloured	1·10	30

972 Gaston Lagaffe (cartoon character)

1992. "Philately for the Young".

3147	**972**	15f. multicoloured	1·50	45

973 Star, "B" and Map

1992. European Single Market.

3148	**973**	15f. multicoloured	1·10	40

974 Okapi

1992. 150th Anniv of Antwerp Zoo. Mult.

3149		15f. Type **974**	1·10	40
3150		30f. Golden-headed tamarin	2·30	50

975 "Place Royale in Winter" (Luc de Decker)

1992. Christmas.

3151	**975**	11f. multicoloured	75	30

976 "Man with Pointed Hat" (Adriaen Brouwer)

1993. Belgian Red Cross. Paintings. Mult.

3152		15f.+3f. Type **976**	2·40	2·40
3153		28f.+7f. "Nereid and Triton" (Peter Paul Rubens) (horiz)	4·75	4·75

977 Council of Leptines, 743

1993. Historical Events. Multicoloured.

3154		11f. Type **977**	75	40
3155		15f. Queen Beatrix and King Matthias I Corvinus of Hungary (detail of "Missale Romanum") (77×24 mm)	1·30	40
3156		30f. Battle scene (Battles of Neerwinden, 1673 and 1773)	2·50	75
MS3157		105×155 mm. 28f. Illustration from Matthias I Corvinus's *Missale Romanum*, 1485 (54×39 mm)	2·50	2·50

978 Town Hall

1993. Antwerp, European City of Culture. Mult.

3158		15f. Panorama of Antwerp (76×24 mm)	1·30	30
3159		15f. Type **978**	1·30	30
3160		15f. "Study of Women's Heads and Male Torso" (Jacob Jordaens)	1·30	30
3161		15f. St. Job's altarpiece, Schoonbroek	1·30	30
3162		15f. "Angels" (stained glass window by Eugeen Yoors, Mother of God Chapel, Marie-Josee Institute, Elisabethville) (vert)	1·30	30

979 1893 2f. Stamp

1993. Stamp Day.

3163	**979**	15f. multicoloured	1·10	30

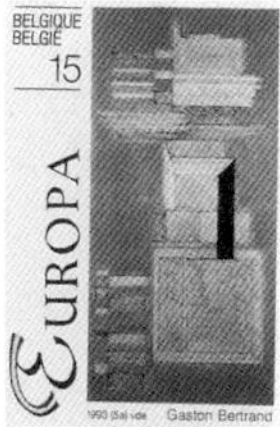

980 "Florence 1960" (Gaston Bertrand)

1993. Europa. Contemporary Art. Multicoloured.

3164		15f. Type **980**	1·30	30
3165		28f. "The Gig" (Constant Permeke)	2·50	75

981 Red Admiral ("Vanessa atalanta")

1993. Butterflies. Multicoloured.

3166		15f. Type **981**	1·10	40
3167		15f. Purple emperor ("Apatura iris")	1·10	40
3168		15f. Peacock ("Inachis io")	1·10	40
3169		15f. Small tortoiseshell ("Aglais urticae")	1·10	40

982 Knot

1993. 150th Anniv of Alumni of Free University of Brussels Association.

3170	**982**	15f. blue and black	1·10	30

983 Mayan Warrior (statuette)

1993. "Europalia 93 Mexico" Festival.

3171	**983**	15f. multicoloured	1·10	30

984 Ommegang, Brussels

1993. Folklore Festivals. Multicoloured.

3172		11f. Type **984**	95	45
3173		15f. Royale Moncrabeau, Namur	1·10	30
3174		28f. Stilt-walkers, Merchtem (vert)	1·90	75

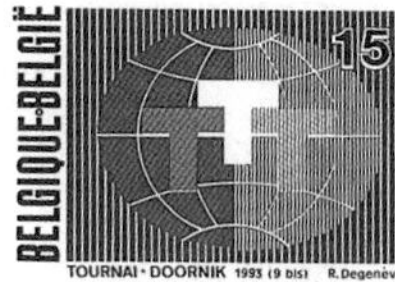

985 La Hulpe Castle

1993. Tourist Publicity.

3175	**985**	15f. black and blue	1·10	30
3176	-	15f. black and lilac	1·10	30
3177	-	15f. black and grey	1·10	30
3178	-	15f. black and pink	1·10	30
3179	-	15f. black and green	1·10	30

DESIGNS—HORIZ: No. 3176, Cortewalle Castle, Beveren; 3177, Jehay Castle; 3179, Raeren Castle. VERT: No. 3178, Arenberg Castle, Heverlee.

986 Emblem

1993. 2nd International Triennial Textile Exhibition, Tournai.

3180	**986**	15f. blue, red and black	1·10	30

987 Presidency Emblem

1993. Belgian Presidency of European Community Council.

3181	**987**	15f. multicoloured	1·10	30

988 Magritte

1993. 25th Death Anniv (1992) of Rene Magritte (artist).

3182	**988**	30f. multicoloured	2·20	90

989 King Baudouin

1993. King Baudouin Commemoration.

3183	**989**	15f. black and blue	1·30	25

990 Red and White Cat

1993. Cats. Multicoloured.

3184		15f. Type **990**	1·40	75
3185		15f. Tabby and white cat standing on rock	1·40	75
3186		15f. Silver tabby lying on wall	1·40	75

3187 15f. Tortoiseshell and white cat sitting by gardening tools 1·40 75

991 Highlighted Cancer Cell

1993. Anti-cancer Campaign.
3188 **991** 15f.+3f. multicoloured 1·90 1·90

992 Frontispiece

1993. 450th Anniv of "De Humani Corporis Fabrica" (treatise on human anatomy) by Andreas Vesalius.
3189 **992** 15f. black, brown & red 1·10 30

993 Natacha (cartoon character)

1993. "Philately for the Young".
3190 **993** 15f. multicoloured 1·40 50

994 Sun's Rays

1993. 50th Anniv of Publication of "Le Faux Soir" (resistance newspaper).
3191 **994** 11f. multicoloured 80 50

995 "Madonna and Child" (statue, Our Lady of the Chapel, Brussels)

1993. Christmas.
3192 **995** 11f. multicoloured 75 30

1993 . 14 bis Serge Creuz
996 Child looking at Globe

1993. Children's Town Councils.
3193 **996** 15f. multicoloured 1·10 30

997 King Albert II **998** King Albert II

1993
3194 **997** 16f. multicoloured 1·70 15
3195 **997** 16f. turquoise and blue 1·30 20
3196 **997** 20f. brown and stone 1·70 25
3197 **997** 30f. purple and mauve 1·90 25
3198 **997** 32f. orange and yellow 2·20 15
3199 **997** 40f. red and mauve 3·00 15
3200 **997** 50f. myrtle and green 5·25 25
3201 **998** 100f. multicoloured 7·50 45
3202 **998** 200f. multicoloured 16·00 65

999 "Ma Toute Belle" (Serge Vandercam)

1994. Painters' Designs. Multicoloured.
3210 16f. Type **999** 1·10 40
3211 16f. "The Malleable Darkness" (Octave Landuyt) (horiz) 1·10 40

1000 Olympic Flames and Rings

1994. Sports. Multicoloured.
3212 16f.+3f. Type **1000** (cent of International Olympic Committee) 2·20 2·20
3213 16f.+3f. Footballers (World Cup Football Championship, U.S.A.) 2·20 2·20
3214 16f.+3f. Skater (Winter Olympic Games, Lillehammer, Norway) 2·20 2·20

1001 Hanriot HD-1

1994. Biplanes. Multicoloured.
3215 13f. Type **1001** 1·10 45
3216 15f. Spad XIII 1·30 40
3217 30f. Schrenck FBA.H flying boat 2·20 75
3218 32f. Stampe SV-4B biplane 2·30 65

1002 Masthead of "Le Jour-Le Courrier" (centenary)

1994. Newspaper Anniversaries. Multicoloured.
3219 16f. Type **1002** 1·10 40
3220 16f. Masthead of "La Wallonie" (75th anniv) (horiz) 1·10 40

1003 "Fall of the Golden Calf" (detail, Fernand Allard l'Olivier)

1994. Centenary of Charter of Quaregnon (social charter).
3221 **1003** 16f. multicoloured 1·10 45

1004 1912 5f. Stamp

1994. Stamp Day. 60th Death Anniv of King Albert I.
3222 **1004** 16f. purple, mauve & bl 1·10 40

1005 Reconciliation of Duke John I and Arnold, Squire of Wezemaal

1994. 700th Death Anniv of John I, Duke of Brabant. Illustrations from 15th-century "Brabantse Yeesten". Multicoloured.
3223 13f. Type **1005** 95 45
3224 16f. Tournament at wedding of his son John to Margaret of York, 1290 1·10 40
3225 30f. Battle of Woeringen (77×25 mm) 2·40 90

1006 Georges Lemaitre (formulator of expanding Universe and of "big bang" theory)

1994. Europa. Discoveries and Inventions. Mult.
3226 16f. Type **1006** 1·30 40
3227 30f. Gerardus Mercator (inventor of Mercator projection in cartography) 2·50 90

1007 Father Damien (missionary and leprosy worker)

1994. Visit of Pope John Paul II. Mult.
3228 16f. Type **1007** (beatification) 1·10 30
3229 16f. St. Mutien-Marie (5th anniv of canonization) 1·10 30

1008 St. Peter's Church, Bertem

1994. Tourist Publicity. Multicoloured.
3230 16f. Type **1008** 1·10 40
3231 16f. St. Bavo's Church, Kanegem (vert) 1·10 40
3232 16f. Royal St. Mary's Church, Schaarbeek 1·10 40
3233 16f. St. Gery's Church, Aubechies 1·10 40
3234 16f. Sts. Peter and Paul's Church, St.-Severin en Condroz (vert) 1·10 40

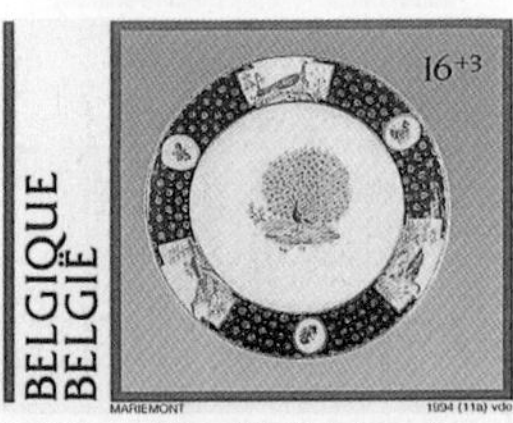

1009 Tournai Porcelain Plate from Duke of Orleans Service (Mariemont Museum)

1994. Museum Exhibits. Multicoloured.
3235 16f.+3f. Type **1009** 1·90 1·90
3236 16f.+3f. Etterbeek porcelain coffee cup and saucer (Louvain Municipal Museum) 1·90 1·90
MS3237 125×90 mm. 50f.+11f. Delft containers (Pharmacy Museum, Maaseik) 9·50 9·50

1010 Guillame Lekeu (composer)

1994. Anniversaries. Multicoloured.
3238 16f. Type **1010** (death cent) 1·10 40
3239 16f. Detail of painting by Hans Memling (500th death anniv) 1·10 40

1011 Generals Crerar, Montgomery and Bradley and Allied Troops (image scaled to 61% of original size)

1994. 50th Anniv of Liberation.
3240 **1011** 16f. multicoloured 1·30 40

1012 Marsh Marigold ("Caltha palustris")

1994. Flowers. Multicoloured.
3241 16f. Type **1012** 1·60 75
3242 16f. White helleborine ("Cephalanthera damasonium") 1·60 75
3243 16f. Sea bindweed ("Calystegia soldanella") 1·60 75
3244 16f. Broad-leaved helleborine ("Epipactis helleborine") 1·60 75

1013 Cubitus (cartoon character)

1994. "Philately for the Young".
3245 **1013** 16f. multicoloured 1·60 50

1014 Simenon and Bridge of Arches, Liege

1994. 5th Death Anniv of Georges Simenon (novelist).
3246 **1014** 16f. multicoloured 1·60 40

The depiction of the bridge alludes to Simenon's first novel "Au Pont des Arches".

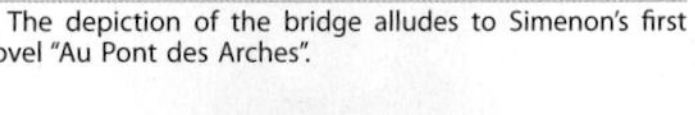

1015 Deaf Man and Butterfly

1994. "Solidarity".
3247 **1015** 16f.+3f. mult 1·50 1·50

1016 Santa Claus on Rooftop

1994. Christmas.

3248	**1016**	13f. multicoloured	95	40

1017 Field and Flax Knife (Flax Museum, Courtrai)

1995. Museums. Multicoloured.

3249	16f.+3f. Type **1017**	1·40	1·40
3250	16f.+3f. River and pump (Water and Fountain Museum, Genval)	1·40	1·40
MS3251	125×90 mm. 34f.+6f. Mask (International Carnival and Mask Museum, Binche)	3·75	3·75

The premium was for the promotion of philately.

1018 Emblem

1995. Anniversaries. Anniversary emblems.

3252	**1018**	16f. red, blue & black	1·10	40
3253	-	16f. multicoloured	1·10	40
3254	-	16f. multicoloured	1·10	40
3255	-	16f. red, black & brown	1·10	40

ANNIVERSARIES: No. 3252, 50th anniv of August Vermeylen Fund; 3253, Centenary of Touring Club of Belgium; 3254, Centenary of Federation of Belgian Enterprises; 3255, 50th anniv of Social Security in Belgium.

1019 "Hibiscus rosa-sinensis"

1995. Ghent Flower Show. Multicoloured.

3256	13f. Type **1019**	95	50
3257	16f. Azalea	1·30	40
3258	30f. Fuchsia	2·20	75

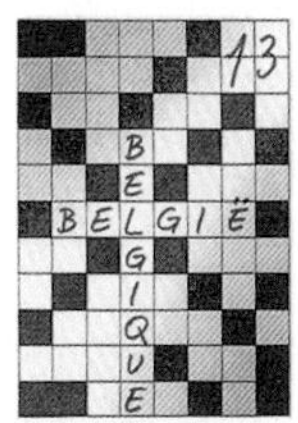

1020 Crossword Puzzle

1995. Games and Pastimes. Multicoloured.

3259	13f. Type **1020**	95	45
3260	16f. King (chess piece)	1·10	40
3261	30f. Scrabble	2·20	75
3262	34f. Queen (playing cards)	2·30	95

1021 Frans de Troyer (promoter of thematic philately)

1995. Post Day.

3263	**1021**	16f. black, stone & orge	1·10	40

1022 Watch Tower and Barbed Wire Fence

1995. Europa. Peace and Freedom. Mult.

3264	16f. Type **1022** (50th anniv of liberation of concentration camps)	2·50	90
3265	30f. Nuclear cloud (25th anniv of Non-Proliferation Treaty)	4·50	90

1023 Soldiers of the Irish Brigade and Memorial Cross

1995. 250th Anniv of Battle of Fontenoy.

3266	**1023**	16f. multicoloured	1·30	30

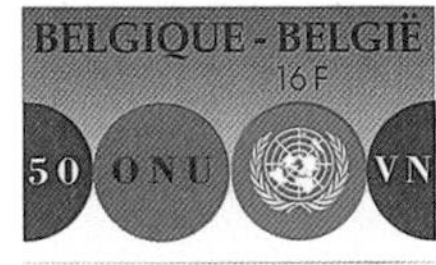

1024 U.N. Emblem

1995. 50th Anniv of U.N.O.

3267	**1024**	16f. multicoloured	1·10	40

1025 "Sauvagemont, Maransart" (Pierre Alechinsky)

1995. Artists' Philatelic Creations.

3268	**1025**	16f. red, black & yellow	1·10	40
3269	-	16f. multicoloured	1·10	40

DESIGN: No. 3269, "Telegram-style" (Pol Mara).

1026 Paul Cauchie (Brussels)

1995. Tourist Publicity. Art nouveau house facades by named architects. Multicoloured.

3270	16f. Type **1026**	1·10	40
3271	16f. Frans Smet-Verhas (Antwerp)	1·10	40
3272	16f. Paul Jaspar (Liege)	1·10	40

1027 Anniversary Emblem

1995. Cent of Royal Belgian Football Assn.

3273	**1027**	16f.+4f. mult	1·60	1·60

1028 "Mercator" (Belgian cadet barque)

1995. Sailing Ships. Multicoloured.

3274	16f. Type **1028**	1·40	75
3275	16f. "Kruzenshern" (Russian cadet barque) (inscr "Kruzenstern")	1·40	75
3276	16f. "Sagres II" (Portuguese cadet barque)	1·40	75
3277	16f. "Amerigo Vespucci" (Italian cadet ship)	1·40	75

1029 Princess Astrid and Globe

1995. Red Cross. Multicoloured.

3278	16f.+3f. Type **1029** (Chairwoman)	1·40	1·40
3279	16f.+3f. Wilhelm Rontgen (discoverer of X-rays) and X-ray of hand	1·40	1·40
3280	16f.+3f. Louis Pasteur (chemist) and microscope	1·40	1·40

1030 1908 Minerva

1995. Motorcycles. Multicoloured.

3281	13f. Type **1030**	95	50
3282	16f. 1913 FN (vert)	1·10	40
3283	30f. 1929 La Mondiale	2·00	75
3284	32f. 1937 Gillet (vert)	2·20	65

1031 Sammy (cartoon character)

1995. "Philately for the Young".

3285	**1031**	16f. multicoloured	1·40	45

1032 Couple and Condom in Wrapper

1995. "Solidarity". AIDS Awareness.

3286	**1032**	16f.+4f. mult	1·40	1·40

1033 King Albert II and Queen Paola (photograph by Christian Louis)

1995. King's Day.

3287	**1033**	16f. multicoloured	1·30	40

1034 "Nativity" (from 15th-century breviary)

1995. Christmas.

3288	**1034**	13f. multicoloured	95	40

1035 Puppets, Walloon Museum, Liege

1996. Museums. Multicoloured.

3289	16f.+4f. Type **1035**	1·40	1·40
3290	16f.+4f. National Gin Museum, Hasselt	1·40	1·40
MS3291	126×90 mm. 34f.+6f. "Fall of Saul" (detail of title panel), Butchers' Guild Hall Museum, Antwerp	3·75	3·75

The premium was used for the promotion of philately.

1036 "Emile Mayrisch"

1996. 70th Death Anniv of Theo van Rysselberghe (painter). No value expressed.

3292	**1036**	A (16f.) mult	1·30	40

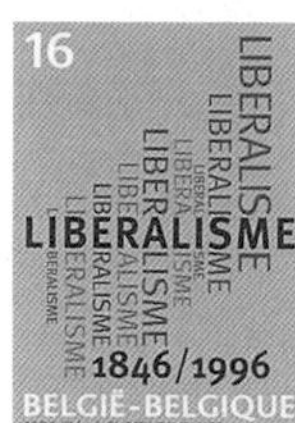

1037 "LIBERALISME"

1996. 150th Anniv of Liberal Party.

3293	**1037**	16f. dp blue, violet & bl	1·30	40

1038 Oscar Bonnevalle (stamp designer) and "Gelatenheid"

1996. Stamp Day.

3294	**1038**	16f. multicoloured	1·30	40

1039 Dragonfly ("Sympetrum sanguineum")

1996. 150th Anniv of Royal Institute of Natural Sciences of Belgium. Insects. Multicoloured.

3295	16f. Type **1039**	90	70
3296	16f. Buff-tailed bumble bee ("Bombus terrestris")	90	70
3297	16f. Stag beetle ("Lucanus cervus")	90	70
3298	16f. May beetle ("Melolontha melolontha")	90	70

3299	16f. European field cricket ("Gryllus campestris")	90	70
3300	16f. Seven-spotted ladybird ("Coccinella septempunctata")	90	70

1040 Yvonne Nevejean (rescuer of Jewish children)

1996. Europa. Famous Women. Multicoloured.

3301	16f. Type **1040**	1·00	40
3302	30f. Marie Gevers (poet)	2·10	90

1996. Birds (3rd series). As T 841. Mult.

3303	1f. Crested tit ("Mesange Huppee")	25	15
3304	2f. Redwing ("Grive mauvis")	30	25
3305	3f. Eurasian skylark ("Alouette des champs")	30	25
3306	4f. Pied flycatcher ("Gore-mouche noir")	45	40
3307	5f. Common starling ("Etourneau sansonnet")	45	25
3308	6f. Spruce siskin ("Tarin des aulnes")	50	30
3309	7f. Yellow wagtail ("Bergeronnette printaniere")	45	15
3310	7f.50 Great grey shrike ("Pie-Grienche Grise")	50	40
3311	9f. Green woodpecker ("Pic Vert")	65	50
3312	10f. Turtle dove ("Tourterelle des Bois")	65	40
3313	15f. Willow tit ("Mesange boreale")	1·20	25
3314	16f. Coal tit ("Mesange noire")	1·00	30
3315	21f. Fieldfare ("Grive Litorne") (horiz)	1·40	80
3316	150f. Black-billed magpie ("Pie bavarde") (35×25 mm)	10·50	25

1042 King Albert II

1996. 62nd Birthday of King Albert II.

3327	**1042**	16f. multicoloured	1·40	25

1043 Han sur Lesse Grottoes

1996. Tourist Publicity. Multicoloured.

3328	16f. Type **1043**	1·20	40
3329	16f. Statue of beguine, Begijnendijk (vert)	1·20	40

1044 Royal Palace

1996. Brussels, Heart of Europe. Mult.

3330	16f. Type **1044**	1·30	40
3331	16f. St. Hubert Royal Galleries	1·30	40
3332	16f. Le Petit Sablon, Egmont Palace (horiz)	1·30	40
3333	16f. Jubilee Park (horiz)	1·30	40

1045 1900 Germain 6CV Voiturette

1996. Cent of Motor Racing at Spa. Mult.

3334	16f. Type **1045**	1·20	40
3335	16f. 1925 Alfa Romeo P2	1·20	40
3336	16f. 1939 Mercedes Benz W154	1·20	40

3337	16f. 1967 Ferrari 330P	1·20	40

1046 Table Tennis

1996. Olympic Games, Atlanta. Mult.

3338	16f.+4f. Type **1046**	1·60	1·60
3339	16f.+4f. Swimming	1·60	1·60
MS3340	125×90 mm. 34f.+6f. High jumping (41×34 mm)	3·50	3·50

1996

3341	16f. blue	1·20	30
3342	17f. blue	1·40	15
3343	18f. green	1·30	50
3344	19f. lilac	1·60	40
3344a	20f. brown	1·40	20
3345	25f. brown	1·70	40
3346	28f. brown	2·40	50
3347	32f. violet	2·10	20
3348	34f. blue	1·90	40
3349	36f. blue	2·30	25
3350	50f. green	4·00	30

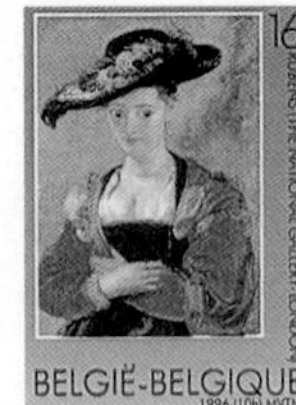

1047 "The Straw Hat" (Peter Paul Rubens)

1996. Paintings by Belgian Artists in the National Gallery, London. Multicoloured.

3351	14f. "St. Ivo" (Rogier van der Weyden)	1·20	40
3352	16f. Type **1047**	1·40	40
3353	30f. "Man in a Turban" (Jan van Eyck)	2·75	65

1048 Philip the Fair

1996. 500th Anniv of Marriage of Philip the Fair and Joanna of Castile and Procession into Brussels. Details of triptych by the Master of Affligem Abbey at Zierikzee Town Hall. Multicoloured.

3354	16f. Type **1048**	4·00	40
3355	16f. Joanna of Castile	1·30	40

1049 Cloro (cartoon character)

1996. "Philately for the Young".

3356	**1049**	16f. multicoloured	1·40	40

1050 Title of First Issue and Charles Letellier (founder)

1996. 150th Anniv of "Mons Almanac".

3357	**1050**	16f. black, yell & mve	1·30	40

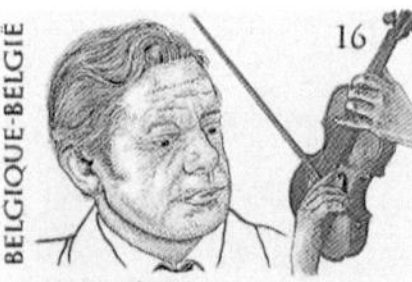

1051 Arthur Grumiaux (violinist, 10th death anniv)

1996. Music and Literature Anniversaries.

3358	**1051**	16f. multicoloured	1·30	40
3359	-	16f. multicoloured	1·30	40
3360	-	16f. black and brown	1·30	40
3361	-	16f. multicoloured	1·30	40

DESIGNS: No. 3359, Flor Peeters (organist, 10th death anniv); 3360, Christian Dotremont (poet, 5th death anniv); 3361, Paul van Ostaijen (writer, birth centenary) and cover drawing by Oscar Jespers for "Bezette Stad".

1052 Globe and Children of Different Races

1996. "Solidarity". 50th Anniv of UNICEF.

3362	**1052**	16f.+4f. mult	1·40	1·40

1053 Christmas Trees

1996. Christmas. Sheet 185×145 mm containing T 1053 and similar horiz designs. Multicoloured.

MS3363	14f. Type **1053**; 14f. "Happy Christmas" in Flemish, German and French; 14f. Church; 14f. Cake stall; 14f. Stall with cribs; 14f. Meat stall; 14f. Father Christmas; 14f. Crowd including man smoking pipe; 14f. Crowd including man carrying holly	9·25	9·25

1054 Students

1997. Centenary of Catholic University, Mons.

3364	**1054**	17f. multicoloured	1·30	30

1055 Barbed Wire and Buildings

1997. Museums. Multicoloured.

3365	17f.+4f. Type **1055** (Deportation and Resistance Museum, Dossin Barracks, Malines)	1·60	1·60
3366	17f.+4f. Foundryman pouring molten metal (Fourneau Saint-Michel Iron Museum)	1·60	1·60
MS3367	90×125 mm. 41f.+9f. Horta Museum, Saint-Giles	5·75	5·75

The premium was used for the promotion of philately.

1056 Deer and Landscape (image scaled to 64% of original size)

1997. "Cantons of the East" (German-speaking Belgium).

3368	**1056**	17f. black and brown	1·30	40

1057 Marie Sasse

1997. Opera Singers. Multicoloured.

3369	17f. Type **1057**	1·20	40
3370	17f. Ernest van Dijck	1·20	40
3371	17f. Hector Dufranne	1·20	40
3372	17f. Clara Clairbert	1·20	40

1058 Soldier on Duty

1997. Belgian Involvement in United Nations Peacekeeping Forces.

3373	**1058**	17f. multicoloured	1·20	40

1059 The Goat Riders

1997. Europa. Tales and Legends. Mult.

3374	17f. Type **1059**	1·40	40
3375	30f. Jean de Berneau	2·50	90

1060 Spinoy working on Recess Plate

1997. Stamp Day. 4th Death Anniv of Constant Spinoy (engraver).

3376	**1060**	17f. brown, yell & blk	1·20	40

BELGIQUE

Paul Delvaux (1897-1994)

BELGIË 15

1061 "The Man in the Street" (detail)

1997. Birth Centenary of Paul Delvaux (artist). Multicoloured.

3377	15f. Type **1061**	1·00	50
3378	17f. "The Public Voice" (horiz)	1·30	40
3379	32f. "The Messenger of the Night"	2·50	80

1062 Flower Arrangement

1997. 2nd International Flower Show, Liege.

3380	**1062**	17f. multicoloured	1·30	40

1063 Men's Judo

1997. Judo. Each black and red.

3381 17f.+4f. Type **1063** 1·40 1·30

3382 17f.+4f. Women's judo (showing female symbol) 1·40 1·30

1064 Queen Paola and Belvedere Villa

1997. 60th Birthday of Queen Paola.

3383 **1064** 17f. multicoloured 1·30 40

1065 Jommeke, Flip and Filiberke (comic strip characters)

1997. "Philately for the Young".

3384 **1065** 17f. multicoloured 1·60 45

1066 "Rosa damascena" "Coccinea"

1997. Roses. Illustrations by Pierre-Joseph Redoute. Multicoloured.

3385 17f. Type **1066** 1·30 40

3386 17f. "Rosa sulfurea" 1·30 40

3387 17f. "Rosa centifolia" 1·30 40

1067 St. Martin's Cathedral, Hal

1997. Tourist Publicity. Multicoloured.

3388 17f. Type **1067** 1·30 40

3389 17f. Notre-Dame Church, Laeken (horiz) 1·30 40

3390 17f. St. Martin's Cathedral, Liege 1·30 40

1068 Stonecutter

1997. Trades. Multicoloured.

3391 17f. Type **1068** 1·30 30

3392 17f. Bricklayer 1·30 30

3393 17f. Carpenter 1·30 30

3394 17f. Blacksmith 1·30 30

1069 Queen amidst Workers

1997. Centenary of Apimondia (International Apicultural Association) and 35th Congress, Antwerp. Bees. Multicoloured.

3395 17f. Type **1069** 1·30 90

3396 17f. Development of egg 1·30 90

3397 17f. Bees emerging from cells 1·30 90

3398 17f. Bee collecting nectar from flower 1·30 90

3399 17f. Bee fanning at hive entrance and worker arriving with nectar 1·30 90

3400 17f. Worker feeding drone 1·30 90

1070 "Belgica" (polar barque) ice-bound

1997. Cent of Belgian Antarctic Expedition.

3401 **1070** 17f. multicoloured 1·30 50

1071 Mask

1997. Centenary of Royal Central Africa Museum, Tervuren. Multicoloured.

3402 17f. Type **1071** 1·30 40

3403 17f. Museum (74×24 mm) 1·30 40

3404 34f. Statuette 2·50 1·00

1073 "Fairon" (Pierre Grahame)

1997. Christmas.

3408 **1073** 15f. multicoloured 1·20 40

1074 Disjointed Figure

1997. "Solidarity". Multiple Sclerosis.

3409 **1074** 17f.+4f. black & blue 1·60 1·60

1997. Willow Tit. As No. 3318 but horiz.

3410 15f. multicoloured 1·50 1·40

1075 Azalea "Mrs. Haerens A"

1997. Self-adhesive.

3411 **1075** (17f.) multicoloured 1·30 20

1076 Female Symbol

1998. 50th Anniv of Women's Suffrage in Belgium.

3412 **1076** 17f. red, brown & sepia 1·20 40

1077 Thalys High Speed Train on Antoing Viaduct

1998. Paris–Brussels–Cologne–Amsterdam High Speed Rail Network.

3413 **1077** 17f. multicoloured 1·30 40

1078 Gerard Walschap

1998. Writers' Birth Centenaries. Mult.

3414 17f. Type **1078** 1·20 40

3415 17f. Norge (Georges Mogin) 1·20 40

1079 King Leopold III

1998. Kings of Belgium (1st series).

3416 **1079** 17f.+8f. green 1·70 1·70

3417 - 32f.+15f. brown 3·00 3·00

MS3418 125×90 mm. 50f.+25f. red 7·00 7·00

KINGS: 32f. Baudouin I; 50f. Albert II.

The premium was used for the promotion of philately.

See also Nos. 3466/8 and **MS**3508.

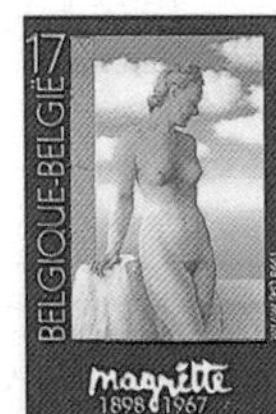

1080 "Black Magic"

1998. Birth Centenary of Rene-Ghislain Magritte (artist) (1st issue). Multicoloured.

3419 17f. Type **1080** 1·30 40

3420 17f. "The Sensitive Chord" (horiz) 1·30 40

3421 17f. "The Castle of the Pyrenees" 1·30 40

See also No. 3432.

1081 "La Foire aux Amours" (Felicien Rops)

1998. Art Anniversaries. Multicoloured.

3422 17f. Type **1081** (death cent) 1·20 1·00

3423 17f. "Hospitality for the Strangers" (Gustave van de Woestijne) (bicentenary of Museum of Fine Arts, Ghent) 1·20 1·00

3424 17f. "Man with Beard" (self-portrait of Felix de Boeck, birth centenary) 1·20 1·00

3425 17f. "black writing mixed with colours..." (Karel Appel and Christian Dotremont) (50th anniv of Cobra art movement) 1·20 1·00

1082 Anniversary Emblem

1998. 75th Anniv of Belgian Postage Stamp Dealers' Association.

3426 **1082** 17f. multicoloured 1·20 40

1083 Avro RJ85 Airplane

1998. 75th Anniv of Sabena Airlines.

3427 **1083** 17f. multicoloured 1·30 40

1084 Fox

1998. Wildlife of the Ardennes. Mult.

3428 17f. Type **1084** 1·30 50

3429 17f. Red deer ("Cervus elaphus") 1·30 50

3430 17f. Wild boar ("Sus scrofa") 1·30 50

3431 17f. Roe deer ("Capreolus capreolus") 1·30 50

1085 "The Return" (Magritte)

1998. Birth Centenary of Rene-Ghislain Magritte (artist) (2nd issue).

3432 **1085** 17f. multicoloured 1·30 50

1086 Struyf

1998. Stamp Day. 2nd Death Anniv of Edmond Struyf (founder of Pro-Post (organization for promotion of philately)).

3433 **1086** 17f. black, red & yellow 1·20 40

1087 Guitarist (Torhout and Werchter Festival)

1998. Europa. National Festivals.
3434 **1087** 17f. violet and yellow 1·40 40
3435 - 17f. violet and mauve 1·40 40
DESIGN: No. 3435, Music conductor (Wallonie Festival).

1088 Pelote

1998. Sports. Multicoloured.
3436 17f.+4f. Type **1088** 1·50 1·50
3437 17f.+4f. Handball 1·50 1·50
MS3438 123×88 mm. 30f.+7f. Goalkeeper (World Cup Football Championship, France) 3·00 3·00

1089 Emblem

1998. European Heritage Days. Mult.
3439 17f. Type **1089** 1·20 50
3440 17f. Bourla Theatre, Antwerp 1·20 50
3441 17f. La Halle, Durbuy 1·20 50
3442 17f. Halletoren, Kortrijk 1·20 50
3443 17f. Louvain Town Hall 1·20 50
3444 17f. Perron, Liege 1·20 50
3445 17f. Royal Theatre, Namur 1·20 50
3446 17f. Aspremont-Lynden Castle, Rekem 1·20 50
3447 17f. Neo-Gothic kiosk, Saint Nicolas 1·20 50
3448 17f. Saint-Vincent's Chapel, Tournai 1·20 50
3449 17f. Villers-la-Ville Abbey 1·20 50
3450 17f. Saint-Gilles Town Hall 1·20 50

1090 Marnix van Sint-Aldegonde

1998. 400th Death Anniv of Philips van Marnix van St. Aldegonde (writer).
3451 **1090** 17f. multicoloured 1·20 40

1091 Face

1998. Bicentenary of "Amis Philanthropes" (circle of free thinkers).
3452 **1091** 17f. black and blue 1·20 40

1092 Mniszech Palace

1998. Belgium Embassy, Warsaw, Poland.
3453 **1092** 17f. multicoloured 1·20 40

1093 King Albert II

1998
3454 **1093** 19f. lilac 1·70 1·60
No. 3454 was for use on direct mail by large companies.

1094 "The Eighth Day" (dir. Jaco van Dormael)

1998. 25th Anniv of Brussels and Ghent Film Festivals. Multicoloured.
3455 17f. Type **1094** 1·30 40
3456 17f. "Daens" (dir. Stijn Coninx) 1·30 40

1096 Chick Bill and Ric Hochet

1998. "Philately for the Young". Comic Strip Characters.
3460 **1096** 17f. multicoloured 1·30 50

1097 "Youth and Space"

1998. 14th World Congress of Association of Space Explorers.
3461 **1097** 17f. multicoloured 1·30 45

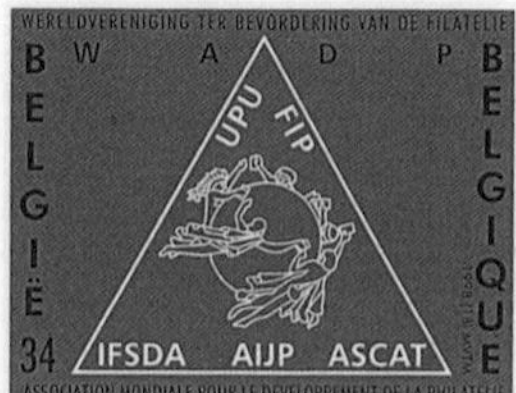

1098 Universal Postal Union Emblem

1998. World Post Day.
3462 **1098** 34f. blue & ultramarine 2·50 1·30

1099 "The Three Kings" (Michel Provost)

1998. Christmas. No value indicated.
3463 **1099** (17f.) multicoloured 1·20 40

1100 Detail of Triptych by Constant Dratz

1998. Cent of General Belgium Trade Union.
3464 **1100** 17f. multicoloured 1·20 40

1101 Blind Man with Guide Dog

1998. "Solidarity". Guide Dogs for the Blind.
3465 **1101** 17f.+4f. multicoloured 1·60 1·60
The face value is embossed in Braille.

1999. Kings of Belgium (2nd series). As T 1079.
3466 17f.+8f. deep green & green 1·90 1·90
3467 32f.+15f. black 3·25 3·25
MS3468 125×90 mm. 50f.+25f. brown and purple 5·75 5·75
KINGS: 17f. Albert I; 32f. Leopold II; 50f. Leopold I.
The premium was used for the promotion of philately.

1102 Candle ("Happy Birthday")

1999. Greetings stamps. No value expressed. Mult.
3469 (17f.) Type **1102** 1·20 50
3470 (17f.) Stork carrying heart ("Welcome" (new baby)) 1·20 50
3471 (17f.) Wristwatch ("Take your Time" (retirement)) 1·20 50
3472 (17f.) Four-leafed clover ("For your pleasure") 1·20 50
3473 (17f.) White doves ("Congratulations" (marriage)) 1·20 50
3474 (17f.) Arrow through heart ("I love you") 1·20 50
3475 (17f.) Woman with heart as head ("Happy Mother's Day") 1·20 50
3476 (17f.) Man with heart as head ("Happy Father's Day") 1·20 50

1103 Barn Owl

1999. Owls. Multicoloured.
3477 17f. Type **1103** 1·30 40
3478 17f. Little owl ("Athene noctua") 1·30 40
3479 17f. Tawny owl ("Strix aluco") 1·30 40
3480 17f. Long-eared owl ("Asio otus") 1·30 40

1104 Leopard Tank (Army)

1999. 50th Anniv of North Atlantic Treaty Organization. Multicoloured.
3481 17f. Type **1104** 1·20 40
3482 17f. Lockhead Martin F-16 Fighting Falcon (Air Force) 1·20 40
3483 17f. "De Wandelaar" (frigate) (Navy) 1·20 40
3484 17f. Field hospital (Medical Service) 1·20 40
3485 17f. Display chart of military operations (General Staff) 1·20 40

1105 Envelopes and World Map

1999. 125th Anniv of U.P.U.
3486 **1105** 34f. multicoloured 2·30 65

1106 De Bunt Nature Reserve, Hamme

1999. Europa. Parks and Gardens. Multicoloured.
3487 17f. Type **1106** 1·40 40
3488 17f. Harchies Marsh 1·40 40

1107 1849 10c. "Epaulettes" Stamp

1999. Stamp Day. 150th Anniv of First Belgian Postage Stamp. Multicoloured.
3489 17f. Type **1107** 1·10 30
3490 17f. 1849 20c. "Epaulettes" stamp 1·10 30

1108 Racing

1999. Sport. Belgian Motor Cycling. Multicoloured.
3491 17f.+4f. Type **1108** 1·60 1·60
3492 17f.+4f. Trial (vert) 1·60 1·60
MS3493 90×125 mm. 30f.+7f. Motocross (vert) 3·25 3·25

1109 "My Favourite Room"

1999. 50th Death Anniv of James Ensor (artist) (1st issue).
3494 **1109** 17f. mullticoloured 1·10 40
See also Nos. 3501/3.

1110 Giant Family, Geraardsbergen

1999. Tourist Publicity. Multicoloured.
3495 17f. Type **1110** 1·10 40
3496 17f. Members of Confrerie de la Misericorde in Car d'Or procession, Mons (horiz) 1·10 40

1111 Harvesting of Cocoa Beans

1999. Belgian Chocolate. Multicoloured.
3497 17f. Type **1111** 1·10 40
3498 17f. Chocolate manufacture 1·10 40
3499 17f. Selling product 1·10 40

1112 Photographs of 1959 and 1999

1999. 40th Wedding Anniv of King Albert and Queen Paola.

3500	**1112**	17f. multicoloured	1·30	40

1113 "Woman eating Oysters"

1999. 50th Death Anniv of James Ensor (artist) (2nd issue).

3501	**1113**	17f. multicoloured	1·10	40
3502	-	30f. black, brown and grey	1·90	80
3503	-	32f. multicoloured	2·10	80

DESIGNS—30f. "Triumph of Death"; 32f. "Old Lady with Masks".

1999. "Bruphila '99" National Stamp Exhibition, Brussels. Kings of Belgium (3rd series). Sheet 191×121 mm containing vert designs as T 1079. Each deep blue and blue.

MS3508 17f. As No. 3466; 17f. Type **1079**; 32f. As No. 3467; 32f. As No. 3417; 50f. As No. **MS**3468; 50f. As No. **MS**3418 26·00 26·00

1115 Henri la Fontaine (President of International Peace Bureau), 1913

1999. Belgian Winners of Nobel Peace Prize.

3509	**1115**	17f. red and gold	1·10	40
3510	-	21f. blue and gold	1·30	80

DESIGNS: 3510, Auguste Beernaert (Prime Minister 1884–94), 1909.

DENOMINATION. From No. 3511 Belgian stamps are denominated both in Belgian francs and in euros.

1116 King Albert II 1116a King Albert II

1999

3511	**1116**	17f. multicoloured	1·20	15
3512	**1116**	17f. blue	1·20	15
3513	**1116**	19f. purple	1·30	40
3514	**1116**	20f. brown	1·30	30
3515	**1116**	25f. brown	2·50	2·30
3516	**1116**	30f. purple	2·10	25
3517	**1116**	32f. green	1·90	25
3518	**1116**	34f. blue	2·30	65
3519	**1116**	36f. brown	2·30	15
3520	**1116a**	50f. blue	3·25	65
3521	**1116a**	200f. lilac	13·00	1·60

1117 "Corentin" (Paul Cuvelier)

1999. "Philately for the Young". Comic Strips. Sheet 185×145 mm containing T 1117 and similar horiz designs. Multicoloured.

MS3525 17f. Type **1117**; 17f. "Jerry Spring" (Jije); 17f. "Gil Jourdan" (Maurice Tillieux); 17f. "Beaver Patrol" (Mitacq); 17f. Entrance Hall, Belgian Comic Strip Centre; 17f. "Hassan and Kadour" (Jacques Laudy); 17f. "Buck Danny" (Victor Hubinon); 17f. "Tif and Tondu" (Fernand Dineur); 17f. "Les Timour" (Sirius) 11·50 11·50

1118 Geranium "Matador"

1999. Flowers. No value expressed (geranium) or inscr "ZONE A PRIOR" (tulip). Multicoloured. Self-adhesive.

3528	(17f.) Type **1118**	1·60	45
3529	(21f.) Tulip (21×26 mm)	1·20	40

The geranium design was for use on inland letters up to 20g. and the tulip design for letters within the European Union up to 20g.

1119 Reindeer holding Glass of Champagne

1999. Christmas.

3530	**1119**	17f. multicoloured	1·20	40

1120 Child bandaging Teddy Bear

1999. "Solidarity". Red Cross. Multicoloured.

3531	17f.+4f. Type **1120**	1·50	1·50
3532	17f.+4f. Child and teddy bear cleaning teeth (vert)	1·50	1·50

1121 Prince Philippe and Mathilde d'Udekem d'Acoz

1999. Engagement of Prince Philippe and Mathilde d'Udekem d'Acoz.

3533	17f. Type **1121**	1·60	50

MS3534 120×89 mm. 21f. Prince Philippe and Mathilde d'Udekem d'Acoz (different) 1·80 1·80

1122 Pope John Paul XXIII

1999. The Twentieth Century (1st issue). Personalities, Sports and Leisure. Sheet 166×200 mm containing T 1122 and similar vert designs. Multicoloured.

MS3535 17f. Type **1122**; 17f. King Baudouin; 17f. Willy Brandt (German statesman); 17f. John F. Kennedy (U.S. President, 1961–3); 17f. Mahatma Gandhi (Indian leader); 17f. Martin Luther King (civil rights leader); 17f. Vladimir Lenin (Prime Minister of Russia, 1917–24; 17f. Che Guevara (revolutionary); 17f. Golda Meir (Prime Minister of Israel, 1969–74); 17f. Nelson Mandela (Prime Minister of South Africa, 1994–99); 17f. Jesse Owens (American athlete) (modern Olympics); 17f. Football; 17f. Eddy Merckx (racing cyclist) (Tour de France); 17f. Edith Piaf (French singer); 17f. The Beatles (English pop band); 17f. Charlie Chaplin (English film actor and director); 17f. Postcards (tourism); 17f. Children around campfire (youth movements); 17f. Tintin and Snowy (comic strip); 17f. Magnifying glass over stamp (hobbies) 23·00 23·00

See also Nos. **MS**3613 and **MS**3656.

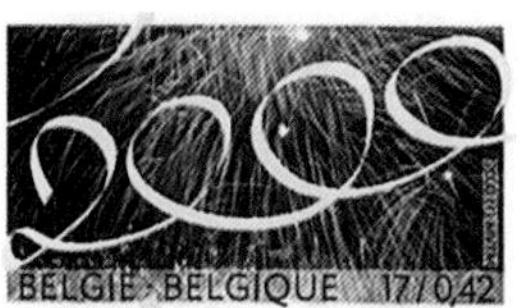

1123 Fireworks and Streamer forming "2000"

2000. New Year.

3536	**1123**	17f. multicoloured	1·30	25

1124 Red-backed Shrike

2000. Birds. Multicoloured.

3537	50c. Goldcrest ("Roitelet Huppe")	15	25
3538	1f. Red crossbill ("Beccroisé des Sapins")	25	15
3539	2f. Short-toed treecreeper ("Grimpereau des Jardins")	25	15
3540	3f. Meadow pipit ("Pipit Farlouse")	25	15
3541	5f. Brambling ("Pinson du Nord")	30	15
3542	7f.50 Great grey shrike ("Pie-Grieche Grise")	50	50
3543	8f. Great tit ("Mesange Charbonniere")	65	30
3544	10f. Wood warbler ("Pouillot Siffleur")	65	40
3545	16f. Type **1124**	1·10	40
3546	16f. Common tern ("Sterne Pierregarin")	1·10	25
3547	21f. Fieldfare ("Grive Litorne") (horiz)	1·30	50
3548	150f. Black-billed magpie ("Pie Bavarde") (36×25 mm)	9·75	65

1125 Brussels Skyline and Group of People

2000. Brussels, European City of Culture. Mult.

3555	17f. Type **1125**	1·10	50
3556	17f. Toots Tielmans (jazz musician), Anne Teresa de Keersmaeker (gymnast) and skyline	1·10	50
3557	17f. Lockhead L-1011 Tristar, train and skyline	1·10	50

Nos. 3555/7 were issued together, se-tenant, forming a composite design showing the Brussels skyline.

1126 Queen Astrid

2000. Queens of Belgium (1st series).

3558	**1126**	17f.+8f. green and deep green	1·90	1·90
3559	-	32f.+15f. brown and black	3·25	3·25

MS3560 125×89 mm. 50f.+25f. deep purple and purple 4·75 4·75

DESIGNS: 32f. Queen Fabiola; 50f. Queen Paola.

The premium was used for the promotion of philately. See also Nos. 3615/**MS**3617 and **MS**3618.

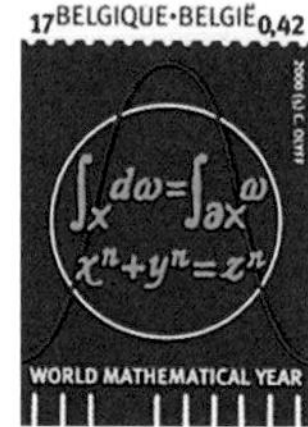

1127 Mathematical Formulae

2000. World Mathematics Year.

3561	**1127**	17f. multicoloured	1·10	40

1128 Globe and Technology (Joachim Beckers)

2000. "Stampin' the Future". Winning Entries in Children's International Painting Competition.

3562	**1128**	17f. multicoloured	1·10	40

1129 "Charles V as Sovereign Master of the Order of the Golden Fleece" (anon)

2000. 500th Birth Anniv of Charles V, Holy Roman Emperor. Paintings of Charles V. Multicoloured.

3563	17f. Type **1129**	1·10	40
3564	21f. "Charles V" (Corneille de la Haye)	1·30	75

MS3565 125×88 mm. 34f. "Charles V on Horseback" (Titian) 2·50 2·50

1130 Common Adder

2000. Amphibians and Reptiles. Multicoloured.

3566	17f. Type **1130**	1·10	40
3567	17f. Sand lizard (*Lacerta agilis*) (vert)	1·10	40
3568	17f. Common tree frog (*Hyla arborea*) (vert)	1·10	40
3569	17f. Spotted salamander (*Salamander salamander*)	1·10	40

1131 Children flying Kites

2000. Red Cross and Red Crescent Movements.

3570	**1131**	17f.+4f. multicoloured	1·50	1·50

1132 Players Celebrating

2000. European Football Championship, Belgium and The Netherlands. Multicoloured. (a) With face value. Size 26×38 mm.

3571	17f. Type **1132**	1·30	25
3572	21f. Football	1·60	40

(b) Size 20×26 mm. Self-adhesive.

3573	(17f.) As Type **1132**	1·60	40

Nos. 3571/3 were printed together, se-tenant, with the backgrounds forming the composite design of a crowd of spectators and the Belgian flag.

1133 Cat and Rabbit reading Book

2000. Stamp Day. Winning Entry in Stamp Design Competition.

3574	**1133**	17f. black, blue and red	1·10	40

1134 Francois de Tassis (detail of tapestry)

2000. "Belgica 2001" Int Stamp Exhibition, Brussels, (1st issue).

3575	**1134**	17f. multicoloured	1·10	50

See also Nos. 3629/33.

1135 *Iris spuria*

2000. Ghent Flower Show. Multicoloured.

3576	16f. Type **1135**	1·30	50
3577	17f. Rhododendron (horiz)	1·50	40
3578	21f. Begonia (vert)	1·60	75

1136 Prince Philippe

2000. 2nd Anniv of Prince Philippe (cultural organization).

3579	**1136**	17f. brn, grey & sil	1·10	40

1137 Harpsichord

2000. 250th Death Anniv of Johann Sebastian Bach. No value expressed. Multicoloured.

3580	(17f.) Type **1137**	1·30	1·00
3581	(17f.) Violin	1·30	1·00
3582	(17f.) Two tenor lutes	1·30	1·00
3583	(17f.) Treble viol	1·30	1·00
3584	(17f.) Three trumpets	1·30	1·00
3585	(17f.) Bach	1·30	1·00

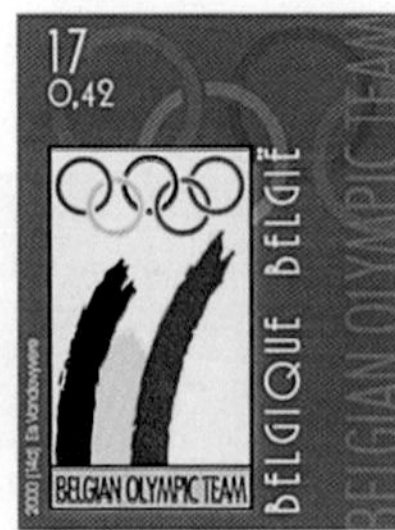
1138 Belgium Team Emblem and Olympic Rings

2000. Olympic Games, Sydney. Multicoloured.

3586	17f. Type **1138**	1·00	50
3587	17f.+4f. Tae-kwon-do	1·40	1·40
3588	17f.+4f. Paralympic athlete (horiz)	1·40	1·40
MS3589	125×90 mm. 30f.+7f. Swimmer (horiz)	2·50	2·50

1139 "Building Europe"

2000. Europa.

3590	**1139**	21f. multicoloured	1·50	75

1140 Flemish Beguinages

2000. UNESCO World Heritage Sites in Belgium. Multicoloured.

3591	17f. Type **1140**	1·10	30
3592	17f. Grand-Place, Brussels	1·10	30
3593	17f. Four lifts, Centre Canal, Wallonia	1·10	30

1141 Baroque Organ, Norbertine Abbey Church, Grimbergen

2000. Tourism. Churches and Church Organs. Mult.

3594	17f. Type **1141**	1·10	40
3595	17f. St. Wandru Abbey, Mons	1·10	40
3596	17f. O.-L.-V. Hemelvaartkerk (former abbey church), Ninove	1·10	40
3597	17f. St. Peter's Church, Bastogne	1·10	40

1142 Red-backed Shrike ("Pie grieche ecorcheur")

2000

3598	**1142**	16f. multicoloured	2·20	1·60
3599	-	17f. mult (51×21 mm)	3·50	2·50
3600	-	23f. lilac	2·50	2·00

DESIGNS: 17f. Francois de Tassis (detail of tapestry) and Belgica 2001 emblem; 23f. King Albert II.

1143 Marcel, Charlotte, Fanny and Konstantinopel

2000. "Philately for the Young". Kiekeboe (cartoon series created by Robert Merhottein).

3601	**1143**	17f. multicoloured	1·10	50

1144 "Springtime"

2000. Hainaut Flower Show.

3602	**1144**	17f. multicoloured	1·10	40

1145 Pansies

2000. Flowers. No value expressed. Self-adhesive.

3603	**1145**	(17f.) multicoloured	1·30	25

1147 "Bing of the Ferro Lusto X" (Panamarenko)

2000. Modern Art. Multicoloured.

3608	17f. Type **1147**	1·10	65
3609	17f. "Construction" (Anne-Mie van Kerckhoven) (vert)	1·10	65
3610	17f. "Belgique eternelle" (Jacques Charlier)	1·10	65
3611	17f. "Les Belles de Nuit" (Marie Jo Lafontaine)	1·10	65

1148 Postman

2000. Christmas.

3612	**1148**	17f. multicoloured	1·10	40

1149 Soldiers at Yser Front, West Flanders (First World War, 1914–18)

2000. The Twentieth Century (2nd issue). War, Peace and Art. Sheet 200×166 mm containing T 1149 and similar horiz designs. Multicoloured.

MS3613 17f. Type **1149**; 17f. German concentration camp and prisoners (black and scarlet); 17f. Atomic cloud and Hiroshima (atomic bomb, 1945); 17f. Winston Churchill, Franklin D. Roosevelt and Joseph Stalin (Yalta conference, 1945); 17f. Headquarters (United Nations established, 1945); 17f. Joseph Kasavubu (first President) and map of Africa (independence of Belgian Congo, 1960); 17f. American soldiers and Boeing CH-14 Chinook(Vietnam War); 17f. Collapse of Berlin Wall, 1989; 17f. Campaign for Nuclear Disarmament emblem and crowd; 17f. Dome of the Rock (Middle East conflict); 17f. Rene Magritte (artist); 17f. Le Corbusier (architect) and building; 17f. Bertolt Brecht (dramatist and poet) and actors; 17f. James Joyce (novelist); 17f. Anne Teresa de Keersmaeker (choreographer); 17f. Bila Bartok (composer); 17f. Andy Warhol (artist); 17f. Maria Callas (opera singer); 17f. Henry Moore (sculptor) and sculpture; 17f. Charlie Parker (alto saxophonist and composer) and Toots Thielemans (composer and jazz musician) 23·00 23·00

1150 Stars

2000. New Year.

3614	**1150**	17f. gold, blue & blk	1·30	50

2001. Queens of Belgium (2nd series). As T 1126.

3615	17f.+8f. green & dp green	1·90	1·90
3616	32f.+15f. black and green	3·25	3·25
MS3617	126×91 mm. 50f.+25f. deep brown and brown	4·75	4·75

DESIGNS: 17f. Queen Elisabeth; 32f. Queen Marie-Henriette; 50f. Queen Louise-Marie.

The premium was used for the promotion of philately.

2001. Queens of Belgium (3rd series). Vert designs as T 1126. Each blue, deep blue and ochre.

MS3618 190×121 mm. 17f. As No. 3615; 17f. As Type **1126**; 32f. As No. 3616; 32f. As No. 3559; 50f. As No. **MS**3617; 50f. As No. **MS**3560 23·00 23·00

1151 Movement of a Dynamo

2001. Death Centenary of Zenobe Gramme (physicist).

3619	**1151**	17f. black, red & black	1·10	40

1152 Virgin and Child (statue)

2001. 575th Anniv of Louvain Catholic University.

3620	**1152**	17f. multicoloured	1·10	40

2001. As T 998 but with face value expressed in francs and euros.

3621	100f. multicoloured	6·25	55

1153 Willem Elsschot (poet)

2001. Music and Literature.

3622	**1153**	17f. brown and black	1·10	40
3623	-	17f. grey and black	1·10	40
MS3624 125×90 mm. 21f. orange and brown			1·50	1·50

DESIGNS—VERT: No. 3623, Albert Ayguesparse (poet). HORIZ: **MS**3624 21f. Queen Elisabeth and emblem (50th anniv of Queen Elisabeth International Music Competition).

1154 Boy washing Hands

2001. Europa. Water Resources.

3625	**1154**	21f. multicoloured	1·40	75

1155 Type 12 Steam Locomotive

2001. 75th Anniv of National Railway Company. Multicoloured.

3626	17f. Type **1155**	1·10	65
3627	17f. Series 06 dual locomotive No. 671	1·10	65
3628	17f. Series 03 locomotive No. 328	1·10	65

Nos. 3626/8 were issued together, se-tenant, forming a composite design.

1156 16th-century Postman on horseback

2001. "Belgica 2001" International Stamp Exhibition, Brussels (2nd issue). 500th Anniv of European Post. Multicoloured.

3629	17f. Type **1156**	1·40	65
3630	17f. 17th-century postman with walking staff (vert)	1·40	65
3631	17f. 18th-century postman and hand using quill (vert)	1·40	65
3632	17f. Steam locomotive and 19th-century postman (vert)	1·40	65
3633	17f. 20th-century forms of communication (vert)	1·40	65
MS3634 190×120 mm. 150f. Female postal worker (35×46 mm)		20·00	20·00

1157 Hassan II Mosque, Casablanca

2001. Places of Worship. Multicoloured.

3635	17f. Type **1157**	1·10	40
3636	34f. Koekelberg Basilica	2·30	1·00

1158 "Winter Landscape with Skaters" (Pieter Bruegel the Elder)

2001. Art. Multicoloured.

3637	17f. Type **1158**	1·10	95
3638	17f. "Heads of Negros" (Peter Paul Rubens)	1·10	95
3639	17f. "Sunday" (Frits van den Berghe)	1·10	95
3640	17f. "Mussels" (Marcel Broodthaers)	1·10	95

1159 Pottery Vase

2001. Chinese Pottery. Multicoloured.

3641	17f. Type **1159**	1·10	30
3642	34f. Teapot	2·30	80

1160 Luc Orient

2001. "Philately for the Young". Cartoon Characters.

3643	**1160**	17f. multicoloured	1·10	50

1161 Cyclists (World Cycling Championship, Antwerp)

2001. Sports. Multicoloured.

3644	17f.+4f. Type **1161**	1·40	1·40
3645	17f.+4f. Gymnast (World Gymnastics Championships, Ghent)	1·40	1·40

1162 Emblem

2001. Belgian Presidency of European Union.

3646	**1162**	17f. multicoloured	1·10	50

1163 Binche

2001. Town Hall Belfries.

3647	**1163**	17f. mauve and black	1·10	40
3648	-	17f. blue, mauve & blk	1·10	40

DESIGN: No. 3648, Dlksmuide.

1164 Damme

2001. Large Farmhouses. Multicoloured.

3649	17f. Type **1164**	1·10	40
3650	17f. Beauvechain	1·10	40
3651	17f. Louvain	1·10	40
3652	17f. Honnelles	1·10	40
3653	17f. Hasselt	1·10	40

1165 Red Cross and Doctor

2001. Red Cross.

3654	**1165**	17f.+4f. multicoloured	1·40	1·40

1166 Stam and Pilou

2001. Stamp Day. No value expressed. Self-adhesive.

3655	**1166**	(17f.) multicoloured	1·40	50

No. 3655 was for use on inland standard letters up to 20g.

1167 Ovide Decroly (educational psychologist) and Road Sign

2001. The Twentieth Century. Science and Technology. Sheet 166×200 mm. Multicoloured.

MS3656 17f. Type **1167**; 17f. Dandelion and windmills (alternative energy sources); 17f. Globe, signature and map (first solo non-stop crossing of North Atlantic by Charles Lindbergh); 17f. Man with head on lap (Sigmund Freud, founder of psychoanalysis); 17f. Astronaut and foot print on moon surface (Neil Armstrong, first man on the moon, 1969); 17f. Claude Levi-Strauss (anthropologist); 17f. DNA double helix and athletes (human genetic code); 17f. Pierre Teilhard de Chardin (theologian palaeontologist and philosopher); 17f. Max Weber (sociologist) and crowd; 17f. Albert Einstein (physicist) (Theory of Relativity); 17f. Knight and jacket of pills (discovery of Penicillin, 1928); 17f. Ilya Prigogine (theoretical chemist and clock face; 17f. Text and Roland Barthes (writer and critic); 17f. Simone de Beauvoir (feminist writer); 17f. Globe and technology highway (computer science); 17f. John Maynard Keynes (economist) and folded paper; 17f. Marc Bloch (historian) and photographs; 17f. Tools and Julius Robert Oppenheimer (nuclear physicist); 17f. Marie and Pierre Curie, discoverers of radioactivity, 1896); 17f. Caricature of Ludwig Josef Wittgenstein (philosopher)	23·00	23·00

1168 Nativity

2001. Christmas.

3657	**1168**	15f. multicoloured	1·10	45

1169 Sunset

2001. Bereavement. No value expressed.

3658	**1169**	(17f.) multicoloured	1·60	40

See also Nos. 3732 and 3856.

1170 Daffodil

2001. Flowers. No value expressed. Self-adhesive. (a) Without service indicator. Multicoloured.

3659	(17f.) Type **1170**	1·30	40

(b) Inscr "ZONE A PRIOR".

3660	(21f.) Tulip "Darwin" (vert)	1·40	50

No. 3659 was for use on inland letters up to 20g. and No. 3660 was for use on letters within the European Union up to 20g.

1171 Tintin

2001. 70th Anniv of Tintin in Congo (cartoon strip). Multicoloured.

3661	17f. Type **1171**	1·30	65
MS3662 123×88 mm. 34f. Tintin, Snowy and guide in car (48×37 mm)		3·25	3·25

1172 King Albert II **1173** King Albert II

2002

3663	**1173**	7c. blue and red (postage)	25	15
3666	**1172**	42c. red	1·10	40
3667	**1172**	47c. green	1·30	50
3668	**1173**	49c. red	1·30	50
3669	**1173**	52c. blue	1·40	50
3670	**1172**	59c. blue	1·80	55
3671	**1172**	60c. blue	1·20	90
3672	**1173**	79c. blue and red	2·50	65
3674	**1173**	€4.21 brown and red	10·00	2·50
3674a	**1172**	70c. blue (air)	1·50	65
3674b	**1172**	60c. blue	1·80	65
3674c	**1172**	80c. purple and red	2·00	65

Nos. 3663, 3668 and 3672 are inscribed "PRIOR" at left.

1174 Female Tennis Player

2002. Centenary of Royal Belgian Tennis Federation. Multicoloured.

3675	42c. Type **1174**	1·30	50
3676	42c. Male tennis player	1·30	50

1175 Cyclist

2002. International Cycling Events held at Circuit Zolder. Multicoloured.

3677	42c. Type **1175** (World Cyclo-Cross Championships)	1·30	50
3678	42c. Cyclist with hand raised (Road Cycling Championships)	1·30	50

1176 Dinosaur

2002. Winning Entry in Children's Stamp Design Competition at "Belgica 2001".

3679	**1176**	42c.+10c. mult	1·50	1·50

The premium was used for the promotion of philately.

1177 Antwerp from River

2002. 150th Anniv of Antwerp University.

3680 **1177** 42c. blue and black 1·10 45

1178 Buildings and Architectural Drawing

2002. "Bruges 2002", European City of Culture. Multicoloured.

3681 42c. Type **1178** 1·30 45
3682 42c. Organ pipes and xylophone 1·30 45
3683 42c. Octopus 1·30 45

1179 16th-century Manuscript (poem, Anna Bijns)

2002. Women and Art. Multicoloured.

3684 42c. Type **1179** 1·30 45
3685 84c. Woman writing (painting, Anna Boch) (vert) 2·10 1·00

1180 Fountain Pen and Writing

2002. Stamp Day.

3686 **1180** 47c. multicoloured 1·40 55

1181 Papillon

2002. Centenary of Flanders Canine Society. Multicoloured.

3687 42c. Type **1181** 1·30 65
3688 42c. Brussels griffon 1·30 65
3689 42c. Bloodhounds 1·30 65
3690 42c. Bouvier des Ardennes 1·30 65
3691 42c. Schipperke 1·30 65

1182 Stock Dove ("Pigeon Colombin-Holenduif")

2002. Birds. Multicoloured.

3692 1c. Nightingale ("Rossignol philomele-Nachtegaal") (postage) 15 15
3693 2c. Snipe ("Becassine des Marais-Watersnip") 15 15
3693a 3c. Marsh tit ("Mesange Nonnette-Glanskopmees") 15 15
3693aa 5c. Little grebe ('Dodaars-Grebe castagneux') (23x27mm) 20 15
3693b 5c. Cirl bunting ("Bruant Zizi-Cirlors") 20 15
3693c 5c. Teal ("Wintertaling-Sarcelle D'Hiver") 20 15
3693d 6c. Little owl ('Steenuil-Chouette Cheveche') 25 15
3694 7c. Type **1182** 25 15
3694a 10c. Tengmalm's owl ("Chouette De Tengmalm-Ruigpootuil") 30 20
3694b 10c. Hedge sparrow (Heggemus-Accentor Maichet) (air/prior) 1·00 35
3694c 15c. Spotted nutcracker (Cassenoix Mouchete-Notenkracker) (air/prior) 1·00 35
3695 10c. Hedge Sparrow ('Heggemus-accenentor Mouchet') (AIRPRIOR) 30 20
3696 15c. Spotted nutcracker ('Cassenoix Mouchete-Noutenkotenkrake')(AIRPRIOR) 40 25
3697 20c. Mediterranean gull ("Zwartkopmeeuw-Mouette Melanocephale") 50 30
3697a 23c. Black-necked grebe ("Greb a Cou Noir - Geoorde Fuut") 55 30
3697b 23c. Jackdaw ("Kauw-Choucas des Tours") 55 30
3698 25c. Oystercatcher ("Scholekster-Huîtrier Pie") 65 40
3698a 27c. Eurasian woodcock ('Houtsnip-becasse des bois') 70 40
3699 30c. Corncrake ("Rale des Genets—Kwartelkoning") 95 40
3700 35c. Spotted woodpecker ("Pic Epeiche-Grote Bonte Specht") 1·00 45
3700a 40c. Spotted flycatcher ("Grauwe vliegenvanger-Gobemouche gris") 1·00 50
3700b 40c. Long-eared owl ("Hibou Moyen-Duc-Ransuil") 1·00 50
3701 41c. Collared dove ("Tourterelle Turque") 1·30 65
3701a 44c. House martin ("Hirondelle de fenetre-Huiszwaluw") 1·30 65
3701b 44c. Wood pigeon ("Hourduif-Pigeon Ramier") 1·30 65
3701c 46c. Avocet ("Kluut—Avocette") 1·30 70
3701d 52c. Hoopoe ("Hop-Huppe Fasciee") 1·40 75
3701e 55c. Plover ("Kleine plevier-Petit gravelot") 1·40 80
3702 57c. Black tern ("Guifette Noire") 1·40 90
3702a 60c. Partridge ("Perdrix Crise-Patrijs") 1·50 1·00
3703 65c. Black-headed gull ("Mouette rieuse-Kapmeeuw") 1·60 1·10
3704 70c. Redshank ("Chevalier Gambette") 2·10 1·10
3704a 70c. Swallow ('Aprus apus') 1·90 1·20
3704aa 75c. Golden plover ("Goudplevier-Pluvier dore") 1·90 1·20
3704b 75c. Firecrest ("Rottelet Triple-Bandeau Vuurgoudhaatje") 1·90 1·20
3704ba 75c. Kestrel ('Falco tinnunculus') 1·90 1·20
3704c 78c. Black-tailed godwit ("Gritto-Barge A Queue Noir") 2·30 1·30
3705 €1 Wheatear ("Traquet Motteux") (38×27 mm) 3·00 1·50
3706 €2 Ringed plover ("Grand Gravelot") (38x27 mm) 6·00 2·50
3707 €3.72 Moorhen ("Waterhoen-Poule d'eau") (38x27 mm) 11·50 3·25
3708 €4 Eagle owl ("Hibou grand-duc-Oehoe") (38x27 mm) 13·00 5·25
3708a €4.30 Grebe ("Fuut-Grebe Huppe") 14·00 5·75
3708aa €4.09 Pheasant ("Faisan de Colchide") (32x24 mm) (14.6.10) 13·50 5·25
3708b €4.40 Peregrine falcon (Slechtwalk-Faucon Pelerin) (38x28 mm) 14·50 6·00
3708c € 4.60 Golden eagle 15·00 6·25
3708ca € 4.60 Barn owl ('Couette effraie-kerkuil') 15·00 6·25
3709 €5 Ruff ("Combattant Varie") (38x27 mm) 16·00 7·00

1183 Big Top, Ringmaster, Seal and Clown

2002. Europa. Circus. Winning Entry in Children's Drawing Competition.

3710 **1183** 52c. multicoloured 2·50 1·00

1184 Paramedic, Patient and Damaged Buildings

2002. Red Cross.

3711 **1184** 84c.+12c. multicoloured 2·50 2·50

1185 Abbey Buildings

2002. 850th Anniv of Leffe Abbey.

3712 **1185** 42c. multicoloured 1·50 50

1186 Loppem Castle

2002. Tourism. Castles. Sheet 161×141 mm containing T 1186 and similar horiz designs showing castles. Multicoloured.

MS3713 42c. Type **1186**; 42c. Horst; 42c. Wissekerke; 42c. Chimay; 42c. Ecaussinnes-Lalaing; 42c. Reinhardstein; 42c. Modave; 42c. Ooidonk; 42c. Corroy-le-Chateau; 42c. Alden Biesen 11·50 11·50

1187 Show Jumping

2002. Horses. Designs showing equestrian events. Multicoloured.

3714 40c. Type **1187** 1·00 45
3715 42c. Carriage driving (vert) 1·10 50

MS3716 126x91 mm. 52c. Two Brabant draught horses' heads (Centenary of St. Paul's horse procession, Opwijk) (37×48 mm) 1·60 1·60

1188 Golden Spur and Battle Scene

2002. 700th Anniv of Battle of the Golden Spurs (Flemish–French battle), Kortrijk. Multicoloured.

3717 42c. Type **1188** 1·10 40
3718 52c. Broel towers 1·30 75

MS3719 126x91 mm. 57c. Flemish and French soldiers, river and knight on horseback (48x38 mm) 1·60 1·60

1189 Onze-Lieve-Vrouw-Lombeek, Roosdaal

2002. Windmills. Multicoloured.

3720 42c. Type **1189** 1·10 40
3721 52c. Faial Island, Azores, Portugal 1·40 75

Stamps of a similar design were issued by Portugal.

1190 Liedekerke Lacework and Statue of Lace-maker

2002. Lace-making. Multicoloured.

3722 42c. Type **1190** 1·10 40
3723 74c. Pag lacework 2·00 90

Stamps of a similar design were issued by Croatia.

1191 Bakelandt, Red Zita and Stagecoach

2002. "Philately for the Young". Bakelandt (comic strip created by Hec Leemans).

3724 **1191** 42c. multicoloured 1·30 65

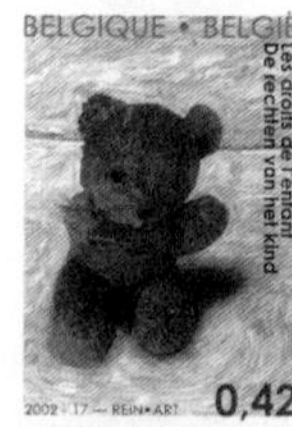

1192 Teddy Bear

2002. "The Rights of the Child".

3725 **1192** 42c. multicoloured 1·30 40

1193 Rey

2002. Birth Centenary of Jean Rey (politician).

3726 **1193** 52c. blue and cobalt 1·60 75

1194 Princess Elisabeth

2002. 1st Birthday of Princess Elisabeth. Multicoloured.

3727 49c. Type **1194** 1·60 50
3728 59c. Princess Elisabeth with parents (horiz) 1·90 75

MS3729 123×88 mm 84c. Princess Elisabeth (different) (59x38 mm) 2·75 2·75

No. 3727 was issued with a se-tenant label inscribed "PRIOR".

1195 Church, Ice Cream Van and Family

2002. Christmas. Sheet 166×40 mm containing T 1195 and similar vert designs. Multicoloured.

MS3730 41c. Type **1195**; 41c. Skier in snowy fir tree; 41c. Tobogganist and bird wearing hat; 41c. Skier wearing kilt; 41c. Skiers holding candles; 41c. Boy holding snowman-shaped ice cream; 41c. Children throwing snowballs; 41c. Children, snowman, and elderly man; 41c. Brazier, refreshment hut and people; 41c. Hut, robbers, cow and policeman 12·50 12·50

HABITATIONS SOCIALES
SOCIALE HUISVESTING
BELGIQUE-BELGIË 0,41 2002 C. OLYFF

1196 Bricks

2002. The Twentieth Century. Society. Sheet 200×166 mm containing T 1196.

MS3731 41c. purple, red and pink (Type **1196** (social housing)); 41c. deep purple, orange and purple ("MEI/MAI 68" and rubble (student protests)); 41c. slate, grey and green (telephone telecommunications)); 41c. red, orange and brown (slabs (gap between wealth and poverty)); 41c. brown, bistre and blue (broken crucifix (secularization of society)); 41c. multicoloured (towers of blocks (urbanization)); 41c. pink, violet and purple (combined female and male symbols (universal suffrage)); 41c. blue, orange and grey (enclosed circle (social security)); 41c. grey, green and bistre (schoolbag (equality in education)); 41c. grey, purple and deep purple (elderly man (ageing population)); 41c. blue, green and emerald ("E" (European Union)); 41c. chestnut, brown and yellow (stylized figure (declaration of Human Rights)); 41c. bistre, orange and light orange (pyramid of blocks (growth of consumer society)); 41c. blue, mauve and green (female symbol (feminism)); 41c. brown, sepia and light brown (mechanical arm (de-industrialization)); 41c. brown and green (dripping nozzle (oil crises)); 41c. multicoloured (vehicle (transportation)); 41c. lilac, brown and purple (sperm and egg (contraception)); 41c. green, red and grey (television (growth of television and radio)); 41c. pink, violet and blue (electric plug (increase in home appliances)) 25·00 25·00

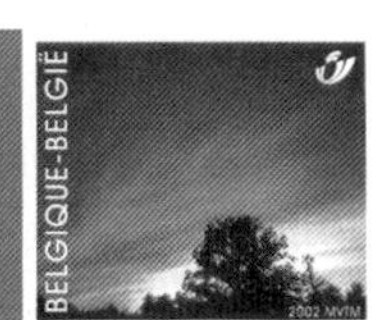

1197 Sunset

2002. Bereavement. No value expressed.

3732 **1197** (49c.) multicoloured 1·50 65

1198 Crocus

2002. Flowers. No value expressed. Ordinary or self-adhesive gum.

3733 **1198** (49c.) multicoloured 1·50 65

No. 3733 was for use on inland letters up to 50 g.

1199 Nero and Adhemar (cartoon characters)

2003. 80th (2002) Birth Anniv of Marc Sleen (cartoonist). Multicoloured.

3735 49c. Type **1199** 1·60 60

MS3736 121×91 mm 82c. Nero and Marc Sleen (49×38 mm) 2·75 2·75

1200 Firefighters, Engine and Ladders

2003. Public Services (Nos. 3737/41) and St. Valentine (3742). Multicoloured.

3737 49c. Type **1200** 1·60 60

3738 49c. Traffic police men and policewoman 1·60 60

3739 49c. Civil defence workers mending flood defences 1·60 60

3740 49c. Elderly woman wearing breathing mask, hand holding syringe and theatre nurse 1·60 60

3741 49c. Postman riding bicycle and obtaining signature for parcel 1·60 60

3742 49c. Hearts escaping from birdcage 1·60 60

1201 Van de Velde and New House, Tervuren

2003. 140th Birth Anniv of Henry van de Velde (architect). Multicoloured.

3743 49c. Type **1201** 1·60 60

3744 59c. Van de Velde and Belgian pavilion, Paris International Exhibition, 1937 (vert) 1·90 70

3745 59c. Van de Velde and Book Tower, Central Library, Ghent University (vert) 1·90 70

MS3746 91×125 mm 84c. Woman and Art Nouveau newel post 2·75 2·75

1202 Bowls

2003. Traditional Sports. Multicoloured.

3747 49c. Type **1202** 1·80 65

3748 49c. Archery 1·80 65

MS3749 91×126 mm. 82c. Pigeon racing 3·00 3·00

1203 Berlioz

2003. Birth Bicentenary of Hector Berlioz (composer).

3750 **1203** 59c. multicoloured 2·10 75

1204 Statue of Men Conversing

2003. Anniversaries. Multicoloured.

3751 49c. Type **1204** (150th anniv of engineers' association) 1·80 65

3752 49c. Statue of seated man (centenary of Solvay Business School) 1·80 65

1205 Papy Ferdinand

2003. Red Cross. Cartoon characters in rescue attempt. Multicoloured.

3753 41c. + 9c. Type **1205** 2·10 1·30

3754 41c. + 9c. Pilou holding light 2·10 1·30

3755 41c. + 9c. Stam running for help 2·10 1·30

Nos. 3753/5 were issued together, se-tenant, forming a composite design.

1206 Bouquet

2003. 3rd International Flower Show, Liege.

3756 **1206** 49c. multicoloured 2·00 65

1207 "Maigret" (film poster)

2002. Birth Centenary of Georges Simenon (writer). Multicoloured.

3757 49c. Type **1207** 2·00 65

3758 59c. "Le chat" (film poster) 2·40 80

MS3759 91×126 mm. 84c. Simenon (38×49 mm) 3·25 3·25

1208 Bells of St. Rumbold's Cathedral, Maline

2003. 150th Anniv of Belgium–Russia Diplomatic Relations. Multicoloured.

3760 59c. Type **1208** 2·40 80

3761 59c. Bells of St. Peter and Paul's Cathedral, St. Petersburg 2·40 80

1209 Eternity Symbol and "Mail Art"

2003. Stamp Day. Mail Art.

3762 **1209** 49c. multicoloured 2·10 65

1210 Roland on Horseback

2003. "Philately for the Young". The Valiant Knight (comic strip created by Francois Craenhals).

3763 **1210** 49c. multicoloured 2·10 65

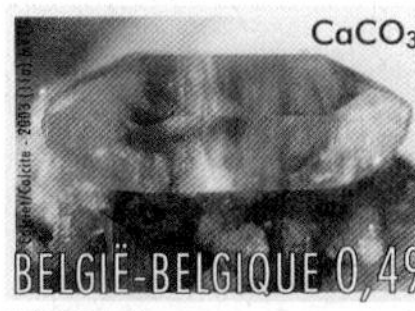

1211 Calcite

2003. Minerals. Multicoloured.

3764 49c. Type **1211** 2·10 65

3765 49c. Quartz 2·10 65

3766 49c. Barytes 2·10 65

3767 49c. Galena 2·10 65

3768 49c. Turquoise 2·10 65

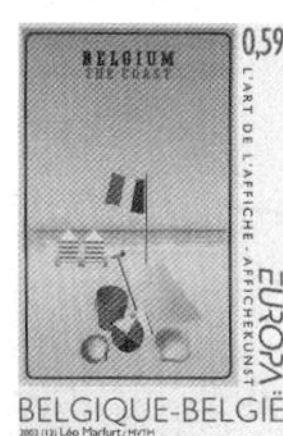

1212 "Belgium, The Coast" (Leo Marfut)

2003. Europa. Poster Art.

3769 **1212** 59c. multicoloured 2·75 1·40

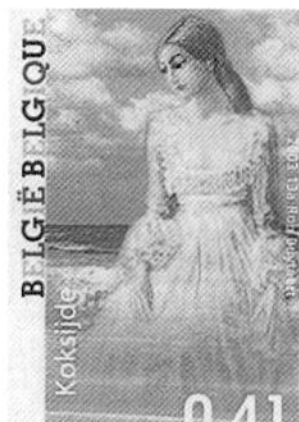

1213 "La Robe de Mariee" (Paul Delvaux, Koksijde)

2003. "This is Belgium" (1st series). Sheet 167×200 mm containing T 1213 and similar vert designs showing sites from smaller Belgian towns. Multicoloured.

MS3770 41c. Type **1213**; 41c. Mural, Town Hall, Oudenaarde; 41c. "De viust" (sculpture, Rik Poot) and Town Hall, Vilvoorde; 41c. Turnhout chateau; 41c. Ambiorix (sculpture), Gallo-Roman museum, Tongeren; 41c. Fountain (sculpture, Pol Bury), La Louviere; 41c. Town Hall, Braine; 52c. Mardasson Memorial, Bastogne; 52c. Tower and snow scene, Sankt Vith; 57c. Saxophone and Citadel, Dinant 20·00 11·00

See also Nos. **MS**3809, **MS**3943 and **MS**4033.

1214 *Monument to the Seasonal Worker, Rillaar* (Jan Peirelinck)

2003. Tourism. Statues. Multicoloured.

3771 49c. Type **1214** 2·20 70

3772 49c. La Tionade, Treignes (Yves and Claude Rahir) 2·20 70

3773 49c. Textile Teut, Town Hall, Hamont-Achel (Teo Groenen) 2·20 70

3774 49c. The Canal Guy, Brussels (Tom Frantzen) 2·20 70

3775 49c. The Maca, Wavre (Jean Godart) 2·20 70

1215 King Baudouin and Prince Albert

2003. 10th Anniv of the Accession of King Albert. Multicoloured.

3776 49c. Type **1215** 2·20 70

MS3777 90×125 mm. 59c. King Baudouin (38×48 mm); 84c. King Albert (38×48 mm) 6·75 5·50

1216 "Argenteuil" (Edouard Manet)

2003. Art.

3778 **1216** 49c. + 11c. multicoloured 2·75 1·80

No. 3778 was issued with a se-tenant label inscribed "PRIOR".

1217 "Still Life" (Giorgio Morandi)

2003. "Europhalia 2003 Italy" Festival. Italian Presidency of European Union. Multicoloured.

3779 49c. Type **1217** 2·20 75

3780 59c. Cistalia 202 (1947) 2·75 90

No. 3779 was issued with a se-tenant label inscribed "PRIOR".

Stamps of the same design were issued by Italy.

1218 Elderly Couple, Family and Young People

2003. Social Cohesion.
3781 **1218** 49c. multicoloured 2·20 80

No. 3781 was issued with a se-tenant label inscribed "PRIOR".

1219 St. Nicholas

2003. Christmas.
3782 **1219** 49c. multicoloured 2·20 80

No. 3782 was issued with a se-tenant label inscribed "PRIOR".

1220 King Albert II

2003

3783	**1220**	49c. red	2·20	80
3784	**1220**	50c. red	2·20	80
3785	**1220**	79c. blue and red	3·50	1·30
3786	**1220**	80c. violet and red	3·50	1·30

Nos. 3783/6 are inscribed "PRIOR" at left.

1221 Woman holding Cat ("Jardin extraordinaire")

2003. 50th Anniv of Belgian Television. Sheet 166×140 mm containing T 1221 and similar vert designs. Multicoloured.
MS3795 41c.×5 Type **1221**; Cameraman and camera; Broadcasting tower; Brothers Cassiers and Jef Burm; Scene from "Schipper naast Mathide" 9·00 6·50

1222 Man leaning against Pile of Books

2003. The Book. Multicoloured.

3796	49c. Type **1222**	2·20	80
3797	49c. Man rolling through printing machine (horiz)	2·20	80
3798	49c. Books on shelves	2·20	80

Nos. 3796/8 were each issued with an attached label inscribed "Prior".

1223 Maurice Gilliams

2003. Writers.

3799	**1223**	49c. brown, sepia and light brown	2·20	80
3800	-	59c. brown and orange	2·75	95

DESIGN: 59c. Marguerite Yourcenar (Maugerite de Crayencour).

No. 3799 was issued with an attached label inscribed "Prior".

1224 Tulip

2003. Flowers. No value expressed. Self-adhesive.
3801 **1224** (59c.) multicoloured 2·50 95

No. 3801 was for use on inland letters up to 50g.

1225 Herbeumont Church

2003. Christmas and New Year.
3802 **1225** 41c. multicoloured 1·70 65

1226 Justin Henin Hardenne

2003. Belgian Tennis Champions. Multicoloured.

3803	49c. Type **1226** (2003 Roland Garros and U.S. Open champion)	2·30	80
3804	49c. Kim Clijsters (2002 Masters Cup and 2003 WTA No. 1 champion) (horiz)	2·30	80

Nos. 3803/4 were each issued with an attached label inscribed "Prior", either at top or bottom (vert) or left or right (horiz).

1227 XIII and Lighthouse

2004. "Philately for the Young". XIII (comic strip created by Jean van Damme and William Vance).
3805 **1227** 41c. multicoloured 1·80 65

1228 "Portrait of Marguerite Khonopff"

2004. Fernand Khnopff (artist) Commemoration. Sheet 160×140 mm containing T 1228 and similar multicoloured designs.
MS3806 41c.×4, Type **1228**; "Caresses" (55×24 mm); "The Abandoned City"; "Brown Eyes and a Blue Flower" (55×24 mm) 5·25 4·75

1229 Carnation

2004. Flowers. No value expressed. Self-adhesive.
3807 **1229** (49c.) multicoloured 1·80 80

No. 3807 was for use on inland letters up to 50g.

1230 Profile, Stamp and Kiss

2004. Stamp Day.
3808 **1230** 41c. multicoloured 1·40 65

1231 Peter Piot (AIDS agency director)

2004. "This is Belgium" (2nd series). Sheet 166×200 mm containing T 1231 and similar vert designs showing Belgian personalities. Multicoloured.
MS3809 57c.×10, Type **1231**; Nicole Van Goethem (film maker); Dirk Frimout and Frank de Winnie (astronaut and cosmonaut); Jaques Rogge (president, International Olympic Committee); Christian de Duve (winner, Nobel Prize for Medicine); Gabrielle Petit (war heroine); Catherine Verfaillie (director, Stem Cell Institute, Minnesota) and Christine Van Broeckhoven (director, Molecular Biology Laboratory, University of Antwerp); Jaques Stilbe (philatelist); Queen Fabiola; Adrien van der Burch (organizer, Brussels Exhibition, 1935) 18·00 14·50

1232 Herg and Models of Rocket and Tintin

2004. 75th Anniv of Tintin (cartoon character created by Georges Remi (Herge)). Sheet 163×126 mm containing T 1232 and similar vert designs. Multicoloured.
MS3810 41c.×5, Type **1232**; Technical sketch for Destination Moon; Tintin and Snowy (Bobbie); Tintin climbing up rocket (*Explorers on the Moon*); Tintin, Captain Haddock and Snowy on the moon (cover illustration, *Explorers on the Moon*) 7·25 6·50

1233 Sugar Beet

2004. Sugar Industry. Multicoloured.

3811	**49c.**	Type **1233**	1·60	70
3812	**49c.**	49c. Sugar refinery	1·60	70
3813	**49c.**	49c. Tienen city	1·60	70

Nos. 3811/13 were each issued with a se-tenant label inscribed "Prior".

1234 Stars

2004. European Elections.
3814 **1234** 22c. cobalt, ultramarine and yellow 80 35

1235 "Temptation" (Salvador Dali)

2004. Birth Centenary of Salvador Dali (artist).
3815 **1235** 49c.+11c. multicoloured 2·10 1·90

No. 3815 was issued with a se-tenant label inscribed "Prior".

1236 Chapel, Buggenhout

2004. Tourism. Places of Pilgrimage.

3816	**1236**	49c. green	1·60	70
3817	-	49c. agate	1·60	70
3818	-	49c. purple	1·60	70
3819	-	49c. indigo	1·60	70

DESIGNS: No. 3817, Banneux; 3818, Scherpenheuvet; 3819, Beauraing (horiz).

Nos. 3816/19 were each issued with a se-tenant label inscribed "Prior".

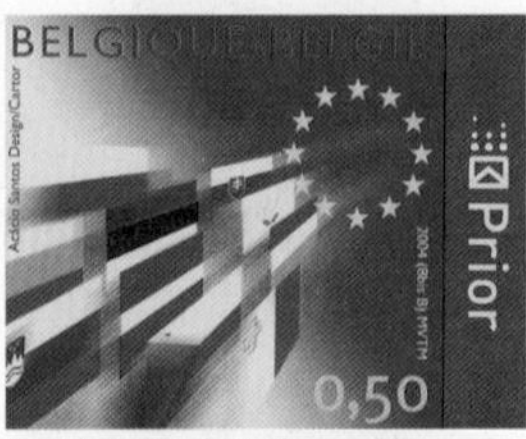

1237 New Member's Flags and EU Emblem

2004. Enlargement of European Union (1st issue). Sheet 125×90 mm containing T 1237 and similar horiz designs. Multicoloured.
MS3820 50c.×2 Type **1237**×2; 60c.×2 Parliament building; As No. 3814 8·00 7·25

See also Nos. 3835/44.

1238 Le Faune Mordu (sculpture) (Jef Lambeaux), Boverie Park

2004. Liege ("Lidje todi"). Multicoloured.

3821	49c. Type **1238**	1·40	65
3822	49c. Bridge (Santiago Calatrava)	1·40	65

MS3823 90×125 mm. 75c. Blast furnace, Seraing (38×49 mm) 2·50 2·30

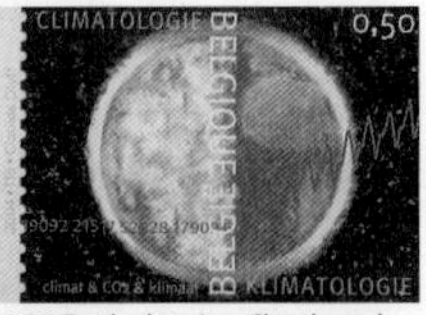

1239 Earth showing Clouds and Ozone Layer (climate and CO2)

2004. Climatology. Multicoloured.

3824	50c. Type **1239**	1·60	65
3825	65c. Sun and earth (earth–sun relationship)	2·00	85
3826	80c. Earth showing continent and viewed from space (earth)	2·50	1·00
3827	80c. Sun viewed through telescope and showing spots	2·50	1·00

Nos. 3824 and 3826 were issued with a se-tenant label inscribed "Prior".

1240 Edgar Jacobs

2004. Birth Centenary of Edgar Pierre Jacobs (creator of Blake and Mortimer (comic strip)). Black and yellow (60c.) or multicoloured (other).

3828 60c. Type **1240** 2·20 90

MS3829 125×90 mm. €1.20 Blake and Mortimer (45×36 mm) 3·75 3·00

Stamps of a similar design were issued by France.

1241 Django Reinhardt

2004. Jazz Musicians. Multicoloured.

3830 50c. Type **1241** (guitarist) 1·60 65

3831 50c. Fud Candrix (saxophonist) 1·60 65

3832 50c. Rene Thomas (guitarist) 1·60 65

3833 50c. Jack Sels (composer and saxophonist) 1·60 65

3834 50c. Bobby Jaspar (flautist and saxophonist) 1·60 65

Nos. 3830/4 were each issued with a se-tenant label inscribed "Prior".

1242 EU Emblem and Cyprus Flag

2004. Enlargement of European Union (2nd issue). Designs showing emblem and new member flag. Multicoloured. Self-adhesive.

3835 44c. Type **1242** 1·60 65

3836 44c. Estonia 1·60 65

3837 44c. Hungary 1·60 65

3838 44c. Latvia 1·60 65

3839 44c. Lithuania 1·60 65

3840 44c. Malta 1·60 65

3841 44c. Poland 1·60 65

3842 44c. Czech Republic 1·60 65

3843 44c. Slovakia 1·60 65

3844 44c. Slovenia 1·60 65

1243 King Albert II

2004. 70th Birthday of King Albert II. Each black and gold.

3845 50c. Type **1243** 1·60 65

MS3846 90×125 mm. 80c. As No. 3845 (38×48 mm) 2·50 2·10

No. 3845 was issued with a se-tenant label inscribed "Prior".

1244 Wind Break (Belgian Coast)

2004. Europa. Holidays. Winning Designs in Photographic Competition. Multicoloured.

3847 55c. Type **1244** (Muriel Vekemans) 1·70 1·40

3848 55c. Semois valley (Belgian Ardennes) (Freddy Deburghgraeve) 1·70 1·40

1245 Female Basketball Player

2004. Olympic Games, Athens 2004. Multicoloured.

3849 50c. Type **1245** 1·70 65

3850 55c. Cyclist (horiz) 1·80 75

3851 60c. Pole vaulter (horiz) 2·00 80

MS3852 136×90 mm. 80c. Olympic flame 2·75 2·10

No. 3849 was issued with a se-tenant label inscribed "Prior".

1246 Red Cross Workers

2004. Red Cross.

3853 **1246** 50c.+11c. multicoloured 2·00 1·60

No. 3853 was issued with a se-tenant label inscribed "Prior".

1247 "L'appel"

2004. 10th Death Anniv of Idel Ianchelevici (sculptor). Multicoloured.

3854 50c. Type **1247** 1·70 65

3855 55c. "Perennis perdurat poeta" 1·80 75

No. 3854 was issued with a se-tenant label inscribed "Prior".

Stamps of the same design were issued by Romania.

2004. Mourning Stamp. As T 1197.

3856 **1197** 50c. multicoloured 1·70 65

1248 Squirrel and Blackcap

2004. Forest Week. Sheet 90×125 mm containing T 1248 and similar vert designs. Multicoloured.

MS3857 44c.×4, Type **1248**; Nightingale, robin and red admiral butterfly; Bee, vole and weasel; Jay and peacock butterfly 6·50 5·25

The stamps and margin of **MS**3857 form a composite design of a forest scene.

1249 Volunteer Medal

2004. War Volunteers.

3858 **1249** 50c. multicoloured 1·70 65

1250 Impatiens

2004. Flowers. No value expressed. Self-adhesive.

3859 **1250** (50c.) multicoloured 1·70 65

No. 3859 was for use on inland letters up to 50g.

1251 Foal

2004. Belgica 2006 International Stamp Exhibition, Brussels (1st issue). Sheet 166×140 mm containing T 1251 and similar vert designs. Multicoloured.

MS3860 44c.×5, Type **1251**; Robin; Cat; Puppy; Fish 17·00 14·50

See also Nos. 3892/**MS**3897.

1252 Jack O' Lantern

2004. Halloween. Self-adhesive. Multicoloured.

3861 44c. Type **1252** 1·70 65

3862 44c. Witch, cat and bats 1·70 65

1253 Raymond Jean de Kramer

2004. Writers' Death Anniversaries. Multicoloured.

3863 50c. Type **1253** (writing as Jean Ray or John Flanders) (40th) 1·70 65

3864 75c. Johan Daisne (26th) 2·50 1·00

3865 80c. Thomas Owen (2nd) (vert) 2·75 1·10

Nos. 3863 and 3865 were issued with a se-tenant label inscribed "Prior".

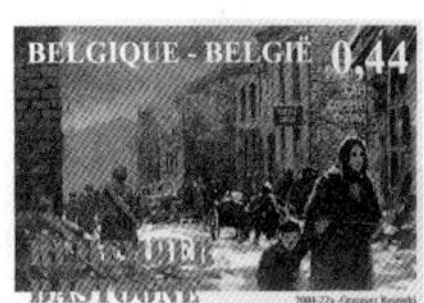

1254 Soldiers, Mother and Child on Snow-covered Street

2004. 60th Anniv of Attack on Bastogne. Multicoloured.

3866 44c. Type **1254** 1·70 65

3867 55c. Soldiers assisting wounded (vert) 1·80 75

3868 65c. Soldiers amongst trees 2·10 85

1255 "Flight into Egypt"

2004. Christmas (1st issue). Paintings by Peter Paul Rubens. Multicoloured.

3869 44c. Type **1255** 1·70 65

3870 44c. "Adoration of the Magi" 1·70 65

Stamps of the same design were issued by Germany.

See also No. 3872.

1256 Rene Baeten

2004. Belgian International Motocross Champions. Sheet 151×166 mm containing T 1256 and similar horiz designs.

MS3871 50c.×12, (23bis a, d, e, f, g, i, j, k and l) multicoloured; (23bis b) green and brown; (23bis c) brown, lemon and deep brown; (23bis h) blue and brown 20·00 16·00

DESIGNS: Type **1256**; Jacky Martens; Georges Jobe; Joel Roberts; Eric Geboers; Roger de Coster; Stefan Everts; Gaston Rahier; Joel Smets; Harry Everts; Andre Malherbe and Steve Ramon.

The stamps of **MS**3871 were arranged around a central label, showing a motocross rider, each with a se-tenant label inscribed "Prior" attached at either left or right. The Belgium Post identification number is given in brackets to assist identification.

2004. Christmas (2nd issue). Paintings by Peter Rubens. Self-adhesive.

3872 44c. As No. 3870 (22×22 mm) 1·70 65

1257 Stylized Posthorn

2005

3873 **1257** 6c. scarlet 35 15

3874 **1257** 10c. blue 85 40

3877 **1257** 1 (52c.) scarlet 1·00 90

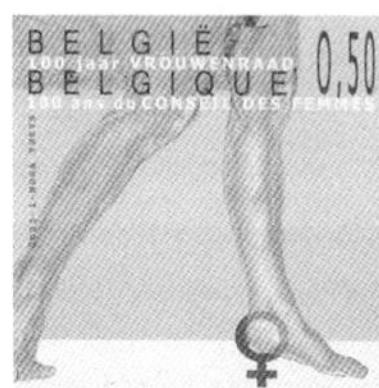

1258 Woman's Legs

2005. Centenary of Women's Council.

3882 **1258** 50c. multicoloured 1·70 65

No. 3882 was issued with a se-tenant label inscribed "Prior".

1259 Michel Vaillant

2005. "Philately for the Young". Michel Vaillant (comic strip created by Jean Graton).

3883 **1259** 50c. multicoloured 1·70 65

No. 3883 was issued with a se-tenant label inscribed "Prior".

1260 "The Violinist" (Kees van Dongen)

2005. "Promotion of Philately".

3884 **1260** 50c.+12c. multicoloured 2·10 1·70

1261 "www.175-25.be"

2005. 175th Anniv of Independence (1st issue). 25th Anniv of Federal State. No value expressed. Self-adhesive.

3885 **1261** (50c.) multicoloured 1·70 65

See also No. **MS**3889 and **MS**3891.

1262 Johan Hendrick van Dale and "van Dale" (Dutch dictionary)

2005. Language. Multicoloured.

3886 55c. Type **1262** 1·80 75

3887 55c. Maurice Grevisse and "le bon usage" (French grammar) 1·80 75

1263 Child receiving Polio Vaccine

2005. Centenary of Rotary International (charitable organization). Polio Eradication Campaign.

3888	**1263**	80c. multicoloured	2·75	1·30

1264 First Railway Journey from Brussels to Malines (1835)

2005. 175th Anniv of Independence (2nd issue). Sheet 166×200 mm containing T 1264 and similar horiz designs. Multicoloured.

MS3889 44c.×10, Type **1264** (transport); Bakuba dancers, Congo; Early school children (education); Factory workers (industrialization); Family (social development); Bombardment of Edingen, 1940; Brussels Expo, 1958 (trade); Rue de la Loi, Wetstraat (federalization); Berlaymont building, Brussels (Europe); "The Shadow and its Shadow" (Rene Mgritte) (art) 15·00 13·50

1265 "TSUNAMI" and Sea

2005. Red Cross. Support for Victims of Tsunami Disaster.

3890	**1265**	50c.+12c. multicoloured	2·10	1·70

No. 3890 was issued with a se-tenant label inscribed "Prior".

1266 King Albert II and Queen Paola

2005. 175th Anniv of Independence (3rd issue). Sheet 126×90 mm.

MS3891 **1266** 75c. multicoloured 2·50 2·00

1267 Go-Kart

2005. Belgica 2006 International Stamp Exhibition, Brussels (2nd issue). Multicoloured. (a) Self-adhesive.

3892	44c. Type **1267**	1·50	60
3893	44c. Motor boat	1·50	60
3894	44c. Train	1·50	60
3895	44c. Airplane	1·50	60
3896	44c. Spacecraft	1·50	60

(b) Size 27×39 mm. Miniature Sheet. Ordinary gum.

MS3897 166×131 mm. Nos. 3892/5 17·00 13·50

1268 Rose "Belinda"

2005. Ghent Flower Show. Multicoloured.

3898	44c. Type **1268**	1·50	60
3899	70c. Rose "Pink Iceberg" (vert)	2·30	95
3900	80c. Rose "Old Master"	2·75	1·10

Nos. 3898/3900 were impregnated with the scent of roses.

No. 3900 was issued with a se-tenant label inscribed "Prior".

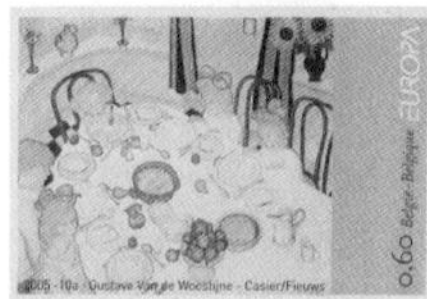

1269 "The Children's Table" (Gustave van de Woestijne)

2005. Europa. Gastronomy. Multicoloured.

3901	60c. Type **1269**	2·00	1·60
3902	60c. "Still Life with Oysters, Fruit and Pastry"	2·00	1·60

1270 Black Stork

2005. Stamp Day.

3903	**1270**	€4 multicoloured	13·00	5·25

1271 Soldiers

2005. 55th Anniv of Korean War.

3904	**1271**	44c. multicoloured	1·50	60

1272 Celebration

2005. 60th Anniv of End of World War II. Multicoloured.

3905	44c. Type **1272**	1·50	60
3906	44c. Camp prisoner	1·50	60
3907	44c. Returning service men and prisoners	1·50	60

1273 Zimmer Tower, Lier, Flanders

2005. Tourism. Clock Towers.

3908	**1273**	44c. black	1·50	60
3909	-	44c. agate	1·50	60
3910	-	44c. chocolate	1·50	60

DESIGNS: No. 3908 Type **1273**; 3909 Belfry, Mons, Wallonia; 3910 Mont des Arts Clock, Brussels.

1274 Hiker (Ardennes)

2005. Holidays. Multicoloured.

3911	50c. Type **1274**	1·70	65
3912	50c. Sunbather	1·70	65

Nos. 3911/12 were each issued with a se-tenant label inscribed "Prior".

1275 Hearts

2005. Greetings Stamps. Multicoloured. Self-adhesive.

3913	(50c.) Type **1275**	1·70	65
3914	80c. Doves (wedding)	2·75	1·10
3915	80c. Two rings (wedding)	2·75	1·10
3916	80c. Boy (birth)	2·75	1·10
3917	80c. Girl (birth)	2·75	1·10

No. 3913 was for use on inland letters up to 50g.

1276 Tulip

2005. Air. Flowers. No value expressed. Multicoloured. Self-adhesive.

3918	**1276**	(70c.) multicoloured	2·30	95

1277 "L'humanitie assaillie par les sept Peches capiteux" (Seven Deadly Sins) (16th-century tapestry, Brussels)

2005. Carpets and Tapestries. Multicoloured.

3919	44c. Type **1277**	1·50	60
3920	60c. Carpet, Hereke, Turkey	2·00	80

Stamps of a similar design were issued by Turkey.

1278 Radio Waves

2005. 75th Anniv of Radio.

3921	**1278**	50c. magenta and black	1·70	65

No. 3921 was issued with a se-tenant label inscribed "Prior".

1279 Robert Van de Walle

2005. Belgian International Judo Champions. Sheet 100×167 mm containing T 1279 and similar horiz designs. Multicoloured.

MS3922 50c.×6, Type **1279**; Ingrid Berghmans; Ulla Werbrouck; Gella Vandecaveye; Christel Deliege; Johan Laats 10·00 8·00

The stamps of **MS**3922 were each issued with a se-tenant label inscribed "Prior" attached at either left or right.

1280 King Albert II

2005

3923	**1280**	50c. multicoloured (postage)	1·00	85
3923a	**1280**	52c. multicoloured	1·00	70
3928	**1280**	70c. blue and light (air)	2·30	95
3928a	**1280**	80c. blue, grey and black	95	65
3928b	**1280**	83c. multicoloured	1·00	70
3929	**1280**	90c. blue, grey and black	2·75	1·10

Nos. 3923 and 3928/9 were inscribed "Prior".

1281 *Buccinum undatum*

2005. Molluscs. Sheet 161×130 mm containing T 1281 and similar designs. Multicoloured. Self-adhesive.

MS3933 44c.×6, Type **1281**; *Epitonium clathrus; Cepea nemoralis* and *Arion rufus; Donax vittatus; Anodonta cygnea; Anodonta cygnea* (different) 9·00 7·25

1282 Centre for Comic Strip Art, Brussels

2005. Architecture. Multicoloured.

3934	44c. Type **1282**	1·50	60
3935	44c. Museum of Musical Instruments, Brussels	1·50	60
3936	65c. Bukit Pasoh Road, Singapore	2·10	85
3937	65c. Kandahar Street, Singapore	2·10	85

Stamps of the same design were issued by Singapore.

1283 Chrysanthemum

2005. Flowers. No value expressed. Self-adhesive.

3938	**1283**	(50c.) multicoloured	1·70	65

No. 3938 was for use on inland letters up to 50g.

1284 "The Reaper" (Kasimir Malevich)

2005. "Europhalia 2005—Russia" Festival. Multicoloured.

3939	50c. Type **1284**	1·70	65
3940	70c. "Allegory" (Sergei Sudeikin)	2·30	95

No. 3939 was issued with a se-tenant label inscribed "Prior".

1285 Shrine of Our Lady, Tournai

2005. 800th Anniv of Shrine of Our Lady by Nicolas of Verdun.

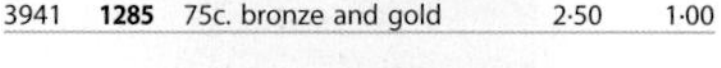

3941	**1285**	75c. bronze and gold	2·50	1·00

1286 Asterix

2005. Asterix (comic strip written by Rene Goscinny and illustrated by Albert Uderzo). Sheet 161×130 mm containing T 1286 and similar designs showing characters. Multicoloured.

MS3942 60c.×6, Type **1286**; Cacofonix (27×41 mm.); Getafix (41×27 mm.); Obelix (41×27 mm.); Abraracourcix (27×41 mm.); Asterix feasting (39×34 mm.)	11·50	10·50

1287 "Objet" (Joelle Tuerlinckx)

2005. "This is Belgium" (3rd series). Art. Sheet 166×201 mm containing T 1287 and similar designs.

MS3943 44c.×10, black and claret (Type **1287**); multicoloured ("ABC" (Jef Geys)); multicoloured ("La Traviata" (Lili Dujourie)); multicoloured ("Representation d'un corps rond" (Ann Veronica Janssens)); black ("Portrait of an Artist by Himself (XIII)" (Jan Vercuysse)); multicoloured ("Donderwolk" (Panamarenko)); multicoloured ("Tournus" (Marthe Wery)); multicoloured ("Figuur op de rug gezien (la nuque)" (Luc Tuymans)); black and bright carmine ("Jeu de mains" (Michel Francois)); "Mur de la montee des Anges" (Jan Fabre))	13·00	12·00

The stamps of No. **MS**3943 form a composite design.

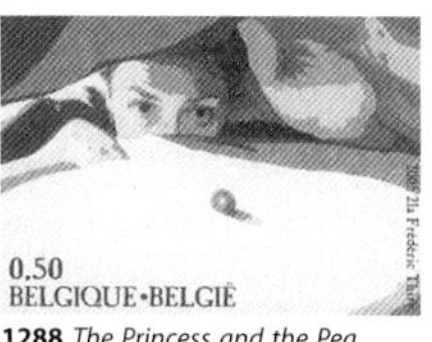

1288 *The Princess and the Pea*

2005. Birth Bicentenary of Hans Christian Andersen (writer). Multicoloured. (a) Ordinary gum.

3944	50c. Type **1288b**	1·70	65
3945	50c. *The Ugly Duckling*	1·70	65
3946	50c. *Thumbelina*	1·70	65
3947	50c. *The Little Mermaid*	1·70	65
3948	50c. *The Emperor's New Clothes*	1·70	65

(b) Size 28×22 mm. Self-adhesive.

3949	50c. As No. 3944	1·70	65
3950	50c. As No. 3945	1·70	65
3951	50c. As No. 3946	1·70	65
3952	50c. As No. 3947	1·70	65
3953	50c. As No. 3948	1·70	65

Nos. 3944/8 each have a label inscribed "Prior" attached at left.

1289 Father Christmas

2005. Christmas. (a) Ordinary gum.

3954	**1289**	44c. multicoloured	1·50	60

(b) Size 23×28 mm. Self-adhesive.

3955	44c. multicoloured	1·50	60

1290 Maurits Sabbe

2005. Popular Literature. Writers. Multicoloured.

3956	44c. Type **1290**	1·50	60
3957	44c. Arthur Masson	1·50	60

1291 Queen Astrid

2005. Birth Centenary of Queen Astrid. Each black and gold.

3958	44c. Type **1291**	1·50	60
MS3959	90×125 mm. 80c. Queen Astrid and Prince Albert (38×49 mm)	2·75	2·10

1292 Drum

2005. Music. Brass Bands. Multicoloured.

3960	50c. Type **1292**	1·70	70
3961	50c. Cornet	1·70	70
3962	50c. Sousaphone	1·70	70
3963	50c. Clarinet	1·70	70
3964	50c. Tuba	1·70	70

Nos. 3960/4 each have a label inscribed "Prior" attached at foot.

1293 Donkey

2006. Farm Animals. Multicoloured. Self-adhesive.

3965	46c. Type **1293**	1·40	65
3966	46c. Hens	1·40	65
3967	46c. Ducks	1·40	65
3968	46c. Pigs	1·40	65
3969	46c. Cow	1·40	65
3970	46c. Goat	1·40	65
3971	46c. Rabbits	1·40	65
3972	46c. Horses	1·40	65
3973	46c. Sheep	1·40	65
3974	46c. Geese	1·40	65

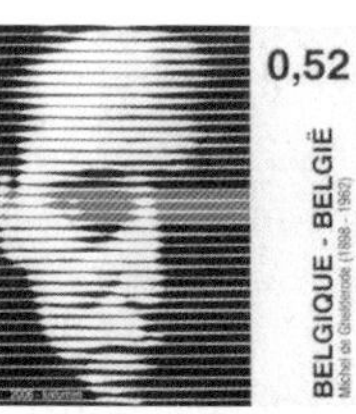

1294 Michel de Ghelderode

2006. Writers Commemorations.

3975	**1294**	52c. black and blue	1·60	70
3976	-	78c. black and magenta	1·90	85

DESIGN: 78c. Herman Terlinck.

No. 3975 has a label inscribed "Prior" attached at left.

1295 Guillaume Dufay and Gilles Binchois

2006. Renaissance Polyphonists (part song writers). Multicoloured.

3977	60c. Type **1295**	1·80	75
3978	60c. Johannes Ockeghem	1·80	75
3979	60c. Jacob Obrecht	1·80	75
3980	60c. Adriaan Willaert	1·80	75
3981	60c. Orlandus Lassus	1·80	75

1296 Musical Score and Mozart

2006. 250th Birth Anniv of Wolfgang Amadeus Mozart.

3982	**1296**	70c. multicoloured	2·30	1·00

1297 Cross Bowman **1298** Cross Bowman

2006. Cross Bowmen. (a) Ordinary gum.

3983	**1297**	46c. multicoloured	1·50	65

(b) Size 24×32 mm. Self-adhesive gum.

3984	**1298**	(52c.) multicoloured	1·70	70

1299 Senate

2006. 175th Anniv of Democracy. Sheet 200×83 mm containing T 1299 and similar multicoloured designs.

MS3985 46c.×3, Type **1299**; King Leopold (vert); Chamber of representatives	4·50	3·75

1300 Head with Open Mouth

2006. Freedom of the Press. Sheet 197×100 mm containing T 1300 and similar multicoloured designs.

MS3986 52c.×5, Type **1300** ×3; Blue sky ×2 (horiz)	8·25	7·25

The stamps of **MS**3986 each have a label inscribed "Prior" attached at foot. The stamp depicting a blue sky shows a woman's face when tilted.

1301 Mouth and Script

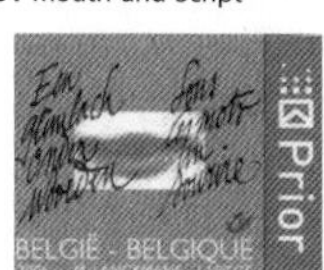

1302 Mouth and Script

2006. Stamp Festival. Winning Entry in Design a Stamp Competition. (a) Ordinary gum.

3987	**1301**	46c. multicoloured	1·50	65

(b) Size 29×25 mm. Self-adhesive gum.

3988	**1302**	(52c.) multicoloured	1·70	70
3988a	**1302**	(52c.) As Type **1302** but design reversed	1·70	70

Nos. 3988/a were each issued with a se-tenant label inscribed "Prior".

1303 Justus Lipsius

2006. 400th Death Anniv of Justus Lipsius (writer and scientist).

3989	**1303**	70c. brown and cinnamon	2·30	1·00

1304 Winner and Trophy

2006. 1st Four Stages—Giro Italia (cycle race), Wallonia.

3990	**1304**	52c. multicoloured	1·70	70

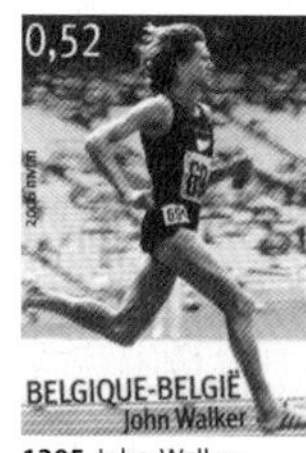

1305 John Walker

2006. 30th Anniv of Memorial Van Damme Track and Field Event. Sheet 167×100 mm containing T 1305 and similar vert designs. Multicoloured.

MS3991 52c.×5, Type **1305**; Alberto Juantorena; Ivo Van Damme; Sebastian Coe; Steve Ovett	8·25	7·25

The stamps of **MS**3991 were each issued with a label inscribed "Prior" at foot.

1306 Clement Van Hassel

2006. Belgian World Champions—Billiards. Sheet 153×167 mm containing T 1306 and similar horiz designs. Multicoloured.

MS3992 52c.×12, Type **1306**; Tony Schrauwen; Leo Corin; Emile Wafflard; Ludo Dielis; Jos Vervest; Frederic Caudron; Laurent Boulanger; Paul Stroobants, Eddy Leppens and Peter De Backer; Raymond Ceulemans; Raymond Steylaerts; Jozef Philipoom	18·00	16·00

The stamps of **MS**3992 were each issued with a label inscribed "Prior" at either left or right.

The stamps of **MS**3992 were not for sale separately.

1307 "L'offrande de Joachim Refusee" (Lambert Lombard)

2006. Art. 500th Birth Anniv of Lambert Lombard (3393/4) or 150th Birth Anniv of Leon Spilliaert (3395/6). Multicoloured.

3993	65c. Type **1307**	2·10	90
3994	65c. "August et la Sybille de Tibur" (Lambert Lombard)	2·10	90
3995	65c. "Duizeling" (Leon Spilliaert)	2·10	90
3996	65c. "De Dame met de Hoed" (Leon Spilliaert)	2·10	90

1308 Ostend Lighthouse

2006. Lighthouses.Multicoloured.

3997	46c. Type **1308**	1·50	65
3998	46c. Blankenberge	1·50	65
3999	46c. Nieuwport	1·50	65
4000	46c. Heist	1·50	65

1309 Dogfish

2006. North Sea Fish. Sheet 146×124 mm containing T 1309 and similar multicoloured designs.

MS4001 46c.×5, Type **1309**; Cod (47×26 mm); Thornback skate; Plaice (33×26 mm); Herring (33×26 mm) 7·50 6·50

The stamps and margins of **MS**4001 form a composite design.

1310 Emblem

1311 Emblem

2006. Belgica 2006 International Stamp Exhibition. (a) Ordinary Gum.

4002	**1310**	46c. multicoloured	1·50	65

(b) Size 24×28 mm. Self-adhesive gum.

4003	**1311**	(52c.) multicoloured	1·50	65

1312 Nurse, Patients and Bandages

1313 Nurse, Patients and Bandages

2006. Red Cross. Benjamin Secouriste (children's Red Cross certificate scheme). (a) Ordinary Gum.

4004	**1312**	52c.+12c. multicoloured	2·00	85

(b) Size 24×28 mm. Self-adhesive gum.

4005	**1313**	(52c.) multicoloured	1·70	70
4005a	**1313**	(52c.) As Type **1313** but design reversed	1·70	70

No. 4005/a were issued with a se-tenant label inscribed "Prior".

1314 Emblem

2006. Centenary of BOIC (Belgian Olympic and Interfederal Committee).

4006	**1314**	52c. multicoloured	1·70	70

No. 4006 was issued with a se-tenant label inscribed "Prior".

1315 Deigne

2006. Tourism. Wallonia. Showing village scenes. Multicoloured.

4007	52c. Type **1315**	1·70	70
4008	52c. Mein	1·70	70
4009	52c. Celles	1·70	70
4010	52c. Lompret	1·70	70
4011	52c. Ny	1·70	70

Nos. 4007/11 were each issued with a se-tenant label inscribed "Prior".

1316 Part of Football

2006. World Cup Football Championship, Germany. Sheet 126×90 mm.

MS4012 **1316** €1.30 multicoloured 4·25 3·75

1317 *Centauria*

2006. Flowers. No value expressed. Self-adhesive.

4013	**1317**	(52c.) multicoloured	1·70	70

No. 4013 was for use on inland letters up to 50g.

1318 Miner

2006. 50th Anniv of Marcinelle Mine Disaster.

4014	**1318**	70c. multicoloured	2·30	1·00

1319 Tulip

2006. Air. Flowers. No value expressed. Self-adhesive. Multicoloured.

4015	**1319**	(70c.) multicoloured	2·30	1·00

No. 4015 was for use on letters of up to 50g. within Europe.

1320 "Oosterlinghuis" (beguinage (religious community), Bruges) (painting)

2006. 650th Anniv of Hanseatic League. Multicoloured.

4016	70c. Type **1320**	2·30	1·00
4017	80c. "Oosters Huis" (Bremen town hall) (painting)	2·50	1·10

1321 Institute Building

2006. Centenary of the Institute of Tropical Medicine.

4018	**1321**	80c. multicoloured	2·50	1·10

1322 "ABA"

2006. Academie de Philatelie de Belgique.

4019	**1322**	52c. multicoloured	1·60	70

No. 4019 was issued with a se-tenant label inscribed "Prior" attached at top.

1323 "Le Kleptomane" (Theodore Gericault)

2006. Foreign Masterpieces in Belgian Collections.

4020	**1323**	52c.+12c. multicoloured	2·10	95

No. 4020 was issued with a label inscribed "Prior" attached at left. The premium was for the promotion of philately.

1324 Ying Yang Symbol

2006. Belgica 2006 International Stamp Exhibition. Young Philatelist World Championship. Two sheets containing T 1324 and similar vert designs. Multicoloured.

MS4021 (a) 166×133 mm. 46c.×5, Type **1324**; Tulips as wine glasses; Butterflies as four leaf clover; Tent at night; Comic page containing all designs. (b) 190×120 mm. €1.95 Emblem (38×49 mm) 29·00 26·00

Nos. **MS**4021a/b were each sold for €5, the premium for the promotion of philately.

1325 Animals (Nassira Tadmiri)

2006. Europa. Integration. Multicoloured.

4022	52c. Type **1325**	1·60	70
4023	52c. Children of many nations and rainbow (Lize-Maria Verhaeghe)	1·60	70

1326 "New Skin" (Pierre Alechinsky)

1327 "New Skin" (Pierre Alechinsky)

2006. CoBrA (artistic movement). Multicoloured. (a) Miniature sheet. Ordinary gum.

MS4024 125×90 mm. 46c. Type **1326**; 70c. "Untitled" (Asger Jorn) 3·75 3·25

(b) Size 28×25 mm. No value expressed. Self-adhesive gum.

4025	(52c.) Type **1327**	1·60	70

Stamps of similar design were issued by Denmark.

1328 Rock and Roll

1329 Rock and Roll

2006. Dance. Multicoloured.

(a) Size 30×26 mm. No value expressed. Self-adhesive gum.

4026	(52c.) Type **1329**	1·60	70
4027	(52c.) Waltz	1·60	70
4028	(52c.) Tango	1·60	70
4029	(52c.) Cha-cha-cha	1·60	70
4030	(52c.) Samba	1·60	70

(b) Miniature sheet. Ordinary gum.

MS4031 166×125 mm. 60c.×5, Type **1328**; Waltz; Tango; Cha-cha-cha; Samba 8·75 8·75

1330 Kramikske

2006. Youth Philately. Kramikske Briochon, cartoon character created by Jean-Pol Vandenbroek.

4032	**1330**	46c. multicoloured	1·50	70

1331 Tomato and Shrimps

2006. "This is Belgium" (4th series). Food. Sheet 154×186 mm containing T 1331 and similar multicoloured designs.

MS4033 46c.×10, Type **1331**; Trappist beer (vert); Jenever (spirit) (vert); Chicory au gratin; Ham and sausages (vert); Waffles (vert); Stewed eels in chervil sauce; Chocolate; Mussels and fries (vert); Gueuze (beer) (vert) 13·50 13·00

1332 Angel playing Psaltery (detail)

1333 Angel playing Psaltery (detail)

2006. Christmas. Altarpiece by Hans Memling. Showing angel musicians. Multicoloured. (a) Ordinary gum.

4034	46c. Type **1332**	1·50	70
4035	46c. Tromba marina	1·50	70
4036	46c. Lute	1·50	70
4037	46c. Trumpet	1·50	70

4038	46c. Shawn	1·50	70

(b) Size 25×29 mm. Self-adhesive.

4039	46c. Type **1333**	1·50	70
4040	46c. Tromba marina	1·50	70
4041	46c. Lute	1·50	70
4042	46c. Trumpet	1·50	70
4043	46c. Shawn	1·50	70

Nos. 4034/8 were issued together, se-tenant, forming a composite design.

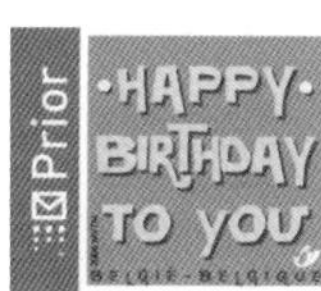

1334 "HAPPY BIRTHDAY TO YOU"

2006. Greetings Stamps. Self-adhesive. Multicoloured. No value expressed.

4044	(52c.) Type **1334**	1·50	70
4045	(52c.) Birthday cake (Prior at right)	1·50	70
4046	(52c.) As No. 4045 (Prior at left)	1·50	70
4047	(52c.) As No. 4044 (Prior at right)	1·50	70

1335 Cycle Wheel (cyclocross)

2007. Sport. Multicoloured. (a) Ordinary gum.

4048	46c. Type **1335**	1·40	65
4049	60c. Ball and skittles (bowling)	1·80	85
4050	65c. Club and ball (golf)	2·00	95

(b) Size 25×29 mm. Self-adhesive. No Value Expressed.

4051	(52c.) As Type **1335**	1·50	70
4052	(52c.) As No. 4049	1·50	70
4053	(52c.) As No. 4050	1·50	70

1336 "Nu Assis" (Amedo Modigliani)

2007. Sheet 90×125 mm.

MS4054	**1336** 60c.+30c. multicoloured	2·75	2·50

The premium was for the promotion of philately.

1337 Alix

2007. "Philately for the Young". Alix (comic strip created by Jacques Martin).

4055	**1337** 52c. multicoloured	1·70	80

1338 Piano Accordion

2007. Bellows-driven Aerophones. Sheet 166×100 mm containing T 1338 and similar vert designs. Multicoloured.

MS4056	52c.×5 Type **1338**; Concertina; Button accordion; Melodeon; Melodeon (different)	7·50	7·25

The stamps of **MS**4056 each have a se-tenant label inscribed "Prior" attached at foot.

The stamps of **MS**4056 were not for sale separately.

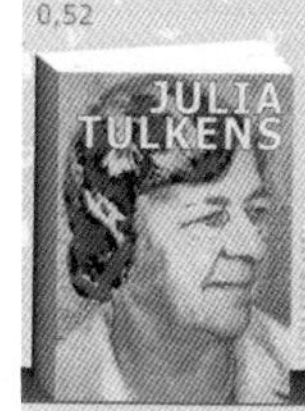

1339 Julia Tulkens

2007. Women in Literature. Sheet 166×100 mm containing T 1339 and similar vert designs. Multicoloured.

MS4057	52c.×5 Type **1339**; Madeleine Bourdhouxhe; Christine d'Haen; Jacqueline Harpman; Maria Rosseels	7·50	7·25

The stamps of **MS**4057 each have a se-tenant label inscribed "Prior" attached at foot and form a composite background design.

1340 Hospital Librarian and Patient

1341 Hospital Librarian and Patient

2007. Red Cross. Multicoloured. (a) Self-adhesive gum.

4058	(52c.) Type **1340**	1·50	70
4059	(52c.) As No. 4058 but with "Prior" at right	1·50	70

(b) Size 39×27 mm. Ordinary gum.

4060	52c.+25c. Type **1341**	2·40	1·10

No. 4060 has a label inscribed "Prior" attached at right.

1342 "Tati l'periki" (Tati the hairdresser) (Edouard Remouchamps)

2007. Belgian Popular Theatre. Sheet 198×83 mm containing T 1342 and similar multicoloured designs.

MS4061	46c.×3, Type **1342**; Romain DeConinck (vert); "Le Mariage de Melle Beulemans" (Jean-Francois Fonson and Fernand Wicheler)	4·50	4·25

The stamps of **MS**4061 form a composite background design.

1343 Stoclet Palace (interior) (Josef Hoffman)

2007. Architecture. Multicoloured.

4062	46c. Type **1343**	1·70	80
4063	80c. Stoclet Palace (exterior)	2·40	1·10

No. 4063 has a label inscribed "Prior" attached at top.

Stamps of a similar design were issued by Czech Republic.

1344 Robert Baden-Powell (founder)

2007. Europa. Centenary of Scouting. Multicoloured.

4064	52c. Type **1344**	1·60	80
MS4065	90×125 mm. 75c. Scouts (38×48 mm)	2·50	2·50

The stamp and margins of **MS**4065 form a composite background design.

1345 Country Identification Letters of Signatories (image scaled to 75% of original size)

2007. 50th Anniv of Treaty of Rome.

4066	**1345** 80c. multicoloured	2·50	1·30

1346 'Tintin au pays de Soviets' (Tintin in the land of Soviets) (French)

2007. Birth Centenary of Georges Remi (Herge) (creator of Tintin). Designs showing Tintin book covers in different languages. Multicoloured.

4067	46c. Type **1346**	1·60	80
4068	46c. Tintin in the Congo (Danish)	1·60	80
4069	46c. Tintin in America	1·60	80
4070	46c. Cigars of the Pharaoh (Luxembourg)	1·60	80
4071	46c. The Blue Lotus (Chinese)	1·60	80
4072	46c. The Broken Ear (Portuguese)	1·60	80
4073	46c. The Black Island (Bengali)	1·60	80
4074	46c. King Ottokar's Sceptre (Slovakian)	1·60	80
4075	46c. The Crab with the Golden Claws (Russian)	1·60	80
4076	46c. The Shooting Star (Icelandic)	1·60	80
4077	46c. The Secret of the Unicorn (Polish)	1·60	80
4078	46c. Red Rackham's Treasure (Afrikaans)	1·60	80
4079	46c. Herge	1·60	80
4080	46c. The Seven Crystal Balls (Arabic)	1·60	80
4081	46c. Prisoners of the Sun (Spanish)	1·60	80
4082	46c. Land of Black Gold (German)	1·60	80
4083	46c. Destination Moon (Finnish)	1·60	80
4084	46c. Explorers of the Moon (Swedish)	1·60	80
4085	46c. The Calculus Affair (Japanese)	1·60	80
4086	46c. The Red Sea Sharks (Turkish)	1·60	80
4087	46c. Tintin in Tibet (Tibetan)	1·60	80
4088	46c. The Castifiore Emerald (Italian)	1·60	80
4089	46c. Flight 714 (Indonesian)	1·60	80
4090	46c. Tintin and the Picaros (Greek)	1·60	80
4091	46c. Tintin and the Alph-Art (Dutch)	1·60	80

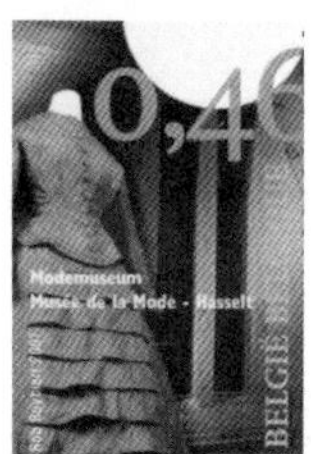

1347 Dress (Museum of Fashion, Hasselt)

2007. Small Museums. Multicoloured.

4092	46c. Type **1347**	1·60	80
4093	75c. Skeleton and woman (Notre-Dame a la Rose Hospital Cultural Museum, Lessines)	2·40	1·20
4094	92c. Beaker (Jewish Museum, Brussels)	3·00	1·50

1348 Men carrying Canoe **1349** Men carrying Canoe

2007. Summer Stamps. No Value Expressed. Multicoloured. (a) Self-adhesive.

4095	(52c.) Type **1348**	1·60	80
4096	(52c.) As No. 4095 but with "Prior" at left	1·60	80
4097	(52c.) Couple with kite	1·60	80
4098	(52c.) As No. 4097 but with "Prior" at left	1·60	80

(b) Ordinary gum.

4099	52c. Type **1349**	1·60	80
4100	52c. As No. 4098	1·60	80

1350 Building

2007. 50th Anniv of King Baudouin Antarctic Base (1st Belgian Antarctic research station). Sheet 90×125 mm.

MS4101	75c. multicoloured	2·50	2·50

1351 Cyclists

2007. Tour de France Cycle Race.

4102	**1351** 52c. multicoloured	1·70	85

1352 Ship in Port **1353** Ship in Port

2007. Centenary of Zeebrugge. No Value Expressed. Multicoloured. (a) Self-adhesive.

4103	(52c.) Type **1352**	1·70	85
4104	(52c.) As No. 4103 but with 'Prior' at left	1·70	85

(b) Ordinary gum.

4105	€1.04 Type **1353** but with 'Prior' at left	3·50	1·80

1354 Athenee Royal Francois Bovesse, Namur

2007. Tourism. Multicoloured.

4106	52c. Type **1354**	1·90	1·10
4107	52c. Saint Michel College, Brussels	1·90	1·10
4108	52c. Heilig Hart College	1·90	1·10

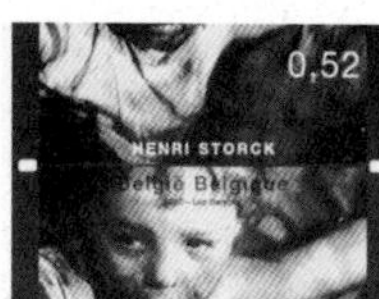

1355 Scene from *Misere au Boringage* (film by Henri Storck)

2007. Belgium Cinema. Birth Centenary of Henri Storck (filmmaker). Sheet 98×167 mm containing T 1355 and similar horiz designs. Multicoloured.

MS4109 52c.×5, Type **1355**; Boy sleeping (*Les Fils* by Luc and Jean-Pierre Dardenne); Haircut (*L'homme au crane rase* (Man who had his hair cut short) by Andre Delvaux); Bedside scene (*Malpertius* by Harry Kumel); Seated woman (*Dust* by Marion Hansel) 8·50 8·50

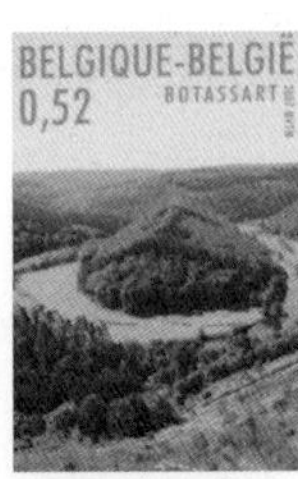

1356 Tombeau du Geant, Botassart

2007. Luxembourg European Capital of Culture–2007. Multicoloured.

4110	52c. Type **1356**	1·90	1·10
4111	80c. Rotunda, Luxembourg Train Station	3·00	1·70

Stamp of a similar design was issued by Luxembourg.

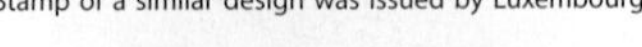

1357 Queen Paola

2007. 70th Birth Anniv of Queen Paola. Sheet 125×90 mm.

MS4112 **1357** €1.04 multicoloured 3·75 3·75

1358 King Albert II

2007

4113	**1358**	1 (52c.) red and vermilion	1·80	1·10
4114	**1358**	2 (€1.04) olive, green and slate	3·50	2·10
4115	**1358**	3 (€1.56) blue, indigo and slate	5·25	3·25
4116	**1358**	5 (€2.60) violet, purple and slate	9·00	5·25
4117	**1358**	7 (€3.64) brown, deep brown and slate	12·50	7·50

This set is to introduce the new franking system which is in multiples of base price (currently 52c.). 1 (52c.) is for use on standard domestic mail from 0–50 grams, 2 (€1.04 (ie twice base rate of 52c.)) is for use on non-standard domestic mail from 0–100 grams, 3 (€1.56) is for use on non-standard domestic mail from 100–350 grams, 5 (€2.60) is for use on non-standard domestic mail from 350 grams–1 kilo, 7 (€3.64) is for use on non-standard domestic mail from 1–2 kilos.

1359 Pears

2007. Fruit. Multicoloured. Self-adhesive.

4118	1 (52c.) Type **1359**	1·80	1·10
4119	1 (52c.) Strawberries	1·80	1·10
4120	1 (52c.) Red currants	1·80	1·10
4121	1 (52c.) Apples	1·80	1·10
4122	1 (52c.) Grapes	1·80	1·10
4123	1 (52c.) Cherries	1·80	1·10
4124	1 (52c.) Raspberries	1·80	1·10
4125	1 (52c.) Peaches	1·80	1·10
4126	1 (52c.) Plums	1·80	1·10
4127	1 (52c.) Blackberries	1·80	1·10

1360 Remington (20th-century)

1361 Remington (20th-century)

2007. Stamp Festival. Typewriters. Multicoloured. (a) Self-adhesive.

4128	1 (52c.) Type **1360**	1·80	1·10
4129	1 (52c.) Royal (1925)	1·80	1·10
4130	1 (52c.) Olympia (1950)	1·80	1·10
4131	1 (52c.) Olivetti (1972)	1·80	1·10
4132	1 (52c.) Laptop word processor	1·80	1·10

(b) Ordinary gum.

MS4133 100×165 mm. 1 (52c.)×5, Type **1361**; As No. 4129; As No. 4130; As No. 4131; As No. 4132 9·00 9·00

1362 Dahlia

2007. Flowers. Multicoloured. Self-adhesive.

4134	1 (52c.) Type **1362**	1·80	1·10
4135	2 (€1.04) Petunia	3·50	2·10

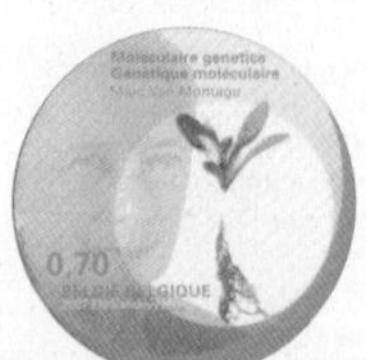

1363 Marc Van Montagu (molecular genetics)

2007. This Belgium. Science. Sheet 166×193 mm containing T 1363 and similar circular designs. Multicoloured. Self-adhesive.

MS4136 70c.×9, Type **1363**; Paul Janssen (medicine); Lise Thirly (microbiology/virology); Chris Van den Wyngaert (international criminal law); Peter Carmeliet (molecular medicine); Philippe Van Parijs (social philosophy); Marie-Claire Foblets (anthropology); Andre Berger (climate studies); Pierre Rene Deligne (mathematics) 18·00 18·00

1364 Tulip 'Peach Blossom'

2007. Self-adhesive.

4137 **1364** A (80c.) multicoloured 2·75 1·70

1365 Sunset

2007. Bereavement. No value expressed.

4138 **1365** 1 (52c.) multicoloured 1·80 1·10

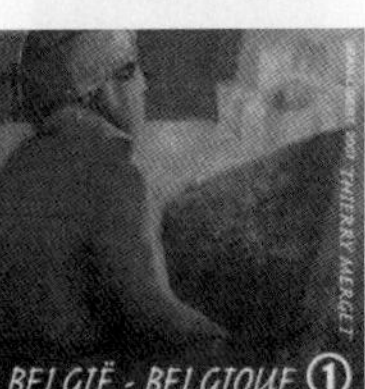

1366 *Les chemins de la liberte* (*Le voyage*) (Thierry Merget)

2007. Postal Art.

4139 **1366** 1 (52c.) multicoloured 1·80 1·10

1367 Couple in Wedding Outfits

2007. Greetings Stamps. Multicoloured. Self-adhesive.

4140	1 (52c.) Type **1367**	1·80	1·10
4141	1 (52c.) Father holding boy baby	1·80	1·10
4142	1 (52c.) Mother holding girl baby	1·80	1·10

2007. Belgian Billiards World Champions. Sheet 80×140 mm containing horiz designs as T 1306. Multicoloured.

MS4143 1 (52c.)×9, Piet J. Van Duppen; Albert Collette; Gustaaf Van Belle; Piet Sels; Gaston De Doncker; Theo Moons; Rene Gabriels; Victor Luypaerts; Rene Vingerhoerdt 14·50 14·50

See also **MS**3992.

1368 Christmas Tree

2007. Christmas and New Year. (a) Ordinary gum.

4144 **1368** 1 (52c.) multicoloured (postage) 1·80 1·10

1369 Christmas Tree

(b) Self-adhesive.

4145 **1369** 1 (52c.) multicoloured 1·80 1·10

1370 Christmas Tree

(c) Self-adhesive.

4146 **1370** A (80c.) multicoloured (air) 2·75 1·70

1371 *The Man From the Sea*

2008. Rene Magritte (artist) Commemoration. Sheet 80×140 mm containing T 1371 and similar multicoloured designs.

MS4147 1 (52c.)×5, Type **1371**; *Scheherazade*; *The Midnight Marriage*; *Georgette* (32×41 mm); *The Ignorant Fairy* (49×37 mm) 9·00 9·00

1372 Give Blood

2008. Red Cross. Give Blood Campaign. (a) Self-adhesive.

4148 **1372** 1 (52c.) multicoloured 1·80 1·10

1373 Give Blood

(b) Ordinary gum.

4149 **1373** 1 (52c.)+25c. multicoloured 2·75 1·70

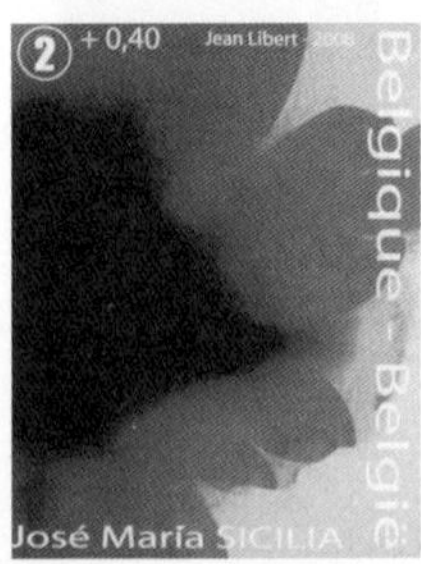

1374 *La Luz que se Apaga* (Jose Maria Sicilia)

2008. Art. Sheet 90×125 mm.

MS4150 **1374** 2 (€1.04)+40c. multicoloured 5·25 5·25

1375 Jeremiah and Kurdy Malloy

2008. 'Philately for the Young'. Jeremiah (comic strip created by Hermann Huppen (Hermann)).

4151 **1375** 1 (52c.) multicoloured 2·10 1·30

1376 Car

2008. Toys. Self-adhesive. Multicoloured.

4152	1 (52c.) Type **1376**	2·10	1·30
4153	1 (52c.) Pram	2·10	1·30
4154	1 (52c.) Doll	2·10	1·30
4155	1 (52c.) Airplane	2·10	1·30
4156	1 (52c.) Horse	2·10	1·30
4157	1 (52c.) Tram	2·10	1·30
4158	1 (52c.) Diablo	2·10	1·30
4159	1 (52c.) Teddy	2·10	1·30
4160	1 (52c.) Top	2·10	1·30
4161	1 (52c.) Wooden scooter	2·10	1·30

1377 Flowers

2008. Bicentenary of Ghent Flower Show. Sheet 90×125 mm.

MS4162 **1377** 80c. multicoloured 3·00 3·00

1378 Suzy Delair as Mila Malou and Pierre Fresnay as Wens (scene from film *L'assassin habite au 21*)

2008. Detective Novels. Multicoloured.

4163	1 (52c.) Type **1378** (novel by Stanislas-Andre Steeman)	2·10	1·30
4164	1 (52c.) Jan Decleir as Angelo Ledda (scene from film *De zaak Alzheimer*) (novel by Jef Geeraerts)	2·10	1·30

1379 Menorah

2008. Bicentenary of Belgian Jewish Community.
4165 **1379** 90c. blue and black 3·50 2·10

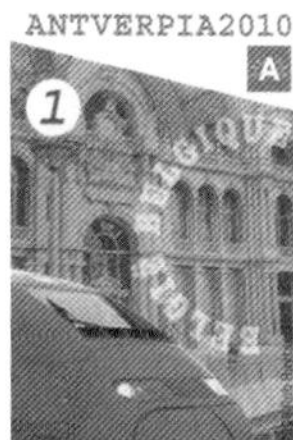

1380 Central Station

2008. Antverpia 2010 European Philatelic Championship, Antwerp. 120th Anniv of Royal National Association of Stamp Collectors. Sheet 161×141 mm containing T 1380 and similar vert designs. Multicoloured.
MS4166 1 (54c.)×5, Type **1380**; Cathedral of Our Lady and Pieter Paul Rubens memorial; Port; Fashion; Diamond necklace by Reena Ahluwalia 17·00 17·00
No. **MS**4166 was sold for €5.

1381 Comte de Champignac

2008. 70th Anniv of Spirou (cartoon character drawn by Andre Franquin). Sheet 166×100 mm containing T 1381 and similar vert designs. Multicoloured.
MS4167 1 (54c.)×5, Type **1381**; Fantasio; Spirou and Spip; Seccotine; Zorglub 10·50 10·50

1382 Coastal Route

2008. Trams. Trams enroute. Multicoloured.
4168 1 (54c.) Type **1382** 2·10 1·30
4169 80c. Charleroi 3·00 1·90
4170 90c. Brussels 3·50 2·10

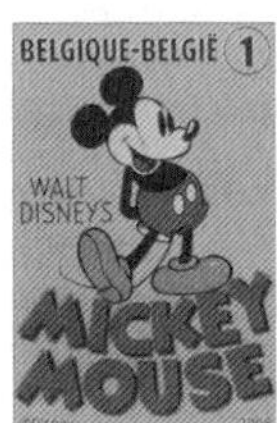

1383 Mickey Mouse

2008. 80th Anniv of Mickey Mouse (cartoon character created by Walt Disney).
4171 **1383** 1 (54c.) multicoloured 2·10 1·30

1384 Letterbox and Envelope

1385 Letterbox and Envelope

2008. Europa. The Letter. (a) Self-adhesive gum.
4172 **1384** 1 (54c.) multicoloured 2·10 1·30

(b) Size 40×27 mm. Ordinary gum.
4173 **1385** 80c. multicoloured 3·00 1·90

1386 *Tagetes portula*

2008. Flowers. Multicoloured. Self-adhesive.
4174 1 (54c.) Type **1386**(postage) 2·10 1·30

No value expressed.
4175 (80c.) Tulip 'Orange Favourite' (air) 3·00 1·90

1387 Artificial Hand and Hands of Many Nations

2008. Diversity in the Workplace.
4176 **1387** 2 (€1.08) multicoloured 4·25 2·50

1388

2008. Freemasonry. Sheet 125×90 mm.
MS4177 **1388** 3 multicoloured 6·25 6·25

1389 Family hiking

1390 Family hiking

2008. Summer Stamps. Multicoloured. (a) Ordinary gum.
4178 1 (52c.) Type **1389** 2·10 1·30
4179 1 (52c.) Family cycling 2·10 1·30

(b) Size 30×25 mm. Self-adhesive.
4180 1 (52c.) Type **1390** 2·10 1·30
4181 1 (52c.) Family cycling 2·10 1·30

1391 Queen Fabiola and King Baudouin

2008. 80th Birth Anniv of Queen Fabiola. Sheet 170×120 mm containing T 1391 and similar vert designs. Multicoloured.
MS4182 1 (52c.)×3, Type **1391**; Portrait of Queen Fabiola; Queen Fabiola and King Baudouin, older, wearing casual dress 6·25 6·25

1392 Woman (George Grard), Musee George Grard, Gijverinkhove

2008. Tourism. Multicoloured.
4183 1 (52c.) Type **1392** 2·20 1·40
4184 80c. *Imago* (Emile Desmedt), Musee en Plein Air du Sart-Tilman, Liege 3·25 2·00
4185 90c. *Autoportrait* (Gerald Dederen), Jardin de sculptures de l'UCL, Brussels 3·50 2·30

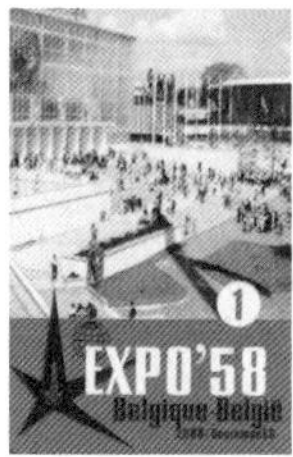

1393 USSR Pavilion

2008. 50th Anniv of EXPO'58, Brussels. Multicoloured.
MS4186 1 (54c.)×5, Type **1393**; Thailand pavilion; Hostesses carrying flags; Expo logo as lighting; Atomium 10·50 10·50
The stamps of **MS**4186 were not for sale individually.

1394 Planting of May Tree (tree of joy), Brussels (700th anniv)

2008. Folklore and Traditions. Multicoloured.
4187 1 (54c.) Type **1394** 2·20 1·40
4188 1 (54c.) Hops, beer barrel, bonfire and hop devil, Asse (Hopduvelfeesten) (horiz) 2·20 1·40
4189 1 (54c.) Jugglers (Eupen carnival) 2·20 1·40
4190 1 (54c.) Men on stage (centenary (2007) of *La Royale Compagnie du Cabaret Wallon Tournaisien*) (philanthropic and literary company) 2·20 1·40

1395 BMX

2008. Olympic Games, Beijing. Multicoloured.
4191 1 (54c.) Type **1395** 2·30 1·50
4192 90c. Relay (horiz) 3·75 2·40
MS4193 125×90 mm. (2) €1.08 Tennis (49×38 mm) 4·50 4·50

1396 Angel Gabriel

2008. Stamp Day. 50th Anniv of Cercle St-Gabriel. 50th Anniv of Thematic Philately in Belgium.
4194 **1396** 1 (54c.) multicoloured 2·30 1·50

1397 Marten

1398 Marten

2008. Nature. Mustelidae. Multicoloured. (a) Self-adhesive gum.
4195 1 (54c.) Type **1397** 2·30 1·50
4196 1 (54c.) Stone marten 2·30 1·50
4197 1 (54c.) Polecat 2·30 1·50
4198 1 (54c.) Otter 2·30 1·50
4199 1 (54c.) Badger 2·30 1·50

(b) Ordinary gum. Sheet 178×146 mm.
MS4200 1 (54c.)×6, Type **1398** (48×38 mm); Ermine (38×42 mm); Stone marten (48×38 mm); Polecat (38×42 mm); Otter (38×48 mm); Badger (48×38 mm) 12·00 12·00

1399 Smurf

1400 Smurf and Smurfette

2008. The Smurfs (characters created by Peyo (Pierre Culliford)). Multicoloured. (a) Self-adhesive gum.
4201 1 (54c.) Type **1399** 2·30 1·50
4202 1 (54c.) Smurfette 2·30 1·50
4203 1 (54c.) Papa Smurf 2·30 1·50
4204 1 (54c.) Smurf and drum (horiz) 2·30 1·50
4205 1 (54c.) Poet Smurf 2·30 1·50
4206 1 (54c.) Jokey Smurf 2·30 1·50
4207 1 (54c.) Smurf carrying bag and envelope 2·30 1·50
4208 1 (54c.) Brainy Smurf 2·30 1·50
4209 1 (54c.) Gargamel 2·30 1·50
4210 1 (54c.) Harmony Smurf (horiz) 2·30 1·50

(b) Ordinary gum. Sheet 186×153 mm.
MS4211 1 (54c.)×5, Type **1400** (42×33 mm); Smurf in party hat (42×33 mm); Two smurfs (42×33 mm); Smurf carrying cake (42×33 mm); Smurf eating cake (38×42 mm) 12·00 12·00

1401 Mothers and Children (Tim Driven)

2008. Belgian Photographers. Sheet 100×166 mm containing 1401 and similar horiz designs. Multicoloured.
MS4212 80c.×5, Type **1401**; Jars (Paul Ausloos); Woman carrying pail (Leonard Misonne); Coloured lights in trees (Harry Gruyaert); Woman cycling (Stephan Vanfleteren) 16·00 16·00

1402 1909 Belgian Congo 1f. Stamp (As No. 40B)

2008. Centenary of Belgian Congo.
4213 **1402** 1 (54c.) multicoloured 2·30 1·50

1403 National Museum of Shoes, Izegem

2008. Museums. Multicoloured.

4214 1 (54c.) Type **1403** 2·30 1·50
4215 80c. Piconrue Museum (religious museum), Bastogne 3·25 2·10
4216 80c. David and Alice van Buuren Museum , Brussels 3·25 2·10

1404 Menin Gate, Ypres

2008. 90th Anniv of End of First World War. Sheet 201×85 mm containing T 1404 and similar vert designs. Multicoloured.

MS4217 90c.×3, Type **1404**; King Albert I (statue); Poppies 10·50 10·50

1405 The Nativity **1406** The Nativity

1407 Cardinal Mercier

2008. Christmas. Multicoloured. (a) Self-adhesive.

4218 1 (54c.) Type **1405** 2·40 1·70
4219 (80c.) Type **1406** 3·50 2·40

(b) Ordinary gum. Sheet 127×124 mm.

MS4220 1 (54c.)×5, Type **1407**; St. Francis; Mary and Joseph; Friar; Infant Jesus 12·00 12·00

No. 4219 was inscribed 'INTERNATIONAL' and was originally on sale for 80c.

No. **MS**4220 includes four labels which, with the stamps form a composite design of a stained glass window.

1408 Queen Elisabeth (Concours Reine Elisabeth (Queen Elisabeth International Music Competition))

2008. This Belgium. Music. Sheet 166×200 mm containing T 1408 and similar square designs. Multicoloured.

MS4221 80c.×10, Type **1408**; Jose van Dam (bass-baritone); Rock Werchter Festival; Philippe Herreweghe and Collegium Vocale Gent (music ensemble); dEus (rock band); Il Novecento (orchestra) and Robert Groslot (conductor); Philip Catherine (jazz guitarist); Dani Klein (singer with Vaya con Dios); Salvatore Adamo (composer and ballad singer); Jaques Brel (singer–songwriter) 32·00 32·00

The stamps of **MS**4136 were not for sale separately.

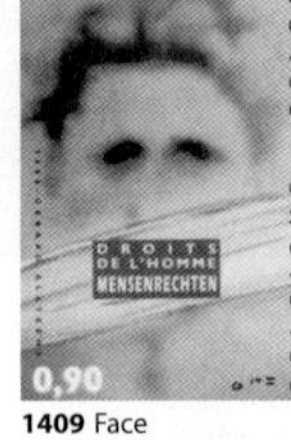

1409 Face

2008. Universal Declaration of Human Rights.

4222 **1409** 90c. multicoloured 4·25 3·00

1410 *Tulipa bakeri*

2009. Air. Flowers. Self-adhesive.

4223 **1410** 1 (90c.) multicoloured 4·25 3·00

1411 King Albert II

2009. Air.

4224 **1411** 1 (90c.) multicoloured 4·25 3·00
4225 **1411** 1 (€1.05) multicoloured 5·00 3·50
4226 **1411** 3 (€2.40) multicoloured 11·00 7·75
4227 **1411** 3 (€2.70) multicoloured 12·00 8·50

No. 4224 and 4225 were for use on airmail within Europe, Nos. 4226 and 4227 for use on international airmail.

See also 4113/17.

1412 '€'

2009. 10th Anniv of European Union. Self-adhesive.

4228 **1412** 1 (59c.) multicoloured 2·75 2·00

1413 Monument

2009. Regions. German Community. Sheet 150×183 mm containing T 1413 and similar multicoloured designs.

MS4229 1 (90c.)×5, Type **1413**; Three handled pitcher; Lake Butgenbach; Eupen sanatorium (33×40 mm); Shooting (49×37 mm) 19·00 19·00

The stamps of **MS**4229 were not for sale separately.

1414 Hands 'reading' Braille

2009. Birth Bicentenary of Louis Braille (inventor of Braille writing for the blind).

4230 **1414** 1 (59c.) multicoloured 2·75 2·00

1415 Child and Tap

2009. Red Cross. Water.

4231 **1415** 1 (59c.) + 25c. black and vermillion 4·00 2·75

1416 Barge

2009. Transportation. Inland Waterways.

4232 **1416** 2 (€1.18) multicoloured 5·50 4·00

1417 Figure and Postbox (Emitis Mohsenin)

2009. Post Day.

4233 **1417** 1 (59c.) multicoloured 2·75 2·00

1418 Marthe Boel (promoter of women's issues)

2009. Women in Action. Multicoloured.

4234 1 (59c.) Type **1418** 2·75 2·00
4235 1 (59c.) Lily Boeykens (lawyer and journalist) 2·75 2·00

1419 Penguins

2009. Preserve Polar Regions and Glaciers. Sheet 120×80 mm containing T 1419 and similar multicoloured design.

MS4236 2 (€1.05)×2, Type **1419**; Polar bear 9·25 9·25

The stamps of **MS**4236 were for use on international priority mail and not for sale separately.

1420 Bob

2009. Bob and Bobette (comic series created by Willy Vandersteen) in Les Diables du Texas (animated film).Showing characters from the film. Multicoloured. Self-adhesive.

4237 1 (59c.) Type **1420** 2·75 2·00
4238 1 (59c.) Bobette 2·75 2·00
4239 1 (59c.) Jerome 2·75 2·00
4240 1 (59c.) Lambik 2·75 2·00
4241 1 (59c.) Aunt Sidonie 2·75 2·00

1421 Telescope and Globe

2009. Europa. Astronomy. Sheet 125×90mm.

MS4242 **1421** 1 (59c.) multicoloured 4·25 4·25

No. **MS**4242 was for use on mail within Europe.

1422 Neolithic Flint Mines, Spiennes

2009. World Heritage Sites. Sheet 166×100 mm containing T 1422 and similar vert designs. Multicoloured.

MS4243 1 (€1.05)×5, Type **1422**; Notre Dame Cathedral, Tournai; Plantin-Moretus Museum, Antwerp; Historic Centre, Bruges; Maison de Maitre (Victor Horta), Brussels 23·00 23·00

No. **MS**4243 was for use on International mail.

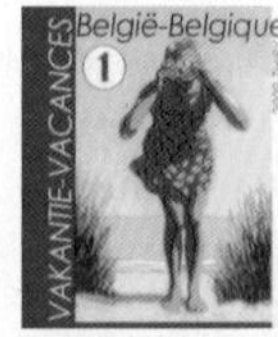

1423 Girl with Camera

2009. Summer Stamps. Holidays in Wallonia and Flanders. Multicoloured. Self-adhesive.

4244 1 (59c.) Type **1423** 2·75 2·00
4245 1 (59c.) Boy with camera 2·75 2·00

1424 Muhka and *Flemish Village* (Luc Tuymans)

2009. Antverpia 2010–International Stamp Exhibition, Antwerp. Artistic Antwerp (1st series). Sheet 180×64 mm containing T 1424 and similar vert designs. Multicoloured.

MS4246 1 (59c.)×5, Type **1424**; *Orbino* (Luc Deleu), Middelheim Sculpture Museum;Bourla Theater and Toneelhuis theatre company; *Hollywood on the Scheldt*, Robbe De Hert, Roma Cinema; *Willem Elschot* (writer) (sculpture by Wilfred Pas) and manuscript of *Kass* 23·00 23·00

See also Nos. **MS**4290.

1425 Henry Purcell (350th birth anniv)

2009. Composers Anniversaries. Sheet 180×64 mm containing T 1425 and similar vert designs. Multicoloured.

MS4247 1 (90c.)×5, Type **1425**; George Frideric Handel (250th death anniv); Franz Joseph Haydn (death bicentenary); Jakob Ludwig Felix Mendelssohn Bartholdy (birth bicentenary); Clara Schumann (nee Clara Josephine Wieck) (190th birth anniv) 21·00 21·00

The stamps and margins of **MS**4247 form a composite design.

The stamps of **MS**4247 were for use on mail within Europe

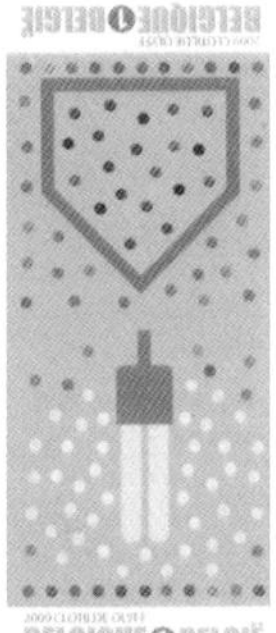

1426 Low Energy Lightbulb

2009. Green Stamps. Environmental Preservation. Multicoloured. Self-adhesive.

4248	1 (59c.) Type **1426**	2·75	2·00
4249	1 (59c.) Wind turbine	2·75	2·00
4250	1 (59c.) Shared transport	2·75	2·00
4251	1 (59c.) Solar panels	2·75	2·00
4252	1 (59c.) Insulated house	2·75	2·00

1427 International Space Station, 2009

2009. Aviation, From Bleriot to De Winne. Multicoloured.

4253	1 (59c.) Type **1427** (Frank de Winne, first European Space Agency astronaut to command mission)	2·75	2·00
4254	1 (59c.) Apollo 11, 1969 (first men on the moon)	2·75	2·00
4255	1 (59c.) Concorde, 1969 (first supersonic flight)	2·75	2·00
4256	1 (59c.) LZ 127 Graf Zeppelin, 1929 (flight around the world)	2·75	2·00
4257	1 (59c.) *Bleriot XI*, 1909 (first flight over English Channel)	2·75	2·00

1428 Yoko Tsuno

2009. Youth Philately. Yoko Tsuno (comic created by Roger Leloup).

4258 **1428** 1 (59c.) multicoloured 2·75 2·00

1429 King Albert and Queen Paola

2009. 50th Anniv of Wedding of King Albert and Queen Paola. Sheet 209×104 mm.

MS4259 **1429** 3 multicoloured 7·25 7·25

1430 Citroen 2CV Delivery Van, c. 1959

2009. Postal Vehicles. Multicoloured.

4260	1 (59c.) Type **1430**	2·75	2·00
4261	1 (59c.) Bedford van, c. 1960	2·75	2·00
4262	1 (59c.) Large Renault van, c. 1970	2·75	2·00
4263	1 (59c.) Renault 4 Fourgonnette van, c. 1980	2·75	2·00
4264	1 (59c.) Modern Citroen van	2·75	2·00

1431 Orchestra

2009. The Circus. Multicoloured. Self-adhesive.

4265	1 (59c.) Type **1431**	2·75	2·00
4266	1 (59c.) Highwire artistes	2·75	2·00
4267	1 (59c.) Illusionist	2·75	2·00
4268	1 (59c.) Acrobat pyramid	2·75	2·00
4269	1 (59c.) Trapeze artiste	2·75	2·00
4270	1 (59c.) Clowns	2·75	2·00
4271	1 (59c.) Acrobats balancing	2·75	2·00
4272	1 (59c.) Illusionist with tophat, rabbit and doves	2·75	2·00
4273	1 (59c.) Equestrian artiste	2·75	2·00
4274	1 (59c.) Clown juggling on uni-cycle	2·75	2·00

1432 Maurice Bejart

2009. Maurice Bejart (dancer) Commemoration.

4275 **1432** 1 (90c.) multicoloured 4·00 3·00

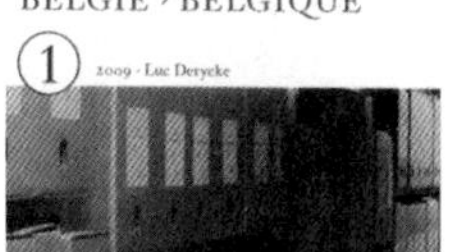

1433 Archives of Belgium

2009. Monts des Arts. Sheet 200×166 mm containing T 1433 and similar multicoloured designs.

MS4276 1 (59c.)×10, Type **1433**; Royal Museum of Fine Arts; Royal Library; Square Meeting Centre; Brussels Palace (38×49 mm); Saint Jaques sur Coudenberg Church and Protestant Chapel (49×38 mm); Palace of Fine Arts; Royal Belgian Filmarchive (Cinematheque Royale de Belgique); Belvue Museum; Musical Instruments Museum 25·00 25·00

1434 Seven Sacraments Altarpiece (detail)

2009. Master of Passions

4277 **1434** 2 (€1.18) multicoloured 5·00 4·00

1435 Lion Mask

2009. Europalia International Arts Festival, China. Self-adesive.

4278 **1435** 1 (59c.) multicoloured 2·75 2·00

1436 Mettoy Streamline Train, 1950

2009. Miniature Trains. Sheet 160×200 mm containing T 1436 and similar square designs. Multicoloured.

MS4279 1 (59c.)×10, Type **1436**; Bavarian locomotive *Aloisus*; Locomotive tender; Diesel locomotive; Locomotive tender *Storchenbein*; Locomotive Type 16; Tin toy train; ICE Deutsche Bahn; Wooden toy train with wagon; Blue and red wooden toy train 28·00 28·00

1437 Pine Tree

2009. La Foret de Soignes (Sonian Forest). Sheet 166×100 mm containing T 1437 and similar vert designs. Multicoloured.

MS4280 2 (€2.18)×5, Type **1437**; Beech; Birch; Larch; Oak 25·00 25·00

1438 Father Damien

2009. Canonization of Father Damien (Jozef De Veuster) (Roman Catholic missionary who ministered to lepers on the Hawaiian island of Molokai).

4281 **1438** 1 Europe (90c.) multicoloured 4·00 3·00

1439 Emblem

2009. 20th Anniv of Comic Strip Art Museum. Sheet 90×120 mm.

MS4282 **1439** 1 (59c.) multicoloured 4·50 3·25

1440 Tom Lanoye

2009. This is Belgium. Literature. Sheet 160×200 mm containing T 1440 and similar multicoloured designs.

MS4283 1 (59c.)×10, Type **1440**; Hugo Claus; Anne Provoost; Poeziezomers, Watou (summer poetry festival) (vert); Redu, Book Village (vert); Book Fair, Antwerp (vert); Book Fair, Brussels (vert); Pierre Mertens; Amelie Northomb; Henri Vernes 25·00 25·00

1441 Gold Baubles

2009. Christmas. Multicoloured. Self-adhesive.

4284	1 (59c.) Type **1441**	2·75	2·00
4285	1 (90c.) Blue baubles	2·75	2·00

No. 4284 were for use on domestic mail and were originally on sale for 59c.

No. 4285 were for use on international mail were originally on sale for 90c.

1442 1920 65c. Stamp (As No. 308b)

2009. Monacophil 2009. Promotion of Philately. Sheet 120×170 mm.

MS4286 **1442** 1 multicoloured 5·75 4·25

The premium was for the promotion of philately.

1443 Sunset

2010. Bereavement. Self-adhesive.

4288 **1443** (59c.) multicoloured 2·75 2·00

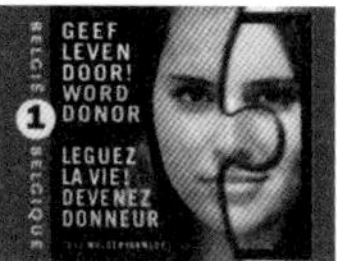

1444 Face as Jigsaw

2010. Organ Donation Awareness Campaign. Self-adhesive.

4289 **1444** (59c.) multicoloured 2·75 2·00

1445 Magnifying Glass

2010. Antverpia 2010–International Stamp Exhibition, Antwerp (2nd series). Sheet 160×140 mm containing T 1445 and similar vert designs. Multicoloured. Phosphorescent paper.

MS4290 (59c.)×6, Type **1445** (120th anniv of Royal Federation of Belgian Philatelic Circles); Commercial centre, Antwerp: Giraffes and Kai-Mook (elephant), Antwerp Zoo; painting by Eugeen van Mieghem and model, Museum aan de Stroom (MAS); *Self-portrait* and house of Peter Paul Rubens; City Hall and Cathedral, Old City Centre 15·00 15·00

No. **MS**4290 was on sale, above face value, at €6.50, the premium for the promotion of philately.

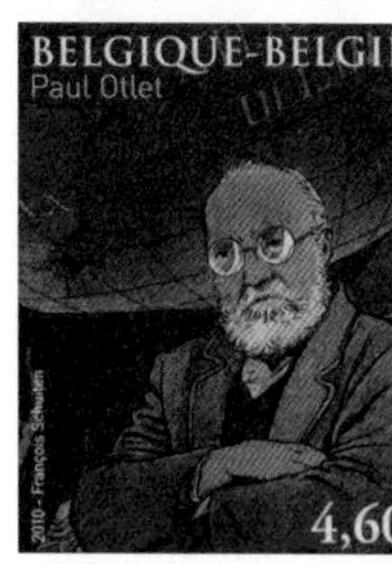

1446 Paul Otlet

2010. From Mundaneum (system for information storage, using Universal Decimal Classification, invented by Paul Otlet and Henri La Fontaine in 1910), the Internet. Sheet 90×125 mm.

MS4291 **1446** €4.60 multicoloured 12·00 12·00

1447 Largo Winch

2010. Youth Philately. Largo Winch (comic created by Philip Francq and writer Jean Van Hamme).

4292 **1447** 1 (59c.) multicoloured 2·75 2·00

1448 Paul Verlane and Arthur Rimbaud

2010. Literary Walk through Brussels. Sheet 180×64 mm containing T 1448 and similar vert designs. Multicoloured.

MS4293	2 (€1.18)×5, Type **1448**; Charles Baudelaire; Multatuli (Eduard Douwes Dekker); Charlotte and Emily Bronte; Victor Hugo	9·00	9·00

The stamps and margins of **MS**4293 form a composite design.

The stamps of **MS**4293 were for use on mail within Europe

1449 *Nicotiana alata*

2010. Ghent Flower Show. Multicoloured.

4294	1 (59c.) Type **1449**	2·75	2·00
4295	1 (59c.) *Lychnis coronaria*	2·75	2·00

1450 Chicks

2010. Young Animals. Multicoloured. Self-adhesive.

4296	1 (59c.) Type **1450**	2·75	2·00
4297	1 (59c.) Rabbits	2·75	2·00
4298	1 (59c.) Kitten	2·75	2·00
4299	1 (59c.) Ducklings	2·75	2·00
4300	1 (59c.) Foal cantering	2·75	2·00
4301	1 (59c.) Labrador puppy	2·75	2·00
4302	1 (59c.) Long-haired dachshund puppy	2·75	2·00
4303	1 (59c.) Two kittens	2·75	2·00
4304	1 (59c.) Foal, head and shoulders	2·75	2·00
4305	1 (59c.) Two lambs	2·75	2·00

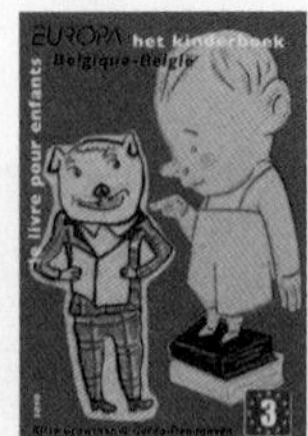
1451 Dog reading to Boy

2010. Europa. Childrens' Books. Sheet 80×120 mm containing T 1451 and similar vert design. Multicoloured.

MS4306	3 Europe (€2.70)×2, Type **1451**; Cat reading to girl	12·00	12·00

1452 Seas and Oceans (Igor Volt)

2010. Environmental Protection. Winning Designs in Childrens' Drawing Competition. Multicoloured.

4307	1 (59c.) Type **1452**	2·75	2·00
4308	1 (59c.) Forest (Lander Keyaerts)	2·75	2·00
4309	1 (59c.) Endangerd species (Eva Sterkens)	2·75	2·00
4310	1 (59c.) Climate (Lucie Octave)	2·75	2·00
4311	1 (59c.) Energy (Louise van Goylen)	2·75	2·00

1453 Natan

2010. This is Belgium. Fashion. Sheet 200×160 mm containing T 1453 and similar multicoloured designs.

MS4312	1 (59c.)×10, Type **1453**; Walter Van Beirendonck; Veronique Branquinho (43×35 mm); A.F. Vandevorst (33×44 mm); Ann Demeulemeester (44×26 mm); Olivier Theyskens (32×48 mm); Dirk Bikkembergs (48×38 mm); Cathy Pill (38×48 mm); Veronique Leroy (29×33 mm); Martin Margiela (48×38 mm)	6·50	6·50

1454 Exhibition Emblem

2010. Antverpia 2010–International Stamp Exhibition, Antwerp (3rd issue). Sheet 190×120 mm.

MS4313	**1454** 3 multicoloured	7·75	7·75

1455 Gyrfalcon (inscr 'Buizerd–Buse Variable')

2010. 25th Anniv of Birds on Stamps drawn by André Buzin. Sheet 160×140 mm containing T 1455 and similar vert designs. Multicoloured.

MS4314	1 Europe (90c.)×5, Type **1455**; Hobby (Faucon hoberau–Boomvalk); Sparrow hawk (Sperwer–Epermer d'Europe); Red Kite (Milan Royal–Rode Wouw); Goshawk (Havik–Autour des Palombes)	25·00	25·00

See also No. 3692 etc.

1456 Prince Philippe

2010. 50th Birth Anniv of Prince Philippe, Duke of Brabant, Prince of Belgium.

4315	**1456** 2 (€1.18) multicoloured	5·00	4·00

1457 Early Steam and Modern High Speed Locomotives

2010. 175th Anniv of Belgian Railways

4316	**1457** 2 (€1.18) multicoloured	4·25	3·00

Nos. 4317/21 have wavy edges (simulating perforations) on two or three sides depending on position.

1458 Profiles and Party Favours

2010. Greetings Stamps. Multicoloured.

4317	1 (59c.) Type **1458**	2·75	2·00
4318	1 (59c.) Hands holding present and bouquet	2·75	2·00
4319	1 (59c.) Hand holding lantern and profile wearing mask	2·75	2·00
4320	1 (59c.) Hands holding tray of glasses and cake	2·75	2·00
4321	1 (59c.) Children	2·75	2·00

1459 Zebra-striped Ball and Player's Boot

2010. World Cup Football Championships, South Africa

4322	**1459** 1 (90c.) multicoloured	3·75	2·75

1460 Winners' Podiums and Athlete

2010. Youth Olympic Games, Singapore

4323	**1460** 1 (€1.05) multicoloured	4·25	3·00

1461 Child and Map as Flag

2010. 50th Anniv of Congo Independence

4324	**1461** 1 (€1.05) multicoloured	4·25	3·00

1462 Eddie Merckx

2010. 65th Birth Anniv of Edouard Louis Joseph Merckx (world champion cyclist)

4325	**1462** 2 (€1.08) multicoloured	5·00	3·50

1463 'eu'

2010. Belgium's Presidency of the European Union

4326	**1463** 1 (90c.) multicoloured	1·90	1·30

1464 Cyclist riding on Fietsknooppunten

2010. Tourism. Multicoloured.

4327	1 (59c.) Type **1464**	2·30	1·60
4328	1 (59c.) Tourist information board and cyclist, The Ravel	2·30	1·60

1465 Ford Bureau de Poste Vehicle (1953)

2010. Postal Transport. Multicoloured.

4329	1 (59c.) Type **1465**	2·30	1·60
4330	1 (59c.) Independent postal train (1931)	2·30	1·60
4331	1 (59c.) Bedford truck (1979)	2·30	1·60
4332	1 (59c.) Independent postal train (1968)	2·30	1·60
4333	1 (59c.) Volvo truck (2009)	2·30	1·60

1466 Le Tonneau, Brussels (S. Jasinsky)

2010. Pre-1960 Architecture. Multicoloured.

MS4334	1 (90c.)×5, Type **1466**; Saint-Maartensdal (Renaat Braem and A33 Architects), Louvain; Le fer à cheval (J. J. Eggericx and R.Verwilghen), Brussels; Boerentoren, Anvers (J. Vanhoenacker, J. Smolderen & E. Van Averbeke); Cité de Droixhe, Liège (EGAU architectural group)	18·00	18·00

1467 Fruit Trees, Saint-Trond

2010. Regions. Multicoloured.

MS4335	1 (90c.)×5, Type **1467**; Fruit blossom; Wine and glasses; Building façade, Hélécine (33×40 mm); Ploughed field and farm buildings, Perwez (49×37 mm)	18·00	18·00

1468 Leisure Centre, Rotselar (de Mena Brewery)

2010. Breweries, Change of Use. Multicoloured.

4336	1 (90c.) Type **1468**	3·25	2·25
4337	1 (€1.05) Telematics Support Centre, Marche-en-Famenne (Carmelite monastery and brewery)	4·00	2·75
4338	2 (€1.18) Weils Contemporary Art Centre, Brussels	5·25	3·50

1469 Shoe Making

2010. Craft Trades. Multicoloured.

4339	1 (59c.) Type **1469**	2·50	1·70
4340	1 (59c.) Clog making	2·50	1·70
4341	1 (59c.) Blacksmithing	2·50	1·70
4342	1 (59c.) Spinning	2·50	1·70
4343	1 (59c.) Laundry	2·50	1·70

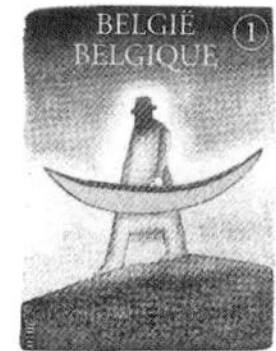

1470 *Voyage dans la lune*

2010. Tenth Anniv of Folon Foundation. Multicoloured.

4344	1 (59c.) Type **1470**	2·50	1·70
4345	1 (59c.) *Pays de connaissance*	2·50	1·70
4346	1 (59c.) *Un cri* (horiz)	2·50	1·70
4347	1 (59c.) *La mer ce grand sculpteur* (Knokke) (horiz)	2·50	1·70
4348	1 (59c.) *L'étranger* (horiz)	2·50	1·70
4349	1 (59c.) *Oiseau* (horiz)	2·50	1·70
4350	1 (59c.) *Pluie* (La Hulpe)	2·50	1·70
4351	1 (59c.) Stained glass window, Eglise de Waha (Marche-en-Famenne)	2·50	1·70
4352	1 (59c.) *L'aube*	2·50	1·70
4353	1 (59c.) *Un monde*	2·50	1·70

1471 Virgin and Child (Caen)

2010. Flemish Primitive Art in French and Belgian Collections. Multicoloured.

MS4354	3 (€2.07)×2, Type **1471**; *Portrait of Laurent Froimont* (Brussels)	18·00	18·00

Stamps of a similar design were issued by France.

1472 Santa in his Sleigh

2010. Christmas. Multicoloured.

4355	1 (59c.) Type **1472**	2·75	2·00
4356	1 (90c.) Santa in his sleigh (different)	5·25	3·50

1473 '1-1-11'

2011. Liberalization of Postal Market from 1st January 2011

4357	**1473**	1 (59c.) multicoloured	2·75	2·00

EXPRESS LETTER STAMPS

E107 Ghent

1929

E530	-	1f.75 blue	70	35
E531	**E107**	2f.35 red	2·20	50
E581	-	2f.45 green	23·00	3·00
E532	-	3f.50 purple	14·00	14·00
E533	-	5f.25 olive	13·50	13·00

DESIGNS: 1f.75, Town Hall, Brussels; 2f.45, Eupen; 3f.50, Bishop's Palace, Liege; 5f.25, Antwerp Cathedral.

1932. No. E581 surch 2 Fr 50 and cross.

E608	2f.50 on 2f.45 green	16·00	2·30

MILITARY STAMPS

1967. As T 289 (Baudouin) but with letter "M" within oval at foot.

M2027	1f.50 green	25	20

1971. As No. 2207/8a and 2209a but with letter "M" within oval at foot.

M2224	1f.75 green	35	35
M2225	2f.25 green	30	40
M2226	2f.50 green	25	25
M2227	3f.25 plum	30	30

NEWSPAPER STAMPS

1928. Railway Parcels stamps of 1923 optd JOURNAUX DAGBLADEN 1928.

N443	**P 84**	10c. red	60	35
N444	**P 84**	20c. green	60	35
N445	**P 84**	40c. olive	60	35
N446	**P 84**	60c. orange	85	35
N447	**P 84**	70c. brown	85	35
N448	**P 84**	80c. violet	1·20	60
N449	**P 84**	90c. slate	10·50	3·50
N450	-	1f. blue	2·30	60
N451	-	2f. olive	4·75	85
N452	-	3f. red	4·75	85
N453	-	4f. red	4·75	85
N454	-	5f. violet	4·75	85
N455	-	6f. brown	7·25	2·00
N456	-	7f. orange	20·00	3·50
N457	-	8f. brown	14·50	2·30
N458	-	9f. purple	41·00	10·50
N459	-	10f. green	14·50	3·50
N460	-	20f. pink	41·00	14·50

1929. Railway Parcels stamps of 1923 optd JOURNAUX DAGBLADEN only.

N505	**P 84**	10c. red	1·20	60
N506	**P 84**	20c. green	60	60
N507	**P 84**	40c. olive	60	60
N508	**P 84**	60c. orange	85	60
N509	**P 84**	70c. brown	60	60
N510	**P 84**	80c. violet	1·20	1·20
N511	**P 84**	90c. slate	7·75	6·50
N512	-	1f. blue	1·70	60
N513	-	1f.10 brown	5·75	1·70
N514	-	1f.50 blue	5·75	1·70
N515	-	2f. olive	3·75	1·20
N516	-	2f.10 slate	17·00	12·00
N517	-	3f. red	3·75	1·20
N518	-	4f. red	3·75	1·20
N519	-	5f. violet	3·75	1·20
N520	-	6f. brown	8·75	1·70
N521	-	7f. orange	26·00	1·70
N522	-	8f. brown	17·00	1·70
N523	-	9f. purple	35·00	19·00
N524	-	10f. green	20·00	4·75
N525	-	20f. pink	49·00	17·00

PARCEL POST STAMPS

1928. Optd COLIS POSTAL POSTCOLLO.

B470	**81**	4f. brown	8·75	2·00
B471	**81**	5f. bistre	8·75	2·00

B106 G.P.O., Brussels

1929

B526	**B106**	3f. sepia	1·50	30
B527	**B106**	4f. slate	1·50	30
B528	**B106**	5f. red	1·50	30
B529	**B106**	6f. purple	36·00	36·00

1933. Surch X4 4X.

B645	4f. on 6f. purple	32·00	45

POSTAGE DUE STAMPS

D21

1870

D63	**D21**	10c. green	4·75	3·00
D64	**D21**	20c. blue	95·00	5·75

D35

1895

D96a	**D35**	5c. green	15	15
D97	**D35**	10c. brown	26·00	2·30
D101	**D35**	10c. red	15	10
D98a	**D35**	20c. green	15	15
D102	**D35**	30c. blue	20	15
D99	**D35**	50c. brown	26·00	7·00
D103	**D35**	50c. grey	45	45
D100	**D35**	1f. red	23·00	13·00
D104	**D35**	1f. yellow	5·75	5·75

1919. As Type D 35, but value in colour on white background.

D251	5c. green	60	30
D323	5c. grey	10	10
D252b	10c. red	1·70	30
D324	10c. green	10	10
D253b	20c. green	8·75	1·50
D325	20c. brown	10	10
D254	30c. blue	4·75	60
D326	30c. red	80	60
D327	35c. green	25	15
D328	40c. brown	25	15
D329	50c. blue	1·50	25
D330	50c. grey	25	10
D331	60c. red	30	15
D1146	65c. green	7·50	3·50
D332	70c. brown	30	15
D333	80c. grey	30	15
D334	1f. violet	50	25
D335	1f. purple	60	30
D336	1f.20 olive	65	25
D337	1f.40 green	65	60
D338	1f.50 olive	65	60
D1147	1f.60 mauve	14·50	7·00
D1148	1f.80 red	16·00	5·75
D339	2f. mauve	65	30
D1149	2f.40 lavender	9·25	3·50
D1150	3f. red	1·70	60
D340	3f.50 blue	65	30
D1151	4f. blue	11·00	60
D1152	5f. brown	3·50	30
D1153	7f. violet	3·50	1·70
D1154	8f. purple	13·00	10·50
D1155	10f. violet	7·50	3·25

D218

1945. Inscr "A PAYER" at top and "TE BETALEN" at bottom, or vice versa.

D1130A	**D218**	10c. olive	10	10
D1131A	**D218**	20c. blue	10	10
D1132A	**D218**	30c. red	10	10
D1133A	**D218**	40c. blue	10	10
D1134A	**D218**	50c. green	10	10
D1135A	**D218**	1f. brown	10	10
D1136A	**D218**	2f. orange	10	10

D462

1966

D2812	**D462**	1f. mauve	10	10
D2813	**D462**	2f. green	10	10
D2814	**D462**	3f. blue	1·40	25
D2815	**D462**	4f. green	25	25
D1985ab	**D462**	5f. purple	30	30
D2816	**D462**	5f. lilac	30	30
D1986	**D462**	6f. brown	85	15
D1987	**D462**	7f. red	70	†
D2818	**D462**	7f. orange	45	45
D2819	**D462**	8f. grey	45	45
D2820	**D462**	9f. red	50	50
D2821	**D462**	10f. brown	60	60
D1988	**D462**	20f. green	1·30	50
D2822	**D462**	20f. green	1·20	1·20

On No. D1988 the "F" is outside the shield; on No. D2822 it is inside.

RAILWAY PARCELS STAMPS

P21

1879

P63	**P21**	10c. brown	£160	10·50
P64	**P21**	20c. blue	£400	29·00
P65	**P21**	25c. green	£550	17·00
P66	**P21**	50c. red	£2750	14·50
P67	**P21**	80c. yellow	£3000	85·00
P68	**P21**	1f. grey	£400	†

In Belgium the parcels service is largely operated by the Belgian Railways for which the following stamps were issued.

Certain stamps under this heading were also on sale at post offices in connection with a "small parcels" service. These show a posthorn in the design except for Nos. P1116/18.

P22

1882

P69	**P22**	10c. brown	35·00	3·00
P73	**P22**	15c. grey	14·50	10·50
P75	**P22**	20c. blue	£100	5·75
P77	**P22**	25c. green	£100	6·00
P78	**P22**	50c. red	£100	1·20
P81	**P22**	80c. yellow	£110	3·00
P84	**P22**	80c. brown	£110	3·00
P86	**P22**	1f. grey	£600	4·75
P87	**P22**	1f. purple	£650	5·75
P88	**P22**	2f. buff	£350	£100

P35

1895. Numerals in black except 1f. and 2f.

P96	**P35**	10c. brown	14·50	1·20
P97	**P35**	15c. slate	14·50	11·50
P98	**P35**	20c. blue	23·00	2·30
P99	**P35**	25c. green	23·00	3·50
P100	**P35**	30c. orange	28·00	2·50
P101	**P35**	40c. green	41·00	2·50
P102	**P35**	50c. red	41·00	1·20
P103	**P35**	60c. lilac	75·00	1·20
P104	**P35**	70c. blue	75·00	2·00
P105	**P35**	80c. yellow	75·00	2·00
P106	**P35**	90c. red	£110	3·00
P107	**P35**	1f. purple	£300	4·75
P108	**P35**	2f. buff	£350	23·00

P37 Winged Railway Wheel

1902

P109a		10c. slate and brown	30	30
P110		15c. purple and slate	30	30
P111		20c. brown and blue	30	30
P112		25c. red and green	30	30
P113		30c. green and orange	30	30
P114		35c. green and brown	30	30
P115		40c. mauve and green	30	30
P116		50c. mauve and pink	30	30
P117		55c. blue and purple	30	30
P118		60c. red and lilac	30	30
P119		70c. red and blue	30	30
P120		80c. purple and yellow	30	30
P121		90c. green and red	30	30
P122	**P37**	1f. orange and purple	30	30
P123	**P37**	1f.10 black and red	30	30
P124	**P37**	2f. green and bistre	30	30
P125	**P37**	3f. blue and black	30	30
P126	**P37**	4f. red and green	2·00	2·00
P127	**P37**	5f. green and orange	1·20	1·20
P128	**P37**	10f. purple and yellow	1·20	1·20

1915. Stamps of 1912–14 optd CHEMINS DE FER SPOORWEGEN and Winged Railway Wheel.

P160	**44**	5c. green	£225
P161	**46**	10c. red	£250
P162	**46**	20c. green	£300
P163	**46**	25c. blue	£300
P164	**45**	35c. brown	£400
P165	**46**	40c. green	£350
P166	**45**	50c. grey	£375
P167	**45**	1f. orange	£350
P168	**45**	2f. violet	£2000
P169	-	5f. purple (No. 143)	£4000

P59 Winged Railway Wheel

P60 Steam Locomotive

1915				
P196	**P59**	10c. blue	1·20	60
P197	**P59**	15c. olive	2·00	2·00
P198	**P59**	20c. red	1·70	1·20
P199	**P59**	25c. brown	1·70	1·20
P200	**P59**	30c. mauve	1·70	1·20
P201	**P59**	35c. grey	2·00	1·20
P202	**P59**	40c. orange	3·25	3·00
P203	**P59**	50c. bistre	3·00	1·20
P204	**P59**	55c. brown	3·50	3·25
P205	**P59**	60c. lilac	3·00	1·20
P206	**P59**	70c. green	2·00	1·20
P207	**P59**	80c. brown	2·00	1·20
P208	**P59**	90c. blue	3·00	1·50
P209	**P60**	1f. grey	2·00	1·20
P210	**P60**	1f.10 bl (FRANKEN)	44·00	33·00
P211	**P60**	1f.10 blue (FRANK)	3·00	1·20
P212	**P60**	2f. red	65·00	1·70
P213	**P60**	3f. violet	65·00	1·70
P214	**P60**	4f. green	75·00	3·25
P215	**P60**	5f. brown	£150	4·25
P216	**P60**	10f. orange	£200	3·75

P69 Winged Railway Wheel

P70 Steam Train

1920				
P259	**P69**	10c. green	2·30	1·20
P280	**P69**	10c. red	60	30
P281	**P69**	15c. green	60	30
P261	**P69**	20c. red	2·30	1·20
P282	**P69**	20c. green	2·00	30
P262	**P69**	25c. brown	3·50	1·20
P283	**P69**	25c. blue	85	30
P263	**P69**	30c. mauve	38·00	34·00
P284	**P69**	30c. brown	85	30
P285	**P69**	35c. brown	85	45
P286	**P69**	40c. orange	85	30
P265	**P69**	50c. bistre	11·50	2·00
P287	**P69**	50c. red	85	30
P266	**P69**	55c. brown	13·00	9·50
P288	**P69**	55c. yellow	7·00	5·75
P267	**P69**	60c. purple	15·00	1·70
P289	**P69**	60c. red	85	30
P290	**P69**	70c. green	4·00	60
P269	**P69**	80c. brown	65·00	2·00
P291	**P69**	80c. violet	3·00	45
P270	**P69**	90c. blue	17·00	1·70
P292	**P69**	90c. yellow	46·00	43·00
P293	**P69**	90c. purple	8·75	45
P271	**P70**	1f. grey	£120	2·00
P272	**P70**	1f.10 blue	38·00	2·00
P273	**P70**	1f.20 green	23·00	†
P274	**P70**	1f.40 brown	23·00	1·70
P275	**P70**	2f. red	£170	1·70
P276	**P70**	3f. mauve	£200	1·20
P277	**P70**	4f. green	£200	1·70
P278	**P70**	5f. brown	£200	1·20
P279	**P70**	10f. orange	£200	1·70

On Nos. P271/9 the engine has one head lamp.

1920. Three head lamps on engine.				
P294	**P70**	1f. brown	8·75	30
P296	**P70**	1f.10 blue	3·00	30
P297	**P70**	1f.20 orange	3·75	30
P298	**P70**	1f.40 yellow	21·00	3·50
P299	**P70**	1f.60 green	38·00	70
P300	**P70**	2f. red	41·00	30
P301	**P70**	3f. red	41·00	30
P302	**P70**	4f. green	41·00	30
P303	**P70**	5f. violet	41·00	30
P304	**P70**	10f. yellow	£225	23·00
P305	**P70**	10f. brown	50·00	30
P306	**P70**	15f. red	50·00	30
P307	**P70**	20f. blue	£600	3·75

P75

1921				
P312	**P75**	2f. black	11·50	95
P313	**P75**	3f. brown	£100	95
P314	**P75**	4f. green	26·00	95
P315	**P75**	5f. red	26·00	95
P316	**P75**	10f. brown	26·00	95
P317	**P75**	15f. red	26·00	1·50
P318	**P75**	20f. blue	£190	3·75

P84

1923				
P375	**P84**	5c. brown	25	25
P376	**P84**	10c. red	10	10
P377	**P84**	15c. blue	30	30
P378	**P84**	20c. green	15	10
P379	**P84**	30c. purple	15	10
P380	**P84**	40c. olive	15	10
P381	**P84**	50c. red	15	10
P382	**P84**	60c. orange	15	10
P383	**P84**	70c. brown	15	10
P384	**P84**	80c. violet	15	10
P385	**P84**	90c. slate	1·00	10
		Similar type, but horiz.		
P386		1f. blue	30	15
P388		1f.10 orange	2·30	85
P389		1f.50 green	2·30	60
P390		1f.70 brown	60	60
P391		1f.80 red	3·50	85
P392		2f. olive	30	30
P393		2f.10 green	6·50	1·70
P394		2f.40 violet	3·00	1·70
P395		2f.70 grey	45·00	1·70
P396		3f. red	30	25
P397		3f.30 brown	70·00	1·70
P398		4f. red	30	25
P399		5f. violet	60	25
P400		6f. brown	30	25
P401		7f. orange	60	25
P402		8f. brown	60	25
P403		9f. purple	2·00	85
P404		10f. green	85	25
P405		20f. pink	1·20	25
P406		30f. green	4·00	60
P407		40f. slate	55·00	1·70
P408		50f. bistre	7·75	60

See Nos. P911/34.

1924. No. P394 surch 2F30.				
P409		2f.30 on 2f.40 violet	5·75	85

P139 Type 5 Steam locomotive "Goliath", 1930

1934				
P655	**P139**	3f. green	14·50	2·50
P656	**P139**	4f. mauve	5·75	30
P657	**P139**	5f. red	80·00	30

P149 Diesel Locomotive

1935. Centenary of Belgian Railway.				
P689	**P149**	10c. red	35	30
P690	**P149**	20c. violet	35	30
P691	**P149**	30c. brown	60	30
P692	**P149**	40c. blue	60	30
P693	**P149**	50c. orange	60	30
P694	**P149**	60c. green	65	30
P695	**P149**	70c. blue	65	30
P696	**P149**	80c. black	65	30
P697	**P149**	90c. red	1·20	60
		Horiz type. Locomotive "Le Belge", 1835.		
P698		1f. purple	85	30
P699		2f. black	2·30	30
P700		3f. orange	3·25	30
P701		4f. purple	3·25	30
P702		5f. purple	4·75	30
P703		6f. green	6·50	30
P704		7f. violet	26·00	30
P705		8f. black	26·00	35
P706		9f. blue	29·00	35
P707		10f. red	29·00	35
P708		20f. green	55·00	35
P709		30f. violet	£150	5·75
P710		40f. brown	£150	5·75
P711		50f. red	£200	5·25
P712		100f. blue	£375	85·00

P162 Winged Railway Wheel and Posthorn

1938				
P806	**P162**	5f. on 3f.50 green	26·00	25
P807	**P162**	5f. on 4f.50 purple	30	10
P808	**P162**	6f. on 5f.50 red	60	10
P1162	**P162**	8f. on 5f.50 brown	60	15
P1163	**P162**	10f. on 5f.50 blue	85	15
P1164	**P162**	12f. on 5f.50 violet	1·50	25

P176 Seal of the International Railway Congress

1939. International Railway Congress, Brussels.				
P856	**P176**	20c. brown	5·25	5·25
P857	**P176**	50c. blue	5·25	5·25
P858	**P176**	2f. red	5·25	5·25
P859	**P176**	9f. green	5·25	5·25
P860	**P176**	10f. purple	5·25	5·25

1939. Surch M. 3Fr.				
P867	**P162**	3f. on 5f.50 red	30	25

1940. Optd B in oval and two vert bars.				
P878	**P84**	10c. red	10	10
P879	**P84**	20c. green	10	10
P880	**P84**	30c. purple	10	10
P881	**P84**	40c. olive	10	10
P882	**P84**	50c. red	10	10
P883	**P84**	60c. orange	75	70
P884	**P84**	70c. brown	10	10
P885	**P84**	80c. violet	10	10
P886	**P84**	90c. slate	30	30
P887	**P84**	1f. blue	15	15
P888	**P84**	2f. olive	25	25
P889	**P84**	3f. red	25	25
P890	**P84**	4f. red	25	25
P891	**P84**	5f. violet	25	25
P892	**P84**	6f. brown	30	25
P893	**P84**	7f. orange	30	25
P894	**P84**	8f. brown	30	25
P895	**P84**	9f. purple	30	25
P896	**P84**	10f. green	30	25
P897	**P84**	20f. pink	75	45
P898	**P84**	30f. green	1·20	1·20
P899	**P84**	40f. slate	3·00	2·50
P900	**P84**	50f. bistre	1·70	1·70

1940. As Type P 84 but colours changed.			
P911	10c. olive	10	10
P912	20c. violet	10	10
P913	30c. red	10	10
P914	40c. blue	10	10
P915	50c. green	10	10
P916	60c. grey	10	10
P917	70c. green	10	10
P918	80c. orange	30	10
P919	90c. lilac	3·00	10
	Similar design, but horizontal.		
P920	1f. green	30	10
P921	2f. brown	35	10
P922	3f. grey	35	10
P923	4f. olive	40	10
P924	5f. lilac	45	10
P925	5f. black	85	10
P926	6f. red	85	10
P927	7f. violet	85	10
P928	8f. green	85	10
P929	9f. blue	1·20	10
P930	10f. mauve	1·20	25
P931	20f. blue	3·50	50
P932	30f. yellow	5·75	1·00
P933	40f. red	7·25	1·00
P934	50f. red	11·50	85

No. P925 was for use as a railway parcels tax stamp.

P195 Engine Driver

1942. Various designs.				
P1090	**P195**	10c. grey	30	25
P1091	**P195**	20c. violet	30	25
P1092	**P195**	30c. red	30	25
P1093	**P195**	40c. blue	30	25
P1094	**P195**	50c. blue	30	25
P1095	**P195**	60c. black	30	25
P1096	**P195**	70c. green	45	25
P1097	**P195**	80c. orange	45	25
P1098	**P195**	90c. brown	45	25
P1099	-	1f. green	30	25
P1100	-	2f. purple	30	25
P1101	-	3f. black	1·50	30
P1102	-	4f. blue	30	25
P1103	-	5f. brown	30	25
P1104	-	6f. green	1·50	60
P1105	-	7f. violet	30	25
P1106	-	8f. red	30	25
P1107	-	9f. blue	60	25
P996	-	9f.20 red	60	60
P1108	-	10f. red	3·25	35
P1109	-	10f. brown	2·30	45
P997	**P195**	12f.30 green	60	60
P998	-	14f.30 red	60	60
P1110	-	20f. green	1·20	25
P1111	-	30f. violet	1·20	25
P1112	-	40f. red	1·20	25
P1113	-	50f. blue	20·00	1·20
P999	-	100f. blue	24·00	24·00

DESIGNS—As Type P **195**: 1f. to 9f.20, Platelayer; 10f. and 14f.30 to 50f. Railway porter; 24½×34½ mm: 100f. Electric train.

No. P1109 was for use as a railway parcels tax stamp.

P216 Mercury

1945. Inscribed "BELGIQUE-BELGIE" or vice-versa.				
P1116A	**P216**	3f. green	30	15
P1117A	**P216**	5f. blue	30	15
P1118A	**P216**	6f. red	30	15

P224 Level Crossing

1947				
P1174	**P224**	100f. green	7·25	30

P230 Archer

1947				
P1193	**P230**	8f. brown	1·20	40
P1194	**P230**	10f. blue and black	1·20	30
P1195	**P230**	12f. violet	1·70	30

1948. Surch.			
P1229	9f. on 8f. brown	1·50	25
P1230	11f. on 10f. blue and black	1·50	40
P1231	13f.50 on 12f. violet	2·00	25

P246 "Parcel Post"

1948				
P1250	**P246**	9f. brown	8·75	35
P1251	**P246**	11f. red	7·50	25
P1252	**P246**	13f.50 black	13·00	25

P254 Type 1 Locomotive, 1867 (dated 1862)

1949. Locomotives.

P1277	-	½f. brown	35	25
P1278	**P254**	1f. red	60	25
P1279	-	2f. blue	80	25
P1280	-	3f. red (1884)	2·50	25
P1281	-	4f. green (1901)	1·70	25
P1282	-	5f. red (1902)	1·70	25
P1283	-	6f. purple (1904)	2·50	25
P1284	-	7f. green (1905)	4·00	25
P1285	-	8f. blue (1906)	5·25	25
P1286	-	9f. brown (1909)	5·75	25
P1287	-	10f. olive (1910)	14·00	3·50
P1288	-	10f. black and red (1905)	7·00	25
P1289	-	20f. orange (1920)	13·00	25
P1290	-	30f. blue (1928)	23·00	25
P1291	-	40f. red (1930)	41·00	25
P1292	-	50f. mauve (1935)	70·00	25
P1293	-	100f. red (1939)	£120	30
P1294	-	300f. violet (1951)	£170	60

DESIGNS: 50c. Locomotive "Le Belge", 1835; 2f. Type 29 locomotive, 1875; 3f. Type 25 locomotive, 1884; 4f. Type 18 locomotive, 1901; 5f. Type 22 locomotive, 1902; 6f. Type 53 locomotive, 1904; 7f. Type 8 locomotive, 1905; 8f. Type 16 locomotive, 1906; 9f. Type 10 locomotive, 1909; 10f. (P1287) Type 36 locomotive, 1910; 10f. (P 1288) Type 38 locomotive, 1905; 20f. Type 38 locomotive, 1920; 30f. Type 48 locomotive, 1928; 40f. Type 5 locomotive, 1935; 50f. Type 1 Pacific locomotive, 1935; 100f. Type 12 locomotive, 1939; 300f. Two-car electric train, 1951.

The 300f. is larger (37½×25 mm).

1949. Electrification of Charleroi–Brussels Line. As Type P254.

P1296		60f. brown	2·00	1·50

DESIGN: 60f. Type 101 electric locomotive, 1945.

P258 Loading Parcels

1950

P1307	-	11f. orange	5·75	25
P1308	-	12f. purple	22·00	2·00
P1309	-	13f. green	7·50	25
P1310	-	15f. blue	16·00	30
P1311	**P258**	16f. grey	5·75	25
P1312	-	17f. brown	7·50	25
P1313	**P258**	18f. red	16·00	25
P1314	**P258**	20f. orange	7·50	30

DESIGNS—HORIZ: 11, 12, 17f. Dispatch counter; 13, 15f. Sorting compartment.

P271 Mercury

1951. 25th Anniv of National Belgian Railway Society.

P1375	**P271**	25f. blue	15·00	13·00

1953. Nos. P1307, P1310 and P1313 surch.

P1442	-	13f. on 15f. blue	65·00	5·75
P1443	-	17f. on 11f. orange	32·00	1·20
P1444	**P258**	20f. on 18f. red	17·00	3·50

P288 Electric Train and Brussels Skyline

1953. Inauguration of Nord-Midi Junction.

P1451	**P288**	200f. green	£250	85
P1452	**P288**	200f. green & brown	£275	3·75

P291 Nord Station **P292** Central Station

1953. Brussels Railway Stations.

P1485	**P291**	1f. ochre	30	25
P1486	**P291**	2f. black	45	25
P1487	**P291**	3f. green	60	30
P1488	**P291**	4f. orange	85	40
P1489	**P291**	5f. brown	3·00	25
P1490	-	5f. brown	10·50	25
P1491	**P291**	6f. purple	1·20	25
P1492	**P291**	7f. green	1·20	25
P1493	**P291**	8f. red	1·50	25
P1494	**P291**	9f. blue	2·00	25
P1495	-	10f. green	2·40	25
P1496	-	10f. black	1·50	30
P1497	-	15f. red	14·50	45
P1498	-	20f. blue	4·00	25
P1498a	-	20f. green	2·30	45
P1499	-	30f. purple	6·50	25
P1500	-	40f. mauve	8·75	25
P1501	-	50f. mauve	10·50	25
P1501a	-	50f. blue	3·50	70
P1502	-	60f. violet	22·00	25
P1503	-	80f. purple	35·00	25
P1504	**P292**	100f. green	20·00	50
P1505	**P292**	200f. blue	£120	1·00
P1506	**P292**	300f. mauve	£200	1·70

DESIGNS—VERT: 5f. (P1490), 10f. (P1496), 15, 20f. (P1498a), 50f. (P1501a), Congress Station; 10f. (P1495), 20f. (P1498) to 50f. (P1501), Midi Station. HORIZ: 60, 80f. Chapelle Station.

Nos. P1490, P1496/7, P1498a and P1501a were for use as railway parcels tax stamps.

P295 Electric Train Type 121 and Nord Station, Brussels

1953

P1517	**P295**	13f. brown	23·00	30
P1518	**P295**	18f. blue	23·00	30
P1519	**P295**	21f. mauve	23·00	30

1956. Surch in figures.

P1585	14f. on 13f. brown	8·25	30
P1586	19f. on 18f. blue	8·25	30
P1587	22f. on 21f. mauve	8·25	30

P326 Mercury and Railway Winged Wheel

1957

P1600	**P326**	14f. green	8·25	25
P1601	**P326**	19f. sepia	8·25	25
P1602	**P326**	22f. red	8·25	40

1959. Surch 20 F.

P1678	20f. on 19f. sepia	29·00	30
P1679	20f. on 22f. red	29·00	70

P357 Brussels Nord Station, 1861–1954

1959

P1695	**P357**	20f. olive	14·50	25
P1696	-	24f. red	5·75	30
P1697	-	26f. blue	5·75	3·50
P1698	-	28f. purple	5·75	3·50

DESIGNS—VERT: 24f. Brussels Midi station, 1869–1949. HORIZ: 26f. Antwerp Central station, 1905; 28f. Ghent St. Pieter's station.

P368 Congress Seal, Type 202 Diesel and Type 125 Electric Locomotives

1960. 75th Anniv of Int Railway Congress Assn.

P1722	**P368**	20f. red	50·00	35·00
P1723	**P368**	50f. blue	50·00	35·00
P1724	**P368**	60f. purple	50·00	35·00
P1725	**P368**	70f. green	50·00	35·00

1961. Nos. P1695/8 surch.

P1787	**P357**	24f. on 20f. olive	60·00	30
P1788	-	26f. on 24f. red	5·75	30
P1789	-	28f. on 26f. blue	5·75	30
P1790	-	35f. on 28f. purple	5·75	30

P477 Arlon Station

1967

P2017	**P477**	25f. ochre	9·25	45
P2018	**P477**	30f. green	2·30	45
P2019	**P477**	35f. blue	3·00	45
P2020	**P477**	40f. red	26·00	70

P488 Type 122 Electric Train

1968

P2047	**P488**	1f. bistre	30	30
P2048	**P488**	2f. green	30	30
P2049	**P488**	3f. green	60	30
P2050	**P488**	4f. orange	60	30
P2051	**P488**	5f. brown	60	30
P2052	**P488**	6f. plum	60	30
P2053	**P488**	7f. green	60	30
P2054	**P488**	8f. red	90	30
P2055	**P488**	9f. blue	1·50	30
P2056	-	10f. green	3·00	30
P2057	-	20f. blue	1·80	30
P2058	-	30f. lilac	5·50	30
P2059	-	40f. violet	6·00	30
P2060	-	50f. purple	7·50	30
P2061	-	60f. violet	11·00	30
P2062	-	70f. brown	48·00	30
P2063	-	80f. purple	7·50	30
P2063a	-	90f. green	7·25	50
P2064	-	100f. green	12·00	30
P2065	-	200f. violet	15·00	60
P2066	-	300f. mauve	27·00	1·50
P2067	-	500f. yellow	42·00	2·10

DESIGNS: 10f. to 40f. Type 126 electric train; 50, 60, 70, 80, 90f. Type 160 electric train; 100, 200, 300f. Type 205 diesel-electric train; 500f. Type 210 diesel-electric train.

1970. Surch.

P2180	**P477**	37f. on 25f. ochre	65·00	7·75
P2181	**P477**	48f. on 35f. blue	6·00	6·00
P2182	**P477**	53f. on 40f. red	6·00	6·00

P551 Ostend Station

1971. Figures of value in black.

P2192	**P551**	32f. ochre	1·80	1·50
P2193	**P551**	37f. grey	16·00	15·00
P2194	**P551**	42f. blue	2·40	1·80
P2195	**P551**	44f. mauve	2·40	1·80
P2196	**P551**	46f. violet	2·75	1·80
P2197	**P551**	50f. red	2·40	1·80
P2198	**P551**	52f. brown	17·00	16·00
P2199	**P551**	54f. green	6·75	6·00
P2200	**P551**	61f. blue	3·50	2·75

1972. Nos. P2192/5 and P2198/200 surch in figures.

P2256	34f. on 32f. ochre	2·75	1·20
P2257	40f. on 37f. grey	2·75	1·20
P2258	47f. on 44f. mauve	3·00	1·20
P2259	53f. on 42f. blue	4·00	1·20
P2260	56f. on 52f. brown	3·50	1·20
P2261	59f. on 54f. green	4·00	1·20
P2262	66f. on 61f. blue	4·25	1·20

P575 Emblems within Bogie Wheels

1972. 50th Anniv of Int Railways Union (U.I.C.).

P2266	**P575**	100f. black, red and green	9·00	2·40

See also No. 2274.

P624 Global Emblem

1974. 4th International Symposium of Railway Cybernetics, Washington.

P2353	**P624**	100f. black, red and yellow	7·00	2·30

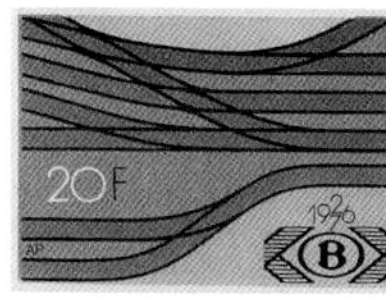

P671 Railway Junction

1976

P2431	**P671**	20f. black, bl & lilac	1·50	1·50
P2432	**P671**	50f. black, green and turquoise	2·50	1·50
P2433	**P671**	100f. black & orange	5·25	2·00
P2434	**P671**	150f. black, mauve and deep mauve	8·25	2·00

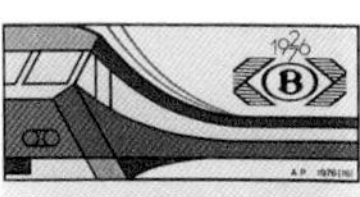

P677 Modern Electric Train

1976. 50th Anniv of National Belgian Railway Company.

P2445	**P677**	6f.50 multicoloured	50	15

P698 Railway Station at Night

1977

P2505	**P698**	1000f. mult	60·00	29·00

P753 Goods Wagon, Type 2216 A8

1980. Values in black.

P2615	**P753**	1f. ochre	30	30
P2616	**P753**	2f. red	30	30
P2617	**P753**	3f. blue	30	30
P2618	**P753**	4f. blue	30	30
P2619	**P753**	5f. brown	30	30
P2620	**P753**	6f. orange	45	45
P2621	**P753**	7f. violet	60	60
P2622	**P753**	8f. black	60	60
P2623	**P753**	9f. green	60	60
P2624	-	10f. brown	60	60
P2625	-	20f. blue	1·50	60
P2626	-	30f. ochre	2·30	60
P2627	-	40f. mauve	2·75	60

P2628	-	50f. purple	3·25	80
P2629	-	60f. olive	3·75	80
P2630	-	70f. blue	5·00	3·50
P2631	-	80f. purple	6·00	1·20
P2632	-	90f. mauve	6·50	4·00
P2633	-	100f. red	7·25	1·70
P2634	-	200f. brown	15·00	2·00
P2635	-	300f. olive	21·00	3·00
P2636	-	500f. purple	37·00	5·00

DESIGNS: 10f. to 40f. Packet wagon, Type 3614 A5; 50f. to 90f. Self-discharging wagon, Type 1000 D; 100f. to 500f. Tanker wagon, Type 2000 G.

P833 Electric Train entering Station

1985. 150th Anniv of Belgian Railways. Paintings by P. Delvaux. Multicoloured.

P2824	250f. Type P **833**	17·00	11·50
P2825	500f. Electric trains in station	41·00	20·00

RAILWAY PARCEL TAX STAMPS

1940. As Nos. P399 and P404 but colours changed.

P876	**P84**	5f. brown	60	60
P877	**P84**	10f. black	6·50	6·50

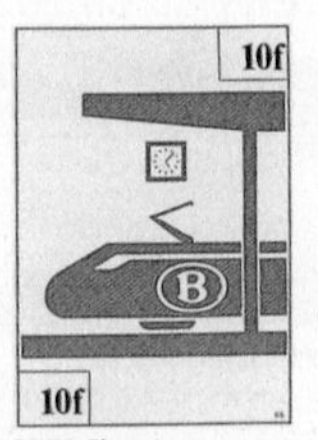

P779 Electric Locomotive at Station

1982

P2703	**P779**	10f. red & black	2·00	30
P2704	**P779**	20f. green & blk	2·30	1·50
P2705	**P779**	50f. brown & blk	4·25	85
P2706	**P779**	100f. blue & blk	7·50	1·20

P877 Buildings and Electric Locomotive

1987

P2923	**P877**	10f. red	1·20	60
P2924	**P877**	20f. green	1·80	1·50
P2925	**P877**	50f. brown	5·50	2·10
P2926	**P877**	100f. purple	9·75	4·25
P2927	**P877**	150f. brown	15·00	5·50

RAILWAY OFFICIAL STAMPS

1929. Stamps of 1922 optd with winged wheel.

O481	**81**	5c. slate	35	30
O482	**81**	10c. green	35	30
O483	**81**	35c. green	45	30
O484	**81**	60c. olive	60	30
O485	**81**	1f.50 blue	19·00	9·25
O486	**81**	1f.75 blue	2·30	1·20

For use on the official mail of the Railway Company.

1929. Stamps of 1929 optd with winged wheel.

O534	**104**	5c. green	30	15
O535	**104**	10c. bistre	30	15
O536	**104**	25c. red	2·50	45
O537	**104**	35c. green	80	25
O538	**104**	40c. purple	80	25
O539	**104**	50c. blue	40	25
O540	**104**	60c. mauve	23·00	11·50
O541	**104**	70c. brown	4·00	1·40
O542	**104**	75c. blue	8·25	1·20

1932. Stamps of 1931–34 optd with winged wheel.

O620	**126**	10c. green	85	60
O677	**127**	35c. green	17·00	65
O678	**142**	70c. green	5·75	40
O679	**121**	75c. brown	2·50	50

1936. Stamps of 1936 optd with winged wheel.

O721	**152**	10c. olive	15	15
O722	**152**	35c. green	15	15
O723	**152**	40c. lilac	25	25
O724	**152**	50c. blue	60	60
O725	**153**	70c. brown	4·75	4·75
O726	**153**	75c. olive	60	60

1941. Optd B in oval frame.

O948	**152**	10c. green	15	15
O949	**152**	40c. lilac	15	15
O950	**152**	50c. blue	25	25
O951	**153**	1f. red (No. 747)	30	30
O952a	**153**	1f. red (No. 748)	60	60
O953	**153**	2f.25 black	70	70
O954	**155**	2f.25 violet	35	35

1942. Nos. O722, O725 and O726 surch.

O983	**152**	10c. on 35c. green	10	15
O984	**153**	50c. on 70c. brown	10	15
O985	**153**	50c. on 75c. olive	25	25

O221

1946. Designs incorporating letter "B".

O1156	**O 221**	10c. green	10	10
O1157	**O 221**	20c. violet	3·75	1·20
O1158	**O 221**	50c. blue	10	10
O1159	**O 221**	65c. purple	5·25	1·50
O1160	**O 221**	75c. mauve	25	15
O1161	**O 221**	90c. violet	6·00	35
O1240	-	1f.35 brn (as 1219)	3·00	60
O1241	-	1f.75 green (as 1220)	7·50	60
O1242	**239**	3f. purple	35·00	10·50
O1243	**240**	3f.15 blue	14·00	8·75
O1244	**240**	4f. blue	28·00	11·50

O283

1952

O1424	**O 283**	10c. orange	40	15
O1425	**O 283**	20c. red	4·25	85
O1426	**O 283**	30c. green	1·70	60
O1427	**O 283**	40c. brown	40	15
O1428	**O 283**	50c. blue	35	15
O1429	**O 283**	60c. mauve	85	30
O1430	**O 283**	65c. purple	35·00	29·00
O1431	**O 283**	80c. green	5·75	1·50
O1432	**O 283**	90c. blue	8·75	1·50
O1433	**O 283**	1f. red	60	15
O1433a	**O 283**	1f.50 grey	25	25
O1434	**O 283**	2f.50 brown	30	15

1954. As T 289 (King Baudouin) but with letter "B" incorporated in design.

O1523	1f.50 black	40	15
O1524	2f. red	46·00	40
O1525	2f. green	45	15
O1526	2f.50 brown	37·00	85
O1527	3f. mauve	2·00	15
O1528	3f.50 green	85	15
O1529	4f. blue	1·20	35
O1530	6f. red	2·00	60

1971. As Nos. 2209/20 but with letter "B" incorporated in design.

O2224	3f. green	1·30	90
O2225	3f.50 brown	50	30
O2226	4f. blue	1·50	60
O2227	4f.50 purple	40	30
O2228	4f.50 blue	30	30
O2229	5f. violet	30	30
O2230	6f. red	50	30
O2231	6f.50 violet	60	30
O2232a	7f. red	35	25
O2233	8f. black	60	30
O2233a	9f. brown	60	30
O2234	10f. red	60	30
O2235	15f. violet	60	30
O2236	25f. purple	1·80	60
O2237	30f. brown	1·90	90

1977. As T 684 but with letter "B" incorporated in design.

O2455	50c. brown	25	25
O2456	1f. mauve	25	25
O2457	2f. orange	25	25
O2458	4f. brown	30	30
O2459	5f. green	30	30

Pt. 7

BERGEDORF

A German city on the Elbe, governed by Hamburg and Lubeck until 1867 when it was purchased by the former. In 1868 became part of North German Confederation.

16 schilling = 1 Hamburg mark.

1

1861. Various sizes. Imperf.

1	**1**	½s. black on lilac	£600	
2	**1**	½s. black on blue	60·00	£950
4	**1**	1s. black on white	60·00	£500
5	**1**	1½s. black on yellow	26·00	£1800
6	**1**	3s. black on red	£900	
7	**1**	3s. blue on red	32·00	£2750
8	**1**	4s. black on brown	32·00	£3000

Pt. 7

BREMEN

A free city of the Hanseatic League, situated on the R. Weser in northern Germany. Joined the North German Confederation in 1868.

72 grote = 1 thaler (internal).
22 grote = 10 silbergroschen (overseas mail)

1

1855. Imperf.

1	**1**	3g. black on blue	£275	£425

2 **3**

1856. Imperf.

3	**2**	5g. black on red	£200	£425
4	**2**	7g. black on yellow	£325	£950
5	**3**	5sg. green	£200	£475

4 **5**

1861. Zigzag roulette or perf.

17	**4**	2g. orange	£130	£425
19	**1**	3g. black on blue	£110	£400
20	**2**	5g. black on red	£170	£400
21	**2**	7g. black on yellow	£200	£6000
22	**5**	10g. black	£250	£1500
24	**3**	5sg. green	£700	£275

Pt. 7

BRUNSWICK

Formerly a duchy of N. Germany. Joined North German Confederation in 1868.

30 silbergroschen = 1 thaler.

1

1852. Imperf.

1	**1**	1sg. red	£2750	£400
2	**1**	2sg. blue	£1900	£350
3	**1**	3sg. red	£1900	£350

1853. Imperf.

4	¼gg. black on brown	£1100	£350
5	⅓gg. black	£190	£425
15	½sg. black on green	32·00	£325
7	1sg. black on buff	£550	85·00
8	2sg. black on blue	£425	85·00
11	3sg. black on red	£750	£225

3

1857. Imperf.

12	**3**	4/4gg. black on brown	55·00	£130

1864. Rouletted.

22	**1**	⅓gg. black	£650	£3000
23	**1**	½sg. black on green	£275	£4250
24	**1**	1sg. black on yellow	£4250	£2000
25	**1**	1sg. yellow	£550	£190
26	**1**	2sg. black on blue	£550	£450
27	**1**	3sg. pink	£1100	£700

4

1865. Roul.

28	**4**	⅓g. black	37·00	£475
29	**4**	1g. red	3·25	70·00
32	**4**	2g. blue	11·50	£170
34	**4**	3g. brown	9·50	£200

Pt. 11

DENMARK

A kingdom in N. Europe, on a peninsula between the Baltic and the North Sea.

1851. 96 rigsbank skilling = 1 rigsdaler.
1875. 100 ore = 1 krone.

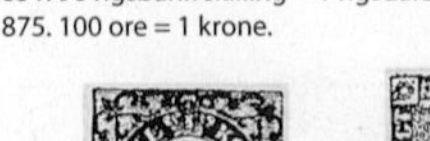

1 **2**

1851. Imperf.

3	**1**	2r.b.s. blue	£2750	£1000
4	**2**	4r.b.s. brown	£650	37·00

4

1854. Dotted background. Brown burelage. Imperf.

8	**4**	2sk. blue	65·00	55·00
9b	**4**	4sk. orange	£500	9·75
12	**4**	8sk. green	£275	75·00
13	**4**	16sk. lilac	£450	£190

5

1858. Background of wavy lines. Brown burelage. Imperf.

15	**5**	4sk. brown	70·00	9·75
18	**5**	8sk. green	£650	£110

1863. Brown burelage. Roul.

20		4sk. brown	£110	14·00
21	**4**	16sk. mauve	£1300	£600

7

1864. Perf.

22	**7**	2sk. blue	60·00	35·00
25	**7**	3sk. mauve	80·00	65·00
28	**7**	4sk. red	41·00	7·50
29	**7**	8sk. bistre	£300	£130
30a	**7**	16sk. green	£475	£130

8

1870. Value in "skilling".

37	**8**	48sk. lilac and brown	£425	£225
39	**8**	2sk. blue and grey	50·00	25·00
42	**8**	3sk. purple and grey	90·00	85·00
44	**8**	4sk. red and grey	43·00	7·50
46	**8**	8sk. brown and grey	£190	65·00
48	**8**	16sk. green and grey	£225	£140

1875. As T **8**, but value in "ore".

56	5ore blue and red	28·00	55·00
72	20ore grey and red	95·00	26·00
80	3ore grey and blue	4·00	2·40
81	4ore blue and grey	4·25	40
82	8ore red and grey	4·25	40
83	12ore purple and grey	5·00	3·25
84	16ore brown and grey	17·00	3·25
85	25ore green and grey	9·00	3·50
86	50ore purple and brown	27·00	17·00
87	100ore orange and grey	27·00	10·00

10

1882

96	**10**	1ore orange	70	50
97	**10**	5ore green	4·25	20
98	**10**	10ore red	3·50	20
99	**10**	15ore mauve	11·50	1·10
100	**10**	20ore blue	18·00	3·00
101	**10**	24ore brown	6·75	4·25

1904. No. 82 and 101 surch.

102	**8**	4ore on 8ore red & grey	2·30	3·75
103	**10**	15ore on 24ore brown	3·50	5·75

14 King Christian IX

1904

104	**14**	10ore red	1·70	35
105	**14**	20ore blue	14·50	1·90
106	**14**	25ore brown	17·00	4·25
107	**14**	50ore lilac	60·00	60·00
108	**14**	100ore brown	9·00	33·00
119	**14**	5ore green	2·75	20

15

1905. Solid background.

173	**15**	1ore orange	30	25
174	**15**	2ore red	2·75	30
175	**15**	3ore grey	4·00	35
176	**15**	4ore blue	5·75	40
177	**15**	5ore brown	90	25
178	**15**	5ore green	2·20	25
179	**15**	7ore green	4·00	5·00
180	**15**	7ore violet	18·00	3·25
181	**15**	8ore grey	7·25	2·20
114	**15**	10ore pink	4·25	25
182	**15**	10ore green	1·20	25
183	**15**	10ore brown	3·00	25
184	**15**	12ore lilac	25·00	6·00
115	**15**	15ore mauve	14·00	70
116	**15**	20ore blue	28·00	75

For stamps with lined background but without hearts, see Nos. 265/76k.

17 King Frederik VIII

1907

121	**17**	5ore green	1·00	20
122	**17**	10ore red	2·50	20
124	**17**	20ore blue	9·25	1·70
125	**17**	25ore brown	22·00	80
127	**17**	35ore orange	3·50	3·00
128	**17**	50ore purple	22·00	4·25
130	**17**	100ore brown	75·00	2·75

1912. (a) Nos. 84 and 72 surch **35 ORE**.

131	**8**	35ore on 16ore brn & grey	9·75	31·00
132	**8**	35ore on 20ore grey and red	18·00	44·00

(b) No. O98 surch **35 ORE FRIMAERKE**.

133	**O9**	35ore on 32ore green	17·00	55·00

20 G.P.O., Copenhagen

1912

134	**20**	5k. red	£200	90·00

21 King Christian X **22**

1913

135	**21**	5ore green	85	20
136	**21**	7ore orange	2·00	80
137	**21**	8ore grey	6·75	3·25
138	**21**	10ore red	1·30	20
139	**21**	12ore grey	5·25	5·75
141a	**21**	15ore mauve	1·50	20
142	**21**	20ore blue	7·75	35
143	**21**	20ore brown	1·00	25
144	**21**	20ore red	1·40	25
145	**21**	25ore brown	9·50	40
146	**21**	25ore black and brown	55·00	4·25
147	**21**	25ore red	3·50	80
148	**21**	25ore green	3·25	40
149	**21**	27ore black and red	20·00	32·00
150	**21**	30ore black and green	39·00	1·60
151	**21**	30ore orange	3·25	1·20
152	**21**	30ore blue	1·60	40
153	**21**	35ore yellow	15·00	2·40
154	**21**	35ore black and yellow	5·00	3·25
155	**21**	40ore black and violet	12·00	2·40
156	**21**	40ore blue	4·00	80
157	**21**	40ore yellow	1·40	80
158	**21**	50ore purple	25·00	3·25
159	**21**	50ore black and purple	43·00	80
160a	**21**	50ore grey	6·75	40
161	**21**	60ore blue and brown	36·00	3·25
162	**21**	60ore blue	6·75	75
163	**21**	70ore green and brown	17·00	2·40
164	**21**	80ore green	30·00	8·75
165	**21**	90ore red and brown	10·50	2·40
166	**22**	1k. brown	65·00	80
167	**21**	1k. blue and brown	34·00	1·20
168	**22**	2k. black	95·00	4·75
169	**21**	2k. purple and grey	45·00	11·50
170	**22**	5k. violet	10·50	5·75
171	**21**	5k. brown and mauve	5·75	4·00
172	**21**	10k. green and red	£180	24·00

1915. (a) No. O94 surch **DANMARK 80 ORE POSTFRIM**.

186	**O9**	80ore on 8ore red	28·00	80·00

(b) No. 83 surch **80 ORE**.

187	**8**	80ore on 12ore pur & grey	27·00	75·00

1918. Newspaper stamps surch **POSTFRIM. ORE 27 ORE DANMARK.**

197	**N18**	27ore on 1ore green	2·75	6·50
198	**N18**	27ore on 5ore blue	7·00	14·50
199	**N18**	27ore on 7ore red	2·75	6·50
200	**N18**	27ore on 8ore green	4·00	8·00
201	**N18**	27ore on 10ore lilac	2·75	5·75
202	**N18**	27ore on 20ore green	4·00	8·00
203	**N18**	27ore on 29ore orge	2·75	5·75
204	**N18**	27ore on 38ore orge	23·00	60·00
205	**N18**	27ore on 41ore brn	6·50	29·00
194	**N18**	27ore on 68ore brn	5·50	16·00
206	**N18**	27ore on 1k. pur & grn	2·50	6·50
195	**N18**	27ore on 5k. grn & pk	5·00	13·50
196	**N18**	27ore on 10k. bl & stone	5·50	18·00

1919. No. 135 surch **2 ORE**.

207	**21**	2ore on 5ore green	£950	£650

27 Castle of Kronborg, Elsinore **29** Roskilde Cathedral

1920. Recovery of Northern Schleswig.

208	**27**	10ore red	4·00	25
209	**27**	10ore green	7·50	35
210	**-**	20ore slate	3·50	25
211	**29**	40ore brown	11·50	3·50
212	**29**	40ore blue	43·00	6·50

DESIGN—HORIZ: 20ore Sonderborg Castle.

1921. Nos. 136 and 139 surch **8 8**.

217	**21**	8 on 7ore orange	1·70	2·40
213	**21**	8 on 12ore green	1·70	5·25

1921. Red Cross. Nos. 209/10 surch with figure of value between red crosses.

214	**27**	10ore+5ore green	17·00	40·00
215	**-**	20ore+10ore grey	20·00	44·00

1921. No. 175 surch *8*.

216	**15**	8 on 3ore grey	2·75	2·40

33 King Christian IV **34** King Christian X

1924. 300th Anniv of Danish Post. A. Head facing to left.

218A	**33**	10ore green	6·50	4·75
221A	**34**	10ore green	6·50	4·75
219A	**33**	15ore mauve	6·50	4·75
222A	**34**	15ore mauve	6·50	4·75
220A	**33**	20ore brown	6·50	4·75
223A	**34**	20ore brown	6·50	4·75

B. Head facing to right.

218B	**33**	10ore green	6·50	4·75
221B	**34**	10ore green	6·50	4·75
219B	**33**	15ore mauve	6·50	4·75
222B	**34**	15ore mauve	6·50	4·75
220B	**33**	20ore brown	6·50	4·75
223B	**34**	20ore brown	6·50	4·75

35

1925. Air.

224	**35**	10ore green	28·00	34·00
225	**35**	15ore lilac	55·00	55·00
226	**35**	25ore red	39·00	55·00
227	**35**	50ore grey	£110	£120
228	**35**	1k. brown	£110	£120

1926. Surch **20 20**.

229	**21**	20 on 30ore orange	4·00	10·00
230	**21**	20 on 40ore blue	4·50	11·50

38 **39**

1926. 75th Anniv of First Danish stamps.

231	**38**	10ore olive	85	40
232	**39**	20ore red	1·40	40
233	**39**	30ore blue	5·00	1·40

1926. Various stamps surch.

234	**15**	7 on 8ore grey	1·40	2·75
235	**21**	7 on 20ore red	55	1·40
236	**21**	7 on 27ore black & red	3·50	10·00
237	**21**	12 on 15ore lilac	2·40	3·25

1926. Official stamps surch **DANMARK 7 ORE POSTFRIM.**

238	**O9**	7ore on 1ore orange	4·00	10·50
239	**O9**	7ore on 3ore grey	9·00	19·00
240	**O9**	7ore on 4ore blue	4·00	10·50
241	**O9**	7ore on 5ore green	45·00	75·00
242	**O9**	7ore on 10ore green	4·00	10·50
243	**O9**	7ore on 15ore lilac	4·25	10·50
244	**O9**	7ore on 20ore blue	19·00	43·00

40 Caravel

1927. Solid background.

246	**40**	15ore red	4·50	20
247	**40**	20ore grey	10·00	1·80
248	**40**	25ore blue	80	35
249	**40**	30ore yellow	1·00	35
250	**40**	35ore red	17·00	1·00
251	**40**	40ore green	16·00	35

For stamps with lined background see Nos. 277b, etc.

41

1929. Danish Cancer Research Fund.

252	**41**	10ore (+5ore) green	4·25	5·50
253	**41**	15ore (+5ore) red	8·25	10·50
254	**41**	25ore (+5ore) blue	31·00	37·00

42 King Christian X

1930. 60th Birthday of King Christian X.

255	**42**	5ore green	2·75	20
256	**42**	7ore violet	6·75	3·00
257	**42**	8ore grey	23·00	20·00
258	**42**	10ore brown	4·25	15
259	**42**	15ore red	8·00	15
260	**42**	20ore grey	23·00	5·75
261	**42**	25ore blue	7·25	1·20
262	**42**	30ore yellow	9·00	1·90
263	**42**	35ore red	10·00	3·50
264	**42**	40ore green	9·00	1·10

43 Numeral

1933. Lined background.

265	**43**	1ore green	20	20
266	**43**	2ore red	20	20
267	**43**	4ore blue	35	20
268	**43**	5ore green	1·10	25
268c	**43**	5ore purple	20	15
268d	**43**	5ore orange	20	15
268e	**43**	6ore orange	30	20
269	**43**	7ore violet	1·80	25
269a	**43**	7ore green	1·60	45
269b	**43**	7ore brown	30	25
270	**43**	8ore grey	50	20
270a	**43**	8ore green	30	20
271	**43**	10ore orange	8·75	25
271b	**43**	10ore brown	6·50	15
271c	**43**	10ore violet	60	20
271d	**43**	10ore green	20	15
272	**43**	12ore green	30	25
272a	**43**	15ore green	25	15
272c	**43**	20ore blue	20	15
272e	**43**	25ore green	40	15
272f	**43**	25ore blue	25	15
273	**43**	30ore green	20	15
273a	**43**	30ore orange	25	15
273c	**43**	40ore orange	25	15
273d	**43**	40ore purple	20	20
274	**43**	50ore brown	20	15
274d	**43**	60ore green	1·40	40
274e	**43**	60ore grey	60	55
275	**43**	70ore red	75	20
275a	**43**	70ore green	30	20
275d	**43**	80ore green	35	20
275e	**43**	80ore brown	50	30
276	**43**	100ore green	45	20
276a	**43**	100ore blue	40	15
276b	**43**	125ore brown	55	25
276c	**43**	150ore green	55	30
276ca	**43**	150ore violet	45	30

276d	**43**	200ore green	50	20
276e	**43**	230ore green	95	40
276f	**43**	250ore green	95	30
276g	**43**	270ore green	75	35
276h	**43**	300ore green	90	20
276i	**43**	325ore green	1·20	65
276j	**43**	350ore green	1·10	40
276k	**43**	375ore green	1·10	30
276l	**43**	400ore green	75	45

45 King Christian X

1933. T **40** with lined background.

277b	**40**	15ore red	2·75	20
277de	**40**	15ore green	5·75	60
278a	**40**	20ore grey	3·75	20
278b	**40**	20ore red	90	50
279	**40**	25ore blue	75·00	19·00
279ab	**40**	25ore brown	95	25
280a	**40**	30ore orange	65	20
280b	**40**	30ore blue	1·60	20
281	**40**	35ore violet	65	25
282	**40**	40ore green	3·75	20
282b	**40**	40ore blue	1·30	20
283	**45**	50ore grey	1·40	20
283a	**45**	60ore green	2·75	20
283b	**45**	75ore blue	50	25
284	**45**	1k. brown	4·00	20
284a	**45**	2k. red	5·75	85
284b	**45**	5k. violet	10·00	2·40

1934. Nos. 279 and 280a surch.

285	**40**	4 on 25ore blue	65	40
286	**40**	10 on 30ore orange	2·75	2·20

47 Fokker FVIIa over Copenhagen

1934. Air.

287	**47**	10ore orange	85	1·10
288	**47**	15ore red	3·25	4·50
289	**47**	20ore green	3·75	5·00
290	**47**	50ore green	3·75	5·00
291	**47**	1k. brown	13·00	17·00

49 Hans Andersen

1935. Centenary of Hans Andersen's Fairy Tales.

292	-	5ore green	4·25	20
293	**49**	7ore violet	3·00	2·75
294	-	10ore orange	6·50	20
295	**49**	15ore red	15·00	20
296	**49**	20ore grey	15·00	1·10
297	**49**	30ore blue	2·75	35

DESIGNS: 5ore "The Ugly Duckling"; 10ore "The Little Mermaid".

51 St. Nicholas's Church, Copenhagen

52 Hans Tausen

53 Ribe Cathedral

1936. 400th Anniv of Reformation.

298	**51**	5ore green	1·40	20
299	**51**	7ore mauve	1·70	3·00
300	**52**	10ore brown	2·10	20
301	**52**	15ore red	3·00	20
302	**53**	30ore blue	15·00	95

54 Dybbol Mill

1937. H. P. Hanssen (North Schleswig patriot) Memorial Fund.

303	**54**	5ore+5ore green	70	1·10
304	**54**	10ore+5ore brown	3·25	5·75
305	**54**	15ore+5ore red	3·25	5·75

56 King Christian X

1937. Silver Jubilee of King Christian X.

306	-	5ore green	1·40	20
307	**56**	10ore brown	1·40	20
308	-	15ore red	1·40	20
309	**56**	30ore blue	20·00	1·90

DESIGNS—HORIZ: 5ore Marselisborg Castle and "Rita" (King's yacht); 15ore Amalienborg Castle.

1937. Copenhagen Philatelic Club's 50th Anniv Stamp Exhibition. No. 271b optd **K.P.K. 17.-26. SEPT. 19 37** (="Kobenhavns Philatelist Klub").

310	**43**	10ore brown	1·40	1·60

58 Emancipation Monument

1938. 150th Anniv of Abolition of Villeinage.

311	**58**	15ore red	70	20

59 B. Thorvaldsen

1938. Centenary of Return of Sculptor Thorvaldsen to Denmark.

312	**59**	5ore purple	30	20
313	-	10ore violet	45	20
314	**59**	30ore blue	1·90	60

DESIGN: 10ore Statue of Jason.

61 Queen Alexandrine

1939. Red Cross Charity. Cross in red.

314a	**61**	5ore+3ore purple	30	35
315	**61**	10ore+5ore violet	30	20
316	**61**	15ore+5ore red	35	40

1940. Stamps of 1933 (lined background) surch.

317	**43**	6 on 7ore green	25	25
318	**43**	6 on 8ore grey	25	20
319a	**40**	15 on 40ore green	95	95
320	**40**	20 on 15ore red	1·20	20
321	**40**	40 on 30ore blue	1·10	25

65 Queen Ingrid (when Princess) and Princess Margrethe

1941. Child Welfare.

322	**65**	10ore+5ore violet	30	25
323	**65**	20ore+5ore red	30	25

66 Bering's Ship "Sv. Pyotr"

1941. Death Bicent of Vitus Bering (explorer).

324	**66**	10ore violet	30	20
325	**66**	20ore brown	65	25
326	**66**	40ore blue	50	35

67 King Christian X

1942

327	**67**	10ore violet	20	15
328	**67**	15ore green	25	15
329	**67**	20ore red	30	15
330	**67**	25ore brown	50	30
331	**67**	30ore orange	40	15
332	**67**	35ore purple	40	30
333	**67**	40ore blue	50	15
333a	**67**	45ore olive	50	20
334	**67**	50ore grey	75	20
335	**67**	60ore green	55	20
335a	**67**	75ore blue	75	25

68 Round Tower of Trinity Church

1942. Tercentenary of the Round Tower.

336	**68**	10ore violet	30	20

69 Focke-Wulf Fw 200 Condor

1943. 25th Anniv of D.D.L. Danish Airlines.

337	**69**	20ore red	30	20

1944. Red Cross. No. 336 surch 5 and red cross.

338	**68**	10ore+5ore violet	30	20

70 Osterlars Church

1944. Danish Churches.

339	-	10ore violet	30	20
340	**70**	15ore green	30	25
341	-	20ore red	25	15

DESIGNS: 10ore Ejby Church; 20ore Hvidbjerg Church.

71 Ole Romer

1944. Birth Tercent of Romer (astronomer).

342	**71**	20ore brown	30	20

72 King Christian X

1945. King Christian's 75th Birthday.

343	**72**	10ore mauve	20	15
344	**72**	20ore red	30	15
345	**72**	40ore blue	55	25

73 Arms

1946

346	**73**	1k. brown	65	15
346a	**73**	1k.10 purple	4·00	1·30
346b	**73**	1k.20 grey	2·40	20
346c	**73**	1k.20 blue	1·20	25
346d	**73**	1k.25 orange	2·40	20
346e	**73**	1k.30 green	90	20
346f	**73**	1k.50 purple	1·30	15
346g	**73**	2k. red	1·30	15
347	**73**	2k.20 orange	2·00	20
347a	**73**	2k.50 olive	1·40	25
347b	**73**	2k.80 grey	1·70	25
347c	**73**	2k.80 olive	95	55
347d	**73**	2k.80 green	85	45
347e	**73**	2k.90 purple	3·25	25
347f	**73**	3k. green	80	15
347g	**73**	3k.10 purple	4·50	25
347h	**73**	3k.30 red	95	55
347i	**73**	3k.50 purple	1·50	25
347j	**73**	3k.50 blue	2·30	2·20
347k	**73**	4k. grey	1·00	25
347l	**73**	4k.10 brown	4·50	25
347m	**73**	4k.30 brown	3·00	3·25
347n	**73**	4k.30 green	3·75	3·75
347o	**73**	4k.50 brown	3·75	25
347p	**73**	4k.60 grey	3·00	3·25
347q	**73**	4k.70 purple	2·75	3·50
348	**73**	5k. blue	1·00	35
348a	**73**	5k.50 blue	2·00	75
348b	**73**	6k. black	1·40	15
348c	**73**	6k.50 green	1·70	45
348d	**73**	6k.60 green	3·00	3·25
348e	**73**	7k. mauve	1·70	20
348f	**73**	7k.10 purple	2·10	1·80
348g	**73**	7k.30 green	3·50	3·50
348h	**73**	7k.50 green	2·00	1·90
348i	**73**	7k.70 purple	2·75	1·30
348j	**73**	8k. orange	1·90	30
348k	**73**	9k. brown	2·00	20
348l	**73**	10k. yellow	2·20	25
348la	**73**	10k.50 blue	3·25	85
348m	**73**	11k. brown	3·75	1·60
348ma	**73**	11k.50 blue	3·00	2·10
348n	**73**	12k. brown	3·25	45
348o	**73**	14k. brown	4·00	55
348p	**73**	16k. red	4·25	45
348q	**73**	17k. red	6·00	95
348r	**73**	18k. brown	7·00	85
348s	**73**	20k. blue	4·50	45
348t	**73**	22k. red	5·00	1·00
348u	**73**	23k. green	6·50	1·10
348v	**73**	24k. green	6·50	85
348w	**73**	25k. green	5·75	30
348x	**73**	26k. green	8·25	1·40
348z	**73**	50k. red	11·50	1·80

74 Tycho Brahe

1946. 400th Birth Anniv of Tycho Brahe (astronomer).

349	**74**	20ore red	35	20

75 Symbols of Freedom

1947. Liberation Fund.

350	**75**	15ore+5ore green	50	30
351	-	20ore+5ore red (Bombed railways)	50	30
352	-	40ore+5ore blue (Flag)	1·00	90

77 Class H Steam Goods Train

1947. Centenary of Danish Railways.

353		15ore green	50	20
354	**77**	20ore red	70	20
355	-	40ore blue	2·75	1·30

DESIGNS—HORIZ: 15ore First Danish locomotive "Odin"; 40ore Diesel-electric train *Lyntog* and train ferry *Fy*".

79 I. C. Jacobsen

1947. 60th Death Anniv of Jacobsen and Centenary of Carlsberg Foundation for Promotion of Scientific Research.

356	**79**	20ore red	30	10

80 King Frederick IX

1948

357a	**80**	15ore green	85	20
358	**80**	15ore violet	50	15
359a	**80**	20ore red	55	15
360	**80**	20ore brown	30	15
361	**80**	25ore brown	1·00	15
362	**80**	25ore red	3·25	15
362a	**80**	25ore blue	70	25
362b	**80**	25ore violet	25	20
363	**80**	30ore orange	9·25	30
363b	**80**	30ore red	40	25
364	**80**	35ore green	40	30
365	**80**	40ore blue	3·25	60
366	**80**	40ore grey	75	15
367	**80**	45ore bistre	1·20	15
368	**80**	50ore grey	1·20	15
369	**80**	50ore blue	2·20	20
369a	**80**	50ore green	40	25
370	**80**	55ore brown	20·00	1·40
371a	**80**	60ore blue	50	25
371b	**80**	65ore grey	40	20
372	**80**	70ore green	1·70	15
373	**80**	75ore purple	1·10	15
373a	**80**	80ore orange	70	25
373b	**80**	90ore bistre	2·75	25
373c	**80**	95ore orange	60	25

81 *The Constituent Assembly of the Kingdom* (after Constantin Hansen)

1949. Centenary of Danish Constitution.

374	**81**	20ore brown	35	20

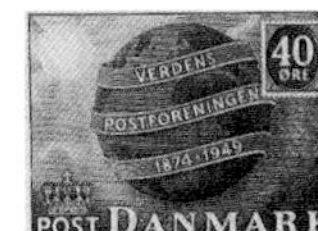
82 Globe

1949. 75th Anniv of U.P.U.

375	**82**	40ore blue	50	40

83 Kalundborg Transmitter

1950. 25th Anniv of State Broadcasting.

376	**83**	20ore brown	35	20

84 Princess Anne-Marie

1950. National Children's Welfare Assn.

377	**84**	25ore+5ore red	55	55

85 *Fredericus Quartus* (warship)

1951. 250th Anniv of Naval Officers' College.

378	**85**	25ore red	55	30
379	**85**	50ore blue	3·00	60

86 *H. C. Oersted* (after C. A. Jensen)

1951. Death Centenary of Oersted (physicist).

380	**86**	50ore blue	1·20	55

87 Mail Coach

1951. Danish Stamp Centenary.

381	**87**	15ore violet	50	25
382	**87**	25ore red	50	25

88 Hospital Ship *Jutlandia*

1951. Danish Red Cross Fund.

383	**88**	25ore +5ore red	60	60

89 *Life-Saving* (relief, H. Solomon)

1952. Centenary of Danish Life-Saving Service.

384	**89**	25ore red	40	30

1953. Netherlands Flood Relief Fund. Surch **NL+10**.

385	**80**	30ore+10ore red	1·10	1·00

91 Memorial Stone, Skamlings-banken

1953. Danish Border Union Fund.

386	**91**	30ore+5ore red	1·10	1·10

92 Runic Stone at Jelling

1953. 1,000 years of Danish Kingdom. Inscr "KONGERIGE i 1000 AR". (a) 1st series.

387	**92**	10ore green	25	20
388	-	15ore lilac	25	20
389	-	20ore brown	25	20
390	-	30ore red	25	20
391	-	60ore blue	35	20

DESIGNS: 15ore Vikings' camp, Trelleborg; 20ore Kalundborg Church; 30ore Nyborg Castle; 60ore Goose Tower, Vordinborg.

(b) 2nd series.

392	10ore green	25	15
393	15ore lilac	25	15
394	20ore brown	25	15
395	30ore red	25	15
396	60ore blue	55	20

DESIGNS: 10ore Spottrup Castle; 15ore Hammershus Castle; 20ore Copenhagen Stock Exchange; 30ore King Frederik V statue; 60ore Soldier's Statue (H. V. Bissen).

93 Telegraph Table, 1854

1954. Telecommunications Centenary.

397	**93**	30ore brown	30	25

94 Head of Statue of King Frederik V at Amalienborg

1954. Bicent of Royal Academy of Fine Arts.

398	**94**	30ore red	50	35

1955. Liberty Fund. Nos. 350/1 surch.

399	**75**	20+5 on 15ore +5ore grn	50	35
400	-	30+5 on 20ore +5ore red	1·10	1·10

1955. Nos. 268e, 269b, 359a and 362 surch.

401	**43**	5ore on 6ore orange	1·10	1·10
402	**43**	5ore on 7ore brown	15	15
403	**80**	30ore on 20ore red	15	15
404	**80**	30ore on 25ore red	50	30

98 S. Kierkegaard (philosopher)

1955. Death Centenary of Kierkegaard.

405	**98**	30ore red	30	20

99 Ellehammer 11 Aircraft

1956. 50th Anniv of 1st Flight by J. C. H. Ellehammer.

406	**99**	30ore red	45	20

100 Whooper Swans

1956. Northern Countries' Day.

407	**100**	30ore red	1·50	15
408	**100**	60ore blue	1·20	70

1957. Danish Red Cross Hungarian Relief Fund. No. 373c surch **Ungarns-hjaelpen 30 + 5**.

409	**80**	30ore+5ore on 95ore orange	50	45

102 National Museum

1957. 150th Anniv of National Museum.

410	**102**	30ore red	65	15
411	-	60ore blue	70	50

DESIGN: 50ore *Sun-God's Chariot* (bronze age model).

103 Harvester

1958. Centenary of Danish Royal Veterinary and Agricultural College.

412	**103**	30ore red	25	20

1959. Greenland Fund. No. 363b surch **Gronlands-fonden + 10**.

413	**80**	30ore+10ore red	75	70

The Greenland Fund was devoted to the relatives of the crew and passengers of the "Hans Hedtoft", the Greenland vessel lost at sea on 30 January 1959.

105 King Frederik IX

1959. 60th Birthday of King Frederik IX.

414	**105**	30ore red	30	15
415	**105**	35ore purple	40	25
416	**105**	60ore blue	40	25

106 Margrethe Schanne in *La Sylphide*

1959. Danish Ballet and Music Festival, 1959.

417	**106**	35ore purple	25	20

See also Nos. 445 and 467.

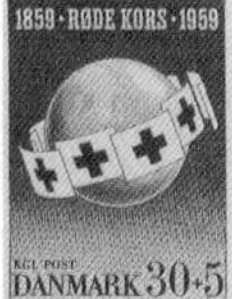
107

1959. Centenary of Red Cross.

418	**107**	30ore+5ore red	50	45
419	**107**	60ore+5ore red & blue	65	60

1960. World Refugee Year. Surch 30 Verdensflygtningeåret 1959-60 and uprooted tree.

420	**80**	30ore on 15ore violet	20	15

109 Sowing Machine

1960. First Danish Food Fair.

421	**109**	12ore green	20	15
422	-	30ore red	25	15
423	-	60ore blue	50	35

DESIGNS: 30ore Combine-harvester; 60ore Plough.

110 King Frederik and Queen Ingrid

1960. Royal Silver Wedding.

424	**110**	30ore red	35	15
425	**110**	60ore blue	50	45

111 Ancient Bascule Light

1960. 400th Anniv of Danish Lighthouse Service.

426	**111**	30ore red	30	20

112 N. Finsen

1960. Birth Cent of Niels R. Finsen (physician).

427	**112**	30ore red	25	20

113 Mother and Child

1960. W.H.O. 10th European Regional Committee Meeting.

428	**113**	60ore blue	50	40

113a Conference Emblem

1960. Europa.

429	**113a**	60ore blue	65	55

114 Queen Ingrid

1960. 25th Year of Queen Ingrid's Service in Girl Guides.

430	**114**	30ore+10ore red	1·00	95

115 Douglas DC-8

1961. Tenth Anniv of Scandinavian Airlines System (SAS).

431	**115**	60ore blue	75	35

116 Coastal Scene

1961. 50th Anniv of Society for Preservation of Danish National Amenities.

432	**116**	30ore red	20	20

117 King Frederik IX

1961

433	**117**	20ore brown	35	15
434	**117**	25ore brown	25	15
435	**117**	30ore red	45	15
436	**117**	35ore green	55	35
437	**117**	35ore red	25	15
438	**117**	40ore grey	1·00	15
438a	**117**	40ore brown	25	15
439	**117**	50ore turquoise	45	15
439a	**117**	50ore red	70	15
439b	**117**	50ore brown	55	15
440	**117**	60ore blue	80	15
440a	**117**	60ore red	55	20
441	**117**	70ore green	1·00	20
442	**117**	80ore orange	1·00	15
442a	**117**	80ore blue	70	45
442b	**117**	80ore green	55	15
443	**117**	90ore olive	3·50	20
443a	**117**	90ore blue	55	30
444	**117**	95ore purple	80	65

1962. Danish Ballet and Music Festival, 1962. As T **106** but inscr "15–31 MAJ".

445		60ore blue	25	20

118 Borkop Watermill

1962. "Dansk Fredning" (Preservation of Danish Natural Amenities and Ancient Monuments) and Centenary of Abolition of Mill Monopolies.

446	**118**	10ore brown	20	20

119 African Mother and Child

1962. Aid for Under-developed Countries.

447	**119**	30ore+10ore red	85	85

120 *Selandia*

1962. 50th Anniv of Freighter *Selandia*.

448	**120**	60ore blue	1·50	1·10

121 "Tivoli"

1962. 150th Birth Anniv of George Carstensen (founder of Tivoli Pleasure Gardens, Copenhagen).

449	**121**	35ore purple	25	20

122 Cliffs, Island of Mon

1962. "Dansk Fredning" (Preservation of Danish Natural Amenities and Ancient Monuments).

450	**122**	20ore brown	20	15

123 Wheat

1963. Freedom from Hunger.

451	**123**	35ore red	20	20

124 Rail and Sea Symbols

1963. Opening of Denmark–Germany Railway ("Bird-flight Line").

452	**124**	15ore green	25	20

125 19th-century Mail Transport

1963. Centenary of Paris Postal Conference.

453	**125**	60ore blue	35	30

126 Hands

1963. Danish Cripples Foundation Fund.

454	**126**	35ore+10ore red	85	85

127 Prof. Niels Bohr

1963. 50th Anniv of Bohr's Atomic Theory.

455	**127**	35ore red	25	15
456	**127**	60ore blue	65	30

128 Ancient Bridge, Immervad

1964. Danish Border Union Fund.

457	**128**	35ore+10ore red	60	75

129 "Going to School" (child's slate)

1964. 150th Anniv of Institution of Primary Schools.

458	**129**	35ore brown	20	15

130 Princesses Margrethe, Benedikte and Anne-Marie

1964. Danish Red Cross Fund.

459	**130**	35ore+10ore red	50	45
460	**130**	60ore+10ore blue & red	85	85

131 "Exploration of the Sea"

1964. International Council for the Exploration of the Sea Conference, Copenhagen.

461	**131**	60ore blue	35	30

132 Danish Stamp "Watermarks, Perforations and Varieties"

1964. 25th Anniv of Stamp Day.

462	**132**	35ore pink	35	20

133 Landscape, R. Karup

1964. "Dansk Fredning" (Preservation of Danish Natural Amenities and Ancient Monuments).

463	**133**	25ore brown	20	20

134 Office Equipment

1965. Centenary of 1st Commercial School.

464	**134**	15ore green	20	20

135 Morse Key, Teleprinter Tape and I.T.U. Emblem

1965. Centenary of I.T.U.

465	**135**	80ore blue	40	25

136 C. Nielsen

1965. Birth Centenary of Carl Nielsen (composer).

466	**136**	50ore red	20	20

1965. Danish Ballet and Music Festival, 1965. As T B but inscr "15-31 MAJ".

467		50ore red	20	15

137 Child in Meadow

1965. Child Welfare.

468	**137**	50ore+10ore red	60	60

138 Bogo Windmill

1965. "Dansk Fredning" (Preservation of Danish Natural Amenities and Ancient Monuments).

469	**138**	40ore brown	20	15

139 Titles of International Red Cross Organizations

1966. Danish Red Cross Fund.

470	**139**	50ore+10ore red	50	60
471	**139**	80ore+10ore bl & red	75	85

140 Heathland

1966. Centenary of Danish Heath Society.

472	**140**	25ore green	20	20

141 C. Kold

1966. 150th Birth Anniv of Christen Kold (educationist).

473	**141**	50ore red	20	15

142 Almshouses, Copenhagen

143 Trees at Bregentved

1966. "Dansk Fredning" (Preservation of Danish Natural Amenities and Ancient Monuments).

474	**142**	50ore red	20	20
475	**143**	80ore blue	35	30

144 G. Jensen

1966. Birth Cent of Georg Jensen (silversmith).

476	**144**	80ore blue	60	30

145 Fund Emblem

1966. "Refugee 66" Fund.

477	**145**	40ore+10ore brown	65	70
478	**145**	50ore+10ore red	60	65
479	**145**	80ore+10ore blue	1·10	1·10

146 Barrow in Jutland

1966. "Dansk Fredning" (Preservation of Danish Natural Amenities and Ancient Monuments).

480	**146**	1k.50 green	70	25

147 Musical Instruments

1967. Cent of Royal Danish Academy of Music.

481	**147**	50ore red	20	15

148 Cogwheels

1967. European Free Trade Assn.

482	**148**	80ore blue	75	25

149 Old City and Windmill

1967. 800th Anniv of Copenhagen.

483	**149**	25ore green	25	20
484	-	40ore brown	25	20
485	-	50ore brown	25	20
486	-	80ore blue	85	65

DESIGNS: 40ore Old bank and ship's masts; 50ore Church steeple and burgher's house; 80ore Building construction.

150 Princess Margrethe and Prince Henri de Monpezat

1967. Royal Wedding.

487	**150**	50ore red	30	20

151 H. C. Sonne

1967. 150th Anniv of Hans Sonne (founder of Danish Co-operative Movement).

488	**151**	60ore red	25	20

152 "Rose"

1967. The Salvation Army.

489	**152**	60ore+10ore red	55	55

153 Porpoise and Cross-anchor

1967. Centenary of Danish Seamen's Church in Foreign Ports.

490	**153**	90ore blue	45	35

154 Esbjerg Harbour

1968. Cent of Esbjerg Harbour Construction Act.

491	**154**	30ore green	20	15

155 Koldinghus Castle

1968. 700th Anniv of Koldinghus Castle.

492	**155**	60ore red	20	15

156 "The Children in the Round Tower" (Greenlandic legend)

1968. Greenlandic Child Welfare.

493	**156**	60ore+10ore red	60	60

157 Shipbuilding

1968. Danish Industries.

494	**157**	30ore green	20	15
495	-	50ore brown	20	15
496	-	60ore red	20	20
497	-	90ore blue	80	75

INDUSTRIES: 50ore Chemicals, 60ore Electric power, 90ore Engineering.

158 *The Sower*

1969. Bicentenary of Danish Royal Agricultural Society.

498	**158**	30ore green	20	15

159 Viking Ships (from old Swedish coin)

1969. 50th Anniv of Northern Countries' Union.

499	**159**	60ore red	70	30
500	**159**	90ore blue	1·10	1·10

160 King Frederik IX

1969. King Frederik's 70th Birthday.

501	**160**	50ore brown	25	25
502	**160**	60ore red	35	30

161 Colonnade

1969. Europa.

503	**161**	90ore blue	85	70

162 Kronborg Castle

1969. 50th Anniv of "Danes Living Abroad" Association.

504	**162**	50ore brown	20	15

163 Fall of Danish Flag

1969. 750th Anniv of "Danish Flag Falling from Heaven".

505	**163**	60ore red, blue & black	25	20

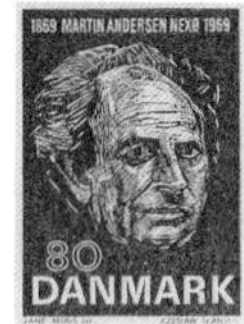
164 M. A. Nexo

1969. Birth Cent of Martin Andersen Nexo (poet).

506	**164**	80ore green	40	20

165 Niels Stensen (geologist)

1969. 300th Anniv of Stensen's "On Solid Bodies".

507	**165**	1k. sepia	40	20

166 "Abstract"

1969. "Non-figurative" stamp.

508	**166**	60ore red, rose and blue	25	20

167 Symbolic "P"

1969. Birth Cent of Valdemar Poulsen (inventor).

509	**167**	30ore green	20	15

168 Princess Margrethe, Prince Henri and Prince Frederik (baby)

1969. Danish Red Cross.

510	**168**	50ore+10ore brn & red	55	60
511	**168**	60ore+10ore brn & red	55	60

169 "Postgiro"

1970. 50th Anniv of Danish Postal Giro Service.

512	**169**	60ore and orange	20	15

170 School Safety Patrol

1970. Road Safety.

513	**170**	50ore brown	30	30

171 Child appealing for Help

1970. 25th Anniv of Save the Children Fund.

514	**171**	60ore+10ore red	55	55

172 Candle in Window

1970. 25th Anniv of Liberation.

515	**172**	50ore black, yellow & bl	45	20

173 Red Deer in Park

1970. 300th Anniv of Jaegersborg Deer Park.

516	**173**	60ore brown, red & grn	20	15

174 Ship's Figurehead (*Elephanten*)

1970. 300th Anniv of "Royal Majesty's Model Chamber" (Danish Naval Museum).

517	**174**	30ore multicoloured	20	15

175 "The Reunion"

1970. 50th Anniv of North Schleswig's Reunion with Denmark.

518	**175**	60ore violet, yellow & grn	20	15

176 Electromagnetic Apparatus

1970. 150th Anniv of Oersted's Discovery of Electromagnetism.

519	**176**	80ore green	40	20

177 Bronze-age Ship (from engraving on razor)

1970. Danish Shipping.

520	**177**	30ore purple and brown	25	15
521	-	50ore brn and purple	25	15
522	-	60ore brown and green	25	15
523	-	90ore blue and green	95	90

DESIGNS: 50ore Viking shipbuilders (Bayeux Tapestry); 60ore *Emanuel* (schooner); 90ore *A. P. Moller* (tanker).

178 Strands of Rope

1970. 25th Anniv of United Nations.

524	**178**	90ore red, green & blue	95	90

179 B. Thorvaldsen from self-portrait

1970. Birth Bicentenary of Bertel Thorvaldsen (sculptor).

525	**179**	2k. blue	65	45

180 Mathilde Fibiger (suffragette)

1971. Centenary of Danish Women's Association ("Kvindesamfund").

526	**180**	80ore green	40	25

181 Refugees

1971. Aid for Refugees.

527	**181**	50ore brown	30	20
528	**181**	60ore red	30	20

182 Danish Child

1971. National Children's Welfare Association.

529	**182**	60ore+10ore red	60	60

183 Hans Egede

1971. 250th Anniv of Hans Egede's Arrival in Greenland.

530	**183**	1k. brown	40	20

184 Swimming

1971. Sports.

531	**184**	30ore green and blue	25	20
532	-	50ore dp brown & brown	25	15
533	-	60ore yellow, blue & grey	50	20
534	-	90ore violet, green & bl	75	55

DESIGNS: 50ore Hurdling; 60ore Football; 90ore Yachting.

185 Georg Brandes

1971. Centenary of First Lectures by Georg Brandes (writer).

535	**185**	90ore blue	40	30

186 Beet Harvester

1972. Centenary of Danish Sugar Production.

536	**186**	80ore green	40	20

187 Meteorological Symbols

1972. Cent of Danish Meteorological Office.

537	**187**	1k.20 brown, blue & pur	65	60

188 King Frederik IX

1972. King Frederik IX-In Memoriam.

538	**188**	60ore red	20	15

189 *N. F. S. Grundtvig* (pencil sketch, P. Skovgaard)

1972. Death Centenary of N. F. S. Grundtvig (poet and clergyman).

539	**189**	1k. brown	50	45

190 Locomotive *Odin*, Ship and Passengers

1972. 125th Anniv of Danish State Railways.

540	**190**	70ore red	30	20

191 Rebild Hills

1972. Nature Protection.

541	**191**	1k. green, brown & blue	45	25

192 Marsh Marigold

1972. Centenary of "Vanforehjemmet" (Home for the Disabled).

542	**192**	70ore+10ore yellow & bl	75	85

193 "The Tinker" (from Holberg's satire)

1972. 250th Anniv of Theatre in Denmark and of Holberg's Comedies.

543	**193**	70ore red	30	20

194 W.H.O. Building, Copenhagen

1972. Inauguration of World Health Organization Building, Copenhagen.

544	**194**	2k. black, blue and red	75	50

195 Little Belt Bridge

1972. Danish Construction Projects.

545	**195**	40ore green	25	20
546	-	60ore brown	30	20
547	-	70ore red	30	20
548	-	90ore green	45	40

DESIGNS: 60ore Hanstholm port; 70ore Limfjord Tunnel; 90ore Knudshoved port.

196 House, Aeroskobing

1972. Danish Architecture.

549	**196**	40ore black, brown & red	25	20
550	-	60ore blue, green & brn	25	20
551	-	70ore brown, red & verm	25	20
552	-	1k.20 grn, brn & dp brn	80	75

DESIGNS—28×21 mm: 60ore Farmhouse, East Bornholm; 37×21 mm: 1k.20, Farmhouse, Hvide Sande; 21×37 mm: 70ore House, Christanshavn.

197 Johannes Jensen

1973. Birth Cent of Johannes Jensen (writer).

553	**197**	90ore green	35	15

198 Cogwheels and Guardrails

1973. Centenary of 1st Danish Factory Act.

554	**198**	50ore brown	20	15

199 P. C. Abildgaard (founder)

1973. Bicentenary of Royal Veterinary College, Christianshavn.

555	**199**	1k. blue	45	35

200 "Rhododendron impeditum"

1973. Cent of Jutland Horticultural Society.

556	**200**	60ore violet, green & brn	45	20
557	-	70ore pink, green & red	45	20

DESIGN: 70ore "Queen of Denmark" rose.

201 Nordic House, Reykjavik

1973. Nordic Countries' Postal Co-operation.

558	**201**	70ore multicoloured	60	30
559	**201**	1k. multicoloured	1·30	1·10

202 Stella Nova and Sextant

1973. 400th Anniv of Tycho Brahe's *De Novc Stella* (book on astronomy).

560	**202**	2k. blue	60	25

203 "St. Mark the Evangelist" (Book of Dalby)

1973. 300th Anniv of Royal Library.

561	**203**	1k.20 multicoloured	70	65

204 Heimaey Eruption

1973. Aid for Victims of Heimaey Eruption, Iceland.

562	**204**	70ore+20ore red and blue	65	65

205 *Devil and Scandalmongers* (Fanefjord Church)

1973. Church Frescoes. Each red, turquoise and yellow on cream.

563	70ore Type **205**	1·10	30
564	70ore *Queen Esther and King Xerxes* (Tirsted Church)	1·10	30
565	70ore *The Harvest Miracle* (Jetsmark Church)	1·10	30
566	70ore *The Crowning with Thorns* (Biersted Church)	1·10	30
567	70ore *Creation of Eve* (Fanefjord Church)	1·10	30

206 Drop of Blood and Donors

1974. Blood Donors Campaign.

568	**206**	90ore red and violet	35	20

207 Queen Margrethe

1974

569	**207**	60ore brown	35	30
570	**207**	60ore orange	35	25
571	**207**	70ore red	25	15
572	**207**	70ore brown	25	20
573	**207**	80ore green	40	20
574	**207**	80ore brown	35	20
575	**207**	90ore purple	40	15
576	**207**	90ore red	40	15
577	**207**	90ore olive	40	25
577a	**207**	90ore grey	2·00	2·00
578	**207**	100ore blue	45	25
579	**207**	100ore grey	45	25
580	**207**	100ore red	45	20
580a	**207**	100ore brown	40	15
580b	**207**	110ore orange	60	40
580c	**207**	110ore brown	45	25
581	**207**	120ore grey	65	40
581b	**207**	120ore red	35	15
582	**207**	130ore blue	1·40	1·40
582a	**207**	130ore red	40	15
582b	**207**	130ore brown	45	40
582c	**207**	140ore orange	1·50	1·70
582d	**207**	150ore blue	70	55
582e	**207**	150ore red	55	50
582f	**207**	160ore blue	70	70
582g	**207**	160ore red	50	15
582h	**207**	180ore green	50	25
582i	**207**	180ore blue	95	90
582j	**207**	200ore blue	80	55
582k	**207**	210ore grey	1·60	1·80
582l	**207**	230ore green	70	30
582m	**207**	250ore green	85	60

208 Theatre Facade

1974. Centenary of Tivoli Pantomime Theatre, Copenhagen.

583	**208**	100ore blue	40	25

209 Hverringe

1974. Provincial Series.

584	**209**	50ore multicoloured	35	30
585	-	60ore grn, dp grn & mve	50	45
586	-	70ore multicoloured	45	45
587	-	90ore multicoloured	35	15
588	-	120ore grn, red & orge	50	45

DESIGNS—HORIZ: 60ore Carl Nielsen's birthplace, Norre Lyndelse; 70ore Hans Christian Andersen's birthplace, Odense; 1k.20, Hindsholm. VERT: 90ore Hessselagergaard.

210 Orienteering

1974. World Orienteering Championships.

589	**210**	70ore brown and blue	55	50
590	-	80ore blue and brown	25	25

DESIGN: 80ore Compass.

211 *Iris spuria*

1974. Cent of Botanical Gardens, Copenhagen.

591	**211**	90ore blue, green & brn	30	15
592	-	120ore red, green and blue	55	50

DESIGN: 120ore *Dactylorhiza purpurella* (orchid).

212 Mail-carriers of 1624 and 1780

1974. 350th Anniv of Danish Post Office.

593	**212**	70ore bistre and purple	35	30
594	-	90ore green and purple	35	25

DESIGN: 90ore Johan Colding's mail balloon (1808) H.M.S. *Edgar* and H.M.S. *Dictator*.

213 Pigeon with Letter

1974. Centenary of U.P.U.

595	**213**	120ore blue	40	25

214 Stamp Essay (Arms)

1975. "Hafnia 76" Stamp Exhibition (1st issue). Sheet 67×93 mm containing T **214** and similar vert designs.

MS596	70ore grey and green; 80ore grey and green; 90ore brown and green; 100ore brown and green (sold at 5k.)	6·75	6·75

DESIGNS: 80ore King Frederik VII; 90ore King Frederik VII (different); 100ore Mercury.

See also Nos. **MS**617 and 629/**MS**630.

215 Radio Equipment of 1925

1975. 50th Anniv of Danish Broadcasting.

597	**215**	90ore pink	40	20

216 Queen Margrethe and I.W.Y. Emblem

1975. International Women's Year.

598	**216**	90ore+20ore red	80	80

217 Floral Decorated Plate

1975. Danish Porcelain.

599	**217**	50ore green	20	15
600	-	90ore red	40	15
601	-	130ore blue	85	85

DESIGNS: 90ore Floral decorated tureen; 130ore Floral decorated vase and tea-caddy.

218 Moravian Brethren Church Christiansfeld

1975. European Architectural Heritage Year.

602	**218**	70ore brown	50	45
603	-	120ore green	55	45
604	-	150ore blue	45	30

DESIGNS—HORIZ: 120ore Farmhouse, Lejre. VERT: 150ore Anna Queenstraede (street), Helsingore.

219 *Numskull Jack* (V. Pedersen)

1975. 170th Birth Anniv of Hans Christian Andersen.

605	**219**	70ore grey and brown	65	60
606	-	90ore brown and red	80	15
607	-	130ore brown and blue	1·30	1·50

DESIGNS: 90ore Hans Andersen (from photograph by G. E. Hansen); 130ore *The Marshking's Daughter* (L. Frolich).

220 Watchman's Square, Aabenraa

1975. Provincial series. South Jutland.

608	**220**	70ore multicoloured	40	30
609	-	90ore brown, red & blue	30	20
610	-	100ore multicoloured	40	25
611	-	120ore blue, black & grn	50	30

DESIGNS—VERT: 90ore, Haderslev Cathedral. HORIZ: 100ore, Mogeltonder Polder; 120ore, Estuary of Vidaaen at Hojer floodgates.

221 River Kingfisher

1975. Danish Endangered Animals.

612	**221**	50ore blue	40	30
613	-	70ore brown	40	30
614	-	90ore brown	40	15
615	-	130ore blue	1·10	95
616	-	200ore black	60	25

DESIGNS: 70ore West European hedgehog; 90ore Cats; 130ore Pied avocets; 200ore European otter.

The 90ore also commemorates the centenary of the Danish Society for the Prevention of Cruelty to Animals.

1975. "Hafnia 76" Stamp Exhibition (2nd issue). Sheet 69×93 mm containing vert designs similar to T **214** showing early Danish stamps.

MS617	50ore brown and buff; 70ore blue, brown and buff; 90ore blue, brown and buff; 130ore brown, olive and buff (sold at 5k.)	3·00	4·00

DESIGNS: 50ore 1851 4 R.B.S. stamp; 70ore 1851 2 R.B.S. stamp; 90ore 1864 2sk. stamp; 130ore 1870 8sk. stamp with inverted frame.

222 Viking Longship

1976. Bicentenary of American Revolution.

618	**222**	70ore+20ore brown	65	75
619	-	90ore+20ore red	65	75
620	-	100ore+20ore green	65	75
621	-	130ore+20ore blue	80	85

DESIGNS: 90ore Freighter *Thingvalla*; 100ore Liner *Frederik VIII*; 130ore Cadet full-rigged ship *Danmark*.

223 "Humanity"

1976. Centenary of Danish Red Cross.

622	**223**	100ore+20ore black and red	40	45
623	**223**	130ore+20ore black, red and blue	55	60

224 Old Copenhagen

1976. Provincial Series. Copenhagen.

624	**224**	60ore multicoloured	35	25
625	-	80ore multicoloured	35	25
626	-	100ore red & vermilion	35	20
627	-	130ore grn, dp brn & brn	1·30	1·20

DESIGNS—VERT: 80ore View from the Round Tower; 100ore Interior of the Central Railway Station. HORIZ: 130ore Harbour buildings.

225 Handicapped Person in Wheelchair

1976. Danish Foundation for the Disabled.
628 **225** 100ore+20ore black and red 50 45

226 Mail Coach Driver (detail from "A String of Horses outside an Inn" (O. Bache))

1976. "Hafnia 76" Stamp Exhibition.
629 **226** 130ore multicoloured 1·00 95
MS630 103×82 mm. **226** 130ore multicoloured 9·50 11·00

227 Prof. Emil Hansen

1976. Centenary of Carlsberg Foundation.
631 **227** 100ore red 35 20

228 Moulding Glass

1976. Danish Glass Industry.
632 **228** 60ore green 25 25
633 - 80ore brown 25 20
634 - 130ore blue 75 70
635 - 150ore red 40 25
DESIGNS: 80ore Removing glass from pipe; 130ore Cutting glass; 150ore Blowing glass.

229 Five Water Lilies

1977. Northern Countries Co-operation in Nature Conservation and Environment Protection.
636 **229** 100ore multicoloured 40 30
637 **229** 130ore multicoloured 1·40 1·20

230 "Give Way"

1977. Road Safety.
638 **230** 100ore brown 45 20

231 Mother and Child

1977. 25th Anniv of Danish Society for the Mentally Handicapped.
639 **231** 100ore+20ore green, blue and brown 80 75

232 Allinge

1977. Europa.
640 **232** 1k. brown 45 15
641 - 1k.30 blue 4·50 3·25
DESIGN: 1k.30, Farm near Ringsted.

233 Kongeaen

1977. Provincial Series. South Jutland.
642 **233** 60ore green and blue 1·10 95
643 - 90ore multicoloured 60 45
644 - 150ore multicoloured 60 40
645 - 200ore grn, pur & emer 60 40
DESIGNS: 90ore Skallingen; 150ore Torskind; 200ore Jelling.

234 Hammers and Horseshoes

1977. Danish Crafts.
646 **234** 80ore brown 35 20
647 - 1k. red 35 20
648 - 1k.30 blue 85 50
DESIGNS: 1k. Chisel, square and plane; 1k.30, Trowel, ceiling brush and folding rule.

235 Globe Flower

1977. Endangered Flora.
649 **235** 1k. green, yellow & brn 45 20
650 - 1k.50 green, ol & brn 1·00 95
DESIGN: 1k.50, *Cnidium dubium*.

236 Handball Player and Emblem

1978. Men's Handball World Championship.
651 **236** 1k.20 red 50 20

237 Christian IV on Horseback

1978. Centenary of National History Museum, Frederiksborg.
652 **237** 1k.20 brown 50 15
653 - 1k.80 black 65 25
DESIGN: 1k.80, North-west aspect of Frederiksborg Castle.

238 Jens Bang's House, Aalborg

1978. Europa.
654 **238** 1k.20 brown 45 20
655 - 1k.50 blue and dp blue 1·30 80
DESIGN: 1k.50, Plan and front elevation of Frederiksborg Castle, Copenhagen.

239 Kongenshus Memorial Park

1978. Provincial Series. Central Jutland.
656 **239** 70ore multicoloured 40 25
657 - 1k.20 multicoloured 50 25
658 - 1k.50 multicoloured 90 65
659 - 1k.80 blue, brn & grn 60 45
DESIGNS: 1k.20, Post office, Aarhus Old Town; 1k.50, Lignite fields, Soby; 1k.80, Church wall, Stadil Church.

240 Boats in Harbour

1978. Fishing Industry.
660 **240** 70ore green 40 30
661 - 1k. brown 45 25
662 - 1k.80 black 55 30
663 - 2k.50 brown 95 40
DESIGNS: 1k. Eel traps; 1k.80, Fishing boats on the slipway; 2k.50, Drying ground.

241 Campaign Emblem

1978. 50th Anniv of Danish Cancer Campaign.
664 **241** 120ore+20ore red 75 75

242 Common Morel

1978. Mushrooms.
665 **242** 1k. brown 75 45
666 - 1k.20 red 75 25
DESIGN: 1k.20, Satan's mushroom.

243 Early and Modern Telephones

1979. Centenary of Danish Telephone System.
667 **243** 1k.20 red 65 20

244 Child

1979. International Year of the Child.
668 **244** 1k.20+20ore red & brn 75 75

245 University Seal

1979. 500th Anniv of Copenhagen University.
669 **245** 1k.30 red 40 15
670 - 1k.60 black 55 40
DESIGN: 1k.60, Pentagram representing the five faculties.

246 Letter Mail Cariole

1979. Europa.
671 **246** 1k.30 red 90 30
672 - 1k.60 blue 2·40 85
DESIGN: 1k.60, Morse key and sounder.

247 Pendant

1979. Viking "Gripping Beast" Decorations.
673 **247** 1k.10 brown 35 25
674 - 2k. green 80 35
DESIGN: 2k. Key.

248 Mols Bjerge

1979. Provincial Series. North Jutland.
675 **248** 80ore green, ultram & brown 40 25
676 - 90ore multicoloured 1·40 1·20
677 - 200ore grn, orge & red 75 25
678 - 280ore slate, sepia & brn 90 60
DESIGNS. 90ore Orslev Kloster; 200ore Trans; 280ore Bovbjerg.

249 Silhouette of Oehlenschlager

1979. Birth Bicentenary of Adam Oehlenschlager (poet).
679 **249** 1k.30 red 50 20

250 Music, Violin and Dancers (birth cent of Jacob Gade (composer))

1979. Anniversaries.
680 **250** 1k.10 brown 40 30
681 - 1k.60 blue 60 45
DESIGN: 1k.60, Dancer at bar (death centenary of August Bournonville (ballet master)).

251 Royal Mail Guards' Office, Copenhagen (drawing, Peter Klaestrup)

1980. Bicentenary of National Postal Service.
682 **251** 1k.30 red 50 20

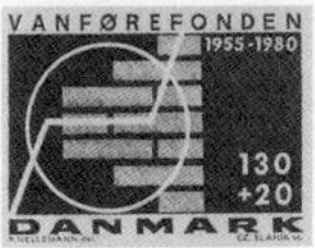

252 Stylized Wheelchair

1980. 25th Anniv of Foundation for the Disabled.
683 **252** 130ore+20ore red 75 55

253 Karen Blixen (writer)

1980. Europa.
684 **253** 1k.30 red 50 20

685	-	1k.60 blue	1·50	75

DESIGN: 1k.60, August Krogh (physiologist).

254 Symbols of Employment, Health and Education

1980. U.N. Decade for Women World Conference.

686	**254**	1k.60 blue	75	50

255 Lindholme Hoje

1980. Provincial Series. Jutland North of Limfjorden. Multicoloured.

687	80ore Type **255**	45	35
688	110ore Skagen lighthouse (vert)	60	35
689	200ore Borglum	65	25
690	280ore Fishing boats at Vorupor	1·50	1·20

256 Silver Pitcher, c. 1641

1980. Nordic Countries Postal Co-operation.

691	**256**	1k.30 black and red	50	20
692	-	1k.80 blue & dp blue	1·10	85

DESIGN: 1k.80, Bishop's bowl.

257 Earliest Danish Coin, Hedeby (c. 800)

1980. Coins from the Royal Collection.

693	**257**	1k.30 red and brown	55	25
694	-	1k.40 olive and green	1·00	85
695	-	1k.80 blue and grey	90	80

DESIGNS: 1k.40, Silver coin of Valdemar the Great and Bishop Absalon (1152–82); 1k.80, Christian VII gold current ducat (1781).

258 Lace Pattern

1980. Lace Patterns. Various designs showing lace.

696	**258**	1k.10 brown	55	40
697	-	1k.30 red	50	25
698	-	2k. green	55	25

259 Children Playing in Yard

1981. National Children's Welfare Association.

699	**259**	1k.60+20ore red	80	70

260 Original Houses, 1631

1981. 350th Anniv of Nyboder (Naval Barracks), Copenhagen.

700	**260**	1k.30 red and yellow	70	55
701	-	1k.60 red and yellow	55	20

DESIGN: 1k.60, 18th-century terraced houses.

261 Tilting at a Barrel (Shrovetide custom)

1981. Europa.

702	**261**	1k.60 red	60	20
703	-	2k. blue	1·40	60

DESIGN: 2k. Midsummer bonfire.

262 Soro

1981. Provincial Series. Zealand and Surrounding Islands.

704	**262**	100ore blue and brown	40	25
705	-	150ore black and green	60	40
706	-	160ore brown and green	60	25
707	-	200ore multicoloured	80	45
708	-	230ore blue and brown	90	45

DESIGNS: 150ore N. F. S. Grundtvig's childhood home, Udby; 160ore Kaj Munk's childhood home, Opager; 200ore Gronsund; 230ore Bornholm.

263 Rigensgade District, Copenhagen

1981. European Urban Renaissance Year.

709	**263**	1k.60 red	50	20

264 Decaying Tree

1981. International Year for Disabled Persons.

710	**264**	2k.+20ore blue	1·10	1·10

265 Ellehammer II at Lindholm, 1906

1981. History of Aviation.

711	**265**	1k. green and black	55	40
712	-	1k.30 brown & dp brn	80	55
713	-	1k.60 vermilion & red	55	20
714	-	2k.30 blue & dp blue	80	60

DESIGNS: 1k.30, Captain P.A. Botved's Fokker C.VE biplane R-1 (Copenhagen–Tokyo, 1926); 1k.60, Hojriis Hillig's Bellanca J-300 Special NR-797 *Liberty* (U.S.A.–Denmark, 1931); 2k.30. Douglas DC-7C *Seven Seas* (first Polar flight, 1957).

266 Queen Margrethe II

1982

715	**266**	1k.60 red	50	20
716	**266**	1k.60 green	2·75	2·50
717	**266**	1k.80 brown	60	40
718	**266**	2k. red	65	15
719	**266**	2k.20 green	2·20	1·90
720	**266**	2k.30 violet	85	85
721	**266**	2k.50 red	75	20
722	**266**	2k.70 blue	90	40
723	**266**	2k.70 red	75	20
724	**266**	2k.80 red	90	20
725	**266**	3k. violet	75	20
726	**266**	3k. red	75	20
727	**266**	3k.20 violet	85	50
727a	**266**	3k.20 red	1·00	15
728	**266**	3k.30 black	1·30	45
729	**266**	3k.40 green	2·20	2·40
730	**266**	3k.50 blue	1·00	25
730a	**266**	3k.50 purple	1·10	55
730b	**266**	3k.50 red	1·00	20
731	**266**	3k.70 blue	1·00	40
732	**266**	3k.75 green	1·50	1·40
733	**266**	3k.80 blue	1·10	50
734	**266**	3k.80 purple	1·60	1·70
735	**266**	4k.10 blue	1·60	25
736	**266**	4k.20 violet	2·20	1·60
737	**266**	4k.40 blue	1·50	40
738	**266**	4k.50 purple	1·90	1·60
739	**266**	4k.75 blue	1·80	25

267 Revenue Cutter "Argus"

1982. 350th Anniv Customs Service.

740	**267**	1k.60 red	50	15

268 Skater

1982. World Figure Skating Championships, Copenhagen.

741	**268**	2k. blue	60	35

269 Villein (Abolition of adscription, 1788)

1982. Europa.

742	**269**	2k. brown	1·00	30
743	-	2k.70 blue	2·10	65

DESIGN: 2k.70, Procession of women (Enfranchisement of women, 1915).

270 Distorted Plant

1982. 25th Anniv of Danish Multiple Sclerosis Society.

744	**270**	2k.+40ore red	1·80	1·50

271 Dairy Farm at Hjedding and Butter Churn

1982. Centenary of Co-operative Dairy Farming.

745	**271**	1k.80 brown	70	45

272 Hand holding Quill Pen

1982. 400th Anniv of Record Office.

746	**272**	2k.70 green	1·00	35

273 Blicher (after J. V. Gertner)

1982. Birth Bicent of Steen Steensen Blicher (poet).

747	**273**	2k. red	75	15

274 Odense Printing Press, 1482

1982. 500th Anniv of Printing in Denmark.

748	**274**	1k.80 brown	80	55

275 Petersen and the Number Men

1982. Birth Centenary of Robert Storm Petersen (cartoonist).

749	**275**	1k.50 red and blue	55	30
750	-	2k. green and red	80	30

DESIGN—HORIZ: 2k. Peter and Ping with dog.

276 Library Seal

1982. 500th Anniv University Library.

751	**276**	2k.70 brown and black	95	40

277 "Interglobal Communications"

1983. World Communications Year.

752	**277**	2k. orange, red & blue	85	25

278 Nurse tending Patient

1983. Red Cross.

753	**278**	2k.+40ore blue & red	1·40	1·60

279 Clown and Girl with Balloon

1983. 400th Anniv of Dyrehavsbakken Amusement Park.

754	**279**	2k. multicoloured	75	15

280 Lene Koppen

1983. World Badminton Championships.

755	**280**	2k.70 blue	1·00	35

281 Burin and Engraving of lore Numeral Stamp

1983. 50th Anniv of Danish Recess-printed Stamps.

756	**281**	2k.50 red	80	15

282 Egeskov Castle

1983. Nordic Countries Postal Co-operation. "Visit the North".

757	**282**	2k.50 dp brown & brn	75	20
758	-	3k.50 dp blue & blue	1·10	65

DESIGN: 3k.50, Troldkirken long barrow, North Jutland.

283 Kildeskovshallen Recreation Centre, Copenhagen

1983. Europa.

759	**283**	2k.50 red and brown	1·20	15
760	-	3k.50 dp blue & blue	1·50	65

DESIGN: 3k.50, Sallingsund Bridge.

284 Weights and Measures

1983. 300th Anniv of Weights and Measures Ordinance.

761	**284**	2k.50 red	80	15

285 Title Page of Law

1983. 300th Anniv of King Christian V's Danish Law (code of laws for Norway).

762	**285**	5k. dp brown & brown	1·80	60

286 Crashed Car and Hand with Eye (Police)

1983. Life-saving Services.

763	**286**	1k. brown	45	25
764	-	2k.50 red	80	20
765	-	3k.50 blue	1·30	65

DESIGNS: 2k.50 Ladder, stretcher and fire-hose (ambulance and fire services); 3k.50 Lifebelt and lifeboat (sea-rescue services).

287 Family Group

1983. The Elderly in Society.

766	**287**	2k. green	65	45
767	-	2k.50 red	85	15

DESIGN: 2k.50 Elderly people in train.

288 Grundtvig (after Constantin Hansen)

1983. Birth Bicentenary of Nicolai Frederik Severin Grundtvig (writer).

768	**288**	2k.50 brown	80	30

289 Perspective Painting

1983. Birth Bicentenary of Christoffer Wilhelm Eckersberg (painter).

769	**289**	2k.50 red	75	25

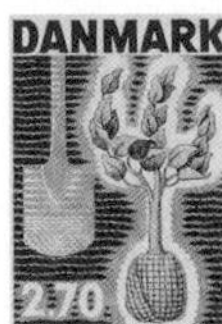
290 Spade and Sapling

1984. Plant a Tree Campaign.

770	**290**	2k.70 yellow, red and green	1·00	25

291 Billiards

1984. World Billiards Championships.

771	**291**	3k.70 green	1·20	40

292 Athletes

1984. Olympic Games, Los Angeles.

772	**292**	2k.70+40ore mult	1·90	2·00

293 Compass Rose

1984. Bicentenary of Hydrographic Department (2k.30) and 300th Anniv of Pilotage Service (2k.70).

773	**293**	2k.30 green	95	65
774	-	2k.70 red	80	25

DESIGN: 2k.70, Pilot boat.

294 Parliament Emblem

1984. Second Direct Elections to European Parliament.

775	**294**	2k.70 yellow and blue	1·00	30

295 Girl Guides

1984. Scout Movement.

776	**295**	2k.70 multicoloured	95	25

296 Bridge

1984. Europa. 25th Anniv of European Post and Telecommunications Conference.

777	**296**	2k.70 red	1·50	25
778	**296**	3k.70 blue	2·40	1·30

297 Anchor (memorial to Danish Sailors)

1984. 40th Anniv of Normandy Invasion.

779	**297**	2k.70 purple	1·30	30

298 Prince Henrik

1984. 50th Birthday of Prince Henrik.

780	**298**	2k.70 brown	1·00	25

299 Old Danish Inn

1984

781	**299**	3k. multicoloured	1·10	80

300 Shoal of Fish (research)

1984. Danish Fisheries and Shipping.

782	**300**	2k.30 blue and green	1·30	1·40
783	-	2k.70 blue and red	90	30
784	-	3k.30 blue and violet	1·30	1·40
785	-	3k.70 blue & ultramarine	1·20	1·20

DESIGNS: 2k.70, Ships (sea transport); 3k.30, *Bettina*"(deep sea fishing boat); 3k.70, Deck of trawler *Jonna Tornby*.

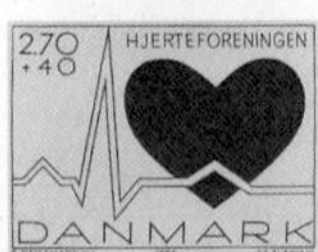
301 Heart and Cardiograph

1984. Heart Foundation.

786	**301**	2k.70+40ore red	1·90	1·60

302 Bird with Letter

1984

787	**302**	1k. multicoloured	50	15

303 "Holberg meeting Officer and Dandy" (Wilhelm Marstrand)

1984. 300th Birth Anniv of Ludvig Holberg (historian and playwright).

788	**303**	2k.70 black, stone & red	1·00	15

304 Woman and Sabbath Candles

1984. 300th Anniv of Jewish Community.

789	**304**	3k.70 multicoloured	1·20	75

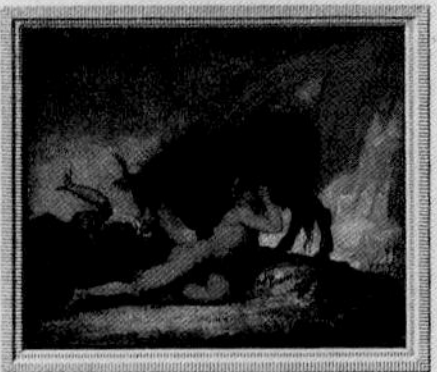
305 *Ymer sucking Milk from the Cow Odhumble* (Nicolai Abildgaard)

1984. Paintings. Multicoloured.

790	5k. *Carnival in Rome* (Christoffer Wilhelm Eckersberg) (horiz)	2·40	1·90
791	10k. Type **305**	4·00	3·50

306 Gothersgade Reformed Church, Copenhagen

1985. 300th Anniv of French and German Reformed Church in Denmark.

792	**306**	2k.80 red	1·00	15

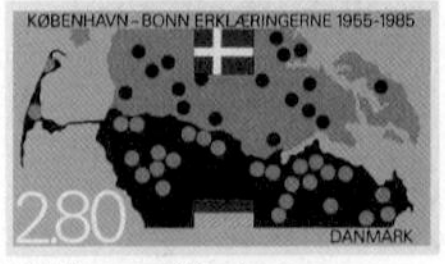
307 Flags and Border

1985. 30th Anniv of Copenhagen–Bonn Declarations.

793	**307**	2k.80 multicoloured	1·30	40

308 Flag, Girl and Boy

1985. International Youth Year.

794	**308**	3k.80 multicoloured	1·10	80

309 Statue on Postmen

1985. "Hafnia 87" International Stamp Exhibition, Copenhagen (1st issue). Sheet 70×95 mm containing T **309** and similar vert designs, each black, ochre and red.

MS795	200ore Type **309**; 250ore 1711 mandate on disinfection of letters; 280ore 1775 decree granting postal monopoly to Danish Post Office; 380ore 1851 title page of *Law on Postal Mail* (sold at 15k.)	4·75	4·75

See also Nos. **MS**817, **MS**836 and 851/**MS**852.

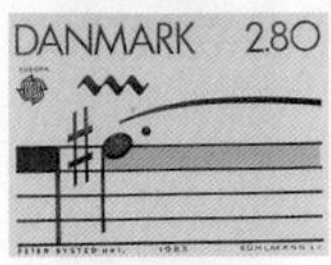
310 Music Score

1985. Europa. Music Year.

796	**310**	2k.80 yell, red & verm	1·60	40
797	-	3k.80 black, bl & grn	2·50	1·30

DESIGN: 3k.80, Music score (different).

311 Flames and Houses

1985. 40th Anniv of Liberation.

798	**311**	2k.80+50ore mult	1·80	1·60

The surtax was for the benefit of Resistance veterans.

312 Queen Ingrid and *Chrysanthemum frutescen* "Sofieri"

1985. 50th Anniv of Queen Ingrid's Arrival in Denmark.
799 **312** 2k.80 multicoloured 1·00 25

313 Faro Bridges

1985. Inauguration of Faro Bridges.
800 **313** 2k.80 multicoloured 1·00 25

314 St. Canute and Lund Cathedral

1985. 900th Anniv of St. Canute's Deed of Gift to Lund.
801 **314** 2k.80 black and red 85 25
802 - 3k. black and red 1·80 1·30
DESIGN: 3k. St. Canute and Helsingborg.

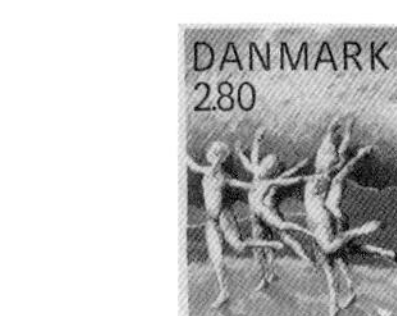

315 Gymnastics

1985. Sports. Multicoloured.
803 2k.80 Type **315** 1·10 15
804 3k.80 Canoeing 1·40 65
805 6k. Cycling 2·00 95

316 Woman Cyclist

1985. United Nations Women's Decade.
806 **316** 3k.80 multicoloured 1·20 95

317 Kronborg Castle

1985. 400th Anniv of Kronborg Castle, Elsinore.
807 **317** 2k.80 multicoloured 1·00 25

318 Dove and U.N. Emblem

1985. 40th Anniv of U.N.O.
808 **318** 3k.80 multicoloured 1·20 80

319 Niels and Margrethe Bohr

1985. Birth Centenary of Niels Bohr (nuclear physicist).
809 **319** 2k.80 multicoloured 1·20 1·20

320 Tapestry (detail) by Caroline Ebbesen

1985. 25th Anniv of National Society for Welfare of the Mentally Ill.
810 **320** 2k.80+40ore mult 1·60 1·20

321 "D" in Sign Language

1985. 50th Anniv of Danish Association of the Deaf.
811 **321** 2k.80 brown & black 1·10 30

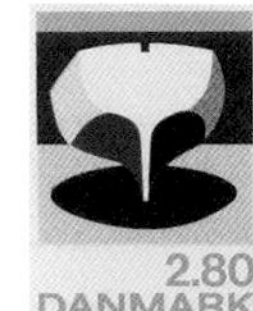

322 Stern of Boat

1985
812 **322** 2k.80 multicoloured 1·00 30

323 "Head"

1985
813 **323** 3k.80 multicoloured 2·50 2·00

324 Leaves and Barbed Wire

1986. 25th Anniv of Amnesty International.
814 **324** 2k.80 multicoloured 1·00 15

325 Girl with Bird

1986
815 **325** 2k.80 multicoloured 1·20 95

326 Reichhardt as Papageno in *The Magic Flute*

1986. First Death Anniv of Poul Reichhardt (actor).
816 **326** 2k.80+50ore mult 1·50 1·50

327 Holstein Carriage, 1840

1986. "Hafnia 87" International Stamp Exhibition, Copenhagen (2nd issue). Sheet 70×94 mm containing T **327** and similar vert designs. Multicoloured.
MS817 100ore Type **327** 250ore Ice boat, 1880; 280ore Mail van, 1908; 380ore Friedrichshafen FF-49 seaplane, 1919 (sold at 15k.) 7·00 7·00

328 Hands reading Braille

1986. 75th Anniv of Danish Society for the Blind.
818 **328** 2k.80+50ore red, brown and black 1·50 1·50

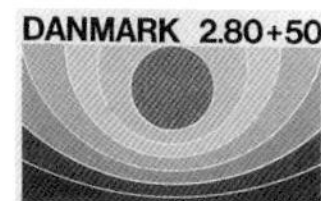

329 Bands of Colour

1986. 50th Anniv of Danish Arthritis Association.
819 **329** 2k.80+50ore mult 1·50 1·50

330 Changing the Guard at Barracks

1986. Bicentenary of Royal Danish Life Guards Barracks, Rosenborg.
820 **330** 2k.80 multicoloured 1·00 25

331 Academy and Arms

1986. 400th Anniv of Soro Academy.
821 **331** 2k.80 multicoloured 1·00 25

332 Hands reaching out

1986. International Peace Year.
822 **332** 3k.80 multicoloured 1·20 80

333 Prince Frederik

1986. 18th Birthday of Crown Prince Frederik.
823 **333** 2k.80 black and red 1·30 30

334 Station

1986. Inaug of Hoje Tastrup Railway Station.
824 **334** 2k.80 black, bl & red 1·00 25

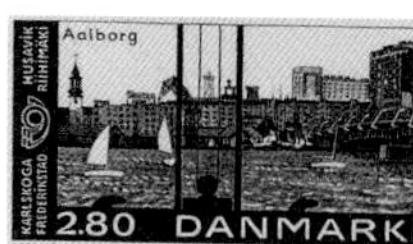

335 Aalborg

1986. Nordic Countries Postal Co-operation. Twinned Towns.
825 **335** 2k.80 black 1·10 25
826 - 3k.80 blue and red 1·30 50
DESIGN: 3k.80, Thisted.

336 Common Raven

1986. Birds. Multicoloured.
827 2k.80 Type **336** 1·60 55
828 2k.80 Common starling (*Sturnus vulgaris*) 1·60 55
829 2k.80 Mute swan (*Cygnus olor*) 1·60 55
830 2k.80 Northern lapwing (*Vanellus vanellus*) 1·60 55
831 2k.80 Eurasian skylark (*Alauda arvensis*) 1·60 55

337 Post Box, Wires and Telephone

1986. 19th International Postal Telegraph and Telephone Congress, Copenhagen.
832 **337** 2k.80 multicoloured 1·00 25

338 Sports Pictograms

1986. 125th Anniv of Danish Rifle, Gymnastics and Sports Clubs.
833 **338** 2k.80 multicoloured 1·00 25

339 Roadsweeper

1986. Europa.
834 **339** 2k.80 red 1·50 30
835 - 3k.80 blue 2·10 75
DESIGN: 3k.80, Refuse truck.

340 Stagecoach, 1840

1986. "Hafnia 87" International Stamp Exhibition, Copenhagen (3rd issue). Sheet 70×94 mm containing T **340** and similar vert design. Multicoloured.
MS836 100ore Type **340**; 250ore Postmaster, 1840; 280ore Postman, 1851; 380ore Rural Postman, 1893 (sold at 15k.) 7·00 7·00

341 Man fleeing

1986. Aid for Refugees.
837 **341** 2k.80 blue, brown & blk 1·00 25

342 Cupid

1986. Bicentenary of First Performance of *The Whims of Cupid and the Ballet Master* by V. Galeotti and J. Lolle.
838 **342** 3k.80 multicoloured 1·20 55

343 Lutheran Communion Service in Thorslunde Church

1986. 450th Anniv of Reformation.
839 **343** 6k.50 multicoloured 2·30 95

344 Graph of Danish Economic Growth and Unemployment Rate

1986. 25th Anniv of Organization of Economic Co-operation and Development.
840 **344** 3k.80 multicoloured 1·70 1·40

345 Abstract

1987
841 **345** 2k.80 multicoloured 1·00 15

346 Price Label through Magnifying Glass

1987. 40th Anniv of Danish Consumer Council.
842 **346** 2k.80 black and red 1·00 15

347 Fresco

1987. Ribe Cathedral. Multicoloured.
843 3k. Type **347** 1·00 45
844 3k.80 Stained glass window (detail) 1·40 95
845 6k.50 Mosaic (detail) 2·40 1·60

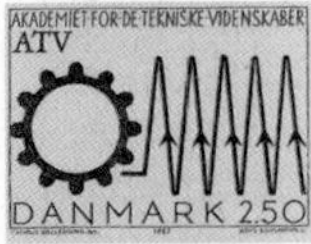

348 Cog and Oscillating Waves

1987. 50th Anniv of Danish Academy of Technical Sciences.
846 **348** 2k.50 black and red 1·30 1·00

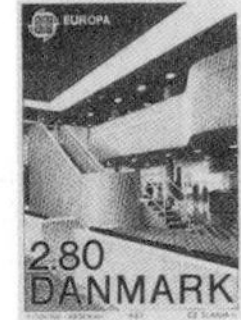

349 Gentofte Central Library

1987. Europa. Architecture.
847 **349** 2k.80 red 1·60 30
848 - 3k.80 blue 2·40 1·00
DESIGN—HORIZ: 3k.80, Hoje Tastrup Senior School.

350 Ball and Ribbons

1987. Eight Gymnaestrada (World Gymnastics Show), Herning.
849 **350** 2k.80 multicoloured 1·00 15

351 Pigs

1987. Centenary of First Co-operative Bacon Factory, Horsens.
850 **351** 3k.80 multicoloured 1·20 80

352 1912 5k. Stamp, Steam Locomotive and Mail Wagon

1987. "Hafnia 87" International Stamp Exhibition, Copenhagen.
851 **352** 280ore multicoloured 1·30 95
MS852 70×95 mm. No. 851 (sold at 45k.) 22·00 22·00

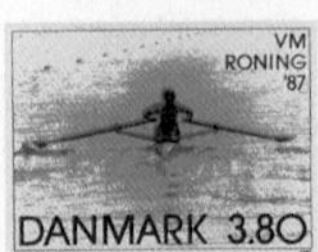

353 Single Scull

1987. World Rowing Championships, Bagsvaerd Lake.
853 **353** 3k.80 indigo and blue 1·20 70

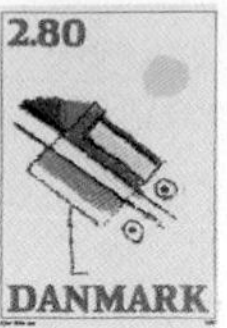

354 Abstract

1987
854 **354** 2k.80 multicoloured 1·00 15

355 Waves

1987. 25th Anniv of Danish Epileptics Association.
855 **355** 2k.80+50ore blue, red and green 1·80 1·40

356 Rask

1987. Birth Bicentenary of Rasmus Kristjan Rask (philologist).
856 **356** 2k.80 red and brown 1·00 15

357 Association Badge

1987. 125th Anniv of Clerical Association for Home Mission in Denmark.
857 **357** 3k. brown 1·00 20

358 Lions supporting Monogram

1988. 400th Anniv of Accession of King Christian IV.
858 **358** 3k. gold and blue 1·00 15
859 - 4k.10 multicoloured 1·30 45
DESIGN: 4k.10, Portrait of Christian IV by P. Isaacsz.

359 Worm and Artefacts

1988. 400th Birth Anniv of Ole Worm (antiquarian).
860 **359** 7k.10 brown 2·10 1·60

360 St. Canute's Church

1988. Millenary of Odense.
861 **360** 3k. brown, black & green 1·00 15

361 African Mother and Child

1988. Danish Church Aid.
862 **361** 3k.+50ore mult 1·80 1·50

362 Sirens, Workers and Emblem

1988. 50th Anniv of Civil Defence Administration.
863 **362** 2k.70 blue and orange 85 80

363 Blood Circulation of Heart

1988. 40th Anniv of W.H.O.
864 **363** 4k.10 red, blue and black 1·30 85

364 Postwoman on Bicycle

1988. Europa. Transport and Communications. Multicoloured.
865 3k. Type **364** 1·60 35
866 4k.10 Mobile telephone 3·00 95

365 *King Christian VII riding past Liberty Monument* (C. W. Eckersberg)

1988. Bicentenary of Abolition of Villeinage.
867 **365** 3k.20 multicoloured 1·10 80

366 *"Men of Industry* (detail, P. S. Kroyer)

1988. 150th Anniv of Federation of Danish Industries.
868 **366** 3k. multicoloured 1·00 35

367 Speedway Riders

1988. World Speedway Championships.
869 **367** 4k.10 multicoloured 1·30 55

368 Glass Mosaic (Niels Winkel)

1988. Centenary of Danish Metalworkers' Union.
870 **368** 3k. multicoloured 1·00 25

369 College

1988. Bicent of Tonder Teacher Training College.
871 **369** 3k. brown 1·00 25

370 "Tribute to Leon Degand" (Robert Jacobsen)

1988. Franco-Danish Cultural Co-operation.
872 **370** 4k.10 red and black 2·50 2·40

371 Emblem

1988. 5th Anniv of National Council for the Unmarried Mother and Her Child.

873	**371**	3k.+50ore red	1·80	1·50

372 Lumby Windmill

1988. Mills.

874	**372**	3k. black, red & orange	1·00	15
875	-	7k.10 black, ultramarine and blue	2·20	1·70

DESIGN: 7k.10, Veistrup water mill.

373 *Bathing Boys 1902* (Peter Hansen)

1988. Paintings. Multicoloured.

876		4k.10 Type **373**	2·75	2·40
877		10k. *Hill at Overkoerby. Winter 1917* (Fritz Syberg)	5·25	4·75

374 *The Little Mermaid* (statue, Edvard Eriksen), Copenhagen

1989. Centenary of Danish Tourist Association.

878	**374**	3k.20 green	1·20	15

375 Army Members in Public House

1989. 102nd Anniv of Salvation Army in Denmark.

879	**375**	3k.20+50ore mult	2·10	1·60

376 Footballer

1989. Centenary of Danish Football Association.

880	**376**	3k.20 red, blk & lt red	1·10	15

377 Emblem

1989. 40th Anniv of N.A.T.O.

881	**377**	4k.40 bl, cobalt & gold	1·50	80

378 *Valby Woman*

1989. Nordic Countries' Postal Co-operation. Traditional Costumes. Engravings by Christoffer Wilhelm Eckersberg. Multicoloured.

882	3k.20 Type **378**	1·00	15
883	4k.40 *Pork Butcher*	1·60	1·00

379 "Parliament Flag

1989. 3rd Direct Elections to European Parliament.

884	**379**	3k. blue and yellow	1·20	95

380 Lego Bricks

1989. Europa. Children's Toys. Multicoloured.

885	3k.20 Type **380**	1·60	15
886	4k.40 Wooden guardsmen by Kay Bojesen	2·40	95

381 Tractor, 1917

1989. Centenary of Danish Agricultural Museum.

887	**381**	3k.20 red	1·10	15

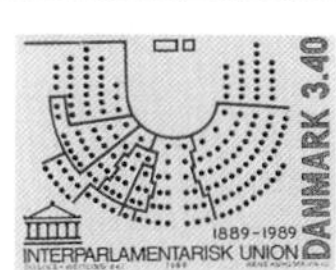

382 Diagram of Folketing (Parliament) Chamber

1989. Centenary of Interparliamentary Union.

888	**382**	3k.40 red and black	2·30	2·00

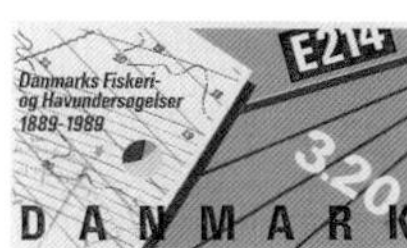

383 Chart and Boat Identity Number

1989. Centenary of Danish Fishery and Marine Research Institute.

889	**383**	3k.20 multicoloured	1·20	25

384 *Ingemann* (after J. V. Gertner)

1989. Birth Bicentenary of Bernhard Severin Ingemann (poet).

890	**384**	7k.70 green	2·20	95

385 Scene from *They Caught the Ferry* (50th anniv of Danish Government Film Office)

1989. Danish Film Industry.

891	**385**	3k. blue, black & orge	1·10	75
892	-	3k.20 pink, blk & orge	1·00	35
893	-	4k.40 brown, blk & orge	1·30	55

DESIGNS: 3k.20, Scene from *The Golden Smile* (birth cent of Bodil Ipsen, actress); 4k.40, Carl Th. Dreyer (director, birth cent).

386 Stamps

1989. 50th Stamp Day.

894	**386**	3k.20 salmon, orge & brn	1·10	25

387 *Part of Northern Citadel Bridge* (Christen Kobke)

1989. Paintings. Multicoloured.

895	4k.40 Type **387**	2·10	1·60
896	10k. *A Little Girl, Elise Kobke, with Cup* (Constantin Hansen)	4·25	3·50

388 Silver Coffee Pot (Axel Johannes Kroyer, 1726)

1990. Centenary of Museum of Decorative Art, Copenhagen.

897	**388**	3k.50 black and blue	1·10	20

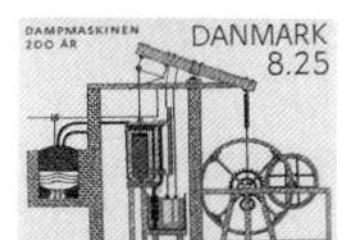

389 Andrew Mitchell's Steam Engine

1990. Bicent of Denmark's First Steam Engine.

898	**389**	8k.25 brown	2·50	1·50

390 Queen Margrethe II

1990

910	**390**	3k.50 red	1·10	15
911	**390**	3k.75 green	2·75	2·40
912	**390**	3k.75 red	1·10	25
913	**390**	4k. brown	1·10	55
914	**390**	4k.50 violet	1·30	90
915	**390**	4k.75 blue	1·30	40
916	**390**	4k.75 violet	1·40	85
917	**390**	5k. blue	1·40	40
918	**390**	5k.25 black	1·60	80
919	**390**	5k.50 green	1·80	1·70

391 Royal Monogram over Door of Haderslev Post Office

1990. Europa. Post Office Buildings.

930	**391**	3k.50 yellow, red & blk	2·40	25
931	-	4k.75 multicoloured	3·25	60

DESIGN: 4k.75, Odense Post Office.

392 Main Guardhouse, Rigging Crane and Ships (after C. O. Willars)

1990. 300th Anniv of Nyholm.

932	**392**	4k.75 black	1·50	55

393 Covered Ice Dish

1990. Bicentenary of Flora Danica Banquet Service. Multicoloured.

933	3k.50 Type **393**	1·50	1·20
934	3k.50 Sauce boat	1·50	1·20
935	3k.50 Lidded ice pot	1·50	1·20
936	3k.50 Serving dish	1·50	1·20

394 Marsh Mallow

1990. Endangered Flowers. Multicoloured.

937	3k.25 Type **394**	1·10	95
938	3k.50 Red helleborine	1·90	25
939	3k.75 Purple orchis	1·40	1·00
940	4k.75 Lady's slipper	1·70	65

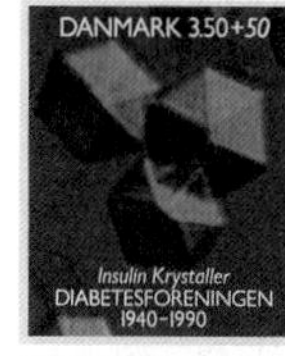

395 Insulin Crystals

1990. 50th Anniv of Danish Diabetes Association.

941	**395**	3k.50+50ore mult	2·50	2·10

396 Gjellerup Church

1990. Jutland Churches. Each brown.

942	3k.50 Type **396**	1·10	20
943	4k.75 Veng Church	1·30	55
944	8k.25 Bredsten Church (vert)	2·50	1·20

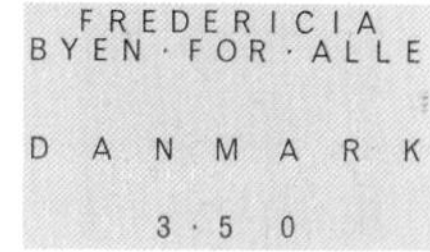

397 Slogan and Braille

1990. Fredericia: "Town for Everybody" (access for the handicapped project).

945	**397**	3k.50 red and black	1·10	45

398 *Tordenskiold and Karlsten's Commandant* (Otto Bache)

1990. 300th Birth Anniv of Admiral Tordenskiold (Peter Wessel).

946	**398**	3k.50 multicoloured	1·20	20

399 Bicycle (Bicycle stealing)

1990. Campaigns.

947	**399**	3k.25 multicoloured	1·20	80
948	-	3k.50 black, bl & mve	1·10	20

DESIGN: 3k.50, Glass and car (Drunken driving).

400 IC3 Diesel Passenger Train, 1990

1991. Railway Locomotives.

949	**400**	3k.25 blue, red & green	1·30	95
950	-	3k.50 black and red	1·10	20
951	-	3k.75 brown & dp brn	1·50	95
952	-	4k.75 black and red	1·30	80

DESIGNS: 3k.50, Class A steam locomotive, 1882; 3k.75, Class MY diesel-electric locomotive, 1954; 4k.75, Class P steam locomotive, 1907.

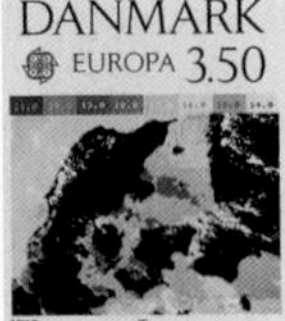

401 Satellite Picture of Denmark's Water Temperatures

1991. Europa. Europe in Space. Mult.

953	3k.50 Type **401**	2·50	30
954	4k.75 Denmark's land temperatures	3·50	80

402 First Page of 1280s Manuscript

1991. 750th Anniv of Jutland Law.

955	**402**	8k.25 multicoloured	2·75	1·70

403 Fano

1991. Nordic Countries' Postal Co-operation. Tourism. Multicoloured.

956	3k.50 Type **403**	1·30	20
957	4k.75 Christianso	1·60	65

404 Child using Emergency Helpline

1991. 15th Anniv of Living Conditions of Children (child welfare organization).

958	**404**	3k.50+50ore blue	1·70	1·70

405 Stoneware Vessels (Christian Poulsen)

1991. Danish Design. Multicoloured.

959	3k.25 Type **405**	1·10	80
960	3k.50 Chair, 1949 (Hans Wegner) (vert)	1·10	25
961	4k.75 Silver cutlery, 1938 (Kay Bojesen) (vert)	1·50	80
962	8k.25 "PH5" lamp, 1958 (Poul Henningsen)	2·75	2·40

406 Man cleaning up after Dog

1991. "Keep Denmark Clean".

963	**406**	3k.50 red	1·10	25
964	-	4k.75 blue	1·30	80

DESIGN: 4k.75, Woman putting litter into bin.

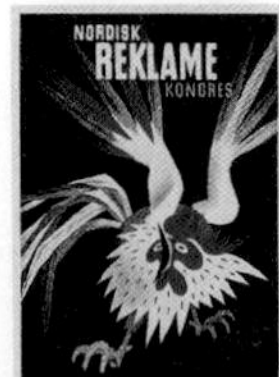

407 Nordic Advertising Congress 1947 (Arne Ungermann)

1991. Posters. Multicoloured.

965	3k.50 Type **407**	1·10	20
966	4k.50 Poster Exhibition, Copenhagen Zoo, 1907 (Valdemar Andersen)	2·00	1·70
967	4k.75 Douglas DC-3 of D.D.L. (Danish Airlines, 1945) (Ib Andersen)	1·50	95
968	12k. Casino's *The Sinner*, 1925 (Sven Brasch)	4·00	2·75

408 *Lady at Her Toilet* (Harald Giersing)

1991. Paintings. Multicoloured.

969	4k.75 Type **408**	2·30	2·20
970	14k. *Road through Wood* (Edvard Weie)	5·50	5·25

409 Skarpsalling Earthenware Bowl

1992. Re-opening of National Museum, Copenhagen. Exhibits from Prehistoric Denmark Collection.

971	**409**	3k.50 brown and lilac	1·10	25
972	-	4k.50 green and blue	2·00	1·40
973	-	4k.75 black & brown	1·50	80
974	-	8k.25 purple & green	2·75	2·00

DESIGNS: 4k.50, Grevensvaenge bronze figure of dancer; 4k.75, Bottom plate of Gundestrup Cauldron; 8k.25, Hindsgavl flint knife.

410 Aspects of Engineering

1992. Centenary of Danish Society of Chemical, Civil, Electrical and Mechanical Engineers.

975	**410**	3k.50 red	1·10	30

411 Queen Margaret I (detail, Vastra Sallerup Church fresco)

1992. "Nordia 94" International Stamp Exhibition, Arhus. Sheet 70×94 mm containing T **411** and similar vert design, each brown, slate and red.

MS976	3k.50, Type **411**; 4k.75 Alabaster bust of Queen Margaret I (attr. Johannes Junge) (sold at 12k.)	5·75	5·75

412 Potato Plant

1992. Europa. 500th Anniv of Discovery of America by Columbus.

977	**412**	3k.50 green & brown	1·30	30
978	-	4k.75 green & yellow	4·50	1·30

DESIGN: 4k.75, Head of maize.

413 Royal Couple in 1992 and in Official Wedding Photograph

1992. Silver Wedding of Queen Margrethe and Prince Henrik.

979	**413**	3k.75 multicoloured	1·50	95

414 Hare, Eurasian Sky Lark and Cars

1992. Environmental Protection. Multicoloured.

980	3k.75 Type **414**	1·10	20
981	5k. Atlantic herrings and sea pollution	1·50	60
982	8k.75 Felled trees and saplings (vert)	2·50	1·60

415 Celebrating Crowd

1992. Denmark, European Football Champion.

983	**415**	3k.75 multicoloured	1·90	30

416 Danish Pavilion

1992. "Expo '92" World's Fair, Seville.

984	**416**	3k.75 blue	1·10	25

417 "Word"

1992. 50th Anniv of Danish Dyslexia Association.

985	**417**	3k.75+50ore multicoloured	2·20	2·20

418 *A Hug*

1992. Danish Cartoon Characters.

986	**418**	3k.50 purple, red & gold	1·60	70
987	-	3k.75 violet and red	1·20	25
988	-	4k.75 black and red	2·00	1·50
989	-	5k. blue and red	1·50	50

DESIGNS: 3k.75, *Love Letter*; 4k.75, *Domestic Triangle*; 5k. *The Poet and his Little Wife.*

419 Abstract

1992. European Single Market.

990	**419**	3k.75 blue and yellow	1·20	35

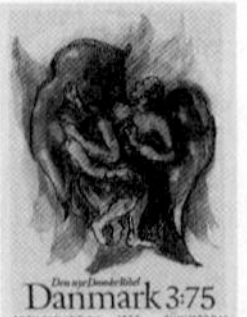

420 *Jacob's Fight with the Angel* (bible illustration by Bodil Kaalund)

1992. Publication of New Danish Bible.

991	**420**	3k.75 multicoloured	1·10	20

421 *Landscape from Vejby, 1843* (Johan Thomas Lundbye)

1992. Paintings. Multicoloured.

992	5k. Type **421**	1·90	1·90
993	10k. *Motif from Halleby Brook, 1847* (Peter Christian Skovgaard)	3·75	3·75

422 Funen Guldgubber

1993. Danish Treasure Trove. Guldgubber (anthropomorphic gold foil figures). Mult.

994	3k.75 Type **422**	1·10	20
995	5k. Bornholm guldgubber (vert)	1·50	55

423 Small Tortoiseshell

1993. Butterflies. Multicoloured.

996	3k.75 Type **423**	1·20	20
997	5k. Large blue	1·60	60
998	8k.75 Marsh fritillary	3·25	2·40
999	12k. Red admiral	3·50	2·75

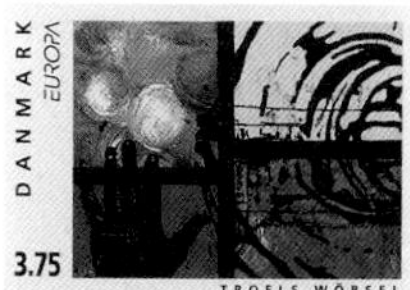

424 Untitled Painting (Troels Worsel)

1993. Europa. Contemporary Art. Multicoloured.

1000	3k.75 Type **424**	1·20	65
1001	5k. "The 7 Corners of the Earth" (Stig Brogger) (vert)	1·90	90

425 *Pierrot* (Thor Bogelund, 1947)

1993. Nordic Countries' Postal Co-operation. Tourism. Publicity posters for Tivoli Gardens, Copenhagen. Multicoloured.

1002	3k.75 Type **425**	1·10	30
1003	5k. Child holding balloons (Wilhelm Freddie, 1987) (vert)	1·50	60

426 *Danmark*

1993. Training Ships. Multicoloured.

1004	3k.75 Type **426**	1·20	25
1005	4k.75 *Jens Krogh* (25×30 mm)	2·30	2·20
1006	5k. *Georg Stage*	1·80	80
1007	9k.50 *Marilyn Anne* (36×26 mm)	4·00	3·50

427 Map

1993. Inauguration of Denmark–Russia Submarine Cable and 500th Anniv of Friendship Treaty.

1008	**427**	5k. green	1·80	45

428 Prow of Viking Ship

1993. Children's Stamp Design Competition.

1009	**428**	3k.75 multicoloured	1·10	20

429 Emblem

1993. 75th Anniv of Social Work of Young Men's Christian Association.

1010	**429**	3k.75+50ore green, red and black	1·50	1·30

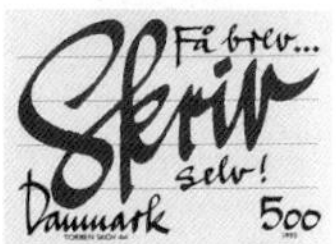

430 "If you want a Letter... Write one Yourself"

1993. Letter-writing Campaign.

1011	**430**	5k. ultram, bl & blk	1·60	75

431 Silver Brooch and Chain, North Falster

1993. Traditional Jewellery. Multicoloured.

1012	3k.50 Type **431**	1·30	80
1013	3k.75 Gilt-silver brooch with owner's monogram, Amager	1·30	30
1014	5k. Silver buttons and brooches, Laeso	1·70	45
1015	8k.75 Silver buttons, Romo	3·25	2·30

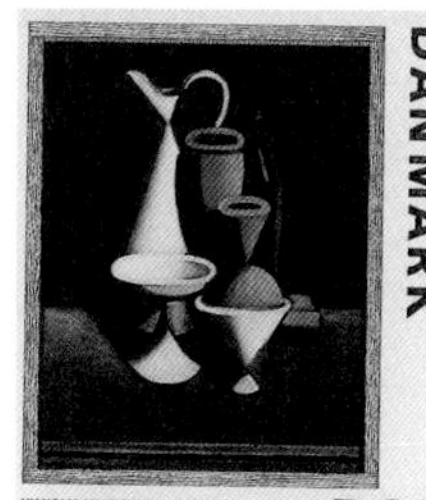

432 *Assemblage* (Vilhelm Lundstrom)

1993. Paintings. Multicoloured.

1016	5k. Type **432**	2·20	2·10
1017	15k. *Composition* (Franciska Clausen)	5·25	5·00

433 Duck

1994. Save Water and Energy Campaign.

1018	**433**	3k.75 multicoloured	1·10	20
1019	-	5k. green, red & black	1·40	50

DESIGN: 5k. Spade (in Danish "spar" = save) and "CO2".

434 Marselisborg Castle, Aarhus

1994. Royal Residences.

1020	**434**	3k.50 dp brn, grn & brn	1·10	75
1021	-	3k.75 multicoloured	1·10	20
1022	-	5k. grn, dp brn & brn	1·80	65
1023	-	8k.75 dp brn, grn & brn	3·00	2·30

DESIGNS: 3k.75, Amalienborg Castle, Copenhagen; 5k. Fredensborg Castle, North Zealand; 8k.75, Graasten Castle, South Jutland.

435 *Danmark* and Wegener's Weather Balloon, Danmarkshavn

1994. Europa. Discoveries. "Danmark" Expedition to North-East Greenland, 1906–08.

1024	**435**	3k.75 purple	1·30	30
1025	-	5k. black	1·80	55

DESIGN: 5k. Johan Peter Koch and theodolite.

436 Copenhagen Tram No. 2, 1911

1994. Trams. Multicoloured.

1026	3k.75 Type **436**	1·00	30
1027	4k.75 Aarhus tram, 1928	2·00	1·60
1028	5k. Odense tram, 1911 (vert)	1·80	95
1029	12k. Copenhagen horse tram *Honen*, 1880 (37×21 mm)	4·75	4·00

437 Prince Henrik

1994. Danish Red Cross Fund. 60th Birthday of Prince Henrik, the Prince Consort.

1030	**437**	3k.75+50ore mult	1·50	1·50

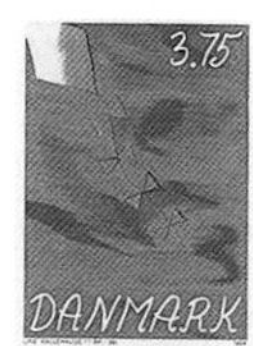

438 Kite

1994. Children's Stamp Design Competition.

1031	**438**	3k.75 multicoloured	1·20	45

439 Emblem

1994. 75th Anniv of I.L.O.

1032	**439**	5k. multicoloured	1·50	50

440 House Sparrows

1994. Protected Animals. Multicoloured.

1033	3k.75 Type **440**	1·00	30
1034	4k.75 Badger	2·30	2·10
1035	5k. Red squirrel (vert)	1·60	65
1036	9k.50 Pair of black grouse	4·25	3·75
1037	12k. Black grass snake (36×26 mm)	4·25	3·75

441 Teacher

1994. 150th Anniv of Folk High Schools.

1038	**441**	3k.75 multicoloured	1·20	30

442 Study for *Italian Woman with Sleeping Child* (Wilhelm Marstrand)

1994. Paintings. Multicoloured.

1039	5k. Type **442**	1·70	1·70
1040	15k. *Interior from Amaliegade with the Artist's Brothers* Wilhelm Bendz)	4·75	4·50

443 The Red Building (architect's drawing, Hack Kampmann)

1995. 800th Anniv of Aarhus Cathedral School.

1041	**443**	3k.75 multicoloured	1·20	30

444 Anniversary Emblem

1995. 50th Anniv of United Nations Organization. U.N. World Summit for Social Development, Copenhagen.

1042	**444**	5k. multicoloured	1·50	45

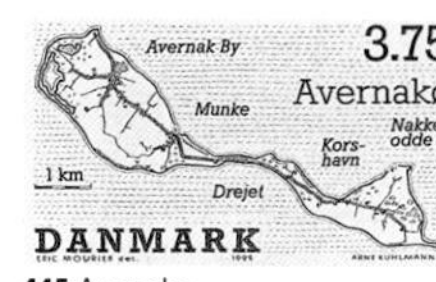

445 Avernako

1995. Danish Islands. Each brown, blue and red.

1043	3k.75 Type **445**	1·10	20
1044	4k.75 Fejo	1·90	1·80
1045	5k. Fur	1·50	65
1046	9k.50 Endelave	3·00	3·00

446 Field-Marshal Montgomery and Copenhagen Town Hall

1995. Europa. Peace and Freedom. Multicoloured.

1047	3k.75 Type **446**	1·10	30
1048	5k. White coaches (repatriation of Danes from German concentration camps) (horiz)	1·50	65
1049	8k.75 Dropping of supplies from Lockheed C-130 Hercules (horiz)	2·50	1·90
1050	12k. Jews escaping by boat to Sweden (horiz)	4·50	4·00

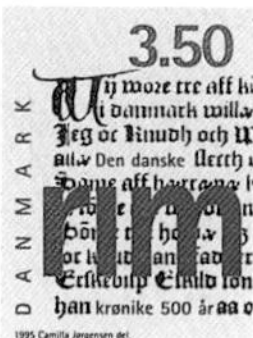

447 Detail of Page

1995. 500th Anniv of *The Rhymed Chronicle* by Friar Niels (first book printed in Danish).

1051	**447**	3k.50 multicoloured	1·10	65

448 Stage

1995. Nordic Countries' Postal Co-operation. Music Festivals. Multicoloured.

1052	3k.75 Type **448** (25th anniv of Roskilde Festival)	1·10	30
1053	5k. Violinist (21st anniv of Tonder Festival) (20×38 mm)	1·70	80

449 Broken Feather

1995. 50th Anniv of National Society of Polio and Accident Victims.
1054 **449** 3k.75+50ore red 1·80 1·70

450 *Midsummer Eve* (Jens Sondergaard)

1995. Paintings. Multicoloured.
1055 10k. Type **450** 3·50 3·50
1056 15k. *Landscape at Gudhjem* (Niels Lergaard) 5·75 5·50

451 Sextant

1995. 450th Birth Anniv of Tycho Brahe (astronomer). Multicoloured.
1057 3k.75 Uraniborg (Palace Observatory) 1·10 25
1058 5k.50 Type **451** 1·80 1·50

452 TEKNO Model Vehicles

1995. Danish Toys. Multicoloured.
1059 3k.75 Type **452** 1·10 20
1060 5k. Edna (celluloid doll), Kirstine (china doll) and Holstebro teddy bear 1·40 60
1061 8k.75 Toy bin-plate locomotives and rolling stock 2·30 2·00
1062 12k. Glud & Marstrand horse-drawn fire engine and carriage 3·50 3·75

453 The Round Tower

1996. Copenhagen, European Cultural Capital. Multicoloured.
1063 3k.75 Type **453** 1·10 30
1064 5k. Christiansborg 1·50 65
1065 8k.75 Dome of Marble Church as hot-air balloon 2·50 1·90
1066 12k. *The Little Mermaid* on stage 3·50 3·25

454 Disabled Basketball Player

1996. Sport. Multicoloured.
1067 3k.75 Type **454** 1·10 20
1068 4k.75 Swimming 1·50 1·30
1069 5k. Yachting 1·50 65
1070 9k.50 Cycling 3·00 2·40

455 Businessmen

1996. Cent of Danish Employers' Confederation.
1071 **455** 3k.75 multicoloured 1·10 50

456 Asta Nielsen (actress)

1996. Europa. Famous Women.
1072 - 3k.75 brown & dp brn 1·20 50
1073 **456** 5k. grey and blue 1·70 80
DESIGN: 3k.75, Karin Blixen (writer).

457 Roskilde Fjord Boat

1996. Wooden Sailing Boats.
1074 **457** 3k.50 brn, bl & red 1·20 95
1075 - 3k.75 lilac, grn & red 1·10 30
1076 - 12k.25 blk, brn & red 4·50 4·50
DESIGNS—As T **457**: 12k.25, South Funen Archipelago smack; 20×38 mm: 3k.75, Limfjorden skiff.

458 Fornaes

1996. Lighthouses. Multicoloured.
1077 3k.75 Type **458** 1·20 30
1078 5k. Blavandshuk 1·50 60
1079 5k.25 Bovbjerg 1·60 1·40
1080 8k.75 Mon 2·50 1·90

459 Ribbons forming Hearts within Star

1996. AIDS Foundation.
1081 **459** 3k.75+50ore red & blk 1·80 1·60

460 Vase

1996. 150th Birth Anniv of Thorvald Bindesboll (ceramic artist). Multicoloured.
1082 3k.75 Type **460** 1·10 30
1083 4k. Portfolio cover 1·30 95

461 *At Lunch* (Peder Kroyer)

1996. Paintings. Multicoloured.
1084 10k. Type **461** 3·25 2·50
1085 15k. *Girl with Sunflowers* (Michael Ancher) 4·00 3·75

462 Queen Margrethe waving to Children

1997. Silver Jubilee of Queen Margrethe. Multicoloured.
1086 3k.50 Queen Margrethe and Prince Henrik 1·00 75
1087 3k.75 Queen Margrethe and Crown Prince Frederik 1·20 30
1088 4k. Queen Margrethe at desk 1·10 1·00
1089 5k.25 Type **462** 1·60 1·30

463 Queen Margrethe

1997
1092 **463** 3k.75 red 1·10 45
1093 **463** 4k. green 1·10 65
1094 **463** 4k. red 1·10 25
1095 **463** 4k.25 brown 1·40 1·30
1096 **463** 4k.50 blue 1·40 95
1097 **463** 4k.75 brown 1·60 1·50
1098 **463** 5k. violet 1·40 45
1099 **463** 5k.25 blue 1·50 55
1100 **463** 5k.50 red 1·40 1·20
1101 **463** 5k.75 blue 1·50 1·00
1104 **463** 6k.75 green 1·60 1·60

464 Karlstrup Post Mill, Zealand

1997. Centenary of Open Air Museum, Lyngby. Construction Drawings by B. Ehrhardt.
1111 **464** 3k.50 brown & purple 1·10 85
1112 - 3k.75 lilac and green 1·20 30
1113 - 5k. green and lilac 1·50 65
1114 - 8k.75 green & brown 2·50 1·60
DESIGNS: 3k.75, Ellested water mill, Funen; 5k. Fjellerup Manor Barn, Djursland; 8k.75, Toftum farm, Romo.

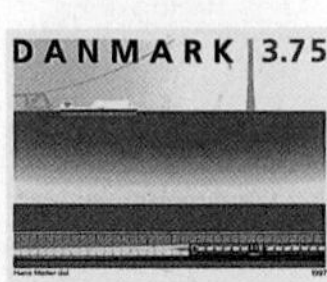

465 The East Tunnel

1997. Inauguration of Railway Section of the Great Belt Link. Multicoloured.
1115 3k.75 Type **465** 1·00 30
1116 4k.75 The West Bridge 1·40 1·30

466 Sneezing

1997. Asthma Allergy Association.
1117 **466** 3k.75+50ore mult 1·90 1·80

467 Electric Trains under New Carlsberg Bridge

1997. 150th Anniv of Copenhagen–Roskilde Railway. Multicoloured.
1118 3k.75 Type **467** 1·10 30
1119 8k.75 Steam train under original Carlsberg bridge (after H. Holm) 2·50 1·60

468 King Erik and Queen Margrete I

1997. 600th Anniv of Kalmar Union (of Denmark, Norway and Sweden). Multicoloured.
1120 4k. Type **468** 1·30 1·10
1121 4k. The Three Graces 1·30 1·10
Nos. 1120/1 were issued, *se-tenant*, forming a composite design of a painting by an unknown artist.

469 Post Office Cars on Great Belt Ferry

1997. Closure of Travelling Post Offices.
1122 **469** 5k. multicoloured 1·40 60

470 *The Tinder-box*

1997. Europa. Tales and Legends by Hans Christian Andersen.
1123 **470** 3k.75 dp brn & brn 1·10 30
1124 - 5k.25 red, dp grn & grn 1·50 1·20
DESIGN: 5k.25, *Thumbelina*.

471 *Dust dancing in the Sun* (Vilhelm Hammershoi)

1997. Paintings. Multicoloured.
1125 9k.75 Type **471** 3·25 2·75
1126 13k. *Woman Mountaineer* (Jens Willumsen) 4·25 3·75

472 Faaborg Chair (Kaare Klint)

1997. Danish Design. Multicoloured.

1127	3k.75 Type **472**	1·10	25
1128	4k. Margrethe bowls (Sigvard Bernadotte and Acton Bjorn)	1·10	1·00
1129	5k. The Ant chairs (Arne Jacobsen) (horiz)	1·70	40
1130	12k.25 Silver bowl (Georg Jensen)	3·75	3·50

473 Workers

1998. Centenary of Danish Confederation of Trade Unions. Multicoloured.

1131	3k.50 Type **473** (General Workers' Union in Denmark)	1·10	75
1132	3k.75 Crowd at meeting (Danish Confederation of Trade Unions)	1·20	30
1133	4k.75 Nurse (Danish Nurses' Organization)	1·50	1·40
1134	5k. Woman using telephone (Union of Commercial and Clerical Employees in Denmark)	1·60	65

474 Roskilde Cathedral and Viking Longship

1998. Millenary of Roskilde.

1135	**474**	3k.75 multicoloured	1·10	40

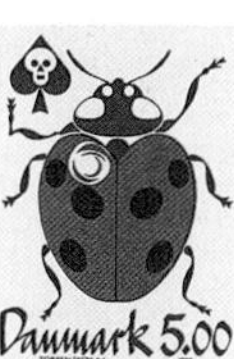

475 Seven-spotted Ladybird

1998. Environmental Issues. Gardening Without Chemicals.

1136	**475**	5k. red and black	1·30	50

476 Postman, 1922

1998. Post and Tele Museum, Copenhagen.

1137	3k.75 Type **476**	1·10	30
1138	4k.50 Morse operator, 1910	1·30	1·00
1139	5k.50 Telephonist, 1910	1·80	1·30
1140	8k.75 Postman, 1998	3·00	2·00

477 The West Bridge

1998. Inauguration of Road Section of the Great Belt Link. Each blue, black and red.

1141	5k. Type **477**	1·30	75
1142	5k. The East Bridge	1·30	75

478 Harbour Master

1998. Nordic Countries' Postal Co-operation. Shipping. Multicoloured.

1143	6k.50 Type **478**	2·10	1·50
1144	6k.50 Sextant and radar image of Copenhagen harbour	2·10	1·50
MS1145	106×75 mm. Nos. 1143/4	6·25	6·00

Nos. 1143/4 were issued together, *se-tenant*, forming a composite design.

479 Horse (Agriculture Show)

1998. Europa. National Festivals. Multicoloured.

1146	3k.75 Type **479**	1·10	50
1147	4k.50 Aarhus Festival Week	1·40	1·20

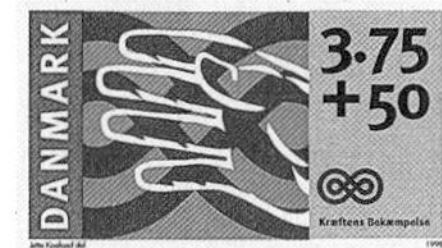

480 Reaching Hand

1998. Anti-cancer Campaign.

1148	**480**	3k.75+50ore red, orange and black	1·60	1·50

481 *Danish Autumn* (Per Kirkeby)

1998. Philatelic Creations. Multicoloured.

1149	3k.75 Type **481**	1·20	1·30
1150	5k. *Alpha* (Mogens Andersen) (vert)	1·80	1·50
1151	8k.75 *Imagery* (Ejler Bille) (vert)	3·00	2·20
1152	19k. *Celestial Horse* (Carl-Henning Pedersen)	6·00	4·75

482 Ammonite (from "Museum Wormianum" by Ole Worm)

1998. Fossils. Designs reproducing engravings from geological works. Each black and red on cream.

1153	3k.75 Type **482**	1·10	50
1154	4k.50 Shark's teeth (from *De Solido* by Niels Stensen)	1·60	1·30
1155	5k.50 Sea urchin (from *Stevens Klint* by Soren Abildgaard)	1·70	1·50
1156	15k. Pleurotomariida (from *Den Danske Atlas*"by Erich Pontoppidan)	4·00	3·75
MS1157	114×142 mm. Nos. 1153/6	8·25	8·00

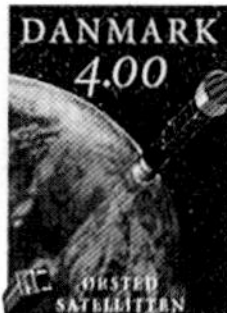

483 Satellite and Earth

1999. Launch of "Orsted" Satellite (Danish research satellite).

1158	**483**	4k. multicoloured	1·10	25

484 Beech

1999. Deciduous Trees. Multicoloured.

1159	4k. Type **484**	1·20	35
1160	5k. Ash (vert)	1·60	1·10
1161	5k.25 Small-leaved lime (vert)	1·70	65
1162	9k.25 Pendunculate oak	2·75	1·80

485 Home Guard

1999. 50th Anniv of Home Guard.

1163	**485**	3k.75 multicoloured	1·20	1·10

486 Northern Lapwing and Eggs

1999. Harbingers of Spring. Multicoloured.

1164	4k. Type **486**	1·10	25
1165	5k.25 Greylag goose with chicks	1·50	55
MS1166	99×82 mm. Nos. 1164/5	3·75	3·75

487 Emblem and Lockheed Martin F-16 Fighting Falcon

1999. 50th Anniv of North Atlantic Treaty Organization.

1167	**487**	4k.25 multicoloured	1·30	1·10

488 Vejlerne

1999. Europa. Parks and Gardens. Multicoloured.

1168	4k.50 Type **488**	1·10	1·00
1169	5k.50 Langli Island	1·80	1·40

489 Anniversary Emblem

1999. 50th Anniv of Council of Europe.

1170	**489**	9k.75 blue	2·50	2·00

490 "g" and Paragraph Sign

1999. 150th Anniv of Danish Constitution.

1171	**490**	4k. red and black	1·10	35

491 Kjeld Petersen and Dirch Passer

1999. 150th Anniv of Danish Revue.

1172	**491**	4k. red	1·10	40
1173	-	4k.50 black	1·60	1·40
1174	-	5k.25 blue	1·70	1·10
1175	-	6k.75 mauve	1·50	2·00

DESIGNS: 4k.50, Osvald Helmuth; 5k.25, Preben Kaas and Jorgen Ryg; 6k.75, Liva Weel.

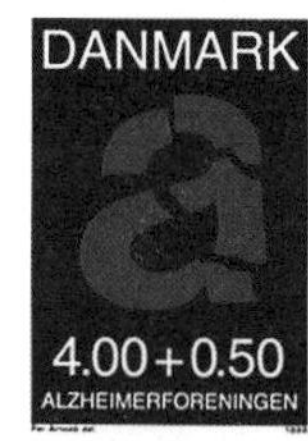

492 Emblem

1999. Alzheimer's Disease Association.

1176	**492**	4k.+50ore. red and blue	1·20	1·10

493 The "Black Diamond"

1999. Inauguration of Royal Library Extension, Copenhagen.

1177	**493**	8k.75 black	3·25	2·75

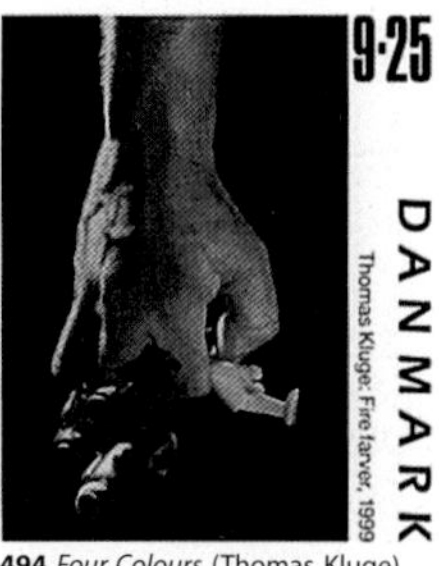

494 *Four Colours* (Thomas Kluge)

1999. Paintings. Multicoloured.

1178	9k.25 Type **494**	2·20	1·90
1179	16k. *Boy* (Lise Malinovsky)	4·25	3·75

495 Barn Swallows

1999. Migratory Birds. Multicoloured.

1180	4k. Type **495**	1·20	35
1181	5k.25 Greylag geese with goslings	1·60	70
1182	5k.50 Eiders	1·80	1·20
1183	12k.25 Arctic tern feeding chick	3·25	2·50
MS1184	Two sheets, each 116×72 mm. (a) Nos. 1180/1. (b) Nos. 1182/3	8·00	7·75

496 Hearts

1999. New Millennium. Multicoloured.

1185		4k. Type **496**	1·10	40
1186		4k. Horizontal wavy lines	1·10	40

497 Johan Henrik Deuntzer (Prime Minister) on Front Page of *Aftenposten* (newspaper)

2000. The Twentieth Century (1st series).

1187	**497**	4k. black and cream	1·10	40
1188	-	4k.50 multicoloured	1·30	1·30
1189	-	5k.25 multicoloured	1·40	1·10
1190	-	5k.75 multicoloured	1·80	1·20

DESIGNS—4k. Type **497** (Venstre (workers') party victory in election, 1901); 4k.50, Caricature of Frederik Borgbjerg (party member, Alfred Schmidt) (first Social Democrat Lord Mayor in Denmark, 1903); 5k.25, Asta Nielson and Poul Reumert (actors) in scene from *The Abyss* (film), 1910; 5k.75, Telephone advertising poster, 1914.

See also Nos. 1207/10, 1212/15 and 1221/4.

498 Queen Margrethe II (Pia Schutzmann)

2000. 60th Birthday of Queen Margrethe II.

1191	**498**	4k. black and red	1·00	45
1192	**498**	5k.25 black and blue	1·40	55
MS1193 63×60 mm. Nos. 1191/2			2·75	2·75

499 Queen Margrethe II

2000

1194	**499**	4k. red	1·10	20
1195	**499**	4k.25 blue	1·70	1·60
1195a	**499**	4k.25 red	1·10	20
1196a	**499**	4k.50 red	7·25	20
1196b	**499**	4k.75 brown	1·10	20
1196d	**499**	4k.75 rosine	1·40	1·10
1197	**499**	5k. green	1·40	1·00
1198	**499**	5k.25 blue	1·40	45
1199	**499**	5k.50 violet	1·70	55
1199a	**499**	5k.50 red	2·25	1·50
1200	**499**	5k.75 green	1·70	85
1201	**499**	6k. brown	1·70	1·10
1201a	**499**	6k.25 green	1·70	1·60
1201b	**499**	6k.50 green	2·30	1·60
1201c	**499**	6k.50 blue	2·50	1·60
1202	**499**	6k.75 red	2·00	1·50
1203	**499**	7k. purple	2·00	1·60
1203a	**499**	7k.25 brown	2·00	1·90
1203b	**499**	7k.50 ultramarine	2·00	1·90
1203c	**499**	7k.75 agate	3·25	2·10
1203d	**499**	8k. black	1·80	1·70
1203e	**499**	8k.25 blue	2·50	2·00
1204	**499**	8k.50 blue	2·75	2·10
1204a	**499**	8k.50 blue	4·00	2·60
1204b	**499**	9k. blue	4·75	3·00

500 Map of Oresund Region

2000. Inauguration of Oresund Link (Denmark–Sweden road and rail system).

1205	**500**	4k.50 blue, white & blk	1·40	1·10
1206	-	4k.50 blue, green & blk	1·40	1·10

DESIGN: No. 1206, Oresund Bridge.

501 Suffragette on Front Page of *Politiken* (newspaper)

2000. The Twentieth Century (2nd series).

1207	**501**	4k. red, blk & cream	1·10	30
1208	-	5k. multicoloured	1·40	1·10
1209	-	5k.50 multicoloured	1·60	1·10
1210	-	6k.75 multicoloured	2·00	1·60

DESIGNS—4k. Type **501** (women's suffrage, 1915); 5k. Caricature of Thorvald Stauning (Prime Minister 1924–26 and 1929–42) (Herluf Jensenius) (The Kanslergade Agreement (economic and social reforms)), 1933; 5k.50, Poster for *The Wheel of Fortune* (film), 1927; 6k.75, Front page of *Radio Weekly Review* (magazine), 1925.

502 "Building Europe"

2000. Europa.

1211	**502**	9k.75 multicoloured	2·75	2·20

503 Front Page of *Kristeligt Dagblad* (newspaper), 5 May 1945

2000. The Twentieth Century (3rd series).

1212	**503**	4k. black and cream	1·10	20
1213	-	5k.75 multicoloured	1·70	85
1214	-	6k.75 multicoloured	2·00	1·60
1215	-	12k.25 multicoloured	3·00	2·50

DESIGNS—4k. Type **503** (Liberation of Denmark); 5k.75, Caricature of Princess Margrethe (Herlif Jenserius) (adoption of new constitution, 1953); 6k.75, Ib Schonberg and Hvid Moller (actors) in a scene from *Cafe Paradise* (film), 1950; 12k.25, Front cover of brochure for Danish Arena televisions, 1957.

504 Linked Hands

2000. Cerebral Palsy Association.

1216	**504**	4k.+50ore blue and red	1·40	1·30

505 Lockheed C-130 Hercules Transport Plane

2000. 50th Anniv of Royal Danish Air Force.

1217	**505**	9k.75 black and red	2·50	2·10
MS1218 116×60 mm. No. 1217			3·00	3·00

506 *Pegasus* (Kurt Trampedach)

2000. Paintings. Multicoloured.

1219		4k. Type **506**	1·40	1·10
1220		5k.25 *Untitled* (Nina Sten-Knudsen)	1·70	1·30

507 Front Page of *Berlingske Tidende* (newspaper), 3 October 1972

2000. The Twentieth Century (4th series).

1221	**507**	4k. red, blk & cream	1·10	55
1222	-	4k.50 multicoloured	1·40	1·10
1223	-	5k.25 blk, red & cream	1·70	1·10
1224	-	5k.50 multicoloured	2·00	1·30

DESIGNS: 4k. Type **507** (referendum on entry to European Economic Community); 4k.50, Caricature from *Blaeksprutten* (magazine), 1969 (The Youth Revolt); 5k.25, Poster for *The Olsen Gang* (film, 1968); 5k.50, Web page (development of the internet).

508 Kite

2001. 40th Anniv of Amnesty International.

1225	**508**	4k.+50 ore blk & red	1·40	1·10

509 Palm House

2001. 400th Anniv of Copenhagen University Botanical Gardens. Multicoloured.

1226		4k. Type **509**	1·10	55
1227		6k. Lake (28×21 mm)	1·40	85
1228		12k.25 Giant lily-pad (28×21 mm)	2·75	3·00

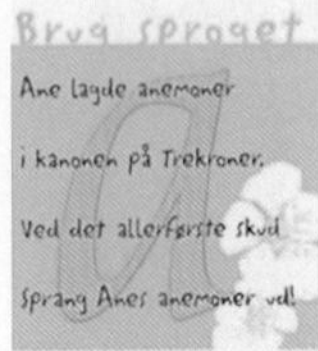

510 "a", Text and Flowers

2001. Reading. Danish Children's Book *ABC* (first reader) by Halfdan Rasmussen. Multicoloured.

1229		4k. Type **510**	1·10	55
1230		7k. "Z" and text	1·70	1·60

511 Martinus William Ferslew (designer and engraver)

2001. 150th Anniv of First Danish Stamp. Each black, red and brown.

1231		4k. Type **511**	1·10	55
1232		5k.50 Andreas Thiele (printer)	1·40	1·10
1233		6k. Frantz Christopher von Jessen (Copenhagen postmaster)	1·70	1·30
1234		10k.25 Magrius Otto Sophus (Postmaster-General)	2·40	2·30

512 Hands catching Water

2001. Europa. Water Resources. Multicoloured.

1235		4k.50 Type **512**	1·40	1·10
1236		9k.75 Woman in shower	2·75	2·75

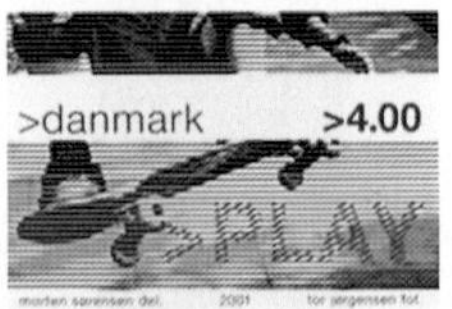

513 Skateboarder

2001. Youth Culture. Multicoloured.

1237		4k. Type **513**	1·10	35
1238		5k.50 Couple kissing	1·50	1·30
1239		6k. Mixing records	1·60	1·40
1240		10k.25 Pierced tongue	2·75	2·50
MS1241 121×70 mm. Nos. 1237/40			7·75	7·50

514 *Missus* (Jorn Larsen)

2001. Paintings.

1242	**514**	18k. black and red	4·50	3·75
1243	-	22k. multicoloured	5·75	5·50

DESIGN: 22k. *Postbillede* (Henning Damgaard-Sorensen).

515 Queen Margrethe II with 1984 Prince Henrik and 1994 Marselisborg Castle Stamps

2001. "HAFNIA '01" International Stamp Exhibition, Copenhagen. Multicoloured.

1244		4k. Type **515**	1·10	65
1245		4k.50 King Frederik IX with 1985 Queen Ingrid and 1994 Graasten Castle stamps	1·20	85
1246		5k.50 King Christian X with 1994 Amalienborg Castle and 1939 Queen Alexandrine stamps	1·50	1·40
1247		7k. King Christian IX with 1994 Fredensborg Castle and 1907 King Frederick VIII stamps	2·00	1·90
MS1248 90×100 mm. Nos. 1244/7			6·75	6·50

516 *Bukken-Bruse*

2001. Ferries.

1249	**516**	3k.75 black, green and emerald	1·00	65
1250	-	4k. black, brown and green	1·10	75
1251	-	4k.25 black, green and blue	1·20	85
1252	-	6k. grey, black and red	1·70	1·60

DESIGNS: 4k. *Ouro*; 4k.25, *Hjarno*; 6k. *Barsofargen*.

517 *Rasmus Klump* (Vilhelm Hansen)

2002. Danish Cartoons. Multicoloured.

1253 4k. Type **517** 1·10 30
1254 5k.50 Valhalla (Peter Madsen) 1·20 1·30
1255 6k.50 Jungo and Rita (Flemming Quist Moller) 1·50 1·50
1256 10k.50 Cirkleen (Hanne and Jannik Hastrup) 2·30 2·30
MS1257 142×80 mm. Nos. 1253/6 7·50 7·25

518 Back View

2002. Nordic Countries' Postal Co-operation. Modern Art. Showing "The Girls in the Airport" (sculpture, Hanne Varming). Each black, bronze on cream.

1258 4k. Type **518** 1·10 55
1259 5k. Front view 1·50 1·30

519 Face

2002. L.E.V. National Association (mental health foundation).

1260 **519** 4k. +50ore brown, agate on cream 1·40 1·30

520 Clown (Luna Ostergard)

2002. Europa. Circus. Winning Entries in Stamp Design Competition. Multicoloured.

1261 4k. Type **520** 1·10 55
1262 5k. Clown (different) (Camille Wagner Larsen) 1·40 1·10

521 Jon's Chapel, Bornholm

2002. Landscape Photographs by Kirsten Klein.

1263 **521** 4k. black and brown 1·10 40
1264 - 6k. black 1·60 1·10
1265 - 6k.50 deep green and green 1·70 1·30
1266 - 12k.50 black and blue 3·00 2·75

DESIGNS: 6k. Trees, Vestervig; 6k.50, Woods, Karskov, Langeland; 12k.50, Cliffs and beach, Stenbjerg, West Jutland.

522 1953 Nimbus Motorcycle and Sidecar

2002. Postal Vehicles. Multicoloured.

1267 4k. Type **522** 1·10 40
1268 5k.50 1962 Bedford CA van 1·40 1·10
1269 10k. 1984 Renault 4 van 2·50 1·60
1270 19k. 1998 Volvo FH12 lorry 5·00 4·25

523 *Dana* (marine research ship) and Atlantic Cod

2002. Centenary of International Council for the Exploration of the Sea. Multicoloured.

1271 4k. Type **523** 1·10 40
1272 10k. Hirtshals lighthouse and atlantic cod 3·00 2·50
MS1273 186×61 mm. 4k. Type **523**; 10k.50 Lighthouse and atlantic cod 4·25 4·00

Stamps of a similar design were issued by Faroe Islands and Greenland.

524 *Children's Corner* (Jens Birkemose)

2002. Paintings.

1274 **524** 5k. red and blue 1·60 1·50
1275 - 6k.50 multicoloured 2·00 1·90

DESIGN: 6k.50 "Maleren og modellen" (Frans Kannik).

525 Underground Train

2002. Inauguration of Copenhagen Metro.

1276 **525** 5k.50 black, green and brown on cream 1·70 1·30

526 Dianas Have, Horsholm (Vandkunsten Design Studio)

2002. Domestic Architecture (1st series). Multicoloured.

1277 4k. Type **526** 90 45
1278 4k.25 Bapistry, Long House and Gate (Poul Ingemann) Blangstedgard, Odense 1·10 1·10
1279 5k.50 Dansk Folkeferie, Karrebaeksminde (Stephan Kappel) 1·40 1·30
1280 6k.50 Terrasser, Fredensborg (Jorn Utzon) 1·50 1·50
1281 9k. Soholm, Klampenborg (Arne Jacobsen) 2·30 2·20

See also Nos. 1296/1300, 1369/73 and 1398/1402.

527 Football

2003. Youth Sports. Multicoloured.

1282 4k.25 Type **527** 1·00 30
1283 5k.50 Swimming 1·40 1·10
1284 8k.50 Gymnastics 2·00 1·70
1285 11k.50 Basketball 3·25 2·75

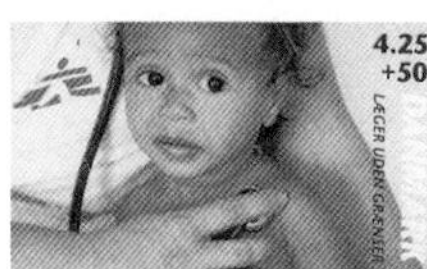

528 Child and Doctor

2003. Medicins sans Frontieres (medical charity).

1286 **528** 4k.25+50ore multicoloured 1·40 1·10

529 Expedition Members

2003. Centenary of the Danish Literary Expedition to Greenland.

1287 **529** 4k.25 blue 1·10 40
1288 - 7k. brown, green and blue (60×22 mm) 2·30 1·90
MS1289 167×61 mm. Nos. 1287/81 2·75 2·75

DESIGN: 7k. Tents and mountains.

Stamps of a similar design were issued by Greenland.

530 Mayfly (*Ephemera danica*)

2003. Insects. Multicoloured.

1290 4k.25 Type **530** 1·00 40
1291 6k.50 Water beetle (*Dysticus latissimus*) 1·70 1·30
1292 12k. Dragonfly (*Cordulegaster boltoni*) (20×39 mm) 3·25 3·00
MS1293 80×76 mm. Nos. 1290/2 6·75 6·00

531 Fools Festival Poster' (Ole Flick)

2003. Europa. Poster Art.

1294 **531** 4k.25 multicoloured 1·00 40
1295 - 5k.50 black 1·40 75

DESIGN: 5k.50, *Thorvaldsen's Museum* (Ole Woldbye).

2003. Domestic Architecture (2nd series). As T 526. Multicoloured.

1296 4k. Bellahoj, Copenhagen (Tage Nielsen and Mogens Irming) 1·00 85
1297 4k.25 Anchersvej Christiansholm Fort, Klampenborg (Mogens Lasen) 1·10 45
1298 5k.25 Gerthasminde, Odense (Anton Rosen) 1·50 1·10
1299 9k. Solvang, Vallekilde (Anton Bentsen) 2·50 2·20
1300 15k. Stenbrogard, Brorup (Peder Holden Hansen) 4·00 3·25

532 *Baering* (Sys Hindsbo)

2003. Paintings. Multicoloured.

1301 5k.50 Type **532** 1·70 1·40
1302 19k. *The Forgotten Land* (Poul Anker Bech) 5·00 4·75

533 Thyra's Stone

2003. UNESCO World Heritage Site. Royal Jelling Open Air Museum.

1303 **533** 4k.25 black, sepia and brown 1·00 40
1304 - 5k.50 black, brown and sepia 1·50 1·10
1305 - 8k.50 black and bistre 2·30 1·90
1306 - 11k.50 black and deep olive 3·25 2·20

DESIGNS: Type **533**; 5k.50, Gorm's cup; 8k.50, Harald's stone; 11k.50, Jelling church.

534 *Towards the Light* (statue, Rudolph Tegner)

2003. Centenary of Niels Finsen's Nobel Prize for Physiology and Medicine.

1307 **534** 6k.50 indigo 1·70 1·40

2004. Arms. As T **73**

(a) Ordinary gum

1307a **73** 10k. bistre 2·30 2·20
1307b **73** 10k.50 carmine 2·50 2·30
1308 **73** 12k.50 indigo 3·00 2·75
1309 **73** 13k. orange 3·25 3·00
1310 **73** 13k.50 green 3·50 3·25
1311 **73** 15k. blue 3·75 3·25
1311a **73** 16k. green 5·75 5·50
1312 **73** 16k.50 brown 4·25 4·00
1313 **73** 17k. green 4·50 4·25
1314 **73** 17k.50 purple 5·25 5·00
1315 **73** 20k. ultramarine 5·50 5·25
1315a **73** 20k.50 lilac 10·25 10·00
1316 **73** 22k. maroon 5·75 5·50

(b) Self-adhesive gum

1316a **73** 10k. pale olive-bistre 5·50 3·50
1332 **73** 15k. blue 6·50 4·50
1333 **73** 20k. dull ultramarine 15·00 13·00
1333a **73** 25k. deep blue-green 7·00 6·25
1317 **73** 30k. chestnut 7·50 6·50
1334 **73** 30k. chestnut 13·50 11·00
1335 **73** 50k. pale carmine 25·00 22·00

535 Butterfly and Caterpillar

2004. Centenary of Children's Aid Day (fund raising charity).

1368 **535** 4k.25+50ore multicoloured 1·30 1·10

2004. Domestic Architecture (3rd series). As T **526**. Multicoloured.

1369 4k.50 Spurveskjul, Virum Copenhagen (Nicolai Abildgaard) 1·10 85
1370 6k. Liselund, Møn (Andreas Kirkerup) 1·50 1·30
1371 7k. Kampmann's Yard, Varde (Hans Ollgaard) 1·80 1·60
1372 12k.50 Harsdorff's House, Copenhagen (Caspar Harsdorff) 3·00 2·75
1373 15k. Nyso, Praesto (Jens Lauridsen) 3·75 3·25

536 Heimdal carrying Gjallar Horn on Bifrost Bridge

2004. Nordic Mythology. Each sepia, blue and black.

1374 4k.50 Type **536** 1·10 60
1375 6k. Gefion ploughing Sealand out of Sweden 1·50 1·30
MS1376 105×71 mm. Nos. 1374/5 2·75 2·75

Stamps of a similar theme were issued by Aland Islands, Faroe Islands, Finland, Greenland, Iceland, Norway and Sweden.

537 Artist's Wooden Figure and Academy Seal

2004. 250th Anniv of Academy of Fine Arts, Copenhagen.

1377	**537**	5k.50 multicoloured	1·50	1·20

538 Fountain viewed through Doorway

2004. 300th Anniv of Frederiksberg Palace. Multicoloured.

1378	4k.25 Type **538**	1·10	90
1379	4k.50 Courtyard viewed through arch	1·10	50
1380	6k.50 Aerial view of palace (57×33 mm)	1·80	1·50
MS1381	125×78 mm. Nos. 1378/80	4·00	3·75

539 Prince Frederik and Mary Donaldson

2004. Marriage of Crown Prince Frederik and Mary Elizabeth Donaldson. Multicoloured.

1382	4k.50 Type **539**	1·20	90
1383	4k.50 As No. 1382 but with design reversed	1·20	90
MS1384	130×65 mm. Nos. 1382/3	2·75	2·50

Stamps of same design were issued by Faroe Islands and Greenland.

540 Prince Henrik

2004. 70th Birthday of Prince Henrik.

1385	**540**	4k.50 multicoloured	1·10	50

541 Cycling

2004. Europa. Holidays. Multicoloured.

1386	6k. Type **541**	1·50	1·30
1387	9k. Sailing	2·30	2·10

542 Trial Sailing of Skuldelev Reconstruction

2004. Viking Ship Museum, Roskilde. Multicoloured.

1388	4k.50 Type **542**	1·10	50
1389	5k.50 Reconstructed hull	1·50	1·10
1390	6k.50 Exhibition	1·80	1·30
1391	12k.50 Excavation	3·00	2·75

543 *Senses the Body Landscape* (Lars Ravn)

2004. Paintings. Multicoloured.

1392	13k. Type **543**	3·25	3·00
1393	21k. *The Dog Bites* (Lars Norgard)	5·25	5·00

544 Kestrel (*Falco tinnunculus*)

2004. Birds of Prey. Multicoloured.

1394	4k.50 Type **544**	1·10	50
1395	5k.50 Northern sparrow hawk (*Accipter nisus*)	1·50	1·10
1396	6k. Common buzzard (*Buteo buteo*)	1·60	1·40
1397	7k. Western marsh harrier (*Circus aeruginosus*)	1·90	1·60

2005. Domestic Architecture (4th series). As T **526**. Multicoloured.

1398	4k.25 Hjarup Manse, Vamdrup	1·10	90
1399	4k.50 Ejdersted Farm, South-West Schleswig (Adriaen Alberts Hauwert)	1·20	50
1400	7k.50 Provstegade, Randers	1·90	1·60
1401	9k.50 Smith's Yard, Kirkestræde, Koge	2·30	2·10
1402	16k.50 Carmelite Monastery, Elsinore	4·25	3·50

545 Boys

2005. SOS Children's Villages.

1403	**545**	4k.50 +50 ore multicoloured	1·30	1·20

546 Hans Christian Andersen

2005. Birth Bicentenary of Hans Christian Andersen (writer).

1404	**546**	4k.50 black	1·20	55
1405	-	5k.50 multicoloured (23×38 mm)	1·50	1·20
1406	-	6k.50 multicoloured (23×38 mm)	1·80	1·50
1407	-	7k.50 multicoloured (23×38 mm)	2·00	1·80

DESIGNS: 5k.50 Paper cut-out; 6k.50 Duckling, script, quill and ink pot; 7k.50 Boots.

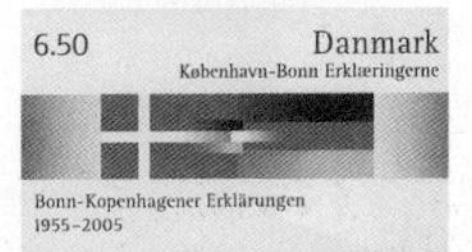

547 Danish and German Flags

2005. 50th Anniv of Copenhagen—Bonn Declarations (tolerance for minorities).

1408	**547**	6k.50 multicoloured	1·80	1·70

548 August Bournonville

2005. Birth Bicentenary of August Bournonville (choreographer).

1409	**548**	4k.50 blue, deep blue and black	1·00	95
1410	-	5k.50 yellow, claret and black	1·30	1·20
MS1411		106×70 mm. Nos. 1409/10	2·30	2·20

DESIGN: 5k.50, Pas de Deux.

549 Ships at Sea

2005. 60th Anniv of End of World War II.

1412	**549**	4k.50 blackish brown	1·00	95
1413	-	7k.50 greenish black	1·70	1·60

DESIGN: 7k.50, Unloading.

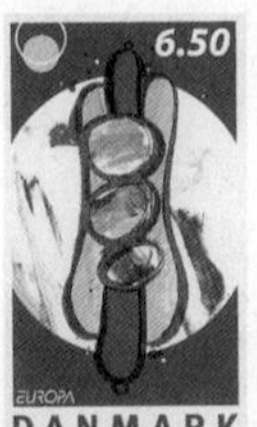

550 Hotdog

2005. Europa. Gastronomy. Multicoloured.

1414	6k.50 Type **550**	1·40	1·40
1415	9k.50 Fish	2·20	2·10

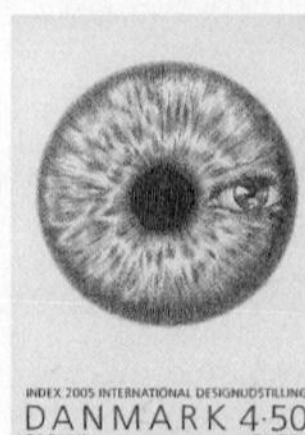

551 Iris containing Eye

2005. Index 2005 International Design Exhibition, Copenhagen.

1416	**551**	4k.50 black	1·10	1·00

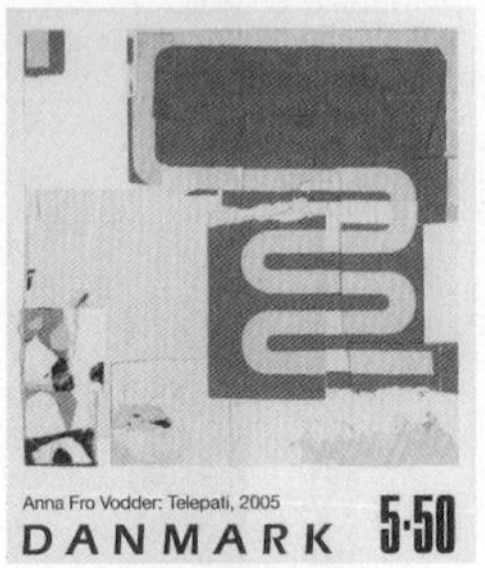

552 *Telepathy* (Anna Fro Vodder)

2005. Paintings. Multicoloured.

1417	5k.50 Type **552**	1·30	1·20
1418	6k.50 "Home Again" (Kaspar Bonnen)	1·40	1·40
1419	7k.50 *Unrest* (John Korner)	1·70	1·60
1420	12k.50 *Palace in the Morning* (Tal R) (horiz)	2·75	2·75

553 Numeral

2005. Centenary of Wavy Line

(a) Ordinary gum

1421	**553**	25ore indigo	10	10
1422	**553**	50ore brown	15	15
1423	**553**	100ore blue	25	20
1424	**553**	200ore green	50	45
1425	**553**	450ore green	1·10	1·00
1425a	**553**	500ore green	2·50	2·50

(b) Self-adhesive gum

1431	**553**	50ö brown	30	20
1432	**553**	100ö blue	50	35
1433	**553**	200ö deep blue-green	85	70
1434	**553**	300ö pale orange	1·90	1·40
1435	**553**	400ö grey-lilac	2·10	1·50
1436	**553**	500ö light green	2·40	1·70
1440	**553**	30k. deep reddish lilac	95	60

554 Harbour Seal (*Phoca vitulina*)

2005. Seals.

1450	**554**	4k.50 black, brown and indigo	1·00	95
1451	-	5k.50 black and indigo	1·30	1·20
MS1452		105×70 mm. Nos. 1450/1	2·30	2·20

DESIGNS: Type **554**; 5k.50 Grey seal (*Halichoerus grypus*).

555 *Galanthus nivalis*

2006. Spring Flowers. Multicoloured.

1453	4k.75 Type **555**	1·10	50
1454	5k.50 *Eranthis hyemalis*	1·20	1·20
1455	7k. *Crocus vernus*	1·60	1·30
1456	8k. *Anemone nemorosa*	1·80	1·60

556 Refugees

2006. Danish Refugee Council.

1457	**556**	4k.75+50ore brown and black	1·30	1·20

557 Castle

2006. 400th Anniv of Rosenborg Castle. Multicoloured.

1458	4k.75 Type **557**	1·10	50
1459	5k.50 Thrones and silver lion	1·30	1·20
1460	13k. Ceiling decoration	3·25	3·00

558 Elf Mound, Elf King and Elvish Women

2006. Nordic Mythology. Multicoloured.

1461	4k.75 Type **558**	1·10	50
1462	7k. Werewolves, hel-horse, incubi, gnome and troll	1·60	1·30
MS1463	105×70 mm. Nos. 1461/2	2·75	2·50

Stamps of a similar theme were issued by Aland Islands, Greenland, Faröe Islands, Finland, Iceland, Norway and Sweden.

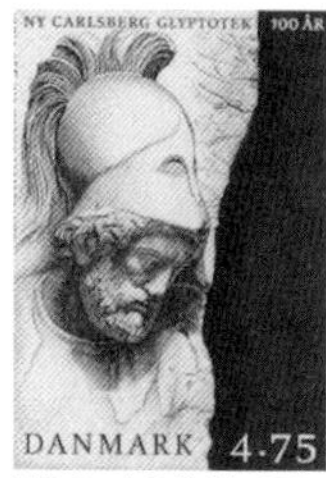

559 Greek Relief (c. 330 BC)

2006. Centenary of New Carlsberg Glyptotek (museum). Multicoloured.
1464 **559** 4k.75 green and black 1·00 50
1465 - 5k.50 drab and black 1·30 1·20
1466 - 8k. bistre and black 1·80 1·60
MS1467 105×70 mm. Nos. 1464/6 4·00 4·00
DESIGNS: 4k.75 Type **559**; 5k.50 Conservatory dome; 8k. *Dancer looking at the Sole of her Right Foot* (Edgar Degas).

560 Alfa Dana Midget and SWEBE-JAP

2006. Vintage Race Cars. Multicoloured.
1468 4k.75 Type **560** 1·10 55
1469 5k.50 Alfa Romeo GTA, Ford Cortina GT and Austin Cooper S 1·30 1·20
1470 10k. Volvo P 1800 and Jaguar E-Type 2·30 1·90
1471 17k. Renault Alpine A 110 and Lotus Elan 3·50 3·00

561 Ellehammer, 1906

2006. Vintage Aircraft. Multicoloured.
1472 4k.50 Type **561** 1·70 90
1473 4k.75 KZ 11, 1946 1·80 1·00
1474 5k.50 KZ IV, 1944 2·50 1·70
1475 13k. KZ V11 Lark, 1947 6·00 3·50

562 Faces (Rikke Veber Rasmussen)

2006. Europa. Integration. Winning designs in Children's Drawing Competition.
1476 **562** 4k.75 multicoloured 1·80 1·20
1477 - 7k. black and green 3·00 2·00
DESIGNS: 4k.75 Type **562**; 7k. Two youths (Anette Bertram Nielsen).

563 *Untitled* (Asger Jorn)

2006. CoBrA (artistic movement). Multicoloured.
1478 4k.75 Type **563** 1·90 1·20
1479 5k.50 *Landscape of the Night* (Else Alfelt) (vert) 2·50 1·70
1480 7k. *New Skin* (Pierre Alechinsky) 3·00 2·00
1481 8k. *The Olive Eater* (Asger Jorn) (vert) 3·50 2·50
Stamps of similar design were issued by Belgium.

563a Askov Windmill (1891)

2007. Windmills.
1482 **563a** 4k.50 agate 1·70 90
1483 - 4k.75 crimson 1·90 1·20
1484 - 6k. green 2·50 1·70
1485 - 8k.50 blue 4·00 3·00
DESIGNS: 4k.50 Type **563a**; 4k.75 Gedser (1957); 6k. Bogø (1989); 8k.50 Middlegrunden (2000).

564 Emblem and Eye

2007. 50th Anniv of Danish United Nations Soldiers.
1486 **564** 4k.75 blue, vermilion and black 2·00 1·30

565 Royal Family

2007. Charity Stamp.
1487 **565** 4k.75+50ore maroon and black 2·30 1·50

566 Carved Figures

2007. International Polar Year. Multicoloured.
1488 7k.25 Type **566** 2·75 2·00
1489 13k.50 de Havilland Canada DH-6 Twin Otter research plane 5·50 3·75
MS1490 100×70 mm. Nos. 1488/9 8·25 6·50

567 Globe of Fish

2007. Galathea 3 Scientific Research Voyage. Multicoloured.
1491 4k.75 Type **567** 2·00 1·30
1492 7k.25 Route 3·00 2·25
MS1493 106×70 mm. Nos. 1491/2 5·00 3·75

568 Ceremonial Axe Heads, Vendsyssel

2007. Bicentenary of National Museum.
1494 **568** 4k.75 blue and black 2·00 1·30
1495 - 6k. brown and black 2·50 1·70
1496 - 8k.25 yellow and black 3·50 2·75
1497 - 10k.25 blue, black and yellow 5·25 4·00
DESIGNS: 4k.75 Type **568**; 6k. Funen aquamanile; 8k.25 Armillary sphere, Germany; 10k.25 Mask, Borneo.

569 Scouts

2007. Europa. Centenary of Scouting. Multicoloured.
1498 4k.75 Type **569** 2·00 1·30
1499 7k.25 Campfire and tent 3·00 2·25

570 *The Traveller* (Arne Haugen Sorensen)

2007. Art. Multicoloured.
1500 4k.75 Type **570** 2·00 1·30
1501 8k.25 *Trionfale* (Seppo Mattinen) 3·50 2·75

571 Hands enclosing Measurement

2007. Centenary of Metric System.
1502 **571** 4k.75 black and rose 2·10 1·30

572 Niobe Fritillary Butterfly

2007. Rabjerg Dune's Flora and Fauna. Multicoloured.
1503 4k.75 Type **572** 2·20 1·30
1504 6k. Northern dune tiger beetle 2·50 1·70
1505 7k.25 Sand lizard 3·25 2·25
1506 13k.50 Seaside pansy 6·25 4·25
MS1507 151×71 mm. Nos. 1503/6 13·00 10·50

573 Poul Henningsen

2007. Personalities.
1508 **573** 4k.75 carmine, red and black 2·20 1·70
1509 - 6k. blue and black 2·50 1·90
1510 - 7k.25 green, rosine and black 3·25 2·25
1511 - 8k.25 violet and black 3·75 2·75
DESIGNS: 4k.75 Type **573** (designer and social commentator) and 'Artichoke' lamp; 6k. Victor Borge (entertainer) and piano; 7k.25 Arne Jacobsen (architect and designer) and 'Egg' chair; 8k.25 Piet Hein (designer, artist, poet and mathematician) and 'superellipse'.

574 Old Stage Theatre, Kongens Nytorv

2008. Inauguration of New Royal Danish Playhouse, Royal Theatre Complex. Multicoloured.
1512 5k.50 Type **574** 3·00 2·20
1513 6k.50 Playhouse Theatre, Kvæsthusbroen 3·25 2·50
1514 7k.75 Opera House, Holmen, Copenhagen 4·00 3·00

575 Woman

2008. Breast Cancer Awareness Campaign. Danish Cancer Society.
1515 **575** 5k.50+50ore vermilion and black 3·00 2·20

576 Lindholm High

2008. Norse Mythology. Mythical Places. Each black.
1516 5k.50 Type **576** 3·00 2·20
1517 7k.75 Feggeklit 3·50 2·75
MS1518 105×70 mm. Nos. 1516/17 7·50 7·50

577 Gala Uniform

2008. 350th Anniv of Royal Life Guards. Multicoloured.
1519 5k.50 Type **577** 3·00 2·20
1520 10k. On parade 4·50 3·75
MS1521 106×71 mm. Nos. 1519/20 7·50 7·50

578 Allotment, Hjelm, Aabenraa

2008. Centenary of Allotment Association. Multicoloured.
1522 5k.50 Type **578** 2·50 1·90
1523 6k.50 Summer house, Vennelyst, Klovermarken 3·25 2·75

579 Boy and Symbols of Letter Writing

2008. Europa. The Letter. Multicoloured.
1524 5k.50 Type **579** 2·50 1·90
1525 7k.75 Girl and symbols of letter writing 4·00 3·00

580 *The Old Villa, Figures in Landscape* (Roy Lichtenstein) and *I am in You* (video installation) (Doug Aitken)

2008. 50th Anniv of Louisiana Museum of Modern Art. Multicoloured.
1526 5k.50 Type **580** 2·00 1·10
1527 7k.50 *I am in You* (different), glass corridor and *A Closer Grand Canyon* (David Hockney) 3·25 2·50
1528 8k.75 *Reclining Figure* (Henry Moore), *Walking Man* and *Big Head* (Alberto Giacometti) and *Slender Ribs* (Alexander Calder) 4·50 3·50
1529 16k. *Slender Ribs* (different), children and concert hall 8·25 7·00
Although not *se-tenant* Nos. 1526/7 and 1528/9, respectively, each form a composite design.

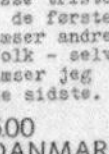

581 Halfdan Rasmussen

2008. Personalities. Multicoloured.

1530	5k. claret and black	2·20	1·70
1531	5k.50 blue, green and black	3·00	2·20
1532	6k.50 red, mauve and black	3·75	2·75
1533	10k. mauve, indigo and black	5·00	4·25

DESIGNS: 5k. Type **581** (poet); 5k.50 Eric Balling (film director); 6k.50 Bodil Kjer (actor); 10k. Neils-Henning Orsted Pedersen (musician).

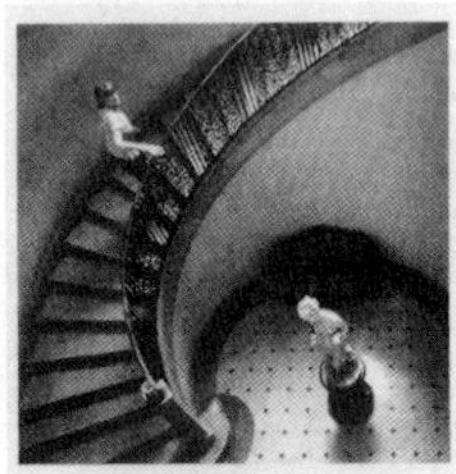

582 *Trappe* (Viggo Raval)

2008. Art Photographs. Both black.

1534	5k.50 Type **582**	2·75	1·70
1535	7k.75 *Berlin* (Krass Clement) (horiz)	4·25	3·25

583 Holly Berries (*Ilex aquifolium*)

2008. Winter Flora. Multicoloured.

1536	5k.50 Type **583**	2·10	1·30
1537	6k.50 Christmas rose (*Hellebore niger*)	2·75	1·90
1538	7k.75 Yew berries (*Taxus baccata*)	4·00	3·00
1539	8k.75 Snowberries (*Symphoricarpos rivularis*)	5·25	4·25

584 Mintmaster's Mansion and Town Drummer

2009. Centenary of Old Town, Aarhus (open air museum). Multicoloured.

1540	5k.50 Type **584**	2·10	1·30
1541	6k.50 Mayor's House	2·75	1·90
1542	8k. Clocks and Watches Museum	3·75	3·00
1543	10k.50 Kertminde School	5·50	4·75
MS1544	151×70 mm. Nos. 1540/3	12·50	12·50

585 Bioenergy

2009. COP15—United Nations Climate Change Conference, Copenhagen. Each indigo.

1545	5k.50 Type **585**	2·10	1·30
1546	9k. Low energy building	5·25	4·25

586 Prince Henrik

2009. World Wildlife Fund. 75th Birth Anniv of Prince Henrik (president of Danish World Wildlife Fund).

1547	**586**	5k.50 + 50 multicoloured	3·00	2·20
1547	**586**	5k.50 + 50 multicoloured	3·00	2·20

The premium is for the World Wildlife Fund.

587 *Anacamptis pyramidalis* (pyramidal orchid)

2009. Flora and Fauna of Mons Klint. Multicoloured.

1548	5k. Type **587**	2·40	1·50
1549	5k.50 *Falco peregrinus* (peregrine)	3·00	1·80
1550	8k. *Zygaena purpuralis* (transparent burnet)	4·50	2·75
1551	17k. *Mosasaurus lemonnieri* (fossil)	10·50	10·50
MS1552	151×71 mm. Nos. 1549/51	20·00	20·00

588 Round Towers

2009. Europa. Astronomy. Multicoloured.

1553	5k.50 Type **588**	3·25	2·00
1554	8k. Tyco Brahe Planetarium	4·75	2·75

589 Rhinoceros

2009. 150th Anniv of Copenhagen Zoo. Multicoloured.

1555	5k.50 Type **589**	2·75	1·70
1556	6k.50 Elephants	3·50	2·10
1557	8k. Red-eyed tree frog and flamingoes	4·50	3·25
1558	9k. Royal python and golden lion tamarin	5·25	3·25

590 First Official Map of Denmark, 1841

2009. Early Maps. Multicoloured.

1559	5k.50 Type **590**	2·40	1·50
1560	6k.50 Map by Johannes Mejer, 1650 (24×40 mm)	6·75	4·00
1561	12k. Map by Marcus Jordan, 1585 (24×40 mm)	6·75	4·00
1562	18k. First printed map of Denmark by Abraham Ortelius, 1570 (24×40 mm)	9·00	5·50

591 *Houses in Motion* (Jes Fomsgaard)

2009. Art.

1563	**591**	5k.50 multicoloured	3·25	2·00

592 Hans Scherfig and Metropolitanskole Building, Fiolstraede, Frue Plads c.1816

2009. Metropolitanskole (Metropolitan School), Copenhagen.

1564	5k.50 black and carmine	2·75	1·70
1565	6k.50 black and bottle-green	4·25	2·50

DESIGNS: 5k.50 Type **592**; 6k.50 Modern Metropolitanskole building, Struenseegade.

2009. COP15—United Nations Climate Change Conference, Copenhagen (2nd issue). As T **585**. Indigo.

1566	5k.50 Fuel cell	3·25	2·00
1567	8k.50 Wind turbine	4·50	2·75

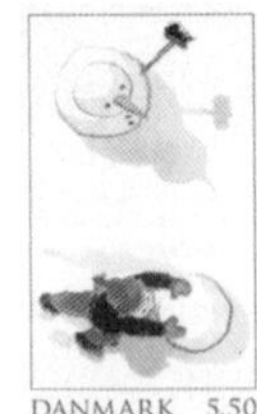

593 Making Snowman

2009. Playing in Snow. Multicoloured. (a) Self-adhesive.

1568	5k.50 Type **593**	2·75	1·70
1569	6k.50 Sledging	4·00	2·40
1570	8k. Snowball fight	4·50	2·75
1571	9k. Making snow angels	5·75	3·50

(b) Sheet 150×70 mm. Ordinary gum.

MS1572	As Nos. 1568/70	17·00	17·00

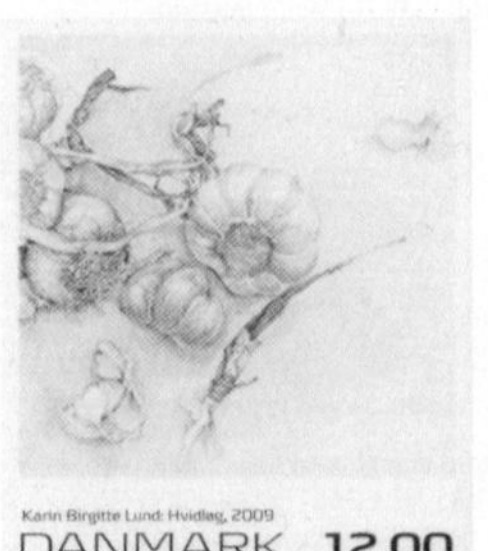

594 *Garlic* (Karin Birgitte Lund)

2009. Art.

1573	**594**	12k. multicoloured	7·00	4·25

597 70th Birthday Portrait of Queen Margrethe II

2010. Queen Margrethe II

1581	**597**	5k.50 bright red and black	2·75	1·70
1581a		6k. bright deep turquoise-green and black	4·00	2·50
1582		6k.50 bright deep turquoise-green and black	4·25	2·50
1582a		8k. bright red and black	4·50	2·75
1583		8k.50 deep bright apple green and black	4·75	2·75
1583a		9k. deep bright apple green and black	5·75	3·50
1584		9k.50 dull ultramarine and black	5·25	4·25
1585		11k. deep ultramarine and black	5·25	4·25

Numbers have been left for additions to this series.

598 Royal Family

2010. 70th Birth Anniv of Queen Margrethe II

1590	**598**	5k.50 multicoloured	2·75	1·70

599 Ribe Cathedral

2010. 1300th Anniv of Ribe. Each black.

1591	5k.50 Type **599**	2·75	1·70
1592	6k.50 Queen Dagmar (statue)	4·25	2·50

600 Lindø Shipyard

2010. Life at the Coast. Multicoloured.

(a) Self-adhesive

1593	5k.50 Type **600**	2·75	1·70
1594	8k.50 Aarhus Port	4·50	2·75

(b) Miniature sheet. Ordinary gum

MS1595	105×70 mm. As Nos. 1593/4	7·25	4·75

Stamps of a similar theme were issued by Aland, Greenland, Faröe Islands, Finland, Iceland, Norway and Sweden.

601 Gasolin 3 (painting by Tage Hansen)

2010. 50th Anniv of P4 Radio Station

1596	**601**	5k.50 multicoloured	3·50	2·25

602 Flower and Posthorn

2010. Greetings Stamps. Multicoloured.

1597	5k.50 Type **602**	2·75	1·70
1598	5k.50 Parcel	2·75	1·70
1599	5k.50 'Tillykke' (congratulations)	2·75	1·70
1600	5k.50 Flag	2·75	1·70
1601	5k.50 Heart	2·75	1·70

603 *Iver Huitfeldt* (frigate)

2010. 500th Anniv of Royal Danish Navy. Each rosine and black, ship's colour given.

1602	5k.50 Type **603**	2·75	1·70
1603	6k.50 *Niels Iuel* (artillery ship) (black)	4·00	2·25
1604	8k.50 *Tordenskjold* (ironclad warship) (rosine)	4·50	2·75
1605	9k.50 *Jylland* (screw frigate) (black)	5·75	3·50
1606	16k. *Maria* (caravel) (rosine)	9·00	7·00

Spørge-Jørgen
Danmark
5.50

604 Sporge Jorgen

2010. Europa. Children's Books. Multicoloured.

1607	5k.50 Type **604** (*Spørge Jørgen* written by Kamma Laurents, illustrated by Robert Storm Petersen)	3·25	2·00
1608	8k.50 Orla Frø-Snapper (*Orla Frø-Snapper* written and illustrated by Ole Lund Kirkegard) (vert)	4·50	2·75

605 Race Horses

2010. Centenary of Copenhagen Racecourse. Multicoloured.

1609	5k.50 Type **605**	4·25	2·75
1610	24k. Derby Day race-goers and race horse	18·75	16·00

606 Cyclist

2011. Post Danmark Rundt Bicycle Race. Multicoloured.

MS1611	5k.50×10, Type **606**; Racing on country road; Group of cyclists, head and shoulders, striped helmets; Two cyclists; Side view of large group of cyclists; Single cyclist wearing white outfit with red inserts; Cyclist, wearing red; Large group of cyclist, facing front; Three cyclists, facing left; Cyclist with arms raised in celebration	28·00	28·00

607 Dan Turèll (poet, lecturer, essayist and crime writer)

2010. Personalities

1612	5k.50 dull violet, bright carmine and black	2·75	1·70
1613	6k.50 bright carmine, new blue and black	4·25	2·50
1614	9k.50 deep magenta, apple green and black	5·75	3·50
1615	12k.50 carmine-lake and black	6·75	4·00

Designs:- 5k.50 Type **607**; 6k.50 Tove Ditlevsen (writer); 9k.50 Henry Heerup (painter, sculptor and graphic artist);12k.50 Dea Trier Mørch (writer and visual artist)

608 *Two Roses* (Inge Ellegaard)

2010. Art. Multicoloured.

1616	5k.50 Type **608**	2·75	1·70
1617	18k.50 *Night Flower* (Kirstine Roepstorff) (horiz)	12·00	9·00

609 Lonely Girl

2010. Winter Stamps. Multicoloured.

(a) Self-adhesive

1618	5k.50 Type **609**	2·75	1·70
1619	6k.50 Lonely girl embracing snowman	4·25	2·50
1620	8k.50 Lonely girl kissing snowman	4·50	2·50
1621	12k.50 Ice man with black and white dog offering lonely girl flowers	7·00	4·25

(b) Miniature sheet. Ordinary gum

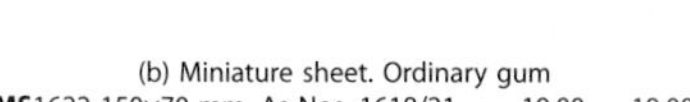

MS1622	150×70 mm. As Nos. 1618/21	19·00	19·00

610 'One in Eight'

2010. Danish Rheumatism Association (1st issue)

1623	**610** 5k.50+50ö. black and scarlet-vermilion	3·50	2·20

2011. Danish Rheumatism Association (2nd issue)

1623a	8k.+50ö As Type **610**	4·25	3·00

611 Excerpt from Supreme Court Decree of 1661

2011. 350th Anniv of Supreme Court. Multicoloured.

(a) Sheet stamps. Self-adhesive

1624	6k. Type **611**	4·00	2·75
1625	8k. Judges outside Supreme Court	4·25	3·00

(b) Miniature sheet. Ordinary gum

MS1626	150×70 mm. As Nos. 1624/5	8·25	5·75

Nos. 1624/5 were issued in sheets with the surplus paper around the stamps removed

612 Man's Torso and Caravan Window

2011. Camping. Multicoloured.

1627	6k. Type **612**	4·00	2·75
1628	8k. Gnome and caravan door	4·25	3·00

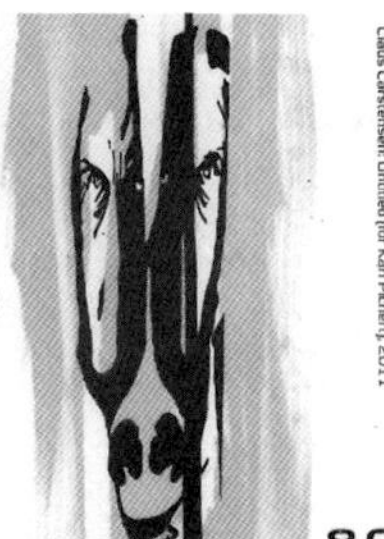

613 Untitled (for Karl Pichert) (Claus Carstensen)

2011. Art on Stamps

1629	8k. black and grey	4·50	4·25
1630	13k. multicoloured	7·50	7·25

Designs:-8k. Type **613**; 13k. *I wonder how you would like this place* (Lise Harlev).

614 Nørre Vosborg

2011. Manor Houses. Multicoloured.

1631	6k. Type **614**	4·00	2·75
1632	6k. Voergaard Castle	4·00	2·75
1633	8k. Engelsholm Castle	4·25	3·00
1634	8k. Gammel Estrup	4·25	3·00

615 Pale Tussock Moth Caterpillar on Spring Branch

2011. Europa. Forests. Multicoloured.

(a) Sheet stamps

1635	8k. Type **615**	4·25	3·00
1636	11k. Red squirrel climbing up tree trunk and Autumn branch	5·25	4·25

(b) Booklet stamp

1637	8k. As Type **615**	4·25	3·00

616 Carsten Niebuhrs wearing Arab Dress

2011. 250th Anniv of Carsten Niebuhr's Arabian Expedition. Multicoloured.

(a) Sheet stamps

1638	8k. Type **616**	4·25	3·00
1639	13k. Horse driven grain mill, Cairo	7·50	7·25
MS1640	150×70 mm. Nos. 1638/9 plus stamp size label showing scarab	12·00	12·00

(b) Booklet stamp

1541	8k. As Type **616**	4·25	3·00

617 Poppy in Bud (*Papaver rhoeas*)

2011. Flowers. Multicoloured.

(a) Sheet stamps. Self-adhesive

1642	2k. Type **617**	1·50	1·00
1643	6k. *Geranium* (Cranesbill)	4·00	2·75
1644	8k. *Astrantia major* (Masterwort)	4·25	3·00
1645	10k. *Papaver nudicaule* (Siberian poppy)	5·75	4·75

(b) Booklet stamp. Self-adhesive

1646	6k. *Geranium* (Cranesbill)	4·00	2·75

(c) Miniature sheet. Ordinary gum

MS1647	150×70 mm. As Nos. 1642/5	14·50	14·50

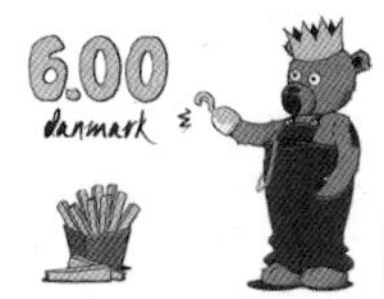

618 Bruno the Bear

2011. Danish Children's Television. Multicoloured.

(a) Sheet stamps

1648	6k. Type **618**	4·00	2·75
1649	8k. Teddy	4·25	3·00

(b) Booklet stamps

1650	6k. As Type **618**	4·00	2·75
1651	8k. As No. 1649	4·25	3·00

619 *Hjejlen*

2011. 150th Anniv of *Hjejlen* (paddle steamer)

1652	**619** 8k. multicoloured	4·25	3·00

620 Woman's Dress

2011. Danish Fashion. Copenhagen Fashion Week

1653	6k. black	4·00	2·75
1654	8k. deep bluish-green	4·25	3·00
MS1655	150×70 mm. As Nos. 1653/4	8·25	8·25

Designs: 6k. Type **620**; 8k. Men's accessories.

621 Two Hearts

2011. UCI Road World Championships-2011, Denmark

1656	**621** 8k. multicoloured	4·25	3·00

2011. Danish Rheumatism Association (3rd issue)

1623a	8k.+50ö As Type **610**	4·25	3·00

622

2011. Greetings Stamps (2nd series). Multicoloured.

1658	8k. Type **622**	4·25	3·00
1659	8k. Flag on small mound	4·25	3·00
1660	8k. 'Tillykke' (congratulations)	4·25	3·00
1661	8k. Envelope containing letter with heart	4·25	3·00
1662	8k. Flower facing left	4·25	3·00

MILITARY FRANK STAMPS

1917. Nos. 135 and 138 optd **S F** (= "Soldater Frimaerke").

M188	**21**	5ore green	13·00	34·00
M189	**21**	10ore red	13·00	34·00

NEWSPAPER STAMPS

N18

1907

N131	**N18**	1ore green	11·00	3·00
N132	**N18**	5ore blue	27·00	10·50
N133	**N18**	7ore red	15·00	1·20
N188	**N18**	8ore green	35·00	2·00
N134	**N18**	10ore lilac	34·00	2·75
N135	**N18**	20ore green	25·00	1·60
N191	**N18**	29ore orange	42·00	3·25
N136	**N18**	38ore orange	34·00	1·90
N193	**N18**	41ore brown	50·00	3·50
N137	**N18**	68ore brown	85·00	24·00
N138	**N18**	1k. purple & green	25·00	2·10
N139	**N18**	5k. green and pink	£160	24·00
N140	**N18**	10k. blue and stone	£170	28·00

OFFICIAL STAMPS

O9

1871. Value in "skilling".

O51a	**O9**	2sk. blue	£130	90·00
O52	**O9**	4sk. red	50·00	18·00
O53	**O9**	16sk. green	£350	£180

1875. Value in "ore".

O185		1ore orange	90	1·20
O100		3ore lilac	1·20	85
O186		3ore grey	3·75	6·50
O101		4ore blue	1·80	1·40
O188		5ore green	1·00	40
O189		5ore brown	5·25	21·00
O94		8ore red	8·75	2·40
O104		10ore red	2·50	1·20
O191		10ore green	3·50	4·25
O192		20ore lilac	13·50	28·00
O193		20ore blue	19·00	9·50
O98		32ore green	25·00	23·00

PARCEL POST STAMPS

1919. Various types optd **POSTFAERGE**.

P208	**21**	10ore red	39·00	60·00
P209	**15**	10ore green	32·00	12·00
P210	**15**	10ore brown	23·00	9·50
P211	**21**	15ore lilac	19·00	28·00
P212	**21**	30ore orange	17·00	25·00
P213	**21**	30ore blue	5·00	5·50
P214	**21**	50ore black & purple	£225	£225
P215a	**21**	50ore grey	25·00	16·00
P216	**22**	1k. brown	£110	£150
P217	**21**	1k. blue and brown	70·00	32·00
P218	**21**	5k. brown & mauve	1·80	1·90
P219	**21**	10k. green and red	75·00	75·00

1927. Stamps of 1927 (solid background) optd **POSTFAERGE**.

P252	**40**	15ore red	18·00	9·75
P253	**40**	30ore yellow	13·50	16·00
P254	**40**	40ore green	23·00	11·50

1936. Stamps of 1933 (lined background) optd **POSTFAERGE**.

P491	**43**	5ore purple	40	40
P299	**43**	10ore orange	18·00	15·00
P300	**43**	10ore brown	1·40	1·30
P301	**43**	10ore violet	25	25
P302	**43**	10ore green	60	30
P303a	**40**	15ore red	55	1·30
P304	**40**	30ore blue	4·50	4·50
P305	**40**	30ore orange	55	65
P306	**40**	40ore green	4·50	5·25
P307	**40**	40ore blue	45	85
P308	**45**	50ore grey	90	1·00
P309	**45**	1k. brown	1·00	85

1945. Stamps of 1942 optd **POSTFAERGE**.

P346	**67**	30ore orange	2·75	1·40
P347	**67**	40ore blue	1·30	1·30
P348	**67**	50ore grey	1·50	1·30

1949. Stamps of 1946 and 1948 optd **POSTFAERGE**.

P376	**80**	30ore orange	3·75	1·60
P377	**80**	30ore red	1·50	1·40
P378	**80**	40ore blue	3·00	1·60
P379	**80**	40ore grey	1·50	1·40
P380	**80**	50ore grey	17·00	3·25
P381	**80**	50ore green	1·50	1·40
P382	**80**	70ore green	1·50	1·40
P383	**73**	1k. brown	1·90	1·30
P384	**73**	1k.25 orange	6·75	8·25
P495	**73**	2k. red	2·50	2·40
P496	**73**	5k. blue	6·25	5·75

1967. Optd **POSTFAERGE**.

P488	**117**	40ore brown	65	65
P492	**117**	50ore brown	45	40
P489	**117**	80ore blue	80	75
P493	**117**	90ore blue	1·00	85

1975. Optd **POSTFAERGE**.

P597	**207**	100ore blue	1·50	1·30

POSTAGE DUE STAMPS

1921. Stamps of 1905 and 1913 optd **PORTO**.

D214	**15**	1ore orange	2·30	1·70
D215	**21**	5ore green	4·50	2·00
D216	**21**	7ore orange	3·50	2·00
D217	**21**	10ore red	20·00	9·75
D218	**21**	20ore blue	17·00	5·75
D219	**21**	25ore black and brown	23·00	2·75
D220	**21**	50ore black & purple	10·00	3·50

D32

1921. Solid background.

D221	**D32**	1ore orange	70	80
D222	**D32**	4ore blue	1·70	2·75
D223	**D32**	5ore brown	2·30	1·20
D224	**D32**	5ore green	1·70	80
D225	**D32**	7ore green	11·50	19·00
D226	**D32**	7ore violet	28·00	32·00
D227	**D32**	10ore green	2·30	80
D228	**D32**	10ore brown	1·70	80
D229	**D32**	20ore blue	1·10	95
D230	**D32**	20ore grey	2·30	2·00
D231	**D32**	25ore red	2·75	1·60
D232	**D32**	25ore lilac	2·75	2·75
D233	**D32**	25ore blue	4·50	3·25
D234	**D32**	1k. blue	70·00	6·50
D235	**D32**	1k. blue and brown	8·50	4·75
D236	**D32**	5k. violet	17·00	7·25

For stamps with lined background see Nos. D285/97.

1921. Military Frank stamp optd **PORTO**.

D237	**21**	10ore red (No. M189)	8·00	5·75

1934. Lined background.

D285	**D32**	1ore grey	25	15
D286	**D32**	2ore red	25	15
D287	**D32**	5ore green	25	15
D288	**D32**	6ore green	35	15
D289	**D32**	8ore mauve	2·20	2·00
D290	**D32**	10ore orange	25	15
D291	**D32**	12ore blue	45	25
D292	**D32**	15ore violet	45	30
D293	**D32**	20ore grey	25	15
D294	**D32**	25ore blue	35	15
D295	**D32**	30ore green	55	25
D296	**D32**	40ore purple	65	50
D297	**D32**	1k. brown	55	15

1934. Surch **PORTO 15**.

D298	**15**	15 on 12ore lilac	4·50	4·50

SPECIAL FEE STAMPS

1923. No. D227 optd **GEBYR GEBYR**.

S218	**D32**	10ore green	10·00	3·25

S36

1926. Solid background.

S229	**S36**	10ore green	6·75	95
S230	**S36**	10ore brown	8·50	95

1934. Lined background.

S285		5ore green	20	20
S286		10ore orange	20	20

Pt. 11

FAROE ISLANDS

A Danish possession in the North Atlantic Ocean. Under British Administration during the German Occupation of Denmark, 1940/5.

100 ore = 1 krone.

1940. Stamps of Denmark surch with new value (twice on Type **43**).

2	**43**	20ore on 1ore green	45·00	65·00
3	**43**	20ore on 5ore purple	45·00	27·00
1	**40**	20ore on 15ore red	70·00	15·00
4	**43**	50ore on 5ore purple	£350	65·00
5	**43**	60ore on 6ore orange	£140	£200

2 1673 Map of the Faroe Islands

3 *Vidoy and Svinoy* (E. Nohr)

1975

6	**2**	5ore brown	25	20
7	-	10ore blue and green	25	20
8	**2**	50ore blue	25	20
9	-	60ore brown and blue	1·10	95
10	-	70ore black and blue	1·10	95
11	-	80ore brown and blue	55	55
12	**2**	90ore red	1·00	85
13	-	120ore blue and deep blue	90	45
14	-	200ore black and blue	90	85
15	-	250ore green, brown & blue	90	75
16	-	300ore green, brown & blue	5·75	2·20
17	**3**	350ore multicoloured	1·10	95
18	-	450ore multicoloured	1·10	1·10
19	-	500ore multicoloured	1·10	1·10

DESIGNS—As Type **2** but HORIZ: 10, 60, 80, 120ore Northern map (A. Ortelius); 70, 200ore West Sandoy; 250, 300ore Streymoy and Vagar. As Type **3**: 450ore *Nes* (R. Smith); 500ore *Hvitanes and Skalafjordur* (S. Joensen-Mikines).

4 Rowing Boat

1976. Inauguration of Faroese Post Office.

20	**4**	125ore red	2·00	1·40
21	-	160ore multicoloured	70	45
22	-	800ore green	2·30	1·20

DESIGNS—24×34 mm: 160ore Faroese flag. 24×31 mm: 800ore Faroese postman.

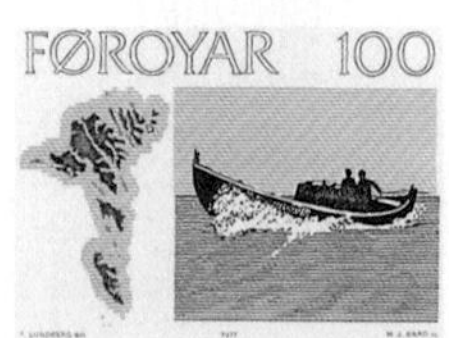

5 Motor Fishing Boat

1977. Faroese Fishing Vessels.

23	**5**	100ore black, lt green & green	5·75	4·50
24	-	125ore black, rose and red	80	75
25	-	160ore black, lt blue & blue	1·20	1·10
26	-	600ore black, ochre & brown	1·70	1·20

DESIGNS: 125ore *Niels Pauli* (inshore fishing cutter); 160ore *Krunborg* (seine fishing boat); 600ore *Polarfisk* (deep-sea trawler).

6 Common Snipe

1977. Birds. Multicoloured.

27	70ore Type **6**	35	30
28	180ore Oystercatcher	50	50
29	250ore Whimbrel	75	70

7 Atlantic Puffins over North Coast

1978. Views of Mykines Island. Multicoloured.

30	100ore Type **7**	25	25
31	130ore Mykines village (horiz)	35	35
32	140ore Cultivated fields (horiz)	55	50
33	150ore Aerial view of Mykines	45	45
34	180ore Map of Mykines (37×26 mm)	45	45

8 Northern Gannet

1978. Sea Birds. Multicoloured.

35	140ore Type **8**	75	60
36	180ore Atlantic puffin	95	90
37	400ore Common guillemot	1·20	1·10

9 Old Library Building

1978. 150th Anniv of National Library.

38	**9**	140ore olive and blue	55	55
39	-	180ore brown and flesh	70	70

DESIGN: 180ore New National Library building.

10 Guide, Tent and Campfire

1978. 50th Anniv of Girl Guides.

40	**10**	140ore multicoloured	65	60

11 Ram

1979. Sheep-rearing.

41	**11**	25k. multicoloured	6·25	3·75

12 Bisect of Denmark 4ore Blue, 1919

1979. Europa. Multicoloured.

42	**12**	140ore bl & yell on stone	60	55
43	-	180ore ol & mve on stone	70	70

DESIGN: 180ore Denmark 1919 2ore surcharge on 5ore.

13 Girl in Festive Costume

1979. International Year of the Child. Multicoloured designs showing childrens' drawings.

44	110ore Type **13**	50	45
45	150ore Man fishing from boat	50	45
46	200ore Two friends	55	50

14 Sea Plantain

1980. Flowers. Multicoloured.

47	90ore Type **14**	30	25
48	110ore Glacier buttercup	35	35
49	150ore Purple saxifrage	50	45
50	200ore Starry saxifrage	60	45
51	400ore Faroese lady's mantle	1·00	90

15 Jakob Jakobsen (linguist and folklorist)

1980. Europa.

52	**15**	150ore green	40	40
53	-	200ore brown	45	45

DESIGN: 200ore Vensel Ulrich Hammershaimb (theologian and linguist).

16 Virgin and Child

1980. Pews of Kirkjubour Church (1st series).

54	**16**	110ore multicoloured	45	35
55	-	140ore multicoloured	45	35
56	-	150ore multicoloured	45	35
57	-	200ore black and buff	50	45

DESIGNS: 140ore St. John the Baptist; 150ore St. Peter; 200ore St. Paul.

See also Nos. 90/3.

17 Timber Houses, Torshavn

1981. Old Torshavn. Designs show different views.

58	**17**	110ore green	45	35
59	-	140ore black	45	35
60	-	150ore brown	45	35
61	-	200ore blue	50	45

18 Garter Dance

1981. Europa.

62	**18**	150ore green and brown	40	40
63	-	200ore brown and green	50	45

DESIGN: 200ore Ring dance.

19 Rune Stone

1981. Historic Writings of the Faroes.

64	**19**	10ore blue, black and grey	25	15
65	-	1k. lt brown, black & brn	35	25
66	-	3k. grey, black and red	1·10	55
67	-	6k. red, black and grey	2·20	1·10
68	-	10k. stone, brown and black	2·75	2·00

DESIGNS: 1k. Score of folksong, 1846; 3k. Manuscript of Sheep Farming Law, 1298; 6k. Seal showing heraldic ram, 1533; 10k. Title page of *Faeroae et Faeroa Reserata* and library.

20 Map of Viking Voyages in North Atlantic

1982. Europa.

69	**20**	1k.50 blue	50	45
70	-	2k. black	75	70

DESIGN: 2k. Archaeological excavations at Kvivik village.

21 Gjogv

1982. Villages.

71	**21**	180ore black and blue	50	45
72	-	220ore black and brown	1·10	70
73	-	250ore black and brown	75	70

DESIGNS: 220ore Hvalvik; 250ore Kvivik.

22 Elinborg's Promise to remain Faithful

1982. *The Ballad of Harra Paetur and Elinborg.* Multicoloured.

74	220ore Type **22**	75	55
75	250ore Elinborg longing for Paetur	75	55
76	350ore Paetur in disguise greets Elinborg	1·00	85
77	450ore Elinborg and Paetur sail away	1·30	1·10

23 *Arcturus*

1983. Old Cargo Liners on the Faroes Run. Multicoloured.

78	220ore Type **23**	65	60
79	250ore Laura	75	65
80	700ore *Thyra*	2·30	1·90

24 King

1983. 19th-century Chess Pieces by Pol i Bud from Nolsoy.

81	**24**	250ore brown and black	1·90	1·70
82	-	250ore blue and black	1·90	1·70

DESIGN: No. 82, Queen.

25 Niels R. Finsen (founder of phototherapy)

1983. Europa.

83	**25**	250ore blue	85	80
84	-	400ore purple	1·50	1·40

DESIGN: 400ore Sir Alexander Fleming (discoverer of penicillin).

26 Torsk

1983. Fishes. Multicoloured.

85	250ore Type **26**	75	70
86	280ore Haddock	95	90
87	500ore Atlantic halibut	1·50	1·40
88	900ore Atlantic wolffish	2·75	2·50

27 Greenland, Halsingland (Sweden) and Iceland Costumes

1983. Inauguration of Nordic House (cultural centre), Torshavn. Sheet 120×67 mm containing T **27** and similar horiz designs.

MS89	250ore Type **27**; 250ore Finnmark (Norway), Funen (Denmark) and Aland costumes; 250ore Telemark (Norway), Faroes and Ostra Nyland (Finland) costumes	11·50	12·50

1984. Pews of Kirkjubour Church (2nd series). As T **16**.

90	250ore multicoloured	75	60
91	300ore lt brown, black & brn	1·30	95
92	350ore brown, grey & black	1·10	1·00
93	400ore multicoloured	1·50	1·30

DESIGNS: 250ore St. John; 300ore St. Jacob; 350ore St. Thomas; 400ore Judas Taddeus.

28 Bridge

1984. Europa. 25th Anniv of European Post and Telecommunications Conference.

94	**28**	250ore red	75	70
95	**28**	500ore blue	1·80	1·70

29 Sverri Patursson

1984. Writers.

96	**29**	200ore green	60	55
97	-	250ore red	90	80
98	-	300ore blue	95	90
99	-	450ore violet	1·50	1·40

DESIGNS: 250ore Joannes Patursson; 300ore Janus Djurhuus; 450ore Hans Andrias Djurhuus.

30 Fisherman

1984. Fishing Industry.

100		280ore blue	80	75
101		300ore brown	95	90
102	**30**	12k. green	4·00	3·75

DESIGNS—HORIZ: 280ore Fishing ketch "*Westward Ho.* VERT: 300ore Fishermen on deck.

31 *Beauty of the Veils*

1984. Fairy Tales. Designs showing woodcuts by Elinborg Lutzen.

103	**31**	140ore blue, green & brn	5·50	5·00
104	-	280ore green and brown	5·50	5·00
105	-	280ore dp green, grn & brn	5·50	5·00
106	-	280ore brown and green	5·50	5·00
107	-	280ore dp green, grn & brn	5·50	5·00
108	-	280ore brn, grn & dp brn	5·50	5·00

DESIGNS: No. 104, *Beauty of the Veils* (different); 105, *The Shy Prince*; 106, *The Glass Sword*; 107, *Little Elin*; 108, "The Boy and the Ox".

32 Torshavn

1985. J. T. Stanley's Expedition to the Faroes, 1789. Paintings by Edward Dayes.

109	**32**	250ore brown and blue	80	70
110	-	280ore brown, green & bl	95	90
111	-	550ore green, brown & bl	1·70	1·80
112	-	800ore brown, green & bl	2·75	2·50

DESIGNS: 280ore Mount Skaeling; 550ore Hoyvik; 800ore The Rocking Stones, Eysturoy.

33 Cellist, Pianist and Flautist

1985. Europa. Music Year. Multicoloured.

113	280ore Type **33**	1·20	1·10
114	550ore Drummer, guitarist and saxophonist	2·20	2·10

34 *Self-portrait* (Ruth Smith)

1985. Paintings. Multicoloured.

115	280ore *The Garden, Hoyvik* (Tummas Arge) (horiz)	1·40	1·30
116	450ore Type **34**	2·00	1·90
117	550ore *Winter's Day in Nolsoy* (Steffan Danielsen) (horiz)	2·75	2·50

35 Nolsoy Lighthouse

1985. Lighthouses. Multicoloured.

118	270ore Type **35**	1·60	1·50
119	320ore Torshavn	1·90	1·80
120	350ore Mykines	2·00	1·90
121	470ore Map of the Faroes showing lighthouse sites	2·50	2·30

36 Douglas DC-3, Faroe Airways

1985. Aircraft. Multicoloured.

122	300ore Type **36**	2·75	2·50
123	300ore Fokker F.27 Friendship, Flugfelag Islands	2·75	2·50
124	300ore Boeing 737 Special, Maersk Air	2·75	2·50
125	300ore Beech 50 Twin Bonanza, Bjorum Fly	2·75	2·50
126	300ore Bell 212 helicopter, Snipan	2·75	2·50

37 Peasant in Forest

1986. Skrimsla (dancing ballad). Multicoloured.

127	300ore Type **37**	1·10	1·00
128	420ore Giant challenges peasant to chess game	1·80	1·60
129	550ore Peasant beats giant	2·00	1·90
130	650ore Peasant and castle	2·40	2·10

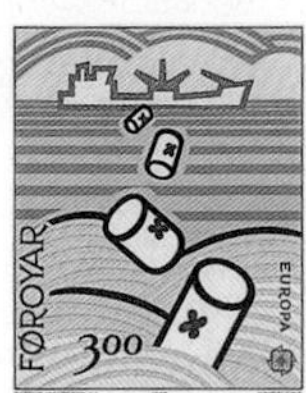

38 Ship dumping Dangerous Canisters at Sea

1986. Europa. Multicoloured.

131	3k. Type **38**	1·30	1·50
132	5k.50 Contents of damaged canister escaping into sea	2·40	2·40

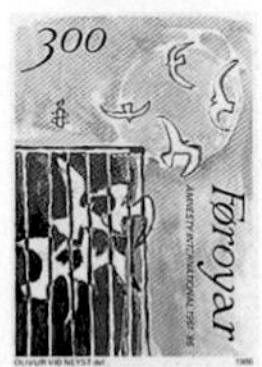

39 Birds escaping from Cage

1986. 25th Anniv of Amnesty International. Multicoloured.

133	3k. Type **39**	1·50	1·40
134	4k.70 Faces (horiz)	1·80	1·70
135	5k.50 Man behind bars and woman with children	2·30	2·20

40 Ship at Anchor in Bay

1986. "Hafnia 87" International Stamp Exhibition, Copenhagen (1st issue). Sheet 108×76 mm containing T **40** and similar vert designs showing *Torshavn East Bay* (watercolour) by Christian Rosenmeyer. Multicoloured.

MS136	3k. Type **40**; 4k.70 Rowing boat in bay; 6k.50 Houses (sold at 20k.)	13·50	12·50

See also No. **MS**154.

41 Glyvrar Bridge, Eysturoy

1986. Bridges.

137	**41**	2k.70 brown	2·40	2·20
138	-	3k. blue	2·30	2·20
139	-	13k. green	5·75	5·25

DESIGNS—VERT: 3k. Leypanagjogv, Vagar. HORIZ: 13k. Skaelingur, Streymoy.

42 Farmhouse, Depli

1987. Farm Buildings.

140	**42**	300ore dp blue & blue	1·40	1·30
141	-	420ore brown & lt brown	2·75	2·50
142	-	470ore green & lt green	2·75	2·50
143	-	650ore black & grey	3·25	3·00

DESIGNS: 420ore Barn, Depli; 470ore Cowshed and blacksmith's, Frammi vid Gjonna; 650ore Farmhouse, Frammi vid Gjonna.

43 Windows

1987. Europa. Architecture. Details of Nordic House, Torshavn (by O. Steen and K. Ragnarsdottir).

144	**43**	300ore blue	1·30	1·20
145	-	550ore brown	2·40	2·30

DESIGN: 550ore Entrance.

44 *Joannes Patursson*

1987. Trawlers. Multicoloured.

146	300ore Type **44**	1·30	1·20
147	550ore *Magnus Heinason* (side trawler)	2·50	2·30
148	800ore "*Sjurdarberg* (stern trawler)	4·75	4·00

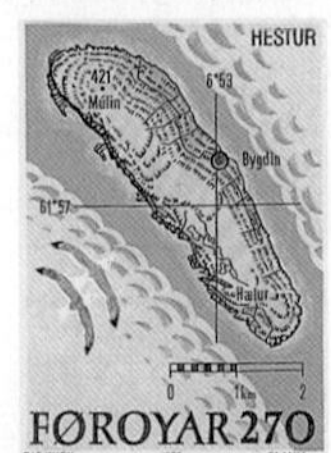

45 Map

1987. Hestur Island. Multicoloured.

149	270ore Type **45**	1·20	1·10
150	300ore Harbour (horiz)	1·10	1·00
151	420ore Alvastakkur needle	1·90	1·80
152	470ore Fagradalsvatn Lake (horiz)	2·00	1·80
153	550ore Bygdin village	2·20	2·10

46 Ships in Bay

1987. "Hafnia 87" International Stamp Exhibition, Copenhagen (2nd issue). Sheet 75×54 mm showing *Torshavn West Bay* (watercolour) by Christian Rosenmeyer.

MS154 **46**	3k. multicoloured (sold at 4k.)	3·75	3·50

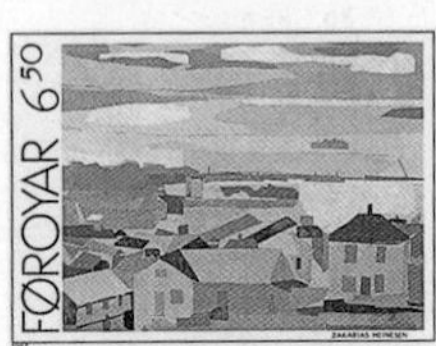

47 *West Bay*

1987. Torshavn Views. Collages by Zacharias Heinesen. Multicoloured.

155	4k.70 "East Bay"	2·20	2·00
156	6k.50 Type **47**	3·00	2·75

48 Daisy

1988. Flowers. Multicoloured.

157	2k.70 Type **48**	1·40	1·30
158	3k. Heath spotted orchid	1·20	1·10
159	4k.70 Tormentil	2·20	2·00
160	9k. Common butterwort	3·75	3·25

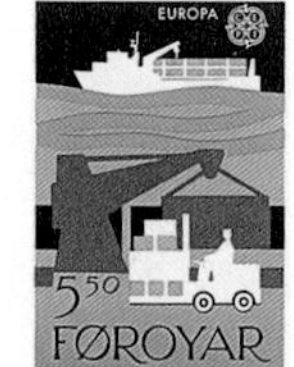

49 Container Ship and Dockside Scene

1988. Europa. Transport and Communications. Multicoloured.

161	3k. Dish aerial and satellite	1·20	1·10
162	5k.50 Type **49**	2·40	2·30

50 Jorgen-Frantz Jacobsen

1988. Writers.

163	**50**	270ore green	1·70	1·50
164	-	300ore red	1·10	1·00
165	-	470ore blue	1·90	1·80
166	-	650ore brown	3·00	2·75

DESIGNS: 300ore Christian Matras; 470ore William Heinesen; 650ore Hedin Bru.

51 Notice of Christmas Meeting and Conveners

1988. Centenary of Christmas Meeting to Establish National Movement. Multicoloured.

167	3k. Type **51**	1·10	1·00
168	3k.20 Drawing by William Heinesen of a People's Meeting, 1908, and conveners	1·60	1·50
169	12k. Opening words of Joannes Patursson's poem *Now the Hour has Come*, conveners and oystercatcher	5·25	5·00

52 Exterior View of Cathedral

1988. Kirkjubour Cathedral Ruins.

170	**52**	270ore green	2·40	2·20
171	-	300ore blue	1·40	1·30
172	-	470ore brown	2·40	2·10
173	-	550ore purple	2·75	2·20

DESIGNS—VERT: 300ore Window; 470ore Crucifixion (relief). HORIZ: 550ore Nave.

53 Church

1989. Bicentenary of Torshavn Church.

174	**53**	350ore green	1·40	1·30
175	-	500ore brown	2·30	2·20
176	-	15k. blue	6·00	5·25

DESIGNS—VERT: 500ore *The Last Supper* (altarpiece); 15k. Bell from *Norske Love* (shipwreck).

54 Wooden Toy Boat

1989. Europa. Children's Toys. Multicoloured.

177	3k.50 Type **54**	1·30	1·40
178	6k. Wooden horse	2·40	2·30

55 Sjostuka Man

1989. Nordic Countries' Postal Co-operation. Traditional Costumes. Multicoloured.

179	350ore Type **55**	1·30	1·40
180	600ore Stakkur woman	2·20	2·30

56 Rowing

1989. Sports. Multicoloured.

181	200ore Type **56**	1·10	1·00
182	350ore Handball	1·50	1·40
183	600ore Football	2·50	2·30
184	700ore Swimming	3·00	2·75

57 Tvoran

1989. Bird Cliffs of Suduroy. Each brown, green and blue.

185	320ore Type **57**	1·20	1·10
186	350ore Skuvanes	1·50	1·30
187	500ore Beinisvord	1·90	1·80
188	600ore Asmundarstakkur	2·75	2·50

58 Unloading Boxes of Fish from Trawler

1990. Fish Processing Industry. Multicoloured.

189	3k.50 Type **58**	1·20	1·10
190	3k.70 Cleaning Atlantic cod	1·50	1·30
191	5k. Filleting fish	2·40	2·00
192	7k. Packed processed fish	2·75	2·50

59 Old Post Office, Gjogv

1990. Europa. Post Office Buildings. Multicoloured.

193	3k.50 Type **59**	1·90	1·80
194	6k. Klaksvik post office	2·75	2·50

60 Faroese Flag

1990. 50th Anniv of Official Recognition of Faroese Flag. Sheet 116×75 mm containing T **60** and similar vert designs. Multicoloured.

MS195	3k.50 Type **60**; 3k.50 "Nyggjaberg" (trawler); 3k.50 "Sanna" (schooner)	5·50	5·00

61 Sowerby's Beaked Whale

1990. Whales. Multicoloured.

196	320ore Type **61**	1·60	1·50
197	350ore Bowhead whale	1·80	1·60
198	600ore Black right whale	2·75	2·20
199	700ore Northern bottle-nosed whale	3·50	3·00

62 Nolsoy from Hilltop

1990. Nolsoy. Paintings by Steffan Danielsen. Multicoloured.

200	50ore Type **62**	20	25
201	350ore Church	1·20	1·00
202	500ore Village	2·20	2·00
203	1000ore Cliffs by moonlight	4·25	3·75

63 Ribwort Plantain

1991. Anthropochora. Multicoloured.

204	3k.70 Type **63**	1·80	1·50
205	4k. Northern dock	2·40	1·90
206	4k.50 Black beetle	3·25	2·20
207	6k.50 Earthworm	3·50	3·00

64 Town Hall

1991. 125th Anniv of Torshavn as Capital. Multicoloured.

208	3k.70 Type **64**	1·60	1·70
209	3k.70 Eastern Tinganes (old part of Torshavn)	1·60	1·70

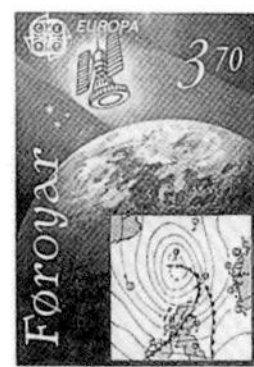

65 Satellite, Earth and Weather Map

1991. Europa. Europe in Space. Multicoloured.

210	3k.70 Type **65**	1·60	1·40
211	5k.50 Chart of Plough constellation and Pole Star, and sailors navigating by stars	2·50	2·50

66 Arctic Terns

1991. Birds. Multicoloured.

212	3k.70 Type **66**	1·80	1·40
213	3k.70 Black-legged kittiwakes	1·80	1·40

67 Saksun

1991. Nordic Countries' Postal Co-operation. Tourism. Multicoloured.

214	370ore Type **67**	1·30	1·20
215	650ore Vestmanna cliffs	2·50	2·30

68 *Handanagardur*

1991. 85th Birth Anniv of Samal Joensen-Mikines (painter). Multicoloured.

216	340ore *Funeral Procession*	1·70	1·40
217	370ore *The Farewell*	1·60	1·30
218	550ore Type **68**	2·10	1·70
219	1300ore *Winter Morning*	5·75	4·25

69 *Ruth*

1991. Mail Ships. Multicoloured.

220	200ore Type **69**	1·10	1·00
221	370ore *Ritan*	1·60	1·10
222	550ore *Sigmundur*	2·40	1·50
223	800ore *Masin*	3·25	2·50

70 Map and Viking Ship (Leif Eriksson)

1992. Europa. 500th Anniv of Discovery of America by Columbus. Multicoloured.

224	3k.70 Type **70**	2·50	2·00
225	6k.50 Map and "Santa Maria"	3·00	2·50
MS226	85×67 mm. Nos. 224/5	5·50	4·50

71 Grey Seal (*Halichoerus grypus*)

1992. Seals. Multicoloured.

227	3k.70 Type **71**	1·60	1·30
228	3k.70 Common seal (*Phoca vitulina*)	1·60	1·30

72 Desmine

1992. Minerals. Multicoloured.

229	370ore Type **72**	1·60	1·40
230	650ore Mesolite	2·40	2·30

73 Glyvra Hanus's House

1992. Old Houses in Nordragota, Eysturoy. Multicoloured.

231	3k.40 Type **73**	1·40	1·20
232	3k.70 Village and church	1·70	1·40
233	6k.50 Blasastova	3·00	2·30
234	8k. Jakupsstova	3·25	2·50

74 Musicians at Jazz, Folk and Blues Festival

1993. Tenth Anniv of Nordic House, Torshavn. Multicoloured.

235	400ore "The Lost Musicians" (William Heinesen)	1·60	1·30
236	400ore Joannes Andreassen (pianist)	1·60	1·30
237	400ore Type **74**	1·60	1·30
MS238	140×80 mm. Nos. 235/7	6·00	5·75

75 Landscape

1993. Nordic Countries' Postal Co-operation. Gjogv. Multicoloured.

239	4k. Type **75**	1·50	1·40
240	4k. Village	1·50	1·40

76 *Reflection*

1993. Europa. Contemporary Art. Bronzes by Hans Pauli Olsen. Multicoloured.

241	4k. Type **76**	1·70	1·30
242	7k. *Movement*	2·40	2·30

77 Horse's Head

1993. Horses.

243	**77**	400ore brown	1·40	1·30
244	-	20k. lilac	7·00	6·00

DESIGN—HORIZ: 20k. Mare and foal.

78 *Apamea zeta*

1993. Butterflies and Moths. Multicoloured.

245	350ore Type **78**	1·60	1·20
246	400ore *Hepialus humuli*	1·60	1·50
247	700ore Red admiral	3·00	2·30
248	900ore *Perizoma albulata*	3·75	2·75

79 Three-spined Stickleback

1994. Fish. Multicoloured.

249	10ore Type **79**	20	15
250	4k. False boarfish	1·80	1·40
251	7k. Brown trout	2·40	2·00
252	10k. Orange roughy	5·00	3·25

80 St. Brendan discovering Faroe Islands

1994. Europa. St. Brendan's Voyages. Multicoloured.

253	4k. Type **80**	1·60	1·30
254	7k. St. Brendan visiting Iceland	2·40	2·00
MS255	81×76 mm. Nos. 253/4	8·00	5·75

81 Sailing Ship and Sailor using Sextant

1994. Centenary (1993) of Faroese Nautical School, Torshavn. Multicoloured.

256	3k.50 Type **81**	1·90	1·50
257	7k. Modern ship and sailor using modern equipment	2·40	2·10

82 Dog and Sheep

1994. Sheepdogs. Multicoloured.

258	4k. Type **82**	1·60	1·50
259	4k. Dog's head (18×25 mm)	1·60	1·50

83 Viking Ship

1994. *Brusajokil's Lay* (traditional song). Multicoloured.

260	1k. Type **83**	35	30
261	4k. Asbjorn at entrance to Brusajokil's cave	1·60	1·30
262	6k. Trolls appearing after Ormar had killed cat	2·10	1·90
263	7k. Ormar pulling off Brusajokil's beard	2·75	2·50

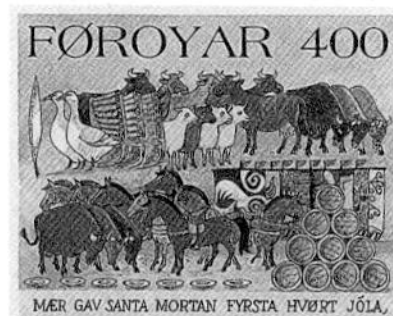

84 First to Tenth Days

1994. Christmas. Designs illustrating *On the First Day of Christmas St. Martin gave to Me.* Multicoloured.

264	400ore Type **84**	1·50	1·40
265	400ore 11th to 15th days	1·50	1·40

85 *Ulopa reticulata*

1995. Leafhoppers. Multicoloured.

266	50ore Type **85**	25	25
267	4k. *Streptanus sordidus*	1·40	1·30
268	5k. *Anoscopus flavostriatus*	1·60	1·50
269	13k. *Macrosteles alpinus*	5·00	4·25

86 Vatnsdalur

1995. Nordic Countries' Postal Co-operation. Tourism. Multicoloured.

270	400ore Type **86**	1·60	1·30
271	400ore Fomjin	1·60	1·30

87 Vidar, Vali and Baldur

1995. Europa. Peace and Freedom. Multicoloured.

272	4k. Type **87**	1·50	1·40
273	7k. Liv and Livtrasir	2·75	2·50

88 Museum of Art, Torshavn

1995. 50th Anniv of Nordic Artists Association. Multicoloured.

274	2k. Type **88**	80	70
275	4k. *Woman* (Frimod Joensen) (vert)	1·50	1·40
276	5k.50 Self-portrait (Joensen) (vert)	2·20	2·00

89 Common Raven

1995. The Raven. Multicoloured.

277	400ore Type **89**	1·50	1·30
278	400ore White speckled raven	1·50	1·30

90 St. Olaf

1995. Birth Millenary of St. Olaf.

279	**90**	4k. multicoloured	1·50	1·30

91 Dairy Maids

1995. Rural Life.

280	**91**	4k. green	1·50	1·30
281	-	6k. brown	2·50	1·90
282	-	15k. blue	5·00	4·75

DESIGNS—VERT: 6k. Sheep shearing; 15k. Fishermen.

92 St. Mary's Catholic Church

1995. Christmas. Multicoloured.

283	400ore Type **92**	1·60	1·50
284	400ore Stained glass window, St. Mary's Church	1·60	1·50

93 Risin and Kellingin (rocks)

1996

285	**93**	450ore multicoloured	1·50	1·40

94 *Ptilota plumosa*

1996. Seaweed. Multicoloured.

286	4k. Type **94**	1·50	1·20
287	5k.50 Flat wrack	2·20	1·60
288	6k. Knotted wrack	2·40	2·00
289	9k. Forest kelp	3·00	2·40

95 *Young Girl*

1996. Europa. Famous Women. Paintings by Samal Joensen-Mikines. Multicoloured.

290	4k.50 Type **95**	1·60	1·40
291	7k.50 Old Woman (vert)	2·75	2·20

96 Bohemian Waxwing

1996. Birds (1st series). Multicoloured.

292	4k.50 Type **96**	1·50	1·40
293	4k.50 Red crossbill (*Loxia curvirostra*)	1·50	1·40

See also Nos. 321/2, 336/7 and 355/6.

97 Faroe Islands and Compass Rose

1996. Maps.

301	**97**	10k. multicoloured	2·40	2·40
302	**97**	11k. multicoloured	2·75	2·50
303	**97**	14k. multicoloured	3·50	3·50
304	**97**	15k. multicoloured	3·75	3·50
305	**97**	16k. multicoloured	4·25	4·25
306	**97**	18k. multicoloured	4·25	4·50
309	**97**	22k. multicoloured	5·25	5·00

98 Boy Playing with Hoop (Bugvi)

1996. "Nordatlantex 96" Stamp Exhibition, Torshavn. Children's Drawings. Sheet 98×61 mm containing T **98** and similar vert designs. Multicoloured.

MS314	4k.50 Type **98**; 4k.50 Girls and traffic lights (Gudrid); 4k.50 Street and child on bicycle (Herborg)	4·75	4·50

99 "Flock of Sheep"

1996. Paintings by Janus Kamban. Multicoloured.

315	4k.50 Type **99**	1·50	1·40
316	6k.50 *Fishermen on way Home*	2·00	1·80
317	7k.50 *View from Torshavn's Old Quarter*	2·40	2·30

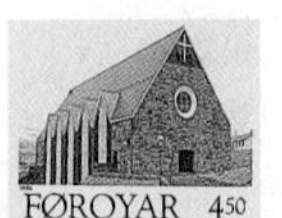

100 Klaksvik Church

1996. Christmas. Multicoloured.

318	4k.50 Type **100**	1·50	1·30
319	4k.50 Altarpiece depicting biblical scenes (21×38 mm)	1·50	1·30

101 Queen Margrethe in Faroese National Costume

1997. Silver Jubilee of Queen Margrethe. Sheet 81×61 mm.

MS320	**101**	450ore multicoloured	3·00	2·75

1997. Birds (2nd series). As T **96**. Multicoloured.

321	4k.50 Redpolls (*Carduelis flammea*)	1·30	1·20
322	4k.50 Northern bullfinches (*Pyrrhula pyrrhula*)	1·30	1·20

102 *Hygrocybe helobia*

1997. Fungi. Multicoloured.

323	4k.50 Type **102**	1·50	1·30
324	6k. *Hygrocybe chlorophana*	2·20	1·60
325	6k.50 Snowy wax cap	2·30	2·00
326	7k.50 Parrot wax cap	2·50	2·20

103 Seal

1997. 600th Anniv of Kalmar Union (of Denmark, Norway and Sweden).

327	**103**	4k.50 violet	1·30	1·20

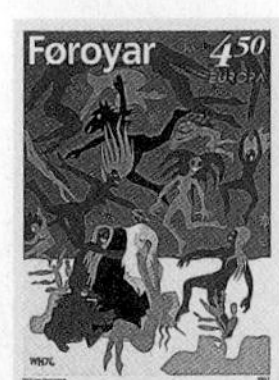

104 *Temptations of Saint Anthony*

1997. Europa. Tales and Legends. Illustrations by William Heinesen. Multicoloured.

328	4k.50 Type **104**	1·60	1·30
329	7k.50 *The Merman* (eating fish bait)	2·75	2·20

105 Hvalvik Church

1997. Christmas. Multicoloured.

330	4k.50 Type **105**	1·30	1·20
331	4k.50 Church interior	1·30	1·20

106 Arrival of Poul Aggerso

1997. *Barbara* (film from novel by Jorgen-Frantz Jacobsen). Scenes from the film. Multicoloured.

332	4k.50 Type **106**	1·30	1·20
333	6k.50 Annike van der Lippe and Lars Simonsen as Barbara and Aggerso	1·90	1·80
334	7k.50 Barbara and men in boat	2·40	2·00
335	9k. Barbara in rowing boat	2·75	2·50

107 Blackbird

1998. Birds (3rd series). Multicoloured.

336	4k.50 Type **107**	1·30	1·20
337	4k.50 Common starling (*Sturnus vulgaris*)	1·30	1·20

108 Wall of Fire around King Budle and Brynhild

1998. *Brynhild's Ballad* (traditional poem). Multicoloured.

338	450ore Type **108**	1·30	1·20
339	650ore Sigurd on his horse Grane jumps through the flames	1·80	1·60
340	750ore Golden rings around Sigurd and Brynhild	2·10	2·00
341	1000ore Gudrun (Sigurd's widow) leading Grane	3·00	2·75

109 Atlantic White-sided Dolphin

1998. International Year of the Ocean. Whales and Dolphins. Multicoloured.

342	4k. Type **109**	1·20	1·10
343	4k.50 Killer whale	1·30	1·20
344	7k. Bottle-nosed dolphin	2·40	1·90
345	9k. White whale	2·75	2·50

110 Procession with Flags

1998. Europa. National Festivals. St. Olav's Day. Multicoloured.

346	4k.50 Type **110**	1·30	1·20
347	7k.50 Members of Parliament and clergy processing through the streets	2·30	2·10

111 Hands cradling Family

1998. 50th Anniv of Universal Declaration of Human Rights.

348	**111**	750ore multicoloured	2·10	2·00

112 Interior of Frederik's Church, Nes

1998. Christmas. Multicoloured.

349	4k.50 Type **112**	1·30	1·20
350	4k.50 Exterior of church	1·30	1·20

113 *Hagamynd*

1998. Paintings by Hans Hansen. Multicoloured.

351	4k.50 Type **113**	1·30	1·20
352	5k.50 *Bygdarmynd*	1·80	1·50
353	6k.50 *Portrait of a Man*	1·90	1·70
354	8k. *Self-portrait*	2·75	2·10

114 Winter Wren

1999. Birds (4th series). Multicoloured.

355	4k.50 Type **114**	1·20	1·10
356	4k.50 House sparrow (*Passer domesticus*)	1·20	1·10

115 *Smiril* (ferry), 1896

1999. Suduroy–Torshavn Passenger Ferries. Multicoloured.

357	4k.50 Type **115**	1·10	1·00
358	5k. *Smiril*, 1932	1·30	1·30
359	8k. *Smyril*, 1967	2·20	2·00
360	13k. *Smyril* (car ferry), 1975	3·50	3·50

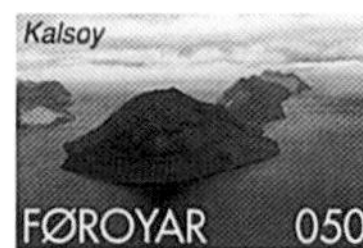

116 Kalsoy

1999. Islands of the Faroes. Multicoloured.

361	50ore Type **116**	25	20
362	100ore Vidoy	25	25
363	200ore Skuvoy	60	60
365	400ore Svinoy	1·20	1·10
366	450ore 50 Fugloy	1·60	1·30
367	500ore Bour	1·60	1·30
368	500ore Gasadalur	1·60	1·30
368a	550ore Stora Dimun	1·70	1·30
369	600ore Kunoy	1·60	1·50
370	650ore Hestoy	2·00	1·40
370a	700ore Litla Dimun	1·90	1·60
371	750ore Koltur	2·30	1·70
372	800ore Bardoy	2·30	2·20
375	1000ore Nolsoy	3·25	2·30

117 Svartifossur, Hoydalar

1999. Europa. Waterfalls. Multicoloured.

379	6k. Type **117**	1·80	1·60
380	8k. Foldarafossur, Hov	2·10	2·10

118 Adam and Eve

1999. Christmas. Multicoloured.

381	450ore Type **118**	1·30	1·20
382	600ore The Annunciation	1·70	1·60

119 *Bygd*

1999. Paintings by Ingalvur av Renyi. Multicoloured.

383	4k.50 Type **119**	1·20	1·10
384	6k. "Husavik"	1·70	1·40
385	8k. "Reytt regn" (vert)	1·90	1·90
386	20k. "Genta" (vert)	4·50	4·50

120 Rasmus Rasmussen and Simun av Skardi (founders)

2000. Centenary (1999) of Folk High School, Torshavn. Multicoloured.

387	4k.50 Type **120**	1·30	1·10
388	4k.50 Sanna av Skardi and Anna Suffia Rasmussen (housekeepers and teachers)	1·30	1·10

121 Arrival of Sigmundur

2000. One Thousand Years of Christianity on the Faroe Islands. Multicoloured.

389	4k.50 Type **121**	1·20	1·10
390	5k.50 Killing of bishop by rebels	1·30	1·20
391	8k. People with flags of Denmark and Faroe Islands	1·90	1·80
392	16k. Children on shore and sun rising	4·25	3·75

122 "Building Europe"

2000. Europa.

393	**122**	8k. multicoloured	2·10	1·90

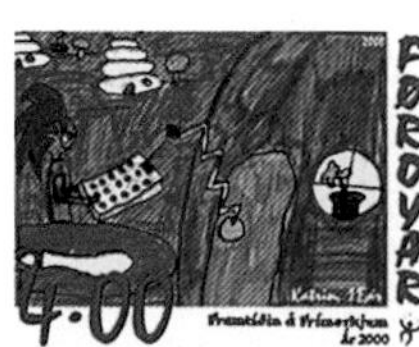

123 Girl unlocking Door by Remote Control and House (Katrin Mortensen)

2000. "Stampin' the Future". Winning Entries in Children's International Painting Competition Multicoloured.

394	4k. Type **123**	1·00	95
395	4k.50 Boy dreaming of future (Sigga Andreassen)	1·20	1·10
396	6k. Offshore oil rig (Steingrimur Joensen)	1·50	1·40
397	8k. Spaceman and television (Dion Dam Frandsen)	2·10	1·80

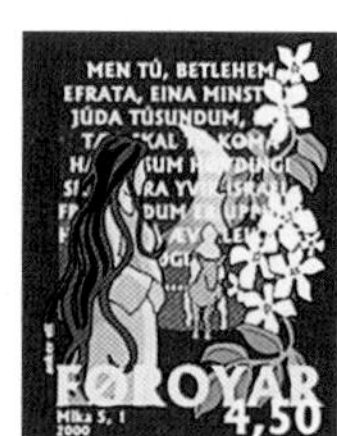

124 Mary and Joseph

2000. Christmas. Multicoloured.

398	4k.50 Type **124**	1·20	1·10
399	6k. Mary holding Jesus	1·50	1·40

125 Apostle holding Cross

2001. Pew Gables, St. Olav's Church, Kirkjubour.

400	**125**	450ore buff, black & grey	1·40	1·40
401	-	650ore buff, black & cinn	1·70	1·60
402	-	800ore buff, black & grn	3·00	2·75
403	-	18k. buff, black and brown	6·50	6·00

DESIGNS: 650ore Apostle holding knife; 800ore Apostle holding book in right hand; 18k. Apostle holding book in left hand.

126 Elderly Woman

2001. 75th Anniv of Faroese Red Cross. Multicoloured.

404	4k.50 Type **126**	1·10	1·00
405	6k. Red Cross volunteers carrying patient on stretcher	1·40	1·30

127 Skjuts (early postal service) Boat

2001. 25th Anniv of Faroese Postal Administration. Sheet 138×101 mm containing T **127** and similar vert designs. Each buff, black and silver.

MS406	4k.50 Type **127**; 4k.50 First Post Office, Torshavn; 4k50 Postman	4·25	4·00

128 Hognis and Tidrik Tattneson (*Hognis Ballad*)

2001. Nordic Myths and Legends. Multicoloured.

407	6k. Type **128**	1·50	1·40
408	6k. Tree and birds nests (*The Tree of the Year*)	1·50	1·40
409	6k. Woman beside river (*The Harp*)	1·50	1·40
410	6k. Sigurd the Dragonslayer's horse Grane and sword Gram	1·50	1·40
411	6k. Sigurd fighting dragon (*Ballad of Nornagest*)	1·50	1·40
412	6k. Hogni Jukeson and brothers on ship "*Hognis Ballad*)	1·50	1·40

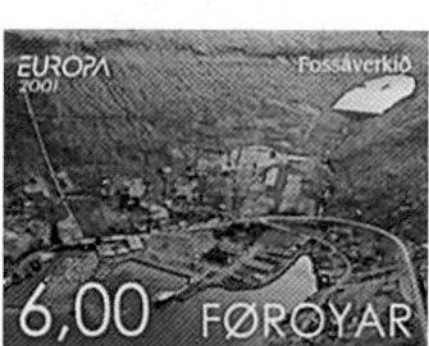

129 Hydro-electric Power Station, Fossaverkio, Vestmanna

2001. Europa. Water Resources. Multicoloured.

413	6k. Type **129**	1·80	1·60
414	8k. Hydro-electric power station, Eidisverkio, Eysturoy	2·30	2·20

130 *The Artist's Mother*

2001. Paintings by Zacharias Heinesen. Multicoloured.

415	4k. Type **130**	1·00	95
416	4k.50 *Uti a Reyni*	1·20	1·10
417	10k. *Ur Vagunum*	2·75	2·50
418	15k. *Sunrise*	4·00	3·75

131 Sperm Whale (*Physeter macrocephalus*)

2001. Whales. Multicoloured.

419 4k.50 Type **131** 1·20 1·10
420 6k.50 Fin whales (*Balaenoptera physalus*) 1·80 1·70
421 9k. Blue whales (*Balaenoptera musculus*) 2·30 2·20
422 20k. Sei whales (*Balaenoptera borealis*) 5·25 4·75

132 Simeon and Mary

2001. Christmas. Multicoloured.

423 5k. Type **132** 1·30 1·20
424 6k.50 Flight into Egypt 1·70 1·60

133 Atlantic Bob-tailed Squid (*Sepiola atlantica*)

2002. Molluscs. Multicoloured.

425 5k. Type **133** 1·30 1·20
426 7k. Horse mussel (*Modiolus modiolus*) 1·70 1·60
427 7k.50 Sea slug (*Polycera faeroensis*) 1·80 1·70
428 18k. Common northern whelk (*Buccinum undatum*) 4·25 4·00

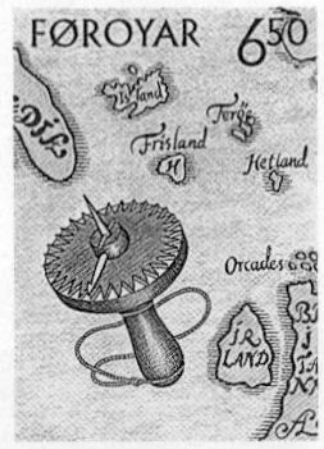

134 Primitive Compass

2002. Viking Voyages. Sheet 160×70 mm containing T **134** and similar vert designs. Multicoloured.

MS429 6k.50 Type **134**; 6k.50 Viking sailor using compass; 6k.50 Viking ship 6·00 5·75

135 *Depths of the Ocean*

2002. Nordic Countries' Postal Co-operation. Art by Trondur Patursson. Multicoloured.

430 5k. Type **135** 1·30 1·20
431 6k.50 *Cosmic Space* 1·60 1·50

136 Clowns (Anna Katrina Olsen)

2002. Europa. Circus. Showing winning designs in children's painting competition. Multicoloured.

432 6k.50 Type **136** 1·70 1·50
433 8k. Animals in Circus Tent (Sara Zachariasardottir) 2·00 1·80

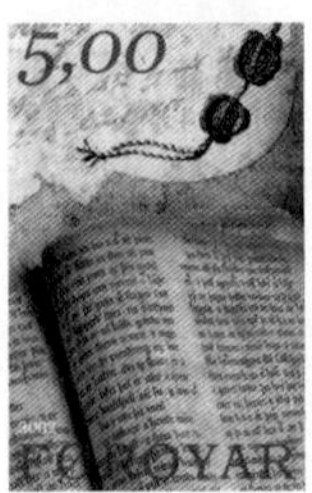

137 Kongsbokin (Royal Book)

2002. 150th Anniv of Foroya Logting (Faroese Representative Council). Sheet 100×70 mm containing T **137** and similar vert design. Multicoloured.

MS434 5k. Type **137**; 6k.50, Introduction of the 1852 Logting protocol 3·75 3·50

138 Whimbrel (*Numenius phaeopus*)

2002. Birds. Showing chicks and eggs. Multicoloured.

435 5k. Type **138** 1·30 1·20
436 7k.50 Common snipe (*Gallinago gallinago*) 1·80 1·70
437 12k. Oystercatcher (*Haematopus ostralegus*) 3·00 2·75
438 20k. Golden plover (*Pluvialis apricaria*) 5·25 4·75

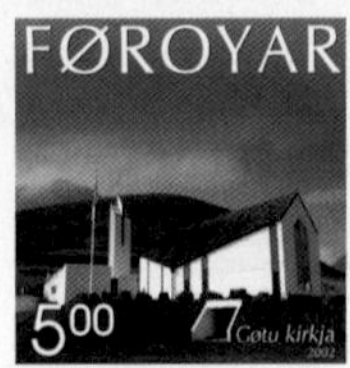

139 Church

2002. Gøta Church. Multicoloured.

439 5k. Type **139** 1·40 1·30
440 6k.50 Church interior 1·80 1·70

140 Cliffs and Blue Whiting (*Micromesistius poutassou*)

2002. Centenary of International Council for the Exploration of the Sea. Sheet 186×61 mm, containing T **140** and similar vert design. Multicoloured.

MS441 8k. Type **140**; 8k. *Magnus Heinason* (trawler) and blue whiting 4·75 4·50

Stamps of a similar design were issued by Denmark and Greenland.

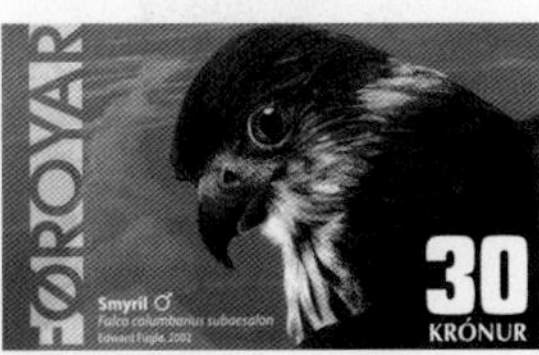

141 Male Merlin (*Falco columbarius subaesalon*)

2002

442 **141** 30k. multicoloured 8·00 7·50

142 Engine Drilling

2003. Completion of Vagatunnilin (tunnel under Vestmannasund). Multicoloured.

443 5k. Type **142** 1·40 1·30
444 5k. Miners and equipment 1·40 1·30

143 Heid

2003. Norse Myths and Legends. Voluspa. Multicoloured.

445 6k.50 Type **143** 1·50 1·40
446 6k.50 Creation of the universe 1·50 1·40
447 6k.50 Creation of humans 1·50 1·40
448 6k.50 Norns (deities of fate) and Yggdrasil (world tree) 1·50 1·40
449 6k.50 Thor with raised hammer 1·50 1·40
450 6k.50 Odin hurling spear 1·50 1·40
451 6k.50 Baldur dying and his infant brother Hodlyn 1·50 1·40
452 6k.50 Ship and Nidhog (giant serpent) 1·50 1·40
453 6k.50 Hodlyn killing serpent 1·50 1·40
454 6k.50 Hodur and Baldur 1·50 1·40

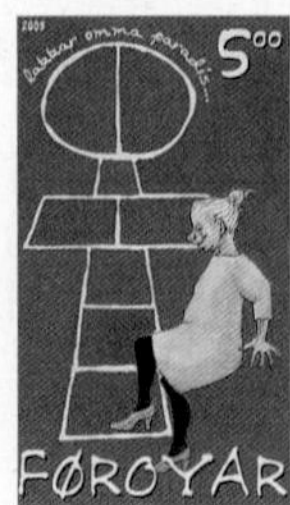

144 *Omma Ludvik*

2003. Children's Songs. Sheet 166×80 mm containing T **144** and similar vert designs. Multicoloured.

MS455 5k.×10, Type **144** and nine different designs depicting children's songs 12·50 11·50

145 *Fish Tree* (tapestry) (Astrid Andreasen)

2003. Europa. Poster Art. Multicoloured.

456 6k.50 Type **145** 1·70 1·50
457 8k. *Chrysalis*, "*Reclining Form* and *Jazz III* (ceramics) (Gudrid Poulsen) 2·00 1·80

146 Fuglafjordur

2003. Island Post Office Centenaries. Sheet 170×120 mm containing T **146** and similar horiz designs. Each black and grey.

MS458 5k. Type **146**; 5k. Strendur; 5k. Sandur; 5k. Eidi; 5k. Vestmanna; 5k. Vagur; 5k. Midvagur; 5k. Hvalba 9·75 9·00

147 Jesper Rasmussen Brochmand

2003. Theologians. Multicoloured.

459 5k. Type **147** 1·20 1·20
460 6k.50 Thomas Kingo 1·70 1·60

148 *Dance in Main Room* (Emil Krause)

2003. Czeslaw Slania's 100th Stamp for Faroese Posts. Sheet 88×72 mm.

MS461 **148** 25k. multicoloured 6·25 5·75

149 Sandvok

2004. Settlements on Suduroy Island. Sheet 135×204 mm containing T **149** and similar horiz designs. Multicoloured.

MS462 5k.×10, Type **149**; Hvalba; Frodba; Oravok; Fámjin; Hov; Porkeri; Akrar; Sumba; Akraberg 20·00 17·00

150 Thor (god) and the Midgard Serpent

2004. Nordic Mythology. Sheet 105×70 mm containing T **150** and similar vert design. Multicoloured.

MS463 6k.50×2, Type **150**; Ran (sea goddess) 5·25 4·25

Stamps of a similar theme were issued by Aland Islands, Denmark, Finland, Greenland, Iceland, Norway and Sweden.

151 Gasholmur and Tindholmur

2004. 150th Anniv of *Journal of Cruise of Maria* (yacht) by Samuel Rathbone and E. H. Greig. Sheet 176×140 mm containing T **151** and similar horiz designs showing illustrations from the journal. Multicoloured.

MS464 6k.50×8, Type **151**; *Diamantunum* (yacht); Houses; Mylingur; Mylingur (different); Kalsoyggin; Yacht and rowing boats; Kunoynni 20·00 17·00

152 Prince Frederik and Mary Donaldson

2004. Marriage of Crown Prince Frederik and Mary Elizabeth Donaldson. Multicoloured.

MS465 130×65 mm. 5k. Type **152**; 6k.50 As 5k. but with design reversed 4·75 3·75

Stamps of same design were issued by Denmark and Greenland.

153 Club Emblems and Players

2004. Football Centenaries. Multicoloured.

466	5k. Type **153** (KI) (Klasvik) and HB (Torshavn) football clubs	1·40	1·20
467	6k.50 Tackling for ball (FIFA)	2·00	1·80

154 Cliffs and Yacht, Hestur

2004. Europa. Holidays. Multicoloured.

468	6k.50 Type **154**	2·00	1·80
469	8k. Walking on foreshore, Stora Dimun	3·75	2·50

155 Vagur Church

2004. Christmas. Churches. Multicoloured.

470	5k.50 Type **155**	1·80	1·50
471	7k.50 Tvoroyri church	3·50	2·00

156 Sea, Woman and Columns

2004. Poems by Jens Hendrik Oliver (Janus) Djurhuus. Sheet 158×126 mm containing T **156** and similar vert designs. Multicoloured.

MS472 7k.50×10, Type **156** (*Atlantis*); Woman, children, man and ship (*Grimur Kamban*); Face in storm (*Gandkvædi Trondar*); Seated man (*Til Faroya I-II*); Woman and sea (*Min sorg*); Snake, woman and man (*Loki*); Birds, wren and crows (*I buri og Slatur*); Giantess and ship at sea (*Heimferd Nolsyar Pals*); Moses and stone tablets (*Moses a Sinai fjalli*); Cello and man wearing raincoat and hat (*Cello*) 30·00 25·00

157 Vikar

2005. Settlements on Vagar Island. Sheet 135×206 mm containing T **157** and similar horiz designs. Multicoloured.

MS473 5k.50×10, Type **157**; Gasadalur; Bour; Slaettanes; Kvigandalsa; Sorvagur; Sandavagur; Vatnsoyrar; Fjallavatn; Miovagur 22·00 19·00

158 Farmers and Sheep

2005. Everyday Life in Viking Age. Sheet 161×70 mm containing T **158** and similar vert designs. Multicoloured.

MS474 7k.50×3, Type **158**; Making hay; Woman milking cow 9·00 7·75

The stamps and margin of **MS**474 form a composite design of a Viking community.

159 White Snow Hare

2005. Faroese Snow Hare (Lepus timidus). Multicoloured.

475	5k.50 Type **159**	2·20	1·80
476	5k.50 Dark (blue) hare	2·20	1·80

160 Lambs' Heads, Stew, Bread and Fish (image scaled to 68% of original size)

2005. Europa. Gastronomy. Multicoloured.

477	7k.50 Type **160**	3·00	2·00
478	10k. Fish heads, rhubarb and stuffed puffins	3·50	2·75

161 Leach's Storm Petrel (*Oceanodroma leucorhoa*)

2005. Petrels. Multicoloured.

479	8k.50 Type **161**	4·00	2·75
480	9k. British storm petrel (*Hydrobates pelagicus*)	4·25	3·00
481	12k. Leach's storm petrel	6·00	4·25
482	20k. British storm petrel	8·00	5·75

162 *Christmas Song*

2005. Christmas. Religious Songs. Multicoloured.

483	5k.50 Type **162**	1·80	1·50
484	7k.50 *The Rudis Ballad*	3·50	2·00

163 Soldiers

2005. British Occupation during World War II, 1940–45.

485	163	5k.50 black and azure	1·80	1·50
486	-	9k. black and stone	4·25	3·00

DESIGN: 9k. Soldiers with children.

164 Landscape

2005. Art. Paintings by Jogvan Waagstein. Multicoloured.

487	7k.50 Type **164**	2·75	2·00
488	7k.50 Houses and sea	2·75	2·00
489	7k.50 Inlet	2·75	2·00
490	7k.50 Road through hills	2·75	2·00
491	7k.50 Large pool and sea	2·75	2·00
492	7k.50 Coastline	2·75	2·00
493	7k.50 Road and rocks	2·75	2·00
494	7k.50 Sea, houses and road	2·75	2·00
495	7k.50 Church	2·75	2·00

165 *Himantolophus groenlandicus*

2006. Deepwater Fish. Multicoloured.

496	5k.50 Type **165**	1·80	1·50
497	5k.50 *Gonostoma elongatum*	1·80	1·50
498	5k.50 *Sebastes mentella*	1·80	1·50
499	5k.50 *Neoraja caerulea*	1·80	1·50
500	5k.50 *Rhinochimaera atlantica*	1·80	1·50
501	5k.50 *Linophryne Lucifer*	1·80	1·50
502	5k.50 *Ceratias holboelli*	1·80	1·50
503	5k.50 *Lampris guttatus*	1·80	1·50
504	5k.50 *Argyropelecus olfersi*	1·80	1·50
505	5k.50 *Lophius piscatorius*	1·80	1·50

166 Syorugota

2006. Villages. Multicoloured.

506	7k. Type **166**	2·75	2·00
507	12k. Fuglafjorour	5·50	4·25
508	20k. Lerivik	7·75	6·75

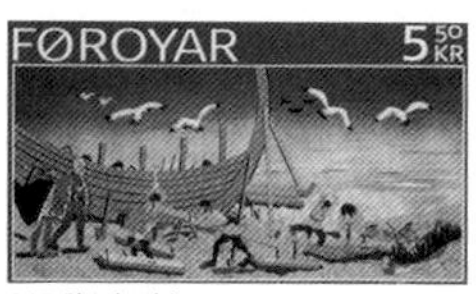
167 Shipbuilding

2006. Ormurin Langi (ballad of *The Long Serpent*). Multicoloured.

509/18 5k. 50×10, Type **167**; Launch; King Olaf on throne; Fleet at sea; Ships watched by enemies ashore; Long Serpent with Ulf the Red at the helm; King Olaf and Erik the Archer on the quarterdeck; Battle scene; Boarding and capture; Battle over 20·00 13·50

168 Nornur (fate)

2006. Nordic Mythology. Multicoloured.

MS519 105×70 mm. 7k.50×2, Type **168**; Sjodreygil (sea ghost) 6·00 4·75

Stamps of a similar theme were issued by Aland Islands, Denmark, Greenland, Finland, Iceland, Norway and Sweden.

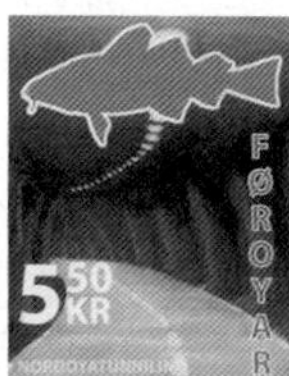
169 Tunnel, Road and Fish

2006. Nordoyatunnilin (tunnel between Eystruroy and Bordoy). Multicoloured.

520	5k.50 Type **169**	2·20	1·20
521	5k.50 Tunnel, road and boat	2·20	1·20

170 Clasped Hands

2006. Europa. Integration. Multicoloured.

522	7k.50 Type **170**	3·00	2·50
523	10k. Downward clasped hands	3·75	3·00

171 Weathervane

2006. Sandur—Oldest Faroese Church. Multicoloured.

524	5k.50 Type **171**	2·00	1·20
525	7k.50 Door, window and pews	3·25	2·50

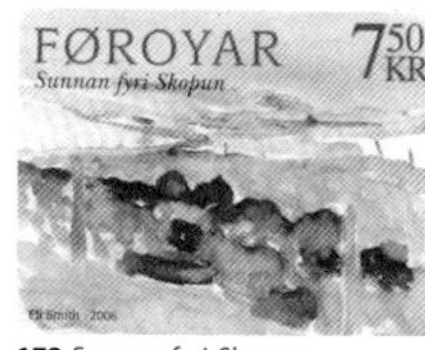
172 Sunnan fyri Skopun

2006. Settlements on Sandoy Island. Sheet 180×121 mm containing T **172** and similar horiz designs. Multicoloured.

MS526 7k.50×8, Type **172**; Dalur; Soltuvik; Skalavik; Skopun; Sandur; Skarvanes; Husavik 19·00 17·00

173 Man watching Seal

2007. Myths and Legends. Kopakonan (seal woman). Multicoloured.

527	5k.50 Type **173**	1·80	1·20
528	5k.50 Seal women dancing	1·80	1·20
529	5k.50 Stealing seal woman's skin	1·80	1·20
530	5k.50 Seal woman and farmer	1·80	1·20
531	5k.50 Seal woman and mate	1·80	1·20
532	5k.50 Seal woman and small children	1·80	1·20
533	5k.50 Seal woman and children	1·80	1·20
534	5k.50 Seal woman and man	1·80	1·20
535	5k.50 Farmer killing seal woman's mate and cubs	1·80	1·20
536	5k.50 Seal woman as she-troll	1·80	1·20

174 *Le Recherche*

2007. Lithographs by Barthelemy Lauvergne. Multicoloured.

537	5k.50 Type **174**	2·00	1·40
538	7k.50 *Skaelingsfjall*	3·25	2·50

175 Wave

2007. Tenth Anniv of West Nordic Council. Tidal Energy.

539	**175**	7k.50 multicoloured	3·25	2·50

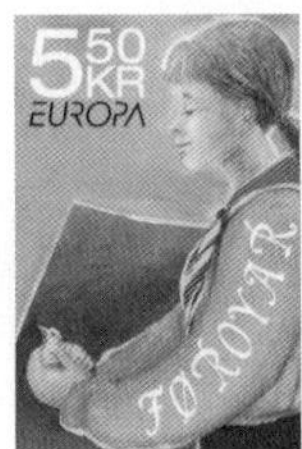

176 Scout

2007. Europa. Centenary of Scouting. Multicoloured.

No.	Description	Unused	Used
540	5k.50 Type **176**	2·20	1·40
541	10k. Tent	4·25	3·50

177 Ketil killing Whale

2007. *Feogar a fero* (Old Man and his Sons) novel by Heoin Bru. Multicoloured.

No.	Description	Unused	Used
542	7k.50 Type **177**	2·25	1·80
543	7k.50 Klavus with broken leg	2·25	1·80
544	7k.50 Kalvur and Klavusardottir	2·25	1·80
545	7k.50 Ketil and Klavur fishing	2·25	1·80
546	7k.50 Ketil's wife arguing with her daughter-in-law	2·25	1·80
547	7k.50 Ketil catching fulmars	2·25	1·80
548	7k.50 Kalvur	2·25	1·80
549	7k.50 Ketil and Kalvur with cow	2·25	1·80

178 Jakup Dahl

2007. Faroese Bible Translators. Sheet 110×70 mm containing T **178** and similar vert designs. Multicoloured.

MS550 5k.50×3, Type **178**; Kristian O. Videro; Victor Danielsen 7·00 6·50

The stamps of **MS**550 form a composite design.

179 Chickens

2007. Domestic Fowl. Multicoloured.

No.	Description	Unused	Used
551	9k. Type **179**	3·50	2·75
552	20k. Ducks	7·00	5·75
553	25k. Geese	9·00	8·25

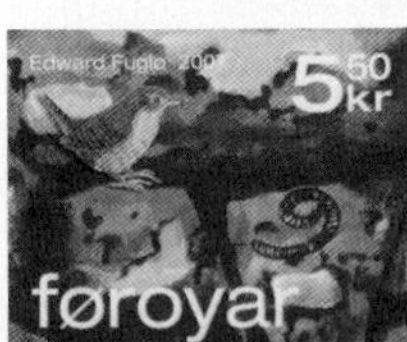

180 Wren and Millipede

2007. Wildlife of Stone Fences. Sheet 170×100 mm containing T **180** and similar horiz designs. Multicoloured.

MS554 5k.50×8, Type **180**; Beetles; Mouse; Crane fly; Storm petrel and hawkbit; Wheatear and buttercup; Earwigs; Starling and eggs 17·00 16·00

The stamps and margins of **MS**554 form a composite design.

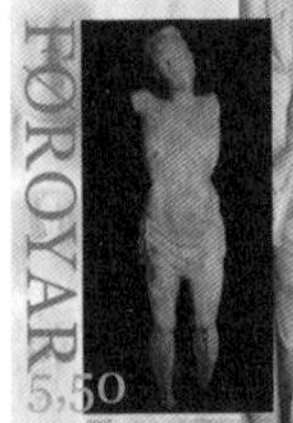

181 Christ Figurine

2007. Statues from Small White Church. Multicoloured.

No.	Description	Unused	Used
555	5k.50 Type **181**	2·00	1·80
556	7k.50 Madonna of Kirkjubour	3·50	3·00

182 Coastline, Hoyvik

2007. SEPAC (small European mail services).

No.	Type	Description	Unused	Used
557	**182**	7k.50 multicoloured	3·25	2·75

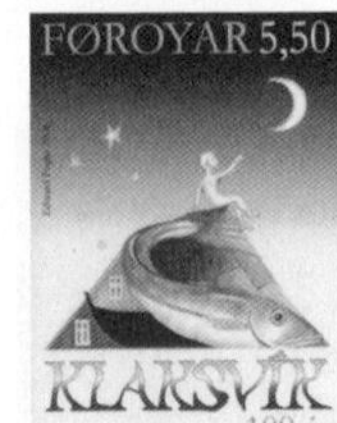

183 Symbols of Klaksvik

2008. Centenary of Klaksvik.

No.	Type	Description	Unused	Used
558	**183**	5k.50 multicoloured	2·75	2·50

184 Patients and Sanatorium

2008. Centenary of Tuberculosis Sanatorium, Hoydalar. Multicoloured.

No.	Description	Unused	Used
559	5k.50 Type **184**	2·75	2·50
560	9k. Dr. Vilhelm Magnussen (pioneer specialist) X-raying patient and child being vaccinated	4·00	3·75

185 Mountain and Houses

2008. Illustrations by Elinborg Eutzens. Sheet 130×83 mm containing T 185 and similar multicoloured designs.

MS561 10k.×6, Type **185**; Milkmaids (30×30 mm); Houses; Underwater reef; Cockerel (30×30 mm); Wharf 22·00 21·00

186 Buildings (rebuilt after fire in 1673)

2008. Tinganes (ancient parliament).

No.	Type	Description	Unused	Used
562	**186**	14k. multicoloured	6·50	6·25

187 Alvheyggur

2008. Norse Mythology. Mythical Places. Sheet 101×70 mm containing T **187** and similar horiz designs. Multicoloured.

MS563 7k.50×2, Type **187**; Klovin-gasteinur 7·25 6·25

188 Niels Winther

2008. Cultural Personlities. Sheet 96×102 mm containing T **188** and similar vert designs. Multicoloured.

MS564 5k.50×6, Type **188** (politician); Susanna Patursson (writer); Rasmus Effersoe (writer and nationalist); Jorgvan Poulsen (writer); Friorikur Petersen (writer); Andreas Evensen (writer, educationalist and politician) 14·50 13·50

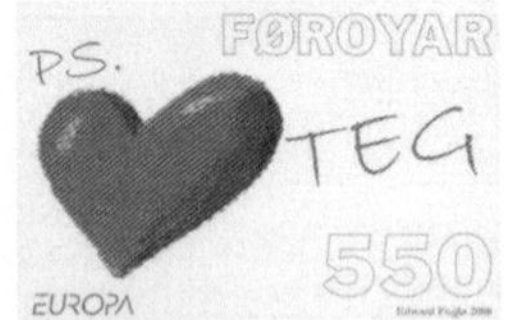

189 Heart, 'PS' and 'TEG'

2008. Europa. The Letter. Multicoloured.

No.	Description	Unused	Used
565	5k.50 Type **189**	2·75	2·50
566	7k. 50 @	3·25	2·75

190 *Caltha palustris*

2008. Marsh Marigold—National Flower.

No.	Type	Description	Unused	Used
567	**190**	30k. multicoloured	14·00	13·00

191 Processional Cross, Kirkjubour

2008. Ancient Crosses. Multicoloured.

No.	Description	Unused	Used
568	6k. Type **191**	3·00	2·30
569	10k. Wooden Cross, Leirvik	5·25	4·75

192 *Gymnocarpium dryopteris*

2008. Ferns. Multicoloured.

No.	Description	Unused	Used
570	8k. Type **192**	4·00	3·50
571	8k. *Polypodium vulgare*	4·00	3·25
572	8k. *Dryopteris dilatata*	4·00	3·25
573	8k. *Asplenium adiantum nigrum*	4·00	3·25
574	8k. *Athyrium felix femina*	4·00	3·25
575	8k. *Dryopteris felix mas*	4·00	3·25
576	8k. *Cystopteris fragilis*	4·00	3·25
577	8k. *Phegopteris connectilis*	4·00	3·25
578	8k. *Polystichum lonchitis*	4·00	3·25
579	8k. *Asplenium trichomanes*	4·00	3·25

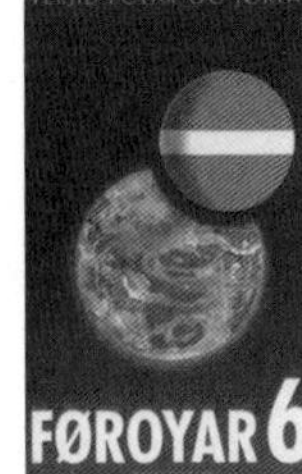

193 Globe and Stop Sign

2009. Global Warming Awareness Campaign. Multicoloured.

No.	Description	Unused	Used
580	6k. Type **193**	3·00	2·30
581	8k. Globe as water droplet	4·00	3·25
MS582	120×80 mm. Nos. 580/1	7·00	5·50

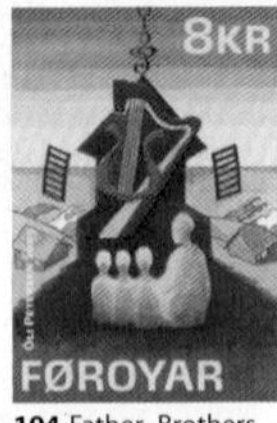

194 Father, Brothers and Aeolian Harp

2009. *The Lost Musicians* (De Fortabte Spilemaend) by William Heinesen. Designs showing scenes from the book. Multicoloured.

No.	Description	Unused	Used
583	8k. Type **194**	4·00	3·25
584	8k. Dancers	4·00	3·25
585	8k. The brothers	4·00	3·25
586	8k. Moritz and Eliana	4·00	3·25
587	8k. Playing the cello	4·00	3·25
588	8k. Playing to the old men	4·00	3·25
589	8k. Orpheus listening	4·00	3·25
590	8k. Orpheus leaving to study	4·00	3·25

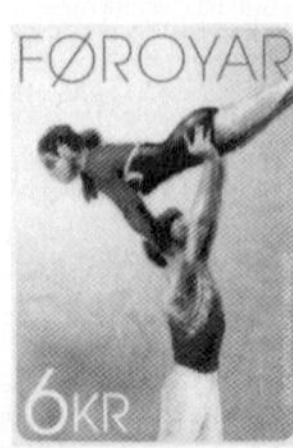

195 Pair of Gymnasts

2009. Centenary of Faroese Gymnastics. Multicoloured. (a) Ordinary gum.

No.	Description	Unused	Used
591	6k. Type **195**	3·00	2·30
592	10k. Handstand	5·25	4·75
593	26k. Using rings	10·00	9·25

(b) Self-adhesive.

No.	Description	Unused	Used
594	6k. As Type **195**	3·00	2·30
595	10k. As No. 592	5·25	4·75

196 Volcano, Lava and Trees

2009. Origins of Faroe Islands. Sheet 119×94 mm containing T **196** and similar horiz designs. Multicoloured.

MS596 10k.×6, Type **196**; Volcano and ash; 60 million years ago; 15 million years ago; Mid Atlantic ridge; Ice age and rock erosion 22·00 21·00

The stamps of **MS**596 share a common background design.

197 Saturn

2009. Europa. Astronomy. Multicoloured.

No.	Description	Unused	Used
597	10k. Type **197**	5·25	4·75
598	12k. Jupiter	6·00	4·50

198 Altarpiece, Vestmanna

2009. Christmas. Altarpieces. Multicoloured.

599	6k. Type **198**	3·00	2·30
600	10k. Altarpiece (Oggi Lamhauge), Hattarvik (41×20 mm)	5·25	4·75

199 Sheep grazing, Leynar

2009. SEPAC (small European mail services).

601	199	10k. multicoloured	5·25	4·75

200 Two Pigeons

2009. Rock Pigeon (Columba livia). Multicoloured.

602	14k. Type **200**	6·50	6·25
603	36k. Pigeon and two in flight	19·00	16·00

201 Seaweeds

2010. Marine Life. Multicoloured.

604	1k. Type **201**	50	45
605	6k. Seaweeds, with red extrusion, at left	3·00	2·30
606	8k. Seaweeds, tall and brightly coloured	4·00	3·25
607	12k. Seaweeds, tall, with crab, at centre	4·50	1·80

202 *Inachis io*

2010. Butterflies and Moths. Multicoloured.

608	6k. Type **202**	3·00	2·30
609	8k. *Vanessa cardui*	4·00	3·25
610	14k. *Agrius convolvuli*	3·00	2·20
611	16k. *Acherontia atropos*	7·75	6·50

203 *Globicephala melas*

2010. Long-finned Pilot Whale.

612	203	50k. black and silver	26·00	23·00

204 Salmon

2010. Life at the Coast. Aquaculture. Sheet 105×70 mm containing T 204 and similar vert design. Multicoloured.

MS613	10k.×2, Type **204**; Aquaculture operative	10·50	10·50

The stamps and margins of **MS**613 form a composite design.

Stamps of a similar theme were issued by Denmark, Greenland, Aland Islands, Finland, Iceland, Norway and Sweden.

205 *A Dog, a Cat and a Mouse* (Barour Oskarsson)

2010. Europa. Children's Books. Multicoloured. (a) Ordinary gum.

614	10k. Type **205**	5·25	4·75
615	12k. *Moss Mollis' Journey* (Janus á Husagaroi)	6·00	4·50

(b) Self-adhesive.

616	10k. As Type **205**	5·25	4·75
617	12k. As No. 615	6·00	4·50

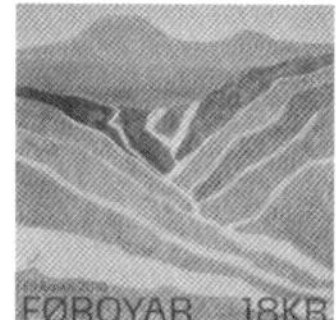
206 Valley

2010. Art. Landscape Paintings by Eli Smith using Pigments found on Faroes Islands. Multicoloured.

618	18k. Type **206**	9·50	8·00
619	24k. Flower, coastline and figure	12·00	9·00

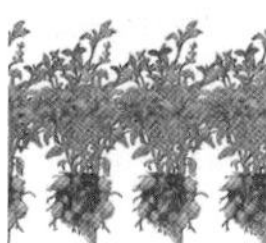

207 Potato

2010. Root Vegetables. Multicoloured.

620	6k. Type **207**	3·25	2·50
621	8k. Turnip	4·50	3·50

208 Lítla fitta nissa mín (Alexander Kristinsen)

2010. Christmas. Faroese Carols. Multicoloured.

622	6k. Type **208**	3·25	2·50
623	10k. *Á barnaárum ungu* (Hans Andreas Djurhuus)	5·75	5·00

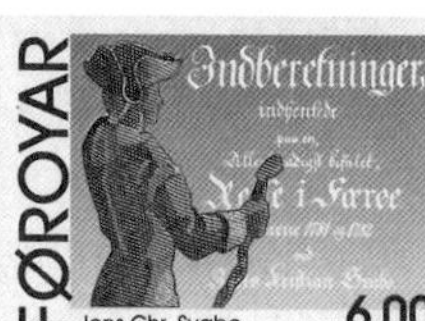
209 Jens Christian Svabo

2010. Jens Christian Svabo (writer and ballad collector) Commemoration. Multicoloured.

624	6k. pale grey-blue and black	3·00	2·50
625	12k. pale orange-brown and black	6·50	5·75
626	14k. pale grey-blue and black	8·00	6·25
627	22k. pale orange-brown and black	11·50	9·75

Designs:- 6k. Type **209**; 12k. Writing at his desk; 14k. Writing whilst standing; 22k. As older man with pile of papers and inkwell.

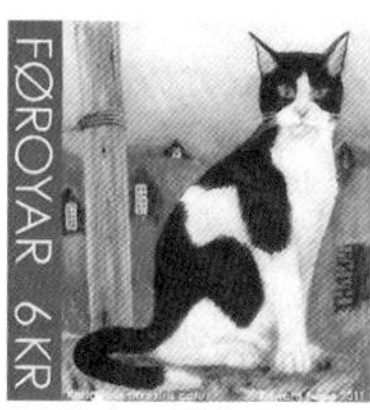
210 Black and White Cat

2011. Domestic Cats. Multicoloured.

(a) Sheet stamps. Ordinary gum

628	6k. Type **210**	3·25	2·50
629	10k. Ginger and white	5·75	5·00

(b) Booklet stamps. Self-adhesive

630	6k. As Type **210**	3·25	2·50
631	10k. As No. 629	5·75	5·00

211 Nursing

2011. Traditional Female Professions. Multicoloured.

632	6k. Type **211**	3·25	2·50
633	16k. Midwifery	9·00	7·50

212 Symbols of Womanhood

2011. Centenary of International Women's Day

634	212	10k. multicoloured	5·75	5·00

213 Annika i Dimun

2011. Annika i Dimun. Multicoloured.

MS635	10k.×3, Type **213**; Seated with two guards; Bound and entering the sea	17·00	17·00

214 *Sterjut strond*

2011. Art. Multicoloured.

636	2k. Type **214**	1·00	80
637	24k. *Ur Nólsay*	11·50	9·25

215 *Urtagarður*

2011. Art. Multicoloured.

638	6k. Type **215**	3·00	2·30
639	26k. *Kona*	12·00	9·50

216 Hurricane Damaged Trees, Tórshavn

2011. Europa. Multicoloured.

640	10k. Type **216**	5·25	4·75
641	12k.641 New plantation, Kunoy (vert)	6·00	4·50

217 *Silene dioica* (campion)

2011. Flora. Multicoloured.

642	14k. Type **217**	6·50	4·50
643	20k. *Geranium sylvaticum*	9·50	7·75

Pt. 11

FINLAND

A country to the east of Scandinavia. A Russian Grand-Duchy until 1917, then a Republic.

1856. 100 kopeks = 1 rouble.
1865. 100 pennia = 1 markka.
2002. 100 cents = 1 euro.

1

1856. Imperf.

1	1	5k. blue	£5500	£1100
2	1	10k. pink	£6500	£300

Used prices are for stamps with penmark cancellation only. Stamps with postmark as well are worth more.

2

1860. Values in "KOP". Roul.

10	2	5k. blue on blue	£800	£160
13	2	10k. pink on pink	£600	50·00

1866. As T **2**, but values in "PEN" and "MARK". Roul.

19	5p. brown on grey	£300	£140
46	8p. black on green	£275	£140
31	10p. black on buff	£700	£225
36	20p. blue on blue	£600	55·00
40	40p. pink on lilac	£550	70·00
49	1m. brown	£1800	£850

5

1875. Perf.

81	5	2p. grey	12·50	11·00
82	5	5p. yellow	45·00	5·25
83	5	5p. red	60·00	6·00
97	5	5p. green	18·00	55
71	5	8p. green	£180	50·00
85	5	10p. brown	95·00	17·00
99	5	10p. pink	25·00	2·20
87	5	20p. blue	45·00	1·70
102	5	20p. orange	27·00	50
89	5	25p. red	45·00	7·25
103	5	25p. blue	55·00	2·20
79	5	32p. red	£300	32·00
90	5	1m. mauve	£325	34·00
105	5	1m. grey and pink	37·00	15·00
106	5	5m. green and pink	£550	£275
107	5	10m. brown and pink	£700	£450

6

1889

108	6	2p. grey	1·10	1·00
148	6	5p. green	85	30
149	6	10p. red	1·10	30
150	6	20p. yellow	1·10	30
151	6	25p. blue	1·10	50
119	6	1m. grey and pink	5·50	3·00
120a	6	5m. green and red	29·00	44·00
122	6	10m. brown and red	44·00	70·00

7 8 9

10

11

1891. Similar to Russian types, but with circles added in designs.

133	7	1k. yellow	5·25	7·00
134	7	2k. green	6·50	6·75
135	7	3k. pink	11·50	12·00
136	8	4k. pink	11·00	11·50
137	7	7k. blue	7·50	2·00
138	8	10k. blue	15·00	11·50
139	9	14k. red and blue	21·00	17·00
140	8	20k. red and blue	16·00	13·50
141	9	35k. green and purple	24·00	32·00
142	8	50k. green and purple	30·00	26·00
143	10	1r. orange and brown	80·00	60·00
144	11	3½r. grey and black	£275	£275
145	11	7r. yellow and black	£225	£190

12 13 14

15

1901. Similar to Russian types, but value in Finnish currency.

161	12	2p. orange	65	90
162b	12	5p. green	1·80	40
169a	13	10p. red	45	25
170	12	20p. blue	55	25
165a	14	1m. green and purple	90	40
166	15	10m. grey and black	£140	38·00

16 17 18

1911

176	16	2p. orange	30	30
177	16	5p. green	30	15
180	17	10p. red	65	40
181	16	20p. blue	30	15
182	18	40p. blue and purple	30	20

19

1917

187a	19	5p. green	25	20
188	19	5p. grey	25	20
189	19	10p. red	25	20
190	19	10p. green	2·20	65
191a	19	10p. blue	35	25
192	19	20p. orange	25	20
193	19	20p. red	65	25
194	19	20p. brown	1·10	50
195	19	25p. blue	45	25
196	19	25p. brown	25	20
234	19	30p. green	55	40
198a	19	40p. purple	25	20
246	19	40p. green	45	85
200	19	50p. brown	60	40
201	19	50p. blue	4·25	50
247	19	50p. green	35	45
237	19	60p. purple	45	35
204	19	75p. yellow	25	40
205	19	1m. black and pink	13·50	25
248	19	1m. orange	30	35
207	19	1½m. purple and green	30	35
208a	19	2m. black and green	4·50	50
250	19	2m. blue	30	35
251	19	3m. black and blue	35	40
242	19	5m. black and purple	90	40
212	19	10m. black and bistre	1·10	90
213	19	25m. orange and red	1·30	21·00

20

1918. With white circle round figure of value.

214	20	5p. green	30	65
215	20	10p. pink	30	65
216	20	30p. grey	90	1·70
217	20	40p. lilac	30	65
218	20	50p. brown	60	1·70
219	20	70p. brown	2·20	10·50
220	20	1m. black and red	60	1·00
221	20	5m. black and lilac	49·00	65·00

1919. Surch with new figure of value three times.

222	19	10 on 5p. green	25	30
223	19	20 on 10p. red	35	30
224	19	50 on 25p. blue	1·30	35
225	19	75 on 20p. orange	25	30

1921. Surch with value, P and bars.

226	30p. on 10p. green	90	25
227	60p. on 40p. purple	3·50	65
228	90p. on 20p. red	40	35
229	1½m. on 50p. blue	2·20	25

23

1922. Red Cross.

230	23	1m.+50p. red and grey	1·30	8·50

26

1927. Tenth Anniv of Independence.

255	26	1½m. mauve	25	35
256	26	2m. blue	35	1·30

1928. Philatelic Exhibition. Optd *Postim. naytt. 1928 Frim. utstalln.*

258	19	1m. orange	10·50	13·00
259	19	1½m. purple and green	10·50	13·00

28 Freighter "*Bore* leaving Turku (Abo)

1929. 700th Anniv of Abo.

260	28	1m. olive	2·75	3·75
261	-	1½m. brown	6·25	3·00
262	-	2m. grey	1·30	3·75

DESIGNS—VERT: 1½m. Cathedral. HORIZ: 2m. Castle.

31

32 Olavinlinna

1930

263	31	5p. brown	25	25
264	31	10p. lilac	25	25
265	31	20p. green	55	35
266	31	25p. brown	25	20
267	31	40p. green	3·00	40
268	31	50p. yellow	90	35
268a	31	50p. green	30	20
269	31	60p. grey	55	40
371	31	75p. orange	35	35
270	31	1m. orange	90	35
372	31	1m. green	30	20
271	31	1m.20 red	45	55
271a	31	1m.25 yellow	35	30
272	31	1½m. mauve	4·50	25
272a	31	1½m. red	45	25
272b	31	1½m. grey	30	15
272c	31	1m.75 yellow	90	40
273	31	2m. blue	45	25
273a	31	2m. mauve	9·00	25
273b	31	2m. red	45	20
373	31	2m. orange	45	25
373a	31	2m. green	70	25
273c	31	2½m. blue	4·50	30
374	31	2½m. red	30	20
425	31	2½m. green	60	20
273d	31	2m.75 purple	25	15
375	31	3m. red	45	20
375a	31	3m. yellow	60	40
426	31	3m. grey	60	40
274a	31	3½m. blue	13·50	40
427	31	3m. green	3·75	35
376	31	3½m. green	30	20
377	31	4m. green	50	15
378	31	4½m. blue	25	20
275	32	5m. blue	45	25
379	31	5m. blue	90	20
379a	31	5m. violet	1·00	30
379b	31	5m. yellow	2·20	20
379c	31	6m. red	90	25
429	31	6m. green	1·10	40
430	31	7m. red	1·20	1·20
379d	31	8m. violet	50	15
431	31	8m. green	2·75	1·90
432	31	9m. red	90	25
433	31	9m. orange	1·30	30
276b	-	10m. lilac	1·10	25
379e	31	10m. blue	2·20	25
434	31	10m. violet	2·75	20
435	31	10m. brown	8·25	20
436	31	10m. green	3·50	20
437	31	12m. blue	3·00	20
438	31	12m. red	1·60	20
410	32	15m. purple	2·20	25
439	31	15m. blue	4·75	20
440	31	15m. purple	18·00	20
441	31	15m. red	3·00	20
442	31	20m. blue	8·00	20
443	31	24m. purple	2·00	40
277	-	25m. brown	2·75	35
444	31	25m. blue	3·50	20
445	32	35m. violet	7·00	25
445a	-	40m. brown	3·50	25

DESIGNS—As Type **32**: 10m. Lake Saimaa; 25, 40m. Wood-cutter.

35

1930. Red Cross Fund.

278	35	1m.+10p. red & orange	2·75	9·25
279	-	1½m.+15p. red & green	2·00	8·75
280	-	2m.+20p. red and blue	4·00	35·00

DESIGNS: 1½m. Drapery; 2m. Viking longship.

1930. Air. No. 276b optd **ZEPPELIN 1930**.

281	10m. lilac	£150	£190

39 Church at Hattula

1931. Red Cross Fund.

282	39	1m.+10p. green & red	3·00	9·25
283	-	1½m.+15p. brown & red	22·00	13·00
284	-	2m.+20p. blue & red	2·20	17·00

DESIGNS: 1½m. Hameen Castle; 2m. Viipuri Castle.

40 Elias Lonnrot

1931. Finnish Literary Society's Centenary.

285	40	1m. brown	4·50	3·75

286	-	1½m. blue	28·00	3·75

DESIGN—HORIZ: 1½m. Society's seal with inscr as T **40**.

42

1931. 75th Anniv of First Finnish Postage Stamps.

287	**42**	1½m. red	3·75	5·25
288	**42**	2m. blue	3·75	5·25

43

1931. Granberg Collection Fund.

289	**43**	1m.+4m. black	17·00	35·00

1931. Surch.

290	**31**	50PEN. on 40p. green	1·80	40
291	**31**	1,25 MK. on 50p. yellow	6·25	1·40

45

1931. President Svinhufvud's 70th Birthday.

292	**45**	2m. black and blue	3·00	2·10

47 St. Nicholas Cathedral

1932. Red Cross Fund.

293	-	1¼m.+10p. bistre & red	2·75	11·50
294	**47**	2m.+20p. purple & red	1·10	6·00
295	-	2½m.+25p. blue & red	1·30	20·00

DESIGNS—HORIZ: 1¼m. University Library, Helsinki; 2½m. Houses of Parliament.

48 Magnus Tawast

1933. Red Cross Fund.

296	**48**	1¼m.+10p. brown & red	6·25	8·00
297	-	2m.+20p. purple & red	90	2·10
298	-	2½m.+25p. blue & red	1·20	4·50

DESIGNS: 2m. Michael Agricola; 2½m. Isacus Rothovius.

51 Evert Horn

1934. Red Cross Fund.

299	**51**	1¼m.+10p. brown & red	90	2·30
300	-	2m.+20p. mauve & red	3·25	4·50
301	-	2½m.+25p. blue & red	1·30	3·25

DESIGNS: 2m. Torsten Stalhandske; 2½m. Jacob de la Gardie ("Lazy Jack").

52 Aleksis Kivi, after medallion by V. Aaltonen

1934. Birth Centenary of Kivi (poet).

302	**52**	2m. purple	3·50	3·25

53 Calonius

1935. Red Cross Fund. Cross in red.

303	**53**	1¼m.+15p. brown	90	2·00
304	-	2m.+20p. mauve	3·50	4·75
305	-	2½m.+25p. blue	1·30	1·80

PORTRAITS: 2m. H. G. Porthan. 2½m. A. Chydenius.

54 Finnish Bards

1935. Centenary of Publication of *Kalevala* (Finnish National Poems).

306	**54**	1¼m. red	1·80	1·50
307	-	2m. brown	5·25	1·20
308	-	2½m. blue	4·50	1·50

DESIGNS: 2m. Louhi's failure to recover the "Sampo"; 2½m. Kullervo's departure to war.

57 R. H. Rehbinder

1936. Red Cross Fund. Cross in red.

309	**57**	1¼m.+15p. brown	90	2·20
310	-	2m.+20p. purple	5·25	5·00
311	-	2½m.+25p. blue	90	2·20

PORTRAITS: 2m. G. M. Armfeldt. 2½m. Arvid Horn.

58 *Lodbrok*, 1771

1937. Red Cross Fund. Warships. Cross in red.

312		1¼m.+15p. brown	1·30	2·40
313	**58**	2m.+20p. red	22·00	8·25
314	-	3½m.+35p. blue	1·60	3·75

DESIGNS—HORIZ: 1¼m. *Thorborg* (inscr "Uusiman"); 3½m. *Styrbjorn* (inscr "Hameenmaa").

1937. Surch **2 MARKKAA**.

315	**31**	2m. on 1½m. red	8·00	90

60 Marshal Mannerheim

1937. Marshal Mannerheim's 70th Birthday.

316	**60**	2m. blue	90	80

61 A. Makipeska

1938. Red Cross Fund. Cross in red.

317	**61**	50p.+5p. green	60	1·30
318	-	1¼m.+15p. brown	90	2·00
319	-	2m.+20p. red	8·00	6·75
320	-	3½m.+35p. blue	90	2·50

PORTRAITS: 1¼m. R. I. Orn. 2m. E. Bergenheim, 3½m. J. M. Nordenstam.

62 Cross-country Skiing

1938. International Skiing Contest, Lahti.

321	**62**	1m.25+75p. black	4·50	8·00
322	-	2m.+1m. red	4·50	8·00
323	-	3m.50+1m.50 blue and light blue	4·50	8·00

DESIGNS: 2m. Ski jumping; 3m.50, Downhill skiing contest.

63 War Veteran

1938. Disabled Soldiers' Relief Fund. 20th Anniv of Independence.

324	**63**	2m.+½m. blue	3·00	3·50

64 Colonizers felling Trees

1938. Tercentenary of Scandinavian Settlement in America.

325	**64**	3½m. brown	1·80	2·10

65 Ahvenkoski P.O., 1787

1938. Tercentenary of Finnish Postal Service.

326	**65**	50p. green	45	65
327	-	1¼m. blue	1·80	2·10
328	-	2m. red	1·80	90
329	-	3½m. grey	7·00	5·75

DESIGNS: 1¼m. Sledge-boat; 2m. Junkers Ju 52/3m mail plane; 3½m. G.P.O., Helsinki.

66 Battlefield of Solferino

1939. Red Cross Fund and 75th Anniv of International Red Cross. Cross in red.

330	**66**	50p.+5p. green	1·30	1·70
331	**66**	1¼m.+15p. brown	1·60	2·50
332	**66**	2m.+20p. red	18·00	10·50
333	**66**	3½m.+35p. blue	1·30	2·50

67 G.P.O., Helsinki

1939

334	**67**	4m. brown	45	25

See also Nos. 382/4.

68 Crossbowman

1940. Red Cross Fund. Cross in red.

335	**68**	50p.+5p. green	1·30	1·60
336	-	1¼m.+15p. brown	1·30	2·40
337	-	2m.+20p. red	1·80	2·50
338	-	3½m.+35p. blue	1·80	4·50

DESIGNS: 1¼m. Mounted cavalrymen; 2m. Unmounted cavalrymen; 3½m. Officer and infantryman.

69 Lion of Finland

1940. National Defence Fund.

339	**69**	2m.+2m. blue	45	1·30

70 Helsinki University

1940. 300th Anniv of Founding of Helsinki University.

340	**70**	2m. deep blue and blue	45	1·10

1940. Surch.

341	**31**	1m.75 on 1m.25 yellow	1·30	2·00
342	**31**	2m.75 on 2m. red	6·75	60

72 Builder

1941. Red Cross Fund. Cross in red.

343	**72**	50p.+5p. green	45	75
344	-	1m.75+15p. sepia	90	1·70
345	-	2m.75+25p. brown	6·25	9·00
346	-	3m.50+35p. blue	1·30	2·20

DESIGNS: 1m.75, Farmer; 2m.75, Mother and child; 3m.50, Flag.

See also Nos. 405/8.

73 Farewell Review

1941. President Kallio Memorial.

347	**73**	2m.75 black	45	80

74 Knight

1941. "Brothers-in-Arms" Welfare Fund.

348	**74**	2m.75+25p. blue	45	1·10

75 Viipuri Castle

1941. Reconquest of Viipuri.

349	**75**	1m.75 orange	35	1·00
350	**75**	2m.75 purple	30	65
351	**75**	3m.50 blue	90	1·50

76 Pres. Risto Ryti

77 Marshal Mannerheim

1941. (a) President Ryti.

352	**76**	50p. green	70	1·10
353	**76**	1m.75 brown	80	1·10
354	**76**	2m. red	70	1·10
355	**76**	2m.75 violet	90	1·10
356	**76**	3m.50 blue	75	1·10
357	**76**	5m. grey	75	1·10

(b) Marshal Mannerheim.

358	**77**	50p. green	70	1·30
359	**77**	1m.75 brown	70	1·30
360	**77**	2m. red	70	1·30
361	**77**	2m.75 violet	90	1·30
362	**77**	3m.50 blue	90	1·30
363	**77**	5m. grey	90	1·30

79 Aland

1942. Red Cross Fund. Cross in red.

364	**79**	50p.+5p. green	90	1·50
365	-	1m.75+15p. brown	1·30	2·75
366	-	2m.75+25p. red	1·60	2·75
367	-	3m.50+35p. blue	1·30	3·00
368	-	4m.75+45p. grey	1·20	2·75

ARMS: 1m.75, Uusimaa (Nyland); 2m.75, Finland Proper; 3m.50, Karelia; 4m.75, Satakunta.

80 Tampere

1942

369	**80**	50m. brown	2·75	40
370	-	100m. blue	3·00	40

DESIGN: 100m. Helsinki Harbour.
For 100m. in green without "mk" see No. 557b.

81 New Testament

82 Mediaeval Press

1942. Tercentenary of Introduction of Printing into Finland.

380	**81**	2m.75 brown	45	80
381	**82**	3m.50 blue	65	1·50

1942

382	**67**	7m. brown	90	25
383	**67**	9m. mauve	60	25
384	**67**	20m. brown	1·60	25

83 Lapland

1943. Red Cross Fund. Cross in red.

385	**83**	50p.+5p. green	45	80
386	-	2m.+20p. brown	70	1·90
387	-	3m.50+35p. red	70	1·90
388	-	4m.50+45p. blue	1·80	8·50

ARMS: 2m. Hame (Tavastland); 3m.50, Pohjanmaa (Oster-botten); 4m.50, Savo (Savolaks).

1943. Surch **3½mk.**

389	**31**	3½m. on 2m.75 purple	25	25

85 Military Tokens

1943. National Relief Fund.

390	**85**	2m.+50p. brown	45	75
391	-	3m.50+1m. purple	45	75

DESIGN—VERT: 3m.50, Widow and Orphans.

87 Red Cross Train

1944. Red Cross Fund. Inscr "1944". Cross in red.

392	**87**	50p.+25p. green	25	40
393	-	2m.+50p. violet	35	80
394	-	3m.50+75p. red	35	80
395	-	4m.50+1m. blue	65	3·50

DESIGNS: 2m. Ambulance; 3m.50, Hospital, Helsinki; 4m.50, Airplane.

88 Minna Canth

1944. Birth Cent of Minna Canth (authoress).

396	**88**	3m.50 green	45	75

89 Douglas DC-2 Mail Plane

1944. Air. 20th Anniv of Air Mail Service.

397	**89**	3m.50 brown	45	90

90 Pres. Svinhufvud

1944. Mourning for Pres. P. E. Svinhufvud.

398	**90**	3½m. black	45	75

91

1944. National Relief Fund.

399	**91**	3m.50+1m.50 brown	45	90

92 Wrestling

1945. Sports Fund.

400	**92**	1m.+50p. green	25	65
401	-	2m.+1m. red	25	65
402	-	3m.50+1m.75 violet	25	65
403	-	4m.50+2m.25 blue	25	65
404	-	7m.+3m.50 brown	70	1·90

DESIGNS: 2m. Vaulting; 3m.50, Running; 4m.50, Skiing; 7m. Throwing the javelin.

1945. Red Cross Fund. As Nos. 343/6, but dated "1945". Cross in red.

405	1m.+25p. green	25	50
406	2m.+50p. brown	25	65
407	3m.50+75p. brown	25	65
408	4m.50+1m. blue	60	1·30

DESIGNS: 1m. Builder; 2m. Farmer; 3m.50, Mother and child; 4m.50, Flag.

93 Pres. Stahlberg

1945. 80th Birth Anniv of Pres. K. J. Stahlberg.

409	**93**	3m.50 violet	35	55

94 Sibelius

1945. 80th Birthday of Sibelius (composer).

411	**94**	5m. green	1·00	35

95 Fishermen

1946. Red Cross Fund. Cross in red.

412	**95**	1m.+25p. green	25	40
413	-	3m.+75p. purple	30	40
414	-	5m.+1m.25 red	30	40
415	-	10m.+2m.50 blue	45	65

DESIGNS: 3m. Butter-making; 5m. Harvesting; 10m. Logging.

1946. Surch with bold figures and bars.

416	**31**	8m. on 5m. violet	35	25
416a	**31**	12m. on 10m. violet	90	25

97 Athletes

1946. National Games.

417	**97**	8m. purple	45	50

98 Nurse and Children

1946. Anti-tuberculosis Fund.

418	**98**	5m.+1m. green	30	60
419	-	8m.+2m. purple	30	60

DESIGN: 8m. Lady doctor examining child.

99 Uto Lighthouse, and Sailing Ship

1946. 250th Anniv of Foundation of Pilotage Institution.

420	**99**	8m. violet	45	50

100 Postal Motor Coach

1946

421	**100**	16m. black	70	75
421a	**100**	30m. black	1·60	25

101 Town Hall

1946. 600th Anniv of Founding of Porvoo (Borga).

422	**101**	5m. black	30	40
423	-	8m. purple	30	40

DESIGN—VERT: 8m. Bridge and church.

103 Tammisaari

1946. 400th Anniv of Tammisaari (Ekenas).

424	**103**	8m. green	35	40

104 Pres. Paasikivi

1947

446	**104**	10m. black	35	40

1947. Anti-tuberculosis Fund. Nos. 418/19 surch.

447	**98**	6+1 on 5m.+1m. grn	35	90
448	-	10+2 on 8m.+2m. pur	35	90

106 Bank Emblem

1947. 60th Anniv of Finnish Postal Savings Bank.

449	**106**	10m. purple	40	50

107 Athletes

1947. National Sports Festival.

450	**107**	10m. blue	40	50

108 Ilmarinen Ploughing

1947. Conclusion of Peace Treaty.

451	**108**	10m. black	40	50

109 Emblem of Savings Bank Association

1947. 125th Anniv of Savings Bank Assn.

452	**109**	10m. brown	40	50

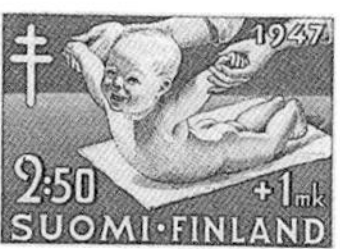

110 Physical Exercise

1947. Anti-tuberculosis Fund.

453	**110**	2m.50+1m. green	40	1·00
454	-	6m.+1m.50 red	45	1·10
455	-	10m.+2m.50 brown	45	1·10
456	-	12m.+3m. blue	60	1·60
457	-	20m.+5m. mauve	70	2·20

DESIGNS—VERT: 6, 10, 20m. Various infant exercises. HORIZ: 12m. Mme. Paasikivi and child.

111 Sower

1947. 150th Anniv of Central League of Agricultural Societies.

458	**111**	10m. grey	35	40

112 Heights of Koli

1947. 60th Anniv of Tourist Society.

459	**112**	10m. blue	35	40

113 Z. Topelius

1948. Red Cross Fund. Dated "1948". Cross in red.

460	**113**	3m.+1m. green	45	75
461	-	7m.+2m. red	55	1·10
462	-	12m.+3m. blue	55	1·10
463	-	20m.+5m. violet	60	1·50

PORTRAITS: 7m. Fr. Pacius; 12m. J. L. Runeberg; 20m. F. R. Cygnaeus.

1948. Anti-tuberculosis Fund. Nos. 454/5 and 457 surch.

464	7m.+2m. on 6m.+1m.50 red	1·20	2·20
465	15m.+3m. on 10m.+2m.50 brown	1·30	2·20
466	24m.+6m. on 20m.+5m. mauve	1·80	3·50

115 Michael Agricola (after sculpture by C. Sjostrand)

1948. 400th Anniv of Translation of New Testament into Finnish by Michael Agricola.

467	**115**	7m. purple	90	1·30
468	-	12m. blue	90	1·40

DESIGN: 12m. Agricola translating New Testament (after painting by A. Edelfelt).

116 King's Gate, Suomenlinna

1948. Bicentenary of Suomenlinna (Sveaborg).

469	**116**	12m. green	1·90	1·70

117 Finnish Mail-carrier's Badge

1948. Helsinki Philatelic Exhibition.

470	**117**	12m. green	8·00	14·50

Sold only at the Exhibition, at 62m. (including 50m. entrance fee).

118 Girl Bundling Twigs

1949. Red Cross Fund. Inscr "SAUNA BASTU 1949". Cross in red.

471	**118**	5m.+2m. green	45	65
472	-	9m.+3m. red	45	90
473	-	15m.+5m. blue	55	75
474	-	30m.+10m. brown	90	2·75

DESIGNS: 9m. Bathing scene; 15m. Heating sauna in winter; 30m. Bathers leaving sauna for plunge in lake.

119 Anemone

1949. Tuberculosis Relief Fund.

475	**119**	5m.+2m. green	50	65
476	-	9m.+3m. red	50	90
477	-	15m.+5m. brown	70	90

DESIGNS: 9m. Rose; 15m. Coltsfoot.

120 Trees and Papermill

1949. Third World Forestry Congress. Inscr "IIIE CONGRES FORESTIER MONDIAL 1949.

478	**120**	9m. brown	2·20	2·50
479	-	15m. green (Tree and Globe)	2·20	2·50

121 Girl with Torch

1949. 50th Anniv of Labour Movement.

480	**121**	5m. green	4·50	8·50
481	-	15m. red (Man with mallet)	4·50	8·50

122 Kristiinankaupunki

1949. Tercent of Kristiinankaupunki (Kristinestad).

482	**122**	15m. blue	1·50	2·20

123 *Salmetar* (lake steamer), Lappeenranta

1949. Tercent of Lappeenranta (Villmanstrand).

483	**123**	5m. green	90	75

124 Church, Raahe

1949. Tercentenary of Raahe (Brahestad).

484	**124**	9m. purple	90	1·00

125 Seal of Technical High School

1949. Cent of Technical High School, Helsinki.

485	**125**	15m. blue	90	90

126 Hannes Gebhard (founder)

1949. 50th Anniv of Finnish Co-operative Movement.

486	**126**	15m. green	90	90

127

1949. 75th Anniv of U.P.U.

487	**127**	15m. blue	90	1·10

128 Douglas DC-6

1950. Air.

488	**128**	300m. blue	11·00	5·50

For 300m. stamp without "mk" see No. 585 and for 3m. stamp see No. 679.

129 White Water-lily

1950. Tuberculosis Relief Fund.

489	**129**	5m.+2m. green	1·30	1·50
490	-	9m.+3m. mauve	1·00	1·50
491	-	15m.+5m. blue	1·00	1·50

DESIGNS: 9m. Pasque flower; 15m. Clustered bellflower.

130 Plan of Helsinki, 1550

1950. 400th Anniv of Helsinki.

492	**130**	5m. green	45	65
493	-	9m. brown	60	1·30
494	-	15m. blue	60	75

DESIGNS: 9m. J. A. Ehrenstrom and C. L. Engel; 15m. Town Hall and Cathedral.

131 President Paasikivi

1950. President's 80th Birthday.

495	**131**	20m. blue	60	45

132 Hospital, Helsinki

1951. Red Cross Fund. Cross in red.

496	**132**	7m.+2m. brown	90	90
497	-	12m.+3m. violet	90	90
498	-	20m.+5m. red	1·10	1·90

DESIGNS: 12m. Blood donor and nurse; 20m. Blood donor's badge.

133 Town Hall

1951. 300th Anniv of Kajaani (Kajana).

499	**133**	20m. brown	60	65

134 Western Capercaillie

1951. Tuberculosis Relief Fund.

500	**134**	7m.+2m. green	2·20	2·50
501	-	12m.+3m. lake	2·20	2·50
502	-	20m.+5m. blue	2·20	2·50

DESIGNS: 12m. Common Cranes; 20m. Caspian Terns.

135 Diving

1951. 15th Olympic Games, Helsinki.

503	**135**	12m.+2m. red	1·20	1·40
504	-	15m.+2m. green	1·20	1·40
505	-	20m.+3m. blue	1·20	1·50
506	-	25m.+4m. brown	1·60	1·60

DESIGNS—HORIZ: 15m. Football; 25m. Running. VERT: 20m. Olympic stadium.

138 Marshal Mannerheim

1952. Red Cross Fund. Cross in red.

No.	Type	Description	Unused	Used
507	**138**	10m.+2m. black	1·10	1·50
508	**138**	15m.+3m. purple	1·10	1·90
509	**138**	25m.+5m. blue	1·10	1·50

139 Arms of Pietarsaari

1952. 300th Anniv of Founding of Pietarsaari (Jakobstad).

No.	Type	Description	Unused	Used
510	**139**	25m. blue	60	80

140 Vaasa

1952. Centenary of Fire of Vaasa (Vasa).

No.	Type	Description	Unused	Used
511	**140**	25m. brown	60	90

141 Knight, Rook and Chessboard

1952. Tenth Chess Olympiad, Helsinki.

No.	Type	Description	Unused	Used
512	**141**	25m. black	1·60	2·20

142 Great Tit

1952. Tuberculosis Relief Fund. Birds.

No.	Type	Description	Unused	Used
513	**142**	10m.+2m. green	1·80	2·10
514	-	15m.+3m. red	1·80	2·10
515	-	25m.+5m. blue	1·80	2·10

BIRDS: 15m. Spotted Flycatchers; 25m. Eurasian Swifts.

143 "Flame of Temperance"

1953. Cent of Finnish Temperance Movement.

No.	Type	Description	Unused	Used
516	**143**	25m. blue	90	90

144 Aerial view of Hamina

1953. 300th Anniv of Hamina (Fredrikshamn).

No.	Type	Description	Unused	Used
517	**144**	25m. slate	60	80

145 Eurasian Red Squirrel

1953. Tuberculosis Relief Fund.

No.	Type	Description	Unused	Used
518	**145**	10m.+2m. brown	2·20	2·50
519	-	15m.+3m. violet	2·20	2·50
520	-	25m.+5m. green	2·20	2·50

DESIGNS: 15m. Brown bear; 25m. Elk.

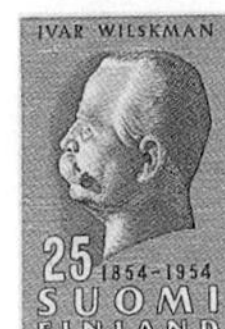

146 Wilskman

1954. Birth Centenary of Ivar Wilskman (gymnast).

No.	Type	Description	Unused	Used
521	**146**	25m. blue	70	80

147 Mother and Children

1954. Red Cross Fund. Cross in red.

No.	Type	Description	Unused	Used
522	**147**	10m.+2m. green	70	1·20
523	-	15m.+3m. blue	90	1·10
524	-	25m.+5m. brown	90	1·10

DESIGNS: 15m. Old lady knitting; 25m. Blind man and dog.

148

1954

No.	Type	Description	Unused	Used
525	**148**	1m. brown	45	40
526	**148**	2m. green	45	25
527	**148**	3m. orange	35	25
527a	**148**	4m. grey	45	35
528	**148**	5m. blue	60	25
529	**148**	10m. green	90	35
530	**148**	15m. red	2·75	25
530a	**148**	15m. orange	7·00	25
531	**148**	20m. purple	8·50	40
531a	**148**	20m. red	1·80	25
532	**148**	25m. blue	2·75	25
532a	**148**	25m. purple	11·00	25
532b	**148**	30m. blue	2·00	25

See also Nos. 647, etc.

149 *In the Outer Archipelago* (after Edelfelt)

1954. Birth Centenary of A. Edelfelt (painter).

No.	Type	Description	Unused	Used
533	**149**	25m. black	60	80

150 White-tailed Bumble Bees collecting Pollen

1954. Tuberculosis Relief Fund. Cross in red.

No.	Type	Description	Unused	Used
534	**150**	10m.+2m. brown	1·30	1·30
535	-	15m.+3m. red	1·80	1·60
536	-	25m.+5m. blue	1·80	1·60

DESIGNS: 15m. Apollo (butterfly) and wild rose; 25m. *Aeshna juncea* (dragonfly).

151 J. J. Nervander

1955. 150th Birth Anniv of Nervander (astronomer and poet).

No.	Type	Description	Unused	Used
537	**151**	25m. blue	70	90

152 Parliament Building

1955. National Philatelic Exhibition, Helsinki.

No.	Type	Description	Unused	Used
538	**152**	25m. black	6·75	12·50

153 St. Henry

1955. 800th Anniv of Establishment of Christianity in Finland.

No.	Type	Description	Unused	Used
539	**153**	15m. purple	65	75
540	-	25m. green	65	75

DESIGN: 25m. Arrival of Christian preachers in 1155.

154 Conference in Session

1955. Interparliamentary Conference, Helsinki.

No.	Type	Description	Unused	Used
541	**154**	25m. green	1·10	1·30

155 Barque *Ilma* and Cargo

1955. 350th Anniv of Oulu (Uleaborg).

No.	Type	Description	Unused	Used
542	**155**	25m. brown	1·10	1·30

156 Eurasian Perch

1955. Tuberculosis Relief Fund. Cross in red.

No.	Type	Description	Unused	Used
543	**156**	10m.+2m. green	1·30	1·30
544	-	15m.+3m. brown (Northern pike)	1·80	1·50
545	-	25m.+5m. blue (Atlantic salmon)	1·80	1·50

157 Town Hall, Lahti

1955. 50th Anniv of Lahti.

No.	Type	Description	Unused	Used
546	**157**	25m. blue	90	1·50

158 J. Z. Duncker

1955. Red Cross. Cross in red.

No.	Type	Description	Unused	Used
547	-	10m.+2m. blue	70	1·10
548	**158**	15m.+3m. brown	80	1·30
549	-	25m.+5m. green	80	1·30

DESIGNS: 10m. Von Dobeln on horseback; 25m. Young soldier.

159 "Telegraphs"

1955. Centenary of Telegraphs in Finland. Inscr "1855–1955 Telegrafen".

No.	Type	Description	Unused	Used
550	**159**	10m. green	1·10	1·10
551	-	15m. violet	1·10	1·00
552	-	25m. blue	1·30	1·50

DESIGNS: 15m. Otto Nyberg; 25m. Telegraph pole.

160 Lighthouse at Porkkala

1956. Return of Porkkala to Finland.

No.	Type	Description	Unused	Used
553	**160**	25m. blue	60	75

161 Lammi Church

1956. Value expressed as "5" etc.

No.	Type	Description	Unused	Used
553a	-	5m. green	35	20
554	**161**	30m. green	70	35
555	-	40m. lilac	2·20	25
556	**161**	50m. green	5·25	25
557	-	60m. purple	9·75	25
557a	-	75m. black	3·50	25
557b	-	100m. green	20·00	25
557c	-	125m. green	19·00	50

DESIGNS: 5m. View of lake, Keuru; 40m. Houses of Parliament; 60m. Olavinlinna; 75m. Pyhakoski Dam; 100m. Helsinki Harbour; 125m. Turku Castle.

No. 557b differs from No. 370 in that "FINLAND" is without the scroll, the figures "100" are upright and "mk" is omitted.

See also Nos. 660, etc.

162 J. V. Snellman (after sculpture by E. Wikstrom)

1956. 150th Birth Anniv of Snellman (statesman).

No.	Type	Description	Unused	Used
558	**162**	25m. brown	90	75

163 Athletes

1956. Finnish Games.

No.	Type	Description	Unused	Used
559	**163**	30m. blue	90	80

164

1956. Centenary of First Finnish Postage Stamp and International Philatelic Exhibition, Helsinki. Roul.

No.	Type	Description	Unused	Used
560	**164**	30m. blue	3·75	4·50

165 Bohemian Waxwing

1956. Tuberculosis Relief Fund. Cross in red.

561	**165**	10m.+2m. brown	1·30	95
562	-	20m.+3m. green	1·80	1·60
563	-	30m.+5m. blue	1·80	1·60

DESIGNS: 20m. Eagle Owl; 30m. Mute Swan.

166 Vaasa Town Hall

1956. 350th Anniv of Vaasa.

564	**166**	30m. blue	90	90

1956. Northern Countries' Day. As T 100 of Denmark.

565	20m. red	2·20	1·20
566	30m. blue	6·75	1·20

167 P. Aulin

1956. Red Cross. Inscr "1956". Cross in red.

567	**167**	5m.+1m. green	90	80
568	-	10m.+2m. brown	1·10	1·10
569	-	20m.+3m. red	1·60	2·00
570	-	30m.+5m. blue	1·60	1·60

PORTRAITS: 10m. L. von Pfaler; 20m. G. Johansson; 30m. V. M. von Born.

168 University Hospital, Helsinki

1956. Bicentenary of National Health Service.

571	**168**	30m. green	1·60	90

169 Scout Badge and Saluting Hand

1957. 50th Anniv of Boy Scout Movement.

572	**169**	30m. blue	1·60	1·00

171 "In Honour of Work"

1957. 50th Anniv of Finnish Trade Union Movement.

573	**171**	30m. red	70	80

172 *Lex* (sculpture by W. Runeberg)

1957. 50th Anniv of Finnish Parliament.

574	**172**	30m. olive	1·00	80

173 Wolverine

1957. Tuberculosis Relief Fund. Inscr "1957". Cross in red.

575	**173**	10m.+2m. purple	1·30	1·10
576	-	20m.+3m. sepia	1·50	1·40
577	-	30m.+5m. blue	1·80	1·40

DESIGNS: 20m. Lynx; 30m. Reindeer.

See also Nos. 642/4.

174 Factories within Cogwheel

1957. 50th Anniv of Central Federation of Finnish Employers.

578	**174**	20m. blue	70	75

175 Red Cross Flag

1957. Red Cross Fund and 80th Anniv of Finnish Red Cross. Cross in red.

579	**175**	10m.+2m. green	1·40	1·90
580	**175**	20m.+3m. lake	1·40	1·90
581	**175**	30m.+5m. blue	1·40	1·90

176 Ida Aalberg (after Edelfelt)

1957. Birth Cent of Ida Aalberg (actress).

582	**176**	30m. maroon & purple	70	75

177 Arms of Finland

1957. 40th Anniv of Independence.

583	**177**	30m. blue	90	80

178 Bust of Sibelius (Waino Aaltonen)

1957. Death of Sibelius (composer).

584	**178**	30m. black	1·10	1·00

1958. Air. As No. 488 but with "mk" omitted.

585	**128**	300m. blue	33·00	1·10

See also No. 679.

179 Ski Jumping

1958. World Ski Championships.

586	**179**	20m. green	90	1·30
587	-	30m. blue	90	1·30

DESIGN—VERT: 30m. Cross-country skiing.

180 *March of the Bjorneborgienses* (after Edelfelt)

1958. 400th Anniv of Founding of Pori (Bjorneborg).

588	**180**	30m. purple	1·10	75

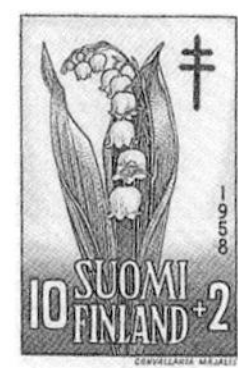

181 Lily of the Valley

1958. Tuberculosis Relief Fund. Cross in red.

589	**181**	10m.+2m. green	1·10	1·10
590	-	20m.+3m. red	1·80	1·60
591	-	30m.+5m. blue	1·80	1·60

DESIGNS: 20m. Red clover; 30m. Anemone.

182 Lyceum Seal

1958. Centenary of Jyvaskyla Lyceum (secondary school).

592	**182**	30m. red	1·10	95

183 Convair CV 340 OH-LRD over Lakes

1958. Air.

593	**183**	34m. blue	90	80
594	**183**	45m. blue	1·80	1·70

See also Nos. 678/a.

184 Cloudberry

1958. Red Cross Fund. Cross in red.

595	**184**	10m.+2m. orange	90	1·10
596	-	20m.+3m. red	1·60	1·50
597	-	30m.+5m. blue	1·60	1·50

DESIGNS: 20m. Cowberry; 30m. Blueberry.

185 Missionary Emblem and Globe

1959. Centenary of Finnish Missionary Society.

598	**185**	30m. purple	70	55

186 Opening of Diet, 1809

1959. 150th Anniv of Re-convening of Finnish Diet at Porvoo.

599	**186**	30m. blue	70	55

1959. Air. No. 593 surch **45**.

600	45m. on 34m. blue	1·80	3·75

188 Multiple Saws

1959. Centenaries of Kestila Sawmill (10m.) and Finnish Forestry Department (30m.).

601	**188**	10m. brown	45	55
602	-	30m. grn (Forest firs)	45	60

1959. Tuberculosis Relief Fund. As T **181** but inscr "1959". Cross in red.

603	10m.+2m. green	1·80	1·50
604	20m.+3m. brown	2·20	2·10
605	30m.+5m. blue	2·20	2·10

DESIGNS: 10m. Marguerite; 20m. Cowslip; 30m. Cornflower.

189 Gymnast

1959. Birth Centenary of Elin Oihonna Kallio (Women's Gymnastics pioneer).

606	**189**	30m. purple	70	65

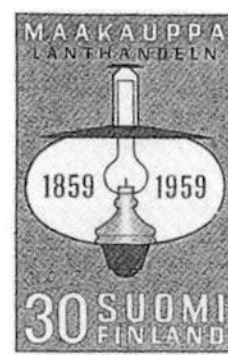

190 Oil Lamp

1959. Cent of Trade Freedom in Finland.

607	**190**	30m. blue	60	65

191 Arms of the Towns

1960. Extra Privileges for Finnish Towns–Hyvinkaa, Kouvola, Riihimaki, Rovaniemi, Salo and Seinajoki.

608	**191**	30m. violet	1·00	75

192 5k. "Serpentine Roulette" Stamp of 1860

1960. Stamp Exhibition, Helsinki, and Centenary of "Serpentine Roulette" stamps. Roul.

609	**192**	30m. blue and grey	6·25	7·50

193 Refugees and Symbol

1960. World Refugee Year.

610	**193**	30m. red	45	50
611	**193**	40m. blue	45	50

194 J. Gadolin

1960. Birth Bicent of Johan Gadolin (chemist).

612	**194**	30m. brown	70	65

195 H. Nortamo

1960. Birth Cent of H. Nortamo (writer).
613 **195** 30m. green 70 65

196 European Cuckoo

1960. Karelian National Festival, Helsinki.
614 **196** 30m. red 80 75

197 "Geodesy" (Geodetic instrument)

1960. 12th International Geodesy and Geophysics Union Assembly, Helsinki.
615 **197** 10m. sepia and blue 45 50
616 **-** 30m. brn, red & verm 45 65
DESIGN: 30m. "Geophysics" (representation of Northern Lights).

198 Pres. Kekkonen

1960. President Kekkonen's 60th Birthday.
617 **198** 30m. blue 80 50

1960. Europa. As T **373** of Belgium but size 31×20½ mm.
618 30m. blue and ultramarine 70 65
619 40m. purple and sepia 70 65

199 Pastor Cygnaeus

1960. 150th Birth Anniv of Pastor Uno Cygnaeus (founder of elementary schools).
620 **199** 30m. purple 90 65

200 Reindeer

1960. Red Cross Fund. Cross in red.
621 **200** 10m.+2m. purple 1·10 1·30
622 **-** 20m.+3m. violet 1·80 1·70
623 **-** 30m.+5m. purple 1·60 1·70
DESIGNS: 20m. Hunter with lasso; 30m. Mountain and lake.

201 *Pommern* (barque)

1961. Cent of Marianhamina (Mariehamn).
624 **201** 30m. blue 2·20 2·10

202 Savings Bank's New Emblem

1961. 75th Anniv of Finnish Postal Savings Bank.
625 **202** 30m. blue 90 50

203 Symbol of Standardization

1961. General Assembly of Int. Organization for Standardization, Helsinki.
626 **203** 30m. green & orange 70 65

1961. Tuberculosis Relief Fund. As T **173**. Cross in red.
627 10m.+2m. purple 1·10 1·30
628 20m.+3m. blue 1·80 1·50
629 30m.+5m. green 1·80 1·80
ANIMALS: 10m. Muskrat; 20m. European otter; 30m. Ringed seal.

204 J. Aho

1961. Birth Centenary of Aho (writer).
630 **204** 30m. brown 80 65

205 Helsinki Cathedral

1961. 150th Anniv of Finnish Central Building Board.
631 **205** 30m. black 80 65

206 A. Jarnefelt

1961. Birth Centenary of Arvid Jarnefelt (writer).
632 **206** 30m. purple 80 65

207 Bank Facade

1961. 150th Anniv of Bank of Finland.
633 **207** 30m. purple 80 65

208 First locomotive, *Ilmarinen*

1962. Centenary of Finnish Railways.
634 **208** 10m. green 1·30 65
635 **-** 30m. blue 1·30 65
636 **-** 40m. purple 3·00 65
LOCOMOTIVES: 30m. Class Hr-1 steam locomotive and Type Hk wagon; 40m. Class Hr-12 diesel locomotive and passenger carriages.

209 Mora Stone

1962. 600th Anniv of Finnish People's Political Rights.
637 **209** 30m. purple 80 65

210 Senate Place, Helsinki

1962. 150th Anniv of Proclamation of Helsinki as Finnish Capital.
638 **210** 30m. brown 80 65

211 Customs Board Crest

1962. 150th Anniv of Finnish Customs Board.
639 **211** 30m. red 1·00 65

212 Emblem of Commerce

1962. Cent of 1st Finnish Commercial Bank.
640 **212** 30m. green 1·00 65

213 S. Alkio

1962. Birth Cent of Santeri Alkio (writer and founder of Young People's Societies' Movement).
641 **213** 30m. purple 1·00 65

1962. Tuberculosis Relief Fund. As T **173**. Cross in red.
642 10m.+2m. black 1·40 1·30
643 20m.+3m. purple 1·80 1·60
644 30m.+5m. blue 1·80 1·60
DESIGNS: 10m. Brown hare; 20m. Pine marten; 30m. Stoat.

214 Finnish Labour Emblem on Conveyor Belt

1962. Home Production.
645 **214** 30m. purple 80 40

215 Hunting Pembroke making Aerial Survey

1962. 150th Anniv of Finnish Land Survey Board.
646 **215** 30m. green 90 75

216

1963. (a) Lion Type.
647 **216** 1p. brown 20 25
648 **216** 2p. green 20 15
649 **216** 4p. grey 55 40
650 **216** 5p. blue 45 20
651 **216** 10p. green 60 40
652 **216** 15p. orange 1·30 35
653a **216** 20p. red 90 20
654a **216** 25p. purple 90 40
656 **216** 30p. blue 1·30 40
657 **216** 35p. blue 1·20 20
657a **216** 35p. yellow 70 30
658 **216** 40p. blue 1·30 40
658b **216** 40p. orange 90 40
659 **216** 50p. blue 2·50 25
659a **216** 50p. purple 70 25
659b **216** 60p. blue 60 25

(b) Views. Values expressed as "0,05" (pennia values) or "1,00" (mark values).
660 - 5p. green (As No. 553a) (postage) 55 25
661 - 25p. multicoloured 45 25
662 - 30p. multicoloured 1·30 25
663 - 40p. lilac (As No. 555) 5·25 25
664 **161** 50p. green 4·50 25
665 - 60p. purple (As No. 557) 10·50 25
666 - 65p. purple (As No. 557) 1·30 30
667 - 75p. black (As No. 557a) 1·80 25
668 - 80p. multicoloured 4·75 35
669 - 90p. multicoloured 1·20 45
670 - 1m. green (As No. 557b) 3·00 25
671 - 1m.25 green (As No. 557c) 1·80 35
672 - 1m.30 multicoloured 90 40
673 - 1m.50 green 3·50 25
674 - 1m.75 blue 1·20 25
675 - 2m. green 13·50 25
676 - 2m.50 blue & yellow 5·50 40
677 - 5m. green 18·00 35
678 **183** 45p. blue (air) 1·30 35
678a **183** 57p. blue 2·00 1·00
679 - 3m. blue (585) 18·00 55
NEW DESIGNS: As Type **161**—VERT: 30p. Nasinneula Tower, Tampere; 80p. Keuruu church; 1m.30, Helsinki Railway Station. HORIZ: 25p. Country mail bus; 90p. Hameen Bridge, Tampere; 1m.50, Loggers afloat; 1m.75, Parainen Bridge; 2m. Country house by lake; 2m.50, Aerial view of Punkaharju; 5m. Ristikallio Gorge.
No. 679 is as No. 585, but with a comma after "3".

217 Mother and Child

1963. Freedom from Hunger.
680 **217** 40p. brown 70 50

218 Hands reaching for Red Cross

1963. Centenary of Red Cross.
681 **218** 10p.+2p. brn & red 60 75
682 **218** 20p.+3p. violet & red 90 1·40
683 **218** 30p.+5p. green & red 90 1·60

219 Crown of Thorns

1963. Lutheran World Federation Assembly, Helsinki.
684 **219** 10p. lake 45 35
685 - 30p. green 60 65
DESIGN: 30p. Head of Christ.

220 "Co-operation"

1963. Europa.
686 **220** 40p. purple 2·40 75

221 House of Estates, Helsinki

1963. Cent of Finnish Representative Assembly.

687	**221**	30p. purple	60	55

222 Convair CV 440 Metropolitan Airliner

1963. 40 Years of Finnish Civil Aviation.

688	**222**	35p. green	70	65
689	-	40p. blue	70	50

DESIGN: 40p. Sud-Aviation SE 210 Caravelle in flight.

223 M. A. Castren (after E. J. Lofgren)

1963. 150th Birth Anniv of M. A. Castren (explorer and scholar).

690	**223**	35p. blue	80	50

224 Soapstone Elk's Head

1964. "For Art" (centenary of Finnish Artists' Society).

691	**224**	35p. green and buff	90	40

225 E. N. Setala

1964. Birth Centenary of Emil Setala (philologist and statesman).

692	**225**	35p. brown	90	55

226 Doctor tending Patient on Sledge

1964. Red Cross Fund. Cross in red.

693	**226**	15p.+3p. blue	90	80
694	-	25p.+4p. green	1·20	1·00
695	-	35p.+5p. purple	1·20	1·00
696	-	40p.+7p. green	1·30	1·00

DESIGNS: 25p. Red Cross hospital ship; 35p. Military sick parade; 40p. Distribution of Red Cross parcels.

227 Emblem of Medicine

1964. 18th General Assembly of World Medical Association.

697	**227**	40p. green	90	55

228 Ice Hockey Players

1965. World Ice Hockey Championships.

698	**228**	35p. blue	90	55

229 Centenary Medal

1965. Cent of Finnish Communal Self-Government.

699	**229**	35p. green	90	55

230 K. J. Stahlberg and Runeberg's sculpture, *Lex*

1965. Birth Cent of K. J. Stahlberg (statesman).

700	**230**	35p. brown	90	55

231 I.C.Y. Emblem

1965. International Co-operation Year.

701	**231**	40p. multicoloured	80	55

232 *The Fratricide*

1965. Birth Centenary of A. Gallen-Kallela (artist). Multicoloured.

702		25p. Type **232**	1·20	75
703		35p. "Head of a Young Girl"	1·20	75

233 Spitz

1965. Tuberculosis Relief Fund. Dogs.

704	**233**	15p.+3p. brn & red	1·20	1·10
705	-	25p.+4p. blk & red	1·80	1·60
706	-	35p.+5p. sep & red	1·80	1·60

FINNISH DOGS: 25p. Karelian bear dog. 35p. Finnish stovare.

234 Piano, Profile and Score of *Finlandia*

1965. Birth Centenary of Sibelius (composer).

707	**234**	25p. violet	70	50
708	-	35p. green	70	75

DESIGN: 35p. Part of score of "Finlandia" and dove.

235 Dish Aerial

1965. Centenary of I.T.U.

709	**235**	35p. blue	75	65

236 *Winter Day* (after P. Halonen)

1965. Birth Cent of Pekka Halonen (painter).

710	**236**	35p. multicoloured	75	50

237 Europa "Sprig"

1965. Europa.

711	**237**	40p. multicoloured	2·00	50

238 "Kiss of Life"

1966. Red Cross Fund. Multicoloured.

712		15p.+3p. Type **238**	70	1·10
713		25p.+4p. Diver and submerged car	70	1·10
714		35p.+5p. Sud-Aviation SE 3130 Alouette II Red Cross helicopter	70	1·10

239 "Growing Up"

1966. Cent of Finnish Elementary School Decree.

715	**239**	35p. bl & ultramarine	65	50

240 Old Post Office

1966. "Nordia 1966" Stamp Exn., Helsinki, and Centenary of 1st Postage Stamps in Finnish Currency.

716	**240**	35p. blue, brown & yell	4·50	5·75

241 Globe and UNESCO Emblem

1966. 20th Anniv of UNESCO.

717	**241**	40p. multicoloured	80	55

242 Police Emblem

1966. 150th Anniv of Finnish Police Force.

718	**242**	35p. silver, black & blue	90	55

243 Anniversary Medal (after K. Kallio)

1966. 150th Anniv of Finnish Insurance.

719	**243**	35p. olive and lake	80	55

244 U.N.I.C.E.F Emblem

1966. 20th Anniv of UNICEF.

720	**244**	15p. violet, green & blue	75	35

245 FINEFTA Symbol

1967. Abolition of Industrial Customs Tariffs by European Free Trade Association.

721	**245**	40p. blue	80	50

246 Windmill

1967. 350th Anniv of Uusikaupunki (Nystad).

722	**246**	40p. multicoloured	85	40

247 Birch Tree and Foliage

1967. Tuberculosis Relief Fund. Multicoloured.

723		20p.+3p. Type **247**	90	90
724		25p.+4p. Pine and foliage	1·00	1·10
725		40p.+7p. Spruce and foliage	1·00	1·10

See also Nos. 753/5.

248 Mannerheim Statue (A. Tukiainen)

1967. Birth Cent of Marshal Mannerheim.

726	**248**	40p. multicoloured	70	40

249 "Solidarity"

1967. Finnish Settlers in Sweden.

727	**249**	40p. multicoloured	70	40

250 Watermark of Thomasbole Factory

1967. 300th Anniv of Finnish Paper Industry.

728	**250**	40p. blue and bistre	70	40

251 Martin Luther (from painting by Lucas Cranach the Elder)

1967. 450th Anniv of the Reformation.

729	**251**	40p. multicoloured	70	40

252 Horse-drawn Ambulance

1967. Red Cross Fund. Multicoloured.

730		20p.+3p. Type **252**	60	1·00
731		25p.+4p. Modern ambulance	80	1·00
732		40p.+7p. Red Cross emblem	80	1·00

253 Northern Lights

1967. 50th Anniv of Independence.

733	**253**	20p. green and blue	60	40
734	-	25p. blue & light blue	60	35
735	-	40p. mauve and blue	60	35

DESIGNS: 25p. Flying swan; 40p. Ear of wheat.

254 Z. Topelius and *Bluebird*

1968. 150th Anniv of Zacharias Topelius (writer).

736	**254**	25p. multicoloured	55	50

255 Skiing

1968. Winter Tourism.

737	**255**	25p. multicoloured	55	75

256 *Paper- making* (from wood relief by H. Autere)

1968. 150th Anniv of Tervakoski Paper Factory.

738	**256**	45p. brown, buff & red	45	40

257 W.H.O. Emblem

1968. 20th Anniv of W.H.O.

739	**257**	40p. multicoloured	55	35

258 *Infantryman* (statue by L. Leppanen, Vaasa)

1968. 50th Anniv of Finnish Army. Multicoloured.

740		20p. Type **258**	70	50
741		25p. Memorial (V. Aaltonen), Hietaniemi cemetery	70	50
742		40p. Modern soldier	70	50

259 Holiday Camp

1968. Tourism.

743	**259**	25p. multicoloured	75	1·00

260 Pulp Bale (with outline of tree in centre) and Paper Reel

1968. Finnish Wood-processing Industry.

744	**260**	40p. multicoloured	55	40

261 O. Merikanto

1968. Birth Cent of Oskar Merikanto (composer).

745	**261**	40p. multicoloured	55	40

262 Mustola Lock

1968. Opening of Saima Canal.

746	**262**	40p. multicoloured	55	40

263 Dock Cranes, *Ivalo* (container ship) and Chamber of Commerce Emblem

1968. "Finnish Economic Life". 50th Anniv of Finnish Central Chamber of Commerce.

747	**263**	40p. multicoloured	55	40

264 Welding

1968. Finnish Metal Industry.

748	**264**	40p. multicoloured	55	30

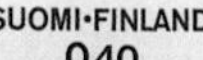

265 Lyre Emblem

1968. Finnish Student Unions.

749	**265**	40p. brn, bl & ultram	55	40

1969. 50th Anniv of Northern Countries' Union. As T **159** of Denmark.

750		40p. blue	1·20	50

266 City Hall and Arms, Kemi

1969. Centenary of Kemi (Kemin).

751	**266**	40p. multicoloured	55	40

267 Colonnade

1969. Europa.

752	**267**	40p. multicoloured	6·50	70

1969. Tuberculosis Relief Fund. As T **247**, but inscr "1969". Multicoloured.

753		20p.+3p. Juniper and berries	65	90
754		25p.+4p. Aspen and catkins	80	1·00
755		40p.+7p. Wild cherry and flowers	80	1·00

268 I.L.O. Emblem

1969. 50th Anniv of I.L.O.

756	**268**	40p. blue, lt blue & red	55	35

269 A. Jarnefelt (after V. Sjostrom)

1969. Birth Cent of Armas Jarnefelt (composer).

757	**269**	40p. multicoloured	55	35

270 Fairs Symbol

1969. Finnish National and Int. Fairs.

758	**270**	40p. multicoloured	55	35

271 J. Linnankoski

1969. Birth Centenary of Johannes Linnankoski (writer).

759	**271**	40p. multicoloured	55	40

272 Board Emblems

1969. Centenary of Central Schools Board.

760	**272**	40p. violet, green & grey	55	40

273 Douglas DC-8-62F over Helsinki Airport

1969. Aviation.

761	**273**	25p. multicoloured	90	90

274 Golden Eagle and Eyrie

1970. Nature Conservation Year.

762	**274**	30p. multicoloured	2·20	1·00

275 "Fabric" Factories

1970. Finnish Textile Industry.

763	**275**	50p. multicoloured	55	40

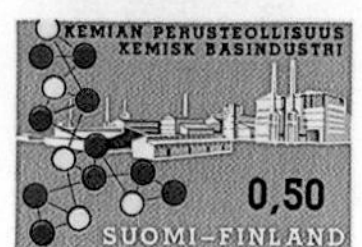

276 "Molecular Structure" and Factories, Nysta

1970. Finnish Chemical Industry.

764	**276**	50p. multicoloured	55	40

277 UNESCO Emblem and Lenin

1970. Finnish Co-operation with United Nations.

765	**277**	30p. multicoloured	55	40
766	-	30p. multicoloured	55	40
767	-	50p. gold, ultram & bl	55	40

DESIGNS—VERT: 30p. (No. 765), Type **277** (Lenin Symposium of UNESCO, Tampere); 30p. (No. 766), "Nuclear data" (Int. Atomic Energy Agency Conference, Otaniemi). HORIZ: 50p. U. N. emblem and globe (United Nations 25th Anniv).

278 *The Seven Brothers*

1970. Red Cross Fund. Multicoloured.

768		25p.+5p. Type **278**	60	90
769		30p.+6p. "Juhani on top of Impivaara" (vert)	60	90
770		50p.+10p. "The Pale Maiden"	60	90

279 Invalid playing Handball

1970. 30th Anniv of Finnish Invalids League.

771	**279**	50p. black, red & orange	55	40

280 *Aurora Society Meeting* (E. Jarnefelt)

1970. Bicentenary of Aurora Society.

772	**280**	50p. multicoloured	55	35

281 City Hall and Old Schoolhouse, Uusikaarlepyy

1970. 350th Anniv of Uusikaarlepyy (Nykarleby) and Kokkola (Gamlakarleby) (towns). Multicoloured.

773		50p. Type **281**	55	40
774		50p. Kokkola and arms	55	40

282 Pres. Kekkonen (from medal by A. Tukiainen)

1970. President Urho Kekkonen's 70th Birthday.

775	**282**	50p. silver and blue	55	40

283 "S.A.L.T." and Globe

1970. Strategic Arms Limitation Talks, Helsinki.

776	**283**	50p. multicoloured	55	40

284 Pres. Paasikivi (after sculpture by E. Renvall)

1970. Birth Centenary of President Paasikivi.

777	**284**	50p. black, blue & gold	55	35

285 Cogwheels

1971. Finnish Industry.

778	**285**	50p. multicoloured	55	40

286 Felling Trees

1971. Tuberculosis Relief Fund. Timber Industry. Multicoloured.

779	25p.+5p. Type **286**	45	90
780	30p.+6p. Tug and log raft	55	1·00
781	50p.+10p. Sorting logs	55	1·10

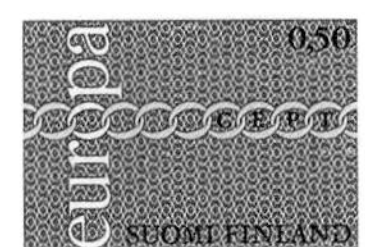

287 Europa Chain

1971. Europa.

782	**287**	50p. yellow, pink & blk	4·50	90

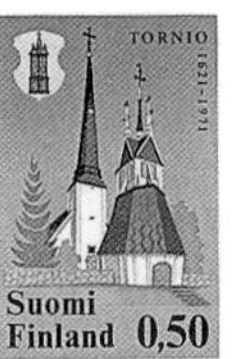

288 Tornio Church

1971. 350th Anniv of Tornio (Torneaa).

783	**288**	50p. multicoloured	75	40

289 *Front-page News* (in Swedish, Finnish and French)

1971. Bicentenary of Finnish Press.

784	**289**	50p. multicoloured	70	40

290 Hurdling, High-jumping and Discus-throwing

1971. European Athletic Championships, Helsinki. Multicoloured.

785	30p. Type **290**	1·10	65
786	50p. Throwing the javelin and running	1·70	65

These two designs form a composite picture when placed side by side.

291 "Lightning" Dinghies

1971. Int "Lightning" Class Sailing Championships, Helsinki.

787	**291**	50p. multicoloured	90	50

292 Silver Pot, Seal and Tools

1971. 60th Anniv of Jewellery and Precious-metal Crafts.

788	**292**	50p. multicoloured	70	30

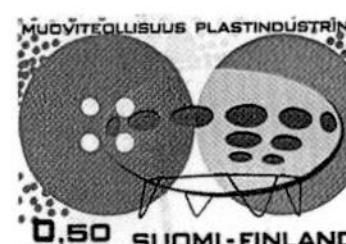

293 Plastic Buttons

1971. Finnish Plastics Industry.

789	**293**	50p. multicoloured	80	40

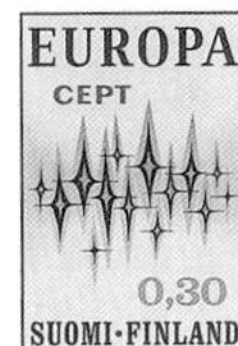

294 "Communications"

1972. Europa.

790	**294**	30p. multicoloured	2·75	50
791	**294**	50p. multicoloured	4·50	50

295 National Theatre Building

1972. Centenary of Finnish National Theatre.

792	**295**	50p. multicoloured	75	50

296 Globe

1972. Conclusion of the Strategic Arms Limitation Talks, Helsinki.

793	**296**	50p. multicoloured	90	35

297 Map and Arms

1972. 50th Anniv of Local Self-government for the Aland Islands.

794	**297**	50p. multicoloured	2·40	75

298 Cadet Ship *Suomen Joutsen*

1972. Start of the Tall Ships' Race, Helsinki.

795	**298**	50p. multicoloured	90	40

299 Post Office, Tampere

1972. Multicoloured.. Multicoloured..

797	40p. Type **299**	70	20
798	60p. National Museum (28×40 mm)	75	40
799	70p. Market Place, Helsinki (39×27 mm)	80	20
800	80p. As 70p.	70	25

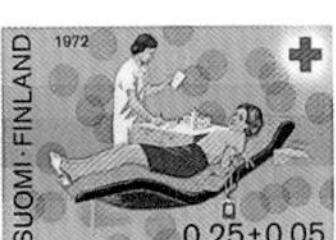

301 Blood Donation

1972. Red Cross Fund. Blood Service. Mult.

820	25p.+5p. Type **301**	65	1·00
821	30p.+6p. Laboratory research (vert)	65	1·00
822	50p.+10p. Blood transfusion	90	1·10

302 Voyri Man

1972. Ancient and National Costumes. Multicoloured.

823	50p. Pernio woman	1·80	40
824	50p. Married couple, Tenala	1·80	40
825	50p. Nastola girl	1·80	40
826	50p. Type **302**	1·80	40
827	50p. Lapp winter costumes	1·80	40
828	60p. Kaukola girl	3·00	35
829	60p. Jaaski woman	3·00	35
830	60p. Koivisto couple	3·00	35
831	60p. Mother and son, Sakyla	3·00	35
832	60p. Heinavesi girl	3·00	35

303 "European Co-operation"

1972. European Security and Co-operation Conf, Helsinki (1st issue).

833	**303**	50p. multicoloured	2·40	50

See also No. 839.

304 *Treaty* and National Colours

1973. 25th Anniv of Friendship Treaty with Russia.

834	**304**	60p. multicoloured	75	50

305 Pres. K. Kallio

1973. Birth Cent of Pres. Kyosti Kallio.

835	**305**	60p. multicoloured	75	30

306 Europa "Posthorn"

1973. Europa.

836	**306**	60p. green, turq & blue	1·60	50

1973. Nordic Countries' Postal Co-operation. As T **201** of Denmark.

837	60p. multicoloured	90	35
838	70p. multicoloured	90	35

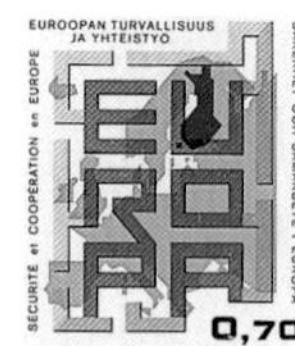

307 "EUROPA" on Map

1973. European Security and Co-operation Conf, Helsinki (2nd issue).

839	**307**	70p. multicoloured	90	50

308 Canoe Paddle

1973. World Canoeing Championships, Tampere.

840	**308**	60p. multicoloured	75	40

309 Radiosonde Balloon

1973. Cent of World Meteorological Organization.

841	**309**	60p. multicoloured	75	40

310 E. Saarinen

1973. Birth Cent of Eliel Saarinen (architect).

842	**310**	60p. multicoloured	75	50

311 *Young Girl with Lamb* (H. Simberg)

1973. Tuberculosis Relief Fund. Artists' Birth Centenaries. Multicoloured.

843	30p.+5p. Type **311**	90	90
844	40p.+10p. *Summer Evening* (W. Sjostrom)	1·20	1·30
845	60p.+15p. *At a Mountain Spring* (J. Rissanen)	1·20	1·30

312 Douglas DC-10-30

1973. 50th Annivs. of Finnair (airline) and Regular Air Services in Finland.

846	**312**	60p. multicoloured	90	40

313 Santa Claus

1973. Christmas.

847	**313**	30p. multicoloured	90	35

314 Scene from *The Barber of Seville*

1973. Centenary of Finnish State Opera Company.

848	**314**	60p. multicoloured	75	40

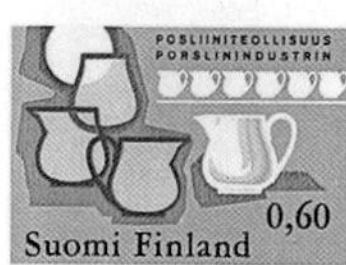

315 Porcelain Products

1973. Finnish Porcelain Industry.

849	**315**	60p. green, blk & bl	80	40

316 "Paavo Nurmi" (Statue by W. Aaltonen)

1973. Paavo Nurmi (Olympic athlete) Commem.

850	**316**	60p. multicoloured	90	40

317 Hanko Casino, Harbour and Map

1974. Centenary of Hanko (Hango).

851	**317**	60p. multicoloured	75	40

318 Arms of Finland, 1581

1974

852	**318**	10m. multicoloured	3·00	35
852a	-	20m. multicoloured	7·00	50

DESIGN: 20m. Arms as in T **318** but different border.

319 Ice Hockey Players

1974. World and European Ice Hockey Championships.

853	**319**	60p. multicoloured	90	35

320 Herring Gulls

1974. Baltic Area Marine Environmental Conference, Helsinki.

854	**320**	60p. multicoloured	80	35

321 *Goddess of Victory bestowing Wreath on Youth* (W. Aaltonen)

1974. Europa.

855	**321**	70p. multicoloured	3·75	50

322 Ilmari Kianto

1974. Birth Centenary of Ilmari Kianto ("Iki Kianto") (writer).

856	**322**	60p. multicoloured	75	40

323 Society Emblem

1974. Finnish Society for Popular Education.

857	**323**	60p. multicoloured	75	40

324 "Rationalization"

1974. Finnish Rationalization in Social Development.

858	**324**	60p. multicoloured	75	40

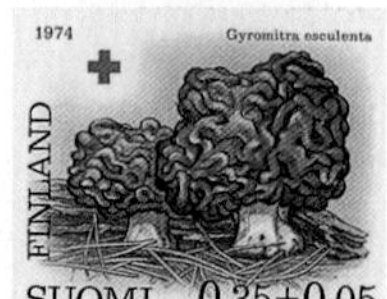

325 Beefsteak Morel

1974. Red Cross Fund. Mushrooms (1st series). Multicoloured.

859		35p.+5p. Type **325**	1·10	80
860		50p.+10p. Chanterelle	1·60	1·70
861		60p.+15p. Cep	1·60	1·70

See also Nos. 937/9 and 967/9.

326 U.P.U. Emblem

1974. Centenary of Universal Postal Union.

862	**326**	60p. multicoloured	65	30
863	**326**	70p. multicoloured	65	30

327 Christmas Gnomes

1974. Christmas.

864	**327**	35p. multicoloured	1·10	50

328 Aunessilta Granite Bridge and Modern Reinforced Concrete Bridge

1974. 175th Anniv of Finnish Road and Waterways Board.

865	**328**	60p. multicoloured	75	35

329 National Arms

1975

865a	**329**	10p. purple	20	15
865c	**329**	20p. yellow	20	15
865d	**329**	30p. red	25	15
866	**329**	40p. orange	30	15
867	**329**	50p. green	30	15
868	**329**	60p. blue	35	15
869	**329**	70p. brown	40	15
870	**329**	80p. red and green	45	15
871	**329**	90p. violet	45	15
872	**329**	1m. brown	40	20
873	**329**	1m.10 yellow	50	15
874	**329**	1m.20 blue	50	15
875	**329**	1m.30 green	50	25
875a	**329**	1m.40 violet	60	15
875b	**329**	1m.50 blue	60	15
875c	**329**	1m.60 red	60	15
875d	**329**	1m.70 grey	60	15
875e	**329**	1m.80 green	75	15
875f	**329**	1m.90 orange	65	15
1161	**329**	2m. green	1·60	65

330 Finnish 32p. Stamp of 1875

1975. "Nordia 1975" Stamp Exhibition.

876	**330**	70p. brown, black & buff	3·00	3·25

331 *A Girl Combing Her Hair* (M. Enckell)

1975. Europa. Multicoloured.

877		70p. Type **331**	2·20	45
878		90p. *Washerwomen* (T. Sallinen)	2·20	45

332 Office Seal

1975. 150th Anniv of State Economy Controllers' Office.

879	**332**	70p. multicoloured	65	35

333 *Niilo Saarinen* (lifeboat) and Sinking Ship

1975. 12th International Salvage Conference, Helsinki.

880	**333**	70p. multicoloured	75	35

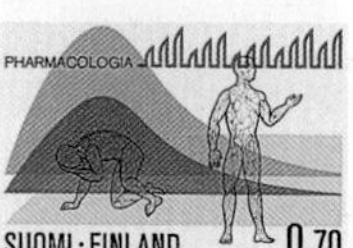

334 "Pharmacology"

1975. Sixth International Pharmacological Congress, Helsinki.

881	**334**	70p. multicoloured	75	35

335 Olavinlinna Castle

1975. 500th Anniv of Olavinlinna Castle.

882	**335**	70p. multicoloured	75	35

336 Finlandia Hall (Conference Headquarters) and Barn Swallow

1975. European Security and Co-operation Conference, Helsinki.

883	**336**	90p. multicoloured	90	35

337 *Echo* (E. Thesleff)

1975. Tuberculosis Relief Fund. Paintings by female artists. Multicoloured.

884		40p.+10p. Type **337**	65	90
885		60p.+15p. *Portrait of Hilda Wiik* (Maria Wiik)	90	1·10
886		70p.+20p. *At Home* (Helene Schjerfbeck)	90	1·10

338 Men and Women supporting Globe

1975. International Women's Year.

887	**338**	70p. multicoloured	75	40

339 Graphic Quarter- circle

1975. Centenary of Finnish Society of Industrial Art.

888	**339**	70p. multicoloured	75	35

340 Nativity Play

1975. Christmas.

889	**340**	40p. multicoloured	75	35

341 State Debenture

1975. Cent. of Finnish State Treasury.
890 **341** 80p. multicoloured 70 30

342 Finnish Glider

1976. 15th World Gliding Championships, Rayskala.
891 **342** 80p. multicoloured 80 35

343 Disabled Ex-servicemen's Association Emblem

1976. Finnish War Invalids Fund.
892 **343** 70p.+30p. mult 90 65

344 Cheese Frames

1976. Traditional Finnish Arts.

893	-	1m.50 multicoloured	75	40
893a	-	2m. multicoloured	1·20	25
893b	-	2m.20 multicoloured	80	30
894	**344**	2m.50 multicoloured	90	40
895	-	3m. multicoloured	1·10	40
896	-	4m.50 multicoloured	1·60	40
896b	-	4m.80 multicoloured	1·50	65
897	-	5m. multicoloured	1·80	40
898	-	6m. multicoloured	1·80	25
899	-	7m. multicoloured	2·75	35
899a	-	8m. brown and black	2·75	35
899b	-	9m. black and blue	3·00	65
899c	-	12m. ochre, drab & brn	4·00	75

DESIGNS—VERT: 1m.50, Rusko drinking bowl, 1542; 4m.50, Spinning distaffs; 5m. Weathercock, Kirvu (metalwork); 6m. Kaspaikka (Karelian towel); 7m. Bridal rug, 1815; 8m. Arsenal door, Hollola church (iron forging). HORIZ: 2m., 4m.80, Old-style sauna; 2m.20, Kerimaki Church and belfry (peasant architecture); 3m. Shuttle and raanu (patterned cover); 9m. Four-pronged fish spear, c. 1000; 12m. Damask with tulip pattern.

345 Heikki Klemetti

1976. Birth Centenary of Professor Heikki Klemetti (composer).
900 **345** 80p. multicoloured 75 30

346 Map of Finnish Dialect Regions

1976. Centenary of Finnish Language Society.
901 **346** 80p. multicoloured 75 30

347 *Aino Ackte in Paris* (A. Edelfelt)

1976. Birth Cent of Aino Ackte (opera singer).
902 **347** 70p. multicoloured 75 35

348 Ancient Knives and Belts

1976. Europa.
903 **348** 80p. multicoloured 5·50 45

349 "Radio Broadcasting"

1976. 50th Anniv of Radio Broadcasting in Finland.
904 **349** 80p. multicoloured 70 30

350 Wedding Dance

1976. Tuberculosis Relief Fund. Traditional Wedding Customs. Multicoloured.
905 50p.+10p. Wedding procession (horiz) 65 65
906 70p.+15p. Type **350** 65 90
907 80p.+20p. Wedding breakfast (horiz) 90 90

351 Sleigh arriving at Church

1976. Christmas.
908 **351** 50p. multicoloured 75 30

352 Medieval Seal and Text

1976. 700th Anniv of Cathedral Chapter, Turku.
909 **352** 80p. multicoloured 70 30

353 Hugo Alvar Aalto and Finlandia Hall, Helsinki

1976. Hugo Alvar Aalto (architect) Commem.
910 **353** 80p. multicoloured 70 40

354 *Disaster Relief*

1977. Red Cross Fund. Centenary of Finnish Red Cross. Multicoloured.
911 50p.+10p. Type **354** 65 90
912 80p.+15p. "Community Work" 65 90
913 90p.+20p. "Blood Transfusion Service" 90 90

355 Figure Skating

1977. European Figure Skating Championships, Helsinki.
914 **355** 90p. multicoloured 75 30

1977. Northern Countries' Co-operation in Nature Conservation and Environment Protection. As T **229** of Denmark.
915 90p. multicoloured 80 35
916 1m. multicoloured 80 35

356 *Urho* (ice-breaker) and Freighter

1977. Centenary of Winter Navigation between Finland and Sweden.
917 **356** 90p. multicoloured 70 30

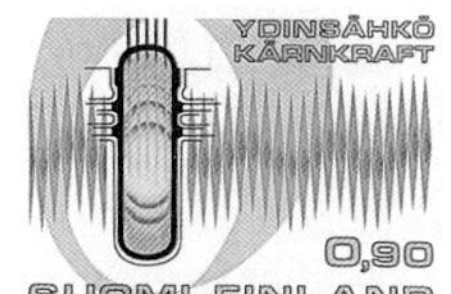

357 "Nuclear Reactor"

1977. Inauguration of Hastholm Island Nuclear Power Station.
918 **357** 90p. multicoloured 70 30

358 Autumn Landscape

1977. Europa.
919 **358** 90p. multicoloured 3·50 45

359 Tree with Nest

1977. 75th Anniv of Co-operative Banks.
920 **359** 90p. multicoloured 70 30

360 New Church of Valamo Cloister, Heinavesi

1977. 800th Anniv of Finnish Orthodoxy and Inauguration of Valamo Cloister.
921 **360** 90p. multicoloured 65 30

361 Paavo Ruotsalainen

1977. Birth Centenary of Paavo Ruotsalanen (leader of Pietistic Movement).
922 **361** 90p. multicoloured 70 30

362 "Defence and Protection"

1977. Civil Defence.
923 **362** 90p. multicoloured 65 30

363 Volleyball

1977. European Volleyball Championships.
924 **363** 90p. multicoloured 65 30

364 Women's Relay Skiing

1977. World Ski Championships, Lahti. Multicoloured.
925 80p.+40p. Type **364** 1·80 1·90
926 1m.+50p. Ski jumper 1·80 1·70

365 Children taking Water to the Sauna

1977. Christmas.
927 **365** 50p. multicoloured 70 30

366 Finnish Flag

1977. 60th Anniv of Independence.
928 **366** 80p. multicoloured 60 30
929 **366** 1m. multicoloured (37×25½ mm) 90 30

367 Early and Modern Telephones

1977. Centenary of Finnish Telephone.
930 **367** 1m. multicoloured 55 30

368 Kotka Harbour

1978. Centenary of Kotka.
931 **368** 1m. multicoloured 75 30

369 Sanatorium, Paimio

1978. Europa. Multicoloured.

932		1m. Type **369**	5·00	1·50
933		1m.20 Studio House, Hvittrask (37×25½ mm)	9·75	7·25

370 Buses

1978. Provincial Bus Service.

934	**370**	1m. multicoloured	60	30

371 Eino Leino

1978. Birth Cent of Eino Leino (poet).

935	**371**	1m. multicoloured	75	30

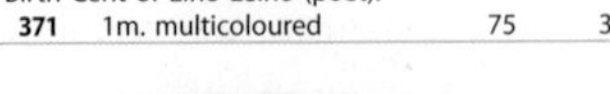

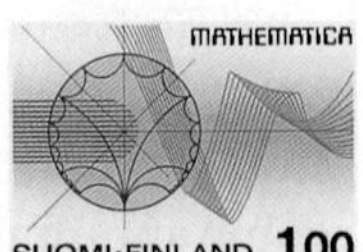

372 Function Theory Diagram

1978. International Congress of Mathematicians, Finland.

936	**372**	1m. multicoloured	75	30

1978. Red Cross Fund. Mushrooms (2nd series). As T **325**. Multicoloured.

937		50p.+10p. *Lactarius deterrimus*	90	75
938		80p.+15p. Parasol mushroom (vert)	1·10	1·10
939		1m.+20p. The gypsy	1·20	1·10

373 Girl feeding Corn to Great Tits

1978. Christmas.

940	**373**	50p. multicoloured	75	30

374 Child, Hearts and Flowers

1979. International Year of the Child.

941	**374**	1m.10 multicoloured	1·50	35

375 Orienteer

1979. Eighth World Orienteering Championships.

942	**375**	1m.10 multicoloured	80	30

376 Old Training College, Hamina, and Academy Flag

1979. Bicentenary of Officer Training.

943	**376**	1m.10 multicoloured	75	30

377 Turku Buildings

1979. 750th Anniv of Turku (Abo).

944	**377**	1m.10 multicoloured	75	30

378 Tram in City Street

1979. Helsinki Tram Service.

945	**378**	1m.10 multicoloured	75	30

379 *Tammerkoski Waterfall* (lithograph, P. Gaimard)

1979. Bicent of Tampere (Tammerfors) (1st issue).

946	**379**	90p. brown, buff & black	60	30

See also No. 953.

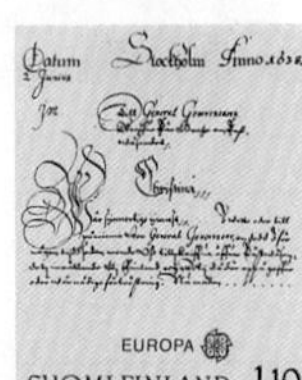

380 Letter establishing Finnish Postal Service, 1638

1979. Europa.

947	**380**	1m.10 blk, brn and ochre	2·75	35
948	-	1m.30 blk, brn and grey	5·75	1·00

DESIGN—HORIZ: 1m.30, A. E. Edelcrantz's optical telegraph, 1796.

381 Pehr Kalm and Title Page

1979. Tuberculosis Relief Fund. Finnish Scientists. Multicoloured.

949		60p.+10p. Type **381**	65	90
950		90p.+15p. Wheat and title page of Pehr Gadd's *Svenska Landt-skot-selen* (vert)	65	1·00
951		1m.10+20p. Petter Forsskaal and title page	90	1·00

382 Town Street with Trade-signs

1979. Centenary of Business and Industry Law.

952	**382**	1m.10 multicoloured	75	30

383 Stylized View of Tampere

1979. Bicentenary of Tampere (2nd issue).

953	**383**	1m.10 multicoloured	75	30

384 Early and Modern Cars at Pedestrian Crossing

1979. The Private Car.

954	**384**	1m.10 multicoloured	65	30

385 House of Korppi, Lapinjarvi, Uusimaa

1979. Peasant Architecture. Multicoloured.

955		1m.10 Type **385**	65	50
956		1m.10 House of Syrjala, Tammela, Hame (left-hand part)	65	50
957		1m.10 House of Syrjala (right-hand part)	65	50
958		1m.10 House of Murtovaarsa, Valtimo, North Karelia	65	50
959		1m.10 House of Antila, Lapua, Pohjanmaa	65	50
960		1m.10 Gable loft of Lu-ukila, Haukipudas and loft of Keskikangas, Yliharma, Pohjanmaa	65	50
961		1m.10 Gate, house of Kanajarvi, Kalvola, Hame	65	50
962		1m.10 Porch, house of Havusel-ka, Kauhajoki, Pohjanmaa	65	50
963		1m.10 Dinner bell and House of Maki-Rasinpera, Kuortane, Pohjanmaa	65	50
964		1m.10 Gable and eaves of granary of Rasula, Kuortane, Pohjanmaa	65	50

See also Nos. 1024/33.

386 "Brownies" feeding Horse

1979. Christmas.

965	**386**	60p. multicoloured	75	30

387 Maria Jotuni

1980. Birth Centenary of Maria Jotuni (writer).

966	**387**	1m.10 multicoloured	75	30

1980. Finnish Red Cross Fund. Mushrooms (3rd series). As T **325**. Multicoloured.

967		60p.+10p. Woolly milk cap	65	75
968		90p.+15p. Red cap	80	1·10
969		1m.10+20p. *Russula paludosa*	1·10	1·10

388 Frans Eemil Sillanpaa

1980. Europa. Finnish Nobel Prize Winners. Multicoloured.

970		1m.10 Type **388** (Literature, 1939)	1·60	50
971		1m.30 Artturi Ilmari Virtanen (Chemistry, 1945) (vert)	3·00	1·00

389 Pres. Kekkonen

1980. President Urho Kekkonen's 80th Birthday.

973	**389**	1m.10 multicoloured	70	30

390 Back-piece Harness

1980. Nordic Countries' Postal Co-operation. Multicoloured.

974		1m.10 Type **390**	65	35
975		1m.30 Collar harness (vert)	65	35

391 Biathlon

1980. Biathlon World Championship, Lahti.

976	**391**	1m.10 multicoloured	70	30

392 Trials of Strength

1980. Christmas. Multicoloured.

977		60p. Type **392**	60	30
978		1m.10 "To put out the shoe maker's eye" (children's game)	85	30

393 Kauhaneva Swamps, Kauhajoki

1981. National Parks.

979	**393**	70p. pink, brown & grn	45	40
980	-	1m.60 multicoloured	65	40
981	-	1m.80 multicoloured	75	40
982	-	2m.40 multicoloured	90	35
983	-	4m.30 multicoloured	1·30	85

DESIGNS—VERT: 1m.60, Forest of Multiharju, Seitseminen National Park. HORIZ: 1m.80, Razorbills, Eastern Gulf National Park; 2m.40, Urho Kekkonen National Park; 4m.30, Archipelago National Park.

394 Boxing

1981. European Boxing Championships, Tampere.

990	**394**	1m.10 multicoloured	70	40

395 Glass-blowing and 19th-century Bottle

1981. 300th Anniv of Finnish Glass Industry.

991	**395**	1m.10 multicoloured	80	40

396 *Furst Menschikoff* (paddle-steamer)

1981. "Nordia 1981" Stamp Exhibition, Helsinki.

992	**396**	1m.10 brown & stone	2·75	3·25

397 Rowing to Church

1981. Europa. Multicoloured.

993	1m.10 Type **397**	1·10	35
994	1m.50 Midsummer Eve celebrations	2·00	65

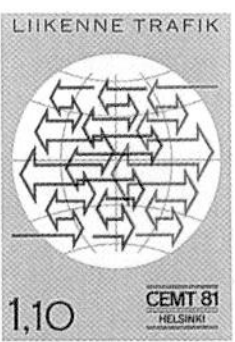

398 "International Traffic Movement"

1981. Council Session of European Conference of Ministers of Transport, Finland.

995	**398**	1m.10 multicoloured	70	30

399 Children on Winged Horse

1981. Centenary of Finnish Youth Associations.

996	**399**	1m. multicoloured	70	40

400 Fuchsia

1981. Tuberculosis Relief Fund. Potted Plants. Multicoloured.

997	70p.+10p. Type **400**	65	75
998	1m.+15p. African violet (*Saintpaulia ionantha*)	75	75
999	1m.10+20p. Pelargonium	90	75

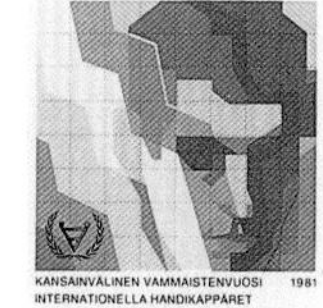

401 Face on Graph

1981. International Year of Disabled Persons.

1000	**401**	1m.10 multicoloured	70	40

402 Children bringing Home Christmas Tree

1981. Christmas. Multicoloured.

1001	70p. Type **402**	65	30
1002	1m.10 Decorating the Christmas tree (vert)	70	30

404 Hame Castle

1982

1007	**404**	90p. brown	45	35
1008	-	1m. brown and blue	65	40

DESIGN—VERT: 1m. Windmill, Harrstrom.

405 First Issue of *Om konsten att ratt Behaga* and Modern Periodical

1982. Bicentenary of Finnish Periodicals.

1015	**405**	1m.20 multicoloured	70	30

406 Kuopio Cathedral and Puijo Tower

1982. Bicentenary of Kuopio.

1016	**406**	1m.20 multicoloured	70	30

407 Neck of Stringed Instrument and Staves of Music

1982. Music Jubilee.

1017	**407**	1m.20 multicoloured	70	30

408 Flats, Factories and Houses

1982. Centenary of Electricity in Finland.

1018	**408**	1m.20 multicoloured	70	30

409 Vegetable and Fruit Garden

1982. Cent of First Finnish Horticultural Society.

1019	**409**	1m.10 multicoloured	70	30

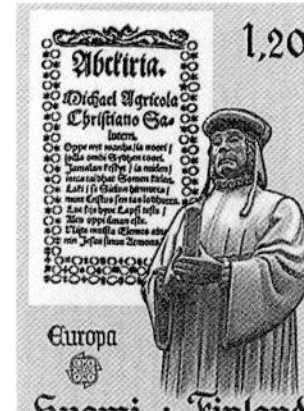

410 Cover of *Abckiria* and sculpture of M. Agricola by O. Jauhiainen

1982. Europa. Multicoloured.

1020	1m.20 Type **410**	2·00	45
1021	1m.50 *Turku Academy Inaugural Procession in 1640* (fresco copied by Johannes Gebhard from painting by Albert Edelfelt) (47×31 mm)	3·00	65

411 Emblems and Symbolic Design

1982. International Monetary Fund and World Bank Committees' Meetings, Helsinki.

1022	**411**	1m.60 multicoloured	70	30

412 Interior of Parliament and *Future* (sculpture by W. Aaltonen)

1982. 75th Anniv of Single Chamber Parliament.

1023	**412**	2m.40 blue, dp bl & blk	1·00	65

1982. Manor Houses. As T **385**. Multicoloured.

1024	1m.20 Kuitia, 1490s	70	50
1025	1m.20 Louhisaari, 1655	70	50
1026	1m.20 Frugard, 1780	70	50
1027	1m.20 Jokioinen, 1798	70	50
1028	1m.20 Moisio, 1820	70	50
1029	1m.20 Sjundby, 1560s	70	50
1030	1m.20 Fagervik, 1773	70	50
1031	1m.20 Mustio, 1792	70	50
1032	1m.20 Fiskars, 1818	70	50
1033	1m.20 Kotkaniemi, 1836	70	50

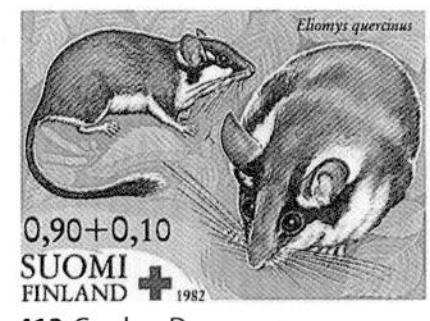

413 Garden Dormouse

1982. Red Cross Fund. Endangered Mammals. Multicoloured.

1034	90p.+10p. Type **413**	60	90
1035	1m.10+15p. Siberian flying squirrel (vert)	90	1·00
1036	1m.20+20p. European mink	1·00	1·00

414 Brownie Children feeding Forest Animals

1982. Christmas. Multicoloured.

1037	90p. Type **414**	65	30
1038	1m.20 Brownie children eating porridge	65	30

415 Gold Prospector

1983. Nordic Countries' Postal Co-operation. "Visit the North". Multicoloured.

1039	1m.20 Type **415**	65	30
1040	1m.30 Descending the Kitajoki river rapids	65	30

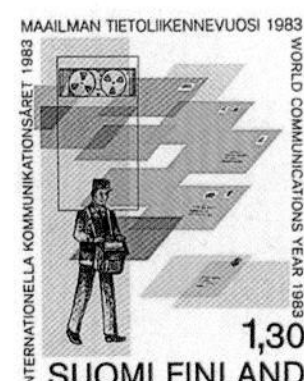

416 Postman, Letters and Computer

1983. World Communications Year. Multicoloured.

1041	1m.30 Type **416**	60	30
1042	1m.70 Modulated wave, pulse stream and optical cables	80	40

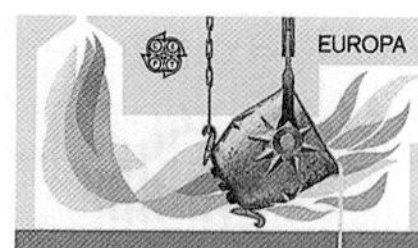

418 Flash Smelting

1983. Europa. Multicoloured.

1044	1m.30 Type **418**	4·00	35
1045	1m.70 Interior of Temppeliaukio Church (Timo and Tuomo Suomalainen)	9·25	1·10

419 President Relander

1983. Birth Centenary of Lauri Kristian Relander (President, 1925–1931).

1046	**419**	1m.30 multicoloured	70	30

420 Throwing the Javelin

1983. World Athletics Championships, Helsinki. Multicoloured.

1047	1m.20 Type **420**	65	35
1048	1m.30 Running (vert)	70	30

421 Kuula and Ostrobothnia

1983. Birth Cent of Toivo Kuula (composer).

1049	**421**	1m.30 multicoloured	70	30

422 Chickweed Wintergreen

1983. Tuberculosis Relief Fund. Wild Flowers. Multicoloured.

1050	1m.+20p. Type **422**	60	80
1051	1m.20+25p. Marsh Violet	65	80
1052	1m.30+30p. Marsh Marigold	1·10	85

423 *Santa Claus* (Eija Myllyviita)

1983. Christmas. Children's Drawings.

1053	**423**	1m. blue & deep blue	65	30
1054	-	1m.30 multicoloured	70	35

DESIGN—VERT: 1m.30, *Two Candles* (Camilla Lindberg).

424 Koivisto

1983. President Mauno Henrik Koivisto's 60th Birthday.

1055	**424**	1m.30 bl, blk & dp bl	65	30

425 Second Class Letters

1984. Re-classification of Postal Items.
1056 **425** 1m.10 green 45 20
1057 - 1m.40 orange & red 45 20
DESIGN—VERT: 1m.40, First class letter.

426 Hydraulic Turbine Manufacture

1984. "Work and Skill" Centenary of Workers' Associations.
1058 **426** 1m.40 multicoloured 70 30

427 Crossbow, Pot and Chalice

1984. Museum Activities.
1059 **427** 1m.40 multicoloured 70 30

428 Bridge

1984. Europa. 25th Anniv of European Post and Telecommunications Conference.
1060 **428** 1m.40 orange, deep orange and black 3·75 45
1061 **428** 2m. blue, violet and black 6·75 1·00

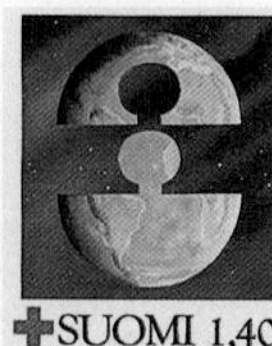

429 Globe as Jigsaw Puzzle

1984. Finnish Red Cross Fund. Multicoloured.
1062 1m.40+35p. Type **429** 80 90
1063 2m.+40p. Spheres around globe 90 1·20

430 Teeth and Dentist treating Patient

1984. International Dental Federation Congress, Helsinki.
1064 **430** 1m.40 multicoloured 90 30

431 Observatory, Planets and Sun

1984. Cent of University of Helsinki Observatory.
1065 **431** 1m.10 multicoloured 70 30

432 Statute Book and Title Page

1984. 250th Anniv of 1734 Common Law.
1066 **432** 2m. multicoloured 85 50

433 *Mother and Child* (Waino Aaltonen) and Lines from *Song of my Heart*

1984. 150th Birth Anniv of Aleksis Kivi (writer).
1067 **433** 1m.40 grey and black 70 30

434 Father Christmas and Brownie

1984. Christmas.
1068 **434** 1m.10 multicoloured 65 30

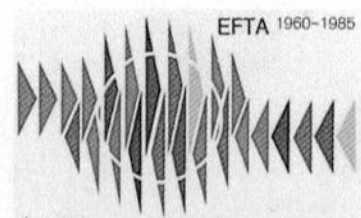

435 Symbolic Representation of International Trade

1985. 25th Anniversary of European Free Trade Association.
1069 **435** 1m.20 multicoloured 70 40

436 Medal of Johan Ludwig Runeberg (by Walter Runeberg) and Emblem

1985. Centenary of Society of Swedish Literature in Finland.
1070 **436** 1m.50 multicoloured 65 30

437 *Saints Sergei and Herman* (icon, Petros Sasaki)

1985. Centenary of Saint Sergei and Saint Herman Order (home missionary organization of Finnish Orthodox Church).
1071 **437** 1m.50 multicoloured 70 30

438 Pedri Semeikka (rune singer)

1985. 150th Anniv of *Kalevala* (Karelian poems collected by Elias Lonnrot). Multicoloured.
1072 1m.50 Type **438** 65 40
1073 2m.10 Larin Paraske (legend teller) (after Albert Edelfelt) 1·10 65

439 *Mermaid* (Ville Vallgren)

1985. "Nordia 1985" International Stamp Exhibition, Helsinki.
1074 **439** 1m.50 black, grey and blue 3·50 4·50

440 1886 5m. Banknote

1985. Centenary of Finnish Banknote Printing. Multicoloured.
1075 1m.50 Type **440** 90 50
1076 1m.50 1909 50m. banknote showing sailing ship (horiz) 90 50
1077 1m.50 50m. banknote showing waterfall 90 50
1078 1m.50 1000m. banknote showing lake (left side) 90 50
1079 1m.50 1000m. banknote showing lake (right side) 90 50
1080 1m.50 500m. banknote showing harvesters 90 50
1081 1m.50 1000m. banknote showing arms and tree, and part of 50m. banknote (horiz) 90 50
1082 1m.50 1955 5000m. banknote showing J. V. Snellman 90 50

441 Children playing Recorders

1985. Europa. Music Year. Multicoloured.
1083 1m.50 Type **441** 3·50 35
1084 2m.10 Cathedral columns and score of "Ramus Virens Olivarum" 12·00 1·40

442 Finlandia Hall and Barn Swallow

1985. Tenth Anniv of European Security and Cooperation Conference, Helsinki.
1085 **442** 2m.10 multicoloured 1·00 75

443 Provincial Arms and Seal of Per Brahe

1985. 350th Anniv of Provincial Administration.
1086 **443** 1m.50 multicoloured 70 30

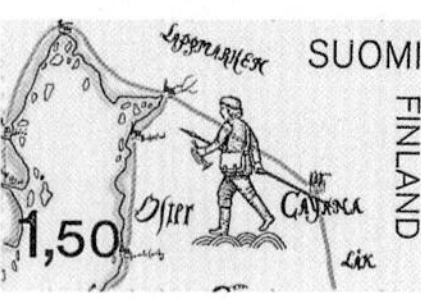

444 Foot Messenger

1985. "Finlandia 88" International Stamp Exhibition, Helsinki (1st issue). Sheet 135×90 mm containing T **444** and similar multicoloured designs forming a composite design of 1698 postal map of Sweden and Finland.
MS1087 1m.50 Type **444**; 1m.50 Raft; 1m.50 Mounted messanger (vert); 1m.50 Iceboat (sold at 8m.) 9·00 8·75
See also Nos. **MS**1107, **MS**1122, 1149 and **MS**1152.

445 I.Y.Y. Emblem

1985. International Youth Year.
1088 **445** 1m.50 multicoloured 70 30

446 Bird Decoration and Tulips

1985. Christmas. Multicoloured.
1089 1m.20 Type **446** 65 30
1090 1m.20 St. Thomas's cross and hyacinths 65 30

447 Orbicular Granite

1986. Centenary of Geological Society. Multicoloured.
1091 1m.30 Type **447** 60 40
1092 1m.60 Rapakivi (granite) 60 30
1093 2m.10 Veined gneiss 85 40

448 Saimaa Ringed Seal

1986. Europa. Multicoloured.
1094 1m.60 Type **448** 4·50 55
1095 2m.20 Landscape seen through window 8·00 1·10

449 Baghdad Conference Palace (Kaija and Heikki Siren)

1986. Modern Architecture. Multicoloured.
1096 1m.60 Type **449** 80 50
1097 1m.60 Lahti Theatre (Pekka Salminen and Esko Koivisto) (value in blue) 80 50
1098 1m.60 Kuusamo Municipal Offices (Marja and Keijo Petaja) (value in red) 80 50
1099 1m.60 Hamina police and court building (Timo and Tuomo Suomalainen) and Greek church (value in green) 80 50
1100 1m.60 Finnish Embassy, New Delhi (Raili and Reima Pietila) (value in green) 80 50
1101 1m.60 Day care centre, Western Sakyla (Kari Jarvinen and Timo Airas) (value in red) 80 50

450 Orange-tip

1986. Finnish Red Cross Fund. Butterflies. Multicoloured.
1102 1m.60+40p. Type **450** 90 90
1103 2m.10+45p. Camberwell beauty 1·10 1·60
1104 5m.+50p. Apollo 2·20 2·50

451 Auditorium, Joensuu

1986. Nordic Countries' Postal Co-operation. Twinned Towns. Multicoloured.
1105 1m.60 Type **451** 80 35
1106 2m.20 Emblem of University of Jyvaskyla 1·00 1·30

452 Paddle-steamer *Aura*

1986. "Finlandia 88" International Stamp Exhibition, Helsinki (2nd issue). Sheet 135×90 mm containing T **452** and similar designs, each deep brown and buff.
MS1107 1m.60 Type **452**; 1m.60 Steamship *Alexander*; 2m.20 Steamship *Nicolai*; 2m.20 Ice-breaker *Express II* (vert) (sold at 10m.) 9·00 8·75

453 Maupertuis, Globe, Quadrant and Sledge

1986. 250th Anniv of Measurement of Arcs of Meridian.
1108 **453** 1m.60 bl, ultram & blk 1·00 30

454 Kekkonen

1986. Urho Kekkonen (President, 1956–81). Commemoration.
1109 **454** 5m. black 1·80 95

455 Cloud, Rainbow and Emblem

1986. International Peace Year.
1110 **455** 1m.60 multicoloured 75 30

456 Angels and Garland

1986. Christmas. Multicoloured.
1111 1m.30 Type **456** 75 30
1112 1m.30 Angels and garland (different) 75 30
1113 1m.60 Brownies and garland 85 30

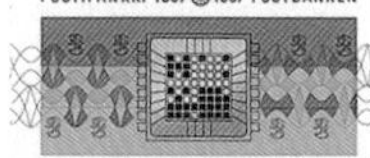

457 Microchip

1987. Centenary of Postal Savings Bank.
1114 **457** 1m.70 multicoloured 75 30

458 Prototype Metre Measuring Bar as Parcel

1987. Centenary of Metric System in Finland.
1115 **458** 1m.40 multicoloured 70 50

459 *Borea* (liner), Diesel Train, Snow Scene and Skier

1987. Tourism. Multicoloured.
1116 1m.70 Type **459** 60 35
1117 2m.30 Douglas DC-10 airplane, bus, yachts on lake and hiker 85 75

460 Wrestlers

1987. European Wrestling Championships, Helsinki.
1118 **460** 1m.70 multicoloured 85 30

461 Madetoja and Score of Cradlesong

1987. Birth Centenary of Leevi Madetoja (composer).
1119 **461** 2m.10 multicoloured 90 30

462 Balls and Pins

1987. 11th World Ten Pin Bowling Championships.
1120 **462** 1m.70 multicoloured 85 30

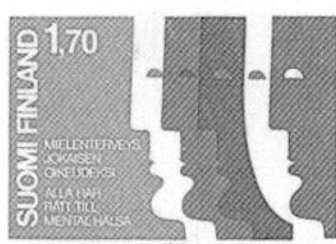

463 Profiles

1987. 90th Anniv of Finnish Association for Mental Health.
1121 **463** 1m.70 multicoloured 85 30

464 Locomotive *Lemminkainen*, 1862

1987. "Finlandia 88" International Stamp Exhibition, Helsinki (3rd issue). Sheet 135×90 mm containing T **464** and similar horiz designs, depicting trains on the Helsinki–Hameenlinna and Riihimaki–St. Petersburg routes.
MS1122 1m.70 green, orange and blue (Type **464**); 1m.70 multicoloured (Mail van No. 9935, 1871); 1m.70 multicoloured (Mail van No. 9991, 1899); 2m.30 green and blue (Locomotive No. 57, 1874) (sold at 10m.) 9·00 8·75

465 *Strawberry Girl* (Nils Schillmark)

1987. Centenary of Ateneum Art Museum. Paintings. Multicoloured.
1123 1m.70 Type **465** 1·40 65
1124 1m.70 *Still Life on a Lady's Work-table* (Ferdinand von Wright) 1·40 65
1125 1m.70 *Old Woman with Basket* (Albert Edelfelt) 1·40 65
1126 1m.70 *Boy and Crow* (Akseli Gallen-Kallela) 1·40 65
1127 1m.70 *Late Winter* (Tyko Sallinen) 1·40 65

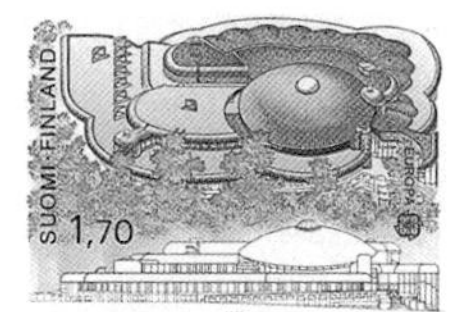

466 Tampere Main Library (Railia and Reima Pietila)

1987. Europa. Art and Architecture. Multicoloured.
1128 1m.70 Type **466** 5·25 35
1129 2m.30 "Stoa" (Hannu Siren) 13·00 1·30

467 Arrows

1987. Seventh European Physics Society General Conference.
1130 **467** 1m.70 multicoloured 70 30

468 Outline Maps of Finland

1987. 70th Anniv of Independence.
1131 **468** 1m.70 silver, grey & bl 85 30
1132 **468** 10m. silver, blue and azure (26×37 mm) 4·00 1·30

469 Baby with Ball and Prof. Ylppo

1987. 100th Birthday of Arvo Ylppo (paediatrician).
1133 **469** 1m.70 multicoloured 75 30

470 Father Christmas and Brownies

1987. Christmas. Multicoloured.
1134 1m.40 Type **470** 55 30
1135 1m.70 Mother Christmas and brownie (vert) 90 30

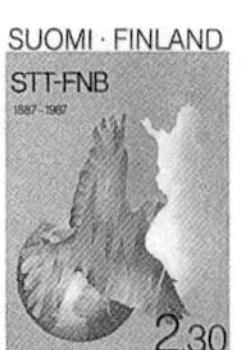

471 Birds flying from Globe to Finland

1987. Centenary of Finnish News Agency.
1136 **471** 2m.30 multicoloured 85 90

472 Pihkala

1988. Birth Centenary of Lauri Pihkala ("Tahko") (writer and sport organizer).
1137 **472** 1m.80 deep blue, blue and black 85 30

473 Telephone and Mail Boxes

1988. 350th Anniv of Posts and Telecommunications Services (1st issue). Multicoloured.
1138 1m.80 Type **473** 70 30
1139 1m.80 Airplane and lorry 70 30
1140 1m.80 Fork-lift truck carrying parcels 70 30
1141 1m.80 Postman 70 30
1142 1m.80 Woman receiving letter 70 30

Nos. 1138/42 were printed together, I, Nos. 1141/2 forming a composite design.

See also Nos. 1165/70.

474 Conifer Branches (Christmas)

1988. Finnish Red Cross Fund. Festivals. Multicoloured.
1143 1m.40+40p. Type **474** 80 1·10
1144 1m.80+45p. Narcissi (Easter) 1·20 75
1145 2m.40+50p. Rose (Midsummer) 1·30 2·00

475 Weather Chart and Measuring Equipment

1988. 150th Anniv of Meteorological Institute.
1146 **475** 1m.40 multicoloured 70 45

476 Map, Settlers, Indians, *Calmare Nyckel* and *Fagel Grip*

1988. 350th Anniv of Founding of New Sweden (Finnish and Swedish settlement in North America).
1147 **476** 3m. multicoloured 1·90 1·00

477 Matti Nykanen (triple gold medal winner)

1988. Finnish Success at Winter Olympic Games, Calgary.

1148	**477**	1m.80 multicoloured	85	35

478 Agathon Faberge (philatelist)

1988. "Finlandia 88" International Stamp Exhibition, Helsinki.

1149	**478**	5m. multicoloured	13·50	13·50

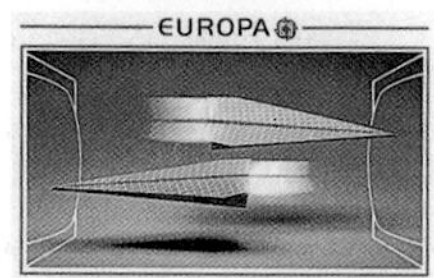

479 Paper Airplanes between VDUs

1988. Europa. Transport and Communications. Multicoloured.

1150	1m.80 Type **479**	4·00	45
1151	2m.40 Horse tram, 1890	8·50	1·30

480 Breguet 14 Biplane with Skis

1988. "Finlandia 88" International Stamp Exhibition, Helsinki (5th issue). Sheet 135×90 mm containing T **480** and similar horiz designs.

MS1152	1m.80 blue and red (Type **480**); 1m.80 blue and mauve (Junkers F-13); 1m.80 blue and orange (Douglas DC-3); 2m.40 ultramarine and blue (Douglas DC-10-30) (sold at 11m.)	10·50	10·00

481 Steam-driven Fire Pump, Turku Fire Brigade

1988. 150th Anniv of Fire Brigades in Finland.

1163	**481**	2m.20 multicoloured	85	50

482 *Missale Aboense* and Illuminated Page

1988. 500th Anniv of Publishing of *Missale Aboense* (first printed book for Finland).

1164	**482**	1m.80 multicoloured	85	30

483 1638 Postal Tariffs

1988. 350th Anniv of Posts and Telecommunications Services (2nd issue). Multicoloured.

1165	1m.80 Type **483**	1·00	50
1166	1m.80 Rural postman, 1860s	1·00	50
1167	1m.80 Postman delivering from mail van	1·00	50
1168	1m.80 Malmi Post Office	1·00	50
1169	1m.80 Skiers using mobile telephone	1·00	50
1170	1m.80 Communications satellite	1·00	50

484 Teacher with Children

1988. Church Playgroups.

1171	**484**	1m.80 multicoloured	75	30

485 Decorations

1988. Christmas.

1172	**485**	1m.40 multicoloured	80	30
1173	**485**	1m.80 multicoloured	90	30

486 Market Place, Town Plan and Arms

1989. 350th Anniv of Hameenlinna Town Charter.

1174	**486**	1m.90 multicoloured	85	30

487 Skier

1989. World Skiing Championships, Lahti.

1175	**487**	1m.90 multicoloured	85	30

488 Photographer with Box Camera on Tripod

1989. 150th Anniv of Photography.

1176	**488**	1m.50 multicoloured	75	40

489 Christmas Collection

1989. Cent of Salvation Army in Finland.

1177	**489**	1m.90 multicoloured	85	30

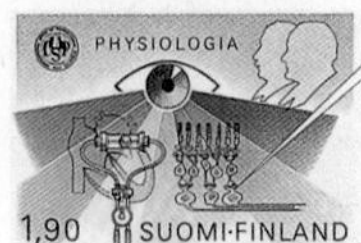

490 Professors Tigerstedt and Granit and Research Fields

1989. 31st International Physiological Sciences Congress, Helsinki.

1178	**490**	1m.90 multicoloured	90	30

491 Skiing

1989. Sport. Multicoloured.

1179	1m.90 Type **491**	85	60
1180	1m.90 Jogging	85	60
1181	1m.90 Cycling	85	60
1182	1m.90 Canoeing	85	60

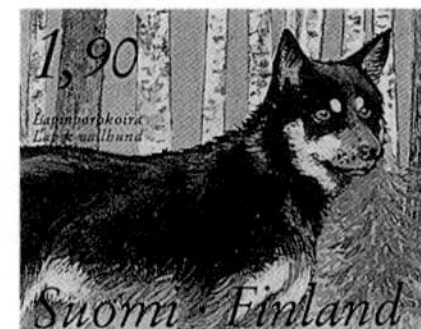

492 Lapponian Herder

1989. Centenary of Finnish Kennel Club. Sheet 114×90 mm containing T **492** and similar horiz designs. Multicoloured.

MS1183	1m.90 Type **492**; 1m.90 Finnish spitz; 1m.90 Karelian bear dog; 1m.90 Finnish hound	3·50	3·25

493 Hopscotch

1989. Europa. Children's Activities. Multicoloured.

1184	1m.90 Type **493**	3·00	45
1185	2m.50 Sledging	5·75	1·00

494 Man from Sakyla

1989. Nordic Countries' Postal Co-operation. Traditional Costumes. Multicoloured.

1186	1m.90 Type **494**	85	30
1187	2m.50 Woman from Veteli	1·20	80

495 Foxglove and Pharmaceutical Equipment

1989. 300th Anniv of Pharmacies in Finland.

1188	**495**	1m.90 multicoloured	95	30

496 Snow Leopard

1989. Cent of Helsinki Zoo. Multicoloured.

1189	1m.90 Type **496**	85	30
1190	2m.50 Markhor goat	1·30	80

497 Savonlinna

1989. 350th Anniv of Savonlinna.

1191	**497**	1m.90 multicoloured	85	30

498 Brown Bear

1989

1192	**498**	50m. multicoloured	18·00	10·50

499 Open Book and Mercury's Staff

1989. 150th Anniv of Commercial Studies in Finland.

1193	**499**	1m.50 multicoloured	80	40

500 Emblem and Columns in Finland's Parliament

1989. Cent of Interparliamentary Union.

1194	**500**	1m.90 multicoloured	90	30

501 Bridges

1989. Accession of Finland to, and 40th Anniv of Council of Europe.

1195	**501**	2m.50 multicoloured	1·20	80

502 Kolehmainen winning 5000 m, Olympic Games, 1912

1989. Birth Cent of Hannes Kolehmainen (runner).

1196	**502**	1m.90 multicoloured	90	30

503 Students, Open Book and Keyboard

1989. Centenary of Folk High Schools.

1197	**503**	1m.90 multicoloured	85	40

504 Decorated Street

1989. Christmas. Multicoloured.

1198	1m.50 Type **504**	80	25
1199	1m.90 Sodankyla Church, Lapland	90	25

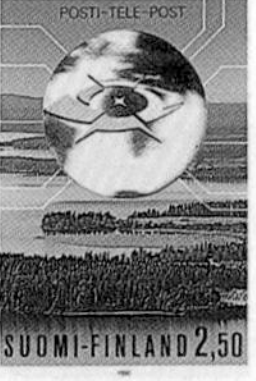

505 Emblem and Lake Paijanne

1990. Formation of Posts and Telecommunications into State Commercial Company.

1200	**505**	1m.90 multicoloured	1·00	80
1201	**505**	2m.50 multicoloured	1·00	1·30

506 Wood Anemone (Uusimaa province)

1990. Provincial Plants. Multicoloured.

1205	2m. Type **506**	70	25
1206	2m.10 Rowan (Northern Savo)	65	60
1207	2m.70 Heather (Kainuu)	90	35
1208	2m.90 Shrub sea buck-thorn (Satakunta)	1·00	35
1209	3m.50 Oak (Varsinais Suomi)	1·20	50

No. 1206 also comes self-adhesive and imperforate.
See also Nos. 1273/4, 1303, 1309, 1327 and 1354.

507 Erik Ferling (first orchestra leader) conducting

1990. Bicentenary of Foundation of Turku Musical Society (first Finnish orchestra).

1220	**507**	1m.90 multicoloured	90	30

508 Snowflake

1990. 50th Anniv of End of Russo–Finnish Winter War.

1221	**508**	2m. blue & ultramarine	90	25

509 Disabled Ex-serviceman

1990. 50th Anniv of Disabled Ex-servicemen's Association.

1222	**509**	2m. multicoloured	85	25

510 Nuvvus Postal Agency

1990. Europa. Post Office Buildings. Multicoloured.

1223	2m. Type **510**	4·50	45
1224	2m.70 Turku Postal Centre	8·00	90

511 Queen Christina

1990. 350th Anniv of Grant of Charter to Turku Academy (later Helsinki University). Multicoloured.

1225	2m. Type **511**	85	30
1226	3m.20 Main building of Helsinki University	1·20	1·00

512 Scarce Copper on Goldrod

1990. Finnish Red Cross Fund. Butterflies. Multicoloured.

1227	1m.50+40p. Type **512**	80	80
1228	2m.+50p. Amanda's blue on meadow vetchling	80	1·00
1229	2m.70+60p. Peacock on tufted vetch	1·20	1·30

See also Nos. 1279/81.

513 Postman at Larsmo, 1890, and Modern Address Sign

1990. Compilation of Address Register and Centenary of Rural Postal Service.

1230	**513**	2m. multicoloured	85	25

514 *Ali Baba and the Forty Thieves*

1990. Birth Centenary of Rudolf Koivu (artist). Designs showing Koivu's illustrations of fairy tales. Multicoloured.

1231	2m. Type **514**	1·00	50
1232	2m. *The Great Musician* (Raul Roine)	1·00	50
1233	2m. *The Giants, the Witches and the Daughter of the Sun* (Koivu)	1·00	50
1234	2m. *The Golden Bird, the Golden Horse and the Princess* (Grimm Brothers)	1·00	50
1235	2m. *Lamb Brother* (Koivu)	1·00	50
1236	2m. *The Snow Queen* (Hans Christian Andersen)	1·00	50

515 Youth feeding Horse

1990. Youth Hobbies. Horse Riding. Sheet 118×63 mm containing T **515** and similar vert designs. Multicoloured.

MS1237 2m. Type **515**; 2m. Two riders; 2m. Girl saddling pony; 2m. Girl grooming horse	4·50	4·50

516 Brownies dealing with Father Christmas's Mail

1990. Christmas. Multicoloured.

1238	1m.70 Type **516**	85	30
1239	2m. Father Christmas and reindeer	90	30

517 Player and Turku Castle

1991. World Ice Hockey Championship, Turku, Tampere and Helsinki.

1246	**517**	2m.10 multicoloured	85	30

518 Teacher and Pupils preparing Meal

1991. Cent of Domestic Science Teacher Training.

1247	**518**	2m.10 multicoloured	85	25

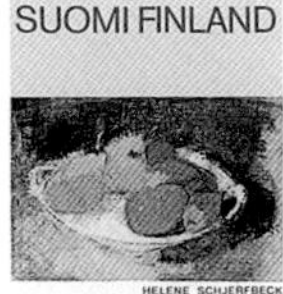

519 *Green Still Life*

1991. Pro Filatelia. Paintings by Helene Schjerfbeck. Multicoloured.

1248	2m.10+50p. Type **519**	1·60	1·80
1249	2m.10+50p. "The Little Convalescent"	1·60	1·80

520 Great Tit

1991. Birds (1st series). Multicoloured.

1250	10p. Type **520**	45	30
1251	60p. Pair of chaffinches	90	55
1252	2m.10 Northern bullfinch	65	45

See also Nos. 1282/4 and 1322/4.

521 Fly-fishing for RainbowTrout

1991. Centenary of Central Fishery Organization. Multicoloured.

1253	2m.10 Type **521**	75	50
1254	2m.10 Stylized Eurasian perch and float	75	50
1255	2m.10 Stylized fish and crayfish	75	50
1256	2m.10 Trawling for Baltic herring	75	50
1257	2m.10 Restocking with white-fish from lorry	75	50

522 Seurasaari Island

1991. Nordic Countries' Postal Co-operation. Multicoloured.

1258	2m.10 Type **522**	85	35
1259	2m.90 Saimaa ferry	1·20	90

523 Map of Europe and Human Figures

1991. Europa. Europe in Space. Multicoloured.

1260	2m.10 Type **523**	4·50	55
1261	2m.90 Map of Europe, satellites and dish aerials	11·00	1·20

524 Iris Vase

1991. 61st Death Anniv of Alfred Finch (painter and ceramic artist). Multicoloured.

1262	2m.10 Type **524**	75	30
1263	2m.90 *The English Coast at Dover*	1·60	95

525 Kittens and "Kiss-Kiss" Sweet

1991. Centenary of Opening of Karl Fazer's Confectionery (beginning of Finnish Sweet Industry).

1264	**525**	2m.10 multicoloured	90	25

526 *Sun* (Kaisa Niemi)

1991. Children's Stamp Design Competition Winners. Sheet 100×60 mm containing T **526** and similar horiz design. Multicoloured.

MS1265 2m.10 Type **526**; 2m.10 "Rainbow" (Elina Aro); 2m.10 "Cows grazing" (Noora Kaunisto)	2·75	2·75

527 Leisure Skiing

1991. Youth Hobbies. Skiing. Sheet 118×64 mm containing T **527** and similar vert designs. Multicoloured.

MS1266 2m.10 Type **527**; 2m.10 Ski-boarding; 2m.10 Freestyle skiing; 2m.10 Speed skating	3·50	3·25

528 Iisalmi

1991. Centenary of Granting of Town Rights to Iisalmi.

1267	**528**	2m.10 multicoloured	85	40

529 Forest Animals and Elf

1991. Christmas. Multicoloured.

1268	1m.80 Type **529**	85	25
1269	2m.10 Father Christmas in sleigh over new Arctic Circle post office (vert)	85	25

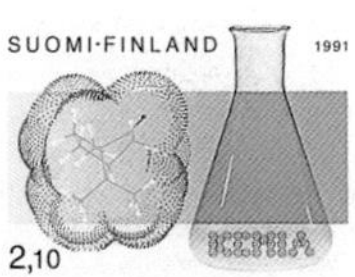

530 Camphor Molecule and Erlenmeyer Flask

1991. Cent of Organized Chemistry in Finland.

1270	**530**	2m.10 multicoloured	90	30

No. 1270 covers either of two stamps which were issued together as a horizontal gutter pair, the stamps differing very slightly in the diagram of the molecule. The gutter pair is stated to produce a three-dimensional image without use of a special viewer.

531 Skiing

1992. Winter Olympic Games, Albertville (1271) and Summer Games, Barcelona (1272). Multicoloured.

1271	2m.10 Type **531**	85	35
1272	2m.90 Swimming	1·10	60

532 Globe Flower (Lapland)

1992. Provincial Plants. With service indicator. Multicoloured.

1273 2KLASS (1m.60) Type **532** 85 25
1274 1KLASS (2m.10) Hepatica (Hame) 1·20 30

See also Nos. 1303, 1309, 1327 and 1354.

533 Finnish Exhibition Emblem

1992. "Expo '92" World's Fair, Seville.

1275 **533** 3m.40 multicoloured 1·40 90

534 Map of Europe

1992. Third Meeting of Council of Foreign Ministers of European Security and Co-operation Conference, Helsinki.

1276 **534** 16m. multicoloured 5·75 3·75

535 Church of the Holy Cross, Town Hall and Brigantine

1992. 550th Anniv of Rauma Town Charter.

1277 **535** 2m.10 multicoloured 85 25

536 Thoughts within Head

1992. Healthy Brains Campaign.

1278 **536** 3m.50 multicoloured 1·60 1·30

1992. Finnish Red Cross Fund. Centenary of Training of Visually Handicapped. Moths. As T **512**. Multicoloured.

1279 1m.60+40p. Taiga dart 85 90
1280 2m.10+50p. Fjeld tiger 1·00 1·10
1281 5m.+60p. Baneberry looper moth 1·80 2·30

537 Pied Wagtail

1992. Birds (2nd series). Multicoloured.

1282 10p. Type **537** 45 50
1283 60p. European robin 90 1·10
1284 2m.10 Three Bohemian waxwings 65 50

538 *Santa Maria* and Route Map

1992. Europa. 500th Anniv of Discovery of America by Columbus. Multicoloured.

1285 2m.10 Type **538** 1·80 45
1286 2m.10 Route map and Columbus 1·80 45

Nos. 1285/6 were issued together, *se-tenant*, forming a composite design.

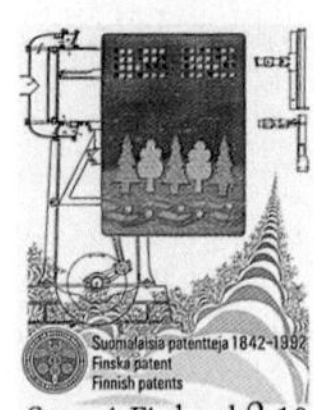

539 Blowing Machine (first Finnish patent, 150th anniv)

1992. Technology. Multicoloured.

1287 2m.10 Type **539** (50th anniv of National Board of Patents and Registration of Trademarks) 1·00 85
1288 2m.90 Triangles and circuits (Finnish chairmanship of EUREKA (European technology development scheme)) 1·10 1·00
1289 3m.40 Inverted triangles (50th anniv of Government Technology Research Centre) 1·40 90

540 Currant Harvesting

1992. Cent of National Board of Agriculture.

1290 **540** 2m.10 multicoloured 85 25

541 Aurora Karamzin

1992. Notable Finnish Women. Multicoloured.

1291 2m.10 Type **541** (founder of Helsinki Deaconesses' Institution) 90 65
1292 2m.10 Sophie Mannerheim (nursing pioneer) 90 65
1293 2m.10 Laimi Leidenius (Professor of Obstetrics and Gynaecology, Helsinki University) 90 65
1294 2m.10 Miina Sillanpaa (first woman Cabinet Minister) 90 65
1295 2m.10 Edith Sodergran (poet) 90 65
1296 2m.10 Kreetta Haapasalo (folk singer) 90 65

542 Flag in Garden (Niina Pennanen)

1992. 75th Anniv of Independence.

1297 **542** 2m.10 multicoloured 85 25
MS1298 116×53 mm. 2m.10 Birds and birch grove (29×36 mm) 1·10 95

543 Moomin looking into River (*Moominland Midwinter*)

1992. "Nordia 1993" International Stamp Exhibition. Stamp Day. Designs showing illustrations from her stories by Tove Jansson. Multicoloured.

1299 2m.10 Type **543** 1·80 65
1300 2m.10 Moomin and trolls (*Moominland Midwinter*) 1·80 65
1301 2m.10 Theatre performance on water (*Moomin Summer Madness*) 1·80 65
1302 2m.10 Moomin and inhabitants (*Tales from Moomin Valley*) 1·80 65

544 Rosebay Willowherb (Etela-Pohjanmaa)

1992. Provincial Plants. With service indicator. Self-adhesive. Imperf.

1303 **544** 1KLASS (2m.10) mult 1·20 70

545 Computerized and Hot Metal Typesetting

1992. 350th Anniv of Printing in Finland.

1304 **545** 2m.10 multicoloured 85 55

546 St. Lawrence's Church, Vantaa

1992. Christmas. Multicoloured.

1305 1m.80 Type **546** 70 25
1306 2m.10 Stained glass window, Karkkila Church (vert) 85 25

547 Couple

1993. 75th Anniv of Central Chamber of Commerce.

1307 **547** 1m.60 multicoloured 70 50

548 Birds, Flowers and Envelope within Heart

1993. Friendship.

1308 **548** 1KLASS (2m.10) multicoloured 1·10 50

549 Iris (Kymenlaakso)

1993. Provincial Plants. With service indicator. Self-adhesive. Imperf.

1309 **549** 2KLASS (1m.90) mult 1·10 55

550 Fox in Winter Coat

1993. Endangered Species. The Arctic Fox. Multicoloured.

1310 2m.30 Type **550** 1·20 65
1311 2m.30 Two foxes in winter coat 1·20 65
1312 2m.30 Mother with young in summer coat 1·20 65
1313 2m.30 Two foxes in summer coat 1·20 65

551 *Autumn Landscape of Lake Pielisjarvi* (left half)

1993. Pro Filatelia. 130th Birth Anniv of Eero Jarnefelt (painter). Multicoloured.

1314 2m.30+70p. Type **551** 1·20 1·30
1315 2m.30+70p. *Autumn Landscape of Lake Pielisjarvi* (right half) 1·20 1·30

Nos. 1314/15 were issued together, se-tenant, forming a composite design of the entire painting.

552 *Rumba* (Martti Aiha)

1993. Europa Contemporary Art. Sculptures. Multicoloured.

1316 2m. Type **552** 1·20 35
1317 2m.90 *Complete Works* (Kari Caven) 2·10 90

553 Burnet Rose

1993. Centenary of Helsinki Philatelic Association.

1318 **553** 2m.30 multicoloured 1·30 60

554 Castle and Courier Route Map

1993. 700th Anniv of Vyborg Castle.

1319 **554** 2m.30 multicoloured 1·10 50

555 Naantali

1993. Nordic Countries' Postal Co-operation. Tourism. Multicoloured.

1320 2m.30 Type **555** 1·00 45
1321 2m.90 Imatra 1·10 65

556 Tengmalm's Owl

1993. Birds (3rd series). Multicoloured.

1322 10p. Type **556** 55 75
1323 20p. Common redstart 60 75
1324 2m.30 White-backed woodpecker 1·10 75

557 Finnish Landscape in Soldier's Silhouette

1993. 75th Anniv of Military Forces. Multicoloured.
1325 2m.30 Type **557** 80 25
1326 3m.40 Checkpoint of Finnish soldiers serving with U.N. peacekeeping force 1·20 75

558 Labrador Tea (Northern Ostrobothnia)

1993. Provincial Plants. With service indicator. Self-adhesive. Imperf.
1327 **558** 1KLASS (2m.30) mult 1·20 30

559 Child skiing (cover illustration from *Kotiliesi*)

1993. Birth Centenary of Martta Wendelin (artist). Multicoloured.
1328 2m.30 Type **559** 1·10 60
1329 2m.30 Mother and daughter knitting (illustration from *First Book of the Home and School*) 1·10 60
1330 2m.30 Children making snow-man (illustration from *First Book of the Home and School*) 1·10 60
1331 2m.30 Rural scene (postcard) 1·10 60
1332 2m.30 Young girl and lamb (cover illustration from *Kotiliesi*) 1·10 60

560 Flock of Black-throated Divers

1993. Water Birds. Multicoloured.
1333 2m.30 Type **560** 1·30 1·00
1334 2m.30 Pair of black-throated divers (*Gavia arctica*) (53×28 mm) 1·30 1·00
1335 2m.30 Goosander (*Mergus merganser*) (26×39 mm) 1·30 1·00
1336 2m.30 Mallards (*Anas platyrhynchos*) (26×39 mm) 1·30 1·00
1337 2m.30 Red-breasted merganser (*Mergus serrator*) (26×39 mm) 1·30 1·00

561 Gymnastics and Football

1993. 150th Anniv of Compulsory Physical Education in Schools.
1338 **561** 2m.30 multicoloured 85 25

562 *Ostobothnians* (Leevi Madetoja)

1993. Inauguration of New National Opera House. Sheet 120×80 mm containing T **562** and similar horiz designs showing scenes from operas and ballets. Multicoloured.
MS1339 2m.30 Type **562**; 2m.30 *The Faun* (Claude Debussy, choreographed by Jorma Uotinen); 2m.90 *The Magic Flute* (Mozart); 3m.40 *Giselle* (Adolphe Adam) 5·00 4·50

563 Brownies and Christmas Tree (Anna Kymalainen)

1993. Christmas. Children's Drawings. Multicoloured.
1340 1m.80 Type **563** 70 25
1341 2m.30 Three angels and star (Taina Tuomola) 80 25

564 Koivisto

1993. 70th Birthday of President Mauno Koivisto.
1342 **564** 2m.30 multicoloured 80 25

565 "Moominland Winter"

1994. Moomin. With service indicator. Illustrations from her stories by Tove Jansson. Multicoloured.
1343 1klass (2m.30) Type **565** 1·30 30
1344 1klass (2m.30) "Moominland Storm" 1·30 30

566 Marja-Liisa Kirvesniemi and Marjo Matikainen

1994. "Finlandia 95" International Stamp Exhibition, Helsinki (1st issue) and Centenary of International Olympic Committee. Sheet 120×80 mm containing T **566** and similar vert designs showing Finnish Winter Olympic Games Competitors. Multicoloured.
MS1345 4m.20 Type **566**; 4m.20 Clas Thunberg; 4m.20 Veikko Kankkonen; 4m.20 Veikko Hakulinen 6·25 6·25

567 "Peace"

1994. Birth Centenary of Waino Aaltonen (sculptor). Multicoloured.
1346 2m. Type **567** 75 25
1347 2m. "Muse" 75 25

568 Postal Clerk and Customer

1994. Centenary of Postal Service Civil Servants Federation.
1348 **568** 2m.30 multicoloured 90 25

569 Ploughing

1994. Finnish Red Cross Fund. Horses. Multicoloured.
1349 2m. Type **569** 1·10 90
1350 2m.30 Marinka (trotting horse) 1·30 1·10
1351 4m.20 Cavalry horses (vert) 1·80 2·00

570 Paper Roll, Nitrogen-fixing Technique, Padlock and *Fennica* (ice-breaker)

1994. Europa. Discoveries and Inventions. Multicoloured.
1352 2m.30 Type **570** 1·40 65
1353 4m.20 Balloon, radiosonde, mobile telephone, fishing lure and lake oxygenation equipment 2·10 1·50

571 Rose (North Karelia)

1994. Provincial Plants. With service indicator. Self-adhesive. Imperf.
1354 **571** 1KLASS (2m.30) mult 1·20 30

572 Riitta Salin and Pirjo Haggman (runners)

1994. "Finlandia 95" International Stamp Exhibition (2nd issue) and European Athletics Championships, Helsinki. Sheet 120×80 mm containing T **572** and similar vert designs showing Finnish athletes. Multicoloured.
MS1355 4m.20 Type **572**; 4m.20 Lasse Viren (runner); 4m.20 Tiina Lillak (javelin thrower); 4m.20 Pentti Nikula (pole vaulter) 6·25 6·25

573 Seven-spotted Ladybirds

1994. "Finlandia 95" International Stamp Exhibition, Helsinki.
1356 **573** 16m. multicoloured 6·25 6·25
See also No. 1393.

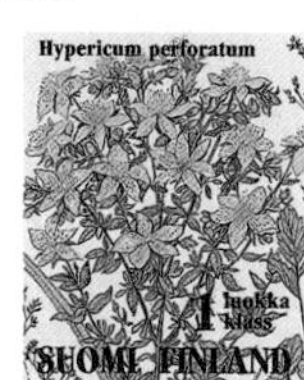

574 Perforate St. John's Wort (*Hypericum perforatum*)

1994. Flowers. With service indicator. Multicoloured.
1357 1klass (2m.30) Type **574** 1·30 45
1358 1klass (2m.30) Sticky catchfly (*Lychnis viscaria*) 1·30 45
1359 1klass (2m.30) Harebell (*Campanula rotundifolia*) 1·30 45
1360 1klass (2m.30) Clustered bellflower (*Campanula glomerata*) 1·30 45
1361 1klass (2m.30) Bloody cranesbill (*Geranium sanguineum*) 1·30 45

1362 1klass (2m.30) Wild strawberry (*Fragaria vesca*) 1·30 45
1363 1klass (2m.30) Germander speedwell (*Veronica chamaedrys*) 1·30 45
1364 1klass (2m.30) Meadow saxifrage (*Saxifraga granulata*) 1·30 45
1365 1klass (2m.30) Wild pansy (*Viola tricolor*) 1·30 45
1366 1klass (2m.30) Silver-weed (*Potentilla anserina*) 1·30 45

575 Patrik Sjoberg (high jump)

1994. Sweden–Finland Athletics Meeting, Stockholm. Multicoloured.
1367 2m.40 Sepo Raty (javelin) 1·10 35
1368 2m.40 Type **575** 1·10 35

576 Crowd on Registration List

1994. 450th Anniv of Population Registers.
1369 **576** 2m.40 multicoloured 85 25

577 Emblem

1994. International Year of the Family.
1370 **577** 3m.40 multicoloured 1·20 65

578 Postman greeting Woman

1994. Stamp Day. Dog Hill Kids (cartoon characters) at the Post Office. Sheet 112×88 mm containing T **578** and similar horiz designs. Multicoloured.
MS1371 2m.80 Type **578**; 2m.80 Postmaster handing letter to postman; 2m.80 Messenger playing bugle; 2m.80 Couple posting letters 6·25 6·25

579 Northern Bullfinches on Reindeer's Antlers

1994. Christmas. Multicoloured.
1372 2m.10 Type **579** 75 25
1373 2m.80 Father and son selecting Christmas tree (vert) 90 35

580 Postman delivering Letter to Alien

1995. Greetings stamps. Multicoloured.
1374 2m.80 Type **580** 1·30 65
1375 2m.80 Cat writing letter 1·30 65
1376 2m.80 Postman delivering letter to elderly dog 1·30 65
1377 2m.80 Teenage dog writing letter 1·30 65

1378 2m.80 Dog receiving postcard 1·30 65
1379 2m.80 Dog on train reading letter 1·30 65
1380 2m.80 Guitarist dog with Valentine greeting 1·30 65
1381 2m.80 Baby dog 1·30 65

581 Paivi Ikola (Pesapallo)

1995. "Finlandia 95" International Stamp Exhibition, Helsinki (4th issue). Team Sports. Sheet containing T **581** and similar vert designs. Multicoloured.
MS1382 3m.40 Type **581**; 3m.40 Jari Kurri (ice hockey); 3m.40 Jari Litmanen (football); 3m.40 Lea Hakala (basketball) 5·00 5·00

582 Shooting Star and Stars

1995. Admission of Finland to European Union.
1383 **582** 3m.50 blue, yell & blk 1·20 90

583 *Boys playing on the Shore*

1995. Pro Filatelia. Paintings by Albert Edelfelt. Multicoloured.
1384 2m.40+60p. Type **583** 1·30 1·00
1385 2m.40+60p. *Queen Blanche* (21×30½ mm) 1·30 1·00

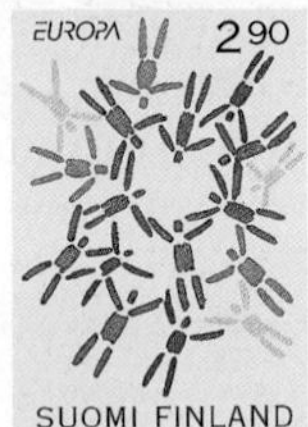

584 Figures forming Parachute

1995. Europa. Peace and Freedom.
1386 **584** 2m.90 multicoloured 2·00 50

585 Lynx

1995. Endangered Animals. Multicoloured.
1387 2m.90 Type **585** 1·10 1·00
1388 2m.90 Landscape 1·10 1·00
1389 2m.90 Shoreline 1·10 1·00
1390 2m.90 Ringed seal 1·10 1·00

586 Daisy (Keski-Suomi)

1995. Provincial Plants. With service indicator. Self-adhesive. Imperf.
1391 **586** 1KLASS (2m.80) mult 1·20 30

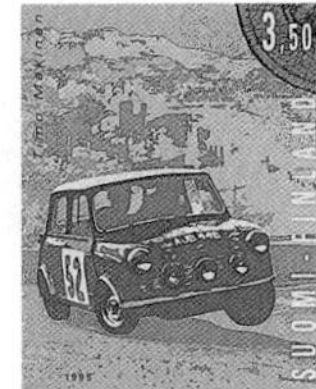

587 Mini

1995. "Finlandia 95" International Stamp Exhibition, Helsinki (5th issue). Motor Sports. Sheet 120×80 mm containing T **587** and similar vert designs. Multicoloured.
MS1392 3m.50 Type **587** (Timo Makinen, rally driver); 3m.50 Rally car (Juha Kankkunen, rally driver); 3m.50 Tommi Ahvala on motor cycle (trials); 3m.50 Heikki Mikkola on motor cycle (motocross) 6·25 5·75

588 Dung Beetle

1995. "Finlandia 95" International Stamp Exhibition, Helsinki.
1393 **588** 19m. multicoloured 7·50 7·00

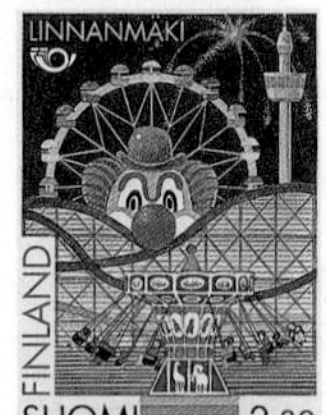

589 Linnanmaki Amusement Park, Helsinki

1995. Nordic Countries' Postal Co-operation. Tourism. Multicoloured.
1394 2m.80 Type **589** 90 40
1395 2m.90 Mantyharju church (400th anniv of parish) 1·00 80

590 Loviisa Market and Church

1995. 250th Anniv of Loviisa.
1396 **590** 3m.20 multicoloured 1·20 75

591 Silver Birch (incorrectly inscr "Betula pendula")

1995. 20th International Union of Forestry Research Organizations World Congress, Tampere. Leaves and flowers of trees. Multicoloured.
1397 2m.80 Type **591** 2·00 60
1398 2m.80 Scots pine (*Pinus sylvestris*) 2·00 60
1399 2m.80 Norway spruce (*Picea abies*) 2·00 60
1400 2m.80 Propagating tree from needle 2·00 60

592 Rontgen Tube and X-Ray Theory

1995. Centenary of Discovery of X-Rays by Wilhelm Rontgen.
1401 **592** 4m.30 multicoloured 1·60 1·00

593 Somali

1995. Cats. Multicoloured.
1402 2m.80 Type **593** 1·10 60
1403 2m.80 Siamese 1·10 60
1404 2m.80 Domestic cat in grass (58×35 mm) 1·10 60
1405 2m.80 Norwegian forest cat 1·10 60
1406 2m.80 Colourpoint Persian 1·10 60
1407 2m.80 Kittens playing in grass (58×35 mm) 1·10 60
Nos. 1404 and 1407 form a composite design.

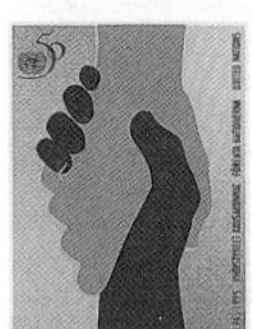

594 Handshake

1995. 50th Anniv of U.N.O.
1408 **594** 3m.40 multicoloured 1·30 75

595 Father Christmas on Skates

1995. Christmas. Multicoloured.
1409 2m. Type **595** 1·30 25
1410 2m.80 Poinsettias in snow (horiz) 90 40

596 "O"

1996. Greeting Stamps. Letters of the Alphabet.
1411 **596** 1m. vio, grn & blk ("M") 50 40
1412 **596** 1m. bl, mauve and black (Type **596**) 50 40
1413 **596** 1m. red, yell & blk ("I") 50 40
1414 **596** 1m. bl, red & blk ("H") 50 40
1415 **596** 1m. red, grn & blk ("E") 50 40
1416 **596** 1m. yell, bl & blk ("J") 50 40
1417 **596** 1m. grn, red & blk ("A") 50 40
1418 **596** 1m. yellow, mauve and black ("N") 50 40
1419 **596** 1m. yell, grn & blk ("T") 50 40
1420 **596** 1m. red, bl & blk ("P") 50 40
1421 **596** 1m. lt bl, bl & blk ("U") 50 40
1422 **596** 1m. yell, mve & blk ("S") 50 40
Nos. 1411/22 were intended to be arranged on envelopes to spell out a desired message.

597 "Smile" (Mauno Paavola)

1996. 50th Anniv of UNICEF.
1423 **597** 2m.80 multicoloured 1·10 35

598 Hoop Exercise

1996. Centenary of Women's Gymnastics Associations in Finland.
1424 **598** 2m.80 multicoloured 1·10 35

599 Mother and Children at Polling Station

1996. Europa. 90th Anniv of Women's Suffrage in Finland.
1425 **599** 3m.20 multicoloured 4·25 75

600 Chicks

1996. Finnish Red Cross Fund. Chickens. Multicoloured.
1426 2m.80+60p. Type **600** 1·20 1·30
1427 3m.20+70p. Hens 1·60 1·50
1428 3m.40+70p. Cock (vert) 1·80 1·70

601 J. Gronroos (circus director) at Film Projector

1996. Centenary of Motion Pictures. Multicoloured.
1429 2m.80 Valle Saikko and Irma Seikkula in *Juha* 1·20 65
1430 2m.80 Alli Riks and Theodor Tugai in *Wide Road* (*Den Breda Vagen*) 1·20 65
1431 2m.80 Ake Lindman in *The Unknown Soldier* (*Okana Soldat*) 1·20 65
1432 2m.80 Type **601** 1·20 65
1433 2m.80 Antti Litja in *Year of the Hare* (*Harens Ar*) 1·20 65
1434 2m.80 Mirjami Kuosmanen in *The White Forest* (*Den Vita Renen*) 1·20 65
1435 2m.80 Ansa Ikonen and Tauno Palo in *Complete Love* (*Alla Alskar*) 1·20 65
1436 2m.80 Matti Pellonpaa in *Shadow in Paradise* (*Skuggor i Paradiset*) 1·20 65

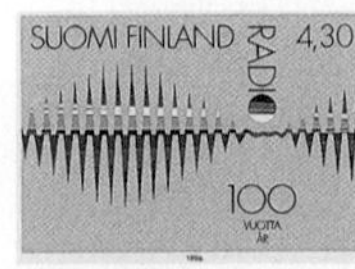

602 Radio Waves

1996. Centenary (1995) of First Radio Transmission.
1437 **602** 4m.30 multicoloured 1·50 1·40

603 Canoeing

1996. Centenary of Modern Olympic Games. Watersports. Multicoloured.
1438 3m.40 Type **603** 1·40 1·10
1439 3m.40 Sailing 1·40 1·10
1440 3m.40 Rowing 1·40 1·10
1441 3m.40 Swimming 1·40 1·10

604 White Water Lily (Southern Savonia)

1996. Provincial Plants. With service indicator. Self-adhesive. Imperf.
1442 **604** 1KLASS (2m.80) mult 1·20 30

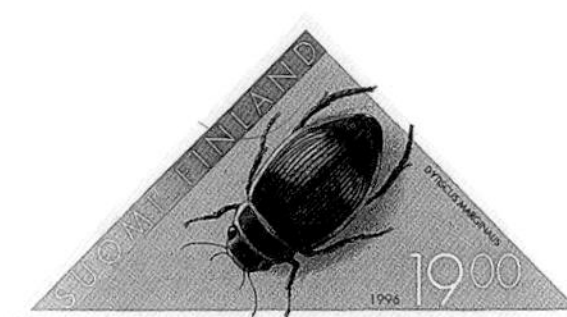
605 Great Diving Beetle

1996
1443 **605** 19m. multicoloured 7·00 7·50

606 Common Snipe (*Gallinago gallinago*)

1996. Stamp Day. Wading Birds. Sheet 121× 72 mm containing T **606** and similar vert designs. Multicoloured.
MS1444 2m.80 Curlew ("Numenius arquata") (29×53 mm); 2m.80 Type **606**; 2m.80 Oystercatcher ("Haematopus ostralegus"); 2m.80 Woodcock ("Scolopax rusticola"); 2m.80 Lapwing ("Vanellus vanellus") 5·75 5·50

607 Professor Itikaisen (Ilmari Vainio)

1996. Centenary of Comic Strips. Each red and black.
1445 2m.80 Type **607** 1·10 65
1446 2m.80 Pekka Puupaa (Peter Blockhead) receiving letter from booth (Ola Fogelberg) 1·10 65
1447 2m.80 Joonas resting chin on hand (Veikko Savolainen) 1·10 65
1448 2m.80 Posti-Aune from *Mammila* in motor cycle helmet (Tarmo Koivisto) 1·10 65
1449 2m.80 Rymy-Eetu smoking pipe (Erkki Tanttu) 1·10 65
1450 2m.80 Kieku (duck) writing letter (Asmo Alho) 1·10 65
1451 2m.80 Pikku Risunen from *Hyvissa naimisissa* (Well-married) in headdress with big ears (Riitta Uusitalo) 1·10 65
1452 2m.80 Kiti from *Vihrea Rapsodia* (Green Rhapsody) holding pencil (Kati Kovacs) 1·10 65

608 Father Christmas and Musicians

1996. Christmas. Multicoloured.
1453 2m. Type **608** 75 30
1454 2m.80 Reindeer and hare 90 30
1455 3m.20 Father Christmas reading letters (vert) 1·20 65

609 Player

1997. World Ice Hockey Championship, Helsinki, Turku and Tampere.
1456 **609** 2m.80 multicoloured 1·10 25

610 Parcel

1997. Cent of Mail Order Sales in Finland.
1457 **610** 2m.80 multicoloured 1·10 65

611 Angels

1997. Greetings Stamps. With service indicator. Old Scrapbook Illustrations. Multicoloured.
1458 1klass (2m.80) Type **611** 1·30 60
1459 1klass (2m.80) Basket of mixed flowers 1·30 60
1460 1klass (2m.80) Barn swallow on hand extended through wreath of roses 1·30 60
1461 1klass (2m.80) Children playing 1·30 60
1462 1klass (2m.80) Child and four-leaf clovers in envelope 1·30 60
1463 1klass (2m.80) Man's and woman's hands extended through heart-shaped wreaths of roses 1·30 60
1464 1klass (2m.80) Roses 1·30 60
1465 1klass (2m.80) Angel 1·30 60

612 Arctic Hares

1997. Easter.
1466 **612** 2m.80 multicoloured 90 30

613 Golden Merganser casting Reflection of Girl

1997. Europa. Tales and Legends. *The Girl who turned into a Golden Merganser* (folktale). Illustrations by Mika Launis. Multicoloured.
1467 3m.20 Type **613** 1·60 65
1468 3m.40 Girl falling into water 2·00 1·00

614 Bird Cherry (Birkaland)

1997. Provincial Plants. With service indicator. Self-adhesive. Imperf.
1469 **614** 1KLASS (2m.80) mult 1·20 35

615 Nurmi running 3000 m (Olympic Games, Paris, 1924)

1997. Birth Cent of Paavo Nurmi (runner).
1470 **615** 3m.40 multicoloured 1·00 75

616 Couple dancing in Meadow

1997. The Tango. With service indicator.
1471 **616** 1klass (2m.80) black and pink 1·20 45

617 *Astrid* (galeasse)

1997. Centenary of Finnish Lifeboat Society. Sailing Ships. Multicoloured.
1472 2m.80 Type **617** 1·30 65
1473 2m.80 *Jacobstads Wapen* (replica of schooner) 1·30 65
1474 2m.80 *Suomen Joutsen* (cadet ship) (48×25 mm) 1·30 65
1475 2m.80 *Tradewind* (brigantine) 1·30 65
1476 2m.80 *Merikokko* (lifeboat) 1·30 65
1477 2m.80 *Sigyn* (barque) (48×25 mm) 1·30 65

618 Globe and Ahtisaari

1997. 60th Birthday of President Martii Ahtisaari.
1478 **618** 2m.80 multicoloured 1·00 30

619 Clouds (Summer)

1997. 80th Anniv of Independence. The Four Seasons. Multicoloured.
1479 2m.80 Lily of the valley (Spring) 1·30 65
1480 2m.80 Type **619** 1·30 65
1481 2m.80 Leaves (Autumn) 1·30 65
1482 2m.80 Snowflakes (Winter) 1·30 65

620 Crane with Chick

1997. The Common Crane (*Grus grus*). Sheet 120×80 mm containing T **620** and similar multicoloured designs.
MS1483 2m.80 Type **620**; 2m.80 Adults, one with frog in beak; 2m.80 Court-ing dance; 2m.80 Adults in flight (31×34 mm) 5·00 5·00

621 Vainamoinen proposing to Aino

1997. Pro Filatelia. *Aino* (triptych) by Akseli Gallen-Kallela. Multicoloured.
1484 2m.80+60p. Type **621** 1·40 1·20
1485 2m.80+60p. Aino in water escaping from Vainamoinen (33×47 mm) 1·40 1·20
1486 2m.80+60p. Mermaids luring Aino into water 1·40 1·20

622 *Seven Brothers* (Aleksis Kivi)

1997. Centenary of Finnish Writers' Association. Book Covers. Multicoloured.
1487 2m.80 Type **622** 1·20 65
1488 2m.80 *Sinuhe the Eyptian* (Mika Waltari) 1·20 65
1489 2m.80 *Under the North Star* (Vaino Linna) 1·20 65
1490 2m.80 *Farewell River Iijoki* (Kalle Paatalo) 1·20 65
1491 2m.80 *Eagle, My Beloved* (Kaari Utrio) 1·20 65
1492 2m.80 *Midsummer Dance* (Hannu Salama) 1·20 65
1493 2m.80 *Manilla Rope* (Veijo Meri) 1·20 65
1494 2m.80 *Uppo-Nalle ja Kumma* (Elina Karjalainen) 1·20 65

623 Church and Houses

1997. Christmas. Multicoloured.
1495 2m. Type **623** 60 35
1496 2m.80 Candelabra, Petajavesi Church (vert) 90 50
1497 3m.20 St. John's Church, Eira, Helsinki (35×24 mm) 1·20 65

624 Zander

1998. Provincial Birds and Fish (1st series). Uusimaa. With service indicator. Mult. Self-adhesive.
1498 2klass (2m.40) Type **624** 1·10 65
1499 1KLASS (2m.80) Blackbird 1·30 30

625 Moominpappa writing Play

1998. Moomin. Illustrations from her stories by Tove Jansson. With service indicator. Multicoloured.
1500 1klass (2m.80) Type **625** 1·40 50
1501 1klass (2m.80) Moomin-mamma making jam 1·40 50
1502 1klass (2m.80) Too-ticky playing barrel organ and Littly My dancing 1·40 50
1503 1klass (2m.80) Moomintroll dancing with the Snork Maiden 1·40 50

626 Nurses of 1898 and 1998

1998. Cent of Finnish Federation of Nurses.
1504 **626** 2m.80 multicoloured 1·00 25

627 Gold Heart and Musical Notes

1998. St. Valentine's Day. With service indicator. Multicoloured.

1505	1klass (2m.80) Type **627**	1·20	75
1506	1klass (2m.80) Gold heart and elephant	1·20	75
1507	1klass (2m.80) Gold heart and puppy on blanket	1·20	75
1508	1klass (2m.80) Gold heart and kittens	1·20	75
1509	1klass (2m.80) Gold heart and dog	1·20	75
1510	1klass (2m.80) Gold heart and flowers	1·20	75

The gold hearts could be scratched off to reveal a complete design.

628 Harebell (Central Ostrobothnia)

1998. Provincial Plants. With service indicator. Self-adhesive. Imperf.

1511	**628**	1KLASS (2m.80) mult	1·20	30

629 Sow and Litter

1998. Finnish Red Cross Fund. Pigs. Multicoloured.

1512	2m.80+60p. Type **629**	1·20	1·30
1513	3m.20+70p. Three piglets	1·50	1·50
1514	3m.40+70p. Boar	1·80	1·60

630 Coltsfoot

1998. Spring.

1515	**630**	2m.80 multicoloured	1·10	30

631 Students with Balloons (Labour Day)

1998. Europa. National Festivals. Multicoloured.

1516	3m.20 Type **631**	1·60	50
1517	3m.40 Couple by lake (Midsummer)	2·00	1·30

632 *Aranda* (research vessel)

1998. Nordic Countries' Postal Co-operation. Shipping. Multicoloured.

1518	2m.80 Type **632** (80th anniv of Finnish Marine Research Institute)	1·00	40
1519	3m.20 *Vega* (120th anniv of Nils Nordenskjöld's navigation of the North-east Passage)	1·30	90

633 Flag and Score

1998. 150th Anniv of First Performance of *Our Country* (national anthem).

1520	**633**	5m. multicoloured	1·80	1·00

634 Bernese Mountain Dog

1998. World Dog Show, Helsinki. With service indicator. Multicoloured.

1521	1klass (2m.80) Type **634**	1·20	65
1522	1klass (2m.80) Pumis	1·20	65
1523	1klass (2m.80) Boxers	1·20	65
1524	1klass (2m.80) Bichon frises	1·20	65
1525	1klass (2m.80) Finnish lap-phounds	1·20	65
1526	1klass (2m.80) Dachshunds	1·20	65
1527	1klass (2m.80) Cairn terriers	1·20	65
1528	1klass (2m.80) Labrador retrievers	1·20	65

635 Downhill Competitor and 19th-century Cyclist

1998. Centenary of Cycling Union of Finland.

1529	**635**	3m. multicoloured	90	60

636 Eagle Owl *Bubo bubo*

1998. Stamp Day. Owls. Sheet 120×80 mm containing T **636** and similar multicoloured designs.

MS1530 3m. Type **636**; 3m. Wing-tip of eagle owl (25×49 mm); 3m. Tengmalm's owl ("Aegolius funereus") (23×42 mm); 3m. Great grey owl ("Stris nebulosa") (24×42 mm); 3m. Snowy owl ("Nyctea scandiaca") (29×42 mm) 5·50 4·50

637 Kilta Tableware (Kaj Franck)

1998. Finnish Industrial Design. Multicoloured.

1531	3m. Savoy Vase (Alvar Aalto)	1·30	85
1532	3m. Karuselli 412 chair (Yrjo Kukkapuro) (29×34 mm)	1·30	85
1533	3m. Tasaraita T-shirts (Annika Rimala) (29×34 mm)	1·30	85
1534	3m. Type **637**	1·30	85
1535	3m. Cast-iron cooking pot (Timo Sarpaneva) (29×34 mm)	1·30	85
1536	3m. Carelia cutlery (Bertel Gardberg) (29×34 mm)	1·30	85

638 Children and Christmas Tree

1998. Christmas. Multicoloured.

1537	2m. Type **638**	60	30
1538	3m. Children tobogganing (horiz)	90	40
1539	3m.20 Snow-bound cottage on island (horiz)	90	50

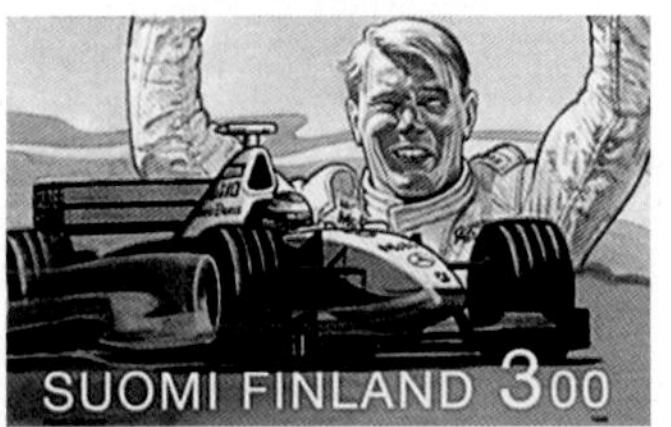

639 Hakkinen and Racing Car

1999. Mika Hakkinen, Formula 1 World Champion 1998. Sheet 115×70 mm.

MS1540 **639** 3m. multicoloured 1·50 1·30

640 Atlantic Salmon

1999. Provincial Birds and Fish (2nd series). Lapland. With service indicator. Multicoloured. Self-adhesive.

1541	2klass (2m.40) Type **640**	80	50
1542	1KLASS (3m.) Bluethroat (vert)	1·00	40

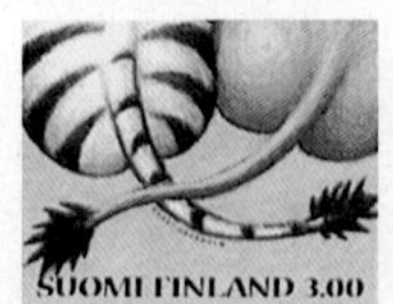

641 Zebra and Lion Tails

1999. Friendship. Multicoloured. Self-adhesive.

1543	3m. Type **641**	1·10	90
1544	3m. Cat and dog tails	1·10	90

642 Monument to Eetu Salin (founder) (Aimo Tukiainen)

1999. Centenary of Founding of Finnish Labour Party (predecessor of Social Democrat Party).

1545	**642**	4m.50 multicoloured	1·30	1·20

643 Horse Brooch

1999. 150th Anniv of New Kalevala (Karelian poems collected by Elias Lonnrot). Sheet 120×74 mm containing T **643** and similar vert designs. Multicoloured.

MS1546 3m. Type **643**; 3m. Kuhmoinen Cocks brooch; 3m. Virusmaki brooch 3·25 3·25

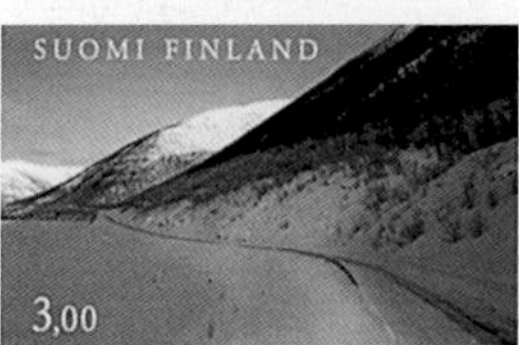

644 Road by River Tenojoki, Utsjoki

1999. Bicentenary of National Road Administration. Multicoloured.

1547	3m. Type **644**	1·50	65
1548	3m. Motorway intersection, Jyvaskyla	1·50	65
1549	3m. Raippaluoto bridge, Vaasa	1·50	65
1550	3m. North Karelian forest road, Kitee	1·50	65

645 Esplanade, Helsinki

1999. Europa. Parks and Gardens. Multicoloured.

1551	2m.70 Type **645**	1·50	75
1552	3m.20 Ruissalo island, Turku	2·00	90

646 Martha Circle

1999. Centenary of Martha Organization (for education and development of women).

1553	**646**	3m. multicoloured	90	35

647 Crocuses

1999. Easter.

1554	**647**	3m. multicoloured	1·20	40

648 Cowslip (Aland Islands)

1999. Provincial Plants. With service indicator. Self-adhesive. Imperf.

1555	**648**	1KLASS (3m.) mult	1·20	35

649 Nightingale (*Luscinia luscinia*)

1999. Nocturnal Summer Birds. Sheet 120×80 mm containing T **649** and similar multicoloured designs.

MS1556 3m. Type **649**; 3m. European cuckoo ("Cuculus canorus) (24×39½ mm); 3m. Eurasian bittern ("Botaurus stellaris") (44×29 mm); 3m. European nightjar ("Caprimulgus europaeus") (24½×36 mm); 3m. Corncrake ("Crex crex") (24½×37 mm) 6·75 5·00

650 Figure reaching for E.U. Stars

1999. Finland's Presidency of European Union.

1557	**650**	3m.50 multicoloured	1·10	60

651 Harmony Sisters

1999. Entertainers. Multicoloured.

1558 3m.50 Type **651** 1·30 75
1559 3m.50 Olavi Virta (tango and jazz singer) (29×34 mm) 1·30 75
1560 3m.50 Georg Malmsten (composer and band leader) (29×34 mm) 1·30 75
1561 3m.50 Topi Karki (composer) and Reino Helismaa (lyricist) 1·30 75
1562 3m.50 Tapio Rautavaara (composer and folk singer) (29×34 mm) 1·30 75
1563 3m.50 Esa Pakarinen (folk artist and actor) (29×34 mm) 1·30 75

652 *Garden of Death*

1999. Pro Filatelia. Paintings by Hugo Simberg. Multicoloured.

1564 3m.50+50p. Type **652** 1·30 1·20
1565 3m.50+50p. *Wounded Angel* 1·30 1·20

653 Fiskars Secateurs and Pruning Shears Designed by Olavi Linden

1999. Finnish Industrial Design. Multicoloured.

1566 3m.50 Type **653** 1·30 85
1567 3m.50 Zoel Versoul guitar (Kari Nieminen) (29×34½ mm) 1·30 85
1568 3m.50 Ergo II Silenta hearing protectors (Jyrki Jarvinen) (29×34½ mm) 1·30 85
1569 3m.50 Ponsse Cobra HS10 harvester (Pentti Hukkanen, Jorma Hyvonen, Jouko Kelppe and Heikki Koivurova) 1·30 85
1570 3m.50 Suunto sailing compass (Heikki Metsa-Ketela and Erikki Vainio) (29×34½ mm) 1·30 85
1571 3m.50 Exel Avanti QLS ski stick (Pasi Jarvinen, Matti Lyly and Mika Vesalainen) (29×34½ mm) 1·30 85

654 Santa Claus

1999. Christmas. Multicoloured.

1572 2m.50 Type **654** 80 40
1573 3m. "Nativity" (Giorgio de Chirico) (horiz) 1·10 60
1574 3m.50 Two hares (horiz) 1·20 50

655 Earth, Sun and Moon

2000. Friendship. Multicoloured.

1575 3m.50 Type **655** 1·30 75
1576 3m.50 Painting a smile on Jupiter 1·30 75
1577 3m.50 Birds using Neptune as balloon 1·30 75
1578 3m.50 Martian using magnet to rescue traveller from Mars 1·30 75
1579 3m.50 People on Saturn's rings 1·30 75
1580 3m.50 Pluto as igloo and polar bear 1·30 75

656 Herring Market

2000. 450th Anniv of Helsinki (European City of Culture, 2000). Multicoloured.

1581 3m.50 Type **656** 1·10 90
1582 3m.50 Museum of Contemporary Art, Kiasma (24×48 mm) 1·60 1·60
1583 3m.50 Statue and Cathedral, Senate Square (42×24 mm) 1·60 1·60
1584 3m.50 Finlandia Hall (42×24 mm) 1·60 1·60
1585 3m.50 Glass Palace Film and Media Centre (24×48 mm) 1·60 1·60
1586 3m.50 "Looking for the Lost Crown" (children's tour), Suomenlin Sea Fortress (24×48 mm) 1·60 1·60
1587 3m.50 Type **656** 1·60 1·60
1588 3m.50 "Forces of Light" celebration (42×24 mm) 1·60 1·60
1589 3m.50 Open-air concert, Kaivopuisto Park (24×48 mm) 1·60 1·60

657 Fortifications at Sveaborg

2000. Sveaborg Fortress.

1590 **657** 7m.20 multicoloured 2·50 1·80

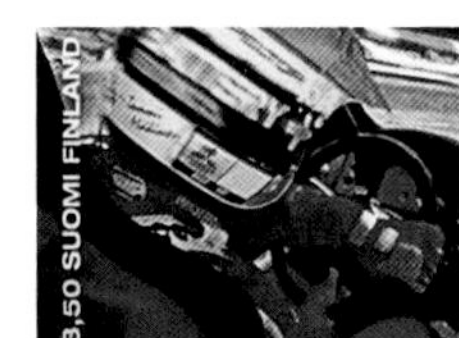

658 Makinen at Wheel of Rally Car

2000. Tommi Makinen, Rally World Champion (1999). Sheet 109×80 mm containing T **658** and similar horiz design. Multicoloured.

MS1591 3m.50 Type **658**; 3m.50 Mitsubishi Lancer rally car 2·75 2·75

659 Marsh Marigold

2000. Spring.

1592 **659** 3m.50 multicoloured 1·20 40

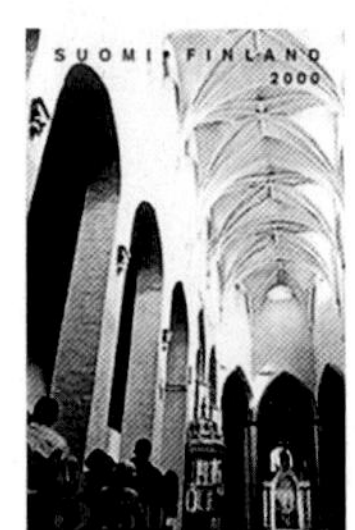

660 Interior of Turku Cathedral

2000. Holy Year 2000. 700th Anniv of Turku Cathedral. Multicoloured.

1593 3m.50 Type **660** 1·40 1·00
1594 3m.50 Woman lighting candle 1·40 1·00
1595 3m.50 *Transfiguration of Christ* (altarpiece) 1·40 1·00
1596 3m.50 Christening 1·40 1·00

661 Emma the Theatre Rat and Moomins at Table

2000. Moomin. Illustrations from her stories by Tove Jansson. With service indicator. Multicoloured.

1597 1klass (3m.50) Type **661** 1·20 65
1598 1klass (3m.50) Park keeper and Hattifatteners growing from the grass 1·20 65
1599 1klass (3m.50) Snufkin walking through forest 1·20 65
1600 1klass (3m.50) Snufkin surrounded by forest children 1·20 65

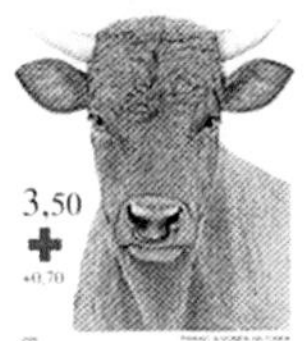

662 Bull

2000. Finnish Red Cross Fund. Cattle. Multicoloured.

1601 3m.50+70p. Type **662** 1·30 1·20
1602 4m.80+80p. Cow and calf (horiz) 1·90 1·80

663 "Building Europe"

2000. Europa.

1603 **663** 3m.50 multicoloured 1·70 95

664 Spring Anemone (South Karelia)

2000. Provincial Plants. With service indicator. Self-adhesive. Imperf.

1604 **664** 1KLASS (3m.50) multicoloured 1·20 30

665 Girls in Laboratory

2000. Heureka Science Centre. Sheet 120×80 mm containing T **665** and similar multicoloured designs.

MS1605 3m.50 Type **665**; 3m.50 DNA double helix and man's face (parallelogram, 20×20 mm); 3m.50 Man's face and Sierinski Triangle aerial (27×27 mm) 3·75 3·50

666 Common Whitefish

2000. Provincial Birds and Fish (3rd series). Southern Lapland. With service indicator. Multicoloured. Self-adhesive.

1606 2klass (2m.70) Type **666** 90 40
1607 1KLASS (3m.30) Willow grouse 1·10 65

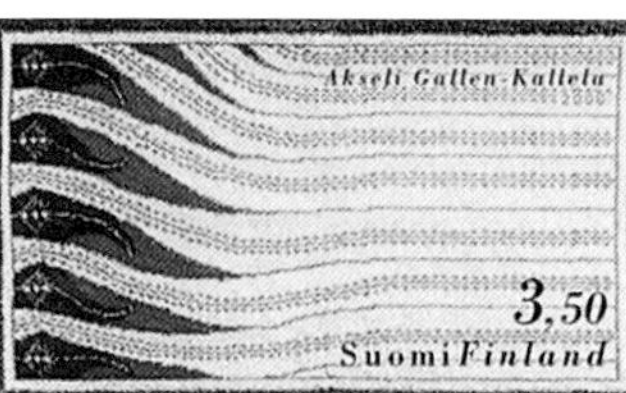

667 *Flame* Rug (Akseli Gallen-Kallela)

2000. Finnish Industrial Design. Multicoloured.

1608 3m.50 Type **667** 1·30 85
1609 3m.50 Pearl Bird (Birger Kaipiainen) (29×34 mm) 1·30 85
1610 3m.50 Pot (Kyllikki Salmenhaara) (29×34 mm) 1·30 85
1611 3m.50 *Leaf* platter (Tapio Wirkkala) 1·30 85
1612 3m.50 *Lichen* (furnishing fabric pattern, Dora Jung) (29×34 mm) 1·30 85
1613 3m.50 Glass vase (Valter Jung) (29×34 mm) 1·30 85

668 Three Wise Men and Star

2000. Christmas. Multicoloured. Self-adhesive.

1614 2m.50 Type **668** 80 35
1615 3m.50 Northern bullfinch sitting on wreath (vert) 1·00 60

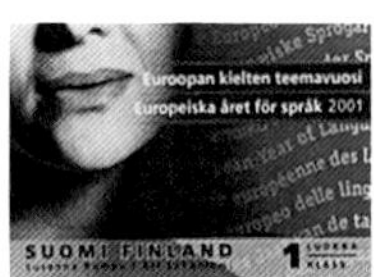

669 Woman's Head

2001. European Year of Languages. With service indicator.

1616 **669** 1KLASS (3m.50) mult 1·20 35

670 Janne Ahonen (ski jumper)

2001. Nordic World Skiing Championships, Lahti. Multicoloured.

1617 3m.50 Type **670** 1·10 40
1618 3m.50 Mika Myllyla 1·10 40

671 Garland of Flowers

2001. Greetings Stamps. Flowers. Multicoloured. Self-adhesive.

1619 1KLASS (3m.50) Type **671** 1·20 65
1620 1KLASS (3m.50) Basket of flowers 1·20 65
1621 1KLASS (3m.50) Heart-shaped garland 1·20 65
1622 1KLASS (3m.50) Bouquet 1·20 65
1623 1KLASS (3m.50) Flowers, cake and cups 1·20 65
1624 1KLASS (3m.50) Flowers and heart-shaped cake 1·20 65

672 Cover of First Magazine published in Finland, 1951

2001. 50th Anniv of The Donald Duck Magazine in Finland. Sheet 130×80 mm containing T **672** and similar vert designs. Multicoloured.

MS1625 1klass Type **672**; 1klass Silhouette of boy and page from magazine; 1klass Toy carrying flag and Chip and Dale (24×30 mm); 1klass Silhouette of Donald Duck and Vainamoinen; 1klass Donald Duck and Helsinki Cathedral 6·00 5·75

673 Father Christmas in Sleigh

2001. Santa Claus. With service indicator. Self-adhesive.

1630 **673** 1klass (3m.50) multi-coloured 1·10 1·00

674 Face of Chick

2001. Easter. Multicoloured.

1631 3m.60 Type **674** 2·10 70
1632 3m.60 Easter egg 2·10 70

675 Roof of Mill and Trees

2001. Verla Groundwood and Board Mill Museum, Jaala. Sheet 80×120 mm containing T **676** and similar vert designs. Multicoloured.

MS1633 3m.60 Type **675**; 3m.60 Mill manager's house, mill building and river; 3m.60 Main mill building and river; 3m.60 Mill building and river 5·25 5·00

676 Lesser Spotted Woodpecker (*Dendrocopos minor*)

2001. Woodpeckers. Sheet 79×119 mm containing T **677** and similar vert designs. Multicoloured.

MS1634 3m.60 Type **676**; 3m.60 Three-toed woodpecker (*Picoides tridactylus*) (28×35 mm); 3m.60 White-backed woodpecker (*Dendrocopos leucotos*) (32×41 mm); 3m.60 Great spotted woodpecker (*Dendrocopos major*) (28×41 mm); 3m.60 Grey-headed green woodpecker (*Picus canus*) (32×41 mm); 3m.60 Black woodpecker (*Dryocopus martius*) (28×41 mm) 6·75 6·75

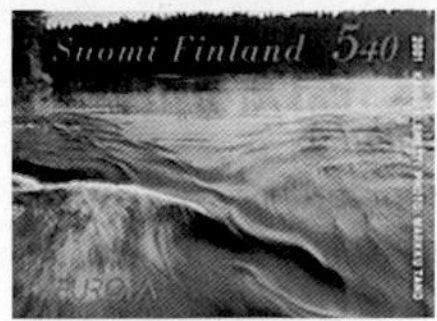

677 Haapavitja Rapids, Runna

2001. Europa. Water Resources.

1635 **674** 5m.40 multicoloured 3·00 1·70

678 Compass and Emblem

2001. Orienteering World Championship, Tampere.

1636 **678** 3m.60 multicoloured 1·00 40

679 Cornflower (Pajat-Hame)

2001. Provincial Flowers. With service indicator. Self-adhesive.

1637 1KLASS (3m.50) Type **679** 1·20 40
1638 1KLASS (3m.50) Pasque flower (Kanta-Hame) 1·20 40

680 Lampern (*Lampetra fluviatilis*) (Satakunta)

2001. Provincial Fish. With service indicator. Multicoloured. Self-adhesive.

1639 2klass (2m.70) Type **680** 1·00 60
1640 2klass (2m.70) Asp (*Aspius aspius*) (Pirkanmaa) 1·00 60
1641 2klass (2m.70) Vendace (*Coregonus albula*) (Savonia) 1·00 60

681 Golden Oriole (*Oriolus oriolus*) (Satakunta)

2001. Provincial Birds. With service indicator. Multicoloured. Self-adhesive.

1642 1KLASS (3m.60) Type **681** 1·10 60
1643 1KLASS (3m.60) Blue tit (*Parus caeruleus*) (Pirkanmaa) 1·10 60
1644 1KLASS (3m.60) Pied wagtail (*Motacilla alba*) (South Savonia) 1·10 60

682 18th-century Captain's Quarters, Merchant Ship

2001. Gulf of Finland (1st series). Multicoloured.

1645 1KLASS (3m.60) Type **682** 1·20 65
1646 1KLASS (3m.60) Uto Lighthouse (32×27 mm) 1·20 65
1647 1KLASS (3m.60) *Sankt Mikael* (Dutch sailing ship) (33×27 mm) 1·20 65
1648 1KLASS (3m.60) Diver on *Sankt Mikael* and treasure (33×27 mm) 1·20 65
1649 1KLASS (3m.60) Opossum shrimp, isopod and bladder wrack (33×27 mm) 1·20 65

See also Nos. 1675/9 and 1753/7.

683 Elf Girl reading

2001. Christmas. Multicoloured. Self-adhesive.

1650 2m.50 Type **683** 80 35
1651 3m.60 Elf boy sledding (horiz) 1·00 40

684 Water Forget-me-not (*Myosotis scorpoides*)

2002. Flowers. Showing water forget-me-nots (5c.) or lily-of-the-valley (10c.). Multicoloured. Self-adhesive.

1652 5c. Type **684** 15 15
1653 5c. Four flowers 15 15
1654 5c. One open flower and four buds 15 15
1655 5c. Spray of flowers 15 15
1656 5c. Five flower heads 15 15
1657 10c. Spray of five lily-of-the-valley flowers (*Convallaria majallis*) 25 25
1658 10c. Spray of eight flowers between two leaves 25 25
1659 10c. Two flowers 25 25
1660 10c. Spray of six flowers against leaf 25 25
1661 10c. Lily-of-the-valley growing through grass 25 25

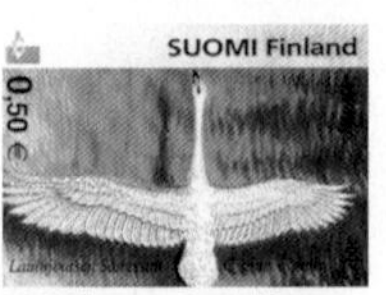

685 Whooper Swan (*Cygnus cygnus*)

2002. Self-adhesive.

1662 **685** 50c. multicoloured 95 40

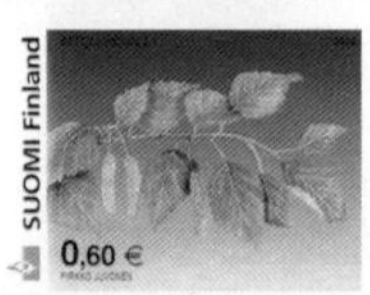

686 Birch (*Betula pendula*)

2002. Trees. Self-adhesive.

1663 60c. Type **686** 1·20 60
1664 €2.50 Norway spruce (*Picea abies*) 4·50 2·50
1665 €3.50 Scots pine (*Pinus sylvestris*) 6·25 3·75

687 National Flag .

2002. With service indicator. Self-adhesive.

1666 **687** 1klass (60c.) mult 1·20 1·00

No. 1666 was for use on domestic first class mail.

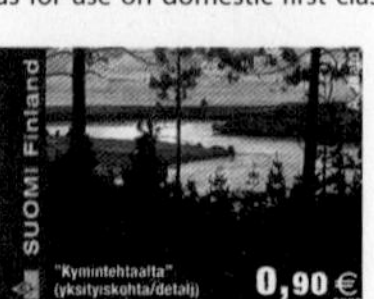

688 *Kymintehtaalta* (Victor Westerholm)

2002. Finnish Landscapes. Self-adhesive. Multicoloured.

1667 90c. Type **688** 1·70 1·50
1668 €1.30 Granite substrata 2·30 1·30

689 Heraldic Lion

2002. Winning entry in Stamp Design Competition. Multicoloured. Self- adhesive.

1669 €1 Type **689** 1·80 1·00
1670 €5 No. 1669 9·00 7·50

690 Witch riding Broomstick

2002. Easter. Self-adhesive.

1671 **690** 60c. multicoloured 1·20 50

691 Plantain

2002. Birth Bicentenary of Elias Lonnrot (linguist, botanist and physician). Sheet 120×80 mm, containing T **691** and similar vert designs. Multicoloured.

MS1672 60c. Type **691**; 60c. Tip of feather and text; 60c. Base of feather and text; 60c. Elias Lonnrot 4·75 4·25

692 Houses

2002. UNESCO World Heritage Site. 560th Anniv of Rauma. Sheet 82×122 mm, containing T **692** and similar vert designs. Multicoloured.

MS1673 60c. Type **692**; 60c. Church of the Holy Cross; 60c. Left side of Rauma museum (face value at left); 60c. Right side of museum (face value at right) 4·75 4·25

693 Circus Performers

2002. Europa. Circus.

1674 **693** 60c. multicoloured 3·00 65

694 Fishing Boat and Net

2002. Gulf of Finland (2nd series). Multicoloured.

1675 1KLASS (60c.) Type **694** 1·20 1·00
1676 1KLASS (60c.) Arctic terns, island and perch (fish) (32×27 mm) 1·20 1·00
1677 1KLASS (60c.) Island, dinghy and buoy (32×27 mm) 1·20 1·00
1678 1KLASS (60c.) Flounder (32×27 mm) 1·20 1·00
1679 1KLASS (60c.) Zooplankton, herring and cod (32×27 mm) 1·20 1·00

Nos. 1675/9 were issued together, I, forming a composite design.

695 *Passio Muscicae* (Sibelius Monument) (sculpture, Eila Hiltunen)

2002. Nordic Countries' Postal Co-operation. Modern Art.

1680 **695** 60c. multicoloured 1·10 40

696 Juniper (*Juniperus communis*)

2002. Self-adhesive.

1681	**696**	60c. multicoloured	1·20	40

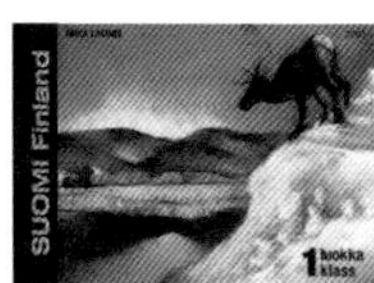
697 Reindeer, Lapland

2002. Self-adhesive.

1682	**697**	60c. multicoloured	1·20	50

698 Horse-drawn Sleigh

2002. Christmas. Multicoloured. Self-adhesive.

1683	45c. Type **698**	90	75
1684	60c. Angel (vert)	1·30	1·00

699 Northern Pike (*Esox lucius*)

2003. Provincial Fish. With service indicator. Multicoloured. Self-adhesive.

1685	2KLASS (50c.) Type **699**	1·00	90
1686	2KLASS (50c.) Bream (*Abramis brama*)	1·00	90
1687	2KLASS (50c.) Lake trout (*Salmo trutta lacustris*)	1·00	90

700 European Cuckoo (*Cuculus canorus*)

2003. Provincial Birds. With service indicator. Multicoloured. Self-adhesive.

1688	1KLASS (60c.) Type **700**	1·20	1·00
1689	1KLASS (60c.) Eurasian sky lark (*Alauda arvensis*)	1·20	1·00
1690	1KLASS (60c.) Siberian jay (*Perisoreus infaustus*)	1·20	1·00

701 Viivi and Wagner

2003. Friendship. With service indicator. Showing Viivi and Wagner (cartoon characters). Multicoloured. Self-adhesive.

1691	1KLASS (60c.) Type **701**	1·20	1·00
1692	1KLASS (60c.) Dancing	1·20	1·00
1693	1KLASS (60c.) Viivi writing letter	1·20	1·00
1694	1KLASS (60c.) In bed	1·20	1·00
1695	1KLASS (60c.) Kissing	1·20	1·00
1696	1KLASS (60c.) Wagner receiving letter	1·20	1·00

702 Games Mascot

2003. World Ice Hockey Championships, Helsinki, Tampere and Turku.

1697	**702**	65c. multicoloured	1·40	1·10

703 Pansy (*Viola wittrockiana*)

2003. Self-adhesive.

1698	**703**	65c. multicoloured	1·40	1·10

704 St. Birgitta (Bridget) (detail, altar screen, Naantali Convent Church)

2003. 700th Birth Anniv of St. Birgitta.

1699	**704**	65c. multicoloured	1·40	1·10

705 Aerospatvale Super Caravelle

2003. Centenary of First Powered Flight. 80th Anniv of Finnair. Multicoloured.

1700	65c. Type **705**	1·20	90
1701	65c. Airbus Industries Airbus 320	1·20	90
1702	65c. Junkers Ju 52/3m	1·20	90
1703	65c. Douglas DC-3	1·20	90

706 *The Fighting Capercailles* (Ferdinand von Wright)

2003. Self-adhesive.

1704	**706**	90c. multicoloured	2·30	1·60

707 Heart (Lasse Hietala)

2003. Europa. Poster Art. Design showing *Someone is waiting for your letter* posters by Lasse Hietala. Multicoloured.

1705	65c. Type **707**	1·80	1·10
1706	65c. Mother	1·80	1·10

708 Butterfly

2003. Summer. T **708** and similar multicoloured designs.

MS1707 65c. Type **708**; 65c. Dragonfly (45×35 mm); 65c. Flowers and caterpillar; 65c. Frog (45×36 mm); 65c. Magpie (36×46 mm) (vert); 65c. Hedgehogs (45×29 mm)	8·50	7·00

709 Moomin Family

2003. Moomins. With service indicator. Illustrations from Moominland Midwinter by Tove Jansson. Multicoloured. Self-adhesive.

1708	1klass (65c.) Type **709**	1·20	1·10
1709	1klass (65c.) Tooticky, Little My and Moomintroll sitting by stove	1·20	1·10
1710	1klass (65c.) Moomintroll performing handstand and Little My	1·20	1·10
1711	1klass (65c.) Moonmintroll and squirrel	1·20	1·10
1712	1klass (65c.) Tooticky, Moominmamma and Little My in snow	1·20	1·10
1713	1klass (65c.) Snufkin walking through forest	1·20	1·10

710 Ligonberry (*Vaccinium vitis-idaea*)

2003. Self-adhesive.

1714	**710**	65c. multicoloured	1·50	1·10

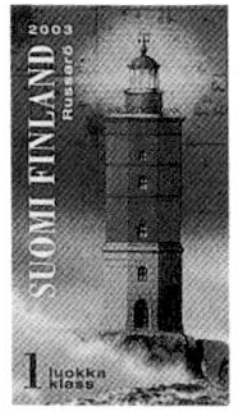
711 Russaro Lighthouse

2003. Lighthouses. With service indicator. Sheet 120×80 mm containing T **711** and similar vert designs. Multicoloured.

MS1715 1klass (65c.) Bengtskar (29×40 mm); 1klass (65c.) Type **711**; 1klass (65c.) Ronnskar; 1klass (65c.) Harmaja Grahara; 1klass (65c.) Soderskar	7·25	6·25

712 Maria and Juho Lallukka

2003. Scientific and Cultural Patrons. Multicoloured.

1716	65c. Type **712**	1·20	1·10
1717	65c. Emil Aaltonen (vert)	1·20	1·10
1718	65c. Heikki Huhtamaki (vert)	1·20	1·10
1719	65c. Jenny and Antti Wihuri	1·20	1·10
1720	65c. Alfred Kordelin (vert)	1·20	1·10
1721	65c. Amos Andersson (vert)	1·20	1·10

713 Elf Boy posting Letters

2003. Christmas. Multicoloured. Self-adhesive.

1722	45c. Type **713**	85	90
1723	65c. Elf girl holding ginger bread on tray (vert)	1·20	1·10

714 President Halonen

2003. 60th Birth Anniv of Tarja Halonen, President of Finland.

1724	**714**	65c. multicoloured	2·00	1·50

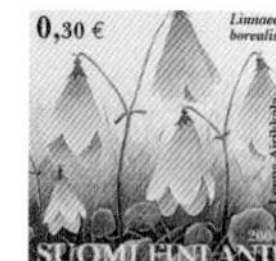
715 *Linnaea borealis*

2004. Self-adhesive.

1725	**715**	30c. multicoloured	1·10	90

716 Jean Sibelius' Hands playing Piano

2004. Ainola Museum (Jean Sibelius (composer)'s house). Multicoloured. Self-adhesive.

1726	2klass (55c.) Type **716**	1·80	1·40
1727	2klass (55c.) Swans and score	1·80	1·40
1728	2klass (55c.) *En Saga Jean Sibelius* (painting, Akseli Gallen-Kalhla)	1·80	1·40
1729	1klass (65c.) *Voices Intimae* score (detail)	2·00	1·60
1730	1klass (65c.) Drawing of Ainola	2·00	1·60
1731	1klass (65c.) *Aino Sibelius* (Eero Järnfelt) and *Jean Sibelius* (Albert Edelfelt)	2·00	1·60

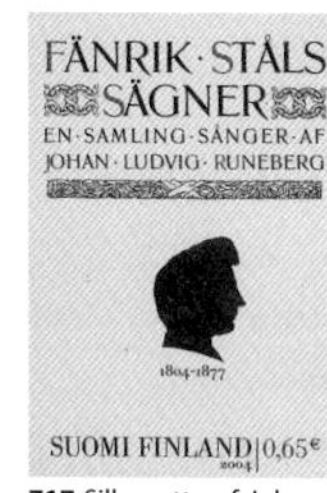
717 Silhouette of Johan Runeberg

2004. Birth Bicentenary of Johan Ludvig Runeberg (writer). Sheet 118×80 mm containing T **717** and similar vert designs. Each stone, black and red.

MS1732 65c.×4, Type **717**; Sven Dufa at the Battle of Koljonvirta (Albert Edelfelt) Landscape (Albert Edelfelt) and Värt Land (national anthem); Johan Runeberg (statue, Walter Runeberg)	7·50	7·00

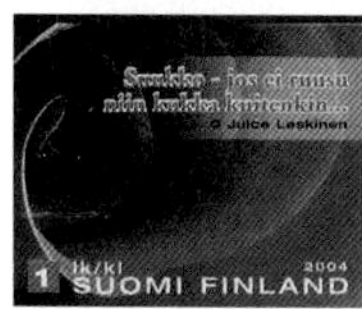
718 Rose

2004. Greetings Stamps. Each black and red. Self-adhesive.

1733	1klass (65c.) Type **718**	2·00	1·60
1734	1klass (65c.) Pursed lips	2·00	1·60
1735	1klass (65c.) Eye	2·00	1·60
1736	1klass (65c.) Man and woman	2·00	1·60
1737	1klass (65c.) Elderly woman	2·00	1·60
1738	1klass (65c.) Hand and flower	2·00	1·60

719 Bear Cub

2004. Self-adhesive.

1739	**719**	2klass (55c.) mult	1·80	1·40

720 Rose

2004. Self-adhesive.

1740	**720**	1klass (65c.). mult	2·00	1·60

721 Daffodils, Narcissi and Grape Hyacinths

2004. Easter. Self-adhesive.

1741	**721**	65c. multicoloured	2·00	1·60

2004. As T **689**. Self-adhesive.

1742	**689**	€3 multicoloured	8·50	8·00

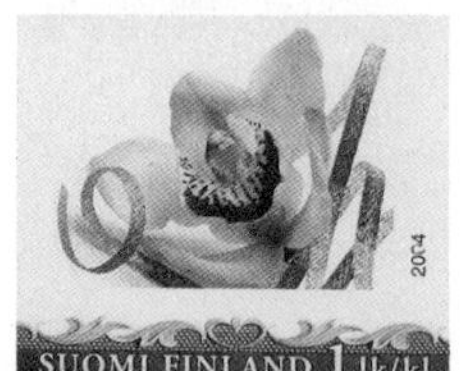

722 Orchid

2004. Greetings Stamps. Multicoloured. Self-adhesive gum.

1743	1 klass (65c.) Type **722**	2·00	1·60
1744	1 klass (65c.) Swallow and martins	2·00	1·60

723 *Luonnotar* (detail) (Akseli Gallen-Kallela)

2004. Nordic Mythology. Sheet 105×70 mm containing T **723** and similar multicoloured design.

MS1745 65c.×2, Type **723**; "Luonnotar" (different) (22×42 mm)	3·75	3·50

Stamps of a similar theme were issued by Aland Islands, Denmark, Faroe Islands, Greenland, Iceland, Norway and Sweden.

724 Wild Strawberry

2004. Self-adhesive.

1746	**724**	65c. multicoloured	2·00	1·60

725 *From the Luxembourg Gardens* (Albert Edelfelt)

2004. Self-adhesive.

1747	**725**	1 klass (65c.) mult	2·00	1·60

726 Fire on Beach

2004. Europa. Holidays. Multicoloured.

1748	65c. Type **726**	1·80	1·50
1749	65c. Rowers	1·80	1·50

727 Red Squirrel

2004. Fauna. Sheet 80×120 mm containing T **727** and similar multicoloured designs.

MS1750 65c.×6, Type **727**; Crow (40×31 mm); Rabbit; Weasels; Lizard; Fox (40×40 mm)	11·00	10·50

728 Snufkin and Moomin Troll

2004. 90th Birth Anniv of Tove Jansson (artist and writer). 50th Anniv of Moomins (cartoon strip by Tove Jansson).

1751	**728**	1 klass (65c.) mult	2·00	1·60

729 Trees and Stone Wall

2004. UNESCO World Heritage Sites. Sammallahdenmäki Bronze Age Ruins. Sheet 120×80 mm containing T **729** and similar square design. Multicoloured.

MS1752 65c.×2, Type **729**; Lichen covered stones	4·00	3·75

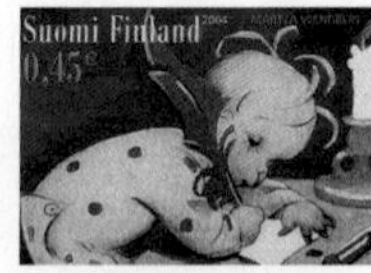

730 Jug (*Egelskar*)

2004. Gulf of Finland (3rd series). Showing artefacts from ships. Multicoloured.

1753	1 klass (65c.) Type **730**	2·00	1·60
1754	1 klass (65c.) Seal (*Vrouw Maria*)	2·00	1·60
1755	1 klass (65c.) Gold watch (*St. Michael*)	2·00	1·60
1756	1 klass (65c.) Figurehead (*St. Nikolai*) (24×40 mm)	2·00	1·60
1757	1 klass (65c.) Powder box (*Mulan*)	2·00	1·60

731 Child writing Letter (Martta Wendelin)

2004. Christmas. Drawings by Martta Wendelin. Self-adhesive.

1758	45c. Type **731**	1·60	1·40
1759	65c. Tree decorations (vert)	2·00	1·60

732 Two Girls

2004. 25th Anniv of United Nations Convention on Rights of the Child. Multicoloured.

1760	65c. Type **732**	2·00	1·60
1761	65c. Boy painting	2·00	1·60

733 World Map of Rotary Emblems

2005. Centenary of Rotary International (charitable organization).

1762	**733**	65c. ultramarine and gold	2·30	2·00

734 Child with Bucket and Spade

2005. 400th Anniv of Oulu City. Multicoloured.

1763	65c. Type **734**	2·00	1·60
1764	65c. Cyclist	2·00	1·60

Nos. 1763/4 were issued together, *se-tenant*, pairs forming a composite design.

735 Sibelius Concert Hall

2005. Centenary of Lahti City. Multicoloured.

1765	65c. Type **735**	2·00	1·60
1766	65c. Radio masts	2·00	1·60

736 Lion and Tiger

2005. Toys. Multicoloured. Self-adhesive.

1767	1 klass (65c.) Type **736**	2·00	1·60
1768	1 klass (65c.) Elephant and dog	2·00	1·60
1769	1 klass (65c.) Airplane, car and train	2·00	1·60
1770	1 klass (65c.) Teddy bear and rabbit	2·00	1·60

737 Earth and Moon (waxing moon)

2005. 300th Anniv of First Finnish Almanac. Self-adhesive.

1771	**737**	65c. multicoloured	2·00	1·60

738 Door Decoration

2005. Hvittrask (Art Nouveau house), Kirkkonummi. Multicoloured. Self-adhesive.

1772	2 klass (55c.) Type **738** (Eliel Saarinen and Santtu Hartman)	1·90	1·60
1773	2 klass (55c.) Copper stove door	1·90	1·60
1774	2 klass (55c.) Chair (detail)	1·90	1·60
1775	1 klass (65c.) Stained glass window (Olga Gummerus-Ehrstrom)	2·10	1·80
1776	1 klass (65c.) Living room	2·10	1·80
1777	1 klass (65c.) Facade	2·10	1·80

739 Woman Auxiliary feeding Soldier and Veteran Organization Emblems

2005. 65th Anniv of End of 105-day Winter War.

1778	**739**	65c. multicoloured	2·30	2·00

740 Apple Blossom

2005. Self-adhesive.

1779	**740**	1 klass (65c.) mult	2·30	2·00

741 Easter Witch carrying Bouquet

2005. Easter. Self-adhesive.

1780	**741**	65c. multicoloured	2·30	2·00

742 Zeus (miniature Schnauzer)

2005. Greetings Stamps. Self-adhesive.

1781	**742**	1 klass (65c.) mult	2·00	1·60

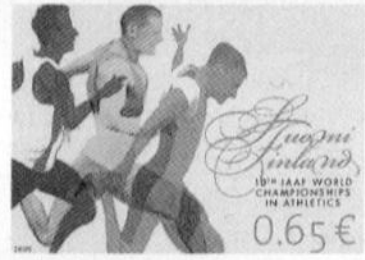

743 Coach (1940)

2005. Centenary of Buses in Finland. Self-adhesive.

1782	**743**	65c. black	2·00	1·60

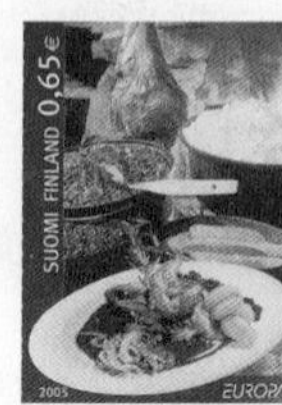

744 Runners

2005. Tenth IAAF World Athletics Championships, Helsinki. Self-adhesive.

1783	**744**	65c. multicoloured	2·00	1·60

745 Reindeer Meat

2005. Europa. Gastronomy. Multicoloured.

1784	65c. Type **745**	2·00	1·60
1785	65c. Fish and beetroot tartare	2·00	1·60

746 Golfer

2005. Golf. Sheet 121×81 mm containing T **746** and similar multicoloured designs.

MS1786 65c.×4, Type **746**; Girl holding flag (vert); Boy putting (vert); Putter and ball	7·75	7·25

The stamps and margins of **MS**1786 were issued together, se-tenant, forming a composite design.

747 Icelandic Pony

2005. Ponies. Self-adhesive. Multicoloured.

1787	1 klass (65c.) Type **747**	1·90	1·50
1788	1 klass (65c.) Welsh pony	1·90	1·50
1789	1 klass (65c.) New Forest pony	1·90	1·50
1790	1 klass (65c.) Shetland pony	1·90	1·50

748 Cloudberry (*Rubus chamaemorus*)

2005. Self-adhesive.

1791	**748**	1 klass (65c.) mult	2·10	1·70

749 *Urho*

2005. Icebreakers (ships). Multicoloured.

1792	1 klass (65c.) Type **749**	1·90	1·50
1793	1 klass (65c.) *Otso*	1·90	1·50
1794	1 klass (65c.) *Fennica*	1·90	1·50
1795	1 klass (65c.) *Botnica*	1·90	1·50

750 Bell Tower

2005. Petajavesi Church. Sheet 80×120 mm containing T **750** and similar vert designs. Multicoloured.
MS1796 65c.×4, Type **750**; Church building (34×40 mm.); Angel (26×38 mm.); Chandelier (26×38 mm.) 7·75 7·25

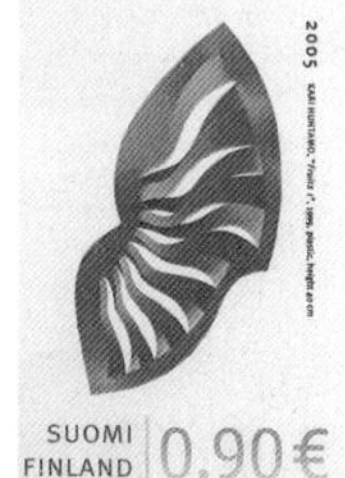
751 "Fruits" (Kari Huhtamo)

2005. Greetings Stamps. Self-adhesive.

1797	**751**	90c. multicoloured	3·00	2·75

752 Father Christmas reading Letters

2005. Christmas. Drawings by Mauri Kunnas. Multicoloured. Self-adhesive.

1798	50c. Type **752**	1·50	1·20
1799	1 klass (65c.) Father and Mrs Christmas dancing (horiz)	2·00	1·60

753 Wood Anemones

2005. 150th Anniv of First Finnish Stamp (1st issue). Sheet 160×97 mm containing T **753** and similar horiz design showing Winter Egg designed by Alma Pihl-Klee and made by Carl Faberge.
MS1800 €3.50×2, Type **753**; Surface of egg 21·00 20·00

754 Early and Modern Postman

2006. Centenary of Postal Union (PAU).

1801	**754**	65c. multicoloured	2·10	1·70

755 Heart

2006. St. Valentine's Day. Self-adhesive.

1802	**755**	65c. pink	2·10	1·70

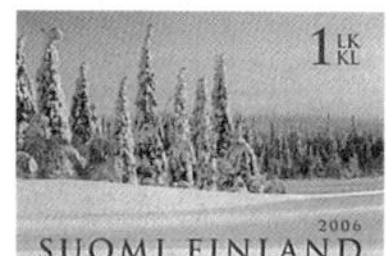
756 Winter Landscape

2006. Self-adhesive.

1803	**756**	1 klass (65c.) mult	2·10	1·70

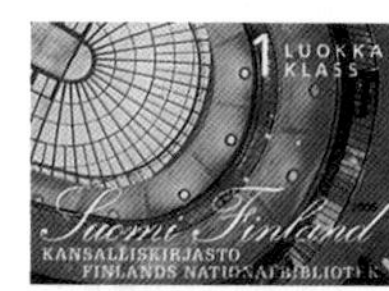
757 Atrium

2006. Inauguration of National Library. Self-adhesive.

1804	**757**	1 klass (65c.) mult	2·10	1·70

758 Oldsmobile (1906)

2006. Centenary of Taxis. Each sepia and yellow. Self-adhesive.

1805	65c. Type **758**	1·90	1·50
1806	65c. Chevrolet (1929)	1·90	1·50
1807	65c. Pobeda (1957)	1·90	1·50
1808	65c. Modern Mercedes-Benz	1·90	1·50

759 J. V. Snellman (drawing)

2006. Birth Bicentenary of Johan Vilhelm Snellman (philosopher and journalist). Sheet 140×90 mm containing T **759** and similar horiz designs. Multicoloured.
MS1809 65c.×4, Type **759**; J. V. Snellman on banknote; J. V. Snellman and railway map; Locomotive Ilmarinen 7·75 7·25

760 Emblem

2006. Centenary of Finnish Parliament. Self-adhesive.

1810	**760**	1 klass (65c.) gold, black and lemon	2·10	1·70

761 Bil-Bol (car advertisement) (1907)

2006. Posters by Akseli Gallen-Kallela. Self-adhesive Coil Stamps. Multicoloured.

1811	2 klass (55c.) Type **761**	1·90	1·50
1812	2 klass (55c.) Eroittaja 2 (Helsinki art exhibition) (1906)	1·90	1·50
1813	2 klass (55c.) Concert Finnois (Finnish concert, World Fair, Paris) (1900)	1·90	1·50

762 Flag

2006. 150th Anniv of Finnish Stamps (1st issue). National Flag.

1814	**762**	1 klass (65c.) mult	2·10	1·70

763 Lilac

2006. Self-adhesive.

1815	**763**	1 klass (65c.) mult	2·30	1·90

764 Chick

2006. Easter. Self-adhesive.

1816	**764**	65c. multicoloured	2·10	1·70

765 *Madonna*

2006. Tarvaspaa, Gallen-Kallela Museum. 140th Birth Anniv of Akseli Gallen-Kallela (artist). Self-adhesive. Multicoloured.

1817	1 klass (65c.) Type **765**	2·20	1·80
1818	1 klass (65c.) *Self-portrait*	2·20	1·80
1819	1 klass (65c.) Tarvaspaa building	2·20	1·80

766 *Fortune Teller* (Helene Schjerfbeck)

2006. Self-adhesive.

1820	**766**	95c. multicoloured	3·00	2·50

767 Fairy

2006. Nordic Mythology. Book Illustrations by Rudolf Koivu. Sheet 105×70 mm containing T **767** and similar multicoloured design.
MS1821 65c.×2, Type **767**; Fairy and elf (vert) 4·00 3·75

Stamps of a similar theme were issued by Aland Islands, Denmark, Faroe Islands, Greenland, Iceland, Norway and Sweden.

768 Tandem

2006. Europa. Integration.

1822	**768**	65c. multicoloured	2·10	1·70

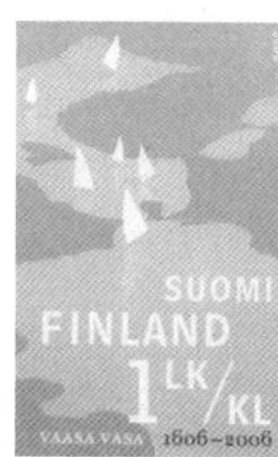
769 Waterway and Sailboats

2006. 400th Anniv of Vaasa.

1823	**769**	1klass (65c.) mult	2·10	1·70

770 Postman's Badge

2006. Personalized Stamp. Self-adhesive.

1824	**770**	1klass (65c.) multicoloured	2·10	1·70

771 King's Port and Pojama Class Frigate

2006. Sveaborg Fortress, Suomenlinna—World Heritage Site. Multicoloured.

1825	1klass Type **771**	2·10	1·70
1826	1klass Von Fersen's Tenaille and Turkoma class frigate	2·10	1·70
1827	1klass Hjarne Bastion and Udema class frigate	2·10	1·70

Stamps of the same design were issued by Sweden.

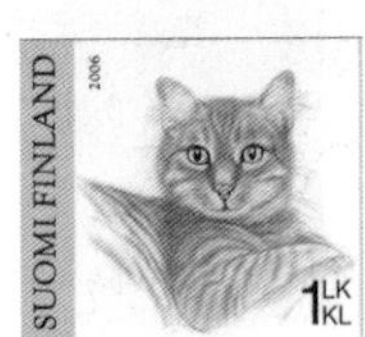
772 Ginger Shorthair

2006. Cats. Self-adhesive. Multicoloured.

1828	1klass (65c.) Type **772**	2·10	1·70
1829	1klass (65c.) British blue shorthair	2·10	1·70
1830	1klass (65c.) Ragdoll	2·10	1·70
1831	1klass (65c.) Persian	2·10	1·70

773 Fishing

2006. Summer. Self-adhesive. Multicoloured.

1832	1klass (65c.) Type **773**	2·10	1·70
1833	1klass (65c.) Children making daisy chains	2·10	1·70
1834	1klass (65c.) Man seated by lake	2·10	1·70
1835	1klass (65c.) Woman picking flowers	2·10	1·70

774 Blueberry (*Vaccinium myrtillus*)

2006. Self-adhesive.

1836	**774**	1klass (70c.) mult	2·30	2·00

775 Family watching Television

2006. Family Life. Self-adhesive.

1837	1 klass (70c.) Type **775**	2·30	2·00
1838	1 klass (70c.) Wife writing letter to husband	2·30	2·00

776 Newspaper Banner and Text

2006. Newspaper Journalism. Self-adhesive.

1839	**776**	70c. black and vermilion	2·30	2·00

777 "Points" (Ritva Puotila)

2006. Personal Stamp. Textile Art. Self-adhesive.

1840	**777**	1klass (70c.) mult	2·30	2·00

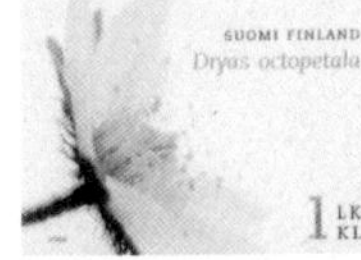
778 *Dryas octopetala*

2006. Self-adhesive.

1841	**778**	1klass (70c.) mult	2·30	2·00

779 Horse (Steve Brice, Charles Dash, Carl Eady and Michael Gresham)

2006. Snow Art (ice sculpture). Self-adhesive. Multicoloured.

1842	1klass (70c.) Type **779**	2·30	2·00
1843	1klass (70c.) Snow Castle, Kemi	2·30	2·00
1844	1klass (70c.) Wall (Kimmo Frosti)	2·30	2·00
1845	1klass (70c.) Lantern of snow balls	2·30	2·00

780 Boy and Great Tit

2006. Christmas. Multicoloured. Self-adhesive.

1846	50c. Type **780**	1·80	1·40
1847	1klass (70c.) Waxwing (vert)	2·00	1·60

781 1930 Heraldic Lion (from stamp drawn by Signe Hammarsten-Jansson)

2006. 150th Anniv of First Stamp. Sheet 120×74 mm containing T **781** and similar vert designs.

MS1848 70c. ultramarine and vermilion; 95c. red, ultramarine and vermilion; €1.40 gold, ultramarine, vermilion and red	9·00	8·50

DESIGNS: 70c. Type **781**; 95c. 1856 10k. oval stamp (detail); €1.40 1975 coat of arms (from stamp drawn by Pirkko Vahtero) (detail).

782 Cameraman

2007. 50th Anniv of Television. Self-adhesive.

1849	**782**	70c. multicoloured	2·30	2·00

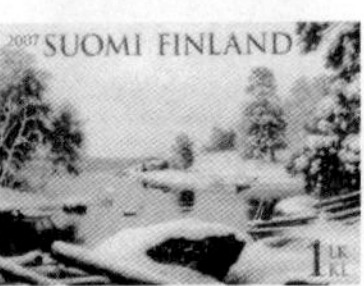
783 Winter Landscape, Haminalahti (Ferdinand von Wright)

2007. Self-adhesive.

1850	**783**	1 klass (70c.) multicoloured	2·30	2·00

784 Faces (Aino-Maija Metsola)

2007. St. Valentine's Day. Self-adhesive.

1851	**784**	70c. multicoloured	2·30	2·00

785 Polar Landscape and Snow Crystal (image scaled to 46% of original size)

2007. International Polar Year. Sheet 105×70 mm as T **785**.

MS1852 70c.×2, Landscape; Snow crystal	4·25	3·75

The stamps of **MS**1852 overlap and share a central area containing hologram of a snow crystal.

786 Logging Truck in Snow (image scaled to 58% of original size)

2007. Centenary of Truck Transport. Self-adhesive. Multicoloured.

1853	70c. Type **786**	2·00	1·60
1854	70c. Milk truck	2·00	1·60
1855	70c. Tipper truck	2·00	1·60
1856	70c. Truck and trailer	2·00	1·60

787 *Sunset* (Aino-Maija Metsola)

2007. Self-adhesive.

1857	**787**	€1.40 multicoloured	2·30	2·00

788 Rabbit with Basket of Eggs

2007. Easter. Self-adhesive.

1858	**788**	1klass (70c.) multicoloured	2·30	2·00

789 Lily "Enchantment"

2007. Self-adhesive.

1859	**789**	1klass (70c.) multicoloured	2·30	2·00

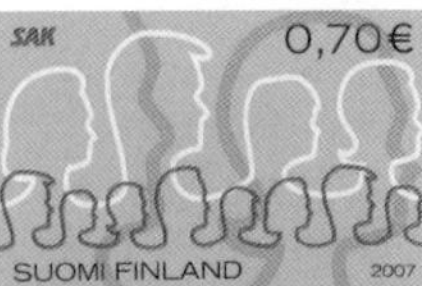
790 Heads

2007. Centenary of Central Organization of Finnish Trade Unions.

1860	**790**	70c. multicoloured	2·30	2·00

791 Young Players

2007. Centenary of Finnish Football Association. Self-adhesive.

1861	**791**	70c. multicoloured	2·30	2·00

No. 1861 has a brief description of Finnish football history on the backing paper.

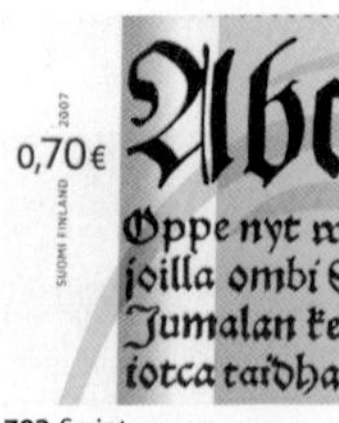
792 Script

2007. 450th Birth Anniv of Mikael Agricola (church reformer and founder of written Finnish). Sheet 140×80 mm containing T **792** and similar vert design. Multicoloured.

MS1862 70c.×2, Type **792**; Preacher	4·25	3·75

793 "Eurovision"

2007. Eurovision Song Contest, Helsinki. Sheet 63×130 mm containing T **793** and similar multicoloured designs. Self-adhesive.

MS1863 70c.×4, Type **793**; Laila Kinunen, Marion Rung, Kirka Babitzin and Katri Helena (49×29 mm); Lordi (band) (49×23 mm); Mr Lordi (Tomi Putaansu) (singer) (35×29 mm)	8·50	8·00

794 Sea Scouts

2007. Europa. Centenary of Scouting. Multicoloured.

1864	70c. Type **794**	2·10	1·70
1865	70c. Girl scouts and campfire	2·10	1·70

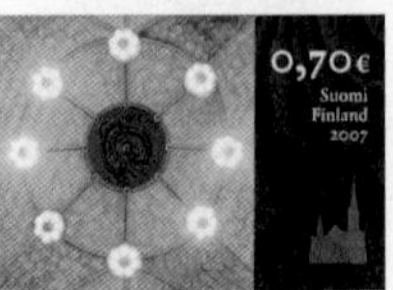
795 Ceiling Vault

2007. Centenary of Tampere Cathedral.

1866	**795**	70c. multicoloured	2·30	2·00

796 Commuter Train

2007. Public Transport. Multicoloured. Self-adhesive. Multicoloured.

1867	1 klass (70c.) Type **796**	2·10	1·70
1868	1 klass (70c.) City tram	2·10	1·70
1869	1 klass (70c.) Metro train	2·10	1·70
1870	1 klass (70c.) Kamppi Bus Terminal	2·10	1·70

797 Little My

2007. Moomins. Multicoloured. Self-adhesive.

1871	1 klass (70c.) Type **797**	2·10	1·70
1872	1 klass (70c.) Moomintroll	2·10	1·70
1873	1 klass (70c.) Moominpappa	2·10	1·70
1874	1 klass (70c.) Snork Maiden	2·10	1·70
1875	1 klass (70c.) Moomin-momma	2·10	1·70
1876	1 klass (70c.) Snufkin	2·10	1·70

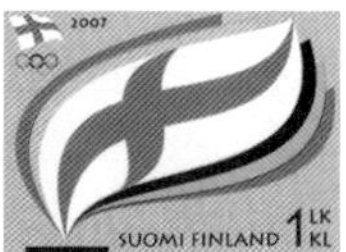
798 Emblem

2007. Centenary of National Olympic Committee. Self-adhesive.

1877	**798**	1 klass (70c.) mult	2·30	2·00

799 Raspberry (*Rubus idaeus*)

2007. Self-adhesive.

1878	**799**	1 klass (70c.) mult	2·30	2·00

800 Wall and Skylight, St John's Church, Mannisto (designed by Juha Leiviska)

2007. Personal Stamp. Architecture. Self-adhesive.

1879	**800**	1 klass (70c.) mult	2·30	2·00

801 *Porvoo Garland* Wallpaper (Biedermeier)

2007. Antiques. Multicoloured. Self-adhesive.

1880	1 klass (70c.) Type **801**	2·30	2·00
1881	1 klass (70c.) '2+3' wallpaper (Ilmari and Annikki Tapiovaara) and 20th-century Paimio chair (Alvar Aalto)	2·30	2·00

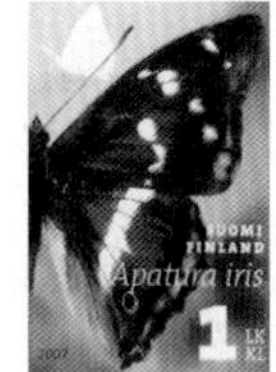
802 *Apatura iris* and 19th-century Empire-style Chair

2007. Butterflies. Multicoloured. Self-adhesive.

1882	1 klass (70c.) Type **802**	2·40	2·00
1883	1 klass (70c.) *Scolitantides orion*	2·40	2·00
1884	1 klass (70c.) *Colias palaeno*	2·40	2·00

803 Hauling Wood

2007. Memories of Finland. 90th Anniv of Finnish Independence. Winning Designs in Photography Competition. Sheet 160×104 mm containing T **803** and similar horiz designs. Multicoloured.

MS1885 70c.×8, Type **803** (c.1930); Bonfire (1999); Toddler blowing birch horn (1943); Boy ski jumping (1999); Two pairs of twins on skis (c.1950); Boy leaping into lake (2005); Making coffee outdoors (1958); Ice fisher (2005) 16·00 4·50

804 Qing Dynasty Carved Chair

2007. Woodcraft. Sheet 106×70 mm containing T 804 and similar horiz design. Multicoloured.

MS1886 106×70 mm. 70c.×2, Type **804**; Wooden bowls 4·75 4·00

Stamps of a similar design were issued by Hong Kong.

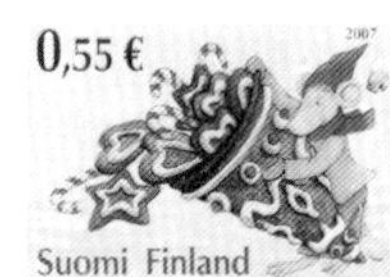
805 Mouse with Gingerbread Cornucopia

2007. Christmas. Multicoloured. Self-adhesive.

1887	55c. Type **805**	1·75	1·50
1888	1 klass (70c.) Mouse and Christmas straw goat (vert)	2·50	2·30

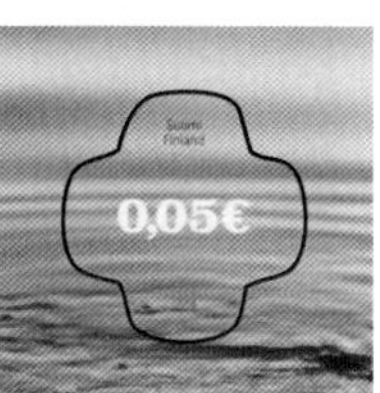
806 Water

807 Water

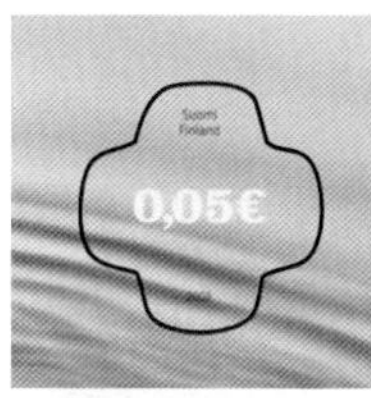
808 Water

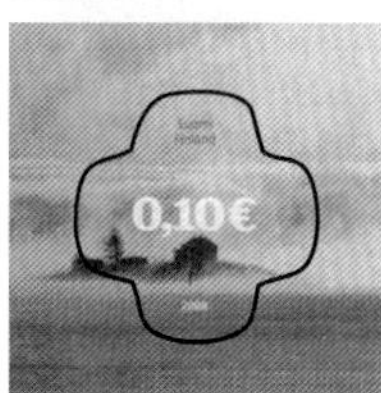
809 Archipelago

810 Archipelago

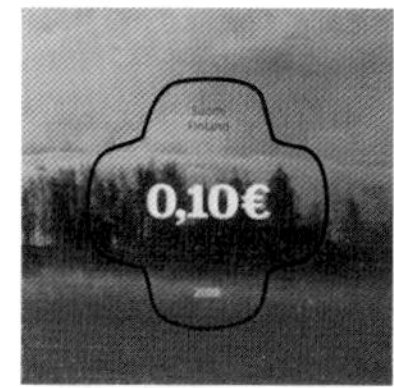
811 Archipelago

2008. Landscapes. Water and Archipelago.

1889	**806**	5c. multicoloured	40	20
1890	**807**	5c. multicoloured	40	20
1891	**808**	5c. multicoloured	40	20
1892	**809**	10c. multicoloured	40	20
1893	**810**	10c. multicoloured	40	20
1894	**811**	10c. multicoloured	40	20

Nos. 1889/91 form a composite design of rippling water and 1892/4 form a composite design of an archipelago.

812 Robot

2008. Centenary of University of Technology, Helsinki. Sheet 130×80 mm containing T **812** and similar horiz design.

MS1895 1 Klass (70c.)×2, Type **812**; University building, Otaniemi 5·00 4·50

The stamps and margins of **MS**1895 form a composite design.

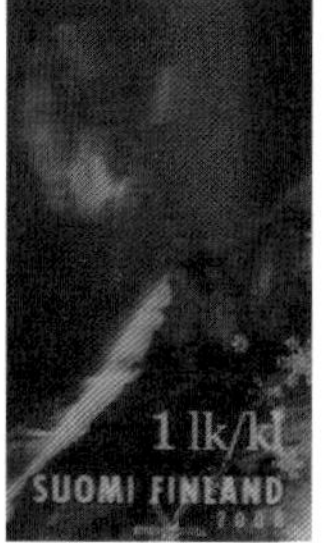
813 Matti Raty (free-skier)

2008. Alpine Sports. Sheet containing T **813** and similar multicoloured designs.

MS1896 1 Klass (70c.)×4, Type **813**; Antti Autti (snow-boarder) (*horiz*); Tapio (Arska) Saarimaki (downhill skiing); Tanja Poutianen (slalom) 9·50 9·00

The stamps and margins of **MS**1896 form a composite design.

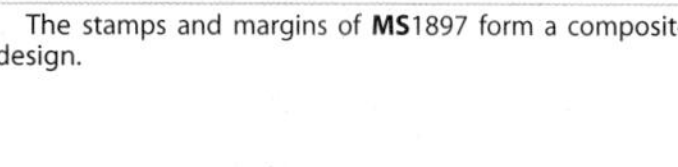
814 Airplane towing Heart

2008. Greetings Stamps. Sheet 90×130 mm containing T **814** and similar multicoloured designs.

MS1897 1 Klass (70c.)×5, Type **814**; Bird carrying envelope; Heart shaped clouds; Heart shaped air balloon; Hearts in a bottle afloat 12·00 11·00

The stamps and margins of **MS**1897 form a composite design.

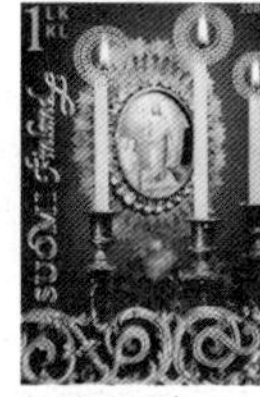
815 Icon and Candlestick

2008. Easter. Self-adhesive.

1898	**815**	1 Klass (70c.) mult	2·75	2·50

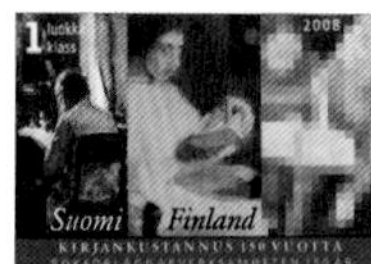
816 *Master Carl Gustaf Swann at his Desk* (Eero Jarnfelt), *Reading Girls* (Helene Schjerfbeck) and Pixel Mosaic of Children Reading

2008. 150th Anniv of Finnish Book Publishers Association. Self-adhesive.

1899	**816**	1 Klass (70c.) mult	2·75	2·50

817 Sweet Pea Flowers and Braille Letters

2008. 80th Anniv of Finnish Federation of Visually Impaired. Self-adhesive.

1900	**817**	1 Klass (70c.) mult	2·75	2·50

818 Red Fin on Perch (dry weather)

2008. Folklore Weather Forecasting. Multicoloured. Self-adhesive.

1901	1 Klass (70c.) Type **818**	2·75	2·50
1902	1 Klass (70c.) Sheep gambolling (wet weather)	2·75	2·50
1903	1 Klass (70c.) Frogs taking long hops (dry weather)	2·75	2·50
1904	1 Klass (70c.) Low flying swallows (wet weather)	2·75	2·50
1905	1 Klass (70c.) Snail with feelers extended (dry weather)	2·75	2·50

819 Desk, Porcelain Clock (Arabia) and Lamp

2008. Antiques. Art Nouveau. Self-adhesive.

1906	**819**	€1.05 multicoloured	4·00	4·00

820 Rock God of Astuvansalmi

2008. Norse Mythology. Mythical Places. Sheet 105×70 mm containing T **820** and similar vert design.

MS1907 70c.×2, Type **820**; Amber head (found at Astuvansalmi) 5·50 5·25

Stamps of a similar theme were issued by Aland Islands, Denmark, Faroe Islands, Greenland, Iceland, Norway and Sweden.

821 Script and Pekka Halonen

2008. Europa. The Letter. Letters between Pekka Halonen and his Wife, Maija. Multicoloured.

1908	70c. Type **821**	2·75	2·50
1909	70c. Script and Maija Halonen	2·75	2·50

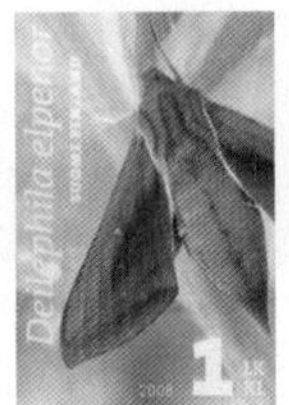

822 *Deilephila elpenor*

2008. Moths. Multicoloured. Self-adhesive.

1910	1 Klass (70c.) Type **822**	2·75	2·50
1911	1 Klass (70c.) *Aglia tau*	2·75	2·50
1912	1 Klass (70c.) *Arctia caja*	2·75	2·50

Nos. 1910/12 each include a clear varnish overprint showing the wing of the relevant insect.

823 Melting Cake

2008. Greetings Stamps. Multicoloured. Self-adhesive.

1913	1 Klass (70c.) Type **823**	2·75	2·50
1914	1 Klass (70c.) Guitars	2·75	2·50
1915	1 Klass (70c.) Winged face	2·75	2·50
1916	1 Klass (70c.) High-heeled boots	2·75	2·50
1917	1 Klass (70c.) Balloons	2·75	2·50
1918	1 Klass (70c.) Stilt walkers	2·75	2·50
1918	1 Klass (70c.) Stilt walkers	2·75	2·50

No. 1913/18 form a composite design.

824 *Sinista ja punaista/Blatt och vitt* (Sam Vanni)

2008. Art. Multicoloured. Self-adhesive.

1919	1 Klass (70c.) Type **824**	2·75	2·50
1920	1 Klass (70c.) *Merirosvolaiva/Sjorovarfartyg* (Kimmo Kaivanto)	2·75	2·50
1921	1 Klass (70c.) *Hiljaisuuden kuuntelija/Lyssnar till tystnaden* (Juhani Linnovaara)	2·75	2·50
1922	1 Klass (70c.) *Odotan kevaan tuloa/Jag väntar pa varen* (Goran Auguston)	2·75	2·50
1923	1 Klass (70c.) *Minaa/Jag* (Carolus Enckell)	2·75	2·50
1924	1 Klass (70c.) *Poyta, Bord* (Reino Heitanen)	2·75	2·50

825 Rising Island and Scale

2008. Kvarken Archipelago—UNESCO World Heritage Site. Self-adhesive.

1925	**825**	€1.50 black and vermilion	5·50	5·25

826 Fireworks

2008. Personal Stamp.

1925a	**826**	1klass (80c.) indigo	3·25	3·00

827 Mika Waltari

2008. Birth Centenary of Mika Waltari (writer). Sheet 100×80 mm containing T **827** and similar vert design. Multicoloured.

MS1926 80c.×2, Type **827**; Cover of *Komisario Palmun Erehdys* (novel) (drawn by Eeeli Jaatinen) 6·25 6·25

828 Kimi Raikkonen

2008. Kimi Raikkonen—2007 Formula One World Champion. Sheet 132×70 mm containing T 828 and similar vert design. Multicoloured.

MS1927 1klass (80c.)×2, Type **828**; Ferrari race car (74×31 mm) 6·25 6·25

829 Finnish Spitz

2008. Dogs. Self-adhesive gum. Multicoloured.

1928	1 Klass (80c.) Type **829**	3·25	3·00
1929	1 Klass (80c.) Collie	3·25	3·00
1930	1 Klass (80c.) Boxer	3·25	3·00
1931	1 Klass (80c.) Finnish hound	3·25	3·00
1932	1 Klass (80c.) King Charles spaniel	3·25	3·00
1933	1 Klass (80c.) Jack Russell terrier	3·25	3·00

830 Adolf Nordenskiold

2008. 140th Anniv of Adolf Erik Nordenskiold's Arctic Expedition to Svalbard. Sheet 165×60 mm containing T 830 and similar multicoloured design.

MS1934 1klass (80c.)×2, Type **830**; *Sofia* (expedition ship), 1883 (date of voyage to Greenland) (58×33 mm) 6·00 6·00

831 Bear's and their Christmas Tree

2008. Christmas. Multicoloured.

1935	60c. Type **831**	2·75	2·50
1936	1klass (80c.) Animals encircling Christmas tree (horiz)	3·50	3·25

832 Snowflake

2008. Frosty Night. Transparent plastic.

1937	**832**	1klass (80c.) multicoloured	3·50	3·25

833 Martti Ahtisaari

2008. Martti Ahtisaari–Nobel Peace Prize Winner, 2008.

1938	**833**	80c. blue	3·75	3·50

834 Nurses

2009. In Praise of Hospital Workers.

1939	**834**	80c. multicoloured	3·50	3·25

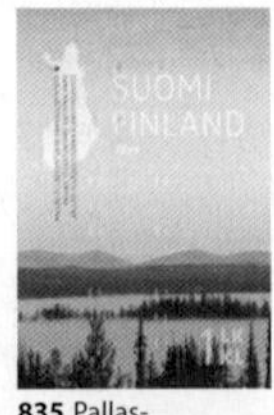

835 Pallas-Yllastunturi, Lapland

2009. National Parks. Self-adhesive.

1940	**835**	1 klass (80c.) multicoloured	3·00	2·75

836 Tsar Alexander I of Russia

2009. Bicentenary of Nationhood. Sheet 147×105 mm containing T **836** and similar vert designs. Multicoloured.

MS1941 80c.×4, Type **836**; George Magnus Sprengtporten; Carl Erik Mannerheim; Gustaf Mauritz Armfelt 13·00 13·00

837 Boy as Policeman

2009. Multicultural Finland. Showing children. Multicoloured. Self-adhesive.

1942	1 klass (80c.) Type **837**	3·25	3·00
1943	1 klass (80c.) As doctor	3·25	3·00
1944	1 klass (80c.) As fire crew	3·00	3·25
1945	1 klass (80c.) As skier	3·25	3·00
1946	1 klass (80c.) As construction worker	3·25	3·00

838 Dressing Up

2009. Greetings Stamps. Sheet 103×100 mm containing T **838** and similar droplet shaped designs. Multicoloured. Self-adhesive.

MS1947 1 klass (80c.) ×5, Type **838**; Cupid; Temple; Bear holding heart; Two swans with necks entwined 16·00 16·00

839 Peony

2009. Self-adhesive.

1948	**839**	€1.10 multicoloured	1·00	1·00

840 Roast Lamb, Potatoes and Chocolate Mousse

2009. Easter. Self-adhesive.

1949	**840**	1 Klass (80c.) multicoloured	3·25	3·00

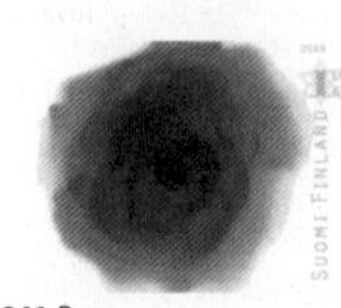

841 Rose

2009. Self-adhesive.

1950	**841**	1 Klass (80c.) multicoloured	3·25	3·00

842 Emblem and Sky

2009. Preserve Polar Regions and Glaciers. Sheet 80×120 mm containing T **842** and similar circular design. Multicoloured.

MS1951 1 Klass (80c.)×2, Type **842**; Emblem and polar sea 6·50 6·50

843 Parcel and Tulips

2009. Greetings Stamps. Multicoloured.

1952	1 Klass (80c.) Type **843**	3·25	3·00
1953	1 Klass (80c.) Strawberries and cake	3·25	3·00
1954	1 Klass (80c.) Dahlias	3·25	3·00
1955	1 Klass (80c.) Cup of coffee	3·25	3·00
1956	1 Klass (80c.) Dove	3·25	3·00

844 Moon, Celestial Phenomena and Lake

2009. Europa. Astronomy. Multicoloured.

1957	80c. Type **844**	3·50	3·25
1958	80c. Celestial phenomena, lake, Saturn and planets	3·50	3·25

Nos. 1957/8 were printed, *se-tenant*, in horizontal pairs within the sheet, each pair forming a composite design.

845 Dress (Anna and Tuomas Laiten)

2009. Fashion. Sheet 160×110 mm containing T **845** and similar multicoloured designs. Self-adhesive.
MS1959 1 Klass (80c.)×5, Type **845**; Handbag (Lumi (Sanna Kantola)) (29×34 mm); Dress (Jasmin Santanen); Red shoes (Minna Parikka) (29×25 mm); Grey shoes (Finsk by Julia Lundsten) (29×31 mm) 16·00 16·00

846 Moominmama

2009. Moomins (cartoon strip by Tove Jansson). Each lemon and black, colour of face value given. Self-adhesive.

1960	1 Klass (80c.) Type **846**	3·50	3·25
1961	1 Klass (80c.) Moominpappa (bright yellow-green)	3·50	3·25
1962	1 Klass (80c.) Little My (new blue)	3·50	3·25
1963	1 Klass (80c.) Snork Maiden (magenta)	3·50	3·25
1964	1 Klass (80c.) Moomintroll and Snufkins (bright yellow-green)	3·50	3·25
1965	1 Klass (80c.) Moominpappa trips (bright orange)	3·50	3·25

847 Towels, Bucket and Birch Twigs

2009. Sauna. Multicoloured. Self-adhesive.

1966	1 Klass (80c.) Type **843**	3·50	3·25
1967	1 Klass (80c.) Men in sauna	3·50	3·25
1968	1 Klass (80c.) Lake and sauna building	3·50	3·25
1969	1 Klass (80c.) Birch twigs (vert)	3·50	3·25
1970	1 Klass (80c.) Bowls (vert)	3·50	3·25

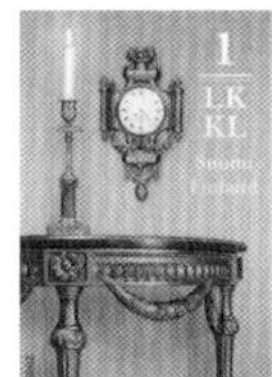

849 Desk, Porcelain Clock (Arabia) and Lamp

2009. Antiques. Gustavian. Self-adhesive.

1971	**849**	1 Klass (80c.) multicoloured	3·50	3·25

No. 1971 has a brief description of the stamp on the backing paper.

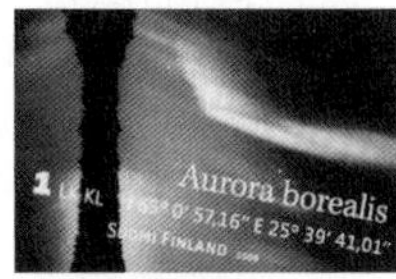

850 Aurora borealis

2009. Aurora borealis. Multicoloured. Self-adhesive.

1972	1 Klass (80c.) Type **850**	3·50	3·25
1973	1 Klass (80c.) Aurora borealis, blue, central burst	3·50	3·25
1974	1 Klass (80c.) Aurora borealis, green, conifers at left	3·50	3·25

851 *Leijonankitoja* (Helene Schjerfbeck)

2009. Art. Multicoloured. Self-adhesive.

1975	1 Klass (80c.) Type **851**	3·50	3·25
1976	1 Klass (80c.) Irises (*Kukkivat iirikset* (Waino Aaltonen))	3·50	3·25
1977	1 Klass (80c.) Peonies (*Juhannusruusuja* (Eero Jarnefelt))	3·50	3·25
1978	1 Klass (80c.) Arum (*Yksinainen kalla* (Ester Helenius))	3·50	3·25
1979	1 Klass (80c.) Amaryllis blooms in vase (*Amaryllisasetelma* (Birger Carlstedt))	3·50	3·25
1980	1 Klass (80c.) Carnation (*Neilikka-asetelma* (Tuomas von Boehm))	3·50	3·25

852 Wreath

2009. Christmas is Near (Finnish carol). Multicoloured. Self-adhesive.

1981	60c. Type **852**	2·75	2·50
1982	60c. Girl with apples	2·75	2·50

853 Amaryllis

2009. Christmas. Self-adhesive.

1983	**853**	1st Klass (80c.) multicoloured	3·50	3·25

854 Reindeer

2009. Personal Stamp. Winter Magic. Self-adhesive.

1984	**854**	1st Klass (80c.) multicoloured	3·50	3·25

855 *Antennaria dioica*

2010. Flora. Self-adhesive.

1985	**855**	1st Klass (80c.) multicoloured	3·50	3·25

856 Seated Flower Fairy

2010. St Valentine's Day. Fairies. Sheet 110×130 mm containing T **856** and similar vert designs. Multicoloured. Self-adhesive.
MS1986 1k.×5, Type **856**; Fairy carrying red heart; Fairy on swing; Fairy playing violin; Fairy with string of stars 18·00 18·00

Several techniques were used to print **MS**1986 giving an effect of varnish and glitter, the whole forming a composite design.

857 Eppu Normaali

2010. Rock and Pop Musicians. Multicoloured. Self-adhesive.

1987	1k. Type **857**	3·50	3·25
1988	1k. Yo	3·50	3·25
1989	1k. Maarit	3·50	3·25
1990	1k. Dingo	3·50	3·25
1991	1k. Popeda	3·50	3·25
1992	1k. Mamba	3·50	3·25

858 Rings (designed by Kirsti Doukas)

2010. My Easter. Self-adhesive.

1993	**858**	1k. multicoloured	3·50	3·25

859 Rabbit Twins

2010. Easter. Self-adhesive.

1994	**859**	1k. multicoloured	3·50	3·25

860 Tomato

2010. Funny Vegetables. Multicoloured. Self-adhesive.

1995	1k. Type **860**	3·50	3·25
1996	1k. Two onions	3·50	3·25
1997	1k. Pumpkin	3·50	3·25
1998	1k. Marrow	3·50	3·25
1999	1k. Aubergine	3·50	3·25
2000	1k. Carrot	3·50	3·25
2001	1k. Broccoli	3·50	3·25
2002	1k. Potato	3·50	3·25

861 Children with Fish

2010. Romance of the Countryside. Each brownish black and gold.

2003	1k. Type **861**	2·75	2·50
2004	1k. Barn, pony, girls and wild strawberries	2·75	2·50
2005	1k. Old style tractor	2·75	2·50
2006	1k. Hay stooks, milk churns and woman milking by hand	2·75	2·50
2007	1k. Musicians and dancers	2·75	2·50

862 Rita-Liisa Pohjalinen (jewelry, clothing and art designer)

2010. Famous Finnish Women. Multicoloured.

2008	1k. Type **862**	2·75	2·50
2009	1k. Elina Haavio-Mannila (sociologist)	2·75	2·50
2010	1k. Aira Samulin (dance instructor and entrepreneur)	2·75	2·50
2011	1k. Maria-Liisa Nevala (literary scholar and National Theatre director)	2·75	2·50
2012	1k. Laila Hirvisaari (writer)	2·75	2·50
2013	1k. Leena Palotie (geneticist)	2·75	2·50

863 Trawler

2010. Life at the Coast. Norden by the Sea. Multicoloured.
MS2014 105x70 mm. 1k. x 2, Type **863**; Yacht (vert) 5·25 5·25

The stamps and margins of **MS**2008 form a composite design.

Stamps of a similar theme were issued by Aland, Denmark, Greenland, Faröe Islands, Iceland, Norway and Sweden.

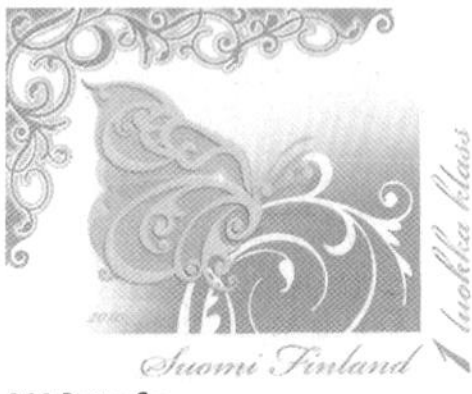

864 Butterfly

2010. Personal Stamp

2015	**864**	1k. multicoloured	3·00	3·00

865 Children, Book Cover as Door and Characters

2010. Europa. Multicoloured.

2016	80c. Type **865**	2·75	2·50
2017	80c. Boy and characters reading	2·75	2·50

866 Posthorn as Leaves

2010. Carbon Neutral Stamp

2018	**866**	1klass (80c.)+5c. apple green and black	3·00	2·75

The premium was for funding of Solar Power Plant.

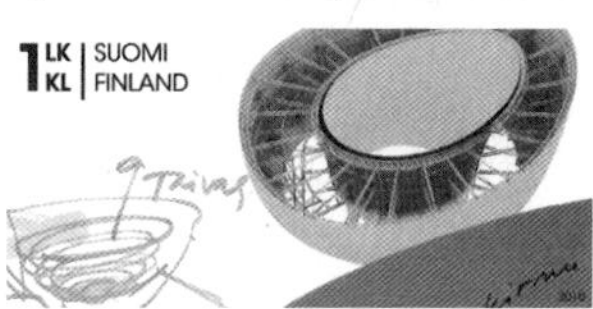

867 Kirnu, Aerial View

2010. Expo 2010, Shanghai. Kirnu (giant's kettle) (Finnish pavillion). Multicoloured.
MS2019 130x70 mm. 1k.x2, Type **867**; Kirnu, external view 5·50 5·50

868 Male Figure

2010. Greetings Stamps. Multicoloured, figure colour given.
MS2020 195x95 mm. 1k.x5, Type **868**; Female figure (magenta); Female (yellow); Male (new blue); Female (bright blue-green) 13·50 13·50

869 Hymy (Kain Tapper)

2010. Finnish Sculpture. Multicoloured.

2021	1k. Type **869**	2·75	2·50
2022	1k. *Hefaistos* (Laila Pullinen)	2·75	2·50
2023	1k. *Polkupyöräilija* (Pekko Aarnio)	2·75	2·50
2024	1k. *Konstructio* (Kari Huhtamo)	2·75	2·50
2025	1k. *Salvos* (Mauno Hartman) (55×21 mm)	2·75	2·50
2026	1k. *Joy* (Miina Äkkijrkka) (55×21 mm)	2·75	2·50

870 Iconic Designs of 1960's

2010. 1960's Pop Antiques

2027	**870**	1k. multicoloured	2·75	2·50

871 Tree and Moorland

2010. Torronsuo National Park

2028	**871**	1k. multicoloured	2·75	2·50

872 Freshwater Crayfish

2010. Autumn. Multicoloured.

MS2029 130x70 mm. 1k.x3, Type **872**; Mallard; Elk — 7·75 — 7·75

No. **MS**2029 was embossed with the stamp values and country name in Braille.

873 Santa Claus

2010. Finland–Japan Winter Stamps. Multicoloured.

MS2030 187x68 mm. 55c.x5, Type **873**; Poinsettias with bell and ribbon; Santa's sleigh flying over church (horiz); Heart-shaped wreath; Reindeer — 9·50 — 9·50

Stamps of the same design were issued by Japan.

874 Santa Claus

2010. Christmas. Multicoloured.

2031	55c. Type **874**	90	80
2032	55c. Santa's reindeer	90	80
2033	1 Klass (80c.) Santa's sleigh flying over Finnish landscape (horiz)	2·20	2·00

Stamps of a similar design were issued by Japan.

875 Bud

2011. Birch. Multicoloured.

2034	20c. Type **875**	1·00	90
2035	30c. Leaves and catkins	1·20	1·10

876 Bird perching

2011. Spring Stamps. Multicoloured.

2036	2k. Type **876**	2·50	2·40
2037	2k. Bird in flight, facing left	2·50	2·40
2038	2k. Flowers	2·50	2·40
2039	2k. Bird perching, singing, facing left	2·50	2·40
2040	2k. Bird in flight, facing right	2·50	2·40

877 Scene from The Red Line (Aulis Sallinen)

2011. Centenary of Finnish National Opera. Multicoloured.

MS2041 80x120 mm. 2k.x4, Type **877**; Couple running towards each other (*Der Rosenkavalier* (Richard Strauss)) (horiz); Couple embracing (*Der Rosenkavalier*) (horiz); Woman wearing red (*The Last Temptations* (Joonas Kokkonen)) — 10·00 — 10·00

878 Bird

879 Friendship (image scaled to 40% of original size)

2011. Friendship Day (St. Valetine's Day). T **878** forming overall design T **879**. Multicoloured.

MS2042 120x120 mm. 2k.x5, Type **878**; Magenta bird, blue background with yellow baubles; Green bird, orange background with green baubles; Large green bird, yellow background with purple baubles; Blue bird, magenta background with blue baubles — 12·50 — 12·50

880 Mailbox

2011. Mailboxes. Multicoloured.

2043	2k. Type **880**	2·50	2·40
2044	2k. Snow-covered, house-shaped mailbox	2·50	2·40
2045	2k. Boy collecting mail from green mailbox	2·50	2·40
2046	2k. Shelter and mailbox inscribed '012'	2·50	2·40
2047	2k. Top opening metal mailbox inscribed '4' and 'POSTI'	2·50	2·40

881 Siniristilippu ('Blue Cross Flag')

2011. National Flag

2048	**881**	2k. ultramarine	2·75	2·50

882 Dahlia

2011. Dahlias. Multicoloured.

2049	1K. Type **882**	2·20	2·00
2050	1K. Pale green and orange dahlia, shaded at lower right	2·25	2·00

883 Tulips

2011. Tulips

2051	**883**	2K. multicoloured	2·50	2·40

884 Kitchen Equipment

2011. Birth Centenary of Kaj Franck (designer). Multicoloured.

MS2052 2K.x5, Type **884**; Carafes (19x46 mm); Wine glasses, carafe and hand sprinkling grains (24x31 mm); Cup, saucer and pot with lid (22x31 mm); Eggs, mug and teapot spout (2331 mm) — 10·50 — 10·50

885 Maisa and Kaarina

2011. Centenary of National Council of Women of Finland. Fantastic Women, Maisa and Kaarina. Booklet Stamps. Multicoloured.

2053	2K. Type **885**	2·50	2·40
2054	2K. Knitting star-studed blanket	2·50	2·00
2055	2K. Holding racquets	2·50	2·40
2056	2K. Maisa taking photograph of Kaarina wearing star-shaped spectacles	2·50	2·40
2057	2K. Kaarina wearing one star, Maisa wearing two stars	2·50	2·40
2058	2K. With layered cake	2·50	2·40

886 Säätytalo (House of the Estates)

2011. Bicentenary of Government Buildings. Booklet Stamps. Multicoloured.

2059	2K. Type **886** (1890)	2·50	2·40
2060	2K. Finnish Embassy, New Delhi (1985)	2·50	2·40
2061	2K. Musiikkitalo (Helsinki Music Centre) (2011)	2·50	2·40
2062	2K. Valtioneuvoston linna (Senate Building), Helsinki (1828)	2·50	2·40
2063	2K. Helsinki-Malmin lentoasema (Helsinki-Malmi Airport) (1938)	2·50	2·40
2064	2K. (Metlan Joensuun tutkimuskeskus) (Finnish Forest Research Institute, Joensuu Research Unit) (2004)	2·50	2·40

887 Lake, Forest and Diagram of Arc

2011. Struve Geodetic Arc. UNESCO World Heritage Site. Multicoloured.

MS2065 2K.x2, Type **887**; Map of Finland — 4·50 — 4·50

888 Forest reflected in Lake

2011. Europa. Multicoloured.

2066	2K. Type **888**	2·30	2·20
2067	2K. Forest and lake in autumn	2·30	2·20

889 Balloons and Parcels

2011. Spring and Summer. The Happiness Tree. Multicoloured.

MS2068 2K.x5, Type **889**; Two birds; Butterfly and cake (34x29 mm); Bird house (34x29 mm); Couple — 10·50 — 10·50

890 Moomintroll carrying Milk

2011. *The Book about Moomin, Mymble and Little My* (by Tove Jansson). Multicoloured.

2069	2K. Type **890** (clod-shaped)	2·50	2·40
2070	2K. Mymble crying (25x29 mm, five unequal sides)	2·50	2·40
2071	2K. Little My and umbrella (27x27 mm, circular)	2·50	2·40
2072	2K. Moomintroll, Moominmama and empty milk churn (3526 mm, xoval)	2·50	2·40
2073	2K. Hemulen (27x39 mm, four unequal sides)	2·50	2·40
2074	2K. Hattifatteners (26x37 mm, straight sides and foot with arched top edge)	2·50	2·40

891 Stack of Paper

2011. 150th Birth Anniv of Juhani Aho (journalist and writer). Multicoloured.

MS2075 2K.x2, Type **891**; Juhani Aho on skis — 5·25 — 5·25

892 *Kili ja Possu* (Olavi Vikainen)

2011. Centenary of Finnish Comics. Multicoloured.

MS2076 2K.×6, Type **292**; *Unto Uneksija* (Joonas); *Herra Kerhonen* (Gösta Thilén); *Antti Puuhaara* (Aarne Nopsanen); *Janne Ankkanen* (Ola Fogelberg); *Olli Pirtea* (Hjalmar Löfving)	15·00	15·00

2011. Finnish Lion. Multicoloured.

2077	€2 As Type **689**, green	8·50	8·00
2078	€4 As Type **689**, purple	17·00	16·00

As Type **689**.

MILITARY FIELD POST

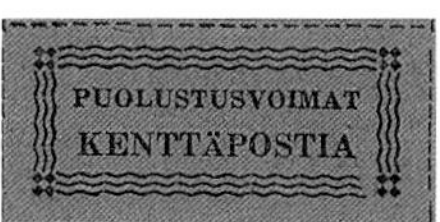

M76

1941. No value indicated. Imperf.

M352	**M76**	(-) black on red	30	60

M86

1943. No value indicated.

M392	**M86**	(-) green	30	35
M393	**M86**	(-) purple	30	40

1943. Optd **KENTTA-POSTI FALTPOST**.

M394	**31**	2m. orange	30	65
M395	**31**	3½m. blue	30	50

1944. As Type **M86**, but smaller (20×16 mm) and inscr "1944".

M396	(-) violet	25	25
M397	(-) green	25	30

M222

1963. No value indicated.

M688	**M222**	(-) violet	£120	£130

1983. No. M688 optd **1983**.

M1043	(-) violet	£150	£110

PARCEL POST STAMPS

P118

1949. Printed in black on coloured backgrounds. Roul.

P471	**P118**	1m. green	2·20	3·25
P472	**P118**	5m. red	16·00	16·00
P473	**P118**	20m. orange	29·00	27·00
P474	**P118**	50m. blue	14·00	12·50
P475	**P118**	100m. brown	14·00	12·50

P137

1952

P507	**P137**	5m. red	3·50	3·75
P508	**P137**	20m. orange	8·00	4·75
P509	**P137**	50m. blue	18·00	10·00
P510	**P137**	100m. brown	24·00	16·00

P216

1963. Figures of value in black.

P647	**P216**	5p. mauve	2·40	2·00
P648	**P216**	20p. orange	2·75	3·25
P649	**P216**	50p. blue	3·00	3·00
P650	**P216**	1m. brown	2·20	4·25

P403 "SISU" Bus

1981. Figures of values in black.

P1003	**P403**	50p. blue	90	3·75
P1004	**P403**	1m. brown	1·30	4·00
P1005	**P403**	5m. green	3·50	8·50
P1006	**P403**	10m. purple	4·50	17·00

Pt. 6

FRANCE

A republic in the W. of Europe.

1849. 100 centimes = 1 franc.
2002. 100 cents = 1 euro.

NOTE. Stamps in types of France up to the 1877 issue were also issued for the French Colonies and where the values and colours are the same they can only be distinguished by their shade or postmark or other minor differences which are outside the scope of this Catalogue. They are priced here by whichever is the lower of the quotations under France or French Colonies in the Stanley Gibbons Catalogue, Part 6 (France). Numbers with asterisks are French Colonies numbers.

1 Ceres

1849. Imperf.

157	**1**	5c. green	£300	£200
15*	**1**	10c. bistre	£325	£130
4	**1**	15c. green	£2750	£1100
6	**1**	20c. black	£550	65·00
17*	**1**	20c. blue	£450	£120
18*	**1**	25c. blue	£140	7·25
22*	**1**	30c. brown	£120	22·00
19*	**1**	40c. orange	£225	14·50
23*	**1**	80c. red	£450	£130
17	**1**	1f. orange	£26000	£3000
19	**1**	1f. red	£15000	£1000

For 10c. brown on pink and 15c. bistre, imperf, see French Colonies Nos. 16 and 20.

2 Louis Napoleon, President

1852. Imperf.

37a	**2**	10c. yellow	£45000	£750
39	**2**	25c. blue	£3750	44·00

3 Napoleon III, Emperor of the French

1853. Imperf.

42	**3**	1c. olive	£275	£110
45	**3**	5c. green	£1100	£110
50	**3**	10c. yellow	£500	13·00
51	**3**	20c. blue	£325	2·20
63	**3**	25c. blue	£3000	£325
64	**3**	40c. orange	£3000	20·00
70	**3**	80c. red	£2750	60·00
72	**3**	1f. red	£8500	£3500

1862. Perf.

87	1c. green	£225	50·00
89	5c. green	£300	13·00
91	10c. bistre	£2000	3·25
95	20c. blue	£475	2·20
97	40c. orange	£1800	6·50
98	80c. pink	£1800	44·00

4 Head with Laurel Wreath

5 Head with Laurel Wreath

1863. Perf.

102	**4**	1c. green	32·00	17·00
104	**4**	2c. brown	£100	33·00
109	**4**	4c. grey	£325	65·00
113a	**5**	10c. bistre	£325	7·75
115a	**5**	20c. blue	£275	2·20
116	**5**	30c. brown	£950	22·00
120	**5**	40c. orange	£1000	14·50
122	**5**	80c. pink	£1200	30·00

For imperforate stamps in these designs see French Colonies.

6

1869

131	**6**	5f. lilac	£7000	£1100

7 Ceres

1870. Imperf.

148	**7**	1c. green	£180	£190
152	**7**	2c. brown	£300	£275
156	**7**	4c. grey	£425	£350

For 1c. green on blue, 2c. brown on yellow and 5c. green as Type **7** and imperf, see French Colonies.

1870. Perf.

185	**7**	1c. green	95·00	22·00
187	**7**	2c. brown	£180	20·00
189	**7**	4c. grey	£425	55·00
192	**7**	5c. green	£300	13·00
136	**1**	10c. bistre	£800	95·00
194	**1**	10c. bistre on pink	£400	15·00
204	**1**	15c. bistre	£550	6·50
137	**1**	20c. blue	£350	8·75
198	**1**	25c. blue	£160	2·20
205	**1**	30c. brown	£850	8·75
140	**1**	40c. orange	£700	8·75
142	**1**	40c. red	£750	11·00
208	**1**	80c. red	£900	17·00

10 Peace and Commerce

1876

212	**10**	1c. green	£200	£100
245	**10**	1c. black on blue	10·50	1·10
225	**10**	2c. green	£170	22·00
248	**10**	2c. brown on buff	12·50	2·20
249	**10**	3c. brown on yellow	£325	55·00
251	**10**	3c. grey	9·50	2·20
214	**10**	4c. green	£225	75·00
252	**10**	4c. brown on grey	12·50	2·20
254	**10**	4c. purple on blue	18·00	4·50
282	**10**	5c. green	32·00	2·20
216	**10**	10c. green	£1300	22·00
284	**10**	10c. black on lilac	42·00	3·25
232	**10**	15c. lilac	£900	2·75
279	**10**	15c. blue	13·50	55
219	**10**	20c. brown on yellow	£850	19·00
260	**10**	20c. red on green	65·00	5·50
234	**10**	25c. blue	£650	1·10
262	**10**	25c. black on red	£1600	28·00
263	**10**	25c. bistre on yellow	£425	5·50
267	**10**	25c. black on pink	£130	1·10
237	**10**	30c. brown	£140	1·70
268	**10**	35c. brown on yellow	£800	39·00
269	**10**	40c. red on yellow	£170	2·20
273	**10**	50c. red	£325	3·50
223	**10**	75c. red	£1500	8·75
274	**10**	75c. brown on orange	£350	50·00
240	**10**	1f. green	£200	7·75
287	**10**	2f. brown on blue	£200	44·00
277	**10**	5f. mauve on lilac	£650	£100

For imperforate stamps in this design see French Colonies.

For 5f. red, perf, see No. 412.

11 "Blanc" type

12 "Mouchon" type

13 "Olivier Merson" type

1900

288	**11**	1c. grey	85	55
289	**11**	2c. purple	1·10	35
290	**11**	3c. red	1·10	70
292a	**11**	4c. brown	3·75	2·20
295	**11**	5c. green	£110	33·00
300	**12**	10c. red	35·00	2·20
301	**12**	15c. orange	9·50	55
297	**12**	20c. brown	65·00	11·00
302	**12**	25c. blue	£160	2·40
299	**12**	30c. mauve	95·00	6·50
303	**13**	40c. red and blue	17·00	90
304	**13**	45c. green and blue	37·00	2·75
305	**13**	50c. brown and lilac	£120	1·80
306	**13**	1f. red and green	33·00	90
369	**13**	1f. red and yellow	60·00	1·50
307	**13**	2f. lilac and buff	£1000	£100
308	**13**	5f. blue and buff	£110	5·50

For further values in these designs, see 1920 issues (following No. 379).

14 "Mouchon" type redrawn

1902

309	**14**	10c. red	55·00	1·40
310	**14**	15c. red	12·50	55
311	**14**	20c. brown	£100	18·00
312	**14**	25c. blue	£110	2·50
313	**14**	30c. mauve	£300	19·00

15 Sower

1903

314	**15**	10c. red	15·00	35
316c	**15**	15c. green	5·25	35
317	**15**	20c. purple	£130	2·20
318	**15**	25c. blue	£150	1·70
319	**15**	30c. lilac	£350	7·25

16 Ground below Feet

1906

325	**16**	10c. red	3·25	2·20

18 No Ground

1906

331	**18**	5c. green	2·10	15
333	**18**	10c. red	2·10	15

337	18	20c. brown	6·25	70
339	18	25c. blue	3·25	15
343	18	30c. orange	21·00	1·70
345	18	35c. violet	11·50	1·10

See also Nos. 497 etc. and 454/a.

1914. Red Cross Fund. Surch with red cross and 5c.

351		10c.+5c. red	6·25	6·50

20

1914. Red Cross Fund.

352	20	10c.+5c. red	42·00	4·50

21 War Widow

23 Woman replaces Man

26 Spirit of War

1917. War Orphans' Fund.

370	21	2c.+3c. red	5·25	5·50
371	-	5c.+5c. green	26·00	13·00
372	23	15c.+10c. green	37·00	31·00
373	23	25c.+15c. blue	95·00	70·00
374	-	35c.+25c. violet and grey	£180	£150
375	-	50c.+50c. brown	£300	£225
376	26	1f.+1f. red	£500	£475
377	26	5f.+5f. blue and black	£2000	£2000

DESIGNS—As Type **21**: 5c. Orphans. As Type **26**: 35c. Front line trench; 50c. Lion of Belfort.
See also Nos. 450/3.

27 Sinking of *Charles Roux* Hospital Ship, and Bombed Hospital

1918. Red Cross Fund.

378	27	15c.+5c. red & green	£150	75·00

1919. Surch ½ centime.

379	11	½c. on 1c. grey	30	35

1920

497	18	1c. bistre	15	35
497a	18	1c. brown	15	35
498	18	2c. green	15	35
499	18	3c. red	15	35
380	18	5c. orange	1·50	35
500	18	5c. mauve	15	35
413	11	7½c. mauve*	1·10	1·10
381	18	10c. green	70	55
413a	11	10c. lilac	4·75	55
501	18	10c. blue	2·00	35
414	18	15c. brown	55	15
415	18	20c. mauve	30	20
415b	18	25c. brown	55	20
382a	18	30c. mauve	1·40	90
416	18	30c. blue	4·75	55
503	18	30c. red	55	35
505	18	35c. green	85	70
417	18	40c. green	1·60	55
418	18	40c. red	3·25	55
418a	18	40c. violet	2·40	1·10
418b	18	40c. blue	1·60	55
419	15	45c. violet	7·50	2·40
420	15	50c. green	8·00	1·40
421	15	50c. red	1·20	35
592	15	50c. blue	1·90	55
384	13	60c. violet and blue	1·10	55
385	15	60c. violet	7·25	2·00
385a	15	65c. red	3·25	1·70
422	15	65c. green	8·50	2·50
423	15	75c. mauve	6·50	70
424	15	80c. red	32·00	10·00
386	15	85c. red	16·00	2·75
425	15	1f. blue	7·50	90
426	18	1f.05 red	10·50	5·75
427	18	1f.10 mauve	13·00	2·75
428	18	1f.40 mauve	22·00	25·00
387	13	2f. orange and green	60·00	55
428a	18	2f. green	17·00	1·80
429	13	3f. violet and blue	32·00	8·75
430	13	3f. mauve and red	65·00	2·50
431	13	10f. green and red	£150	19·00
432	13	20f. mauve and green	£250	44·00

***PRECANCEL.** No. 413 was issued only pre-cancelled. The "unused" price is for stamp with full gum and the used price for stamp without gum.

1922. War Orphans' Fund. Nos. 370/7 surch with new value, cross and bars.

388	21	1c. on 2c.+3c. red	55	55
389	-	2½c. on 5c.+5c. green	85	85
390	23	5c. on 15c.+10c. green	1·50	1·50
391	23	5c. on 25c.+15c. blue	3·00	3·00
392	-	5c. on 35c.+25c. violet and grey	17·00	17·00
393	-	10c. on 50c.+50c. brn	28·00	28·00
394	26	25c. on 1f.+1f. red	38·00	38·00
395	26	1f. on 5f.+5f. blue and black	£180	£180

30 Pasteur

1923

396	30	10c. green	85	35
396a	30	15c. green	2·00	35
396b	30	20c. green	3·50	1·10
397	30	30c. red	1·10	2·00
397a	30	30c. green	85	55
398	30	45c. red	2·75	2·50
399	30	50c. blue	5·50	55
400	30	75c. blue	4·75	1·40
400a	30	90c. red	13·50	4·50
400b	30	1f. blue	26·00	55
400c	30	1f.25 blue	33·00	11·00
400d	30	1f.50 blue	6·50	35

1923. Optd CONGRES PHILATELIQUE DE BORDEAUX 1923.

400e	13	1f. red and green	£600	£700

31 Stadium and Arc de Triomphe

1924. Olympic Games.

401	31	10c. green & light green	2·75	1·20
402	-	25c. deep red and red	3·75	1·00
403	-	30c. red and black	10·50	14·50
404	-	50c. ultramarine & blue	31·00	5·50

DESIGNS—HORIZ: 25c. Notre Dame and Pont Neuf. VERT: 30c. Milan de Crotone (statue); 50c. The victor.

35 Ronsard

1924. 400th Birth Anniv of Ronsard.

405	35	75c. blue	2·40	2·00

36

1924. International Exhibition of Modern Decorative Arts. Dated "1925".

406	36	10c. yellow and green	85	1·10
407	-	15c. green & deep green	85	1·20
408	-	25c. red and purple	85	55
409	-	25c. mauve and blue	1·80	1·10
410	-	75c. blue and grey	4·00	3·00
411	36	75c. blue and deep blue	21·00	8·50

DESIGNS—HORIZ: 25c. (No. 408); 75c. (No. 410) Potter and vase; 25c. (No. 409), Chateau and steps. VERT: 15c. Stylized vase.

1925. Paris Int Philatelic Exhibition.

412	10	5f. red	£170	£170
MS412a		140×220 mm. No. 412 in block of four	£1600	£1600

1926. Surch with new value and bars.

433	18	25c. on 30c. blue	30	55
434	18	25c. on 35c. violet	30	55
436	15	50c. on 60c. violet	1·50	1·40
437	15	50c. on 65c. red	85	65
438	30	50c. on 75c. blue	4·00	2·20
439	15	50c. on 80c. red	1·50	1·40
440	15	50c. on 85c. red	2·40	1·20
441	18	50c. on 1f.05 red	1·50	90
442	30	50c. on 1f.25 blue	3·25	2·75
443	15	55c. on 60c. violet*	£180	75·00
444	18	90c. on 1f.05 red	3·00	3·50
445	18	1f.10 on 1f.40 red	1·20	1·10

***PRECANCEL.** No. 443 was issued only precancelled. The "unused" price is for stamp with full gum and the used price for stamp without gum.

1926. War Orphans' Fund.

450	21	2c.+1c. purple	2·10	1·70
451	-	50c.+10c. brn (as No. 375)	26·00	17·00
452	26	1f.+25c. red	65·00	55·00
453	26	5f.+1f. blue and black	£130	£120

1927. Strasbourg Philatelic Exhibition.

454	18	5f. blue	£325	£325
454a	18	10f. red	£325	£325
MS454b		110×140 mm. 5f.+10f. and label inscr "STRASBOURG 1927"	£1400	£1400

1927. Air. 1st International Display of Aviation and Navigation, Marseilles. Optd with Bleriot XI airplane and Poste Aerienne.

455	13	2f. red and green	£275	£275
456	13	5f. blue and yellow	£275	£275

44 Marcelin Berthelot

1927. Birth Centenary of Berthelot.

457	44	90c. red	2·40	70

45 Lafayette, Washington, "Paris" (liner) and Lindbergh's Ryan NYP "Spirit of St. Louis"

1927. Visit of American Legion.

458	45	90c. red	2·00	1·50
459	45	1f.50 blue	4·75	2·50

1927. Sinking Fund. Surch Caisse d'Amortissement or C A and premium.

460	18	40c.+10c. blue	6·25	6·50
461	15	50c.+25c. green	9·50	10·00
462	30	1f.50+50c. orange	19·00	17·00

See also Nos. 466/8, 476/8, 485/7 and 494/6.

48

1928. Sinking Fund.

463	48	1f.50+8f.50 blue	£190	£200

1928. Air ("Ile de France"). Surch 10 FR. and bars.

464	44	10f. on 90c. red	£3250	£3250
465	30	10f. on 1f.50 blue	£14000	£14000

1928. Sinking Fund. Surch as Nos. 460/2.

466	18	40c.+10c. violet	12·50	11·00
467	15	50c.+25c. red	37·00	33·00
468	30	1f.50+50c. mauve	65·00	50·00

50 Joan of Arc

1929. 500th Anniv of Relief of Orleans.

469	50	50c. blue	2·40	35

1929. Optd EXPOSITION LE HAVRE 1929 PHILATELIQUE.

470	13	2f. red and green	£900	£900

52 Reims Cathedral

53 Mont St. Michel

1929. Views.

470a	-	90c. mauve	4·25	1·20
471	-	2f. red	44·00	1·10
472	52	3f. blue	80·00	3·25
473a	53	5f. brown	26·00	90
474b	-	10f. blue	£130	20·00
475b	-	20f. brown	£350	46·00

DESIGNS—HORIZ: 90c. Le Puy-en-Velay; 2f. Arc de Triomphe; 10f. Port de la Rochelle; 20f. Pont du Gard.

1929. Sinking Fund. Surch as Nos. 460/2.

476	18	40c.+10c. green	21·00	19·00
477	15	50c.+25c. mauve	37·00	33·00
478	30	1f.50+50c. brown	70·00	70·00

54 Bay of Algiers

1930. Centenary of French Conquest of Algeria.

479	54	50c. red and blue	3·25	55

55 *Le Sourire de Reims*

1930. Sinking Fund.

480	55	1f.50+3f.50 purple	£110	£110

1930. I.L.O. Session, Paris. Optd CONGRES DU B.I.T. 1930.

481	15	50c. red	3·00	2·50
482	30	1f.50 blue	22·00	17·00

57 Farman F.190 over Notre Dame de la Garde, Marseilles

1930. Air.

483	57	1f.50 red	27·00	5·00
484	57	1f.50 blue	27·00	2·50

1930. Sinking Fund. Surch as Nos. 460/2.

485	18	40c.+10c. red	26·00	26·00
486	15	50c.+25c. brown	47·00	44·00
487	18	1f.50+50c. violet	85·00	85·00

58 Woman of the Fachi tribe

59 *French Colonies*

1930. International Colonial Exhibition.

488	58	15c. black	1·50	55
489	58	40c. brown	2·75	55
490	58	50c. red	1·10	15
491	58	1f.50 blue	11·50	70
492	59	1f.50 blue	55·00	2·40

60 *French Provinces*

1931. Sinking Fund.

493	**60**	1f.50+3f.50 green	£180	£190

1931. Sinking Fund. Surch as Nos. 460/2.

494	**18**	40c.+10c. green	65·00	44·00
495	**15**	50c.+25c. violet	£150	£120
496	**18**	1f.50+50c. red	£130	£120

61 Peace

1932

502	**61**	30c. green	1·10	70
506	**61**	40c. mauve	30	35
507	**61**	45c. brown	2·10	1·40
508	**61**	50c. red	20	15
508d	**61**	55c. violet	85	35
508e	**61**	60c. bistre	30	55
509	**61**	65c. purple	55	45
509a	**61**	65c. blue	30	15
510	**61**	75c. green	20	35
510a	**61**	80c. orange	20	35
511	**61**	90c. red	44·00	2·50
511a	**61**	90c. green	20	15
511b	**61**	90c. blue	1·10	15
512	**61**	1f. orange	3·75	35
512a	**61**	1f. pink	4·75	55
513	**61**	1f.25 olive	90·00	6·00
513a	**61**	1f.25 red	2·75	2·20
513b	**61**	1f.40 mauve	7·50	6·50
514	**61**	1f.50 blue	30	20
515	**61**	1f.75 mauve	5·25	55

1933. Surch ½ centime.

515a	**18**	½c. on 1c. bistre	30	55
515b	**18**	½c. on 1c. brown	1·10	1·70

62 Briand

1933. Portraits.

516	**62**	30c. green	32·00	10·00
517	-	75c. mauve (Doumer)	32·00	1·70
518	-	1f.25 red (Victor Hugo)	7·50	2·50

65 Dove of Peace

1934

519	**65**	1f.50 blue	65·00	19·00

66 J. M. Jacquard

1934. Death Centenary of Jacquard.

520	**66**	40c. blue	4·25	1·10

67 Jacques Cartier, *Grande Hermine* and *Petite Hermine*

1934. 4th Cent of Cartier's Discovery of Canada.

521	**67**	75c. mauve	32·00	2·50
522	**67**	1f.50 blue	55·00	5·00

68 Bleriot XI

1934. Air. 25th Anniv of Channel Flight.

523	**68**	2f.25 violet	26·00	7·75

1934. Surch in figures and bars.

524	**61**	50c. on 1f.25 olive	4·75	70
524a	**61**	80c. on 1f. orange	55	70

69 Breton River Scene

1935

525	**69**	2f. green	42·00	1·10

70 *Normandie*

1935. Maiden Trip of Liner "Normandie".

526	**70**	1f.50 blue	16·00	2·50

71 St. Trophime, Arles

1935

527	**71**	3f.50 brown	34·00	5·00

72 B. Delessert

1935. Opening of Int Savings Bank Congress.

528	**72**	75c. green	23·00	1·70

73 Victor Hugo

1935. 50th Death Anniv of Victor Hugo.

529	**73**	1f.25 purple	5·75	2·50

74 Cardinal Richelieu

1935. Tercentenary of French Academy by Richelieu.

530	**74**	1f.50 red	26·00	1·70

75 Jacques Callot

1935. Death Tercentenary of Callot (engraver).

531	**75**	75c. red	12·50	70

77 Symbolic of Art

1935. Unemployed Intellectuals' Relief Fund. Inscr "POUR L'ART ET LA PENSEE".

532	-	50c.+10c. blue	3·25	3·25
533	**77**	50c.+2f. red	70·00	60·00

DESIGN—HORIZ: No. 532, Help for intellectuals (inscr "POUR LES CHOMEURS INTELLECTUELS").

78 Caudron C-635 Simoun over Paris

1936. Air.

534	**78**	85c. green	3·25	2·75
535	**78**	1f.50 blue	13·50	6·50
536	**78**	2f.25 violet	25·00	8·25
537	**78**	2f.50 red	32·00	10·00
538	**78**	3f. blue	26·00	2·50
539	**78**	3f.50 brown	80·00	30·00
540	**78**	50f. green	£1200	£450

79 Caudron C-635 Simoun over Paris

1936. Air.

541	**79**	50f. blue and pink	£950	£450

80 Statue of Liberty

1936. Nansen (Refugee) Fund.

541a	**80**	50c.+25c. blue	4·75	5·00
542	**80**	75c.+50c. violet	13·00	12·00

81 Andre-Marie Ampere

1936. Death Centenary of Ampere.

543	**81**	75c. brown	24·00	2·50

82 Daudet's Mill, Fontvieille

1936

544	**82**	2f. blue	5·25	55

83 Children of the Unemployed

1936. Children of the Unemployed Fund.

545	**83**	50c.+10c. red	6·50	5·50

84 Pilatre de Rozier and Montgoldier Balloon

1936. 150th Death Anniv of Pilatre de Rozier.

546	**84**	75c. blue	24·00	3·25

85 Rouget de Lisle

1936. Death Centenary of Rouget de Lisle, Composer of the "Marseillaise".

547	**85**	20c. green	4·50	2·50
548	-	40c. brown	7·25	4·25

DESIGN—HORIZ: 40c. Female figure inscr "LA MARSEILLAISE".

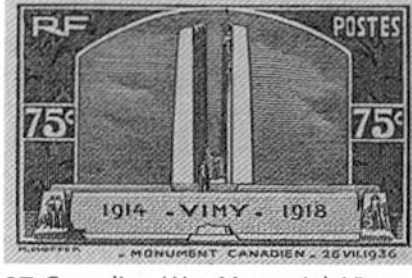

87 Canadian War Memorial, Vimy

1936. Unveiling of Canadian War Memorial, Vimy Ridge.

549	**87**	75c. red	12·00	2·50
550	**87**	1f.50 blue	21·00	11·00

88 Jean Jaures as an Orator

1936. Jaures Commemoration.

551	**88**	40c. brown	4·75	1·80
552	-	1f.50 blue	18·00	4·50

The 1f.50 has a head and shoulders portrait of Jaures.

91 Latecoere 300 Flying Boat

1936. 100th Flight between France and S. America.

553	**91**	1f.50 blue	24·00	6·00
554	**91**	10f. green	£450	£170

DESIGN—VERT: 1f.50, Airplane and old-time sailing ship.

92 Herald **93** "World Exhibition"

1936. Paris International Exhibition.

555	**92**	20c. mauve	60	70
556	**92**	30c. green	3·50	2·00
557	**92**	40c. blue	1·90	90
558	**92**	50c. orange	1·70	45
559	**93**	90c. red	16·00	9·50
560	**93**	1f.50 blue	44·00	5·00

94 "Vision of Peace"

1936. Universal Peace Propaganda.

561	**94**	1f.50 blue	20·00	5·00

1936. Unemployed Intellectuals' Fund. No. 533 surch + 20c.

562	**77**	20c. on 50c.+2f. red	4·75	4·75

96 Jacques Callot

1936. Unemployed Intellectuals' Fund. Inscr as in T 96.

563	**96**	20c.+10c. lake	3·50	3·25
564	-	40c.+10c. green	3·50	4·50

565	-	50c.+10c. red	6·00	4·50
566	-	1f.50+50c. blue	27·00	24·00

DESIGNS: 40c. Hector Berlioz; 50c. Victor Hugo; 1f.50, Louis Pasteur.

See also Nos. 603/5 and 607.

97 Ski Jumper

1937. Chamonix-Mont Blanc Skiing Week.

567	**97**	1f.50 blue	9·00	2·00

98 Pierre Corneille (author)

1937. 300th Anniv of First Performance of "Le Cid" (play).

568	**98**	75c. red	2·75	1·80

99 France and Minerva

1937. Paris International Exhibition.

569	**99**	1f.50 blue	3·25	1·40

100 Mermoz

101 Jean Mermoz Memorial

1937. Mermoz Commemoration.

570	**100**	30c. green	60	90
571	**101**	3f. violet	8·25	4·50

102 Paris–Orleans Midi Electric Train

1937. 13th International Railway Congress, Paris.

572	**102**	30c. green	1·20	1·80
573	-	1f.50 blue	10·00	9·25

DESIGN: 1f.50, Nord streamlined steam locomotive.

103 Rene Descartes

1937. 300th Anniv of Publication of "Discours". (a) Wrongly inscr "DISCOURS SUR LA METHODE".

574	**103**	90c. red	2·75	1·80

(b) Corrected to "DISCOURS DE LA METHODE".

575	90c. red	8·25	2·20

104 Anatole France

1937. Unemployed Intellectuals' Relief Fund.

576	**104**	30c.+10c. green	2·75	3·25
577	-	90c.+10c. red	8·25	7·75

DESIGN—HORIZ: 90c. Auguste Rodin.

See also Nos. 602 and 606.

107 Ramblers

1937. Postal Workers' Sports Fund.

578		20c.+10c. brown	2·20	2·50
579		40c.+10c. lake	2·20	2·50
580	**107**	50c.+10c. purple	2·20	2·50

DESIGNS—HORIZ: 20c. Tug-of-War; 40c. Runners and discus thrower.

1937. Inter Philatelic Ex, Paris. As T **1**, printed in miniature sheets of four (578×858ins.) inscr "PEXIP PARIS 1937" between stamps.

MS581 5c. brown and blue; 15c. carmine and red; 30c. red and blue; 50c. brown and red	£550	£450

108 Pierre Loti and Constantinople

1937. Pierre Loti Memorial Fund.

585	**108**	50c.+20c. red	5·50	4·50

109 *Victory of Samothrace*

1937. National Museums.

586	**109**	30c. green	£100	55·00
587	**109**	55c. red	£100	55·00

110 "France" and Child

1937. Public Health Fund.

588	**110**	65c.+25c. purple	4·50	3·25
588a	**110**	90c.+30c. blue	3·00	3·25

111 France congratulating U.S.A.

1937. 150th Anniv of U.S. Constitution.

589	**111**	1f.75 blue	3·50	2·50

112 Iseran Pass

1937. Opening of Col de l'Iseran Road.

590	**112**	90c. green	2·75	35

113 Ceres

1938

591	**113**	1f.75 blue	95	65
591a	**113**	2f. red	35	20
591b	**113**	2f.25 blue	12·00	1·10
591c	**113**	2f.50 green	2·00	90
591d	**113**	2f.50 blue	80	90
591e	**113**	3f. mauve	80	55

1938. Shipwrecked Mariners Society. As T **104** but portrait of Jean Charcot.

593	65c.+35c. green	1·90	3·25
593a	90c.+35c. purple	16·00	14·50

113a Gambetta

1938. Birth Centenary of Leon Gambetta (politician).

594	**113a**	55c. lilac	60	70

113b Champagne Girl

1938

594a	-	90c. red on blue	1·20	1·40
595	**113b**	1f.75 blue	5·50	4·50
596	-	2f. brown	1·20	75
597	-	2f.15 purple	6·00	1·10
598	-	3f. red	18·00	5·00
599	-	5f. blue	95	55
600	-	10f. purple on blue	2·40	2·20
601	-	20f. green	60·00	23·00

DESIGNS—VERT: 2f.15, Coal miners; 10f. Vincennes. HORIZ: 90c. Chateau de Pau; 2f. Arc de Triomphe at Orange; 3f. Papal Palace, Avignon; 5f. Carcassonne; 20f. St. Malo.

1938. Unemployed Intellectuals' Relief Fund. As Nos. 563/6 and 576/7, inscr "POUR LES CHOMEURS INTELLECTUELS".

602	30c.+10c. red	2·40	2·40
603	35c.+10c. green	3·50	3·50
604	55c.+10c. violet	8·25	5·00
605	65c.+10c. blue	8·25	5·00
606	1f.+10c. red	7·25	6·50
607	1f.75+25c. blue	24·00	22·00

PORTRAITS—As Type **96**: 35c. Callot; 55c. Berlioz; 65c. Victor Hugo; 1f.75, Louis Pasteur. As No. 577: 1f. Auguste Rodin. As Type **104**: 30c. Anatole France.

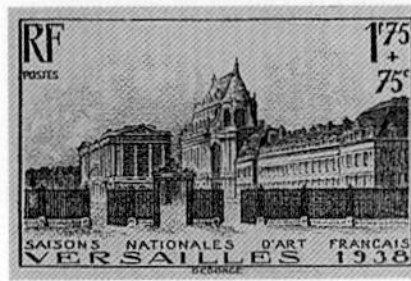

114 Palais de Versailles

1938. French National Music Festivals.

608	**114**	1f.75+75c. blue	27·00	24·00

115 Soldier in Trench

1938. Infantry Monument Fund.

609	**115**	55c.+70c. purple	6·50	6·00
610	**115**	65c.+1f.10 blue	6·50	6·00

116 Medical Corps Monument at Lyons

1938. Military Medical Corps' Monument Fund.

611	**116**	55c.+45c. red	16·00	14·50

117 Saving a Goal

1938. World Football Cup.

612	**117**	1f.75 blue	18·00	17·00

117a Clement Ader and 'Avion III'

1938. Clement Ader (air pioneer).

612a	**117a**	50f. blue	£130	90·00

118 Jean de La Fontaine

1938. La Fontaine (writer of fables).

613	**118**	55c. green	80	1·40

1938. Reims Cathedral Restoration Fund. As T 52, but inscr "REIMS 10.VII.1938".

614	65c.+35c. blue	12·00	14·00

119 Houses of Parliament, "Friendship" and Arc de Triomphe

1938. Visit of King George VI and Queen Elizabeth to France.

615	**119**	1f.75 blue	80	1·40

120 "France" welcoming Frenchmen repatriated from Spain

1938. French Refugees' Fund.

616	**120**	65c.+60c. red	5·25	6·50

121 Pierre and Marie Curie

1938. International Anti-cancer Fund. 40th Anniv of Discovery of Radium.

617	**121**	1f.75+50c. blue	12·00	14·00

122 Arc de Triomphe and Allied Soldiers

1938. 20th Anniv of 1918 Armistice.

618	**122**	65c.+35c. red	4·50	5·00

123 Mercury

1938. Inscr "REPUBLIQUE FRANCAISE".

618a	**123**	1c. brown	25	20
619	**123**	2c. green	25	20
620	**123**	5c. red	20	15
621	**123**	10c. blue	20	15
622	**123**	15c. orange	20	35
622a	**123**	15c. brown	90	90
623	**123**	20c. mauve	20	15
624	**123**	25c. green	20	15
625	**123**	30c. red	20	15
626	**123**	40c. violet	20	15
627	**123**	45c. green	60	90
627b	**123**	50c. green	60	70
627c	**123**	50c. blue	25	20
628	**123**	60c. orange	20	35
629	**123**	70c. mauve	25	35
629a	**123**	75c. brown	5·50	3·00

For similar stamps inscr "POSTES FRANCAISES", see Nos. 750/3.

124 Nurse and Patient

1938. Students' Fund.

630	**124**	65c.+60c. blue	11·00	10·00

125 Blind Radio Listener

1938. "Radio for the Blind" Fund.

631	**125**	90c.+25c. purple	10·50	11·00

126 Monument to Civilian War Victims, Lille

1939. War Victims' Monument Fund.

632	**126**	90c.+35c. brown	12·00	12·00

127 Paul Cezanne

1939. Birth Cent of Paul Cezanne (painter).

633	**127**	2f.25 blue	4·75	4·50

128 Red Cross Nurse

1939. 75th Anniv of Red Cross Society. Cross in red.

634	**128**	90c.+35c. blue & black	9·50	9·25

129 Military Engineer

1939. To the Glory of French Military Engineers.

635	**129**	70c.+50c. red	8·25	8·50

130 Ministry of Posts, Telegraphs and Telephones

1939. P.T.T. Orphans' Fund.

636	**130**	90c.+35c. blue	27·00	25·00

131 "Dunkerque" Class Battleship

1939. Laying down Keel of Battleship "Clemenceau".

637	**131**	90c. blue	80	90

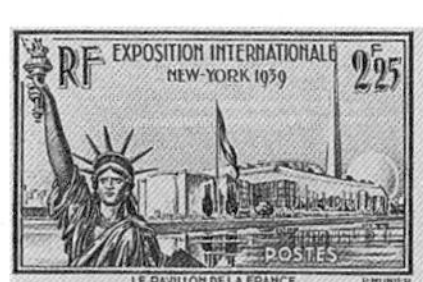

132 French Pavilion, New York Exhibition

1939. New York World's Fair.

638	**132**	2f.25 blue	10·50	7·75
638a	**132**	2f.50 blue	13·00	12·00

133 Mother and Child

1939. Children of the Unemployed Fund.

639	**133**	90c.+35c. red	3·25	3·00

134 Niepce and Daguerre

1939. Photographic Centenary.

640	**134**	2f.25 blue	9·50	7·75

135 Eiffel Tower

1939. 50th Anniv of Erection of Eiffel Tower.

641	**135**	90c.+50c. purple	11·00	10·00

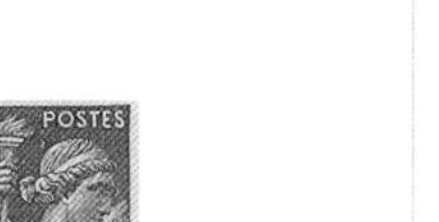

136 Iris

1939

642	**136**	80c. brown	25	35
643	**136**	1f. green	95	35
643a	**136**	1f. red	35	35
643b	**136**	1f.30 blue	20	35
643c	**136**	1f.50 orange	20	35

See also Nos. 861/8.

137 Marly Water Works

1939. International Water Exhibition, Liege.

644	**137**	2f.25 blue	16·00	6·00

138 Balzac

1939. Unemployed Intellectuals' Fund.

645	-	40c.+10c. red	1·50	1·00
646	-	70c.+10c. purple	5·50	3·00
647	**138**	90c.+10c. mauve	4·75	3·25
648	-	2f.25+25c. blue	20·00	14·50

PORTRAITS—VERT: 40c. Puvis de Chavannes. HORIZ: 70c. Claude Debussy; 2f.25, Claude Bernard.

See also Nos 667b/d.

139 St. Gregory of Tours

1939. 1400th Birth Anniv of St. Gregory of Tours.

649	**139**	90c. red	60	90

140 Mother and Children

1939. Birth-rate Development Fund.

650	-	70c.+80c. vio, bl & grn	4·50	5·00
651	**140**	90c.+60c. brn, pur & sep	6·25	6·50

DESIGN: 70c. Mother and children admiring infant in cot.

141 Oath of the Tennis Court

1939. 150th Anniv of French Revolution.

652	**141**	90c. green	2·50	2·40

142 Strasbourg Cathedral

1939. 5th Centenary of Completion of Strasbourg Cathedral Spire.

653	**142**	70c. red	1·20	1·70

143 Porte Chaussee, Verdun

1939. 23rd Anniv of Battle of Verdun.

654	**143**	90c. grey	80	1·20

144 "The Letter"

1939. Postal Museum Fund.

655	**144**	40c.+60c. brown	3·25	4·25

145 Statue to Sailors lost at Sea

1939. Boulogne Monument Fund.

656	**145**	70c.+30c. plum	17·00	15·00

146 Languedoc

1939

657	**146**	70c. black on blue	60	70

147 Lyons

1939

658	**147**	90c. purple	80	1·10

148 French Soldier and Strasbourg Cathedral

1940. Soldiers' Comforts Fund.

659	**148**	40c.+60c. purple	2·75	3·25
660	-	1f.+50c. blue	2·75	3·25

DESIGN: 1f. Veteran French colonial soldier and African village.

149 French Colonial Empire

1940. Overseas Propaganda Fund.
661 **149** 1f.+25c. red 2·40 3·00
See also Nos. 708 and 953.

150 Marshal Joffre

1940. War Charities. Inscr as in T **150**.
662 **150** 80c.+45c. brown 6·00 7·75
663 - 1f.+50c. violet 10·00 7·75
664 - 1f.50+50c. red 5·25 5·00
665 - 2f.50+50c. blue 10·50 14·00
DESIGNS—HORIZ: 1f.50, General Gallieni; 2f.50, Ploughing. VERT: 1f. Marshal Foch.

151 Nurse and Wounded Soldier

1940. Red Cross. Cross in red.
666 80c.+1f. green 6·50 7·75
667 **151** 1f.+2f. brown 8·25 7·75
DESIGN: 80c. Doctor, nurse, soldier and family.

152 G. Guynemer (pilot)

1940
667a **152** 50f. blue 12·00 11·00

1940. Unemployed Intellectuals' Fund. As T **138**. Inscr "POUR LES CHOMEURS INTELLECTUELS".
667b 80c.+10c. brown 6·50 10·00
667c 1f.+10c. purple 6·50 10·00
667d 2f.50+25c. blue 6·50 10·00
PORTRAITS: 80c. Debussy; 1f. Balzac.; 2f.50, Bernard.

153 Nurse, wounded Soldier and Family

1940. War Victim's Fund.
667e **153** 1f.+2f. violet 1·30 1·40

154 Harvesting

1940. National Relief Fund. Inscr "SECOURS NATIONAL".
668 **154** 80c.+2f. sepia 2·20 2·75
669 - 1f.+2f. brown 2·20 2·75
670 - 1f.50+2f. violet 2·40 2·75
671 - 2f.50+2f. green 3·25 2·75
DESIGNS: 1f. Sowing; 1f.50, Gathering grapes; 2f.50, Cattle.

1940. Surch with new value and with bars on all except T 113.
672 **18** 30c. on 35c. green 20 40
673 **61** 50c. on 55c. violet 20 40
674 **61** 50c. on 65c. blue 20 15
675 **61** 50c. on 75c. green 20 40
676 **123** 50c. on 75c. brown 20 40
677 **61** 50c. on 80c. orange 20 40
678 **61** 50c. on 90c. blue 20 15
679 **61** 1f. on 1f.25 red 20 40
680 **61** 1f. on 1f.40 mauve 20 55
681 **61** 1f. on 1f.50 blue 1·20 1·50
682 **113** 1f. on 1f.75 blue 25 40
683 - 1f. on 2f.15 purple (No. 597) 40 55
684 **113** 1f. on 2f.25 blue 25 40
685 **113** 1f. on 2f.50 green 1·20 1·90
686 - 2f.50 on 5f. blue (No. 599) 40 55
687 - 5f. on 10f. purple on blue (No. 600) 1·70 2·50
688 - 10f. on 20f. green (No. 601) 1·30 2·20
689 **117a** 20f. on 50f. blue 48·00 50·00

155 Marshal Petain

1940
690 **155** 40c. brown 35 55
691 **155** 80c. green 35 70
692 **155** 1f. red 25 35
693 **155** 2f.50 blue 1·30 1·50
See also Nos. 774/5.

156 Prisoners of War

1941. Prisoners of War Fund.
696 **156** 80c.+5f. green 1·30 2·10
697 - 1f.+5f. red 1·50 2·20
DESIGN: 1f. Group of soldiers.

157 Frederic Mistral

1941. Frederic Mistral (poet).
698 **157** 1f. red 20 35

158 Science against Cancer

1941. Anti-cancer Fund.
699 **158** 2f.50+50c. blk and brn 1·30 1·90

159 Beaune Hospital, 1443

1941. Views.
700 **159** 5f. brown 35 35
701 - 10f. violet 60 70
702 **159** 15f. red 50 70
703 - 20f. brown 95 1·40
DESIGNS: 10f. Angers; 20f. Ramparts of St. Louis, Aigues-Mortes.

1941. National Relief Fund. Surch + 10c.
704 **155** 1f.+10c. red 20 15

160

1941. Winter Relief Fund. Inscr as in T 160.
705 **160** 1f.+2f. purple 2·20 1·80
706 - 2f.50+7f.50 blue 7·00 3·25
DESIGN: 2f.50, "Charity" helping a pauper.

162 Liner "Pasteur"

1941. Seamen's Dependants Relief Fund. Surch.
707 **162** 1f.+1f. on 70c. green 35 55

1941. As No. 661, but without "R.F." and dated "1941".
708 **149** 1f.+1f. multicoloured 60 70

163 **164** Marshal Petain **165**

1941. Frame in T 164 is 17×20½ mm.
709 **163** 20c. purple 20 15
710 **163** 30c. red 20 15
711 **163** 40c. blue 20 15
712 **164** 50c. green 20 15
713 **164** 60c. violet 20 15
714 **164** 70c. blue 20 15
715 **164** 70c. orange 20 15
716 **164** 80c. brown 20 20
717 **164** 80c. green 20 15
718 **164** 1f. red 20 15
719 **164** 1f.20 brown 20 15
720 **165** 1f.50 pink 20 15
721 **165** 1f.50 brown 20 15
722 **165** 2f. green 20 15
723 **165** 2f.40 red 20 35
724 **165** 2f.50 blue 35 1·10
725 **165** 3f. orange 20 15
725a **164** 4f. blue 20 35
725b **164** 4f.50 green 60 90
See also Nos. 740/1.

166 Fisherman

1941. National Seamen's Relief Fund.
726 **166** 1f.+9f. green 80 1·20

167 Arms of Nancy

1942. National Relief Fund.
727 **167** 20c.+30c. black 2·40 3·25
728 - 40c.+60c. brown 2·40 3·25
729 - 50c.+70c. blue 2·40 3·25
730 - 70c.+80c. red 2·40 3·25
731 - 80c.+1f. red 2·40 3·25
732 - 1f.+1f. black 2·40 3·25
733 - 1f.50+2f. blue 2·40 3·25
734 - 2f.+2f. violet 2·40 3·75
735 - 2f.50+3f. green 2·40 3·75
736 - 3f.+5f. brown 2·40 3·75
737 - 5f.+6f. blue 2·40 3·75
738 - 10f.+10f. red 2·40 3·75
DESIGNS—As Type **167**. Nos. 728/38 show respectively the Arms of Lille, Rouen, Bordeaux, Toulouse, Clermont-Ferrand, Marseilles, Lyons, Rennes, Reims, Montpellier and Paris.
See also Nos. 757/68.

168 Jean-Francois de La Perouse, "L'Astrolabe" and "La Boussole"

1942. Birth Bicentenary of La Perouse (navigator and explorer) and National Relief Fund.
739 **168** 2f.50+7f.50 blue 1·30 2·00

1942. Frame 18×21½ mm.
740 **164** 4f. blue 25 35
741 **164** 4f.50 green 25 35

169 Potez 63-11 Bombers

1942. Air Force Dependants Relief Fund.
742 **169** 1f.50+3f.50 violet 2·20 3·25

170 Alexis Emmanuel Chabrier

1942. Birth Centenary of Chabrier (composer) and Musicians' Mutual Assistance Fund.
743 **170** 2f.+3f. brown 95 1·80

171 Symbolical of French Colonial Empire

1942. Empire Fortnight and National Relief Fund.
744 **171** 1f.50+8f.50 black 95 1·50

172 Marshal Petain

173 Marshal Petain

1942
745 **172** 5f. green 25 35
746 **173** 50f. black 3·75 5·50
See also Nos. 772/3.

174 Jean de Vienne

1942. 600th Birth Anniv of Jean de Vienne (admiral) and Seamen's Relief Fund.
748 **174** 1f.50+8f.50 brown 95 1·80

175 Jules Massenet

1942. Birth Centenary of Massenet (composer).
749 **175** 4f. green 25 35

1942. As T 123, but inscr "POSTES FRANCAISES".
750 10c. blue 15 15
751 30c. red 15 15
752 40c. violet 15 35
753 50c. blue 15 15

1942. National Relief Fund. Surch + 50 S N.
754 **165** 1f.50+50c. blue 20 15

177 Stendhal (Marie Henri Beyle)

1942. Death Centenary of Stendhal (novelist).

755	177	4f. brown and red	60	70

178 Andre Blondel

1942. Andre Blondel (physicist).

756	178	4f. blue	60	70

1942. National Relief Fund. Arms of French towns as T **167**.

757	50c.+60c. black	3·50	5·00
758	60c.+70c. green	2·75	4·25
759	80c.+1f. red	2·75	4·25
760	1f.+1f.30 green	2·75	4·25
761	1f.20+1f.50 red	2·75	4·50
762	1f.50+1f.80 blue	2·75	4·75
763	2f.+2f.30 red	2·75	4·75
764	2f.40+2f.80 green	3·00	4·75
765	3f.+3f.50 violet	3·00	4·75
766	4f.+5f. blue	3·50	4·75
767	4f.50+6f. red	3·50	4·75
768	5f.+7f. lilac	3·50	5·00

DESIGNS: Nos. 757/68 respectively show the Arms of Chambery, La Rochelle, Poitiers, Orleans, Grenoble, Angers, Dijon, Limoges, Le Havre, Nantes, Nice and St. Etienne.

179 Legionary and Grenadiers

1942. Tricolor Legion.

769	179	1f.20+8f.80 blue	8·25	14·00
770	179	1f.20+8f.80 red	8·25	14·00

180 Belfry, Arras Town Hall

1942

771	180	10f. green	20	35

1943. National Relief Fund.

772	173	1f.+10f. blue	1·90	3·25
773	173	1f.+10f. red	1·90	3·25
774	155	2f.+12f. blue	1·90	3·25
775	155	2f.+12f. red	1·90	3·25

182 Arms of Lyonnais

1943. Provincial Coats of Arms.

776	182	5f. red, blue & yellow	35	55
777	-	10f. black and brown	60	70
778	-	15f. yellow, blue & red	1·70	1·90
779	-	20f. yellow, blue & brn	1·20	2·10

ARMS: 10f. "Bretagne"; 15f. "Provence"; 20f. "Ile-de-France".
For other provinces in this series, see Nos. 814/7, 971/4, 1049/53, 1121/5, 1178/83, 1225/31, 1270/3.
For arms of French towns, see Nos. 1403/10, etc.

183 "Work"   184 Marshal Petain

1943. National Relief Fund.

780		1f.20+1f.40 purple	14·50	20·00
781	183	1f.50+2f.50 red	14·50	20·00
782	-	2f.40+7f. brown	14·50	20·00
783	-	4f.+10f. violet	14·50	20·00
784	184	5f.+15f. brown	14·50	20·00

DESIGNS: 1f.20, Marshal Petain bareheaded; 2f.40, "Family"; 4f. "Country".

185 Lavoisier

1943. Birth Bicentenary of Lavoisier (chemist).

785	185	4f. blue	25	35

186 Lake Lerie and the Meije Peak

1943

786	186	20f. green	95	1·20

187 Nicholas Rolin and Guisone de Salins

1943. 500th Anniv of Beaune Hospital.

787	187	4f. blue	20	35

188 Victims of Bombed Towns

1943. National Relief Fund.

788	188	1f.50+3f.50 black	60	70

189 Prisoners' Families' Relief Work

1943. Prisoners' Families Relief Fund. Inscr as in T 189.

789	-	1f.50+8f.50 brown	95	1·20
790	189	2f.40+7f.60 green	95	1·20

DESIGN—VERT: 1f.50, Prisoner's family.

190 Chevalier de Bayard

1943. National Relief Fund.

791	-	60c.+80c. green	1·70	2·75
792	-	1f.20+1f.50 black	1·70	2·75
793	-	1f.50+3f. blue	1·70	2·75
794	190	2f.40+4f. red	1·70	2·75
795	-	4f.+6f. brown	1·70	3·00
796	-	5f.+10f. green	1·90	3·00

PORTRAITS: 60c. Michel de Montaigne (essayist); 1f.20, Francois Clouet (painter); 1f.50, Ambroise Pare (surgeon); 4f. Duc de Sully (King Henri IV's finance minister); 5f. King Henri IV.

191 Picardy

1943. National Relief Fund. Provincial costumes.

797	191	60c.+1f.30 brown	2·10	2·75
798	-	1f.20+2f. violet	2·10	2·75
799	-	1f.50+4f. blue	2·10	2·75
800	-	2f.40+5f. red	2·10	2·75
801	-	4f.+6f. blue	2·40	4·00
802	-	5f.+7f. red	2·40	4·00

DESIGNS: 1f.20, "Bretagne"; 1f.50, "Ile de France"; 2f.40, "Bourgogne"; 4f. "Auvergne"; 5f. "Provence".

196 Admiral de Tourville

1944. 300th Birth Anniv of Admiral de Tourville.

810	196	4f.+6f. red	80	1·10

197 Branly

1944. Birth Centenary of Branly (physicist).

811	197	4f. blue	25	35

198 Gounod

1944. 50th Death Anniv of Gounod (composer).

812	198	1f.50+3f.50 brown	80	1·10

200 Flanders

1944. Provincial Coats of Arms.

814	200	5f. black, orange & red	20	35
815	-	10f. yellow, red & brown	20	35
816	-	15f. yellow, blue & brown	85	1·10
817	-	20f. yellow, red & blue	1·20	1·40

ARMS: 10f. "Languedoc"; 15f. "Orleanais"; 20f. "Normandie".

201 Marshal Petain

202 Petain gives France Workers' Charter

1944. Petain's 88th Birthday.

818	201	1f.50+3f.50 brown	3·25	5·00
819	-	2f.+3f. blue	60	90
820	202	4f.+6f. red	60	90

DESIGN—As Type **202**: 2f. inscr "Le Marechal institua la Corporation Paysanne" (Trans. "The Marshal set up the Peasant Corporation").

203 Paris-Rouen Travelling Post Office Van, 1844

1944. Centenary of Mobile Post Office.

821	203	1f.50 green	60	90

204 Chateau of Chenonceaux

1944

822	204	15f. brown	35	70
823	204	25f. black	60	90

The 15f. is inscr "FRANCE".

205 Louis XIV

1944. National Relief Fund.

824	-	50c.+1f.50 red	1·90	2·75
825	-	80c.+2f.20 green	1·30	2·10
826	-	1f.20+2f.80 black	1·30	2·10
827	-	1f.50+3f.50 blue	1·30	2·10
828	-	2f.+4f. brown	1·30	2·10
829	205	4f.+6f. orange	1·30	2·10

DESIGNS: 50c. Moliere (dramatist); 80c. Jean Hardouin-Manzart (scholar); 1f.20, Blaise Pascal (mathematician); 1f.50, Louis, Prince de Conde; 2f. Jean-Baptiste Colbert (King Louis XIV's chief minister).

206 Old and Modern Locomotives

1944. National Relief Fund. Centenary of Paris-Orleans and Paris-Rouen Railways.

830	206	4f.+6f. black	1·90	2·50

207 Claude Chappe

1944. 150th Anniv of Invention of Semaphore Telegraph.

831	207	4f. blue	20	35

208 Gallic Cock

209 "Marianne"

1944

832	**208**	10c. green	25	20
833	**208**	30c. lilac	35	55
834	**208**	40c. blue	25	20
835	**208**	50c. red	25	20
836	**209**	60c. brown	25	20
837	**209**	70c. mauve	25	20
838	**209**	80c. green	95	1·50
839	**209**	1f. violet	25	35
840	**209**	1f.20 red	25	35
841	**209**	1f.50 blue	25	20
842	**208**	2f. blue	25	20
843	**209**	2f.40 red	1·30	2·00
844	**209**	3f. green	25	35
845	**209**	4f. blue	25	35
846	**209**	4f.50 black	25	20
847	**209**	5f. blue	4·00	6·00
848	**208**	10f. violet	4·50	6·50
849	**208**	15f. brown	4·75	6·50
850	**208**	20f. green	4·00	6·00

210 Arc de Triomphe, Paris

1944

851	**210**	5c. purple	20	15
852	**210**	10c. grey	20	15
853	**210**	25c. brown	20	15
854	**210**	50c. green	20	15
855	**210**	1f. green	20	15
856	**210**	1f.50 pink	20	15
857	**210**	2f.50 violet	20	15
858	**210**	4f. blue	20	15
859	**210**	5f. black	35	35
860	**210**	10f. orange	26·00	30·00

See also Nos. 936/45.

1944. New colours and values.

861	**136**	80c. green	20	35
862	**136**	1f. blue	20	15
863	**136**	1f.20 violet	20	15
864	**136**	1f.50 brown	20	15
865	**136**	2f. brown	20	15
866	**136**	2f.40 red	20	35
867	**136**	3f. orange	20	15
868	**136**	4f. blue	20	35

211 "Marianne"

1944

869	**211**	10c. blue	25	15
870	**211**	30c. brown	25	15
871	**211**	40c. blue	25	15
872	**211**	50c. orange	25	15
873	**211**	60c. blue	25	15
874	**211**	70c. brown	25	15
875	**211**	80c. green	25	15
876	**211**	1f. lilac	25	15
877	**211**	1f.20 green	25	15
878	**211**	1f.50 red	25	15
879	**211**	2f. brown	25	15
880	**211**	2f.40 red	25	15
881	**211**	3f. olive	25	15
882	**211**	4f. blue	25	35
883	**211**	4f.50 grey	25	35
884	**211**	5f. orange	25	35
885	**211**	10f. green	25	35
886	**211**	15f. red	25	35
887	**211**	20f. orange	1·30	2·00
888	**211**	50f. violet	2·75	3·25

212 St. Denis Basilica

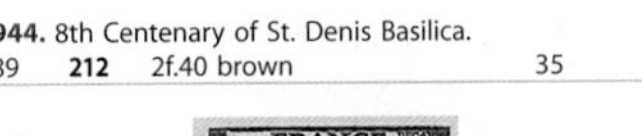
1944. 8th Centenary of St. Denis Basilica.

889	**212**	2f.40 brown	35	55

213 Marshal Bugeaud

1944. Centenary of Battle of Isly.

890	**213**	4f. green	25	35

214 Angouleme Cathedral

1944. Cathedrals of France (1st issue).

891	**214**	50c.+1f.50 black	80	1·10
892	-	80c.+2f.20 purple	80	1·10
893	-	1f.20+2f.80 red	80	1·10
894	-	1f.50+3f.50 blue	80	1·10
895	-	4f.+6f. red	80	1·10

DESIGNS: 80c. Chartres; 1f.20, Amiens; 1f.50, Beauvais; 4f. Albi.

1944. Nos. 750/3 optd RF.

896	10c. blue	20	15
897	30c. red	20	15
898	40c. violet	20	15
899	50c. blue	20	15

215 Arms of De Villayer

1944. Stamp Day.

900	**215**	1f.50+3f.50 brown	20	35

216 "France" exhorting Resistance Forces

1945. Liberation.

901	**216**	4f. blue	60	55

217 Shield and Broken Chains

218 Ceres

219 Marianne

220 Marianne

1945

902	**217**	10c. brown	20	15
903	**217**	30c. green	20	15
904	**217**	40c. mauve	20	15
905	**217**	50c. blue	20	15
906	**218**	60c. blue	20	15
907	**218**	80c. green	20	15
908	**218**	90c. green*	95	70
909	**218**	1f. red	20	15
910	**218**	1f.20 black	20	15
997	**218**	1f.30 blue	20	20
911	**218**	1f.50 purple	20	15
912	**219**	1f.50 red	20	15
913	**219**	2f. green	20	15
914	**218**	2f. green	20	15
915	**219**	2f.40 red	60	55
916	**218**	2f.50 brown	20	15
997a	**219**	2f.50 brown*	3·50	1·90
917	**219**	3f. brown	20	15
918	**219**	3f. red	20	15
998	**219**	3f. green	3·00	60
999	**219**	3f. mauve	40	35
1000	**219**	3f.50 brown and red	1·30	80
919	**219**	4f. blue	20	15
920	**219**	4f. violet	20	15
1001	**219**	4f. green	40	35
1001a	**219**	4f. orange	5·00	1·40
1002	**219**	4f.50 blue	40	20
921	**219**	5f. green	35	15
1003	**219**	5f. red	20	20
1004	**219**	5f. blue	40	35
1004b	**219**	5f. violet	80	20
922	**219**	6f. blue	35	35
1005	**219**	6f. red	40	20
1005a	**219**	6f. green	10·50	85
1006	**219**	8f. blue	65	35
924	**219**	10f. orange	95	70
928	**219**	10f. blue	1·90	70
1007	**219**	10f. violet	40	20
1007a	**219**	12f. blue	5·00	60
1007b	**219**	12f. orange	1·30	35
926	**219**	15f. purple	4·75	2·50
1007c	**219**	15f. red	1·60	25
1007d	**219**	15f. blue	55	20
1007e	**219**	18f. red	27·00	2·10
930	**219**	20f. green	1·90	70
932	**220**	20f. green	1·90	1·50
931	**219**	25f. red	13·00	2·00
933	**220**	25f. violet	2·40	1·80
934	**220**	50f. brown	2·75	2·75
935	**220**	100f. red	18·00	8·50

***PRECANCELS.** See note below No. 432.

1945

936	**210**	30c. black and orange	20	15
937	**210**	40c. black and grey	20	15
938	**210**	50c. black and green	20	15
939	**210**	60c. black and violet	20	15
940	**210**	80c. black and green	20	15
941	**210**	1f.20 black and brown	20	15
942	**210**	1f.50 black and red	20	15
943	**210**	2f. black and yellow	20	15
944	**210**	2f.40 black and red	20	15
945	**210**	3f. black and purple	20	15

221 Arms of Strasbourg

1945. Liberation of Metz and Strasbourg.

946	-	2f.40 blue	40	35
947	**221**	4f. brown	40	35

DESIGN: 2f.40, Arms of Metz.

222 Patient in Deck Chair

1945. Anti-tuberculosis Fund.

948	**222**	2f.+1f. orange	40	35

223 Refugee Employee and Family

1945. Postal Employees War Victims' Fund.

949	**223**	4f.+6f. brown	40	35

224 Sarah Bernhardt

1945. Birth Cent of Sarah Bernhardt (actress).

950	**224**	4f.+1f. brown	65	60

225 Alsatian and Lorrainer in Native Dress

1945. Liberation of Alsace-Lorraine.

951	**225**	4f. brown	40	35

226 Children in Country

1945. Fresh Air Crusade.

952	**226**	4f.+2f. green	40	35

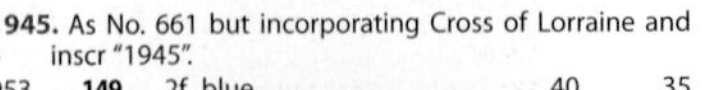
1945. As No. 661 but incorporating Cross of Lorraine and inscr "1945".

953	**149**	2f. blue	40	35

227 Destruction of Oradour

1945. Destruction of Oradour-sur-Glane.

954	**227**	4f.+2f. brown	40	35

228 Louis XI

1945. Stamp Day.

955	**228**	2f.+3f. blue	85	80

229 Dunkirk

1945. Devastated Towns.

956	**229**	1f.50+1f.50 red	85	80
957	-	2f.+2f. violet	85	80
958	-	2f.40+2f.60 blue	85	80
959	-	4f.+4f. black	85	80

DESIGNS: 2f. Rouen; 2f.40c. Caen; 4f. St. Malo.

230 Alfred Fournier

1946. Prophylaxis Fund.

960	230	2f.+3f. red	65	60
961	230	2f.+3f. blue	65	60

231 Henri Becquerel

1946

962	231	2f.+3f. violet	65	60

1946. Surcharged 3F.

963	222	3f. on 2f.+1f. orange	40	35

233 "Les Invalides"

1946. War Invalids' Relief Fund.

964	233	4f.+6f. brown	65	60

234 "Emile Bertin" (cruiser) and "Lorraine" (battleship)

1946. Naval Charities.

965	234	2f.+3f. black	1·30	1·20

235 "The Letter"

1946. Postal Museum Fund.

966	235	2f.+3f. red	85	80

236 Iris

237 Jupiter carrying off Egine

1946. Air.

967	-	40f. green	1·30	60
968	236	50f. pink	1·30	60
969	237	100f. blue	11·50	1·60
970	-	200f. red	9·00	2·40

DESIGNS—VERT: 40f. Centaur. HORIZ: 200f. Apollo and chariot.

239 Arms of Corsica

1946. Provincial Coats of arms.

971	239	10c. black and blue	20	20
972	-	30c. black, red and yellow	20	20
973	-	50c. brown, yellow & red	20	20
974	-	60c. red, blue & black	20	20

DESIGNS: 30c. Alsace; 50c. Lorraine; 60c. Nice.

241 Fouquet de la Varane

1946. Stamp Day.

975	241	3f.+2f. brown	1·10	1·00

244 Luxembourg Palace

245 Roc-Amadour

1946. Views.

976	-	5f. mauve	40	35
977	-	6f. red	2·50	1·00
978	244	10f. blue	40	35
979	244	12f. red	5·00	1·00
980	245	15f. purple	7·00	80
980a	244	15f. red	1·30	1·20
981	-	20f. blue	2·10	35
982	-	25f. brown	7·00	60
982a	-	25f. blue	19·00	2·00

DESIGNS—HORIZ: 5f. Vezelay; 6f. Cannes; 20f. Pointe du Raz; 25f. (both) Stanislas Place, Nancy.

248 "Peace"

1946. Peace Conference.

983	248	3f. green	40	35
984	-	10f. blue	40	35

DESIGN: 10f. Woman releasing dove.

250 Francois Villon

1946. National Relief Fund. 15th-century Figures.

985	250	2f.+1f. blue	2·50	2·40
986	-	3f.+1f. blue	2·50	2·40
987	-	4f.+3f. red	2·50	2·40
988	-	5f.+4f. blue	2·75	2·50
989	-	6f.+5f. brown	2·75	2·50
990	-	10f.+6f. orange	2·75	2·50

DESIGNS: 3f. Jean Fouquet; 4f. Philippe de Commynes; 5f. Joan of Arc; 6f. Jean Gerson; 10f. Charles VII.

251

1946. UNESCO Conference, Paris.

991	251	10f. blue	40	35

252 St. Julien Cathedral, Le Mans

1947. National Relief Fund. Cathedrals of France (2nd issue). As T 214 and 252.

992	-	1f.+1f. red	1·70	1·60
993	-	3f.+2f. black	5·00	4·50
994	-	4f.+3f. red	2·50	2·40
995	252	6f.+4f. blue	2·50	2·40
996	-	10f.+6f. green	5·00	4·50

DESIGNS—VERT: 1f. St. Sernin, Toulouse; 3f. Notre-Dame du Port, Clermont-Ferrand; 10f. Notre-Dame, Paris. HORIZ: 4f. St. Front, Perigueux.

253 Louvois

1947. Stamp Day.

1008	253	4f.50+5f.50 red	2·50	2·30

254 The Louvre Colonnade

255 Herring Gull over Ile de la Cite

1947. 12th U.P.U. Congress.

1009	254	3f.50 purple (postage)	65	60
1010	-	4f.50 grey	95	60
1011	-	6f. red	1·90	1·50
1012	-	10f. blue	1·90	1·50
1013	255	500f. green (air)	85·00	65·00

DESIGNS—As Type 254: 4f.50, La Conciergerie; 6f. La Cite; 10f. Place de la Concorde.

256 Auguste Pavie

1947. Birth Cent of Auguste Pavie (explorer).

1014	256	4f.50 purple	65	60

257 Fenelon

1947. Fenelon, Archbishop of Cambrai.

1015	257	4f.50 brown	65	60

258 St. Nazaire Monument

1947. 5th Anniv of British Commando Raid on St. Nazaire.

1016	258	6f.+4f. blue	1·10	1·00

259

1947. Boy Scouts' Jamboree.

1017	259	5f. brown	65	60

260 Milestone on Road of Liberty

1947. Road Maintenance Fund.

1018	260	6f.+4f. green	1·70	1·50

261 "Resistance"

1947. Resistance Movement.

1019	261	5f. purple	1·10	1·00

1947. No. 997 surch 1F.

1020	218	1f. on 1f.30 blue	25	25

263 Conques Abbey

1947

1021	263	15f. red	7·00	1·50
1022	263	18f. blue	7·00	60

No. 1022 is inscribed "FRANCE".

264 Louis Braille

1948. Louis Braille (inventor of system of writing and printing for the blind).

1023	264	6f.+4f. violet	65	60

265 A. de Saint-Exupery (pilot and writer) and Douglas DB-7

1948. Air. Famous Airmen.

1024	**265**	50f.+30f. purple	5·25	4·75
1025	-	100f.+70f. blue	6·75	5·75
1026	-	40f.+10f. blue	2·75	2·30

DESIGNS: 40f. "Avion III" and Douglas DB-7 (Clement Ader); 100f. Jean Dagnaux. Douglas DB-7.

267 Etienne Arago

1948. Stamp Day and Centenary of First French Adhesive Postage Stamps.

1027	**267**	6f.+4f. violet	1·10	1·00

268 Lamartine

1948. National Relief Fund and Cent of 1848 Revolution. Dated "1848 1948".

1028	**268**	1f.+1f. green	2·10	2·00
1029	-	3f.+2f. red	2·10	2·00
1030	-	4f.+3f. purple	2·10	2·00
1031	-	5f.+4f. blue	5·25	5·00
1032	-	6f.+5f. blue	4·00	3·75
1033	-	10f.+6f. red	4·00	3·75
1034	-	15f.+7f. blue	5·25	5·00
1035	-	20f.+8f. violet	5·25	5·00

PORTRAITS: 3f. Alexandre-Auguste Ledru-Rollin; 4f. Louis Blanc; 5f. A. M. Albert; 6f. Pierre Joseph Proudhon; 10f. Louis-Auguste Blanqui; 15f. Armand Barbes; 20f. Denis-Auguste Affre.

269 Dr. Calmette

1948. 1st International B.C.G. (Vaccine) Congress.

1036	**269**	6f.+4f. slate	1·30	1·00

270 Gen. Leclerc

1948. Gen. Leclerc Memorial.

1037	**270**	6f. black	65	60

See also Nos. 1171/a.

271 Chateaubriand

1948. Death Centenary of Chateaubriand.

1038	**271**	18f. blue	65	60

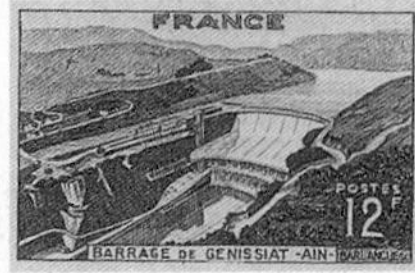
272 Genissiat Barrage

1948. Inauguration of Genissiat Barrage.

1039	**272**	12f. red	1·30	1·20

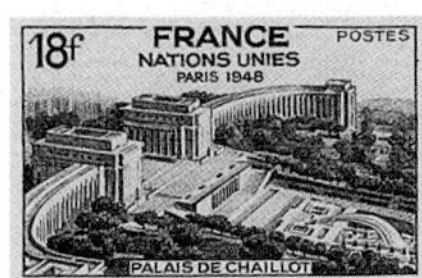
273 Aerial View of Chaillot Palace

1948. U.N. Assembly, Paris.

1040	-	12f. red	85	80
1041	**273**	18f. blue	85	80

DESIGN: 12f. Ground level view of Chaillot Palace.

274 Paul Langevin

1948. Transfer of Ashes of Paul Langevin and Jean Perrin to the Pantheon.

1042	**274**	5f. brown	65	35
1043	-	8f. green (Perrin)	65	35

1949. Surch 5F.

1044	**219**	5f. on 6f. red	40	35

276 Ploughing

1949. Workers.

1045	**276**	3f.+1f. purple	1·60	1·00
1046	-	5f.+3f. blue	1·60	1·20
1047	-	8f.+4f. blue	1·60	1·20
1048	-	10f.+6f. red	1·90	1·50

DESIGNS: 5f. Fisherman; 8f. Miner; 10f. Industrial worker.

277 Arms of Burgundy

1949. Provincial Coats of Arms.

1049	**277**	10c. red, yellow & blue	20	20
1050	-	50c. yellow, red & blue	20	20
1051	-	1f. red and brown	85	60
1052	-	2f. red, yellow & green	85	35
1053	-	4f. blue, yellow & red	65	60

ARMS: 50c. "Guyenne"; 1f. "Savoie"; 2f. "Auvergne"; 4f. "Anjou".

See also Nos. 1121/5, 1178/83, 1225/31 and 1270/3.

278 Due de Choiseul

1949. Stamp Day.

1054	**278**	15f.+5f. green	1·90	1·70

279 Lille

279a Paris

1949. Air. Views.

1055	**279**	100f. purple	1·90	60
1056	-	200f. green	22·00	1·20
1057	-	300f. violet	26·00	16·00
1058	-	500f. red	£100	8·25
1059	**279a**	1000f. purple & black	£200	36·00

DESIGNS—As Type **279**: 200f. Bordeaux; 300f. Lyons; 500f. Marseilles.

280 Polar Scene

1949. Polar Expeditions.

1060	**280**	15f. blue	65	60

1949. French Stamp Centenary. (a) Imperf.

1061	**1**	15f. red	5·25	4·75
1062	**1**	25f. blue	5·25	4·75

(b) Perf.

1063	**219**	15f. red	5·25	4·75
1064	**219**	25f. blue	5·25	4·75

281 Collegiate Church of St. Bernard, Romans

1949. 600th Anniv of Cession of Dauphiny to King of France.

1065	**281**	12f. brown	65	60

282 Emblems of U.S.A. and France

1949. Franco-American Amity.

1066	**282**	25f. blue and red	1·00	95

284 St. Wandrille Abbey

1949. Views.

1067	-	20f. red	40	35
1068	**284**	25f. blue	65	35
1068a	**284**	30f. blue	7·75	6·00
1068b	-	30f. blue	1·60	35
1069	-	40f. green	24·00	60
1070	-	50f. purple	3·75	35

DESIGNS: 20f. St. Bertrand de Comminges; 30f. (1068b) Arbois (Jura); 40f. Valley of the Meuse (Ardennes); 50f. Mt. Gerbier-de-Jone, Vivarais.

285 Jean Racine

1949. 250th Death Anniv of Racine (dramatist).

1071	**285**	12f. purple	65	60

1949. French Stamp Centenary ("CITEX"). T **1** with dates "1849 1949" below, repeated ten times (2×5) with "1849–1949" centred above.

MS1071a	280×155 mm. 10f. (+100f.) orange-red.	85·00	65·00

286 Claude Chappe

287 Alexander III Bridge and "Petit Palais"

1949. International Telephone and Telegraph Congress, Paris.

1072	**286**	10f. red (postage)	1·40	1·30
1073	-	15f. violet	1·60	1·50
1074	-	25f. red	3·75	3·25
1075	-	50f. blue	7·25	5·75
1076	**287**	100f. red (air)	11·50	8·25

PORTRAITS—As Type **286**: 15f. Arago and Ampere; 25f. Emile Baudot; 50f. Gen. Ferrie.

288 Allegory of Commerce

1949. French Chambers of Commerce.

1077	**288**	15f. red	40	35

289 Allegory

1949. 75th Anniv of U.P.U.

1078	**289**	5f. green	40	35
1079	**289**	15f. red	65	35
1080	**289**	25f. blue	2·10	1·30

290 Montesquieu

1949. National Relief Fund.

1081	**290**	5f.+1f. green	5·25	4·75
1082	-	8f.+2f. blue	5·25	4·75
1083	-	10f.+3f. brown	6·00	5·50
1084	-	12f.+4f. violet	6·00	5·50
1085	-	15f.+5f. red	7·75	7·25
1086	-	25f.+10f. blue	10·00	9·25

PORTRAITS: 8f. Voltaire; 10f. Watteau; 12f. Buffon; 15f. Dupleix; 25f. Turgot.

291 "Spring"

1949. National Relief Fund. Seasons.

1087	**291**	5f.+1f. green	2·75	2·50
1088	-	8f.+2f. yellow	3·50	3·25
1089	-	12f.+3f. violet	3·75	3·25
1090	-	15f.+4f. blue	6·50	5·50

DESIGNS: 8f. "Summer"; 12f. "Autumn"; 15f. "Winter".

292 Postman

1950. Stamp Day.

1091	**292**	12f.+3f. blue	5·50	4·00

293 Raymond Poincare

1950. Honouring Poincare.

1092	**293**	15f. blue	60	55

294 Charles Peguy

1950. Honouring Charles Peguy (writer).

1093	**294**	12f. purple	60	55

295 Francois Rabelais

1950. Honouring Francois Rabelais (writer).

1094	**295**	12f. lake	1·20	1·10

296 Andre Chenier

1950. National Relief Fund (revolutionaary celebrities). Frames in blue.

1095	**296**	5f.+2f. purple	16·00	15·00
1096	-	8f.+3f. sepia	16·00	15·00
1097	-	10f.+4f. red	17·00	16·00
1098	-	12f.+5f. brown	19·00	18·00
1099	-	15f.+6f. green	20·00	20·00
1100	-	20f.+10f. blue	20·00	20·00

PORTRAITS: 8f. Louis David; 10f. Lazare Carnot; 12f. Danton; 15f. Robespierre; 20f. Hoche.

297 Chateaudun

1950

1101	**297**	8f. brown & lt brown	1·20	80
1102	-	12f. brown	1·60	1·10

DESIGN: 12f. Palace of Fontainebleau.

298 Madame Recamier

1950

1103	**298**	12f. green	95	80
1104	-	15f. blue	95	80

PORTRAIT: 15f. Madame de Sevigne.

299 "L'Amour" (after Falconet)

1950. Red Cross. Cross in red.

1105		8f.+2f. blue	3·25	3·25
1106	**299**	15f.+3f. purple	4·00	3·50

DESIGN: 8f. Bust of Alexandre Brongniart (after Houdon).

300 T.P.O. Sorting Van

1951. Stamp Day.

1107	**300**	12f.+3f. violet	5·50	5·25

301 J. Ferry (statesman)

1951

1108	**301**	15f. red	80	75

302 Shuttle

1951. Textile Industry.

1109	**302**	25f. blue	1·50	90

303 De La Salle

1951. Birth Tercentenary of Jean Baptiste de la Salle (educational reformer).

1110	**303**	15f. brown	95	75

304 Anchor and Map

1951. 50th Anniv of Formation of Colonial Troops.

1111	**304**	15f. blue	1·20	80

305 Vincent D'Indy

1951. Birth Centenary of Vincent D'Indy (composer).

1112	**305**	25f. green	2·75	2·75

306 A. de Musset

1951. National Relief Fund. Frames in sepia.

1113	**306**	5f.+1f. green	9·50	9·25
1114	-	8f.+2f. purple	11·50	11·00
1115	-	10f.+3f. green	9·50	9·25
1116	-	12f.+4f. brown	11·50	11·00
1117	-	15f.+5f. red	11·50	11·00
1118	-	30f.+10f. blue	18·00	18·00

PORTRAITS: 8f. Delacroix; 10f. Gay-Lussac; 12f. Surcouf; 15f. Talleyrand; 30f. Napoleon.

307 Nocard, Bouley and Chauveau

1951. French Veterinary Research.

1119	**307**	12f. mauve	85	75

308 Picque, Roussin and Villemin

1951. Military Health Service.

1120	**308**	15f. purple	85	75

1951. Provincial Coats of Arms as T 277.

1121	10c. yellow, blue and red	20	15
1122	50c. black, red and green	20	15
1123	1f. red, yellow and blue	35	35
1124	2f. yellow, blue and red	1·30	55
1125	3f. yellow, blue and red	1·20	55

ARMS: 10c. "Artois"; 50c. "Limousin"; 1f. "Bearn"; 2f. "Touraine"; 3f. "Franche-Comte".

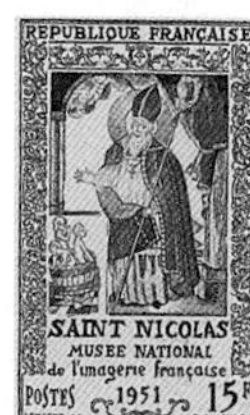
309 St. Nicholas

1951. Popular Pictorial Art Exhibition, Epinal. Multicoloured centre.

1126	**309**	15f. blue	2·00	1·50

310 Seal of Mercantile Guild

1951. Bimillenary of Paris.

1127	**310**	15f. brown, blue & red	95	55

311 M. Nogues

1951. M. Nogues (aviator).

1128	**311**	12f. indigo and blue	1·30	1·10

312 C. Baudelaire

1951. Famous French Poets.

1129	**312**	8f. violet	1·20	1·00
1130	-	12f. grey	1·20	1·00
1131	-	15f. green	1·20	1·00

DESIGNS: 12f. Paul Verlaine; 15f. Arthur Rimbaud.

313 Eiffel Tower and Chaillot Palace

1951. U.N.O. General Assembly.

1132	**313**	18f. red	1·70	1·10
1133	**313**	30f. blue	3·00	1·60

314 L. G. Clemenceau (statesman)

1951. 110th Birth Anniv of Clemenceau and 33rd Anniv of Armistice.

1134	**314**	15f. sepia	80	75

315 Chateau Clos-Vougeot

1951. 400th Anniv of Chateau Clos-Vougeot.

1135	**315**	30f. dp brown & brown	9·00	3·50

316 15th-century Child

1951. Red Cross. Cross in red.

1136	**316**	12f.+3f. brown	4·50	4·50
1137	-	15f.+5f. blue	5·50	5·25

DESIGN: 15f. 18th-century child (De La Tour).

317 Observatory, Pic du Midi de Bigorre

1951

1138	**317**	40f. violet	8·25	35
1139	-	50f. brown	7·25	35

VIEW—VERT: 50f. Church of St. Etienne, Caen.

319 19th-cent Mail Coach

1952. Stamp Day.

1140	**319**	12f.+3f. green	6·50	6·25

320 Marshal de Lattre de Tassigny

1952

1140a	**320**	12f. indigo and blue	2·75	1·80
1141	**320**	15f. brown	1·50	90

321 Gate of France, Vaucouleurs

1952

1142	**321**	12f. brown	1·90	1·40

322 French Monument, Narvik

1952. Battle of Narvik.

1143	**322**	30f. blue	4·75	3·25

323 Chambord Chateau

1952

1144	**323**	20f. violet	80	35

324 Council of Europe Building, Strasbourg

1952. Council of Europe Assembly.

1145	**324**	30f. green	11·50	8·00

325 Bir Hakeim Monument

1952. 10th Anniv of Battle of Bir Hakeim.

1146	**325**	30f. lake	5·25	2·75

326 Abbey of the Holy Cross, Poitiers

1952. 1400th Anniv of Abbey of the Holy Cross, Poitiers.

1147	**326**	15f. red	80	75

327 Medaille Militaire, in 1852 and 1952

1952. Centenary of Medaille Militaire.

1148	**327**	15f. brown, yell & grn	95	80

328 Garabit Railway Viaduct

1952

1149	**328**	15f. blue	95	75

329 Leonardo, Amboise Chateau and Town of Vinci

1952. 500th Birth Anniv of Leonardo da Vinci.

1150	**329**	30f. blue	12·00	9·75

330 Flaubert (after E. Giraud)

1952. National Relief Fund. Frames in sepia.

1151	**330**	8f.+2f. blue	10·00	9·75
1152	-	12f.+3f. blue	10·00	9·75
1153	-	15f.+4f. green	10·00	9·75
1154	-	18f.+5f. sepia	13·50	13·00
1155	-	20f.+6f. red	13·50	13·00
1156	-	30f.+7f. violet	13·50	13·00

PORTRAITS: 12f. Manet; 15f. Saint-Saens; 18f. H. Poincare; 20f. Haussmann (after Yvon); 20f. Thiers.

331 R. Laennec (physician)

1952

1157	**331**	12f. green	1·20	85

332 "Cherub" (bas-relief)

1952. Red Cross Fund. Sculptures from Basin of Diana, Versailles. Cross in red.

1158	**332**	12f.+3f. green	7·25	7·00
1159	-	15f.+5f. blue	7·25	7·00

DESIGN: 15f. "Cherub" (facing left).

333 Versailles Gateway

1952

1160	**333**	18f. purple	4·25	2·75
1160a	**333**	18f. indigo, blue & brn	13·00	8·75

334 Count D'Argenson

1953. Stamp Day.

1161	**334**	12f.+3f. blue	4·75	4·50

335 "Gargantua" (Rabelais)

337 Mannequin and Place Vendome, Paris

1953. Literary Figures and National Industries.

1162	**335**	6f. lake and red	50	35
1163	-	8f. blue and indigo	50	35
1164	-	12f. green and brown	50	35
1165	-	18f. sepia and purple	90	55
1166	-	25f. sepia, red & brown	20·00	75
1166a	-	25f. blue and black	1·50	35
1167	**337**	30f. violet and blue	1·40	55
1167a	-	30f. blue & turquoise	3·50	35
1168	-	40f. brown & chocolate	6·00	55
1169	-	50f. brn, turq & blue	3·50	35
1170	-	75f. lake and red	20·00	1·60

DESIGNS—As Types **335/337**: 8f. "Celimene" (Moliere); 12f. "Figaro" (Beaumarchais); 18f. "Hernani" (Victor Hugo); 25f. (No. 1166) Tapestry; 25f. (No. 1166a) Mannequin modelling gloves; 30f. (No. 1167a) Rare books and book-binding; 40f. Porcelain and cut-glass; 50f. Gold plate and jewellery; 75f. Flowers and perfumes.

1953. General Leclerc. As T **270** but inscr "GENERAL LECLERC MARECHAL DE FRANCE".

1171	**270**	8f. brown	1·50	1·30
1171a	**270**	12f. turquoise & green	4·50	2·75

338 Olivier de Serres

1953. National Relief Fund.

1172	-	8f.+2f. blue	9·50	9·25
1173	**338**	12f.+3f. green	9·50	9·25
1174	-	15f.+4f. lake	16·00	15·00
1175	-	18f.+5f. blue	16·00	15·00
1176	-	20f.+6f. violet	16·00	15·00
1177	-	30f.+7f. brown	17·00	16·00

PORTRAITS: 8f. St. Bernard; 15f. Rameau; 18f. Monge; 20f. Michelet; 30f. Marshal Lyautey.

1953. Provincial Coats of Arms as T **277**.

1178	50c. yellow, red and blue	35	35
1179	70c. yellow, blue and red	35	35
1180	80c. yellow, red and blue	35	35
1181	1f. yellow, red and black	35	35
1182	2f. yellow, blue and brown	70	55
1183	3f. yellow, blue and red	95	55

ARMS: 50c. "Picardie"; 70c. "Gascogne"; 80c. "Berri"; 1f. "Poitou"; 2f. "Champagne"; 3f. "Dauphine".

339 Cyclists and Map

1953. 50th Anniv of "Tour de France" Cycle Race.

1184	**339**	12f. black, blue & red	3·25	1·80

340 Swimming

1953. Sports.

1185	**340**	20f. brown and red	3·50	35
1186	-	25f. brown and green	19·00	80
1187	-	30f. brown and blue	3·50	55
1188	-	40f. indigo and brown	17·00	80
1189	-	50f. brown and green	12·00	35
1190	-	75f. lake and orange	50·00	18·00

SPORTS: 25f. Running; 30f. Fencing; 40f. Canoeing; 50f. Rowing; 75f. Horse-jumping.

See also Nos. 1297/1300.

341 Mme. Vigee-Lebrun and Daughter (self- portrait)

1953. Red Cross Fund. Cross in red.

1191	**341**	12f.+3f. brown	12·00	9·75
1192	-	15f.+5f. blue	16·00	14·00

DESIGN: 15f. "The Return from the Baptism" (L. Le Nain).

1953. Surch 15F.

1193	**219**	15f. on 18f. red	80	75

343 Fouga Magister CM-170

1954. Air.

1194	-	100f. brown and blue	4·25	35
1195	-	200f. purple and blue	13·50	55
1196	**343**	500f. red and orange	£300	18·00
1197	-	1000f. blue, pur & turq	£160	23·00

AIRCRAFT: 100f. Dassault Mystere IVA; 200f. Nord 2501 Noratlas; 1000f. Breguet Br 763 Provence.

See also No. 1457.

344 Harvester

345 Gallic Cock

1954. (a) Precancelled*.

1198	**344**	4f. blue	35	25
1198a	**345**	5f. brown	60	30
1199	**344**	6f. red	8·25	1·70
1199a	**345**	8f. violet	95	35
1199b	**345**	10f. blue	3·00	55
1200	**345**	12f. mauve	5·50	1·10
1200b	**345**	15f. purple	3·75	1·10
1200c	**345**	20f. green	2·75	1·40
1201	**345**	24f. green	29·00	7·00
1201a	**345**	30f. red	17·00	4·50
1201b	**345**	40f. red	6·50	3·50
1201c	**345**	45f. green	32·00	20·00
1201d	**345**	55f. green	27·00	16·00

(b) Without precancel.

1201e	**344**	6f. brown	20	15
1201f	**344**	10f. green	1·20	15
1201g	**344**	12f. purple	35	35

***PRECANCELS.** See note below No. 432. See also Nos. 1470/3.

346 Lavallette

1954. Stamp Day.

1202	**346**	12f.+3f. green & brown	6·50	5·25

347 Exhibition Buildings

1954. 50th Anniv of Paris Fair.

1203	**347**	15f. lake and blue	60	55

348 "D-Day"

1954. 10th Anniv of Liberation.

1204	**348**	15f. red and blue	3·00	2·00

349 Lourdes

1954. Views.

1205	**349**	6f. indigo, blue & grn	70	55
1206	-	8f. green and blue	50	35
1207	-	10f. brown and blue	50	15
1208	-	12f. lilac and violet	70	15
1209	-	12f. brown & chocolate	2·40	2·10
1210	-	18f. indigo, blue & grn	4·75	1·30
1211	-	20f. brn, chestnut & bl	4·25	35
1211a	**349**	20f. brown and blue	60	35

VIEWS—HORIZ: 8f. Seine Valley at Andelys; 10f. Royan; 12f. (No. 1209), Limoges; 18f. Cheverny Chateau; 20f. (No. 1211), Ajaccio Bay. VERT: 12f. (No. 1208), Quimper.

350 Jumieges Abbey

1954. 13th Centenary of Jumieges Abbey.

1212	**350**	12f. indigo, blue & grn	2·40	1·70

351 Abbey Church of St. Philibert, Tournus

1954. 1st Conference of Romanesque Studies, Tournus.

1213	**351**	30f. blue and indigo	7·25	6·25

352 Stenay

1954. Tercent of Return of Stenay to France.

1214	**352**	15f. brown and sepia	1·20	90

353 St. Louis

1954. National Relief Fund.

1215	**353**	12f.+4f. blue	31·00	30·00
1216	-	15f.+5f. violet	31·00	30·00
1217	-	18f.+6f. sepia	31·00	30·00
1218	-	20f.+7f. red	43·00	41·00
1219	-	25f.+8f. blue	43·00	41·00
1220	-	30f.+10f. purple	43·00	41·00

PORTRAITS: 15f. Bossuet; 18f. Sadi Carnot; 20f. A. Bourdelle; 25f. Dr. E. Roux; 30f. Paul Valery.

354 Villandry Chateau

1954. Four Centuries of Renaissance Gardens.

1221	**354**	18f. green and blue	7·25	5·75

355 Cadet and Flag

1954. 150th Anniv of St. Cyr Military Academy.

1222	**355**	15f. indigo, blue & red	1·90	1·80

356 Napoleon Conferring Decorations

1954. 150th Anniv of First Legion of Honour Presentation.

1223	**356**	12f. red	2·40	1·70

357 "Basis of Metric System"

1954. 150th Anniv of Metric System.

1224	**357**	30f. sepia and blue	7·25	6·25

1954. Provincial Coats of Arms as T **277**.

1225		50c. yellow, blue and black	35	35
1226		70c. yellow, red and green	35	35
1227		80c. yellow, blue and red	35	35
1228		1f. yellow, blue and red	20	15
1229		2f. yellow, red and black	20	15
1230		3f. yellow, red and brown	20	15
1231		5f. yellow and blue	20	15

ARMS: 50c. "Maine"; 70c. "Navarre"; 80c. "Nivernais"; 1f. "Bourbonnais"; 2f. "Angoumois"; 3f. "Aunis"; 5f. "Saintonge".

359 "Young Girl with Doves" (J.-B. Greuze)

1954. Red Cross Fund. Cross in red.

1232	-	12f.+3f. indigo & blue	17·00	14·50
1233	**359**	15f.+5f. brn & dp brn	19·00	16·00

DESIGN: 12f. "The Sick Child" (E. Carriere).

360 Saint-Simon

1955. Death Bicentenary of Saint-Simon (writer).

1234	**360**	12f. purple & brown	95	90

361 "Industry", "Agriculture" and Rotary Emblem

1955. 50th Anniv of Rotary International.

1235	**361**	30f. orange, blue and deep blue	4·00	2·30

362 "France"

1955

1236	**362**	6f. brown	4·25	2·75
1237	**362**	12f. green	4·75	1·80
1238	**362**	15f. red	35	15
1238a	**362**	18f. green	1·80	1·10
1238b	**362**	20f. blue	70	15
1238c	**362**	25f. red	2·10	15

363 Thimonnier and Sewing-machines

1955. French Inventors (1st series).

1239	-	5f. blue & light blue	1·10	1·00
1240	**363**	10f. brown & chestnut	1·30	1·30
1241	-	12f. green	1·80	1·70
1242	-	18f. blue and grey	4·25	4·00
1243	-	25f. violet and plum	4·75	3·50
1244	-	30f. vermilion & red	4·75	3·50

DESIGNS: 5f. Le Bon (gaslight); 12f. Appert (food canning); 18f. Sainte-Claire Deville (aluminium); 25f. Martin (steel); 30f. Chardonnet (artificial silk).

See also Nos. 1324/7.

364 Mail Balloon "Armand Barbes", 1870

1955. Stamp Day.

1245	**364**	12f.+3f. brown, green and blue	7·25	6·25

365 Florian and Pastoral scene

1955. Birth Bicent of Florian (fabulist).

1246	**365**	12f. turquoise	1·20	90

366 Eiffel Tower and Television Aerials

1955. Television Development.

1247	**366**	15f. blue & deep blue	1·50	1·30

367 Observation Tower and Fence

1955. 10th Anniv of Liberation of Concentration Camps.

1248	**367**	12f. black and grey	1·50	1·30

368 Electric Locomotive

1955. Electrification of Valenciennes–Thionville Railway Line.

1249	**368**	12f. brown and grey	3·00	1·80

369 The "Jacquemart" (campanile), Moulins

1955

1250	**369**	12f. brown	2·20	1·80

370 Jules Verne and Capt. Nemo on the "Nautilus"

1955. 50th Death Anniv of Jules Verne (author).

1251	**370**	30f. blue	10·50	7·00

371 Maryse Bastie (airwoman) and Caudron C-635 Simoun F-ANXH

1955. Air. Maryse Bastie Commemoration.

1252	**371**	50f. claret and red	9·50	5·75

372 Vauban

1955. National Relief Fund.

1253	-	12f.+5f. violet	24·00	22·00
1254	-	15f.+6f. blue	24·00	22·00
1255	**372**	18f.+7f. green	26·00	24·00
1256	-	25f.+8f. slate	36·00	30·00
1257	-	30f.+9f. lake	38·00	34·00
1258	-	50f.+15f. turquoise	43·00	40·00

PORTRAITS: 12f. King Philippe-Auguste; 15f. Malherbe; 25f. Vergennes; 30f. Laplace; 50f. Renoir.

373 A. and L. Lumiere

1955. 60th Anniv of French Cinema Industry.

1259	**373**	30f. brown	9·00	6·25

374 Jacques Coeur (merchant prince)

1955

1260	**374**	12f. violet	3·25	2·20

375 "La Capricieuse"

1955. Centenary of Voyage of "La Capricieuse" (sail warship).

1261	**375**	30f. blue & turquoise	7·25	6·25

376 Marseilles

1955. Views.

1262	-	6f. red	50	35
1263	**376**	8f. blue	95	35
1264	-	10f. blue	50	35
1265	-	12f. brown and grey	50	35
1265a	-	15f. indigo and blue	85	75
1266	-	18f. blue and green	1·20	35
1267	-	20f. violet & dp violet	4·75	35
1268	-	25f. brown & chestnut	1·80	35
1268a	-	35f. turquoise & green	5·50	1·30
1268b	-	70f. black and green	29·00	2·75

DESIGNS—HORIZ: 6f., 35f. Bordeaux; 10f. Nice; 12f., 70f. Valentre Bridge, Cahors; 18f. Uzerche; 20f. Mount Pele, Martinique; 25f. Ramparts of Brouage. VERT: 15f. Douai Belfry.

377 Gerard de Nerval

1955. Death Centenary of De Nerval (writer).

1269	**377**	12f. sepia and red	60	55

1955. Provincial Coats of Arms as T **277**.

1270	50c. multicoloured	25	25
1271	70c. yellow, blue and red	25	25
1272	80c. yellow, red & brown	25	25
1273	1f. yellow, red and blue	25	25

ARMS: 50c. "Comte de Foix"; 70c. "Marche"; 80c. "Roussillon"; 1f. "Comtat Venaissin".

379 "Child and Cage" (after Pigalle)

1955. Red Cross Fund. Cross in red.

1274	**379**	12f.+3f. lake	12·00	11·50
1275	-	15f.+5f. blue	7·75	7·50

DESIGN: 15f. "Child and goose" (Greek sculpture).

380

1956. National Deportation Memorial.

1276	**380**	15f. sepia and brown	95	75

381 Colonel Driant

1956. Birth Centenary of Col. Driant.

1277	**381**	15f. blue	65	55

382 Trench Warfare

1956. 40th Anniv of Battle of Verdun.

1278	**382**	30f. blue and brown	2·75	2·10

383 Francis of Taxis

1956. Stamp Day.

1279	**383**	12f.+3f. brn, grn & bl	4·25	4·00

384 J. H. Fabre (entomologist)

1956. French Scientists.

1280	**384**	12f. dp brown & brn	1·50	90
1281	-	15f. black and grey	1·50	90
1282	-	18f. blue	2·75	2·30
1283	-	30f. green & dp green	6·75	4·00

DESIGNS: 15f. C. Tellier (refrigeration engineer); 18f. C. Flammarion (astronomer); 30f. P. Sabatier (chemist).

385 Grand Trianon, Versailles

1956

1284	**385**	12f. brown, green & blk	2·30	1·40

386 "Latin America" and "France"

1956. Franco-Latin American Friendship.

1285	**386**	30f. brown and sepia	3·00	2·30

387 "Reims" and "Florence"

1956. Reims-Florence Friendship.

1286	**387**	12f. green and black	1·20	1·10

388 Order of Malta and Leper Colony

1956. Order of Malta Leprosy Relief.

1287	**388**	12f. red, brown & sepia	85	75

389 St. Yves de Treguier

1956. St. Yves de Treguier Commemoration.

1288	**389**	15f. black and grey	65	55

390 Marshal Franchet d'Esperey

1956. Birth Centenary of Marshal d'Esperey.

1289	**390**	30f. purple	4·00	2·75

391 Monument

1956. Centenary of Montceau-les-Mines.

1290	**391**	12f. sepia	85	75

392 Bude

1956. National Relief Fund.

1291	**392**	12f.+3f. blue	8·25	8·00
1292	-	12f.+3f. grey	8·25	8·00
1293	-	12f.+3f. red	8·25	8·00
1294	-	15f.+5f. green	12·00	11·50
1295	-	15f.+5f. brown	12·00	11·50
1296	-	15f.+5f. violet	12·00	11·50

PORTRAITS: No. 1292, Goujon; No. 1293, Champlain; No. 1294, Chardin; No. 1295, Barres; No. 1296, Ravel.

393 Pelota

1956. Sports.

1297		30f. black and grey	2·10	35
1298	**393**	40f. purple and brown	8·50	55
1299	-	50f. violet and purple	3·00	35
1300	-	75f. grn, black & blue	17·00	3·25

DESIGNS: 30f. Basketball; 50f. Rugby; 75f. Alpine climbing.

394

1956. Europa.

1301	**394**	15f. red and pink	1·50	35
1302	**394**	30f. ultramarine and blue	8·50	1·40

395 Donzere-Mondragon Barrage

1956. Technical Achievements.

1303	**395**	12f. grey and brown	2·40	1·60
1304	-	18f. blue	4·75	3·25
1305	-	30f. blue and indigo	20·00	8·75

DESIGNS—VERT: 18f. Aiguille du Midi cable railway. HORIZ: 30f. Port of Strasbourg.

396 A. A. Parmentier (agronomist)

1956. Parmentier Commemoration.

1306	**396**	12f. brown and sepia	1·30	90

397 Petrarch

1956. Famous Men.

1307	**397**	8f. green	1·20	90
1308	-	12f. purple (Lully)	1·20	90
1309	-	15f. red (Rousseau)	1·80	90
1310	-	18f. blue (Franklin)	4·00	3·25
1311	-	20f. violet (Chopin)	5·50	2·50
1312	-	30f. turq (Van Gogh)	8·25	4·25

398 Pierre de Coubertin (reviver of Olympic Games)

1956. Coubertin Commemoration.

1313	**398**	30f. purple and grey	3·00	2·10

399 "Jeune Paysan" (after Le Nain)

1956. Red Cross Fund. Cross in red.

1314	**399**	12f.+3f. olive	4·25	4·00
1315	**399**	15f.+5f. lake	4·25	4·25

DESIGN: 15f. "Gilles" (after Watteau).

400 Pigeon and Loft

1957. Pigeon-fanciers' Commemoration.

1316	**400**	15f. blue, indigo & pur	65	55

401 Sud Aviation SE 212 Caravelle

1957. Air.

1318	-	300f. olive & turquoise	9·50	4·50
1319	**401**	500f. black and blue	42·00	5·25
1320	-	1000f. black, vio & sep	90·00	31·00

AIRCRAFT: 300f. Morane Saulnier MS-760 Paris I airplane; 1000f. Sud Aviation SE3130 Alouette II helicopter.

See also Nos. 1458/60.

402 Victor Schoelcher (slavery abolitionist)

1957. Schoelcher Commem.

1321	**402**	18f. mauve	95	90

403 18th-century Felucca

1957. Stamp Day.

1322	**403**	12f.+3f. black & grey	2·75	2·20

404 "La Baigneuse" (after Falconet) and Sevres Porcelain

1957. Bicentenary of National Porcelain Industry at Sevres.

1323	**404**	30f. blue and light blue	1·20	90

405 Plante and Accumulators

1957. French Inventors (2nd series).

1324	**405**	8f. purple and sepia	70	70
1325	-	12f. black, blue & green	85	80
1326	-	18f. lake and red	2·00	2·00
1327	-	30f. myrtle and green	3·50	3·50

DESIGNS: 12f. Beclere (radiology); 18f. Terrillon (antiseptics); 30f. Oehmichen (helicopter).

406 Uzes Chateau

1957

1328	**406**	12f. black, brown & bl	60	55
1334	-	8f. green	20	15
1335	-	15f. black and green	20	15

DESIGNS—VERT: 8f., 15f. Le Quesnoy.

407 Jean Moulin

1957. Heroes of the Resistance (1st issue). Inscr as in T **407**.

1329	**407**	8f. chocolate & brown	1·60	75
1330	-	10f. blue and black	1·60	75
1331	-	12f. green and brown	1·60	1·30
1332	-	18f. black and violet	2·75	2·10
1333	-	20f. blue & turquoise	2·40	1·40

PORTRAITS: 10f. H. d'Estienne d'Orves; 12f. R. Keller; 18f. P. Brossolette; 20f. J.-B. Lebas.

See also Nos. 1381/4, 1418/22, 1478/82 and 1519/22.

409 Emblems of Auditing

1957. 150th Anniv of Court of Accounts.

1336	**409**	12f. blue and green	35	35

410 Joinville

1957. National Relief Fund.

1337	**410**	12f.+3f. olive & sage	4·00	3·75
1338	-	12f.+3f. black & turq	4·00	3·75
1339	-	15f.+5f. red & verm	5·25	5·25
1340	-	15f.+5f. bl & ultram	5·25	5·00
1341	-	18f.+7f. black & grn	6·25	6·00
1342	-	18f.+7f. choc & brn	6·25	6·00

PORTRAITS: No. 1338, Bernard Palissy; No. 1339, Quentin de la Tour; No. 1340, Lamennais; No. 1341, George Sand; No. 1342, Jules Guesde.

See also Nos. 1390/5.

411 "Public Works"

1957. French Public Works.

1343	**411**	30f. brn, dp brn & grn	3·00	1·80

412 Port of Brest

1957

1344	**412**	12f. green and brown	1·70	1·60

413 Leo Lagrange (founder) and Stadium

1957. Universities World Games.

1345	**413**	18f. black and grey	80	75

414 Auguste Comte

1957. Death Centenary of Auguste Comte (philosopher).

1346	**414**	35f. sepia and brown	60	55

415 "Agriculture and Industry"

1957. Europa.

1347	**415**	20f. green and brown	90	40
1348	**415**	35f. blue and sepia	1·70	1·30

416 Roman Theatre, Lyons

1957. Bimillenary of Lyons.

1349	**416**	20f. purple & brown	60	55

417 Sens River, Guadeloupe

1957. Tourist Publicity Series.

1350	**417**	8f. brown and green	25	15
1351	-	10f. chocolate & brown	25	15
1351a	-	15f. multicoloured	60	55
1352	-	18f. brown and blue	40	35
1353	-	25f. brown and grey	1·00	35
1353a	-	30f. green	3·75	35
1354	-	35f. mauve and red	40	15
1355	-	50f. brown & green	85	15
1356	-	65f. blue and indigo	1·00	55
1356a	-	85f. purple	5·50	55
1356b	**417**	100f. violet	45·00	55

DESIGNS—HORIZ: 10f., 30f., Palais de l'Elysee, Paris; 15f. Chateau de Foix; 25f. Chateau de Valencay; 50f. Les Antiques, Saint Remy; 65f., 85f. Evian-les-Bains. VERT: 18f. Beynac-Cazenac (Dordogne); 35f. Rouen Cathedral.

418 Copernicus

1957. Famous Men.

1357	**418**	8f. brown	1·30	90
1358	-	10f. green	1·30	90
1359	-	12f. violet	1·30	1·10
1360	-	15f. brown & dp brown	1·70	1·30
1361	-	18f. blue	2·40	1·50
1362	-	25f. purple and lilac	2·40	1·50
1363	-	35f. blue	2·75	2·00

PORTRAITS: 10f. Michelangelo; 12f. Cervantes; 15f. Rembrandt; 18f. Newton; 25f. Mozart; 35f. Goethe.

See also Nos. 1367/74.

419 L.-J. Thenard

1957. Death Centenary of Thenard (chemist).

1364	**419**	15f. green and bistre	60	55

420 "The Blind Man and the Beggar" (after J. Callot)

1957. Red Cross Fund. Cross in red.

1365	**420**	15f.+7f. blue	6·00	5·75
1366	-	20f.+8f. brown	7·75	7·50

DESIGN: 20f. "The Beggar and the One-eyed Woman" (after J. Callot).

1958. French Doctors. As T **418**.

1367	8f. brown	1·30	90
1368	12f. violet	1·30	90
1369	15f. blue	2·00	1·10
1370	35f. black	2·50	1·60

PORTRAITS: 8f. Dr. Pinel; 12f. Dr. Widal; 15f. Dr. C. Nicolle; 35f. Dr. R. Leriche.

1958. French Scientists. As T **418**.

1371	8f. violet and blue	1·30	90
1372	12f. grey and brown	1·60	90
1373	15f. green and deep green	2·50	1·30
1374	35f. red and lake	3·50	1·80

PORTRAITS: 8f. Lagrange (mathematician); 12f. Le Verrier (astronomer); 15f. Foucault (physicist); 35f. Berthollet (chemist).

421 Rural Postal Services

1958. Stamp Day.

1375	**421**	15f.+5f. deep green, green and brown	2·50	1·80

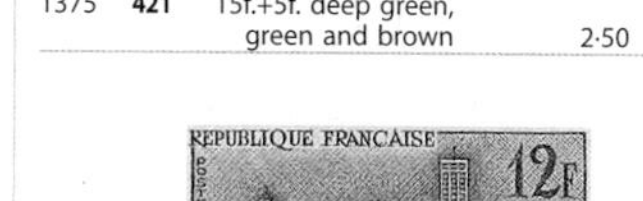

422 Le Havre

1958. Municipal Reconstruction.

1376	**422**	12f. red and olive	95	75
1377	-	15f. brown and violet	95	75
1378	-	18f. indigo and blue	1·60	1·10
1379	-	25f. brown, turq & blue	1·90	1·10

DESIGNS—VERT: 15f. Maubeuge; 18f. Saint-Die. HORIZ: 25f. Sete.

423 French Pavilion

1958. Brussels International Exhibition.

1380	**423**	35f. green, blue & brn	35	35

1958. Heroes of the Resistance (2nd issue). Portraits inscr as in T **407**.

1381	8f. black and violet	1·10	1·00
1382	12f. green and blue	1·10	1·00
1383	15f. grey and sepia	2·75	1·40
1384	20f. blue and brown	2·10	1·60

PORTRAITS: 8f. Jean Cavailles; 12f. Fred Scamaroni; 15f. Simone Michel-Levy; 20f. Jacques Bingen.

424 Boules

1958. French Traditional Games.

1385	**424**	12f. brown and red	1·50	1·30
1386	-	15f. dp grn, grn & bl	1·90	1·40
1387	-	18f. brown and green	3·50	1·80
1388	-	25f. blue and brown	5·00	2·75

DESIGNS—HORIZ: 15f. Nautical jousting. VERT: 18f. Archery; 25f. Breton wrestling.

425 Senlis Cathedral

1958. Senlis Cathedral Commemoration.

1389	**425**	15f. blue and indigo	60	55

1958. Red Cross Fund. French Celebrities as T **410**.

1390	12f.+4f. green	2·50	2·50
1391	12f.+4f. blue	2·50	2·50
1392	15f.+5f. purple	2·75	2·75
1393	15f.+5f. blue	3·00	2·75
1394	20f.+8f. red	3·00	2·75
1395	35f.+15f. green	3·75	3·75

PORTRAITS: No. 1390, J. du Bellay; No. 1391, Jean Bart; No. 1392, D. Diderot; No. 1393, G. Courbet; No. 1394, J. B. Carpeaux; No. 1395, Toulouse-Lautrec.

426 Fragment of the Bayeux Tapestry

1958

1396	**426**	15f. red and blue	65	65

1958. Europa. As T 345 of Belgium. Size 22×36 mm.

1397	20f. red	60	45
1398	35f. blue	1·80	1·30

427 Town Halls of Paris and Rome

1958. Paris–Rome Friendship.

1399	**427**	35f. grey, blue & red	60	55

428 UNESCO Headquarters, Paris

1958. Inauguration of UNESCO Building.

1400	**428**	20f. bistre and turq	25	25
1401	-	35f. red and myrtle	35	35

DESIGN: 35f. Different view of building.

429 Flanders Grave

1958. 40th Anniv of First World War Armistice.

1402	**429**	15f. blue and green	85	55

430 Arms of Marseilles

1958. Arms of French Towns.

1403	**430**	50c. blue & deep blue	20	15
1404	-	70c. multicoloured	20	15
1405	-	80c. red, yellow & bl	20	15
1406	-	1f. red, yellow & blue	20	15
1407	-	2f. red, green & blue	20	15
1408	-	3f. multicoloured	20	15
1409	-	5f. red and brown	20	15
1410	-	15f. multicoloured	35	15

ARMS: 70c. "Lyon"; 80c. "Toulouse"; 1f. "Bordeaux"; 2f. "Nice"; 3f. "Nantes"; 5f. "Lille"; 15f. "Alger".

See also Nos. 1452, 1454, 1498a/99f, 1700/1 and 1735.

431 St. Vincent de Paul

1958. Red Cross Fund. Cross in red.

1411	**431**	15f.+7f. green	1·90	1·80
1412	-	20f.+8f. violet	1·90	1·80

PORTRAIT: 20f. J. H. Dunant (founder).

432 Arc du Carrousel and Flowers

1959. Paris Flower Festival.

1413	**432**	15f. multicoloured	80	55

433 Symbols of Learning and "Academic Palms"

1959. 150th Anniv of "Academic Palms".

1414	**433**	20f. black, vio & lake	35	35

434 Father Charles de Foucauld (missionary)

1959. Charles de Foucauld Commem.

1415	**434**	50f. multicoloured	80	75

435 Douglas DC-3 Mail Plane making Night-landing

1959. Stamp Day.

1416	**435**	20f.+5f. mult	95	90

See also No. 1644.

436 Miner's Lamp, Picks and School Building

1959. 175th Anniv of School of Mines.

1417	**436**	20f. turq, blk & red	35	35

437 "Five Martyrs"

1959. Heroes of the Resistance (3rd series).

1418	**437**	15f. black and violet	65	35
1419	-	15f. violet and purple	65	65
1420	-	20f. brown & chestnut	65	65
1421	-	20f. turquoise & green	90	85
1422	-	30f. violet and purple	1·10	90

PORTRAITS—As T **407**: No. 1419, Yvonne Le Roux; No. 1420, Martin Bret; No. 1421, Mederic-Vedy; No. 1422, Moutardier.

438 Foum el Gherza Dam

1959. French Technical Achievements.

1423	**438**	15f. turq and brown	60	35
1424	-	20f. purple, red & brn	85	80
1425	-	30f. brn, turq & blue	85	80
1426	-	50f. blue and green	1·30	90

DESIGNS—VERT: 20f. Marcoule Atomic Power Station; 30f. Oil derrick and pipe-line at Hassi-Messaoud, Sahara. HORIZ: 50f. National Centre of Industry and Technology, Paris.

439 C. Goujon and C. Rozanoff (test pilots)

1959. Goujon and Rozanoff Commem.

1427	**439**	20f. brown, red & blue	80	75

440 Villehardouin (chronicler)

1959. Red Cross Fund.

1428	**440**	15f.+5f. blue	1·90	1·80
1429	-	15f.+5f. myrtle	1·90	1·80
1430	-	20f.+10f. bistre	1·90	1·80
1431	-	20f.+10f. grey	2·10	2·10
1432	-	30f.+10f. lake	2·10	2·10
1433	-	30f.+10f. brown	2·40	2·10

PORTRAITS: No. 1429, Le Notre (Royal gardener); No. 1430, D'Alembert (philosopher); No. 1431, D'Angers (sculptor); No. 1432, Bichat (physiologist); No. 1433, Bartholdi (sculptor).

441 M. Desbordes-Valmore

1959. Death Centenary of Marceline Desbordes-Valmore (poetess).

1434	**441**	30f. brown, blue & grn	35	35

442 "Marianne" in Ship of State

1959

1437	**442**	25f. red and black	60	15

See also No. 1456.

443 Tancarville Bridge

1959. Inauguration of Tancarville Bridge.

1438	**443**	30f. green, brown & blue	60	55

444 Jean Jaures

1959. Birth Centenary of Jean Jaures (socialist leader).

1439	**444**	50f. brown	60	55

1959. Europa. As T **360** of Belgium but size 22×36 mm.

1440	25f. green	60	25
1441	50f. violet	2·40	1·60

445 "Giving Blood"

1959. Blood Donors.

1442	**445**	20f. grey and red	35	35

446 Clasped Hands of Friendship

1959. Tercent of Treaty of the Pyrenees.

1443	**446**	50f. red, blue & mauve	80	55

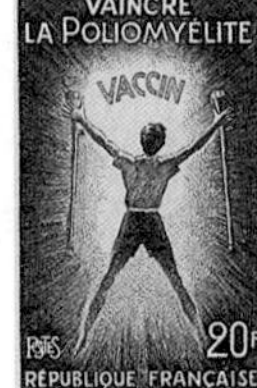

447 Youth throwing away Crutches

1959. Infantile Paralysis Relief Campaign.

1444	**447**	20f. blue	35	35

448 Henri Bergson

1959. Birth Centenary of Bergson (philosopher).

1445	**448**	50f. brown	60	55

449 Avesnes-sur-Helpe

1959

1446	**449**	20f. blue, brown & blk	60	35
1447	-	30f. brown, purple & bl	60	55

DESIGN: 30f. Perpignan Castle.

450 Abbe C. M. de l'Epee (teacher of deaf mutes)

1959. Red Cross Fund. Cross in red.

1448	**450**	20f.+10f. purple & blk	3·00	3·00
1449	-	25f.+10f. black & blue	3·50	3·50

PORTRAIT: 25f. V. Hauy (teacher of the blind).

451 N.A.T.O. Headquarters, Paris

1959. Tenth Anniv of N.A.T.O.

1450	**451**	50f. brown, green & bl	80	75

1959. Frejus Disaster Fund. Surch FREJUS + 5f.

1451	**442**	25f.+5f. red & black	35	35

453 Sower

1960. T **453** and previous designs but new currency.

1452	-	5c. red & brn (as 1409)	7·25	25
1453	**344**	10c. green	80	15
1454	-	15c. mult (as 1410)	1·20	25
1455	**453**	20c. red & turquoise	35	15
1456	**442**	25c. blue and red	3·25	15
1456a	**453**	30c. blue and indigo	2·40	55

1960. Air. As previous designs but new currency and new design (No. 1457b).

1457	-	2f. pur & blk (as 1195)	2·40	35
1457b	-	2f. indigo and blue	1·40	35
1458	-	3f. brn & bl (as 1318)	2·40	25
1459	**401**	5f. black and blue	4·75	1·10
1460	-	10f. black, violet and brown (as 1320)	19·00	2·75

DESIGN: No. 1457b, Dassault Berguet Mystere Falcon.

454 Laon Cathedral

1960. Tourist Publicity.

1461	**454**	15c. indigo and blue	60	35
1462	-	30c. pur, grn & blue	3·75	45
1463	-	45c. vio, pur & sepia	1·20	35
1464	-	50c. purple and green	2·50	15
1465	-	65c. brn, grn & blue	1·90	35
1466	-	85c. sepia, grn & blue	3·75	35
1467	-	1f. violet, grn & turq	3·75	30

DESIGNS—HORIZ: 30c. Fougeres Chateau; 65c. Valley of the Sioule; 85c. Chaumont Railway Viaduct. VERT: 45c. Kerrata Gorges, Algeria; 50c. Tlemcen Mosque, Algeria; 1f. Cilaos Church and Great Bernard Mountains, Reunion.

See also Nos. 1485/7.

455 Pierre de Nolhac

1960. Birth Centenary (1959) of Pierre de Nolhac (historian).

1468	**455**	20c. black	80	55

456 St. Etienne Museum

1960. Museum of Art and Industry, St. Etienne.

1469	**456**	30c. brown, red & blue	80	55

1960. As T **345** but with values in new currency.

1470	**345**	8c. violet	1·20	25
1471	**345**	20c. green	3·75	80
1472	**345**	40c. red	13·50	3·00
1473	**345**	55c. green	43·00	23·00

Nos. 1470/3 were only issued precancelled (see note below No. 432).

457 Assembly Emblem and View of Cannes

1960. 5th Meeting of European Mayors Assembly.

1474	**457**	50c. brown and green	1·20	90

458 "Ampere" (cable-laying ship)

1960. Stamp Day.

1475	**458**	20c.+5c. blue & turq	2·30	1·70

459 Girl of Savoy

1960. Centenary of Attachment of Savoy and Nice to France.

1476	**459**	30c. green	1·00	80
1477	-	50c. brown, red and yellow (Girl of Nice)	1·00	55

1960. Heroes of the Resistance (4th series). Portraits as T **407**.

1478	20c. black and brown	2·50	1·70
1479	20c. lake and red	2·50	1·70
1480	30c. violet & deep violet	3·75	2·30
1481	30c. blue and indigo	3·75	2·30
1482	50c. brown and green	5·00	3·50

PORTRAITS: No. 1478, E. Debeaumarche; No. 1479, P. Masse; No. 1480, M. Ripoche; No. 1481, L. Vieljeux; No. 1482, Abbe Rene Bonpain.

460 Child Refugee

1960. World Refugee Year.

1483	**460**	25c.+10c. bl, brn & grn	60	55

461 "The Road to Learning"

1960. 150th Anniv of Strasbourg Teachers' Training College.

1484	**461**	20c. violet, pur & blk	35	35

1960. Views as T **454**.

1485	15c. sepia, grey and blue	60	55
1485a	20c. blue, green and buff	35	35
1486	30c. sepia, green and blue	1·20	90
1487	50c. brown, green & red	1·00	90

DESIGNS: 15c. Lisieux Basilica; 20c. Bagnoles de l'Orne; 30c. Chateau de Blois; 50c. La Bourboule.

462 L'Hospital (statesman)

1960. Red Cross Fund.

1488	**462**	10c.+5c. violet & red	2·50	2·30
1489	-	20c.+10c. turq & grn	3·75	3·50
1490	-	20c.+10c. green & brn	3·75	3·50
1491	-	30c.+10c. blue & vio	5·00	4·50
1492	-	30c.+10c. crim & red	5·00	4·50
1493	-	50c.+15c. blue and slate	6·25	5·75

DESIGNS: No. 1489, Boileau (poet); No. 1490, Turenne (military leader); No. 1491, Bizet (composer); No. 1492, Charcot (neurologist); No. 1493, Degas (painter).

463 "Marianne"

1960

1494	**463**	25c. grey and red	35	15

464 Cross of Lorraine

1960. 20th Anniv of De Gaulle's Appeal.

1495	**464**	20c. brown, grn & sep	1·00	55

465 Jean Bouin and Olympic Stadium

1960. Olympic Games.

1496	**465**	20c. brown, red & blue	60	55

1960. Europa. As T **373** of Belgium, but size 36×22½ mm.

1497	25c. turquoise and green	35	25
1498	50c. purple and red	1·00	55

1960. Arms. As T **430**.

1498a	1c. blue and yellow	20	15
1498b	2c. yellow, green and blue	20	15
1499	5c. multicoloured	20	15
1499a	5c. red, yellow and blue	20	15
1499b	10c. blue, yellow and red	20	15
1499c	12c. red, yellow and black	20	15
1499d	15c. yellow, blue and red	20	15
1499e	18c. multicoloured	60	55
1499f	30c. red and blue	75	15

ARMS: 1c. "Niort"; 2c. "Gueret"; 5c. (No. 1499) "Oran"; 5c. (No. 1499a) "Amiens"; 10c. "Troyes"; 12c. "Agen"; 15c. "Nevers"; 18c. "Saint-Denis (Reunion)"; 30c. "Paris".

466 Madame de Stael (after Gerard)

1960. Madame de Stael (writer).

1500	**466**	30c. olive and purple	60	55

467 Gen. Estienne, Morane Saulnier Type L Airplane and Tank

1960. Birth Centenary of Gen. Estienne.

1501	**467**	15c. sepia and lilac	60	55

468 Sangnier

1960. 10th Death Anniv of Marc Sangnier (patriot).

1502	**468**	20c. black, violet & blue	35	35

469 Order of the Liberation

1960. 20th Anniv of Order of the Liberation.

1503	**469**	20c. green and black	60	55

470 Atlantic Puffins at Les Sept Iles

1960. Nature Protection.

1504	**470**	30c. multicoloured	35	35
1505	-	50c. multicoloured	1·20	55

DESIGN: 50c. European bee eaters, Camargue.

471 A. Honnorat

1960. 10th Death Anniv of Andre Honnorat (philanthropist).

1506	**471**	30c. black, green & blue	35	35

472 Mace of St. Martin's Brotherhood

1960. Red Cross Fund. Cross in red.

1507	**472**	20c.+10c. lake	5·00	4·50
1508	-	25c.+10c. blue	5·00	4·50

DESIGN: 25c. St. Martin (after 16th-cent. wood-carving).

473 St. Barbe and College

1960. 500th Anniv of St. Barbe College.

1509	**473**	30c. multicoloured	60	55

474 Northern Lapwings

1960. Study of Bird Migration. Inscr "ETUDE DES MIGRATIONS".

1510	**474**	20c. multicoloured	35	35
1511	-	45c. multicoloured	1·00	1·10

DESIGN: 45c. Green-winged teal.

475 "Mediterranean" (after Maillol)

1961. Birth Cent of Aristide Maillol (sculptor).

1512	**475**	20c. blue and red	35	35

476 "Marianne"

1961

1513	**476**	20c. red and blue	35	15

477 Orly Airport

1961. Opening of New Installations at Orly Airport.

1514	**477**	50c. turq, blue & blk	80	55

478 Georges Melies

1961. Birth Centenary of Georges Melies (cinematograph pioneer).

1515	**478**	50c. blue, brown & vio	1·20	90

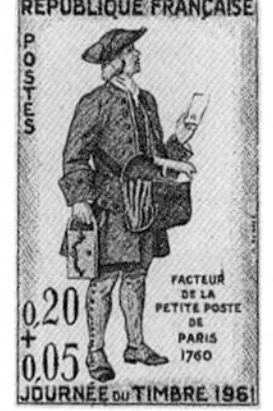
479 Postman of Paris "Little Post" 1760

1961. Stamp Day and Red Cross Fund.

1516	**479**	20c.+5c. grn, red & brn	1·20	90

480 Jan Nicquet and Tobacco Flowers and Leaves

1961. 400th Anniv of Introduction of Tobacco into France.

1517	**480**	30c. red, brown & grn	35	35

The portrait on No. 1517 is of Jan Nicquet, a Flemish merchant, and not Jean Nicot as inscribed.

481 Father Lacordaire (after Chasseriau)

1961. Death Centenary of Father Lacordaire (theologian).

1518	**481**	30c. black and brown	60	55

1961. Heroes of the Resistance (5th issue). Portrait inscr as in T **407**.

1519	20c. violet and blue	1·50	90
1520	20c. blue and green	1·50	90
1521	30c. black and brown	2·50	1·30
1522	30c. black and blue	2·00	1·50

PORTRAITS: No. 1519, J. Renouvin; No. 1520, L. Dubray; No. 1521, P. Gateaud; No. 1522, Mother Elisabeth.

482 Dove, Globe and Olive Branch

1961. World Federation of Old Soldiers Meeting, Paris.

1523	**482**	50c. red, blue & green	60	55

483 Deauville, 1861

1961. Centenary of Deauville.

1524	**483**	50c. lake	2·75	2·00

484 Du Guesclin (Constable of France)

1961. Red Cross Fund.

1525	**484**	15c.+5c. black & pur	2·50	2·30
1526	-	20c.+10c. green & blue	3·75	3·50
1527	-	20c.+10c. crimson & red	3·75	3·50
1528	-	30c.+10c. black & brn	3·75	3·50
1529	-	45c.+10c. brown & grn	5·00	4·50
1530	-	50c.+15c. violet & red	5·00	4·50

PORTRAITS: No. 1526, Puget (sculptor); No. 1527, Coulomb (physicist); No. 1528, General Drouot; No. 1529, Daumier (caricaturist); No. 1530, Apollinaire (writer).

485 Champmesle ("Roxane")

1961. French Actors and Actresses. Frames in red.

1531	**485**	20c. brown and green	1·50	55
1532	-	30c. brown and red	1·50	75
1533	-	30c. myrtle and green	1·50	75
1534	-	50c. brown & turquoise	2·10	1·10
1535	-	50c. brown and olive	2·00	90

PORTRAITS: No. 1532, Talma ("Oreste"); No. 1533, Rachel ("Phedre"); No. 1534, Raimu ("Cesar"); No. 1535, Gerard Philipe ("Le Cid").

486 Mont Dore, Snow Crystal and Cable Rly

1961. Mont Dore.

1536	**486**	20c. purple and orange	35	35

487 Thann

1961. 800th Anniv of Thann.

1537	**487**	20c. violet, brn & grn	1·00	75

488 Pierre Fauchard

1961. Birth Bicentenary of Pierre Fauchard (dentist).

1538	**488**	50c. black and green	80	75

489 Doves

1961. Europa.

1539	**489**	25c. red	35	25
1540	**489**	50c. blue	1·00	55

490 Sully-sur-Loire

1961. Tourist Publicity.

1541	-	15c. slate, pur & turq	20	15
1542	-	20c. brown and green	35	35
1543	-	30c. blue, grn & sepia	35	35
1544	-	30c. black, grey & grn	1·90	1·10
1545	**490**	45c. brown, green & blue	35	15
1546	-	50c. myrt, turq & grn	2·00	35
1547	-	65c. blue, brown & myrt	60	35
1548	-	85c. blue, brown & myrt	80	55
1549	-	1f. brown, blue & myrt	6·25	55
1550	-	1f. brown, green & blue	80	15

VIEWS—HORIZ: 15c. Saint-Paul; 30c. (No. 1543), Arcachon; 30c. (No. 1544), Law Courts, Rennes; 50c. Cognac; 65c. Dinan; 85c. Calais; 1f. (No. 1549), Medea, Algeria; 1f. (No. 1550), Le Touquet-Paris-Plage, golf-bag and Handley Page H.P.R.7 Dart Herald airplane. VERT: 20c. Laval, Mayenne.

See also Nos. 1619/23, 1654/7, 1684/8, 1755/61, 1794, 1814/18, 1883/5, 1929/33, 1958/61, 2005/8, 2042/4, 2062/4, 2115/20, 2187/97, 2258/64, 2310/15, 2360/5, 2403/10, 2503/8, 2566/70, 2630/4, 2652/6, 2710/14, 2762/6, 2834/6, 2883/6, 2973/6, 3024/6, 3077/80, 3124/9, 3180/3, 3240/3, 3330/3, 3375/9, 3487/91, 3580/3, 3642/5, 3720/3, 3800/1, 3908/11, 3946/9 and 4084/7.

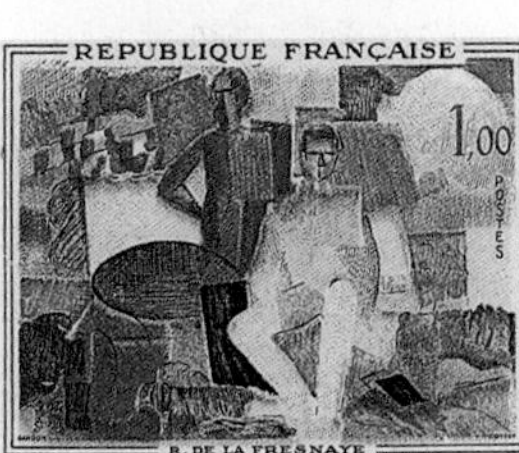

491 "14th July" (R. de la Fresnaye)

1961. Modern French Art.

1551		50c. multicoloured	5·00	2·30
1552		65c. blue, green & violet	7·50	3·50
1553		85c. red, bistre and blue	3·75	2·30
1554	**491**	1f. multicoloured	6·25	3·50

PAINTINGS: 50c. "The Messenger" (Braque); 65c. "Blue Nudes" (Matisse); 85c. "The Cardplayers" (Cezanne).

See also Nos. 1590/2, 1603/6, 1637/9, 1671/4, 1710/4, 1742/5, 1786/9, 1819/22, 1877/80, 1908/10, 1944/7, 1985/8, 2033/6, 2108/13, 2159/60, 2243, 2290/2, 2338/41, 2398/9, 2531/4, 2580/2, 2608/12, 2672/6, 2710/5, 2721/5, 2773/6, 2850/3, 2858/60, 2966/8, 3008/9, 3085, 3245/7, 3306/7, 3368/9, 3483/6, 3561/3, 3638/4, 3702/5, 3899, 3990, 3902, 3951/4 and 4074/7.

493 "It is so sweet to love" (Wood-carving from Rouault's "Miserere")

1961. Red Cross Fund. Cross in red.

1555	**493**	20c.+10c. black & pur	3·50	3·25
1556	-	25c.+10c. black & pur	4·25	4·00

DESIGN: 25c. "The blind leading the blind" (from Rouault's "Miserere").

494 Liner "France"

1962. Maiden Voyage of Liner "France".

1557	**494**	30c. black, red & blue	1·20	75

495 Skier at Speed

1962. World Ski Championships, Chamonix.

1558	**495**	30c. violet and blue	35	35
1559	-	50c. green, blue & vio	80	55

DESIGN: 50c. Slalom-racer.

496 M. Bourdet

1962. 60th Birth Anniv of Maurice Bourdet (journalist and radio commentator).

1560	**496**	30c. grey	35	35

497 Dr. P.-F. Bretonneau

1962. Death Centenary of Dr. Pierre-Fidele Bretonneau (medical scientist).

1561	**497**	50c. violet and blue	60	55

498 Gallic Cock

1962

1562	**498**	25c. red, blue & brown	35	15
1562a	**498**	30c. red, green & brn	1·20	15

499 Royal Messenger of late Middle Ages

1962. Stamp Day.

1563	**499**	20c.+5c. brn, bl & red	1·20	1·10

500 Vannes

1962

1564	**500**	30c. blue	1·20	1·10

501 Globe and Stage Set

1962. World Theatre Day.

1565	**501**	50c. lake, grn & ochre	80	55

502 Harbour Installations

1962. 300th Anniv of Cession of Dunkirk to France.

1566	**502**	95c. purple, brown & green	1·90	90

503 Mount Valerien Memorial

1962. Resistance Fighters' Memorials (1st issue).

1567	**503**	20c. myrtle and drab	1·20	90
1568	-	30c. blue	1·20	90
1569	-	50c. indigo and blue	1·50	1·10

MEMORIALS—VERT: 30c. Vercors; 50c. Ile de Sein.

See also Nos. 1609/10.

504 Emblem and Swamp

1962. Malaria Eradication.

1570	**504**	50c. red, blue & green	60	45

505 Nurses and Child

1962. National Hospitals Week.

1571	**505**	30c. brown, grey & grn	35	35

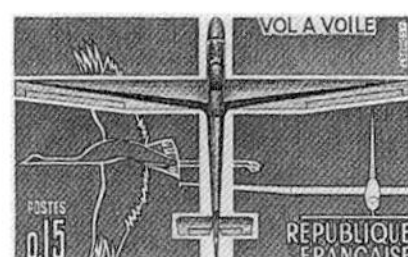

506 Gliders and Stork

1962. Civil and Sports Aviation.

1572	**506**	15c. brown and chest	80	55
1573	-	20c. red and purple	80	55

DESIGN: 20c. Jodel Ambassadeur and early aircraft.

507 Emblem and School of Horology

1962. Cent of School of Horology, Besancon.

1574	**507**	50c. vio, brown & red	80	55

508 "Selecting a Tapestry"

1962. Tercentenary of Manufacture of Gobelin Tapestries.

1575	**508**	50c. turq, red & grn	80	55

509 Pascal

1962. Death Tercent of Pascal (philosopher).

1576	**509**	50c. red and green	80	55

510 Denis Papin (inventor)

1962. Red Cross Fund.

1577	15c.+5c. sepia & turquoise	2·50	2·30
1578	20c.+10c. brown and red	3·75	3·50
1579	20c.+10c. blue and grey	3·75	3·50
1580	30c.+10c. indigo and blue	3·75	3·50
1581	45c.+15c. pur and brown	3·75	3·50
1582	50c.+20c. black and blue	3·75	3·50

DESIGNS: No. 1577, Type **510**; 1578, Edme Bouchardon (sculptor); 1579, Joseph Lakanal (politician); 1580, Gustave Charpentier (composer); 1581, Edouard Estauni (writer); 1582, Hyacinthe Vincent (scientist).

511 "Modern" Rose

1962. Rose Culture.

1583	**511**	20c. red, green & olive	1·00	55
1584	-	30c. red, myrt & olive	1·00	75

DESIGN: 30c. "Old fashioned" rose.

512 Europa "Tree"

1962. Europa.

1585	**512**	25c. violet	35	25
1586	**512**	50c. brown	1·00	55

513 Telecommunications Centre, Pleumeur-Bodou

1962. 1st Trans-Atlantic Telecommunications Satellite Link.

1587	**513**	25c. buff, green & grey	35	35
1588	-	50c. bl, grn & indigo	80	55
1589	-	50c. brown and blue	80	55

DESIGNS: 50c. (No. 1588), "Telstar" satellite, globe and television receiver; 50c. (No. 1589), Radio telescope, Nancay (Cher).

1962. French Art. As T **491**.

1590	50c. multicoloured	5·00	2·30
1591	65c. multicoloured	5·00	2·30
1592	1f. multicoloured	7·50	3·50

PAINTINGS—HORIZ: 50c. "Bonjour, Monsieur Courbet" (Courbet); 65c. "Madame Manet on a Blue Sofa" (Manet). VERT: 1f. "Officer of the Imperial Horse Guards" (Gericault).

514 "Rosalie Fragonard" (after Fragonard)

1962. Red Cross Fund. Cross in red.

1593	**514**	20c.+10c. brown	1·90	1·70
1594	-	25c.+10c. green	3·00	2·75

PORTRAIT: 25c. "Child as Pierrot" (after Fragonard).

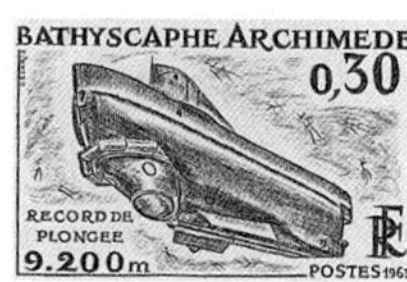

515 Bathyscaphe "Archimede"

1963. Record Undersea Dive.

1595	**515**	30c. black and blue	35	35

516 Flowers and Nantes Chateau

1963. Nantes Flower Show.

1596	**516**	30c. blue, red & green	35	35

517 Jacques Amyot (Bishop of Auxerre)

1963. Red Cross Fund.

1597	**517**	20c.+10c. purple, violet and grey	1·50	1·40
1598	-	20c.+10c. deep brown, brown and blue	1·90	1·70
1599	-	30c.+10c. grn & pur	1·50	1·40
1600	-	30c.+10c. black, green and brown	1·90	1·70
1601	-	50c.+20c. grn, brn & bl	1·90	1·70
1602	-	50c.+20c. blk, bl & brn	2·50	2·30

DESIGNS: No. 1598, Etienne Mehul (composer); No. 1599 Pierre de Marivaux (dramatist); No. 1600, N.-L. Vauquelin (chemist); No. 1601, Jacques Daviel (oculist); No. 1602, Alfred de Vigny (poet).

1963. French Art. As T **491**.

1603	50c. multicoloured	5·00	3·50
1604	85c. multicoloured	2·75	1·80
1605	95c. multicoloured	1·00	90
1606	1f. multicoloured	6·25	4·50

DESIGNS—VERT: 50c. "Jacob's Struggle with the Angel" (Delacroix); 85c. "The Married Couple of the Eiffel Tower" (Chagall); 95c. "The Fur Merchants" (stained glass window, Chartres Cathedral); 1f. "St. Peter and the Miracle of the Fishes" (stained glass window, Church of St. Foy de Conches).

518 Roman Post Chariot

1963. Stamp Day.

1607	**518**	20c.+5c. purple & brn	35	35

519 Woman reaching for Campaign Emblem

1963. Freedom from Hunger.

1608	**519**	50c. brown & myrtle	60	55

520 Glieres Memorial

1963. Resistance Fighters' Memorials (2nd issue).

1609	**520**	30c. olive and brown	80	75
1610	-	50c. black	80	75

DESIGN: 50c. Deportees Memorial, Ile de la Cite (Paris).

521 Beethoven (West Germany)

1963. Celebrities of European Economic Community Countries.

1611	**521**	20c. blue, brown & grn	60	55
1612	-	20c. black, violet & red	60	55
1613	-	20c. blue, pur & olive	60	55
1614	-	20c. brown, pur & brn	60	55
1615	-	30c. sepia, violet & brn	60	55

PORTRAITS AND VIEWS: No. 1611, Birthplace and modern Bonn; No. 1612, Emile Verhaeren (Belgium: Family grave and residence, Roisin); No. 1613, Giuseppe Mazzini (Italy: Marcus Aurelius statue and Appian Way, Rome); No. 1614, Emile Mayrisch (Luxembourg: Colpach Chateau and Steel Plant, Esch); No. 1615, Hugo de Groot (Netherlands: Palace of Peace, The Hague, and St. Agatha's Church, Delft).

522 Hotel des Postes, Paris

1963. Centenary of Paris Postal Conference.

1616	**522**	50c. sepia	60	55

523 College Building

1963. 400th Anniv of Louis the Great College, Paris.

1617	**523**	30c. myrtle	35	35

524 St. Peter's Church and Castle Keep, Caen

1963. 36th French Philatelic Societies Federation Congress, Caen.

1618	**524**	30c. brown and blue	35	35

1963. Tourist Publicity. As T **490**. Inscr "196…

1619	30c. ochre, blue & green		
1620	50c. red, blue & turquoise		
1621	60c. red, turquoise & blue	1·…	
1622	85c. purple, turquoise & grn	2·1…	
1623	95c. black	1·20	35

DESIGNS—HORIZ: 30c. Amboise Chateau; 50c. Cote d'Azur, Var; 85c. Vittel. VERT: 60c. Saint-Flour; 95c. Church and cloisters, Moissac.

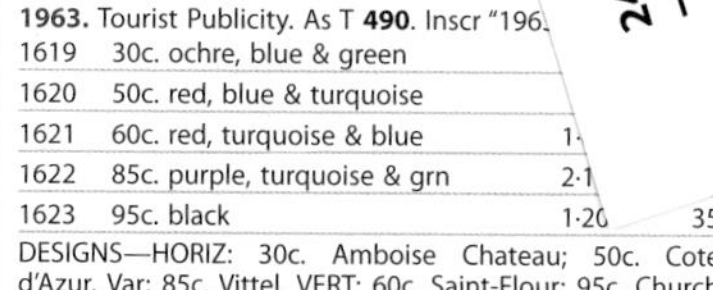

525 Water-skiing

1963. World Water-skiing Championships, Vichy.

1624	**525**	30c. black, red & turq	35	35

526 "Co-operation"

1963. Europa.

1625	**526**	25c. brown	50	35
1626	**526**	50c. green	75	55

527 "Child with Grapes" (Angers)

1963. Red Cross Fund. Cross in red.

1627	**527**	20c.+10c. black	1·20	1·10
1628	-	25c.+10c. green	1·20	1·10

DESIGN: 25c. "The Piper" (Manet).

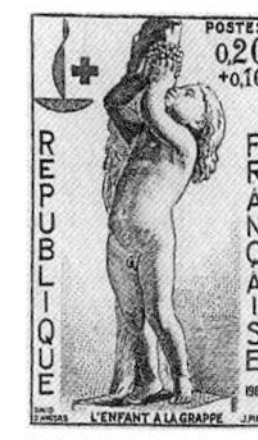

528 "Philately"

1963. "PHILATEC 1964" International Stamp Exhibition, Paris (1st issue).

1629	**528**	25c. red, green & grey	35	35

See also Nos. 1640/3 and 1651.

529 Radio-T.V. Centre

1963. Opening of Radio-T.V. Centre, Paris.

1630	**529**	20c. slate, ol & brn	35	35

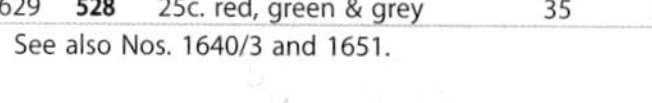

530 Emblems of C.P. Services

1964. Civil Protection.

1631	**530**	30c. blue, red & orange	60	55

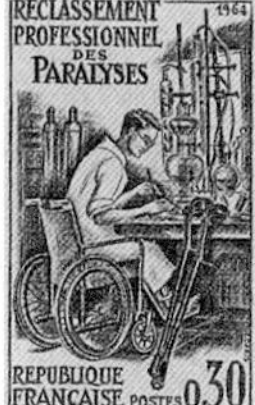

531 Paralytic at Work in Invalid Chair

1964. Professional Rehabilitation of Paralytics.

1632	**531**	30c. brn, chestnut & grn	35	35

532 18th-century Courier

1964. Stamp Day.

1633	**532**	20c.+5c. myrtle	35	35

533 "Deportation"

1964. 20th Anniv of Liberation (1st issue).

1634	**533**	20c.+5c. slate	1·00	90
1635	-	50c.+5c. green	1·20	1·10

DESIGN: 50c. "Resistance" (memorial).
See also Nos. 1652/3 and 1658.

534 Pres. Rene Coty

1964. Pres. Coty Commemoration.

1636	**534**	30c.+10c. brown & red	60	55

1964. French Art. As T **491**.

1637	1f. multicoloured	2·50	1·80
1638	1f. multicoloured	1·90	1·40
1639	1f. multicoloured	1·00	90

DESIGNS—VERT: No. 1637, Jean le Bon (attributed to Girard of Orleans); No. 1638, Tomb plaque of Geoffrey IV (12th-century "champleve" (grooved) enamel from Limousin); No. 1639, "The Lady with the Unicorn" (15th-century tapestry).

535 "Blanc" 2c. Stamp of 1900

1964. "PHILATEC 1964" International Stamp Exhibition, Paris (2nd issue).

1641	**535**	25c. purple and bistre	60	55
1642	-	25c. blue and bistre	60	55
1640	-	30c. blue, black & brn	60	55
1643	-	30c. red, black & blue	60	55

DESIGNS: No. 1640, "Postal Mechanization" (letter-sorting equipment and parcel conveyor); No. 1642, "Mouchon" 25c. stamp of 1900; No. 1643, "Telecommunications" (telephone dial, teleprinter and T.V. tower).

1964. 25th Anniv of Night Airmail Service. As T **435** but additionally inscr "25E ANNIVERSAIRE" and colours changed.

1644	**435**	25c. multicoloured	35	35

536 Stained Glass Window

1964. 800th Anniv of Notre Dame, Paris.

1645	**536**	60c. multicoloured	80	75

537 Calvin

1964. 400th Death Anniv of Calvin (reformer).

1646	**537**	30c.+10c. brown, sepia and turquoise	60	55

538 Gallic Coin

1964. Pre-cancels.

1647	**538**	10c. brown and green	60	35
1647a	**538**	15c. brown & orange	35	35
1647b	**538**	22c. violet and green	85	55
1647c	**538**	25c. brown and violet	60	75
1647d	**538**	26c. brown & purple	1·00	35
1647e	**538**	30c. brn & lt brown	1·00	90
1647f	**538**	35c. blue and red	1·90	90
1648	**538**	45c. brown and green	2·50	1·10
1648a	**538**	50c. brown and blue	1·20	1·30
1648b	**538**	70c. brown and blue	8·00	4·50
1649	**538**	90c. brown and red	3·00	1·80

See note below No. 432 (1920).
For stamps as Type **538** but inscribed "FRANCE", see Nos. 2065a/1.

539 Pope Sylvester II

1964. Pope Sylvester II Commemoration.

1650	**539**	30c.+10c. pur & grey	60	55

540 Rocket and Horseman

1964. "PHILATEC 1964" International Stamp Exhibition, Paris (3rd issue).

1651	**540**	1f. blue, red & brown	37·00	29·00
MS1651a		145×285 mm. No. 1651 ×8 plus labels bearing "PHILATEC" emblem	£375	£275

Sold at 4f. incl. entrance fee to Exhibition.

541 Landings in Normandy and Provence

1964. 20th Anniv of Liberation (2nd issue).

1652	**541**	30c.+5c. sep, brn & bl	1·20	1·10
1653	-	30c.+5c. red, sep & brn	1·20	1·10

DESIGN: No. 1653, Taking prisoners in Paris, and tank in Strasbourg.

1964. Tourist Publicity. As T **490**. Inscr "1964".

1654	40c. brown, green & chest	50	35
1655	70c. purple, turquoise & blue	60	15
1656	1f.25 green, blue & bistre	1·20	45
1657	1f.30 chestnut, choc & brn	2·20	55

DESIGNS—HORIZ: 40c., 1f.25, Notre-Dame Chapel, Haut-Ronchamp (Haute-Saone). VERT: 70c. Caesar's Tower, Provins; 1f.30, Joux Chateau (Doubs).

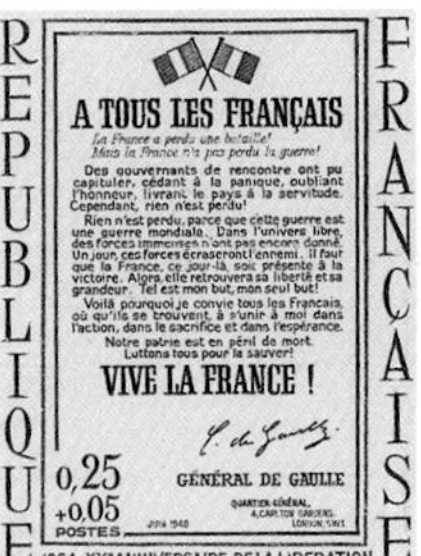

542 De Gaulle's Appeal of 18th June, 1940

1964. 20th Anniv of Liberation (3rd issue).

1658	**542**	25c.+5c. blk, red & bl	1·50	1·40

543 Judo

1964. Olympic Games, Tokyo.

1659	**543**	50c. purple and blue	60	55

544 G. Mandel

1964. 20th Death Anniv of Georges Mandel (statesman).

1660	**544**	30c. purple	35	35

545 Soldiers departing for the Marne by Taxi-cab

1964. 50th Anniv of Victory of the Marne.

1661	**545**	30c. black, red & blue	35	35

546 Europa "Flower"

1964. Europa.

1662	**546**	25c. red, brown & grn	35	25
1663	**546**	50c. red, green & vio	1·00	35

547 Co-operation

1964. French, Africa and Malagasy Co-operation.

1664	**547**	25c. choc, blue & brn	35	35

548 J. N. Corvisart (physician)

1964. Red Cross Fund.

1665	**548**	20c.+10c. black and red	60	55
1666	-	25c.+10c. black and red	60	55

DESIGN: 25c. D. Larrey (military surgeon).

549 La Rochefoucauld

1965. Red Cross Fund. Inscr "1965".

1667	**549**	30c.+10c. blue & brn	60	55
1668	-	30c.+10c. brown & red	80	75
1669	-	40c.+10c. slate and brown	80	75
1670	-	40c.+10c. brown, blue and chestnut	80	75

PORTRAITS: No. 1668, Nicolas Poussin (painter); No. 1669, Paul Dukas (composer); No. 1670, Charles d'Orleans.

1965. French Art. As T **491**.

1671	1f. multicoloured	75	55
1672	1f. multicoloured	60	55
1673	1f. multicoloured	60	55
1674	1f. black, rose and red	60	55

DESIGNS—VERT: No. 1671, "L'Anglaise du `Star' au Havre" (Toulouse-Lautrec); No. 1673, "The Apocalypse" (14th-century tapestry). HORIZ: No. 1672, "Hunting with Falcons" (miniature from manuscript "Les Tres Riches Heures du Duc de Berry", by the Limbourg brothers); No. 1674, "The Red Violin" (R. Dufy).

550 "La Guienne" (steam packet)

1965. Stamp Day.

1675	**550**	25c.+10c. blk, grn & bl	1·20	1·10

551 Deportees

1965. 20th Anniv of Return of Deportees.

1676	**551**	40c. green	80	55

552 Youth Club

1965. 20th Anniv of Youth Clubs ("Maisons des Jeunes et de la Culture").

1677	**552**	25c. blue, brn & grn	35	35

553 Girl with Bouquet

1965. "Welcome and Friendship" Campaign.

1678	**553**	60c. red, orge & grn	60	55

554 Allied Flags and Broken Swastika

1965. 20th Anniv of Victory in World War II.

1679	**554**	40c. red, blue & black	60	35

555 I.T.U. Emblem, "Syncom", Morse Key and Pleumeur-Bodou Centre

1965. Centenary of I.T.U.

1680	**555**	60c. brown, black & bl	80	75

556 Croix de Guerre

1965. 50th Anniv of Croix de Guerre.

1681	**556**	40c. brown, red & green	80	75

557 Bourges Cathedral

1965. National Congress of Philatelic Societies, Bourges.

1682	**557**	40c. brown and blue	60	55

558 Stained Glass Window

1965. 800th Anniv of Sens Cathedral.

1683	**558**	1f. multicoloured	75	55

1965. Tourist Publicity. As T **490**. Inscr "1965".

1684	50c. blue, green and bistre	60	25
1685	60c. brown and blue	1·20	40
1686	75c. brown, green & blue	2·00	1·40
1687	95c. brown, green & blue	6·25	1·40
1688	1f. grey, green and brown	2·20	30

DESIGNS—HORIZ: 50c. Moustiers Ste. Marie (Basses-Alpes); 95c. Landscape, Vendee; 1f. Monoliths, Carnac. VERT: 60c. Yachting, Aix-les-Bains; 75c. Tarn gorges.

559 Mont Blanc from Chamonix

1965. Opening of Mont Blanc Road Tunnel.

1689	**559**	30c. violet, blue & plum	35	35

560 Europa "Sprig"

1965. Europa.

1690	**560**	30c. red	1·00	35
1691	**560**	60c. grey	1·60	90

561 Etienne Regnault and "Le Taureau"

1965. Tercent of Colonisation of Reunion.

1692	**561**	30c. blue and red	35	35

562 "One Million Hectares"

1965. Reafforestation.

1693	**562**	25c. brown, yellow & grn	35	35

563 Atomic Reactor and Emblems

1965. 20th Anniv of Atomic Energy Commission.

1694	**563**	60c. black and blue	80	75

564 Aviation School, Salon-de-Provence

1965. 30th Anniv of Aviation School.

1695	**564**	25c. green, indigo & blue	60	35

565 Rocket "Diamant"

1965. Launching of 1st French Satellite.

1696	**565**	30c. blue, turq & ind	35	35
1697	-	60c. blue, turq & ind	60	35

DESIGN: 60c. Satellite "A1".

566 "Le Bebe a la Cuiller"

1965. Red Cross Fund. Paintings by Renoir.

1698	**566**	25c.+10c. blue and red	35	35
1699	-	30c.+10c. brown & red	60	55

DESIGN: 30c. "Coco ecrivant" (portrait of Renoir's small son writing).

1966. Arms. As T **430**.

1700	5c. red and blue	20	15
1701	25c. blue and brown	1·40	35

DESIGNS: 5c. "Auch"; 25c. "Mont-de-Marsan".

568 St. Pierre Fourier and Basilica, Mattaincourt (Vosges)

1966. Red Cross Fund.

1702	**568**	30c.+10c. brown & grn	60	55
1703	-	30c.+10c. purple & grn	60	55
1704	-	30c.+10c. bl, brn & grn	60	55
1705	-	30c.+10c. blue & brn	60	55
1706	-	30c.+10c. brown & grn	60	55
1707	-	30c.+10c. black & brn	60	55

DESIGNS: No. 1703, F. Mansart (architect) and Carnavalet House, Paris; No. 1704, M. Proust (writer) and St. Hilaire Bridge, Illiers (Eure-et-Loir); No. 1705, G. Faure (composer), statuary and music; No. 1706, Hippolyte Taine (philosopher) and birthplace; No. 1707, Elie Metchnikoff (scientist), microscope and Pasteur Institute.

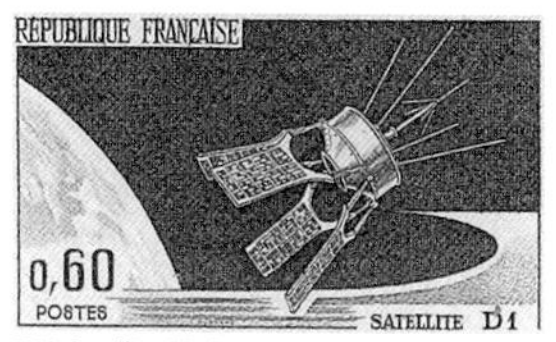

569 Satellite "D1"

1966. Launching of Satellite "D1".

1708	**569**	60c. red, blue & green	35	35

570 Engraving a die

1966. Stamp Day.

1709	**570**	25c.+10c. deep brown, grey and brown	35	35

1966. French Art. As T **491**.

1710	1f. bronze, green & purple	60	55
1711	1f. multicoloured	60	55
1712	1f. multicoloured	60	55
1713	1f. multicoloured	60	55
1714	1f. multicoloured	60	55

DESIGNS—HORIZ: No. 1710, Detail of Vix Crater (wine-bowl); No. 1711, "The New-born Child" (G. de la Tour); No. 1712, "Baptism of Judas" (stained glass window, Sainte Chapelle, Paris); No. 1714, "Crispin and Scapin" (after H. Daumier). VERT: No. 1713, "The Moon and the Bull" (Lurcat tapestry).

571 Knight and Chessboard

1966. International Chess Festival, Le Havre.

1715	**571**	60c. grey, brown & vio	1·00	90

572 Pont St. Esprit Bridge

1966. 700th Anniv of Pont St. Esprit.

1716	**572**	25c. black and blue	35	35

573 St. Michel

1966. Millenary of Mont St. Michel.

1717	**573**	25c. multicoloured	35	35

574 King Stanislas, Arms and Palace

1966. Bicentenary of Reunion of Lorraine and Barrois with France.

1718	**574**	25c. brown, grn & blue	35	35

575 Niort

1966. National Congress of Philatelic Societies, Niort.

1719	**575**	40c. slate, green & blue	60	35

576 "Angel of Verdun"

1966. 50th Anniv of Verdun Victory.

1720	**576**	30c.+5c. slate, bl & grn	35	35

577 Fontenelle

1966. Tercentenary of Academy of Sciences.

1721	**577**	60c. brown and lake	60	55

578 William the Conqueror, Castle and Landings

1966. 900th Anniv of Battle of Hastings.

1722	**578**	60c. brown and blue	80	55

579 Globe and Railway Track

1966. 19th International Railway Congress, Paris.

1723	**579**	60c. brown, blue & lake	1·20	90

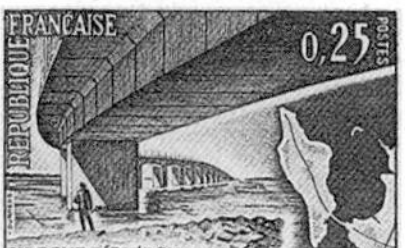

580 Oleron Bridge

1966. Opening of Oleron Bridge.

1724	**580**	25c. brown, green & bl	35	35

581 Europa "Ship"

1966. Europa.

1725	**581**	30c. blue	60	35
1726	**581**	60c. red	1·20	55

582 Vercingetorix

1966. History of France (1st series). Inscr "1966".

1727	**582**	40c. brown, blue & grn	60	55
1728	-	40c. brown and black	60	55
1729	-	60c. red, brown & violet	80	55

DESIGNS—VERT: 40c. (No. 1728), Clovis. 60c. Charlemagne.

See also Nos. 1769/71, 1809/11, 1850/2, 1896/8, 1922/4, 1975/7 and 2017/19.

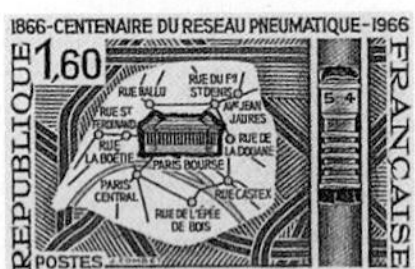

583 Route Map

1966. Centenary of Paris Pneumatic Post.

1730	**583**	1f.60 blue, lake & brn	1·20	90

584 Chateau de Val

1966. Chateau de Val.

1731	**584**	2f.30 brown, grn & bl	2·50	55

585 Rance Barrage

1966. Inauguration of Rance River Tidal Power Station.

1732	**585**	60c. slate, grn & brn	80	75

586 Nurse tending wounded soldier (1859)

1966. Red Cross Fund. Cross in red.

1733	**586**	25c.+10c. green	80	75
1734	-	30c.+10c. blue	80	75

DESIGN: 30c. Nurse tending young girl (1966).

1966. Arms. As T **430**. Multicoloured.

1735		20c. "Saint-Lo"	20	15

588 Beaumarchais (playwright)

1967. Red Cross Fund.

1736	**588**	30c.+10c. violet & red	60	55
1737	-	30c.+10c. blue & indigo	60	55
1738	-	30c.+10c. purple & brn	60	55
1739	-	30c.+10c. violet & bl	60	55

PORTRAITS: No. 1737, Emile Zola (writer); No. 1738, A. Camus (writer); No. 1739, St. Francois de Sales (reformer).

589 Congress Emblem

1967. 3rd International Congress of European Broadcasting Union (U.E.R.).

1740	**589**	40c. red and blue	35	35

590 Postman of the Second Empire

1967. Stamp Day.

1741	**590**	25c.+10c. grn, red & bl	35	35

1967. French Art. As T **491**.

1742		1f. multicoloured	60	55
1743		1f. multicoloured	60	55
1744		1f. brown, blue and black	60	55
1745		1f. multicoloured	60	55

DESIGNS—HORIZ: No. 1742, "Old Juniet's Trap" (after H. Rousseau); No. 1745, "The Window-makers" (stained glass window, St. Madeleine's Church, Troyes). VERT: No. 1743, "Francois I" (after Jean Clouet); No. 1744, "The Bather" (Ingres).

591 Winter Olympics Emblem

1967. Publicity for Winter Olympic Games, Grenoble (1968).

1746	**591**	60c. red, lt blue & bl	60	55

592 French Pavilion

1967. World Fair, Montreal.

1747	**592**	60c. green and blue	60	55

593 Cogwheels

1967. Europa.

1748	**593**	30c. blue and grey	60	35
1749	**593**	60c. brown and blue	1·60	90

594 Nungesser, Coli Lavasseur PL-8 and "L'Oiseau Blanc"

1967. 40th Anniv of Trans-Atlantic Flight Attempt by Nungesser and Coli.

1750	**594**	40c. blue, brown & pur	80	55

595 Great Bridge, Bordeaux

1967. Inauguration of Great Bridge, Bordeaux.

1751	**595**	25c. black, olive & brn	35	35

596 Gouin Mansion, Tours

1967. National Congress of Philatelic Societies, Tours.

1752	**596**	40c. brown, blue & red	80	75

597 Gaston Ramon (vaccine pioneer) and College Gates

1967. Bicentenary of Alfort Veterinary School.

1753	**597**	25c. brown, green & bl	35	35

598 Esnault-Pelterie, Rocket and Satellite

1967. 10th Death Anniv of Robert Esnault-Pelterie (rocket pioneer).

1754	**598**	60c. indigo and blue	80	75

1967. Tourist Publicity. As T **490**. Inscr "1967".

1755		50c. brown, dp blue & blue	60	35
1756		60c. brown, dp blue & blue	85	80
1757		70c. brown, blue and red	60	15
1758		75c. blue, red and brown	1·90	1·30
1759		95c. violet, green & blue	1·90	1·80
1760		1f. blue	1·00	15
1761		1f.50 red, blue and green	1·90	55

DESIGNS—VERT: 50c. Town Hall, St. Quentin (Aisne); 60c. Clock-tower and gateway, Vire (Calvados); 1f. Rodez Cathedral; 1f.50, Morlaix–views and carved buttress. HORIZ: 70c. St. Germain-en-Laye Chateau; 75c. La Baule; 95c. Boulogne-sur-Mer.

599 Orchids

1967. Orleans Flower Show.

1762	**599**	40c. red, purple & violet	1·20	90

600 Scales of Justice

1967. 9th Int Accountancy Congress, Paris.

1763	**600**	60c. brown, blue & pur	1·00	90

601 Servicemen and Cross of Lorraine

1967. 25th Anniv of Battle of Bir-Hakeim.

1764	**601**	25c. ultramarine, bl & brn	35	35

602 Marie Curie and Pitchblende

1967. Birth Centenary of Marie Curie.

1765	**602**	60c. ultramarine & blue	60	55

603 Lions Emblem

1967. 50th Anniv of Lions International.

1766	**603**	40c. violet and lake	1·20	75

604 "Republique"

1967

1767	**604**	25c. blue	60	55
1768	**604**	30c. purple	60	25
1768b	**604**	40c. red	60	25
1843	**604**	30c. green	35	25

See also No. 1882.

1967. History of France (2nd series). As T **582**, but inscr "1967".

1769		40c. ultramarine, grey & bl	60	55
1770		40c. black and slate	60	55
1771		60c. green and brown	80	55

DESIGNS—HORIZ: No. 1769, Hugues Capet elected King of France. VERT: No. 1770, Philippe-Auguste at Bouvines; 1771, Saint-Louis receiving poor.

605 "Flautist"

1967. Red Cross Fund. Ivories in Dieppe Museum. Cross in red.

1772	**605**	25c.+10c. brown & vio	80	75
1773	-	30c.+10c. brown & grn	80	75

DESIGNS: 30c. "Violinist".

606 Anniversary Medal

1968. 50th Anniv of Postal Cheques Service.

1774	**606**	40c. bistre and green	35	35

607 Cross-country Skiing and Ski Jumping

1968. Winter Olympic Games, Grenoble.

1775	**607**	30c.+10c. brown, grey & red	60	55
1776	-	40c.+10c. pur, bis & dp pur	60	55
1777	-	60c.+20c. red, purple & grn	80	75
1778	-	75c.+25c. brown, grn & pur	80	75
1779	-	95c.+35c. brown, mve & bl	85	80

DESIGNS: 30c. Type **607**; 40c. Ice hockey; 60c. Olympic flame; 75c. Figure skating; 95c. Slalom.

608 Road Signs

1968. Road Safety.
1780 **608** 25c. red, blue and purple 35 35

609 Rural Postman of 1830

1968. Stamp Day.
1781 **609** 25c.+10c. indigo, blue and red 35 35

610 F. Couperin (composer) and Concert Instruments

1968. Red Cross Fund. Inscr "1968".

1782	**610**	30c.+10c. lilac & vio	35	35
1783	-	30c.+10c. brown & grn	35	35
1784	-	30c.+10c. red & brown	35	35
1785	-	30c.+10c. purple & lil	35	35

DESIGNS: No. 1783, General Desaix, and death scene at Marengo; No. 1784, Saint Pol-Roux (poet) and "Evocation of Golgotha"; No. 1785, Paul Claudel (poet) and "Joan of Arc".

1968. French Art. As T **491**.

1786	1f. multicoloured	80	75
1787	1f. multicoloured	1·00	75
1788	1f. olive and red	1·00	55
1789	1f. multicoloured	1·20	75

DESIGNS—HORIZ: No. 1786, Wall painting, Lascaux; No. 1787, "Arearea" (Gauguin). VERT: No. 1788, "La Danse" (relief by Bourdelle in Champs-Elysees Theatre, Paris); No. 1789, "Portrait of a Model" (Renoir).

611 Congress Palace, Royan

1968. World Co-operation Languages Conf, Royan.
1790 **611** 40c. blue, brown & grn 60 55

612 Europa "Key"

1968. Europa.
1791 **612** 30c. brown and purple 60 25

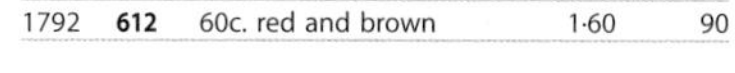

1792 **612** 60c. red and brown 1·60 90

613 Alain R. Le Sage

1968. 300th Birth Anniv of Le Sage (writer).
1793 **613** 40c. purple and blue 35 35

1968. Tourist Publicity. As T **490**, but inscr "1968".
1794 60c. blue, purple & green 95 75
DESIGN—HORIZ: 60c. Langeais Chateau.

614 Pierre Larousse (encyclopedist)

1968. Larousse Commem.
1795 **614** 40c. brown & violet 60 55

615 Forest Trees

1968. Link of Black and Rambouillet Forests.
1796 **615** 25c. brown, green & blue 60 55

616 Presentation of the Keys, and Map

1968. 650th Anniv of Papal Enclave, Valreas.
1797 **616** 60c. violet, bistre & brn 80 75

617 Louis XIV, and Arms of Flanders and France

1968. 300th Anniv of (First) Treaty of Aix-la-Chapelle.
1798 **617** 40c. lake, bistre & grey 35 35

618 Martrou Bridge, Rochefort

1968. Inauguration of Martrou Bridge.
1799 **618** 25c. black, brown & blue 35 35

619 Letord 4 Lorraine Bomber and Route Map

1968. 50th Anniv of 1st Regular Internal Airmail Service.
1800 **619** 25c. indigo, blue & red 80 55

620 Tower of Constance, Aigues-Mortes

1968. Bicent. of Release of Huguenot Prisoners.
1801 **620** 25c. purple, brown & bl 35 35

621 Cathedral and Old Bridge, Beziers

1968. National Congress of Philatelic Societies, Beziers.
1802 **621** 40c. ochre, green & blue 1·20 75

622 "Victory" and White Tower, Salonika

1968. 50th Anniv of Armistice on Salonika Front.
1803 **622** 40c. purple & lt purple 35 35

623 Louis XV and Arms of Corsica and France

1968. Bicent of Union of Corsica and France.
1804 **623** 25c. blue, green & blk 35 35

624 Relay-racing

1968. Olympic Games, Mexico.
1805 **624** 40c. blue, green & brn 80 75

625 Polar Landscape

1968. French Polar Exploration.
1806 **625** 40c. turq, red & blue 60 55

626 "Ball of the Little White Beds" (opera) and Bailby

1968. 50th Anniv of "Little White Beds" Children's Hospital Charity.
1807 **626** 40c. red, orge & brn 35 35

627 "Angel of Victory" over Arc de Triomphe

1968. 50th Anniv of Armistice on Western Front.
1808 **627** 25c. blue and red 35 35

1968. History of France (3rd series). Designs as T **582**, but inscr "1968".

1809	40c. green, grey and red	60	55
1810	40c. blue, green & brown	60	55
1811	60c. brown, blue & ultram	1·00	75

DESIGNS—HORIZ: No. 1809, Philip the Good presiding over States-General. VERT: No. 1810, Death of Du Guesclin; No. 1811, Joan of Arc.

628 "Spring"

1968. Red Cross Fund. Cross in red.

1812	**628**	25c.+10c. blue & vio	60	55
1813	-	30c.+10c. red & brown	60	55

DESIGN: 30c. "Autumn".
See also Nos. 1853/4.

1969. Tourist Publicity. Similar to T **490** but inscr "1969".

1814	45c. green, brown and blue	35	25
1815	70c. brown, indigo and blue	60	55
1816	80c. brown, purple & bistre	60	20
1817	85c. grey, blue and green	1·20	1·00
1818	1f.15 lt brown, brown & blue	1·20	95

DESIGNS—HORIZ: 45c. Brou Church, Bourg-en-Bresse (Ain); 70c. Hautefort Chateau; 80f. Vouglans Dam, Jura; 85f. Chantilly Chateau; 1f.15, La Trinite-sur-Mer, Morbihan.

1969. French Art. As T **491**.

1819	1f. brown and black	1·00	75
1820	1f. multicoloured	1·00	75
1821	1f. multicoloured	1·00	75
1822	1f. multicoloured	1·00	75

DESIGNS—VERT: No. 1819, "February" (bas-relief, Amiens Cathedral); No. 1820, "Philippe le Bon" (Rogier de la Pasture, called Van der Weyden); No. 1822, "The Circus" (Georges Seurat). HORIZ: No. 1821, "Savin and Cyprien appearing before Ladicius" (Romanesque painting, Church of St. Savin, Vienne).

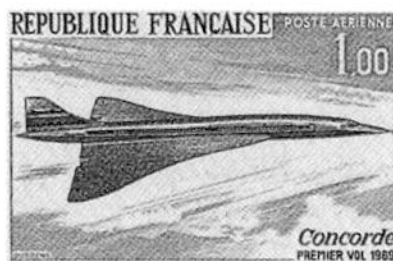

629 Concorde in Flight

1969. Air. 1st Flight of Concorde.
1823 **629** 1f. indigo and blue 1·40 85

630 Postal Horse-bus of 1890

1969. Stamp Day.
1824 **630** 30c.+10c. green, brown and black 35 35

631 A. Roussel (composer)

1969. Red Cross Fund. Celebrities.

1825	**631**	50c.+10c. blue	60	55
1826	-	50c.+10c. red	60	55
1827	-	50c.+10c. grey	60	55

1828	-	50c.+10c. brown	60	55
1829	-	50c.+10c. purple	60	55
1830	-	50c.+10c. green	60	55

PORTRAITS: No. 1826, General Marceau; No. 1827, C. A. Sainte-Beuve (writer); No. 1828, Marshal Lannes; No. 1829, G. Cuvier (anatomist and naturalist); No. 1830, A. Gide (writer).

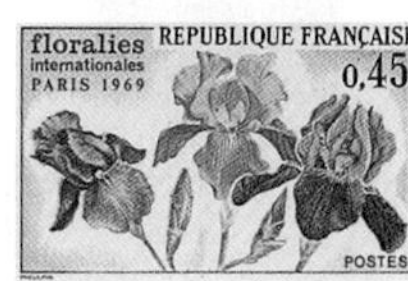

632 Irises

1969. International Flower Show, Paris.

1831	**632**	45c. multicoloured	60	55

633 Colonnade

1969. Europa.

1832	**633**	40c. mauve	60	25
1833	**633**	70c. blue	1·00	55

634 Battle of the Garigliano (Italy)

1969. 25th Anniv of "Resistance and Liberation".

1834	**634**	45c. black and violet	80	75
1835	-	45c. ultram, bl & grey	1·90	75
1836	-	45c. grey, blue & green	1·20	90
1837	-	45c. brown and grey	1·50	90
1838	-	45c. indigo, blue & red	1·20	1·10
1839	-	45c.+10c. green & grey	1·50	1·40
1840	-	70c.+10c. grn, pur & brn	3·75	3·50

DESIGNS—VERT: No. 1835, Parachutists and Commandos ("D-Day Landings"); 1836, Memorial and Resistance fighters (Battle of Mont Mouchet). HORIZ: No. 1837, Troops storming beach (Provence Landings); 1838, French pilot, Soviet mechanic and Yakovlev Yak-9 fighter aircraft (Normandy-Niemen Squadron); 1839, General Leclerc, troops and Les Invalides (Liberation of Paris); 1840, As No. 1839 but showing Strasbourg Cathedral (Liberation of Strasbourg).

635 "Miners" (I.L.O. Monument, Geneva) and Albert Thomas (founder)

1969. 50th Anniv of I.L.O.

1841	**635**	70c. brn, bl & dp brn	60	55

636 Chalons-sur-Marne

1969. National Congress of Philatelic Societies, Chalons-sur-Marne.

1842	**636**	45c. ochre, blue & grn	60	55

637 Canoeing

1969. World Kayak-Canoeing Championships, Bourg-St. Maurice.

1844	**637**	70c. brown, green & blue	60	55

638 Napoleon as Young Officer, and Birthplace

1969. Birth Bicent of Napoleon Bonaparte.

1845	**638**	70c. grn, violet & blue	60	55

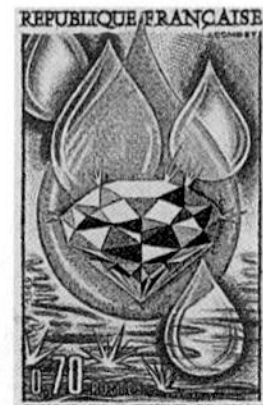

639 "Diamond Crystal" in Rain Drop

1969. European Water Charter.

1846	**639**	70c. black, green & bl	60	55

640 Mouflon

1969. Nature Conservation.

1847	**640**	45c. black, brn & grn	1·00	75

641 Aerial View of College

1969. College of Arts and Manufactures, Chatenay-Malabry.

1848	**641**	70c. grn, orge & dp grn	60	55

642 "Le Redoutable"

1969. 1st French Nuclear Submarine "Le Redoutable".

1849	**642**	70c. green, emer & bl	60	55

1969. History of France (4th series). As T **582** but inscr "1969".

1850	80c. bistre, brown & green	80	55
1851	80c. brown, blk & lt brn	80	55
1852	80c. blue, black and violet	80	55

DESIGNS—HORIZ: No. 1850, Louis XI and Charles the Bold; 1852, Henry IV and Edict of Nantes, VERT: No. 1851, Bayard at the Battle of Brescia.

1969. Red Cross Fund. Paintings by N. Mignard. As T **628**. Cross in red.

1853	40c.+15c. brown & choc	80	75
1854	40c.+15c. blue & violet	80	75

DESIGNS: No. 1853, "Summer"; 1854, "Winter".

643 Gerbault aboard "Firecrest"

1970. Alain Gerbault's World Voyage, 1923–29.

1855	**643**	70c. indigo, grey & blue	1·00	75

644 Gendarmerie Badge and Activities

1970. National Gendarmerie.

1856	**644**	45c. blue, green & brown	1·50	75

645 L. Le Vau (architect)

1970. Red Cross Fund.

1857	**645**	40c.+10c. lake	60	55
1858	-	40c.+10c. blue	60	55
1859	-	40c.+10c. green	60	55
1860	-	40c.+10c. brown	60	55
1861	-	40c.+10c. slate	60	55
1862	-	40c.+10c. blue	60	55

DESIGNS: No. 1858, Prosper Merimee (writer); 1859, Philbert de l'Orme (architect); 1860, Edouard Branly (scientist); 1861, Maurice de Broglie (physicist); 1862, Alexandre Dumas (pere) (writer).

646 Handball Player

1970. 7th World Handball Championship.

1863	**646**	80c. green	80	55

647 Marshal Alphonse Juin and Les Invalides, Paris

1970. Marshal Juin Commem.

1864	**647**	45c. brown and blue	60	35

648 Gas-turbine Monorail Aerotrain "Orleans 1-80"

1970. 1st Aerotrain in Service.

1865	**648**	80c. drab and violet	1·00	70

649 Postman of 1830 and Paris Scene

1970. Stamp Day.

1866	**649**	40c.+10c. black, blue and red	60	55

650 P.-J. Pelletier and J. B. Caventou with Formula

1970. 150th Anniv of Discovery of Quinine.

1870	**650**	50c. green, mauve & bl	60	55

651 Greater Flamingo

1970. Nature Conservation Year.

1871	**651**	45c. mauve, grey & grn	60	35

652 Rocket and Dish Aerial

1970. Launching of "Diamant B" Rocket from Guyana.

1872	**652**	45c. green	1·00	75

653 "Health and Sickness"

1970. W.H.O. "Fight Cancer" Day (7th April).

1873	**653**	40c.+10c. mauve, brown and blue	35	35

654 "Flaming Sun"

1970. Europa.

1874	**654**	40c. red	60	35
1875	**654**	80c. blue	1·00	80

655 Marshal de Lattre de Tassigny and Armistice Meeting

1970. 25th Anniv of Berlin Armistice.

1876	**655**	40c.+10c. blue & turq	1·00	90

1970. French Art. As T **491**.

1877	1f. multicoloured	80	75
1878	1f. chestnut	80	75
1879	1f. multicoloured	1·20	90
1880	1f. multicoloured	1·20	90

DESIGNS—VERT: No. 1877, 15-cent. Savoy Primitive painting on wood; No. 1880, "The Ballet-dancer" (Degas). HORIZ: No. 1878, "The Triumph of Flora" (sculpture by J. B. Carpeaux); No. 1879, "Diana's Return from the Hunt" (F. Boucher).

656 Arms of Lens, Miner's Lamp and Pithead

1970. 43rd French Federation of Philatelic Societies Congress, Lens.

1881	**656**	40c. red	35	35

657 "Republique" and Perigueux

1970. Transfer of French Govt Printing Works to Perigueux.

1882	**657**	40c. red	60	35

The above stamp and label which together comprise No. 1882 were issued together se-tenant in sheets for which special printing plates were laid down. The stamp is virtually indistinguishable from the normal 40c. definitive, No. 1768b.

1970. Tourist Publicity. As T **490**, but inscr "1970".

1883	50c. purple, blue & green	60	15
1884	95c. brown, red and olive	1·50	1·10
1885	1f. green, blue and red	1·00	20

DESIGNS: 50c. Diamond Rock, Martinique; 95c. Chancelade Abbey (Dordogne); 1f. Gosier Island, Guadeloupe.

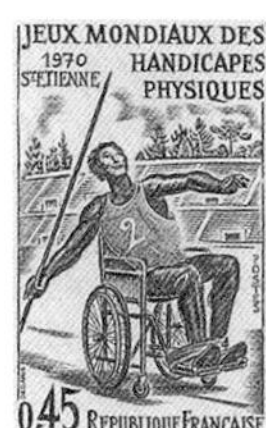

658 Javelin-thrower in Wheelchair

1970. World Games for the Physically Handicapped, St.-Etienne.

1886	**658**	45c. red, green & blue	70	55

659 Hand and Broken Chain

1970. 25th Anniv of Liberation from Concentration Camps.

1887	**659**	45c. brown, ultram & bl	80	55

660 Observatory and Nebula

1970. Haute-Provence Observatory.

1888	**660**	1f.30 violet, blue & grn	2·50	1·40

661 Pole Vaulting

1970. 1st European Junior Athletic Championships, Paris.

1889	**661**	45c. indigo, blue & purple	75	55

662 Didier Daurat, Raymond Vanier and Douglas DC-4

1970. Air. Pioneer Aviators.

1890	**662**	5f. brown, green & blue	3·75	35
1891	-	10f. grey, violet & red	7·50	55
1892	-	15f. grey, mauve & brn	11·00	90
1893	-	20f. indigo and blue	15·00	1·00

DESIGNS: 10f. Helene Boucher, Maryse Hilsz and de Havilland Gipsy Moth and Caudron monoplane; 15f. Henri Guillaumet, Paul Codos, "Lieutenant de Vaisseau Paris" (flying boat) and wreck of Potez 25A2 airplane; 20f. Jean Mermoz, Antoine de Saint-Exupery and Concorde.

663 Bath-House, Arc-et-Senans (Doubs)

1970. Royal Salt Springs, Chaux (founded by N. Ledoux).

1895	**663**	80c. brown, grn & bl	85	70

1970. History of France (5th series). As T **582**, but inscr "1970".

1896	45c. mauve, grey & black	1·00	75
1897	45c. brown, green & yellow	1·00	75
1898	45c. grey, brown & orange	1·00	90

DESIGNS: No. 1896, Richelieu and siege of La Rochelle, 1628; 1897, King Louis XIV; 1898, King Louis XV at Battle of Fontenoy (after painting by H. Vernet).

664 U.N. Emblem, New York Headquarters and Palais des Nations, Geneva

1970. 25th Anniv of United Nations.

1899	**664**	80c. violet, green & blue	80	55

665 Bordeaux and "Ceres" Stamp

1970. Centenary of Bordeaux "Ceres" Stamp Issue.

1900	**665**	80c. violet and blue	80	55

666 Col. Denfert-Rochereau and "Lion of Belfort" (after Bartholdi)

1970. Centenary of Belfort Siege.

1901	**666**	45c. blue, brown & grn	60	55

667 "Lord and Lady" (c. 1500)

1970. Red Cross Fund. Frescoes from Dissay Chapel, Vienne. Cross in red.

1902	**667**	40c.+15c. green	1·00	90
1903	-	40c.+15c. red	1·00	90

DESIGN: No. 1903, "Angel with instruments of mortification".

668 "Marianne"

1971

1904	**668**	45c. blue	60	20
1904ap	**668**	60c. green	1·00	20
1904b	**668**	80c. green	1·00	20
1905	**668**	50c. red	60	20
1905bp	**668**	80c. red	1·00	20
1905d	**668**	1f. red	80	20

669 Balloon "Ville d'Orleans" leaving Paris

1971. Air. Centenary of Paris Balloon Post.

1907	**669**	95c. multicoloured	1·20	90

1971. French Art. As T 491.

1908	1f. brown	1·20	90
1909	1f. multicoloured	1·00	75
1910	1f. multicoloured	1·00	75

DESIGNS: No. 1908, "St. Matthew" (sculpture, Strasbourg Cathedral); No. 1909, "The Winnower" (Millet); No. 1910, "Songe Creux" (G. Rouault).

670 Ice Skaters

1971. World Ice Skating Championships, Lyon.

1911	**670**	80c. ultramarine, blue and indigo	80	75

671 Diver and Bathysphere

1971. "Oceanexpo" Exhibition, Bordeaux.

1912	**671**	80c. turquoise & blue	80	55

672 General D. Brosset and Fourviere Basilica, Lyon

1971. Red Cross Fund. Celebrities.

1913	**672**	50c.+10c. brown & grn	85	80
1914	-	50c.+10c. brn & choc	85	80
1915	-	50c.+10c. brown & red	85	80
1916	-	50c.+10c. lilac & blue	85	80
1917	-	50c.+10c. pur & plum	85	80
1918	-	50c.+10c. bl & indigo	85	80

DESIGNS: No. 1914, Esprit Auber (composer) and manuscript of "Fra Diavolo"; 1915, Victor Grignard (chemist) and Nobel Prize for Chemistry; 1916, Henri Farman (aviation pioneer) and Farman Voisin No. 1 bis (airplane); 1917, General C. Delestraint (Resistance leader) and "Secret Army" proclamation; 1918, J. Robert-Houdin (magician) and levitation act.

673 Field Post Office, World War I

1971. Stamp Day.

1919	**673**	50c.+10c. blue, brown and bistre	80	55

674 Barque "Antoinette"

1971. French Sailing Ships.

1920	**674**	80c. violet, indigo & bl	1·50	90

See also Nos. 1967, 2011 and 2100.

675 Chamois

1971. Inaug of Western Pyrenees National Park.

1921	**675**	65c. brown, bl & choc	85	75

1971. History of France (6th series). As T 582 but inscr "1971".

1922	45c. purple, blue & red	80	55
1923	45c. red, brown & blue	1·00	70
1924	65c. brown, purple & blue	1·20	90

DESIGNS: No. 1922, Cardinal, noble and commoner (Opening of the States-General, 1789); No. 1923, Battle of Valmy, 1792; No. 1924, Fall of the Bastille, 1789.

676 Basilica of Santa Maria, Venice

1971. Europa.

1925	**676**	50c. brown and blue	95	55
1926	-	80c. purple	1·20	80

DESIGN: 80c. Europa chain.

677 View of Grenoble

1971. 44th French Federation of Philatelic Societies Congress, Grenoble.

1927	**677**	50c. red, pink & brown	60	35

678 A.F.R. Emblem and Town

1971. 25th Anniv (1970) of Rural Family Aid.

1928	**678**	40c. blue, violet & green	60	35

1971. Tourist Publicity. As T 490, but inscr "1971".

1929	60c. black, blue and green	75	35
1930	65c. black, violet & brown	1·00	35
1931	90c. brown, green & ochre	1·00	35
1932	1f.10 brown, blue & green	1·00	90
1933	1f.40 purple, blue & green	1·20	35

DESIGNS—VERT: 60c. Sainte Chapelle, Riom; 65c. Church and fountain, Dole; 90c. Gate-tower and houses, Riquewihr; 1f.40, Ardeche gorges. HORIZ: 1f.10, Fortress, Sedan.

679 Bourbon Palace, Paris

1971. 59th Interparliamentary Union Conference, Paris.

1934	**679**	90c. blue	1·00	90

680 Embroidery and Instrument-making

1971. 40th Anniv of 1st Meeting of Crafts Guilds Association.

1935	**680**	90c. purple and red	1·00	55

681 Reunion Chameleon

1971. Nature Conservation.

1936	**681**	60c. green, brn & yell	1·20	90

682 De Gaulle in Uniform (June 1940)

1971. 1st Death Anniv of General Charles de Gaulle.

1937	**682**	50c. black	1·20	1·10
1938	-	50c. blue	1·20	1·10
1939	-	50c. red	1·20	1·10
1940	-	50c. black	1·20	1·10

DESIGNS: No. 1938, De Gaulle at Brazzaville, 1944; No. 1939, Liberation of Paris, 1944; No. 1940, De Gaulle as President of the French Republic, 1970.

683 Baron Portal (1st President) and First Assembly

1971. 150th Anniv of National Academy of Medicine.

1941	**683**	45c. plum and purple	60	55

684 "Young Girl with Little Dog"

1971. Red Cross Fund. Paintings by J.-B. Greuze. Cross in red.

1942	**684**	30c.+10c. blue	1·00	90
1943	-	50c.+10c. red	1·00	90

DESIGN: No. 1943. "The Dead Bird".

1972. French Art. As T 491. Multicoloured.

1944	1f. "L'Etude" (portrait of a young girl) (Fragonard) (vert)	1·20	90
1945	1f. "Women in a Garden" (Monet) (vert)	2·00	1·00
1946	2f. "St. Peter presenting Pierre de Bourbon" (Master of Moulins) (vert)	2·50	1·70
1947	2f. "The Barges" (A. Derain)	3·75	2·50

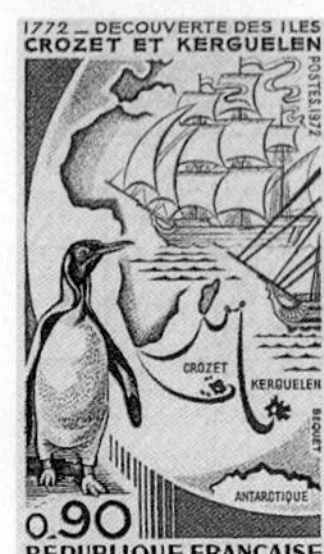

685 King Penguin, Map and "Le Mascarin" (Dufresne)

1972. Bicentenary of Discovery of Crozet Islands and Kerguelen (French Southern and Antarctic Territories).

1948	**685**	90c. black, blue & orge	1·00	75

686 Skier and Emblem

1972. Winter Olympic Games, Sapporo, Japan.

1949	**686**	90c. red and green	80	55

687 Aristide Berges (hydro-electric engineer)

1972. Red Cross Fund. Celebrities.

1950	**687**	50c.+10c. black, emerald and green	1·00	80
1951	-	50c.+10c. black, blue and ultramarine	1·00	80
1952	-	50c.+10c. black, purple and plum	1·00	80
1953	-	50c.+10c. black, red and crimson	1·00	80
1954	-	50c.+10c. black, chestnut and brown	1·00	80
1955	-	50c.+10c. black, orange and red	1·00	80

DESIGNS: No. 1951, Paul de Chomedey, Maisonneuve (founder of Montreal); No. 1952, Edouard Belin (communications scientist); No. 1953, Louis Bleriot (pioneer airman) and Bleriot XI., No. 1954, Theophile Gautier (writer); No. 1955, Admiral Francois de Grasse.

688 Rural Postman of 1894

1972. Stamp Day.

1956	**688**	50c.+10c. blue, drab and yellow	1·20	90

689 Heart and W.H.O. Emblems

1972. World Heart Month.

1957	**689**	45c. red, orange & grey	60	55

1972. Tourist Publicity. As Type 490, but inscr "1972".

1958	1f. brown and yellow	95	35
1959	1f.20 blue and brown	1·00	45
1960	2f. purple and green	1·60	55
1961	3f.50 brown, red and blue	2·50	90

DESIGNS—VERT: 1f. Red deer stag and forest, Sologne Nature Reserve. HORIZ: 1f.20, Charlieu Abbey; 2f. Bazoches-du-Morvand Chateau; 3f.50, St. Just Cathedral, Narbonne.

690 Eagle Owl

1972. Nature Conservation.

1962	-	60c. black, green & bl	3·00	1·70
1963	**690**	65c. brown, bis & grey	1·20	90

DESIGN—HORIZ: 60c. Atlantic salmon.

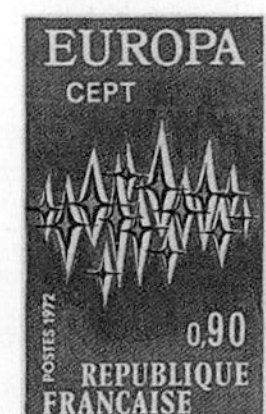

691 "Communications"

1972. Europa.

1964	-	50c. purple, yellow & brn	1·00	45
1965	**691**	90c. multicoloured	1·20	80

DESIGN: 50c. Aix-la-Chapelle Cathedral.

692 "Tree of Hearts"

1972. 20th Anniv of Post Office Employees' Blood-donors Association.

1966	**692**	40c. red	35	35

693 "Cote d'Emeraude" Grand Banks Fishing barquentine

1972. French Sailing Ships.

1967	**693**	90c. blue, green & orge	1·20	90

694 St.-Brieuc Cathedral (from lithograph of 1840)

1972. 45th French Federation of Philatelic Societies Congress, St.-Brieuc.

1968	**694**	50c. red	35	35

695 Hand and Code Emblems

1972. Postal Code Campaign.

1969	**695**	30c. red, black & green	25	15
1970	**695**	50c. yellow, black & red	60	35

696 Old and New Communications

1972. 21st World Congress of Post Office Trade Union Federation (I.P.T.T.), Paris.

1971	**696**	45c. blue and grey	60	35

697 Hurdling

1972. Olympic Games, Munich.

1972	**697**	1f. green	80	55

698 Hikers on Road

1972. "Walking Tourism Year".

1973	**698**	40c. multicoloured	1·60	90

699 Cycling

1972. World Cycling Championships.

1974	**699**	1f. brown, purple & grey	1·90	1·30

1972. History of France (7th series). The Directory. As T 582 but dated "1972".

1975	45c. purple, olive & green	60	55
1976	60c. blue, red and black	1·20	75
1977	65c. purple, brown & blue	1·40	90

DESIGNS—VERT: 45c. "Incroyables et Merveilleuses" (fashionable Parisians), 1794; 60c. Napoleon Bonaparte at the Bridge of Arcole, 1796; 65c. Discovery of antiquities, Egyptian Expedition, 1798.

700 J.-F. Champollion and Hieroglyphics

1972. 150th Anniv of Champollion's Translation of Egyptian Hieroglyphics.

1978	**700**	90c. brown, blue & blk	80	55

701 Nicholas Desgenettes (military physician)

1972. Red Cross Fund. Doctors of the 1st Empire. Cross in red.

1979	**701**	30c.+10c. green and bronze	1·00	90
1980	-	50c.+10c. red & brown	1·00	90

DESIGN: No. 1980, Francois Broussais (pathologist).

702 St. Theresa and Porch of Notre Dame, Alencon

1973. Birth Centenary of St. Theresa of Lisieux.

1981	**702**	1f. indigo & turquoise	1·20	75

703 Anthurium

1973. Martinique Flower Cultivation.

1982	**703**	50c. multicoloured	60	55

704 National Colours of France and West Germany

1973. 10th Anniv of Franco-German Co-operation Treaty.

1983	**704**	50c. multicoloured	60	55

705 Polish Immigrants

1973. 50th Anniv of Polish Immigration.

1984	**705**	40c. red, green & brown	35	35

1973. French Art. As T 491.

1985	2f. multicoloured	1·90	1·40
1986	2f. red and yellow	1·90	1·40
1987	2f. maroon and brown	1·90	1·40
1988	2f. multicoloured	1·90	1·40

DESIGNS: No. 1985, "The Last Supper" (carved capital, St. Austremoine Church, Issoire); No. 1986, "Study of a Kneeling Woman" (Charles le Brun); No. 1987, Wood-carving, Moutier d'Ahun; No. 1988, "La Finette" (girl with lute) (Watteau).

706 Admiral G. de Coligny (Protestant leader)

1973. Red Cross Fund. Celebrities' Annivs.

1989	**706**	50c.+10c. blue, brown and purple	1·00	90
1990	-	50c.+10c. mauve, grey and orange	1·00	90
1991	-	50c.+10c. green, purple and yellow	1·00	90
1992	-	50c.+10c. red, purple and bistre	1·00	90
1993	-	50c.+10c. grey, purple and brown	1·00	90
1994	-	50c.+10c. brown, lilac and blue	1·00	90
1995	-	50c.+10c. blue, purple and brown	1·00	90

DESIGNS: No. 1989, 400th death anniv (1972); 1990, Ernest Renan (philologist and writer, 150th birth anniv); 1991, Santos-Dumont (pioneer aviator, birth centenary); and "Balloon No. 6", "Balloon No.14" and biplane 14bis; 1992, Colette (writer, birth centenary); 1993, Duguay-Trouin (naval hero, 300th birth anniv); 1994, Louis Pasteur (scientist, 150th birth anniv 1972); 1995, Tony Garnier (architect, 25th death anniv).

707 Mail Coach, c. 1835

1973. Stamp Day.

1996	**707**	50c.+10c. blue	60	55

708 Tuileries Palace and New Telephone Exchange

1973. French Technical Achievements.

1997	**708**	45c. blue, grey & green	35	35
1998	-	90c. black, blue & pur	85	75
1999	-	3f. black, blue & grn	2·50	1·80

DESIGNS: 90c. Francois I Lock, Le Havre; 3f. Airbus Industrie A300B2-100 airplane.

709 Town Hall, Brussels

1973. Europa.

2000	**709**	50c. brown and red	95	55
2001	-	90c. multicoloured	2·20	1·30

DESIGN—HORIZ: 90c. Europa "Posthorn".

710 Guadeloupe Racoon

1973. Nature Conservation.

2002	**710**	40c. mauve, grn & pur	60	35
2003	-	60c. black, red & blue	85	75

DESIGN: 60c. White storks.

711 Masonic Emblem

1973. Bicentenary of Masonic Grand Orient Lodge of France.

2004	**711**	90c. blue and purple	80	55

1973. Tourist Publicity. As T 490, but inscr "1973".

2005	60c. blue, green and light blue	60	35
2006	65c. violet and red	60	35
2007	90c. brown, dp blue & bl	80	35
2008	1f. green, brown and blue	80	35

DESIGNS—VERT: 60c. Waterfall, Doubs; 1f. Clos-Luce Palace, Amboise; HORIZ: 65c. Palace of the Dukes of Burgundy, Dijon; 90c. Gien Chateau.

712 Globe and "Heart"

1973. 50th Anniv of Academy of Overseas Sciences.

2009	**712**	1f. green, brown & pur	80	55

713 Racing-car at Speed

1973. 50th Anniv of Le Mans 24-hour Endurance Race.

2010	**713**	60c. blue and brown	1·00	75

714 Five-masted Barque "France II"

1973. French Sailing Ships.

2011	**714**	90c. lt blue, indigo & bl	1·50	90

715 Bell-tower, Toulouse

1973. 46th French Federation of Philatelic Societies Congress, Toulouse.

2012	**715**	50c. brown and violet	60	35

716 Dr. G. Hansen

1973. Centenary of Hansen's Identification of Leprosy Bacillus.

2013	**716**	45c. brown, olive & grn	60	35

717 Eugene Ducretet (radio pioneer)

1973. 75th Anniv of Eiffel Tower–Pantheon Experimental Radio Link.

2014	**717**	1f. green and red	80	75

718 Moliere as "Sganarelle"

1973. 300th Death Anniv of Moliere (playwright).

2015	**718**	1f. brown and red	80	55

719 Pierre Bourgoin (parachutist) and Philippe Kieffer (Marine Commando)

1973. Heroes of World War II.

2016	**719**	1f. claret, blue & red	80	55

1973. History of France (8th series). As Type 582, but inscr "1973".

2017	45c. purple, grey and blue	80	55
2018	60c. brown, bistre & green	80	75
2019	1f. red, brown and green	1·00	75

DESIGNS—HORIZ: 45c. Napoleon and Portalis (Preparation of Civil Code, 1800–1804); 60c. Paris Industrial Exhibition, Les Invalides, 1806. VERT: 1f. "The Coronation of Napoleon, 1804" (David).

720 Eternal Flame, Arc de Triomphe

1973. 50th Anniv of Tomb of the Unknown Soldier, Arc de Triomphe.

2020	**720**	40c. red, blue and lilac	60	35

721 "Mary Magdalene"

1973. Red Cross Fund. Tomb Figures, Tonnerre.

2021	**721**	30c.+10c. grn & red	80	75
2022	-	50c.+10c. blk & red	80	75

DESIGN: 50c. Female saint.

722 Weathervane

1973. 50th Anniv of French Chambers of Agriculture.

2023	**722**	65c. black, blue & green	60	55

723 Figure and Human Rights Emblem

1973. 25th Anniv of Declaration of Human Rights.

2024	**723**	45c. brown, orge & red	60	35

724 Facade of Museum

1973. Opening of New Postal Museum Building.

2025	**724**	50c. lt brown, pur & brn	60	25

725 Exhibition Emblem

1974. "ARPHILA 75" International Stamp Exhibition, Paris.

2026	**725**	50c. brown, blue & pur	35	35

726 St. Louis-Marie Grignion de Montfort

1974. Red Cross Fund. Celebrities.

2027	**726**	50c.+10c. brown, green and red	75	70
2028	-	50c.+10c. red, purple and blue	75	70
2029	-	80c.+15c. purple, deep purple & blue	80	75
2030	-	80c.+15c. blue, black and purple	80	75

DESIGNS: No. 2028, Francis Poulenc (composer); No. 2029, Jean Giraudoux (writer); No. 2030, Jules Barbey d'Aurevilly (writer).

727 Automatic Letter-sorting

1974. Stamp Day.

2031	**727**	50c.+10c. brn, red & grn	60	55

728 Concorde over Airport

1974. Opening of Charles de Gaulle Airport, Roissy.

2032	**728**	60c. violet and brown	60	55

1974. "Arphila 1975" Stamp Exhibition. French Art. As Type 491. Multicoloured.

2033	2f. "Cardinal Richelieu" (P. de Champaigne)	1·90	1·40
2034	2f. "Abstract after Original Work" (J. Miro)	1·90	1·40
2035	2f. "Loing Canal" (A. Sisley)	1·90	1·60
2036	2f. "Homage to Nicolas Fouquet" (E. de Mathieu)	1·90	1·60

729 French Alps and Gentian

1974. Centenary of French Alpine Club.

2037	**729**	65c. vio, grn & blue	60	55

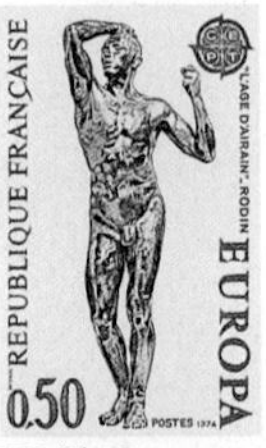
730 "The Brazen Age" (Rodin)

1974. Europa. Sculptures.

2038	**730**	50c. black and purple	95	55
2039	-	90c. brown and bistre	1·50	80

DESIGN—HORIZ: 90c. "The Expression" (reclining woman) (A. Maillol).

731 Shipwreck and "Pierre Loti" (lifeboat)

1974. French Lifeboat Service.

2040	**731**	90c. blue, red & brown	80	55

732 Council Headquarters, Strasbourg

1974. 25th Anniv of Council of Europe.

2041	**732**	45c. blue, lt blue & brn	60	55

733 "Cornucopia of St. Florent" (Corsica)

1974. Tourist Publicity.

2042	-	65c. brown and green	60	55
2043	-	1f.10 brown & green	80	55
2044	-	2f. purple and blue	1·50	55
2045	**733**	3f. blue, red & green	2·00	90

DESIGNS—As Type **490**. HORIZ: 65c. Salers; 1f.10, Lot Valley; VERT: 2f. Basilica of St. Nicolas-de-Port.

734 European Bison

1974. Nature Conservation.

2046	**734**	40c. purple, bl & brn	60	35
2047	-	65c. grey, green & blk	60	55

DESIGN: 65c. Giant Armadillo of Guiana.

735 Normandy Landings

1974. 30th Anniv of Liberation.

2048	**735**	45c. blue, red & green	1·20	90
2049	-	1f. red, brown & violet	80	55
2050	-	1f. brown, blk & red	1·00	75
2051	-	1f.+10c. brn, grn & blk	1·00	90

DESIGNS—HORIZ: No. 2050, Resistance medal and torch; 2051, Order of Liberation and honoured towns. VERT: No. 2049, General Koenig and liberation monuments.

736 Colmar

1974. 47th Congress of French Philatelic Societies.

2052	**736**	50c. red, purple & brn	35	35

737 Board and Chess Pieces

1974. 21st Chess Olympiad, Nice.

2053	**737**	1f. red, brown & blue	1·00	55

738 Commemorative Medallion

1974. 300th Anniv of "Hotel des Invalides".

2054	**738**	40c. black, brn & bl	35	35

739 French Turbotrain TGV 001

1974. Completion of Turbotrain TGV 001 Project.

2055	**739**	60c. red, black & blue	1·40	90

740 "Nuclear Power"

1974. Completion of Phenix Nuclear Generator.

2056	**740**	65c. brown, mve & red	60	55

741 Peacocks with Letter

1974. Centenary of Universal Postal Union.

2057	**741**	1f.20 red, green & blue	80	55

742 Copernicus and Heliocentric System

1974. 500th Birth Anniv (1973) of Nicolas Copernicus (astronomer).

2058	**742**	1f.20 mauve, brn & blk	80	55

743 Children playing on Beach

1974. Red Cross Fund. Seasons. Cross in red.

2059	**743**	60c.+15c. red, brown and blue	80	75
2060	-	80c.+15c. red, brown and blue	1·00	90

DESIGN: 80c. Child in garden looking through window. See also 2098/9.

744 Dr. Albert Schweitzer

1975. Birth Centenary of Dr. Albert Schweitzer.

2061	**744**	80c.+20c. brown, red and green	85	80

1975. Tourist Publicity. As Type 490 but inscr "1975".

2062	85c. blue and brown	80	35
2063	1f.20 brown, dp brn & bl	80	35
2064	1f.40 blue, brown & green	1·00	55

DESIGNS—HORIZ: 85c. Law Courts, Rouen; 1f.40, Chateau de Rochechouart. VERT: 1f.20, St. Pol-de-Leon.

745 Little Egrets

1975. Nature Conservation.

2065	**745**	70c. brown and blue	70	55

1975. Precancels. As T 538, but inscribed "France".

2065a	42c. red and orange	2·30	90
2065b	48c. red and turquoise	1·90	1·70
2065c	50c. brown & turquoise	1·90	1·10
2065d	52c. brown and red	60	90
2065e	60c. brown and mauve	2·50	2·00
2065f	62c. brown & mauve	1·90	1·70
2065g	70c. red and mauve	3·75	2·10
2065h	90c. brown and pink	3·75	2·50
2065i	95c. brown and sepia	1·90	1·70
2065j	1f.35 red and green	4·00	2·30
2065k	1f.60 brown and violet	6·25	4·00
2065l	1f.70 brown and blue	5·00	3·50

See note below No. 432 (1920).

746 Edmond Michelet (politician)

1975. Red Cross Fund. Celebrities.

2066	**746**	80c.+20c. ind & bl	80	75
2067	-	80c.+20c. blk & bl	1·20	1·10
2068	-	80c.+20c. blk & bl	80	75
2069	-	80c.+20c. blk, turq & bl	80	75

DESIGNS—VERT: No. 2067, Robert Schuman (statesman); No. 2068, Eugene Thomas (former Telecommunications Minister). HORIZ: No, 2069, Andre Siegfried (geographer and humanist).

747 Eye

1975. "Arphila 75" International Stamp Exhibition, Paris.

2070	**747**	1f. orange, vio & red	60	55
2071	-	2f. black, red & green	1·20	90
2072	-	3f. green, grey & brown	1·90	1·30
2073	-	4f. green, red & orange	2·50	1·80
MS2074		152×143 mm. 2f. blue and red (Type **747**); 3f. deep blue, red and blue (as No. 2071); 4f. blue, deep blue and red (as No. 2072); 6f. deep blue, blue and red (as No. 2073)	12·50	11·50

DESIGNS: 2f. Capital; 3f. "Arphila 75 Paris"; 4f. Head of Ceres.

748 Postman's Badge

1975. Stamp Day.

2075	**748**	80c.+20c. blk, yell & bl	80	75

749 Pres. G. Pompidou

1975. Pres. Georges Pompidou Commem.

2076	**749**	80c. black and blue	60	35

750 "Paul as Harlequin" (Picasso)

1975. Europa. Multicoloured.

2077	80c. Type **750**	95	55
2078	1f.20 "In the Square" or "Woman leaning on Balcony" (Van Dongen) (horiz)	1·40	1·00

751 Machine Tools and Emblem

1975. 1st World Machine-Tools Exhibition, Paris.
2079 **751** 1f.20 black, red & blue 1·50 55

752 First Assembly at Luxembourg Palace

1975. Centenary of French Senate.
2080 **752** 1f.20 bistre, brn & red 1·00 75

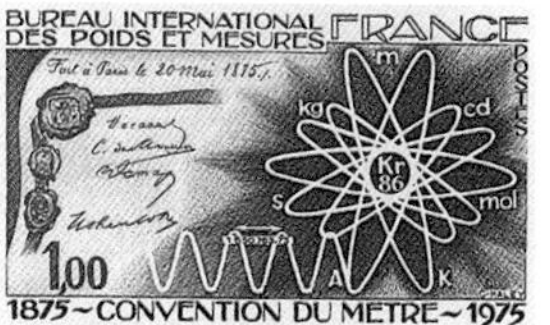

753 Seals, Signatures and Symbols

1975. Centenary of Metre Convention.
2081 **753** 1f. purple, mve & brn 80 55

754 Sud Aviation SA 341 Gazelle Helicopter

1975. Development of Gazelle Helicopter.
2082 **754** 1f.30 green and blue 1·00 80

755 Youth and Health Symbols

1975. Students' Health Foundation.
2083 **755** 70c. black, purple & red 60 55

756 Underground Train

1975. Opening of Metro Regional Express Service.
2084 **756** 1f. deep blue and blue 1·20 80

757 Bussang Theatre and M. Pottecher (founder)

1975. 80th Anniv of People's Theatre, Bussang.
2085 **757** 85c. lilac, brown & blue 60 55

758 Picardy Rose

1975. Regions of France.
2086 **758** 85c. orange, turq & blue 1·00 55

2087 - 1f. lake, red & yellow 1·00 55
2088 - 1f.15 green, bl & ochre 1·00 55
2089 - 1f.30 black, red & blue 1·20 75
2090 - 1f.90 blue, bistre & blk 1·50 80
2091 - 2f.80 blue, red, & black 2·10 1·40

DESIGNS—VERT: 1f. Bourgogne agriculture emblems; 1f.15, Loire scene; 1f.30, Auvergne (bouquet of carnations); 1f.90, Allegory, Poitou-Charentes. HORIZ: 2f.80, "Nord-Pas-de-Calais".

See also Nos. 2102/6, 2150/7, 2246/8, 2329, 2508, 2555 and 2613.

759 Concentration Camp Victims

1975. 30th Anniv of Liberation of Concentration Camps.
2092 **759** 1f. green, blue and red 80 55

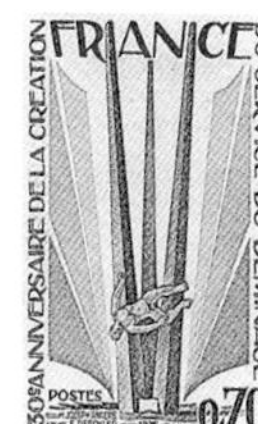

760 "Ballon d'Alsace" (Mine-clearers Monument)

1975. 30th Anniv of Mine Clearance Service.
2093 **760** 70c. green, bistre & blue 60 35

761 "Urban Development"

1975. New Towns.
2094 **761** 1f.70 blue, grn & brn 1·20 90

762 St. Nazaire Bridge

1975. Opening of St. Nazaire Bridge.
2095 **762** 1f.40 black, bl & grn 1·00 55

763 Rainbow over Women's Faces

1975. International Women's Year.
2096 **763** 1f.20 multicoloured 80 55

764 French and Russian Flags

1975. 50th Anniv of Franco-Soviet Diplomatic Relations.
2097 **764** 1f.20 yellow, red & blue 80 55

1975. Red Cross Fund. "The Seasons". As T 743.
2098 60c.+15c. red and green 80 75
2099 80c.+20c. brn, orge & red 1·00 90

DESIGNS: 60c. Child on swing; 80c. Rabbits under umbrella.

765 Cadet Ship "La Melpomene"

1975. French Sailing Ships.
2100 **765** 90c. blue, orge & red 1·40 70

766 Concorde

1976. Air. Concorde's First Commercial Flight, Paris–Rio de Janeiro.
2101 **766** 1f.70 black, blue & red 1·20 75

1976. Regions of France. As T 758.
2102 25c. green and blue 35 35
2103 60c. green, blue & purple 35 35
2104 70c. blue, green, & black 85 55
2105 1f.25 blue, brown & green 1·00 90
2106 2f.20 multicoloured 1·70 1·40

DESIGNS—HORIZ: 25c. Industrial complex in the Central region; 60c. Aquitaine; 2f.20, Pyrenees. VERT: 70c. Limousin; 1f.25, Guiana.

1976. French Art. As T 491.
2108 2f. grey and blue 1·70 1·40
2109 2f. yellow and brown 1·50 1·30
2110 2f. multicoloured 1·70 1·40
2111 2f. multicoloured 1·50 1·10
2112 2f. multicoloured 1·50 1·10
2113 2f. multicoloured 1·50 1·10

DESIGNS—VERT: No. 2108, "The Two Saints", St.-Genis-des-Fontaines (wood-carving); No. 2109, "Venus of Brassempouy" (ivory sculpture); No. 2110, "La Joie de Vivre" (Robert Delaunay). HORIZ: No. 2111, Rameses II in war-chariot (wall-carving); No. 2112, Painting by Carzou; No. 2113, "Still Life with Fruit" Maurice de Vlaminck).

767 French Stamp Design of 1876

1976. International Stamp Day.
2114 **767** 80c.+20c. lilac & blk 60 55

1976. Tourist Publicity. As T 490, but dated "1976".
2115 1f. brown, green and red 60 35
2116 1f.10 blue 80 55
2117 1f.40 blue, green & brown 1·00 35
2118 1f.70 purple, green & blue 1·20 35
2119 2f. mauve, red and brown 1·40 35
2120 3f. brown, blue and green 1·70 55

DESIGNS—HORIZ: 1f. Chateau Bonaguil; 1f.40, Basque coast, Biarritz. 3f. Chateau de Malmaison. VERT: 1f.10, Lodeve Cathedral; 1f.70, Thiers. 2f. Ussel.

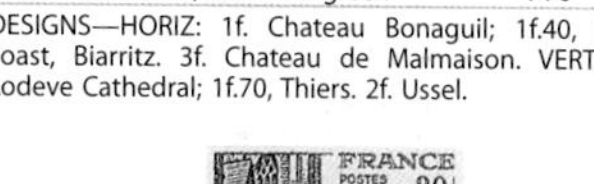

768 Old Rouen

1976. 49th Congress of French Philatelic Societies.
2121 **768** 80c. green and brown 60 35

769 "Duguay Trouin VIII" (cruiser), "Duguay Trouin IX" (destroyer) and Naval Emblem

1976. 50th Anniv of Central Marine Officers' Reserve Association.
2122 **769** 1f. yellow, blue & red 85 55

770 Youth

1976. "Juvarouen 76" Youth Stamp Exhibition, Rouen.
2123 **770** 60c. indigo, blue & red 60 35

771 Strasbourg Jug

1976. Europa. Multicoloured.
2124 80c. Type **771** 95 45
2125 1f.20 Sevres plate 1·50 85

772 Vergennes and Franklin

1976. Bicentenary of American Revolution.
2126 **772** 1f.20 black, red & blue 80 55

773 Marshal Moncey

1976. Red Cross. Celebrities.
2127 **773** 80c.+20c. purple, black and brown 80 75
2128 - 80c.+20c. grn & brn 80 75
2129 - 80c.+20c. mve & grn 80 75
2130 - 1f.+20c. black, light blue and blue 85 80
2131 - 1f.+20c. blue, mauve and purple 85 80
2132 - 1f.+20c. grey & red 85 80

DESIGNS: No. 2128, Max Jacob (poet); 2129, Mounet-Sully (tragedian); 2130, General Daumesnil; 2131, Eugene Fromentin (writer and painter); 2132, Anna de Noailles.

774 People talking

1976. "Communication".
2133 **774** 1f.20 black, red & yell 80 75

775 Verdun Memorial

1976. 60th Anniv of Verdun Offensive.

2134	**775**	1f. red, brown & green	80	55

776 Troncais Forest

1976. Nature Conservation.

2135	**776**	70c. brown, green & blue	60	35

777 Cross of Lorraine Emblem

1976. 30th Anniv of Free French Association.

2136	**777**	1f. red, dp blue & blue	1·00	55

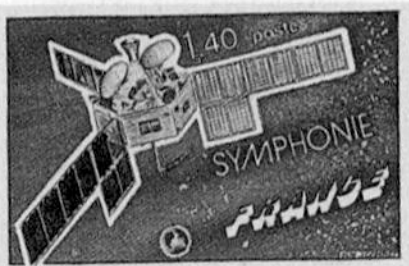

778 Satellite "Symphonie"

1976. Launch of "Symphonie No. 1" Satellite.

2137	**778**	1f.40 brn, choc & vio	1·00	75

779 Carnival Figures

1976. "La Fete" (Summer Festivals Exhibition, Tuileries, Paris).

2138	**779**	1f. red, green & blue	80	55

780 Yachting

1976. Olympic Games, Montreal.

2139	**780**	1f.20 ind, ultram & bl	1·00	55

781 Officers in Military and Civilian Dress

1976. Centenary of Reserve Officers Corps.

2140	**781**	1f. grey, red & blue	80	35

782 Early and Modern Telephones

1976. Telephone Centenary.

2141	**782**	1f. grey, brown & blue	80	35

783 Bronze Statue and Emblem

1976. 10th Anniv of International Tourist Film Association.

2142	**783**	1f.40 brown, red & grn	1·00	75

784 Police and Emblems

1976. 10th Anniv of National Police Force.

2143	**784**	1f.10 green, red & blue	80	55

785 Symbol of Nuclear Science

1976. European Research into Nuclear Science.

2144	**785**	1f.40 multicoloured	1·20	90

786 Fair Emblem

1976. 50th Anniv of French Fairs and Exhibitions Federation.

2145	**786**	1f.50 blue, green & brn	1·20	75

787 St. Barbara

1976. Red Cross Fund. Statuettes in Brou Church.

2146	**787**	80c.+20c. vio & red	80	75
2147	-	1f.+25c. brn & red	1·20	1·10

DESIGN: 1f. Cumaean Sybil.

788 "Douane" Symbol

1976. French Customs Service.

2148	**788**	1f.10 multicoloured	80	75

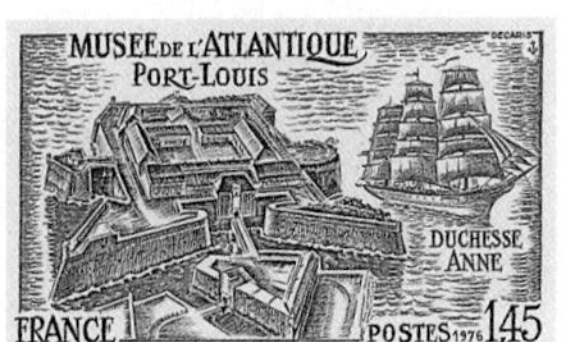

789 Museum and "Duchesse Anne" (cadet ship)

1976. Atlantic Museum, Port Louis.

2149	**789**	1f.45 brown, blue & blk	1·00	75

1977. Regions of France. As T 758.

2150		1f.45 mauve and green	1·00	55
2151		1f.50 multicoloured	1·00	75
2152		2f.10 yellow, blue & green	1·50	1·10
2153		2f.40 brown, green & blue	1·70	55
2154		2f.50 multicoloured	1·70	1·10
2155		2f.75 green	2·20	1·10
2156		3f.20 brown, green & blue	2·50	1·30
2157		3f.90 red, brown and blue	3·25	2·00

DESIGNS—HORIZ: 1f.45, Birds and flowers (Reunion); 2f.40, Coastline (Bretagne); 2f.75, Mountains (Rhone-Alpes). VERT: 1f.50, Banana tree (Martinique); 2f.10, Arms and transport (Franche-Comte); 2f.50, Fruit and yachts (Languedoc-Roussillon); 3f.20, Champagne and scenery (Champagne-Ardenne); 3f.90, Village church (Alsace).

790 Centre Building

1977. Opening of Georges Pompidou National Centre of Arts and Culture, Paris.

2158	**790**	1f. red, blue & green	60	35

1977. French Art. As T 491.

2159		2f. multicoloured	1·50	1·10
2160		2f. multicoloured	1·90	1·10

DESIGNS—HORIZ: No. 2159, "Mantes Bridge" (Corot). VERT: No. 2160, "Virgin and Child" (Rubens).

791 Dunkirk Harbour

1977. Dunkirk Port Extensions.

2161	**791**	50c. blue, indigo & brn	35	35

792 Torch and Dagger Emblem

1977. 90th Anniv of "Le Souvenir Francais" (French War Graves Organization).

2162	**792**	80c. brown, red & blue	80	55

793 Marckolsheim Post Relay Sign

1977. Stamp Day.

2163	**793**	1f.+20c. grey & blue	80	75

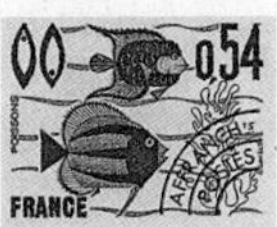

794 "Pisces"

1977. Precancels. Signs of the Zodiac.

2164	**794**	54c. violet	1·00	55
2165	-	58c. green	1·20	55
2166	-	61c. blue	80	55
2167	-	68c. brown	1·00	75
2168	-	73c. red	1·90	1·10
2169	-	78c. orange	1·20	75
2170	-	1f.05 mauve	2·10	1·80
2171	-	1f.15 orange	3·00	2·30
2172	-	1f.25 green	1·50	1·40
2173	-	1f.85 green	4·50	2·30
2174	-	2f. turquoise	3·75	3·50
2175	-	2f.10 mauve	2·30	1·80

DESIGNS: 58c. Cancer; 61c. Sagittarius; 68c. Taurus; 73c. Aries; 78c. Libra; 1f.05, Scorpio; 1f.15, Capricorn; 1f.25, Leo; 1f.85, Aquarius; 2f. Virgo; 2f.10, Gemini.

See note below No. 432 (1920).

795 "Geometric Design" (Victor Vasarely)

1977. Philatelic Creations. Works of Art by Modern Artists.

2176	**795**	3f. green and lilac	2·30	1·10
2177	-	3f. black and red	2·50	1·80
2178	-	3f. multicoloured	2·50	1·80

DESIGNS—VERT: No. 2177, Profile heads of man and hawk (Pierre-Yves Tremois). HORIZ: No. 2178, Abstract in Blue (R. Excoffon).

See also Nos. 2249, 2331/2, 2346/8, 2434/5, 2547 and 2578/9.

796 Flowers and Ornamental Garden

1977. 50th Anniv of National Horticultural Society.

2179	**796**	1f.70 red, brown & grn	1·20	75

797 Provencal Village

1977. Europa.

2180	**797**	1f. red, brown & blue	95	45
2181	-	1f.40 blk, brn & grn	1·50	55

DESIGN: 1f.40, Breton port.

798 Stylized Plant

1977. International Flower Show, Nantes.

2182	**798**	1f.40 mve, yell & bl	1·20	90

799 Battle of Cambrai

1977. 300th Anniv of Reunification of Cambrai with France.

2183	**799**	80c. mauve, brown & bl	60	55

800 Church, School and Map

1977. Centenary of French Catholic Institutes.

2184	**800**	1f.10 brown, bl & choc	80	75

801 Modern Constructions

1977. Meeting of European Civil Engineering Federation, Paris.

2185	**801**	1f.10 red, bistre & blue	80	55

802 Annecy

1977. 50th Congress of French Philatelic Societies.

2186	**802**	1f. brown, grn & olive	80	55

1977. Tourist Publicity. As T 490.

2187	1f.25 grey, brown & red	80	55
2188	1f.40 blue, purple & pink	1·00	55
2189	1f.45 sepia, brown & blue	1·00	55
2190	1f.50 olive, red & brown	1·00	55
2191	1f.90 yellow and black	1·40	65
2192	2f.40 bistre, green & black	1·50	55

DESIGNS—HORIZ: 1f.25, Premontres Abbey, Pont-a-Mousson; 1f.50, Statue and cloisters, Fontenay Abbey, Cote d'Or; 2f.40, Chateau de Vitre. VERT: 1f.40, Abbey tower of St. Amand-les-Eaux, Nord; 1f.45, Le Dorat Church, Haute-Vienne; 1f.90, Bayeux Cathedral.

803 School Building

1977. Polytechnic School, Palaiseau.

2193	**803**	1f.70 green, red & blue	1·20	55

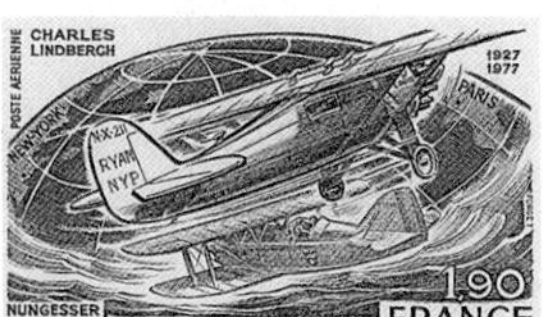
804 "Spirit of St. Louis" and "L'Oiseau Blanc"

1977. Air. 50th Anniv of North Atlantic Flights.

2194	**804**	1f.90 indigo, blue & grn	1·20	90

805 French Football Cup and Players

1977. 60th Anniv of French Football Cup.

2195	**805**	80c. bistre, blue & red	1·20	80

806 De Gaulle Memorial

1977. 5th Anniv of General de Gaulle Memorial.

2196	**806**	1f. multicoloured	1·20	90

807 "Map of France"

1977. 25th Anniv of Junior Chambers of Commerce.

2197	**807**	1f.10 blue and red	80	55

808 Battle of Nancy

1977. 500th Anniv of Battle of Nancy.

2198	**808**	1f.10 slate and blue	1·40	90

809 Seal of Burgundy

1977. 500th Anniv of Union of Burgundy with France.

2199	**809**	1f.25 green and olive	80	55

810 Compass on Globe

1977. 10th Anniv of International Association of French Language Parliaments.

2200	**810**	1f.40 red and blue	1·00	55

811 Red Cicada

1977. Nature Protection.

2201	**811**	80c. multicoloured	80	55

812 Hand and Examples of Craftsmanship

1977. French Craftsmanship.

2202	**812**	1f.40 brown and olive	1·20	75

813 Edouard Herriot (statesman)

1977. Red Cross Fund. Celebrities.

2203	**813**	1f.+20c. black	95	85
2204	-	1f.+20c. brn & grn	95	85
2205	-	1f.+20c. brn, bis & grn	95	85
2206	-	1f.+20c. bl, lt bl & red	95	85

DESIGNS: No. 2204, Abbe Breuil (archaeologist); 2205, Guillaume de Machault (poet); 2206, Charles Cros (poet).

814 "Agriculture and Industry"

1977. 30th Anniv of Economic and Social Council.

2207	**814**	80c. bistre, green & brn	60	35

815 "Old Man"

1977. Red Cross Fund. Carved Christmas Crib Figures from Provence.

2208	**815**	80c.+20c. black & red	80	75
2209	-	1f.+25c. green & red	1·00	90

DESIGN: 1f. "Old Woman".

816 "Sabine" (after Louis David)

1977. Inscr "FRANCE".

2210	**816**	1c. black	20	20
2211	**816**	2c. blue	20	20
2212	**816**	5c. green	20	15
2213	**816**	10c. red	20	15
2214	**816**	15c. blue	60	55
2215	**816**	20c. green	20	15
2216	**816**	30c. orange	20	15
2216a	**816**	40c. brown	35	35
2217	**816**	50c. violet	35	15
2217a	**816**	60c. red	35	35
2218	**816**	70c. blue	35	35
2219	**816**	80c. green	1·20	35
2220	**816**	80c. yellow	35	35
2221	**816**	90c. mauve	60	55
2222	**816**	1f. red	1·20	15
2223	**816**	1f. emerald	1·00	15
2224	**816**	1f. olive	60	15
2225	**816**	1f.10 green	1·00	35
2226	**816**	1f.20 red	1·00	15
2226a	**816**	1f.20 green	80	15
2227	**816**	1f.30 red	1·00	15
2228	**816**	1f.40 blue	2·20	90
2228a	**816**	1f.40 red	1·00	15
2229	**816**	1f.60 violet	1·50	55
2230	**816**	1f.70 blue	1·40	75
2230a	**816**	1f.80 brown	1·40	90
2231	**816**	2f. green	1·20	15
2232	**816**	2f.10 purple	1·40	35
2233	**816**	3f. brown	1·70	55
2233a	**816**	3f.50 green	2·10	90
2234	**816**	4f. red	2·75	80
2234a	**816**	5f. blue	50·00	35

For values inscr "REPUBLIQUE FRANÇAISE" see Nos. 2423/5.

817 Table Tennis

1977. 50th Anniv of French Table Tennis Federation.

2240	**817**	1f.10 grn, pur & orge	3·50	1·70

818 Percheron

1978. Nature Conservation.

2241	**818**	1f.70 multicoloured	1·50	1·10
2242	-	1f.80 brn, olive & grn	1·40	75

DESIGN—VERT: (23×37 mm) 1f.80, Osprey.

1978. French Art. As T 491.

2243	2f. black	3·00	1·70

DESIGN: 2f. Tournament under Louis XIV, Les Tuileries, 1662.

819 Flags of France and Sweden of 1878

1978. Centenary of Return of St. Barthelemy Island to France.

2244	**819**	1f.10 brn, red & mve	80	55

820 College Building

1978. Centenary of National Telecommunications College.

2245	**820**	80c. blue	60	45

1978. Regions of France. As T 758.

2246	1f. red, blue and black	80	35
2247	1f.40 blue, orange & green	1·20	75
2248	1f.70 gold, red and black	1·70	90

DESIGNS—VERT: 1f. Symbol of Ile de France. HORIZ: 1f.40, Flower and port (Haute-Normandie); 1f.70, Ancient Norman ship (Basse-Normandie).

1978. "Philatelic Creations". As T 795.

2249	3f. multicoloured	3·00	1·80
2250	3f. multicoloured	2·50	1·60

DESIGNS—HORIZ: No. 2249 "Institut de France and Pont des Arts, Paris" (B. Buffet); 2250, "Camargue Horses" (Yves Brayer).

821 Marie Noel (poet)

1978. Red Cross Fund. Celebrities.

2251	**821**	1f.+20c. indigo & bl	95	85

2252	-	1f.+20c. green, brown and blue	95	85
2253	-	1f.+20c. mve & vio	95	85
2254	-	1f.+20c. green & brn	95	85
2255	-	1f.+20c. mve & red	95	85
2256	-	1f.+20c. black, brown and red	95	85

DESIGNS: No. 2252, Georges Bernanos (writer); 2253, Leconte de Lisle (poet); 2254, Leo Tolstoy (novelist); 2255, Voltaire and J.-J. Rousseau; 2256, Claude Bernard (physician).

822 Jigsaw Map of France

1978. 15th Anniv of Regional Planning Boards.

2257	**822**	1f.10 green & violet	80	45

1978. Tourist Publicity. As T 490.

2258	50c. green, blue & dp green	35	35
2259	80c. dp green, blue & grn	60	35
2260	1f. black	60	35
2261	1f.10 violet, brown & grn	1·00	55
2262	1f.10 brown, blue & green	1·00	55
2263	1f.25 brown and red	1·20	55
2264	1f.70 black and brown	1·50	90

DESIGNS—VERT: 50c. Verdon Gorge; 1f. Church of St. Saturnin, Puy de Dome. HORIZ: 80c. Pont-Neuf, Paris; 1f.10 (No. 2261), Notre-Dame du Bec-Hellouin Abbey; 1f.10 (No. 2262), Chateau d'Esquelbecq; 1f.25, Abbey Church of Aubazine; 1f.70, Fontevraud Abbey.

823 Head of Girl

1978. "Juvexniort" Youth Philately Exhibition, Niort.

2265	**823**	80c. brn, choc & mve	60	35

824 Postman emptying Pillar Box, 1900

1978. Stamp Day.

2266	**824**	1f.+20c. grn & blue	80	75

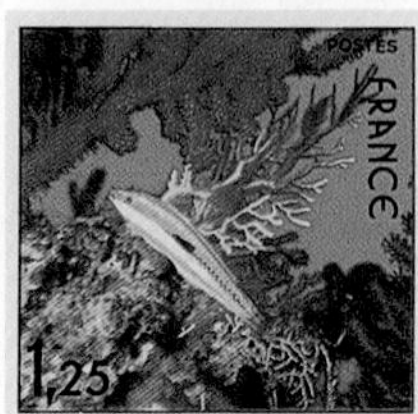

825 Underwater Scene and Rainbow Wrasse

1978. Port Cros National Park.

2267	**825**	1f.25 multicoloured	1·50	1·40

826 Floral Arch and Garden

1978. "Make France Bloom".

2268	**826**	1f.70 red, blue & green	1·90	75

827 Hands encircling Sun

1978. Energy Conservation.

2269	**827**	1f. yellow, brn & bistre	80	55

828 War Memorial, Notre Dame de Lorette

1978. Hill of Notre Dame de Lorette (War Cemetery).

2270	**828**	2f. brown and bistre	1·50	70

829 Fontaine des Innocents, Paris

1978. Europa. Fountains.

2271	**829**	1f. blk, bistre & blue	1·20	40
2272	-	1f.40 brn, grn & blue	1·50	70

DESIGN: 1f.40, Fontaine du Parc Floral, Paris.

830 Hotel de Mauroy, Troyes

1978. 51st Congress of French Philatelic Societies.

2273	**830**	1f. black, red & blue	80	55

831 Tennis Player and Stadium

1978. 50th Anniv of Roland Garros Tennis Stadium.

2274	**831**	1f. grey, brown & blue	3·00	70

832 Open Hand

1978. Handicrafts.

2275	**832**	1f.30 brown, grn & red	80	55

833 Citadel and Church

1978. 300th Anniv of Reunification of Franche-Comte with France.

2276	**833**	1f.20 grey, blue & grn	80	45

834 Emblem

1978. State Printing Office.

2277	**834**	1f. green, black & blue	60	45

835 Valenciennes and Maubeuge

1978. 300th Anniv of Return of Valenciennes and Maubeuge to France.

2278	**835**	1f.20 brown, vio & grey	80	55

836 Sower

1978. 50th Anniv of Academie de Philatelie.

2279	**836**	1f. blue, purple & violet	80	55

837 Morane-Saulnier Type H and Route

1978. Air. 65th Anniv of First Airmail Flight Villacoublay–Pauillac.

2280	**837**	1f.50 brown, blue & grn	1·20	80

838 Gymnasts, White Stork and Strasbourg Cathedral

1978. 19th World Gymnastics Championships, Strasbourg.

2281	**838**	1f. red, sepia & brown	85	55

839 Sporting Activities

1978. Sport for All.

2282	**839**	1f. violet, mauve & blue	1·20	90

840 "Freedom holding Dying Warrior" (A. Greck)

1978. Polish Fighters' War Memorial.

2283	**840**	1f.70 lake, red & green	1·20	90

841 Railway Carriage, Rethondes, and Armistice Monument

1978. 60th Anniv of Armistice.

2284	**841**	1f.20 black	1·20	55

842 Symbols of Readaptation

1978. Help for Convalescents.

2285	**842**	1f. red, brown & orge	80	55

843 "The Hare and the Tortoise"

1978. Red Cross Fund. Fables of La Fontaine.

2286	**843**	1f.+25c. brown, red and green	1·00	90
2287	-	1f.20+30c. green, red and brown	1·20	1·10

DESIGN: 1f.20, "The Town and the Country Mouse".

844 Human Figures balanced on Globe

1978. 30th Anniv of Human Rights.

2288	**844**	1f.70 blue and brown	1·20	55

845 Seated Child

1979. International Year of the Child.
2289 **845** 1f.70 red, vio & brn 4·25 2·30

1979. French Art. As T 491.
2290 2f. multicoloured 1·90 1·10
2291 2f. brown, black & dp brn 1·90 1·40
2292 2f. multicoloured 4·00 1·70
DESIGNS—HORIZ: No. 2290, "Music" (15th century miniature by Robinet Testart). VERT: No. 2291, "Diana in her Bath" (mantelpiece originally from Chalons-sur-Marne, now in Chateau d'Ecouen); 2292, "Auvers-sur-Oise Church" (Vincent van Gogh).

846 Marshal de Bercheny (Cavalry leader)

1979. Red Cross Fund. Celebrities.
2293 **846** 1f.20+30c. brown, blue and deep blue 1·20 1·10
2294 - 1f.20+30c. black and yellow 1·20 1·10
2295 - 1f.20+30c. deep brown, red & brown 1·20 1·10
2296 - 1f.20+30c. blue, mauve and red 1·20 1·10
2297 - 1f.30+30c. red and brown 1·20 1·10
2298 - 1f.30+30c. blue and ultramarine 1·20 1·10
DESIGNS: No. 2294, Leon Jouhaux (Nobel Peace Prize winner); 2295, Abelard and Heloise; 2296, Georges Courteline (playwright); 2297, Simone Weil (social philosopher); 2298, Andre Malraux (writer and politician).

847 "Amanita caesarea"

1979. Precancelled. Mushrooms.
2299 **847** 64c. red 80 35
2300 - 83c. brown 80 55
2301 - 1f.30 yellow 1·40 90
2302 - 2f.25 lilac 2·00 1·60
DESIGNS: 83c. "Craterellus comucopioides"; 1f.30, "Omphalotus olearius"; 2f.20, "Ramaria botrytis".
See note below No. 432 (1920).

848 Segalen, Pirogue, Pagoda and "Durance"

1979. 60th Death Anniv of Victor Segalen (writer and explorer).
2303 **848** 1f.50 turq, brn & red 1·00 55

849 Hibiscus Flower

1979. International Flower Show, Martinique.
2304 **849** 35c. lilac, mve & grn 35 35

850 Seated Buddha

1979. Borobudur Temple Preservation.
2305 **850** 1f.80 turquoise & green 1·40 55

851 Head Post Office, Paris

1979. Stamp Day.
2306 **851** 1f.20+30c. blue, red and brown 1·00 75

852 Street Urchin

1979. Birth Centenary of Francisque Poulbot (artist).
2307 **852** 1f.30 multicoloured 1·00 55

853 "Apis mellifera"

1979. Nature Conservation.
2308 **853** 1f. green, brown & orge 1·20 55

854 St.-Germain-des-Pres Abbey

1979. St.-Germain-des-Pres Abbey Restoration.
2309 **854** 1f.40 red, grey and blue 1·00 55

1979. Tourist Publicity. As T 490.
2310 45c. violet, blue & ultram 35 35
2311 1f. green, dp grn & lt grn 60 55
2312 1f. sepia, brown and lilac 60 55
2313 1f.20 brown, blue and green 80 55
2314 1f.50 sepia, red & brown 1·00 55
2315 1f.70 blue and brown 1·00 90
DESIGNS—VERT: No. 2311, Interiors of Abbeys of Bernay and St. Pierre-sur-Dives, Normandy; 2312, Auray; 2313, Windmill at Steenvoorde, Dunkirk (after Pierre Spas). HORIZ: No. 2310, Chateau de Maisons-Laffitte; 2314, Niaux Grotto; 2315, Palace of Kings of Majorca, Perpignan.

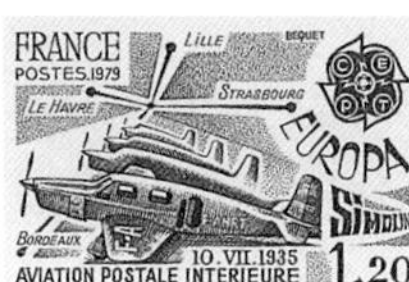

855 Caudron C.635 Monoplanes

1979. Europa.
2316 **855** 1f.20 blue, grn & turq 1·20 35
2317 - 1f.70 green, turq & red 2·50 80
DESIGN: 1f.70, Boule de Moulins (floating container used to carry letters during the Siege of Paris).

856 Sailing Ship at Nantes

1979. Federation of French Philatelic Societies Congress, Nantes.
2318 **856** 1f.20 blue, vio & grey 80 55

857 "Camille Desmoulins addressing Crowd" (engraving by Huyot)

1979. 190th Anniv of Palais Royal, Paris.
2319 **857** 1f. red and violet 60 35

858 Flags of Member Countries and Strasbourg Cathedral

1979. First Direct Elections to European Assembly.
2320 **858** 1f.20 multicoloured 80 35

859 Joan of Arc Monument, Rouen

1979. National Monument.
2321 **859** 1f.70 mauve 1·20 75

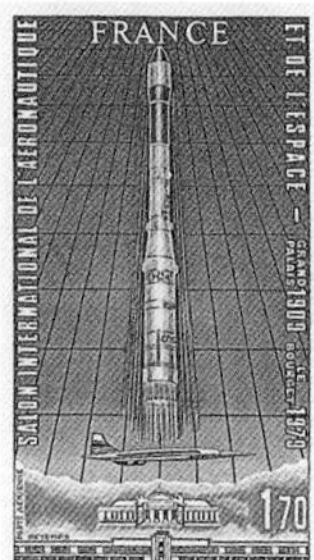

860 "Ariane" Rocket and Concorde over Grand Palais, Paris and Le Bourget Airport

1979. Air. International Aeronautics and Space Exhibition, Le Bourget.
2322 **860** 1f.70 bl, orge & brn 1·70 1·30

861 Felix Guyon (urologist)

1979. 18th Congress of International Society of Urologists, Paris.
2323 **861** 1f.80 blue and brown 1·20 55

862 Lantern Tower, La Rochelle

1979. Pre-cancelled. Historic Monuments (1st series).
2324 **862** 68c. lilac 60 55
2325 - 88c. blue 60 75
2326 - 1f.40 green 1·20 90
2327 - 2f.35 brown 1·90 1·40
DESIGNS: 88c. Cathedral towers, Chartres; 1f.40, Cathedral towers, Bourges; 2f.35, Cathedral towers, Amiens.
See note below No. 432 (1920).
See also Nos. 2342/5, 2383/6 and 2509/12.

863 "Telecom 79"

1979. Third World Telecommunications Exhibition, Geneva.
2328 **863** 1f.10 brn, turq & grn 80 35

1979. Regions of France. As T 758.
2329 2f.30 black, yellow & red 1·50 55
DESIGN: 2f.30, Thistle, Lorraine.

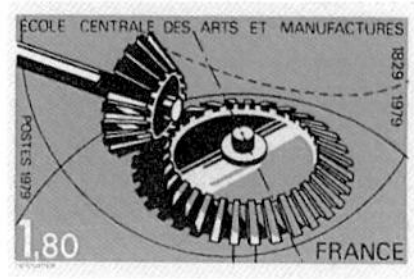

864 Gear-wheels

1979. 150th Anniv of Central Technical School, Paris.
2330 **864** 1f.80 yellow, blk & grn 1·20 90

1979. "Philatelic Creations". As T 795.
2331 3f. multicoloured 2·20 1·40
2332 3f. brown and green 2·30 1·40
DESIGNS: No. 2331, "Marianne" (Salvador Dali); 2332, "Fire Dancer from 'The Magic Flute'" (Chapelain-Midy).

865 Judo

1979. World Judo Championships, Paris.
2333 **865** 1f.60 blk, lt grn & grn 1·00 55

866 Woman's Head

1979. Red Cross Fund. Stained Glass Windows, Church of St. Joan of Arc, Rouen.
2334 **866** 1f.10+30c. brown, green and red 80 75
2335 - 1f.30+30c. brown, green and red 1·20 90
DESIGN: 1f.30, Simon the Magician.
The windows came originally from the Church of St. Vincent, Rouen, destroyed during the Second World War.

867 Violins

1979. Handicrafts. Violin Manufacture.
2336 **867** 1f.30 blk, red & lake 1·00 55

868 Eurovision Satellite

1980. 25th Anniv of Eurovision (European Broadcasting Union).
2337 **868** 1f.80 bl, dp bl & blk 1·40 1·10

1980. French Art. Design similar to T 491.

2338		3f. brown, ochre & green	2·30	1·40
2339		3f. multicoloured	2·50	1·50
2340		3f. multicoloured	2·50	1·50
2341		4f. multicoloured	3·00	1·60

DESIGNS—VERT: No. 2338, "Woman with Fan" (sculpture by Ossip Zadkine); 2340, "The Peasant Family" (Louis le Nain); 2341, "Woman with Blue Eyes" (Modigliani). HORIZ: No. 2339, "Homage to J. S. Bach" (tapestry by Jean Picart Le Doux).

1980. Pre-cancelled. Historic Monuments (2nd series). Designs as T 862.

2342		76c. turquoise	60	35
2343		99c. green	60	55
2344		1f.60 red	1·20	1·10
2345		2f.65 brown	1·90	1·40

DESIGNS: 76c. Chateau d'Angers; 99c. Chateau de Kerjean; 1f.60, Chateau de Pierrefonds; 2f.65, Chateau de Tarascon.
See note below No. 432 (1920).

1980. Philatelic Creations. Design similar to T 795.

2346		3f. blue, black and brown	2·30	1·40
2347		4f. multicoloured	3·00	1·70
2348		4f. black and blue	3·00	1·70

DESIGNS—As T **795**: HORIZ: No. 2346, Abstract (Raoul Ubac). VERT: No. 2348, Abstract (Hans Hartung). 43×49 mm: No. 2347, "Message of Peace" (Yaacov Agam).

869 Processional Figures and Carnival Crowd

1980. "Giants of the North" Festival.

2349	**869**	1f.60 red, grn & blue	1·00	55

870 Viollet-le-Duc (architect and writer)

1980. Red Cross Fund. Celebrities.

2350	**870**	1f.30+30c. black and grey	1·20	90
2351	-	1f.30+30c. brown and green	2·00	1·80
2352	-	1f.40+30c. deep blue and blue	1·20	90
2353	-	1f.40+30c. black	1·20	90
2354	-	1f.40+30c. grey and black	1·20	90
2355	-	1f.40+30c. turquoise and green	1·20	90

DESIGN—VERT: No. 2351, Jean Monnet (statesman); 2352, Jean-Marie de la Mennais (Christian educationalist) (portrait after Paulin-Guerin); 2353, Frederic Mistral (poet); 2355, Saint-John Perse (poet and diplomat). HORIZ: No. 2354, Pierre Paul de Riquet (constructor of Canal du Midi).

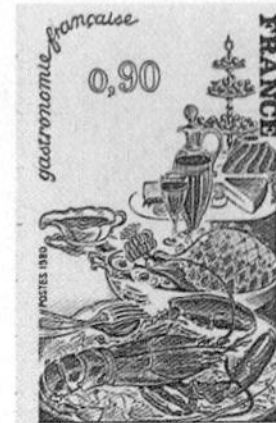

871 French Cuisine

1980. French Gastronomical Exn, Paris.

2356	**871**	90c. brown and red	1·20	90

872 "The Letter to Melie" (Mario Avati)

1980. Stamp Day.

2357	**872**	1f.30+30c. mult	1·00	90

873 "Woman Embroidering" (Toffoli)

1980. Handicrafts. Embroidery.

2358	**873**	1f.10 blue, yell & brn	80	55

874 Smoker and Non-smoker (poster)

1980. Anti-smoking Campaign.

2359	**874**	1f.30 blue, red & black	80	45

1980. Tourist Publicity. Designs as T 490.

2360		1f.50 orange, brown & blue	1·00	35
2361		2f. black and red	1·20	55
2362		2f.20 brown, blue & green	1·40	55
2363		2f.30 green, brown & blue	1·50	55
2364		2f.50 blue, violet and mauve	1·50	35
2365		3f.20 brown and blue	2·10	80

DESIGNS—VERT: 1f.50, Cordes; 2f.30, Montauban; 2f.50, Praying nun and St. Peter's Abbey, Solesmes; 3f.20, Puy Cathedral. HORIZ: 2f. Chateau de Maintenon; 2f.20, Chateau de Rambouillet.

875 Aristide Briand (statesman)

1980. Europa.

2366	**875**	1f.30 multicoloured	1·20	45
2367	-	1f.80 red and brown	1·90	85

DESIGN: 1f.80, St. Benedict (illuminated letter from manuscript).

876 La Rouchefoucauld-Liancourt (founder) and Map

1980. Bicentenary of National Technical High School.

2368	**876**	2f. green and violet	1·20	70

877 Town Hall and Cranes, Dunkirk

1980. Federation of French Philatelic Societies Congress, Dunkirk.

2369	**877**	1f.30 bl, red & ultram	80	35

878 Isabel

1980. Nature Conservation.

2370	**878**	1f.10 multicoloured	1·20	75

879 Albert Durer (self portrait)

1980. "Philexfrance 82" International Stamp Exhibition, Paris (1st issue).

2371	**879**	2f. multicoloured	2·10	2·00

See also Nos. 2415/16, 2520/1 and **MS**2539.

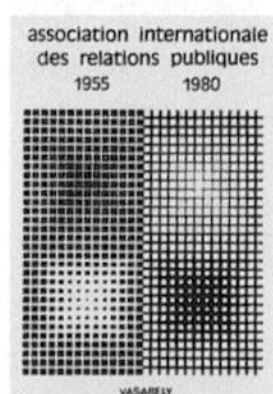

880 Symbolic Design

1980. 25th Anniv of International Public Relations Association.

2372	**880**	1f.30 blue and red	1·00	55

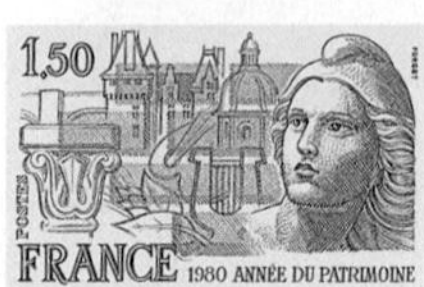

881 "Marianne" and Architecture

1980. Heritage Year.

2373	**881**	1f.50 blue and black	1·00	55

882 Sources of Energy

1980. 26th International Geological Congress, Paris.

2374	**882**	1f.60 red, brown & ol	1·20	75

883 Rochambeau landing at Newport

1980. Bicentenary of Rochambeau's arrival at Newport, Rhode Island.

2375	**883**	2f.50 mve, red & grey	1·90	1·10

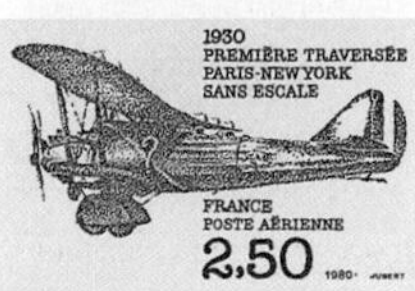

884 Breguet 19 Super TR "Point d'Interrogation"

1980. Air. 50th Anniv of First Non-stop Paris–New York Flight.

2376	**884**	2f.50 purple and blue	1·70	55

885 Golf

1980. French Golf Federation.

2377	**885**	1f.40 brown & green	1·00	55

886 Comedie-Francaise

1980. 300th Anniv of Comedie-Francaise.

2378	**886**	2f. blue, red and grey	1·40	75

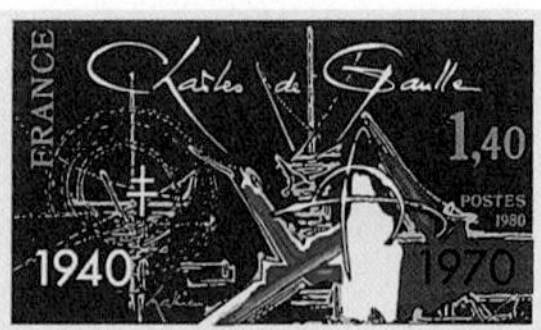

887 Abstract based on Lorraine Cross and French Flag

1980. 40th Anniv of Appeal by, and 10th Death Anniv of, General de Gaulle.

2379	**887**	1f.40 multicoloured	1·70	75

888 Guardsman

1980. Centenary of Reorganization and Naming of Republican Guard.

2380	**888**	1f.70 blue and red	1·40	75

889 "Filling the Granaries"

1980. Red Cross Fund. Stall Carvings from Amiens Cathedral.

2381	**889**	1f.20+30c. brown and red	1·00	90
2382	-	1f.40+30c. brown and red	1·20	1·10

DESIGN: 1f.40, "Grapes from the Promised Land".

1981. Pre-cancelled. Historic Monuments (3rd series). Horiz designs as T 862.

2383		88c. mauve	60	35
2384		1f.14 blue	60	55
2385		1f.84 green	1·20	1·10
2386		3f.05 brown	1·90	1·50

DESIGNS: 88c. Imperial Chapel, Ajaccio; 1f.14, Astronomical Clock, Besancon; 1f.84, Castle ruins, Coucy-le-Chateau; 3f.05, Cave paintings, Font-de Gaume, Les Eyzies-de Tayac.
See note below No. 432 (1920).

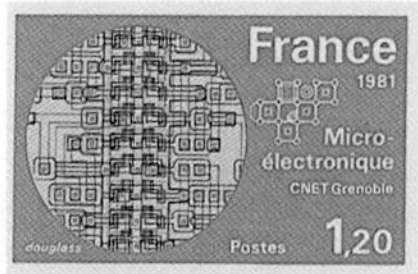

890 Micro-electronics

1981. Technology.

2387	**890**	1f.20 multicoloured	80	55
2388	-	1f.20 multicoloured	80	55
2389	-	1f.40 multicoloured	1·00	55
2390	-	1f.80 dp bl, bl & yell	1·20	90
2391	-	2f. blue, red and black	1·50	1·10

DESIGNS: No. 2388, Biology; 2389, New energy sources; 2390, Sea bed exploitation; 2391, Telematics.

891 Louis Armand (engineer and Academician)

1981. Red Cross Fund. Celebrities.

2392	**891**	1f.20+30c. green and brown	1·00	90
2393	-	1f.20+30c. mult	1·00	90
2394	-	1f.40+30c. deep green and green	1·20	1·10
2395	-	1f.40+30c. blue and black	1·20	1·10
2396	-	1f.40+30c. blue and violet	1·40	1·30
2397	-	1f.40+30c. brown and bistre	1·50	1·40

DESIGNS—VERT: No. 2393, Louis Jouvet (theatre and film director and actor); 2396, R. P. Pierre Teilhard de Chardin (palaeontologist and philosopher). HORIZ: No. 2394, Anne-Marie Javouhey (missionary); 2395, Jacques Offenbach (composer); 2397, Pastor Marc Boegner.

1981. French Art. As T 491. Multicoloured.

2398	2f. "The Footpath" (Camille Pissarro) (horiz)	1·50	1·30
2399	4f. "Composition 1920/23" (Albert Gleizes) (vert)	2·75	1·30

892 "The Love Letter" (Goya)

1981. Stamp Day.

2400	**892**	1f.40+30c. mult	1·20	1·10

893 Angel pouring Water on France

1981. Water.

2401	**893**	1f.40 red, blue & blk	1·00	55

1981. Tourist Publicity. Designs similar to T 490.

2403	1f.40 brown and red	1·00	35
2404	1f.70 brown, green & blue	1·40	75
2405	2f. black and red	1·50	75
2406	2f.20 black and blue	1·50	75
2407	2f.20 sepia and brown	1·50	75
2408	2f.50 brown, blue & green	1·50	55
2409	2f.60 red and green	1·70	55
2410	2f.90 green	2·00	35

DESIGNS—VERT: 1f.40, St. John's Cathedral, Lyon; 1f.70, Maison Carree, Nimes; 2f.20 (2406), St. Anne's Church, Auray; 2f.90, Crest. HORIZ: 2f. Interior, Notre Dame Abbey, Vaucelles; 2f.20 (2407), Notre Dame Church, Louviers; 2f.50, Chateau de Sully, Rosny-sur-Seine; 2f.60, Saint-Emilion.

894 Bookbinding Press

1981. Handicrafts. Bookbinding.

2411	**894**	1f.50 olive and red	1·20	75

895 Bourree Croisee dance

1981. Europa.

2412	**895**	1f.40 brown, blk & grn	1·20	35
2413	-	2f. black, brn & blue	1·90	90

DESIGN: 2f. Sardane (Catalan dance).

896 Military and Sporting Scenes

1981. Cent of Saint-Maixent Military Academy.

2414	**896**	2f.50 mauve, blue & vio	1·50	55

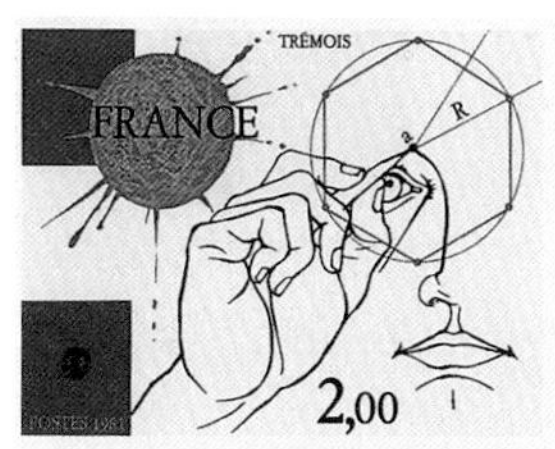

897 "France"

1981. "Philexfrance 82" International Stamp Exhibition, Paris (2nd issue). Multicoloured.

2415	2f. Type **897**	1·70	1·30
2416	2f. "Paris"	1·70	1·30

898 Theophraste Renaudot and Emile de Girardin

1981. 350th Anniv of First French Newspaper "La Gazette", Death Centenary of Emile de Girardin (founder of newspaper "La Presse") and Cent of Law on Freedom of the Press.

2417	**898**	2f.20 black and red	1·50	90

899 Thermal Waters of Vichy

1981. Federation of French Philatelic Societies Congress, Vichy.

2418	**899**	1f.40 brown, bl & grn	1·00	55

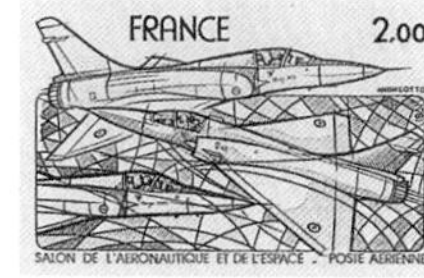

900 Dassault Mirage 2000 Aircraft

1981. Air. 34th International Aeronautics and Space Exhibition.

2419	**900**	2f. mauve, blue & violet	2·50	90

901 "HEC"

1981. Centenary of Paris Commercial College.

2420	**901**	1f.40 blue, green & red	1·00	55

902 Grey Heron and La Palissade, Camargue

1981. Conservation of Littoral Regions.

2421	**902**	1f.60 green, brn & red	1·40	90

903 Fencing

1981. World Fencing Championships, Clermont-Ferrand.

2422	**903**	1f.80 black & brown	1·40	90

1981. Vert designs as T 816 but inscr "REPUBLIQUE FRANCAISE".

2423	1f.40 green	1·00	20
2424	1f.60 red	1·00	20
2425	2f.30 blue	2·75	1·30

904 Car colliding with Glass

1981. Campaign against Drinking and Driving.

2428	**904**	1f.60 brown, red & olive	1·40	55

905 Costes, Le Brix and Breguet 19 Super TR "Nungesser et Coli"

1981. Air. Dieudonne Costes and Joseph Le Brix (pilots of first non-stop South Atlantic flight) Commemoration.

2429	**905**	10f. black, brn & red	6·25	90

906 Bird

1981. 45th International Congress of P.E.N. Club, Lyon and Paris.

2430	**906**	2f. black, violet & grn	1·40	55

907 Stylized Bird

1981. Centenary of National Savings Bank.

2431	**907**	1f.40 green, bl & red	1·00	35
2432	**907**	1f.60 carmine, blue & red	1·20	45

908 Jules Ferry (education reformer)

1981. Cent of National Education System.

2433	**908**	1f.60 vio, brn & blk	1·20	55

1981. Philatelic Creations. As T 795. Mult.

2434	4f. "The Divers" (Edouard Pignon) (horiz)	2·75	1·30
2435	4f. "Alleluia" (Alfred Manessier)	2·75	1·30

909 "Borda" (warship) and Naval School, Lanveoc-Poulmic

1981. 150th Anniv of Naval School.

2436	**909**	1f.40 brown, blue & red	1·20	55

910 "Vision of St. Hubert" (15th-cent sculpture)

1981. Hunting and Nature Museum, Hotel de Guenegaud, Paris.

2437	**910**	1f.60 brown & stone	1·40	55

911 J. Moulin, J. Jaures, V. Schoelcher and Pantheon

1981. Pantheon.

2438	**911**	1f.60 purple and blue	1·20	45

912 Disabled Draughtsman

1981. International Year of Disabled Persons.

2439	**912**	1f.60 black, bl & red	1·00	55

913 Pastoral Scene (2nd-century mosaic)

1981. 2000th Death Anniv of Virgil (poet).

2440	**913**	2f. multicoloured	1·90	1·30

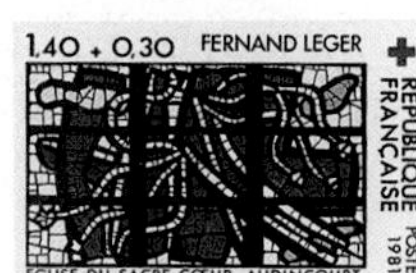

914 "Scourges of the Passion"

1981. Red Cross Fund. Stained Glass Windows by Fernand Leger from the Church of the Sacred Heart, Audincort. Multicoloured.

2441	1f.40+30c. Type **914**	1·20	1·10
2442	1f.60+30c. "Peace"	1·40	1·10

915 Memorial (Antoine Rohal)

1981. Martyrs of Chateaubriant (Second World War victims).

2443	**915**	1f.40 black, purple & bl	1·00	55

916 "Liberty" (from "Liberty guiding the People" by Delacroix)

1982

2444	**916**	5c. green	35	35
2445	**916**	10c. brown	20	15
2446	**916**	15c. purple	60	55
2447	**916**	20c. green	20	15
2448	**916**	30c. orange	20	15
2449	**916**	40c. brown	35	35
2450	**916**	50c. mauve	35	15
2451	**916**	60c. brown	35	15
2452	**916**	70c. blue	60	35
2453	**916**	80c. green	60	15
2454	**916**	90c. mauve	60	35
2455	**916**	1f. green	60	35
2456	**916**	1f.40 green	1·20	15
2457	**916**	1f.60 red	1·00	15
2458	**916**	1f.60 green	1·20	20
2460	**916**	1f.80 red	1·20	20
2461	**916**	1f.80 green	1·20	20
2464	**916**	2f. red	1·20	20
2465	**916**	2f. green	1·20	20
2466	**916**	2f.10 red	1·20	20
2467	**916**	2f.20 red	1·20	20
2468	**916**	2f.30 blue	2·75	1·60
2469	**916**	2f.60 blue	2·50	1·40
2470	**916**	2f.80 blue	2·50	1·30
2471	**916**	3f. brown	1·90	35
2472	**916**	3f. blue	2·50	90
2473	**916**	3f.20 blue	3·75	1·10
2474	**916**	3f.40 blue	2·50	1·10
2475	**916**	3f.60 blue	1·90	75
2476	**916**	3f.70 purple	1·90	55
2477	**916**	4f. red	2·20	35
2478	**916**	5f. blue	3·25	20
2479	**916**	10f. violet	5·00	20
2484	**916**	1f.70 green	1·20	75
2487	**916**	1f.90 green	1·90	55

1982. Tourist Publicity. As T 490.

2503	1f.60 blue, green and black	1·20	35
2504	2f. red and mauve	1·20	55
2505	2f.90 green, dp brn & brn	1·90	1·10
2506	3f. deep blue and blue	1·70	75
2507	3f. red, yellow and blue	1·70	55

DESIGNS—VERT: No. 2503, Fishing boats and map of St. Pierre et Miquelon. HORIZ: No. 2504, Aix-en-Provence; 2505, Chateau de Ripaille, Haute-Savoie; 2506, Chateau Henri IV, Pau; 2507, Collonges-la-Rouge.

1982. Regions of France. As T 758.

2508	1f.90 blue and red	1·20	55

DESIGN: 1f.90, Map of Corsica, containing sun and sea, superimposed on mountain.

1982. Pre-cancelled. Historic Monuments (4th series). As T 862.

2509	97c. green	60	35
2510	1f.25 red	60	55
2511	2f.03 brown	1·20	1·10
2512	3f.36 blue	1·90	1·40

DESIGNS: 97c. Chateau de Tanlay; 1f.25, Salses Fort; 2f.03, Montlhery Tower; 3f.36, Chateau d'If.
See note below No. 432 (1920).

918 Guillaume Postel (scholar)

1982. Red Cross Fund. Celebrities.

2513	**918**	1f.40+30c. black and brown	1·40	1·30
2514	-	1f.40+30c. brown and grey	1·40	1·30
2515	-	1f.60+30c. lilac, violet and purple	1·40	1·30
2516	-	1f.60+40c. blue and brown	1·40	1·30
2517	-	1f.60+40c. blue	1·50	1·40
2518	-	1f.80+40c. brown	1·70	1·60

DESIGNS: No. 2514, Henri Mondor (doctor and writer); 2515, Andre Chantemesse (doctor and bacteriologist); 2516, Louis Pergaud (writer); 2517, Robert Debre (professor of medicine); 2518, Gustave Eiffel (engineer).

919 St. Francis of Assisi

1982. 800th Birth Anniv of St. Francis of Assisi.

2519	**919**	2f. black and blue	1·40	75

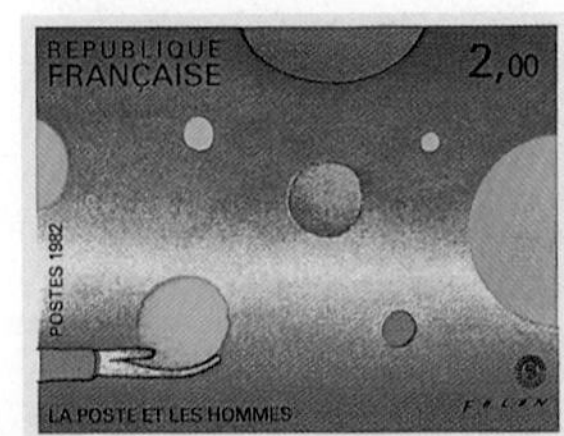

920 "The Post and Man"

1982. "Philexfrance 82" International Stamp Exhibition, Paris (3rd issue). Multicoloured.

2520	2f. Type **920**	3·75	2·75
2521	2f. Cogwheels ("The Post and Technology")	3·75	2·75

921 Lord Baden-Powell and Scouts

1982. 75th Anniv of Boy Scout Movement and 125th Birth Anniv of Lord Baden-Powell (founder).

2522	**921**	2f.30 black & green	1·40	55

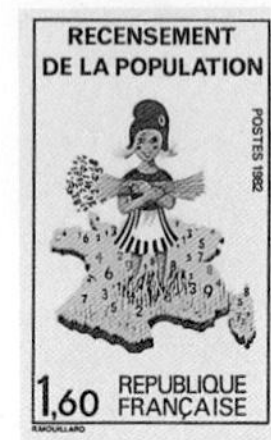

922 "Marianne" on Map of France

1982. Population Census.

2523	**922**	1f.60 multicoloured	1·00	45

923 Basel-Mulhouse Airport

1982

2524	**923**	1f.90 blue, brn & red	1·50	75

924 Clasped Wrists

1982. Anti-racism Campaign.

2525	**924**	2f.30 orange & brown	1·50	75

925 "Woman Reading" (Picasso)

1982. Stamp Day.

2526	**925**	1f.60+40c. mult	1·40	90

926 "Blacksmith" (Toffoli)

1982. Handicrafts. Iron Work.

2527	**926**	1f.40 yellow, red & blk	1·00	75

927 Map of Europe and Seal (Treaty of Rome)

1982. Europa.

2528	**927**	1f.60 blue	1·50	75
2529	-	2f.30 brn, blk & grn	1·90	75

DESIGN: 2f.30, Seal of Charles the Bald (Treaty of Verdun, 843).

928 Goalkeeper and Stadium

1982. World Cup Football Championship, Spain.

2530	**928**	1f.80 green, red & bl	2·30	55

1982. Art. Designs as T 491.

2531	4f. yellow, blue and brown	2·75	1·30
2532	4f. multicoloured	2·75	1·30
2533	4f. multicoloured	2·75	1·40
2534	4f. pink and grey	2·75	1·40

DESIGNS—VERT: No. 2531, "Ephebus of Agde" (ancient Greek bronze sculpture); 2533, "The Lacemaker" (Vermeer); 2534, "The Family" (sculpture, Marc Boyan). HORIZ: 2532, "Embarkation of St. Paul at Ostia" (Claude Gellee (Le Lorrain)).

929 Festival Poster (Federico Fellini)

1982. 35th International Film Festival, Cannes.

2535	**929**	2f.30 multicoloured	1·50	1·10

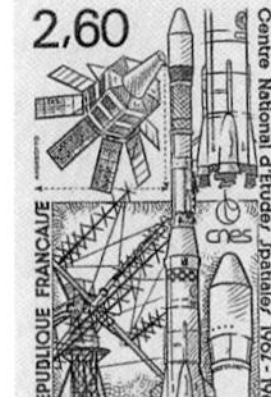

930 "Eole" Satellite, "Ariane" Rocket and Antenna

1982. 20th Anniv of National Space Studies Centre.

2536	**930**	2f.60 dp blue, bl & red	1·50	90

931 Interlocking Lines

1982. Industrialized Countries Summit, Versailles.

2537	**931**	2f.60 multicoloured	1·50	90

932 Valles

1982. 150th Birth Anniv of Jules Valles (journalist).

2538	**932**	1f.60 dp green & green	1·20	45

933 "Marianne"

1982. "Philexfrance 82" International Stamp Exhibition, Paris (4th issue). Sheet 100×71 mm.

MS2539 **933** 4f. blue and red; 6f. red and blue	19·00	19·00

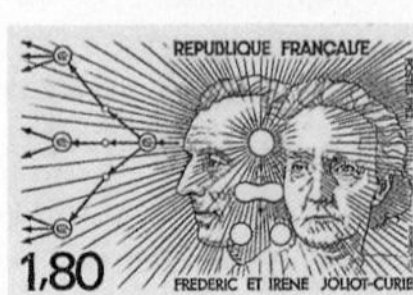

934 The Joliot-Curies

1982. Frederic and Irene Joliot-Curie (nuclear physicists) Commemoration.

2540	**934**	1f.80 pur, mve & vio	1·20	55

935 Grenoble Street Scene

1982. Centenary of Electric Street Lighting.

2541	**935**	1f.80 purple, bl & vio	1·20	35

936 Firemen

1982. Cent of National Federation of Fire Fighters.
2542 **936** 3f.30 brown and red 2·30 80

937 Marionnettes

1982
2543 **937** 1f.80 red, blue & lilac 1·20 55

938 Rugby

1982
2544 **938** 1f.60 blue, grn & red 2·50 90

939 Lecture Room

1982. Teacher Training Colleges.
2545 **939** 1f.80 grey & brown 1·20 55

940 Lille

1982
2546 **940** 1f.80 red and green 1·20 55

1982. Philatelic Creations. As T 795. Mult.
2547 4f. "The Turkish Room" (Balthus) 2·75 1·40

941 Dr. Robert Koch, Microscope and Bacillus

1982. Cent of Discovery of Tubercle Bacillus.
2548 **941** 2f.60 black and red 1·50 75

942 "Five Weeks in a Balloon"

1982. Red Cross Fund. Works by Jules Verne.
2549 **942** 1f.60+30c. brown & red 1·40 90
2550 - 1f.80+40c. green & red 1·40 90
DESIGN: 1f.80, "20,000 Leagues Under the Sea".

943 St. Theresa of Avila

1982. 400th Death Anniv of St. Theresa of Avila.
2551 **943** 2f.10 brn, blk & grn 1·40 75

944 Latecoere 300 Flying Boat F-AKGF "Croix du Sud"

1982. Air. 46th Anniv of Disappearance of "Croix du Sud".
2552 **944** 1f.60 lilac and blue 1·20 1·10

945 Cavelier de la Salle and Map of Louisiana

1982. 300th Anniv of Discovery of Louisiana.
2553 **945** 3f.25 brn, red & grn 1·90 80

946 Leon Blum

1982. 110th Birth Anniv of Leon Blum (politician).
2554 **946** 1f.80 brown & lt brn 1·20 45

1983. Regions of France. As T 758.
2555 1f. multicoloured 80 35
DESIGN—HORIZ: 1f. Map and coastline, Provence, Alpes, Cote d'Azur.

947 Andre Messager (composer)

1983. Red Cross Fund. Celebrities.
2556 **947** 1f.60+30c. blk & bl 1·40 1·30
2557 - 1f.60+30c. blk & yell 1·40 1·30
2558 - 1f.80+40c. blk & vio 1·50 1·40
2559 - 1f.80+40c. blk & red 1·50 1·40
2560 - 2f.+40c. blk & grn 1·60 1·50
2561 - 2f.+40c. black & bl 1·60 1·50
DESIGNS: No. 2557, Jacques-Ange Gabriel (architect); 2558, Hector Berlioz (composer); 2559, Max-Pol Fouchet (writer); 2560, Rene Cassin (diplomat); 2561, Stendhal (writer).

948 Budding Plant (spring)

1983. Pre-cancelled. The Four Seasons.
2562 **948** 1f.05 green 60 55
2563 - 1f.35 red 60 55
2564 - 2f.19 brown 1·20 1·10
2565 - 3f.63 violet 1·90 1·40
DESIGNS: 1f.35, Wheat (summer); 2f.19, Berries (autumn); 3f.63, Tree in snow (winter).
See note below No. 432 (1920).

949 Charleville Mezieres (image scaled to 61% of original size)

1983. Tourist Publicity.
2566 1f.80 brown, grn & bl 1·20 35
2567 2f. brown and black 1·20 55
2568 3f. brown and blue 1·70 90
2569 **949** 3f.10 brown and red 2·00 1·10
2570 - 3f.60 black, brn & bl 2·30 55
DESIGNS—As T **490**: 1f.80, Brantome, Perigord; 2f. Jarnac; 3f. Concarneau; 3f.60, Noirlac Abbey.
See also Nos. 2838 and 3642/5.

950 Martin Luther

1983. 500th Birth Anniv of Martin Luther (Protestant reformer).
2571 **950** 3f.30 brown & stone 2·10 80

951 Woman reading and Globe

1983. Centenary of French Alliance (language-teaching and cultural institute).
2572 **951** 1f.80 blue, red & brn 1·20 55

952 "Man dictating Letter" (Rembrandt)

1983. Stamp Day.
2573 **952** 1f.80+40c. stone and black 1·50 1·10

953 Danielle Casanova (resistance leader)

1983. International Women's Day.
2574 **953** 3f. brown and black 1·70 70

954 Figure within Globe releasing Dove

1983. World Communications Year.
2575 **954** 2f.60 multicoloured 1·50 1·10

955 Montgolfier Brothers' Hot-air Balloon

1983. Bicentenary of Manned Flight. Mult.
2576 2f. Type **955** (first manned flight by Pilatre de Rozier and Marquis d'Arlandes, Nov 1783) 1·50 90
2577 3f. Hydrogen balloon over Tuileries, Paris (flight by J. Charles and M. N. Robert, Dec 1783) 1·90 1·10

1983. Philatelic Creations. As T 795. Mult.
2578 4f. "Aurora-Set" (Dewasne) (horiz) 2·75 1·40
2579 4f. "Marianne" licking envelope (Jean Effel) (vert) 2·75 1·40

1983. Art. As T 491.
2580 4f. brown and buff 2·75 1·40
2581 4f. black and red 2·75 1·40
2582 4f. multicoloured 2·75 1·40
DESIGNS—VERT: No. 2580, "Venus and Psyche" (preparatory sketch for fresco, Raphael); 2581, "Blue-beard giving Keys to his wife" from Perrault's "Tales" (engraving by Gustave Dore). HORIZ: 2582, "The agile Rabbit Inn" (Utrillo).

956 Thistle

1983. Flowers. Engravings from Paris Natural History Museum Library. Multicoloured.
2583 1f. Type **956** 60 35
2584 2f. Turk's cap lily (after Nicolas Robert) 1·40 45
2585 3f. Aster (after Nicolas Robert) 2·00 80
2586 4f. Aconite 2·75 80

957 Camera Diaphragm (photography)

1983. Europa. Each brown and deep brown.
2587 1f.80 Type **957** 2·20 55
2588 2f.60 Light rays entering eye and film (cinema) 2·50 1·10

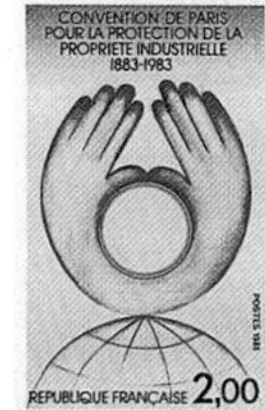

958 Hands on Globe

1983. Centenary of Paris Convention for the Protection of Industrial Property.
2589 **958** 2f. multicoloured 1·20 45

959 Marseille

1983. Federation of French Philatelic Societies Congress, Marseille.
2590 **959** 1f.80 red and blue 1·20 55

960 Air France Colours and Emblem

1983. 50th Anniv of Air France.
2591 **960** 3f.45 blue, red & black 2·30 1·30

961 "France defending U.S.A. from England" (medal by Augustin Dupre)

1983. Bicentenary of Treaties of Versailles and Paris.
2592 **961** 2f.80 brown & black 1·70 90

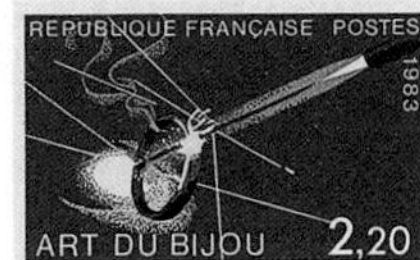

962 Forging a Ring

1983. Handicrafts. Jewellery.
2593 **962** 2f.20 multicoloured 1·20 55

963 Customs Museum, Bordeaux

1983. 30th Anniv of Customs Co-operation Council.
2594 **963** 2f.30 blk, dp grn & grn 1·20 75

964 Pierre and Ernest Michaux's Bicycle

1983. The Bicycle.
2595 **964** 1f.60 black, blue & red 1·90 55

965 Globe and Weather-Satellite and Map

1983. National Meteorology.
2596 **965** 1f.50 dp blue, brn & bl 1·00 45

966 Renee Levy

1983. Heroines of the Resistance.
2597 **966** 1f.60 brown & blue 1·00 55
2598 - 1f.60 brown and green 1·00 55
DESIGN: No. 2598, Berthie Albrecht.

967 Virgin and Child, Baillon

1983. Red Cross Fund. Wood Sculptures.
2599 **967** 1f.60+40c. brn & red 1·20 90
2600 - 2f.+40c. blue & red 1·40 90
DESIGN: 2f. Virgin and Child, Genainville.

968 Pierre Mendes France

1983. 1st Death Anniv of Pierre Mendes France (statesman).
2601 **968** 2f. black and red 1·20 45

969 Emile Littre (lexicographer and writer)

1984. Red Cross Fund. Celebrities.
2602 **969** 1f.60+40c. purple and black 1·20 1·10
2603 - 1f.60+40c. green and black 1·20 1·10
2604 - 1f.70+40c. violet and black 1·40 1·30
2605 - 2f.+40c. grey and black 1·40 1·30
2606 - 2f.10+40c. brown and black 1·40 1·30
2607 - 2f.10+40c. blue and black 1·40 1·30
DESIGNS: No. 2603, Jean Zay (politician); 2604, Pierre Corneille (dramatist); 2605, Gaston Bachelard (philosopher and poet); 2606, Jean Paulhan (writer); 2607, Evariste Galois (mathematician).

1984. Art. As T 491. Multicoloured.
2608 4f. "Cesar" film award (Cesar Baldaccini) (vert) 2·75 1·30
2609 4f. "The Four Corners of Heaven" (Jean Messagier) (horiz) 2·75 1·40
2610 4f. "Corner of Dining Room at Cannet" (Pierre Bonnard) (horiz) 2·75 1·40
2611 5f. "Pythia" (Andre Masson) (vert) 3·75 1·40
2612 5f. "The Painter trampled by his Model" (Jean Helion) (vert) 3·75 1·40

1984. Regions of France. As T 758.
2613 2f.30 violet, purple & red 1·20 55
DESIGN—HORIZ: 2f.30, Map and dancers, Guadeloupe.

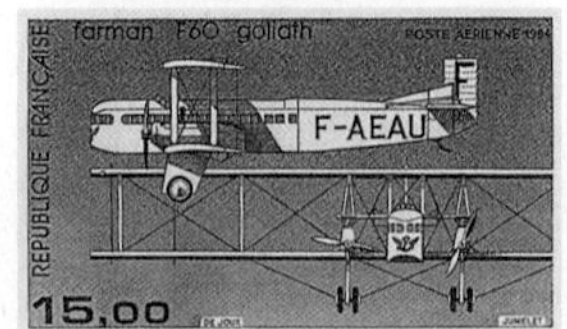

970 Farman F60 Goliath

1984. Air.
2614b - 20f. red 10·00 90
2641 **970** 15f. blue 7·50 90
2614c - 30f. violet 15·00 2·30
2614d - 50f. green 20·00 7·00
DESIGNS: 20f. CAMS 53 flying boat; 30f. Wibault 283 trimotor; 50f. Dewoitine D-338 trimotor.

971 Flora Tristan

1984. International Women's Day.
2615 **971** 2f.80 purple and black 1·70 75

972 "Diderot" (L. M. van Loo)

1984. Stamp Day.
2616 **972** 2f.+40c. blue & blk 1·50 1·30

973 Pierre Waldeck-Rousseau (politician)

1984. Centenary of Trade Union Legislation.
2617 **973** 3f.60 black and blue 2·10 55

974 Emblem

1984. 2nd Direct Elections to European Parliament.
2618 **974** 2f. orange, yell & bl 1·20 45

975 Hearts

1984. Precancels. Playing Cards.
2619 **975** 1f.14 violet and red 60 55
2620 - 1f.47 blue and black 1·00 70
2621 - 2f.38 brown and red 1·50 1·10
2622 - 3f.95 green and black 1·90 1·60
DESIGNS: 1f.47, Spades; 2f.38, Diamonds; 3f.95, Clubs.
See note below No. 432 (1920).

976 Jacques Cartier and "Grande Hermine"

1984. 450th Anniv of Jacques Cartier's Voyage to Canada.
2623 **976** 2f. multicoloured 1·20 35

977 Children and "Sower" Stamp

1984. "Philex-Jeunes 84" Stamp Exhibition, Dunkirk.
2624 **977** 1f.60 brn, red & vio 1·00 55

978 Bridge

1984. Europa. 25th Anniv of European Post and Telecommunications Conference.
2625 **978** 2f. red 1·90 70
2626 **978** 2f.80 blue 2·50 1·00

979 Legionnaires at Camerone, Mexico, 1863

1984. Foreign Legion.
2627 **979** 3f.10 red, grn & blk 1·90 80

980 Resistance Fighter

1984. 40th Anniv of Liberation.
2628 **980** 2f. red, brown and black 1·20 80
2629 - 3f. red, brown and black 2·00 90
DESIGN: 3f. Soldiers disembarking.

1984. Tourist Publicity. As T 490.
2630 1f.70 blue and red 1·20 45
2631 2f.10 brown, green & red 1·40 45
2632 2f.50 brown, green & blue 1·50 55
2633 3f.50 purple and black 2·75 55
2634 3f.70 purple, violet & red 2·10 55
DESIGNS—HORIZ: 1f.70, Monastery of Grande, Chartreuse; 2f.10, Cheval's Ideal Palace, Hauterives; 2f.50, Vauban's Citadel, Belle-Ile-en-Mer, Brittany; 3f.70, Chateau de Montsegur. VERT: 3f.50, Cordouan lighthouse, Gironde.

981 Olympic Sports (image scaled to 61% of original size)

1984. Olympic Games, Los Angeles, and 90th Anniv of International Olympic Committee.
2635 **981** 4f. lilac, blue & green 2·50 1·40

982 Engraver

1984. Handicrafts. Engraving.
2636 **982** 2f. brown, blk & grn 1·20 40

983 Bordeaux

1984. Federation of French Philatelic Societies Congress, Bordeaux.
2637 **983** 2f. red 1·20 40

984 Anniversary Emblem

1984. 40th Anniv of National Centre for Telecommunications Studies.
2638 **984** 3f. blue and deep blue 1·70 65

985 Contour Map of Alps (image scaled to 61% of original size)

1984. 25th International Geography Congress, Paris.
2639 **985** 3f. blue, black & orge 1·70 85

986 "Telecom 1"

1984. "Telecom 1" Communications Satellite.
2640 **986** 3f.20 multicoloured 2·10 85

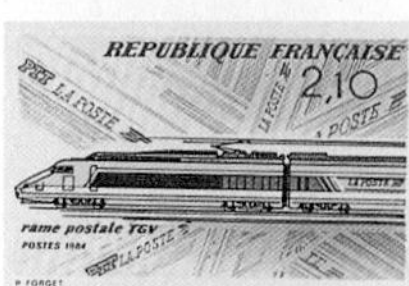

987 TGV Mail Train

1984. Inauguration of TGV High-speed Paris–Lyon Mail Service.
2641 **987** 2f.10 multicoloured 1·90 45

988 Marx Dormoy

1984. Marx Dormoy (politician) Commemoration.
2642 **988** 2f.40 black and blue 1·50 65

989 Lammergeier

1984. Birds of Prey. Multicoloured.

2643	1f. Type **989**		60	40
2644	2f. Short-toed eagle		1·50	65
2645	3f. Northern sparrowhawk		2·10	1·30
2646	5f. Peregrine falcon		3·50	90

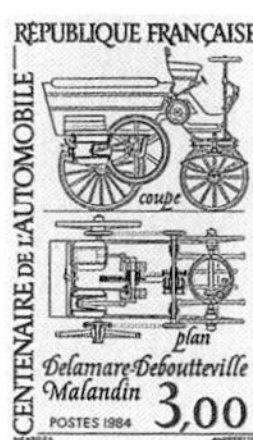

990 Delmare-Debouteville Malandin Automobile

1984. Centenary of Motor Car.

2647	**990**	3f. brown, blue & red	2·30	65

991 Vincent Auriol

1984. Birth Centenary of Vincent Auriol (President, 1947–54).

2648	**991**	2f.10 brown & green	1·20	40

992 "The Pink Basket" (Caly)

1984. Red Cross Fund.

2649	**992**	2f.10+50c. mult	1·50	1·40

993 Emblem

1984. 9th Five-year Plan.

2650	**993**	2f.10 blue, red and black	1·40	50

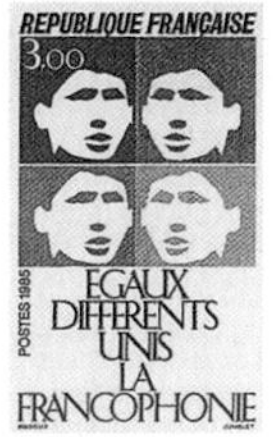

994 Four Heads

1985. Promotion of French Language.

2651	**994**	3f. deep blue & blue	1·70	65

1985. Tourist Publicity. As T 490.

2652	1f.70 green, olive & brown	1·20	40
2653	2f.10 brown and orange	1·40	65
2654	2f.20 multicoloured	1·40	40
2655	3f. brown, red and blue	1·70	95
2656	3f.90 brown, red and blue	2·50	65

DESIGNS—HORIZ: 1f.70, Vienne, Isere; 2f.10, Montpellier Cathedral; 3f. Talmont Church; 3f.90, Solutre. VERT: 2f.20, St. Michael of Cuxa Abbey.

995 Coloured Dots

1985. 50th Anniv of French Television.

2657	**995**	2f.50 multicoloured	1·50	85

996 Snowflake (January)

1985. Precancels. Months of the Year (1st series).

2658	**996**	1f.22 violet and lilac	1·20	65
2659	-	1f.57 grey and blue	1·50	1·30
2660	-	2f.55 brown & green	1·90	2·00
2661	-	4f.23 green & orange	3·50	2·75

DESIGNS: 1f.57, Bare branch and bird (February); 2f.55, Rain-drops and sun-rays (March); 4f.23, Flowers (April).

See note below No. 432 (1920).

See also Nos. 2699/2702 and 2750/3.

997 Couple, Heart-shaped Letter-box and Cherubs

1985. St. Valentine's Day.

2662	**997**	2f.10 multicoloured	1·40	40

998 Jean-Paul Sartre

1985. Red Cross Fund. Writers.

2663	**998**	1f.70+40c. violet and purple	3·50	3·25
2664	-	1f.70+40c. purple and violet	3·50	3·25
2665	-	1f.70+40c. violet and deep violet	3·50	3·25
2666	-	2f.10+50c. deep violet and violet	3·50	3·25
2667	-	2f.10+50c. violet and purple	3·50	3·25
2668	-	2f.10+50c. purple and violet	3·50	3·25

DESIGNS: No. 2664, Romain Rolland; 2665, Jules Romains; 2666, Francois Mauriac; 2667, Victor Hugo; 2668, Roland Dorgeles.

1000 Pauline Kergomard

1985. International Women's Day. 60th Death Anniv of Pauline Kergomard (reformer of infant schools).

2670	**1000**	1f.70 blue and brown	1·20	55

1001 Daguin Cancelling Machine

1985. Stamp Day.

2671	**1001**	2f.10+50c. brown, grey and black	1·50	1·50

1985. Art. As T 491.

2672	5f. multicoloured	3·75	1·70
2673	5f. multicoloured	3·75	1·70
2674	5f. multicoloured	3·75	1·70
2675	5f. red, green and black	3·75	1·70
2676	5f. black and yellow	3·75	1·70

DESIGNS—VERT: No. 2672, "Judgement of Solomon" (stained glass window, Strasbourg Cathedral); 2675, Painting by Pierre Alechinsky. HORIZ: No. 2673, "Still Life with Candlestick" (Nicholas de Stael); 2674, Painting by Dubuffet; 2676, "The Dog" (sculpture by Alberto Giacometti).

1002 Landevennec Abbey

1985. 1500th Anniv of Landevennec Abbey.

2677	**1002**	1f.70 green & purple	1·20	55

1003 Modern Housing, Givors (Jean Renaudie)

1985. Contemporary Architecture.

2678	**1003**	2f.40 blk, grn & orge	1·50	85

1004 Adam de la Halle (composer)

1985. Europa. Music Year.

2679	**1004**	2f.10 dp bl, bl & blk	1·60	85
2680	-	3f. black, bl & dp bl	2·50	1·30

DESIGN: 3f. Darius Milhaud (composer).

1005 Soldier with Rifle

1985. 40th Anniv of V.E. (Victory in Europe) Day.

2681	**1005**	2f. black, red & blue	1·20	85
2682	-	3f. black, red & blue	1·70	1·10

DESIGN: 3f. Prisoners of war.

1006 Tours Cathedral

1985. Federation of French Philatelic Societies Congress, Tours.

2683	**1006**	2f.10 indigo and blue	1·40	65

1007 Vaccinating Patient (after Le Riverend)

1985. Centenary of Anti-rabies Vaccination.

2684	**1007**	1f.50 brn, grn & red	1·00	40

1008 Mystere/Falcon

1985. 36th International Aeronautics and Space Exhibition, Le Bourget.

2685	**1008**	10f. blue	5·75	3·00

1009 Capsized Boat and Lifeboat

1985. Centenary of Lake Geneva International Life-Saving Society.

2686	**1009**	2f.50 black, red & bl	1·50	85

1010 U.N. Emblem

1985. 40th Anniv of U.N.O.

2687	**1010**	3f. blue, grey & dp bl	1·70	65

1011 Huguenot Cross

1985. French Huguenots (300th Anniv of Revocation of Edict of Nantes).

2688	**1011**	2f.50 brown, red & bl	1·50	85

1012 Beech

1985. Trees.

2689	**1012**	1f. black, green & blue	80	40
2690	-	2f. black, green & red	1·50	45
2691	-	3f. black, green & violet	2·00	1·10
2692	-	5f. black, green & brn	3·00	1·30

DESIGNS: 2f. Scotch elm; 3f. Pedunculate oak; 5f. Norwegian spruce.

1013 "Marianne"

1985. National Memorial Day.

2693	**1013**	1f.80 pur, orge & blk	1·20	40

1014 Dullin and Theatre

1985. Birth Centenary of Charles Dullin (actor).

2694	**1014**	3f.20 black & blue	1·90	85

1015 World Map on Open Book and Keyboard

1985. 40th Anniv of French Information Service.

2695	**1015**	2f.20 black and red	1·20	40

1016 "Concert of Angels" (M. Grunewald) (detail, Isenheim Altarpiece)

1985. Red Cross Fund.

2696	**1016**	2f.20+50c. mult	1·50	1·30

1017 Siamese Envoys before King Louis XIV

1986. 300th Anniv of Diplomatic Relations with Thailand.

2697	**1017**	3f.20 purple & black	2·10	1·10

1018 "Leisure Activities" (Fernand Leger)

1986. 50th Anniv of Popular Front.

2698	**1018**	2f.20 multicoloured	1·20	40

1986. Precancels. Months of the Year (2nd series). As T 996.

2699	1f.28 pink and green	1·20	65
2700	1f.65 green & turquoise	1·20	1·30
2701	2f.67 blue and red	1·90	2·00
2702	4f.44 orange and brown	3·75	2·75

DESIGNS: 1f.28, Butterflies (May); 1f.65, Flowers (June); 2f.67, Phrygian cap (July); 4f.44, Sun (August).

See note below No. 432 (1920).

1019 Masked Revellers

1986. Venetian Carnival in Paris.

2703	**1019**	2f.20 multicoloured	1·20	40

1020 Francois Arago (physicist and politician)

1986. Red Cross Fund. Celebrities.

2704	**1020**	1f.80+40c. black, blue & turquoise	1·20	1·10
2705	-	1f.80+40c. black, blue & turquoise	1·20	1·10
2706	-	1f.80+40c. black, blue & turquoise	1·20	1·10
2707	-	2f.20+50c. black, turquoise & blue	1·60	1·30
2708	-	2f.20+50c. black, turquoise & blue	1·60	1·30
2709	-	2f.20+50c. brown	1·90	2·00

DESIGNS: No. 2705, Henri Moissan (chemist); 2706, Henri Fabre (engineer) and seaplane "Hydravion"; 2707, Marc Seguin (locomotive engineer); 2708, Paul Heroult (chemist); 2709, Pierre Cot (politician).

1986. Tourist Publicity. As T 490 and 949.

2710	1f.80 multicoloured	1·20	40
2711	2f. blue and black	1·40	95
2712	2f.20 brown, blue & green	1·40	65
2713	2f.50 dp brown & brown	1·70	65
2714	3f.90 orange and black	3·00	1·30

DESIGNS: As T **490**—HORIZ: 1f.80, Filitosa, Corsica; 2f. Chateau de Loches; 2f.20, Manor of St. Germain de Livet, Calvados. VERT: 2f.50, Cloisters, Notre Dame en Vaux, Marne. As T **949**: 3f.90, Monpazier, Dordogne.

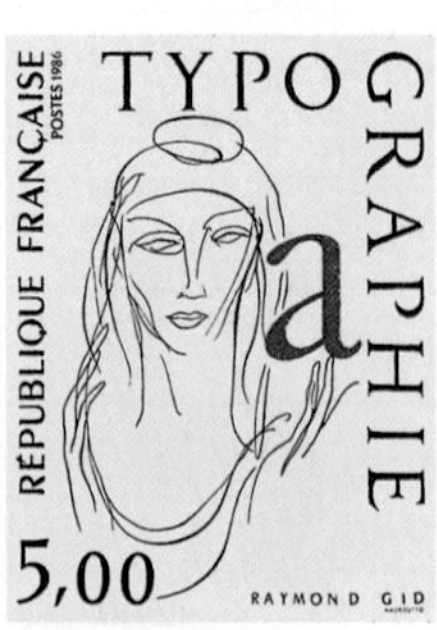

1021 Woman's Head

1986. Typography.

2715	**1021**	5f. black and red	3·75	1·70

1022 Louise Michel (writer)

1986. International Women's Day.

2716	**1022**	1f.80 black and red	1·20	40

1023 La Villette

1986. Science and Industry City, La Villette.

2717	**1023**	3f.90 multicoloured	2·50	85

1024 Britska Mail Coach

1986. Stamp Day.

2718	**1024**	2f.20+60c. pink and brown	1·70	1·70
2719	**1024**	2f.20+60c. yellow and black	1·90	1·90

1025 Map and Latitude Lines

1986. 50th Anniv of African and Asian Studies Centre.

2720	**1025**	3f.20 multicoloured	1·90	65

1986. Art. As T 491.

2721	5f. multicoloured	3·75	1·90
2722	5f. multicoloured	3·75	1·90
2723	5f. multicoloured	3·75	1·90
2724	5f. multicoloured	3·75	1·90
2725	5f. grey, black & violet	3·75	1·90

DESIGNS—HORIZ: No. 2721, "Skibet" (Maurice Esteve); 2722, "Virginia" (Alberto Magnelli); 2725, Abstract by Pierre Soulages. VERT: 2723, "The Dancer" (Hans Arp); 2724, "Isabelle d'Este" (Leonardo da Vinci).

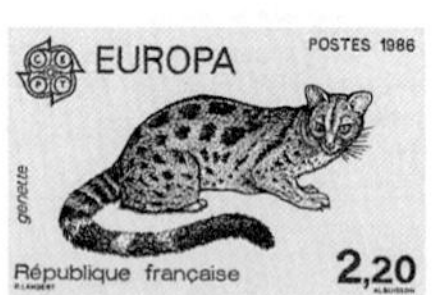

1026 Genet

1986. Europa.

2726	**1026**	2f.20 black and red	1·90	55
2727	-	3f.20 black and red	2·50	1·10

DESIGN: 3f.20, Lesser horseshoe bat.

1027 Victor Basch

1986. International Peace Year.

2728	**1027**	2f.50 black & green	1·50	65

1028 Vianney

1986. Birth Bicentenary of Saint J. M. B. Vianney, Cure d'Ars.

2729	**1028**	1f.80 brown, deep brown and orange	1·20	40

1029 City Gate

1986. Federation of French Philatelic Societies Congress, Nancy.

2730	**1029**	2f. blue and green	1·20	45

1030 Players

1986. Men's World Volleyball Championships.

2731	**1030**	2f.20 purple, vio & red	1·20	65

1031 Head of Statue

1986. Centenary of Statue of Liberty.

2732	**1031**	2f.20 blue and red	1·20	40

1032 "Liberty" (after Delacroix)

1986. No value expressed.

2733	**1032**	(1f.90) green	1·20	40

See also Nos. 2784 and 2949/50.

1033 Mont Blanc, J. Balmat and M. G. Paccard

1986. Bicentenary of First Ascent of Mont Blanc.

2734	**1033**	2f. blue, dp bl & brn	1·20	85

1034 Maupertuis and La Condamine

1986. 250th Anniv of Measurement of Arcs of Meridian.

2735	**1034**	3f. black, lt bl & bl	1·90	85

1035 Marcasite

1986. Minerals.

2736	**1035**	2f. multicoloured	1·40	40
2737	-	3f. multicoloured	1·70	55
2738	-	4f. blue, brown & mve	2·50	1·30
2739	-	5f. turq, mve & bl	3·00	1·10

DESIGNS: 3f. Quartz; 4f. Calcite; 5f. Fluorite.

1036 Musidora in "The Vampires" (dir. Louis Feuillade)

1986. 50th Anniv of French Film Institute. Sheet 143×179 mm containing T 1036 and similar horiz designs, each black, deep grey and deep grey-brown.

MS2740 2f.20 Type **1036**; 2f.20 Max Linder; 2f.20 Sacha Guitry in "Story of a Cheat" (dir. Guitry); 2f.20 Pierre Fresnay and Eric von Stroheim in "The Great Illusion" (dir. Jean Renoir); 2f.20 Raimu and Ginette Leclerc in "The Baker's Wife" (dir. Marcel Pagnol); 2f.20 Rene Ferte in "The Triple Mirror" (dir. Jean Epstein); 2f.20 Gerard Philipe and Martine Carol in "Beauties in the Night" (dir. Rene Clair); 2f.20 Jean Gabin and Mireille Balin in "Face of Love" (dir. Jean Gremillon); 2f.20 Simone Signoret in "Casque d'Or" (Golden Marie) (dir. Jacques Becker); 2f.20 Francois Truffaut and Jean-Pierre Cargol in "The Wild Child" (dir. Truffaut) 19·00 17·00

1037 Woman's Head, Printed Circuit and Drawing Instruments

1986. Centenary of Technical Education.
2741 **1037** 1f.90 blue & mauve 1·20 40

1038 Scene from "Le Grand Meaulnes"

1986. Birth Centenary of Henri Alain-Fournier (writer).
2742 **1038** 2f.20 brown & red 1·20 65

1039 Emblem

1986. World Energy Conference, Cannes.
2743 **1039** 3f.40 blue, mve & red 2·10 1·10

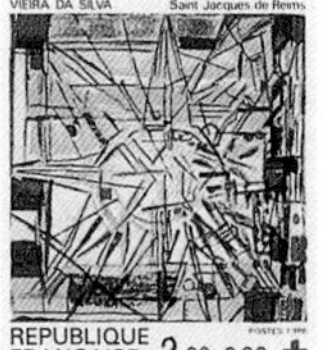

1041 Detail of Window by Vieira da Silva, St. John's Church, Rheims

1986. Red Cross Fund.
2745 **1041** 2f.20+60c. mult 1·70 1·50

1042 Car, Steam Locomotive and Carpet

1986. Mulhouse Technical Museums.
2746 **1042** 2f.20 red, black & blue 1·90 1·10

1043 Museum Facade

1986. Quai d'Orsay Museum.
2747 **1043** 3f.70 dp blue & blue 2·10 1·10

1044 Underground Train in Tunnel

1987. 50th Death Anniv (1986) of Fulgence Bienvenue (designer of Paris Metro).
2748 **1044** 2f.50 pur, grn & brn 1·90 1·10

1045 Raoul Follereau

1987. 10th Death Anniv of Raoul Follereau (leprosy pioneer).
2749 **1045** 1f.90 dp grn & grn 1·30 1·00

1987. Precancels. Months of the Year (3rd series). As T 996.
2750 1f.31 brown and orange 1·30 1·00
2751 1f.69 orange and purple 1·60 1·30
2752 2f.74 grey and blue 2·20 1·80
2753 4f.56 green and mauve 3·75 3·00
DESIGNS: 1f.31, Grapes (September); 1f.69, Posthorn (October); 2f.74, Falling leaves (November); 4f.56, Christmas tree (December).
See note below No. 432 (1920).

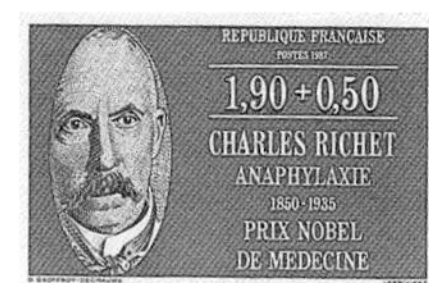

1046 Charles Richet (physiologist)

1987. Red Cross Fund. Medical Celebrities.
2754 **1046** 1f.90+50c. blue 1·30 1·00
2755 - 1f.90+50c. lilac 1·30 1·00
2756 - 1f.90+50c. grey 1·30 1·00
2757 - 2f.20+50c. grey 1·40 1·10
2758 - 2f.20+50c. blue 1·40 1·10
2759 - 2f.20+50c. lilac 1·40 1·10
DESIGNS: No. 2755, Eugene Jamot (sleeping sickness pioneer); 2756, Bernard Halpern (immunologist); 2757, Alexandre Yersin (bacteriologist, discoverer of plague bacillus); 2758, Jean Rostand (geneticist); 2759, Jacques Monod (molecular biologist).

1047 Grinding Blades

1987. Handicrafts. Thiers Cutlery.
2760 **1047** 1f.90 black and red 1·30 90

1048 "Liberty" and "Philexfrance 89"

1987. "Philexfrance 89" International Stamp Exhibition, Paris (1st issue).
2761 **1048** 2f.20 red 1·30 90
The stamp and label which together comprise No. 2761 were printed together se-tenant. For stamp without label, see No. 2466.
See also No. 2821.

1987. Tourist Publicity. As T 490 and 949.
2762 2f.20 green, grey & mauve 1·30 90
2763 2f.20 multicoloured 1·30 90
2764 2f.50 green and blue 1·80 1·30
2765 2f.50 black, red and blue 1·80 1·30
2766 3f. brown and violet 2·10 1·50
2767 3f.70 blue, lilac & brown 2·50 1·80
DESIGNS—As T **490**: No. 2762, Redon Abbey; 2763, Etretat (after Eugene Delacroix); 2764, Azay-le-Rideau Chateau; 2765, Montbenoit le Saugeais; 2766, Les Baux-de-Provence. As T **949**: No. 2767, Cotes de Meuse.

1049 Berlin

1987. Stamp Day.
2768 **1049** 2f.20+60c. brown and yellow 1·80 1·30
2769 **1049** 2f.20+60c. deep blue and blue 1·90 1·40

1050 "Divine Proportion"

1987. Birth Centenary of Charles-Edouard Jeanneret "Le Corbusier" (architect).
2770 **1050** 3f.70 multicoloured 1·90 1·40

1051 "57 Metal", Boulogne-Billancourt (Claude Vasconi)

1987. Europa. Architecture.
2771 **1051** 2f.20 blue and green 1·90 1·40
2772 - 3f.40 brown & green 2·50 1·80
DESIGN: 3f.40, Rue Mallet-Stevens, Paris (Robert Mallet-Stevens).

1987. Art. As T 491.
2773 5f. multicoloured 3·75 2·75
2774 5f. multicoloured 3·75 2·75
2775 5f. multicoloured 3·75 2·75
2776 5f. brn, lt brn & blk 3·75 2·75
DESIGNS—HORIZ: No. 2773, "Abstract" (Bram van Velde); 2774, "Woman with Parasol" (Eugene Boudin); 2776, "World" (sculpture, Antoine Pevsner). VERT: No. 2775, "Pre-Cambrian" (Camille Bryen).

1052 Gaspard of the Mountains

1987. Birth Centenary of Henri Pourrat (writer).
2777 **1052** 1f.90 brown and green 1·30 90

1053 Lens

1987. Federation of French Philatelic Societies Congress, Lens.
2778 **1053** 2f.20 red & brown 1·30 90

1054 Gen. Pershing, Soldiers and U.S. Flag

1987. 70th Anniv of Entry of U.S. Troops into First World War.
2779 **1054** 3f.40 red, blue & green 2·20 1·40

1055 Cable Cars

1987. 6th International Cable Transport Congress, Grenoble.
2780 **1055** 2f. black, bl & grn 1·40 90

1056 Noyon Cathedral and Symbol

1987. Millenary of Election of Hugues Capet as King of France.
2781 **1056** 1f.90 black and blue 1·30 75

1057 Prytanee

1987. Prytanee National Military School (for French Soldiers' Children), La Fleche.
2782 **1057** 2f.20 black, grn & red 1·30 90

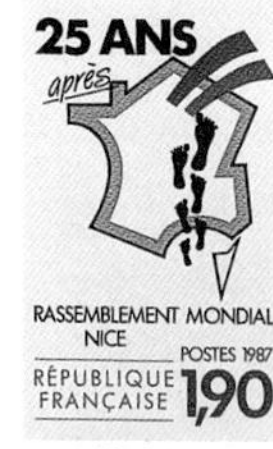

1058 Black Footprints on Map of France

1987. "25 Years After" World Assembly of Repatriated French-Algerians, Nice.
2783 **1058** 1f.90 multicoloured 1·30 75

1987. No value expressed. As T 1032 but inscr "B".
2784 (2f.) green 1·30 55

1059 Globe and Wrestlers

1987. World Wrestling Championship, Clermont-Ferrand.
2785 **1059** 3f. brown, grey & vio 1·50 90

1060 "Gyroporus cyanescens"

1987. Fungi.
2786 **1060** 2f. multicoloured 1·40 65
2787 - 3f. multicoloured 1·80 1·20
2788 - 4f. black, bistre & brn 2·50 1·40
2789 - 5f. multicoloured 3·25 1·80
DESIGNS: 3f. "Gomphus clavatus"; 4f. "Morchella conica"; 5f. "Russula virescens".

1061 Bayeux Tapestry (detail)

1987. 900th Death Anniv of William the Conqueror.

2790	**1061**	2f. multicoloured	1·30	90

1062 Institute

1987. Centenary of Pasteur Institute.

2791	**1062**	2f.20 red and blue	1·30	90

1063 Cendrars (after Modigliani)

1987. Birth Centenary of Blaise Cendrars (writer).

2792	**1063**	2f. buff, black and green	1·30	90

1064 "Flight into Egypt" (Melchior Broederlam) (detail, Champmol Charterhouse retable)

1987. Red Cross Fund.

2793	**1064**	2f.20+60c. mult	1·60	90

1065 Leclerc, Oasis, Tank, Pantheon and Strasbourg Cathedral

1987. 40th Death Anniv of Marshal Leclerc.

2794	**1065**	2f.20 blk, brn & dp brn	1·60	90

1066 Treaty Document, Brunehaut, Childebert II and King Guntram of Burgundy

1987. 1400th Anniv of Treaty of Andelot.

2795	**1066**	3f.70 blk, dp bl & bl	2·40	1·10

1067 Dr. Konrad Adenauer (West German Chancellor) and Charles de Gaulle (French President)

1988. 25th Anniv of Franco-German Co-operation Treaty.

2796	**1067**	2f.20 purple & black	1·90	90

1068 Dassault and Aircraft

1988. 2nd Death Anniv of Marcel Dassault (aircraft engineer).

2797	**1068**	3f.60 brown, red & bl	2·50	1·40

1069 People on Airplane flying around Globe (Rene Pellos)

1988. Communications. Designs by comic strip artists. Multicoloured.

2798	2f.20 Type **1069**	1·30	90
2799	2f.20 Monkey writing in light from table lamp (Jean-Marc Reiser)	1·30	90
2800	2f.20 Sitting Bull and smoke signals (Marijac (Jacques Dumas))	1·30	90
2801	2f.20 Couple with love letter (Fred (Othon Aristides))	1·30	90
2802	2f.20 Man watching levitating letter (Moebius (Jean Giraud))	1·30	90
2803	2f.20 Globe and astronaut (Paul Gillon)	1·30	90
2804	2f.20 Man playing letter and pen "guitar" (Claire Bretecher)	1·30	90
2805	2f.20 Hand posting letter in talking letter-box (Jean-Claude Forest)	1·30	90
2806	2f.20 Rocket behind astronaut reading letter (Jean-Claude Mezieres)	1·30	90
2807	2f.20 Woman with mystery letter (Jacques Tardi)	1·30	90
2808	2f.20 Baby reading letter in pram with attached letter-box (Jacques Lob)	1·30	90
2809	2f.20 Woman pilot with letters (Enki Bilal)	1·30	90

1070 Bird flying (Air)

1988. Precancels. The Elements.

2810	**1070**	1f.36 blue and black	1·30	90
2811	-	1f.75 blue and black	1·60	1·10
2812	-	2f.83 red and black	2·20	1·60
2813	-	4f.75 green & black	3·75	2·75

DESIGNS: 1f.70, Splash of water (Water); 2f.83, Flames (Fire); 4f.75, Tree (Earth).

See note below No. 432 (1920).

1071 Dove and Interior

1988. Rue Victoire Synagogue, Paris.

2814	**1071**	2f. black and gold	1·30	90

1072 Abraham Duquesne and Map

1988. Red Cross Fund. Explorers. Each blue, brown and black.

2815	2f.+50c. Type **1072**	1·30	90
2816	2f.+50c. Pierre Andre de Suffren Saint Tropez	1·30	90
2817	2f.+50c. Jean Francois de Galaup, Comte de La Perouse	1·30	90
2818	2f.+50c. Bertrand Francois Mahe de La Bourdonnais	1·30	90
2819	2f.20+50c. Louis Antoine de Bougainville	1·30	90
2820	2f.20+50c. Jules Dumont d'Urville	1·30	90

1073 "Liberty" and Emblem

1988. "Philexfrance 89" International Stamp Exhibition, Paris (2nd issue).

2821	**1073**	2f.20 red, black & bl	1·30	55

1074 Mail Coach

1988. Stamp Day.

2822	**1074**	2f.20+60c. purple and mauve	1·80	1·10
2823	**1074**	2f.20+60c. brown and flesh	1·80	1·10

1075 Emblem

1988. Centenary of Post Office National College.

2824	**1075**	3f.60 bl, grn & red	2·20	1·00

1076 "Stamps"

1988. "Philex-Jeunes 88" Stamp Exhibition, Nevers.

2825	**1076**	2f. blue, violet & mve	1·30	75

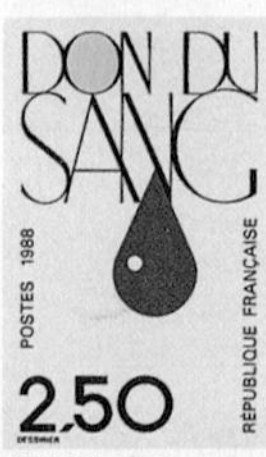

1077 Blood Drop

1988. Blood Donation Service.

2826	**1077**	2f.50 red, blk & yell	1·60	90

1988. No. 2467 surch ECU 0,31.

2827	**916**	0.31ECU on 2f.20 red	1·90	90

ECU stands for European Currency Unit.

1079 Cable and Satellite Communications

1988. Europa. Transport and Communications.

2828	**1079**	2f.20 grey, black & bl	1·90	1·40
2829	-	3f.60 pur, blk & lt pur	2·50	1·80

DESIGN: 3f.60, Two-car electric train.

1080 Monnet

1988. Birth Centenary of Jean Monnet (statesman).

2830	**1080**	2f.20 blue and brown	1·60	90

1081 Town Hall and Roman Carved Stone Heads

1988. Federation of French Philatelic Societies Congress, Valence.

2831	**1081**	2f.20 orge, dp bl & bl	1·30	90

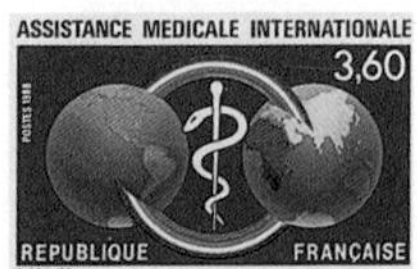

1082 Rod of Aesculapius, Globes and Rainbows

1988. International Medical Assistance.

2832	**1082**	3f.60 multicoloured	2·20	90

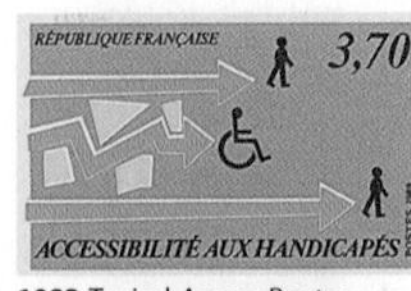

1083 Typical Access Routes

1988. Easy Access for the Handicapped.

2833	**1083**	3f.70 multicoloured	2·20	90

1988. Tourist Publicity.

2834	2f. multicoloured	1·30	75
2835	2f.20 brown, bl & turq	1·30	90
2836	2f.20 blue, turq & grn	1·30	90
2837	3f. violet, green and brown	1·80	90
2838	3f.70 black, blue and red	2·10	1·50

DESIGNS—As T **490**. HORIZ: No. 2834, Ship Museum, Douarnenez; 2836, Perouges; 2837, Cirque de Gavarnie (rock formation). VERT: No. 2835, Sedieres Chateau, Correze. As T **949**: No. 2838, "Double-headed Hermes of Frejus" (Roman sculpture).

1084 Otters

1988. Animals. Illustrations from "Natural History" by Comte de Buffon.

2839	**1084**	2f. black and green	1·30	45
2840	-	3f. black and red	1·80	90
2841	-	4f. black and mauve	2·40	1·40
2842	-	5f. black and blue	3·00	1·80

DESIGNS: 3f. Stag; 4f. Fox; 5f. Badger.

1085 "Assembly of the Three Estates, Vizille" (Alexandre Debelle)

1988. Bicentenary of French Revolution (1st issue). Each black, blue and red.

2843	3f. Type **1085**	1·80	1·10
2844	4f. "Day of the Tiles, Grenoble" (Alexandre Debelle)	2·20	1·30

See also Nos. 2857, 2863/8, 2871/3, **MS**2889, **MS**2890, **MS**3005 and **MS**3083.

1086 Soldiers of 1888 and 1988

1988. Centenary of Alpine Troops.

2845	**1086**	2f.50 dp bl, bl & red	1·90	1·40

1087 Bleriot XI

1988. Birth Centenary of Roland Garros (aviator).

2846	**1087**	2f. green, olive and blue	1·60	90

1088 Soldiers

1988. 70th Anniv of Armistice.

2847	**1088**	2f.20 multicoloured	1·60	90

1089 "Tribute to Leon Degand" (Robert Jacobsen)

1988. French–Danish Cultural Year.

2848	**1089**	5f. red & black on grey	3·75	1·70

1090 City Arms

1988. 2000th Anniv of Strasbourg.

2849	**1090**	2f.20 multicoloured	1·40	90

1988. Art. As T 491.

2850	5f. brown	3·75	1·70
2851	5f. multicoloured	3·75	1·70
2852	5f. multicoloured	3·75	1·70
2853	5f. multicoloured	3·75	1·70

DESIGNS—48×38 mm: No. 2850, St. Mihiel's Sepulchre (Ligier Richier); 2851, "Composition" (Serge Poliakoff); 2852, "Meta" (Tinguely). 48×43 mm: No. 2853, "Pieta de Villeneuve-les-Avignon" (Enguerrand Quarton).

1091 Activities at Spas

1988. Thermal Spas.

2854	**1091**	2f.20 red, blue & grn	1·30	90

1092 Cross

1988. Red Cross Fund.

2855	**1092**	2f.20+60c. red, blue and black	1·60	90

1093 Earth

1988. 40th Anniv of Universal Declaration of Human Rights.

2856	**1093**	2f.20 dp blue & blue	1·90	1·10

1094 Birds

1989. Bicentenary of French Revolution (2nd issue).

2857	**1094**	2f.20 blue, red & blk	1·30	90

1989. Art. As T 491. Multicoloured.

2858	5f. "Anthropometry of the Blue Era" (Yves Klein)	3·50	1·50
2859	5f. "Oath of the Tennis Court" (sketch, David)	3·50	1·50
2860	5f. "Regetta with Wind Astern" (Lapicque) (vert)	3·50	1·50

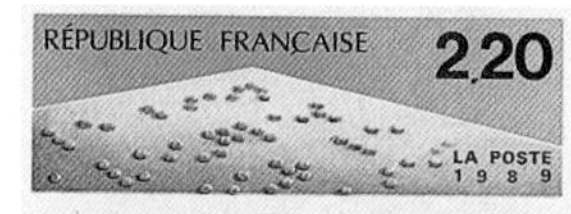

1095 Page of Braille

1989. The Blind.

2861	**1095**	2f.20 bl, orge & mve	1·30	90

1096 "E"

1989. Centenary of Estienne School.

2862	**1096**	2f.20 blk, grey & red	1·30	90

1097 Comte de Sieyes

1989. Red Cross Fund. Bicentenary of French Revolution (3rd issue). Personalities. Mult.

2863	2f.20+50c. Type **1097**	1·40	1·10
2864	2f.20+50c. Comte de Mirabeau	1·40	1·10
2865	2f.20+50c. Vicomte de Noailles	1·40	1·10
2866	2f.20+50c. Marquis de Lafayette	1·40	1·10
2867	2f.20+50c. Antoine Barnave	1·40	1·10
2868	2f.20+50c. Jean Baptiste Drouet	1·40	1·10

1098 Emblem on Spectrum

1989. Direct Elections to European Parliament.

2869	**1098**	2f.20 multicoloured	1·30	90

1099 Flags, Astronauts and Satellite

1989. French–Soviet Space Flight.

2870	**1099**	3f.60 multicoloured	2·50	1·40

1100 "Liberty"

1989. Bicentenary of French Revolution (4th issue) and Declaration of Rights of Man (1st issue). Paintings by Roger Druet. Multicoloured.

2871	2f.20 Type **1100**	1·30	90
2872	2f.20 "Equality"	1·30	90
2873	2f.20 "Fraternity"	1·30	90

1101 Paris–Lyon Stage Coach

1989. Stamp Day.

2874	**1101**	2f.20+60c. deep blue and blue	1·50	1·00
2875	**1101**	2f.20+60c. lilac and mauve	1·80	1·10

1102 Arche de la Defense

1989. Paris Panorama. Multicoloured.

2876	2f.20 Type **1102**	1·60	90
2877	2f.20 Eiffel Tower	1·60	90
2878	2f.20 Pyramid, Louvre	1·60	90
2879	2f.20 Notre Dame Cathedral	1·60	90
2880	2f.20 Bastille Opera House	1·60	90

1103 Hopscotch

1989. Europa. Children's Games. Mult.

2881	2f.20 Type **1103**	2·50	45
2882	3f.60 Ball game	3·75	1·60

1989. Tourist Publicity. As T 490 and 949.

2883	2f.20 green, brown & orge	1·40	75
2884	3f.70 red, blue and black	2·40	90
2885	3f.70 black and brown	2·40	1·30
2886	4f. blue	2·50	1·40

DESIGNS—As T **490**. HORIZ: No. 2883, Fontainebleau forest. VERT: No. 2884, Malestroit. As T **949**: No. 2885, Chateau of Vaux-le-Vicomte; 2886, La Brenne.

1104 Emblems and Buildings

1989. International Telecommunications Union Plenipotentiaries Conference, Nice.

2887	**1104**	3f.70 red, blue & orge	2·20	1·10

1105 Cyclists

1989. International Cycling Championships, Chambery.

2888	**1105**	2f.20 multicoloured	1·80	90

1106 Madame Roland

1989. Bicentenary of French Revolution (5th issue). Personalities. Sheet 78×105 mm containing T 1106 and similar vert designs. Multicoloured.

MS2889 2f.20 Type **1106**; 2f.20 Camille Desmoulins; 2f.20 Marquis de Condorcet; 2f.20 Major-Gen. Francois Kellerman — 5·75 — 5·50

1107 "LES repesentans du people Francois,..."

1989. Bicentenary of French Revolution (6th issue) and Declaration of Rights of Man (2nd issue). Sheet 130×143 mm containing T 1107 and similar horiz designs. Multicoloured.

MS2890 5f. Type **1107**; 5f. "NUL home ne peut etre accuse..."; 5f. "LE but de toute association politique..."; 5f. "LA garantie des droits de l'homme..." (sold at 50f.) — 26·00 — 26·00

1108 Arche de la Defense

1989. Summit Conference of Industrialised Countries, Paris.

2891	**1108**	2f.20 multicoloured	1·30	90

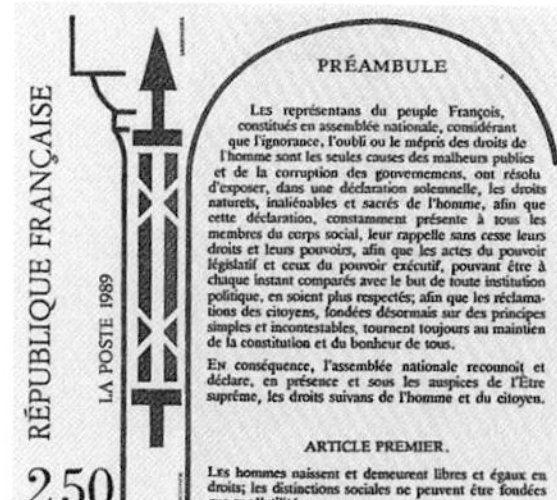

1109 Preamble

1989. Bicentenary of Declaration of Rights of Man (3rd issue). Multicoloured.

2892	2f.50 Type **1109**	1·40	90
2893	2f.50 Articles II to VI	1·40	90
2894	2f.50 Articles VII to XI	1·40	90
2895	2f.50 Articles XII to XVII	1·40	90

1110 Harp

1989. Precancels. Musical Instruments (1st series).

2896	**1110**	1f.39 lt blue & blue	1·30	65
2897	-	1f.79 brn & lt brn	1·50	90

2898	-	2f.90 orange & brn	2·50	1·40
2899	-	4f.84 orange & brn	3·75	2·75

DESIGNS: 1f.79, Piano; 2f.90, Trumpet; 4f.84, Violin.
See note below No. 432 (1920).
See also Nos. 2993/9, 3052/62, 3095/8 and 3145/8.

1111 Train

1989. TGV "Atlantique" Express Train.

2900	**1111**	2f.50 blue, silver & red	2·50	1·20

1112 Tram

1989. Cent of Clermont-Ferrand Electric Tramway.

2901	**1112**	3f.70 black & brown	2·50	1·10

1113 King Francois I

1989. 450th Anniv of Villers-Cotterets Ordinance.

2902	**1113**	2f.20 red and black	1·30	90

1114 Cauchy, Graphs and Formula

1989. Birth Bicentenary of Augustin Louis Cauchy (mathematician).

2903	**1114**	3f.60 blue, blk & red	2·20	1·10

1115 Marshal Lattre de Tassigny

1989. Birth Centenary of Marshal Jean de Lattre de Tassigny.

2904	**1115**	2f.20 black, blue & red	1·60	90

1116 Bird feeding Chicks (18th-century silk painting)

1989. Red Cross Fund.

2905	**1116**	2f.20+60c. mult	1·60	1·00

1117 Harkis

1989. Harkis (French North African troops).

2906	**1117**	2f.20 multicoloured	1·60	90

1118 "Marianne"

1989. Imperf (2943), perf or imperf (2910, 2915, 2916), perf (others).

2907	**1118**	10c. brown	25	20
2908	**1118**	20c. green	25	20
2909	**1118**	50c. violet	25	20
2943b	**1118**	70c. brown	14·00	5·50
2910	**1118**	1f. orange	65	45
2911	**1118**	2f. green	1·30	45
2912	**1118**	2f. blue	1·30	45
2913	**1118**	2f.10 green	1·30	45
2914	**1118**	2f.20 green	1·90	60
2916	**1118**	2f.30 red	1·30	75
2917	**1118**	2f.40 green	1·60	45
2918	**1118**	2f.50 red	1·90	90
2919	**1118**	2f.70 green	1·80	65
2920	**1118**	3f.20 blue	2·20	90
2921	**1118**	3f.40 blue	2·10	90
2922	**1118**	3f.50 green	2·20	45
2923	**1118**	3f.80 mauve	2·40	90
2924	**1118**	3f.80 blue	2·20	90
2925	**1118**	4f. mauve	3·00	90
2926	**1118**	4f.20 mauve	2·50	90
2927	**1118**	4f.40 blue	2·50	90
2928	**1118**	4f.50 mauve	2·50	1·20
2929	**1118**	5f. blue	2·75	90
2930	**1118**	10f. violet	5·50	90

The imperforate stamps are self-adhesive.
For designs as T **1118** but inscr "D" for face value, see Nos. 3036/7, and with no value at all see No. 3122.

1990. No value expressed. As T 1032 but inscr "C".

2949	(2f.10) green	1·30	45
2950	(2f.30) red	1·30	45

1119 Lace

1990

2951	**1119**	2f.50 white and red	1·60	90

1120 Games Emblem

1990. Winter Olympic Games, Albertville (1992) (1st issue).

2952	**1120**	2f.50 multicoloured	1·60	90

See also Nos. 2953/62 and 3048.

1121 Emblem and Ice Skaters

1990. Winter Olympic Games, Albertville (1992) (2nd issue). Each black, blue and red.

2953	2f.30+20c. Type **1121**	1·60	90
2954	2f.30+20c. Ski jumping	1·60	90
2955	2f.30+20c. Speed skiing	1·60	90
2956	2f.30+20c. Slalom	1·60	90
2957	2f.30+20c. Cross-country skiing	1·60	90
2958	2f.30+20c. Ice hockey	1·60	90
2959	2f.50+20c. Luge	1·60	90
2960	2f.50+20c. Curling	1·60	90
2961	2f.50+20c. Artistic skiing	1·60	90
2962	2f.50+20c. Downhill skiing	1·60	90
MS2963	143×126 mm. 10 ×2f.50+20c. As Nos. 2953/62	19·00	19·00

1122 Cross of Lorraine and De Gaulle

1990. Birth Centenary of Charles de Gaulle (President, 1959–69).

2964	**1122**	2f.30 blue, black & vio	1·90	1·20

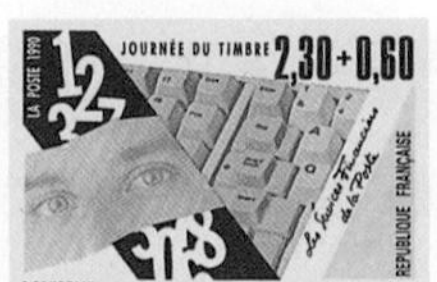

1123 Aircraft and Hymans

1990. 90th Birth Anniv of Max Hymans (civil aviation pioneer).

2965	**1123**	2f.30 green, violet & bl	1·30	90

1990. Art. As T 491.

2966	5f. multicoloured	3·50	1·40
2967	5f. blue, brown and ochre	3·50	1·40
2968	5f. multicoloured	3·50	1·40
2969	5f. multicoloured	3·50	1·40

DESIGNS—VERT: No. 2966, "Woman's Profile" (Odilon Redon); 2967, "Seated Cambodian Woman" (Auguste Rodin); 2968, "Head of Christ of Wissembourg"; 2969, "Yellow and Grey" (Roger Bissiere).

1124 Eyes and Keyboard

1990. Stamp Day.

2970	**1124**	2f.30+60c. blue, ultramarine and yellow	1·90	1·20
2971	**1124**	2f.30+60c. deep green, green, blue and yellow	1·90	1·40

1125 Guehenno

1990. Birth Cent of Jean Guehenno (writer).

2972	**1125**	3f.20 brown & lt brn	1·90	1·10

1990. Tourist Publicity. As T 490.

2973	2f.30 orange, blue & black	1·50	90
2974	2f.30 black, blue & green	1·50	90
2975	3f.80 brown and green	2·50	1·20
2976	3f.80 purple, brown & blue	2·50	1·20

DESIGNS: No. 2973, Cluny; 2974, Aqueduct, Briare Canal; 2975, Flaran-Gers Abbey; 2976, Cap Canaille Cassis.

1126 Macon Post Office

1990. Europa. Post Office Buildings.

2978	**1126**	2f.30 black, ochre and blue	1·90	85
2979	-	3f.20 multicoloured	2·50	1·30

DESIGN: 3f.20, Cerizay post office.

1127 Crowd

1990. Centenary of Labour Day.

2980	**1127**	2f.30 multicoloured	1·30	90

1128 Quimper Faience Plate

1990. Red Cross Fund.

2981	**1128**	2f.30+60c. mult	1·80	1·00

1129 Institute Building

1990. Arab World Institute.

2982	**1129**	3f.80 dp blue, bl & red	2·40	1·10

1130 Detail of Stonework, Notre Dame des Marais

1990. Federation of French Philatelic Societies Congress, Villefranche-sur-Saone.

2983	**1130**	2f.30 black, grn & red	1·30	90

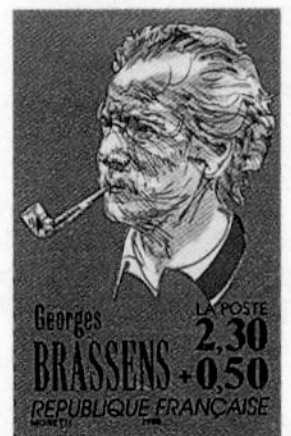

1131 "La Poste"

1990. Round the World Yacht Race.

2984	**1131**	2f.30 multicoloured	1·30	90

1132 Georges Brassens

1990. Red Cross Fund. French Singers. Mult.

2985	2f.30+50c. Aristide Bruant	1·60	1·20
2986	2f.30+50c. Maurice Chevalier	1·60	1·20
2987	2f.30+50c. Tino Rossi	1·60	1·20
2988	2f.30+50c. Edith Piaf	1·60	1·20
2989	2f.30+50c. Jacques Brel	1·60	1·20
2990	2f.30+50c. Type **1132**	1·60	1·20

1133 Cross of Lorraine and Marianne

1990. 50th Anniv of De Gaulle's Call to Resist.

2991	**1133**	2f.30 red, blue & blk	1·60	90

1134 Aerial View of House

1990. 5th Anniv of France–Brazil House, Rio de Janeiro.

2992	**1134**	3f.20 multicoloured	2·10	1·10

1990. Precancels. Musical Instruments (2nd series). As T **1110**.

2993	1f.46 emerald and green	1·60	90
2994	1f.80 brown and orange	1·90	90
2995	1f.93 green & deep green	1·60	90
2996	2f.39 mauve and purple	1·90	1·30
2997	2f.74 violet and blue	3·00	1·70
2998	3f.06 blue and deep blue	2·50	1·80
2999	5f.10 violet and purple	4·25	2·75

DESIGNS: 1 f 46, Accordion; 1f.89, Breton bagpipe; 1f.93, Harp; 2f.39, Piano; 2f.74, Violin; 3f.06, Provencal drum; 5f.10, Hurdy-gurdy.

See note below No. 432 (1920).

1135 Relief Map of France

1990. 50th Anniv of National Geographical Institute.

3000	**1135**	2f.30 multicoloured	1·60	90

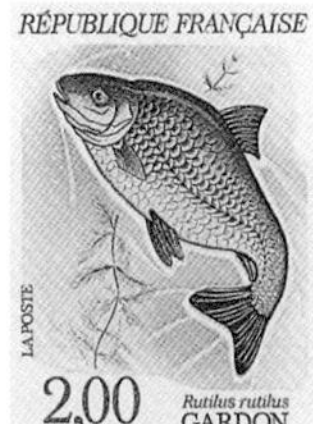
1136 Roach

1990. Freshwater Fishes. Multicoloured.

3001	2f. Type **1136**	1·30	65
3002	3f. Eurasian perch	1·80	1·00
3003	4f. Atlantic salmon	2·50	1·40
3004	5f. Northern pike	3·00	1·70

1137 Gaspard Monge (Navy Minister)

1990. Bicentenary of French Revolution (7th issue). Sheet 79×106 mm containing T 1137 and similar vert designs.

MS3005	2f.50 Type **1137**; 2f.50 Abbe Henri Gregorie; 2f.50 Creation of national flag; 2f.50 Creation of departments	6·50	6·50

1138 Genevoix

1990. Birth Centenary of Maurice Genevoix (writer).

3006	**1138**	2f.30 green & black	1·30	90

1139 World Map

1990. 30th Anniv of Organization for Economic Co-operation and Development.

3007	**1139**	3f.20 blue & ultram	1·90	1·10

1991. Art. As T 491.

3008	5f. multicoloured	3·50	1·70
3009	5f. black and stone	3·50	1·70
3010	5f. black	3·50	1·70
3011	5f. multicoloured	3·50	1·70

DESIGNS—VERT: No. 3008, "The Swing" (Auguste Renoir); 3009, "The Black Knot" (Georges Seurat); 3010, "Volta faccia" (Francois Rouan). HORIZ: No. 3011, "Oh Black Painting" (Roberto Matta).

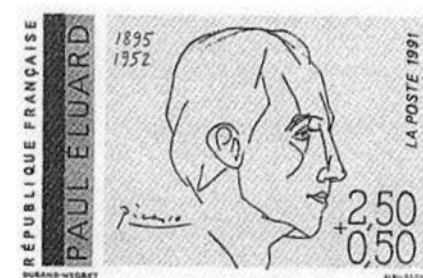
1140 Paul Eluard (after Pablo Picasso)

1991. Red Cross Fund. French Poets. Each grey, black and blue.

3013	2f.50+50c. Type **1140**	1·80	1·30
3014	2f.50+50c. Andre Breton (after Man Ray)	1·80	1·30
3015	2f.50+50c. Louis Aragon (after Henri Matisse)	1·80	1·30
3016	2f.50+50c. Francis Ponge (after Stella Mertens)	1·80	1·30
3017	2f.50+50c. Jacques Prevert (after Picasso)	1·80	1·30
3018	2f.50+50c. Rene Char (after Valentine Hugo)	1·80	1·30

1141 Mail Sorting by Hand and by Machine

1991. Stamp Day. Multicoloured, colour of machine given.

3019	**1141**	2f.50+60c. blue	1·80	1·10
3020	**1141**	2f.50+60c. violet	1·90	1·40

1142 Children, Bicycle and Dove

1991. "Philexjeunes 91" Youth Stamp Exhibition, Cholet.

3021	**1142**	2f.50 multicoloured	1·60	90

1143 Mozart and Globe

1991. Death Bicentenary of Wolfgang Amadeus Mozart (composer).

3022	**1143**	2f.50 black, blue & red	1·60	90

1144 Eyes and Forms of Writing

1991. 350th Anniv of State Printing Office.

3023	**1144**	4f. multicoloured	2·40	1·30

1991. Tourist Publicity. As T 490.

3024	2f.50 multicoloured	1·60	90
3025	2f.50 multicoloured	1·60	90
3026	4f. lilac	2·40	1·10

DESIGNS—VERT: No. 3024, Chevire Bridge, Nantes. HORIZ: No. 3025, Carennac; 3026, Munster Valley.

1145 Poster

1991. 90th Anniv of Concours Lepine (French Association of Small Manufacturers and Inventors).

3028	**1145**	4f. multicoloured	2·40	1·30

1146 "Ariane" Rocket and Map of French Guiana

1991. Europa. Europe in Space. Each blue, red and green.

3029	2f.50 Type **1146**	1·90	90
3030	3f.50 "TDF-1" broadcasting satellite, eyes and globe	3·75	1·80

1147 Perpignan

1991. Federation of French Philatelic Societies Congress, Perpignan.

3031	**1147**	2f.50 red, grey & blue	1·60	90

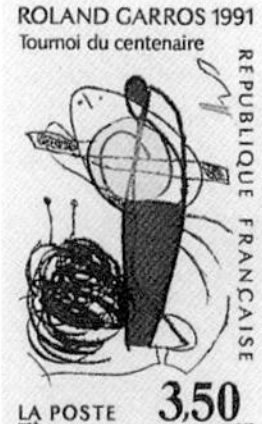
1148 Painting by Joan Miro

1991. Centenary of French Open Tennis Championships.

3032	**1148**	3f.50 multicoloured	2·40	1·30

1149 La Tour d'Auvergne ("First Grenadier of France")

1991. Bicentenary of French Revolution (8th issue). Sheet 105×80 mm containing T 1149 and similar horiz designs. Multicoloured.

MS3033	2f.50 Type **1149**; 2f.50 Tree of Liberty; 2f.50 Mounted gendarme; 2f.50 Louis Saint-Just	6·50	6·50

1150 Organ Pipes

1991. Organ of St. Nicholas's, Wasquehal.

3034	**1150**	4f. buff and brown	2·50	1·20

1151 Illustration from Gaston's "Book of Hunting"

1991. 600th Death Anniv of Gaston III Phoebus, Count of Foix.

3035	**1151**	2f.50 multicoloured	1·60	90

1991. No value expressed. As T 1118 but inscr "D". Imperf (self-adhesive) or perf (3037), perf (3036).

3036	(2f.20) green	1·60	45
3037	(2f.50) red	1·60	45

1152 Brown Bear

1991. Nature. Multicoloured.

3039	2f. Type **1152**	1·40	90
3040	3f. Hermann's tortoise	1·80	90
3041	4f. Eurasian beaver	2·50	1·40
3042	5f. River kingfisher	3·25	1·40

1153 Forest

1991. 10th World Forestry Congress, Paris.

3043	**1153**	2f.50 green, bl & blk	1·60	90

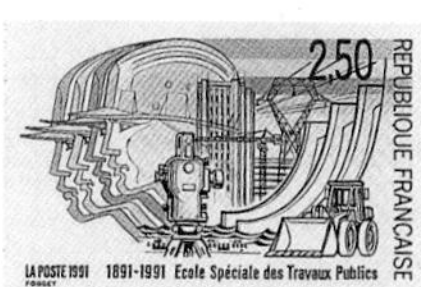
1154 Aspects of Public Works

1991. Centenary of School of Public Works.

3044	**1154**	2f.50 multicoloured	1·60	90

1155 "Bird Monument" (detail)

1991. Birth Centenary of Max Ernst (painter).

3045	**1155**	2f.50 multicoloured	1·90	1·10

1156 Cerdan

1991. 75th Birth Anniv of Marcel Cerdan (boxer).

3046	**1156**	2f.50 black and red	1·60	90

1157 "Amnesty International"

1991. 30th Anniv of Amnesty International.

3047	**1157**	3f.40 bl, mve & blk	2·20	1·10

1158 Stylized Flame

1991. Winter Olympic Games, Albertville (1992) (3rd issue).

3048	**1158**	2f.50 blue, blk & red	1·60	1·00

1159 "Toulon" (Francois Nardi)

1991. Red Cross Fund.

3049	**1159**	2f.50+60c. mult	1·80	1·10

1160 Bird

1991. 5th Paralympic Games, Tignes (1992).

3050	**1160**	2f.50 blue	1·60	90

1161 Shore

1991. 150th Anniv of Voluntary Adhesion of Mayotte to France.

3051	**1161**	2f.50 multicoloured	1·60	90

1992. Precancels. Musical Instruments (3rd series). As T 1110.

3052a	1f.60 brown and orange	7·75	5·50
3053	1f.98 bistre and ochre	6·00	3·00
3054	2f.08 orange and yellow	3·00	1·80
3055	2f.46 violet	3·00	1·80
3056	2f.98 lilac and mauve	3·00	1·80
3057	3f.08 purple and red	8·75	4·50
3058	3f.14 green and turquoise	3·75	2·30
3059	3f.19 grey and black	10·50	4·50
3060	5f.28 green and lt green	6·50	4·50
3061	5f.30 ultramarine & blue	5·00	3·50
3062	5f.32 brown & dp brown	5·00	3·50

DESIGNS: 1f.60, Guitar; 1f.98, Accordion; 2f.08, Saxophone; 2f.46, Breton bagpipe; 2f.98, Banjo; 3f.08, Provencal drum; 3f.14, Hurdy-gurdy; 3f.19, Harp; 5f.28, Xylophone; 5f.30, Piano; 5f.32, Violin.

See note below No. 432 (1920).

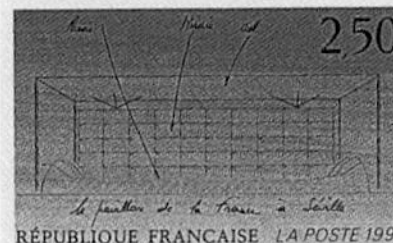

1162 Plan of French Pavilion

1992. "Expo '92" World's Fair, Seville.

3063	**1162**	2f.50 blue, blk & grn	1·60	90

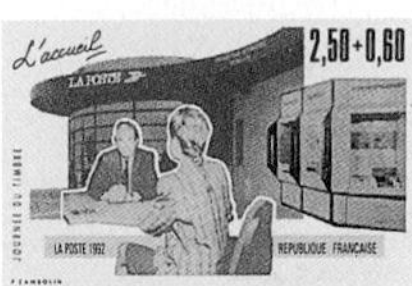

1163 Post Office, Reception Area and Postal Self-service Machines

1992. Stamp Day.

3064	**1163**	2f.50+60c. black, blue and yellow	1·80	1·00
3065	**1163**	2f.50+60c. red, blue, black & yell	1·90	1·20

1164 Runner

1992. Olympic Games, Barcelona.

3066	**1164**	2f.50 multicoloured	1·90	90

1165 Cesar Franck

1992. Red Cross Fund. Composers. Mult.

3067	2f.50+50c. Type **1165**	1·80	1·30
3068	2f.50+50c. Erik Satie	1·80	1·30
3069	2f.50+50c. Florent Schmitt	1·80	1·30
3070	2f.50+50c. Arthur Honegger	1·80	1·30
3071	2f.50+50c. Georges Auric	1·80	1·30
3072	2f.50+50c. Germaine Tailleferre	1·80	1·30

1166 Marguerite d'Angouleme (after Clouet)

1992. 500th Birth Anniv of Marguerite d'Angouleme, Queen of Navarre.

3073	**1166**	3f.40 multicoloured	2·20	1·10

1167 "Madonna, Child and Angel" (Botticelli)

1992. 500th Anniv of Ajaccio.

3074	**1167**	4f. multicoloured	2·40	1·30

1168 Navigational Instruments and Map

1992. Europa. 500th Anniv of Discovery of America by Columbus. Multicoloured.

3075	2f.50 Type **1168**	1·90	90
3076	3f.40 Caravel, map and compass rose	3·75	1·80

1992. Tourist Publicity. As T 490.

3077	2f.50 brown, blue & green	1·60	90
3078	3f.40 brown, green & blue	2·20	1·20
3079	4f. blue, black and green	2·40	1·10
3080	4f. green, lt green & brown	2·40	1·30

DESIGNS—VERT: No. 3077, Chateau de Biron, Dordogne; 3078, Mont Aiguille, Isere (500th anniv of first ascent). HORIZ: No. 3079, 4f. L'Ourcq Canal; 3080, Lorient.

1169 Wheat, Poppies and Loaves

1992. International Bread and Cereals Congress.

3081	**1169**	3f.40 multicoloured	2·20	1·30

1170 Couple leaping through Stamp

1992. Federation of French Philatelic Societies Congress, Niort.

3082	**1170**	2f.50 multicoloured	1·90	90

1171 Olympic Rings

1992. Winter Olympic Games, Albertville, and Summer Games, Barcelona.

3083	**1171**	2f.50 multicoloured	1·90	90

1172 Tautavel Man

1992

3084	**1172**	3f.40 multicoloured	2·20	1·20

1992. Art. As T 491.

3085	5f. black and stone	3·50	1·70

DESIGN—VERT: 5f. "Portrait of Claude Deruet" (Jacques Callot).

1173 Sand Lily

1992. Flowers. Multicoloured.

3086	2f. Type **1173**	1·30	45
3087	3f. Sundew	1·80	90
3088	4f. "Orchis palustris"	2·30	1·40
3089	5f. Yellow water lily	3·00	1·80

1174 Marianne and National Colours

1992. Bicentenary of Year One of First Republic.

3090	**1174**	2f.50 multicoloured	1·60	90

1175 Marianne

1992. Bicentenary of Declaration of First Republic. Each red.

3091	2f.50 Type **1175**	1·60	90
3092	2f.50 Tree of Liberty	1·60	90
3093	2f.50 Marianne as cockerel	1·60	90
3094	2f.50 "Republique Francaise"	1·60	90

1992. Precancels. Musical Instruments (4th series). As T 1110.

3095	1f.73 deep green & green	1·30	60
3096	2f.25 red and orange	1·60	90
3097	3f.51 ultramarine & blue	3·25	1·40
3098	5f.40 red and mauve	3·75	2·10

DESIGNS: 1f.73, Guitar; 2f.25, Saxophone; 3f.51, Banjo; 5f.40, Xylophone.

See note below No. 432 (1920).

1176 Symbol of Market

1992. European Single Market.

3099	**1176**	2f.50 multicoloured	1·60	90

1177 Farman HF16 and Boeing 737-500

1992. 80th Anniv of Nancy–Luneville Air Mail Service.

3100	**1177**	2f.50 multicoloured	1·60	90

1178 Paul and Electricity Pylon

1992. 10th Death Anniv of Marcel Paul (politician).

3101	**1178**	4f.20 blue & purple	3·00	1·20

1179 "Woman at Window" (Paul Delvaux)

1992. Contemporary Art.

3102	**1179**	5f. multicoloured	3·00	1·40
3103	-	5f. multicoloured	3·00	1·40
3104	-	5f. black, mauve & yell	3·00	1·40
3105	-	5f. black and yellow	3·00	1·40

DESIGNS: No. 3103, "Portrait of Man" (Francis Bacon); 3104, Abstract (Alberto Burri); 3105, Abstract (Antoni Tapies).

See also Nos. 3154, 3176, 3285 and 3301/2.

1180 Birds holding Strings (T. Ungerer)

1992. Red Cross Fund. Mutual Aid Meeting, Strasbourg.

3106	**1180**	2f.50+60c. mult	1·80	1·00

1181 Horse, Guitar and Dancer

1992. Gypsies.

3107 **1181** 2f.50 multicoloured 1·60 90

1182 Smew Pair

1993. Ducks. Multicoloured.

3108	2f. Type **1182**	1·30	65
3109	3f. Ferruginous duck and drake	1·90	1·10
3110	4f. Common sheldrake pair	2·50	1·50
3111	5f. Red-breasted merganser pair	3·25	1·80

1183 "La Poste" (yacht) and Globe

1993. "Postmen around the World". Post Office Team Participation in Around the World Yacht Race.

3112	**1183**	2f.50 yell, ultram & bl	2·10	1·10
3113	**1183**	2f.80 yell, ultram & bl	2·50	1·10

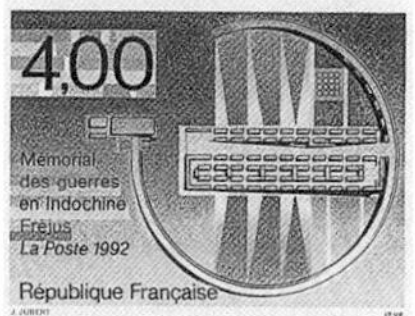

1184 Memorial

1993. Indo-China Wars Memorial, Frejus.

3114 **1184** 4f. multicoloured 2·40 1·50

1185 Postman with Bicycle

1993. Stamp Day.

3115	**1185**	2f.50 multicoloured	1·90	90
3116	**1185**	2f.50+60c. mult	1·80	1·20

1186 Yacht and Runner

1993. Mediterranean Games, Agde and Roussillon (Languedoc).

3117 **1186** 2f.50 multicoloured 1·60 1·10

1187 Maria Deraismes and Georges Martin (founders)

1993. Centenary of Le Droit Humain (International Mixed Freemasons Order).

3118 **1187** 3f.40 black and blue 2·20 1·30

1188 "Red Rhythm Blue" (Olivier Debre)

1993. Europa. Contemporary Art. Mult.

3119	2f.50 Type **1188**	1·90	1·30
3120	3f.40 "Le Griffu" (bronze, Germaine Richier) (vert)	2·50	2·00

1993. As T 1118 but no value expressed. Imperf (self-adhesive) or perf.

3122 **1118** (-) red 1·30 55

No. 3122 was sold at the current inland rate (at time of issue 2f.50).

1993. Tourist Publicity. As T 490 and 949.

3124	2f.80 green, brown and blue	1·90	1·10
3125	3f.40 red, green and blue	2·40	1·30
3126	4f.20 dp green, green & brn	2·50	1·70
3127	4f.20 brown and green	2·50	1·70
3128	4f.40 black, green and red	2·50	1·80
3129	4f.40 multicoloured	2·50	1·80

DESIGNS—As T **490**. HORIZ: No. 3124, La Chaise-Dieu Abbey, Haute-Loire; 3128, Montbeliard-Doubs. VERT: No. 3125, Artouste train, Laruns; 3126, Minerve-Herault; 3129, Le Jacquemard, Lambesc. As T **949**: No. 3127, Chinon.

1189 Guy de Maupassant

1993. Red Cross Fund. Writers. Mult.

3131	2f.50+50c. Type **1189**	1·80	1·50
3132	2f.50+50c. Alain	1·80	1·50
3133	2f.50+50c. Jean Cocteau	1·80	1·50
3134	2f.50+50c. Marcel Pagnol	1·80	1·50
3135	2f.50+50c. Andre Chamson	1·80	1·50
3136	2f.50+50c. Marguerite Yourcenar	1·80	1·50

1190 Map of Europe and Liberty

1993. 9th European Constitutional Court Conference on Human Rights.

3137 **1190** 2f.50 multicoloured 1·60 1·10

1191 Reinhardt

1993. 40th Death Anniv of Django Reinhardt (guitarist).

3138 **1191** 4f.20 multicoloured 2·50 1·70

1192 Weiss

1993. Birth Centenary of Louise Weiss (women's rights campaigner).

3139 **1192** 2f.50 blk, orge & red 1·90 1·10

1193 TGV and Eurostar Trains at Lille

1993. Federation of French Philatelic Societies Congress, Lille.

3140 **1193** 2f.50 lt bl, bl & mve 1·60 1·10

1194 Emblem

1993. Bicentenary of National Natural History Museum, Paris.

3141 **1194** 2f.50 multicoloured 1·60 1·10

1195 Bas-relief (Georges Jeanclos) (left half)

1993. Martyrs and Heroes of the Resistance. Multicoloured.

3142	2f.50 Type **1195**	1·80	90
3143	4f.20 Right half of bas-relief	2·50	1·40

Nos. 3142/3 were issued together, se-tenant, forming a composite design.

1196 Central Telegraph Tower, Paris

1993. Bicentenary of Chappe's Optical Telegraph.

3144 **1196** 2f.50 black, stone and blue 1·60 1·10

1993. Precancels. Musical Instruments (5th series). As T 1110.

3145	1f.82 grey and black	1·30	70
3146	2f.34 brown and orange	1·60	1·10
3147	3f.86 red and pink	3·25	1·70
3148	5f.93 violet and mauve	3·75	2·50

DESIGNS: 1f.82, Trumpet; 2f.34, Drum; 3f.86, Hurdy-gurdy; 5f.93, Xylophone.

1197 Map of Corsica and "Casabianca" (submarine)

1993. 50th Anniv of Liberation of Corsica.

3149 **1197** 2f.80 black, red & bl 1·90 1·10

1993. Art. As T 491. Multicoloured.

3150	5f. "Saint Thomas" (Georges de la Tour) (vert)	3·50	1·90
3151	5f. "The Muses" (Maurice Denis) (vert)	3·25	1·80

1198 Le Val-de-Grace, Paris

1993. Bicentenary of Conversion of Monastery of Le Val-de-Grace to Military Hospital (now museum).

3152 **1198** 3f.70 black, grn & brn 2·20 1·30

1199 Clowns

1993. National Centre for Circus Arts, Chalons-sur-Marne.

3153 **1199** 2f.80 multicoloured 1·90 1·10

1993. Contemporary Art. As T 1179.

3154	5f. red and black	3·00	1·70
3155	5f. multicoloured	3·00	1·70

DESIGNS: No. 3154, Abstract (Takis); 3155, "Enhanced Engraving" (Maria Elena Vieira da Silva).

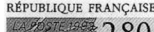

1200 Girl studying Flower ("Happy Holiday") (C. Wendling)

1993. Greetings Stamps. "The Pleasure of Writing". Designs by comic strip artists. Multicoloured.

3156A	2f.80 Type **1200**	1·70	1·40
3157A	2f.80 Clowns ("Happy Holiday") (B. Olivie)	1·70	1·40
3158A	2f.80 Cat on birthday cake ("Happy Birthday") (S. Colman)	1·70	1·40
3159A	2f.80 Girl with cake ("Happy Birthday") (G. Sorel)	1·70	1·40
3160A	2f.80 Man courting woman on balcony ("With Passion") (J. M. Thiriet)	1·70	1·40
3161A	2f.80 Man playing large fountain pen ("Pleasure of Writing") (E. Davodeau)	1·70	1·40
3162A	2f.80 Pig with letter ("Greetings") (J. de Moor)	1·70	1·40
3163A	2f.80 Jester in horseshoe ("Good Luck") (Mezzo)	1·70	1·40
3164A	2f.80 Clowns running ("Best Wishes") (N. de Crecy)	1·70	1·40
3165A	2f.80 Girl and cat watching tree fairy ("Best Wishes") (F. Magnin)	1·70	1·40
3166A	2f.80 Cards tumbling from Santa Claus's sack ("Happy Christmas") (T. Robin)	1·70	1·40
3167A	2f.80 Mouse dressed as Santa Claus ("Happy Christmas") (P. Prugne)	1·70	1·40

1201 Rhododendron

1993. 1st European Stamp Salon, Flower Gardens, Paris (1994) (1st issue). Sheet 106×78 mm containing T 1201 and similar horiz design. Multicoloured.

MS3168 2f.40 Type **1201**; 2f.40 View of Gardens (sold at 15f.) 19·00 18·00

1202 Louvre, 1793

1993. Bicentenary of Louvre Museum. Mult.

3169	2f.80 Type **1202**	2·20	1·90
3170	4f.40 Louvre, 1993	2·50	2·00

Nos. 3169/70 were issued together, se-tenant, forming a composite design.

1203 "St. Nicholas"

1993. Red Cross Fund. Metz Engravings.

3171	**1203**	2f.80+60c. mult	2·20	1·70

1204 Cast-iron Sign at Metro Entrance, Paris (detail, Hector Guimard)

1994. Art Nouveau. Multicoloured.

3172	2f.80 Type **1204**	1·60	1·10
3173	2f.80 "Roses of France Cup" (vase, Emile Galle)	1·60	1·10
3174	4f.40 Drawing-room table with bronze water-lily decoration (Louis Majorelle)	2·20	1·70
3175	4f.40 Stoneware teapot (Pierre-Adrien Dalpayrat)	2·20	1·70

1994. Contemporary Art. As T 1179. Mult.

3176	6f.70 Abstract (Sean Scully)	3·75	2·40
3177	6f.70 "Couple" (Georg Baselitz)	3·75	2·40

1205 "Death of St. Stephen"

1994. 12th-century Stained Glass Window, Le Mans Cathedral.

3179	**1205**	6f.70 multicoloured	3·75	2·40

1994. Tourist Publicity. As T 490.

3180	2f.80 multicoloured	1·70	1·10
3181	2f.80 blue	1·70	1·10
3182	3f.70 brown, dp green & grn	2·50	1·40
3183	4f.40 brown and blue	2·40	1·70
3184	4f.40 brown and red	2·40	1·70

DESIGNS—HORIZ: No. 3180, "Mount Sainte Victoire" (Paul Cezanne); 3181, Bridge at Rupt aux Nonains, Saulx Region, Meuse; 3184, Argentat. VERT: No. 3182, La Grand Cascade, Saint-Cloud Park; 3183, Old port and St. John the Baptist Church, Bastia.

1206 European Union Flag

1994. European Parliament Elections.

3185	**1206**	2f.80 blue, yell & grey	1·90	1·10

1207 Mourguet and Guignol

1994. 150th Death Anniv of Laurent Mourguet (creator of Guignol (puppet)).

3186	**1207**	2f.80 multicoloured	1·60	1·10

1208 Emblem

1994. Bicent of Polytechnic Institute, Paris.

3187	**1208**	2f.80 multicoloured	1·60	1·10

1209 "Marianne"

1994. Stamp Day. 50th Anniv of Edmond Dulac's "Marianne" Design.

3188	**1209**	2f.80 red and blue	1·80	1·50
3190	**1209**	2f.80+60c. red & bl	1·90	1·80

1210 "The Vikings" (detail, Bayeux Tapestry)

1994. Franco-Swedish Cultural Relations. Mult.

3191	2f.80 Type **1210**	3·75	3·25
3192	2f.80 Viking longships (different detail)	3·75	3·25
3193	2f.80 Costume design for sailor by Fernand Leger in Swedish Ballet production of "Skating Rink"	3·75	3·25
3194	2f.80 Costume design for gentleman in "Skating Rink"	3·75	3·25
3195	3f.70 "Banquet for Gustav III at the Trianon, 1784" (Niclas Lafrensen the younger)	5·25	4·50
3196	3f.70 Swedish and French flags	5·25	4·50

Nos. 3195/6 are larger, 49×37 mm.

1211 Mountain Ambush

1994. 50th Anniv of Liberation. The Maquis (resistance movement).

3197	**1211**	2f.80 multicoloured	1·60	1·10

1212 Pompidou

1994. 20th Death Anniv of Georges Pompidou (Prime Minister 1962–68, President 1969–74).

3198	**1212**	2f.80 brown	1·60	1·10

1213 Boy netting Stamps

1994. "Philex Jeunes 94" Youth Stamp Exhibition, Grenoble.

3199	**1213**	2f.80 multicoloured	1·60	1·10

1214 AIDS Virus

1994. Europa. Discoveries. Multicoloured.

3200	2f.80 Type **1214** (11th anniv of discovery)	1·90	1·10
3201	3f.70 Wavelength formula (70th anniv of Louis de Broglie's proof of undulatory theory of matter)	3·25	1·70

1215 Bank Emblem

1994. 27th Assembly of Asian Development Bank, Nice.

3202	**1215**	2f.80 multicoloured	1·60	1·10

1216 British Lion and French Cockerel over Tunnel

1994. Opening of Channel Tunnel. Mult.

3203	2f.80 Type **1216**	1·60	1·10
3204	2f.80 Symbolic hands over Eurostar express train	1·60	1·10
3205	4f.30 Type **1216**	2·50	1·70
3206	4f.30 As No. 3204	2·50	1·70

1217 Martigues inside Fish

1994. Federation of French Philatelic Societies Congress, Martigues.

3207	**1217**	2f.80 violet, bl & grn	1·60	1·10

1218 Court Building, Ile de la Cite, Paris

1994. Court of Cassation.

3208	**1218**	2f.80 multicoloured	1·60	1·10

1219 Landing Forces and Beach Defences

1994. 50th Anniv of Normandy Landings.

3209	**1219**	4f.30 red, ind & bl	2·50	1·70

1220 Allied Forces

1994. 50th Anniv of Liberation.

3210	**1220**	4f.30 multicoloured	2·50	1·70

1221 Sorbonne University and Pierre de Coubertin (founder)

1994. Centenary of International Olympic Committee.

3211	**1221**	2f.80 multicoloured	2·40	1·10

1222 Organ Pipes

1994. Poitiers Cathedral Organ.

3212	**1222**	4f.40 multicoloured	2·50	1·70

1223 Flag, Map and Soldier

1994. 50th Anniv of Allied Landings in Southern France.

3213	**1223**	2f.80 multicoloured	1·90	1·30

1224 Oak

1994. Precancels. Leaves.

3321	-	1f.87 brown & green	1·40	65
3214	**1224**	1f.91 olive & green	1·30	75
3322	-	2f.18 red and lake	1·80	90
3215	-	2f.46 green & lt green	1·90	1·00
3216	-	4f.24 red and orange	2·75	1·50
3323	-	4f.66 yellow & green	3·25	1·80
3217	-	6f.51 turquoise & blue	4·25	2·75
3324	-	7f.11 turquoise & blue	4·50	2·75

DESIGNS: 1f.87, Ash; 2f.18, Beech; 2f.46, Plane; 4f.24, Chestnut; 4f.66, Walnut; 6f.51, Holly; 7f.11, Elm.

1225 "Moses and the Daughters of Jethro" (drawing) (image scaled to 61% of original size)

1994. 400th Birth Anniv of Nicolas Poussin (artist).

3218	**1225**	4f.40 brown & black	2·50	1·70

1226 Yvonne Printemps (singer and actress)

1994. Entertainers. Multicoloured.

3219	2f.80+60c. Type **1226**	1·90	1·70
3220	2f.80+60c. Fernandel (Fernand Contandin) (actor)	1·90	1·70
3221	2f.80+60c. Josephine Baker (music hall performer)	1·90	1·70

3222 2f.80+60c. Bourvil (Andre Raimbourg) (actor) 1·90 1·70
3223 2f.80+60c. Yves Montand (singer and actor) 1·90 1·70
3224 2f.80+60c. Coluche (Michel Colucci) (comedian) 1·90 1·70

1227 Map and Foucault's Pendulum

1994. Bicentenary of National Conservatory of Arts and Craft.
3225 **1227** 2f.80 pur, bl & red 1·60 1·10

1228 Doorway

1994. Bicent of Ecole Normale Superieure.
3226 **1228** 2f.80 blue and red 1·60 1·10

1229 Simenon and Quai des Orfevres, Paris

1994. 5th Death Anniv of Georges Simenon (novelist).
3227 **1229** 2f.80 multicoloured 1·90 1·10

1230 Headless Drug Addict (after Vladimir Velickovic)

1994. National Drug Addiction Prevention Day.
3228 **1230** 2f.80 multicoloured 1·60 1·10

1231 Gardens

1994. 1st European Stamp Salon, Flower Gardens, Paris (2nd issue). Sheet 106×78 mm containing T 1231 and similar multicoloured designs.
MS3229 2f.80 Type **1231**; 2f.80 Dahlias (25×39 mm) (sold at 16f.) 20·00 18·00

1232 Lodge Emblem and Symbols of Freemasonry

1994. Centenary of Grand Lodge of France.
3230 **1232** 2f.80 brown, red & bl 1·60 1·10

1233 Stormy Sea and Colas

1994. 16th Death Anniv of Alain Colas (yachtsman).
3231 **1233** 3f.70 blk, grn & emer 2·40 1·70

1234 St. Vaast

1994. Red Cross Fund. 15th-century Arras Tapestry.
3232 **1234** 2f.80+60c. mult 2·20 1·70

1235 AIDS Virus (image scaled to 61% of original size)

1994. AIDS Day.
3233 **1235** 2f.80 multicoloured 2·50 2·20

The stamp and se-tenant label, as illustrated, comprise No. 3233. For stamp without attached label, see No. 3200.

1236 Slogan

1994. 50th Anniv of National Press Federation.
3234 **1236** 2f.80 purple & yellow 1·60 1·10

1237 Champs Elysees (image scaled to 61% of original size)

1994. New Year.
3235 **1237** 4f.40 multicoloured 3·00 1·10

1238 Projector and Scene from Film

1995. Centenary of Motion Pictures. Sheet 105×78 mm containing T 1238 and similar horiz designs. Multicoloured.
MS3236 2f.80 Type **1238**; 2f.80 Projector and head of man in cap; 2f.80 Projector and monster's head; 2f.80 Reel of films and Indian's head 7·75 6·50

1239 Normandy Bridge (image scaled to 61% of original size)

1995. Inauguration of Normandy Bridge (over Seine between Le Havre and Honfleur).
3237 **1239** 4f.40 multicoloured 3·00 1·70

1240 Emblem

1995. European Public Notaries.
3238 **1240** 2f.80 multicoloured 1·60 1·10

1241 Pasteur

1995. Death Centenary of Louis Pasteur (chemist).
3239 **1241** 3f.70 multicoloured 2·50 1·30

1995. Tourist Publicity. As T 490.
3240 2f.80 green and olive 1·70 1·00
3241 2f.80 green, brown & blue 1·70 1·00
3242 4f.40 multicoloured 2·50 1·40
3243 4f.40 black, lilac & green 2·50 1·40

DESIGNS—HORIZ: No. 3240, Malt works, Stenay; 3241, Remiremont, Vosges; 3242, Nyons Bridge, Drome. VERT: No. 3243, Margot gate and St. Martial's Church, Correze.

1995. Art. As T 491.
3245 6f.70 black, yellow & red 3·75 2·40
3246 6f.70 black, blue & dp blue 3·75 2·40
3247 6f.70 multicoloured 3·75 2·40
3248 6f.70 multicoloured 3·75 2·40

DESIGNS—VERT: No. 3245, Reliquary of St. Taurin, Evereux; 3248, "The Cradle" (Berthe Morisot). HORIZ: No. 3246, Study for "The Dream of Happiness" (Pierre Prud'hon); 3247, Seascape (Zao Wou-Ki).

1242 Band-tailed Pigeons

1995. Bird Paintings by John James Audubon (ornithologist). Multicoloured.
3249 2f.80 Type **1242** 1·60 1·10
3250 2f.80 Snowy egret 1·60 1·10
3251 4f.30 Common tern 2·20 1·70
3252 4f.40 Rough-legged buzzards 2·20 1·70
MS3253 113×120 mm. Nos. 2149/52 9·00 8·25

1243 "Marianne"

1995. Stamp Day. 50th Anniv of Pierre Gandon's "Marianne" Design.
3255 **1243** 2f.80 green, bl & red 5·25 4·50
3256 **1243** 2f.80+60c. green, ultramarine & red 2·50 2·20

1244 Hour Glass

1995. 50th Anniv of Works Councils.
3257 **1244** 2f.80 brown, lt bl & bl 1·60 1·10

1245 Means of Communications

1995. Centenary (1994) of Advanced Institute of Electricity.
3258 **1245** 3f.70 lt blue, bl & red 2·20 1·40

1246 Forms of Writing

1995. Bicentenary of School of Oriental Languages.
3259 **1246** 2f.80 multicoloured 1·60 1·10

1247 Giono

1995. Birth Centenary of Jean Giono (writer).
3260 **1247** 3f.70 blk, blue & red 2·50 1·40

1248 "Ariane" Rocket and Map of French Guiana

1995. French Space Centre in French Guiana.
3261 **1248** 2f.80 blue, grn & red 2·10 1·10

1249 Steel and Worker

1995. Lorraine's Iron and Steel Industry.
3262 **1249** 2f.80 multicoloured 1·60 1·10

1250 "Freedom"

1995. Europa. Peace and Freedom. Mult.
3263 2f.80 Type **1250** 1·90 1·10
3264 3f.70 "Peace" 3·25 2·20

1251 Lumberjack

1995. Forestry in the Ardennes.
3265 **1251** 4f.40 brn, blk & grn 2·50 1·70

1252 Paris Landmarks and Charles de Gaulle

1995. 50th Anniv of End of Second World War.
3266 **1252** 2f.80 multicoloured 2·20 1·10

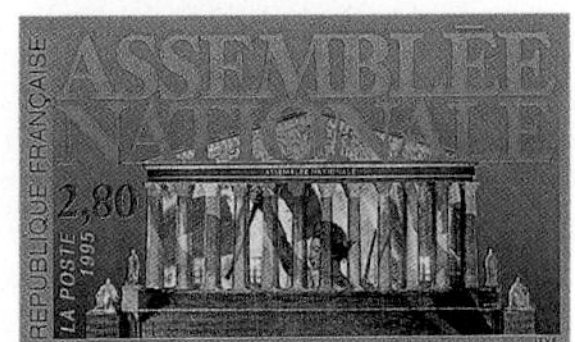

1253 Marianne in Assembly Building

1995. National Assembly.

3267	**1253**	2f.80 multicoloured	1·70	1·00

1254 "King Louis XIII on Horseback" (Saumur tapestry)

1995. Red Cross Fund.

3268	**1254**	2f.80+60c. mult	2·20	1·70

1255 Winged Hand

1995. 50th Anniv of French People's Relief Association (welfare organization).

3270	**1255**	2f.80 multicoloured	1·70	1·00

1256 Brittany

1995. Landscapes.

3271	**1256**	2f.40 green	1·30	90
3272	-	2f.40 green	1·30	90
3273	-	2f.80 red	1·60	1·00
3274	-	2f.80 red	1·60	1·00

DESIGNS: No. 3272, Vosges; 3273, Auvergne; 3274, Camargue.

1257 Orleans

1995. Federation of French Philatelic Societies Congress, Orleans.

3275	**1257**	2f.80 multicoloured	1·60	1·10

1258 "The Grasshopper and The Ant"

1995. 300th Death Anniv of Jean de la Fontaine (writer of fables). Multicoloured.

3276	2f.80 Type **1258**	2·10	1·40
3277	2f.80 "The Fat Frog and the Ox"	2·10	1·40
3278	2f.80 "The Wolf and the Lamb"	2·10	1·40
3279	2f.80 "The Raven and the Fox"	2·10	1·40
3280	2f.80 "The Cat, the Weasel and the Little Rabbit"	2·10	1·40
3281	2f.80 "The Hare and the Tortoise"	2·10	1·40

1259 Flower, Star and Wire

1995. 53rd Anniv of Internment of Jews in Velodrome d'Hiver, Paris.

3282	**1259**	2f.80 multicoloured	1·60	1·10

1260 Maginot and Roof

1995. 63rd Death Anniv of Andre Maginot (politician and instigator of Maginot Line (fortifications on French–German border)).

3283	**1260**	2f.80 brown, grn & red	1·60	1·10

1261 Lodge Emblem

1995. 50th Anniv of Women's Grand Masonic Lodge of France.

3284	**1261**	2f.80 multicoloured	1·60	1·10

1995. Contemporary Art. As T 1179. Mult.

3285	6f.70 Abstract (Kirkeby)	3·75	2·20

1262 Apothecary and Molecules

1995. 500th Anniv of Hospital Pharmacies.

3286	**1262**	2f.80 multicoloured	1·60	1·10

1263 "Thatched Cottages in Barbizon" (Narcisse Diaz de a Pena)

1995. 170th Anniv of Barbizon School (artists' settlement).

3287	**1263**	4f.40 multicoloured	2·50	1·70

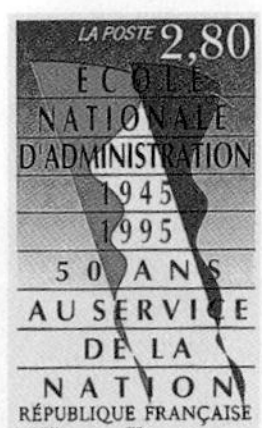

1264 Institute Emblem

1995. 50th Anniv of National Civil Servants' Training Institute, Paris.

3288	**1264**	2f.80 multicoloured	1·60	1·10

1265 Institute Building

1995. Bicentenary of French Institute, Paris.

3289	**1265**	2f.80 black, red & grn	1·60	1·10

1266 New and Old Motor Vehicles and Headquarters

1995. Centenary of French Automobile Club.

3290	**1266**	4f.40 black, bl & red	2·50	1·70

1267 Dove, Blue Helmet and Anniversary Emblem

1995. 50th Anniv of U.N.O.

3291	**1267**	4f.30 multicoloured	2·50	1·70

1268 Shepherd

1995. Red Cross Fund. Crib Figures from Provence. Multicoloured.

3292	2f.80+60c. Type **1268**	1·90	1·70
3293	2f.80+60c. Miller	1·90	1·70
3294	2f.80+60c. Simpleton and tambourine player	1·90	1·70
3295	2f.80+60c. Fishmonger	1·90	1·70
3296	2f.80+60c. Knife grinder	1·90	1·70
3297	2f.80+60c. Elderly couple	1·90	1·70

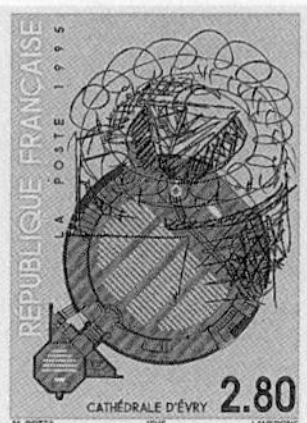

1269 Jammes

1995. 127th Birth Anniv of Francis Jammes (poet).

3298	**1269**	3f.70 black and blue	2·20	1·40

1270 Architect's Plans

1995. Completion of Evry Cathedral.

3299	**1270**	2f.80 multicoloured	1·80	1·10

1271 Pitch and Balls

1995. World Cup Football Championship, France (1998).

3300	**1271**	2f.80 multicoloured	1·60	1·10

1996. Contemporary Art. As T 1179.

3301	6f.70 black, red and blue	3·75	2·20
3302	6f.70 multicoloured	3·75	2·20

DESIGNS: No. 3301, "Sculpture" (Lucien Wercollier); 3302, "Horizon" (Jan Dibbets).

1272 Pottery Dog

1996. Completion of Archaeological Excavations in Saint-Martin Island, Guadeloupe.

3305	**1272**	2f.80 multicoloured	1·60	1·10

1996. Art. As T 491.

3306	6f.70 multicoloured	3·75	2·20
3307	6f.70 multicoloured	3·75	2·20
3308	6f.70 gold, copper & blk	3·75	2·20

DESIGNS—HORIZ: No. 3306, "Narni Bridge" (Camille Corot); 3308, "Cellos" (Arman). VERT: No. 3307, Bronze horse (found at Neuvy-en-Sullias).

1273 "St. Patrick" (stained glass window, Evie Hone)

1996. "L'imaginaire Irlandais" Festival of Contemporary Irish Arts, France.

3311	**1273**	2f.80 multicoloured	1·60	1·10

1274 "The Sower"

1996. Stamp Day. 93rd Anniv of Louis-Oscar Roty's "The Sower" design.

3313	**1274**	2f.80 mauve & violet	5·00	4·50
3314	**1274**	2f.80+60c. mauve and violet	2·50	1·90

1275 Rueff and New 1 Franc Coin of 1960

1996. Birth Centenary of Jacques Rueff (economist).

3315	**1275**	2f.80 black, bl & brn	1·60	1·10

1276 Descartes (after Frans Hals)

1996. 400th Birth Anniv of Rene Descartes (philosopher and scientist).

3316	**1276**	4f.40 red	2·50	1·70

1277 Lightbulb and Flame

1996. 50th Anniv of Electricite de France and Gaz de France.
3317 **1277** 3f. multicoloured 1·90 1·10

1278 Eurasian Beaver and Columbine, Cevennes

1996. National Parks. Multicoloured.
3318 3f. Type **1278** 1·80 1·00
3319 4f.40 Lammergeier and saxifrage, Mercantour 2·75 1·40
3320 4f.40 Ibex and gentian, Vanoise 2·75 1·40
See also Nos. 3380/3.

1280 Mme. de Sevigne (writer)

1996. Europa. Famous Women.
3325 **1280** 3f. multicoloured 1·80 1·30

1281 Test Tubes and Flower held with Tweezers

1996. 50th Anniv of National Institute for Agronomic Research.
3326 **1281** 3f.80 multicoloured 2·50 1·40

1282 Joan of Arc's Cottage, Domremy la Pucelle, Vosges

1996. 75th Anniv (1995) of Canonization of Joan of Arc.
3327 **1282** 4f.50 multicoloured 2·75 1·70

1283 Fishes, Sea and Coastline

1996. 20th Anniv of Ramoge Agreement on Environmental Protection of the Mediterranean.
3328 **1283** 3f. multicoloured 2·50 1·10

1284 Notre-Dame de Clermont and the Jacquemart (Cathedral clock)

1996. Federation of French Philatelic Societies Congress, Clermont-Ferrand.
3329 **1284** 3f. green, brown & red 1·90 1·10

1996. Tourist Publicity. As T 490.
3330 3f. multicoloured 1·90 1·10
3331 3f. multicoloured 1·90 1·10
3332 3f.80 brown and mauve 2·10 1·30
3333 4f.50 multicoloured 2·40 1·70
DESIGN—HORIZ: 3f. (No. 3330), Bitche Castle, Moselle; 3f. (No. 3331), Sanguinaries Islands, Corsica; 3f.80, Cloisters, Thoronet Abbey, Var; 4f.50, Detail of trompe l'oeil by Casimir Vicario, Chambery Cathedral.

1285 Lens

1996. World Cup Football Championship, France (1998) (1st issue). Host Cities. Multicoloured.
3335 3f. Type **1285** 1·80 1·30
3336 3f. Montpellier 1·80 1·30
3337 3f. Saint-Etienne 1·80 1·30
3338 3f. Toulouse 1·80 1·30
See also Nos. 3401/4, 3464/5 and 3472.

1286 Throwing the Discus

1996. Centenary of Modern Olympic Games.
3339 **1286** 3f. multicoloured 1·90 1·10

1287 Marette

1996. 12th Death Anniv of Jacques Marette (journalist and politician).
3340 **1287** 4f.40 lilac 2·50 1·80

1288 Diesel Railcar Set

1996. Centenary of Ajaccio–Vizzavona Railway, Corsica.
3341 **1288** 3f. multicoloured 1·90 1·10

1289 Basilica

1996. Centenary of Our Lady of Fourviere Basilica, Lyon.
3342 **1289** 3f. black and yellow 1·90 1·10

1290 Baptism of Clovis (illus from "Grandes Chroniques de France")

1996. Inauguration of Committee for Commemoration of Origins: from Gaul to France. 1500th Anniv of Baptism of Clovis.
3343 **1290** 3f. multicoloured 1·90 1·10

1291 Arsene Lupin (Maurice Leblanc)

1996. Red Cross Fund. Heroes of Crime Novels. Multicoloured.
3344 3f.+60c. Rocambole (Pierre Ponson du Terrail) 2·10 1·80
3345 3f.+60c. Type **1291** 2·10 1·80
3346 3f.+60c. Joseph Rouletabille (Gaston Leroux) 2·10 1·80
3347 3f.+60c. Fantomas (Pierre Souvestre and Marcel Allain) 2·10 1·80
3348 3f.+60c. Commissioner Maigret (Georges Simenon) 2·10 1·80
3349 3f.+60c. Nestor Burma (Leo Malet) 2·10 1·80

1292 School Building

1996. Bicentenary of Henri IV School, Paris.
3350 **1292** 4f.50 blue, brn & grn 2·50 1·70

1293 Children of Different Nations

1996. 50th Anniv of UNICEF.
3351 **1293** 4f.50 multicoloured 2·50 1·70

1294 Iena Palace (headquarters)

1996. 50th Anniv of Economic and Social Council.
3352 **1294** 3f. black, red & blue 1·90 1·10

1295 Headquarters, Paris

1996. 50th Anniv of UNESCO.
3353 **1295** 3f.80 multicoloured 2·20 1·30

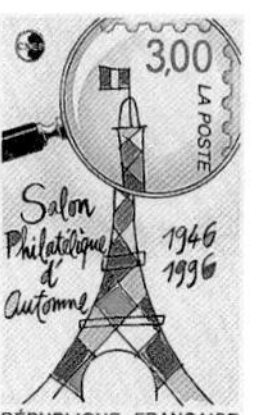

1296 Magnifying Glass over Eiffel Tower

1996. 50th Anniv of Autumn Stamp Show, Paris.
3354 **1296** 3f. multicoloured 1·90 1·10

1297 "Woman"

1996. 50th Anniv of Creation of French Overseas Departments of Martinique, Guadeloupe, Guiana and La Reunion.
3355 **1297** 3f. multicoloured 1·90 1·10

1298 Snowman and Polar Bear in Hot-air Balloon

1996. Red Cross Fund. Christmas.
3356 **1298** 3f.+60c. mult 2·20 1·70

1299 Temple, Delphi

1996. 150th Anniv of French School in Athens.
3357 **1299** 3f. multicoloured 1·90 1·10

1300 Malraux

1996. 20th Death Anniv of Andre Malraux (writer and politician).
3358 **1300** 3f. blue 1·90 1·10

1301 Clapperboard, Camera and Golden Palm

1996. 50th Int Film Festival, Cannes.
3359 **1301** 3f. multicoloured 1·90 1·10

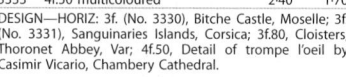

1302 New Building

1996. Inauguration of New National Library Building, Paris.
3360 **1302** 3f. yellow, blue & red 1·90 1·10

1303 Mitterrand

1997. Francois Mitterrand (President, 1981–95) Commemoration.
3361 **1303** 3f. multicoloured 1·90 1·10

1304 Wire Figures

1997. "Participatory Innovation" (suggestions schemes).
3362 **1304** 3f. multicoloured 1·90 1·10

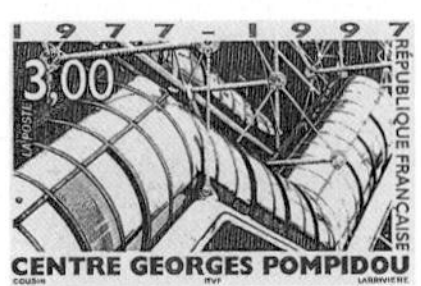

1305 Detail of Building

1997. 20th Anniv of Georges Pompidou National Centre of Art and Culture.
3363 **1305** 3f. multicoloured 1·90 1·10

1306 "bonne fete" (Happy Holiday)

1997. Greetings stamps. Multicoloured.
3364 3f. Type **1306** 1·90 1·10
3365 3f. "joyeux anniversaire" (Happy Birthday) 1·90 1·10

1307 New Building, Marne-la-Vallee

1997. 250th Anniv of National School of Bridges and Highways.
3366 **1307** 3f. multicoloured 1·90 1·10

1308 Gateway and Buildings

1997. National Historic Landmark Status of Former Penal Colony, Saint-Laurent-du-Maroni, French Guiana.
3367 **1308** 3f. multicoloured 1·90 1·10

1997. Art. As T **491**.
3368 6f.70 Fresco (detail), St. Nicholas's Church, Tavant (Indre et Loire) (vert) 3·75 2·20
3369 6f.70 Abstract (Bernard Moninot) 3·75 2·20
3370 6f.70 "The Thumb" (sculpture, Cesar Baldaccini) (vert) 3·75 2·20
3371 6f.70 "Grapes and Pomegranates" (Jean Baptiste Chardin) 3·75 2·20

1309 "Mouchon" type

1997. Stamp Day. 97th Anniv of Louis-Eugene Mouchon's Design.
3372 **1309** 3f.+60c. blue, mauve and silver 2·20 1·40
3373 **1309** 3f. blue, mauve & silver 3·75 2·75

1997. Tourist Publicity. As T **490**.
3375 3f. emerald, dp green & grn 1·90 1·10
3376 3f. green, red and orange 1·90 1·10
3377 3f. brown, blue and green 1·90 1·10
3378 3f. brown, choc & green 1·90 1·10
3379 3f. green, blue and brown 1·90 1·10

DESIGN—VERT: No. 3375, Millau, Aveyron; 3376, Buttress of "Calvary" and church, Guimiliau. HORIZ: No. 3377, Sable-sur-Sarthe; 3378, St. Maurice's Cathedral, Epinal; 3379, Sceaux estate.

1997. National Parks. As T **1278**. Mult.
3380 3f. Golden eagle and blue thistle, Ecrins 1·80 1·10
3381 3f. Racoon and La Soufriere (volcano), Guadeloupe 1·80 1·10
3382 4f.50 Manx shearwater and coves, Port-Cros 2·40 1·40
3383 4f.50 Chamois and mountain, Pyrenees 2·40 1·40

1310 "Puss in Boots" (engraving by Gustav Dore)

1997. Europa. Tales and Legends.
3384 **1310** 3f. blue 1·90 1·70

1311 Teenager "flying" Stamp

1997. "Philexjeunes 97" Youth Stamp Exhibition, Nantes.
3385 **1311** 3f. multicoloured 1·90 1·10

1312 Envelope writing Letter

1997. The Journey of a Letter. Multicoloured. Ordinary or self-adhesive gum.
3392 3f. Type **1312** 2·20 1·90
3393 3f. Smiling letter climbing up to post box 2·20 1·90
3394 3f. Letter as van 2·20 1·90
3395 3f. Letters holding hands and postman carrying letter 2·20 1·90
3396 3f. Girl kissing letter 2·20 1·90
3397 3f. Girl reading long letter 2·20 1·90

1313 Soldier and Map

1997. French Army Operations in North Africa, 1952–62.
3398 **1313** 3f. multicoloured 1·90 1·10

1314 Palace of Versailles (image scaled to 62% of original size)

1997. 70th Federation of French Philatelic Societies Congress, Versailles.
3399 **1314** 3f. multicoloured 1·90 1·70

1315 Chateau du Plessis-Bourre

1997
3400 **1315** 4f.40 multicoloured 2·40 1·70

1997. World Cup Football Championship, France (1998) (2nd issue). Host Cities. As T 1285. Multicoloured.
3401 3f. Lyon 1·80 1·10
3402 3f. Marseille 1·80 1·10
3403 3f. Nantes 1·80 1·10
3404 3f. Paris 1·80 1·10

1316 Detail of Fresco

1997. Restoration of Frescoes in St. Eutrope's Church, Les Salles-Lavauguyon.
3405 **1316** 4f.50 multicoloured 2·40 1·70

1317 St. Martin (from Tours Missal)

1997. 1600th Death Anniv of St. Martin, Bishop of Tours.
3406 **1317** 4f.50 multicoloured 2·50 1·70

1318 "Marianne of 14 July"

1997. No value expressed.
3407 **1318** (3f.) red 1·50 1·10

1997
3415 **1318** 10c. brown 25 20
3416 **1318** 20c. green 25 20
3417 **1318** 50c. violet 25 20
3418 **1318** 1f. orange 50 45
3419 **1318** 2f. blue 90 75
3420 **1318** 2f.70 green 1·40 1·20
3423 **1318** 3f.50 green 1·50 1·30
3425 **1318** 3f.80 blue 1·70 1·40
3427 **1318** 4f.20 red 1·80 1·50
3428 **1318** 4f.40 blue 1·90 1·70
3429 **1318** 4f.50 mauve 2·10 1·80
3430 **1318** 5f. blue 2·50 2·20
3431 **1318** 6f.70 green 3·25 2·75
3432 **1318** 10f. violet 4·50 3·75
MS3439 (a) Nos. 3415/19, 3430 and 3432; (b) Nos. 3407, 3420/9 and 3431 26·00 22·00

1319 Rowers

1997. World Rowing Championships, Lake Aiguebelette, Savoie.
3440 **1319** 3f. mauve, bl & red 1·90 1·10

1320 Sailors and Privateer Ship

1997. Basque Corsairs.
3441 **1320** 3f. multicoloured 1·90 1·10

1321 Horse-drawn Fish Cart

1997. Fresh Fish Merchants from Boulogne.
3442 **1321** 3f. green, violet & blue 1·90 1·10

1322 Kudara Kannon (statue from Horyu Temple, Nara) and Japanese Cultural Centre, Paris

1997. Japan Year.
3443 **1322** 4f.90 blue, orge & blk 2·75 1·70

1323 Contest

1997. World Judo Championships, Paris.
3444 **1323** 3f. multicoloured 1·90 1·10

1324 Emblem

1997. Sar-Lor-Lux (Saarland–Lorraine–Luxembourg) European Region.
3445 **1324** 3f. multicoloured 1·90 1·10

1325 College and King Francois I (founder)

1997. Le College de France.
3446 **1325** 4f.40 green, brn & blk 2·40 1·70

1326 Team with Coloured Ribbons

1997. French Movement for Quality.
3447 **1326** 4f.50 multicoloured 1·90 1·70

1327 Lancelot (Chretien de Troyes)

1997. Red Cross Fund. Literary Heroes. Multicoloured.
3448 3f.+60c. Type **1327** 2·10 1·80
3449 3f.+60c. Pardaillan (Michel Zevaco) 2·10 1·80
3450 3f.+60c. D'Artagnan ("The Three Musketeers" by Alexandre Dumas) 2·10 1·80
3451 3f.+60c. Cyrano de Bergerac (Edmond Rostand) 2·10 1·80
3452 3f.+60c. Captain Fracasse (Theophile Gautier) 2·10 1·80
3453 3f.+60c. Lagardere as Le Bossu (Paul Feval) 2·10 1·80

1328 Teddy Bear with Gifts in Spaceship

1997. Red Cross Fund. Christmas.

3454 **1328** 3f.+60c. mult 2·20 1·70

1329 Mouse giving Gift to Cat

1997. "Best Wishes".

3455 **1329** 3f. multicoloured 1·90 1·10

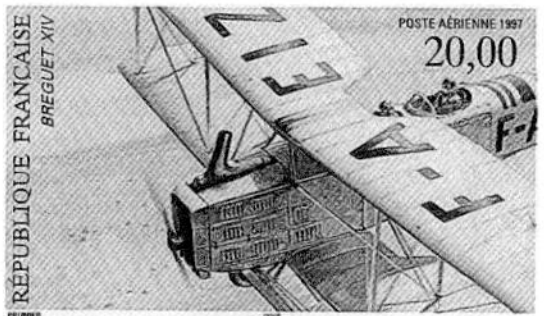

1330 Breguet 14 Biplane

1997. Air.

3456 **1330** 20f. multicoloured 7·75 3·25

1331 Teddy Bear holding Toy Windmill

1997. Protection of Abused Children Campaign.

3457 **1331** 3f. multicoloured 1·90 1·10

1332 Flying Postman

1997. "Best Wishes".

3458 **1332** 3f. multicoloured 1·90 1·10

1333 Cross of Lorraine on Map of France and Leclerc

1997. 50th Death Anniv of Marshal Leclerc.

3459 **1333** 3f. multicoloured 1·90 1·10

1334 "Marianne of 14 July" and Emblem

1997. "Philexfrance 99" International Stamp Exhibition, Paris.

3460 **1334** 3f. red and blue 1·90 1·10

1335 Carving and Buildings

1997. Millenary of Foundation of Moutier D'Ahun Monastery, Creuse.

3461 **1335** 4f.40 multicoloured 2·50 1·70

1336 Debre

1998. 2nd Death Anniv of Michel Debre (Prime Minister, 1958–62).

3462 **1336** 3f. black, blue & red 1·90 1·10

1337 Anniversary Emblem

1998. Bicentenary of National Assembly.

3463 **1337** 3f. red and blue 1·90 1·10

1998. World Cup Football Championship, France (3rd issue). Host Cities. As T 1285. Multicoloured.

3464 3f. Bordeaux 1·90 1·10

3465 3f. Saint-Denis, Paris 1·90 1·10

MS3466 148×140 mm. Nos. 3335/8, 3401/4 and 3464/5 13·00 11·00

1338 Cherub with Letter and Flowers

1998. St. Valentine's Day.

3467 **1338** 3f. multicoloured 1·90 1·10

1339 Mediator and People

1998. 25th Anniv of Mediator of the Republic (ombudsman).

3468 **1339** 3f. multicoloured 1·90 1·10

1340 "Blanc" Type

1998. Stamp Day. 98th Anniv of Joseph Blanc's Design.

3469 **1340** 3f.+60c. red, green and silver 2·20 1·40

3470 **1340** 3f. red, grn & silver 4·75 2·75

1341 Football

1998. World Cup Football Championship, France (4th issue). Ordinary or self-adhesive gum.

3472 **1341** 3f. multicoloured 1·90 1·10

MS3474 No. 3472 plus 7 labels showing the World Cup mascot demonstrating various shots 10·50 10·00

1342 Stock

1998. 50th Death Anniv of Father Franz Stock (wartime prison chaplain).

3475 **1342** 4f.50 blue 2·40 1·70

1343 "Happy Birthday"

1998. Greeting Stamp.

3476 **1343** 3f. multicoloured 1·90 1·10

1344 Citeaux Abbey

1998. 900th Anniv of Founding of Citeaux Abbey.

3477 **1344** 3f. multicoloured 1·90 1·10

1345 Mulhouse, 1798

1998. Bicentenary of Union of Mulhouse with France.

3478 **1345** 3f. multicoloured 1·90 1·10

1346 Sub-prefect's Residence, Saint-Pierre

1998. Reunion's Architectural Heritage.

3479 **1346** 3f. multicoloured 1·90 1·10

1347 "The Return"

1998. Birth Centenary of Rene-Ghislain Magritte (painter).

3480 **1347** 3f. multicoloured 1·90 1·10

1348 King Henri IV

1998. 400th Anniv of Edict of Nantes.

3481 **1348** 4f.50 multicoloured 2·50 1·70

1349 Slave wearing Cap of Liberty

1998. 150th Anniv of Abolition of Slavery by France.

3482 **1349** 3f. multicoloured 1·90 1·10

1998. Art. As T **491**. Multicoloured.

3483 6f.70 "The Crusaders' Arrival in Constantinople" (detail, Eugene Delacroix) (vert) 3·75 2·20

3484 6f.70 "Spring" (Pablo Picasso) 3·75 2·20

3485 6f.70 "Nine Idiot Bachelors" (Marcel Duchamp) 3·75 2·20

3486 6f.70 "Vision after the Sermon" (Paul Gaugin) 3·75 2·20

1998. Tourist Publicity. As T **490**.

3487 3f. multicoloured 1·90 1·10

3488 3f. multicoloured 1·90 1·10

3489 3f. green, blue and cream 1·90 1·10

3490 3f. multicoloured 1·90 1·10

3491 4f.40 multicoloured 2·50 1·70

DESIGNS—As Type **490**: No. 3487, Le Gois Causeway, Noirmoutiers Island; 3489, Crussol Chateau, Ardeche; 3490, Liberty Tower, Saint-Die, Vosges. 26×38 mm: No. 3488, Bay of Somme. 26×36 mm: No. 3491, Mantes-la-Jolie collegiate church, Yvelines.

1350 Dove Carrying Letter to Noah's Ark

1998. History of the Letter. Multicoloured. Ordinary or self-adhesive gum.

3492 3f. Type **1350** 1·90 1·10

3493 3f. Egyptian carving tablet 1·90 1·10

3494 3f. Ancient Greek carrying letter from Marathon to Athens 1·90 1·10

3495 3f. Knight on horseback carrying letter and pen 1·90 1·10

3496 3f. Man writing with quill 1·90 1·10

3497 3f. Spaceman posting letter 1·90 1·10

1351 Figure with Butterfly Wings

1998. Cent of League of Human Rights.

3504 **1351** 4f.40 multicoloured 2·40 1·70

1352 Collet

1998. 47th Death Anniv of Henri Collet (composer).

3505 **1352** 4f.50 black & stone 2·40 1·70

1353 Statue of Jean Bart, Cathedral and "Sandettie II" (light-ship)

1998. Federation of French Philatelic Societies Congress, Dunkirk.

3506 **1353** 3f. red, orange & blue 1·90 1·10

1354 Mont Saint Michel

1998

3507 **1354** 3f. multicoloured 1·90 1·10

1355 Pan playing Flute (Festival of Music)

1998. Europa. National Festivals.

3508	**1355**	3f. multicoloured	1·90	1·10

1998. France, World Cup Football Champion. As No. 3472 but additionally inscribed "Champion du Monde FRANCE".

3509	3f. multicoloured	1·90	1·10

1356 Potez 25 Biplane

1998. Air.

3510	**1356**	30f. multicoloured	13·00	8·75

1357 Convolvulus

1998. Precancels. Flowers. Multicoloured.

3511	1f.87 Type **1357**	1·40	55
3512	2f.18 Poppy	1·80	90
3513	4f.66 Violet	3·25	1·80
3514	7f.11 Buttercup	4·50	2·75

1358 Mallarme

1998. Death Centenary of Stephane Mallarme (poet).

3515	**1358**	4f.40 multicoloured	2·40	1·70

1359 Balloon and Early Airplane

1998. Centenary of Aero Club of France.

3516	**1359**	3f. multicoloured	1·90	1·10

1360 The Little Prince

1998. "Philexfrance 99" International Stamp Exhibition, Paris (1st issue). "The Little Prince" (novel) by Antoine de Saint-Exupery. Multicoloured.

3517	3f. Type **1360**	1·90	1·10
3518	3f. On wall watching snake (vert)	1·90	1·10
3519	3f. On planet (vert)	1·90	1·10
3520	3f. Watering flower (vert)	1·90	1·10
3521	3f. On hillside with fox	1·90	1·10
MS3522	111×157 mm. Nos. 3517/21 (sold at 25f.)	11·00	10·00

See also No. **MS**3576.

1361 Hall of Supreme Harmony, Forbidden City, Peking, China

1998. Cultural Heritage. Multicoloured.

3523	3f. Type **1361**	1·90	1·10
3524	4f.90 Louvre Palace, Paris	2·50	1·70

1362 Violin and Ballet Dancer

1998. National Opera House, Paris.

3525	**1362**	4f.50 multicoloured	2·50	1·70

1363 Camargue

1998. Horses. Multicoloured.

3526	2f.70 Type **1363**	1·80	1·00
3527	3f. French trotter	1·90	1·10
3528	3f. Pottok	1·90	1·10
3529	4f.50 Ardennais	2·50	1·70

1364 Dion-Bouton and Racing Cars

1998. Centenary of Paris Motor Show.

3530	**1364**	3f. multicoloured	1·90	1·10

1365 Marianne and Flag

1998. 40th Anniv of Constitution of Fifth Republic.

3531	**1365**	3f. multicoloured	1·90	1·10

1366 Romy Schneider

1998. Film Stars. Multicoloured.

3532	3f.+60c. Type **1366**	2·10	1·80
3533	3f.+60c. Simone Signoret	2·10	1·80
3534	3f.+60c. Jean Gabin	2·10	1·80
3535	3f.+60c. Louis de Funes	2·10	1·80
3536	3f.+60c. Bernard Blier	2·10	1·80
3537	3f.+60c. Lino Ventura	2·10	1·80

1367 State Flags

1998. 80th Anniv of Signing of First World War Armistice.

3538	**1367**	3f. multicoloured	1·90	1·10

1368 Flora and Fauna, Child and Emblem

1998. 50th Anniv of International Union for the Conservation of Nature and Natural Resources.

3539	**1368**	3f. multicoloured	1·90	1·10

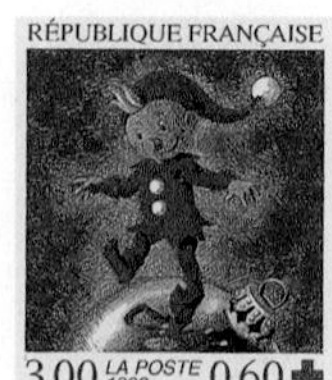

1369 Elf on Christmas Bauble

1998. Red Cross Fund. Christmas.

3540	**1369**	3f.+60c. mult	2·10	1·20

1370 Father Christmas Snowboarding

1998. Christmas and New Year. Multicoloured.

3541	3f. Type **1370** (violet background)	1·90	1·10
3542	3f. Decorated house (daytime)	1·90	1·10
3543	3f. Type **1370** (bright yellow background)	1·90	1·10
3544	3f. Decorated house (night-time)	1·90	1·10
3545	3f. Type **1370** (green background)	1·90	1·10

1371 Child expressing Ambition and People of Different Nations

1998. Medecins sans Frontieres (volunteer medical and relief organization).

3546	**1371**	3f. multicoloured	1·90	1·10

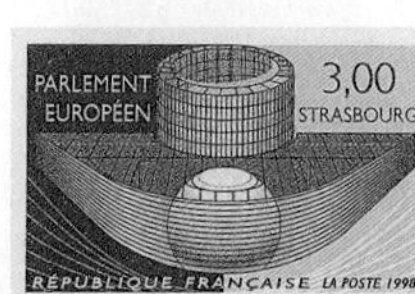

1372 Architectural Drawing

1998. Construction of New European Parliament Building, Strasbourg (designed by Architecture Studio Europe).

3547	**1372**	3f. multicoloured	1·90	1·10

1373 Rene Cassin, Eleanor Roosevelt and Palais de Chaillot

1998. 50th Anniv of Universal Declaration of Human Rights. Multicoloured.

3548	3f. Type **1373**	1·90	1·10
3549	3f. Globe and people of different races	1·90	1·10

1374 Radium

1998. Centenary of Discovery of Radium by Marie and Pierre Curie and 50th Anniv of ZOE Reactor, Chatillon.

3550	**1374**	3f. multicoloured	1·90	1·10

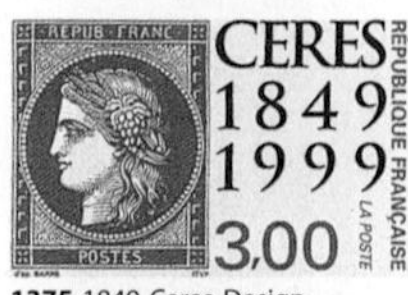

1375 1849 Ceres Design

1999. 150th Anniv of First French Postage Stamp (1st issue).

3551	**1375**	3f. black and red	6·50	5·50
3552	-	3f. black and red	1·90	1·10

DESIGN: No. 3552, As Type **1375** but with stamp and text transposed.

See also No. 3596.

1376 Euro Symbol

1999. Introduction of the Euro (European currency). Ordinary or self-adhesive gum.

3553	**1376**	3f. red and blue	2·20	1·30

No. 3553 is denominated both in French francs and in euros.

1377 Open Hands

1999. 150th Anniv of Public Welfare Hospitals of Paris (administration of Paris health services).

3555	**1377**	3f. blue, mve & grn	1·90	1·10

1378 Flags of France and Israel

1999. 50th Anniv of Diplomatic Relations between France and Israel.

3556	**1378**	4f.40 multicoloured	2·50	1·70

1379 Heart

1999. St. Valentine's Day. Multicoloured. Ordinary and self-adhesive gum.

3557	3f. Type **1379**	1·90	1·10
3558	3f. Heart-shaped rose	1·90	1·10

1999. Art. As T **491**.

3561	6f.70 brown and orange	3·50	2·40
3562	6f.70 multicoloured	3·50	2·40
3563	6f.70 multicoloured	3·50	2·40
3564	6f.70 multicoloured	3·50	2·40

DESIGNS—VERT: No. 3561, "St. Luke the Evangelist" (sculpture, Jean Goujon); 3562, Stained glass window (Arnaud de Moles), Chapelle de la Compassion, Auch Cathedral; 3564, "Charles I, King of England" (Anton van Dyck). HORIZ: No. 3563, "Water Lilies, Effect of Evening" (Claude Monet).

1380 Flowers on Map of France

1999. 33rd Population Census.

3565	**1380**	3f. multicoloured	1·90	1·10

1381 "The Capture of Europa" (mosaic from Byblos)

1999. Cultural Heritage of Lebanon.

3566	**1381**	4f.40 multicoloured	2·40	1·70

1382 Asterix

1999. Stamp Day. Asterix the Gaul (cartoon character) by Albert Uderzo and Rene Goscinny.

3567	**1382**	3f. multicoloured	1·90	1·10
3569	**1382**	3f.+60c. mult	3·25	2·75
MS3570		102×77 mm. No. 3569	3·75	3·75

1383 Council Emblem on World Map

1999. 50th Anniv of Council of Europe.

3571	**1383**	3f. multicoloured	1·90	1·10

1384 Two Doves and Hearts (wedding)

1999. Greetings Stamps. Multicoloured.

3572	3f. Type **1384**	1·90	1·10
3573	3f. "Thank you" in different languages	1·90	1·10
3574	3f. Stork carrying blue bundle ("It's a boy")	1·90	1·10
3575	3f. Stork carrying pink bundle ("It's a girl")	1·90	1·10

1385 "Venus de Milo" (statue)

1999. "Philexfrance 99" International Stamp Exhibition, Paris (2nd issue). Art. Sheet 159×111 mm containing T 1385 and similar designs.

MS3576 5f. sepia (Type **1385**); 5f. multicoloured ("Mona Lisa" (Leonardo da Vinci)) (37×49 mm); 10f. multicoloured ("Liberty guiding the People" (Eugene Delacroix)) (36×37 mm) (sold at 50f.) 50·00 55·00

1386 Branches and Hand reaching for Star

1999. European Parliament Elections.

3577	**1386**	3f. multicoloured	1·90	1·10

1387 Richard the Lion Heart (from "Historia Anglorum")

1999. 800th Death Anniv of King Richard I of England.

3578	**1387**	3f. multicoloured	1·90	1·10

1388 Airbus A300-B4

1999. Air.

3579	**1388**	15f. multicoloured	9·00	7·75

1389 Dieppe Castle

1999. Tourist Publicity.

3580	**1389**	3f. multicoloured	1·90	1·10
3581	-	3f. multicoloured	1·90	1·10
3582	-	3f. multicoloured	1·90	1·10
3583	-	3f. multicoloured	1·90	1·10

DESIGNS—As T **949**: No. 3581, Haut-Koenigsbourg Castle, Lower Rhine. As T **490**: No. 3582, Place des Ecritures, Figeac; 3583, Arnac-Pompadour Chateau.

No. 3583 is denominated in both francs and euros.

1390 The Camargue

1999. Europa. Parks and Gardens.

3584	**1390**	3f. multicoloured	1·90	1·10

1391 Cake and Music Notes ("Happy Birthday")

1999. Greetings Stamps. Multicoloured.

3585	3f. Type **1391**	1·90	1·10
3586	3f. Seagull and sun wearing sunglasses ("Have a nice holiday")	1·90	1·10
3587	3f. Float on water ("Long live holidays") (vert)	1·90	1·10

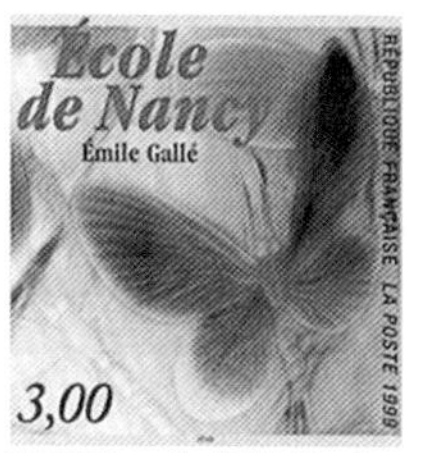

1392 St. Pierre and Mt. Pelee

1999. Heritage of Martinique.

3588	**1392**	3f. multicoloured	1·90	1·10

1393 "Noctuelles" Dish (detail, Emile Galle)

1999. Nancy School (art movement).

3589	**1393**	3f. multicoloured	1·90	1·10

1394 "Mme. Alfred Carriere"

1999. Old Roses. Sheet 111×160 mm containing T **1394** and similar vert designs. Multicoloured.

MS3590 3f. Type **1394**; 4f.50 "Mme. Caroline Testout"; 4f.50 "La France" 11·50 11·00

1395 Ruins, Grape Vines and Seal

1999. 800th Anniv of Granting of City Rights to Saint-Emilion and 50th Anniv of Re-institution of the Jurade (controllers of St.-Emilion wine appellation).

3591	**1395**	3f.80 multicoloured	2·20	1·40

1396 The Mint, Paris

1999

3592	**1396**	4f.50 red, blue & black	2·50	1·70

1397 Model Girls

1999. Birth Bicentenary of Countess de Segur (children's writer).

3593	**1397**	3f. multicoloured	1·90	1·10

1398 Sun and Doves in Mosaic

1999. Post Office "Pleasure to Welcome" Customer Campaign.

3594	**1398**	3f. multicoloured	1·90	1·10

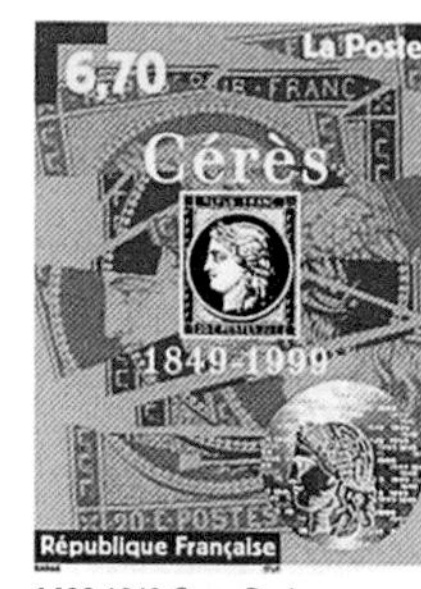

1399 Caillie

1999. Birth Bicentenary of Rene Caillie (explorer).

3595	**1399**	4f.50 violet, yellow and orange	2·50	1·70

1400 1849 Ceres Design

1999. 150th Anniv of First French Postage Stamp (2nd issue).

3596	**1400**	6f.70 multicoloured	4·50	2·40

DENOMINATION. From No. 3597 to 3769 French stamps were denominated both in francs and in euros. As no cash for the latter was in circulation, the catalogue refers to the franc value.

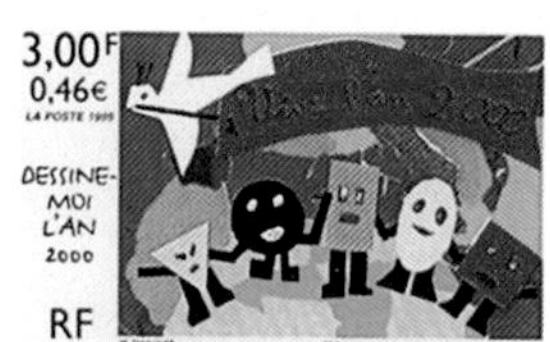

1401 Spinning Globe

1999. Year 2000.

3597	**1401**	3f. multicoloured	1·90	1·10

1402 Winning Entry by Morgane Toulouse

1999. "Design a Stamp for Year 2000" Children's Drawing Contest.

3598	**1402**	3f. multicoloured	1·90	1·10

1403 Total Eclipse

1999. Solar Eclipse (11 August).

3599	**1403**	3f. multicoloured	1·90	1·10

1404 "Simon Bolivar" (Venezuelan cadet barque)

1999. "Armada of the Century", Rouen. Sailing Ships. Multicoloured.

3600	1f. Type **1404**	65	55
3601	1f. "Iskra" (Polish cadet ship)	65	55
3602	1f. "Statsraad Lehmkuhl" (barque)	65	55
3603	1f. "Asgard II" (cadet brigantine)	65	55
3604	1f. "Belle Poule" (sail frigate)	65	55
3605	1f. "Belem" (barque)	65	55
3606	1f. "Amerigo Vespucci" (cadet ship)	65	55
3607	1f. "Sagres" (cadet barque)	65	55
3608	1f. "Europa" (barque)	65	55
3609	1f. "Cuauhtemoc" (barque)	65	55

1405 "School, 1956" (Robert Doisneau)

1999. French Photographers. Multicoloured.

3610	3f.+60c. Type **1405**	2·20	1·90
3611	3f.+60c. "St. James's Tower, View of Notre Dame, 1936" (Gilberte Brassai)	2·20	1·90
3612	3f.+60c. "Renee on the way to Paris, Aix-les-Bains" (Jacques Henri Lartigue)	2·20	1·90
3613	3f.+60c. "Hyeres, France, 1932" (Henri Cartier-Bresson)	2·20	1·90
3614	3f.+60c. "Travelling Salesman" (Eugene Atget)	2·20	1·90
3615	3f.+60c. "Debureau at the Camera" (Nadar)	2·20	1·90

1406 Players

1999. 4th World Cup Rugby Championship, Great Britain, Ireland and France.

3616	**1406**	3f. multicoloured	1·70	1·00

1407 Ozanam (after Louis Janmot)

1999. 146th Death Anniv of Frederic Ozanam (historian and social campaigner).

3617	**1407**	4f.50 deep green, brown and red	2·30	1·50

1408 People holding Hands

1999. 50th Anniv of Emmaus Movement (welfare organization).

3618	**1408**	3f. multicoloured	1·70	1·00

1409 Chartreuse Cat

1999. Domestic Pets. Multicoloured.

3619	2f.70 Type **1409**	1·40	1·00
3620	3f. European tabby cat	1·40	1·00
3621	3f. Pyrenean mountain dog	1·40	1·00
3622	4f.50 Brittany spaniel	2·30	2·00

1410 Chopin (after George Sand)

1999. 150th Death Anniv of Frederic Chopin (composer).

3623	**1410**	3f.80 blue, deep violet and orange	1·40	1·20

1411 Star playing Drum with Clock Face

1999. Red Cross Fund. New Year.

3624	**1411**	3f.+60c. mult	1·80	1·30

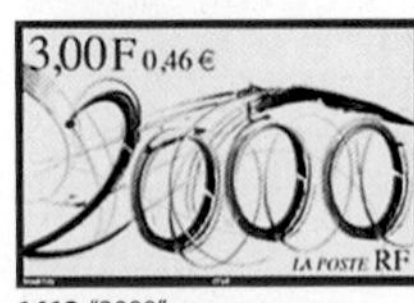

1412 "2000"

1999. Year 2000. Multicoloured.

3625	3f. Type **1412**	1·50	1·00
3626	3f. Half-unwrapped parcel (vert)	1·50	1·00

1413 Metro Signs

1999. Centenary of Paris Metro.

3627	**1413**	3f. multicoloured	1·50	1·00

1414 Column and Pediment

1999. Bicentenary of Council of State.

3628	**1414**	3f. blue and grey	1·50	1·00

1415 San Juan de Salvamento and La Rochelle Lighthouses

2000. Reconstruction of San Juan de Salvamento Lighthouse, Staten Island.

3629	**1415**	3f. multicoloured	1·50	1·00

1416 Snakes forming Heart

2000. Yves St. Laurent (couturier). Multicoloured. Ordinary or self-adhesive gum.

3630	3f. Type **1416**	1·50	1·00
3631	3f. Woman's face	1·50	1·00
MS3632	95×150 mm. Nos. 3630 ×3 and No. 3631 ×2	6·75	6·50

1417 Bank Entrance

2000. Bicentenary of Bank of France.

3635	**1417**	3f. multicoloured	1·10	1·00

1418 Couzinet 70 *Arc en Ciel*

2000. Air.

3636	**1418**	50f. multicoloured	22·00	19·00

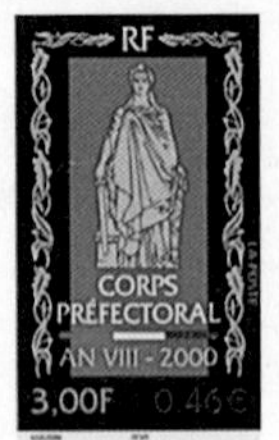

1419 Emblem

2000. Bicentenary of Prefectorial Corps.

3637	**1419**	3f. multicoloured	1·10	1·00

2000. Art. As T **491**.

3638	6f.70 multicoloured (vert)	3·25	2·00
3639	6f.70 multicoloured (vert)	3·25	2·00
3640	6f.70 multicoloured (vert)	3·25	2·00

DESIGNS: No. 3638, Detail of "Venus and the Graces offering Gifts to a Young Girl" (Sandro Botticelli); 3639, "The Waltz" (sculpture, Camille Claudel); 3640, "Visage Rouge" (Gaston Chaissac).

2000. Tourist Publicity. As T **949**.

3642	3f. multicoloured	1·10	1·00
3643	3f. multicoloured	1·10	1·00
3644	3f. multicoloured	1·10	1·00
3645	3f. multicoloured	1·10	1·00

DESIGNS: No. 3642, Carcassonne. As Type **490**: 37×27 mm—No. 3643, Saint Guilhem le Desert, Herault; 3644, Valley of the Lakes, Gerardmer. 36×23 mm—No. 3645, Ottmarsheim Abbey church.

1420 Tintin and Snowy

2000. Tintin (cartoon character) by Georges Renu (Herge).

3646	**1420**	3f. multicoloured	1·60	1·00
3648	**1420**	3f.+60c. mult	2·75	2·00
MS3649		101×76 mm. No. 3648	3·50	3·00

1421 Parliament Building

2000. Restoration of Breton Regional Parliament, Rennes.

3650	**1421**	3f. multicoloured	1·10	1·00

1422 Periwinkle

2000

3651	**1422**	4f.50 multicoloured	1·70	1·50

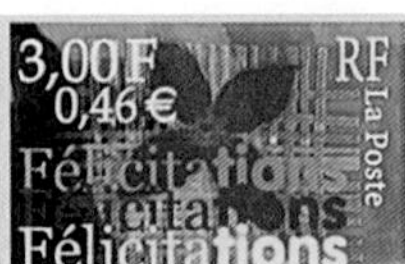

1423 "Congratulations"

2000. Greetings Stamp. Multicoloured.

3652	3f. Type **1423**	1·10	1·00
3653	3f. "bonnes vacances"	1·10	1·00

1424 Football World Cup Trophy (France, World Champions, 1998)

2000. The Twentieth Century (1st series). Sporting Achievements. Sheet 185×245 mm containing five different 3f. designs as T **1424**, each ×2. Multicoloured.

MS3654	3f. Type **1424**; 3f. Marcel Cerdan (World Middleweight Champion, 1948); 3f. Carl Lewis (Olympic Gold medallist 100m, 200m, 100m relay and long jump, 1984) (vert); 3f. Charles Lindbergh and *Spirit of St. Louis* (first solo Atlantic crossing,1927); 3f. Jean-Claude Killy (Winter Olympic Gold medallist downhill, giant slalom and special slalom, 1968) (vert)	14·00	13·00

See also No. **MS**3687, **MS**3710, **MS**3756, **MS**3814 and **MS**3861.

1425 Bugatti 35

2000. "Philexjeunes 2000" International Youth Stamp Exhibition, Annely. Vintage Cars. Multicoloured.

3655	1f. Type **1425**	45	40
3656	1f. Citroen Traction	45	40
3657	1f. Renault 4CV	45	40
3658	1f. Simca Chamord	45	40
3659	1f. Hispano Suiza K6	45	40
3660	2f. Volkswagen Beetle	90	80
3661	2f. Cadillac 62	90	80
3662	2f. Peugeot 203	90	80
3663	2f. Citroen DS19	90	80
3664	2f. Ferrari 250 GTO	90	80

1426 "Building Europe"

2000. Europa.

3665	**1426**	3f. multicoloured	2·30	2·00

1427 Du Monceau

2000. 300th Birth Anniv of Henry-Louis Duhamel du Monceau (technologist and natural scientist).

3666	**1427**	4f.50 multicoloured	1·70	1·50

1428 Porte du Croux and Earthenware Jug

2000. 73rd French Philatelic Federation Congress, Nevers.

3667	**1428**	3f. multicoloured	1·10	1·00

1429 Mountaineers

2000. 50th Anniv of French Ascent of Mt. Annapurna, Himalayas.

3668	**1429**	3f. multicoloured	1·10	1·00

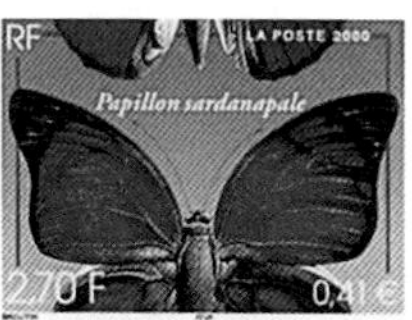

1430 *Agrias sardanapalus*

2000. National Museum of Natural History. Mult.

3669	2f.70 Type **1430**	1·10	1·00
3670	3f. Giraffe (vert)	1·10	1·00
3671	3f. Allosaurus	1·10	1·00
3672	4f.50 *Tulipa lutea* (vert)	1·70	1·50
MS3673	110×160 mm. Nos. 3669/72	5·75	5·75

1431 Saint-Exupery and Caudron C.690

2000. Birth Centenary of Antoine de Saint-Exupery (aviator and writer).

3674	**1431**	3f. multicoloured	1·10	1·00

1432 Train

2000. Centenary of the Yellow Train (Villefranch de Conflent–Latourde Card service), Cerdagne.

3675	**1432**	3f. multicoloured	1·10	1·00

1433 "Folklores" and Characters

2000

3676	**1433**	4f.50 multicoloured	1·70	1·50

1434 Cycling, Fencing and Relay

2000. Olympic Games, Sydney. Multicoloured.

3677	3f. Type **1434**	1·40	1·00
3678	3f. Relay, judo and diving	1·40	1·00
MS3679	210×143 mm. Nos. 3677/8, each ×5 plus label	15·00	15·00

Nos. 3677/8 were issued together, se-tenant, forming a composite design.

1435 Eric Tabarly (yachtsman)

2000. French Adventurers. Multicoloured.

3680	3f.+60c. Type **1435**	2·00	1·70
3681	3f.+60c. Alexandra David-Neel (explorer)	2·00	1·70
3682	3f.+60c. Haroun Tazieff (geologist and vulcanologist)	2·00	1·70
3683	3f.+60c. Paul-Emile Victor (polar explorer)	2·00	1·70
3684	3f.+60c. Jacques-Yves Cousteau (underwater explorer)	2·00	1·70
3685	3f.+60c. Norbert Casteret (archeologist and speleologist)	2·00	1·70

1436 Stanke

2000. 25th Death Anniv of Brother Alfred Stanke (German wartime prison hospital Chaplain who helped French prisoners).

3686	**1436**	4f.40 brown, ultramarine and blue	1·70	1·50

1437 Edwin E. Aldrin on Moon (first manned Moon landing, 1969)

2000. The Twentieth Century (2nd series). Sheet 185×245 mm containing five different 3f. designs as T **1437**, each ×2. Multicoloured.

MS3687	VERT: 3f. Type **1437**. HORIZ: 3f. Family paddling in sea (entitlement to paid holiday, 1936); 3f. Modern washing machine (invention of washing machine, 1901); 3f. Women posting voting slips (women given right to vote, 1944); 3f. Graffiti (Declaration of Human Rights, 1948)	14·00	14·00

S.O.S amitié 1960-2000
RF 0,46€ 3,00F

1438 Man telephoning Helpline

2000. 40th Anniv of S.O.S. Amitie (telephone support service).

3688	**1438**	3f. multicoloured	1·10	1·00

1439 Globe and Methods of Communication

2000. New Millennium.

3689	**1439**	3f. multicoloured	1·10	1·00

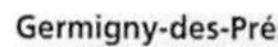

1440 Detail of Mosaic

2000. Germigny-des-Pres Mosaic, Loire Valley.

3690	**1440**	6f.70 multicoloured	2·75	2·00

1441 Young Couple and Bandstand (R. Peynet)

2000

3691	**1441**	3f. multicoloured	2·30	1·00

1442 Brown Kiwi (New Zealand)

2000. Endangered Species. Multicoloured.

3692	3f. Type **1442**	1·40	1·00
3693	5f.20 Lesser kestrel (France)	2·30	2·00

1443 Toy Aeroplane and Gifts

2000. Red Cross Fund. New Year.

3694	**1443**	3f.+60c. mult	1·50	1·30

1444 World Map in Envelope

2000. Third Millennium.

3695	**1444**	3f. multicoloured	1·40	1·10

1445 "Bonne annee" and Snowflakes

2000. Christmas and New Year. Multicoloured.

3696	3f. Type **1445**	1·10	1·00
3697	3f. "Meilleurs voeux", Globe and gifts	1·10	1·00

1446 Eiffel Tower and Space Rocket

2000. Centenary of Union of Metallurgy and Mining Industries.

3698	**1446**	4f.50 multicoloured	1·80	1·50

1447 Emblem

2001. World Handball Championship, France.

3699	**1447**	3f. multicoloured	1·10	1·00

1448 Stone covered Heart

2001. St. Valentine's Day.

3700	**1448**	3f. multicoloured	1·10	1·00
MS3701		136×143 mm. No. 3700 ×5	7·00	7·00

2001. Art. As T **491**.

3702	6f.70 multicoloured	2·75	2·00
3703	6f.70 multicoloured	2·75	2·00
3704	6f.70 multicoloured	2·75	2·00
3705	6f.70 multicoloured	2·75	2·00

DESIGNS—Horiz: No. 3702, "The Peasant Dance" (Pieter Brugel the Elder); 3703, St. James of Compostela and Angel (mural, hospital of Order of St. John of Jerusalem, Toulouse), 3705, "Honfleur at Low Tide" (Johan Barthold Jongkind). VERT: 3704, "Yvette Guilbert singing Linger, Longer Loo" (Henri Toulouse-Lautrec).

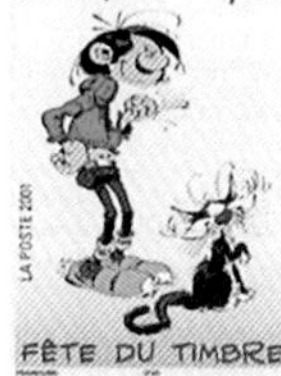

1449 Gaston Lagaffe

2001. Gaston Lagaffe (cartoon character) by Andre Franquin.

3706	**1449**	3f. multicoloured	1·10	1·00
3708	**1449**	3f.+60c. multicoloured	2·75	1·50
MS3709		101×75 mm. No. 3708	3·50	3·50

1450 Nounours, Pimprenelle and Nicolas from "Bonne Nuit les Petits" (chilren's televison programme, 1965)

2001. The Twentieth Century (3rd series). Forms of Communication. Sheet 186×245 mm containing five different 3f. designs as T 1450, each ×2. Multicoloured.

MS3710	3f. Type **1450**; 3f. Hand holding compact disc (development of analogue technology); 3f. The Little Miner and road sign (cinema advertising character created by Jean Mineur, 1950); 3f. Couple dancing and early radio (*Salut les Copians* (first broadcast by popular radio programme, 1959)); 3f. Baby, mobile phone and globe (development of digital mobile phone technology, 1991)	14·00	14·00

1451 Flower ("merci")

2001. Greetings Stamps. Multicoloured.

3711	3f. Type **1451**	1·20	1·00
3712	3f. Teddy bear wearing bow tie ("c'est un garcon")	1·20	1·00
3713	3f. Teddy bear wearing yellow ribbon ("c'est une fille")	1·20	1·00
3714	4f.50 Two hearts ("oui")	1·80	1·50

1452 Eurasian Red Squirrel

2001. Animals. Multicoloured.

3715	2f.70 Type **1452**	1·20	1·00
3716	3f. Roe deer (horiz)	1·20	1·00

3717		3f. West European hedgehog (horiz)	1·20	1·00
3718		4f.50 Stoat	1·80	1·50
MS3719		161×111 mm. Nos. 3715/18	6·00	6·00

2001. Tourist Publicity. As T 490. Multicoloured.

3720	3f. Nogent-le-Rotrou (vert)	1·20	1·00
3721	3f. Besancon, Doubs	1·20	1·00
3722	3f. Calais	1·20	1·00
3723	3f. Chateau de Grignan, Drome	1·20	1·00

1453 Water Droplet and Globe

2001. Europa. Water Resources.

3724	**1453**	3f. multicoloured	1·80	1·50

1454 Gardens (image scaled to 64% of original size)

2001. Versailles Palace Gardens.

3725	**1454**	4f.40 multicoloured	1·80	1·50

1455 Lyon

2001

3726	**1455**	3f. multicoloured	1·20	1·00

1456 Claude Francois

2001. Singers. Multicoloured.

3727	3f. Type **1456**	1·20	1·00
3728	3f. Leo Ferre	1·20	1·00
3729	3f. Serge Gainsbourg	1·20	1·00
3730	3f. Dalida	1·20	1·00
3731	3f. Michel Berger	1·20	1·00
3732	3f. Barbara	1·20	1·00
MS3733	135×143 mm. Nos. 3727/32 (sold at 28f.)	14·50	14·50

1457 Craftsman, Wilson Bridge and St. Gatien Cathedral

2001. 74th French Philatelic Federation Congress, Tours.

3734	**1457**	3f. multicoloured	1·20	1·00

1458 Vilar

2001. 30th Death Anniv of Jean Vilar (theatre director).

3735	**1458**	3f. multicoloured	1·20	1·00

1459 Footprint in Sand

2001. Greetings Stamps. Holidays. Ordinary or self-adhesive gum.

3736	**1459**	3f. multicoloured	1·20	1·00

1460 1 Euro Coin

2001. The European Currency.

3738	**1460**	3f. multicoloured	1·80	1·00

1461 Caquot, Airship and Bridge

2001. 120th Birth Anniv of Albert Caquot (civil engineer).

3739	**1461**	4f.50 multicoloured	1·80	1·50

1462 Jigsaw Pieces

2001. Centenary of Freedom of Association Law.

3740	**1462**	3f. multicoloured	1·20	1·00

1463 Eurostar Express Train

2001. Locomotives. Multicoloured.

3741	1f.50 Type **1463**	70	60
3742	1f.50 American 220 steam locomotive	70	60
3743	1f.50 Ae 6/8 "Crocodile" locomotive	70	60
3744	1f.50 Crampton steam locomotive	70	60
3745	1f.50 Garratt type 59 steam locomotive	70	60
3746	1f.50 Pacific Chapelon steam locomotive	70	60
3747	1f.50 LNER Class A4 steam locomotive No. 4468 *Mallard*, 1938, Great Britain	70	60
3748	1f.50 Capitole electric locomotive	70	60
3749	1f.50 Autorail	70	60
3750	1f.50 230 Class P8 type 230 steam locomotive	70	60

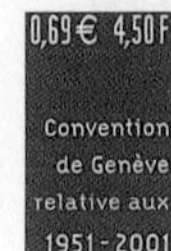

1464 Emblem

2001. 50th Anniv of United Nations High Commissioner for Refugees.

3751	**1464**	4f.50 green, magenta and blue	1·80	1·50

2001. No value expressed. As T **1318** but with "RF" in lower left corner and "LA POSTE" in upper right corner.

3752	(3f.) red	1·20	50

1465 Fermat and Mathematical Equations

2001. 400th Birth Anniv of Pierre de Fermat (mathematician).

3755	**1465**	4f.50 multicoloured	1·80	1·50

1466 Yuri Gagarin and Vostok 1 (first man in space, 1961)

2001. The Twentieth Century (4th issue). Science. Sheet 185×244 mm containing five different 3f. designs as T 1466, each×2. Multicoloured.

MS3756	3f. Type **1466**; 3f. Human body and DNA double helix (identification of DNA molecule, 1953); 3f. Hand holding credit card (development of chip card) (horiz); 3f. Laser treatment for correcting eye sight (development of laser technology); 3f. Bacteriologist and penicillin culture (discovery of penicillin, 1928) (horiz)	14·50	14·50

1467 Astrolabe (sculpture, Alain Le Boucher)

2001. 25th Anniv of Val-de-Reuil.

3757	**1467**	3f. multicoloured	1·20	1·00

1468 Pumpkin

2001. Halloween.

3758	**1468**	3f. multcoloured	1·20	1·00
MS3759		135×144 mm. No. 3759 ×5	6·00	6·00

1469 Father Christmas

2001. Red Cross Fund. Christmas.

3760	**1469**	3f.+60c. multicoloured	1·40	1·20

1470 Pierre-Bloch

2001. 2nd Death Anniv of Jean Pierre-Bloch (politician).

3761	**1470**	4f.50 blue, ultramarine and deep blue	1·80	1·50

1471 Eiffel Tower and Arc de Triomphe dancing

2001. Birth Centenary of Albert Decaris (artist and engraver).

3762	**1471**	3f. violet, brown and blue	1·50	1·00

1472 Children and Snowman

2001. New Year. Multicoloured. Self-adhesive or ordinary gum.

3763	3f. Type **1472**	1·20	1·00
3764	3f. Children and wheelbarrow	1·20	1·00

1473 Chaban-Delmas

2001. Jaques Chaban-Delmas (politician) Commemoration.

3767	**1473**	3f. multicoloured	1·30	1·00

1474 Nejjarine Fountain, Fez, Morocco

2001. French–Moroccan Cultural Heritage. Fountains. Multicoloured.

3768	3f. Type **1474**	1·30	1·00
3769	3f.80 Wallace Fountain, Paris	2·50	1·50

After the adoption by France of the euro currency on 1 January 2002, No. 3752 were sold at 46c.

2002. As T 1318 but with "RF" in lower left corner, "LAPOSTE" in upper right corner and values expressed in euros. (a) Sheet stamps.

3770	1c. yellow	20	15
3771	2c. brown	20	15
3772	5c. green	20	15
3773	10c. violet	40	15
3774	20c. orange	65	20
3775	41c. green	1·60	40
3776	50c. blue	1·90	50
3777	53c. green	1·90	80
3778	58c. blue	1·90	1·30
3778a	58c. green	1·90	50
3779	64c. orange	2·50	1·00
3780	67c. blue	2·50	1·30
3781	69c. mauve	2·50	1·00
3782	70c. green	2·50	70
3783	75c. blue	2·50	70
3784	90c. blue	3·25	1·50
3785	€1 turquoise	3·75	1·00
3786	€1.02 green	3·75	1·00
3787	€1.11 purple	3·75	1·10
3788	€1.90 purple	6·50	2·00
3789	€2 violet	6·50	2·00

(b) Coil stamp. (i) With face value.

3790	(41c.) green	2·50	1·00
3792	(46c.) red	1·50	1·00

(ii) No value expressed.

3791	41c. green	2·50	1·00

(c) Miniature sheets. Two sheets, each 145×143 mm.

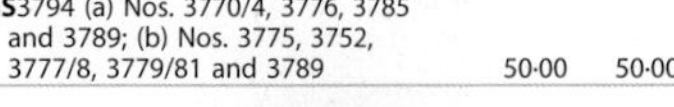

MS3794	(a) Nos. 3770/4, 3776, 3785 and 3789; (b) Nos. 3775, 3752, 3777/8, 3779/81 and 3789	50·00	50·00

1475 *Orchis insularis*

2002. Orchids. Multicoloured.

3795	29c. Type **1475**	1·50	1·20
3796	33c. *Orphrys fuciflora*	1·70	1·30

Nos. 3795/6 were only issued precancelled.

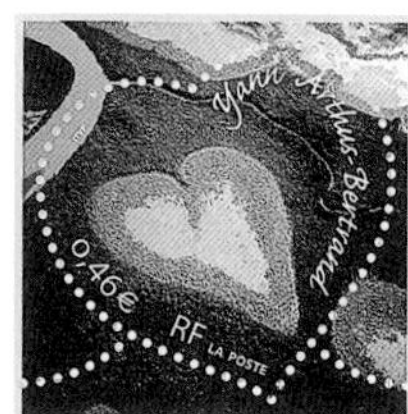

1476 Heart Shape in Landscape, New Caledonia

2002. St. Valentine's Day.
3797 **1476** 46c. multicoloured 1·30 1·00
MS3798 135×142 mm. No. 3797×5 6·50 6·50

1477 Snowboarder

2002. Winter Olympic Games, Salt Lake City, U.S.A.
3799 **1477** 46c. multicoloured 1·30 1·00

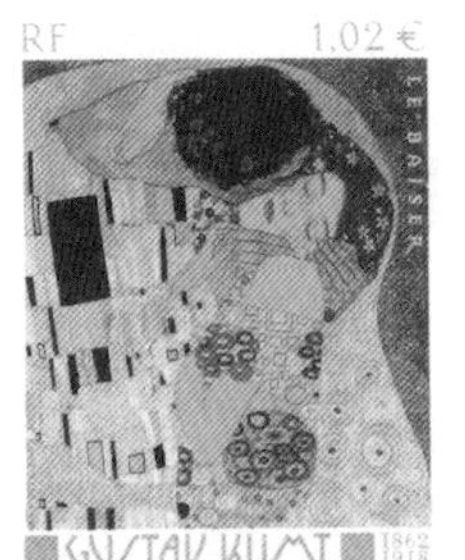

1478 The Kiss (Gustav Klimt)

2002. Art. Designs as T 1478. Multicoloured.
3800 €1.02 "The Kiss" (Gustav Klimt) 3·25 2·00
3801 €1.02 "The Dancers" (painting, Fernando Botero) 3·25 2·00

1479 Bosquet

2002. 4th Death Anniv of Alain Bosquet (Anatole Bisk) (writer).
3804 **1478** 58c. brown, orange and blue 1·70 1·30

1480 Bee wearing Crown ("c'est une fille")

2002. Greetings Stamps. Multicoloured.
3805 46c. Type **1479** 1·30 1·00
3806 46c. Bee wearing cap ("c'est un garcon") 1·30 1·00
3807 69c. "Oui" in flowers 1·90 1·50

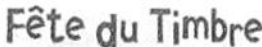

1481 Elephant, Performers and Horse

2002. Europa. Circus.
3808 **1481** 46c. multicoloured 1·90 1·50

1482 Boule, Bill and Birds

2002. Boule and Bill (cartoon characters) by Jean Roba. Multicoloured.
3809 46c. Type **1482** 1·30 1·00
3811 46c. + 9c. Boule, Bill and ball 2·50 2·00
MS3812 100×75 mm. As No. 3811 3·25 3·25

1483 Amphitheatre, Nimes

2002
3813 **1483** 46c. multicoloured 1·30 1·00

1484 Concorde (first flight, 1969)

2002. The Twentieth Century (5th series).Transport. Sheet 185×245 mm, containing five different 46c. designs as T 1484, each×2. Multicoloured.
MS3814 46c. Type **1484**; 46c. TGV train (high speed passenger train); 46c. "La Mobylette" (motorcycle) (vert); 46c. *France* (transatlantic passenger liner) (vert); 46c. 2CV (motor car) (vert) 19·00 19·00

1485 Matthew Flinders, Map of Australia and H.M.S. *Investigator* (ship of the line)

2002. France—Australia Joint Issue. Bicentenary of Nicolas Baudin–Matthew Flinders Meeting at Encounter Bay, Australia. Multicoloured.
3815 46c. Type **1485** 1·30 1·00
3816 79c. *Geographie* (corvette), map of Australia and Nicolas Baudin 2·50 1·60

1486 La Charite-sur-Loire Church, Nievre

2002. UNESCO. World Heritage Site.
3817 **1486** 46c. multicoloured 1·40 1·00

1487 Butterflies and Gift ("Anniversaire")

2002. Greetings Stamps. Multicoloured.
3818 46c. Type **1487** 1·40 1·00
3819 46c. Bird and envelopes ("Invitation") 1·40 1·00

1488 Cyclists

2002. 100th Paris–Roubaix Cycle Race.
3820 **1488** 46c. multicoloured 1·40 1·00

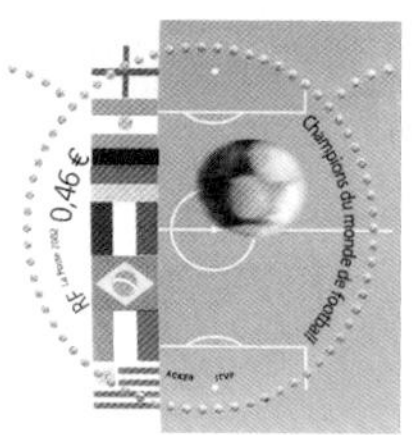

1489 Winners' Flags and Football

2002. World Cup Football Championship, Japan and South Korea. Multicoloured.
3821 46c. Type **1489** 1·40 1·00
3822 46c. Footballer 1·40 1·00
MS3823 143×210 mm. Nos. 3821/2, each ×5 17·00 17·00

No. **MS**3823 was inscribed on the back, with the groups around the edge and with facilities for recording the results between the stamps, over the gum.

1490 Leatherback Turtle

2002. Animals. Multicoloured.
3824 41c. Type **1490** 1·40 1·00
3825 46c. Killer whale (horiz) 1·40 1·00
3826 46c. Bottle-nosed dolphin (horiz) 1·40 1·00
3827 69c. Common seal 2·75 2·00
MS3828 109×160 mm. Nos. 3824/7 4·50 4·50

1491 Old Port, Marseille (image scaled to 63% of original size)

2002. 75th French Federation of Philatelic Societies Congress, Marseille.
3829 **1491** 46c. multicoloured 1·40 1·00

1492 Medal

2002. Bicentenary of Legion d'Honneur (medal).
3830 **1492** 46c. multicoloured 1·40 1·00

1493 Rocamadour, Lot

2002
3831 **1493** 46c. multicoloured 1·40 1·00

1494 Delgres

2002. Death Bicentenary of Louis Delgres (soldier and anti-slavery campaigner).
3832 **1494** 46c. multicoloured 1·40 1·00

1495 Woman in Hammock

2002. Holidays. Ordinary or self-adhesive gum.
3833 **1495** 46c. multicoloured 1·40 1·00

1496 Wheelchair Racers

2002. World Disabled Athletics Championship, Lille-Villeneuve-d'Ascq.
3835 **1496** 46c. multicoloured 1·40 1·00

1497 Collioure Lighthouse (painting, Andre Derain)

2002. Collioure, Pyrenees.
3836 **1497** 46c. multicoloured 1·40 1·00

1498 Chapel

2002. Saint-Ser Chapel, Puyloubier, Bouches-du-Rhone.
3837 **1498** 46c. multicoloured 1·40 1·00

1499 Stained Glass Window (Mark Chagall)

2002. Metz Cathedral.
3838 **1499** 46c. multicoloured 1·70 1·00

2002. Tourist Publicity. As Type 490. Multicoloured.
3839 46c. Lacronan, Finistere (vert) 1·40 1·00
3840 46c. Neufchateau, Vosges 1·40 1·00

1500 Louis Armstrong

2002. Jazz. Multicoloured.

3841	46c. Type **1500**	1·40	1·00
3842	46c. Ella Fitzgerald	1·40	1·00
3843	46c. Duke Ellington	1·40	1·00
3844	46c. Stephane Grappelli	1·40	1·00
3845	46c. Michel Petrucciani (horiz)	1·40	1·00
3846	46c. Sidney Bechet (horiz)	1·40	1·00
MS3847	135×143 mm. Nos. 3841/6 (sold at €4.36)	17·00	17·00

No. **MS**3847 was sold with a premium of €1.60 for the benefit of the Red Cross.

1501 Building Facade

2002. 150th Anniv of Notre-Dame de la Salette, Isere.

3848	**1501**	46c. multicoloured	1·40	1·00

1502 Hands (image scaled to 63% of original size)

2002. Choreography.

3849	**1502**	53c. multicoloured	2·10	1·10

1503 Honda CB 750 Four

2002. Motorcycles. Multicoloured.

3850	16c. Type **1503**	55	40
3851	16c. Terrot 500 RGST	55	40
3852	16c. Majestic 350	55	40
3853	16c. Norton Commando 750	55	40
3854	16c. Voxon 1000 Cafe Racer	55	40
3855	30c. BMW R 90 S	1·10	60
3856	30c. Harley Davidson FL Hydra-Glide	1·10	60
3857	30c. Triumph T120 Bonneville 650	1·10	60
3858	30c. Ducati 916	1·10	60
3859	30c. Yamaha 500 XT	1·10	60

1504 Perec

2002. 20th Death Anniv of Georges Perec (writer).

3860	**1504**	46c. multicoloured	1·40	1·00

1505 Family on Motor Scooter

2002. The Twentieth Century (6th series). Everyday Life. Sheet 185×243 mm, containing five different 46c. designs as T 1505, each× 2. Multicoloured.

MS3861	46c. Type **1505**; 46c. Man with horse and cart (horiz); 46c. Woman ironing (horiz); 46c. Boy at water pump; 46c. Girl at school desk	17·00	17·00

1506 Zola

2002. Death Centenary of Emile Zola (writer).

3862	**1506**	46c. multicoloured	1·40	1·00

1507 Self-portrait (Uffizi museum, Florence)

2002. 160th Death Anniv of Elisabeth Vigee-Lebrun (artist).

3863	**1507**	€1.02 multicoloured	3·50	2·00

1508 Airbus

2002. 30th Anniv of First Flight of Airbus A300-B1.

3864	**1508**	€3 multicoloured	9·75	6·00

1509 "Sleeping Jesus" (Giovanni Battista Salvi)

2002. Red Cross Fund. Christmas.

3865a	**1509**	46c.+9c. multicoloured	1·70	80

1510 Trevi Fountain

2002. European Capitals. Rome. Sheet 144×36 mm containing T 1510 and similar multicoloured designs.

MS3866	46c. Type **1510**; 46c. Coliseum (horiz); 46c. Trinita dei Monti church; 46c. St. Peter's Basilica (horiz)	8·25	8·25

1511 World embedded in Computer Circuit

2002. Enterprise.

3867	**1511**	46c. multicoloured	1·40	1·00

1512 Snow-covered House

2002. New Year. Ordinary or Self-adhesive gum.

3868	**1512**	46c. multicoloured	1·40	1·00

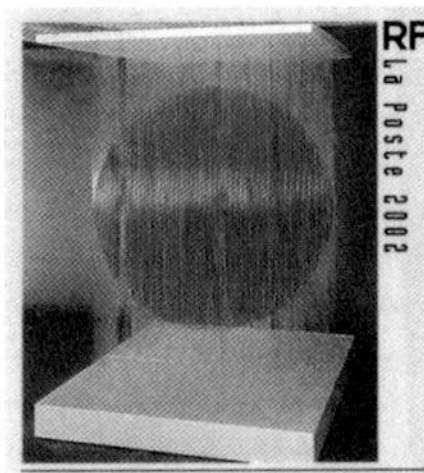

1513 "Sphere Concorde" (Jesus Rafael)

2002

3870	**1513**	75c. multicoloured	2·75	1·50

1514 Dumas

2002. Birth Bicentenary of Alexandre Dumas (writer).

3871	**1514**	46c. multicoloured	1·40	1·00

1515 Senghor

2002. 1st Death Anniv of Leopold Sedar Senghor (writer and linguist).

3872	**1515**	46c. multicoloured	1·40	1·00

1516 Baby and "naissance"

2003. Greetings Stamps. Multicoloured.

3873	46c. Type **1516**	1·40	1·00
3874	46c. "MERCI" and oak leaf	1·40	1·00

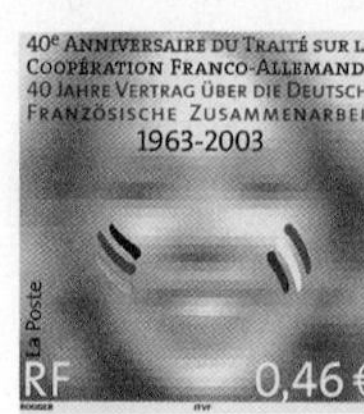

1517 Heart

2003. St. Valentine's Day. Multicoloured.

3875	46c. Type **1517**	1·40	1·00
3876	69c. Heart and roses	2·10	1·50
MS3877	136×144 mm. As No. 3875×5	7·00	7·00

1518 Face

2003. 40th Anniv of French–German Co-operation Treaty.

3878	**1518**	46c. multicoloured	2·75	2·00

1519 Map

2003. 40th Anniv of Delegation for Land Use Planning and Regional Action (DATAR).

3879	**1519**	46c. multicoloured	1·40	1·00

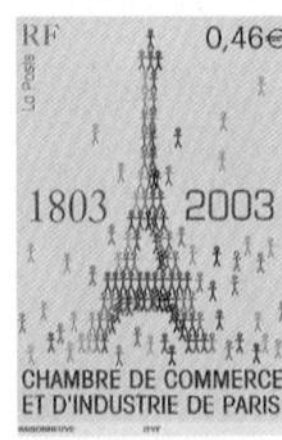

1520 Genevieve De Gaulle Anthioniz

2003. 1st Death Anniv of Genevieve De Gaulle Anthioniz (resistance fighter and writer).

3880	**1520**	46c. multicoloured	1·40	1·00

1521 Eiffel Tower

2003. Bicentenary of Chamber of Commerce and Industry.

3881	**1521**	46c. multicoloured	1·40	1·00

1522 Lucky Luke

2003. Lucky Luke (cartoon character) by Morris. Multicoloured.

3882	46c. Type **1522**	1·40	1·00
3884	46c.+9c. Lucky Luke and Rantanplan (dog)	2·10	1·10
MS3885	101×75 mm. 46c. As No. 3882	3·50	3·50

1523 Blue-headed Hummingbird

2003. Birds. Multicoloured.

3886	41c. Type **1523**	1·10	80
3887	46c. Toucan	1·40	1·00
3888	46c. Purple-throated carib	1·40	1·00
3889	69c. Mascarene paradise fly-catcher	2·10	1·50
MS3890	110×160 mm. Nos. 3886/9	7·00	7·00

1524 Tram and Nantes Town Hall

2003. Nantes City.

3891	**1524**	46c. multicoloured	1·40	1·00

1525 Pierre Beregovoy

2003. 10th Death Anniv of Pierre Beregovoy (resistance fighter and politician).

3892	**1525**	46c. multicoloured	1·40	1·00

1526 Milan Stefanik

2003. Milan Rastislav Stefanik Commemoration (founder of Czechoslovakia).
3893 **1526** 50c. multicoloured 1·40 1·00

1527 Monsavon Cow and Dubonnet Man (Raymond Savignac)

2003. Europa. Poster Art.
3894 **1527** 50c. multicoloured 2·10 1·50

1528 *Charles de Gaulle* (aircraft carrier) and Dassault Rafale M

2003
3895 **1528** 50c. multicoloured 2·10 1·50

1529 Figure with Winged Shadow

2003. European Union Charter of Fundamental Rights.
3896 **1529** 50c. multicoloured 2·10 1·50

1530 Beach Huts

2003. Regions (1st issue). Sheet 286×110 mm containing T 1530 and similar multicoloured designs.
MS3897 50c. Type **1530**; 50c. Fishing hut; 50c. Vinyards; 50c. Camembert cheese (vert); 50c. Foie gras; 50c. Petanque; 50c. "Guignol" (puppet) (vert); 50c. Crepes (vert); 50c. Cassoulet (casserole); 50c. Porcelain 17·00 17·00

See also Nos. **MS**4083, **MS**4121, **MS**4169, **MS**4209, **MS**4269, **MS**4329, **MS**4379, **MS**4493.

2003. Art. Design as T 491. Multicoloured.
3898 75c. "La Boulee Rouge" (Paul Signac) 2·75 1·50
3899 75c. "The Dying Slave" and "The Rebel Slave" (sculptures, Michelangelo) 2·75 1·50
3900 €1.11 "Untitled" (Vassily Kandinsky) 3·50 2·20

1531 Marsupilami (cartoon character) (Andre Franquin)

2003. Greetings Stamp. Birthday.
3902 **1531** 50c. multicoloured 1·40 1·00

2003. Orchids. As T 1475. Multicoloured.
3903 30c. *Platanthera chlorantha* 1·70 60
3904 35c. *Dactylorhiza savogiensis* 1·80 70

1532 Mulhouse Museums Building and Bugatti Car

2003. 76th French Federation of Philatelic Associations Congress.
3905 **1532** 50c. multicoloured 1·40 1·00

1533 Woman and Children Sunbathing

2003. Holidays. Ordinary or self-adhesive gum.
3906 **1533** 50c. multicoloured 1·80 1·00

2003. Tourist Publicity. As T 490.
3908 50c. multicoloured 1·50 1·00
3909 50c. lilac, orange and green 1·50 1·00
3910 50c. multicoloured 1·50 1·00
3911 50c. multicoloured 1·50 1·00

DESIGNS: No. 3908, Tulle (35×26 mm); No. 3909, Notre-Dame de l'Epine (vert). 50c. Arras (80×24 mm). 50c. Pontarlier (25×39 mm).

1534 Jaqueline Auriol and Dassault Mirage III Fighter

2003. Air. 3rd Death Anniv of Jaqueline Auriol (aviation pioneer).
3912 **1534** €4 multicoloured 12·00 8·00

1535 Square and Compass

2003. 1275th Anniv of French Freemasonry.
3913 **1535** 50c. blue, orange and red 1·50 1·00

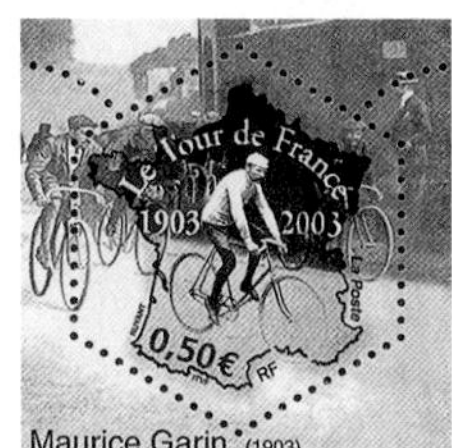

1536 Maurice Garin (1903 race winner)

2003. Centenary of Tour de France Cycle Race. Multicoloured.
3914 50c. Type **1536** 1·50 1·00
3915 50c. Modern competitor 1·50 1·00

1537 Saint-Pere-sous-Vezelay Church, Yonne

2003
3916 **1537** 50c. multicoloured 1·50 1·00

1538 Athletes (image scaled to 64% of original size)

2003. 9th IAAF World Athletics Championships, Paris and Saint Denis.
3917 **1538** 50c. multicoloured 1·50 1·00

1539 Eugene-Francois Vidocq (undercover police officer and writer)

2003. Literature. Multicoloured.
3918 50c. Type **1539** 1·50 1·00
3919 50c. Esmeralda (character from *The Hunchback of Notre Dame*, Victor Hugo) 1·50 1·00
3920 50c. Claudine (character from Claudine novels, *Colette*) 1·50 1·00
3921 50c. Nana (character from *Nana*, Emile Zola) 1·50 1·00
3922 50c. Edmond Dantes (character from *The Count of Monte-Cristo*, Alexandre Dumas) 1·50 1·00
3923 50c. Gavroche (character from Les *Miserables*, Victor Hugo) 1·50 1·00
MS3924 135×144 mm. 50c. ×6 Nos. 3918/23 15·00 15·00

No. **MS**3924 was sold with a premium of €1.60 for the benefit of the Red Cross.

1540 Ahmad Massoud

2003. 50th Birth Anniv of Ahmad Shah Massoud (Afghan resistance fighter).
3925 **1540** 50c. multicoloured 1·50 1·00

2003. Regions (2nd issue). Sheet 286×110 mm containing multicoloured designs as T 1530.
MS3926 50c. Chenonceau Chateau; 50c. Alsatian house; 50c. Dormer windows, Hospices de Beaune; 50c. Genoese tower, Cap Corse (vert); 50c. Arc de Triomphe, Paris (vert); 50c. Mas (country house), Provence; 50c. Pointe de Raz (vert); 50c. Mont Blanc (vert); 50c. Basque house; 50c. Pont du Gard (Roman bridge) 18·00 18·00

1541 Buttes-Chaumont Park, Paris

2003. French Gardens. Sheet 286×109 mm containing T 1541 and similar design. Multicoloured.
MS3927 €1.90 Type **1541**; €1.90 Luxembourg Gardens 12·00 12·00

See also No. **MS**3978.

1542 Isobloc Type 648 DP 102 Coach (1954)

2003. Philexjeunes 2003 International Stamp Exhibition, Annely. Utility Vehicles. Sheet 108×183 mm containing T 1542 and similar horiz designs. Multicoloured.
MS3928 20c.×5 Type **1542**; SVF Type 302 tractor (1950); Delahaye Fire appliance with ladder (1938); Renault Kangoo postal van; Renault Type TN6 coach (1932); 30c.×5 Berliet 22 HP Type M delivery truck (1910); Berliet T 100 (1957); Citroen Police van (1960); Heuliez and Citroen DS ambulance; Hotchkiss Type PL 50 rescue truck (1964) 9·00 9·00

1543 "Meilleurs Voeux"

2003. New Year. Ordinary or self-adhesive gum.
3929 **1543** 50c. multicoloured 1·50 1·00

No. 3929 was intended for use by corporate customers.

1544 Robin

2003. New Year. Ordinary or Self-adhesive gum.
3930 **1544** 50c. multicoloured 3·75 2·00

1545 "The Virgin of the Grapes" (Pierre Mignard)

2003. Red Cross Fund. Christmas.
3932 **1545** 50c. multicoloured 2·30 1·30

1546 "The Sower"

2003. Centenary of "The Sower" (sculpture, O. Roty). Self-adhesive.
3933 **1546** 50c. red 3·00 2·00

1547 Notre-Dame Cathedral

2003. European Capitals. Luxembourg. Sheet 144×136 mm containing T 1547 and similar multicoloured designs.
MS3934 50c.×4, Type **1547**; Saint Esprit plateau (vert); Grand Ducal Palace; Adolphe Bridge (vert) 7·50 7·50

1548 "Marilyn"

2003. 16th Death Anniv of Andy Warhol (artist).
3935 **1548** €1.11 multicoloured 3·75 2·20

1549 Cockerel amongst Foliage

2003. 15th-century Illuminations. Multicoloured.

3936 50c. Type **1549** 1·50 1·00

3937 90c. Peacock 3·00 2·00

Stamps of a similar design were issued by India.

1550 *Queen Mary 2*

2003. Launch of Queen Mary 2 (ocean liner).

3938 **1550** 50c. multicoloured 2·30 1·00

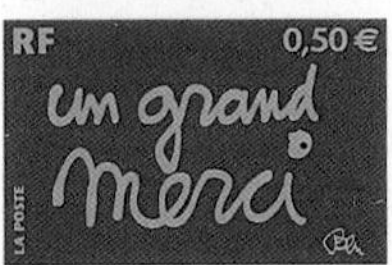

1551 "ceci est une invitation"

2004. Greetings Stamps. Multicoloured.

3939 50c. Type **1551** 2·00 1·00

3940 50c. "un grand merci" 2·00 1·00

See also Nos. 4072/3.

1552 Baby wearing Bee Costume ("c'est une fille")

2004. Greetings Stamps. Multicoloured. Self-adhesive.

3941 50c. Type **1552** 2·00 1·00

3942 50c. Baby wearing butterfly costume ("c'est un garcon") 2·00 1·00

1553 Perfume Bottle

2004. St. Valentine's Day. Multicoloured.

3943 50c. Type **1553** 1·80 1·00

3944 75c. Eiffel tower and woman 3·00 1·50

MS3945 135×143 mm. No. 3944×5 8·25 8·25

2004. Tourist Publicity. As T 490. Multicoloured.

3946 50c. Lille (European capital of culture, 2004) 2·00 1·00

3947 50c. Bridge and tram, Gironde, Bordeaux (79×25 mm) 2·00 1·00

3948 50c. Vaux sur Mer, Charente–Maritime 2·00 1·00

3949 50c. Lucon cathedral, Vendee (vert) 2·00 1·00

2004. Art. As T 491.

3951 75c. multicoloured 2·75 1·50

3952 90c. green, red and gold 3·00 2·00

3953 € 1.11 multicoloured 3·75 2·20

3954 €1.11 multicoloured 3·75 2·20

DESIGN: No. 3951, "La Meridienne d'apres Millet" (Vincent van Gogh); 3952, " The statue of Liberty" (sculpture, Auguste Barthodli) (horiz); 3953, €1.11 "Cock Fight" (Jean-Leon Gerome); 3954 "Galatee aux Spheres" (Salvador Dali).

1554 Eleanor of Aquitaine

2004. 600th Death Anniv of Eleanor of Aquitaine (wife of King Henry II of England).

3955 **1554** 50c. multicoloured 1·70 1·00

1555 Mickey Mouse

2004. 75th Anniv of Mickey Mouse (cartoon character). Multicoloured.

3956 45c. Donald Duck 4·25 2·00

3957 50c. Type **1555** 1·70 1·00

3958 75c. Minnie Mouse 2·50 1·50

1556 Emblem

2004. Bicentenary of Civil Code.

3959 **1556** 50c. blue, black and red 1·70 1·00

1557 George Sand

2004. Birth Bicentenary of George Sand (Aurore Dupin) (writer).

3960 **1557** 50c. multicoloured 1·70 1·00

1558 Vercingetorix (Gaullist leader) (statue) (Auguste Bartholdi)

2004. Clermont-Ferrand, Puy-de-Dome, Auvergne.

3961 **1558** 50c. multicoloured 1·70 1·00

2004. Regions (3rd issue). Sheet 286×110 mm containing multicoloured designs as T 1530.

MS3962 50c.×10 Cutlery; Vegetables of Provence (vert); Grapes, Beaujolais (vert); Bread; Madras cotton Creole headdress (vert); Oyster (vert); Quiche Lorraine; Course Landes, Aquitaine; Clafoutis (fruit flan); Pipe band 20·00 20·00

1559 "Coccinelle" (Sonia Delaunay)

2004. Centenary of the Entente Cordiale. Contemporary Paintings.

3963 **1559** 50c. grey, black and rose 1·70 1·00

3964 - 75c. multicoloured 2·50 1·50

DESIGN: 75c. "Lace 1 (trial proof) 1968" (Sir Terry Frost). Stamps of similar designs were issued by Great Britain.

1560 Heart-shaped Seat Belt Buckle and Body as Map

2004. Road Safety. Two phosphor bands.

3965 **1560** 50c. multicoloured 1·70 1·00

1561 Rabbit

2004. Farm Animals. Multicoloured.

3966 45c. Type **1561** 1·50 90

3967 50c. Hen and chicks 1·70 1·00

3968 50c. Cow (vert) 1·70 1·00

3969 75c. Donkey (vert) 3·00 1·50

MS3970 160×110 mm. Nos. 3966/9 8·25 8·25

1562 Map of EU as Flags

2004. Enlargement of European Union.

3971 **1562** 50c. multicoloured 1·70 1·00

1563 Soldiers and Douglas C-47 Skytrain

2004. 50th Anniv of Battle of Dien Bieen Phu.

3972 **1563** 50c. multicoloured 1·70 1·00

1564 Yachts (painting) (Raoul Dufy)

2004. Europa. Holidays. Ordinary or self-adhesive gum.

3973 **1564** 50c. multicoloured 1·70 1·00

1565 Emblem as Graffiti and Blake and Mortimer

2004. Birth Centenary of Edgar Pierre Jacobs (creator of Blake and Mortimer (comic strip)). Multicoloured.

3975 50c. Type **1565** 1·70 1·00

3976 €1 Blake and Mortimer (horiz) 3·25 2·00

Stamps of a similar design were issued by Belgium.

1566 FIFA Emblem

2004. Centenary of FIFA (Federation Internationale de Football Association).

3977 **1566** 50c. multicoloured 1·70 1·00

2004. French Gardens. Sheet 286×109 mm containing designs as T 1541. Multicoloured.

MS3978 €1.90 Jardin des Tuileries; €1.90 Parc Floral de Paris 13·00 13·00

1567 Woman throwing Flowers to Soldiers

2004. 60th Anniv of Liberation of France.

3979 **1567** 50c. multicoloured 1·70 1·00

1568 Smiling Hand and Organs

2004. Organ Donation Campaign.

3980 **1568** 50c. multicoloured 1·70 1·00

1569 Mounted Rifleman

2004. Napoleon I's Imperial Guard. Multicoloured.

3981 50c. Type **1569** 1·70 1·00

3982 50c. Gunner (horiz) 1·70 1·00

3983 50c. Dragoon 1·70 1·00

3984 50c. Mameluk 1·70 1·00

3985 50c. Napoleon I 1·70 1·00

3986 50c. Bombardier 1·70 1·00

MS3987 135×143 mm. Nos. 3981/6 17·00 17·00

No. **MS**3987 was sold at €4.60, the premium for the benefit of the Red Cross.

1570 Pierre Dugua de Mons (founder of Arcadia)

2004. 400th Anniv of French Landing in Maine, USA and Nova Scotia.

3988 **1570** 90c. blue and ochre 3·25 2·00

1571 Eiffel Tower holding Postcard

2004. 77th French Federation of Philatelic Associations Congress.

3989	**1571**	50c. multicoloured	1·80	1·00

1572 Canoeist, Tennis Player and Show Jumper

2004. Olympic Games Athens 2004. Sheet 183×108 mm containing T 1572 and similar horiz designs. Multicoloured.

MS3990 50c.×10, Type **1572**×5; Early Greek athletes×5 18·00 18·00

2004. French Gardens. Salon du Timber. Sheet 210×143 mm Containing design as T 1541. Multicoloured.

MS3990a As Nos. **MS**3927 and **MS**3978 27·00 27·00

1573 Marie Marvingt and Bleriot XI

2004. 40th Death Anniv (2003) of Marie Marvingt (aviation pioneer).

3991	**1573**	€5 multicoloured	20·00	11·00

1574 Waiter carrying Candlelit Cake

2004. Greetings Stamp.

3992	**1574**	50c. multicoloured	1·80	1·00

MS3993 135×143 mm. No. 3992×5 9·00 9·00

1575 Marianne and Emblem

2004. Campaign to Combat AIDS, Tuberculosis and Malaria.

3994	**1575**	(50c.) bright scarlet	1·80	1·00

1576 Skateboarding

2004. Sport. Multicoloured.

MS3995 108×184 mm. 20c.×5, Type **1576**; Parachuting; Windsurfing; Surfing; Tobogganing; 30c.×5, BMX cycling; Paragliding; Jet skiing; Snowboarding; Roller skating 9·00 9·00

2004. Regions (4th issue). Sheet 286×110 mm containing multicoloured designs as T 1530.

MS3996 50c.×10 Thatched house, Normandy; Chateau, Chambord; Gorge, Tarn (vert); Notre Dame cathedral, Paris (vert); Northern windmill (vert); Troglodyte houses; Stream, Cassis (vert); Lighthouse, Cap Ferrat (vert); Cathar chateau; Alpine chalet 20·00 20·00

1577 Pumpkin and Witch

2004. Halloween.

3997	**1577**	50c. multicoloured	1·80	1·00

1578 Felix Eboue

2004. 120th Birth Anniv of Felix Eboue (politician).

3998	**1578**	50c. multicoloured	1·80	1·00

1579 Lighthouse, Ouistreham

2004

3999	**1579**	50c. multicoloured	1·80	1·00

1580 Virgin and Child (15th-century Cretan school)

2004. Red Cross Fund. Christmas.

4000	**1580**	50c. multicoloured	2·75	1·50

2004. 60th Anniv of "Marianne d'Alger". Two phosphor bands. Self-adhesive.

4001	**209**	50c. scarlet	2·50	2·00

1581 Academy

2004. European Capitals. Athens. Sheet 144×134 mm containing T 1581 and similar multicoloured designs.

MS4002 50c.×4, Type **1581**; Parthenon; Odeon of Herode Atticus; Church of the Holy Apostles (vert) 9·00 9·00

1582 "Meilleurs Voeux"

2004. Christmas and New Year.

4003	**1582**	50c. multicoloured	1·80	1·00

1583 "Meilleurs Voeux" and Bird

2004. Christmas and New Year. Multicoloured. Ordinary gum or self-adhesive gum.

4004		50c. Type **1583**	3·50	1·60
4005		50c. Baubles hanging from branch	3·50	1·60
4006		50c. Stars holding snowballs	3·50	1·60
4007		50c. Star holding flower	3·50	1·60
4008		50c. Stars	3·50	1·60

1584 Henri Wallon

2004. Death Centenary of Henri Wallon (politician).

4014	**1584**	50c. multicoloured	1·80	1·00

1585 Millau Viaduct (image scaled to 63% of original size)

2004

4015	**1585**	50c. multicoloured	2·75	1·00

1586 "Marianne de Francais"

2005. (i) With face value.

4016	**1586**	1c. yellow	35	15
4017	**1586**	5c. agate	35	15
4018	**1586**	10c. black	55	15
4019	**1586**	10c. violet	55	15
4025	**1586**	55c. ultramarine	2·75	50
4027	**1586**	58c. yellow	2·75	85
4028	**1586**	60c. ultramarine	2·30	30
4030	**1586**	64c. green	2·75	60
4031a	**1586**	70c. green	2·75	40
4031b	**1586**	72c. green	2·75	40
4032	**1586**	75c. blue	2·75	75
4034	**1586**	82c. rose	3·50	80
4034a	**1586**	85c. violet	3·50	80
4034b	**1586**	86c. rose	3·50	80
4034c	**1586**	88c. rose	3·50	80
4035	**1586**	90c. indigo	3·50	1·50
4036	**1586**	€1 orange	5·25	1·00
4040	**1586**	€1.11 purple	6·25	2·00
4040a	**1586**	€1.15 blue	4·00	50
4041	**1586**	€1.22 purple	5·25	1·30
4041a	**1586**	€1.25 cobalt	4·50	55
4042	**1586**	€1.30 purple	4·50	65
4042a	**1586**	€1.33 purple	5·25	60
4045	**1586**	€1.90 brown	6·75	1·80
4046	**1586**	€1.98 purple	8·50	1·80
4048	**1586**	€2.11 claret	7·50	1·00
4048a	**1586**	€2.18 chocolate	8·00	85

(ii) Without face value.

4050	(45c.) emerald	1·80	15
4051	(50c.) scarlet	2·10	20
4052	(65c.) blue	3·50	60

(iii) Self-adhesive.

4057	(50c.+20c.) scarlet	2·20	20
4058	(65c.) blue	3·50	1·00

1587 "Solidarite Asie"

2005. Red Cross Fund. For Victims of the Tsunami Disaster.

4060	**1587**	(50c.)+20c. scarlet	2·50	1·40

1588 Rashi

2005. 900th Death Anniv of Rabbi Solomon bar Isaac (Rashi) of Troyes (Biblical and Talmudic scholar).

4061	**1588**	50c. ultramarine, green and brown	1·80	1·00

1589 Rooster

2005. New Year. "Year of the Rooster".

4062	**1589**	(50c.) multicoloured	1·80	1·00

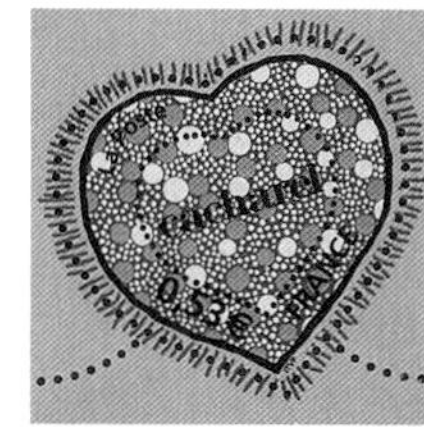
1590 Heart

2005. St. Valentine's Day. Multicoloured.

4063	53c. Type **1590**	2·00	1·10
4064	82c. Heart containing bird	3·00	1·70

MS4065 136×144 mm. 53c.×5, As No. 4063×5 9·75 9·75

2005. Orchids. Aas T 1475.

4066	**1475**	39c. multicoloured	1·80	1·00

No. 4066 was only issued pre-cancelled in black.

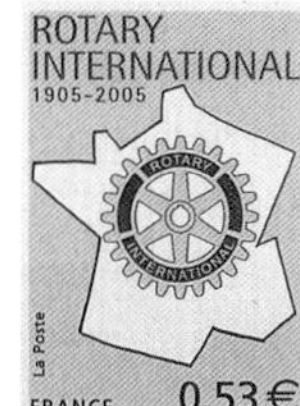
1591 Emblem

2005. Centenary of Rotary International (charitable organization). Ordinary or self-adhesive gum.

4067	**1591**	53c. lemon, ultramarine and vermilion	1·80	1·10

1592 Manu

2005. Titeuf (cartoon created by Philippe Chappuis (Zep). Multicoloured.

4069	(45c.) Type **1592**	3·25	2·00
4068	(50c.) Titeuf	1·60	1·00
4071	(90c.) Nadia	3·00	1·80

2005. Greetings Stamps. As T 1551. Multicoloured.

4072	(53c.) As No. 3939	1·80	1·10
4073	(53c.) As No. 3940	1·80	1·10

Nos. 4072/3 were for use on mail within France weighing 20 grams or less.

2005. Art Design. As T 491.

4074	82c. multicoloured	2·75	1·70
4075	90c. multicoloured	3·00	1·80
4076	€1.22 multicoloured	4·00	2·50
4077	€1.22 multicoloured	4·00	2·50

DESIGNS: No. 4074, 82c. "Le guitariste" (Jean-Baptiste Greuze) (36×48 mm); 4075, "Ours Blanc" (sculpture, Francois Pompon) (48×38 mm); 4706, "Sicile" (painting, Nicolas de Stael) (48×38 mm); 4077, €1.22 Les Halles Centrales (Victor Baltard) (architect) (birth bicentenary)) (48×38 mm).

1593 *Paphiopedilum* "Mabel Saunders"

2005. Orchids. Multicoloured.

4078	53c. Type **1593**	1·80	1·10
4079	53c. *Cypripedium calceolus*	1·80	1·10
4080	55c. *Oncidium papilio*	1·80	1·10
4081	82c. *Paphinia cristata* (horiz)	2·75	1·70
MS4082	110×160 mm. Nos. 4078/81	8·00	8·00

2005. Regions (5th issue). Sheet 286×110 mm containing multicoloured designs as T 1530.

MS4083 53c.×10 Nautical jousting; Clocks (vert); Cantal cheese (vert); Accordion player; Bouillabaisse (soup); Le P'tit Quinquin (statue), Lille (vert); Les rillettes (pig meat); La choucroute (fermented cabbage, sausages, pork and potatoes); Pelote player (vert); Sugar cane (vert) 18·00 18·00

2005. Tourist Publicity. As T 490. Multicoloured.

4084	53c. Aix-en-Provence	1·80	1·10
4085	53c. Golfe du Mobihan (75×23 mm)	1·80	1·10
4086	53c. Villefranche-sur-Mer	1·80	1·10
4087	53c. La Roque-Gageac	1·80	1·10

1594 Becassine (character created by Caumery and Pinchon)

2005. Greetings Stamp. Birthday.

4088	**1594**	(53c.) multicoloured	1·80	1·10

1595 Albert Einstein

2005. 50th Death Anniv of Albert Einstein (physicist). International Year of Physics.

4089	**1595**	53c. multicoloured	1·80	1·10

1596 Alexis de Tocqueville

2005. Birth Bicentenary of Alexis de Tocqueville (sociologist).

4090	**1596**	90c. multicoloured	3·00	1·80

1597 Prisoner supported by American and Russian Soldiers

2005. 60th Anniv of Liberation of Concentration Camps.

4091	**1597**	53c. multicoloured	1·80	1·10

1598 Napoleon I

2005. Bicentenary of the Battle of Austerlitz.

4092	**1598**	55c. multicoloured	1·80	1·10

A stamp of the same design was issued by Czech Republic.

1599 Stanislas Place, Nancy (image scaled to 62% of original size)

2005. Federation of French Philatelic Association Congress, Nancy.

4093	**1599**	53c. multicoloured	1·80	1·10

1600 Chef and Table

2005. Europa. Gastronomy.

4094	**1600**	53c. multicoloured	1·80	1·10

1601 Jardin de la Fontaine, Nimes

2005. French Gardens. Sheet 285×110 mm containing T 1601 and similar design. Mult.

MS4095 €1.98×2, Type **1601**; Cherubs and vase 13·00 13·00

1602 Woman and Beach Huts

2005. Holidays. Self-adhesive. No value expressed.

4096	**1602**	(53c.) multicoloured	1·80	1·10

No. 4096 was for use on letters up 20g.

1603 Octopus (*20,000 Leagues under the Sea*)

2005. Death Centenary of Jules Verne (writer). Multicoloured.

4097	53c. Type **1603**	1·80	1·10
4098	53c. *Five Weeks in a Balloon*	1·80	1·10
4099	53c. *Around the World in Eighty Days*	1·80	1·10
4100	53c. *From the Earth to the Moon*	1·80	1·10
4101	53c. *Michael Strogoff* (horiz)	1·80	1·10
4102	53c. *Voyage to the Centre of the Earth* (horiz)	1·80	1·10
MS4103	135×144 Nos. 4097/4102 (sold at €4.80)	16·00	16·00

No. **MS**4103 was sold with a premium of €1.62 for the benefit of the Red Cross.

1604 Formula 1 Race Car

2005. Centenary of First French Gordon Bennett Cup Race. Multicoloured.

4104	53c. Type **1604**	1·80	1·10
4105	53c. Van in sand (Paris—Dakar race)	1·80	1·10
4106	53c. Two rally cars (horiz)	1·80	1·10
4107	53c. Race car (Endurance race) (horiz)	1·80	1·10
4108	53c. Early race car facing right (horiz)	1·80	1·10
4109	53c. Early race car facing left (horiz)	1·80	1·10

1605 Hands, Swallow and Mountain (image scaled to 61% of original size)

2005. Environmental Charter.

4110	**1605**	53c. multicoloured	1·80	1·10

1606 Hand holding Figure

2005. February 11th Law (equal rights for the disabled).

4111	**1606**	53c. multicoloured	1·80	1·10

1607 Baby asleep in Flower ("c'est une fille")

2005. Greetings Stamps. No value expressed. Self-adhesive. Multicoloured.

4112	(53c.) Type **1607**	1·80	1·10
4113	(53c.) Baby facing right ("c'est un garcon")	1·80	1·10

Nos. 4112/13 were for use on letters up to 20g.

2005. Valentine's Day. As T 1553 and T 1590. Self-adhesive.

4114	50c. As Type No. 1553	1·60	1·00
4115	53c. As Type **1590**	1·80	1·10
4116	75c. As No. 3944	2·40	1·50
4117	82c. As No. 4064	2·75	1·70

1608 Horse's Head and Building Facade

2005. Le Haras du Pin (Royal stud and stables).

4118	**1608**	53c. multicoloured	1·80	1·10

1609 Brandenburg Gate

2005. European Capitals. Berlin. Sheet 144×134 mm containing T 1609 and similar multicoloured designs.

MS4119 53c.×4, Type **1609**; Kaiser Wilhelm Memorial Church (vert); Philharmonie; Reichstag 7·00 7·00

2005. Orchids. As T 1475.

4120	**1475**	39c. multicoloured	1·50	95

2005. Regions (6th issue). Sheet 286×110 mm containing multicoloured designs as T 1530.

MS4121 53c.×10 D'Annecy Lake; Les falaises d'Etretat (vert); Pigeon loft (vert); Pool Lavoir; Banks of Seine; Megaliths, Carnac, Solognote house; Dunes, Pilat; Old lighthouse, Stiff (vert); Borie (dry stone hut) (vert) 18·00 18·00

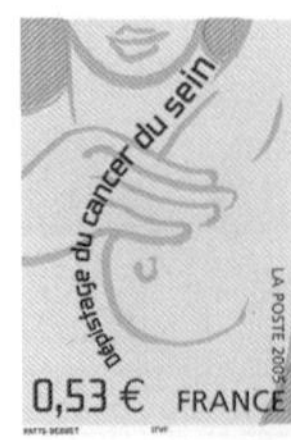

1610 Self-Examination

2005. Breast Cancer Awareness Campaign.

4122	**1610**	53c. multicoloured	1·80	1·10

1611 Cat holding Stamp

2005. "Sourires". Designs showing "Cat" (cartoon character created by Philippe Geluck). Multicoloured. Self-adhesive.

4123	(53c.) Type **1611**	1·80	1·10
4124	(53c.) Seated at typewriter	1·80	1·10
4125	(53c.) With female cat	1·80	1·10
4126	(53c.) With diagram of human	1·80	1·10
4127	(53c.) Wearing satchel containing envelopes	1·80	1·10
4128	(53c.) Holding letter	1·80	1·10
4129	(53c.) Writing letter	1·80	1·10
4130	(53c.) With folded arms/paws	1·80	1·10
4131	(53c.) On stage	1·80	1·10
4132	(53c.) Holding stamps (different)	1·80	1·10

Nos. 4123/32 were issued in booklets of ten stamps for use on mail within France weighing 20 grams or less.

1612 Raymond Aron

2005. Birth Centenary of Raymond Aron (philosopher).

4133	**1612**	53c. blue, indigo and black	1·80	1·10

1613 Adrienne Bolland, Andes and Caudron G3

2005. 30th Death Anniv of Adrienne Bolland (1st woman to fly over the Andes).

4134	**1613**	€2 multicoloured	6·50	4·00

1614 Link

2005. Video Game Characters. Sheet 109×184 mm containing T 1614 and similar horiz designs. Multicoloured.

MS4135 20c.×5, Type **1614**; Pac-Man; Prince of Persia; Spyro; Donkey Kong. 33c.×5, Mario; Adibou; Rayman; Lara Croft; Les Sims 9·75 9·75

1615 "Marianne Dulac"

2005. 60th Anniv of "Marianne Dulac" (stamp designed by Edmond Dulac). Self-adhesive. 60th Anniv of "Marianna Dula" (stamp designed by Edmond Dulac).

4136 **1615** 53c. scarlet 1·80 1·10

1616 Virgin and Child (Hans Memling)

2005. Red Cross Fund. Christmas.

4137 **1616** 53c. multicoloured 2·20 1·40

1617 "The Annunciation"

2005. Art. "The Annunciation" by Raffello Sanzio (Raphael). Sheet 131×86 mm containing T 1617 and similar horiz design.

MS4138 53c. Type **1617**; 55c. "The Annunciation" (different) 3·50 3·50

Stamps of a similar design were issued by Vatican City.

1618 Avicenne

2005. 1025th Birth Anniv of Avicenne (Ibn Sina) (doctor and philosopher).

4139 **1618** 53c. multicoloured 1·80 1·10

1619 Bear and Penguin pulling Sledge

2005. Christmas and New Year. No Value expressed. Self-adhesive . Multicoloured.

4140 (53c.) Type **1619** 1·80 1·10

4141 (53c.) Penguins, deer and snowman 1·80 1·10

4142 (53c.) Penguins and deer on sledge 1·80 1·10

4143 (53c.) Penguins holding snowballs 1·80 1·10

4144 (53c.) Bear and penguins on sledge 1·80 1·10

Nos. 4140/4 were for use on letters weighing up to 20 grams.

1620 Jacob Kaplan

2005. 110th Birth Anniv of Jacob Kaplan (chief Rabbi).

4145 **1620** 53c. multicoloured 1·80 1·10

1621 Church Tower and Document

2005. Centenary of Law separating Church and State.

4146 **1621** 53c. multicoloured 1·80 1·10

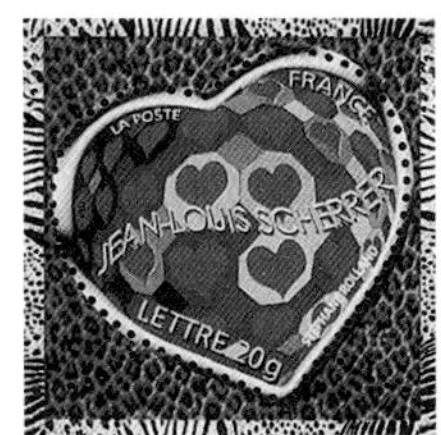

1622 Heart containing Hearts

2006. St. Valentine's Day. No value expressed. Multicoloured.

4147 (53c.) Type **1622** 1·80 1·10

4148 (82c.) Heart containing jewelled heart 2·75 1·70

MS4148a 136×144 mm. 53c.×5, As No. 4147×5 9·25 9·25

No. 4147/8 also come self-adhesive.

No. 4147 was for use on letters up to 20 grams and Nos. 4148 and 4150 for letters up to 50 grams.

1623 Dog

2006. New Year. Year of the Dog. No value expressed.

4151 **1623** (53c.) multicoloured 1·80 1·10

No. 4151 was for use on letters up to 20 grams.

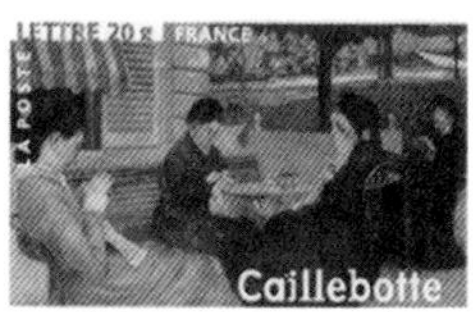

1624 "Portraits a la Campagne" (Gustave Caillebotte)

2006. Impressionist Paintings. Multicoloured. Self-adhesive.

4152 (53c.) Type **1624** 1·80 1·10

4153 (53c.) "La Chasse aux Papillons" (Berthe Morisot) 1·80 1·10

4154 (53c.) "Mere et Enfant" (Mary Cassat) 1·80 1·10

4155 (53c.) "Jeunes Filles au Piano" (Auguste Renoir) 1·80 1·10

4156 (53c.) "La Beregere" (Camille Pissarro) 1·80 1·10

4157 (53c.) "Mademoiselle Gachet dans son Jardin" (Vincent van Gogh) 1·80 1·10

4158 (53c.) "L'air du Soir" (Henri-Edmond Cross) 1·80 1·10

4159 (53c.) "Danseuses" (Edgar Degas) 1·80 1·10

4160 (53c.) "Le Dejeuner sur L'Herbe (Eduard Manet) 1·80 1·10

4161 (53c.) "Femmes de Tahiti" (Paul Gauguin) 1·80 1·10

Nos. 4152/61 were for use on letters up to 20 grams.

1625 Biathlon

2006. Winter Olympic Games, Turin.

4162 **1625** 53c. multicoloured 1·80 1·10

1626 Spirou

2006. 70th Anniv of Spirou (cartoon character drawn by Jose Luis Munuera). Multicoloured.

4164 (48c.) Spirou and Fantasio 1·40 90

4163 (53c.) Type **1626** 1·80 1·10

4165 (90c.) Fantasio 2·75 1·80

No. 4163 was for use on second class, No. 4164 was for use on first class and No. 4165 was for use on international mail up to 20 grams.

1627 Miner

2006. Centenary of Courrieres Mine Disaster.

4166 **1627** 53c. multicoloured 1·80 1·10

1628 Graves and Cloister

2006. Douaumont Ossuary (war grave).

4167 **1628** 53c. green, blue and brown 1·80 1·10

1629 Village from Lake

2006. 700th Anniv of Yvoire, Haute-Savoie.

4168 **1629** 53c. multicoloured 1·80 1·10

2006. Regions (7th issue). Sheet 286×110 mm containing multicoloured designs as T 1530.

MS4169 53c.×10, Fruit (La mirabelle); Les marais salant; Butter (le beurre); Roquefort cheese (vert); Olive oil (vert); Child in headdress (Le carnaval) (vert), Grapes (Les vendanges) (vert); Waiter (vert); Crops and punt (Les hortillomages) 18·00 18·00

1630 Well of Moses (Claus Sluter) and St. Benigne Church

2006. Dijon, Cote-d'Or.

4170 **1630** 53c. multicoloured 1·80 1·10

1631 "The Bathers"

2006. Death Centenary of Paul Cezanne (artist).

4171 **1631** 82c. multicoloured 2·75 1·70

1632 Girl holding Kitten

2006. Young Domestic Animals. Multicoloured.

4172 53c. Type **1632** 1·90 1·10

4173 53c. Puppy 1·90 1·10

4174 55c. Foal (horiz) 1·90 1·10

4175 82c. Lamb (horiz) 2·75 1·70

MS4176 110×161 mm. Nos. 4173/5 8·00 8·00

The stamps and margins of **MS**4176 form a composite design of children and young animals.

1633 Parc de la Valle aux Loups

2006. French Gardens. Sheet 285×110 mm containing T 1633 and similar design. Multicoloured.

MS4177 €1.98×2, Type **1633**; Bridge, Albert Kahn gardens 13·50 13·50

1634 Faces and Stars

2006. Europa. Integration.

4178 **1634** 53c. multicoloured 1·90 1·10

1635 Pierre Bayle

2006. 300th Death Anniv of Pierre Bayle (philosopher).

4179 **1635** 53c. green, blue and brown 1·90 1·10

1636 Figure connected to Broken Chain

2006. Abolition of Slavery Day.

4180 **1636** 53c. multicoloured 1·90 1·10

1637 Animals

2006. 50th Anniv of Discovery of Rouffignac Caves, Dordogne.

4181 **1637** 55c. multicoloured 2·00 1·20

1638 Substitutes

2006. World Cup Football Championship, Germany. Sheet 211×143 mm containing T 1639 and similar multicoloured designs.

MS4182 53c.×10, Type **1638**; Supporters; Ball at chest (Controle) (circular) (32×32 mm); Centre (circular) (32×32 mm); Throw in (Degagement) (circular) (32×32 mm); Kicking from horizontal (Retourne) (circular) (32×32 mm); Tackling (Feitne de corps) (circular) (32×32 mm); Referee (vert); Trainers; Journalists 17·00 17·00

1639 Woman in Hammock

2006. Holidays. Self Adhesive.

4183 **1639** (53c.) multicoloured 1·90 1·10

No. 4182 was issued for use on internal mail weighing up to 20 grams.

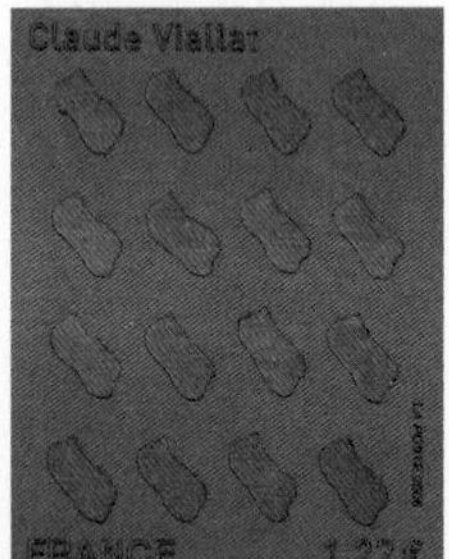

1640 Untitled

2006. 70th Birth Anniv of Claude Viallat (artist).

4184 **1640** €1.22 magenta and green 4·00 2·50

1641 "The Abduction from the Seraglio" (Varona)

2006. Operas by Wolfgang Amadeus Mozart. Costume Designs. Multicoloured.

4185 53c. Type **1641** 1·90 1·10
4186 53c. "Cosi fan Tutte" (Erte) 1·90 1·10
4187 53c. "The Magic Flute" (Chapelin-Midy) 1·90 1·10
4188 53c. "Don Giovanni" (Marillier) 1·90 1·10
4189 53c. "The Marriage of Figaro" (Enzio Frigerio) 1·90 1·10
4190 53c. "The Clemency of Titus" (Graf) 1·90 1·10
MS4191 136×143 mm. Nos. 4185/90 14·50 14·50

1642 Provins

2006. World Heritage Sites. Multicoloured.

4192 53c. Type **1642** 1·90 1·10
4193 90c. Mont Saint Michel 3·00 1·80

Stamps of a similar design were issued by United Nations.

2006. Salon de Timbre (European Stamp Salon). Sheet 212×143 mm containing vert designs as T 1601. Multicoloured.

MS4194 €1.98×4, Jardin de la Fontaine, Nimes (T **1601**) (**MS**4095); Cherubs and vase (**MS**4095); Parc de la Vallee aux Loups; Bridge (**MS**4177); Albert Kahn gardens (**MS**4177) 19·00 19·00

1643 Building Facade

2006. Opera Garnier. 79th French Philatelic Association Congress.

4195 **1643** 53c. olive, blue and lemon 1·90 1·10

1644 Babar

2006. Greetings Stamp. Birthdays.

4196 **1644** (53c.) multicoloured 1·90 1·10

No. 4196 was for use on letters up to 20g.

1645 Chrysaliniotissa Church

2006. European Capitals. Nicosia. Sheet 144×134 mm containing T 1645 and similar horiz designs. Multicoloured.

MS4197 53c.×4, Type **1645**; Archaeological Museum; Famagouste Gate; Archbishop's Palace 7·50 7·50

1646 Dancers

2006. Tango. Multicoloured.

4198 53c. Type **1646** 1·90 1·10
4199 90c. Musician 3·00 1·80

Stamps of a similar design were issued by Argentina.

1647 "@"

2006. 10th Anniv of La Poste's Business Foundation.

4200 **1647** (53c.) orange, rosine and black 1·90 1·10

No. 4200 was for use on letters up to 20g.

1648 Airbus A380

2006. Air.

4201 **1648** €3 multicoloured 10·00 6·00

1649 Golfers

2006. France Open Golf Tournament.

4202 **1649** 53c. blue and rosine 1·90 1·10

1649a Arms and Football

2006. Thank you "Les Bleus" (celebration of French team reaching semi-final of World Cup Football Championship).

4203 **1649a** 53c. multicoloured 1·90 1·90

1650 Statue and Building (image scaled to 61% of original size)

2006. Opening of Quai Branley Museum (designed by Jean Nouvel).

4204 **1650** 53c. multicoloured 1·90 1·10

1651 Receiving Legion d'Honneur

2006. Centenary of Rehabilitation of Captain Richard Dreyfus.

4205 **1651** 53c. multicoloured 1·90 1·10

1652 Rouget de Lisle

2006. 170th Death Anniv of Rouget de Lisle (writer of "Marsailles" (national anthem)).

4205 **1652** 53c. multicoloured 1·90 1·10

1653 Town and Walls

2006. Antibes Juan-les-Pins.

4207 **1653** 53c. multicoloured 1·90 1·10

1654 Pablo Casals

2006. 130th Birth Anniv of Pablo Casals (cellist).

4208 **1654** 53c. multicoloured 1·90 1·10

2006. Regions (8th issue). Sheet 251×110 mm containing multicoloured designs as T 1530.

MS4209 54c.×10, Castle on rocks (Tours catalanes); Beach (La Croisette); Grave (La foret de Broceliande); Tree-covered crater (Les volcans d'Auvergne) (vert); Building at night (Les Invalides) (vert); Le chateau de Chaumont-sur-Loire, Rock bridge (Les gorges de l'Ardeche) (vert); Le moulin de Valmy (vert); La grotte de Lourdes; Cliffs (Calanche de Piana) 16·00 16·00

1657 Thionville, Moselle

2006

4210 **1657** 54c. multicoloured 1·90 1·10

1658 Cubitus as Stamp on Letter to Senechal

2006. "Sourires". Designs showing "Cubitus" (cartoon character created by Dupa (Luc Dupanloup)). Multicoloured. Self-adhesive.

4211 (54c.) Type **1658** 1·90 1·10
4212 (54c.) With stamp stuck on nose 1·90 1·10
4213 (54c.) With puppy 1·90 1·10
4214 (54c.) With Senechal, Semaphore and puppy 1·90 1·10
4215 (54c.) Holding envelopes by open letterbox 1·90 1·10
4216 (54c.) Dressed as Marianne 1·90 1·10
4217 (54c.) Holding letter with hearts 1·90 1·10
4218 (54c.) With Semaphore 1·90 1·10
4219 (54c.) With snail 1·90 1·10
4220 (54c.) Hand stroking Cubitus 1·90 1·10

Nos. 4211/20 were for use on mail within France weighing 20 grams or less.

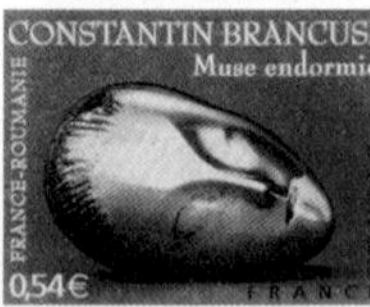

1659 "Muse endormie"

2006. 130th Birth Anniv of Constantin Brancusi (sculptor). Multicoloured.

4221 54c. Type **1659** 1·90 1·10
4222 85c. "Le sommeil" 2·75 1·70

Stamps of a similar design were issued by Romania.

1660 Cesssna 208 Caravan, Child and Aid Box

2006. Aviation Sans Frontieres (humanitarian organization).

4223 **1660** 54c. multicoloured 1·90 1·10

1661 Henri Moisson

2006. Death Centenary (2007) of Henri Moissan (winner of Nobel Prize for Chemistry—1906).

4224 **1661** 54c. multicoloured 1·90 1·10

1662 "Memoire Partagee" (shared memory)

2006. UNESCO First International Conference—"Memory of the World".

4225 **1662** 54c. multicoloured 1·90 1·10

1663 Marianne

2006. 60th Anniv of Marianne de Gandon (stamp designed by P. Gandon). Multicoloured. Self-adhesive.

4226 54c. Type **1663** 1·90 1·10
4227 (54c.) As No. 4051 1·90 1·10

1664 Helicopter (helicoptere) (Gustave de Ponton d'Amecourt) (1863)

2006. Flying Machines. Multicoloured.

4228 54c. Type **1664** 1·90 1·10
4229 54c. *Demoiselle* (Alberto Santos-Dumont) (1908) (horiz) 1·90 1·10
4230 54c. Flying boat (barque ailee) (Jean-Marie le Bris) (1856) (horiz) 1·90 1·10
4231 54c. *Avion III* (Clement Ader) (1897) (horiz) 1·90 1·10
4232 54c. Hydravion (hydravion) (Henri Fabre) (1910) (horiz) 1·90 1·10
4233 54c. Balloon with oars (ballon a rames) (Jean-Pierre Blanchard) (1784) 1·90 1·10

1665 "Three Beggars at the Door of a House" (etching)

2006. 400th Birth Anniv of Rembrandt Harmenszoon van Rijn (artist).

4234 **1665** €1.30 sepia, brown and red 4·50 2·50

1666 Engine

2006. Tram-Train (from Aulnay-sous-Bois to Bondy) (1st issue).

4235 **1666** 54c. multicoloured 1·90 1·10

1667 "Fleur" (Yacine Lorafy)

2006. Red Cross Fund. Christmas. Children's Paintings. Multicoloured.

4236 (54c.) Type **1667** 1·90 1·10
4237 (54c). "Petite fleur" (Margot Deram) 1·90 1·10

Nos. 4236/7 were for use on letters weighing up to 20 grams.

1668 Penguins pulling Sledge carrying Reindeer

2006. Christmas and New Year. No Value expressed. Multicoloured. Self-adhesive.

4238 (54c.) Type **1668** 1·90 1·10
4239 (54c.) Reindeer and penguins fishing 1·90 1·10
4240 (54c.) Reindeer and penguins dressing tree 1·90 1·10
4241 (54c.) Reindeer skating 1·90 1·10
4242 (54c.) Reindeer, penguins and parcels 1·90 1·10

Nos. 4238/42 were for use on letters weighing up to 20 grams.

1669 Square and Compass

2006. National Grand Lodge of Masons.

4243 **1669** 54c. ultramarine and grey 1·90 1·10

1670 Alain Poher

2006. 10th Death Anniv of Alain Poher (politician and twice interim president).

4244 **1670** 54c. multicoloured 1·90 1·10

1671 Tram

2006. Paris Tramway (return of trams to southern Paris).

4245 **1671** 54c. multicoloured 1·90 1·10

2007. Orchids. As T 1475. Multicoloured.

4246 31c. As No. 3903 1·10 65
4247 36c. As No. 3904 1·30 75
4248 43c. As Type **1475** 1·60 95

Nos. 3246/8 were only issued pre-cancelled in black.

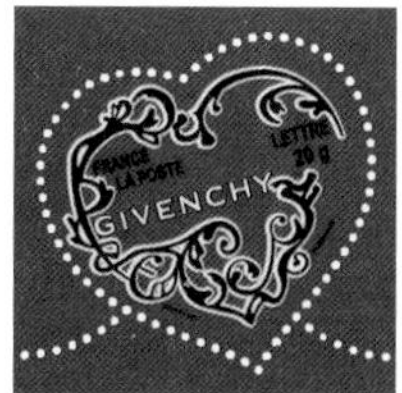

1672 Decorated Heart

2007. St. Valentine's Day. No value expressed. Multicoloured. Ordinary gum.

4249 **1672** (54c.) scarlet and black 1·90 1·10
4250 **1672** (86c.) black and vermilion 2·75 1·70
MS4251 136×144 mm. (54c.)×5, As No. 4249×5 9·25 9·25

(b) Self-adhesive

4252 (54c.) scarlet and black 1·90 1·10
4253 (86c.) black and vermillion 2·75 1·70

No. 4249 and 4251 were for use on letters up to 20 grams and No. 4250 and 4252 for letters up to 50 grams.

1673 Pig

2007. New Year. Year of the Pig. No value expressed.

4254 **1673** (54c.) multicoloured 1·90 1·10

No. 4254 was for use on letters up to 20 grams.

1674 Hippopotamus (Egypt)

2007. Antiquities. No Value expressed. Multicoloured. Self-adhesive.

4255 (54c.) Type **1674** 1·90 1·10
4256 (54c.) Aphrodite (Greece) 1·90 1·10
4257 (54c.) Victory of Samothrace (Greece) 1·90 1·10
4258 (54c.) Fresco from Pompeii (Rome) 1·90 1·10
4259 (54c.) Amenemhat III (Egypt) 1·90 1·10
4260 (54c.) Juno (Rome) 1·90 1·10
4261 (54c.) Harpist (Egypt) 1·90 1·10
4262 (54c.) Etruscan sarcophagus 1·90 1·10
4263 (54c.) Scribe (Egypt) 1·90 1·10
4264 (54c.) Pericles (Greece) 1·90 1·10

Nos. 4255/64 were for use on letters weighing up to 20 grams.

1675 Watteau Fountain

2007. Valenciennes.

4265 **1675** 54c. blue and vermilion 1·90 1·10

1676 Pantheon, Paris

2007. Justes de France.

4266 **1676** 54c. blue and black 1·90 1·10

1677 Illuminated Letter

2007. Humanist Library, Selestat.

4267 **1677** 60c. multicoloured 2·00 1·20

1678 Eurocopter EC130

2007. Centenary of the Helicopter.

4268 **1678** €3 multicoloured 10·00 7·00

2007. Regions (9th issue). Sheet 251×110 mm containing multicoloured designs as T 1530.

MS4269 54c.×10, Hill town (Les Baux-de-Provence); Beach (Bords de Loire); Mountains (Le massif de la Grande-Chartreuse); Harbour (Saint Tropez); Waterfall (Cascade Doubs) (vert); Rocks and trees (Le foret de Fontainebleau) (vert); Chateau reflected in water (Le chateau de Chantilly); Seawall (Saint-Malo); Flowers (Le ballon d'Alsace) (vert); Towpath (Le canal du Midi) (vert) 17·00 17·00

1679 Harry Potter (Daniel Radcliffe)

2007. Fete du Timbres. "Harry Potter" (character created by J. K. Rowling). No Value expressed. Multicoloured.

4270 (54c.) Type **1679** 1·90 1·10
4271 (54c.) Hermione Granger (Emma Watson) 1·90 1·10
4272 (54c.) Ron Weasley (Rupert Grint) 1·90 1·10

1680 Albert Londres

2007. Albert Londres (journalist) Commemoration.

4273 **1680** 54c. blue, green and sepia 1·90 1·10

1681 Building Facade

2007. Bicentenary of Court of Auditors. Ordinary or self-adhesive gum.

4274 **1681** 54c. blue and vermilion 1·90 1·10

1682 Haute-Vienne, Limoges

2007

4275 **1682** 54c. multicoloured 1·90 1·10

1683 Cut-out Figures

2007. 50th Anniv of Treaty of Rome.

4276 **1683** 54c. multicoloured 1·90 1·10

1684 Vauban

2007. 300th Death Anniv of Sebastian le Preste, Marquis de Vauban (Marshall of France, military strategist and engineer).

4277 **1684** 54c. claret, green and orange 1·90 1·10

1685 Players

2007. Rugby. "Allez les Petits" (catchphrase of Roger Coudrec (sports commentator)).

4278 **1685** 54c. multicoloured 1·90 1·10

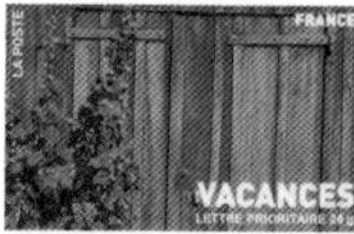

1686 Blue Doors

2007. Holidays. No value expressed. Multicoloured. Self-adhesive.

4279 (54c.) Type **1686** 1·90 1·10
4280 (54c.) Angelfish 1·90 1·10
4281 (54c.) Gentians 1·90 1·10
4282 (54c.) Blueberries 1·90 1·10
4283 (54c.) Boats 1·90 1·10
4284 (54c.) Drying wool 1·90 1·10
4285 (54c.) Snow peaks 1·90 1·10
4286 (54c.) Palm tree 1·90 1·10
4287 (54c.) Beach umbrellas 1·90 1·10
4288 (54c.) Colour pigment boxes 1·90 1·10

Nos. 4279/88 were for use on letters weighing up to 20 grams.

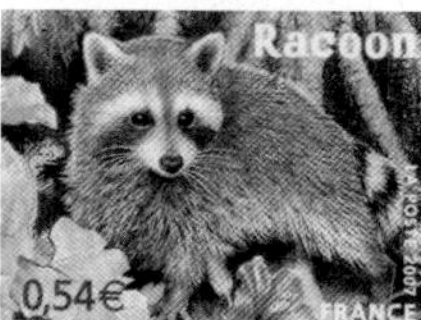

1687 Racoon

2007. Endangered Species of Overseas Departments. Multicoloured.

4289	54c. Type **1687**	1·90	1·10
4290	54c. Iguana (*vert*)	1·90	1·10
4291	60c. Jaguar	2·00	1·20
4292	86c. Barau's petrel	2·75	1·70
MS4293	110×161 mm. Nos. 4289/92	8·50	8·50

1688 Flowers and Pergola

2007. Salon du Timbres et de l'Ecrit 2008. French Gardens. Parc de la Tete d'Or. Sheet 285×110 mm containing T 1688 and similar design. Multicoloured.

MS4294 €2.11×2, Type **1688**; Path and glass house 14·00 14·00

No. **MS**4294 was divided into five parts by four lines of rouletting, the whole forming a composite design.

1689 Scouts

2007. Europa. Centenary of Scouting.

4295	**1689**	60c. multicoloured	2·00	1·20

1690 Yachts (image scaled to 58% of original size)

2007. Centenary of International Sailing Federation.

4296	**1690**	85c. multicoloured	2·75	1·70

1691 Tintin and Snowy

2007. Birth Centenary of Georges Remi (Herge) (creator of Tintin). Showing characters from Tintin graphic novels. Multicoloured.

4297	54c. Type **1691**	1·90	1·10
4298	54c. Bianca Castafiore	1·90	1·10
4299	54c. Captain Haddock	1·90	1·10
4300	54c. Thompson and Thompson	1·90	1·10
4301	54c. Professor Calculus	1·90	1·10
4302	54c. Chang	1·90	1·10
MS4303	136×142 mm. Nos. 4297/302	15·00	15·00

No. **MS**4303 was sold for €5, the premium for the benefit of the Red Cross.

1692 Arcachon, Gironde

2007

4304	**1692**	54c. multicoloured	1·90	1·10

1693 The Nativity (15th-century miniature)

2007. Year of Armenia in France. Multicoloured.

4305	54c. Type **1693**	1·90	1·10
4306	85c. 'L'Ange au sourire' (the angel with a smile), Rheims Cathedral	2·75	1·70

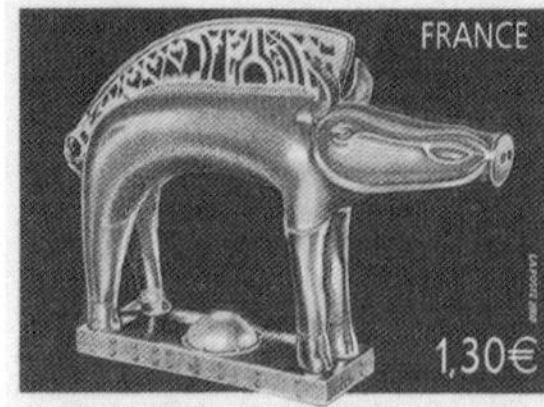

1694 Boar

2007. Gallic Boar (military ensign), Art and Archaeology Museum, Soulac-sur-Mer.

4307	**1694**	€1.30 multicoloured	4·50	2·50

1695 TGV

2007. TGV Europe.

4308	**1695**	54c. multicoloured	1·90	1·10

1696 Notre Dame la Grande

2007. 80th French Federation of Philatelic Associations Conference, Poitiers.

4309	**1696**	54c. brown and yellow	1·90	1·10

1697 Scrum, Player and Ball (melee)

2007. Rugby World Cup Championship (1st issue). Sheet 210×143 mm containing T 1697 and similar multicoloured designs.

MS4310 54c.×10, Type **1697**; Two players (attaque); One player prone (essai); Players reaching for ball (touche) (elliptical); Player kicking conversion (transformation) (elliptical); Passing the ball (passe); Player defending the ball (raffut); New Zealand team (haka); Tackle (plaquage); Fans (supporteurs) 17·00 17·00

See also No. 4315.

1698 Maison du Roi

2007. European Capitals. Brussels. Sheet 144×134 mm containing T 1698 and similar horiz designs. Multicoloured.

MS4311 54c.×4, Type **1698**; Hotel de Ville (vert); Manneken Pis (vert); Atomium 7·50 7·50

1699 Marianne

2007. Centenary of the Association of Mayors.

4312	**1699**	54c. multicoloured	1·90	1·10

1700 Pierre Pflimlin

2007. Birth Centenary of Pierre Pflimlin (mayor of Strasbourg 1959–83 and president of European Union 1984–7).

4313	**1700**	60c. multicoloured	2·00	1·20

1701 Garden

2007. Castres, Tarn.

4314	**1701**	54c. green, deep green and violet	1·90	1·10

1702 Player

2007. Rugby World Cup, France (2nd issue).

4315	**1702**	€3 multicoloured	6·75	5·00

2007. Greetings Stamps. Sheet 90×220 mm. As T 1704. Multicoloured.

MS4315a (54c.)×5, As Type **1704**; As No. 4319; As No. 4318; As No. 4321; As No. 4320 9·50 4·75

1703 Sylvain, Sylvette and Cake (cartoon characters created by Maurice Cuvillier)

2007. Greetings Stamp. 'Happy Birthday'.

4316	**1703**	(54c.) multicoloured	1·90	1·10

No. 4316 was for use on letters weighing up to 20 grams.

1704 Box and Butterflies

2007. Greetings Stamps. No value expressed. Multicoloured. Self-adhesive.

4317	(54c.) Type **1704**	1·90	1·10
4318	(54c.) Box and hearts	1·90	1·10
4319	(54c.) Box and flowers	1·90	1·10
4320	(54c.) Box and bubbles	1·90	1·10
4321	(54c.) Box and musical notes	1·90	1·10

Nos. 4317/21 were for use on letters weighing up to 20 grams. Firminy, Loire.

2007. Greeting Stamps. Sheet 90×220 mm. Vert stamps as T 1704 Multicoloured.

MS4321a (54c.)×5 As Type **1704**; As No. 4319; As No. 4318; As No. 4321; As No. 4320 9·25 9·25

No. **MS**4294 was divided into five parts by four lines of rouletting, the whole forming a composite design.

1705 St. Peter's Church, Firminy, Loire (Le Corbusier)

2007

4322	**1705**	54c. blue, black and green	1·90	1·10

1706 Sully Prudhomme Firminy, Loire

2007. Death Centenary of Sully Prudhomme (poet) (winner of Nobel Prize for Literature, 1901).

4323	**1706**	€1.30 ultramarine, blue and green	4·50	2·50

1707 Cow licking Stamps

2007. "Sourires". No value expressed. Multicoloured. Self-adhesive.

4324	(54c.) Type **1707**	1·90	1·10
4325	(54c.) Cow covered in stamps	1·90	1·10
4326	(54c.) Cow posting milk bottle with stamp	1·90	1·10
4327	(54c.) Cow date stamped	1·90	1·10
4328	(54c.) Cow singing	1·90	1·10

Nos. 4324/8 were issued for use on mail within France weighing 20 grams or less.

2007. Regions (10th issue). Sheet 251×110 mm containing multicoloured designs as T 1530.

MS4329 54c.×10, Sevres porcelain; Parfum de Grasse (perfume); Christmas market; Marseille soap; Les geants (giants), (vert); Basque beret (vert); Aubusson tapestry; Le bouchon Lyonnais (restaurant); Les charentaises (slippers) (vert); Melon (vert) 16·00 16·00

1708 Satellites

2007. 50th Anniv of Space Exploration.

4330	**1708**	85c. multicoloured	3·00	1·70

1709 *La Barriere Fleurie*

2007. 70th Death Anniv of Paul Serusier (artist).

4331	**1709**	86c. multicoloured	3·00	1·70

1710 Researcher

2007. 60th Anniv of Medical Research Foundation.

4332	**1710**	54c. multicoloured	1·90	1·10

1711 Guy Moquet

2007. Guy Moquet (17 year old communist resister, executed, 1941) Commemoration.

4333	**1711**	54c. violet and buff	2·00	1·10

1712 Dole, Jura (Louis Pasteur's birthplace)

2007

4334	**1712**	54c. multicoloured	2·00	1·10

1713 Marianne de Cheffer

2007. 40th Anniv of Marianne de Cheffer (stamp drawn by Henry Cheffer). Each scarlet. Self-adhesive.

4335	54c. Type **1713**	2·00	1·10
4336	(54c.) As No. 4057	2·00	1·10

1714 Jean-Baptiste Charcot

2007. Jean-Baptiste Charcot (arctic explorer) Commemoration. Multicoloured.

4337	**1714**	54c. blue, ultramarine and brown	2·00	1·10
4338	-	60c. multicoloured	2·10	1·20

DESIGNS: 54c. Type **1714**; 60c. *Pourquoi-Pas?*(55×33 mm).

1715 Cap Frehel Lighthouse

2007. Lighthouses. Sheet 143×105 mm containing T 1715 and similar multicoloured designs showing lighthouses.

MS4339 54c.×6, Type **1715**; L'Espiguette; D'Ar-Men; Grand-LEon; Porquerolles (horiz); Chassiron (horiz) 11·50 11·50

1716 Players

2007. Women's World Handball Championship, France.

4340	**1716**	54c. multicoloured	2·00	1·10

1717 Galerie de Glaces (mirror gallery) (designed by Jules Hardoui-Mansart), Chateau de Versailles

2007. Ordinary or self-adhesive gum.

4341	**1717**	85c. multicoloured	3·00	1·70

1718 'LES ENFANTS=AMOUR'

2007. Red Cross. No value expressed. Multicoloured. Self-adhesive.

4342	(54c.) Type **1718**	2·10	1·20
4343	(54c.) QUE TOUS LES ENFANTS DU MONDE SOIENT HEUREUX	2·10	1·20

Nos. 4342/3 were for use on letters weighing up to 20 grams.

1719 Squirrel

2007. Christmas and New Year. No value expressed. Multicoloured. Self-adhesive.

4344	(54c.) Type **1719**	2·00	1·10
4345	(54c.) Bird	2·00	1·10
4346	(54c.) Hedgehog	2·00	1·10
4347	(54c.) Puppy	2·00	1·10
4348	(54c.) Deer	2·00	1·10

Nos. 4344/8 were issued for use on letters weighing up to 20 grams.

1720 Heart containing Faces

2008. St. Valentine's Day. No value expressed. Multicoloured.

(a) Ordinary gum.

4349	(54c.) Type **1720**	2·00	1·10
4350	(83c.) Heart containing hearts as plant	3·00	1·70

MS4351 136×144 mm. 53c.×5, As No. 4349×5 10·00 10·00

(b) Self-adhesive.

4351a	(54c.) As No. 4349	2·00	1·10

Nos. 4349 was for use on letters up to 20 grams and No. 4350 for letters up to 50 grams.

1721 Rat and Grapes

2008. New Year. 'Year of the Rat'.

4352	**1721**	(54c.) multicoloured	2·00	1·10

1722 *Scenes from the life of Saint Francis* (Giotto di Bondone)

2008. Art. Multicoloured. Self-adhesive.

4353	(54c.) Type **1722**	2·00	1·10
4354	(54c.) *Sea Port at Sunset* (La Lorrain)	2·00	1·10
4355	(54c.) *Girl with a Pearl Earring* (Johannes Vermeer) (vert)	2·00	1·10
4356	(54c.) *La Joconde* (Leonardo de Vinci) (vert)	2·00	1·10
4357	(54c.) *The Money Lender and his Wife* (Quentin Metsys) (vert)	2·00	1·10
4358	(54c.) *The Birth of Venus* (Sandro Botticelli)	2·00	1·10
4359	(54c.) *Bonaparte* (Jacques Louis David)	2·00	1·10
4360	(54c.) *La Belle Jardiniere* (Madonna and Child with Saint John the Baptist) (Raphael) (vert)	2·00	1·10
4361	(54c.) *L'Ete* (summer) (Guiseppe Arcimboldo) (vert)	2·00	1·10
4362	(54c.) *L'Infante Marie Marguerite* (Diego Velasquez) (vert)	2·00	1·10

1723 Stadium

2008. 10th Anniv of Stade de France Stadium, Saint-Denis.

4363	**1723**	54c. multicoloured	2·10	1·20

1724 Loir-et-Cher, Vendome

2008

4364	**1724**	54c. multicoloured	2·10	1·20

1725 Globes and Detail

2008. Coronelli Globes (Marly globes).

4365	**1725**	85c. multicoloured	3·25	1·80

DESIGN: Two globes, terrestial globe, showing the world as it was known in the late 17th century and celestial globe, shows stars and their constellations, made by Vincenzo Coronelli in 1681 and 1683 for Louis XIV.

1726 Abd el-Kader

2008. Birth Bicentenary of Abd al-Qadir al-Jaza'iri (Abd el-Kader) (Algerian Islamic scholar, Sufi, political and military leader).

4366	**1726**	54c. multicoloured	2·10	1·20

1727 *Aquilegia*

2008. Flowers. Multicoloured.

4367	37c. Type **1727**	1·60	90
4368	38c. *Tulipa*	1·60	90
4369	44c. *Bellis perennis*	1·90	1·10
4370	45c. *Primula veris*	1·90	1·10

No. 4367/70 were only issued pre-cancelled in black.

1728 Droopy

2008. Stamp Day. Birth Centenary of Tex Avery (cartoonist and animator). Designs showing Droopy and characters from Red Hot Riding Hood. Multicolourd. (a) Ordinary gum.

4371	55c. Type **1728**	2·10	1·20
4372	55c. The Girl (Red)	2·10	1·20
4373	55c. The Wolf (Wolfie)	2·10	1·20

MS4374 105×72 mm. €2.18 Droopy (40×30 mm) 8·25 8·25

(b) Self adhesive.

4375	(55c.) As Type **1728**	2·40	1·40
4376	(55c.) As No. 4373	2·40	1·40
4377	(55c.) As No. 4372	2·40	1·40

The stamp of **MS**4374 contains an area, which when rubbed, shows a message in English.

1729 Book, CD and Ear

2008. 35th (2007) Anniv of Audio Book Readers Association.

4378	**1729**	55c. multicoloured	2·10	1·20

2008. Regions (11th issue). Sheet 251×110 mm containing multicoloured designs as T 1530.

MS4379 55c.×10, Le chateau d'Usse; Vezelay; Le Marais, Paris; Le Marais, Poitevin (boats); Le moulin de Cugarel (windmill); La cote de granit rose (shoreline); Honfleur (harbour); La Petite France (waterfront); Sarlat-la-Caneda; Le cirque de Mafate, La Reunion 19·00 19·00

1730 Saint-George Bridge, Lyon, Rhone

2008

4380	**1730**	55c. multicoloured	2·10	1·20

1731 Saint-Nicolas Tower, Old Port and La Chaine Tower, La Rochelle (image scaled to 62% of original size)

2008

4381	**1731**	55c. multicoloured	2·10	1·20

1732 Water Garden, Parc Longchamp, Marseille

2008. Salon du Timbre et de l'Ecrit 2008. French Gardens. Sheet 285×110 mm containing T 1732 and similar design. Multicoloured.

MS4382 €2.18×2, Type **1732**; Pagoda, Parc Borely, Marseille 15·00 15·00

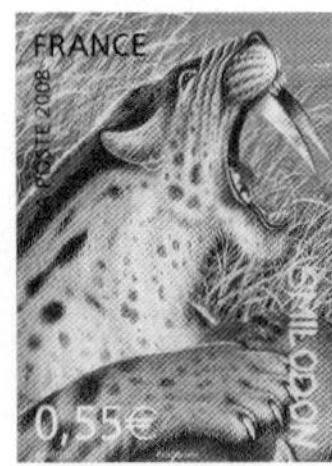

1733 Smilodon

2008. Prehistoric Animals.

No.	Description	Mint	Used
4383	55c. Type **1733**	2·10	1·20
4384	55c. Phorusrhacos	2·10	1·20
4385	65c. Megaloceros	2·50	1·50
4386	88c. Mammoth	3·25	1·80
MS4387	110×160 mm. Nos. 4383/6	9·75	9·75

1734 Bandaged Heart

2008. 40th Anniv of First Heart Transplant in Europe.

No.	Type	Description	Mint	Used
4388	**1734**	55c. multicoloured	2·10	1·20

1735 Bridge

2008. 700th Anniv of Pont Valentre de Cahors.

No.	Type	Description	Mint	Used
4389	**1735**	55c. multicoloured	2·10	1·20

1736 Quill

2008. Europa. The Letter. Ordinary or self-adhesive gum.

No.	Type	Description	Mint	Used
4390	**1736**	55c. multicoloured	2·30	1·30

1737 Samuel de Champlain's Ship, Native Canoe and New Settlement of Quebec, 1608

2008. 400th Anniv of City of Quebec.

No.	Type	Description	Mint	Used
4391	**1737**	85c. multicoloured	3·50	2·00

A stamp in a similar design was issued by Canada.

1738 Noddy (character created by Enid Blyton)

2008. Greetings Stamp. Happy Birthday.

No.	Type	Description	Mint	Used
4392	**1738**	(55c.) multicoloured	2·30	1·30

No. 4392 was inscribed 'Lettre prioritaire 20g' and was for use on domestic mail up to 20 grams.

1739 Teddy

2008. Congratulations. Multicoloured. Self-adhesive gum.

No.	Description	Mint	Used
4393	(55c.) Type **1739**	2·30	1·30
4394	(55c.) Duck	2·30	1·30

Nos. 4393/4 was inscribed 'Lettre prioritaire 20g' and was for use on domestic mail up to 20 grams.

Nos. 4393/4 includes an area which when rubbed reveals the child is a boy.

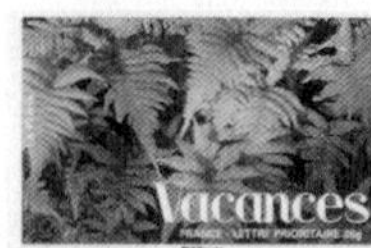

1740 Ferns

2008. Holidays. No value expressed. Multicoloured. Self-adhesive.

No.	Description	Mint	Used
4395	(55c.) Type **1740**	2·30	1·30
4396	(55c.) Butterfly	2·30	1·30
4397	(55c.) Leaves	2·30	1·30
4398	(55c.) Coconut tree	2·30	1·30
4399	(55c.) Park	2·30	1·30
4400	(55c.) Golf putt	2·30	1·30
4401	(55c.) Water lily	2·30	1·30
4402	(55c.) Watering cans	2·30	1·30
4403	(55c.) Kiwi fruit slices	2·30	1·30
4404	(55c.) Peas	2·30	1·30

No. 4395/404 were inscribed 'Lettre prioritaire 20g' and was for use on domestic mail up to 20 grams.

1741 Beffroi d'Evreux (Evreux belfry)

2008

No.	Type	Description	Mint	Used
4405	**1741**	55c. multicoloured	2·30	1·30

1742 Grand Palais

2008

No.	Type	Description	Mint	Used
4406	**1742**	55c. indigo, brown and orange	2·30	1·30

1743 Marianne of Europe

2008. Marianne of Europe

(aii) Without face value.

No.	Description	Mint	Used
4417	(50c.) emerald	2·10	1·10
4418	(55c.) scarlet	2·30	1·30
4418a	(55c.) black (one phosphor band) (1.7.11)	2·30	1·30
4418b	(60c.) scarlet (two phosphor bands (1.7.11)	2·40	1·40
4419	(65c.) ultramarine	2·75	1·50
4419a	(77c.) blue (two phosphor bands) (1.7.11)	3·00	1·70
4419b	(89c.) bright violet (two phosphor bands (1.7.11)	4·00	2·20
4419c	(€1) brown-rose (two phosphor bands (1.7.11)	3·75	2·25
4419d	(€1.45) bright purple (two phosphor bands) (1.7.11)	6·25	3·75
4419e	(€2.40) chocolate (two phosphor bands (1.7.11)	4·50	2·75

(b) Coil stamps.

No.	Description	Mint	Used
4420	(50c.) emerald	3·00	1·60
4421	(55c.) scarlet	3·00	1·70
4422	(65c.) ultramarine	3·75	2·10

(c) Self-adhesive

No.	Description	Mint	Used
4439	(55c.) black (one phosphor band) (1.7.11)	2·30	1·30
4440a	(60c.) scarlet (two phosphor bands (1.7.11)	2·75	1·50
4442b	(77c.) blue (two phosphor bands) (1.7.11)	4·25	2·30
4443a	(89c.) bright violet (two phosphor bands (1.7.11)	5·25	2·75
4444a	(€1) brown-rose (two phosphor bands (1.7.11)	7·25	4·00
4446a	(€1.45) bright purple (two phosphor bands (1.7.11)	11·00	6·50
4448	(€2.40) chocolate (two phosphor bands (1.7.11)	12·00	8·00
4440	(55c.) scarlet	2·30	1·30
4441	(65c.) ultramarine	2·75	1·50
4442	73c. green	4·25	2·30
4442a	75c. olive-green (1 band)	4·25	2·30
4443b	90c. rose	5·25	2·75
4443	87c. bright violet (2 bands)	5·25	2·75
4444	95c. brown-rose (2 bands)	7·25	4·00
4444b	€1.30 blue	7·25	4·00
4445a	€1.35 purple	7·50	4·25
4445b	€1.35 new blue (2 bands)	7·50	4·25
4446	€1.40 bright purple (2 bands)	11·00	6·50
4446b	€2.22 claret	10·50	5·75
4447	€2.30 deep claret (2 bands) (1.7.10)	12·00	8·00

Nos. 4418b; 4419c/e; 4439; 4440a; 4444; 4446a and 4448 were inscribed 'Lettre Prioritaire'.

No. 4418a and 4439 were inscribed 'Ecopli'; Nos. 4419a and 4442b were inscribed 'Europe'; Nos. 4419b and 4443a were inscribed 'Monde'.

Nos. 4449/57 are left vacant for possible additions to this series.

1744 Tree (paperless office)

2008. Environmental Protection. Sustainability. Multicoloured. Self-adhesive.

No.	Description	Mint	Used
4459	(55c.) Type **1744**	2·30	1·30
4460	(55c.) Bicycle (transport)	2·30	1·30
4461	(55c.) Map (green tourism)	2·30	1·30
4462	(55c.) VDU and keyboard (electronics recycling)	2·30	1·30
4463	(55c.) Water droplets (water conservation)	2·30	1·30
4464	(55c.) Sun (renewable energy)	2·30	1·30
4465	(55c.) Detergent bottles (cleaning)	2·30	1·30
4466	(55c.) Plastic bottles (plastics recycling)	2·30	1·30
4467	(55c.) Apple core (sustainable food production)	2·30	1·30
4468	(55c.) Strawberry (food security)	2·30	1·30

1745 Hand holding Tree

2008. Marianne, Democracy and Environment. Self-adhesive.

No.	Description	Mint	Used
4469	55c. scarlet	2·30	1·30
4470	55c. scarlet	2·30	1·30
4471	55c. scarlet	2·30	1·30
4472	65c. ultramarine	2·75	1·50
4473	65c. ultramarine	2·75	1·50
4474	65c. ultramarine	2·75	1·50

DESIGNS: 4470, Type **1745**; 4471, Dove and olive branch; 4472, Hand and ballot box; 4473, As Type **1745**; 4474, As No. 4471; 4475, As No. 4472.

2008. Salon du Timbres et de l'Ecrit 2008. French Gardens. Planete Timbre. Sheet 210×143 mm containing T 1688 and similar design. Multicoloured.

No.	Description	Mint	Used
MS4475	€2.11×2, Type **1688**; Glass house and path (as **MS**4294); €2.18×2, Type **1732**; Pagoda Parc Borely (as **MS**4382)	31·00	31·00

1746 Trapeze Artiste

2008. Circus. Multicoloured.

No.	Description	Mint	Used
4476	55c. Type **1746**	2·30	1·30
4477	55c. Bareback rider (vert)	2·30	1·30
4478	55c. L'Auguste (clown) (vert)	2·30	1·30
4479	55c. Lion tamer (vert)	2·30	1·30
4480	55c. Le clown blanc (white faced clown) (vert)	2·30	1·30
4481	55c. Juggler (vert)	2·30	1·30
MS4482	135×143 mm. Nos. 4476/81	19·00	19·00

No. **MS**4482 was on sale for €5.10, the premium was for the benefit of French Red Cross Society.

1747 Show Jumping and Cycling

2008. Olympic Games, Beijing. Sheet 210×143 mm containing T 1747 and similar multicoloured designs.

No.	Description	Mint	Used
MS4483	55c.×10, Type **1747**×2; Swimming and rowing×3 (horiz); Judo and fencing×3 (horiz); Tennis and athletics×2	20·00	20·00

1748 Charles de Gaulle Memorial, Colomby-les-Deux-Eglises

2008

No.	Type	Description	Mint	Used
4484	**1748**	55c. indigo, green and brown	2·30	1·30

1749 '€' and €1 Coin (Euro)

2008. European Projects. Sheet 143×105 mm containing T 1749 and similar multicoloured designs.

No.	Description	Mint	Used
MS4485	55c.×4, Type **1749**; Flag (French presidency of EU) (horiz); Satellite (Galileo) (horiz); Young people and flags (Erasmus)	9·25	9·25

1750 Untitled (Gerard Garouste)

2008. Art.

No.	Type	Description	Mint	Used
4486	**1750**	€1.33 multicoloured	5·50	3·00

1751 *Grande Hermine* (Jacques Cartier)

2008. Famous Ships. Sheet 143×105 mm containing T 1751 and similar multicoloured designs.

No.	Description	Mint	Used
MS4487	55c.×6, Type **1751**; *Boudeuse* (Louis Antoine de Bougainville); *La Confiance* (Robert Surcouf) (vert); *La Boussole* (Jean-Francois de Galaup de La Perouse) (vert); *Astrolabe*; *Hermione* (Marquis de La Fayette);	14·00	14·00

The stamps and margins of **MS**4487 form a composite design.

1752 Amazon Rain Forest

2008. Landscapes. Multicoloured.

4488	55c. Type **1752**	2·30	1·30
4489	85c. Mer de Glace	3·50	2·00

Nos. 4488/9 were issued in se-tenant forming a composite design.

Stamps of a similar design were issued by Brazil.

1753 Port

2008. Toulon, Var.

4490	**1753**	55c. multicoloured	2·30	1·30

1754 Gate and Cardinal Richelieu (statue)

2008. Richelieu, Indre-et-Loire.

4491	**1754**	55c. multicoloured	2·30	1·30

1755 Olive Tree

2008. Mediterranean Union Summit, Paris.

4492	**1755**	55c. multicoloured	2·30	1·30

2008. Regions (12th issue). Living France. Sheet 251×110 mm containing multicoloured designs as T 1530.

MS4493 55c.×10, Les espadrille; Le pot au feu; La Chataigne (chestnuts); Le Feux d'artifice (fireworks); L'image d'Epinal; La lentille (lentils); Le reblochon (cheese); Le calisson (biscuits); Les echasses (stilt walker); La moutade (mustard) 21·00 21·00

1756 Town Hall

2008. Le Havre.

4494	**1756**	55c. multicoloured	2·30	1·30

1757 Fly Past

2008. Air. La Patrouille de France (precision aerobatic demonstration team of the French Air Force).

4495	**1757**	€3 multicoloured	12·50	8·00

1758 Garfield and Letterbox

2008. "Sourires". Garfield (character created by Jim Davis). No Value Expressed. Designs showing Garfield. Multicoloured. Self-adhesive.

4496	(55c.) Type **1758**	2·30	1·30
4497	(55c.) Wearing glasses	2·30	1·30
4498	(55c.) Eating pizza	2·30	1·30
4499	(55c.) Odie licking Garfield	2·30	1·30
4500	(55c.) Eating envelope	2·30	1·30
4501	(55c.) Taking envelope from letterbox	2·30	1·30
4502	(55c.) Kicking Odie	2·30	1·30
4503	(55c.) With Arlene holding envelope	2·30	1·30
4504	(55c.) Holding extra large pencil	2·30	1·30
4505	(55c.) Lying in letterbox	2·30	1·30

1759 Castle

2008. Josselin, Morbihan.

4506	**1759**	55c. multicoloured	2·30	1·30

1760 Charles de Gaulle, Constitution and Coin

2008. 50th Anniv of Fifth Republic.

4507	**1760**	55c. multicoloured	2·30	1·30

1761 'Je Suis Sport'

2008. Sport.

4508	**1761**	55c. multicoloured	2·30	1·30

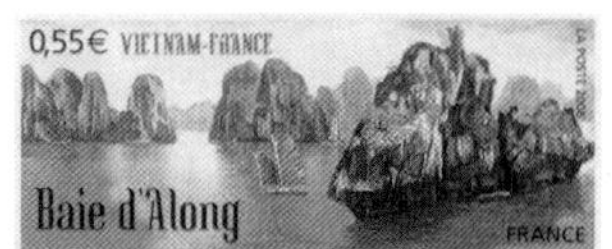
1762 Baie d'Along, Vietnam

2008. France–Vietnam Relations. Multicoloured.

4509	55c. Type **1762**	2·30	1·30
4510	85c. Strait of Bonifacio, France	3·50	2·00

Stamps of a similar design were issued by Vietnam.

1763 *Jeune Fille se Chauffant les Mains a un Grand Poele* (Jean-Jaques Henner)

2008. Art.

4511	**1763**	88c. multicoloured	3·75	2·10

1764 Marianne in Ship of State (Andre Reganon) (1959) (As Type **442**)

2008. Marianne–Symbol of the Republic. Designs showing Marianne. Self-adhesive.

4512	55c. multicoloured	2·30	1·30
4513	55c. multicoloured	2·30	1·30
4514	55c. multicoloured	2·30	1·30
4515	55c. multicoloured	2·30	1·30
4516	55c. multicoloured	2·30	1·30
4517	55c. multicoloured	2·30	1·30
4518	55c. scarlet	2·30	1·30
4519	55c. scarlet	2·30	1·30
4520	55c. vermilion	2·30	1·30
4521	55c. vermilion	2·30	1·30
4522	55c. vermilion	2·30	1·30
4523	55c. vermilion	2·30	1·30

DESIGNS: 4512 Type **1764**; 4513 Marianne (Albert Ducaris) (1960) (As Type **463**); 4514 Marianne (Jean Cocteau) (1961) (As Type **476**); 4515 Gallic cock (Albert Ducaris) (1962) (As Type **498**); 4516 'Republique' (Henri Cheffer) (1967) (As Type **604**); 4517 Marianne (Pierre Bequet) (1971) (As Type **668**); 4518 'Sabine' (after Louis David) (Pierre Gandon) (1977) (As Type **816**); 4519 'Liberty' (from *Liberty guiding the People* by Delacroix) (Pierre Gandon) (1982) (As Type **916**); 4520 Marianne (Louis Briat) (1989) (As Type **1118**); 4521 'Marianne of 14 July' (Eve Luquet) (1997) (As Type **1318**); 4522 'Marianne de Francais' (Thierry Lamouche) (2004) (As Type **1586**); 4523 Marianne of Europe (Yves Beaujard) (2008) (As Type **1743**).

1765 Air France DC3, Envelope and Haifa

2008. 60th Anniv of France–Israel Relations. 60th Anniv of First Flight from Israel to France. Multicoloured.

4524	55c. Type **1765**	2·30	1·30
4525	85c. Paris, envelope and aircraft	3·50	2·00

Stamps of a similar design were issued by Israel.

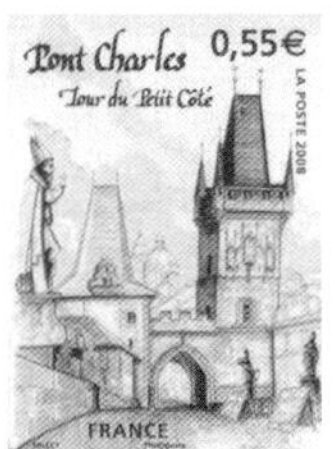
1766 Charles Bridge Tower

2008. European Capitals. Prague. Sheet 143×135 mm containing T 1766 and similar multicolored designs.

MS4526 55c.×4, Type **1766**; Old Town Hall Tower and astronomical clock; Church of Our Lady before Tyn; Prague Castle 9·00 9·00

1767 *Un Guichet de Theatre*

2008. Birth Bicentenary of Honore Daumier (artist).

4527	**1767**	€1.33 indigo and maroon	5·50	3·00

1768 Stylized Figure

1769 Dancing Feet

2008. Greetings Stamps. Winning Designs in Students Design-a-Stamp Competition. No Value Expressed. Multicoloured. Self-adhesive.

4528	(55c.) Type **1768** (20×26 mm)	2·30	1·30
4529	(55c.) Smile (20×26 mm)	2·30	1·30
4530	(55c.) Stars (20×26 mm)	2·30	1·30
4531	(55c.) Type **1769** (37×23 mm)	2·30	1·30
4532	(55c.) Hearts and flowers (37×23 mm)	2·30	1·30
4533	(55c.) Female figure with lizard's head (37×23 mm)	2·30	1·30
4534	(55c.) Balloons (37×23 mm)	2·30	1·30
4535	(55c.) Stylized planets (20×26 mm)	2·30	1·30
4536	(55c.) String figure jumping (20×26 mm)	2·30	1·30
4537	(55c.) Heart containing symbols of celebration (20×26 mm)	2·30	1·30
4538	(55c.) Figure swinging from moon (37×23 mm)	2·30	1·30
4539	(55c.) Bonnes Fetes	2·30	1·30
4540	(55c.) Bonnes Fetes	2·30	1·30
4541	(55c.) Family (37×23 mm)	2·30	1·30

Nos. 4528/41 were issued for use on mail within France weighing 20 grams or less.

1770 Globe, Animals, Rainbow and Butterflies

2008. Red Cross. Winning Designs in Childrens Design-a-Stamp Competition. No value expressed. Multicoloured. Self-adhesive.

4542	(55c.) Type **1770**	3·00	1·60
4543	(55c.) Globe showing northern and southern hemispheres	3·00	1·60

Nos. 4542/3 were for use on letters weighing up to 20 grams.

1771 Soldiers and Families

2008. 90th Anniv of End of First World War.

4544	**1771**	55c. blue, black and brown	2·40	1·40

1772 *Helianthus annuus*

2008. Flowers. Multicoloured.

4545	31c. Type **1772**	1·30	75
4546	38c. *Magnolia*	1·50	85

No. 4545/6 were only issued pre-cancelled in black.

1773 Oak, Map of Mediterranean and Cedar Tree

2008. France–Lebanon Relations.

4547	**1773**	85c. multicoloured	3·75	2·10

A stamp of a similar design was issued by Lebanon.

1774 Louis Braille

2009. Birth Bicentenary of Louis Braille (inventor of Braille writing for the blind).

4548	**1774**	55c. black and violet	2·40	1·40

1775 Ox

2009. Chinese New Year. Year of the Ox. No value expressed.

4549	**1775**	(55c.) multicoloured	2·40	1·40

No. 4549 was for use on letters weighing up to 20 grams and was originally on sale for 55c.

1776 Glasswork

2009. Artistic Trades. No value expressed. Multicoloured. Self-adhesive.

No.	Description	Mint	Used
4550	(55c.) Type **1776**	2·40	1·40
4551	(55c.) Horology	2·40	1·40
4552	(55c.) Marquetry	2·40	1·40
4553	(55c.) Faience (tin-glazed pottery)	2·40	1·40
4554	(55c.) Fresco	2·40	1·40
4555	(55c.) Tapestry	2·40	1·40
4556	(55c.) Stained glass	2·40	1·40
4557	(55c.) Fine woodwork	2·40	1·40
4558	(55c.) Ironwork	2·40	1·40
4559	(55c.) Mosaic	2·40	1·40
4560	(55c.) Jewellery	2·40	1·40
4561	(55c.) Crystal	2·40	1·40

Nos. 4550/61 were for use on letters weighing up to 20 grams and were originally on sale for 55c.

1777 Rene of Anjou

2009. 600th Birth Anniv of Rene of Anjou (Duke of Anjou and King of Naples (1438–1442)).

No.	Description	Mint	Used
4562	**1777** 55c. multicoloured	2·50	1·50

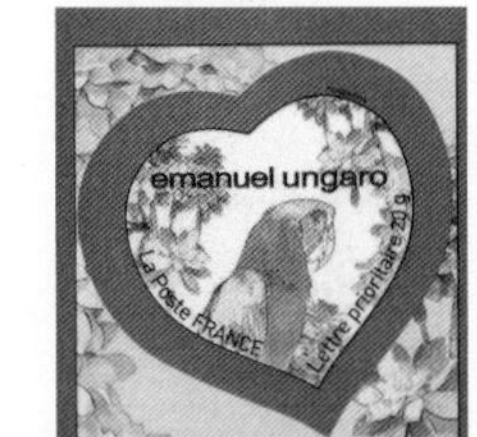

1778 Heart enclosing Parrot

2009. St. Valentine's Day. No value expressed. Multicoloured. (a) Ordinary gum.

No.	Description	Mint	Used
4563	(55c.) Type **1778**	2·40	1·40
4564	(85c.) Heart enclosing two parrots	4·00	2·20
MS4565	143×136 mm. (55c.)×5, As No. 4563×5	12·50	12·50
	(b) Self-adhesive gum.		
4566	(85c.) As No. 4563	4·00	2·20

No. 4563 was for use on letters up to 20 grams and Nos. 4564/5 for letters up to 50 grams.

1779 Les Sables d'Olonne, Vendee

2009

No.	Description	Mint	Used
4567	**1779** 55c. multicoloured	2·50	1·50

1780 Combined

2009. Alpine Skiing World Championship, Val d' Isere. Sheet 143×105 containing T 1780 and similar horiz designs. Multicoloured.

No.	Description	Mint	Used
MS4568	55c.×5, Type **1780**; Slalom; Downhill; Giant Slalom; Competitors	12·00	12·00

1781 Tree of Hands

2009. 40th Anniv of Fondation de France (charity).

No.	Description	Mint	Used
4569	**1781** 55c. multicoloured	2·50	1·40

1782 Cherub

2009. Cathedrale Sainte-Cecile, Albi. Ordinary or self-adhesive gum.

No.	Description	Mint	Used
4570	85c. multicoloured	3·75	2·10

1783 Menton, Alpes-Maritimes

2009

No.	Description	Mint	Used
4572	**1783** 56c. multicoloured	2·50	1·40

1784 Coyote and Road Runner

2009. Stamp Day. Designs showing characters from Looney Tunes (cartoon series by Warner Brothers). Multicoloured. (a) Ordinary gum.

No.	Description	Mint	Used
4573	56c. Type **1784**	2·50	1·40
4574	56c. Sylvester and Tweetie Pie	2·50	1·40
4575	56c. Bugs Bunny	2·50	1·40
MS4576	105×72 mm. €1 Looney Tunes characters (80×26 mm)	4·50	2·50
	(b) No value expressed. Self-adhesive.		
4577	(56c.) As Type **1784**	2·50	1·40
4578	(56c.) As No. 4574	2·50	1·40
4579	(56c.) As No. 4575	2·50	1·40

1785 Emblem

2009. 50th Anniv (2008) of Constitutional Council (Conseil Constitutionnel). Ordinary of self-adhesive gum.

No.	Description	Mint	Used
4580	**1785** 56c. multicoloured	2·50	1·40

1786 Palais de Papes, Avignon

2009

No.	Description	Mint	Used
4581	**1786** 70c. multicoloured	3·00	1·70

1787 Helena (USA)

2009. Women of the World. No Value Expressed. Designs showing women. Multicoloured. Self-adhesive.

No.	Description	Mint	Used
4582	(56c.) Type **1787**	2·50	1·40
4583	(56c.) Dayu (Indonesia)	2·50	1·40
4584	(56c.) Deborah (France)	2·50	1·40
4585	(56c.) Kabari (Bangladesh)	2·50	1·40
4586	(56c.) Mei Mei (China)	2·50	1·40
4587	(56c.) Malika (Morocco)	2·50	1·40
4588	(56c.) Dayan (Colombia)	2·50	1·40
4589	(56c.) Francine (Rwanda)	2·50	1·40
4590	(56c.) Blessing (Nigeria)	2·50	1·40
4591	(56c.) Nandita (India)	2·50	1·40
4592	(56c.) Elmas (Turkey)	2·50	1·40
4593	(56c.) Nadia (Brazil)	2·50	1·40

1788 Macon, Saone-et-Loire

2009

No.	Description	Mint	Used
4594	**1788** 56c. multicoloured	2·50	1·40

1789 Polar Landscape

2009. Preserve Polar Regions and Glaciers. Sheet 143×105 mm containing T 1789 and similar multicoloured design.

No.	Description	Mint	Used
MS4595	56c.×2, Type **1789**; Emperor penguins (horiz)	6·25	6·25

1790 Aime Cesaire

2009. Aime Cesaire (writer and politician) Commemoration.

No.	Description	Mint	Used
4596	**1790** 56c. multicoloured	2·50	1·40

1791 Quetsche Plum, Alsace

2009. Regional Flora. No Value Expressed. Multicoloured. Self-adhesive.

No.	Description	Mint	Used
4597	(56c.) Type **1791**	2·50	1·40
4598	(56c.) Mirabelle plum, Lorraine	2·50	1·40
4599	(56c.) Birch trees, Centre	2·50	1·40
4600	(56c.) Bee orchid, Champagne–Ardenne	2·50	1·40
4601	(56c.) Lily, Paris	2·50	1·40
4602	(56c.) Blue bells, Ile de France	2·50	1·40
4603	(56c.) Gorse, Bretagne	2·50	1·40
4604	(56c.) Lily of the Valley, Pays de la Loire	2·50	1·40
4605	(56c.) Apples, Basse Normandie	2·50	1·40
4606	(56c.) Beech leaves, Haute Normandie	2·50	1·40
4607	(56c.) Rose, Picardie	2·50	1·40
4608	(56c.) Potatoes, Pas le Calais	2·50	1·40
4609	(56c.) Olives and lavender field, Provence–Alpes–Cote d'Azur	2·50	1·40
4610	(56c.) Chestnut, Corse	2·50	1·40
4611	(56c.) Thyme, Languedoc–Rous-sillon	2·50	1·40
4612	(56c.) Yellow gentian, Auvergne	2·50	1·40
4613	(56c.) Fungi, Limousin	2·50	1·40
4614	(56c.) Salicorne Salicornia, Poitou–Charentes	2·50	1·40
4615	(56c.) Maritime pine, Aquitaine	2·50	1·40
4616	(56c.) Spruce, Franche–Covete	2·50	1·40
4617	(56c.) Cordyline, Guyane	2·50	1·40
4618	(56c.) Violet, Midi-Pyrenees	2·50	1·40
4619	(56c.) Myrtle berries, Rhone–Alpes	2·50	1·40
4620	(56c.) Blackcurrant, Baugogne	2·50	1·40

Nos. 4597/620 were for use on mail within France weighing 20 grams or less.

1792 Saturn

2009. Europa. Astronomy. Sheet 143×105 mm containing T **1792** and similar vert design. Multicoloured.

No.	Description	Mint	Used
MS4621	70c.×2, Type **1792**; Exoplanet	6·25	6·25

1793 Director's Chair

1794 Cockerel

2009. Holidays. No Value Expressed. Multicoloured. Self-adhesive.

No.	Description	Mint	Used
4622	(56c.) Type **1793** (20×26 mm)	2·50	1·40
4623	(56c.) Ladybird (20×26 mm)	2·50	1·40
4624	(56c.) Tomatoes (20×26 mm)	2·50	1·40
4625	(56c.) Type **1794** (37×23 mm)	2·50	1·40
4626	(56c.) Poppy (37×23 mm)	2·50	1·40
4627	(56c.) Bonaire, Netherlands Antilles vehicle number plate (37×23 mm)	2·50	1·40
4628	(56c.) Butterfly (37×23 mm)	2·50	1·40
4629	(56c.) Tennis ball and court (20×26 mm)	2·50	1·40
4630	(56c.) Turban (20×26 mm)	2·50	1·40
4631	(56c.) Air bed (20×26 mm)	2·50	1·40
4632	(56c.) Raspberries (37×23 mm)	2·50	1·40
4633	(56c.) Door knocker (37×23 mm)	2·50	1·40
4634	(56c.) 11	2·50	1·40
4635	(56c.) Mooring rope (37×23 mm)	2·50	1·40

1795 Timber-framed House, Alsace

2009. France on Stamps. No Value Expressed. Multicoloured. Self-adhesive.

No.	Description	Mint	Used
4636	(68c.) Type 1795	3·00	1·70
4637	(68c.) Chateau, Azay-le-Rideau	3·00	1·70
4638	(68c.) Notre Dame Cathedral, Paris	3·00	1·70
4639	(68c.) Vineyards, Bordeaux	3·00	1·70
4640	(68c.) Promenade des Anglais, Nice	3·00	1·70
4641	(68c.) Mont Saint Michel	3·00	1·70
4642	(68c.) Eiffel Tower, Paris	3·00	1·70
4643	(68c.) Saint-Paul-de-Vence, Provence	3·00	1·70

Nos. 4636/43 were issued for use on International mail weighing 20 grams or less.

1796 'CHAUMONT'

2009. Chaumont, Haute-Marne. 20th International Poster and Graphic Arts Festival.

No.	Description	Mint	Used
4644	**1796** 56c. multicoloured	2·50	1·40

1799 John Calvin

2009. 500th Birth Anniv of Jean Calvin (religious reformer).

No.	Description	Mint	Used
4647	**1799** 56c. multicoloured	2·50	1·40

1800 Cocoa Fruit

2009. 400th Anniv of Arrival of Chocolate in France. Sheet 160×110 mm containing T **1800** and similar vert designs. Multicoloured.
MS4648 56c.×10, Type **1800**; Quetzacoatl; Hernan Cortes; Alhambra de Granada, Spain; Map and 'BAYONNE 1609'; Anne of Austria and Louis XIII of France; Chocolate factory; Chocolate block; Pot of hot chocolate and cup; Eating bar of chocolate 23·00 23·00

The stamps and margins of No. **MS**4648 form a composite design of a chocolate bar and produce the scent of chocolate when rubbed.

1801 Chateau de la Batie d'Urfe, Loire

2009
4649 **1801** 56c. multicoloured 2·50 1·40

1802 Tarbes

2009
4650 **1802** 56c. multicoloured 2·50 1·40

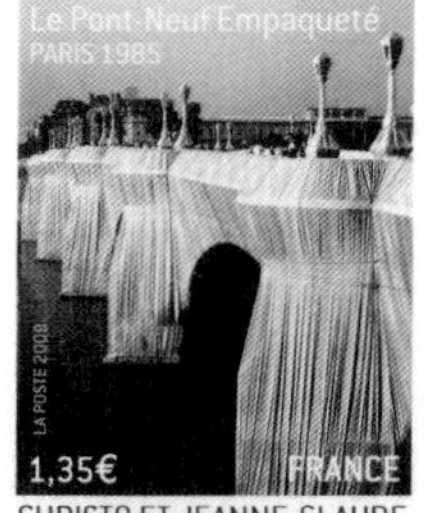
1803 *Le Pont Neuf Wrapped*, 1985 (Christo and Jeanne-Claude)

2009. Art. Self-adhesive or ordinary gum.
4651 **1803** €1.35 multicoloured 5·75 3·25

1804 Place Royale (now Place de la Bourse) (image scaled to 63% of original size)

2009. Bordeaux, Gironde
4652 **1804** 56c. multicoloured 2·50 1·40

1805 Jean Moulin

2009. Jean Moulin (member of the French Resistance) Commemoration. Self-adhesive or ordinary gum.
4653 **1805** 56c. multicoloured 2·50 1·40

1805a Giant Panda

2009. Endangered Species. Multicoloured.

4654	56c. Type **1805a**	2·50	1·40
4655	56c. Rhinocerus	2·50	1·40
4656	70c. Auroch (horiz)	3·00	1·60
4657	90c. Californian condor (horiz)	10·50	5·75
MS4658	160×110 mm. Nos. 4654/7	11·00	11·00

1805b Early Aircraft

2009. Centenary of Coupe Aeronautique Gordon-Bennett.
4659 **1805b** 56c. deep brown and black 2·50 1·40

1806 Etienne Dolet

2009. 500th Birth Anniv of Etienne Dolet (scholar, translator and printer).
4660 **1806** 56c. deep brownish grey, dull orange and dull vermilion 2·50 1·40

1807 Louis Bleriot and *Bleriot XI*

2009. Centenary of Bleriot's Cross Channel Flight.
4661 **1807** €2 multicoloured 8·00 5·00

1808 Chair-O-Plane ('Les Chaise Volante')

2009. The Funfair. Sheet 143×135 mm containing T 1808 and similar vert designs. Multicoloured.
MS4662 56c.×6, Type **1808**; Big Wheel ('La Grande Roue'); Roller Coaster ('Les Montagnes Russes'); Carousel ('Le Manege'); Toffee apple ('La Pomme D'Amour'); Fishing for ducks ('La Peche aux Canards') 14·50 14·50

1809 Woman wearing Green Dress

1810 Woman wearing Trousers

2009. Greetings Stamps. No Value Expressed. Multicoloured. Self-adhesive.

4663	(56c.) Type **1809** (20×26 mm)	2·50	1·40
4664	(56c.) Rear view of seated girl holding balloons (20×26 mm)	2·00	1·40
4665	(56c.) Cakes (20×26 mm)	2·50	1·50
4666	(56c.) Type **1810** (37×23 mm)	2·50	1·40
4667	(56c.) Figure with arms and legs raised (37×23 mm)	2·50	1·40
4668	(56c.) Woman holding letter facing left (37×23 mm)	2·50	1·40
4669	(56c.) Clown (37×23 mm)	2·50	1·40
4670	(56c.) Woman wearing tiered dress holding letters (20×26 mm)	2·50	1·40
4671	(56c.) Bird (20×26 mm)	2·50	1·40
4672	(56c.) Acrobat (20×26 mm)	2·50	1·40
4673	(56c.) Figure wearing blue tiered trousers facing left (37×23 mm)	2·50	1·40
4674	(56c.) Cake, cake slice and heart (37×23 mm)	2·50	1·40
4675	(56c.) Cow holding flowers (37×23 mm)	2·50	1·40
4676	(56c.) Grey haired woman (37×23 mm)	2·50	1·40

Nos. 4663/76 were issued for use on mail within France weighing 20 grams or less.

1811 'Geoffroy'

1812 'Chouette, des nouvelles'

2009. Sourires

4677	(56c.) Type **1811** (20×26 mm)	2·50	1·40
4678	(56c.) Nicolas	2·50	1·40
4679	(56c.) Joachim	2·50	1·40
4680	(56c.) Type **1812** (37×23 mm)	2·50	1·40
4681	(56c.) Vous me ferez cent lignes!	2·50	1·40
4682	(56c.) J	2·50	1·40
4683	(56c.) C	2·50	1·40
4684	(56c.) Nicolas	2·50	1·40
4685	(56c.) Eudes	2·50	1·40
4686	(56c.) Nicolas	2·50	1·40
4687	(56c.) Nicolas writing on typewriter (37×23 mm)	2·50	1·40
4688	(56c.) Chere Maman	2·50	1·40
4689	(56c.) C	2·50	1·40
4690	(56c.) moi, je vieux pas grand chose reellement	2·50	1·40

Nos. 4677/90 were issued for use on mail within France weighing 20 grams or less.

1813 Eugene Vaille

2009. 50th Death Anniv of Eugene Vaille (first curator of the Postal Museum of France, the forerunner of the Museum of La Poste). Self-adhesive.
4692 **1813** 56c. brown, black and orange-brown 2·50 1·40

1814 Henry Dunant

2009. Red Cross. 150th Anniv of Battle of Solferino (witnessed by Henry Dunant who instigated campaign resulting in establishment of Geneva Conventions and Red Cross). Sheet 160×110 mm containing T **1814** and similar designs. Each black, ultramarine and scarlet-vermilion.
MS4693 56c.×5, Type **1814**; Wounded, Battle of Solferino; *Pelias Et Nelee* (Georges Braque) (horiz); Committee members, Geneva Convention; Globe (International Federation of Red Cross and Red Crescent) 21·00 21·00

1815 Bandstand

2009. Salon de Timbre. Gardens of France. Jardin des Plantes, Paris. Sheet 95×110 mm containing T 1815 and similar vert design. Multicoloured.
MS4694 €2.22×2, Type **1815**; Mexican Hothouse, built by Rohault de Fleury 19·00 19·00

1816 Abbaye de Royaumont, Val d'Oise

2009
4695 **1816** 56c. multicoloured 2·50 1·40

1817 Rene de Saint-Marceaux (sculptor and creator of statue used as emblem of Universal Postal Union) and UPU Monument

2009. Centenary of UPU Monument. Rene de Saint-Marceaux (sculptor and creator of statue used as emblem of Universal Postal Union) Commemoration.
4696 **1817** 70c. multicoloured 3·00 1·70

1818 Porcelain Doll

2009. Dolls. Multicoloured.
MS4697 144×105 mm. 56c.×6, Type **1818**; Inscr 'Poupée GéGé' (horiz); Rag doll (horiz); Bella doll (horiz); Inscr 'Baigneur petitcollin' (horiz); Bisque doll 17·00 17·00

1819 *Le Promenade* (Jean-Jaques Waltz (Hansi))

2009. Art. Ordinary or self-adhesive gum.
4698 **1819** 90c. multicoloured 4·00 2·20

1820 Telegraph Machine and Juliette Dodu

2009. Birth Centenary of Juliette Dodu (spy and heroine of 1870 war). Ordinary or self-adhesive gum.
4700 **1820** 56c. multicoloured 2·50 1·40

1821 Jeronimos Monastery

2009. European Capitals. Lisbon. Sheet 143×135 mm containing T 1821 and similar multicoloured designs.
MS4702 56c.×4, Type **1821**; Bario Alto quarter (vert); Belem Tower; Discoveries Monument 10·00 10·00

2009. Marianne of Europe. The Colours of Marianne. Sheet 141×139 containing vert designs as T 1743.

MS4703 1c. chrome yellow; 5c. agate; 10c. agate; (51c.) emerald; (56c.) scarlet; (70c.) dull ultramarine; 73c. olive-green; 85c. bright violet; 90c. brown-rose; €1 bright orange; €1.30 new blue; €1.35 bright purple; €2.22 deep claret 44·00 44·00

1822 *Monsieur et Madame Bernheim de Villers*

2009. Art. Paintings by Auguste Renoir. Sheet 143×105 mm containing T 1822 and similar vert design. Multicoloured.

MS4704 85c. Type **1822**; €1.35 *Gabrielle a la Rose* 9·50 9·50

1823 Francisco Miranda

2009. Sebastian Francisco de Miranda y Rodriguez (Francisco Miranda) (Venezuelan revolutionary) Commemoration.

4705 **1823** 85c. multicoloured 3·75 2·10

A stamp of a similar design was issued by Venezuela.

1824 Map of Mediterranean and Emblem

2009. Euromed Postal Conference, Egypt.

4706 **1824** 56c. multicoloured 2·50 1·40

1825 Flowers and Window

2009. Christmas and New Year. No Value Expressed. Multicoloured. Self-adhesive.

4707 (56c.) Type **1825** 2·50 1·40
4708 (56c.) Ladder, woman's face and lantern 2·50 1·40
4709 (56c.) Faces and baubles 2·50 1·40
4710 (56c.) Blonde woman wearing orange dress 2·50 1·40
4711 (56c.) Sprite riding blue lion 2·50 1·40
4712 (56c.) Two older women exchanging presents 2·50 1·40
4713 (56c.) Santa releasing doves holding envelopes 2·50 1·40
4714 (56c.) Flowers and stylized dove 2·50 1·40
4715 (56c.) Guitarist 2·50 1·40
4716 (56c.) Bouquet and tiny women on arm 2·50 1·40
4717 (56c.) Blonde woman kneeling 2·50 1·40
4718 (56c.) Figure in air balloon basket throwing symbols of good luck 2·50 1·40
4719 (56c.) Figure in Zeppelin basket throwing symbols of good luck 2·50 1·40
4720 (56c.) Woman catching gifts in box 2·50 1·40

Nos. 4707/20 were issued for use on mail within France weighing 20 grams or less.

1826 *Jeanne d'Arc*

2009. *Jeanne d'Arc* (French Navyhelicopter cruiser). Multicoloured.

4721 56c. Type **1826** 2·50 1·40
4722 56c. Crew members (29×35 mm) 2·50 1·40

1827 Asterix

2009. 50th Anniv of Asterix (character created by writer Rene Goscinny and illustrated by Albert Uderzo). Red Cross (MS4724). Multicoloured.

4723 56c. Type **1827** 2·50 1·40

MS4724 205×95 mm. 56c.×6, Cacofonix bound, hanging from tree (40×30 mm); As Type **1827**; Villagers queuing for potion from Getafix (80×26 mm); Panacea (30×40 mm); Dogmatix and bone (22×18 mm); Obelix carrying menhir (49×100 mm) 15·00 15·00

No. **MS**4724 was sold for €5.20, the premium being for the benefit of the Red Cross.

1828 Woman reading

2010. St. Valentine's Day. Multicoloured.

4725 56c. Type **1828** 2·50 1·40
4726 90c. Woman with arms raised 4·00 2·20

MS4727 143×136 mm. 56c.×5, As Type **1828** 12·50 12·50

Nos. 4728/9 are left for stamps not yet received.

1829 Tiger

2010. Chinese New Year. Year of the Tiger.

4730 **1829** 56c. multicoloured 2·50 1·40

1830 'Solidarite Haiti'

2010. Red Cross Fund. For Victims of Haiti Earthquake. (a) Ordinary gum

4731 **1830** (56c.) + 44c. scarlet 4·00 2·25

(b) Self-adhesive gum

4732 **1830** (56c.) + 44c. scarlet 4·00 2·25

1831 Abbe Pierre

2010. Abbe Pierre (Henri Marie Joseph Groues) (member of WWII resistance and founder of Emmaus movement, helping the poor, homeless and refugees) Commemoration. Ordinary or self-adhesive gum.

4733 **1831** 56c. dull aquamarine, greenish blue and deep reddish purple 2·50 1·40

1832 Angel playing Harp (Gustav Moreau)

2010. Music . Multicoloured.

4735 (56c.) Type **1832** 2·50 1·40
4736 (56c.) Woman playing concert harp (Francois Andre Vincent) 2·50 1·40
4737 (56c.) Woman and man playing cello (Karl Gustav Klingstedt) 2·50 1·40
4738 (56c.) Woman playing guitar (Camille Roqueplan) 2·50 1·40
4739 (56c.) Horn players (Daniel Rabel) 2·50 1·40
4740 (56c.) Man playing saxaphone (Marthe and Juliette Vesque) 2·50 1·40
4741 (56c.) Ornate pipe organ (Francois Garas) 2·50 1·40
4742 (56c.) Soldier holding cornet (Auguste Mayer) 2·50 1·40
4743 (56c.) Man playing violin and woman playing harpsichord (Carmontelle) 2·50 1·40
4744 (56c.) Woman playing piano (Pierre-Desire Lamy) 2·50 1·40
4745 (56c.) Woman playing tambourine (Theodore Chasseriau) 2·50 1·40
4746 (56c.) Horse mounted drums (Jaques-Antoine Delaistre) 2·50 1·40

1833 Figure Skater

2010. Winter Olympic Games, Vancouver. Multicoloured.

4747 85c. Type **1833** 3·75 2·10
4748 85c. Alpine skier 3·75 2·10

Nos. 4747/8 were printed, se-tenant, each pair forming a composite design.

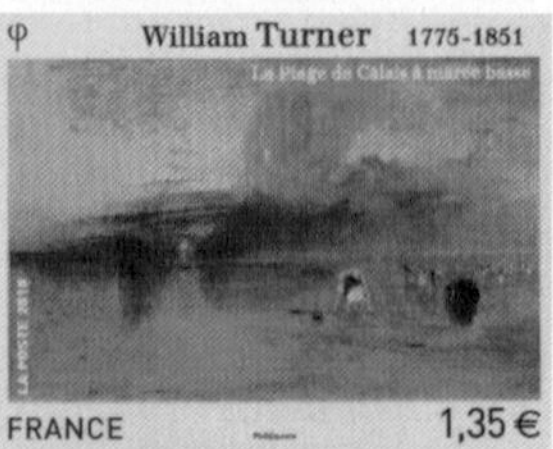

1834 *Calais Beach at Low Tide*

2010. Joseph Mallord William Turner (artist) Commemoration. Ordinary or self-adhesive gum.

4749 **1834** €1.35 multicoloured 5·75 3·25

No. 4751 and Type **1835** are left for Stamp Day (1st issue) issued on 27 February 2010, not yet received.

1836 Dolphins (sea mammals)

2010. Stamp Day (2nd issue). Water. Multicoloured. Self-adhesive.

4752 (56c.) Type **1836** 2·50 1·40
4753 (56c.) Oil covered sea bird (black seas) 2·50 1·40
4754 (56c.) 5 M 2·50 1·40
4755 (56c.) Waterfalls (water sources) 2·50 1·40
4756 (56c.) Electricity pylon (hydro-electric power) 2·50 1·40
4757 (56c.) Hot springs (geo-thermal power) 2·50 1·40
4758 (56c.) Paddy fields (irrigation) 2·50 1·40
4759 (56c.) Surf and African children 2·50 1·40
4760 (56c.) Sewage pipe (algae growth) 2·50 1·40
4761 (56c.) Cracked soil and watering can (drought) 2·50 1·40
4762 (56c.) Factory chimney and denuded forest (acid rain) 2·50 1·40
4763 (56c.) Polar bear (melting glaciers) 2·50 1·40

1837 Horse

2010. Stamp Day (3rd issue). Apollo Fountain, Palace of Versailles. Sheet 105×72 mm.

MS4764 multicoloured 8·00 5·00

1838 Conifer, Alpine Meadow, Mountain and Treaty

2010. 150th Anniv of Treaty of Turin (formalizing attachment of Duchy of Savoy to France). (a) Ordinary gum

4765 **1838** 56c. multicoloured 2·50 1·40

(b) Self-adhesive gum

4766 56c. multicoloured 2·50 1·40

1839 Henri Fabre and *Le Canard*

2010. Air. Centenary of First Seaplane (invented, manufactured and piloted by Henri Fabre) to take off from Water under its Own Power.

4767 **1839** €3 multicoloured 12·00 7·50

1840 Fort Saint Andre

2010. Villeneuve-lez-Avignon.

(a) Ordinary gum

4768 **1840** 56c. multicoloured 2·50 1·40

(b) Self-adhesive

4769 **1840** 56c. multicoloured 2·50 1·40

1841 Women

2010. International Year of Violence against Women Awareness Campaign

4770 (56c.) Type **1841** 2·50 1·40
4771 (56c.) Woman at microphone with raised arms 2·50 1·40
4772 Woman standing with hand over face (vert) 2·50 1·40
4773 (56c.) Woman standing with arms folded (vert) 2·50 1·40
4774 (56c.) Girl wearing black head-covering (vert) 2·50 1·40
4775 (56c.) Woman wearing necklaces and headcovering with central safety pin (vert) 2·50 1·40
4776 (56c.) School girls wearing blue and yellow uniforms 2·50 1·40
4777 (56c.) School girls wearing red t-shirts 2·50 1·40
4778 (56c.) Woman with braided hair facing left (vert) 2·50 1·40

4779 (56c.) Older woman with very short hair (vert) 2·50 1·40
4780 (56c.) Girl wearing multicoloured woven poncho (vert) 2·50 1·40
4781 (56c.) Older woman wearing sari (vert) 2·50 1·40

1842 Little Venice and La Maison des Têtes Hotel

2010. Colmar Haut-Rhin

(a) Ordinary gum
4782 **1842** 56c. multicoloured 2·50 1·40

(b) Self-adhesive
4783 **1842** 56c. multicoloured 2·50 1·40

1843 Merino Ram and Buildings

2010. Bergerie, Rambouillet (national centre for agricultural education, sustainable agriculture, local development and rural tourism)
4784 **1843** 90c. multicoloured 3·75 2·10

1844 Girl reading and Characters from Children's Literature

2010. Europa
4785 **1844** 70c. multicoloured 3·25 1·90

1845 Building Façade

2010. Orcival Basilica, Puy-de-Dôme
4786 **1845** 56c. multicoloured 2·50 1·40

1846 Franklin Delano Roosevelt

2010. 150th Anniv of Bourse aux Timbres (stamp show). Each black, ochre and red-brown.
MS4787 56c.×5, Type **1846**; Lucien Berthelot; Louis Yvert (horiz); Arthur Mauray (horiz); Alberto Bolaffi 13·00 13·00

1847 '2010' and Beach

2010. 150th Anniv of Deauville
4788 **1847** 85c. multicoloured 3·50 2·00

1848 Pool and Exhibits

2010. Museum of Art and Industry (The Pool), Roubaix

(a) Ordinary gum
4789 **1848** 85c. multicoloured 1·80 1·00

(b) Self-adhesive
4790 **1848** 85c. multicoloured 1·80 1·00

1849 Castle and Old Port

2010. Pornic, Loire-Atlantique
4791 **1849** 56c. multicoloured 2·50 1·40

1850 Mother Teresa

2010. Birth Centenary of Agnes Gonxha Bojaxhiu (Mother Teresa) (founder of Missionaries of Charity)

(a) Ordinary gum
4792 **1850** 85c. blue, brown-purple and black 1·80 1·00

(b) Self-adhesive
4793 **1850** 85c. blue, brown-purple and black 1·80 1·00

1851 Abbe Breuil, Prince Albert I, Institute Building and Grimaldi Caves

2010. Centenary of Institute of Human Paleontology, Paris
4794 **1851** 56c. multicoloured 2·50 1·40

1852 Players

2010. Football
4795 **1852** €5 silver 20·00 17·00

1853 Nice

2010. 150th Anniv of Affiliation of Nice to France

(a) Ordinary gum
4796 **1853** 56c. multicoloured 2·40 1·40

(b) Self-adhesive
4797 **1853** 56c. multicoloured 2·50 1·40

1854 Eclade

2010. Flavours of France. Multicoloured.
4798 (56c.) Type **1854** 2·50 1·40
4799 (56c.) Baeckaoffe 2·50 1·40
4800 (56c.) Tomme des Pyrénées 2·50 1·40
4801 (56c.) Tarte aux mirabelles 2·50 1·40
4802 (56c.) Potage au cresson 2·50 1·40
4803 (56c.) Flamiche 2·50 1·40
4804 (56c.) Pont l'Evêque 2·50 1·40
4805 (56c.) Blanc-manger 2·50 1·40
4806 (56c.) Caviar 2·50 1·40
4807 (56c.) Chapon 2·50 1·40
4808 (56c.) Fourme d'Ambert 2·50 1·40
4809 (56c.) Tarte Tatin 2·50 1·40
4810 (56c.) Quenelles 2·50 1·40
4811 (56c.) Escalope normande 2·50 1·40
4812 (56c.) Maroilles 2·50 1·40
4813 (56c.) Clafoutis 2·50 1·40
4814 (56c.) Gougères 2·50 1·40
4815 (56c.) Tian 2·50 1·40
4816 (56c.) Brocciu 2·50 1·40
4817 (56c.) Abricots rouge au miel 2·50 1·40
4818 (56c.) Homard breton 2·50 1·40
4819 (56c.) Brochet au beurre blanc 2·50 1·40
4820 (56c.) Chaource 2·50 1·40
4821 (56c.) Paris-Brest 2·50 1·40

1855 Launch Pad

2010. Launch of Soyuz Spacecraft from Sinnamary, Guyana

(a) Ordinary gum
4823 **1855** 85c. multicoloured 3·50 2·75

(b) Self-adhesive
4824 **1855** 85c. multicoloured 3·50 2·75

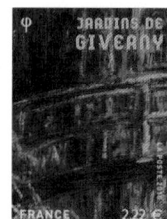

1856 Bridge at Giverny (detail)

2010. Gardens of Giverny. *Le Bassin aux nymphéas* by Claude Monet . Multicoloured.
MS4825 €2.22×2, Type **1856**; Pond at Giverny (detail) 17·00 17·00

2010. Salon de Timbres, Gardens of France. Jardin des Plantes, Paris and Gardens of Giverny. Multicoloured.
MS4826 €2.22×4, As Type **1815**; Mexican Hothouse, built by Rohault de Fleury; As Type **1856**; Pond at Giverny (detail, *Le Bassin aux nymphéas* by Claude Monet) 35·00 35·00
No. **MS**4826 contains the stamps of **MS** and **MS**4825.

1857 'tu y crois?' (do you believe?) **1858** a fond!' ('flat out!')

2010. World Cup Football Championships, South Africa (1st issue)
4827 **1857** 56c. multicoloured 2·50 1·40
4828 **1858** 56c. multicoloured 2·50 1·40

1859 Players Legs and Ball

2010. World Cup Football Championships, South Africa (2nd issue)
MS4829 85c.×4, Type **1859**; Players, rear view (vert); Parliament Building, Pretoria (vert); Cape Town, South Africa 11·50 11·50

1860 Bas-relief, Tournus

2010. Romanesque Art. Multicoloured.

(a) Booklet stamps
4830 (56c.) Type **1860** 2·50 1·40
4831 (56c.) Arched nave, Léoncel 2·50 1·40
4832 (56c.) Beatus (Apocalypse) (detail), St.-Sever 2·50 1·40
4833 (56c.) Serrabone Abbey, Boule d'Amont 2·50 1·40
4834 (56c.) Carved stone birds, L'Île-Bouchard 2·50 1·40
4835 (56c.) Illuminated letter from Book of Job, Citeaux Abbey 2·50 1·40
4836 (56c.) Fresco, St. Martin's Church, Nohant-Vic 2·50 1·40
4837 (56c.) Bas-relief, Clermont-Ferrand Cathedral 2·50 1·40
4838 (56c.) Fresco, St. Jacques des Guérets church 2·50 1·40
4839 (56c.) Stone carving, Angoulême Cathedral 2·50 1·40
4840 (56c.) Illuminated manuscript, Cluny Abbey 2·50 1·40
4841 (56c.) Carved tympanum, Conques church 2·50 1·40

(b) Sheet stamps
4842 (56c.) As No. 4831 2·50 1·40
4843 (56c.) As No. 4834 2·50 1·40

1861 Montbrun-Lauragais

2010. Windmills. Multicoloured.
MS4844 56c.×6, Type **1861**; Cassel; Aigremonts Bléré (horiz); Daudet Fontveille (horiz) ; Villeneuve-d'Ascq; Birlot Île-de-Bréhat (horiz) 14·00 14·00

1862 Young People and Singapore Skyline

2010. Youth Olympic Games, Singapore
4845 **1862** 85c. multicoloured 3·00 1·70

1863 Maman

2010. Louise Joséphine Bourgeois (artist and sculptor) Commemoration

(a) Ordinary gum
4846 **1863** €1.35 multicoloured 6·00 3·25

(b) Self-adhesive
4847 **1863** €1.35 multicoloured 6·00 3·25

1864 General de Gaulle and Microphone

2010. 70th Anniv of Appeal of 18 June 1940 by Charles de Gaulle, leader of Free French Forces (origin of French Resistance)

MS4848 **1864** 56c. multicoloured 10·00 10·00

1865 La Conciergerie

2010. Fédération Françaises des Associations Philatélique (FFAP) Congress, Paris

4849 **1865** 56c. multicoloured 2·50 1·40

No. 4849 has a half stamp size illustrated label attached at right.

1866 French Pavilion

2010. Expo 2010, Shanghai

4850 **1866** 85c. multicoloured 3·50 2·75

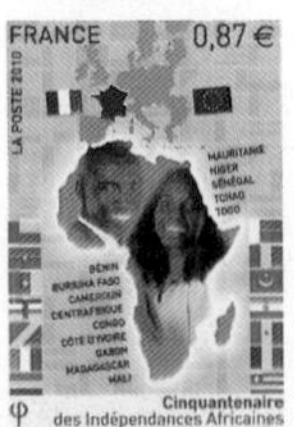
1867 Couple enclosed in Map of Africa

2010. 50th Anniv of French African Colonies Independence

(a) Ordinary gum

4851 **1867** 87c. multicoloured 2·50 1·40

(b) Self-adhesive

4852 **1867** 87c. multicoloured 2·50 1·40

1868 *Morpho menelaus* (blue morpho)

2010. Butterflies. Multicoloured.

4853 58c. Type **1868** 2·50 1·40

MS4854 110×160 mm. 58c. As Type **1868**; 58c.*Cerura vinula* (caterpillar)75c. *Thersamolycaena dispar* (vert); 95c. *Callophrys rubi* 10·00 10·00

1869 Children writing in Hebrew and French

2010. 150th Anniv of France–Israel Alliance

4855 **1869** 58c. multicoloured 2·50 1·40

1870 Arcueil and Cachan Aqueduct

2010. Arcueil and Cachan Aqueduct, Val-de-Marne

4856 **1870** 58c. multicoloured 2·50 1·40

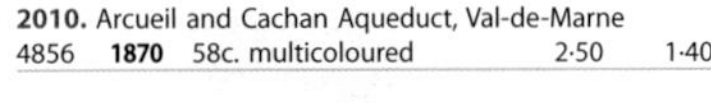

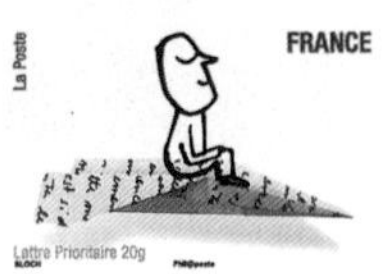
1871 Figure riding Paper Airplane

2010. Sourire (humour). Booklet Stamps. No Value Expressed. Multicoloured.

4857	(58c.) Type **1871**	2·50	1·40
4858	(58c.) Female figure with paper hat and scarf	2·50	1·40
4859	(58c.) Male figure wearing glasses and riding paper horse	2·50	1·40
4860	(58c.) Male figure on paper island	2·50	1·40
4861	(58c.) Couple in paper house	2·50	1·40
4862	(58c.) Male figure with telescope in paper boat	2·50	1·40
4863	(58c.) Couple joined by paper heart	2·50	1·40
4864	(58c.) Male figure in paper vehicle	2·50	1·40
4865	(58c.) Two figures and paper speech bubble	2·50	1·40
4866	(58c.) Boy wearing paper hat and carrying sword	2·50	1·40
4867	(58c.) Hands picking petals from paper flower	2·50	1·40
4868	(58c.) Male figure declaiming from paper stage	2·50	1·40

1872 Elise Deroche (first woman to receive pilot's licence) and Caudron G-3

2010. Pioneers of Aviation. Multicoloured.

(a) Ordinary gum

4869 58c. Type **1872** 2·75 1·70

MS4870 135×143 mm. 58c.×6, Hubert Latham (first attempt to cross English Channel) and *Antoinette* monoplane; As Type **1872**; Orville and Wilbur Wright (first manned flight) and *Wright Flyer*; Henry Farman (first cross-country flight) and Voisin biplane; Jules Vedrines (first flight over 100 mph, 1912) and Deperdussin racing monoplane; Léon Delagrange (first flight with passenger) and Voisin biplane 32·00 32·00

(b) Self-adhesive

4871 58c. As Type **1872** 2·75 1·70

1873 Able-bodied and Wheelchair Competitors

2010. World Fencing Championships, Grand Palais, Paris. Multicoloured.

4872 58c. Type **1873** 2·75 1·70

4873 87c. Two competitors attacking 4·00 2·20

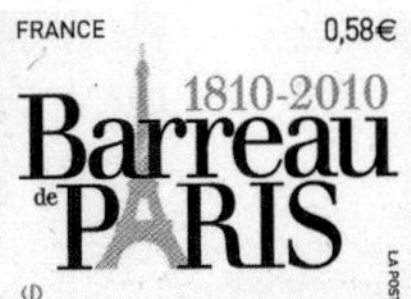
1874 Eiffel Tower and 'Barreau de Paris'

2010. Bicentenary of Barreau de Paris (Paris bar)

(a) Ordinary gum

4874 **1874** 58c. multicoloured 2·75 1·70

(b) Self-adhesive

4875 **1874** 58c. black and new blue 2·75 1·70

1875 Bridge, Villeneuve-sur-Lot

2010. Villeneuve-sur-Lot, Lot-et-Garonne

4876 **1875** 58c. multicoloured 2·50 1·40

1876 Stars and Cherub

2010. Greetings. Booklet Stamps. Multicoloured.

4877	(58c.) Type **1876**	2·50	1·40
4878	(58c.) Santa Claus and children	2·50	1·40
4879	(58c.) Christmas tree bauble and flowers	2·50	1·40
4880	(58c.) Couple, baubles, flowers and striped ribbon	2·50	1·40
4881	(58c.) Parcel outline, Santa Claus decorations and baubles	2·50	1·40
4882	(58c.) Reindeer, tree and rose	2·50	1·40
4883	(58c.) Swallow carrying flowers and silver coloured heart	2·50	1·40
4884	(58c.) Flying fish, tag and flower outlines	2·50	1·40
4885	(58c.) Champagne bottle and star-shaped baubles	2·40	1·50
4886	(58c.) Green and red buttonhole decoration and tag inscribed 'DREAM'	2·40	1·50
4887	(58c.) Inscribed outline heart and multicoloured swallow	2·50	1·40
4888	(58c.) Outline yule log, mother and daughter	2·50	1·40
4889	(58c.) Christmas tree and outline trumpe	2·50	1·40
4890	(58c.) Gerbera flower, candles, lily-of-the-valley and horse shoe	2·50	1·40

1877 Emergency Phone-call

2010. French Red Cross. Multicoloured (except Red Cross emblem).

MS4891 58c.×5, Type **1877**; Recovery position; Red Cross emblem (bright vermilion and ultramarine) (horiz); Heimlich manoeuvre; Giving CPR (Cardiopulmonary resuscitation) 20·00 20·00

1878 Arc de Triomphe

2010. European Capitals. Multicoloured.

MS4892 58c.×4, Type **1878**; Notre Dame Cathedral; Palais Garnier Opera House; Eiffel Tower (vert) 9·75 9·75

1879 Spring (detail)

2010. 500th Death Anniv of Sandro Botticelli (1st issue). Multicoloured.

MS4893 87c. Type **1879**; €1.40 Three dancers (*Spring* (detail)) 9·50 9·50

1880 Virgin and Child (Caen)

2010. Flemish Primitive Art in French and Belgian Collections. Multicoloured.

MS4894 €1.80×2, Type **1880**; *Portrait of Laurent Froimont* (Brussels) 15·00 15·00

1881 Tax Stamp

2010. 150th Anniv of First Tax Stamp

4895 **1881** (58c.) chocolate 2·50 1·40

2010. 500th Death Anniv of Sandro Botticelli (2nd issue). Multicoloured.

4896 87c. *Spring* (detail) (As Type **1879**) 3·75 2·10

4897 €1.40 Three dancers (*Spring* (detail)) 6·00 3·75

1882 Map of Central and South America and Libertarian Authors' Names on Book Covers

2010. Bicentenary of Latin American Freedom from Colonialism

4898 **1882** 87c. multicoloured 3·75 2·20

1883 Rabbit

2011. Chinese New Year

4899 **1883** 58c. multicoloured 2·50 1·40

1883a Tram Train

2011. Tram-Train, Mulhouse-Thur Valley

4899a **1883a** 58c. multicoloured 2·50 1·40

1884 Heart

2011. St. Valentine's Day. Multicoloured.

(a) Self-adhesive gum

4900 58c. Type **1884** 2·50 1·40

4901 95c. Red heart 4·25 2·50

(b) Miniature sheet. Ordinary gum

MS4902 135×142 mm. (55c.)×5, As No. 4900×5 15·00 15·00

1885 France

2011. World Fabrics. Multicoloured.

4903 (55c.) Type **1885** 2·50 1·40
4904 (55c.) Ivory Coast 2·50 1·40
4905 (55c.) Polynesia 2·50 1·40
4906 (55c.) Italy 2·50 1·40
4907 (55c.) Iran 2·50 1·40
4908 (55c.) Egypt 2·50 1·40
4909 (55c.) India 2·50 1·40
4910 (55c.) China 2·50 1·40
4911 (55c.) Japan 2·50 1·40
4912 (55c.) Japan 2·50 1·40
4913 (55c.) Morocco 2·50 1·40
4914 (55c.) France (different) 2·50 1·40

1886 Marie Curie

2011. International Year of Chemistry

(a) Ordinary gum

4915 **1886** 87c. blue-black and chestnut 3·75 2·10

(b) Self-adhesive

4915a **1886** 87c. blue-black and chestnut 3·75 2·10

1887 *La Kiosque des Noctambules* (Kiosk of the Night Birds)

2011. Art. Jean-Michel Othoniel

(a) Ordinary gum

4916 **1887** €1.40 multicoloured 6·25 5·00

(b) Self-adhesive

4916a **1887** €1.40 multicoloured 6·25 5·00

1888 Henri Péquet

2011. Centenary of First Bulk Airmail Flight (Henri Pequet carried 6,500 letters from Allahabad, India to Naini, India)

4917 **1888** €2 multicoloured 4·00 2·40

1889 Leaf suspended from Cliff

2011. Stamp Day

(a) Sheet stamps. No value expressed. Self-adhesive

4918 (58c.) Type **1889** 2·50 1·40
4919 (58c.) Symbols of plant life emerging from globe 2·50 1·40
4920 (58c.) Hands holding young tree 2·40 1·50

(b) Booklet stamps. No value expressed. Self-adhesive.

4921 (58c.) As No. 4920 2·50 1·40
4922 (58c.) As Type **1889** 2·50 1·40
4923 (58c.) Hedgehog 2·50 1·40
4924 (58c.) Riverlets 2·50 1·40
4925 (58c.) Tree with many different fruit 2·50 1·40
4926 (58c.) Man pushing globe in wheelbarrow 2·50 1·40
4927 (58c.) Three heart-shaped plants in pots 2·50 1·40
4928 (58c.) Hands holding saplings gathered from soil 2·50 1·40
4929 (58c.) Animals following man on steps watering tree on globe 2·50 1·40
4930 (58c.) Man watering plant enclosing globe 2·50 1·40
4931 (58c.) House, figure, dead trees and cypresses 2·50 1·40
4931a (58c.) As No. 4919 2·50 1·40

(c) Ordinary gum. With face value. Recess and litho

4931b 58c. Hand holding seedling and Marianne de Europe 2·50 1·40

MS4931c 106×72 mm €2 Ruby Strawberry (painted by Alfred Riocreux and engraved by Picart Philibert) (41×52 mm) 4·00 4·00

1889a *Les amours jaunes* (detail) and Tristan Corbière

2011. Édouard-Joachim Corbière (Tristan Corbière) (poet) Commemoration

4931d **1889a** 75c. yellow-ochre, black and carmine-vermilion

1890 'FEMME DE L'ÊTRE'

2011. Miss Tic (visual artist and poet). Each black and vermilion.

4932 60c. Type **1890** 25 15
4933 60c. 'JE SUIS LA VOYELLE DU MOT VOYOU' 25 15
4934 60c. 'FEMME DE TÊTE MAIS L'ESPRIT DE CORPS' 25 15
4935 60c. 'TOUT ACHEVER SAUF LE DÉSIR' 25 15
4936 60c. 'SOYONS HEUREUSES EN ATTENDENT LE BONHEUR' 25 15
4937 60c. 'JE CROIS EN L'ÉTERNEL FÉMININ' 25 15
4938 60c. 'L'HOMME EST LE PASSÉ DE LA FEMME' 25 15
4939 60c. 'LE MASCULIN L'EMPORTE MAIS OÙ' 25 15
4940 60c. 'JE NE ME SUIS PAS LAISSÉ DEFAIRÉ' 25 15
4941 60c. 'MIEUX QUE RIEN C'EST PAS ASSEZ' 25 15
4942 60c. 'IL FAIT UN TEMPS DE CHIENNE' 25 15
4943 60c. 'CUEILLIR L'ÉROS DE LA VIE' 25 15

No. 4944 is vacant.

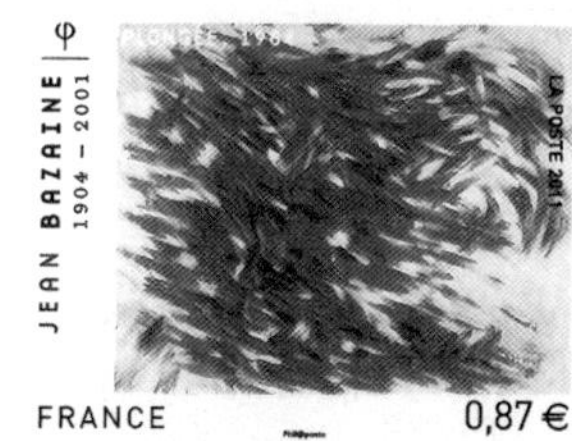

1891 *Plongée*

2011. Art

(a) Ordinary gum

4945 **1891** 87c. multicoloured 3·75 2·10

(b) Self-adhesive

4945a **1891** 87c. multicoloured 3·75 2·20

1892 Parliament Buildings

2011. European Capitals. Budapest

MS4945b 58c.×4, Type **1891a**; Széchenyi Chain Bridge; Royal Palace; Szechenyi Baths (vert) 10·00 10·00

1893 Le Bouddha

2011. Art. Odilon Redon

(a) Ordinary gum

4946 **1893** €1.40 multicoloured 6·00 3·75

(b) Self-adhesive

4946a **1893** €1.40 multicoloured 6·00 3·75

1894 Bridge from Below

2011. Pont en Bois de Crest, Drome

4947 **1894** 58c. multicoloured 2·50 1·40

1895 Riverside

2011. Angers, Maine-et-Loire

4948 **1895** 58c. multicoloured 2·50 1·40

1896 Statues, Saint Etienne Cathedral, Sens

2011. Gothic Art. Multicoloured.

4949 (58c.) Type **1896** 2·50 1·40
4950 (58c.) Stained glass window, Notre Dame Cathedral, Chartres 2·50 1·40
4951 (58c.) Circular window, Notre Dame Cathedral, Laon 2·50 1·40
4952 (58c.) Ribbed vault, Saint Etienne Cathedral, Metz 2·50 1·40
4953 (58c.) Internal view of clerestory, Saint-Pierre Cathedral, Beauvais 2·50 1·40
4954 (58c.) Stained glass, Saint Etienne Cathedral, Bourges 2·50 1·40
4955 (58c.) Circular stained glass window, Notre Dame Cathedral, Strasbourg 2·50 1·40
4956 (58c.) Corbels, Notre Dame, Amiens 2·50 1·40
4957 (58c.) Arches, Notre Dame Cathedral, Bayeux 2·50 1·40
4958 (58c.) External view of clerestory, Notre Dame Cathedral, Rouen 2·50 1·40
4959 (58c.) Lower level, Sainte-Chapelle, Paris 2·50 1·40
4960 (58c.) Basilica of Saint Denis 2·50 1·40

1897 Labrador

2011. Dogs. Multicoloured.

4961 58c. Type **1897** 2·50 1·40

MS4962 160×110 mm 58c. Type **1897**; 58c. German shepherd (vert); 75c. Poodle; 95c. Yorkshire terrier (vert) 15·00 15·00

1898 Carloman II of France

2011. 800th Anniv of Reims Cathedral. Multicoloured.

MS4963 58c. Type **1898**; 87c. Stained glass window 6·25 6·25

1899 Leaves, Squirrel, Fungi and Woodpecker

2011. Europa

(a) Ordinary gum

4964 **1899** 75c. multicoloured 3·25 1·75

(b) Self-adhesive

4965 **1899** 75c. multicoloureed 3·75 1·75

1900 St-Lazare Cathedral, Temple of Janus and Statues of Urseline Nuns

2011. Autun, Saône-et-Loire

4966 **1900** 58c. mullticoloured 2·50 1·40

1901 Claude Bourgelat (founder)

2011. 250th Anniversary of First Veterinary School, Lyon

(a) Ordinary gum

4967 **1901** 58c. indigo 2·50 1·40

(b) Self-adhesive

4968 **1901** 58c. indigo 2·50 1·40

1901a Théâtre des Cabotans (Picardie)

2011. Festivals and Traditions. Multicoloured.

4969 (60c.) Type **1901a** 25 15
4970 (60c.) Fireworks, 14 July (Paris) 25 15
4971 (60c.) La Braderie (flea market) (Nord Pas de Calais) 25 15
4972 (60c.) Médiévales de Provins (annual festival) (Ile-de-France) 25 15
4973 (60c.) La Bénédiction de la Mer (blessing the sea) (Basse-Normandie) 25 15
4974 (60c.) La Fête du Hareng (herring festival) (Haute Normandie) 25 15

4975	(60c.) La Fête des Brodeuses (embroidery festival) (Brittany)	25	15
4976	(60c.) Fête des Chalands Fleuris (flower barges) (Pays de la Loire)	25	15
4977	(60c.) La Force Basque (strength contest) (Aquitaine),	25	15
4978	(60c.) lLes Nuits Romanes (Poitou-Charentes)	25	15
4979	(60c.) La Sardane (Languedoc-Roussillon)	25	15
4980	(60c.) La Fête de la Transhumance (movement of livestock festival) (Midi-Pyrénées)	25	15
4981	(60c.) St Nicolas (Lorraine)	25	15
4982	(60c.) Le Mariage de l'Ami Fritz (folk festival) (Alsace)	25	15
4983	(60c.) Les Fêtes Johanniques (Champagne-Ardenne)	25	15
4984	(60c.) Les Soufflaculs (Franche Comté)	25	15
4985	(60c.) La Fête de l'Estive (movement of livestock festival) (Auvergne)	25	15
4986	(60c.) La St Vincent Tournante (viticultural event, to patron St Vincent) (Bourgogne)	25	15
4987	(60c.) La Foire aux Potirons (Centre)	25	15
4988	(60c.) La Frairie des Petits Ventres (Limousin)	25	15
4989	(60c.) La Fête du Citron (lemon festival) (Provence Alpes-Côte d'Azur)	25	15
4990	(60c.) La Fête des Lumières (light festival) (Rhône-Alpes)	25	15
4991	(60c.) L'Abolition de l'Esclavage (abolition of slavery) (Réunion)	25	15
4992	(60c.) Les Chants Corses (song festival) (Corse)	25	15

Nos. 4993/4 are vacant

1902 St. Etienne Cathedral, Metz

2011. La Fédération Française des Associations Philatéliques (FFAP) Congress, Metz

4995	**1902**	58c. multicoloured	2·75	1·70

1903 *Draisienne* (invented by Drais de Sauerbrunn)

2011. History of Bicycle. Multicoloured.

MS4996 58c.x6, Type **1903**; The Boneshaker (invented by Michaux and Lallement); Bicycle with pneumatic tyres (vert); Grand-bi (penny farthing) (vert); Woman's bicycle with chain, chain guard and parcel rack; Man's bicycle with chain, gears and headlamp — 1·50 — 90

1904 Georges Pompidou

2011. Birth Centenary of Georges Jean Raymond Pompidou (prime minister 1962 to 1968, and president 1969 to 1974)

4997	**1904**	58c. slate-green and new blue	2·75	1·70

1905 Church of St. Valery

2011. Varengeville-sur-Mer

4998	**1905**	58c. multicoloured	2·75	1·70

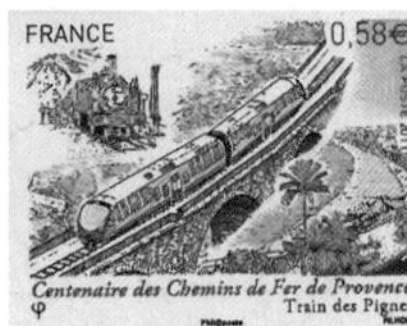

1906 Early Steam Locomotive and Modern Train

2011. Centenary of Train des Pignes

4999	**1906**	58c. multicoloured	2·75	1·70

1907 Anniversary Emblem

2011. 50th Anniv of Organisation for Economic Co-operation and Development (OECD) (Organisation de coopération et de développement économiques, OCDE)

5000	**1907**	87c. multicoloured	4·00	2·40

1908 *Aquilegia*

2011. Flowers. Multicoloured.

5001	(38c.) Type **1908**	1·10	75
5002	(39c.) Tulips (*Tulipa*)	1·10	75
5003	(46c.) Daisy (*Bellis perennis*)	3·50	2·75
5004	(47c.) Cowslip (*Primula veris*)	3·50	2·75

1909 Three Judo Moves and Japanese Ideogram meaning 'The Gentle Way'

2011. World Judo Championships, Paris Bercy

5005	**1909**	89c. multicoloured	4·25	2·30

1910 Emblem

2011. France's Presidency of G20-G8, 2011

(a) Ordinary gum

5006	**1910**	89c. multicoloured	4·25	2·30

(b) Self-adhesive

5007	**1910**	89c. multicoloured	4·25	3·00

1911 Player passing Ball from Scrum

2011. Rugby World Cup, New Zealand. Multicoloured.

(a) Ordinary gum

MS5008 143×105 mm. 89c.x4, Type **1911**; Player with ball (vert);Auckland Skyline (vert); Lake — 17·00 — 17·00

(b) Self-adhesive

5009	€5 Two players	20·00	20·00

FRANK STAMP

1939. Optd F.

F652	**61**	90c. blue	2·75	3·25

MILITARY FRANK STAMPS

1901. Optd F. M.

M309	**12**	15c. orange	90·00	8·75

1903. Optd F. M.

M314	**14**	15c. red	90·00	8·75

1904. Optd F. M.

M323	**15**	10c. red	47·00	10·00
M324	**15**	15c. green	85·00	10·00

1907. Optd F. M.

M348	**18**	10c. red	2·10	1·10

1929. Optd F. M.

M471	**15**	50c. red	6·25	1·10

1933. Optd F. M.

M516	**61**	50c. red	4·25	90
M517	**61**	65c. blue	55	55
M518	**61**	90c. blue	70	70

M 236

1946. No value indicated.

M967	**M 236**	green	2·40	1·90
M968	**M 236**	red	65	35

M545 Flag

1964. No value indicated.

M1661	**M 545**	multicoloured	60	55

NEWSPAPER STAMPS

J6

1868. With or without gum. (a) Imperf.

J131	**J6**	2c. mauve	£375	95·00
J132	**J6**	2c. blue	£750	£375

(b) Perf.

J133	**J 6**	2c. mauve	65·00	28·00
J134	**J 6**	2c. blue	95·00	44·00
J135	**J 6**	2c. pink	£325	£130
J136	**J 6**	5c. mauve	£1600	£800

POSTAGE DUE STAMPS

D4

1859

D87	**D4**	10c. black	47·00	22·50
D88	**D4**	15c. black	55·00	17·00
D212	**D4**	25c. black	£200	70·00
D213	**D4**	30c. black	£325	£180
D214	**D4**	40c. blue	£550	£650
D216	**D4**	60c. yellow	£650	£1700
D217	**D4**	60c. blue	£110	£170

D11

1882

D279	**D11**	1c. black	3·25	2·75
D280	**D11**	2c. black	55·00	33·00
D281	**D11**	3c. black	75·00	31·00
D282	**D11**	4c. black	95·00	50·00
D283	**D11**	5c. black	£190	39·00
D297	**D11**	5c. blue	30	50
D284	**D11**	10c. black	£225	2·75
D298	**D11**	10c. brown	30	50
D285	**D11**	15c. black	£130	13·00
D317	**D11**	15c. green	37·00	1·90
D286	**D11**	20c. black	£550	£170
D300	**D11**	20c. green	8·00	85
D301	**D11**	25c. red	8·00	5·00
D287	**D11**	30c. black	£325	2·75
D302	**D11**	30c. red	30	35
D288	**D11**	40c. black	£225	75·00
D304	**D11**	40c. red	16·00	5·50
D305	**D11**	45c. green	10·50	6·00
D289	**D11**	50c. black	£950	£275
D306	**D11**	50c. purple	55	55
D290	**D11**	60c. black	£950	70·00
D307	**D11**	60c. green	1·10	55
D291	**D11**	1f. black	£1200	£500
D308	**D11**	1f. pink on yellow	£800	£500
D309	**D11**	1f. brown on yellow	11·50	55
D310	**D11**	1f. brown	1·40	55
D293	**D11**	2f. black	£2000	£1000
D294	**D11**	2f. brown	£300	£190
D311	**D11**	2f. red	£375	85·00
D312	**D11**	2f. mauve	85	1·30
D313	**D11**	3f. mauve	85	1·20
D295	**D11**	5f. black	£4250	£22500
D296	**D11**	5f. brown	£700	£450
D314	**D11**	5f. orange	3·75	3·00

D19

1908

D348	**D19**	1c. olive	1·20	1·70
D349	**D19**	10c. violet	1·50	55
D350	**D19**	20c. bistre	55·00	1·70
D351	**D19**	30c. bistre	15·00	55
D352	**D19**	50c. red	£450	75·00
D353	**D19**	60c. red	3·25	5·50

1917. Surch.

D378	20c. on 30c. bistre	42·00	5·00
D379	40c. on 50c. red	12·50	5·00
D433	50c. on 10c. violet	4·25	5·00
D434	60c. on 1c. olive	7·50	6·00
D435	1f. on 60c. red	24·00	17·00
D436	2f. on 60c. red	24·00	17·00

D43

1927

D454	**D43**	1c. green	1·60	1·80
D455	**D43**	10c. red	2·40	2·75
D456	**D43**	30c. bistre	6·25	55
D457	**D43**	60c. red	6·25	55
D458	**D43**	1f. purple	18·00	4·00
D459	**D43**	1f. green	21·00	1·00
D460	**D43**	2f. blue	£110	55·00
D461	**D43**	2f. brown	£190	34·00

1929. Surch.

D471	1f.20 on 2f. blue	55·00	18·00
D472	5f. on 1f. purple	75·00	19·00

1931. Surch UN FRANC.

D494	1f. on 60c. red	37·00	2·20

D187 Wheat Sheaves

1943. Inscr "CHIFFRE-TAXE".

D787	**D187**	10c. brown	20	20
D788	**D187**	30c. purple	20	20
D789	**D187**	50c. green	20	20
D790	**D187**	1f. blue	20	20
D791	**D187**	1f.50 red	20	35
D792	**D187**	2f. blue	20	35
D793	**D187**	3f. red	20	35
D794	**D187**	4f. violet	4·50	3·75
D795	**D187**	5f. pink	50	45
D796	**D187**	10f. orange	3·00	2·50
D797	**D187**	20f. bistre	9·00	3·75

1946. As Type D 187 but inscr "TIMBRE TAXE".

D985	10c. brown	1·80	1·70
D986	30c. purple	1·80	1·70
D987	50c. green	37·00	13·50
D988	1f. blue	40	35
D989	2f. blue	40	35
D990	3f. red	40	35
D991	4f. violet	40	35
D992	5f. pink	40	35

D993	10f. red	40	35
D994	20f. brown	2·75	60
D995	50f. green	38·00	2·00
D996	100f. green	£120	9·50

D457

1960. New Currency.

D1474	**D457**	5c. mauve	5·00	90
D1475	**D457**	10c. red	7·50	80
D1476	**D457**	20c. brown	6·25	35
D1477	**D457**	50c. green	19·00	1·60
D1478	**D457**	1f. green	75·00	2·75

D539 Poppies

1964

D1650	-	5c. red. grn & pur	20	15
D1651	-	10c. bl, grn & pur	20	15
D1652	**D 539**	15c. red, green & brown	35	35
D1653	-	20c. pur, grn & turq	20	15
D1654	-	30c. bl, grn & brn	20	15
D1655	-	40c. yell, red & turq	35	35
D1656	-	50c. red, grn & bl	35	35
D1657	-	1f. vio, grn & bl	1·00	35

DESIGNS: 5c. Knapweed; 10c. Gentian; 20c. Little periwinkle; 30c. Forget-me-not; 40 c Columbine; 50c. Clover; 1f. Soldanella.

D917 "Ampedus cinnabarinus"

1982. Beetles.

D2493	**D917**	10c. brown & black	20	15
D2494	-	20c. black	20	15
D2495	-	30c. red, brn & blk	35	35
D2496	-	40c. bl, brn & blk	60	35
D2497	-	50c. red and black	35	35
D2498	-	1f. black	60	55
D2499	-	2f. yellow and black	1·20	90
D2500	-	3f. black and red	1·90	55
D2501	-	4f. brown and black	2·75	90
D2502	-	5f. bl, red & blk	2·75	55

DESIGNS: 20c. "Dorcadion fuliginator"; 30c. "Leptura cordigera"; 40c. "Paederus littoralis"; 50c. "Pyrochroa coccinea"; 1f. "Scarites laevigatus"; 2f. "Trichius gallicus"; 3f. "Adalia alpina"; 4f. "Apoderus coryli"; 5f. "Trichodes alvearius".

COUNCIL OF EUROPE STAMPS

Until March 25th, 1960, these stamps could only be used by delegates and permanent officials of the Council of Europe on official correspondence at Strasbourg. From that date they could be used on all correspondence posted within the Council of Europe building.

1950. No. 1354 optd CONSEIL DE L'EUROPE.

C1	35f. mauve and red	1·70	3·25

C2 Council Flag

1958

C2	**C2**	8f. blue, orange & pur	35	35
C3	**C2**	20f. blue, yellow & brn	35	35
C4	**C2**	25f. blue, pur & myrtle	70	70
C5	**C2**	35f. blue and red	55	55
C6	**C2**	50f. blue and purple	1·40	1·40

1963

C7	20c. blue, yellow & brn	1·40	1·40
C8	25c. blue, pur & myrt	2·75	2·00
C9	25c. multicoloured	1·40	1·10
C10	30c. blue, yellow & red	1·10	1·10
C11	40c. multicoloured	1·70	1·50
C12	50c. blue and purple	3·25	2·75
C13	50c. multicoloured	3·25	2·20
C14	60c. multicoloured	1·70	1·70
C15	70c. multicoloured	5·50	4·00

1975. As Type C 2, but inscr "FRANCE".

C16	60c. multicoloured	1·70	1·50
C17	80c. yellow, blue and red	2·20	1·90
C18	1f. multicoloured	4·50	4·50
C19	1f.20 multicoloured	6·50	5·00

C3 New Council of Europe Building, Strasbourg

1977

C20	**C3**	80c. red, lt brn & brn	1·10	1·10
C21	**C3**	1f. brown, blue & grn	55	55
C22	**C3**	1f.40 grey, grn & brn	2·50	2·50
C23	**C3**	1f.40 green	1·10	1·10
C24	**C3**	2f. blue	1·40	1·40

1978. 25th Anniv of European Convention on Human Rights. As Type C 3 with the addition of the Human Rights emblem.

C25	1f.20 black, purple & grn	70	70
C26	1f.70 turquoise, blue & grn	1·10	1·10

C5 Exterior and Interior of New Council Building, Strasbourg

1981

C27	**C5**	1f.40 violet, blue & pur	90	90
C28	**C5**	1f.60 green & brown	90	90
C29	**C5**	1f.70 green	1·10	1·10
C30	**C5**	1f.80 red, green & pur	1·20	1·20
C31	**C5**	2f. red, green & blue	1·10	1·10
C32	**C5**	2f.10 red	1·20	1·20
C33	**C5**	2f.30 green, turq & bl	1·10	1·10
C34	**C5**	2f.60 purple, bl & grey	1·40	1·40
C35	**C5**	2f.80 brown, dp bl & bl	1·40	1·40
C36	**C5**	3f. blue	1·70	1·70

C6 Foot Breaking through Shell

1985

C37	**C6**	1f.80 green	1·10	1·10
C38	**C6**	2f.20 red	1·40	1·40
C39	**C6**	3f.20 blue	1·70	1·70

C7 Council of Europe Building, Strasbourg

1986

C40	**C7**	1f.90 green	1·40	1·40
C41	**C7**	2f. green	1·40	1·40
C42	**C7**	2f.20 red	1·50	1·50
C43	**C7**	3f.40 blue	2·20	2·20
C44	**C7**	3f.60 blue	2·20	2·20

C8 Stars, Doves and Girl

1989. 40th Anniv of Council of Europe.

C45	**C8**	2f.20 multicoloured	1·70	1·70
C46	**C8**	3f.60 multicoloured	2·20	2·20

C9 Map of Europe

1990

C47	**C9**	2f.30 multicoloured	1·70	1·70
C48	**C9**	2f.50 multicoloured	1·70	1·70
C49	**C9**	3f.20 multicoloured	2·20	2·20
C50	**C9**	3f.40 multicoloured	2·20	2·20

C10 "36 Heads" (Friedensreich Hundertwasser)

1994

C51	**C10**	2f.80 multicoloured	2·40	2·00
C52	**C10**	3f.70 multicoloured	3·00	2·40

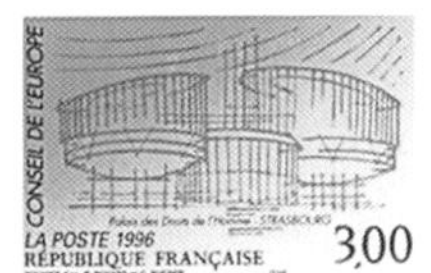

C11 Palace of Human Rights, Strasbourg

1996

C53	**C11**	3f. multicoloured	2·75	2·75
C54	**C11**	3f.80 multicoloured	3·25	3·25

C12 "Charioteer of Delphi" (replica of ancient Greek statue)

1999. Sculptures presented by Member states.

C55	3f. Type **C12**	3·00	3·00
C56	3f.80 "Nike" (Petras Mazuras)	3·50	3·50

C13 "I am black, I am white, I am black and white" (drawing, Tom Ungerer)

2001

C57	**C13**	3f. multicoloured	3·25	3·25
C58	**C13**	3f.80 multicoloured	3·75	3·75

C14 "Walking on Stars" (drawing, Tom Ungerer)

2003

C59	**C14**	50c. multicoloured	2·75	3·75
C60	**C14**	75c. multicoloured	3·25	3·25

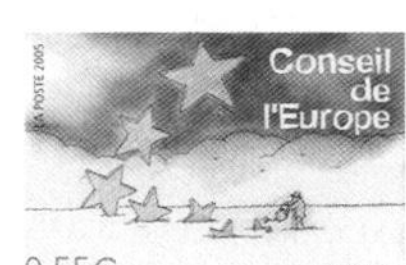

C15 "Conseil de l'Europe, semeur d'espoirs" (drawing, Tom Ungerer)

2005. Two phosphor bands. Multicoloured.

C61	55c. Type **C15**	2·75	2·75
C62	75c. Clouds in flag (Rafal Olbinski)	3·25	3·25

C16 Emblem and Globe

2007. Multicoloured.. Multicoloured..

C63	60c. Type **C16**	2·20	2·20
C64	85c. Statues (Mariano Gonzalez Beltran)	2·75	2·75

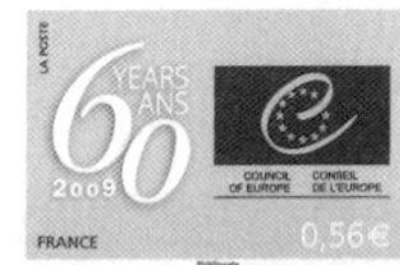

C17 '60'

2009. 60th Anniv of Council of Europe. Multicoloured.

C65	56c. Type **C17**	2·50	2·50
C66	70c. Court Building (50th Anniv of European Court of Human Rights)	2·75	2·75

C18 Tree and Roots (institutional communications emblem)

2010. 60th Anniv of European Convention on Human Rights. Multicoloured.

C67	75c. Type **C18**	3·50	3·50
C68	87c. Broken chain as '60' (anniversary emblem)	4·00	4·00

UNESCO STAMPS

For use on correspondence posted within the UNESCO headquarters building.

U1 Buddha and Hermes

1961

U1	**U1**	20c. bistre, blue & brown	55	55
U2	**U1**	25c. purple, green & blk	55	55
U3	**U1**	30c. brown & dp brown	1·40	1·10
U4	**U1**	50c. red, violet & black	1·40	1·40
U5	**U1**	60c. brown, mauve & bl	2·00	1·70

U2 Open Book and Globe

1966

U6	**U2**	25c. brown	55	55
U7	**U2**	30c. red	85	85
U8	**U2**	60c. green	1·40	1·40

U3 "Human Rights"

1969

U9	**U3**	30c. red, green & brown	90	90
U10	**U3**	40c. red, mauve & brn	1·10	90
U11	**U3**	50c. red, blue & brown	2·00	1·80
U12	**U3**	70c. red, violet & blue	3·00	2·75

U4 "Leaf"

1976

U16	**U4**	80c. blue, brown & pur	1·10	1·10
U17	**U4**	1f. orange, green & blue	55	55
U18	**U4**	1f.20 blue, red & green	70	70
U19	**U4**	1f.40 brn, mve & orge	2·50	2·50
U20	**U4**	1f.70 red, green & brn	1·10	90

U5 Old Slave Dungeons, Goree, Senegal

1980. Sites in Need of Protection.

U21	**U5**	1f.20 blue, green & red	85	85
U22	-	1f.40 mauve, blue & grn	1·10	1·10
U23	-	2f. violet, green & red	1·40	1·40

DESIGNS: 1f.40, Moenjodaro, Pakistan; 2f. Palace of Sans-Souci, Haiti.

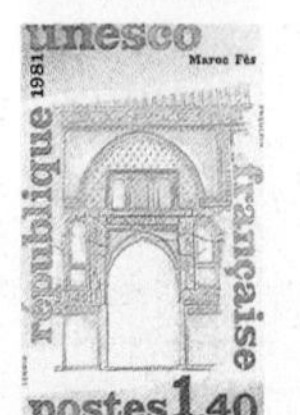

U6 Gateway, Fez, Morocco

1981. Sites in Need of Preservation.

U24	**U6**	1f.40 brown, blue & red	90	90
U25	-	1f.60 blue, red & grn	90	90
U26	-	1f.80 violet, pur & bl	1·20	1·20
U27	-	2f.30 brown, grn & bl	1·10	1·10
U28	-	2f.60 black, bl & red	1·40	1·40

DESIGNS—VERT: 1f.60, Seated Buddha Sukhotai, Thailand; 1f.80, Hue, Vietnam; 2f.60, Sao Miguel Cathedral, Brazil. HORIZ: 2f.30, Fort St. Elmo, Malta.

U7 Chinguetti Mosque, Mauritania

1983. Sites in Need of Preservation.

U29		1f.70 brown and green	1·10	1·10
U30	**U 7**	2f. brown, blue & blk	1·10	1·10
U31	-	2f.10 brown, bl & turq	1·20	1·20
U32	-	2f.80 black, bl & brn	1·40	1·40
U33	-	3f. orange, brn & grn	1·70	1·70

DESIGNS: 1f.70, Lalibela Church, Ethiopia; 2f.10, Sana'a, Yemen Arab Republic; 2f.80, City walls, Istanbul, Turkey; 3f. St. Mary's Church, Kotor, Yugoslavia.

U8 Amphitheatre, Carthage

1985. Protected Sites. Each grey, green and blue.

U34	1f.80 Type **U8**	1·60	1·40
U35	2f.20 Old Square, Havana, Cuba	1·60	1·40
U36	3f.20 Temple of Anuradhapura, Sri Lanka	2·75	2·75

U9 Temple of Tikal, Guatemala

1986. Protected Sites. Each grey, brown and green.

U37	1f.90 Type **U9**	1·70	1·70
U38	3f.40 Bagerhat Mosque, Bangladesh	3·00	3·00

1975. As Type **U3**, but inscribed "France".

U13	60c. red, green and brown	1·70	1·40
U14	80c. red, brown and lake	2·20	1·70
U15	1f.20 red, blue and purple	4·50	4·50

U10 Acropolis, Athens

1987. Protected Sites. Each brown, chestnut and blue.

U39	2f. Type **U10**	1·90	1·90
U40	3f.60 Philae Temple, Egypt	3·00	3·00

U11 St. Francis's Monastery, Lima, Peru

1990. Protected Sites.

U41	**U11**	2f.30 brn, grn & blk	2·00	2·00
U42	-	3f.20 brn, orge & bl	2·75	2·75

DESIGN—HORIZ: 3f.20 Shibam, People's Democratic Republic of Yemen.

U12 Temple of Bagdaon, Nepal

1991. Protected Sites.

U43	**U12**	2f.50 brown and red	2·00	2·00
U44	-	3f.40 brown & green	3·00	3·00

DESIGN—HORIZ: 3f.40, Herat Fort, Afghanistan.

U13 Angkor, Cambodia

1993. Protected Sites. Multicoloured.

U45	2f.80 Type **U13**	2·00	2·00
U46	3f.70 Cave paintings, Tassili n'Ajjer National Park, Algeria (horiz)	2·75	2·75

U14 Ayers Rock, Uluru, Australia

1996. Protected Sites. National Parks. Mult.

U47	3f. Type **U14**	2·75	2·75
U48	3f.80 Glacier, Los Glaciares, Argentine Republic	3·25	3·25

U15 Detail of Fresco from Villa of Mysteries, Pompeii

1998. Protected Sites. Multicoloured.

U49	3f. Type **U15**	3·00	3·00
U50	3f.80 Statues, Easter Island (horiz)	3·50	3·50

U16 Sphinx and Pyramids, Giza, Egypt

2001. Protected Sites. Multicoloured.

U51	3f. Type **U16**	3·25	3·25
U52	3f.80 Komodo National Park, Indonesia	3·75	3·75

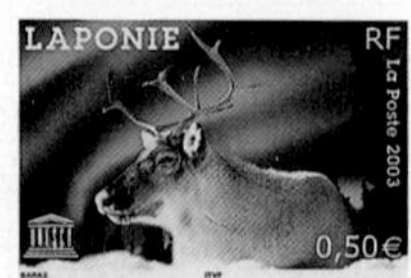

U 17 Reindeer, Lapland

2003. Protected Sites. Multicoloured.

U53	50c. Type **U17**	2·75	2·75
U54	75c. Church of the Resurrection, St. Petersburg (300th anniv) (vert)	3·25	3·25

U18 Bison, Bialowieza Forest

2005. Protected Sites. Multicoloured.

U55	55c. Type **U18**	2·75	2·75
U56	90c. Rock building, Jordan (horiz)	3·25	3·25

U19 Tiger, Siberia

2006. Protected Sites. Multicoloured.

U57	60c. Type **U19**	2·20	2·20
U58	85c. Luang Prabang, Laos (horiz)	2·75	2·75

U20 Ksar of Ait-Ben-Haddou, Morocco

2007. Protected Sites. Multicoloured.

U59	60c. Type **U20**	2·20	2·20
U60	85c. Koala bear, Austalia (vert)	2·75	2·75

U21 Mountain Gorilla, Virunga National Park

2008. Protected Sites. Multicoloured.

U61	65c. Type **U21**	2·20	2·20
U62	85c. Machu Picchu, Peru	2·75	2·75

U22 Alhambra, Granada, Spain

2010. Cultural and Natural Heritage. Multicoloured.

U63	75c. Type **U22**	3·50	3·50
U64	87c. Alpaca	3·50	3·50

Pt. 7

GERMAN OCCUPATION OF ALSACE

100 pfennig = 1 mark.

1940. Stamps of Germany optd Elsa

1	**94**	3pf. brown	35	75
2	**94**	4pf. slate	75	1·50
3	**94**	5pf. green	35	75
4	**94**	6pf. green	35	75
5	**94**	8pf. orange	35	75
6	**94**	10pf. brown	35	1·10
7	**94**	12pf. red	35	75
8	**94**	15pf. red	75	1·50
9	**94**	20pf. blue	75	1·50
10	**94**	25pf. blue	1·10	2·10
11	**94**	30pf. olive	1·50	2·30
12	**94**	40pf. mauve	1·50	2·30
13	**94**	50pf. black and green	2·10	3·75
14	**94**	60pf. black and red	2·40	4·25
15	**94**	80pf. black and blue	3·50	6·25
16	**94**	100pf. black and yellow	5·00	5·75

Pt. 4

GERMAN OCCUPATION OF BELGIUM

German occupation of E. Belgium during the war of 1914–18.

100 centimes = 1 franc.

Stamps of Germany inscr "DEUTSCHES REICH" surcharged

1914. Surch Belgien and value thus: 3 Centimes, 1Franc or 1Fr.25C.

1	**10**	3c. on 3pf. brown	40	40
2	**10**	5c. on 5pf. green	40	40
3	**10**	10c. on 10pf. red	40	40
4	**10**	25c. on 20pf. blue	2·10	2·10
5	**10**	50c. on 40pf. black and red	5·25	5·75
6	**10**	75c. on 60pf. purple	2·75	2·75
7	**10**	1f. on 80pf. black and red on rose	2·75	2·75
8	**12**	1f.25 on 1m. red	26·00	17·00
9	**13**	2f.50 on 2m. blue	23·00	21·00

1916. Surch Belgien and value, thus: 2 Cent.,1F., or 1F.25Cent.

10	**24**	2c. on 2pf. grey	30	1·50
11	**10**	3c. on 3pf. brown	95	2·10
12	**10**	5c. on 5pf. green	95	3·25
13	**24**	8c. on 7½pf. orange	95	2·75
14	**10**	10c. on 10pf. red	1·30	2·10
15	**24**	15c. on 15pf. brown	1·60	2·75
16	**24**	15c. on 15pf. violet	1·30	2·75
17	**10**	20c. on 25pf. black and red on yellow	40	1·90
18	**10**	25c. on 20pf. blue	1·30	2·30
19	**10**	40c. on 30pf. black and orange on buff	40	1·30
20	**10**	50c. on 40pf. black and red	1·30	2·75
21	**10**	75c. on 60pf. mauve	1·80	42·00
22	**10**	1f. on 80f. black and red on rose	2·10	9·00
23a	**12**	1f.25 on 1m. red	6·25	8·00
24	**13**	2f.50 on 2m. blue	25·00	37·00
25	**15**	6f.25 on 5m. red and black	32·00	48·00

Pt. 7

GERMAN OCCUPATION OF LORRAINE

100 pfennig = 1 mark.

1940. Stamps of Germany optd **Lothringen**.

1	94	3pf. brown	55	85
2	94	4pf. slate	55	85
3	94	5pf. green	55	85
4	94	6pf. green	55	40
5	94	8pf. orange	55	85
6	94	10pf. brown	55	65
7	94	12pf. red	55	65
8	94	15pf. lake	55	1·30
9	94	20pf. blue	80	1·30
10	94	25pf. blue	80	1·60
11	94	30pf. olive	1·10	1·90
12	94	40pf. mauve	1·10	1·90
13	94	50pf. black and green	1·90	3·25
14	94	60pf. black and red	2·10	3·75
15	94	80pf. black and blue	2·75	4·25
16	94	100pf. black and yellow	4·75	7·50

Pt. 7

GERMANY

A country in Northern Central Europe. A federation of states forming the German Reich. An empire till November 1918 and then a republic until the collapse of Germany in 1945. Until 1949 under Allied Military Control when the German Federal Republic was set up for W. Germany and the German Democratic Republic for E. Germany. See also notes before No. 899.

Germany.
1872. Northern areas including Alsace and Lorraine: 30 groschen = 1 thaler. Southern areas: 90 kreuzer = 1 gulden.
1875. Throughout Germany: 100 pfennig = 1 mark.
1923. 100 renten-pfennig = 1 rentenmark (gold currency).
1928. 100 pfennig = 1 reichsmark.

Allied Occupation.
100 pfennige = 1 Reichsmark.
21.6.48. 100 pfennige = 1 Deutsche Mark (West).
24.6.48. 100 pfennige = 1 Deutsche Mark (East).

German Federal Republic.
1949. 100 pfennig = 1 Deutsche Mark (West).
2002. 100 cents = 1 euro.

West Berlin.
1948. 100 pfennig = 1 Deutsche Mark (East).
1949. 100 pfennig = 1 Deutsche Mark (West).

German Democratic Republic (East Germany).
1949. 100 pfennig = 1 Deutsche Mark (East).
1990. 100 pfennig = 1 Deutsche Mark (West).

I. GERMANY 1871–1945

1

A

1872. Arms embossed as Type A.

1	1	¼g. violet	£300	£130
2	1	⅓g. green	£650	55·00
3	1	½g. red	£1400	60·00
4	1	½g. yellow	£1600	65·00
5	1	1g. red	£425	8·50
6	1	2g. blue	£2250	21·00
7	1	5g. bistre	£1300	£130
8	1	1k. green	£950	75·00
9	1	2k. red	£850	£425
10	1	2k. yellow	55·00	£225
11	1	3k. red	£2500	18·00
12	1	7k. blue	£3500	£130
13	1	18k. bistre	£700	£550

2

B

1872

14	2	10g. grey	75·00	£1900
15	-	30g. blue	£150	£3500
38d	2	2m. purple	90·00	7·50

On the 30g. the figures are in a rectangular frame.

1872. Arms embossed as Type B.

16	1	¼g. purple	£110	£140
17	1	⅓g. green	48·00	21·00
18	1	½g. orange	55·00	12·50
19	1	1g. red	£110	8·50
20	1	2g. blue	32·00	9·50
21	1	2½g. brown	£2750	£110
22	1	5g. olive	42·00	42·00
23	1	1k. green	48·00	48·00
24	1	2k. orange	£650	£3250
25	1	3k. red	32·00	9·50
26	1	7k. blue	42·00	95·00
27	1	9k. brown	£650	£600
28	1	18k. olive	48·00	£3000

1874. Surch with bold figures over arms.

29	"2½" on 2½g. brown	55·00	60·00
30	"9" on 9k. brown	£110	£650

5

6

1875. "PFENNIGE" with final "E".

31	5	3pf. green	80·00	7·50
32	5	5pf. mauve	£140	5·25
33	6	10pf. red	60·00	2·10
34a	6	20pf. blue	£650	2·10
35	6	25pf. brown	£700	25·00
36	6	50pf. grey	£2250	16·00
37	6	50pf. green	£2250	19·00

1880. "PFENNIG" without final "E".

39a	5	3pf. green	4·25	1·90
40a	5	5pf. purple	2·10	1·90
41b	6	10pf. red	16·00	1·90
42a	6	20pf. blue	8·50	2·10
43b	6	25pf. brown	21·00	7·50
44a	6	50pf. green	15·00	1·90

8

9

1889

45	8	2pf. grey	1·30	1·30
46	8	3pf. brown	3·25	1·60
47a	8	5pf. green	2·10	1·60
48b	9	10pf. red	3·25	1·60
49	9	20pf. blue	10·50	1·60
50b	9	25pf. yellow	42·00	2·10
51b	9	50pf. brown	37·00	1·60

10 "Germania"

12 General Post Office, Berlin

13 Allegory of Union of N. and S. Germany (after Anton von Werner)

14 Unveiling of Kaiser Wilhelm I Memorial in Berlin (after W. Pape)

15 25th Anniv of German Empire Address by Wilhelm II (after W. Pape)

1899. Types 10 to 15 inscr "REICHSPOST".

52	10	2pf. grey	1·20	85
53	10	3pf. brown	1·20	1·50
54	10	5pf. green	2·10	85
55	10	10pf. red	3·25	1·10
56	10	20pf. blue	10·50	85
57a	10	25pf. black & red on yellow	19·00	5·75
58a	10	30pf. black & orge on rose	26·00	1·30
59a	10	40pf. black and red	32·00	1·70
60a	10	50pf. black & pur on rose	32·00	1·40
61a	10	80pf. black and red on rose	55·00	3·25
62	12	1m. red	£150	3·75
63	13	2m. blue	£110	9·50
64	14	3m. black	£140	65·00
65b	15	5m. red and black	£475	£550

1902. T 10 to 15 inscr "DEUTSCHES REICH".

67	10	2pf. grey	2·10	85
68	10	3pf. brown	1·10	1·40
84a	10	5pf. green	85	1·90
85	10	10pf. red	4·25	1·90
86d	10	20pf. blue	1·10	1·90
87	10	25pf. black & red on yellow	55·00	3·00
88a	10	30pf. black & orge on buff	1·10	1·90
89a	10	40pf. black and red	1·60	1·90
90a	10	50pf. black & pur on buff	1·10	1·90
91a	10	60pf. purple	2·10	1·90
92a	10	80pf. black and red on rose	1·60	2·75
93B	12	1m. red	3·75	3·25
94B	13	2m. blue	7·50	6·75
95B	14	3m. black	4·25	6·25
96B	15	5m. red and black	4·25	6·75

No. 93 has three pedestrians in front of the carriage in the right foreground and has no tram in the background. See No. 113 for redrawn design.

24 Unshaded background

26

27

28

1916. Inscr "DEUTSCHES REICH".

97	24	2pf. grey	40	4·25
98	24	2½pf. grey	30	2·75
140	10	5pf. brown	30	2·75
99a	24	7½pf. yellow	40	3·25
141	10	10pf. orange	20	2·10
100	24	15pf. brown	4·25	3·25
101	24	15pf. violet	30	2·75
102	24	15pf. purple	4·25	4·25
142	10	20pf. green	30	3·25
143a	10	30pf. blue	20	2·10
103	24	35pf. brown	40	3·25
144a	10	40pf. red	20	2·75
145a	10	50pf. purple	85	3·25
146	10	60pf. olive	20	2·10
104	10	75pf. black and green	40	3·25
147a	10	75pf. purple	85	2·75
148a	10	80pf. blue	30	3·25
113	12	1m. red	2·75	3·25
149	10	1m. green and violet	20	3·25
114	12	1m.25 green	2·10	2·50
150	10	1¼m. purple and red	20	2·75
115	12	1m.50 brown	65	2·50
151	10	2m. blue and red	85	2·10
116a	13	2m.50 red	65	3·25
152	10	4m. red and black	20	3·25

No. 113 has one pedestrian behind the carriage in the right foreground and a tram in the background.

1919. War Wounded Fund. Surch 5 Pf. fur Kriegs=beschadigte.

105		10pf.+5pf. (No. 85a)	65	5·75
106	24	15pf.+5pf. (No. 101)	65	6·25

1919. National Assembly, Weimar.

107	26	10pf. red	20	2·10
108	27	15pf. blue and brown	20	2·10
109	28	25pf. red and green	20	2·10
110	28	30pf. red and purple	20	3·25

29

30 L.V.G. Schneider Biplane

1919. Air.

111	29	10pf. orange	30	3·75
112	30	40pf. green	30	4·25

1920. Stamps of Bavaria optd Deutsches Reich.

117	26	5pf. green	20	2·10
118	26	10pf. orange	20	2·10
119	26	15pf. red	20	2·10
120	27	20pf. purple	20	2·10
121	27	30pf. blue	20	2·10
122	27	40pf. brown	20	2·10
123	28	50pf. red	20	3·25
124	28	60pf. green	20	1·90
125	28	75pf. purple	65	6·75
126	28	80pf. blue	55	3·75
127	29	1m. red and grey	65	3·75
128	29	1¼m. blue and bistre	65	3·75
129	29	1½m. green and grey	75	4·75
130	29	2m. violet and bistre	1·10	5·25
131	29	2½m. black and grey	20	3·75
132	30	3m. blue	3·75	11·50
133	30	4m. red	4·25	13·50
134	30	5m. yellow	3·75	12·50
135	30	10m. green	6·75	21·00
136	30	20m. black	8·00	17·00

1920. Surch with new value and stars.

137	12	1m.25 on 1m. green	55	8·50
138	12	1m.50 on 1m. brown	55	9·50
139	13	2m.50 on 2m. purple	12·50	£275

35

36 Blacksmiths

37 Miners

38 Reapers

40

41 Ploughman

1921

153	35	5pf. red	20	2·10
154	35	10pf. olive	20	2·75
155	35	15pf. blue	20	1·90
156	35	25pf. brown	20	2·10
157	35	30pf. green	20	1·90
158	35	40pf. orange	20	1·90
182	35	50pf. purple	30	2·10
160	36	60pf. red	20	1·90
184	35	75pf. blue	20	3·75
161	36	80pf. red	20	7·50
186	37	100pf. green	20	2·10
163	37	120pf. blue	20	2·10
188	38	150pf. orange	20	1·90
165	38	160pf. green	20	12·50
193	40	5m. orange	40	2·75
194	40	10m. red	40	2·75
195	41	20m. blue and green	20	3·75

1921. 1902 stamps surch.

172	10	1m.60 on 5pf. brown	20	3·25
173	10	3m. on 1¼m. purple and red	20	3·75
174	10	5m. on 75pf. purple	30	3·25
175	10	10m. on 75pf. purple	55	3·25

39 Posthorn

1921

190	39	2m. violet and pink	20	1·90
204	39	2m. purple	30	2·10
191	39	3m. red and yellow	20	1·90

205	39	3m. red	20	2·10
192	39	4m. green and light green	20	1·90
206	39	4m. green	30	2·10
207	39	5m. orange and yellow	20	3·00
208	39	5m. orange	30	2·10
209	39	6m. blue	30	2·10
210	39	8m. green	30	2·10
211	39	10m. red and pink	20	2·10
212	39	20m. violet and red	55	2·10
213	39	20m. violet	30	2·10
214	39	30m. brown and yellow	20	2·10
215	39	30m. brown	30	9·50
216	39	40m. green	30	3·25
217	39	50m. green and purple	20	2·10

47 Arms of Munich

1922. Munich Exhibition.

198	47	1¼m. red	30	2·75
199	47	2m. violet	30	2·75
200	47	3m. red	20	2·75
201	47	4m. blue	20	2·75
202	47	10m. brown on buff	85	3·75
203	47	20m. red on rose	5·25	16·00

48

1922. Air.

218	48	25pf. brown	55	25·00
219	48	40pf. orange	55	34·00
220	48	50pf. purple	30	11·50
221	48	60pf. red	75	27·00
222	48	80pf. green	55	27·00
223	-	1m. green	20	5·25
224	-	2m. red and grey	20	5·25
225	-	3m. blue and grey	30	6·25
226	-	5m. orange and yellow	20	5·25
227	-	10m. purple and red	20	12·50
228	-	25m. brown and yellow	20	11·50
229	-	100m. olive and red	20	9·50

The mark values are larger (21×27 mm).
See also Nos. 269/73 and 358/64.

1922. New values.

235	40	50m. black	30	2·10
230	40	100m. purple on buff	30	1·90
231	40	200m. red on buff	20	1·90
238	40	300m. green on buff	20	1·90
239	40	400m. brown on buff	20	1·90
240	40	500m. orange on buff	20	1·90
241	40	1000m. grey	20	1·90
242	40	2000m. blue	40	2·75
243	40	3000m. brown	30	2·10
244	40	4000m. violet	20	2·10
245	40	5000m. green	40	2·10
246	40	100000m. red	20	1·90

50 Allegory of Charity

1922. Fund for the Old and for Children.

247	50	6m.+4m. blue and bistre	20	32·00
248	50	12m.+8m. red and lilac	20	32·00

51 Miners

1923

249	51	5m. orange	20	17·00
250	38	10m. blue	20	1·90
251	38	12m. red	20	1·90
252	51	20m. purple	20	1·90
253	38	25m. bistre	20	1·90
254	51	30m. olive	20	3·25
255	38	40m. green	30	2·10
256	51	50m. blue	55	£160

1923. Relief Fund for Sufferers in the Rhine and Ruhr Occupation Districts. Surch Rhein=Ruhr=Hilfe and premium.

257		5+100m. orange	20	12·50
259	41	20+1000m. blue and green	2·75	£120
258	38	25+500m. bistre	20	32·00

54

1923. T = Tausend (thousand).

261	54	100m. purple	30	2·10
262	54	200m. red	20	2·10
263	54	300m. green	20	1·90
264	54	400m. brown	20	8·00
265	54	500m. red	20	8·50
266	54	1000m. grey	20	1·90
312	54	5T. blue	20	23·00
313	54	50T. brown	20	2·10
314	54	75T. purple	20	15·00

55 Wartburg Castle

1923

267	55	5000m. blue	40	4·25
268	-	10,000m. olive	40	5·25

DESIGN—VERT: 10,000m. Cologne Cathedral.

1923. Air. As T 48, but larger (21×27 mm).

269		5m. orange	20	60·00
270		10m. purple	20	13·50
271		25m. brown	20	13·50
272		100m. green	20	16·00
273		200m. blue	20	48·00

1923. Surch with new value in Tausend or Millionen (marks). Perf or rouletted.

274	35	5T. on 40pf. orange	10	2·30
275a	35	8T. on 30pf. green	10	2·10
276	38	15T. on 40m. green	30	2·10
277	38	20T. on 12m. red	10	2·10
278	38	20T. on 25m. brown	10	3·25
279	54	20T. on 200m. red	30	3·25
280	38	25T. on 25m. brown	10	19·00
281	38	30T. on 10m. blue	10	1·90
282	54	30T. on 200m. blue	10	2·10
283	54	75T. on 300m. green	10	19·00
284	54	75T. on 400m. green	30	2·10
285	54	75T. on 1000m. green	30	3·75
286	54	100T. on 100m. purple	30	3·25
287	54	100T. on 400m. green	10	1·90
288	54	125T. on 1000m. red	10	2·75
289	54	250T. on 200m. red	10	7·50
290	54	250T. on 300m. green	10	23·00
291	54	250T. on 400m. brown	10	26·00
292	54	250T. on 500m. pink	10	2·10
293	54	250T. on 500m. orange	10	26·00
306	35	400T. on 15pf. brown	20	6·25
307	35	400T. on 25pf. brown	20	6·25
308	35	400T. on 30pf. green	20	6·25
309	35	400T. on 40pf. brown	20	6·25
294	35	800T. on 5pf. green	20	5·75
295	35	800T. on 10pf. green	20	6·75
296	54	800T. on 200m. red	20	£110
297	54	800T. on 300m. green	20	6·75
298	54	800T. on 400m. green	20	5·25
299	54	800T. on 400m. brown	20	17·00
300	54	800T. on 500m. green	20	£2000
301	54	800T. on 1000m. green	30	2·10
302	54	2M. on 200m. red	20	3·00
303	54	2M. on 300m. green	20	3·00
304	54	2M. on 500m. red	20	8·50
305	54	2M. on 5T. red	20	12·50

62

1923. Perf or rouletted.

315	62	500T. brown	20	3·75
316	62	1M. blue	20	2·30
317	62	2M. purple	20	27·00
318	62	4M. green	20	2·10
319	62	5M. red	20	2·10
320	62	10M. red	20	2·10
321	62	20M. blue	20	2·75
322	62	30M. purple	20	12·50
323	62	50M. green	30	2·75
324	62	100M. grey	20	2·10
325	62	200M. brown	20	2·10
326	62	500M. olive	20	1·90

1923. As T 62, but value in "Milliarden". Perf or roul.

327	1Md. brown	40	2·75
328	2Md. green and flesh	20	2·75
329	5Md. brown and yellow	20	2·10
330	10Md. green & light green	20	2·10
331	20Md. brown and green	20	2·75
332	50Md. blue	30	48·00

1923. Surch in Milliarden. Perf or roul.

342	54	1Md. on 100m. purple	30	40·00
343	62	5Md. on 2M. purple	30	£180
344	62	5Md. on 4M. green	20	32·00
345	62	5Md. on 10M. red	20	3·75
346	62	10Md. on 20M. blue	30	6·25
347	62	10Md. on 50M. green	20	6·25
348	62	10Md. on 100M. grey	20	10·50

1923. As T 62, but without value in words and tablet blank.

352	3pf. brown	55	30
353	5pf. green	55	30
354	10pf. red	55	30
355	20pf. blue	1·60	55
356	50pf. orange	3·75	1·40
357	100pf. purple	11·50	1·60

The values of this and the following issues are expressed on the basis of the gold mark.

1924. Air.

358	48	5pf. green	1·80	3·25
359	48	10pf. red	1·80	3·25
360	48	20pf. blue	9·50	7·50
361	48	50pf. orange	16·00	37·00
362	48	100pf. purple	42·00	80·00
363	48	200pf. blue	80·00	£110
364	48	300pf. grey	£140	£150

65

1924. Welfare Fund.

365	65	5+15pf. green	2·10	4·75
366	-	10+30pf. red	2·10	4·75
367	-	20+60pf. blue	9·50	11·50
368	-	50+1m.50 brown	32·00	90·00

DESIGNS: St. Elizabeth feeding the hungry (5pf.); giving drink to the thirsty (10pf.); clothing the naked (20pf.); and caring for the sick (50pf.).

66

1924

369	66	3pf. brown	40	55
370	66	5pf. green	40	55
371	66	10pf. red	55	55
372	66	20pf. blue	2·75	55
373	66	30pf. red	2·75	65
374	66	40pf. olive	18·00	95
375	66	50pf. orange	21·00	1·60

67 Rheinstein

1924

376	67	1m. green	16·00	4·75
377	-	2m. blue (A)	26·00	4·75
458	-	2m. blue (B)	37·00	20·00
378	-	3m. red	32·00	7·50
379	-	5m. green	48·00	21·00

DESIGNS: 2m. Cologne. (A) inscr "Zwei Mark"; (B) inscr "ZWEI REICHSMARK"; 3m. Marienburg; 5m. Speyer Cathedral.

71 Dr. von Stephan

1924. 50th Anniv of U.P.U.

380	71	10pf. green	85	40
381	71	20pf. blue	2·10	85
382	-	60pf. brown	5·25	1·10
383	-	80pf. deep green	13·50	2·10

DESIGN: Nos. 382/3. Similar to Type **71** but with border changed.

73 German Eagle and Rhine

1925. Rhineland Millenary.

384	73	5pf. green	55	55
385	73	10pf. red	1·30	55
386	73	20pf. blue	6·75	1·50

74

1925. Munich Exhibition.

387	74	5pf. green	4·50	7·50
388	74	10pf. red	5·50	13·50

75 Arms of Prussia

1925. Welfare Fund. Arms dated "1925".

389	75	5pf.+5pf. yell, blk & grn	75	2·75
390	-	10pf.+10pf. brn, bl & red	1·60	2·75
391	-	20pf.+20pf. brn, grn & bl	9·00	19·00

ARMS: 10pf. Bavaria; 20pf. Saxony.
See also Nos. 413/16a, 446/50 and 451/5.

76

1926. Air.

392	76	5pf. green	1·40	1·60
393	76	10pf. red	2·10	1·60
394	76	15pf. purple	2·75	2·75
395	76	20pf. blue	2·75	2·75
396	76	50pf. orange	25·00	7·50
397	76	1m. red and black	25·00	8·50
398	76	2m. blue and black	25·00	32·00
399	76	3m. olive and black	75·00	£130

78 Goethe

1926. Portraits.

400	78	3pf. brown	1·60	55
402	-	5pf. green (Schiller)	1·60	55
404	-	8pf. green (Beethoven)	2·10	55
405	-	10pf. red (Frederick the Great)	2·10	55
406	-	15pf. red (Kant)	3·25	55
407	-	20pf. deep green (Beethoven)	15·00	1·60
408	78	25pf. blue	4·75	1·30
409	-	30pf. olive (Lessing)	9·00	85
410	-	40pf. violet (Leibniz)	16·00	85
411	-	50pf. brown (Bach)	20·00	10·50
412	-	80pf. brown (Durer)	42·00	6·75

1926. Welfare Fund. As T 75. Arms, dated "1926".

413	5pf.+5pf. multicoloured	1·40	3·25
414	10pf.+10pf. red, gold and rose	2·10	4·25
415	25pf.+25pf. blue, yell & red	16·00	26·00

416a		50pf.+50pf. multicoloured	60·00	£140

ARMS: 5pf. Wurttemberg; 10pf. Baden; 25pf. Thuringia; 50pf. Hesse.

79 Pres. von Hindenburg

1927. Welfare Fund. President's 80th Birthday.

417	**79**	8pf.+7pf. green	1·20	2·10
418	**79**	15pf.+15pf. red	1·30	3·25
419	**79**	25pf.+25pf. blue	8·50	30·00
420	**79**	50pf.+50pf. brown	14·50	34·00

1927. International Labour Office Session, Berlin. Optd I.A.A. 10.–15. 10. 1927.

421	-	8pf. green (No. 404)	24·00	90·00
422	-	15pf. red (No. 406)	24·00	90·00
423	**78**	25pf. blue	24·00	90·00

81 Pres. Ebert

82 Pres. von Hindenburg

1928

424	**81**	3pf. brown	30	85
425	**82**	4pf. blue	1·30	1·70
426	**82**	5pf. green	55	85
427	**81**	6pf. olive	1·10	95
428	**81**	8pf. green	30	85
429	**81**	10pf. red	2·75	3·25
430	**81**	10pf. purple	1·30	1·10
431	**82**	12pf. orange	1·60	95
432	**82**	15pf. red	85	85
433	**81**	20pf. deep green	9·00	5·25
434	**81**	20pf. grey	8·50	1·10
435	**82**	25pf. blue	10·50	1·30
436	**81**	30pf. olive	7·50	1·30
437	**82**	40pf. violet	21·00	1·30
438	**81**	45pf. orange	12·50	4·25
439	**82**	50pf. brown	13·50	3·75
440	**81**	60pf. brown	16·00	4·25
441	**82**	80pf. brown	32·00	9·50
442	**82**	80pf. yellow	13·00	3·25

83 Airship LZ-127 "Graf Zeppelin"

1928. Air.

443	**83**	1m. red	34·00	48·00
444	**83**	2m. blue	60·00	70·00
445	**83**	4m. brown	37·00	48·00

1928. Welfare Fund. As T 75, dated "1928".

446		5pf.+5pf. green, red & yellow	75	5·25
447		8pf.+7pf. multicoloured	75	5·25
448		15pf.+15pf. red, bl & yellow	1·10	5·25
449		25pf.+25pf. blue, red & yellow	12·50	70·00
450		50pf.+50pf. multicoloured	65·00	£130

ARMS: 5pf. Hamburg; 8pf. Mecklenburg-Schwerin; 15pf. Oldenburg; 25pf. Brunswick; 50pf. Anhalt.

1929. Welfare Fund. As T 75, dated "1929".

451		5pf.+2pf. green, yellow & red	85	2·75
452		8pf.+4pf. yellow, red & green	85	2·75
453		15pf.+5pf. yellow, blk & red	1·10	2·40
454		25pf.+10pf. multicoloured	16·00	70·00
455		50pf.+40pf. yellow, red & brn	60·00	£130

ARMS: 5pf. Bremen; 8pf. Lippe; 15pf. Lubeck; 25pf. Mecklenburg-Strelitz; 50pf. Schaumburg-Lippe.

1930. Air. LZ-127 "Graf Zeppelin" 1st S. American Flight. T 83 inscr "I. SUDAMERIKA FAHRT".

456		2m. blue	£350	£425
457		4m. brown	£425	£550

1930. Evacuation of Rhineland by Allied Forces. Optd 30. JUNI 1930.

459	**81**	8pf. green	2·10	1·30
460	**82**	15pf. red	2·10	1·30

86 Aachen

1930. International Philatelic Exhibition, Berlin.

461	**86**	8pf.+4pf. green	42·00	£150
462	-	15pf.+5pf. red	42·00	£150
463	-	25pf.+10pf. blue	42·00	£150
464	-	50pf.+40pf. brown	42·00	£150
MS464a		195×148 mm. Nos. 461/4 (sold at 2m.70 in the exhibition)	£550	£2000

DESIGNS: 15p. Berlin; 25pf. Marienwerder; 50pf. Wurzburg.

1930. Welfare Fund.

465	**86**	8pf.+4pf. green	55	1·30
466	-	15pf.+5pf. red	65	1·70
467	-	25pf.+10pf. blue	10·50	32·00
468	-	50pf.+40pf. brown	32·00	£120

DESIGNS: 15pf. Berlin; 25pf. Marienwerder; 50pf. Wurzburg.

1931. Air. LZ-125 "Graf Zeppelin" Polar Flight. Optd POLAR-FAHRT 1931.

469	**83**	1m. red	£160	£150
470	**83**	2m. blue	£225	£275
471	**83**	4m. brown	£600	£950

92 Heidelberg Castle

1931. Welfare Fund.

472	-	8pf.+4pf. green	40	1·60
473	-	15pf.+5pf. red	65	1·60
474	**92**	25pf.+10pf. blue	10·50	42·00
475	-	50pf.+40pf. brown	48·00	£110

DESIGNS—VERT: 8pf. The Zwinger, Dresden; 15pf. Town Hall, Breslau; 50pf. The Holstentor, Lubeck.

See also Nos. 485/9.

1932. Welfare Fund. Nos. 472/3 surch.

476		6+4pf. on 8pf.+4pf. green	5·25	13·50
477		12+3pf. on 15pf.+5pf. red	7·50	16·00

94 President von Hindenburg

1932. 85th Birthday of Pres. von Hindenburg.

478	**94**	4pf. blue	75	85
496B	**94**	5pf. green	20	55
480	**94**	12pf. orange	6·25	85
481	**94**	15pf. red	4·25	13·50
503B	**94**	25pf. blue	65	55
483	**94**	40pf. violet	24·00	2·10
484	**94**	50pf. brown	8·50	15·00

See also Nos. 493/509 and 545/50.

1932. Welfare Fund. As T 92.

485		4pf.+2pf. blue	40	1·60
486		6pf.+4pf. olive	50	1·60
487		12pf.+3pf. red	70	1·60
488		25pf.+10pf. blue	10·50	25·00
489		40pf.+40pf. purple	37·00	90·00

CASTLES: 4pf. Wartburg; 6pf. Stolzenfels; 12pf. Nuremberg; 25pf. Lichtenstein; 40pf. Marburg.

96 Frederick the Great (after A. von Menzel)

1933. Opening of Reichstag in Potsdam.

490	**96**	6pf. green	80	1·30
491	**96**	12pf. red	80	1·30
492	**96**	25pf. blue	55·00	30·00

1933

493B	**94**	1pf. black	20	55
494B	**94**	3pf. brown	20	55
495B	**94**	4pf. grey	20	55
497B	**94**	6pf. green	20	55
498B	**94**	8pf. orange	20	55
499B	**94**	10pf. brown	20	55
500B	**94**	12pf. red	20	55
501B	**94**	15pf. red	40	55
502B	**94**	20pf. blue	65	55
504B	**94**	30pf. green	1·10	55
505B	**94**	40pf. mauve	2·10	55
506B	**94**	50pf. black and green	4·25	55
507B	**94**	60pf. black and red	1·10	55
508B	**94**	80pf. black and blue	3·25	1·70
509B	**94**	100pf. black and yellow	4·25	1·60

1933. Air. LZ-127 "Graf Zeppelin" Chicago World Exhibition Flight. Optd Chicagofahrt Weltausstellung 1933.

510	**83**	1m. red	£950	£550
511	**83**	2m. blue	95·00	£275
512	**83**	4m. brown	95·00	£275

99 Tannhauser

1933. Welfare Fund. Wagner's Operas.

513	**99**	3pf.+2pf. brown	2·40	8·00
514	-	4pf.+2pf. blue	1·90	3·25
515	-	5pf.+2pf. green	4·75	9·50
516	-	6pf.+4pf. green	1·90	3·25
517	-	8pf.+4pf. orange	3·00	5·25
518	-	12pf.+3pf. red	3·00	3·75
519a	-	20pf.+10pf. light blue	£150	£140
520	-	25pf.+15pf. blue	37·00	55·00
521	-	40pf.+35pf. mauve	£150	£170

OPERAS: 4pf. "The Flying Dutchman"; 5pf. "Rhinegold"; 6pf. "The Mastersingers"; 8pf. "The Valkyries"; 12pf. "Siegfried"; 20pf. "Tristan and Isolde"; 25pf. "Lohengrin"; 40pf. "Parsifal".

1933. Welfare Fund. Stamps as 1924, issued together in sheets of four, each stamp optd 1923–1933.

522	**65**	5+15pf. green	£130	£550
523	-	10+30pf. red	£130	£550
524	-	20+60pf. blue	£130	£550
525	-	50pf.+1.50m. brown	£130	£550
MS525a		210×148 mm. Nos. 522/5	£1900	£14000

100 Golden Eagle, Globe and Swastika

101 Count Zeppelin and Airship LZ-127 "Graf Zeppelin"

1934. Air.

526	**100**	5pf. green	1·60	1·30
527	**100**	10pf. red	1·60	1·30
528	**100**	15pf. blue	2·50	1·70
529	**100**	20pf. blue	5·00	2·30
530	**100**	25pf. brown	6·25	2·75
531	**100**	40pf. mauve	9·50	1·60
532	**100**	50pf. green	17·00	1·30
533	**100**	80pf. yellow	5·25	5·25
534	**100**	100pf. black	10·50	3·75
535	-	2m. grey and green	23·00	26·00
536	**101**	3m. grey and blue	42·00	60·00

DESIGN—As Type **101**: 2m. Otto Lilienthal and Lilienthal biplane glider.

103 Franz A. E. Luderitz

1934. German Colonizers' Jubilee.

537	**103**	3pf. brown and chocolate	3·25	8·50
538	-	6pf. brown and green	1·60	2·10
539	-	12pf. brown and red	2·75	2·10
540	-	25pf. brown and blue	13·00	27·00

DESIGNS: 6pf. Gustav Nachtigal; 12pf. Karl Peters; 25pf. Hermann von Wissmann.

104 "Saar Ownership"

1934. Saar Plebiscite.

541	**104**	6pf. green	4·00	85
542	-	12pf. red	6·25	85

DESIGN: 12pf. Eagle inscribed "Saar" in rays from a swastika-eclipsed sun.

105 Nuremberg Castle

1934. Nuremberg Congress.

543	**105**	6pf. green	4·00	85
544	**105**	12pf. red	6·25	85

1934. Hindenburg Memorial. Portrait with black borders.

545	**94**	3pf. brown	1·10	65
546	**94**	5pf. green	1·10	75
547	**94**	6pf. green	1·90	65
548	**94**	8pf. orange	3·25	65
549	**94**	12pf. red	3·25	65
550	**94**	25pf. blue	10·00	11·50

106 Blacksmith

1934. Welfare Fund.

551	-	3pf.+2pf. brown	1·20	2·10
552	**106**	4pf.+2pf. black	1·10	2·10
553	-	5pf.+2pf. green	8·00	10·50
554	-	6pf.+4pf. green	80	85
555	-	8pf.+4pf. red	1·20	2·75
556	-	12pf.+3pf. red	65	85
557	-	20pf.+10pf. green	19·00	30·00
558	-	25pf.+15pf. blue	21·00	30·00
559	-	40pf.+35pf. lilac	60·00	95·00

DESIGNS: 3pf. Merchant; 5pf. Mason; 6pf. Miner; 8pf. Architect; 12pf. Farmer; 20pf. Scientist; 25pf. Sculptor; 40pf. Judge.

107 Friedrich von Schiller

1934. 175th Birth Anniv of Schiller.

560	**107**	6pf. green	3·75	85
561	**107**	12pf. red	6·25	85

108 "The Saar comes home"

1935. Saar Restoration.

562	**108**	3pf. brown	95	1·60
563	**108**	6pf. green	95	1·10
564	**108**	12pf. red	3·00	1·10
565	**108**	25pf. blue	10·50	11·50

109 "Steel Helmet"

1935. War Heroes' Day.

566	**109**	6pf. green	1·20	2·10
567	**109**	12pf. red	1·20	2·10

110 "Victor's Crown"

1935. Apprentices Vocational Contest.

568	**110**	6pf. green	1·10	1·90
569	**110**	12pf. red	1·30	1·90

111 Heinrich Schutz

1935. Musicians' Anniversaries.

570	**111**	6pf. green	65	1·10
571	-	12pf. red (Bach)	85	1·10
572	-	25pf. blue (Handel)	2·10	1·30

112 Allenstein Castle

1935. International Philatelic Exhibition, Konigsberg. In miniature sheets.

573	**112**	3pf. brown	48·00	55·00
574	-	6pf. green	48·00	55·00
575	-	12pf. red	48·00	55·00
576	-	25pf. blue	48·00	55·00
MS576a 148×105 mm. Nos. 573/6			£1200	£950

DESIGNS: 6pf. Tannenberg Memorial; 12pf. Konigsberg Castle; 25pf. Heilsberg Castle.

113 Stephenson Locomotive "Adler", 1835

1935. German Railway Centenary. Locomotive types inscr "1835–1935".

577	**113**	6pf. green	1·40	1·10
578	-	12pf. red	1·40	1·10
579	-	25pf. blue	8·00	2·50
580	-	40pf. purple	13·00	2·50

DESIGNS: 12pf. Class 03 steam train, 1930s; 25pf. Diesel train "Flying Hamburger"; 40pf. Class 05 streamlined steam locomotive No. 001, 1935.

114 Trumpeter

1935. World Jamboree of "Hitler Youth".

581	**114**	6pf. green	1·60	3·25
582	**114**	15pf. red	2·10	4·25

115 Nuremberg

1935. Nuremberg Congress.

583	**115**	6pf. green	1·10	75
584	**115**	12pf. red	2·75	75

116 East Prussia

1935. Welfare Fund. Provincial Costumes.

585	**116**	3pf.+2pf. brown	30	55
586	-	4pf.+3pf. blue	1·10	2·10
587	-	5pf.+3pf. green	30	1·40
588	-	6pf.+4pf. green	20	55
589	-	8pf.+4pf. brown	2·40	2·10
590	-	12pf.+6pf. red	30	55
591	-	15pf.+10pf. brown	5·25	8·00
592	-	25pf.+15pf. blue	10·50	8·50
593	-	30pf.+20pf. grey	16·00	27·00
594	-	40pf.+35pf. mauve	12·50	20·00

COSTUMES: 4pf. Silesia; 5pf. Rhineland; 6pf. Lower Saxony; 8pf. Kurmark; 12pf. Black Forest; 15pf. Hesse; 25pf. Upper Bavaria; 30pf. Friesland; 40pf. Franconia.

117 S.A. Man and Feldherrnhalle, Munich

1935. 12th Anniv of 1st Hitler Putsch.

595	**117**	3pf. brown	40	95
596	**117**	12pf. red	1·10	95

118 Skating

1935. Winter Olympic Games, Garmisch-Partenkirchen.

597	**118**	6pf.+4pf. green	85	1·90
598	-	12pf.+6pf. red	1·60	1·70
599	-	25pf.+15pf. blue	8·50	10·50

DESIGNS: 12pf. Ski jumping; 25pf. Bobsleighing.

119 Heinkel He 70 Blitz

1936. 10th Anniv of Lufthansa Airways.

600	**119**	40pf. blue	8·50	4·25

120 Gottlieb Daimler

1936. Berlin Motor Show. 50th Anniv of Invention of First Motor Car.

601	**120**	6pf. green	80	1·40
602	**120**	12pf. red (Carl Benz)	1·10	1·40

121 Airship LZ-129 "Hindenburg"

1936. Air.

603	**121**	50pf. blue	25·00	1·10
604	**121**	75pf. green	27·00	1·50

122 Otto von Guericke

1936. 250th Death Anniv of Otto von Guericke (scientist).

605	**122**	6pf. green	40	65

123 Gymnastics

1936. Summer Olympic Games, Berlin.

606	**123**	3pf.+2pf. brown	50	65
607	-	4pf.+3pf. blue	40	1·10
608	-	6pf.+4pf. green	50	65
609	-	8pf.+4pf. red	3·50	1·80
610	-	12pf.+6pf. red	55	65
611	-	15pf.+10pf. red	6·75	4·25
612	-	25pf.+15pf. blue	4·50	5·25
613	-	40pf.+35pf. violet	8·75	10·50
MS613a Two sheets, each 148×105 mm. (a) Nos. 606/8 and 613; (b) Nos. 609/12			85·00	£140

DESIGNS: 4pf. Diver; 6pf. Footballer; 8pf. Javelin thrower; 12pf. Olympic torchbearer; 15pf. Fencer; 25pf. Double scullers; 40pf. Show jumper.

124 Symbolical of Local Government

1936. 6th Int Local Government Congress.

614	**124**	3pf. brown	35	40
615	**124**	5pf. green	35	40
616	**124**	12pf. red	80	85
617	**124**	25pf. blue	1·50	1·50

125 "Brown Ribbon" Race

1936. "Brown Ribbon of Germany". Single stamp in miniature sheet.

MS618	**125**	42pf. brown	10·50	19·00

126 "Leisure Time"

1936. Int Recreational Congress, Hamburg.

619	**126**	6pf. green	65	75
620	**126**	15pf. red	95	1·40

127 Saluting the Swastika

1936. Nuremberg Congress.

621	**127**	6pf. green	65	85
622	**127**	12pf. red	80	85

128 Luitpoldhain Heroes Memorial, Nuremberg

1936. Winter Relief Fund.

623	-	3pf.+2pf. brown	20	55
624	-	4pf.+3pf. black	30	65
625	**128**	5pf.+3pf. green	20	55
626	-	6pf.+4pf. green	20	55
627	-	8pf.+4pf. brown	1·30	1·80
628	-	12pf.+6pf. red	30	55
629	-	15pf.+10pf. brown	3·00	4·75
630	-	25pf.+15pf. blue	2·40	5·25
631	-	40pf.+35pf. mauve	4·00	10·50

DESIGNS: 3pf. Munich frontier road; 4pf. Air Ministry, Berlin; 6pf. Bridge over River Saale; 8pf. Deutschlandhalle, Berlin; 12pf. Alpine road; 15pf. Fuhrerhaus, Munich; 25pf. Bridge over River Mangfall; 40pf. German Art Museum, Munich.

129 R(eichs) L(uftschutz) B(und) = Civil Defence Union

1937. 4th Anniv of Civil Defence Union.

632	**129**	3pf. brown	55	55
633	**129**	6pf. green	55	55
634	**129**	12pf. red	1·30	1·10

130 Adolf Hitler

1937. Hitler's Culture Fund and 48th birthday. Four stamps in miniature sheet (148×105 mm). Perf or Imperf.

MS635	**130**	6+19pf. green	25·00	17·00

1937. "Brown Ribbon of Germany". No. MS618 optd with German eagle and ornamental border surrounding, "1. AUGUST 1937 MUNCHEN-REIM" in red.

MS637a	**125**	42pf. (+108pf.) brown	85·00	£140

1937. Nuremberg Congress. Four stamps in miniature sheet, as No. MS637, but optd REICHSPARTEITAG NURNBERG 1937 in panels of stamps.

MS638	**130**	6+19pf. green	£110	65·00

131 Fishing Smacks

1937. Winter Relief Fund.

639	-	3pf.+2pf. brown	20	55
640	-	4pf.+3pf. black	1·40	1·60
641	**131**	5pf.+3pf. green	20	55
642	-	6pf.+4pf. green	20	55
643	-	8pf.+4pf. orange	1·10	1·60
644	-	12pf.+6pf. red	25	55
645	-	15pf.+10pf. brown	2·75	5·25
646	-	25pf.+15pf. blue	5·25	5·25
647	-	40pf.+35pf. purple	9·00	10·50

DESIGNS: 3pf. "Bremen" (lifeboat), 1931; 4pf. "Burgemeister Oswald" (lightship); 6pf. "Wilhelm Gustloff" (liner); 8pf. "Padua" (barque); 12pf. "Tannenberg" (liner); 15pf. "Schwerin" (train ferry); 25pf. "Hamburg" (liner); 40pf. "Europa" (liner).

132 Hitler Youth

1938. Hitler Culture Fund. 5th Anniv of Hitler's Leadership.

648	**132**	6pf.+4pf. green	1·30	2·75
649	**132**	12pf.+8pf. red	1·30	2·75

133 "Unity"

1938. Austrian Plebiscite.

650	**133**	6pf. green	1·10	85

134 Adolf Hitler

1938. Hitler's Culture Fund and 49th Birthday.

652	**134**	12pf.+38pf. red	2·75	3·75

See also No. 660.

135 Breslau Cathedral

1938. 16th German Sports Tournament, Breslau. Inscr as in T 135.

653	**135**	3pf. brown	35	75
654	-	6pf. green	40	75
655	-	12pf. red	75	75
656	-	15pf. brown	1·40	1·10

DESIGNS: 6pf. Hermann Goering Stadium; 12pf. Breslau Town Hall; 15pf. Centenary Hall.

136 Airship Gondola and Airship LZ-127 "Graf Zeppelin"

1938. Air. Birth Cent of Count Zeppelin.

657		25pf. blue	3·50	2·10
658	**136**	50pf. green	5·00	2·10

DESIGN: 25pf. Count Zeppelin and airship LZ-5.

137 Horsewoman

1938. "Brown Ribbon of Germany".

659	**137**	42pf.+108pf. brown	30·00	65·00

1938. Nuremberg Congress and Hitler's Culture Fund. As No. 652, but inscr "Reichsparteitag 1938".

660	**134**	6pf.+19pf. green	3·25	5·75

138 Saarpfalz Gautheater, Saarbrucken

1938. Opening of Gautheater and Hitler's Culture Fund.

661	**138**	6pf.+4pf. green	1·40	2·75
662	**138**	12pf.+8pf. red	2·75	3·75

139 Forchtenstein Castle, Burgenland

1938. Winter Relief.

663	**139**	3pf.+2pf. brown	25	65
664	-	4pf.+3pf. blue	2·10	1·60
665	-	5pf.+3pf. green	20	65
666	-	6pf.+4pf. green	20	65
667	-	8pf.+4pf. red	2·10	1·60
668	-	12pf.+6pf. red	30	65
669	-	15pf.+10pf. red	4·75	6·25
670	-	25pf.+15pf. blue	4·50	6·25
671	-	40pf.+35pf. mauve	9·50	10·50

DESIGNS: 4pf. Flexenstrasse; 5pf. Zell am See; 6pf. Grossglockner; 8pf. Augstein Castle, Wachau; 12pf. Wien (Prince Eugene Statue, Vienna); 15pf. Erzberg, Steiermark; 25pf. Hall-in-Tirol; 40pf. Braunau.

140 Sudeten Miner and Wife

1938. Acquisition of Sudetenland and Hitler's Culture Fund.

672	**140**	6pf.+4pf. green	2·10	4·25
673	**140**	12pf.+8pf. red	3·25	4·25

141 Racing Cars

1939. Int Motor Show, Berlin, and Hitler's Culture Fund.

674	-	6pf.+4pf. green	3·75	4·75
675	**141**	12pf.+8pf. red	3·75	4·75
676	-	25pf.+10pf. blue	10·50	8·50

DESIGNS: 6pf. Early Benz and Daimler cars; 25pf. Volkswagen car.

142 Eagle and Laurel Wreath

1939. Apprentices' Vocational Contest.

677	**142**	6pf. green	1·60	5·25
678	**142**	12pf. red	2·40	5·25

143 Adolf Hitler in Braunau

1939. Hitler's 50th Birthday and Culture Fund.

679	**143**	12pf.+38pf. red	2·10	6·25

144 Horticultural Exhibition Entrance and Arms of Stuttgart

1939. Stuttgart Horticultural Exhibition and Hitler's Culture Fund.

680	**144**	6pf.+4pf. green	1·40	4·25
681	**144**	15pf.+5pf. red	1·60	4·25

145 Adolf Hitler Speaking

1939. National Labour Day and Hitler's Culture Fund.

682	**145**	6pf.+19pf. brown	5·25	6·75

See also No. 689.

1939. Nurburgring Races and Hitler's Culture Fund. Nos. 674/6 optd Nurburgring-Rennen.

683	-	6pf.+4pf. green	30·00	37·00
684	**141**	12pf.+8pf. red	30·00	37·00
685	-	25pf.+10pf. blue	30·00	37·00

147 "Investment" and Jockey

1939. 70th Anniv of German Derby.

686	**147**	25pf.+50pf. blue	21·00	21·00

148 Training Thoroughbred Horses

1939. "Brown Ribbon of Germany" and Hitler's Culture Fund.

687	**148**	42pf.+108pf. brown	21·00	34·00

149 "Young Venetian Woman" after Durer

1939. German Art Day.

688	**149**	6pf.+19pf. green	7·50	13·50

1939. Nuremberg Congress and Hitler's Culture Fund. As T 145, but inscr "REICHS-PARTEITAG 1939".

689		6pf.+19pf. brown	5·75	12·50

150 Mechanics at Work and Play

1939. Postal Employees' and Hitler's Culture Funds. Inscr "Kameradschaftsblock der Deutschen Reichspost".

690	-	3pf.+2pf. brown	2·75	7·50
691	-	4pf.+3pf. blue	2·75	7·50
692	**150**	5pf.+3pf. green	95	2·10
693	-	6pf.+4pf. green	95	2·10
694	-	8pf.+4pf. orange	95	2·10
695	-	10pf.+5pf. brown	95	2·75
696	-	12pf.+6pf. red	1·10	2·75
697	-	15pf.+10pf. red	95	3·25
698	-	16pf.+10pf. green	95	3·25
699	-	20pf.+10pf. blue	1·10	3·25
700	-	24pf.+10pf. olive	2·75	5·25
701	-	25pf.+15pf. blue	2·75	4·25

DESIGNS: 3pf. Postal employees' rally; 4pf. Review in Vienna; 6pf. Youths on parade; 8pf. Flag bearers; 10pf. Distributing prizes; 12pf. Motor race; 15pf. Women athletes; 16pf. Postal police; 20pf. Glider workshop; 24pf. Mail coach; 25pf. Sanatorium, Konigstein.

See also Nos. 761/6 and 876/81.

151 St. Mary's Church, Danzig

1939. Occupation of Danzig. Inscr "DANZIG IST DEUTSCH".

702	**151**	6pf. green	30	95
703	-	12pf. red (Crane Gate)	40	1·20

1939. Stamps of Danzig surch Deutsches Reich and new values.

704	**28**	Rpf. on 3pf. brown	85	3·00
705	**28**	4Rpf. on 35pf. blue	85	3·25
706	**28**	Rpf. on 5pf. orange	85	3·75
707	**28**	Rpf. on 8pf. green	1·40	5·25
708	**28**	Rpf. on 10pf. green	2·75	5·25
709	**28**	12Rpf. on 7pf. green	1·90	3·00
710	**28**	Rpf. on 15pf. red	8·00	15·00
711	**28**	Rpf. on 20pf. grey	3·75	10·50
712	**28**	Rpf. on 25pf. red	5·75	13·50
713	**28**	Rpf. on 30pf. purple	2·75	5·75
714	**28**	Rpf. on 40pf. blue	3·25	7·50
715	**28**	Rpf. on 50pf. red and blue	4·75	9·00
716	**42**	1Rm on 1g. black & orge	18·00	75·00
717	-	2Rm on 2g. black and red (No. 206)	23·00	75·00

155 Elbogen Castle

1939. Winter Relief Fund.

718	**155**	3pf.+2pf. brown	20	65
719	-	4pf.+3pf. black	1·90	2·75
720	-	5pf.+3pf. green	20	75
721	-	6pf.+4pf. green	20	55
722	-	8pf.+4pf. red	1·90	2·30
723	-	12pf.+6pf. red	25	1·10
724	-	15pf.+10pf. brown	3·25	6·25
725	-	25pf.+15pf. blue	3·50	6·25
726	-	40pf.+35pf. purple	4·00	8·50

DESIGNS: 4pf. Drachenfels; 5pf. Goslar Castle; 6pf. Clocktower, Graz; 8pf. The Romer, Frankfurt; 12pf. City Hall, Klagenfurt; 15pf. Ruins of Schreckenstein Castle; 25pf. Salzburg Fortress; 40pf. Hohentwiel Castle.

156 Leipzig Library and Gutenberg

1940. Leipzig Fair.

727	**156**	3pf. brown	40	65
728	-	6pf. green	40	65
729	-	12pf. red	55	65
730	-	25pf. blue	85	1·60

DESIGNS: 6pf. Augustusplatz; 12pf. Old Town Hall; 25pf. View of Fair.

157 Courtyard of Chancellery, Berlin

1940. 2nd Berlin Philatelic Exhibition.

731	**157**	24pf.+76pf. green	8·50	23·00

158 Hitler and Child

1940. Hitler's 51st Birthday.

732	**158**	12pf.+38pf. red	4·25	8·50

159 Wehrmacht Symbol

1940. National Fete Day and Hitler's Culture Fund.

733	**159**	6pf.+4pf. green	40	1·80

160 Horseman

1940. Hamburg Derby and Hitler's Culture Fund.

734	**160**	25pf.+100pf. blue	5·75	16·00

161 Chariot

1940. Hitler's Culture Fund and "Brown Ribbon" Race.

735	**161**	42pf.+108pf. brown	32·00	37·00

162 Malmedy

1940. Eupen and Malmedy reincorporated in Germany, and Hitler's Culture Fund. Inscr "Eupen-Malmedy wieder Deutsch".

736	**162**	6pf.+4pf. green	1·20	4·00
737	-	12pf.+8pf. red	1·20	4·00

DESIGNS: 12pf. View of Eupen.

163 Heligoland

1940. 50th Anniv of Cession of Heligoland to Germany and Hitler's Culture Fund.

738	**163**	6pf.+94pf. red and green	8·00	16·00

164 Artushof, Danzig

1940. Winter Relief Fund.

739	**164**	3pf.+2pf. brown	10	65
740	-	4pf.+3pf. blue	60	1·10
741	-	5pf.+3pf. green	25	65
742	-	6pf.+4pf. green	25	65
743	-	8pf.+4pf. orange	95	1·20
744	-	12pf.+6pf. red	25	65
745	-	15pf.+10pf. brown	1·20	3·75
746	-	25pf.+15pf. blue	1·90	3·75
747	-	40pf.+35pf. purple	3·00	8·50

DESIGNS: 4pf. Town Hall, Thorn; 5pf. Kaub Castle; 6pf. City Theatre, Posen; 8pf. Heidelberg Castle; 12pf. Porta Nigra, Trier; 15pf. New Theatre, Prague; 25pf. Town Hall, Bremen; 40pf. Town Hall, Munster.

165 Emil von Behring (bacteriologist)

1940. 50th Anniv of Development of Diphtheria Antitoxin.

748	**165**	6pf.+4pf. green	75	2·30
749	**165**	25pf.+10pf. blue	1·30	3·25

166 Postilion and Globe

1941. Stamp Day.

750	**166**	6pf.+24pf. green	1·60	4·25

167 Mussolini and Hitler

1941. Hitler's Culture Fund.

751	**167**	12pf.+38pf. red	1·60	5·75

168 House of Nations, Leipzig

1941. Leipzig Fair. Buildings. Inscr "REICHSMESSE LEIPZIG 1941".

752	**168**	3pf. brown	30	1·40
753	-	6pf. green	30	1·40
754	-	12pf. red	40	1·60
755	-	25pf. blue	85	2·10

DESIGNS: 6pf. Cloth Hall; 12pf. Exhibition Building; 25pf. Railway Station.

169 Dancer

1941. Vienna Fair.

756	**169**	3pf. brown	30	75
757	-	6pf. green	40	75
758	-	12pf. red	50	85
759	-	25pf. blue	1·10	2·10

DESIGNS: 6pf. Arms and Exhibition Building; 12pf. Allegory and Municipal Theatre; 25pf. Prince Eugene's Equestrian Monument.

170 Adolf Hitler

1941. Hitler's 52nd Birthday and Culture Fund.

760	**170**	12pf.+38pf. red	1·60	4·25

1941. Postal Employees' and Hitler's Culture Funds. Inscr "Kameradschaftsblock der Deutschen Reichspost" as Nos. 693/4, 696 and 698/700, but premium values and colours changed.

761	6pf.+9pf. green	80	3·25
762	8pf.+12pf. red	1·10	2·10
763	12pf.+18pf. red	1·10	2·75
764	16pf.+24pf. black	1·30	5·25
765	20pf.+30pf. blue	1·30	5·25
766	24pf.+36pf. violet	6·25	16·00

171 Racehorse

1941. 72nd Anniv of Hamburg Derby.

767	**171**	25pf.+100pf. blue	4·25	10·50

172 Two Amazons

1941. "Brown Ribbon of Germany".

768	**172**	42pf.+108pf. brown	2·75	6·75

173 Adolf Hitler

1941

769	**173**	1pf. grey	20	40
770	**173**	3pf. brown	20	40
771	**173**	4pf. slate	20	40
772	**173**	5pf. green	20	40
773	**173**	6pf. violet	20	40
774	**173**	8pf. red	20	40
777	**173**	10pf. brown	55	65
776	**173**	12pf. red	30	40
779	**173**	15pf. lake	40	2·10
780	**173**	16pf. green	20	2·10
781	**173**	20pf. blue	20	55
782	**173**	24pf. brown	20	2·10
783	**173**	25pf. blue	20	65
784	**173**	30pf. olive	20	65
785	**173**	40pf. mauve	20	65
786	**173**	50pf. green	20	65
787	**173**	60pf. brown	20	65
788	**173**	80pf. blue	20	65

Nos. 783/8 are larger (21½×26 mm).

174 Brandenburg Gate, Berlin

1941. Berlin Grand Prix and Hitler's Culture Fund.

789	**174**	25pf.+50pf. blue	3·75	9·50

175 Belvedere Palace, Vienna

176 Belvedere Gardens, Vienna

1941. Vienna Fair and Hitler's Culture Fund.

790	**175**	12pf.+8pf. red	95	3·75
791	**176**	15pf.+10pf. violet	1·10	4·25

177 Marburg

178 Veldes

1941. Annexation of Northern Slovenia, and Hitler's Culture Fund.

792	**177**	3pf.+7pf. brown	1·10	3·25
793	**178**	6pf.+9pf. violet	1·10	3·25
794	-	12pf.+13pf. red	1·30	3·75
795	-	25pf.+15pf. blue	1·90	3·75

DESIGNS: 12pf. Pettau; 25pf. Triglav.

179 Mozart

1941. 150th Death Anniv of Mozart and Hitler's Culture Fund.

796	**179**	6pf.+4pf. purple	20	1·30

180 Philatelist

1942. Stamp Day and Hitler's Culture Fund.

797	**180**	6pf.+24pf. violet	75	4·00

181 Symbolical of Heroism

1942. Heroes' Remembrance Day and Hitler's Culture Fund.

798	**181**	12pf.+38pf. slate	65	2·30

182 Adolf Hitler

1942

799a	**182**	1m. green	65	6·25
800a	**182**	2m. violet	2·10	6·25
801	**182**	3m. red	2·10	21·00
802a	**182**	5m. blue	3·25	13·50

183 Adolf Hitler

1942. Hitler's 53rd Birthday and Culture Fund.

803	**183**	12pf.+38pf. red	2·10	8·50

184 Jockey and Three-year-old Horse

1942. Hamburg Derby and Hitler's Culture Fund.

804	**184**	25pf.+100pf. blue	6·25	16·00

185 Equine Trio

1942. "Brown Ribbon of Germany" and Hitler's Culture Fund.

805	**185**	42pf.+108pf. brown	2·10	7·50

186 Cream Jug and Loving Cup

1942. 10th Anniv of National Goldsmiths' Institution.

806	**186**	6pf.+4pf. red	35	2·10
807	**186**	12pf.+88pf. green	75	3·25

187 Badge of Armed S.A.

1942. S.A. Military Training Month.

808	**187**	6pf. violet	20	1·10

188 Peter Henlein

1942. 400th Death Anniv of Henlein (inventor of the watch).

809	**188**	6pf.+24pf. violet	65	2·10

189 Mounted Postilion

1942. European Postal Congress, Vienna.

810	-	3pf.+7pf. blue	40	2·10
811	-	6pf.+14pf. brown & blue	65	2·10
812	**189**	12pf.+38pf. brown & red	85	3·75

DESIGNS—HORIZ: 3pf. Postilion and map of Europe. VERT: 6pf. Mounted postilion and globe.

1942. Signing of European Postal Union Agreement. Nos. 810/2 optd 19.Okt.1942.

813	-	3pf.+7pf. blue	90	3·75
814	-	6pf.+14pf. brown & blue	90	3·75
815	**189**	12pf.+38pf. brown & red	1·60	6·25

191 Mail Coach

1943. Stamp Day and Hitler's Culture Fund.

816	**191**	6pf.+24pf. brn, yell & bl	20	1·30

192 Brandenburg Gate and Torchlight Parade

1943. 10th Anniv of Third Reich.

817	**192**	54pf.+96pf. red	65	3·25

193

1943. Philatelic Cancellation Premium.

818	**193**	3pf.+2pf. bistre	20	1·30

194 Machine Gunners

1943. Armed Forces' and Heroes' Day.

819	-	3pf.+2pf. brown	55	1·70
820	**194**	4pf.+3pf. brown	55	1·70
821	-	5pf.+4pf. green	55	1·70
822	-	6pf.+9pf. violet	55	1·70
823	-	8pf.+7pf. red	55	1·70
824	-	12pf.+8pf. red	55	1·70
825	-	15pf.+10pf. purple	55	1·70
826	-	20pf.+14pf. blue	55	1·70
827	-	25pf.+15pf. blue	55	1·70
828	-	30pf.+30pf. green	85	2·75
829	-	40pf.+40pf. purple	85	2·75
830	-	50pf.+50pf. green	1·20	4·25

DESIGNS: 3pf. U-boat Type VIIA (submarine); 5pf. Armed motor cyclists; 6pf. Wireless operators; 8pf. Engineers making pontoon; 12pf. Grenade thrower; 15pf. Heavy artillery; 20pf. Anti-aircraft gunners; 25pf. Junkers Ju 87B "Stuka" dive bombers; 30pf. Parachutists; 40pf. Tank; 50pf. "S-22" (motor torpedo-boat).

195 Hitler Youth

1943. Youth Dedication Day.

831	**195**	6pf.+4pf. green	30	1·80

196 Adolf Hitler

1943. Hitler's 54th Birthday and Culture Fund.

832	**196**	3pf.+7pf. black	65	2·10
833	**196**	6pf.+14pf. green	65	2·10
834	**196**	8pf.+22pf. blue	65	2·10
835	**196**	12pf.+38pf. red	65	2·10
836	**196**	24pf.+76pf. purple	1·10	4·75
837	**196**	40pf.+160pf. olive	1·10	4·75

197 Attestation

1943. Labour Corps.

838	**197**	3pf.+7pf. brown	10	1·10
839	-	5pf.+10pf. green	10	85
840	-	6pf.+14pf. blue	10	85
841	-	12pf.+18pf. red	30	1·90

DESIGNS: 5pf. Harvester sharpening scythe; 6pf. Labourer wielding sledge-hammer; 12pf. "Pick and shovel fatigue".

198 Huntsman

1943. "Brown Ribbon of Germany".

842	**198**	42pf.+108pf. brown	30	1·70

199 Birthplace of Peter Rosegger **200** Peter Rosegger

1943. Birth Cent of Peter Rosegger (poet).

843	**199**	6pf.+4pf. green	20	1·30
844	**200**	12pf.+8pf. red	30	1·30

201 Racehorse

1943. Grand Prix, Vienna.

845	**201**	6pf.+4pf. violet	30	1·70
846	**201**	12pf.+88pf. red	30	1·70

202 Mother and Children

1943. 10th Anniv of Winter Relief Fund.

847	**202**	12pf.+38pf. red	30	1·70

203 St George and the Dragon

1943. 11th Anniv of National Goldsmiths' Institution.

848	**203**	6pf.+4pf. green	25	1·10
849	**203**	12pf.+88pf. purple	30	1·60

204 Lubeck

1943. 800th Anniv of Lubeck.

850	**204**	12pf.+8pf. red	20	1·60

205

1943. 20th Anniv of Munich Rising.

851	**205**	24pf.+26pf. red	20	2·10

206 Dr. Robert Koch

1944. Birth Centenary of Dr. Robert Koch (bacteriologist).

852	**206**	12pf.+38pf. sepia	20	1·60

207 Adolf Hitler

1944. 11th Anniv of Third Reich.

853	**207**	54pf.+96pf. brown	30	2·30

208 Focke Wulf Fw 200 Condor over Tempelhof Airport **209** Dornier Do-26 Flying Boat

1944. 25th Anniv of Air Mail Services.

854	**208**	6pf.+4pf. green	20	1·60
855	**209**	12pf.+8pf. purple	20	1·60
856	-	42pf.+108pf. blue	40	3·25

DESIGNS—VERT: 42pf. Junkers Ju 90B airplane seen from above.

210 Day Nursery **211** "Mothers' Help"

1944. 10th Anniv of "Mother and Child" Organization.

857	**210**	3pf.+2pf. brown	10	95
858	**211**	6pf.+4pf. green	10	95
859	-	12pf.+8pf. red	10	95
860	-	15pf.+10pf. purple	20	1·10

DESIGNS: 12pf. Child auscultation; 15pf. Mothers at convalescent home.

212 Landing Craft

1944. Armed Forces' and Heroes' Day.

861	**212**	3pf.+2pf. brown	50	1·60
862	-	4pf.+3pf. blue	50	1·60
863	-	5pf.+3pf. green	20	75
864	-	6pf.+4pf. violet	20	75
865	-	8pf.+4pf. red	20	85
866	-	10pf.+5pf. brown	20	75
867	-	12pf.+6pf. red	20	75
868	-	15pf.+10pf. purple	20	1·10
869	-	16pf.+10pf. green	40	1·70
870	-	20pf.+10pf. blue	50	2·75
871	-	24pf.+10pf. brown	50	2·75
872	-	25pf.+15pf. blue	1·10	5·25
873	-	30pf.+20pf. olive	1·10	5·25

DESIGNS: 4pf. Caterpillar tricar; 5pf. Parachutists; 6pf. Submarine officer; 8pf. Mortar-firing party; 10pf. Searchlight unit; 12pf. Machine gunners; 15pf. Tank; 16pf. "S-128" (motor torpedo-boat); 20pf. Arado Ar 196A seaplane; 24pf. Railway gun; 25pf. Rocket projectiles; 30pf. Alpine trooper.

213 Fulda Monument

1944. 1200th Anniv of Fulda.

874	**213**	12pf.+38pf. brown	20	1·30

214 Adolf Hitler

1944. Hitler's 55th Birthday.

875	**214**	54pf.+96pf. red	40	3·50

215 Postwoman

1944. Postal Employees' and Hitler's Culture Funds. Inscr "Kameradschaftsblock der Deutschen Reichspost".

876	**215**	6pf.+9pf. blue	20	1·10
877	-	8pf.+12pf. grey	20	1·10
878	-	12pf.+18pf. mauve	20	1·10
879	-	16pf.+24pf. green	20	1·10
880	-	20pf.+30pf. blue	25	2·00
881	-	24pf.+36pf. violet	55	2·00

DESIGNS—As Type **150**: 8pf. Mail coach; 16pf. Motor-car race; 20pf. Postal police march; 24pf. Glider workshop. As Type **215**: 12pf. The Field Post on Eastern Front.

216 Girl Worker **217** Labourer

1944. Labour Corps.

882	**216**	6pf.+4pf. green	20	95
883	**217**	12pf.+8pf. red	20	95

218 Riflemen

1944. 7th Innsbruck Shooting Competition.

884	**218**	6pf.+4pf. green	20	1·20
885	**218**	12pf.+8pf. red	20	1·20

219 Duke Albrecht

1944. 400th Anniv of Albert University, Konigsberg.

886	**219**	6pf.+4pf. green	30	1·70

220 Racehorse and Foal

1944. "Brown Ribbon of Germany".

887	**220**	42pf.+108pf. brown	30	2·75

221 Racehorse and Laurel Wreath

1944. Vienna Grand Prix.

888	**221**	6pf.+4pf. green	20	1·50
889	**221**	12pf.+88pf. red	20	1·50

222 Chambered Nautilus Beaker

1944. National Goldsmiths' Institution.

890	**222**	6pf.+4pf. green	20	1·50
891	**222**	12pf.+88pf. red	20	1·50

223 Posthorn

1944. Stamp Day.

892	**223**	6pf.+24pf. green	20	1·70

224 Eagle and Dragon

1944. 21st Anniv of Munich Rising.

893	**224**	12pf.+8pf. red	20	1·70

225 Adolf Hitler

1944

894	**225**	42pf. green	20	2·75

226 Count Anton Gunther

1945. 600th Anniv of Oldenburg.

895	**226**	6pf.+14pf. purple	20	1·70

227 "Home Guard"

1945. Mobilization of "Home Guard".

896	**227**	12pf.+8pf. red	45	3·75

228 S.S. Troopers

1945. 12th Anniv of Third Reich.

897	**228**	12pf.+38pf. red	16·00	70·00
898	-	12pf.+38pf. red	10·50	70·00

DESIGN: No. 898, S.A. man with torch.

For Nos. 899 onwards see section B of Allied Occupation.

MILITARY FIELDPOST STAMPS

M184 Junkers Ju 52/3m

1942. Air. No value indicated. Perf. or roul.

M804	**M184**	(-) blue	50	65

M185

1942. Parcel Post. Size 28×23 mm. No value indicated. Perf or roul.

M805	**M185**	(-) brown	35	16·00

Nos. M804/5 also exist overprinted **INSELPOST** in various types for use in Crete and the Aegean Islands and there are various other local fieldpost issues.

1944. Christmas Parcel Post. Size 22½×18 mm. No value indicated. Perf.

M895		(-) green	85	4·00

1944. For 2 kilo parcels. No value indicated. No. 785 optd FELDPOST 2kg.

M896	**173**	(-) on 40pf. mauve	85	4·25

NEWSPAPER STAMPS

N156 Newspaper Messenger and Globe

1939

N727	**N156**	5pf. green	75	7·50
N728	**N156**	10pf. brown	75	7·50

OFFICIAL STAMPS

O23

1903

O82	**O23**	2pf. grey	1·60	5·25
O83	**O23**	3pf. brown	1·60	5·25
O84	**O23**	5pf. green	30	75
O85	**O23**	10pf. red	30	75
O86	**O23**	20pf. blue	30	75
O87	**O23**	25pf. black and red on yellow	1·10	2·30
O88	**O23**	40pf. black and red	1·10	2·75
O89	**O23**	50pf. blk & pur on buff	1·30	2·75

O24

1905

O90	**O24**	2pf. grey	75·00	£110
O91	**O24**	3pf. brown	8·50	15·00
O92	**O24**	5pf. green	5·75	12·50
O93	**O24**	10pf. red	1·10	3·00
O94	**O24**	20pf. blue	2·10	4·25
O95	**O24**	25pf. black and red on yellow	42·00	75·00

O31 **O32**

1920. Numeral designs as Types O 31 and O 32.

O117		5pf. green	30	4·25
O118		10pf. red	1·10	2·10
O119		15pf. brown	20	3·25
O120		20pf. blue	20	2·75
O121		30pf. orange on pink	20	2·10
O122		50pf. violet on pink	40	2·10
O123		1m. red on pink	11·50	5·25

1920. Similar designs but without figures "21".

O124		5pf. brown on yellow	1·30	19·00
O125		10pf. red	20	2·30
O126		10pf. orange	85	£650
O127		15pf. purple	20	3·25
O128		20pf. blue	20	2·75
O129		30pf. orange on pink	20	2·75
O130		40pf. red	20	2·75
O131		50pf. violet on pink	20	2·75
O132		60pf. brown	40	2·10
O133		1m. red on pink	20	2·75
O134		1m.25 blue on yellow	20	5·25
O135a		2m. blue	20	2·10
O136		5m. brown on yellow	1·60	4·25

1920. Official stamps of Bavaria optd Deutsches Reich.

O137	**O31**	5pf. green	20	4·25
O138	**O31**	10pf. orange	20	2·50
O139	**O31**	15pf. red	20	2·75
O140	**O31**	20pf. purple	20	2·10
O141	**O31**	30pf. blue	20	2·10
O142	**O31**	40pf. brown	20	2·10
O143	**O32**	50pf. red	20	2·75
O144	**O32**	60pf. green	20	2·10
O145	**O32**	70pf. violet	2·75	3·75
O146	**O32**	75pf. red	40	1·90
O147	**O32**	80pf. blue	20	1·90
O148	**O32**	90pf. olive	2·10	4·75
O149	**O33**	1m. brown	20	2·75
O150	**O33**	1¼m. green	20	2·75
O151	**O33**	1½m. red	20	2·75
O152	**O33**	2½m. blue	20	2·75
O153	**O33**	3m. red	20	2·75
O154	**O33**	5m. black	11·50	34·00

1920. Municipal Service stamps of Wurttemberg optd Deutsches Reich.

O155	**M5**	5pf. green	5·25	13·50
O156	**M5**	10pf. red	3·25	6·25
O157	**M5**	15pf. violet	3·25	6·75
O158	**M5**	20pf. blue	5·25	11·50
O159	**M5**	50pf. purple	6·25	23·00

1920. Official stamps of Wurttemberg optd Deutsches Reich.

O160	**O5**	5pf. green	3·25	5·25
O161	**O5**	10pf. red	2·10	4·25
O162	**O5**	15pf. purple	2·10	4·25
O163	**O5**	20pf. blue	2·10	2·10
O164	**O5**	30pf. black and orange	2·10	5·25
O165	**O5**	40pf. black and red	2·10	4·25
O166	**O5**	50pf. purple	2·10	5·25
O167	**O5**	1m. black and grey	3·25	10·50

O48 **O50**

1922. Figure designs.

O247	-	3m. brown on red	20	2·10
O248	**O50**	10m. green on red	20	2·10
O249	**O48**	75pf. blue	30	10·50
O251	**O50**	20m. blue on red	20	2·10
O252	**O50**	50m. violet on red	20	2·10
O253	**O50**	100m. red on rose	20	2·10

1923. Postage stamps optd Dienstmarke.

O274	**51**	20m. purple	40	10·50
O275	**51**	30m. olive	20	48·00
O276	**38**	40m. green	40	4·25
O277	**54**	200m. red	20	2·10
O278	**54**	300m. green	20	2·10
O279	**54**	400m. brown	20	2·10
O280	**54**	500m. orange	20	2·10
O342	**62**	100M. grey	20	£200
O343	**62**	200M. brown	40	£200
O344	**62**	2Md. green and pink	20	£160
O345	**62**	5Md. brown and yellow	20	£120
O346	**62**	10Md. green and light green	5·25	£190
O347	**62**	20Md. brown and green	5·25	£200
O348	**62**	50Md. blue	2·75	£275

1923. Official stamps of 1920 and 1922 surch Tausend or Millionen and figure.

O312	-	5T. on 5m. brown on yellow	10	4·25
O313	-	20T. on 30pf. orange on rose (No. O129)	10	4·25
O317	**O50**	75T. on 50m. violet on rose	10	4·25
O314	-	100T. on 15pf. purple	10	4·25
O315	-	250T. on 10pf. red (No. O125)	10	4·25
O318	-	400T. on 15pf. purple	10	38·00
O319	-	800T. on 30pf. orge on rose (No. O129)	40	6·25
O320	**O48**	1M. on 75pf. blue	10	55·00
O321	-	2M. on 10pf. red (No. O125)	40	5·25
O322	**O50**	5M. on 100m. red on rose	10	8·00

1923. Nos. 352/7 optd Dienstmarke.

O358	**64**	3pf. brown	30	1·10
O359	**64**	5pf. green	30	1·10
O360	**64**	10pf. red	30	1·10
O361	**64**	20pf. blue	85	1·60
O362	**64**	50pf. orange	85	2·10
O363	**64**	100pf. purple	5·25	10·50

1924. Optd Dienstmarke.

O376	**66**	3pf. brown	55	3·25
O377	**66**	5pf. green	40	1·10
O378	**66**	10pf. red	40	1·10
O379	**66**	20pf. blue	40	1·10
O380	**66**	30pf. red	1·40	1·10
O381	**66**	40pf. olive	1·40	1·10
O382	**66**	50pf. orange	10·50	5·25
O384	**72**	60pf. brown	2·75	5·25
O385	**72**	80pf. grey	10·50	50·00

O81

1927

O424	**O81**	3pf. brown	50	1·10
O425	**O81**	4pf. blue	40	1·30
O427	**O81**	5pf. green	20	1·10
O428	**O81**	6pf. green	55	1·30
O429	**O81**	8pf. green	40	1·10
O430	**O81**	10pf. red	10·50	8·50
O432	**O81**	10pf. mauve	40	1·30
O433	**O81**	10pf. brown	5·25	12·50
O434	**O81**	12pf. orange	55	1·30
O436	**O81**	15pf. red	55	1·30
O437	**O81**	20pf. green	7·50	4·25
O438	**O81**	20pf. grey	2·10	1·60
O439	**O81**	30pf. green	1·30	1·30
O440	**O81**	40pf. violet	1·30	1·30
O441	**O81**	60pf. brown	1·60	2·75

O100

1934

O809	**O100**	3pf. brown	30	1·60
O527	**O100**	4pf. blue	40	1·30
O528	**O100**	5pf. green	20	1·60
O529	**O100**	6pf. green	20	1·30
O812	**O100**	6pf. violet	30	1·60
O813	**O100**	8pf. red	30	1·60
O531	**O100**	10pf. brown	40	10·50
O532	**O100**	12pf. red	2·40	2·10
O533	**O100**	15pf. red	1·30	12·50
O534	**O100**	20pf. blue	55	2·10
O535	**O100**	30pf. green	95	2·10
O536	**O100**	40pf. mauve	95	2·10
O537	**O100**	50pf. yellow	1·40	5·25
O820	**O100**	50pf. green	4·00	£425

SPECIAL STAMPS FOR USE BY OFFICIALS OF THE NATIONAL SOCIALIST GERMAN WORKERS' PARTY

P132 Party Badge

1938

O648	**P132**	1pf. black	1·20	4·25
O799	**P132**	3pf. brown	30	1·60
O650	**P132**	4pf. blue	1·20	1·10
O651	**P132**	5pf. green	1·20	2·10
O652	**P132**	6pf. green	1·20	2·10
O802	**P132**	6pf. violet	30	3·25
O803	**P132**	8pf. red	30	3·25
O804	**P132**	12pf. red	30	1·60
O655	**P132**	16pf. grey	1·60	12·50
O805	**P132**	16pf. blue	2·10	£110
O656	**P132**	24pf. green	2·50	6·75
O806	**P132**	24pf. brown	65	42·00
O657	**P132**	30pf. green	1·90	10·50
O658	**P132**	40pf. mauve	1·90	16·00

II. ALLIED OCCUPATION

A. Allied Military Post (British and American Zones)

The defeat of Germany in May 1945 resulted in the division of the country into four zones of occupation (British, American, French and Russian), while Berlin was placed under joint allied control. Allied Military Post Stamps came into use in the British and American zones, the French issued special stamps in their zone and in the Russian zone the first issues were made by local administrations.

The territory occupied by the Anglo-American and French Zones subsequently became the German Federal Republic (West Germany) which was set up in September 1949. By the Nine Power Agreement of 3 October 1954, the occupation of West Germany was ended and full sovereignty was granted to the German Federal Government as from 5 May 1955 (see Section III).

The territory in the Russian Zone became the German Democratic Republic (East Germany) which was set up on 7 October 1949 (see Section V).

Separate issues for the Western Sectors of Berlin came into being in 1948 (see Section IV). The Russian Zone issues inscribed "STADT BERLIN" were for use in the Russian sector of the city and Brandenburg and these were superseded first by the General Issues of the Russian Zone and then by the stamps of East Germany.

A1

1945

A16	**A1**	1pf. black	55	6·75
A10	**A1**	3pf. violet	30	85
A11	**A1**	4pf. grey	30	85
A3	**A1**	5pf. green	30	55
A4	**A1**	6pf. yellow	30	55
A5	**A1**	8pf. orange	30	55
A6	**A1**	10pf. brown	30	55
A15	**A1**	12pf. purple	40	85
A8	**A1**	15pf. red	30	2·10
A25	**A1**	16pf. green	55	19·00
A26	**A1**	20pf. blue	55	5·25
A27a	**A1**	24pf. brown	55	17·00
A9	**A1**	25pf. blue	40	2·20
A29	**A1**	30pf. olive	55	2·75
A30	**A1**	40pf. mauve	75	4·25
A31	**A1**	42pf. green	55	3·25
A32	**A1**	50pf. slate	55	21·00
A33	**A1**	60pf. plum	1·10	26·00
A34b	**A1**	80pf. blue	42·00	£425
A35	**A1**	1m. green	8·50	£700

Values 30pf. to 80pf. are size 22×25 mm and 1m. is size 25×29½ mm.

Nos. A36 etc continue in Section C.

Used prices are for cancelled-to-order.

B. American, British and Russian Zones 1946–48

From February 1946 to June 1948 these zones used the same stamps (Nos. 899/956). It had been intended that they should be used throughout all four zones but until the creation of the German Federal Republic, in September 1949, the French Zone always had its own stamps, while after the revaluation of the currency in June 1948 separate stamps were again issued for the Russian Zone.

229 Numeral

1946

899	**229**	1pf. black	20	4·25
900	**229**	2pf. black	20	30
901	**229**	3pf. brown	20	4·75
902	**229**	4pf. blue	20	6·25
903	**229**	5pf. green	20	85
904	**229**	6pf. violet	20	20
905	**229**	8pf. red	20	30
906	**229**	10pf. brown	20	30
907	**229**	12pf. red	20	30
908	**229**	12pf. grey	20	30
909	**229**	15pf. red	20	9·50
910	**229**	15pf. green	20	30
911	**229**	16pf. green	20	30
912	**229**	20pf. blue	20	30
913	**229**	24pf. brown	20	30
914	**229**	25pf. blue	20	8·50
915	**229**	25pf. orange	20	1·60
916	**229**	30pf. green	20	30
917	**229**	40pf. purple	20	30
918	**229**	42pf. green	3·00	42·00
919	**229**	45pf. red	20	40
920	**229**	50pf. green	20	30
921	**229**	60pf. red	20	30
922	**229**	75pf. blue	20	30
923	**229**	80pf. blue	20	30
924	**229**	84pf. green	20	30
925	**229**	1m. green (24×30 mm)	20	30
MS925a 107×51 mm. Nos. 912/13 and 917 (sold at 5m.)			90·00	£300

231 1160: Leipzig obtains Charter

1947. Leipzig Spring Fair. Inscr "LEIPZIGER MESSE 1947".

926	**231**	24pf.+26pf. brown	1·60	6·75
927	-	60pf.+40pf. blue	1·60	6·75

DESIGN: 60pf. 1268: Foreign merchants at Leipzig Fair.

See also Nos. 951/4.

233 Gardener

237 "Dove of Peace"

1947

928	**233**	2pf. black	20	55
929	**233**	6pf. violet	30	30
930	**A**	8pf. red	30	55
931	**A**	10pf. green	30	55
932	**B**	12pf. grey	30	30
933	**233**	15pf. brown	55	5·25
934	**C**	16pf. green	30	55
935	**A**	20pf. blue	30	1·60
936	**C**	24pf. brown	30	55
937	**233**	25pf. orange	30	1·60
938	**B**	30pf. red	55	4·25
939	**A**	40pf. mauve	30	55
940	**C**	50pf. blue	55	2·75
941	**B**	60pf. red	30	55
942	**B**	60pf. brown	30	1·10
943	**B**	80pf. blue	30	1·60
944	**C**	84pf. green	55	2·75
945	**237**	1m. green	40	55
946	**237**	2m. violet	40	1·60
947	**237**	3m. lake	40	26·00
948	**237**	5m. blue	3·75	£110

DESIGNS: A, Sower; B, Labourer; C, Bricklayer and reaper.

238 Dr. von Stephan

1947. 50th Death Anniv of Von Stephan.

949	**238**	24pf. brown	30	2·10
950	**238**	75pf. blue	30	2·10

1947. Leipzig Autumn Fair. As T 231.

951		12pf. red	65	2·75
952		75pf. blue	65	3·75

DESIGNS: 12pf. 1497: Maximilian I granting Charter; 75pf. 1365: Assessment and Collection of Ground Rents.

1948. Leipzig Spring Fair. As T 231 but dated "1948".

953		50pf. blue	65	2·10
954		84pf. green	65	3·25

DESIGNS: 50pf. 1388: At the customs barrier; 84pf. 1433: Bringing merchandise.

For similar types, dated "1948", "1949" or "1950", but with premium values, see Nos. R31/2, R51/2, R60/1 of Russian Zone and E7/8 of East Germany.

239 Weighing Goods

1948. Hanover Trade Fair.

955	**239**	24pf. red	40	2·10
956	**239**	50pf. blue	40	3·25

C. British and American Zones 1948–49

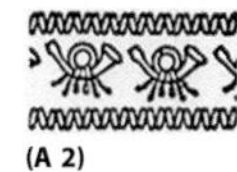
(A 2)

1948. Currency Reform. (a) On Pictorial issue of 1947, Nos. 928/44. (i) Optd with Type A 2.

A36	2pf. black	65	65
A37	6pf. violet	65	65
A38	8pf. red	65	65
A39	10pf. green	65	65
A40	12pf. grey	65	65
A41	15pf. brown	11·50	21·00
A42	16pf. green	1·90	3·25
A43	20pf. blue	85	1·30
A44	24pf. brown	65	65
A45	25pf. orange	65	65
A46	30pf. red	3·75	6·25
A47	40pf. mauve	1·10	2·10
A48	50pf. blue	1·20	1·30
A49	60pf. brown	1·10	1·30
A50	60pf. red	85·00	£325
A51	80pf. blue	1·70	3·25
A52	84pf. green	6·25	8·50

(ii) Optd with multiple posthorns over whole stamp.

A53	2pf. black	1·30	1·90
A54	6pf. violet	1·30	1·90
A55	8pf. red	1·30	1·90
A56	10pf. green	65	65
A57	12pf. grey	1·50	2·10
A58	15pf. brown	65	95
A59	16pf. green	2·10	3·25
A60	20pf. blue	65	65
A61	24pf. brown	1·10	2·10
A62	25pf. orange	10·50	21·00
A63	30pf. red	65	95
A64	40pf. mauve	65	85
A65	50pf. blue	65	85
A66	60pf. brown	65	95
A67	60pf. red	3·25	5·25
A68	80pf. blue	65	1·10
A69	84pf. green	2·10	1·90

(b) On Numeral issue of 1946, Nos. 900 to 924. (i) Optd with Type A 2.

A70	**229**	2pf. black	8·50	44·00
A71	**229**	8pf. red	16·00	90·00
A72	**229**	10pf. brown	1·30	6·75
A73	**229**	12pf. red	11·50	75·00
A74	**229**	12pf. grey	£190	£800
A75	**229**	15pf. red	11·50	75·00
A76	**229**	15pf. green	3·75	23·00
A77	**229**	16pf. green	60·00	£275
A78	**229**	24pf. brown	£110	£300
A79	**229**	25pf. blue	21·00	90·00
A80	**229**	25pf. orange	1·90	12·50
A81	**229**	30pf. olive	3·25	12·50
A82	**229**	40pf. purple	85·00	£300
A83	**229**	45pf. red	4·25	11·50
A84	**229**	50pf. green	2·75	10·50
A85	**229**	75pf. blue	7·50	34·00
A86	**229**	84pf. green	8·50	34·00

(ii) Optd with multiple posthorns over whole stamp.

A87	2pf. black	32·00	95·00
A88	8pf. red	55·00	£190
A89	10pf. brown	55·00	£200
A90	12pf. red	17·00	95·00
A91	12pf. grey	£400	£1500
A92	15pf. red	17·00	70·00
A93	15pf. green	2·10	11·50
A94	16pf. green	60·00	£225
A95	24pf. brown	65·00	£300
A96	25pf. blue	17·00	90·00
A97	25pf. orange	60·00	£275
A98	30pf. olive	2·75	9·50
A99	40pf. purple	85·00	£350
A100	45pf. red	5·25	17·00
A101	50pf. green	5·25	17·00
A102	75pf. blue	3·75	17·00
A103	84pf. green	5·25	18·00

A4 Crowned Head

A7 Cologne Cathedral

1948. 700th Anniv of Cologne Cathedral and Restoration Fund.

A104	**A4**	6pf.+4pf. brown	1·10	1·10
A105	-	12pf.+8pf. blue	2·10	2·75
A106	-	24pf.+16pf. red	5·75	5·25
A107	**A7**	50pf.+50pf. blue	10·50	13·50

DESIGNS—As Type A **4**: 12pf. The Three Wise Men; 24pf. Cologne Cathedral.

A9 The Romer, Frankfurt am Main

A10 Frauenkirche, Munich

A13 Holstentor Lubeck

1948. Various designs.

A108	**A9**	2pf. black	55	65
A109	**A10**	4pf. brown	55	65
A110a	**A**	5pf. blue	85	65
A111	**A10**	6pf. brown	55	1·30
A112	**A10**	6pf. orange	65	65
A113	**A9**	8pf. yellow	65	85
A114	**A10**	8pf. slate	55	65
A115a	**A**	10pf. green	65	65
A116	**A10**	15pf. orange	2·75	6·25
A117	**A9**	15pf. violet	1·50	65
A118	**A9**	16pf. green	85	85
A119	**A9**	20pf. blue	1·30	4·25
A120	**B**	20pf. red	95	65
A121	**B**	24pf. red	65	65
A122	**A**	25pf. red	1·30	65
A123	**B**	30pf. blue	1·60	65
A124	**A10**	30pf. red	3·75	7·50
A125	**A**	40pf. mauve	2·10	65
A126	**B**	50pf. blue	1·60	3·25
A127	**A10**	50pf. green	2·10	65
A128a	**A**	60pf. purple	3·25	65
A129	**B**	80pf. mauve	3·75	65
A130	**A10**	84pf. purple	2·30	8·50
A131	**A**	90pf. mauve	3·75	65
A132	**A13**	1Dm. green	42·00	85
A133	**A13**	2Dm. violet	37·00	1·10
A134	**A13**	3Dm. mauve	42·00	3·75
A135	**A13**	5Dm. blue	65·00	30·00

DESIGNS—As Type A **9/10**: A, Cologne Cathedral; B, Brandenburg Gate.

A15 Brandenburg Gate, Berlin

1948. Aid to Berlin.

A140	**A15**	10pf.+5pf. green	8·50	10·50
A141	**A15**	20pf.+10pf. red	8·50	10·50

A16 Herman Hillebrant Wedigh (after Holbein)

1949. Hanover Trade Fair.

A142	**A16**	10pf. green	4·25	3·75
A143	**A16**	20pf. red	4·25	3·25
A144	**A16**	30pf. blue	6·25	4·75
MSA145 110×65 mm. Nos. A142/4 (sold at 1Dm.)			£120	£375

A17 Racing Cyclists

1949. Trans-Germany Cycle Race.

A146	**A17**	10pf.+5pf. green	6·25	8·50
A147	**A17**	20pf.+10pf. brown	17·00	23·00

A18 Goethe in Italy

A19 Goethe

1949. Birth Bicentenary of Goethe (poet).

A148	**A18**	10pf.+5pf. green	5·25	5·75
A149	**A19**	20pf.+10pf. red	7·50	10·50
A150	-	30pf.+15pf. blue	32·00	32·00

DESIGN—VERT: 30pf. Profile portrait.

OBLIGATORY TAX STAMPS

AT14

1948. Aid for Berlin. Perf or imperf.

AT136	**AT14**	2pf. blue	1·10	30

The Anglo-American Zones, together with the French Zone, became the Federal German Republic (West Germany) in September 1949.

D. French Zone.

(a) General Issues, 1945–46.

F1 Arms of the Palatinate

F2 Goethe

1945. (a) Arms.

F1	**F1**	1pf. green, black & yellow	30	30
F2	-	3pf. yellow, black and red	30	30
F3	-	5pf. black, yellow & brn	30	30
F4	-	8pf. red, yellow and brown	30	30
F5	**F1**	10pf. green, brown & yell	16·00	80·00
F6	-	12pf. yellow, black & red	30	30
F7	-	15pf. blue, black and red	30	30
F8	-	20pf. black, yellow & red	30	30
F9	-	24pf. blue, black and red	30	30
F10	-	30pf. red, yellow & black	30	30

ARMS: 3, 12pf. Rhineland; 5, 20pf. Wurttemberg; 8, 30pf. Baden; 15, 24pf. Saar.

(b) Poets.

F11	**2**	1m. brown	4·75	25·00
F12	-	2m. blue (Schiller)	4·75	75·00
F13	-	5m. red (Heine)	5·25	95·00

(b) Baden, 1947–49.

FB1 J. P. Hebel

FB2 Rastatt Castle

FB3 Hollental Black Forest

FB4 Freiburg Cathedral

1947. Inscr "BADEN".

FB1	**FB1**	2pf. grey	30	55
FB2	-	3pf. brown	30	55
FB3	-	10pf. blue	30	55
FB4	**FB1**	12pf. green	30	55
FB5	-	15pf. violet	30	55
FB6	**FB2**	16pf. green	30	2·10
FB7	-	20pf. blue	30	55
FB8	**FB2**	24pf. red	30	55
FB9	-	45pf. mauve	30	1·30
FB10	**FB1**	60pf. orange	30	55
FB11	-	75pf. blue	30	2·75
FB12	**FB3**	84pf. green	30	2·75
FB13	**FB4**	1m. brown	40	1·10

DESIGNS—18×23 mm: 3, 15, 45pf. Badensian girl and yachts; 10, 20, 75pf. Hans Baldung Grien.

1948. Currency Reform. As 1947 issue. (a) Value in "PF".

FB14	**FB1**	2pf. orange	30	40
FB15	-	6pf. brown	30	40
FB16	-	10pf. brown	55	40
FB17	**FB1**	12pf. red	55	40
FB18	-	15pf. blue	65	85
FB19	**FB2**	24pf. green	75	40
FB20	-	30pf. mauve	1·50	1·60
FB21	-	50pf. blue	1·50	40

(b) New currency. Value in "D.PF" or "D.M." (="Deutschpfennig" or "Deutschmark").

FB22		8dpf. green	75	1·60
FB23	**FB2**	16dpf. violet	1·60	2·75
FB24	-	20dpf. brown	5·25	1·40
FB25	**FB1**	60dpf. grey	7·50	85
FB26	**FB3**	84dpf. red	9·50	6·25
FB27	**FB4**	1dm. blue	8·50	6·25

DESIGNS—As Types FB **1/2**: 6, 15pf. Badensian girl and yachts; 10pf., 20dpf. Hans Baldung Grien; 8dpf., 30pf. Black Forest girl in festive headdress; 50pf. Grand-Duchess Stephanie of Baden.

Nos. FB14/21 were sold on the new currency basis though not inscribed "D.PF.".

1948. As 1947 issue, but "PF" omitted.

FB28	**FB1**	2pf. orange	1·60	75
FB29	-	4pf. violet	1·10	65
FB30	-	5pf. blue	1·40	85
FB31	-	6pf. brown	34·00	19·00
FB32	-	8pf. brown	1·60	1·50
FB33	-	10pf. green	3·25	75
FB34	-	20pf. mauve	1·90	55
FB35	-	40pf. brown	80·00	£110
FB36	**FB1**	80pf. red	13·50	8·75
FB37	**FB3**	90pf. red	80·00	£110

DESIGNS—18×23 mm: 4pf., 40pf. Rastatt; 5pf., 6pf. Badensian girl and yachts; 8pf. Black Forest girl in festive headdress; 10pf., 20pf. Portrait of Hans Baldung Grien.

FB5 Cornhouse, Freiburg

1949. Freiburg Rebuilding Fund.

FB38	**FB5**	4pf.+16pf. violet	19·00	55·00
FB39	-	10pf.+20pf. green	19·00	55·00
FB40	-	20pf.+30pf. red	19·00	55·00
FB41	-	30pf.+50pf. blue	21·00	65·00
MSFB41a		65×78 mm. Nos. FB38/41	80·00	£300
MSFB41b		Ditto but imperf	80·00	£300

DESIGNS: 10pf. Freiburg Cathedral; 20pf. Trumpeting angel, Freiburg; 30pf. "Fischbrunnen," Freiburg.

FB6 Arms of Baden

1949. Red Cross Fund.

FB42	**FB6**	10pf.+20pf. green	26·00	£110
FB43	**FB6**	20pf.+40pf. lilac	26·00	£110
FB44	**FB6**	30pf.+60pf. blue	26·00	£110
FB45	**FB6**	40pf.+80pf. grey	26·00	£110
MSFB45a		90×100 mm. Nos. FB42/5	£120	£1600

FB7 Seehof Hotel, Constance

1949. Engineers' Congress, Constance.

FB46	**FB7**	30pf. blue	27·00	90·00

FB8 Goethe

1949. Birth Bicentenary of Goethe (poet).

FB47	**FB8**	10pf.+5pf. green	10·50	26·00
FB48	-	20pf.+10pf. red	12·50	26·00
FB49	-	30pf.+15pf. blue	16·00	65·00

FB9 Carl Schurz and Revolutionary Scene

1949. Cent of Rastatt Insurrection.

FB50	**FB9**	10pf.+5pf. green	12·50	40·00
FB51	**FB9**	20pf.+10pf. mauve	12·50	40·00
FB52	**FB9**	30pf.+15pf. blue	15·00	40·00

FB10 Conradin Kreutzer

1949. Death Centenary of Conradin Kreutzer (composer).

FB53	**FB10**	10pf. green	4·75	16·00

FB11 1849 Mail Coach

1949. German Stamp Centenary.

FB54	**FB11**	10pf. green	6·75	15·00
FB55	-	20pf. brown	6·75	15·00

DESIGN: 20pf. Postal motor-coach with trailer and Douglas DC-4 airliner.

FB12 Posthorn and Globe

1949. 75th Anniv of U.P.U.

FB56	**FB12**	20pf. red	7·50	15·00
FB57	**FB12**	30pf. blue	7·50	12·50

(C) Rhineland Palatinate, 1947–49.

FR1 "Porta Nigra", Trier

FR2 Karl Marx

FR4 Statue of Charlemagne

1947. Inscr "RHEINLAND-PFALZ".

FR1	-	2pf. grey	30	40
FR2	-	3pf. brown	30	40
FR3	-	10pf. blue	30	40
FR4	**FR1**	12pf. green	30	40
FR5	**FR2**	15pf. violet	30	40
FR6	-	16pf. green	30	1·50
FR7	-	20pf. blue	30	40
FR8	-	24pf. red	30	40
FR9	-	30pf. mauve	20	3·25
FR10	-	45pf. mauve	20	85
FR11	-	50pf. blue	30	3·25
FR12	-	60pf. orange	30	40
FR13	-	75pf. blue	30	85
FR14	-	84pf. green	40	1·90
FR15	**FR4**	1m. brown	40	1·10

DESIGNS—SMALL SIZE: 2pf., 60pf. Beethoven's death mask; 3pf. Baron von Ketteler, Bishop of Mainz; 10pf. Girl vintager; 16pf. Rocks at Arnweiler; 20pf. Palatinate village house; 24pf. Worms Cathedral; 30pf., 75pf. Gutenberg (printer); 45pf., 50pf. Mainz Cathedral. LARGE SIZE—HORIZ: 84pf. Gutenfels Castle and Rhine.

1948. Currency Reform. As 1947 issue. (a) Value in "PF".

FR16	-	2pf. orange	30	40
FR17	-	6pf. brown	30	40
FR18	-	10pf. brown	55	40
FR19	**FR1**	12pf. red	55	40
FR20	**FR2**	15pf. blue	1·60	85
FR21	-	24pf. green	55	40
FR22	-	30pf. mauve	1·60	55
FR23	-	50pf. blue	2·10	55

(b) New currency. Value in "D.PF." or "D.M." (= "Deutschpfennig" or "Deutschmark").

FR24	**FR1**	8dpf. green	55	1·60
FR25	-	16dpf. violet	85	1·90
FR26	-	20dpf. brown	4·25	85
FR27	-	60dpf. grey	10·50	55
FR28	-	84dpf. red	6·75	8·00
FR29	**FR4**	1dm. blue	7·50	8·00

DESIGNS—SMALL SIZE: 6pf. Baron von Ketteler; 30pf. Mainz Cathedral; 50pf. Gutenberg (printer). Others as 1947 issue.

Nos. FR16/23 were sold on the new currency basis though not inscribed "D.PF.".

FR5 St. Martin

1948. Ludwigshafen Explosion Relief Fund.

FR30	**FR5**	20pf.+30pf. mauve	2·75	80·00
FR31	-	30pf.+50pf. blue	2·75	80·00

DESIGN: 30pf. St. Christopher.

1948. Inscr "RHEINLAND-PFALZ". As 1947 issue, but "PF" omitted.

FR32		2pf. orange	1·10	55
FR33		4pf. violet	1·10	55
FR34	**FR2**	5pf. blue	1·10	85
FR35	-	6pf. brown	37·00	21·00
FR36	**FR1**	8pf. red	95·00	£550
FR37	-	10pf. green	1·40	55
FR38	-	20pf. mauve	1·40	55
FR39	-	40pf. brown	5·25	5·25
FR40	**FR1**	80pf. red	6·25	6·75
FR41	-	90pf. red	10·50	21·00

DESIGNS—SMALL SIZE: 4pf. Rocks at Arnweiler; 40pf. Worms Cathedral. LARGE SIZE—HORIZ: 90pf. Gutenfels Castle and Rhine. Others as 1947–48 issues.

1949. Red Cross Fund. As Type FB 6 of Baden, but Arms of Rhineland and inscr "RHEINLANDPFALZ".

FR42	10pf.+20pf. green	23·00	£120
FR43	20pf.+40pf. lilac	23·00	£120
FR44	30pf.+60pf. blue	23·00	£120
FR45	40pf.+80pf. grey	23·00	£120
MSFR45a	90×100 mm. Nos. FR42/5	£130	£1600

1949. Birth Bicentenary of Goethe. As Nos. FB47/9 of Baden.

FR46	10pf.+5pf. green	8·50	25·00
FR47	20pf.+10pf. mauve	8·50	25·00
FR48	30pf.+15pf. blue	16·00	60·00

1949. Centenary of German Postage Stamp. As Nos. FB54/5 of Baden.

FR49	10pf. green	11·50	26·00
FR50	20pf. brown	11·50	26·00

1949. 75th Anniv of U.P.U. As Nos. FB56/7 of Baden.

FR51	20pf. red	8·00	16·00
FR52	30pf. blue	8·00	13·50

FW1 Fr. von Schiller

FW2 Bebenhausen Monastery

FW3 Lichtenstein Castle

1947. Inscr "WURTTEMBERG".

FW1	**FW1**	2pf. grey	30	85
FW2	-	3pf. brown	30	40
FW3	-	10pf. blue	30	55
FW4	**FW1**	12pf. green	30	40
FW5	-	15pf. violet	30	65
FW6	**FW2**	16pf. green	30	1·70
FW7	-	20pf. blue	30	1·70
FW8	**FW2**	24pf. red	30	40
FW9	-	45pf. mauve	30	1·70
FW10	**FW1**	60pf. orange	30	1·10
FW11	-	75pf. blue	55	1·90
FW12	**FW3**	84pf. green	55	1·90
FW13	-	1m. brown	55	1·90

DESIGNS—SMALL SIZE: 3pf., 15pf., 45pf. Holderlin (poet); 10pf., 20pf., 75pf. Wangen Gate. LARGE SIZE—VERT: 1m. Zwiefalten Monastery Church.

1948. Currency Reform. As 1947 issue. (a) Value in "PF".

FW14	**FW1**	2pf. orange	30	55
FW15	-	6pf. brown	30	40
FW16	-	10pf. brown	30	55
FW17	**FW1**	12pf. red	30	40
FW18	-	15pf. blue	1·10	55
FW19	**FW2**	24pf. green	1·60	85
FW20	-	30pf. mauve	1·60	85
FW21	-	50pf. blue	3·25	85

(b) Value in "D.PF" (= Deutsch Pfennig) or "D.M." (= Deutsch Mark).

FW22		8dpf. green	1·60	3·25
FW23	**FW2**	16dpf. violet	1·30	2·10
FW24	-	20dpf. brown	2·75	1·60
FW25	**FW1**	60dpf. grey	16·00	85
FW26	**FW3**	84dpf. red	4·25	6·25
FW27	-	1dm. blue	4·25	6·25

DESIGNS—SMALL SIZE: 6pf., 15pf. Fr. Holderlin (poet); 8 dpf., 30pf. Waldsee Castle; 50pf. Ludwig Uhland (poet). Others as 1947 issue.

Nos. FW14/21 were sold on the new currency basis though not inscribed "D.PF.".

1948. Inscr "WURTTEMBERG". As 1947 issue, but "PF" omitted.

FW28	**FW1**	2pf. orange	1·40	85
FW29	**FW2**	4pf. violet	3·25	55
FW30	-	5pf. blue	8·00	3·25
FW31	-	6pf. brown	10·50	8·00
FW32	-	8pf. red	10·50	3·25
FW33	-	10pf. green	9·50	55
FW34	-	20pf. mauve	10·50	55
FW35	**FW2**	40pf. brown	26·00	55·00
FW36	**FW1**	80pf. red	55·00	55·00
FW37	**FW3**	90pf. red	85·00	£140

DESIGNS—SMALL SIZE: 5pf., 6pf. Holderlin. Others as 1947 and 1948 issues.

FW4 Isny and Coat of Arms

1949. Ski Championships (Northern Combination) at Isny/Allgau.

FW38	**FW4**	10pf.+4pf. green	10·50	32·00
FW39	-	20pf.+6pf. lake	10·50	32·00

DESIGN: 20pf. Skier and view of Isny.

1949. Red Cross Fund. As Type FB 6 of Baden, but Arms of Wurttemberg and inscr "WURTTEMBERG".

FW40	10pf.+20pf. green	42·00	£130
FW41	20pf.+40pf. lilac	42·00	£130
FW42	30pf.+60pf. blue	42·00	£130
FW43	40pf.+80pf. grey	42·00	£130
MSFW43a	90×100 mm. Nos. FW40/3	£160	£1900

1949. Birth Bicentenary of Goethe. As Nos. FB47/9 of Baden.

FW44	10pf.+5pf. green	9·50	26·00
FW45	20pf.+10pf. mauve	13·50	37·00
FW46	30pf.+15pf. blue	13·50	55·00

FW5 Gustav Werner

1949. Centenary of Christian Institution "Zum Bruderhaus".

FW47	**FW5**	10pf.+5pf. green	6·75	18·00
FW48	**FW5**	20pf.+10pf. purple	6·75	18·00

1949. German Stamp Centenary. As Nos. FB54/5 of Baden.

FW49	10pf. green	8·50	17·00
FW50	20pf. brown	8·50	17·00

1949. 75th Anniv of U.P.U. As Nos. FB56/7 of Baden.

FW51	20pf. red	6·75	14·50
FW52	30pf. blue	6·75	12·50

E. Russian Zone.

For a list of the stamps issued by the Russian Zone Provincial Administrations of Berlin (Brandenburg), Mecklenburg-Vorpommern, Saxony (Halle, Leipzig and Dresden) and Thuringia, see Stanley Gibbons Part 7 Catalogue.

In February 1946, the Provincial Issues were replaced by the General Issues, Nos. 899/956, until the revaluation of the currency in June 1948, when Nos. 928/44 were brought into use handstamped with District names and numbers as a control measure pending the introduction of the following overprinted stamps on 3rd July. There are over 1,900 different types of district handstamp.

1948. Optd Sowjetische Besatzungs Zone. (a) On Pictorial issue of 1947, Nos. 928/44.

R1	2pf. black	55	55
R2	6pf. violet	55	55
R3	8pf. red	55	55
R4	10pf. green	55	65
R5	12pf. grey	55	55
R6	15pf. brown	65	65
R7	16pf. green	55	85
R8	20pf. blue	55	65
R9	24pf. brown	55	40
R10	25pf. orange	55	40
R11	30pf. red	2·75	65
R12	40pf. mauve	55	65
R13	50pf. blue	85	2·10
R14	60pf. brown	1·60	2·10
R15	60pf. red	75·00	£180
R16	80pf. blue	3·25	4·25
R17	84pf. green	3·75	4·25

(b) On Numerical issue of 1946, Nos. 903, etc.

R18	**229**	5pf. green	1·10	2·10
R19	**229**	30pf. olive	1·70	4·25
R20	**229**	45pf. red	85	1·60
R21	**229**	75pf. blue	85	1·60
R22	**229**	84pf. green	1·90	4·25

Sowjetische Besatzungs Zone
(R1)

(c) On stamps inscr "STADT BERLIN".

R23	**R1**	5pf. green	55	2·10
R25	-	6pf. violet	55	2·10
R26	-	8pf. orange	55	2·75
R27	-	10pf. brown	55	2·75
R28	-	12pf. red	75	21·00
R29	-	20pf. blue	55	1·30
R30	-	30pf. olive	55	9·00

DESIGNS: 6pf. Bear with spade; 8pf. Bear on shield; 10pf. Bear holding brick; 12pf. Bear carrying plank; 20pf. Bear on small shield; 30pf. Oak sapling amid ruins.

1948. Leipzig Autumn Fair. As T 231 but dated "1948".

R31	16pf.+9pf. purple	95	85
R32	50pf.+25pf. blue	95	85

DESIGNS: 16pf. 1459: The first Spring Fair; 50pf. 1469: Foreign merchants displaying cloth.

R3 Kathe Kollwitz

1948. Politicians, Artists and Scientists.

R33	**R3**	2pf. grey	2·10	2·10
R34	-	6pf. violet	2·10	2·10
R35	-	8pf. red	2·10	2·10
R36	-	10pf. green	2·10	1·60
R37	-	12pf. blue	5·00	1·10
R38	-	15pf. brown	1·60	3·25
R39	-	16pf. blue	4·75	3·25
R40	**R3**	20pf. purple	2·10	2·10
R41	-	24pf. red	5·25	2·10
R42	-	25pf. olive	2·10	2·75
R43	-	30pf. red	5·25	3·25
R44	-	40pf. purple	21·00	3·75
R45	-	50pf. blue	2·10	2·75
R46	-	60pf. green	10·50	3·75
R47	-	80pf. blue	2·10	2·10
R48	-	84pf. brown	3·50	6·25
E95	-	80pf. red	17·00	12·00

PORTRAITS: 6, 40pf. Gerhart Hauptmann; 8, 50pf. Karl Marx; 10, 84pf. August Bebel; 12, 30pf. Friedrich Engels; 15, 60pf. G. F. W. Hegel; 16, 25pf. Rudolf Virchow; 24, 80pf. Ernst Thalmann.

R4

1948. Stamp Day.

R49	**R4**	12pf.+3pf. red	1·10	1·40

R5 Liebknecht and Rosa Luxemburg

1949. 30th Death Anniv of Karl Liebknecht and Rosa Luxemburg (revolutionaries).

R50	**R5**	24pf. red	1·10	1·40

1949. Leipzig Spring Fair. As T 231 but dated "1949".

R51	30pf.+15pf. red	5·00	5·75
R52	50pf.+25pf. blue	5·75	6·25

DESIGNS: 30pf. 1st Neubau Town Hall bazaar, 1556; 50pf. Italian merchants at Leipzig, 1536.

R6 Dove

1949. 3rd German Peoples' Congress.

R53	**R6**	24pf. red	2·10	3·00

1949. Optd 3. Deutscher Volkskongreß 29.-30 Mai 1949.

R54	24pf. red	2·75	4·00

R8 Goethe

1949. Birth Bicent of Goethe. Portraits of Goethe.

R55	**R8**	6pf.+4pf. violet	3·25	3·75
R56	-	12pf.+8pf. brown	3·25	3·75
R57	-	24pf.+16pf. lake	2·75	3·25
R58	-	50pf.+25pf. blue	2·75	3·25
R59	-	84pf.+36pf. grey	4·75	6·25

1949. Goethe Festival Week, Weimar. Sheet 106×104 mm.

MSR59a R **9** 50pf. (+Dm. 4.50) blue	£225	£650

1949. Leipzig Autumn Fair. As T 231 but dated "1949".

R60	12pf.+8pf. slate	6·25	10·50
R61	24pf.+16pf. lake	7·50	12·50

DESIGNS: 12pf. Russian merchants, 1650; 24pf. Goethe at Fair, 1765.

The Russian Zonee was incorporated in East Germany in October 1949.

III. GERMAN FEDERAL REPUBLIC

The Federal Republic was set up on 23 May 1949.Until October 1990 it comprised the territory whixh formerly came under the British, American and French Zones. On 3 October 1990 the former territory of East Germany (German Democratic Republic) was absorbed into the Federal Republic.

257 Constructing Parliament Building

1949. Opening of West German Parliament, Bonn.

1033	**257**	10pf. green	55·00	26·00
1034	**257**	20pf. red	60·00	31·00

258 Reproduction of T **1** of Bavaria

1949. Centenary of 1st German Stamps.

1035	**258**	10pf.+2pf. black & grn	19·00	33·00
1036	-	20pf. blue and red	44·00	49·00
1037	-	30pf. brown and blue	55·00	75·00

DESIGN: 20pf., 30pf. Reproductions of T **2** of Bavaria.

259 Dr. von Stephan, Old G.P.O., Berlin and Standehaus, Berne

1949. 75th Anniv of U.P.U.

1038	**259**	30pf. blue	80·00	49·00

260 St. Elisabeth of Thuringia

1949. Refugees' Relief Fund. Inscr as in T 260.

1039	**260**	8pf.+2pf. purple	25·00	28·00
1040	-	10pf.+5pf. green	19·00	16·00
1041	-	20pf.+10pf. red	19·00	16·00
1042	-	30pf.+15pf. blue	£110	£140

PORTRAITS: 10pf. Paracelsus von Hohenheim; 20pf. F. W. A. Froebel; 30pf. J. H. Wichern.

261 J. S. Bach's Seal

1950. Death Bicent of Bach (composer).

1043	**261**	10pf.+2pf. green	80·00	55·00
1044	**261**	20pf.+3pf. red	90·00	60·00

262 Numeral and Posthorn

1951

1045	**262**	2pf. green	6·50	1·40
1046	**262**	4pf. brown	5·00	45
1047	**262**	5pf. purple	15·00	45
1048	**262**	6pf. orange	24·00	4·50
1049	**262**	8pf. grey	25·00	10·50
1050	**262**	10pf. green	10·00	45
1051	**262**	15pf. violet	49·00	1·40
1052	**262**	20pf. red	7·75	45
1053	**262**	25pf. plum	£120	7·75
1054	**262**	30pf. blue	65·00	90
1055	**262**	40pf. purple	£180	90
1056	**262**	50pf. grey	£225	90
1057	**262**	60pf. brown	£160	90
1058	**262**	70pf. yellow	£550	21·00
1059	**262**	80pf. red	£600	3·25
1060	**262**	90pf. green	£600	3·75

The 30pf. to 90pf. are 20×24½ mm.

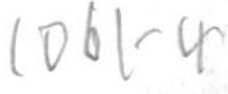

264 Figures

1951. 700th Anniv of St. Mary's Church, Lubeck.

1065	**264**	10pf.+5pf. black & grn	£110	90·00
1066	**264**	20pf.+5pf. black & red	£120	£110

265 Stamps under Magnifier

1951. National Philatelic Exn, Wuppertal.

1067	**265**	10pf.+2pf. yellow, black and green	55·00	60·00
1068	**265**	20pf.+3pf. yellow, black and red	60·00	65·00

266 St. Vincent de Paul

1951. Humanitarian Relief Fund.

1069	**266**	4pf.+2pf. brown	11·00	12·50
1070	-	10pf.+3pf. green	16·00	10·50
1071	-	20pf.+5pf. red	16·00	10·50
1072	-	30pf.+10pf. blue	£120	£140

PORTRAITS: 10pf. F. Von Bodelschwingh; 20pf. Elsa Brandstrom; 30pf. J. H. Pestalozzi.

267 W. C. Rontgen (physicist)

1951. 50th Anniv of Award to Rontgen of 1st Nobel Prize for Physics.

1073	**267**	30pf. blue	95·00	22·00

268 Mona Lisa

1952. 500th Birth Anniv of Leonardo da Vinci.

1074	**268**	5pf. multicoloured	1·80	3·25

269 Martin Luther

1952. Lutheran World Federation Assembly, Hanover.

1075	**269**	10pf. green	17·00	6·75

270 A. N. Otto and Diagram

1952. 75th Anniv of Otto Gas Engine.

1076	**270**	30pf. blue	37·00	20·00

271 Nuremberg Madonna

1952. Centenary of German National Museum, Nuremberg.

1077	**271**	10pf.+5pf. green	22·00	26·00

272 Trawler "Senator Schaffer" off Heligoland

1952. Rehabilitation of Heligoland.

1078	**272**	20pf. red	21·00	8·50

273 Carl Schurz

1952. Centenary of Arrival of Schurz in America.

1079	**273**	20pf. pink, black and blue	24·00	11·00

274 Boy Hikers

1952. Youth Hostels Fund. Inscr "JUGENDMARKE 1952".

1080	**274**	10pf.+2pf. green	24·00	27·00
1081	-	20pf.+3pf. red	24·00	27·00

DESIGN: 20pf. Girl hikers.

275 Elizabeth Fry

1952. Humanitarian Relief Fund.

1082	**275**	4pf.+2pf. brown	11·50	9·25
1083	-	10pf.+5pf. green	11·50	9·25
1084	-	20pf.+10pf. lake	23·00	19·00
1085	-	30pf.+10pf. blue	95·00	£120

PORTRAITS: 10pf. Dr. C. Sonnenschein; 20pf. T. Fliedner; 30pf. H. Dunant.

276 Postman, 1852

1952. Thurn and Taxis Stamp Centenary.

1086	**276**	10pf. multicoloured	10·50	3·50

277 P. Reis

1952. 75th Anniv of German Telephone Service.

1087	**277**	30pf. blue	60·00	21·00

278 Road Accident Victim

1953. Road Safety Campaign.

1088	**278**	20pf. multicoloured	23·00	7·00

279

1953. 50th Anniv of Science Museum, Munich.

1089	**279**	10pf.+5pf. green	33·00	41·00

280 Red Cross and Compass

1953. 125th Birth Anniv of Henri Dunant (founder of Red Cross).

1090	**280**	10pf. red and green	26·00	8·75

281 Prisoner of War

1953. Commemorating Prisoners of War.

1091	**281**	10pf. black and grey	8·25	60

282 J. von Liebig

1953. 150th Birth Anniv of Liebig (chemist).

1092	**282**	30pf. blue	60·00	29·00

283 "Rail Transport"

1953. Transport Exn, Munich. Inscr as in T 283.

1093	**283**	4pf. brown	8·25	5·75
1094	-	10pf. green	16·00	9·25
1095	-	20pf. red	22·00	11·50
1096	-	30pf. blue	60·00	29·00

DESIGNS: 10pf. "Air" (dove and aeroplanes); 20pf. "Road" (traffic lights and cars); 30pf. "Sea" (buoy and ships).

284 Gateway, Thurn and Taxis Palace

1953. International Philatelic Exhibition, Frankfurt am Main. Inscr "IFRABA 1953".

1097	**284**	10pf.+2pf. brown, black and green	29·00	33·00
1098	-	20pf.+3pf. grey, blue and red	29·00	33·00

DESIGN: 20pf. Telecommunications Buildings, Frankfurt am Main.

285 A. H. Francke

1953. Humanitarian Relief Fund.

1099	**285**	4pf.+2pf. brown	7·00	10·50
1100	-	10pf.+5pf. green	11·00	10·50
1101	-	20pf.+10pf. red	16·00	13·00
1102	-	30pf.+10pf. blue	70·00	85·00

PORTRAITS: 10pf. S. Kneipp; 20pf. J. C. Senckenberg; 30pf. F. Nansen.

286 Pres. Heuss

1954. (a) Size 18½×22½ mm or 18×22 mm.

1103	**286**	2pf. green	35	35
1104	**286**	4pf. brown	35	35
1105	**286**	5pf. mauve	35	35
1106	**286**	6pf. brown	60	1·20
1107	**286**	7pf. green	35	45
1108	**286**	8pf. grey	35	95
1109	**286**	10pf. green	35	35
1110	**286**	15pf. blue	95	70
1111	**286**	20pf. red	35	35
1112	**286**	25pf. purple	1·60	80
1122a	**286**	30pf. green	60	95
1122c	**286**	40pf. blue	2·75	45
1122e	**286**	50pf. olive	1·50	45
1122f	**286**	60pf. brown	4·50	70
1122g	**286**	70pf. violet	14·00	70
1122h	**286**	80pf. orange	8·25	3·00
1122i	**286**	90pf. green	22·00	1·50

(b) Size 20×24 mm.

1113	30pf. blue	17·00	7·00
1114	40pf. purple	7·00	45
1115	50pf. slate	£225	70
1116	60pf. brown	50·00	95
1117	70pf. olive	21·00	3·00
1118	80pf. red	3·50	7·00
1119	90pf. green	17·00	3·50

(c) Size 25×30 mm.

1120	1Dm. olive	2·00	45
1121	2Dm. lavender	3·50	1·70
1122	3Dm. purple	9·25	3·50

287 P. Ehrlich and E. von Behring

1954. Birth Centenaries of Ehrlich and Von Behring (bacteriologists).

1123	**287**	10pf. green	14·00	5·25

288 Gutenburg and Printing-press

1954. 500th Anniv of Gutenberg Bible.

1124	**288**	4pf. brown	1·70	95

289 Sword-pierced Mitre

1954. 1,200th Anniv of Martyrdom of St. Boniface.

1125	**289**	20pf. red and brown	10·50	5·75

290 Kathe Kollwitz

1954. Humanitarian Relief Fund.

1126	**290**	7pf.+3pf. brown	4·75	4·75
1127	-	10pf.+5pf. green	2·30	2·30
1128	-	20pf.+10pf. red	11·50	7·00
1129	-	40pf.+10pf. blue	42·00	50·00

PORTRAITS: 10pf. L. Werthmann; 20pf. J. F. Oberlin; 40pf. Bertha Pappenheim.

291 C. F. Gauss

1955. Death Cent of Gauss (mathematician).

1130	**291**	10pf. green	7·00	95

292 "Flight"

1955. Re-establishment of "Lufthansa" Airways.
1131 **292** 5pf. mauve and black 1·50 1·20
1132 **292** 10pf. green and black 1·90 1·70
1133 **292** 15pf. blue and black 9·25 8·25
1134 **292** 20pf. red and black 27·00 9·25

293 O. von Miller

1955. Birth Centenary of Von Miller (electrical engineer).
1135 **293** 10f. green 7·50 2·10

295 Schiller

1955. 150th Death Anniv of Schiller (poet).
1136 **295** 40pf. blue 21·00 7·50

296 Motor-coach, 1906

1955. 50th Anniv of Postal Motor Transport.
1137 **296** 20pf. black and red 16·00 6·50

297 Arms of Baden-Wurttemburg

1955. Baden-Wurttemberg Agricultural Exhibition, Stuttgart.
1138 **297** 7pf. black, brn & bistre 6·50 5·25
1139 **297** 10pf. black, grn & bistre 7·75 3·50

298 "Earth and Atom"

1955. Cosmic Research.
1140 **298** 20pf. lake 14·00 1·50

299 Refugees

1955. 10th Anniv of Expulsion of Germans from beyond the Oder-Neisse Line.
1141 **299** 20pf. red 5·25 80
See also No. 1400.

300 Orb, Arrows and Waves

1955. Millenary of Battle of Lechfeld.
1142 **300** 20pf. purple 11·50 4·75

301 Magnifying Glass and Carrier Pigeon

1955. West European Postage Stamp Exn.
1143 **301** 10pf.+2pf. green 5·75 8·25
1144 - 20pf.+3pf. red 14·00 17·00
DESIGN: 20pf. Tweezers and posthorn.

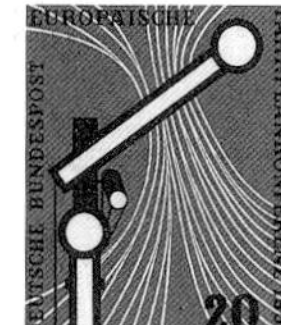

302 Railway Signal

1955. Railway Timetable Conference.
1145 **302** 20pf. black and red 13·00 3·50

303 Stifter Monument

1955. 150th Birth Anniv of Stifter (Austrian poet).
1146 **303** 10pf. green 5·25 3·50

304 U.N. Emblem

1955. U.N. Day.
1147 **304** 10pf. green and brown 5·25 5·75

305 Amalie Sieveking

1955. Humanitarian Relief Fund.
1148 **305** 7pf.+3pf. brown 4·50 4·75
1149 - 10pf.+5pf. green 3·50 2·30
1150 - 20pf.+10pf. red 3·50 2·30
1151 - 40pf.+10pf. blue 42·00 50·00
PORTRAITS: 10pf. A. Kolping; 20pf. Dr. S. Hahnemann; 40pf. Florence Nightingale.

306

1955
1152 **306** 1pf. grey 35 60

307 Von Stephan's Signature

1955. 125th Birth Anniv of H. von Stephan.
1153 **307** 20pf. red 10·00 4·00

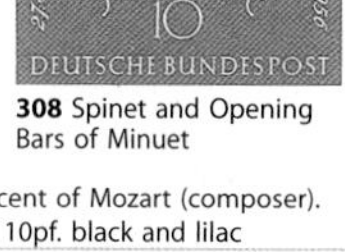

308 Spinet and Opening Bars of Minuet

1956. Birth Bicent of Mozart (composer).
1154 **308** 10pf. black and lilac 1·40 60

309 Heinrich Heine

1956. Death Centenary of Heine (poet).
1155 **309** 10pf. green and black 4·50 4·75

310 Old Houses and Crane

1956. Millenary of Luneburg.
1156 **310** 20pf. red 10·50 11·50

311

1956. Olympic Year.
1157 **311** 10pf. green 1·30 95

312 Boy and Dove

1956. Youth Hostels' Fund. Inscr "JUGEND".
1158 **312** 7pf.+3pf. grey, black and brown 3·00 4·75
1159 - 10pf.+5pf. grey black and green 9·25 11·50
DESIGN: 10pf. Girl playing flute and flowers.

313 Robert Schumann

1956. Death Centenary of Schumann (composer).
1160 **313** 10pf. black, red & bistre 1·00 70

314

1956. Evangelical Church Convention, Frankfurt am Main.
1161 **314** 10pf. green 5·25 5·25
1162 **314** 20pf. red 6·50 7·00

315 T. Mann (author)

1956. Thomas Mann Commemoration.
1163 **315** 20pf. red 4·75 3·25

316

1956. 800th Anniv of Maria Laach Abbey.
1164 **316** 20pf. grey and red 3·50 3·00

317 Ground Plan of Cologne Cathedral and Hand

1956. 77th Meeting of German Catholics, Cologne.
1165 **317** 10pf. green and brown 4·25 4·00

318

1956. International Police Exhibition, Essen.
1166 **318** 20pf. green, orange & blk 4·75 4·00

1956. Europa. As Nos. 1582/3 of Belgium.
1167 10pf. green 1·60 25
1168 40pf. blue 9·25 1·50

320 Midwife and Baby

1956. Humanitarian Relief Fund. Centres in black.
1169 **320** 7pf.+3pf. brown 2·30 3·50
1170 - 10pf.+5pf. green 1·70 1·20
1171 - 20pf.+10pf. red 1·70 1·20
1172 - 40pf.+10pf. blue 23·00 22·00
DESIGNS: 10pf. I. P. Semmelweis and cot; 20pf. Mother, and baby in cradle; 40f. Nurse maid and children.

321 Carrier Pigeon

1956. Stamp Day.
1173 **321** 10pf. green 2·30 1·00

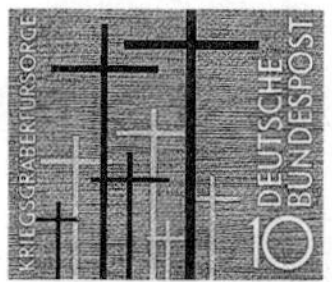

322 "Military Graves"

1956. War Graves Commission.
1174 **322** 10pf. green 2·30 1·00

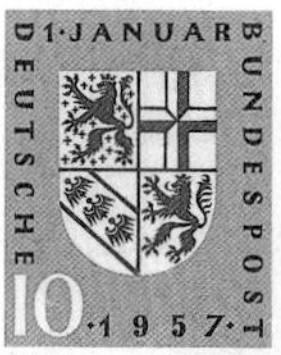

323 Arms

1957. Return of the Saar to West Germany.
1175 **323** 10pf. brown and green 80 70

324 Children with Luggage

1957. Berlin Children's Holiday Fund.

1176	**324**	10pf.+5pf. orange and green	1·70	3·00
1177	-	20pf.+10pf. blue and orange	4·00	5·25

DESIGN: 20pf. Girl returning from holiday.

325 Heinrich Hertz

1957. Birth Cent of Hertz (physicist).

1178	**325**	10pf. black and green	2·00	95

326 Paul Gerhardt

1957. 350th Birth Anniv of Paul Gerhardt (hymn-writer).

1179	**326**	20pf. red	95	80

327 "Flora and Philately"

1957. Exhibition and 8th Congress of Int Federation of "Constructive Philately".

1180	**327**	20pf. orange	95	80

328 Emblem of Aschaffenburg

1957. Millenary of Aschaffenburg.

1181	**328**	20pf. red and black	95	80

329 University Class

1957. 500th Anniv of Freiburg University.

1182	**329**	10pf. black, red & green	70	60

330 "Bayernstein" (freighter)

1957. German Merchant Shipping Day.

1183	**330**	15pf. black, red and blue	1·60	1·50

331 Justus Liebig University

1957. 350th Anniv of Justus Liebig University, Giessen.

1184	**331**	10pf. green	70	70

332 Albert Ballin

1957. Birth Centenary of Albert Ballin (director of Hamburg-America Shipping Line).

1185	**332**	20pf. black and red	2·00	70

333 Television Screen

1957. Publicizing West German Television Service.

1186	**333**	10pf. green and blue	70	70

334 "Europa" Tree

1957. Europa.

1187	**334**	10pf. green and blue	60	25
1188	**334**	40pf. blue	5·75	60

335 Young Miner

1957. Humanitarian Relief Fund.

1189	**335**	7pf.+3pf. black & brn	1·70	2·30
1190	-	10pf.+5pf. black & grn	1·20	1·20
1191	-	20pf.+10pf. black & red	1·70	1·20
1192	-	40pf.+10pf. black & bl	23·00	26·00

DESIGNS: 10pf. Miner drilling coal-face; 20pf. Miner with coal-cutting machine; 40pf. Operator at mine lift-shaft.

336 Water Lily

1957. Nature Protection Day.

1193	**336**	10pf. orange, yell & grn	70	60
1194	-	20pf. multicoloured	80	70

DESIGN—VERT: 20pf. European robin.

337 Carrier Pigeons

1957. International Correspondence Week.

1195	**337**	20pf. black and red	1·30	80

338 Baron von Stein

1957. Birth Bicentenary of Baron von Stein (statesman).

1196	**338**	20pf. red	2·30	95

339 Dr Leo Baeck (philosopher)

1957. 1st Death Anniv of Dr. Leo Baeck.

1197	**339**	20pf. red	2·30	95

340 Wurttemberg Parliament House

1957. 500th Anniv of First Wurttemberg Parliament.

1198	**340**	10pf. olive and green	1·30	80

341 Stage Coach

1957. Death Centenary of Joseph von Eichendorff (novelist).

1199	**341**	10pf. green	1·20	80

342 "Max and Moritz" (cartoon characters)

1958. 50th Death Anniv of Wilhelm Busch (writer and illustrator).

1200	**342**	10pf. olive and black	35	30
1201	-	20pf. red and black	1·20	95

DESIGN: 20pf. Wilhelm Busch.

343 "Prevent Forest Fires"

1958. Forest Fires Prevention Campaign.

1202	**343**	20pf. black and red	1·00	80

344 Rudolf Diesel and First Oil Engine

1958. Birth Centenary of Rudolf Diesel (engineer).

1203	**344**	10pf. myrtle	60	60

345 "The Fox who stole the Goose"

1958. Berlin Students' Fund. Inscr "Fur die Jugend".

1204	**345**	10pf.+5pf. red, black and green	2·30	3·00
1205	-	20pf.+10pf. brown, green and red	4·00	4·75

DESIGN: 20pf. "A hunter from the Palatinate" (horseman).

346 Giraffe and Lion

1958. Centenary of Frankfurt am Main Zoo.

1206	**346**	10pf. black and green	80	60

347 Old Munich

1958. 800th Anniv of Munich.

1207	**347**	20pf. red	80	60

348 Trier and Market Cross

1958. Millenary of Trier Market.

1208	**348**	20pf. red and black	80	60

349 Deutsche Mark (coin)

1958. 10th Anniv of Currency Reform.

1209	**349**	20pf. black and orange	1·00	1·70

350 Emblem of Gymnastics

1958. 150th Anniv of German Gymnastics.

1210	**350**	10pf. black, green & grey	60	70

351 H. Schulze-Delitzsch

1958. 150th Birth Anniv of Schulze-Delitzsch (pioneer of German co-operative movement).

1211	**351**	10pf. green	70	60

1958. Europa. As No. 643 of Luxembourg, size 24½×30 mm.

1212	10pf. blue and green	60	35
1213	40pf. red and blue	4·75	60

352 Friedrich Raiffeisen (philanthropist)

353 Dairymaid

1958. Humanitarian Relief and Welfare Funds.

1214	**352**	7pf.+3pf. brown, deep brown and chestnut	70	70
1215	**353**	10pf.+5pf. red, yellow and green	70	70
1216	-	20pf.+10pf. blue, green and red	70	70
1217	-	40pf.+10pf. yellow, orange and blue	8·75	10·50

DESIGNS— As Type **353**: 20pf. Vine-dresser; 40pf. Farm labourer.

354 Cardinal Nicholas of Cues (founder)

1958. 500th Anniv of Hospice of St. Nicholas.

1218	**354**	20pf. black and mauve	70	60

1959. As Type B 53 of West Berlin but without "BERLIN".

1219	7pf. green	35	30
1220	10pf. green	60	35
1221	20pf. red	60	35
1222	40pf. blue	19·00	1·40
1223	70pf. violet	5·75	1·20

355 Jakob Fugger (merchant prince)

1959. 500th Birth Anniv of Jakob Fugger.

1224	**355**	20pf. black and red	60	70

356 Adam Riese (mathematician)

1959. 400th Death Anniv of Adam Riese.

1225	**356**	10pf. black and green	60	70

357 A. von Humboldt (naturalist)

1959. Death Cent of Alexander von Humboldt.

1226	**357**	40pf. blue	2·50	2·00

358 First Hamburg Stamp of 1859

1959. International Stamp Exhibition, Hamburg, and Centenary of First Stamps of Hamburg and Lubeck.

1228	**358**	10pf.+5pf. brown & grn	35	1·20
1230	-	20pf.+10pf. brn & red	35	1·20

DESIGN: 20pf. First Lubeck stamp of 1859.

359 Buxtehude

1959. Millenary of Buxtehude.

1231	**359**	20pf. red, black and blue	60	60

360 Holy Tunic of Trier

1959. Holy Tunic of Trier Exhibition.

1232	**360**	20pf. black, buff & purple	60	60

361 Congress Emblem

1959. German Evangelical Church Day and Congress, Munich.

1233	**361**	10pf. violet, green & blk	45	45

1959. Inauguration of Beethoven Hall, Bonn. T 361a and similar horiz designs in sheet 148×104 mm with extract from Beethoven's music notebooks.

MS1233a	10pf. green (Handel); 15pf. blue (Spohr); 20pf. red (T **361a**); 25pf. brown (Haydn); 40pf. blue (Mendelssohn)	33·00	70·00

1959. Europa. As Nos. 659/60 of Luxembourg, but size 24½×30 mm.

1234	10pf. green	45	25
1235	40pf. blue	1·90	60

362 "Feeding the Poor"

1959. Humanitarian Relief and Welfare Funds.

1236	**362**	7pf.+3pf. sepia & yellow	35	60
1237	-	10pf.+5pf. green & yell	35	60
1238	-	20pf.+10pf. red & yell	45	60
1239	-	40pf.+10pf. mult	4·75	6·50

DESIGNS: 10pf. "Clothing the Naked"; 20pf. "Bounty from Heaven" (scenes from the Brothers Grimm story "The Star Thaler"); 40pf. The Brothers Grimm.

363 "Uprooted Tree"

1960. World Refugee Year.

1240	**363**	10pf. black, purple & grn	35	35
1241	**363**	40pf. black, red and blue	3·25	3·25

364 P. Melanchthon

1960. 400th Death Anniv of Philip Melanchthon (Protestant reformer).

1242	**364**	20pf. black and red	2·00	1·70

365 Cross and Symbols of the Crucifixion

1960. Oberammergau Passion Play.

1243	**365**	10pf. grey, ochre and blue	45	45

366

1960. 37th World Eucharistic Congress, Munich.

1244	**366**	10pf. green	80	60
1245	**366**	20pf. red	1·20	1·20

367 Wrestling

1960. Olympic Year. Inscr as in T 367.

1246	**367**	7pf. brown	35	25
1247	-	10pf. green	60	25
1248	-	20pf. red	60	25
1249	-	40pf. blue	2·00	1·90

DESIGNS: 10pf. Running; 20pf. Javelin and discus-throwing; 40pf. Chariot-racing.

368 Hildesheim Cathedral

1960. Birth Millenary of Bishops St. Bernward and St. Godehard.

1250	**368**	20pf. purple	1·20	70

368a Conference Emblem

1960. Europa.

1251	**368a**	10pf. green and olive	35	35
1252	**368a**	20pf. vermilion and red	1·20	40
1253	**368a**	40pf. light blue and blue	1·70	1·50

369 Little Red Riding Hood meeting Wolf

1960. Humanitarian Relief and Welfare Funds.

1254	**369**	7pf.+3pf. black, red and bistre	70	70
1255	-	10pf.+5pf. black, red and green	70	60
1256	-	20pf.+10pf. black, green and red	70	60
1257	-	40pf.+20pf. black, red and blue	3·50	5·75

DESIGNS: 10pf. Red Riding Hood and wolf disguised as grandmother; 20pf. Woodcutter and dead wolf; 40pf. Red Riding Hood with grandmother.

1960. 1st Death Anniv of Gen. George C. Marshall. Portrait as T 364.

1258	40pf. black and blue	4·00	3·25

371 "Adler", 1835

1960. 125th Anniv of German Railway.

1259	**371**	10pf. black and bistre	45	60

372 St. George and the Dragon

1961. Pathfinders (German Boy Scouts) Commemoration.

1260	**372**	10pf. green	35	45

1961. Famous Germans. As Nos. B194, etc of West Berlin but without "BERLIN".

1261	5pf. olive	25	25
1262	7pf. brown	25	25
1263	8pf. violet	25	35
1264	10pf. green	25	35
1265a	15pf. blue	25	25
1266a	20pf. red	25	25
1267	25pf. brown	35	30
1268	30pf. sepia	35	30
1269	40pf. blue	35	30
1270	50pf. brown	45	35
1271	60pf. red	45	35
1272	70pf. green	35	35
1273	80pf. brown	60	60
1274	90pf. bistre	45	30
1275	1Dm. violet	80	35
1276	2Dm. green	4·00	80

PORTRAIT: 90pf. Franz Oppenheimer (economist).

373 Early Daimler Motor Car

1961. 75th Anniv of Daimler-Benz Patent.

1277	**373**	10pf. green and black	35	25
1278	-	20pf. red and black	45	45

DESIGN: 20pf. Early Benz motor car.

374 Nuremberg Messenger of 1700

1961. "The Letter during Five Centuries" Exhibition, Nuremberg.

1279	**374**	7pf. black and red	35	45

375 Speyer Cathedral

1961. 900th Anniv of Speyer Cathedral.

1280	**375**	20pf. red	45	70

376 Doves

1961. Europa.

1281	**376**	10pf. green	35	35
1282	**376**	40pf. blue	60	80

377 Hansel and Gretel in the Wood

1961. Humanitarian Relief and Welfare Funds. Multicoloured.

1283	7pf.+3pf. Type **377**	35	45
1284	10pf.+5pf. Hansel, Gretel and the Witch	35	45
1285	20pf.+10pf. Hansel in the Witch's cage	35	45
1286	40pf.+20pf. Hansel and Gretel reunited with their father	1·40	2·75

378 Telephone Apparatus

1961. Centenary of Philipp Reis's Telephone.

1287	**378**	10pf. green	45	60

379 Baron W. E. von Ketteler

1961. 150th Birth Anniv of Baron W. E. von Ketteler (Catholic leader).

1288	**379**	10pf. black and green	45	60

380 Drusus Stone

1962. Bimillenary of Mainz.

1289	**380**	20pf. purple	45	60

381 Apollo

1962. Child Welfare. Butterflies. Mult.

1290	7pf.+3pf. Type **381**	60	80
1291	10pf.+5pf. Camberwell beauty	60	80
1292	20pf.+10pf. Small tortoiseshell	1·20	1·60
1293	40pf.+20pf. Scarce swallowtail	1·70	2·75

382 Part of "In Dulci Jubilo", from "Musae Sioniae" (M. Praetorius)

1962. "Song and Choir" (Summer Music Festivals).

1294	**382**	20pf. red and black	45	70

383 "Belief, Thanksgiving and Service"

1962. Catholics' Day.

1295	**383**	20pf. mauve	45	70

384 Open Bible

1962. 150th Anniv of Wurttembergische Bibelanstalt (Bible publishers).

1296	**384**	20pf. black and red	45	70

385 Europa "Tree"

1962. Europa.

1297	**385**	10pf. green	35	35
1298	**385**	40pf. blue	70	80

386 Snow White and the Seven Dwarfs

1962. Humanitarian Relief and Welfare Funds. Scenes from "Snow White and the Seven Dwarfs" (Brothers Grimm). Multicoloured.

1299	7pf.+3pf. The "Magic Mirror"	35	35
1300	10pf.+5pf. Type **386**	35	35
1301	20pf.+10pf. "The Poisoned Apple"	35	35
1302	40pf.+20pf. Snow White and Prince Charming	1·20	1·90

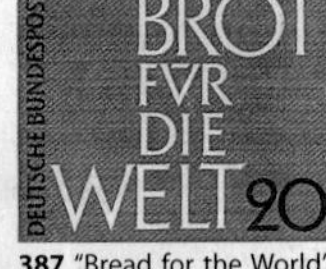

387 "Bread for the World"

1963. Freedom from Hunger.

1303	**387**	20pf. brown and black	45	70

388 Relief Distribution

1963. CRALOG and CARE Relief Organizations.

1304	**388**	20pf. red	35	60

389 Ears of Wheat, Cross and Globe

1963. Freedom from Hunger.

1305	**389**	20pf. black, red and grey	35	60

390 Snake's Head Lily

1963. "Flora and Philately" Exhibition, Hamburg. Multicoloured.

1306	10pf. Type **390**	35	35
1307	15pf. Lady's slipper orchid	35	35
1308	20pf. Columbine	35	35
1309	40pf. Sea holly	50	65

391 "Heidelberger Catechismus"

1963. 400th Anniv of Heidelberg Catechism.

1310	**391**	20pf. black, red and orange	45	60

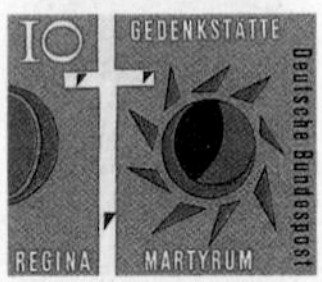

392 Cross, Sun and Moon

1963. Consecration of Regina Martyrum Church, Berlin.

1311	**392**	10pf. multicoloured	35	45

393 Emblems of Conference Participating Countries

1963. Centenary of Paris Postal Conference.

1312	**393**	40pf. blue	60	80

394 Map and Flags

1963. Opening of Denmark–Germany Railway ("Vogelfluglinie").

1313	**394**	20pf. multicoloured	45	45

395 Red Cross Emblem

1963. Red Cross Centenary.

1314	**395**	20pf. red, purple & yell	45	45

396 Hoopoe

1963. Child Welfare. Bird designs inscr "FUR DIE JUGEND 1963". Multicoloured.

1315	10pf.+5pf. Type **396**	70	95
1316	15pf.+5pf. Golden oriole	60	95
1317	20pf.+10pf. Northern bullfinch	60	95
1318	40pf.+20pf. River kingfisher	2·50	3·75

397 Congress Emblem

1963. German Evangelical Church Day and Congress, Dortmund.

1319	**397**	20pf. black and brown	45	60

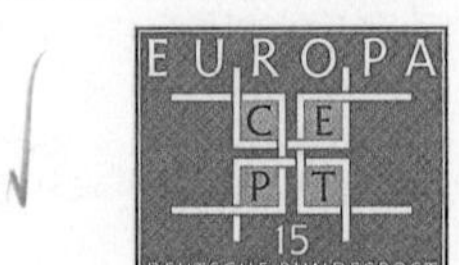

398 "Co-operation"

1963. Europa.

1320	**398**	15pf. green	35	45
1321	**398**	20pf. red	35	35

399 Mother Goat warning kids

1963. Humanitarian Relief and Welfare Funds.

1322	**399**	10pf.+5pf. mult	35	35
1323	-	15pf.+5pf. mult	35	35
1324	-	20pf.+10pf. mult	35	35
1325	-	40pf.+20pf. mult	95	1·60

DESIGNS: 15pf. Wolf entering house; 20pf. Wolf in house, threatening kids; 40pf. Mother Goat and Kids dancing round wolf in well. From Grimm's "Wolf and the Seven Kids".

400 Atlantic Herring

1964. Child Welfare. Fish designs inscr "Fur die Jugend 1964". Multicoloured.

1326	10pf.+5pf. Type **400**	35	50
1327	15pf.+5pf. Redfish	35	50
1328	20pf.+10pf. Mirror carp	50	70
1329	40pf.+20pf. Atlantic cod	1·40	2·75

401 Old Town Hall, Hanover

1964. Capitals of the Federal Lands. Mult.

1330	20pf. Type **401**	35	45
1331	20pf. Hamburg	35	45
1332	20pf. Kiel	35	45
1333	20pf. Munich	35	45

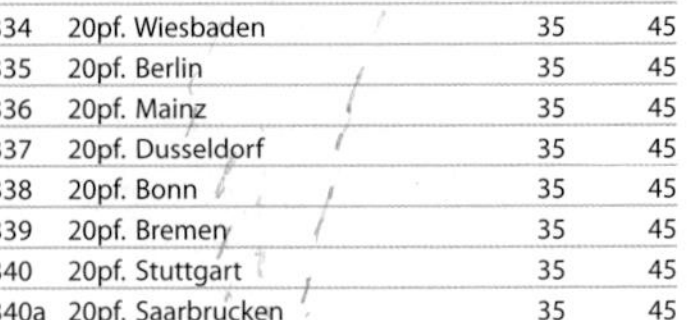

1334	20pf. Wiesbaden	35	45
1335	20pf. Berlin	35	45
1336	20pf. Mainz	35	45
1337	20pf. Dusseldorf	35	45
1338	20pf. Bonn	35	45
1339	20pf. Bremen	35	45
1340	20pf. Stuttgart	35	45
1340a	20pf. Saarbrucken	35	45

DESIGNS: No. 1331, Liner "Lichtenfels" and St. Michael's Church (775th anniv); 1332, Ferry "Kronprinz Harald"; 1333, National Theatre; 1334, Kurhaus; 1335, Reichstag; 1336, Gutenberg Museum; 1337, Jan Wellen's Monument and Town Hall; 1338, Town Hall; 1339, Market Hall; 1340, Town view; 1340a, Ludwig's Church.

402 Ottobeuren Abbey

1964. 1200th Anniv of Benedictine Abbey, Ottobeuren.

1341	**402**	20pf. black, red and pink	35	45

1964. Re-election of Pres. Lubke. As Type B 67 of West Berlin, inscr "DEUTSCHE BUNDESPOST" only.

1342	20pf. red	35	35
1343	40pf. blue	35	45

402b Sophie Scholl

1964. 20th Anniv of Attempt on Hitler's Life. Anti-Hitlerite Martyrs. Each black and grey.

1343a	20pf. Type **402b**	95	1·70
1343b	20pf. Ludwig Beck	95	1·70
1343c	20pf. Dietrich Bonhoeffer	95	1·70
1343d	20pf. Alfred Delp	95	1·70
1343e	20pf. Karl Friedrich Goerdeler	95	1·70
1343f	20pf. Wilhelm Leuschner	95	1·70
1343g	20pf. Helmuth James (Von Moltke)	95	1·70
1343h	20pf. Claus Schenk (Von Stauffenberg)	95	1·70

403 Calvin

1964. World Council of Reformed Churches.

1344	**403**	20pf. black and red	35	45

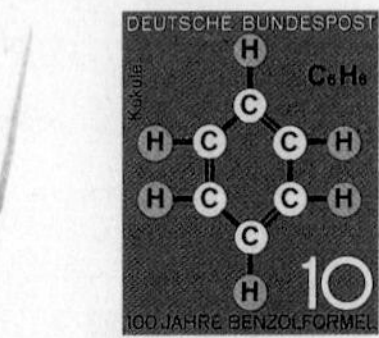

404 Diagram of Benzene Formula

1964. Scientific Anniversaries (1st series).

1345	10pf. green, black and brown	35	35
1346	15pf. multicoloured	35	35
1347	20pf. green, black and red	35	35

DESIGNS: 10pf. Type **404** (centenary of publication of Kekule's benzene formula); 15pf. Diagram of nuclear reaction (25th anniv of publication of Hahn-Strassman treatise on splitting the nucleus of the atom); 20pf. Gas engine (centenary of Otto-Langen internal-combustion engine).

See also Nos. 1426/7 and 1451/3.

405 F. Lassalle

1964. Death Centenary of Ferdinand Lassalle (Socialist founder and leader).

1348	**405**	20pf. black and blue	35	45

406 "The Sun"

1964. 80th Catholics' Day.

1349	**406**	20pf. red and blue	35	45

407 Europa "Flower"

1964. Europa.

1350	**407**	15pf. violet and green	25	25
1351	**407**	20pf. violet and red	25	25

408 "The Sleeping Beauty"

1964. Humanitarian Relief and Welfare Funds.

1352	**408**	10pf.+5pf. mult	35	35
1353	-	15pf.+5pf. mult	35	35
1354	-	20pf.+10pf. mult	35	35
1355	-	40pf.+20pf. mult	65	1·40

DESIGNS: 15pf., 20pf., 40pf. Various scenes from Grimm's "The Sleeping Beauty".

409 Judo

1964. "Olympic Year".

1356	**409**	20pf. multicoloured	35	45

410 Prussian Eagle

1964. 250th Anniv of German Court of Accounts.

1357	**410**	20pf. orange and black	35	45

411 Pres. Kennedy

1964. Pres. Kennedy Commemoration.

1358	**411**	40pf. blue	45	45

412 Castle Gateway, Ellwangen (Jagst)

1964. Twelve Centuries of German Architecture. (a) Size 18½×22 mm. Plain background.

1359	-	10pf. brown	35	35
1360	-	15pf. green	35	35
1361	-	20pf. brown	40	35
1362	-	40pf. blue	40	35
1363	**412**	50pf. brown	70	35
1364	-	60pf. red	1·60	60
1365	-	70pf. green	1·90	60
1366	-	80pf. brown	1·60	50

(b) Size 19½×24 mm. Coloured background.

1367	5pf. brown	30	15
1368	10pf. brown	30	15
1369	20pf. green	35	15
1370	30pf. green	35	15
1371	30pf. red	35	20
1372	40pf. brown	45	35
1373	50pf. blue	60	25
1374	60pf. orange	3·75	2·10
1375	70pf. green	1·60	35
1376	80pf. brown	3·00	2·10
1377	90pf. black	1·20	45
1378	1Dm. blue	1·00	35
1379	1Dm.10 brown	1·20	60
1380	1Dm.30 green	3·00	2·10
1381	2Dm. purple	3·00	95

BUILDINGS: 5pf. Berlin Gate, Stettin; 10pf. Zwinger pavilion, Dresden; 15pf. Tegel Castle, Berlin; 20pf. Monastery Gate, Lorsch; 30pf. North Gate, Flensburg; 40pf. Trifels Castle (Palatinate); 60pf. Treptow Portal, Neubrandenburg; 70pf. Osthofen Gate, Soest; 80pf. Ellingen Portal, Weissenburg (Bavaria); 90pf. Zschokk's Convent, Konigsberg; 1Dm. Melanchthon House, Wittenberg; 1Dm.10, Trinity Hospital, Hildesheim; 1Dm.30, Tegel Castle, Berlin (diff); 2Dm. Burghers' Hall, Lowenberg Town Hall (Silesia).

413 Owl, Hat, Walking-stick and Satchel

1965. 150th Death Anniv of Matthias Claudius (poet).

1383	**413**	20pf. black and red on grey	35	45

414 Eurasian Woodcock

1965. Child Welfare. Inscr "FUR DIE JUGEND 1965". Multicoloured.

1384	10pf.+5pf. Type **414**	35	45
1385	15pf.+5pf. Common pheasant	35	45
1386	20pf.+10pf. Black grouse	35	45
1387	40pf.+20pf. Western capercaillie	45	1·40

415 Bismarck (statesman)

1965. 150th Birth Anniv of Otto von Bismarck.

1388	**415**	20pf. black and red	35	45

416 Boeing 727-100 Airliner and Space Capsule

1965. Int Transport Exn, Munich. Mult.

1389	5pf. Traffic lights and road signs	35	45
1390	10pf. "Syncom" satellite and tracking station	35	45
1391	15pf. Old and modern postal buses	35	45
1392	20pf. Old semaphore station and modern signal tower	35	45
1393	40pf. Locomotive "Adler" (1835) and Class E.10.12 electric locomotive (1960s)	35	45
1394	60pf. Type **416**	35	45
1395	70pf. "Bremen" (liner) and "Hammonia" (19th-century steamship)	45	45

No. 1394 was also issued to mark the 10th anniv of Lufthansa's renewed air services.

417 Bouquet

1965. 75th Anniv of "May 1st" (Labour Day).

1396	**417**	15pf. multicoloured	30	35

418 I.T.U. Emblem

1965. Centenary of I.T.U.

1397	**418**	40pf. black and blue	45	60

419 A. Kopling

1965. Death Centenary of Adolf Kolping (miners' padre).

1398	**419**	20pf. black, red and grey	35	45

420 Rescue Vessel "Theodor Heuss"

1965. Cent of German Sea-rescue Service.

1399	**420**	20pf. violet, black & red	35	45

1965. 20th Anniv of Influx of East German Refugees. As T 299 but inscr "ZWANZIG JAHRE VERTREIBUNG 1945 1965".

1400	20pf. purple	35	45

421 Evangelical Church Emblem

1965. German Evangelical Church Day and Synod, Cologne.

1401	**421**	20pf. black, turq & bl	35	45

422 Radio Tower

1965. Radio Exhibition, Stuttgart.

1402	**422**	20pf. black, blue & mve	35	45

423 Thurn and Taxis 1, 2 and 5sgr. Stamps of 1852

1965. 125th Anniv of 1st Postage Stamp.

1403	**423**	20pf. multicoloured	35	45

424 Europa "Sprig"

1965. Europa.

1404	**424**	15pf. green	35	35
1405	**424**	20pf. red	35	35

425 Cinderella with Birds

1965. Humanitarian Relief Funds. Mult.

1406	10pf.+5pf. Type **425**	35	35
1407	15pf.+5pf. Cinderella and birds with dress	35	35
1408	20pf.+10pf. Prince offering slipper to Cinderella	35	35
1409	40pf.+20pf. Cinderella and Prince on horse	70	1·00

426 N. Soderblom

1966. Birth Centenary of Nathan Soderblom (Archbishop of Uppsala).

1410	**426**	20pf. black and lilac	35	45

427 Cardinal von Galen

1966. 20th Death Anniv of Cardinal Clemens von Galen.

1411	**427**	20pf. red, mauve & black	35	45

428 Brandenburg Gate, Berlin

1966

1412	**428**	10pf. brown	35	25
1413	**428**	20pf. green	50	35
1414	**428**	30pf. red	50	35
1415	**428**	50pf. blue	1·90	60
1415a	**428**	100pf. blue	14·50	95

429 Roe deer

1966. Child Welfare. Multicoloured.

1416	10pf.+5pf. Type **429**	35	40
1417	20pf.+10pf. Chamois	35	40
1418	30pf.+15pf. Fallow deer	35	40
1419	50pf.+25pf. Red deer	95	1·40

430 Christ and Fishermen (Miracle of the Fishes)

1966. Catholics' Day.

1420	**430**	30pf. black and salmon	35	45

431 19th-cent Postman

1966. F.I.P. Meeting, Munich. Multicoloured.

1421	30pf.+15pf. Bavarian mail coach	60	1·00
1422	50pf.+25pf. Type **431**	80	1·00

432 G. W. Leibniz

1966. 250th Death Anniv of Gottfried Leibniz (scientist).
1423 **432** 30pf. black and mauve 35 45

433 Europa "Ship"

1966. Europa.
1424 **433** 20pf. multicoloured 35 45
1425 **433** 30pf. multicoloured 35 30

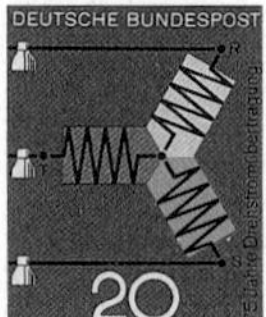

434 Diagram of A.C. Transmission (75th Anniv)

1966. Scientific Annivs (2nd series). Mult.
1426 20pf. Type **434** 30 35
1427 30pf. Diagram of electric dynamo (cent) 35 35

435 Princess and Frog

1966. Humanitarian Relief Funds. Mult.
1428 10pf.+5pf. Type **435** 30 30
1429 20pf.+10pf. Frog dining with Princess 30 35
1430 30pf.+15pf. Prince and Princess 30 35
1431 50pf.+25pf. In coach 60 1·40
Designs from Grimm's "The Frog Prince".

436 UNICEF Emblem

1966. Award of Nobel Peace Prize to United Nations Children's Fund.
1432 **436** 30pf. sepia, black and red 35 45

437 W. von Siemens (electrical engineer)

1966. 150th Birth Anniv of Werner von Siemens (electrical engineer).
1433 **437** 30pf. red 35 45

438 Common Rabbit

1967. Child Welfare. Multicoloured.
1434 10pf.+5pf. Type **438** 35 60
1435 20pf.+10pf. Stoat 35 60
1436 30pf.+15pf. Common hamster 70 1·20
1437 50pf.+25pf. Red fox 1·50 2·30
See also Nos. 1454/7.

439 Cogwheels

1967. Europa.
1438 **439** 20pf. multicoloured 45 45
1439 **439** 30pf. multicoloured 35 35

440 Francis of Taxis

1967. 450th Death Anniv of Francis of Taxis.
1440 **440** 30pf. black and orange 35 45

441 Evangelical Symbols

1967. 13th German Evangelical Churches Day.
1441 **441** 30pf. black and mauve 35 45

442 Friedrich von Bodelschwingh (Head of Hospital 1910–46)

1967. Cent of Bethel Hospital, Bielefeld.
1442 **442** 30pf. black and brown 35 45

443 Frau Holle at Spinning-wheel

1967. Humanitarian Relief Funds. Mult.
1443 10pf.+5pf. Type **443** 35 35
1444 20pf.+10pf. In the clouds 35 35
1445 30pf.+15pf. With shopping-basket and cockerel 35 35
1446 50pf.+25pf. Covered with soot 80 1·60
Designs from Grimm's "Frau Holle" ("Mother Carey").

1967. Re-election of Pres. Lubke. As Type B 67 of West Berlin, but inscr "DEUTSCHE BUNDESPOST".
1447 30pf. red 35 45
1448 50pf. blue 60 60

444 Wartburg (castle), Eisenach

1967. 450th Anniv of Luther's "Theses" and the Reformation.
1449 **444** 30pf. red 45 60

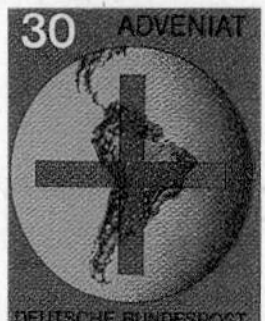

445 Cross on South American Map

1967. "Adveniat" (Aid for Catholic Church in Latin America).
1450 **445** 30pf. multicoloured 35 45

446 Koenig's Printing Machine

1968. Scientific Anniv (3rd series). Mult.
1451 10pf. Type **446** 25 25
1452 20pf. Ore Crystals 25 25
1453 30pf. Lens Refraction 35 35

ANNIVS: 10pf. 150th anniv; 20pf. Millenary of ore mining in Harz Mountains; 30pf. Centenary of Abbe-Zeiss Scientific Microscope.

1968. Child Welfare. As T 438 but inscr "1968". Multicoloured.
1454 10pf.+5pf. Wildcat 35 70
1455 20pf.+10pf. European otter 60 1·20
1456 30pf.+15pf. Eurasian badger 80 1·60
1457 50pf.+25pf. Eurasian beaver 3·00 4·00

447 Trade Symbols

1968. German Crafts and Trades.
1458 **447** 30pf. multicoloured 45 60

448 Dr. Adenauer

1968. Adenauer Commemoration (1st issue). T 448 and similar horiz designs in sheet 149×106 mm.
MS1459 10pf. brown and black; 20pf. green and black; 30pf. red and black; 50pf. blue and black 3·50 3·50
DESIGNS: 10pf. Sir Winston Churchill; 20pf. Alcide de Gasperi; 30pf. Robert Schuman.
See also No. 1469.

449 Europa "Key"

1968. Europa.
1460 **449** 20pf. yellow, brn & grn 35 45
1461 **449** 30pf. yellow, brn & red 35 35

450 Karl Marx

1968. 150th Birth Anniv of Karl Marx.
1462 **450** 30pf. red, black & grey 35 45

451 F. von Langen (horseman)

1968. Olympic Games (1972) Promotion Fund (1st series).
1463 **451** 10pf.+5pf. black & grn 45 40
1464 - 20pf.+10pf. black & grn 45 40
1465 - 30pf. black and lilac 45 40
1466 - 30pf.+15pf. black & red 80 75
1467 - 50pf.+25pf. black & bl 1·30 1·30
DESIGN: 20pf. R. Harbig (runner); 30pf. (No. 1465) Pierre de Coubertin (founder of Olympics); 30pf. (No. 1466) Helene Mayer (fencer); 50pf. Carl Diem (sports organiser).
See also Nos. 1493/6, 1524/7, 1589/92, 1621/4, **MS**1625 and 1629/32.

452 Opening Bars of "The Mastersingers"

1968. Centenary of 1st Performance of Richard Wagner's Opera "The Mastersingers".
1468 **452** 30pf. multicoloured 35 45

453 Dr. Adenauer

1968. Adenauer Commemoration (2nd issue).
1469 **453** 30pf. black and orange 45 45

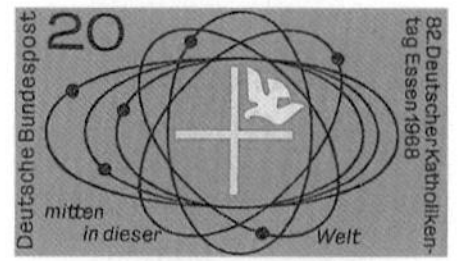

454 Cross, Dove and "The Universe"

1968. Catholics' Day.
1470 **454** 20pf. violet, yellow & grn 35 45

455 Northern District 1g. and Southern District 7k. stamps of 1868

1968. Cent of North German Postal Confederation and First Stamps.
1471 **455** 30pf. red, blue and black 35 45

456 Arrows

1968. Cent of German Trade Unions.
1472 **456** 30pf. multicoloured 35 45

457 Doll of 1878

1968. Humanitarian Relief Funds. Mult.
1473 10pf.+5pf. Type **457** 35 35
1474 20pf.+10pf. Doll of 1850 35 35
1475 30pf.+15pf. Doll of 1870 35 35
1476 50pf.+25pf. Doll of 1885 80 1·30

458 Human Rights Emblem

1968. Human Rights Year.
1477 **458** 30pf. multicoloured 35 45

459 Pony

1969. Child Welfare.
1478 **459** 10pf.+5pf. brown, black and yellow 45 60
1479 - 20pf.+10pf. brown, black and buff 45 60
1480 - 30pf.+15pf. brown, black and red 85 1·20
1481 - 50pf.+25pf. mult 2·50 2·30
HORSES: 20pf. Draught-horse; 30pf. Saddle-horse; 50pf. Thoroughbred.

460 Junkers Ju 52/3m "Boelke"

1969. 50th Anniv of German Airmail Services. Multicoloured.

1482		20pf. Type **460**	60	35
1483		30pf. Boeing 707 airliner	95	35

461 Colonnade

1969. Europa.

1484	**461**	20pf. yellow, grn & bl	45	35
1485	**461**	30pf. yellow, red & violet	45	35

462 "The Five Continents"

1969. 50th Anniv of I.L.O.

1486	**462**	30pf. multicoloured	70	45

463 Eagle Emblems of Weimar and Federal Republics

1969. 20th Anniv of German Federal Republic.

1487	**463**	30pf. black, gold and red	1·40	70

464 "War Graves"

1969. 50th Anniv of German War Graves Commission.

1488	**464**	30pf. blue and yellow	70	45

465 Lakeside Landscape

1969. Nature Protection. Multicoloured.

1489		10pf. Type **465**	35	35
1490		20pf. Highland landscape	95	60
1491		30pf. Alpine landscape	45	35
1492		50pf. River landscape	1·40	80

466 "Running Track"

1969. Olympic Games (1972). Promotion Fund (2nd series). Multicoloured.

1493		10pf.+5pf. Type **466**	35	35
1494		20pf.+10pf. "Hockey"	60	45
1495		30pf.+15pf. "Shooting target"	80	70
1496		50pf.+25pf. "Sailing"	1·70	1·40

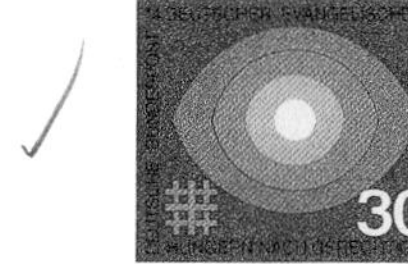

467 "Longing for Justice"

1969. 14th German Protestant Congress, Stuttgart.

1497	**467**	30pf. multicoloured	70	45

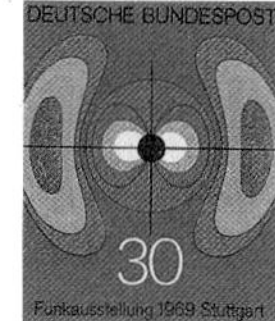

468 "Electromagnetic Field"

1969. German Radio Exhibition, Stuttgart.

1498	**468**	30pf. multicoloured	70	45

469 Marie Juchacz

1969. "Fifty Years of German Women's Suffrage". Sheet 102×61 mm containing T 469 and similar vert portraits of women politicians.

MS1499		10pf. olive; 20pf. green; 30pf. red	1·60	1·20

DESIGNS: 20pf. Marie-Elizabeth Luders; 30pf. Helene Weber.

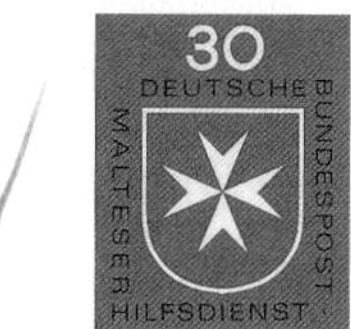

470 Maltese Cross Symbol

1969. "Malteser Hilfsdienst" (welfare organization).

1500	**470**	30pf. red and black	70	45

471 Bavaria 3k. Stamp of 1867

1969. German Philatelic Federation Congress and Exn, Garmisch-Partenkirchen.

1501	**471**	30pf. red and slate	70	45

472 Map of Pipeline

1969. 350th Anniv of Bad Reichenhall–Traunstein Brine Pipeline.

1502	**472**	20pf. multicoloured	70	45

473 Rothenburg ob der Tauber

1969. Tourism.

1503	**473**	30pf. black and red	70	45

See also Nos. 1523, 1558, 1564, 1587, 1606, 1641/2, 1655/6 and 1680/2.

474 Mahatma Gandhi

1969. Birth Centenary of Mahatma Gandhi.

1504	**474**	20pf. black and green	45	45

475 Pope John XXIII

1969. Pope John XXIII Commemoration.

1505	**475**	30pf. red	60	45

476 "Adler" (1835)

1969. Humanitarian Relief Funds. Pewter Figurines. Mult.

(a) Inscr. "WOHLFAHRTSMARKE".

1506		10pf.+5pf. Type **476**	30	30
1507		20pf.+10pf. Woman watering flowers (1780)	35	35
1508		30pf.+15pf. Bird salesman (1850)	45	45
1509		50pf.+25pf. Mounted dignitary (1840)	1·40	1·70

(b) Christmas. Inscr "WEIHNACHTSMARKE".

1510		10pf.+5pf. "Child Jesus in crib" (1850)	50	45

477 E. M. Arndt

1969. Birth Bicent of Ernst Arndt (writer).

1511	**477**	30pf. lake and bistre	60	45

478 "H. von Rugge"

1970. Child Welfare. Minnesinger Themes. Multicoloured.

1512		10pf.+5pf. Type **478**	60	45
1513		20pf.+10pf. "W. von Eschenbach"	95	60
1514		30pf.+15pf. "W. von Metz"	1·20	95
1515		50pf.+25pf. "W. von der Vogelweide"	2·50	2·30

479 Beethoven

1970. Birth Bicentenaries.

1516	**479**	10pf. black and blue	1·20	35
1517	-	20pf. black and olive	70	35
1518	-	30pf. black and pink	70	35

DESIGNS: 20pf. G. W. Hegel (philosopher); 30pf. F. Holderlin (poet).

480 Saar 1m. Stamp of 1947

1970. "Sabria 70" Stamp Exn, Saarbrucken.

1519	**480**	30pf. green, black and red	60	45

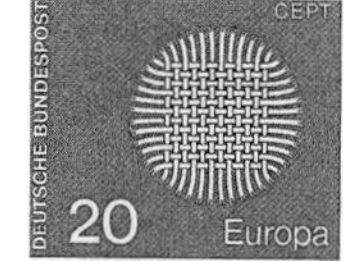

481 "Flaming Sun"

1970. Europa.

1520	**481**	20pf. green	45	35
1521	**481**	30pf. red	50	35

482 Von Munchhausen on Severed Horse

1970. 250th Birth Anniv of Baron H. von Munchhausen.

1522	**482**	20pf. multicoloured	60	45

1970. Tourism. As T 473, but with view of Oberammergau.

1523		30pf. black and orange	60	45

483 Royal Palace

1970. Olympic Games (1972). Promotion Fund (3rd series).

1524	**483**	10pf.+5pf. brown	35	35
1525	-	20pf.+10pf. turquoise	70	60
1526	-	30pf.+15pf. red	95	80
1527	-	50pf.+25pf. blue	1·50	1·50

DESIGNS (Munich buildings): 20pf. Propylaea; 30pf. Glyptothek; 50pf. "Bavaria" (statue and colonnade).

484 Liner "Kungsholm IV" and Road-tunnel

1970. 75th Anniv of Kiel Canal.

1528	**484**	20pf. multicoloured	60	45

485 Nurse with Invalid

1970. Voluntary Relief Services. Mult.

1529		5pf. Oxygen-lance operator	30	35
1530		10pf. Mountain rescue	35	35
1531		20pf. Type **485**	45	35
1532		30pf. Fireman with hose	1·20	35
1533		50pf. Road-accident casualty	1·20	60
1534		70pf. Rescue from drowning	1·40	1·20

486 President Heinemann

1970

1535	**486**	5pf. black	35	35
1536	**486**	10pf. brown	35	35
1537	**486**	20pf. green	35	35

1538	**486**	25pf. green	50	35
1539	**486**	30pf. brown	45	35
1540	**486**	40pf. orange	45	35
1541	**486**	50pf. blue	2·10	35
1542	**486**	60pf. blue	95	35
1543	**486**	70pf. brown	1·20	45
1544	**486**	80pf. green	1·20	45
1545	**486**	90pf. red	2·10	1·70
1546	**486**	1Dm. green	1·50	45
1547	**486**	110pf. grey	1·70	1·20
1548	**486**	120pf. brown	2·00	1·20
1549	**486**	130pf. brown	2·10	1·20
1550	**486**	140pf. green	2·20	1·40
1551	**486**	150pf. red	2·20	1·20
1552	**486**	160pf. orange	3·25	1·60
1553	**486**	170pf. orange	2·75	1·20
1554	**486**	190pf. purple	3·50	1·30
1555	**486**	2Dm. violet	3·75	60

487 Illuminated Cross

1970. Catholic Church World Mission.

1556	**487**	20pf. yellow and green	45	35

488 Stylized Cross

1970. Catholics Day and 83rd German Catholic Congress, Trier.

1557	**488**	20pf. multicoloured	45	35

1970. Tourism. As T 473.

1558	20pf. black and green	70	45

DESIGN: 20pf. View of Cochem.

489 "Jester"

1970. Humanitarian Relief Funds. Puppets. Multicoloured. (a) Relief Funds.

1559		10pf.+5pf. Type **489**	35	35
1560		20pf.+10pf. "Buffoon"	35	45
1561		30pf.+15pf. "Clown"	60	60
1562		50pf.+25pf. "Harlequin"	1·50	1·50

(b) Christmas.

1563		10pf.+5pf. "Angel"	45	40

1970. Tourism. As T 473, but with view of Freiburg im Breisgau.

1564	20pf. brown and green	70	45

490 A. J. Comenius (scholar)

1970. Int Education Year and 300th Death Anniv of Comenius (Jan Komensky).

1565	**490**	30pf. red and black	70	45

491 Engels as Young Man

1970. 150th Birth Anniv of Friedrich Engels.

1566	**491**	50pf. blue and red	2·10	1·20

492 German Eagle

1971. Centenary of German Unification.

1567	**492**	30pf. black, red & orange	2·10	45

493 "Ebert" Stamp of 1928 and inscr "To the German People"

1971. Birth Centenary of Friedrich Ebert (Chancellor 1918 and President 1919–25).

1568	**493**	30pf. green, black and red	2·10	45

494 "King of Blackamoors"

1971. Child Welfare. Children's Drawings. Multicoloured.

1569		10pf.+5pf. Type **494**	45	45
1570		20pf.+10pf. "Flea"	60	60
1571		30pf.+15pf. "Puss-in-Boots"	95	95
1572		50pf.+25pf. "Serpent"	1·50	1·50

495 Molecular Chain

1971. 125 Years of Chemical Fibre Research.

1573	**495**	20pf. black, red & green	45	35

496 Road-crossing Patrol

1971. New Road Traffic Regulations (1st series).

1574	**496**	10pf. black, blue and red	25	25
1575	-	20pf. black, red & green	45	35
1576	-	30pf. red, black and grey	70	35
1577	-	50pf. black, blue and red	1·20	75

ROAD SIGNS: 20pf. "Right-of-way across junction"; 30pf. "STOP"; 50pf. "Pedestrian Crossing".

See also Nos. 1579/82.

497 Luther before Charles V

1971. 450th Anniv of Diet of Worms.

1578	**497**	30pf. black and red	95	45

1971. New Traffic Regulations (2nd series). Horiz designs similar to T 496.

1579	5pf. red, black and blue	30	30
1580	10pf. multicoloured	35	30
1581	20pf. red, black and green	60	30
1582	30pf. yellow, black and red	1·00	30

NEW HIGHWAY CODE: 5pf. Overtaking; 10pf. Warning of obstruction; 20pf. Lane discipline; 30pf. Pedestrian Crossing.

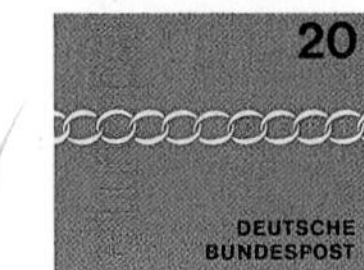

498 Europa Chain

1971. Europa.

1583	**498**	20pf. gold, green & black	40	35
1584	**498**	30pf. gold, red and black	45	35

499 Thomas a Kempis writing "The Imitation of Christ"

1971. 500th Death Anniv of Thomas a Kempis (devotional writer).

1585	**499**	30pf. black and red	80	45

500 Durer's Monogram

1971. 500th Birth Anniv of Albrecht Durer.

1586	**500**	30pf. brown & red	1·90	45

1971. Tourism. As T 473, but with view of Nuremburg.

1587	30pf. black and red	70	45

501 Meeting Emblem

1971. Whitsun Ecumenical Meeting, Augsburg.

1588	**501**	30pf. black, orange & red	70	45

502 Ski Jumping

1971. Olympic Games (1972). Promotion Fund (4th series). Winter Games, Sapporo.

1589	**502**	10pf.+5pf. black & brn	35	25
1590	-	20pf.+10pf. black & grn	70	45
1591	-	30pf.+15pf. black & red	1·30	95
1592	-	50pf.+25pf. black & bl	2·00	1·90
MS1593		112×66 mm. Nos. 1589/92	4·75	4·00

DESIGNS: 20pf. Ice dancing; 30pf. Skiing start; 50pf. Ice hockey.

503 Astronomical Calculus

1971. 400th Birth Anniv of Johann Kepler (astronomer).

1594	**503**	30pf. gold, red and black	80	45

504 Dante

1971. 650th Death Anniv of Dante Alighieri.

1595	**504**	10pf. black	35	35

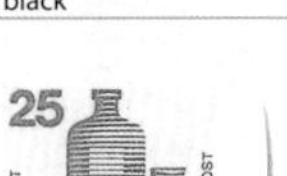

505 Alcohol and front of Car ("Don't Drink and Drive")

1971. Accident Prevention.

1596	-	5pf. orange	35	15
1597	-	10pf. brown	35	15
1598	-	20pf. violet	45	30
1599	**505**	25pf. green	60	30
1600	-	30pf. red	60	30
1601	-	40pf. mauve	60	30
1602	-	50pf. blue	3·00	30
1603	-	60pf. blue	2·00	70
1603a	-	70pf. blue and green	1·70	45
1604	-	1Dm. green	3·00	35
1605	-	1Dm.50 brown	7·50	1·70

DESIGNS: 5pf. Man within flame, and spent match ("Fire Prevention"); 10pf. Fall from ladder; 20pf. Unguarded machinery ("Factory Safety"); 30pf. Falling brick and protective helmet; 40pf. Faulty electric plug; 50pf. Protruding nail in plank; 60pf., 70pf. Ball in front of car ("Child Road Safety"); 1Dm. Crate on hoist; 1Dm.50, Open manhole.

1971. Tourism. As T 473 but with view of Goslar.

1606	20pf. black and green	70	60

506 Women churning Butter

1971. Humanitarian Relief Funds. Wooden Toys. Mult. (a) Inscr. "WOHLFAHRTSMARKE".

1607	20pf.+10pf. Type **506**	35	30
1608	25pf.+10pf. Horseman on wheels	35	30
1609	30pf.+15pf. Nutcracker man	70	70
1610	60pf.+30pf. Dovecote	1·90	1·90

(b) Christmas. Inscr "WEIHNACHTSMARKE".

1611	20pf.+10pf. Angel with three candles	80	60

507 Deaconess and Nurse

1972. Death Cent of Johann Wilhelm Lohe (founder of Deaconesses Mission, Neuendettelsau).

1612	**507**	25pf. slate, black & green	70	45

508 Ducks crossing Road

1972. Child Welfare. Annimal Protection. Multicoloured.

1613	20pf.+10pf. Type **508**	80	70
1614	25pf.+10pf. Hunter scaring deer	70	50
1615	30pf.+15pf. Child protecting bird from cat	1·40	1·40
1616	60pf.+30pf. Boy annoying mute swans	2·30	2·40

509 Senefelder's Press

1972. "175 Years of Offset Lithography".

1617	**509**	25pf. multicoloured	70	45

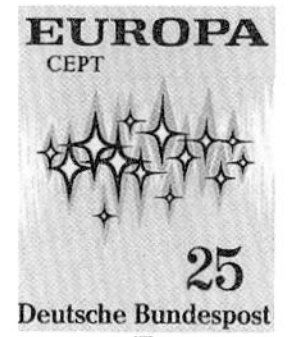

510 "Communications"

1972. Europa.
1618 **510** 25pf. multicoloured 60 30
1619 **510** 30pf. multicoloured 65 35

511 Lucas Cranach

1972. 500th Birth Anniv of Lucas Cranach the Elder (painter).
1620 **511** 25pf. black, stone & grn 80 45

512 Wrestling

1972. Olympic Games, Munich (5th series). Multicoloured.
1621 20pf.+10pf. Type **512** 70 60
1622 25pf.+10pf. Sailing 70 60
1623 30pf.+15pf. Gymnastics 70 60
1624 60pf.+30pf. Swimming 2·50 2·30
See also Nos. 1629/32.

513 Gymnastics Stadium

1972. Olympic Games, Munich (6th series). Sheet 148×105 mm containing T 513 and similar multicoloured designs.
MS1625 25pf.+10pf. Type **513**; 30pf.+15pf. Athletics stadium; 40pf.+20pf. Tented area; 70pf.+35pf. TV tower 6·50 6·50

514 Invalid Archer

1972. 21st Int Games for the Paralysed, Heidelberg.
1626 **514** 40pf. red, black & yellow 95 45

515 Posthorn and Decree

1972. Cent of German Postal Museum.
1627 **515** 40pf. multicoloured 1·30 45

516 K. Schumacher

1972. 20th Death Anniv of Kurt Schumacher (politician).
1628 **516** 40pf. black and red 1·90 45

1972. Olympic Games, Munich (7th series). As Type 512. Multicoloured.
1629 25pf.+5pf. Long jumping 70 70
1630 30pf.+10pf. Basketball 1·90 1·80
1631 40pf.+10pf. Throwing the discus 2·50 2·40
1632 70pf.+10pf. Canoeing 1·30 1·20
MS1633 111×66 mm. Nos. 1629/32 6·50 6·50

517 Open Book

1972. International Book Year.
1634 **517** 40pf. multicoloured 95 45

518 Music and Signature

1972. 300th Death Anniv of Heinrich Schutz (composer).
1635 **518** 40pf. multicoloured 1·20 45

519 Knight

1972. Humanitarian Relief Funds. Mult. (a) 19th-century Faience Chessmen. Inscr "WOHLFAHRTSMARKE".
1636 25pf.+10pf. Type **519** 45 45
1637 30pf.+15pf. Rook 45 35
1638 40pf.+20pf. Queen 80 35
1639 70pf.+35pf. King 3·00 2·75

(b) Christmas. Inscr "WEIHNACHTSMARKE".
1640 30pf.+15pf. "The Three Wise Men" (horiz) 1·20 80

1972. Tourism. As T 473.
1641 30pf. black and green 70 35
1642 40pf. black and orange 80 35
VIEWS: 30pf. Heligoland; 40pf. Heidelberg.

520 Revellers

1972. 150th Anniv of Cologne Carnival.
1643 **520** 40pf. multicoloured 1·40 45

521 H. Heine

1972. 175th Birth Anniv of Heinrich Heine (poet).
1644 **521** 40pf. black, red and pink 1·40 45

522 "Brot fur die Welt"

1972. Freedom from Hunger Campaign.
1645 **522** 30pf. red and green 70 70

523 Wurzburg Cathedral (seal)

1972. Catholic Synod '72.
1646 **523** 40pf. black, purple & red 80 45

524 National Colours of France and Germany

1973. 10th Anniv of Franco-German Treaty.
1647 **524** 40pf. multicoloured 1·60 50

525 Osprey

1973. Youth Welfare. Birds of Prey. Multicoloured.
1648 25pf.+10pf. Type **525** 1·40 1·20
1649 30pf.+15pf. Common buzzard 1·70 1·40
1650 40pf.+20pf. Red kite 2·30 2·10
1651 70pf.+35pf. Montagu's harrier 5·00 5·25

526 Copernicus

1973. 500th Birth Anniv of Copernicus.
1652 **526** 40pf. black and red 1·90 45

527 Radio Mast and Transmission

1973. 50th Anniv of Interpol.
1653 **527** 40pf. black, red and grey 70 45

528 Weather Chart

1973. Cent of Int Meteorological Organization.
1654 **528** 30pf. multicoloured 70 45

1973. Tourism. As T 473.
1655 40pf. black and red 1·40 35
1656 40pf. black and orange 1·20 35
VIEWS: No. 1655, Hamburg; 1656, Rudesheim.

529 "Gymnast" (poster)

1973. Gymnastics Festival, Stuttgart.
1657 **529** 40pf. multicoloured 70 45

530 Kassel (Hesse) Sign

1973. "I.B.R.A. Munchen 73" International Stamp Exhibition, Munich. F.I.P. Congress. Post-house Signs. Multicoloured.
1658 40pf.+20pf. Type **530** 1·00 1·00
1659 70pf.+35pf. Prussia 1·90 1·90

MS1660 74×105 mm. 40pf.+20pf. Wurttemberg; 70pf.+35pf. Kurpfalz (Bavaria) (sold at 2.20Dm.) 5·25 5·75

531 Europa "Posthorn"

1973. Europa.
1661 **531** 30pf. yell, myrtle & grn 70 35
1662 **531** 40pf. yellow, lake & pink 80 35

532 "R" Motif

1973. 1000th Death Anniv of Roswitha von Gandersheim (poetess).
1663 **532** 40pf. yellow, black & red 80 45

533 M. Kolbe

1973. Father Maximilian Kolbe (Concentration camp victim) Commemoration.
1664 **533** 40pf. red, brown & black 80 45

534 "Profile" (from poster)

1973. 15th German Protestant Church Conference.
1665 **534** 30pf. multicoloured 60 35

535 Environmental Conference Emblem and Waste

1973. "Protection of the Environment". Multicoloured.
1666 25pf. Type **535** 60 35
1667 30pf. Emblem and "Water" 60 35
1668 40pf. Emblem and "Noise" 1·20 35
1669 70pf. Emblem and "Air" 1·90 1·00

536 Schickard's Calculating Machine

1973. 350th Anniv of Schickard's Calculating Machine.
1670 **536** 40pf. black, red and orange 80 60

537 Otto Wels

1973. Birth Centenary of Otto Wels (Social Democratic Party leader).
1671 **537** 40pf. purple and lilac 95 45

538 Lubeck Cathedral

1973. 800th Anniv of Lubeck Cathedral.

1672	**538**	40pf. multicoloured	1·40	45

539 U.N. and German Eagle Emblems

1973. Admission of German Federal Republic to U.N. Organization.

1673	**539**	40pf. multicoloured	2·00	45

540 French Horn

1973. Humanitarian Relief Funds. Multicoloured. (a) Musical Instruments. Inscr "WOHLFAHRTSMARKE".

1674	25pf.+10pf. Type **540**	80	45
1675	30pf.+15pf. Grand piano	85	45
1676	40pf.+20pf. Violin	1·20	70
1677	70pf.+70pf. Harp	3·00	2·50

(b) Christmas. Inscr "WEIHNACHTSMARKE".

1678	30pf.+15pf. Christmas star	1·20	80

541 Radio set of 1923

1973. "50 Years of German Broadcasting".

1679	**541**	30pf. multicoloured	60	35

1974. Tourism. As Type 473.

1680	30pf. black and green	95	35
1681	40pf. black and red	95	35
1682	40pf. black and red	95	35

VIEWS: No. 1680, Saarbrucken; 1681, Aachen; 1682, Bremen.

542 Louise Otto-Peters

1974. Women in German Politics. Each black and orange.

1683	40pf. Type **542**	95	70
1684	40pf. Helene Lange	95	70
1685	40pf. Rosa Luxemburg	95	70
1686	40pf. Gertrud Baumer	95	70

543 Drop of Blood and Emergency Light

1974. Blood Donor and Accident/Rescue Services.

1687	**543**	40pf. red and blue	1·30	45

544 "Deer in Red" (Franz Marc)

1974. German Expressionist Paintings. Mult.

1688	30pf. Type **544**	70	35
1689	30pf. "Girls under Trees" (A. Macke)	95	40
1690	40pf. "Portrait in Blue" (A. von Jawiensky) (vert)	95	35
1691	50pf. "Pechstein asleep" (E. Heckel) (vert)	95	45
1692	70pf. "Still Life with Telescope" (Max Beckmann)	1·40	1·20
1693	120pf. "Old Peasant" (L. Kirchner) (vert)	2·75	2·30

545 St. Thomas teaching Pupils

1974. 700th Death Anniv of St. Thomas Aquinas.

1694	**545**	40pf. black and red	80	45

546 Disabled Persons in Outline

1974. Rehabilitation of the Handicapped.

1695	**546**	40pf. red and black	1·30	45

547 Construction (Bricklayer)

1974. Youth Welfare. Youth Activities. Multicoloured.

1696	25pf.+10pf. Type **547**	80	70
1697	30pf.+15pf. Folk dancing	1·40	1·20
1698	40pf.+20pf. Study	2·30	2·10
1699	70pf.+35pf. Research	4·25	4·25

548 "Ascending Youth" (W. Lehmbruck)

1974. Europa.

1700	**548**	30pf. black, green & sil	75	35
1701	-	40pf. black, red and lilac	80	35

DESIGN: 40pf. "Kneeling Woman" (W. Lehmbruck).

549 Immanuel Kant

1974. 250th Birth Anniv of Immanuel Kant (philosopher).

1702	**549**	90pf. red	3·00	70

550 Federal Arms and National Colours

1974. 25th Anniv of Formation of Federal Republic. Sheet 94×64 mm.

MS1703	**550**	40pf. multicoloured	2·10	2·75

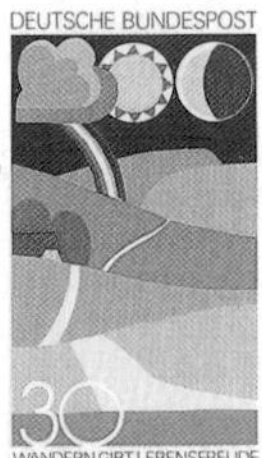

551 Country Road

1974. Rambling, and Birth Centenaries of Richard Schirrman and Wilhelm Munker (founders of Youth Hostelling Assn).

1704	**551**	30pf. multicoloured	60	45

552 Friedrich Klopstock

1974. 250th Birth Anniv of Friedrich Gottlieb Klopstock (poet).

1705	**552**	40pf. black and red	80	40

553 "Crowned Cross" Symbol

1974. 125th Anniv of German Protestant Church Diaconal Association (charitable organization).

1706	**553**	40p. multicoloured	80	45

554 Goalkeeper saving Goal

1974. World Cup Football Championship. Multicoloured.

1707	30pf. Type **554**	1·20	35
1708	40pf. Mid-field melee	2·50	35

555 Hans Holbein (self-portrait)

1974. 450th Death Anniv of Hans Holbein the Elder (painter).

1709	**555**	50pf. black and red	1·20	45

556 Broken Bars of Prison Window

1974. Amnesty International Commemoration.

1710	**556**	70pf. black and blue	1·60	70

557 "Man and Woman looking at the Moon"

1974. Birth Bicentenary of Caspar David Friedrich (artist).

1711	**557**	50pf. multicoloured	1·50	45

558 Campion

1974. Humanitarian Relief Funds. Flowers. Multicoloured. (a) 25th Anniv of Welfare Stamps. Inscr "25 JAHRE WOHLFAHRTSMARKE".

1712	30pf.+15pf. Type **558**	45	45
1713	40pf.+20pf. Foxglove	60	45
1714	50pf.+25pf. Mallow	70	60
1715	70pf.+35pf. Campanula	2·00	2·00

(b) Christmas. Inscr "WEIHNACHTSMARKE".

1716	40pf.+20pf. Poinsettia	1·40	80

559 Early German Post-boxes

1974. Cent of Universal Postal Union.

1717	**559**	50pf. multicoloured	1·90	60

560 Annette Kolb

1975. International Women's Year. Women Writers.

1718	30pf. Type **560**	95	45
1719	40pf. Ricarda Huch	80	45
1720	50pf. Else Lasker-Schuler	80	45
1721	70pf. Gertrud von le Fort	1·40	1·40

561 Hans Bockler (Trade Union leader)

1975. Birth Centenaries.

1722	**561**	40pf. black and green	1·00	45
1723	-	50pf. black and red	95	45
1724	-	70pf. black and blue	2·75	1·20

DESIGNS: 50pf. Matthias Erzberger (statesman); 70pf. Albert Schweitzer (medical missionary).

562 Mother and Child and Emblem

1975. 25th Anniv of Organization for the Rest and Recuperation of Mothers.

1725	**562**	50pf. multicoloured	1·00	45

563 Detail of Ceiling Painting, Sistine Chapel

1975. 500th Birth Anniv of Michelangelo.

1726	**563**	70pf. black and blue	2·10	2·00

564 Plan of St. Peter's, Rome within a cross

1975. "Holy Year (Year of Reconcillation)".

1727	**564**	50pf. multicoloured	1·00	45

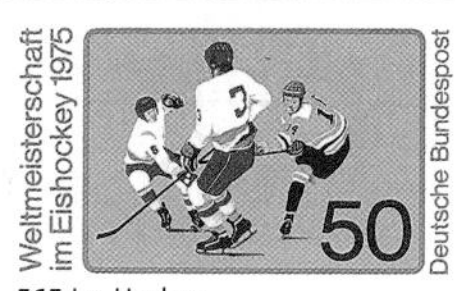

565 Ice Hockey

1975. World Ice Hockey Championships, Munich and Dusseldorf.

1728	**565**	50pf. multicoloured	1·50	45

566 Class 218 Diesel Locomotive

1975. Youth Welfare. Railway Locomotives. Multicoloured.

1729	30pf.+15pf. Type **566**	70	60
1730	40pf.+20pf. Class 103 electric locomotive	1·00	95
1731	50pf.+25pf. Class 403 electric railcar	1·50	1·40
1732	70pf.+35pf. Transrapid Maglev train (model)	2·50	2·30

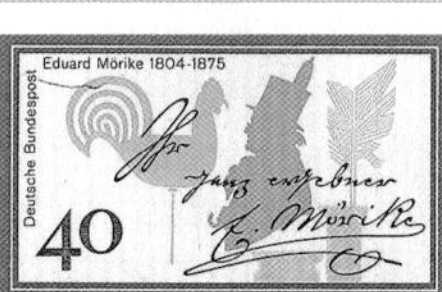

567 "Concentric Group"

1975. Europa. Paintings by Oskar Schlemmer. Multicoloured.

1733	40pf. Type **567**	75	35
1734	50pf. "Bauhaus Staircase"	1·10	35

568 Morike's Silhouette and Signature

1975. Death Cent of Eduard Morike (writer).

1735	**568**	40pf. multicoloured	50	35

569 "Nuis" (woodcarving)

1975. 500th Anniv of Siege of Neuss.

1736	**569**	50pf. multicoloured	1·00	50

570 Jousting Contest

1975. 500th Anniv of "Landshut Wedding" (festival).

1737	**570**	50pf. multicoloured	1·50	50

571 Mainz Cathedral

1975. Millenary of Mainz Cathedral.

1738	**571**	40pf. multicoloured	1·50	50

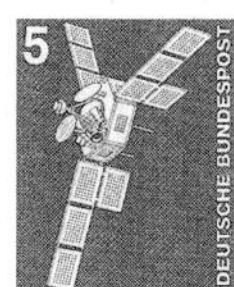

572 Tele-communication Satellite

1975. Industry and Technology.

1739	**572**	5pf. green	25	25
1740	-	10pf. mauve	25	25
1741	-	20pf. red	30	25
1742	-	30pf. lilac	35	30
1743	-	40pf. green	50	35
1744	-	50pf. mauve	60	35
1745	-	60pf. red	1·00	35
1746	-	70pf. blue	1·00	35
1747	-	80pf. green	1·10	35
1748	-	100pf. brown	1·20	35
1748a	-	110pf. purple	2·40	1·00
1749	-	120pf. blue	1·60	50
1749a	-	130pf. red	2·75	1·00
1750	-	140pf. red	1·80	60
1751	-	150pf. red	4·00	1·20
1752	-	160pf. green	2·40	1·00
1753	-	180pf. brown	3·25	1·20
1753a	-	190pf. brown	3·75	1·00
1754	-	200pf. purple	2·75	50
1754a	-	230pf. purple	5·00	1·50
1754b	-	250pf. green	5·50	2·30
1754c	-	300pf. green	6·00	2·30
1755	-	500pf. black	6·75	1·80

DESIGNS: 10pf. Electric train; 20pf. Modern lighthouse; 30pf. MBB-Bolkow Bo 105C rescue helicopter; 40pf. Space laboratory; 50pf. Dish aerial; 60pf. X-ray apparatus; 70pf. Ship-building; 80pf. Farm tractor; 100pf. Lignite excavator; 110pf. Colour television camera; 120pf. Chemical plant; 130pf. Brewery plant; 140pf. Power station; 150, 190pf. Mechanical shovel; 160pf. Blast furnace; 180pf. Wheel loader; 200pf. Marine drilling platform; 230, 250pf. Frankfurt Airport; 300pf. Electromagnetic monorail; 500pf. Radio telescope.

573 Town Hall and Market, Alsfeld

1975. European Architectural Heritage Year. German Buildings. Multicoloured.

1756	50pf. Type **573**	1·20	85
1757	50pf. Plonlein corner, Siebers tower and Kobelzeller gate, Rothenburg-on-Tauber	1·20	85
1758	50pf. Town Hall ("The Steipe") Trier	1·20	85
1759	50pf. View of Xanten	1·20	85

574 Effects of Drug-taking

1975. Campaign to Fight the Abuse of Drugs and Intoxicants.

1760	**574**	40pf. multicoloured	60	50

575 Posthouse Sign, Royal Prussian Establishment for Transport 1776

1975. Stamp Day.

1761	**575**	10pf. multicoloured	60	35

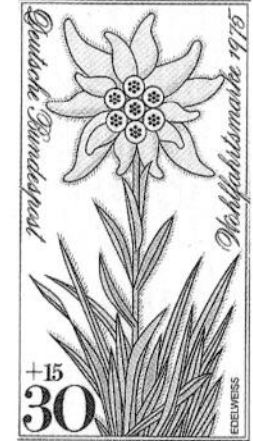

576 Edelweiss

1975. Humanitarian Relief Funds. Alpine Flowers. Multicoloured. (a) Inscr "Wohlfartsmarke 1975".

1762	30pf.+15pf. Type **576**	60	50
1763	40pf.+20pf. Trollflower	60	50
1764	50pf.+25pf. Alpine rose	1·00	75
1765	70pf.+35pf. Pasque-flower	2·20	2·10

(b) Inscr "Weihnachtsmarke 1975".

1766	40pf.+20pf. Christmas rose	1·70	1·50

See also Nos. 1796/9, 1839/42, 1873/6 and 1905/8.

577 Gustav Stresemann (statesman)

1975. German Nobel Peace Prize Winners. Sheet 100×70 mm containing T 577 and similar vert designs in black.

MS1767	50pf. Type **577**; 50pf. Ludwig Quidde (Reichstag deputy); 50pf. Carl von Ossietzky (journalist)	3·00	2·75

578 Stylized Ski-runners

1975. Winter Olympic Games, Innsbruck.

1768	**578**	50pf. multicoloured	1·50	50

579 Konrad Adenauer

1976. Birth Centenary of Konrad Adenauer (Chancellor 1949–63).

1769	**579**	50pf. green	3·00	50

580 Cover Pages from Hans Sachs' Books

1976. 400th Death Anniv of Hans Sachs (poet and composer).

1770	**580**	40pf. multicoloured	1·00	50

581 Junkers F-13 "Herta"

1976. 50th Anniv of Lufthansa (German civil airline).

1771	**581**	50pf. multicoloured	1·50	50

582 Emblem and Commemorative Inscription

1976. 25th Anniv of Federal Constitutional Court.

1772	**582**	50pf. multicoloured	1·20	50

583 Letters "E G" representing Steel Girders

1976. 25th Anniv of European Coal and Steel Community.

1773	**583**	40pf. multicoloured	1·20	50

584 Monorail Train

1976. 75th Anniv of Wuppertal Monorailway.

1774	**584**	50pf. multicoloured	1·20	50

585 Basketball

1976. Youth Welfare. Training for the Olympics. Multicoloured.

1775	30pf.+15pf. Type **585**	75	50
1776	40pf.+20pf. Rowing	1·30	1·00
1777	50pf.+25pf. Gymnastics	1·70	1·50
1778	70pf.+35pf. Volleyball	2·30	2·10

586 Swimming

1976. Olympic Games, Montreal. Mult.

1779	40pf.+25pf. Type **586**	1·20	75
1780	50pf.+25pf. High jumping	1·70	1·20
MS1781	110×70 mm. 30pf.+15pf. black, orange-red and pale yellow; 70pf. + 35pf. black, new blue and pale blue	3·00	2·50

DESIGNS: 30pf. Hockey; 50pf. High jumping; 70pf. Rowing four.

587 Girl selling Trinkets and Copperplate Prints

1976. Europa. Ludwigsburg China Figures. Multicoloured.

1782	40pf. Type **587**	80	35
1783	50pf. Boy selling copperplate prints	85	35

588 Carl Sonnenschein

1976. Birthday Centenary of Dr. Carl Sonnenschein (clergyman).

1784	**588**	50pf. multicoloured	1·00	50

589 Opening bars of Hymn "Entrust Yourself to God"

1976. 300th Birth Anniv of Paul Gerhardt (composer).

1785	**589**	40pf. multicoloured	60	35

590 Carl Maria von Weber conducting

1976. 150th Death Anniv of Carl Maria von Weber (composer).

1786	**590**	50pf. black and brown	1·20	50

591 Carl Schurz

1976. Bicent of American Revolution.

1787	**591**	70pf. multicoloured	1·60	60

592 Wagnerian Stage

1976. Centenary of Bayreuth Festival.

1788	**592**	50pf. multicoloured	2·00	50

593 Bronze Ritual Chariot

1976. Archaeological Heritage. Mult.

1789		30pf. Type **593**	60	50
1790		40pf. Gold-ornamental bowl	85	50
1791		50pf. Silver necklet	1·20	75
1792		120pf. Roman gold goblet	2·75	2·50

594 Golden Plover

1976. Bird Protection.

1793	**594**	50pf. multicoloured	1·70	50

595 Mythical Creature

1976. 300th Death Anniv of J. J. C. von Grimmelshausen (writer).

1794	**595**	40pf. multicoloured	1·70	50

596 18th-century Posthouse Sign, Hochst-am-Main

1976. Stamp Day.

1795	**596**	10pf. multicoloured	50	35

1976. Humanitarian Relief Funds. Garden Flowers. Designs similar to T 576. Multicoloured.

1796		30pf.+15pf. Phlox	75	60
1797		40pf.+20pf. Marigolds	1·00	85
1798		50pf.+25pf. Dahlias	1·10	1·00
1799		70pf.+35pf. Pansies	1·80	1·70

597 Sophie Schroder ("Sappho")

1976. Famous German Actresses. Mult.

1800		30pf. Carolin Neuber ("Medea")	85	35
1801		40pf. Type **597**	85	35
1802		50pf. Louise Dumont ("Hedda Gabler")	1·00	55
1803		70pf. Hermine Korner ("Macbeth")	2·00	1·60

598 "Madonna and Child" ("Marienfenster" window, Frauenkirche, Esslingen)

1976. Christmas. Sheet 71×101 mm.

MS1804	**598**	50pf.+25pf. multicoloured	1·50	1·30

599 Eltz Castle

1977. German Castles.

1805	-	10pf. blue	25	20
1805c	-	20pf. orange	25	20
1805d	-	25pf. red	60	35
1806	-	30pf. bistre	50	25
1806c	-	35pf. red	85	50
1807	**599**	40pf. green	75	20
1807a	-	40pf. brown	85	35
1808	-	50pf. red	85	30
1808b	-	50pf. green	1·10	35
1809	-	60pf. brown	1·20	30
1809a	-	60pf. red	1·10	50
1810	-	70pf. blue	1·20	35
1810a	-	80pf. green	1·60	35
1810c	-	90pf. blue	1·80	60
1810d	-	120pf. violet	2·40	85
1811	-	190pf. red	3·00	1·20
1812	-	200pf. green	3·75	1·20
1812a	-	210pf. brown	5·00	1·80
1812b	-	230pf. green	5·00	1·80
1812c	-	280pf. blue	5·00	85
1812d	-	300pf. orange	5·75	60

DESIGNS: 10pf. Glucksburg; 20, 190pf. Pfaueninsel, Berlin; 25pf. Gemen; 30pf. Ludwigstein, Werratal; 35pf. Lichtenstein; 40pf. (1807a) Wolfsburg; 50pf. (1808) Neuschwanstein; 50pf. (1808b) Inzlingen; 60pf. (1809) Marksburg; 60pf. (1809a) Rheydt; 70pf. Mespelbrunn; 80pf. Wilhelmsthal; 90pf. Vischering; 120pf. Charlottenburg, Berlin; 200pf. Burresheim; 210pf. Schwanenburg; 230pf. Lichtenberg; 280pf. Ahrensburg; 300pf. Herrenhausen, Hanover.

600 Palais de l'Europe

1977. Inauguration of Palais de l'Europe (Council of Europe buildings), Strasbourg.

1813	**600**	140pf. green and black	2·75	85

601 Book Illustrations

1977. "Till Eulenspiegel" (popular fable).

1814	**601**	50pf. multicoloured	85	50

602 Floral Ornament

1977. German "Nouveau" Art. Sheet 116×86 mm containing T 602 and similar vert designs. Multicoloured.

MS1815		30pf. Type **602**; 70pf. Woman's head; 90pf. Chair	4·00	2·75

603 Jean Monnet

1977. Award of "Citizen of Europe" honour to Jean Monnet (French statesman).

1816	**603**	50pf. black, grey & yell	1·00	50

604 "Flower"

1977. 25th Anniv of Federal Horticultural Show.

1817	**604**	50pf. multicoloured	1·30	50

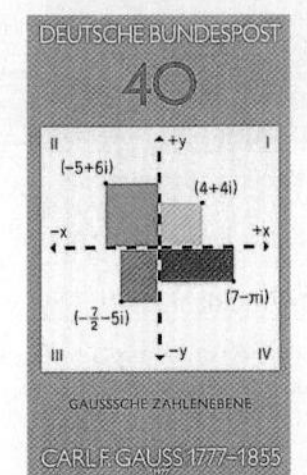

605 Plane of Complex Numbers

1977. Birth Bicentenary of Carl Friedrich Gauss (mathematician).

1818	**605**	40pf. multicoloured	2·00	50

606 "Wappen von Hamburg" (warship)

1977. Youth Welfare. Ships. Multicoloured.

1819		30pf.+15pf. Type **606**	85	75
1820		40pf.+20pf. "Preussen" (full-rigged sailing ship)	1·10	1·00
1821		50pf.+25pf. "Bremen" (liner)	1·50	1·30
1822		70pf.+35pf. "Sturmfels" (container ship)	2·10	2·00

607 Head of Barbarossa

1977. Staufer Year, Baden-Wurttemberg.

1823	**607**	40pf. multicoloured	2·00	50

608 Rhon Autobahn

1977. Europa.

1824	**608**	40pf. black and green	90	35
1825	-	50pf. black and red	1·00	35

DESIGN: 50pf. Rhine landscape.

609 "Self-Portrait" (Rubens)

1977. 400th Birth Anniv of Peter Paul Rubens.

1826	**609**	30pf. black	1·30	50

610 Ulm Cathedral

1977. 600th Anniv of Ulm Cathedral.

1827	**610**	40pf. brown, green & bl	85	50

611 Rector's Seal, Mainz University (500th Anniv)

1977. University Anniversaries.

1828	**611**	50pf. black and red	1·20	50
1829	-	50pf. black and red	1·20	50
1830	-	50pf. black and red	1·50	50

DESIGNS: No. 1829, Great Seal, Marburg University (450th anniv); No. 1830, Great Seal, Tubingen University (500th anniv).

612 "Morning"

1977. Birth Bicentenary of Phillipp Otto Runge (artist).

1831	**612**	60pf. multicoloured	1·50	60

613 Ketteler's Coat of Arms

1977. Death Centenary of Bishop Wilhelm Emmanuel von Ketteler.
1832 **613** 50pf. multicoloured 1·00 50

614 Fritz von Bodelschwingh

1977. Birth Centenary of Pastor Fritz von Bodelschwingh (pioneer of welfare work for the disabled).
1833 **614** 50pf. multicoloured 1·20 50

615 Golden Hat

1977. Archaeological Heritage. Multicoloured.
1834 30pf. Type **615** 60 50
1835 120pf. Gilt helmet 2·40 1·80
1836 200pf. Bronze centaur head 3·25 2·75

616 Operator and Switchboard

1977. Centenary of Telephone in Germany.
1837 **616** 50pf. multicoloured 1·70 50

617 19th-century Posthouse Sign, Hamburg

1977. Stamp Day.
1838 **617** 10pf. multicoloured 60 35

1977. Humanitarian Relief Funds. Meadow Flowers. As T 576. Multicoloured.
1839 30pf.+15pf. Caraway 65 50
1840 40pf.+20pf. Dandelion 80 60
1841 50pf.+25pf. Red clover 1·00 75
1842 70pf.+35pf. Meadow sage 2·00 1·80

618 Travelling Surgeon

1977. 250th Death Anniv of Dr. Johann Andreas Eisenbarth.
1843 **618** 50pf. multicoloured 1·20 50

619 Wilhelm Hauff

1977. 150th Death Anniv of Wilhelm Hauff (poet and novelist).
1844 **619** 40pf. multicoloured 60 35

620 "King presenting Gift" (stained glass window, Basilica of St. Gereon, Cologne)

1977. Christmas. Sheet 70×105 mm.
MS1845 **620** 50pf.+25pf. multicoloured 1·50 1·30

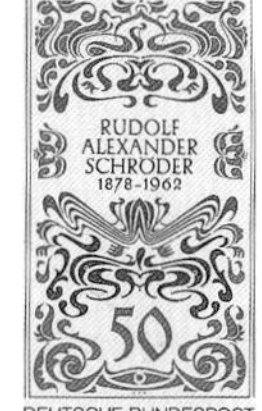

621 Book Cover Designs

1978. Birth Centenary of Rudolph Alexander Schroder (writer).
1846 **621** 50pf. multicoloured 1·00 50

622 Refugees

1978. 20th Anniv of Friedland Aid Society.
1847 **622** 50pf. multicoloured 1·00 50

623 Skiing

1978. Sport Promotion Fund. Multicoloured.
1848 50pf.+25pf. Type **623** 2·20 1·80
1849 70pf.+35pf. Show jumping 4·75 4·25

624 Gerhart Hauptmann

1978. German Winners of Nobel Prize for Literature. Multicoloured.
1850 30pf. Type **624** 75 35
1851 50pf. Hermann Hesse 1·00 50
1852 70pf. Thomas Mann 1·20 85
MS1853 120×70 mm. Nos. 1850/2 3·25 2·20

625 Martin Buber

1978. Birth Centenary of Martin Buber (religious philosopher).
1854 **625** 50pf. multicoloured 1·10 50

626 Museum Tower and Cupola

1978. 75th Anniv of German Scientific and Technical Museum, Munich.
1855 **626** 50pf. black, yellow & red 1·10 50

627 Wilhelmine Reichart's Balloon, Munich October Festival, 1820

1978. Youth Welfare. Aviation History (1st series). Multicoloured.
1856 30pf.+15pf. Type **627** 90 75
1857 40pf.+20pf. Airship LZ-1, 1900 1·10 1·00
1858 50pf.+25pf. Bleriot XI monoplane, 1909 1·50 1·30
1859 70pf.+35pf. Hans Grade's monoplane, 1909 2·00 1·80
See also Nos. 1886/9 and 1918/21.

628 Old Town Hall, Bamberg

1978. Europa. Multicoloured.
1860 40pf. Type **628** 85 35
1861 50pf. Old Town Hall, Regensburg 1·20 35
1862 70pf. Old Town Hall, Esslingen am Neckar 1·60 90

629 Piper and Children

1978. Pied Piper of Hamelin.
1863 **629** 50pf. multicoloured 1·20 50

630 Janusz Korczak

1978. Birth Centenary of Janusz Korczak (educational reformer).
1864 **630** 90pf. multicoloured 1·70 85

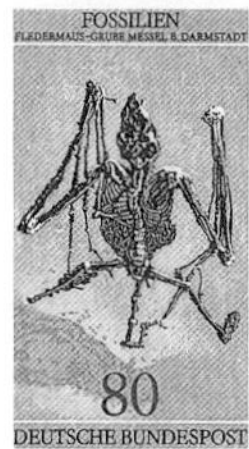

631 Fossil Bat

1978. Archaeological Heritage, Fossils. Mult.
1865 80pf. Type **631** 2·50 2·20
1866 200pf. Horse ("eohippus") skeleton 2·75 2·40

632 Parliament Building, Bonn

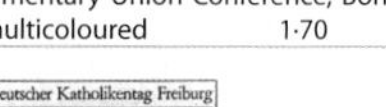

1978. 65th Interparliamentary Union Conference, Bonn.
1867 **632** 70pf. multicoloured 1·70 60

633 Rose Window, Freiburg Minster

1978. 85th Conference of German Catholics, Freiburg.
1868 **633** 40pf. multicoloured 75 50

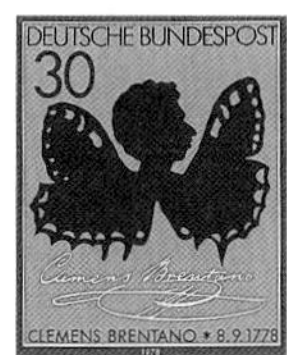

634 Silhouette

1978. Birth Bicent of Clemens Brentano (poet).
1869 **634** 30pf. multicoloured 75 50

635 Text

1978. 25th Anniv of European Convention for the Protection of Human Rights.
1870 **635** 50pf. multicoloured 1·20 50

636 Baden Post-house Sign

1978. Stamp Day and World Philatelic Movement. Multicoloured.
1871 40pf. Type **636** 75 35
1872 50pf. 1850 3pf. stamp of Saxony 75 35

1978. Humanitarian Relief Funds. Woodland Flowers. As T 576. Multicoloured.
1873 30pf.+15pf. Arum 60 50
1874 40pf.+20pf. Weasel-snout 85 75
1875 50pf.+25pf. Turk's-cap lily 1·20 1·10
1876 70pf.+35pf. Liverwort 1·60 1·50

1978. Impressionist Paintings. Multicoloured.
1877 50pf. Type **637** 1·10 75
1878 70pf. "Horseman on the Shore turning Left" (Max Liebermann) (vert) 1·60 1·00
1879 120pf. "Lady with a Cat" (Max Slevogt) (vert) 2·40 2·20

638 "Christ Child" (stained glass window, Frauenkirche, Munich)

1978. Christmas. Sheet 65×93 mm.
MS1880 **638** 50pf.+25pf. multicoloured 1·20 1·20

639 Child

1979. International Year of the Child.
1881 **639** 60pf. multicoloured 1·50 50

640 Agnes Miegel

1979. Birth Cent of Agnes Miegel (poet).

1882 **640** 60pf. multicoloured 1·10 50

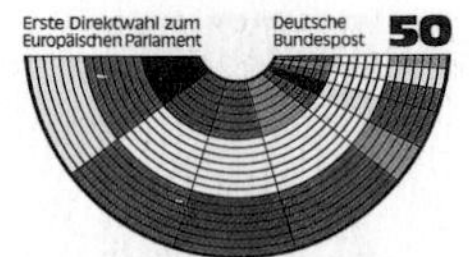

641 Seating Plan

1979. First Direct Elections to European Parliament.

1883 **641** 50pf. multicoloured 1·50 50

642 Film

1979. 25th West German Short Film Festival.

1884 **642** 50pf. black and turquoise 1·20 50

643 Rescue Services Emblems

1979. Rescue Services on the Road.

1885 **643** 50pf. multicoloured 1·20 50

1979. Youth Welfare. History of Aviation (2nd series). As T 627. Multicoloured.

1886 40pf.+20pf. Dornier Do-J Wal flying boat, 1922 85 85

1887 50pf.+25pf. Heinkel He 70 Blitz, 1932 1·20 1·20

1888 60pf.+30pf. Junkers W.33 "Bremen", 1928 1·50 1·50

1889 90pf.+45pf. Focke Achgelis Fa 61 helicopter, 1936 2·00 2·00

644 Handball

1979. Sport Promotion Fund. Multicoloured.

1890 60pf.+30pf. Type **644** 1·50 1·30

1891 90pf.+45pf. Canoeing 2·20 2·00

645 Telegraph Office, 1863

1979. Europa. Multicoloured.

1892 50pf. Type **645** 1·00 35

1893 60pf. Post Office counter, 1854 1·20 35

646 Anne Frank

1979. 50th Birth Anniv of Anne Frank (concentration camp victim and diary writer).

1894 **646** 60pf. black, grey and red 1·30 50

647 Werner von Siemens's Electric Railway, 1879

1979. International Transport Exhibition. Hamburg.

1895 **647** 60pf. multicoloured 1·50 50

648 Hand operating Radio Dial

1979. World Administrative Radio Conference, Geneva.

1896 **648** 60f. multicoloured 1·30 50

649 "Moses receiving the Tablets of the Law" (woodcut, Cranach the Elder)

1979. 450th Anniv of Publication of Martin Luther's Catechisms.

1897 **649** 50pf. black and green 1·50 50

650 Cross and Orb

1979. Pilgrimage to Aachen.

1898 **650** 50pf. multicoloured 1·00 50

651 Hildegard von Bingen

1979. 800th Death Anniv of Hildegard von Bingen (writer and mystic).

1899 **651** 110pf. multicoloured 1·70 85

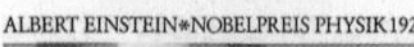

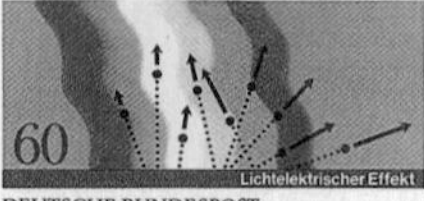

652 Photo-electric Effect

1979. Birth Centenaries of Nobel Prize Winners. Multicoloured.

1900 60pf. Type **652** (Albert Einstein, Physics, 1921) 1·20 60

1901 60pf. Splitting of uranium nucleus (Otto Hahn, Chemistry, 1944) 2·40 60

1902 60pf. Diffraction pattern of X-rays passed through crystal (Max von Laue, Physics, 1914) 1·20 60

653 Pilot and Helmsman

1979. 300th Anniv of 1st Pilotage Regulations.

1903 **653** 60pf. brown and claret 1·00 50

654 Posthouse Sign, Altheim, Saar (German side), 1754

1979. Stamp Day.

1904 **654** 60pf.+30pf. mult 1·70 1·60

1979. Humanitarian Relief Funds. Woodland Flowers and Fruit. As T 576. Multicoloured.

1905 40pf.+20pf. Red beech (horiz) 75 75

1906 50pf.+25pf. English oak (horiz) 1·00 1·00

1907 60pf.+30pf. Hawthorn (horiz) 1·10 1·10

1908 90pf.+45pf. Mountain pine (horiz) 1·80 1·70

656 "Bird Garden"

1979. Birth Cent of Paul Klee (artist).

1909 **656** 90pf. multicoloured 1·60 85

657 Faust and Mephistopheles

1979. Doctor Johannes Faust.

1910 **657** 60pf. multicoloured 1·80 50

658 Lightbulb

1979. "Save Energy".

1911 **658** 40pf. multicoloured 1·00 50

659 "Nativity" (Altenberg medieval manuscript)

1979. Christmas.

1912 **659** 60pf.+30pf. mult 1·50 1·50

660 "Iphigenia"

1980. Death Centenary of Anselm Feuerbach (artist).

1913 **660** 50pf. multicoloured 1·70 50

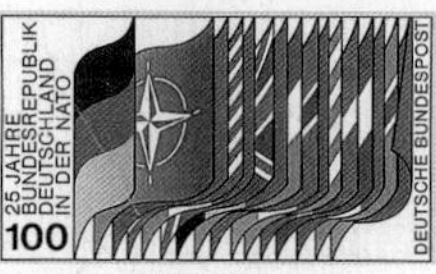

661 Flags of NATO Members

1980. 25th Anniv of NATO Membership.

1914 **661** 100pf. multicoloured 2·75 1·20

662 Town Hall, St. Mary's Church, and St Peter's Cathedral

1980. 1200th Anniv of Osnabruck Town and Bishopric.

1915 **662** 60pf. multicoloured 1·20 50

663 "Gotz von Berlichingen" (glass picture)

1980. 500th Birth Anniv of Gotz von Berlichingen (Frankish knight).

1916 **663** 60pf. multicoloured 1·20 50

664 Texts from 1880 and 1980 Duden Dictionaries

1980. Centenary of Konrad Duden's 1st Dictionary.

1917 **664** 60pf. multicoloured 1·20 50

1980. Youth Welfare. Aviation History (3rd series). As T 627. Multicoloured.

1918 40pf.+20pf. Phoenix FS 24 glider, 1957 60 60

1919 50pf.+25pf. Lockheed L.1049G Super Constellation 1·00 1·00

1920 60pf.+30pf. Airbus Industrie A300B2, 1972 1·30 1·30

1921 90pf.+45pf. Boeing 747-100, 1969 2·00 2·00

No. 1919 is incorrectly dated "1950".

665 Emblems of Association Members

1980. Centenary of German Association of Welfare Societies.

1922 **665** 60pf. blue, red and black 1·20 50

666 "Frederick I with his sons" (Welf Chronicle)

1980. 800th Anniv of Imperial Diet of Gelnhausen.

1923 **666** 60pf. multicoloured 1·60 50

667 Football

1980. Sport Promotion Fund. Multicoloured.

1924 50pf.+25pf. Type **667** 85 75

1925 60pf.+30pf. Dressage 1·20 1·00

1926 90pf.+45pf. Skiing 2·20 2·20

668 Albertus Magnus (scholar)

1980. Europa. Multicoloured.

1927 50pf. Type **668** 1·20 35

1928 60pf. Gottfried Leibniz (philosopher) 1·20 35

669 Reading the Augsburg Confession (engraving, G Kohler)

1980. 450th Anniv of Augsburg Confession.
1929 **669** 50pf. black, yellow & grn 1·10 50

670 Nature Reserve

1980. Nature Conservation.
1930 **670** 40pf. multicoloured 1·60 50

671 Ear and Oscillogram Pulses

1980. International Congress for the Training and Education of the Hard of Hearing, Hamburg.
1931 **671** 90pf. multicoloured 1·80 60

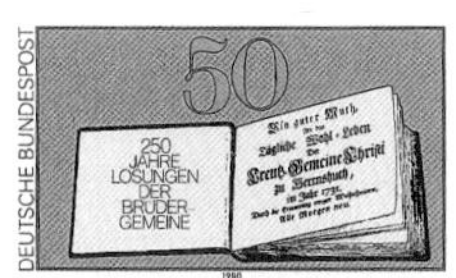

672 First Book of Daily Bible Readings, 1731

1980. 250th Anniv of Moravian Brethren's Book of Daily Bible Readings.
1932 **672** 50pf. multicoloured 1·10 50

673 St. Benedict

1980. 1500th Birth Anniv of St. Benedict of Nursia (founder of Benedictine Order).
1933 **673** 50pf. multicoloured 1·00 50

674 Helping Hand

1980. Birth Bicentenary of Friedrich Joseph Haass (philanthropist).
1934 **674** 60pf. multicoloured 1·20 50

675 Marie von Ebner-Eschenbach

1980. 150th Birth Anniv of Marie von Ebner-Eschenbach (novelist).
1935 **675** 60pf. buff, black & orge 1·20 50

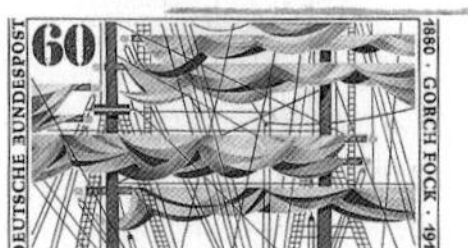

676 Rigging

1980. Birth Centenary of Johan Kinau ("Gorch Fock") (poet).
1936 **676** 60pf. multicoloured 2·40 50

677 Positioning Keystone of South Tower Finial (engraving)

1980. Centenary of Completion of Cologne Cathedral.
1937 **677** 60pf. multicoloured 2·40 50

678 "Ceratocephalus falcatus"

1980. Humanitarian Relief Funds. Endangered Wildflowers. Multicoloured.
1938 40pf.+20pf. Type **678** 85 75
1939 50pf.+25pf. Yellow Vetchling 1·10 1·00
1940 60pf.+30pf. Corn Cockle 1·20 1·20
1941 90pf.+45pf. Tassel Hyacinth 2·00 2·00

See also Nos. 1972/5.

679 Wine-making (woodcuts)

1980. Bimillenary of Vine Growing in Central Europe.
1942 **679** 50pf. multicoloured 1·20 50

680 Posthouse Sign, Altheim, Saar, 1754 (French side)

1980. 49th International Philatelic Federation Congress, Essen.
1943 **680** 60pf.+30pf. mult 1·20 1·10

681 "Nativity" (Altomunster manuscript)

1980. Christmas.
1944 **681** 60pf.+30pf. mult 1·60 1·50

682 "Landscape with Two Fir Trees" (etching)

1980. 500th Birth Anniv of Albrecht Altdorfer (painter, engraver and architect).
1945 **682** 40pf. lt brown, blk & brn 1·00 50

683 Elly Heuss-Knapp

1981. Birth Centenary of Elly Heuss-Knapp (social reformer).
1946 **683** 60pf. multicoloured 1·20 50

684 Society accepting the Handicapped

1981. International Year of Disabled Persons.
1947 **684** 60pf. multicoloured 1·20 50

685 Old Town Houses

1981. European Campaign for Urban Renaissance.
1948 **685** 60pf. multicoloured 1·20 50

686 Telemann and Title Page of "Singet dem Herrn"

1981. 300th Birth Anniv of Georg Philipp Telemann (composer).
1949 **686** 60pf. multicoloured 1·20 50

687 Visiting a Foreign Family

1981. Integration of Guest Worker Families.
1950 **687** 50pf. multicoloured 1·30 50

688 Polluted Butterfly, Fish and Plant

1981. Preservation of the Environment.
1951 **688** 60pf. multicoloured 2·00 50

689 Patent Office Emblem and Scientific Signs

1981. Establishment of European Patent Office, Munich.
1952 **689** 60pf. grey, red and black 1·20 50

690 Scintigram showing Distribution of Radioactive Isotope

1981. Cancer Prevention through Medical Check-ups.
1953 **690** 40pf. multicoloured 1·00 50

691 Borda Circle, 1800

1981. Youth Welfare. Optical Instruments. Multicoloured.
1954 40pf.+20pf. Type **691** 85 60
1955 50pf.+25pf. Reflecting telescope, 1770 1·50 1·20
1956 60pf.+30pf. Binocular microscope, 1860 1·50 1·20
1957 90pf.+45pf. Octant, 1775 2·10 2·00

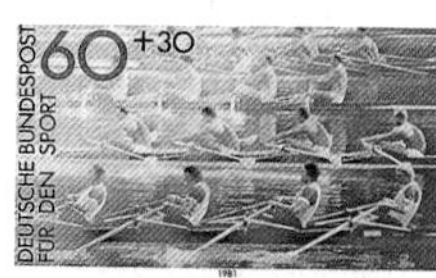

692 Rowing

1981. Sport Promotion Fund. Multicoloured.
1958 60pf.+30pf. Type **692** 1·50 1·20
1959 90pf.+45pf. Gliding 2·20 2·00

693 South German Dancers

1981. Europa. Multicoloured.
1960 50pf. Type **693** 1·10 35
1961 60pf. North German dancers 1·20 35

694 Convention Cross

1981. 19th German Protestant Convention, Hamburg.
1962 **694** 50pf. multicoloured 1·20 50

695 Group from Crucifixion Altar

1981. 450th Death Anniv of Tilman Riemenschneider (woodcarver).
1963 **695** 60pf. multicoloured 1·20 50

696 Georg von Neumayer Antarctic Research Station

1981. Polar Research.
1964 **696** 110pf. multicoloured 2·75 75

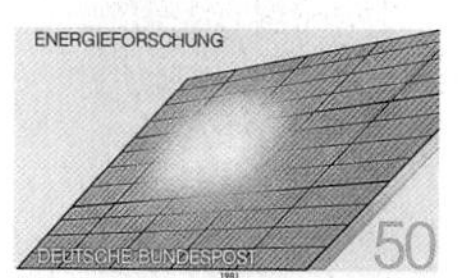

697 Solar Generator

1981. Energy Research.
1965 **697** 50pf. multicoloured 1·60 50

698 Hand holding Baby Black Coot

1981. Animal Protection.
1966 **698** 60pf. multicoloured 2·00 50

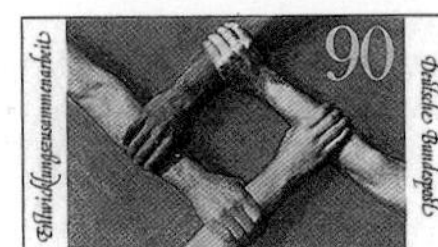

699 Arms of different Races forming Square

1981. Co-operation with Developing Countries.
1967 **699** 90pf. multicoloured 2·00 75

700 Wilhelm Raabe

1981. 150th Birth Anniv of Wilhelm Raabe (poet).
1968 **700** 50pf. light green & green 1·20 50

701 Constitutional Freedom

1981. Fundamental Concepts of Democracy. Article 20 of the Basic Law. Multicoloured.
1969 40pf. Type **701** 1·30 35
1970 50pf. Separation of Powers 1·30 35
1971 60pf. Sovereignty of the People 2·00 35

1981. Humanitarian Relief Funds. Endangered Wildflowers. As T 678. Multicoloured.
1972 40pf.+20pf. Water nut 75 60
1973 50pf.+25pf. Floating Heart 1·00 85
1974 60pf.+30pf. Water gilly-flower 1·20 1·20
1975 90pf.+45pf. Water lobelia 2·20 2·10

702 Posthouse Scene c. 1855

1981. Stamp Day.
1976 **702** 60pf. multicoloured 2·00 50

703 "Nativity" (glass painting)

1981. Christmas.
1977 **703** 60pf.+30pf. mult 1·60 1·20

704 St. Elisabeth

1981. 750th Death Anniv of St. Elisabeth of Thuringia.
1978 **704** 50pf. multicoloured 1·60 50

705 Clausewitz (after W. Wach)

1981. 150th Death Anniv of General Carl von Clausewitz (military writer).
1979 **705** 60pf. multicoloured 1·60 50

706 People forming Figure "100"

1981. Cent of Social Insurance.
1980 **706** 60pf. multicoloured 1·30 50

707 Map of Antarctica

1981. 20th Anniv of Antarctic Treaty.
1981 **707** 100pf. blue, lt blue & blk 2·20 75

708 Pot with Lid

1982. 300th Birth Anniv of Johann Friedrich Bottger (founder of Meissen China Works).
1982 **708** 60pf. multicoloured 1·30 50

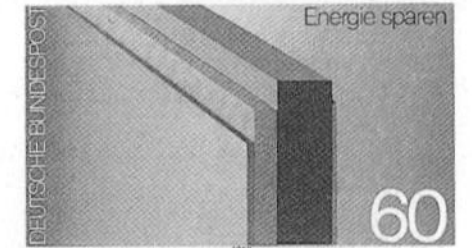

709 Insulated Wall

1982. Energy Conservation.
1983 **709** 60pf. multicoloured 1·30 50

710 Silhouette (Dora Brandenburg-Polster)

1982. "The Town Band of Bremen" (German fairy tale).
1984 **710** 40pf. black and red 1·00 50

711 Goethe (after Georg Melchior Kraus)

1982. 150th Death Anniv of Johann Wolfgang von Goethe (writer).
1985 **711** 60pf. multicoloured 3·75 50

712 Robert Koch

1982. Centenary of Discovery of Tubercle Bacillus.
1986 **712** 50pf. multicoloured 4·25 50

713 Benz Patent "Motorwagen", 1886

1982. Youth Welfare. Motor Cars. Mult.
1987 40pf.+20pf. Type **713** 85 75
1988 50pf.+25pf. Mercedes "Tourenwagen", 1913 1·10 1·00
1989 60pf.+30pf. Hannomag "Kommissbrot", 1925 1·50 1·20

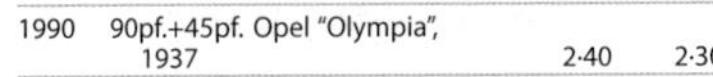
1990 90pf.+45pf. Opel "Olympia", 1937 2·40 2·30

714 Jogging

1982. Sport Promotion Fund. Multicoloured.
1991 60pf.+30pf. Type **714** 1·50 1·30
1992 90pf.+45pf. Disabled archers 2·20 2·10

715 "Good Helene"

1982. 150th Birth Anniv of Wilhelm Busch (writer and illustrator).
1993 **715** 50pf. black, green & yell 1·60 50

716 "Procession to Hambach Castle, 1832" (wood engraving)

1982. Europa.
1994 **716** 50pf. black, yellow & red 1·60 35
1995 - 60pf. multicoloured 2·10 35
DESIGN: 60pf. Excerpt from Treaty of Rome (instituting European Economic Community), 1957, and flags.

717 Racing Yachts

1982. Centenary of Kiel Regatta Week.
1996 **717** 60pf. multicoloured 1·60 50

718 Young Couple

1982. Centenary of Young Men's Christian Association in Germany.
1997 **718** 50pf. multicoloured 1·20 50

719 Polluted Sea

1982. "Prevent the Pollution of the Sea".
1998 **719** 120pf. multicoloured 4·25 60

720 Battered Licence Plate

1982. "Don't Drink and Drive".
1999 **720** 80pf. multicoloured 1·60 50

721 Doctor examining Leper

1982. 25th Anniv of German Lepers' Welfare Organization.
2000 **721** 80pf. multicoloured 1·60 50

722 Franck and Born

1982. Birth Centenaries of James Franck and Max Born (physicists and Nobel Prize Winners).
2001 **722** 80pf. grey, black and red 2·00 50

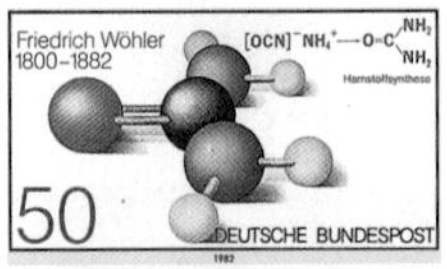

723 Atomic Model of Urea

1982. Death Centenary of Friedrich Wohler (chemist).
2002 **723** 50pf. multicoloured 1·50 50

724 "St. Francis preaching to the Birds" (fresco by Giotto)

1982. 87th German Catholics' Congress, Dusseldorf and 800th Birth Anniv of St. Francis of Assisi.
2003 **724** 60pf. multicoloured 1·50 50

725 Hybrid Tea Rose

1982. Humanitarian Relief Funds. Roses. Multicoloured.
2004 50pf.+20pf. Type **725** 85 75
2005 60pf.+30pf. Floribunda 1·10 1·00
2006 80pf.+40pf. Bourbon 1·70 1·60
2007 120pf.+60pf. Polyantha hybrid 2·40 2·20

726 Letters on Desk

1982. Stamp Day.
2008 **726** 80pf. multicoloured 2·20 50

727 Gregorian Calendar by Johannes Rasch, 1586

1982. 400th Anniv of Gregorian Calendar.
2009 **727** 60pf. multicoloured 1·50 50

728 Theodor Heuss

1982. Presidents of the Federal Republic. Sheet 130×100 mm containing T 728 and similar horiz designs. Multicoloured.
MS2010 80pf. Type **728**; 80pf. Heinrich Lubke; 80pf. Gustav Heinemann; 80pf. Walter Scheel; 80pf. Karl Carstens 7·25 6·75

729 "Nativity" (detail from St. Peter Altar by Master Bertram)

1982. Christmas.
2011 **729** 80pf.+40pf. mult 2·40 1·70

730 Edith Stein

1983. 40th Death Anniv (1982) of Edith Stein (philosopher).
2012 **730** 80pf. lt grey, grey & blk 2·40 75

731 White Rose and Barbed Wire

1983. Persecution and Resistance 1933–45.
2013 **731** 80pf. multicoloured 2·40 75

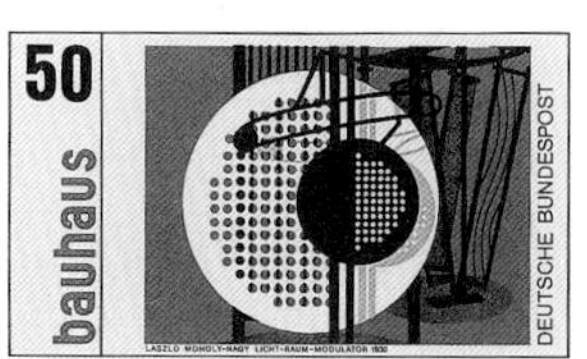

732 "Light Space Modulator" (Laszlo Moholy-Nagy)

1983. Birth Cent of Walter Gropius (founder of Bauhaus School of Art, Weimar). Bauhaus Art. Multicoloured.
2014 50pf. Type **732** 1·20 50
2015 60pf. "Sanctuary" (lithograph by Josef Albers) 1·70 50
2016 80pf. Skylights from Bauhaus Archives, Berlin (Walter Gropius) 2·00 55

733 Federahannes (Rottweil carnival figure)

1983. Carnival.
2017 **733** 60pf. multicoloured 1·60 50

734 Daimler-Maybach, 1885

1983. Youth Welfare. Motor Cycles. Mult.
2018 50pf.+20pf. Type **734** 85 75
2019 60pf.+30pf. N.S.U., 1901 1·10 1·00
2020 80pf.+40pf. Megola "Sport", 1922 2·00 1·80
2021 120pf.+60pf. B.M.W. world record holder, 1936 3·00 2·75

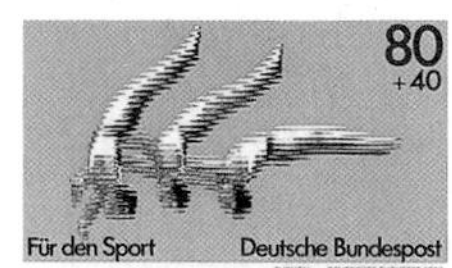

735 Gymnastics (German Festival, Frankfurt am Main)

1983. Sports Promotion Fund. Multicoloured.
2022 80pf.+40pf. Type **735** 1·80 1·60
2023 120pf.+60pf. Modern pentathlon (world championships, Warendorf) 3·00 2·75

736 Stylized Flower

1983. 4th International Horticultural Show. Munich.
2024 **736** 60pf. multicoloured 1·60 50

737 Modern Type and Gutenberg Letters

1983. Europa. Multicoloured.
2025 60pf. Type **737** 3·00 60
2026 80pf. Resonant circuit and electric flux lines 1·80 60

738 Johannes Brahms

1983. 150th Birth Anniv of Johannes Brahms (composer).
2027 **738** 80pf. multicoloured 2·40 75

739 Kafka's Signature and Teyn Church, Prague

1983. Birth Cent of Franz Kafka (writer).
2028 **739** 80pf. multicoloured 2·40 75

740 Brewing (frontispiece of 1677 treatise)

1983. 450th Anniv of Beer Purity Law.
2029 **740** 80pf. multicoloured 2·40 75

741 "Concord"

1983. 300th Anniv of First German Settlers in America.
2030 **741** 80pf. multicoloured 2·75 75

742 Children crossing Road

1983. Children and Road Traffic.
2031 **742** 80pf. multicoloured 2·40 75

743 Flags forming Car

1983. 50th International Motor Show, Frankfurt-on-Main.
2032 **743** 60pf. multicoloured 1·20 50

744 Warburg (after Oberland)

1983. Birth Centenary of Otto Warburg. (physiologist and chemist).
2033 **744** 50pf. multicoloured 1·50 75

745 Wieland (after G. B. Bosio)

1983. 250th Birth Anniv of Cristoph Martin Wieland (writer).
2034 **745** 80pf. multicoloured 2·00 75

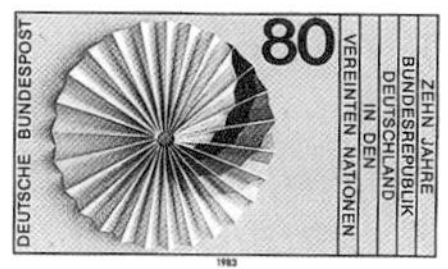

746 Rosette in National Colours

1983. 10th Anniv of U.N. Membership.
2035 **746** 80pf. multicoloured 2·75 75

747 "Das Rauhe Haus" and Children

1983. 150th Anniv of "Das Rauhe Haus" (children's home, Hamburg).
2036 **747** 80pf. multicoloured 2·10 75

748 Surveying Maps

1983. International Geodesy and Geophysics Union General Assembly, Hamburg.
2037 **748** 120pf. multicoloured 2·75 85

749 Swiss Androsace

1983. Humanitarian Relief Funds. Endangered Alpine Flowers. Multicoloured.
2038 50pf.+20pf. Type **749** 85 75
2039 60pf.+30pf. Krain groundsel 1·10 1·00
2040 80pf.+40pf. Fleischer's willow herb 2·00 1·80
2041 120pf.+60pf. Alpine sow-thistle 3·00 2·75

750 Horseman with Posthorn

1983. Stamp Day.
2042 **750** 80pf. multicoloured 2·20 75

751 Luther (engraving by G. Konig after Cranach)

1983. 500th Birth Anniv of Martin Luther (Protestant reformer).
2043 **751** 80pf. multicoloured 3·75 75

752 Interwoven National Colours

1983. Federation, Lander and Communities Co-operation.
2044 **752** 80pf. multicoloured 2·75 75

753 Customs Stamps

1983. 150th Anniv of German Customs Union.
2045 **753** 60pf. multicoloured 2·75 50

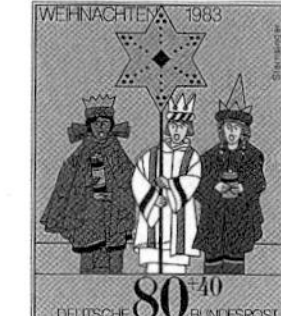

754 Epiphany Carol Singers

1983. Christmas.
2046 **754** 80pf.+40pf. mult 2·75 2·00

755 Black Gate, Trier

1984. 2000th Anniv of Trier.
2047 **755** 80pf. multicoloured 2·75 75

756 Reis and Telephone Apparatus

1984. 150th Birth Anniv of Philipp Reis (telephone pioneer).
2048 **756** 80pf. multicoloured 2·75 75

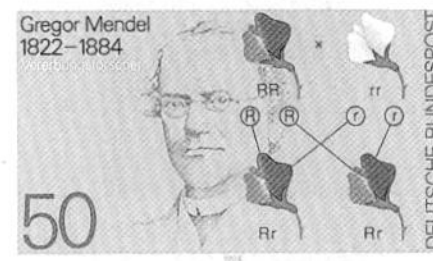

757 Mendel and Genetic Diagram

1984. Death Cent of Gregor Mendel (geneticist).
2049 **757** 50pf. multicoloured 1·60 50

758 Town Hall

1984. 500th Anniv of Michelstadt Town Hall.
2050 **758** 60pf. multicoloured 1·60 50

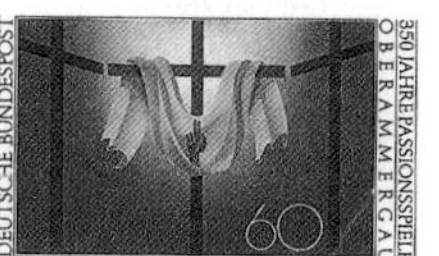

759 Cloth draped on Cross

1984. 350th Anniv of Oberammergau Passion Play.
2051 **759** 60pf. multicoloured 1·60 50

760 Bee-eating Beetle

1984. Youth Welfare. Pollinating Insects. Multicoloured.

2052 50pf.+20pf. Type **760**	1·00	85
2053 60pf.+30pf. Red admiral	1·70	1·60
2054 80pf.+40pf. Honey bee	2·20	2·10
2055 120pf.+60pf. "Chrysotoxum festivium" (hover fly)	3·00	3·00

761 Throwing the Discus

1984. Sport Promotion Fund. Multicoloured.

2056 60pf.+30pf. Type **761**	1·70	1·20
2057 80pf.+40pf. Rhythmic gymnastics	2·20	2·00
2058 120pf.+60pf. Windsurfing	4·00	3·75

762 Parliament Emblem

1984. 2nd Direct Elections to European Parliament.

2059 **762** 80pf. yellow, blue and light blue	3·00	85

763 Bridge

1984. Europa. 25th Anniv of European Post and Telecommunications Conference.

2060 **763** 60pf. blue, lt blue & blk	2·00	60
2061 **763** 80pf. purple, red & black	2·00	60

764 St. Norbert (sculpture)

1984. 850th Death Anniv of St. Norbert von Xanten.

2062 **764** 80pf. green & deep green	2·00	75

765 Nursery Rhyme Illustration

1984. Death Centenary of Ludwig Richter (illustrator).

2063 **765** 60pf. black and brown	1·20	50

766 Cross and Shadow

1984. 50th Anniv of Protestant Churches' Barmen Theological Declaration.

2064 **766** 80pf. multicoloured	2·00	75

767 Letter sorting, 1800s

1984. 19th Universal Postal Union Congress, Hamburg. Sheet 138×104 mm containing T 767 and similar square designs.

MS2065 60pf. brown and black; 80pf. multicoloured; 120pf. green, black and grey	5·00	4·25

DESIGNS: 80pf. Modern automatic letter sorting machine scanning device; 120pf. Heinrich von Stephan (founder of U.P.U.).

768 Groom leading Horse (detail from tomb of Oclatius)

1984. 2000th Anniv of Neuss.

2066 **768** 80pf. multicoloured	2·00	75

769 Bessel

1984. Birth Bicentenary of Friedrich Wilhelm Bessel (astronomer and mathematician).

2067 **769** 80pf. grey, black and red	2·00	75

770 Eugenio Pacelli (Pope Pius XII)

1984. 88th German Catholics' Congress, Munich.

2068 **770** 60pf. multicoloured	1·60	50

771 Town Hall

1984. 750th Anniv of Duderstadt Town Hall.

2069 **771** 60pf. multicoloured	1·50	50

772 Medieval Document and Visual Display Unit

1984. 10th International Archives Congress, Bonn.

2070 **772** 70pf. multicoloured	2·00	75

773 Knoop Lock

1984. Bicent of Schleswig-Holstein Canal.

2071 **773** 80pf. multicoloured	2·40	75

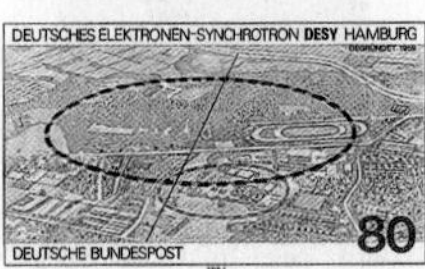

774 Research Centre and Storage Rings

1984. 25th Anniv of German Electron Synchrotron (physics research centre), Hamburg-Bahrenfeld.

2072 **774** 80pf. multicoloured	2·75	75

775 "Aceras anthropophorum"

1984. Humanitarian Relief Funds. Orchids. Multicoloured.

2073 50pf.+20pf. Type **775**	1·20	1·10
2074 60pf.+30pf. "Orchis ustulata"	1·20	1·10
2075 80pf.+40pf. "Limodorum abortivum"	1·80	1·70
2076 120pf.+60pf. "Dactylorhiza sambucina"	3·25	3·25

776 Taxis Posthouse, Augsburg

1984. Stamp Day.

2077 **776** 80pf. multicoloured	2·75	75

777 Burning Match

1984. Anti-smoking Campaign.

2078 **777** 60pf. multicoloured	1·70	50

778 Male and Female Symbols

1984. Equal Rights for Men and Women.

2079 **778** 80pf. black, mauve & bl	2·40	75

779 Ballot Slip

1984. For Peace and Understanding.

2080 **779** 80pf. grey, black & blue	2·00	75

780 St. Martin giving Cloak to Beggar

1984. Christmas.

2081 **780** 80pf.+40pf. mult	2·20	2·00

781 Emperor Augustus (bust), Buildings and Arms

1985. 2000th Anniv of Augsburg.

2082 **781** 80pf. multicoloured	2·40	60

782 Spener (engraving by Bartholome Kilian after Johann Georg Wagner)

1985. 350th Birth Anniv of Philipp Jakob Spener (church reformer).

2083 **782** 80pf. black and green	2·00	75

783 Grimm Brothers (engraving by Lazarus Sichling)

1985. Birth Bicentenaries of Grimm Brothers (folklorists) and 7th International Union for German Linguistics and Literature Congress, Gottingen.

2084 **783** 80pf. black, grey and red	2·75	75

784 Romano Guardini

1985. Birth Centenary of Romano Guardini (theologian).

2085 **784** 80pf. multicoloured	2·00	75

785 Verden

1985. Millenary of Market and Coinage Rights in Verden.

2086 **785** 60pf. multicoloured	2·75	50

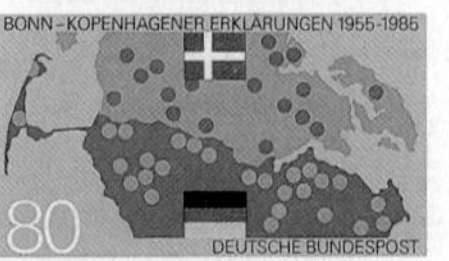

786 Flags and German-Danish Border

1985. 30th Anniv of Bonn-Copenhagen Declarations.

2087 **786** 80pf. multicoloured	3·00	1·00

787 Bowling

1985. Sport Promotion Fund. Multicoloured.

2088 80pf.+40pf. Type **787** (cent. of German Nine-pin Bowling Association)	2·00	1·70
2089 120pf.+60pf. Kayak (world rapid-river and slalom canoeing championships)	3·25	3·00

788 Kisch

1985. Birth Centenary of Egon Erwin Kisch (journalist).

2090 **788** 60pf. multicoloured	1·60	50

789 "Hebel and the Margravine"

1985. 225th Birth Anniv of Johann Peter Hebel (poet).

2091 **789** 80pf. multicoloured	2·00	75

790 Draisienne Bicycle, 1817

1985. Youth Welfare International Youth Year. Cycles. Multicoloured.

2092 50pf.+20pf. Type **790**	1·20	1·20

2093	60pf.+30pf. NSU Germania "ordinary", 1866	1·50	1·50
2094	80pf.+40pf. Cross-frame low bicycle, 1887	1·80	1·80
2095	120pf.+60pf. Adler tricycle, 1888	3·50	3·50

791 Handel

1985. Europa. Composers' 300th Birth Anniversaries. Multicoloured.

2096	60pf. Type **791**	2·75	60
2097	80pf. Bach	2·75	60

792 Saint George's Cathedral

1985. 750th Anniv of Limburg Cathedral.

2098	**792**	60pf. multicoloured	1·50	75

793 Capital (presbytery, "Wies" Church)

1985. 300th Birth Anniv of Dominikus Zimmermann (architect).

2099	**793**	70pf. multicoloured	1·80	75

794 Josef Kentenich

1985. Birth Centenary of Father Josef Kentenich (founder of International Schonstatt (Catholic laymen's) Movement).

2100	**794**	80pf. multicoloured	2·00	75

795 Clock and Forest

1985. Save the Forests.

2101	**795**	80pf. multicoloured	2·75	75

796 Tug of War and Scouting Emblem

1985. 30th World Scouts Conference, Munich.

2102	**796**	60pf. multicoloured	1·70	75

797 "Sunday Walk"

1985. Death Cent of Carl Spitzweg (artist).

2103	**797**	60pf. multicoloured	2·75	75

798 Horses and Postilion

1985. "Mophila 1985" Stamp Exhibition, Hamburg. Multicoloured.

2104	60pf.+20pf. Type **798**	3·25	3·00
2105	80pf.+20pf. Mail coach	3·25	3·00

Nos. 2104/5 were printed se-tenant, forming a composite design.

799 Stock Exchange

1985. 400th Anniv of Frankfurt Stock Exchange.

2106	**799**	80pf. black, red and grey	2·40	75

800 Flowers and Butterfly

1985. Humanitarian Relief Funds. Designs depict motifs from borders of medieval prayer book. Multicoloured.

2107	50pf.+20pf. Type **800**	1·20	1·00
2108	60pf.+30pf. Flowers, bird and butterfly	1·50	1·20
2109	80pf.+40pf. Flowers, berries and snail	1·70	1·60
2110	120pf.+60pf. Flowers, snail and butterfly	2·75	2·75

801 Fritz Reuter

1985. 175th Death Anniv of Fritz Reuter (writer).

2111	**801**	80pf. black, grey and blue	3·00	75

802 "Inauguration of First German Railway" (Heim)

1985. 150th Anniv of German Railways and Birth Bicent. of Johannes Scharrer (joint founder).

2112	**802**	80pf. multicoloured	3·00	75

803 Carpentry Joint in National Colours

1985. 40th Anniv of Integration of Refugees.

2113	**803**	80pf. multicoloured	3·00	75

804 Iron Cross and National Colours

1985. 30th Anniv of Federal Armed Forces.

2114	**804**	80pf. red, black & yellow	4·25	75

805 "Nativity" (detail, High Altar, Freiburg)

1985. Christmas. 500th Birth Anniversary of Hans Baldung Grien (artist).

2115	**805**	80pf.+40pf. mult	2·30	2·30

806 Early and Modern Cars

1986. Centenary of Motor Car.

2116	**806**	80pf. multicoloured	3·00	75

807 Town Buildings

1986. 1250th Anniv of Bad Hersfeld.

2117	**807**	60pf. multicoloured	2·00	75

808 "Self-portrait"

1986. Birth Centenary of Oskar Kokoschka (artist and writer).

2118	**808**	80pf. black, grey and red	2·00	75

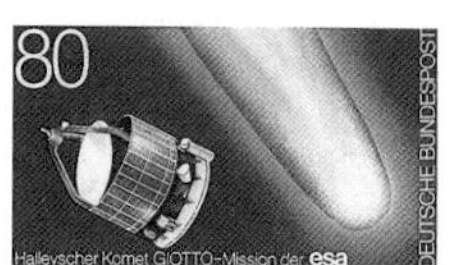

809 Comet and "Giotto" Space Probe

1986. Appearance of Halley's Comet.

2119	**809**	80pf. multicoloured	3·00	85

810 Running

1986. Sport Promotion Fund. Multicoloured.

2120	80pf.+40pf. Type **810** (European Athletics Championships, Stuttgart)	2·40	2·40
2121	120pf.+55pf. Bobsleigh (World Championships, Konigsee)	3·75	3·75

811 Optician

1986. Youth Welfare. Trades (1st series). Multicoloured.

2122	50pf.+25pf. Type **811**	1·60	1·50
2123	60pf.+30pf. Bricklayer	1·80	1·70
2124	70pf.+35pf. Hairdresser	2·10	2·00
2125	80pf.+40pf. Baker	3·00	2·75

See also Nos. 2179/82.

812 Walsrode Monastery

1986. Millenary of Walsrode.

2126	**812**	60pf. multicoloured	2·00	75

813 Ludwig and Neuschwanstein Castle

1986. Death Centenary of King Ludwig II of Bavaria.

2127	**813**	60pf. multicoloured	3·50	75

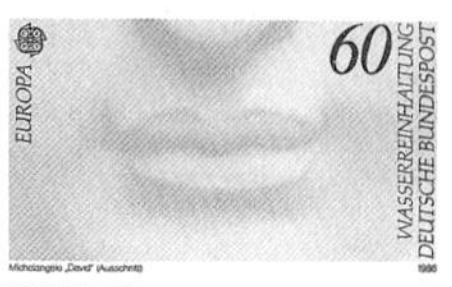

814 Mouth

1986. Europa. Details of "David" (sculpture) by Michelangelo. Multicoloured.

2128	60pf. Type **814**	1·80	60
2129	80pf. Nose	1·80	60

815 Karl Barth

1986. Birth Centenary of Karl Barth (theologian).

2130	**815**	80pf. black, red & purple	2·20	75

816 Ribbons

1986. Union of German Catholic Students' Societies 100th Assembly, Frankfurt am Main.

2131	**816**	80pf. multicoloured	2·20	75

817 Weber and Score of "Gloria"

1986. Birth Bicentenary of Carl Maria von Weber (composer).

2132	**817**	80pf. brown, black & red	3·00	75

818 "TV-Sat" and Earth

1986. Launch of German "TV-Sat" and French "TDF-1" Broadcasting Satellites.

2133	**818**	80pf. multicoloured	3·00	85

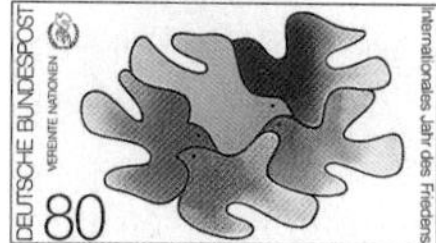

819 Doves

1986. International Peace Year.

2134	**819**	80pf. multicoloured	2·75	75

820 Liszt

1986. Death Centenary of Franz Liszt (composer).

2135	**820**	80pf. blue and orange	2·75	75

821 Reichstag, Berlin

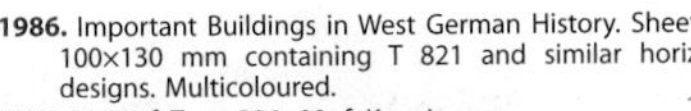

1986. Important Buildings in West German History. Sheet 100×130 mm containing T 821 and similar horiz designs. Multicoloured.

MS2136 80pf. Type **821**; 80pf. Koenig Museum, Bonn (venue of 1948–49 Parliamentary Council); 80pf. Bundeshaus, Bonn (parliamentary building) 5·50 5·00

822 Pollution Damage of Stained Glass Window

1986. Protection of Monuments.

2137	**822**	80pf. multicoloured	3·00	75

823 Frederick the Great (after Anton Graff)

1986. Death Bicentenary of Frederick the Great.

2138	**823**	80pf. multicoloured	4·25	75

824 Congress Card

1986. Centenary of First German Skat Congress and 24th Congress, Cologne.

2139	**824**	80pf. multicoloured	3·00	75

825 Opposing Arrows

1986. 25th Anniv of Organization for Economic Co-operation and Development.

2140	**825**	80pf. multicoloured	2·20	75

826 Old University

1986. 600th Anniv of Heidelberg University.

2141	**826**	80pf. multicoloured	2·75	75

827 Fan of Stamps behind Stagecoach

1986. 50th Anniv of Stamp Day.

2142	**827**	80pf. multicoloured	2·75	75

828 Ornamental Flask, 300 A.D.

1986. Humanitarian Relief Funds. Glassware. Multicoloured.

2143	50pf.+25pf. Type **828**	1·10	1·00
2144	60pf.+30pf. Goblet with decorated stem, 1650	1·50	1·30
2145	70pf.+35pf. Imperial Eagle tankard, 1662	1·70	1·50
2146	80pf.+40pf. Engraved goblet, 1720	2·00	1·80

829 "Dance in Silence" from "Autumnal Dances"

1986. Birth Centenary of Mary Wigman (dancer).

2147	**829**	70pf. multicoloured	1·60	75

830 Cross over Map

1986. 25th Anniv of Adveniat (Advent collection for Latin America).

2148	**830**	80pf. green, blue & blk	1·60	75

831 "Adoration of the Infant Jesus" (Ortenberg altarpiece)

1986. Christmas.

2149	**831**	80pf.+40pf. mult	2·20	2·10

832 Christine Teusch (politician)

1986. Famous German Women. Inscr "Deutsche Bundespost".

2150	-	5pf. brown and grey	50	35
2151	-	10pf. brown and violet	60	35
2152	-	20pf. blue and red	1·20	60
2152a	-	30pf. bistre and purple	60	50
2153	-	40pf. red and blue	1·20	35
2154	**832**	50pf. green and brown	1·20	35
2155	-	60pf. lilac and green	1·50	35
2155a	-	70pf. green and red	1·80	1·00
2156	-	80pf. brown and green	1·50	35
2156a	-	80pf. brown and blue	1·30	75
2157	-	100pf. grey and red	1·80	60
2157a	-	100pf. bistre and lilac	1·30	75
2158	-	120pf. green and brown	2·40	1·50
2159	-	130pf. violet and blue	3·75	1·20
2160	-	140pf. ochre and blue	4·25	2·20
2161	-	150pf. blue and red	5·00	2·20
2162	-	170pf. purple and green	3·00	1·80
2163	-	180pf. purple and blue	3·75	1·80
2164	-	200pf. red and brown	3·00	1·20
2165	-	240pf. brown and green	4·25	3·00
2166	-	250pf. blue and mauve	5·75	3·00
2167	-	300pf. green and purple	3·75	1·80
2168	-	350pf. brown and black	6·00	3·75
2168a	-	400pf. black and red	6·75	5·25
2168b	-	450pf. ultramarine & bl	8·00	5·75
2169	-	500pf. red and green	8·00	5·00

DESIGNS: 5pf. Emma Ihrer (politician and trade unionist); 10pf. Paula Modersohn-Becker (painter); 20pf. Cilly Aussem (tennis player); 30pf. Kathe Kollwitz (artist); 40pf. Maria Sibylla Merian (artist and naturalist); 60pf. Dorothea Erxleben (first German woman Doctor of Medicine); 70pf. Elisabet Boehm (founder of Agricultural Association of Housewives); 80pf. (2156), Clara Schumann (pianist and composer); 80pf. (2156a), Rahel Varnhagen von Ense (humanist) (after Wilhelm Hensel); 100pf. (2157), Therese Giehse (actress); 100pf. (2157a), Luise Henriette of Orange (mother of King Friedrich I of Prussia) (after Gerhard von Honthorst); 120pf. Elisabeth Selbert (politician); 130pf. Lise Meitner (physicist); 140pf. Cecile Vogt (medical researcher); 150pf. Sophie Scholl (resistance member); 170pf. Hannah Arendt (sociologist); 180pf. Lotte Lehmann (opera singer); 200pf. Bertha von Suttner (novelist and pacifist); 240pf. Mathilda Franziska Anneke (women's rights activist); 250pf. Queen Louise of Prussia; 300pf. Fanny Hensel (composer) (after Eduard Magnus); 350pf. Hedwig Dransfeld (politician); 400pf. Charlotte von Stein (friend of Goethe); 450pf. Hedwig Courths-Mahler (novelist); 500pf. Alice Salomon (women's rights activist).

For similar designs inscribed "Deutschland", see Nos. 2785/95.

833 Berlin Landmarks

1987. 750th Anniv of Berlin.

2170	**833**	80pf. multicoloured	3·25	1·00

834 Staircase, Residenz Palace, Wurzburg

1987. 300th Birth Anniv of Balthasar Neumann (architect).

2171	**834**	80pf. grey, black and red	2·40	75

835 Erhard

1987. 90th Birth Anniv of Ludwig Erhard (former Chancellor).

2172	**835**	80pf. multicoloured	3·00	75

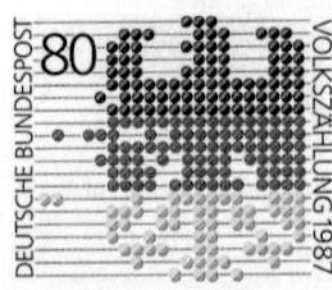

836 Abacus Beads forming Eagle

1987. Census.

2173	**836**	80pf. multicoloured	2·75	75

837 Clemenswerth Castle

1987. 250th Anniv of Clemenswerth Castle.

2174	**837**	60pf. multicoloured	2·10	75

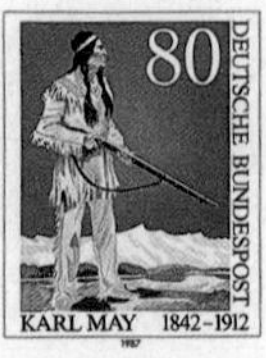

838 Chief Winnetou (from book cover)

1987. 75th Death Anniv of Karl May (writer).

2175	**838**	80pf. multicoloured	2·30	75

839 Solar Spectrum

1987. Birth Bicentenary of Joseph von Fraunhofer (optician and physicist).

2176	**839**	80pf. multicoloured	2·10	75

840 World Sailing Championships, Kiel

1987. Sport Promotion Fund. Multicoloured.

2177	80pf.+40pf. Type **840**	2·10	2·10
2178	120pf.+55pf. World Nordic Skiing Championships, Oberstdorf	3·25	3·25

1987. Youth Welfare. Trades (2nd series). As T 811. Multicoloured.

2179	50pf.+25pf. Plumber	1·80	1·70
2180	60pf.+30pf. Dental technician	2·20	2·10
2181	70pf.+35pf. Butcher	2·40	2·20
2182	80pf.+40pf. Bookbinder	3·25	3·00

841 Clefs, Notes and Leaves

1987. 125th Anniv of German Choir Association.

2183	**841**	80pf. multicoloured	2·30	75

842 Pope's Arms, Madonna and Child and Kevelaer

1987. Visit of Pope John Paul II to Kevelaer (venue for 17th Marian and 10th Mariological Congresses).

2184	**842**	80pf. multicoloured	2·75	75

843 Dulmen's Wild Horses

1987. European Environment Year.

2185	**843**	60pf. multicoloured	2·75	75

844 German Pavilion, International Exhibition, Barcelona, 1929 (Ludwig Mies van der Rohe)

1987. Europa. Architecture. Multicoloured.

2186	60pf. Type **844**	2·00	75
2187	80pf. Kohlbrand Bridge, Hamburg (Thyssen Engineering)	2·40	75

845 Emblem and Globe

1987. Rotary International Convention, Munich.

2188	**845**	70pf. ultram, yell & bl	2·20	75

846 "Without Title (With an Early Portrait)"

1987. Birth Centenary of Kurt Schwitters (artist and writer).

2189	**846**	80pf. multicoloured	2·20	75

847 Organ Pipes and Signature

1987. 350th Birth Anniv of Dietrich Buxtehude (composer).

2190	**847**	80pf. black, stone and red	1·60	75

JOHANN ALBRECHT BENGEL 1687 1752 DEUTSCHE BUNDESPOST 80

848 Bengal

1987. 300th Birth Anniv of Johann Albrecht Bengel (theologian).

2191	**848**	80pf. brown, ochre & blk	2·20	75

849 Wilhelm Kaisen

1987. Birth Centenary of Wilhelm Kaisen (Senate president and Mayor of Bremen).

2192	**849**	80pf. multicoloured	2·20	75

850 Charlemagne, Bishop Willehad, Bremen Cathedral and City Arms (after mural)

1987. 1200th Anniv of Bremen Bishopric.

2193	**850**	80pf. multicoloured	2·00	75

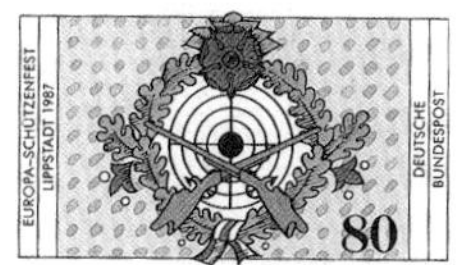

851 Target, Crossed Rifles and Wreath

1987. 7th European Riflemen's Festival, Lippstadt.

2194	**851**	80pf. multicoloured	2·00	75

852 4th-century Roman Bracelet

1987. Humanitarian Relief Funds. Precious Metal Work. Multicoloured.

2195		50pf.+25pf. Type **852**	1·80	1·70
2196		60pf.+30pf. 6th-century East Gothic buckle	1·80	1·70
2197		70pf.+35pf. 7th-century Merovingian disc fibula	1·80	1·70
2198		80pf.+40pf. 8th-century reliquary	2·40	2·40

853 Loading and Unloading Mail Train, 1897

1987. Stamp Day.

2199	**853**	80pf. multicoloured	2·00	1·30

854 Corner Tower, Celle Castle

1987. Tourist Sights. Inscr "DEUTSCHE BUNDESPOST".

2200	-	5pf. blue and grey	45	35
2201	-	10pf. blue and indigo	75	25
2202	-	20pf. pink and blue	60	35
2203	**854**	30pf. brown and green	1·00	35
2204	-	33pf. green and red	75	50
2205	-	38pf. grey and blue	1·20	75
2206	-	40pf. brown, red & blue	1·00	75
2206a	-	41pf. grey and yellow	85	60
2207	-	45pf. pink and blue	75	60
2208	-	50pf. brown and blue	1·00	35
2209	-	60pf. green and black	1·20	35
2210	-	70pf. pink and blue	1·30	35
2210a	-	70pf. brown and blue	75	50
2211	-	80pf. grey and green	1·20	35
2212	-	90pf. bistre and yellow	3·50	2·40
2213	-	100pf. green and orange	3·00	50
2214	-	120pf. green and red	2·75	1·10
2215	-	140pf. bistre and yellow	3·00	1·00
2216	-	170pf. grey and yellow	3·25	1·20
2216a	-	200pf. blue and brown	3·25	1·10
2217	-	280pf. grey and blue	5·50	4·00
2218	-	300pf. pink and brown	4·25	75
2219	-	350pf. grey and blue	5·00	1·00
2220	-	400pf. red and brown	5·25	1·00
2220a	-	450pf. blue and brown	6·00	1·80
2220b	-	500pf. stone and purple	6·75	2·20
2220c	-	550pf. brown and blue	7·25	3·50
2220d	-	700pf. green and yellow	9·25	3·75

DESIGNS: 5pf. Brunswick Lion; 10pf. Frankfurt airport; 20, 70 (2210) pf. Head of Nefertiti, Berlin Museum; 33, 120pf. Schleswig Cathedral; 38, 280pf. Statue of Roland, Bremen; 40pf. Chile House, Hamburg; 41, 170pf. Russian Church, Wiesbaden; 45pf. Rastatt Castle; 50pf. Freiburg Cathedral; 60pf. "Bavaria" (bronze statue), Munich; 70pf. (2210a) Heligoland; 80pf. Zollern II Dortmund Mine Industrial Museum, Westphalia; 90, 140pf. Bronze flagon, Reinheim; 100pf. Pilgrimage Chapel, Altotting; 200pf. Magdeburg Cathedral; 300pf. Hambach Castle; 350pf. Externsteine (rock formation), Horn-Bad Meinberg; 400pf. Dresden Opera House; 450pf. New Gate, Neubrandenburg; 500pf. Cottbus State Theatre; 550pf. Suhl-Heinrichs Town Hall, Thuringia; 700pf. National Theatre, Berlin.

The 10, 60, 80 and 100pf. also exist imperforate and self-adhesive from booklets.

For similar designs inscribed "DEUTSCHLAND", see Nos. 2654/66.

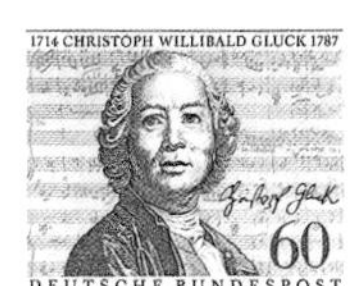

855 Gluck and Score of "Armide"

1987. Death Bicentenary of Christoph Willibald Gluck (composer).

2221	**855**	60pf. black, grey and red	1·60	60

856 Poster by Emil Orlik for "The Weavers"

1987. 125th Birth Anniv of Gerhart Hauptmann (playwright).

2222	**856**	80pf. lt red, black & red	2·40	75

857 Paddy Field

1987. 25th Anniv of German Famine Aid.

2223	**857**	80pf. multicoloured	2·40	75

858 "Birth of Christ" (13th-century Book of Psalms)

1987. Christmas.

2224	**858**	80pf.+40pf. mult	2·40	2·20

859 Jester

1988. 150th Anniv of Mainz Carnival.

2225	**859**	60pf. multicoloured	1·70	75

860 Kaiser

1988. Birth Centenary of Jakob Kaiser (trade unionist and politician).

2226	**860**	80pf. black and grey	1·60	75

861 Stein and Mayer

1988. Beatification of Edith Stein and Father Rupert Mayer.

2227	**861**	80pf. multicoloured	2·00	75

862 Dr Konrad Adenauer (West German Chancellor) and Charles de Gaulle (French President)

1988. 25th Anniv of Franco-German Co-operation Treaty.

2228	**862**	80pf. purple and black	2·75	1·00

863 "Solitude of the Green Woods" (woodcut of poem, Ludwig Richter)

1988. Birth Bicentenary of Joseph von Eichendorff (writer).

2229	**863**	60pf. multicoloured	2·00	75

864 Raiffeisen and Ploughed Field

1988. Death Centenary of Friedrich Wilhelm Raiffeisen (philanthropist and agricultural co-operative founder).

2230	**864**	80pf. green and black	2·75	75

865 Schopenhauer

1988. Birth Bicentenary of Arthur Schopenhauer (philosopher).

2231	**865**	80pf. brown and black	2·40	75

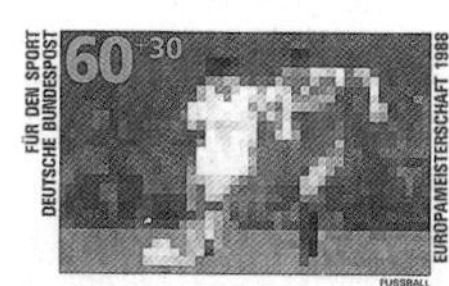

866 Football (European Championship)

1988. Sport Promotion Fund. Multicoloured.

2232		60pf.+30pf. Type **866**	1·80	1·50
2233		80pf.+40pf. Tennis (Olympic Games)	3·00	2·40
2234		120pf.+55pf. Diving (Olympic Games)	3·50	3·00

867 Buddy Holly

1988. Youth Welfare. Pop Music. Mult.

2235		50pf.+25pf. Type **867**	1·80	2·00
2236		60pf.+30pf. Elvis Presley	4·25	3·75
2237		70pf.+35pf. Jim Morrison	2·20	2·20
2238		80pf.+40pf. John Lennon	4·00	3·50

868 Hutten (wood engraving from "Conquestiones")

1988. 500th Birth Anniv of Ulrich von Hutten (writer).

2239	**868**	80pf. multicoloured	2·00	85

869 City Buildings and Jan Wellem Monument

1988. 700th Anniv of Dusseldorf.

2240	**869**	60pf. multicoloured	2·00	75

870 Airbus Industrie A320 and Manufacturing Nations' Flag

1988. Europa. Transport and Communications. Multicoloured.

2241		60pf. Type **870**	1·60	75
2242		80pf. Diagram of Integrated Services Digital Network	1·60	75

871 University Buildings and City Landmarks

1988. 600th Anniv of Cologne University.

2243	**871**	80pf. multicoloured	2·00	75

872 Monnet

1988. Birth Centenary of Jean Monnet (statesman).

2244	**872**	80pf. multicoloured	2·00	75

873 Storm

1988. Death Centenary of Theodor Storm (writer).

2245	**873**	80pf. multicoloured	2·00	75

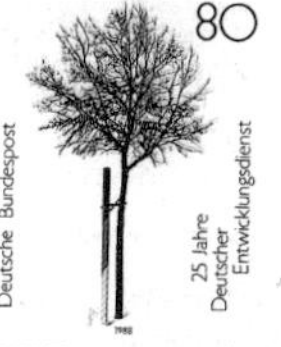

874 Tree supported by Stake in National Colours

1988. 25th Anniv of German Volunteer Service.

2246	**874**	80pf. multicoloured	2·00	75

875 Meersburg

1988. Millenary of Meersburg.

2247	**875**	60pf. multicoloured	1·50	75

876 Gmelin

1988. Birth Bicentenary of Leopold Gmelin (chemist).

2248	**876**	80pf. multicoloured	1·60	75

877 Vernier Caliper Rule in National Colours

1988. "Made in Germany".

2249	**877**	140pf. multicoloured	3·00	1·50

878 Bebel

1988. 75th Death Anniv of August Bebel (Social Democratic Labour Party co-founder).

2250	**878**	80pf. mauve, blue & sil	2·20	75

879 Carrier Pigeon

1988. Stamp Day.

2251	**879**	20pf. multicoloured	1·00	60

880 13th-century Rock Crystal Reliquary

1988. Humanitarian Relief Funds. Precious Metal Work. Multicoloured.

2252	50pf.+25pf. Type **880**	1·00	1·00
2253	60pf.+30pf. 14th-century bust of Charlemagne	1·50	1·50
2254	70pf.+35pf. 10th-cent. crown of Otto III	1·50	1·50
2255	80pf.+40pf. 17th-cent. jewelled flowers	2·20	2·20

881 Red Cross

1988. 125th Anniv of Red Cross.

2256	**881**	80pf. red and black	2·20	75

882 Burning Synagogue, Baden-Baden

1988. 50th Anniv of "Kristallnacht" (Nazi pogrom).

2257	**882**	80pf. purple and black	1·60	75

883 Cancelled Postage Stamps

1988. Centenary of Collection of Used Stamps for the Bethel Charity.

2258	**883**	60pf. multicoloured	1·80	75

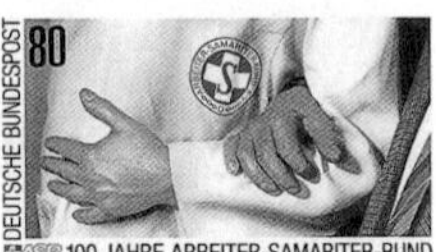

884 Linked Arms

1988. Centenary of Samaritan Workers' (first aid) Association.

2259	**884**	80pf. multicoloured	1·80	75

885 "Adoration of the Magi" (illus from Henry the Lion's Gospel Book)

1988. Christmas.

2260	**885**	80pf.+40pf. mult	2·20	2·00

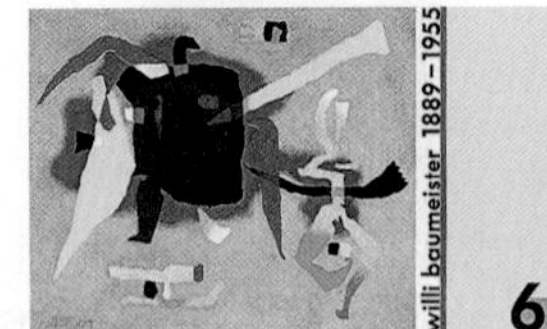

886 "Bluxao I"

1989. Birth Centenary of Willi Baumeister (painter).

2261	**886**	60pf. multicoloured	1·60	75

887 Bonn

1988. 2000th Anniv of Bonn.

2262	**887**	80pf. multicoloured	2·40	1·10

888 Grass growing from Dry, Cracked Earth

1989. 30th Anniversaries of Misereor and Bread for the World (Third World relief organizations).

2263	**888**	80pf. multicoloured	1·80	75

889 "Cats in the Attic" (woodcut)

1989. Birth Cent of Gerhard Marcks (artist).

2264	**889**	60pf. black, stone and red	1·60	75

890 Table Tennis (World Championships)

1989. Sport Promotion Fund. Multicoloured.

2265	100pf.+50pf. Type **890**	3·00	2·75
2266	140pf.+60pf. Gymnastics (World Championships)	4·25	4·00

891 Elephants

1989. Youth Welfare. Circus. Multicoloured.

2267	60pf.+30pf. Type **891**	2·40	2·40
2268	70pf.+30pf. Acrobat on horseback	3·00	3·00
2269	80pf.+35pf. Clown	4·25	3·75
2270	100pf.+50pf. Caravans and Big Top	5·50	4·25

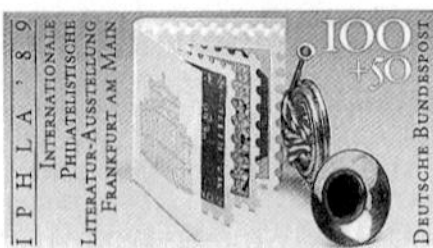

892 Posthorn and Book of Stamps

1989. "IPHLA '89" International Philatelic Literature Exhibition, Frankfurt.

2271	**892**	100pf.+50pf. mult	4·25	4·00

893 European and Members' Flags

1989. 3rd Direct Elections to European Parliament.

2272	**893**	100pf. multicoloured	3·25	1·50

894 Shipping

1989. 800th Anniv of Hamburg Harbour.

2273	**894**	60pf. multicoloured	2·20	75

895 Asam (detail of fresco, Weltenburg Abbey)

1989. 250th Death Anniv of Cosmas Damian Asam (painter and architect).

2274	**895**	60pf. multicoloured	1·20	75

896 Kites

1989. Europa. Children's Toys. Multicoloured.

2275	60pf. Type **896**	1·80	60
2276	100pf. Puppet show	2·40	60

897 Emblem, National Colours and Presidents' Signatures

1989. 40th Anniv of German Federal Republic.

2277	**897**	100pf. multicoloured	3·00	1·10

898 Council Assembly and Stars

1989. 40th Anniv of Council of Europe.

2278	**898**	100pf. blue and gold	2·75	1·20

899 Gabelsberger and Shorthand

1989. Birth Bicentenary of Franz Xaver Gabelsberger (shorthand pioneer).

2279	**899**	100pf. multicoloured	2·75	85

900 Score of "Lorelei" and Silhouette of Silcher

1989. Birth Bicentenary of Friedrich Silcher (composer).

2280	**900**	80pf. multicoloured	1·60	75

901 Saints Kilian, Totnan and Colman (from 12th-century German manuscript)

1989. 1300th Death Anniversaries of Saints Kilian, Colman and Totnan (Irish missionaries to Franconia).

2281	**901**	100pf. multicoloured	2·40	1·00

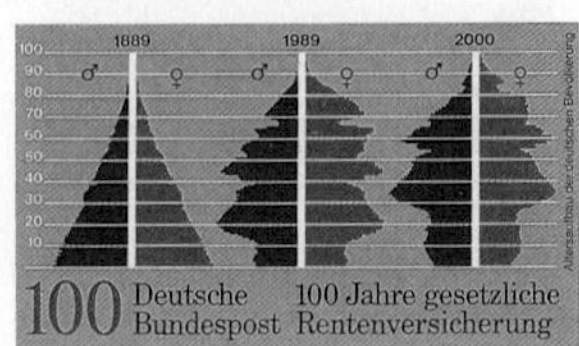

902 Age Graphs of Men and Women

1989. Centenary of National Insurance.

2282	**902**	100p. blue, red & lt blue	2·40	1·00

903 "Summer Evening" (Heinrich Vogler)

1989. Cent of Worpswede Artists' Village.

2283	**903**	60pf. multicoloured	1·30	75

904 Schneider

1989. 50th Death Anniv of Reverend Paul Schneider (concentration camp victim).

2284	**904**	100pf. blk, lt grey & grey	2·10	85

905 List (after Kriehuber) and Train

1989. Birth Bicentenary of Friedrich List (economist).

2285	**905**	170pf. black and red	3·75	1·50

906 Cathedral

1989. 750th Anniv of Frankfurt Cathedral.
2286 **906** 60pf. multicoloured 2·00 75

907 Children building House

1989. "Don't Forget the Children".
2287 **907** 100pf. multicoloured 2·10 85

908 Ammonite and Union Emblem

1989. Centenary of Mining and Power Industries Trade Union.
2288 **908** 100pf. multicoloured 2·10 85

909 18th-century Mounted Courier, Thurn and Taxis

1989. Humanitarian Relief Funds. Postal Deliveries. Multicoloured.
2289 60pf.+30pf. Type **909** 1·80 1·70
2290 80pf.+35pf. Hamburg postal messenger, 1808 2·75 2·40
2291 100pf.+50pf. Bavarian mail coach, 1900 4·00 3·75

910 Maier

1989. Birth Centenary of Reinhold Maier (politician).
2292 **910** 100pf. multicoloured 2·20 85

911 Organ Pipes

1989. 300th Anniv of Arp Schnitger Organ, St. James's Church, Hamburg.
2293 **911** 60pf. multicoloured 2·00 75

912 Angel

1989. Christmas. 16th-century Carvings by Veit Stoss, St. Lawrence's Church, Nuremberg. Multicoloured.
2294 60pf.+30pf. Type **912** 2·00 1·70
2295 100pf.+50pf. "Nativity" 2·40 2·20

913 Speyer

1990. 2000th Anniv of Speyer.
2296 **913** 60pf. multicoloured 2·00 75

914 "Courier" (Albrecht Durer)

1990. 500th Anniv of Regular European Postal Services.
2297 **914** 100pf. deep brown, light brown and brown 3·25 1·00

915 Vine forming Initial "R"

1990. 500 Years of Riesling Grape Cultivation.
2298 **915** 100pf. multicoloured 2·00 1·00

916 Old Lubeck

1990. UNESCO World Heritage Site, Old Lubeck.
2299 **916** 100pf. multicoloured 2·00 1·00

917 15th-century Seal and Grand Master's Arms

1990. 800th Anniv of Teutonic Order.
2300 **917** 100pf. multicoloured 2·40 1·00

918 Frederick II's Seal and Fair Entrance Hall

1990. 750th Anniv of Granting of Fair Privileges to Frankfurt.
2301 **918** 100pf. multicoloured 2·40 1·00

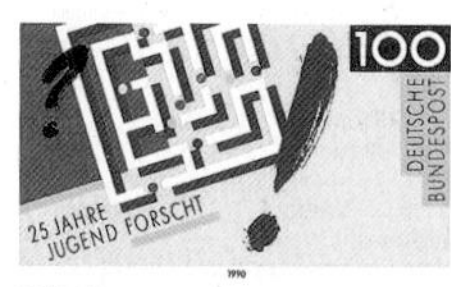

919 Maze

1990. 25th Anniv of Youth Research Science Competition.
2302 **919** 100pf. multicoloured 2·40 1·00

920 Wildlife

1990. North Sea Protection.
2303 **920** 100pf. multicoloured 3·00 1·00

921 Handball

1990. Sport Promotion Fund. Multicoloured.
2304 100pf.+50pf. Type **921** 4·00 2·40
2305 140pf.+60pf. Keep-fit 4·75 3·75

922 Widow Bolte

1990. Youth Welfare. 125th Anniv of Max and Moritz (characters from books by Wilhelm Busch). Multicoloured.
2306 60pf.+30pf. Type **922** 1·30 1·20
2307 70pf.+30pf. Max asleep 2·00 1·80
2308 80pf.+35pf. Moritz watching Max sawing through bridge 2·75 2·40
2309 100pf.+50pf. Max and Moritz 3·25 3·00

923 "1.MAI" and Factory Silhouette

1990. Centenary of Labour Day.
2310 **923** 100pf. red and black 2·00 1·00

924 Woman's Face

1990. 75th Anniv of German Association of Housewives.
2311 **924** 100pf. multicoloured 2·00 1·00

925 Collection Box

1990. 125th Anniv of German Lifeboat Institution.
2312 **925** 60pf. multicoloured 1·80 85

926 Thurn and Taxis Palace, Frankfurt

1990. Europa. Post Office Buildings. Mult.
2313 60pf. Type **926** 2·20 85
2314 100pf. Postal Giro Office, Frankfurt 2·40 85

927 St Philip's Church, Protestant Church Flag and Candle Flames

1990. Centenary of Rummelsberg Diaconal Institution.
2315 **927** 100pf. multicoloured 2·00 1·00

928 Leuschner

1990. Birth Centenary of Wilhelm Leuschner (trade unionist and member of anti-Hitler Resistance).
2316 **928** 100pf. black and lilac 2·40 1·00

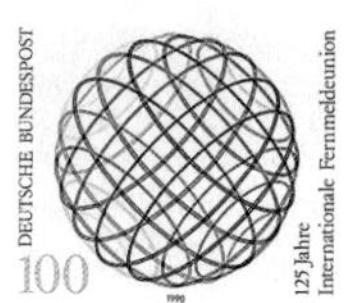

929 Globe

1990. 125th Anniv of I.T.U.
2317 **929** 100pf. multicoloured 2·00 1·00

930 National Colours and Students

1990. 175th Anniv of German Students' Fraternity and of their Colours (now national colours).
2318 **930** 100pf. multicoloured 2·40 1·00

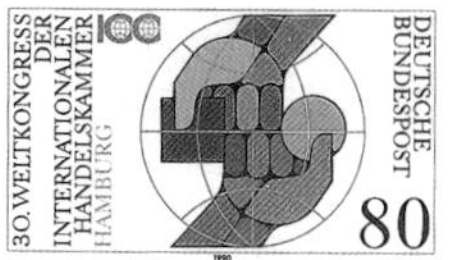

931 Hands exchanging Money and Goods

1990. 30th World Congress of International Chamber of Commerce, Hamburg.
2319 **931** 80pf. multicoloured 2·00 1·20

40 JAHRE CHARTA DER DEUTSCHEN HEIMATVERTRIEBENEN

WIR RUFEN VÖLKER UND MENSCHEN AUF, DIE GUTEN WILLENS SIND, HAND ANZULEGEN ANS WERK, DAMIT AUS SCHULD, UNGLÜCK, LEID, ARMUT UND ELEND FÜR UNS ALLE DER WEG IN EINE BESSERE ZUKUNFT GEFUNDEN WIRD.

DEUTSCHE BUNDESPOST 100

932 Closing Sentence of Charter

1990. 40th Anniv of Expelled Germans Charter.
2320 **932** 100pf. multicoloured 2·40 85

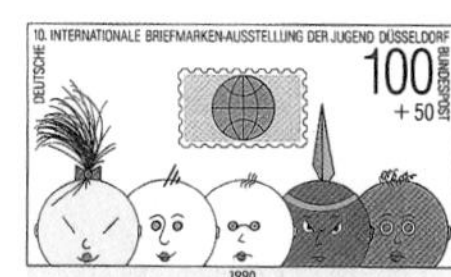

933 Children of Different Races

1990. 10th International Youth Philatelic Exhibition, Dusseldorf. Sheet 165×101 mm.
MS2321 **933** 6×100pf.+50pf. multi-coloured 27·00 30·00

934 Claudius

1990. 250th Birth Anniv of Matthias Claudius (writer).
2322 **934** 100pf. blue, black and red 2·20 75

935 Mail Motor Wagon, 1900

1990. Humanitarian Relief Funds. Posts and Telecommunications. Multicoloured.
2323 60pf.+30pf. Type **935** 1·30 1·30
2324 80pf.+35pf. Telephone ex-change, 1890 2·20 2·20
2325 100pf.+50pf. Parcel sorting office, 1900 3·25 3·25

936 "German Unity" and National Colours

1990. Reunification of Germany.
2326 **936** 50pf. black, red & yellow 1·80 60
2327 **936** 100pf. black, red & yell 2·40 85

937 Schliemann and Lion Gate, Mycenae

1990. Death Centenary of Heinrich Schliemann (archaeologist).

2328	**937**	60pf. multicoloured	2·00	75

938 Penny Black, Bavaria 1k. and West Germany 1989 100pf. Stamps

1990. Stamp Day. 150th Anniv of the Penny Black.

2329	**938**	100pf. multicoloured	2·20	75

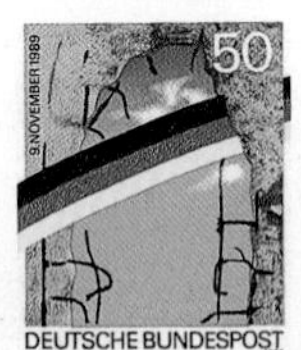

939 National Colours spanning Breach in Wall

1990. 1st Anniv of Opening of Berlin Wall.

2330	50pf. Type **939**	1·80	1·10
2331	100pf. Brandenburg Gate and crowd	2·40	1·10
MS2332	146×100 mm. As Nos. 2330/1	5·00	5·00

940 Angel with Candles

1990. Christmas. Multicoloured.

2333	50pf.+20pf. Type **940**	1·20	1·20
2334	60pf.+30pf. Figure of man smoking	1·50	1·50
2335	70pf.+30pf. "Soldier" nutcrackers	2·00	2·00
2336	100pf.+50pf. Tinsel angel	3·00	3·00

941 Kathe Dorsch in "Mrs Warren's Profession"

1990. Birth Centenary of Kathe Dorsch (actress).

2337	**941**	100pf. violet and red	2·20	1·00

942 View of City

1991. 750th Anniv of Hanover.

2338	**942**	60pf. multicoloured	2·00	75

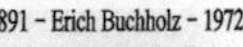

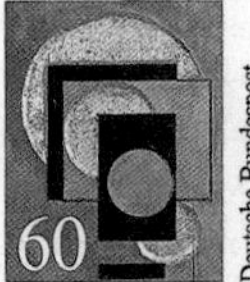

943 "Three Golden Circles with a Full Circle in Blue" (relief in wood)

1991. Birth Centenary of Erich Buchholz (artist).

2339	**943**	60pf. multicoloured	1·60	75

944 Miniature from 13th-century French Code

1991. 750th Anniv of Promulgation of Pharmaceutical Ethics in Germany.

2340	**944**	100pf. multicoloured	2·40	1·00

945 Brandenburg Gate (from "Old Engravings of Berlin")

1991. Bicentenary of Brandenburg Gate.

2341	**945**	100pf. black, red and grey	2·75	75

946 Eucken

1991. Birth Centenary of Walter Eucken (economist).

2342	**946**	100pf. multicoloured	2·10	1·00

947 Globe and "25" (poster)

1991. 25th International Tourism Fair, Berlin.

2343	**947**	100pf. multicoloured	2·10	1·00

948 Two-man Bobsleigh

1991. World Bobsleigh Championships, Altenberg. Sheet 55×80 mm.

MS2344	**948**	100pf. multicoloured	3·00	3·75

949 Weightlifting (World Championships)

1991. Sport Promotion Fund. Multicoloured.

2345	70pf.+30pf. Type **949**	2·20	2·20
2346	100pf.+50pf. Cycling (world championships)	2·40	2·40
2347	140pf.+60pf. Basketball (centenary)	3·00	3·00
2348	170pf.+80pf. Wrestling (European championships)	3·75	3·75

950 Title Page of "Cautio Criminalis" (tract against witch trials), Langenfeld and Score of "Trutz-Nachtigall"

1991. 400th Birth Anniv of Friedrich Spee von Langenfeld (poet and human rights pioneer).

2349	**950**	100pf. multicoloured	2·20	75

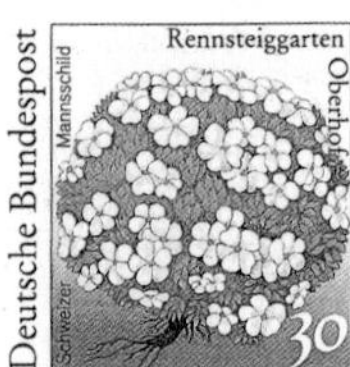

951 Androsace

1991. Plants in Rennsteiggarten (botanical garden), Oberhof. Multicoloured.

2350	30pf. Type **951**	60	60
2351	50pf. Primula	85	85
2352	80pf. Gentian	1·50	60
2353	100pf. Cranberry	2·10	85
2354	350pf. Edelweiss	6·75	5·00

952 Werth (attr Wenzel Hollar)

1991. 400th Birth Anniv of Jan von Werth (military commander).

2355	**952**	60pf. multicoloured	1·60	75

953 Windthorst

1991. Death Centenary of Ludwig Windthorst (politician).

2356	**953**	100pf. multicoloured	2·20	75

954 Junkers F-13, 1930

1991. Historic Mail Aircraft. Multicoloured.

2357	30pf. Type **954**	60	60
2358	50pf. Hans Grade's monoplane, 1909	85	60
2359	100pf. Fokker F.III, 1922	2·40	60
2360	165pf. Airship LZ-127 "Graf Zeppelin", 1928	3·75	3·50

955 Mountain Clouded Yellow

1991. Youth Welfare. Endangered Butterflies. Multicoloured.

2361	30pf.+15pf. Type **955**	60	60
2362	50pf.+25pf. Poplar admiral	75	75
2363	60pf.+30pf. Purple emperor	1·50	1·50
2364	70pf.+30pf. Violet copper	1·60	1·60
2365	80pf.+35pf. Swallowtail	2·00	2·00
2366	90pf.+45pf. Small apollo	2·40	2·40
2367	100pf.+50pf. Moorland clouded yellow	3·00	3·00
2368	140pf.+60pf. Large copper	3·75	3·75

See also Nos. 2449/53.

956 Academy Building, 1830

1991. Bicentenary of Choral Academy, Berlin.

2369	**956**	100pf. multicoloured	2·20	1·00

957 Typesetting School, 1875

1991. 125th Anniv of Lette Foundation (institute for professional training of women).

2370	**957**	100pf. multicoloured	2·20	1·00

958 Battle (detail of miniature, Schlackenwerth Codex, 1350)

1991. 750th Anniv of Battle of Legnica.

2371	**958**	100pf. multicoloured	2·40	1·50

959 Arms

1991. 700th Anniv of Granting of Charters to Six Towns of Trier.

2372	**959**	60pf. multicoloured	1·60	75

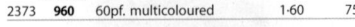

960 Speeding Train

1991. Inauguration of Inter-City Express (ICE) Railway Service.

2373	**960**	60pf. multicoloured	1·60	75

961 "ERS-1" European Remote Sensing Satellite

1991. Europa. Europe in Space. Mult.

2374	60pf. Type **961**	1·80	60
2375	100pf. "Kopernikus" telecommunications satellite	2·75	60

962 Reger and Organ Pipes

1991. 75th Death Anniv of Max Reger (composer).

2376	**962**	100pf. multicoloured	2·40	75

963 Ruffs

1991. Seabirds. Multicoloured.

2390	60pf. Type **963**	1·20	75
2391	80pf. Little terns	1·80	1·20
2392	100pf. Brent geese	1·80	1·20
2393	140pf. White-tailed sea eagles	3·00	2·40

964 Wilhelm August Lampadius (gas pioneer)

1991. 18th World Gas Congress, Berlin. Each black and blue.

2394	60pf. Type **964**	1·20	50
2395	100pf. Gas street lamp, Berlin	1·80	75

965 Wallot (after Franz Wurbel) and Reichstag Building, Berlin

1991. 150th Birth Anniv of Paul Wallot (architect).

2396	**965**	100pf. multicoloured	2·40	75

966 "Libellula depressa"

1991. Dragonflies. Multicoloured.

2397	50pf. Type **966**	1·00	60
2398	60pf. Type **966**	1·80	1·00
2399	60pf. "Sympetrum sanguineum"	1·80	1·00
2400	60pf. "Cordulegaster boltonii"	1·80	1·00
2401	60pf. "Aeshna viridis"	1·80	1·00
2402	70pf. As No. 2399	1·80	1·20
2403	80pf. As No. 2400	1·80	1·20
2404	100pf. As No. 2401	1·80	1·20

967 Hand clutching Cloak

1991. 40th Anniv of Geneva Convention on Refugees.

2405	**967**	100pf. lilac and black	2·20	70

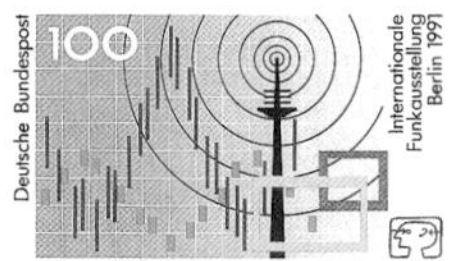

968 Radio Waves and Mast

1991. International Radio Exhibition, Berlin.

2406	**968**	100pf. multicoloured	2·20	70

969 Pedestrians and Traffic

1991. Road Safety Campaign.

2407	**969**	100pf. multicoloured	2·40	95

970 Lilienthal

1991. Centenary of First Heavier-than-Air Manned Flight by Otto Lilienthal and "Lilienthal '91" European Airmail Exhibition, Dresden. Sheet 57×82 mm.

MS2408	**970** 100pf.+50pf. brown, blue and red	5·00	4·50

971 August Heinrich Hoffmann von Fallersleben (lyricist) and Third Verse

1991. 150th Anniv of "Song of the Germans" (national anthem).

2409	**971**	100pf. red, black & green	2·20	70

972 Thadden-Trieglaff

1991. Birth Cent of Reinold von Thadden-Trieglaff (founder of German Protestant Convention).

2410	**972**	100pf. multicoloured	2·10	70

973 Transmission Test between Lauffen am Neckar and Frankfurt am Main

1991. Centenary of Three-phase Energy Transmission.

2411	**973**	170pf. multicoloured	3·50	1·80

974 Quill, Pen and Sword

1991. Birth Bicentenary of Theodor Korner (poet). Sheet 55×80 mm containing T 974 and similar vert designs. Multicoloured.

MS2412	60pf. Type **974**; 100pf. Korner	3·50	4·25

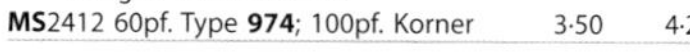

975 Albers in "The Winner"

1991. Birth Centenary of Hans Albers (actor).

2413	**975**	100pf. multicoloured	2·75	70

976 Harbour

1991. 275th Anniv of Rhine-Ruhr Port, Duisburg.

2414	**976**	100pf. multicoloured	2·20	70

977 Bethel Post Office

1991. Humanitarian Relief Funds. Postal Buildings. Multicoloured.

2415	30pf.+15pf. Type **977**	95	70
2416	60pf.+30pf. Budingen post station	1·50	1·40
2417	70pf.+30pf. Stralsund post office	1·80	1·70
2418	80pf.+35pf. Lauscha post office	2·40	2·10
2419	100pf.+50pf. Bonn post office	3·00	2·75
2420	140pf.+60pf. Weilburg post office	3·50	3·50

978 Postal Delivery in Spreewald Region

1991. Stamp Day.

2421	**978**	100pf. multicoloured	2·10	70

979 "Bird Monument" (detail)

1991. Birth Centenary of Max Ernst (painter).

2422	**979**	100pf. multicoloured	2·20	70

980 "Portrait of the Dancer Anita Berber"

1991. Birth Cent of Otto Dix (painter). Mult.

2423	60pf. Type **980**	1·20	70
2424	100pf. "Self-portrait in Right Profile"	2·40	85

981 "The Violinist and the Water Sprite"

1991. Sorbian Legends. Multicoloured.

2425	60pf. Type **981**	1·40	70
2426	100pf. "The Midday Woman and the Woman from Nochten"	2·10	85

982 Angel (detail of "The Annunciation")

1991. Christmas. Works by Martin Schongauer. Multicoloured.

2427	60pf.+30pf. Type **982**	1·50	1·40
2428	70pf.+30pf. Virgin Mary (detail of "The Annunciation")	1·90	1·80
2429	80pf.+35pf. Angel (detail of "Madonna in a Rose Garden")	3·75	3·25
2430	100pf.+50pf. "Nativity"	4·50	4·00

983 Leber

1991. Birth Cent of Julius Leber (politician).

2431	**983**	100pf. multicoloured	2·10	70

984 Nelly Sachs

1991. Birth Centenary of Nelly Sachs (writer).

2432	**984**	100pf. dp violet & violet	2·20	70

985 Mozart

1991. Death Bicentenary of Wolfgang Amadeus Mozart (composer). Sheet 82×56 mm.

MS2433	**985** 100pf. lilac and brown	3·50	4·00

986 Base of William I Monument and City Silhouette

1992. 2000th Anniv of Koblenz.

2434	**986**	60pf. multicoloured	2·40	85

987 Niemoller

1992. Birth Centenary of Martin Niemoller (theologian).

2435	**987**	100pf. multicoloured	1·80	70

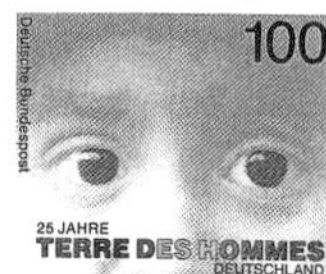

988 Child's Eyes

1992. 25th Anniv of Terre des Hommes (child welfare organization) in Germany.

2436	**988**	100pf. multicoloured	2·40	95

989 Arms of Baden-Wurttemberg

1992. Lander of the Federal Republic.

2437	**989**	100pf. multicoloured	2·20	1·10

See also Nos. 2448, 2465, 2470, 2474, 2479, 2506, 2526, 2527, 2534, 2539, 2556, 2567, 2580, 2584 and 2597.

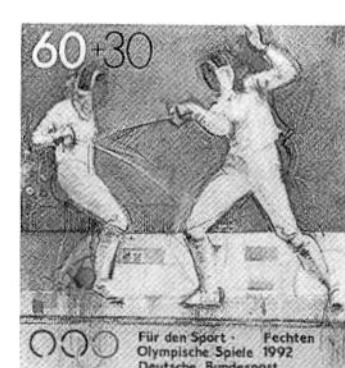

990 Fencing

1992. Sport Promotion Fund. Olympic Games, Albertville and Barcelona. Multicoloured.

2438	60pf.+30pf. Type **990**	1·40	1·40
2439	80pf.+40pf. Rowing eight	1·70	1·70
2440	100pf.+50pf. Dressage	3·50	3·50
2441	170pf.+80pf. Skiing (slalom)	5·25	5·25

991 Honegger and Score of Ballet "Semiramis"

1992. Birth Centenary of Arthur Honegger (composer).

2442	**991**	100pf. black and brown	2·40	1·10

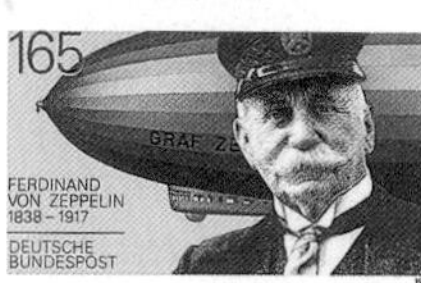

992 Zeppelin and LZ-127 "Graf Zeppelin"

1992. 75th Death Anniv of Ferdinand von Zeppelin (airship manufacturer).

2443	**992**	165pf. multicoloured	3·50	1·90

993 Kiel City and Harbour

1992. 750th Anniv of Kiel.

2444	**993**	60pf. multicoloured	1·80	85

994 Andreas Marggraf, Beet, Franz Achard and Carl Scheibler

1992. 125th Anniv of Berlin Sugar Institute.
2445 **994** 100pf. multicoloured 2·20 1·10

The stamp depicts the discoverer of beet sugar, the founder of the beet sugar industry and the founder of the Institute respectively.

995 Horses and Renz

1992. Death Centenary of Ernst Jakob Renz (circus director).
2446 **995** 100pf. multicoloured 2·20 85

996 Adenauer

1992. 25th Death Anniv of Konrad Adenauer (Chancellor, 1949–63).
2447 **996** 100pf. brn & cinnamon 2·75 85

1992. Lander of the Federal Republic. As T 989. Multicoloured.
2448 100pf. Bavaria 2·20 1·10

1992. Youth Welfare. Endangered Moths. As T 955. Multicoloured.
2449 60pf.+30pf. Purple tiger moth 2·10 2·10
2450 70pf.+30pf. Hawk moth 2·40 2·40
2451 80pf.+40pf. "Noctuidae sp." 3·00 3·00
2452 100pf.+50pf. Tiger moth 3·25 3·25
2453 170pf.+80pf. "Arichanna melanaria" 3·75 3·75

997 Schall

1992. 400th Birth Anniv of Adam Schall von Bell (missionary astronomer).
2454 **997** 140pf. black, yellow & bl 3·00 1·50

998 Cathedral and St. Severus's Church

1992. 1250th Anniv of Erfurt.
2455 **998** 60pf. multicoloured 1·70 85

999 Woodcut from 1493 Edition of Columbus's Letters

1992. Europa. 500th Anniv of Discovery of America by Columbus. Multicoloured.
2456 60pf. Type **999** 1·80 70
2457 100pf. "Rene de Laudonniere and Chief Athore" (Jacques le Moyne de Morgues, 1564) 2·40 85

1000 "Consecration of St. Ludgerus" (from "Vita Liudgeri" by Altfridus)

1992. 1250th Birth Anniv of St. Ludgerus (first Bishop of Munster).
2458 **1000** 100pf. multicoloured 2·10 95

1001 Arithmetic Sum

1992. 500th Birth Anniv of Adam Riese (mathematician).
2459 **1001** 100pf. multicoloured 2·40 85

1002 Order of Merit

1992. 150th Anniv of Civil Class of Order of Merit (for scientific or artistic achievement).
2460 **1002** 100pf. multicoloured 2·10 85

1003 "Landscape with Horse" (Franz Marc)

1992. 20th-century German Paintings (1st series). Multicoloured.
2461 60pf. Type **1003** 1·20 95
2462 100pf. "Fashion Shop" (August Macke) 1·80 95
2463 170pf. "Murnau with Rainbow" (Wassily Kandinsky) 3·00 2·50

See also Nos. 2507/9, 2590/2, 2615/17 and 2704/6.

1004 Lichtenberg

1992. 250th Birth Anniv of Georg Christoph Lichtenberg (physicist and essayist).
2464 **1004** 100pf. multicoloured 2·10 95

1992. Lander of the Federal Republic. As T 989. Multicoloured.
2465 100pf. Berlin 2·20 1·10

1005 Rainforest

1992. "Save the Tropical Rain Forest".
2466 **1005** 100pf.+50pf. mult 2·75 2·75

The premium was for the benefit of environmental projects.

1006 Garden

1992. Leipzig Botanical Garden.
2467 **1006** 60pf. multicoloured 1·50 85

1007 Stylized House and Globe

1992. 17th International Home Economics Congress, Hanover.
2468 **1007** 100pf. multicoloured 2·40 95

1008 Family

1992. Family Life.
2469 **1008** 100pf. multicoloured 2·40 85

1992. Lander of the Federal Republic. As T 989. Multicoloured.
2470 100pf. Brandenburg 2·20 1·10

1009 "Assumption of the Virgin Mary" (Rohr Monastery Church)

1992. 300th Birth Anniv of Egid Quirin Asam (sculptor).
2471 **1009** 60pf. multicoloured 1·80 85

1010 Opera House (Georg von Knobelsdorff)

1992. 250th Anniv of German State Opera House, Berlin.
2472 **1010** 80pf. multicoloured 2·00 85

1011 Masked Actors

1992. Centenary of German Amateur Theatres Federation.
2473 **1011** 100pf. multicoloured 2·40 85

1992. Lander of the Federal Republic. As T 989. Multicoloured.
2474 100pf. Bremen 2·20 1·10

1012 Globe

1992. 500th Anniv of Martin Behaim's Terrestrial Globe.
2475 **1012** 60pf. multicoloured 1·90 85

1013 1890 Pendant and 1990 Clock

1992. 225th Anniv of Jewellery and Watch-making in Pforzheim.
2476 **1013** 100pf. multicoloured 2·00 85

1014 Bergengruen (after Hanni Fries)

1992. Birth Centenary of Werner Bergengruen (writer).
2477 **1014** 100pf. grey, blue & blk 2·00 85

1015 Neue Holzbrucke Bridge, nr Essing

1992. Inauguration of Main–Donau Canal.
2478 **1015** 100pf. multicoloured 2·00 85

1992. Lander of the Federal Republic. As T 989. Multicoloured.
2479 100pf. Hamburg 2·20 1·10

1016 Turret Clock, 1400

1992. Humanitarian Relief Funds. Clocks. Multicoloured.
2480 60pf.+30pf. Type **1016** 1·70 1·50
2481 70pf.+30pf. Astronomical mantel clock, 1738 2·00 1·90
2482 80pf.+40pf. Flute clock, 1790 2·10 2·00
2483 100pf.+50pf. Figurine clock, 1580 2·50 2·40
2484 170pf.+80pf. Table clock, 1550 3·50 3·25

1017 Distler and Score of "We Praise Our Lord Jesus Christ"

1992. 50th Death Anniv of Hugo Distler (composer).
2485 **1017** 100pf. black and violet 2·40 85

1018 Balloon Post

1992. Stamp Day.
2486 **1018** 100pf. multicoloured 2·40 95

1019 Otto Engine, 1892, Cogwheel and Laser Beam

1992. Centenary of German Plant and Machine Builders Association.
2487 **1019** 170pf. multicoloured 2·75 1·70

1020 "Adoration of the Magi"

1992. Christmas. Carvings by Franz Maidburg, St. Anne's Church, Annaberg-Buchholz. Mult.
2488 60pf.+30pf. Type **1020** 1·70 1·50

2489 100pf.+50pf. "Birth of Christ" 2·40 2·10

1021 Blucher (after Simon Meister)

1992. 250th Birth Anniv of Field Marshal Gebhard Leberecht von Blucher.
2490 **1021** 100pf. multicoloured 2·40 85

1022 Werner von Siemens

1992. Death Centenary of Werner von Siemens (electrical engineer).
2491 **1022** 100pf. brown & dp brn 2·40 85

1023 Klepper

1992. 50th Death Anniv of Jochen Klepper (writer).
2492 **1023** 100pf. multicoloured 2·40 85

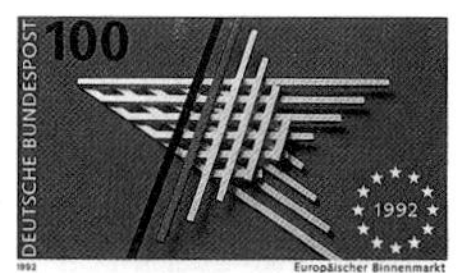

1024 Star in German Colours

1992. European Single Market.
2493 **1024** 100pf. multicoloured 2·75 95

1025 Cathedral and Uberwasser Church

1993. 1200th Anniv of Munster.
2494 **1025** 60pf. multicoloured 1·50

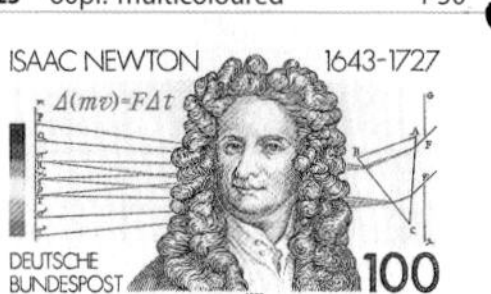

1026 Newton, Sketch of Refraction of Light and Formula

1993. 350th Birth Anniv of Sir Isaac Newton (scientist).
2495 **1026** 100pf. multicoloured 2·10 85

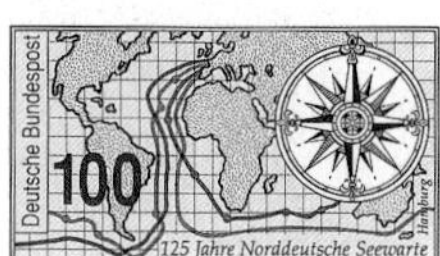

1027 Route Map and Compass Rose

1993. 125th Anniv of North German Naval Observatory, Hamburg.
2496 **1027** 100pf. multicoloured 1·90 85

1028 Emblem and Safety Stripes

1993. European Year of Health, Hygiene and Safety in the Workplace.
2497 **1028** 100pf. blue, yell & blk 1·90 85

1029 Wires and Wall Socket forming House

1993. Centenary of German Association of Electrical Engineers.
2498 **1029** 170pf. multicoloured 2·75 1·70

1030 Ski-jumping Hill, Garmisch-Partenkirchen

1993. Sport Promotion Fund. German Olympic Venues. Multicoloured.
2499 60pf.+30pf. Type **1030** 2·40 2·10
2500 80pf.+40pf. Olympia-park, Munich 3·00 2·75
2501 100pf.+50pf. Olympic Stadium, Berlin 3·75 3·50
2502 170pf.+80pf. Olympic Harbour, Kiel 4·50 4·25

1031 Stylised Sound Vibration

1993. 250th Anniv of Leipzig Gewandhaus Orchestra.
2503 **1031** 100pf. gold and black 1·90 85

1032 Statue of St. John and Charles Bridge, Prague

1993. 600th Death Anniv of St. John of Nepomuk.
2504 **1032** 100pf. multicoloured 2·10 85

1033 Diagram explaining New Postcodes

1993. Introduction of Five-digit Postcode System.
2505 **1033** 100pf. multicoloured 2·40 85

1993. Lander of the Federal Republic. As T 989. Multicoloured.
2506 100pf. Hesse 2·00 1·10

1993. 20th-century German Paintings (2nd series). As T 1003. Multicoloured.
2507 100pf. multicoloured 2·00 1·20
2508 100pf. black, grey and mauve 2·00 1·20
2509 100pf. multicoloured 2·00 1·20

DESIGNS: No. 2507, "Cafe" (George Grosz); 2508, "Sea and Sun" (Otto Pankok); 2509, "Audience" (Andreas Paul Weber).

1034 Abbeys

1993. 900th Anniversaries of Maria Laach and Bursfelde Benedictine Abbeys.
2510 **1034** 80pf. multicoloured 2·10 85

1035 Alpine Longhorn Beetle

1993. Youth Welfare. Endangered Beetles. Multicoloured.
2511 80pf.+40f. Type **1035** 2·40 2·40
2512 80pf.+40pf. Rose chafer 2·40 2·40
2513 100pf.+50pf. Stag beetle 2·75 2·75
2514 100pf.+50pf. Tiger beetle 2·75 2·75
2515 200pf.+50pf. Cockchafer 4·25 4·25

1036 Plants

1993. 5th International Horticultural Show, Stuttgart.
2516 **1036** 100pf. multicoloured 1·90 85

1037 Horse Race

1993. 125th Anniv of Hoppegarten Racecourse.
2517 **1037** 80pf. multicoloured 1·70 95

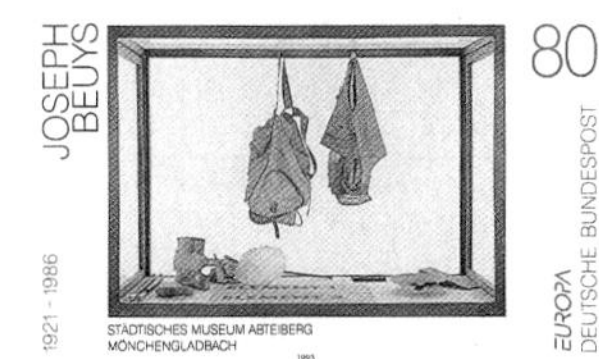

1038 "Storage Place" (Joseph Beuys)

1993. Europa. Contemporary Art. Mult.
2518 80pf. Type **1038** 1·80 1·00
2519 100pf. "Homage to the Square" (Josef Albers) 1·80 1·00

1039 Church and Pupils

1993. 450th Anniv of Pforta School.
2520 **1039** 100pf. multicoloured 1·90 85

1040 Students, Flag, City Hall and Castle

1993. 125th Anniv of Coburg Association of University Student Unions.
2521 **1040** 100pf. black, grn & red 1·90 85

1041 "Hohentwiel" (lake steamer) and Flags

1993. Lake Constance European Region.
2522 **1041** 100pf. multicoloured 2·00 85

1042 "Old Market—View of St. Nicholas's Church" (detail, Ferdinand von Arnim)

1993. Millenary of Potsdam.
2523 **1042** 80pf. multicoloured 2·00 85

1043 Holderlin (after Franz Hiemer)

1993. 150th Death Anniv of Friedrich Holderlin (poet).
2524 **1043** 100pf. multicoloured 2·00 85

1044 "If People can fly to the Moon, why can't they do anything about so many Children dying?"

1993. 40th Anniv of German United Nations Children's Fund Committee.
2525 **1044** 100pf. multicoloured 1·90 85

1993. Lander of the Federal Republic. As T 989. Multicoloured.
2526 100pf. Mecklenburg-Vorpommern 2·00 1·10

1993. Lander of the Federal Republic. As T 989. Multicoloured.
2527 100pf. Lower Saxony 2·00 1·10

1045 Fallada (after E. O. Plauen)

1993. Birth Centenary of Hans Fallada (writer).
2528 **1045** 100pf. green, brn & red 2·10 85

1046 Harz Mountain Range

1993. Landscapes (1st series). Multicoloured.
2529 100pf. Type **1046** 2·00 1·10
2530 100pf. Rugen 2·00 1·10
2531 100pf. Hohe Rhon 2·00 1·10

See also Nos. 2585/8, 2646/9, 2709/12 and 2806/8.

1047 Stages of Manufacture

1993. 250th Death Anniv of Mathias Klotz (violin maker).
2532 **1047** 80pf. multicoloured 1·70 70

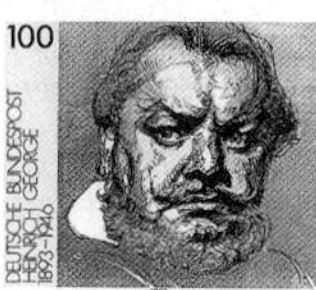

1048 George as Gotz von Berlichingen in Goethe's "Urgotz"

1993. Birth Centenary of Heinrich George (actor).
2533 **1048** 100pf. multicoloured 1·90 85

1993. Lander of the Federal Republic. As T 989. Multicoloured.
2534 100pf. Nordrhein-Westfalen 2·00 1·10

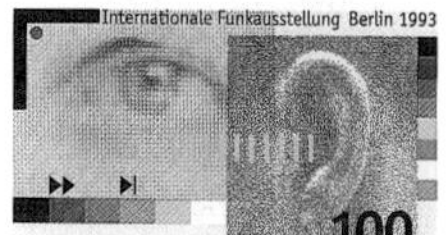

1049 Digitalised Eye and Ear

1993. International Radio Exhibition, Berlin.
2535 **1049** 100pf. multicoloured 1·90 85

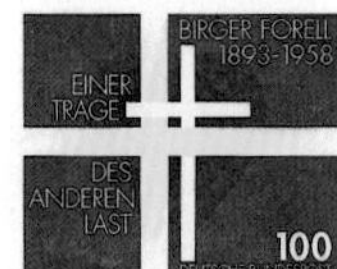

1050 Swedish Flag, Heart and Cross

1993. Birth Centenary of Birger Forell (founder of Espelkamp (town for war refugees)).
2536 **1050** 100pf. yell, ultram & bl 2·40 85

1051 "Tuledu Bridge" (engraving)

1993. Birth Centenary of Hans Leip (writer and artist).
2537 **1051** 100pf. black, red & blue 2·40 85

1052 Singing Clown

1993. "For Us Children". Sheet 49×83 mm.
MS2538 **1052** 100pf. multicoloured 2·50 2·50

1993. Lander of the Federal Republic. As T 989. Multicoloured.
2539 100pf. Rheinland-Pfalz 2·00 1·10

1053 Postman delivering Letter

1993. Stamp Day.
2540 **1053** 100pf.+50pf. mult 2·40 2·40

1054 "Swan Lake"

1993. Death Centenary of Pyotr Tchaikovsky (composer).
2541 **1054** 80pf. multicoloured 2·00 85

1055 Fohr, Schleswig-Holstein

1993. Humanitarian Relief Funds. Traditional Costumes (1st series). Multicoloured.
2542 80pf.+40pf. Type **1055** 2·10 2·10
2543 80pf.+40pf. Rugen, Mecklenburg-Vorpommern 2·10 2·10
2544 100pf.+50pf. Oberndorf, Bavaria 2·40 2·40
2545 100pf.+50pf. Schwalm, Hesse 2·40 2·40
2546 200pf.+40pf. Ernstroda, Thuringia 4·00 4·00

See also Nos. 2598/2602.

1056 St. Jadwiga (miniature, Schlackenwerther Codex)

1993. 750th Death Anniv of St. Jadwiga of Silesia.
2547 **1056** 100pf. multicoloured 2·40 85

1057 Reinhardt on Stage

1993. 50th Death Anniv of Max Reinhardt (theatrical producer).
2548 **1057** 100pf. black, brn & red 2·40 85

1058 Brandt

1993. 80th Birth Anniv of Willy Brandt (statesman).
2549 **1058** 100pf. multicoloured 3·00 1·40

1059 Monteverdi

1993. 350th Death Anniv of Claudio Monteverdi (composer).
2550 **1059** 100pf. multicoloured 2·40 85

1060 Paracelsus (after Augustin Hirschvogel)

1993. 500th Birth Anniv of Paracelsus (physician and philosopher).
2551 **1060** 100pf. ochre, brown and green 2·40 85

1061 "Adoration of the Magi"

1993. Christmas. Carvings from Altar Triptych, Blaubeuren Minster. Multicoloured.
2552 80pf.+40pf. Type **1061** 1·40 1·40
2553 100pf.+50pf. "Birth of Christ" 2·50 2·40

1062 Quayside Buildings, Town Hall and St. Cosmas's Church

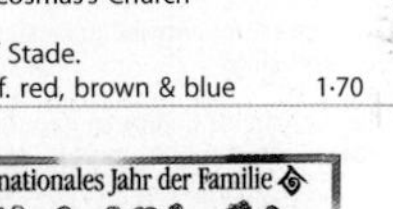

1994. Millenary of Stade.
2554 **1062** 80pf. red, brown & blue 1·70 85

1063 "FAMILIE"

1994. International Year of the Family.
2555 **1063** 100pf. multicoloured 2·10 1·10

1994. Lander of the Federal Republic. As T 989. Multicoloured.
2556 100pf. Saarland 2·00 1·10

1064 Hertz and Electromagnetic Waves

1994. Death Centenary of Heinrich Hertz (physicist).
2557 **1064** 200pf. black, red and drab 4·00 1·70

1065 Frankfurt am Main

1994. 1200th Anniv of Frankfurt am Main.
2558 **1065** 80pf. multicoloured 1·70 85

1066 Ice Skating

1994. Sport Promotion Fund. Sporting Events and Anniversaries. Multicoloured.
2559 80pf.+40pf. Type **1066** (Winter Olympic Games, Lillehammer, Norway) 2·20 2·10
2560 100pf.+50pf. Football and trophy (World Cup Football Championship, U.S.A.) 2·50 2·40
2561 100pf.+50pf. Flame (cent of International Olympic Committee) 2·50 2·40
2562 200pf.+80pf. Skier (Winter Paralympic Games, Lillehammer) 4·25 4·00

1067 Cathedral, St. Michael's Church and Castle

1994. 1250th Anniv of Fulda.
2563 **1067** 80pf. multicoloured 1·90 85

1068 Council Emblem

1994. Cent of Federation of German Women's Associations—German Women's Council.
2564 **1068** 100pf. black, red & yell 2·10 95

1069 Members' Flags as Stars

1994. 4th Direct Elections to European Parliament.
2565 **1069** 100pf. multicoloured 2·40 1·10

1070 People holding Banner

1994. "Living Together" (integration of foreign workers in Germany).
2566 **1070** 100pf. multicoloured 2·40 1·10

1994. Lander of the Federal Republic. As T 989. Multicoloured.
2567 100pf. Saxony 2·00 1·10

1071 Johnny Head-in-the-Air

1994. Youth Welfare. Death Centenary of Heinrich Hoffmann (writer). Designs illustrating characters from "Slovenly Peter". Multicoloured.
2568 80pf.+40pf. Type **1071** 2·40 2·40
2569 80pf.+40pf. Little Pauline 2·40 2·40
2570 100pf.+50pf. Naughty Friederich 2·50 2·50
2571 100pf.+50pf. Slovenly Peter 2·50 2·50
2572 200pf.+80pf. Fidget-Philipp 3·75 3·75

1072 Frauenkirche

1994. 500th Anniv of Frauenkirche, Munich.
2573 **1072** 100pf. multicoloured 2·75 1·20

1073 Resistor and Formula

1994. Europa. Discoveries. Multicoloured.
2574 80pf. Type **1073** (Ohm's Law) 1·50 70
2575 100pf. Radiation from black body and formula (Max Planck's Quantum Theory) 1·90 70

1074 Pfitzner (after Emil Orlik)

1994. 125th Birth Anniv of Hans Pfitzner (composer).
2576 **1074** 100pf. deep blue, blue and red 2·10 95

1075 Hegenbeck and Animals

1994. 150th Anniversaries. Sheet 77×108 mm containing T 1075 and similar horiz design. Multicoloured.
MS2577 100pf. Type **1075** (birth anniv of Carl Hagenbeck (circus owner and founder of first zoo without bars)); 200pf. Animals and entrance to Berlin Zoo 5·00 6·00

1076 Spandau Castle

1994. 400th Anniv of Spandau Castle.
2578 **1076** 80pf. multicoloured 1·80 85

1077 Village Sign showing Society Emblem

1994. Centenary of Herzogsagmuhle (Society for the Domestic Missions welfare village).
2579 **1077** 100pf. multicoloured 1·90 95

1994. Lander of the Federal Republic. As T 989. Multicoloured.
2580 100pf. Saxony-Anhalt 2·00 1·10

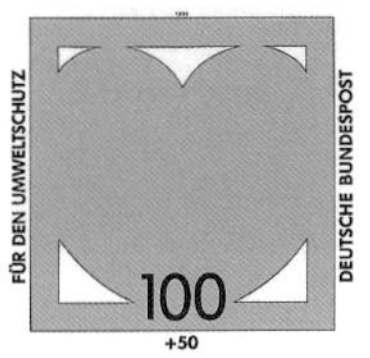

1078 Heart inside Square

1994. Environmental Protection.
2581 **1078** 100pf.+50pf. green and black 2·40 2·40

1079 Friedrich II (13th-century miniature, "Book of Falcons")

1994. 800th Birth Anniv of Emperor Friedrich II.
2582 **1079** 400pf. multicoloured 6·50 6·00

1080 "20 JULY 1944" behind Bars

1994. 50th Anniv of Attempt to Assassinate Hitler. Sheet 105×70 mm.
MS2583 **1080** 100pf. black, yellow and red 3·00 3·00

1994. Lander of the Federal Republic. As T 989. Multicoloured.
2584 100pf. Schleswig-Holstein 2·00 1·10

1994. Landscapes (2nd series). As T 1046. Multicoloured.
2585 100pf. The Alps 1·70 1·20
2586 100pf. Erzgebirge 1·70 1·20
2587 100pf. Main valley 1·70 1·20
2588 100pf. Mecklenburg lakes 1·70 1·20

1081 Herder (after Anton Graff)

1994. 250th Birth Anniv of Johann Gottfried Herder (philosopher).
2589 **1081** 80pf. multicoloured 1·50 85

1994. 20th-century German Paintings (3rd series). As T 1003. Multicoloured.
2590 100pf. "Maika" (Christian Schad) 1·40 95
2591 200pf. "Dresden Landscape" (Erich Heckel) 2·75 2·40
2592 300pf. "Aleksei Javlensky and Marianne Werefkin" (Gabriele Munter) 4·25 3·75

1082 Early 20th-century Makonde Mask (Tanzania)

1994. 125th Anniv of Leipzig Ethnology Museum.
2593 **1082** 80pf. multicoloured 1·80 85

1083 Helmholtz, Eye and Colour Triangle

1994. Death Centenary of Hermann von Helmholtz (physicist).
2594 **1083** 100pf. multicoloured 2·10 85

1084 Richter

1994. Birth Cent of Willi Richter (President of Confederation of German Trade Unions).
2595 **1084** 100pf. brown, purple and black 2·10 85

1085 "Flying on Dragon"

1994. "For Us Children". Sheet 106×61 mm.
MS2596 **1085** 100pf. multicoloured 3·00 3·00

1994. Lander of the Federal Republic. As T 989. Multicoloured.
2597 100pf. Thuringia 2·00 1·10

1994. Humanitarian Relief Funds. Traditional Costumes (2nd series). As T 1055. Multicoloured.
2598 80pf.+40pf. Buckeburg 1·80 1·80
2599 80pf.+40pf. Halle an der Saale 1·80 1·80
2600 100pf.+50pf. Minden 2·40 2·40
2601 100pf.+50pf. Hoyerswerda 2·40 2·40
2602 200pf.+70pf. Betzingen 3·75 3·75

1086 St. Wolfgang with Church Model (woodcut)

1994. Death Millenary of St. Wolfgang, Bishop of Regensburg.
2603 **1086** 100pf. gold, cream and black 1·90 95

1087 Sachs

1994. 500th Birth Anniv of Hans Sachs (mastersinger and poet).
2604 **1087** 100pf. purple and green on greyish 1·90 95

1088 Spreewald Postman, 1900

1994. Stamp Day.
2605 **1088** 100pf. multicoloured 1·90 95

1089 Quedlinburg

1994. Millenary of Quedlinburg.
2606 **1089** 80pf. multicoloured 1·50 85

1090 "Adoration of the Magi"

1994. Christmas. 500th Death Anniv of Hans Memling (painter). Details of his triptych in St. John's Hospice, Bruges. Multicoloured.
2607 80pf.+40pf. Type **1090** 2·00 1·90
2608 100pf.+50pf. "Nativity" 2·50 2·40

1091 Steuben and "Surrender of Cornwallis at Yorktown" (detail, John Trumbull)

1994. Death Bicentenary of Gen. Friedrich Wilhelm von Steuben (Inspector General of Washington's Army).
2609 **1091** 100pf. multicoloured 1·90 95

1092 Cemetery

1994. 75th Anniv of National Assn for the Preservation of German Graves Abroad.
2610 **1092** 100pf. black and red 1·90 95

1093 Obersuhl Checkpoint, 11 November 1989

1994. 5th Anniv of Opening of Borders between East and West Germany.
2611 **1093** 100pf. multicoloured 1·90 95

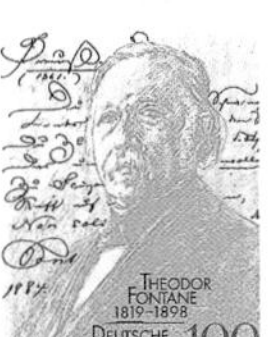

1094 Fontane (after Max Liebermann) and Lines from "Prussian Song"

1994. 175th Birth Anniv of Theodor Fontane (writer).
2612 **1094** 100pf. green, black and mauve 1·90 95

1095 Simson Fountain, Town Hall and St. Mary's and St Salvator's Churches

1995. Millenary of Gera.
2613 **1095** 80pf. multicoloured 1·80 85

1096 Emperor Friedrich III, First Page of "Libellus" and Zur Munze (venue)

1995. 500th Anniv of Diet of Worms.
2614 **1096** 100pf. black and red 1·80 95

1995. 20th-century German Paintings (4th series). As T 1003. Multicoloured.
2615 100pf. "The Water Tower, Bremen" (Franz Radziwill) 1·80 85
2616 200pf. "Still Life with Cat" (Georg Schrimpf) 2·75 2·40
2617 300pf. "Estate in Dangast" (Karl Schmidt-Rottluff) 4·00 3·50

1097 Canoeing

1995. Sport Promotion Fund. Multicoloured.
2618 80pf.+40pf. Type **1097** (27th World Canoeing Championships, Duisburg) 1·80 1·80
2619 100pf.+50pf. Hoop exercises (10th Int Gymnastics Festival, Berlin) 1·80 1·80
2620 100pf.+50pf. Boxing (8th World Amateur Boxing Championships, Berlin) 1·80 1·80
2621 200pf.+80pf. Volleyball (centenary) 3·75 3·75

1098 Friedrich Wilhelm (after A. Romandon)

1995. 375th Birth Anniv of Friedrich Wilhelm of Brandenburg, The Great Elector.
2622 **1098** 300pf. multicoloured 4·75 3·75

1099 Deed of Donation (995) and Arms of Mecklenburg-Vorpommern

1995. Millenary of Mecklenburg.
2623 **1099** 100pf. multicoloured 1·50 95

1100 Computer Image of Terminal and Lion

1995. 250th Anniv of Carolo-Wilhelmina Technical University, Braunschweig.
2624 **1100** 100pf. multicoloured 1·50 95

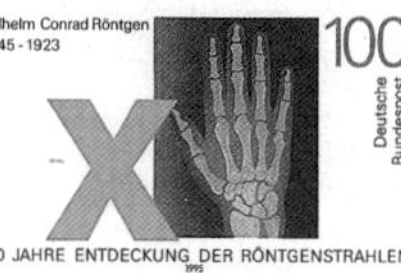

1101 X-ray of Hand

1995. 150th Birth Anniv of Wilhelm Rontgen and Centenary of his Discovery of X-rays.
2625 **1101** 100pf. multicoloured 1·50 95

1102 Globe and Rainbow

1995. 1st Conference of Signatories to General Convention on Climate, Berlin.
2626 **1102** 100pf. multicoloured 1·50 95

1103 Old Town Hall Reliefs

1995. 750th Anniv of Regensburg.
2627 **1103** 80pf. multicoloured 1·30 85

1104 Bonhoeffer

1995. 50th Death Anniv of Dietrich Bonhoeffer (theologian).

2628	**1104**	100pf. black, bl & grey	1·50	95

1105 Symbols of Speech, Writing and Pictures

1995. Freedom of Expression.

2629	**1105**	100pf. multicoloured	1·50	95

1106 St. Clement's Church, Munster

1995. 300th Birth Anniv of Johann Conrad Schlaun (architect).

2630	**1106**	200pf. multicoloured	3·00	2·50

1107 Friedrich Schiller, Signature and Schiller Museum, Marbach

1995. Centenary of German Schiller Society.

2631	**1107**	100pf. multicoloured	1·50	95

1108 St. Vincent de Paul

1995. 150th Anniv of Vincent Conferences (charitable organization) in Germany.

2632	**1108**	100pf. multicoloured	1·50	1·10

1109 Number on Cloth and Barbed Wire

1995. 50th Anniv of Liberation of Concentration Camps. Sheet 105×70 mm.

MS2633 **1109** 100pf. grey, blue and black		2·40	2·50

1110 City Ruins

1995. 50th Anniv of End of Second World War. Sheet 104×70 mm containing T 1110 and similar square design. Multicoloured.

MS2634 100pf. Type **1110**; 100pf. Refugees	4·00	4·25

1111 Returning Soldiers ("End of War")

1995. Europa. Peace and Freedom.

2635	**1111**	100pf. black and red	1·80	1·20
2636	-	200pf. blue, yell & blk	2·50	2·40

DESIGN: 200pf. Emblem of European Community ("Moving towards Europe").

1112 Shipping Routes before and after 1895

1995. Centenary of Kiel Canal.

2637	**1112**	80pf. multicoloured	1·80	85

1113 Guglielmo Marconi and Wireless Equipment

1995. 100 Years of Radio.

2638	**1113**	100pf. multicoloured	1·90	1·30

1114 U.N. Emblem

1995. 50th Anniv of U.N.O.

2639	**1114**	100pf. lilac, gold and grey	1·50	95

1115 Munsterlander

1995. Youth Welfare. Dogs (1st series). Mult.

2640	80pf.+40pf. Type **1115**	1·80	1·80
2641	80pf.+40pf. Giant schnauzer	1·80	1·80
2642	100pf.+50pf. Wire-haired dachshund	2·00	2·00
2643	100pf.+50pf. German shepherd	2·00	2·00
2644	200pf.+80pf. Keeshund	3·50	3·50

See also Nos. 2696/2700.

1116 Opening Bars of "Carmina Burana" and Characters

1995. Birth Centenary of Carl Orff (composer).

2645	**1116**	100pf. multicoloured	1·50	95

1995. Landscapes (3rd series). As T 1046. Multicoloured.

2646	100pf. Franconian Switzerland	1·40	1·20
2647	100pf. River Havel, Berlin	1·40	1·20
2648	100pf. Oberlausitz	1·40	1·20
2649	100pf. Sauerland	1·40	1·20

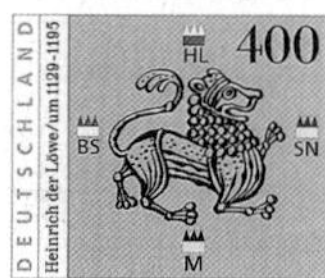

1117 Lion (from 12th-century coin)

1995. 800th Death Anniv of Henry the Lion, Duke of Saxony and Bavaria.

2650	**1117**	400pf. multicoloured	4·75	4·75

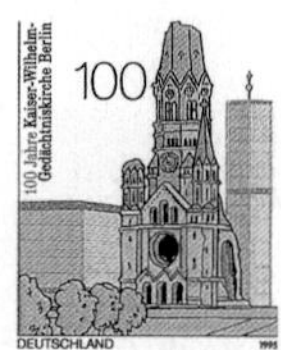

1118 Kaiser Wilhelm Memorial Church

1995. Centenary of Kaiser Wilhelm Memorial Church, Berlin.

2651	**1118**	100pf. multicoloured	1·70	95

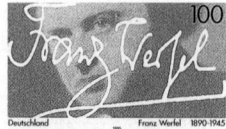

1119 Werfel and Signature

1995. 50th Death Anniv of Franz Werfel (writer).

2652	**1119**	100pf. mauve, bl & blk	1·50	95

1995. Tourist Sights. As T 854 but inscr "DEUTSCHLAND".

2654	47pf. green and black	85	70
2656	100pf. blue and black	1·20	1·20
2657	110pf. cinnamon and brown	1·30	60
2658	110pf. orange and blue	1·50	95
2659	220pf. green and black	2·40	1·20
2661	440pf. orange and blue	6·00	5·25
2663	510pf. red and blue	6·00	6·00
2665	640pf. blue and brown	8·25	4·75
2666	690pf. black and green	8·50	5·25

DESIGNS: 47pf. Berus Monument, Uberherrn; 100pf. Goethe-Schiller Monument, Weimar; 110pf. (2657) Bellevue Castle, Berlin; 110pf. (2658) Emblem of "Expo 2000" World's Fair, Hanover; 220pf. Bruhl's Terrace, Dresden; 440pf. Town Hall, Bremen; 510pf. Holsten Gate, Lubeck; 640pf. Speyer Cathedral; 690pf. St. Michael's Church, Hamburg.

1120 Strauss

1995. 80th Birth Anniv of Franz Josef Strauss (politician).

2675	**1120**	100pf. multicoloured	1·80	1·20

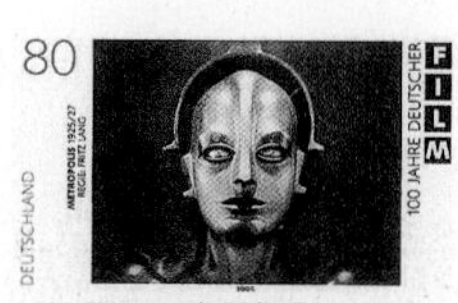

1121 Postwoman

1995. Stamp Day.

2676	**1121**	200pf.+100pf. mult	4·25	4·25

1122 "Metropolis" (dir. Fritz Lang)

1995. Centenary of Motion Pictures. Sheet 100×130 mm containing T 1122 and similar horiz designs showing frames from films. Multicoloured.

MS2677 80pf. Type **1122**; 100pf. "Little Superman" (dir. Wolfgang Staudte); 200pf. "The Sky over Berlin" (dir. Wim Wenders)	7·00	8·25

1123 Eifel

1995. Humanitarian Relief Funds. Farmhouses (1st series). Multicoloured.

2678	80pf.+40pf. Type **1123**	1·70	1·50
2679	80pf.+40pf. Saxony	1·70	1·50
2680	100pf.+50pf. Lower Germany	1·90	1·80
2681	100pf.+50pf. Upper Bavaria	1·90	1·80
2682	200pf.+70pf. Mecklenburg	3·50	3·50

See also Nos. 2742/6.

1124 Schumacher

1995. Birth Centenary of Kurt Schumacher (politician).

2683	**1124**	100pf. multicoloured	1·50	95

1125 Animals gathered on Hill

1995. "For Us Children". Sheet 110×60 mm.

MS2684 **1125** 80pf. multicoloured	4·00	4·50

1126 Ranke

1995. Birth Bicentenary of Leopold von Ranke (historian).

2685	**1126**	80pf. multicoloured	1·20	85

1127 Hindemith

1995. Birth Centenary of Paul Hindemith (composer).

2686	**1127**	100pf. multicoloured	1·50	95

1128 Alfred Nobel and Will

1995. Centenary of Nobel Prize Trust Fund.

2687	**1128**	100pf. multicoloured	1·90	1·40

1129 "CARE" in American Colours

1995. 50th Anniv of CARE (Co-operative for Assistance and Remittances Overseas).

2688	**1129**	100pf. multicoloured	1·50	95

1130 Berlin Wall

1995. Commemorating Victims of Political Oppression, 1945–89.

2689	**1130**	100pf. multicoloured	1·50	95

1131 "The Annunciation"

1995. Christmas. Stained Glass Windows in Augsburg Cathedral. Multicoloured.

2690	80pf.+40pf. Type **1131**	1·80	1·70
2691	100pf.+50pf. "Nativity"	2·40	2·40

1132 Dribbling

1995. Borussia Dortmund, German Football Champions.

2692	**1132** 100pf. multicoloured	2·10	1·20

1133 Auguste von Sartorius (founder)

1996. 150th Anniv of German Institute for Children's Missionary Work.

2693	**1133** 100pf. multicoloured	1·40	1·10

1134 Bodelschwingh

1996. 50th Death Anniv of Friedrich von Bodelschwingh (theologian).

2694	**1134** 100pf. black and red	1·40	1·10

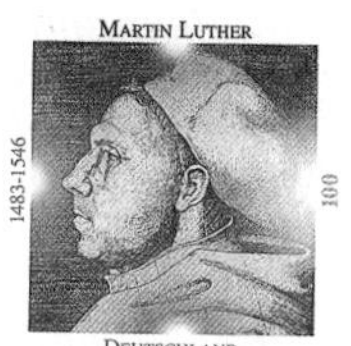

1135 Luther (after Lucas Cranach)

1996. 450th Death Anniv of Martin Luther (Protestant reformer).

2695	**1135** 100pf. multicoloured	1·50	1·30

1996. Youth Welfare. Dogs (2nd series). As T 1115. Multicoloured.

2696	80pf.+40pf. Borzoi	1·90	1·90
2697	80pf.+40pf. Chow chow	1·90	1·90
2698	100pf.+50pf. St. Bernard	2·40	2·40
2699	100pf.+50pf. Rough collie	2·40	2·40
2700	200pf.+80pf. Briard	3·50	3·50

1136 Siebold

1996. Birth Bicentenary of Philipp Franz von Siebold (physician and Japanologist).

2701	**1136** 100pf. multicoloured	1·50	1·30

1137 Cathedral Square

1996. Millenary of Cathedral Square, Halberstadt.

2702	**1137** 80pf. multicoloured	1·10	70

1138 Galen

1996. 50th Death Anniv of Cardinal Count Clemens von Galen, Bishop of Munster.

2703	**1138** 100pf. grey, blue & gold	1·40	95

1996. 20th-century German Paintings (5th series). As T 1003. Multicoloured.

2704	100pf. "Seated Female Nude" (Max Pechstein)	1·40	1·40
2705	200pf. "For Wilhelm Runge" (Georg Muche)	2·75	2·40
2706	300pf. "Still Life with Guitar, Book and Vase" (Helmut Kolle)	3·50	3·50

1139 Detail of Ceiling Fresco, Prince-bishop's Residence, Wurzburg

1996. 300th Birth Anniv of Giovanni Battista Tiepolo (artist).

2707	**1139** 200pf. multicoloured	2·50	2·20

1140 Post Runner

1996. "For Us Children". Sheet 83×67 mm.

MS2708	**1140** 100pf. multicoloured	2·10	2·40

1996. Landscapes (4th series). As T 1046. Multicoloured.

2709	100pf. Eifel	1·40	1·20
2710	100pf. Holstein Switzerland	1·40	1·20
2711	100pf. Saale	1·40	1·20
2712	100pf. Spreewald	1·40	1·20

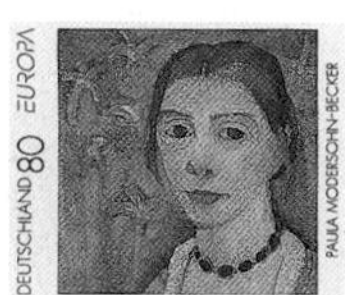

1141 Paula Modersohn-Becker (self-portrait)

1996. Europa. Famous Women.

2713	**1141** 80pf. multicoloured	1·40	60
2714	- 100pf. black, grey and mauve	1·50	1·20

DESIGN: 100pf. Kathe Kollwitz (self-portrait).

1142 Opening Lines of Document and Town (1642 engraving, Matthaeus Merian)

1996. Millenary of Granting to Freising the Right to hold Markets.

2715	**1142** 100pf. multicoloured	1·40	1·10

1143 Borchert

1996. 75th Birth Anniv of Wolfgang Borchert (writer).

2716	**1143** 100pf. multicoloured	1·40	1·10

1144 Emblem

1996. 50th Anniv of Ruhr Festival, Recklinghausen.

2717	**1144** 100pf. multicoloured	1·40	1·10

1145 Ticket and Stage Curtain

1996. 150th Anniv of German Theatre Assn.

2718	**1145** 200pf. multicoloured	2·50	1·80

1146 Leibniz and Mathematical Diagram

1996. 350th Birth Anniv of Gottfried Leibniz.

2719	**1146** 100pf. red and black	1·40	1·10

1147 Kneeling Figure and Motto forming "A"

1996. 300th Anniv of Berlin Academy of Arts.

2720	**1147** 100pf. multicoloured	1·40	1·10

1148 Carl Schuhmann (wrestling, equestrian sports and gymnastics, 1896)

1996. Sport Promotion Fund. Centenary of Modern Olympic Games. German Olympic Champions. Multicoloured.

2721	80pf.+40pf. Type **1148**	3·00	2·40
2722	100pf.+50pf. Josef Neckermann (dressage, 1964 and 1968)	3·50	2·75
2723	100pf.+50pf. Annie Hubler-Horn (ice skating, 1908)	3·50	2·75
2724	200pf.+80pf. Alfred and Gustav Flatow (gymnastics, 1896)	5·00	4·00

1149 Townscape

1996. 800th Anniv of Heidelberg.

2725	**1149** 100pf. multicoloured	1·40	1·10

1150 Children's Handprints

1996. 50th Anniv of UNICEF.

2726	**1150** 100pf. multicoloured	1·40	1·10

1151 "Wedding" (illustration by Bruno Paul)

1996. 75th Death Anniv of Ludwig Thoma (satirist).

2727	**1151** 100pf. multicoloured	1·40	1·10

1152 Beach

1996. Western Pomerania National Park. Sheet 166×111 mm containing T 1152 and similar horiz designs showing Park landscapes. Multicoloured.

MS2728	100pf. Type **1152**; 200pf. Mudflat; 300pf. Sea inlet	8·75	8·75

1153 Map and Tropical Wildlife

1996. Environmental Protection. Preservation of Tropical Habitats.

2729	**1153** 100pf.+50pf. mult	2·10	2·40

1154 Volklingen Blast Furnace

1996. UNESCO World Heritage Sites.

2730	**1154** 100pf. multicoloured	1·40	1·10

1155 Lincke

1996. 50th Death Anniv of Paul Lincke (composer and conductor).

2731	**1155** 100pf. multicoloured	1·40	1·10

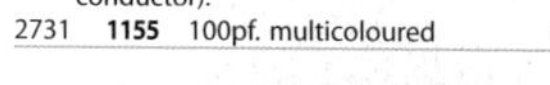

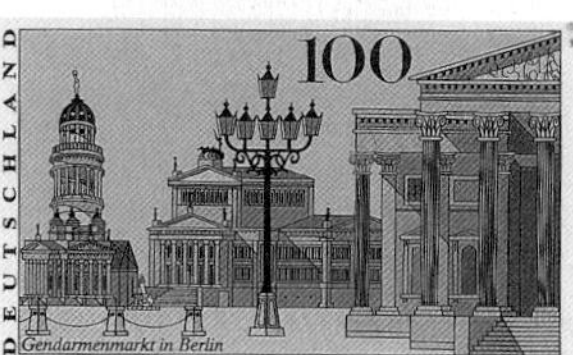

1156 Gendarmenmarkt, Berlin

1996. Images of Germany.

2732	**1156** 100pf. multicoloured	1·40	1·10

1157 "50" comprising Stamp under Magnifying Glass

1996. Stamp Day. 50th Anniv of Association of German Philatelists.

2733	**1157** 100pf. multicoloured	1·40	1·10

1158 Book

1996. Centenary of German Civil Code.
2734 **1158** 300pf. multicoloured 3·75 3·50
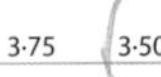

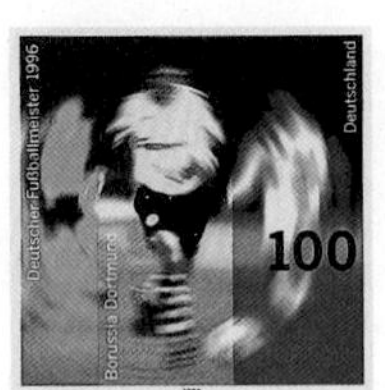

1159 Players

1996. Borussia Dortmund, German Football Champions.
2735 **1159** 100pf. multicoloured 1·40 1·10

1160 Bamburg Old Town

1996. UNESCO World Heritage Sites.
2736 **1160** 100pf. multicoloured 1·40 1·10

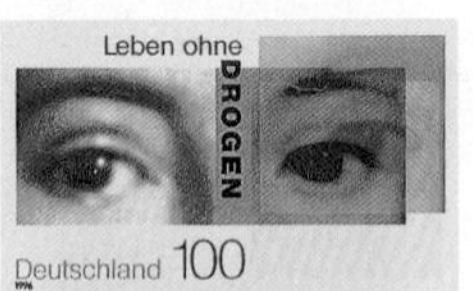

1161 Eyes

1996. "Life without Drugs".
2737 **1161** 100pf. multicoloured 1·40 1·10

1162 "Like will Cure Like" and Samuel Hahnemann (developer of principle)

1996. Bicentenary of Homeopathy.
2738 **1162** 400pf. multicoloured 4·50 4·50

1163 Bruckner and Symphony No. III

1996. Death Centenary of Anton Bruckner (composer).
2739 **1163** 100pf. multicoloured 1·40 1·10

1164 Mueller, Map and Plants

1996. Death Centenary of Ferdinand von Mueller (botanist).
2740 **1164** 100pf. multicoloured 1·40 1·10

1165 Score by John Cage

1996. 75th Anniv of Donaueschingen Music Festival.
2741 **1165** 100pf. blue, blk & mve 1·40 1·10

1996. Humanitarian Relief Funds. Farmhouses (2nd series). As T 1123. Multicoloured.
2742 80pf.+40pf. Spree Forest 1·40 1·20
2743 80pf.+40pf. Thuringia 1·40 1·20
2744 100pf.+50pf. Black Forest 1·70 1·70
2745 100pf.+50pf. Westphalia 1·70 1·70
2746 200pf.+70pf. Schleswig-Holstein 3·25 3·25

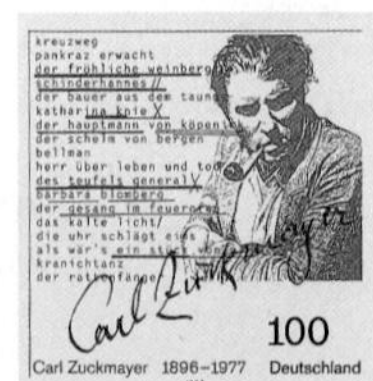

1166 Titles of Plays and Zuckmayer

1996. Birth Centenary of Carl Zuckmayer (dramatist).
2747 **1166** 100pf. multicoloured 1·40 1·10

1167 "Adoration of the Magi"

1996. Christmas. Illustrations from Henry II's "Book of Pericopes" (illuminated manuscript of readings from the Gospels). Multicoloured.
2748 80pf.+40pf. Type **1167** 1·80 1·80
2749 100pf.+50pf. "Nativity" 2·10 2·40

1168 Schmid

1996. Birth Centenary of Carlo Schmid (politician and writer).
2750 **1168** 100pf. multicoloured 1·40 1·10

1169 "Friends of Schubert in Afzenbrugg" (detail, L. Kupelwieser)

1997. Birth Bicentenary of Franz Schubert (composer).
2751 **1169** 100pf. multicoloured 1·40 1·10

1170 Pitch, Player and Herberger

1997. Birth Centenary of Sepp Herberger (national football team coach, 1936–64).
2752 **1170** 100pf. green, red & blk 1·40 1·10

1171 Motor Cars

1997. "More Safety for Children" (road safety campaign).
2752a **1171** 10pf. multicoloured 45 35
2753 **1171** 100pf. multicoloured 1·40 1·10

1172 Melanchthon (after Lucas Cranach the younger)

1997. 500th Birth Anniv of Philipp Melanchthon (religious reformer).
2754 **1172** 100pf. multicoloured 1·40 1·10

1173 Revellers "Wiggling"

1997. 175th Anniv of Cologne Carnival.
2755 **1173** 100pf. multicoloured 1·40 1·10

1174 Erhard

1997. Birth Centenary of Ludwig Erhard (Chancellor, 1963–66).
2756 **1174** 100pf. black and red 1·40 1·10

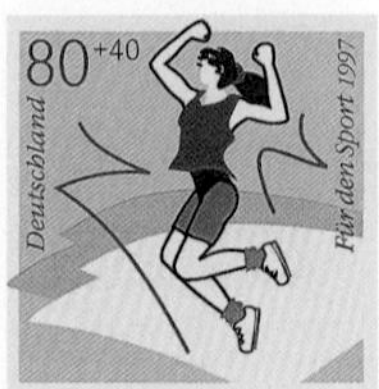

1175 Aerobics

1997. Sport Promotion Fund. Fun Sports. Multicoloured.
2757 80pf.+40pf. Type **1175** 1·70 1·90
2758 100pf.+50pf. Inline skating 1·90 2·10
2759 100pf.+50pf. Streetball 1·90 2·10
2760 200pf.+80pf. Freeclimbing 3·50 4·00

1176 New Pavilion

1997. 500th Anniv of Granting of Imperial Fair Rights to Leipzig.
2761 **1176** 100pf. silver, red & blue 1·40 1·10

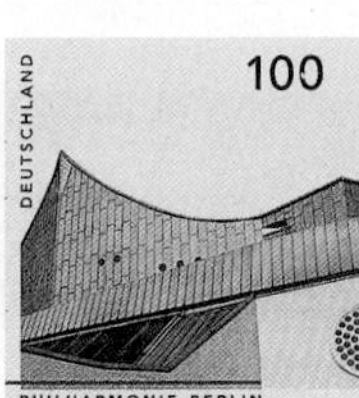

1177 Philharmonic, Berlin (Hans Scharoun)

1997. Post-1945 German Architecture. Sheet 137×101 mm containing T 1177 and similar square designs. Multicoloured.
MS2762 100pf. Type **1177**; 100pf. National Gallery, Berlin (Ludwig Miles van der Rohe); 100pf. St. Mary, Queen of Peace Pilgrimage Church, Neviges (Gottfried Bohm); 100pf. German Pavilion, 1967 World's Trade Fair, Montreal (Frei Otto) 6·00 6·25

1178 Straubing

1997. 1100th Anniv of Straubing.
2763 **1178** 100pf. multicoloured 1·40 1·10

1179 Stephan, Telephone and Postcards

1997. Death Centenary of Heinrich von Stephan (founder of U.P.U.).
2764 **1179** 100pf. multicoloured 1·40 1·10

1180 Augustusburg and Falkenlust Castles

1997. UNESCO World Heritage Sites.
2765 **1180** 100pf. multicoloured 1·40 1·10

1181 Diamonds

1997. 500th Anniv of Idar-Oberstein Region Gem Industry.
2766 **1181** 300pf. multicoloured 4·25 3·50

1182 St. Adalbert

1997. Death Millenary of St. Adalbert (Bishop of Prague).
2767 **1182** 100pf. lilac 1·40 1·10

1183 "The Fisherman and His Wife" (Brothers Grimm)

1997. Europa. Tales and Legends. Mult.
2768 80pf. Type **1183** 1·40 95
2769 100pf. "Rubezahl" 1·70 1·20

1184 Knotted Ribbons

1997. 50th Anniv of Town Twinning Movement.

2770 **1184** 100pf. multicoloured 1·40 1·10

1185 Deciduous Trees

1997. 50th Anniv of Society for the Protection of the German Forest. Sheet 105×70 mm containing T 1185 and similar square design. Multicoloured.

MS2771 100pf. Type **1185**; 200pf. Evergreen trees 4·75 4·75

1186 Kneipp

1997. Death Cent of Father Sebastian Kneipp (developer of naturopathic treatments).

2772 **1186** 100pf. multicoloured 1·40 1·10

1187 United States Flag, George Marshall and Bomb Site

1997. 50th Anniv of Marshall Plan (European Recovery Program).

2773 **1187** 100pf. multicoloured 1·40 1·10

1188 Rheno-German Heavy Horse

1997. Youth Welfare. Horses. Multicoloured.

2774 80pf.+40pf. Type **1188** 1·50 1·50
2775 80pf.+40pf. Shetland ponies 1·50 1·50
2776 100pf.+50pf. Frisian 1·80 1·80
2777 100pf.+50pf. Haflinger 1·80 1·80
2778 200pf.+80pf. Hanoverian with foal 3·75 3·75

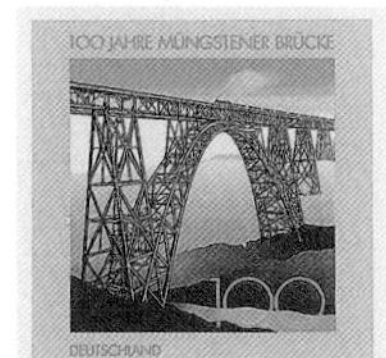

1189 Train on Bridge

1997. Centenary of Mungsten Railway Bridge.

2779 **1189** 100pf. multicoloured 1·40 1·10

1190 "Composition" (Fritz Winter)

1997. 10th "Documenta" Modern Art Exhibition, Kassel. Sheet 137×97 mm containing T 1190 and similar horiz designs. Multicoloured.

MS2780 100pf. Type **1190**; 100pf. "Mouth No. 15" (Tom Wesselmann); 100pf. "Quathlamba" (Frank Stella); 100pf. "Beuys/Bois" (Nam June Paik) 6·50 6·50

1191 Children holding Envelopes

1997. "For Us Children". Sheet 70×105 mm.

MS2781 **1191** 100pf. multicoloured 2·40 2·40

1997. Famous Women. As T 832 but inscr "Deutschland".

2785 100pf. brown and green 1·50 1·00
2786 110pf. drab and violet 1·50 1·00
2790 220pf. ultramarine and blue 3·00 2·75
2792 300pf. brown and blue 3·50 3·00
2795 440pf. brown and violet 6·25 6·00

DESIGNS: 100pf. Elisabeth Schwarzhaupt (politician); 110pf. Marlene Dietrich (actress); 220pf. Marie-Elisabeth Luders (politician); 300pf. Maria Probst (social reformer and politician); 440pf. Gret Palucca (dancer).

1192 Arms of Brandenburg

1997. Flood Relief Funds.

2805 **1192** 110pf.+90pf. mult 2·75 2·75

1997. Landscapes (5th series). As T 1046. Multicoloured.

2806 110pf. Bavarian Forest 1·50 1·40
2807 110pf. North German Moors 1·50 1·40
2808 110pf. Luneburg Heath 1·50 1·40

1193 Rudolf Diesel and First Oil Engine

1997. Centenary of Diesel Engine.

2809 **1193** 300pf. black and blue 4·00 3·50

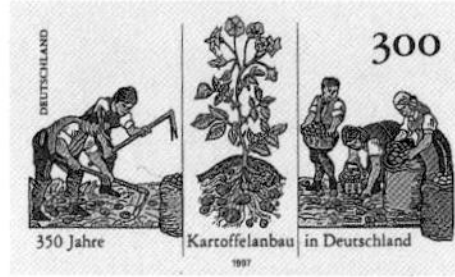

1194 Potato Plant and Cultivation

1997. 350th Anniv of Introduction of the Potato to Germany.

2810 **1194** 300pf. multicoloured 4·00 3·50

1195 Biplane and Motorized Tricycle

1997. Stamp Day. Sheet 70×105 mm.

MS2811 **1195** 440pf.+220pf. multi-coloured 8·25 8·50

1196 Mendelssohn-Bartholdy and Music Score

1997. 150th Death Anniv of Felix Mendelssohn-Bartholdy (composer).

2813 **1196** 110pf. green, olive & yell 1·50 1·20

1197 Watermill, Black Forest

1997. Humanitarian Relief Funds. Mills. Multicoloured.

2814 100pf.+50pf. Type **1197** 2·75 2·75
2815 110pf.+50pf. Watermill, Hesse 3·00 3·00
2816 110pf.+50pf. Post mill, Lower Rhine 3·00 3·00
2817 110pf.+50pf. Scoop windmill, Schleswig-Holstein 3·00 3·00
2818 220pf.+80pf. Dutch windmill 4·75 4·75

1198 Emblem

1997. Saar–Lor–Lux European Region.

2819 **1198** 110pf. multicoloured 1·70 1·20

1199 Team celebrating

1997. Bayern Munchen, German Football Champions.

2820 **1199** 110pf. multicoloured 1·70 1·20

1200 Dehler

1997. Birth Centenary of Thomas Dehler (politician).

2821 **1200** 110pf. multicoloured 1·40 1·20

1201 Heine (after Wilhelm Hensel)

1997. Birth Bicentenary of Heinrich Heine (journalist and poet).

2822 **1201** 110pf. multicoloured 1·40 1·20

1202 Tree and Title of Hymn

1997. 300th Birth Anniv of Gerhard Tersteegen (religious reformer).

2823 **1202** 110pf. brown, grey and black 1·40 1·20

1203 Emblem

1997. Cent of Deutscher Caritas Verband (Catholic charitable association).

2824 **1203** 110pf. multicoloured 1·40 1·20

1204 Three Kings

1997. Christmas. Multicoloured.

2825 100pf.+50pf. Type **1204** 1·90 1·80
2826 110pf.+50pf. Nativity 2·20 2·20

The premium was for the benefit of the Federal Association of Free Welfare Work, Bonn.

1205 Monastery Plan and Church

1998. UNESCO World Heritage Site. Maulbronn Monastery.

2827 **1205** 100pf. multicoloured 1·40 1·20

1206 Walled City

1998. 1100th Anniv of Nordlingen.

2828 **1206** 110pf. multicoloured 1·40 1·20

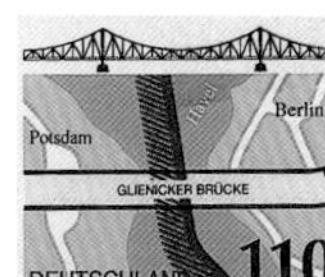

1207 Glienicke Bridge, Potsdam–Berlin

1998. Bridges. (1st series).

2829 **1207** 110pf. multicoloured 1·40 1·20

See also Nos. 2931, 2956 and 3046.

1208 Football

1998. Sport Promotion Fund. International Championships. Multicoloured.

2830 100pf.+50pf. Type **1208** (World Cup Football Championship, France) 2·40 2·40
2831 110pf.+50pf. Ski jumping (Winter Olympic Games, Nagano, Japan) 2·75 2·75
2832 110pf.+50pf. Rowing (World Rowing Championships, Cologne) 2·75 2·75
2833 300pf.+100pf. Disabled skier (Winter Paralympic Games, Nagano) 6·00 6·00

1209 Characters in Brecht's Head

1998. Birth Centenary of Bertolt Brecht (dramatist).

2834	**1209**	110pf. multicoloured	1·40	1·20

1210 X-ray Photographs of Moon, Ionic Lattice Structure and Nerve of Goldfish and Founding Assembly

1998. 50th Anniv of Max Planck Society for the Advancement of Science.

2835	**1210**	110pf. multicoloured	1·40	1·20

1211 Bad Frankenhausen

1998. Millenary of First Documentary Mention of Bad Frankenhausen.

2836	**1211**	110pf. multicoloured	1·40	1·20

1212 Signatories

1998. 350th Anniv of Peace of Westphalia (settlements ending Thirty Years' War).

2837	**1212**	110pf. blk, grey & mve	1·70	1·20

1213 Baden-Wurttemberg (Kurt Viertel)

1998. Federal State Parliament Buildings (1st series). Multicoloured.

2838	110pf. Type **1213**	1·50	1·20
2839	110pf. Bavaria (designed Friedrich Burklein)	1·50	1·20
2840	110pf. Chamber of Deputies, Berlin (Friedrich Schulze)	1·50	1·20
2841	110pf. Brandenburg (Franz Schwechten)	1·50	1·20

See also Nos. 2885, 2893/4, 2897, 2953, 2957, 2978, 3025, 3043, 3052, 3064 and 3071.

1214 Hildegard's Vision of Life Cycle

1998. 900th Birth Anniv of Hildegard of Bingen (writer and mystic).

2842	**1214**	100pf. multicoloured	1·40	1·20

1215 Marine Life

1998. "For Us Children". Sheet 110×66 mm.

MS2843 **1215** 110pf. multicoloured 2·40 2·40

1216 St. Marienstern Abbey

1998. 750th Anniv of St. Marienstern Abbey, Panschwitz-Kuckau.

2844	**1216**	110pf. multicoloured	1·40	1·20

1217 Auditorium (image scaled to 74% of original size)

1998. 250th Anniv of Bayreuth Opera House.

2845	**1217**	300pf. multicoloured	3·75	3·50

1218 Junger

1998. Ernst Junger (writer) Commemoration.

2846	**1218**	110pf. multicoloured	1·40	1·20

1219 Doves and Tree (German Unification Day)

1998. Europa. National Festivals.

2847	**1219**	110pf. multicoloured	1·80	1·20

1220 Association Manifesto

1998. 50th Anniv of German Rural Women's Association.

2848	**1220**	110pf. grn, emer & blk	1·40	1·20

1221 Opening Session of Parliamentary Council, 1948

1998. Parliamentary Anniversaries. Sheet 105×70 mm containing T 1221 and similar square design. Multicoloured.

MS2849 110pf. Type **1221**; 220pf. First German National Assembly, St. Paul's Church, Frankfurt, 1848 4·75 4·75

1222 Coast and Ocean

1998. Environmental Protection.

2850	**1222**	110pf.+50pf. mult	2·40	2·50

1223 "The Mouse"

1998. Youth Welfare. Children's Cartoons. Multicoloured.

2851	100pf.+50pf. Type **1223**	1·90	1·90
2852	100pf.+50pf. "The Sandman"	1·90	1·90
2853	110pf.+50pf. "Maja the Bee"	2·10	2·10
2854	110pf.+50pf. "Captain Bluebear"	2·10	2·10
2855	220pf.+80pf. "Pumuckl"	3·75	3·75

1224 Crowds of People and Cross

1998. 150th Anniv of First Congress of German Catholics.

2856	**1224**	110pf. multicoloured	1·40	1·10

1225 One Deutschmark Coin

1998. 50th Anniv of the Deutschmark.

2857	**1225**	110pf. multicoloured	2·10	1·40

1226 Harvesting Hops

1998. 1100 Years of Hop Cultivation in Germany.

2858	**1226**	110pf. multicoloured	1·40	1·20

1227 Euro Banknotes forming "EZB"

1998. Inauguration of European Central Bank, Frankfurt am Main.

2859	**1227**	110pf. multicoloured	1·40	1·20

1228 Rock Face, Elbe Sandstone Mountains

1998. Saxon Switzerland National Park. Sheet 105×70 mm containing T 1228 and similar square design. Multicoloured.

MS2860 110pf. Type **1228**; 220pf. Elbe Sandstone Mountains 4·75 4·75

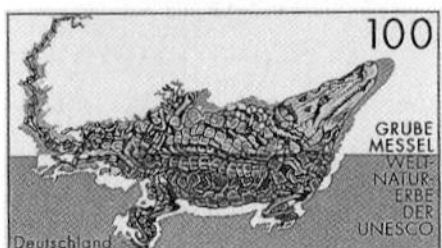

1229 Skeleton of Crocodile

1998. UNESCO World Heritage Sites. Grube Messel Fossil Deposits.

2861	**1229**	100pf. multicoloured	1·40	1·10

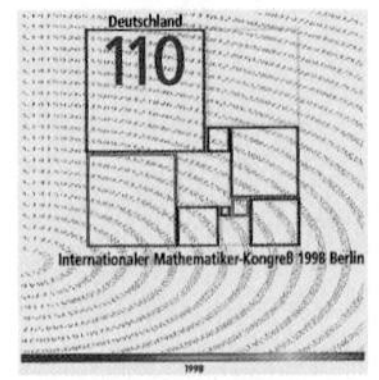

1230 Coloured Squares and Ludolphian Number

1998. 23rd International Congress of Mathematicians, Berlin.

2862	**1230**	110pf. multicoloured	1·40	1·20

1231 Wurzburg Palace

1998. UNESCO World Heritage Sites. Multicoloured.

2863	110pf. Type **1231**	1·50	1·10
2864	110pf. Puning Temple, Chengde, China	1·50	1·10

1232 Glasses (Peter Behrens)

1998. Contemporary Design (1st series). Sheet 138×97 mm containing T 1232 and similar horiz designs. Multicoloured.

MS2865 110pf. Type **1232**; 110pf. Tea-pot (Marianne Brandt); 110pf. Table lamp (Wilhelm Wagenfeld); 110pf. "Wassily" chair (Marcel Breuer) 6·50 6·50

See also No. **MS**2922.

1233 Players, Ball and Pitch

1998. 1st FC Kaiserslautern, National Football Champions, 1998.

2866	**1233**	110pf. multicoloured	1·70	1·20

1234 Main Building

1998. 300th Anniv of Francke Charitable Institutions, Halle.

2867	**1234**	110pf. multicoloured	1·40	1·20

1235 Hausmann and Book Cover

1998. Birth Centenary of Manfred Hausmann (writer).
2868 **1235** 100pf. multicoloured 1·40 1·20

1236 Hands on T-shirt

1998. Child Protection.
2869 **1236** 110pf. red and black 1·40 1·20

1237 Hen Harriers and Chicks

1998. Humanitarian Relief Funds. Birds. Multicoloured.
2870 100pf.+50pf. Type **1237** 1·90 1·90
2871 110pf.+50pf. Great bustards 2·10 2·10
2872 110pf.+50pf. Ferruginous ducks 2·10 2·10
2873 110pf.+50pf. Aquatic warblers on reeds 2·10 2·10
2874 220pf.+80pf. Woodchat shrike 3·50 3·50

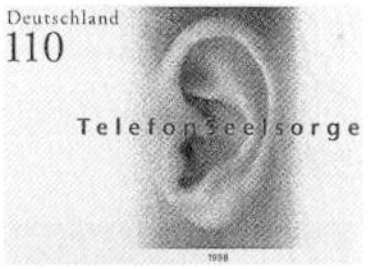

1238 Ear

1998. Telephone Help Lines.
2875 **1238** 110pf. black and orange 1·40 1·20

1239 "Hiorten" (sailing packet), 1692

1998. Stamp Day.
2876 **1239** 110pf. multicoloured 1·40 1·20

1240 Ramin

1998. Birth Centenary of Gunther Ramin (choir leader and organist).
2877 **1240** 300pf. multicoloured 3·75 3·50

1241 Shepherds following Star

1998. Christmas. Multicoloured.
2878 100pf.+50pf. Type **1241** 1·90 1·80
2879 110pf.+50pf. Baby Jesus 2·00 1·80

1242 Dove

1998. 50th Anniv of Declaration of Human Rights.
2880 **1242** 110pf. multicoloured 1·40 1·20

For charity stamp for Kosovo Relief Fund in similar design see No. 2899.

1243 Conductor's Hands and Baton

1998. 450th Anniv of Saxony State Orchestra, Dresden.
2881 **1243** 300pf. multicoloured 4·00 3·50

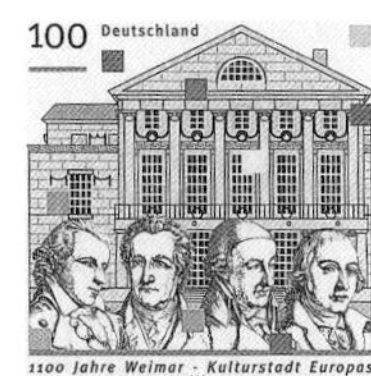

1244 National Theatre, Schiller, Goethe, Wieland and Herder

1999. 1100th Anniv of Weimar, European City of Culture.
2882 **1244** 100pf. multicoloured 1·40 1·30

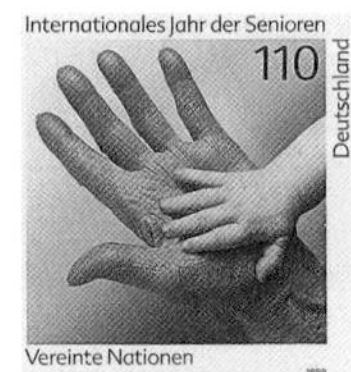

1245 Hands of Elderly Person and Child

1999. International Year of the Elderly.
2883 **1245** 110pf. multicoloured 1·50 1·30

1246 Katharina von Bora

1999. 500th Birth Anniv of Katharina von Bora (wife of Martin Luther).
2884 **1246** 110pf. multicoloured 1·50 1·30

1999. Federal State Parliament Buildings (2nd series). As T 1213.
2885 110pf. Hesse (Richard Goerz) (former palace of Dukes of Hesse) 1·50 1·30

1247 Cycle Racing

1999. Sport Promotion Fund. Multicoloured.
2886 100pf.+50pf. Type **1247** 2·20 2·20
2887 110pf.+50pf. Horse racing 2·40 2·40
2888 110pf.+50pf. Motor racing 2·40 2·40
2889 300pf.+100pf. Motor cycle racing 4·75 4·75

1248 Cover Illustration (by Walter Trier) of "Emil and the Detectives" (novel)

1999. Birth Centenary of Erich Kastner (writer).
2890 **1248** 300pf. multicoloured 3·75 3·50

1249 Coloured Diodes

1999. 50th Anniv of Fraunhofer Society (for applied research).
2891 **1249** 110pf. multicoloured 1·50 1·30

1250 Emblem and Initials

1999. 50th Anniv of North Atlantic Treaty Organization.
2892 **1250** 110pf. multicoloured 1·50 1·30

1999. Federal State Parliament Buildings (3rd series). As T 1213. Multicoloured.
2893 110pf. City Parliament of Hamburg 1·50 1·30
2894 110pf. Mecklenburg-Western Pomerania (Schwerin Castle, rebuilt by Georg Demmler and Friedrich Stuler) 1·50 1·30

1251 Maybach Cabriolet of 1936 and Club Emblem

1999. Centenary of German Automobile Club.
2895 **1251** 110pf. multicoloured 1·50 1·30

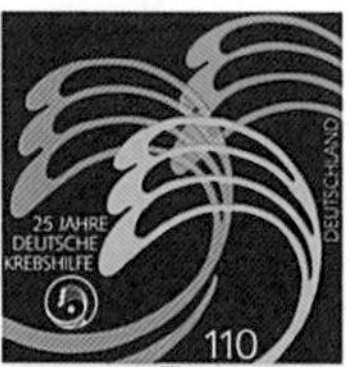

1252 Emblem

1999. 25th Anniv of German Cancer Relief.
2896 **1252** 110pf. multicoloured 1·50 1·30

1999. Federal State Parliament Buildings (4th series). As T 1213.
2897 110pf. Bremen (Wassili Luckhardt) 1·50 1·30

1253 "Man, Nature, Technology"

1999. "EXPO 2000" World's Fair, Hanover (1st issue).
2898 **1253** 110pf. multicoloured 1·50 1·30

See also Nos. 2936, 2959 and 2979.

1999. Kosovo Relief Fund. As T 1242 but with inscription changed to "KOSOVO–HILFE 1999".
2899 110pf.+100pf. multicoloured 3·00 3·00

1254 Bavaria 1849 1k. and Saxony 1850 3pf. Stamps

1999. "iBRA'99" International Stamp Exhibition, Nuremberg. Sheet 140×100 mm.
MS2900 **1254** 300pf.+110pf. black, red and gold/cream 6·00 6·00

1255 Berchtesgaden National Park

1999. Europa. Parks and Gardens. Sheet 110×66 mm.
MS2901 **1255** 110pf. multicoloured 3·25 3·25

1256 Cross of St. John

1999. 900th Anniv of Order of Knights of St. John of Jerusalem.
2902 **1256** 110pf. multicoloured 1·50 1·30

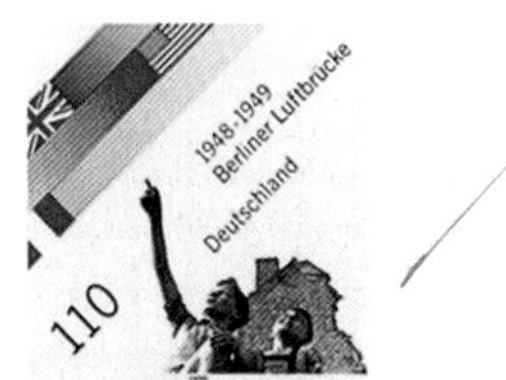

1257 Flags and Children

1999. 50th Anniv of Berlin Airlift of 1948–49.
2903 **1257** 110pf. multicoloured 1·50 1·30

1258 Emblem

1999. 50th Anniv of Council of Europe.
2904 **1258** 110pf. multicoloured 1·70 1·30

1259 State Arms and Article 1

1999. 50th Anniv of German Basic Law. Sheet 110×66 mm.
MS2905 **1259** 110pf. multicoloured 2·40 3·00

1260 Politicians and New Parliament Chamber, Berlin

1999. 50th Anniv of Federal Republic of Germany. Sheet 138×97 mm containing T 1260 and similar horiz designs. Multicoloured.

MS2906	110pf. Type **1260**; 110pf. Child playing in rubble and child among flowers; 110pf. Berlin Wall and its fall; 110pf. Soldiers confronting civilians and debating chamber	6·00	6·50

1261 Lars, the Little Polar Bear

1999. Youth Welfare. Cartoon Characters. Mult.

2907	100pf.+50pf. Type **1261**	2·10	2·10
2908	100pf.+50pf. Rudi the Crow	2·10	2·10
2909	110pf.+50pf. Twipsy (mascot of "Expo 2000" World's Fair, Hanover)	2·40	2·40
2910	110pf.+50pf. Mecki (hedgehog)	2·40	2·40
2911	220pf.+80pf. Tabaluga (dragon)	3·50	3·50

1262 Cross Clasp, Altar, Cathedral Spire and Time-line

1999. 1200th Anniv of Paderborn Diocese.

2912	**1262**	110pf. multicoloured	1·50	1·20

1263 House (child's painting)

1999. 50th Anniv of S.O.S. Children's Villages.

2913	**1263**	110pf. multicoloured	1·50	1·20

1264 "Ball at the Viennese Hofburg" and Score

1999. Death Centenary of Johann Strauss the younger (composer).

2914	**1264**	300pf. multicoloured	4·00	3·50

1265 Children at Desks (tapestry)

1999. 115th Anniv of Dominikus-Ringeisen Institute for Disabled People, Ursberg.

2915	**1265**	110pf. multicoloured	1·50	1·20

1266 Heinemann

1999. Birth Centenary of Gustav Heinemann (President 1969–74).

2916	**1266**	110pf. grey and red	1·50	1·20

1267 "Old Woman laughing" (Ernst Barlach)

1999. Cultural Foundation of the Federal States (1st series). Sculptures. Multicoloured.

2917	110pf. Type **1267**	1·50	1·20
2918	220pf. "Bust of a Thinker" (Wilhelm Lehmbruck)	2·50	2·40

See also Nos. 2960/1.

1268 Participating Countries and Dove

1999. Centenary of First Peace Conference, The Hague.

2919	**1268**	300pf. grey, red and blue	3·75	3·25

1269 Goethe (after J. K. Stieler)

1999. 250th Birth Anniv of Johann Wolfgang von Goethe (poet and playwright).

2920	**1269**	110pf. multicoloured	1·50	1·30

1270 Mouse carrying Letter

1999. "For Us Children". Sheet 105×71 mm.

MS2921	**1270**	110pf. multicoloured	2·40	2·75

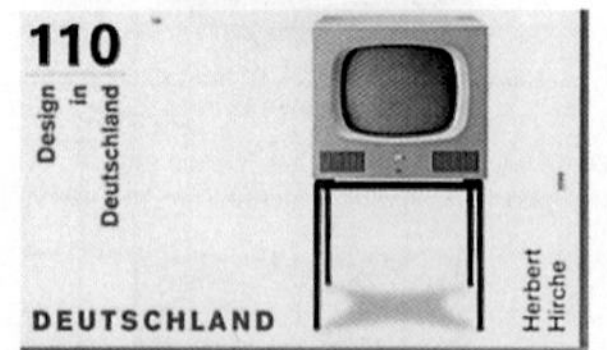

1271 HF1 Television Set (Herbert Hirche)

1999. Contemporary Design (2nd series). Sheet 138×97 mm containing T 1271 and similar horiz designs. Multicoloured.

MS2922	110pf. Type **1271**; 110pf. "Mono-a" cutlery (Peter Raacke); 110pf. Pearl bottles (Gunter Kupetz); 110pf. Transrapid Maglev train (Alexander Neumeister)	6·00	6·50

1272 Player

1999. FC Bayern Munich, National Football Champions.

2923	**1272**	110pf. multicoloured	1·50	1·30

1273 Book and Bookmark

1999. 50th Anniv of Federal Association of German Book Traders' Peace Prize.

2924	**1273**	110pf. multicoloured	1·50	1·30

1274 Strauss and Poster from "Salome" (opera)

1999. 50th Death Anniv of Richard Strauss (composer).

2925	**1274**	300pf. multicoloured	4·00	3·75

1275 Andromeda Galaxy

1999. Humanitarian Relief Funds. Outer Space. Multicoloured.

2926	100pf.+50pf. Type **1275**	1·90	1·90
2927	100pf.+50pf. Swan constellation	1·90	1·90
2928	110pf.+50pf. X-ray image of exploding star	2·10	2·10
2929	110pf.+50pf. Comet colliding with Jupiter	2·10	2·10
2930	300pf.+100pf. Gamma ray image of sky	5·00	5·00

1276 Goltzsch Valley Railway Bridge

1999. Bridges (2nd series).

2931	**1276**	110pf. multicoloured	1·50	1·30

1277 "DGB"

1999. 50th Anniv of German Federation of Trade Unions.

2932	**1277**	110pf. black and bright red	1·50	1·30

1278 Greater Horseshoe Bats

1999. Endangered Species.

2933	**1278**	100pf. multicoloured	1·40	1·30

1279 The Annunciation

1999. Christmas. Multicoloured.

2934	100pf.+50pf. Type **1279**	1·90	1·80
2935	110pf.+50pf. Nativity	2·00	1·90

1280 Emblem and Eye

2000. "EXPO 2000" World's Fair, Hanover (2nd issue).

2936	**1280**	100pf. multicoloured	1·40	1·30

1281 Emblem

2000. Holy Year 2000.

2937	**1281**	110pf. multicoloured	1·50	1·30

1282 Charlemagne and Plan of Palace Chapel

2000. 1200th Anniv of Aachen Cathedral.

2938	**1282**	110pf. multicoloured	1·50	1·30

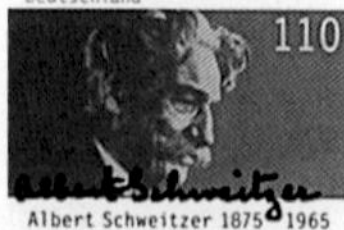

1283 Schweitzer and Signature

2000. 125th Birth Anniv of Albert Schweitzer (missionary doctor).

2939	**1283**	110pf. multicoloured	1·80	1·30

1284 Football

2000. Centenary of German Football Association.

2940	**1284**	110pf. multicoloured	1·70	1·30

1285 Wehner

2000. 10th Death Anniv of Herbert Wehner (politician).

2941	**1285**	110pf. multicoloured	1·50	1·30

1286 Woman

2000. Prevention of Violence Against Women.

2942	**1286**	110pf. red, grey and black	1·50	1·30

1287 "2000" in Moving Film Sequence

2000. 50th Berlin International Film Festival.

2943	**1287**	100pf. multicoloured	1·40	1·30

1288 Boxing

2000. Sport Promotion Fund. Multicoloured.
2944 100pf.+50pf. Type **1288** (fair play) 1·90 1·90
2945 110pf.+50pf. Rhythmic gymnastics (beauty) 2·10 2·10
2946 110pf.+50pf. Running (competition) 2·10 2·10
2947 300pf.+100pf. Raised hands (culture of interaction) 4·75 4·75

1289 Gutenberg (after engraving by A. Thevet) and Letters from Gutenberg Bible

2000. 600th Birth Anniv of Johannes Gutenberg (inventor of printing press).
2948 **1289** 110pf. black and red 1·50 1·30

1290 Jester

2000. 175th Anniv of First Dusseldorf Carnival.
2949 **1290** 110pf. multicoloured 1·70 1·30

1291 Ebert

2000. 75th Death Anniv of Friedrich Ebert (President, 1919–25).
2950 **1291** 110pf. multicoloured 1·50 1·30

1292 Weill at Rehearsal of "One Touch of Venus" (musical), 1943

2000. Birth Centenary of Kurt Weill (composer).
2951 **1292** 300pf. blk, stone & red 4·00 3·75

1293 Passau

2000. Images of Germany.
2952 **1293** 110pf. multicoloured 1·50 1·30

2000. Federal State Parliament Buildings (5th series). As T 1213. Multicoloured.
2953 110pf. Leine Palace, Lower Saxony 1·50 1·30

1294 Trees

2000. Hainich National Park. Sheet 105×70 mm.
MS2954 **1294** 110pf. multicoloured 2·50 2·50

1295 Toy Windmill and "Post!"

2000
2955 **1295** 110pf. multicoloured 1·80 1·70

1296 "Blue Wonder" Bridge, Dresden

2000. Bridges (3rd series).
2956 **1296** 100pf. multicoloured 1·40 1·20

2000. Federal State Parliament Buildings (6th series). As T 1213. Multicoloured.
2957 110pf. North-Rhine/Westphalia (Fritz Eller) 1·80 1·30

1297 City Buildings

2000. 750th Anniv of Greifswald.
2958 **1297** 110pf. multicoloured 1·50 1·30

2000. "EXPO 2000" World's Fair, Hanover (3rd issue). As No. 2898 but self-adhesive.
2959 **1253** 110pf. multicoloured 6·50 6·00

1298 "Expulsion from Paradise" (Leonhard Kern)

2000. Cultural Foundation of the Federal States. Sculptures. Multicoloured.
2960 110pf. Type **1298** 2·10 1·70
2961 220pf. Silver table fountain (Melchior Gelb) 2·50 2·40

1299 "Building Europe"

2000. Europa. Ordinary or self-adhesive gum.
2962 **1299** 110pf. multicoloured 2·00 1·40

1300 Von Zinzendorf and Natives

2000. 300th Birth Anniv of Nikolaus Ludwig von Zinzendorf (leader of Moravian Brethren).
2964 **1300** 110pf. multicoloured 1·70 1·20

1301 Countryside

2000. Environmental Protection.
2965 **1301** 110pf.+50pf. mult 2·40 2·40

1302 Crowd at Music Festival

2000. Youth Welfare. "EXPO 2000" World's Fair, Hanover (4th issue). Multicoloured.
2966 100pf.+50pf. Type **1302** 2·00 2·00
2967 100pf.+50pf. Back-packers 2·00 2·00
2968 110pf.+50pf. Map of Africa and text 2·10 2·10
2969 110pf.+50pf. Eye of Buddha 2·10 2·10
2970 110pf.+50pf. Chinese calligraphy 2·10 2·10
2971 300pf.+100pf. Psychedelic swirl 4·75 4·75

1303 Front Page of Issue 17, 1650, and Modern Pages of Newspaper

2000. 350th Anniv of Einkommende Zeitungen (first German daily newspaper).
2972 **1303** 110pf. multicoloured 1·70 1·30

1304 Emblem

2000. Centenary of Chambers of Handicrafts.
2973 **1304** 300pf. orange and black 3·75 3·50

1305 Meteorological Station

2000. Centenary of the Zugspitze Meteorological Station.
2974 **1305** 100pf. multicoloured 1·80 1·30

1306 Road Sign and Flashing Light

2000. 50th Anniv of Technisches Hilfwerk (Federal disaster relief organization).
2975 **1306** 110pf. multicoloured 1·80 1·30

1307 Bach

2000. 250th Death Anniv of Johann Sebastian Bach (composer).
2976 **1307** 110pf. multicoloured 1·80 1·30

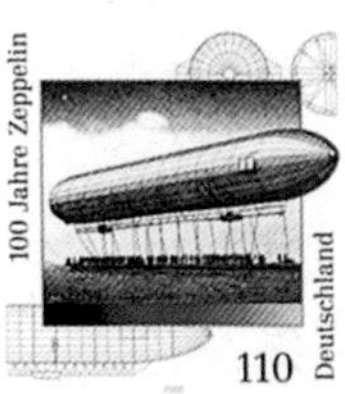

1308 LZ-1

2000. Centenary of Inaugural Flight of LZ-1 (Zeppelin airship), 1900.
2977 **1308** 110pf. multicoloured 1·70 1·30

2000. Federal State Parliament Buildings (7th series). As T 1213. Multicoloured.
2978 110pf. Rhineland-Palatinate, Mainz 1·70 1·30

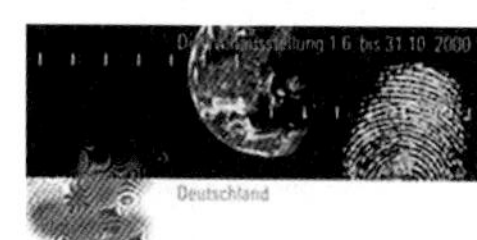

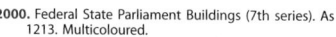

1309 Emblem, Globe and Fingerprint

2000. "EXPO 2000" World's Fair, Hanover (5th issue).
2979 **1309** 110pf. multicoloured 1·70 1·30

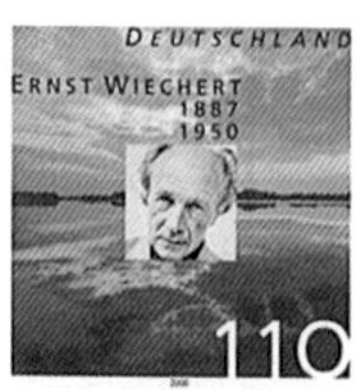

1310 Wiechert

2000. 50th Death Anniv of Ernst Wiechert (writer).
2980 **1310** 110pf. multicoloured 1·70 1·30

1311 Nietzsche (Edvard Munch)

2000. Death Centenary of Friedrich Nietzsche (philosopher).
2981 **1311** 110pf. multicoloured 1·70 1·30

1312 "For You"

2000. Greetings Stamp.
2982 **1312** 100pf. multicoloured 1·40 1·30

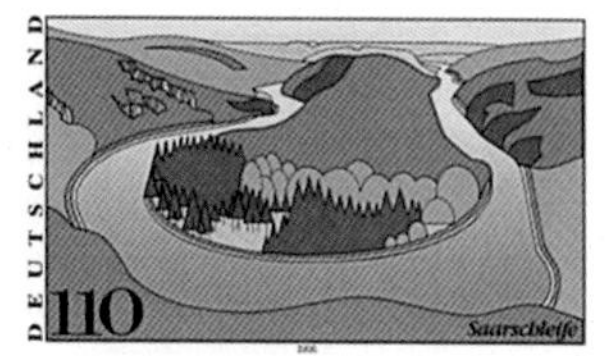

1313 Saar River, Mettlach

2000. Images of Germany.
2983 **1313** 110pf. multicoloured 1·50 1·30

1314 Adolph Kopling

2000. 150th Anniv of Kopling Society (voluntary organization).
2984 **1314** 110pf. multicoloured 1·50 1·30

1315 Building

2000. 50th Anniv of Federal Court of Justice.
2985 **1315** 110pf. multicoloured 1·40 1·30

1316 Clown's Face

2000. "For Us Children". Sheet 55×82 mm.

MS2986	**1316**	110pf. multicoloured	2·40	2·40

1317 Nocht (founder), World Map and Microscope Images of Pathogens

2000. Centenary of Bernard Nocht Institute for Tropical Medicine.

2987	**1317**	300pf. multicoloured	4·50	4·25

1318 Town Hall, Wernigerode

2000. Tourist Sights. Showing face values in German currency and euros.

2988	**1318**	10pf. grey, orge & slate	70	35
2989	-	20pf. orange and black	70	60
2990	-	47pf. mauve and green	70	70
2991	-	50pf. brown and red	1·20	95
2992	-	80pf. green and brown	1·10	95
2993	-	100pf. blue and brown	1·80	1·70
2994	-	110pf. pur, brn & orge	1·70	1·20
2997	-	220pf. blue and brown	3·00	2·75
3000	-	300pf. brown and blue	3·50	3·25
3001	-	400pf. brown and red	4·75	4·50
3002	-	440pf. black and grey	5·00	4·75
3003	-	510pf. pink and red	6·25	6·00
3004	-	720pf. purple & mauve	8·25	8·25

DESIGNS: 20pf. Bottcherstrasse, Bremen; 47pf. Wilhelmshohe Park, Kassel; 50pf. Ceiling decoration, Kircheim Castle; 80pf. St. Reinoldi Church, Dortmund; 100pf. Schwerin Castle, Mecklenberg; 110pf. Stone bridge, Regensburg; 220pf. St. Nikolai Cathedral, Greifswald; 300pf. Town Hall Grimma; 400pf. Wartburg Castle, Eisenach; 440pf. Cologne Cathedral; 510pf. Heidelberg Castle; 720pf. Town Hall, Hildesheim.

Nos. 2988, 2993/4 also come self-adhesive.

1319 National Colours

2000. 10th Anniv of Reunification of Germany.

3010	**1319**	110pf. black, red & yell	1·50	1·30

1320 Curd Jurgens

2000. Humanitarian Relief Funds. Actors. Mult.

3011	100pf.+50pf. Type **1320**	2·10	2·10
3012	100pf.+50pf. Lilli Palmer	2·10	2·10
3013	110pf.+50pf. Heinz Ruhmann	2·40	2·40
3014	110pf.+50pf. Romy Schneider	2·40	2·40
3015	300pf.+100pf. Gert Frobe	4·75	4·75

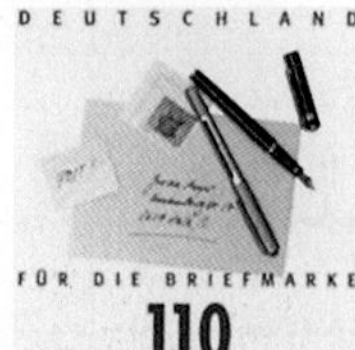

1321 Pens, Envelope and 1999 110pf. Stamp

2000. Stamp Day.

3016	**1321**	110pf. multicoloured	1·40	1·30

1322 Grethe Weiser (actress and singer)

2000. Famous German Women.

3017	**1322**	100pf. green and brown	1·30	1·20
3018	-	110pf. red and green	1·40	1·20
3019	-	220pf. brown and green	2·50	2·40
3020	-	300pf. purple and brown	3·25	3·00

DESIGNS: 110pf. Kate Strobel (politician); 200pf. Marielu-ise Fleisser (writer); 300pf. Nelly Sachs (writer).

2000. Federal State Parliament Buildings (8th series). As T 1213. Multicoloured.

3025	110pf. Saarland	1·50	1·30

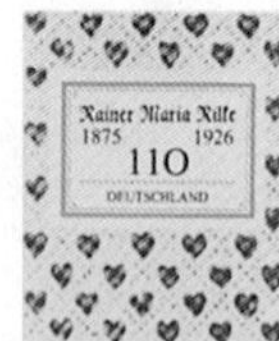

1323 Book Cover

2000. 125th Birth Anniv of Rainer Maria Rilke (poet).

3026	**1323**	110pf. multicoloured	1·50	1·30

1324 Bode

2000. Birth Centenary of Arnold Bode (artist).

3027	**1324**	110pf. black and red	1·50	1·30

1325 "Birth of Christ" (Conrad von Soest)

2000. Christmas. Multicoloured.

3028	100pf.+50pf. Type **1325**	1·80	1·70
3029	110pf.+50pf. Nativity	2·00	1·80

1326 Indian Pepper (illustration from *New Book of Herbs*)

2001. 500th Birth Anniv of Leonhart Fuchs (physician and botanist).

3030	**1326**	100pf. multicoloured	1·20	1·10

1327 "VdK"

2001. 50th Anniv (2000) of Disabled War Veterans' Association.

3031	**1327**	110pf. multicoloured	1·30	1·20

1328 Prussian Eagle

2001. 300th Anniv of the Kingdom of Prussia.

3032	**1328**	110pf. multicoloured	1·30	1·20

1329 Lortzing and Music Score

2001. Birth Bicent of Albert Lortzing (composer).

3033	**1329**	110pf. multicoloured	1·30	1·20

1330 Telephone Handset and Number

2001. National Federation of Child and Youth Telephone Helplines.

3034	**1330**	110pf. yellow, red & blk	1·30	1·20

1331 Bucer

2001. 450th Death Anniv of Martin Bucer (teacher and Protestant reformer).

3035	**1331**	110pf. multicoloured	1·50	1·30

1332 Children running

2001. Sport Promotion Fund. Multicoloured.

3036	100pf.+50pf. Type **1332**	2·00	2·00
3037	110pf.+50pf. Disabled and able-bodied athletes	2·20	2·20
3038	110pf.+50pf. Adult and children skating	2·20	2·20
3039	300pf.+100pf. Men playing basketball	5·00	5·25

1333 Hand holding Quill

2001. 250th Birth Anniv of Johann Heinrich Voss (writer and translator). (a) Ordinary gum.

3040	**1333**	300pf. multicoloured	3·75	3·75

(b) Self-adhesive gum.

3040a	€1.53 multicoloured	5·50	5·00

1334 Ollenhauer

2001. Birth Centenary of Erich Ollenhauer (politician).

3041	**1334**	110pf. red, black & sil	1·30	1·20

1335 Arnold

2001. Birth Centenary of Karl Arnold (politician).

3042	**1335**	110pf. black, green & red	1·30	1·20

2001. Federal State Parliament Buildings (9th series). As T 1213. Multicoloured.

3043	110pf. Saxony	1·30	1·20

1336 Badge

2001. 50th Anniv of Federal Border Police.

3044	**1336**	110pf. multicoloured	1·30	1·20

1337 Suspension Railway

2001. Centenary of Suspension Railway, Wuppertal.

3045	**1338**	110pf.+50pf. mult	2·20	2·00

1338 Rendsberg Railway Viaduct

2001. Bridges (4th series).

3046	100pf. multicoloured	1·30	1·20

1339 "Post!"

2001

3047	**1339**	110pf. multicoloured	1·30	1·20

1340 Accordion

2001. Folk Music.

3048	**1340**	110pf. multicoloured	1·30	1·20

1341 World Map

2001. 50th Anniv of Goethe Institute.

3049	**1341**	300pf. multicoloured	3·75	3·75

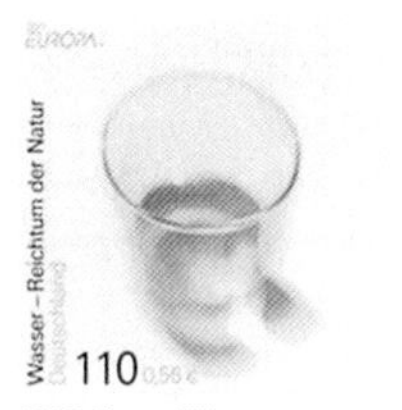

1342 Glass of Water

2001. Europa. Water Resources.
3050 **1342** 110pf. multicoloured 1·80 1·30

1343 Egk

2001. Birth Centenary of Werner Egk (composer and conductor).
3051 **1343** 110pf. multicoloured 1·30 1·30

2001. Federal State Parliament Buildings (10th series). As T 1213. Multicoloured.
3052 110pf. Saxony-Anhalt 1·30 1·30

1344 Mountain Gorilla with Young

2001. Endangered Species. Multicoloured. Ordinary or self-adhesive gum.
3053 110pf. Type **1344** 1·70 1·50
3054 110pf. Indian rhinoceros with young 1·70 1·50

1345 Pinocchio

2001. Youth Welfare. Characters from Children's Stories. Multicoloured.
3057 100pf.+50pf. Type **1345** 2·00 2·00
3058 100pf.+50pf. Pippi Longstocking 2·00 2·00
3059 110pf.+50pf. Heidi and Peter 2·20 2·20
3060 110pf.+50pf. Jim Knopf 2·20 2·20
3061 300pf.+100pf. Tom Sawyer and Huckleberry Finn 5·00 5·00

1346 St. Catherine's Monastery and Oceanographic Chart

2001. 750th Anniv of St. Catherine's Monastery and 50th Anniv of German Oceanographic Museum, Stralsund.
3062 **1346** 110pf. multicoloured 1·30 1·20

1347 Church Exterior and Plan

2001. 250th Anniv of Catholic Court Church, Dresden.
3063 **1347** 110pf. multicoloured 1·30 1·20

2001. Federal State Parliament Buildings (11th series). As T 1213. Multicoloured.
3064 110pf. Schleswig-Holstein 1·30 1·20

1348 Church Bell Tower, Canzow

2001
3065 **1348** 110pf. black, blue and mauve 1·30 1·20

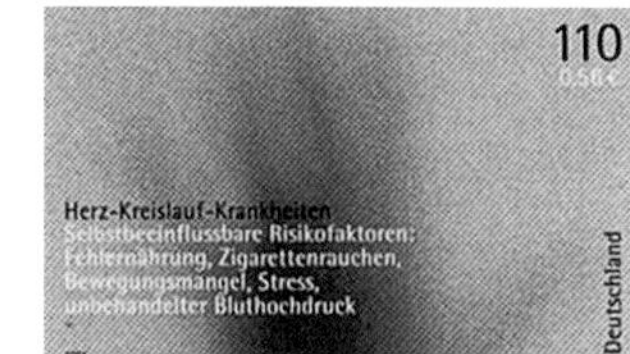

1349 Hand (circulatory disease)

2001. Health Awareness Campaign. Sheet 138×110 mm containing T 1349 and similar horiz designs. Multicoloured.
MS3066 110pf. Type **1349**; 110pf. Torso (cancer); 110pf. Lower body (infectious diseases); 110pf. Man holding head (depression) 7·25 7·25

1350 Emblem

2001. Dragon Lancing Festival, Furth im Wald.
3067 **1350** 100pf. multicoloured 1·20 1·10

1351 Lime Tree, Himmelsberg

2001. Natural Heritage. Ordinary or self-adhesive gum.
3068 **1351** 110pf. multicoloured 1·30 1·20

1352 "Schoolmaster Lampel" (Wilhelm Busch) and Text

2001. Lifelong Learning.
3070 **1352** 110pf. multicoloured 1·30 1·20

1353 Felix standing on Cat

2001. "For Us Children". Sheet 110×66 mm.
MS3071 **1353** 110pf. multicoloured 1·80 1·80

2001. Federal State Parliament Buildings (12th series). As T 1213. Multicoloured.
3072 110pf. Thuringia 1·30 1·20

1354 "Justice" (sculpture)

2001. 50th Anniv of Federal Constitutional Court.
3073 **1354** 110pf. multicoloured 1·30 1·20

1355 Members' Flags

2001. 1st Union Network International World Congress, Berlin.
3074 **1355** 110pf. multicoloured 1·30 1·20

1356 Museum Floor Plan

2001. Jewish Museum, Berlin.
3075 **1356** 110pf. multicoloured 1·30 1·20

1357 Marilyn Monroe

2001. Humanitarian Relief Funds. Film Industry. Multicoloured.
3076 100pf.+50pf. Type **1357** 2·00 2·00
3077 100pf.+50pf. Charlie Chaplin 2·00 2·00
3078 110pf.+50pf. Greta Garbo 2·20 2·20
3079 110pf.+50pf. Film reel 2·20 2·20
3080 300pf.+100pf. Jean Gabin 5·00 5·00
MS3080a 205×156 mm. As Nos. 3076/80 16·00 16·00

1358 Ribbon and "fur Dich"

2001. Greetings Stamp.
3081 **1358** 110pf. red and black 1·30 1·20

1359 "Virgin and Child" (Alfredo Roldan)

2001. Christmas. Religious Paintings. Mult.
3082 100pf.+50pf. Type **1359** 1·80 1·80
3083 110pf.+50pf. "The Shepherd's Adoration" (Jusepe de Ribera) 2·00 2·00
MS3083a 106×133 mm. Nos. 3082/3 and 3788/9 of Spain 6·00 6·00

1360 *Gauss* (survey barquentine)

2001. Centenary of German Antarctic Research. Sheet 135×105 mm containing T 1360 and similar horiz design. Multicoloured.
MS3084 110pf. Type **1360**; 220pf. *Polarstern* (exploration ship) 5·00 5·00

1361 Heisenberg

2001. Birth Centenary of Werner Heisenberg (physicist).
3085 **1361** 300pf. black and blue 4·25 3·75

1362 Bautzen

2002. Millenary of Bautzen. Ordinary or self-adhesive gum.
3086 **1362** 56c. multicoloured 1·30 1·20

1363 Von Dohnanyi

2002. Birth Centenary of Hans von Dohnanyi (German resistance co-ordinator).
3087 **1363** 56c. multicoloured 1·30 1·20

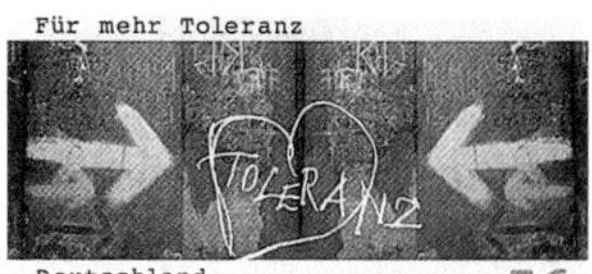

1364 Graffiti

2002. "Tolerance".
3088 **1364** 56c. multicoloured 1·30 1·20

1365 " € "

2002. New Currency. Ordinary or self-adhesive gum.
3089 **1365** 56c. yellow and blue 2·00 1·80

1366 Mountains

2002. International Year of Mountains.
3091 **1366** 56c.+26c. multicoloured 1·80 1·20
No. 3091 was sold with a premium towards environmental protection.

1367 Cross-country Skier (biathlon)

2002. Winter Olympic Games, Salt Lake City, U.S.A. Multicoloured.
3092 51c.+26c. Type **1367** 2·00 2·00
3093 56c.+26c. Ice skater (speed skating) 2·20 2·20
3094 56c.+26c. Skier (ski jumping) 2·20 2·20
3095 153c.+51c. Man in helmet (luge) 5·00 5·00
MS3096 142×98 mm. As Nos. 3092/5 14·50 14·50
Nos. 3092/**MS**3096 were sold with a premium towards "Foundation for the Promotion of Sport in Germany".

1368 Knigge and Books

2002. 250th Birth Anniv of Adolf Freiherr Knigge (author of Uber den Umgang mit Menschen (book on etiquette)).
3097 **1368** 56c. multicoloured 1·50 1·30

1369 Front of Train Carriage

2002. Centenary of Berlin Subway.
3098 **1369** 56c. multicoloured 1·50 1·30

1370 Deggendorf

2002. Millenary of Deggendorf.
3099 **1370** 56c. multicoloured 1·50 1·30

1371 Mechanical Calculator (Johann Christoph Schuster)

2002. Cultural Foundation of the Federal States.
3100 **1371** 56c. multicoloured 1·50 1·30

1372 Ecksberg Pilgrimage Church

2002. 150th Anniv of Ecksberg Foundation (for people with disabilities).
3101 **1372** 56c. multicoloured 1·50 1·30

1373 Exhibits and Building

2002. Centenary of Freemason's Museum, Bayreuth.
3102 **1373** 56c. multicoloured 1·50 1·30

1374 Armorial Lions

2002. 50th Anniv of Baden-Württemberg State.
3103 **1374** 56c. black, gold and yellow 1·50 1·30

1375 "post"

2002
3104 **1375** 56c. multicoloured 1·50 1·30

1376 Emblem

2002. 50th Anniv of Federal Employment Services.
3105 **1376** €1.53 red and black 4·00 3·75

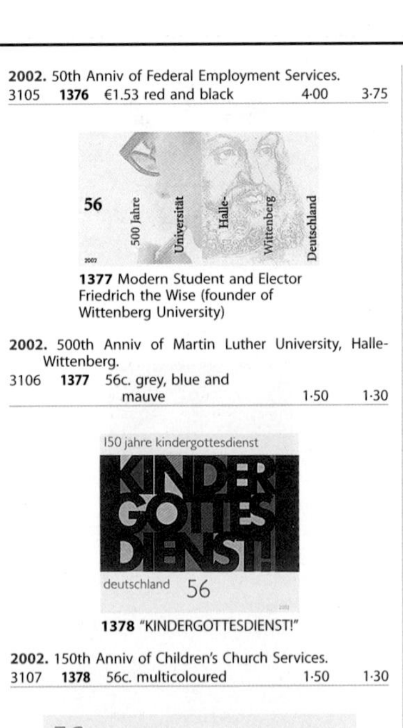

1377 Modern Student and Elector Friedrich the Wise (founder of Wittenberg University)

2002. 500th Anniv of Martin Luther University, Halle-Wittenberg.
3106 **1377** 56c. grey, blue and mauve 1·50 1·30

1378 "KINDERGOTTESDIENST!"

2002. 150th Anniv of Children's Church Services.
3107 **1378** 56c. multicoloured 1·50 1·30

1379 "Documenta11"

2002. 11th "Documenta" Modern Art Exhibition, Kassel. Sheet 100×70 mm.
MS3108 **1379** 56c. ultramarine, lilac and blue 1·70 1·70

1380 Flags of Championship Winners and Football

2002. 20th-century World Cup Football Champions. Multicoloured.
3109 56c. Type **1380** 1·50 1·50
3110 56c. German Footballer 1·50 1·50

1381 Clown

2002. Europa. Circus. Ordinary or self-adhesive gum.
3111 **1381** 56c. black, red and green 1·50 1·30

1382 Dessau-Worlitz

2002. UNESCO World Heritage Site. Dessau-Worlitz Gardens. Ordinary or self-adhesive gum.
3113 **1382** 56c. multicoloured 1·50 1·30

1383 Thaer

2002. 250th Birth Anniv of Albrecht Daniel Thaer (agronomist).
3115 **1383** €2.25 multicoloured 6·00 6·00

1384 Desmoulin's Whorl Snail

2002. Endangered Species. Molluscs. Multicoloured.
3116 51c. Type **1384** 1·20 1·20
3117 56c. Freshwater pearl mussel 1·30 1·30

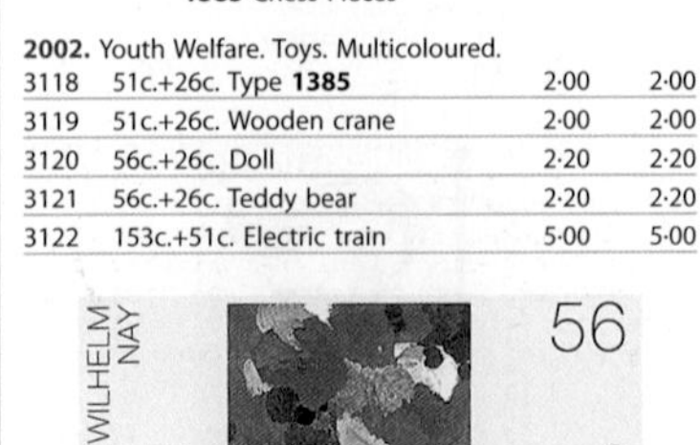

1385 Chess Pieces

2002. Youth Welfare. Toys. Multicoloured.
3118 51c.+26c. Type **1385** 2·00 2·00
3119 51c.+26c. Wooden crane 2·00 2·00
3120 56c.+26c. Doll 2·20 2·20
3121 56c.+26c. Teddy bear 2·20 2·20
3122 153c.+51c. Electric train 5·00 5·00

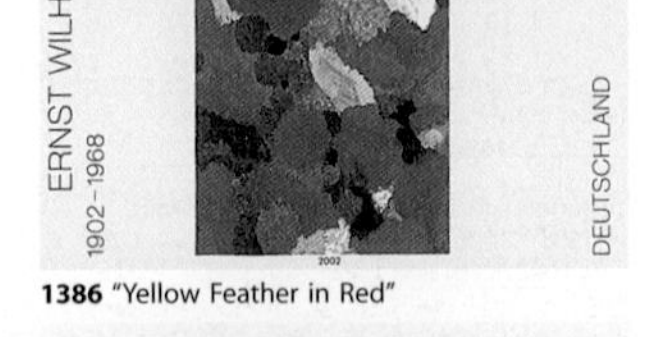

1386 "Yellow Feather in Red"

2002. Birth Centenary of Ernst Wilhelm Nay (artist).
3123 **1386** 56c. multicoloured 1·50 1·30

1387 Leaves and Silhouettes

2002. 40th Anniv of "Deutsche Welthungerhilfe" (humanitarian aid organization).
3124 **1387** 51c. multicoloured 1·30 1·20

1388 "Way of Human Rights" (sculpture, Danni Karavan)

2002. 150th Anniv of National Museum of German Art and Culture, Nuremberg.
3125 **1388** 56c. multicoloured 1·50 1·30

1389 Hesse

2002. 125th Birth Anniv of Hermann Hesse (writer).
3126 **1389** 56c. blue and yellow 1·50 1·30

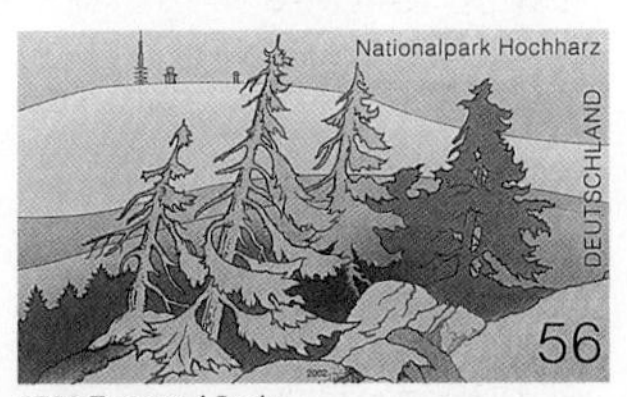

1390 Trees and Rocks

2002. Hochharz National Park. Sheet 110×66 mm.
MS3127 **1390** 56c. multicoloured 2·10 2·10

1391 Felder

2002. 2nd Death Anniv of Josef Felder (politician and journalist).
3128 **1391** 56c. multicoloured 1·50 1·30

1392 Museum Buildings

2002. UNESCO World Heritage Site. Museum Island, Berlin.
3129 **1392** 56c. black and green 1·50 1·30

1393 Firemen fighting Fire

2002. Voluntary Fire Brigades.
3130 **1393** 56c. multicoloured 1·50 1·30

1394 Building Facade

2002. 130th Anniv of Communications Museum, Berlin.
3131 **1394** 153c. multicoloured 3·75 3·50

2002. Flood Relief. As T 1222 but with "HOCHWASSERHILFE 2002" inscribed at left and new face value.
3132 56c.+44c. multicoloured 3·25 2·75

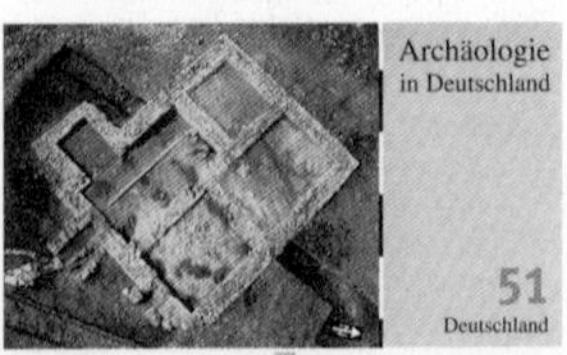

1395 Walls of Roman Bathhouse, Wurmlingen (illustration from *Die Alammannen* by Konrad Theiss)

2002. Archaeology.
3133 **1395** 51c. multicoloured 1·50 1·30

1396 Face painted on Child's Toe

2002. "For Us Children". Sheet 110×66 mm.
MS3134 **1396** 56c. multicoloured 2·10 2·00

1397 "Rotes Elisabeth-Ufer" (painting, Ernst Ludwig Kirchner)

2002
3135 **1397** 112c. multicoloured 3·00 2·50

1398 Von Kleist (miniature, Peter Friedel)

2002. 225th Birth Anniv of Heinrich von Kleist (writer).

3136	**1398**	56c. multicoloured	1·50	1·30

1399 Jochum rehearsing

2002. Birth Centenary of Eugen Jochum (conductor).

3137	**1399**	56c. multicoloured	1·50	1·30

1400 Diagram of Planets (Copernicus), Horsemen and Sphere

2002. 400th Birth Anniv of Otto von Guericke (engineer and physicist).

3138	**1400**	153c. multicoloured	4·25	3·50

1401 Angel (detail, "The Annunciation")

2002. Christmas. Paintings by Rogier van der Weyden. Multicoloured.

3139	51c.+26c. Type **1401**	2·20	2·00
3140	56c.+26c. The Holy Family (detail, Miraflores alterpiece)	2·40	2·10

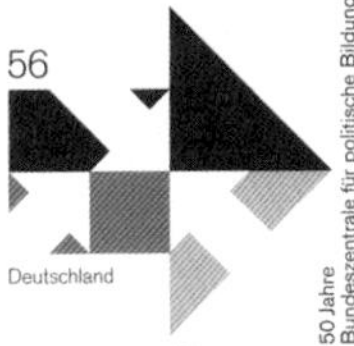

1402 Arrows

2002. 50th Anniv of Federal Agency for Civic Education.

3141	**1402**	56c. black, red and yellow	1·50	1·30

1403 Clock and Eye

2002. 50th Anniv of German Television.

3142	**1403**	56c. multicoloured	1·50	1·30

1404 BMW Isetta 300

2002. Cars. Multicoloured.

3144	45c.+20c. Type **1404**	2·20	2·10
3145	55c.+25c. Volkswagen Beetle	2·40	2·20
3146	55c.+25c. Mercedes Benz 300 SL	2·40	2·20
3147	55c.+25c. VEB Sachsenring Trabant P50	2·40	2·20
3148	144c.+56c. Borgward Isabella Coupe	5·50	5·25

See also Nos. 3238/42.

1405 "Halle Market Church" (Lyonel Feininger)

3149	**1405**	55c. multicoloured	1·50	1·30

2002. Tourist Sights. As T 1318 but with face value in new currency.

3150	5c. brown and green	25	25
3151	25c. olive and violet	60	55
3153	40c. multicoloured	1·00	90
3154	44c. yellow and black	1·20	1·10
3155	45c. pink and black	1·20	1·10
3156	55c. yellow and black	1·50	1·40
3157	€1 grey and black	2·40	2·00
3158	€1.44 pink and green	3·50	3·25
3159	€1.60 grey, black and orange	3·75	3·50
3160	€1.80 green and chestnut	5·00	4·00
3161	€2 red and green	5·00	4·75
3162	€2.20 blue and black	5·50	5·00
3163	€2.60 blue and red	6·00	5·75
3164	€4.10 purple and blue	9·25	8·50

DESIGNS: 5c. Erfuster Cathedral; 25c. Schloss Arolsen; 40c. J.S. Bach (statue), Leipzig; 44c. Philharmonic Hall, Berlin; 45c. Canal warehouse, Tonning; 55c. Old Opera House, Frankfurt; €1 Porta Niga (black gate), Trier; €1.44 Beethoven's birthplace, Bonn; €1.60 Bauhaus, Dessau; €1.80 Staatsgalerie, Stuttgart; €2 Bamberger Reister (statue); €2.20 Theodor Fontane monument, Neuruppin; €2.60 *Seute Dern* (four-mast barque), Maritime Museum, Bremerhaven; €4.10 Houses, Wismar.

Nos. 3151 and 3155/6 also come self-adhesive.

2002. Famous German Women. As T 1322 but with face value in new currency.

3190	45c. green and blue	1·20	1·10
3191	55c. red and black	1·30	1·30
3192	€1 purple and blue	2·40	2·30
3193	€1.44 brown and blue	3·25	3·00

DESIGNS: 45c. Annette von Droste-Hulshoff (writer); 55c. Hildegard Knef (actress); €1 Marie Juchacz (politician); €1.44 Esther von Kirchbach (writer).

1406 Town Buildings

2003. Millenary of Kronach.

3194	**1406**	45c. multicoloured	1·20	1·00

1407 Georg Elser

2003. Birth Centenary of Georg Elser (attempted assassination of Adolf Hitler).

3195	**1407**	55c. multicoloured	1·50	1·30

1408 Bridge joined by Heart

2003. 40th Anniv of German–French Co-operation Treaty.

3196	**1408**	55c. multicoloured	1·50	1·30

1409 Hand and Page

2003. Year of the Bible.

3197	**1409**	55c. multicoloured	1·50	1·30

1410 "Proun 30t" (El Lissitzky)

2003. Cultural Foundation of the Federal States.

3198	**1410**	€1.44 multicoloured	3·75	3·50

1411 St. Thomas Church Choir, Leipzig

2003. Boys' Choirs. Sheet 172×77 mm containing T 1411 and similar horiz designs. Multicoloured.

MS3199	45c. Type **1411**; 55c. Dresden Church choir; 100c. St. Peter's Cathedral choir, Regensburg	5·50	5·00

1412 Rose

2003. Greetings Stamp. Ordinary or self-adhesive gum.

3200	**1412**	55c. multicoloured	1·50	1·20

1413 "Junger Argentier" (Max Beckman)

2003. Artists' Anniversaries. Multicoloured.

3202	55c. Type **1413** (53rd death anniv)	1·70	1·30
3203	€1 "Komposition" (Adolf Holzel) (150th birth anniv)	2·50	2·30

1414 Footballer

2003. Sports Promotion Fund. World Cup Football Championship (2006), Germany. Multicoloured.

3204	45c.+20c. Type **1414**	2·00	2·00
3205	55c.+25c. Boys playing football	2·20	2·20
3206	55c.+25c. Fan with arms raised	2·20	2·20
3207	55c.+25c. Young player heading ball	2·20	2·20
3208	€1.44+56c. Boy kicking ball to older man	5·00	5·00

1415 Building Facade

2003. UNESCO World Heritage Sites. Cologne Cathedral. Ordinary or self-adhesive gum.

3209	**1415**	55c. grey, red and black	1·50	1·30

1416 Flower

2003. International Horticultural Exhibition, Rostock.

3211	**1416**	45c. multicoloured	1·30	1·20

1417 Oskar von Miller (founder) and Technological Symbols

2003. Centenary of Deutsches Museum, Munich.

3212	**1417**	55c. multicoloured	1·50	1·30

1418 Cut-out Figures

2003. 50th Anniv of Deutscher Kinderschutzbund (children's organization).

3213	**1418**	55c. multicoloured	1·50	1·30

1419 Map and Representation of Radio Waves

2003. 50th Anniv of Deutsche Welle (radio station).

3214	**1419**	55c. multicoloured	1·50	1·30

1420 Aviators and Junkers W.33 Bremen

2003. 75th Anniv East–West North Atlantic Flight.

3215	**1420**	144c.+56c. multicoloured	5·50	5·00

1421 1960s Posters

2003. Europa. Poster Art.

3216	**1421**	55c. multicoloured	1·50	1·30

1422 Justus von Liebig

2003. Birth Bicentenary of Justus von Liebig (chemist).

3217	**1422**	55c. multicoloured	1·50	1·30

1423 Reinhold Schneider and Text

2003. Birth Centenary of Reinhold Schneider (writer).

3218	**1423**	55c. multicoloured	1·50	1·30

1424 Eurocopter EC135 and Patrol Vehicle

2003. Centenary of ADAC (automobile association).
3219 **1424** 55c. multicoloured 1·50 1·30

1425 Rainbow

2003. Ecumenical Church Conference, Berlin.
3220 **1425** 55c. multicoloured 1·50 1·30

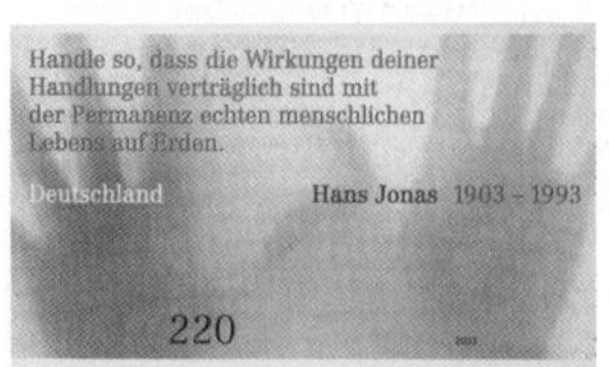

1426 Hands and Text

2003. Birth Centenary of Hans Jonas (philosopher).
3221 **1426** 220c. multicoloured 5·75 5·00

1427 Hand with Face and Feet

2003. 10th Anniv of Postal Codes.
3222 **1427** 55c. multicoloured 1·50 1·30

1428 Bridge over Salzach River

2003. Centenary of Oberndorf–Laufen Bridge. Ordinary or self-adhesive gum.
3223 **1428** 55c. multicoloured 1·50 1·50

A stamp of the same design was issued by Austria.

1429 Lake, Trees and Islands

2003. Unteres Odertal National Park. Sheet 111×66 mm.
MS3225 **1429** 55c. multicoloured 1·80 1·70

1430 Protesters and Tanks

2003. 50th Anniv of Uprising in East Berlin.
3226 **1430** 55c.+25c. multicoloured 2·20 2·10

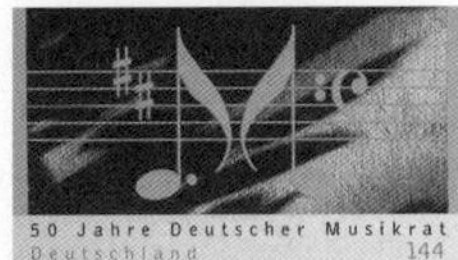

1431 Musical Notations

2003. 50th Anniv of Deutscher Musikrat (music education). Ordinary or self-adhesive gum.
3227 **1431** €1.44 silver and blue 4·00 3·75

1432 Father chasing Son

2003. "For Us Children". "Father and Son" (cartoon by E.O. Plauen (Erich Ohser)). Sheet 111×191 mm containing T 1432 and similar horiz designs. Multicoloured.
MS3228 45c.+20c. Type **1432**; 55c.+25c. Father and son falling; 55c.+25c. Father looking over shoulder at son running away; 55c.+25c. Father chasing son in a circle; €1.44+56c. Father and son sliding 13·50 13·00

1433 Winding Gear and Trees

2003. Ruhr District Industrial Landscape.
3229 **1433** 55c. multicoloured 1·50 1·30

1434 Andres Hermes

2003. 125th Birth Anniv of Andreas Hermes (politician).
3230 **1434** 55c. multicoloured 1·50 1·30

1435 Market Stalls, Munich

2003. German Cities. Multicoloured.
3231 45c. Type **1435** 1·30 1·20
3232 55c. Building facades, Altstadt Gorlitz 1·50 1·30

No. 3231 also comes self-adhesive.

1436 Petrified Forest, Chemnitz

2003
3234 **1436** 144c. multicoloured 3·75 3·50

1437 Viaduct and Enz River

2003. 150th Anniv of Enztal Viaduct (railway).
3235 **1437** 55c. multicoloured 1·80 1·40

1438 Theodor Adorno and Manuscript

2003. Birth Centenary of Theodor Adorno (philosopher and sociologist).
3236 **1438** 55c. multicoloured 1·80 1·40

1439 Elephant and Bird

2003. "For Us Children". Sheet 111×65 mm.
MS3237 **1439** 55c. multicoloured 2·00 1·80

2003. Cars. As T 1404. Multicoloured.
3238 45c.+20c. Wartburg 311 Coupe 2·00 2·00
3239 55c.+25c. Ford Taunus 17 M P3 2·40 2·10
3240 55c.+25c. Porsche 356 B Coupe 2·40 2·10
3241 55c.+25c. Opel Olympia Rekord P1 2·40 2·10
3242 144c.+56c. Auto Union 1000 S 5·50 5·00

1440 Letter Box

2003. Post.
3243 **1440** 55c. multicoloured 1·80 1·40

1441 Lifeguards

2003. 90th Anniv of DLRG (safety organization).
3244 **1441** 144c. multicoloured 4·50 3·50

1442 Nativity Figures (19th-century)

2003. Christmas. Multicoloured.
3245 45c.+20c. Type **1442** 2·10 1·60
3246 55c.+25c. Holy Family 2·50 2·00

1443 Dresden Opera House

2003. Birth Bicentenary of Gottfried Semper (architect).
3247 **1443** 55c. multicoloured 1·80 1·40

1444 Hands and Women

2003. Centenary of German Catholic Women's Federation.
3248 **1444** 55c. multicoloured 1·80 1·40

1445 Stars

2003. 10th Anniv of Maastricht Treaty.
3249 **1445** 55c. blue and yellow 1·80 1·40

1446 St. Martin's Church

2004. 800th Anniv of Landshut.
3250 **1446** 45c. multicoloured 1·50 1·20

1447 Cathedral and Images of Schleswig

2004. 1200th Anniv of Schleswig.
3251 **1447** 55c. multicoloured 1·90 1·50

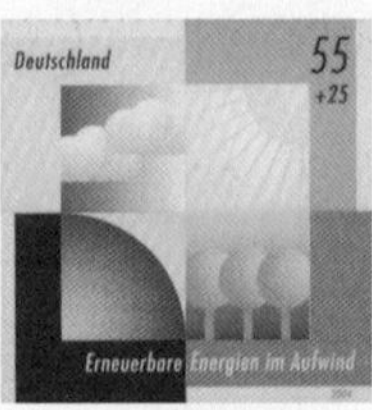

1448 Clouds, Sun and Trees

2004. Environmental Protection and Renewable Energy.
3252 **1448** 55c.+25c. multicoloured 2·75 2·20

1449 Football Players

2004. Sport Promotion Fund. Multicoloured.
3253 45c.+20c. Type **1449** (European Football Championship) 2·50 2·10
3254 55c.+25c. Wheelchair athlete (Paralympics) 2·75 2·20
3255 55c.+25c. Runner (Olympic Games, Greece) 2·75 2·20
3256 55c.+25c. Footballer (50th anniv of Germany winning World Cup) 2·75 2·20
3257 144c.+56c. Hands holding trophy (Centenary of FIFA) 6·50 5·50

1450 Paper Airplanes

2004. Post.
3258 **1450** 55c. multicoloured 1·90 1·50

1451 Buildings

2004. 1300th Anniv of Arnstadt.
3259 **1451** 55c. multicoloured 1·90 1·50

Wilhelm Tell.
Deutschland 45

1452 Shadow of Boy, Apple and Arrow

2004. Classic Theatre. Sheet 102×73 mm containing T 1452 and similar square design. Multicoloured.
MS3260 45c. Type **1452** (William Tell (Friedrich von Schiller) (200th anniv)); 100c. Faust and the devil (Faust II (Johann Wolfgang von Goethe) (150th anniv)) 5·00 4·75

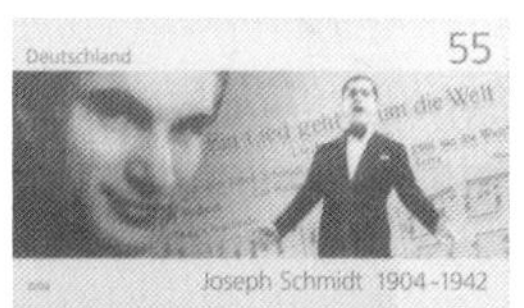

1453 Joseph Schmidt

2004. Birth Centenary of Joseph Schmidt (singer).
3261 **1453** 55c. brown 1·90 1·50

1454 Paul Ehrlich (chemistry) and Emil von Behring (medicine)

2004. 150th Birth Anniv of Nobel Prize Winners.
3262 **1454** 144c. multicoloured 4·75 3·75

1455 White Stork in Flight

2004. Endangered Species. White Stork (Circona circona).
3263 **1455** 55c. black, blue and red 1·90 1·50

1456 Master House, Dessau

2004. Bauhaus (design group).
3264 **1456** 55c. multicoloured 1·90 1·50

1457 Kurt Kiesinger

2004. Birth Centenary of Kurt Georg Kiesinger (politician).
3265 **1457** 55c. multicoloured 1·90 1·50

1458 Early and Modern Light Bulbs

2004. 150th Anniv of Electric Light Bulb.
3266 **1458** 220c. multicoloured 6·75 6·50

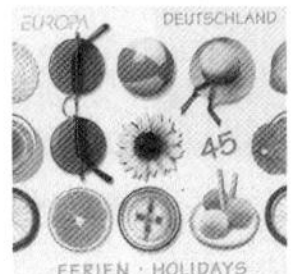

1459 Sunflower and Holiday Symbols

2004. Europa. Holidays.
3267 **1459** 45c. multicoloured 1·70 1·30

1460 New Members' Flags as Cones

2004. Enlargement of European Union.
3268 **1460** 55c. multicoloured 1·90 1·50

1461 Reinhard Schwarz-Schilling

2004. Birth Centenary of Reinhard Schwarz-Schilling (composer).
3269 **1461** 55c. sepia 1·90 1·50

1462 St. Boniface under Attack

2004. 350th Anniv of Martyrdom of St. Boniface (papal envoy to Germany).
3270 **1462** 55c. multicoloured 1·90 1·50

1463 Schloss Ludwigsburg

2004. 300th Anniv of Schloss Ludwigsburg.
3271 **1463** €1.44 multicoloured 4·50 4·00

1464 Two Kittens playing with String

2004. "For Us Children". Cats. Multicoloured.
3272 45c.+20c. Type **1464** 2·40 2·00
3273 55c.+25c. Three kittens playing with ball 2·50 2·20
3274 55c.+25c. Mother and kitten 2·50 2·20
3275 55c.+25c. Cat washing paw 2·50 2·20
3276 €1.44+56c. Two kittens asleep 6·75 5·75

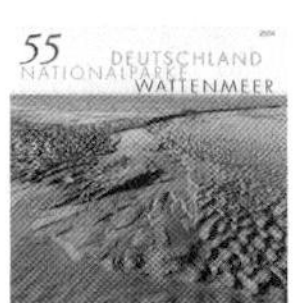

1465 Sea and Sand

2004. Wattenmeer National Park.
3277 **1465** 55c. multicoloured 1·90 1·50

1466 National Flags as Heart-shaped Kite

2004. 21st-century German—Russian Youth Forum.
3278 **1466** 55c. multicoloured 1·90 1·50

1467 Greifswalder Oie, Baltic Sea

2004. Lighthouses. Multicoloured. (a) Ordinary gum.
3279 45c. Type **1467** 1·70 1·30
3280 55c. Roter Sands 1·90 1·50

(b) Self-adhesive gum.
3281 55c. As No. 3280 (35×35 mm) 1·90 1·50

1468 *Bremen* (passenger ship) and New York Harbour

2004. Bremen—1929 Winner of Blue Ribbon (Europe to America speed record). Ordinary or self-adhesive gum.
3282 **1468** 55c. multicoloured 1·90 1·50

1469 Ludwig Fuerbach

2004. Birth Bicentenary of Ludwig Fuerbach (philosopher).
3284 **1469** 144c. rosine and black 4·50 3·75

1470 Camellia

2004. Greetings Stamp. Ordinary or Self-adhesive gum.
3285 **1470** 55c. multicoloured 1·90 1·50

1471 Church Facade

2004. Centenary of Protestant Regional Church, Speyer.
3287 **1471** 55c. multicoloured 1·90 1·50

1472 Scene from "Hansel and Gretel" and Engelbert Humperdinck

2004. 150th Birth Anniv of Engelbert Humperdinck (composer).
3288 **1472** 45c. multicoloured 1·70 1·30

1473 Ink Pot, Quill Pen, Manuscript and Glasses

2004. Birth Bicentenary of Eduard Morike (writer).
3289 **1473** 55c. multicoloured 1·90 1·50

1474 Feet and Hand Prints forming Face

2004. "For Us Children".
3290 **1474** 55c. multicoloured 1·90 1·50

1475 Kaiser Wilhelm Cathedral church, Berlin and Egon Eiermann

2004. Birth Centenary of Egon Eiermann (architect).
3291 **1475** 100c. multicoloured 3·50 2·75

1476 Court Seal

2004. 50th Anniv of Federal Social Court.
3292 **1476** 144c. multicoloured 4·50 3·75

1477 Iceberg, Greenland

2004. Climate Zones. Multicoloured.
3293 45c.+20c. Type **1477** (arctic) 2·50 2·20
3294 55c.+25c. Mountains, Tibet (alpine) 3·00 2·50
3295 55c.+25c. River and grazing animals, Mecklenburg-Vorpommern (temperate) 3·00 2·50
3296 55c.+25c. Dunes, Sahara (desert) 3·00 2·50
3297 144c.+56c. Rainforest, Galapagos Islands (tropics) 6·75 5·75

1478 Flying Boat Dornier Do-X (1930)

2004. Stamp Day.
3298 **1478** 55c. ultramarine and vermilion 2·10 1·60

1479 "Flight into Egypt"

2004. Christmas. Paintings by Peter Paul Rubens. Multicoloured.
3299 45c.+20c. Type **1479** 2·50 2·10
3300 55c.+25c. "Adoration of the Magi" 3·00 2·40
Stamps of the same design were issued by Belgium.

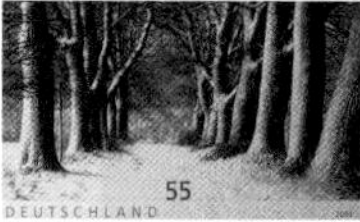

1480 Snow-covered Avenue

2004. Post.
3301 **1480** 55c. multicoloured 2·10 1·60

1481 "Das Geheimnis"

2004. Birth Centenary of Felix Nussbaum (artist).
3302 **1481** 55c. multicoloured 2·10 1·60

1482 International Space Station

2004
3303 **1482** 55c. multicoloured 2·10 1·60

1483 City Hall

2005. 1200th Anniv of Forchheim.
3304 **1483** 45c. multicoloured 1·70 1·30

1484 Three Kings (board painting, Cologne (c. 1350))

2005. Art.

3305	**1484**	55c. multicoloured	2·10	1·60

1485 Sunflower

2005. Flowers. Multicoloured.

(a) Ordinary gum

3306	5c. Crocus	35	35
3306a	10c. Tulip	45	40
3307	20c. Tagetes	75	65
3307a	25c. Carnation	95	80
3308	25c. Mallow	95	80
3308a	35c. Dahlia	1·30	1·10
3308b	40c. Blue flower	1·50	1·30
3310	45c. Daisy	1·50	1·30
3310a	45c. Lily of the Valley (6.5.10)	1·50	1·30
3311	50c. Aster	1·70	1·50
3312	55c. Poppy	1·90	1·60
3313	55c. Red rose	1·90	1·60
3314	65c. Rudbeckia	2·40	2·10
3315	70c. Pink flower	2·50	2·30
3315a	75c. Balloon flower (*Platycodon grandiflorus*) (3.1.11)	2·75	2·40
3318	90c. Narcissus	3·00	2·50
3320	95c. Type **1485**	3·00	2·50
3320a	100c. *Dicentra spectabilis*	3·25	3·00
3320b	145c. Iris	4·25	3·75
3320c	200c. *Eschscholzia californica*	7·50	6·50
3320d	220c. Edlweiss	7·75	6·75
3320e	390c. Lily	12·50	11·00
3320f	€4.10 Ladies slipper	19·00	16·00
3321	€4.30 Larkspur	13·00	11·50
3322	€5 Gentian (7.7.11)	14·00	12·00

(b) Self-adhesive

3324	35c. Dahlia	1·30	1·10
3324a	45c. As No. 3310a (lily-of-the-valley) (1.3.11)	1·50	1·30
3325	55c. Poppy	1·90	1·60
3326	55c. Red rose	1·90	1·60
3327	65c. As No. 3314	2·20	2·00
3328	70c. As No. 3315	2·40	2·10
3330	90c. As No. 3318 (Narcissus)	3·25	2·75

1486 Celtic Statue, Glauberg

2005. Archaeology.

3335	**1486**	€1.44 multicoloured	5·00	4·25

1487 Championship Mascot (⅔-size illustration)

2005. Sport Promotion Fund. Multicoloured.

3336	45c.+20c. Type **1487** (World Cup Football Championship, Germany 2006)	2·75	2·40
3337	55c.+25c. Footballers (World Cup Football Championships, Germany 2006)	3·00	2·50
3338	55c.+25c. Skier (Nordic World Ski Championships, Oberstdorf)	3·00	2·50
3339	55c.+25c. Gymnasts (International German Gymnastics Festival, Berlin)	3·00	2·50
3340	144c.+56c. Fencers (Fencing World Championships, Leipzig)	7·00	6·00

1488 Pillar

2005. 150th Anniv of Advertisement Pillars.

3341	**1488**	55c. multicoloured	2·10	1·60

1489 Cathedral Facade

2005. Centenary of Berlin Cathedral. Ordinary or self-adhesive gum.

3342	**1489**	95c. multicoloured	3·25	2·50

1490 Postman walking in Mountains

2005. Postal Service (1st series). Multicoloured.

3344	55c. Type **1490**	2·10	1·60
3345	55c. Postman cycling	2·10	1·60

See also Nos. 3370/1.

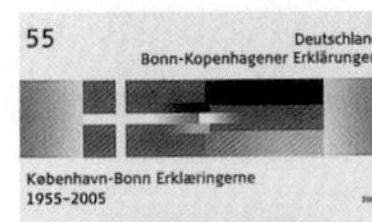

1491 Danish and German Flags

2005. 50th Anniv of Germany—Denmark Relations.

3346	**1491**	55c. multicoloured	2·10	1·60

A stamp of the same design was issued by Denmark.

1492 Lockheed L-1049 Super Constellation

2005. 50th Anniv of Resumption of German Air Traffic.

3347	**1492**	155c. multicoloured	5·25	4·25

1493 Aquaduct

2005. Centenary of Mittelland Canal.

3348	**1493**	45c. multicoloured	1·70	1·50

1494 Rock, Ferns and Tree

2005. National Parks. Bavarian Forest.

3349	**1494**	55c. multicoloured	2·10	1·60

1495 Silhouettes of Characters

2005. Birth Bicentenary of Hans Christian Andersen (writer). Ordinary or self-adhesive gum.

3350	**1495**	144c. light orange, orange and black	4·75	4·00

1496 Book Bindings and Signature

2005. Birth Bicentenary of Friedrich Schiller (poet). Schiller Year.

3352	**1496**	55c. multicoloured	2·10	1·60

1497 Signatories.

2005. 50th Anniv of Paris Agreements (establishing Federal Democratic Republic of Germany in Western European Union (WEU) and North Atlantic Treaty Organization (NATO).

3353	**1497**	55c. black and vermilion	2·10	1·60

1498 "Sitzende Franzi" (woodcut) (Erich Heikel)

2005. Centenary of Die Brucke (The Bridge) (group of Expressionist artists).

3354	**1498**	55c. black, vermilion and stone	2·10	1·60

1499 Wine Glass, Wine Bottle, Candle and Cup

2005. Europa. Gastronomy.

3355	**1499**	55c. chocolate, orange and rose	2·10	1·60

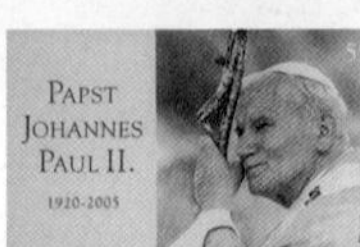

1500 Pope John Paul II

2005. Pope John Paul II Commemoration.

3356	**1500**	55c. multicoloured	2·10	1·60

1501 Kraftpost Omnibus

2005. Stamp Day. Centenary of Post Bus.

3357	**1501**	55c.+25c. multicoloured	3·00	2·50

1502 *Greif* ("Reach") (training ship)

2005. Youth Welfare. Ships. Multicoloured.

3358	45c.+20c. Type **1502**	2·75	2·40
3359	55c.+25c. *Passat* ("Trade Wind") (four-mast bark)	3·00	2·50
3360	55c.+25c. *Rickmer Rickmers* (cargo ship)	3·00	2·50
3361	55c.+25c. *Grand Duchess Elizabeth* (schooner)	3·00	2·50
3362	144c.+56c. *Deutschland* (training ship)	7·00	6·00

1503 Numbers as Map of Europe

2005. EUROSAI (European Organization of Supreme Audit Institutions) Conference, Bonn.

3363	**1503**	55c. multicoloured	2·10	1·60

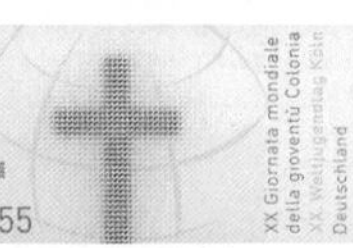

1504 Cross and Globe

2005. World Youth Day.

3364	**1504**	55c. multicoloured	2·10	1·60

A stamp of the same design was issued by Vatican City.

1505 Brunsbuttel Lighthouse

2005. Lighthouses. Multicoloured. Ordinary or self-adhesive gum.

3365	45c. Type **1505**	1·70	1·50
3366	55c. Westerheversand	2·10	1·50

See also Nos. 3429/30.

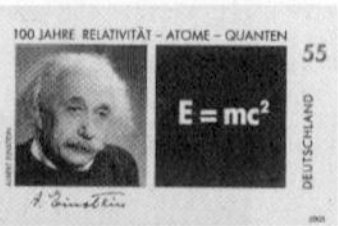

1506 Albert Einstein and "E=mc²"

2005. Centenary of Special Theory of Relativity by Albert Einstein (physicist).

3368	**1506**	55c. black and scarlet	2·10	1·60

1507 New Palace, Sanssouci Park, Potsdam

2005. Prussian Schlosses. Sheet 98×70 mm.

MS3369	**1507**	220c. multicoloured	7·50	7·00

2005. Postal Service (2nd issue). As T 1490. Multicoloured.

3370	55c. Postman with trolley	2·10	1·60
3371	55c. Postman in boat	2·10	1·60

1508 Tree and Figure

2005. Centenary of NaturFreunde Deutschlands (conservation organization).

3372	**1508**	144c. green and rose	5·25	4·50

1509 Chickens

2005. "For us Children".

3373	**1509**	55c. multicoloured	2·10	1·60

1510 City from River (15th-century woodcut)

2005. 1200th Anniv of Magdeburg.

3374	**1510**	55c. multicoloured	2·10	1·60

1511 Angel

2005. 450th Anniv of Religious Freedom.

3375	**1511**	55c. multicoloured	2·10	1·60

1512 Max Schmeling

2005. Birth Centenary of Max Schmeling (boxer).
3376 **1512** 100c. black and vermilion 2·10 1·60

1513 Church

2005. Completion of Reconstruction of Frauenkirche (Church of our Lady) Dresden (2004).
3377 **1513** 55c. multicoloured 2·10 1·60

1514 Script and Pen Nib

2005. Birth Bicentenary of Adalbert Stifter (writer).
3378 **1514** 55c. multicoloured 3·50 3·00

1515 Horse-drawn Procession

2005. 150th Anniv of Bad Tolz Leonhardifahrt (festival).
3379 **1515** 45c. multicoloured 1·70 1·30

1516 "Adoration of the Child Jesus"

2005. Christmas. Paintings by Stefan Lochner. Multicoloured.
3380 45c.+20c. Type **1516** 2·50 2·10
3381 55c.+25c. "Madonna of the Rose Bush" 3·25 2·40

1517 Israeli and German Flags

2005. 40th Anniv of Diplomatic Relations with Israel.
3382 **1517** 55c. multicoloured 2·10 1·60

1518 Bertha von Suttner and "Die Waffen nieder"

2005. Centenary of Bertha von Suttner's Nobel Peace Prize.
3383 **1518** 55c. multicoloured 2·10 1·60

1519 "50 JAHRE BUNDES WEHR"

2005. 50th Anniv of German Federal Armed Forces.
3384 **1519** 55c. multicoloured 2·10 1·60

1520 Robert Koch and Microscope

2005. Centenary of Robert Koch's Nobel Prize for Physiology and Medicine.
3385 **1520** 55c. multicoloured 5·00 4·00

2005. Prussian Schlosses. New Palace, Sanssouci Park, Potsdam (2nd issue). Self-adhesive Stamp.
3386 **1507** 220c. multicoloured 7·50 6·50

1521 *Gonepteryx rhamni*

2005. Butterflies and Moths. Multicoloured Ordinary gum.
3387 45c.+20c. Type **1521** 2·50 2·30
3388 55c.+25c. *Panaxia quadripunctaria* 3·00 2·40
3389 55c.+25c. *Inachis io* 3·00 2·40
3390 145c.+55c. *Brintesia circe* 6·50 5·75

(b) Self-adhesive.
3391 55c.+25c. As No. 3389 3·00 2·50

1522 Sights of Halle

2006. 1200th Anniv of Halle.
3392 **1522** 45c. multicoloured 1·70 1·30

1523 Wolfgang Mozart

2006. 250th Birth Anniv of Wolfgang Amadeus Mozart (composer).
3393 **1523** 55c. multicoloured 2·10 1·60

1524 Snow-covered Tree

2006. Winter.
3394 **1524** 55c. multicoloured 2·10 1·60

1525 Clouds over Earth

2006. Climate Protection Awareness.
3395 **1525** 55c.+25c. multicoloured 3·25 2·75

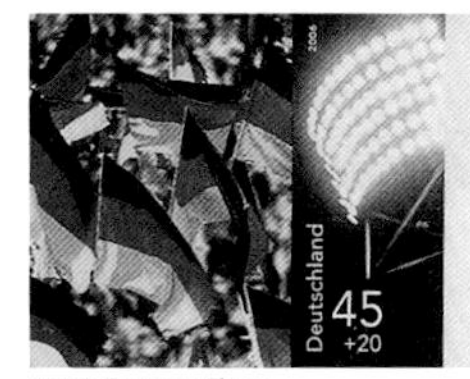

1526 Bull (detail) and Charles IV's Seal

2006. 650th Anniv of Charles IV's Golden Bull (document creating constitutional structure). (a) Ordinary or Self-adhesive gum.
3396 **1526** 145c. multicoloured 5·25 4·50

1527 German Flags

2006. Sport Promotion Fund. World Cup Football Championship, Germany. Multicoloured.
3398 45c.+20c. Type **1527** 2·50 2·10
3399 55c.+25c. Horse and rider (World Equestrian Games, Aachen 2006) 2·75 2·30
3400 55c.+25c. Stadium lights (opening game) 2·75 2·30
3401 55c.+25c. Pitch (final) 2·75 2·30
3402 145c.+56c. Fireworks and emblem 6·50 5·50

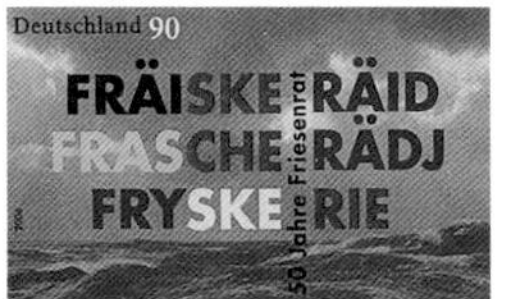

1528 Rooftops

2006. 850th Anniv of Michaelskirche, Schwäbisch Hall.
3403 **1528** 55c. multicoloured 2·10 1·60

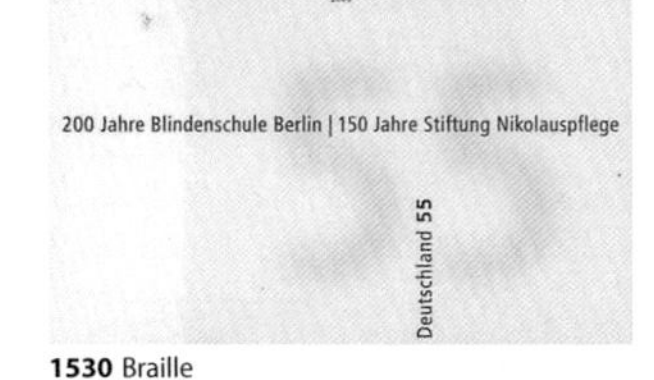

1529 "Fraiske Räid"

2006. 50th Anniv of Friesenrat (Frisian council).
3404 **1529** 90c. multicoloured 3·25 2·75

1530 Braille

2006. Bicentenary of Blind School, Berlin. 150th Anniv of Nikolauspflege (charitable organization).
3405 **1530** 55c. black and grey 2·10 1·60

1531 Early Town and Map

2006. 1200th Anniv of Ingolstadt.
3406 **1531** 55c. multicoloured 2·10 1·60

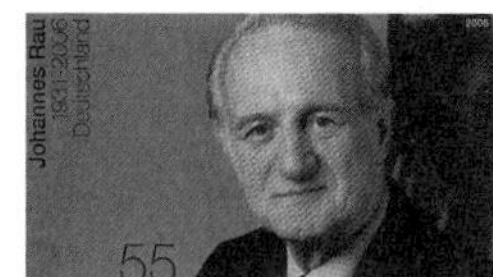

1532 Altes Museum, Lustgarten

2006. 225th Birth Anniv of Karl Friedrich Schinkel (architect). Ordinary or self-adhesive gum.
3407 **1532** 55c. multicoloured 2·10 1·60

1533 Johannes Rau

2006. Johannes Rau (president 1999—2004) Commemoration.
3408 **1533** 55c. multicoloured 2·10 1·60

1534 Emblem

2006. 500th Anniv of European University Viadrina Frankfurt (Oder).
3409 **1534** 55c. blue and black 2·10 1·60

1535 Blossom-covered Trees

2006. Spring.
3410 **1535** 55c. multicoloured 2·10 1·60

1536 Self-Portrait (Albrecht Durer)

2006. Art.
3411 **1536** 145c. blue and black 5·25 4·25

2006. World Cup Football Championship, Germany. Sheet 130×180 mm containing T 1527 and similar horiz designs. Multicoloured.
MS3412 130×180 mm. Nos. 3398, 3400/2 15·00 14·00

1537 "Integration" on Jacket

2006. Europa. Integration.
3413 **1537** 55c. multicoloured 2·10 1·60

1538 Rhine Valley

2006. Upper Central Rhine Valley (Oberes Mittelrheintal). World Heritage Site. Ordinary or self-adhesive gum.
3414 **1538** 55c. multicoloured 2·10 1·60

1539 Gerd Bucerius

2006. Birth Centenary of Gerd Bucerius (politician).
3416 **1539** 85c. multicoloured 3·25 2·50

1540 Pine Marten

2006. Youth Welfare. Animals. Multicoloured.
3417 45c.+20c. Type **1540** 2·20 2·00
3418 55c.+25c. Hares 2·75 2·40
3419 55c.+25c. Red squirrel 2·75 2·40
3420 55c.+25c. Roe deer and fawn 2·75 2·40

3421 145c.+55c. Wild boar and young 6·75 5·75

1541 Stripes

2006. Birth Centenary of Stefan Andres (writer).

3422 **1541** 55c. multicoloured 2·10 1·60

1542 Brooklyn Bridge, New York

2006. Birth Bicentenary of Johan August Robling (architect).

3423 **1542** 145c. multicoloured 5·25 4·00

1543 Car Number Plates

2006. Centenary of First Number Plates.

3424 **1543** 45c. multicoloured 1·90 1·50

1544 Berghauser Castle, Burganlage

2006

3425 **1544** 55c. multicoloured 2·10 1·60

1545 Flowering Rapeseed

2006. Summer.

3426 **1545** 55c. multicoloured 2·10 1·60

1546 "Saskia van Uylenburgh"

2006. 400th Birth Anniv of Rembrandt Harmenszoon van Rijn (Rembrandt) (artist).

3427 **1546** 55c. multicoloured 2·50 2·10

2006. Lighthouses. As T 1505. Multicoloured.

3429 45c. Neuland 1·90 1·50

3430 55c. Hohe Weg 2·10 1·60

1547 Valley

2006. Tourism. Schwarzwald. Sheet 145×70 mm.

MS3432 **1547** 55c. multicoloured 2·20 2·10

1548 Valley and Skull

2006. 150th Anniv of Discovery of Neanderthal Skull.

3433 **1548** 220c. multicoloured 7·50 6·50

1549 Cat and Envelopes

2006. For us Children

3434 **1549** 55c. multicoloured 2·10 1·60

1550 Hauptmann von Kopenick

2006. Centenary of Hauptmann von Kopenick (fraudulent identity of William Voigt) Affair.

3435 **1550** 55c. multicoloured 2·10 1·60

1551 Shipping and Trade

2006. 650th Anniv of Hanseatic league (Stadtehanse).

3436 **1551** 70c. multicoloured 2·75 2·40

1552 Fliegender Hamburger VT 877

2006. Welfare. Trains. Multicoloured. (a) Ordinary gum.

3437 45c.+20c. Type **1552** 2·50 2·30

3438 55c.+25c. Intercity Express ET 403 2·75 2·40

3439 55c.+25c. Trans Europe Express VT 11.5 2·75 2·40

3440 145c.+55c. Henschel-Wegmann-Zug 61 001 7·00 6·00

(b) Self-adhesive.

3441 55c.+25c. As No. 3438 3·00 2·50

1553 Postcard, 1896

2006. Stamp Day.

3442 **1553** 55c. multicoloured 2·10 1·60

1554 Woodland

2006. Autumn.

3443 **1554** 55c. multicoloured 2·10 1·60

1555 Hannah Arendt

2006. Birth Centenary of Hannah Arendt (political theorist and philosopher).

3444 **1555** 145c. multicoloured 5·00 4·50

1556 Eugen Bolz

2006. 125th Birth Anniv of Eugen Anton Bolz (Catholic politician).

3445 **1556** 45c. blue and yellow 1·90 1·30

1557 The Nativity

2006. Christmas. Paintings by Meister Franke. Multicoloured.

3446 45c.+20c. Type **1557** 2·20 2·00

3447 55c.+25c. Three Kings 2·75 2·40

1558 Cardinal Hoffner

2006. Birth Centenary of Cardinal Joseph Hoffner (Bishop of Munster and Archbishop of Cologne).

3448 **1558** 55c. multicoloured 2·10 1·60

2006. Seasons. Multicoloured.

3449 55c. As Type **1535** 2·10 1·60

3450 55c. As Type **1545** 2·10 1·60

3451 55c. As Type **1554** 2·10 1·60

3452 55c. As Type **1524** 2·10 1·60

1559 Werner Forbmann

2006. 50th Anniv of Werner Forbmann's (surgeon and inventor of the heart catheter) Nobel Prize for Medicine.

3453 **1559** 90c. multicoloured 3·25 3·00

1560 Street

2007. Furth Millenary. (a) Ordinary or self-adhesive gum.

3454 **1560** 45c. multicoloured 1·90 1·50

1561 Stars

2007. Germany's Presidency of European Union.

3456 **1561** 55c. black, vermilion and yellow 2·10 1·60

1562 Imperial Cathedral Facade

2007. Bamberg Diocese Millenary.

3457 **1562** 55c. rosine, blue and gold 2·10 1·60

1563 Symbols of Saarland

2007. 50th Anniv of Federal Republic of Saarland. (a) Ordinary or self-adhesive gum.

3458 **1563** 55c. multicoloured 2·10 1·60

1564 Ball and Hands

2007. Sport Promotion Fund (1st issue). World Handball Championship, Germany.

3460 **1564** 55c.+25c. multicoloured 3·25 2·75

See also Nos. 3462/4.

1565 Engine Diagram and NSU Ro80

2007. 50th Anniv of Rotary Engine designed by Felix Wankel.

3461 **1565** 145c. multicoloured 5·00 4·50

2007. Sport Promotion Fund (2nd issue). As T 1564. Multicoloured.

3462 45c.+20c. Canoeing (world championships, Wedau Park) 2·50 2·30

3463 55c.+25c. Gymnastics (world championships, Stuttgart) 3·00 2·50

3464 145c.+55c. Swimming (world pentathlon championships, Berlin) 6·00 5·25

1566 Johann Senckenberg and Institute Building

2007. 300th Birth Anniv of Johann Christian Senckenberg (physician and health reformer).

3465 **1566** 90c. multicoloured 3·25 3·00

1567 Claus Schenk Graf von Stauffenberg and Helmuth James Graf von Moltke

2007. Birth Centenaries.

3466 **1567** 55c. vermilion and black 2·10 1·60

1568 Star of David

2007. Jewish Centre, Munich.

3467 **1568** 55c. multicoloured 2·10 1·60

1569 "Die Ausgrabung der Kreuze" (Adam Elsheimer)

2007

3468 **1569** 55c. multicoloured 2·10 1·60

1570 Signatories

2007. 50th Anniv of Treaty of Rome.

3469 **1570** 55c. multicoloured 2·10 1·60

1571 Paul Gerhardt and Score

2007. 400th Birth Anniv of Paul Gerhardt.

3470 **1571** 55c. multicoloured 2·10 1·60

1572 LZ 127 *Graf Zeppelin*

2007. Stamp Day. Sheet 105×70 mm.

MS3471 **1572** 170c.+70c. mult 8·75 7·75

1573 Writing a Letter

2007. Post. Each yellow, black and vermilion.

3472	55c. Type **1573**	2·10	1·60
3473	55c. Posting letter	2·10	1·60

1574 Pope Benedict XVI

2007. 80th Birthday of Pope Benedict XVI.

3474	**1574** 55c. multicoloured	2·10	1·60

1575 "Universalis Cosmographia"

2007. 500th Anniv of World Map drawn by Martin Waldseemüller.

3475	**1575** €2.20 multicoloured	8·00	7·00

1576 Scouts

2007. Europa. Centenary of Scouting.

3476	**1576** 45c. multicoloured	1·70	1·30

2007. 40th Anniv of Sport Promotion Fund. As T 1564. Multicoloured.

MS3477	45c.+20c. As No. 3462; 55c.+25c. As No. 3460; 55c.+25c. As No. 3463; 145c.+55c. As No. 3464	13·00	11·50

1577 Schloss

2007. Bellevue Schloss. Ordinary or self-adhesive gum.

3478	**1577** 55c. multicoloured	2·10	1·60

1578 Schloss and Sculptures

2007. 700th Anniv of Moyland Schloss.

3480	**1578** 85c. multicoloured	3·25	2·50

1579 Early Festival Goers

2007. 175th Anniv of Hambacher Fest (democratic festival). (a) Ordinary or Self-adhesive gum.

3481	**1579** 145c. multicoloured	5·00	4·00

1580 Sawing legs from Chair

2007. 125th Birth Anniv of Valentin Ludwig Fey (Karl Valentin) (comedian and writer).

3483	**1580** 45c. multicoloured	1·90	1·50

1581 'Nichts Schonres gab's fur Tante Lotte Als Schwarze-Heidelbeer-Kompotte' (Behold Aunt Lotte's choicest snack: Blueberry compote, sweet and black)

2007. For the Young. 175th Birth Anniv of Wilhelm Busch (poet and cartoonist). Sheet 165×75 mm containing T 1581 and similar square designs showing scenes from illustrated poem Hans Huckebein-der Unglucksrabe (the unlucky raven) by Wilhelm Busch. Multicoloured.

MS3484	45c.+20c. Type **1581**; 55c.+25c. Doch Huckebein verschleudert nur Die schone Gabe der Natur (But Huckebein, unused to thrift, Just squanders nature's precious gift); 55c.+25c. Die Tante naht voll Zorn und Schrecken; Hans Huckebein verlaßt das Becken (The aunt descends in shock and wrath. Hans Huckebein deserts his bath); 145c.+55c. Und schnell betritt er, angstbeflugelt, Die Wasche, welche frisch gebugelt (And tramples, on the wings of fright, The ironed laundry, clean and white)	13·00	11·50

1582 Paul Klinger and Nadia Grey (poster for film 'Hengst Maestoso Austria')

2007. Birth Centenary of Paul Karl Heinrich Klinksik (Paul Klinger) (actor).

3485	**1582** 55c. multicoloured	2·75	2·40

2007. Lighthouses. As T 1467. Multicoloured.

3486	45c. Bremerhaven Oberfeuer	1·90	1·50
3487	55c. Hornum	2·10	1·60

1583 House of Blackheads, Riga

2007. World Heritage Sites, Riga and Wismar. Multicoloured.

3488	65c. Type **1583**	2·20	2·00
3489	70c. City Hall and St. George's Church, Wismar	2·40	2·10

Stamps of a similar design were issued by Latvia.

1584 Banknotes and Coins from Various Currency Epochs

2007. 50th Anniv of German Bundesbank (Federal bank).

3490	**1584** 55c. multicoloured	2·20	1·60

1585 Saale River Plain

2007. 75th Anniv of Saaletalsperre Bleiloch (dam across Saale valley).

3491	**1585** 55c. multicoloured	2·20	1·60

1586 Kaiser Wilhelm Bridge

2007. Centenary of Kaiser Wilhelm Bridge, Wilhelmshaven.

3492	**1586** 145c. multicoloured	5·25	4·50

1587 Hedgehog and Hearts

2007. For us Children

3493	**1587** 55c. multicoloured	2·20	1·60

1588 Receiving a Letter

2007. Post. Multicoloured.

3494	55c. Type **1588**	2·10	1·60
3495	55c. Reading letter	2·10	1·60

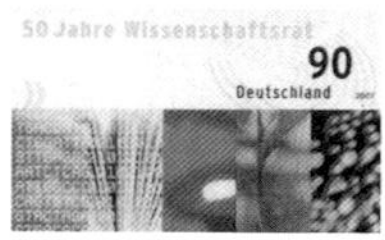

1589 Symbols of Science

2007. 50th Anniv of Wissenschaftsrat (government scientific advisors).

3496	**1589** 90c. multicoloured	3·50	3·00

1590 Stylized Building

2007. Centenary of Deutscher Werkbund (artistic design group).

3497	**1590** 55c. multicoloured	2·10	1·60

1591 Section of 'Limes' and Watch Towers

2007. World Heritage Site. 'The Roman Limes' (Roman camp, castle and walls). Sheet 105×70 mm.

MS3498	55c. multicoloured	2·10	2·00

1592 Karl Freiherr Vom Stein

2007. 250th Birth Anniv of Heinrich Friedrich Carl Freiherr Vom und Zum Stein (statesman and reformer).

3499	**1592** 145c. multicoloured	5·00	4·50

1593 Three Kings

2007. Christmas. Multicoloured.

3500	45c+20c. Type **1593**	2·50	2·30
3501	55c.+25c. Virgin and Child	2·75	2·50

1594 St. Elizabeth feeding Invalid

2007. 800th Birth Anniv of St. Elizabeth von Thuringen.

3502	**1594** 55c. multicoloured	2·10	1·60

1595 Astrid Lindgren and Emil from Lönneberga (character from book)

2007. Birth Centenary of Astrid Lindgren (children's author).

3503	**1595** 100c. multicoloured	3·50	3·25

A stamp of the same design was issued by Sweden.

1596 Brandenburg Gate, Berlin

2007. 275th Birth Anniv of Carl Gotthard Langhans (architect). Ordinary or self-adhesive gum.

3504	**1596** 55c. multicoloured	2·10	1·60

1597 Guinea Pigs

2007. Welfare. Pets. Showing animals and young. Multicoloured. (a) Ordinary gum.

3506	45c.+20c. Type **1597**	2·50	2·30
3507	55c.+25c. Dogs	2·75	2·40
3508	55c.+25c. Horses	2·75	2·40
3509	145c.+55c. Rabbits	6·75	6·00

(b) Self-adhesive.

3510	55c.+25c. As No. 3508	3·25	3·00

1598 Liturgical Book and Gothic Wall Painting (detail), Reichenau Abbey

2008. World Heritage Site. Ordinary or self-adhesive gum.

3511	**1598** 45c. multicoloured	1·80	1·50

1599 *Old Berlin Distillery*

2008. 150th Birth Anniv of Heinrich Zille (artist).

3513	**1599** 55c. multicoloured	2·10	1·80

1600 '50 Jahre Bundeskartellamt'

2008. 50th Anniv of Bundeskartellamt (monopolies commission).
3514 **1600** 90c. multicoloured 3·50 3·25

1601 Cathedral Square

2008. 1100th Anniv of Eichstatt. Ordinary or self-adhesive gum.
3515 **1601** 145c. multicoloured 5·50 5·00

1602 Decorative Pot with Shell Insert

2008. 500th Birth Anniv of Wenzel Jamnitzer (goldsmith).
3517 **1602** 220c. multicoloured 8·25 7·50

1603 *Der Arme Poet*

2008. Birth Bicentenary of Carl Spitzweg (artist). Ordinary or self-adhesive gum.
3518 **1603** 55c. multicoloured 2·20 2·10

1604 Fish and Heart ('Herzlichen Gluckwunsch') (Congratulations)

2008. Post. Multicoloured.
3519 55c. Type **1604** 2·20 2·10
3520 55c. Cats ('Alles Gute') (All Good) 2·20 2·10

1605 Church Facade

2008. Millenary of Bochum-Stiepel Village Church.
3521 **1605** 145c. multicoloured 5·50 5·00

1606 Glider World Championships, Lusse

2008. Sports Promotion Fund. Multicoloured.
3522 45c.+20c. Type **1606** 2·40 2·20
3523 55c.+25c. European Football Championships, Austria and Switzerland 2·75 2·40
3524 55c.+25c. Chess Olympiad, Dresden 2·75 2·40
3525 145c.+55c. Olympic Games, Beijing 7·00 6·25

1607 Helmut Kautner

2008. Birth Centenary of Helmut Kautner (film director).
3526 **1607** 55c. multicoloured 2·30 2·00

1608 Gnu Herd

2008. 150th Anniv of Frankfurt Zoological Society.
3527 **1608** 65c. multicoloured 2·50 2·30

2008. 50th Anniv of Bundeskartellamt (monopolies commission) (2nd issue). Self adhesive.
3528 **1600** 90c. multicoloured 3·50 3·25

1609 Birds

2008. Centenary of State Bird Sanctuary, Seebach.
3529 **1609** 45c. multicoloured 2·10 1·60

1610 Max Planck

2008. 150th Birth Anniv of Max Planck (physicist, Nobel Prize Winner–1918).
3530 **1610** 55c. multicoloured 2·30 2·00

1611 Johann Wichern

2008. Birth Bicentenary of Johann Hinrich Wichern (theologian).
3531 **1611** 55c. multicoloured 2·30 2·00

1612 Knut (hand reared polar bear cub)

2008. Environmental Protection.
3532 **1612** 55c.+25c. multicoloured 3·25 3·00

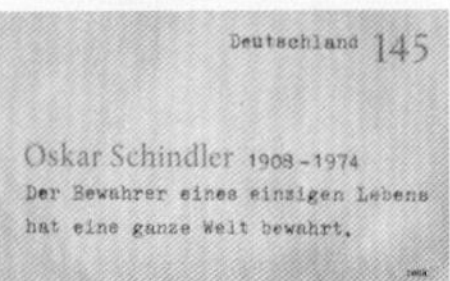

1613 'Der Bewahrer eines einzigen Lebens hat eine ganze Welt bewahrt' ((he who saves a single life saves the whole world) (translation of Hebrew engraving on Oskar Schindler's ring, gift of farewell from rescuee on 8 May 1945))

2008. Birth Centenary of Oskar Schindler (industrialist who saved Jews during WWII).
3533 **1613** 145c. multicoloured 5·50 5·00

1614 Photograph of German Players (5 April 1908) and Parts of Original Poster

2008. Centenary of German Soccer Internationals.
3534 **1614** 170c. multicoloured 6·50 6·00

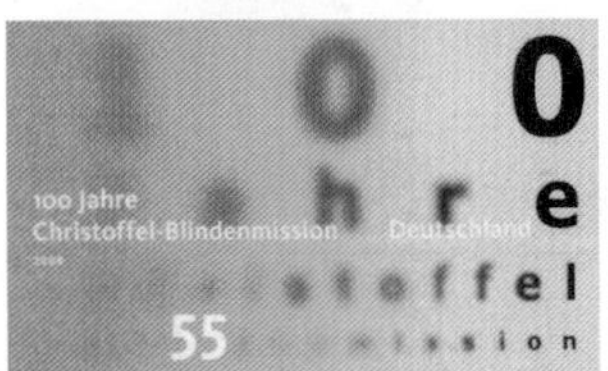

1615 Blurred Script

2008. Centenary of Christoffel Blind Mission. (Christoffel Blindoffmission) (charity founded by pastor Ernst Jakob Christoffel for sopport of the blind worldwide.
3535 **1615** 55c. multicoloured 2·30 2·00

1616 Sun and Moon ('Herzliche Grube (cordial greetings)')

2008. Greetings Stamps. Europa. The Letter (3536/8). Multicoloured. (a) Ordinary gum.
3536 55c. Type **1616** 2·30 2·00
3537 55c. Hands holding bird and flower ('Danke' (thank you)) 2·30 2·00

(b) Self-adhesive.
3538 55c. As Type **1616** 2·30 2·00
3539 55c. As No. 3520 2·30 2·00
3540 55c. As No. 3519 2·30 2·00
3541 55c. As No. 3537 2·30 2·00

1617 Dornier Do J *Wal*

2008. Welfare. Aircraft. Multicoloured. (a) Ordinary gum.
3542 45c.+20c. Type **1617** 3·00 2·75
3543 55c.+25c. A380 Airbus 3·00 3·00
3544 55c.+25c. Junkers Ju 52 3·00 3·00
3545 145c.+55c. Messerschmitt-Bolkow-Blohm (MBB) BO 105 7·50 7·00

(b) Self-adhesive.
3546 55c.+25c. As No. 3543 3·75 3·50

1618 Faces

2008. Community Service.
3547 **1618** 55c. multicoloured 2·30 2·00

1619 Steam Locomotive, Early Station and Passengers

2008. 125th Anniv of Drachenfels Railway (Drachenfelsbahn) (rack railway line from Konigswinter to summit of Drachenfels).
3548 **1619** 45c. multicoloured 2·00 1·90

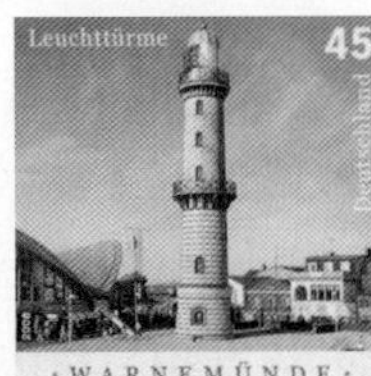

1620 Warnemunde

2008. Lighthouses. Multicoloured. (a) Ordinary gum.
3549 45c. Type **1620** 2·10 1·80
3550 55c. Amrum 2·30 2·00

(b) Self-adhesive.
3551 55c. Hornum 2·30 2·00
3552 55c. As No. 3550 2·30 2·00

1621 Man at Table (drawing by Franz Kafka)

2008. 125th Birth Anniv of Franz Kafka (Czech writer).
3553 **1621** 55c. black 2·40 2·10

1622 *Selbstportrat mit Ruckenakt* and *Morgensonne*

2008. 150th Birth Anniv of Lovis Corinth (artist).
3554 **1622** 145c. multicoloured 6·00 5·75

1623 *Gorch Fock*

2008. 50th Anniv of Gorch Fock (sail training ship).
3555 **1623** 55c. multicoloured 2·50 2·30

1624 Silhouette *Ringelnatz* (Ernst Moritz Engert)

2008. 125th Birth Anniv of Joachim Ringelnatz (writer and artist).
3556 **1624** 85c. blue and black 3·75 3·75

1625 Herman Schulze-Delitzsch

2008. Birth Bicentenary of Herman Schulze-Delitzsch (politician and founder of German cooperative system).
3557 **1625** 90c. multicoloured 4·00 3·75

1626 Triceratops

2008. Youth Stamp. Dinosaurs. Sheet 190×110 mm containing T 1626 and similar horiz designs. Multicoloured.
MS3558 45c.+20c. Type **1626**; 55c.+25c. Tyrannosaurus; 55c.+25c. Diplodocus; 145c.+55c. Plateosaurus 17·00 17·00

1627 Arrival of First Mail Coach in Ohrdruff

2008. Stamp Day. Philatelic Treasures.

3559	**1627**	55c. multicoloured	2·50	2·30

1628 Ronald, Gunni and Jenny the Rat riding Blue Horse

2008. For us Children

3560	**1628**	55c. multicoloured	2·50	2·30

1629 Old Bridge, Bad Sackingen–Stein/Aargau

2008. Bridges.

3561	**1629**	70c. multicoloured	3·00	2·75

A stamp of a similar design was issued by Switzerland.

1630 Livestock Market

2008. 500th Anniv of Gallimarkt (annual fair), Leer.

3562	**1630**	45c. multicoloured	2·00	1·80

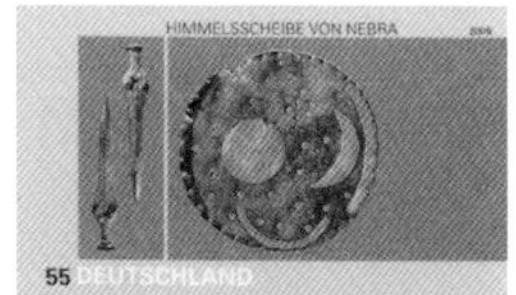

1631 Disc and Two Bronze Swords

2008. Archaeology. Sky Disc of Nebra (bronze plate with apparent astronomical phenomena and religious themes).

3563	**1631**	55c. multicoloured	2·50	2·30

1632 Lorenz Werthmann

2008. 150th Birth Anniv of Lorenz Werthmann (founder and first president of the German Caritas association).

3564	**1632**	55c. multicoloured	2·50	2·30

1633 Aircraft in Flight

2008. Centenary of Hans Grade's First Powered Flight in Germany.

3565	**1633**	145c. multicoloured	6·00	5·50

2008. Winter. 450th Anniv (2005) of the 'Peace of Augsburg' (treaty marking the beginning of peaceful cohabitation of Catholics and Protestants) (3566). As Types 1484 and 1511. Multicoloured. Self-adhesive.

3566	55c. As Type **1484**	2·50	2·30
3567	55c. As Type **1511**	2·50	2·30

Type **1634** is vacant.
See also Nos. 3305 and 3375.

1635 *The Nativity* (Albrecht Durer)

2008. Christmas. Multicoloured.

3568	45c.+20c. Type **1635**	3·00	2·75
3569	55c.+25c. *The Nativity* (Raffaello Santi) (horiz)	3·75	3·50

1636 Association Emblem

2008. 30th Anniv of 'Heart for Children' Association (children's charity).

3570	**1636**	55c. vermilion and black	2·50	2·30

1637 'Leben'

2008. 50th Anniv of Federal Association of Life (intellectual diasablities charity).

3571	**1637**	55c. multicoloured	2·50	2·30

1638 *Nils Holgersson with Ganz* (book illustration by Wilhelm Schultz)

2008. 150th Birth Anniv of Selma Ottilia Lovisz Lagerlof (winner of Nobel Prize for Literature–1909).

3572	**1638**	100c. multicoloured	4·50	4·00

1639 Building Facade

2009. 500th Anniv of Frankenberg Hall. Multicoloured. Ordinary or self-adhesive gum.

3573	45c. Type **1639**	2·30	2·00

1640 Plates with Cereal Grains

2009. 50th Anniv of MISEREOR and Bread for the World (church charities).

3575	**1640**	55c. multicoloured	2·75	2·50

1641 Rainbow

2009. Welfare Stamps. Celestial Phenomena. Multicoloured. (a) Ordinary gum.

3576	45c.+20c. Type **1641**	3·75	3·50
3577	55c.+25c. Aurora borealis	4·00	3·75
3578	55c.+25c. Sunset	4·00	3·75
3579	145c.+55c. Lightning	9·75	9·00

(b) Self-adhesive.

3580	55c.+25c. As No. 3678	4·25	4·00

1642 Tangermunde Castle

2009. Tangermunde Castle Millennary.

3581	**1642**	90c. multicoloured	4·25	4·00

1643 Theodor Heuss

2009. 125th Birth Anniv of Theodor Heuss (politician, writer and first FDR Head of State).

3582	**1643**	145c. multicoloured	7·00	6·50

1644 Heinz Erhardt

2009. Birth Centenary of Heinz Erhardt (comedian).

3583	**1644**	55c. multicoloured	2·50	2·40

1645 Felix Mendelssohn

2009. Birth Bicentenary of Jakob Ludwig Felix Mendelssohn Bartholdy (composer).

3584	**1645**	65c. multicoloured	3·00	2·75

1646 *The Propylaea in Munich*

2009. 225th Birth Anniv of Leo von Klenze (architect).

3585	**1646**	70c. multicoloured	3·25	3·00

1647 *The Firebird*

2009. Birth Centenary of Helmut Andreas Paul (HAP) Grieshaber (artist).

3586	**1647**	165c. multicoloured	7·25	6·50

1648 Golo Mann

2009. Birth Centenary of Angelus Gottfried Thomas Mann (Golo) Mann (historian and writer).

3587	**1648**	45c. multicoloured	2·30	2·10

1649 Applying Stamp

2009. Post. Multicoloured.

3588	55c. Type **1649**	2·75	2·50
3589	55c. Post Office	2·75	2·50

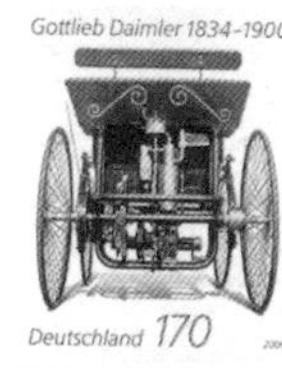

1650 Stahlradwagen

2009. 175th Birth Anniv of Gottlieb Wilhelm Daimler (engineer and motor vehicle pioneer).

3590	**1650**	170c. multicoloured	8·00	7·50

1651 Hurdler

2009. Sports Promotion Fund. International Association of Athletics Federations World Championship—Berlin 2009. Multicoloured.

3591	45c.+20c. Type **1651**	3·25	3·00
3592	55c.+25c. Pole vaulter	4·00	3·75
3593	55c.+25c. Runners	4·00	3·75
3594	145c.+55c. Discus	9·75	9·00

1652 Bernhard Grzimek

2009. Birth Centenary of Bernhard Grzimek (film maker).

3595	**1652**	55c. multicoloured	2·75	2·50

1653 Planets

2009. Europa. Astronomy. 400th Anniv of Kepler's Laws.

3596	**1653**	55c. multicoloured	2·75	2·50

2009. Post. As T 1649. Multicoloured.

3597	55c. Transport	2·75	2·50
3598	55c. Delivery	2·75	2·50

1654 Eichstatt Letter (showing first German stamps, franked 1849)

2009. Stamp Day.

3599	**1654**	55c.+25c. multicoloured	4·00	3·75

1655 Luther Memorials, Eisleben and Wittenberg

2009. World Heritage Sites.

3600	**1655**	145c. multicoloured	6·75	6·25

1656 First Exhibition Poster, Frankfurt 1909

2009. Centenary of International Areospace Exhibition.

3601	**1656**	55c. multicoloured	2·50	2·40

1657 *Mask* (Christian Grovermann), *Emperor Agustus* (Jochen Hahnel), Hermann Monument, Teutoburg Forest and *Forest* (Thomas Serres)

2009. Bimillennary of Varus (Teutoburg Forest) Battle. Multicoloured. Ordinary or self-adhesive gum.

3602	55c. Type **1657**		2·50	2·40

1658 Illustration from *Struwwelpeter*

2009. Birth Bicentenary of Heinrich Hoffman (children's author and politician).

3604	**1658**	85c. multicoloured	4·00	3·50

1659 Eifel National Park

2009. Sheet 105×70 mm.

MS3605	**1659**	220c. multicoloured	9·75	8·75

1660 Norderney

2009. Lighthouses. Multicoloured.

3606	45c. Type **1660**	2·10	1·90
3607	55c. Dornbusch	2·50	2·40

1661 Early Campus

2009. 600th Anniv of Leipzig University. Multicoloured. (a) Ordinary gum.

3608	55c. Type **1661**	2·50	2·40

(b) Size 38×22 mm. Self-adhesive.

3609	55c. As Type **1661**	2·50	2·40

1662 John Calvin

2009. 500th Birth Anniv of John Calvin (religious reformer).

3610	**1662**	70c. black	3·50	3·00

1663 Loading

2009. Centenary of Sassnitz to Trelleborg Ferry.

3611	**1663**	145c. multicoloured	6·75	6·25

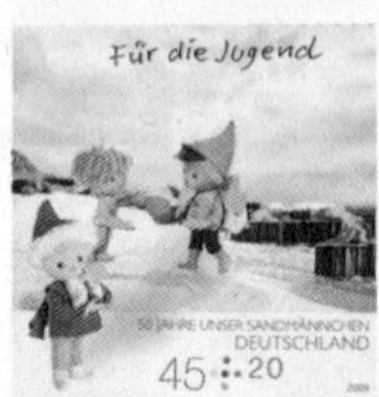

1664 Baltic Sea Beach

2009. Youth Stamps. 50th Anniv of Unser Sandmannchen (children's television programme). Multicoloured.

3612	45c.+20c. Type **1664**	3·00	2·75
3613	55c.+25c. Flying machine	4·00	3·50
3614	55c.+25c. Harz narrow-gauge railway	4·00	3·50
3615	145c.+55c. Planet Gugel	9·25	8·50

1665 Houses and Young People

2009. Centenary of Jugendherbergen (youth hostels).

3616	**1665**	55c. multicoloured	2·50	2·40

2009. Centenary of International Aerospace Exhibition. Self-adhesive.

3616a	**1656**	55c. multicoloured	2·50	2·40

1666 Early Race Cars

2009. Historic Motorsport. 115th Anniv of First Automobile Race between Paris and Rouen in France. Sheet 105×70 mm.

MS3617	**1666**	85c. multicoloured	4·25	3·75

1667 Cathedral

2009. Millenary of Mainz Cathedral (Mainzer Dom) Consecration.

3618	**1667**	90c. multicoloured	4·25	3·75

1668 Cowboy and Indian

2009. For us Children

3619	**1668**	55c. multicoloured	2·50	2·40

1669 Celebration

2009. 60th Anniv of Basic Law and 20th Anniv of Fall of Berlin Wall.

3620	**1669**	55c. multicoloured	2·50	2·40

1670 Bundestag, Reichstag Building (parliament)

2009. Government. Sheet 130×90 mm containing T 1670 and similar horiz design. Multicoloured.

MS3621	55c. Type **1670**; 90c. Bundesrat, Prussian Manor, Berlin (federal council)	7·00	6·25

1671 '20'

2009. 20th Anniv of Opening of Border between Austria and Hungary.

3622	**1671**	70c. multicoloured	3·50	3·00

A stamp of a similar design was issued by Austria and Hungary.

1672 *Still Life with Cherries* (Georg Flegel)

2009. Art.

3623	**1672**	45c. multicoloured	2·10	1·90

1673 Crowd and Nikolai Church, Leipzig

2009. 20th Anniv of Peaceful Revolution.

3624	**1673**	55c. multicoloured	2·50	2·40

1674 Adoration of the Magi

2009. Christmas. The Hoya Missal. Multicoloured.

3625	45c.+20c. Type **1674**	3·00	2·75
3626	55c.+25c. Holy Family	4·00	3·50

1675 Badger

2009. Animal of the Year.

3627	**1675**	55c. multicoloured	2·50	2·40

1676 Marion Grafin Donhoff

2009. Birth Centenary of Marion Grafin Donhoff (political Journalist).

3628	**1676**	55c. multicoloured	2·50	2·40

1677 'Die Kunste ist eine Tochter der Freiheit'

2009. Birth Bicentenary of Johann Christoph Friedrich von Schiller.

3629	**1677**	145c. black, ultramarine and brownish grey	6·75	6·25

1678 Exhibits

2010. Bicentenary of Natural History Museum, Berlin. Ordinary or self-adhesive gum.

3630	**1678**	45c. multicoloured	2·30	2·10

1679 *Malus domestica* (apple)

2010. Welfare Stamps. Fruit. Multicoloured. (a) Ordinary gum.

3632	45c.+20c. Type **1679**	3·25	3·00
3633	55c.+25c. *Citrus limon* (lemon)	4·00	3·75
3634	55c.+25c. *Fragaria ananassa* (strawberry)	4·00	3·75
3635	145c.+55c. *Vaccinium myrtillus* (bilberry)	9·75	8·75

(b) Self-adhesive.

3636	55c.+25c. As No. 3634 (strawberry)	4·00	3·75

1680 'Ruhr 2010'

2010. Ruhr–European Capital of Culture, 2010.

3637	**1680**	55c. multicoloured	2·75	2·50

1681 *Limburg an der Lahn* (George Clarkson Stanfield)

2010. 1100th Anniv of Limburg an der Lahn. Ordinary or self-adhesive gum.
3638 **1681** 145c. multicoloured 7·25 7·00

1682 St Michael's Church, Hildesheim

2010. Millennary of St Michael's Church, Hildesheim. UNESCO World Heritage Site. Ordinary or self-adhesive gum.
3640 **1682** 220c. multicoloured 11·00 10·50

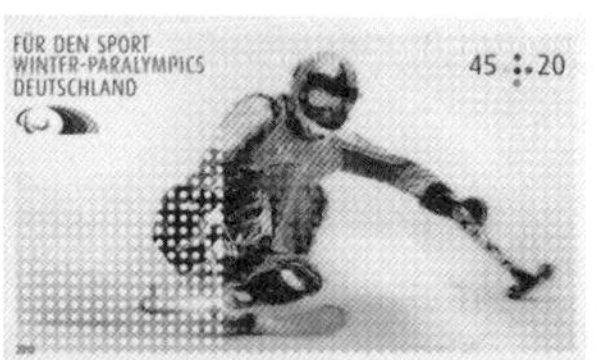

1683 Disabled Athlete

2010. Sports Promotion Fund. Winter Paralympics (45c.+20c.) or Winter Olympic Games, Vancouver (55c.+25c.). Multicoloured.
3642 45c.+20c. Type **1683** 3·25 3·00
3643 55c.+25c. Skier 4·25 4·00

1684 Family playing

2010. Mensch argere dich nicht (board game designed by Joseph Friedrich Schmidt).
3644 **1684** 55c. multicoloured 2·75 2·50

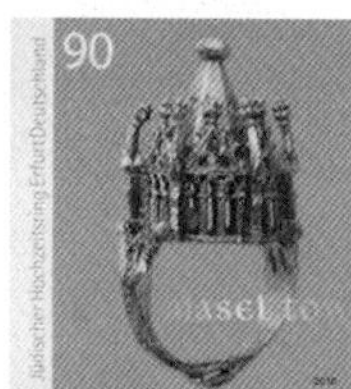

1685 Ring

2010. 14th-century Jewish Wedding Ring found at Erfurt.
3645 **1685** 90c. multicoloured 4·75 4·50

1686 Ship

2010. Post. Greeting Stamps (1st issue). Multicoloured.
3646 55c. Type **1686** 2·75 2·50
3647 55c. Rainbow 2·75 2·50

1687 *Ariadne abandoned by Theseus*

2010. Art. Painting by Maria Anna Catharina Angelica (Angelica) Kauffmann.
3648 **1687** 260c. multicoloured 13·00 12·00

2010. Post. Greeting Stamps (2nd issue). Multicoloured.
3649 55c. Dove 2·75 2·50
3650 55c. Angel carrying heart 2·75 2·50

1688 Footballers

2010. Sports Promotion Fund. Football World Cup Championships, South Africa (55c.+25c) or 2010 Ice Hockey World Cup, Germany (145c.+55c.). Multicoloured.
3651 55c.+25c. Type **1688** 4·25 4·00
3652 145c.+55c. Ice hockey players 10·00 9·25

1689 Birds and Cliffs

2010. Centenary of Helgoland Ornithological Institute

(a) Sheet 105×70 mm. Ordinary gum
MS3653 **1689** 145c. multicoloured 7·25 6·75

(b) Coil stamp. Self-adhesive
3654 **1689** 145c. multicoloured 7·25 6·75

1690 Robert Schumann

2010. Birth Bicentenary of Robert Alexander Schumann (composer)
3655 **1690** 55c. multicoloured 2·75 2·50

1691 Zampino the Magical Bear

2010. Europa. Children's Books
3656 **1691** 55c. multicoloured 2·75 2·50

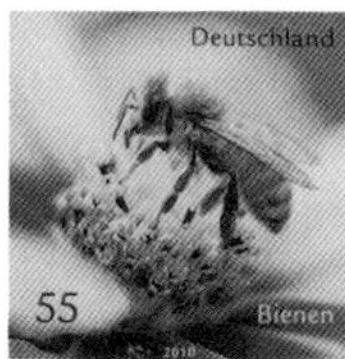

1692 Bee

2010. Bee Awareness Campaign

(a) Ordinary gum
3657 **1692** 55c. multicoloured 2·75 2·50

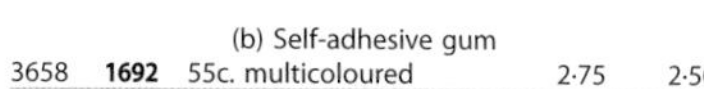

(b) Self-adhesive gum
3658 **1692** 55c. multicoloured 2·75 2·50

1693 Grey Seals

2010. Environmental Protection
3659 **1693** 55c.+25c. multicoloured 4·25 4·00
The premium was for marine conservation.

1694 Neuwerk

2010. Lighthouses. Multicoloured.
3660 45c. Type **1694** 2·20 2·10
3661 55c. Falshöft 2·75 2·50

1695 Konrad Zuse

2010. Birth Centenary of Konrad Zuse (engineer and computer pioneer)
3662 **1695** 55c. steel blue, pale blue and yellow-olive 2·75 2·50

1696 Ship and Figure holding Wine Glass (Andrea Doria)

2010. Illustrations of Songs by Udo Lindenburg (rock musician and artist). Multicoloured.

(a) Sheet stamps. Ordinary gum
3663 45c. Type **1696** 2·20 2·10
3664 55c. Train (*Sonderzug nach Pankow*) 2·75 2·50

(b) Size 38×22 mm. Booklet stamps. Self-adhesive
3665 45c. As Type **1696** 2·20 2·10
3666 55c. As No. 3664 2·75 2·50

1697 Johann Friedrich Böttger (inventor of first process) demonstrates to August the Strong (painting by Paul Kießling)

2010. 300th Anniv of Porcelain Production in Europe
3667 **1697** 55c. multicoloured 2·75 2·50

1698 Four Seater Stagecoach

2010. Historic Mail Coaches
3668 **1698** 145c. multicoloured 7·25 6·75

1699 *Germany*

2010. Youth Stamps. Multicoloured.
3669 45c.+20c. Type **1699** 2·50 2·30
3670 55c.+25c. *Imperator* 3·25 3·00
3671 55c.+25c. *Aller* 3·23 3·00
3672 145c.+55c. *Columbus* 3·25 3·00

1700 Bf 108 Taifun (D-EBEI) and Elly Beinhorn

2010. 75th Anniv of Elly Beinhorn's Long distance flight from Gliwice to Berlin, via Istanbul
3673 **1700** 55c. black and carmine 2·50 2·20

1701 Mother Teresa

2010. Birth Centenary of Agnes Gonxha Bojaxhiu (Mother Teresa) (founder of Missionaries of Charity)
3674 **1701** 70c. black and new blue 3·00 2·75

1702 Jorge Luis Borges

2010. Frankfurt Bookfair
3675 **1702** 170c. black, silver and scarlet-vermilion 8·00 7·50

2010. 300th Anniv of Porcelain Production in Europe. Self-adhesive
3676 **1697** 55c. multicoloured 2·50 2·20

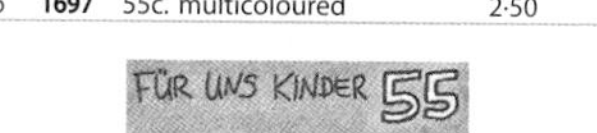

1703 Bear cradling Child

2010. For Us Children
3677 **1703** 55c. multicoloured 2·50 2·20

1704 *Imperial German Post to Helgoland, Norderney, Sylt* (poster, 1880)

2010. Stamp Day
3678 **1704** 55c. multicoloured 2·50 2·20

1705 Merry-go-Round

2010. Bicentenary of Oktoberfest
3679 **1705** 55c. multicoloured 2·50 2·20

1706 Celebration of German Unity in Berlin

2010. 20th Anniv of Re-unification of Germany

(a) Ordinary gum
3680 **1706** 55c. multicoloured 2·50 2·20

(b) Coil stamp. Self-adhesive
3681 **1706** 55c. multicoloured 2·50 2·20

1707 Castle, Schweinspoint

2010. 150th Anniv of St John Foundation for the Disabled

3682 **1707** 90c. multicoloured 4·00 3·75

1708 Baumann'sche House (Upper German), Eppingen (1582)

2010. Half-timbered Architecture. Multicoloured.

3683 45c. Type **1708** 2·00 1·80

3684 55c. Farmhouse (Low German), Trebel-Dunsche (1734) 2·50 2·20

1709 Ear of Corn

2010. Thanksgiving

3685 **1709** 55c. multicoloured 2·50 2·20

1710 Friedrich Loeffler and Pathogen

2010. Centenary of Friedrich Loeffler Institute

3686 **1710** 85c. multicoloured 4·25 4·00

2010. Post. Greeting Stamps (3rd issue). Self-adhesive. Multicoloured.

3686a 55c. As No. 3649 2·50 2·20

3686b 55c. As No. 3650 2·50 2·20

1711 Madonna and Child

2010. Christmas. Multicoloured.

3687 45c.+20c. Type **1711** 2·50 2·30

3688 55c.+25c. Adoration of the Magi 3·25 3·00

The premium was for the benefit of Federal Association of Voluntary Welfare Association

1712 Adler Locomotive on First Journey from Nuremberg to Fürth on Bavarian Ludwig Railway

2010. 175th Anniv of German Railways

3689 **1712** 55c. multicoloured 2·50 2·20

1713 Giant Slalom

2010. Alpine Ski World Championships 2011, Garmisch-Partenkirchen

3690 **1713** 55c. multicoloured 2·50 2·50

1714 'WENN EINER DAUHN DEIHT.....' and Fritz Reuter

2010. Birth Bicentenary of Fritz Reuter (writer)

3691 **1714** 100c. multicoloured 4·50 4·00

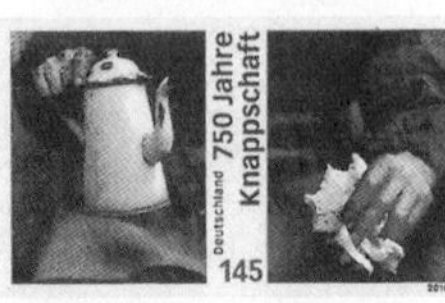

1715 Hands holding Coffeepot and Sandwich

2010. 750th Anniv of Knappschaft (providing sickness, accident, and death benefits for miners)

3692 **1715** 145c. black and carmine 6·25 6·00

1716 Glider, 1920

2011. Rhön Gliding Competitions at Wasserkuppe

3693 **1716** 45c. multicoloured 2·25 2·00

1717 Wanderer above the Sea of Fog (Caspar David Friedrich)

2011. German Painting

(a) Ordinary gum

3694 **1717** 55c. multicoloured 2·75 2·50

(b) Self-adhesive

3694a **1717** 55c. multicoloured 2·75 2·50

1718 Dr. Sommer and Bello being Interviewed (The Talking Dog)

2011. Welfare Stamps. Multicoloured.

(a) Ordinary gum

3695 45c.+20c. Type **1718** 2·50 2·20

3696 55c.+25c. Kloebner and Mueller-Luedenscheidt in the bath (*The Bathtub*) 3·50 3·25

3697 55c.+25c. Two racegoers (*At the Racecourse*) 3·50 3·25

3698 145c.+55c. Berta and her husband eating breakfast (*The Breakfast Egg*) 8·50 8·00

(b) Self-adhesive

3699 55c.+25c. As No. 3697 3·75 3·50

1719 National Park-Edersee Keller

2011. National Parks

3700 **1719** 145c. multicoloured 6·50 6·00

1720 Franz Liszt

2011. Birth Bicentenary of Franz Liszt (pianist and composer)

3701 **1720** 55c. dull violet 2·75 2·50

2011. Post. Greeting Stamps (4th issue). Self-adhesive. Multicoloured.

3701a 55c. As No. 3646 2·50 2·40

3701b 55c. As No. 3647 2·50 2·40

1721 Main Hall and Great Hall Pagodas, Old City, Nara Yakushi-ji

2011. World Heritage Sites. Multicoloured.

(a) Ordinary gum

3702 55c. Type **1721** 2·75 2·50

3703 75c. Regensburg Cathedral 3·50 3·25

(b) Self-adhesive

3703a 75c. As No. 3703 (3.3.11) 3·50 3·25

3703b 75c. Regensburg Cathedral 3·50 3·25

1722 Hanstein Castle (ruin) and Ludwigstein Castle

2011. Werratal, View of Two Castles

(a) Ordinary gum

3704 **1722** 90c. multicoloured 4·25 4·00

(b) Self-adhesive

3704a **1722** 90c. multicoloured 4·25 4·00

1722a Droplets on Leaf (water)

2011. Post. Multicoloured.

3705 55c. Type **1722a** 2·50 2·40

3706 55c. Dunes (earth) 2·50 2·40

3707 55c. Erupting volcano (fire) 2·50 2·40

3708 55c. Clouds (air) 2·50 2·40

1723 Alsfeld Town Hall

2011. Half-timbered Architecture. Multicoloured.

3709 45c. Type **1723** 2·30 2·10

3710 55c. White Horse Inn, Hartenstein 2·50 2·30

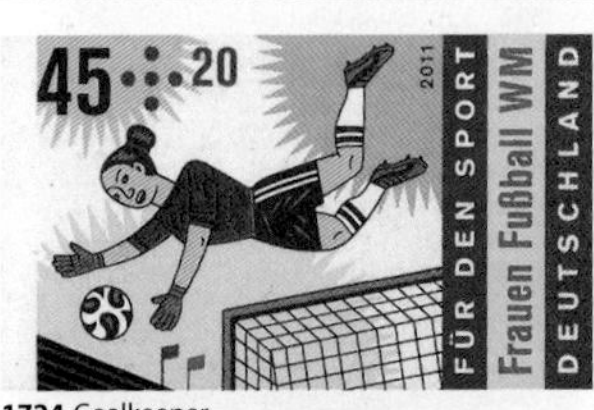

1724 Goalkeeper

2011. Sports Promotion Fund, 2011. Women's Football World Cup (45c.+20c., 55c.+25c.), European Gymnastics Championships, Berlin (55c.+25c.) or Mönchengldbach Hockey Championship (145c.+55c.). Multicoloured.

3711 (45c.+20c.) Type **1724** 2·50 2·20

3712 (55c.+25c.) Player kicking ball 3·50 3·25

3713 (55c.+25c.) Male gymnast using bars 3·50 3·25

3714 (145c.+55c.) Player with raised stick and ball 8·50 8·00

1719 National Park-Edersee Keller

2011. National Parks. Booklet Stamp

3714a **1719** 145c. multicoloured 6·50 6·00

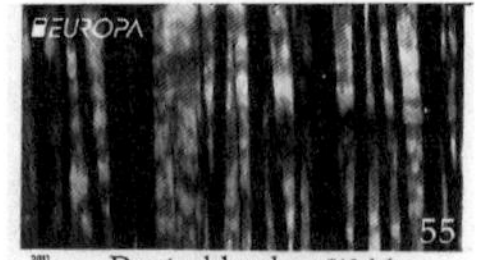

1725 Light through Tree Trunks

2011. Europa

3716 **1725** 55c. multicoloured 2·75 2·50

1726 Benz Patent-Motorwagen and Patent Details

2011. 125th Anniv of First Automobile

3717 **1726** 55c. multicoloured 2·75 2·50

1727 External and Interior of Museum

2011. 150th Anniv of Wallraff-Richartz-Museum

3718 **1727** 85c. multicoloured 4·00 3·75

1728 Chamber of Commerce Offices in Germany and DIHK Emblem

2011. 150th Anniv of Industry and Commerce Organization (DIHK)

3719 **1728** 145c. multicoloured 6·75 6·50

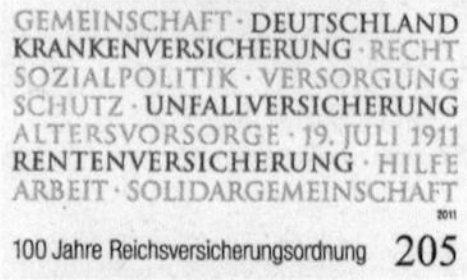

GEMEINSCHAFT · DEUTSCHLAND
KRANKENVERSICHERUNG · RECHT
SOZIALPOLITIK · VERSORGUNG
SCHUTZ · UNFALLVERSICHERUNG
ALTERSVORSORGE · 19. JULI 1911
RENTENVERSICHERUNG · HILFE
ARBEIT · SOLIDARGEMEINSCHAFT
100 Jahre Reichsversicherungsordnung 205

1729 Reich Insurance Code

2011. Centenary of Insurance Code (Reich Insurance Code (RVO))

3720 **1729** 205c. scarlet-vermilion, silver and black 10·00 9·50

1730 Train

2011. 125th Anniv of Mecklenburg Bäderbahn Steam-operated Narrow Gauge Railway ('Molli')

3721 **1730** 45c. multicoloured 2·30 2·10

1731 *Light at the end of a Tunnel*

2011. 50th Anniv of Amnesty International

3722 **1731** 55c. multicoloured 2·75 2·40

1732 The First Gymnasium in Germany (lithograph)

2011. Bicentenary of Friedrich Ludwig Jahn Turnplatz (first open air gymnasium)

3723	**1732**	165c. black and scarlet-vermilion	8·25	8·00

1733 Paddle Steamer

2011. 175th Anniv of Saxon Steamship Company

(a) Ordinary gum. Sheet 105×70 mm

MS3724 **1733** 220c. multicoloured		10·00	10·00

(b) Self-adhesive. Booklet stamp

3724a	220c. As Type **1733**	10·00	10·00

1734 Till Eulenspiegel

2011. 500th Anniv of Till Eulenspiegel (folklore trickster figure)

3725	**1734**	55c. multicoloured	2·75	2·40

1735 Arngast Lighthouse

2011. Lighthouses. Multicoloured.

3726	55c. Type **1735**	2·00	1·80
3727	90c. Dahmeshöved	2·30	2·10

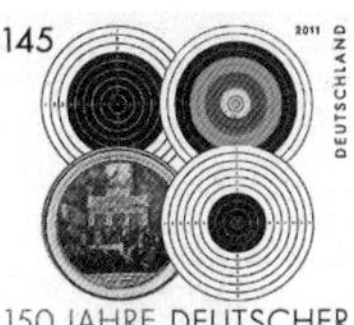

1736 Targets and 1861 Awards Ceremony

2011. 150th Anniv of German Shooting Federation

3728	**1736**	145c. multicoloured	4·25	4·00

1737 Horse Head Nebula

2011. For Us Children. Astronomy. Multicoloured.

3729	45c.+20c. Type **1737**	2·50	2·20
3730	55c.+25c. Solar System (left)	3·50	3·25
3731	55c.+25c. Solar System (right)	3·50	3·25
3732	145c.+55c. Pleiades	8·50	8·00

1738 Archaeopteryx Fossil

2011. 150th Anniv of Discovery of Archaeopteryx

3733	**1738**	55c. multicoloured	2·75	2·50

1739 Anniversary Emblem

2011. 75th Anniv of Stamp Day in Germany

3734	**1739**	55c.+ 25c. multicoloured	3·50	3·25

IV. WEST BERLIN

The Russian Government withdrew from the four-power control of Berlin on 1 July 1948, with the Western Sectors remaining under American, British and French control. West Berlin was constituted a "Land" of the Federal Republic on 1 September 1950. The Russian Zone issues inscribed "STADT BERLIN" (which we do not list unoverprinted in this Catalogue), were not intended for use throughout Berlin, but were for the Russian sector of the city and for Brandenburg.

The first stamps to be used in the Western Sectors were Nos. A4/5 and A7 of the Anglo-American Zones, followed by Nos. A36/52, which were on sale from 24 June to 31 August 1948, and remained valid until 19 September 1948.

1948. Pictorial issue of 1947 (Nos. 928/48) optd BERLIN.

B21	2pf. black	3·75	3·00
B2	6pf. violet	5·25	6·25
B3	8pf. red	2·20	6·25
B4	10pf. green	2·75	1·90
B5	12pf. grey	2·20	1·90
B25	15pf. brown	13·50	2·75
B7	16pf. green	4·25	2·75
B26	20pf. blue	4·50	1·40
B9	24pf. brown	2·10	65
B10	25pf. orange	26·00	65·00
B11	30pf. red	7·50	10·50
B12	40pf. mauve	10·50	10·50
B13	50pf. blue	15·00	37·00
B14	60pf. brown	6·25	65
B15	80pf. blue	16·00	32·00
B16	84pf. green	21·00	£120
B17	1m. olive	70·00	£190
B18	2m. violet	75·00	£650
B19	3m. red	£100	£900
B20	5m. blue	£130	£900

B2 Schoneberg

1949. Inscr "DEUTSCHE POST". Berlin Views. (a) Small size.

B35	-	1pf. grey	55	55
B36	**B2**	4pf. brown	1·10	55
B36c	-	4pf. brown	6·25	5·25
B37	-	5pf. green	1·30	55
B38	-	6pf. purple	2·30	1·60
B39	**B2**	8pf. orange	2·30	1·70
B40	-	10pf. green	1·10	40
B41	**B3**	15pf. brown	20·00	1·30
B42	-	20pf. red	6·25	55
B42b	-	20pf. red	85·00	3·25
B43	-	25pf. yellow	34·00	1·40
B44	-	30pf. blue	18·00	1·70
B45	**B2**	40pf. lake	26·00	1·50
B46	-	50pf. olive	26·00	55
B47	-	60pf. red	90·00	55
B48	-	80pf. blue	22·00	1·60
B49	-	90pf. green	26·00	2·10

B3 Douglas C-54 over Tempelhof Airport

(b) Large size.

B50	**B3**	1Dm. olive	34·00	1·60
B51	-	2Dm. purple	95·00	2·10
B52	-	3Dm. red	£375	21·00
B53	-	5Dm. blue	£180	21·00

DESIGNS—As Type B **2**: 1pf. Brandenburg Gate; 4pf. (B36c) Exhibition Building; 5, 25pf. "Tegel Schloss". 6, 50pf. Reichstag Building. 10, 30pf. "Kleistpark". 20 (B42), 80, 90pf. Technical High School; 20pf. (B42b) Olympia Stadium; 60pf. National Gallery. As Type B **3**: 2Dm. "Gendarmenmarkt"; 3Dm. Brandenburg Gate; 5Dm. "Tegel Schloss".

For similar views inscribed "DEUTSCHE POST BERLIN" see Nos. B118/19.

B4 Stephan Monument and Globe

B5 Heinrich von Stephan Monument

1949. 75th Anniv of U.P.U.

B54	**B4**	12pf. grey	39·00	12·50
B55	**B4**	16pf. green	60·00	25·00
B56	**B4**	24pf. orange	46·00	1·10
B57	**B4**	50pf. olive	£250	60·00
B58	**B4**	60pf. brown	£275	55·00
B59	**B5**	1Dm. olive	£190	£170
B60	**B5**	2Dm. purple	£200	£110

B6 Goethe and Scene from "Iphigenie"

1949. Birth Bicent of Goethe (poet). Portraits of Goethe and scenes from his works.

B61	**B6**	10pf. green	£190	90·00
B62	-	20pf. red	£200	£100
B63	-	30pf. blue	50·00	70·00

DESIGNS—Scenes from: 20pf. "Reineke Fuchs"; 30pf. "Faust".

1949. Numeral and pictorial issues of 1946/7 surch BERLIN and bold figures.

B64	**229**	5pf. on 45pf. red	6·25	65
B65	**C**	10pf. on 24pf. brown	25·00	65
B66	**B**	20pf. on 80pf. blue	95·00	21·00
B67	**237**	1m. on 3m. lake	£225	24·00

B9 Alms Bowl and Bear

1949. Berlin Relief Fund.

B68	**B9**	10pf.+5pf. green	£130	£250
B69	**B9**	20pf.+5pf. red	£160	£250
B70	**B9**	30pf.+5pf. blue	£170	£300
MSB70a		111×65 mm. Nos. B68/70 (sold at 1Dm.)	£1200	£3000

B10

1950. European Recovery Programme.

B71	**B10**	20pf. red	£130	50·00

B11 Harp

1950. Restablishment of Berlin Philharmonic Orchestra.

B72	**B11**	10pf.+5pf. green	65·00	50·00
B73	-	30pf.+5pf. blue	£140	£110

DESIGN: 30pf. "Singing Angels" (after H. and J. van Eyck).

B13 G. A. Lortzing

1951. Death Cent of Lortzing (composer).

B74	**B13**	20pf. brown	75·00	70·00

B14 Freedom Bell

1951. (a) Clapper at left.

B75	**B14**	5pf. brown	3·00	11·00
B76	**B14**	10pf. green	23·00	33·00
B77	**B14**	20pf. red	12·00	27·00
B78	**B14**	30pf. blue	80·00	£100
B79	**B14**	40pf. purple	18·00	55·00

(b) Clapper at right.

B82	5pf. green	3·00	2·75
B83	10pf. green	8·75	5·50
B84	20pf. red	29·00	22·00
B85	30pf. blue	75·00	60·00
B86	40pf. red	29·00	22·00

(c) Clapper in centre.

B101	5pf. brown	1·60	1·40
B102	10pf. green	3·25	2·20
B103	20pf. red	8·75	4·50
B104	30pf. blue	16·00	15·00
B105	40pf. violet	80·00	44·00

B15 Boy Stamp Collectors

1951. Stamp Day.

B80	**B15**	10pf.+3pf. green	37·00	38·00
B81	**B15**	20pf.+2pf. red	42·00	45·00

B16 Mask of Beethoven (taken from life, 1812)

1952. 125th Death Anniv of Beethoven (composer).

B87	**B16**	30pf. blue	55·00	37·00

B17 Olympic Torch

1952. Olympic Games Festival, Berlin.

B88	**B17**	4pf. brown	1·30	3·00
B89	**B17**	10pf. green	15·00	21·00
B90	**B17**	20pf. red	23·00	32·00

B18 W. von Siemens (electrical engineer)

1952. Famous Berliners.

B91	-	4pf. brown	75	75
B92	-	5pf. blue	1·50	75

B93	-	6pf. purple	8·75	12·00
B94	-	8pf. brown	3·25	3·75
B95	-	10pf. green	4·50	85
B96	-	15pf. lilac	23·00	21·00
B97	B18	20pf. red	3·75	1·20
B98	-	25pf. green	70·00	9·75
B99	-	30pf. purple	25·00	12·00
B100	-	40pf. black	40·00	3·75

PORTRAITS: 4pf. Zelter (musician); 5pf. Lilienthal (aviator); 6pf. Rathenau (statesman); 8pf. Fontane (writer); 10pf. Von Menzel (artist); 15pf. Virchow (pathologist); 25pf. Schinkel (architect); 30pf. Planck (physicist); 40pf. W. von Humboldt (philologist).

B19 Church before Bombing

1953. Kaiser Wilhelm Memorial Church Reconstruction Fund.

B106	B19	4pf.+1pf. brown	65	22·00
B107	B19	10pf.+5pf. green	1·90	60·00
B108	-	20pf.+10pf. red	4·50	60·00
B109	-	30pf.+15pf. blue	25·00	£130

DESIGN: 20pf., 30pf. Church after bombing.

B20 Chainbreaker

1953. East German Uprising. Inscr "17. JUNI 1953".

B110	B20	20pf. black	9·00	2·20
B111	-	30pf. red	46·00	44·00

DESIGN: 30pf. Brandenburg Gate.

B21 Ernst Reuter

1954. Death of Ernst Reuter (Mayor of West Berlin).

B112	B21	20pf. brown	10·50	2·50

B22 Conference Buildings

1954. Four-Power Conference, Berlin.

B113	B22	20pf. red	11·50	5·75

B23 O. Mergenthaler and Linotype Machine

1954. Birth Cent of Mergenthaler (inventor).

B114	B23	10pf. green	4·75	3·75

1954. West German Presidential Election. No. B103 optd Wahl des Bundesprasidenten in Berlin 17. Juli 1954.

B115	B14	20pf. red	6·75	7·50

B25 "Germany in Bondage"

1954. 10th Anniv of Attempt on Hitler's Life.

B116	B25	20pf. grey and red	7·50	6·25

B26 Prussian Postilion, 1827

1954. National Stamp Exhibition.

B117	B26	20pf.+10pf. mult	21·00	42·00

1954. Berlin Views. As Type B 2 but inscr "DEUTSCHE POST BERLIN".

B118		7pf. green	8·00	2·10
B119		70pf. olive	£130	26·00

DESIGNS: 7pf. Exhibition building; 70pf. Grunewald hunting lodge.

B27 Memorial Library

1954

B120	B27	40pf. purple	13·50	4·25

B28 Richard Strauss

1954. 5th Death Anniv of Strauss (composer).

B121	B28	40pf. blue	13·50	4·75

B29 Blacksmiths forging Rail

1954. Death Cent of A. Borsig (industrialist).

B122	B29	20pf. brown	10·00	2·75

B30 "Berlin" (liner)

1955

B123	B30	10pf. green	1·60	1·10
B124	B30	25pf. blue	9·50	5·00

B31 Wilhelm Furtwangler (conductor)

1955. 1st Death Anniv of Furtwangler.

B125	B31	40pf. blue	26·00	25·00

B32

1955. Federal Parliament Session, Berlin.

B126	B32	10pf. black, yell & red	75	1·10
B127	B32	20pf. black, yell & red	7·00	11·50

B33 Prussian Rural Postilion, 1760

1955. Stamp Day and Philatelic Fund.

B128	B33	25pf.+10pf. mult	8·00	17·00

B34 St. Otto

1955. 25th Anniv of Berlin Bishopric.

B129	B34	7pf.+3pf. brown	1·10	3·25
B130	-	10pf.+5pf. green	1·60	3·75
B131	-	20pf.+10pf. mauve	2·75	5·00

DESIGNS: 10pf. St. Hedwig; 20pf. St. Peter.

B35 Radio Tower and Exhibition Hall

1956. Berlin Buildings and Monuments.

B133	-	1pf. grey	30	25
B133b	-	3pf. violet	30	25
B134	-	5pf. mauve	30	25
B132	B35	7pf. turquoise (A)	11·50	3·25
B135	-	7pf. turquoise (B)	30	25
B136	-	8pf. grey	65	55
B136a	-	8pf. red	40	55
B137	-	10pf. green	30	25
B138	-	15pf. blue	65	30
B139	-	20pf. red	65	25
B140	-	25pf. brown	65	65
B141	-	30pf. green	1·30	1·30
B142	-	40pf. blue	13·50	10·50
B143	-	50pf. green	1·30	1·30
B144	-	60pf. brown	1·30	1·30
B145	-	70pf. violet	36·00	17·00
B146	-	1Dm. green	2·75	3·25
B146a	-	3Dm. red	7·75	23·00

DESIGNS—As Type B **35** (B)—HORIZ: 1pf., 3pf. Brandenburg Gate; 5pf. P.O. Headquarters; 20pf. Free University; 40pf. Charlottenburg Castle; 60pf. Chamber of Commerce and Bourse; 70pf. Schiller Theatre. VERT: 8pf. Town Hall, Neukolln; 10pf. Kaiser Wilhelm Memorial Church; 15pf. Airlift Monument; 25pf. Lilienthal Monument; 30pf. Pfaueninsel Castle; 50pf. Reuter Power-station. LARGER (24×30 mm): 1Dm. "The Great Elector" (statue, after Schluter). (29½×25 mm): 3Dm. Congress Hall, Berlin.

7pf. (A) Type B **35**. (B) As Type B **35** but with inscription at top.

B37 Eagle and Arms of Berlin

1956. Federal Council Meeting.

B147	B37	10pf. black, yell & red	1·60	1·10
B148	B37	25pf. black, yell & red	6·25	6·00

B38

1956. Centenary of German Engineers' Union.

B149	B38	10pf. green	2·75	2·10
B150	B38	20pf. red	6·25	6·75

1956. Flood Relief Fund. As No. B 77 (colour changed) surch +10 Berlinhilfe fur die Hochwassergeschadigten DEUTSCHE BUNDESPOST-BERLIN and bar.

B151	B14	20pf.+10pf. bistre	4·25	4·75

B40 P. Lincke

1956. 10th Death Anniv of Lincke (composer).

B152	B40	20pf. red	3·50	4·00

B41 Wireless Transmitter

1956. Industrial Exhibition.

B153	B41	25pf. brown	8·50	12·50

B42 Brandenburg Postilion, 1700

1956. Stamp Day and Philatelic Fund.

B154	B42	25pf.+10pf. mult	3·75	4·75

B43 Spandau

1957. 725th Anniv of Spandau.

B155	B43	20pf. olive and brown	85	1·10

B44 Model of Hansa District

1957. International Building Exn, Berlin.

B156	B44	7pf. brown	40	40
B157	-	20pf. red	1·10	1·10
B158	-	40pf. blue	2·75	3·25

DESIGNS—HORIZ: 20pf. Aerial view of Exhibition; 40pf. Exhibition Congress Hall.

B45 Friedrich K. von Savigny (jurist)

1957. Portraits as Type B 45.

B159		7pf. brown and green	30	25
B160		8pf. brown and grey	30	25
B161		10pf. brown and green	30	25
B162		15pf. sepia and blue	55	1·10
B163		20pf.+10pf. sepia and red	1·10	1·30
B164		20pf. brown and red	30	25
B165		25pf. sepia and lake	1·30	1·50
B166	B45	30pf. sepia and green	3·25	3·75
B167	-	40pf. sepia and blue	1·30	1·50
B168	-	50pf. sepia and olive	5·75	9·50

PORTRAITS—VERT: 7pf. T. Mommsen (historian); 8pf. H. Zille (painter); 10pf. E. Reuter (Mayor of Berlin); 15pf. F. Haber (chemist); 20pf. (No. B164), F. Schleiermacher (theologian); 20pf. (B163), L. Heck (zoologist); 25pf. Max Reinhardt (theatrical producer); 40pf. A. von Humboldt (naturalist); 50pf. C. D. Rauch (sculptor).

The premium on No. B163 was for the Berlin Zoo. No. B167 commemorates Humboldt's death centenary.

B46 Uta von Naumburg (statue)

1957. German Cultural Congress.

B169	**B46**	25pf. brown	1·30	1·60

B47 "Unity Justice and Freedom"

1957. 3rd Federal Parliament Assembly.

B170	**B47**	10pf. black, ochre & red	55	1·10
B171	**B47**	20pf. black, ochre & red	3·25	4·25

B48 Postilion, 1897–1925

1957. Stamp Day.

B172	**B48**	20pf. multicoloured	1·30	1·50

B49 Torch of Remembrance

1957. 7th World War Veterans Congress.

B173	**B49**	20pf. myrtle, yell & grn	1·60	1·10

B50 Elly Heuss-Knapp (social worker)

1957. Mothers' Convalescence Fund.

B174	**B50**	20pf.+10pf. red	2·30	3·50

B51 Christ and Symbols of the Cosmos

1958. German Catholics' Day.

B175	**B51**	10pf. black and green	75	85
B176	**B51**	20pf. black and mauve	1·40	2·10

B52 Otto Suhr

1958. 1st Death Anniv of Burgomaster Otto Suhr.

B177	**B52**	20pf. red	1·60	2·75

See also Nos. B187 and B193.

B53 Pres. Heuss

1959

B178	**B53**	7pf. green	40	55
B179	**B53**	10pf. green	40	55
B180	**B53**	20pf. red	75	55
B181	**B53**	40pf. blue	3·50	6·25
B182	**B53**	70pf. violet	12·00	15·00

B54 Symbolic Airlift

1959. 10th Anniv of Berlin Airlift.

B183	**B54**	25pf. black and red	75	70

B55 Brandenburg Gate, Berlin

1959. 14th World Communities Congress, Berlin.

B184	**B55**	20pf. blue, red & lt blue	1·20	65

B56 Schiller

1959. Birth Bicentenary of Schiller (poet).

B185	**B56**	20pf. brown and red	55	65

B57 Robert Koch

1960. 50th Death Anniv of Robert Koch (bacteriologist).

B186	**B57**	20pf. purple	55	65

1960. 4th Death Anniv of Walther Schreiber (Mayor of Berlin, 1951–53). As Type B 52.

B187	20pf. red	75	95

DESIGN: Portrait of Schreiber.

B58 Boy at Window

1960. Berlin Children's Holiday Fund. Inscr "FERIENPLATZE FUR BERLINER KINDER".

B188	**B58**	7pf.+3pf. dp brown, brown & light brown	30	40
B189	-	10pf.+5pf. deep green, olive and green	30	40
B190	-	20pf.+10pf. brown, red and pink	70	75
B191	-	40pf.+20pf. deep blue, blue & light blue	1·80	4·75

DESIGNS: 10pf. Girl in street; 20pf. Girl blowing on Alpine flower; 40pf. Boy on beach.

B59 Hans Boeckler

1961. 10th Anniv of Hans Boeckler (politician).

B192	**B59**	20pf. black and red	50	55

1961. Louise Schroeder Commemoration. As Type B 52.

B193	20pf. brown	55	55

DESIGN: Portrait of Schroeder.

B60 Durer

1961. Famous Germans.

B194	5pf. olive (Magnus)	30	30
B195	7pf. brown (St. Elizabeth of Thuringia)	30	55
B196	8pf. violet (Gutenberg)	30	55
B197	10pf. green (Type B **60**)	30	30
B198	15pf. blue (Luther)	30	55
B199	20pf. red (Bach)	30	30
B200	25pf. brown (Neumann)	30	55
B201	30pf. brown (Kant)	40	75
B202	40pf. blue (Lessing)	80	1·30
B203	50pf. brown (Goethe)	55	1·40
B204	60pf. red (Schiller)	55	1·60
B205	70pf. green (Beethoven)	80	1·60
B206	80pf. brown (Kleist)	4·50	10·50
B207	1Dm. violet (Annette von Droste-Hulshoff)	2·00	4·75
B208	2Dm. green (Hauptmann)	2·75	6·75

B61 "Five Crosses" Symbol and St. Mary's Church

1961. 10th Evangelical Churches' Day. Crosses in violet.

B210	**B61**	10pf. green	30	25
B211	-	20pf. purple	35	30

DESIGN: 20pf. "Five Crosses" and Kaiser Wilhelm Memorial Church.

B62 Exhibition Emblem

1961. West Berlin Radio and Television Exn.

B212	**B62**	20pf. brown and red	40	55

B63 "Die Linden" (1650)

1962. "Old Berlin" series.

B213	**B63**	7pf. sepia and brown	30	25
B214	-	10pf. sepia and green	30	25
B215	-	15pf. black and blue	30	25
B216	-	20pf. sepia and brown	30	25
B217	-	25pf. sepia and olive	30	25
B218	-	40pf. black and blue	40	50
B219	-	50pf. sepia and purple	55	55
B220	-	60pf. sepia and mauve	65	65
B221	-	70pf. black and purple	65	65
B222	-	80pf. sepia and red	85	95
B223	-	90pf. sepia and brown	90	1·10
B224	-	1Dm. sepia and green	1·10	1·60

DESIGNS: 10pf. "Waisenbrucke" (Orphans' Bridge), 1783; 15pf. Mauerstrasse, 1780; 20pf. Berlin Castle, 1703; 25pf. Potsdamer Platz, 1825; 40pf. Bellevue Castle, c. 1800; 50pf. Fischer Bridge, 1830; 60pf. Halle Gate, 1880; 70pf. Parochial Church, 1780; 80pf. University, 1825; 90pf. Opera House, 1780; 1Dm. Grunewald Lake, c. 1790.

B64 Euler Gelberhund Biplane, 1912, and Boeing 707 Airliner

1962. 50th Anniv of German Airmail Transport.

B225	**B64**	60pf. black and blue	75	75

B65 Exhibition Emblem

1963. West Berlin Broadcasting Exn.

B226	**B65**	20pf. ultram, grey & bl	40	40

B66 Town Hall Schoneberg

1964. 700th Anniv of Schoneberg.

B227	**B66**	20pf. brown	40	40

B67 Pres. Lubke

1964. Re-election of Pres. Lubke.

B228	**B67**	20pf. red	30	25
B229	**B67**	40pf. blue	55	50

See also Nos. B308/9.

WEST BERLIN DESIGNS. Except where illustrated the following are the same or similar designs to German Federal Republic additonally inscr "BERLIN".

1964. Capitals of the Federal Lands. As No. 1335.

B230	20pf. multicoloured	55	55

1964. Humanitarian Relief and Welfare Funds. As Nos. 1352/5.

B231	10pf.+5pf. multicoloured	30	30
B232	15pf.+5pf. multicoloured	30	30
B233	20pf.+10pf. multicoloured	55	40
B234	40pf.+20pf. multicoloured	75	1·30

1964. Pres. Kennedy Commem. As Type 411.

B235	40pf. blue	65	75

1964. Twelve Centuries of German Architecture. (a) Size 18½×22½ mm. As Nos. 1359/66. Plain backgrounds.

B236	10pf. brown	30	30
B237	15pf. green	30	30
B238	20pf. red	30	30
B239	40pf. blue	90	1·60
B240	50pf. bistre	1·90	2·10
B241	60pf. red	1·50	1·60
B242	70pf. green	2·75	4·75
B243	80pf. brown	2·75	2·10

(b) Size 19½×24 mm. As Nos. 1367/81. Coloured backgrounds.

B244	5pf. bistre	30	30
B245	8pf. red	30	30
B246	10pf. purple	30	30
B247	20pf. green	30	30
B248	30pf. olive	30	30
B249	30pf. red	30	30
B250	40pf. bistre	80	1·10
B251	50pf. blue	60	65
B252	60pf. red	2·10	2·75
B253	70pf. bronze	1·10	1·10
B254	80pf. brown	1·40	2·75
B255	90pf. black	80	1·10
B256	1Dm. blue	80	1·10
B257	1Dm.10 brown	1·90	1·90
B258	1Dm.30 green	3·25	3·25
B259	2Dm. purple	3·25	2·75

BUILDINGS: 8pf. Palatine Castle, Kaub. Others as Nos. 1359/81 of German Federal Republic.

1965. Child Welfare. As Nos. 1384/7.

B261	10pf.+5pf. Eurasian woodcock	30	30
B262	15pf.+5pf. Common pheasant	30	30
B263	20pf.+10pf. Black grouse	30	30
B264	40pf.+20pf. Western capercaillie	65	1·10

B68 Kaiser Wilhelm Memorial Church

1965. "New Berlin". Multicoloured.

B265	10pf. Type B **68**	30	30
B266	15pf. Opera House (horiz)	30	30
B267	20pf. Philharmonic Hall (horiz)	30	30
B268	30pf. Jewish Community Centre (horiz)	30	30
B269	40pf. Regina Martyrum Memorial Church (horiz)	30	30
B270	50pf. Ernst-Reuter Square (horiz)	30	40
B271	60pf. Europa Centre	40	55
B272	70pf. Technical University, Charlottenburg (horiz)	65	65
B273	80pf. City Motorway	65	65
B274	90pf. Planetarium (horiz)	80	1·10
B275	1Dm. Telecommunications, Tower	85	1·30
B276	1Dm.10 University Clinic, Steglitz (horiz)	90	1·40

1965. Humanitarian Relief Funds. As Nos. 1406/9.

B277	10pf.+5pf. Type **425**	30	30
B278	15pf.+5pf. Cinderella and birds with dress	30	30
B279	20pf.+10pf. Prince offering slipper to Cinderella	30	30
B280	40pf.+20pf. Cinderella and Prince on horse	60	1·10

1966. As Nos. 1412/15a.

B281	10pf. brown	30	30
B282	20pf. green	30	30
B283	30pf. red	30	30
B284	50pf. blue	75	55
B284a	100pf. blue	5·75	5·50

1966. Child Welfare. As Nos. 1416/19.

B285	10pf.+5pf. Type **429**	30	30
B286	20pf.+10pf. Chamois	30	30
B287	30pf.+15pf. Fallow deer	30	40
B288	50pf.+25pf. Red deer	80	1·10

1966. Humanitarian Relief Funds. As Nos. 1428/31.

B289	10pf.+5pf. Type **435**	30	30
B290	20pf.+10pf. Frog dining with Princess	30	30
B291	30pf.+15pf. Frog Prince and Princess	55	30
B292	50pf.+25pf. In coach	65	1·10

Designs from Grimm's "The Frog Prince".

1967. Child Welfare. As Nos. 1434/7.

B293	10pf.+5pf. Common rabbit	30	30
B294	20pf.+10pf. Stoat	30	30
B295	30pf.+15pf. Common hamster	55	40
B296	50pf.+25pf. Red fox	1·30	1·90

B69 "Bust of a Young Man" (after C. Meit)

1967. Berlin Art Treasures.

B297	**B69**	10pf. sepia and bistre	30	30
B298	-	20pf. olive and blue	30	30
B299	-	30pf. brown and olive	30	30
B300	-	50pf. sepia and grey	55	55
B301	-	1Dm. black and blue	1·10	1·10
B302	-	1Dm.10 brn & chest	1·60	2·10

DESIGNS: 20pf. Head of "The Elector of Brandenburg" (statue by Schluter); 30pf. "St. Mark" (statue by Riemenschneider); 50pf. Head from Quadriga, Brandenburg Gate. 1Dm. "Madonna" (carving by Feuchtmayer). (22½×39 mm) 1Dm.10, "Christ and St. John" (after carving from Upper Swabia, c. 1320).

B70 Broadcasting Tower and T.V. Screen

1967. West Berlin Broadcasting Exn.

B303	**B70**	30pf. multicoloured	40	55

1967. Humanitarian Relief Funds. As Nos. 1443/6.

B304	10pf.+5pf. multicoloured	30	30
B305	20pf.+10pf. multicoloured	30	30
B306	30pf.+15pf. multicoloured	30	55
B307	50pf.+25pf. multicoloured	75	1·10

1967. Re-election of President Lubke. As Type B 67.

B308	**B67**	30pf. red	30	30
B309	**B67**	50pf. blue	55	60

1968. Child Welfare. As Nos. 1454/7.

B310	10pf.+5pf. Wild cat	30	65
B311	20pf.+10pf. European otter	40	65
B312	30pf.+15pf. Eurasian badger	75	1·30
B313	50pf.+25pf. Eurasian beaver	2·30	2·75

B71 Former Court-house

1968. 500th Anniv of Berlin Magistrates' Court.

B314	**B71**	30pf. black	50	55

B72 Festival Emblems

1968. Athletics Festival, Berlin.

B315	**B72**	20f. red, black and grey	40	50

1968. Humanitarian Relief Funds. As Nos. 1473/6.

B316	10pf.+5pf. Doll of 1878	30	30
B317	20pf.+10pf. Doll of 1850	30	30
B318	30pf.+15pf. Doll of 1870	30	30
B319	50pf.+25pf. Doll of 1885	75	1·10

B74 "The Newspaper Seller" (C. W. Allers, 1889)

1969. 19th-cent Berliners. Contemporary Art.

B320	-	5pf. black	25	20
B321	**B74**	10pf. purple	25	20
B322	-	10pf. brown	25	20
B323	-	20pf. green	30	30
B324	-	20pf. turquoise	30	30
B325	-	30pf. brown	80	55
B326	-	30pf. brown	80	55
B327	-	50pf. blue	2·10	2·50

DESIGNS—HORIZ: 5pf. "The Cab-driver" (H. Zille, 1875). VERT: 10pf. "The Bus-driver" (C. W. Allers, 1890); 20pf. (No. B323) "The Cobblers Boy" (F. Kruger, 1839); 20pf. (No. B324) "The Cobbler" (A. von Menzel, 1833); 30pf. (No. B325) "The Borsig Forge" (P. Meyerheim, 1878); 30pf. (No. B326) "Three Berlin Ladies" (F. Kurger, 1839); 50pf. "At the Brandenburg Gate" (C. W. Allers, 1889).

1969. Child Welfare. As Nos. 1478/81.

B328	10pf.+5pf. brn, blk & yell	30	40
B329	20pf.+10pf. brown, black and buff	40	75
B330	30pf.+15pf. brn, blk & red	65	1·10
B331	50pf.+25pf. grey, yellow, black and blue	1·70	2·10

B75 Orang-Utan Family

1969. 125th Anniv of Berlin Zoo. Sheet 99×74 mm containing Type B 75 and similar horiz designs.

MSB332	10pf. black and brown; 20pf. black and green; 30pf. black and purple; 50pf. black and blue (sold for 1Dm.30)	2·75	2·75

DESIGNS: 20pf. Dalmatian pelican family; 30pf. Gaur and calf; 50pf. Common zebra and foal.

B76 Postman

1969. 20th Congress of Post Office Trade Union Federation (I.P.T.T.), Berlin.

B333	**B76**	10pf. olive	30	30
B334	-	20pf. brown and buff	30	30
B335	-	30pf. violet and ochre	75	85
B336	-	50pf. blue and light blue	1·50	1·70

DESIGNS: 20pf. Telephonist; 30pf. Technician; 50pf. Airmail handlers.

B77 J. Joachim (violinist and director, after A. von Menzel)

1969. Anniversaries. Multicoloured.

B337	30pf. Type B **77**	75	65
B338	50pf. Alexander von Humboldt (after J. Stieler)	1·30	1·70

ANNIVERSARIES: 30pf. Centenary of Berlin Academy of Music; 50pf. Birth bicentenary of Humboldt.

B78 Railway Carriage (1835)

1969. Humanitarian Relief Funds. Pewter Models. Multicoloured. (a) Inscr "WOHLFAHRTSMARKE".

B339	10pf.+5pf. Type B **78**	30	30
B340	20pf.+10pf. Woman feeding chicken (1850)	30	30
B341	30pf.+15pf. Market stall (1850)	55	55
B342	50pf.+25pf. Mounted postilion (1860)	1·40	1·40

(b) Christmas. Inscr "WEIHNACHTSMARKE".

B343	10pf.+5pf. "The Three Kings"	55	40

B79 T. Fontane

1970. 150th Birth Anniv of Theodor Fontane (writer).

B344	**B79**	20pf. multicoloured	55	40

B80 Heinrich von Stretlingen

1970. Miniatures of Minnesingers. Mult.

B345	10pf.+5pf. Type B **80**	30	30
B346	20pf.+10pf. Meinloh von Sevelingen	55	65
B347	30pf.+15pf. Burkhart von Hohenfels	75	85
B348	50pf.+25pf. Albrecht von Johannsdorf	1·70	2·00

B81 Film "Title"

1970. 20th International Film Festival, Berlin.

B349	**B81**	30pf. multicoloured	65	75

1970. Pres. Heinemann. As Nos. 1535/55.

B350	**486**	5pf. black	30	20
B351	**486**	8pf. brown	1·10	1·40
B352	**486**	10pf. brown	30	20
B353	**486**	15pf. bistre	30	40
B354	**486**	20pf. green	30	30
B355	**486**	25pf. green	1·30	75
B356	**486**	30pf. brown	1·40	65
B357	**486**	40pf. orange	75	30
B358	**486**	50pf. blue	65	25
B359	**486**	60pf. blue	1·30	75
B360	**486**	70pf. brown	1·10	85
B361	**486**	80pf. green	1·30	1·20
B362	**486**	90pf. red	2·50	3·25
B363	**486**	1Dm. green	1·30	95
B364	**486**	110pf. grey	1·60	1·50
B365	**486**	120pf. brown	1·60	1·30
B366	**486**	130pf. brown	2·30	2·10
B367	**486**	140pf. green	2·30	2·10
B368	**486**	150pf. red	2·30	1·60
B369	**486**	160pf. orange	3·25	2·75
B370	**486**	170pf. orange	2·30	2·20
B371	**486**	190pf. purple	2·75	2·50
B372	**486**	2Dm. violet	2·75	1·90

B82 Allegory of Folklore

1970. 20th Berlin Folklore Week.

B373	**B82**	30pf. multicoloured	75	65

B83 "Caspar"

1970. Humanitarian Relief Funds. Puppets. Multicoloured. (a) Relief Funds.

B374	10pf.+5pf. Type B **83**	30	30
B375	20pf.+10pf. "Polichinelle"	35	30
B376	30pf.+15pf. "Punch"	75	65
B377	50pf.+25pf. "Pulcinella"	1·30	1·50

(b) Christmas.

B378	10pf.+5pf. "Angel"	40	40

B84 L. von Ranke (after painting by J. Schrader)

1970. 175th Birth Anniv of Leopold von Ranke (historian).

B379	**B84**	30pf. multicoloured	65	55

1971. Centenary of German Unification.

B380	**492**	30pf. black, red & orange	75	75

B85 Class ET 165.8 Electric Train, 1933

1971. Berlin Rail Transport. Multicoloured.

B381	5pf. Class T.12 steam train, 1925	30	25
B382	10pf. Electric tram, 1890	30	25
B383	20pf. Horse tram, 1880	30	30
B384	30pf. Type B **85**	65	55
B385	50pf. Electric tram, 1950	2·30	1·90
B386	1Dm. Underground train No. 2431, 1971	2·75	2·50

B86 "Fly"

1971. Child Welfare. Children's Drawings. Multicoloured.

B387	10pf.+5pf. Type B **86**	40	40
B388	20pf.+10pf. "Fish"	40	40
B389	30pf.+15pf. "Porcupine"	65	75
B390	50pf.+25pf. "Cockerel"	1·70	1·80

B87 "The Bagpiper" (copper engraving, Durer, c. 1514)

1971. 500th Birth Anniv of Albrecht Durer.
B391 **B87** 10pf. black and brown 65 40

B88 Communications Tower and Dish Aerials

1971. West Berlin Broadcasting Exhibition.
B392 **B88** 30pf. indigo, blue & red 1·10 85

B89 Bach and part of 2nd Brandenburg Concerto

1971. 250th Anniv of Bach's Brandenburg Concertos.
B393 **B89** 30pf. multicoloured 95 85

B90 H. von Helmholtz (from painting by K. Morell-Kramer)

1971. 150th Anniv of Hermann von Helmholtz (scientist).
B394 **B90** 25pf. multicoloured 75 55

B91 "Opel" Racing-car (1921)

1971. 50th Anniv of Avus Motor-racing Track. Sheet 100×75 mm containing horiz designs as Type B 91. Multicoloured.
MSB395 10pf. Type B **91**; 25pf. "Auto-Union" (1936); 30pf. "Mercedes-Benz SSKL" (1931); 60pf. "Mercedes" racing with "Auto-Union" (1937) 2·10 1·90

1971. Accident Prevention. As Nos. 1596/1605.

B396	5pf. orange	30	40
B397	10pf. brown	30	25
B398	20pf. violet	30	25
B399	25pf. green	55	85
B400	30pf. red	55	65
B401	40pf. mauve	55	75
B402	50pf. blue	2·50	1·60
B403	60pf. blue	2·75	3·25
B404	70pf. blue and green	2·00	1·50
B405	100pf. green	2·75	1·60
B406	150pf. brown	8·00	9·50

B92 Dancing Men

1971. Humanitarian Relief Funds. Wooden Toys. Mult. (a) Inscr "WOHLFAHRTSMARKE".

B407	10pf.+5pf. Type B **92**	25	25
B408	25pf.+10pf. Horseman on wheels	30	30
B409	30pf.+15pf. Acrobat	75	75
B410	60pf.+30pf. Nurse and babies	1·40	1·60

(b) Christmas. Inscr "WEIHNACHTSMARKE".
B411 10pf.+5pf. Angel with two candles 55 40

B93 Microscope

1971. Birth Centenary of Material-testing Laboratory, Berlin.
B412 **B93** 30pf. multicoloured 65 55

B94 F. Gilly (after bust by Schadow)

1972. Birth Bicentenary of Friedrich Gilly (architect).
B413 **B94** 30pf. black and blue 75 55

B95 Boy raiding Bird's-nest

1972. Child Welfare. Animal Protection. Multicoloured.

B414	10pf.+5pf. Type B **95**	30	30
B415	25pf.+10pf. Care of kittens	40	40
B416	30pf.+15pf. Man beating watch-dog	75	75
B417	60pf.+30pf. Animals crossing road at night	1·80	1·80

B96 "Grunewaldsee" (A. von Riesen)

1972. Paintings of Berlin Lakes. Multicoloured.

B418	10pf. Type B **96**	30	30
B419	25pf. "Wannsee" (Max Liebermann)	75	75
B420	30pf. "Schlachtensee" (W. Leistikow)	1·40	85

B97 E. T. A. Hoffman

1972. 150th Death Anniv of E. T. A. Hoffman (poet and musician).
B421 **B97** 60pf. black and violet 1·50 1·50

B98 Max Liebermann (self-portrait)

1972. 125th Birth Anniv of Max Liebermann (painter).
B422 **B98** 40pf. multicoloured 95 65

B99 Stamp Printing-press

1972. Stamp Day.
B423 **B99** 20pf. blue, black & red 65 40

1972. Humanitarian Relief Funds. Multicoloured. (a) 19th-century Faience Chessmen. As Nos. 1636/40 of West Germany. Inscr "WOLHFAHRTSMARKE".

B424	20pf.+10pf. Knight	40	40
B425	30pf.+15pf. Rook	65	65
B426	40pf.+20pf. Queen	1·80	1·80
B427	70pf.+35pf. King	2·50	2·50

(b) Christmas. Inscr "WEIHNACHTSMARKE".
B428 20pf.+10pf. "The Holy Family" 75 65

B100 Prince von Hardenberg (after Tischbein)

1972. 150th Death Anniv of Karl August von Hardenberg (statesman).
B429 **B100** 40pf. multicoloured 85 65

B101 Northern Goshawk

1973. Youth Welfare. Birds of Prey. Mult.

B430	20pf.+10pf. Type B **101**	65	65
B431	30pf.+15pf. Peregrine falcon	95	95
B432	40pf.+20pf. Northern sparrow hawk	1·40	1·40
B433	70pf.+35pf. Golden eagle	2·30	2·30

B102 Horse-bus, 1907

1973. Berlin Buses. Multicoloured.

B434	20pf. Type B **102**	55	40
B435	20pf. Trolley bus, 1933	55	40
B436	30pf. Motor bus, 1919	1·10	65
B437	30pf. Double-decker, 1970	1·50	65
B438	40pf. Double-decker, 1925	1·60	95
B439	40pf. "Standard" bus, 1973	1·60	95

B103 L. Tieck

1973. Birth Bicentenary of Ludwig Tieck (poet and writer).
B440 **B103** 40pf. multicoloured 95 65

B104 J. J. Quantz

1973. Death Bicentenary of Johann Quantz (composer).
B441 **B104** 40pf. black 1·10 85

B105 Radio Set, 1926

1973. "50 Years of German Broadcasting". Sheet 148×105 mm containing horiz designs as Type B 105.
MSB442 20pf. black and yellow; 30pf. black and green; 40pf. black and red; 70pf. black and blue (sold at 1.80Dm) 5·25 5·25

DESIGNS: 30pf. Hans Bredow and microphone of 1924; 40pf. Girl with TV and video tape-recorder; 70pf. TV camera.

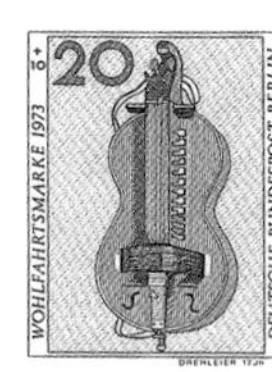

B106 17th-century Hurdy-Gurdy

1973. Humanitarian Relief Funds. Mult. (a) Musical Instruments. Inscr "WOHLFAHRTSMARKE".

B443	20pf.+10pf. Type B **106**	55	55
B444	30pf.+15pf. 16th century drum	1·10	1·10
B445	40pf.+20pf. 18th century lute	1·30	1·30
B446	70pf.+35pf. 16th century organ	1·80	1·80

(b) Christmas. Inscr "WEIHNACHTSMARKE".
B447 20pf.+10pf. Christmas star 75 75

B107 G. W. Knobelsdorff

1974. 275th Birth Anniv of Georg W. von Knobelsdorff (architect).
B448 **B107** 20pf. brown 65 40

B108 G. R. Kirchoff

1974. 150th Birth Anniv of Gustav R. Kirchhoff (physicist).
B449 **B108** 30pf. green and grey 55 55

B109 A. Slaby

1974. 125th Birth Anniv of Adolf Slaby (radio pioneer).
B450 **B109** 40pf. black and red 75 65

B110 Airlift Memorial

1974. 25th Anniv of Berlin Airlift.

B451	**B110**	90pf. multicoloured	3·25	2·10

B111 Photography

1974. Youth Welfare. Youth Activities. Multicoloured.

B452	20pf.+10pf. Type B **111**	55	65
B453	30pf.+15pf. Athletics	55	65
B454	40pf.+20pf. Music	1·30	1·40
B455	70pf.+35pf. Voluntary service (Nurse)	1·80	1·90

B112 School Seal

1974. 400th Anniv of Evangelical Grammar School, Berlin.

B456	**B112**	50pf. grey, brn & gold	95	65

B113 Spring Bouquet

1974. Humanitarian Relief Funds. Flowers. Multicoloured.
(a) 25th Anniv of Humanitarian Relief Stamps. Inscr "25 JAHRE WOHLFAHRTSMARKE".

B457	30pf.+15pf. Type B **113**	55	55
B458	40pf.+20pf. Autumn bouquet	95	95
B459	50pf.+25pf. Bouquet of roses	1·10	1·10
B460	70pf.+35pf. Winter bouquet	1·60	1·60

(b) Christmas. Inscr "WEIHNACHTSMARKE".

B461	30pf.+15pf. Christmas bouquet	1·10	1·20

B114 Tegel Airport

1974. Opening of Tegel Airport. Berlin.

B462	**B114**	50pf. violet, bl & grn	1·50	85

B115 "Venus" (F. E. Meyer)

1974. Berlin Porcelain Figures. Mult.

B463	30pf. Type B **115**	75	65
B464	40pf. "Astronomy" (W. C. Meyer)	85	75
B465	50pf. "Justice" (J. G. Muller)	95	90

B116 Gottfried Schadow

1975. 125th Death Anniv of Gottfried Schadow (sculptor).

B466	**B116**	50pf. brown	1·10	75

B117 "Prinzess Charlotte"

1975. Berlin Pleasure Boats. Multicoloured.

B467	30pf. Type B **117**	85	40
B468	40pf. "Siegfried"	75	40
B469	50pf. "Sperber"	1·60	1·10
B470	60pf. "Vaterland"	1·60	1·10
B471	70pf. "Moby Dick"	2·10	1·90

B118 Steam Locomotive "Drache", 1848

1975. Youth Welfare. Railway Locomotives. Multicoloured.

B472	30pf.+15pf. Type B **118**	1·10	85
B473	40pf.+20pf. Class 89 tank locomotive	1·10	1·10
B474	50pf.+25pf. Class 050 steam locomotive	2·10	1·80
B475	70pf.+35pf. Class 010 steam locomotive	3·25	2·75

B119 Ferdinand Sauerbruch (surgeon)

1975. Birth Cent of Ferdinand Sauerbruch.

B476	**B119**	50pf. dp brn, brn & pk	1·10	75

B120 Gymnastics Emblem

1975. Gymnaestrada (Gymnastic Games), Berlin.

B477	**B120**	40pf. black, gold and green	75	55

1975. Industry and Technology. As Nos. 1742/55.

B478	-	5pf. green	30	20
B479	-	10pf. purple	30	20
B480	-	20pf. red	30	20
B481	-	30pf. violet	40	30
B482	572	40pf. green	65	30
B483	-	50pf. red	65	30
B483a	-	60pf. red	1·10	55
B484	-	70pf. blue	1·20	65
B485	-	80pf. green	1·20	35
B486	-	100pf. brown	1·20	65
B486a	-	110pf. purple	1·80	1·60
B487	-	120pf. blue	1·60	1·30
B487a	-	130pf. red	3·00	1·90
B488	-	140pf. red	1·60	1·80
B488a	-	150pf. red	3·75	1·60
B489	-	160pf. green	3·25	1·80
B489a	-	180pf. brown	3·75	2·75
B489b	-	190pf. brown	3·75	3·25
B490	-	200pf. purple	2·10	1·10
B490a	-	230pf. purple	3·25	2·75
B490b	-	250pf. green	5·25	3·00
B490c	-	300pf. green	5·25	3·25
B491	-	500pf. black	7·50	5·25

B121 "Lovis Corinth" (self-portrait)

1975. 50th Death Anniv of Lovis Corinth (painter).

B492	**B121**	50pf. multicoloured	1·10	75

B122 Buildings in Naunynstrasse, Berlin-Kreuzberg

1975. European Architectural Heritage Year.

B493	**B122**	50pf. multicoloured	1·10	85

B123 Yellow Gentian

1975. Humanitarian Relief Funds. Alpine Flowers. Multicoloured.

B494	30pf.+15pf. Type B **123**	75	75
B495	40pf.+20pf. Arnica	75	75
B496	50pf.+25pf. Cyclamen	90	90
B497	70pf.+35pf. Blue gentian	1·50	1·50

1975. Christmas. As Type B 123, inscr "WEIHNACHTSMARKE". Mult.

B498	30pf.+15pf. Snow heather	1·10	1·10

See also Nos. B508/11, B540/3 and B557/60.

B124 Paul Lobe

1975. Birth Cent of Paul Lobe (politician).

B499	**B124**	50pf. red	1·10	75

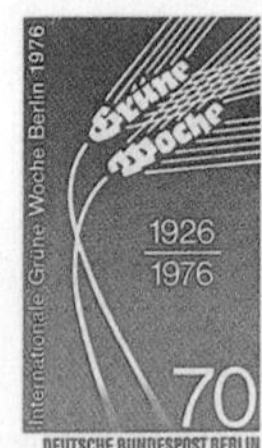

B125 Ears of Wheat, with inscription "Grune Woche"

1976. "International Agriculture Week", Berlin.

B500	**B125**	70pf. yellow and green	1·10	95

B126 Putting the Shot

1976. Youth Welfare. Training for the Olympics. Multicoloured.

B501	30pf.+15pf. Type B **126**	1·10	1·10
B502	40pf.+20pf. Hockey	1·10	1·10
B503	50pf.+25pf. Handball	1·20	1·20
B504	70pf.+35pf. Swimming	2·20	2·20

B127 Hockey

1976. Women's World Hockey Championships.

B505	**B127**	30pf. green	95	55

B128 Treble Clef

1976. German Choristers' Festival.

B506	**B128**	40pf. multicoloured	1·10	75

B129 Fire Service Emblem

1976. 125th Anniv of Berlin Fire Service.

B507	**B129**	50pf. multicoloured	1·70	1·10

1976. Humanitarian Relief Funds. Garden Flowers. As Type B 123. Multicoloured.

B508	30pf.+15pf. Iris	55	55
B509	40pf.+20pf. Wallflower	55	55
B510	50pf.+25pf. Dahlia	1·10	1·10
B511	70pf.+35pf. Larkspur	1·50	1·50

B130 Julius Tower, Spandau

1976. Berlin Views (1st series).

B512	-	30pf. black and blue	75	55
B513	**B130**	40pf. black and brown	1·10	55
B514	-	50pf. black and green	1·20	60

DESIGNS: 30pf. Yacht on the Havel; 50pf. Lake and Victory Column, Tiergarten park.

See also Nos. B562/4, B605/7 and B647/9.

B131 "Annunciation to the Shepherds" (window, Frauenkirche, Esslingen)

1976. Christmas. Sheet 71×101 mm.

MSB515	B **131** 30pf.+15pf. multicoloured	1·10	1·00

1977. Coil Stamps. German Castles. As Nos. 1805/12d.

B516	10pf. blue	30	20
B517	20pf. orange	30	25
B517a	25pf. red	85	55
B518	30pf. brown	35	30
B518c	35pf. red	50	40
B519	40pf. green	40	30
B519a	40pf. brown	75	40
B520	50pf. red	75	30
B520b	50pf. green	85	40
B521	60pf. brown	1·40	65
B521a	60pf. red	1·30	65
B522	70pf. blue	1·40	65
B522a	80pf. green	85	40
B522b	90pf. blue	1·40	1·10
B522c	120pf. violet	1·50	1·30
B523	190pf. red	1·90	1·80
B524	200pf. green	2·20	1·90
B524a	210pf. brown	2·75	2·10
B524b	230pf. green	2·75	2·10
B524c	280pf. blue	4·75	3·25
B524d	300pf. orange	4·75	3·25

B132 "Eugenie d'Alton" (Cristian Rauch)

1977. Birth Bicentenary of Christian Daniel Rauch (sculptor).

B525	**B132**	50pf. black	1·10	75

B133 "Eduard Gaertner" (self-portrait)

1977. Death Cent of Eduard Gaertner (artist).

B526	**B133**	40pf. black, green and deep green	75	55

B134 Bremen Kogge, 1380

1977. Youth Welfare. Ships. Multicoloured.

B527	30pf.+15pf. Type B **134**	65	65
B528	40pf.+20pf. "Helena Sloman" (steamship), 1850	75	75
B529	50pf.+25pf. "Cap Polonio" (liner), 1914	1·30	1·30
B530	70pf.+35pf. "Widar" (bulk carrier), 1971	1·60	1·60

B135 Female Figure

1977. Birth Cent of Georg Kolbe (sculptor).

B531	**B135**	30pf. green and black	75	55

B136 Crosses and Text

1977. 17th Evangelical Churches Day.

B532	**B136**	40pf. yellow, blk & grn	75	55

B137 Telephones of 1905 and 1977

1977. International Telecommunications Exhibition and Centenary of German Telephone Service.

B533	**B137**	50pf. buff, black & red	2·50	1·40

B138 Imperial German Patent Office, Berlin-Kreuzberg

1977. Centenary of German Patent Office.

B534	**B138**	60pf. black, red & grey	2·10	95

B139 Untitled Painting (G. Grosz)

1977. 15th European Art Exhibition.

B535	**B139**	70pf. multicoloured	1·40	1·30

B140 Picassco Triggerfish

1977. 25th Anniv of Reopening of Berlin Aquarium. Multicoloured.

B536	20pf. Type B **140**	70	65
B537	30pf. Paddlefish	95	85
B538	40pf. Radiated tortoise	1·40	1·10
B539	50pf. Rhinoceros iguana	1·90	1·30

1977. Humanitarian Relief Funds. Meadow Flowers. As Type B 123. Multicoloured.

B540	30pf.+15pf. Daisy	40	40
B541	40pf.+20pf. Marsh marigold	75	75
B542	50pf.+25pf. Sainfoin	1·10	1·10
B543	70pf.+35pf. Forget-me-not	1·60	1·60

B141 "Madonna and Child" (stained glass window, Basilica of St. Gereon, Cologne)

1977. Christmas. Sheet 70×105 mm.

MSB544 B **141** 30pf.+15pf. multicoloured	1·10	1·10

B142 Walter Kollo

1978. Birth Cent of Walter Kollo (composer).

B545	**B142**	50pf. brown and red	1·50	95

B143 Emblem of U.S. Chamber of Commerce

1978. 75th Anniv of U.S. Chamber of Commerce in Germany.

B546	**B143**	90pf. blue and red	1·80	1·70

1978. Youth Welfare. Aviation History (1st series). As T 627. Multicoloured.

B547	30pf.+15pf. Montgolfier balloon, 1783	55	65
B548	40pf.+20pf. Lilienthal glider, 1891	75	75
B549	50pf.+25pf. Wright Type A biplane	95	95
B550	70pf.+35pf. Etrich/Rumpler Taube, 1910	1·80	1·80

See also Nos. B567/70 and B589/92.

1978. Sport Promotion Fund. As T 623. Multicoloured.

B551	50pf.+25pf. Cycling	1·30	85
B552	70pf.+35pf. Fencing	1·70	1·50

B146 Albrecht von Graefe

1978. 150th Birth Anniv of Albrecht von Graefe (pioneer of medical eye services).

B553	**B146**	30pf. black and brown	75	55

B147 Friedrich Ludwig Jahn

1978. Birth Bicentenary of F. L. Jahn (pioneer of physical education).

B554	**B147**	50pf. red	1·10	75

B148 Swimming

1978. 3rd World Swimming Championships.

B555	**B148**	40pf. multicoloured	1·50	1·20

B149 "The Boat" (Karl Hofer)

1978. Birth Centenary of Karl Hofer (Impressionist painter).

B556	**B149**	50pf. multicoloured	1·10	85

1978. Humanitarian Relief Funds. Woodland Flowers. As Type B 123. Multicoloured.

B557	30pf.+15pf. Solomon's seal	65	65
B558	40pf.+20pf. Wood primrose	75	75
B559	50pf.+25pf. Red helle-borine	1·10	1·10
B560	70pf.+35pf. Bugle	1·60	1·60

B150 Prussian State Library

1978. Opening of New Prussian State Library Building.

B561	**B150**	90pf. olive and red	1·90	1·50

1978. Berlin Views (2nd series). As Type B 130.

B562	40pf. black and green	85	55
B563	50pf. black and purple	1·10	85
B564	60pf. black and brown	1·30	95

DESIGNS: 40pf. Belvedere; 50pf. Landwehr Canal; 60pf. Village church, Lichtenrade.

B151 "Madonna" (stained glass window, Frauenkirche, Munich)

1978. Christmas. Sheet 65×92 mm.

MSB565 B **151** 30pf.+15pf. multicoloured	1·10	1·10

B152 Congress Centre

1979. Opening of International Congress Centre, Berlin.

B566	**B152**	60pf. black, blue & red	1·50	95

1979. Youth Welfare. History of Aviation (2nd series). As T 627. Multicoloured.

B567	40pf.+20pf. Vampyr glider, 1921	75	75
B568	50pf.+25pf. Junkers Ju 52/3m D-2202 "Richthofen", 1932	1·10	1·10
B569	60pf.+30pf. Messerschmitt Bf 108 D-1010, 1934	1·40	1·40
B570	90pf.+45pf. Douglas DC-3 NC-14988, 1935	2·10	2·10

B153 Relay Runners

1979. Sport Promotion Fund. Multicoloured.

B571	60pf.+30pf. Type B **153**	1·40	1·30
B572	90pf.+45pf. Archers	1·80	1·70

B154 Old and New Arms

1979. Centenary of State Printing Works, Berlin.

B573	**B154**	60pf. multicoloured	2·00	1·50

B155 Arrows and Target

1979. World Archery Championships.

B574	**B155**	50pf. multicoloured	1·10	75

B156 Television Screen

1979. International Telecommunications Exhibition, Berlin.

B575	**B156**	60pf. black, grey & red	1·50	1·10

B157 Moses Mendelssohn

1979. 250th Birth Anniv of Moses Mendelssohn (philosopher).

B576	**B157**	90pf. black	1·70	1·10

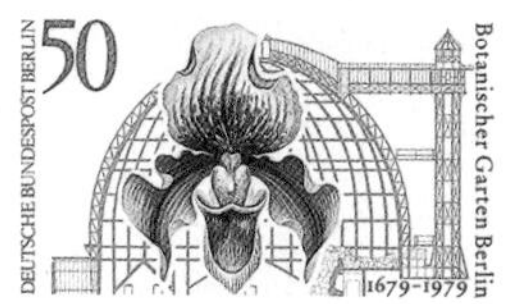

B158 Venus Slipper Orchid and Great Tropical House

1979. 300th Anniv of Berlin Botanical Gardens.

B577	**B158**	50pf. multicoloured	1·10	75

B159 Gas Lamp, Kreuzberg District

1979. 300th Anniv of Street Lighting.

B578	**B159**	10pf. green, bl & grey	55	30
B579	-	40pf. green, bis & grey	1·10	85
B580	-	50pf. green, brn & grey	1·50	95
B581	-	60pf. green, red & grey	1·60	1·50

DESIGNS: 40pf. Electric carbon-arc lamp, Hardenbergstrasse; 50pf. Gas Lamps, Wittenberg-platz; 60pf. Five-armed chandelier, Charlottenburg.

1979. Humanitarian Relief Funds. Woodland Flowers and Fruit. As Type B 123, but horiz. Multicoloured.

B582	40pf.+20pf. Larch	85	65
B583	50pf.+25pf. Hazelnut	1·10	95
B584	60pf.+30pf. Horse chestnut	1·50	1·40
B585	90pf.+45pf. Blackthorn	1·90	1·80

B161 Advertisement Pillar

1979. 125th Anniv of Advertisement Pillars.

B586	**B161**	50pf. red and lilac	2·00	1·10

B162 "Nativity" (Altenberg medieval manuscript)

1979. Christmas.

B587	**B162**	40pf.+20pf. mult	1·30	1·10

B163 Map showing Wegener's Theory of Continental Drift

1980. Birth Centenary of Alfred Wegener (explorer and geophysicist).

B588	**B163**	60pf. black, orange and blue	1·70	1·40

1980. Youth Welfare. Aviation History (3rd series). As T 627. Multicoloured.

B589	40pf.+20pf. Vickers Viscount 810	95	95
B590	50pf.+25pf. Fokker Friendship "Condor"	1·10	1·10
B591	60pf.+30pf. Sud Aviation Caravelle F-BKSZ, 1955	1·40	1·40
B592	90pf.+45pf. Sikorsky S-55 helicopter OO-SHB, 1949	1·90	1·90

Nos. B589/90 are incorrectly dated.

B164 Throwing the Javelin

1980. Sport Promotion Fund. Multicoloured.

B593	50pf.+25pf. Type B **164**	95	95
B594	60pf.+30pf. Weightlifting	1·10	1·10
B595	90pf.+45pf. Water polo	1·60	1·60

B165 Cardinal Preysing

1980. 86th German Catholics Congress.

B596	**B165**	50pf. red and black	1·10	75

B166 "Operatio" (enamel medallion)

1980. 150th Anniv of Prussian Museums. Multicoloured.

B597	40pf. Type B **166**	1·10	65
B598	60pf. "Monks Reading" (oak sculpture, Ernst Barlach)	1·50	85

B167 Robert Stolz

1980. Birth Centenary of Robert Stolz (composer).

B599	**B167**	60pf. multicoloured	1·50	1·10

B168 Von Steuben

1980. 250th Birth Anniv of Friedrich Wilhelm von Steuben (American general).

B600	**B168**	40pf. multicoloured	1·50	75

B169 Orlaya grandiflora

1980. Humanitarian Relief Funds. Endangered Wild Flowers. Multicoloured.

B601	40pf.+20pf. Type B **169**	95	95
B602	50pf.+25pf. Yellow gagae	1·20	1·20
B603	60pf.+30pf. Summer pheasant's-eye	1·20	1·20
B604	90p.+45pf. Venus's looking-glass	2·00	2·00

See also Nos. B622/5.

1980. Berlin Views (3rd series). As Type B 130.

B605	40pf. black and green	1·10	60
B606	50pf. black and brown	1·20	95
B607	60pf. black and blue	1·80	1·10

DESIGNS: 40pf. Lilienthal Monument; 50pf. "Grosse Neugierde"; 60pf. Grunewald Tower.

B170 "Message to the Shepherds" (Altomunster manuscript)

1980. Christmas.

B608	**B170**	40pf.+20pf. mult	1·30	1·20

B171 Von Arnim (after Strohling)

1981. Birth Bicentenary of Achim von Arnim (poet).

B609	**B171**	60pf. green	1·30	85

B172 Von Chamisso (bronze medallion, David d'Angers)

1981. Birth Bicentenary of Adelbert von Chamisso (poet and naturalist).

B610	**B172**	60pf. brown, deep brown and ochre	1·30	85

B173 Von Gontard

1981. 250th Birth Anniv of Karl Phillipp von Gontard (architect).

B611	**B173**	50pf. red, black & grey	1·30	85

B174 Kreuzberg War Memorial

1981. Birth Bicentenary of Karl Friedrich Schinkel (architect).

B612	**B174**	40pf. green and brown	1·50	1·10

B175 Theodolite, c. 1810

1981. Youth Welfare. Optical Instruments. Multicoloured.

B613	40pf.+20pf. Type B **175**	75	75
B614	50pf.+25pf. Equatorial telescope, 1820	1·10	1·10
B615	60pf.+30pf. Microscope, 1790	1·40	1·40
B616	90pf.+45pf. Sextant, 1830	2·10	2·10

B176 Group Gymnastics

1981. Sport Promotion Fund. Multicoloured.

B617	60pf.+30pf. Type B **176**	1·30	1·20
B618	90pf.+45pf. Cross-country race	1·90	1·80

B177 "Cupid and Psyche"

1981. 150th Birth Anniv of Reinhold Begas (sculptor).

B619	**B177**	50pf. black and blue	1·10	75

B178 Badge of Order "Pour le Merite"

1981. Prussian Exhibition, Berlin-Kreuzberg.

B620	**B178**	40pf. multicoloured	1·10	75

B179 Broadcasting House, Charlottenburg

1981. International Telecommunications Exhibition, Berlin.

B621	**B179**	60pf. multicoloured	1·70	1·10

1981. Humanitarian Relief Funds. Endangered Wild Flowers. As Type B 169. Multicoloured.

B622	40pf.+20pf. Common bistort	1·10	95
B623	50pf.+25pf. Moor-king	1·20	1·10
B624	60pf.+30pf. "Gladiolus palustris"	1·30	1·10
B625	90pf.+45pf. Siberian iris	2·50	2·10

B180 "Three Kings" (glass painting)

1981. Christmas.

B626	**B180**	40pf.+20pf. mult	1·30	95

B181 Peter Beuth

1981. Birth Bicentenary of Peter Beuth (constitutional lawyer).

B627	**B181**	60pf. black and brown	1·10	95

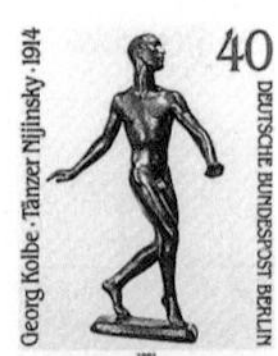

B182 "Dancer Nijinsky" (Georg Kolbe)

1981. 20th Century Sculptures. Mult.

B628	40pf. Type B **182**	75	55
B629	60pf. "Mother Earth II" (Ernst Barlach)	1·30	85
B630	90pf. "Flora Kneeling" (Richard Scheibe)	1·70	1·50

B183 Arms and View of Spandau, c. 1700

1982. 750th Anniv of Spandau.

B631	**B183**	60pf. multicoloured	1·70	1·30

B184 Daimler Steel-wheeled Car, 1889

1982. Youth Welfare Fund. Motor Cars. Multicoloured.

B632	40pf.+20pf. Type B **184**	95	95
B633	50pf.+25pf. Wanderer "Puppchen", 1911	1·10	1·10
B634	60pf.+30p. Adler limousine, 1913	1·30	1·30
B635	90pf.+45pf. DKW "F 1", 1913	2·10	2·10

B185 Sprinting

1982. Sport Promotion Fund. Multicoloured.

B636	60pf.+30pf. Type B **185**	1·40	1·10
B637	90pf.+45pf. Volleyball	2·00	1·50

B186 Harp

1982. Centenary of Berlin Philharmonic Orchestra.

B638	**B186**	60pf. grey, red & green	1·50	95

B187 "Emigrants reaching Prussian Frontier" (woodcut after drawing by Adolph von Menzel)

1982. 250th Anniv of Salzburg Emigrants' Arrival in Prussia.

B639	**B187**	50pf. stone, deep brown and brown	1·10	75

B188 "Italian Stone Carriers" (Max Pechstein)

1982. Paintings. Multicoloured.

B640	50pf. Type B **188**	1·30	95
B641	80pf. "Two Girls Bathing" (Otto Mueller)	1·90	1·50

B189 Floribunda-Grandiflora

1982. Humanitarian Relief Funds. Roses. Multicoloured.

B642	50pf.+20pf. Type B **189**	1·40	1·20
B643	60pf.+30pf. Hybrid tea	1·70	1·30
B644	80pf.+40pf. Floribunda	2·10	2·00
B645	120pf.+60pf. Miniature rose	3·50	3·50

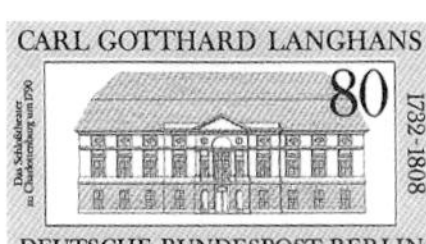

B190 Castle Theatre, Charlottenburg

1982. 250th Birth Anniv of Carl Gotthard Langhans (architect).

B646	**B190**	80pf. red, grey and black	2·30	1·70

1982. Berlin Views (4th series). As Type B 130.

B647	50pf. black and blue	1·50	95
B648	60pf. black and red	1·60	1·20
B649	80pf. black and brown	2·10	1·30

DESIGNS: 50pf. Villa Borsig; 60pf. Sts. Peter and Paul Church; 80pf. Villa von der Heydt.

B191 "Adoration of the Kings" (detail from St. Peter altar by Master Bertram)

1982. Christmas.

B650	**B191**	50pf.+20pf. mult	1·30	1·10

B192 Water Pump, Klausenerplatz

1983. Street Water Pumps. Multicoloured.

B651	50pf. Type B **192**	1·60	1·10
B652	60pf. Chamissoplatz	1·90	1·20
B653	80pf. Schloss-strasse	2·30	1·70
B654	120pf. Kuerfurstendamm	3·25	2·75

B193 Royal Prussian Telegraphy Inspectors at St. Anne's Church

1983. 150th Anniv of Berlin–Coblenz Optical-Mechanical Telegraph.

B655	**B193**	80pf. brown	2·50	2·00

B194 Hildebrand & Wolfmuller, 1894

1983. Youth Welfare. Motor Cycles. Mult.

B656	50pf.+20pf. Type B **194**	1·10	75
B657	60pf.+30pf. Wanderer, 1908	1·60	1·40
B658	80pf.+40pf. D.K.W.-Lomos, 1922	1·80	1·50
B659	120pf.+60pf. Mars, 1925	4·00	3·75

B195 Latin-American Dancing

1983. Sport Promotion Fund. Multicoloured.

B660	80pf.+40pf. Type B **195**	2·10	1·60
B661	120pf.+60pf. Ice hockey	3·25	2·75

B196 "La Barbarina" (painting of Barbara Campanini)

1983. 300th Birth Anniv of Antoine Pesne (artist).

B662	**B196**	50pf. multicoloured	1·30	95

B197 Ringelnatz (silhouette by E. M. Engert)

1983. Birth Centenary of Joachim Ringelnatz (poet and painter).

B663	**B197**	50pf. green, brn & red	1·50	1·10

B198 Paul Nipkow's Picture Transmission System, 1884

1983. International Broadcasting Exn, Berlin.

B664	**B198**	80pf. multicoloured	2·30	1·80

B199 Mountain Windflower

1983. Humanitarian Relief Funds. Endangered Alpine Flowers. Multicoloured.

B665	50pf.+20pf. Type B **199**	85	85
B666	60pf.+30pf. Alpine auricula	1·30	1·30
B667	80pf.+40pf. Little primrose	2·30	2·30
B668	120pf.+60pf. Einsele's aquilegia	3·50	3·50

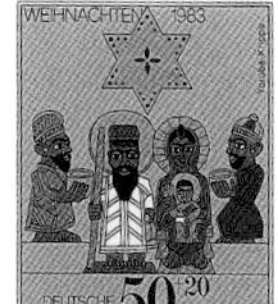

B200 Nigerian Yoruba Crib

1983. Christmas.

B669	**B200**	50pf.+20pf. mult	1·30	1·20

B201 Queen Cleopatra VII (Antikenmuseum)

1984. Art Objects in Berlin Museums. Multicoloured.

B670	30pf. Type B **201**	1·40	1·10
B671	50pf. Statue of seated couple from Giza Necropolis (Egyptian Museum)	1·80	1·50
B672	60pf. Goddess with pearl turban (Ethnology Museum)	2·30	1·90
B673	80pf. Majolica dish (Applied Arts Museum)	3·00	2·75

B202 "Trichius Fasciatus"

1984. Youth Welfare. Pollinating Insects. Multicoloured.

B674	50pf.+20pf. Type B **202**	1·40	95
B675	60pf.+30pf. "Agrumenia carniolica"	1·40	1·10
B676	80pf.+40pf. "Bombus terrestris"	2·75	1·90
B677	120pf.+60pf. "Eristalis tenax"	3·25	3·00

B203 Hurdling

1984. Sport Promotion Fund. Multicoloured.

B678	60pf.+30pf. Type B **203**	2·10	1·50
B679	80pf.+40pf. Cycling	2·75	1·50
B680	120pf.+60pf. Four-seater kayaks	3·75	3·50

B204 Klausener

1984. 50th Death Anniv of Dr. Erich Klausener (chairman of Catholic Action).

B681	**B204**	80pf. green & dp green	1·50	1·10

B205 "Electric Power" (K. Sutterlin)

1984. Centenary of Berlin Electricity Supply.

B682	**B205**	50pf. yell, orge & blk	1·30	95

B206 Conference Emblem

1984. 4th European Ministers of Culture Conference, Berlin.

B683	**B206**	60pf. multicoloured	1·60	1·10

B207 Brehm and White Stork

1984. Death Centenary of Alfred Brehm (zoologist).

B684	**B207**	80pf. multicoloured	2·50	1·80

B208 Heim (bust, Freidrich Tieck)

1984. 150th Death Anniv of Ernst Ludwig Heim (medical pioneer).

B685	**B208**	50pf. black and red	1·50	1·10

B209 "Listera cordata"

1984. Humanitarian Relief Funds. Orchids. Multicoloured.

B686	50pf.+20pf. Type B **209**	2·30	1·50
B687	60pf.+30pf. "Ophrys insectifera"	2·30	1·50
B688	80pf.+40pf. "Epipactis palustris"	3·75	3·50
B689	120pf.+60pf. "Ophrys coriophora"	5·75	5·25

B210 "Sunflowers on Grey Background"

1984. Birth Centenary of Karl Schmidt-Rottluff (artist).

B690	**B210**	60pf. multicoloured	1·50	1·10

B211 St. Nicholas

1984. Christmas.

B691	**B211**	50pf.+20pf. mult	1·60	1·50

B212 Bettina von Arnim

1985. Birth Bicentenary of Bettina von Arnim (writer).

B692	**B212**	50pf. black, brn & red	1·30	1·20

B213 Humboldt (statue, Paul Otto)

1985. 50th Death Anniv of Wilhelm von Humboldt (philologist).

B693	**B213**	80pf. black, blue & red	2·00	1·80

B214 Ball in Net

1985. Sport Promotion Fund. Multicoloured.

B694	80pf.+40pf. Type B **214** (50th anniv of basketball in Germany and European championships, Stuttgart)	1·90	1·90
B695	120pf.+60pf. Table tennis (60th anniv of German Table Tennis Association)	3·25	3·25

B215 Stylized Flower

1985. Federal Horticultural Show, Berlin.

B696	**B215**	80pf. multicoloured	1·80	1·50

B216 Bussing Bicycle, 1868

1985. Youth Welfare. International Youth Year. Bicycles. Multicoloured.

B697	50pf.+20pf. Type B **216**	1·60	1·60
B698	60pf.+30pf. Child's tricycle, 1885	1·60	1·60
B699	80pf.+40pf. Jaray bicycle, 1925	2·10	2·10
B700	120pf.+60pf. Opel racing bicycle, 1925	4·75	4·75

B217 Stock Exchange, 1863–1945

1985. 300th Anniv of Berlin Stock Exchange.

B701	**B217**	50pf. multicoloured	1·50	1·20

B218 Otto Klemperer

1985. Birth Centenary of Otto Klemperer (orchestral conductor).

B702	**B218**	60pf. blue	1·80	1·50

B219 Association Emblem

1985. 11th International Gynaecology and Obstetrics Association Congress, Berlin.

B703	**B219**	60pf. multicoloured	1·50	1·20

B220 "FE 3" Television Camera, 1935

1985. International Broadcasting Exn, Berlin.

B704	**B220**	80pf. multicoloured	2·50	2·10

B221 Seal of Brandenburg-Prussia and Preamble of Edict

1985. 300th Anniv of Edict of Potsdam (admitting Huguenots to Prussia).

B705	**B221**	50pf. lilac and black	1·30	95

B222 Flowers, Strawberries and Ladybirds

1985. Humanitarian Relief Funds. Motifs from borders of medieval prayer book. Multicoloured.

B706	50pf.+20pf. Type B **222**	1·60	1·60
B707	60pf.+30pf. Flowers, bird and butterfly	2·10	2·10
B708	80pf.+40pf. Flowers, bee and butterfly	2·10	2·10
B709	120pf.+60pf. Flowers, berries, butterfly and snail	3·25	3·25

B223 "Adoration of the Kings" (detail, Epiphany Altar)

1985. Christmas. 500th Birth Anniv of Hans Baldung Grien (artist).

B710	**B223**	50pf.+20pf. mult	1·70	1·50

B224 Kurt Tucholsky

1985. 50th Death Anniv of Kurt Tucholsky (writer and journalist).

B711	**B224**	80pf. multicoloured	2·30	1·50

B225 Furtwangler and Score

1986. Birth Centenary of Wilhelm Furtwangler (composer and conductor).

B712	**B225**	80pf. multicoloured	2·50	2·30

B226 Rohe and National Gallery

1986. Birth Centenary of Ludwig Mies van der Rohe (architect).

B713	**B226**	50pf. multicoloured	1·60	1·50

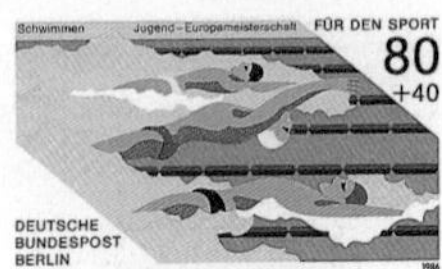

B227 Swimming

1986. Sport Promotion Fund. Multicoloured.

B714	80pf.+40pf. Type B **227** (European Youth Championships, Berlin)	2·75	2·30
B715	120pf.+55pf. Show-jumping (World Championships, Aachen)	3·25	3·00

B228 Glazier

1986. Youth Charity. Trades (1st series). Multicoloured.

B716	50pf.+25pf. Type B **228**	1·60	1·60
B717	60pf.+30pf. Locksmith	2·10	2·10
B718	70pf.+35pf. Tailor	2·10	2·10
B719	80pf.+40pf. Carpenter	2·75	2·75

See also Nos. B765/8.

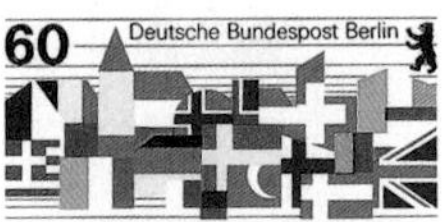

B229 Flags

1986. 16th European Communities Day.

B720	**B229**	60pf. multicoloured	1·40	1·30

B230 Ranke

1986. Death Centenary of Leopold von Ranke (historian).

B721	**B230**	80pf. brown and grey	2·30	1·80

B231 Benn

1986. Birth Centenary of Gottfried Benn (poet).

B722	**B231**	80pf. blue	2·30	1·80

B232 Charlottenburg Gate

1986. Gateways. Multicoloured.

B723	50pf. Type B **232**	1·90	1·90
B724	60pf. Griffin Gate, Glienicke Palace	2·00	2·00
B725	80pf. Elephant Gate, Berlin Zoo	2·20	2·20

B233 "The Flute Concert" (detail, Adolph von Menzel)

1986. Death Bicentenary of Frederick the Great.

B726	**B233**	80pf. multicoloured	2·30	1·80

B234 Cantharus, 1st century A.D.

1986. Humanitarian Relief Funds. Glassware. Multicoloured.

B727	50pf.+25pf. Type B **234**	2·75	1·60
B728	60pf.+30pf. Beaker, 200 A.D.	2·10	2·10
B729	70pf.+35pf. Jug, 3rd century A.D.	2·10	2·10
B730	80pf.+40pf. Diatreta 4th century A.D.	2·75	2·75

B235 "Adoration of the Three Kings" (Ortenberg altarpiece)

1986. Christmas.

B731	**B235**	50pf.+25pf. mult	1·40	1·30

1986. Famous German Women. As Nos. 2149a/54, 2158, 2161, 2166/9a.

B732	5pf. brown and grey	55	3·00
B733	10pf. brown and violet	65	2·10
B734	20pf. blue and red	2·20	5·25
B735	40pf. red and blue	1·70	5·25
B736	50pf. green and brown	2·75	3·75
B737	60pf. lilac and green	1·60	5·25
B738	80pf. brown and green	1·90	3·75
B739	100pf. grey and red	2·75	2·10
B740	130pf. violet and blue	5·25	16·00
B741	140pf. brown and blue	6·25	16·00
B742	170pf. purple and green	3·50	12·50
B743	180pf. purple and blue	5·00	18·00
B744	240pf. brown and blue	4·50	18·00
B745	250pf. blue and mauve	10·00	30·00
B746	300pf. green and plum	10·50	26·00
B747	350pf. brown and black	7·50	21·00
B748	500pf. red and green	11·50	48·00

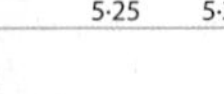

B236 Berlin, 1650

1987. 750th Anniv of Berlin. (a) As No. 2170.

B760	**833**	80pf. multicoloured	2·50	2·10

(b) Sheet 130×100 mm containing Type B 236 and similar horiz designs. Multicoloured.

MSB761	40pf. Type B **236**; 50pf. Charlottenburg Castle, 1830; 60pf. Turbine Hall; 80pf. Philharmonic and Chamber Music Concert Hall	5·25	5·25

B237 Louise Schroeder

1987. Birth Centenary of Louise Schroeder (Mayor of Berlin).

B762	**B237**	50pf. brown and orange on light brown	1·50	1·50

B238 German Gymnastics Festival, Berlin

1987. Sport Promotion Fund. Multicoloured.

B763	80pf.+40pf. Type B **238**	2·10	2·10
B764	120pf.+55pf. World Judo Championships, Essen	3·25	3·25

1987. Youth Welfare. Trades (2nd series). As Type B 228. Multicoloured.

B765	50pf.+25pf. Cooper	1·60	1·60
B766	60pf.+30pf. Stonemason	1·60	1·60
B767	70pf.+35pf. Furrier	2·10	2·10
B768	80pf.+40pf. Painter/ lacquerer	2·10	2·10

B239 "Bohemian Refugees" (detail of relief, King Friedrich Wilhelm Monument, Berlin-Neukolln)

1987. 250th Anniv of Bohemian Settlement, Rixdorf.

B769	**B239**	50pf. brown and green	1·30	1·10

B240 New Buildings

1987. International Building Exhibition, Berlin.

B770	**B240**	80pf. silver, black & bl	1·80	1·60

B241 Tree in Arrow Circle

1987. 14th International Botanical Congress, Berlin.

B771	**B241**	60pf. multicoloured	1·40	1·30

B242 Compact Disc and Gramophone

1987. International Broadcasting Exhibition, Berlin. Centenary of Gramophone Record.

B772	**B242**	80pf. multicoloured	1·70	1·60

B243 5th-century Bonnet Ornament

1987. Humanitarian Relief Funds. Precious Metal Work. Multicoloured.

B773	50pf.+25pf. Type B **243**	1·10	1·10
B774	60pf.+30pf. Athene plate, 1st-century B.C.	1·60	1·60
B775	70pf.+35pf. "Armilla" armlet, 1180	1·90	1·90
B776	80pf.+40pf. Snake bracelet, 300 B.C.	2·30	2·30

1987. Tourist Sights. As Nos. 2200/19.

B777	5pf. blue and grey	40	65
B778	10pf. blue and indigo	55	50
B779	20pf. flesh and blue	55	1·10
B780	30pf. brown and green	1·40	1·30
B781	40pf. brown, red and blue	1·80	3·00
B782	50pf. ochre and blue	2·10	1·60
B783	60pf. green and black	2·10	1·60
B784	70pf. flesh and blue	2·10	3·75
B785	70pf. brown and blue	3·00	6·25
B786	80pf. grey and green	2·20	1·60
B787	100pf. green and orange	1·70	2·10
B788	120pf. green and red	3·25	4·75
B789	140pf. bistre and yellow	3·25	5·75
B790	300pf. flesh and brown	6·25	6·00
B791	350pf. brown and blue	6·25	9·50

B244 "Adoration of the Magi" (13th-century Book of Psalms)

1987. Christmas.

B797	**B244**	50pf.+25pf. mult	1·30	1·20

B245 Heraldic Bear

1988. Berlin, European City of Culture.

B798	**B245**	80pf. multicoloured	2·75	2·50

B246 Old and New Buildings

1988. Centenary of Urania Science Museum.

B799	**B246**	50pf. multicoloured	1·90	1·80

B247 "Large Pure-bred Foal" (bronze)

1988. Birth Centenary of Rene Sintenis (sculptor).

B800	**B247**	60pf. multicoloured	1·30	1·30

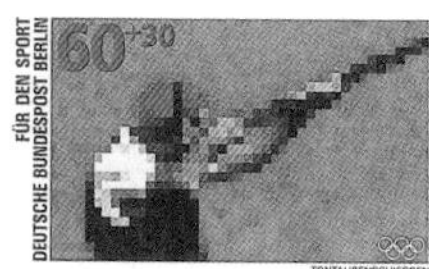
B248 Clay-pigeon Shooting

1988. Sport Promotion Fund. Olympic Games. Multicoloured.

B801	60pf.+30pf. Type B **248**	2·10	1·90
B802	80pf.+40pf. Figure skating (pairs)	2·10	1·90
B803	120pf.+55pf. Throwing the hammer	2·75	2·75

B249 Piano, Violin and Cello

1988. Youth Welfare. Music. Multicoloured.

B804	50pf.+25pf. Type B **249**	1·60	1·60
B805	60pf.+30pf. Wind quintet	2·10	2·10
B806	70pf.+35pf. Guitar, recorder and mandolin	2·10	2·10
B807	80pf.+40pf. Children's choir	3·25	3·25

B250 Great Elector and Family in Berlin Castle Gardens

1988. 300th Death Anniv of Friedrich Wilhelm, Great Elector of Brandenburg.

B808	**B250**	50pf. multicoloured	1·50	1·40

B251 Globe

1988. International Monetary Fund and World Bank Boards of Governors Annual Meetings, Berlin.

B809	**B251**	70pf. multicoloured	1·60	1·40

B252 First Train leaving Potsdam Station

1988. 150th Anniv of Berlin–Potsdam Railway.

B810	**B252**	10pf. multicoloured	75	65

B253 "The Collector" (bronze statue)

1988. 50th Death Anniv of Ernst Barlach (artist).

B811	**B253**	40pf. multicoloured	95	75

B254 18th-century Breast Ornament

1988. Humanitarian Relief Funds. Precious Metal Work. Multicoloured.

B812	50pf.+25pf. Type B **254**	1·50	1·50
B813	60pf.+30pf. 16th-century lion-shaped jug	1·70	1·70
B814	70pf.+35pf. 16th-century goblet	1·90	1·90
B815	80pf.+40pf. 15th-century cope clasp	2·30	2·30

B255 "Annunciation to the Shepherds" (illus from Henry the Lion's Gospel Book)

1988. Christmas.

B816	**B255**	50pf.+25pf. mult	1·70	1·60

B256 Volleyball (European Championships)

1989. Sport Promotion Fund. Multicoloured.

B817	100pf.+50pf. Type B **256**	3·25	3·25
B818	140pf.+60pf. Hockey (Champions Trophy)	4·50	4·50

B257 Tigers and Tamer

1989. Youth Welfare. Circus. Multicoloured.

B819	60pf.+30pf. Type B **257**	2·10	2·10
B820	70pf.+30pf. Trapeze artistes	2·75	2·75
B821	80pf.+35pf. Sealions	3·75	3·75
B822	100pf.+50pf. Jugglers	4·50	4·50

B258 U.S. and U.K. Flags forming Airplane

1989. 40th Anniv of Berlin Airlift.

B823	**B258**	60pf. multicoloured	1·70	1·60

B259 Emblem

1989. 13th International Organization of Chief Accountants Congress.

B824	**B259**	80pf. multicoloured	1·80	1·80

B260 Reuter

1989. Birth Centenary of Ernst Reuter (politician and Mayor of Berlin).

B825	**B260**	100pf. multicoloured	2·50	2·30

B261 Satellite Radio Waves and T.V. Screen

1989. International Broadcasting Exn, Berlin.

B826	**B261**	100pf. multicoloured	2·10	2·00

B262 Plan of Berlin Zoo and Lenne

1989. Birth Bicentenary of Peter Joseph Lenne (landscape designer).

B827	**B262**	60pf. multicoloured	2·10	1·80

B263 Ossietzky and Masthead of "Die Weltbuhne"

1989. Birth Centenary of Carl von Ossietzky (journalist and peace activist).

B828	**B263**	100pf. multicoloured	2·30	2·10

B264 Former School Building

1989. 300th Anniv of Berlin Lycee Francais.

B829	**B264**	40pf. multicoloured	1·30	1·20

B265 St. Nicholas's Church, Berlin-Spandau

1989. 450th Anniv of Reformation.

B830	**B265**	60pf. multicoloured	1·30	1·20

B266 15th-century Letter Messenger

1989. Humanitarian Relief Funds. Postal Deliveries. Multicoloured.

B831	60pf.+30pf. Type B **266**	3·25	3·25
B832	80pf.+35pf. Brandenburg mail coach, 1700	4·25	4·25
B833	100pf.+50pf. 19th-century Prussian postal messengers	5·25	5·25

B267 "Journalists"

1989. Birth Centenary of Hannah Hoch (painter).

B834	**B267**	100pf. multicoloured	2·50	2·10

B268 Angel

1989. Christmas. 16th-century Carvings by Veit Stoss, St. Lawrence's Church, Nuremberg. Multicoloured.

B835		40pf.+20pf. Type B **268**	1·60	1·60
B836		60pf.+30pf. "Adoration of the Magi"	2·75	2·75

B269 Horse-drawn Passenger Vehicle

1990. 250th Anniv of Public Transport in Berlin.

B837	**B269**	60pf. multicoloured	2·50	2·10

B270 Rudorff

1990. 150th Birth Anniv of Ernst Rudorff (founder of conservation movement).

B838	**B270**	60pf. multicoloured	2·50	2·10

1990. 500th Anniv of Regular European Postal Services. As No. 2297.

B839	**914**	100pf. deep brown, light brown and brown	3·50	3·00

B271 Curtain and Theatre

1990. Cent of National Free Theatre, Berlin.

B840	**B271**	100pf. multicoloured	2·75	2·75

B272 Facade

1990. 40th Anniv of Bundeshaus, Berlin.

B841	**B272**	100pf. multicoloured	3·75	3·00

B273 Water Polo

1990. Sport Promotion Fund. Multicoloured.

B842		100pf.+50pf. Type B **273**	4·25	4·75
B843		140pf.+60pf. Wheelchair basketball	7·50	8·50

B274 Moritz filling Pipe with Gunpowder

1990. Youth Welfare. 125th Anniv of Max and Moritz (characters from books by Wilhelm Busch). Multicoloured.

B844		60pf.+30pf. Type B **274**	2·40	2·40
B845		70pf.+30pf. Max and Moritz running off	3·50	3·50
B846		80pf.+35pf. Moritz slashing sack open	3·75	3·75
B847		100pf.+50pf. Insect on Uncle Fritz's nose	3·75	3·75

B275 Poster

1990. 90th German Catholic Day.

B848	**B275**	60pf. multicoloured	2·30	2·10

B276 "Street Singer" (etching, Ludwig Knaus)

1990. Bicentenary of Barrel-organ.

B849	**B276**	100pf. multicoloured	2·75	2·50

B277 Pestle and Mortar and Diagram of Aspirin Molecule

1990. Centenary of German Pharmaceutical Society.

B850	**B277**	100pf. multicoloured	5·25	4·25

B278 Diesterweg

1990. Birth Bicentenary of Adolph Diesterweg (educationist).

B851	**B278**	60pf. multicoloured	3·75	4·00

B279 Travelling Post Office, 1900

1990. Humanitarian Relief Funds. Posts and Telecommunications. Multicoloured.

B852		60pf.+30pf. Type B **279**	2·75	2·75
B853		80pf.+35pf. Installing telephone lines, 1900	3·75	3·75
B854		100pf.+50pf. Electric parcels van, 1930	5·25	5·25

With the absorption of East Germany into the Federal Republic of Germany on 3 October 1990, separate issues for West Berlin ceased.

GERMAN DEMOCRATIC REPUBLIC (East Germany)

The German Democratic Republic was set up in October 1949 and comprised the former Russian Zone. Its stamps were used in East Berlin.

On 3 October 1990 the territory was absorbed into the German Federal Republic.

E1 Pigeon and Globe

1949. 75th Anniv of U.P.U.

E1	**E1**	50pf. blue and deep blue	15·00	12·50

E2 Postal Workers and Globe

1949. Postal Workers' Congress.

E2	**E2**	12pf. blue	11·50	13·50
E3	**E2**	30pf. red	18·00	23·00

E3 Type **1** of Bavaria and Magnifying Glass

1949. Stamp Day.

E4	**E3**	12pf.+3pf. black	9·00	7·50

E4 Skier

1950. 1st Winter Sports Meeting, Schierke.

E5	**E4**	12pf. violet	9·00	5·25
E6	-	24pf. blue	11·50	8·50

DESIGN: 24pf. Girl skater.

1950. Leipzig Spring Fair. As T 231 but dated "1950".

E7		24pf.+12pf. purple	12·50	12·50
E8		30pf.+14pf. red	15·00	15·00

DESIGNS: 24pf. First Dresden China Fair, 1710; 30pf. First Sample Fair, 1894.

E5 Globe and Sun

1950. 60th Anniv of Labour Day.

E9	**E5**	30pf. red	24·00	19·00

E6 Wilhelm Pieck

E7 Wilhelm Pieck

1950

E68	**E6**	5pf. green	13·00	5·00
E10	**E6**	12pf. blue	34·00	2·75
E70	**E6**	24pf. brown	34·00	2·00
E12	**E7**	1Dm. green	43·00	6·00
E13	**E7**	2Dm. red	26·00	5·75
E14	**E7**	5Dm. blue	11·50	2·10

For 1 and 2Dm. with different portrait of president, see Nos. E320/1 (1953).

E8 Shepherd Playing Pipes

1950. Death Bicentenary of J. S. Bach (composer).

E15	**E8**	12pf.+4pf. green	9·00	6·25
E16	-	24pf.+6pf. olive	9·00	6·25
E17	-	30pf.+8pf. red	17·00	13·50
E18	-	50pf.+16pf. blue	26·00	21·00

DESIGNS: 24pf. Girl playing hand-organ; 30pf. Bach; 50pf. Three singers.

E9 Dove, Globe and Stamp

1950. Philatelic Exhibition (DEBRIA), Leipzig.

E19	**E9**	84pf.+41pf. red	60·00	14·50

E10 L. Euler

1950. 250th Anniv of Academy of Science, Berlin.

E20	**E10**	1pf. grey	6·00	2·40
E21	-	5pf. green	8·50	6·00
E22	-	6pf. violet	17·00	6·00
E23	-	8pf. brown	23·00	13·00
E24	-	10pf. green	21·00	13·00
E25	-	12pf. blue	18·00	5·00
E26	-	16pf. blue	24·00	23·00
E27	-	20pf. purple	22·00	18·00
E28	-	24pf. red	24·00	5·00
E29	-	50pf. blue	37·00	24·00

PORTRAITS: 5pf. A. von Humboldt; 6pf. T. Mommsen; 8pf. W. von Humboldt; 10pf. H. von Helmholtz; 12pf. M. Planck; 16pf. J. Grimm; 20pf. W. Nernst; 24pf. G. W. Leibniz; 50pf. A. von Harnack.

1950. German Stamp Exhibition, "DEBRIA". Sheet 92×52 mm.

MSE29a	Nos. E4 and E19	£200	£200

E11 Miner

1950. 750th Anniv of Mansfeld Copper Mines.

E30	**E11**	12pf. blue	8·50	9·75
E31	-	24pf. red	13·50	10·50

DESIGN: 24pf. Copper smelting.

E12 Ballot Box

1950. East German Elections.

E32	**E12**	24pf. brown	20·00	6·00

E13 Hand, Dove and Burning Buildings

1950. Peace Propaganda. Inscr "ERKAMPFT DEN FRIEDEN".

E33	-	6pf. blue	5·50	4·25
E34	**E13**	8pf. brown	5·50	2·40
E35	-	12pf. blue	7·25	5·50
E36	-	24pf. red	7·50	3·75

DESIGNS (all include hand and dove): 6pf. Tank; 12pf. Atom bomb explosion; 24pf. Rows of gravestones.

E14 Tobogganing

1951. 2nd Winter Sports Meeting, Oberhof.

E37	**E14**	12pf. blue	12·00	9·75
E38	-	24f. red (ski jumper)	16·00	12·00

E15

1951. Leipzig Spring Fair.

E39	**E15**	24pf. red	23·00	14·50
E40	**E15**	50pf. blue	23·00	14·50

E16 Presidents Pieck and Bierut

1951. Visit of Polish President to Berlin.

E41	**E16**	24pf. red	27·00	22·00
E42	**E16**	50pf. blue	27·00	22·00

E17 Mao Tse-tung

E18 Chinese Land Reform

1951. Friendship with China.

E43	**E17**	12pf. green	£120	30·00
E44	**E18**	24pf. red	£140	37·00
E45	**E17**	50pf. blue	£120	37·00

E19 Youth Hoisting Flag

1951. 3rd World Youth Festival. Inscr as in Type E 19. On coloured papers.

E46	**E19**	12pf. brown	17·00	8·50
E47	-	24pf. green and red	17·00	5·00
E48	**E19**	30pf. buff and green	20·00	9·25
E49	-	50pf. red and blue	20·00	9·25

DESIGN: 24pf., 50pf. Three girls dancing.

E20 Symbols of Agriculture & Industry

1951. Five Year Plan.

E50	**E20**	24pf. multicoloured	6·75	3·00

E21 K. Liebknecht

1951. 80th Birth Anniv of Liebknecht (revolutionary).

E51	**E21**	24pf. slate and red	7·50	3·00

E22 Instructing Young Collectors

1951. Stamp Day.

E52	**E22**	12pf. blue	9·50	3·75

E23 P. Bykow and E. Wirth

1951. German–Soviet Friendship.

E53	**E23**	12pf. blue	6·75	5·00
E54	-	24pf. red	8·00	6·50

DESIGN: 24pf. Stalin and Pres. Pieck.

E24 Skier

1952. 3rd Winter Sports Meeting. Oberhof.

E55	**E24**	12pf. green	8·75	5·00
E56	-	24pf. blue	9·50	6·00

DESIGN: 24pf. Ski jumper.

E25 Beethoven

1952. 125th Death Anniv of Beethoven (composer).

E57		12pf. blue and light blue	3·25	1·20
E58	**E25**	24pf. brown and grey	4·75	1·80

DESIGN: 12pf. Full face portrait.

E26 President Gottwald

1952. Czechoslovak–German Friendship.

E59	**E26**	24pf. blue	5·25	3·00

E27 Bricklayers

1952. National Reconstruction Fund.

E60	-	12pf.+3pf. violet	3·25	1·00
E61	**E27**	24pf.+6pf. red	2·75	1·20
E62	-	30pf.+10pf. green	3·25	1·30
E63	-	50pf.+10pf. blue	4·00	2·40

DESIGNS: 12pf. Workers clearing debris; 30pf. Carpenters; 50pf. Architect and workmen.

E28 Cyclists

1952. 5th Warsaw–Berlin–Prague Cycle Race.

E64	**E28**	12pf. blue	6·00	3·00

E29 Handel

1952. Handel Festival, Halle.

E65	**E29**	6pf. brown	4·25	1·80
E66	-	8pf. red	5·00	3·00
E67	-	50pf. blue	5·00	3·75

COMPOSERS: 8pf. Lortzing; 50pf. Weber.

E31 Victor Hugo

1952. Cultural Anniversaries.

E73	**E31**	12pf. brown	5·00	6·00
E74	-	20pf. green	5·00	6·00
E75	-	24pf. red	5·00	6·00
E76	-	35pf. blue	7·25	7·50

PORTRAITS: 20pf. Leonardo da Vinci; 24pf. N. Gogol; 35pf. Avicenna.

E32 Machinery, Dove and Globe

1952. Leipzig Autumn Fair.

E77	**E32**	24pf. red	4·50	2·40
E78	**E32**	35pf. blue	4·50	3·00

E33 F. L. Jahn

1952. Death Centenary of Jahn (patriot).

E79	**E33**	12pf. blue	2·75	2·40

E34 University Building

1952. 450th Anniv of Halle-Wittenberg University.

E80	**E34**	24pf. green	2·75	1·50

E35 Dove, Stamp and Flags

1952. Stamp Day.

E81	**E35**	24pf. brown	3·50	1·60

E36 Dove, Globe and St. Stephen's Cathedral, Vienna

1952. Vienna Peace Congress.

E97	**E36**	24pf. red	2·75	2·75
E98	**E36**	35pf. blue	2·75	5·00

E37 President Pieck

1953. President's Birthday.

E320	**E37**	1Dm. olive	3·50	2·30
E321	**E37**	2Dm. brown	6·75	2·30

E38 Karl Marx

1953. 70th Death Anniv of Marx.

E102	-	6pf. red and green	2·00	1·00
E103	-	10pf. brown and green	5·75	1·20
E104	-	12pf. red and green	1·70	1·00
E105	-	16pf. blue and red	4·50	3·00
E106	-	20pf. brown and yellow	2·00	1·30
E107	**E38**	24pf. brown and red	4·50	1·20
E108	-	35pf. yellow and purple	4·50	4·25
E109	-	48pf. brown and green	2·75	1·20
E110	-	60pf. red and brown	5·75	4·25
E111	-	84pf. brown and blue	4·50	3·00

MSE111a Two sheets, each 148×104 mm. (a) the six vert, and (b) the four horiz designs Set of 2 sheets £250 £375

DESIGNS—VERT: 6pf. Flag and foundry; 12pf. Flag and Spassky Tower, Kremlin; 20pf. Marx reading from "Das Kapital"; 35pf. Marx addressing meeting; 48pf. Marx and Engels. HORIZ: 10pf. Marx, Engels and "Communist Manifesto"; 16pf. Marching crowd; 60pf. Flag and workers; 84pf. Marx in medallion and Stalin Avenue, Berlin.

In each case the flag shows heads of Marx, Engels, Lenin and Stalin.

E39 Gorky

1953. 85th Birth Anniv of Maksim Gorky (writer).

E112	**E39**	35pf. brown	80	75

E40 Cyclists

1953. 6th International Cycle Race.

E113	**E40**	24pf. green	3·50	3·00
E114	-	35pf. blue	1·70	1·80
E115	-	60pf. brown	2·30	2·40

DESIGNS—VERT: 35pf. Cyclists and countryside; 60pf. Cyclists in town.

E41 H. Von Kleist

1953. 700th Anniv of Frankfurt-on-Oder.

E116	**E41**	16pf. brown	2·30	2·75
E117	-	20pf. green	1·70	2·75
E118	-	24pf. red	2·30	2·75
E119	-	35pf. blue	2·30	4·00

DESIGNS—HORIZ: 20pf. St. Mary's Church; 24pf. Frankfurt from R. Oder; 35pf. Frankfurt Town Hall and coat of arms.

E42 Miner

1953. Five Year Plan. (a) Design in minute dots.

E120	**E42**	1pf. black	2·30	80
E121	-	5pf. green	2·75	1·60
E122	-	6pf. violet	2·75	1·40
E123	-	8pf. brown	4·00	1·60
E124	-	10pf. blue	2·75	1·40
E125	-	12pf. blue	4·00	1·50
E126	-	15pf. violet	4·50	2·50
E127	-	16pf. violet	9·00	3·50
E128	-	20pf. green	6·75	3·50
E129	-	24pf. red	17·00	1·70
E130	-	25pf. green	9·00	4·50
E131	-	30pf. red	11·50	6·00
E132	-	35pf. blue	23·00	6·25
E133	-	40pf. red	19·00	5·75
E134	-	48pf. mauve	19·00	5·00
E135	-	60pf. blue	19·00	7·25
E136	-	80pf. turquoise	19·00	6·75
E137	-	84pf. brown	19·00	20·00

(b) Design in lines.

E153	**E42**	1pf. black	1·10	25
E310A	-	5pf. green	55	30
E155	-	6pf. violet	5·00	55
E156	-	8pf. brown	5·25	45
E311B	-	10pf. blue	35	35
E312A	-	10pf. green	80	55
E159	-	12pf. turquoise	5·00	45
E160	-	15pf. lilac	23·00	80
E313B	-	15pf. violet	45	35
E162	-	16pf. violet	5·75	1·10
E163	-	20pf. green	£100	1·10
E314A	-	20pf. red	55	30
E165	-	24pf. red	9·00	45
E315A	-	25pf. green	55	35
E316B	-	30pf. red	45	35
E168	-	35pf. blue	6·25	1·40
E169	-	40pf. red	13·50	1·40
E317B	-	40pf. mauve	45	35
E171	-	48pf. mauve	13·50	2·00
E318B	-	50pf. blue	50	35

E173 - 60pf. blue 23·00 2·30
E319B - 70pf. brown 50 35
E175 - 80pf. turquoise 5·75 2·30
E176 - 84pf. brown 23·00 2·30

DESIGNS—VERT: 5pf. Woman turning wheel; 6pf. Workmen shaking hands; 8pf. Students; 10pf. grn Engineers; 10pf. bl and 12pf. Agricultural and industrial workers; 15pf. mve Tele-typist; 15pf. vio and 16pf. Foundry worker; 20pf. grn Workers' health centre, Elster; 20pf. red and 24pf. Stalin Avenue, Berlin; 25pf. Locomotive construction workers; 30pf. Folk dancers; 35pf. Stadium; 40pf. red, Scientist; 40pf. mve, 48pf. Zwinger, Dresden; 50pf., 60pf. Launching ship; 80pf. Farm workers; 70pf., 84pf. Workman and family.

E43 Mechanical Grab

1953. Leipzig Autumn Fair.
E138 **E43** 24pf. brown 3·50 3·00
E139 - 35pf. green 4·25 3·50
DESIGN: 35pf. Potato-harvester.

E44 G. W. von Knobelsdorff and Opera House, Berlin

1953. German Architects.
E140 **E44** 24pf. mauve 2·30 1·40
E141 - 35pf. slate 2·75 2·30
DESIGN: 35pf. B. Neumann and Wurzburg Palace.

E45 Lucas Cranach

1953. 400th Death Anniv of Cranach (painter).
E142 **E45** 24pf. brown 4·00 1·70

E46 Nurse and Patient

1953. Red Cross.
E143 **E46** 24pf. red and brown 3·50 2·30

E47 Postman delivering Letters

1953. Stamp Day.
E144 **E47** 24pf. blue 4·50 1·10

E48 Lion

1953. 75th Anniv of Leipzig Zoo.
E145 **E48** 24pf. brown 3·00 1·10

E49 Muntzer and Peasants

1953. German Patriots.
E146 **E49** 12pf. brown 2·00 90
E147 - 16pf. brown 2·00 90
E148 - 20pf. red 2·00 55
E149 - 24pf. blue 2·00 55
E150 - 35pf. green 3·50 2·30
E151 - 48pf. sepia 3·50 1·80

DESIGNS: 16pf. Baron vom Stein and scroll; 20pf. Von Schill and cavalry; 24pf. Blucher and infantry; 35pf. Students marching; 48pf. Barricade, 1848 Revolution.

E50 Franz Schubert

1953. 125th Death Anniv of Schubert.
E152 **E50** 48pf. brown 4·00 2·30

E52 G. E. Lessing (writer)

1954. 225th Birth Anniv of Lessing.
E177 **E52** 20pf. green 3·50 1·40

E53 Conference Table and Crowd

1954. Four-Power Conference, Berlin.
E178 **E53** 12pf. blue 2·50 1·40

E54 Stalin

1954. 1st Death Anniv of Stalin.
E179 **E54** 20pf. brown, orange and grey 4·25 1·50

E55 Racing Cyclists

1954. 7th International Cycle Race.
E180 **E55** 12pf. brown 2·30 1·10
E181 - 24pf. green 2·75 1·70
DESIGN: 24pf. Cyclists racing through countryside.

E56 Folk Dancing

1954. 2nd German Youth Assembly.
E182 **E56** 12pf. green 1·70 1·40
E183 - 24pf. red 1·70 1·40
DESIGN: 24pf. Young people and flag.

E57 F. Reuter

1954. 80th Death Anniv of Reuter (author).
E184 **E57** 24pf. brown 2·50 1·60

E58 Dam and Forest

1954. Flood Relief Fund.
E185 **E58** 24pf.+6pf. green 1·40 1·10

E59 E. Thalmann

1954. 10th Death Anniv of Thalmann (politician).
E186 **E59** 24pf. brown, bl & orge 1·90 1·30

E60 Exhibition Buildings

1954. Leipzig Autumn Fair.
E187 **E60** 24pf. red 1·30 1·10
E188 **E60** 35pf. blue 1·40 1·10

1954. (a) Nos. E155, etc surch in figures.
E189 5pf. on 6pf. violet 1·50 45
E190 5pf. on 8pf. brown 2·00 45
E191 10pf. on 12pf. turquoise 1·70 45
E192 15pf. on 16pf. lilac 1·50 45
E194 20pf. on 24pf. red 2·75 70
E195 40pf. on 48pf. mauve 4·50 1·10
E196 50pf. on 60pf. blue 4·50 1·10
E197 70pf. on 84pf. brown 12·00 1·10

(b) No. E129 similarly surch.
E193a 20pf. on 24pf. red 1·60 70

E62 President Pieck

1954. 5th Anniv of German Democratic Republic.
E198 **E62** 20pf. brown 4·00 1·80
E199 **E62** 35pf. blue 4·00 2·00

E63 Stamp of 1953

1954. Stamp Day.
E200 **E63** 20pf. mauve 2·50 1·10
MSE200b 60×80 mm. No. E200 imperf (sold at Dm.30) 65·00 65·00

E64 Russian Pavilion

1955. Leipzig Spring Fair.
E201 **E64** 20pf. purple 1·70 1·40
E202 - 35pf. blue (Chinese Pavilion) 2·30 2·30

1955. Flood Relief Fund. Surch in figures.
E203 **E58** 20+5pf. on 24pf.+6pf. green 1·40 80

E66 "Women of All Nations"

1955. 45th Anniv of International Women's Day.
E204 **E66** 10pf. green 1·60 70
E205 **E66** 20pf. red 1·60 70

E67 Parade of Workers

1955. International Conference of Municipal Workers, Vienna.
E206 **E67** 10pf. black and red 1·40 1·40

E68 Monument to Fascist Victims, Brandenburg

1955. International Liberation Day.
E207 **E68** 10pf. blue 1·30 1·40
E208 **E68** 20pf. mauve 1·60 1·80
MSE208a 73×99 mm. Nos. E207/8 23·00 36·00

E69 Monument to Russian Soldiers, Treptow

1955. 10th Anniv of Liberation.
E209 **E69** 20pf. mauve 2·50 1·70

E70 Schiller (poet)

1955. 150th Death Anniv of Schiller.
E210 **E70** 5pf. green 4·00 3·50
E211 - 10pf. blue 80 55
E212 - 20pf. brown 80 55
MSE212a 73×100 mm. Nos. E210/12 (+15pf.) 27·00 38·00
PORTRAITS OF SCHILLER: 10pf. Full-face; 20pf. Facing left.

E71 Cyclists

1955. 8th International Cycle Race.
E213 **E71** 10pf. turquoise 1·10 90
E214 **E71** 20pf. red 1·40 1·10

E72 Karl Liebknecht

1955. German Labour Leaders.
E215 **E72** 5pf. green 45 35
E216 - 10pf. blue 70 35
E217 - 15pf. violet 9·00 6·00
E218 - 20pf. red 70 35
E219 - 25pf. blue 70 35
E220 - 40pf. red 3·50 35
E221 - 60pf. brown 70 35
PORTRAITS: 10pf. A. Bebel; 15pf. F. Mehring; 20pf. E. Thalmann; 25pf. Clara Zetkin; 40pf. Wilhelm Liebknecht; 60pf. Rosa Luxemburg.

E73 Pottery

1955. Leipzig Autumn Fair.

E222		10pf. blue	1·50	80
E223	**E73**	20pf. green	1·50	80

DESIGN: 10pf. Camera and microscope.

E74 Workers and Charter

1955. 10th Anniv of Land Reform.

E224	**E74**	5pf. green	8·00	6·75
E225	-	10pf. blue	1·10	55
E226	-	20pf. red	1·10	55

DESIGNS—VERT: 10pf. Bricklayers at work. HORIZ: 20pf. Combine-harvesters.

E75 "Solidarity"

1955. 10th Anniv of People's Solidarity Movement.

E227	**E75**	10pf. blue	1·00	80

E76 Engels Speaking

1955. 135th Birth Anniv of Engels.

E228	**E76**	5pf. blue and yellow	45	25
E229	-	10pf. violet and yellow	90	25
E230	-	15pf. green and yellow	90	25
E231	-	20pf. brown and orange	1·80	25
E232	-	30pf. brown and grey	11·00	11·50
E233	-	70pf. green and red	4·50	45
MSE233a 148×105 mm. Nos. E228/33			85·00	£130

DESIGNS: 10pf. Engels and Marx; 15pf. Engels and newspaper; 20pf. Portrait facing right; 30pf. Portrait facing left; 70pf. 1848 Revolution scene.

E77 Magdeburg Cathedral

1955. Historic Buildings.

E234	**E77**	5pf. sepia	1·10	55
E235	-	10pf. green	1·10	55
E236	-	15pf. purple	1·10	55
E237	-	20pf. red	1·10	1·10
E238	-	30pf. brown	14·00	17·00
E239	-	40pf. blue	2·30	1·10

DESIGNS: 10pf. State Opera House, Berlin; 15pf. Old Town Hall, Leipzig; 20pf. Town Hall, Berlin; 30pf. Erfurt Cathedral; 40pf. Zwinger, Dresden.

E78 Georg Agricola

1955. 400th Death Anniv of Agricola (scholar).

E240	**E78**	10pf. brown	1·00	80

E79 "Portrait of a Young Man" (Durer)

1955. Dresden Gallery Paintings. (1st series).

E241	**E79**	5pf. brown	90	30
E242	-	10pf. brown	90	30
E243	-	15pf. purple	34·00	32·00
E244	-	20pf. sepia	90	30
E245	-	40pf. green	90	55
E246	-	70pf. blue	2·30	1·10

PAINTINGS: 10pf. "The Chocolate Girl" (Liotard); 15pf. "Portrait of a Boy" (Pinturicchio); 20pf. "Self-portrait with Saskia" (Rembrandt); 40pf. "Maiden with Letter" (Vermeer); 70pf. "Sistine Madonna" (Raphael).

See also Nos. E325/30 and E427/31.

E80 Mozart

1956. Birth Bicent of Mozart (composer).

E247	**E80**	10pf. green	17·00	13·50
E248	-	20pf. brown	5·75	2·75

PORTRAIT: 20pf. Facing left.

E81 Ilyushin Il-14P DDR-ABA

1956. Establishment of East German Lufthansa Airways.

E249		5pf. multicoloured	19·00	13·50
E250	**E81**	10pf. green	1·10	55
E251	-	15pf. blue	1·10	55
E252	-	20pf. red	1·10	55

DESIGNS: 5pf. Lufthansa flag; 15pf. View of Ilyushin Il-14P DDR-ABF airplane from below; 20pf. Ilyushin Il-14P DDR-ABA airplane facing left.

E82 Heinrich Heine (poet)

1956. Death Centenary of Heine.

E253	**E82**	10pf. green	16·00	8·50
E254	-	20pf. red	3·50	90

PORTRAIT: 20pf. Full-face.

E83 Mobile Cranes

1956. Leipzig Spring Fair.

E255	**E83**	20pf. red	1·40	80
E256	**E83**	35pf. blue	2·00	1·30

E84 E Thalmann

1956. 70th Birth Anniv of Thalmann (communist leader).

E257	**E84**	20pf. black, brn & red	90	55
MSE257a 73×100 mm. No. E257			13·50	36·00

E85 Hand, Laurels and Cycle Wheel

1956. 9th International Cycle Race.

E258	**E85**	10pf. green	1·10	50
E259	-	20pf. red	1·10	50

DESIGN: 20pf. Arms of Warsaw, Berlin and Prague and cycle wheel.

E86 New Buildings, Old Market-place

1956. 750th Anniv of Dresden.

E260	**E86**	10pf. green	55	25
E261	-	20pf. red	55	25
E262	-	40pf. violet	2·75	3·00

DESIGNS: 20pf. Elbe Bridge; 40pf. Technical High School.

E87 Workman

1956. 10th Anniv of Industrial Reforms.

E263	**E87**	20pf. red	70	35

E88 Robert Schumann

1956. Death Centenary of Schumann (composer). (a) Type E 88 (wrong music).

E264	**E88**	10pf. green	3·00	2·00
E265	**E88**	20pf. red	1·10	25

E88a Robert Schumann

(b) Type E 88a (correct music).

E266	**E88a**	10pf. green	6·75	2·75
E267	**E88a**	20pf. red	4·00	55

E89 Footballers

1956. 2nd Sports Festival, Leipzig.

E268	**E89**	5pf. green	45	35
E269	-	10pf. blue	45	35
E270	-	15pf. purple	3·25	2·50
E271	-	20pf. red	45	35

DESIGNS: 10pf. Javelin thrower; 15pf. Hurdlers; 20pf. Gymnast.

E90 T. Mann (author)

1956. 1st Death Anniv of Thomas Mann.

E272	**E90**	20pf. black	1·80	80

E91 J. B. Cisinski

1956. Birth Centenary of Cisinski (poet).

E273	**E91**	50pf. brown	1·50	80

E92 Lace

1956. Leipzig Autumn Fair.

E274	**E92**	10pf. green and black	70	55
E275	-	20pf. pink and black (Sailing dinghy)	70	55

E93 Buchenwald Memorial

1956. Concentration Camp Memorials Fund.

E276	**E93**	20pf.+80pf. red	1·60	5·75

For similar stamp see No. E390.

E94 Torch and Olympic Rings

1956. Olympic Games.

E277	**E94**	20pf. brown	80	55
E278	-	35pf. slate	1·10	80

DESIGN: 35pf. Greek athlete.

E95

1956. 500th Anniv of Greifswald University.

E279	**E95**	20pf. red	90	55

E96 Postal Carrier, 1450

1956. Stamp Day.

E280	**E96**	20pf. red	90	55

E97 E. Abbe

1956. 110th Anniv of Zeiss Factory, Jena.

E281	**E97**	10pf. green	45	25
E282	-	20pf. brown	45	25
E283	-	25pf. blue	70	45

DESIGNS—HORIZ: 20pf. Factory buildings; 25pf. Carl Zeiss.

E98 "Negro"

1956. Human Rights Day.

E284 5pf. green on olive 1·80 1·60
E285 **E98** 10pf. brown on pink 35 35
E286 - 25pf. blue on lavender 35 35

DESIGNS: 5pf. "Chinese"; 25pf. "European".

E99 Indian Elephants

1956. Berlin Zoological Gardens. Centres in grey.

E287 **E99** 5pf. black 35 25
E288 - 10pf. green 35 25
E289 - 15pf. purple 6·25 4·50
E290 - 20pf. red 35 25
E291 - 25pf. brown 40 25
E292 - 30pf. blue 45 25

DESIGNS: 10pf. Greater flamingos; 15pf. Black rhinoceros; 20pf. Mouflon; 25pf. European bison; 30pf. Polar bear.

1956. Egyptian Relief Fund. No. E237 surch HELFT AGYPTEN +10.

E293 20pf.+10pf. red 1·00 55

1956. Hungarian Socialists' Relief Fund. No. E237 surch HELFT DEM SOZIALISTISCHEN UNGARN +10.

E294 20pf.+10pf. red 1·00 55

E103 "Frieden" (freighter)

1957. Leipzig Spring Fair.

E295 **E103** 20pf. red 45 25
E296 - 25pf. blue 45 25

DESIGN: 25pf. Class E251 electric locomotive.

E104 Silver Thistle

1957. Nature Protection Week.

E297 **E104** 5pf. brown 35 25
E298 - 10pf. green 3·50 3·25
E299 - 20pf. brown 35 25

DESIGNS: 10pf. Green lizard; 20pf. Lady's slipper orchid.

E105 Friedrich Froebel and Children

1957. 175th Birth Anniv of Froebel (educator).

E300 10pf. black and green 1·80 1·40
E301 **E105** 20pf. black and brown 35 25

DESIGN: 10pf. Children at play.

E106 Ravensbruck Memorial

1957. Concentration Camp Memorials Fund.

E302 **E106** 5pf.+5pf. green 45 35
E303 - 20pf.+10pf. red 55 60

DESIGN—HORIZ: 20pf. Memorial and environs.

For similar stamp to No. E303 see No. E453.

E107 Cycle Race Route

1957. 10th International Cycle Race.

E304 **E107** 5pf. orange 55 45

E108 Miner

1957. Coal Mining Industry.

E305 - 10pf. green 35 30
E306 - 20pf. brown 35 30
E307 **E108** 25pf. blue 3·50 2·00

DESIGNS (39×21 mm): 10pf. Mechanical shovel and coal trucks; 20pf. Gantry.

E109 Henri Dunant and Globe

1957. Int Red Cross Day. Cross in red.

E308 **E109** 10pf. brown and green 35 35
E309 - 25pf. brown and blue 35 35

DESIGN: 25pf. H. Dunant wearing hat, and globe.

E110 Joachim Jungius (botanist)

1957. Scientists' Anniversaries.

E322 **E110** 5pf. brown 2·30 1·70
E323 - 10pf. green 35 30
E324 - 20pf. brown 35 30

PORTRAITS: 10pf. L. Euler (mathematician); 20pf. H. Hertz (physicist).

1957. Dresden Gallery Paintings (2nd series). As Type E 79.

E325 5pf. sepia 45 35
E326 10pf. green 45 35
E327 15pf. brown 45 35
E328 20pf. red 45 35
E329 25pf. purple 45 35
E330 40pf. grey 6·75 3·00

PAINTINGS—VERT: 5pf. "The Holy Family" (Mantegna); 10pf. "The Dancer, Barbarina Campani" (Carriera); 15pf. "Portrait of Morette" (Holbein the Younger); 20pf. "The Tribute Money" (Titian); 25pf. "Saskia with a Red Flower" (Rembrandt); 40pf. "A Young Standard-bearer" (Piazetta).

E111 Clara Zetkin and Flower

1957. Birth Cent of Clara Zetkin (patriot).

E331 **E111** 10pf. green and red 1·00 45

E112 Bertolt Brecht (dramatist)

1957. 1st Death Anniv of Bertolt Brecht.

E332 **E112** 10pf. green 45 35
E333 **E112** 25pf. blue 85 35

E113 Congress Emblem

1957. 4th World Trade Unions Congress.

E334 **E113** 20pf. black and red 90 45

E114 Fair Emblem

1957. Leipzig Autumn Fair.

E335 **E114** 20pf. red 40 35
E336 **E114** 25pf. blue 45 35

E115 Savings Bank Book

1957. Savings Week.

E337 **E115** 10pf. black and green on grey 1·10 90
E338 **E115** 20pf. black and mauve on grey 45 45

E116 Postrider of 1563

1957. Stamp Day.

E339 **E116** 5pf. blue on brown 80 35

E117 Revolutionary's Rifle and Red Flag

1957. 40th Anniv of Russian Revolution.

E340 **E117** 10pf. green and red 35 35
E341 **E117** 25pf. blue and red 35 35

E118 Artificial Satellite

1957. International Geophysical Year.

E342 **E118** 10pf. blue 55 40
E343 - 20pf. red 80 25
E344 - 25pf. blue 3·00 2·00

DESIGNS: 20pf. Stratosphere balloon; 25pf. Ship using echo-sounder.

E119 Professor Ramin

1957. "National Prize" Composers.

E345 **E119** 10pf. black and green 1·50 1·40
E346 - 20pf. black and orange 35 25

PORTRAIT: 20pf. Professor Abendroth.

E120 Ernst Thalmann

1957. National Memorials Fund. East German War Victims. Portraits in grey.

E347 **E120** 20pf.+10pf. mauve 35 25
E348 - 25pf.+15pf. blue 35 25
E349 - 40pf.+20pf. violet 55 70
MSE349a 140×95 mm. Nos. E347/9 (+20pf.) 70·00 £150

PORTRAITS: 25pf. R. Breitscheid; 40pf. Father P. Schneider.

For other stamps as Type E **120** see Nos. E374/8, E448/52, E485/7, E496/500, E540/4 and E588/92.

E121

E122

1957. Air.

E350 **E121** 5pf. black and grey 4·00 25
E351 **E121** 20pf. black and red 35 25
E352 **E121** 35pf. black and violet 35 25
E353 **E121** 50pf. black and brown 45 25
E354 **E122** 1Dm. olive and yellow 1·60 25
E355 **E122** 3Dm. brown & yellow 2·50 70
E356 **E122** 5Dm. blue and yellow 5·75 1·00

E123 Fair Emblem

1958. Leipzig Spring Fair.

E357 **E123** 20pf. red 45 25
E358 **E123** 25pf. blue 55 35

E124 Transmitting Aerial and Posthorn

1958. Communist Postal Conf, Moscow.

E359 **E124** 5pf. black and grey 1·10 90
E360 - 20pf. red 55 25

DESIGN—HORIZ: 20pf. Aerial as in 5pf. but posthorn above figures of value.

E125 "Zille at play"

1958. Birth Cent of Heinrich Zille (painter).

E361 **E125** 10pf. drab and green 3·75 2·00
E362 - 20pf. drab and red 90 35

DESIGN—VERT: 20pf. Self-portrait of Zille.

E126 Max Planck

1958. Birth Cent of Max Planck (physicist).

E363		10pf. olive	1·70	1·60
E364	**E126**	20pf. mauve	55	35

DESIGN—VERT: 10pf. "h" (symbol of Planck's Constant).

E127 Breeding Cow

1958. 6th Markkleeberg Agricultural Exn. Inscr "6 Landwirtschaftausstellung der DDR in Markkleeberg".

E365	**E127**	5pf. grey	3·50	2·00
E366	-	10pf. green	55	35
E367	-	20pf. red	55	35

DESIGNS (39×22½ mm): 10pf. Chaff-cutter; 20pf. Beet-harvester.

E128 Charles Darwin

1958. Centenary of Darwin's Theory of Evolution and Bicentenary of Linnaeus's Plant Classification System. Portraits in black.

E368	**E128**	10pf. green	2·00	1·70
E369	-	20pf. red	35	30

PORTRAIT—HORIZ: 20pf. Linnaeus (Carl von Linne) inscr "200 JAHRE SYSTEMA NATURAE".

E129 Congress Emblem

1958. 5th German Socialist Unity Party Congress.

E370	**E129**	10pf. red	55	45

E130 "The Seven Towers of Rostock", Liner and Freighters

1958. Rostock Port Reconstruction.

E371	-	10pf. green	35	25
E372	**E130**	20pf. orange	1·10	45
E373	-	25pf. blue	1·60	1·70

DESIGNS: 10pf. "Freundschaft" (freighter) at quayside; 25pf. "Frieden" (freighter) in Rostock harbour.

1958. "Resistance Fighters". As Type E 120. Portraits in grey.

E374	5pf.+5pf. brown	45	1·10
E375	10pf.+5pf. green	45	1·10
E376	15pf.+10pf. violet	45	4·50
E377	20pf.+10pf. brown	45	1·10
E378	25pf.+15pf. black	1·40	17·00

PORTRAITS—VERT: 5pf. A. Kuntz; 10pf. R. Arndt; 15pf. Dr. K. Adams; 20pf. R. Renner; 25pf. W. Stoecker.

E131 Mare and Foal

1958. "Grand Prix of the D.D.R." Horse Show.

E379	**E131**	5pf. sepia	3·50	3·75
E380	-	10pf. green	35	35
E381	-	20pf. brown	35	35

DESIGNS: 10pf. Horse-trotting; 20pf. Racing horses.

E132 J. A. Komensky ("Comenius")

1958. Komensky Commem. Centres in black.

E382	**E132**	10pf. green	2·30	1·60
E383	-	20pf. brown	35	30

DESIGN: 20pf. Komensky with pupils (from an old engraving).

E133 Camp Bugler

1958. 10th Anniv of East German "Pioneer" Organization.

E384	**E133**	10pf.+5pf. green	50	35
E385	-	20pf.+10pf. red	55	35

DESIGN—VERT: 20pf. Young Pioneer saluting.

E134 University Seal

1958. 400th Anniv of Friedrich Schiller University, Jena.

E386	**E134**	5pf. black and grey	2·00	1·60
E387	-	20pf. grey and red	45	30

DESIGN: 20pf. University building.

E135 Model with Hamster-lined Coat, and Leipzig Central Railway Station

1958. Leipzig Autumn Fair.

E388	**E135**	10pf. brown and green	40	30
E389	-	25pf. black and blue	45	35

DESIGN: 25pf. Model with Karakul fur coat, and Leipzig Old Town Hall.

1958. Concentration Camp Memorials Fund. As Type E 93 but additionally inscr "14. SEPTEMBER 1958" in black.

E390	20pf.+20pf. red	90	80

E136 Soldier climbing Wall

1958. 1st Summer Military Games, Leipzig.

E391	**E136**	10pf. brown and green	2·30	1·50
E392	-	20pf. yellow and brown	45	35
E393	-	25pf. red and blue	45	35

DESIGNS: 20pf. Games emblem; 25pf. Marching athletes with banner.

E137 Warding off the Atomic Bomb

1958. Campaign Against Atomic Warfare.

E394	**E137**	20pf. red	45	25
E395	**E137**	25pf. blue	70	35

E138 17th-century Mail Cart

1958. Stamp Day.

E396	**E138**	10pf. green	2·75	1·70
E397	-	20pf. red	55	25

DESIGN: 20pf. Modern postal sorting train and Baade-Bonin 152 jetliner.

E139 Revolutionary and Soldier

1958. 40th Anniv of November Revolution.

E398	**E139**	20pf. purple and red	12·50	22·00

E140 Brandenburg Gate, Berlin

1958. Brandenburg Gate Commemoration.

E399	**E140**	20pf. red	55	25
E400	**E140**	25pf. blue	3·75	2·30

E141 "Girl's Head" (bas-relief)

1958. Antique Art Treasures.

E401	**E141**	10pf. black and green	2·00	1·60
E402	-	20pf. black and red	35	25

DESIGN: 20pf. "Large Head" (from Pergamon frieze).
See also Nos. E475/8.

E142 Negro and European Youths

1958. 10th Anniv of Declaration of Human Rights.

E403	**E142**	10pf. black and green	35	30
E404	-	25pf. black and blue	2·75	1·60

DESIGN: 25pf. Chinese and European girls.

E143 O. Nuschke

1958. 1st Death Anniv of Vice-Premier Otto Nuschke.

E405	**E143**	20pf. red	45	40

E144 "The Red Flag" (Party Newspaper)

1958. 40th Anniv of German Communist Party.

E406	**E144**	20pf. red	55	45

E145 Pres. Pieck

1959. Pres. Pieck's 83rd Birthday.

E407	**E145**	20pf. red	70	35

For 20pf. black see No. E517.

E146 Rosa Luxemburg (revolutionary)

1959. 40th Death Anniv of Rosa Luxemburg and Karl Liebknecht. Centres in black.

E408	**E146**	10pf. green	3·00	1·80
E409	-	20pf. red	35	25

DESIGN—HORIZ: 20pf. Liebknecht-(revolutionary).

E147 Concert Hall, Leipzig

1959. 150th Birth Anniv of Felix Mendelssohn-Bartholdy (composer).

E410	**E147**	10pf. green on green	80	80
E411	-	25pf. blue on blue	2·30	4·00

DESIGN—HORIZ: 25pf. Opening theme of Symphony in A Major ("The Italian").

E148 "Schwarze Pumpe" plant

1959. Leipzig Spring Fair. Inscr as in Type E 148.

E412	**E148**	20pf. red	45	25
E413	-	25pf. blue	55	30

DESIGN—HORIZ: 25pf. Various cameras.

E149 Boy holding Book for Girl

1959. 5th Anniv of "Youth Consecration".

E414	**E149**	10pf. black on green	2·30	1·50
E415	-	20pf. black on salmon	35	25

DESIGN: 20pf. Girl holding book for boy.

E150 Handel's Statue, Oboe and Arms of Halle

1959. Death Bicentenary of Handel. Centre in black.

E416	**E150**	10pf. green	2·50	1·60
E417	-	20pf. red	35	30

DESIGN: 20pf. Portrait of Handel (after oil painting by Thomas Hudson).

E151 A. von Humboldt and Jungle Scene

1959. Death Centenary of Alexander von Humboldt (naturalist).

E418	**E151**	10pf. green	2·00	1·60
E419	-	20pf. red	45	25

DESIGN: 20pf. As Type E **151** but with view of sleigh in forest.

E152 Posthorn

1959. Socialist Countries' Postal Ministers Conference, Berlin.

E420 **E152** 20pf. black, yell & red 45 25
E421 **E152** 25pf. black, yell & bl 1·10 1·10

E153 Grey Heron

1959. Nature Preservation.

E422 **E153** 5pf. lilac, black & blue 35 25
E423 - 10pf. brn, sep & turq 35 25
E424 - 20pf. multicoloured 35 25
E425 - 25pf. multicoloured 55 25
E426 - 40pf. yell, blk & grey 8·50 5·00

DESIGNS: 10pf. Eurasian bittern; 20pf. Lily of the valley and "Inachis io" (butterfly); 25pf. Eurasian beaver; 40pf. "Apis mellifera" (bee) and willow catkin.

1959. Dresden Gallery Paintings as Type E 79 (3rd series).

E427 5pf. olive 35 25
E428 10pf. green 35 25
E429 20pf. orange 35 25
E430 25pf. brown 55 35
E431 40pf. red 8·00 4·00

PAINTINGS—VERT: 5pf. "The Vestal Virgin" (Kauffman); 10pf. "The Needlewoman" (Metsu); 20pf. "Mlle. Lavergne reading a letter" (Liotard); 25pf. "Old woman with a brazier" (Rubens); 40pf. "Young man in black coat" (Hals).

E154 Great Cormorant

1959. "Birds of the Homeland". Centres and inscriptions in black.

E432 **E154** 5pf. yellow 35 25
E433 - 10pf. green 35 25
E434 - 15pf. violet 7·50 4·00
E435 - 20pf. pink 35 25
E436 - 25pf. blue 35 25
E437 - 40pf. red 35 25

BIRDS: 10pf. Black Stork; 15pf. Eagle Owl; 20pf. Black Grouse; 25pf. Hoopoe; 40pf. Peregrine Falcon.

E155

1959. 7th World Youth Festival, Vienna.

E438 **E155** 20pf. red 45 35
E439 - 25pf. blue 1·40 1·10

DESIGN—HORIZ: 25pf. White girl embracing negro girl.

E156 Hoop Exercises

1959. 3rd German Gymnastic and Sports Festival, Leipzig.

E440 **E156** 5pf.+5pf. brown 35 25
E441 - 10pf.+5pf. green 35 25
E442 - 20pf.+10pf. red 35 25
E443 - 25pf.+10pf. blue 35 25
E444 - 40pf.+20pf. purple 2·50 1·10

DESIGNS: 10pf. High jumping; 20pf. Vaulting; 25pf. Club exercises; 40pf. Fireworks over Leipzig Stadium.

E157 Modern Leipzig Building

1959. Leipzig Autumn Fair.

E445 **E157** 20pf. grey and red 55 45

See also Nos. E483/4.

E158 Glass Tea-set

1959. 75 Years of Jena Glassware.

E446 **E158** 10pf. turquoise 30 25
E447 - 25pf. blue 2·75 1·70

DESIGN—VERT: 25pf. Laboratory retorts.

1959. Ravensbruck Concentration Camp Victims. As Type E 120. Portraits in black.

E448 5pf.+5pf. brown 35 30
E449 10pf.+5pf. green 35 30
E450 15pf.+10pf. violet 35 30
E451 20pf.+10pf. mauve 35 30
E452 25pf.+15pf. blue 70 1·50

PORTRAITS: 5pf. T. Klose; 10pf. K. Niederkirchner; 15pf. C. Eisenblatter; 20pf. O. Benario-Prestes; 25pf. M. Grollmuss.

1959. Concentration Camp Memorials Fund. As No. E303 but inscr "12. SEPTEMBER 1959" in black.

E453 20pf.+10pf. red 80 45

E159 "Russian Pennant on the Moon"

1959. Landing of Russian Rocket on the Moon.

E454 **E159** 20pf. red 90 55

E160 E. German Flag and Combine-harvester

1959. 10th Anniv of German Democratic Republic. Designs as Type E 160 showing E. German flag in black, red and yellow. Inscriptions in black and red on coloured paper.

E455 **E160** 5pf. buff 25 25
E456 - 10pf. grey 25 25
E457 - 15pf. pale yellow 25 25
E458 - 20pf. lilac 25 25
E459 - 25pf. pale olive 25 25
E460 - 40pf. yellow 25 25
E461 - 50pf. salmon 25 25
E462 - 60pf. turquoise 25 25
E463 - 70pf. pale green 25 25
E464 - 1Dm. brown 55 65

DESIGNS—East German flag and: 10pf. "Fritz Heckert" convalescent home; 15pf. Zwinger Palace, Dresden; 20pf. Steel worker; 25pf. Industrial chemist; 40pf. Leipzig Stadium; 50pf. Woman tractor-driver; 60pf. Ilyushin Il-14M airplane; 70pf. Shipbuilding; 1Dm. East Germany's first atomic reactor.

E161 J. R. Becher

1959. 1st Death Anniv of Becher (poet).

E465 **E161** 20pf. slate and red 1·80 35

E162 Schiller

1959. Birth Bicentenary of Schiller (poet).

E466 - 10pf. green on green 2·20 1·60
E467 **E162** 20pf. lake on pink 80 25

DESIGN: 10pf. Schiller's house, Weimar.

E163 18th-century Courier and Milestone

1959. Stamp Day.

E468 **E163** 10pf. green 1·90 1·50
E469 - 20pf. lake 35 25

DESIGN: 20pf. Postwoman on motor cycle.

E164 Eurasian Red Squirrels

1959. Forest Animals.

E470 **E164** 5pf. red, brown & grey 55 25
E471 - 10pf. lt brn, brn & grn 70 25
E472 - 20pf. multicoloured 70 25
E473 - 25pf. multicoloured 80 35
E474 - 40pf. yellow, brown and blue 15·00 5·00

ANIMALS: 10pf. Brown hares; 20pf. Roe deer; 25pf. Red deer; 40pf. Lynx.

1959. Antique Art Treasures (2nd series). As Type E 141.

E475 5pf. black and yellow 45 25
E476 10pf. black and green 45 25
E477 20pf. black and red 45 25
E478 25pf. black and blue 1·80 1·10

DESIGNS: 5pf. Attic goddess (about 580 B.C.); 10pf. Princess of Tell el-Amarna (about 1360 B.C.); 20pf. Bronze horse of Toprak-Kale, Armenia (7th-century B.C.). HORIZ: (49×28 mm): 25pf. Altar of Zeus, Pergamon (about 160 B.C.).

E165 Boxing

1960. Olympic Games. As Type E 165 inscr "OLYMPISCHE SOMMERSPIELE 1960" or "WINTERSPIELE" etc (20pf.). Centres and inscriptions in bistre.

E479 **E165** 5pf. brown 6·75 3·50
E480 - 10pf. green 35 25
E481 - 20pf. red 35 25
E482 - 25pf. blue 35 25

DESIGNS: 10pf. Running; 20pf. Ski jumping; 25pf. Sailing.

1960. Leipzig Spring Fair. As Type E 157 but inscr "LEIPZIGER FRUHJAHRSMESSE 1960".

E483 20pf. grey and red 30 25
E484 25pf. grey and blue 35 25

DESIGNS: 20pf. Northern Entrance, Technical Fair; 25pf. Ring Fair Building.

1960. Sachsenhausen Concentration Camp Victims (1st issue). As Type E 120. Portraits in black.

E485 5pf.+5pf. drab 35 30
E486 10pf.+5pf. myrtle 35 30
E487 20pf.+10pf. purple 35 30

PORTRAITS: 5pf. L. Erdmann; 10pf. E. Schneller; 20pf. L. Horn.

See also Nos. E496/500.

E166 Purple Foxglove

1960. Medicinal Flowers. Background in pale drab.

E488 **E166** 5pf. red and green 35 25
E489 - 10pf. olive and green 35 25
E490 - 15pf. red and green 35 25
E491 - 20pf. violet & turq 35 25
E492 - 40pf. red, green & brn 7·50 3·50

FLOWERS: 10pf. Camomile; 15pf. Peppermint; 20pf. Poppy; 40pf. Wild Rose.

E167 Lenin

1960. 90th Birth Anniv of Lenin.

E493 **E167** 20pf. red 55 35

1960. Re-opening of Rostock Port. No. E371 optd Inbetriebnahme des Hochsee-hafens 1. Mai 1960.

E494 10pf. green 90 55

E169 Russian Soldier and Liberated Prisoner

1960. 15th Anniv of Liberation.

E495 **E169** 20pf. red 55 45

1960. Sachsenhausen Concentration Camp Victims (2nd issue). As Type E 120. Portraits in black.

E496 10pf.+5pf. green 35 25
E497 15pf.+5pf. violet 1·10 80
E498 20pf.+10pf. lake 35 25
E499 25pf.+10pf. blue 35 35
E500 40pf.+20pf. brown 2·50 3·50

PORTRAITS: 10pf. M. Lademann; 15pf. L. Breunig; 20pf. M. Thesen; 25pf. G. Sandtner; 40pf. H. Rothbarth.

E170 Model and Plan of "Fritz Heckert" (Liner)

1960. Launching of Cruise Liner "Fritz Heckert".

E501 **E170** 5pf. slate, red & yell 35 25
E502 - 10pf.+5pf. black, red and yellow 35 25
E503 - 20pf.+10pf. black, red and blue 35 25
E504 - 25pf. black, yellow and blue 6·25 6·75

DESIGNS: 10pf. Liner under construction at Wismar; 20pf. Liner off Stubbenkammer; 25pf. Liner and Russian cruiser "Aurora" at Leningrad.

E171 Lenin Statue, Eisleben

1960. Lenin-Thalmann Statues.

E505 **E171** 10pf. green 35 35
E506 - 20pf. red 35 35

DESIGN: 20pf. Thalmann statue, Pushkin, U.S.S.R.

E172 Masked Dancer (statuette)

1960. 250th Anniv of Porcelain Industry, Meissen. Centres and inscriptions in blue. Figures in colours given.

E507	**E172**	5pf. orange	35	25
E508	-	10pf. green	35	25
E509	-	15pf. purple	5·00	5·00
E510	-	20pf. red	35	25
E511	-	25pf. olive	35	25

DESIGNS: 10pf. Dish inscr with swords and years "1710 1960"; 15pf. Otter; 20pf. Potter; 25pf. Coffee-pot.

E173 Racing Cyclist

1960. World Cycling Championships.

E512	**E173**	20pf.+10pf. mult	35	35
E513	-	25pf.+10pf. brown, drab and blue	2·00	4·00

DESIGN (38½×21 mm): 25pf. Racing cyclists on track.

E174 Opera House, Leipzig

1960. Leipzig Autumn Fair.

E514	**E174**	20pf. grey and red	45	25
E515	-	25pf. brown and blue	45	45

DESIGN: 25pf. Export goods.

E175 Sachsenhausen Memorial

1960. Concentration Camp Memorials Fund.

E516	**E175**	20pf.+10pf. red	55	45

1960. President Pieck Mourning issue.

E517	**E145**	20pf. black	70	45
MSE517a 88×108 mm. No. E517. Imperf			2·00	3·25

E176 18th-century Rook

1960. 14th Chess Olympiad, Leipzig. German Chessmen.

E518	**E176**	10pf.+5pf. green	35	25
E519	-	20pf.+10pf. purple	35	25
E520	-	25pf.+10pf. blue	1·40	4·00

DESIGNS: 20pf. 18th-century knight; 25pf. 14th-century knight.

E177 Mail Vans

1960. Stamp Day.

E521	**E177**	20pf. yell, blk & mve	35	30
E522	-	25pf. mauve, blk & bl	4·25	2·30

DESIGN: 25pf. 19th-century railway mail coach.

E178 Medal of 1518 showing Hans Burgkmair (painter)

1960. 400th Anniv of Dresden Art Collections.

E523	**E178**	20pf. ochre, green and buff	35	30
E524	-	25pf. black and blue	2·30	2·75

DESIGN: 25pf. "Dancing Peasants" (after Durer).

E179 Count N. von Gneisenau

1960. Birth Bicent of Count N. von Gneisenau.

E525	**E179**	20pf. black and red	35	30
E526	-	25pf. blue	1·90	1·90

DESIGN: 25pf. Similar portrait but vert.

E180 R. Virchow

1960. 250th Anniv of Berlin Charity and 150th Anniv of Humboldt University, Berlin. Centres in black.

E527	**E180**	5pf. ochre	35	25
E528	-	10pf. green	35	25
E529	-	20pf. brown	35	25
E530	-	25pf. blue	35	25
E531	-	40pf. red	3·50	2·20

DESIGNS—As Type E **180** (Berlin Charity); 10pf. Robert Koch; 40pf. W. Griesinger. (Humboldt University); 20pf. University building and statues of William and Alexander von Humboldt; 25pf. Plaque with profiles of Von Humboldt brothers.

E181 Scientist with Notebook

1960. Chemical Workers' Day.

E532	**E181**	5pf. grey and red	25	20
E533	-	10pf. green and orange	25	20
E534	-	20pf. red and blue	25	20
E535	-	25pf. blue and yellow	2·50	3·25

DESIGNS: 10pf. Chemical worker with fertiliser; 20pf. Girl worker with jar, and Trabant car; 25pf. Laboratory assistant and synthetic dress.

E182 "Young Socialists' Express" (double-deck train)

1960. 125th Anniv of German Railways.

E536	**E182**	10pf. black and green	35	35
E537	-	20pf. black and red	35	35
E538	-	25pf. black and blue	6·75	6·75

DESIGNS—As Type E **182**: 25pf. Stephenson locomotive "Adler" (1835) and Class V180 diesel locomotive. (43×25½ mm): 20pf. Sassnitz Harbour station and train ferry "Sassnitz".

E183 President Pieck

1961. 85th Birth Anniv of President Pieck.

E539	**E183**	20pf. red and black	55	45

1961. Concentration Camp Victims. As Type E 120. Portraits in black.

E540	5pf.+5pf. green	25	25
E541	10pf.+5pf. green	25	25
E542	15pf.+5pf. violet	1·80	3·25
E543	20pf.+10pf. red	25	25
E544	25pf.+10pf. blue	25	25

PORTRAITS: 5pf. W. Kube; 10pf. H. Gunther; 15pf. Elvira Eisenschneider; 20pf. Hertha Lindner; 25pf. H. Tschape.

E184 High-voltage Switchgear

1961. Leipzig Spring Fair. Inscr as in Type E 184.

E545	**E184**	10pf. slate and green	45	30
E546	-	25pf. slate and blue	55	35

DESIGN: 25pf. Ilyushin Il-12 over Fair Press Centre.

E185 Lilienstein Saxony

1961. Landscapes and Historical Buildings.

E547		5pf. grey	25	25
E548		10pf. green	25	25
E549	**E185**	20pf. brown	25	35
E550	-	20pf. red	25	25
E551	-	25pf. blue	25	35

DESIGNS—VERT: 5pf. Ruins of Rudelsburg; 10pf. Wartburg; 20pf. (No. E550), Town Hall, Wernigerode. HORIZ: 25pf. Brocken, Oberharz.

E186 "Ros" (Trawler)

1961. Deep Sea Fishing Industry.

E552	**E186**	10pf. green	25	20
E553	-	20pf. purple	25	20
E554	-	25pf. blue	25	20
E555	-	40pf. violet	3·25	2·50

DESIGNS: 20pf. Hauling nets; 25pf. "Robert Koch" (trawler); 40pf. Processing Atlantic cod.

E187 Cosmonaut in Capsule

1961. 1st Manned Space Flight. Inscr "12.4.1961".

E556		10pf. red and green	1·70	1·10
E557	**E187**	20pf. red	1·70	1·10
E558	-	25pf. blue	6·25	6·75

DESIGNS: 10pf. Space rocket leaving globe; 25pf. Capsule's parachute descent.

E188 Marx, Engels, Lenin and Demonstrators

1961. 15th Anniv of German Socialist Unity Party.

E559	**E188**	20pf. red	70	45

E189 Common Zebra

1961. Centenary of Dresden Zoo.

E560	**E189**	10pf. black and green	6·75	6·75
E561	-	20pf. black and mauve	1·10	55

DESIGN: 20pf. Eastern black-and-white colobus.

E190 Pioneers playing Volleyball

1961. Pioneers Meeting, Erfurt. Mult.

E562	10pf.+5pf. Type E **190**	25	20
E563	20pf.+10pf. Folk dancing	25	20
E564	25pf.+10pf. Model airplane construction	4·25	3·50

E191 High Jump

1961. 3rd European Women's Gymnastic Championships, Leipzig.

E565	**E191**	10pf. green	25	20
E566	-	20pf. mauve	25	20
E567	-	25pf. blue	6·75	6·25

DESIGNS—VERT: 20pf. Gymnast. HORIZ: 25pf. Exercise on parallel bars.

E192 Salt Miners and Castle

1961. Halle (Saale) Millenary.

E568	**E192**	10pf. black, yell & grn	3·75	2·00
E569	-	20pf. black, yell & red	25	25

DESIGN: 20pf. Scientist and Five Towers of Halle.

E193 Canadian Canoe

1961. World Canoeing Championships.

E570		5pf. blue and grey	4·25	3·75
E571	**E 193**	10pf. green and grey	25	20
E572	-	20pf. purple and grey	25	20

DESIGNS: 5pf. Folding canoe; 20pf. Canadian two-seater canoe.

E194 Line-casting

1961. World Angling Championships.

E573	**E194**	10pf. green and blue	3·50	3·25
E574	-	20pf. lake and blue	55	25

DESIGN: 20pf. River-fishing.

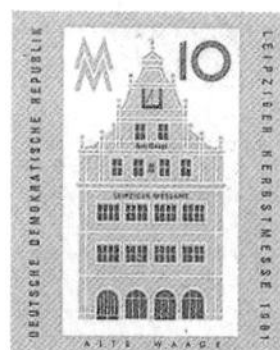

E195 Old Weigh-house, Leipzig

1961. Leipzig Autumn Fair.

E575	**E195**	10pf. olive and green	25	20
E576	-	25pf. blue & ultram	1·50	45

DESIGN: 25pf. Old Stock Exchange, Leipzig.
See also Nos. E612/14.

E196 Walter Ulbricht

1961. Type E 196 or larger, 24×29 mm (Dm. values).

E577	5pf. blue	35	35
E578	10pf. green	45	55
E579	15pf. purple	80	25
E580	20pf. red	65	50
E581	25pf. turquoise	45	25
E582	30pf. red	25	25
E582a	35pf. green	80	55
E583	40pf. violet	25	25
E584	50pf. blue	35	25
E584a	60pf. green	45	35
E585	70pf. brown	45	25
E585a	80pf. blue	70	55
E586	1Dm. green	1·10	80
E587	2Dm. brown	2·30	80

See also Nos. E805/6, E1197/8 and E1255.

1961. Concentration Camps Memorials Fund. As Type E 120. Portraits in grey and black.

E588	5pf.+5pf. green	25	35

E589	10pf.+5pf. green	25	35
E590	20pf.+10pf. mauve	25	35
E591	25pf.+10pf. blue	25	35
E592	40pf.+20pf. lake	2·75	7·50

PORTRAITS: 5pf. C. Schonhaar; 10pf. H. Baum; 20pf. Liselotte Herrmann. HORIZ: (41×32½ mm): 25pf. Sophie and Hans Scholl; 40pf. Hilde and Hans Coppi.

E197 Dahlia

1961. International Horticultural Exn.

E593	-	10pf. red, yellow & grn	45	35
E594	**E197**	20pf. red, yellow & brn	45	35
E595	-	40pf. red, yellow & bl	11·50	12·50

FLOWERS: 10pf. Tulip. 40pf. Rose.

E198 Liszt and Berlioz (after Von Kaulbach and Prinzhofer)

1961. 150th Birth Anniv of Liszt (composer).

E596	**E198**	5pf. black	35	25
E597	-	10pf. green	2·75	3·25
E598	-	20pf. red	35	25
E599	-	25pf. blue	3·50	3·75

DESIGNS: 10pf. Young hand of Liszt (from French sculpture, Liszt Museum, Budapest); 20pf. Liszt (after Rietschel); 25pf. Liszt and Chopin (after Bartolini and Bovy).

E199 TV Camera and Screen

1961. Stamp Day.

E600	**E199**	10pf. black and green	2·30	3·75
E601	-	20pf. black and red	25	35

DESIGNS: 20pf. Studio microphone and radio tuning-scale.

E200 G. S. Titov with Young Pioneers

1961. 2nd Russian Manned Space Flight.

E602	**E200**	5pf. violet and red	35	25
E603	-	10pf. green and red	35	25
E604	-	15pf. mauve and blue	11·50	12·50
E605	-	20pf. red and blue	35	25
E606	-	25pf. blue and red	35	25
E607	-	40pf. blue and red	2·00	70

DESIGNS—HORIZ: 15pf. Titov in space-suit; 20pf. Titov receiving Karl Marx Order from Ulbricht; 25pf. "Vostok 2" rocket in flight; 40pf. Titov and Ulbricht in Berlin. VERT: 10pf. Titov in Leipzig.

E201 "Formica ruta" (Ant)

1962. Fauna Protection Campaign (1st series).

E608	**E201**	5pf. yellow, brn & blk	5·00	8·50
E609	-	10pf. brown and green	25	20
E610	-	20pf. brown and red	25	20
E611	-	40pf. yellow, blk & vio	80	55

DESIGNS: 10pf. Weasels; 20pf. Eurasian common shrews; 40pf. Common long-eared bat.

See also Nos. E699/703.

1962. Leipzig Spring Fair. As Type E 195.

E612	10pf. sepia and green	25	25
E613	20pf. black and red	45	25
E614	25pf. purple and blue	1·10	1·10

BUILDINGS: 10pf. Zum Kaffeebaum; 20pf. Gobliser Schlosschen; 25pf. Romanus-Haus.

E203 Pilot and Mikoyan Gurevich MiG-17 Jet Fighters

1962. 6th Anniv of East German People's Army.

E615	**E203**	5pf. blue	35	25
E616	-	10pf. green	35	25
E617	-	20pf. red	35	25
E618	-	25pf. blue	35	50
E619	-	40pf. brown	2·75	2·00

DESIGNS: 10pf. Soldier and armoured car; 20pf. Factory guard; 25pf. Sailor and Habich I class minesweeper; 40pf. Tank and driver.

E204 Danielle Casanova

1962. Concentration Camps Memorial Fund. Camp Victims.

E620	**E204**	5pf.+5pf. black	25	20
E621	-	10pf.+5pf. green	25	20
E622	-	20pf.+10pf. purple	25	20
E623	-	25pf.+10pf. blue	35	25
E624	-	40pf.+20pf. purple	2·30	3·25

PORTRAITS: 10pf. Julius Fucik; 20pf. Johanna J. Schaft; 25pf. Pawel Finder; 40pf. Soja A. Kosmodemjanskaja.

E205 Racing Cyclists and Prague Castle

1962. 15th Int Peace Cycle Race. Mult.

E625	10pf. Type E **205**	25	20
E626	20pf.+10pf. Cyclists and Palace of Culture and Science, Warsaw	25	25
E627	25pf. Cyclist and Town Hall, East Berlin	1·90	1·90

E206 Johann Fichte

1962. Birth Bicent of Fichte (philosopher).

E628	-	10pf. green and black	3·25	2·75
E629	**E206**	20pf. red and black	35	35

DESIGN: 10pf. Fichte's birthplace, Ramenau.

E207 Cross of Lidice

1962. 20th Anniv of Destruction of Lidice.

E630	**E207**	20pf. red and black	35	25
E631	**E207**	25pf. blue and black	1·40	1·80

E208 Dimitrov at Leipzig

1962. 80th Birth Anniv of G. Dimitrov (Bulgarian statesman).

E632	**E208**	5pf. black & turquoise	80	55
E633	-	20pf. black and red	35	25

DESIGN: 20pf. Dimitrov as Premier of Bulgaria.

E209 Maize-planting machine

1962. 10th D.D.R. Agricultural Exhibition, Markkleeberg. Multicoloured.

E634	10pf. Type E **209**	25	20
E635	20pf. Milking shed	25	20
E636	40pf. Combine-harvester	2·30	2·10

E210 "Frieden" (freighter)

1962. 5th Baltic Sea Week, Rostock.

E637	-	10pf. turquoise & blue	25	20
E638	-	20pf. red and yellow	25	20
E639	**E210**	25pf. bistre and blue	3·00	2·75

DESIGNS—HORIZ: 10pf. Map of Baltic Sea inscr "Meer des Friedens" ("Sea of Peace"). VERT: 20pf. Hochhaus, Rostock.

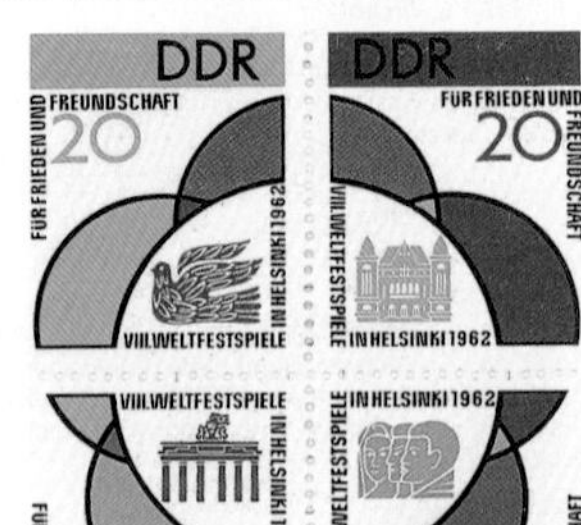

E211/E212 Brandenburg Gate, Berlin and Youth of Three Races

E213-E214 Folk Dancers and Youth of Three Nations

1962. World Youth Festival Games, Helsinki. Multicoloured.

E640	5pf. Type E **211**	2·75	3·50
E641	5pf. Type E **212**	2·75	3·50
E642	10pf.+5pf. Type E **213**	45	30
E643	15pf.+5pf. Type E **214**	45	30
E644	20pf. Dove	2·75	3·50
E645	20pf. National Theatre, Helsinki	2·75	3·50

Nos. 640/11 and 644/5 were issued together as a se-tenant block of four and Nos. 642/3 in horizontal pairs, both forming composite designs.

E217 Free-style Swimming

1962. 10th European Swimming Championships, Leipzig. Design in blue: value colours given.

E646	**E217**	5pf. orange	25	20
E647	-	10pf. blue	25	20
E648	-	20pf.+10pf. mauve	25	20
E649	-	25pf. blue	25	20
E650	-	40pf. violet	1·70	1·70
E651	-	70pf. brown	25	20

DESIGNS: 10pf. Back stroke; 20pf. High diving; 25pf. Butterfly stroke; 40pf. Breast stroke; 70pf. Water-polo.

On Nos. E649/51 the value, etc, appears at the foot of the design.

E218 Municipal Store, Leipzig

1962. Leipzig Autumn Fair.

E652	**E218**	10pf. black and green	25	25
E653	-	20pf. black and red	45	30
E654	-	25pf. black and blue	1·20	1·10

DESIGNS: 20pf. Madler Arcade, Leipzig; 25pf. Leipzig Airport and Ilyushin Il-14M airplane.

E219 "Transport and Communications"

1962. 10th Anniv of "Friedrich List" Transport High School, Dresden.

E655	**E219**	5pf. black and blue	50	30

E219a P. Popovich and A. Nikolaev

1962. "Vostok 3" and "Vostok 4" Space Flights. Sheet 89×108 mm.

MSE655a	E **219a** 70pf. green, blue and yellow	4·00	6·75

E220 Rene Blieck

1962. Concentration Camp Victims. Memorials Fund.

E656	**E220**	5pf.+5pf. blue	25	20
E657	-	10pf.+5pf. green	25	20
E658	-	15pf.+5pf. violet	25	20
E659	-	20pf.+10pf. purple	30	25
E660	-	70pf.+30pf. brown	2·50	3·75

PORTRAITS—As Type E **220**: 10pf. Dr. A. Klahr; 15pf. J. Diaz; 20pf. J. Alpari. HORIZ: (39×21 mm): 70pf. Seven Cervi brothers.

E221 Television Screen and Call-sign

1962. Stamp Day and 10th Anniv of German Television.

E661	**E221**	20pf. purple and green	25	25
E662	-	40pf. purple & mauve	2·30	2·75

DESIGN: 40pf. Children with stamp album (inscr "TAG DER BRIEFMARKE 1962").

E222 G. Hauptmann

1962. Birth Centenary of Gerhart Hauptmann (author).

E663	**E222**	20pf. black and red	60	30

E222a Gagarin and "Vostok 1"

1962. Five Years of Russian Space Flights. Sheet 127×108 mm. Multicoloured.
MSE663a 5pf. Dogs "Belka" and "Strelka", 10pf. Type E**222a**; 15pf. "Sputniks 1, 2 and 3"; 20pf. Titov and "Vostok 2"; 25pf. "Luniks 1 and 2"; 30pf. Nikolaev and Popovich; 40pf. Interplanetary station and spacecraft; 50pf. "Lunik 3" 46·00 70·00

E223 Pierre de Coubertin

1963. Birth Centenary of Pierre de Coubertin (reviver of Olympic Games).
E664 **E223** 20pf. red and grey 25 25
E665 - 25pf. blue and ochre 2·30 3·50
DESIGN: 25pf. Stadium.

E224 Party Flag

1963. 6th Socialists Unity Party Day.
E666 **E224** 10pf. red, black & yell 45 30

E225 Insecticide Sprayer

1963. Malaria Eradication.
E667 **E225** 20pf. black, red & orge 25 25
E668 - 25pf. multicoloured 25 25
E669 - 50pf. multicoloured 1·70 1·90
DESIGNS: 25pf. Rod of Aesculapius; 50pf. Mosquito. Map is common to all values.

E226 Red Fox (Silver Fox race)

1963. International Fur Auctions, Leipzig.
E670 **E226** 20pf. blue and red 25 25
E671 - 25pf. indigo and blue 2·00 3·25
DESIGN: 25pf. Karakul lamb.

E227 Barthels Hof, Leipzig (1748–1872)

1963. Leipzig Spring Fair.
E672 **E227** 10pf. black and yellow 25 25
E673 - 20pf. black and brown 45 35
E674 - 25pf. black and blue 1·70 1·80
LEIPZIG BUILDINGS: 20pf. New Town Hall; 25pf. Clock-tower, Karl-Marx Square.

E227a Laboratory Worker and Apparatus

1963. "Chemistry for Freedom and Socialism". Sheet 105×74 mm with Type E 227a and similar horiz design. Imperf. No gum.
MSE674a 50pf. blue and black (E **227a**); 70pf. blue and grey (oil refinery) 5·75 30·00

E228 J. G. Seume (poet) and Scene from "Syracuse Walk" (Birth Bicent)

1963. Cultural Anniversaries. Design and portrait in black.
E675 **E228** 5pf. yellow 25 25
E676 - 10pf. turquoise 25 25
E677 - 20pf. orange 25 25
E678 - 25pf. blue 2·30 2·75
DESIGNS: 10pf. F. Hebbel (poet) and scene from "Mary Magdalene" (150th birth anniv); 20pf. G. Buchner (poet) and scene from "Woyzeck" (150th birth anniv); 25pf. R. Wagner (composer) and scene from "The Flying Dutchman" (150th birth anniv).

E229 Nurse bandaging Patient

1963. Centenary of Red Cross.
E679 **E229** 10pf. multicoloured 1·60 1·60
E680 - 20pf. black, grey and red 25 25
DESIGN: 20pf. Barkas type "B 1000" ambulance.

E230 W. Bohne (runner)

1963. Concentration Camps Memorial Fund. Sportsmen Victims (1st series). Designs in black.
E681 **E230** 5pf.+5pf. yellow 25 35
E682 - 10pf.+5pf. green 25 35
E683 - 15pf.+5pf. mauve 25 35
E684 - 20pf.+10pf. pink 25 35
E685 - 25pf.+10pf. blue 2·75 8·00
SPORTSMEN: 10pf. W. Seelenbinder (wrestler); 15pf. A. Richter (cyclist); 20pf. H. Steyer (footballer); 25pf. K. Schlosser (mountaineer).
See also Nos. E704/8.

E231 Gymnastics

1963. 4th East German Gymnastics and Sports Festival, Leipzig. Inscr in black.
E686 **E231** 10pf.+5pf. yellow and green 25 20
E687 - 20pf.+10pf. violet and red 30 25
E688 - 25pf.+10pf. green and blue 4·50 4·25
DESIGNS: 20pf. Dederon kerchief exercises; 25pf. Relay-racing.

E232 E. Pottier (lyricist) and Opening Bars of the "Internationale"

1963. 75th Anniv of "Internationale" (song).
E689 **E232** 20pf. black and red 25 25
E690 - 25pf. black and blue 1·60 1·80
DESIGN: 25pf. As 20pf. but portrait of P.-C. Degeyter.

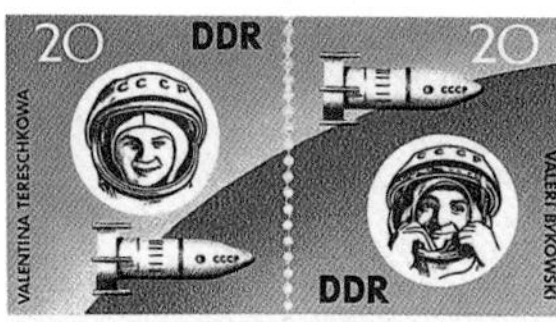

E 233 V. Tereshkova and "Vostok 6"
E 234 V. Bykovsky and "Vostok 5"

1963. 2nd "Team" Manned Space Flights.
E691 **E233** 20pf. black, grey & bl 1·10 35
E692 **E234** 20pf. black, grey & bl 1·10 35
Nos. E691/2 were printed together, se-tenant, forming a composite design.

E235 Motor Cyclist competing in "Motocross", Apolda

1963. World Motor Cycle Racing Championships.
E693 **E235** 10pf. emerald & green 4·50 5·00
E694 - 20pf. red and pink 35 35
E695 - 25pf. blue & light blue 35 35
DESIGNS—HORIZ (39×22 mm): 20pf. Motor cyclist; 25pf. Two motor cyclists cornering.

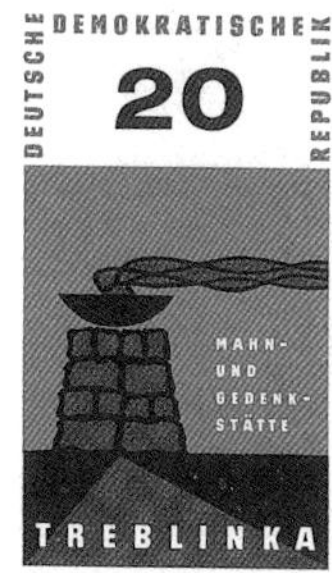

E236 Treblinka Memorial

1963. Erection of Treblinka Memorial, Poland.
E696 **E236** 20pf. blue and red 45 35

E237/E238 Transport

1963. Leipzig Autumn Fair.
E697 **E237** 10pf. multicoloured 1·00 25
E698 **E238** 10pf. multicoloured 1·00 25
Nos. E697/8 were printed together, se-tenant, forming a composite design.

1963. Fauna Protection Campaign (2nd series). As Type E 201. Fauna in natural colours, background colours given.
E699 10pf. green 25 20
E700 20pf. red 25 20
E701 30pf. red 25 25
E702 50pf. blue 4·50 4·50
E703 70pf. brown 80 80
DESIGNS: 10pf. Stag-beetle; 20pf. Salamander; 30pf. European pond tortoise; 50pf. Green toad; 70pf. West European hedgehogs.

1963. Concentration Camps Memorial Fund. Sportsmen Victims (2nd series). As Type E 230. Designs in black.
E704 5pf.+5pf. yellow 25 25
E705 10pf.+5pf. green 25 25
E706 15pf.+5pf. violet 25 25
E707 20pf. 10pf. red 25 25
E708 40pf.+20pf. blue 3·50 5·00
SPORTSMEN: 5pf. H. Tops (Gymnast); 10pf. Kate Tucholla (hockey-player); 15pf. R. Seiffert (swimmer); 20pf. E. Grube (athlete); 40pf. K. Biedermann (canoeist).

E239 N. von Gneisenau and G. L. von Blucher

1963. 150th Anniv of German War of Liberation.
E709 **E239** 5pf. black, buff & yell 25 20
E710 - 10pf. black, buff & grn 25 20
E711 - 20pf. blk, buff & orge 25 20
E712 - 25pf. black, buff & bl 25 20
E713 - 40pf. black, buff & red 3·25 1·80
DESIGNS: 10pf. "Cossacks and (German) Soldiers in Berlin" (Ludwig Wolf); 20pf. E. M. Arndt and Baron vom Stein; 25pf. Lutzow corps in battle order (detail from painting by Hans Kohlschein); 40pf. G. von Scharnhorst and Prince Kutuzov.

E240 V. Tereshkova

1963. Visit of Soviet Cosmonauts to East Berlin.
E714 **E240** 10pf. green and blue 25 20
E715 - 20pf. black, red & buff 25 20
E716 - 20pf. green, red & buff 25 20
E717 - 25pf. orange and blue 5·75 3·50
DESIGNS—SQUARE: No. E717, Tereshkova in capsule. VERT: (24×32 mm). No. E715, Tereshkova with bouquet; No. E716, Gagarin (visit to Berlin).

E241 Synagogue aflame

1963. 25th Anniv of "Kristallnacht" (Nazi pogrom).
E718 **E241** 10pf. multicoloured 45 45

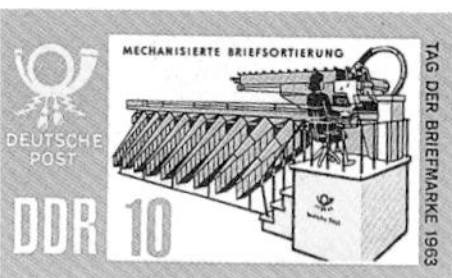

E242 Letter-sorting Machine

1963. Stamp Day. Multicoloured.
E719 10pf. Type E **242** 2·50 2·75
E720 20pf. Fork-lift truck loading mail train 25 25

E243 Ski Jumper commencing Run

1963. Winter Olympic Games, Innsbruck, 1964. Rings in different colours; skier in black.
E721 **E243** 5pf. yellow 25 20
E722 - 10pf. green 25 20
E723 - 20pf.+10pf. red 25 20
E724 - 25pf. blue 3·00 3·25
DESIGNS: Ski jumper—10pf. Taking-off; 20pf. In mid-air; 25pf. Landing.

E244 "Vanessa atlanta"

1964. Butterflies. Butterflies in natural colours; inscr in black.
E725 **E244** 10pf. olive 55 25
E726 - 15pf. lilac 55 25
E727 - 20pf. orange 55 25
E728 - 25pf. blue 55 25
E729 - 40pf. blue 7·50 3·50
BUTTERFLIES: 15pf. "Parnassius phoebus"; 20pf. "Papilio machaon"; 25pf. "Colius croceus"; 40pf. "Nymphalis polychloros".

E245 Shakespeare (b. 1564)

1964. Cultural Anniversaries.
E730 20pf. blue and pink 35 25
E731 25pf. purple and blue 35 25
E732 **E245** 40pf. blue and lilac 1·80 1·60
DESIGNS: 20pf. Quadriga, Brandenburg Gate (J. G. Schadow, sculptor, b. 1764); 25pf. Portal keystone, German Historical Museum (A. Schluter, sculptor, b. 1664).

E246 "Elektrotecknik" Hall

1964. Leipzig Spring Fair.

E733	**E246**	10pf. black and green	3·50	45
E734	-	20pf. black and red	3·50	45

DESIGN: 20pf. Braunigkes Hof, c. 1700.

E247 A. Saefkow

1964. Concentration Camp Victims. Memorials Fund.

E735	**E247**	5pf.+5pf. brown & bl	35	20
E736	-	10pf.+5pf. brn & ol	35	20
E737	-	15pf.+5pf. brn & vio	35	20
E738	-	20pf.+5pf. olive and red	35	25
E739	-	25pf.+10pf. blue & ol	55	35
E740	-	40pf.+10pf. ol & brn	1·70	2·30

PORTRAITS—As Type E **247**: 10pf. F. Jacob; 15pf. B. Bastlein; 20pf. H. Schulze-Boysen; 25pf. Dr. A. Kuckhoff. (49×27½ mm): 40pf. Dr. A. and Mildred Harnack.

E248 Mr. Khrushchev with East German Officials

1964. Mr. Khrushchev's 70th Birthday.

E741	**E248**	25pf. blue	35	25
E742	-	40pf. black and purple	4·00	3·00

DESIGN: 40pf. Mr. Khrushchev with cosmonauts Tereshkova and Gagarin.

E249 Boys and Girls

1964. German Youth Meeting, Berlin. Multicoloured.

E743	10pf. Type E **249**	25	20
E744	20pf. Young gymnasts	25	20
E745	25pf. Youth with accordion and girl with flowers	2·30	1·30

E250 Flax, Krumel and Struppi, the dog

1964. Children's Day. Multicoloured.

E746	5pf. Type E **250**	35	20
E747	10pf. Master Nadelohr	35	20
E748	15pf. Pittiplatsch	35	20
E749	20pf. Sandmannschen (sandman)	35	20
E750	40pf. Bummi (teddy bear) and Schnatterinchen (duckling)	2·30	2·50

The designs show characters from children's T.V. programmes.

E251 Governess and Child (with portrait of Jenny Marx)

1964. East German Women's Congress. Mult.

E751	20pf. Type E **251**	45	20
E752	25pf. Switchboard technicians	1·50	1·30
E753	70pf. Farm girls	45	20

E252 Cycling

1964. Olympic Games, Tokyo. Multicoloured. (a) 1st Series. As Type E 252.

E754	5pf. Type E **252**	35	35
E755	10pf. Volleyball	35	35
E756	20pf. Judo	35	35
E757	25pf. Diving	35	35
E758	40pf.+20pf. Running	35	35
E759	70pf. Horse-jumping	2·40	2·40

E253 Diving

(b) 2nd Series. As Type E 253.

E760	10pf. Type E **253**	3·50	4·00
E761	10pf.+5pf. Horse-jumping	3·50	4·00
E762	10pf. Volleyball	3·50	4·00
E763	10pf. Cycling	3·50	4·00
E764	10pf.+5pf. Running	3·50	4·00
E765	10pf. Judo	3·50	4·00

Nos. E760/5 were printed together in se-tenant blocks of six (3×2) within sheets of 60 (6×10), and with an overall pattern of the five Olympic "rings" in each block.

E254 Young Artists

1964. 5th Young Pioneers' Meeting, East Berlin. Multicoloured.

E766	10pf.+5pf. Type E **254**	2·30	60
E767	20pf.+10pf. Planting tree	2·30	60
E768	25pf.+10pf. Playing with ball	5·75	6·00

E255 Leningrad Memorial

1964. Victims of Leningrad Siege Commem.

E769	**E255**	25pf. black, yellow and blue	1·40	35

E256 F. Joliot-Curie

1964. "World Peace".

E770	**E256**	20pf. sepia and red	35	25
E771	-	25pf. black and blue	35	25
E772	-	50pf. black and lilac	1·80	1·30

PORTRAITS (Campaigners for "World Peace"): 25pf. B. von Suttner; 50pf. C. von Ossietzky.

E257 Ancient Glazier's Shop

1964. Leipzig Autumn Fair. Multicoloured.

E773	10pf. Type E **257**	85	25
E774	15pf. Jena glass factory	85	25

E258 I.W.M.A. Cachet

1964. Centenary of "First International".

E775	**E258**	20pf. black and red	25	20
E776	**E258**	25pf. black and blue	95	95

E259 "Rostock Port" Stamp of 1958

1964. National Stamp Exn, East Berlin.

E777	**E259**	10pf.+5pf. green and orange	35	25
E778	-	20pf.+10pf. blue and purple	45	35
E779	-	50pf. brown and grey	2·75	2·10

DESIGNS: 20pf., 12pf. "Peace" stamp of 1950; 50pf., 5pf. "Dresden Paintings" stamp of 1955.

E260 Modern Buildings and Flag ("Reconstruction")

1964. 15th Anniv of German Democratic Republic. Multicoloured.

E780	10pf. Type E **260**	45	35
E781	10pf. Surveyor and conveyor ("Coal")	45	35
E782	10pf. Scientist and chemical works ("Chemical Industry")	45	35
E783	10pf. Guard and chemical works ("Chemical Industry")	45	35
E784	10pf. Milkmaid and dairy pen ("Agriculture")	45	35
E785	10pf. Furnaceman and mills ("Steel")	45	35
E786	10pf. Student with microscope, and lecture hall ("Education")	45	35
E787	10pf. Operator and lathe ("Engineering")	45	35
E788	10pf. Scientist and planetarium ("Optics")	45	35
E789	10pf. Girl with cloth, and loom ("Textiles")	45	35
E790	10pf. Docker and ship at quayside ("Shipping")	45	35
E791	10pf. Leipzig buildings and "businessmen" formed of Fair emblem ("Exports")	45	35
E792	10pf. Building worker and flats ("New Construction")	45	35
E793	10pf. Sculptor modelling and Dresden gateway ("Culture")	45	35
E794	10pf. Girl skier and holiday resort ("Recreation")	45	35
MSE794a	210×285 mm. Nos. E780/94	75·00	£110

E261 Monchgut (Rugen) Costume

1964. Provincial Costumes (1st series). Mult.

E795	5pf. Type E **261**	12·50	8·25
E796	5pf. Monchgut (male)	12·50	8·25
E797	10pf. Spreewald (female)	1·10	60
E798	10pf. Spreewald (male)	1·10	60
E799	20pf. Thuringen (female)	1·10	60
E800	20pf. Thuringen (male)	1·10	60

See Nos. E932/7 and E1073/6.

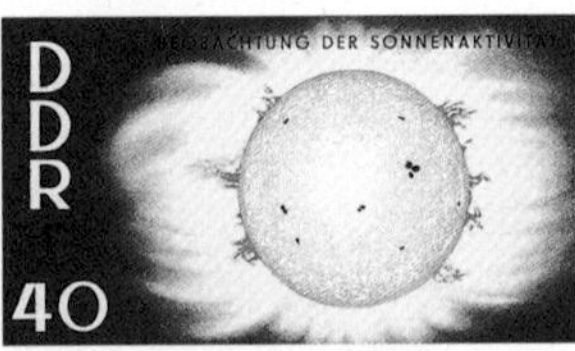

E261a Observation of Sun's Activity

1964. Quiet Sun Year. Three sheets, each 108×90 mm incorporating stamp as Type E 261a. Multicoloured.

MSE801	(a) 25pf. Rocket over part of Earth. (b) 40pf. Type E **261a**. (c) 70pf. Earth and rocket routes	14·50	24·00

E262 Dr. Schweitzer and Lambarene River

1965. 90th Birthday of Dr. Albert Schweitzer.

E802	**E262**	10pf. yellow, blk & grn	55	20
E803	-	20pf. yellow, blk & red	55	20
E804	-	25pf. yellow, blk & bl	4·50	3·00

DESIGNS: 20pf. Schweitzer and "nuclear disarmament" marchers; 25pf. Schweitzer and part of a Bach organ prelude.

1965. As Nos. E586/7 but values expressed in "MDN" (Deutschen Notenbank Marks) instead of "DM".

E805	1MDN. green	70	1·20
E806	2MDN. brown	80	1·80

E263 A. Bebel

1965. 125th Birth Anniv of August Bebel (founder of Social Democratic Party).

E807	**E263**	20pf. yellow, brn & red	55	25

See also Nos. E814/15, E839, E842 and E871.

E264 Fair Medal (obverse)

1965. Leipzig Spring Fair and 800th Anniv of Leipzig Fair.

E808	**E264**	10pf. gold and mauve	35	20
E809	-	15pf. gold and mauve	35	20
E810	-	25pf. multicoloured	80	35

DESIGNS: 15pf. Fair medal (reverse); 25pf. Chemical Works.

E265 Giraffe

1965. 10th Anniv of East Berlin Zoo.

E811	**E265**	10pf. grey and green	25	20
E812	-	25pf. grey and blue	35	25
E813	-	30pf. grey and sepia	3·00	2·10

ANIMALS—HORIZ: 25pf. Iguana; 30pf. Black wildebeest.

1965. 120th Birth Anniv of W. C. Rontgen (physicist). As Type E 263 but portrait of Rontgen.

E814	10pf. yellow, brown and green	70	25

1985. 700th Birth Anniv of Dante. As Type E 263 but portrait of Dante.

E815	50pf. yellow, brown & lemon	2·50	35

E266 Belyaev and Leonov

1965. Space Flight of "Voskhod 2".

E816	**E266**	10pf. red	45	25
E817	-	25pf. blue	3·00	2·40

DESIGN: 25pf. Leonov in space.

E267 Boxing Gloves

1965. European Boxing Championships, Berlin.

E818	**E267**	10pf.+5pf. mult	25	20
E819	-	20pf. gold, black and red	1·20	1·20

DESIGN: 20pf. Boxing glove.

E268 Dimitrov denouncing Fascism

1965. 20th Anniv of Liberation. Multicoloured.

E820	5pf.+5pf. Type E **268**	35	25
E821	10pf.+5pf. Distributing "Communist Manifesto"	35	25
E822	15pf.+5pf. Soldiers of International Brigade fighting in Spain	35	25
E823	20pf.+10pf. "Freedom for Ernst Thalmann" demonstration	35	25
E824	25pf.+10pf. Founding of "Free Germany" National Committee (Moscow)	35	25
E825	40pf. Ulbricht and Weinert distributing "Manifesto" on Eastern Front	35	25
E826	50pf. Liberation of concentration camps	35	25
E827	60pf. Hoisting Red Flag on Reichstag	4·00	4·00
E828	70pf. Bilateral demonstration of Communist and Socialist parties	35	25

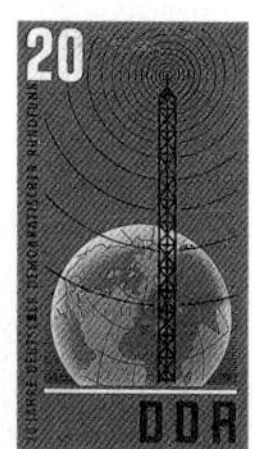

E269 Transmitter Aerial and Globe

1965. 20th Anniv of East German Broadcasting Service.

E829	**E269**	20pf. black, red and cerise	45	20
E830	-	40pf. black and blue	2·00	95

DESIGN: 40pf. Radio workers.

E270 I.T.U. Emblem and Radio Circuit Diagram

1965. Centenary of I.T.U.

E831	**E270**	20pf. black, yell & ol	55	20
E832	-	25pf. black, mve & vio	3·00	70

DESIGN: 25pf. I.T.U. emblem and switch diagram.

E271 F.D.G.B. Emblem

1965. 20th Anniv of Free German (F.D.G.B.) and World Trade Unions.

E833	**E271**	20pf. gold and red	55	25
E834	-	25pf. black, bl & gold	1·70	70

DESIGN—HORIZ (39×21½ mm): 25pf. Workers of "two hemispheres" (inscr "20 JAHRE WELTGEWERKSCHAFTSBUND").

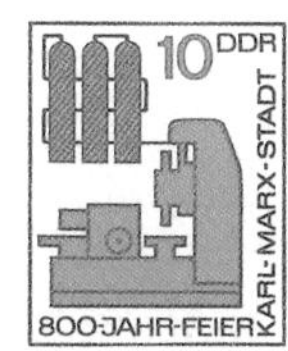

E272 Industrial Machine

1965. 800th Anniv of Karl-Marx-Stadt (formerly Chemnitz).

E835	**E272**	10pf. green and gold	35	20
E836	-	20pf. red and gold	35	20
E837	-	25pf. blue and gold	1·60	70

DESIGNS: 20pf. Red Tower, Chemnitz; 25pf. Town Hall, Chemnitz.

E273 Marx and Lenin

1965. Socialist Countries' Postal Ministers Conference, Peking.

E838	**E273**	20pf. black, yell & red	80	30

1965. 90th Birth Anniv of Dr. Wilhelm Kulz (politician). As Type E 263 but portrait of Kulz.

E839	25pf. yellow, brown and blue	1·30	30

E274 Congress Emblem

1965. World Peace Congress, Helsinki.

E840	**E274**	10pf.+5pf. green and blue	35	20
E841	**E274**	20pf.+5pf. blue and red	70	50

1965. 75th Birth Anniv of Erich Weinert (poet). As Type E 263, but portrait of Weinert.

E842	40pf. yellow, brown and red	70	30

1965. "Help for Vietnam". Surch Hilfe fur VIETNAM +10.

E843	**E260**	10pf.+10pf. mult	55	30

E276 Rebuilt Weigh-house and Modern Buildings, Katharinenstrasse

1965. 800th Anniv of Leipzig.

E844	**E276**	10pf. purple, bl & gold	25	20
E845	-	25pf. orge, sep & gold	25	20
E846	-	40pf. multicoloured	35	20
E847	-	70pf. blue and gold	2·75	1·30

DESIGNS: 25pf. Old Town Hall; 40pf. Opera House and new G.P.O.; 70pf. "Stadt Leipzig" Hotel.

E277 "Praktica" and "Praktisix" Cameras

1965. Leipzig Autumn Fair.

E848	**E277**	10pf. blk, gold & grn	45	25
E849	-	15pf. multicoloured	45	25
E850	-	25pf. multicoloured	1·00	35

DESIGNS: 15pf. Clavichord and electric guitar; 25pf. "Zeiss" microscope.

1965. Leipzig Philatelic Exhibition, "INTERMESS III". Nos. E844/7 in two miniature sheets each 137×99 mm.

MSE851	(a) Nos. E844 and E847. (b) Nos. E845/6 (sold for 1 MDN.75)	7·25	9·50

E278 Show Jumping

1965. World Modern Pentathlon Championships, Leipzig. Multicoloured.

E852	10pf. Type E **278**	35	20
E853	10pf. Swimming	35	20
E854	10pf. Running	3·50	3·50
E855	10pf.+5pf. Fencing	35	20
E856	10pf.+5pf. Pistol-shooting	35	20

E279 E. Leonov

1965. Soviet Cosmonauts Visit to East Germany.

E857	**E279**	20pf. blue, silver & red	80	85
E858	-	20pf. blue, silver & red	80	85
E859	-	25pf. multicoloured	80	85

DESIGNS—As Type E **275**. No. E858, Belyaev. HORIZ (48×29 mm): No. E859, "Voskhod 2" and Leonov in space.

E280 Memorial at Putten, Netherlands

1965. Putten War Victims Commem.

E860	**E280**	25pf. black, yell & bl	90	30

E281 Stoking Furnace (from old engraving)

1965. Bicent of Mining School, Freiberg. Multicoloured.

E861	10pf. Type E **281**	35	25
E862	15pf. Mining ore (old engraving)	90	1·20
E863	20pf. Ore	35	25
E864	25pf. Sulphur	35	25

E282 Red Kite

1965. Birds of Prey. Multicoloured.

E865	5pf. Type E **282**	25	20
E866	10pf. Lammergeier	25	20
E867	20pf. Common Buzzard	35	20
E868	25pf. Common Kestrel	35	20
E869	40pf. Northern Goshawk	55	25
E870	70pf. Golden Eagle	5·00	3·25

1965. 150th Birth Anniv of A. von Menzel (painter). As Type E 263 but portrait of Menzel.

E871	10pf. yellow, brown and red	1·00	30

E283 Otto Grotewohl

1965. Grotewohl Commemoration.

E872	**E283**	20f. black	1·00	30

E284 Extract from Newsletter

1966. 50th Anniv of Spartacus Group Conference. Miniature sheet 138×98 mm. Type E 284 and similar horiz design.

MSE873	20pf. black and red (Type E **284**); 50pf. black and red (Karl Liebknecht and Rosa Luxemburg)	2·75	7·00

E285 Ladies' Single-seater

1966. World Tobogganing Championships, Friedrichroda.

E874	**E285**	10pf. green and olive	25	20
E875	-	20pf. blue and red	25	20
E876	-	25pf. indigo and blue	1·70	1·20

DESIGNS: 20pf. Men's double-seater; 25pf. Men's single seater.

E286 Electronic Punch-card Computer

1966. Leipzig Spring Fair. Multicoloured.

E877	10pf. Type E **286**	35	25
E878	15pf. Drilling and milling plant	1·30	35

E287 Soldier and National Gallery, Berlin

1966. 10th Anniv of National People's Army.

E879	**E287**	5pf. black, olive & yell	35	20
E880	-	10pf. black, ol & yell	35	20
E881	-	20pf. black, ol & yell	35	20
E882	-	25pf. black, ol & yell	1·60	1·20

DESIGNS: Soldier and—10pf. Brandenburg Gate; 20pf. Industrial plant; 25pf. Combine-harvester.

E288 J. A. Smoler (Sorb patriot and savant)

1966. 150th Birth Anniv of Jan Smoler.

E883	**E288**	20pf. black, red & blue	25	20
E884	-	25pf. black, red & blue	80	70

DESIGN: 25pf. House of the Sorbs, Bautzen.

E289 "Good Knowledge" Badge

1966. 20th Anniv of "Freie Deutsche Jugend" (Socialist Youth Movement).

E885	**E289**	20pf. multicoloured	80	30

E290 "Luna 9" on Moon

1966. Moon Landing of "Luna 9".

E886	**E290**	20pf. multicoloured	2·75	60

E291 Road Signs

1966. Road Safety.

E887	**E291**	10pf. red, bl & ultram	25	20
E888	-	15pf. black, yell & grn	25	20
E889	-	25pf. black, blue & bis	25	20
E890	-	50pf. black, yell & red	1·50	1·00

DESIGNS: 15pf. Child on scooter crossing in front of car; 25pf. Cyclist and hand-signal; 50pf. Motor cyclist, glass of beer and ambulance.

E292 Marx and Lenin Banner

1966. 20th Anniv of Socialist Unity Party (S.E.D.).

E891		5pf. multicoloured	25	20
E892	**E292**	10pf. yellow, blk & red	25	20
E893	-	15pf. black and green	35	20
E894	-	20pf. black and red	35	20
E895	-	25pf. black, yell & red	2·30	1·80

DESIGNS—VERT: 5pf. Party badge and demonstrators; 15pf. Marx, Engels and manifesto; 20pf. Pieck and Grotewohl. HORIZ: 25pf. Workers greeting Ulbricht.

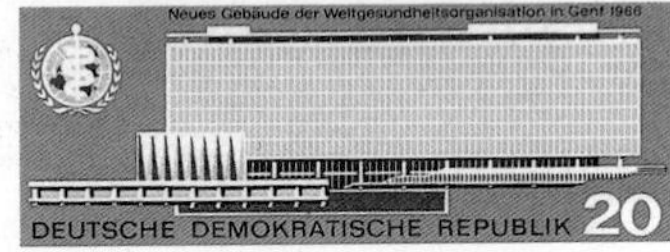

E293 W.H.O. Building

1966. Inaug of W.H.O. Headquarters, Geneva.

E896	**E293**	20pf. multicoloured	55	45

E294 Spreewald

1966. National Parks. Multicoloured.

E897	10pf. Type E **294**	25	20
E898	15pf. Konigsstuhl (Isle of Rugen)	25	20
E899	20pf. Sachsische Schweiz	25	20
E900	25pf. Westdarss	35	20
E901	30pf. Teufelsmauer	35	25
E902	50pf. Feldberg Lakes	2·50	1·50

E295 Lace "Flower"

1966. Plauen Lace. Floral Patterns as Type E 295.

E903	**E295**	10pf. myrtle and green	25	20
E904	-	20pf. indigo and blue	25	20
E905	-	25pf. red and rose	35	25
E906	-	50pf. violet and lilac	3·25	1·80

E296 Lily of the Valley

1966. Int Horticultural Show, Erfurt. Mult.

E907	20pf. Type E **296**	25	20
E908	25pf. Rhododendrons	35	25
E909	40pf. Dahlias	45	35
E910	50pf. Cyclamen	5·50	5·25

E297 Parachutist on Target

1966. 8th World Parachute Jumping Championships, Leipzig.

E911	**E297**	10pf. blue, black & bis	25	20
E912	-	15pf. multicoloured	80	80
E913	-	20pf. black, bistre & bl	25	20

DESIGNS: 15pf. Group descent; 20pf. Free fall.

E298 Hans Kahle and Music of "The Thalmann Column"

1966. 30th Anniv of International Brigade in Spain. Multicoloured.

E914	5pf. Type E **298**	35	25
E915	10pf.+5pf. W. Bredel and open-air class	35	25
E916	15pf. H. Beimler and Madrid street-fighting	35	25
E917	20pf.+10pf. H. Rau and march-past after Battle of Brunete	35	25
E918	25pf.+10pf. H. Marchwitza and soldiers	35	25
E919	40pf.+10pf. A. Becker and Ebro battle	1·90	1·80

E299 Canoeing

1966. World Canoeing Championships, Berlin. Multicoloured.

E920	10pf.+5pf. Type E **299**	35	25
E921	15pf. Kayak doubles	1·60	1·40

E300 Television Set

1966. Leipzig Autumn Fair. Multicoloured.

E922	10pf. Type E **300**	90	25
E923	15pf. Electric typewriter	2·00	35

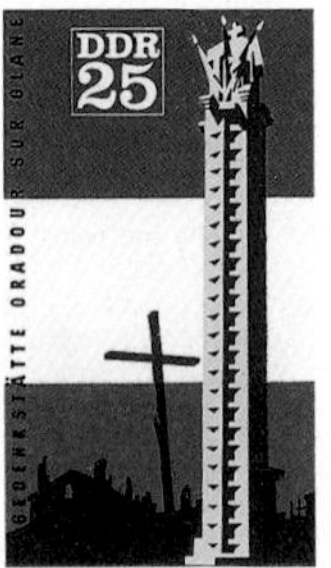

E301 Oradour Memorial

1966. Oradour-sur-Glane War Victims Commem.

E924	**E301**	25pf. black, blue & red	55	35

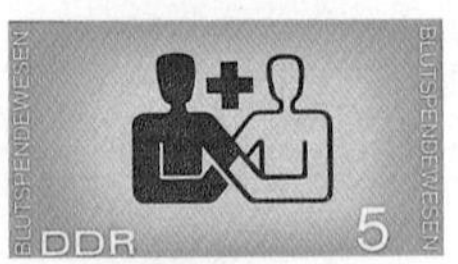

E302 "Blood Donors"

1966. International Health Co-operation.

E925	**E302**	5pf. red and green	35	25
E926	-	20pf.+10pf. red and violet	55	25
E927	-	40pf. red and blue	2·50	85

DESIGNS—HORIZ: 20pf. I.C.Y. emblem. VERT: 40pf. Health symbol.

E303 Weightlifting ("snatch")

1966. World and European Weightlifting Championships, Berlin.

E928	**E303**	15pf. black and brown	2·00	2·10
E929	-	20pf.+5pf. black and blue	55	25

DESIGN: 20pf. Weightlifting ("jerk").

E304 Congress Hall

1966. 6th Int Journalists' Congress, Berlin.

E930	**E304**	10pf. multicoloured	70	60
E931	-	20pf. yellow and blue	25	20

DESIGN—VERT: 20pf. Emblem of Int Organization of journalists.

1966. Provincial Costumes (2nd series). As Type E 261. Multicoloured.

E932	5pf. Altenburg (female)	55	30
E933	10pf. Altenburg (male)	55	30
E934	10pf. Mecklenburg (female)	55	30
E935	15pf. Mecklenburg (male)	55	30
E936	20pf. Magdeburger Borde (female)	2·75	2·50
E937	30pf. Magdeburger Borde (male)	2·75	2·50

E305 "Vietnam is Invincible"

1966. Aid for Vietnam.

E938	**E305**	20pf.+5pf. black and pink	55	35

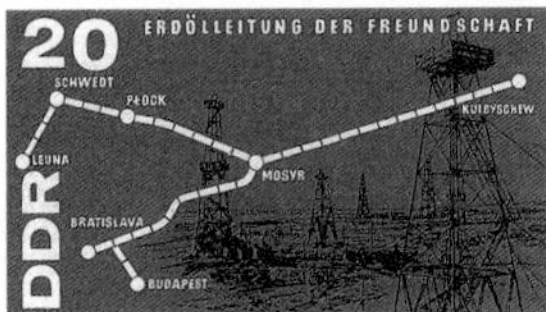

E306 Oil Rigs and Pipeline Map

1966. Inaug of Int "Friendship" Oil Pipeline.

E939	**E306**	20pf. black and red	30	25
E940	-	25pf. black and blue	1·30	60

DESIGN: 25pf. "Walter Ulbricht" Oil Works, Leuna and pipeline map.

E307 Black Phantom Tetra

1966. Aquarium Fishes. Multicoloured.

E941	5pf. Type E **307**	25	20
E942	10pf. Cardinal tetra	25	20
E943	15pf. Rio Grande cichlid	3·50	3·00
E944	20pf. Blue gularis	25	20
E945	25pf. Ramirez's dwarf cichlid	35	25
E946	40pf. Honey gourami	45	30

E308 "Horse" (detail from Ishtar Gate)

1966. Babylonian Art Treasures, Vorderasiatisches Museum, Berlin. Multicoloured.

E947	10pf. Type E **308**	25	20
E948	20pf. Mythological animal, Ishtar Gate	25	20
E949	25pf. Lion facing right (vert)	25	20
E950	50pf. Lion facing left (vert)	90	1·70

E309 The Wartburg from the East

1966. 900th Anniv of Wartburg Castle.

E951	**E309**	10pf.+5pf. slate	35	25
E952	-	20pf. green	35	25
E953	-	25pf. purple	80	55

DESIGNS: 20pf. Castle bailiwick; 25pf. Residence.

E310 "Gentiana pneumonanthe"

1966. Protected Plants (1st series). Mult.

E954	10pf. Type E **310**	25	20
E955	20pf. "Cephalanthera rubra"	35	25
E956	25pf. "Arnica montana"	1·90	1·30

See also Nos. E1177/82 and E1284/9.

E311 Son leaves Home

1966. Fairy Tales (1st series). "The Wishing Table". Multicoloured.

E957	5pf. Type E **311**	35	45

E958 10pf. Setting the table 35 45
E959 20pf. The thieving inn-keeper 90 1·10
E960 25pf. The magic donkey 90 1·10
E961 30pf. The cudgel in the sack 35 45
E962 50pf. Return of the son 35 45

See also Nos. E1045/50, E1147/52, E1171/6, E1266/71, E1437/42, E1525/30, E1623/8, E1711/16, E1811/13, E1902/7, E1996/2001 and E2092/7.

E312 Worlitz Castle

1967. Principal East German Buildings. (1st series). Multicoloured.

E964 5pf. Type E **312** 25 20
E965 10pf. Stralsund Town Hall (vert) 25 20
E966 15pf. Chorin Monastery (vert) 35 20
E967 20pf. Ribbeck House, Berlin 35 20
E968 25pf. Moritzburg, Zeitz (vert) 35 20
E969 40pf. Old Town Hall, Potsdam (vert) 1·80 1·30

See also Nos. E1100/3 and E1155/60.

E313 Rifle-shooting

1967. World Biathlon Championships, Altenburg.

E970 **E313** 10pf. blue, drab & mve 20 15
E971 - 20pf. olive, blue & grn 20 15
E972 - 25pf. green, blue & ol 1·00 70

DESIGNS: 20pf. Shooting on skis; 25pf. Riflemen racing on skis.

E314 "Multilock" Loom

1967. Leipzig Spring Fair.

E973 **E314** 10pf. green, grey & pur 25 20
E974 - 15pf. bistre & blue 1·10 35

DESIGN: 15pf. Zeiss tracking telescope.

E315 Mother and Child

1967. 20th Anniv of German Democratic Women's Federation.

E975 **E315** 20pf. grey, red and purple 35 25
E976 - 25pf. brown, turquoise and brown 90 1·10

DESIGN: 25pf. Professional woman.

E316 Industrial Control Desk

1967. Socialist Party Rally. Multicoloured.(a) 1st series.

E977 10pf. Type E **316** 35 25
E978 20pf. Ulbricht meeting workers 35 25
E979 25pf. Servicemen guarding industrial plants 35 25
E980 40pf. Agricultural workers and harvesters 80 1·20

Each with inset portraits of Marx, Engels and Lenin.

(b) 2nd series. As Type E 316 but vert.

E981 5pf. Agricultural worker 25 25
E982 10pf. Teacher and pupil 25 25
E983 15pf. Socialist family 55 55
E984 20pf. Servicemen 25 25

Each with inset portraits as above.

E317 "Portrait of a Girl" (after F Hodler)

1967. Dresden Gallery Paintings (1st series). Multicoloured.

E985 20pf. Type E **317** 25 20
E986 25pf. "Peter at the Zoo" (H. Hakenbeck) 25 20
E987 30pf. "Venetian Episode" (R. Bergander) 25 20
E988 40pf. "Tahitian Women" (Gauguin) (horiz) 25 20
E989 50pf. "The Grandchild" (J. Scholtz) 2·50 2·10
E990 70pf. "Cairn in the Snow" (C. D. Friedrich) (horiz) 45 35

See also Nos. E1114/19 and E1249/54.

E318 Barn Owl

1967. Protected Birds. Multicoloured.

E991 5pf. Type E **318** 25 20
E992 10pf. Common Crane 25 20
E993 20pf. Peregrine Falcon 25 20
E994 25pf. Northern bullfinches 25 20
E995 30pf. River kingfisher 5·25 3·50
E996 40pf. European roller 45 20

E319 Cycle Wheels

1967. 20th Warsaw–Berlin–Prague Cycle Race.

E997 **E319** 10pf. violet, black and yellow 25 20
E998 - 25pf. red and blue 70 60

DESIGN: 25pf. Racing cyclists.

E320 "Tom Cat"

1967. Int Children's Day. Multicoloured.

E999 5pf. Type E **320** 25 20
E1000 10pf. "Snow White" 25 20
E1001 15pf. "Fire Brigade" 25 20
E1002 20pf. "Cockerel" 25 20
E1003 25pf. "Vase of Flowers" 25 20
E1004 30pf. "Children Playing with Ball" 1·50 1·20

E321 "Girl with Grapes" (Gerard Dou)

1967. Paintings Missing from German National Galleries (after World War II).

E1005 **E 321** 5pf. blue 25 20
E1006 - 10pf. brown 25 20
E1007 - 20pf. green 25 20
E1008 - 25pf. purple 25 20
E1009 - 40pf. olive 25 20
E1010 - 50pf. sepia 2·20 1·80

DESIGNS—VERT: 25pf. "Portrait of W Schroeder-Devrient" (after K. Begas); 40pf. "Young Girl in Straw Hat" (after S. Bray); 50pf. "The Four Evangelists" (after Jordaens). HORIZ: 5pf. "Three Horsemen" (after Rubens); 20pf. "Spring Idyll" (after H. Thoma).

E322 Exhibition Emblem

1967. 15th Agricultural Exn, Markkleeberg.

E1011 **E322** 20pf. red, green and yellow 45 35

E323 Marie Curie (Birth Cent)

1967. Birth Anniversaries.

E1012 - 5pf. brown 35 20
E1013 **E323** 10pf. blue 35 20
E1014 - 20pf. red 35 20
E1015 - 25pf. sepia 35 20
E1016 - 40pf. green 1·10 85

PORTRAITS: 5pf. G. Herwegh (poet—150th); 20pf. Kathe Kollwitz (artist—cent); 25pf. J. J. Winckelmann (archaeologist—250th); 40pf. T. Storm (poet—150th).

E324 Jack of Diamonds

1967. German Playing-cards. Multicoloured.

E1017 5pf. Type E **324** 25 20
E1018 10pf. Jack of Hearts 25 20
E1019 20pf. Jack of Spades 25 20
E1020 25pf. Jack of Clubs 7·25 4·00

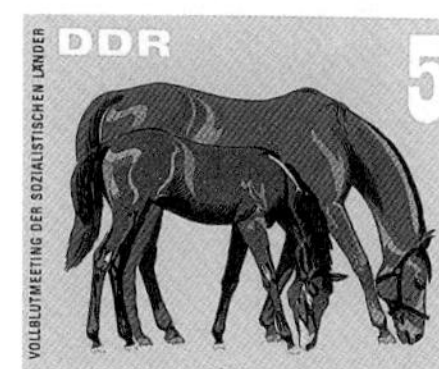

E325 Mare and Filly

1967. Thoroughbred Horse Meeting, Berlin. Multicoloured.

E1021 5pf. Type E **325** 30 20
E1022 10pf. Stallion 30 20
E1023 20pf. Horse-racing 35 25
E1024 50pf. Two fillies (vert) 4·25 3·00

E326 Kitchen Equipment

1967. Leipzig Autumn Fair. Multicoloured.

E1025 10pf. Type E **326** 55 25
E1026 15pf. Fur coat and "Interpelz" brand-mark 1·40 60

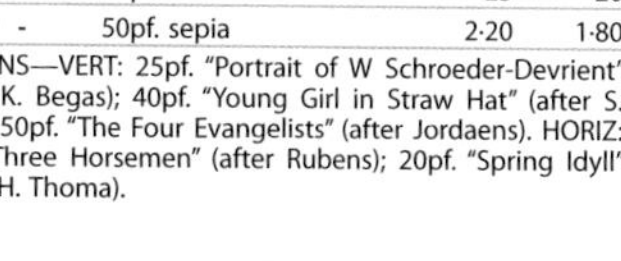

E327 Max Reichpietsch and "Friedrich der Grosse" (battleship), 1914–18

1967. 50th Anniv of Revolutionary Sailors' Movement. Multicoloured.

E1027 10pf. Type E **327** 25 20
E1028 15pf. Albin Kobis and "Prinzregent Luitpold" (battleship), 1914–18 1·70 85
E1029 20pf. Sailors' demonstration and "Seydlitz" (battle cruiser), 1914–18 55 20

E328 Kragujevac Memorial

1967. Victims of Kragujevac (Yugoslavia) Massacre.

E1030 **E328** 25pf. black, yellow and red 1·00 45

E329 Worker and Dam ("Electrification")

1967. 50th Anniv of October Revolution.

E1031 - 5pf. black, orange and red 25 20
E1032 **E 329** 10pf. black, red and bistre 25 20
E1033 - 15pf. black, red and grey 25 20
E1034 - 20pf. black, red and orange 45 20
E1035 - 40pf. black, red and orange 3·50 3·00
MSE1036 127×83 mm. Nos. E1034/5. Imperf (sold for 85pf.) 2·00 5·25

DESIGNS: 5pf. Worker and newspaper headline "Hands off Soviet Russia!"; 15pf. Treptow Memorial ("Victory over Fascism"); 20pf. German and Soviet soldiers ("Friendship"); 40pf. Lenin and "Aurora" (Russian cruiser) . Each with hammer and sickle.

E330 Martin Luther (from engraving by Lucas Cranach the Elder)

1967. 450th Anniv of Reformation.

E1037 **E330** 20pf. black & mauve 25 20
E1038 - 25pf. black and blue 25 20
E1039 - 40pf. black and bistre 3·00 1·40

DESIGNS—HORIZ: 25pf. Luther's house, Wittenberg. VERT: 40pf. Castle church, Wittenberg.

E331 Young Workers

1967. 10th "Masters of Tomorrow" Fair, Leipzig.

E1040 **E 331** 20pf. black, gold and blue 70 60
E1041 - 20pf. black, gold and blue 70 60
E1042 - 25pf. multicoloured 70 60

DESIGNS—VERT: No. E1041, Young man and woman. HORIZ: (51×29 mm): No. E1042, Presentation of awards.

E332 Goethe's House, Weimar

1967. Cultural Places.

E1043 **E332** 20pf. blk, brn & grey 35 20

E1044 - 25pf. olive, brn & yell 2·20 85

DESIGN: 25pf. Schiller's House, Weimar.

E333 Queen and Courtiers

1967. Fairy Tales (2nd series). "King Thrushbeard". Designs showing different scenes.

E1045 **E333** 5pf. multicoloured 35 35

E1046 - 10pf. multicoloured 35 35

E1047 - 15pf. multicoloured 1·40 1·40

E1048 - 20pf. multicoloured 1·40 1·40

E1049 - 25pf. multicoloured 35 35

E1050 - 30pf. multicoloured 35 35

E334 Peasants and Modern Farm Buildings

1967. 15th Anniv of Agricultural Co-operatives.

E1052 **E334** 10pf. sepia, green and olive 45 25

E335 Nutcracker and Two "Smokers"

1967. Popular Art of the Erzgebirge. Multicoloured.

E1053 10pf. Type E **335** 90 60

E1054 20pf. "Angel" and miner with candles (carved figures) 25 20

E336 Ice Skating

1968. Winter Olympic Games, Grenoble.

E1055 **E336** 5pf. blue, red and light blue 25 20

E1056 - 10pf.+5pf. blue, red and turquoise 25 20

E1057 - 15pf. multicoloured 25 20

E1058 - 20pf. ultramarine, red and blue 25 20

E1059 - 25pf. multicoloured 25 20

E1060 - 30pf. ultramarine, red and blue 4·50 1·90

DESIGNS: 10pf. Tobogganing; 15pf. Slalom; 20pf. Ice hockey; 25pf. Figure skating (pairs); 30pf. Cross-country skiing.

E337 Actinometer

1968. 75th Anniv of Potsdam Meteorological Observatory and World Meteorological Day (23 March).

E1061 **E337** 10pf. blk, red & pur 55 55

E1062 - 20pf. multicoloured 55 55

E1063 - 25pf. blk, yell & grn 55 55

DESIGNS—VERT: 25pf. Cornfield by day and night. HORIZ—(50×28 mm): 20pf. Satellite picture of clouds.

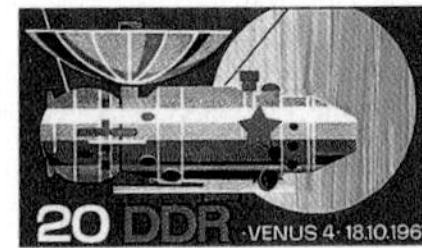

E338 "Venus 4"

1968. Soviet Space Achievements. Mult.

E1064 20pf. Type E **338** 25 20

E1065 25pf. Coupled satellites "Cosmos 186" and "188" 1·50 85

E339 "Illegal Struggle" (man, wife and child)

1968. Stained-glass Windows, Sachsenhausen National Memorial Museum. Multicoloured.

E1066 10pf. Type E **339** 25 20

E1067 20pf. "Liberation" 25 20

E1068 25pf. "Partisans' Struggle" 70 45

E340 Type DE1 Diesel-electric Locomotive (built for Brazil)

1968. Leipzig Spring Fair. Multicoloured.

E1069 10pf. Type E **340** 45 30

E1070 15pf. Deep sea trawler 1·30 60

E341 Gorky

1968. Birth Cent of Maxim Gorky (writer).

E1071 **E341** 20pf. purple and red 45 30

E1072 - 25pf. purple and red 90 55

DESIGN: 25pf. Fulmar (from "Song of the Stormy Petrel"—poem).

1968. Provincial Costumes (3rd series). As Type E 261. Multicoloured.

E1073 10pf. Hoyerswerda (female) 25 20

E1074 20pf. Schleife (female) 25 20

E1075 40pf. Crostwitz (female) 35 25

E1076 50pf. Spreewald (female) 3·75 1·50

E342 Common Pheasants

1968. Small Game. Multicoloured.

E1077 10pf. Type E **342** 25 25

E1078 15pf. Grey Partridges 25 25

E1079 20pf. Mallards 25 25

E1080 25pf. Greylag Geese 25 25

E1081 30pf. Wood Pigeon 25 25

E1082 40pf. Brown hares 4·00 7·00

E343 Karl Marx

1968. 150th Birth Anniv of Karl Marx.

E1083 - 10pf. black and green 35 35

E1084 **E343** 20pf. black, yell & red 35 35

E1085 - 25pf. blk, brn & yell 35 35

MSE1086 126×86 mm. Nos. E1083/5. Imperf 2·00 5·25

DESIGNS: 10pf. Title-page of "Communist Manifesto"; 25pf. Title-page of "Das Kapital".

E344 "Fritz Heckert" (after E. Hering)

1968. 7th Confederation of Free German Trade Unions Congress. Multicoloured.

E1087 10pf. Type E **344** 25 25

E1088 20pf. Young workers and new tenements 35 35

E345 Hammer and Anvil ("The right to work")

1968. Human Rights Year.

E1089 **E345** 5pf. mauve & purple 25 20

E1090 - 10pf. bistre & brown 25 20

E1091 - 25pf. blue & turq 1·00 70

DESIGNS: 10pf. Tree and Globe ("The right to live"); 25pf. Dove and Sun ("The right to peace").

E346 Vietnamese Mother and Child

1968. Aid for Vietnam.

E1092 **E346** 10pf.+5pf. mult 35 25

E347 Angling (World Angling Championships, Gustrow)

1968. Sporting Events.

E1093 **E347** 20pf. blue, grn & red 25 20

E1094 - 20pf. blue, turq & grn 25 20

E1095 - 20pf. purple, red & bl 1·10 95

DESIGNS: No. E1094, Sculling (European Women's Rowing Championships, Berlin); No. E1095, High jumping (2nd European Youth Athletic Competitions).

E348 Brandenburg Gate and Torch

1968. German Youth Sports Day. Mult.

E1096 10pf. Type E **348** 25 20

E1097 25pf. Stadium plan and torch 1·30 85

E349 Festival Emblem

1968. Peace Festival, Sofia.

E1098 **E349** 20pf.+5pf. mult 45 25

E1099 **E349** 25pf. multicoloured 1·00 65

1968. Principal East German Buildings (2nd series). As Type E 312. Multicoloured.

E1100 10pf. Town Hall, Wernigerode 25 20

E1101 20pf. Moritzburg Castle, Dresden 25 20

E1102 25pf. Town Hall, Greifswald 25 20

E1103 30pf. New Palace, Potsdam 1·00 1·30

DESIGN SIZES—VERT: 10pf., 25pf. (24×29 mm). HORIZ: 20pf., 30pf. (51½×29½ mm).

E350 Walter Ulbricht

1968. 75th Birthday of Walter Ulbricht (Chairman of Council of State).

E1104 **E350** 20pf. black, red and orange 55 30

E351 Ancient Rostock

1968. 750th Anniv of Rostock. Mult.

E1105 20pf. Type E **351** 25 20

E1106 25pf. Rostock, 1968 75 65

E352 Dr K. Landsteiner (physician and pathologist, birth cent)

1968. Celebrities' Annivs. (1st series).

E1107 **E352** 10pf. grey 25 20

E1108 - 15pf. black 25 20

E1109 - 20pf. brown 25 20

E1110 - 25pf. blue 25 20

E1111 - 40pf. red 1·10 85

DESIGNS: 15pf. Dr. E. Lasker (chess master, birth cent); 20pf. Hans Eisler (composer, 70th birth anniv); 25pf. Ignaz Semmelweis (physician, 150th birth anniv); 40pf. Max von Pettenkofer (hygienist, 150th birth anniv).

See also Nos. E1161/4 and E1256/61.

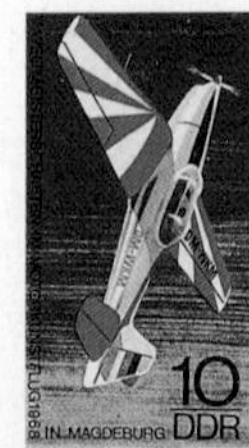

E353 Zlin Z-226 Trener 6 DM-WKM looping

1968. Aerobatics World Championships, Magdeburg. Multicoloured.

E1112 10pf. Type E **353** 25 20

E1113 25pf. Stunt flying 75 60

E354 "At the Seaside" (Womacka)

1968. Dresden Gallery Paintings (2nd series). Multicoloured.

E1114 10pf. Type E **354** 25 20

E1115 15pf. "Peasants Mowing Mountain Meadow" (Egger-Lienz) 25 20

E1116 20pf. "Portrait of a Farmer's Wife" (Liebl) (vert) 25 20

E1117 40pf. "Portrait of my Daughter" (Venturelli) (vert) 55 25

E1118 50pf. "High-School Girl" (Michaelis) (vert) 55 25

E1119 70pf. "Girl with Guitar" (Castelli) (vert) 2·75 1·80

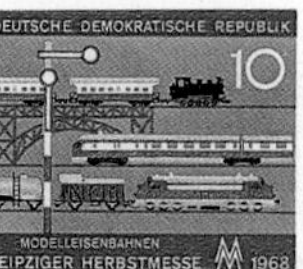

E355 Model Trains

1968. Leipzig Autumn Fair.
E1120 **E355** 10pf. multicoloured 45 35

E356 Spremberg Dam

1968. East German Post-War Dams. Multicoloured.

E1121	5pf. Type E **356**	25	20
E1122	10pf. Pohl Dam (vert)	25	20
E1123	15pf. Ohra Valley Dam (vert)	70	70
E1124	20pf. Rappbode Dam	35	35

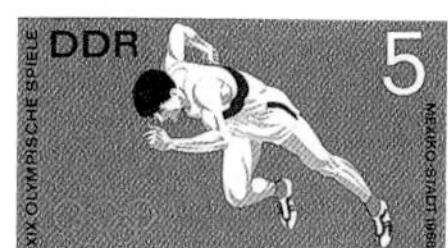

E357 Sprinting

1968. Olympic Games, Mexico. Multicoloured.

E1125	5pf. Type E **357**	25	20
E1126	10pf.+5pf. Pole-vaulting (vert)	25	20
E1127	20pf.+10pf. Football (vert)	25	20
E1128	25pf. Gymnastics (vert)	25	20
E1129	40pf. Water-polo (vert)	35	25
E1130	70pf. Sculling	2·00	1·90

E358 Breendonk Memorial, Belgium

1968. Breendonk War Victims Commem.
E1131 **E358** 25pf. multicoloured 55 25

E359 "Cicindela campestris"

1968. "Useful Beetles". Multicoloured.

E1132	10pf. Type E **359**	25	20
E1133	15pf. "Cychrus caraboides"	25	20
E1134	20pf. "Adalia bipunctata"	25	20
E1135	25pf. "Carabus arvensis" ("arcensis")	2·75	2·50
E1136	30pf. "Hister bipustulatus"	35	25
E1137	40pf. "Clerus mutillarius" ("Pseudoclerops mutillarius")	35	25

E360 Lenin and Letter to Spartacus Group

1968. 50th Anniv of German November Revolution.

E1138	**E 360**	10pf. black, red and yellow	25	20
E1139	-	20pf. black, red and yellow	25	20
E1140	-	25pf. black, red and yellow	70	65

DESIGNS: 20pf. Revolutionaries and title of Spartacus newspaper "Die Rote Fahne"; 25pf. Karl Liebknecht and Rose Luxemburg.

E361 "Lailio-cattleya alba rubra" ("Maggie Raphaela")

1968. Orchids. Multicoloured.

E1141	5pf. Type E **361**	25	20
E1142	10pf. "Paphiopedilum albertianum"	25	20
E1143	15pf. "Cattleya fabia"	25	20
E1144	20pf. "Cattleya aclaniae"	25	20
E1145	40pf. "Sobralia macrantha"	35	25
E1146	50pf. "Dendrobium alpha"	2·75	1·90

E362 Trying on the Boots

1968. Fairy Tales (3rd series). "Puss in Boots". As Type E 362. Designs showing different scenes.

E1147	5pf. multicoloured	25	25
E1148	10pf. multicoloured	25	25
E1149	15pf. multicoloured	1·40	1·40
E1150	20pf. multicoloured	1·40	1·40
E1151	25pf. multicoloured	25	25
E1152	30pf. multicoloured	25	25

E363 Young Pioneers

1968. 20th Anniv of Ernst Thalmann's "Young Pioneers." Multicoloured.

E1153	10pf. Type E **363**	25	20
E1154	15pf. Young pioneers (diff)	95	45

1969. Principal East German Buildings (3rd series). As Type E 312. Multicoloured.

E1155	5pf. Town Hall, Tangermunde (vert)	25	20
E1156	10pf. State Opera House, Berlin	25	20
E1157	20pf. Rampart Pavilion, Dresden Castle (vert)	25	20
E1158	25pf. Patrician's House, Luckau (vert)	1·40	95
E1159	30pf. Dornburg Castle	25	20
E1160	40pf. "Zum Stockfisch" Inn, Erfurt (vert)	35	25

1969. Celebrities' Annivs. (2nd series). As Type E 352.

E1161	10pf. olive	25	20
E1162	20pf. brown	25	20
E1163	25pf. blue	1·10	60
E1164	40pf. brown	25	20

DESIGNS: 10pf. M. A. Nexo (Danish poet—birth cent.); 20pf. O. Nagel (painter—75th birth anniv); 25pf. A. von Humboldt (naturalist—bicent. of birth); 40pf. T. Fontane (writer—150th birth anniv).

E364 Pedestrian Crossing

1969. Road Safety. Multicoloured.

E1165	5pf. Type E **364**	25	20
E1166	10pf. Traffic lights	25	20
E1167	20pf. Class 103 electric locomotive and railway crossing sign	25	20
E1168	25pf. Motor-vehicle overtaking	75	60

E365 "E-512" Combine- harvester

1969. Leipzig Spring Fair. Multicoloured.

E1169	10pf. Type E **365**	25	20
E1170	15pf. "Planeta-Variani" lithograph printing-press	35	30

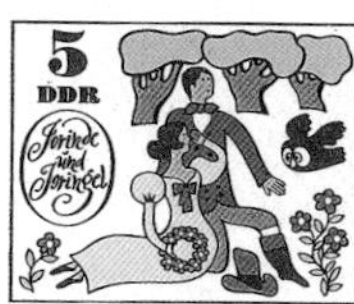

E366 Jorinde and Joringel

1969. Fairy Tales (4th series). "Jorinde and Joringel". As Type E 366, showing different scenes.

E1171	5pf. multicoloured	25	35
E1172	10pf. multicoloured	25	35
E1173	15pf. multicoloured	70	85
E1174	20pf. multicoloured	70	85
E1175	25pf. multicoloured	25	35
E1176	30pf. multicoloured	25	35

E367 Spring Snowflake

1969. Protected Plants (2nd series). Mult.

E1177	5pf. Type E **367**	25	20
E1178	10pf. Yellow pheasant's-eye ("Adonis vernalis")	25	20
E1179	15pf. Globe flower ("Trollius europaeus")	25	20
E1180	20pf. Martagon lily ("Lilium martagon")	25	20
E1181	25pf. Sea holly ("Eryngium maritmum")	3·75	2·40
E1182	30pf. "Dactylorchis latifolia"	45	25

See also Nos. E1284/9.

E368 Plantation of Young Conifers

1969. Forest Fires Prevention. Mult.

E1183	5pf. Type E **368**	35	25
E1184	10pf. Lumber, and resin extraction	35	25
E1185	20pf. Forest stream	35	25
E1186	25pf. Woodland camp	2·50	1·40

E369 Symbols of the Societies

1969. 50th Anniv of League of Red Cross Societies. Multicoloured.

E1187	10pf. Type E **369**	35	25
E1188	15pf. Similar design with symbols in oblong	1·70	70

E370 Erythrite (Schneeberg)

1969. East German Minerals. Multicoloured.

E1189	5pf. Type E **370**	25	20
E1190	10pf. Fluorite (Halsbrucke)	25	20
E1191	15pf. Galena (Neudorf)	25	20
E1192	20pf. Smoky Quartz (Lichtenberg)	25	20
E1193	25pf. Calcite (Niederrabenstein)	1·10	95
E1194	50pf. Silver (Freiberg)	35	25

E371 Women and Symbols

1969. 2nd D.D.R. Women's Congress.

E1195	**E371**	20pf. red and blue	25	20
E1196	-	25pf. blue and red	1·30	55

DESIGN: 25pf. Woman and Symbols (different).

1969. As Nos. E586/7 (Ulbricht), but with face values expressed in "M" (Mark).

E1197	1M. green	55	1·80
E1198	2M. brown	70	2·00

E372 Badge of D.D.R. Philatelists' Association

1969. 20th Anniv of D.D.R. Stamp Exhibition, Magdeburg (1st issue).
E1199 **E372** 10pf. gold, blue and red 45 25

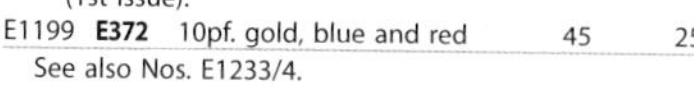
See also Nos. E1233/4.

E373 Armed Volunteers

1969. Aid for Vietnam.
E1200 **E373** 10pf.+5pf. mult 45 25

E374 "Development of Youth"

1969. Int Peace Meeting, East Berlin. Mult.

E1201	10pf. Type E **374**	85	1·20
E1202	20pf.+5pf. Berlin landmarks (50×28 mm)	85	1·20
E1203	25pf. "Workers of the World"	85	1·20

E375 Inaugural Ceremony

1969. 5th Gymnastics and Athletic Meeting, Leipzig. Multicoloured.

E1204	5pf. Type E **375**	25	20
E1205	10pf.+5pf. Gymnastics	25	20
E1206	15pf. Athletes' parade	25	20
E1207	20pf.+5pf. "Sport" Art Exhibition	25	20
E1208	25pf. Athletic events	2·20	85
E1209	30pf. Presentation of colours	25	20

E376 Pierre de Coubertin (from bust by W. Forster)

1969. 75th Anniv of Pierre de Coubertin's Revival of Olympic Games' Movement.

E1210	**E376**	10pf. sepia, black & bl	25	20
E1211	-	25pf. sepia, blk & red	1·10	1·10

DESIGN: 25pf. Coubertin monument, Olympia.

E377 Knight

1969. World Sports Championships. Mult.

E1212	**E377**	20pf. gold, red & pur	35	25
E1213	-	20pf. multicoloured	35	25
E1214	-	20pf. multicoloured	35	25

DESIGNS AND EVENTS: No. E1212, 16th World Students' Team Chess Championship, Dresden; No. E1213, Cycle Wheel (World Covered Court Cycling Championships, Erfurt); No. E1214, Ball and net (2nd World Volleyball Cup).

E378 Fair Display Samples

1969. Leipzig Autumn Fair.

E1215	**E378**	10pf. multicoloured	35	35

E379 Rostock

1969. 20th Anniv of German Democratic Republic. (1st issue). Multicoloured.

E1216	10pf. Type E **379**	25	20
E1217	10pf. Neubrandenburg	25	20
E1218	10pf. Potsdam	25	20
E1219	10pf. Eisenhuttenstadt	25	20
E1220	10pf. Hoyerswerda	25	20
E1221	10pf. Magdeburg	25	20
E1222	10pf. Halle-Neustadt	25	20
E1223	10pf. Suhl	25	20
E1224	10pf. Dresden	25	20
E1225	10pf. Leipzig	25	20
E1226	10pf. Karl-Marx Stadt	25	20
E1227	10pf. East Berlin	25	20
MSE1228	88×110 mm. 1m. East Berlin and D.D.R. emblem (30×52 mm)	2·75	5·50

E380 Flags and Rejoicing Crowd (image scaled to 59% of original size)

1969. 20th Anniv of German Democratic Republic (2nd issue). Sheet 110×154 mm.

MSE1229	E **380** 1m. multicoloured	3·00	5·00

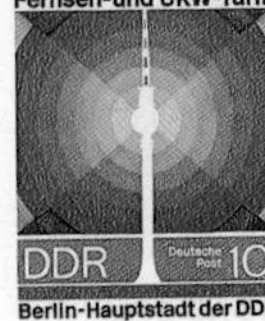

E381 T.V. Tower, East Berlin

1969. 20th Anniv of German Democratic Republic (3rd issue). Completion of East Berlin T.V. Tower. Type E 381 and similar vert designs. Multicoloured.

E1230	10pf. Type E **381**	25	20
E1231	20pf. "Globe" of Tower on T.V. screen	35	25
MSE1232	96×115 mm. 1m. T.V. Tower and receiver	2·10	6·00

The design of No. **MS**E1232 is larger, 21½×60½ mm.

E382 O. von Guericke Memorial, Cathedral and Hotel International, Magdeburg

1969. 20th Anniv of D.D.R. Stamp Exhibition, Magdeburg (2nd issue). Multicoloured.

E1233	20pf. Type E **382**	25	20
E1234	40pf.+10pf. Von Guericke's vacuum experiment	1·60	1·00

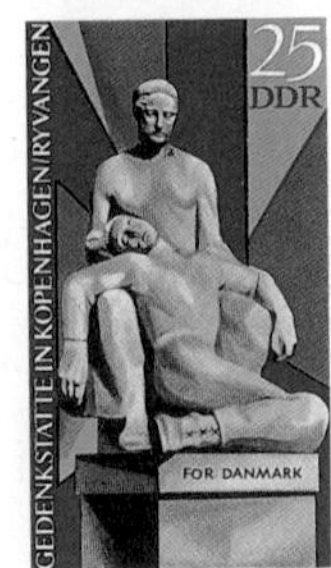

E383 Ryvangen Memorial

1969. War Victims' Memorial, Ryvangen (Copenhagen).

E1235	**E383**	25pf. multicoloured	1·00	25

E384 U.F.I. Emblem

1969. 36th Int Fairs Union (U.F.I.) Congress, Leipzig.

E1236	**E384**	10pf. multicoloured	25	25
E1237	**E384**	15pf. multicoloured	2·20	50

E385 I.L.O. Emblem

1969. 50th Anniv of I.L.O.

E1238	**E385**	20pf. silver and green	25	20
E1239	**E385**	25pf. silver & mauve	2·20	50

E386 University Seal and Building

1969. 550th Anniv of Rostock University. Multicoloured.

E1240	10pf. Type E **386**	35	20
E1241	15pf. Steam-turbine rotor and curve (University emblem)	1·80	40

E387 "Horseman" Pastry-mould

1969. Lausitz Folk Art.

E1242	**E387**	10pf. brn, blk & flesh	1·50	1·50
E1243	-	20pf.+5pf. mult	50	50
E1244	-	50pf. multicoloured	2·40	2·40

DESIGNS: 20pf. Plate; 50pf. Pastry in form of Negro couple.

E388 Antonov An-24B

1969. Interflug Aircraft. Multicoloured.

E1245	20pf. Type E **388**	25	20
E1246	25pf. Ilyushin Il-18	1·70	1·50
E1247	30pf. Tupolev Tu-134	25	25
E1248	50pf. Mil Mi-8 helicopter DM-SPA	35	25

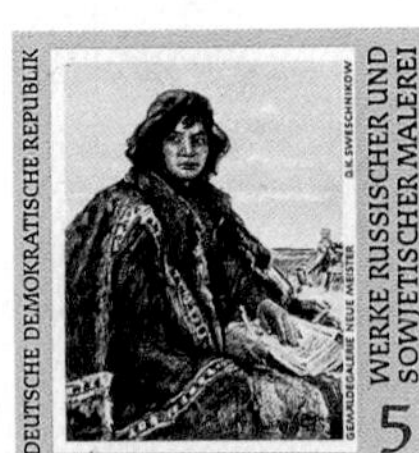

E389 "Siberian Teacher" (Svechnikov)

1969. Dresden Gallery Paintings (3rd series). Multicoloured.

E1249	5pf. Type E **389**	25	20
E1250	10pf. "Steel-worker" (Serov)	25	20
E1251	20pf. "Still Life" (Aslamasjan)	25	20
E1252	25pf. "A Warm Day" (Romas)	1·50	1·50
E1253	40pf. "Springtime Again" (Kabatchek)	35	25
E1254	50pf. "Man by the River" (Makovsky)	35	25

1970. Coil Stamp. As Nos. E577 etc, but value expressed in "M".

E1255	**E196**	1m. olive	1·20	4·25

1970. Celebrities Annivs. (3rd series). As Type E 352.

E1256	5pf. blue	35	20
E1257	10pf. brown	35	20
E1258	15pf. blue	35	20
E1259	20pf. purple	50	20
E1260	25pf. blue	3·00	1·00
E1261	40pf. red	60	25

DESIGNS: 5pf. E. Barlach (sculptor and playwright; birth cent); 10pf. J. Gutenberg (printer; 500th death anniv) (1968); 15pf. K. Tucholsky (author; 80th birth anniv); 20pf. Beethoven (birth bicent); 25pf. F. Holderlin (poet; birth bicent); 40 pf G. W. F. Hegel (philosopher; birth bicent).

E390 Red fox

1970. Int Fur Auction, Leipzig. Mult.

E1262	10pf. Rabbit	25	20
E1263	20pf. Type E **390**	25	20
E1264	25pf. European mink	4·00	3·75
E1265	40pf. Common hamster	50	25

E391 "Little Brother and Little Sister"

1970. Fairy Tales (5th series). "Little Brother and Little Sister".

E1266	**E 391**	5pf. multicoloured	35	50
E1267	-	10pf. multicoloured	35	50
E1268	-	15pf. multicoloured	85	1·00
E1269	-	20pf. multicoloured	85	1·00
E1270	-	25pf. multicoloured	35	50
E1271	-	30pf. multicoloured	35	50

DESIGNS: 10pf. to 30pf. showing different scenes.

E392 Telephone and Electrical Switchgear

1970. Leipzig Spring Fair. Multicoloured.

E1272	10pf. Type E **392**	25	20
E1273	15pf. High-voltage transformer (vert)	75	35

E393 Horseman's Gravestone (A.D. 700)

1970. Archaeological Discoveries.

E1274	**E393**	10pf. olive, blk & grn	35	25
E1275	-	20pf. black, yell & red	35	25
E1276	-	25pf. grn, blk & yell	1·20	1·70
E1277	-	40pf. chestnut, black and brown	35	25

DESIGNS: 20pf. Helmet (A.D. 500); 25pf. Bronze basin (1000 B.C.); 40pf. Clay drum (2500 B.C.).

E394 Lenin and "Iskra" (= the Spark) press

1970. Birth Centenary of Lenin. Multicoloured.

E1278	10pf. Type E **394**	25	20
E1279	20pf. Lenin and Clara Zetkin	25	20
E1280	25pf. Lenin and "State and Revolution" (book)	2·75	2·20
E1281	40pf. Lenin Monument, Eisleben	25	20
E1282	70pf. Lenin Square, East Berlin	50	25
MSE1283	118×84 mm. 1m. Lenin (vert)	2·75	6·00

1970. Protected Plants (3rd series). Vert designs as Type E 367. Multicoloured.

E1284	10pf. Sea kale ("Crambe maritima")	25	20
E1285	20pf. Pasque flower ("Pulsatilla vulgaris")	25	20
E1286	25pf. Fringed gentian ("Gentiana ciliata")	2·40	2·75
E1287	30pf. Military orchid ("Orchis militaris")	25	25
E1288	40pf. Labrador tea ("Ledum palustre")	35	25
E1289	70pf. Round-leaved wintergreen ("Pyrola rotundifolia")	50	35

E395 Capture of the Reichstag, 1945

1970. 25th Anniv of "Liberation from Fascism". Multicoloured.

E1290	10pf. Type E **395**	35	20
E1291	20pf. Newspaper headline, Kremlin and State Building, East Berlin	35	20
E1292	25pf. C.M.E.A. Building, Moscow and flags	1·80	1·00
MSE1293	135×105 mm. 70pf. Buchenwald Monument (horiz)	2·40	5·00

E396 Shortwave Aerial

1970. 25th Anniv of D.D.R. Broadcasting Service. Multicoloured.

E1294	10pf. Type E **396**	85	85
E1295	15pf. Radio Station, East Berlin (horiz) (50×28 mm)	1·20	1·20

E397 Globe and Ear of Corn

1970. 5th World Corn and Bread Congress, Dresden. Multicoloured.

E1296	20pf. Type E **397**	1·20	1·20
E1297	25pf. Palace of Culture and ear of corn	1·20	1·20

E398 Fritz Heckert Medal

1970. 25th Annivs of German Confederation of Trade Unions and World Trade Union Federation ("Federation Syndicale Mondiale"). Mult.

E1298	20pf. Type E **398**	25	20
E1299	25pf. F.S.M. Emblem	85	75

E399 Gods Amon, Shu and Tefnut

1970. Sudanese Archaeological Excavations by Humboldt University Expedition. Multicoloured.

E1300	10pf. Type E **399**	25	20
E1301	15pf. King Arnekhamani	25	20
E1302	20pf. Cattle frieze	25	20
E1303	25pf. Prince Arka	1·50	1·00
E1304	30pf. God Arensnuphis (vert)	25	20
E1305	40pf. War elephants and prisoners	25	20
E1306	50pf. God Apedemak	25	20

The above designs reproduce carvings unearthed at the Lions' Temple, Musawwarat, Sudan.

E400 Road Patrol

1970. 25th Anniv of "Deutsche Volkspolizei" (police force). Multicoloured.

E1307	5pf. Type E **400**	35	25
E1308	10pf. Policewoman with children	35	25
E1309	15pf. Radio patrol car	35	25
E1310	20pf. Railway policeman and Class SVT18.16 diesel-hydraulic locomotive	35	25
E1311	25pf. River police in patrol boat	3·00	60

E401 D.K.B. Emblem

1970. 25th Anniv of "Deutscher Kulturbund" (cultural assn).

E1312	**E401**	10pf. brown, silver and blue	3·25	3·75
E1313	-	25pf. brown, gold and blue	3·25	3·75

DESIGN: 25pf. Johannes Becher medal.

E402 Arms of D.D.R. and Poland

1970. 20th Anniv of Gorlitz Agreement on Oder-Neisse Border.

E1314	**E402**	20pf. multicoloured	50	30

E403 Vaulting

1970. 3rd Children and Young People's Sports Days. Multicoloured.

E1315	10pf. Type E **403**	25	20
E1316	20pf.+5pf. Hurdling	60	25

E404 Boy Pioneer with Neckerchief

1970. 6th Young Pioneers Meeting. Cottbus. Multicoloured.

E1317	10pf.+5pf. Type E **404**	35	50
E1318	25pf.+5pf. Girl pioneer with neckerchief	35	50

Nos. E1317/18 were issued together, se-tenant, forming a composite design.

E405 Cecilienhof Castle

1970. 25th Anniv of Potsdam Agreement.

E1319	**E405**	10pf. yellow, red and black	35	45
E1320	-	20pf. black, red and yellow	35	45
E1321	-	25pf. black and red	35	45

DESIGNS—VERT: 20pf. "Potsdam Agreement" in four languages. HORIZ (77×28 mm): 25pf. Conference delegates around the table.

E406 Pocket-watch and Wristwatch

1970. Leipzig Autumn Fair.

E1322	**E406**	10pf. multicoloured	50	25

E407 T. Neubauer and M. Poser

1970. "Anti-Fascist Resistance".

E1323	**E407**	20pf. purple, red & bl	25	25
E1324	-	25pf. olive and red	35	35

DESIGN—VERT: 25pf. "Motherland"—detail from Soviet War Memorial, Treptow, Berlin.

E408 Pres. Ho-Chi-Minh

1970. Aid for Vietnam and Ho-Chi-Minh. Commemoration.

E1325	**E408**	20pf.+5pf. black, red and pink	60	25

E409 Compass and Map

1970. World "Orienteering" Championships. East Germany. Multicoloured.

E1326	10pf. Type E **409**	25	20

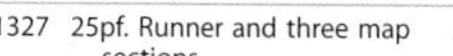

E1327	25pf. Runner and three map sections	1·70	50

OTTO NAGEL 1935

10 DDR

E410 "Forester Scharf's Birthday" (Nagel)

1970. "The Art of Otto Nagel, Kathe Kollwitz and Ernst Barlach".

E1328	**E410**	10pf. multicoloured	25	20
E1329	-	20pf. multicoloured	25	20
E1330	-	25pf. brown & mauve	1·50	1·60
E1331	-	30pf. black and pink	25	20
E1332	-	40pf. black and yellow	25	20
E1333	-	50pf. black and yellow	35	25

DESIGNS: 20pf. "Portrait of a Young Girl" (Nagel); 25pf. "No More War" (Kollwitz); 30pf. "Mother and Child" (Kollwitz); 40pf. Sculptured head from Gustrow Cenotaph (Barlach); 50pf. "The Flute-player" (Barlach).

E411 "The Little Trumpeter" (Weineck Memorial, Halle)

1970. 2nd National Youth Stamp Exhibition, Karl-Marx-Stadt. Multicoloured.

E1334	10pf. Type E **411**	25	50
E1335	15pf.+5pf. East German 25pf. stamp of 1959	25	50

E412 Flags Emblem

1970. "Comrades-in-Arms". Warsaw Pact Military Manoeuvres.

E1336	**E412**	10pf. multicoloured	25	25
E1337	**E412**	20pf. multicoloured	35	35

E413 Musk Ox

1970. Animals in East Berlin "Tierpark" (Zoo). Multicoloured.

E1338	10pf. Type E **413**	50	25
E1339	15pf. Whale-headed Stork	50	25
E1340	20pf. Addax	85	50
E1341	25pf. Sun bear	7·25	7·25

E414 U.N. Emblem and Headquarters, New York

1970. 25th Anniv of United Nations.

E1342	**E414**	20pf. multicoloured	75	35

E415 Engels

1970. 150th Birth Anniv of Friedrich Engels.

E1343	**E415**	10pf. black, grey and orange	35	20
E1344	-	20pf. blk, grn & orge	35	20
E1345	-	25pf. blk, red & orge	1·80	1·00

DESIGNS: 20pf. Engels, Marx and "Communist Manifesto"; 25pf. Engels and "Anti-Duhring".

DDR 5

E416 "Epiphyllum hybr"

1970. Cacti Cultivation in D.D.R. Mult.

E1346	5pf. Type E **416**	25	20
E1347	10pf. "Astrophytum myriostigma"	25	20
E1348	15pf. "Echinocereus salmdyckianus"	25	20
E1349	20pf. "Selenicereus grandiflorus"	25	20
E1350	25pf. "Hamatoc setispinus"	2·40	2·20
E1351	30pf. "Mamillaria boolii"	30	20

1970. Birth Bicentenary of Beethoven. As No. E1259, but colour and face value changed, in sheet 81×55 mm.

MSE1352	1m. green	2·40	3·00

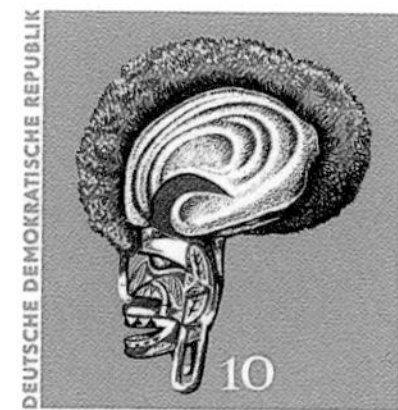

E417 Dancer's Mask, Bismarck Archipelago

1971. Exhibits from the Ethnological Museum, Leipzig.

E1353	**E417**	10pf. multicoloured	25	20
E1354	-	20pf. brown & orange	25	20
E1355	-	25pf. multicoloured	1·10	85
E1356	-	40pf. brown and red	35	20

DESIGNS: 20pf. Bronze head, Benin; 25pf. Tea-pot, Thailand; 40pf. Zapotec earthenware Jaguar-god, Mexico.

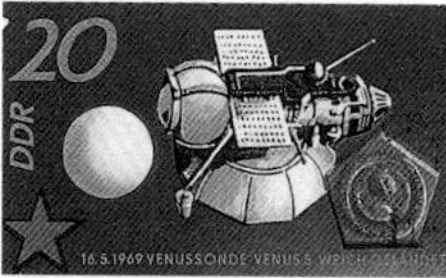

E418 "Venus 5"

1971. Soviet Space Research. Multicoloured.

E1357	20pf. Type E **418**	35	50
E1358	20pf. Orbital space station	35	50
E1359	20pf. "Luna 10" and "Luna 16"	75	85
E1360	20pf. Various "Soyuz" spacecraft	75	85
E1361	20pf. "Proton 1" satellite and "Vostok" rocket	75	85
E1362	20pf. "Molniya 1" communications satellite	75	85
E1363	20pf. Gagarin and "Vostok 1"	35	50
E1364	20pf. Leonov in space	35	50

E419 K. Liebknecht

1971. Birth Centenaries of Karl Liebknecht and Rosa Luxemburg (revolutionaries).

E1365 **E419** 20pf. mauve, gold and black 60 60
E1366 - 25pf. mauve, gold and black 60 60

DESIGN: 25pf. Rosa Luxemburg.

E420 J. R. Becher (poet)

1971. Celebrities' Birth Anniversaries.

E1367 **E420** 5pf. brown 25 20
E1368 - 10pf. blue 25 20
E1369 - 15pf. black 25 20
E1370 - 20pf. purple 25 20
E1371 - 25pf. green 1·00 85
E1372 - 50pf. blue 35 25

DESIGNS: 5pf. (80th birth anniv); 10pf. H. Mann (writer—birth cent); 15pf. J. Heartfield (artist—80th birth anniv); 20pf. W. Bredel (70th birth anniv); 25pf. F. Mehring (politician—125th birth anniv); 50pf. J. Kepler (astronomer—400th birth anniv).

See also Nos. E1427 and E1451/5.

E421 Soldier and Army Badge

1971. 15th Anniv of National People's Army.

E1373 **E421** 20pf. multicoloured 50 30

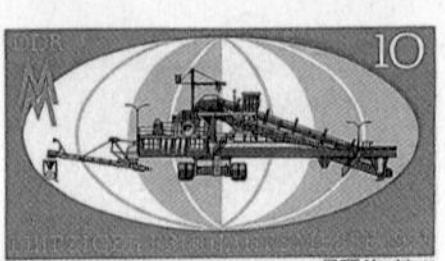

E422 "Sket" Mobile Ore-crusher

1971. Leipzig Spring Fair. Multicoloured.

E1374 10pf. Type E **422** 25 20
E1375 15pf. Dredger "Takraf" 25 20

E423 Proclamation of the Commune

1971. Centenary of Paris Commune.

E1376 **E423** 10pf. black, brown and red 35 25
E1377 - 20pf. black, brown and red 35 25
E1378 - 25pf. black, brown and red 80 75
E1379 - 30pf. black, grey and red 35 25

DESIGNS: 20pf. Women at the Place Blanche barricade; 25pf. Cover of "L'Internationale"; 30pf. Title page of Karl Marx's "The Civil War in France".

E424 "Lunokhod 1" on Moon's Surface

1971. Moon Mission of "Lunokhod 1".

E1380 **E424** 20pf. turquoise, blue and red 85 50

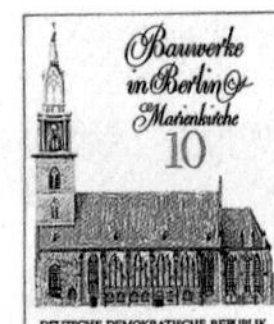

E425 St. Mary's Church

1971. Berlin Buildings. Multicoloured.

E1381 10pf. Type E **425** 25 20
E1382 15pf. Kopenick Castle (horiz) 25 20
E1383 20pf. Old Library (horiz) 25 20
E1384 25pf. Ermeler House 4·00 3·50
E1385 50pf. New Guardhouse (horiz) 35 25
E1386 70pf. National Gallery (horiz) 50 25

E426 "The Discus-thrower"

1971. 20th Anniv of D.D.R. National Olympics Committee.

E1387 **E426** 20pf. multicoloured 1·10 35

E427 Handclasp and XXV Emblem

1971. 25th Anniv of Socialist Unity Party.

E1388 **E427** 20pf. black, red and gold 50 25

E428 Schleife Costume

1971. Sorbian Dance Costumes. Mult.

E1389 10pf. Type E **428** 25 25
E1390 20pf. Hoyerswerda 25 25
E1391 25pf. Cottbus 1·00 1·20
E1392 40pf. Kamenz 35 35

For 10pf. and 20pf. in smaller size, see Nos. E1443/4.

E429 Self-portrait, c. 1500

1971. 500th Birth Anniv of Albrecht Durer. Paintings. Multicoloured.

E1393 10pf. Type E **429** 35 25
E1394 40pf. "The Three Peasants" 35 25
E1395 70pf. "Philipp Melanchthon" 2·40 1·20

E430 Construction Worker

1971. 8th S.E.D. Party Conference.

E1396 **E430** 5pf. multicoloured 25 20
E1397 - 10pf. multicoloured 25 20
E1398 - 20pf. multicoloured 25 20
E1400 - 20pf. gold, red and mauve 50 25
E1399 - 25pf. multicoloured 55 50

DESIGNS: 10pf. Technician; 20pf. (No. E1398) Farm girl; 20pf. (No. E1400) Conference emblem (smaller, 23×29 mm); 25pf. Soldier.

E432 "Internees"

1971. 20th Anniv of International Resistance Federation (F.I.R.). Lithographs from Fritz Cremer's "Buchenwaldzyklus".

E1401 **E432** 20pf. black & yellow 75 85
E1402 - 25pf. black and blue 75 85

DESIGN: 25pf. "Attack on Guard".

E433 Cherry stone with 180 Carved Heads

1971. Art Treasures of Dresden's Green Vaults. Multicoloured.

E1403 5pf. Type E **433** 25 20
E1404 10pf. Insignia of the Golden Fleece, c. 1730 25 20
E1405 15pf. Nuremberg jug, c. 1530 25 20
E1406 20pf. Mounted Moorish drummer figurine, c. 1720 25 20
E1407 25pf. Writing-case, 1562 1·00 1·10
E1408 30pf. St. George medallion, c. 1570 25 20

E434 Mongolian Arms

1971. 50th Anniv of Mongolian People's Republic.

E1409 **E434** 20pf. multicoloured 50 35

E435 Child's Face

1971. 25th Anniv of UNICEF.

E1410 **E435** 20pf. multicoloured 50 30

E436 Servicemen

1971. 10th Anniv of Berlin Wall. Mult.

E1411 20pf. Type E **436** 1·00 35
E1412 35pf. Brandenburg Gate 2·30 1·60

E437 "Ivan Franko" (liner)

1971. East German Shipbuilding Industry.

E1413 **E437** 10pf. brown 25 20
E1414 - 15pf. blue and brown 25 20
E1415 - 20pf. green 25 20
E1416 - 25pf. blue 1·60 1·50
E1417 - 40pf. brown 25 20
E1418 - 50pf. blue 25 20

DESIGNS: 15pf. "Irkutsk" (freighter); 20pf. "Rostock" freighter, 1966; 25pf. "Junge Welt" (fish-factory ship); 40pf. "Hansel" (container ship); 50pf. "Akademik Kurchatov" (research ship).

E438 Vietnamese Woman and Child

1971. Aid for Vietnam.

E1419 **E438** 10pf.+5pf. mult 50 30

E439 MAG-Butadien Plant

1971. Leipzig Autumn Fair.

E1420 **E439** 10pf. vio, mve & grn 25 20
E1421 - 25pf. violet, grn & bl 40 35

DESIGN: 25pf. SKL reactor plant.

E440 Upraised Arms (motif by J. Heartfield)

1971. Racial Equality Year.

E1422 **E440** 35pf. black, sil & bl 50 30

E441 Tupolev Tu-134 Mail Plane at Airport

1971. Philatelists' Day.

E1423 **E441** 10pf.+5pf. blue, red and green 35 25
E1424 - 25pf. red, green & bl 65 60

DESIGN: 25pf. Milestone and Zurner's measuring cart.

E442 Wiltz Memorial, Luxembourg

1971. Monuments. Multicoloured.

No.	Description		
E1425	25pf. Type E **442**	35	25
E1426	35pf. Karl Marx monument, Karl-Marx-Stadt	60	25

1971. 150th Birth Anniv of R. Virchow (physician). As Type E 420.

No.	Description		
E1427	40pf. plum	60	25

E443 German Violin

1971. Musical Instruments in Markneukirchen Museum. Multicoloured.

No.	Description		
E1428	10pf. North African "darbuka"	25	20
E1429	15pf. Mongolian "morin chuur"	25	20
E1430	20pf. Type E **443**	25	20
E1431	25pf. Italian mandolin	25	20
E1432	40pf. Bohemian bagpies	25	25
E1433	50pf. Sudanese "kasso"	1·50	1·50

E444 "Dahlta O 10 A" Theodolite

1971. 125th Anniv of Carl Zeiss Optical Works, Jena.

No.	Type	Description		
E1434	**E444**	10pf. black, red & bl	75	75
E1435	-	20pf. black, red & bl	75	75
E1436	-	25pf. blue, yellow and ultramarine	75	75

DESIGNS—VERT: 20pf. "Ergaval" microscope. HORIZ (52×29 mm) 25pf. Planetarium.

E445 Donkey and Windmill

1971. Fairy Tales (6th series). As Type E 445. "The Town Musicians of Bremen".

No.	Description		
E1437	5pf. multicoloured	30	30
E1438	10pf. multicoloured	30	30
E1439	15pf. multicoloured	85	1·20
E1440	20pf. multicoloured	85	1·20
E1441	25pf. multicoloured	30	30
E1442	30pf. multicoloured	30	30

1971. Sorbian Dance Costumes. As Nos. E1389/90 but smaller, size 23×28 mm.

No.	Type	Description		
E1443	**E428**	10pf. multicoloured	35	25
E1444	-	20pf. multicoloured	85	60

E446 Tobogganing

1971. Winter Olympic Games, Sapporo, Japan (1972).

No.	Type	Description		
E1445	**E 446**	5pf. black, green and mauve	25	20
E1446	-	10pf.+5pf. blk, bl & mve	25	20
E1447	-	15pf.+5pf. black, grn & bl	25	20
E1448	-	20pf. black, mauve & violet	25	20
E1449	-	25pf. black, violet & mauve	2·10	1·70
E1450	-	70pf. black, blue and violet	35	25

DESIGNS: 10pf. Figure skating; 15pf. Speed skating; 20pf. Cross-country skiing; 25pf. Biathlon; 70pf. Ski jumping.

1972. German Celebrities. As Type E 420.

No.	Description		
E1451	10pf. green	25	20
E1452	20pf. mauve	25	20
E1453	25pf. blue	25	20
E1454	35pf. brown	25	20
E1455	50pf. lilac	1·60	1·80

CELEBRITIES: 10pf. J. Tralow (writer); 20pf. L. Frank (writer); 25pf. K. A. Kocor (composer); 35pf. H. Schliemann (archaeologist); 50pf. Caroline Neuber (actress).

E447 Gypsum from Eisleben

1972. Minerals. Multicoloured.

No.	Description		
E1456	5pf. Type E **447**	35	25
E1457	10pf. Zinnwaldite, Zinnwald	35	25
E1458	20pf. Malachite, Ullersreuth	35	25
E1459	25pf. Amethyst, Wiesenbad	35	25
E1460	35pf. Halite, Merkers	35	25
E1461	50pf. Proustite, Schneeberg	1·60	1·60

E448 Vietnamese Woman

1972. Aid for Vietnam.

No.	Type	Description		
E1462	**E448**	10pf.+5pf. mult	50	25

E449 Soviet Exhibition Hall

1972. Leipzig Spring Fair. Multicoloured.

No.	Description		
E1463	10pf. Type E **449**	25	20
E1464	25pf. East German and Soviet flags	35	35

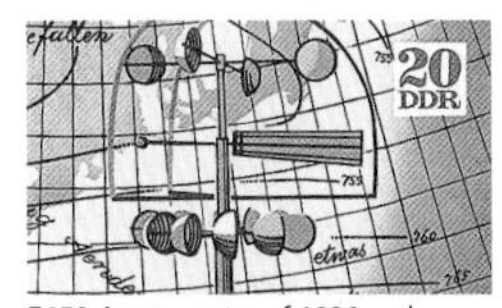

E450 Anemometer of 1896 and Koppen's Chart of 1876

1972. International Meteorologists Meeting, Leipzig. Three sheets, each 85×57 mm. Multicoloured.

No.	Description		
MSE1465	20pf. Type E **450**; 35pf. Weather station and clouds; 70pf. Satellite and weather map	3·25	4·00

E451 W.H.O. Emblem

1972. World Health Day.

No.	Type	Description		
E1466	**E451**	35pf. ultramarine, silver and blue	50	30

E452 Kamov Ka-26 Helicopter

1972. East German Aircraft. Multicoloured.

No.	Description		
E1467	5pf. Type E **452**	25	25
E1468	10pf. Letov Z-37 Cmelak crop-sprayer DM-SMC	25	25
E1469	35pf. Ilyushin Il-62M	35	25
E1470	1m. Ilyushin Il-62M	1·80	1·80

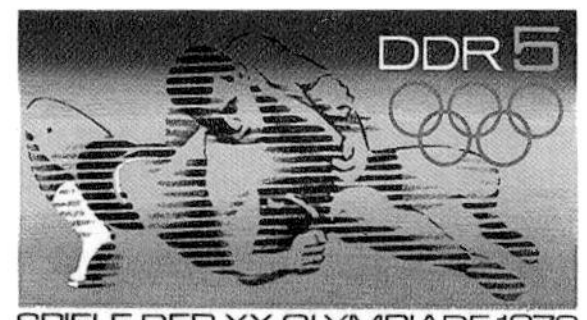

E453 Wrestling

1972. Olympic Games, Munich. Mult.

No.	Description		
E1471	5pf. Type E **453**	25	20
E1472	10pf.+5pf. High-diving	25	20
E1473	20pf. Pole-vaulting	25	20
E1474	25pf.+10pf. Rowing	25	25
E1475	35pf. Handball	35	25
E1476	70pf. Gymnastics	4·00	2·75

E454 Soviet and East German Flags

1972. 25th Anniv of German–Soviet Friendship Society. Multicoloured.

No.	Description		
E1477	10pf. Type E **454**	1·60	1·20
E1478	20pf. Brezhnev (U.S.S.R.) and Honecker (D.D.R.)	1·60	1·20

E455 Steel Workers

1972. Trade Unions Federation Congress.

No.	Type	Description		
E1479	**E455**	10pf. pur, orge & brn	50	30
E1480	-	35pf. blue and brown	50	30

DESIGN: 35pf. Students.

E456 "Karneol" Rose

1972. International Rose Exhibition. German Species. Multicoloured.

No.	Description		
E1481	5pf. Type E **456**	25	20
E1482	10pf. "Berger's Rose"	25	20
E1497	10pf. "Berger's Rose"	25	25
E1483	15pf. "Charme"	2·10	2·10
E1484	20pf. "Izetka Spreeathen"	25	20
E1485	25pf. "Kopernicker Sommer"	25	20
E1498	25pf. "Kopernicker Sommer"	1·70	75
E1486	35pf. "Professor Knoll"	25	20
E1499	35pf. "Professor Knoll"	1·70	75

Nos. E1497/9 are smaller, size 24×28 mm.

E457 "Portrait of Young Man"

1972. 500th Birth Anniv of Lucas Cranach the Elder. Multicoloured.

No.	Description		
E1487	5pf. Type E **457**	25	25
E1488	20pf. "Mother and Child"	25	25
E1489	25pf. "Margarete Luther"	35	35
E1490	70pf. "Nymph" (horiz)	3·00	4·25

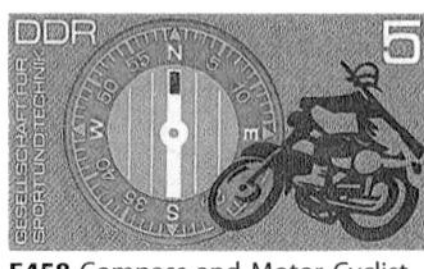

E458 Compass and Motor Cyclist

1972. Sports and Technical Sciences Association. Multicoloured.

No.	Description		
E1491	5pf. Type E **458**	25	25
E1492	10pf. Light airplane and parachute	25	25
E1493	20pf. Target and obstacle race	25	25
E1494	25pf. Radio set and Morse key	1·00	1·00
E1495	35pf. "Wilhelm Pieck" (brigantine) and propeller	25	25

E459 "Young Worker Reading" (J. Damme)

1972. Int Book Year.

No.	Type	Description		
E1496	**E459**	50pf. multicoloured	85	50

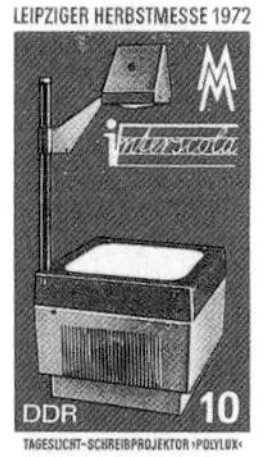

E460 Overhead Projector

1972. Leipzig Autumn Fair.

No.	Type	Description		
E1500	**E460**	10pf. black and red	25	25
E1501	-	25pf. black and green	35	35

DESIGN—HORIZ: 25pf. Slide projector.

E461 G. Dimitrov

1972. 90th Birth Anniv of Georgi Dimitrov (Bulgarian statesman).

No.	Type	Description		
E1502	**E461**	20pf. black and red	60	35

E462 "Catching Birds" (Egyptian relief painting, c. 2400 B.C.)

1972. "Interartes" Stamp Exhibition, East Berlin. Multicoloured.

E1503	10pf. Type E **462**	25	20
E1504	15pf.+5pf. "Persian Spearman" (glazed tile, c. 500 B.C.)	1·20	1·10
E1505	20pf. Anatolian tapestry c. 1400 B.C	25	20
E1506	35pf.+5pf. "The Grapesellers" (Max Lingner, 1949) (horiz)	25	20

E463 Red Cross Team and Patient

1972. East German Red Cross.

E1507	**E463**	10pf. ultramarine, blue and red	50	35
E1508	-	15pf. ultramarine, blue and red	50	35
E1509	-	35pf. red, blue and ultramarine	50	35

DESIGNS—VERT: 15pf. Sea-rescue launch. HORIZ (50½×28 mm): 35pf. World map on cross, and transport.

E464 Terrestrial Globe (J. Praetorius, 1568)

1972. Terrestrial and Celestial Globes. Mult.

E1510	5pf. Arab celestial globe, 1279	25	25
E1511	10pf. Type E **464**	25	25
E1512	15pf. Globe clock (J. Reinhold and G. Roll, 1586)	3·25	3·25
E1513	20pf. Globe clock (J. Burgi, 1590)	25	25
E1514	25pf. Armillary sphere (J. Moeller, 1687)	25	25
E1515	35pf. Heraldic celestial globe, 1690	35	35

E465 Monument

1972. German–Polish Resistance Memorial, Berlin, Inauguration.

E1516	**E465**	25pf. multicoloured	60	30

E466 Educating Juveniles

1972. Juvenile Inventions Exhibition. Mult.

E1517	10pf. Type E **466**	35	35
E1518	25pf. Youths with welding machine	35	35

E467 "Mauz and Hoppel" (Cat and Hare)

1972. Children's T.V. Characters. Mult.

E1519	5pf. Type E **467**	30	35
E1520	10pf. "Fuchs and Elster" (Fox and Magpie)	30	35
E1521	15pf. "Herr Uhn" (Eagle Owl)	1·10	1·20
E1522	20pf. "Frau Igel and Borstel" (Hedgehogs)	1·10	1·20
E1523	25pf. "Schuffel and Pieps" (Dog and Mouse)	30	35
E1524	35pf. "Paulchen" (Paul from the children's library)	30	35

E468 "The Snow Queen"

1972. Fairy Tales (7th series). As Type E 468. "The Snow Queen" (Hans Christian Andersen).

E1525	5pf. multicoloured	30	40
E1526	10pf. multicoloured	85	1·20
E1527	15pf. multicoloured	30	40
E1528	20pf. multicoloured	30	40
E1529	25pf. multicoloured	85	1·20
E1530	35pf. multicoloured	30	40

E469 H. Heine

1972. 175th Birth Anniv of Heinrich Heine (poet). Sheet 60×86 mm.

MSE1531	E **469** 1m. black, red and green	2·40	2·40

E470 Arms of U.S.S.R.

1972. 50th Anniv of U.S.S.R.

E1532	**E470**	20pf. multicoloured	60	30

E471 Leninplatz, East Berlin

1973. (a) Size 29×24 mm.

E1533	-	5pf. green	35	35
E1534	-	10pf. green	60	35
E1535	-	15pf. mauve	60	35
E1536	**E471**	20pf. mauve	1·20	45
E1537	-	25pf. green	1·50	35
E1538	-	30pf. orange	60	35
E1539	-	35pf. blue	1·20	50
E1540	-	40pf. violet	75	35
E1541	-	50pf. blue	85	35
E1542	-	60pf. purple	1·20	35
E1543	-	70pf. brown	1·10	35
E1544	-	80pf. blue	1·50	35
E1545	-	1m. green	1·80	35
E1546	-	2m. red	2·50	35
E1546a	-	3m. mauve	4·25	1·20

(b) Size 22×18 mm.

E2197		5pf. green	25	20
E1548		10pf. green	60	45
E2198		10pf. green	35	20
E2199		15pf. mauve	60	35
E2200	**E471**	20pf. mauve	75	25
E1549a		25pf. green	60	35
E2202	-	30pf. orange	75	60
E2203	-	35pf. blue	75	50
E2204	-	40pf. violet	1·50	60
E2205	-	50pf. blue	85	50
E2206	-	60pf. purple	1·10	55
E2207	-	70pf. brown	1·10	75
E2208	-	80pf. blue	1·30	85
E2209	-	1m. green	1·50	1·00
E2210	-	2m. red	2·75	1·50
E2211	-	3m. mauve	4·25	1·80

DESIGNS: 5pf. Eastern white pelican and Alfred Brehm House, Tierpark, Berlin; 10pf. (Nos. E1534, E1548) Neptune Fountain and Rathausstrasse, Berlin; 10pf. (No. E2198) Palace of the Republic, Berlin; 15pf. Apartment Blocks, Fishers' Island, Berlin; 20pf. TV Tower, Alexander Square, Berlin; 30 pf, Workers' Memorial, Halle; 35pf. Karl-Marx-Stadt; 40pf. Brandenburg Gate Berlin; 50pf. New Guardhouse, Berlin; 60pf. Crown Gate and Zwinger, Dresden; 70pf. Old Town Hall, Leipzig; 80pf. Rostock-Warnemunde; 1m. Soviet War Memorial, Treptow; 2, 3m. Arms of East Germany.

E472 M. da Caravaggio

1973. Cultural Anniversaries.

E1551	**E472**	5pf. brown	1·10	1·10
E1552	-	10pf. green	25	20
E1553	-	20pf. purple	25	20
E1554	-	25pf. blue	25	20
E1555	-	35pf. red	25	20

PORTRAITS AND ANNIVERSARIES: 5pf. (painter, 400th birth anniv); 10pf. Friedrich Wolf (dramatist, 85th birth anniv); 20pf. Max Reger (composer, birth cent.); 25pf. Max Reinhardt (impressario, birth cent.); 35pf. Johannes Dieckmann (politician, 80th birth anniv).

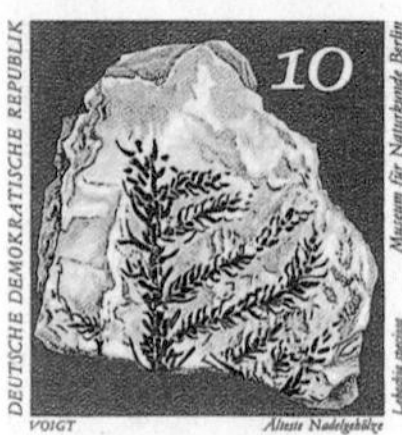

E473 "Lebachia speciosa"

1973. Fossils in Palaeontological Collection, Berlin Natural History Museum. Multicoloured.

E1556	10pf. Type E **473**	25	20
E1557	15pf. "Spheronopteris hollandica"	25	20
E1558	20pf. "Pterodactylus kochi"	25	20
E1559	25pf. "Botryopteris"	25	20
E1560	35pf. "Archaeopteryx lithographica"	25	20
E1561	70pf. "Odontopleura ovata"	2·20	2·10

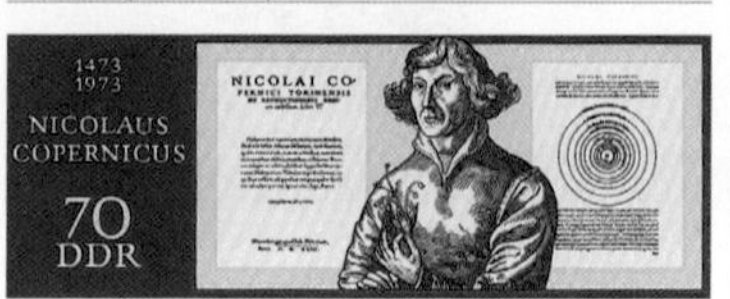

E474 Copernicus (image scaled to 63% of original size)

1973. 500th Birth Anniv of Copernicus.

E1562	**E474**	70pf. multicoloured	1·20	60

E475 National Flags

1973. 10th World Youth Festival, Berlin (1st issue). Multicoloured.

E1563	10pf.+5pf. Type E **475**	25	25
E1564	25pf.+5pf. Youths and peace dove	35	35

See also Nos. E1592/6.

E476 Bobsleigh Course

1973. 15th World Bobsleigh Championships, Oberhof.

E1565	**E476**	35pf. multicoloured	60	50

E477 Combine Harvester

1973. Leipzig Spring Fair. Multicoloured.

E1566	10pf. Type E **477**	25	25
E1567	25pf. Automatic lathe	50	50

E478 Firecrests

1973. Songbirds. Multicoloured.

E1568	5pf. Type E **478**	25	25
E1569	10pf. White-winged crossbill	25	25
E1570	15pf. Bohemian waxwing	25	25
E1571	20pf. Bluethroats	25	25
E1572	25pf. Eurasian goldfinch	25	25
E1573	35pf. Golden oriole	25	25
E1574	40pf. Grey wagtail	25	25
E1575	60pf. Wallcreeper	3·75	3·75

E479 Class 211 Electric Locomotive No. 200-3

1973. Railway Rolling Stock. Multicoloured.

E1576	5pf. Type E **479**	35	25
E1577	10pf. Refrigerator wagon	35	25
E1578	20pf. Long-distance passenger carriage	35	25
E1579	25pf. Tank wagon	35	25
E1580	35pf. Double-deck carriage	35	25
E1581	85pf. Passenger carriage	3·00	3·00

E480 "King Lear" (directed by W. Langhoff)

1973. Famous Theatrical Productions. Mult.

E1582	10pf. Type E **480**	25	20
E1583	25pf. "A Midsummer Night's Dream" (opera) (Benjamin Britten) (directed by Walter Felsenstein)	25	20
E1584	35pf. "Mother Courage" (directed by Berthold Brecht)	1·10	1·00

E481 H. Matern

1973. 80th Birth Anniv of Hermann Matern (politician).

E1585	**E481**	40pf. red	60	35

E482 Goethe and House

1973. Cultural Celebrities and Houses in Weimar. Multicoloured.

E1586	10pf. Type E **482**	25	20
E1587	15pf. C. M. Wieland (writer)	25	20
E1588	20pf. F. Schiller (writer)	25	20

E1589 25pf. J. G. Herder (writer) 25 20
E1590 35pf. Lucas Cranach the Elder (painter) 25 20
E1591 50pf. Franz Liszt (composer) 3·00 2·00

E483 Firework Display

1973. World Festival of Youth and Students, East Berlin (2nd issue). Multicoloured.
E1592 5pf. Type E **483** 25 20
E1593 15pf. Students ("Int Solidarity") 25 20
E1594 20pf. Young workers ("Economic Integration") 25 20
E1595 30pf. Students ("Aid for Young Nations") 1·60 75
E1596 35pf. Youth and Students' Emblems 25 20
MSE1597 86×107 mm. 50pf. Emblem and Brandenburg Gate (26.7) 1·70 1·20

E484 W. Ulbricht

1973. Death of Walter Ulbricht.
E1598 **E484** 20pf. black 85 50

E485 Power Network

1973. 10th Anniv of "Peace" United Energy Supply System.
E1599 **E485** 35pf. orge, pur & bl 60 50

E486 "Leisure Activities"

1973. Leipzig Autumn Fair. Multicoloured.
E1600 10pf. Type E **486** 25 20
E1601 25pf. Yacht, guitar and power drill 50 35

E487 Militiaman and Emblem

1973. 20th Anniv of Workers Militia. Mult.
E1602 10pf. Type E **487** 25 20
E1603 20pf. Militia guard 50 30
MSE1604 61×87 mm. 50pf. Militiamen (vert) 1·60 1·60

E488 Red Flag encircling Globe

1973. 15th Anniv of "Problems of Peace and Socialism".
E1605 **E488** 20pf. red and gold 75 35

E489 Langenstein-Zwieberge Memorial

1973. Langenstein-Zwieberge Monument.
E1606 **E489** 25pf. multicoloured 75 35

E490 U.N. H.Q. and Emblems

1973. Admission of German Democratic Republic to United Nations Organization.
E1607 **E490** 35pf. multicoloured 80 35

E491 "Young Couple" (G. Glombitza)

1973. Philatelists' Day and 3rd Young Philatelists' Stamp Exhibition, Halle.
E1608 **E491** 20pf.+5pf. mult 50 30

E492 Congress Emblem

1973. 8th World Trade Union Congress, Varna, Bulgaria.
E1609 **E492** 35pf. multicoloured 60 50

E493 Vietnamese Child

1973. "Solidarity with Vietnam".
E1610 **E493** 10pf.+5pf. mult 50 30

E494 Launching Rocket

1973. Soviet Science and Technology Days. Multicoloured.
E1611 10pf. Type E **494** 25 20
E1612 20pf. Soviet map and emblem (horiz) 25 20
E1613 25pf. Oil refinery 1·20 1·10

E495 L. Corvalan

1973. Solidarity with the Chilean People. Multicoloured.
E1614 10pf.+5pf. Type E **495** 30 30
E1615 25pf.+5pf. Pres. Allende 60 60

E496 "Child with Doll" (C. L. Vogel)

1973. Paintings by Old Masters. Mult.
E1616 10pf. Type E **496** 25 25
E1617 15pf. "Madonna with Rose" (Parmigianino) 25 25
E1618 20pf. "Woman with Fair Hair" (Rubens) 25 25
E1619 25pf. "Lady in White" (Titian) 25 25
E1620 35pf. "Archimedes" (D. Fetti) 25 25
E1621 70pf. "Flower Arrangement" (Jan D. de Heem) 3·50 2·40

E497 Flame Emblem

1973. 25th Anniv of Declaration of Human Rights.
E1622 **E497** 35pf. multicoloured 75 50

E498 "Catching the Pike"

1973. Fairy Tales (8th series). As Type E 498. "At the Bidding of the Pike".
E1623 5pf. multicoloured 30 35
E1624 10pf. multicoloured 1·20 1·80
E1625 15pf. multicoloured 30 35
E1626 20pf. multicoloured 30 35
E1627 25pf. multicoloured 1·20 1·80
E1628 35pf. multicoloured 30 35

E499 E. Hoernle

1974. Socialist Personalities.
E1629 **E499** 10pf. grey 35 25
E1630 - 10pf. lilac 35 25
E1631 - 10pf. blue 35 25
E1632 - 10pf. brown 35 25
E1633 - 10pf. green 35 25
E1634 - 10pf. brown 35 25
E1635 - 10pf. blue 35 25
E1636 - 10pf. brown 35 25

PERSONALITIES: No. E1630, Etkar Andre; E1631, Paul Merker; E1632, Hermann Duncker; E1633, Fritz Heckert; E1634, Otto Grotewohl; E1635, Wilhelm Florin; E1636, Georg Handke.

See also Nos. E1682/4.

E500 Pablo Neruda

1974. Pablo Neruda (Chilean poet) Commem.
E1637 **E500** 20pf. multicoloured 60 35

E501 "Comecon" Emblem

1974. 25th Anniv of Council for Mutual Economic Aid.
E1638 **E501** 20pf. multicoloured 60 30

E502 "Echinopsis multiplex"

1974. Cacti. Multicoloured.
E1639 5pf. Type E **502** 25 25
E1640 10pf. "Lobivia haageana" 25 25
E1641 15pf. "Parodia sanguiniflora" 3·00 3·00
E1642 20pf. "Gymnocal monvillei" 25 25
E1643 25pf. "Neoporteria rapifera" 25 25
E1644 35pf. "Notocactus concinnus" 35 35

E503 Handball Players

1974. 8th Men's World Indoor Handball Championships.
E1645 **E503** 5pf. multicoloured 50 50
E1646 - 10pf. multicoloured 50 50
E1647 - 35pf. multicoloured 50 50

Nos. E1645/7 were issued together, se-tenant, forming a composite design of a handball match.

E504 High-tension Testing Plant

1974. Leipzig Spring Fair. Multicoloured.
E1648 10pf. Type E **504** 25 20
E1649 25pf. "Robotron" computer (horiz) 50 35

E505 "Rhodophyllus sinuatus"

1974. Poisonous Fungi. Multicoloured.
E1650 5pf. Type E **505** 25 20
E1651 10pf. "Boletus satanas" 25 20
E1652 15pf. "Amanita pantherina" 25 20
E1653 20pf. "Amanita muscaria" 25 20
E1654 25pf. "Gyromitra esculenta" 25 20
E1655 30pf. "Inocybe patouillardii" 35 25
E1656 35pf. "Amanita phalloides" 35 25
E1657 40pf. "Clitocybe dealbata" 2·30 2·10

E506 Gustav Kirchhoff

1974. Celebrities' Birth Anniversaries.

E1658	**E506**	5pf. black and grey	25	20
E1659	-	10pf. ultram & bl	25	20
E1660	-	20pf. red and pink	25	25
E1661	-	25pf. green & turq	25	25
E1662	-	35pf. choc & brn	1·00	1·00

PORTRAITS AND ANNIVERSARIES: 5pf. (physicist, 150th); 10pf. Immanuel Kant (philosopher, 250th); 20pf. Elm Welk (writer, 90th); 25pf. Johann Herder (author, 230th); 35pf. Lion Feuchtwanger (novelist, 90th).

E507 Globe and "PEACE"

1974. 25th Anniv of 1st World Peace Congress.

E1663	**E507**	35pf. multicoloured	60	50

E508 Tractor Driver

1974. 25th Anniv of German Democratic Republic. Multicoloured.

E1664	10pf. Type E **508**	25	20
E1665	20pf. Students	25	20
E1666	25pf. Woman worker	25	25
E1667	35pf. East German family	1·30	1·20

E509 Buk Lighthouse, 1878

1974. Lighthouses (1st series). Multicoloured.

E1668	10pf. Type E **509**	25	20
E1669	15pf. Warnemunde lighthouse, 1898	25	20
E1670	20pf. Darsser Ort lighthouse, 1848	25	20
E1671	35pf. Arkona lighthouse in 1827 and 1902	25	20
E1672	40pf. Greifswalder Oie lighthouse, 1855	1·70	1·50

See also Nos. E1760/4.

E510 "Man and Woman looking at the Moon"

1974. Birth Bicentenary of Caspar Friedrich (painter). Multicoloured.

E1673	10pf. Type E **510**	25	20
E1674	20pf. "The Stages of Life" (seaside scene)	25	20
E1675	25pf. "Heath near Dresden"	2·40	2·40
E1676	35pf. "Trees in the Elbe Valley"	35	25
MSE1677	80×55 mm. E **511** 70pf. sepia	2·00	2·50

E512 Lace Pattern

1974. Plauen Lace.

E1678	**E512**	10pf. black and violet	25	20
E1679	-	20pf. brown, black and bistre	25	20
E1680	-	25pf. black, blue and turquoise	1·80	1·60
E1681	-	35pf. black, mauve and pink	25	25

DESIGNS: Nos. E1679/81, Lace patterns similar to Type E **512**.

1974. Socialist Personalities. As Type E 499.

E1682	10pf. blue	35	25
E1683	10pf. violet	35	25
E1684	10pf. brown	35	25

DESIGNS: No. E1682, R. Breitscheid; No. E1683, K. Burger; No. E1684, C. Moltmann.

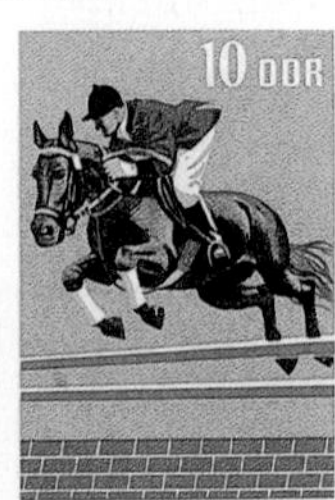

E513 Show Jumping

1974. International Horse-breeders' Congress, Berlin. Multicoloured.

E1685	10pf. Type E **513**	25	20
E1686	20pf. Horse & trap (horiz)	25	20
E1687	25pf. Haflinger draught horses (horiz)	2·20	2·75
E1688	35pf. Horse-racing (horiz)	35	25

E514 Crane lifting Diesel Locomotive

1974. Leipzig Autumn Fair. Multicoloured.

E1689	10pf. Type E **514**	35	25
E1690	25pf. Agricultural machine	50	35

E515 "The Porcelain Shop"

1974. "Mon Plaisir". Exhibits in Dolls' Village, Castle Museum, Arnstadt. Mult.

E1691	5pf. Type E **515**	25	20
E1692	10pf. "Fairground Crier"	25	20
E1693	15pf. "Wine-tasting in Cellar"	25	20
E1694	20pf. "Cooper and Apprentice"	25	20
E1695	25pf. "Bagpiper playing for Dancing Bear"	2·00	2·10
E1696	35pf. "Butcher's Wife and Crone"	25	25

E516 Ardeatine Caves Memorial, Rome

1974. International War Memorials.

E1697	**E516**	35pf. black, grn & red	50	50
E1698	-	35pf. black, bl & red	50	50

DESIGN: No. E1698, Resistance Memorial, Chateaubriant, France.

E517 Arms of East Germany and Family

1974. 25th Anniv of German Democratic Republic. Sheet 90×108 mm.

MSE1699	E **517** 1m. multicoloured	2·40	2·40

E518 "James Watt" (paddle-steamer) and Modern Freighter

1974. Centenary of U.P.U. Multicoloured.

E1700	10pf. Type E **518**	25	20
E1701	20pf. Steam and diesel railway locomotives	25	20
E1702	25pf. Early airliner and Tupolev Tu-134	25	20
E1703	35pf. Early mail coach and modern truck	1·50	1·20

E519 "The Revolutionaries" (E. Rossdeutscher)

1974. "DDR 74" Stamp Exhibition. Sculptures in Karl-Marx-Stadt. Each black, bistre and green.

E1704	10pf.+5pf. Type E **519**	35	35
E1705	20pf. "The Dialectics"	35	35
E1706	25pf. "The Party"	35	35

E520 "The Sun shines for all" (G. Milosch)

1974. Children's Paintings. Multicoloured.

E1707	20pf. Type E **520**	50	50
E1708	20pf. "My Friend Sascha" (B. Ozminski)	50	50
E1709	20pf. "Carsten the Best Swimmer" (M. Kluge)	50	50
E1710	20pf. "Me and the Blackboard" (P. Westphal)	50	50

E521 "The Woodchopper"

1974. Fairy Tales (9th series). "Twittering To and Fro" by A. Tolstoi.

E1711	**E521**	10pf. multicoloured	25	25
E1712	-	15pf. multicoloured	1·30	1·30
E1713	-	20pf. multicoloured	25	25
E1714	-	30pf. multicoloured	25	25
E1715	-	35pf. multicoloured	1·30	1·30
E1716	-	40pf. multicoloured	25	25

DESIGNS: Nos. E1712/16, Scenes from "Twittering To and Fro" fairy tale, similar to Type E **521**.

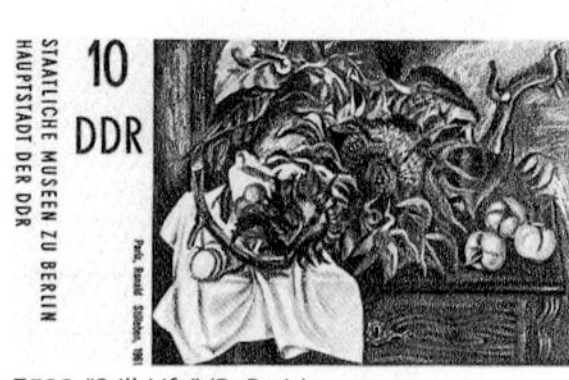

E522 "Still Life" (R. Paris)

1974. Paintings from Berlin Museums. Mult.

E1717	10pf. Type E **522**	25	20
E1718	15pf. "Girl in Meditation" (W. Lachnit) (vert)	25	20
E1719	20pf. "Fisherman's House" (H. Hakenbeck) (vert)	25	20
E1720	35pf. "Girl in Red" (R. Bergander)	35	20
E1721	70pf. "Parents" (W. Sitte) (vert)	2·40	2·10

E523 Banded Jasper

1974. Gem-stones in Freiberg Mining Academy Collection. Multicoloured.

E1722	10pf. Type E **523**	25	20
E1723	15pf. Smoky quartz	25	20
E1724	20pf. Topaz	25	20
E1725	25pf. Amethyst	25	20
E1726	35pf. Aquamarine	35	20
E1727	70pf. Agate	2·40	2·10

E524 Martha Arendsee

1975. 90th Birth Anniv of Martha Arendsee (Socialist).

E1728	**E524**	10pf. red	50	30

E525 Peasants doing Forced Labour

1975. 450th Anniv of Peasants' War.

E1729	**E525**	5pf. black, green and grey	50	50
E1730	-	10pf. black, brown and grey	50	50
E1731	-	20pf. black, blue and grey	50	50
E1732	-	25pf. black, yellow and grey	85	85
E1733	-	35pf. black, lilac and grey	85	85
E1734	-	50pf. black, grey and light grey	50	50

DESIGNS: 10pf. "Paying Tithe"; 20pf. Thomas Muntzer (leader); 25pf. "Armed Peasants"; 35pf. "Liberty" flag; 50pf. Peasants on trial.

E526 Women and Emblem

1975. International Women's Year.

E1735	**E526**	10pf. multicoloured	35	35
E1736	-	20pf. multicoloured	35	35
E1737	-	25pf. multicoloured	35	35

DESIGNS: 20pf., 25pf. Similar to Type E **526**.

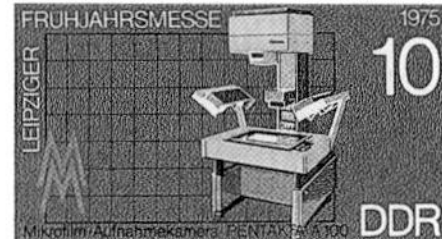

E527 Pentakta "A-100" (microfilm camera)

1975. Leipzig Spring Fair. Multicoloured.

E1738	10pf. Type E **527**	30	25
E1739	25pf. "SKET" (cement works)	45	35

E528 Hans Otto (actor) (1900–33)

1975. Celebrities' Birth Anniversaries.

E1740	**E528**	5pf. blue	25	20
E1741	-	10pf. red	25	20
E1742	-	20pf. green	25	20
E1743	-	25pf. brown	25	20
E1744	-	35pf. blue	1·20	95

PORTRAITS AND ANNIVERSARIES: 10pf. Thomas Mann, author (1875–1955); 20pf. Dr. A. Schweitzer (1875–1965); 25pf. Michelangelo (1475–1564); 35pf. Andre-Marie Ampere, scientist (1775–1836).

E529 Blue and Yellow Macaws

1975. Zoo Animals. Multicoloured.

E1745	5pf. Type E **529**	35	25
E1746	10pf. Orang-utan	35	25
E1747	15pf. Ibex	35	25
E1748	20pf. Indian rhinoceros (horiz)	35	25
E1749	25pf. Pygmy hippopotamus (horiz)	35	25
E1750	30pf. Grey seals (horiz)	35	25
E1751	35pf. Tiger (horiz)	35	25
E1752	50pf. Common zebra	2·30	2·40

E530 Soldiers, "Industry" and "Agriculture"

1975. 20th Anniv of Warsaw Treaty.

E1753	**E530**	20pf. multicoloured	1·60	50

E531 Soviet Memorial, Berlin-Treptow

1975. 30th Anniv of Liberation. Mult.

E1754	10pf. Type E **531**	25	20
E1755	20pf. Detail of Buchenwald memorial	25	20
E1756	25pf. Woman voluntary worker	25	20
E1757	55pf. "Socialist economic integration"	1·00	1·00
MSE1758	109×90 mm. 50pf. Soldier planting Red flag on Reichstag. Imperf	1·60	1·80

E532 Ribbons with "Komsomol" and "F.D.J." Badges

1975. 3rd Youth Friendship Festival, Halle.

E1759	**E532**	10pf. mult	60	30

1975. Lighthouses (2nd series). As Type E 509. Multicoloured.

E1760	5pf. Trimmendorf lighthouse	35	25
E1761	10pf. Gellen lighthouse	35	25
E1762	20pf. Sassnitz lighthouse	35	25
E1763	25pf. Dornbusch lighthouse	35	25
E1764	35pf. Peenemunde lighthouse	1·40	1·20

E533 Wilhelm Leibknecht and August Bebel

1975. Centenary of Marx's "Programmkritik" and Gotha Unity Congress.

E1765	**E533**	10pf. deep brown, brown and red	35	35
E1766	-	20pf. multicoloured	35	35
E1767	-	25pf. deep brown, brown and red	35	35

DESIGNS: 20pf. Tivoli (meeting place at Gotha) and title-page of Minutes of Unity Congress; 25pf. Karl Marx and Friedrich Engels.

E534 Dove and "Scientific Co-operation between Socialist Countries"

1975. 25th Anniv of Eisenhuettenstadt.

E1768	**E534**	20pf. multicoloured	50	30

E535 Construction Workers

1975. 30th Anniv of Free-German Trade Union Association.

E1769	**E535**	20pf. multicoloured	50	30

E536 Automatic Clock, 1585

1975. Ancient Clocks. Multicoloured.

E1770	5pf. Type E **536**	25	20
E1771	10pf. Astronomical Mantlepiece clock, 1560	25	20
E1772	15pf. Automatic clock, 1600	2·10	2·10
E1773	20pf. Mantlepiece Clock, 1720	25	20
E1774	25pf. Mantlepiece Clock, 1700	25	20
E1775	35pf. Astronomical Clock, 1738	25	25

E537 Jacob and Wilhelm Grimm's German Dictionary

1975. 275th Anniv of Academy of Science.

E1776	**E537**	10pf. black, grn & red	25	20
E1777	-	20pf. black and blue	25	20
E1778	-	25pf. blk, yell & grn	25	20
E1779	-	35pf. multicoloured	1·30	1·30

DESIGNS: 20pf. Karl Schwarzschildt observatory, Tautenberg; 25pf. Electron microscope and chemical plant; 35pf. Intercosmic satellite.

E538 Runner with Torch

1975. 5th National Youth Sports Day.

E1780	**E538**	10pf. black and pink	25	20
E1781	-	20pf. black and yellow	25	20
E1782	-	25pf. black and blue	25	20
E1783	-	35pf. black and green	1·30	1·30

DESIGNS: 20pf. Hurdling; 25pf. Swimming; 35pf. Gymnastics.

E539 Map of Europe

1975. European Security and Co-operation Conference, Helsinki.

E1784	**E539**	20pf. multicoloured	60	35

E540 Asters

1975. Flowers. Multicoloured.

E1785	5pf. Type E **540**	25	20
E1786	10pf. Pelargoniums	25	20
E1787	20pf. Gerberas	25	20
E1788	25pf. Carnation	25	20
E1789	35pf. Chrysanthemum	35	25
E1790	70pf. Pansies	3·50	3·00

E541 "Medimorph" (Anaesthetizing machine)

1975. Leipzig Autumn Fair. Multicoloured.

E1791	10pf. Type E **541**	30	20
E1792	25pf. Zschopau "TS-250" motor-cycle (horiz)	60	35

E542 School Crossing

1975. Road Safety. Multicoloured.

E1793	10pf. Type E **542**	25	20
E1794	15pf. Policewoman controlling traffic	2·00	1·30
E1795	20pf. Policeman assisting motorist	25	20
E1796	25pf. Car having check-up	25	20
E1797	35pf. Road safety instruction	25	20

E543 Launch of "Soyuz"

1975. "Apollo"–"Soyuz" Space Link. Mult.

E1798	10pf. Type E **543**	25	20
E1799	20pf. Spaceships in linking manoeuvre	25	20
E1800	70pf. The completed link (88×33 mm)	2·40	2·20

E544 Clenched Fist and Red Star

1975. "International Solidarity".

E1801	**E544**	10pf.+5pf. black, red and olive	50	30

E545 "Weimar in 1650" (Merian)

1975. Millenary of Weimar.

E1802	**E545**	10pf. brown, light green and green	25	20
E1803	-	20pf. multicoloured	25	20
E1804	-	35pf. multicoloured	75	65

DESIGNS:—VERT: 20pf. Buchenwald memorial. HORIZ: 35pf. Weimar buildings (975–1975).

E546 Vienna Memorial (F. Cremer)

1975. Austrian Patriots Monument, Vienna.

E1805	**E546** 35pf. multicoloured	60	30

E547 Louis Braille

1975. International Braille Year. Mult.

E1806	20pf. Type E **547**	25	20
E1807	35pf. Hands reading braille	25	20
E1808	50pf. An eye-ball, eye shade and safety goggles	2·00	1·80

E548 Post Office Gate, Wurzen

1975. National Philatelists' Day. Mult.

E1809	10pf.+5pf. Type E **548**	65	65
E1810	20pf. Post Office, Barenfels	25	25

E549 Hans Christian Andersen and scene from "The Emperor's New Clothes" (image scaled to 73% of original size)

1975. Fairy Tales (10th series). "The Emperor's New Clothes".

E1811	**E549** 20pf. multicoloured	60	60
E1812	- 35pf. multicoloured	1·00	1·00
E1813	- 50pf. multicoloured	60	60

DESIGNS: 35, 50pf. Different scenes.

E550 Tobogganing

1975. Winter Olympic Games, Innsbruck (1976). Multicoloured.

E1814	5pf. Type E **550**	25	20
E1815	10pf.+5pf. Bobsleigh track	25	20
E1816	20pf. Speed-skating rink	25	20
E1817	25pf.+5pf. Ski-jump	35	25
E1818	35pf. Skating-rink	35	25
E1819	70pf. Skiing	2·75	2·30
MSE1820	80×55 mm. 1m. Innsbruk (33×28 mm)	3·00	2·40

E551 W. Pieck

1975. Birth Cent of President Pieck (statesman).

E1821	**E551** 10pf. brown & blue	35	25

1976. Members of German Workers' Movement. As Type E 551.

E1822	10pf. brown and red	30	25
E1823	10pf. brown and green	30	25
E1824	10pf. brown and orange	30	25
E1825	10pf. brown and violet	30	25

PORTRAITS: No. E1822, Ernst Thalmann; E1823, Georg Schumann; E1824, Wilhelm Koenen; E1825, John Schehr.

E552 Organ, Rotha

1976. Gottfried Silbermann (organ builder) Commemoration. Multicoloured.

E1826	10pf. Type E **552**	25	20
E1827	20pf. Organ, Freiberg	25	20
E1828	35pf. Organ, Fraureuth	25	20
E1829	50pf. Organ, Dresden	1·80	1·20

E553 Richard Sorge

1976. Dr. Richard Sorge (Soviet agent) Commemoration. Sheet 82×65 mm.

MSE1830	E **553** 1m. black and pale olive-grey	2·75	2·75

E554 Servicemen and Emblem

1976. 20th Anniv of National Forces (N.V.A.). Multicoloured.

E1831	10pf. Type E **554**	30	20
E1832	20pf. N.V.A. equipment	50	35

E555 Telephone and Inscription

1976. Centenary of Telephone.

E1833	**E555** 20pf. blue	50	30

E556 Block of Flats, Leipzig

1976. Leipzig Spring Fair. Multicoloured.

E1834	10pf. Type E **556**	30	25
E1835	25pf. "Prometey" (deep sea trawler) (horiz)	60	35

E557 Palace of the Republic, Berlin

1976. Opening of Palace of Republic, Berlin.

E1836	**E557** 10pf. multicoloured	1·10	30

E558 Telecommunications Satellite Tracking Radar

1976. "Intersputnik".

E1837	**E558** 20pf. multicoloured	50	25

E559 Marx, Engels, Lenin and Socialist Party Emblem

1976. 9th East German Socialist Party Congress.

E1838	**E559** 10pf. red, gold and deep red	30	25
E1839	- 20pf. multicoloured	35	30
MSE1840	110×91 mm. E **557** 1m. multicoloured	2·10	2·10

DESIGN—HORIZ: 20pf. Industrial site, housing complex and emblem.

E560 Cycling

1976. Olympic Games, Montreal. Mult.

E1841	5pf. Type E **560**	25	20
E1842	10pf.+5pf. Modern swimming pool	25	20
E1843	20pf. Modern sports hall	25	20
E1844	25pf. Regatta course	25	20
E1845	35pf.+10pf. Rifle-range	35	25
E1846	70pf. Athletics	3·00	2·75
MSE1847	81×55 mm. 1m. Modern sports stadium (33×28 mm)	2·30	2·30

E561 Intertwined Ribbon and Emblem

1976. 10th Youth Parliament Conference, Berlin. Multicoloured.

E1848	10pf. Type E **561**	25	25
E1849	20pf. Members of Youth Parliament and stylised industrial plant	35	35

E562 "Himantoglossum bircinum"

1976. Flowers. Multicoloured.

E1850	10pf. Type E **562**	25	20
E1851	20pf. "Dactylorhiza incarnata"	25	20
E1852	25pf. "Anacamptis pyramidalis"	25	20
E1853	35pf. "Dactylorhiza sambucina"	35	25
E1854	40pf. "Orchis coriophora"	35	25
E1855	50pf. "Cypripedium calceolus"	3·50	2·40

E563 "Shetland Pony" (H. Drake)

1976. Statuettes from Berlin Museums.

E1856	**E563** 10pf. black and blue	25	20
E1857	- 20pf. black & brown	25	20
E1858	- 25pf. black & orange	25	20
E1859	- 35pf. black and green	25	20
E1860	- 50pf. black and pink	2·40	2·10

STATUETTES—VERT: 20pf. "Tanzpause" (W. Arnold); 25pf. "Am Strand" (L. Englehardt); 35pf. "Herman Duncker" (W. Howard); 50pf. "Das Gesprach" (G. Weidanz).

E564 Marx, Engels, Lenin and Red Flag

1976. European Communist Parties' Conference.

E1861	**E564** 20pf. blue, deep red and red	60	30

E565 State Carriage, 1790

1976. 19th-century Horse-drawn Vehicles. Multicoloured.

E1862	10pf. Type E **565**	25	20
E1863	20pf. Russian trap, 1800	25	20
E1864	25pf. Carriage, 1840	25	20
E1865	35pf. State carriage, 1860	30	20
E1866	40pf. Stagecoach, 1850	35	25
E1867	50pf. Carriage, 1889	3·75	3·50

E566 Gera, c. 1652

1976. National Philatelists' Day, Gera. Mult.

E1868	10pf.+5pf. Type E **566**	30	30
E1869	20pf. Gera buildings	30	30

E567 Boxer

1976. Domestic Dogs. Multicoloured.

E1870	5pf. Type E **567**	25	25
E1871	10pf. Airedale Terrier	25	25
E1872	20pf. Alsatian	25	25
E1873	25pf. Collie	25	25
E1874	35pf. Schnauzer	25	25
E1875	70pf. Great Dane	3·25	3·25

E568 Oil Refinery

1976. Autumn Fair, Leipzig. Multicoloured.

E1876	10pf. Type E **568**	25	20
E1877	25pf. Library, Leipzig	50	30

E569 Templin Lake Railway Bridge

1976. East German Bridges. Multicoloured.

E1878	10pf. Type E **569**	25	25
E1879	15pf. Adlergestell Railway Bridge, Berlin	25	25
E1880	20pf. River Elbe Railway Bridge, Rosslau	25	25
E1881	25pf. Goltzschtal Viaduct	25	25
E1882	35pf. Elbe River Bridge, Magdeburg	25	25
E1883	50pf. Grosser Dreesch Bridge, Schwerin	2·40	2·40

E570 Memorial Figures

1976. Patriots' Memorial, Budapest.

E1884	**E570** 35pf. multicoloured	60	50

E571 Brass Jug, c. 1500

1976. Exhibits from Applied Arts Museum, Kopenick Castle, Berlin. Multicoloured.

E1885	10pf. Type E **571**	25	25
E1886	20pf. Faience covered vase, c. 1710	25	25
E1887	25pf. Porcelain "fruit-seller" table centre, c. 1768	25	25
E1888	35pf. Silver "basket-carrier" statuette, c. 1700	25	25
E1889	70pf. Coloured glass vase, c. 1900	2·75	2·75

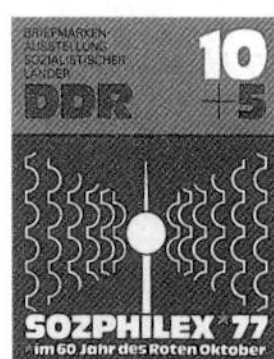

E572 Berlin T.V. Tower

1976. "Sozphilex 77" Stamp Exhibition. East Berlin (1st issue).

E1890	**E572** 10pf.+5pf. blue, black and red	50	30

See also Nos. E1962/3.

E573 Spade-tailed Guppy

1976. Aquarium Fishes – Guppies. Mult.

E1891	10pf. Type E **573**	25	20
E1892	15pf. Lyre-tailed	25	20
E1893	20pf. Flag-tailed	25	20
E1894	25pf. Sword-tailed	25	20
E1895	35pf. Delta	25	20
E1896	70pf. Round-tailed	3·00	2·75

E574 Clay Pots c. 3000 B.C.

1976. Archaeological Discoveries in D.D.R. Multicoloured.

E1897	10pf. Type E **574**	25	20
E1898	20pf. Bronze cult vessel on wheels, c. 1300 B.C.	25	20
E1899	25pf. Roman gold aureus of Tetricus I, A.D. 270–273	25	20
E1900	35pf. Viking cross-shaped pendant, 10th century A.D.	25	20
E1901	70pf. Roman glass beaker, 3rd century A.D.	2·75	2·75

E575 The Miller and the King

1976. Fairy Tales (11th series). "Rumpelstiltskin".

E1902	**E575** 5pf. multicoloured	30	30
E1903	- 10pf. multicoloured	85	85
E1904	- 15pf. multicoloured	30	30
E1905	- 20pf. multicoloured	30	30
E1906	- 25pf. multicoloured	85	85
E1907	- 30pf. multicoloured	30	30

DESIGNS: 10pf. to 30pf. Scenes from the fairy tale.

E576 "The Air" (R. Carriera)

1976. Paintings by Old Masters from the National Art Collection, Dresden. Mult.

E1908	10pf. Type E **576**	25	20
E1909	15pf. "Madonna and Child" (Murillo)	25	20
E1910	20pf. "Viola Player" (B. Strozzi)	25	20
E1911	25pf. "Ariadne Forsaken" (A. Kauffman)	25	20
E1912	35pf. "Old Man in Black Cap" (B. Nazzari)	25	20
E1913	70pf. "Officer reading a Letter" (G. Terborch)	3·00	2·20

E577 Arnold Zweig (author)

1977. German Celebrities.

E1914	**E577** 10pf. black and pink	25	20
E1915	- 20pf. black and grey	25	20
E1916	- 35pf. black and green	25	20
E1917	- 40pf. black and blue	1·20	1·20

DESIGNS: 20pf. Otto von Guericke (scientist); 35pf. Albrecht D. Thaer (agriculturalist); 40pf. Gustav Hertz (physicist).

E578 Spring near Plaue, Thuringia

1977. Natural Phenomena. Multicoloured.

E1918	10pf. Type E **578**	25	20
E1919	20pf. Rock face near Jonsdorf	25	20
E1920	25pf. Oaks near Reuterstadt Stavenhagen	25	20
E1921	35pf. Rocky ledge near Saalburg	25	20
E1922	50pf. Erratic boulder near Furstenwalde/Spree	2·00	2·00

E579 Book Fair Building

1977. Leipzig Spring Fair. Multicoloured.

E1923	10pf. Type E **579**	25	20
E1924	25pf. Aluminium casting machine	35	30

E580 Senftenberg Costume, Zly Komorrow

1977. Sorbian Historical Costumes. Mult.

E1925	10pf. Type E **580**	25	20
E1926	20pf. Bautzen, Budysin	25	20
E1927	25pf. Klitten, Kletno	25	20
E1928	35pf. Nochten, Wochozy	25	20
E1929	70pf. Muskau, Muzakow	3·25	2·40

E581 Carl Friedrich Gauss

1977. Birth Bicentenary of Carl Friedrich Gauss (mathematician).

E1930	**E581** 20pf. black and blue	85	35

E582 Start of Race

1977. 30th International Peace Cycle Race. Multicoloured.

E1931	10pf. Type E **582**	35	35
E1932	20pf. Spurt	35	35
E1933	35pf. Race finish	35	35

E583 Three Flags

1977. 9th Congress of Free German Trade Unions Association.

E1934	**E583** 20pf. multicoloured	50	30

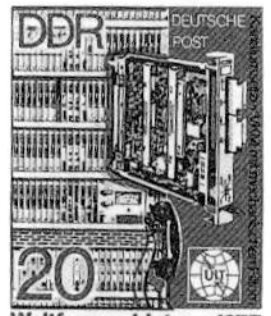

E584 VKM Channel Converter and Filters

1977. World Telecommunications Day.

E1935	**E584** 20pf. black, blue and red	50	30

E585 Shooting

1977. 25th Anniv of Sports and Technical Sciences Association.

E1936	**E585** 10pf. black, grn & red	25	25
E1937	- 20pf. black, bl & mve	25	25
E1938	- 35pf. black, pk & grn	1·20	1·20

DESIGNS: 20pf. Skin diving; 25pf. Radio-controlled model boat.

E586 Accordion, 1900

1977. Old Musical Instruments from Vogtland. Multicoloured.

E1939	10pf. Type E **586**	25	20
E1940	20pf. Treble viola da gamba, 1747	25	20
E1941	25pf. Oboe, 1785, Clarinet, 1830, Flute, 1817	25	20
E1942	35pf. Concert zither, 1891	25	20
E1943	70pf. Trumpet, 1860	3·25	3·00

E587 "Bathsheba at the Fountain"

1977. 400th Birth Anniv of Peter Paul Rubens. Dresden Gallery Paintings. Multicoloured.

E1944	10pf. Type E **587**	25	20
E1945	15pf. "Mercury and Argus" (horiz)	25	20
E1946	20pf. "The Drunk Hercules"	25	20
E1947	25pf. "Diana's Return from Hunting" (horiz)	25	20
E1948	35pf. "The Old Woman with the Brazier"	35	25
E1949	50pf. "Leda with the Swan" (horiz)	4·25	3·25

E588 Soviet and East German Flags

1977. 30th Anniv of German-Soviet Friendship Society. Sheet 80×55 mm.

MSE1950	E **588** 50pf. multicoloured	1·60	1·50

E589 Tractor and Plough

1977. Modern Agricultural Techniques. Multicoloured.

E1951	10pf. Type E **589**	25	20
E1952	20pf. Fertilizer spreader on truck	25	20
E1953	25pf. Potato digger and loader	25	20
E1954	35pf. High pressure collecting press	25	20
E1955	50pf. Milking machine	2·75	2·40

E590 High Jump

1977. 6th Gymnastics and Athletic Meeting and 6th Children and Young People's Sports Days, Leipzig. Multicoloured.

E1956	5pf. Type E **590**	25	20

E1957	10pf.+5pf. Running	25	20
E1958	20pf. Hurdling	25	20
E1959	25pf.+5pf. Gymnastics	25	20
E1960	35pf. Dancing	25	20
E1961	40pf. Torch bearer and flags	2·40	2·40

E591 "Bread for Everybody" (Wolfram Schubert)

1977. "Sozphilex 77" Stamp Exhibition, East Berlin (2nd issue). Multicoloured.

E1962	10pf. Type E **591**	35	25
E1963	25pf. "... when Communists are Dreaming" (Walter Womacka)	75	60
MSE1964	Two sheets, each 77×110 mm. (a) No. E1962 ×4; (b) No. E1963 ×4 Set of 2 sheets	5·00	4·50
MSE1965	85×54 mm. 50pf.+20pf. "World Youth Song" (Lothar Zitzmann) (horiz)	2·10	2·10

E592 "Konsument" Department Store, Leipzig

1977. Leipzig Autumn Fair. Multicoloured.

E1966	10pf. Type E **592**	35	20
E1967	25pf. Carved bowl and Thuringian blown-glass vases	50	35

E593 Bust of Dzerzhinsky and Young Pioneers

1977. Birth Centenary of Feliks E. Dzerzhinsky (founder of Soviet Cheka). Sheet 127×69 mm containing Type E 593 and similar vert design. Multicoloured.

MSE1968	20pf. Type E **593**; 35pf. Portrait	2·30	2·30

E594 Steam Locomotive "Muldenthal", 1861

1977. Transport Museum, Dresden. Mult.

E1969	5pf. Type E **594**	35	25
E1970	10pf. Dresden tram, 1896	35	25
E1971	20pf. Hans Grade's monoplane, 1909	35	25
E1972	25pf. Phanomobil tricar, 1924	35	25
E1973	35pf. River Elbe passenger steamer, 1837	3·75	3·00

E595 "Aurora" (cruiser)

1977. 60th Anniv of October Revolution. Multicoloured.

E1974	10pf. Type E **595**	50	25
E1975	25pf. Assault on Winter Palace	75	60
MSE1976	55×86 mm. 1m. Lenin (vert)	3·00	2·40

E596 Soviet Memorial

1977. Soviet Memorial, Berlin-Schoenholz.

E1977	**E596** 35pf. multicoloured	60	30

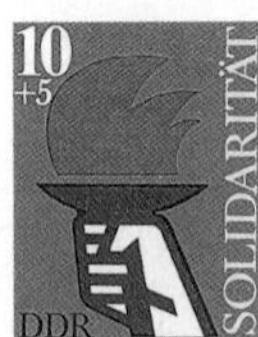

E597 Flaming Torch

1977. "Solidarity".

E1978	**E597** 10pf.+5pf. mult	50	30

E598 Ernst Meyer

1977. Socialist Personalities.

E1979	**E598** 10pf. brown	25	25
E1980	- 10pf. red	25	25
E1981	- 10pf. blue	25	25

PERSONALITIES: No. E1980, A. Frolich; No. E1981, G. Eisler.

E599 H. von Kleist

1977. Birth Bicentenary of Heinrich von Kleist (poet). Sheet 82×54 mm.

MSE1982	E **599** 1m. black and red	3·75	3·00

E600 Rocket pointing Right

1977. 20th "Masters of Tomorrow" Fair, Leipzig.

E1983	**E600** 10pf. red, silver and black	25	25
E1984	- 20pf. blue, gold and black	35	35

DESIGN: 20pf. Rocket pointing left.

E601 Mouflon

1977. Hunting. Multicoloured.

E1985	10pf. Type E **601**	25	20
E1986	15pf. Red deer	3·00	3·00
E1987	20pf. Shooting common pheasant	25	20
E1988	25pf. Red fox and mallard	35	25
E1989	35pf. Tractor driver with roe deer fawn	35	25
E1990	70pf. Wild boars	50	25

E602 Firemen with Scaling Ladders

1977. Fire Brigade. Multicoloured.

E1991	10pf. Type E **602**	25	20
E1992	20pf. Children visiting fire brigade (vert)	25	20
E1993	25pf. Fire engines in countryside	25	20
E1994	35pf. Artificial respiration (vert)	25	20
E1995	50pf. Fire-fighting tug	3·00	2·75

E603 Traveller and King

1977. Fairy Tales (12th series). "Six World Travellers" (Brothers Grimm).

E1996	**E603** 5pf. multicoloured	25	25
E1997	- 10pf. multicoloured	1·20	1·20
E1998	- 20pf. multicoloured	25	25
E1999	- 25pf. multicoloured	25	25
E2000	- 35pf. multicoloured	1·20	1·20
E2001	- 60pf. multicoloured	25	25

DESIGNS: 10pf. to 60pf. Scenes from the fairy tale.

E604 Rosehips

1978. Medicinal Plants. Multicoloured.

E2002	10pf. Type E **604**	25	20
E2003	15pf. Birch leaves	25	20
E2004	20pf. Camomile flowers	25	20
E2005	25pf. Coltsfoot	25	20
E2006	35pf. Lime flowers	25	20
E2007	50pf. Elder flowers	3·25	3·00

E605 Amilcar Cabral

1978. Amilcar Cabral (nationalist leader of Guinea-Bissau) Commemoration.

E2008	**E605** 20pf. multicoloured	60	50

E606 Town Hall, Suhl-Heinrichs

1978. Half-timbered Buildings. Multicoloured.

E2009	10pf. Type E **606**	25	20
E2010	20pf. Farmhouse, Niederodewitz	25	20
E2011	25pf. Farmhouse, Strassen	25	20
E2012	35pf. House, Quedlinburg	25	20
E2013	40pf. House, Eisenach	3·00	2·75

E607 Post Office Van, 1921

1978. Postal Transport. Multicoloured.

E2014	10pf. Type E **607**	25	25
E2015	20pf. Postal truck, 1978	60	60
E2016	25pf. Railway mail coach, 1896	75	75
E2017	35pf. Railway mail coach, 1978	1·00	1·00

E608 Ear-pendant, 11th century

1978. Slavonic Treasures. Multicoloured.

E2018	10pf. Type E **608**	25	20
E2019	20pf. Ear-ring, 10th century	25	20
E2020	25pf. Bronze tag, 10th century	25	20
E2021	35pf. Bronze horse, 12th century	35	25
E2022	70pf. Arabian coin, 8th century	2·40	2·40

E609 "Royal House" Market Square, Leipzig

1978. Leipzig Spring Fair.

E2023	**E609** 10pf. yell, blk & red	30	20
E2024	- 25pf. green, blk & red	60	50

DESIGN: 25pf. Universal measuring instrument, UMK 10/1318.

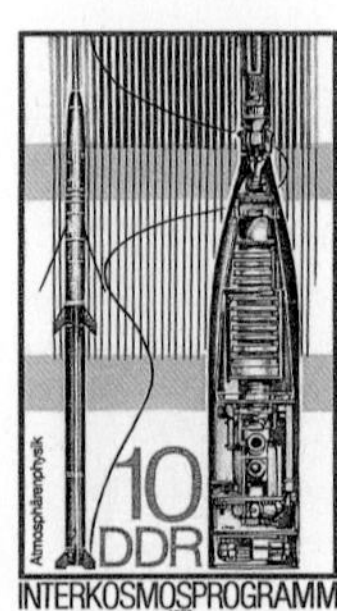

E610 "M-100" Meteorological Rocket

1978. "Interkosmos" Space Programme. Mult.

E2025	10pf. Type E **610**	25	25
E2026	20pf. "Interkosmos 1" satellite	25	25
E2027	35pf. "Meteor" satellite with Fourier spectrometer	1·50	1·50
MSE2028	90×109 mm. 1m. "MKF-6" multispectral camera	3·75	3·00

E611 Samuel Heinicke (founder)

1978. Bicentenary of First National Deaf and Dumb Educational Institution.

E2029	20pf. Type E **611**	25	25
E2030	25pf. Child learning alphabet	1·00	1·00

E612 Radio-range Tower, Dequede, and Television Transmission Van

1978. World Telecommunications Day. Mult.

E2031	10pf. Type E **612**	35	25
E2032	20pf. Equipment in Berlin television tower and Dresden television tower	45	45

E613 Saxon miner in Gala Uniform

1978. 19th-Century Gala Uniforms of Mining and Metallurgical Industries. Multicoloured.
E2033 10pf. Type E **613** 25 20
E2034 20pf. Freiberg foundry worker 25 20
E2035 25pf. School of Mining academician 25 20
E2036 35pf. Chief Inspector of Mines 1·80 1·50

E614 Lion Cub

1978. Centenary of Leipzig Zoo. Multicoloured.
E2037 10pf. Type E **614** 35 25
E2038 20pf. Leopard cub 35 25
E2039 35pf. Tiger cub 35 25
E2040 50pf. Snow leopard cub 2·00 1·90

E615 Loading Container

1978. Container Goods Traffic. Multicoloured.
E2041 10pf. Type E **615** 25 20
E2042 20pf. Placing container on truck 25 20
E2043 35pf. Diesel locomotive and container wagons 25 20
E2044 70pf. Placing containers on "Boltenhagen" 2·75 2·30

E616 Clay Ox (Egyptian Museum, Leipzig)

1978. Ancient African Works of Art in Egyptian Museums at Leipzig and Berlin. Multicoloured.
E2045 5pf. Type E **616** 25 20
E2046 10pf. Clay head of woman (Leipzig) 25 20
E2047 20pf. Gold bangle (Berlin) (horiz) 25 20
E2048 25pf. Gold ring plate (Berlin) 25 20
E2049 35pf. Gold signet-ring plate (Berlin) 25 20
E2050 40pf. Necklace (Berlin) (horiz) 2·00 1·80

E617 Justus von Liebig (agricultural chemist, 175th birth anniv)

1978. Celebrities' Birth Anniversaries.
E2051 **E617** 5pf. black and ochre 25 20
E2052 - 10pf. black and blue 25 20
E2053 - 15pf. black and green 25 20
E2054 - 20pf. black and blue 25 20
E2055 - 25pf. black and red 25 20
E2056 - 35pf. black and green 25 20
E2057 - 70pf. black and drab 2·20 2·00

DESIGNS: 10pf. Joseph Dietzgen (writer, 150th); 15pf. Alfred Doblin (novelist, 100th); 20pf. Hans Loch (politician, 80th); 25pf. Theodor Brugsch (scientist, 100th); 35pf. Friedrich Ludwig Jahn (gymnast, 200th); 70pf. Albrecht von Graefe (ophthalmatician, 150th).

E618 Cottbus, 1730

1978. 5th National Youth Stamp Exhibition, Cottbus. Multicoloured.
E2058 10pf.+5pf. Type E **618** 35 35
E2059 20pf. Modern Cottbus 35 35

E619 Havana Buildings and Festival Emblem

1978. 11th World Youth and Students' Festival, Havana. Multicoloured.
E2060 20pf. Type E **619** 50 50
E2061 35pf. Festival emblem and East Berlin buildings 50 50

E620 "Trooper with Halberd" (Hans Schaufelein)

1978. Drawings in Berlin State Museum. Sheet 110×98 mm containing Type E 620 and similar vert designs, each brownish black and stone.
MSE2062 10pf. Type E **620**; 20pf. "Woman reading a Letter" (Jean Antoine Watteau); 25pf. "Seated Boy" (Gabriel Metsu); 30pf. "Young Man cutting a Loaf" (Cornelis Saftleven); 35pf. "St. Anthony in a Landscape" (Matthias Grunewald); 50pf. "Man seated in an Armchair" (Abraham van Diepenbeeck) 4·50 4·50

E621 "Multicar 25" Truck

1978. Leipzig Autumn Fair. Multicoloured.
E2063 10pf. Type E **621** 30 25
E2064 25pf. "Three Kings" Fair building, Petersstrasse 60 50

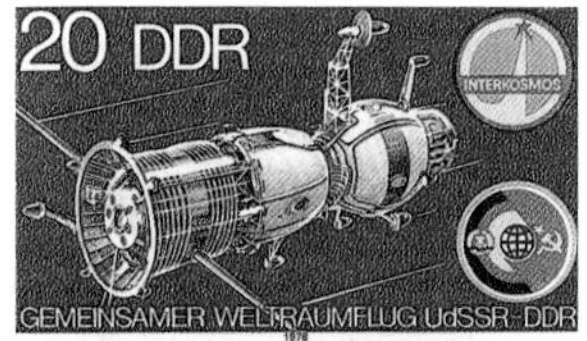

E622 "Soyuz" Spaceship and Emblems

1978. Soviet–East German Space Flight (1st issue).
E2065 **E622** 20pf. multicoloured 60 35
See also Nos. E2069/**MS**2073.

E623 Mauthausen Memorial

1978. War Victims' Memorial, Mauthausen, Austria.
E2066 **E623** 35pf. multicoloured 60 45

E624 W.M.S. Unit on the March

1978. 25th Anniv of Workers' Militia Squads.
E2067 20pf. Type E **624** 60 50
E2068 35pf. Members of Red Army, National People's Army and W.M.S. 60 50

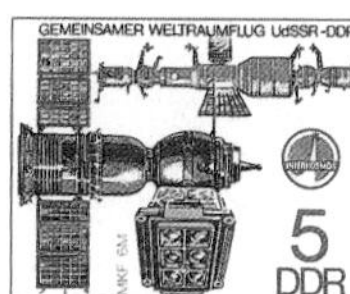

E625 "Soyuz", "MKF 6M" Camera and Space Station

1978. Soviet–East German Space Flight (2nd issue). Multicoloured.
E2069 5pf. Type E **625** 25 20
E2070 10pf. Albert Einstein and "Soyuz" 25 20
E2071 20pf. Sigmund Jahn (first East German cosmonaut) (vert) 25 20
E2072 35pf. "Salyut", "Soyuz" and Lilienthal monoplane glider 1·40 1·20
MSE2073 110×90 mm. 1m. Space station and cosmonauts Valeri Bykovski and Jahn (54×32 mm) 3·00 3·00

E626 Human Pyramid

1978. The Circus. Multicoloured.
E2074 5pf. Type E **626** 50 85
E2075 10pf. Elephant on tricycle 85 1·20
E2076 20pf. Performing horse 1·50 2·20
E2077 35pf. Polar bear kissing girl 2·40 4·25

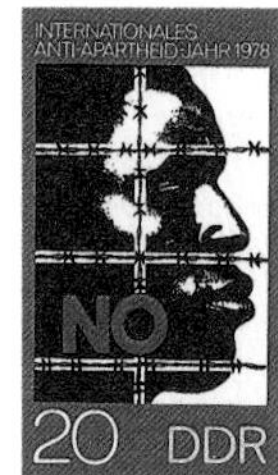

E627 African behind Barbed Wire

1978. International Anti-Apartheid Year.
E2078 **E627** 20pf. multicoloured 60 30

E628 Construction of Natural Gas Pipe Line

1978. Construction of "Friendship Line" (Drushba-Trasse) by East German Youth.
E2079 **E628** 20pf. multicoloured 60 30

E629 "Parides hahneli" ("Papilio hahneli")

1978. 250th Anniv of Dresden Scientific Museums. Multicoloured.
E2080 10pf. Type E **629** 25 20
E2081 20pf. "Agama lehmanni" 25 20
E2082 25pf. Agate 25 20
E2083 35pf. "Palaeobatrachus diluvianus" 25 20
E2084 40pf. Mantlepiece clock, c. 1720 35 25
E2085 50pf. Table telescope, c. 1750 3·00 2·75

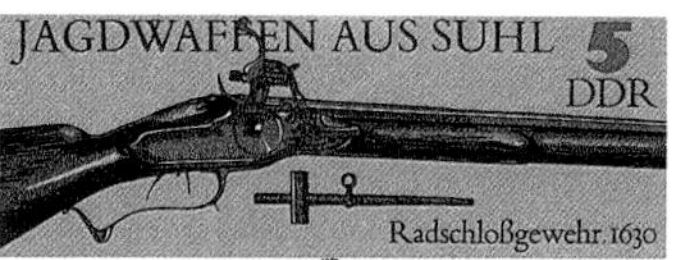

E630 Wheel-lock Gun, 1630

1978. Sporting Guns from Suhl. Multicoloured.
E2086 5pf. Type E **630** 25 25
E2087 10pf. Double-barrelled gun, 1978 25 25
E2088 20pf. Spring-cock gun, 1780 35 35
E2089 25pf. Superimposed double-barrelled gun, 1978 50 50
E2090 35pf. Percussion gun, 1850 75 75
E2091 70pf. Three-barrelled gun, 1978 1·50 1·50

E631 Old Woman and Youth

1978. Fairy Tales. "Rapunzel". Multicoloured.
E2092 10pf. Type E **631** 30 30
E2093 15pf. Old Woman climbing tower on Rapunzel's hair 1·30 1·30
E2094 20pf. Prince calling to Rapunzel 30 30
E2095 25pf. Prince climbing through window 30 30
E2096 35pf. Old woman about to cut Rapunzel's hair 1·30 1·30
E2097 50pf. "Happy ever after" 30 30

E632 Chaffinches

1979. Songbirds. Multicoloured.
E2098 5pf. Type E **632** 35 25
E2099 10pf. Eurasian nuthatch 35 25
E2100 20pf. European robin 35 25
E2101 25pf. Common rosefinch 35 25
E2102 35pf. Blue tit 35 25
E2103 50pf. Linnet 3·50 2·50

E633 Chabo

1979. Poultry. Multicoloured.
E2104 10pf. Type E **633** 25 20
E2105 15pf. Crows head 25 20
E2106 20pf. Porcelain-colour Feather-footed dwarf 25 20
E2107 25pf. Saxonian 25 20
E2108 35pf. Phoenix 25 20
E2109 50pf. Striped Italian 3·00 2·40

E634 Telephone Exchanges in 1900 and 1979

1979. Telephone and Telegraphs Communications. Multicoloured.
E2110 20pf. Type E **634** 25 20
E2111 35pf. Transmitting telegrams in 1800 and 1979 1·10 1·00

E635 Albert Einstein

1979. Birth Centenary of Albert Einstein (physicist). Sheet 55×86 mm.

MSE2112 E **635** 1m. light brown, deep brown and brown 3·25 3·00

E636 Max Klinger Exhibition House, Leipzig

1979. Leipzig Spring Fair. Multicoloured.

E2113	10pf. Type E **636**	30	20
E2114	25pf. Horizontal drill and milling machine	50	35

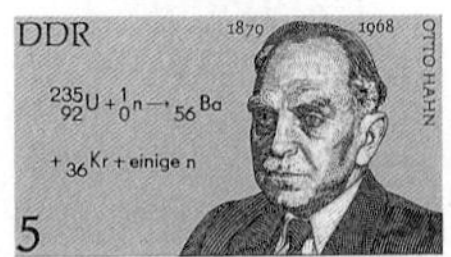

E637 Otto Hahn (physicist, centenary)

1979. Celebrities' Birth Anniversaries.

E2115	**E637**	5pf. black and pink	25	20
E2116	-	10pf. black and blue	25	20
E2117	-	20pf. black and yellow	25	20
E2118	-	25pf. black and green	25	20
E2119	-	35pf. black and blue	25	20
E2120	-	70pf. black and pink	3·00	2·20

DESIGNS: 10pf. Max von Laue (physicist, centenary); 20pf. Arthur Scheunert (physiologist, centenary); 25pf. Friedrich August Kekule (chemist, 150th); 35pf. Georg Forster (explorer and writer, 225th); 70pf. Gotth Ephraim Lessing (playwright and essayist, 250th).

E638 "Radebeul" (container ship), "Sturmvogel" (tug) and Shipping Route Map

1979. World Navigation Day.

E2121	**E638**	20pf. multicoloured	60	35

E639 Horch "8", 1911

1979. Zwickau Motor Industry. Multicoloured.

E2122	20pf. Type E **639**	50	50
E2123	35pf. Trabant "601 S de luxe", 1978	85	85

E640 MXA Electric Train

1979. East German Locomotives and Wagons. Multicoloured.

E2124	5pf. Type E **640**	35	25
E2125	10pf. Self-discharging wagon	35	25
E2126	20pf. Diesel locomotive No. 110836.4	35	25
E2127	35pf. Railway car transporter	1·30	1·10

E641 Durga (18th century)

1979. Indian Miniatures. Multicoloured.

E2128	20pf. Type E **641**	25	20
E2129	35pf. Mahavira (15th/16th century)	25	20
E2130	50pf. Todi Ragini (17th century)	35	25
E2131	70pf. Asavari Ragini (17th century)	3·50	3·25

E642 Children Playing

1979. International Year of the Child. Multicoloured.

E2132	10pf. Type E **642**	25	25
E2133	20pf. Overseas aid for children	60	60

E643 Construction Work on Leipziger Strasse Complex

1979. "Berlin Project" of Free German Youth Organization. Multicoloured.

E2134	10pf. Type E **643**	25	20
E2135	20pf. Berlin-Marzahn building site	50	50

E644 Torchlight Procession of Free German Youth, 1949

1979. National Youth Festival. Mult.

E2136	10pf.+5pf. Type E **644**	35	35
E2137	20pf. Youth rally	35	35

E645 Exhibition Symbol

1979. "agra 79" Agricultural Exhibition, Markkleeberg.

E2138	**E645**	10pf. multicoloured	60	30

E646 "Rostock" (train ferry), 1977

1979. 70th Anniv of Sassnitz–Trelleborg Railway Ferry. Multicoloured.

E2139	20pf. Type E **646**	50	50
E2140	35pf. "Rugen" (train ferry)	50	50

E647 Hospital Classroom

1979. Rehabilitation. Multicoloured.

E2141	10pf. Type E **647**	25	20
E2142	35pf. Wheelchair-bound factory worker	75	70

E648 Cycling

1979. 7th Children's and Young People's Sports Day, Berlin. Multicoloured.

E2143	10pf. Type E **648**	25	20
E2144	20pf. Roller-skating	75	60

E649 Dahlia "Rubens"

1979. "iga" International Garden Exhibition, Erfurt. Dahlias. Multicoloured.

E2145	10pf.+5pf. Type E **649**	25	20
E2146	20pf. "Rosalie"	25	20
E2147	25pf. "Corinna"	25	20
E2148	35pf. "Enzett-Dolli"	25	20
E2149	50pf. "Enzett-Carola"	35	25
E2150	70pf. "Don Lorenzo"	3·75	3·50

E650 Goose-thief Fountain, Dresden

1979. National Stamp Exhibition, Dresden. Multicoloured.

E2151	10pf.+5pf. Type E **650**	75	60
E2152	20pf. Dandelion fountain, Dresden	25	20
MSE2153	86×55 mm. 1m. Dresden buildings (horiz)	3·00	2·75

E651 World Map and Russian Alphabet

1979. 4th International Congress of Russian Language and Literature Teachers, Berlin.

E2154	**E651**	20pf. multicoloured	50	30

E652 Italian Lira de Gamba, 1592

1979. Musical Instruments in Leipzig Museum. Multicoloured.

E2155	20pf. Type E **652**	25	20
E2156	25pf. French serpent, 17th/18th century	25	20
E2157	40pf. French barrel-lyre, 1750	35	25
E2158	85pf. German tenor flugelhorn, 1850	3·50	2·75

E653 Horseracing

1979. 30th International Congress on Horse-breeding in Socialist Countries, Berlin. Multicoloured.

E2159	10pf. Type E **653**	25	20
E2160	25pf. Dressage (pas de deux)	1·20	1·10

E654 Mittelbau-Dora Memorial

1979. Mittelbau-Dora Memorial, Nordhausen.

E2161	**E654**	35pf. black and violet	75	50

E655 Teddy Bear

1979. Leipzig Autumn Fair. Multicoloured.

E2162	10pf. Type E **655**	25	20
E2163	25pf. Grosser Blumenberg building, Richard Wagner Square	45	25

E656 Philipp Dengel

1979. Socialist Personalities.

E2164	**E656**	10pf. black, green and deep green	30	25
E2165	-	10pf. black, bl & ind	30	25
E2166	-	10pf. blk, stone & bis	30	25
E2167	-	10pf. black, red & brn	30	25

DESIGNS: No. E2165, Otto Buchwitz; No. E2166, Bernard Koenen; No. E2167, Heinrich Rau.

E657 Building Worker and Flats

1979. 30th Anniv of German Democratic Republic. Multicoloured.

E2168	5pf. Type E **657**	25	20
E2169	10pf. Boy and girl	25	20
E2170	15pf. Soldiers	75	50
E2171	20pf. Miner and Soviet soldier	25	20
MSE2172	90×110 mm. 1m. Family and flats (29×51 mm)	2·40	2·20

E658 Girl applying Lipstick (1966/7)

1979. Meissen Porcelain. Multicoloured.

E2173	5pf. Type **E 658**	20	20
E2174	10pf. "Altozier" coffee pot (18th cent)	25	25
E2175	15pf. "Gosser Ausschnitt" coffee pot (1973/4)	35	35
E2176	20pf. Vase with lid (18th century)	50	50
E2177	25pf. Parrot with cherry (18th century)	60	60
E2178	35pf. Harlequin with tankard (18th century)	1·00	1·00
E2179	50pf. Flower girl (18th century)	1·30	1·30
E2180	70pf. Sake bottle (18th century)	1·80	1·80

E659 Vietnamese Soldier, Mother and Child

1979. "Invincible Vietnam".

E2181	**E659** 10pf.+5pf. black and red	60	45

E660 Rag-doll, 1800

1979. Dolls. Multicoloured.

E2182	10pf. Type **E 660**	25	25
E2183	15pf. Ceramic doll, 1960	1·50	1·50
E2184	20pf. Wooden doll, 1780	25	25
E2185	35pf. Straw puppet, 1900	25	25
E2186	50pf. Jointed doll, 1800	1·50	1·50
E2187	70pf. Tumbler-doll, 1820	25	25

E661 "Balance on Ice" (Johanna Starke)

1980. Winter Olympic Games, Lake Placid. Multicoloured.

E2188	10pf. "Bobsleigh Start" (Gunter Rechn) (horiz)	25	25
E2189	20pf. Type **E 661**	25	25
E2190	25pf.+10pf. "Ski jumpers" (plastic sculpture, Gunter Schultz)	25	25
E2191	35pf. "Speed Skaters at the Start" (Axel Wunsch)	1·80	1·80
MSE2192	79×55 mm. 1m. "Skiing Girls" (Lothar Zitmann) (29×24 mm)	3·00	2·75

E662 Stille Musik Rock Garden, Grosssedlitz

1980. Baroque Gardens. Multicoloured.

E2193	10pf. Type **E 662**	25	20
E2194	20pf. Belvedere Orangery, Weimar	25	20
E2195	50pf. Flower garden, Dornburg Castle	35	20
E2196	70pf. Park, Rheinsberg Castle	2·20	2·20

E663 Cable-laying Machine and Dish Aerial

1980. Post Office Activities. Multicoloured.

E2212	10pf. Type **E 663**	25	20
E2213	20pf. T.V. Tower, Berlin, and television	35	30

E664 Johann Wolfgang Dobereiner (chemist, bicent)

1980. Celebrities' Birth Anniversaries.

E2214	**E664** 5pf. black and bistre	25	20
E2215	- 10pf. black and red	25	20
E2216	- 20pf. black and green	25	20
E2217	- 25pf. black and blue	25	20
E2218	- 35pf. black and blue	25	20
E2219	- 70pf. black and red	2·00	1·60

DESIGNS: 10pf. Frederic Joliot-Curie (physicist, and chemist, 80th anniv); 20pf. Johann Friedrich Naumann (zoologist, bicent); 25pf. Alfred Wegener (explorer and geophysicist, cent); 35pf. Carl von Clausewitz (Prussian general, bicent); 70pf. Helene Weigel (actress, 80th anniv).

E665 Karl Marx University, Leipzig

1980. Leipzig Spring Fair. Multicoloured.

E2220	10pf. Type **E 665**	25	20
E2221	25pf. "ZT 303" tractor	50	35

E666 Werner Eggerath

1980. 80th Birth Anniv of Werner Eggerath (socialist).

E2222	**E666** 10pf. brown and red	60	50

E667 Cosmonauts and "Interkosmos" Emblem

1980. "Interkosmos" Programme. Sheet 109×89 mm.

MSE2223	E **667** 1m. multicoloured	3·00	2·75

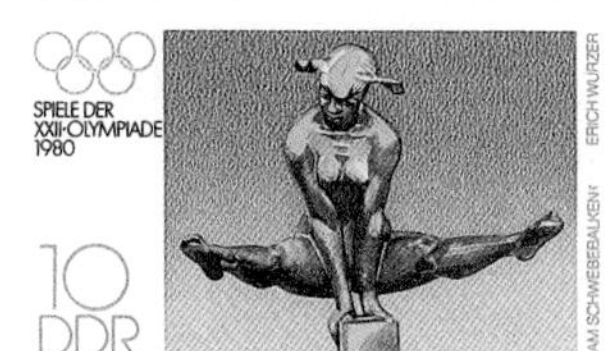

E668 "On the Horizontal Beam" (sculpture, Erich Wurzer)

1980. Olympic Games, Moscow (1st issue). Multicoloured.

E2224	10pf. Type **E 668**	35	25
E2225	20pf.+5pf. "Runners before the Winning Post" (Lothar Zitzmann)	35	25
E2226	50pf. "Coxless Four" (Wilfred Falkenthal)	2·00	1·70

See also Nos. E2247/9.

E669 Flags of Member States

1980. 25th Anniv of Warsaw Pact.

E2227	**E669** 20pf. multicoloured	75	30

E670 Co-operative Society Building (W. Gropius)

1980. Bauhaus Architecture. Multicoloured.

E2228	5pf. Type **E 670**	35	25
E2229	10pf. Socialists' Memorial Place (M. v. d. Rhode) (horiz)	35	25
E2230	15pf. Monument to the Fallen of March 1922 (W. Gropius)	35	25
E2231	20pf. Steel Building 1926 (G. Muche and R. Paulick) (horiz)	35	25
E2232	50pf. Trade Union school (H. Meyer)	50	30
E2233	70pf. Bauhaus building (W. Gropius) (horiz)	3·00	2·75

E671 Rostock Buildings

1980. 18th Workers' Festival, Rostock. Mult.

E2234	10pf. Type **E 671**	30	25
E2235	20pf. Costumed dancers	50	35

E672 Radar Complex, Berlin-Schoenefeld Airport

1980. "Aerosozphilex 1980" International Airmail Exhibition, Berlin. Multicoloured.

E2236	20pf. Type **E 672**	50	50
E2237	25pf. Ilyushin Il-62M at Schonefeld Airport	50	50
E2238	35pf. PZL-106A Kruk crop-spraying airplane	75	75
E2239	70pf. Antonov An-2 aerial photography biplane and multispectrum camera	1·50	1·50
MSE2240	64×95 mm. 1m.+10pf. Ilyushin Il-62M jetliner and globe	3·00	3·00

E673 Okapi

1980. Endangered Animals. Multicoloured.

E2241	5pf. Type **E 673**	25	20
E2242	10pf. Lesser pandas	25	20
E2243	15pf. Maned wolf	25	20
E2244	20pf. Arabian oryx	25	20
E2245	25pf. White-eared pheasant	25	20
E2246	35pf. Musk oxen	2·50	2·00

1980. Olympic Games, Moscow (2nd issue). As Type E 668. Multicoloured.

E2247	10pf. "Judo" (Erhard Schmidt)	25	20
E2248	20pf.+10pf. "Swimmer" (Willi Sitte) (vert)	25	20
E2249	50pf. "Spurt" (sculpture, Siegfried Schreiber)	2·10	1·60
MSE2250	79×55 mm. 1m. "Spinnakers" (Karl Raetsch) (29×24 mm)	3·50	3·00

E674 Suhl, 1700

1980. 6th National Youth Stamp Exhibition, Suhl. Multicoloured.

E2251	10pf.+5pf. Type **E 674**	50	50
E2252	20pf. Modern Suhl	50	50

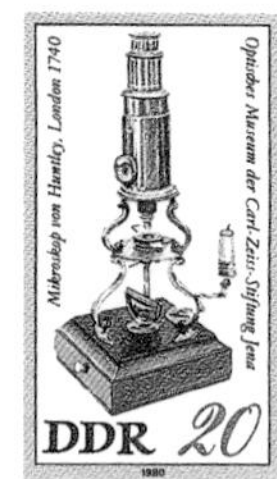

E675 Huntley Microscope

1980. Carl Zeiss Optical Museum, Jena. Mult.

E2253	20pf. Type **E 675**	50	50
E2254	25pf. Magny microscope, 1751	50	50
E2255	35pf. Amici microscope, 1845	85	85
E2256	70pf. Zeiss microscope, 1873	1·40	1·40

E676 Majdanek Memorial

1980. War Victims' Memorial, Majdanek, Poland.

E2257	**E676** 35pf. multicoloured	75	50

E677 Information Centre, Leipzig

1980. Leipzig Autumn Fair. Multicoloured.

E2258	10pf. Type **E 677**	30	25
E2259	25pf. Carpet-knitting machine	75	35

E678 Palace of Republic, Berlin

1980. 67th Interparliamentary Conference, Berlin.

E2260	**E678** 20pf. multicoloured	1·10	35

E679 "Laughing Boy with Flute"

1980. 400th Anniv of Frans Hals (artist). Multicoloured.

E2261	10pf. Type **E 679**	25	20
E2262	20pf. "Portrait of Young Man in Drab Coat"	25	20
E2263	25pf. "The Mulatto"	25	20
E2264	35pf. "Portrait of Young Man in Black Coat"	1·50	1·30
MSE2265	80×55 mm. 1m. brown (Self-portrait) (29×23 mm)	3·00	2·50

E680 Clenched Fist and Star

1980. "Solidarity".

E2266	**E680**	10pf.+5pf. turq & red	60	30

E681 "Leccinum versipelle" ("Leccinum testaceo scabrum")

1980. Edible Mushrooms. Multicoloured.

E2267	5pf. Type E **681**	25	20
E2268	10pf. "Boletus miniatoporus" ("Boletus erythropus")	25	20
E2269	15pf. "Agaricus campestris" ("Agaricus campester")	25	20
E2270	20pf. "Xerocomus badius"	25	20
E2271	35pf. "Boletus edulis"	35	25
E2272	70pf. "Cantharellus cibarius"	2·75	2·50

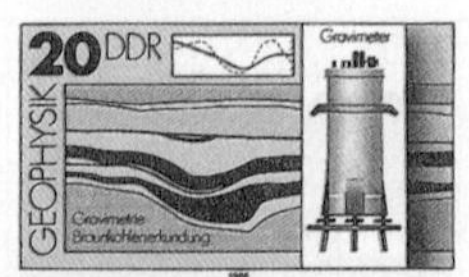

E682 Gravimetry

1980. Geophysics. Multicoloured.

E2273	20pf. Type E **682**	50	30
E2274	25pf. Bore-hole measuring	60	50
E2275	35pf. Seismic prospecting	75	75
E2276	50pf. Seismology	1·20	1·20

E683 Radebeul–Radeburg Steam Locomotive

1980. Narrow-gauge Railways (1st series). Multicoloured.

E2277	20pf. Type E **683**	50	50
E2278	20pf. Bad Doberan–Ostseebad Kuhlungsborn steam locomotive	50	50
E2279	25pf. Radebeul–Radeburg passenger carriage	50	50
E2280	35pf. Bad Doberan–Ostseebad Kuhlungsborn passenger carriage	50	50

See also Nos. E2342/5, E2509/12 and E2576/9.

E684 Toy Steam Locomotive, 1850

1980. Historical Toys. Multicoloured.

E2281	10pf. Type E **684**	35	35
E2282	20pf. Aeroplane, 1914	1·50	1·50
E2283	25pf. Steam-roller, 1920	35	35
E2284	35pf. Sailing ship, 1825	35	35
E2285	40pf. Car, 1900	1·50	1·50
E2286	50pf. Balloon, 1920	35	35

E685 Mozart

1981. 225th Birth Anniv of Wolfgang Amadeus Mozart (composer). Sheet 55×80 mm.

MSE2287	E **685** 1m. black, carmine-rose and stone	3·50	3·00

E686 "Malus pumila"

1981. Rare Plants in Berlin Arboretum. Mult.

E2288	5pf. Type E **686**	25	20
E2289	10pf. "Halesia carolina" (horiz)	25	20
E2290	20pf. "Colutea arborescens"	25	20
E2291	25pf. "Paulownia tomentosa"	25	20
E2292	35pf. "Lonicera periclymenum" (horiz)	35	25
E2293	50pf. "Calycanthus floridus"	3·00	2·75

E687 Heinrich von Stephan

1981. 150th Birth Anniv of Heinrich von Stephan (founder of U.P.U.).

E2294	**E687**	10pf. black and yellow	60	35

E688 Soldiers on Parade

1981. 25th Anniv of National People's Army. Multicoloured.

E2295	10pf. Type E **688**	35	25
E2296	20pf. Marching soldiers	50	25

E689 Marx and Lenin

1981. 10th East German Socialist Party Congress (1st series).

E2297	**E689**	10pf. multicoloured	60	25

See Nos. E2309/**MS**2313.

E690 Counter Clerks

1981. Post Office Training. Multicoloured.

E2298	5pf. Type E **690**	25	20
E2299	10pf. Telephone engineers	25	20
E2300	15pf. Radio communications	25	20
E2301	20pf. Rosa Luxemburg Engineering School, Leipzig	35	25
E2302	25pf. Friedrich List Communications School, Dresden	1·70	1·30

E691 Erich Baron

1981. Socialist Personalities.

E2303	**E691**	10pf. black and green	30	25
E2304	-	10pf. black and yellow	30	25
E2305	-	10pf. black and blue	30	25
E2306	-	10pf. black and brown	30	25

DESIGNS: No. E2304, Conrad Blenkle; E2305, Arthur Ewert; E2306, Walter Stoecker.

E692 Hotel Merkur Leipzig

1981. Leipzig Spring Fair. Multicoloured.

E2307	10pf. Type E **692**	30	20
E2308	25pf. Open-cast mining machine	60	35

E693 "Ernst Thalmann" (Willi Sitte)

1981. 10th East German Socialist Party Congress (2nd series). Multicoloured.

E2309	10pf. Type E **693**	25	20
E2310	20pf. "Brigadier" (Bernhard Heisig)	25	20
E2311	25pf. "Festival Day" (Rudolf Bergander)	1·20	1·10
E2312	35pf. "Comrades in Arms" (Paul Michaelis)	25	20
MSE2313	108×82 mm. 1m. "When Communists are Dreaming" (Walter Womacka)	2·40	2·10

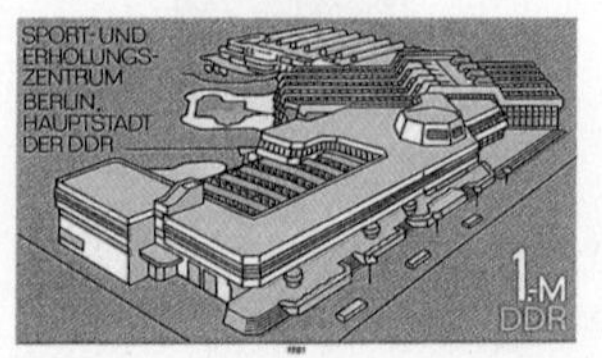

E694 Sports Centre

1981. Sports Centre, Berlin. Sheet 110×90 mm.

MSE2314	E **694** 1m. multicoloured	3·25	3·00

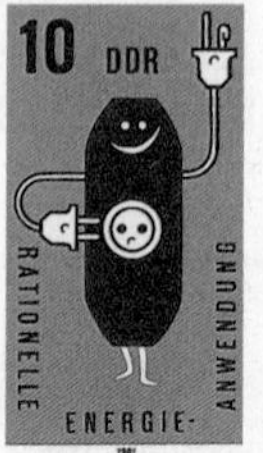

E695 Plugs and Socket

1981. Conservation of Energy.

E2315	**E695**	10pf. black & orange	35	30

E696 Heinrich Barkhausen

1981. Celebrities' Birth Anniversaries.

E2316	**E696**	10pf. black and blue	25	20
E2317	-	20pf. black and red	25	20
E2318	-	25pf. black and brown	3·25	2·40
E2319	-	35pf. black and violet	35	25
E2320	-	50pf. black and green	50	25
E2321	-	70pf. black and brown	75	30

DESIGNS: 10pf. Type E **696** (physicist, birth centenary); 20pf. Johannes R. Becher (writer, 90th birth anniv); 25pf. Richard Dedekind (mathematician, 150th birth anniv); 35pf. Georg Philipp Telemann (composer, 300th anniv); 50pf. Adelbert V. Chamisso (poet and naturalist, bicentenary); 70pf. Wilhelm Raabe (novelist, 150th birth anniv).

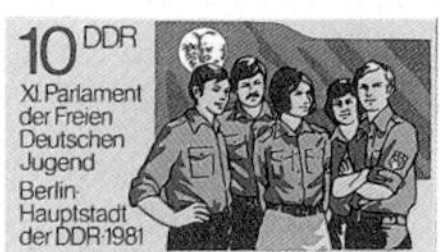

E697 Free German Youth Members and Banner

1981. 11th Free German Youth Parliament. Multicoloured.

E2322	10pf. Type E **697**	35	35
E2323	20pf. Free German Youth members instructing foreign students	35	35

E698 Worlitz Park

1981. Landscaped Parks. Multicoloured.

E2324	5pf. Type E **698**	25	20
E2325	10pf. Tiefurt Park, Weimar	25	20
E2326	15pf. Marxwalde	25	20
E2327	20pf. Branitz Park	25	20
E2328	25pf. Treptow Park, Berlin	2·40	2·20
E2329	35pf. Wiesenburg Park	35	25

E699 Children at Play and Sport

1981. 8th Children's and Young People's Sports Days, Berlin. Multicoloured.

E2330	10pf.+5pf. Type E **699**	85	60
E2331	20pf. Artistic gymnastics	35	30

E700 Berlin Theatre

1981. Birth Bicentenary of Karl Friedrich Schinkel (architect).

E2332	**E700**	10pf. stone and black	1·30	25
E2333	-	25pf. stone and black	3·00	1·30

DESIGN: 25pf. Old Museum, Berlin.

E701 Throwing the Javelin from a Wheel chair

1981. International Year of Disabled Persons. Multicoloured.

E2334	5pf. Type E **701**	35	25
E2335	15pf. Disabled people in art gallery	35	25

E702 House, Zaulsdorf

1981. Half-timbered Buildings. Multicoloured.

E2336	10pf. Type E **702**	25	20
E2337	20pf. "Sugar-loaf" cottage, Gross Zicker (horiz)	25	20
E2338	25pf. Farmhouse, Weckersdorf	25	20
E2339	35pf. House, Pillgram (horiz)	35	25
E2340	50pf. House, Eschenbach	50	30
E2341	70pf. House, Ludersdorf (horiz)	4·25	3·25

1981. Narrow-Gauge Railways (2nd series). As Type E 683. Multicoloured.

E2342	5pf. black and red	35	25
E2343	5pf. black and red	35	25
E2344	15pf. multicoloured	35	25

E2345 20pf. multicoloured 35 25

DESIGNS: Nos. E2342, Freital–Kurort Kipsdorf steam locomotive; E2343, Putbus–Gohren steam locomotive; E2344, Freital–Kurort Kipsdorf luggage van; E2345, Putbus–Gohren passenger carriage.

E703 Chemical Works

1981. Leipzig Autumn Fair. Multicoloured.

E2346 10pf. Type E **703** 30 20
E2347 25pf. New Draper's Hall (horiz) 60 50

E704 Ebers Papyrus (Leipzig University Library)

1981. Precious Books from East German Libraries. Multicoloured.

E2348 20pf. Type E **704** 25 20
E2349 35pf. Maya manuscript (Dresden Library) 25 20
E2350 50pf. Miniature from "Les six visions Messire Francoys Petrarque" (Berlin State Library) 2·20 2·20

E705 Sassnitz Memorial

1981. Resistance Fighters' Memorial, Sassnitz.

E2351 **E705** 35pf. multicoloured 75 50

E706 Henbane and Incense Burner

1981. Early Medical Equipment in the Karl-Sudhoff Institute, Leipzig. Multicoloured.

E2352 10pf. Type E **706** 25 20
E2353 20pf. Dental instruments 25 20
E2354 25pf. Forceps 25 20
E2355 35pf. Bladder knife and hernia shears 35 25
E2356 50pf. Speculum and gynaecological forceps (vert) 3·75 3·75
E2357 85pf. Triploid elevators (vert) 75 50

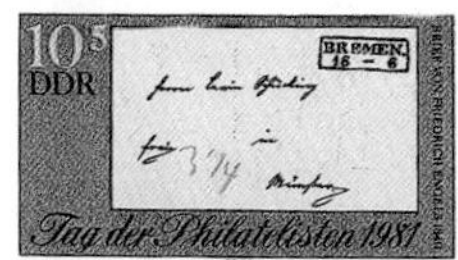

E707 Letter from Friedrich Engels, 1840

1981. Stamp Day. Multicoloured.

E2358 10pf.+5pf. Type E **707** 1·20 85
E2359 20pf. Postcard from Karl Marx, 1878 35 25

E708 African breaking Chains

1981. "Solidarity".

E2360 **E708** 10pf.+5pf. mult 50 25

E709 Tug

1981. Inland Shipping. Multicoloured.

E2361 10pf. Type E **709** 25 20
E2362 20pf. Tug and barges 25 20
E2363 25pf. Diesel-electric paddle-ferry, River Elbe 25 20
E2364 35pf. Ice-breaker in the Oder estuary 35 25
E2365 50pf. "Schonewalde" (motor barge) 50 25
E2366 85pf. Dredger 4·00 3·75

E710 Windmill, Dabel

1981. Windmills. Multicoloured.

E2367 10pf. Type E **710** 25 20
E2368 20pf. Pahrenz 25 20
E2369 25pf. Dresden-Gohlis 25 20
E2370 70pf. Ballstadt 2·40 2·20

E711 Snake, 1850

1981. Historical Toys. Multicoloured.

E2371 10pf. Type E **711** 35 35
E2372 20pf. Teddy bear, 1910 35 35
E2373 25pf. Goldfish, 1935 1·50 1·50
E2374 35pf. Hobby-horse, 1850 1·50 1·50
E2375 40pf. Pull-along duck, 1800 35 35
E2376 70pf. Clockwork frog, 1930 35 35

E712 Coffee Pot, 1715

1982. 300th Birth Anniv of Johann Friedrich Bottger (founder of Meissen China Works). Multicoloured.

E2377 10pf. Type E **712** 25 25
E2378 20pf. Vase decorated with flowers, 1715 50 50
E2379 25pf. "Oberon" (figurine), 1969 75 75
E2380 35pf. Vase "Day and Night", 1979 1·00 1·00
MSE2381 89×110 mm. 50pf. Portrait medal; 50pf. Bottger's seal 4·00 3·00

E713 Post Office, Bad Liebenstein

1982. Post Office Building. Multicoloured.

E2382 20pf. Type E **713** 25 20
E2383 25pf. Telecommunications Centre, Berlin 25 20
E2384 35pf. Head Post Office, Erfurt 35 25

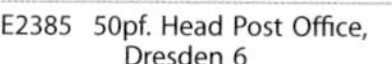

E2385 50pf. Head Post Office, Dresden 6 2·40 2·10

E714 Alpine Marmot

1982. International Fur Auction, Leipzig. Multicoloured.

E2386 10pf. Type E **714** 25 20
E2387 20pf. Polecat 25 20
E2388 25pf. European mink 35 25
E2389 35pf. Beech marten 1·80 1·60

E715 Silhouette of Goethe

1982. Johann Wolfgang von Goethe and Friedrich von Schiller (writers) Commemoration. Sheet 110×90 mm containing Type E 715 and similar vert design. Multicoloured.

MSE2390 50pf. Type E **715** (150th death anniv); 50pf. Silhouette of Schiller (175th death (1980) and 225th birth (1984) annivs) 4·00 3·50

E716 West Entrance to Fairground

1982. Leipzig Spring Fair. Multicoloured.

E2391 10pf. Type E **716** 25 20
E2392 25pf. Seamless steel tube plant, Riesa Zeithain 50 35

E717 Dr. Robert Koch

1982. Centenary of Discovery of Tubercle Bacillus. Sheet 80×55 mm.

MSE2393 E **717** 1m. multicoloured 3·00 2·75

E718 Max Fechner

1982. Socialist Personalities.

E2394 **E718** 10pf. brown 25 20
E2395 - 10pf. green 25 20
E2396 - 10pf. lilac 25 20
E2397 - 10pf. blue 25 20
E2398 - 10pf. green 25 20

DESIGNS: No. E2395, Ottomar Geschke; E2396, Helmut Lehmann; E2397, Herbert Warnke; E2398, Otto Winzer.

E719 Meadow Saffron

1982. Poisonous Plants. Multicoloured.

E2399 10pf. Type E **719** 25 25
E2400 15pf. Bog arum 25 25
E2401 20pf. Labrador tea 25 25
E2402 25pf. Bryony 25 25
E2403 35pf. Monkshood 35 25

E2404 50pf. Henbane 2·00 2·00

E720 Decorative Initial "I"

1982. International "Art of the Book" Exhibition, Leipzig.

E2405 **E720** 15pf. multicoloured 60 60
E2406 - 35pf. brn, red & blk 60 60

DESIGN: 35pf. Exhibition emblem.

E721 "Mother with Child" (W. Womacka)

1982. 10th Free German Trade Unions Association Congress, Berlin.

E2407 **E721** 10pf. black, red and yellow 25 20
E2408 - 20pf. multicoloured 25 20
E2409 - 25pf. multicoloured 90 80

DESIGNS—HORIZ: 20pf. "Discussion by Collective of Innovators" (Willi Neubert). VERT: 25pf. "Young Couple" (Karl-Heinz Jakob).

E722 Osprey

1982. Protected Birds. Multicoloured.

E2410 10pf. Type E **722** 35 25
E2411 20pf. White-tailed sea eagle (horiz) 35 25
E2412 25pf. Little owl 35 25
E2413 35pf. Eagle owl 2·20 1·80

E723 Old and Modern Buildings

1982. 19th Workers' Festival, Neubrandenburg. Multicoloured.

E2414 10pf. Type E **723** 30 30
E2415 20pf. Couple in traditional costume 60 50

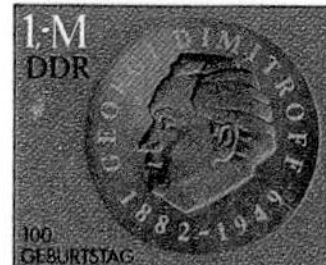

E724 Memorial Medal

1982. Birth Centenary of Georgi Dimitrov (Bulgarian statesman). Sheet 80×55 mm.

MSE2416 E **724** 1m. multicoloured 3·75 3·75

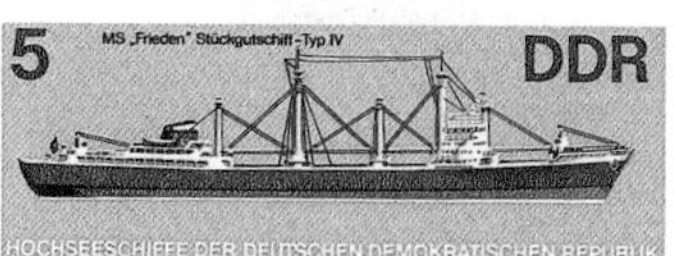

E725 "Frieden" (freighter)

1982. Ocean-going Ships. Multicoloured.

E2417 5pf. Type E **725** 25 20
E2418 10pf. "Fichtelberg" (roll on roll off freighter) 25 20

E2419	15pf. "Brocken" (heavy cargo carrier)	25	20
E2420	20pf. "Weimar" (container ship)	25	20
E2421	25pf. "Vorwarts" (freighter)	25	20
E2422	35pf. "Berlin" (container ship)	2·10	1·80

E726 Members' Activities

1982. 30th Anniv of Sports and Science Association.

E2423	**E726**	20pf. multicoloured	60	30

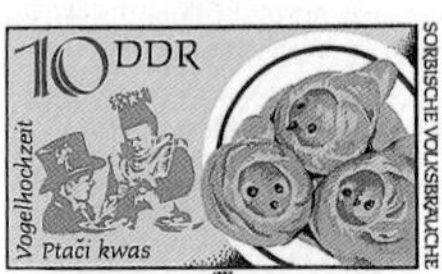

E727 Bird Wedding

1982. Sorbian Folk Customs. Multicoloured.

E2424	10pf. Type E **727**	25	20
E2425	20pf. Shrove Tuesday procession	35	25
E2426	25pf. Egg rolling	50	50
E2427	35pf. Painted Easter eggs	85	85
E2428	40pf. St. John's Day riders	1·00	1·00
E2429	50pf. Distribution of Christmas gifts to hard-working children	1·20	1·20

E728 Schwerin, 1640

1982. 7th National Youth Stamp Exhibition, Schwerin. Multicoloured.

E2430	10pf.+5pf. Type E **728**	50	50
E2431	20pf. Modern Schwerin	50	50

E729 Flag and Pioneers

1982. 7th Pioneers Meeting, Dresden. Mult.

E2432	10pf.+5pf. Type E **729**	75	75
E2433	20pf. Trumpet and drum	25	25

E730 "Stormy Sea" (Ludolf Backhuysen)

1982. Paintings in Schwerin State Museum. Multicoloured.

E2434	5pf. Type E **730**	25	20
E2435	10pf. "Music making at Home" (Frans van Mieris) (vert)	25	20
E2436	20pf. "The Watchman" (Carel Fabritius) (vert)	25	20
E2437	25pf. "Company of Peasants" (Adriaen Brouwer)	35	25
E2438	35pf. "Breakfast Table with Ham" (Willem Claesz Heda)	35	25
E2439	70pf. "River Landscape" (Jan van Goyen)	2·75	2·50

E731 Karl-Marx-Stadt

1982. 13th Socialist Countries' Postal Ministers Conference, Karl-Marx-Stadt.

E2440	**E731**	10pf. multicoloured	75	50

E732 Stentzlers Hof

1982. Leipzig Autumn Fair. Multicoloured.

E2441	10pf. Type E **732**	25	20
E2442	25pf. Amber box, ring and pendant	45	35

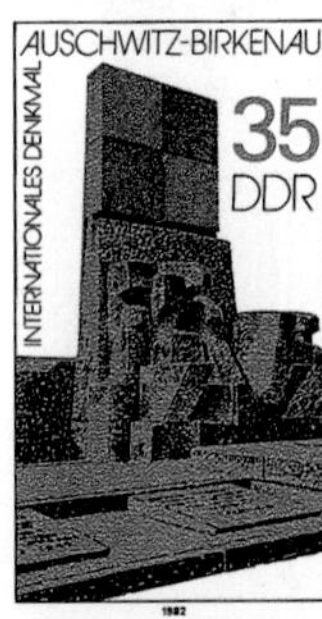

E733 Auschwitz-Birkenau Memorial

1982. War Victims' Memorial, Auschwitz-Birkenau.

E2443	**E733**	35pf. blue, blk & red	60	50

E734 Federation Badge

1982. 9th International Federation of Resistance Fighters Congress, Berlin.

E2444	**E734** 10pf. multicoloured	60	35

E735 "Anemone hupehensis"

1982. Autumn Flowers. Multicoloured.

E2445	5pf. Type E **735**	25	20
E2446	10pf. French marigolds	25	20
E2447	15pf. Gazania	25	20
E2448	20pf. Sunflower	25	20
E2449	25pf. Annual chrysanthemum	35	25
E2450	35pf. Cosmea	3·00	2·30

E736 Palestinian Family

1982. Solidarity with Palestinian People.

E2451	**E736**	10pf.+5pf. mult	60	35

E737 "B 1000" Ambulance

1982. IFA Vehicles. Multicoloured.

E2452	5pf. Type E **737**	25	20
E2453	10pf. Road cleaner	25	20
E2454	20pf. "LD 3000" omnibus	25	20
E2455	25pf. "LD 3000" lorry	35	25
E2456	35pf. "W 50" lorry	35	25
E2457	85pf. "W 50" milk tanker	3·50	2·75

E738 Fair Emblem

1982. 25th "Masters of Tomorrow" Fair, Leipzig.

E2458	**E738**	20pf. multicoloured	50	30

E739 Aircraft and Envelope

1982. Air.

E2459	**E739**	5pf. black and blue	25	25
E2460	**E739**	15pf. black and mauve	25	50
E2461	**E739**	20pf. black and orange	35	25
E2462	**E739**	25pf. black and bistre	60	50
E2463	**E739**	30pf. black and green	35	25
E2464	**E739**	40pf. black and green	50	25
E2465	**E739**	1m. black and blue	1·50	75
E2466	**E739**	3m. black and brown	4·25	2·40
E2467	**E739**	5m. black and red	6·00	2·20

E740 Seal of Eisleben, 1500

1982. 500th Birth Anniv of Martin Luther (Protestant reformer).

E2471	10pf. Type E **740**	30	25
E2472	20pf. Luther as Junker Jog, 1521	35	25
E2473	35pf. Seal of Wittenberg, 1500	60	25
E2474	85pf. Luther (after Cranach)	5·00	3·00

See also No. **MS**2548.

E741 Carpenter

1982. Mechanical Toys. Multicoloured.

E2475	10pf. Type E **741**	30	30
E2476	20pf. Shoemaker	1·70	1·70
E2477	25pf. Baker	30	30
E2478	35pf. Cooper	30	30
E2479	40pf. Tanner	1·70	1·70
E2480	70pf. Wheelwright	30	30

E742 Johannes Brahms

1983. 150th Birth Anniv of Johannes Brahms (composer). Sheet 55×80 mm.

MSE2481	E **742** 1m.15, green, brown and sepia	4·25	3·50

E743 Franz Dahlem

1983. Socialist Personalities.

E2482	**E743**	10pf. brown	25	20
E2483	-	10pf. green	25	20
E2484	-	10pf. green	25	20
E2485	-	10pf. lilac	25	20
E2486	-	10pf. blue	25	20

DESIGN: No. E2483, Karl Maron; E2484, Josef Miller; E2485, Fred Oelssner; E2486, Siegfried Radel.

E744 Telephone Handset and Push-buttons

1983. World Communications Year.

E2487	**E744**	5pf. brown, black and deep brown	25	20
E2488	-	10pf. blue, turquoise and deep blue	25	20
E2489	-	20pf. green, deep green and black	25	20
E2490	-	35pf. multicoloured	1·80	1·30

DESIGNS: 10pf. Aerials and tankers (Rugen Radio); 20pf. Ilyushin Il-62, container ship, letter and parcel; 35pf. Optical fibre cables.

E745 Otto Nuschke

1983. Birth Cent of Otto Nuschke (politician).

E2491	**E745**	20pf. light brown, black and brown	50	35

E746 Stolberg Town Hall

1983. Historic Town Halls. Multicoloured.

E2492	10pf. Type E **746**	25	20
E2493	20pf. Gera (vert)	25	20
E2494	25pf. Possneck (vert)	25	20
E2495	35pf. Berlin	2·00	1·70

E747 Petershof

1983. Leipzig Spring Fair. Multicoloured.

E2496	10pf. Type E **747**	30	25
E2497	25pf. Robotron micro- electronic calculator	50	35

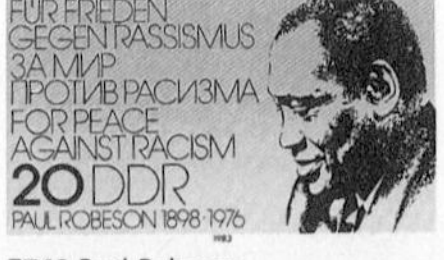

E748 Paul Robeson

1983. 85th Birth Anniv of Paul Robeson (singer).

E2498	**E748**	20pf. multicoloured	50	35

E749 Harnack, Schulze-Boysen and Sieg

1983. 40th Death Annivs of Arvid Harnack, Harro Schulze-Boysen and John Sieg (Resistance workers). Sheet 80×55 mm.

MSE2499	E **749** 85pf. black and green	2·20	2·20

E750 Karl Marx and Newspaper Mastheads

1983. Death Cent of Karl Marx. Multicoloured.

E2500	10pf. Type E **750**	25	25
E2501	20pf. Marx, Lyons silk weavers and title page of "Deutsche-Franzosische Jahrbucher"	25	25
E2502	35pf. Marx, Engels and "Communist Manifesto"	35	25
E2503	50pf. Marx and German, Russian and French versions of "Das Kapital"	35	30

E2504	70pf. Marx and part of letter to Wilhelm Bracke containing commentary on German Workers' Party Programme	60	35
E2505	85pf. Globe and banner portraying Marx, Engels, Lenin	3·75	3·75
MSE2506	81×56 mm. 1m.15 Karl Marx (26×32 mm)	3·75	3·25

E751 "Athene"

1983. Sculptures in State Museum, Berlin.

E2507	**E751**	10pf. brown, light brown and blue	30	20
E2508	-	20pf. brown, light brown and green	60	35

DESIGN: 20pf. "Amazon".

1983. Narrow-gauge Railways (3rd series). As Type E 683.

E2509	15pf. grey, black and red	60	60
E2510	20pf. multicoloured	60	60
E2511	20pf. grey, black and red	60	60
E2512	50pf. brown, black and grey	60	60

DESIGNS: No. E2509, Wernigerode-Nordhausen steam locomotive; E2510, Wernigerode-Nordhausen passenger carriage; E2511, Zittau-Kurort Oybin/Kurort Jonsdorf steam locomotive; E2512, Zittau-Kurort Oybin/Kurort Jonsdorf luggage van.

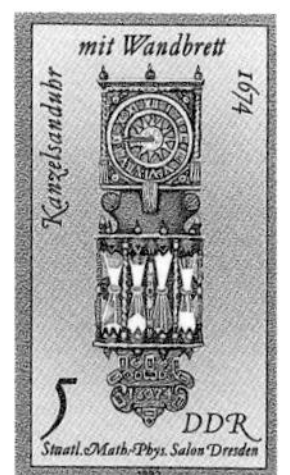

E752 Chancery Hourglass with Wallmount, 1674

1983. Hourglasses and Sundials. Multicoloured.

E2513	5pf. Type E **752**	25	20
E2514	10pf. Chancery hour-glass, 1700	25	20
E2515	20pf. Horizontal table sundial, 1611	25	20
E2516	30pf. Equatorial sundial, 1750	35	25
E2517	50pf. Equatorial sundial, 1760	60	35
E2518	85pf. "Noon Gun" table sundial, 1800	3·50	3·00

E753 "Coryphantha elephantidens"

1983. Cultivated Cacti. Multicoloured.

E2519	5pf. Type E **753**	25	20
E2520	10pf. "Thelocactus schwarzii"	25	20
E2521	20pf. "Leuchtenbergia principis"	25	20
E2522	25pf. "Submatucana madisoniorum"	30	25
E2523	35pf. "Oroya peruviana"	35	25
E2524	50pf. "Copiapoa cinerea"	2·40	2·20

E754 Thimo and Wilhelm

1983. Founders of Naumberg Cathedral. Statues in the West Choir. Multicoloured.

E2525	20pf. Type E **754**	60	60
E2526	25pf. Gepa and Gerburg	75	75
E2527	35pf. Hermann and Reglindis	85	85
E2528	85pf. Eckehard and Uta	2·10	2·10

E755 "Glasewaldt and Zinna defending the Barricade, Berlin, 1848" (Theodor Hosemann)

1983. "Junior Sozphilex 1983" Stamp Exhibition, Berlin.

E2529	**E 755**	10pf.+5pf. brown, black and red	1·00	85
E2530	-	20pf. multicoloured	35	25

DESIGN—HORIZ: 20pf. "Instruction at Polytechnic" (Harald Metzkes).

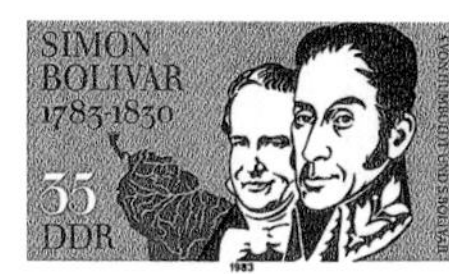

E756 Simon Bolivar and Alexander von Humboldt

1983. Birth Bicentenary of Simon Bolivar.

E2531	**E756**	35pf. black, brown and deep brown	85	50

E757 Exercise with Balls

1983. 7th Gymnastics and Sports Festival and 9th Children and Young People's Sports Days, Leipzig. Multicoloured.

E2532	10pf.+5pf. Type E **757**	85	60
E2533	20pf. Volleyball	30	30

E758 Arms of Cottbus

1983. Town Arms (1st series).

E2534	**E758**	50pf. multicoloured	1·10	1·10
E2535	-	50pf. multicoloured	1·10	1·10
E2536	-	50pf. red, black and silver	1·10	1·10
E2537	-	50pf. multicoloured	1·10	1·10
E2538	-	50pf. black, red and silver	1·10	1·10

DESIGNS: No. E2535, Dresden; E2536, Erfurt; E2537, Frankfurt-on-Oder. (21×39 mm); No. E2538, Berlin.

See also Nos. E2569/73 and E2644/8.

E759 Central Fair Palace

1983. Leipzig Autumn Fair. Multicoloured.

E2539	10pf. Type E **759**	30	20
E2540	25pf. Microchip	75	35

E760 Militiaman

1983. 30th Anniv of Workers' Militia. Sheet 63×86 mm.

MSE2541	E **760** 1m. multicoloured	3·25	2·75

E761 Euler, Formula and Model

1983. Death Bicentenary of Leonhard Euler (mathematician).

E2542	**E761**	20pf. blue and black	75	45

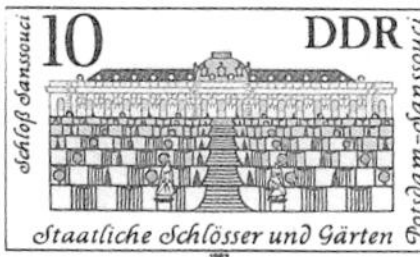

E762 Sanssouci Castle

1983. Public Palaces and Gardens of Potsdam-Sanssouci. Multicoloured.

E2543	10pf. Type E **762**	25	20
E2544	20pf. Chinese tea house	35	25
E2545	40pf. Charlottenhof Palace	60	35
E2546	50pf. Film museum (former stables)	3·75	3·50

E763 "Mother Homeland" (Yevgeni Vuzhetich)

1983. Vologrod War Memorial.

E2547	**E763**	35pf. blue, blk & grn	80	45

E764 "D.M.L." (Dr. Martin Luther)

1983. 500th Birth Anniv of Martin Luther (Protestant reformer) (2nd issue). Sheet 108×83 mm.

MSE2548	E **764** 1m. multicoloured	4·25	3·75

E765 Learning to Read and Write

1983. "Solidarity with Nicaragua".

E2549	**E765**	10pf.+5pf. mult	50	30

E766 Cockerel

1983. Thuringian Glass. Multicoloured.

E2550	10pf. Type E **766**	35	25
E2551	20pf. Beaker	35	25
E2552	25pf. Vase	35	25
E2553	70pf. Goblet	2·75	2·50

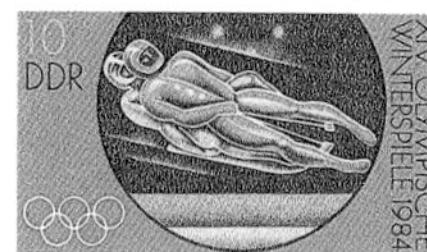

E767 Luge

1983. Winter Olmpic Games, Sarajevo (1984).

E2554	**E767**	10pf.+5pf. multicoloured	25	20
E2555	-	20pf.+10pf. multicoloured	25	20
E2556	-	25pf. multicoloured	25	20
E2557	-	35pf. multicoloured	2·20	1·80
MSE2558		83×57 mm. 85pf. blue and silver	2·75	2·40

DESIGNS: 20pf. Cross-country skiing and ski jumping; 25pf. Cross-country skiing; 35pf. Biathlion; 85pf. Olympic Centre, Sarajevo.

E768 Dove and Greeting in German and English

1983. New Year. Sheet 93×83 mm containing Type E 768 and similar horiz designs, each showing dove and greeting in named languages. Multicoloured.

MSE2559	10pf. Type E **768**; 20pf. German and Russian; 25pf. French and German; 35pf. Spanish and German	2·75	2·40

E769 Dr. Otto Schott (chemist)

1984. Centenary of Jena Glass.

E2560	**E769**	20pf. multicoloured	60	35

E770 Friedrich Ebert

1984. Socialist Personalities.

E2561	**E770**	10pf. black	30	25
E2562	-	10pf. green	30	25
E2563	-	10pf. black	30	25

DESIGNS: No. E2562, Fritz Grosse; E2563, Albert Norden.

E771 Mendelssohn

1984. 175th Birth Anniv of Felix Mendelssohn Bartholdy (composer). Sheet 82×57 mm.

MSE2564	E **771** 85pf. multicoloured	1·70	1·70

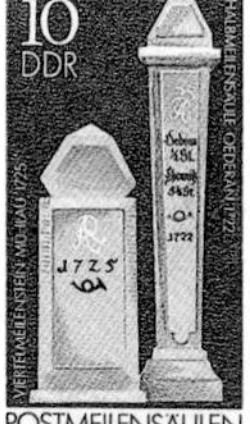

E772 Milestones, Muhlau and Oederan

1984. Postal Milestones. Multicoloured.

E2565	10pf. Type E **772**	25	20
E2566	20pf. Milestones, Johanngeorgenstadt and Schonbrunn	50	35
E2567	35pf. Distance column, Freiberg	60	55
E2568	85pf. Distance column, Pegau	1·20	1·20

1984. Town Arms (2nd series). As Type E 758.

E2569	50pf. multicoloured	75	65
E2570	50pf. red, black and silver	75	65
E2571	50pf. multicoloured	75	65
E2572	50pf. multicoloured	75	65
E2573	50pf. multicoloured	90	85

DESIGNS: No. E2569, Gera; E2570, Halle; E2571, Karl-Marx-Stadt; E2572, Leipzig; E2573, Magdeburg.

E773 Old Town Hall, Leipzig

1984. Leipzig Spring Fair. Multicoloured.

E2574	10pf. Type E **773**	30	25
E2575	25pf. Body stamping press	50	35

1984. Narrow-gauge Railways (4th series). As Type E 683.

E2576	30pf. grey, black and red	35	35
E2577	40pf. grey, black and red	50	50
E2578	60pf. multicoloured	60	60
E2579	80pf. multicoloured	1·00	1·00

DESIGNS: 30pf. Cranzahl–Kurort Oberwiesenthal steam locomotive; 40pf. Selketalbahn steam locomotive; 60pf. Selketalbahn passenger carriage; 80pf. Cranzahl–Kurort Oberwiesenthal passenger carriage.

E774 Town Hall, Rostock

1984. 7th International Society for Preservation of Monuments General Assembly, Rostock and Dresden. Multicoloured.

E2580	10pf. Type E **774**	25	20
E2581	15pf. Albrecht Castle, Meissen	25	25
E2582	40pf. Gateway, Rostock (vert)	75	50
E2583	85pf. Stables, Dresden	1·80	1·60

E775 Telephone, Letter, Pencil and Headquarters

1984. 25th Meeting of Posts and Telecommunications Commission of Council of Mutual Economic Aid, Cracow.

E2584 **E775**	70pf. multicoloured	1·10	50

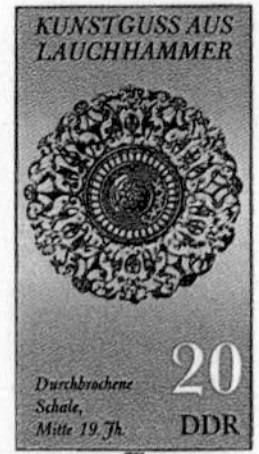

E776 Cast Iron Bowl

1984. Cast Iron from Lauchhammer. Multicoloured.

E2585	20pf. Type E **776**	35	30
E2586	85pf. "Climber" (Fritz Cremer)	1·30	1·30

E777 String Puppet

1984. Puppets. Multicoloured.

E2587	50pf. Type E **777**	85	85
E2588	80pf. Hand puppet	1·50	1·50

E778 Marchers with Flags

1984. National Youth Festival, Berlin. Multicoloured.

E2589	10pf.+5pf. Type E **778**	30	25
E2590	20pf. Young construction workers	35	30

E779 Gera Buildings

1984. 20th Workers' Festival, Gera. Multicoloured.

E2591	10pf. Type E **779**	30	25
E2592	20pf. Couple in traditional costume	35	35

E780 Salt Carrier

1984. National Stamp Exhibition, Halle. Mult.

E2593	10pf.+5pf. Type E **780**	30	25
E2594	20pf. Citizen of Halle with his bride	50	35

E781 Bakers' Seal, Berlin

1984. Historical Seals of 1442. Multicoloured.

E2595	5pf. Type E **781**	50	25
E2596	10pf. Wool weavers, Berlin	85	50
E2597	20pf. Wool weavers, Colln on Spree	1·60	60
E2598	35pf. Shoemakers, Colln on Spree	2·75	2·40

E782 New Flats and Restored Terrace

1984. 35th Anniv of German Democratic Republic (1st issue). Multicoloured.

E2599	10pf. Type E **782**	30	20
E2600	20pf. Surface mining	50	50
MSE2601	80×55 mm. 1m. Privy Council building	1·80	1·80

See also Nos. E2604/**MS**E2607 and E2069/**MS**E2613.

E783 Frege House, Katherine Street

1984. Leipzig Autumn Fair. Multicoloured.

E2602	10pf. Type E **783**	30	25
E2603	25pf. Crystal jar from Olbernhau	50	35

E784 East Ironworks

1984. 35th Anniv of German Democratic Republic (2nd issue). Multicoloured.

E2604	10pf. Type E **784**	25	25
E2605	20pf. Soldiers, Mil Mi-8 helicopter, tank and warship	35	35
E2606	25pf. Petro-chemical complex, Schwedt	50	45
MSE2607	110×90 mm. 1m. bright carmine (Family and new flats) (51×29 mm)	2·00	2·00

E785 "Members of the Resistance" (Arno Wittig)

1984. Resistance Memorial, Georg-Schumann Building, Technical University of Dresden.

E2608 **E785**	35pf. multicoloured	1·10	50

E786 Construction Workers

1984. 35th Anniv of German Democratic Republic (3rd issue). Multicoloured.

E2609	10pf. Type E **786**	25	20
E2610	20pf. Soldiers	35	25
E2611	25pf. Industrial workers	50	45
E2612	35pf. Agricultural workers	60	55
MSE2613	108×88 mm. 1m. Dove and national arms (vert)	1·70	1·70

E787 Magdeburg, 1551

1984. 8th National Youth Exhibition, Magdeburg. Multicoloured.

E2614	10pf.+5pf. Type E **787**	30	30
E2615	20pf. Modern Magdeburg	30	30

E788 "Spring"

1984. Statuettes by Balthasar Permoser in Green Vault, Dresden. Multicoloured.

E2616	10pf. Type E **788**	25	25
E2617	20pf. "Summer"	35	35
E2618	35pf. "Autumn"	60	60
E2619	70pf. "Winter"	1·20	1·20
MSE2620	144×115 mm. No. E 2617×8	3·75	3·75

E789 Entwined Cable and Red Star

1984. "Solidarity".

E2621 **E789**	10pf.+5pf. mult	60	45

E790 Falkenstein Castle

1984. Castles (1st series). Multicoloured.

E2622	10pf. Type E **790**	25	25
E2623	20pf. Kriebstein Castle	35	30
E2624	35pf. Ranis Castle	75	75
E2625	80pf. Neuenburg	1·40	1·40

See also Nos. E2686/9 and E2742/5.

E791 Queen and Princess

1984. Fairy Tales. "Dead Tsar's Daughter and the Seven Warriors" by Pushkin. Multicoloured.

E2626	5pf. Type E **791**	45	35
E2627	10pf. Princess and dog outside cottage	45	35
E2628	15pf. Princess and seven warriors	4·25	2·50
E2629	20pf. Princess holding poisoned apple	4·25	2·50
E2630	35pf. Princess awakened by Prince	45	35
E2631	50pf. Prince and Princess on horse	45	35

E792 Anton Ackermann

1985. Socialist Personalities.

E2632 **E792**	10pf. black	25	25
E2633 -	10pf. brown	25	25
E2634 -	10pf. purple	25	25

DESIGNS: No. E2633, Alfred Kurella; E2634, Otto Schon.

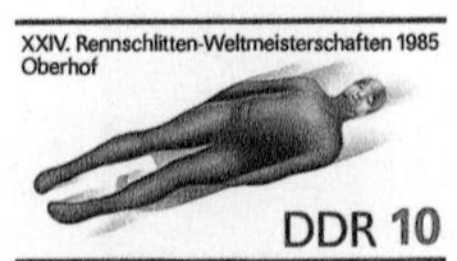

E793 Luge

1985. 24th World Luge Championships, Oberhof.

E2635 **E793**	10pf. multicoloured	50	35

E794 Letter-box, 1850

1984. Letter-boxes.

E2636 **E794**	10pf. brown and black	25	25
E2637 -	20pf. black, brown and red	25	25
E2638 -	35pf. multicoloured	50	50
E2639 -	50pf. brown, black and grey	75	75

DESIGNS: 20pf. Letter-box, 1860; 35pf. Letter-box, 1900; 50pf. Letter-box, 1920.

E795 Semper Opera House, 1985

1985. Re-opening of Semper Opera House, Dresden. Sheet 57×80 mm.

MSE2640 E **795**	85pf. brown, grey and red	1·60	1·60

E796 Bach Statue, Leipzig

1985. Leipzig Spring Fair. Multicoloured.

E2641	10pf. Type E **796**	30	25
E2642	25pf. Meissen porcelain pot	50	35

E797 Johann Sebastian Bach

1985. 300th Birth Annivs of Bach and Handel and 400th Birth Anniv of Schutz (composers). Sheet 90×114 mm containing Type E 797 and similar vert designs, together with se-tenant horiz labels.

MSE2643	10pf. blue and bistre; 20pf. purple and bistre; 85pf. green and bistre	3·50	3·50

DESIGNS: 20pf. Georg Friedrich Handel; 85pf. Heinrich Schutz.

1985. Town Arms (3rd series). As Type E 758. Multicoloured.

E2644	50pf. Neubrandenburg	75	70
E2645	50pf. Potsdam	75	70
E2646	50pf. Rostock	75	70
E2647	50pf. Schwerin	75	70
E2648	50pf. Suhl	85	80

E798 Liberation Monument

1985. Liberation Monument, Seelow Heights.

E2649	**E798**	35pf. multicoloured	75	50

E799 Egon Erwin Kisch

1985. Birth Centenary of Egon Erwin Kisch (journalist).

E2650	**E799**	35pf. multicoloured	75	60

E800 Sigmund Jahn and Valeri Bykovski

1985. 40th Anniv of Defeat of Fascism. Multicoloured.

E2651	10pf. Type E **800**	25	25
E2652	20pf. Adolf Hennecke as miner	35	35
E2653	25pf. Agricultural workers reading paper	45	45
E2654	50pf. Laboratory technicians	85	1·00
MSE2655	55×81 mm. 1m. Soviet war memorial, Berlin-Treptow (22×40 mm)	1·80	1·80

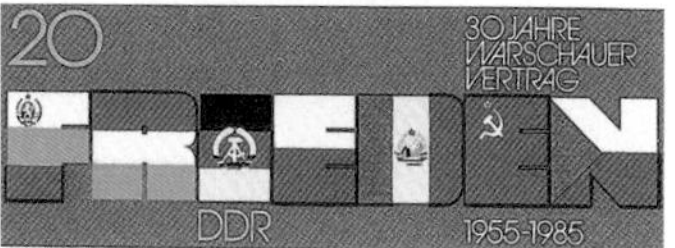

E801 Flags forming "Frieden" (Peace)

1985. 30th Anniv of Warsaw Pact.

E2656	**E801**	20pf. multicoloured	60	35

E802 Emblem and Berlin Buildings

1985. 12th Free German Youth Parliament, Berlin. Multicoloured.

E2657	10pf.+5pf. Type E **802**	35	25

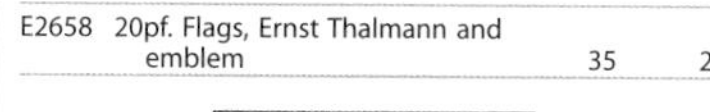

E2658	20pf. Flags, Ernst Thalmann and emblem	35	25

E803 "Solidarity" and Dove on Globe

1985. "Solidarity".

E2659	**E803**	10pf.+5pf. mult	50	30

E804 Olympic Flag

1985. 90th International Olympic Committee Meeting, Berlin.

E2660	**E804**	35pf. multicoloured	1·30	1·00

E805 "40" and Emblem

1985. 40th Anniv of Free German Trade Unions Federation.

E2661	**E805**	20pf. multicoloured	50	35

E806 Harpy Eagle

1985. Protected Animals. Multicoloured.

E2662	5pf. Type E **806**	25	20
E2663	10pf. Red-breasted geese (horiz)	25	20
E2664	20pf. Spectacled bear (horiz)	35	35
E2665	50pf. Bantengs (horiz)	75	60
E2666	85pf. Sunda gavial (horiz)	1·60	1·60

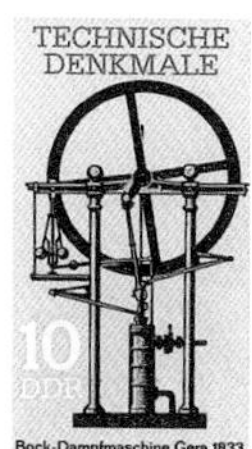

E807 Support Steam-engine, Gera, 1833

1985. Steam Engines. Multicoloured.

E2667	10pf. Type E **807**	30	25
E2668	85pf. Balance steam-engine, Frieberg, 1848	1·50	1·30

E808 Students reading

1985. 12th World Youth and Students' Festival, Moscow. Multicoloured.

E2669	20pf.+5pf. Type E **808**	35	35
E2670	50pf. Students with raised arms	60	60

E809 Diver at Turning Post

1985. Second World Orienteering Diving Championship, Neuglobsow. Multicoloured.

E2671	10pf. Type E **809**	25	25
E2672	70pf. Divers	1·20	1·20

E810 Bose House, Saint Thomas Churchyard

1985. Leipzig Autumn Fair. Multicoloured.

E2673	10pf. Type E **810**	30	25
E2674	25pf. J. Scherzer Bach- trumpet	60	35

E811 Passenger Mail Coach (relief, Hermann Steinemann)

1985. "Sozphilex '85" Stamp Exhibition, Berlin. Multicoloured.

E2675	5pf. Type E **811**	25	25
E2676	20pf.+5pf. Team of horses	35	35

Nos. E2675/6 were printed together, se-tenant, forming a composite design.

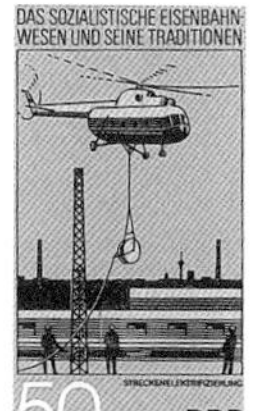

E812 Electrification of Railway

1985. Railways. Multicoloured.

E2677	20pf. Signal box	35	25
E2678	25pf. Andreas Schubert (engineer), his steam locomotive "Saxonia", 1838, and electric locomotive Type BR250	50	35
E2679	50pf. Type E **812**	1·00	85
E2680	85pf. Leipzig Central Station	1·60	1·60

E813 Gertrauden Bridge

1985. Berlin Bridges. Multicoloured.

E2681	10pf. Type E **813**	25	25
E2682	20pf. Jungfern Bridge	35	35
E2683	35pf. Weidendammer Bridge	60	60
E2684	70pf. Marx-Engels Bridge	1·00	1·00
MSE2685	107×128 mm. No. E2673×8	4·50	4·50

1985. Castles (2nd series). As Type E 790. Mult.

E2686	10pf. Hohnstein Castle	25	25
E2687	20pf. Rochsburg	30	30
E2688	35pf. Schwarzenberg Castle	50	50
E2689	80pf. Stein Castle	1·50	1·50

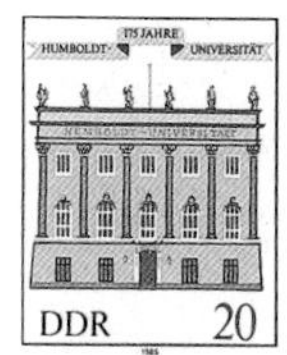

E814 Humboldt University

1985. Anniversaries. Multicoloured.

E2690	20pf. Type E **814** (175th anniv of Humboldt University, Berlin)	35	35
E2691	85pf. New and old Charite buildings (275th anniv of Berlin Charite (training clinic))	1·50	1·50

E815 Cecilienhof Castle and U.N. Emblem

1985. 40th Anniv of U.N.O.

E2692	**E815**	85pf. multicoloured	1·50	75

E816 Elephants on Balls

1985. Circus. Multicoloured.

E2693	10pf. Type E **816**	50	50
E2694	20pf. Trapeze artiste	75	75
E2695	35pf. Acrobats on monocycles	1·50	1·50
E2696	50pf. Tigers and trainer	2·20	2·20

E817 Grimm Brothers

1985. Birth Bicentenaries of Jacob and Wilhelm Grimm (folklorists). Multicoloured.

E2697	5pf. Type E **817**	30	30
E2698	10pf. "The Valiant Tailor"	30	30
E2699	20pf. "Lucky John"	90	1·30
E2700	25pf. "Puss in Boots"	90	1·30
E2701	35pf. "The Seven Ravens"	30	30
E2702	85pf. "The Sweet Pap"	30	30

E818 Water Pump, Berlin, 1900

1986. Water Supply.

E2703	**E818**	10pf. green and red	25	20
E2704	-	35pf. deep brown, brown and green	50	45
E2705	-	50pf. purple & green	85	80
E2706	-	70pf. blue and brown	1·10	1·00

DESIGNS: 35pf. Water tower, Berlin-Altglienicke, 1906; 50pf. Waterworks, Berlin-Friedrichshagen, 1893; 70pf. Rappbode dam, 1959.

E819 Saxon Postilion

1986. Postal Uniforms of 1850. Multicoloured.

E2707A	10pf. Type E **819**	30	25
E2708A	20pf. Prussian postman	50	35
E2709A	85pf. Prussian postal official	1·70	1·60
E2710A	1m. Postal official from Mecklenburg region	2·20	2·20

E820 Flag

1986. 40th Anniv of Free German Youth.
E2711 **E820** 20pf. yellow, bl & blk 60 50

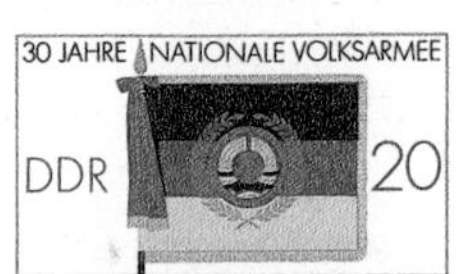

E821 Flag

1986. 30th Anniv of National People's Army.
E2712 **E821** 20pf. multicoloured 1·00 75

E822 Exhibition Hall

1986. Leipzig Spring Fair. Multicoloured.
E2713 35pf. Type E **822** 50 35
E2714 50pf. "Atlantik 488" (factory trawler) 85 60

E823 Yuri Gagarin and "Vostok"

1986. 25th Anniv of Manned Space Flight. Multicoloured.
E2715 40pf. Type E **823** (first man in space) 50 60
E2716 50pf. Cosmonauts Valeri Bykovski and Sigmund Jahn, space station and "Interkosmos" emblem 60 75
E2717 70pf. Space probe "Venera", orbit around Venus and spectrometer 85 1·00
E2718 85pf. Reconnaissance camera MKF-6, photo, "Soyuz 22" spaceship, airplane and research ship 1·10 1·20

E824 Marx, Engels and Lenin

1986. 11th Socialist Unity Party of Germany Day.
E2719 **E824** 10pf. black, red and silver 25 25
E2720 - 20pf. red, black and silver 35 35
E2721 - 50pf. multicoloured 75 75
E2722 - 85pf. black, red and silver 1·50 1·50
MSE2723 80×55 mm. 1m. multicoloured 1·70 1·70
DESIGNS: 20pf. Ernst Thalmann (birth centenary); 50pf. Wilhelm Pieck and Otto Grotewohl, April 1946; 85pf. Family; 1m. Construction worker holding symbolic key.

E825 Memorial

1986. Opening of Ernst Thalmann Park, Berlin.
E2724 **E825** 20pf. multicoloured 60 50

E826 Horse Tram, Dresden, 1886

1986. Trams. Multicoloured.
E2725 10pf. Type E **826** 25 25
E2726 20pf. Leipzig, 1896 35 35
E2727 40pf. Berlin, 1919 85 85
E2728 70pf. Halle, 1928 1·80 1·50

E827 Orang-utan

1986. 125th Anniv of Dresden Zoo. Multicoloured.
E2729 10pf. Type E **827** 35 25
E2730 20pf. Eastern black-and-white colobus 60 50
E2731 50pf. Mandrill 1·20 1·20
E2732 70pf. Ring-tailed lemurs 1·60 1·60

E828 City Seal, 1253

1986. 750th Anniv of Berlin (1st issue).
E2733 **E 828** 10pf. deep brown, bistre and brown 35 25
E2734 - 20pf. olive, grn & brn 75 35
E2735 - 50pf. blk, brn & red 1·50 1·00
E2736 - 70pf. green & brown 2·50 1·90
MSE2737 54×80 mm. 1m. green 2·20 2·20
DESIGNS—HORIZ: 20pf. City map, 1648; 50pf. Oldest City arms. VERT: 70pf. St. Nicolas's Church, 1832; 1m. Cabinet building tower.
See also Nos. E2780/**MS**E2784 and **MS**E2828.

E829 Couple, Tractor and House

1986. 21st Workers' Festival, Magdeburg. Mult.
E2738 20pf. Type E **829** 35 35
E2739 50pf. Port and town of Magdeburg 50 50

E830 Berlin, 1652

1986. 9th Youth Stamp Exhibition, Berlin. Multicoloured.
E2740 10pf.+5pf. Type E **830** 25 25
E2741 20pf. Historic and modern Berlin buildings 35 35

E831 Schwerin Castle

1986. Castles (3rd series). Multicoloured.
E2742 10pf. Type E **831** 25 20
E2743 20pf. Gustrow castle 35 25
E2744 85pf. Rheinsberg castle 1·30 1·30
E2745 1m. Ludwigslust castle 1·80 1·80

E832 Soldiers and Girl before Brandenburg Gate

1986. 25th Anniv of Berlin Wall.
E2746 **E832** 20pf. multicoloured 1·00 60

E833 Doves flying from Emblem

1986. International Peace Year.
E2747 **E833** 35pf. multicoloured 85 60

E834
Ring-Messehaus

1986. Leipzig Autumn Fair. Sheet 82×57 mm containing Type E 834 and similar vert design.
MSE2748 25pf. Type E **834**; 85pf. Merchants displaying cloth 2·00 2·00

E835 Rostock, 1637

1986. Coins.
E2749 **E835** 10pf. black, silver and red 25 20
E2750 - 35pf. black, silver and blue 50 50
E2751 - 50pf. multicoloured 75 75
E2752 - 85pf. black, silver and blue 1·20 1·20
E2753 - 1m. black, silver and green 1·70 1·70
DESIGNS: 35pf. Nordhausen, 1660; 50pf. Erfurt, 1633; 85pf. Magdeburg, 1638; 1m. Stralsund, 1622.

E836 Man with Rifle

1986. 44th World Sports Shooting Championships, Suhl.
E2754 **E836** 20pf. black, green and grey 35 25
E2755 - 70pf. black, red and grey 1·20 1·10
E2756 - 85pf. black, blue and grey 1·50 1·30
DESIGNS: 70pf. Woman with pistol; 85pf. Man with double-barrelled shotgun.

E837 Guard and Boundary Post

1986. 40th Anniv of Border Guards.
E2757 **E837** 20pf. multicoloured 60 50

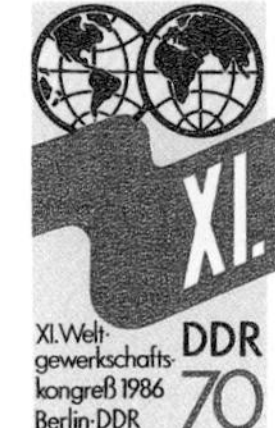

E838 Hemispheres and Red Banner

1986. 11th World Trade Unions Congress, Berlin.
E2758 **E838** 70pf. multicoloured 1·50 1·20

E839 German Members Memorial, Friedrichshain

1986. 50th Anniv of Formation of International Brigades in Spain.
E2759 **E839** 20pf. brown, black and red 60 45

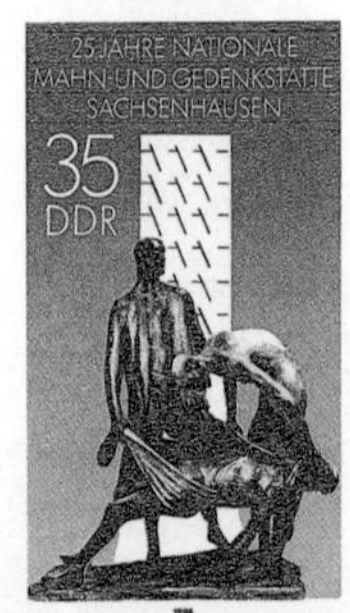

E840 Memorial

1986. 25th Anniv of Sachsenhausen Memorial.
E2760 **E840** 35pf. black, grn & bl 75 50

E841 Double-deck Train Ferry Loading Ramps

1986. Opening of Mukran–Klaipeda Railway Ferry Service. Multicoloured.
E2761 50pf. Type E **841** 60 60
E2762 50pf. "Mukran" (train ferry) 60 60
Nos. E2761/2 were printed together, se-tenant, forming a composite design.

E842 "Help for Developing Countries"

1986. "Solidarity".
E2763 **E842** 10pf.+5pf. mult 50 45

E843 Weber (after F. Jugel)

1986. Birth Bicentenary of Carl Maria von Weber (composer). Sheet 82×57 mm.
MSE2764 E **843** 85pf. multicoloured 1·80 1·70

E844 Indira Gandhi

1986. 2nd Death Anniv of Indira Gandhi (Indian Prime Minister).

E2765	**E844**	10pf. stone & brown	50	35

E845 Candle Holder, 1778

1986. Candle Holders from the Erzgebirge. Multicoloured.

E2766	10pf. Type E **845**	30	30
E2767	20pf. Candle holder, 1796	30	30
E2768	25pf. Candle holder, 1810	85	85
E2769	35pf. Candle holder, 1821	85	85
E2770	40pf. Candle holder, 1830	30	30
E2771	85pf. Candle holder, 1925	30	30

E846 Ronald Statue, Stendal

1987. Statues of Roland (1st series).

E2772	10pf. lt brown, brown & yell	25	20
E2773	20pf. lt brown, brown & bl	35	25
E2774	35pf. lt brown, brown & orge	60	60
E2775	50pf. lt brown, brown & grn	90	90

DESIGNS: Statues at—10pf. Type E **846**; 20pf. Halle; 35pf. Brandenburg; 50pf. Quedlinburg.

See also Nos. E2984/7.

E847 Post Office, Freiberg

1987. Post Offices.

E2776	**E847**	10pf. black, red and blue	25	25
E2777	-	20pf. multicoloured	35	35
E2778	-	70pf. multicoloured	85	85
E2779	-	1m.20 mult	1·80	1·80

DESIGNS: 20pf. Perleberg; 70pf. Weimar; 1m.20, Kirschau.

1987. 750th Anniv of Berlin (2nd issue). As Type E 828.

E2780	20pf. brown and green	30	30
E2781	35pf. green and red	55	55
E2782	70pf. blue and red	1·10	1·10
E2783	85pf. olive and green	1·60	1·60
MSE2784	Four sheets, 75×108 mm (a) or 107×75 mm (others). (a) 10pf. As No. E2780; (b) 10pf. ×4, As No. E2781; (c) 20pf. ×4, As No. E2782; (d) 20pf. ×4, As No. E2783	6·50	7·25

DESIGNS—VERT: 20pf. Ephraim Palace. HORIZ: 35pf. New buildings, Alt Marzahn; 70pf. Marx-Engels Forum; 85pf. Friedrichstadtpalast.

E848 Woman with Flower in Hair

1987. 40th Anniv and 12th Congress (Berlin) of German Democratic Women's Federation.

E2785	**E848**	10pf. blue, red & sil	50	50

E849 Fair Hall 20

1987. Leipzig Spring Fair. Multicoloured.

E2786	35pf. Type E **849**	55	55
E2787	50pf. "Traders at Weighbridge, 1804" (Christian Geissler)	1·00	1·00

E850 Clara Zetkin

1987. Socialist Personalities. Multicoloured.

E2788	**E850**	10pf. purple	35	25
E2789	-	10pf. black	35	25
E2790	-	10pf. black	35	25
E2791	-	10pf. green	35	25

DESIGNS: No. E2789, Fritz Gabler; E2790, Walter Vesper; E2791, Robert Siewert.

E851 Construction Industry

1987. 11th Federation of Free German Trade Unions Congress, Berlin. Multicoloured.

E2792	20pf. Type E **851**	30	30
E2793	50pf. Communications industry	75	75

E852 Flag, World Map and Doves

1987. 10th German Red Cross Congress, Dresden.

E2794	**E852**	35pf. multicoloured	75	50

E853 Museum and Karl August Lingner (founder) (after Robert Sterl)

1987. 75th Anniv of German Hygiene Museum, Dresden.

E2795	**E853**	85pf. multicoloured	1·30	1·20

E854 Old and New Farming Methods

1987. 35th Anniv of Agricultural Co-operatives.

E2796	**E854**	20pf. multicoloured	60	50

E855 Ludwig Uhland (poet)

1987. Birth Anniversaries. Multicoloured.

E2797	10pf. Type E **855** (bicent)	25	25
E2798	20pf. Arnold Zweig (writer, centenary)	35	35
E2799	35pf. Gerhart Hauptmann (writer, 125th anniv)	60	60
E2800	50pf. Gustav Hertz (physicist, centenary)	1·00	1·00

E856 Bream

1987. Freshwater Fishes. Multicoloured.

E2801	5pf. Type E **856**	30	20
E2802	10pf. Brown trout	35	35
E2803	20pf. Wels	35	25
E2804	35pf. European grayling	60	60
E2805	50pf. Barbel	85	60
E2806	70pf. Northern pike	1·20	1·20

E857 Woman holding Baby

1987. "Solidarity" Anti-Apartheid Campaign.

E2807	**E857**	10pf.+5pf. mult	50	35

E858 Horse-drawn Hand-pumped Fire Engine, 1756

1987. Fire Engines. Multicoloured.

E2808	10pf. Type E **858**	25	25
E2809	25pf. Steam engine, 1903	35	35
E2810	40pf. Model "LF 15", 1919	75	75
E2811	70pf. Model "LF 16-TS 8", 1971	1·20	1·20

E859 Ludwig Lazarus Zamenhof (inventor)

1987. Centenary of Esperanto (invented language). Sheet 55×80 mm.

MSE2812	E **859** 85pf. multicoloured	1·50	2·00

E860 Otters

1987. Endangered Animals. European Otter. Multicoloured.

E2813	10pf. Type E **860**	25	20
E2814	25pf. Otter swimming	45	35
E2815	35pf. Otter	60	50
E2816	60pf. Otter's head	1·50	1·40

E861 Tug-of-War

1987. 8th Gymnastics and Sports Festival and 11th Children and Young People's Sports Days, Leipzig. Multicoloured.

E2817	5pf. Type E **861**	25	20
E2818	10pf. Handball	25	20
E2819	20pf.+5pf. Long jumping	35	30
E2820	35pf. Table tennis	50	45
E2821	40pf. Bowling	75	60
E2822	70pf. Running	1·60	1·60

E862 Association Activities

1987. 35th Anniv of Association of Sports and Technical Sciences.

E2823	**E862**	10pf. multicoloured	50	30

E863 Head Post Office, Berlin, 1760

1987. Stamp Day. Multicoloured.

E2824	10pf.+5pf. Type E **863**	30	30
E2825	20pf. Wartenberg Palace	30	30

E864 Market Scene

1987. Leipzig Autumn Fair. Sheet 80×58 mm containing Type E 864 and similar vert design showing "Market Scene" by Christian Geissler.

MSE2826	40pf. multicoloured; 50pf. multicoloured	2·00	2·00

E865 Memorial Statue (Jozsef Somogyi)

1987. War Victims' Memorial, Budapest.

E2827	**E865**	35pf. multicoloured	60	35

E866 Memorial, Ernst Thalmann Park

1987. 750th Anniv of Berlin (3rd issue). Sheet 80×55 mm.

MSE2828	E **866** 1m.35 black, stone and red	2·40	2·40

X. KUNSTAUSSTELLUNG DER DDR · DRESDEN 1987/88

E867 "Weidendamm Bridge" (Arno Mohr)

1987. 10th Art Exhibition, Dresden. Mult.

E2829	10pf. Type E **867**	25	25
E2830	50pf. "They only wanted to learn Reading and Writing (Nicaragua)" (Willi Sitte)	80	80
E2831	70pf. "Big Mourning Man" (Wieland Forster)	1·00	1·00
E2832	1m. Vase (Gerd Lucke) (horiz)	1·90	1·90

E868 Red Flag, Smolny Building (Leningrad), "Aurora" and Lenin

1987. 70th Anniv of Russian Revolution. Multicoloured.

E2833	10pf. Type E **868**	30	20
E2834	20pf. Moscow Kremlin towers	35	25

E869 Youth using Personal Computer

1987. 39th "Masters of Tomorrow" Fair, Leipzig. Multicoloured.

E2835	10pf. Type E **869**	30	20
E2836	20pf. "ZIM 10-S" robot-welder	35	25

E870 Annaberg, 1810

1987. Christmas Pyramids from Erzgebirge. Multicoloured.

E2837	10pf. Type E **870**	35	35
E2838	20pf. Freiberg, 1830	85	85
E2839	25pf. Neustadtel, 1870	35	35
E2840	35pf. Schneeberg, 1870	35	35
E2841	40pf. Lossnitz, 1880	85	85
E2842	85pf. Seiffen, 1910	35	35

E871 Ski Jumping

1988. Winter Olympic Games, Calgary. Mult.

E2843	5pf. Type E **871**	35	25
E2844	10pf. Speed skating	35	25
E2845	20pf.+10pf. Four-man bobsleigh	60	50
E2846	35pf. Biathlon	75	75
MSE2847	80×55 mm. 1m.20 Two-man and single luge (horiz)	2·40	2·10

E872 Berlin-Buch Post Office

1988. Postal Buildings. Multicoloured.

E2848	15pf. Type E **872**	45	25
E2849	20pf. Postal museum	55	25
E2850	50pf. Berlin-Marzahn general post office	1·20	1·00

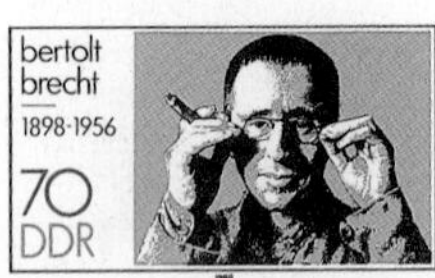

E873 Brecht

1988. 90th Birth Anniv of Bertholt Brecht (writer). Sheet 58×82 mm.

MSE2851	E **873** 70pf. grey, black and red	1·60	1·60

E874 "Tillandsia macrochlamys"

1988. Bromeliads. Multicoloured.

E2852	10pf. Type E **874**	25	20
E2853	25pf. "Tillandsia bulbosa"	35	35
E2854	40pf. "Tillandsia kalmbacheri"	60	60
E2855	70pf. "Guzmania blassii"	1·20	1·20

E875 Madler-passage Entrance

1988. Leipzig Spring Fair. 75th Anniv of Madler-passage (fair building). Each brown, orange and pink.

E2856	20pf. Type E **875**	30	25
E2857	70pf. "Faust and Mephistopheles" (bronze statue, Matthieu Molitor)	1·20	1·00

E876 Eichendorff

1988. Birth Bicentenary of Joseph von Eichendorff (writer). Sheet 82×55 mm.

MSE2858	E **876** 70pf. olive, drab and blue	2·00	1·70

E877 Saddler, Muhlhausen, 1565

1988. Historic Seals. Multicoloured.

E2859	10pf. Type E **877**	25	25
E2860	25pf. Butcher, Dresden, 1564	35	35
E2861	35pf. Smith, Nauen, 16th-century	50	50
E2862	50pf. Clothier, Frankfurt on Oder, 16th-century	65	65

E878 Georg Forster Antarctic Research Station

1988. 12th Anniv of Georg Forster Antarctic Research Station.

E2863	**E878** 35pf. multicoloured	75	50

E879 Wismar

1988. Northern Towns of the Democratic Republic.

E2864	5pf. black, green & turquoise	25	20
E2865	10pf. black, ochre and brown	25	20
E2866	25pf. black, lightt blue & blue	45	30
E2867	60pf. black, pink and red	85	75
E2868	90pf. black, lt green & green	1·20	1·10
E2869	1m.20 black, brown and red	1·60	1·50

DESIGNS: 5pf. Type E **879**.; 10pf. Anklam; 25pf. Ribnitz-Damgarten; 60pf. Stralsund; 90pf. Bergen; 1m.20, Greifswald.

E880 Hutten

1988. 500th Birth Anniv of Ulrich von Hutten (humanist). Sheet 54×80 mm.

MSE2870	E **880** 70pf. black, yellow and ochre	1·70	1·60

E881 Chorin and Neuzelle Monasteries, Industrial and Agricultural Symbols

1988. 22nd Workers' Arts Festival, Frankfurt-on-Oder. Multicoloured.

E2871	20pf. Type E **881**	35	35
E2872	50pf. Buildings of Frankfurt	75	75

E882 Cosmonauts Sigmund Jahn and Valery Bykovski

1988. 10th Anniv of U.S.S.R.–East German Manned Space Flight (1st issue). Multicoloured.

E2873	5pf. Type E **882**	30	25
E2874	10pf. "MKS-M" multi- channel spectrometer	30	25
E2875	20pf. "Mir"–"Soyuz" space complex	35	35

See also Nos. E2894/6.

E883 Erfurt, 1520

1988. 10th Youth Stamp Exhibition, Erfurt and Karl-Marx-Stadt. Multicoloured.

E2876	10pf.+5pf. Type E **883**	25	25
E2877	20pf.+5pf. Chemnitz, 1620	35	35
E2878	25pf. Modern view of Erfurt	35	35
E2879	50pf. Modern view of Karl-Marx-Stadt (formerly Chemnitz)	85	85

E884 Swearing-in Ceremony

1988. 35th Anniv of Workers' Militia Squads. Multicoloured.

E2880	5pf. Type E **884**	35	25
E2881	10pf. Tribute to Ernst Thalmann	35	25
E2882	15pf. Parade	45	45
E2883	20pf. Arms distribution	35	25

E885 Balloons and Doves over Karl-Marx-Stadt

1988. 8th Pioneers Meeting, Karl-Marx-Stadt. Multicoloured.

E2884	10pf. Type E **885**	30	30
E2885	10pf.+5pf. Doves, balloons and Pioneers	30	30

E886 Swimming

1988. Olympic Games, Seoul. Multicoloured.

E2886	5pf. Type E **886**	25	25
E2887	10pf. Handball	25	25
E2888	20pf.+10pf. Hurdling	50	50
E2889	25pf. Rowing	50	50
E2890	35pf. Boxing	75	75
E2891	50pf.+20pf. Cycling	1·10	1·10
MSE2892	55×80 mm. 85pf. Relay race	3·00	3·00

E887 Examining Fair Goods, 1810

1988. Leipzig Autumn Fair and 175th Anniv of Battle of Leipzig. Sheet 110×90 mm containing Type E 887 and similar vert designs. Multicoloured.

MSE2893	5pf. Type E **887**; 15pf. Battle of Leipzig Monument; 100pf. Fair, 1820	2·75	2·75

1988. 10th Anniv of U.S.S.R.–East German Manned space Flight (2nd issue). As Nos. E2873/5 but values changed. Multicoloured.

E2894	10pf. Type E **882**	35	35
E2895	20pf. As No. E2874	50	50
E2896	35pf. As No. E2875	85	85

E888 Buchenwald Memorial (Fritz Cremer)

1988. War Memorials.

E2897	**E888** 10pf. green, black and brown	35	30
E2898	- 35pf. multicoloured	60	50

DESIGN: 35pf. Resistance Monument, Lake Como, Italy (Gianni Colombo).

E889 "'Adolph Friedrich' at Stralsund: Captain C. Leplow" (E. Laschke)

1988. 500th Anniv of Stralsund Shipping Company. Captains' Paintings. Multicoloured.

E2899	5pf. Type E **889**	35	25
E2900	10pf. "'Gartenlaube' of Stralsund: Captain J. F. Kruger" (A. Luschky)	35	25
E2901	70pf. "Brigantina 'Auguste Mathilde' of Stralsund: Captain I. C. Grunwaldt" (Johnsen-Seby Bergen)	1·20	1·20
E2902	1m.20 "Brig 'Hoffnung' of Cologne-on-Rhine: Captain G. A. Luther" (anon)	1·80	1·80

E890 Medical Scene and African Child

1988. "Solidarity".

E2903	**E890** 10pf.+5pf. mult	1·20	1·20

E891 Magdeburg Drawbridge

1988. Drawbridges and Ship Lifts. Mult.

E2904	5pf. Type E **891**	25	20
E2905	10pf. Lift, Magdeburg–Rothensee Canal	25	25
E2906	35pf. Lift, Niederfinow	55	55
E2907	70pf. Bridge and lock, Altfriesack	1·00	1·00
E2908	90pf. Drawbridge, Rugendamm	1·20	1·20

E892 Menorah

1988. 50th Anniv of "Kristallnacht" (Nazi pogrom).

E2909	**E892** 35pf. purple, yellow and black	75	50

E893 "In the Boat"

1988. Birth Centenary of Max Lingner (artist). Multicoloured.

E2910		5pf. Type E **893**	35	25
E2911		10pf. "Mademoiselle Yvonne"	35	25
E2912		20pf. "Free, Strong and Happy"	50	30
E2913		85pf. "New Harvest"	1·60	1·50

E894 Lace (Regine Wengler)

1988. Bobbin Lace from Erzgebirge. Pieces by lacemakers named. Each black, brown and yellow.

E2914		20pf. Type E **894**	35	35
E2915		25pf. Wally Tilp	85	85
E2916		35pf. Elisabeth Mehnert-Pfabe	35	35
E2917		40pf. Ute Siewert	35	35
E2918		50pf. Regine Siebdraht	85	85
E2919		85pf. Elise Schubert	35	35

E895 W.H.O. Emblem

1988. 40th Anniv of W.H.O.

E2920	**E895**	85pf. silver, bl & grey	1·50	75

E896 Dr. Wolf

1988. Birth Centenary of Dr. Freidrich Wolf (writer). Sheet 87×59 mm.

MSE2921	E**896**	110pf. grey, black and vermilion	1·80	1·80

E897 Members' Flags

1989. 40th Anniv of Council of Mutual Economic Aid.

E2922	**E897**	20pf. multicoloured	50	35

E898 Edith Baumann

1989. Socialist Personalities.

E2923	**E898**	10pf. brown	30	20
E2924	-	10pf. green	30	20
E2925	-	10pf. brown	30	20
E2926	-	10pf. blue	30	20

DESIGNS: No. E2924, Otto Meier; E2925, Alfred Oelssner; E2926, Fritz Selbmann.

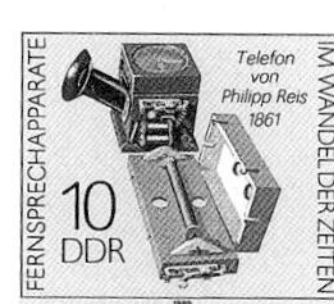

E899 Philipp Reis Telephone, 1861

1989. Telephones. Multicoloured.

E2927		10pf. Type E **899**	25	25
E2928		20pf. Siemens & Halske wall telephone, 1882	35	35
E2929		50pf. "OB 03" wall telephone, 1903	75	75
E2930		85pf. "OB 05" desk telephone, 1905	1·20	1·20

E900 Johann Beckmann (technologist, 250th anniv)

1989. Birth Anniversaries. Multicoloured.

E2931		10pf. Type E **900**	30	20
E2932		10pf. Rudolf Mauersberger and church choir (musician, cent)	30	20
E2933		10pf. Carl von Ossietzky and masthead of "Die Weltbuhne" (journalist and peace activist, centenary)	30	20
E2934		10pf. Ludwig Renn and International Brigades flag (writer, centenary)	30	20
E2935		10pf. Adam Scharrer and cover of "Stateless People" (novelist, centenary)	30	20

E901 Handelshof Fair Building

1989. Leipzig Spring Fair. Multicoloured.

E2936		70pf. Type E **901** (80th anniv)	1·20	1·00
E2937		85pf. Naschmarkt bake-house and bread shop, 1690	1·50	1·30

E902 Muntzer (after Christoph van Stichen and Romeyn de Hooghe)

1989. 500th Birth Anniv of Thomas Muntzer (religious reformer) (1st issue). Sheet 86×66 mm.

MSE2938	E **902**	110pf. black and buff	2·00	2·00

See also Nos. E2967/**MS**2972.

E903 Friedrich List (economist and promoter of railway system)

1989. 150th Anniv of Leipzig–Dresden Railway (first German long-distance service).

E2939	**E903**	15pf. brown, pale brown and green	50	35
E2940	-	20pf. black, green and red	50	25
E2941	-	50pf. black, brown and deep brown	1·00	1·00

DESIGNS: 20pf. Dresdner Station, Leipzig, 1839; 50pf. Leipziger Station, Dresden, 1839.

E904 Tea Caddy

1989. Meissen Porcelain. 250th Anniv of Onion Design. Each brown, blue and ultramarine.

E2942A		10pf. Type E **904**	35	25
E2943A		20pf. Vase	35	30
E2944A		35pf. Bread board	75	75
E2945A		70pf. Coffee pot	1·30	1·30

E905 Renaissance Initial "I"

1989. 7th International Typography Exhibition, Leipzig.

E2946	**E905**	20pf. multicoloured	35	25
E2947	-	50pf. black, yellow and green	75	75
E2948	-	1m.35 red, black and grey	2·10	2·10

DESIGNS: 50pf. Art Nouveau initial "B"; 1m.35, Modern initial "A".

E906 Chollima Statue, Pyongyang

1989. 13th World Youth and Students' Festival, Pyongyang (E2949) and Free German Youth Whitsun Festival, Berlin (E2950). Multicoloured.

E2949		20pf. Type E **906**	50	50
E2950		20pf.+5pf. Berlin buildings	50	50

E907 "Princess Louise"

1989. 225th Birth Anniv of Johann Gottfried Schadow (sculptor). Details of "Princesses". Multicoloured.

E2951		50pf. Type E **907**	1·00	75
E2952		85pf. "Princess Friederike"	1·70	1·50

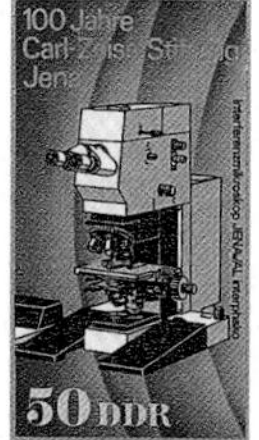

E908 JENEVAL Interference Microscope

1989. Centenary of Carl Zeiss Foundation, Jena. Multicoloured.

E2953		50pf. Type E **908**	65	65
E2954		85pf. "ZKM 01-250 C" bi-coordinate measuring instrument	1·20	1·20

E909 Front Page of Address

1989. Bicentenary of Inaugural Address to Jena University by Friedrich Schiller (writer and philosopher). Each brown, black & grey.

E2955		25pf. Type E **909**	35	35
E2956		85pf. Part of address	1·10	1·10

E910 A. E. Brehm

1989. 160th Birth Anniv of Alfred Edmund Brehm and 125th Death Anniv of Christian Ludwig Brehm (naturalists). Sheet 110×80 mm containing Type E 910 and similar vert design. Multicoloured.

MSE2957		50pf. Type E **910**; 85pf. C. L. Brehm	2·40	13·00

E911 Storming the Bastille

1989. Bicent of French Revolution. Mult.

E2958		5pf. Type E **911**	25	20
E2959		20pf. Sans-culottes	25	25
E2960		90pf. Invading the Tuileries	1·50	1·50

E912 Haflingers

1989. 40th International Horse Breeding in Socialist States Congress, Berlin. Multicoloured.

E2961		10pf. Type E **912**	25	25
E2962		20pf. English thoroughbreds (racehorses)	25	25
E2963		70pf. Heavy horses (plough team)	1·00	1·00
E2964		110pf. Thoroughbreds (dressage)	1·60	1·60

E913 Till Eulenspiegel Fountain

1989. National Stamp Exn, Magdeburg. Fountains by Heinrich Apel. Multicoloured.

E2965		20pf. Type E **913**	30	25
E2966		70pf.+5pf. Devil's fountain	1·20	1·20

E914 "Annunciation to the Peasants"

1989. 500th Birth Anniv of Thomas Muntzer (Protestant reformer) (2nd issue). Details of "Early Bourgeois Revolution in Germany" by Werner Tubke. Multicoloured.

E2967	5pf. Type E **914**	25	20
E2968	10pf. "Fountain of Life"	25	25
E2969	20pf. "Muntzer in the Battle"	35	30
E2970	50pf. "Lutheran Cat Battle"	85	85
E2971	85pf. "Justice, Jester"	1·60	1·60
MSE2972	99×142 mm. No. E2609/4	1·80	1·80

E915 New Fair Building

1989. Leipzig Autumn Fair. Sheet 105×75 mm containing Type E 915 and similar horiz design. Multicoloured.

MSE2973	50pf. Type E **915**; 85pf. New fair building (different)	2·30	2·30

E916 African Children

1989. "Solidarity".

E2974	**E916** 10pf.+5pf. mult	35	35

E917 "Mother Group" (Fritz Cremer)

1989. 30th Anniv of Ravensbruck War Victims' Memorial.

E2975	**E917** 35pf. multicoloured	60	50

E918 "Adriana"

1989. Epiphyllums. Multicoloured.

E2976	10pf. Type E **918**	25	20
E2977	35pf. "Fire Magic"	60	50
E2978	50pf. "Franzisko"	1·00	1·00

E919 Dove, Flag and Schoolchildren

1989. 40th Anniv of German Democratic Republic. Multicoloured.

E2979	5pf. Type E **919**	35	25
E2980	10pf. Combine harvester and agricultural workers	35	25
E2981	20pf. Political activists working together	50	45
E2982	25pf. Industrial workers	75	65
MSE2983	113×93 mm. 135pf. Construction workers (54×32 mm)	6·00	5·00

1989. Statues of Roland (2nd series). As Type E 846. Multicoloured.

E2984	5pf. Zerbst	25	20
E2985	10pf. Halberstadt	25	20
E2986	20pf. Buch-Altmark	35	30
E2987	50pf. Perleberg	85	85

E920 Nehru

1989. Birth Centenary of Jawaharlal Nehru (Indian statesman).

E2988	**E920** 35pf. brown and black	60	60

E921 Schneeberg, 1860

1989. Chandeliers from the Erzgebirge. Mult.

E2989	10pf. Type E **921**	35	35
E2990	20pf. Schwarzenberg, 1850	85	85
E2991	25pf. Annaberg, 1880	35	35
E2992	35pf. Seiffen, 1900	35	35
E2993	50pf. Seiffen, 1930	85	85
E2994	70pf. Annaberg, 1925	35	35

E922 Bee on Apple Blossom

1990. The Honey Bee. Multicoloured.

E2995	5pf. Type E **922**	25	20
E2996	10pf. Bee on heather	25	20
E2997	20pf. Bee on rape	35	35
E2998	50pf. Bee on clover	1·20	1·20

E923 "Courier" (Albrecht Durer)

1990. 500th Anniv of Regular European Postal Services.

E2999	**E923** 35pf. chocolate, light brown and brown	75	75

E924 Erich Weinert

1990. Socialist Personalities.

E3000	**E924** 10pf. blue	45	35
E3001	- 10pf. brown	45	35

DESIGN: No. E3001, Bruno Leuschner.

E925 19th-century Sign, Blankenburg

1990. Posthouse Signs. Multicoloured.

E3002A	10pf. Type E **925**	30	20
E3003A	20pf. Royal Saxony sign (19th century)	35	25
E3004A	50pf. German Empire sign (1870s)	1·00	1·00
E3005A	110pf. German Empire auxiliary station sign (1900s)	2·20	2·20

E926 Bebel

1990. 150th Birth Anniv of August Bebel (politician).

E3006	**E926** 20pf. black, grey and red	75	60

E927 Drawings by Leonardo da Vinci

1990. "Lilienthal '91" European Airmail Exhibition. Historic Flying Machine Designs. Multicoloured.

E3007	20pf. Type E **927**	35	25
E3008	35pf.+5pf. Melchior Bauer's man-powered airplane design, 1764	75	75
E3009	50pf. Albrecht Berblinger's man-powered flying machine, 1811	1·00	1·00
E3010	90pf. Otto Lilienthal's design for a monoplane glider	1·70	1·70

E928 St. Nicholas's Church, Leipzig, and Demonstrators

1990. "We Are The People".

E3011	**E928** 35pf.+15pf. mult	1·30	1·10

E929 Warrior's Head

1990. Museum of German History, Berlin. Stone Reliefs by Andreas Schluter.

E3012	**E929** 40pf. yell, grn & blk	1·00	1·00
E3013	- 70pf. multicoloured	1·30	1·30

DESIGN: 70pf. Warrior's head (different).

E930 Fair Seal, 1268

1990. Leipzig Spring Fair and 825th Anniv of Leipzig. Multicoloured.

E3014	70pf. Type E **930**	2·10	1·10
E3015	85pf. Fair seal, 1497	2·20	1·50

E931 Kurt Tucholsky (writer, centenary)

1990. Birth Anniversaries.

E3016	**E931** 10pf. black, green and deep green	50	50
E3017	- 10pf. black, brown and red	50	50

DESIGN: No. E3017, Friedrich Adolph Wilhelm Diesterweg (educationist, bicent).

E932 "Solidarity of Labour" (Walter Crane)

1990. Centenary of Labour Day.

E3018	**E932** 10pf. grey, black and red	60	60
E3019	- 20pf. red, grey and black	1·20	1·20

DESIGN: 20pf. Red carnation.

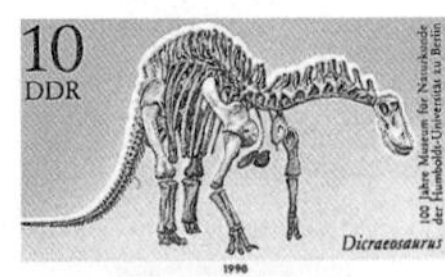

E933 Dicraeosaurus

1990. Centenary of Natural Science Museum, Berlin. Dinosaur Skeletons. Multicoloured.

E3020	10pf. Type E **933**	25	20
E3021	25pf. Kentrurosaurus	45	35
E3022	35pf. Dysalotosaurus	50	50
E3023	50pf. Brachiosaurus (vert)	75	75
E3024	85pf. Skull of brachiosaurus (vert)	1·60	1·60

E934 Penny Black

1990. 150th Anniv of the Penny Black.

E3025	**E934** 20pf. black, mauve and magenta	60	60
E3026	- 35pf.+15pf. red, lilac and black	1·10	1·10
E3027	- 110pf. multicoloured	3·00	3·00

DESIGNS: 35pf. Saxony 1850 3pf. stamp; 110pf. First East Germany stamp, 1949.

E935 Edward Hughes and 1855 Printing Telegraph

1990. 125th Anniv of I.T.U. Multicoloured.

E3028	10pf. Type E **935**	30	30
E3029	20pf. Distribution rods from Berlin-Kopenick post office	50	50
E3030	25pf. Transmitting tower and radio control desk	55	55
E3031	50pf. "Molniya" communications satellite and globe	1·20	1·20
MSE3032	82×56 mm. 70pf. Philipp Reis (telephone pioneer)	3·00	3·00

E936 Pope John Paul II

1990. Pope's 70th Birthday.

E3033	**E936** 35pf. multicoloured	1·20	1·10

E937 Halle (18th-century)

1990. 11th National Youth Stamp Exhibition, Halle. Multicoloured.

E3034	10pf.+5pf. Type E **937**	50	50
E3035	20pf. Modern Halle	50	50

E938 Rules of Order of Teutonic Knights, 1264

1990. Exhibits in German State Library, Berlin. Multicoloured.

E3036	20pf. Type E **938**	60	35
E3037	25pf. World map from "Rudimentum Novitiorum", 1475	85	45
E3038	50pf. "Chosrou and Schirin" by Nizami (18th century Persian manuscript)	1·70	1·10
E3039	110pf. Book cover from Amalia musical library	3·25	2·75

WEST GERMAN CURRENCY

On 1 July 1990 the Ostmark was abolished and replaced by the West German Deutsche Mark.

E939 Albrechts Castle and Cathedral, Meissen

1990. Tourist Sights.

E3040	**E939**	10pf. blue	45	30
E3041	-	30pf. green	50	35
E3042	-	50pf. green	75	60
E3043	-	60pf. brown	1·00	1·00
E3044	-	70pf. brown	1·00	1·00
E3045	-	80pf. red	1·20	1·50
E3046	-	100pf. red	1·60	1·20
E3047	-	200pf. violet	2·75	2·40
E3048	-	500pf. green	7·00	5·75

DESIGNS: 30pf. Goethe-Schiller Monument, Weimar; 50pf. Brandenburg Gate, Berlin; 60pf. Kyffhauser Monument; 70pf. Semper Opera House, Dresden; 80pf. Sanssouci Palace, Potsdam; 100pf. Wartburg Castle, Eisenach; 200pf. Magdeburg Cathedral; 500pf. Schwerin Castle.

E940 Different Alphabets

1990. International Literacy Year.

E3049	**E940**	30pf.+5pf. on 10pf.+5pf. mult	1·50	1·70

No. E3049 was not issued without surcharge.

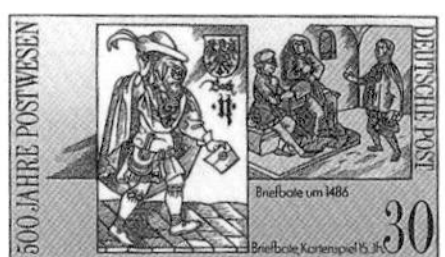

E941 Letter-carrier (from playing card) and Messenger, 1486

1990. 500th Anniv of Regular European Postal Services.

E3050	**E941**	30pf. blk, brn & grn	60	60
E3051	-	50pf. black, red and blue	85	85
E3052	-	70pf. black, brown and red	1·10	1·50
E3053	-	100pf. black, grn & bl	1·80	1·80

DESIGNS: 50pf. "Courier" (Albrecht Durer) and post rider, 1590; 70pf. Open wagon, 1595, and mail carriage, 1750; 100pf. Travelling post office vans, 1842 and 1900.

E942 Louis Lewandowski (choir conductor)

1990. Reconstruction of New Synagogue, Berlin. Multicoloured.

E3054	30pf. Type E **942**	50	50
E3055	50pf.+15pf. New Synagogue	1·00	1·00

E943 Schliemann and Two-handled Vessel

1990. Death Cent of Heinrich Schliemann (archaeologist). Multicoloured.

E3056	30pf. Type E **943**	50	50
E3057	50pf. Schliemann and double pot (horiz)	1·00	1·00

E944 Dresden

1990. 41st International Astronautics Federation Congress, Dresden.

E3058	**E944**	30pf. black and grey	35	35
E3059	-	50pf. multicoloured	75	75
E3060	-	70pf. dp bl, grn & bl	1·20	1·50
E3061	-	100pf. multicoloured	1·70	1·70

DESIGNS: 50pf. Earth; 70pf. Moon; 100pf. Mars.

On 3 October 1990 the territory of the Democratic Republic was absorbed into the Federal Republic of Germany, whose stamps have been used since then.

OFFICIAL STAMPS

EO58 (Cross-piece projects to left)

1954. (a) Design in minute dots.

EO185	**EO58**	5pf. green	45
EO186	**EO58**	6pf. violet	2·30
EO187	**EO58**	8pf. brown	45
EO188	**EO58**	10pf. turquoise	45
EO189	**EO58**	12pf. blue	45
EO190	**EO58**	15pf. violet	45
EO191	**EO58**	16pf. violet	1·70
EO192	**EO58**	20pf. olive	45
EO193	**EO58**	24pf. red	80
EO194	**EO58**	25pf. turquoise	80
EO195	**EO58**	30pf. red	70
EO196	**EO58**	40pf. red	45
EO197	**EO58**	48pf. lilac	6·75
EO198	**EO58**	50pf. lilac	1·00
EO199	**EO58**	60pf. blue	1·10
EO200	**EO58**	70pf. brown	1·00
EO201	**EO58**	84pf. brown	11·50

EO59 (Cross-piece projects to right)

(b) Design in lines.

EO202	**EO59**	5pf. green		70
EO203	**EO59**	10pf. turquoise		55
EO204	**EO59**	12pf. turquoise		55
EO205	**EO59**	15pf. violet		55
EO207	**EO59**	25pf. green		2·50
EO210	**EO59**	50pf. lilac		1·10
EO211	**EO59**	70pf. brown		1·40
EO298	**EO59**	20pf. olive	70	35
EO299	**EO59**	30pf. red	£130	35
EO300	**EO59**	40pf. red	1·10	35

EO84

1956. For internal use.

EO257	**EO84**	5pf. black	4·00	35
EO258	**EO84**	10pf. black	1·40	35
EO259	**EO84**	20pf. black	80	45
EO260	**EO84**	40pf. black	5·75	55
EO261	**EO84**	70pf. black	£200	70

Nos. EO257/61 were not on sale to the public in unused condition, although specimens of all values are available on the market. The used prices are for cancelled-to-order, with segments across the corners of the stamps. Postally used are worth more.

OFFICIAL CENTRAL COURIER SERVICE STAMPS

These were for use on special postal services for confidential mail between Government officials and state-owned enterprises.

EO95

1956. With or without control figures.

EO303	**EO95**	10pf. black & purple	80	1·70
EO304	**EO95**	20pf. black & purple	2·30	1·70
EO305	**EO95**	40pf. black & purple	80	3·50
EO306	**EO95**	70pf. black & purple	4·00	75·00

EO123

1958. With various control figures. (a) With one bar (thick or thin) each side of figure.

EO357	**EO123**	(10pf.) red & yell	55·00	7·50
EO373	**EO123**	(10pf.) brown & bl	28·00	9·00
EO375	**EO123**	(10pf.) violet and orange	34·00	11·50
EO377	**EO123**	(10pf.) red and green	12·50	13·50

(b) With two bars (thick or thin) each side of figure.

EO358	(20pf.) red & yell	55·00	4·50
EO374	(20pf.) brown & bl	70·00	5·75
EO376	(20pf.) violet and orange	90·00	9·00
EO378	(20pf.) red and green	17·00	6·25

Used prices for Nos. EO357/EO378 are for postally used copies.

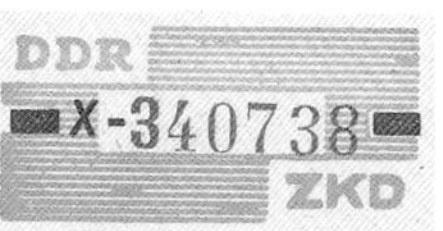

EO149

1959. With various control figures. (a) With one bar each side of figure.

EO414	**EO149**	(10pf.) red, violet and green	13·50	9·00
EO416	**EO149**	(10pf.) black & bl	17·00	85·00
EO418	**EO149**	(10pf.) black, brown and blue	55·00	95·00

(b) With two bars each side of figure.

EO415	(20pf.) blue, brown and yellow	20·00	8·00
EO417	(20pf.) green, blue and red	17·00	11·50
EO419	(20pf.) violet, black and brown	40·00	8·00

REGISTRATION STAMPS

SELF=SERVICE POST OFFICE

These registration labels embody a face value to cover the registration fee and have franking value to this extent. They are issued in pairs from automatic machines together with a certificate of posting against a 50pf. coin. The stamps are serially numbered in pairs and inscribed with the name of the town of issue.

The procedure is to affix one label to the letter (already franked with stamps for carriage of the letter) and complete page 1 of the certificate of posting which is then placed in the box provided together with the letter. The duplicate label is affixed to the second page of the certificate and retained for production as evidence in the event of a claim. They are not obtainable over the post office counter.

Unused prices are for pairs.

ER318

1967

ER992	**ER318**	50pf. red and black	4·75

ER319

1968

ER993	**ER319**	50pf. red	2·30

ER345

1968. For Parcel Post.

ER1089	**ER345**	50pf. black	8·00

Pt. 1

GIBRALTAR

A British colony at the W. entrance to the Mediterranean.

1886. 12 pence = 1 shilling; 20 shillings = 1 pound.
1971. 100 (new) pence = 1 pound.

1886. Stamps of Bermuda (Queen Victoria) optd GIBRALTAR.

1	9	½d. green	18·00	9·50
2	9	1d. red	80·00	4·50
3	9	2d. purple	£140	80·00
4	9	2½d. blue	£180	3·25
5	9	4d. orange	£180	£100
6	9	6d. lilac	£300	£225
7	9	1s. brown	£450	£375

2

1886. Various frames.

39	2	½d. green	11·00	1·75
40	2	1d. red	11·00	50
10	2	2d. purple	30·00	27·00
42	2	2½d. blue	35·00	50
12	2	4d. orange	85·00	80·00
13	2	6d. lilac	£140	£130
14	2	1s. brown	£250	£200

1889. Surch with new value in CENTIMOS.

15	5c. on ½d. green	8·00	29·00
16	10c. on 1d. red	13·00	16·00
17	25c. on 2d. purple	4·75	11·00
18	25c. on 2½d. blue	24·00	2·25
19	40c. on 4d. orange	55·00	75·00
20	50c. on 6d. lilac	55·00	75·00
21	75c. on 1s. brown	55·00	65·00

7

1889

22	7	5c. green	5·50	80
23	7	10c. red	4·50	50
24	7	20c. green and brown	45·00	23·00
25	7	20c. green	15·00	£100
26	7	25c. blue	23·00	70
27	7	40c. orange	3·75	4·00
28	7	50c. lilac	3·25	2·00
29	7	75c. green	32·00	32·00
30	7	1p. brown	75·00	20·00
31	7	1p. brown and blue	4·75	8·00
32	7	2p. black and red	11·00	30·00
33	7	5p. grey	42·00	£100

1898. As 1886.

41	2	2d. purple and blue	24·00	1·75
43	2	4d. brown and green	18·00	4·75
44	2	6d. violet and red	42·00	24·00
45	2	1s. brown and red	38·00	11·00

1903

66	8	½d. green	10·00	1·75
57c	8	1d. purple on red	8·00	85
58a	8	2d. green and red	10·00	11·00
49	8	2½d. purple and black on blue	7·50	60
60a	8	6d. purple and violet	32·00	18·00
61a	8	1s. black and red	55·00	20·00
62a	9	2s. green and blue	95·00	£120
53	9	4s. purple and green	£120	£200
54	9	8s. purple and black on blue	£160	£180
55	9	£1 purple and black on red	£550	£700

8

9

1907

67		1d. red	5·50	60
68		2d. grey	8·50	11·00
69		2½d. blue	6·00	1·60
70		6d. purple	£140	£375
71		1s. black on green	23·00	21·00
72	9	2s. purple and blue on blue	50·00	48·00
73	9	4s. black and red	£150	£170
74	9	8s. purple and green	£225	£225

1912. As T 8/9, but portrait of King George V. (3d. A. Inscr "3 PENCE". B. Inscr "THREE PENCE").

89	½d. green	1·50	1·50
90	1d. red	1·75	1·00
91a	1½d. brown	2·00	30
93	2d. grey	1·25	1·25
79	2½d. blue	10·00	2·00
95a	3d. blue (A)	2·50	1·50
109	3d. blue (B)	7·50	2·00
97a	6d. purple	1·60	3·50
81	1s. black on green	12·00	3·25
102a	1s. olive and black	14·00	18·00
82	2s. purple and blue on blue	26·00	3·50
103	2s. brown and black	10·00	38·00
104	2s.6d. green and black	10·00	25·00
83	4s. black and red	35·00	55·00
105	5s. red and black	16·00	75·00
84	8s. purple and green	85·00	£120
106	10s. blue and black	32·00	80·00
85	£1 purple and black on red	£140	£225
107	£1 orange and black	£180	£275
108	£5 violet and black	£1500	£5500

1918. Optd WAR TAX.

86	½d. green (No. 89)	1·00	1·75

13 The Rock of Gibraltar

1931

110	13	1d. red	2·50	2·50
111	13	1½d. brown	1·75	2·25
112	13	2d. grey	6·50	1·75
113	13	3d. blue	6·00	3·00

1935. Silver Jubilee. As T 10a of Gambia.

114	2d. blue and black	1·60	2·50
115	3d. brown and blue	3·25	5·00
116	6d. green and blue	13·00	19·00
117	1s. grey and purple	15·00	19·00

1937. Coronation. As T 10b of Gambia.

118	½d. green	25	50
119	2d. grey	2·00	3·25
120	3d. blue	2·75	3·25

14 King George VI **15** Rock of Gibraltar

1938. King George VI.

121	14	½d. green	10	40
122b	15	1d. brown	50	60
123	15	1½d. red	35·00	1·00
123b	-	1½d. violet	50	1·50
124a	-	2d. grey	5·00	35
124c	-	2d. red	50	60
125b	-	3d. blue	1·75	30
125c	-	5d. orange	1·25	1·25
126b	-	6d. red and violet	7·50	1·75
127b	-	1s. black and green	3·25	4·25
128b	-	2s. black and brown	7·50	6·50
129b	-	5s. black and red	30·00	17·00
130a	-	10s. black and blue	40·00	25·00
131	14	£1 orange	40·00	48·00

DESIGNS—HORIZ: 2d. The Rock (North side); 3d., 5d. Europa Point; 6d. Moorish Castle; 1s. South-port Gate; 2s. Eliott Memorial; 5s. Government House; 10s. Catalan Bay.

1946. Victory. As T 11a of Gambia.

132	½d. green	10	1·50
133	3d. blue	50	1·25

1948. Silver Wedding. As T 11b/11c of Gambia.

134	½d. green	1·50	3·00
135	£1 orange	60·00	75·00

1949. U.P.U. As T 11d/11g of Gambia.

136	2d. red	1·00	1·25
137	3d. blue	2·00	1·50
138	6d. purple	1·25	2·00
139	1s. green	1·00	3·50

1950. Inauguration of Legislative Council. Optd NEW CONSTITUTION 1950.

140	2d. red (No. 124c)	30	1·50
141	3d. blue (No. 125b)	65	1·00
142	6d. red and violet (No. 126b)	75	2·00
143	1s. black and green (No. 127b)	75	2·00

1953. Coronation. As T 11h of Gambia.

144	½d. black and green	60	1·75

24 Cargo and Passenger Wharves

1953

145	24	½d. blue and green	15	30
146	-	1d. green	1·50	1·00
147	-	1½d. black	1·00	2·25
148	-	2d. brown	2·00	1·00
149a	-	2½d. red	6·50	1·50
150	-	3d. blue	4·75	10
151	-	4d. blue	6·50	3·50
152	-	5d. purple	1·75	1·25
153	-	6d. black and blue	4·00	1·75
154	-	1s. blue and brown	85	1·50
155a	-	2s. orange and violet	28·00	7·00
156	-	5s. brown	40·00	16·00
157	-	10s. brown and blue	45·00	42·00
158	-	£1 red and yellow	50·00	50·00

DESIGNS—HORIZ: 1d. South view from Straits; 1½d. Gibraltar Fish Canneries; 2d. Southport Gate; 2½d. Sailing in the Bay; 3d. Liner; 4d. Coaling wharf; 5d. English Electric Canberra at Gibraltar Airport; 6d. Europa Point; 1s. Straits from Buena Vista; 2s. Rosia Bay and Straits; 5s. Main entrance, Government House. VERT: 10s. Tower of Homage, Moorish Castle; £1 Arms of Gibraltar.

1954. Royal Visit. As No. 150, but inscr "ROYAL VISIT 1954".

159	3d. blue	50	20

38 Gibraltar Candytuft

40 St. George's Hall

1960

160	38	½d. purple and green	15	50
161	-	1d. black and green	20	10
162	-	2d. blue and brown	1·00	20
163a	-	2½d. black and blue	1·25	30
164	-	3d. blue and orange	1·00	10
199	-	4d. brown and turquoise	30	2·50
166	-	6d. brown and green	1·00	70
167	-	7d. blue and red	2·50	1·75
168	-	9d. blue and turquoise	1·00	1·00
169	-	1s. brown and green	1·50	70
170	-	2s. brown and blue	19·00	3·25
171	-	5s. blue and green	8·00	7·50
172	-	10s. yellow and blue	25·00	20·00
173	40	£1 black and brown	20·00	20·00

DESIGNS (As Type **38**):—HORIZ: 1d. Moorish Castle; 2d. St George's Hall; 3d. The Rock by moonlight; 4d. Catalan Bay; 1s. Barbary ape; 2s. Barbary Partridge; 5s. Blue Rock Thrush. VERT: 2½d. The keys; 6d. Map of Gibraltar; 7d. Hawker Siddeley Comet 4 over airport; 9d. American War Memorial; 10s. Rock lily.

1963. Freedom from Hunger. As T 21a of Gambia.

174	40	9d. sepia	3·00	1·50

1963. Centenary of Red Cross. As T 21b of Gambia.

175	1d. red and black	1·00	2·00
176	9d. red and blue	2·50	4·50

1964. 400th Birth Anniv of Shakespeare. As T 35a of Gambia.

177	7d. bistre	60	20

1964. New Constitution. Nos. 164 and 166 optd NEW CONSTITUTION 1964.

178	3d. blue and orange	20	10
179	6d. sepia and green	20	60

52a I.T.U. Emblem

1965. Centenary of I.T.U.

180	52a	4d. green and yellow	2·00	50
181	52a	2s. green and blue	5·50	3·25

52b I.C.Y. Emblem

1965. I.C.Y.

182	52b	½d. green and lavender	20	2·75
183	52b	4d. purple and turquoise	80	50

The value of the ½d. stamp is shown as "1/2".

52c Sir Winston Churchill and St. Paul's Cathedral in Wartime

1966. Churchill Commemoration.

184	52c	½d. blue	20	2·25
185	52c	1d. green	30	10
186	52c	4d. brown	1·25	10
187	52c	9d. violet	1·25	2·50

52d Footballer's legs, ball and Jules Rimet cup

1966. World Cup Football Championships.

188	52d	2½d. multicoloured	75	1·00
189	52d	6d. multicoloured	1·00	50

53 Red Seabream

1966. European Sea Angling Championships. Gibraltar.

190	53	4d. red, blue and black	30	10
191	-	7d. red, green and black	60	70
192	-	1s. brown, green and black	50	30

DESIGNS—HORIZ: 7d. Red scorpionfish. VERT: 1s. Stone bass.

54 W.H.O. Building

1966. Inauguration of W.H.O. Headquarters, Geneva.

193	54	6d. black, green and blue	3·00	1·75
194	54	9d. black, purple and ochre	3·50	3·00

56 "Our Lady of Europa"

1966. Centenary of Re-enthronement of "Our Lady of Europa".

195	56	2s. blue and black	30	80

56a "Education"

56b "Science"

56c "Culture"

1966. 20th Anniv of UNESCO.

196	56a	2d. multicoloured	60	10
197	56b	7d. yellow, violet and olive	2·25	10
198	56c	5s. black, purple & orge	4·50	3·00

57 H.M.S. "Victory"

1967. Multicoloured.. Multicoloured..

200	½d. Type **57**	10	20
201	1d. "Arab" (early steamer)	10	10
202	2d. H.M.S. "Carmania" (merchant cruiser)	15	10
203	2½d. "Mons Calpe" (ferry)	40	30
204	3d. "Canberra" (liner)	20	10
205	4d. H.M.S. "Hood" (battle cruiser)	30	10
205a	5d. "Mirror" (cable ship)	2·00	55
206	6d. Xebec (sailing vessel)	30	50
207	7d. "Amerigo Vespucci" (Italian cadet ship)	30	1·00
208	9d. "Raffaello" (liner)	30	1·75
209	1s. "Royal Katherine" (galleon)	30	35
210	2s. Fairey Swordfish over H.M.S. "Ark Royal" (aircraft carrier, 1937)	4·00	2·50
211	5s. H.M.S. "Dreadnought" (nuclear submarine)	3·50	7·00
212	10s. "Neuralia" (liner)	14·00	23·00
213	£1 "Mary Celeste" (sailing vessel)	14·00	24·00

58 Aerial Ropeway

1967. International Tourist Year. Multicoloured.

214	7d. Type **58**	15	10
215	9d. Shark fishing (horiz)	15	10
216	1s. Skin-diving (horiz)	20	15

59 Mary, Joseph and Child Jesus

1967. Christmas. Multicoloured.

217	2d. Type **59**	15	10
218	6d. Church window (vert)	15	10

61 General Eliott and Route Map

1967. 250th Birth Anniv of General Eliott. Mult.

No.	Type	Description	Unused	Used
219		4d. Type **61**	15	10
220		9d. Heathfield Tower and Monument, Sussex	15	10
221		1s. General Eliott (vert)	15	10
222		2s. Eliott directing rescue operations (55×21 mm)	25	50

65 Lord Baden-Powell

1968. 60th Anniv of Gibraltar Scout Association.

No.	Type	Description	Unused	Used
223	**65**	4d. buff and violet	15	10
224	-	7d. ochre and green	15	20
225	-	9d. blue, orange and black	15	30
226	-	1s. yellow and green	15	30

DESIGNS: 7d. Scout flag over the Rock; 9d. Tent, Scouts and salute; 1s. Scout badges.

66 Nurse and W.H.O. Emblem

1968. 20th Anniv of W.H.O. Multicoloured.

No.	Type	Description	Unused	Used
227		2d. Type **66**	10	15
228		4d. Doctor and W.H.O. emblem	10	10

68 King John signing Magna Carta

1968. Human Rights Year.

No.	Type	Description	Unused	Used
229	**68**	1s. orange, brown and gold	15	10
230	-	2s. myrtle and gold	15	20

DESIGN: 2s. "Freedom" and Rock of Gibraltar.

70 Shepherd, Lamb and Star

1968. Christmas. Multicoloured.

No.	Type	Description	Unused	Used
231		4d. Type **70**	10	10
232		9d. Mary holding Holy Child	15	20

72 Parliament Houses

1969. Commonwealth Parliamentary Association Conference.

No.	Type	Description	Unused	Used
233	**72**	4d. green and gold	10	10
234	-	9d. violet and gold	10	10
235	-	2s. red, gold and blue	15	20

DESIGNS—HORIZ: 9d. Parliamentary emblem and outline of "The Rock". VERT: 2s. Clock Tower, Westminster (Big Ben) and Arms of Gibraltar.

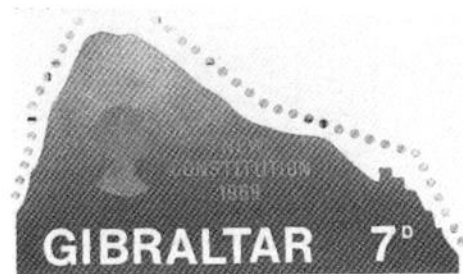

75 Silhouette of Rock and Queen Elizabeth II

1969. New Constitution.

No.	Type	Description	Unused	Used
236	**75**	½d. gold and orange	10	10
237	**75**	5d. silver and green	20	10
238	**75**	7d. silver and purple	20	10
239	**75**	5s. silver and blue	65	1·10

77 Soldier and Cap Badge, Royal Anglian Regiment, 1969

1969. Military Uniforms (1st series). Multicoloured.

No.	Type	Description	Unused	Used
240		1d. Royal Artillery Officer, 1758, and modern cap badge	15	10
241		6d. Type **77**	20	15
242		9d. Royal Engineers' Artificer, 1786, and modern cap badge	30	15
243		2s. Private, Fox's Marines, 1704, and modern Royal Marines' cap badge	75	70

See also Nos. 248/51, 290/3, 300/303, 313/16, 331/4, 340/3 and 363/6.

80 "Madonna of the Chair" (detail, Raphael)

1969. Christmas. Multicoloured.

No.	Type	Description	Unused	Used
244		5d. Type **80**	10	35
245		7d. "Virgin and Child" (detail, Morales)	20	35
246		1s. "The Virgin of the Rocks" (detail, Leonardo da Vinci)	20	40

83 Europa Point

1970. Europa Point.

No.	Type	Description	Unused	Used
247	**83**	2s. multicoloured	45	50

1970. Military Uniforms (2nd series). As T 77. Multicoloured.

No.	Type	Description	Unused	Used
248		2d. Royal Scots Officer (1839) and cap badge	25	10
249		5d. South Wales Borderers Private (1763) and cap badge	35	10
250		7d. Queen's Royal Regiment Private (1742) and cap badge	35	10
251		2s. Royal Irish Rangers piper (1969) and cap badge	1·00	90

88 No. 191a and Rock of Gibraltar

1970. "Philympia 70" Stamp Exhibition, London.

No.	Type	Description	Unused	Used
252	**88**	1s. red and green	15	10
253	-	2s. blue and mauve	25	65

DESIGN: 2s. Stamp and Moorish Castle.

The stamps shown in the designs are well-known varieties with values omitted.

90 "The Virgin and Mary" (stained-glass window Gabriel Loire)

1970. Christmas.

No.	Type	Description	Unused	Used
254	**90**	2s. multicoloured	30	80

91 Saluting Battery, Rosia

92 Saluting Battery, Rosia, Modern View

1971. Decimal Currency.

No.	Type	Description	Unused	Used
255	**91**	½p. multicoloured	20	30
256	**92**	½p. multicoloured	20	30
257	-	1p. multicoloured	80	30
258	-	1p. multicoloured	80	30
259	-	1½p. multicoloured	20	70
260	-	1½p. multicoloured	20	70
317	-	2p. multicoloured	1·25	2·50
318	-	2p. multicoloured	1·25	2·50
263a	-	2½p. multicoloured	40	1·40
264	-	2½p. multicoloured	20	70
265	-	3p. multicoloured	20	20
266	-	3p. multicoloured	20	20
319	-	4p. multicoloured	1·40	2·75
320	-	4p. multicoloured	1·40	2·75
269	-	5p. multicoloured	35	65
270	-	5p. multicoloured	35	65
271	-	7p. multicoloured	65	65
272	-	7p. multicoloured	65	65
273	-	8p. multicoloured	70	80
274	-	8p. multicoloured	70	80
275	-	9p. multicoloured	70	80
276	-	9p. multicoloured	70	80
277	-	10p. multicoloured	80	80
278	-	10p. multicoloured	80	80
279	-	12½p. multicoloured	1·00	1·75
280	-	12½p. multicoloured	1·00	1·75
281	-	25p. multicoloured	1·10	1·75
282	-	25p. multicoloured	1·10	1·75
283	-	50p. multicoloured	1·50	2·75
284	-	50p. multicoloured	1·50	2·75
285	-	£1 multicoloured	2·25	4·25
286	-	£1 multicoloured	2·25	4·25

DESIGNS: The two versions of each value show the same Gibraltar view taken from an early 19th-century print (first design) or modern photograph (second design): HORIZ: 1p. Prince George of Cambridge Quarters and Trinity Church; 1½p. The Wellington Bust, Alameda Gardens; 2p. Gibraltar from the North Bastion; 2½p. Catalan Bay; 3p. Convent Garden; 4p. The Exchange and Spanish Chapel; 5p. Commercial Square and Library; 7p. South Barracks and Rosia Magazine; 8p. Moorish Mosque and Castle; 9p. Europa Pass Road; 10p. South Barracks from Rosia Bay; 12½p. Southport Gates; 25p. Trooping the Colour, The Alameda. VERT: 50p. Europa Pass Gorge; £1 Prince Edward's Gate.

93

1971. Coil Stamps.

No.	Type	Description	Unused	Used
287	**93**	½p. orange	15	30
288	**93**	1p. blue	15	30
289	**93**	2p. green	50	1·10

1971. Military Uniforms (3rd series). As T 77. Multicoloured.

No.	Type	Description	Unused	Used
290		1p. The Black Watch (1845)	35	30
291		2p. Royal Regimental of Fusiliers (1971)	55	30
292		4p. King's Own Royal Border Regiment (1704)	75	50
293		10p. Devonshire and Dorset Regiment (1801)	2·75	3·00

94 Regimental Arms

1971. Presentation of Colours to the Gibraltar Regiment.

No.	Type	Description	Unused	Used
294	**94**	3p. black, gold and red	55	30

95 Nativity Scene

1971. Christmas. Multicoloured.

No.	Type	Description	Unused	Used
295		3p. Type **95**	40	60
296		5p. Mary and Joseph going to Bethlehem	40	65

96 Soldier Artificer, 1773

1972. Bicentenary of Royal Engineers in Gibraltar. Multicoloured.

No.	Type	Description	Unused	Used
297		1p. Type **96**	50	60
298		3p. Modern tunneller	60	80
299		5p. Old and new uniforms and badge (horiz)	70	90

1972. Military Uniforms (4th series). As T 77. Multicoloured.

No.	Type	Description	Unused	Used
300		1p. The Duke of Cornwall's Light Infantry, 1704	50	20
301		3p. King's Royal Rifle Corps, 1830	1·25	40
302		7p. 37th North Hampshire, Officer, 1825	2·00	70
303		10p. Royal Navy, 1972	2·25	1·50

97 "Our Lady of Europa"

1972. Christmas.

No.	Type	Description	Unused	Used
304	**97**	3p. multicoloured	10	20
305	**97**	5p. multicoloured	10	35

98 Keys of Gibraltar and "Narcissus niveus"

1972. Royal Silver Wedding.

No.	Type	Description	Unused	Used
306	**98**	5p. red	25	20
307	**98**	7p. green	25	20

99 Flags of Member Nations and E.E.C. Symbol

1973. Britain's Entry into E.E.C.
308 **99** 5p. multicoloured 40 50
309 **99** 10p. multicoloured 60 1·00

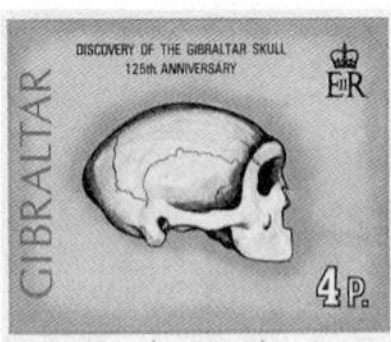

100 Skull

1973. 125th Anniv of Gibraltar Skull Discovery. Multicoloured.
310 4p. Type **100** 1·25 60
311 6p. Prehistoric man 1·50 1·25
312 10p. Prehistoric family 2·00 2·50
No. 312 is size 40×26 mm.

1973. Military Uniforms (5th series). As T 77. Multicoloured.
313 1p. King's Own Scottish Borderers, 1770 50 50
314 4p. Royal Welsh Fusiliers, 1800 1·25 80
315 6p. Royal Northumberland Fusiliers, 1736 1·75 1·75
316 10p. Grenadier Guards, 1898 2·50 4·00

101 "Nativity" (Danckerts)

1973. Christmas.
321 **101** 4p. violet and red 30 15
322 **101** 6p. mauve and blue 40 1·10

101a Princess Anne and Captain Mark Phillips

1973. Royal Wedding.
323 **101a** 6p. multicoloured 10 10
324 **101a** 14p. multicoloured 20 20

102 Victorian Pillar-box

1974. Centenary of U.P.U. Multicoloured.
325 2p. Type **102** 15 30
326 6p. Pillar-box of George VI 20 35
327 14p. Pillar-box of Elizabeth II 30 80
Nos. 325/7 also come self-adhesive from booklet panes.

1974. Military Uniforms (6th series). As T 77. Multicoloured.
331 4p. East Lancashire Regiment, 1742 50 50
332 6p. Somerset Light Infantry, 1833 70 70
333 10p. Royal Sussex Regiment, 1790 1·00 1·40
334 16p. R.A.F. officer, 1974 2·25 4·00

103 "Madonna with the Green Cushion" (Solario)

1974. Christmas. Multicoloured.
335 4p. Type **103** 40 30
336 6p. "Madonna of the Meadow" (Bellini) 60 95

104 Churchill and Houses of Parliament

1974. Birth Centenary of Sir Winston Churchill. Multicoloured.
337 **104** 6p. black, purple and lavender 25 15
338 - 20p. black, brown and red 35 45
MS339 114×93 mm. Nos. 337/8 4·50 6·50
DESIGN: 20p. Churchill and "King George V" (battleship).

1975. Military Uniforms (7th series). As T 77. Multicoloured.
340 4p. East Surrey Regiment, 1846 35 20
341 6p. Highland Light Infantry, 1777 50 40
342 10p. Coldstream Guards, 1704 70 70
343 20p. Gibraltar Regiment, 1974 1·25 2·50

105 Girl Guides' Badge

1975. 50th Anniversary of Gibraltar Girl Guides.
346 **105** 5p. gold, blue and violet 25 55
347 **105** 7p. gold, brown and light brown 35 60
348 - 15p. silver, black and brown 50 1·25
No. 348 is as Type **105** but shows a different badge.

106 Child at Prayer

1975. Christmas. Multicoloured.
349 6p. Type **106** 40 60
350 6p. Angel with lute 40 60
351 6p. Child singing carols 40 60
352 6p. Three children 40 60
353 6p. Girl at prayer 40 60
354 6p. Boy and lamb 40 60

107 Bruges Madonna

1975. 500th Birth Anniv of Michelangelo. Multicoloured.
355 6p. Type **107** 20 25
356 9p. Taddei Madonna 20 40
357 15p. Pieta 30 1·10
Nos. 355/7 also come self-adhesive from booklet panes.

108 Bicentennial Emblem and Arms of Gibraltar

1976. Bicentenary of American Revolution.
361 **108** 25p. multicoloured 50 50
MS362 85×133 mm. No. 361×4 2·75 4·50

1976. Military Uniforms (8th series). As T 24. Multicoloured.
363 1p. Suffolk Regiment, 1795 20 20
364 6p. Northamptonshire Regiment, 1779 40 30
365 12p. Lancashire Fusiliers, 1793 50 60
366 25p. Ordnance Corps, 1896 60 1·40

109 The Holy Family

1976. Christmas. Multicoloured.
367 6p. Type **109** 25 15
368 9p. Madonna and Child 35 25
369 12p. St. Bernard 50 60
370 20p. Archangel Michael 85 1·40
Nos. 367/70 show different stained-glass windows from St. Joseph's Church, Gibraltar.

110 Queen Elizabeth II, Royal Arms and Gibraltar Arms

1977. Silver Jubilee. Multicoloured.
371 **110** 6p. red 15 20
372 **110** £1 blue 1·10 2·00
MS373 124×115 mm. Nos. 371/2 1·25 1·50

111 Toothed Orchid

1977. Birds, Flowers, Fish and Butterflies. Multicoloured.
374 ½p. Type **111** 60 2·50
375 1p. Red mullet (horiz) 15 70
376 2p. "Maculinea arion" (butterfly) (horiz) 30 1·75
377 2½p. Sardinian warbler 1·75 2·75
378 3p. Giant squill 20 10
379 4p. Grey wrasse (horiz) 30 10
380 5p. "Vanessa atalanta" (butterfly) (horiz) 50 1·00
381 6p. Black kite 2·25 55
382 9p. Shrubby scorpion-vetch 70 70
383 10p. John dory (fish) (horiz) 40 20
384 12p. "Colias crocea" (butterfly) (horiz) 1·00 35
384b 15p. Winged asparagus pea 1·50 55
385 20p. Audouin's gull 2·00 3·25
386 25p. Barbary nut (iris) 1·25 2·00
387 50p. Swordfish (horiz) 2·00 2·50
388 £1 "Papilio machaon" (butterfly) (horiz) 4·25 5·00
389 £2 Hoopoe 9·00 12·00
389a £5 Arms of Gibraltar 10·00 12·00

112 "Our Lady of Europa" Stamp

1977. "Amphilex '77" Stamp Exhibition, Amsterdam. Multicoloured.
390 6p. Type **112** 10 20
391 12p. "Europa Point" stamp 15 30
392 25p. "E.E.C. Entry" stamp 20 50

113 "The Annunciation" (Rubens)

1977. Christmas and 400th Birth Anniv of Rubens. Multicoloured.
393 3p. Type **113** 10 10
394 9p. "The Adoration of the Magi" 25 25
395 12p. "The Adoration of the Magi" (horiz) 30 50
396 15p. "The Holy Family under the Apple Tree" 30 55
MS397 110×200 mm. Nos. 393/6 2·75 4·00

114 Aerial View of Gibraltar

1978. Gibraltar from Space. Multicoloured.
398 12p. Type **114** 25 50
MS399 148×108 mm. 25p. Aerial view of Straits of Gibraltar 80 80

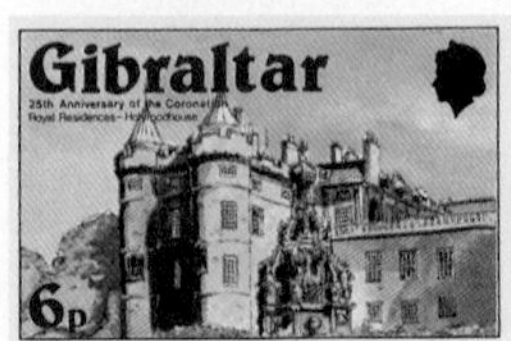

115 Holyroodhouse

1978. 25th Anniv of Coronation. Multicoloured.
400 6p. Type **115** 20 15
401 9p. St. James's Palace 25 15
402 12p. Sandringham 30 30
403 18p. Balmoral 40 85
406 25p. Windsor Castle 1·00 2·00
Nos. 402/3 also exist as self-adhesive stamps from booklet panes, No. 406 only coming in this form.

116 Short S.25 Sunderland, 1938–58

1978. 60th Anniv of Royal Air Force. Multicoloured.
407 3p. Type **116** 15 10
408 9p. Caudron G-3, 1918 35 40
409 12p. Avro Shackleton M.R.2, 1953–66 40 55
410 16p. Hawker Hunter F.6, 1954–77 45 1·00
411 18p. Hawker Siddeley H.S.801 Nimrod M.R.1, 1969–78 50 1·10

117 "Madonna with Animals"

1978. Christmas. Paintings by Durer. Multicoloured.

412		5p. Type **117**	20	10
413		9p. "The Nativity"	25	15
414		12p. "Madonna of the Goldfinch"	30	40
415		15p. "Adoration of the Magi"	35	1·00

118 Sir Rowland Hill and 1d. Stamp of 1886

1979. Death Centenary of Sir Rowland Hill.

416	**118**	3p. multicoloured	10	10
417	-	9p. multicoloured	15	15
418	-	12p. multicoloured	15	20
419	-	25p. black, purple yellow	25	50

DESIGNS: 9p. 1971 1p. coil stamp; 12p. 1840 Post Office Regulations; 25p. "G" cancellation.

119 Posthorn, Dish Antenna and Early Telephone

1979. Europa. Communications.

420	**119**	3p. green and pale green	15	10
421	**119**	9p. brown and ochre	30	90
422	**119**	12p. blue and violet	35	1·25

120 African Child

1979. Christmas. International Year of the Child. Multicoloured.

423		12p. Type **120**	25	30
424		12p. Asian child	25	30
425		12p. Polynesian child	25	30
426		12p. American Indian child	25	30
427		12p. Nativity and children of different races	25	30
428		12p. European child	25	30

121 Early Policeman

1980. 150th Anniv of Gibraltar Police Force. Multicoloured.

429		3p. Type **121**	20	10
430		6p. Policemen of 1895, early 1900s and 1980	20	15
431		12p. Police officer and police ambulance	25	20
432		37p. Policewoman and police motor-cyclist	55	1·25

122 Peter Amigo (Archbishop)

1980. Europa. Personalities. Multicoloured.

433		12p. Type **122**	20	30
434		12p. Gustavo Bacarisas (artist)	20	30
435		12p. John Mackintosh (philanthropist)	20	30

123 Queen Elizabeth the Queen Mother

1980. 80th Birthday of The Queen Mother.

436	**123**	15p. multicoloured	30	30

124 "Horatio Nelson" (J. F. Rigaud)

1980. 175th Death Anniv of Nelson. Paintings. Multicoloured.

437		3p. Type **124**	15	10
438		9p. "H.M.S. Victory' (horiz)	25	25
439		15p. "Horatio Nelson" (Sir William Beechey)	35	35
440		40p. "H.M.S. Victory' being towed into Gibraltar" (Clarkson Stanfield) (horiz)	80	1·00
MS441		159×99 mm. No. 439	1·00	1·50

125 Three Kings

1980. Christmas.

442	**125**	15p. brown and yellow	25	35
443	-	15p. brown and yellow	25	35

DESIGN: No. 443, Nativity scene.

126 Hercules creating the Mediterranean

1981. Europa. Multicoloured.

444		9p. Type **126**	20	15
445		15p. Hercules and Pillars of Hercules	25	35

127 Dining-room

1981. 450th Anniv of The Convent (Governor's Residence). Multicoloured.

446		4p. Type **127**	10	10
447		14p. King's Chapel	15	15
448		15p. The Convent	15	15
449		55p. Cloister	60	80

128 Prince Charles and Lady Diana Spencer

1981. Royal Wedding.

450	**128**	£1 multicoloured	1·25	1·25

129

1981

451	**129**	1p. black	50	60
452	**129**	4p. blue	50	50
453	**129**	15p. green	30	40

130 Paper Airplane

1981. 50th Anniv of Gibraltar Airmail Service. Multicoloured.

454		14p. Type **130**	15	15
455		15p. Airmail letters, post box and aircraft tail fin	15	15
456		55p. Jet airliner circling globe	60	80

131 Carol Singers

1981. Christmas. Children's Drawings. Multicoloured.

457		15p. Type **131**	30	15
458		55p. Postbox (vert)	1·00	85

132 I.Y.D.P. Emblem and Stylized Faces

1981. International Year for Disabled Persons.

459	**132**	14p. multicoloured	30	30

133 Douglas DC-3

1982. Aircraft. Multicoloured.

460		1p. Type **133**	25	2·00
461		2p. Vickers Viking 1B	30	2·00
462		3p. Airspeed A.S.57 Ambassador G-ALZN	30	1·75
463		4p. Vickers 953 Viscount 800	40	20
464		5p. Boeing 727-100	90	60
465		10p. Vickers Vanguard	1·75	50
466		14p. Short Solent 2	1·75	4·00
467		15p. Fokker F.27 Friendship	2·75	4·00
468		17p. Boeing 737	1·00	75
469		20p. B.A.C. One Eleven 500G-AWYV	1·00	65
470		25p. Lockheed Constellation	4·00	5·00
471		50p. de Havilland Comet 4B	4·00	2·25
472		£1 Saro Windhover G-ABJP "General Godley"	5·50	2·25
473		£2 Hawker Siddeley Trident 2E	6·50	5·00
474		£5 De Havilland D.H.89A Dragon Rapide	8·00	14·00

134 Crest, H.M.S. "Opossum"

1982. Naval Crests (1st series). Multicoloured.

475		½p. Type **134**	10	30
476		15½p. H.M.S. "Norfolk"	40	55
477		17p. H.M.S. "Fearless"	40	60
478		60p. H.M.S. "Rooke"	85	2·75

See also Nos. 493/6, 510/13, 522/5, 541/4, 565/8, 592/5, 616/19 and 651/4.

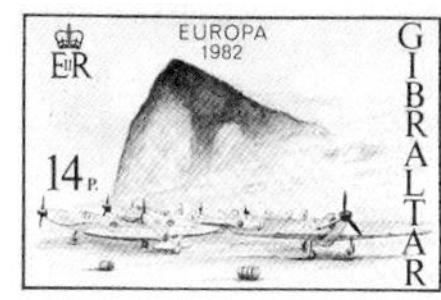

135 Hawker Hurricane Mk I and Supermarine Spitfires at Gibraltar

1982. Europa. Operation Torch. Multicoloured.

479		14p. Type **135**	25	70
480		17p. General Giraud, General Eisenhower and Gibraltar	35	80

136 Gibraltar Chamber of Commerce Centenary

1982. Anniversaries. Multicoloured.

481		½p. Type **136**	10	65
482		15½p. British Forces Postal Service centenary	45	30
483		60p. 75th anniv of Gibraltar Scout Association	1·25	2·00

137 Printed Circuit forming Map of World

1982. International Direct Dialling.

484	**137**	17p. black, blue and orange	35	35

138 Gibraltar illuminated at Night and Holly

1982. Christmas. Multicoloured.

485		14p. Type **138**	50	30
486		17p. Gibraltar illuminated at night and mistletoe	50	35

139 Yacht Marina

1983. Commonwealth Day. Multicoloured.

487		4p. Type **139**	10	10
488		14p. Scouts and Guides Commonwealth Day Parade	20	15
489		17p. Flag of Gibraltar (vert)	25	20
490		60p. Queen Elizabeth II (from photo by Tim Graham) (vert)	70	1·00

140 St. George's Hall Gallery

1983. Europa.

491	**140**	16p. black and brown	35	50
492	-	19p. black and blue	40	75

DESIGN: 19p. Water catchment slope.

1983. Naval Crests (2nd series). As T 134. Multicoloured.

493	4p. H.M.S. "Faulknor"	30	10
494	14p. H.M.S. "Renown"	70	35
495	17p. H.M.S. "Ark Royal"	75	40
496	60p. H.M.S. "Sheffield"	1·75	1·50

141 Landport Gate, 1729

1983. Fortress Gibraltar in the 18th Century. Multicoloured.

497	4p. Type **141**	15	10
498	17p. Koehler Gun, 1782	35	30
499	77p. King's Bastion, 1779	1·00	1·25
MS500	97×145 mm. Nos. 497/9	2·25	1·50

142 "Adoration of the Magi" (Raphael)

1983. Christmas. 500th Birth Anniv of Raphael. Multicoloured.

501	4p. Type **142**	25	10
502	17p. "Madonna of Foligno" (vert)	70	35
503	60p. "Sistine Madonna" (vert)	1·75	1·40

143 1932 2d. Stamp and Globe

1984. Europa, Posts and Telecommunications. Multicoloured.

504	17p. Type **143**	45	50
505	23p. Circuit board and globe	55	1·00

144 Hockey

1984. Sports. Multicoloured.

506	20p. Type **144**	70	80
507	21p. Basketball	70	80
508	26p. Rowing	70	1·25
509	29p. Football	70	1·50

1984. Naval Crests (3rd series). As T 134. Multicoloured.

510	20p. H.M.S. "Active"	1·75	2·25
511	21p. H.M.S. "Foxhound"	1·75	2·50
512	26p. H.M.S. "Valiant"	2·00	2·50
513	29p. H.M.S. "Hood"	2·50	2·75

145 Mississippi River Boat Float

1984. Christmas. Epiphany Floats. Multicoloured.

514	20p. Type **145**	30	30
515	80p. Roman Temple float	1·40	2·75

146 Musical Symbols, and Score from Beethoven's 9th (Choral) Symphony

1985. Europa. European Music Year. Multicoloured.

516	**146**	20p. multicoloured	30	30
517	-	29p. multicoloured	40	1·50

DESIGN: The 29p. is as T **146**, but shows different symbols.

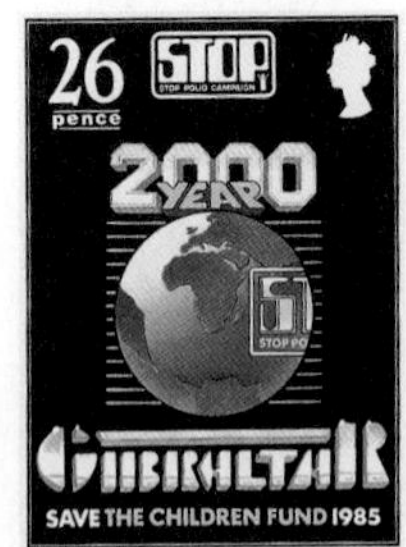

147 Globe and Stop Polio Campaign Logo

1985. Stop Polio Campaign.

518	26p. multicoloured (Type **147**)	90	1·40
519	26p. multicoloured ("ST" visible)	90	1·40
520	26p. multicoloured ("STO" visible)	90	1·40
521	26p. multicoloured ("STOP" visible)	90	1·40

Each design differs in the position of the logo across the centre of the globe. On No. 518 only the letter "S" is fully visible, on No. 519 "ST", on No. 520 "STO" and on No. 521 "STOP". Other features of the design also differ, so that the word "Year" moves towards the top of the stamp and on No. 521 the upper logo is omitted.

1985. Naval Crests (4th series). As T 134. Multicoloured.

522	4p. H.M.S. "Duncan"	70	10
523	9p. H.M.S. "Fury"	1·25	50
524	21p. H.M.S. "Firedrake"	2·50	2·00
525	80p. H.M.S. "Malaya"	4·50	6·00

148 I.Y.Y. Logo

1985. International Youth Year. Multicoloured.

526	4p. Type **148**	35	10
527	20p. Hands passing diamond	1·40	1·10
528	80p. 75th anniv logo of Girl Guide Movement	3·25	3·75

149 St. Joseph

1985. Christmas. Centenary of St. Joseph's Parish Church. Multicoloured.

529	4p. Type **149**	65	1·00
530	4p. St. Joseph's Parish Church	65	1·00
531	80p. Nativity crib	4·50	5·50

150 "Papilio machaon" (butterfly) and The Convent

1986. Europa. Nature and the Environment. Multicoloured.

532	22p. Type **150**	1·00	50
533	29p. Herring gull and Europa Point	1·50	4·25

151 1887 Queen Victoria 6d. Stamp

1986. Centenary of First Gibraltar Postage Stamps. Designs showing stamps. Multicoloured.

534	4p. Type **151**	30	10
535	22p. 1903 Edward VII 2½d.	1·00	1·00
536	32p. 1912 George V 1d.	1·50	2·00
537	36p. 1938 George VI £1	1·60	2·50
538	44p. 1953 Coronation ½d. (29×46 mm)	2·00	3·00
MS539	102×73 mm. 29p. 1886 "GIBRALTAR" overprinted on Bermuda 1d.	3·25	3·75

152 Queen Elizabeth II in Robes of Order of the Bath

1986. 60th Birthday of Queen Elizabeth II.

540	**152**	£1 multicoloured	1·75	3·00

1986. Naval Crests (5th series). As T 134. Multicoloured.

541	22p. H.M.S. "Lightning"	1·75	1·00
542	29p. H.M.S. "Hermione"	2·00	1·75
543	32p. H.M.S. "Laforey"	2·25	3·25
544	44p. H.M.S. "Nelson"	2·75	5·50

153 Prince Andrew and Miss Sarah Ferguson

1986. Royal Wedding. Sheet 115×85 mm.

MS545	**153** 44p. multicoloured	1·40	2·25

154 Three Kings and Cathedral of St. Mary the Crowned

1986. Christmas. International Peace Year. Multicoloured.

546	18p. Type **154**	1·00	50
547	32p. St. Andrew's Church	1·50	3·00

155 Neptune House

1987. Europa. Architecture. Multicoloured.

563	22p. Type **155**	1·25	50
564	29p. Ocean Heights	2·00	4·25

1987. Naval Crests (6th series). As T 134. Multicoloured.

565	18p. H.M.S. "Wishart"	1·60	75
566	22p. H.M.S. "Charybdis"	1·75	1·10
567	32p. H.M.S. "Antelope"	2·50	3·50
568	44p. H.M.S. "Eagle"	3·00	4·50

156 13-inch Mortar, 1783

1987. Guns. Multicoloured.

569	1p. Type **156**	20	70
570	2p. 6-inch coastal gun, 1909	30	70
571	3p. 8-inch howitzer, 1783	40	1·00
572	4p. Bofors "L40/70" AA gun, 1951	40	10
573	5p. 100 ton rifled muzzle-loader, 1882	40	70
574	10p. 5.25 inch heavy AA gun, 1953	40	70
575	18p. 25-pounder gun-how, 1943	65	1·00
576	19p. 64-pounder rifled muzzle-loader, 1873	70	1·25
577	22p. 12-pounder gun, 1758	70	50
578	50p. 10-inch rifled muzzle-loader, 1870	1·40	3·00
579	£1 Russian 24-pounder gun, 1854	2·50	2·50
580	£3 9.2 inch "Mk 10" coastal gun, 1935	3·00	12·00
581	£5 24-pounder gun, 1779	5·00	14·00

157 Victoria Stadium

1987. Bicentenary of Royal Engineers' Royal Warrant. Multicoloured.

582	18p. Type **157**	1·25	65
583	32p. Freedom of Gibraltar scroll and casket	1·75	3·25
584	44p. Royal Engineers' badge	2·50	4·50

158 The Three Kings

1987. Christmas. Multicoloured.

585	4p. Type **158**	20	10
586	22p. The Holy Family	1·00	1·00
587	44p. The Shepherds	1·90	3·50

159 "Canberra" (liner) passing Gibraltar

1988. Europa. Transport and Communications. Multicoloured.

588	22p. Type **159**	1·50	2·25
589	22p. "Gibline I" (ferry), dish aerial and Boeing 737 airliner	1·50	2·25
590	32p. Horse-drawn carriage and modern coach	2·00	2·75
591	32p. Car, telephone and Rock of Gibraltar	2·00	2·75

1988. Naval Crests (7th series). As T 134.

592	18p. multicoloured	1·50	65
593	22p. black, brown and gold	2·00	1·25
594	32p. multicoloured	2·25	3·50
595	44p. multicoloured	3·00	4·75

DESIGNS: 18p. H.M.S. "Clyde"; 22p. H.M.S. "Foresight"; 32p. H.M.S. "Severn"; 44p. H.M.S. "Rodney".

160 European Bee Eater

1988. Birds. Multicoloured.

596	4p. Type **160**	75	20
597	22p. Atlantic puffin	1·75	90
598	32p. Western honey buzzard ("Honey Buzzard")	2·25	2·50
599	44p. Blue rock thrush	2·75	4·00

161 "Zebu" (brigantine)

1988. Operation Raleigh. Multicoloured.

600	19p. Type **161**	65	60
601	22p. Miniature of Sir Walter Raleigh and logo	75	70
602	32p. "Sir Walter Raleigh" (expedition ship) and world map	1·10	2·00
MS603	135×86 mm. 22p. As No. 601; 44p. "Sir Walter Raleigh" (expedition ship) passing Gibraltar	4·50	5·50

162 "Snowman" (Rebecca Falero)

1988. Christmas. Children's Paintings. Mult.

604	4p. Type **162**	15	10
605	22p. "The Nativity" (Dennis Penalver)	55	60
606	44p. "Father Christmas" (Gavin Key) (23×31 mm)	1·00	2·40

163 Soft Toys and Toy Train

1989. Europa. Children's Toys. Multicoloured.

607	25p. Type **163**	1·25	75
608	32p. Soft toys, toy boat and doll's house	1·75	2·75

164 Port Sergeant with Keys

1989. 50th Anniv of Gibraltar Regiment. Mult.

609	4p. Type **164**	50	10
610	22p. Regimental badge and colours	1·40	1·10
611	32p. Drum major	1·90	3·50
MS612	124×83 mm. 22p. As No. 610; 44p. Former Gibraltar Defence Force badge	4·75	5·50

165 Nurse and Baby

1989. 125th Anniv of International Red Cross.

613	**165**	25p. black, red and brown	1·00	60
614	-	32p. black, red and brown	1·25	1·75
615	-	44p. black, red and brown	1·50	3·50

DESIGNS: 32p. Famine victims; 44p. Accident victims.

1989. Naval Crests (8th series). As T 134.

616	22p. multicoloured	1·50	75
617	25p. black and gold	1·50	1·50
618	32p. gold, black and red	2·00	3·25
619	44p. multicoloured	3·00	5·50

DESIGNS: 22p. H.M.S. "Blankney"; 25p. H.M.S. "Deptford"; 32p. H.M.S. "Exmoor"; 44p. H.M.S. "Stork".

166 One Penny Coin

1989. New Coinage. T 166 and similar vert designs in two miniature sheets.

MS620	72×94 mm. 4p. bronze, black and red (Type **166**); 4p. bronze, black and brown (two pence); 4p. silver, black and yellow (ten pence); 4p. silver, black and green (five pence)	1·25	2·25
MS621	100×95 mm. 22p. silver, black and green (fifty pence); 22p. gold, black and blue (five pounds); 22p. gold, black and brown (two pounds); 22p. gold, black and green (one pound); 22p. gold, black and violet (obverse of coin series); 22p. silver, black and blue (twenty pence)	5·50	7·50

167 Father Christmas in Sleigh

1989. Christmas. Multicoloured.

622	4p. Type **167**	20	10
623	22p. Shepherds and sheep	90	70
624	32p. The Nativity	1·40	1·75
625	44p. The Three Wise Men	2·25	4·00

168 General Post Office Entrance

1990. Europa. Post Office Buildings. Multicoloured.

626	22p. Type **168**	1·25	1·75
627	22p. Interior of General Post Office	1·25	1·75
628	32p. Interior of South District Post Office	1·50	2·50
629	32p. South District Post Office	1·50	2·50

169 19th-century Firemen

1990. 125th Anniv of Gibraltar Fire Service. Multicoloured.

630	4p. Type **169**	1·00	15
631	20p. Early fire engine (horiz)	2·50	1·10
632	42p. Modern fire engine (horiz)	3·00	3·75
633	44p. Modern fireman in breathing apparatus	3·00	3·75

170 Henry Corbould (artist) and Penny Black

1990. 150th Anniv of the Penny Black. Multicoloured.

634	19p. Type **170**	1·10	1·00
635	22p. Bath Royal Mail coach	1·25	1·00
636	32p. Sir Rowland Hill and Penny Black	2·50	4·50
MS637	145×95 mm. 44p. Penny Black with Maltese Cross cancellation	4·75	6·00

1990. Naval Crests (9th series). As T 134. Multicoloured.

638	22p. H.M.S. "Calpe"	1·75	70
639	25p. H.M.S. "Gallant"	1·90	1·75
640	32p. H.M.S. "Wrestler"	2·50	3·25
641	44p. H.M.S. "Greyhound"	3·00	6·50

171 Model of Europort Development

1990. Development Projects. Multicoloured.

642	22p. Type **171**	75	80
643	23p. Construction of building material factory	75	1·50
644	25p. Land reclamation	95	1·50

172 Candle and Holly

1990. Christmas. Multicoloured.

645	4p. Type **172**	15	10
646	22p. Father Christmas	75	65
647	42p. Christmas tree	1·50	2·50
648	44p. Nativity crib	1·50	2·50

173 Space Laboratory and Spaceplane (Columbus Development Programme)

1991. Europa. Europe in Space. Multicoloured.

649	25p. Type **173**	75	75
650	32p. "ERS-1" earth resources remote sensing satellite	1·00	2·25

1991. Naval Crests (10th series). As T 134.

651	4p. black, blue and gold	60	10
652	21p. multicoloured	1·75	1·25
653	22p. multicoloured	1·75	1·25
654	62p. multicoloured	3·75	7·00

DESIGNS: 4p. H.M.S. "Hesperus"; 21p. H.M.S. "Forester"; 22p. H.M.S. "Furious"; 62p. H.M.S. "Scylla".

174 Shag

1991. Endangered Species. Birds. Multicoloured.

655	13p. Type **174**	1·40	1·60
656	13p. Barbary partridge	1·40	1·60
657	13p. Egyptian vulture	1·40	1·60
658	13p. Black stork	1·40	1·60

1991. No. 580 surch £1.05.

659	£1.05 on £3 9.2-inch "Mk.10" coastal gun, 1935	3·50	1·60

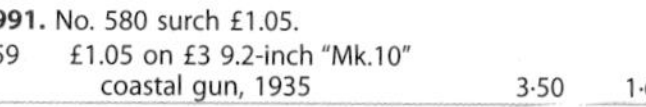

176 "North View of Gibraltar" (Gustavo Bacarisas)

1991. Local Paintings. Multicoloured.

660	22p. Type **176**	85	50
661	26p. "Parson's Lodge" (Elena Mifsud)	1·00	1·00
662	32p. "Governor's Parade" (Jacobo Azagury)	1·50	2·25
663	42p. "Waterport Wharf" (Rudesindo Mannia) (vert)	2·25	4·50

177 "Once in Royal David's City"

1991. Christmas. Carols. Multicoloured.

664	4p. Type **177**	40	10
665	24p. "Silent Night"	1·75	70
666	25p. "Angels We Have Heard on High"	1·75	1·25
667	49p. "O Come All Ye Faithful"	2·50	6·00

178 "Danaus chrysippus"

1991. "Phila Nippon '91" International Stamp Exhibition, Tokyo. Sheet 116×91 mm.

MS668	**178** £1.05, multicoloured	3·25	4·50

179 Columbus and "Santa Maria"

1992. Europa. 500th Anniv of Discovery of America by Columbus. Multicoloured.

669	24p. Type **179**	1·25	2·00
670	24p. Map of Old World and "Nina"	1·25	2·00
671	34p. Map of New World and "Pinta"	1·50	2·50
672	34p. Map of Old World and look-out	1·50	2·50

Nos. 669/70 and 671/2 were issued together, se-tenant, each pair forming a composite design.

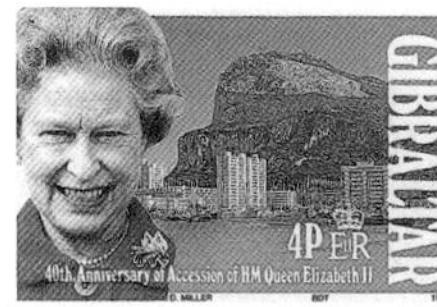

179a Gibraltar from North

1992. 40th Anniv of Queen Elizabeth II's Accession. Multicoloured.

673	4p. Type **179a**	15	10
674	20p. H.M.S. "Arrow" (frigate) and Gibraltar from south	60	60
675	24p. Southport Gates	75	80
676	44p. Three portraits of Queen Elizabeth	1·25	1·60
677	54p. Queen Elizabeth II	1·60	1·90

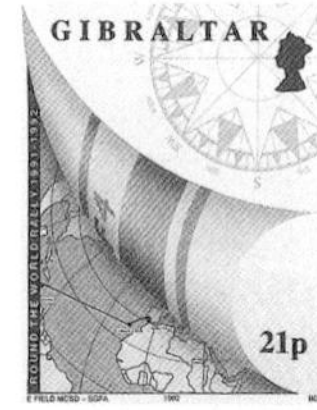

180 Compass Rose, Sail, and Atlantic Map

1992. Round the World Yacht Rally. Multicoloured designs, each incorporating compass rose and sail.

678	21p. Type **180**	75	80
679	24p. Map of Indonesian Archipelago (horiz)	95	1·40
680	25p. Map of India Ocean (horiz)	95	1·75
MS681	108×72 mm. 21p. Type **180**; 49p. Map of Mediterranean and Red Sea	2·50	3·50

181 Holy Trinity Cathedral

1992. 150th Anniv of Anglican Diocese of Gibraltar-in-Europe. Multicoloured.

No.	Description	Unused	Used
682	4p. Type **181**	20	10
683	24p. Diocesan crest and map (horiz)	1·00	65
684	44p. Construction of Cathedral and Sir George Don (horiz)	1·75	3·00
685	54p. Bishop Tomlinson	2·00	3·50

182 Sacred Heart of Jesus Church

1992. Christmas. Churches. Multicoloured.

No.	Description	Unused	Used
686	4p. Type **182**	35	10
687	24p. Cathedral of St. Mary the Crowned	1·50	55
688	34p. St. Andrew's Church of Scotland	2·00	2·50
689	49p. St. Joseph's Church	2·50	5·50

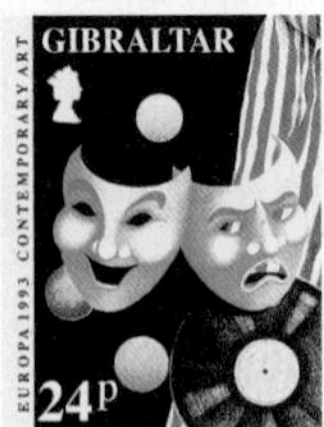

183 "Drama and Music"

1993. Europa. Contemporary Art. Multicoloured.

No.	Description	Unused	Used
690	24p. Type **183**	1·50	2·00
691	24p. "Sculpture, Art and Pottery"	1·50	2·00
692	34p. "Architecture"	2·00	2·75
693	34p. "Printing and Photography"	2·00	2·75

184 H.M.S. "Hood" (battle cruiser)

1993. Second World War Warships (1st series). Sheet 120×79 mm, containing T 184 and similar horiz designs. Multicoloured.

MS694 24p. Type **184**; 24p. H.M.S. "Ark Royal" (aircraft carrier, 1937); 24p. H.M.A.S. "Waterhen" (destroyer); 24p. U.S.S. "Gleaves" (destroyer) — 11·00 — 11·00

See also Nos. **MS**724, **MS**748, **MS**779 and **MS**809.

185 Landport Gate

1993. Architectural Heritage. Multicoloured.

No.	Description	Unused	Used
695	1p. Type **185**	30	1·25
696	2p. St. Mary the Crowned Church (horiz)	50	1·25
697	3p. Parsons Lodge Battery (horiz)	50	1·50
698	4p. Moorish Castle (horiz)	65	1·25
699	5p. General Post Office	65	30
699a	6p. House of Assembly	2·00	1·25
699b	7p. Bleak House (horiz)	2·00	1·25
699c	8p. General Eliott Memorial	2·00	1·25
699d	9p. Supreme Court Building (horiz)	2·00	1·25
700	10p. South Barracks (horiz)	50	60
700a	20p. The Convent (horiz)	3·00	1·25
701	21p. American War Memorial	1·00	80
702	24p. Garrison Library (horiz)	1·10	80
703	25p. Southport Gates	1·10	80
704	26p. Casemates Gate (horiz)	4·00	2·00
704a	30p. St. Bernard's Hospital	4·00	1·25
704b	40p. City Hall (horiz)	4·00	2·00
705	50p. Central Police Station (horiz)	2·50	2·25
706	£1 Prince Edward's Gate	2·25	2·75
706a	£2 Church of the Sacred Heart of Jesus	8·50	8·00
707	£3 Lighthouse, Europa Point	11·00	11·00
708	£5 Coat of Arms and fortress keys	10·00	15·00

186 £sd and Decimal British Coins (25th anniv of decimal currency)

1993. Anniversaries. Multicoloured.

No.	Description	Unused	Used
709	21p. Type **186**	1·00	65
710	24p. R.A.F. crest with Handley Page 0/400 and Panavia Tornado F Mk 3 (75th anniv)	1·75	75
711	34p. Garrison Library badge and building (bicent)	1·60	2·25
712	49p. Sir Winston Churchill and air raid (50th anniv of visit)	4·00	5·00

187 Mice decorating Christmas Tree

1993. Christmas. Multicoloured.

No.	Description	Unused	Used
713	5p. Type **187**	25	10
714	24p. Mice pulling cracker	1·10	70
715	44p. Mice singing carols	2·25	3·00
716	49p. Mice building snowman	2·75	3·75

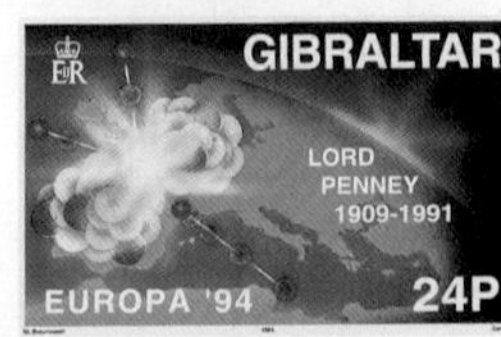

188 Exploding Atom (Lord Penney)

1994. Europa. Scientific Discoveries. Mult.

No.	Description	Unused	Used
717	24p. Type **188**	1·00	1·50
718	24p. Polonium and radium experiment (Marie Curie)	1·00	1·50
719	34p. First oil engine (Rudolph Diesel)	1·25	2·00
720	34p. Early telescope (Galileo)	1·25	2·00

189 World Cup and Map of U.S.A.

1994. World Cup Football Championship, U.S.A. Multicoloured.

No.	Description	Unused	Used
721	26p. Type **189**	80	55
722	39p. Players and pitch in shape of U.S.A.	1·25	2·00
723	49p. Player's legs (vert)	1·60	2·75

1994. Second World War Warships (2nd series). Sheet 112×72 mm, containing horiz designs as T 184. Multicoloured.

MS724 5p. H.M.S. "Penelope" (cruiser); 25p. H.M.S. "Warspite" (battleship); 44p. U.S.S. "McLanahan" (destroyer); 49p. "Isaac Sweers" (Dutch destroyer) — 10·00 — 11·00

190 Pekingese

1994. "Philakorea '94" International Stamp Exhibition, Seoul. Sheet 102×76 mm.

MS725 **190** £1.05, multicoloured — 2·50 — 4·00

191 Golden Star Coral

1994. Marine Life. Multicoloured.

No.	Description	Unused	Used
726	21p. Type **191**	75	45
727	24p. Star fish	90	55
728	34p. Gorgonian sea-fan	1·50	2·25
729	49p. Peacock wrasse ("Turkish wrasse")	2·00	3·50

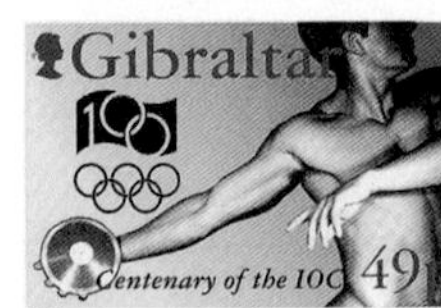

192 Throwing the Discus and Centenary Emblem

1994. Centenary of Int Olympic Committee. Mult.

No.	Description	Unused	Used
730	49p. Type **192**	1·75	2·25
731	54p. Javelin throwing and emblem	1·75	2·50

193 Great Tit

1994. Christmas. Songbirds. Multicoloured.

No.	Description	Unused	Used
732	5p. Type **193**	80	10
733	24p. European robin (horiz)	2·25	70
734	34p. Blue tit (horiz)	2·50	1·50
735	54p. Eurasian goldfinch ("Goldfinch")	3·25	5·50

194 Austrian Flag, Hand and Star

1995. Expansion of European Union. Multicoloured.

No.	Description	Unused	Used
736	24p. Type **194**	60	55
737	26p. Finnish flag, hand and star	60	60
738	34p. Swedish flag, hand and star	90	1·50
739	49p. Flags of new members and European Union emblem	1·60	3·25

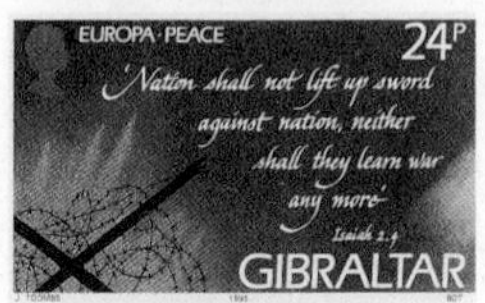

195 Barbed Wire and Quote from Isaiah Ch 2.4

1995. Europa. Peace and Freedom. Multicoloured.

No.	Description	Unused	Used
740	24p. Type **195**	1·40	1·60
741	24p. Rainbow and hands releasing peace dove	1·40	1·60
742	34p. Shackles on wall and quote from Isaiah ch 61.1	1·60	2·25
743	34p. Hands and sea birds	1·60	2·25

196 Fairey Swordfish, I Class Destroyer and Rock of Gibraltar

1995. 50th Anniv of End of Second World War. Sheet 101×66 mm.

MS744 **196** £1.05, multicoloured — 3·25 — 4·25

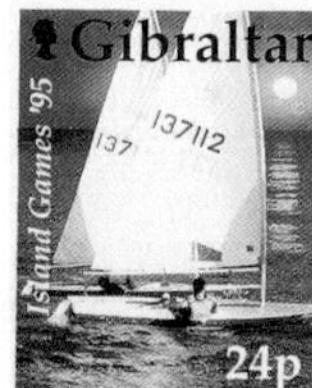

197 Yachting

1995. Island Games '95. Multicoloured.

No.	Description	Unused	Used
745	24p. Type **197**	70	60
746	44p. Athlete on starting blocks	1·60	2·50
747	49p. Swimmer at start of race	1·60	2·50

1995. Second World War Warships (3rd series). Sheet 133×85 mm, containing horiz designs as T 184. Multicoloured.

MS748 5p. H.M.S. "Calpe" (destroyer); 24p. H.M.S. "Victorious" (aircraft carrier); 44p. U.S.S. "Weehawken" (attack transport); 49p. "Savorgan de Brazza" (French destroyer) — 10·00 — 11·00

198 Bee Orchid

1995. "Singapore '95" International Stamp Exhibition. Orchids. Multicoloured.

No.	Description	Unused	Used
749	22p. Type **198**	1·40	1·60
750	23p. Brown bee orchid	1·40	1·60
751	24p. Pyramidal orchid	1·40	1·60
752	25p. Mirror orchid	1·40	1·60
753	26p. Sawfly orchid	1·40	1·60

199 Handshake and United Nations Emblem

1995. 50th Anniv of United Nations. Multicoloured.

No.	Description	Unused	Used
754	34p. Type **199**	1·50	1·10
755	49p. Peace dove and U.N. emblem	1·75	3·00

200 Marilyn Monroe

1995. Centenary of Cinema. T 200 and similar horiz designs showing film stars. Multicoloured.

MS756 Two sheets, each 116×80 mm. (a) 5p. Type **200**; 25p. Romy Schneider; 28p. Yves Montand; 38p. Audrey Hepburn. (b) 24p. Ingrid Bergman; 24p. Vittorio de Sica; 24p. Marlene Dietrich; 24p. Laurence Olivier Set of 2 sheets — 4·50 — 5·50

201 Father Christmas

1995. Christmas. Multicoloured.

No.	Description	Unused	Used
757	5p. Type **201**	40	10
758	24p. Toys in sack	1·25	55
759	34p. Reindeer	1·75	1·25
760	54p. Sleigh over houses	3·00	4·50

202 Shih Tzu

1996. Puppies. Multicoloured.

761	5p. Type **202**	40	85
762	21p. Dalmatians	75	95
763	24p. Cocker spaniels	80	1·10
764	25p. West Highland white terriers	80	1·10
765	34p. Labrador	90	1·25
766	35p. Boxer	90	1·25

No. 762 is inscr "Dalmation" in error.

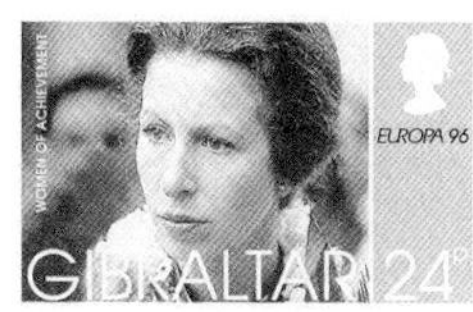

203 Princess Anne

1996. Europa. Famous Women.

767	**203**	24p. black and yellow	1·60	1·60
768	-	24p. black and green	1·60	1·60
769	-	34p. black and red	2·00	2·25
770	-	34p. black and purple	2·00	2·25

DETAILS: Nos. 768, Princess Diana; 769, Queen Elizabeth II; 770, Queen Elizabeth the Queen Mother.

204 West German Player, 1980

1996. European Football Championship, England. Players from previous winning teams. Multicoloured.

771	21p. Type **204**	55	45
772	24p. French player, 1984	65	55
773	34p. Dutch player, 1988	95	1·10
774	£1.20 Danish player, 1992	2·50	4·75
MS775	135×91 mm. As Nos. 771/4	5·50	7·50

205 Ancient Greek Athletes

1996. Centenary of Modern Olympic Games.

776	**205**	34p. black, purple & orge	95	90
777	-	49p. black and brown	1·40	1·75
778	-	£1.05 multicoloured	3·00	4·50

DESIGNS: 49p. Start of early race; £1.05, Start of modern race.

1996. Second World War Warships (4th series). Sheet 118×84 mm, containing horiz designs as T 184. Multicoloured.

MS779 5p. H.M.S. "Starling" (sloop); 25p. H.M.S. "Royalist" (cruiser); 49p. U.S.S. "Philadelphia" (cruiser); 54p. H.M.C.S. "Prescott" (corvette) 7·50 8·50

206 Asian Children

1996. 50th Anniv of UNICEF.

780	**206**	21p. multicoloured	60	80
781	-	24p. multicoloured	70	90
782	-	49p. multicoloured	1·25	2·00
783	-	54p. multicoloured	1·40	2·25

DESIGNS: 24p. to 54p. Children from different continents.

207 Red Kites in Flight

1996. Endangered Species. Red Kite. Multicoloured.

784	34p. Type **207**	1·60	1·90
785	34p. Red kite on ground	1·60	1·90
786	34p. On rock	1·60	1·90
787	34p. Pair at nest	1·60	1·90

208 Christmas Pudding

1996. Christmas. Designs created from "Lego" Blocks. Multicoloured.

788	5p. Type **208**	15	15
789	21p. Snowman face	70	45
790	24p. Present	80	55
791	34p. Father Christmas face	1·10	1·25
792	54p. Candle	1·50	2·75

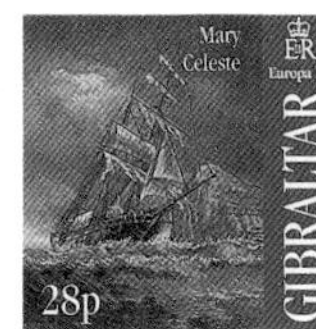

209 "Mary Celeste" passing Gibraltar

1997. Europa. Tales and Legends. "The Mary Celeste". Multicoloured.

793	28p. Type **209**	1·40	1·40
794	28p. Boarding the "Mary Celeste"	1·40	1·40
795	30p. Crew leaving "Mary Celeste"	1·40	1·60
796	30p. "Mary Celeste" found by "Dei Gratia"	1·40	1·60

210 American Shorthair Silver Tabby

1997. Kittens. Multicoloured.

797	5p. Type **210**	40	1·00
798	24p. Rumpy Manx red tabby	75	1·25
799	26p. Blue point birmans	75	1·25
800	28p. Red self longhair	80	1·25
801	30p. British shorthair tortoise-shell and white	80	1·25
802	35p. British bicolour shorthairs	90	1·40
MS803	132×80 mm. Nos. 797/802 with "HONG KONG '97" International Stamp Exhibition logo at bottom left	5·00	8·00

211 "Anthocharis belia euphenoides"

1997. Butterflies. Multicoloured.

804	23p. Type **211**	70	50
805	26p. "Charaxes jasius"	85	60
806	30p. "Vanessa cardui"	95	90
807	£1.20 "Iphiclides podalirius"	3·25	5·00
MS808	135×90 mm. Nos. 804/7	5·25	6·50

1997. Second World War Warships (5th series). Sheet 117×82 mm, containing horiz designs as T 184. Multicoloured.

MS809 24p. H.M.S. "Enterprise" (cruiser); 26p. H.M.S. "Cleopatra" (cruiser); 38p. U.S.S. "Iowa" (battleship); 50p. "Orkan" (Polish destroyer) 4·00 5·00

212 Queen Elizabeth and Prince Philip at Carriage-driving Trials

1997. Golden Wedding of Queen Elizabeth and Prince Philip. Multicoloured.

810	£1.20 Type **212**	4·75	5·50
811	£1.40 Queen Elizabeth in Trooping the Colour uniform	4·75	5·50

213 Christian Dior Evening Dress

1997. Christian Dior Spring/Summer '97 Collection. Multicoloured.

812	30p. Type **213**	80	1·25
813	35p. Tunic top and skirt	1·00	1·60
814	50p. Ballgown	1·00	1·75
815	62p. Two-piece suit	1·25	2·25
MS816	110×90 mm. £1.20, Ballgown (different)	2·25	3·50

214 "Our Lady and St. Bernard" (St. Joseph's Parish Church)

1997. Christmas. Stained Glass Windows. Mult.

817	5p. Type **214**	25	10
818	26p. "The Epiphany" (Our Lady of Sorrows Church)	1·00	60
819	38p. "St. Joseph" (Our Lady of Sorrows Church)	1·25	95
820	50p. "The Holy Family" (St. Joseph's Parish Church)	1·50	2·25
821	62p. "The Miraculous Medal" (St. Joseph's Parish Church)	1·75	3·25

215 Sir Joshua Hassan

1997. Sir Joshua Hassan (former Chief Minister) Commemoration.

822	**215**	26p. black	1·50	75

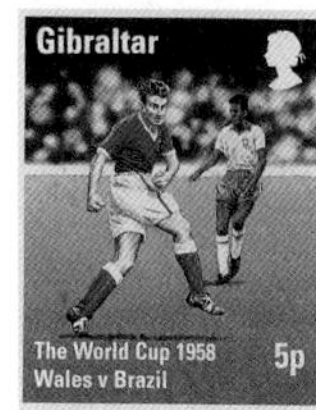

216 Wales v Brazil (1958)

1998. World Football Championship, France (1998). Multicoloured.

823	5p. Type **216**	25	10
824	26p. Northern Ireland v France (1958)	1·00	60
825	38p. Scotland v Holland (1978)	1·25	90
826	£1.20 England v West Germany (1966)	2·25	4·75
MS827	153×96 mm. Nos. 823/6	4·25	6·00

1998. Diana, Princess of Wales Commemoration. Sheet 145×70 mm, containing vert designs as T 177 of Ascension. Multicoloured.

MS828 26p. Wearing jacket with white fur collar, 1988; 26p. Wearing pink checked suit and hat; 38p. Wearing black jacket, 1995; 38p. Wearing blue jacket with gold embroidery, 1987 (sold at £1.28+20p. charity premium) 2·25 3·75

216b Saunders Roe (Saro) London (flying boat)

1998. 80th Anniv of Royal Air Force. Multicoloured.

829	24p. Type **216b**	70	55
830	26p. Fairey Fox	75	60
831	38p. Handley Page Halifax GR.VI	95	1·25
832	50p. Hawker Siddeley Buccaneer S.2B	1·25	2·50
MS833	110×77 mm. 24p. Sopwith Strutter; 26p. Bristol M.IB; 38p. Supermarine Spitfire XII; 50p. Avro York 685 York	3·50	4·50

217 Miss Gibraltar saluting

1998. Europa. Festivals. National Day. Mult.

834	26p. Type **217**	1·10	1·25
835	26p. In black bodice and long red skirt	1·10	1·25
836	38p. In black bodice and short red skirt, with Gibraltar flag	1·40	1·60
837	38p. In Genoese-style costume	1·40	1·60

218 Striped Dolphin

1998. International Year of the Ocean. Sheet 155×64 mm, containing T 218 and similar multicoloured designs.

MS838 5p. Type **218**; 5p. Common dolphin (vert); 26p. Killer whale (vert); £1.20, Blue whale 5·50 6·50

219 Nileus (dog) with Hat and Telescope

1998. Bicentenary of Battle of the Nile. Multicoloured.

839	12p. Type **219**	1·00	1·25
840	26p. Rear-Admiral Sir Horatio Nelson	1·00	80
841	28p. Frances Nisbet, Lady Nelson	1·75	2·00
842	35p. H.M.S. "Vanguard" (ship of the line)	1·75	2·25
843	50p. Battle of the Nile (47×29 mm)	1·75	3·25

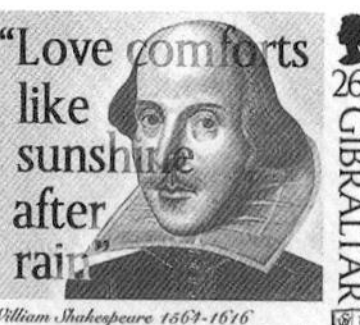

220 "Love comforts like Sunshine after Rain" (William Shakespeare)

1998. Famous Quotations. Multicoloured.

844	26p. Type **220**	90	1·00
845	26p. "The price of greatness is responsibility" (Sir Winston Churchill)	90	1·00
846	38p. "Hate the sin, love the sinner" (Mahatma Gandhi)	1·10	1·50
847	38p. "Imagination is more important than knowledge" (Albert Einstein)	1·10	1·50

221 The Nativity

1998. Christmas. Multicoloured.

848	5p. Type **221**	35	10
849	26p. Star and stable	1·25	70
850	30p. King with gold	1·40	75
851	35p. King with myrrh	1·40	1·25
852	50p. King with frankincense	1·75	3·25

222 Barbary Macaque

1999. Europa. Parks and Gardens. Upper Rock Nature Reserve. Multicoloured.

853	30p. Type **222**	1·75	1·50
854	30p. Dartford warbler	2·00	1·50
855	42p. Dusky grouper	2·00	2·50
856	42p. River kingfisher ("Common Kingfisher")	2·25	2·50

223 Queen Elizabeth II

1999. (a) Ordinary gum.

857	**223**	1p. purple	10	70
858	**223**	2p. brown	10	70
859	**223**	4p. blue	20	60
860	**223**	5p. green	20	30
861	**223**	10p. orange	40	30
862	**223**	12p. red	45	40
863	**223**	20p. green	1·00	45
864	**223**	28p. mauve	1·25	60
865	**223**	30p. orange	1·50	65
866	**223**	40p. grey	2·00	85
867	**223**	42p. green	2·00	90
868	**223**	50p. bistre	2·00	1·25
869	**223**	£1 black	3·50	2·75
869a	**223**	£1.20 red	4·50	4·00
869b	**223**	£1.40 blue	4·50	4·25
870	**223**	£3 blue	8·50	11·00

(b) Self-adhesive.

871	(1st) orange	1·00	60

Nos. 868/71 are larger, 22×28 mm.
No. 871 was initially sold at 26p.

224 Roman Marine and Galley

1999. Maritime Heritage. Multicoloured.

872	5p. Type **224**	25	10
873	30p. Arab sailor, medieval galley house and dhow	95	65
874	42p. Marine officer and British ship of the line (1779–83)	1·50	1·50
875	£1.20 Naval rating, Queen Alexandra Dry Dock and H.M.S. "Berwick" (cruiser) (1904)	3·25	4·25
MS876	116×76 mm. Nos. 872/5	6·00	7·00

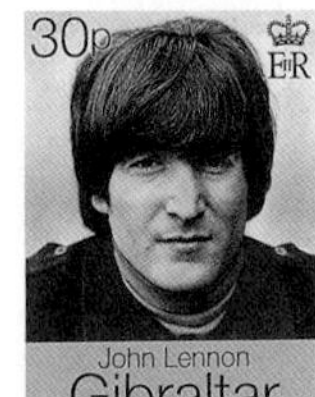

225 John Lennon (musician)

1999. 30th Wedding Anniv of John Lennon and Yoko Ono. Designs showing John Lennon.

877	-	20p. multicoloured	1·00	55
878	**225**	30p. black and blue	1·25	90
879	-	40p. multicoloured	1·50	1·90

MS880 Two sheets, each 62×100 mm. (a) £1 black and blue. (b) £1 multicoloured Set of 2 sheets 8·50 8·50

DESIGNS 20p. With flower over left eye; 40p. Wearing orange glasses; £1 (No. **MS**880a), Holding marriage certificate; £1 (No. **MS**880b), Standing on aircraft steps.

226 Postal Van at Dockside, 1930s

1999. 125th Anniv of U.P.U. Multicoloured.

881	5p. Type **226**	25	25
882	30p. Space shuttle and station	75	1·25

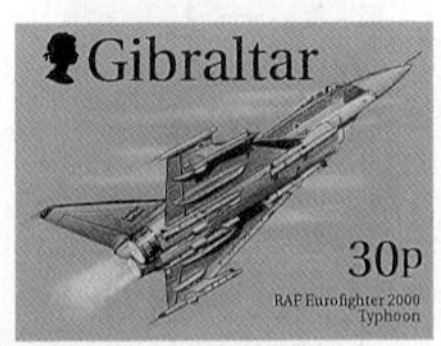

227 Eurofighter EF-2000 Typhoon

1999. "Wings of Prey" (1st series). Birds of Prey and R.A.F. Fighter Aircraft. Multicoloured.

883	30p. Type **227**	1·25	1·40
884	30p. Panavia Tornado F.Mk3	1·25	1·40
885	30p. BAe Harrier II GR7	1·25	1·40
886	42p. Lesser kestrel	1·40	1·60
887	42p. Peregrine falcon	1·40	1·60
888	42p. Common kestrel ("Kestrel")	1·40	1·60

MS889 Two sheets, each 105×86 mm. (a) Nos. 883/5. (b) Nos. 886/8 Set of 2 sheets 8·00 8·50

See also Nos. 943/8 and 982/7.

228 Prince Edward and Sophie Rhys-Jones

1999. Royal Wedding. Multicoloured.

890	30p. Type **228**	1·25	65
891	42p. Prince Edward and Sophie Rhys-Jones holding hands (vert)	1·60	1·00
892	54p. In carriage on wedding day	2·00	2·50
893	66p. On Chapel steps after wedding (vert)	2·50	3·00

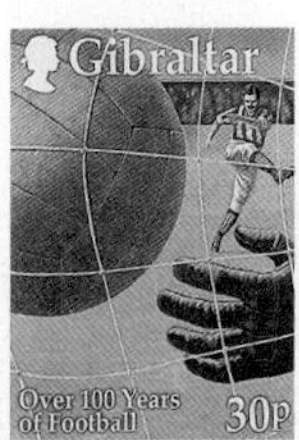

229 Football

1999. Local Sporting Centenaries. Multicoloured.

894	30p. Type **229**	75	65
895	42p. Rowing	1·00	90
896	£1.20 Cricket	3·25	4·25

230 "Seasons Greetings"

1999. Christmas. Multicoloured.

897	5p. Type **230**	15	10
898	5p. "Happy Christmas"	15	10
899	30p. "Happy Millennium"	80	80
900	30p. "Happy Christmas" and Santa with reindeer	80	80
901	42p. Santa Claus in chimney	1·25	1·75
902	54p. Santa Claus leaving presents	1·40	2·50

231 "People travelling with Environmentally-friendly Jet-packs" (Colin Grech)

2000. "Stampin' the Future" (children's stamp design competition). Multicoloured.

903	30p. Type **231**	1·50	1·60
904	42p. "Robotic Postman" (Kim Barea)	1·50	1·60
905	54p. "Living on the Moon" (Stephan Williamson-Fa)	1·50	1·60
906	66p. "Jet-powered Cars" (Michael Podesta)	1·50	1·60

232 Dutch Football Player and Flag, 1988

2000. European Football Championship, Belgium and Netherlands. Multicoloured.

907	30p. Type **232**	85	90
908	30p. French player and flag, 1984	85	90
909	42p. German player scoring and flag, 1996	1·10	1·40
910	42p. Danish player and flag, 1992	1·10	1·40

MS911 Two sheets, each 115×85 mm. (a) 54p.×4, English player and flag. (b) Nos. 907/10 Set of 2 sheets 11·00 12·00

233 Fountain of Stars

2000. Europa. Multicoloured.

912	30p. Type **233**	1·00	80
913	40p. Exchanging star	1·25	1·40
914	42p. Stars and airplane	1·25	1·40
915	54p. Stars and end of rainbow	1·75	2·75

234 3000 m Waterfall between Gibraltar and North African Coast, 5 Million B.C.

2000. New Millennium. History of Gibraltar. Multicoloured (except Nos. 926/30).

916	5p. Type **234**	30	50
917	5p. Sabre-tooth tiger, 2 million B.C.	30	50
918	5p. Neanderthal hunting goat, and skull, 30,000 B.C.	30	50
919	5p. Phoenician traders and galley, 700 B.C.	30	50
920	5p. Roman warship, 100 B.C.	30	50
921	5p. Tarik-Ibn-Zayad, ape and Moorish Castle, 711 A.D.	30	50
922	5p. Coat of arms, 1502	30	50
923	5p. Admiral George Rooke and Union Jack, 1704	30	50
924	30p. General Eliott at The Great Siege, 1779–83	1·00	1·25
925	30p. H.M.S. *Victory*, 1805	1·00	1·25
926	30p. Queen Alexandra in horse-drawn carriage, 1903 (brown, silver and black)	1·00	1·25
927	30p. 100 ton gun, 1870s (grey, silver and black)	1·00	1·25
928	30p. Evacuees, 1940 (purple, silver and black)	1·00	1·25
929	30p. Tank and anti-aircraft gun, 1940s (brown, silver and black)	1·00	1·25
930	30p. Queen Elizabeth II in Gibraltar, 1954 (grey, silver and black)	1·00	1·25
931	30p. Aerial view of office district, 2000	1·00	1·25

235 Princess Diana holding Prince William, 1982

2000. 18th Birthday of Prince William. Multicoloured.

932	30p. Type **235**	90	65
933	42p. Prince William as a toddler	1·25	90
934	54p. Prince William with Prince Charles	1·50	2·00
935	66p. Prince William at 18	1·75	2·75
MS936	115×75 mm. Nos. 932/5	5·00	6·00

236 Lady Elizabeth Bowes-Lyon signing Book

2000. Queen Elizabeth the Queen Mother's 100th Birthday.

937	**236**	30p. black and blue	90	65
938	-	42p. black and brown	1·25	90
939	-	54p. multicoloured	1·50	2·00
940	-	66p. multicoloured	1·75	2·75
MS941		115×75 mm. Nos. 937/40	4·75	6·00

DESIGNS: 42p. Duke and Duchess of York; 54p. Queen Mother with bouquet; 66p. Queen Mother in orange coat and hat.

237 Moorish Castle

2000

942	**237**	£5 black, silver and gold	13·00	14·00

The Queen's head on this stamp is printed in optically variable ink, which changes colour from gold to green when viewed from different angles.

2000. "Wings of Prey" (2nd series). Birds of Prey and R.A.F. Second World War Aircraft. As T 227. Multicoloured.

943	30p. Supermarine Spitfire Mk IIA *Gibraltar*	1·75	1·75
944	30p. Hawker Hurricane Mk IIC	1·75	1·75
945	30p. Avro Lancaster BI-III *City of Lincoln*	1·75	1·75
946	42p. Merlin (male)	2·00	2·00
947	42p. Merlin (female)	2·00	2·00
948	42p. Bonelli's eagle	2·00	2·00

MS949 Two sheets, each 105×85 mm. (a) Nos. 943/5. (b) Nos. 946/8 Set of 2 sheets 10·00 10·00

238 Infant Jesus

2000. Christmas. Multicoloured.

950	5p. Type **238**	25	15

951 30p. Virgin Mary with infant Jesus 85 65
952 30p. Journey to Bethlehem 85 65
953 40p. Mary and Joseph with innkeeper 1·10 1·00
954 42p. The Nativity 1·10 1·25
955 54p. Visit of the Wise Men 1·60 2·25

239 Wedding of Queen Victoria and Prince Albert

2001. Death Centenary of Queen Victoria.
956 **239** 30p. blue, violet and black 1·00 65
957 - 42p. myrtle, green & black 1·40 1·00
958 - 54p. purple, red and black 2·00 2·50
959 - 66p. brown, gold & black 2·25 3·25
DESIGNS: 42p. Victoria as Empress of India; 54p. Queen Victoria in carriage; 66p. Queen Victoria standing by chair.

240 Grass Snake

2001. Snakes. Multicoloured.
960 5p. Type **240** 25 40
961 5p. Ladder snake 25 40
962 5p. Montpellier snake 25 40
963 30p. Viperine snake 85 1·00
964 30p. Southern smooth snake 85 1·00
965 30p. False smooth snake 85 1·00
966 66p. Horseshoe whip snake (30×62 mm) 1·75 2·50
MS967 155×87 mm. Nos. 960/6 7·00 7·50
No. **MS**967 also commemorates the Chinese New Year "Year of the Snake".
No. 962 and **MS**967 are inscribed "MONTPELIER" in error.

241 Long-snouted Seahorse

2001. Europa. Water and Nature. Multicoloured.
968 30p. Type **241** 1·75 80
969 40p. Snapdragon 2·25 1·25
970 42p. Herring gull ("Yellow-legged Gull") 3·25 1·75
971 54p. Goldfish 2·75 5·00

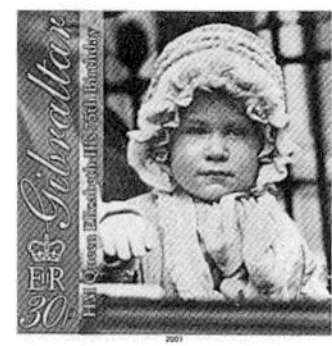

242 Queen Elizabeth II as a Baby

2001. 75th Birthday of Queen Elizabeth II.
972 **242** 30p. black and mauve 85 75
973 - 30p. black and violet 85 75
974 - 42p. black and red 1·25 1·50
975 - 42p. black and violet 1·25 1·50
976 - 54p. multicoloured 1·60 2·25
MS977 101×89 mm. £2 multicoloured 5·50 6·50
DESIGNS—HORIZ: No. 973, Queen Elizabeth as teenager; 974, On wedding day, 1947; 975, After Coronation, 1953; 976, Queen Elizabeth in blue hat. VERT: (35×49 mm)—No. **MS**977, Queen Elizabeth II, 2001 (photo by Fiona Hanson).
No. **MS**977 marks a successful attempt on the record for the fastest produced stamp issue. The miniature sheet was on sale in Gibraltar 10 hours and 24 minutes after the artwork was approved at Buckingham Palace.

243 Battle of Trafalgar, 1805

2001. Bicentenary of The Gibraltar Chronicle (newspaper). Each black.
978 30p. Type **243** 1·50 65
979 42p. Invention of the telephone, 1876 1·25 90
980 54p. Winston Churchill (Victory in Second World War, 1945) 2·50 2·50
981 66p. Footprint on Moon (Moon landing, 1969) 2·50 3·75

2001. "Wings of Prey" (3rd series). Birds of Prey and Modern Military Aircraft. As T 227. Multicoloured.
982 40p. Royal Navy Sea Harrier FA MK.2 1·25 1·50
983 40p. Western marsh harrier ("Marsh Harrier") 1·25 1·50
984 40p. R.A.F. Hawk T MK.1 1·25 1·50
985 40p. Northern sparrowhawk ("Sparrowhawk") 1·25 1·50
986 40p. R.A.F. SEPECAT Jaguar GR1B 1·25 1·50
987 40p. Northern hobby ("Hobby") 1·25 1·50
MS988 Two sheets, each 103×84 mm. (a) Nos. 982, 984 and 986. (b) Nos. 983, 985 and 987 Set of 2 sheets 6·50 7·00

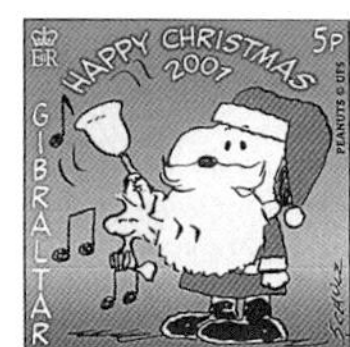

244 Snoopy as Father Christmas with Woodstock

2001. Christmas. Peanuts (cartoon characters by Charles Schulz). Multicoloured.
989 5p. Type **244** 25 15
990 30p. Charlie Brown and Snoopy with Christmas tree 85 65
991 40p. Snoopy asleep in wreath 1·10 1·00
992 42p. Snoopy with plate of biscuits 1·25 1·25
993 54p. Snoopy asleep on kennel 1·75 2·50
MS994 140×85 mm. Nos. 989/93 4·75 5·50

245 One Cent Coin

2002. Introduction of Euro Currency by European Union. Coins. Sheet 165×105 mm, containing T 245 and similar square designs showing coins. Multicoloured.
MS995 5p. Type **245**; 12p. 2 cents; 30p. 5 cents; 35p. 10 cents; 40p. 20 cents; 42p. 50 cents; 54p. 1 Euro; 66p. 2 Euros. 7·00 7·50

2002. Golden Jubilee. As T 219 of Falkland Islands.
996 30p. black, red and gold 1·25 1·40
997 30p. agate, red and gold 1·25 1·40
998 30p. multicoloured 1·25 1·40
999 30p. multicoloured 1·25 1·40
1000 75p. multicoloured 2·25 3·00
MS1001 162×95 mm. Nos. 996/1000 7·00 8·00
DESIGNS—HORIZ: No. 996, Princess Elizabeth and Princess Margaret making radio broadcast, 1940; 997, Princess Elizabeth in Girl Guide uniform, 1942; 998, Queen Elizabeth in evening dress, 1961; 999, Queen Elizabeth in Chelsea, 1993. VERT (38×51 mm): No 1000, Queen Elizabeth after Annigoni.

246 Joshua Grimaldi

2002. Europa. Circus. Famous Clowns. Multicoloured.
1002 30p. Type **246** 90 65
1003 40p. Karl Wettach ("Grock") 1·25 1·25
1004 42p. Nicolai Polakovs ("Coco") 1·25 1·25
1005 54p. Charlie Cairoli 1·75 2·50

247 Bobby Moore holding Jules Rimet Trophy, 1966

2002. World Cup Football Championship, Japan and Korea (2002). England's Victory, 1966. Multicoloured.
1006 30p. Type **247** 80 65
1007 42p. Kissing Trophy 1·25 90
1008 54p. Bobby Moore with Queen Elizabeth II 1·50 2·00
1009 66p. Bobby Moore in action 1·75 2·75
MS1010 135×90 mm. Nos. 1006/9 5·50 6·00

248 Barbary Macaque

2002. Wildlife. Multicoloured.
1011 30p. Type **248** 90 80
1012 30p. Red fox (horiz) 90 80
1013 40p. White-toothed shrew (horiz) 1·25 85
1014 £1 Rabbit 2·75 3·50
MS1015 125×100 mm. Nos. 1011/14 6·00 7·00

249 Gibraltar from the North

2002. Views of the Rock of Gibraltar. Multicoloured.
1016 30p. Type **249** 1·25 1·25
1017 30p. View from the south 1·25 1·25
1018 £1 View from the east (50×40 mm) 2·75 3·50
1019 £1 View from the west (50×40 mm) 2·75 3·50
Nos. 1016/19 were printed together, se-tenant, with powdered particles of the Rock sintered to their surface using thermography.

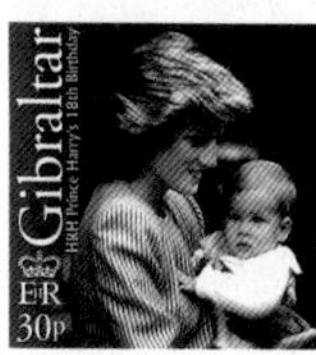

250 Princess Diana holding Prince Harry

2002. 18th Birthday of Prince Harry. Multicoloured.
1020 30p. Type **250** 90 65
1021 42p. Prince Harry waving 1·25 90
1022 54p. Prince Harry skiing 1·50 1·60
1023 66p. Wearing dark suit 1·90 2·75
MS1024 115×75 mm. Nos. 1020/3 5·50 6·50

251 Crib, Cathedral of St. Mary the Crowned

2002. Christmas. Cribs from Gibraltar Cathedrals and Churches. Multicoloured.
1025 5p. Type **251** 35 10
1026 30p. St. Joseph's Parish Church 1·25 65
1027 40p. St. Theresa's Parish Church 1·50 85
1028 42p. Our Lady of Sorrows Church 1·50 90
1029 52p. St. Bernard's Church 1·75 2·50
1030 54p. Cathedral of the Holy Trinity 1·75 2·50

252 Archbishop of Canterbury crowning Queen Elizabeth II

2003. 50th Anniv of the Coronation. Each black, grey and purple.
1031 30p. Type **252** 90 85
1032 30p. Queen Elizabeth II in Coronation robes 90 85
1033 40p. Queen Elizabeth holding the Orb and Sceptre 1·40 85
1034 £1 Queen Elizabeth in Coronation Coach 3·00 3·50
MS1035 116×76 mm. Nos. 1031/4 5·50 6·50

253 Young Prince William with Princess Diana

2003. 21st Birthday of Prince William of Wales. Each black, grey and violet.
1036 30p. Type **253** 1·50 1·00
1037 30p. Prince William at Eton College 1·50 1·00
1038 40p. Prince William 2·00 1·00
1039 £1 Prince William in Operation Raleigh sweatshirt 3·75 4·50
MS1040 115×75 mm. Nos. 1036/9 7·00 7·50

254 Drama Festival Poster

2003. Europa. Poster Art. Multicoloured.
1041 30p. Type **254** 80 65
1042 40p. Spring Festival poster 1·00 1·00
1043 42p. Art Festival poster 1·00 1·00
1044 54p. Dance festival poster 1·50 2·50

255 Wright Brothers' *Flyer I*, 1903

2003. Centenary of Powered Flight. Aircraft.
1045 **255** 30p. multicoloured 90 65
1046 - 40p. black and brown 1·25 1·25
1047 - 40p. black and blue 1·25 1·25
1048 - 42p. black and blue 1·25 1·25
1049 - 44p. multicoloured 1·40 1·40
1050 - 66p. multicoloured 2·00 3·25
MS1051 140×110 mm. Nos. 1045/50 7·75 8·25
DESIGNS—HORIZ: (37×28 mm) 40p. (No. 1046) Charles Lindbergh and *Spirit of St. Louis* (first Transatlantic solo flight, 1927); 40p. (No. 1047) Boeing 314 *Yankee Clipper* flying boat (first Transatlantic scheduled air service, 1939). (77×28 mm)—42p. Saunders Roe (Saro) A21 Windhover (first scheduled air service between Gibraltar and Tangier, 1931); 44p. Aerospatiale/BAe Concorde (first supersonic airliner, 1976). VERT (37×58 mm)—66p. Space shuttle *Columbia* (first shuttle flight in Space orbit, 1981).

256 Flag of St. George

2003. 1700th Death Anniv of St. George. Multicoloured.

1052	30p. Type **256**	1·00	65
1053	40p. Cross of Military Constantinian Order of St. George	1·25	95
1054	£1.20 "St. George and the Dragon" (stained glass window, St. Joseph's Church, Gibraltar) (32×63 mm)	3·50	4·50
MS1055	150×100 mm. Nos. 1052/4	5·25	6·00

257 Big Ben, Swift and Rock of Gibraltar

2003

1056	**257**	(£3) multicoloured†	8·00	8·50

No. 1056 is inscribed "UK express" and was initially sold at £3.

†The Queen's head on this stamp is printed in optically variable ink which changes colour from gold to green when viewed from different angles.

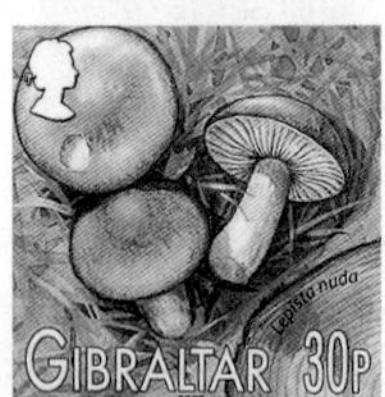

258 Wood Blewit (*Lepista nuda*)

2003. Mushrooms of Gibraltar. Multicoloured.

1057	30p. Type **258**	1·00	1·00
1058	30p. Blue-green funnel-cap (*Clitocybe odora*)	1·00	1·00
1059	30p. Sulphur tuft (*Hypholoma fasciculare*)	1·00	1·00
1060	£1.20 Field mushrooms (*Agaricus campestris*)	3·50	4·25
MS1061	105×90 mm. Nos. 1057/60	6·00	7·00

259 Daisy (Latvia), Cornflower (Estonia) and Rue (Lithuania)

2003. Enlargement of the European Union (2004). Designs showing the national flowers of new member countries. Multicoloured.

1062	30p. Type **259**	1·25	80
1063	40p. Rose (Cyprus) and Maltese Centaury (Malta)	1·50	1·25
1064	42p. Tulip (Hungary), Carnation (Slovenia) and Dog Rose (Slovakia)	1·50	1·25
1065	54p. Corn Poppy (Poland) and Scented Thyme (Czech Republic)	2·00	3·25

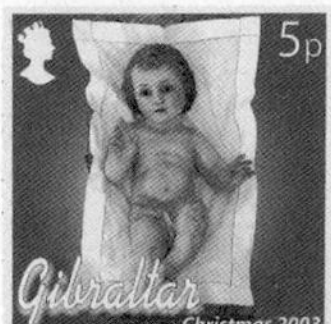

260 Baby Jesus Crib Figure, Our Lady of Sorrows Church

2003. Christmas. Multicoloured.

1066	5p. Type **260**	20	10
1067	30p. Children making Crib	90	65
1068	40p. Three Kings Cavalcade	1·25	1·00
1069	42p. Children's provisions for Santa and reindeer	1·25	1·00
1070	54p. Cathedral of St. Mary the Crowned lit for Christmas Eve Midnight Mass	1·75	3·00
MS1071	100×80 mm. £1 Cartoon characters from Peanuts carol singing around Christmas tree (50×40 mm)	4·25	5·00

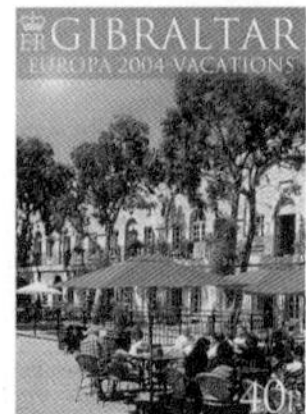

261 Street Cafe

2004. Europa. Holidays. Multicoloured.

1072	40p. Type **261**	1·25	1·40
1073	40p. St. Michael's Cave	1·25	1·40
1074	54p. Dolphins	1·75	2·25
1075	54p. Harbourside restaurant	1·75	2·25

262 Arms

2004. 300th Anniv of British Gibraltar (1st series). Multicoloured.

1076	8p. Type **262**	65	65
MS1077	144×114 mm. 30p. Royal Katarine flying Red Ensign, 1704; 30p. Landing party, 1704; 30p. Soldiers of 1704; 30p. Arms of Gibraltar on military uniform; 30p. Royal Gibraltar police helmet and red phone box; 30p. Post Office arms and red pillar box; 30p. Graduates and University of Cambridge examination certificate; 30p. Crowd waving Union Jacks and Gibraltar flags; £1.20 Union Jack	12·00	13·00

See also **MS**1095.

263 Queen Elizabeth holding Bouquet

2004. 50th Anniv of Visit of Queen Elizabeth II.

1078	**263**	38p. multicoloured	1·10	85
1079	-	40p. black and yellow	1·10	85
1080	-	47p. multicoloured	1·25	1·25
1081	-	£1 black	2·75	4·00
MS1082		95×110 mm. £1.50 black	3·75	4·50

DESIGNS: 38p. Type **263**; 40p.Queen Elizabeth holding out keys; 47p. Queen and Duke of Edinburgh in car; £1 Queen, Prince Charles and Princess Anne with members of British armed forces; £1.50 Queen waving with Duke of Edinburgh.

264 Scoring a Goal

2004. European Football Championships 2004, Portugal. Multicoloured.

1083	30p. Type **264**	90	65
1084	40p. Two defenders blocking a goal attempt	1·25	1·25
1085	40p. Overhead kick	1·25	1·25
1086	£1 Player performing header	2·75	4·00
MS1087	Two sheets. (a) 102×77 mm. £1.50 Player celebrating with arms in air (51×39 mm) (b) 105×105 mm (circular). Nos. 1083/6	8·00	8·50

265 Landing at St. Aubin, 1944

2004. 60th Anniv of D-Day Landings. Each black, brown and red.

1088	38p. Type **265**	1·25	85
1089	40p. Cruiser tank Mk VIII Cromwell	1·25	85
1090	47p. Handley Page Halifax plane	1·60	1·60
1091	£1 HMS *Belfast*	3·00	4·00
MS1092	170×100 mm. Nos. 1088/91	6·00	7·00

266 Union Jack Flag

2004. 300th Anniv of British Gibraltar (2nd series). Elton John Tercentenary Concert. Circular sheet 105×105 mm.

MS1093	**266** £1.20 multicoloured	3·00	3·25

Stamp in No. **MS**1093 is similar in design to the £1.20 stamp in No. **MS**1077.

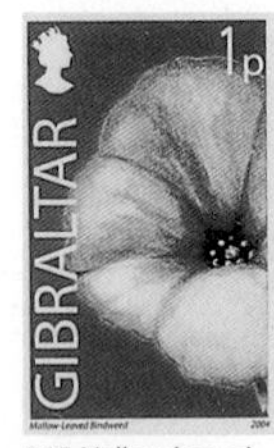

267 Mallow-leaved Bindweed

2004. Wild Flowers. Multicoloured.

1094	1p. Type **267**	15	35
1095	2p. Gibraltar sea lavender	25	35
1095b	3p. Gibraltar restharrow	30	40
1096	5p. Gibraltar chickweed	30	30
1097	(7p.) Romulea	45	20
1098	10p. Common centaury	60	30
1099	(12p.) Pyramidal orchid	75	75
1099b	15p. Paper-white narcissus	75	50
1100	(28p.) Friars cowl	1·25	60
1101	(38p.) Corn poppy	1·40	85
1102	(40p.) Giant Tangier fennel	1·40	65
1103	(47p.) Snapdragon	1·75	1·10
1104	50p. Common gladiolus	1·75	1·50
1104b	53p. Gibraltar campion	2·00	1·60
1105	£1 Yellow horned poppy	3·50	3·50
1105b	£1.60 Sea daffodil	4·75	4·75
1106	£3 Gibraltar candytuft	9·50	10·00

Nos. 1097 and 1099/103 are inscribed "G", "G1", "S", "UK", "E" and "U" and were initially sold for 7p., 12p., 28p., 38p., 40p. and 47p. respectively.

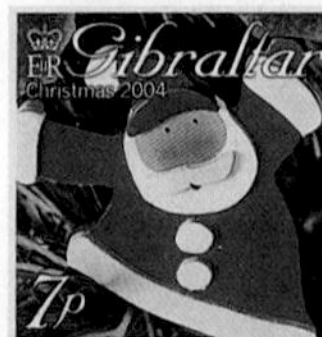

268 Father Christmas

2004. Christmas. Decorations. Multicoloured.

1107	7p. Type **268**	30	20
1108	28p. Cherub	1·25	60
1109	38p. Red star	1·40	80
1110	40p. Gold conical tree	1·40	85
1111	47p. Red bauble	1·60	1·25
1112	53p. Gold star	1·90	3·50

269 Ferrari F2003 GA

2004. Ferrari. Multioloured.

1113	5p. Type **269**	35	40
1114	5p. F2004	35	40
1115	30p. F2001	1·00	1·00
1116	30p. F2002	1·00	1·00
1117	75p. F399	2·50	3·00
1118	75p. F1-2000	2·50	3·00
MS1119	161×116 mm. Nos. 1113/18	7·00	7·50

270 Soldier guarding Nelson's Body

2005. Bicentenary of the Battle of Trafalgar. Multicoloured.

1120	38p. Type **270**	1·75	75
1121	40p. HMS *Entreprenante*	1·75	85
1122	47p. Admiral Nelson (vert)	2·00	1·50
1123	£1.60 HMS *Victory*	5·50	7·50
MS1124	120×80 mm. £2 HMS *Victory* (44×44 mm)	12·00	12·00

Nos. 1120/4 contain traces of powdered wood from HMS *Victory*.

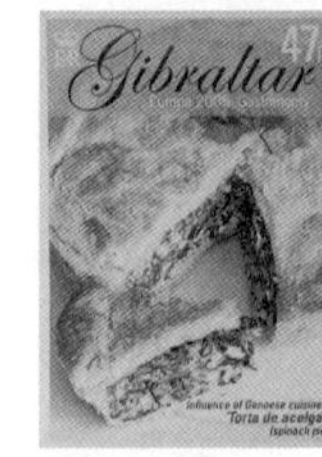

271 Spinach Pie

2005. Europa. Gastronomy. Multicoloured.

1125	47p. Type **271**	1·75	2·00
1126	47p. Grilled sea-bass	1·75	2·00
1127	47p. Veal "Birds"	1·75	2·00
1128	47p. Sherry trifle	1·75	2·00

272 Churchill giving Victory Salute

2005. 60th Anniv of VE Day. Multicoloured.

1129	38p. Type **272**	1·40	90
1130	40p. Family with Union Jack flags	1·40	90
1131	47p. VE Day celebrations	1·60	1·50
1132	£1 Returning Gibraltar people on dockside	3·75	4·75
MS1133	150×100 mm. Nos. 1129/32	7·25	7·50

273 *Circassia*

2005. Cruise Ships (1st series). Multicoloured.

1134	38p. Type **273**	1·40	90
1135	40p. *Nevasa*	1·40	90
1136	47p. *Black Prince*	1·60	1·50
1137	£1 *Arcadia*	3·75	4·75
MS1138	150×85 mm. Nos. 1134/7	7·25	7·50

See also Nos. 1180/**MS**1184 and 1207/**MS**1211.

274 Early and Modern Police Officers

2005. Anniversaries. Multicoloured.

1139	38p. Type **274** (175th anniv of Royal Gibraltar Police)	2·00	1·00
1140	47p. Skull, plate and ceramic horses (75th anniv of Gibraltar Museum)	1·50	1·00
1141	£1 Charter of Justice (175th anniv)	3·75	5·00

The back of Nos. 1139/41 is printed with a brief description of the subject of the stamp.

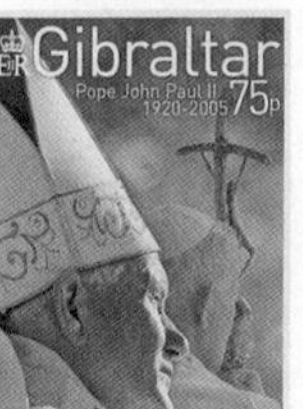

275 Pope John Paul II

2005. Pope John Paul II Commemoration.
1142 **275** 75p. multicoloured 2·50 2·75

276 Map of Europe and 1979 Europa 12p. Stamp

2005. 50th Anniv of Europa Stamps.
1143 **276** £5 multicoloured 14·00 16·00

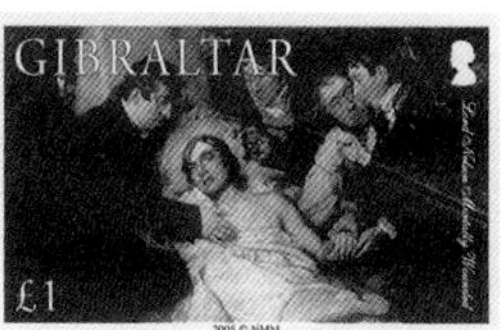

277 "Death of Nelson" (William Devis)

2005. Bicentenary of the Battle of Trafalgar and Death of Admiral Lord Nelson. Multicoloured.
MS1144 120×80 mm. £1 Type **277** 3·25 4·00
MS1145 170×75 mm. £1 As Type **277**, but 50×31 mm together with £1 stamp from Isle of Man No. **MS**1264 6·50 7·00

No. **MS**1145 was also issued by Isle of Man.

278 Two Angels

2005. Christmas. Angels. Multicoloured.
1146 7p. Type **278** 25 20
1147 38p. Angel with children by Christmas tree 1·25 80
1148 40p. Angel with toys 1·25 80
1149 47p. Angel with hymn book and top of Christmas tree 1·75 1·40
1150 53p. Angel with basket of fruit 2·00 2·75
MS1151 168×86 mm. Nos. 1146/50 6·00 7·00

279 Giant Devil Ray

2006. Endangered Species. Giant Devil Ray (Mobula mobular). Multicoloured.
1152 38p. Type **279** 1·25 1·75
1153 40p. Giant devil ray and trail of bubbles 1·40 1·75
1154 47p. Two giant devil rays 1·75 2·00
1155 £1 Upperside of giant devil ray 3·75 4·00

280 Queen Elizabeth II

2006. 80th Birthday of Queen Elizabeth II. Each showing 1950s and more recent photograph. Multicoloured.
1156 38p. Type **280** 2·00 2·00
1157 40p. In evening dress, c. 1955 and wearing purple hat 2·00 2·00
1158 47p. Smelling carnation, c. 1955 and wearing yellow hat 2·25 2·25
1159 £1 Princess Elizabeth, c. 1950 and Queen wearing red and black hat 3·75 4·25
MS1160 Two sheets, each 142×82 mm. (a) Nos. 1156 and 1159. (b) Nos. 1157/8 8·00 9·00

281 Uruguay

2006. World Cup Football Championship, Germany. Showing children with flags painted on faces. Multicoloured.
1161 38p. Type **281** 1·25 1·40
1162 38p. Italy 1·25 1·40
1163 38p. Germany 1·25 1·40
1164 38p. Brazil 1·25 1·40
1165 38p. England 1·25 1·40
1166 38p. Argentina 1·25 1·40
1167 38p. France 1·25 1·40

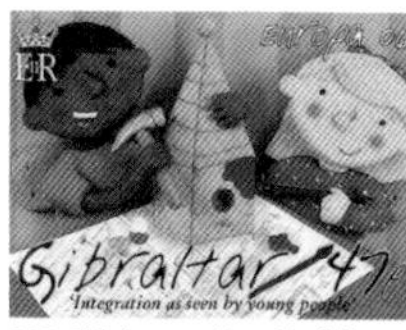

282 Children making Model Building

2006. Europa. Integration. Multicoloured.
1168 47p. Type **282** 1·50 1·50
1169 47p. Boy and girl 1·50 1·50
1170 47p. Children playing football 1·50 1·50
1171 47p. Children playing music 1·50 1·50

283 *Cornwallis*

2006. Bicentenary of the Gibraltar Packet Agency. Designs showing packet ships of the 1800s. Multicoloured.
1172 8p. Type **283** 60 35
1173 40p. *Meteor* 2·00 1·00
1174 42p. *Carteret* 2·00 1·00
1175 68p. *Prince Regent* 3·00 5·00

284 Saunders Roe (Saro) A21 Windhover Flying Boat, 1931

2006. 75th Anniv of Gibraltar Airmail Service. Multicoloured.
1176 8p. Type **284** 60 30
1177 40p. Vickers Vanguard, 1959 2·00 90
1178 49p. Vickers Viscount 2·75 1·50
1179 £1.60 Boeing 737 6·50 8·50

285 *Coral*

2006. Cruise Ships (2nd series). Multicoloured.
1180 40p. Type **285** 1·60 1·25
1181 42p. *Legend of the Seas* 1·75 1·40
1182 66p. *Saga Ruby* 2·75 3·50
1183 78p. *Costa Concordia* 3·25 5·00
MS1184 100×80 mm. Nos. 1180/83 8·50 10·00

286 St. Nicholas and Christmas Tree

2006. Christmas. St. Nicholas. Multicoloured.
1185 8p. Type **286** 40 15
1186 40p. St. Nicholas (in red) carrying presents 1·50 80
1187 42p. St. Nicholas giving present to young girl 1·60 85
1188 49p. St. Nicholas (in green) carrying sack of toys 2·00 1·75
1189 55p. St. Nicholas (in white) carrying sack and small Christmas tree 2·25 3·75
MS1190 165×80 mm. Nos. 1185/8 7·00 7·50

287 Navigational Instruments

2006. 500th Death Anniv of Christopher Columbus. Multicoloured.
1191 40p. Type **287** 1·50 1·25
1192 42p. Columbus writing report of voyage, 1492 1·50 1·25
1193 66p. *Santa Maria* 2·50 3·00
1194 78p. Columbus and Arawak chief 3·00 4·00
MS1195 95×74 mm. £1.60 Columbus' fleet, 1492 (47×47 mm) 5·75 6·50

288 Engagement, 1947

2007. Diamond Wedding of Queen Elizabeth II and Prince Philip. Multicoloured.
1196 40p. Type **288** 1·50 1·25
1197 42p. Wedding photograph, 1947 1·60 1·40
1198 66p. Silver Wedding anniversary, 1972 2·40 2·75
1199 78p. Ruby Anniversary, 1987 2·75 3·50
MS1200 105×105 mm. £1.60 Wedding photograph with bridesmaids and pageboys, 1947 (diamond shape, 84×83 mm) 5·75 6·50

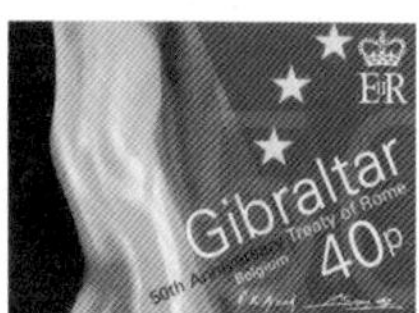

289 Flag of Belgium

2007. 50th Anniv of the Treaty of Rome. Sheet 137×100 mm containing T 289 and similar horiz designs showing national flags. Multicoloured.
MS1201 40p.×6 Type **289**; Germany; France; Italy; Luxembourg; Netherlands 6·00 7·00

290 Princess Diana

2007. 10th Death Anniv of Princess Diana. Multicoloured.
1202 8p. Type **290** 40 25
1203 40p. Seen full-face, eyes looking sideways 1·40 1·40
1204 42p. In half profile, smiling 1·40 1·40
1205 £1.60 Seen full-face, smiling 5·50 7·00
MS1206 165×92 mm. Nos. 1202/5 8·00 9·00

2007. Cruise Ships (3rd series). As T 285. Multicoloured.
1207 40p. *Oriana* 1·50 1·25
1208 42p. *Oceana* 1·60 1·40
1209 66p. *Queen Elizabeth 2* 2·75 3·25
1210 78p. *Queen Mary 2* 3·00 4·75
MS1211 168×67 mm. Nos. 1207/10 8·00 9·50

291 Gibraltar Scout, 1908

2007. Europa. Centenary of World Scouting. Multicoloured.
1212 8p. Type **291** 40 30
1213 40p. Scout, 1950s 1·40 1·25
1214 42p. Sea scout, 1980s 1·50 1·40
1215 £1 Modern scout 3·50 5·00

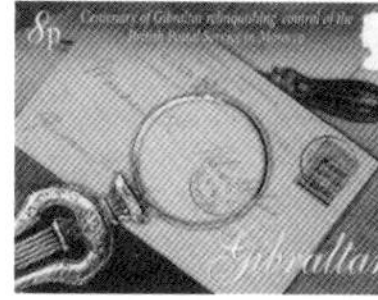
292 Postcard from Fez, 1907

2007. Gibraltar Postal Anniversaries. Multicoloured.
1216 8p. Type **292** (Cent of Gibraltar relinquishing control of British Postal Service in Morocco) 55 30
1217 40p. Gibraltar date stamp of Packet Agency, 1857 (150th anniv of Gibraltar Post Office) 2·00 1·25
1218 42p. Letter with British postage stamps cancelled 'G' (150th anniv of the introduction of British postage stamps in Gibraltar) 2·00 1·40
1219 £1 Earliest known letter from Morocco via Gibraltar (150th anniv of first British Postal Agency in Morocco) 4·50 5·50

Nos. 1216/19 have information about the anniversaries commemorated printed on the reverse (gummed) side of the stamps.

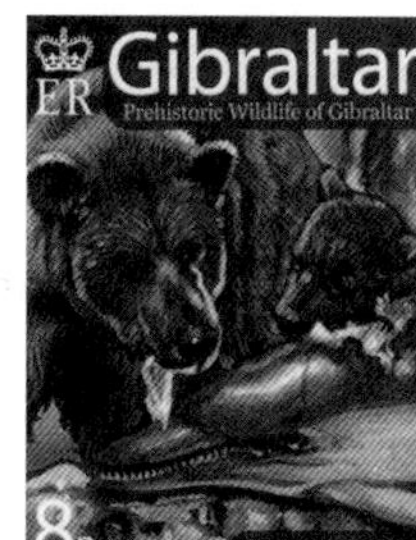

293 Bear and Cub feeding on Dolphin

2007. Prehistoric Wildlife of Gibraltar. Mult.
1220 8p. Type **293** 40 40
1221 40p. Eagle owl 1·50 1·50
1222 42p. Great auk and eagle 1·60 1·60
1223 55p. Red deer and boar 1·75 2·50
1224 78p. Wolf and vulture feeding on wild horse 2·75 4·50
MS1225 154×100 mm. £2 Ibex 7·00 8·50

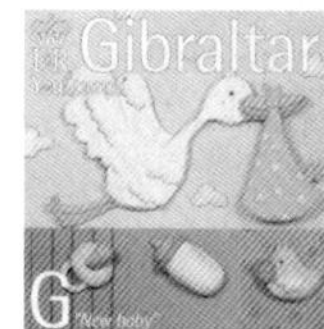

294 Stork ('New baby')

2007. YouStamps
1226 (8p.) Type **294** 40 40
1227 (8p.) Lion, sheep and dog wearing party hats ('Let's celebrate') 40 40
1228 (8p.) Crab finding heart written in beach sand ('With love') 40 40
1229 (8p.) Heart enclosed in wedding ring ('Commitment') 40 40
1230 (8p.) Dolphins and Rock of Gibraltar ('Greetings from Gibraltar') 40 40
1231 (40p.) As Type **294** 1·40 1·40
1232 (40p.) As No. 1227 1·40 1·40
1233 (40p.) As No. 1228 1·40 1·40
1234 (40p.) As No. 1229 1·40 1·40
1235 (40p.) As No. 1230 1·40 1·40

Nos. 1226/30 are inscr 'G' and sold for 8p. each. Nos. 1231/5 are inscr 'E' and sold for 40p. each.

295 Rock of Gibraltar

2007. Panoramic Views of Gibraltar. Multicoloured.

1236	40p. Type **295**	1·40	1·25
1237	42p. Beach and Rock of Gibraltar	1·60	1·40
1238	55p. Rock of Gibraltar at sunset	2·00	2·50
1239	78p. Town and Rock of Gibraltar	3·25	4·00
MS1240	114×67 mm. £1.70 Gibraltar Trinity Lighthouse (52×20 mm)	6·50	6·50

No. 1236 is inscr 'sepac'.

296 Joseph

2007. Christmas. Porcelain Figurines. Multicoloured.

1241	8p. Type **296**	25	25
1242	8p. Baby Jesus	25	25
1243	40p. Mary	1·25	80
1244	42p. King Melchoir	1·40	90
1245	49p. King Balthasar	1·60	1·60
1246	55p. King Gaspar	1·75	3·00
MS1247	124×105 mm. Nos. 1241/6	6·50	7·00

Nos. 1241/6 have biblical quotations printed on the reverse (gummed) side of the stamps.

297 Woodchat Shrike

2008. Birds of the Rock. Multicoloured.

1248	1p. Type **297**	10	10
1249	2p. Balearic shearwater	15	15
1250	5p. Eagle owl	20	15
1251	(8p.) Egyptian vulturel	40	35
1252	10p. Razorbil	50	45
1252a	10p. Black stalk	75	80
1253	(30p.) European bee-eater	90	85
1254	(40p.) Hoopoe	1·25	1·10
1255	(42p.) Bonelli's eagle	1·40	1·25
1256	(49p.) Blue rock thrush	1·50	1·25
1257	50p. Greater flamingo	1·50	1·25
1258	55p. Mediterranean shag	1·60	1·50
1258a	59p. Barbary partridge	2·00	1·90
1258b	76p. Ortolan bunting	2·50	2·50
1259	£1 Honey buzzard (34×47 mm)	3·00	3·00
1259a	£2 Northern gannett (35×48 mm)	6·00	6·50
1259b	£2 Pallid swift	6·50	7·00
1259c	£3 Osprey (35×38 mm)	9·25	9·50
1260	£5 Lesser kestrel (34×47 mm)	12·00	13·00

Nos. 1251 and 1255/8 are inscribed 'S', 'G', 'E', 'U' and 'UK' and were sold for 8p, 30p, 40p, 42p and 49p respectively.

298 Short 184 and Saro London

2008. 90th Anniv of the Royal Air Force. Multicoloured.

1261	40p. Type **298**	2·00	2·00
1262	40p. Spitfire IV and Hurricane IIc	2·00	2·00
1263	42p. Beaufighter II and Lancaster TS III	2·00	2·00
1264	42p. Hunter Mk.6 and Shackleton MR2	2·00	2·00
1265	49p. Vulcan and Mosquito	2·50	2·50
1266	49p. Tornado GR4 and Jaguar GR3	2·50	2·50
MS1267	107×75 mm. £2 Felixstowe F.3 of No. 265 Squadron on anti-submarine patrol, Gibraltar, 1918	9·50	9·50

299 HMS *La Minerve*

2008. 250th Birth Anniv of Admiral Lord Nelson. Multicoloured.

1268	40p. Type **299**	2·00	2·00
1269	40p. HMS *Agamemnon*	2·00	2·00
1270	42p. HMS *Vanguard*	2·00	2·00
1271	42p. HMS *Captain*	2·00	2·00
1272	49p. HMS *Victory*	2·50	2·50
1273	49p. HMS *Amphion*	2·50	2·50
MS1274	120×80 mm. £2 Birthplace at Burnham Thorpe, Norfolk (horiz)	7·00	8·00

300 Sir Winston Churchill

2008. Europa. Writing Letters. Multicoloured.

1275	10p. Type **300**	75	50
1276	42p. Lord Nelson	1·75	1·25
1277	44p. President John F. Kennedy	1·75	1·50
1278	£1 Mahatma Ghandi	5·50	6·00

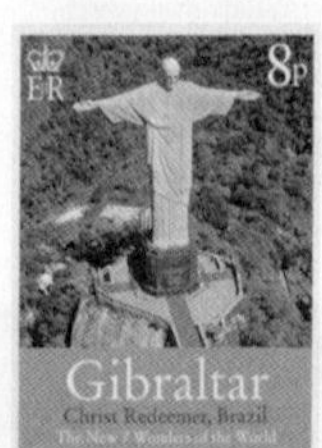

301 Christ the Redeemer Statue, Rio de Janeiro, Brazil

2008. The New Seven Wonders of the World. Multicoloured.

1279	8p. Type **301**	35	35
1280	8p. Colosseum, Rome, Italy	35	35
1281	38p. Petra, Jordan	1·50	1·50
1282	38p. The Great Wall of China	1·50	1·50
1283	40p. Machu Picchu, Peru	1·50	1·50
1284	40p. Chichen Itza	1·50	1·50
1285	66p. Taj Mahal, India	3·25	3·25

2008. Cruise Ships (4th series). As T 285. Multicoloured.

1286	40p. *Century*	1·75	1·25
1287	42p. *Grand Princess*	1·75	1·25
1288	66p. *Queen Victoria*	2·75	3·00
1289	78p. *Costa Mediterranea*	3·75	4·50
MS1290	168×66 mm. Nos. 1286/9	9·00	9·00

302 *Launch of Apollo 11*

2008. 50th Anniv of NASA (US National Aeronautics and Space Administration). Sheet 144×98 mm containing T 302 and similar square designs. Multicoloured.

MS1291	10p. Type **302**; 17p. The Earth seen from the Moon; 42p. Lunar module; £2 US flag on the Moon	8·50	8·50

303 Gibraltar Volunteer Corps, World War I

2008. Royal Gibraltar Regiment. Multicoloured.

1292	10p. Type **303**	45	45
1293	10p. Gibraltar Defence Force, World War II	45	45
1294	10p. Buena Vista Barracks (National Service)	45	45
1295	42p. Thomson's Battery 1958–91 (Gibraltar Regiment)	1·40	1·40
1296	42p. Infantry Company 1958–99 (Gibraltar Regiment)	1·40	1·40
1297	44p. Air Defence Troop 1958–91 (Gibraltar Regiment)	1·40	1·40
1298	44p. 'Guarding the Rock' (Royal Gibraltar Regiment)	1·40	1·40
1299	51p. Training African Peace-keepers (Royal Gibraltar Regiment)	1·90	2·00
1300	51p. Operations in Iraq (Royal Gibraltar Regiment)	1·90	2·00
1301	£2 Operations in Afghanistan (Royal Gibraltar Regiment)	7·00	8·00

304 *When Santa got stuck in a Chimney*

2008. Christmas. Christmas Songs and Carols. Multicoloured.

1302	10p. Type **304**	45	20
1303	42p. *Rudolph the Red-nosed Reindeer*	1·50	1·25
1304	44p. *Oh Christmas Tree*	1·50	1·25
1305	51p. *Away in a Manger*	1·90	1·90
1306	59p. *Jingle Bells*	2·25	2·75

305 Catherine of Aragon

2009. 500th Anniv of the Coronation of King Henry VIII. Multicoloured.

1307	10p. Type **305**	45	45
1308	10p. Anne Boleyn	45	45
1309	42p. Jane Seymour	1·75	1·50
1310	42p. Anne of Cleves	1·75	1·50
1311	44p. Catherine Howard	1·75	1·50
1312	44p. Katherine Parr	1·75	1·50
1313	51p. King Henry VIII	2·25	2·75
1314	51p. *Mary Rose* (galleon)	2·25	2·75
MS1315	120×80 mm. £2 King Henry VIII and Hampton Court Palace	7·50	8·00

306 Virgin and Child (shrine of Our Lady of Europe at Europa Point, Gibraltar)

2009. 700th Anniv of Our Lady of Europe.

1316	**306**	61p. multicoloured	3·50	3·50

Stamps of a similar design were issued by Vatican City.

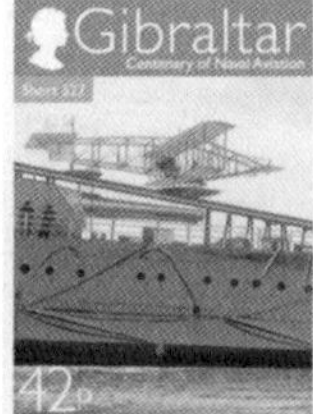

307 Short S27

2009. Centenary of Naval Aviation. Multicoloured.

1317	42p. Type **307**	1·90	1·90
1318	42p. Morane-Saulnier Type L and Zeppelin LZ 37	1·90	1·90
1319	42p. Short Type 184 seaplane	1·90	1·90
1320	42p. SS Type Non Rigid Airship	1·90	1·90
1321	42p. Caudron Gill	1·90	1·90
1322	42p. Avro 504	1·90	1·90
MS1323	120×80 mm. £2 Short Type 184 seaplane hoisted over stern of First World War seaplane carrier and Hawker Siddeley Sea Harrier on ramp of modern Invincible Class CVS aircraft carrier	8·00	8·00

The stamp within No. **MS**1323 has text printed on the back describing the aircraft and ships depicted on the miniature sheet.

308 Peter Phillips

2009. Queen Elizabeth II's Grandchildren. Multicoloured.

1324	42p. Type **308**	1·50	1·50
1325	42p. Zara Phillips	1·50	1·50
1326	42p. Prince William of Wales	1·50	1·50
1327	42p. Prince Henry of Wales	1·50	1·50
1328	42p. Princess Beatrice of York	1·50	1·50
1329	42p. Princess Eugenie of York	1·50	1·50
1330	42p. Lady Louise Windsor	1·50	1·50
1331	42p. Viscount Severn	1·50	1·50

309 Aristotle (early Greek philosopher and scientist)

2009. Europa. International Year of Astronomy. Multicoloured.

1332	10p. Type **309**	40	30
1333	42p. Galileo Galilei (astronomer, mathematician and philosopher)	1·75	1·25
1334	44p. Nicolaus Copernicus (astronomer)	2·25	1·50
1335	£1.50 Sir Isaac Newton (scientist and mathematician)	4·50	6·00

310 Road to the Frontier

2009. Old Views of Gibraltar. Showing scenes from postcards. Multicoloured.

1336	10p. Type **310**	40	30
1337	42p. Catalan Bay village	1·60	1·25
1338	44p. The Rock of Gibraltar	1·60	1·25
1339	51p. The Moorish Castle	2·00	1·90
1340	59p. South Barracks	2·25	2·75
MS1341	163×79 mm. 10p. Garrison Library; 42p. The Piazza; 44p. The Plazza – Casemates; £1 Main Street	6·75	7·50

310a Charles Darwin, *Zoology of the Beagle* and *Voyages of the Adventure and Beagle*

2009. Birth Bicentenary of Charles Darwin (naturalist and evolutionary theorist). Multicoloured.

1341a	10p. Type **310a**	45	30
1341b	42p. Charles Darwin and *The Descent of Man*	1·50	1·25
1341c	44p. Charles Darwin and *Animals and Plants under Domestication*	1·50	1·40
1341d	£2 Charles Darwin and *On the Origin of Species*	7·00	7·50
MS1341e	126×86 mm. £2.42 Charles Darwin, The Mount, Shrewsbury (his birthplace) and *On the Origin of Species*	9·50	9·50

311 Santa Tree Decoration

2009. Christmas. Multicoloured.

1342	10p. Type **311**	45	30
1343	42p. Angel	1·50	1·25
1344	44p. Teddy bear	1·50	1·40
1345	51p. Filigree Christmas tree	1·90	1·60
1346	£2 Bells and baubles	6·75	7·50

312 '100 Ton' Gun, Napier of Magdala Battery, Gibraltar, 1880

2010. '100 Ton' Guns. Multicoloured.

MS1347	118x102 mm. 75p.×4 Type **312**; '100 ton' gun, Napier of Magdala Battery, Gibraltar, 2010; '100 ton' gun, Fort Rinella, Malta, 2010; '100 ton' gun, Fort Rinella, Malta, 1882	10·00	11·00

A miniature sheet containing the same designs was issued by Malta.

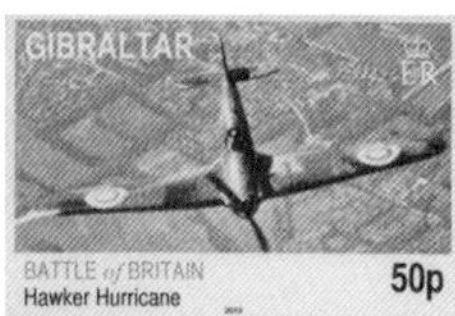

313 Hawker Hurricane

2010. 70th Anniv of the Battle of Britain. Multicoloured.

1348	50p. Type **313**	2·00	2·00
1349	50p. Miles Master	2·00	2·00
1350	50p. Bristol Blenheim	2·00	2·00
1351	50p. Boulton Paul Defiant	2·00	2·00
1352	50p. Gloster Gladiator	2·00	2·00
1353	50p. Supermarine Spitfire	2·00	2·00
MS1354	110×70 mm. £2 Douglas Bader (vert)	7·50	7·50

314 King George V, Queen Mary and Family

2010. Centenary of Accession of King George V. Multicoloured.

1355	10p. Type **314**	50	30
1356	42p. King George V with his stamp collection	1·75	1·25
1357	44p. King George V on horse-back inspecting soldiers	1·74	1·40
1358	£2 King George V in navy uniform and gun battery	8·00	9·00

315 Charlie and the Chocolate Factory

2010. Europa. Children's Books. Multicoloured.

1359	10p. Type **315**	45	30
1360	42p. *Matilda*	1·75	1·25
1361	44p. *The Twits*	1·75	1·40
1362	£1.50 *The BFG*	4·75	5·50

316 Emblem

2010. 'Miss Gibraltar 2009 (Kaiane Aldorino) is Miss World. Sheet 140×84 mm

MS1363	**316** £2 gold and black	6·50	7·50

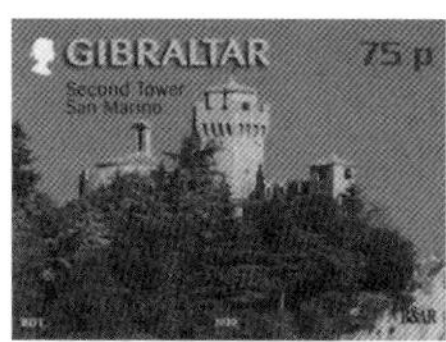

317 Second Tower, San Marino

2010. Gibraltar and San Marino. Multicoloured.

MS1364	137x105 mm. 75p.×4 Type **317**; Moorish Castle, Gibraltar; Mount Titano, San Marino; The Rock of Gibraltar	10·00	11·00

A miniature sheet containing the same designs was issued by San Marino.

318 Elise Deroche (inscr 'Baroness Raymonde de Laroche') flying Voisin Biplane, 8 March 1910

2010. Aviation Centenaries. Multicoloured.

1365	10p. Type **318** (first woman with pilot's licence)	50	30
1366	42p. DELAG's Zeppelin LZ7 (first fare paying passengers), 21 June 1910	1·50	1·25
1367	49p. Hubert Latham sets altitude record at 4,541 ft in *Antoinette VII*, 7 July 1910	2·00	1·75
1368	£2 Clément-Bayard No. 2 (first airship flight across English Channel, 16 October 1910)	6·75	7·50
MS1369	163×75 mm. 10p. Henri Fabre flies *Le Canard*, 28 March 1910; 42p. Supermarine S.6B Schneider Trophy winner, 1931; 49p. Short Sunderland, 204 Squadron, Gibraltar, 1941; £2 Saunders-ROE Princess, 22 August 1952 (centenary of seaplanes)	11·00	12·00

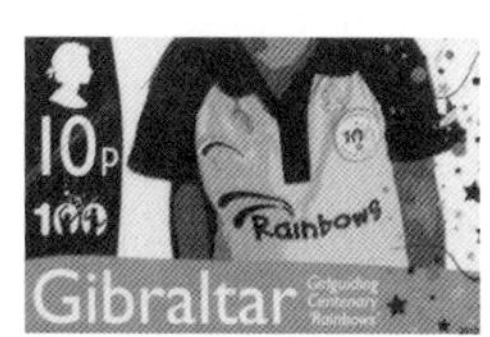

319 Rainbow Uniform

2010. Centenary of Girlguiding. Multicoloured.

1370	10p. Type **319**	50	30
1371	42p. Brownie	1·60	1·25
1372	44p. Guide	1·60	1·40
1373	£2 Senior	6·75	7·50

320 Emblem

2010. Commonwealth Games, Delhi. Sheet 90×103 mm

MS1374	**320** £2 multicoloured	7·50	7·50

321 Interior of Cathedral of St. Mary the Crowned

2010. Centenary of Diocese of Gibraltar. Sheet 114×80 mm

MS1375	**321** £2 multicoloured	6·50	7·00

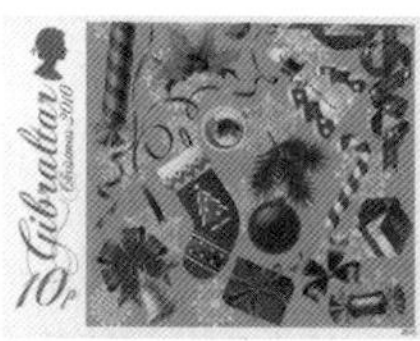

322 Christmas Stocking, Wrapped Presents and Decorations

2010. Christmas. Multicoloured.

1376	10p. Type **322**	45	30
1377	42p. Christmas stockings hanging from mantelpiece	1·50	1·25
1378	44p. Santa's sleigh flying over snowy landscape	1·60	1·40
1379	51p. Three snowmen as musicians with accordion, fiddle and cymbals	1·75	2·25

323 Prince William and Miss Catherine Middleton

2011. Royal Engagement

MS1380	**323** £2 multicoloured	6·50	6·50

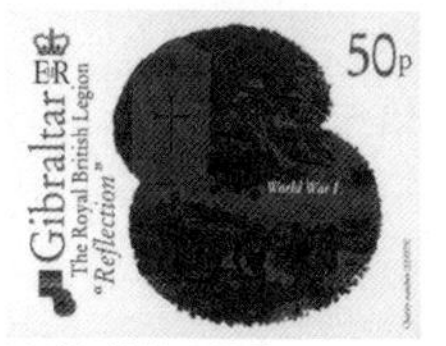

324 World War I ('Reflection')

2011. Royal British Legion. Multicoloured.

1381	50p. Type **324**	1·75	1·75
1382	50p. World War II ('Hope')	1·75	1·75
1383	50p. Northern Ireland ('Selflessness')	1·75	1·75
1384	50p. The Falklands ('Comradeship')	1·75	1·75
1385	50p. The Gulf War ('Welfare')	1·75	1·75
1386	50p. The Balkans ('Service')	1·75	1·75
1387	50p. Iraq ('Representation')	1·75	1·75
1388	50p. Afghanistan ('Remembrance')	1·75	1·75
MS1389	120×80 mm. £2 Statue and poppies	6·50	6·50

325 Queen Elizabeth II

2011. Queen Elizabeth II and Prince Philip. 'Lifetime of Service'. Multicoloured.

1390	10p. Type **325**	45	30
1391	42p. Queen Elizabeth II and Prince Philip, 1960s	1·50	1·25
1392	44p. Queen Elizabeth II (wearing purple) and Prince Philip, c. 2010	1·60	1·40
1393	51p. Queen Elizabeth II and Prince Philip, c. 1952	1·75	2·25
1394	55p. Queen Elizabeth II (wearing tiara) and Prnce Philip, c. 1965	1·90	2·40
1395	£2 Prince Philip, c. 1970	6·50	6·50
MS1397	110×70 mm. £3 Princess Eliizabeth and Duke of Edinburgh on wedding day, 1947	13·50	13·50

No. **MS**1396 is left for a miniature sheet containing the set of six stamps not yet received

POSTAGE DUE STAMPS

D1

1956

D1	**D1**	1d. green	1·50	4·25
D2	**D1**	2d. brown	1·50	2·75
D3	**D1**	4d. blue	1·75	5·00

1971. As Nos. D1/3, but inscr in decimal currency.

D4	½p. green	25	80
D5	1p. brown	25	70
D6	2p. blue	25	1·00

D2

1976

D7	**D2**	1p. orange	15	60
D8	**D2**	3p. blue	15	75
D9	**D2**	5p. red	20	75
D10	**D2**	7p. violet	20	75
D11	**D2**	10p. green	25	75
D12	**D2**	20p. green	45	1·00

D3 Gibraltar Coat of Arms

1984

D13	**D3**	1p. black	25	60
D14	**D3**	3p. red	40	60
D15	**D3**	5p. blue	45	60
D16	**D3**	10p. blue	60	60
D17	**D3**	25p. mauve	1·25	1·00
D18	**D3**	50p. orange	1·50	1·25
D19	**D3**	£1 green	2·50	3·25

D4 Water Port Gates

1996. Gibraltar Landmarks.

D20	**D4**	1p. black, emerald and green	20	75
D21	-	10p. black and grey	70	70
D22	-	25p. black, brown and chestnut	1·50	1·25
D23	-	50p. black and lilac	2·25	2·25
D24	-	£1 black, brown and chestnut	3·50	3·25
D25	-	£2 black and blue	5·50	6·50

DESIGNS: 10p. Naval Dockyard; 25p. Military Hospital; 50p. Governor's Cottage; £1 Swans on the Laguna; £2 Catalan Bay.

D5 Greenfinch

2002. Gibraltar Finches. Type D 5 Multicoloured.

D26	5p. Type D **5**	10	10
D27	10p. Serin	20	15
D28	20p. Siskin	40	45
D29	50p. Linnet	1·00	1·10
D30	£1 Chaffinch	2·00	2·10
D31	£2 Goldfinch	4·00	4·25

Pt. 7

HAMBURG

A port in north-west Germany, formerly a Free City. In 1867 it joined the North German Confederation.

16 schillinge = 1 mark.

1

1859. Imperf.

1	1	½s. black	£140	£800
2	1	1s. brown	£140	£130
3	1	2s. red	£140	£140
4	1	3s. blue	£140	£170
6	1	4s. green	£160	£1700
7	1	7s. orange	£140	55·00
10	1	9s. yellow	£275	£2750

3

4

1864. Imperf.

11	3	1¼s. lilac	£850	£1300
15	3	1¼s. grey	£120	£110
17	3	1¼s. blue	£850	£1600
18	4	2½s. green	£190	£190

1864. Perf.

19	1	½s. black	8·50	16·00
20	1	1s. brown	17·00	23·00
21	3	1¼s. mauve	£130	16·00
25	1	2s. red	21·00	26·00
27	4	2½s. green	£160	48·00
30	1	3s. blue	60·00	48·00
33	1	4s. green	£300	55·00
34	1	7s. orange	£200	£160
37	1	7s. mauve	15·00	21·00
38	1	9s. yellow	37·00	£2750

5

1866. Roul.

44	5	1¼s. mauve	55·00	48·00
45	5	1½s. pink	12·50	£170

1867. Perf.

46	1	2½s. green	17·00	£110

Pt. 7

HANOVER

In north-east Germany. An independent kingdom until 1866, when it was annexed by Prussia.

1850. 12 pfennige = 1 gutegroschen.
24 gutengroschen = 1 thaler.
1858. 10 (new) pfennige = 1 (new) groschen.
30 (new) groschen = 1 thaler.

2

1850. On coloured paper. Imperf.

1	2	1ggr. black on blue	£5500	65·00
2	2	1ggr. black on green	£130	11·50
3	2	⅓₀th. black on orange	£160	70·00
4	2	⅓₀th. black on red	£160	70·00
5	2	⅟₁₅th. black on blue	£250	£110
6	2	⅟₁₀th. black on orange	£325	80·00

1853. Imperf.

18	4	3pf. pink	£180	£200

4

1855. With coloured network. Imperf.

12	4	3pf. pink and black	£425	£375
14	2	1ggr. black and green	£110	16·00
15	2	⅓₀th. black and pink	£200	42·00
16	2	⅟₁₅th. black and blue	£160	95·00
10	2	⅟₁₀th. black and orange	£325	£200

5 King George V

1859. Imperf.

23	5	1gr. pink	5·25	5·75
25a	5	2gr. blue	21·00	60·00
28	5	3gr. yellow	£200	£130
29	5	3gr. brown	37·00	65·00
31	5	10gr. green	£325	£1200

6

1860. Imperf.

32a	6	½gr. black	£225	£275

1863. Imperf.

34	4	3pf. green	£550	£1300

1864. Roul.

35a		3pf. green	42·00	80·00
36a	6	½gr. black	£350	£350
37a	5	1gr. pink	16·00	10·50
38	5	2gr. blue	£160	80·00
39a	5	3gr. brown	95·00	95·00

Pt. 1

HELIGOLAND

An island off the N. coast of Germany, ceded to that country by Great Britain in 1890.

1867. 16 schillings = 1 mark.
1875. 100 pfennig = 1 mark.

Many of the Heligoland stamps found in old collections and the majority of those offered at a small fraction of catalogue prices today, are reprints which have very little value.

1

1867. Perf (½, 1, 2 and 6 sch. also roul).

5	1	¼sch. green and red	30·00	£1500
6b	1	½sch. green and red	£100	£160
7	1	¾sch. red and green	40·00	£1100
8a	1	1sch. red and green	£130	£190
9	1	1½sch. green and red	80·00	£250
3	1	2sch. red and green	14·00	60·00
4	1	6sch. green and red	16·00	£250

2

3

4

5

1875

10	2	1pf. (¼d.) green and red	16·00	£500
11	2	2pf. (½d.) red and green	16·00	£600
12a	3	3pf. (⅝d.) green, red and yellow	£160	£850
13	2	5pf. (¾d.) green and red	19·00	19·00
14a	2	10pf. (1½d.) red and green	15·00	22·00
15b	3	20pf. (2½d.) green, red and yellow	21·00	29·00
16	2	25pf. (3d.) green and red	21·00	28·00
17	2	50pf. (6d.) red and green	23·00	40·00
18	4	1m. (1s.) green, red and black	£160	£200
19	5	5m. (5s.) green, red and black	£200	£950

Pt. 11

ICELAND

An island lying S.E. of Greenland. An independent state formerly under the Danish sovereign, now a republic.

1873. 96 skilling = 1 riksdaler.
1876. 100 aurar (singular: eyrir) = 1 krona.

1

1873

1	1	2s. blue	£750	£1500
5	1	3s. grey	£350	£1000
2	1	4s. red	£110	£700
3	1	8s. brown	£225	£800
7	1	16s. yellow	85·00	£450

1876

42		3a. yellow	5·75	16·00
27		4a. grey and red	14·50	16·00
13		5a. blue	£275	£550
28		5a. green	3·25	2·20
29a		6a. grey	13·00	14·00
30		10a. red	7·25	2·20
31		16a. brown	60·00	80·00
18a		20a. mauve	27·00	£375
32a		20a. blue	37·00	28·00
33		25a. blue and brown	23·00	24·00
19		40a. green	80·00	£160
23b		40a. mauve	36·00	30·00
24		50a. red and blue	65·00	70·00
25		100a. purple and brown	60·00	85·00

þrír

(6)

1897. Surch as T 6 with figure 3 under word.

38	3 on 5a. green	£425	£350

1897. Surch as T 6.

40	3 on 5a. green	£500	£375

10 King Christian IX

1902

43	10	3a. orange	5·00	2·40
44	10	4a. red and grey	3·50	1·10
45	10	5a. green	23·00	75
46	10	6a. brown	17·00	6·75
47	10	10a. red	5·75	75
48	10	16a. brown	5·00	7·00
49	10	20a. blue	2·00	3·00
50	10	25a. green and brown	2·30	4·00
51	10	40a. mauve	3·50	4·00
52	10	50a. black and grey	4·50	20·00
53	10	1k. brown and blue	6·25	6·75
54	10	2k. blue and brown	25·00	46·00
55	10	5k. grey and brown	£120	£160

1902. Optd I GILDI '02–'03.

67	1	3a. yellow	85	1·40
68	1	4a. grey and red	27·00	41·00
69	1	5a. green	80	5·75
71	1	6a. grey	85	5·75
73	1	10a. red	85	7·00
74	1	16a. brown	17·00	28·00
75	1	20a. blue	75	7·50
77	1	25a. blue and brown	75	12·00
79	1	40a. mauve	75	32·00
80	1	50a. red and blue	3·00	47·00
65	1	100a. purple and brown	39·00	55·00

12 Kings Christian IX and Frederik VIII

1907

81	12	1e. red and green	1·00	75
82	12	3a. brown	3·50	1·10
83	12	4a. red and grey	2·00	1·20
84	12	5a. green	65·00	75
85	12	6a. grey	36·00	2·50
114	12	10a. red	2·30	1·10
87	12	15a. green and red	5·00	1·10
88	12	16a. brown	6·75	25·00
89	12	20a. blue	6·75	3·50
90	12	25a. green and brown	5·25	7·75
91	12	40a. red	4·50	9·50
92	12	50a. red and grey	5·75	8·25
93	12	1k. brown and blue	18·00	45·00
94	12	2k. green and brown	25·00	55·00
95	12	5k. blue and brown	£170	£225

13 Jon Sigurdsson

1911. Birth Centenary of Jon Sigurdsson (historian and Althing member).

96	13	1e. green	2·00	1·00
97	13	3a. brown	3·50	8·25
98	13	4a. blue	1·10	1·20
99	13	6a. grey	8·00	16·00
100	13	15a. violet	9·50	1·10
101	13	25a. orange	20·00	31·00

1912. As T 13, but portrait of King Frederik VIII and "JON SIGURDSSON" omitted.

102		5a. green	23·00	8·25
103		10a. red	23·00	8·25
104		20a. blue	36·00	10·50
105		50a. red	7·50	26·00
106		1k. yellow	25·00	50·00
107		2k. red	23·00	50·00
108		5k. brown	£120	£150

15 King Christian X

1920

116	15	1e. red and green	85	75
117	15	3a. brown	5·50	10·50
184	15	4a. red and grey	2·20	1·40
119	15	5a. green	1·70	1·20
185	15	6a. grey	2·00	3·00
186	15	7a. green	75	1·10
121	15	8a. brown	8·25	1·40
122	15	10a. red	2·40	6·25
133	15	10a. green	3·00	1·20
187	15	10a. brown	£140	95
123	15	15a. violet	34·00	75
124	15	20a. blue	2·40	11·00
134	15	20a. brown	60·00	1·20
125	15	25a. green and brown	15·00	1·10
135	15	25a. red	12·00	33·00
189	15	30a. green and red	38·00	3·50
127	15	40a. red	42·00	1·90
136	15	40a. blue	75·00	8·75
128	15	50a. red and grey	£200	6·25
191	15	1k. brown and blue	80·00	6·00
130	15	2k. green and brown	£275	20·00
131	15	5k. blue and brown	65·00	10·00
193	15	10k. black and green	£375	£150

1921. Various types surch.

137	10	5a. on 16a. brown	3·75	20·00
138	12	5a. on 16a. brown	1·90	5·75
139	15	10a. on 5a. green	8·00	2·40
140	10	20a. on 25a. green & brn	7·25	4·75
141	12	20a. on 25a. green & brn	4·50	5·75
142	10	20a. on 40a. mauve	8·50	14·00
143	12	20a. on 40a. red	11·00	15·00
144	10	30a. on 50a. grey	31·00	26·00
145	10	50a. on 5k. grey & brown	65·00	38·00
146	15	1k. on 40a. blue	£190	30·00
147	13	2k. on 25a. orange	£160	£100
148	-	10k. on 50a. red (No. 105)	£350	£350
149	-	10k. on 1k. yell (No. 106)	£475	£475
150	10	10k. on 2k. black & brn	90·00	23·00
150a	12	10k. on 5k. black & brn	£400	£450

22 Landing Mails at Vik

1925

151	22	7a. green	55·00	5·75
152	-	10a. brown and blue	55·00	70
153	-	20a. red	55·00	70
154	-	35a. blue	90·00	6·50
155	22	50a. brown and green	90·00	1·50

DESIGNS: 10a., 35a. Reykjavik and Esjaberg (mountain); 20a. National Museum, Reykjavik.

1928. Air. Optd with airplane.

156	15	10a. red	1·20	8·75
157	12	50a. purple and grey	75·00	85·00

24 Discovery of Iceland

25 Gyrfalcon

1930. Parliament Millenary Celebration.

158	-	3a. violet and lilac (postage)	2·10	6·75
159	24	5a. blue and grey	2·10	6·75
160	-	7a. green and dp green	2·10	6·75
161	-	10a. purple and mauve	7·00	11·00
162	-	15a. dp blue & blue	2·10	6·75
163	-	20a. red and pink	34·00	47·00
164	-	25a. brown and lt brown	6·25	8·50
165	-	30a. green and grey	4·75	8·50
166	-	35a. blue & ultramarine	5·50	8·50
167	-	40a. red, blue and grey	4·25	8·50
168	-	50a. dp brown and brown	70·00	£100
169	-	1k. green and grey	70·00	£100
170	-	2k. blue and green	90·00	£120
171	-	5k. orange and yellow	42·00	90·00
172	-	10k. lake and red	42·00	90·00
173	25	10a. blue & dp blue (air)	20·00	42·00

DESIGNS—HORIZ: 3a. Parliament House, Reykjavik; 7a. Encampment at Thingvellir; 10a. Arrival of Ingolf Arnarsson; 15a. Naming the Island; 20a. Chieftains riding to the "Althing" (Parliament); 25a. Discovery of Arnarsson's pillar; 30a. View of Thingvellir; 35a. Queen Aud; 40a. National flag; 50a. Proclamation at Thingvellir; 1k. Map of Iceland; 2k. Winter-bound farmstead; 5k. Woman spinning; 10k. Viking sacrifice to Thor.

26 Snaefellsjokull

1930. Air. Parliamentary Millenary Celebration.

174	26	15a. blue and brown	23·00	38·00
175	-	20a. blue and brown	23·00	38·00
176	-	35a. brown and green	45·00	75·00
177	-	50a. blue and green	45·00	75·00
178	-	1k. red and green	45·00	75·00

DESIGNS: 20a. Old Icelandic fishing boat; 35a. Icelandic pony; 50a. The Gullfoss Falls; 1k. Statue of Arnarsson, Reykjavik.

1931. Air. Optd Zeppelin 1931.

179	15	30a. green and red	34·00	£110
180	15	1k. brown and blue	9·00	£110
181	15	2k. green and brown	55·00	£110

29 Gullfoss Falls

1931

195	29	5a. grey	11·50	60
196	29	20a. red	10·00	20
197	29	35a. blue	17·00	8·25
198	29	60a. mauve	11·50	80
199	29	65a. brown	2·30	80
200	29	75a. blue	90·00	23·00

30 Shipwreck and Breeches-buoy

1933. Philanthropic Associations.

201	30	10a.+10a. brown	1·70	4·50
202	-	20a.+20a. red	1·70	4·50
203	30	35a.+25a. blue	1·70	4·50
204	-	50a.+25a. green	1·70	4·50

DESIGNS: 20a. Children gathering flowers; 50a. Aged fisherman and rowing boat.

1933. Air. Balbo Transatlantic Mass Formation Flight. Optd Hopflug Itala 1933.

205	15	1k. brown and blue	£170	£425
206	15	5k. blue and brown	£425	£1000
207	15	10k. black and green	£1100	£2000

32 Avro 504K Biplane over Thingvellir

1934. Air.

208	32	10a. blue	1·90	1·90
209	32	20a. green	4·00	4·25
210a	-	25a. violet	17·00	13·00
211	-	50a. purple	4·50	6·25
212	-	1k. brown	28·00	26·00
213	-	2k. red	11·50	11·00

DESIGNS: 25a., 50a. Monoplane and Aurora Borealis; 1k., 2k. Monoplane over map of Iceland.

33 Dynjandi Falls

1935

214	33	10a. blue	24·00	20
215	-	1k. green	45·00	25

DESIGN—HORIZ: 1k. Mt. Hekla.

35 Matthias Jochumsson

1935. Birth Centenary of M. Jochumsson (poet).

216	35	3a. green	90	2·75
217	35	5a. grey	17·00	95
218	35	7a. green	24·00	1·20
219	35	35a. blue	75	95

36 King Christian X

1937. Silver Jubilee of King Christian X.

220	36	10a. green	2·10	16·00
221	36	30a. brown	2·10	7·25
222	36	40a. red	2·10	7·25

MS223 128½×112 mm. **36** 15a. violet; 25a. red; 50a. blue (sold at 2k.) 42·00 £225

37 The Great Geyser

1938

226	37	15a. purple	5·75	7·75
227	37	20a. red	28·00	25
228	37	35a. blue	85	65
229	-	40a. brown	14·00	21·00
230	-	45a. blue	75	70
231	-	50a. green	27·00	65
232a	-	60a. blue	5·00	6·75
233	-	1k. blue	2·30	25

The frames of the 40a. to 1k. differ from Type **37**.

37b Leif Eiriksson's Statue, Reykjavik

1938. Leif Eiriksson's Day. Sheet 140×100 mm.
MS233b 30a. red (T **37b**), 40a. violet; 60a. green (sold at 2k.) 4·75 24·00
DESIGNS: 40a. Figure from statue; 60a. Part of globe showing Iceland and Vinland (larger).

38 Reykjavik University

1938. 20th Anniv of Independence.

234	**38**	25a. green	5·75	10·50
235	**38**	30a. brown	5·75	10·50
236	**38**	40a. purple	5·75	10·50

1939. Surch 5.

237	**35**	5 on 35a. blue	90	1·00

40 Trylon and Perisphere

1939. New York World's Fair.

238	**40**	20a. red	3·50	4·75
239	-	35a. blue	3·50	6·50
240	-	45a. green	4·25	7·25
241	-	2k. black	50·00	£120

DESIGNS: 35a. Viking longship and route to America; 45a., 2k. Statue of Thorfinn Karlsefni, Reykjavik.

41 Atlantic Cod **42** Icelandic Flag

1939

242a	**41**	1e. blue	40	2·75
243a	-	3a. violet	40	60
244a	**41**	5a. brown	40	30
245	-	7a. green	4·75	6·75
246	**42**	10a. red and blue	2·50	80
247a	-	10a. green	38·00	45
248	-	10a. black	30	25
249	-	12a. green	40	55
250a	**41**	25a. red	27·00	35
251	**41**	25a. brown	35	35
252	-	35a. red	65	25
253	**41**	50a. green	70	25

DESIGN: 3, 7, 10a. (Nos. 247a/8), 12, 35a. Atlantic herring.

43 Statue of Thorfinn Karlsefni

1939

254	**43**	2k. grey	3·50	20
255	**43**	5k. brown	28·00	30
256	**43**	10k. brown	12·00	1·40

1940. New York World's Fair. Optd 1940.

257	**40**	20a. red	7·50	19·00
258	-	35a. blue (No. 239)	7·50	19·00
259	-	45a. green (No. 240)	7·50	19·00
260	-	2k. black (No. 241)	£110	£325

1941. Surch 25.

261	**35**	25a. on 3a. olive	80	95

46 Statue of Snorri Sturluson (O. Vigeland)

1941. 700th Death Anniv of Snorri Sturluson (historian).

262	**46**	25a. red	85	1·30
263	**46**	50a. blue	1·70	3·50
264	**46**	1k. olive	1·70	3·50

47 Jon Sigurdsson (historian and Althing member)

1944. Proclamation of Republic.

265	**47**	10a. grey	45	65
266	**47**	25a. brown	50	65
267	**47**	50a. green	55	65
268	**47**	1k. black	1·00	65
269	**47**	5k. brown	4·25	8·75
270	**47**	10k. brown	46·00	65·00

48 Grumman G-21 Goose Amphibian over Thingvellir

1947. Air.

271	**48**	15a. orange	65	75
272	-	30a. black	65	1·00
273	-	75a. red	65	75
274	-	1k. blue	65	75
275	-	1k.80 blue	12·50	11·00
276	-	2k. brown	1·30	1·60
277	-	2k.50 green	24·00	1·00
278	-	3k. green	1·30	1·90
279	-	3k.30 blue	6·75	5·50

DESIGNS—HORIZ: 30a. Consolidated PBY-5 Catalina flying boat over Isafjordur; 75a. Douglas DC-3 over Eyjafjord; 1k.80, Douglas DC-3 over Snaefellsjokull; 2k.50, Consolidated PBY-5 Catalina over Eiriksjokull; 3k. Douglas DC-4 over Reykjavik; 3k.30, Douglas DC-4 over Oraefajokull. VERT: 1k. Grumman G-21 Goose over Sethisfjordur, Strandatindur; 2k. Consolidated PBY-5 Catalina over Hvalfjordur, Thyrill.

For stamps as Type **48** but without airplane, see Nos. 346/8.

50 Mt. Hekla in Eruption

1948. Inscr "HEKLA 1947".

280	**50**	12a. purple	20	25
281	-	25a. green	1·30	25
282	-	35a. red	40	30
283	**50**	50a. brown	1·70	20
284	-	60a. blue	6·50	3·00
285	-	1k. brown	14·50	60
286	-	10k. violet	41·00	60

DESIGNS—VERT: 35a., 60a. Mt. Hekla in Eruption (different view). HORIZ: 25a., 1k., 10k. Mt. Hekla.

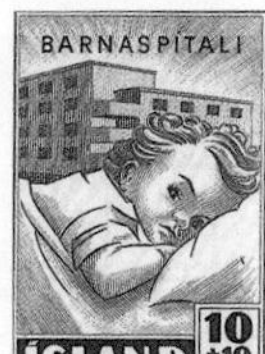
53 Hospital and Child

1949. Red Cross Fund.

287	**53**	10a.+10a. green	65	1·00
288	-	35a.+15a. red	65	1·00
289	-	50a.+25a. brown	75	1·00
290	-	60a.+25a. blue	75	1·10
291	-	75a.+25a. blue	1·10	1·00

DESIGNS: 35a. Nurse and patient; 50a. Nurse arranging patient's bed; 60a. Aged couple; 75a. Freighter and ship's lifeboat.

54 Pony Pack-train

1949. 75th Anniv of U.P.U.

292	**54**	25a. green	40	65
293	-	35a. red	40	65
294	-	60a. blue	55	85
295	-	2k. orange	1·30	1·10

DESIGNS: 35a. Reykjavik; 60a. Map of Iceland; 2k. Almannagja Gorge.

55 "Ingolfur Arnarson" (trawler)

1950

296		5a. brown	20	20
297	**55**	10a. grey	15	25
298	-	20a. brown	20	25
299	**55**	25a. red	20	20
300	-	60a. green	11·50	17·00
301	-	75a. orange	45	35
302	-	90a. red	45	35
303	-	1k. brown	5·00	35
304	**55**	1k.25 purple	23·00	35
305	**55**	1k.50 blue	12·50	35
306	-	2k. violet	21·00	35
307	-	5k. green	34·00	1·20
308	-	25k. black	£150	13·00

DESIGNS—As T **55**: 5, 90a., 2k. Vestmannaeyjar harbour; 20, 75a., 1k. Tractor; 60a., 5k. Flock of sheep; 25k. Parliament Building, Reykjavik (29½×23½ mm).

56 Bishop Jon Arason

1950. 400th Death Anniv of Bishop Arason.

309	**56**	1k.80 red	2·75	2·75
310	**56**	3k.30 green	1·70	2·50

57 Postman, 1776

1951. 175th Anniv of Icelandic Postal Service.

311	**57**	2k. blue	2·50	2·20
312	-	3k. purple	3·25	3·00

DESIGN: 3k. as 2k. but Saab 90 Scandia aeroplane replaces man.

58 President Bjornsson

1952. Death of S. Bjornsson (first President of Iceland).

313	**58**	1k.25 blue	2·20	30
314	**58**	2k.20 green	75	4·25
315	**58**	5k. blue	8·75	1·50
316	**58**	10k. brown	35·00	24·00

1953. Netherlands Flood Relief Fund. Surch Hollandshjalp 1953 + 25.

317	-	75a.+25a. orange (No. 301)	1·30	3·50
318	**55**	1k.25+25a. purple	1·70	3·50

60 "Reykjabok" (Saga of Burnt Njal)

1953

319	**60**	10a. black	20	20
320	-	70a. green	40	30
321	-	1k. red	50	25
322	-	1k.75 blue	23·00	1·10
323	-	10k. brown	10·50	90

DESIGNS: 70a. Hand writing on manuscript; 1k. "Stjorn" (15th century manuscript); 1k.75, Books and candle; 10k. Page from "Skardsbok" (14th century law manuscript).

1954. No. 282 surch 5 AURAR and bars.

324	5a. on 35a. red	40	25

62 Hannes Hafstein

1954. 50th Anniv of Appointment of Hannes Hafstein as First Native Minister of Iceland. Portraits of Hafstein.

325	**62**	1k.25 blue	3·75	35
326	-	2k.45 green	19·00	30·00
327	-	5k. red	19·00	3·75

63 Icelandic Wrestling

1955. Icelandic National Sports.

328	**63**	75a. brown	35	25
329	-	1k.25 blue (Diving)	60	40
330	**63**	1k.50 red	85	25
331	-	1k.75 blue (Diving)	55	25

64 St. Thorlacas

1956. 9th Centenary of Consecration of First Icelandic Bishop and Skalholt Rebuilding Fund. Inscr as in T 64.

332	**64**	75a.+25a. red	35	40
333	-	1k.25+75a. brown	35	40
334	-	1k.75+1k.25 black	90	1·10

DESIGNS—HORIZ: 1k.25, Skalholt Cathedral, 1772. VERT: 1k.75, J. P. Vidalin, Bishop of Skalholt, 1698–1720.

65 Skogafoss

1956. Power Plants and Waterfalls.

335	**65**	15a. blue	25	25
336	-	50a. green	25	25
337	-	60a. brown	2·50	2·75
338	-	1k.50 violet	26·00	20
339	-	2k. brown	1·80	45
340	-	2k.45 black	7·50	7·00
341	-	3k. blue	3·75	75
342	-	5k. green	12·50	1·70

DESIGNS—HORIZ: 50a. Ellidaarvirkjun; 60a. Godafoss; 1k.50, Sogsvirkjun; 2k. Dettifoss; 2k.45, Andakilsarvirkjun; 3k. Laxarvirkjun. VERT: 5k. Gullfoss.

67 Map of Iceland

1956. 50th Anniv of Icelandic Telegraph System.

343	**67**	2k.30 blue	50	85

67a Whooper Swans

1956. Northern Countries' Day.

344	**67a**	1k.50 red	50	75
345	**67a**	1k.75 blue	9·00	9·75

1957. Designs as T 48 but airplane omitted.

346	2k. green	2·50	40
347	3k. blue	2·75	45
348	10k. brown	4·50	55

DESIGNS—HORIZ: 2k. Snaefellsjokull; 3k. Eiriksjokull; 10k. Oraefajokull.

68 Presidential Residence, Bessastadir

1957

349	**68**	25k. black	17·00	3·50

69 Norwegian Spruce

1957. Reafforestation Campaign.

350	**69**	35a. green	20	20
351	-	70a. green	20	20

DESIGN: 70a. Icelandic birch and saplings.

70 Jonas Hallgrimsson

1957. 150th Birth Anniv of Hallgrimsson (poet).

352	**70**	5k. black and green	1·50	55

71 River Beauty

1958. Flowers. Multicoloured.

353	1k. Type **71**	20	20
354	2k.50 Wild pansy	40	35

72 Icelandic Pony

1958

355	**72**	10a. black	20	20
356	**72**	1k. red	40	25
357	**72**	2k.25 brown	55	25

73 Icelandic Flag

1958. 40th Anniv of Icelandic Flag.

358	**73**	3k.50 red and blue	1·30	60
359	**73**	50k. red and blue	6·00	5·00

No. 359 is 23½×26½ mm.

74 Old Government House

1958

360	**74**	1k.50 blue	25	20
361	**74**	2k. green	35	35
362	**74**	3k. red	25	20
363	**74**	4k. brown	65	40

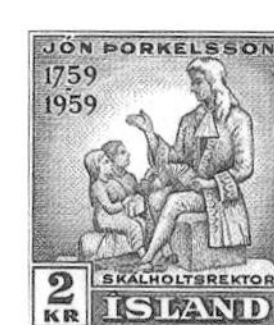

75 Jon Thorkelsson with Children

1959. Death Bicentenary of Jon Thorkelsson (Johannes Thorkillius, Rector of Skalholt).

364	**75**	2k. green	55	55
365	**75**	3k. purple	55	55

76 Vickers Viscount 700 and 1919 Avro 504K Biplane

1959. Air. 40th Anniv of Iceland Civil Aviation.

366	**76**	3k.50 blue	65	60
367	-	4k.05 green	65	80

DESIGN: 4k.05, Douglas DC-4 and Avro 504K aircraft.

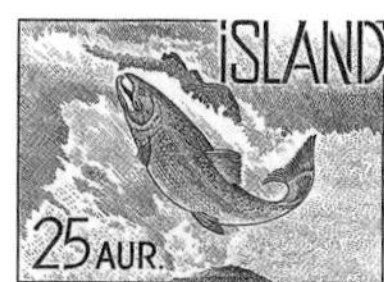

77 Atlantic Salmon

1959

368	**77**	25a. blue	20	20
369	-	90a. black and brown	30	30
370	-	2k. black	45	25
371	**77**	5k. green	7·25	95
372	-	25k. violet and yellow	11·50	12·50

DESIGNS—VERT: 90a., 2k. Eiders; 25k. Gyr falcon.

78 "The Outcast" (after Jonsson)

1960. World Refugee Year.

373	**78**	2k.50 brown	25	25
374	**78**	4k.50 blue	90	85

78a Conference Emblem

1960. Europa.

375	**78a**	3k. green	75	55
376	**78a**	5k.50 blue	1·40	1·60

79 Dandelions

1960. Wild Flowers.

377	-	50a. violet, green and myrtle (Campanulas)	20	20
378	-	1k.20 violet, green and brown (Geraniums)	20	20
379	**79**	2k.50 yellow, green & brn	30	20
380	-	3k.50 yellow, green and blue (Buttercup)	35	20

See also Nos. 412/15 and 446/7.

80 Sigurdsson

1961. 150th Birth Anniv of Jon Sigurdsson (historian and Althing member).

381	**80**	50a. red	25	30
382	**80**	3k. blue	1·40	1·10
383	**80**	5k. purple	55	55

81 Reykjavik Harbour

1961. 175th Anniv of Reykjavik.

384	**81**	2k.50 blue and green	55	25
385	**81**	4k.50 blue and violet	75	30

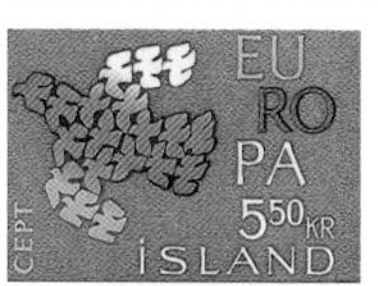

82 Doves

1961. Europa.

386	**82**	5k.50 multicoloured	50	65
387	**82**	6k. multicoloured	50	85

83 B. Sveinsson

1961. 50th Anniv of Iceland University.

388	**83**	1k. brown	25	30
389	-	1k.40 blue	30	30
390	-	10k. green	1·10	85
MS391		99×50 mm. Nos. 388/90. Imperf	1·00	1·20

DESIGNS—VERT: 1k.40, B. M. Olsen (first Vice-chancellor). HORIZ: 10k. University building.

84 Productivity Institute

1962. Icelandic Buildings.

392	**84**	2k.50 blue	35	25
393	-	4k. green	40	25
394	-	6k. brown	60	30

DESIGNS: 4k. Fishing Research Institute; 6k. Agricultural Society's Headquarters.

85 Europa "Tree"

1962. Europa.

395	**85**	5k.50 brown, green & yell	30	25
396	**85**	6k.50 brown, green & yell	55	60

86 Cable Map

1962. Opening of North Atlantic Submarine Telephone Communications.

397	**86**	5k. green, red and lavender	1·00	45
398	**86**	7k. green, red and blue	55	25

87 S. Gudmundsson (scholar and curator)

1963. Centenary of National Museum.

399	**87**	4k. brown and bistre	55	30
400	-	5k.50 brown and olive	45	30

DESIGN: 5k.50, Detail from carving on church door, Valthjofsstad.

88 Herring Catch

1963. Freedom from Hunger.

401	**88**	5k. multicoloured	75	35
402	**88**	7k.50 multicoloured	25	25

89 View of Akureyri

1963

403	**89**	3k. green	30	20

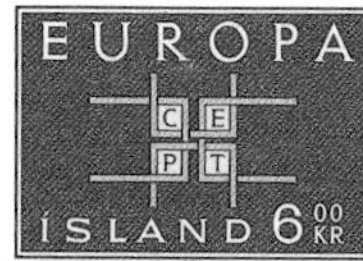

90 "Co-operation"

1963. Europa.

404	**90**	6k. yellow, ochre and brown	60	60
405	**90**	7k. yellow, green and blue	60	60

91 Ambulance

1963. Red Cross Centenary.

406	**91**	3k.+50a. multicoloured	70	1·20
407	**91**	3k.50+50a. mult	70	1·20

92 "Gullfoss" (cargo liner)

1964. 50th Anniv of Iceland Steamship Co.

408	**92**	10k. black, purple and blue	1·80	1·40

93 Scout Emblem

1964. Icelandic Boy Scouts Commemoration.

409	**93**	3k.50 multicoloured	60	25
410	**93**	4k.50 multicoloured	60	25

94 Arms of Iceland

1964. 20th Anniv of Icelandic Republic.

411	**94**	25k. multicoloured	2·00	1·70

1964. Wild Flowers. As T 79. Multicoloured.

412	50a. Mountain avens	20	20
413	1k. Glacier buttercup	20	20
414	1k.50 Bogbean	20	20
415	2k. White clover	20	20

95 Europa "Flower"

1964. Europa.

416	**95**	4k.50 turquoise, cream and brown	65	45
417	**95**	9k. sepia, cream and blue	90	70

96 Running

1964. Olympic Games, Tokyo.

418	**96**	10k. black and green	1·00	65

97 Rock Ptarmigan (summer plumage)

1965. Charity stamps.

419	**97**	3k.50+50a. mult	90	1·50
420	-	4k.50+50a. mult	90	1·50

DESIGN: 4k.50, Rock ptarmigan in winter plumage.

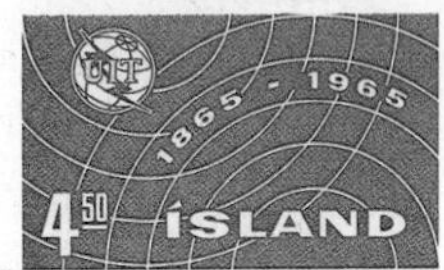

98 "Sound Waves"

1965. Centenary of I.T.U.

421	**98**	4k.50 green	75	65
422	**98**	7k.50 blue	25	25

99 Eruption, November 1963

1965. Birth of Surtsey Island. Multicoloured.

423	1k.50 Type **99**	55	55
424	2k. Surtsey in April 1964 (horiz)	55	55
425	3k.50 Surtsey in September 1964 (horiz)	85	65

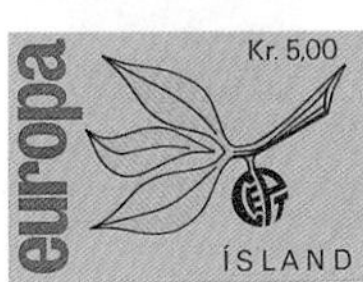

100 Europa "Sprig"

1965. Europa.

426	**100**	5k. green, brown and ochre	1·70	1·40
427	**100**	8k. green, brown & turq	1·40	1·30

101 E. Benediktsson

1965. 25th Death Anniv of Einar Benediktsson (poet).

428	**101**	10k. brown, black and blue	2·75	3·50

102 Girl in National Costume

1965

429	**102**	100k. multicoloured	7·50	7·00

103 White-tailed Sea Eagle

1966. Multicoloured.. Multicoloured..

430	20k. Great northern diver	5·00	4·50
431	50k. Type **103**	8·75	8·75

104 Londrangar

1966. Landscapes (1st series). Multicoloured.

432	2k.50 Type **104**	35	30
433	4k. Myvatn	35	30
434	5k. Bulandstindur	60	30
435	6k.50 Dyrholaey	70	30

See also Nos. 465/8.

105 Europa "Ship"

1966. Europa.

436	**105**	7k. turquoise blue and red	2·20	1·80
437	**105**	8k. brown, cream and red	2·20	1·80

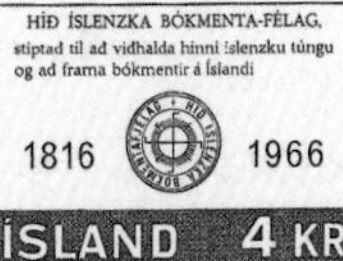

106 Society Emblem

1966. 150th Anniv of Icelandic Literary Society.

438	**106**	4k. blue	35	25
439	**106**	10k. red	75	55

107 Cogwheels

1967. Europa.

440	**107**	7k. blue, brown and yellow	2·20	1·40
441	**107**	8k. blue, grey and green	2·20	1·40

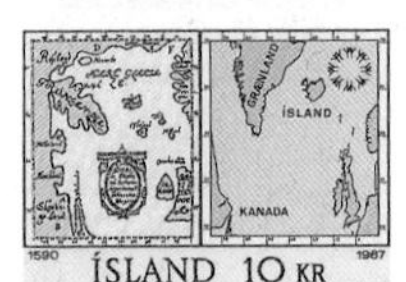

108 Old and New Maps of Iceland

1967. World Fair, Montreal.

442	**108**	10k. multicoloured	50	45

109 Trade Symbols

1967. 50th Anniv of Icelandic Chamber of Commerce.

443	**109**	5k. multicoloured	35	25

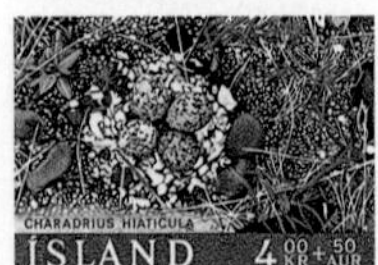

110 Nest and Eggs of Ringed Plover

1967. Charity stamps.

444	**110**	4k.+50a. multicoloured	80	1·50
445	-	5k.+50a. multicoloured	80	1·50

DESIGN: 5k. Nest and eggs of rock ptarmigan.

1968. Wild Flowers. As T 79. Multicoloured.

446	50a. Saxifrage	20	20
447	2k.50 Orchid	20	20

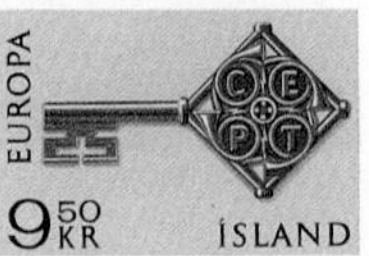

111 Europa "Key"

1968. Europa.

448	**111**	9k.50 mauve, black & yell	1·80	1·10
449	**111**	10k. yellow, sepia & green	1·80	1·10

112 Right-hand Traffic

1968. Adoption of Changed Rule of the Road.

450	**112**	4k. brown and yellow	20	20
451	**112**	5k. brown	20	20

113 "Fridriksson and Boy" (statue by S. Olafsson)

1968. Birth Cent of Pastor Fridrik Fridriksson (founder of Icelandic Y.M.C.A. and Y.W.C.A.).

452	**113**	10k. black and blue	50	35

114 Library Interior

1968. 150th Anniv of National Library.

453	**114**	5k. brown and buff	20	20
454	**114**	20k. ultramarine and blue	1·00	95

115 Jon Magnusson (former Prime Minister)

1968. 50th Anniv of Independence.

455	**115**	4k. lake	30	20
456	**115**	50k. sepia	3·50	3·25

116 Viking Ships

1969. 50th Anniv of Northern Countries' Union.

457	**116**	6k.50 red	50	45
458	**116**	10k. blue	50	45

117 Colonnade

1969. Europa.

459	**117**	13k. multicoloured	3·25	2·40
460	**117**	14k.50 multicoloured	1·10	1·00

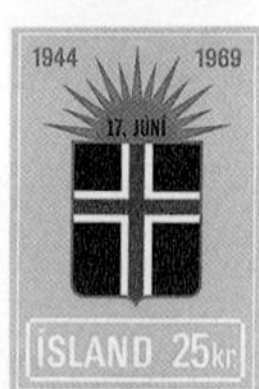

118 Republican Emblem (after S. Jonsson)

1969. 25th Anniv of Republic.

461	**118**	25k. multicoloured	1·10	75
462	**118**	100k. multicoloured	5·75	5·50

119 Boeing 727 Airliner

1969. 50th Anniv of Icelandic Aviation.

463	**119**	9k.50 ultramarine & blue	50	55
464	-	12k. ultramarine and blue	50	55

DESIGN: 12k. Canadair CL-44-D4 (inscr "Rolls-Royce 400").

120 Snaefellsjokull

1970. Landscapes (2nd series). Multicoloured.

465	1k. Type **120**	20	20
466	4k. Laxfoss and Baula	20	20
467	5k. Hattver (vert)	25	25
468	20k. Fjardagil (vert)	1·40	45

121 First Court Session

1970. 50th Anniv of Icelandic Supreme Court.

469	**121**	6k.50 multicoloured	25	20

122 Part of "Skardsbok" (14th-cent law manuscript)

1970. Icelandic Manuscripts. Multicoloured.

470	5k. Type **122**	25	25
471	15k. Part of preface to "Flateyjarbok"	55	65
472	30k. Illuminated initial from "Flateyjarbok"	1·10	1·10

123 "Flaming Sun"

1970. Europa.

473	**123**	9k. yellow and brown	2·75	1·60
474	**123**	25k. brown and green	3·75	2·75

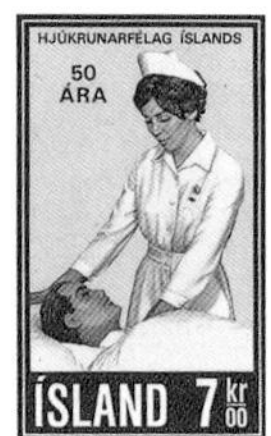

124 Nurse tending Patient

1970. 50th Anniv of Icelandic Nurses Assn.

475	**124**	7k. ultramarine and blue	30	25

125 G. Thomsen

1970. 150th Birth Anniv of Grimur Thomsen (poet).

476	**125**	10k. indigo and blue	55	35

126 "The Halt" (T. B. Thorlaksson)

1970. International Arts Festival, Reykjavik.

477	**126**	50k. multicoloured	1·50	1·30

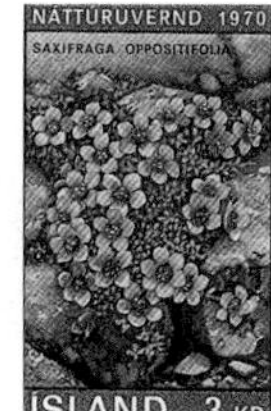

127 Purple Saxifrage

1970. Nature Conservation Year. Mult.

478	3k. Type **127**	25	20
479	15k. Lakagigar (view)	90	85

128 U.N. Emblem and Map

1970. 25th Anniv of United Nations.

480	**128**	12k. multicoloured	50	45

129 "Flight" (A. Jonsson)

1971. "Help for Refugees".

481	**129**	10k. multicoloured	85	75

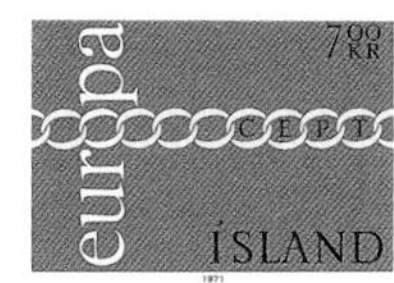

130 Europa Chain

1971. Europa.

482	**130**	7k. yellow, red and black	2·50	1·80
483	**130**	15k. yellow, blue and black	3·50	1·60

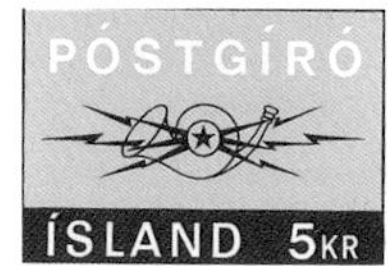

131 Postgiro Emblem

1971. Inauguration of Postal Giro Service.

484	**131**	5k. blue and light blue	25	20
485	**131**	7k. green and light green	30	25

132 Society Emblem

1971. Centenary of Icelandic Patriotic Society.

486	**132**	30k. lilac and blue	1·10	85
487	-	100k. black and grey	5·50	5·50

DESIGN: 100k. T. Gunnarsson (president and editor).

133 Freezing Plant and Haddock ("Melanogrammus aeglefinus")

1971. Icelandic Fishing Industry. Mult.

488	5k. Type **133**	20	20
489	7k. Landing catch and Atlantic cod ("Gadus morhua")	20	20
490	20k. Canning shrimps and "Pandalus borealis"	85	75

134 Mt. Herdubreid

1972

491	**134**	250k. multicoloured	70	30

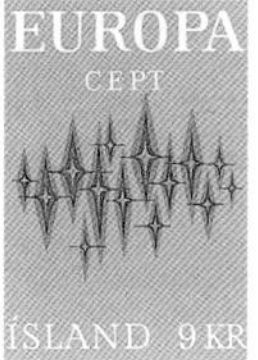

135 "Communications"

1972. Europa.

492	**135**	9k. multicoloured	1·50	75
493	**135**	13k. multicoloured	3·25	1·70

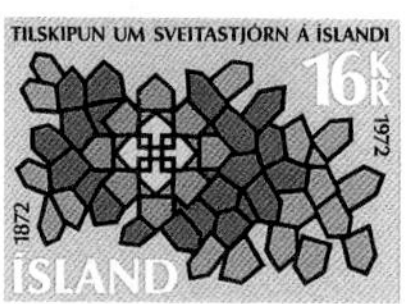

136 "Municipalities"

1972. Centenary of Icelandic Municipal Laws.

494	**136**	16k. multicoloured	25	25

137 World Map on Chessboard

1972. World Chess Championship, Reykjavik.

495	**137**	15k. multicoloured	30	25

138 Tomatoes

1972. Hot-house Plant Cultivation. Mult.

496	8k. Type **138**	20	20
497	12k. Steam source and valve	20	20
498	40k. Rose cultivation	1·10	75

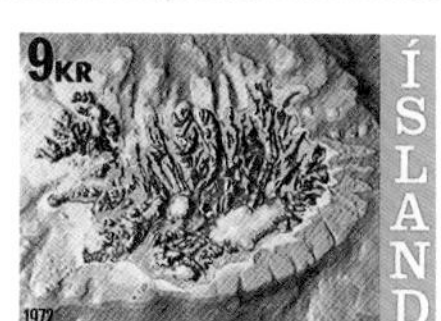

139 Contour Map and Continental Shelf

1972. Iceland's Offshore Claims.

499	**139**	9k. multicoloured	25	25

140 Arctic Tern feeding Young

1972. Charity Stamps.

500	**140**	7k.+1k. multicoloured	55	75
501	**140**	9k.+1k. multicoloured	55	75

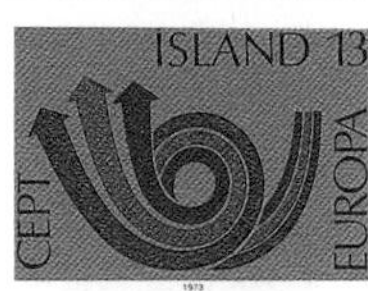

141 Europa "Posthorn"

1973. Europa.

502	**141**	13k. multicoloured	4·75	2·20
503	**141**	25k. multicoloured	95	65

142 Postman and 2s. stamp of 1873

1973. Stamp Centenary. Multicoloured.

504	10k. Type **142**	55	30
505	15k. Pony train	35	30
506	20k. "Esja" (mail steamer)	35	30
507	40k. Mail van	35	30
508	80k. Beech Model 18 mail plane	1·10	85

143 "The Nordic House", Reykjavik

1973. Nordic Countries' Postal Co-operation.

509	**143**	9k. multicoloured	40	35
510	**143**	10k. multicoloured	1·10	85

144 Pres. Asgeirsson

1973. 5th Death Anniv of Asgeir Asgeirsson (politician).

511	**144**	13k. red	35	30
512	**144**	15k. blue	30	25

145 Exhibition Emblem

1973. "Islandia 73" Stamp Exhibition. Mult.

513	17k. Type **145**	35	30
514	20k. Exhibition emblem (different)	30	30

146 "The Elements"

1973. Centenary of I.M.O.

515	**146**	50k. multicoloured	80	45

147 "Ingolfur and High-Seat Pillar" (tapestry, J. Briem)

1974. 1100th Anniv of Icelandic Settlement. Multicoloured.

516	10k. Type **147**	25	20
517	13k. "Grimur Geitskor at Thingvellir" (painting) (horiz)	25	30
518	15k. Bishop G. Thorlaksson of Holar	20	20
519	17k. "Snorri Sturluson slaying the King's messenger" (T. Skulason)	30	25
520	20k. Stained glass window from Hallgrimskirkja, Saurbaer	25	20
521	25k. Illuminated "I", from "Flateyjarbok" (manuscript)	30	25
522	30k. "Christ the King" (mosaic altar-piece, Skalholt Cathedral)	75	50
523	40k. 18th-century wood-carving	75	30
524	60k. "Curing the Catch" (concrete relief by S. Olafsson)	1·00	70
525	70k. "Saemunder smiting the Devil Seal" (bronze)	90	60
526	100k. Altar-cloth, Church of Stafafell (horiz)	1·10	85

148 "Horseman" (17th-century wood-carving)

1974. Europa. Sculptures. Multicoloured.

527		13k. Type **148**	50	20
528		20k. "Through the Sound Barrier" (bronze, A. Sveinsson)	1·50	85

149 Purchasing Stamps

1974. Centenary of Universal Postal Union.

529	**149**	17k. brown, blue & yellow	30	25
530	-	20k. brown, blue & green	30	30

DESIGN: 20k. Postman sorting mail.

150 Village with Erupting Volcano in distance

1975. Volcanic Eruption, Heimaey (1973).

531	**150**	20k. multicoloured	35	40
532	**150**	25k. multicoloured	30	30

151 "Autumn Bird" (T. Skullason)

1975. Europa. Paintings. Multicoloured.

533		18k. Type **151**	55	35
534		23k. "Sun Queen" (J. S. Kjarval) (vert.)	1·10	45

152 Stephan G. Stephansson (poet)

1975. Centenary of Icelandic Settlements in North America.

535	**152**	27k. brown and green	60	30

153 Hallgrimur Petursson (religious poet)

1975. Celebrities.

536	**153**	18k. black and green	20	30
537	-	23k. blue	20	30
538	-	30k. red	30	30
539	-	50k. blue	35	30

PORTRAITS: 23k. Arni Magnusson (historian); 30k. Jon Eiriksson (statesman); 50k. Einar Jonsson (painter and sculptor).

154 Red Cross Flag on Map of Iceland

1975. 50th Anniv of Icelandic Red Cross.

540	**154**	23k. multicoloured	30	25

155 "Abstract" (N. Tryggvadottir)

1975. International Women's Year.

541	**155**	100k. multicoloured	1·00	60

156 "Bertel Thorvaldsen" (self-statue)

1975. Centenary of Thorvaldsen Society (Charity organization).

542	**156**	27k. multicoloured	65	30

157 "Forestry"

1975. Reafforestation.

543	**157**	35k. multicoloured	65	30

158 "Landscape" (Asgrimur Jonsson)

1976. Birth Cent of Asgrimur Jonsson (painter).

544	**158**	150k. multicoloured	1·50	1·00

159 Wooden Bowl

1976. Europa. Old Wooden Crafts. Mult.

545		35k. Type **159**	1·10	85
546		45k. Spinning-wheel (vert)	1·10	95

160 Title page of Postal Services Order

1976. Bicent of Icelandic Postal Services.

547	**160**	35k. brown	40	30
548	-	45k. blue	60	45

DESIGN: 45k. Signature appended to Postal Services Order.

161 Iceland 5a. Stamp with Reykjavik Postmark, 1876

1976. Cent of Icelandic Aurar Currency Stamps.

549	**161**	30k. multicoloured	25	20

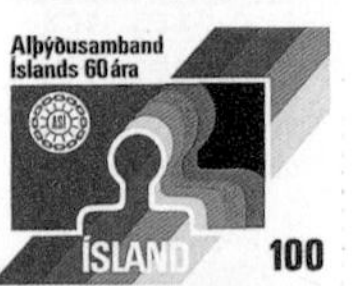

162 "Workers" and Federation Emblem

1976. 60th Anniv of Icelandic Labour Federation.

550	**162**	100k. multicoloured	85	55

163 Water-lilies

1977. Nordic Countries' Co-operation in Nature Conservation and Environment Protection.

551	**163**	35k. multicoloured	70	45
552	**163**	45k. multicoloured	70	45

164 Ofaerufoss, Eldgja

1977. Europa. Multicoloured.

553		45k. Type **164**	2·75	65
554		85k. Kirkufell from Grundarfjord	2·75	60

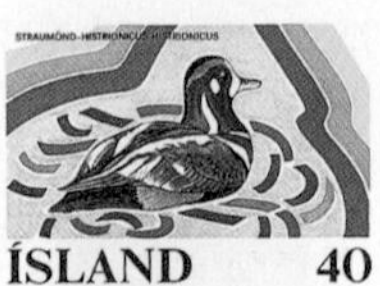

165 Harlequin Duck

1977. European Wetlands Campaign.

555	**165**	40k. multicoloured	40	30

166 Co-operative Emblem

1977. 75th Anniv of Federation of Icelandic Co-operative Societies.

556	**166**	60k. blue and light blue	65	40

167 Thermal Spring and Rheumatic Treatment

1977. World Rheumatism Year.

557	**167**	90k. multicoloured	60	40

168 Cairn and Glacier

1977. 50th Anniv of Icelandic Touring Club.

558	**168**	45k. blue	75	50

169 Thorvaldur Thoroddsen (geologist)

1978. Famous Icelanders.

559	**169**	50k. green and brown	30	25
560	-	60k. brown and green	50	55

DESIGN: 60k. Briet Bjarnhedinsdottir (suffragette).

170 Videy Mansion

1978. Europa. Multicoloured.

561		80k. Type **170**	2·30	55
562		120k. Husavik Church (vert.)	2·30	65

171 Dr. A. Johannesson, Junkers W.34 "Island 1" and Junkers F-13 "Island 2"

1978. 50th Anniv of Domestic Flights.

563	**171**	60k. black and blue	30	30
564	-	100k. multicoloured	60	40

DESIGN: 100k. Fokker F.27 Friendship TF-F1K.

172 Skeidara Bridge

1978. Skeidara Bridge.

565	**172**	70k. multicoloured	25	25

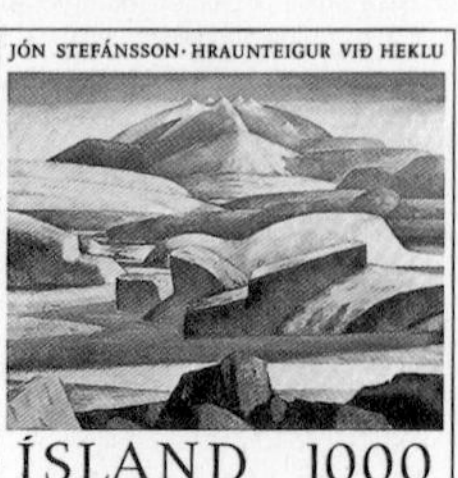

173 "Lava Scene near Mt. Hekla" (J. Stefansson)

1978

566	**173**	1000k. multicoloured	3·50	2·50

174 Wreck of "Sargon" and Breeches-buoy

1978. 50th Anniv of National Life-Saving Association of Iceland.

567	**174**	60k. black	25	20

175 "Reykjanesviti" Lighthouse

1978. Centenary of Lighthouses in Iceland.

568	**175**	90k. multicoloured	55	35

176 Halldor Hermannsson

1978. Birth Centenary of Halldor Hermannsson (scholar and librarian).

569	**176**	150k. blue	45	35

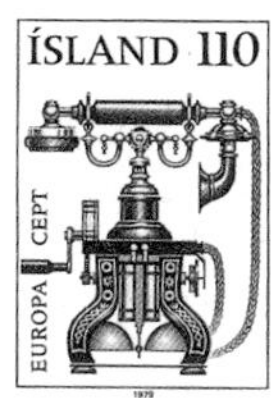

177 Old Telephone

1979. Europa. Multicoloured.

570	110k. Type **177**	2·75	55
571	190k. Posthorn and mailbag	4·25	65

178 Bjarni Thorsteinsson (clergyman and composer)

1979. Famous Icelanders.

572	-	80k. purple	25	25
573	**178**	100k. black	20	20
574	-	120k. red	30	30
575	-	130k. brown	40	45
576	-	170k. red	50	45

DESIGNS: 80k. Ingibjorg H. Bjarnason (headmistress and first female member of Althing); 120k. Petur Gudjohnsen (organist); 130k. Sveinbjorn Sveinbjornson (composer); 170k. Torfhildur Holm (poetess and novelist).

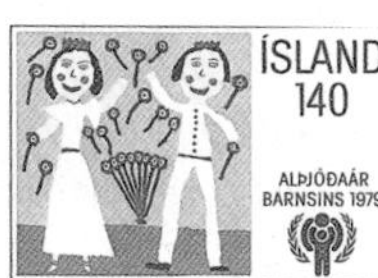

179 Children with Flowers

1979. International Year of the Child.

577	**179**	140k. multicoloured	65	40

180 Icelandic Arms to 1904 and 1904–19

1979. 75th Anniv of Ministry of Iceland.

578	**180**	500k. multicoloured	1·30	85

181 Sigurdsson and I. Einarsdottir

1979. Death Centenaries of Jon Sigurdsson (historian and Althing member) and of his wife, Ingibjorg Einarsdottir.

579	**181**	150k. black	50	40

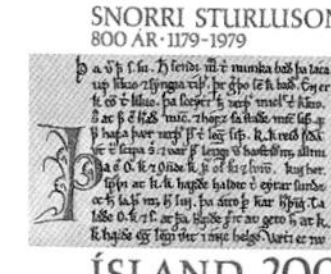

182 Part of Kringla Leaf (MS of "Heimskringla")

1979. 800th Birth Anniv of Snorri Sturluson (saga writer).

580	**182**	200k. multicoloured	60	40

183 Icelandic Dog

1980. Fauna.

581	**183**	10k. black	15	15
582	-	90k. brown	15	15
583	-	160k. purple	75	35
584	-	170k. black	50	45
585	-	190k. brown	25	25

DESIGNS: 90k. Arctic fox; 160k. Greater redfish; 170k. Atlantic puffins; 190k. Common seal.

184 Jon Sveinsson alias Nonni (writer)

1980. Europa.

586	**184**	140k. pink and black	1·40	55
587	-	250k. pink and black	1·40	65

DESIGN: 250k. Gunnar Gunnarsson (writer).

185 Rowan Berries

1980. Year of the Tree.

588	**185**	120k. multicoloured	35	30

186 Sports Complex, Reykjavik

1980. Olympic Games, Moscow.

589	**186**	300k. turquoise	50	50

187 Embroidered Cushion

1980. Nordic Countries' Postal Co-operation. Multicoloured.

590	150k. Carved and painted cabinet door	55	50
591	180k. Type **187**	80	55

188 University Hospital

1980. 50th Anniv of University Hospital.

592	**188**	200k. multicoloured	45	35

189 Loudspeaker

1980. 50th Anniv of State Broadcasting Service.

593	**189**	400k. multicoloured	80	35

190 Magnus Stephensen (Chief Justice and publisher)

1981. Famous Icelanders.

594	**190**	170a. blue	40	30
595	-	190a. green	45	30

DESIGN: 190a. Finnur Magnusson (writer and Keeper of Privy Archives).

191 Loftur the Sorcerer

1981. Europa. Illustrations of Icelandic legends. Multicoloured.

596	180a. Type **191**	1·40	80
597	220a. Witch wading the deeps off Iceland	1·40	80

192 Winter Wren

1981. Birds.

598	**192**	50a. brown	15	15
599	-	100a. blue	20	15
600	-	200a. black	45	25

DESIGNS: 100a. Golden plover; 200a. Common raven.

193 Human Jigsaw

1981. International Year for Disabled Persons.

601	**193**	200a. multicoloured	25	25

194 Skyggnir Dish Aerial

1981. 75th Anniv of Icelandic Telephone Service.

602	**194**	500a. multicoloured	95	50

195 "Hauling the Line" (Gunnlaugur Scheving)

1981

603	**195**	5000a. multicoloured	5·75	3·50

196 Medieval Driftwood crucifix from Alftamyri

1981. Millenary of Missionary Work in Iceland.

604	**196**	200a. lilac	25	25

197 Leaf-bread (star pattern)

1981. Christmas. Multicoloured.

605	200a. Type **197**	60	50
606	250a. Leaf-bread (tree pattern)	60	50

198 Common Northern Whelk

1982. Shells.

607	**198**	20a. red	20	20
608	-	600a. brown	75	30

DESIGN: 600a. Iceland scallop.

199 Casting Dais Post into Sea (first Iceland settlement, 874)

1982. Europa. Multicoloured.

609	350a. Type **199**	5·25	85
610	450a. Discovery of Vinland (America), 1000	5·25	85

200 Sheep

1982. Domestic Animals.

611	**200**	300a. brown	80	45
612	-	400a. red	35	20
613	-	500a. grey	35	20

DESIGNS: 400a. Cow; 500a. Cat.

201 Co-operative Trading House, Husavik

1982. Centenary of Thingeyjar Co-operative Society.

614	**201**	1000a. black and brown	75	40

202 Horseman

1982. Iceland Ponies and Horsemanship.
615 **202** 700a. multicoloured 45 35

203 Holar

1982. Cent of Holar Agricultural College.
616 **203** 1500a. multicoloured 85 70

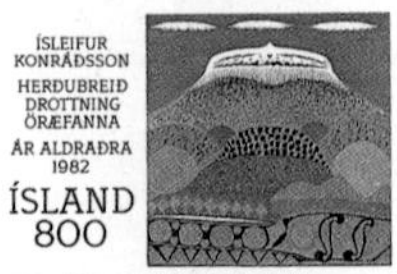

204 "Mount Herdubreid" (Isleifur Konradsson)

1982. Year of the Aged.
617 **204** 800a. multicoloured 75 40

205 T. Sveinsdottir

1982. Famous Icelanders. Thorbjorg Sveindsdottir (midwife and founder of Icelandic Women's Association).
618 **205** 900a. brown 50 40

206 Reynistadur Monastery Seal

1982. "Nordia 84" Stamp Exhibition, Reykjavik (1st issue). Sheet 82×80 mm containing T 206 and similar vert design.
MS619 400a. brown and black; 800a. brown and black (sold at 18k.) 5·25 5·25
DESIGN:—800a. Thingeyrar Monastery seal.
See also Nos. **MS**636 and **MS**645.

207 Doves and Opening of "The Night was such a Splendid One"

1982. Christmas. Multicoloured.
620 300a. Type **207** 75 45
621 350a. Bells and close of "The Night was such a Splendid One" (composed by Sigvaldi Kaldalons from poem by E. Sigurdsson) 80 60

208 Marsh Marigold

1983. Flowers. Multicoloured.
622 7k.50 Type **208** 35 25
623 8k. Alpine catchfly 70 45
624 10k. Marsh cinquefoil 1·00 45
625 20k. Water forgetmenot 2·00 85

209 Mount Sulur

1983. Nordic Countries' Postal Co-operation. "Visit the North". Multicoloured.
626 4k.50 Type **209** 80 65
627 5k. Urridafossar Falls 85 70

210 Thermal Area and Heat-exchange Plant

1983. Europa. Multicoloured.
628 5k. Type **210** 19·00 1·10
629 5k.50 Thermal area heating houses 22·00 1·60

211 Stern Trawler

1983. Fishing Industry.
630 **211** 11k. blue 65 60
631 - 13k. blue 1·10 55
DESIGN: 13k. Line fishing.

212 "Laki Craters" (Finnur Jonsson)

1983. Bicentenary of Skafta Eruption.
632 **212** 15k. multicoloured 85 60

213 Skiing

1983. Outdoor Sports. Multicoloured.
633 12k. Type **213** 80 45
634 14k. Jogging 95 55

214 Aircraft and W.C.Y. Emblem

1983. World Communications Year.
635 **214** 30k. multicoloured 1·80 1·10

215 Seal of Bishop Magnus Eyjolfsson

1983. "Nordia 84" Stamp Exhibition, Reykjavik (2nd issue). Sheet 82×80 mm containing T 215 and similar vert design.
MS636 8k. blue and black; 12k. green and black (sold at 30k.) 6·75 6·50
DESIGN: 12k. seal of Bishop Ogmundur Palsson.

216 Virgin Mary and Child

1983. Christmas. Multicoloured.
637 600a. Type **216** 80 45
638 650a. Visitation of the Angel 80 45

217 Pres. Eldjarn

1983. 1st Death Anniv (September) of Kristjan Eldjarn (President, 1968–80).
639 **217** 6k.50 red 80 55
640 **217** 7k. blue 45 25

218 Burnet Rose

1984. Flowers. Multicoloured.
641 6k. Type **218** 60 45
642 25k. Silverweed 1·20 45
See also Nos. 648/9, 657/60 and 717/18.

219 Bridge

1984. Europa. 25th Anniv of European Post and Telecommunications Conference.
643 **219** 6k.50 deep blue and blue 2·40 70
644 **219** 7k.50 dp purple & purple 1·20 75

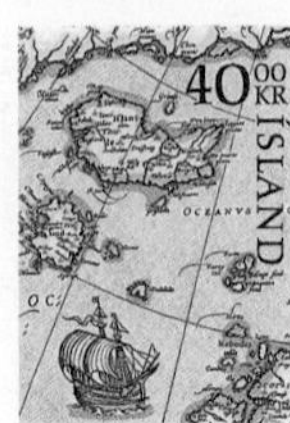

220 Map of North Atlantic by Abraham Ortelius, 1570

1984. "Nordia 84" Stamp Exhibition, Reykjavik (3rd issue). Sheet 114×76 mm.
MS645 **220** 40k. multicoloured (sold at 60k.) 12·50 12·00

221 Icelandic Flags

1984. 40th Anniv of Republic.
646 **221** 50k. multicoloured 4·75 2·40

222 I.O.G.T. Lodge, Akureyri

1984. Centenary of International Order of Good Templars in Iceland.
647 **222** 10k. green 70 40

1984. Flowers. As T 218. Multicoloured.
648 6k.50 Wild azalea 55 40
649 7k.50 Alpine bearberry 65 65

223 Basalt symbolising Industries

1984. 50th Anniv of Confederation of Icelandic Employers.
650 **223** 30k. multicoloured 1·40 1·00

224 Bjorn Bjarnarson (founder) (after J. P. Wildenradt)

1984. Centenary of National Gallery.
651 **224** 12k. black, brown and green 70 50
652 - 40k. black, green and red 1·90 1·20
DESIGN: 40k. New gallery building.

225 Virgin and Child

1984. Christmas.
653 **225** 600a. blue, lt blue & gold 55 30
654 - 650a. red and gold 70 30
DESIGN: 650a. Angel with Christmas rose.

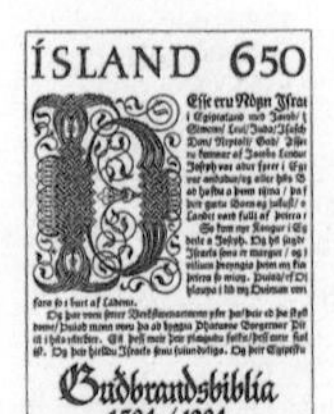

226 Text from Bible

1984. 400th Anniv of Gudbrand's Bible.
655 **226** 6k.50 red 50 30
656 - 7k.50 purple 45 70
DESIGN: 7k.50, Illustration from Bible.

1985. Flowers. As T 218. Multicoloured.
657 8k. Stone bramble 55 30
658 9k. Rock speedwell 70 30
659 16k. Sea pea 1·90 65
660 17k. Alpine whitlow-grass 70 55

227 Lady playing Langspil

1985. Europa. Music Year. Multicoloured.
661 6k.50 Type **227** 3·25 45
662 7k.50 Man playing Icelandic violin 3·25 1·30

228 Swedish Whitebeam

1985. Centenary of Iceland Horticultural Society.

663	**228**	20k. multicoloured	90	60

229 Girl and I.Y.Y. Emblem

1985. International Youth Year.

664	**229**	25k. multicoloured	1·00	75

230 Common Squid

1985. Marine Life.

665	**230**	7k. purple	35	30
666	-	8k. brown	35	30
667	-	9k. red	75	45

DESIGNS: 8k. Common spider crab; 9k. Sea anemone.

231 Rev. Hannes Stephensen (politician)

1985. Famous Icelanders.

668	**231**	13k. red	55	30
669	-	30k. violet	1·40	70

DESIGN: 30k. Jon Gudmundsson (editor and politician).

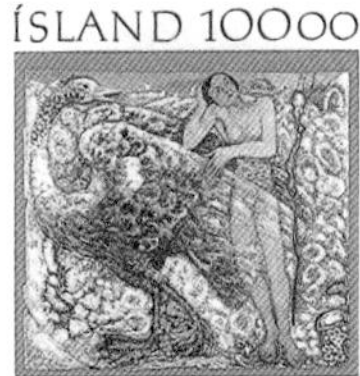

232 "Flight Yearning"

1985. Birth Centenary of Johannes Sveinsson Kjarval (artist).

670	**232**	100k. multicoloured	5·00	3·75

233 Snow Scene

1985. Christmas. Multicoloured.

671	8k. Type **233**	70	30
672	9k. Snow scene (different)	70	65

234 Pied Wagtail

1986. Birds. Multicoloured.

673	6k. Type **234**	35	30
674	10k. Pintail	1·30	55
675	12k. Merlin	95	50
676	15k. Razorbill	90	45

See also Nos. 697/700, 720/1, 726/7, 741/2 and 763/4.

235 Skaftafell National Park

1986. Europa. Multicoloured.

677	10k. Type **235**	13·00	1·40
678	12k. Jokulsargljufur National Park	4·50	85

236 Stykkisholmur

1986. Nordic Countries' Postal Co-operation. Twinned Towns. Multicoloured.

679	10k. Type **236**	1·10	60
680	12k. Seydisfjordur	1·10	55

237 Head Office, Reykjavik

1986. Centenary of National Bank. Mult.

681	**237**	13k. green	65	55
682	-	250k. brown	10·00	6·50

DESIGN: 250k. Reverse of first National Bank 5k. note.

238 First Official Seal

1986. Bicentenary of Reykjavik.

683	**238**	10k. red	60	45
684	-	12k. brown	60	45
685	-	13k. green	60	45
686	-	40k. blue	1·50	75

DESIGNS: 12k. "Reykjavik pond, 1856" (illustration from "Journey in the Northern Seas" by Charles Edmond); 13k. Women washing clothes in natural hot water brook, Laugardalur; 40k. City Theatre.

239 Early Telephone Equipment

1986. 80th Anniv of Icelandic Telephone and Telegraph Service. Multicoloured.

687	10k. Type **239**	45	25
688	20k. Modern digital telephone system	1·10	70

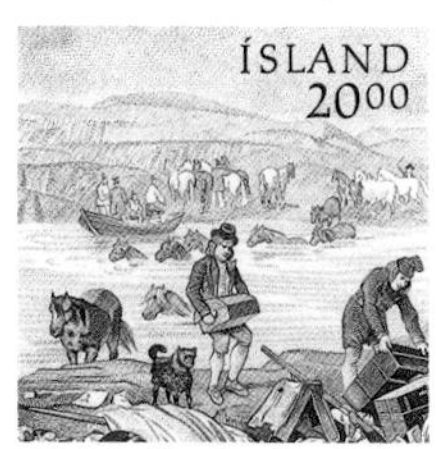

240 Hvita River Crossing, 1836 (after Auguste Mayer)

1986. Stamp Day. Sheet 95×67 mm.

MS689 **240**	20k. black (sold at 30k.)	5·00	4·75

241 "Christmas at Peace"

1986. Christmas. Multicoloured.

690	10k. Type **241**	70	35
691	12k. "Christmas Night"	60	35

242 "Svanur" (ketch) anchored off Olafsvik

1987. 300th Anniv of Olafsvik Trading Station.

692	**242**	50k. purple	2·30	1·40

243 Terminal and Boeing 727 Tail

1987. Opening of Leif Eiriksson Terminal, Keflavik Airport.

693	**243**	100k. multicoloured	4·25	1·70

244 Christ carrying Cross

1987. Europa. Stained Glass Windows by Leifur Breidfoerd, Fossvogur Cemetery Chapel. Multicoloured.

694	12k. Type **244**	1·80	70
695	15k. Soldiers and peace dove	3·00	90

245 Rask

1987. Birth Bicentenary of Rasmus Kristjan Rask (philologist).

696	**245**	20k. black	90	65

1987. Birds. As T 234. Multicoloured.

697	13k. Short-eared owl	65	30
698	40k. Redwing	1·70	80
699	70k. Oystercatcher	2·50	1·20
700	90k. Mallard	4·00	2·10

246 Girl Brushing Teeth

1987. Dental Protection.

701	**246**	12k. multicoloured	55	45

247 Vulture

1987. National Guardian Spirits. Each red.

702	13k. Type **247**	70	95
703	13k. Dragon	70	95
704	13k. Bull	70	95
705	13k. Giant	70	95

See also Nos. 713/16, 732 and 743/50.

248 Djupivogur Trading Station, 1836 (after Auguste Mayer)

1987. Stamp Day. Sheet 95×67 mm.

MS706 **248**	30k. black (sold at 45k.)	5·00	5·50

249 Christmas Tree

1987. Christmas. Multicoloured.

707	13k. Type **249**	70	45
708	17k. "Christmas Light"	85	70

250 Steinn Steinarr (poet)

1988. Famous Icelanders. Multicoloured.

709	16k. Type **250**	70	30
710	21k. David Stefansson (writer)	90	55

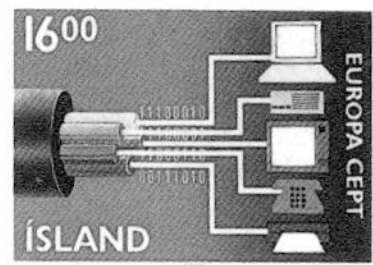

251 Transmission of Messages by Modern Data System

1988. Europa. Communications. Multicoloured.

711	16k. Type **251**	95	45
712	21k. Phone pad and globe within envelope (transmission of letters by facsimile machine)	4·25	1·90

1988. National Guardian Spirit. As Nos. 702/5 but values and colour changed.

713	16k. black (Type **247**)	70	65
714	16k. black (Dragon)	70	65
715	16k. black (Bull)	70	65
716	16k. black (Giant)	70	65

1988. Flowers. As T 218. Multicoloured.

717	10k. Tufted vetch	55	25
718	50k. Wild thyme	2·30	70

252 Handball

1988. Olympic Games, Seoul.

719	**252**	18k. multicoloured	90	45

1988. Birds. As T 234. Multicoloured.

720	5k. Black-tailed godwit	30	20
721	30k. Long-tailed duck	1·40	55

253 "Nupsstadur Farm, Fljotshverfi, 1836" (after Auguste Mayer)

1988. Stamp Day. Sheet 95×67 mm.
MS722 **253** 40k. black (sold at 60k.) 4·50 4·50

254 Mother and Baby

1988. 40th Anniv of W.H.O. "Health for All in 2000".
723 **254** 19k. multicoloured 95 45

255 Fisherman with Haul of Fish

1988. Christmas. Multicoloured.
724 19k. Type **255** 70 40
725 24k. Trawler and buoy 1·10 70

1989. Birds. As T 234. Multicoloured.
726 19k. Red-necked phalarope 70 40
727 100k. Snow buntings 4·50 3·25

256 Peysufot (dress costume)

1989. Nordic Countries' Postal Co-operation. Traditional Costumes. Multicoloured.
728 21k. Type **256** 1·10 60
729 26k. Upphlutur (everyday wear) 1·10 70

257 Children at Seaside

1989. Europa. Childrens' Toys and Games. Multicoloured.
730 21k. Type **257** 6·50 80
731 26k. Girl with hoop and boy with hobby-horse 6·50 80

1989. National Guardian Spirits. As No. 703 but colour and value changed.
732 500k. brown (Dragon) 19·00 11·00

258 Mount Skeggi, Arnarfjord

1989. Landscapes. Multicoloured.
733 35k. Type **258** 1·20 65
734 45k. Namaskard thermal spring 1·20 75
See also Nos. 757/8 and 765/6.

259 College

1989. Cent of Hvanneyri Agricultural College.
735 **259** 50k. multicoloured 1·40 85

260 Seaman throwing Barrels at Whales

1989. Stamp Day. "Nordia 91" Stamp Exhibition, Reykjavik (1st issue). Sheet 114×74 mm containing T 260 and similar vert designs, showing details of the 1539 Carta Marina by Olaus Magnus.
MS736 30k. Type **260**; 30k. Ship harpooning whale; 30k. Sea serpent encircling ship (sold at 130k.) 8·50 8·00
See also Nos. **MS**760 and **MS**771.

261 Stefan Stefansson (co-founder) and Flowers

1989. Centenary of Icelandic Natural History Society. Multicoloured.
737 21k. Type **261** 90 45
738 26k. Bjarni Saemundsson (first Chairman) and Atlantic cod 90 45

262 "Virgin and Child"

1989. Christmas. Multicoloured.
739 21k. Type **262** 90 45
740 26k. "Three Wise Men" 1·00 65

1990. Birds. As T 234. Multicoloured.
741 21k. European wigeons 1·10 45
742 80k. Pink-footed goose and goslings 2·75 1·10

1990. National Guardian Spirits. As Nos. 702/5 but value and colours changed.
743 5k. green (Type **247**) 35 35
744 5k. green (Dragon) 35 35
745 5k. green (Bull) 35 35
746 5k. green (Giant) 35 35
747 21k. blue (Type **247**) 70 70
748 21k. blue (Dragon) 70 70
749 21k. blue (Bull) 70 70
750 21k. blue (Giant) 70 70

263 Gudrun Larusdottir (writer and politician) (after Halldor Petursson)

1990. 110th Birth Anniversaries. Mult.
751 21k. Type **263** 80 45
752 21k. Ragnhildur Petursdottir (women's educationist) (after Asgrimur Jonsson) 80 45

264 Posthouse Street, Reykjavik, Post Office and Old Scales

1990. Europa. Post Office Buildings. Mult.
753 21k. Type **264** 3·75 85
754 40k. Thoenglabakki 4, Reykjavik, Post Office and modern scales 5·25 1·80

265 Archery

1990. Sport. Multicoloured.
755 21k. Type **265** 80 55
756 21k. Football 80 55

1990. Landscapes. As T 258. Multicoloured.
757 25k. Hvitserkur, Hunafjord 1·10 55
758 200k. Lomagnupur 6·25 2·75

266 Bird, Stars and Map

1990. European Tourism Year.
759 **266** 30k. multicoloured 1·10 80

267 Denmark

1990. Stamp Day. "Nordia 91" Stamp Exhibition, Reykjavik (2nd issue). Sheet 114×74 mm containing T 267 and similar vert designs, showing details of the 1539 Carta Marina by Olaus Magnus.
MS760 40k. Type **267**; 40k. Sweden; 40k. Gotland and sailing ship (sold at 170k.) 9·25 9·00

268 Children around Christmas Tree

1990. Christmas. Multicoloured.
761 25k. Type **268** 1·20 60
762 30k. Carol singers 1·40 75

1991. Birds. As T 234. Multicoloured.
763 25k. Slavonian grebes 1·00 30
764 100k. Northern gannets 4·50 1·30

1991. Landscapes. As T 258. Multicoloured.
765 10k. Mt. Vestrahorn 45 30
766 300k. Kverkfjoll range 9·50 3·75

269 Meteorological Information

1991. Europa. Europe in Space. Mult.
767 26k. Type **269** 8·50 1·10
768 47k. Telecommunications satellite 13·50 1·90

270 Jokulsarlon

1991. Nordic Countries' Postal Co-operation. Tourism. Multicoloured.
769 26k. Type **270** 1·40 70
770 31k. Strokkur hot spring 1·50 80

271 Western Iceland

1991. "Nordia 91" Stamp Exhibition (3rd issue). Sheet 114×74 mm containing T 271 and similar vert designs, showing details of the 1539 Carta Marina by Olaus Magnus.
MS771 50k. Type **271**; 50k. Arms and central part of Iceland; 50k. Eastern Iceland, ice floes and compass rose (sold at 215k.) 11·00 10·50

272 Golf

1991. Sports. Multicoloured.
772 26k. Type **272** 90 55
773 26k. Glima (wrestling) 90 55

273 Pall Isolfsson (composer) (after Hans Muller)

1991. Famous Icelanders. Multicoloured.
774 60k. Ragnar Jonsson (founder of Reykjavik College of Music) (after Joannes Kjarval) (horiz) 1·70 1·10
775 70k. Type **273** 2·30 1·60

274 College Building and Student using Sextant

1991. Cent of College of Navigation, Reykjavik.
776 **274** 50k. multicoloured 1·70 90

275 "Soloven" (mail brigantine)

1991. Stamp Day. Ships. Multicoloured.
777 30k. Type **275** 2·75 1·50
778 30k. "Arcturus" (cargo liner) 2·75 1·50
779 30k. "Gullfoss I" (cargo liner) 2·75 1·50
780 30k. "Esja II" (cargo liner) 2·75 1·50

276 "Light of Christmas"

1991. Christmas. Multicoloured.
781 30k. Type **276** 1·00 60
782 35k. Star 1·10 85

277 Skiing

1992. Sport. Multicoloured.

783 30k. Type **277** 1·00 55
784 30k. Volleyball 1·00 55

278 Map and "Santa Maria"

1992. Europa. 500th Anniv of Discovery of America by Columbus. Multicoloured.

785 55k. Map and Viking ship (Leif Eriksson) 6·50 1·60
786 55k. Type **278** 6·50 1·60
MS787 85×67 mm. Nos. 785/6 10·50 9·50

279 Agricultural and Industrial Symbols

1992. 75th Anniv of Iceland Chamber of Commerce (30k.) and 50th Anniv of Icelandic Freezing Plants Corporation (35k.). Multicoloured.

788 30k. Type **279** 1·00 65
789 35k. Trawler and Atlantic cod 1·00 70

280 River Fnjoska Bridge, Skogar

1992. Bridges. Multicoloured.

790 5k. Type **280** 25 20
791 250k. River Olfusa bridge, Selfoss 8·00 5·75

See also Nos. 804/5.

281 Ford "TT", 1920–26

1992. Postal Vehicles. Multicoloured.

792 30k. Type **281** 2·10 1·10
793 30k. Citroen snowmobile, 1929 2·10 1·10
794 30k. Mail/passenger transport car "RE 231", 1933 2·10 1·10
795 30k. Ford bus, 1946 2·10 1·10

282 Face and Candle reflected in Window

1992. Christmas. Multicoloured.

796 30k. Type **282** 1·10 65
797 35k. Full moon 1·10 75

283 Gyr Falcon with Chicks

1992. Endangered Species. The Gyr Falcon. Multicoloured.

798 5k. Type **283** 1·20 30
799 10k. Beating wings 1·40 40
800 20k. Eating 2·00 80
801 35k. On ground 2·50 1·40

284 Handball

1993. Sport. Multicoloured.

802 30k. Type **284** 90 50
803 30k. Running 90 50

1993. Bridges. As T 280. Multicoloured.

804 90k. River Hvita bridge, Ferjukot 3·00 1·60
805 150k. River Jokulsa a Fjollum bridge, Grimsstadir 5·25 3·25

285 The Blue Lagoon, Svartsengi

1993. Nordic Countries' Postal Co-operation. Tourism. Multicoloured.

806 30k. Type **285** 1·00 75
807 35k. Perlan (The Pearl), Reykjavik 1·40 90

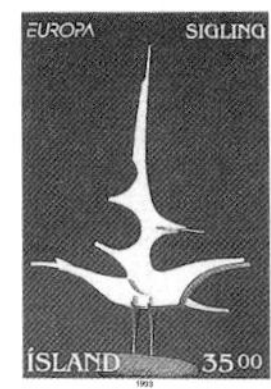

286 "Sailing" (Jon Gunnar Arnason)

1993. Europa. Contemporary Art. Mult.

808 35k. Type **286** 1·70 1·00
809 55k. "Hatching of the Jet" (Magnus Tomasson) 2·75 1·80

287 1933 1k. Balbo Flight Stamp

1993. 60th Anniv of Balbo Transatlantic Mass Formation Flight. Sheet 110×76 mm containing T 287 and similar vert designs. Multicoloured.

MS810 10k. Type **287**; 50k. 1933 5k. Balbo flight stamp; 100k. 1933 10k. Balbo flight stamp (sold at 200k.) 6·75 6·50

288 Junkers "F-13" Seaplane "Sulan" D-483

1993. 65th Anniv of 1st Icelandic Postal Flight. Multicoloured.

811 30k. Type **288** 1·90 75
812 30k. Waco YKS-7 seaplane TF-ORH 1·90 75
813 30k. Grumman G-21 Goose amphibian TF-VK 1·90 75
814 30k. Consolidated PBY-5 Catalina flying boat "Old Peter" TF-TSP 1·90 75

289 Three Wise Men adoring Child

1993. Christmas. Multicoloured.

815 30k. Type **289** 1·00 75
816 35k. Madonna and Child 1·20 95

290 Swimming

1994. Sport. Multicoloured.

817 30k. Type **290** 1·00 45
818 30k. Weightlifting 1·00 45

291 Finger Puppets

1994. International Year of the Family.

819 **291** 40k. multicoloured 1·00 75

292 St. Brendan visiting Iceland

1994. Europa. St. Brendan's Voyages. Multicoloured.

820 35k. Type **292** 1·30 95
821 55k. St. Brendan discovering Faroe Islands 2·00 1·60
MS822 81×76 mm. Nos. 820/1 3·50 3·50

293 Conductor and Instruments

1994. 50th Anniv of Independence. Art and Culture. Multicoloured.

823 30k. Type **293** (44th anniv of Icelandic Symphony Orchestra) 85 45
824 30k. Pottery (55th anniv of College of Arts and Crafts) 85 45
825 30k. Cameraman and actors (16th anniv of National Film Fund) 85 45
826 30k. Ballerina and modern dancers (21st anniv of Icelandic Dance Company) 85 45
827 30k. Theatre masks (44th anniv of Icelandic National Theatre) 85 45

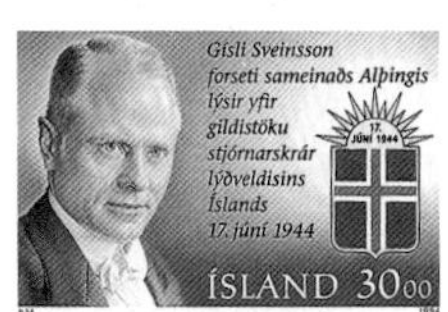

294 Gisli Sveinsson (President of United Althing, 1944)

1994. 50th Anniv of New Constitution.

828 **294** 30k. multicoloured 90 75

295 Sveinn Bjornsson (1944–52)

1994. 50th Anniv of Republic. Presidents. Sheet 118×71 mm containing T 295 and similar vert designs. Multicoloured.

MS829 50k. Type **295**; 50k. Asgeir Asgeirsson (1952–68); 50k. Kristjan Eldjarn (1968–80); 50k. Vigdis Finnbogadottir (1980 onwards) 6·75 6·50

296 Children looking at Stamp Album

1994. Stamp Day. Stamp Collecting. Sheet 120×50 mm containing T 296 and similar square designs. Multicoloured.

MS830 30k. Type **296**; 35k. Magnifying glass over stamps; 100k. Girl and elderly man studying globe (sold at 200k.) 8·50 8·00

297 Woman and Stars

1994. Christmas. Multicoloured.

831 30k. Type **297** 90 65
832 35k. Man and stars 1·00 75

298 Emblem and Airplane

1994. 50th Anniv of I.C.A.O.

833 **298** 100k. multicoloured 3·25 2·20

299 Flag and Salvation Army Members

1995. Anniversaries. Multicoloured.

834 35k. Type **299** (centenary of Salvation Army in Iceland) 1·00 75
835 90k. Map of fjord (centenary of Seydisfjordur) 2·75 1·60

300 Geyser

1995. 14th World Men's Handball Championship. Multicoloured.

836 35k. Type **300** 1·30 1·80
837 35k. Stadium 1·30 1·80
838 35k. Volcano 1·30 1·80
839 35k. Entrance to fjord 1·30 1·80

301 Laufas

1995. Nordic Countries' Postal Co-operation. Tourism. Multicoloured.

840 30k. Type **301** 1·00 75
841 35k. Fjallsjokull Glacier 1·40 85

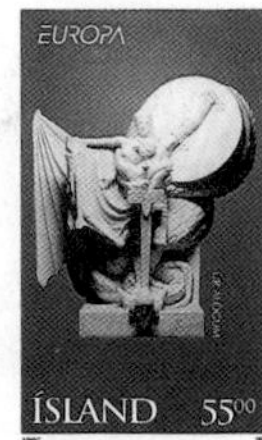
302 "Spell-broken" (sculpture, Einar Jonsson)

1995. Europa. Peace and Freedom.

842	**302**	35k. multicoloured	1·20	1·00
843	**302**	55k. multicoloured	2·00	1·50

303 *Laura* (mail ship)

1995. Mail Ships. Multicoloured.

844	30k. Type **303**	1·10	1·00
845	30k. *Dronning Alexandrine*	1·10	1·00
846	30k. *Laxfoss*	1·10	1·00
847	30k. *Godafoss III*	1·10	1·00

304 Redpoll ("Acanthis flammea")

1995. European Nature Conservation Year. Birds. Multicoloured.

848	25k. Type **304**	75	55
849	250k. Common snipe ("Gallinago gallinago")	7·25	6·25

305 Boeing 757

1995. 40th Anniv of Iceland–Luxembourg Air Link.

850	**305**	35k. multicoloured	1·00	85

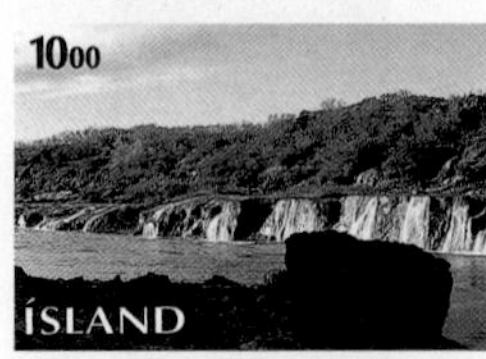
306 Hraunfossar Waterfalls (left detail)

1995. "Nordia 96" Stamp Exhibition, Reykjavik (1st issue). Sheet 105×65 mm containing T 306 and similar horiz design. Multicoloured.

MS851	10k. Type **306**; 150k. Waterfalls (right detail) (sold at 200k.)	8·00	7·50

The stamps form a composite design.
See also No. **MS**871.

307 Snowman and Snowwoman

1995. Christmas. Multicoloured.

852	30k. Type **307**	90	60
853	35k. Coloured fir trees	1·10	70

308 Anniversary Emblem

1995. 50th Anniv of U.N.O.

854	**308**	100k. multicoloured	2·75	1·80

309 Common Cormorant ("Phalacrocorax carbo")

1996. Birds. Multicoloured.

855	20k. Type **309**	55	45
856	40k. Barrow's goldeneye ("Bucephala islandica")	1·10	95

310 "Seamen in a Boat" (Gunnlaugur Scheving)

1996. Paintings. Multicoloured.

857	100k. Type **310**	2·75	1·50
858	200k. "At the Washing Springs" (Kristin Jonsdottir)	5·00	3·50

311 Halldora Bjarnadottir (founder of women's societies)

1996. Europa. Famous Women. Mult.

859	35k. Type **311**	1·40	1·00
860	55k. Olafia Johannsdottir (women's rights campaigner and temperance worker)	1·70	1·50

312 1931 Buick

1996. Post Buses. Multicoloured.

861	35k. Type **312**	1·10	95
862	35k. 1933 Studebaker	1·10	95
863	35k. 1937 Ford	1·10	95
864	35k. 1946 Reo	1·10	95

313 Running

1996. Olympic Games, Atlanta. Mult.

865	5k. Type **313**	20	15
866	25k. Javelin	70	60
867	45k. Long jumping	1·10	1·10
868	65k. Shot put	1·70	1·60

314 Hospital Ward

1996. Centenary of Order of the Sisters of St. Joseph in Iceland.

869	**314**	65k. black, stone & purple	1·70	1·50

315 School

1996. 150th Anniv of Reykjavik School.

870	**315**	150k. multicoloured	4·00	3·25

316 Godafoss Waterfalls (central detail)

1996. "Nordia 96" Stamp Exhibition, Reykjavik (2nd issue). Sheet 105×65 mm containing T 316 and similar square designs. Multicoloured.

MS871	45k. Type **316**; 65k. Waterfalls (right detail); 90k. Waterfalls (left detail) (sold at 300k.)	8·75	8·25

The stamps form a composite design.

317 Reykjavik Cathedral

1996. Bicentenary of Reykjavik Cathedral.

872	**317**	45k. multicoloured	1·40	1·10

318 "Virgin Mary holding Child Jesus" (ivory figurine)

1996. Christmas. Exhibits from National Museum of Iceland. Multicoloured.

873	35k. Type **318**	1·00	65
874	45k. Pax depicting Nativity	1·50	1·40

319 Red-breasted Merganser ("Mergus serrator")

1997. Ducks. Multicoloured.

875	10k. Type **319**	40	40
876	500k. Green-winged teal ("Anas crecca")	12·50	12·00

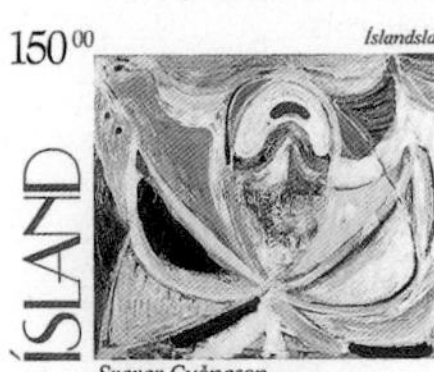
320 "Song of Iceland" (Svavar Gudnason)

1997. Paintings. Multicoloured.

877	150k. Type **320**	4·00	3·25
878	200k. "The Harbour" (Thorvaldur Skulason)	5·75	4·25

321 De Havilland D.H.89A Dragon Rapide

1997. Mail Planes. Multicoloured.

879	35k. Type **321**	1·10	80
880	35k. Stinson S.R. 8B Reliant seaplane	1·10	80
881	35k. Douglas DC-3 Dakota	1·10	80
882	35k. De Havilland D.H.C.6 Twin Otter	1·10	80

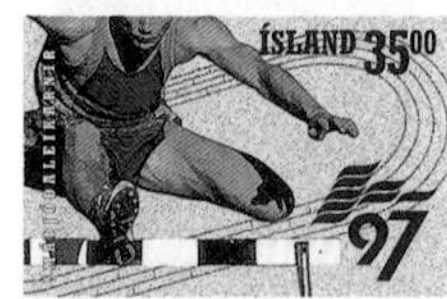
322 Hurdling

1997. 7th European Small States' Games. Multicoloured.

883	35k. Type **322**	1·10	90
884	45k. Sailing	1·50	1·20

323 "The Deacon of Myrka"

1997. Europa. Tales and Legends. Paintings by Asgrimur Jonsson. Multicoloured.

885	45k. Type **323**	1·50	1·30
886	65k. "Surtla at Blalandseyjar"	2·00	1·50

324 Printer's Colour Control and Pieces of Type

1997. Centenary of Formation of Icelandic Printers' Association (now part of Union of Icelandic Graphic Workers).

887	**324**	90k. multicoloured	2·75	2·20

325 Stefania Gudmundsdattir and Idno Theatre

1997. Centenary of Reykjavik Theatre.

888	**325**	100k. multicoloured	2·75	2·40

The actress is shown in the role of the Fairy in "New Year's Night" by Indridi Einarsson.

326 Western Islands Eight-oared Fishing Boat

1997. Stamp Day. Icelandic Boats. Sheet 110×76 mm containing T 326 and similar square designs. Each black, brown and chestnut.

MS889	35k. Type **326**; 65k. Engey six-oared sailing boat, 1912; 100k. Egil (Breidafjordur boat), 1904 (sold at 250k.)	6·25	6·00

327 Wise Men

1997. Christmas. Multicoloured.

890	35k. Type **327**	1·10	95
891	45k. Nativity	1·40	1·10

328 Mounted Mail Carrier

1997. Rural Post.

892	**328**	50k. multicoloured	1·40	1·20

329 Downhill Skiing

1998. Winter Olympic Games, Nagano, Japan. Multicoloured.

893	35k. Type **329**	1·00	85
894	45k. Cross-country skiing	1·50	1·20

330 Sailing Dinghies

1998. Nordic Countries' Postal Co-operation. Sailing. Multicoloured.

895	35k. Type **330**	1·00	85
896	45k. Yachts	1·50	1·10

331 Lumpsucker ("Cyclopterus lumpus")

1998. Fishes (1st series). Multicoloured.

897	5k. Type **331**	20	20
898	10k. Atlantic cod ("Gadus morhua")	25	20
899	60k. Skate ("Raja batis")	1·70	1·60
900	300k. Atlantic wolffish ("Anarhichas lupus")	8·00	7·50
MS901	100×68 mm. Nos. 897/900	10·00	9·75

See also Nos. 913/14, 972/3 and 983/4.

332 Children waving Flags

1998. Europa. National Festivals. National Day. Multicoloured.

902	45k. Type **332**	1·40	1·30
903	65k. Statue of President Jon Sigurdsson and flags	2·10	1·70

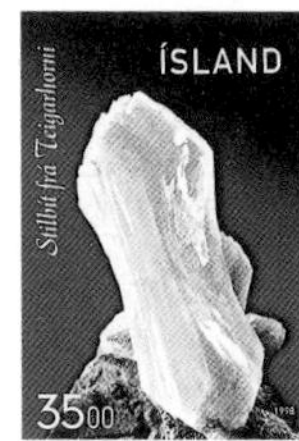

333 Scolecite

1998. Minerals (1st series). Multicoloured.

904	35k. Type **333**	1·00	90
905	45k. Stilbite	1·40	1·10

See also Nos. 933/4.

334 Hospital

1998. Centenary of Founding of Leprosy Hospital, Laugarnes.

906	**334**	70k. multicoloured	1·80	1·60

335 Anniversary Emblem

1998. 125th Anniv of First Iceland Stamps.

907	**335**	35k. multicoloured	1·10	90

336 Peat-cutter

1998. Stamp Day. Agricultural Tools. Sheet 110×76 mm containing T 336 and similar square designs.

MS908	35k. green, black and grey; 65k. ochre, black and grey; 100k. blue, black and grey (sold at 250k.)	7·00	6·75

DESIGNS: 65k. Mower; 100k. Grinder.

337 Cat and Houses (Thelma Ingolfsdottir)

1998. Christmas. Multicoloured.

909	35k. Type **337**	90	80
910	45k. Two angels (Telma Thrastardottir)	1·40	1·10

338 Writing and Hand forming Fist

1998. 50th Anniv of Universal Declaration of Human Rights.

911	**338**	50k. black, green and red	1·50	1·40

339 Leifs

1999. Birth Centenary of Jon Leifs (composer).

912	**339**	35k. multicoloured	1·10	95

1999. Fishes (2nd series). As T 331. Multicoloured.

913	35k. Plaice ("Pleuronectes platessa")	1·10	1·00
914	55k. Atlantic herring ("Clupea harengus")	1·60	1·30

340 Killer Whale ("Orcinus orca")

1999. Marine Mammals (1st series). Multicoloured.

915	35k. Type **340**	1·00	80
916	45k. Sperm whale ("Physeter macrocephalus")	1·40	1·10
917	65k. Blue whale ("Balaenoptera musculus")	1·80	1·60
918	85k. Common porpoise ("Phocoena phocoena")	2·30	2·00
MS919	100×80 mm. Nos. 915/19	6·25	6·00

See also Nos. 966/9 and 1000/3.

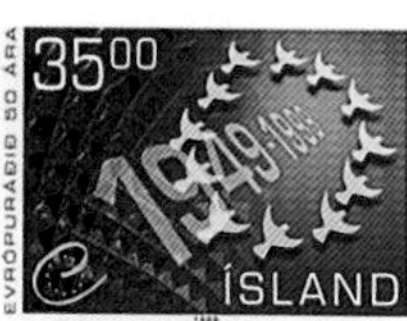

341 Arnold Jung's Steam Locomotive "Minor", 1892

1999. Transport. Multicoloured.

920	25k. Type **341**	90	85
921	50k. Type **341**	1·40	1·30
922	75k. "Sigurfari" (fishing cutter)	2·30	2·20

342 Dates and Doves

1999. 50th Anniv of Council of Europe.

923	**342**	35k. multicoloured	1·70	1·10

343 Larch Boletes ("Suillus grevillei")

1999. Fungi (1st series). Multicoloured.

924	35k. Type **343**	1·00	75
925	75k. Field mushrooms ("Agaricus campestris")	2·00	1·60

See also Nos. 954/5.

344 Skutustadagigar, Lake Myvatn

1999. Europa. Parks and Gardens. Multicoloured.

926	50k. Type **344**	1·40	1·10
927	75k. Arnarstapi Point	2·00	1·60

345 Wheat ("Land Graedsla")

1999. Nature Conservation. Multicoloured.

928	35k. Type **345**	1·00	90
929	35k. Rainbow and tree within sun ("Loft")	1·00	90
930	35k. Nest with eggs ("Vot Lendis")	1·00	90
931	35k. Tree stump ("Skog Raekt")	1·00	90
932	35k. Fish and birds ("Stlendur")	1·00	90

1999. Minerals (2nd series). As T 333. Mult.

933	40k. Calcite	1·20	1·00
934	50k. Heulandite	1·40	1·20

346 "Facescape" (Erro)

1999. Reykjavik, European Cultural City. Mult.

935	35k. Type **346**	1·10	1·00
936	50k. Cultural symbols	1·50	1·30

347 "Danish Sailing Ship off Drangey" (Carl Baagoe)

1999. Stamp Day. Sheet 110×65 mm.

MS937	**347** 200k. brown and black (sold at 250k.)	7·25	7·00

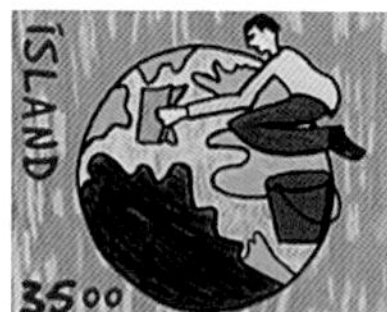

348 Man cleaning Globe (Jona Greta Gudmundsdottir)

1999. "Stampin' the Future". Winning Entries in Children's International Painting Competition.

938	**348**	35k. multicoloured	1·10	90

349 Goblin (Stiff-legs)

1999. Christmas. Yule Goblins. Multicoloured.

939	35k. Type **349**	1·10	95
940	35k. Leaping over rock (Gully-gawk)	1·10	95
941	35k. With arm raised (Stubby)	1·10	95
942	35k. Licking spoon (Spoon-licker)	1·10	95
943	35k. With hand in cooking pot (Pot-scraper)	1·10	95
944	35k. With finger in mouth (Bowl-licker)	1·10	95
945	35k. Opening door (Door-slammer)	1·10	95
946	35k. Drinking from ladle (Skyr-gobbler)	1·10	95
947	35k. Carrying sausages (Sausage-swiper)	1·10	95
948	35k. Looking through window (Window-peeper)	1·10	95
949	50k. With nose raised (Door-sniffer)	1·40	1·30
950	50k. With leg of meat (Meat-hook)	1·40	1·30
951	50k. With candles (Candle-beggar)	1·40	1·30

350 Embroidered Altar Frontal, Holar Cathedral

2000. Millenary of Christianity in Iceland. Mult.

952	40k. Type **350**	1·10	1·00
MS953	70×46 mm. 40k. Family singing hymns (29×39 mm)	1·00	95

351 Chanterelle (*Cantharellus cibarius*)

2000. Fungi (2nd series). Multicoloured.

954	40k. Type **351**	1·10	95
955	50k. Shaggy ink cap (*Coprinus comatus*)	1·40	1·10

352 Statue of Thorfinn Karlsefni (early settler) and Globe

2000. Millenary of Discovery of the Americas by Leif Eriksson. Multicoloured.

956	40k. Type **352**	1·00	95
957	50k. Viking longship under sail	1·40	1·30
958	75k. Longship on shore	1·80	1·70
959	90k. Leif Eriksson and globe	2·40	2·30
MS960	96×76 mm. Nos. 956/9	6·75	6·50

353 Quill and Profile

2000. New Millennium. Multicoloured.

961	40k. Type **353**	1·10	95
962	50k. Family tree, man and computer chip	1·40	1·10

354 Steam Roller

2000. Transport. Multicoloured.

963	50k. Type **354**	1·40	1·30
964	75k. Fire engine	2·00	1·90

355 "Building Europe"

2000. Europa.

965	**355** 50k. multicoloured	1·70	1·60

2000. Marine Mammals (2nd series). As T 340. Mult.

966	5k. Bottlenose whale (*Hyperoodon ampullatus*)	25	20
967	40k. Atlantic white-sided dolphin (*Lagenorhynchus actus*)	90	95
968	50k. Humpback whale (*Megaptera novaeangliae*)	1·40	1·30
969	75k. Minke whale (*Balaenoptera acutorostrata*)	2·00	1·90

356 Pansy (*Violea x wittrockiana*)

2000. Summer Flowers (1st series). Multicoloured.

970	40k. Type **356**	1·10	95
971	50k. Petunia (*Petunia x hybrida*)	1·30	1·10

See also Nos. 986/7.

2000. Fishes (3rd series). As T 331. Multicoloured.

972	10k. Haddock (*Melanogrammus aeglefinus*)	25	20
973	250k. Capelin (*Mallotus villosus*)	7·25	7·00

357 Dark Marbled Carpet (*Chioroclysta citrata*)

2000. Butterflies. Multicoloured.

974	40k. Type **357**	1·10	95
975	50k. Antler (*Cerapteryx graminis*)	1·40	1·30

358 "Icelandic settlers on the Shore of Lake Winnipeg" (Arni Sigurdsson)

2000. Stamp Day. Sheet 88×73 mm.

MS976	**358** 200k. multicoloured (sold at 250k.)	6·50	6·25

359 Viking Settler's House

2000. Early Dwellings. Multicoloured.

977	45k. Type **359**	1·00	95
978	75k. Viking turf houses, Stong Thjorsardal	1·70	1·60

360 Leppaludi

2000. Christmas. Ogres. Multicoloured.

979	40k. Type **360**	90	90
980	50k. Gryla	1·20	1·10
MS981	105×75 mm. As Nos. 979/80, but 21×36 mm	2·50	2·40

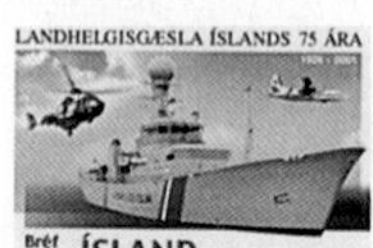

361 Super Puma Helicopter, Fokker 27 Airplane and *Tyr* (ship)

2001. 75th Anniv of Coast Guard Service in Iceland.

982	**361** 20k. multicoloured	90	85

2001. Fishes. As T 331. Multicoloured.

983	55k. Greenland halibut (*Reinhardtius hippogolossides*)	1·20	1·20
984	80k. Saithe (*Pollachius virens*)	1·80	1·70

362 Man's Face, Tents and Emblem

2001. 50th Anniv of United Nations Commissioner for Refugees.

985	**362** 50k. black and brown	1·10	1·10

363 Marigold (*Calendula officinalis*)

2001. Summer Flowers. Multicoloured.

986	55k. Type **363**	1·30	1·20
987	65k. Livingstone daisy (*Dorotheanthus bellidformis*)	1·50	1·40

364 Dog

2001. Icelandic Sheepdogs. Multicoloured.

988	40k. Type **364**	90	85
989	80k. Black and white dog	1·80	1·70

365 Olsen-Jonasson Ognin

2001. Airplanes. Multicoloured.

990	55k. Type **365**	1·20	1·20
991	80k. Klemm KL-25E	1·80	1·70

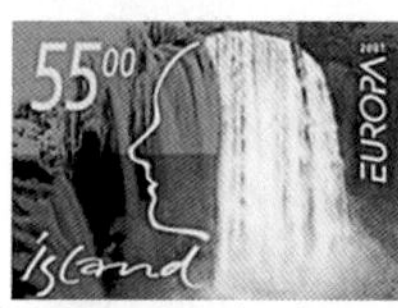

366 Woman's Head and Waterfall

2001. Europa. Water Resources. Multicoloured.

992	55k. Type **366**	1·30	1·20
993	80k. Cupped hands and wave	1·80	1·70

367 Walking

2001. Horses. Multicoloured.

994	40k. Type **367**	90	85
995	50k. Running walk	1·10	1·10
996	55k. Trotting	1·20	1·20
997	60k. Pacing	1·40	1·30
998	80k. Cantering	1·80	1·70

2001. Domestic Letter Rate. No. 915 optd Bref 50g.

999	(35k.) multicoloured	1·10	1·10

2001. Marine Mammals (3rd series). As T 340. Multicoloured.

1000	5k. Large-beaked dolphin (*Lagenorhynchus albirostris*)	25	20
1001	40k. Fin whale (*Balaenoptera physalus*)	90	85
1002	80k. Sei whale (*Balaenoptera borealis*)	1·80	1·70
1003	100k. Long-finned pilot whale (*Globicephala melas*)	2·30	2·20

369 Grimsey

2001. Islands (1st series). Multicoloured.

1004	40k. Type **369**	90	85
1005	55k. Papey	1·20	1·10

See also Nos. 1031/2, 1061/2 and 1094/5.

370 Esja Mountain

2001. Stamp Day. Sheet 105×48 mm.

MS1006	**370** 250k. multicoloured	6·50	6·25

371 Brautarholt Church, Kjalarnes

2001. Christmas. Multicoloured.

1007	(42k.) Type **371**	1·10	1·10
1008	55k Viomyri Church, Skagafjorour	1·20	1·20

372 Northern Wheatear (*Oenanthe oenanthe*)

2001. Birds (1st series). Multicoloured.

1009	42k. Type **372**	90	85
1010	250k. Ringed plover (*Charadrius hiaticula*)	6·00	5·75

See also Nos. 1036/7,1055/6 and 1092/3.

373 Brown Birch Bolete (*Leccinum scabrum*)

2002. Fungi. Multicoloured. (a) Inscr "Bref 20g".

1011	(42k.) Type **373**	90	85

(b) With face value.

1012	85k. Hedgehog fungus (*Hydnum repandum*)	1·80	1·70

No. 1011 was for use on domestic mail up to 20 grammes.

374 Stanley and 2 h.p. Mollerup Engine

2002. Centenary of First Motorboat in Iceland.

1013	**374** 60k. multicoloured	1·30	1·20

375 Mount Snæfell

2002. International Year of the Mountain. Inscr "Bref 20g".

1014	**375** (42k.) multicoloured	1·50	1·50

No. 1014 was for use on domestic mail up to 20 grammes.

376 Laxness

2002. Birth Centenary of Halldor Laxness (writer and Nobel Prize winner).

1015	**376** 100k. multicoloured	2·10	2·00
MS1016	75×45 mm. No. 1015	2·10	2·00

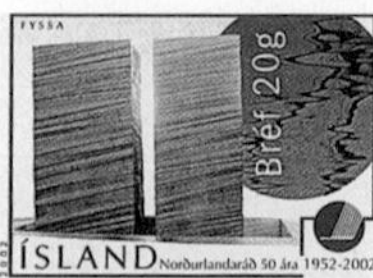

377 "Waterfall" (sculpture, Ruri) and Emblem

2002. Nordic Countries' Postal Co-operation. Modern Art. Multicoloured. (a) Inscr "Bref 20g".

1017	(42k.) Type **377** (50th anniv of Nordic Council)	90	85

(b) With face value.

1018	60k. "Tension" (sculpture, Hafsteinn Austmann) and emblem	1·40	1·30

No. 1017 was for use on domestic mail up to 20 grammes.

378 Grotta

2002. Lighthouses. Multicoloured.

1019	60k. Type **378**	1·40	1·30
1020	85k. Kogur	1·90	1·80

379 House and Sesselja Sigmundsdottir

2002. Birth Centenary of Sesselja H. Sigmundsdottir (mental health pioneer and environmentalist).

1021	**379**	45k. multicoloured	1·00	95

380 Trapeze Artists and Clown

2002. Europa. Circus. Multicoloured.

1022	60k. Type **380**	1·40	1·30
1023	85k. Marionette's head and lion leaping through flaming hoop	1·80	1·70

381 Lobelia (*Lobelia erinus*)

2002. Summer Flowers. Multicoloured.

1024	10k. Type **381**	25	20
1025	200k. Cornflower (*Centaurea cyanus*)	4·25	4·00

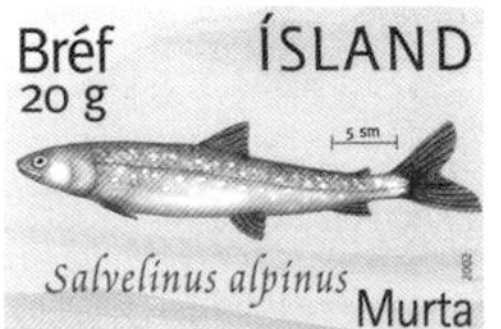

382 Arctic Charr (*Salvelinus alpinus*)

2002. Fish from Lake Thingvallavatn. Multicoloured. (a) Inscr "Bref 20g".

1026	(45k.) Type **382**	1·10	1·00

(b) Inscr "Bréf 50g".

1027	(55k.) Brown trout (*Salmo trutta*) (vert)	1·40	1·40

(c) With face value.

1028	60k. Arctic charr (*Salvelinus alpinus*)	1·50	1·40
1029	90k. Arctic charr (*Salvelinus alpinus*)	2·10	2·00
1030	200k. Arctic charr (*Salvelinus alpinus*)	4·75	4·75

No. 1026 was for use on domestic mail up to 20 grammes.

No. 1027 was for use on domestic mail up to 50 grammes.

2002. Islands (2nd series). As T 369. Multicoloured.

1031	45k. Vigur	1·00	95
1032	55k. Flatey	1·20	1·10

383 South Street, Reykjavik, and Mount Keilir (volcano)

2002. Stamp Day. Sheet 85×55 mm.

MS1033 **383**	250k. multicoloured	6·25	6·00

384 Bauble, Flags and Gift

2002. Christmas. Multicoloured.

1034	45k. Type **384**	1·00	95
1035	60k. Gifts	1·30	1·20

385 Common Redshank (*Tringa totanus*)

2002. Birds (2nd series). Multicoloured.

1036	50k. Type **385**	1·10	1·00
1037	85k. Grey phalarope (*Phalaropus fulicarius*)	1·80	1·70

386 Modern Policemen

2003. Bicentenary of Icelandic Police Force. Multicoloured.

1038	45k. Type **386**	1·00	95
1039	55k. 1803 policeman	1·20	1·10

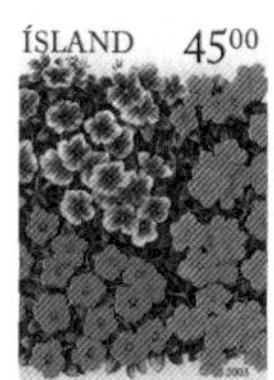

387 Annual Phlox (*Phlox drummondii*)

2003. Summer Flowers. Multicoloured.

1040	45k. Type **387**	1·00	95
1041	60k. Treasure flower (*Gazania x hybrida*)	1·30	1·20

388 Bull and Audhumla (mythological cow)

2003. Icelandic Cattle. Multicoloured.

1042	45k. Type **388**	1·00	95
1043	85k. Red-mottled cow	1·90	1·80

389 Map, Crow and Sailing Ship

2003. Nordia 2003 International Stamp Exhibition, Rekjavik. Sheet 86×76 mm.

MS1044 **389**	250k. multicoloured	6·50	6·25

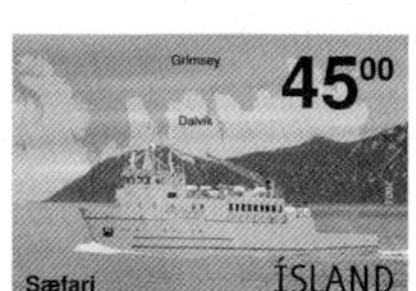

390 *Saefari*

2003. Ferries. Multicoloured.

1045	45k. Type **390**	1·00	95
1046	45k. *Saevar*	1·00	95
1047	60k. *Herjolfur*	1·40	1·30
1048	60k. *Baldur*	1·40	1·30

391 Church

2003. Centenary of Free Church, Reykjavik.

1049	**391**	200k. multicoloured	4·25	4·00

392 Hen and Cockerel

2003. Icelandic Poultry.

1050	**392**	45k. multicoloured	1·00	95

393 Posters

2003. Europa. Poster Art. Multicoloured.

1051	60k. Type **393**	1·40	1·30
1052	85k. Posters (different)	1·80	1·70

394 Friendship (Orn Agustsson)

2006. Winning Entry in Children's Stamp Design Competition.

1053	**394**	45k. multicoloured	1·00	95

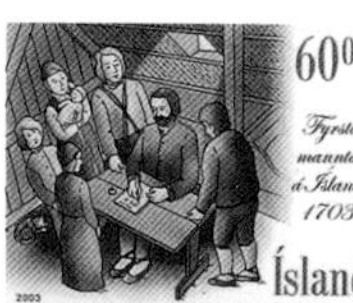

395 District Officer and Family

2003. 300th Anniv of First Census.

1054	**395**	60k. multicoloured	1·30	1·20

2003. Birds (3rd series). As T 385. Multicoloured.

1055	70k. Meadow pipit (*Anthus pratensis*)	1·60	1·50
1056	250k. Whimbrel (*Numenius phaeopus*)	5·25	5·00

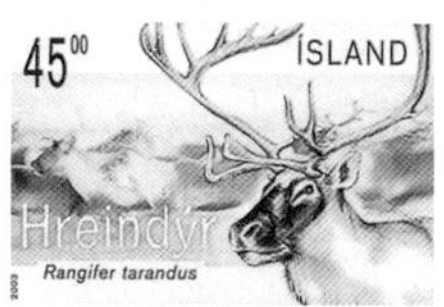

396 Reindeer (*Rangifer tarandus*)

2003

1057	**396**	45k. multicoloured	1·00	95

397 Barrack converted to House

2003. Stamp Day. Sheet 120×58 mm.

MS1058 **397**	250k. multicoloured	5·25	5·25

398 Girl hanging Baubles on Tree

2003. Christmas. Multicoloured.

1059	45k. Type **398**	1·00	95
1060	60k. Boy lighting candles	1·30	1·20

2003. Islands (3rd series). As T 369.

1061	85k. Heimaey	1·80	1·70
1062	200k. Hrisey	4·25	4·00

399 Marigolds (*Tagetes patula*)

2004. Summer Flowers. Multicoloured.

1063	50k. Type **399**	1·30	1·00
1064	55k. Begonias (*begonia x tuberhybrida*)	1·50	1·20

400 Hannes Hafstein (first minister)

2004. Centenary of Icelandic Home Rule. Multicoloured.

1065	150k. Type **400**	4·00	3·75
MS1066	79×50 mm. No. 1065	4·00	3·75

401 *Coot* (trawler)

2004

1067	**401**	50k. blue and black	1·30	1·10

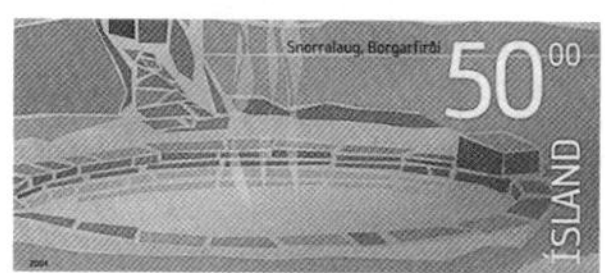

402 Snorralaug Thermal Pool

2004. Geo-thermal Energy. Multicoloured.

1068	50k. Type **402**	1·40	1·20
1069	55k. Vent, dome and steam (30×48 mm)	1·60	1·40
1070	60k. Pipeline	2·00	1·80
1071	90k. Turbine	3·00	2·75
1072	250k. Map of Iceland, mid Atlantic ridge and clouds (30×48 mm)	6·25	5·75

403 Odin

2004. Norse Mythology. Sheet 105×70 mm containing T 403 and similar horiz design (1st issue). Multicoloured.

MS1073 50k. Type **403**; 60k. Sleipnir (Odin's horse)	3·50	3·25

Stamps of a similar theme were issued by Aland Islands, Denmark, Faroe Islands, Finland, Greenland, Norway and Sweden.

See also No. **MS**1137.

404 Ford Fairlane Victoria, 1956

2004. Cars. Multicoloured.

1074	60k. Type **404**	2·00	1·80
1075	60k. Pobeta, 1954	2·00	1·80
1076	85k. Chevrolet Bel Air, 1955	2·75	2·50
1077	85k. Volkswagen, 1952	2·75	2·50

405 Woman reaching into Barrel of Fish

2004. Centenary of Herring Production.

1078	**405** 65k. multicoloured	1·60	1·40

406 Cyclists

2004. Europa. Holidays. Multicoloured.

1079	65k. Type **406**	1·60	1·40
1080	90k. Four-wheel drive vehicles in snow	2·40	2·20

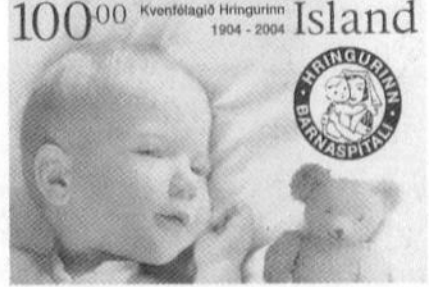

407 Baby and Emblem

2004. Centenary of Hringurinn (women's charitable organization).

1081	**407** 100k. multicoloured	2·50	2·30

408 Hand holding Light Bulb

2004. Centenary of Electrification.

1082	**408** 50k. multicoloured	1·30	1·10

409 Grisette (*Amanita vaginata*)

2004. Fungi. Multicoloured.

1083	50k. Type **409**	1·40	1·20
1084	60k. *Camarophyllus pratensis*	1·60	1·40

410 Cudell (1901)

2004. Centenary of First Motor Car in Iceland.

1085	**410** 100k. black	2·50	2·30

411 Ground Beetle (*Nebria gyllenhali*)

2004. Insects. Multicoloured.

1086	50k. Type **411**	1·60	1·40
1087	70k. White-tailed bumble bee (*Bombus lucorum*)	1·80	1·60

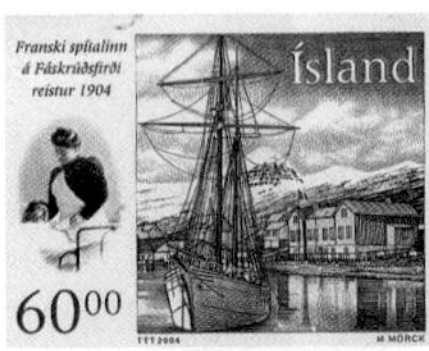

412 Ship and Hospital Building

2004. Centenary of French Hospital, Faskrudsfirdi.

1088	**412** 60k. multicoloured	1·50	1·30

413 Rock, Hvita River, Bruarhlod

2004. Stamp Day. Sheet 85×55 mm.

MS1089	250k. multicoloured	6·50	6·25

414 Ptarmigan in Winter Plumage

2004. Christmas. Multicoloured.

1090	45k. Type **414**	1·30	1·10
1091	65k. Reindeer	1·70	1·50

2004. Birds (4th series). As T 385. Multicoloured.

1092	55k. Sandpiper (*Caladris maritime*)	1·50	1·30
1093	75k. Dunlin (*Caladris alpine*)	2·00	1·80

2005. Islands (4th series). As T 369.

1094	5k. Videy	25	20
1095	90k. Flatey	2·30	2·20

415 Forest

2005. Centenary of Forestation Programme.

1096	**415** 45k. multicoloured	1·30	1·10

416 Brooch (11th-century)

2005. 60th Anniv of Foundation, and Re-opening (2004) of National Museum. Sheet 105×75 mm containing T 416 and similar vert designs. Multicoloured.

MS1097	100k. Type **416**; 150k. Thor (10th-century statue)	7·00	6·75

417 Field Mouse (*Apodemus sylvaticus*)

2005. Mice. Multicoloured.

1098	45k. Type **417**	1·50	1·30
1099	125k. House mouse (*Mus musculus*)	3·50	3·25

418 Rose

2005. Greetings Stamps. Flowers. Multicoloured.

1100	50k. Type **418**	1·60	1·40
1101	50k. Gerbera	1·60	1·40
1102	50k. Zantedeschia	1·60	1·40
1103	70k. Tulip	2·20	2·00

419 *Araneus diadematus*

2005. Insect and Spider. Multicoloured.

1104	50k. Type **419**	1·40	1·20
1105	70k. *Musca domestica*	2·10	1·90

420 Vorour PH 4

2005. Old Fishing Boats. Multicoloured.

1106	70k. Type **420**	2·10	1·90
1107	70k. *Karl VE 47*	2·10	1·90
1108	95k. *Sædis IS 67*	2·50	2·30
1109	95k. *Guobjorg NK 74*	2·50	2·30

421 Bridge over Sogid River, Grimsnes

2005. Bridges.

1110	**421** 50k. violet, silver and black	1·60	1·40
1111	- 95k. ultramarine, silver and black	3·00	2·75
1112	- 165k. blue, silver and black	5·00	4·75

DESIGNS: 50k. Type **421**; 95k. Over Lagarfljot river; 165k. Over Jokulsa river, Oxarfjordur.

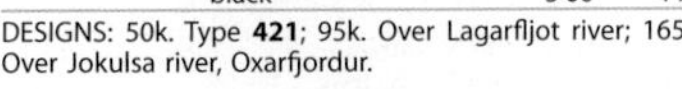

422 Fish Fillets, Cutlery, Smoked Fish and Water

2005. Europa. Gastronomy. Multicoloured.

1113	70k. Type **422**	1·90	1·60
1114	90k. Cutlery, chillies and fish fillets, smoked fish and flowers	2·50	2·30

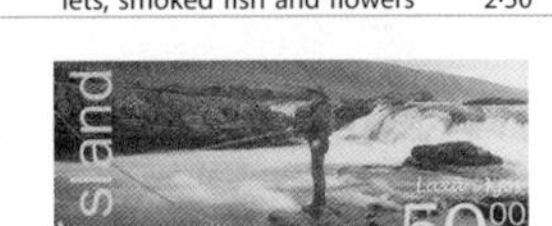

423 Fisherman and Red Frances Fly

2005. Salmon Fishing. Multicoloured.

1115	50k. Type **423**	1·50	1·30
1116	60k. Fishing from boat and Laxa Blue fly (vert)	1·70	1·50

424 *Vaccinium uliginosum*

2005. Berries. Multicoloured.

1117	65k. Type **424**	1·80	1·70
1118	90k. *Fragaria vesca*	2·30	2·10

425 Motorcyclist

2005. Centenary of First Motorcycle.

1119	**425** 50k. multicoloured	1·50	1·30

426 Couple dancing

2005. Centenary of Commercial College.

1120	**426** 70k. multicoloured	1·90	1·70

427 Reykjavik

2005. Stamp Day. Sheet 105×55 mm.

MS1121	**427** 200k. multicoloured	6·00	5·75

428 Apple

2005. Christmas.

1122	**428** 50k. vermilion and gold	1·50	1·30
1123	- 70k. green and gold	1·90	1·70

DESIGNS: 50k. Type **428**; 70k. Pine tree.

Nos. 1122/3 were impregnated with the scent of apples and pine, respectively, which was released when rubbed.

429 Greylag (*Anser anser*)

2005. Birds. Multicoloured.

1124	60k. Type **429**	1·80	1·60
1125	105k. Starling (*Sturnus vulgaris*)	2·75	2·50

430 *Dryas octopetala*

2006. National Flower.
1126 **430** 50k. multicoloured 1·50 1·30

431 Record Label, Cadillac, Guitar and Dancers

2006. 50th Anniv of Rock and Roll Music in Iceland.
1127 **431** 60k. multicoloured 1·80 1·60

432 Hands, Dove and Barbed Wire

2006. 50th Anniv of First Refugees.
1128 **432** 70k. multicoloured 2·10 1·90

433 1969 14k.50 Europa Stamp (As Type **117**)

2006. 50th Anniv of Europa Stamps. Sheet 80×49 mm containing T 433 and similar horiz design. Multicoloured.
MS1129 150k.×2, Type **433**; 1968 9k.50 Europa stamp (As Type **111**) 8·25 8·00

434 Camera, Programme and First Cinema

2006. Centenary of Cinema in Iceland. Mult.
1130 50k. Type **434** 2·50 2·30
1131 95k. Faces, projector and tickets 3·00 2·75
1132 160k. Helmeted warrior, clapperboard, popcorn and cameraman 4·25 4·00

435 Landrover (1951)

2006. First Four-wheel Drive Vehicles in Iceland.
1133 70k. Type **435** 1·90 1·90
1134 70k. Willys jeep (1946) 1·90 1·90
1135 90k. Austin Gypsy (1965) 2·75 2·50
1136 90k. Gaz-69 (1955) 2·75 2·50

436 "Mythical Beings" (Johann Briem)

2004. Norse Mythology (2nd issue). Sheet 105×70 mm.
MS1137 **436** 50k. multicoloured 2·50 2·30

Stamps of a similar theme were issued by Aland Islands, Denmark, Faröe Islands, Greenland, Finland, Norway and Sweden.

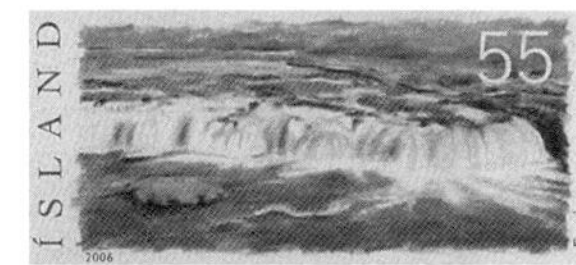

437 Faxi

2006. Waterfalls. Multicoloured.
1138 55k. Type **437** 1·50 1·30
1139 65k. Oxararfoss (30×48 mm) 1·70 1·50
1140 75k. Glymur (30×48 mm) 1·90 1·70
1141 95k. Hjalparfoss 2·75 2·50
1142 220k. Skeifarfoss 6·00 5·75

438 Enclosed Heart

2006. Europa. Integration. Ordinary or self-adhesive gum.
1143 **438** 75k. scarlet and black 1·90 1·70
1144 - 95k. blue and black (horiz) 2·75 2·50

DESIGNS: No. 1143, Type **438**; 1144, Arrows, one joining from right.

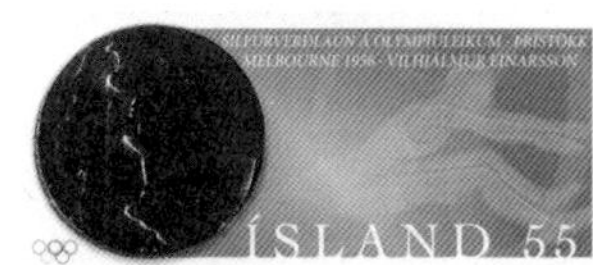

439 Medal and Athlete

2006. 50th Anniv of First Icelandic Olympic Gold Medal.
1147 **439** 55k. multicoloured 1·40 1·30

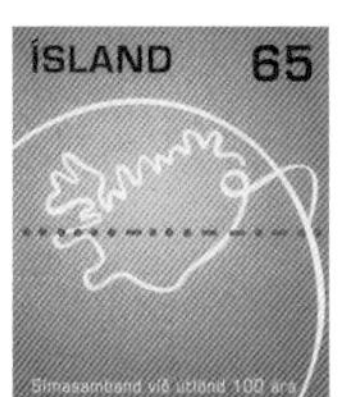

440 Iceland outlined in Cable

2006. Centenary of Telephony in Iceland.
1148 **440** 65k. multicoloured 1·60 1·40

441 *Empetrum nigrum*

2006. Berries. Multicoloured.
1149 75k. Type **441** 1·80 1·60
1150 130k. *Rubus saxatilis* 3·25 3·00

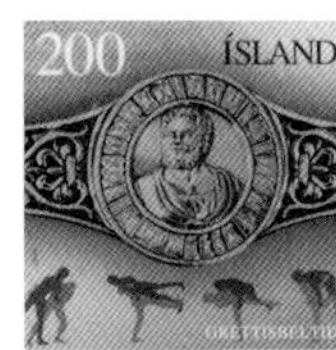

442 Girdle of Grettir (trophy)

2006. Centenary of Wrestling (Glima) Tournament. Sheet 80×47 mm.
MS1151 **442** 200k. multicoloured 5·00 4·75

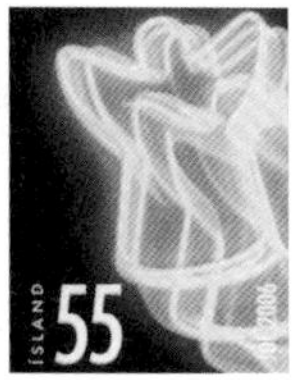

443 Angel

2006. Christmas. Multicoloured.
1152 55k. Type **443** 1·50 1·30
1153 75k. Heart 1·80 1·60

No. 1152 also comes self-adhesive.

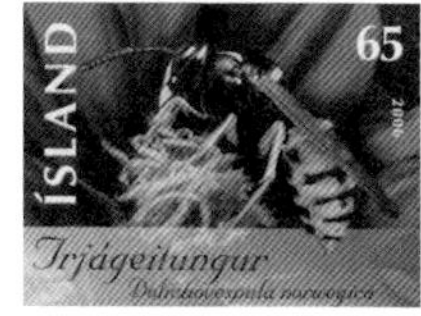

444 *Dolchiovespula norwegica*

2006. Insects. Multicoloured.
1155 65k. Type **444** 1·70 1·50
1156 110k. *Coccinella undecim-punctata* 2·75 2·50

445 *Xerocomus subtomentosus*

2006. Fungi. Multicoloured.
1157 70k. Type **445** 1·80 1·60
1158 90k. *Kuehneromyces mutablis* 2·50 2·30

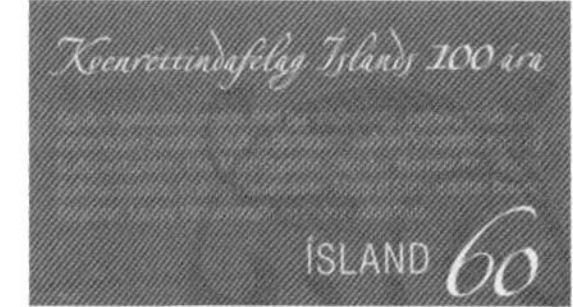

446 Emblem

2007. Centenary of Icelandic Women's Society.
1159 **446** 60k. multicoloured 1·60 1·40

447 *Jon foseti*

2007. Centenary of Jon foseti (first Icelandic deep sea trawler).
1160 **447** 65k. multicoloured 1·70 1·50

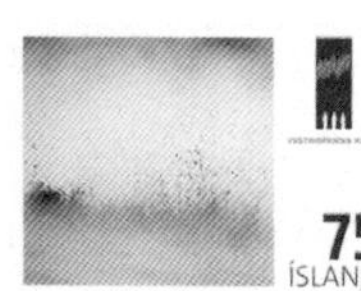

448 Eruption

2007. Tenth Anniv of West Nordic Council. Geothermal Power.
1161 **448** 75k. multicoloured 1·90 1·70

449 Volcano erupting

2007. International Polar Year. Sheet 105×70 mm containing T 449 and similar square design. Multicoloured.
MS1162 75k. Type **449**; 95k. Taking radio echo soundings 3·75 3·50

450 Leaves and Catkins

2007. Centenary of Forestry and Soil Conservation Act. Multicoloured.
1163 10k. Type **450** 20 10
1164 60k. Red leaves 1·60 1·40

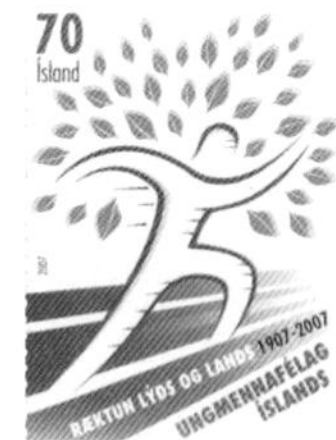

451 Figure as Tree

2007. Centenary of National Youth Organization.
1165 **451** 70k. multicoloured 1·80 1·60

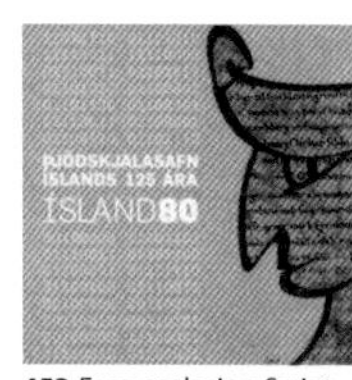

452 Face enclosing Script

2007. 125th Anniv of National Archives.
1166 **452** 80k. multicoloured 2·00 1·80

453 *Hamrafell*

2007. Cargo Ships. Multicoloured.
1167 80k. Type **453** 2·00 1·80
1168 80k. *Trollafoss* 2·00 1·80
1169 105k. *Langjokull* 2·50 2·30
1170 105k. *Akranes* 2·50 2·30

454 Breioamerkurjokull

2007. Glaciers. Multicoloured.
1171 5k. Type **453** 10 10
1172 60k. Langjokull (vert) 1·60 1·40
1173 80k. Hofsjokull 2·00 1·80
1174 115k. Snaefellsjokull 3·00 2·75
1175 300k. Oraefajokull (70×30 mm) 7·25 7·00

455 Dunes and Grasses

2007. Centenary of Soil Conservation. (a) No Value expressed. Self-adhesive.
1176 **455** (60k.) multicoloured 1·60 1·40

(b) Ordinary gum.
1177 (60k.) multicoloured 1·60 1·40

456 Fleur de Lys

2007. Europa. Centenary of Scouting. Multicoloured. Ordinary or self-adhesive gum.

1178	80k. Type **456**	2·00	1·80
1179	105k. Clover leaf	2·75	2·50

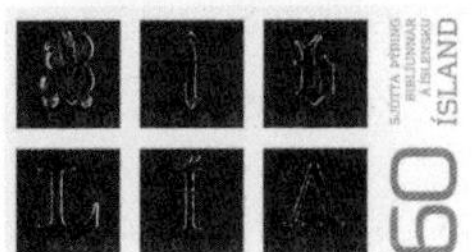

457 'BibLLA' and Dates of Translations

2007. New Translation of the Bible into Icelandic.

1182	**457** 60k. brown and gold	1·50	1·30

458 *Vaccinium myrtillus*

2007. Berries. Multicoloured.

1183	120k. Type **458**	3·00	2·75
1184	145k. *Cornus suecica*	3·25	3·00

459 King Frederick VIII

2007. Centenary of King Frederick VIII's visit to Iceland. Sheet 80×56 mm.

MS1185	250k. brown and gold	6·50	6·25

460 Selfoss Waterfall, Jokulsarglijufur

2007. SEPAC (small European mail services) Multicoloured.

1186	80k. Type **460**	2·10	1·90
1187	105k. Selfoss Waterfall, Jokulsarglijufur (right) (30×27 mm)	3·00	2·75

461 Jonas Hallgrimsson

2007. Birth Centenary of Jonas Hallgrimsson (poet).

1188	**461** 65k. brown	1·80	1·60

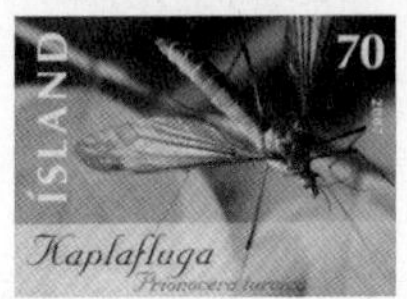

462 *Prionocera turcica* (cranefly)

2007. Insects. Multicoloured.

1189	70k. Type **462**	1·90	1·70
1190	190k. *Euceraphis punctipennis* (birch aphid)	5·00	4·75

463 Hospital Facade

2007. Centenary of Psychiatric Hospital, Kleppur.

1191	**463** 80k. multicoloured	2·10	1·90

464 Leaf Bread

2007. Christmas. Multicoloured. Self-adhesive.

1192	60k. Type **464**	1·60	1·40
1193	80k. Leaf bread (different)	2·10	1·90

465 Older Couple

2008. Greetings Stamps. Multicoloured.

1194	65k. Type **465**	1·90	1·70
1195	65k. Mother and child	1·90	1·70
1196	75k. Adolescents	2·10	1·90
1197	85k. Couple about to kiss	2·00	2·00

466 Early Students

2008. Centenary of University of Education.

1198	**466** 85k. multicoloured	2·10	1·90

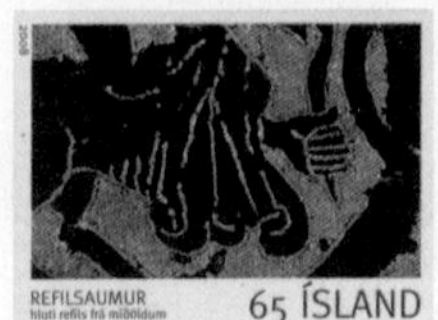

467 'REFILSAUMUR'

2008. Embroidery. Multicoloured.

1199	65k. Type **467**	1·90	1·70
1200	85k. AUGNSAUMUR	2·10	1·90
1201	110k. KROSSSAUMUR	3·00	2·75

468 Ferguson Tractor TF20

2008. Vintage Agricultural Tools. Multicoloured.

1202	85k. Type **468**	2·10	1·90
1203	85k. IHC Bulldozer	2·10	1·90
1204	110k. Scottish plough (introduced by Torfi Bjarnason's agricultural school)	3·00	2·75
1205	110k. Landbaumotor Lanz (turf killer) (used for leveling hay fields)	1·90	2·75

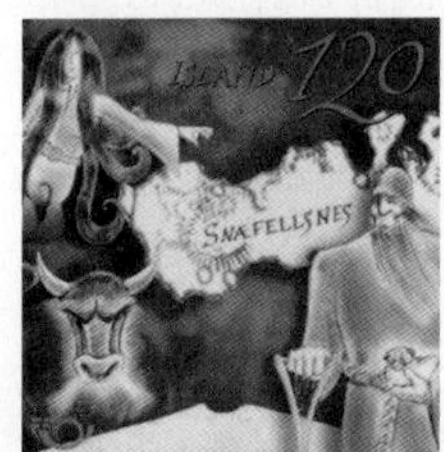

469 Snaefellsnes (home of 9th-century sorcerer Bardur Snaefellsas)

2008. Norse Mythology. Mythical Places. Sheet 105×70 mm.

MS1206	**469** 20k. multicoloured	3·00	2·75

Stamps of a similar theme were issued by Aland Islands, Denmark, Faroe Islands, Greenland, Finland, Norway and Sweden.

470 Proprio Foot (intelligent prosthetic foot)

2008. Icelandic Industrial Design. Multicoloured.

1207	65k. Type **470**	1·70	1·60
1208	120k. Marel *OptiCut* (meat slicer)	2·75	2·50
1209	155k. *Wish* (fly fishing reel)	3·25	3·00
1210	200k. *Gavia* (autonomous underwater vehicle)	4·25	4·00

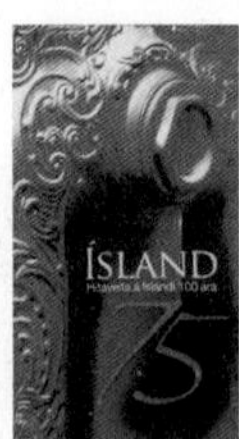

471 Radiator

2008. Centenary of Geothermal Space Heating.

1211	**471** 75k. multicoloured	1·90	1·80

472 Girl skipping

2008. My Stamp

1212	**472** 50g. (75k.) multicoloured	1·80	1·70

473 Buildings

2008. Centenary of HafnarfJorour.

1213	**473** 80k. multicoloured	1·90	1·80

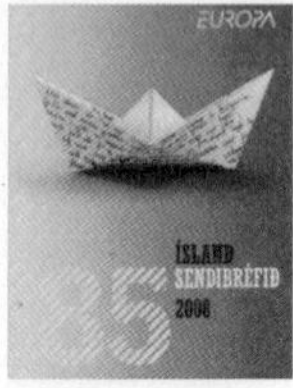

474 Letter as Paper Boat

2008. Europa. The Letter. Multicoloured. Ordinary or self-adhesve gum.

1214	85k. Type **474**	2·00	1·90
1215	110k. Letter as paper airplane	2·50	2·25

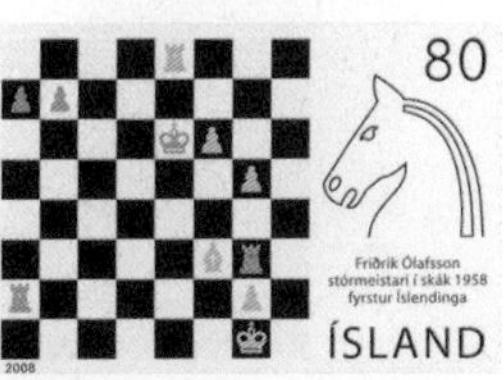

475 Winning Play

2008. Friorik Olafsson—1958 Chess Grandmaster.

1218	**475** 80k. multicoloured	1·80	1·70

476 *por* (coast guard vessel)

2008. 50th Anniv of Extension of Fishery Zone.

1219	**476** 90k. multicoloured	2·00	1·90

477 Algae, Map and Lake Myvatn

2008. Endangered Species. Aegagropila linnaei (lake ball algae).

1220	**477** 140k. multicoloured	3·00	2·75

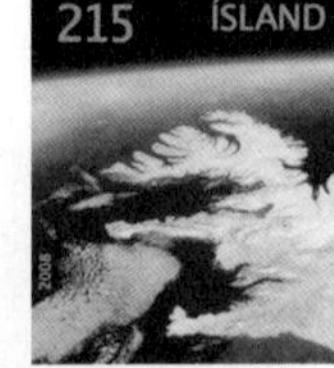

478 Satellite Image of Iceland

2008. International Year of Planet Earth. Sheet 100×55 mm.

MS1221	**478** 215k. multicoloured	4·75	4·50

479 Peace Tower

2008. First Anniv of Peace Tower (John Lennon memorial), Videy.

1222	**479** 120k. multicoloured	2·50	2·25

480 Yule Goblin Stiff-Legs

2008. Christmas. Children's Design a Stamp Competition, Winning Designs by Heioar Jokull Hafsteinsson and Konrao K. Pormarr. Multicoloured. Self adhesive.

1223	70k. Type **480**	1·20	1·10
1224	90k. Christmas Cat	1·60	1·50

481 Snow-covered Trees

2008. Centenary of Forestry in Vaglaskogur.

1225	**481** 400k. multicoloured	7·00	6·75

2009. Islands (5th series). As T 369.

1226	75k. Hjorsey	1·20	1·10
1227	90k. Maimey	1·60	1·50

482 *Psychodidae* (Moth Fly)

2009. Insects. Multicoloured.

1228	80k. Type **482**	1·50	1·40
1229	120k. *Gnaphosa lapponum* (field spider)	2·50	2·40

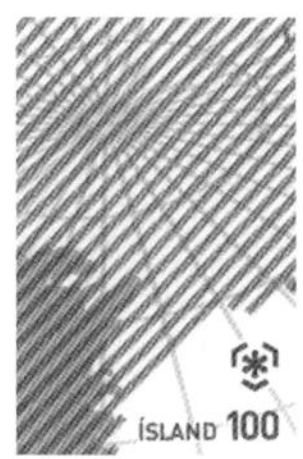

483 Polar Ice

2009. Preserve Polar Regions and Glaciers. Sheet 80×120 mm containing T 483 and similar vert design. Multicoloured.

MS1230	100k. Type **483**; 130k. Iceland	4·50	4·25

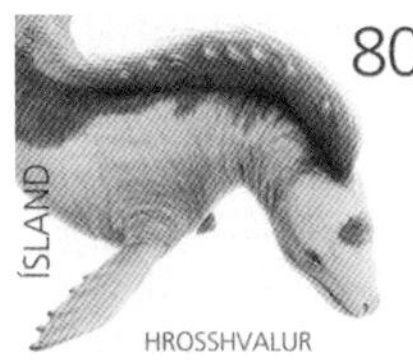

484 Hrosshvalur

2009. Legendary Creatures from Folktales. Multicoloured.

1231	80k. Type **484**	2·00	1·90
1232	80k. Skoffin	2·00	1·90
1233	80k. Mushveli	2·00	1·90
1234	80k. Rauokembingur	2·00	1·90
1235	80k. Selamooir	2·00	1·90
1236	80k. Ofuguggi	2·00	1·90
1237	80k. Saeneyti	2·00	1·90
1238	80k. Skeljaskrimsli	2·00	1·90
1239	80k. Uroarkottur	2·00	1·90
1240	80k. Fjorulalli	2·00	1·90

485 Avro 504K

2009. Civil Aviation. Multicoloured.

1241	90k. Type **485**	2·20	2·10
1242	90k. Waco ZKS-7	2·20	2·10
1243	120k. Boeing 757	3·50	3·25
1244	120k. Fokker 50	3·50	3·25

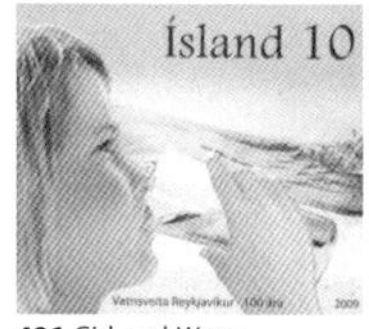

486 Girl and Water

2009. Centenary of Water Works, Reykjavik.

1245	**486**	10k. multicoloured	1·00	85

487 Athletes

2009. Centenary of Iceland Youth Organization (UMFI) National Sports Tournaments.

1246	**487**	105k. multicoloured	2·40	2·20

488

2009. Europa. Astronomy. Multicoloured. (a) Ordinary or self-adhesive gum.

1247	105k. Type **488**	2·40	2·20
1248	140k. Observatory	3·75	3·25

489 Arch and Gateway

2009. Centenary of Skruour Garden, Dyrafjorour.

1251	**489**	140k. multicoloured	3·75	3·25

490 *Fratercula arctica* (puffin)

2009. Nordia 2009–Nordic Philatelic Exhibition, Reykjavik. Sheet 100×60 mm.

MS1252	**490**	190k. multicoloured	4·75	4·75

491 Gathering Sheep from the Hills

2009. Sheep Gathering. Multicoloured.

1253	95k. Type **491**	1·80	1·60
1254	160k. Collection pens (vert)	2·20	2·00

492 Skaftafell

2009. SEPAC (small european mail services). Multicoloured.

1255	120k. Type **492**	2·00	1·80
1256	120k. Skaftafell (right) (30×29 mm)	2·00	1·80

Nos. 1255/6 were printed, se-tenant, each pair forming a composite design of Skaftafell.

493 Heritage Centre

2009. Centenary of National Centre for Cultural Heritage. Sheet 85×57 mm.

MS1257	**493**	150k. multicoloured	4·25	4·25

494 *Sermon on the Mount* (detail) (Gudmundur Einarsson)

2009. Christmas. Multicoloured. Self-adhesive.

1258	(70k.) Type **494**	1·70	1·50
1259	120k. *Holy Mother of God* (Finnur Jónsson)	3·50	3·25

495 *Uria lomvia* (Brunnich's guillemot)

2009. Seabirds. Multicoloured.

1260	110k. Type **495**	2·50	2·40
1261	130k. *Larus hyperboreus* (glaucous gull)	3·50	3·25

496 Thingvellir Church

2009. 150th Anniv of Thingvellir Church.

1262	**496**	190k. multicoloured	4·50	4·25

497 *Phoca vitulina* (harbor seal)

2010. Seals (1st series). Multicoloured.

1263	5k. Type **497**	75	65
1264	220k. *Phoca groenlandica* (harp seal)	4·25	4·00

498 Hanger Tree (Katrín Olina Petursdottir and Michael Young)

2010. Icelandic Design. Furniture. Multicoloured.

1265	75k. Type **498**	1·20	1·00
1266	140k. Tango (chair) (Sigourur Gustafsson)	2·00	1·80
1267	155k. MGO 180 dining table (Guorun M. Olafsdottir and Oddgeir Poroarson) (horiz)	2·75	2·50
1268	165k. Dimon sofa (Erla Solveig Oskarsdottir) (horiz)	3·00	2·75

499 Door of Valbjofsstaoir (13th-century)

2010. Icelandic Design. Carving in Wood and Bone. Multicoloured. (a) Ordinary gum.

1269	10k. Type **499**	40	35
1270	(75k.) 17th-century Judge's drinking horn (Brynjolfur Jónsson)	1·20	1·10
1271	200k. *Play in Leaves* (Sigriour Jona Kristjansottir) (vert)	4·25	4·00

(b) Size 32×28 mm. Self-adhesive.

1272	(75k.) As No. 1269 (drinking horn)	1·20	1·10

Nos. 1270 and 1272 were for use on mail within Iceland up to 50 grams.

500 Man pushing Barrel

2010. Norden by the Sea. Life at the Coast. Sheet 105×70 mm containing T 500 and similar vert design. Multicoloured.

MS1273	75k.×2, Type **500**; Women sorting herrings	1·80	1·60

The stamps and margins of **MS**1273 form a composite design.

501 *Bjarni riddari GK 1*

2010. Trawlers. Multicoloured.

1274	75k. Type **501**	2·20	2·20
1275	75k. *Ingolfur Arnarson RE 201*	2·20	2·20
1276	165k. *Solborg IS 260*	3·75	3·50
1277	165k. *Harobakur EA 3*	3·75	3·50

502 Jónsgarður, Isajörður

2010. Parks. Multicoloured.

1278	90k. Type **502**	1·80	1·60
1279	130k. Helisgerði, Hafnarfjörður	2·10	1·90
1280	285k. Skallagrimsgarður, Borgarnes (horiz)	4·00	3·75

503 Icelandic Pavilion

2010. Expo 2010, Shanghai

MS1281	**503**	130k. multicoloured	2·50	2·50

504 Footballer

2010. Personalised Stamps. Multicoloured.

1282	50g. Type **504**	3·50	3·25
1283	50g. Girl footballer	3·50	3·50

No. 1282 was for mail within Europe, originally on sale for 165k and No. 1283 was for mail outside Europe, originally on sale for 220k.

505 The Fate of the Gods (written by Ingunn Asdisardóttir and illustrated by Kristin Ragna)

2010. Europa. Children's Books. Multicoloured.

(a) Ordinary gum

1284	165k. Type **505**	2·75	2·50
1285	220k. *Good Evening* (written and illustrated by Aslaug Jonsdóttir)	4·00	3·75

(b) Self-adhesive

1286	165k. As Type **505**	2·75	2·50
1287	220k. As No. 1285	4·00	3·75

506 Lava Flow

2010. Eyjafjallajokull Volcanic Eruption. Multicoloured.

1288	50g. (75k.) Type **506**	2·75	2·75
1289	50g. (165k.) Ash cloud	2·75	2·75
1290	50g. (220k.) Eruption	2·75	2·75

Nos. 1288-90 were for mail weighing up to 50g. No. 1288 was for use on mail within Iceland, No. 1289 for mail within Europe and No.1290 for mail outside Europe.

507 Early Patients

2010. Centenary of Vifilsstaðir Sanatorium

1291	**507**	100g. (90k.) multicoloured	1·75	1·50

No. 1291 was for use on local mail weighing up to 100g.

508 Eagle, Fox and Mouse

2010. International Year of Biodiversity. Multicoloured.

MS1292	90k.×2, Type **508**; Leaping salmon and duck	3·25	3·25

509 Athlete

2010. Youth Olympic Games, Singapore

1293	**509**	165k. multicoloured	3·00	1·75

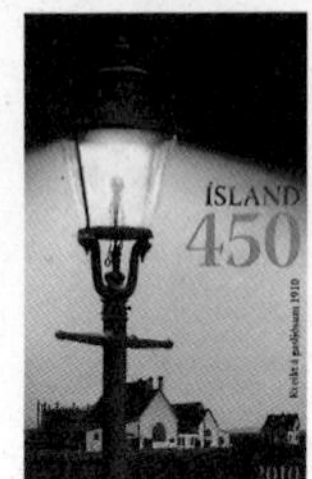

510 Street Lamp

2010. Centenary of Reykjavik Gas Works

1294	**510**	450k. multicoloured	8·25	8·00

511 Bird and Wreath

2010. Christmas. Multicoloured.

1295	50g. (75k.) Type **511**	1·90	1·70
1296	50g. (165k.) Two birds and wreath	2·40	2·20

Nos. 1295/6 were for mail weighing up to 50g. No. 1295 was for use on mail within Iceland and No. 1296 for mail within Europe.

512 Landscape (Isleifur Konráðsson)

2010. Icelandic Visual Art. Multicoloured.

1297	50g. (75k.) Type **512**	1·20	1·00
1298	100g. (90k.) Portrait (Sölvi Helgason) (vert)	1·75	1·50
1299	50g. (165k.) Fisherman in boat (Sigurlaug Jónasdóttir) (vert)	3·00	2·75
1300	50g. (220k.) Dreamscape (Karl Einarsson Dunganon) (vert)	4·00	4·25

Nos. 1297,1299/300 were for mail weighing up to 50g. No. 1297 was for use on mail within Iceland, No. 1299 for mail within Europe and No.1300 for mail outside Europe.
No. 1298 was for use on mail weighing up to 100g. within Iceland.

513 '14 DES 1910' and 'ERAÐ ÞREIFA......'

2010. Centenary of *Visir* (newspaper)

1301	**513**	140k. agate and bistre	2·75	2·50

514 Melanitta nigra (common scoter)

2011. 50th Anniv of World Wide Fund for Nature. Multicoloured.

1302	50g. (75k.) Type **514**	1·50	1·20
1303	50g. (75k.) *Branta leucopsis* (barnacle goose)	1·50	1·20
1304	50g. (165k.) *Anser albifrons* (white-fronted goose)	3·00	2·75
1305	50g. (165k.) *Anas strepera* (gadwall)	3·00	2·75

Nos. 1302/5 were for mail weighing up to 50g. Nos. 1302/3 were for use on mail within Iceland and Nos. 1304/5 for mail within Europe.

515 *Phoca hispida* (ringed seal)

2011. Seals (2nd series). Multicoloured.

1306	100g. (90k.) Type **515**	1·60	1·50
1307	100g. (220k.) *Halichoerus grypus* (grey seal)	4·00	3·75

Nos. 1306/7 were for mail weighing up to 100g. No. 1306 was for use on mail within Iceland and No. 1307 for mail outside Europe.

516 Moto-Cross

2011. Motor Sports. Multicoloured.

1308	50g. (75k.) Type **516**	1·90	1·70
1309	50g. (75k.) Rallying	1·90	1·70
1310	50g. (165k.) Off-roading	2·40	2·20
1311	50g. (165k.) Drag racing	2·40	2·20

Nos. 1308/11 were for mail weighing up to 50g. Nos. 1308/9 were for use on mail within Iceland and Nos. 1310/11 for mail within Europe.

517 Langanesviti

2011. Lighthouses. Multicoloured.

1312	50g. (75k.) Type **517**	1·90	1·70
1313	50g. (165k.) Stokksnes (vert)	2·40	2·20

No. 1312/13 were for mail weighing up to 50g. No. 1312 was for use on mail within Iceland and No. 1313 for mail within Europe.

518 Tree Rings from Log of Siberian Larch (resources)

2011. Europa. Multicoloured.

(a) Ordinary gum

1314	50g. (165k.) Type **518**	2·40	2·20
1315	50g. (220k.) Close-up of leaf (ecosystem)	4·25	4·00

(b) Self-adhesive

1316	50g. (165k.) As Type **518**	2·40	2·20
1317	50g. (220k.) As No. 1315	4·25	4·00

No. 1314/17 were for mail weighing up to 50g. Nos. 1314 and 1316 was for use on mail within Europe, Nos. 1315 and 1317 for mail outside Europe.

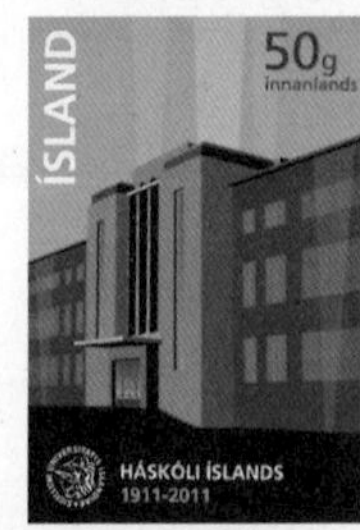

519 University Building

2011. Centenary of University of Iceland

1318	**519**	50g. (75k.) multicoloured	1·90	1·70

520 Building Façade (image scaled to 35% of original size)

2011. Harpa Reykjavik Concert Hall and Conference Centre. As T **520**

MS1319	50g.×5, Part of structure (black) (28×20 mm); Part of structure (brownish grey) (10×25 mm); Part of structure (grey) (25×47 mm); Part of structure (pink) (17×37 mm); Part of structure (yellow) (50×26 mm)	10·50	10·50

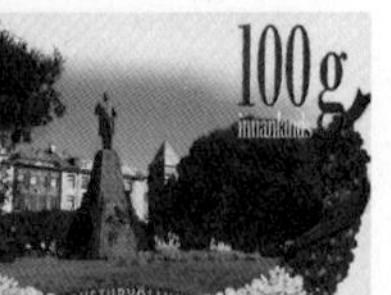

521 Austurvöllur, Reykjavik

2011. Parks. Multicoloured.

1320	100g.(90k.) Type **521**	2·50	2·20
1321	100g.(285k.) Parliament Park (Alþingsgarðurinn)	7·75	7·50

522 Outlines of Athletes and Musicians

2011. Centenary of Melavöllur Stadium

1322	**522**	250g. (130k.) grey, brownish grey and black	4·50	4·25

523 President Jón Sigurðsson

2011. Birth Bicentenary of President Jón Sigurðsson. Each black and bistre.

1323	50g.(75k.) Type **523**	3·00	2·75
1324	1000k. As older man	17·00	16·00
MS1325	100×75 mm.50g. (75k.) as Type **252**; 1000k. As No. 1324	20·00	19·00

OFFICIAL STAMPS

1873. As T 1 but inscr "PJON. FRIM." at foot.

O8	4s. green	60·00	£275
O10	8s. mauve	£350	£450

O4

1876

O36	**O4**	3a. yellow	10·50	20·00
O37	**O4**	4a. grey	21·00	26·00
O21b	**O4**	5a. brown	6·50	11·50
O22a	**O4**	10a. blue	49·00	9·50
O23a	**O4**	16a. red	16·00	35·00
O24a	**O4**	20a. green	14·00	23·00
O25	**O4**	50a. mauve	47·00	65·00

1902. As T 10, but inscr "PJONUSTA".

O81	3a. sepia and yellow	2·50	1·90
O82	4a. sepia and green	3·25	1·20
O83	5a. sepia and brown	2·00	2·75
O84	10a. sepia and blue	2·20	2·75
O85	16a. sepia and red	2·30	10·00
O86	20a. sepia and green	11·00	5·75
O87	50a. sepia and mauve	6·00	7·50

1902. Optd I GILDI '02–'03.

O94	3a. yellow	60	1·60
O95	4a. grey	60	1·60
O96	5a. brown	60	1·60
O97	10a. blue	60	1·60
O91	16a. red	12·00	43·00
O98	20a. green	60	17·00
O93	50a. mauve	£425	41·00

1907. As T 12, but inscr "PJONUSTU".

O99	3a. sepia and yellow	5·75	5·75
O100	4a. sepia and green	2·50	6·00
O101	5a. sepia and brown	7·50	2·75
O102	10a. sepia and blue	2·00	2·40
O103	15a. sepia and blue	3·50	6·00
O104	16a. sepia and red	3·00	21·00
O105	20a. sepia and green	9·25	4·25
O106	50a. sepia and mauve	5·00	7·75

1920. As T 15, but inscr "PJONUSTU".

O132	3a. black and yellow	3·00	2·75
O133	4a. black and green	1·10	2·50
O134	5a. black and orange	1·10	1·00
O135	10a. black and blue	3·75	75
O136	15a. black and blue	1·00	1·00
O137	20a. black and green	39·00	3·00
O138	50a. black and violet	34·00	1·20
O139	1k. black and red	34·00	2·30
O140	2k. black and blue	4·50	13·50
O141	5k. black and brown	28·00	40·00

1922. Optd Pjonusta.

O153	**15**	20a. on 10a. red	19·00	1·60
O151a	**13**	2k. red (No. 107)	23·00	42·00
O152	**13**	5k. brown (No. 108)	£190	£180

1930. Parliamentary Commemoratives of 1930 optd Pjonustumerki.

O174	**24**	3a. violet and lilac (postage)	9·25	24·00
O175	-	5a. blue and grey	9·25	24·00
O176	-	7a. green and dp green	9·25	24·00
O177	-	10a. purple and mauve	9·25	24·00
O178	-	15a. dp blue & blue	9·25	24·00
O179	-	20a. red and pink	9·25	24·00
O180	-	25a. brown & lt brown	9·25	24·00
O181	-	30a. green and grey	9·25	24·00
O182	-	35a. blue & ultramarine	9·25	24·00
O183	-	40a. red, blue and grey	9·25	24·00
O184	-	50a. dp brown & brown	£110	£200
O185	-	1k. green and grey	£110	£200
O186	-	2k. blue and green	£110	£225
O187	-	5k. orange and yellow	£110	£200
O188	-	10k. lake and red	£110	£200
O189	**25**	10a. blue & dp blue (air)	19·00	80·00

1936. Optd Pjonusta.

O220	**15**	7a. green	2·30	21·00
O221	**15**	10a. red	8·00	1·60
O222	**12**	50a. red and grey	18·00	21·00

Pt. 1

IRELAND

Ireland (Eire) consisting of Ireland less the six counties of Ulster, became the Irish Free State in 1922 and left the British Empire in 1949 when it became an independent republic.

1949. 12 pence = 1 shilling; 20 shillings = 1 pound.
1971. 100 (new) pence = 1 pound (Punt).
2002. 100 cents = 1 euro.

Rialtas
Sealadaċ
na
hÉireann
1922

(1) "Provisional Government of Ireland, 1922"

1922. Stamps of Great Britain optd with T 1 (date in thin figures and no full point).

1	**105**	½d. green	2·00	40
2	**104**	1d. red	2·50	40
4b	**104**	2½d. blue	2·00	4·00
5	**106**	3d. violet	4·75	5·00
6	**106**	4d. green	6·00	18·00
7	**107**	5d. brown	4·75	8·50
8	**108**	9d. black	13·00	30·00
9	**108**	10d. blue	9·50	50·00
17	**109**	2s.6d. brown	55·00	85·00
19	**109**	5s. red	85·00	£170
21	**109**	10s. blue	£170	£375

On Nos. 17, 19 and 21 the overprint is in four lines instead of five.

Rialtas
Sealadaċ
na
hÉireann
1922.

(2)

1922. Stamps of Great Britain optd with T 2 (date in thick figures followed by full point).

47	**105**	½d. green	1·00	1·75
31	**104**	1d. red	2·75	50
10	**105**	1½d. brown	2·75	1·25
12	**106**	2d. orange	6·50	50
35	**104**	2½d. blue	6·00	25·00
36	**106**	3d. violet	10·00	2·25
37	**106**	4d. green	4·50	8·50
38	**107**	5d. brown	5·50	10·00
39	**107**	6d. purple	15·00	7·50
40	**108**	9d. black	14·00	22·00
41	**108**	9d. green	6·00	45·00
42	**108**	10d. blue	28·00	75·00
43	**108**	1s. brown	12·00	12·00

Saorstát
Éireann
1922

5 "Irish Free State, 1922"

1922. Stamps of Great Britain optd with T 5.

52		½d. green	2·00	30
53	**104**	1d. red	2·50	50
54	**105**	1½d. brown	3·50	8·50
55	**106**	2d. orange	1·50	1·00
56	**104**	2½d. blue	7·50	10·00
57	**106**	3d. violet	4·50	11·00
58	**106**	4d. green	4·50	9·50
59	**107**	5d. brown	5·50	4·75
60	**107**	6d. purple	3·75	2·00
61	**108**	9d. green	6·50	5·50
62	**108**	10d. blue	21·00	75·00
63	**108**	1s. brown	7·00	11·00
86	**109**	2s.6d. brown	50·00	60·00
87	**109**	5s. red	80·00	£100
88	**109**	10s. blue	£190	£225

6 "Sword of Light"

7 Map of Ireland

8 Arms of Ireland

9 Celtic Cross

1922

71	**6**	½d. green	3·00	90
112	**7**	1d. red	30	10
73	**7**	1½d. purple	2·75	2·50
114	**7**	2d. green	30	10
75	**8**	2½d. brown	4·50	4·25
116	**9**	3d. blue (18½×22½ mm)	70	10
227	**9**	3d. blue (17×21 mm)	40	15
117	**8**	4d. blue	55	10
118	**6**	5d. violet (18½×22½ mm)	1·00	10
228	**6**	5d. violet (17×21 mm)	30	15
119b	**6**	6d. purple	1·25	20
119c	**6**	8d. red	80	1·25
120	**8**	9d. violet	1·50	80
121	**9**	10d. brown	75	80
121b	**9**	11d. red	2·00	3·25
82	**6**	1s. blue	16·00	4·25

12 Daniel O'Connell

1929. Centenary of Catholic Emancipation.

89	**12**	2d. green	70	45
90	**12**	3d. blue	4·25	10·00
91	**12**	9d. violet	4·25	5·00

13 Shannon Barrage

1930. Completion of Shannon Hydro-electric Scheme.

92	**13**	2d. deep brown	1·25	55

14 Reaper

1931. Bicentenary of Royal Dublin Society.

93	**14**	2d. blue	1·00	30

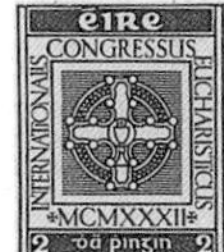
15 The Cross of Cong

1932. International Eucharistic Congress.

94	**15**	2d. green	2·00	30
95	**15**	3d. blue	3·75	6·00

16 Adoration of the Cross

1933. "Holy Year".

96	**16**	2d. green	2·25	15
97	**16**	3d. blue	3·50	2·50

17 Hurler

1934. 50th Anniv of Gaelic Athletic Assn.

98	**17**	2d. green	1·75	55

18 St. Patrick

1937

123b	**18**	2s.6d. green	1·50	3·25
124ca	**18**	5s. purple	4·00	9·50
125ba	**18**	10s. blue	4·00	16·00

19 Ireland and New Constitution

1937. Constitution Day.

105	**19**	2d. red	2·00	20
106	**19**	3d. blue	5·00	3·75

For similar stamps see Nos. 176/7.

20 Father Mathew

1938. Centenary of Temperance Crusade.

107	**20**	2d. black	2·50	50
108	**20**	3d. blue	12·00	6·50

21 George Washington, American Eagle and Irish Harp

1939. 150th Anniv of U.S. Constitution and Installation of First U.S. President.

109	**21**	2d. red	2·25	1·00
110	**21**	3d. blue	3·25	5·50

1941. 25th Anniv of Easter Rising (1916). (a) Provisional issue. Optd with two lines of Irish characters between the dates "1941" and "1916".

126	**7**	2d. orange	2·00	1·00
127	**9**	3d. blue	25·00	11·00

24 Volunteer and G.P.O., Dublin

(b) Definitive Issue.

128	**24**	2½d. black	3·25	1·25

25 Dr. Douglas Hyde

1943. 50th Anniv of Gaelic League.

129	**25**	½d. green	1·25	70
130	**25**	2½d. purple	2·00	10

26 Sir William Rowan Hamilton

1943. Centenary of Announcement of Discovery of Quaternions.

131	**26**	½d. green	40	70
132	**26**	2½d. brown	2·25	20

27 Bro. Michael O'Clery

1944. Death Tercentenary of Michael O'Clery (Franciscan historian) (commemorating the "Annals of the Four Masters").

133	**27**	½d. green	10	10
134	**27**	1s. brown	1·25	10

28 Edmund Ignatius Rice

1944. Death Centenary of Edmund Rice (founder of Irish Christian Brothers).

135	**28**	2½d. slate	1·75	45

29 "Youth sowing Seeds of Freedom"

1945. Death Centenary of Thomas Davis (founder of Young Ireland Movement).

136	**29**	2½d. blue	1·50	75
137	**29**	6d. purple	6·00	6·50

30 "Country and Homestead"

1946. Birth Centenaries of Michael Davitt and Charles Parnell (land reformers).

138	**30**	2½d. red	2·50	25
139	**30**	3d. blue	3·50	4·25

31 Angel Victor over Rock of Cashel

1948. Air. Inscr "VOX HIBERNIAE".

140	**31**	1d. brown	3·00	4·50
141	-	3d. blue	3·00	3·50
142	-	6d. purple	1·00	2·25
142b	-	8d. lake	7·00	9·00
143	-	1s. green	1·00	2·00
143a	**31**	1s.3d. orange	8·50	1·50
143b	**31**	1s.5d. blue	4·00	2·00

DESIGNS: 3d., 8d. Angel Victor over Lough Derg; 6d. Over Croagh Patrick; 1s. Over Glendalough.

35 Theobald Wolfe Tone

1948. 150th Anniv of Insurrection.

144	**35**	2½d. purple	1·00	10
145	**35**	3d. violet	3·25	4·00

36 Leinster House and Arms of Provinces

1949. International Recognition of Republic.

146	**36**	2½d. brown	1·75	10
147	**36**	3d. blue	6·50	4·25

37 J. C. Mangan

1949. Death Centenary of James Clarence Mangan (poet).

148	**37**	1d. green	1·50	35

38 Statue of St. Peter, Rome

1950. Holy Year.

149	**38**	2½d. violet	1·00	40
150	**38**	3d. blue	8·00	12·00
151	**38**	9d. brown	8·00	13·00

39 Thomas Moore

1952. Death Centenary of Thomas Moore (poet).

152	**39**	2½d. purple	1·00	10
153	**39**	3½d. olive	1·75	4·00

40 Irish Harp

1953. "An Tostal" (Ireland at Home) Festival.

154	**40**	2½d. green	1·75	35
155	**40**	1s.4d. blue	19·00	28·00

41 Robert Emmet

1953. 150th Death Anniv of Emmet (patriot).

156	**41**	3d. green	3·00	15
157	**41**	1s.3d. red	45·00	10·00

42 Madonna and Child (Della Robbia)

1954. Marian Year.

158	**42**	3d. blue	1·00	10
159	**42**	5d. green	2·00	3·25

43 Cardinal Newman (first Rector)

1954. Centenary of Founding of Catholic University of Ireland.

160	**43**	2d. purple	1·50	10
161	**43**	1s.3d. blue	16·00	6·00

44 Statue of Commodore Barry

1956. Barry Commemoration.

162	**44**	3d. lilac	1·00	10
163	**44**	1s.3d. blue	4·50	8·00

45 John Redmond

1957. Birth Centenary of John Redmond (politician).

164	**45**	3d. blue	1·00	10
165	**45**	1s.3d. purple	9·00	15·00

46 Thomas O'Crohan

1957. Birth Cent of Thomas O'Crohan (author).

166	**46**	2d. purple	1·00	20
167	**46**	5d. violet	1·00	4·50

47 Admiral Brown

1957. Death Cent of Admiral William Brown.

168	**47**	3d. blue	3·00	20
169	**47**	1s.3d. red	25·00	16·00

48 "Father Wadding" (Ribera)

1957. Death Tercentenary of Father Luke Wadding (theologian).

170	**48**	3d. blue	2·00	10
171	**48**	1s.3d. lake	15·00	8·50

49 Tom Clarke

1958. Birth Centenary of Thomas J. ("Tom") Clarke (patriot).

172	**49**	3d. green	2·00	10
173	**49**	1s.3d. brown	4·00	11·00

50 Mother Mary Aikenhead

1958. Death Centenary of Mother Mary Aikenhead (foundress of Irish Sisters of Charity).

174	**50**	3d. blue	2·00	10
175	**50**	1s.3d. red	11·00	8·00

1958. 21st Anniv of Irish Constitution.

176	**19**	3d. brown	1·00	10
177	**19**	5d. green	1·25	4·50

51 Arthur Guinness

1959. Bicentenary of Guinness Brewery.

178	**51**	3d. purple	3·00	10
179	**51**	1s.3d. blue	12·00	12·00

52 "The Flight of the Holy Family"

1960. World Refugee Year.

180	**52**	3d. purple	40	10
181	**52**	1s.3d. sepia	60	3·75

53 Conference Emblem

1960. 1st Anniv of Europa.

182	**53**	6d. brown	9·00	3·00
183	**53**	1s.3d. violet	23·00	20·00

54 Dublin Airport, de Havilland Dragon Mk 2 EI-ABI "Iolar" and Boeing 720 EI-ALA

1961. Silver Jubilee of Aer Lingus Airlines.

184	**54**	6d. blue	1·75	3·75
185	**54**	1s.3d. green	2·25	5·50

55 St Patrick

1961. 15th Death Centenary of St. Patrick.

186	**55**	3d. blue	1·00	10
187	**55**	8d. purple	2·75	5·50
188	**55**	1s.3d. green	2·75	1·60

56 John O'Donovan and Edugen O'Curry

1962. Death Centenaries of O'Donovan and O'Curry (scholars).

189	**56**	3d. red	30	10
190	**56**	1s.3d. purple	1·25	2·25

57 Europa "Tree"

1962. Europa.

191	**57**	6d. red	70	1·00
192	**57**	1s.3d. turquoise	80	1·50

58 Campaign Emblem

1963. Freedom from Hunger.

193	**58**	4d. violet	50	10
194	**58**	1s.3d. red	2·75	2·75

59 "Co-operation"

1963. Europa.

195	**59**	6d. red	1·25	75
196	**59**	1s.3d. blue	3·50	3·75

60 Centenary Emblem

1963. Centenary of Red Cross.

197	**60**	4d. red and grey	50	10
198	**60**	1s.3d. red, grey and green	1·50	2·25

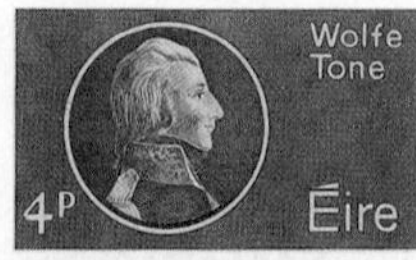

61 Wolfe Tone

1964. Birth Bicentenary of Wolfe Tone (revolutionary).

199	**61**	4d. black	50	10
200	**61**	1s.3d. blue	1·90	2·00

62 Irish Pavilion at Fair

1964. New York World's Fair.

201	**62**	5d. multicoloured	50	10
202	**62**	1s.5d. multicoloured	2·00	2·00

63 Europa "Flower"

1964. Europa.

203	**63**	8d. green and blue	1·50	1·25
204	**63**	1s.5d. brown and orange	7·00	2·75

64 "Waves of Communications"

1965. Centenary of I.T.U.

205	**64**	3d. blue and green	30	10
206	**64**	8d. black and green	1·25	1·60

65 W. B. Yeats (poet)

1965. Birth Centenary of Yeats.

207	**65**	5d. black, brown and green	30	10
208	**65**	1s.5d. black, green & brown	2·25	1·75

66 I.C.Y. Emblem

1965. International Co-operation Year.

209	**66**	3d. blue	60	10
210	**66**	10d. brown	1·00	3·00

67 Europa "Sprig"

1965. Europa.

211	**67**	8d. black and red	1·50	1·00
212	**67**	1s.5d. purple and turquoise	7·00	3·50

68 James Connolly

1966. 50th Anniv of Easter Rising.

213	**68**	3d. black and blue	75	10
214	-	3d. black and bronze	75	10
215	-	5d. black and olive	75	10
216	-	5d. black, orange and green	75	10
217	-	7d. black and brown	75	2·25
218	-	7d. black and green	75	2·25
219	-	1s.5d. black and turquoise	75	1·50
220	-	1s.5d. black and green	75	1·50

DESIGNS: No. 214, Thomas J. Clarke; No. 215, P. H. Pearse; No. 216, "Marching to Freedom"; No. 217, Eamonn Ceannt; No. 218, Sean MacDiarmada; No. 219, Thomas MacDonagh; No. 220, Joseph Plunkett.

76 Roger Casement

1966. 50th Death Anniv of Roger Casement (patriot).

221	**76**	5d. black	15	10
222	**76**	1s. brown	30	50

77 Europa "Ship"

1966. Europa.

223	**77**	7d. green and orange	1·00	40
224	**77**	1s.5d. green and grey	2·00	1·60

78 Interior of Abbey (from lithograph)

1966. 750th Anniv of Ballintubber Abbey.

225	**78**	5d. brown	10	10
226	**78**	1s. black	20	25

79 Cogwheels

1967. Europa.

229	**79**	7d. green, gold and cream	60	40
230	**79**	1s.5d. red, gold and cream	1·90	1·00

80 Maple Leaves

1967. Canadian Centennial.

231	**80**	5d. multicoloured	10	10
232	**80**	1s.5d. multicoloured	20	75

81 Rock of Cashel (from photo by Edwin Smith)

1967. International Tourist Year.

233	**81**	7d. sepia	15	20
234	**81**	10d. blue	15	40

82 1c. Fenian Stamp Essay

1967. Centenary of Fenian Rising.

235	**82**	5d. black and green	10	10
236	-	1s. black and pink	20	30

DESIGN: 1s.24c. Fenian Stamp Essay.

84 Jonathan Swift

1967. 300th Birth Anniv of Jonathan Swift.

237	**84**	3d. black and grey	10	10
238	-	1s.5d. brown and blue	20	30

DESIGN: 1s.5d. Gulliver and Lilliputians.

86 Europa Key

1968. Europa.

239	**86**	7d. red, gold and brown	50	50
240	**86**	1s.5d. blue, gold and brown	75	1·00

87 St Mary's Cathedral, Limerick

1968. 800th Anniv of St. Mary's Cathedral, Limerick.

241	**87**	5d. blue	10	10
242	**87**	10d. green	20	60

88 Countess Markievicz

1968. Birth Centenary of Countess Markievicz (patriot).

243	**88**	3d. black	10	10
244	**88**	1s.5d. indigo and blue	20	20

89 James Connolly

1968. Birth Centenary of James Connolly (patriot).

245	**89**	6d. brown and chocolate	20	75
246	**89**	1s. green, lt green & myrtle	20	10

90 Stylized Dog (brooch)

92 Winged Ox (Symbol of St. Luke)

1968

247	**90**	½d. orange	10	30
248	**90**	1d. green	15	10
249	**90**	2d. ochre	50	10
250	**90**	3d. blue	35	10
251	**90**	4d. red	30	10
252	**90**	5d. green	1·25	75
253	**90**	6d. brown	30	10
254	-	7d. brown and yellow	45	3·75
255	-	8d. brown and chestnut	45	2·50
256	-	9d. blue and green	50	10
257	-	10d. brown and violet	1·50	2·50
258	-	1s. chocolate and brown	40	10
259	-	1s.9d. black and turquoise	4·00	2·75
260	**92**	2s.6d. multicoloured	1·75	30
261	**92**	5s. multicoloured	3·00	3·25
262	-	10s. multicoloured	4·75	4·50

DESIGNS—As Type **90**: 7d., 8d., 9d., 10d., 1s., 1s.9d., Stag. As Type **92**: 10s Eagle (Symbol of St. John The Evangelist).

See also Nos. 287, etc.

94 Human Rights Emblem

1968. Human Rights Year.

263	**94**	5d. yellow, gold and black	15	10
264	**94**	7d. yellow, gold and red	15	40

95 Dail Eireann Assembly

1969. 50th Anniv of Dail Eireann (1st National Parliament).

265	**95**	6d. green	15	10
266	**95**	9d. blue	15	30

96 Colonnade

1969. Europa.

267	**96**	9d. grey, ochre and blue	1·00	1·10
268	**96**	1s.9d. grey, gold and red	1·25	1·40

97 Quadruple I.L.O. Emblems

1969. 50th Anniv of I.L.O.

269	**97**	6d. black and grey	20	10
270	**97**	9d. black and yellow	20	25

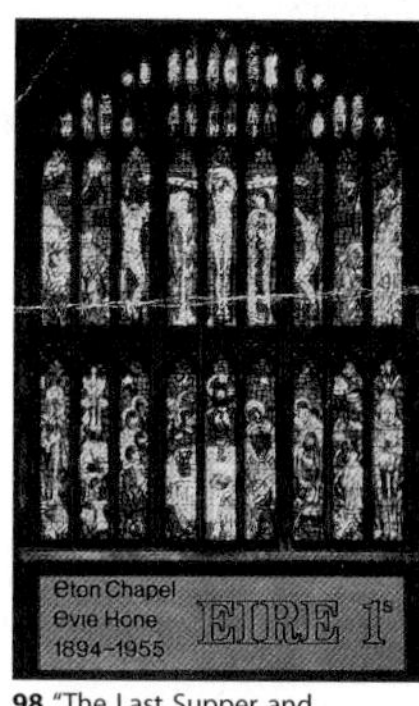

98 "The Last Supper and Crucifixion" (Evie Hone Window, Eton Chapel)

1969. Contemporary Irish Art (1st issue).

271	**98**	1s. multicoloured	30	1·50

See also Nos. 280, 306, 317, 329, 362, 375, 398, 408, 452, 470 and 498.

99 Mahatma Gandhi

1969. Birth Centenary of Mahatma Gandhi.

272	**99**	6d. black and green	50	10
273	**99**	1s.9d. black and yellow	75	90

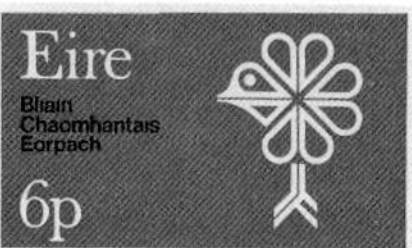

100 Symbolic Bird in Tree

1970. European Conservation Year.

274	**100**	6d. bistre and black	20	10
275	**100**	9d. violet and black	25	80

101 "Flaming Sun"

1970. Europa.

276	**101**	6d. violet and silver	55	10
277	**101**	9d. brown and silver	90	1·25
278	**101**	1s.9d. grey and silver	1·75	2·00

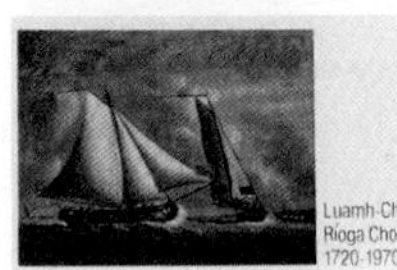

102 "Sailing Boats" (Peter Monamy)

1970. 250th Anniv of Royal Cork Yacht Club.

279	**102**	4d. multicoloured	15	10

103 "Madonna of Eire" (Mainie Jellett)

1970. Contemporary Irish Art (2nd issue).

280	**103**	1s. multicoloured	15	20

104 Thomas MacCurtain

1970. 50th Death Annivs of Irish Patriots.

281	**104**	9d. black, violet and grey	1·00	25
282	-	9d. black, violet and grey	1·00	25
283	**104**	2s.9d. black, blue and grey	1·75	1·50
284	-	2s.9d. black, blue and grey	1·75	1·50

DESIGN: Nos. 282 and 284, Terence MacSwiney.

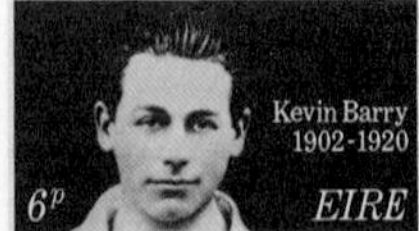

106 Kevin Barry

1970. 50th Death Anniv of Kevin Barry (patriot).

285	**106**	6d. green	30	10
286	**106**	1s.2d. blue	40	1·10

1971. Decimal Currency. As Nos. 247/62 but with face values in new currency, without "p", and some colours changed.

287	**90**	½p. green	10	10
340	**90**	1p. blue	10	10
289	**90**	1½p. red	15	50
341	**90**	2p. green	10	10
291	**90**	2½p. brown	15	10
342	**90**	3p. brown	10	10
293	**90**	3½p. orange	25	10
294	**90**	4p. violet	20	10
295	-	5p. brown and olive	1·00	20
344	**90**	5p. green	60	10
296	-	6p. grey and brown	3·50	1·25
346	**90**	6p. grey	20	10
347	-	7p. blue and green	70	35
348	**90**	7p. green	35	10
297	-	7½p. mauve and brown	50	1·40
349	-	8p. brown and deep brown	60	50
350	**90**	8p. brown	30	10
351	-	9p. black and green	70	30
352	**90**	9p. green	30	10
352a	**90**	9½p. red	35	20
353	**92**	10p. multicoloured	1·25	30
354	-	10p. black and lilac	70	10
354a	**90**	10p. mauve	70	10
355	-	11p. black and red	45	1·00
299b	**92**	12p. multicoloured	60	1·50
355a	-	12p. black and green	55	10
355b	**90**	12p. green	30	10
355c	-	13p. brown	40	1·75
356	**92**	15p. multicoloured	55	40
356a	**90**	15p. blue	40	10
356b	-	16p. black and green	40	1·00
356c	**92**	17p. multicoloured	50	1·40
478	**90**	18p. red	45	50
479	**90**	19p. blue	55	2·00
357	**92**	20p. multicoloured	50	15
480	**90**	22p. blue	65	10
481	**90**	24p. brown	1·25	1·25
482	**90**	26p. green	1·50	40
483	**90**	29p. mauve	2·00	3·00
358	-	50p. multicoloured	1·00	30
359	-	£1 multicoloured	1·75	30

DESIGNS—As Type **90**: 5p. (295); 6p. (296); 7p. (347); 7½p., 8p., 9p. (351) 10p. (354), 11p., 12p. (No. 355a), 13p., 16p. Stag. As Type **92**: 50p., £1, Eagle (symbol of St. John the Evangelist).

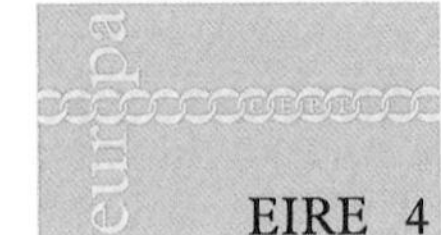

107 "Europa Chain"

1971. Europa.

302	**107**	4p. brown and green	75	10
303	**107**	6p. black and blue	2·75	2·75

108 J. M. Synge

1971. Birth Centenary of J. M. Synge (playwright).

304	**108**	4p. multicoloured	15	10
305	**108**	10p. multicoloured	60	80

109 "An Island Man" (Jack B. Yeats)

1971. Contemporary Irish Art (3rd issue). Birth Centenary of J. B. Yeats (artist).

306	**109**	6p. multicoloured	55	55

110 Racial Harmony Symbol

1971. Racial Equality Year.

307	**110**	4p. red	20	10
308	**110**	10p. black	50	75

111 "Madonna and Child" (statue by J. Hughes)

1971. Christmas.

309	**111**	2½p. black, gold and green	10	10
310	**111**	6p. black, gold and blue	65	65

112 Heart

1972. World Health Day.

311	**112**	2½p. gold and brown	30	15
312	**112**	12p. silver and grey	1·10	1·75

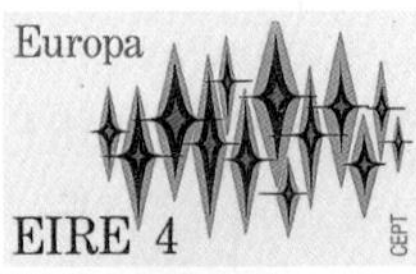

113 "Communications"

1972. Europa.

313	**113**	4p. orange, black and silver	2·50	25
314	**113**	6p. blue, black and silver	7·50	4·75

114 Dove and Moon

1972. Patriot Dead 1922–1923.

315	**114**	4p. multicoloured	10	10
316	**114**	6p. yellow, green & dp grn	65	50

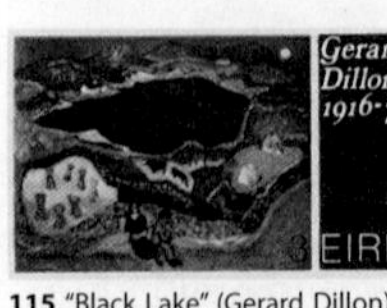

115 "Black Lake" (Gerard Dillon)

1972. Contemporary Irish Art (4th issue).

317	**115**	3p. multicoloured	60	35

116 "Horseman" (Carved Slab)

1972. 50th Anniv of Olympic Council of Ireland.

318	**116**	3p. yellow, black and gold	15	10
319	**116**	6p. pink, black and gold	55	60

117 Madonna and Child (from Book of Kells)

1972. Christmas.

320	**117**	2½p. multicoloured	10	10
321	**117**	4p. multicoloured	25	10
322	**117**	12p. multicoloured	1·00	1·00

118 2d. Stamp of 1922

1972. 50th Anniv of 1st Irish Postage Stamp.

323	**118**	6p. grey and green	60	60
MS324		72×104 mm. No. 323×4	3·75	7·50

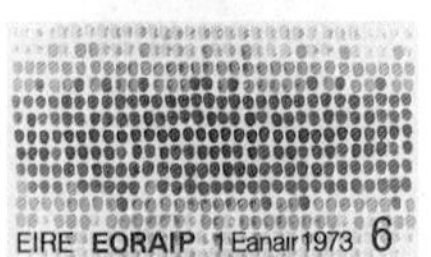

119 Celtic Head Motif

1973. Entry into European Communities.

325	**119**	6p. multicoloured	45	70
326	**119**	12p. multicoloured	65	90

120 Europa "Posthorn"

1973. Europa.

327	**120**	4p. blue	1·75	10
328	**120**	6p. black	3·75	3·25

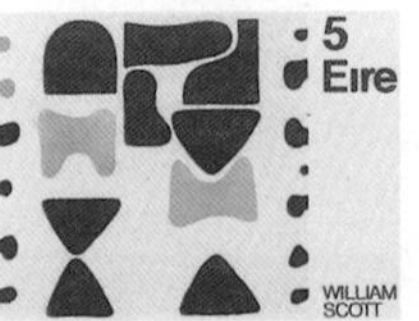

121 "Berlin Blues II" (W. Scott)

1973. Contemporary Irish Art (5th issue).

329	**121**	5p. blue and black	40	30

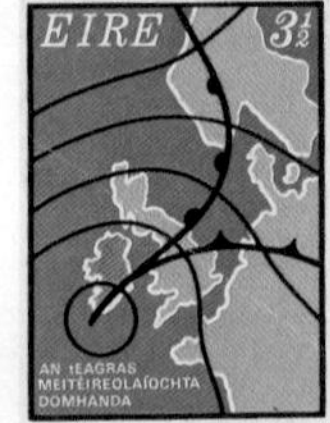

122 Weather Map

1973. Centenary of I.M.O./W.M.O.

330	**122**	3½p. multicoloured	30	10
331	**122**	12p. multicoloured	1·10	2·00

123 Tractor ploughing

1973. World Ploughing Championships, Wellington Bridge.

332	**123**	5p. multicoloured	15	10
333	**123**	7p. multicoloured	1·00	50

124 "Flight into Egypt" (Jan de Cock)

1973. Christmas.

334	**124**	3½p. multicoloured	15	10
335	**124**	12p. multicoloured	1·10	1·50

125 Daunt Island Lightship and "Mary Stanford" (Ballycotton Lifeboat), 1936

1974. 150th Anniv of R.N.L.I.

336 **125** 5p. multicoloured 30 30

126 "Edmund Burke" (statue by J. H. Foley)

1974. Europa.

337 **126** 5p. black and blue 1·50 10

338 **126** 7p. black and green 5·00 2·50

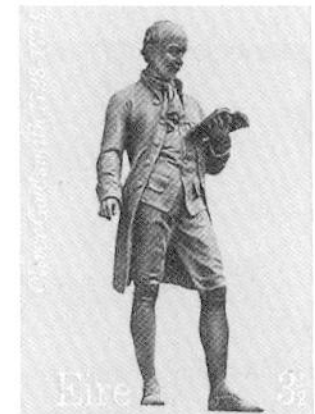

127 "Oliver Goldsmith" (statue by J. H. Foley)

1974. Death Bicentenary of Oliver Goldsmith (writer).

360 **127** 3½p. black and yellow 25 10

361 **127** 12p. black and green 75 1·00

128 "Kitchen Table" (Norah McGuiness)

1974. Contemporary Irish Art (6th issue).

362 **128** 5p. multicoloured 35 30

129 Rugby Players

1974. Centenary of Irish Rugby Football.

363 **129** 3½p. green 50 10

364 **129** 12p. multicoloured 2·00 2·75

130 U.P.U. "Postmark"

1974. Centenary of Universal Postal Union.

365 **130** 5p. green and black 25 10

366 **130** 7p. blue and black 35 55

131 "Madonna and Child" (Bellini)

1974. Christmas.

367 **131** 5p. multicoloured 15 10

368 **131** 15p. multicoloured 60 90

132 "Peace"

1975. International Women's Year.

369 **132** 8p. purple and blue 25 75

370 **132** 15p. blue and green 50 1·25

133 "Castletown Hunt" (R. Healy)

1975. Europa.

371 **133** 7p. grey 2·00 15

372 **133** 9p. green 5·50 2·50

134 Putting

1975. Ninth European Amateur Golf Team Championship, Killarney.

373 **134** 6p. multicoloured 75 45

374 - 9p. multicoloured 1·50 1·50

No. 374 is similar to Type **134** but shows a different view of the putting green.

135 "Bird of Prey" (sculpture by Oisin Kelly)

1975. Contemporary Irish Art (7th issue).

375 **135** 15p. brown 75 75

136 Nano Nagle (founder) and Waifs

1975. Bicentenary of Presentation Order of Nuns.

376 **136** 5p. black and blue 20 10

377 **136** 7p. black and brown 30 30

137 Tower of St. Anne's Church, Shandon

1975. European Architectural Heritage Year.

378 **137** 5p. brown 20 10

379 **137** 6p. multicoloured 40 85

380 - 7p. blue 40 10

381 - 9p. multicoloured 40 80

DESIGN: Nos. 380/1, Interior of Holycross Abbey, Co. Tipperary.

138 St. Oliver Plunkett (commemorative medal by Imogen Stuart)

1975. Canonization of Oliver Plunkett.

382 **138** 7p. black 15 10

383 **138** 15p. brown 55 45

139 "Madonna and Child" (Fra Filippo Lippi)

1975. Christmas.

384 **139** 5p. multicoloured 15 10

385 **139** 7p. multicoloured 20 10

386 **139** 10p. multicoloured 75 60

140 James Larkin (from a drawing by Sean O'Sullivan)

1975. Birth Centenary of James Larkin (Trade Union Leader).

387 **140** 7p. green and grey 20 10

388 **140** 11p. brown and yellow 40 55

141 Alexander Graham Bell

1976. Centenary of Telephone.

389 **141** 9p. multicoloured 20 10

390 **141** 15p. multicoloured 45 50

142 1847 Benjamin Franklin Essay

1976. Bicentenary of American Revolution.

391 - 7p. blue, red and silver 20 10

392 - 8p. blue, red and silver 25 1·10

393 **142** 9p. blue, orange and silver 25 10

394 **142** 15p. red, grey and silver 45 75

MS395 95×75 mm. Nos. 391/4 2·75 8·00

DESIGNS: 7p. Thirteen Stars; 8p. Fifty Stars.

143 Spirit Barrel

1976. Europa. Irish Delft. Multicoloured.

396 9p. Type **143** 1·25 20

397 11p. Dish 3·25 1·60

144 "The Lobster Pots, West of Ireland" (Paul Henry)

1976. Contemporary Irish Art (8th issue).

398 **144** 15p. multicoloured 60 60

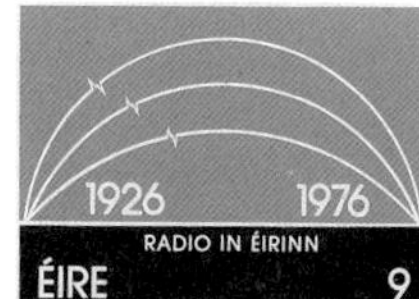

145 Radio Waves

1976. 50th Anniv of Irish Broadcasting Service.

399 **145** 9p. blue and green 20 10

400 - 11p. brown, red and blue 60 1·00

DESIGN—VERT: 11p. Transmitter, radio waves and globe.

146 "The Nativity" (Lorenzo Monaco)

1976. Christmas.

401 **146** 7p. multicoloured 15 10

402 **146** 9p. multicoloured 15 10

403 **146** 15p. multicoloured 55 55

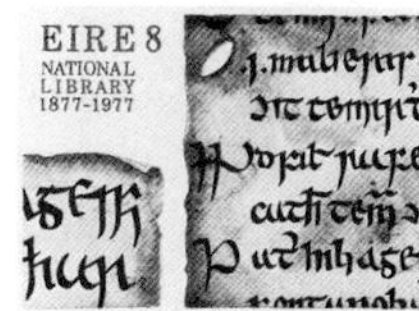

147 16th Century Manuscript

1977. Centenaries of National Library (8p.) and National Museum (10p.). Multicoloured.

404 8p. Type **147** 30 30

405 10p. Prehistoric stone 40 35

148 Ballynahinch, Galway

1977. Europa. Multicoloured.

406 10p. Type **148** 1·50 25

407 12p. Lough Tay, Wicklow 4·50 1·50

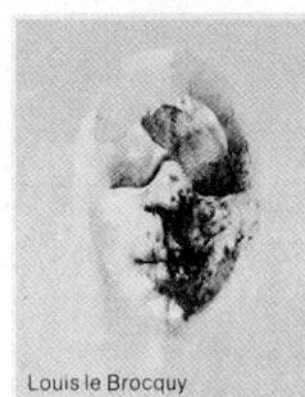

149 "Head" (Louis le Brocquy)

1977. Contemporary Irish Art (9th issue).
408 **149** 17p. multicoloured 65 75

150 Guide and Tents

1977. Scouting and Guiding. Multicoloured.
409 8p. Type **150** 30 10
410 17p. Tent and Scout saluting 80 1·50

151 "The Shanachie" (drawing by Jack B. Yeats)

1977. Anniversaries.
411 **151** 10p. black 35 15
412 - 12p. black 45 1·00
DESIGNS AND EVENTS: 10p. Type **151** (Golden Jubilee of Irish Folklore Society); 12p. The philosopher Eriugena (1100th death anniv).

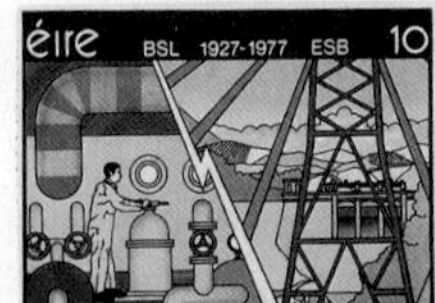

152 "Electricity" (Golden Jubilee of Electricity Supply Board)

1977. Golden Jubilees.
413 **152** 10p. multicoloured 15 10
414 - 12p. multicoloured 30 1·40
415 - 17p. black and brown 65 35
DESIGNS: 12p. Bulls (from Irish coins) (Agricultural Credit Act); 17p. Greyhound (Greyhound Track Racing).

153 "The Holy Family" (Giorgione)

1977. Christmas.
416 **153** 8p. multicoloured 20 10
417 **153** 10p. multicoloured 20 10
418 **153** 17p. multicoloured 75 1·25

154 Junkers W.33 D-1167 "Bremen" in Flight

1978. 50th Anniv of 1st East-West Transatlantic Flight.
419 **154** 10p. black and blue 20 15
420 **154** 17p. black and brown 35 1·10

155 Spring Gentian

1978. Wild Flowers. Multicoloured.
421 8p. Type **155** 25 40
422 10p. Strawberry tree 25 15
423 11p. Large-flowered Butterwort 25 50
424 17p. St. Dabeoc's Heath 45 2·00

156 Catherine McAuley

1978. Anniversaries and Events. Multicoloured.
425 10p. Type **156** (founder of Sisters of Mercy) (birth bicent) 25 10
426 11p. Doctor performing vaccination (Global Eradication of Smallpox) (horiz) 35 80
427 17p. "Self-portrait" Sir William Orpen (painter) (birth cent) 55 1·10

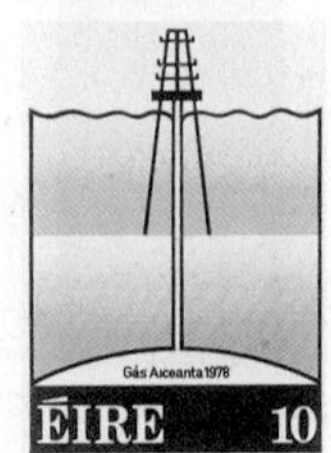

157 Diagram of Drilling Rig

1978. Arrival Onshore of Natural Gas.
428 **157** 10p. multicoloured 30 30

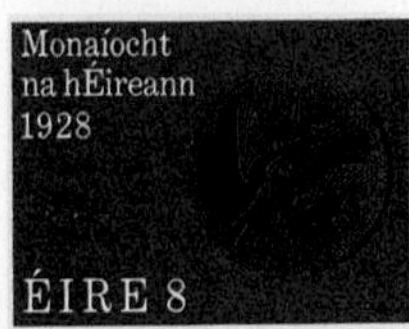

158 Farthing

1978. 50th Anniv of Irish Currency.
429 **158** 8p. black, copper and green 20 20
430 - 10p. black, silver and green 25 10
431 - 11p. black, copper & brn 30 50
432 - 17p. black, silver and blue 40 1·00
DESIGNS: 10p. Florin; 11p. Penny; 17p. Half-crown.

159 "Virgin and Child" (Guercino)

1978. Christmas.
433 **159** 8p. brown, blue and gold 15 10
434 **159** 10p. brown, blue & purple 15 10
435 **159** 17p. brown, blue and green 45 1·40

160 Conolly Folly, Castletown

1978. Europa.
436 **160** 10p. brown 1·50 15
437 - 11p. green 1·50 1·75
DESIGN: 11p. Dromoland Belvedere.

161 Athletes in Cross-country Race

1979. 7th World Cross-country Championships, Limerick. Multicoloured.
438 **161** 8p. multicoloured 20 30

162 "European Communities" (in languages of member nations)

1979. 1st Direct Elections to European Assembly.
439 **162** 10p. green 15 15
440 **162** 11p. violet 15 35

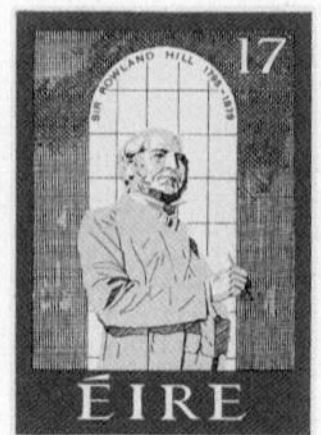

163 Sir Rowland Hill

1979. Death Centenary of Sir Rowland Hill.
441 **163** 17p. black, grey and red 30 60

164 Winter Wren

1979. Birds. Multicoloured.
442 8p. Type **164** 40 80
443 10p. Great crested grebe 40 15
444 11p. White-fronted goose 45 80
445 17p. Peregrine falcon 70 2·00

165 "A Happy Flower" (David Gallagher)

1979. International Year of the Child. Paintings by Children. Multicoloured.
446 10p. Type **165** 20 10
447 11p. "Myself and My Skipping Rope" (Lucy Norman) (vert) 25 60
448 17p. "Swans on a Lake" (Nicola O'Dwyer) 35 85

166 Pope John Paul II

1979. Visit of Pope John Paul II.
449 **166** 12p. multicoloured 30 20

167 Brother with Child

1979. Anniversaries and Events.
450 **167** 9½p. brown and mauve 20 10
451 - 11p. orange, black and blue 20 70
452 - 20p. multicoloured 40 1·40
DESIGNS—VERT: 11p. Windmill and sun (Int Energy Conservation Month). HORIZ: 9½p. Type **167** (Cent of Hospitaller Order of St. John of God in Ireland); 20p. "Seated Figure" (sculpture F. E. McWilliam) (Contemporary Irish Art (10th issue)).

168 Patrick Pearse, "Liberty" and G.P.O., Dublin

1979. Birth Centenary of Patrick Pearse (patriot).
453 **168** 12p. multicoloured 30 15

169 "Madonna and Child" (panel painting from the Domnach Airgid Shrine)

1979. Christmas.
454 **169** 9½p. multicoloured 15 10
455 **169** 20p. multicoloured 30 55

170 Bianconi Long Car, 1836

1979. Europa. Multicoloured.
456 12p. Type **170** 1·25 30
457 13p. Transatlantic cable, Valentia, 1866 1·75 1·40

171 John Baptist de la Salle (founder)

1980. Cent of Arrival of De La Salle Order.
458 **171** 12p. multicoloured 30 30

172 George Bernard Shaw

1980. Europa. Personalities. Multicoloured.

459	12p. Type **172**	1·25	50
460	13p. Oscar Wilde (29×40 mm)	2·00	2·50

173 Stoat

1980. Wildlife. Multicoloured.

461	12p. Type **173**	25	40
462	15p. Arctic hare	25	15
463	16p. Red fox	25	80
464	25p. Red deer	35	1·60
MS465	73×97 mm. Nos. 461/4	1·00	2·75

174 Playing Bodhran and Whistle

1980. Traditional Music and Dance. Mult.

466	12p. Type **174**	15	10
467	15p. Playing Uilleann pipes	20	15
468	25p. Dancing	35	1·10

175 Sean O'Casey

1980. Commemorations.

469	12p. multicoloured	20	10
470	25p. black, buff and brown	35	1·00

DESIGNS AND COMMEMORATIONS: 12p. Type **175** (playwright) (birth centenary); 25p. "Gold Painting No. 57" (P. Scott) (Contemporary Irish Art (11th issue)).

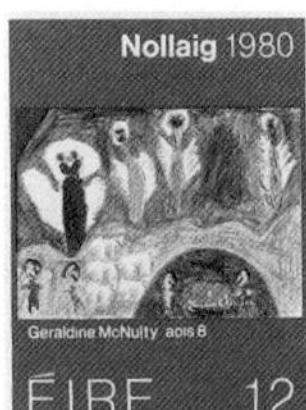

176 Nativity Scene (painting by Geraldine McNulty)

1980. Christmas.

471	**176**	12p. multicoloured	15	10
472	**176**	15p. multicoloured	20	10
473	**176**	25p. multicoloured	40	1·25

177 Boyle Air-pump, 1659

1981. Irish Science and Technology. Mult.

474	12p. Type **177**	20	10
475	15p. Ferguson tractor, 1936	25	10
476	16p. Parsons turbine, 1884	30	90
477	25p. Holland submarine, 1878	35	1·25

178 "The Legend of the Cock and the Pot"

1981. Europa. Folklore. Paintings by Maria Simonds-Gooding.

491	**178**	18p. black, yellow and red	1·25	10
492	-	19p. black, orange & yellow	2·25	1·50

DESIGN: 19p. "The Angel with the Scales of Judgement".

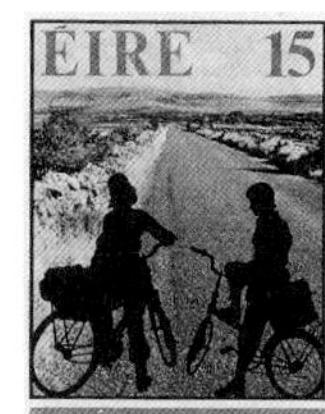

179 Cycling

1981. 50th Anniv of "An Oige" (Irish Youth Hostel Association). Multicoloured.

493	15p. Type **179**	25	40
494	18p. Hill-walking (horiz)	25	10
495	19p. Mountaineering (horiz)	25	95
496	30p. Rock-climbing	40	95

180 Jeremiah O'Donovan Rossa

1981. 150th Birth Anniv of Jeremiah O'Donovan Rossa (politician).

497	**180**	15p. multicoloured	40	30

181 "Railway Embankment" (W. J. Leech)

1981. Contemporary Irish Art (12th issue).

498	**181**	30p. multicoloured	1·00	70

182 James Hoban and White House

1981. 150th Death Anniv of James Hoban (White House architect).

499	**182**	18p. multicoloured	50	30

183 "Arkle" (steeplechaser)

1981. Famous Irish Horses. Multicoloured.

500	18p. Type **183**	50	1·00
501	18p. "Boomerang" (show-jumper)	50	1·00
502	22p. "King of Diamonds" (Draught horse)	50	30
503	24p. "Ballymoss" (flat-racer)	50	70
504	36p. "Coosheen Finn" (Connemara pony)	60	1·00

184 "Nativity" (F. Barocci)

1981. Christmas.

505	**184**	18p. multicoloured	25	10
506	**184**	22p. multicoloured	30	10
507	**184**	36p. multicoloured	80	1·50

185 Eviction Scene

1981. Anniversaries. Multicoloured.

508	18p. Type **185**	50	25
509	22p. Royal Dublin Society emblem	50	30

ANNIVERSARIES: 18p. Centenary of Land Law (Ireland) Act. 22p. Royal Dublin Society (organization for the advancement of agriculture, industry, art and science), 250th Anniv.

186 Upper Lake, Killarney National Park

1982. 50th Anniv of Killarney National Park. Multicoloured.

510	18p. Type **186**	40	20
511	36p. Eagle's Nest	85	1·60

187 "The Stigmatization of St. Francis" (Sassetta)

1982. Religious Anniversaries.

512	**187**	22p. multicoloured	50	15
513	-	24p. brown	75	85

DESIGNS AND ANNIVERSARIES: 22p. Type **187** (St. Francis of Assisi (founder of Franciscan order) (500th birth anniv); 24p. Francis Makemie (founder of American Presbyterianism) and old Presbyterian Church, Ramelton, Co. Donegal (300th anniv of ordination).

188 The Great Famine, 1845–50

1982. Europa. Historic Events.

514	**188**	26p. black and stone	3·50	50
515	-	29p. multicoloured	4·50	5·00

DESIGN—HORIZ: 29p. The coming of Christianity to Ireland.

189 Padraic O. Conaire (writer) (birth centenary)

1982. Anniversaries of Cultural Figures.

516	**189**	22p. black and blue	25	30
517	-	26p. black and brown	55	30
518	-	29p. black and blue	65	1·75
519	-	44p. black and grey	65	1·60

DESIGNS AND ANNIVERSARIES: 26p. James Joyce (writer) (birth centenary); 29p. John Field (musician) (birth centenary); 44p. Charles Kickham (writer) (death centenary).

190 Porbeagle Shark

1982. Marine Life. Multicoloured.

520	22p. Type **190**	60	1·25
521	22p. Common European oyster	60	1·25
522	26p. Atlantic salmon	70	30
523	29p. Dublin Bay prawn	70	1·75

191 "St. Patrick" (Galway hooker)

1982. Irish Boats. Multicoloured.

524	22p. Type **191**	60	1·25
525	22p. Curragh (horiz)	60	1·25
526	26p. "Asgard II" (cadet brigantine) (horiz)	70	30
527	29p. Howth 17 foot yacht	70	1·75

192 "Irish House of Commons" (painting by Francis Wheatley)

1982. Bicentenary of Grattan's Parliament and Birth Centenary of Eamon de Valera. Multicoloured.

528	22p. Type **192**	35	1·25
529	26p. Eamon de Valera (vert)	40	40

193 "Madonna and Child" (sculpture)

1982. Christmas.

530	**193**	22p. multicoloured	30	90
531	**193**	26p. multicoloured	30	35

194 Aughnanure Castle

1983. Irish Architecture.

532	-	1p. blue	10	10
533	-	2p. green	20	10
534	-	3p. black	20	10
535	-	4p. red	20	10
536	-	5p. brown	30	10
537	-	6p. blue	30	15
538	-	7p. green	30	1·25
539	-	10p. black	30	10
540	-	12p. brown	30	1·75
541	**194**	15p. green	45	35
542	**194**	20p. purple	50	45
543	**194**	22p. blue	50	10
544	-	23p. green	85	1·25
544a	-	24p. brown	1·25	35
545	-	26p. black	75	10
545c	-	28p. red	75	45
546	-	29p. green	70	1·00
547	-	30p. black	70	30
547c	-	32p. brown	2·50	3·00
547d	-	37p. blue	1·00	2·75
547e	-	39p. red	2·50	2·75
548	-	44p. black and grey	1·00	70
548b	-	46p. green and grey	6·50	2·00
549	-	50p. blue and grey	1·75	65
550	-	£1 brown and grey	4·50	3·75
550b	-	£1 blue and grey	5·00	1·25
550c	-	£2 green and black	6·50	5·50
551	-	£5 red and grey	12·00	6·00

DESIGNS—HORIZ: (As T **194**): 1 to 5p. Central Pavilion, Dublin Botanic Gardens; 6 to 12p. Dr. Steevens' Hospital, Dublin; 28 to 37p. St. MacDara's Church. (37×21 mm); 46p., £1 (No. 550) Cahir Castle; 50p., £2 Casino Marino. £5 Central Bus Station, Dublin. VERT: (As T **194**): 23 to 26p., 39p. Cormac's Chapel. (21×37 mm); 44p., £1 (No. 550b) Killarney Cathedral.

195 Ouzel Gallery Goblet

1983. Bicentenaries of Dublin Chamber of Commerce (22p.) and Bank of Ireland (26p.). Multicoloured.

552	22p. Type **195**	30	90
553	26p. Bank of Ireland building (horiz)	35	35

196 Padraig O. Siochfhradha (writer and teacher)

1983. Anniversaries. Multicoloured.

554	26p. Type **196** (birth cent)	50	75
555	29p. Young Boys' Brigade member (centenary)	90	1·50

197 Neolithic Carved Pattern, Newgrange Tomb

1983. Europa.

556	**197**	26p. black and yellow	2·50	50
557	-	29p. black, brown & yellow	7·00	5·50

DESIGN: 29p. Sir William Rowan Hamilton's formulae for the multiplication of quaternions.

198 Kerry Blue Terrier

1983. Irish Dogs. Multicoloured.

558	22p. Type **198**	65	35
559	26p. Irish wolfhound	70	45
560	26p. Irish water spaniel	70	45
561	29p. Irish terrier	75	2·25
562	44p. Irish setters	1·25	2·50
MS563	142×80 mm. Nos. 558/62	6·00	8·00

199 Animals (Irish Society for the Prevention of Cruelty to Animals)

1983. Anniversaries and Commemorations.

564	**199**	22p. multicoloured	50	1·00
565	-	22p. multicoloured	50	1·00
566	-	26p. multicoloured	50	60
567	-	26p. multicoloured	50	60
568	-	44p. blue and black	75	2·00

DESIGNS—VERT: No. 565, Sean MacDiarmada (patriot) (birth cent); 567, "St. Vincent de Paul in the Streets of Paris" (150th anniv of Society of St. Vincent de Paul); 568, "Andrew Jackson" (Frank McKelvey) (President of the United States). HORIZ: No. 566, "100" (Centenary of Industrial Credit Company).

200 Postman with Bicycle

1983. World Communications Year. Multicoloured.

569	22p. Type **200**	1·10	75
570	29p. Dish antenna	90	2·00

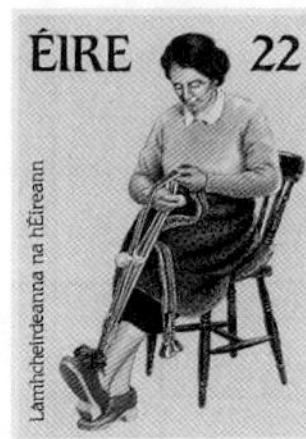

201 Weaving

1983. Irish Handicrafts. Multicoloured.

571	22p. Type **201**	60	50
572	26p. Basket making	60	35
573	29p. Irish crochet	65	1·25
574	44p. Harp making	1·25	2·50

202 "La Natividad" (R. van der Weyden)

1983. Christmas.

575	**202**	22p. multicoloured	40	30
576	**202**	26p. multicoloured	60	30

203 Dublin and Kingstown Railway Steam Locomotive "Princess"

1984. 150th Anniv of Irish Railways. Mult.

577	23p. Type **203**	75	1·25
578	26p. Great Southern Railways steam locomotive "Macha"	75	35
579	29p. Great Northern Railway steam locomotive No. 87 "Kestrel"	85	1·75
580	44p. Two-car electric train Coras Iompair Eireann	1·10	2·25
MS581	129×77 mm. Nos. 577/80	3·75	5·00

204 "Sorbus hibernica"

1984. Irish Trees. Multicoloured.

582	22p. Type **204**	55	70
583	26p. "Taxus baccata fastigiata"	60	30
584	29p. "Salix hibernica"	70	1·75
585	44p. "Betula pubescens"	1·00	2·50

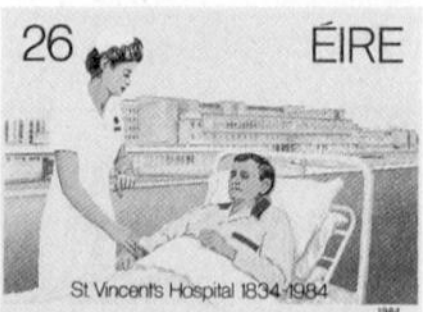

205 St. Vincent's Hospital, Dublin

1984. 150th Anniv of St. Vincent's Hospital and Bicentenary of Royal College of Surgeons. Multicoloured.

586	26p. Type **205**	75	30
587	44p. Royal College and logo	1·25	1·50

206 C.E.P.T. 25th Anniversary Logo

1984. Europa.

588	**206**	26p. blue, dp blue & black	2·50	50
589	**206**	29p. lt green, green & blk	5·00	4·25

207 Flags on Ballot Box

1984. Second Direct Elections to European Assembly.

590	**207**	26p. multicoloured	1·00	70

208 John McCormack

1984. Birth Centenary of John McCormack (tenor).

591	**208**	22p. multicoloured	50	70

209 Hammer-throwing

1984. Olympic Games, Los Angeles.

592	**209**	22p. mauve, black and gold	35	80
593	-	26p. violet, black and gold	40	65
594	-	29p. blue, black and gold	60	1·25

DESIGNS: 26p. Hurdling; 29p. Running.

210 Hurling

1984. Cent of Gaelic Athletic Association. Mult.

595	22p. Type **210**	50	90
596	26p. Irish football (vert)	60	90

211 Galway Mayoral Chain

1984. Anniversaries. Multicoloured.

597	26p. Type **211** (500th anniv of mayoral charter)	35	50
598	44p. St. Brendan (from 15th-cent Bodleian manuscript) (1500th birth anniv) (horiz)	75	1·50

212 Hands passing Letter

1984. Bicentenary of Irish Post Office.

599	**212**	26p. multicoloured	60	70

213 "Virgin and Child" (Sassoferrato)

1984. Christmas. Multicoloured.

600	17p. Christmas star (horiz)	45	80
601	22p. Type **213**	45	1·25
602	26p. Type **213**	65	40

214 "Love" and Heart-shaped Balloon

1985. Greetings Stamps. Multicoloured.

603	22p. Type **214**	50	75
604	26p. Bouquet of hearts and flowers (vert)	60	75

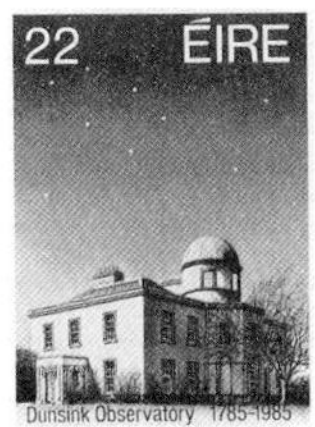

215 Dunsink Observatory (bicentenary)

1985. Anniversaries. Multicoloured.

605	22p. Type **215**	60	50
606	26p. "A Landscape at Tivoli, Cork, with Boats" (Nathaniel Grogan) (800th anniv of City of Cork) (horiz)	60	30
607	37p. Royal Irish Academy (bicentenary)	80	1·75
608	44p. Richard Crosbie's balloon flight (bicentenary of first aeronautic flight by an Irishman)	1·00	1·75

216 "Polyommatus icarus"

1985. Butterflies. Multicoloured.

609	22p. Type **216**	1·50	1·00
610	26p. "Vanessa atalanta"	1·50	70
611	28p. "Gonepteryx rhamni"	1·75	3·00
612	44p. "Eurabyas aurinia"	2·00	3·25

217 Charles Villiers Stanford (composer)

1985. Europa. Irish Composers. Multicoloured.

613	26p. Type **217**	2·50	50
614	37p. Turlough Carolan (composer and lyricist)	5·50	6·00

218 George Frederick Handel

1985. European Music Year. Composers. Mult.

615	22p. Type **218**	1·25	2·50
616	22p. Guiseppe Domenico Scarlatti	1·25	2·50
617	26p. Johann Sebastian Bach	1·50	50

219 U.N. Patrol of Irish Soldiers, Congo, 1960

1985. Anniversaries. Multicoloured.

618	22p. Type **219** (25th anniv of Irish Participation in U.N. Peace-keeping Force)	55	80
619	26p. Thomas Ashe (patriot) (birth cent) (vert)	55	60
620	44p. "Bishop George Berkeley" (James Lathan) (philosopher, 300th birth anniv) (vert)	85	3·00

220 Group of Young People

1985. International Youth Year. Mult.

621	22p. Type **220**	55	50
622	26p. Students and young workers (vert)	55	50

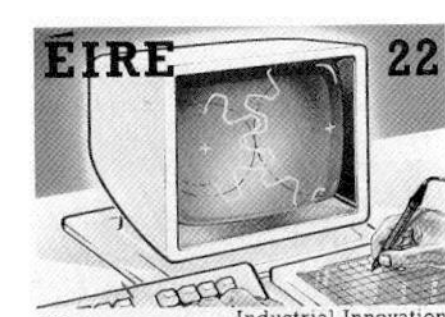

221 Visual Display Unit

1985. Industrial Innovation. Multicoloured.

623	22p. Type **221**	50	75
624	26p. Turf cutting with hand tool and with modern machinery	50	55
625	44p. "The Key Man" (Sean Keating) (150th anniv of Institution of Engineers of Ireland)	1·00	2·50

222 Lighted Candle and Holly

1985. Christmas. Multicoloured.

626	22p. Type **222**	50	50
627	22p. "Virgin and Child in a Landscape" (Adrian van Ijsenbrandt)	80	2·00
628	22p. "The Holy Family" (Murillo)	80	2·00
629	26p. "The Adoration of the Shepherds" (Louis le Nain) (horiz)	80	25

No. 626 was only issued in sheetlets of 16 sold at £3, providing a discount of 52p. off the face value of the stamps.

224 Stylized Love Bird with Letter

1986. Greetings Stamps. Multicoloured.

630	22p. Type **224**	75	90
631	26p. Heart-shaped pillar-box	75	90

225 Hart's Tongue Fern

1986. Ferns. Multicoloured.

632	24p. Type **225**	70	70
633	28p. Rusty-back fern	80	70
634	46p. Killarney fern	1·25	2·10

226 "Harmony between Industry and Nature"

1986. Europa. Protection of the Environment. Multicoloured.

635	28p. Type **226**	6·00	50
636	39p. "Vanessa atalanta" (butterfly) and tractor in field ("Preserve hedgerows") (horiz)	18·00	6·00

227 Boeing 747-200 over Globe showing Aer Lingus Routes

1986. 50th Anniv of Aer Lingus (airline). Multicoloured.

637	28p. Type **227**	1·50	75
638	46p. de Havilland Dragon Mk 2 EI-ABI "Iolar" (first airplane)	2·25	3·00

228 Grand Canal at Robertstown

1986. Irish Waterways. Multicoloured.

639	24p. Type **228**	1·50	1·00
640	28p. Fishing in County Mayo (vert)	1·60	1·00
641	30p. Motor cruiser on Lough Derg	1·75	2·50

229 "Severn" (19th-century paddlesteamer)

1986. 150th Anniv of British and Irish Steam Packet Company. Multicoloured.

642	24p. Type **229**	75	1·00
643	28p. "Leinster" (modern ferry)	85	60

230 Kish Lighthouse and Bell JetRanger III Helicopter

1986. Irish Lighthouses. Multicoloured.

644	24p. Type **230**	1·50	75
645	30p. Fastnet Lighthouse	2·50	2·75

231 J. P. Nannetti (first president) and Linotype Operator (Dublin Council of Trade Unions centenary)

1986. Anniversaries and Commemorations.

646	**231**	24p. multicoloured	50	90
647	-	28p. black and grey	60	80
648	-	28p. multicoloured	60	80
649	-	30p. multicoloured	70	1·00
650	-	46p. multicoloured	80	1·75

DESIGNS:—VERT: No. 647, Arthur Griffith (statesman); 649, Clasped hands (International Peace Year). HORIZ: No. 648, Woman surveyor (Women in Society); 650, Peace dove (International Peace Year).

232 William Mulready and his Design for 1840 Envelope

1986. Birth Bicentenaries of William Mulready (artist) (24p.) and Charles Bianconi (originator of Irish mail coach service) (others). Multicoloured.

651	24p. Type **232**	70	70
652	28p. Bianconi car outside Hearns Hotel, Clonmel (vert)	85	55
653	39p. Bianconi car on the road	1·40	1·75

233 "Adoration of the Shepherds" (Francesco Pascucci)

1986. Christmas. Multicoloured.

654	21p. Type **233**	1·10	1·40
655	28p. "Adoration of the Magi" (Frans Francken III) (vert)	65	60

234 "Butterfly and Flowers" (Tara Collins)

1987. Greetings Stamps. Children's Paintings. Multicoloured.

656	24p. Type **234**	75	1·25
657	28p. "Postman on Bicycle delivering Hearts" (Brigid Teehan) (vert)	1·25	1·25

235 Cork Electric Tram

1987. Irish Trams. Multicoloured.

658	24p. Type **235**	65	65
659	28p. Dublin standard tram No. 29	70	85
660	30p. Howth (Great Northern Railway) tram	80	2·00
661	46p. Galway horse tram	1·25	2·25
MS662	131×85 mm. Nos. 658/61	3·75	5·25

236 Ships from Crest (Bicentenary of Waterford Chamber of Commerce)

1987. Anniversaries.

663	**236**	24p. black, blue and green	70	60
664	-	28p. multicoloured	70	60
665	-	30p. multicoloured	70	2·00
666	-	39p. multicoloured	75	1·75

DESIGNS—HORIZ: 28p. Canon John Hayes and symbols of agriculture and development (birth centenary and 50th anniv of Muintir na Tire programme); 39p. Mother Mary Martin and International Missionary Training Hospital, Drogheda (50th anniv of Medical Missionaries of Mary). VERT: 30p. "Calceolaria burbidgei" and College crest (300th anniv of Trinity College Botanic Gardens, Dublin).

237 Bord na Mona Headquarters and "The Turf Cutter" (sculpture, John Behan), Dublin

1987. Europa. Modern Architecture. Mult.

667	28p. Type **237**	3·00	60
668	39p. St. Mary's Church, Cong	6·50	6·50

238 Kerry Cow

1987. Irish Cattle. Multicoloured.

669	24p. Type **238**	80	75
670	28p. Friesian cow and calf	95	60
671	30p. Hereford bullock	1·00	2·25
672	39p. Shorthorn bull	1·10	2·25

239 Fleadh Nua, Ennis

1987. Festivals. Multicoloured.

673	24p. Type **239**	75	70
674	28p. Rose of Tralee International Festival	80	60
675	30p. Wexford Opera Festival (horiz)	1·50	2·00
676	46p. Ballinasloe Horse Fair (horiz)	1·50	2·00

240 Flagon (1637), Arms and Anniversary Ornament (1987) (350th anniv of Dublin Goldsmiths' Company)

1987. Anniversaries and Commemorations.

677	**240**	24p. multicoloured	80	80
678	-	24p. grey and black	80	80
679	-	28p. multicoloured	1·00	60
680	-	46p. multicoloured	1·40	1·10

DESIGNS—VERT: 24p. (No. 678) Cathal Brugha (patriot); 46p. Woman chairing board meeting (Women in Society). HORIZ: 28p. Arms of Ireland and inscription (50th anniv of Constitution).

241 Scenes from "The Twelve Days of Christmas" (carol)

1987. Christmas. Multicoloured.

681	21p. Type **241**	60	1·00
682	24p. The Nativity (detail, late 15th-century Waterford Vestments) (vert)	75	1·00
683	28p. Figures from Neapolitan crib, c. 1850 (vert)	75	80

242 Acrobatic Clowns spelling "LOVE"

1988. Greetings Stamps. Multicoloured.

684	24p. Type **242**	75	60
685	28p. Pillar box and hearts (vert)	75	65

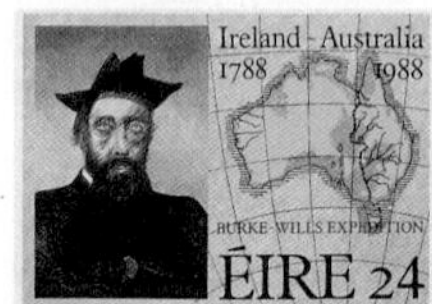

243 "Robert Burke" (Sidney Nolan) and Map of Burke and Wills Expedition Route

1988. Bicent of Australian Settlement. Mult.

686	24p. Type **243**	1·00	60
687	46p. "Eureka Stockade" (mural detail, Sidney Nolan)	1·25	1·75

244 Past and Present Buildings of Dublin

1988. Dublin Millennium.

688	**244**	28p. multicoloured	45	55

245 Showjumping

1988. Olympic Games, Seoul. Multicoloured.

689	28p. Type **245**	1·00	1·40
690	28p. Cycling	1·00	1·40

246 William T. Cosgrave (statesman)

1988. Anniversaries and Events.

691	**246**	24p. grey and black	45	45
692	-	30p. multicoloured	80	1·00
693	-	50p. multicoloured	1·00	1·90

DESIGNS—HORIZ: 30p. Members with casualty and ambulance (50th anniv of Order of Malta Ambulance Corps). VERT: 50p. Barry Fitzgerald (actor) (birth centenary).

247 Air Traffic Controllers and Airbus Industrie A320

1988. Europa. Transport and Communications. Multicoloured.

694	28p. Type **247**	2·25	55
695	39p. Globe with stream of letters from Ireland to Europe	3·25	3·50

248 "Sirius" (paddle-steamer)

1988. Transatlantic Transport Anniversaries. Multicoloured.

696	24p. Type **248** (150th anniv of regular transatlantic steamship services)	1·00	50
697	46p. Short S.20 seaplane "Mercury" G-ADHJ and Short S.21 flying boat G-ADHK "Maia" (Short Mayo composite aircraft) in Foynes Harbour (50th anniv of first commercial transatlantic flight)	1·75	3·00

249 Cottonweed

1988. Endangered Flora of Ireland. Mult.

698	24p. Type **249**	70	55
699	28p. Hart's saxifrage	80	55
700	46p. Purple milk-vetch	1·00	2·75

250 Garda on Duty

1988. Irish Security Forces. Multicoloured.

701	28p. Type **250**	70	1·10
702	28p. Army unit with personnel carrier	70	1·10
703	28p. Navy and Air Corps members with "Eithne" (helicopter patrol vessel)	70	1·10
704	28p. Army and Navy reservists	70	1·10

251 Computer and Abacus

1988. Anniversaries. Multicoloured.

705	24p. Type **251** (Institute of Chartered Accountants in Ireland centenary)	40	40
706	46p. "Duquesa Santa Ana" off Donegal (400th anniv of Spanish Armada) (horiz)	1·25	1·25

252 "President Kennedy" (James Wyeth)

1988. 25th Death Anniv of John F. Kennedy (American statesman).

707	**252**	28p. multicoloured	1·00	80

253 St. Kevin's Church, Glendalough

1988. Christmas. Multicoloured.

708	21p. Type **253**	80	1·00
709	24p. The Adoration of the Magi	50	60
710	28p. The Flight into Egypt	60	45
711	46p. The Holy Family	1·00	3·00

The designs of Nos. 709/11 are from a 15th-century French Book of Hours.

254 Spring Flowers spelling "Love" in Gaelic

1989. Greetings Stamps. Multicoloured.

712	24p. Type **254**	75	55
713	28p. "The Sonnet" (William Mulready) (vert)	75	55

255 Italian Garden, Garinish Island

1989. National Parks and Gardens. Multicoloured.

714	24p. Type **255**	90	55
715	28p. Lough Veagh, Glenveagh National Park	1·10	55
716	32p. Barnaderg Bay, Connemara National Park	1·25	1·25
717	50p. St. Stephen's Green, Dublin	1·75	1·75

256 "Silver Stream", 1908

1989. Classic Irish Cars. Multicoloured.

718	24p Type **256**	50	55
719	28p Benz "Comfortable", 1898	50	55
720	39p "Thomond", 1929	1·25	1·50
721	46p Chambers' 8 h.p. model, 1905	1·50	1·50

257 Ring-a-ring-a-roses

1989. Europa. Children's Games. Multicoloured.

722	28p. Type **257**	75	75
723	39p. Hopscotch	1·00	2·25

258 Irish Red Cross Flag (50th anniv)

1989. Anniversaries and Events.

724	**258**	24p. red and black	55	60

725	-	28p. blue, black and yellow	1·60	1·10

DESIGN: 28p. Circle of twelve stars (third direct elections to European Parliament).

259 Saints Kilian, Totnan and Colman (from 12th-century German manuscript)

1989. 1300th Death Anniv of Saints Kilian, Totnan and Colman.

726	**259**	28p. multicoloured	45	1·10

260 19th-century Mail Coach passing Cashel

1989. Bicentenary of Irish Mail Coach Service.

727	**260**	28p. multicoloured	1·50	75

261 Crest and 19th-century Dividers (150th anniv of Royal Institute of Architects of Ireland)

1989. Anniversaries and Commemorations.

728	-	24p. grey and black	65	55
729	**261**	28p. multicoloured	65	55
730	-	30p. multicoloured	1·75	2·25
731	-	46p. brown	3·00	3·25

DESIGNS—VERT: 24p. Sean T. O'Kelly (statesman) (drawing by Sean O'Sullivan); 46p. Jawaharlal Nehru (birth centenary). HORIZ: 30p. Margaret Burke-Sheridan (soprano) (portrait by De Gennaro) and scene from "La Boheme" (birth centenary).

262 "NCB Ireland' rounding Cape Horn" (Des Fallon)

1989. First Irish Entry in Whitbread Round the World Yacht Race.

732	**262**	28p. multicoloured	1·50	1·25

263 Willow/Red Grouse

1989. Game Birds. Multicoloured.

733	24p. Type **263**	1·00	55
734	28p. Northern lapwing	1·00	55
735	39p. Eurasian woodcock	1·25	2·50
736	46p. Common pheasant	1·25	2·50
MS737	128×92 mm. Nos. 733/6	5·00	7·00

264 "The Annunciation"

1989. Christmas. Multicoloured.

738	21p. Children decorating crib	75	75
739	24p. Type **264**	75	60
740	28p. "The Nativity"	80	55
741	46p. "The Adoration of the Magi"	1·60	2·50

265 Logo (Ireland's Presidency of the European Communities)

1990. European Events. Multicoloured.

742	30p. Type **265**	1·00	60
743	50p. Logo and outline map of Ireland (European Tourism Year)	2·25	3·00

266 Dropping Messages from Balloon

1990. Greetings Stamps.

744	**266**	26p. multicoloured	1·50	1·25
745	-	30p. red, buff and brown	1·50	1·25

DESIGN: 30p. Heart and "Love" drawn in lipstick.

267 Silver Kite Brooch

1990. Irish Heritage.

746	**267**	1p. black and blue	10	10
747	**267**	2p. black and orange	10	10
748	-	4p. black and violet	15	30
749	-	5p. black and green	20	10
750	-	10p. black and orange	30	25
751	-	20p. black and yellow	50	40
752	-	26p. black and violet	1·50	65
809	-	28p. black and orange	1·75	3·00
754	-	30p. black and blue	1·25	1·50
810	-	32p. black and green	50	80
756	-	34p. black and yellow	1·25	1·25
757	-	37p. black and green	1·50	2·25
758	-	38p. black and violet	1·50	2·25
758b	-	40p. black and blue	1·50	1·50
759	-	41p. black and orange	1·50	2·25
760	-	44p. brown and yellow	2·50	3·00
760a	-	45p. black and violet	3·25	2·00
761	-	50p. black and yellow	1·75	2·25
762	-	52p. black and blue	3·25	3·50
763	-	£1 black and yellow	3·25	2·25
764	-	£2 black and green	4·50	3·25
765	-	£5 black and blue	10·00	9·00

DESIGNS: 4, 5p. Dunamase food vessel; 26, 28p. Lismore crozier; 34, 37, 38, 40p. Gleninsheen collar; 41, 44p. Silver thistle brooch; 45, 50, 52p. Broighter boat. 22×38 mm: £5 St. Patrick's Bell Shrine. HORIZ: 10p. Derrinboy armlets; 20p. Gold dress fastener; 30p. Enamelled latchet brooch; 32p. Broighter collar. 38×22 mm: £1 Ardagh Chalice; £2 Tara brooch.

For 32p. value as No. 755 but larger, 29×24 mm, and self-adhesive, see No. 823.

268 Posy of Flowers

1990. Greetings Stamps. Multicoloured.

766	26p. Type **268**	2·00	2·50
767	26p. Birthday presents	2·00	2·50
768	30p. Flowers, ribbon and horseshoe	2·00	2·50
769	30p. Balloons	2·00	2·50

269 Player heading Ball

1990. World Cup Football Championship, Italy. Multicoloured.

770	30p. Type **269**	1·50	2·00
771	30p. Tackling	1·50	2·00

270 Battle of the Boyne, 1690

1990. 300th Anniv of the Williamite Wars (1st issue). Multicoloured.

772	30p. Type **270**	1·75	1·75
773	30p. Siege of Limerick, 1690	1·75	1·75

See also Nos. 806/7.

271 1990 Irish Heritage 30p. Stamp and 1840 Postmark

1990. 150th Anniv of the Penny Black. Mult.

774	30p. Type **271**	90	90
775	50p. Definitive stamps of 1922, 1969, 1982 and 1990	1·25	2·25

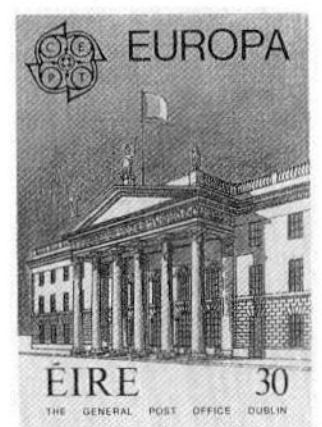
272 General Post Office, Dublin

1990. Europa Post Office Buildings. Mult.

776	30p. Type **272**	1·00	60
777	41p. Westport Post Office, County Mayo	1·75	3·00

273 Medical Missionary giving Injection

1990. Anniversaries and Events.

778	**273**	26p. multicoloured	80	40
779	-	30p. black	1·00	2·75
780	-	50p. multicoloured	1·00	1·75

DESIGNS—VERT: 30p. Michael Collins (statesman) (birth centenary). HORIZ: 50p. Missionaries working at water pump (Irish missionary service).

274 Narcissus "Foundling" and Japanese Gardens, Tully

1990. Garden Flowers. Multicoloured.

781	26p. Type **274**	60	55
782	30p. "Rosa x hibernica" and Malahide Castle gardens	70	80

783	41p. Primula "Rowallane Rose" and Rowallane garden	1·25	2·50
784	50p. "Erica erigena" "Irish Dusk" and Palm House, National Botanical Gardens	1·50	2·75

275 "Playboy of the Western World" (John Synge)

1990. Irish Theatre. Multicoloured.

785	30p. Type **275**	1·25	1·75
786	30p. "Juno and the Pay-cock" (Sean O'Casey)	1·25	1·75
787	30p. "The Field" (John Keane)	1·25	1·75
788	30p. "Waiting for Godot" (Samuel Beckett)	1·25	1·75

276 Nativity

1990. Christmas. Multicoloured.

789	26p. Child praying by bed	75	80
790	26p. Type **276**	60	60
791	30p. Madonna and Child	90	90
792	50p. Adoration of the Magi	1·75	3·50

277 Hearts in Mail Sack and Postman's Cap

1991. Greetings Stamps. Multicoloured.

793	26p. Type **277**	85	1·00
794	30p. Boy and girl kissing	90	1·00

278 Starley "Rover" Bicycle, 1886

1991. Early Bicycles. Multicoloured.

795	26p. Type **278**	90	60
796	30p. Child's horse tricycle, 1875	1·00	1·00
797	50p. "Penny Farthing", 1871	1·75	2·50
MS798	113×72 mm. Nos. 795/7	3·25	4·00

279 "Cuchulainn" (statue by Oliver Sheppard) and Proclamation

1991. 75th Anniv of Easter Rising.

799	**279**	32p. multicoloured	1·00	1·40

280 Scene from "La Traviata" (50th anniv of Dublin Grand Opera Society)

1991. "Dublin 1991 European City of Culture". Multicoloured.

800 28p. Type **280** 1·00 1·00
801 32p. City Hall and European Community emblem 1·10 1·60
802 44p. St. Patrick's Cathedral (800th anniv) 90 1·60
803 52p. Custom House (bicent) (41×24 mm) 1·00 1·60

281 "Giotto" Spacecraft approaching Halley's Comet

1991. Europa. Europe in Space. Multicoloured.

804 32p. Type **281** 1·00 1·00
805 44p. Hubble Telescope orbiting Earth 1·50 3·00

282 Siege of Athlone

1991. 300th Anniv of the Williamite Wars (2nd issue). Multicoloured.

806 28p. Type **282** 1·25 1·75
807 28p. Generals Ginkel and Sarsfield (signatories of Treaty of Limerick) 1·25 1·75

283 John A. Costello (statesman)

1991. Anniversaries.

811 **283** 28p. black 1·25 70
812 - 32p. multicoloured 1·40 1·00
813 - 52p. multicoloured 1·75 2·50

DESIGNS—VERT: 28p. Type **283** (birth cent) (drawing by Sean O'Sullivan); 32p. "Charles Stewart Parnell" (Sydney Hall) (death cent); HORIZ: 52p. Meeting of United Irishmen.

284 Player on 15th Green, Portmarnock (Walker Cup)

1991. Golf Commemorations. Multicoloured.

814 28p. Type **284** 1·00 75
815 32p. Logo and golfer of 1900 (cent of Golfing Union of Ireland) (vert) 1·25 1·00

285 Wicklow Cheviot

1991. Irish Sheep. Multicoloured.

816 32p. Type **285** 1·00 80
817 38p. Donegal Blackface 1·40 1·75
818 52p. Galway (horiz) 2·00 3·50

286 Boatyard

1991. Fishing Fleet. Multicoloured.

819 28p. Type **286** 70 65
820 32p. Traditional inshore trawlers 80 80
821 44p. Inshore lobster pot boat 1·60 2·50
822 52p. "Veronica" (fish factory ship) 1·90 2·75

1991. As No. 755, but larger, 27×21 mm. Self-adhesive.

823a 32p. black and green 1·00 1·25

287 The Annunciation

1991. Christmas.

827 - 28p. multicoloured 1·00 1·00
828 **287** 28p. blue, green and black 1·00 65
829 - 32p. red and black 1·10 75
830 - 52p. multicoloured 2·00 3·25

DESIGNS: No. 827, Three Kings; No. 829, The Nativity; No. 830, Adoration of the Kings.

288 Multicoloured Heart

1992. Greetings Stamps. Multicoloured.

831 28p. Type **288** 1·00 95
832 32p. "LOVE" at end of rainbow (vert) 1·10 1·10

289 Healthy Family on Apple

1992. "Healthy Living" Campaign.

833 **289** 28p. multicoloured 1·25 1·00

290 Boxing

1992. Olympic Games, Barcelona. Mult.

834 32p. Type **290** 75 90
835 44p. Sailing 1·00 2·25
MS836 130×85 mm. Nos. 834/5×2 4·75 6·00

291 "Mari" (cog) and 14th-century Map

1992. Irish Maritime Heritage. Multicoloured.

837 32p. Type **291** 1·00 90
838 52p. "Ovoca" (trawler) and chart (vert) 1·50 2·75

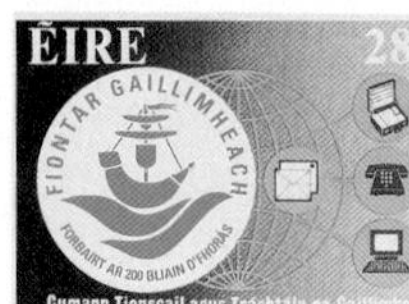

292 Chamber Logo and Commercial Symbols

1992. Bicentenary of Galway Chamber of Commerce and Industry.

839 **292** 28p. multicoloured 1·00 1·00

293 Cliffs and Cove

1992. Greetings Stamps. Multicoloured.

840 28p. Type **293** 90 1·10
841 28p. Meadow 90 1·10
842 32p. Fuchsia and honeysuckle 90 1·10
843 32p. Lily pond and dragonfly 90 1·10

294 Fleet of Columbus

1992. Europa. 500th Anniv of Discovery of America by Columbus. Multicoloured.

844 32p. Type **294** 1·25 90
845 44p. Columbus landing in the New World 2·00 3·00

295 Irish Immigrants

1992. Irish Immigrants in the Americas. Mult.

846 52p. Type **295** 1·75 1·75
847 52p. Irish soldiers, entertainers and politicians 1·75 1·75

296 Pair of Pine Martens

1992. Endangered Species. Pine Marten. Mult.

848 28p. Type **296** 1·00 70
849 32p. Marten on branch 1·00 80
850 44p. Female with kittens 1·60 1·50
851 52p. Marten catching great tit 2·00 2·50

297 "The Rotunda and New Rooms" (James Malton)

1992. Dublin Anniversaries. Multicoloured.

852 28p. Type **297** 70 65
853 32p. Trinity College Library (27×44 mm) 1·00 1·00
854 44p. "Charlemont House" 1·10 2·00
855 52p. Trinity College main gate (27×44 mm) 1·40 2·25

ANNIVERSARIES: 28, 44p. Bicentenary of Publication of Malton's "Views of Dublin"; 32, 52p. 400th anniv of Founding of Trinity College.

298 European Star and Megalithic Dolmen

1992. Single European Market.

856 **298** 32p. multicoloured 55 80

299 Farm Produce

1992. Irish Agriculture. Multicoloured.

857 32p. Type **299** 1·25 1·25
858 32p. Dairy and beef herds 1·25 1·25
859 32p. Harvesting cereals 1·25 1·25
860 32p. Market gardening 1·25 1·25

Nos. 857/60 were printed together, se-tenant, forming a composite design.

300 "The Annunciation" (from illuminated manuscript)

1992. Christmas. Multicoloured.

861 28p. Congregation entering church 80 65
862 28p. Type **300** 80 65
863 32p. "Adoration of the Shepherds" (Da Empoli) 1·10 1·00
864 52p. "Adoration of the Magi" (Rottenhammer) 1·40 1·50

301 Queen of Hearts

1993. Greetings Stamps. Multicoloured.

865 28p. Type **301** 90 75
866 32p. Hot air balloon trailing hearts (horiz) 1·00 85

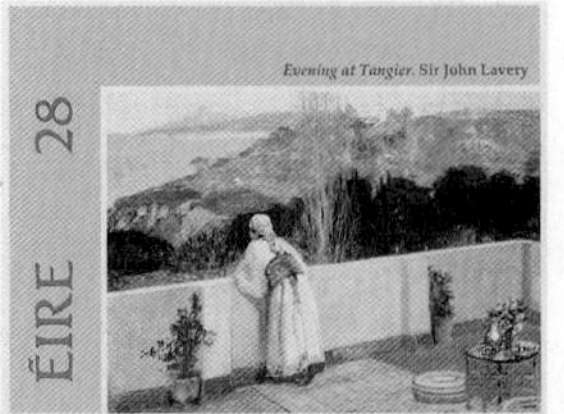

302 "Evening at Tangier" (Sir John Lavery)

1993. Irish Impressionist Painters. Multicoloured.

867 28p. Type **302** 70 60
868 32p. "The Goose Girl" (William Leech) 75 65
869 44p. "La Jeune Bretonne" (Roderic O'Conor) (vert) 75 1·75
870 52p. "Lustre Jug" (Walter Osborne) (vert) 80 2·40

303 Bee Orchid

1993. Irish Orchids. Multicoloured.

871	28p. Type **303**	90	60
872	32p. O'Kelly's orchid	1·10	80
873	38p. Dark red helleborine	1·60	2·25
874	52p. Irish lady's tresses	1·90	2·75
MS875	130×71 mm. Nos. 871/4	5·00	6·00

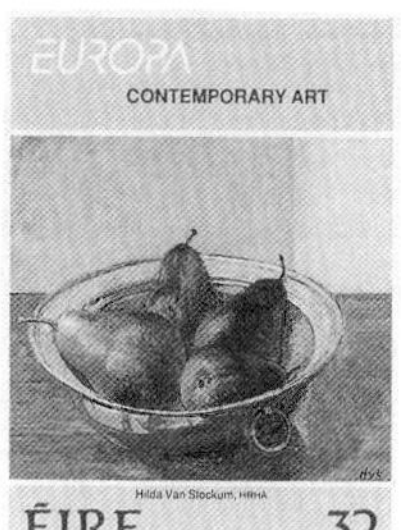

304 "Pears in a Copper Pan" (Hilda van Stockum)

1993. Europa. Contemporary Art. Mult.

876	32p. Type **304**	75	75
877	44p. "Arrieta Orzola" (Tony O'Malley)	1·10	1·10

305 Cultural Activities

1993. Centenary of Conradh Na Gaelige (cultural organization). Multicoloured.

878	32p. Type **305**	85	75
879	52p. Illuminated manuscript cover (vert)	1·50	1·50

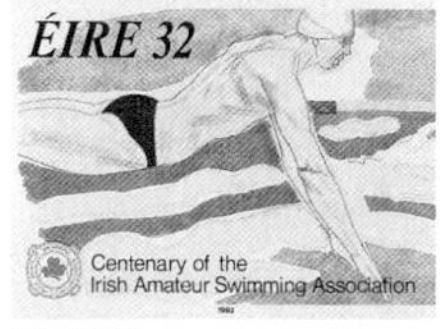

306 Diving

1993. Centenary of Irish Amateur Swimming Association. Multicoloured.

880	32p. Type **306**	1·00	1·50
881	32p. Swimming	1·00	1·50

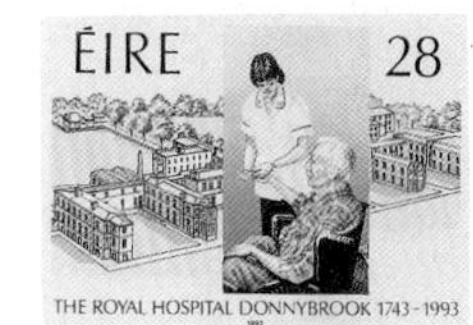

307 Nurse with Patient and Hospital Buildings

1993. Anniversaries and Events. Multicoloured.

882	28p. Type **307** (250th anniv of Royal Hospital, Donnybrook)	1·25	60
883	32p. College building and crest (bicentenary of St. Patrick's College, Carlow) (vert)	80	60
884	44p. Map of Neolithic field system, Ceide (opening of interpretative centre)	1·75	1·60
885	52p. Edward Bunting (musicologist) (150th death anniv) (25×42 mm)	1·75	2·00

308 Great Northern Railways Gardner at Drogheda

1993. Irish Buses. Multicoloured.

886	28p. Type **308**	85	70
887	32p. C.I.E. Leyland Titan at College Green, Dublin	1·00	70
888	52p. Horse-drawn omnibus at Old Baal's Bridge, Limerick	1·75	2·50
889	52p. Char-a-banc at Lady's View, Killarney	1·75	2·50

309 The Annunciation

1993. Christmas. Multicoloured.

890	28p. The flight into Egypt (vert)	80	80
891	28p. Type **309**	80	55
892	32p. Holy Family	90	70
893	52p. Adoration of the shepherds	2·00	2·50

310 Biplane skywriting "Love"

1994. Greetings Stamps. Multicoloured.

894	28p. Type **310**	90	75
895	32p. Couple within heart (vert)	1·00	85

311 Smiling Sun

1994. Greetings Stamps. Multicoloured.

896	32p. Type **311**	1·00	1·50
897	32p. Smiling daisy	1·00	1·50
898	32p. Smiling heart	1·00	1·50
899	32p. Smiling rose	1·00	1·50

1994. "Hong Kong '94" International Stamp Exhibition. Chinese New Year ("Year of the Dog").

MS900	137×74 mm. Nos. 896/8	4·50	6·50

312 Stylized Logo of Macra na Feirme (50th anniv)

1994. Anniversaries and Events.

901	**312**	28p. gold and blue	75	65
902	-	32p. multicoloured	1·00	75
903	-	38p. multicoloured	2·50	2·25
904	-	52p. black, cobalt and blue	1·75	2·50

DESIGNS—38×35 mm: 32p. "The Taking of Christ" (Caravaggio) (loan of painting to National Gallery). 37½×27 mm: 38p. Sir Horace Plunkett with 19th-century milk carts and modern tankers (centenary of Irish Co-operative Organization Society); 52p. Congress emblem (centenary of Irish Congress of Trade Unions).

313 St. Brendan visiting Iceland

1994. Europa. St. Brendan's Voyages. Mult.

905	32p. Type **313**	75	70
906	44p. Discovering Faroe Islands	1·50	2·00
MS907	82×76 mm. Nos. 905/6	2·75	4·00

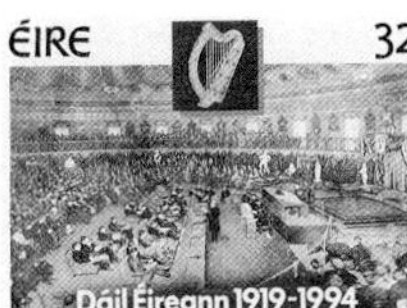

314 First Meeting of Dail, 1919

1994. Parliamentary Anniversaries. Multicoloured.

908	32p. Type **314** (75th anniv)	90	1·00
909	32p. European Parliament (4th direct elections)	90	1·00

315 Irish and Argentine Footballers

1994. Sporting Anniversaries and Events. Multicoloured.

910	32p. Type **315**	80	1·25
911	32p. Irish and German footballers	80	1·25
912	32p. Irish and Dutch women's hockey match (horiz)	2·00	1·25
913	52p. Irish and English women's hockey match (horiz)	2·25	2·50

ANNIVERSARIES AND EVENTS: Nos. 910/11, World Cup Football Championship, U.S.A.; 912, Women's Hockey World Cup, Dublin; 913, Centenary of Irish Ladies' Hockey Union.

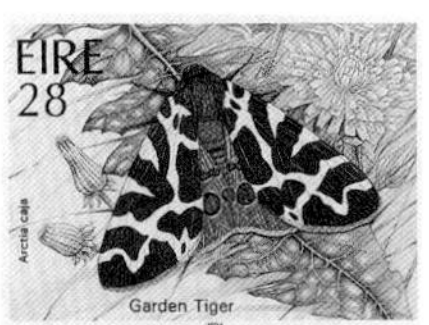

316 "Arctia caja"

1994. Moths. Mult. (a) Size 37×26 mm.

914	28p. Type **316**	65	60
915	32p. "Calamia tridens"	75	70
916	38p. "Saturnia pavonia"	90	1·10
917	52p. "Deilephila elpenor"	1·50	2·00
MS918	120×71 mm. Nos. 914/17	3·50	4·00

(b) Size 34×22 mm. Self-adhesive.

919	32p. "Calamia tridens"	1·25	1·75
920	32p. Type **316**	1·25	1·75
921	32p. "Deilephila elpenor"	1·25	1·75
922	32p. "Saturnia pavonia"	1·25	1·75

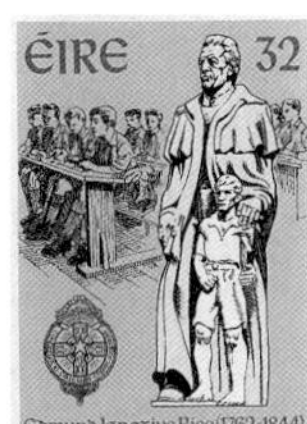

317 Statue of Edmund Rice and Class

1994. Anniversaries and Events. Multicoloured.

923	28p. St. Laurence Gate, Drogheda (44×27 mm)	1·50	1·60
924	32p. Type **317**	1·50	1·60
925	32p. Edmund Burke (politician)	1·50	1·60
926	52p. Vickers FB-27 Vimy and map (horiz)	1·50	1·75
927	52p. Eamonn Andrews (broadcaster)	1·50	1·75

ANNIVERSARIES AND EVENTS: No. 923, 800th anniv of Drogheda; 924, 150th death anniv of Edmund Rice (founder of Irish Christian Brothers); 925, 927, The Irish abroad; 926, 75th anniv of Alcock and Brown's first transatlantic flight.

318 George Bernard Shaw (author) and "Pygmalion" Poster

1994. Irish Nobel Prize Winners. Multicoloured.

928	28p. Type **318**	60	90
929	28p. Samuel Beckett (author) and pair of boots	60	90
930	32p. Sean MacBride (human rights campaigner) and peace doves	70	90
931	52p. William Butler Yeats (poet) and poem	1·10	2·00

319 "The Annunciation" (ivory plaque)

1994. Christmas. Multicoloured.

932	28p. Nativity	70	60
933	28p. Type **319**	80	60
934	32p. "Flight into Egypt" (wood carving)	90	70
935	52p. "Nativity" (ivory plaque)	1·40	2·00

320 Tree of Hearts

1995. Greetings Stamps. Multicoloured.

936	32p. Type **320**	1·10	1·25
937	32p. Teddy bear holding balloon	1·10	1·25
938	32p. Clown juggling hearts	1·10	1·25
939	32p. Bouquet of flowers	1·10	1·25

1995. Chinese New Year ("Year of the Pig").

MS940	137×74 mm. Nos. 936, 938/9	4·50	4·50

321 West Clare Railway Steam Locomotive No. 1 "Kilkee" at Kilrush Station

1995. Transport. Narrow Gauge Railways. Mult.

941	28p. Type **321**	85	60
942	32p. County Donegal Railway tank locomotive No. 2 "Blanche" at Donegal Station	1·10	90
943	38p. Cork and Muskerry Railway tank locomotive No. 1 "City of Cork" on Western Road, Cork	1·40	1·75
944	52p. Cavan and Leitrim Railway tank locomotive No. 3 "Lady Edith" on Arigna Tramway	1·90	2·50
MS945	127×83 mm. Nos. 941/4	4·75	5·50

322 English and Irish Rugby Players

1995. World Cup Rugby Championship, South Africa. Multicoloured.

946	32p. Type **322**	1·00	75
947	52p. Australian and Irish players	1·40	1·75
MS948	108×77 mm. £1 Type **322**	3·00	3·50

323 Peace Dove and Skyscrapers

1995. Europa. Peace and Freedom. Mult. (a) Size 38×26 mm. Ordinary gum.

949	32p. Type **323**	85	75

950	44p. Peace dove and map of Europe and North Africa	1·40	2·00

(b) Size 34½×23 mm. Self-adhesive.

951	32p. Type **323**	90	90
952	32p. As No. 950	90	90

324 Soldiers of the Irish Brigade and Memorial Cross

1995. 250th Anniv of Battle of Fontenoy.

953	**324**	32p. multicoloured	1·25	80

A similar stamp was issued by Belgium.

325 Irish Brigade, French Army, 1745

1995. Military Uniforms. Multicoloured.

954	28p. Type **325**	70	60
955	32p. Tercio Irlanda, Spanish army in Flanders, 1605	80	75
956	32p. Royal Dublin Fusiliers, 1914	80	75
957	38p. St. Patrick's Battalion, Papal Army, 1860	1·10	1·25
958	52p. 69th Regiment, New York State Militia, 1861	1·60	1·75

326 Guglielmo Marconi and Original Radio Transmitter

1995. Centenary of Radio. Multicoloured.

959	32p. Type **326**	1·50	1·75
960	32p. Traditional radio dial	1·50	1·75

327 Bartholomew Mosse (founder) and Hospital Building

1995. Anniversaries. Multicoloured.

961	28p. Type **327** (250th anniv of Rotunda Hospital)	1·40	70
962	32p. St. Patrick's House, Maynooth College (bicent) (25×41 mm)	80	80
963	32p. Laurel wreath and map of Europe (50th anniv of end of Second World War)	80	80
964	52p. Geological map of Ireland (150th anniv of Geological Survey of Ireland) (32½×32½ mm)	1·25	1·50

328 Natterjack Toad

1995. Reptiles and Amphibians. Multicoloured. (a) Size 40×27 mm. Ordinary gum.

965	32p. Type **328**	1·00	1·25
966	32p. Common lizards	1·00	1·25
967	32p. Smooth newts	1·00	1·25
968	32p. Common frog	1·00	1·25

(b) Size 37×25 mm. Self-adhesive.

969	32p. Type **328**	1·25	1·75
970	32p. Common lizard	1·25	1·75
971	32p. Smooth newts	1·25	1·75
972	32p. Common frog	1·25	1·75

Nos. 965/8 were printed together, se-tenant, with the backgrounds forming a composite design.

329 "Crinum moorei"

1995. Bicentenary of National Botanic Gardens, Glasnevin. Flowers. Multicoloured.

973	32p. Type **329**	1·50	70
974	38p. "Sarracenia x moorei"	1·25	1·50
975	44p. "Solanum crispum" "Glasnevin"	1·25	2·50

330 Anniversary Logo and Irish United Nations Soldier

1995. 50th Anniv of United Nations. Mult.

976	32p. Type **330**	80	70
977	52p. Emblem and "UN"	1·25	1·40

331 "Adoration of the Shepherds" (illuminated manuscript) (Benedotto Bardone)

1995. Christmas. Multicoloured.

978	28p. Adoration of the Magi	1·10	65
979	28p. Type **331**	80	65
980	32p. "Adoration of the Magi" (illuminated manuscript) (Bardone)	1·00	70
981	52p. "The Holy Family" (illuminated manuscript) (Bardone)	1·75	2·75

332 Zig and Zag on Heart

1996. Greetings Stamps. Multicoloured.

982	32p. Type **332**	1·25	75
983	32p. Zig and Zag waving	2·50	2·50
984	32p. Zig and Zag in space suits	2·50	2·50
985	32p. Zig and Zag wearing hats	2·50	2·50

1996. Chinese New Year ("Year of the Rat").

MS986	130×74 mm. Nos. 982, 984/5	3·00	3·00

333 Wheelchair Athlete

1996. Olympic and Paralympic Games, Atlanta. Multicoloured.

987	28p. Type **333**	70	65
988	32p. Running	80	80
989	32p. Throwing the discus	80	80
990	32p. Single kayak	80	80

334 Before the Start, Fairyhouse Race Course

1996. Irish Horse Racing. Multicoloured.

991	28p. Type **334**	70	65
992	32p. Steeplechase, Punchestown	80	80
993	32p. On the Flat, The Curragh	80	80
994	38p. Steeplechase, Galway	1·25	1·25
995	52p. After the race, Leopardstown	1·50	1·50

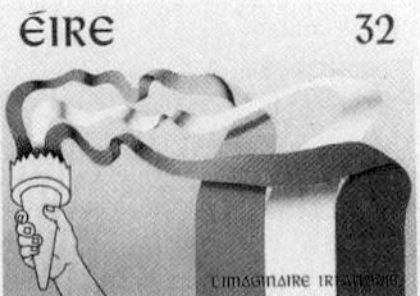

335 Irish and French Coloured Ribbons merging

1996. "L'Imaginaire Irlandais" Festival of Contemporary Irish Arts, France.

996	**335**	32p. multicoloured	1·00	1·00

336 Louie Bennett (suffragette)

1996. Europa. Famous Women. (a) Size 40×29 mm. Ordinary gum.

997	**336**	32p. violet	80	70
998	-	44p. green	1·10	1·25

(b) Size 37×25 mm. Self-adhesive.

999	**336**	32p. violet	1·10	1·25
1000	-	32p. green	1·10	1·25

DESIGN: Nos. 998, 1000, Lady Augusta Gregory (playwright).

337 Newgrange Passage Tomb (Boyne Valley World Heritage Site)

1996. Anniversaries and Events.

1001	**337**	28p. brown and black	1·00	60
1002	-	32p. multicoloured	1·10	90

DESIGN: 32p. Children playing (50th anniv of UNICEF.).

1996. "CHINA '96" 9th Asian International Stamp Exhibition, Peking. Sheet 120×95 mm, containing Nos. 992/3.

MS1003	32p. Steeplechase, Punchestown; 32p. On the Flat, The Curragh	11·00	11·00

338 Stanley Woods

1996. Isle of Man Tourist Trophy Motor Cycle Races. Irish Winners. Multicoloured.

1004	32p. Type **338**	80	70
1005	44p. Artie Bell	1·25	1·50
1006	50p. Alec Bennett	1·50	1·75
1007	52p. Joey and Robert Dunlop	1·50	1·75
MS1008	100×70 mm. 50p. As 52p.	1·75	2·00

339 Michael Davitt (founder of The Land League)

1996. Anniversaries and Events. Multicoloured.

1009	28p. Type **339** (150th birth anniv)	80	60
1010	32p. Presidency logo (Ireland's Presidency of European Union) (horiz)	80	70
1011	38p. Thomas McLaughlin (hydro-electric engineer) and Ardnacrusha Power Station (birth centenary) (horiz)	1·25	1·10
1012	52p. Mechanical peat harvester (50th anniv of Bord na Mona) (horiz)	1·75	1·75

340 "Ciara" (coastal patrol vessel)

1996. 50th Anniv of Irish Naval Service. Multicoloured.

1013	32p. Type **340**	80	70
1014	44p. "Cliona" (corvette)	1·40	1·50
1015	52p. "M-1" (motor torpedo boat) (vert)	1·50	1·60

341 Blind Woman with Child

1996. People with Disabilities. Multicoloured.

1016	28p. Type **341**	1·25	1·25
1017	28p. Man in wheelchair playing bowls	1·25	1·25

342 Green-winged Teal

1996. Freshwater Ducks. Multicoloured.

1018	32p. Type **342**	1·00	70
1019	38p. Common shoveler	1·10	1·25
1020	44p. European wigeon	1·25	1·75
1021	52p. Mallard	1·60	2·00
MS1022	127×85 mm. Nos. 1018/21	4·50	5·50

343 "Man of Aran"

1996. Centenary of Irish Cinema. Multicoloured.

1023	32p. Type **343**	85	1·10
1024	32p. "My Left Foot"	85	1·10
1025	32p. "The Commitments"	85	1·10
1026	32p. "The Field"	85	1·10

344 Visit of the Magi

1996. Christmas. Designs from 16th-century "Book of Hours" (Nos. 1028/30). Multicoloured.

1027	28p. The Holy Family	75	60
1028	28p. Type **344**	60	60
1029	32p. The Annunciation	80	75
1030	52p. The Shepherds receiving new of Christ's birth	1·40	1·60

345 Black-billed Magpie ("Magpie")

1997. Birds. Ordinary gum. Multicoloured. (a) Size 23×26 mm or 26×23 mm.

1031	1p. Type **345**	10	60
1032	2p. Northern gannet ("Gannet") (vert)	15	60
1033	4p. Corn crake (vert)	20	40
1034	5p. Wood pigeon (horiz)	20	80
1035	10p. River kingfisher ("Kingfisher") (vert)	40	1·00
1036	20p. Northern lapwing ("Lapwing") (vert)	65	1·00
1037	28p. Blue tit (horiz)	2·50	50
1038	30p. Blackbird (vert)	85	1·00
1039p	30p. Goldcrest (vert)	1·25	1·25
1040	30p. Common stonechat ("Stonechat") (vert)	1·25	1·25
1041	30p. As No. 1036	1·25	1·25
1042	30p. As No. 1032	1·25	1·25
1043	30p. As No. 1033	1·25	1·25
1044	30p. Type **345**	1·25	1·25
1045	30p. As No. 1035	1·25	1·25
1046	30p. Peregrine falcon (vert)	1·25	1·25
1047	30p. Barn owl (vert)	1·25	1·25
1048	30p. European robin ("Robin") (vert)	1·25	1·25
1049	30p. Song thrush (vert)	1·25	1·25
1050	30p. Winter wren ("Wren") (vert)	2·50	3·25
1051	30p. Pied wagtail (vert)	2·50	3·25
1052	30p. Atlantic puffin ("Puffin") (vert)	1·25	1·25
1053	32p. As No. 1048	2·25	55
1054	35p. As No. 1040	1·00	1·50
1055p	40p. Ringed plover (horiz)	1·50	1·00
1056	44p. As No. 1052	3·50	2·25
1057ac	45p. As No. 1049	1·50	1·50
1058ac	50p. Northern sparrow hawk ("European Sparrow Hawk") (horiz)	2·25	1·25
1059	52p. As No. 1047	4·00	2·00

(b) Size 26×47 mm or 47×26 mm.

1060	£1 White-fronted goose ("Greenland White-fronted Goose") (vert)	2·00	1·60
1061	£2 Northern pintail ("Pintail") (horiz)	3·75	3·50
1062	£5 Common shelduck ("Shelduck") (vert)	8·50	9·00

(c) Size 17×21 mm or 21×17 mm.

1080	4p. Corn crake	1·25	2·00
1081	5p. Wood pigeon	80	1·00
1082	30p. Blackbird	1·60	1·60
1083	30p. Goldcrest	1·00	1·75
1084	32p. European robin ("Robin")	1·00	1·50
1085	32p. Peregrine falcon	1·50	1·50

(d) Size 24×29 mm. Self-adhesive.

1086	30p. Goldcrest	1·00	1·10
1087	30p. Blackbird	1·00	1·10
1088	32p. Peregrine falcon	2·50	4·00
1089	32p. European robin ("Robin")	2·50	4·00

346 Pair of Doves

1997. Greetings Stamps. Multicoloured.

1100	32p. Type **346**	85	50
1101	32p. Cow jumping over moon	1·10	1·25
1102	32p. Pig going to market	1·10	1·25
1103	32p. Cockerel	1·10	1·25

1997. "HONG KONG '97" International Stamp Exhibition. Chinese New Year ("Year of the Ox").

MS1104	124×74 mm. Nos. 1101/3	2·75	2·75

347 Troops on Parade

1997. 75th Anniv of Irish Free State. Mult.

1105	28p. Page from the "Annals of the Four Masters", quill and 1944 ½d. O'Clery stamp	75	55
1106	32p. Type **347**	1·00	1·25
1107	32p. The Dail, national flag and Constitution	1·00	1·25
1108	32p. Athlete, footballer and hurling player	1·00	1·25
1109	32p. Singer, violinist and bodhran player	1·00	1·25
1110	32p. Stained glass window and 1929 9d. O'Connell stamp	1·00	1·00
1111	32p. 1923 2d. map stamp and G.P.O., Dublin	1·00	1·00
1112	52p. Police personnel and Garda badge	1·50	2·00
1113	52p. The Four Courts and Scales of Justice	1·50	2·00
1114	52p. Currency, blueprint and food-processing plant	1·50	2·00
1115	52p. Books, palette and Seamus Heaney manuscript	1·50	2·00
1116	52p. Air Lingus Boeing 737 and 1965 1s.5d. air stamp	1·50	1·50
MS1117	174×209 mm. As Nos. 1105/16, but each with face value of 32p.	12·00	15·00

348 Grey Seals

1997. Marine Mammals. Multicoloured.

1118	28p. Type **348**	75	60
1119	32p. Bottle-nosed dolphins	85	80
1120	44p. Harbour porpoises (horiz)	1·25	1·40
1121	52p. Killer whale (horiz)	1·40	1·50
MS1122	150×68 mm. As Nos. 1118/21	6·00	6·00

349 Dublin Silver Penny of 997

1997. Millenary of Irish Coinage.

1123	**349**	32p. multicoloured	65	65

350 "The Children of Lir"

1997. Europa. Tales and Legends. Multicoloured. (a) Size 38×28 mm. Ordinary gum.

1124	32p. Type **350**	75	60
1125	44p. Oisin and Niamh	1·10	2·00

(b) Size 36×25 mm. Self-adhesive.

1126	32p. Type **350**	1·50	70
1127	32p. Oisin and Niamh	1·50	70

351 Emigrants waiting to board Ship

1997. 150th Anniv of The Great Famine.

1128	**351**	28p. blue, red and stone	1·00	70
1129	-	32p. orange, blue & stone	1·25	70
1130	-	52p. brown, blue & stone	1·75	3·00

DESIGNS: 32p. Family and dying child; 52p. Irish Society of Friends soup kitchen.

1997. "Pacific '97" International Stamp Exhibition, San Francisco. Sheet 100×70 mm, containing No. 1061. Multicoloured.

MS1131	£2 Pintail (48×26 mm)	4·75	6·50

352 Kate O'Brien (novelist) (birth centenary)

1997. Anniversaries. Multicoloured.

1132	28p. Type **352**	85	1·00
1133	28p. St. Columba crossing to Iona (stained glass window) (1400th death anniv)	85	1·00
1134	32p. "Daniel O'Connell" (J. Haverty) (politician) (150th death anniv) (27×49 mm)	95	70
1135	52p. "John Wesley" (N. Hone) (founder of Methodism) (250th anniv of first visit to Ireland)	1·75	2·50

353 The Baily Lighthouse

1997. Lighthouses. Multicoloured.

1136	32p. Type **353**	1·40	1·40
1137	32p. Tarbert	1·40	1·40
1138	38p. Hookhead (vert)	1·40	1·10
1139d	50p. The Fastnet (vert)	1·40	2·00

354 Commemorative Cross

1997. Ireland–Mexico Joint Issue. 150th Anniv of Mexican St. Patrick's Battalion.

1140	**354**	32p. multicoloured	55	60

355 Dracula and Bat

1997. Centenary of Publication of Bram Stoker's "Dracula". Multicoloured.

1141	28p. Type **355**	60	55
1142	32p. Dracula and female victim	65	60
1143	38p. Dracula emerging from coffin (horiz)	80	90
1144	52p. Dracula and wolf (horiz)	1·10	1·75
MS1145	150×90 mm. As Nos. 1141/4	3·25	3·75

356 "The Nativity" (Kevin Kelly)

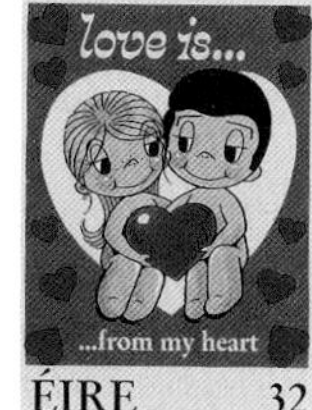

357 Christmas Tree

1997. Christmas. Multicoloured. (a) Stained-glass Windows. Ordinary gum.

1146	28p. Type **356**	70	55
1147	32p. The Nativity (Sarah Purser and A. E. Child)	80	65
1148	52p. The Nativity (A. E. Child)	1·50	1·75

(b) Self-adhesive.

1149	28p. Type **357**	80	80

358 Holding Heart

1998. Greetings Stamps (1st series). Designs based on the "love is ..." cartoon characters of Kim Casali. Multicoloured.

1150	32p. Type **358**	1·10	50
1151	32p. Receiving letter	1·10	1·25
1152	32p. Sitting on log	1·10	1·25
1153	32p. With birthday presents	1·10	1·25

See also Nos. 1173/6.

1998. Chinese New Year ("Year of the Tiger").

MS1154	124×73 mm. Nos. 1151/3	4·50	5·50

359 Lady Mary Heath and Avro Type 581 Avian II over Pyramids

1998. Pioneers of Irish Aviation. Multicoloured.

1155	28p. Type **359**	60	55
1156	32p. Col. James Fitzmaurice and Junkers W.33 "Bremen" over Labrador	65	60
1157	44p. Captain J. P. Saul and Fokker F.VIIa/3m "Southern Cross"	1·25	1·25
1158	52p. Captain Charles Blair and Sikorsky V-S 44 (flying boat)	1·50	1·50

360 Show-jumping

1998. Equestrian Sports. Multicoloured.

1159	30p. Type **360**	90	60
1160	32p. Three-day eventing	95	65
1161	40p. Gymkhana	1·00	1·40
1162	45p. Dressage (vert)	1·00	1·40
MS1163	126×84 mm. Nos. 1159/62	3·50	4·00

361 Figure of "Liberty"

1998. Bicentenary of United Irish Rebellion. Mult.

1164	30p. Type **361**	1·00	1·00
1165	30p. United Irishman	1·00	1·00
1166	30p. French soldiers	1·00	1·00
1167	45p. Wolfe Tone	1·00	1·25
1168	45p. Henry Joy McCracken	1·00	1·25

362 Gathering of the Boats, Kinvara

1998. Europa. Festivals. Multicoloured. (a) Size 39×27 mm.

1169	30p. Type **362**	1·50	80
1170	40p. Puck Fair, Killorglin	1·50	95

(b) Size 34×23 mm. Self-adhesive.

1171	30p. Type **362**	1·50	90
1172	30p. Puck Fair, Killorglin	1·50	90

1998. Greetings Stamps (2nd series). As Nos. 1105/8, but with changed face value. Multicoloured.

1173	30p. As No. 1153	70	95
1174	30p. As No. 1152	70	95
1175	30p. As No. 1151	70	95
1176	30p. Type **358**	70	95

363 Cyclists rounding Bend

1998. Visit of "Tour de France" Cycle Race to Ireland. Multicoloured.

1177	30p. Type **363**	85	85
1178	30p. Two cyclists ascending hill	85	85
1179	30p. "Green jersey" cyclist and other competitor	85	85
1180	30p. "Yellow jersey" (race leader)	85	85

364 Voter and Local Councillors of 1898

1998. Democracy Anniversaries. Multicoloured.

1181	30p. Type **364** (cent of Local Government (Ireland) Act)	60	60
1182	32p. European Union flag and harp symbol (25th anniv of Ireland's entry into European Community)	65	65
1183	35p. Woman voter and suffragettes, 1898 (cent of women's right to vote in local elections)	75	75
1184	45p. Irish Republic flag (50th anniv of Republic of Ireland Act)	1·00	1·25

365 "Asgard II" (cadet brigantine)

1998. "Cutty Sark" International Tall Ships Race, Dublin. Multicoloured. (a) Ordinary gum.

1185	30p. Type **365** (26×38 mm)	1·00	1·00
1186	30p. U.S.C.G. "Eagle" (cadet barque) (26×38 mm)	1·00	1·00
1187	45p. "Boa Esperanza" (replica caravel) (38×26 mm)	1·25	1·00
1188	£1 "Royalist" (training brigantine) (38×26 mm)	2·00	2·75

(b) Self-adhesive.

1189	30p. "Boa Esperanza" (34×23 mm)	85	1·00
1190	30p. Type **365** (23×34 mm)	85	1·00
1191	30p. U.S.C.G. "Eagle" (23×34 mm)	85	1·00
1192	30p. "Royalist" (34×23 mm)	85	85

366 Ashworth Pillbox (1856)

1998. Irish Postboxes. Multicoloured.

1193	30p. Type **366**	75	1·00
1194	30p. Irish Free State wallbox (1922)	75	1·00
1195	30p. Double pillarbox (1899)	75	1·00
1196	30p. Penfold pillarbox (1866)	75	1·00

367 Mary Immaculate College, Limerick (centenary)

1998. Anniversaries. Multicoloured.

1197	30p. Type **367**	75	60
1198	40p. Newtown School, Waterford (bicent) (vert)	1·00	1·50
1199	45p. Trumpeters (50th anniv of Universal Declaration of Human Rights)	1·10	1·75

1998. "Portugal '98" International Stamp Exhibition, Lisbon. Sheet 101×71 mm, containing design as No. 1187.

MS1200	£2 "Boa Esperanza" (caravel) (horiz)	4·50	5·50

368 Cheetah

1998. Endangered Animals. Multicoloured.

1201	30p. Type **368**	1·00	1·25
1202	30p. Scimitar-horned oryx	1·00	1·25
1203	40p. Golden lion tamarin (vert)	1·10	1·25
1204	45p. Tiger (vert)	1·40	1·50
MS1205	150×90 mm. As Nos. 1201/4	3·50	4·25

369 The Holy Family **370** Choir Boys

1998. Christmas. Mult. (a) Ordinary gum.

1206	30p. Type **369**	70	60
1207	32p. Shepherds	75	65
1208	45p. Three Kings	1·00	1·75

(b) Self-adhesive.

1209	30p. Type **370**	80	80

371 Puppy and Heart

1999. Greetings Stamps. Pets. Multicoloured.

1210	30p. Type **371**	80	50
1211	30p. Kitten and ball of wool	80	1·00
1212	30p. Goldfish	80	1·00
1213	30p. Rabbit with lettuce leaf	80	1·00

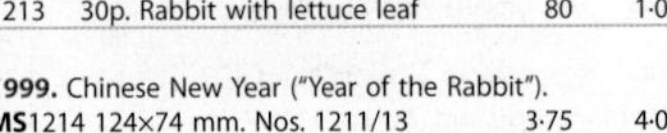

1999. Chinese New Year ("Year of the Rabbit").

MS1214	124×74 mm. Nos. 1211/13	3·75	4·00

372 Micheal Mac Liammoir

1999. Irish Actors and Actresses.

1215	**372**	30p. black and brown	65	60
1216	-	45p. black and green	1·00	1·10
1217	-	50p. black and blue	1·00	1·25

DESIGNS: 45p. Siobhan McKenna, 50p. Noel Purcell.

373 Irish Emigrant Ship

1999. Ireland–U.S.A. Joint Issue. Irish Emigration.

1218	**373**	45p. multicoloured	1·25	1·00

374 "Polly Woodside" (barque)

1999. Maritime Heritage. Multicoloured.

1219	30p. Type **374**	55	60
1220	35p. "Ilen" (schooner)	65	70
1221	45p. R.N.L.I. Cromer class lifeboat (horiz)	80	85
1222	£1 "Titanic" (liner) (horiz)	2·00	2·50
MS1223	150×90 mm. No. 1222×2	3·25	4·00

1999. Ireland—Australia Joint Issue. "Polly Woodside" (barque). Sheet 137×72 mm. Multicoloured.

MS1224	45c. Type **603** of Australia; 30p. Type **374** (No. **MS**1224 was sold at 52p. in Ireland)	1·25	1·75

No. **MS**1224 includes the "Australia '99" emblem on the sheet margin and was postally valid in Ireland to the value of 30p.

The same miniature sheet was also available in Australia.

375 Sean Lemass

1999. Birth Centenary of Sean Lemass (politician).

1225	**375**	30p. black and green	1·40	1·00

376 European Currency Emblem

1999. Introduction of Single European Currency.

1226	**376**	30p. multicoloured	75	65

The face value of No. 1226 is shown in both Irish and euro currency.

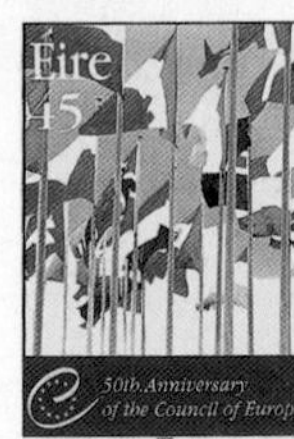

377 European Flags

1999. 50th Anniv of Council of Europe.

1227	**377**	45p. multicoloured	1·00	1·00

378 Whooper Swans, Kilcolman Nature Reserve

1999. Europa. Parks and Gardens. Multicoloured. (a) Size 36×26 mm. Ordinary gum.

1228	30p. Type **378**	90	50
1229	40p. Fallow deer, Phoenix Park	1·00	1·75

(b) Size 34×23 mm. Self-adhesive.

1230	30p. Type **378**	1·50	2·25
1231	30p. Fallow deer, Phoenix Park	1·50	2·25

379 Father James Cullen and St. Francis Xavier Church, Dublin

1999. Centenary of Pioneer Total Abstinence Association.

1232	**379**	32p. brown, bistre and black	75	65

380 Elderly Man and Child using Computer

1999. International Year of Older Persons.

1233	**380**	30p. multicoloured	70	65

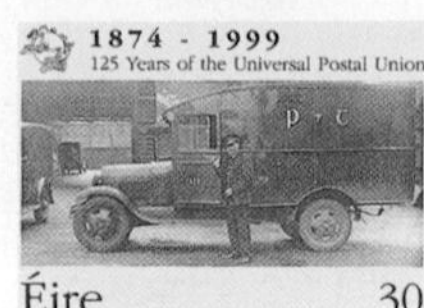

381 Postal Van, 1922

1999. 125th Anniv of Universal Postal Union.

1234	**381**	30p. green and deep green	1·40	1·25
1235	-	30p. multicoloured	1·40	1·25

DESIGN: No. 1235, Modern postal lorries.

382 Danno Keeffe

1999. Gaelic Athletic Association "Millennium Football Team". Multicoloured. (a) Size 37×25 mm. Ordinary gum.

1236	30p. Type **382**	65	70
1237	30p. Enda Colleran	65	70
1238	30p. Joe Keohane	65	70
1239	30p. Sean Flanagan	65	70
1240	30p. Sean Murphy	65	70
1241	30p. John Joe Reilly	65	70
1242	30p. Martin O'Connell	65	70
1243	30p. Mick O'Connell	65	70
1244	30p. Tommy Murphy	65	70
1245	30p. Sean O'Neill	65	70
1246	30p. Sean Purcell	65	70
1247	30p. Pat Spillane	65	70
1248	30p. Mikey Sheehy	65	70
1249	30p. Tom Langan	65	70
1250	30p. Kevin Heffernan	65	70

(b) Size 33×23 mm. Self-adhesive.

1251	30p. Type **382**	1·50	2·50
1252	30p. Enda Colleran	65	80
1253	30p. Joe Keohane	1·50	2·50
1254	30p. Sean Flanagan	65	80
1255	30p. Sean Murphy	1·50	2·50
1256	30p. John Joe Reilly	45	60
1257	30p. Martin O'Connell	45	60

1258	30p. Mick O'Connell	1·50	2·50
1259	30p. Tommy Murphy	55	80
1260	30p. Sean O'Neill	45	60
1261	30p. Sean Purcell	55	80
1262	30p. Pat Spillane	55	80
1263	30p. Mikey Sheehy	55	80
1264	30p. Tom Langan	55	80
1265	30p. Kevin Heffernan	45	60

383 Douglas DC-3

1999. Commercial Aviation. Multicoloured.

1266	30p. Type **383**	65	50
1267	32p. Pilatus-Britten BN-2 Norman Islander	75	55
1268	40p. Boeing 707	80	1·40
1269	45p. Lockheed Constellation	90	1·50

384 Mammoth

1999. Extinct Irish Animals. Multicoloured. (a) Size 26×38 mm (vert) or 38×26 mm (horiz). Ordinary gum.

1270	30p. Type **384**	70	70
1271	30p. Giant deer	70	70
1272	45p. Wolves (horiz)	90	1·25
1273	45p. Brown bear (horiz)	90	1·25
MS1274	150×63 mm. Nos. 1270/3	2·75	3·00

(b) Size 33×23 mm (horiz) or 22×34 mm (vert). Self-adhesive.

1275	30p. Brown bear (horiz)	70	85
1276	30p. Type **384**	70	85
1277	30p. Wolves (horiz)	70	85
1278	30p. Giant deer	70	85

385 Holy Family

1999. Christmas. Children's Nativity Plays. Mult. (a) Size 35×25 mm. Ordinary gum.

1279	30p. Type **385**	60	50
1280	32p. Visit of the Shepherds	65	55
1281	45p. Adoration of the Magi	1·25	1·50

(b) Size 16×26 mm. Self-adhesive.

1282	30p. Angel	70	50

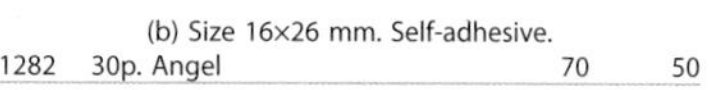

386 Grace Kelly (American actress)

1999. New Millennium (1st issue). Famous People of the 20th Century. Multicoloured.

1283	30p. Type **386**	1·75	2·00
1284	30p. Jesse Owens (American athlete)	1·75	2·00
1285	30p. John F. Kennedy (former American President)	1·75	2·00
1286	30p. Mother Teresa (missionary)	1·75	2·00
1287	30p. John McCormack (tenor)	1·75	2·00
1288	30p. Nelson Mandela (South African statesman)	1·75	2·00

See also Nos. 1289/94, 1300/5, 1315/20, 1377/82 and 1383/88.

387 Ruined Castle (Norman Invasion, 1169)

2000. New Millennium (2nd issue). Irish Historic Events. Multicoloured.

1289	30p. Type **387**	1·75	2·00
1290	30p. Flight of the Earls, 1607	1·75	2·00
1291	30p. Opening of Irish Parliament, 1782	1·75	2·00
1292	30p. Eviction (formation of the Land League)	1·75	2·00
1293	30p. First four Irish Prime Ministers (Irish Independence)	1·75	2·00
1294	30p. Irish soldier and personnel carrier (U.N. Peace-keeping)	1·75	2·00

388 Frog Prince

2000. Greetings Stamps. Mythical Creatures. Multicoloured.

1295	30p. Type **388**	1·00	60
1296	30p. Pegasus	1·00	1·25
1297	30p. Unicorn	1·00	1·25
1298	30p. Dragon	1·00	1·25

2000. Chinese New Year ("Year of the Dragon").

MS1299	124×74 mm. Nos. 1296/8	3·00	3·00

389 Revd. Nicholas Callan (electrical scientist)

2000. New Millennium (3rd issue). Discoveries. Multicoloured.

1300	30p. Type **389**	1·75	2·00
1301	30p. Birr Telescope	1·75	2·00
1302	30p. Thomas Edison (inventor of light bulb)	1·75	2·00
1303	30p. Albert Einstein (mathematical physicist)	1·75	2·00
1304	30p. Marie Curie (physicist)	1·75	2·00
1305	30p. Galileo Galilei (astronomer and mathematician)	1·75	2·00

390 "Jeanie Johnston" (emigrant ship)

2000. Completion of "Jeanie Johnston" Replica.

1306 **390**	30p. multicoloured	70	50

391 "Building Europe"

2000. Europa. (a) 25½×36½ mm.

1307 **391**	32p. multicoloured	80	55

(b) 22×34 mm. Self-adhesive.

1308	30p. multicoloured	75	50

DENOMINATION. From No. 1309 to 1465 some Irish stamps are denominated both in Irish pounds and in euros.

392 Oscar Wilde

2000. Death Centenary of Oscar Wilde (writer). Multicoloured.

1309	30p. Type **392**	1·40	1·40
1310	30p. *The Happy Prince*	1·40	1·40
1311	30p. Lady Bracknell from *The Importance of being Earnest*	1·40	1·40
1312	30p. *The Picture of Dorian Gray*	1·40	1·40
MS1313	150×190 mm. £2 Type **392**	3·25	4·00

A further 30p. exists in a design similar to Type **392**, but 29×29 mm, printed in sheets of 20, each stamp having a se-tenant half-stamp size label attached at right inscribed "Oscar". These sheets could be personalized by the addition of a photograph in place of the inscription on the labels. Such stamps are not listed as they were not available at face value, the sheets of 20 containing the "Oscar" labels being sold for £10.

393 Ludwig van Beethoven (German composer)

2000. New Millennium (4th issue). The Arts. Mult.

1315	30p. Type **393**	1·40	1·50
1316	30p. Dame Ninette de Valois (ballet director)	1·40	1·50
1317	30p. James Joyce (author)	1·40	1·50
1318	30p. "Mona Lisa" (Leonardo da Vinci)	1·40	1·50
1319	30p. "Lady Lavery" (Sir John Lavery)	1·40	1·50
1320	30p. William Shakespeare (playwright)	1·40	1·50

394 Running

2000. Olympic Games, Sydney. Multicoloured.

1321	30p. Type **394**	70	70
1322	30p. Javelin throwing	70	70
1323	50p. Long jumping	1·00	1·25
1324	50p. High jumping	1·00	1·25

395 "Space Rocket over Flowers" (Marguerite Nyhan)

2000. "Stampin' the Future" (children's stamp design competition). Multicoloured.

1325	30p. Type **395**	60	50
1326	32p. "Tree, rocket and hands holding globe in '2000'" (Kyle Staunton) (horiz)	70	55
1327	45p. "People holding hands on globe" (Jennifer Branagan) (horiz)	90	1·10
1328	45p. "Colony on Moon" (Diarmuid O'Ceochain) (horiz)	90	1·10

396 Tony Reddin

2000. "Hurling Team of the Millennium". Multicoloured. (a) Size 36×27 mm.

1329	30p. Type **396**	60	70
1330	30p. Bobby Rackard	60	70
1331	30p. Nick O'Donnell	60	70
1332	30p. John Doyle	60	70
1333	30p. Brian Whelahan	60	70
1334	30p. John Keane	60	70
1335	30p. Paddy Phelan	60	70
1336	30p. Lory Meagher	60	70
1337	30p. Jack Lynch	60	70
1338	30p. Jim Langton	60	70
1339	30p. Mick Mackey	60	70
1340	30p. Christy Ring	60	70
1341	30p. Jimmy Doyle	60	70
1342	30p. Ray Cummins	60	70
1343	30p. Eddie Keher	60	70

(b) Size 33×23 mm. Self-adhesive.

1344	30p. Type **396**	60	1·00
1345	30p. Jimmy Doyle	60	1·00
1346	30p. John Doyle	60	1·00
1347	30p. Paddy Phelan	60	1·60
1348	30p. Jim Langton	60	1·60
1349	30p. Lory Meagher	60	1·00
1350	30p. Eddie Keher	60	1·00
1351	30p. Mick Mackey	60	1·00
1352	30p. Brian Whelahan	60	1·00
1353	30p. John Keane	60	1·00
1354	30p. Bobby Rackard	60	1·00
1355	30p. Nick O'Donnell	60	1·00
1356	30p. Jack Lynch	60	1·00
1357	30p. Ray Cummins	60	1·00
1358	30p. Christy Ring	60	1·00

397 Peacock Butterfly

2000. Butterflies. Multicoloured.

1359	30p. Type **397**	80	50
1360	32p. Small tortoiseshell	85	55
1361	45p. Silver-washed fritillary	1·25	1·75
1362	50p. Orange-tip	1·40	2·50
MS1363	150×90 mm. Nos. 1359/62	3·75	4·50

2000. Military Aviation. Multicoloured. (a) Size 37×26 mm.

1364	30p. Hawker Hurricane Mk IIC	1·25	1·50
1365	30p. Bristol F.2B Mk II	1·25	1·50
1366	45p. de Havilland DH.115 Vampire T 55	1·50	1·75
1367	45p. Eurocopter S.E. 3160 Alouette III (helicopter)	1·50	1·75

(b) Size 33×22 mm. Self-adhesive.

1368	30p. Bristol F.2B Mk II	1·25	1·25
1369	30p. Hawker Hurricane Mk IIC	1·25	1·25
1370	30p. de Havilland DH.115 Vampire T.55	1·25	1·25
1371	30p. Eurocopter SE. 3160 Alouette III	1·25	1·25

398 Tractor ploughing Field

2000. Centenary of An Roinn Talmhaiochta (Department of Agriculture).

1372 **398**	50p. multicoloured	1·00	1·10

399 The Nativity

2000. Christmas. Multicoloured. (a) Size 24×27 mm.

1373	30p. Type **399**	65	25
1374	32p. Three Magi	75	55
1375	45p. Shepherds	1·00	1·50

(b) Size 24×29 mm. Self-adhesive.

1376	30p. Flight into Egypt	90	50

400 Storming the Bastille, Paris, 1789

2000. New Millennium (5th issue). World Events. Multicoloured.

1377	30p. Type **400**	1·75	2·00
1378	30p. Early railway	1·75	2·00
1379	30p. Returning troop ship, 1945	1·75	2·00
1380	30p. Suffragettes	1·75	2·00
1381	30p. Destruction of the Berlin Wall, 1989	1·75	2·00
1382	30p. Internet communications	1·75	2·00

2001. New Millennuim (6th issue). Epic Journeys. As T 400. Multicoloured.

1383	30p. Marco Polo	2·00	2·00
1384	30p. Captain James Cook	2·00	2·00
1385	30p. Burke and Wills expedition crossing Australia, 1860	2·00	2·00
1386	30p. Ernest Shackleton in Antarctica	2·00	2·00
1387	30p. Charles Lindbergh and Ryan NYP Special *Spirit of St. Louis*	2·00	2·00
1388	30p. Astronaut on Moon	2·00	2·00

401 Goldfish

2001. Greetings Stamps. Pets. (a) As Type 401. Mult.

1389	30p. Type **401**	80	50

(b) Designs smaller, 20×30 mm. Self-adhesive.

1390	30p. Lizard	1·00	1·10
1391	30p. Frog	1·00	1·10
1392	30p. Type **401**	1·00	1·10
1393	30p. Snake	1·00	1·10
1394	30p. Tortoise	1·00	1·10

2001. Chinese New Year ("Year of the Snake").

MS1395	124×75 mm. As Nos. 1391 and 1393/4, but larger, 28×39 mm	2·50	2·50

402 Television Presenter and Audience

2001. Irish Broadcasting.

1396	**402**	30p. multicoloured	70	50
1397	-	32p. black, ultramarine and blue	80	55
1398	-	45p. black, brown and orange	1·00	1·10
1399	-	50p. brown, yellow and green	1·00	1·25

DESIGNS: 32p. Radio sports commentators; 45p. Family around radio; 50p. Play on television set.

403 Archbishop Narcissus Marsh and Library Interior

2001. Literary Anniversaries. Multicoloured.

1400	30p. Type **403** (300th anniv of Marsh's Library)	60	50
1401	32p. Book of Common Prayer, 1551 (450th anniv of first book printed in Ireland)	65	1·00

404 Bagpipe Player

2001. 50th Anniv of Comhaltas Ceoltoiri Eireann (cultural organization). Multicoloured.

1402	30p. Type **404**	70	1·00
1403	30p. Bodhran player	70	1·00
1404	45p. Young fiddler and Irish dancer (horiz)	1·00	1·50
1405	45p. Flautist and singer (horiz)	1·00	1·50

405 Jordan Formula 1 Racing Car

2001. Irish Motorsport. Multicoloured. (a) As Type 405.

1406	30p. Type **405**	75	50
1407	32p. Hillman Imp on Tulip Rally	80	55
1408	45p. Mini Cooper S on Monte Carlo Rally	1·25	80
1409	£1 Mercedes SSK, winner of 1930 Irish Grand Prix	2·00	2·50
MS1410	150×90 mm. £2 Type **405**	3·75	4·25

(b) Designs smaller, 33½×22½. Self-adhesive.

1411	30p. Type **405**	90	1·00
1412	30p. Hillman Imp on Tulip Rally	1·40	1·75
1413	30p. Mini Cooper S on Monte Carlo Rally	1·40	1·75
1414	30p. Mercedes SSK, winner of 1930 Irish Grand Prix	1·40	1·75

406 Peter Lalor (leader at Eureka Stockade) and Gold Licence

2001. Irish Heritage in Australia. Multicoloured.

1415	30p. Type **406**	60	60
1416	30p. Ned Kelly (bush ranger) and "Wanted" poster	60	60
1417	45p. Family leaving for Australia and immigrant ship	1·25	1·25
1418	45p. Irish settler and life in gold camp	1·25	1·25
MS1419	150×90 mm. £1 As No. 1416	2·25	2·50

407 Children playing in River

2001. Europa; Water Resources. Multicoloured. (a) Size 36½×26½ mm.

1420	30p. Type **407**	1·25	50
1421	32p. Man fishing	1·50	75

(b) Designs smaller, 33×22 mm. Self-adhesive.

1422	30p. Type **407**	90	90
1423	30p. As 32p	90	90

408 Blackbird

2001. Dual Currency Birds. Vert designs as Nos. 1038, 1050, 1053, 1056/7 and 1060 (some with different face values) showing both Irish currency and euros as in T 408. Multicoloured. (a) Ordinary gum.

1424	30p./38c. Type **408**	1·50	1·00
1425	32p./41c. European robin ("Robin")	1·60	1·00
1426	35p./44c. Atlantic puffin ("Puffin")	1·75	1·75
1427	40p./51c. Winter wren ("Wren")	2·00	2·50
1428	45p./57c. Song thrush	2·25	2·50
1429	£1/€1.27 White-fronted goose ("Greenland White-fronted Goose") (23×44 mm)	5·50	7·00

(b) Designs as Nos. 1038/9, but 25×30 mm. Self-adhesive.

1430	30p./38c. Type **408**	1·50	1·50
1431	30p./38c. Goldcrest	1·50	1·50

409 Irish Pikeman

2001. 400th Anniv of Battle of Kinsale. Nine Years War. Multicoloured.

1432	30p. Type **409**	90	1·00
1433	30p. English cavalry	90	1·00
1434	32p. Spanish pikeman	1·00	80
1435	45p. Town of Kinsale	1·40	1·50

410 Ruffian 23 Yachts

2001. Yachts. Multicoloured. (a) Size 26×37½ mm.

1436	30p. Type **410**	70	60
1437	32p. Howth 17 yacht	75	65
1438	45p. 1720 Sportsboat yacht	1·10	1·25
1439	45p. Glen class cruising yacht	1·10	1·25

(b) Self-adhesive. Size 22×34 mm.

1440	30p. Type **410**	1·00	1·00
1441	30p. Howth 17 yacht	1·00	1·00
1442	30p. Glen class cruising yacht	1·00	1·00
1443	30p. 1720 Sportsboat yacht	1·00	1·00

411 Padraic Carney (footballer)

2001. Gaelic Athletic Association Hall of Fame 2001 (1st series). Multicoloured. (a) Size 36½×27 mm.

1444	30p. Type **411**	90	90
1445	30p. Frank Cummins (hurler)	90	90
1446	30p. Jack O'Shea (footballer)	90	90
1447	30p. Nicky Rackard (hurler)	90	90

(b) Self-adhesive. Size 33½×22½ mm.

1448	30p. Type **411**	70	70
1449	30p. Frank Cummins (hurler)	70	70
1450	30p. Jack O'Shea (footballer)	70	70
1451	30p. Nicky Rackard (hurler)	70	70

See also Nos. 1550/3.

2001. "Belgica 2001" International Stamp Exhibition, Brussels. No. MS1410 with "Belgica 2001" added to the sheet margin.

MS1452	150×90 mm. £2 Type **405**	4·00	4·25

See also Nos. 1550/3.

412 Blackbird

2001. Birds. Vert designs as Nos. 1038/9, 1048 and 1049, but 24×29 mm, each showing a letter in place of face values as in T 412. Multicoloured. Self-adhesive.

1453	(N) Type **408**	1·40	80
1454	(N) Goldcrest	1·40	80
1455	(E) Robin	1·50	70
1456	(W) Song thrush	2·00	1·50

Nos. 1453/6 were intended to cover the changeover period to euros. Nos. 1453/4 were sold for 30p, No. 1455 for 32p. and No. 1456 for 45p.

413 Perch

2001. Freshwater Fish. Multicoloured.

1457	30p. Type **413**	75	50
1458	32p. Arctic charr	80	85
1459	32p. Pike	80	85
1460	45p. Common bream	1·10	1·25

414 "Out of Bounds" (sculpture by Eilis O'Connell)

2001. 50th Anniv of Government Support for Arts.

1461	**414**	50p. multicoloured	1·25	1·40

415 "The Nativity" (Richard King)

2001. Christmas. Paintings by Richard King. Multicoloured. (a) Size 25½×36½ mm.

1462	30p. Type **415**	70	50
1463	32p. "The Annunciation"	75	55
1464	45p. "Presentation in the Temple"	1·10	1·25

(b) Size 25×30 mm. Self-adhesive.

1465	30p. "Madonna and Child"	1·10	50

416 Black-billed Magpie ("Magpie")

2002. New Currency. Birds, as Nos. 1031/62, and new designs, with face values in cents and euros, as T 416. (i) Size 23×26 mm or 26×23 mm.

1466	1c. Type **416**	10	50
1467	2c. Northern gannet ("Gannet")	10	50
1468	3c. Blue tit (horiz)	10	50
1469	4c. Corn crake	10	50
1470	5c. Woodpigeon (horiz)	10	50
1470a	7c. Common stonechat	1·25	75
1471	10c. River kingfisher ("Kingfisher")	30	55
1472	20c. Northern lapwing ("Lapwing")	55	1·00
1473	38c. Blackbird	1·00	75
1474	41c. Chaffinch	70	60
1475	41c. Goldcrest	2·25	2·75
1476	44c. European robin ("Robin")	1·00	65
1477	47c. Kestrel (horiz)	1·25	70
1477a	48c. Peregrine falcon	1·00	70
1477b	48c. Pied wagtail	2·50	3·00
1478	50c. Grey heron (horiz)	1·25	90
1479	51c. Roseate tern (horiz)	1·25	75
1480	55c. Oystercatcher (horiz)	1·25	1·50
1481	57c. Western curlew ("Curlew")	1·25	80
1482	60c. Jay (horiz)	1·25	1·25
1482a	60c. Atlantic puffin	1·75	1·00
1482b	65c. Song thrush	1·50	1·00
1482c	75c. Ringed plover (horiz)	2·75	1·10
1482d	95c. Sparrowhawk (horiz)	2·75	1·40

(ii) Size 47×26 mm or 26×47 mm.

1483	€1 Barnacle goose (horiz)	2·00	1·40
1484	€2 White-fronted goose ("Greenland White-fronted Goose")	3·25	3·00
1485	€5 Northern pintail ("Pintail") (horiz)	7·50	7·00
1486	€10 Common shelduck ("Shelduck")	16·00	18·00

(b) Size 20×23 mm.

1486a	4c. Corncrake	80	1·50
1487	10c. River kingfisher ("King-fisher")	2·50	3·25
1488	36c. Wren	2·75	3·50
1489	38c. Blackbird	70	1·00
1490	41c. Chaffinch	70	80
1490a	48c. Peregrine falcon	75	90

(c) Self-adhesive. Size 24×29 mm.

1491	38c. Blackbird	70	71
1492	38c. Goldcrest	70	70
1493	41c. Chaffinch	90	90
1494	41c. Goldcrest	90	90
1495	44c. Robin	95	95
1495b	(–) Peregrine falcon	1·75	1·75
1495c	(–) Pied wagtail	1·75	1·75
1495d	48c. Peregrine falcon	1·00	1·00
1495e	48c. Pied wagtail	1·00	1·00
1496	50c. Puffin	1·25	1·25
1497	57c. Song thrush	1·10	1·10
1497b	60c. Atlantic puffin	1·40	1·40
1497c	65c. Song thrush	1·75	1·75

Nos. 1495b/c were sold for 48c.

417 Reverse of Irish €1 Coin, 2002

2002. Introduction of Euro Currency. Irish Coins.

1506	38c. Type **417**	75	50
1507	41c. Reverse of 50p. coin, 1971–2001	80	60
1508	57c. Reverse of 1d. coin, 1928–71	1·10	1·25

418 Teddy Bear

2002. Greetings Stamps. Toys. Multicoloured. (a) Design 25×37 mm.

1509	38c. Type **418**	70	50

(b) Designs 20×27 mm. Self-adhesive.

1510	38c. Type **418**	80	80
1511	38c. Rag doll	80	80
1512	38c. Rocking horse	80	80
1513	38c. Train	80	80
1514	38c. Wooden blocks	80	80

2002. Chinese New Year ("Year of the Horse").

MS1515	124×74 mm. As Nos. 1511/13, but 25×37 mm	2·75	2·75

419 Around the Camp Fire

2002. 75th Anniv of Scouting Ireland CSI. Multicoloured.

1516	41c. Type **419**	75	75
1517	41c. Setting up camp	75	75
1518	57c. Scouts canoeing	1·10	1·25
1519	57c. Scouts on hill walk	1·10	1·25

420 "Arkle"

2002. 250th Anniv of Steeplechasing in Ireland. Irish Steeplechasers. Multicoloured.

1520	38c. Type **420**	1·00	1·00
1521	38c. "L'Escargot"	1·00	1·00
1522	38c. "Dawn Run"	1·00	1·00
1523	38c. "Istabraq"	1·00	1·00

421 Badger

2002. Irish Mammals. Multicoloured.

1524	41c. Type **421**	75	60
1525	50c. Otter	90	70
1526	57c. Red squirell (vert)	1·10	80
1527	€1 Hedgehog (vert)	1·75	1·90
MS1528	150×67 mm. €5 As 50c.	7·00	8·50

422 Roy Keane

2002. World Cup Football Championship, Japan and Korea (2002). Irish Footballers. Multicoloured. (a) Size 29×40 mm or 40×29 mm.

1529	41c. Packie Bonner (horiz)	1·00	75
1530	41c. Type **422**	1·00	75
1531	41c. Paul McGrath	1·00	75
1532	41c. David O'Leary	1·00	75

(b) Size 25×37 mm or 37×35 mm. Self-adhesive.

1533	41c. Packie Bonner (horiz)	1·00	1·00
1534	41c. Type **422**	1·00	1·00
1535	41c. Paul McGrath	1·00	1·00
1536	41c. David O'Leary	1·00	1·00

423 Clown

2002. Europa. Circus. Multicoloured. (a) Size 40×29 mm. Ordinary gum.

1537	41c. Type **423**	70	70
1538	44c. Girl on horse	70	70

(b) Self-adhesive. Size 37×25 mm.

1539	41c. Type **423**	70	70
1540	41c. As No. 1538	70	70

424 Padre Pio

2002. Canonisation of St. Pio de Pietrelcina (Padre Pio).

1541	**424**	41c. multicoloured	75	70

425 Brian Boru leading Army

2002. 1000th Anniv of Declaration of Brian Boru as High King of Ireland. Multicoloured.

1542	41c. Type **425**	75	60
1543	44c. Leading fleet	75	60
1544	57c. Receiving surrender of the O'Neills	90	80
1545	£1 Decreeing primacy of bishopric of Armagh in the Irish Church	1·75	1·90

426 "Before the Start" (J. B. Yeats)

2002. 140th Anniv of National Gallery of Ireland (2004) (1st issue). Paintings. Multicoloured.

1546	41c. Type **426**	70	1·00
1547	41c. "The Conjuror" (Nathaniel Hone)	70	1·00
1548	41c. "The Colosseum and Arch of Constantine, Rome" (Giovanni Panini)	70	1·00
1549	41c. "The Gleaners" (Jules Breton)	70	1·00

See also Nos. 1606/9 and 1700/3.

2002. Gaelic Athletic Association Hall of Fame 2002 (2nd series). As T 411.

1550	41c. Peter McDermott (footballer)	1·00	1·00
1551	41c. Jimmy Smyth (hurler)	1·00	1·00
1552	41c. Matt Connor (footballer)	1·00	1·00
1553	41c. Seanie Duggan (hurler)	1·00	1·00

427 Archbishop Thomas Croke

2002. Death Centenary of Archbishop Croke (first patron of Gaelic Athletic Association).

1554	**427**	44c. multicoloured	80	70

428 U2

2002. Irish Rock Legends. Multicoloured.

1555	41c. Type **428**	1·40	1·25
1556	41c. Phil Lynott	1·40	1·25
1557	57c. Van Morrison	1·60	2·00
1558	57c. Rory Gallagher	1·60	2·00
MS1559	Four sheets, each 150×90 mm. (a) €2 Type **428**. (b) €2 No. 1556. (c) €2 No. 1557. (d) €2 No. 1558	9·00	13·00

429 "Adoration of the Magi"

2002. Christmas. Illustrations from "Les Tres Riches Heures du Duc de Berry" (medieval book of hours). Multicoloured. (a) Size 30×41 mm.

1560	41c. Type **429**	70	60
1561	44c. "The Annunciation to the Virgin Mary"	75	60
1562	57c. "The Annunciation to the Shepherds"	1·00	1·10

(b) Size 25×30 mm. Self-adhesive.

1563	41c. "The Nativity"	1·00	60

430 Labrador Puppies

2003. Greetings Stamps. Baby Animals. Multicoloured. (a) 29×40 mm.

1564	41c. Type **430**	80	65

(b) Designs 24×29 mm. Self-adhesive.

1565	41c. Type **430**	80	80
1566	41c. Chicks	80	80
1567	41c. Kids	80	80
1568	41c. Kittens	80	80
1569	41c. Baby rabbits	80	80

2003. Chinese New Year ("Year of the Goat"). Designs as Nos. 1566/8, but 29×40 mm.

MS1570	124×74 mm. 50c. Chicks; 50c. Kids; 50c. Kittens	3·75	4·50

431 St. Patrick

2003. St. Patrick's Day. Multicoloured. Size 29×40 mm.

1571	41c. Type **431**	80	60
1572	50c. St. Patrick's Day Parade passing St. Patrick's Cathedral, Dublin	95	1·00
1573	57c. St. Patrick's Day Parade, New York	1·10	1·25

(b) Size 25×26 mm. Self-adhesive.

1574	41c. St. Patrick	85	90
1575	50c. St. Patrick's Day Parade passing St. Patrick's Cathedral, Dublin	85	1·00
1576	57c. St. Patrick's Day Parade, New York	95	1·25

432 Seven-spotted Ladybird

2003. Irish Beetles. Multicoloured.

1577	41c. Type **432**	90	60
1578	50c. Great diving beetle	1·00	70
1579	57c. Leaf beetle	1·25	80
1580	€1 Green tiger beetle	2·25	2·50
MS1581	150×68 mm. €2 Type **432**	3·75	4·50

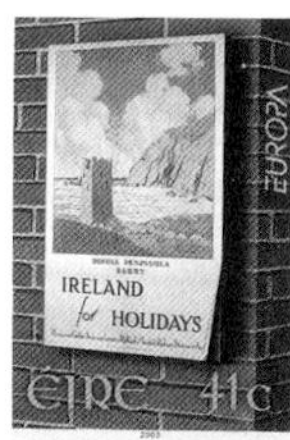

433 Dingle Peninsula ("IRELAND for HOLIDAYS")

2003. Europa. Poster Art. Posters by Paul Henry. Multicoloured.

1582	41c. Type **433**	80	65
1583	57c. Connemara ("IRELAND THIS YEAR")	95	1·10

434 "2003" and EYPD Logo

2003. European Year of People with Disabilities.

1584	**434**	41c. multicoloured	80	65

435 Athletes waving to Crowd

2003. 11th Special Olympics World Summer Games, Dublin. Multicoloured.

1585	41c. Type **435**	75	45
1586	50c. Swimmer	80	60
1587	57c. Athlete on starting block	95	65
1588	€1 Athlete running	2·25	3·25

436 Napier

2003. Centenary of Gordon Bennett Race in Ireland. Racing cars of 1903. Multicoloured. (a) Ordinary gum. Size 39×29 mm.

1589	41c. Type **436**	80	1·00
1590	41c. Mercedes	80	1·00
1591	41c. Mors	80	1·00
1592	41c. Winton	80	1·00

(b) Self-adhesive. Size 36×25 mm.

1593	41c. As No. 1592	80	90
1594	41c. As No. 1591	80	90
1595	41c. As No. 1590	80	90
1596	41c. Type **436**	80	90

437 Henry Ford and Model T Ford, 1908–28

2003. Centenary of the Ford Motor Company.

1597	**437**	41c. multicoloured	80	65

438 Harry Ferguson flying first Irish Monoplane, 1909

2003. Centenary of Powered Flight. Multicoloured.

1598	41c. Type **438**	80	60
1599	50c. Alcock and Brown's Vickers FB.27 Vimy over Galway after first transatlantic flight, 1919	1·10	80
1600	57c. *Wright Flyer I*, 1903	1·25	1·50
1601	57c. Lillian Bland's biplane, 1910	1·25	1·50
MS1602	150×90 mm. €5 As No. 1600	8·50	10·00

439 Robert Emmet

2003. Centenary of Rebellion of 1803. Multicoloured.

1603	41c. Type **439**	80	60
1604	50c. Thomas Russell	1·10	1·10
1605	57c. Anne Devlin	1·40	1·60

2003. 140th Anniv of National Gallery of Ireland (2004) (2nd issue). Paintings. As T 426 but vert. Multicoloured.

1606	48c. "Self-portrait as Timanthes" (James Barry)	1·00	1·25
1607	48c. "Man writing a Letter" (Gabriel Metsu)	1·00	1·25
1608	48c. "Woman reading a Letter" (Gabriel Metsu)	1·00	1·25
1609	48c. "Woman seen from the Back" (Jean-Antoine Watteau)	1·00	1·25

440 Frank O'Connor

2003. Birth Centenary of Frank O'Connor (writer).

1610	**440**	50c. multicoloured	1·00	1·00

441 E. T. S. Walton

2003. Birth Centenary of E. T. S. Walton (Nobel Prize for Physics, 1951).

1611	**441**	57c. cream, black and brown	1·00	1·00

442 Admiral William Brown (founder of the Argentine Navy)

2003. Irish Mariners. Multicoloured. (a) Ordinary gum. Size 40×29 mm.

1612	48c. Type **442**	1·25	1·25
1613	48c. Commodore John Barry (Commanding Officer of US Navy, 1794–1803)	1·25	1·25
1614	57c. Captain Robert Halpin (Commander of cable ship *Great Eastern*)	1·40	1·40
1615	57c. Captain Richard Roberts (captain of *Sirius*, first scheduled passenger steamship London to New York voyage)	1·40	1·40
MS1616	150×90 mm. €5 Commodore John Barry	8·00	8·50

(b) Self-adhesive. Size 36×21 mm.

1617	48c. Commodore John Barry	1·10	1·40
1618	48c. Admiral William Brown	1·10	1·40
1619	48c. Captain Robert Halpin	1·10	1·40
1620	48c. Captain Richard Roberts	1·10	1·40

443 Pope John Paul II

2003. 25th Anniv of the Election of Pope John Paul II. Multicoloured.

1621	48c. Type **443**	1·25	90
1622	50c. Pope in St. Peter's Square, Rome	1·40	95
1623	57c. Making speech at United Nations	1·50	1·40

444 Angel

2003. Christmas. Multicoloured. (a) Ordinary gum.

1624	48c. Flight into Egypt (32×32 mm)	90	80
1625	50c. Type **444**	95	80
1626	57c. Three Kings	1·10	1·25

(b) Self-adhesive. Size 29×24 mm.

1627	48c. Nativity	1·00	70

445 Boyne Bridge

2004. Ireland's Presidency of European Union.

1628	**445**	48c. multicoloured	1·50	1·00

446 "Monkeys in Love"

2004. Greetings Stamps. Animals. Multicoloured. Ordinary gum. Size 29×39 mm.

1629	48c. Type **446**	1·50	1·25
MS1630	124×74 mm. 60c. Type **446**; 60c. "Jolly Panda"; 60c. "Cute Koalas"	3·50	3·75

(b) Self-adhesive. Size 24×29 mm.

1631	48c. Type **446**	1·00	1·00
1632	48c. "Jolly Panda"	1·00	1·00
1633	48c. "Cute Koalas"	1·00	1·00
1634	48c. "Happy Hippo"	1·00	1·00

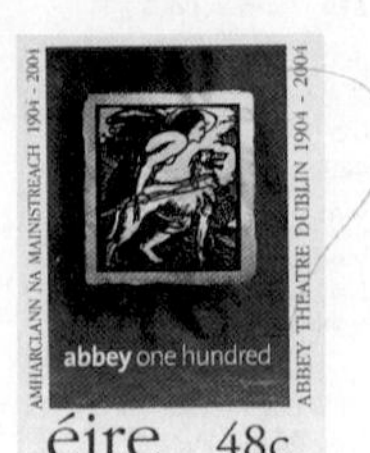

447 St. Patrick and Stained Glass Window from Church of the Holy and Undivided Trinity, Magheralin, Co. Down

2004. St. Patrick's Day.

1635	**447**	65c. multicoloured	1·50	1·50

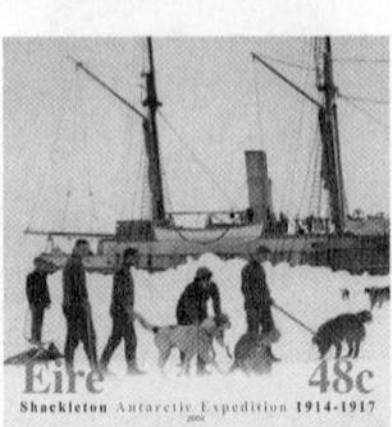

448 Abbey Theatre Logo

2004. Centenary of Abbey Theatre, Dublin.

1636	**448**	48c. multicoloured	1·10	1·10

449 Expedition Members, Dogs and *Endurance* trapped in Ice

2004. 90th Anniv of Shackleton's Antarctic Expedition. Multicoloured.

1637	48c. Type **449**	1·75	1·50
1638	48c. Two crew members, huskies and bow of *Endurance*	1·75	1·50
1639	65c. Crew member looking out of tent	1·50	2·25
1640	65c. Crew members and tented camp on ice	1·50	2·25
MS1641	149×90 mm. €1 As No. 1639; €1 As No. 1640	5·50	5·50

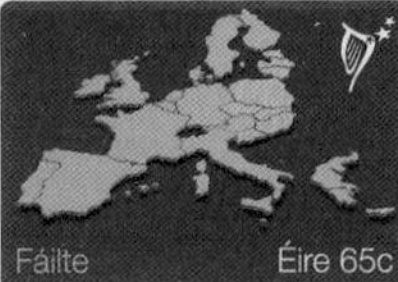

450 Flags, Football and Globe

2004. Centenary of FIFA (Federation Internationale de Football Association).

1642	**450**	60c. multicoloured	1·40	1·40

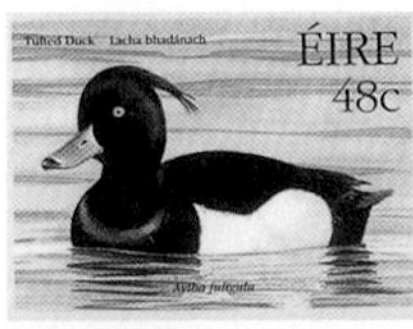

451 Map of Europe showing Acceding Countries

2004. Enlargement of the European Union.

1643	**451**	65c. multicoloured	2·25	1·40

452 Tufted Duck

2004. Ducks. Multicoloured.

1644	48c. Type **452**	1·00	70
1645	60c. Red-breasted merganser	1·50	1·25
1646	65c. Gadwall	1·50	1·25
1647	€1 Garganey	2·50	2·00
MS1648	150×90 mm. Nos. 1644/7	6·00	6·00

453 Ross Castle, Co. Kerry

2004. Europa. Holidays. Multicoloured.

1649	48c. Type **453**	1·25	70
1650	65c. Cliffs of Moher, Co. Clare	1·50	1·50

454 Emblem

2004. 10th Anniv of UN International Year of the Family.

1651	**454**	65c. scarlet, yellow and green	1·25	1·50

455 "Frog" (Daire Lee)

2004. Winning Entries in Children's Painting Competition. Multicoloured.

1652	48c. Type **455**	90	70
1653	60c. "Marmalade Cat" (Cian Colman)	1·25	1·25
1654	65c. "Ralleshin Dipditch" (Daire O'Rourke)	1·25	1·25
1655	€1 "Fish on a Dish" (Ailish Fitzpatrick) (horiz)	1·90	2·00

456 "James Joyce" (Tullio Pericoli)

2004. Centenary of "Leopold Bloom's Adventure" (from Ulysses by James Joyce). Multicoloured.

1656 48c. Type **456** 80 70
1657 65c. James Joyce 1·10 1·40

457 College Entrance

2004. 426th Anniv of Irish College, Paris.

1658 **457** 65c. multicoloured 1·00 1·00

458 LUAS Tram

2004. Introduction of LUAS Tram System, Dublin. Multicoloured.

1659 48c. Type **458** 65 70
1660 48c. People accessing LUAS tram 65 70

459 Javelin Thrower and Olympic Flame

2004. Olympic Games, Athens. Multicoloured.

1661 48c. Type **459** 1·25 70
1662 60c. Discobolus (sculpture, Myron) and Olympic flame 1·50 1·60

460 Two Camogie Players and O'Duffy Cup

2004. Centenary of Camogie (Gaelic game for women). Multicoloured.

1663 48c. Type **460** 95 1·10
1664 48c. Two players and Camogie emblem 95 1·10

461 Common Dog-violet

2004. Wild Flowers. Multicoloured

(a) Ordinary gum. (i) 23 x 26 mm

1665 1c. Bloody crane's-bill 10 10
1666 2c. Irish orchid 10 10
1667 3c. Yellow flag 10 10
1668 4c. Type **461** 10 15
1669 5c. Dandelion 10 15
1670 7c. Fly orchid 15 20
1671 10c. Mountain avens 15 20
1672 12c. Autumn gorse 15 20
1673 20c. Thrift 30 35
1674 25c. Common knapweed 35 40
1675 48c. Daisy 65 70
1676 48c. Primrose 65 70
1677 50c. Biting stonecrop 70 75
1678 55c. Large-flowered butterwort 1·20 1·20
1679 60c. Hawthorn 80 85
1680 65c. Bluebell 90 95
1681 75c. Navelwort 1·00 1·10
1682 78c. Black bog-rush 1·80 1·80
1683 82c. Sea aster 1·20 1·30
1684 90c. Viper's bugloss 1·20 1·30
1685 95c. Purple loosestrife 2·20 2·20

(ii) 26×47 mm (€1, €2) or 47×26 mm (others).

1686 €1 Foxglove 1·40 1·50
1687 €2 Lords-and-ladies 2·75 3·00
1688 €5 Dog-rose 6·75 7·00
1689 €10 Spring Gentian 13·50 14·00

(b) Booklet stamps. Ordinary gum. Size 20×23 mm

1690 5c. Dandelion 45 1·00
1691 25c. Common knapweed 1·00 1·25
1692 55c. Large-flowered butterwort 1·40 1·40

(c) Size 23×29 mm

1693 48c. Daisy 65 65
1694 48c. Primrose 65 65
1695 - (N) Large-flowered butterwort 1·75 1·75
1696 - (N) Blue-eyed grass 1·75 1·75
1697 - 55c. Large-flowered butterwort 1·25 1·25
1698 - 75c. Navelwort 1·70 1·70
1699 - 78c. Black bog-rush 1·75 1·75
1699b - 82c. Sea aster 1·80 1·80

(d) Size 20x24 mm. Self-adhesive

1699c (N) Yellow horned-poppy 1·75 1·75
1699d 55c. Large-flowered butterwort 1·75 1·75
1699e 82c. Sea aster 2·40 2·40

2004. 140th Anniv of National Gallery of Ireland (3rd issue). As T 426. Multicoloured.

1700 48c. "The House Builders" (Walter Osborne) 80 80
1701 48c. "Kitchen Maid with the Supper at Emmaus" (Diego Velazquez) 80 80
1702 48c. "The Lamentation over the Dead Christ" (Nicolas Poussin) 80 80
1703 48c. "The Taking of Christ" (Caravaggio) 80 80

462 William Butler Yeats

2004. Irish Winners of Nobel Prize for Literature. Multicoloured.

1704 (N) Type **462** 1·00 1·00
1705 (N) George Bernard Shaw 1·00 1·00
1706 (N) Samuel Beckett 1·00 1·00
1707 (N) Seamus Heaney 1·00 1·00

Nos. 1706 were inscribed "N" and sold for 48c. each. Stamps of similar designs were issued by Sweden.

463 George Fox (Founder of The Society of Friends ("Quakers"))

2004. 350th Anniv of Quakers in Ireland.

1708 **463** 60c. multicoloured 1·00 1·00

464 Patrick Kavanagh

2004. Birth Centenary of Patrick Kavanagh (poet).

1709 **464** 48c. green and dull green 1·00 75

465 The Holy Family

2004. Christmas. Multicoloured.

(a) Ordinary gum

1710 48c. Type **465** 85 50
1711 60c. The flight into Egypt 1·10 1·25
1712 65c. The Adoration of the Magi 1·25 1·40

(b) Size 24×29 mm. Self-adhesive.

1713 48c. The Holy Family 1·00 70

466 Lovebirds

2005. Love, Greetings and Chinese New Year of the Rooster. Multicoloured. (a) Ordinary gum.

1714 48c. Type **466** 1·00 1·00
MS1715 130×74 mm. 60c. Rooster; 60c. Type **466**; 60c. Owl 4·00 4·00

(b) Self-adhesive. Designs 30×25 mm.

1716 48c. Rooster 1·50 1·50
1717 48c. Stork 1·50 1·50
1718 48c. Type **466** 1·00 1·00
1719 48c. Owl 1·25 1·25

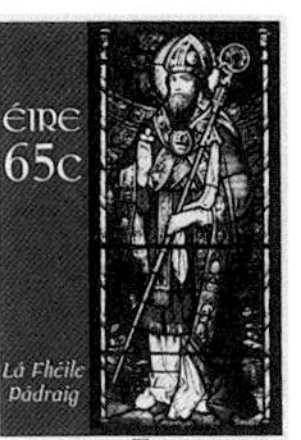

467 St. Patrick

2005. St. Patrick's Day.

1720 **467** 65c. multicoloured 1·25 1·25

468 "Landscape, Co. Wicklow" (Evie Hone)

2005. Female Artists. Multicoloured.

1721 48c. Type **468** 85 95
1722 48c. "Seabird and Landmarks" (Nano Reid) 85 95
1723 65c. "Three Graces" (Gabriel Hayes) (vert) 1·10 1·25
1724 65c. "Threshing" (Mildred Anne Butler) (vert) 1·10 1·25

469 Statue, City Hall and Churches

2005. Cork–European Capital of Culture 2005. Multicoloured.

1725 48c. Type **469** 80 80
1726 48c. Court House and Shandon Steeple (clock tower) 80 80

Nos. 1725/6 were printed together, se-tenant, forming a composite design showing Patrick's Bridge and a montage of landmark buildings and monuments of the city of Cork.

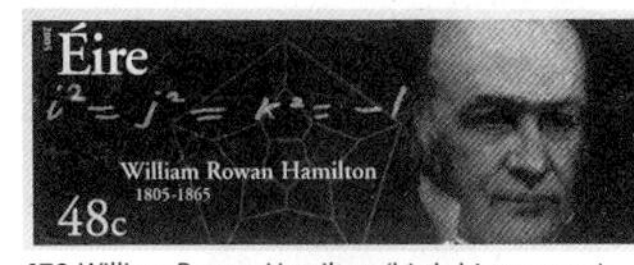

470 William Rowan Hamilton (birth bicentenary)

2005. UNESCO World Year of Physics. Multicoloured.

1727 48c. Type **470** 85 70
1728 60c. UNESCO Headquarters, Paris, trees and reflections of sunlight 1·10 1·25
1729 65c. Albert Einstein (50th death anniv) 1·25 1·40

471 201 Class Diesel Locomotive pulling "Enterprise Express" Train

2005. 150th Anniv of Dublin–Belfast Railway. Multicoloured.

1730 48c. Type **471** 1·00 1·00
1731 48c. V Class 3 steam locomotive No. 85, *Merlin*, arriving at Amiens Street (now Connolly) Station, Dublin, c. 1951 1·00 1·00
1732 60c. Q Class steam locomotive No. 131 crossing Boyne Valley viaduct, Drogheda 1·40 1·40
1733 65c. Modern "Enterprise Express" leaving Belfast Central Station 1·40 1·40
MS1734 150×90 mm. Nos. 1730/3 4·25 4·50

472 Red Deer Stags, Killarney National Park, Ireland

2005. Biosphere Reserves. Multicoloured.

1735 48c. Type **472** 70 70
1736 65c. Saskatoon Berries and Osprey, Waterton Lakes National Park, Alberta, Canada 1·40 1·50
MS1737 150×90 mm. Nos. 1735/6 2·00 2·50

Stamps in similar designs were issued by Canada.

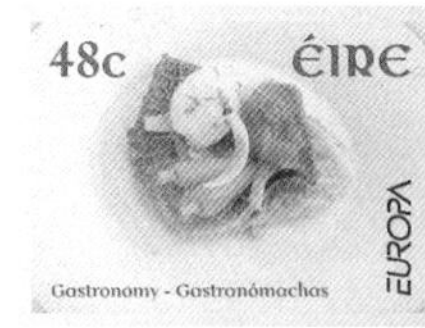

473 Lamb, Cabbage, Carrots and Potato (ingredients of Irish Stew)

2005. Europa. Gastronomy. Multicoloured.

1738 48c. Type **473** 75 70
1739 65c. Oysters 1·00 1·25

474 Small Copper

2005. Butterflies. Multicoloured.

1740 48c. Type **474** 75 70
1741 60c. Green hairstreak 95 90
1742 65c. Painted lady 1·00 1·10
1743 €1 Pearl-bordered fritillary 1·90 2·25
MS1744 150×67 mm. €5 As No. 1742 7·50 9·00

475 *Dunbrody*

2005. Cutty Sark International Tall Ships Race, Waterford. Multicoloured.

1745 48c. Type **475** 85 70
1746 60c. *Tenacious* 1·00 1·10
1747 65c. USCG *Eagle* 1·10 1·25

476 Glendalough, Co. Wicklow

2005. Round Towers of Ireland. Each black.

1748 48c. Type **476** 75 85
1749 48c. Ardmore, Co. Waterford 75 85
1750 48c. Clones, Co. Monaghan 75 85
1751 48c. Kilmacduagh, Co. Galway 75 85

Nos. 1748/51 commemorate the 75th Anniversary of the Monuments of Ireland Act.

477 Bees on Honeycomb

2005. Apimondia 2005 (international bee-keeping conference and exhibition), Dublin.

1752	**477**	65c. multicoloured	1·25	1·25

478 Eamonn Darcy, Christy O'Connor Jnr and Philip Walton holding Ryder Cup

2005. Ireland and the Ryder Cup (golf tournament). Multicoloured.

1753	48c. Type **478**	1·25	1·25
1754	48c. Darren Clarke, Paul McGinley and Padraig Harrington with Ryder Cup	1·25	1·25
1755	60c. Harry Bradshaw, Ronan Rafferty and Christy O'Connor Snr	1·50	1·50
1756	65c. The K Club, Straffan, Co. Kildare (venue of 2006 Ryder Cup)	1·50	1·50

479 Erskine Childers

2005. Birth Centenary of Erskine Childers (President of Ireland 1973–4).

1757	**479**	48c. multicoloured	75	75

480 An Garda Siochana on Overseas Duty

2005. 50th Anniv of Ireland's Membership of United Nations. Multicoloured.

1758	48c. Type **480**	1·00	1·00
1759	48c. Irish Army medical aid in East Timor	1·00	1·00
1760	60c. F. H. Boland (signatory of Ireland's membership), 1955	1·25	1·25
1761	65c. Member of Irish Defence Force in classroom, Lebanon	1·25	1·25

481 "Arthur Griffith" (Leo Whelan) and Title Page of Essay

2005. Centenary of Arthur Griffith's Essays "The Resurrection of Hungary: A Parallel for Ireland".

1762	**481**	48c. multicoloured	75	75

482 Nativity

2005. Christmas. Multicoloured. (a) Ordinary gum.

1763	48c. Type **482**	80	50
1764	60c. Choir of angels with harp	1·10	1·25
1765	65c. Choir of angels with tambourine and trumpet	1·25	1·50

(b) Size 24×29 mm. Self-adhesive.

1766	48c. Type **482**	85	80

483 Patrick Gallagher (founder) and Templecrone Co-operative Store

2006. Centenary of the Templecrone Co-operative Agricultural Society ("The Cope").

1767	**483**	48c. multicoloured	85	85

484 Red Setter and Couple Embracing

2006. Love, Greetings and Chinese New Year of the Dog. Multicoloured. (a) Ordinary gum.

1768	48c. Type **484**	1·00	85
MS1769	130×74 mm. 65c. Two Chinese crested dogs; 65c. As No. 1768.; 65c. Golden labrador	5·00	5·00

(b) Self-adhesive. Size 29×24 mm.

1770	48c. Two Chinese crested dogs	1·75	1·75
1771	48c. Golden Labrador	1·75	1·75
1772	48c. Type **484**	1·75	1·75
1773	48c. Red setter puppy	1·75	1·75

485 "St. Patrick lights the Paschal Fire at Slane" (Sean Keating)

2006. St. Patrick's Day.

1774	**485**	65c. multicoloured	1·75	1·25

486 Sessile Oak ("Quercus petraea")

2006. Trees of Ireland. Multicoloured.

1775	48c. Type **486**	60	85
1776	60c. Yew (*Taxus baccata*)	1·10	1·10
1777	75c. Ash (*Fraxinus excelsior*)	1·40	1·40
1778	€1 Strawberry-tree (*Arbutus unedo*)	1·75	2·00
MS1779	150×90 mm. Nos. 1775/8	6·50	6·50

487 St. Hubert, Church of Ireland, Carnalway, Co. Kildare

2006. 75th Death Anniv of Harry Clarke (stained glass artist).

1780	**487**	48c. multicoloured	1·00	85

488 General Post Office, Dublin

2006. 90th Anniv of the Easter Rising.

1781	**488**	48c. multicoloured	1·00	85

489 Children waving Irish and EU Flags (Katie McMillan)

2006. Europa. Winning Entries in Children's Stamp Design Competition. Multicoloured.

1782	48c. Type **489**	1·25	60
1783	75c. Flags of EU members in flowers (Sarah Naughter)	1·60	2·25

490 EU Flag

2006. 10th Anniv of European Union Flag.

1784	**490**	48c. multicoloured	1·00	85

491 Interior of University Church (Dr. Thomas Ryan)

2006. 150th Anniv of University Church, St. Stephen's Green, Dublin.

1785	**491**	48c. multicoloured	1·00	75

492 Mairtin O Cadhain (Irish language writer) (birth centenary)

2006. Celtic Scholars. Multicoloured.

1786	48c. Type **492**	1·00	1·00
1787	48c. Johann Caspar Zeus (Celtic languages researcher) (birth bicentenary)	1·00	1·00

493 Pebbles and Typewriter Keyboard

2006. 50th Anniv of the Department of the Gaeltacht.

1788	**493**	48c. multicoloured	1·00	75

494 Emblem

2006. 10th Anniv of TG4 (Teilifise Gaeilge 4) Television Channel.

1789	**494**	48c. multicoloured	1·00	75

495 *St. David* (ferry), 1906

2006. Centenary of the Rosslare–Fishguard Ferry Service. Multicoloured.

1790	48c. Type **495**	1·50	1·50
1791	48c. *Stena Lynx* (ferry), 2006	1·50	1·50
MS1792	150×90 mm. Nos. 1790/1	3·00	3·00

496 "The Battle of the Somme (36th Ulster Division)" (J. P. Beadle)

2006. 90th Anniv of the Battle of the Somme.

1793	**496**	75c. multicoloured	3·00	2·50

497 Guide Dog

2006. 30th Anniv of Irish Guide Dogs for the Blind.

1794	**497**	48c. multicoloured	1·75	1·25

498 Golf Ball on Tee

2006. Ryder Cup Golf Tournament, K Club, Straffan, Co. Kildare (1st issue). Multicoloured. (a). Ordinary gum.

1795	48c. Type **498**	1·40	1·40
1796	48c. Golf ball in the rough	1·40	1·40
1797	48c. Golf ball in bunker	1·40	1·40
1798	48c. Golf ball at edge of green	1·40	1·40
MS1799	150×90 mm. Nos. 1795/8	5·00	5·00

See also No. **MS**1808.

(b) Self-adhesive. Size 24×29 mm.

1800	48c. Type **498**	1·40	1·40
1801	48c. As No. 1796	1·40	1·40
1802	48c. As No. 1797	1·40	1·40
1803	48c. As No. 1798	1·40	1·40

499 "Ronnie Delany" (Dr. Thomas Ryan)

2006. 50th Anniv of Ronnie Delany's Gold Medal for 1500 Metres at Olympic Games, Melbourne.

1804	**499**	48c. multicoloured	1·00	75

500 Michael Cusack

2006. Death Centenary of Michael Cusack (founder of Gaelic Athletic Association).

1805 **500** 48c. multicoloured 1·00 75

501 "Michael Davitt" (Sir William Orpen)

2006. Death Centenary of Michael Davitt (founder of Irish National Land League).

1806 **501** 48c. multicoloured 1·00 75

502 RTE National Symphony Orchestra

2006. 25th Anniv of National Concert Hall, Dublin.

1807 **502** 48c. multicoloured 1·00 75

503 Teeing Off

2006. Ryder Cup Golf Tournament, K Club, Straffan, Co. Kildare (2nd issue). Sheet 140×102 mm containing T 503 and similar horiz design. Multicoloured. Self-adhesive.

MS1808 75c. Type **503**; 75c. In bunker 4·50 5·00

504 River Barrow at Graiguenamanagh, Co. Kilkenny

2006. Inland Waterways. Multicoloured.

1809 75c. Type **504** 1·60 1·90
1810 75c. Belturbet Marina, River Erne, Co. Cavan 1·60 1·90
1811 75c. Lock-keepers cottage on Grand Canal, Cornalour, Co. Offaly 1·60 1·90
1812 75c. River Shannon at Meelick Quay 1·60 1·90

505 The Chieftains

2006. Irish Music (1st series). Multicoloured.

1813 48c. Type **505** 1·25 1·00
1814 48c. The Dubliners 1·25 1·00
1815 75c. The Clancy Brothers and Tommy Makem 1·75 2·00
1816 75c. Altan 1·75 2·00
MS1817 150×90 mm. Nos. 1813/16 5·50 6·50

See also Nos. 1919/23.

506 Madonna and Child **507** "The Nativity" (Simon Bening)

2006. Christmas. Multicoloured. (a) Ordinary gum.

1818 48c. Type **506** 1·00 50
1819 75c. Shepherd with lamb 1·75 2·25

(b) Self-adhesive. Size 22×30 mm.

1820 48c. Type **507** 1·25 60

2006. Belgica 2006 International Stamp Exhibition, Brussels. No. MS1817 with Belgica '06 emblem and "16–20 November, 2006" added to the sheet margin.

MS1821 150×90 mm. Nos. 1813/16 5·50 6·50

2006. MonacoPhil 2006 International Stamp Exhibition. No. MS1817 with MonacoPhil 2006 emblem and "1–3 December, 2006" added to the sheet margin.

MS1822 150×90 mm. Nos. 1813/16 5·50 6·50

508 Franciscan and Door to Auditorium of Irish College

2007. 400th Anniv of the Irish Franciscan College, Louvain, Belgium.

1823 **508** 75c. multicoloured 1·75 2·25

509 Father Luke Wadding

2007. 350th Death Anniv of Father Luke Wadding (theologian).

1824 **509** 75c. multicoloured 1·75 2·25

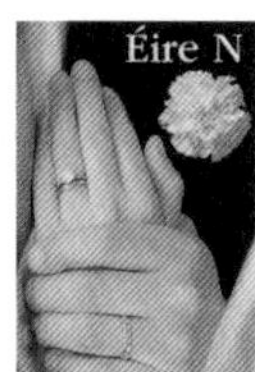

510 Linked Hands

2007. Weddings (1st issue). Chalk-surfaced paper. Self-adhesive.

1825 **510** (N) multicoloured 1·00 70

No. 1825 is inscribed "N" and was sold for 48c. each.

See also Nos. 1862, 1880 and 1929.

511 Cartoon Stamp and Heart

2007. Greetings Stamps. Multicoloured. Self-adhesive.

1826 (48c.) Type **511** 1·10 70
1827 (48c.) Birthday cake 1·10 70

Nos. 1826/7 are inscribed "N" and sold for 48c. each.

512 Two Pigs

2007. Chinese New Year ("Year of the Pig").

1828 **512** 75c. multicoloured 1·75 2·25

MS1829 130×74 mm. 75c.×2 Type **512**; 75c. As Type **512** but green background 5·25 6·75

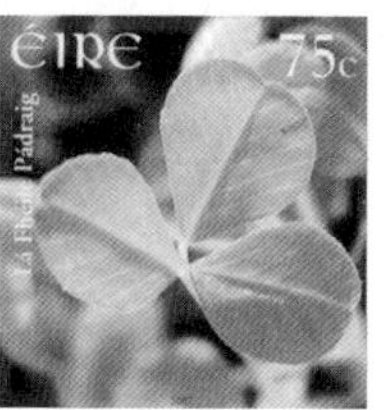

513 Shamrock

2007. St. Patrick's Day.

1830 **513** 75c. multicoloured 2·00 2·50

514 Hugh O'Neill, Earl of Tyrone

2007. 400th Anniv of the Flight of the Earls. Multicoloured.

1831 48c. Type **514** 1·00 1·25
1832 48c. Rory O'Donnell, Earl of Tyrconnell 1·00 1·25
MS1833 150×90 mm. Nos. 1831/2 2·25 2·50

Nos. 1831/2 were printed together, se-tenant, forming a composite background design showing Lough Swilly and map of Europe.

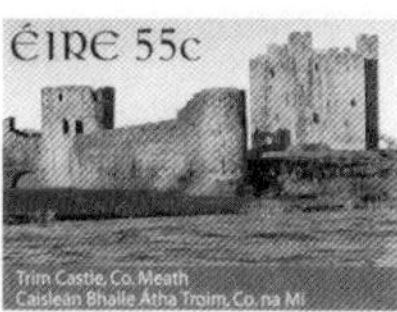

515 Trim Castle, Co. Meath

2007. Castles. Multicoloured.

1834 55c. Type **515** 1·50 1·50
1835 55c. Dunluce Castle, Co. Antrim 1·50 1·50
1836 55c. Lismore Castle, Co. Waterford 1·50 1·50
1837 55c. Portumna Castle, Co. Galway 1·50 1·50
MS1838 150×90 mm. Nos. 1834/7 5·50 5·50

516 EU Flag, Signatures and Palazzo dei Conservatori, Rome

2007. 50th Anniv of the Treaty of Rome.

1839 **516** 55c. multicoloured 1·25 1·25

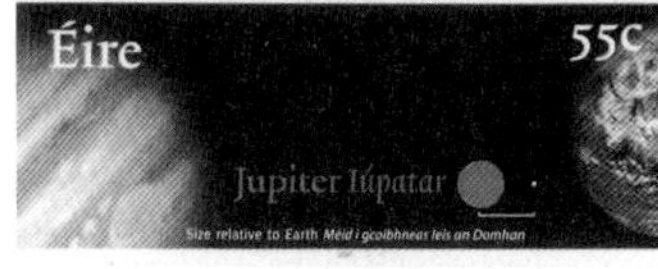

517 Girl Scout at Campsite, c. 2007

2007. Europa. Centenary of Scouting. Multicoloured.

1840 55c. Type **517** 1·50 75
1841 78c. Boy scout camping, c. 1907 2·00 2·50

518 Jupiter

2007. The Planets (1st series). Multicoloured.

1842 55c. Type **518** 1·40 1·50
1843 55c. Neptune 1·40 1·50
1844 78c. Saturn 1·90 2·25
1845 78c. Uranus 1·90 2·25
MS1846 150×90 mm. Nos. 1842/5 6·00 6·75

Nos. 1842/3 and 1844/5 were printed together, se-tenant, forming a composite design showing Planet Earth.

519 St. Charles of Mount Argus, Dublin

2007. Canonisation of Blessed Charles of Mount Argus.

1847 **519** 55c. multicoloured 1·25 1·25

520 Anniversary Emblem

2007. 50th Anniv of the IPA (Institute of Public Administration).

1848 **520** 55c. multicoloured 1·25 1·25

521 RTE National Symphony Orchestra

2007. RTE Performing Groups. Multicoloured. Ordinary or self-adhesive gum.

1849 55c. Type **521** 1·40 1·50
1850 55c. RTE Concert Orchestra 1·40 1·50
1851 55c. RTE Vanbrugh Quartet 1·40 1·50
1852 55c. RTE Philharmonic Choir 1·40 1·50
1853 55c. RTE Cor na nOg children's choir 1·40 1·50

522 Society Seal and Gandon Facade of King's Inns Building

2007. 400th Anniv of Revival of the Honourable Society of King's Inns.

1859 **522** 55c. multicoloured 1·25 1·25

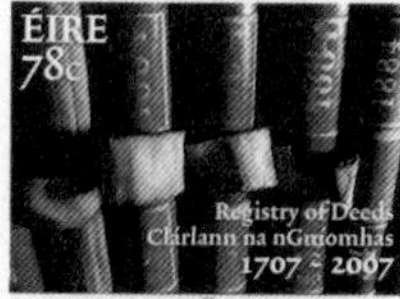

523 Bound Books containing Records in Registry of Deeds

2007. 300th Anniv of the Registry of Deeds Act.

1860 **523** 78c. multicoloured 1·75 1·75

524 Girls Choir from Colaiste Iosagain, Co. Dublin

2007. Centenary of the National Anthem.

1861 **524** 55c. multicoloured 1·25 1·25

2007. Weddings (2nd issue). As T 510 but new value. Self-adhesive.

1862 55c. As Type **510** 1·25 1·25

525 *Skuldelev 2* (Viking longship)

2007. Voyage of the Havhingsten fra Glendalough (replica of Viking longship Skuldelev 2) from Denmark to Dublin. Multicoloured.

1863	55c. Type **525**	1·25	1·25
MS1864	150×90 mm. €3 *Havhingsten fra Glendalough* (replica Viking longship)	6·75	7·50

526 Paul O'Connell

2007. Rugby World Cup, France. Multicoloured.

1865	55c. Type **526**	1·40	1·25
1866	78c. Irish players in lineout, Croke Park, 2007	2·25	2·50
MS1867	Two sheets, each 150×90 mm. (a) No. 1865. (b) No. 1866 Set of 2 sheets	3·00	3·50

527 'Fat Cat'

2007. Celtic Cats

1868	55c. Type **527**	1·25	1·50
1869	55c. Celtic Tigress	1·25	1·50
1870	78c. Cool Cats	2·00	2·25
1871	78c. Kilkenny Cat	2·00	2·25
MS1872	150×90 mm. As Nos. 1868/71 but 18×18 mm	6·00	6·75

528 Fr. Joseph Mullooly in 4th-century Basilica, San Clemente, Rome

2007. 150th Anniv of Archaeological Discoveries, San Clemente, Rome.

1873	**528**	55c. multicoloured	1·25	1·25

529 James Fintan Lalor

2007. Birth Bicentenary of James Fintan Lalor (nationalist and journalist).

1874	**529**	55c. multicoloured	1·25	1·25

530 Giant Elk Antlers

2007. 150th Anniv of the Natural History Museum, Dublin.

1875	**530**	55c. multicoloured	1·25	1·25

531 The Presentation in the Temple

2007. Christmas. Multicoloured. (a) Ordinary gum.

1876	55c. Type **531**	1·25	75
1877	78c. The Three Magi	2·00	3·50

(b) Self-adhesive. Size 24×29 mm.

1878	55c. The Adoration of the Shepherds	1·25	1·25

532 Charles Wesley (*The Lily Portrait*)

2007. 300th Birth Anniv of Charles Wesley (founder of Methodism and hymn writer).

1879	**532**	78c. multicoloured	1·90	2·25

533 Bride and Groom Embracing

2008. Weddings (3rd issue). Self-adhesive.

1880	**533**	55c. multicoloured	1·25	1·40

534 Rat and Candle

2008. Chinese New Year ('Year of the Rat').

1881	**534**	78c. multicoloured	2·00	2·25
MS1882		130×74 mm. No. 1881×3	5·75	6·50

535 Liam Whelan and Munich Memorial Clock, Old Trafford, Manchester

2008. 50th Anniv of the Munich Air Disaster.

1883	**535**	55c. multicoloured	2·00	1·40

536 Juggling Frog

2008. Greetings Stamps. Multicoloured. Self-adhesive.

1884	55c. Trumpeting elephant	1·40	1·40
1885	55c. Type **536**	1·40	1·40

537 St. Patrick (line engraving by Leonard Gaultier)

2008. St. Patrick's Day.

1886	**537**	78c. multicoloured	2·00	2·25

No. 1886 is based on a drawing made in 1619 by Thomas Messingham.

538 Logo

2008. European Year of Intercultural Dialogue.

1887	**538**	55c. multicoloured	1·40	1·40

539 *Hugh Lane* (Antonio Mancini)

2008. Centenary of Hugh Lane Gallery, Dublin.

1888	**539**	55c. multicoloured	1·40	1·40

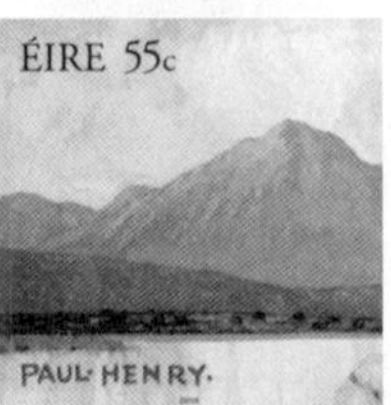

540 *West of Ireland Landscape*

2008. Paul Henry Landscape Paintings. Multicoloured.

1889	55c. Type **540** (signature at left)	1·75	1·75
1890	55c. *West of Ireland Landscape* (rocks in foreground, signature at right)	1·75	1·75
1891	55c. *A Connemara Village* (signature at left)	1·75	1·75
1892	55c. *A Connemara Village* (signature at right)	1·75	1·75

Nos. 1889/92 commemorate the 50th death anniversary of Paul Henry.

541 Logo of Irish League of Credit Unions (ILCU)

2008. 50th Anniv of the Credit Union Movement in Ireland.

1893	**541**	55c. multicoloured	1·50	1·50

542 World Map showing Africa and Asia (Mohammed Rahman)

2008. International Year of Planet Earth. Showing children's plasticine models of Planet Earth. Multicoloured. Self-adhesive.

1894	55c. Type **542**	1·50	1·50
1895	55c. World map showing the Americas and Atlantic Ocean (Conor Reid)	1·40	1·40

543 '50'

2008. 50th Anniv of the Institute of Creative Advertising and Design (ICAD).

1896	**543**	55c. multicoloured	1·50	1·50

544 RMS *Leinster*

2008. 90th Anniv of the Sinking of RMS Leinster.

1897	**544**	55c. multicoloured	2·00	1·50

545 Boy writing Letter

2008. Europa. The Letter. Multicoloured.

1898	55c. Type **545**	1·50	1·50
1899	82c. Girl writing letter	2·00	2·00

546 Aughrim, Co. Wicklow (2007 winner)

2008. 50th Anniv of the Tidy Towns Competition.

1900	**546**	55c. multicoloured	1·50	1·50

547 Lt. Col. McCarthy, Comdt. Higgins, Capt. Lavelle, Comdt. Coughlan and Capt. Henderson

2008. 50th Anniv of the First Irish Defence Forces Mission to the UN.

1901	**547**	55c. multicoloured	2·00	1·50

548 Colm Meaney in *Kings*

2008. Filmed in Ireland

1902	55c. Type **548**	1·50	1·50
1903	55c. Brid Ni Neachtain in *Cre Na Cille*	1·50	1·50
1904	82c. Cillian Murphy in *The Wind that Shakes the Barley*	2·10	2·10
1905	82c. Pat Shortt in *Garage*	2·10	2·10
MS1906	150×90 mm. Nos. 1902/5	7·25	8·00

549 Rowing

2008. Olympic Games, Beijing. Multicoloured.
1907 55c. Type **549** 1·50 1·50
1908 82c. Shot-putt 2·00 2·00
MS1909 150×90 mm. As Nos. 1907/8 optd 'Olympex 2008' 3·50 4·00

2008. Inland Waterways. Multicoloured.
1909a 55c. Type **549a**
1909b 55c. Belturbet Marina, River Erne, Co. Cavan
1909c 55c. River Barrow at Graiguenamanagh, Co. Kilkenny
1909d 55c. River Shannon, Meelick Quay

550 Parasol (*Macrolepiota procera*)

2008. Fungi. Multicoloured.
1910 55c. Type **550** 1·50 1·50
1911 55c. Orange birch bolete (*Leccinum versipelle*) 1·50 1·50
1912 82c. Pink waxcap (*Hygrocybe calyptriformis*) 2·00 2·00
MS1913 150×67 mm. 95c. Scarlet elfcup (*Sarcoscypha austriaca*) 3·50 4·00

551 HMS *Agamemnon* and USS *Niagra* laying Cable, 1858

2008. 150th Anniv of the First Transatlantic Cable Message.
1914 **551** 82c. multicoloured 2·75 2·75

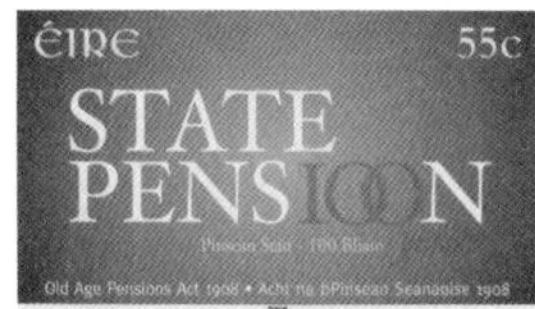

552 'STATE PENSIOON'

2008. Centenary of the Old Age Pensions Act.
1915 **552** 55c. multicoloured 1·50 1·50

553 Open Books forming Star

2008. Centenary of the National University of Ireland.
1916 **553** 55c. multicoloured 1·50 1·50

554 Padraic Mac Piarais and Cullenswood House, Ranelagh, Dublin, 1908–10

2008. Centenary of Opening of Scoil Eanna (bilingual Irish/English school). Showing founder and school premises.
1917 55c. Type **554** 1·50 1·50
1918 55c. Padraic Mac Piariais and The Hermitage, Rathfarnham, 1910–35 1·50 1·50

555 Planxty

2008. Irish Music (2nd series). Multicoloured.
1919 55c. Type **555** 1·75 1·75
1920 55c. De Dannan 1·75 1·75
1921 82c. Tulla Ceili Band 2·25 2·25
1922 82c. The Bothy Band 2·25 2·25
MS1923 150×90 mm. Nos. 1919/22 7·25 8·00

556 Irish Dancer

2008. Traditional Dances. Multicoloured.
1924 55c. Type **556** 1·50 1·50
MS1925 150×90 mm. No. 1924; 82c. Flamenco dancer 4·00 4·50
Stamps in a similar design were issued by Spain.

557 The Flight into Egypt

2008. Christmas. Multicoloured. (a) Ordinary gum.
1926 55c. Type **557** 1·75 1·50
1927 82c. The Annunciation 2·25 2·50

(b) Self-adhesive. Size 25×30 mm.
1928 55c. Infant Jesus in manger 1·50 1·50

558 Pair of Wedding Rings

2009. Weddings (4th issue). Self-adhesive.
1929 **558** 55c. multicoloured 1·60 1·60

559 Eye

2009. Birth Bicentenary of Louis Braille (inventor of Braille writing for the blind).
1930 **559** 55c. black 2·25 1·60
No. 1930 has 'Eire' and '55c' in Braille.

560 Ox

2009. Chinese New Year ('Year of the Ox').
1931 **560** 82c. multicoloured 2·50 2·50
MS1932 130×74 mm. No. 1931×3 7·25 8·00

561 *St. Patrick Climbs Croagh Patrick* (Margaret Clarke)

2009. St. Patrick's Day.
1933 **561** 82c. multicoloured 2·50 2·50

562 Little Girl posting Card, helped by her Father

2009. Greetings Stamps. Multicoloured. Self-adhesive.
1934 55c. Type **562** 1·60 1·60
1935 55c. Girl with opened birthday card and dog 1·60 1·60

563 *Charles Darwin* (pen and ink drawing, Harry Furniss)

2009. Birth Bicentenary of Charles Darwin (naturalist and evolutionary theorist).
1936 **563** 82c. multicoloured 2·40 2·40

564 Scene from *The Playboy of the Western World* (Sean Keating)

2009. Death Centenary of John Millington Synge (writer).
1937 **564** 55c. multicoloured 1·60 1·60

565 *Irish Times* Clock

2009. 150th Anniv of the Irish Times (newspaper).
1938 **565** 55c. multicoloured 1·60 1·60

566 Girl writing Letter

2009. 25th Anniv of An Post. Multicoloured. Self-adhesive. (a) Size 25×30 mm.
1939 55c. Type **566** 2·00 2·00
1940 55c. Girl posting letter 2·00 2·00
1941 55c. Postman emptying pillar box 2·00 2·00
1942 55c. Woman at post office counter 2·00 2·00
1943 55c. An Post van and lorry 2·00 2·00
1944 55c. Flying letters 2·00 2·00
1945 55c. Postman with trolley 2·00 2·00
1946 55c. Postman with mail 2·00 2·00
1947 55c. Seán Kelly cycling team sponsored by An Post 2·00 2·00
1948 55c. G.P.O., Dublin 2·00 2·00

(b) Size 20×24 mm.
1949 55c. As Type **566** 1·60 2·00
1950 55c. As No. 1940 1·60 2·00
1951 55c. As No. 1941 1·60 2·00
1952 55c. As No. 1942 1·60 2·00
1953 55c. As No. 1943 1·60 2·00
1954 55c. As No. 1944 1·60 2·00
1955 55c. As No. 1945 1·60 2·00
1956 55c. As No. 1946 1·60 2·00
1957 55c. As No. 1947 1·60 2·00
1958 55c. As No. 1948 1·60 2·00

567 *Self-portrait*, 1969

2009. Birth Centenary of Francis Bacon (artist). Multicoloured.
1959 55c. Type **567** 1·60 1·60
MS1960 150×90 mm. 82c. Francis Bacon's studio 2·40 2·75

568 James Larkin (union organiser) addressing Crowd, c. 1908

2009. Centenary of IT&GWU (Irish Transport and General Workers Union).
1961 **568** 55c. multicoloured 1·60 1·60

569 *Green Dragon* (Irish entry)

2009. Volvo Ocean Race. Multicoloured.
1962 55c. Type **569** 1·60 1·60
MS1963 150×90 mm. €3 *Green Dragon* and other yachts (27×47 mm) 8·75 9·50

570 Crab Nebula

2009. Europa. Astronomy. Multicoloured.
1964 55c. Type **570** 1·60 1·60
1965 82c. Brown dwarf 2·40 2·40

571 CEPT Logo, '50', Telephone Dial and Pillar Box

2009. 50th Anniv of CEPT (European Conference of Postal and Telecommunications Administration).

1966	**571**	82c. multicoloured	2·25	2·25

572 'Aberann Conan' (Glen of Imaal terrier)

2009. European Dog Show, Dublin.

1967	**572**	55c. multicoloured	1·50	1·50

573 Castle and St. John's Bridge, Kilkenny City

2009. 400th Anniv of City Status for Kilkenny.

1968	**573**	55c. multicoloured	1·75	1·50

574 Anthony Trollope (from albumen print by Julia Margaret Cameron, 1864)

2009. Anthony Trollope (novelist) Commemoration.

1969	**574**	82c. multicoloured	2·25	2·25

575 *Augustine Birrell* (Sir Leslie Ward)

2009. Centenary of the Birrell Land Act (Irish Land Act).

1970	**575**	82c. multicoloured	2·25	2·25

576 *Wolfgang Amadeus Mozart* (Josef Grassi) and Overture of Opera *Don Giovanni*

2009. Classical Composers. Each showing composer and score . Multicoloured.

1971		55c. Type **576**	1·60	1·60
1972		55c. *George Frideric Handel* (Thomas Hudson, 1736) and last folio from opera *Susanna*, 1748	1·60	1·60
1973		82c. *Joseph Haydn* (John Carl Rossler, 1799) and Symphony No. 95	2·25	2·25
1974		82c. *Frederic Chopin* (Ary Schef-fer) and Ballade Number 2 in F	2·25	2·25
MS1975		150×90 mm. Nos. 1971/4	7·50	8·00

577 Arthur Guinness (founder)

2009. 250th Anniv of the Guinness Brewery.

1976	**577**	82c. multicoloured	2·40	2·40

578 'Plantation of Ulster 1609' in Irish

2009. 400th Anniv of the Plantation of Ulster. Multicoloured.

1977		55c. Type **578**	1·60	1·60
1978		55c. 'PLANTATION of ULSTER 1609' in English	1·60	1·60

579 Brian Friel

2009. Modern Irish Playwrights. Multicoloured.

1979		55c. Type **579**	1·90	1·90
1980		55c. Frank McGuinness	1·90	1·90
1981		55c. Tom Murphy	1·90	1·90

580 Irish Bluet (*Coenagrion lunulatum*)

2009. Dragonflies. Multicoloured.

1982		55c. Type **580**	1·75	1·90
1983		55c. Large red damselfly (*Pyrrhosoma nymphula*)	1·75	1·90
1984		82c. Four-spotted chaser (*Libellula quadrimaculata*) (horiz)	2·75	3·00
MS1985		150×65 mm. 95c. Banded demoiselle (*Calopteryx splendens*) (60×26 mm)	2·75	3·00

581 Nativity

2009. Christmas. Illustrations from the Gospel Book, Gamaghiel Monastery, Khizan (1986/7) or the Rosarium of King Philip II of Spain (1988). Multicoloured designs showing illustrations. (a) Ordinary gum.

1986		55c. Type **581**	1·60	1·00
1987		82c. Annunciation	2·40	3·00

(b) Size 25×30 mm. Self-adhesive.

1988		55c. *Virgin and Child* (Simon Bening)	1·60	1·60

The images on Nos. 1986/7 come from the *Gospel Book* from the Monastery of Gamaghiel, Khizan, and on No. 1988 from the Rosarium of Philip II, King of Spain.

582 Dr. Douglas Hyde

2010. 150th Birth Anniv of Douglas Hyde (first President of Ireland 1938–45).

1989	**582**	55c. multicoloured	1·50	1·50

583 Pair of Stylised 'Lovebirds'

2010. Weddings (5th issue). Self-adhesive.

1990	**583**	55c. multicoloured	1·75	1·75

584 Boy Astronaut and Heart

2010. Greetings Stamps. Multicoloured.

1991		55c. Type **584**	1·75	1·75
1992		55c. Girl astronaut riding rocket and birthday cake	1·75	1·75

585 Tiger (18th century Tibetan painting)

2010. Chinese New Year. Year of the Tiger.

1993	**585**	82c. multicoloured	2·25	2·25
MS1994		150×90 mm. No. 1993×3	7·00	7·50

586 St. Patrick (stained glass window, St. Patrick's Cathedral, Co. Armagh)

2010. St. Patrick's Day.

1995	**586**	82c. multicoloured	2·25	2·25

587 Gaisce Symbol and Aras an Uachtarain (President's official residence)

2010. 25th Anniv of Gaisce the President's Award.

1996	**587**	55c. multicoloured	1·60	1·60

588 Women playing Golf, Baking, Exercising and Painting

2010. Centenary of Irish Countrywoman's Association.

1997	**588**	55c. multicoloured	1·50	1·50

589 Monasterboice Cross, Co. Louth

2010. Ireland Series—High Crosses. Each black.

1998		55c. Type **589**	1·75	1·75
1999		55c. Carndonagh Cross, Co. Donegal	1·75	1·75
2000		55c. Drumcliffe Cross, Co. Sligo	1·75	1·75
2001		55c. Ahenny Cross, Co. Tipperary	1·75	1·75

590 The Happy Prince (Oscar Wilde)

2010. Europa. Multicoloured.

2002		55c. Type **590**	2·00	2·00
2003		82c. *Gulliver's Travels* (Jonathan Swift)	2·00	2·00

591 Máirtín Ó Direáin and Aran Islands

2010. Birth Centenary of Máirtín Ó Direáin (poet)

2004	**591**	55c. multicoloured	1·50	1·50

592 The Breton Girl, 1906

2010. 150th Birth Anniv of Roderic O'Conor (artist). Multicoloured.

2005		55c. Type **592**	1·50	1·50
2006		55c. *Self-portrait*, 1928	1·50	1·50

593 Mother Teresa

2010. International Humanitarians. Multicoloured.

2007	55c. Type **593**	1·50	1·50
2008	55c. Henry Dunant (founder of Red Cross) and Battle of Solferino	1·50	1·50

594 Top and Skirt (Paul Costelloe)

2010. Irish Fashion Designers. Multicoloured.

2009	55c. Type **594**	1·50	1·50
2010	55c. Dark blue jacket (Louise Kennedy)	1·50	1·50
2011	55c. Olive-brown crocheted coat (Lainey Keogh)	1·50	1·50
2012	82c. Black dress with ruffled skirt (John Rocha)	2·25	2·25
2013	82c. Black hat with white ribbons (Philip Treacy)	2·25	2·25
2014	82c. Handbag with leaf design (Orla Kiely)	2·25	2·25

595 Mountain Avens (*Dryas octopetala*)

2010. Irish Wild Flowers. Multicoloured.

2015	55c. Type **595**	1·60	1·60
2016	55c. Spring gentian (*Gentiana verna*)	1·60	1·60
2017	55c. Bloody cranes-bill (*Geranium sanguineum*)	1·60	1·60
2018	55c. Common knapweed (*Centaurea nigra*)	1·60	1·60

596 Buzzard (*Buteo buteo*)

2010. Birds of Prey. Multlcoloured.

2019	55c. Type **596**	1·50	1·50
2020	55c. Golden eagle (*Aquila chrysaetos*)	1·50	1·50
2021	82c. Peregrine falcon (*Falco peregrinus*)	2·25	2·25
2022	95c. Merlin (*Falco columbarius*)	2·75	2·75
MS2023	150×90 mm. Nos. 2019/22	8·00	8·00

597 Anneli Alhanko and Per-Arthur Segerström in Romeo and Juliet

2010. Czeslaw Slania (engraver and stamp designer) Commemoration

2024	**597**	55c. black and light brown	2·00	1·60

Stamps in a similar design were issued by Sweden.

598 Oliver Murphy (founding member) and Shane Barker

2010. 50th Anniv of the Irish Wheelchair Association

2025	**598**	55c. multicoloured	1·60	1·60

599 Green Tiger Beetle (*Cicindela campestris*)

2010. Irish Animals and Marine Life (1st series). Multicoloured.

2026	55c. Type **599**	1·60	1·60
2027	55c. Golden eagle (*Aquila chrysaetos*)	1·60	1·60
2028	55c. Tompot blenny (*Parablennius gattorugine*)	1·60	1·60
2029	55c. Red squirrel (*Sciurus vulgaris*)	1·60	1·60
2030	55c. Common octopus (*Octopus vulgaris*)	1·60	1·60
2031	55c. Hermit crab (*Pagurus bernhardus*)	1·60	1·60
2032	55c. Sea slug (*Lomanotus genei*)	1·60	1·60
2033	55c. Bottlenose dolphin (*Tursiops truncates*)	1·60	1·60

600 The Miami Showband

2010. Legendary Showbands. Multicoloured.

2034	55c. Type **600**	1·50	1·50
2035	55c. The Drifters Showband	1·50	1·50
2036	82c. The Royal Showband	2·40	2·40
2037	82c. The Freshmen	2·40	2·40
MS2038	150×90 mm. Nos. 2034/7	7·75	7·50

601 Early Patrolman

2010. Centenary of Automobile Association Ireland

2039	**601**	55c. multicoloured	1·50	1·50

602 John MacKenna

2010. Bicentenary of Chilean Independence. Multicoloured.

2040	82c. Type **602**	1·75	1·75
2041	82c. Bernardo O'Higgins	1·75	1·75

Stamps in similar designs were issued by Chile.

603 The Nativity (St. Brigid's Church, Dangan, Co. Roscommon)

604 Robin

2010. Christmas. Multicoloured.

(a) Sheet stamps. Ordinary gum

2042	55c. Type **603**	1·60	1·60
2043	82c. Annunciation (Church of Our Lady of Perpetual Help, Aughrim, Co. Roscommon)	2·00	2·00

(b) Booklet stamp. Self-adhesive. Size 30×25 mm.

2044	**604**	55c. multicoloured	1·60	1·60

(c) 'Stamps on a roll'. Designs as Nos. 2042/3 but 55x24 mm. Self-adhesive

2045	55c. As Type **603**	1·75	1·75
2046	82c. As No. 2043	2·00	2·00

605 Couple Sharing Umbrella

2011. Weddings (6th issue)

2047	**605**	55c. multicoloured	1·60	1·60

606 Couple sharing Umbrella

2011. Greetings Stamps. Multicoloured.

2048	55c. Type **606**	1·60	1·60
2049	55c. Balloons	1·60	1·60

607 USA and Ireland Flags and Entrance to American Chamber of Commerce, Dublin

2011. 50th Anniv of the American Chamber of Commerce, Ireland

2050	**607**	55c. multicoloured	1·75	1·75

608 Cearbhall Ó Dálaigh

2011. Birth Centenary of Cearbhall Ó Dálaigh (President of Ireland 1974–6)

2051	**608**	55c. multicoloured	1·75	1·75

609 St. Patrick (stone carving from St. Patrick's College Chapel, Maynooth)

2011. St. Patrick's Day

2052	**609**	82c. multicoloured	2·50	2·50

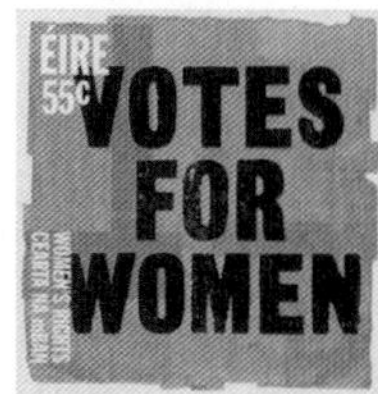

610 'VOTES FOR WOMEN'

2011. Women's Rights. Multicoloured.

2053	55c. Type **610**	1·75	1·75
2054	82c. 'EQUALITY'	2·00	2·00

611 Boxing Match

2011. Centenary of the Irish Amateur Boxing Association

2055	**611**	55c. multicoloured	1·50	1·50

612 Tulip Tree, Knockabbey Gardens

2011. Europa. Forests. Multicoloured.

2056	55c. Type **612**	1·60	1·60
2057	82c. River Walk, Avondale Forest Park	2·50	2·50

613 Ceramic (Deirdre McLoughlin)

2011. Year of Craft. Multicoloured.

2058	55c. Type **613**	1·60	1·60
2059	55c. Glass artwork (Róisín de Buitléar)	1·60	1·60
2060	55c. Jewellery(Inga Reed)	1·60	1·60
2061	55c. Slippers (Helen McAllister)	1·60	1·60
2062	55c. Wooden pot (Liam Flynn)	1·60	1·60

614 Ballycroy National Park

2011. Ireland's National Parks. Multicoloured.

2063	55c. Type **614**	1·60	1·60
2064	55c. The Burren National Park	1·60	1·60
2065	55c. Connemara National Park	1·60	1·60
2066	82c. Glenveagh National Park	2·50	2·50
2067	82c. Killarney National Park	2·50	2·50
2068	82c. Wicklow Mountains National Park	2·50	2·50
MS2069	150×90 mm. Nos. 2063/6	4·50	4·50
MS2070	150×90 mm. Nos. 2066/8	7·00	7·00

615 Hermit Crab (*Pagurus bernhardus*)

2011. Irish Animals and Marine Life

2071	**615**	55c. multicoloured	1·60	1·60

616 Candle wrapped with Barbed Wire

2011. 50th Anniv of Amnesty International

2072	**616**	55c. greenish yellow, black and yellow-green	1·60	1·60

2011. Irish Animals and Marine Life (2nd series). Multicoloured.

2073	55c. Beadlet anemone (*Actinia equina*)	1·60	1·60
2074	55c. Squat lobster (*Munida rugosa*)	1·60	1·60

2075		55c. Cuckoo wrasse (*Labrus mixtus*)	1·60	1·60
2076		55c. Common frog (*Rana temporaria*)	1·60	1·60
2077		55c. Green huntsman spider (*Micrommata virescens*)	1·60	1·60
2078		55c. Elephant hawk-moth (*Deilephila elpenor*)	1·60	1·60
2079		55c. Goldfinch (*Carduelis carduelis*)	1·60	1·60
2080		55c. Red deer stag (*Cervus elaphus*)	1·60	1·60

617 House with Solar Panels

2011. Renewable Energy. Multicoloured.

2081		55c. Type **617**	1·60	1·60
2082		55c. Ardnacrusha hydro electric power station	1·60	1·60
2083		55c. Wind turbines	1·60	1·60
2084		55c. Wave energy	1·60	1·60
2085		55c. Field of rape (Biofuel)	1·60	1·60

618 Coloured Horse

2011. The Irish Horse. Multicoloured.

2086		55c. Type **618**	1·60	1·60
2087		55c. Irish draught horse	1·60	1·60
2088		55c. Thoroughbred	1·60	1·60
2089		55c. Connemara pony	1·60	1·60
MS2090		150×90 mm. Nos. 2086/9	6·25	6·25

POSTAGE DUE STAMPS

D1

1925

D1	**D1**	½d. green	12·00	16·00
D6	**D1**	1d. red	1·50	70
D7	**D1**	1½d. orange	3·25	8·00
D8	**D1**	2d. green	2·75	70
D9	**D1**	3d. blue	3·50	3·75
D10	**D1**	5d. violet	4·50	2·25
D11a	**D1**	6d. plum	15·00	15·00
D12	**D1**	8d. orange	9·00	14·00
D13	**D1**	10d. purple	8·50	8·50
D14	**D1**	1s. green	8·50	11·00

1971. Decimal Currency. Colours changed.

D15		1p. brown	30	60
D16		1½p. green	40	1·50
D17		3p. stone	60	2·00
D18		4p. orange	60	1·25
D19		5p. blue	60	3·00
D20		7p. yellow	40	3·50
D21		8p. red	40	2·75

D2

1980

D25	**D2**	1p. green	30	70
D26	**D2**	2p. blue	30	70
D27	**D2**	4p. green	40	70
D28	**D2**	6p. flesh	40	80
D29	**D2**	8p. blue	40	85
D30	**D2**	18p. green	75	1·25
D31	**D2**	20p. red	2·25	5·50
D32	**D2**	24p. green	75	2·00
D33	**D2**	30p. violet	3·00	7·50
D34	**D2**	50p. pink	3·75	7·50

D3

1988

D35	**D3**	1p. black, red and yellow	10	60
D36	**D3**	2p. black, red and brown	10	60
D37	**D3**	3p. black, red and purple	15	60
D38	**D3**	4p. black, red and violet	15	60
D39	**D3**	5p. black, red and blue	15	60
D40	**D3**	17p. black, red and green	40	65
D41	**D3**	20p. black, red and blue	55	80
D42	**D3**	24p. black, red and green	60	85
D43	**D3**	30p. black, red and grey	80	1·25
D44	**D3**	50p. black, red and grey	1·25	1·75
D45	**D3**	£1 black, red and brown	1·75	2·25

Pt. 8

ITALY

A Republic in S. Europe on the Mediterranean and Adriatic Seas. Originally a kingdom formed by the union of various smaller kingdoms and duchies that issued their own stamps.

1862. 100 centesimi = 1 lira.
2002. 100 cents = 1 euro.

1 King Victor Emmanuel II

1862. Head embossed. Imperf (15c.) or perf (others).

1	**1**	10c. bistre	£10000	£375
5	**1**	15c. blue	£100	65·00
2a	**1**	20c. blue	26·00	47·00
3	**1**	40c. red	£350	£225
4	**1**	80c. yellow	80·00	£1900

For stamps of this type imperf, see Sardinia Nos. 27 etc.

3

1863. Imperf.

7	**3**	15c. blue	8·50	15·00

4 5 6 7 10

1863. Perf.

8	**4**	1c. green	10·50	4·75
9	**5**	2c. brown	37·00	3·25
10	**6**	5c. grey	£2000	5·25
11	**6**	10c. brown	£3500	6·50
21	**6**	10c. blue	£7500	6·50
12	**6**	15c. blue	£3000	4·25
20a	**10**	20c. blue	£900	1·60
22a	**10**	20c. orange	£3750	2·75
13	**6**	30c. brown	15·00	21·00
14	**6**	40c. red	£6000	9·50
15	**6**	60c. mauve	32·00	21·00
16	**7**	2l. red	35·00	£130

1865. Surch C 20 20 C and curved bar.

17	**6**	20c. on 15c. blue	£850	4·25

1878. Official stamps surch 2 C and wavy bars.

23	**O11**	2c. on 2c. red	£190	32·00
24	**O11**	2c. on 5c. red	£225	40·00
25	**O11**	2c. on 20c. red	£900	5·25
26	**O11**	2c. on 30c. red	£750	15·00
27	**O11**	2c. on 1l. red	£650	5·25
28	**O11**	2c. on 2l. red	£700	12·00
29	**O11**	2c. on 5l. red	£900	15·00
30	**O11**	2c. on 10l. red	£650	19·00

12 King Umberto I

1879. Corners vary for each value.

31	**12**	5c. green	12·00	1·60
32	**12**	10c. red	£600	2·10
33	**12**	20c. orange	£550	1·60
34	**12**	25c. blue	£950	8·50
35	**12**	30c. brown	£190	£2250
36	**12**	50c. mauve	27·00	24·00
37	**12**	2l. orange	65·00	£375

13 Arms of Savoy

14

1889. Figures in four corners. Various frames.

38	**13**	5c. green	£1000	2·10
39	**14**	40c. brown	14·00	15·00
40	**14**	45c. green	£2500	7·50
41	**14**	60c. mauve	19·00	30·00
42	**14**	1l. brown and orange	19·00	15·00
43	**14**	5l. red and green	75·00	£750

1890. Surch Cmi. 2 or Cmi 20.

44	**12**	2c. on 5c. green	27·00	65·00
45	**12**	20c. on 30c. brown	£475	12·00
46	**12**	20c. on 50c. mauve	£600	55·00

1890. Parcel Post stamps surch Valevole per le stampe Cmi. 2 and bars.

47	**P13**	2c. on 10c. grey	7·50	8·00
48	**P13**	2c. on 20c. blue	7·50	8·00
49	**P13**	2c. on 50c. pink	85·00	60·00
50	**P13**	2c. on 75c. green	7·50	8·00
51	**P13**	2c. on 1l.25 orange	65·00	43·00
52	**P13**	2c. on 1l.75 brown	29·00	70·00

21 22 23

24

25 26

27

29

1891

53	**21**	1c. brown	10·50	6·50
54	**22**	2c. brown	10·50	5·25
55	**23**	5c. green	£750	2·75
56	**24**	5c. green	43·00	2·10
57	**25**	10c. red	10·50	2·75
58a	**26**	20c. orange	10·50	2·75
59	**27**	25c. blue	10·50	1·60
60	**27**	45c. olive	7·00	3·25
61	**29**	5l. red and blue	95·00	£225

30

31

33 King Victor Emmanuel III

34 King Victor Emmanuel III

1901. Designs vary.

62	**30**	1c. brown	1·10	10
63	**31**	2c. brown	1·10	10
64	**31**	5c. green	90·00	65
65	**33**	10c. red	£120	1·40
66	**33**	20c. orange	21·00	1·40
67	**33**	25c. blue	£170	3·25
68	**33**	40c. brown	£800	10·50
69	**33**	45c. green	12·00	65
70	**33**	50c. violet	£900	18·00
71	**34**	1l. brown and green	6·50	65
72	**34**	5l. blue and pink	36·00	8·50
85	**34**	10l. green and pink	95·00	25·00

See also Nos. 171s, 181, 185 and 186/7.

1905. Surch C. 15.

73	**33**	15c. on 20c. orange	95·00	2·75

37

39

41

1906

75	**37**	5c. green	95	50
76	**37**	10c. red	1·20	10
90	**41**	15c. grey	43·00	1·30
77	**39**	25c. blue	1·60	10
78	**39**	40c. brown	3·25	10
79	**39**	50c. violet	1·60	10

See also Nos. 104 etc, 171d/h and 171j/r.

42 Garibaldi

1910. 50th Anniv of Plebiscite in Naples and Sicily.

81	**42**	5c.(+5c.) green	27·00	32·00
82	**42**	15c.(+5c.) red	48·00	70·00

43

1910. National Plebiscite of Southern States, 1860.

83	**43**	5c.(+5c.) pink	£190	£160
84	**43**	15c.(+5c.) green	£275	£250

45

46

1911. Jubilee of Italian Kingdom.

86	**45**	2c.(+3c.) brown	12·00	5·25
87	**46**	5c.(+5c.) green	17·00	32·00
88	-	10c.(+5c.) red	26·00	48·00
89	-	15c.(+5c.) grey	27·00	75·00

DESIGNS: Symbolic of the Genius of Italy (10c.) and the Glory of Rome (15c.).

50

1912. Re-erection of Campanile of St. Mark, Venice.

91	**50**	5c. black	8·50	16·00
92	**50**	15c. brown	41·00	55·00

1913. Surch 2 2.

93	**46**	2 on 5c. green	2·10	6·50
94	-	2 on 10c. red (No. 88)	2·10	6·50
95	-	2 on 15c. grey (No. 89)	2·10	6·50

53 Banner of United Italy

54 Italian Eagle and Arms of Savoy

1915. Red Cross Society. No. 98 is surch 20.

96	**53**	10c.+5c. red	3·25	10·50
97	**54**	15c.+5c. grey	6·50	10·50
98	**54**	20 on 15c.+5c. grey	10·50	43·00
99	**54**	20c.+5c. orange	18·00	55·00

1916. Surch CENT. 20.

100	**41**	20c. on 15c. grey	24·00	1·60

1917. Air. Express Letter stamp optd ESPERIMENTO POSTA AEREA MAGGIO 1917 TORINO=ROMA=ROMA=TORINO.

102	**E35**	25c. red	20·00	40·00

1917. Air. Express Letter stamp surch IDROVOLANTE NAPOLI-PALERMO NAPOLI 25 CENT 25.

103	**E59**	25c. on 40c. violet	21·00	48·00

1917

104	**37**	15c. grey	1·10	65
105	**41**	20c. orange	5·25	55
178	**39**	20c. orange	2·75	1·30
179	**39**	20c. green	1·10	30
180	**39**	20c. purple	2·10	50
181	**34**	25c. green and light green	2·10	50
182	**39**	25c. green	10·50	14·00
106	**39**	30c. brown	3·00	1·10
183	**39**	30c. grey	3·75	10
107	**39**	55c. purple	17·00	16·00
108	**39**	60c. red	3·25	65
109	**39**	60c. blue	7·00	43·00
184	**39**	60c. orange	8·50	75
185	**34**	75c. red and carmine	6·50	50
110	**39**	85c. brown	10·50	8·50
186	**34**	1l.25 blue and ultramarine	8·50	50
111	**34**	2l. green and orange	32·00	6·50
187	**34**	2l.50 green and orange	70·00	8·50

See also Nos. 171a/c and 171i.

59 Ancient Seal of Republic of Trieste

1921. Union of Venezia Giulia with Italy.

112	**59**	15c. red and black	4·25	43·00
113	**59**	25c. red and blue	4·25	43·00
114	**59**	40c. red and brown	4·25	43·00

60

1921. 600th Death Anniv of Dante.

115	**60**	15c. red	5·25	14·00
116	-	25c. green	5·25	14·00
117	-	40c. brown	6·50	15·00

DESIGNS: 25c. Woman with book; 40c. Dante.

62 "Victory"

1921. Victory of 1918.

118	**62**	5c. green	1·10	2·75
119	**62**	10c. red	1·10	2·75
120	**62**	15c. grey	3·25	10·50
121	**62**	25c. blue	1·10	5·25

1922. 9th Italian Philatelic Congress. Trieste. Optd IX CONGRESSO FILATELICO ITALIANO TRIESTE 1922.

122	**37**	10c. red	£400	£375
123	**37**	15c. grey	£250	£275
124	**39**	25c. blue	£250	£325
125	**39**	40c. brown	£425	£375

64

1922. 50th Death Anniv of Mazzini.

126	**64**	25c. purple	6·50	32·00
127	-	40c. purple	27·00	37·00
128	-	80c. blue	6·50	55·00

DESIGNS—VERT: 40c. Mazzini. HORIZ: 80c. Tomb of Mazzini.

66

1923. Tercentenary of Propagation of the Faith.

129	**66**	20c. orange and green	4·25	80·00
130	**66**	30c. orange and red	4·25	80·00
131	**66**	50c. orange and violet	4·25	80·00
132	**66**	1l. orange and blue	4·25	80·00

The portraits and arms in the corners at right vary for each value.

1923. Surch in words and figures. (15c. surch DIECI only).

133	**39**	7½c. on 85c. brown	55	1·70
135	**30**	10c. on 1c. brown	55	45
136	**31**	10c. on 2c. brown	55	45
137	**37**	10c. on 15c. grey	45	55
138	**39**	20c. on 25c. blue	45	55
139	**33**	25c. on 45c. olive	45	55
140	**39**	25c. on 60c. blue	2·10	1·60
141	**39**	30c. on 50c. mauve	55	55
142	**39**	30c. on 55c. purple	75	55
143	**39**	50c. on 40c. brown	3·25	60
144	**39**	50c. on 55c. purple	32·00	15·00
145	**34**	1l.75 on 10l. olive and red	21·00	32·00

73 **74**

75

1923. 1st Anniv of Fascist March on Rome.

146	**73**	10c. green	4·25	6·50
147	**73**	30c. violet	4·25	6·50
148	**73**	50c. red	6·50	10·50
149	**74**	1l. blue	9·50	10·50
150	**74**	2l. brown	9·50	16·00
151	**75**	5l. black and blue	21·00	65·00

76

1923. Fascist "Black Shirt" Fund.

152	**76**	30c.+30c. brown	37·00	£100
153	**76**	50c.+50c. mauve	37·00	£100
154	**76**	1l.+1l. grey	37·00	£100

77

1923. 50th Death Anniv of A. Manzoni (writer).

155	**77**	10c. black and red	8·50	75·00
156	-	15c. black and green	8·50	75·00
157	-	30c. black	8·50	75·00
158	-	50c. black and brown	8·50	75·00
159	-	1l. black and blue	£110	£325
160	-	5l. black and purple	£750	£2750

DESIGNS: 10c. to 50c. Scenes from Manzoni's "I Promessi Sposi"; 1l. Manzoni's home, Milan; 5l. Portrait of Manzoni.

1924. Victory stamps surch LIRE UNA between stars.

161	**62**	1l. on 5c. green	27·00	£130
162	**62**	1l. on 10c. red	16·00	£130
163	**62**	1l. on 15c. grey	27·00	£130
164	**62**	1l. on 25c. blue	16·00	£130

1924. Trade Propaganda. Optd CROCIERA ITALIANA 1924.

165	**37**	10c. red	2·10	21·00
166	**39**	30c. brown	2·10	21·00
167	**39**	50c. violet	2·10	21·00
168	**39**	60c. blue	10·50	75·00
169	**39**	85c. brown	7·50	75·00
170	**34**	1l. brown and green	65·00	£350
171	**34**	2l. green and orange	55·00	£350

Used on an Italian cruiser which visited South America for trade propaganda.

1924. Previous issues with attached advertising labels (imperf between stamp and label). Colour of label given.

171a	15c. (104) + Columbia (blue)	43·00	43·00
171b	15c. (104) + Bitter Campari (blue)	4·25	19·00
171c	15c. (104) + Cordial Campari (black)	4·25	21·00
171d	25c. (77) + Coen (green)	£250	48·00
171e	25c. (77) + Piperno (brown)	£1600	£750
171f	25c. (77) + Tagliacozzo (brown)	£850	£750
171g	25c. (77) + Abrador (blue)	£120	£110
171h	25c. (77) + Reinach (green)	£100	85·00
171i	30c. (106) + Columbia (green)	34·00	55·00
171j	50c. (79) + Coen (blue)	£1600	85·00
171k	50c. (79) + Columbia (red)	21·00	16·00
171l	50c. (79) + De Montel (blue)	4·25	19·00
171m	50c. (79) + Piperno (green)	£1900	£275
171n	50c. (79) + Reinach (blue)	£225	65·00
171o	50c. (79) + Singer (red)	4·25	8·50
171p	50c. (79) + Tagliacozzo (green)	£2500	£550
171q	50c. (79) + Siero Casali (blue)	21·00	43·00
171r	50c. (79) + Tantal (red)	£400	£120
171s	1l. (71) + Columbia (blue)	£750	£800

81 Church of St. John Lateran

1924. Holy Year (1925).

172	-	20c.+10c. brown & green	3·25	13·00
173	**81**	30c.+15c. brown & choc	3·25	13·00
174	-	50c.+25c. brown & violet	3·25	13·00
175	-	60c.+30c. brown and red	3·25	32·00
176	-	1l.+50c. purple and blue	3·25	32·00
177	-	5l.+2l.50 purple and red	13·00	85·00

DESIGNS: 20c. Church of St. Maria Maggiore; 50c. Church of St. Paul; 60c. St. Peter's; 1l. Pope opening Holy Door; 5l. Pope shutting Holy Door.

82

1925. Royal Jubilee.

188B	**82**	60c. red	1·10	1·10
189B	**82**	1l. blue	2·10	1·10
190A	**82**	1l.25 blue	4·25	2·10

83 Vision of St. Francis

1926. 700th Death Anniv of St. Francis of Assisi.

191	**83**	20c. green	55	1·10
194B	-	30c. black	55	1·10
192	-	40c. violet	55	1·10
193	-	60c. red	1·10	1·10
195B	-	1l.25 blue	1·10	1·10
196	-	5l.+2l.50 brown	14·00	£120

DESIGNS—HORIZ: 40c. St. Damian's Church and Monastery, Assisi; 60c. St. Francis's Monastery, Assisi; 1l.25, Death of St. Francis, from fresco in Church of the Holy Cross, Florence. VERT: 30c., 5l. St. Francis (after Luca della Robbia).

88

1926. Air.

197	**88**	50c. red	4·25	10·50
198	**88**	60c. grey	4·25	10·50
199	**88**	80c. brown and purple	43·00	85·00
200	**88**	1l. blue	8·50	£120
201	**88**	1l.20 brown	19·00	£110
202	**88**	1l.50 orange	19·00	32·00
203	**88**	5l. green	48·00	£110

89 Castle of St. Angelo

1926. 1st National Defence issue.

204	**89**	40c.+20c. black & brown	3·25	7·50
205	-	60c.+30c. brown and red	3·25	7·50
206	-	1l.25+60c. black & grn	3·25	7·50
207	-	5l.+2l.50 black and blue	5·25	15·00

DESIGNS: 60c. Aqueduct of Claudius; 1l.25, Capitol; 5l. Porta del Popolo.

See also Nos. 219/22 and 278/81.

90 Volta

1927. Death Centenary of Volta.

208	**90**	20c. red	1·10	1·10
209	**90**	50c. green	2·10	1·10
210	**90**	60c. purple	4·25	5·25
211	**90**	1l.25 blue	7·50	7·50

91

1927

212	**91**	1l.75 brown	4·75	20
213	**91**	1l.85 black	1·10	1·10
214	**91**	2l.55 red	8·00	10·50
215	**91**	2l.65 purple	8·50	55·00
216	**91**	50c. grey and brown	4·25	45

No. 216 is smaller (17½×21½ mm).

1927. Air. Surch.

217	**88**	50c. on 60c. grey	16·00	55·00
218	**88**	80c. on 1l. blue	43·00	£190

1928. 2nd National Defence issue. As Nos. 204/7.

219	**89**	30c.+10c. black and violet	7·50	27·00
220	-	50c.+20c. black and olive	8·50	27·00
221	-	1l.25+50c. black & blue	27·00	65·00
222	-	5l.+2l. black and red	48·00	£225

92

1928

223	**92**	7½c. brown	4·25	13·00
224	**92**	15c. orange	5·25	25
225	**92**	35c. grey	7·50	12·00
226	**92**	50c. mauve	15·00	10

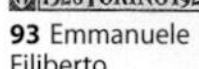
93 Emmanuele Filiberto

94 Soldier of First World War and Statue

95 Statue, Turin (Maroghetti)

1928. 400th Birth Anniv of Emmanuele Filiberto, Duke of Savoy, and 10th Anniv of Victory in World War.

227a	**93**	20c. blue and brown	2·10	6·50
228a	**93**	25c. green and red	2·10	6·50
229a	**93**	30c. brown and green	4·25	10·50
230	**94**	50c. red and blue	2·10	1·10
231	**94**	75c. red and pink	3·25	5·25
232	**95**	1l.25 black and blue	3·25	5·25
233	**94**	1l.75 green and blue	5·25	16·00
234	**93**	5l. green and mauve	16·00	95·00
235	**94**	10l. black and pink	32·00	£225
236	**95**	20l. green and mauve	70·00	£800

96 King Victor Emmanuel II

1929. 50th Death Anniv of King Victor Emmanuel II. Veterans' Fund.

237	**96**	50c.+10c. green	4·25	8·50

97 Fascist Arms of Italy

98 Romulus, Remus and Wolf

99 Julius Caesar

103 King Victor Emmanuel III

1929. Imperial Series.

238	**97**	2c. orange	65	20
239	**98**	5c. brown	20	20
240	**99**	7½c. violet	20	20
241	-	10c. brown	20	20
242	-	15c. green	20	20
243	**99**	20c. red	20	20
244	-	25c. green	20	20
245	**103**	30c. brown	20	20
246	-	35c. blue	20	20
247	**103**	50c. violet	20	20
248	-	75c. red	20	20
249	**99**	1l. violet	25	20
250	-	1l.25 blue	20	20
251	-	1l.75 orange	20	20
252	-	2l. red	20	20
253	**98**	2l.55 green	20	60
254	**98**	3l.70 violet	25	1·10
255	**98**	5l. red	25	20
256	-	10l. violet	2·10	2·75
257	**99**	20l. green	4·25	13·00
258	-	25l. black	10·50	41·00
259	-	50l. violet	15·00	55·00

DESIGNS—As Type **99**: 10c., 1l.75, 25l. Augustus the Great; 15c., 35c., 2l., 10l. Italia (Woman with castle on her head); 25c., 75c., 1l.25, 50l. Profile of King Victor Emmanuel III.

For stamps as above but without Fascist emblems, see Nos. 633 etc, and for stamps with integral label for armed forces see Nos. 563/74.

104 Bramante Courtyard

1929. 1400th Anniv of Abbey of Montecassino.

260	**104**	20c. orange	1·60	2·10
261	-	25c. green	1·60	2·10
262	-	50c.+10c. brown	2·10	16·00
263	-	75c.+15c. red	3·25	27·00
264	**104**	1l.25+25c. blue	4·25	29·00
265	-	5l.+1l. purple	12·00	85·00
266	-	10l.+2l. green	17·00	£180

DESIGNS—HORIZ: 25c. "Death of St. Benedict" (fresco); 50c. Monks building Abbey; 75c., 5l. Abbey of Montecassino. VERT: 10l. St. Benedict.

109

1930. Marriage of Prince Umberto and Princess Marie Jose.

267	**109**	20c. orange	1·10	80
268	**109**	50c.+10c. brown	2·10	4·25
269	**109**	1l.25+25c. blue	3·25	13·00

110 Pegasus

113

1930. Air.

270	-	25c. green	10	10
271	**110**	50c. brown	10	10
272	-	75c. brown	10	10
273	-	80c. orange	10	10
274	-	1l. violet	10	10
275	**113**	2l. blue	10	20
276	**110**	5l. green	50	45
277	**110**	10l. red	65	1·10

DESIGNS—As Type **110**: 25c., 80c. Wings; 75c., 1l. Angel.

1930. 3rd National Defence issue. Designs as Nos. 204/7.

278	**89**	30c.+10c. violet & green	1·10	21·00
279	-	50c.+10c. blue and green	2·10	16·00
280	-	1l.25+30c. green & blue	7·50	48·00
281	-	5l.+1l.50 choc & brn	10·50	£160

114 Ferrucci on Horseback

117 Francesco Ferrucci

1930. 400th Death Anniv of Francesco Ferrucci.

282	**114**	20c. red (postage)	1·10	1·10
283	-	25c. green	2·10	1·10
284	-	50c. violet	1·10	30
285	-	1l.25 blue	10·50	5·25
286	-	5l.+2l. orange	19·00	£150
287	**117**	50c. violet (air)	2·10	13·00
288	**117**	1l. brown	2·10	19·00
289	**117**	5l.+2l. purple	8·50	£140

DESIGNS—HORIZ: 25c., 50c., 1l.25, Ferrucci assassinated by Maramaldo. VERT: 5l. Ferrucci in helmet.

119 Jupiter sending forth Eagle

1930. Birth Bimillenary of Virgil.

290	-	15c. brown (postage)	1·10	2·10
291	-	20c. orange	1·10	2·10
292	-	25c. green	1·10	2·10
293	-	30c. purple	2·10	4·25
294	-	50c. violet	1·10	1·10
295	-	75c. red	2·10	6·50
296	-	1l.25 blue	2·10	6·50
297	-	5l.+1l.50 brown	65·00	£225
298	-	10l.+2l.50 olive	65·00	£275
299	**119**	50c. brown (air)	9·50	21·00
300	**119**	1l. orange	9·50	21·00
301	**119**	7l.70+1l.30 purple	48·00	£275
302	**119**	9l.+2l. blue	60·00	£325

DESIGNS (scenes from "Aeneid" or "Georgics"): 15c. Helenus and Anchises; 20c. The passing legions; 25c. Landing of Aeneas; 30c. Earth's bounties; 50c. Harvesting; 75c. Rural life; 1l.25, Aeneas sights Italy; 5l. A shepherd's hut; 10l. Turnus, King of the Rutuli.

120 Savoia Marchetti S-55A Flying Boats

1930. Air. Transatlantic Mass Formation Flight.

303	**120**	7l.70 blue and brown	£750	£1400

121 St. Antony's Installation as a Franciscan

1931. 700th Death Anniv of St. Antony of Padua.

304	**121**	20c. purple	3·25	1·60
305	-	25c. green	2·10	1·60
306	-	30c. brown	4·25	2·10
307	-	50c. violet	3·25	1·10
308	-	75c. lake	10·50	10·50
309	-	1l.25 blue	16·00	8·50
310	-	5l.+2l.50 olive	48·00	£190

DESIGNS—HORIZ: 25c. Sermon to the Fishes; 30c. Hermitage of Olivares; 50c. Basilica of the Saint at Padua; 75c. Death of St. Antony; 1l.25, St. Antony liberating prisoners. VERT: 5l. Vision of St. Antony.

123 Tower of the Marzocco

1931. 50th Anniv of Naval Academy, Leghorn.

311	**123**	20c. red	5·25	2·10
312	-	50c. violet	5·25	1·10
313	-	1l.25 blue	13·00	5·25

DESIGNS—HORIZ: 50c. Cadet ship "Amerigo Vespucci"; 1l.25, Cruiser "Trento".

124 Dante (1265–1321)

125 Leonardo da Vinci's Drawing "Flying Man"

127 Leonardo da Vinci

1932. Dante Alighieri Society. (a) Postage.

314		10c. brown	2·10	2·10
315		15c. green	2·10	2·10
316		20c. red	2·10	1·10
317		25c. green	2·10	1·10
318		30c. brown	3·25	2·10
319		50c. violet	1·10	1·10
320		75c. red	6·50	6·50
321		1l.25 blue	2·10	4·25
322		1l.75 orange	5·25	6·50
323		2l.75 green	21·00	32·00
324		5l.+2l. red	32·00	£160
325	**124**	10l.+2l.50 olive	43·00	£225

DESIGNS: 10c. Giovanni Boccaccio (writer); 15c. Niccolo Machiavelli (statesman); 20c. Fra Paolo Sarpi (philosopher); 25c. Vittorio Alfieri (poet); 30c. Ugo Foscolo (writer); 50c. Giacomo Leopardi (poet); 75c. Giosue Carducci (poet); 1l.25, Carlo Botta (historian); 1l.75, Torquato Tasso (poet); 2l.75, Francesco Petrarch (poet); 5l. Ludovico Ariosto (poet).

(b) Air.

326	**125**	50c. brown	2·10	6·50
327	-	1l. violet	3·25	7·50
328	-	3l. red	5·25	27·00
329	-	5l. green	5·25	32·00
330	**125**	7l.70+2l. blue	7·50	85·00
331	-	10l.+2l.50 grey	10·50	£140
332	**127**	100l. green and blue	37·00	£450

DESIGN—HORIZ: 1, 3, 5, 10l. Leonardo da Vinci.

128 Garibaldi and Victor Emmanuel

130 Caprera

1932. 50th Death Anniv of Garibaldi.

333	-	10c. blue (postage)	3·25	2·10
334	**128**	20c. brown	3·25	1·20
335	-	25c. green	3·25	2·10
336	**128**	30c. orange	3·25	3·25
337	-	50c. violet	2·10	45
338	-	75c. red	16·00	8·50
339	-	1l.25 blue	21·00	5·25
340	-	1l.75+25c. blue	27·00	95·00
341	-	2l.55+50c. brown	27·00	£130
342	-	5l.+1l. lake	27·00	£140

DESIGNS—HORIZ: 10c. Garibaldi's birthplace, Nice; 25c., 50c. "Here we make Italy or die"; 75c. Death of Anita (Garibaldi's wife); 1l.25, Garibaldi's tomb; 1l.75, Quarto Rock. VERT: 2l.55, Garibaldi's statue in Rome; 5l. Garibaldi.

343	**130**	50c. lake (air)	4·25	8·50
344	-	80c. green	4·25	15·00
345	**130**	1l.+25c. brown	5·25	32·00
346	-	2l.+50c. blue	6·50	48·00
347	-	5l.+1l. green	9·50	60·00

DESIGNS—VERT: 80c. The Ravenna hut; 2l. Anita; 5l. Garibaldi.

132 Agriculture

1932. 10th Anniv of Fascist March on Rome. (a) Postage.

350	**132**	5c. sepia	1·10	1·10
351	-	10c. sepia	1·10	1·10
352	-	15c. green	1·10	1·10
353	-	20c. red	1·10	65
354	-	25c. green	1·10	85
355	-	30c. sepia	2·10	3·25
356	-	35c. blue	5·25	10·50
357	-	50c. violet	2·10	20
358	-	60c. brown	5·25	7·50
359	-	75c. red	3·25	4·25
360	-	1l. violet	6·50	6·50
361	-	1l.25 blue	3·25	2·10
362	-	1l.75 orange	7·50	2·10
363	-	2l.55 green	28·00	43·00
364	-	2l.75 green	29·00	43·00
365	-	5l.+2l.50 red	65·00	£300

DESIGNS: 10c. Fascist soldier; 15c. Fascist coastguard; 20c. Italian youth; 25c. Tools forming a shadow of the Fasces; 30c. Religion; 35c. Imperial highways; 50c. Equestrian statue of Mussolini; 60c. Land reclamation; 75c. Colonial expansion; 1l. Marine development; 1l.25, Italians abroad; 1l.75, Sport, 2l.55, Child Welfare; 2l.75. "O.N.D." Recreation; 5l. Caesar's statue.

(b) Air.

366	50c. brown	3·25	10·50
367	75c. brown	9·50	32·00

DESIGNS: 50c. Savoia Marchetti S-55A flying boat over Eagle (front of Air Ministry Building, Rome); 75c. Aerial view of Italian cathedrals.

134 Airship "Graf Zeppelin"

1933. Air. LZ-127 "Graf Zeppelin" issue.

372	**134**	3l. green and black	10·50	95·00
373	-	5l. brown and green	16·00	£110
374	-	10l. blue and red	16·00	£250
375	-	12l. orange and blue	21·00	£375
376	-	15l. black and brown	21·00	£475
377	-	20l. blue and brown	21·00	£550

DESIGNS (all with airship): 3l. S. Paola Gate and tomb of Consul Caius Cestius; 5l. Appian Way and tomb of Cecilia Metella; 10l. Portion of Mussolini Stadium; 12l. S. Angelo Castle; 15l. Forum Romanum; 20l. Empire Way, Colosseum and Baths of Domitian.

135 Italian Flag / King Victor Emmanuel III / "Flight" (image scaled to 44% of original size)

136 Italian Flag / King Victor Emmanuel III / Rome–Chicago (image scaled to 44% of original size)

1933. Air. Balbo Transatlantic Mass Formation Flight by Savoia Marchetti S-55X Flying Boats.

378	**135**	5l.25+19l.75 red, green and blue	£170	£2250
379	**136**	5l.25+44l.75 red, green and blue	£170	£2250

The first part of the illustration in each group is of the Registered Air Express label and has an abbreviation of one of the pilots' names overprinted on it; the second part is the stamp for Ordinary Postage and the third is the actual Air Mail stamp.

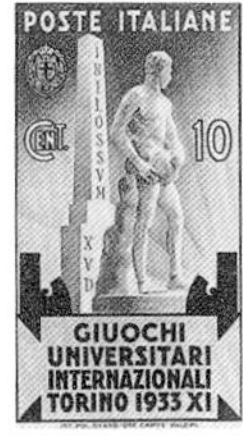

137 Athlete

1933. International University Games, Turin.

380	**137**	10c. brown	55	1·10
381	**137**	20c. red	55	1·10
382	**137**	50c. violet	1·10	60
383	**137**	1l.25 blue	2·10	6·50

138 Dome of St. Peter's **139** St. Peter's and Church of the Holy Sepulchre

1933. "Holy Year". (a) Postage.

384	**138**	20c. red	3·25	1·10
385	-	25c. green	4·25	2·10
386	-	50c. violet	3·25	1·10
387	**138**	1l. 25 blue	4·25	6·50
388	-	2l.55+2l.50 black	10·50	£225

DESIGNS: 25, 50c. Angel with Cross; 2l.55, Cross with Doves of Peace.

(b) Air.

389	**139**	50c.+25c. brown	1·10	16·00
390	**139**	75c.+50c. purple	3·25	27·00

1934. Air. Rome-Buenos Aires Flight. Surch with airplane, 1934 XII PRIMO VOLO DIRETTO ROMA = BUENOS-AYRES TRIMOTORE "LOMBARDI MAZZOTTI", value and fasces.

391	**113**	2l. on 2l. yellow	7·50	65·00
392	**113**	3l. on 2l. green	7·50	£110
393	**113**	5l. on 2l. red	7·50	£225
394	**113**	10l. on 2l. violet	7·50	£325

141 Anchor of the "Emmanuele Filiberto"

1934. 10th Anniv of Annexation of Fiume.

395	**141**	10c. brown (postage)	5·25	4·25
396	**141**	20c. red	30	1·10
397	-	50c. violet	30	1·10
398	-	1l.25 blue	45	6·50
399	-	1l.75+1l. blue	1·10	37·00
400	-	2l.55+2l. purple	1·10	60·00
401	-	2l.75+2l.50 olive	1·10	60·00

DESIGNS: 50c. Gabriele d'Annunzio; 1l.25, St. Vito's Tower barricaded; 1l.75, Hands supporting crown of historical monuments; 2l.55, Victor Emmanuel III's arrival in the "Brindisi" (cruiser); 2l.75, Galley, gondola and battleship.

402	25c. green (air)		25	4·25
403	50c. brown		25	3·25
404	75c. brown		25	10·50
405	1l.+50c. purple		25	16·00
406	2l.+1l.50 blue		25	24·00
407	3l.+2l. black		1·10	24·00

DESIGNS—Marina Fiat MF.5 flying boat over: 25, 75c. Fiume Harbour; 50c., 1l. War Memorial; 2l. Three Venetian lions; 3l. Roman Wall.

142 Antonio Pacinotti

1934. 75th Anniv of Invention of Pacinotti's Dynamo.

411	**142**	50c. violet	55	60
412	**142**	1l.25 blue	1·10	2·75

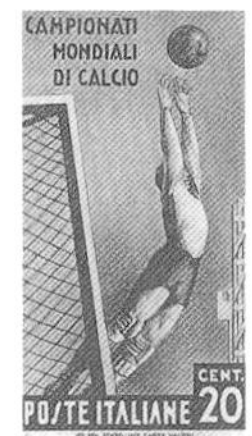

143

1934. World Cup Football Championship, Italy.

413	**143**	20c. red (postage)	10·50	10·50
414	-	25c. green	15·00	3·25
415	-	50c. violet	17·00	1·60
416	-	1l.25 blue	36·00	16·00
417	-	5l.+2l.50 brown	85·00	£400

DESIGNS—VERT: 5l. Players heading the ball. HORIZ: 25c., 50c., 1l.25, Two footballers.

418	50c. red (air)		9·00	21·00
419	75c. blue		9·00	27·00
420	5l.+2l.50 olive		37·00	£225
421	10l.+5l. brown		50·00	£325

DESIGNS—HORIZ: 50c. Marina Fiat MF.5 flying boat over Mussolini Stadium, Turin; 5l. Marina Fiat MF.5 flying boat over Stadium, Rome. VERT: 75c. Savoia Marchetti S-55X flying boat over footballer; 10l. Marina Fiat MF.5 flying boat over Littoral Stadium, Bologna.

145 Luigi Galvani

1934. 1st Int Congress of Electro-radio-biology.

422	**145**	30c. brown on buff	85	1·10
423	**145**	75c. red on pink	1·10	3·25

146 Military Symbol

1934. Military Medal Centenary.

424	**146**	10c. brown (postage)	1·10	2·10
425	-	15c. green	1·10	5·25
426	-	20c. red	1·10	2·10
427	-	25c. green	2·10	2·10
428	-	30c. brown	4·25	8·50
429	-	50c. violet	2·10	1·10
430	-	75c. red	8·50	13·00
431	-	1l.25 blue	9·50	8·50
432	-	1l.75+1l. red	18·00	55·00
433	-	2l.55+2l. purple	20·00	70·00
434	-	2l.75+2l. violet	32·00	75·00

DESIGNS—VERT: 25c. Mountaineers; 1l.75, Cavalry. HORIZ: 15c., 50c. Barbed-wire cutter; 20c. Throwing hand-grenade; 30c. Cripple wielding crutch; 75c. Artillery; 1l.25, Soldiers cheering; 2l.55, Sapper; 2l.75, First Aid.

435	25c. green (air)		2·10	5·25
436	50c. grey		2·10	8·50
437	75c. brown		2·10	10·50
438	80c. blue		2·10	13·00
439	1l.+50c. brown		4·25	34·00
440	2l.+1l. blue		5·25	41·00
441	3l.+2l. black		8·50	48·00

DESIGNS—HORIZ: 25, 80c. Italian "P" Type airship under fire; 50, 75c. Marina Flat MF.5 flying boat and Naval launch; 1l. Caproni Ca 101 airplane and troops in desert; 2l. Pomilio PC type biplane and troops. VERT: 3l. Marina Flat MF.5 flying boat over Unknown soldier's tomb.

148 King Victor Emmanuel III

1934. Air. Rome–Mogadiscio Flight and King's visit to Italian Somaliland.

444	**148**	1l. violet	2·10	35·00
445	**148**	2l. blue	2·10	45·00
446	**148**	4l. brown	5·25	£160
447	**148**	5l. green	5·25	£225
448	**148**	8l. red	24·00	£300
449	**148**	10l. brown	26·00	£375

149 Man with Fasces

1935. University Contests. Inscr "LITTORIALI".

450	**149**	20c. red	1·10	1·10
451	-	30c. brown	3·25	5·25
452	-	50c. violet	1·10	65

DESIGNS: 30c. Eagle and soldier. 50c. Standard-bearer and bayonet attack.

150

1935. National Militia. Inscr "PRO OPERA PREVID. MILIZIA".

453	**150**	20c.+10c. red (postage)	9·50	13·00
454	-	25c.+15c. green	9·50	17·00
455	-	50c.+30c. violet	9·50	24·00
456	-	1l.25+75c. blue	9·50	43·00
457	-	50c.+50c. brown (air)	10·50	37·00

DESIGNS: 25c. Roman standards; 50c. Soldier and cross; 50c.+50c. Wing over Globe; 1l.25, Soldiers and arch.

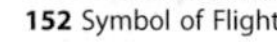
152 Symbol of Flight **153** Leonardo da Vinci

1935. International Aeronautical Exn, Milan.

458	**152**	20c. red	8·50	2·10
459	**152**	30c. brown	25·00	7·50
460	**153**	50c. violet	32·00	1·10
461	**153**	1l.25 blue	36·00	8·50

154 Vincenzo Bellini **155** "Music"

1935. Death Centenary of Bellini (composer).

462	**154**	20c. red (postage)	6·50	3·25
463	**154**	30c. brown	9·50	10·50
464	**154**	50c. violet	9·50	1·10
465	**154**	1l.25 blue	10·50	13·00
466	-	1l.75+1l. orange	36·00	£150
467	-	2l.75+2l. olive	50·00	£170

DESIGNS—VERT: 2l.75, Bellini's villa. HORIZ: 1l.75, Hands at piano.

468	**155**	25c. brown (air)	2·10	10·50
469	**155**	50c. brown	2·10	5·25
470	**155**	60c. red	5·25	16·00
471	-	1l.+1l. violet	10·50	£110
472	-	5l.+2l. green	18·00	£170

DESIGNS: 1l. Angelic musicians; 5l. Mountain landscape (Bellini's birthplace).

156 "Commerce" and Industrial Map of Italy

1936. 17th Milan Fair. Inscr as in T 156.

473	**156**	20c. red	55	60
474	-	30c. brown	55	1·10
475	-	50c. violet	55	60
476	**156**	1l.25 blue	1·60	3·25

DESIGN—HORIZ: 30c., 50c. Cog-wheel and plough.

157 "Fertility"

1936. 2000th Birth Anniv of Horace.

477	**157**	10c. green (postage)	5·25	1·10
478	-	20c. red	3·25	1·10
479	-	30c. brown	6·50	2·10
480	-	50c. violet	6·50	85
481	-	75c. red	13·00	10·50
482	-	1l.25+1l. blue	30·00	£110
483	-	1l.75+1l. red	37·00	£120
484	-	2l.55+1l. blue	43·00	£160

DESIGNS—HORIZ: 20c., 1l.25, Landscape; 75c. Capitol; 2l.55, Dying gladiator. VERT: 30c. Ajax defying lightning; 50c. Horace; 1l.75, Pan.

485	25c. green (air)		3·25	8·50
486	50c. brown		4·25	8·50
487	60c. red		5·25	16·00
488	1l.+1l. violet		13·00	£130
489	5l.+2l. green		19·00	£190

DESIGNS—HORIZ: 25c. Savoia Marchetti S-55A flying boat; 50c., 1l. Caproni Ca 101 airplane over lake; 60c. Eagle and oak tree; 5l. Rome.

159 **160**

1937. Child Welfare. Inscr as in T 159/60.

490	**159**	10c. brown (postage)	3·25	1·10
491	**160**	20c. red	3·25	1·10
492	**159**	25c. green	3·25	2·10
493	-	30c. sepia	3·25	3·25
494	**160**	50c. violet	3·25	60
495	-	75c. red	8·50	10·50
496	**160**	1l.25 blue	10·50	10·50
497	-	1l.75+75c. orange	43·00	£120
498	-	2l.75+1l.25 green	30·00	£130
499	**160**	5l.+3l. blue	37·00	£180

DESIGNS—As Type **159**: 30c., 1l.75, Boy between Fasces; 75c., 2l.75, "Bambino" (after della Robbia).

500	25c. green (air)		8·50	10·50

501		50c. brown	8·50	8·50
502		1l. violet	8·50	10·50
503		2l.+1l. blue	13·00	90·00
504		3l.+2l. orange	17·00	£130
505		5l.+3l. red	19·00	£170

DESIGNS—As Type **160**: 25c., 1l., 3l. Little child with rifle. As Type **159**: 50c., 2l., 5l. Children's heads.

163 Naval Memorial

164 Augustus the Great

1937. 2000th Birth Anniv of Augustus the Great.

506	**163**	10c. green (postage)	3·25	1·10
507	-	15c. brown	3·25	1·40
508	-	20c. red	3·25	1·10
509	-	25c. green	3·25	1·10
510	-	30c. brown	3·25	2·10
511	-	50c. violet	3·25	30
512	-	75c. red	5·25	5·25
513	-	1l.25 blue	8·50	6·50
514	-	1l.75+1l. purple	43·00	£120
515	-	2l.55+2l. black	48·00	£130

DESIGNS—VERT: 15c. Military trophies; 20c. Reconstructing temples of Rome; 25c. Census (with reference to birth of Jesus Christ); 30c. Statue of Julius Caesar; 50c. Election of Augustus as Emperor; 75c. Head of Augustus (conquest of Ethiopia); 1l.25, Constructing new fleet; 1l.75, Building Altar of Peace; 2l.55, The Capitol.

516		25c. purple (air)	6·50	10·50
517		50c. brown	6·50	8·50
518		80c. brown	15·00	13·00
519		1l.+1l. blue	34·00	95·00
520	**164**	5l.+1l. violet	45·00	£150

DESIGNS—HORIZ: 25c. "Agriculture"; 50c. Prosperity of the Romans; 80c. Horses of the Sun Chariot; 1l. Staff and map of ancient Roman Empire.

165 Gaspare Spontini (composer)

1937. Famous Italians.

521	**165**	10c. sepia	1·10	1·10
522	-	20c. red	1·10	1·40
523	-	25c. green	1·10	1·10
524	-	30c. brown	1·10	1·10
525	-	50c. violet	1·10	2·10
526	-	75c. red	2·10	65
527	-	1l.25 blue	3·25	5·25
528	**165**	1l.75 orange	3·25	6·50
529	-	2l.55+2l. green	13·00	£120
530	-	2l.75+2l. brown	16·00	£130

DESIGNS: 20c., 2l.55, Antonio Stradivarius (violin maker); 25, 50c. Giacomo Leopardi (poet); 30, 75c., Giovanni Battista Pergolesi (composer); 1l.25, 2l.75, Giotto di Bondone (painter and architect).

166 Marconi

1938. Guglielmo Marconi (telegraphy pioneer) Commemoration.

531	**166**	20c. red	2·10	1·10
532	**166**	50c. violet	1·10	60
533	**166**	1l.25 blue	2·10	4·75

167 Founding of Rome

168 Victor Emmanuel III

1938. 2nd Anniv of Proclamation of Italian Empire.

534	**167**	10c. brown (postage)	2·10	80
535	-	20c. red	2·10	80
536	-	25c. green	2·10	80
537	-	30c. brown	2·10	1·30
538	-	50c. violet	2·10	80
539	-	75c. red	3·25	1·90
540	-	1l.25 blue	6·50	1·90
541	-	1l.75 violet	8·50	2·75
542	-	2l.75 green	21·00	33·00
543	-	5l. red	38·00	41·00

DESIGNS—VERT: 20c. Emperor Augustus; 25c. Dante; 30c. Columbus; 50c. Leonardo da Vinci; 75c. Garibaldi and Victor Emmanuel II; 1l.25, Italian Unknown Warrior's Tomb; 1l.75, "March on Rome"; 2l.75, Wedding ring on map of Ethiopia; 5l. Victor Emmanuel III.

544	**168**	25c. green (air)	3·25	4·50
545	-	50c. brown	3·25	4·50
546	-	1l. violet	4·25	7·00
547	-	2l. blue	5·25	22·00
548	**168**	3l. red	8·50	30·00
549	-	5l. green	9·50	48·00

DESIGNS—HORIZ: 50c., 1l. Dante: 2, 5l. Leonardo da Vinci.

169 Steam Locomotive and ETR 200 Express Train

1939. Centenary of Italian Railways.

550	**169**	20c. red	1·10	45
551	**169**	50c. violet	1·10	45
552	**169**	1l.25 blue	2·10	4·00

170 Hitler and Mussolini

171 Hitler and Mussolini

1941. Italo-German Friendship.

553	**170**	10c. brown	1·10	1·60
554	**170**	20c. orange	1·10	1·60
555	**170**	25c. green	1·10	1·60
556	**171**	50c. violet	2·10	1·60
557	**171**	75c. red	5·25	4·00
558	**171**	1l.25 blue	6·50	7·25

172 Roman Cavalry

1941. 2000th Birth Anniv of Livy (Latin historian).

559	**172**	20c.+10c. red	30	1·30
560	**172**	30c.+15c. brown	30	1·90
561	-	50c.+25c. violet	45	1·90
562	-	1l.25+1l. blue	55	2·40

DESIGN: 50c., 1l.25, Roman legionary.

1942. War Propaganda. Nos. 244/5 and 247 with attached labels (imperf between stamp and label) to encourage war effort.

563		25c. green (Navy)	45	1·30
564		25c. green (Army)	45	1·30
565		25c. green (Air Force)	45	1·30
566		25c. green (Militia)	45	1·30
567		30c. brown (Navy)	45	5·25
568		30c. brown (Army)	45	5·25
569		30c. brown (Air Force)	45	5·25
570		30c. brown (Militia)	45	5·25
571		50c. violet (Navy)	55	1·30
572		50c. violet (Army)	55	1·30
573		50c. violet (Air Force)	55	1·30
574		50c. violet (Militia)	55	1·30

173 Galileo teaching at Padua

1942. Death Tercentenary of Galileo.

575	**173**	10c. red and orange	55	45
576	-	25c. green and olive	55	45
577	-	50c. violet and purple	60	40
578	-	1l.25 blue and grey	60	3·00

DESIGNS: Galileo at Venice (25c.) and at Arcetri, near Florence (1l.25), 50c. Portrait of Galileo.

174 Rossini

1942. 150th Birth Anniv of Rossini (composer).

579		25c. green	20	60
580		30c. brown	20	60
581	**174**	50c. violet	30	60
582	**174**	1l. blue	30	1·60

DESIGN: 25c., 30c. Rossini Monument, Pescaro.

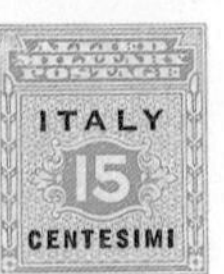

175

1943. Allied Military Government issue.

583	**175**	15c. orange	80	1·20
584	**175**	25c. bistre	80	1·20
585	**175**	30c. grey	80	1·20
586	**175**	50c. violet	80	1·20
587	**175**	60c. yellow	80	1·40
588	**175**	1l. green	80	1·20
589	**175**	2l. red	80	3·00
590	**175**	5l. blue	80	5·50
591	**175**	10l. brown	80	6·75

1943. Allied Military Government issue. Stamps of 1929 optd GOVERNO MILITARE ALLEATO.

592	**99**	20c. red	95	3·00
593	**99**	35c. blue	6·50	20·00
594	**103**	50c. violet	35	1·00

187 Romulus, Remus and Wolf (after Pollaiuolo)

1944

619	**187**	50c. purple	10	2·10

1944. As issue of 1929, but with Fascist emblems removed.

633	-	10c. brown (Augustus the Great)	75	1·10
640	**99**	20c. red	55	20
620	**103**	30c. brown	55	25
621	**103**	50c. violet	1·10	2·75
635	-	50c. violet (Italia)	75	20
636	-	60c. orange (Italia)	75	20
641	**103**	60c. green	55	20
637	**99**	1l. violet	75	20
643	-	1l.20 brown (Italia)	55	20
638	-	2l. red (Italia)	1·30	1·10
645	**98**	5l. red	1·60	20
646	-	10l. violet (Italia)	8·00	7·50

1945. Stamps of Italy surch L. 2,50 (No. 629) and stamps of Italian Social Republic surch POSTE ITALIANE and new value (Nos. 627/8).

627		1l.20 on 20c. red (No. 102)	10	10
628		2l. on 25c. green (No. 103)	15	20
629		2l.50 on 1l.75 orange (No. 251)	15	30

193 "Work, Justice and Family"

195 Planting a Sapling

196 "Peace"

197 "Work, Justice and Family"

1945

647	-	10c. brown	10	10
648	**193**	20c. brown	10	10
649	-	25c. blue	10	20
650	**195**	40c. grey	10	15
651	-	50c. violet	10	15
652	-	60c. green	15	60
653	-	80c. red	10	10
654	**195**	1l. green	20	10
655	-	1l.20 brown	20	50
656	-	2l. brown	20	30
657	-	3l. red	20	10
658	-	4l. red	60	10
659	**193**	5l. blue	4·50	10
660	**195**	6l. violet	11·00	10
661	-	8l. green	6·25	25
662	-	10l. grey	2·00	20
663	**193**	10l. red	41·00	10
664	**195**	15l. blue	16·00	10
665	-	20l. purple	13·00	10
666	**196**	25l. green	34·00	15
667	-	30l. blue	£500	45
668	**196**	50l. purple	14·00	20
669	**197**	100l. red	£550	4·50

DESIGNS: 10, 50, 80c., 8, 10l. (662) Hammer breaking chain ("Freedom"); 25c., 1l.20, 3, 4, 20, 30l. Flaming torch ("Enlightenment"); 60c., 2l. Gardener tying sapling to stake.

198 Clasped Hands and Caproni Campini N-1 Jet

1945. Air.

670	**198**	1l. grey	30	10
671	-	2l. blue	30	10
672	**198**	3l.20 red	45	25
673	-	5l. green	20	15
674	**198**	10l. red	30	15
675	-	25l. blue	15	13·00
676	-	25l. brown	25	10
677	**198**	50l. green	42·00	21·00
678	**198**	50l. violet	25	10

DESIGN: 2, 5, 25l. Barn swallows in flight.

200 Amalfi

1946. Mediaeval Italian Republics.

679	**200**	1l. sepia	20	20
680	-	2l. blue	20	20
681	-	3l. green	20	20
682	-	4l. orange	20	20
683	-	5l. violet	25	20
684	-	10l. red	25	20
685	-	15l. blue	2·40	1·30
686	-	20l. brown	70	45

DESIGNS—VERT: 2l. Lucca; 3l. Siena; 4l. Florence. HORIZ: 5l. Pisa; 10l. Genoa; 15l. Venice; 20l. "The Oath of Pontida".

1947. Air. Surch LIRE 6-.

687	**198**	6l. on 3l.20 orange	45	10

202 Wireless Mast

1947. Air. 50th Anniv of Radio.

688	**202**	6l. violet	20	15
689	-	10l. red	20	15
690	-	20l. orange	1·30	1·10
691	**202**	25l. blue	1·90	1·30
692	-	35l. blue	3·00	2·40
693	-	50l. purple	4·00	3·25

DESIGNS: 10, 35l. Ship's aerial; 20, 50l. Heinkel He 70 Blitz wireless-equipped airplane.

204 Douglas DC-2 over Rome

1948. Air.

911	**204**	100l. green	65	20
912	**204**	300l. mauve	65	30
913	**204**	500l. blue	1·70	1·60
914	**204**	1000l. brown	2·75	2·75

For No. 911 in smaller size see No. 1297.

205 St. Catherine giving her Cloak to a Beggar

206 St. Catherine carrying the Cross

1948. 600th Birth Anniv of St. Catherine of Siena.

698	**205**	3l. blue and green (postage)	20	25
699	-	5l. blue and violet	20	25
700	-	10l. violet and brown	4·50	3·25
701	-	30l. grey and bistre	25·00	21·00
702	**206**	100l. violet and brown (air)	£130	60·00
703	-	200l. blue and bistre	80·00	27·00

DESIGNS—All show St. Catherine. VERT: 5l. Carrying the Cross; 10l. Extending her arms to Italy; 30l. Dictating "The Dialogue" to a Disciple. HORIZ: 200l. Extending her arms to Italy.

207 "Proclamation of New Constitution"

1948. Proclamation of New Constitution.

704	**207**	10l. violet	1·70	1·10
705	**207**	30l. blue	5·50	3·25

208 Rising at Palermo

1948. Centenary of Revolution of 1848.

706	**208**	3l. brown	1·40	70
707	-	4l. purple	1·40	70
708	-	5l. blue	4·50	85
709	-	6l. green	2·75	1·30
710	-	8l. brown	2·50	1·30
711	-	10l. red	4·25	60
712	-	12l. green	16·00	4·25
713	-	15l. black	31·00	3·25
714	-	20l. red	75·00	10·50
715	-	30l. blue	18·00	3·25
716	-	50l. violet	£190	7·50
717	-	100l. blue	£190	27·00

DESIGNS: 4l. Rising at Padua; 5l. Concession of Statute, Turin; 6l. Storming Porta Tosa, Milan; 8l. Proclamation of Venetian Republic; 10l. Defence of Vicenza; 12l. Hero of Curtatone; 15l. Hero of Goito; 20l. Austrian retreat from Bologna; 30l. Fighting at Brescia; 50l. Garibaldi; 100l. Goffredo Mameli (party patriot) on death bed, July 1849.

209 Alpinist and Bassano Bridge

1948. Rebuilding of Bassano Bridge.

718	**209**	15l. green	4·00	2·10

210 Gaetano Donizetti

1948. Death Centenary of Donizetti (composer).

719	**210**	15l. brown	2·75	1·80

211 Exhibition Grounds

1949. 27th Milan Fair.

720	**211**	20l. sepia	17·00	6·00

212

1949. 25th Biennial Art Exhibition. Venice.

721	**212**	5l. red and flesh	1·10	25
722	-	15l. green and cream	7·75	2·75
723	-	20l. brown and buff	13·50	30
724	-	50l. blue and yellow	£110	2·75

DESIGNS: 15l. Clock bell-ringers, St. Mark's Column and Campanile; 20l. Emblem of Venice and "Bucentaur" (state gallery); 50l. Winged lion on St. Mark's Column.

213 Globes and Forms of Transport

1949. 75th Anniv of U.P.U.

725	**213**	50l. blue	£110	10·50

214 Vascello Castle

1949. Centenary of Roman Republic.

726	**214**	100l. brown	£475	£140

215 Worker and Ship

1949. European Recovery Plan.

727	**215**	5l. green	11·00	6·50
728	**215**	15l. violet	50·00	24·00
729	**215**	20l. brown	£120	27·00

216 Statue of Mazzini

1949. Honouring Giuseppe Mazzini (founder of "Young Italy").

730	**216**	20l. black	19·00	6·50

217 V. Alfieri

1949. Birth Bicentenary of Vittorio Alfieri (poet).

731	**217**	20l. brown	13·50	5·25

218 San Giusto Cathedral

1949. 1st Trieste Free Election.

732	**218**	20l. lake	22·00	21·00

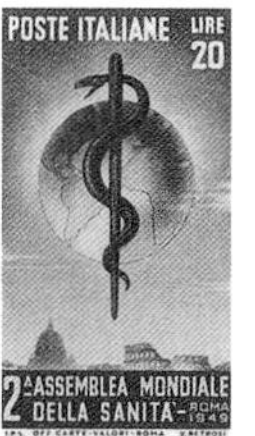
219 Staff of Aesculapius and Globe

1949. 2nd World Health Congress, Rome.

733	**219**	20l. violet	65·00	20·00

220 A. Palladio and Vicenza Basilica

1949. 400th Anniv of Completion of Palladio's Basilica at Vicenza.

734	**220**	20l. violet	22·00	10·50

221 Lorenzo de Medici

1949. 500th Birth Anniv of Lorenzo de Medici "The Magnificent".

735	**221**	20l. blue	19·00	3·75

222 Galleon and Exhibition Buildings

1949. 13th Levant Fair, Bari.

736	**222**	20l. red	13·50	3·75

223 Voltaic Pile

224 Count Alessandro Volta

1949. 150th Anniv of Volta's Discovery of the Electric Cell.

737	**223**	20l. red	11·00	2·75
738	**224**	50l. blue	£170	46·00

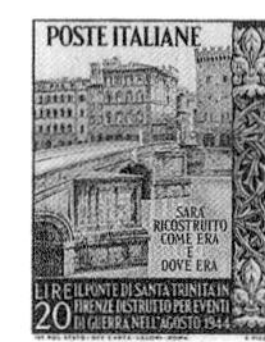
225 Holy Trinity Bridge, Florence

1949. Rebuilding of Holy Trinity Bridge, Florence.

739	**225**	20l. green	22·00	3·75

226 Caius Valerius Catullus

1949. Death Bimillenary of Catullus (poet).

740	**226**	20l. blue	22·00	3·75

227 Domenico Cimarosa

1949. Birth Bicentenary of Cimarosa (composer).

741	**227**	20l. violet	19·00	2·75

228 Entrance to Exhibition

1950. 28th Milan Fair.

742	**228**	20l. brown	6·75	2·75

229 Car and Flags

1950. 32nd Int Automobile Exhibition, Turin.

743	**229**	20l. violet	19·00	2·75

230 Statue of Perseus

1950. 5th General UNESCO Conference, Florence.

744	-	20l. green	17·00	2·10
745	**230**	55l. blue	£100	17·00

DESIGN—HORIZ: 20l. Pitti Palace, Florence.

231 St. Peter's Basilica

1950. Holy Year.

746	**231**	20l. violet	17·00	1·10
747	**231**	55l. blue	£140	3·25

232 Gaudenzio Ferrari

1950. Honouring Gaudenzio Ferrari (painter).

748	**232**	20l. green	32·00	3·25

233 Town Hall, Florence, Statue of Columbus and Wireless Mast

1950. International Radio Conf, Florence.

749	**233**	20l. violet	28·00	13·00
750	**233**	55l. blue	£325	£180

234 L. Muratori

1950. Death Bicentenary of Ludovico Muratori (historian).

751	**234**	20l. brown	11·00	2·75

235 Guido D'Arezzo

1950. 9th Death Cent of D'Arezzo (musician).

752	**235**	20l. green	36·00	3·25

236 Galleon

1950. 14th Levant Fair, Bari.

753	**236**	20l. brown	20·00	2·75

237 Marzotto and Rossi

1950. Pioneers of Wool Industry.

754	**237**	20l. blue	6·75	1·80

238 Tobacco Plant and Factory

1950. European Tobacco Conference, Rome.

755	**238**	5l. green and mauve	4·50	2·75
756	-	20l. green and brown	5·50	1·40
757	-	55l. brown and blue	£120	30·00

DESIGNS: 20l. Plant; 55l. Girl and plant.

239 Seal of Academy

1950. Bicentenary of Academy of Fine Arts, Venice.

758	**239**	20l. lt brown and brown	9·00	2·75

240 A. Righi

1950. Birth Centenary of Augusto Righi (physicist).

759	**240**	20l. black and buff	9·00	2·75

241 Blacksmith

1950. Provincial Occupations. As T 241.

760	**241**	50c. blue	20	25
762	-	2l. brown	35	25
881	-	1l. violet	10	10
763	-	5l. black	1·10	15
764	-	6l. brown	35	25
765	-	10l. green	5·50	15
766	-	12l. green	5·50	25
883	-	15l. blue	1·70	10
768	-	20l. violet	33·00	15
769	-	25l. brown	6·00	15
770	-	30l. purple	4·50	25
771	-	35l. red	24·00	70
772	-	40l. brown	1·10	25
773	-	50l. violet	50·00	15
774	-	55l. blue	3·25	25
775	-	60l. red	7·75	85
776	-	65l. green	2·20	35
777	-	100l. brown	£110	50
778	-	200l. brown	33·00	4·75

DESIGNS: 1l. Motor mechanic; 2l. Stonemason; 5l. Potter; 6l. Girls embroidering and water-carrying; 10l. Weaver; 12l. Fisherman at tiller; 15l. Boat builder; 20l. Fisherman trawling; 25l. Girl packing oranges; 30l. Girl carrying grapes; 35l. Gathering olives; 40l. Carter and wagon; 50l. Shepherd; 55l. Ploughman; 60l. Ox-cart; 65l. Girl harvester; 100l. Women handling maize; 200l. Woodcutter.

242 First Tuscan Stamp

1951. Centenary of First Tuscan Stamp.

779	**242**	20l. red and purple	4·50	1·60
780	**242**	55l. blue and ultramarine	65·00	48·00

243 Car and Flags

1951. 33rd International Motor Show, Turin.

781	**243**	20l. green	24·00	3·75

244 Peace Hall, Rome

1951. Consecration of Hall of Peace, Rome.

782	**244**	20l. violet	17·00	3·75

245 Westland W.81 Helicopter over Fair

246 Fair Building

1951. 29th Milan Fair.

783	**245**	20l. brown	22·00	2·75
784	**246**	55l. blue	£120	75·00

247 Allegory

1951. 10th International Textile Art and Fashion Exhibition, Turin.

785	**247**	20l. violet	40·00	4·25

248 Columbus disembarking

1951. 500th Birth Anniv of Columbus.

786	**248**	20l. green	33·00	4·25

249 Gymnastics Symbols

1951. Int Gymnastic Festival, Florence.

787	**249**	5l. red and brown	50·00	£450
788	**249**	10l. red and green	50·00	£450
789	**249**	15l. red and blue	50·00	£450

250 Montecassino Abbey restored

1951. Restoration of Montecassino Abbey.

790	**250**	20l. violet	11·00	2·75
791	-	55l. blue	£110	65·00

DESIGN: 55l. Abbey in ruins, 1944.

251 Perugino

1951. 500th Birth Anniv of Perugino (painter).

792	**251**	20l. brown and sepia	6·75	4·25

252 Modern Art

1951. Triennial Art Exhibition, Milan.

793	**252**	20l. black and green	13·50	3·25
794	-	55l. pink and blue	65·00	55·00

DESIGN—HORIZ: 55l. Jug and symbols.

253 Cyclist and Globe

1951. World Cycling Championship.

795	**253**	25l. black	20·00	3·75

254 Galleon and Hemispheres

1951. 15th Levant Fair, Bari.

796	**254**	25l. blue	12·00	3·25

255 "Jorio's Daughter"

1951. Birth Centenary of Francesco Paolo Michetti (painter).

797	**255**	25l. brown	11·00	3·25

256 T 1 of Sardinia and Arms of Cagliari

1951. Sardinian Postage Stamp Centenary.

798	**256**	10l. black and sepia	4·00	3·25
799	-	25l. green and red	5·00	2·75
800	-	60l. red and blue	24·00	21·00

DESIGNS: 25l. 20c. stamp and arms of Genoa; 60l. 40c. stamp and arms of Turin.

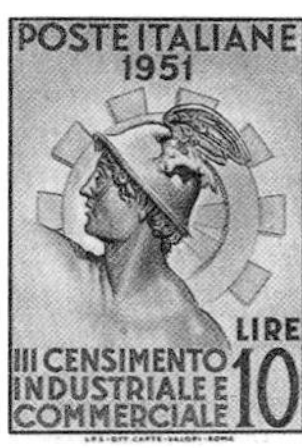
257 "Industry and Commerce"

1951. 3rd Industrial and Commercial Census.

801	257	10l. green	2·20	1·90

258 Census in Ancient Rome

1951. 9th National Census.

802	258	25l. black	9·00	1·90

259 G. Verdi and Roncole Church

1951. 50th Death Anniv of Giuseppe Verdi (composer).

803	-	10l. green and purple	5·50	2·75
804	259	25l. brown and chocolate	11·00	2·75
805	-	60l. blue and green	75·00	21·00

DESIGNS: 10l. Verdi, Theatre Royal and Cathedral, Parma; 60l. Verdi, La Scala Opera House and Cathedral, Milan.

260 Mountain Forest

1951. Forestry Festival. Inscr "FESTA DEGLI ALBERI".

806	260	10l. green and olive	3·25	3·25
807	-	25l. green	11·00	2·10

DESIGN—HORIZ: 25l. Tree and wooded hills.

261 V. Bellini

1952. 150th Birth Anniv of Bellini (composer).

808	261	25l. black	6·75	1·60

262 Royal Palace, Caserta

1952. Bicentenary of Construction of Caserta Palace by Vanvitelli.

809	262	25l. bistre and green	6·75	1·60

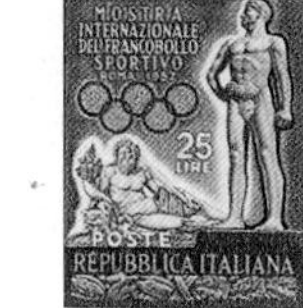
263

1952. 1st Int Sports Stamps Exhibition, Rome.

810	263	25l. brown and black	2·75	1·30

264 Motor-boat Pavilion

1952. 30th Milan Fair.

811	264	60l. blue	75·00	18·00

265 Leonardo da Vinci

1952. 500th Birth Anniv of Leonardo da Vinci.

812	265	25l. orange	65	55
813	-	60l. blue	9·25	8·50
814	265	80l. red	26·00	80

DESIGN—(inscr "LEONARDO DA VINCI 1452–1952"): 60l. "The Virgin of the Rocks".

267 Campaniles and First Stamps

1952. Modena and Parma Stamp Centenary.

815	267	25l. black and brown	1·70	1·60
816	267	60l. indigo and blue	16·00	14·00

268 Hand, Torch and Globe

1952. Overseas Fair, Naples.

817	268	25l. blue	3·25	1·30

269 Lion of St. Mark

1952. 26th Biennial Art Exhibition, Venice.

818	269	25l. black and cream	4·50	1·30

270 Emblem of Fair

1952. 30th Padua Fair.

819	270	25l. red and blue	5·50	1·60

271 San Giusto Cathedral and Flag

1952. 4th Trieste Fair.

820	271	25l. green, red and brown	4·50	1·60

272 Caravel and Bari Fair

1952. 16th Levant Fair, Bari.

821	272	25l. green	2·00	1·30

273 Girolamo Savonarola

1952. 5th Birth Cent of Savonarola (reformer).

822	273	25l. violet	8·25	1·60

274 Savoia Marchetti S.M.95C over Colosseum

1952. 1st Civil Aeronautics Law Conf, Rome.

823	274	60l. blue and ultramarine	28·00	27·00

275 Alpine Climbing Equipment

1952. Alpine Troops National Exhibition.

824	275	25l. black	1·10	85

276 Army, Navy and Air Force Symbols

277 Sailor, Soldier and Airman

1952. Armed Forces Day.

825	276	10l. green	30	10
826	277	25l. sepia and brown	85	30
827	-	60l. black and blue	16·00	6·00

DESIGN—As Type **277**: 60l. Airplane, motor torpedo boat and tank.

278 Cardinal Massaia and Map

1952. Centenary of Mission to Ethiopia.

828	278	25l. deep brown & brown	2·75	2·40

279 V. Gemito

1952. Birth Centenary of Gemito (sculptor).

829	279	25l. brown	1·70	1·10

280 A. Mancini

1952. Birth Centenary of Mancini (painter).

830	280	25l. myrtle	1·70	1·10

281

1952. Centenary of Martyrdom of Belfiore.

831	281	25l. blue and black	4·00	1·10

282 Antonello da Messina

1953. Antonello Exhibition, Messina.

832	282	25l. red	3·25	1·10

283 Cars Racing

1953. 20th "Mille Miglia" Car Race.

833	283	25l. violet	1·70	1·10

284 Bee and Medals

1953. Creation of Orders of Meritorious Labour.

834	284	25l. violet	1·70	1·10

285 Arcangelo Corelli

1953. Birth Tercentenary of Corelli (composer).

835	285	25l. brown	1·70	1·10

286 Coin of Syracuse

1953. (a) Size 17×21 mm.

887	286	1l. black	10	10
888	286	5l. grey	10	10
889	286	6l. brown	10	10
890	286	10l. red	10	10
891	286	12l. green	10	10
892	286	13l. purple	10	10
893	286	15l. grey	10	10
894	286	20l. brown	10	10
895	286	25l. violet	45	10
896	286	30l. brown	30	10
897	286	35l. red	20	10
898	286	40l. mauve	65	10
899	286	50l. green	55	10
900	286	60l. blue	20	20
901	286	70l. green	35	20
902	286	80l. brown	35	20
903	286	90l. brown	65	20
1008	286	100l. brown	35	10

905	**286**	130l. red and grey	35	25
1009	**286**	200l. blue	80	10

(b) Size 22½×28 mm.

904		100l. brown	24·00	25
846		200l. blue	11·00	65

See also Nos. 1202/19b.

287 St. Clare of Assisi

1953. 700th Death Anniv of St. Clare.

847	**287**	25l. red and brown	1·10	75

288 Mountains and Reservoirs

1953. Mountains Festival.

848	**288**	25l. green	2·20	65

289 "Agriculture"

1953. International Agricultural Exn, Rome.

849	**289**	25l. brown	1·70	30
850	**289**	60l. blue	7·75	3·25

290 Rainbow over Atlantic

1953. 4th Anniv of Atlantic Pact.

851	**290**	25l. turquoise and orange	8·25	25
852	**290**	60l. blue and mauve	20·00	4·75

291 L. Signorelli

1953. 500th Birth Anniv of Signorelli (painter).

853	**291**	25l. green and brown	1·30	55

292 A. Bassi

1953. 6th Int Microbiological Congress, Rome.

854	**292**	25l. brown and black	1·10	55

293 Capri

1953. Tourist Series.

855	-	10l. brown and sepia	35	30
856	-	12l. black and blue	55	45
857	-	20l. brown and orange	80	10
858	-	25l. green and blue	2·75	10
859	-	35l. brown and buff	3·25	85
860	**293**	60l. blue and green	6·00	1·10

DESIGNS—VERT: 10l. Siena; 25l. Cortina d'Ampezzo. HORIZ: 12l. Rapallo; 20l. Gardone; 35l. Taormina.

294 Lateran Palace

1954. 25th Anniv of Lateran Treaty.

861	**294**	25l. brown and sepia	80	25
862	**294**	60l. blue and bright blue	5·00	3·75

295 Television Aerial and Screen

1954. Introduction of Television in Italy.

863	**295**	25l. violet	1·90	25
864	**295**	60l. turquoise	9·50	5·25

296 "Everyone Must Contribute to the Public Expense"

1954. "Encouragement to Taxpayers".

865	**296**	25l. violet	2·75	55

297 Vertical Flight Trophy

1954. 1st Experimental Helicopter Mail Flight, Milan–Turin.

866	**297**	25l. green	1·30	75

298 Golden Eagle and Campanile

1954. 10th Anniv of Resistance Movement.

867	**298**	25l. black and brown	60	55

299 A. Catalani

1954. Birth Centenary of Catalani (composer).

868	**299**	25l. green	60	55

300 Marco Polo, Lion of St. Mark, Venice, and Dragon Pillar, Peking

1954. 7th Birth Centenary of Marco Polo.

869	**300**	25l. brown	65	55
870	**300**	60l. green	6·75	6·50

301 Cyclist, Car and Landscape

1954. 60th Anniv of Italian Touring Club.

871	**301**	25l. green and red	80	55

302 "St. Michael the Archangel" (after Guido Reni)

1954. International Police Congress, Rome.

872	**302**	25l. red	55	25
873	**302**	60l. blue	2·20	2·50

303 "Pinocchio"

1954. 64th Death Anniv of Carlo Lorenzini (Collodi) (writer).

874	**303**	25l. red	1·10	55

304 Amerigo Vespucci

1954. 5th Birth Cent of Vespucci (explorer).

875	**304**	25l. purple	65	45
876	**304**	60l. blue	4·00	3·75

305 "Madonna" (Perugino)

1954. Termination of Marian Year.

877	**305**	25l. brown and buff	55	55
878	-	60l. black and cream	2·75	2·75

DESIGN: 60l. Madonna's head (Michelangelo).

306 Silvio Pellico

1955. Death Centenary of Pellico (dramatist).

879	**306**	25l. blue and violet	55	65

308 "The Nation Expects a Faithful Declaration of Your Income"

1955. "Encouragement to Taxpayers".

907	**308**	25l. lilac	2·20	30

309

1955. 4th World Petroleum Congress.

908	**309**	25l. green	55	30
909	-	60l. red	1·30	1·80

DESIGN: 60l. Oil derricks and globe.

310 A. Rosmini

1955. Death Cent of Rosmini (theologian).

910	**310**	25l. brown	1·30	30

311 Girolamo Fracastoro (physician) and Roman Arena, Verona

1955. International Medical Conf, Verona.

915	**311**	25l. brown and black	80	30

312 Basilica of St. Francis

1955. Bicentenary of Elevation of Basilica of St. Francis of Assisi to Papal Chapel.

916	**312**	25l. black and cream	55	30

313 Scholar and Drawing-board

1955. Centenary of "Montani" Institute, Fermo.

917	**313**	25l. green	55	30

314 "The Harvester"

1955. 50th Anniv of Int Agricultural Institute.
918 **314** 25l. brown and red 45 30

315 F.A.O. Building, Rome

1955. 10th Anniv of F.A.O.
919 **315** 60l. violet and black 1·80 1·30

316 G. Matteotti

1955. 70th Birth Anniv of Giacomo Matteotti (politician).
920 **316** 25l. red 1·30 30

317 B. Grassi

1955. 30th Death Anniv of Grassi (biologist).
921 **317** 25l. green 55 30

318 "St. Stephen giving Alms to the Poor"

1955. 5th Death Cent of Fra Angelico (painter).
922 **318** 10l. black and cream 20 20
923 - 25l. blue and cream 35 30
DESIGN—HORIZ: 25l. "St. Lawrence giving goods of the Church to the poor".

319 G. Pascoli

1955. Birth Centenary of Pascoli (poet).
924 **319** 25l. black 55 30

320 G. Mazzini

1955. Air. 150th Birth Anniv of Mazzini (founder of "Young Italy").
925 **320** 100l. green 3·00 1·60

321 "Italia" Ski-jump

1956. 7th Winter Olympic Games, Cortina d'Ampezzo.
926 **321** 10l. green and orange 10 20
927 - 12l. black and yellow 10 30
928 - 25l. purple and orange 45 20
929 - 60l. blue and orange 3·50 3·00
DESIGNS: 12l. Snow Stadium; 25l. Ice Stadium; 60l. Skating Arena, Misurina.

1956. Air. Italian President's Visit to U.S.A. and Canada. Surch 1956 Visita del Presidente della Repubblica negli U.S.A. e nel Canada L. 120.
930 **198** 120l. on 50l. mauve 2·20 2·40

323 Coach and Steam Train

1956. 50th Anniv of Simplon Tunnel.
931 **323** 25l. green 11·00 1·10

324

1956. 10th Anniv of Republic.
932 **324** 10l. grey and blue 30 25
933 **324** 25l. carmine and red 55 25
934 **324** 60l. light blue and blue 6·75 6·50
935 **324** 80l. orange and brown 12·00 70

325 Count Avogadro

1956. Death Centenary of Avogadro (physicist).
936 **325** 25l. black 35 30

326

1956. Europa.
937 **326** 25l. deep green and green 2·20 15
938 **326** 60l. deep blue and blue 14·50 1·40

327

1956. Int Astronautical Congress, Rome.
939 **327** 25l. blue 55 30

328 The Globe

1956. 1st Anniv of Admission to U.N.
940 **328** 25l. red and green on pink 35 20
941 **328** 60l. green and red on green 55 30

329 Savings Bank, Books and Certificates

1956. 80th Anniv of Post Office Savings Bank.
942 **329** 25l. blue and slate 35 30

330 Ovid

1957. Birth Bimillenary of Ovid (poet).
943 **330** 25l. black and olive 45 30

331 St. George (after Donatello)

1957
944a **331** 500l. green 2·75 10
945a **331** 1000l. red 2·75 30

332 Antonio Canova

1957. Birth Bicentenary of Canova (sculptor).
946 **332** 25l. brown 15 20
947 - 60l. slate 40 65
948 - 80l. blue 45 20
DESIGNS—VERT: 60l. Hercules and Lica. HORIZ: 80l. Pauline Borghese (bust).

333 Traffic Lights at Crossroads

1957. Road Safety Campaign.
949 **333** 25l. red, black and green 45 30

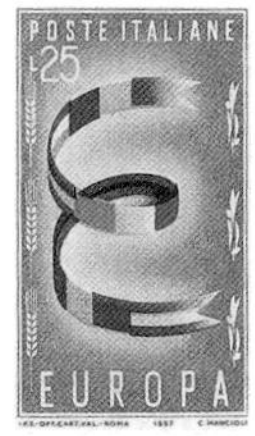

334 "Europa" Flags

1957. Europa. Flags in national colours.
950 **334** 25l. blue 1·10 10
951 **334** 60l. blue 9·00 1·00

335 Giosue Carducci

1957. 50th Death Anniv of Carducci (poet).
954 **335** 25l. sepia 55 30

336 Filippino Lippi (after self-portrait)

1957. 500th Birth Anniv of Filippino Lippi (painter).
955 **336** 25l. brown 35 30

337 Cicero (bust)

1957. Death Bimillenary of Cicero (statesman).
956 **337** 25l. red 35 30

338 Garibaldi (after M. Lorusso)

1957. 150th Birth Anniv of Garibaldi.
957 **338** 15l. grey 20 15
958 - 110l. lilac 35 20
DESIGN—HORIZ: 110l. Statue of Garibaldi on horseback (after Romanelli).

339 St. Domenico Savio and Youths

1957. Death Centenary of St. Domenico Savio.
959 **339** 15l. black and violet 35 30

340 St. Francis of Paola

1957. 450th Death Anniv of St. Francis of Paola.
960 **340** 25l. black 35 30

341 Dams, Peasant and Map of Sardinia

1958. Inaug of Flumendosa–Mulargia Irrigation Scheme, Sardinia.
961 **341** 25l. turquoise 35 30

342 Statue of the Holy Virgin and Lourdes Basilica

1958. Centenary of Apparition of Virgin Mary at Lourdes.

962	**342**	15l. purple	10	10
963	**342**	60l. blue	30	20

343 "The Constitution"

1958. 10th Anniv of Constitution.

964	**343**	25l. green and brown	10	10
965	-	60l. sepia and blue	10	10
966	-	110l. sepia and brown	10	10

DESIGNS—VERT: 60l. Oak tree with new growth. HORIZ: 110l. Montecitorio Palace, Rome.

344 Exhibition Emblem and Ancient Roman Road

1958. Brussels International Exhibition.

967	**344**	60l. yellow and blue	35	30

345 Rodolfo's Attic ("La Boheme")

1958. Birth Centenary of Puccini (operatic composer).

968	**345**	25l. blue	35	30

346 The Prologue ("I Pagliacci")

1958. Birth Centenary of Leoncavallo (operatic composer).

969	**346**	25l. red and indigo	35	30

347 "Ave Maria" (after Segantini)

1958. Birth Centenary of Giovanni Segantini (painter).

970	**347**	110l. green on cream	55	30

348 "Fattori in his Studio" (self-portrait)

1958. 50th Death Anniv of Giovanni Fattori (painter).

971	**348**	110l. brown	55	35

349 Federal Palace, Brasilia and Arch of Titus, Rome

1958. Visit of Pres. Gronchi to Brazil.

972	**349**	175l. green	80	70

349a "Europa"

1958. Europa.

973	**349a**	25l. blue and red	55	15
974	**349a**	60l. red and blue	1·70	20

350 Naples ½ grano stamp of 1858

1958. 1st Naples Postage Stamps Centenary.

975	**350**	25l. brown	10	10
976	-	60l. brown and sepia	10	10

DESIGN: 60l. Naples 1 grano stamp of 1858.

351 "Winged Horse" (sculpture in Sorrento Cathedral)

1958. Visit of Shah of Iran.

977	**351**	25l. sepia and lavender	20	10
978	**351**	60l. blue and pale blue	90	1·10

352 E. Torricelli

1958. 350th Birth Anniv of Evangelista Torricelli (physicist).

979	**352**	25l. red	55	45

353 "Triumphs of Julius Caesar" (after fresco by Mantegna)

1958. 40th Anniv of Victory in World War I.

980	**353**	15l. green	15	10
981	-	25l. slate	15	10
982	-	60l. red	35	20

DESIGNS—HORIZ: 25l. Arms of Trieste, Rome and Trento. VERT: 60l. Memorial bell of Rovereto.

354 Eleonora Duse

1958. Birth Centenary of Eleonora Duse (actress).

983	**354**	25l. blue	35	30

355 "Drama"

1958. 10th Anniv of "Premio Italia" (international contest for radio and television plays).

984	**355**	25l. black, blue and red	10	10
985	-	60l. black and blue	20	20

DESIGN: 60l. "Music" (radio mast and grand piano).

356 Sicily 5gr. stamp of 1859

1959. 1st Sicilian Postage Stamps Centenary.

986		25l. turquoise	10	10
987	**356**	60l. orange	20	20

DESIGN: 25l. Sicily 2gr. stamp of 1859.

357 Capitol, Quirinal Square Obelisk and Dome of St. Peter's

1959. 30th Anniv of Lateran Treaty.

988	**357**	25l. blue	35	30

358 N.A.T.O. Emblem and Map

1959. 10th Anniv of N.A.T.O.

989	**358**	25l. blue and yellow	10	10
990	**358**	60l. blue and green	20	30

359 Arms of Paris and Rome

1959. Rome-Paris Friendship.

991	**359**	15l. red, brown and blue	10	10
992	**359**	25l. red, brown and blue	20	10

360 Olive Branch growing from shattered Tree

1959. Int War Veterans' Assn Convention, Rome.

993	**360**	25l. green	35	30

361 Lord Byron Monument

1959. Unveiling of Lord Byron Monument, Rome.

994	**361**	15l. green	35	30

362 C. Prampolini

1959. Birth Centenary of Camillo Prampolini (politician).

995	**362**	15l. red	9·50	45

363 Quirinal Square Obelisk, Rome

1959. Olympic Games Propaganda. Roman Monuments and Ruins. Inscr "ROMA MCMLX".

996	**363**	15l. sepia and orange	10	10
997	-	25l. sepia and blue	20	20
998	-	35l. sepia and buff	20	20
999	-	60l. sepia and mauve	35	35
1000	-	110l. sepia and yellow	55	20

DESIGNS—VERT: 25l. Tower of City Hall, Quirinal Hill. HORIZ: 35l. Baths of Caracalla; 60l. Arch of Constantine (Colosseum); 110l. Basilica of Massentius.

364 Victor Emmanuel II, Garibaldi, Cavour and Mazzini

1959. Centenary of 2nd War of Independence.

1001	**364**	15l. black	10	10
1002	-	25l. red and brown	10	10
1003	-	35l. violet	20	20
1004	-	60l. blue	20	35
1005	-	110l. lake	45	35

DESIGNS—VERT: 25l. Italian camp after the Battle of Magenta (after painting by Fattori); 110l. Battle of Magenta (after painting by Induno). HORIZ: 35l. Battle of San Fermo (after painting by Trezzini); 60l. Battle of Palestro.

The 25l. is also a Red Cross commemorative.

365 Workers' Monument and I.L.O. Building, Geneva

1959. 40th Anniv of I.L.O.

1006	**365**	25l. violet	10	10
1007	**365**	60l. brown	10	10

366 Romagna 8b. Stamp of 1859

1959. Romagna Postage Stamps Centenary.

1010	**366**	25l. brown and black	10	10
1011	-	60l. green and black	20	20

DESIGN: 60l. Romagna 20b. stamp of 1859.

366a "Europa"

1959. Europa.

1012	**366a**	25l. green	20	20
1013	**366a**	60l. blue	35	35

367

1959. Stamp Day.

1014	**367**	15l. red, black and grey	20	30

368 "The Fire of Borgo" (after Raphael)

1960. World Refugee Year.

1015	**368**	25l. red	20	10
1016	**368**	60l. purple	20	20

369 Garibaldi's Message to Sicilians

1960. Cent of Garibaldi's Expedition to Sicily.

1017	**369**	15l. brown	10	10
1018	-	25l. red	10	10
1019	-	60l. blue	20	20

DESIGNS—VERT: 25l. Garibaldi meeting King Victor Emmanuel II near Naples (after Matania). HORIZ: 60l. Embarkation of volunteers at Quarto, near Genoa (after T. van Elven).

370 "The Discus Thrower" (after Miron)

1960. Olympic Games. Inscr as in T 370.

1020		5l. brown	10	10
1021		10l. blue and orange	10	10
1022		15l. blue	10	10
1023		25l. sepia and lilac	10	10
1024	**370**	35l. red	10	10
1025	-	60l. sepia and green	10	10
1026	-	110l. purple	30	20
1027	-	150l. brown and blue	1·70	1·30
1028	-	200l. green	85	35

DESIGNS—VERT: 5l. Games emblem; 15l. "Starting the Race" (statue); 110l. "Pugilist at rest" (after Apollonius); 200l. "The Apoxiomenos" (after Lisippos). HORIZ: 10l. Olympic Stadium, Rome; 25l. Cycling Stadium, Rome; 60l. Sports Palace, Rome; 150l. Little Sports Palace.

371 Vittorio Bottego (after Ettore Ximenes)

1960. Birth Centenary of Vittorio Bottego (explorer).

1029	**371**	30l. brown	35	30

371a Conference Emblem

1960. Europa.

1030	**371a**	30l. brown and green	20	10
1031	**371a**	70l. orange and blue	20	10

372 Caravaggio

1960. 350th Death Anniv of Caravaggio (painter).

1032	**372**	25l. brown	35	30

373 Coach and Posthorn

1960. Stamp Day.

1033	**373**	15l. sepia and red	35	30

374 Michelangelo

1961. Works of Michelangelo. Frescoes on ceiling of Sistine Chapel. (a) Size 17×20½ mm.

1034	-	1l. black	10	10
1035	-	5l. orange	10	10
1036	-	10l. red	10	10
1037	-	15l. purple	10	10
1038	-	20l. green	10	10
1039	-	25l. brown	10	10
1040	-	30l. purple	10	20
1041	-	40l. red	10	10
1042	-	50l. green	10	10
1043	-	55l. brown	10	30
1044	-	70l. blue	10	10
1045	-	85l. green	10	10
1046	-	90l. mauve	30	50
1047	-	100l. violet	30	10
1048	-	115l. blue	30	30
1049	-	150l. brown	45	20
1050	**374**	200l. blue	65	15

(b) Size 22×26½ mm.

1051		500l. green	5·00	35
1052		1000l. red	3·25	6·75

DESIGNS: 1, 5, 10, 115, 150l. Ignudo (different versions); 15l. Joel; 20l. Libyan Sibyl; 25l. Isaiah; 30l. Erythraean Sibyl; 40l. Daniel; 50l. Delphic Sibyl; 55l. Cumaean Sibyl; 70l. Zachariah; 85l. Jonah; 90l. Jeremiah; 100l. Ezekiel; 500l. Adam; 1000l. Eve.

375 Douglas DC-8 crossing Atlantic Ocean

1961. Visit of President Gronchi to S. America.

1053	**375**	170l. blue (Argentina)	4·50	4·50
1054	**375**	185l. green (Uruguay)	4·50	4·50
1055	**375**	205l. violet (Peru)	13·50	13·50

The countries indicated are shown in deep colours on the map.

376 Pliny the Younger

1961. 19th Birth Cent of Pliny the Younger.

1056	**376**	30l. brown and buff	35	30

377 Ippolito Nievo

1961. Birth Centenary of Ippolito Nievo (poet).

1057	**377**	30l. blue and red	35	30

378 St. Paul in Ship (from 15th-century Bible of Borso d'Este)

1961. 19th Cent of St. Paul's Arrival in Rome.

1058	**378**	30l. multicoloured	20	20
1059	**378**	70l. multicoloured	45	45

379 Cannon and Gaeta Fortress

1961. Cent of Italian Unification and Independence.

1060	**379**	15l. brown and blue	20	10
1061	-	30l. brown and blue	20	20
1062	-	40l. brown and blue	20	45
1063	-	70l. mauve and brown	20	20
1064	-	115l. blue and brown	1·70	20
1065	-	300l. red, brown & green	5·50	5·50

DESIGNS: 30l. Carignano Palace, Turin; 40l. Montecitorio Palace, Rome; 70l. Vecchio Palace, Florence; 115l. Madama Palace, Rome; 300l. Capitals, "Palace of Work", Int. Exn. of Work, Turin.

380 Doves

1961. Europa.

1066	**380**	30l. red	15	10
1067	**380**	70l. green	15	15

381 G. Romagnosi

1961. Birth Bicent of Romagnosi (philosopher).

1068	**381**	30l. green	35	30

382 Imprint of 50c. Provisional Postal Franked Paper of Sardinia, 1819

1961. Stamp Day.

1069	**382**	15l. mauve and black	35	30

383 "The Sweet-burning Lamp" from Pascoli's "La Poesia" (after wood-eng by P. Morbiducci)

1962. 50th Death Anniv of G. Pascoli (poet).

1070	**383**	30l. red	10	10
1071	**383**	70l. blue	10	10

384 Pacinotti's Dynamo (diagram)

1962. 50th Death Anniv of Antonio Pacinotti (physicist).

1072	**384**	30l. black and red	10	10
1073	**384**	70l. black and blue	35	55

385 St. Catherine (after 15th-century woodcut)

1962. 5th Centenary of Canonization of St. Catherine of Siena.

1074	-	30l. violet	10	10
1075	**385**	70l. black and red	55	55

DESIGN: 30l. St. Catherine (after A. Vanni).

386 Camera Lens

1962. 30th Anniv of International Cinematograph Art Fair. Venice.

1076	**386**	30l. black and blue	10	10
1077	-	70l. black and red	35	55

DESIGN: 70l. Lion of St. Mark.

387 Cyclist being paced

1962. World Cycling Championships.

1078	**387**	30l. black and green	30	10
1079	-	70l. blue and black	30	35
1080	-	300l. black and red	3·00	5·50

DESIGNS: 70l. Cyclists road-racing; 300l. Cyclists on track.

388 Europa "Tree"

1962. Europa.

1081	**388**	30l. red and carmine	60	15
1082	**388**	70l. ultramarine and blue	60	35

389 Balzan Medal

1962. International Balzan Foundation.

1083	**389**	70l. red and green	1·00	45

390 Campaign Emblem

1962. Malaria Eradication.

1084	**390**	30l. violet	10	10
1085	**390**	70l. blue	55	55

391 10c. Stamp of 1862 and 30l. Stamp of 1961

1962. Stamp Day.

1086	**391**	15l. multicoloured	35	30

392 "The Pentecost" (from "Codex Syriacus")

1962. Ecumenical Council, Vatican City.

1087	**392**	30l. orange & bl on cream	10	10
1088	**392**	70l. blue & orge on cream	35	35

393 Statue of Cavour (statesman)

1962. Centenary of Court of Accounts.

1089	**393**	30l. green	35	30

394 Pico della Mirandola (scholar)

1963. 5th Birth Cent of G. Pico della Mirandola.

1090	**394**	30l. violet	35	30

395 D'Annunzio

1963. Birth Centenary of Gabriele D'Annunzio (author and soldier).

1091	**395**	30l. green	35	30

396 "Sowing" (bas-relief after G. and N. Pisano)

1963. Freedom from Hunger.

1092	**396**	30l. sepia and red	20	10
1093	-	70l. sepia and blue	35	40

DESIGN: 70l. "Harvesting" (bas-relief after G. and N. Pisano).

397 Monviso, Italian Alps, Ice-axe and Rope

1963. Italian Alpine Club Centenary.

1094	**397**	115l. sepia and blue	35	30

398 "I.N.A." Lighthouse

1963. 50th Anniv of Italian National Insurance Corporation.

1095	**398**	30l. black and green	35	30

399 Posthorn and Globe

1963. Paris Postal Conference Centenary.

1096	**399**	70l. blue and green	35	30

400 Three-dimensional Emblem

1963. Red Cross Centenary.

1097	**400**	30l. red and purple	10	10
1098	**400**	70l. red and blue	55	55

401 "World Tourism"

1963. U.N. Tourism Conference, Rome.

1099	**401**	15l. blue and olive	35	20
1100	**401**	70l. brown and blue	45	45

402 "Co-operation"

1963. Europa.

1101	**402**	30l. brown and red	20	20
1102	**402**	70l. green and brown	65	35

403 "Naples"

1963. 4th Mediterranean Games, Naples. Inscr "NAPOLI 1963".

1103	**403**	15l. ochre and blue	10	10
1104	-	70l. orange and green	20	20

DESIGN: 70l. Greek "Olympic" vase.

404 Mascagni and Costanzi Theatre

1963. 150th Birth Anniv of Verdi (1105) and Birth Centenary of Mascagni (1106) (composers).

1105		30l. brown and green	35	35
1106	**404**	30l. green and brown	35	35

DESIGN: No. 1105, Verdi and La Scala Opera House.

405 G. Belli

1963. Death Centenary of Giuseppe Belli (poet).

1107	**405**	30l. brown	35	30

406 Stamp "Flower"

1963. Stamp Day.

1108	**406**	15l. red and blue	35	30

407 Galileo Galilei

1964. 400th Birth Anniv of Galileo Galilei.

1109	**407**	30l. brown	20	20
1110	**407**	70l. black	35	35

408 Nicodemus (from Michelangelo's "Pieta")

1964. 400th Death Anniv of Michelangelo.

1111	**408**	30l. sepia (postage)	10	10
1112	-	185l. black (air)	55	55

DESIGN: 185l. Michelangelo's "Madonna of Bruges".

410 Carabinieri on Parade

1964. 150th Anniv of Carabinieri (military police).

1113	**410**	30l. red and blue	15	10
1114	-	70l. brown	20	20

DESIGN: 70l. "The Charge at Pastrengo (1848)" (De Albertis).

411 G. Bodoni

1964. 150th Death Anniv (1963) of Giambattista Bodoni (type-designer and printer).

1115	**411**	30l. red	35	30

412 Europa "Flower"

1964. Europa.

1116	**412**	30l. purple	20	15
1117	**412**	70l. blue	45	15

413 European Buildings

1964. 7th European Municipalities' Assembly.

1118	**413**	30l. brown and green	10	10
1119	**413**	70l. brown and blue	30	30
1120	**413**	500l. red	2·20	2·20

414 Victor Emannuel Monument, Rome

1964. War Veterans' Pilgrimage to Rome.

1121	**414**	30l. brown	15	15
1122	**414**	70l. blue	20	20

415 G. da Verrazzano and Verrazano Narrows Bridge

1964. Opening of Verrazano Narrows Bridge, New York.

1123	**415**	30l. black and brown (postage)	30	30
1124	**415**	130l. black and green (air)	65	30

This American bridge is designated "Verrazano" with one "z".

416 Italian Stamps

1964. Stamp Day.

1125	**416**	15l. brown and bistre	35	30

417 Prisoners of War

1965. 20th Anniv of Resistance.

1126	**417**	10l. black	10	10
1127	-	15l. black, red and green	10	10
1128	-	30l. purple	10	10
1129	-	70l. blue	10	10
1130	-	115l. red	10	10
1131	-	130l. brown, green & red	10	10

DESIGNS—VERT: 15l. Servicemen and casualty ("Liberation Army"); 70l. Alpine soldiers ("Resistance in the mountains"). HORIZ: 30l. Gaunt hands and arms on swastika ("Political and Racial Persecution"); 115l. Patriots with banners ("Resistance in the Towns"); 130l. Ruined building and torn flags ("Martyred Cities").

418 I.T.U. Emblem, Meucci and Marconi

1965. I.T.U. Centenary.

1132	**418**	70l. red and green	35	25

419 "Flying Dutchman" Dinghies

1965. World Sailing Championships, Alassio and Naples.

1133	**419**	30l. black and red	10	10
1134	-	70l. black and blue	10	10
1135	-	500l. black and blue	55	55

DESIGNS—VERT: 70l. "5.5 S.1" class yachts. HORIZ: 500l. "Lightning" dinghies.

420 Mont Blanc and Tunnel

1965. Opening of Mont Blanc Road Tunnel.

1136	**420**	30l. black	30	30

421 A. Tassoni and Episode from his "Secchia Rapita"

1965. 400th Birth Anniv of Alessandro Tassoni (poet).

1137	**421**	40l. multicoloured	30	30

422 Europa "Sprig"

1965. Europa.

1138	**422**	40l. green and orange	15	10
1139	**422**	90l. green and blue	40	20

423 "Hell" (Codex, Vatican Library)

1965. 700th Birth Anniv of Dante.

1140	**423**	40l. multicoloured	20	10
1141	-	90l. multicoloured	20	10
1142	-	130l. multicoloured	20	10
1143	-	500l. green	55	55

DESIGNS—VERT: 90l. "Purgatory" (codex, Marciana Library, Venice); 500l. Head of Dante (bronze, Naples Museum). HORIZ: 130l. "Paradise" (codex, British Museum).

424 House and Savings-bank

1965. Savings Day.

1144	**424**	40l. multicoloured	30	30

425 Douglas DC-6B passing Control-tower

1965. Night Airmail Service.

1145	**425**	40l. red and blue	10	10
1146	-	90l. multicoloured	15	15

DESIGN: 90l. Sud Aviation SE 210 Caravelle jetliner within airmail envelope "border".

426 Map of "Highway to the Sun"

1965. Stamp Day.

1147	**426**	20l. multicoloured	30	30

427 Two-man Bobsleigh

1966. World Bobsleigh Championships, Cortina d'Ampezzo.

1148	**427**	40l. red, blue and grey	10	10
1149	-	90l. violet and blue	15	15

DESIGN: 90l. Four-man bobsleigh.

428 Skier carrying Torch

1966. University Winter Games, Turin.

1150	**428**	40l. black and red	20	10
1151	-	90l. violet and red	20	10
1152	-	500l. brown and red	65	50

DESIGNS—VERT: 90l. Ice skating; 500l. Ice hockey.

429 B. Croce

1966. Birth Centenary of Benedetto Croce (philosopher).

1153	**429**	40l. sepia	35	30

430 Arms of Cities of Venezia

1966. Centenary of Union of Venezia and Italy.

1154	**430**	40l. multicoloured	35	30

431 Pine, Palatine Hill, Rome

1966. "Trees and Flowers". Multicoloured.

1155	20l. Type **431**	10	10
1156	25l. Apples	10	10
1157	40l. Carnations	10	10
1158	50l. Irises	10	10
1159	90l. Anthemis (Golden Marguerite)	10	10
1160	170l. Olive tree, Villa Adriana, Tivoli	10	10
1241	55l. Cypresses (26×35½ mm)	15	10
1242	180l. Broom (26×35½ mm)	30	20

432 "Visit Italy"

1966. Tourist Propaganda.

1161	**432**	20l. multicoloured	35	25

433 Capital "I"

1966. 20th Anniv of Republic.

1162	**433**	40l. multicoloured	10	10
1163	**433**	90l. multicoloured	20	20

434 Battle Scene

1966. Centenary of Battle of Bezzecca.

1164	**434**	90l. olive	35	30

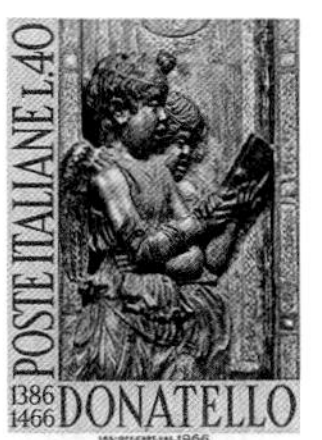

435 "Singing Angels" (from copper panel on altar of St. Antony's Basilica, Padua)

1966. 5th Death Centenary of Donatello.

1165	**435**	40l. multicoloured	35	30

436 Europa "Ship"

1966. Europa.

1166	**436**	40l. violet	20	15
1167	**436**	90l. blue	35	15

437 "Madonna in Maesta" (after Giotto)

1966. Giotto's 700th Birth Anniv.

1168	**437**	40l. multicoloured	35	30

438 Filzi, Battisti, Chiesa and Sauro

1966. 50th Death Annivs of World War I Heroes.

1169	**438**	40l. green and slate	35	30

439 Postal Emblem

1966. Stamp Day.

1170	**439**	20l. multicoloured	30	30

440 Compass and Globe

1967. Centenary of Italian Geographical Society.
1171 **440** 40l. blue and black 35 30

441 Toscanini

1967. Birth Centenary of Arturo Toscanini (orchestral conductor).
1172 **441** 40l. buff and blue 35 30

442 Campidoglio, Rome

1967. 10th Anniv of Rome Treaties.
1173 **442** 40l. brown and black 20 20
1174 **442** 90l. purple and black 20 20

443 Cogwheels

1967. Europa.
1175 **443** 40l. purple and pink 20 15
1176 **443** 90l. blue and cream 35 20

444 Brown Bear (Abruzzo Park)

1967. Italian National Parks. Multicoloured.
1177 20l. Ibex (Gran Paradiso Park) (vert) 10 10
1178 40l. Type **444** 10 10
1179 90l. Red deer stag (Stelvio Park) 20 10
1180 170l. Tree (Circeo Park) (vert) 35 20

445 Monteverdi

1967. 400th Death Anniv of Claudio Monteverdi (composer).
1181 **445** 40l. brown and chestnut 35 30

446 Racing Cyclists

1967. 50th Tour of Italy Cycle Race. Designs showing cyclists.
1182 **446** 40l. multicoloured 15 15
1183 - 90l. multicoloured 15 20
1184 - 500l. multicoloured 1·70 95

447 Pirandello and Stage

1967. Birth Centenary of Luigi Pirandello (dramatist).
1185 **447** 40l. multicoloured 35 30

448 Stylized Mask

1967. Two Worlds Festival, Spoleto.
1186 **448** 20l. black and green 15 10
1187 **448** 40l. black and red 20 10

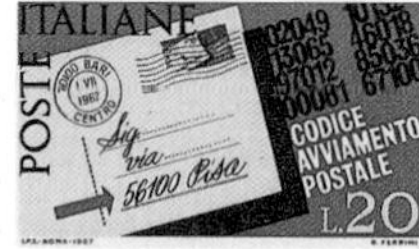

449 Coded Addresses

1967. Introduction of Postal Codes.
1188 **449** 20l. black, blue & yellow 15 10
1189 **449** 25l. black, red and yellow 20 10
1190 **449** 40l. black, purple & yell 15 10
1191 **449** 50l. black, green & yellow 20 10

450 Pomilio PE Type Biplane and Postmark

1967. 50th Anniv of 1st Airmail Stamp.
1192 **450** 40l. black and blue 35 30

451 St. Ivo's Church, Rome

1967. 300th Death Anniv of Francesco Borromini (architect).
1193 **451** 90l. multicoloured 35 30

UMBERTO GIORDANO
1867-1948
POSTE ITALIANE L.20

452 U. Giordano and Music from "Andrea Chenier"

1967. Birth Centenary of Umberto Giordano (composer).
1194 **452** 20l. brown and black 35 30

453 "The Oath of Pontida" (from painting by Adolfo Cao)

1967. 800th Anniv of Oath of Pontida.
1195 **453** 20l. brown 35 30

454 I.T.Y. Emblem

1967. International Tourist Year.
1196 **454** 20l. black, blue and yellow 15 15
1197 **454** 50l. black, blue & orange 20 15

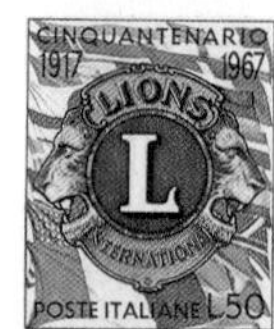

455 Lions Emblem

1967. 50th Anniv of Lions International.
1198 **455** 50l. multicoloured 35 30

456 Sentry

1967. 50th Anniv of Stand on the Piave.
1199 **456** 50l. multicoloured 35 30

457 E. Fermi (scientist) and Reactor

1967. 25th Anniv of 1st Nuclear Chain Reaction.
1200 **457** 50l. black and brown 35 30

458 Stamp and Dove

1967. Stamp Day.
1201 **458** 25l. multicoloured 35 30

1968. As Nos. 887, etc (1952), size 16×20 mm.

1202	**286**	1l. black	10	10
1203	**286**	5l. slate	10	10
1204	**286**	6l. brown	10	10
1205	**286**	10l. red	10	10
1206	**286**	15l. violet	10	10
1207	**286**	20l. sepia	10	10
1208	**286**	25l. violet	10	10
1209	**286**	30l. brown	10	10
1210	**286**	40l. purple	10	10
1211	**286**	50l. olive	10	10
1212	**286**	55l. violet	10	15
1213	**286**	60l. blue	10	15
1214	**286**	70l. green	10	15
1215	**286**	80l. brown	10	15
1215a	**286**	90l. brown	10	10
1216	**286**	100l. brown	10	10
1216a	**286**	120l. blue and green	10	10
1216b	**286**	125l. purple and brown	55	30
1217	**286**	130l. red and grey	10	10
1217a	**286**	150l. violet	20	10
1217b	**286**	170l. green and brown	45	10
1218	**286**	180l. purple and grey	65	30
1218a	**286**	200l. blue	20	10
1219	**286**	300l. green	65	30
1219a	**286**	350l. orange, red & yell	65	15
1219b	**286**	400l. red	65	15

459 Scouts around Campfire

1968. Italian Boy Scouts.
1220 **459** 50l. multicoloured 50 30

460 Europa "Key"

1968. Europa.
1221 **460** 50l. green and pink 15 15
1222 **460** 90l. brown and blue 30 30

461 "Tending the Sick"

1968. 400th Birth Anniv of Luigi Gonzaga (St. Aloysius).
1223 **461** 25l. violet and brown 35 30

462 Boito and "Mephistopheles"

1968. 50th Death Anniv of Arrigo Boito (composer and librettist).
1224 **462** 50l. multicoloured 35 30

463 F. Baracca and "Aerial Combat" (abstract by G. Balla)

1968. 500th Death Anniv of Francesco Baracca (airman of World War I).
1225 **463** 25l. multicoloured 35 30

464 Giambattista Vico (300th Birth Anniv)

1968. Italian Philosophers' Birth Annivs.
1226 **464** 50l. blue 35 30
1227 - 50l. black 35 30
DESIGN: No. 1227, Tommaso Campanella (400th birth anniv).

465 Cycle Wheel and Stadium

1968. World Road Cycling Championships.
1228 **465** 25l. blue, pink and brown 15 10
1229 - 90l. indigo, red and blue 35 20
DESIGN: 90l. Cyclists and Imola Castle.

466 "St. Mark's Square, Venice" (Canaletto)

1968. Death Bicentenary of Canaletto (painter).

1230 **466** 50l. multicoloured 35 30

467 Rossini

1968. Death Centenary of Gioacchino Rossini (composer).

1231 **467** 50l. red 35 30

468 Mobilization

1968. 50th Anniv of Victory in World War I. Multicoloured.

1232 20l. Type **468** 10 10

1233 25l. Trench warfare 10 10

1234 40l. Naval forces 20 10

1235 50l. Air Force 20 10

1236 90l. Battle of Vittorio Veneto 20 15

1237 180l. Tomb of Unknown Soldier 35 15

469 "Conti Correnti Postali"

1968. 50th Anniv of Postal Cheque Service.

1238 **469** 50l. multicoloured 35 30

470 Tracking Equipment and Buildings

1968. Space Telecommunications Centre, Fucino.

1239 **470** 50l. multicoloured 35 30

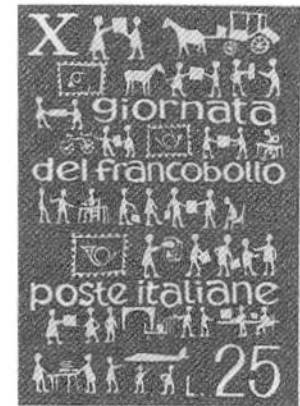

471 "Postal Development"

1968. Stamp Day.

1240 **471** 25l. red and yellow 35 30

472 Commemorative Medal

1969. Centenary of State Audit Department.

1243 **472** 50l. black and pink 35 30

473 Colonnade

1969. Europa.

1244 **473** 50l. multicoloured 20 15

1245 **473** 90l. multicoloured 35 20

474 Machiavelli

1969. 500th Birth Anniv of Niccolo Machiavelli (statesman).

1246 **474** 50l. multicoloured 35 30

475 I.L.O. Emblem

1969. 50th Anniv of I.L.O.

1247 **475** 50l. black and green 20 10

1248 **475** 90l. black and red 35 10

476 Postal Emblem

1969. 50th Anniv of Italian Philatelic Federation.

1249 **476** 50l. multicoloured 35 30

477 Sondrio-Tirano Mailcoach of 1903

1969. Stamp Day.

1250 **477** 25l. blue 35 30

478 Skiing

1970. World Skiing Championships, Val Gardena. Multicoloured.

1251 50l. Type **478** 20 15

1252 90l. Dolomites 35 20

479 "Galatea" (detail of fresco by Raphael)

1970. 450th Death Anniv of Raphael. Mult.

1253 20l. Type **479** 20 10

1254 50l. "Madonna of the Goldfinch" 35 10

480 Symbols of Flight

1970. 50th Anniv of Rome–Tokyo Flight by A. Ferrarin.

1255 **480** 50l. multicoloured 20 10

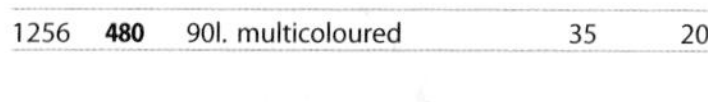

1256 **480** 90l. multicoloured 35 20

481 "Flaming Sun"

1970. Europa.

1257 **481** 50l. yellow and red 20 20

1258 **481** 90l. yellow and green 35 35

482 Erasmo da Narni (from statue by Donatello)

1970. 600th Birth Anniv of Erasmo da Narni "Il Gattamelata" (condottiere).

1259 **482** 50l. green 35 30

483 Running

1970. World University Games, Turin. Mult.

1260 20l. Type **483** 20 10

1261 180l. Swimming 45 30

484 Dr. Montessori and children

1970. Birth Centenary of Dr. Maria Montessori (educationist).

1262 **484** 50l. multicoloured 35 30

485 Map and Cavour's Declaration

1970. Centenary of Union of Rome and Papal States with Italy.

1263 **485** 50l. multicoloured 35 30

486 Loggia of Campanile, St. Mark's Square, Venice

1970. 400th Death Anniv of Jacopo Tatti, "Il Sansovino" (architect).

1264 **486** 50l. brown 35 30

487 "Garibaldi at Dijon" (engraving)

1970. Centenary of Garibaldi's Participation in Franco-Prussian War.

1265 **487** 20l. grey and blue 20 10

1266 **487** 50l. purple and blue 35 10

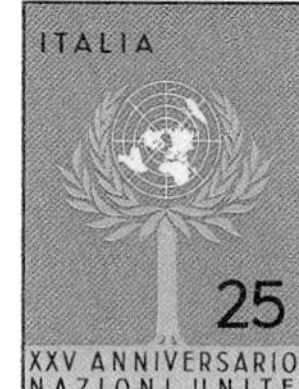

488 U.N. Emblem within Tree

1970. 25th Anniv of United Nations.

1267 **488** 25l. green, black & brown 20 15

1268 **488** 90l. yellow, black and blue 45 15

489 Rotary Emblem

1970. 65th Anniv of Rotary International.

1269 **489** 25l. ultramarine, yell & bl 20 10

1270 **489** 90l. ultramarine, yell & bl 35 15

490 Telephone Dial and "Network"

1970. Completion of Telephone Trunk-dialling System.

1271 **490** 25l. green and red 20 15

1272 **490** 90l. blue and red 35 20

491 Urban Complex and Tree

1970. Nature Conservation Year.

1273 **491** 20l. red and green 20 10

1274 **491** 25l. grey and green 35 10

492 Electric Locomotive "Tartaruga"

1970. Stamp Day.

1275 **492** 25l. black 35 30

493 "The Adoration" (F. Lippi)

1970. Christmas. Multicoloured.

1276 25l. Type **493** (postage) 20 30

1277 150l. "The Adoration of the Magi" (Gentile da Fabriano) (44×35 mm) (air) 35 35

494 Saverio Mercadante

1970. Death Centenary of Saverio Mercadante (composer).

1278	**494**	25l. violet and grey	35	30

495 "Mercury" (part of Cellini's "Perseus with the Head of Medusa")

1971. 400th Death Anniv of Benvenuto Cellini (goldsmith and sculptor).

1279	**495**	50l. blue	35	30

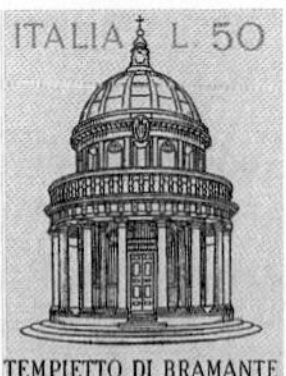

496 Bramante's "Little Temple", St. Peter's Montorio, Rome

1971

1280	**496**	50l. black and brown	35	30

497 Adenauer, Schuman and De Gasperi

1971. 20th Anniv of European Coal and Steel Community.

1281	**497**	50l. brown, black & grn	20	15
1282	**497**	90l. brown, black and red	35	20

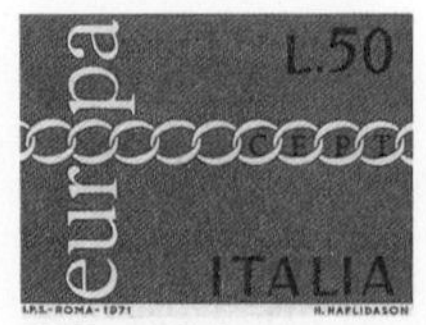

498 Europa Chain

1971. Europa.

1283	**498**	50l. red	30	15
1284	**498**	90l. purple	50	20

499 Mazzini

1971. 25th Anniv of Republic.

1285	**499**	50l. multicoloured	20	15
1286	**499**	90l. multicoloured	35	20

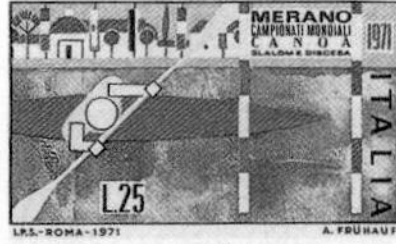

500 Canoeist in Slalom

1971. World Canoeing Slalom and Free Descent Championships, Merano. Multicoloured.

1287	25l. Type **500**	20	10
1288	90l. Canoeist making free descent	35	20

501 Three Sports

1971. Youth Games.

1289	**501**	20l. black, green & brn	10	10
1290	-	50l. black, violet & orge	20	10

DESIGN: 50l. Four other sports.

502 Alitalia Emblem

1971. 25th Anniv of Alitalia State Airline. Multicoloured.

1291	50l. Type **502**	20	10
1292	90l. Emblem and Globe	20	15
1293	150l. Tailplane of Boeing 747	30	20

503 Grazia Deledda

1971. Birth Cent of Grazia Deledda (writer).

1294	**503**	50l. black and brown	35	30

504 Boy in "Savings" Barrel

1971. Postal Savings Bank.

1295	**504**	25l. multicoloured	10	20
1296	**504**	50l. multicoloured	15	15

1971. Air. As No. 911 but smaller, 20×36 mm.

1297	**204**	100l. green	35	30

505 UNICEF Emblem and Paper Dolls

1971. 25th Anniv of UNICEF. Multicoloured.

1301	25l. Type **505**	20	10
1302	90l. Children acclaiming UNICEF emblem	35	20

506 Liner "Tirrenia"

1971. Stamp Day.

1303	**506**	25l. green	35	30

507 "The Nativity"

1971. Christmas. Miniatures from "Matilda's Evangelarium", Nonantola Abbey, Modena. Multicoloured.

1304	25l. Type **507**	20	15
1305	90l. "The Adoration of the Magi"	35	15

508 G. Verga and Sicilian Cart

1972. 50th Death Anniv of Giovanni Verga (writer).

1306	**508**	25l. multicoloured	20	10
1307	**508**	50l. multicoloured	35	10

509 G. Mazzini

1972. Death Cent of Giuseppe Mazzini (statesman).

1308	**509**	25l. green and black	10	10
1309	**509**	90l. grey and black	20	20
1310	**509**	150l. red and black	35	30

510 Stylized Flags

1972. 50th International Fair, Milan.

1311	**510**	25l. green and black	10	10
1312	-	50l. red and black	15	15
1313	-	90l. blue and black	35	20

DESIGNS: 50l. "Windows, stand and pavilions" (abstract); 90l. Abstract general view of Fair.

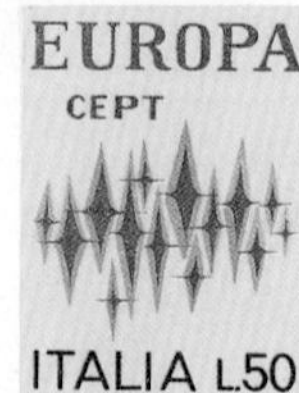

511 "Communications"

1972. Europa.

1314	**511**	50l. multicoloured	55	35
1315	**511**	90l. multicoloured	1·10	45

512 Alpine Soldier

1972. Centenary of Alpine Corps. Multicoloured.

1316	25l. Type **512**	15	15
1317	50l. Soldier's hat	30	20
1318	90l. Soldier and mountains	40	20

513 Brenta Mountains

1972. Centenary of Tridentine Alpinists Society.

1319	25l. Type **513**	15	10
1320	50l. Alpinist	30	20
1321	180l. Mt. Crozzon	35	35

514 Diagram of Conference Hall

1972. 60th Interparliamentary Union Conference, Rome.

1322	**514**	50l. multicoloured	20	10
1323	**514**	90l. multicoloured	35	15

515 "St. Peter Damiani" (miniature, after G. di Paolo)

1972. 900th Death Anniv of St. Peter Damiani.

1324	**515**	50l. multicoloured	35	30

516 "The Three Graces" (Canova)

1972. 150th Death Anniv of Antonio Canova (sculptor).

1325	**516**	50l. green	35	30

517 Initial and First Verse (Foligno edition)

1972. 500th Anniv of "The Divine Comedy". Multicoloured.

1326	50l. Type **517**	20	10
1327	90l. Initial and first verse (Mantua edition) (vert)	45	15
1328	180l. Initial and first verse ("Jesino" edition)	45	30

518 "Angel"

1972. Christmas. Multicoloured.

1329	20l. Type **518**	10	10
1330	25l. "Holy Child in Crib" (horiz)	20	15
1331	150l. "Angel" (looking to left)	35	40

519 Postal Coach

1972. Stamp Day.

1332	**519**	25l. red	35	30

520 L. B. Alberti (from bronze by M. de Pasti, Louvre)

1972. 500th Death Anniv of Leon B. Alberti (writer and savant).

1333	**520**	50l. blue and yellow	35	30

521 L. Perosi

1972. Birth Centenary of Lorenzo Perosi (composer and priest).

1334	**521**	50l. brown and yellow	20	10
1335	**521**	90l. black and green	35	15

522 Don Orione

1972. Birth Centenary of Don Orione (child-welfare pioneer).

1336	**522**	50l. blue and turquoise	20	10
1337	**522**	90l. green and yellow	35	15

523 Oceanic Survey

1973. Centenary of Military Marine Institute of Hydrography.

1338	**523**	50l. multicoloured	35	30

524 Grand Staircase, Royal Palace, Caserta

1973. Death Bicentenary of Luigi Vanvitelli (architect).

1339	**524**	25l. green	35	30

525 Schiavoni Shore

1973. "Save Venice" Campaign. Multicoloured.

1340	20l. Type **525**	35	15
1341	25l. "The Tetrarchs" (sculpture) (vert)	10	10
1342	50l. "The Triumph of Venice" (V. Carpaccio)	10	10
1343	90l. Bronze horses, St. Mark's Basilica (vert)	20	20
1344	300l. Piazzetta S. Marco	90	65

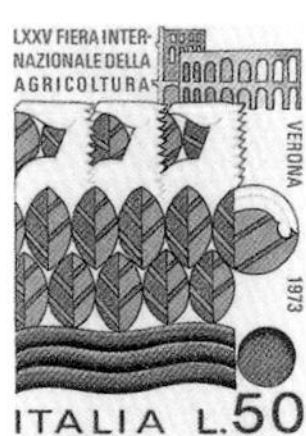

526 Fair Theme

1973. 75th Int Agricultural Fair, Verona.

1345	**526**	50l. multicoloured	35	30

527 Title-page of "Diverse Figure"

1973. 300th Death Anniv of Salvator Rosa (painter and poet).

1346	**527**	25l. black and orange	35	30

528 Formation of Fiat G-91 PAN Acrobatic Jet Aircraft

1973. 50th Anniv of Military Aviation. Mult.

1349	20l. Type **528** (postage)	20	10
1350	25l. Formation of Savoia Marchetti S-55X flying boats	20	10
1351	50l. Fiat G-91Y jet fighters on patrol	20	10
1352	90l. Fiat CR-32 biplanes performing aerobatics	20	20
1353	180l. Caproni Campini N-1 jet airplane	20	30
1354	150l. Lockheed F-104S Starfighter over Aeronautical Academy, Pozzuoli (air)	35	30

529 Football and Pitch

1973. 75th Anniv of Italian Football Association. Multicoloured.

1355	25l. Type **529**	35	30
1356	90l. Players in goalmouth	80	45

530 A. Manzoni (after F. Hayez)

1973. Death Centenary of Alessandro Manzoni (writer and politician).

1357	**530**	25l. brown and black	35	30

531 Palladio's "Rotunda", Vicenza

1973. Andrea Palladio Commemoration.

1358	**531**	90l. multicoloured	35	30

532 Spring and Cogwheels

1973. 50th Anniv of Italian State Supplies Office.

1359	**532**	50l. multicoloured	35	30

533 Europa "Posthorn"

1973. Europa.

1360	**533**	50l. gold, lilac and yellow	20	15
1361	**533**	90l. gold, green & yellow	35	20

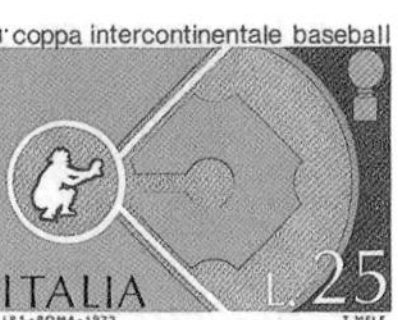

534 "Catcher" and Baseball Field

1973. 1st Intercontinental Baseball Cup. Mult.

1362	25l. Type **534**	20	15
1363	90l. "Striker" and baseball field	35	20

535 Carnival Setting

1973. Viareggio Carnival.

1364	**535**	25l. multicoloured	35	30

536 "Argenta Episode"

1973. 50th Death Anniv of Don Giovanni Minzoni (military chaplain).

1365	**536**	50l. multicoloured	35	30

537 G. Salvemini

1973. Birth Centenary of Gaetano Salvemini (political historian).

1366	**537**	50l. multicoloured	35	30

VIGNOLA 1507-1573

ITALIA L.90

538 Farnese Palace, Caprorola

1973. 400th Birth Anniv of "Vignola" (Jacopa Barozzi—architect).

1367	**538**	90l. purple and yellow	35	30

539 "St. John the Baptist"

1973. 400th Birth Anniv of Caravaggio (painter).

1368	**539**	25l. black and yellow	35	30

540 Leaning Tower of Pisa

1973. Tourism.

1369	**540**	50l. multicoloured	35	30

541 Botticelli

1973. Italian Painters (1st series).

1370	**541**	50l. brown and red	15	15
1371	-	50l. blue and brown	15	15
1372	-	50l. green and emerald	15	15
1373	-	50l. black and red	15	15
1374	-	50l. brown and blue	15	15

PAINTERS: No. 1371, Piranesi; No. 1372, Veronese; No. 1373, Verrocchio; No. 1374, Tiepolo.

See also Nos. 1392/6, 1456/61, 1495/9 and 1518/22.

542 Immacolatella Fountain, Naples

1973. Italian Fountains (1st series). Mult.

1375	25l. Type **542**	10	10
1376	25l. Trevi Fountain, Rome	10	10
1377	25l. Pretoria Fountain, Palermo	10	10

See also Nos. 1418/20, 1453/5, 1503/5, 1529/31, 1570/2 and 1618/20.

543 "Angels"

1973. Christmas. Sculptures by A. di Duccio.

1378	**543**	20l. black and green	15	10
1379	-	25l. black and blue	15	10
1380	-	150l. black and yellow	20	20

DESIGNS: 25l. "Virgin and Child"; 150l. "Angels" (different).

544 Map and Emblems

1973. 50th Anniv of Italian Rotary.

1381	**544**	50l. blue, green and red	35	30

545 Sud Aviation Super Caravelle 12

1973. Stamp Day.

1382	**545**	25l. blue	35	30

546 Military Medal for Valour

1973. 150th Anniv of Holders of the Gold Medal for Military Valour Organisation.

1383	**546**	50l. multicoloured	35	30

547 Caruso as Duke of Mantua in Verdi's "Rigoletto"

1973. Birth Centenary of Enrico Caruso (operatic tenor).

1384	**547**	50l. red	35	30

548 "Christ crowning King Roger" (Martorana Church, Palermo)

1974. Norman Art in Sicily. Mosaics.

1385	**548**	20l. blue and yellow	10	10
1386	-	50l. red and green	15	10

DESIGN: 50l. "King William offering Church to the Virgin Mary" (Monreale Cathedral).

549 Pres. L. Einaudi

1974. Birth Centenary of Luigi Einaudi (President 1948–55).

1387	**549**	50l. green	20	10

550 G. Marconi in Headphones

1974. Birth Centenary of Guglielmo Marconi (radio pioneer).

1388	**550**	50l. brown and green	20	10
1389	-	90l. multicoloured	35	20

DESIGN: 90l. Marconi and world map.

551 "David" (Bernini)

1974. Europa. Sculptures. Multicoloured.

1390		50l. Type **551**	65	35
1391		90l. "Spirit of Victory" (Michelangelo)	85	35

1974. Italian Painters (2nd series). As T 541.

1392		50l. blue and green	15	10
1393		50l. brown and blue	15	10
1394		50l. black and red	15	10
1395		50l. brown and yellow	15	10
1396		50l. blue and brown	15	10

PORTRAITS: No. 1392, Borromini; No. 1393, Carriera; No. 1394, Giambellino (Giovanni Bellini); No. 1395, Mantegna; No. 1396, Raphael.

552 Guards from Lombardy-Venetia (1848), Sardinian Marines (1815) and Tebro Battalion (1849)

1974. Bicentenary of Italian Excise Guards. Uniforms. Multicoloured.

1397		40l. Sardinian chasseurs, 1774 and 1795, and Royal Fusilier of 1817	15	20
1398		50l. Type **552**	20	20
1399		90l. Lieutenant (1866), Sergeant-major of Marines (1892) and guard (1880)	35	20
1400		180l. Helicopter pilot, naval and alpine guards of 1974	45	45

553 Feather Headdress

1974. 50th Anniv of National Bersaglieri Association. Multicoloured.

1401		40l. Type **553**	15	10
1402		50l. Bersaglieri emblem on rosette	30	10

554 Running

1974. European Athletics Championships, Rome. Multicoloured.

1403		40l. Type **554**	15	10
1404		50l. Pole vaulting	15	10

555 Francesco Petrarch

1974. 600th Death Anniv of Francesco Petrarch (poet and scholar).

1405	**555**	40l. multicoloured	10	10
1406	-	50l. blue, yellow & brown	10	10

DESIGN: 50l. Petrarch at work in his study.

556 Portofino

1974. Tourist Publicity (1st series). Mult.

1407		40l. Type **556**	15	10
1408		40l. Gradara	15	10

See also Nos. 1442/4, 1473/5, 1513/14, 1515/17, 1543/5, 1596/9, 1642/5, 1722/5, 1762/5, 1806/9, 1845/8, 1877/80, 1917/20, 1963/6, 1992/5, 2031/4, 2088/91, 2115/18, 2165/8, 2212/15, 2248/51, 2315/16, 2365/8, 2425/8, 2486/9, 2550/3, 2661/4, 2752/5, 2872/4, 2940/2, 3004/6 and 3158/61.

557 Tommaseo's Statue, Sebenico

1974. Death Centenary of Niccolo Tommaseo (writer).

1409	**557**	50l. green and pink	20	10

558 Giacomo Puccini

1974. 50th Death Anniv of Giacomo Puccini (composer).

1410	**558**	40l. multicoloured	25	15

559 Cover Engraving of Ariosto's "Orlando Furioso"

1974. 500th Birth Anniv of Ludovico Ariosto (poet).

1411	**559**	50l. blue and red	25	10

560 Commemoration Tablet (Quotation from Varrone's "Menippean Satire")

1974. 2000th Death Anniv of Marco Varrone (Varrone Reatino) (author).

1412	**560**	50l. lake, red and yellow	25	10

561 "The Month of October" (detail from 15th-century mural)

1974. 14th International Wine Congress.

1413	**561**	50l. multicoloured	25	10

562 "U.P.U." and Emblem

1974. Centenary of Universal Postal Union. Mult.

1414		50l. Type **562**	15	10
1415		90l. "U.P.U." emblem and letters	35	10

563 "The Triumph of St. Thomas Aquinas" (detail—F. Traini)

1974. 700th Death Anniv of St. Thomas Aquinas.

1416	**563**	50l. multicoloured	25	10

564 Detail of Bas-relief, Ara Pacis

1974. Centenary of Italian Order of Advocates.

1417	**564**	50l. black, green & brown	25	10

1974. Italian Fountains (2nd series). As T 542 Multicoloured.

1418		40l. Oceanus Fountain, Florence	15	20
1419		40l. Neptune Fountain, Bologna	15	20
1420		40l. Maggiore Fountain, Perugia	15	20

565 "The Adoration" (Presepe di Greccio)

1974. Christmas.

1421	**565**	40l. multicoloured	25	10

566 Pulcinella

1974. Children's Comic Characters. Mult.

1422		40l. Type **566**	10	10
1423		50l. Clowns	20	10
1424		90l. Pantaloon from Bisognosi	25	15

567 "God admonishing Adam" (Jacopo della Quercia (sculptor) (1374–1438))

1974. Italian Artists' Anniversaries (1st series).

1425	**567**	90l. violet	20	20
1426	-	90l. multicoloured	20	20

DESIGN: No. 1426, Uffizi Gallery, Florence (Giorgio Vasari (architect and painter) (1511–1574)).

See also Nos. 1445/6, 1480/2, 1523/4, 1564/5, 1593/4, 1699/1700, 1731/2, 1774/5, 1824/5, 1885/6, 1949/50 and 1987.

568 "Angel with Tablet"

1975. Holy Year. Multicoloured.

1427		40l. Type **568**	10	10
1428		50l. Angel with column	10	10
1429		90l. Bridge of the Holy Angels, Rome (49×40 mm)	15	20
1430		150l. Angel with crown of thorns	45	20
1431		180l. Angel with cross	70	30

569 "Pitti Madonna"

1975. 500th Birth Anniv of Michelangelo.

1432	**569**	40l. green	15	10
1433	-	50l. brown	15	10
1434	-	90l. red	15	25

DESIGNS: 50l. Sculptured niche, Vatican Palace; 90l. Detail from fresco "Flood of the Universe" (Sistine Chapel).

570 "The Four Days of Naples" (M. Mazzacurati)

1975. 30th Anniv of Italian Resistance Movement. Resistance Monuments. Multicoloured.

1435		70l. Type **570**	10	10
1436		100l. "Martyrs of the Ardeatine Caves" (F. Coccia)	20	10
1437		150l. "The Resistance Fighters of Cuneo" (U. Mastroianni)	40	25

571 "The Flagellation of Christ" (Caravaggio)

1975. Europa. Paintings. Multicoloured.

1438		100l. Type **571**	70	15
1439		150l. "The Appearance of the Angel to Agar and Ishmael in the Desert" (Tiepolo)	95	25

572 Globe and Emblems

1975. International Women's Year.

1440	**572**	70l. multicoloured	25	10

573 "San Marco III" (satellite) and "Santa Rita" (marine launching pad)

1975. Italian Space Project.

1441	**573**	70l. multicoloured	25	10

1975. Tourist Publicity (2nd series). As T 556. Multicoloured.

1442		150l. Cefalu	35	15
1443		150l. Isola Bella	35	15
1444		150l. Montecatini Terme	35	15

1975. Italian Artists' Annivs (2nd series). As T 567. Multicoloured.

1445		90l. "Flora" (Guido Reni (1575–1642))	20	15
1446		90l. "Artist and Model" (Armando Spadini (1883–1925))	20	15

574 Cover Engraving from Palestrina's "Primo Libro delle Messe"

1975. 450th Birth Anniv of Giovanni Pierluigi da Palestrina (composer).

1447	**574**	100l. purple and brown	40	30

575 Boat in Harbour

1975. Italian Emigration.

1448	**575**	70l. multicoloured	25	30

576 Notoriat Emblem

1975. Centenary of Unification of Italian Laws.

1449	**576**	100l. mauve, stone & blue	25	30

577 Railway Steam Locomotive Driving-wheels

1975. 21st International Railway Congress, Bologna.

1450	**577**	70l. multicoloured	30	30

578 "D'Acquisto's Sacrifice" (Vittorio Pisani)

1975. 32nd Death Anniv of Salvo d'Acquisto (carabiniere who sacrificed himself to save 22 hostages).

1451	**578**	100l. multicoloured	25	30

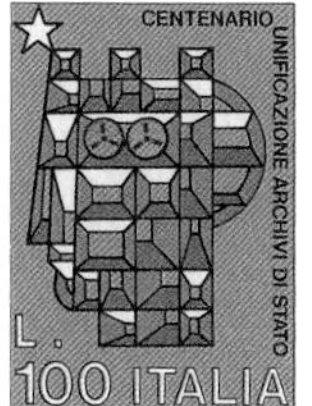

579 Symbolised Head representing Files

1975. Centenary of State Archives Unification.

1452	**579**	100l. multicoloured	25	30

1975. Italian Fountains (3rd series). As T 542. Multicoloured.

1453		70l. Rosello Fountain, Sassari	25	20
1454		70l. 99 Channel Fountain, L'Aquila	25	20
1455		70l. Piazza Fountain, Milan	25	20

1975. Italian Composers. As T 541.

1456		100l. blue, pink and red	25	10
1457		100l. blue, green & deep green	25	10
1458		100l. green, brown & dp brn	25	10
1459		100l. brown, red and lake	25	10
1460		100l. purple, grey and green	25	10
1461		100l. black, lt yellow & yellow	25	10

DESIGNS: No. 1456, Ferruccio Busoni; 1457, Alessandro Scarlatti; 1458, Francesco Cilea; 1459, Antonio Vivaldi; 1460, Franco Alfa; No. 1461, Gaspare Spontini.

581 "Annunciation to the Shepherds"

1975. Christmas. Alatri Cathedral Carvings. Multicoloured.

1462		70l. Type **581**	10	10
1463		100l. "The Nativity"	15	10
1464		150l. "Annunciation to the Kings"	35	25

582 "Children on Horseback"

1975. Stamp Day. Children's Stories. Mult.

1465		70l. Type **582**	10	10
1466		100l. "The Magic Orchard" (vert)	15	10
1467		150l. "Church Procession"	35	25

583 "Boccaccio" (from fresco by A. del Castagno)

1975. 600th Death Anniv of Giovanni Boccaccio. Multicoloured.

1468		100l. Type **583**	15	10
1469		150l. Cover engraving from Boccaccio's "Fiammetta"	25	20

584 Entrance to State Advocate's Office

1976. Centenary of State Advocate's Office.

1470	**584**	150l. multicoloured	35	15

585 "Italia 1976" Emblem

1976. "Italia 76" International Stamp Exhibition, Milan (1st issue).

1471	**585**	150l. red, green and black	25	15
1472	-	180l. multicoloured	25	20

DESIGN: 180l. Exhibition Hall, Milan.
See also Nos. 1487/91.

1976. Tourist Publicity (3rd series). As T 556. Multicoloured.

1473		150l. Fenis Castle, Aosta	30	15
1474		150l. Forio Ischia	30	15
1475		150l. Itria Valley	30	30

586 Majolica Plate

1976. Europa. Italian Crafts. Multicoloured.

1476		150l. Type **586**	75	25
1477		180l. Vase in form of woman's head	1·10	35

587 Republican Flags

1976. 30th Anniv of Republic. Multicoloured.

1478		100l. Type **587**	10	10
1479		150l. Statesmen	30	10

588 "Fortitude" (Giacomo Serpotta) (1656–1732)

1976. Italian Artists' Annivs (3rd series).

1480	**588**	150l. blue	30	15
1481	-	150l. multicoloured	30	15
1482	-	150l. black and red	30	15

DESIGNS: No. 1481, "Woman at Table" (Umberto Boccioni (1882–1916)); 1482, "Gunner's Letter from the Front" (Filippo Tommaso Marinetti (1876–1944)).

589 "The Dragon"

1976. 450th Death Anniv of Vittore Carpaccio (painter).

1483	**589**	150l. red	50	35
1484	-	150l. red	50	35

DESIGN: No. 1484, "St. George".
Nos. 1483/4 form Carpaccio's "St. George and the Dragon".

590 "Flora" (Titian)

1976. 400th Death Anniv of Titian.

1485	**590**	150l. red	40	25

591 St. Francis (13th-century fresco)

1976. 750th Death Anniv of St. Francis of Assisi.

1486	**591**	150l. brown & lt brown	40	15

592 "Cursus Publicus" Post Cart

1976. "Italia 76" International Stamp Exhibition, Milan (2nd issue).

1487	**592**	70l. black, grey and blue	15	10
1488	-	100l. black, grey & yellow	25	15
1489	-	150l. black, grey & brown	40	15
1490	-	200l. multicoloured	55	25
1491	-	400l. multicoloured	70	30

DESIGNS: 100l. Emblem of Royal Sardinian Posts; 150l. 19th-century "Lion's head" letterbox; 200l. Early cancelling machine; 400l. Modern letter-coding machine.

593 Girl with "Protective Umbrella" and Animals

1976. Stamp Day. Nature Protection. Multicoloured.

1492	40l. Type **593**	15	10
1493	100l. "Protective scarf"	20	15
1494	150l. Doctor with bandaged tree	25	20

1976. Italian Painters (3rd series). As T 541.

1495	170l. green, yellow and red	35	10
1496	170l. black, turquoise & green	35	10
1497	170l. black, purple and mauve	35	10
1498	170l. brown, lavender & violet	35	10
1499	170l. black and brown	35	10

DESIGNS: No. 1495, Carlo Dolci; 1496, Lorenzo Ghiberti (sculptor); 1497, Domenico Ghirlandaio; 1498, Giovanni Piazzetta; 1499, "Sassoferrato" (Giovanni Salvi).

594 "The Visit" (S. Lega)

1976. 150th Birth Anniv of Silvestro Lega (painter).

1500	**594**	170l. multicoloured	40	10

595 "Adoration of the Magi" (Bartolo di Fredi)

1976. Christmas. Multicoloured.

1501	70l. Type **595**	20	10
1502	120l. "The Nativity" (Taddao Gaddi)	25	25

1976. Italian Fountains (4th series). As T 542 Multicoloured.

1503	170l. Antique Fountain, Gallipoli	35	15
1504	170l. Erbe Madonna Fountain, Verona	35	15
1505	170l. Fountain of Palazzo Doria, Gerona	35	15

596 Net of Serpents obscuring the Sun

1977. Campaign against Drug Abuse. Mult.

1506	120l. Type **596**	25	15
1507	170l. "Addict" and poppy	30	15

597 Igniting Explosives

1977. 300th Birth Anniv of Pietro Micca (national hero).

1508	**597**	170l. multicoloured	35	25

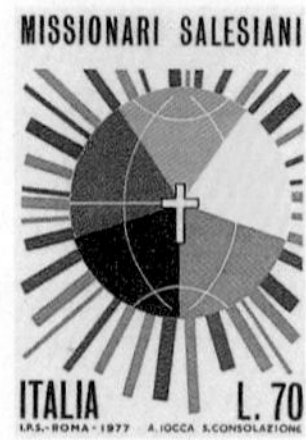

598 "Globe" and Cross

1977. Salesian Missionaries. Multicoloured.

1509	70l. Type **598**	20	10
1510	120l. St. John Bosco and "United people"	15	10

599 Article 53 of the Italian Constitution

1977. "Encouragement to Taxpayers".

1511	**599**	120l. black, brn & stone	20	15
1512	**599**	170l. black, olive & green	20	15

1977. Europa. As T 556 but with C.E.P.T. emblem. Multicoloured.

1513	170l. Mount Etna	90	25
1514	200l. Castel del Monte	2·20	35

1977. Tourist Publicity (4th series). As T 556. Multicoloured.

1515	170l. Canossa Castle	35	20
1516	170l. Castellana Grotto	35	20
1517	170l. Fermo	35	20

1977. Famous Italians. As T 541.

1518	70l. brown, green & dp green	15	20
1519	70l. black, blue and green	15	20
1520	70l. brown, yellow & lt brown	15	20
1521	70l. blue, pink and red	15	20
1522	70l. black, brown & dp brown	15	20

DESIGNS: No. 1518, Filippo Brunelleschi (architect); 1519, Pietro Aretino (satirist); 1520, Carlo Goldoni (dramatist); 1521, Luigi Cherubini (composer); 1522, Edoardo Bassini (surgeon).

1977. Italian Artists' Anniversaries (4th series). As T 567 Multicoloured.

1523	170l. "Winter" (G. Arcimboldi (c. 1527–93))	40	15
1524	170l. "Justice" (Andrea Delitio (15th century))	40	20

601 Paddle-steamer "Ferdinando Primo"

1977. Italian Ship-building (1st series). Multicoloured.

1525	170l. Type **601**	50	15
1526	170l. Sail corvette "Carracciolo"	50	15
1527	170l. Liner "Saturnia"	50	15
1528	170l. Hydrofoil missile boat "Sparviero"	50	15

See also Nos. 1552/5, 1621/4 and 1691/4.

1977. Italian Fountains (5th series). As T 542. Multicoloured.

1529	120l. Pacassi Fountain, Gorizia	35	35
1530	120l. Fraterna Fountain, Isernia	35	35
1531	120l. Palma Fountain, Palmi	35	35

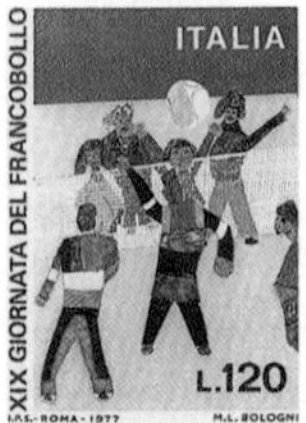

602 Handball

1977. Stamp Day. "Leisure Time". Multicoloured.

1532	120l. Type **602**	25	10
1533	120l. Catching butterflies	25	10
1534	120l. Kites	25	10

603 "Pulse"

1977. "Give Blood". Multicoloured.

1535	70l. Type **603**	40	15
1536	120l. "Transfusion"	55	15

604 Quintino Sella and 1863 1l. Stamps

1977. 150th Birth Anniv of Quintino Sella (statesman).

1537	**604**	170l. green and brown	35	30

605 Dina Galli

1977. Birth Centenary of Dina Galli (actress).

1538	**605**	170l. multicoloured	40	30

606 "Adoration of the Shepherds" (P. Testa)

1977. Christmas.

1539	**606**	70l. black and green	20	15
1540	-	120l. black and green	25	25

DESIGN: 120l. "The Adoration of the Shepherds" (J. Caraglio).

607 La Scala Opera House

1978. Bicentenary of La Scala Opera House.

1541	170l. Type **607**	40	15
1542	200l. Theatre interior	60	30

1978. Tourist Publicity (5th series). As T 556. Multicoloured.

1543	70l. Gubbio	20	10
1544	200l. Udine	55	15
1545	600l. Paestum	1·10	60

608 Dusky Grouper

1978. Environmental Protection. Mediterranean Fauna. Multicoloured.

1546	170l. Type **608**	70	15
1547	170l. Leathery turtle	70	15
1548	170l. Mediterranean monk seal	70	15
1549	170l. Audouin's gull	70	15

609 Maschio Angioino Castle, Naples

1978. Europa. Multicoloured.

1550	170l. Type **609**	95	35
1551	200l. Pantheon, Rome	1·10	45

1978. Italian Ship-building (2nd series). As T 601. Multicoloured.

1552	170l. Brigantine "Fortuna"	60	25
1553	170l. Cruiser "Benedetto Brin"	60	25
1554	170l. Frigate "Lupo"	60	25
1555	170l. Container ship "Africa"	60	25

610 Matilde Serao (writer)

1978. Famous Italians.

1556	**610**	170l. black and red	35	25
1557	-	170l. brown and blue	35	25
1558	-	170l. blue and pale blue	35	25
1559	-	170l. black and green	35	25
1560	-	170l. brown and green	35	25
1561	-	170l. blue and red	35	25

DESIGNS: No. 1557, Vittorino da Feltre (scientist); No. 1558, Victor Emmanuel II; No. 1559, Pope Pius IX; No. 1560, Marcello Malpighi (biologist); No. 1561, Antonio Meucci (telephone pioneer).

See also Nos. 1600/4.

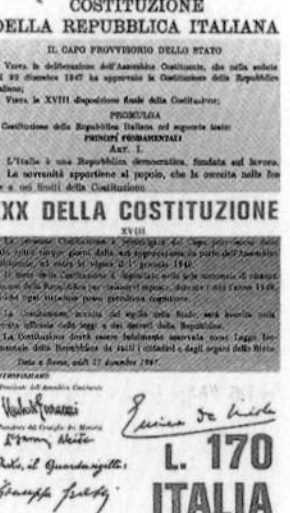

611 First and Last Paragraphs of Constitution

1978. 30th Anniv of Constitution.

1562	**611**	170l. multicoloured	40	30

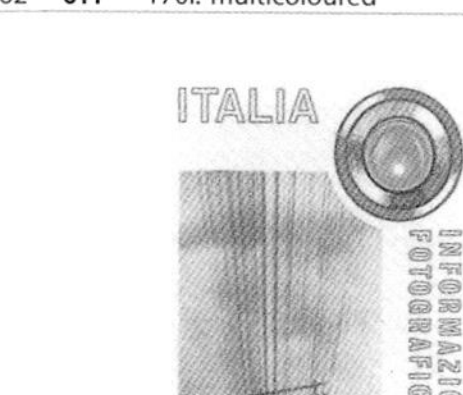

612 Telephone Wires and Lens

1978. Photographic Information.

1563	**612**	120l. grey, blue and green	25	30

1978. Italian Artists' Annivs (5th series). As T 567. Multicoloured.

1564	170l. "The Ivy" (Tranquillo Cremona, 1837–78)	40	15
1565	520l. "The Cook" (Bernardo Strozzi, 1581–1644)	2·30	80

613 The Holy Shroud of Turin

1978. 400th Anniv of Translation of the Holy Shroud from Savoy to Turin.

1566	**613**	220l. yellow, black & red	75	30

614 Volleyball Players

1978. World Volleyball Championships.

1567	**614**	80l. black, red and blue	20	20
1568	-	120l. black, blue & orge	60	20

DESIGN: 120l. Players with ball.

615 Detail from "St. Peter distributing Ananias's Silver"

1978. 550th Death Anniv of Tommaso Guidi (Masaccio).

1569	**615**	170l. blue	40	10

1978. Italian Fountains (6th series). As T 542. Multicoloured.

1570	120l. Neptune Fountain, Trento	30	20
1571	120l. Fountain of Fortune, Fano	30	20
1572	120l. Cavallina Fountain, Genzano di Lucania	30	20

616 "Madonna and Child" (Giorgione)

1978. Christmas.

1573	**616**	80l. red and brown	20	15
1574	-	120l. multicoloured	25	15

DESIGN—HORIZ (48×27 mm): 120l. "Adoration of the Magi" (Giorgione).

617 "Flowers"

1978. Stamp Day. United Europe. Mult.

1575	120l. Type **617**	25	15
1576	120l. Flags and ribbon	25	15
1577	120l. Figures raising globe inscribed "E"	25	15

618

1978

1578	**618**	1500l. multicoloured	1·40	15
1579	**618**	2000l. multicoloured	3·50	15
1580	**618**	3000l. multicoloured	5·50	15
1581	**618**	4000l. multicoloured	7·50	35
1582	**618**	5000l. multicoloured	9·50	60
1583	**618**	10000l. multicoloured	15·00	90
1584	**618**	20000l. multicoloured	30·00	4·50

619 State Polygraphic Institute

1979. 50th Anniv of State Polygraphic Institute. Multicoloured.

1588	170l. Type **619**	25	15
1589	220l. Printing press	45	30

620 "St. Francis washing the Feet of a Leper" (Maestro di Francesco Bardi)

1979. Leprosy Relief.

1590	**620**	80l. multicoloured	35	15

621 Cyclist carrying Bicycle

1979. World Cyclo-cross Championships.

1591	**621**	170l. multicoloured	25	15
1592	**621**	220l. multicoloured	45	35

1979. Italian Artists' Annivs (6th series). As T 567. Multicoloured.

1593	170l. "Annunciation" (Antonella da Messina c. 1430–79)	35	25
1594	520l. "Field with Haystack" (Ardengo Soffici 1879–1964)	1·10	40

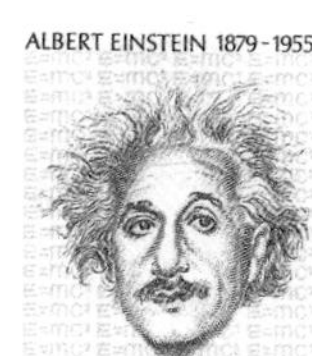

622 Albert Einstein

1979. Birth Centenary of Albert Einstein (physicist).

1595	**622**	120l. purple, grey & bl	30	15

1979. Tourist Publicity (6th series). As T 556. Multicoloured.

1596	70l. Asiago	20	15
1597	90l. Castelsardo, Sardinia	20	15
1598	170l. Orvieto	25	30
1599	220l. Scilla	40	35

1979. Famous Italians. As T 610.

1600	170l. brown, blue and black	30	15
1601	170l. green, yellow and violet	30	15
1602	170l. blue and pink	30	15
1603	170l. brown and ochre	30	15
1604	170l. mauve, brown and green	30	15

DESIGNS: No. 1600, Carlo Maderno (architect); No. 1601, Lazzaro Spallanzani (biologist); No. 1602, Ugo Foscolo (author); No. 1603, Massimo Bontempelli (writer); No. 1604, Francesco Severi (mathematician).

623 Morse Telegraph Apparatus

1979. Europa. Multicoloured.

1605	170l. Type **623**	2·40	35
1606	220l. Carrier pigeon with message tube	2·75	45

624 Flags of Member States forming "E"

1979. First Direct Elections to European Parliament.

1607	**624**	170l. multicoloured	40	15
1608	**624**	220l. multicoloured	35	30

625 Head of Aeneas (bas-relief, Ara Pacis, Rome)

1979. 70th World Rotary Congress, Rome.

1609	**625**	220l. multicoloured	40	30

626 Ball in Basket (poster)

1979. 21st European Basketball Championships.

1610	**626**	80l. multicoloured	25	15
1611	-	120l. lake, black & yellow	35	25

DESIGN: 120l. Two players.

627 "Doctor examining Patient with Stomach Ailment" (woodcut from Giovanni da Cuba's "Hortus Sanitatus")

1979. Prevention of Digestive Illnesses.

1612	**627**	120l. multicoloured	35	25

628 Emblem, Ribbon "3" and Milan Cathedral

1979. Third World Machine Tool Exhibition, Milan.

1613	**628**	170l. multicoloured	45	15
1614	**628**	220l. multicoloured	35	30

629 Ottorino Respighi and Appian Way, Rome

1979. Birth Centenary of Ottorino Respighi (composer).

1615	**629**	120l. multicoloured	35	15

630 Woman with Telephone and Morse Key

1979. 3rd World Telecommunications Exhibition, Geneva.

1616	**630**	170l. black and red	55	15
1617	-	220l. grey and green	40	30

DESIGN: 220l. Woman with early telephone and communications satellite.

1979. Italian Fountains (7th series). As T 542. Multicoloured.

1618	120l. Melograno Fountain, Issogne	40	25
1619	120l. Bollente Fountain, Acqui Terme	40	25
1620	120l. Grand Fountain, Viterbo	40	25

1979. Italian Ship-building (3rd series). As T 601. Multicoloured.

1621	170l. Full-rigged ship "Cosmos"	60	25
1622	170l. Cruiser "Dandolo"	60	25
1623	170l. Ferry "Deledda"	60	25
1624	170l. Submarine "Carlo Fecia di Cossato"	60	25

631 Sir Rowland Hill and Penny Black

1979. Death Centenary of Sir Rowland Hill.

1625	**631**	220l. multicoloured	40	30

632 Christmas Landscape

1979. Christmas.

1626	**632**	120l. multicoloured	35	30

633 Children under Umbrella (Group IIB, Varapodio School)

1979. Stamp Day. International Year of the Child. Drawings by Schoolchildren. Multicoloured.

1627		70l. Children of different races holding hands (L. Carra) (horiz)	15	15
1628		120l. Type **633**	25	25
1629		150l. Children with balloons (V. Fedon) (horiz)	35	25

634 Solar Energy (alternative sources)

1980. Energy Conservation. Multicoloured.

1630		120l. Type **634**	20	15
1631		170l. Oil well (reduction of consumption)	35	25

635 "St. Benedict" (detail, fresco by Sodoma in Monastery of Monteoliveto Maggiore)

1980. 1500th Birth Anniv of St. Benedict of Nursia (founder of Benedictine Order).

1632	**635**	220l. blue	40	25

636 Royal Palace, Naples

1980. "Europa 80" International Stamp Exhibition, Naples.

1633	**636**	220l. multicoloured	40	25

637 Antonio Pigafetta (navigator) and "Vitoria"

1980. Europa. Multicoloured.

1634		170l. Type **637**	1·40	30
1635		220l. Antonio lo Surdo (geo-physicist)	2·00	45

638 St. Catherine (reliquary bust)

1980. 600th Death Anniv of St. Catherine of Siena.

1636	**638**	170l. multicoloured	40	30

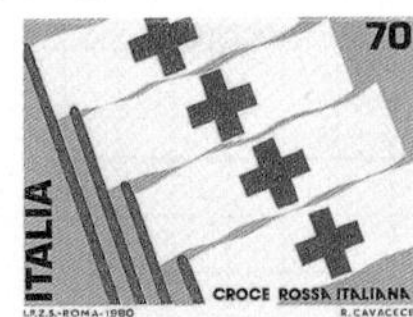

639 Red Cross Flags

1980. 1st International Exhibition of Red Cross Stamps in Italy.

1637	**639**	70l. multicoloured	35	25
1638	**639**	80l. multicoloured	35	25

640 Philae Temples

1980. Italian Work for the World (1st series). Preservation of Philae Temples, Egypt. Multicoloured.

1639		220l. Type **640**	50	15
1640		220l. Right hand view of temples	50	15

Nos. 1639/40 were issued together se-tenant, forming a composite design.

See also Nos. 1720/1, 1758/9, 1780/1, 1830/1, 1865/6 and 1937/40.

641 Footballer

1980. European Football Championship, Italy.

1641	**641**	80l. multicoloured	2·40	2·20

1980. Tourist Publicity (7th series). As T 556. Multicoloured.

1642		80l. Erice	15	30
1643		150l. Ravello	25	25
1644		200l. Roseto degli Abruzzi	45	25
1645		670l. Salsomaggiore Terme	1·40	85

642 "Cosimo I with his Artists" (Vasari)

1980. "Florence and Tuscany of the Medicis in 16th Century Europe" Exhibition. Multicoloured.

1646		170l. Type **642** (ceiling medallion, Palazzo Vecchio, Florence)	30	15
1647		170l. Armillary sphere	30	15

643 Fonte Avellana Monastery

1980. Millenary of Fonte Avellana Monastery.

1648	**643**	200l. dp green, grn & brn	40	50

644 Castel Sant' Angelo, Rome

1980. Castles. (a) Size 22×27 mm.

1649	**644**	5l. blue and red	25	10
1650	-	10l. brown and ochre	25	10
1651	-	20l. brown and blue	25	10
1652	-	30l. orange and blue	25	10
1653	-	40l. brown and blue	25	10
1654	-	50l. multicoloured	25	10
1655	-	60l. green and mauve	25	10
1656	-	70l. multicoloured	25	10
1657	-	80l. multicoloured	25	10
1658	-	90l. multicoloured	25	10
1659	-	100l. multicoloured	25	10
1660	-	120l. blue and pink	25	10
1661	-	150l. violet and brown	35	10
1662	-	170l. black and yellow	80	10
1663	-	180l. blue and pink	1·40	1·20
1664	-	200l. multicoloured	85	10
1665	-	250l. multicoloured	80	10
1666a	-	300l. multicoloured	60	10
1667	-	350l. brown, blue & grn	90	10
1667a	-	380l. multicoloured	80	30
1668	-	400l. blue, green & brn	90	10
1669	-	450l. multicoloured	1·20	10
1670	-	500l. blue, brown & grn	90	10
1670a	-	550l. multicoloured	90	30
1671	-	600l. black and green	1·00	10
1671a	-	650l. multicoloured	1·20	30
1672	-	700l. multicoloured	1·20	10
1673	-	750l. brown, green & bl	1·20	30
1674	-	800l. brown, grn & mve	1·30	15
1675	-	850l. multicoloured	1·40	30
1676	-	900l. multicoloured	1·40	15
1677	-	1000l. multicoloured	1·50	15
1678	-	1400l. brown, blue & vio	2·10	45
		(b) Size 16×21 mm.		
1679		30l. mauve	30	25
1680b		50l. blue	15	15
1680c		100l. brown	15	15
1681		120l. brown	30	30
1682		170l. violet	30	30
1683		200l. violet and blue	2·00	2·00
1684		300l. light green and green	60	60
1685		400l. brown and green	70	60
1686a		450l. green	75	65
1687		500l. blue	90	70
1687a		600l. green	90	90
1688		650l. mauve	90	90
1689		750l. violet	1·00	1·00
1690		800l. red	1·40	85

DESIGNS: 10l. Sforzesco Castle, Milan; 20l. Castel del Monte, Andria; 30l. (1652), L'Aquila Castle; 30l. (1679), 100l. (1680c), Santa Severa Castle; 40l. Ursino Castle, Catania; 50l. (1654), Rocca di Calascio, L'Aquila; 50l. (1680b), Scilla; 60l. Norman Tower, San Mauro; 70l. Aragonese Castle, Reggio Calabria; 80l. Sabbionara, Avio; 90l. Isola Capo Rizzuto; 100l. (1659), Aragonese Castle, Ischia; 120l. (1660), Estense Castle, Ferrara; 120l. (1681), Lombardia Enna; 150l. Miramare, Trieste; 170l. (1662), Ostia; 170l. (1682), 650l. (1688), Serralunga d'Alba; 180l. Castel Gavone, Finale Ligure; 200l. (1664), Cerro al Volturno; 200l. (1683), Svevo Angioina Fortress, Lucera; 250l. Rocca di Mondavio, Pesaro; 300l. (1666a), Norman Castle, Svevo, Bari; 300l. (1684), 500l. (1687), Norman Castle, Melfi; 350l. Mussomeli; 380l. Rocca di Vignola, Modena; 400l. (1668), Emperor's Castle, Prato; 400l. (1685), 750l. (1689), Venafro; 450l. (1669), Bosa; 450l. (1686a) Piobbico Castle, Pesaro; 500l. (1670), Rovereto; 550l. Rocca Sinibalda; 600l. Scaligero Castle, Sirmione; 650l. (1671a), Montecchio; 700l. Ivrea; 750l. (1673), Rocca di Urbisaglia; 800l. Rocca Maggiore, Assisi; 850l. Castello di Arechi, Salerno; 900l. Castello di Saint-Pierre, Aosta; 1000l. Montagnana, Padua; 1400l. Caldoresco Castle, Vasto.

1980. Italian Ship-building (4th series). As T 601. Multicoloured.

1691		200l. Corvette "Gabbiano"	1·60	30
1692		200l. Destroyer "Audace"	1·60	30
1693		200l. Barque "Italia"	1·60	30
1694		200l. Pipe-layer "Castoro Sei"	1·60	30

645 Filippo Mazzei

1980. 250th Birth Anniv of Filippo Mazzei (writer and American revolutionary).

1695	**645**	320l. multicoloured	80	30

646 Villa Foscari Malcontenta, Venice

1980. Italian Villas (1st series). Multicoloured.

1696		80l. Type **646**	65	35
1697		150l. Barbaro Maser, Treviso	1·20	30
1698		170l. Godi Valmarana, Vicenza	1·40	25

See also Nos. 1737/9, 1770/2, 1811/14, 1853/6, 1893/6 and 1943/7.

1980. Italian Artists Anniversaries (7th series). As T 567. Multicoloured.

1699		520l. "Saint Barbara" (Jacopo Palma, the Elder (1480–1528))	95	65
1700		520l. "Apollo and Daphne" (Gian Lorenzo Bernini (1598–1680))	95	65

647 "Nativity" (Federico Brandani)

1980. Christmas.

1701	**647**	120l. green and brown	40	30

648 "My Town" (Treviso)

1980. Stamp Day. Paintings by Schoolchildren entitled "My Town". Multicoloured.

1702		70l. Type **648**	20	15
1703		120l. Sansepolcro	40	15
1704		170l. Sansepolcro (different)	55	25

649 Daniele Comboni and African Village

1981. 150th Birth Anniv and Death Centenary of Daniele Comboni (missionary).

1705	**649**	80l. brown, indigo and blue	30	30

650 Alcide de Gasperi

1981. Birth Centenary of Alcide de Gasperi (politician).

1706	**650**	200l. green	30	30

651 Landscape outlined by Person in Wheelchair

1981. International Year of Disabled Persons.

1707	**651**	300l. multicoloured	70	30

652 Anemone

1981. Flowers (1st series). Multicoloured.

1708		200l. Type **652**	40	30
1709		200l. Oleander	40	30
1710		200l. Rose	40	30

See also Nos. 1753/5 and 1797/9.

653 Human Chess Game, Marostica

1981. Europa. Multicoloured.

1711	300l. Type **653**	4·00	30
1712	300l. "Il Palio" horse race, Siena	4·00	30

654 St. Rita of Cascia

1981. 600th Birth Anniv of St. Rita of Cascia.

1713	**654**	600l. multicoloured	1·20	60

655 Ciro Menotti

1981. 150th Death Anniv of Ciro Menotti (patriot).

1714	**655**	80l. black and brown	30	30

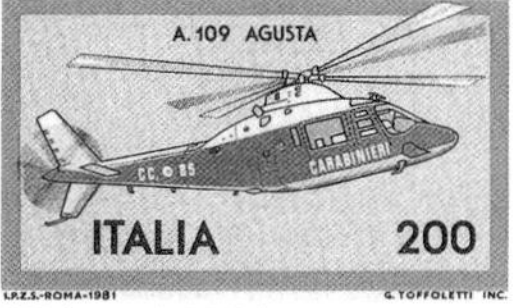

656 Agusta A.109 Helicopter

1981. Italian Aircraft (1st series). Multicoloured.

1715	200l. Type **656**	55	30
1716	200l. Partenavia P.68B Victor-PART airplane	55	30
1717	200l. Aeritalia G.222 transport	55	30
1718	200l. Aermacchi MB 339 jet trainer	55	30

See also Nos. 1748/51 and 1792/5.

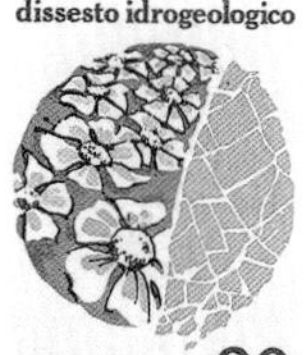

657 Fertile and Barren Soil

1981. Water Conservation.

1719	**657**	80l. multicoloured	35	30

1981. Italian Work for the World (2nd series). As T 640.

1720	300l. blue	70	40
1721	300l. red	70	40

DESIGNS: No. 1720, Sao Simao, Brazil; No. 1721, High Island, Hong Kong.

1981. Tourist Publicity (8th series). As T 556. Multicoloured.

1722	80l. Matera	20	50
1723	150l. Riva del Garda	35	1·20
1724	300l. Santa Teresa di Gallura	75	50
1725	900l. Tarquinia	2·20	90

658 Naval Academy and Badge

1981. Centenary of Naval Academy, Livorno. Multicoloured.

1726	80l. Type **658**	20	10
1727	150l. Aerial view of Academy	40	50
1728	200l. "Amerigo Vespucci" (cadet ship) and sailor using sextant	55	25

659 Spada Palace, Rome, and Decorative Motif from Grand Hall

1981. 150th Anniv of Council of State.

1729	**659**	200l. brown, green & blue	40	30

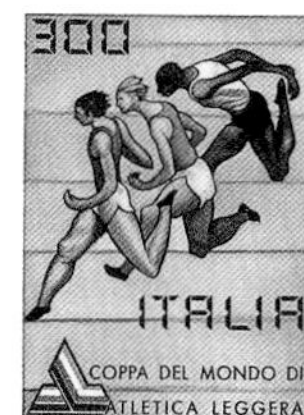

660 Running

1981. World Cup Light Athletics Championships, Rome.

1730	**660**	300l. multicoloured	80	30

1981. Italian Artists' Annivs (8th series). As T 567. Multicoloured.

1731	200l. "Harbour" (Carlo Carra (1881–1966))	40	35
1732	200l. "Nightfall" (Giuseppe Ugonia (1881–1944))	45	35

661 Riace Bronze

1981. Riace Bronzes (ancient Greek statues). Multicoloured.

1733	200l. Type **661**	70	40
1734	200l. Riace bronze (different)	70	40

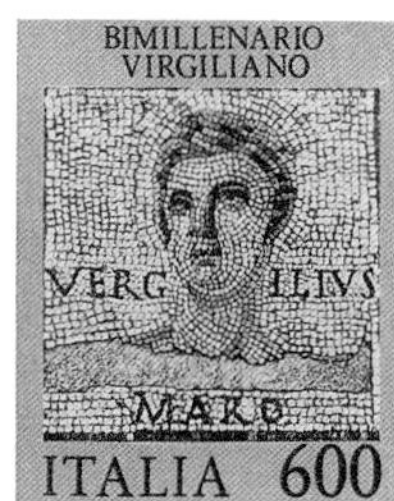

662 Virgil (Treviri mosaic)

1981. Death Bimillenary of Virgil (poet).

1735	**662**	600l. multicoloured	1·30	45

663 "Still-life" (Gregorio Sciltian)

1981. World Food Day.

1736	**663**	150l. multicoloured	45	30

1981. Italian Villas (2nd series). As T 646. Multicoloured.

1737	100l. Villa Campolieto, Ercolano	25	25
1738	200l. Villa Cimbrone, Ravello	45	25
1739	300l. Villa Pignatelli, Naples	1·10	35

664 "Adoration of the Magi" (Giovanni da Campione d'Italia)

1981. Christmas.

1740	**664**	200l. dp blue, brown & bl	45	30

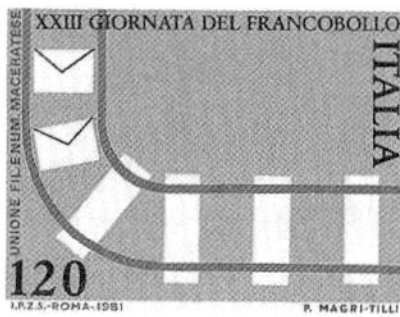

665 Pope John XXIII

1981. Birth Centenary of Pope John XXIII.

1741	**665**	200l. multicoloured	80	30

666 Envelopes forming Railway Track

1981. Stamp Day.

1742	**666**	120l. green, red and black	20	50
1743	-	200l. multicoloured	45	65
1744	-	300l. multicoloured	95	30

DESIGNS—VERT: 200l. Caduceus, chest, envelopes and cherub blowing posthorn. HORIZ: 300l. Letter seal.

667 "St. Francis receiving the Stigmata" (Pietro Cavaro)

1982. 800th Birth Anniv of St. Francis of Assisi.

1745	**667**	300l. brown and blue	80	30

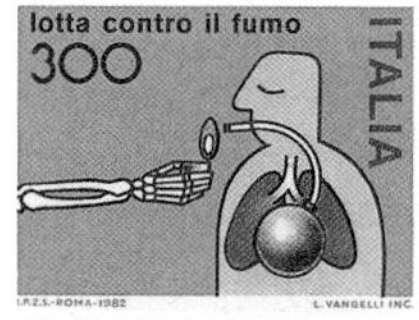

668 Paganini (after Ingres)

1982. Birth Bicentenary of Niccolo Paganini (composer and violinist).

1746	**668**	900l. multicoloured	2·10	90

669 Skeletal Hand lighting Cigarette "Bomb"

1982. Anti-smoking Campaign.

1747	**669**	300l. multicoloured	60	30

1982. Italian Aircraft (2nd series). As T 656. Multicoloured.

1748	300l. Panavia (inscr "Aeritalia") MRCA Tornado jet fighter	1·60	65
1749	300l. Savoia SIAI 260 Turbo I-FAIR trainer	1·60	65
1750	300l. Piaggio P-166 DL-3 Turbo I-PIAE	1·60	65

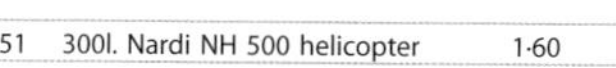

1751	300l. Nardi NH 500 helicopter	1·60	65

670 Church of Santo Spirito o del Vespro, Palermo

1982. 700th Anniv of Sicilian Vespers (uprising).

1752	**670**	120l. red, blue and purple	35	30

1982. Flowers (2nd series). As T 652. Mult.

1753	300l. Camellias	90	90
1754	300l. Carnations	90	90
1755	300l. Cyclamen	90	90

671 Coronation of Charlemagne, 799

1982. Europa.

1756	**671**	200l. brown, black & blue	4·00	1·20
1757	-	450l. multicoloured	4·00	65

DESIGN: 450l. Stars and signatures to Treaty of Rome, 1957.

1982. Italian Work for the World (3rd series). As T 640. Multicoloured.

1758	450l. Radio communication across Red Sea	1·20	30
1759	450l. Automatic letter sorting	1·20	30

672 Garibaldi

1982. Death Centenary of Giuseppe Garibaldi.

1760	**672**	200l. multicoloured	1·10	70

673 Bridge Game, Pisa

1982. Folk Customs (1st series).

1761	**673**	200l. multicoloured	45	35

See also Nos. 1804, 1850, 1875/6, 1914, 1972, 2004, 2028 and 2092.

1982. Tourist Publicity (9th series). As T 556. Multicoloured.

1762	200l. Frasassi Grotto	45	75
1763	200l. Fai della Paganella	45	75
1764	450l. Rodi Garganico	1·40	50
1765	450l. Temples of Agrigento	1·40	50

674 Coxless Four

1982. World Junior Rowing Championships.

1766	**674**	200l. multicoloured	45	35

675 Ducal Palace, Urbino, Montefeltro and Palazzo dei Consoli, Gubbio

1982. 500th Death Anniv of Federico da Montefeltro, Duke of Urbino.
1767 **675** 200l. multicoloured 45 35

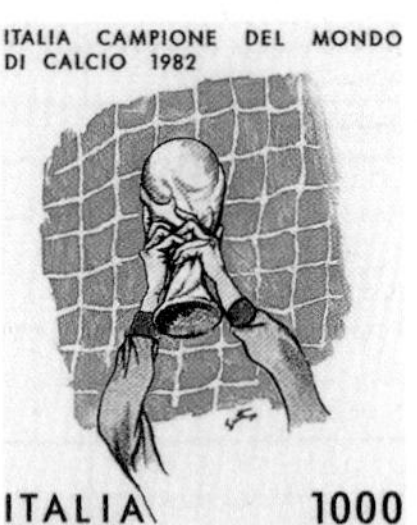

676 Footballer holding aloft World Cup

1982. Italy's World Cup Football Victory.
1768 **676** 1000l. multicoloured 2·40 1·20

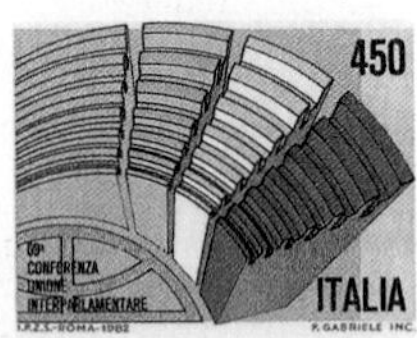

677 Seating Plan

1982. 69th Interparliamentary Union Conference.
1769 **677** 450l. multicoloured 80 30

1982. Italian Villas (3rd series). As T 646. Multicoloured.
1770 150l. Temple of Aesculapius, Villa Borghese, Rome 40 65
1771 250l. Villa D'Este, Tivoli 1·40 35
1772 350l. Villa Lante, Bagnaia, Viterbo 3·00 1·80

678 Francis of Taxis

1982. Commemoration of Establishment of First Public Postal System in Europe.
1773 **678** 300l. red, blue & verm 80 30

1982. Italian Artists' Annivs (9th series). As T 567. Multicoloured.
1774 300l. "Portrait of Antonietta Negroni Prati Morosini as a Child" (Francesco Hayez (1791–1882)) 1·00 60
1775 300l. "The Fortuneteller" (Giovanni Piazzetta (1682–1754)) 1·00 60

679 Tree, Chair and Bed (Maria di Pastena)

1983. Stamp Day. Timber in Human Life. Drawings by Schoolchildren. Multicoloured.
1776 150l. Type **679** 35 35
1777 250l. Tree with timber products in branches (Lucia Andreoli) 60 35
1778 350l. Forest (Marco Gallea) 80 65

680 Microscope

1983. Cancer Control.
1779 **680** 400l. multicoloured 1·30 40

1983. Italian Work for the World (4th series). Automobile Industry. As T 640. Multicoloured.
1780 400l. Factories on globe 1·20 50
1781 400l. Assembly line 1·20 50

681 Academy Emblem

1983. 400th Anniv of Accademia della Crusca (Florentine Academy of Letters).
1782 **681** 400l. red, brown and blue 95 40

682 Shooting

1983. World Biathlon Championships, Antholz.
1783 **682** 200l. multicoloured 80 40

683 Gabriele Rossetti

1983. Birth Centenary of Gabriele Rossetti (poet).
1784 **683** 300l. blue and brown 80 35

684 Guicciardini (after G. Bugiardini)

1983. 500th Birth Anniv of Francesco Guicciardini (lawyer and diplomat).
1785 **684** 450l. brown 1·10 45

685 Saba and Trieste

1983. Birth Centenary of Umberto Saba (poet).
1786 **685** 600l. multicoloured 1·60 35

686 Pope Pius XII

1983. 25th Death Anniv of Pope Pius XII.
1787 **686** 1400l. blue 3·50 1·50

687 Pope and St. Paul's Basilica

1983. Holy Year. Multicoloured.
1788 250l. Type **687** 70 45
1789 300l. Pope John Paul II and Basilica of Santa Maria Maggiore 80 30
1790 400l. Pope and St. John's Basilica 1·00 25
1791 500l. Pope and St. Peter's Cathedral. 1·40 25

1983. Italian Aircraft (3rd series). As T 656. Multicoloured.
1792 400l. Savoia SIAI 211 I-SUE 1·40 65
1793 400l. Agusta A.129 Mangusta helicopter 1·40 65
1794 400l. Caproni C22J glider I-CAVJ 1·40 65
1795 400l. Aeritalia/Aermacchi AM-X jet fighter 1·40 65

688 Launch of Ship

1983. Labour Day.
1796 **688** 1200l. blue 2·75 35

1983. Flowers (3rd series). As T 652. Mult.
1797 200l. Gladiolus 1·10 60
1798 200l. Mimosa 1·10 60
1799 200l. Rhododendron 1·10 60

689 Galileo (after O. Leoni) and Telescope

1983. Europa. Multicoloured.
1800 400l. Type **689** 15·00 1·70
1801 500l. Archimedes (marble bust) and screw 15·00 1·30

690 Moneta and Doves

1983. 150th Birth Anniv of Ernesto Teodoro Moneta (Nobel Peace Prize winner).
1802 **690** 500l. multicoloured 1·10 35

691 Quadriga, Globe and V.D.U.

1983. 3rd International Juridical Information Congress, Rome.
1803 **691** 500l. multicoloured 1·30 35

1983. Folk Customs (2nd series). As T 673. Multicoloured.
1804 300l. Ceri procession, Gubbio 1·10 35

692 Elevation of Host

1983. 20th National Eucharistic Congress, Milan.
1805 **692** 300l. multicoloured 80 35

1983. Tourist Publicity (10th series). As T 556. Multicoloured.
1806 250l. Alghero 95 1·20
1807 300l. Bardonecchia 1·10 1·20
1808 400l. Riccione 1·60 75
1809 500l. Taranto 1·90 50

693 Frescobaldi

1983. 400th Birth Anniv of Girolamo Frescobaldi (composer).
1810 **693** 400l. green, blue & brn 80 35

1983. Italian Villas (4th series). As T 646. Multicoloured.
1811 250l. Villa Fidelia, Spello 1·10 2·40
1812 300l. Villa Imperiale, Pesaro 1·40 30
1813 400l. Michetti Convent, Francavilla al Mare 1·80 25
1814 500l. Villa di Riccia 2·20 25

694 Francesco de Sanctis

1983. Death Centenary of Francesco de Sanctis (writer).
1815 **694** 300l. multicoloured 1·10 35

695 "Madonna of the Chair"

1983. Christmas. 500th Birth Anniv of Raphael (artist). Multicoloured.
1816 250l. Type **695** 35 35
1817 400l. "Sistine Madonna" 75 25
1818 500l. "Madonna of the Candles" 1·90 25

696 Chain of Letters (Roberta Rizzi)

1983. Stamp Day. Drawings by school-children. Multicoloured.
1819 200l. Type **696** 60 50
1820 300l. Space postman delivering letter (Maria Grazia Federico) (vert) 95 35
1821 400l. Steam train leaving envelope and globe (Paolo Bucciarelli) 1·20 30

697 Battered Road Sign

1984. Road Safety. Multicoloured.

1822	300l. Type **697**	80	45
1823	400l. Crashed car and policeman	1·10	60

1984. Italian Artists Anniversaries (10th series). As T 567. Multicoloured.

1824	300l. "Races at Bois de Boulogne" (Giuseppe de Nittis (1846–84))	1·00	60
1825	400l. "Paul Guillaume" (Amedeo Modigliani (1884–1920))	1·50	80

698 Maserati "Biturbo"

1984. Italian Motor Industry (1st series). Multicoloured.

1826	450l. Type **698**	2·50	50
1827	450l. Iveco "190.38 Special" lorry	2·50	50
1828	450l. Same Trattori "Galaxy" tractor	2·50	50
1829	450l. Alfa "33"	2·50	50

See also Nos. 1867/70 and 1933/6.

699 Glassblower, Glasses and Jug

1984. Italian Work for the World (5th series). Ceramic and Glass Industries. Multicoloured.

1830	300l. Ceramic plaque and furnace	95	30
1831	300l. Type **699**	95	30

700 European Parliament Building, Strasbourg

1984. Second European Parliament Direct Elections.

1832	**700**	400l. multicoloured	95	70

701 State Forest Corps Hughes 500 Helicopter

1984. Nature Protection. Forests. Multicoloured.

1833	450l. Type **701**	3·50	75
1834	450l. Forest animals and burning cigarette	3·50	75
1835	450l. River and litter	3·50	75
1836	450l. Wildlife and building construction	3·50	75

702 Ministry of Posts and Telecommunications, Rome

1984. "Italia '85" International Stamp Exhibition, Rome (1st issue). Multicoloured.

1837	450l. Type **702**	1·20	30
1838	550l. Appian Way	1·30	30

See also Nos. 1857/9, 1862/4, 1871/3 and 1898/1911.

703 G. di Vittorio, B. Buozzi and A. Grandi

1984. 40th Anniv of Rome Pact (foundation of Italian Trade Unions).

1839	**703**	450l. multicoloured	1·30	60

704 Bridge

1984. Europa. 25th Anniv of European Post and Telecommunications Conference.

1840	**704**	450l. multicoloured	13·50	2·30
1841	**704**	550l. multicoloured	17·00	5·75

705 Symposium Emblem

1984. Int Telecommunications Symposium, Florence.

1842	**705**	550l. multicoloured	1·60	85

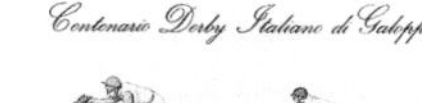

706 Horse-race

1984. Centenary of Italian Derby. Multicoloured.

1843	250l. Type **706**	2·00	1·70
1844	400l. Horse-race (different)	3·25	80

1984. Tourist Publicity (11th series). As T 556. Multicoloured.

1845	350l. Campione d'Italia	1·80	2·10
1846	400l. Chiancianco Terme	1·90	90
1847	450l. Padula	2·20	90
1848	550l. Syracuse	2·75	1·00

1984. Folk Customs (3rd series). As T 673. Multicoloured.

1850	400l. Procession of Shrine of Santa Rosa, Viterbo	1·20	30

708 Harvester, Thresher and Medieval Fields Map

1984. Peasant Farming. Multicoloured.

1851	250l. Type **708**	65	45
1852	350l. Hand oil press, cart and medieval fields map	90	70

1984. Italian Villas (5th series). As T 646. Multicoloured.

1853	250l. Villa Caristo, Stignano	1·60	1·20
1854	350l. Villa Doria Pamphili, Genoa	2·20	90
1855	400l. Villa Reale, Stupinigi	2·50	1·00
1856	450l. Villa Mellone, Lecce	3·00	1·20

709 Etruscan Bronze of Warrior

1984. "Italia '85" International Stamp Exhibition, Rome (2nd issue). Multicoloured.

1857	550l. Type **709**	1·70	60
1858	550l. Exhibition emblem	1·70	60
1859	550l. Etruscan silver-backed mirror	1·70	60

710 Dish Aerial, Globe and Punched Tape

1985. Information Technology.

1860	**710**	350l. multicoloured	80	45

711 Man helping Old Woman

1985. Problems of Elderly People.

1861	**711**	250l. multicoloured	60	45

712 "Venus in her Chariot" (fresco, Raphael)

1985. "Italia '85" International Stamp Exhibition, Rome (3rd issue). Multicoloured.

1862	600l. Type **712**	1·70	35
1863	600l. Exhibition emblem	1·70	35
1864	600l. Warriors (detail of fresco, Baldassare Peruzzi)	1·70	35

713 Plate, Vase and Pot

1985. Italian Work for the World (6th series). Ceramics. Multicoloured.

1865	600l. Type **713**	1·90	35
1866	600l. Decorated plate	1·90	35

1985. Italian Motor Industry (2nd series). As T 698. Multicoloured.

1867	450l. Fiat "Uno"	4·50	65
1868	450l. Lamborghini "Countach LP500"	4·50	65
1869	450l. Lancia "Thema"	4·50	65
1870	450l. Fiat Abarth "100 Bialbero"	4·50	65

714 St. Mary of Peace Church, Rome

1985. "Italia '85" International Stamp Exhibition, Rome (4th issue). Baroque Art. Multicoloured.

1871	250l. Type **714**	85	50
1872	250l. Exhibition emblem	85	50
1873	250l. Fountain obelisk and Saint Agnes's Church, Rome	85	50

715 Pope Sixtus V

1985. 400th Anniv of Election of Pope Sixtus V.

1874	**715**	1500l. multicoloured	3·50	2·10

1985. Folk Customs (4th series). As T 673. Multicoloured.

1875	250l. March of the Turks, Potenza	1·20	75
1876	350l. Republican regatta, Amalfi	1·70	75

1985. Tourist Publicity (12th series). As T 556. Multicoloured.

1877	350l. Bormio	90	1·20
1878	400l. Castellammare di Stabia	1·30	50
1879	450l. Stromboli	1·60	50
1880	600l. Termoli	4·25	85

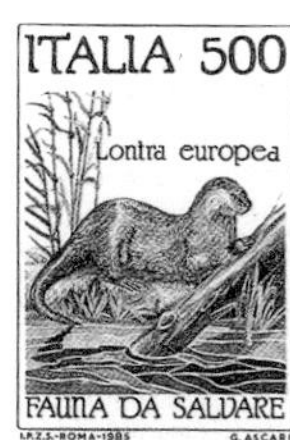

716 European Otter

1985. Nature Protection. Multicoloured.

1881	500l. Type **716**	4·25	65
1882	500l. Primulas	4·25	65
1883	500l. Fir tree	4·25	65
1884	500l. Black-winged stilts	4·25	65

1985. Anniversaries of Italian Artists (11th series). As T 567. Multicoloured.

1885	350l. "Madonna" (Giambattista Salvi (1609–85))	1·70	1·30
1886	400l. "The Pride of Work" (Mario Sironi (1885–1961))	2·10	1·10

717 Aureliano Pertile and Giovanni Martinelli (singers)

1985. Europa. Music Year. Multicoloured.

1887	500l. Type **717**	13·00	1·20
1888	600l. Vicenzo Bellini and Johann Sebastian Bach (composers)	17·00	1·70

718 San Salvatore Abbey

1985. 950th Anniv of San Salvatore Abbey, Mt. Amiata.

1889	**718**	450l. multicoloured	1·20	35

719 Cyclists

1985. World Cycling Championships, Bassano del Grappa.

1890	**719**	400l. multicoloured	1·90	45

720 U.N. and Congress Emblems and Globe

1985. 7th United Nations Crime Prevention Congress, Milan.

1891 **720** 600l. multicoloured 1·90 45

721 Profile and Emblem

1985. International Youth Year.

1892 **721** 600l. multicoloured 1·90 45

1985. Villas (6th series). As T 646. Multicoloured.

1893 300l. Villa Nitti, Maratea 1·90 75
1894 400l. Villa Aldrovandi Mazzacorati, Bologna 2·50 30
1895 500l. Villa Santa Maria, Pula 3·00 45
1896 600l. Villa de Mersi, Villazzano 3·75 50

722 State Emblems of Italy and Vatican City and Medallion (Mario Soccorsi)

1985. Ratification of the Modification of 1929 Lateran Concordat.

1897 **722** 400l. multicoloured 1·10 45

723 Parma Town Hall and 1857 25c. Stamp

724 Basel 1845 2½r. Stamp

1985. "Italia '85" International Stamp Exhibition. Rome (5th issue). Multicoloured. (a) As T 723.

1898 300l. Type **723** 70 45
1899 300l. Naples New Castle and 1858 2g. stamp 70 45
1900 300l. Palermo Cathedral and Sicily 1859 ½g. stamp 70 45
1901 300l. Modena Cathedral and 1852 15c. stamp 70 45
1902 300l. Piazzo Navona, Rome, and Papal States 1852 7b. stamp 70 45
1903 300l. Palazzo Vecchio, Florence, and Tuscany 1851 2c. stamp 70 45
1904 300l. Turin and Sardinia 1861 3l. stamp 70 45
1905 300l. Bologna and Romagna 1859 6b. stamp 70 45
1906 300l. Palazzo Litta, Milan, and Lombardy and Venetia 1850 15c. stamp 70 45

(b) As T 724.

1907 500l. Type **724** 3·25 50
1908 500l. Japan 1871 48m. stamp 3·25 50
1909 500l. United States 1847 10c. stamp 3·25 50
1910 500l. Western Australia 1854 1d. stamp 3·25 50
1911 500l. Mauritius 1848 2d. stamp 3·25 50

(c) Sheet 86×56 mm. Imperf.

MS1912 4000l. Sardinia 1851 5c. stamp and Great Britain "Penny Black" 7·50 7·50

725 Skiers

1986. Cross-country Skiing.

1913 **725** 450l. multicoloured 1·20 45

1986. Folk Customs (5th series). As T 673. Multicoloured.

1914 450l. Le Candelore, Catania 1·20 30

726 Amilcare Ponchielli and Scene from "La Gioconda"

1986. Composers. Multicoloured.

1915 2000l. Type **726** (death centenary) 5·25 90
1916 2000l. Giovan Battista Pergolesi (250th death anniv) 5·25 90

727 Acitrezza

1986. Tourist Publicity (13th series). Mult.

1917 350l. Type **727** 1·30 60
1918 450l. Capri 1·70 90
1919 550l. Merano 2·10 35
1920 650l. San Benedetto del Tronto 2·50 65

728 Heart-shaped Tree (life)

1986. Europa. Multicoloured.

1921 650l. Type **728** 8·25 50
1922 650l. Star-shaped tree (poetry) 8·25 50
1923 650l. Butterfly-shaped tree (colour) 8·25 50
1924 650l. Sun-shaped tree (energy) 8·25 50

729 "Eyes"

1986. 25th International Ophthalmology Congress, Rome.

1925 **729** 550l. multicoloured 1·20 30

730 Italian Police

1986. European Police Meeting, Chianciano Terme.

1926 **730** 550l. multicoloured 3·00 1·40
1927 **730** 650l. multicoloured 3·50 1·60

731 Battle Scene

1986. 120th Anniv of Battle of Bezzecca.

1928 **731** 550l. multicoloured 1·60 60

732 Figure with Flag

1986. National Independence Martyrs' Day.

1929 **732** 2000l. multicoloured 5·25 90

733 Bersagliere and Helmets

1986. 150th Anniv of Turin Bersaglieri Corps (alpine troops).

1930 **733** 450l. multicoloured 1·60 50

734 Dish Aerial, Transmitter and "Messages"

1986. Telecommunications.

1931 **734** 350l. multicoloured 80 60

735 Varallo

1986. Holy Mountain of Varallo.

1932 **735** 2000l. green and blue 5·25 90

1986. Italian Motor Industry (3rd series). As T 698. Multicoloured.

1933 450l. Alfa Romeo "AR 8 Turbo" 4·25 1·20
1934 450l. Innocenti "650 SE" 4·25 75
1935 450l. Ferrari "Testarossa" 4·25 75
1936 450l. Fiatallis "FR 10B" 4·25 75

736 Clothes and Woman (fashion)

1986. Italian Work for the World (7th series). Mult.

1937 450l. Type **736** 3·00 50
1938 450l. Man and clothes (fashion) 3·00 50
1939 650l. Olivetti personal computer, keyboard and screen 4·50 50
1940 650l. Breda steam turbine 4·50 50

737 Airplane flying through "40"

1986. 40th Anniv of Alitalia (national airline). Multicoloured.

1941 550l. Type **737** 1·70 30
1942 650l. Airplane and landing lights 2·10 45

1986. Italian Villas (7th series). As T 646. Mult.

1943 350l. Villa Necker, Trieste 1·20 75
1944 350l. Villa Borromeo, Cassana d'Adda 1·20 75
1945 450l. Villa Palagonia, Bagheria 1·40 65
1946 550l. Villa Medicea, Poggio a Caiano 1·80 50
1947 650l. Issogne Castle 2·20 75

738 "Madonna and Child" (bronze sculpture by Donatello)

1986. Christmas.

1948 **738** 450l. bistre 1·20 30

1986. Anniversaries of Italian Artists (12th series). As T 567.

1949 450l. black and orange 2·10 30
1950 550l. multicoloured 3·00 50

DESIGNS: 450l. Drawing of woman (Andrea del Sarto (1486–1531)); 550l. "Daphne at Pavarola" (Felice Casorati (1883–1963)).

739 Lockheed C130 Hercules Transport dropping Squares in National Colours onto Globe

1986. International Peace Year. Multicoloured.

1951 550l. Type **739** 1·70 45
1952 650l. Airplane, Cross and people (commemoration of Italian airmen killed on mission to Kindu, Congo) 2·00 50

740 Engraving 1862 Stamp

1986. Stamp Day. Francesco Maria Matraire (engraver).

1953 **740** 550l. multicoloured 1·90 30

741 Woven Threads (Marzotto Textile Industry)

1987. Italian Industry.

1954 **741** 700l. multicoloured 1·90 90
1955 - 700l. blue and turquoise 1·90 90

DESIGN: No. 1955, Clouds and flame (Italgas Gas Corporation).

742 River Volturno

1987. Nature Protection. Rivers and Lakes. Multicoloured.

1956 500l. Type **742** 3·00 35
1957 500l. Lake Garda 3·00 35
1958 500l. Lake Trasimeno 3·00 35
1959 500l. River Tirso 3·00 35

743 Gramsci

1987. 50th Death Anniv of Antonio Gramsci (politician).

1960	**743**	600l. grey, black and red	2·10	45

744 Church of the Motorway of the Sun, Florence (Giovanni Michelucci)

1987. Europa. Architecture. Multicoloured.

1961	600l. Type **744**	9·00	90
1962	700l. Termini station, Rome (Nervi)	11·50	90

1987. Tourist Publicity (14th series). As T 556. Multicoloured.

1963	380l. Verbania Pallanza	1·40	65
1964	400l. Palmi	1·70	90
1965	500l. Vasto	2·10	65
1966	600l. Villacidro	2·50	65

745 View of Naples on Football

1987. S.S.C. Naples, National Football Champion, 1986–87.

1967	**745**	500l. multicoloured	3·00	1·60

746 "The Absinthe Drinker" (Edgar Degas)

1987. Anti-alcoholism Campaign.

1968	**746**	380l. multicoloured	1·60	60

747 Liguori and Gulf of Naples

1987. Death Bicentenary of St. Alfonso Maria de Liguori (co-founder of Redemptorists).

1969	**747**	400l. multicoloured	1·10	35

748 Emblem and Olympic Stadium, Rome

1987. World Light Athletics Championships, Rome (1970) and "Olymphilex '87" Stamp Exhibition, Rome (1971).

1970	700l. Type **748**	1·60	25
1971	700l. International Olympic Committee building, Foro Italico, Rome	1·60	25

1987. Folk Customs (6th series). As T 673. Multicoloured.

1972	380l. Joust, Foligno	1·20	45

749 Piazza del Popolo, Ascoli Piceno

1987. Piazzas (1st series). Multicoloured.

1973	380l. Type **749**	1·20	65
1974	500l. Piazza Giuseppe Verdi, Palermo	1·40	25
1975	600l. Piazza San Carlo, Turin	1·70	35
1976	700l. Piazza dei Signori, Verona	2·00	65

See also Nos. 2002/3 and 2023/4.

750 "The Adoration in the Manger" (St. Francis's Basilica, Assisi)

1987. Christmas. Frescoes by Giotto. Mult.

1977	500l. Type **750**	1·70	35
1978	600l. "Epiphany" (Scrovegni Chapel, Padua)	2·10	35

751 Battle Scene

1987. 120th Anniv of Battle of Mentana.

1979	**751**	380l. multicoloured	1·60	60

752 "Christ Pantocrator" (mosaic, Monreale Cathedral)

1987. Artistic Heritage. Multicoloured.

1980	500l. Type **752**	2·30	65
1981	500l. San Carlo Theatre, Naples (18th-century engraving)	2·30	65

753 College and 1787 and 1987 Uniforms

1987. Bicentenary of Nunziatella Military Academy, Naples.

1982	**753**	600l. multicoloured	1·90	45

754 Marco de Marchi (philatelist) and Milan Cathedral

1987. Stamp Day.

1983	**754**	500l. multicoloured	2·00	45

755 Man chipping Flints

1988. "Homo aeserniensis".

1984	**755**	500l. multicoloured	1·20	60

756 Lyceum

1988. E.Q. Visconti Lyceum, Rome.

1985	**756**	500l. multicoloured	1·20	45

See also Nos. 2019, 2109 and 2127.

757 Statue, Bosco and Boy

1988. Death Centenary of St. John Bosco (founder of Salesian Brothers).

1986	**757**	500l. multicoloured	1·20	45

1988. Anniversaries of Italian Artists (13th series). As T 567. Multicoloured.

1987	650l. "Archaeologists" (Giorgio de Chirico (1888–1978))	2·50	70

758 15th-Century Soncino Bible

1988. 500th Anniv of First Printing of Bible in Hebrew.

1988	**758**	550l. multicoloured	1·40	45

759 St. Valentine, Epileptics and Wave Patterns

1988. Anti-epilepsy Campaign.

1989	**759**	500l. multicoloured	1·20	60

760 ETR 450 High Speed Train in Station

1988. Europa. Transport and Communications. Multicoloured.

1990	650l. Type **760**	7·25	1·70
1991	750l. Map and keyboard operator (electronic postal systems)	8·25	2·30

1988. Tourist Publicity (15th series). As T 556. Multicoloured.

1992	400l. Castiglione della Pescaia	1·20	90
1993	500l. Lignano Sabbiadoro	1·40	75
1994	650l. St. Domenico's Church, Noto	1·80	90
1995	750l. Vieste	2·20	1·10

761 Golfer on Ball

1988. Golf.

1996	**761**	500l. multicoloured	1·20	35

762 Stadium and Mascot

1988. World Cup Football Championship, Italy (1990) (1st issue).

1997	**762**	3150l. multicoloured	6·25	3·50

See also Nos. 2049 and 2052/87.

763 Milan Cathedral on Football

1988. A. C. Milan. National Football Champion, 1987–88.

1998	**763**	650l. multicoloured	1·10	85

764 Horse's Head

1988. Artistic Heritage. Pergola Bronzes. Multicoloured.

1999	500l. Type **764**	90	60
2000	650l. Bust of woman	1·20	80

765 Student (bas-relief)

1988. 900th Anniv of Bologna University.

2001	**765**	500l. violet	1·20	45

1988. Piazzas (2nd series). As T 749. Mult.

2002	400l. Piazza del Duomo, Pistoia	1·60	75
2003	550l. Piazza del Unita d'Italia, Trieste	2·30	50

1988. Folk Customs (7th series). As T 673. Multicoloured.

2004	500l. Candle procession, Sassari	2·30	45

766 Emblem and Appian Way

1988. "Roma 88" Int Gastroenterology and Digestive Endoscopy Congress.

2005	**766**	750l. multicoloured	1·90	60

767 "Ossessione" (Luchino Visconti, 1942)

1988. Italian Films. Scenes from and Advertising Posters of named Films. Multicoloured.

2006	500l. Type **767**	1·40	1·50
2007	650l. "Ladri di Biciclette" (Vittorio de Sica, 1948)	1·80	1·80
2008	2400l. "Roma Citta Aperta" (Roberto Rossellini, 1945)	6·75	1·30
2009	3050l. "Riso Amaro" (Giuseppe de Santis, 1949)	8·75	2·50

768 Bird (aluminium)

1988. Italian Industry. Multicoloured.

2010	750l. Type **768**	1·60	65
2011	750l. Oscilloscope display (electronics)	1·60	65
2012	750l. Banknote engraving, 1986 tourism stamp and medals (60th anniv of State Polygraphic Institute)	1·60	65

769 "Holy Family" (Pasquale Celommi)

1988. Christmas (1st issue).

2013	**769**	650l. multicoloured	2·50	30

See also No. 2015.

770 Borromeo and Plague Victims

1988. 450th Birth Anniv of St. Carlo Borromeo, Archbishop of Milan.

2014	**770**	2400l. multicoloured	5·25	1·30

771 "Nativity" (bas-relief)

1988. Christmas (2nd issue).

2015	**771**	500l. green and brown	2·00	45

772 Edoardo Chiossone (stamp designer) and Japanese 1879 2s. "Koban" Stamp

1988. Stamp Day.

2016	**772**	500l. multicoloured	1·20	45

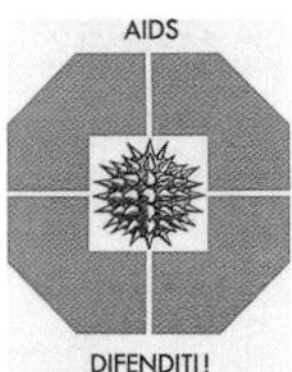

773 AIDS Virus

1989. Anti-AIDS Campaign.

2017	**773**	650l. multicoloured	1·60	25

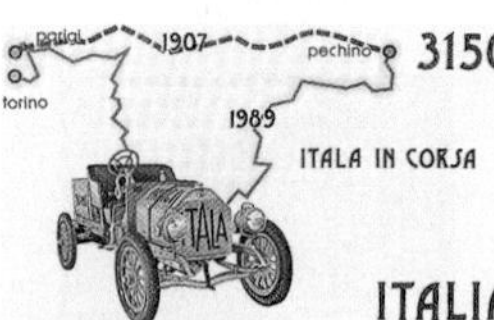

774 1907 Itala Car and Route Map

1989. Re-enactment of 1907 Peking–Paris Car Rally.

2018	**774**	3150l. multicoloured	7·25	4·50

1989. Giuseppe Parini Lyceum, Milan. As T 756.

2019	650l. multicoloured	1·60	45

776 Fresco, Ragione Palace, Padua

1989. Artistic Heritage.

2020	**776**	500l. multicoloured	1·60	75
2021	-	650l. blue	2·00	75

DESIGN: 650l. Crypt, Basilica of St. Nicolas, Bari.

777 Stylized Yachts

1989. World Sailing Championships, Alassio, Naples and Porto Cervo.

2022	**777**	3050l. multicoloured	7·25	2·10

1989. Piazzas (3rd series). As T 749. Mult.

2023	400l. Piazza di Spagna, Rome	1·10	75
2024	400l. Piazza del Duomo, Catanzaro	1·10	75

778 Leap-frog (Luca Rizzello)

1989. Europa. Children's Games. Mult.

2025	500l. Type **778**	4·00	65
2026	650l. Girl dressing up (Serena Forcuti) (vert)	5·25	50
2027	750l. Sack race (Adelise Lahner)	6·00	50

1989. Folk Customs (8th series). As T 673. Multicoloured.

2028	400l. Spello flower paintings	1·10	60

779 Cloisters

1989. Pisa University.

2029	**779**	500l. violet	1·20	50

780 Parliamentary Emblem as Tree on Map

1989. 3rd Direct Elections to European Parliament.

2030	**780**	500l. multicoloured	2·50	45

No. 2030 is also inscribed with the European Currency Unit rate of 0.31 ECU.

1989. Tourist Publicity (16th series). As T 556. Multicoloured.

2031	500l. Grottammare	1·50	85
2032	500l. Spotorno	1·50	85
2033	500l. Pompeii	1·50	85
2034	500l. Giardini Naxos	1·50	85

781 1889 5c. Savoy Arms Stamp

1989. Centenary of Ministry of Posts and Telecommunications. Multicoloured.

2035	500l. Type **781**	1·20	1·80
2036	2400l. Globe within posthorn	6·00	1·80

782 Ball and Club Emblem

1989. Inter Milan, National Football Champion, 1988–89.

2037	**782**	650l. multicoloured	1·20	60

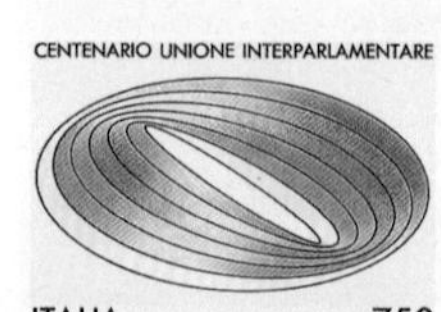

783 Stylized Chamber

1989. Centenary of Interparliamentary Union.

2038	**783**	750l. multicoloured	1·60	45

784 Phrygian Cap

1989. Bicentenary of French Revolution.

2039	**784**	3150l. multicoloured	7·00	4·50

785 Corinaldo Wall

1989. Artistic Heritage. 550th Birth Anniv of Francesco di Giorgio Martini (architect).

2040	**785**	500l. multicoloured	1·40	60

786 Chaplin in Film Scenes

1989. Birth Centenary of Charlie Chaplin (film actor and director).

2041	**786**	750l. black and brown	1·90	60

787 "Inauguration of Naples–Portici Line" (left-hand detail, S Fergola)

1989. 150th Anniv of Naples–Portici Railway. Multicoloured.

2042	550l. Type **787**	1·60	30
2043	550l. Right-hand detail	1·60	30

Nos. 2042/3 were printed together, se-tenant, forming a composite design.

788 Castelfidardo, Accordion and Stradella

1989. Italian Industry. Multicoloured.

2044	450l. Type **788**	1·10	65
2045	450l. Books (Arnoldo Mondadori Publishing House)	1·10	65

789 Madonna and Child

1989. Christmas. Details of "Adoration of the Magi" (Correggio). Multicoloured.

2046	500l. Type **789**	1·20	35
2047	500l. Magi	1·20	35

Nos. 2046/7 were printed together, se-tenant, forming a composite design.

790 Emilio Diena (stamp dealer)

1989. Stamp Day.

2048	**790**	500l. black, brown & blue	1·60	45

791 Monument (Mario Ceroli) and Football Pitch

1989. World Cup Football Championship, Italy (1990) (2nd issue).

2049	**791**	450l. multicoloured	1·10	70

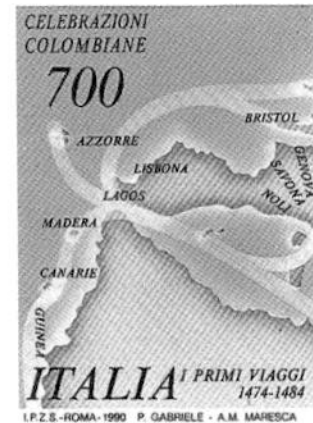

792 Old Map (left half) with Route superimposed

1990. Columbus's First Voyages, 1474–84. Multicoloured.

2050	700l. Type **792**	1·40	35
2051	700l. Right half of map	1·40	35

Nos. 2050/1 were printed together, se-tenant, forming a composite design.

793 Italy

1990. World Cup Football Championship, Italy (3rd issue). Designs showing finalists' emblems or playing venues. Multicoloured.

2052	450l. Type **793**	55	90
2053	450l. U.S.A.	55	90
2054	450l. Olympic Stadium, Rome	55	90
2055	450l. Comunale Stadium, Florence	55	90
2056	450l. Austria	55	90
2057	450l. Czechoslovakia	55	90
2058	600l. Argentina	75	75
2059	600l. U.S.S.R.	75	75
2060	600l. San Paolo Stadium, Naples	75	75
2061	600l. New Stadium, Bari	75	75
2062	600l. Cameroun	75	75
2063	600l. Rumania	75	75
2064	650l. Brazil	85	65
2065	650l. Costa Rica	85	65
2066	650l. Delle Alpi Stadium, Turin	85	65
2067	650l. Ferraris Stadium, Genoa	85	65
2068	650l. Sweden	85	65
2069	650l. Scotland	85	65
2070	700l. United Arab Emirates	90	45
2071	700l. West Germany	90	45
2072	700l. Dall'Ara Stadium, Bologna	90	45
2073	700l. Meazza Stadium, Milan	90	45
2074	700l. Colombia	90	45
2075	700l. Yugoslavia	90	45
2076	800l. Belgium	1·00	75
2077	800l. Uruguay	1·00	75
2078	800l. Bentegodi Stadium, Verona	1·00	75
2079	800l. Friuli Stadium, Udine	1·00	75
2080	800l. South Korea	1·00	75
2081	800l. Spain	1·00	75
2082	1200l. England	1·50	1·10
2083	1200l. Netherlands	1·50	1·10
2084	1200l. Sant'Elia Stadium, Cagliari	1·50	1·10
2085	1200l. La Favorita Stadium, Palermo	1·50	1·10
2086	1200l. Ireland	1·50	1·10
2087	1200l. Egypt	1·50	1·10

See also No. 2104.

1990. Tourist Publicity (17th series). As T 556. Multicoloured.

2088	600l. San Felice Circeo	1·30	65
2089	600l. Castellammare del Golfo	1·30	65
2090	600l. Montepulciano	1·30	65
2091	600l. Sabbioneta	1·30	65

1990. Folk Customs (9th series). As T 673. Multicoloured.

2092	600l. Avelignesi horse race, Merano	1·40	45

794 National Colours

1990. Death Centenary of Aurelio Saffi.

2093	**794**	700l. multicoloured	1·60	45

795 Giovanni Giorgi (inventor)

1990. 55th Anniv of Invention of Giorgi/MKSA System of Electrotechnical Units.

2094	**795**	600l. multicoloured	1·20	45

796 Flags, Globe and Workers (after "The Four States" (Pellizza da Volpedo))

1990. Centenary of Labour Day.

2095	**796**	600l. multicoloured	1·20	35

797 Ball on Map

1990. S. S. C. Naples, National Football Champion, 1989–90.

2096	**797**	700l. multicoloured	1·90	1·20

798 Piazza San Silvestro Post Office, Rome

1990. Europa. Post Office Buildings. Mult.

2097	700l. Type **798**	5·25	50
2098	800l. Fondaco Tedeschi post office, Venice	6·25	50

799 Paisiello

1990. 250th Birth Anniv of Giovanni Paisiello (composer).

2099	**799**	450l. multicoloured	1·10	45

800 Globe, Open Book and Bust of Dante

1990. Centenary of Dante Alighieri Society.

2100	**800**	700l. multicoloured	1·60	35

801 Byzantine Mosaic, Ravenna

1990. Artistic Heritage. Multicoloured.

2101	450l. Type **801**	1·00	75
2102	700l. "Christ and Angels" (detail of Rachis altar, Friuli) (Lombard art)	1·60	50

802 Malatestiana Temple, Rimini

1990. 40th Anniv of Malatestiana Religious Music Festival.

2103	**802**	600l. multicoloured	1·40	60

1990. West Germany, Winner of World Cup Football Championship. As No. 2071 but value changed and additionally inscr "CAMPIONE DEL MONDO".

2104	600l. multicoloured	1·90	70

803 "Still Life"

1990. Birth Cent of Giorgio Morandi (painter).

2105	**803**	750l. black	1·90	90

804 Ancient and Modern Wrestlers

1990. World Greco-Roman Wrestling Championships, Rome.

2106	**804**	3200l. multicoloured	6·75	1·30

805 "New Life" (Emidio Vangelli)

1990. Christmas. Multicoloured.

2107	600l. Type **805**	1·40	50
2108	750l. "Adoration of the Shepherds" (fresco by Pellegrino in St. Daniel's Church, Friuli)	1·80	50

806 Catania University

1990

2109	-	600l. multicoloured	1·40	50
2110	**806**	750l. blue and ultramarine	1·80	50

DESIGN—As T **756**: 600l. Bernardino Telesio High School, Cosenza.

807 Corrado Mezzana (stamp designer, self-portrait)

1990. Stamp Day.

2111	**807**	600l. multicoloured	1·60	60

808 Holy Family

1991. "The Living Tableau", Rivisondoli.

2112	**808**	600l. multicoloured	1·40	60

809 Fair Emblem

1991. "EuroFlora '91" Fair, Genoa.

2113	**809**	750l. multicoloured	1·60	35

810 Emblem

1991. 750th Anniv of Siena University.

2114	**810**	750l. gold, black and blue	1·60	35

1991. Tourist Publicity (18th series). As T 556. Multicoloured.

2115	600l. Cagli	1·30	65
2116	600l. La Maddalena	1·30	65
2117	600l. Roccaraso	1·30	65
2118	600l. Sanremo	1·30	65

812 City and Columbus's Fleet

1991. Europa Youth Meeting, Venice.

2119	**811**	750l. multicoloured	1·60	25

No. 2119 is also valued in ECUs (European Currency Unit).

1991. 500th Anniv (1992) of Discovery of America by Christopher Columbus (1st issue). Multicoloured.

2120	750l. Type **812**	1·40	35
2121	750l. Map, Columbus, seal and King and Queen of Spain	1·40	35

Nos. 2120/1 were printed together, se-tenant, forming a composite design.

See also Nos. 2151/4 and **MS**2158.

813 Belli and View of Rome

1991. Birth Bicentenary of Giuseppe Gioachino Belli (poet).
2122 **813** 600l. brown and blue 1·20 35

814 St Gregory's Church, Rome

1991. Artistic Heritage.
2123 **814** 3200l. multicoloured 7·75 1·50

815 "DRS" Satellite

1991. Europa. Europe in Space. Multicoloured.
2124 750l. Type **815** 6·25 90
2125 800l. "Hermes" spaceship and "Columbus" space station 6·50 50

816 Sta Maria Maggiore Church, Lanciano

1991. Artistic Heritage.
2126 **816** 600l. brown 1·20 60

1991. D. A. Azuni Lyceum, Sassari. As T 756.
2127 600l. multicoloured 1·20 60

817 Football and Genoa Lantern

1991. Sampdoria, National Football Champion, 1990–91.
2128 **817** 3000l. multicoloured 6·50 3·50

818 Hands and Ball

1991. Centenary of Basketball.
2129 **818** 500l. multicoloured 1·10 60

819 Children and Butterflies

1991. United Nations Conference on Rights of the Child. Multicoloured.
2130 600l. Type **819** 1·20 15
2131 750l. Child with balloon on man's shoulders 1·60 50

820 "Youth and Gulls" (sculpture, Pericle Fazzini)

1991. Artistic Heritage. Multicoloured.
2132 **820** 600l. yellow, blue & black 1·20 1·20
2133 - 3200l. multicoloured 6·50 1·50
DESIGN: 3200l. Palazzo Esposizioni, Turin (Pier Luigi Nervi (birth centenary)).

821 Winged Sphinx

1991. Egyptian Museum, Turin.
2134 **821** 750l. gold, green & yellow 1·90 35

822 Luigi Galvani (physiologist) and Experimental Equipment

1991. 100 Years of Radio (1st issue).
2135 **822** 750l. multicoloured 2·00 25
Galvani carried out experiments in electricity.
See also Nos. 2148, 2203, 2241 and 2321/2.

823 Mozart at Spinet

1991. Death Bicentenary of Wolfgang Amadeus Mozart (composer).
2136 **823** 800l. multicoloured 2·10 60

824 Bear

1991. Nature Protection. Multicoloured.
2137 500l. Type **824** 1·60 65
2138 500l. Peregrine falcon 1·60 65
2139 500l. Deer 1·60 65
2140 500l. Marine life 1·60 65

825 "The Angel of Life" (Giovanni Segantini)

1991. Christmas.
2141 **825** 600l. multicoloured 1·60 60

826 Giulio and Alberto Bolaffi (stamp catalogue publishers)

1991. Stamp Day.
2142 **826** 750l. multicoloured 1·60 45

827 Signature and National Flag

1991. Birth Cent of Pietro Nenni (politician).
2143 **827** 750l. multicoloured 1·60 60

828 Runners

1992. 22nd European Indoor Light Athletics Championships, Genoa.
2144 **828** 600l. multicoloured 1·30 60

829 Neptune Fountain, Florence

1992. 400th Death Anniv of Bartolomeo Ammannati (architect and sculptor).
2145 **829** 750l. multicoloured 1·60 60

830 Statue of Marchese Alberto V of Este (founder) and University

1992. 600th Anniv (1991) of Ferrara University.
2146 **830** 750l. multicoloured 1·60 60

831 Pediment

1992. Naples University.
2147 **831** 750l. multicoloured 1·60 45

1992. 100 Years of Radio (2nd issue). As T 822. Multicoloured.
2148 750l. Alessandro Volta (physicist) and Voltaic pile 2·20 60
Volta formulated the theory of current electricity and invented an electric battery.

832 Emblem and Venue

1992. "Genova '92" International Thematic Stamp Exhibition (1st issue).
2149 **832** 750l. multicoloured 1·60 25
See also Nos. 2170/5.

833 Medal of Lorenzo (Renato Beradi)

1992. 500th Death Anniv of Lorenzo de Medici, "The Magnificent".
2150 **833** 750l. multicoloured 1·60 60

834 Columbus before Queen Isabella

1992. 500th Anniv of Discovery of America by Columbus (2nd issue). Multicoloured.
2151 500l. Type **834** 1·10 70
2152 500l. Columbus's fleet 1·10 70
2153 500l. Sighting land 1·10 70
2154 500l. Landing in the New World 1·10 70

835 Scenes from Life of St. Maria Filippini (altar, Montefiascone Cathedral)

1992. 300th Anniv of Maestre Pie Filippini Institute.
2155 **835** 750l. multicoloured 1·60 60

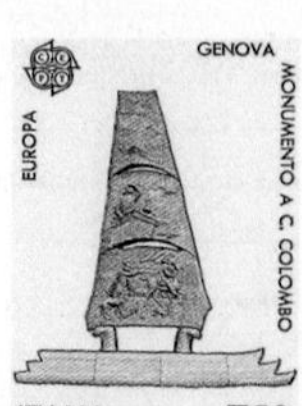

836 Columbus Monument, Genoa (G. Giannetti)

1992. Europa. 500th Anniv of Discovery of America by Columbus. Multicoloured.
2156 750l. Type **836** 5·50 90
2157 850l. Emblem of "Colombo '92" exhibition, Genoa 6·25 65

837 Columbus presenting Natives

1992. 500th Anniv of Discovery of America by Columbus (3rd issue). Six sheets each 113×93 mm containing horiz designs as T 837 reproducing scenes from United States 1893 Columbian Exposition issue.

MS2158 Six sheets (a) 50l. green (Type **837**); 300l. blue (Columbus announcing discovery); 4000l. mauve (Columbus in chains). (b) 100l. lilac (Columbus welcomed at Barcelona); 800l. red (Columbus restored to favour); 3000l. green (Columbus describing third voyage). (c) 200l. blue (Columbus sighting land); 900l. blue (Columbus's fleet); 1500l. red (Queen Isabella pledging jewels). (d) 400l. brown (Columbus soliciting aid of Queen Isabella); 700l. red (Columbus at La Rabida); 1000l. blue (Recall of Columbus). (e) 500l. brown (Landing of Columbus); 600l. green ("Santa Maria"); 2000l. red (Portraits of Queen Isabella and Columbus). (f) 5000l. green ("America", Columbus and "Liberty") Set of 6 sheets 44·00 30·00

838 Seascape and Cyclists

1992. 75th "Tour of Italy" Cycle Race. Mult.

2159	750l. Type **838**	1·60	50
2160	750l. Mountains and cyclists	1·60	50

Nos. 2159/60 were issued together, se-tenant, forming a composite design.

839 Ball, Team Badge and Stylization of Milan Cathedral

1992. A.C. Milan, National Football Champion, 1991–92.

2161	**839**	750l. green, red and black	1·60	70

840 Viareggio

1992. Seaside Resorts. Multicoloured.

2162	750l. Type **840**	1·60	45
2163	750l. Rimini	1·60	60

841 Nuvolari

1992. Birth Centenary of Tazio Nuvolari (racing driver).

2164	**841**	3200l. multicoloured	7·50	1·60

1992. Tourist Publicity (19th series). As T 556. Multicoloured.

2165	600l. Arcevia	1·50	90
2166	600l. Braies	1·50	90
2167	600l. Maratea	1·50	90
2168	600l. Pantelleria	1·50	90

842 "Adoration of the Shepherds" (detail)

1992. 400th Death Anniv of Jacopo da Ponte (painter).

2169	**842**	750l. multicoloured	1·60	60

843 Columbus's House, Genoa

1992. "Genova '92" International Thematic Stamp Exhibition (2nd issue). Multicoloured.

2170	500l. Type **843**	1·00	50
2171	600l. Departure of Columbus's fleet from Palos, 1492	1·20	35
2172	750l. Route map of Columbus's first voyage	1·50	50
2173	850l. Columbus sighting land	1·80	65
2174	1200l. Columbus landing on San Salvador	2·40	70
2175	3200l. Columbus, "Man" (Leonardo da Vinci), "Fury" (Michelangelo) and Raphael's portrait of Michelangelo	6·75	1·80

844 Woman's Eyes and Mouth

1992. Stamp Day. Ordinary or self-adhesive gum.

2176	**844**	750l. multicoloured	1·60	45

845 Map of Europe and Lions Emblem

1992. 75th Anniv of Lions International and 38th Europa Forum, Genoa.

2178	**845**	3000l. multicoloured	6·75	2·10

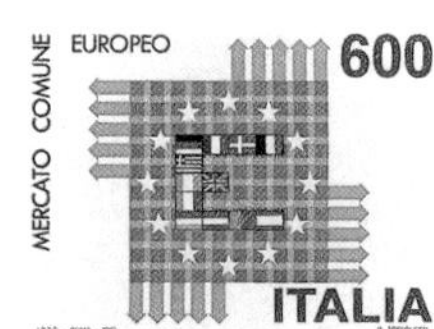

846 European Community Emblem and Members' Flags

1992. European Single Market (1st issue).

2179	**846**	600l. multicoloured	1·30	60

See also Nos. 2182/93.

847 Woman with Food Bowl

1992. International Nutrition Conference, Rome.

2180	**847**	500l. multicoloured	1·10	60

848 Caltagirone Crib

1992. Christmas.

2181	**848**	600l. multicoloured	1·50	45

849 Buildings on Flag of Italy

1993. European Single Market (2nd issue). Designs differing in flag of country and language of inscription. Multicoloured.

2182	750l. Type **849**	1·80	50
2183	750l. Belgium	1·80	50
2184	750l. Denmark	1·80	50
2185	750l. France	1·80	50
2186	750l. Germany	1·80	50
2187	750l. Greece	1·80	50
2188	750l. Ireland	1·80	50
2189	750l. Luxembourg	1·80	50
2190	750l. Netherlands	1·80	50
2191	750l. Portugal	1·80	50
2192	750l. United Kingdom	1·80	50
2193	750l. Spain	1·80	50

850 Russian and Italian Alpine Veterans

1993. 50th Anniv Meeting of Veterans of Battle of Nikolayevka.

2194	**850**	600l. multicoloured	1·60	60

851 Mezzettino, Colombina and Arlecchino

1993. Death Bicentenary of Carlo Goldoni (dramatist). Multicoloured.

2195	500l. Type **851**	1·10	80
2196	500l. Arlecchino and portrait of Goldoni	1·10	80

852 "Africa" (mosaic, Roman villa, Piazza Armerina)

1993. Artistic Heritage.

2197	**852**	750l. multicoloured	1·60	60

853 Wedge stopping Heart-shaped Cog

1993. National Health Day. Campaign against Heart Disease.

2198	**853**	750l. multicoloured	1·60	60

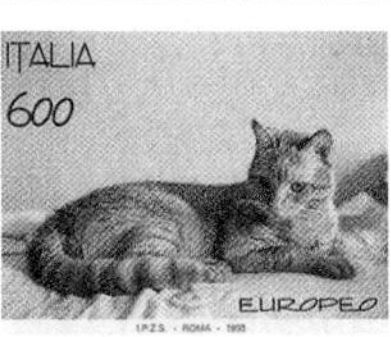

854 Tabby

1993. Domestic Cats. Multicoloured.

2199	600l. Type **854**	1·20	65
2200	600l. White Persian	1·20	65
2201	600l. Devon rex (vert)	1·20	65
2202	600l. Maine coon (vert)	1·20	65

1993. 100 Years of Radio (3rd issue). As T 822. Multicoloured.

2203	750l. Temistocle Calzecchi Onesti (physicist) and apparatus for detecting electromagnetic waves	2·00	35

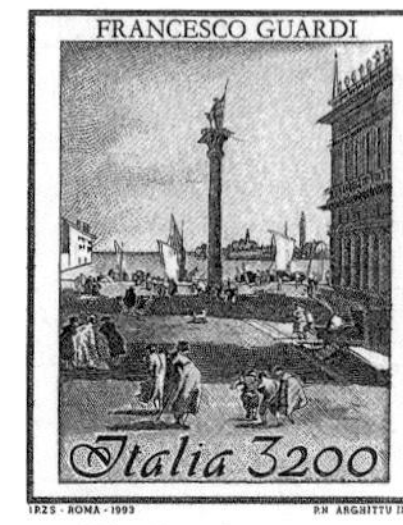

855 "The Piazza"

1993. Death Bicentenary of Francesco Guardi (artist).

2204	**855**	3200l. multicoloured	7·25	2·40

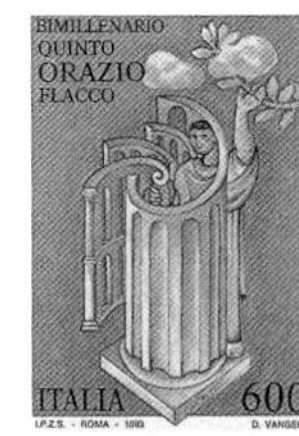

856 Horace

1993. 2000th Death Anniv of Horace (Quintus Horatius Flaccus) (poet).

2205	**856**	600l. multicoloured	1·30	50

857 Cottolengo and Small House of the Divine Providence, Turin

1993. St. Giuseppe Benedetto Cottolengo Commemoration.

2206	**857**	750l. multicoloured	1·60	35

858 "Carousel Horses" (Lino Bianchi Barriviera)

1993. Europa. Contemporary Art. Mult.

2207	750l. Type **858**	2·00	75
2208	850l. "Dynamism of Coloured Shapes" (Gino Severini)	2·40	60

859 Medal (Giuseppe Romagnoli)

1993. 400th Anniv of San Luca National Academy.

2209	**859**	750l. multicoloured	1·60	45

860 Emblem

1993. "Family Fest '93" International Conference, Rome.

2210	**860**	750l. multicoloured	1·60	60

861 Player and Club Badge

1993. Milan, National Football Champion, 1992–93.

2211	**861**	750l. multicoloured	1·60	60

862 Carloforte

1993. Tourist Publicity (20th series). Mult.

2212	600l. Type **862**	1·50	50
2213	600l. Palmanova	1·50	50
2214	600l. Senigallia	1·50	50
2215	600l. Sorrento	1·50	50

See also Nos. 2248/51 and 2315/18.

863 Canoeing

1993. World Canoeing Championships, Trentino.

2216	**863**	750l. multicoloured	1·60	45

864 Observatory

1993. Centenary of Regina Margherita Observatory.

2217	**864**	500l. multicoloured	1·60	50

865 Staircase, St. Salome's Cathedral, Veroli

1993. Artistic Heritage.

2218	**865**	750l. multicoloured	1·60	35

866 Soldier, Boy with Rifle and German Helmet

1993. Second World War 50th Anniversaries (1st issue). Multicoloured.

2219	750l. Type **866** (the Four Days of Naples)	1·60	35
2220	750l. Menorah, people in railway truck and Star of David (deportation of Roman Jews)	1·60	35
2221	750l. Seven Cervi brothers (execution)	1·60	35

See also Nos. 2259/61.

867 Carriage

1993. The Taxis Family in Postal History. Multicoloured.

2222	750l. Type **867**	1·50	25
2223	750l. Taxis arms	1·50	25
2224	750l. Gig	1·50	25
2225	750l. 17th-century postal messenger	1·50	25
2226	750l. 18th-century postal messenger	1·50	25

868 Head Office, Rome

1993. Centenary of Bank of Italy. Mult.

2227	750l. Type **868**	4·50	35
2228	1000l. 1000 lire banknote (first note issued by Bank)	6·25	50

869 Colonies Express Letter Stamp Design

1993. Stamp Day. Centenary of First Italian Colonies Stamps.

2229	**869**	600l. red and blue	1·30	45

870 Tableau Vivant, Corchiano

1993. Christmas. Multicoloured.

2230	600l. Type **870**	1·50	65
2231	750l. "The Annunciation" (Piero della Francesca)	1·90	50

871 17th-century Map of Foggia

1993. Treasures from State Archives and Museums (1st series). Multicoloured.

2232	600l. Type **871** (Foggia Archives)	1·30	65
2233	600l. "Concert" (Bartolomeo Manfredi) (Uffizi Gallery, Florence)	1·30	65
2234	750l. View of Siena from 15th-century illuminated manuscript (Siena Archives) (vert)	1·60	30
2235	850l. "The Death of Adonis" (Sebastiano del Piombo) (Uffizi Gallery)	1·80	65

See also Nos. 2266/9, 2306/9 and 2346/9.

872 Ringmaster and Bareback Riders

1994. The Circus. Multicoloured.

2236	600l. Type **872**	1·40	60
2237	750l. Clowns	1·70	35

873 Mother and Child inside House

1994. "The Housewife, a Presence that Counts".

2238	**873**	750l. multicoloured	2·00	30

874 "Bread" (Dario Piazza)

1994. Paintings of Italian Food. Multicoloured.

2239	500l. Type **874**	1·10	75
2240	600l. "Italian Pasta in the World" (Erminia Scaglione)	1·40	50

1994. 100 Years of Radio (4th issue). As T 822. Multicoloured.

2241	750l. Augusto Righi (physicist) and his Hertzian oscillator	2·00	35

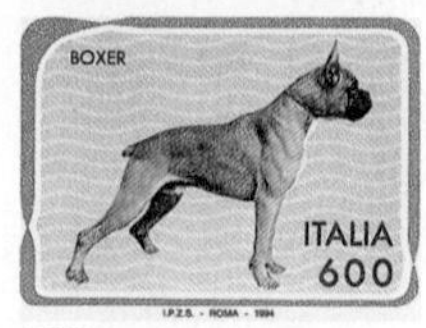
875 Boxer

1994. Dogs. Multicoloured.

2242	600l. Type **875**	1·40	50
2243	600l. Dalmatian	1·40	50
2244	600l. Maremma sheepdog	1·40	50
2245	600l. German shepherd	1·40	50

876 "The Risen Christ" (statue)

1994. Procession of "The Risen Christ", Tarquinia.

2246	**876**	750l. multicoloured	2·00	35

877 Pacioli in Study

1994. 500th Anniv of Publication of "Summary of Arithmetic, Geometry, Proportion and Proportionality" by Fra' Luca Pacioli.

2247	**877**	750l. multicoloured	2·00	35

1994. Tourist Publicity (21st series). As T 862. Multicoloured.

2248	600l. Odescalchi Castle, Santa Marinella	1·40	35
2249	600l. St. Michael's Abbey, Monticchio	1·40	35
2250	600l. Orta San Giulio	1·40	50
2251	600l. Cathedral, Messina	1·40	50

878 Kossuth

1994. Death Centenary of Lajos Kossuth (Hungarian statesman).

2252	**878**	3750l. multicoloured	8·00	2·75

879 Women's High-diving

1994. World Water Sports Championships. Multicoloured.

2253	600l. Type **879**	1·30	50
2254	750l. Water polo	1·70	35

880 Club Badge, Football and Colours

1994. Milan, National Football Champion, 1993–94.

2255	**880**	750l. multicoloured	2·10	60

881 Camillo Golgi (cytologist) and Golgi Cells

1994. Europa. Discoveries. Italian Nobel Prize winners. Multicoloured.

2256	750l. Type **881** (medicine, 1906)	2·20	45
2257	850l. Giulio Natta (chemist) and diagram of polymer structure (chemistry, 1963)	2·50	60

882 "Goddess of Caldevigo" (bronze statuette, 5th century B.C.)

1994. "Ancient Peoples of Italy" Archaeological Exhibition, Rimini.

2258	**882**	750l. multicoloured	2·00	35

883 Destruction of Montecassino

1994. Second World War 50th Anniversaries (2nd issue). Multicoloured.

2259	750l. Type **883**	1·80	30

2260		750l. Bound prisoners (Ardeatine Caves Massacre)	1·80	30
2261		750l. Family (Marzabotto Massacre)	1·80	30

884 Washing of Feet

1994. 22nd National Eucharistic Congress, Siena.

2262	**884**	600l. multicoloured	1·60	45

885 "Ariadne, Venus and Bacchus"

1994. Artistic Heritage. 400th Death Anniv of Tintoretto (artist).

2263	**885**	750l. multicoloured	2·00	45

886 "Piazza del Duomo during the Plague, 1630" (attr Cigoli)

1994. 750th Anniv of Arciconfraternita della Misericordia, Florence.

2264	**886**	750l. multicoloured	2·00	30

887 "E", European Union Emblem and Parliament

1994. European Parliament Elections.

2265	**887**	600l. multicoloured	1·60	45

1994. Treasures from State Archives and Museums (2nd series). As T 871. Multicoloured.

2266	600l. Frontispiece of notary's register, 1623–24 (Catania Archives) (vert)	1·10	50
2267	600l. "Death of Patroclus" (Attic vase, 5th century B.C.) (Agrigento Archaeological Museum) (vert)	1·10	50
2268	750l. "Galata and his Wife" (statue) (National Roman Museum) (vert)	1·40	25
2269	850l. Civic seal, 1745 (Campobasso Archives) (vert)	1·60	35

888 Olympic Rings and Pierre de Coubertin (founder)

1994. Centenary of Int Olympic Committee.

2270	**888**	850l. multicoloured	2·00	45

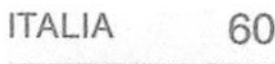

889 Vesuvius and "G 7"

1994. Group of Seven (industrialized countries) Summit, Naples.

2271	**889**	600l. blue, ultram & grn	1·30	45

890 Church of the Holy House and "Madonna and Child"

1994. 700th Anniv of Shrine of the Nativity of the Virgin, Loreto.

2272	**890**	500l. multicoloured	1·60	60

891 Pietro Miliani (papermaker) (after Francesco Rosaspina)

1994. Stamp Day. Multicoloured.

2273	600l. Type **891**	1·30	50
2274	750l. Paper and Watermark Museum (former St. Dominic's Monastery), Fabriano	1·60	35

892 Frederick II (sculpture, Bitonto Cathedral)

1994. 800th Birth Anniv of Frederick II, Holy Roman Emperor.

2275	**892**	750l. multicoloured	2·00	30

893 St. Mark's Basilica

1994. 900th Anniv of Dedication of St. Mark's Basilica, Venice.

2276	**893**	750l. multicoloured	2·20	85
MS2277		80×115 mm. No. 2276 together with No. 1491 of San Marino	4·00	3·50

894 "The Annunciation" (Melozzo da Forli)

1994. Christmas. Multicoloured.

2278		600l. Type **894**	1·50	50
2279		750l. "Sacred Conversation" (detail, Lattanzio da Rimini)	3·25	35

895 Club Emblem on Globe

1994. Centenary of Italian Touring Club.

2280	**895**	600l. multicoloured	1·60	45

896 Headquarters, Rome

1994. 75th Anniv of Credit for Businesses and Public Works.

2281	**896**	750l. multicoloured	4·00	35

897 New Emblem

1994. Incorporation of Italian Post. Size 34×26 mm.

2282	-	600l. red and silver	1·80	50
2283	**897**	750l. black, green and red	2·30	35
2284	**897**	750l. red	2·30	35

DESIGN—VERT: 600l. Palazzo Querini Dubois, Venice (restored with Post Office help).

For 750 and 850l. values, size 26×17 mm, see Nos. 2343/4.

898 Gentile

1994. 50th Death Anniv of Giovanni Gentile (philosopher).

2285	**898**	750l. multicoloured	2·10	45

899 Rainbow, Dove, Olive Tree and Flood

1995. For Flood Victims.

2286	**899**	750l.+2250l. mult	9·25	5·75

900 Skater

1995. World Speed Skating Championships, Baselga di Pine.

2287	**900**	750l. multicoloured	2·00	35

901 First Issue of "La Domenica del Corriere"

1995. 50th Death Anniv of Achille Beltrame (painter).

2288	**901**	500l. multicoloured	1·60	60

902 Rice

1995. Italian Food. Multicoloured.

2289	500l. Type **902**	1·40	65
2290	750l. Olives and olive oil	2·00	50

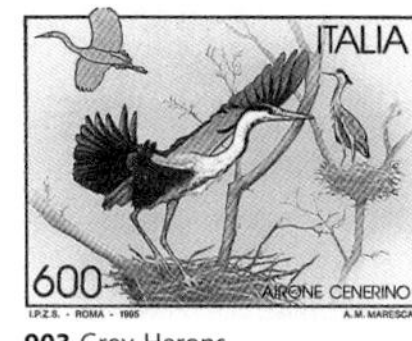

903 Grey Herons

1995. Birds. Multicoloured.

2291	600l. Type **903**	1·40	50
2292	600l. Griffon vultures ("Grifone")	1·40	50
2293	600l. Golden eagles ("Aquila Reale")	1·40	50
2294	600l. White-winged snow finches ("Fringuello Alpino")	1·40	50

904 Anniversary Emblem

1995. 50th Anniv of U.N.O.

2295	**904**	850l. black, blue and gold	2·20	45

905 Detail of Monument (Giuseppe Grande)

1995. Centenary of Monument to the Fallen of the Five Days of Milan (1848 uprising).

2296	**905**	750l. multicoloured	1·60	35

906 Princess Mafalda of Savoy and Concentration Camp

1995. 50th Anniv of End of Second World War. Multicoloured.

2297	750l. Type **906**	1·70	30
2298	750l. DUKW at Anzio	1·70	30
2299	750l. Teresa Gullace and scene of her death	1·70	30
2300	750l. Florence Town Hall and Military Medal	1·70	30
2301	750l. Vittorio Veneto Town Hall and Military Medal	1·70	30
2302	750l. Cagliari Town Hall and Military Medal	1·70	30
2303	750l. Battle of Mount Lungo	1·70	30
2304	750l. Martin B-26 Marauders parachuting supplies in the Balkans	1·70	30
2305	750l. Light cruisers of the Eighth Division in Atlantic	1·70	30

1995. Treasures from State Archives and Museums (3rd series). As T 871. Multicoloured.

2306	500l. "Illuminated letter "P" from statute of Pope Innocent III (Rome Archives) (vert)	1·00	65
2307	500l. "Port of Naples" (detail, Bernardo Strozzi) (St. Martin National Museum, Naples)	1·00	65
2308	750l. Illuminated letter "I" showing the Risen Christ from 1481 document (Mantua Archives) (vert)	1·50	35
2309	850l. "Sacred Love and Profane Love" (Titian) (Borghese Museum and Gallery, Rome)	1·80	65

907 Emblem

1995. Centenary of Venice Biennale.
2310 **907** 750l. blue, gold & yellow 1·80 35

908 Santa Croce Basilica, Florence

1995. Artistic Heritage.
2311 **908** 750l. brown 1·80 35

909 Soldiers and Civilians celebrating

1995. Europa. Peace and Freedom. Mult.

2312	750l. Type **909** (50th anniv of end of Second World War in Europe)	2·40	35
2313	850l. Mostar Bridge, (Bosnia) and Council of Europe emblem	2·75	50

910 Players

1995. Centenary of Volleyball.
2314 **910** 750l. blue, orange & grn 2·00 35

1995. Tourist Publicity (22nd series). As T 862. Multicoloured.

2315	750l. Alatri	1·80	35
2316	750l. Nuoro	1·80	35
2317	750l. Susa	1·80	35
2318	750l. Venosa	1·80	35

911 Experiment demonstrating X-rays

1995. Centenary of Discovery of X-rays by Wilhelm Rontgen.
2319 **911** 750l. multicoloured 1·60 35

912 Player and Club Badge

1995. Juventus, National Football Champion, 1994–95.
2320 **912** 750l. multicoloured 2·00 45

913 Villa Griffone (site of Marconi's early experiments)

1995. 100 Years of Radio (5th issue). Centenary of First Radio Transmission. Multicoloured.

2321	750l. Type **913**	1·80	35
2322	850l. Guglielmo Marconi and transmitter (36×21 mm)	2·10	50

914 St. Antony, Holy Basilica (Padua) and Page of Gospel

1995. 800th Birth Anniv of St. Antony of Padua. Multicoloured.

2323	750l. Type **914**	1·80	35
2324	850l. St. Antony holding Child Jesus (painting, Vieira Lusitano) (horiz)	2·10	50

915 Durazzo Pallavicini, Pegli

1995. Public Gardens (1st series). Multicoloured.

2325	750l. Type **915**	1·70	15
2326	750l. Boboli, Florence	1·70	15
2327	750l. Ninfa, Cisterna di Latina	1·70	15
2328	750l. Parco della Reggia, Caserta	1·70	15

See also Nos. 2439/42.

916 Milan Cathedral and Eye (congress emblem)

1995. 10th European Ophthalmological Society Congress, Milan.
2329 **916** 750l. multicoloured 1·60 35

917 "Sailors' Wives"

1995. Birth Centenary of Massimo Campigli (painter).
2330 **917** 750l. multicoloured 2·20 35

918 Dome of Santa Maria del Fiore (Florence), Galileo and Albert Einstein

1995. 14th World Relative Physics Conference, Florence.
2331 **918** 750l. blue, brown & black 1·60 35

919 Rudolph Valentino in "The Son of the Sheik"

1995. Centenary of Motion Pictures.

2332	**919**	750l. black, blue and red	1·70	50
2333	-	750l. multicoloured	1·70	50
2334	-	750l. multicoloured	1·70	50
2335	-	750l. multicoloured	1·70	50

DESIGNS: No. 2333, Toto in "The Gold of Naples"; 2334, Frederico Fellini's "Cabiria Nights"; 2335, Poster (by Massimo Geleng) for "Cinecitta 95" film festival.

920 Wheatfield and Anniversary Emblem

1995. 50th Anniv of F.A.O.
2336 **920** 850l. multicoloured 2·40 45

921 St. Albert's Stone Coffin (detail) and Basilica

1995. 900th Anniversaries of Pontida Basilica and Death of St. Albert of Prezzate.
2337 **921** 1000l. brown and blue 2·20 60

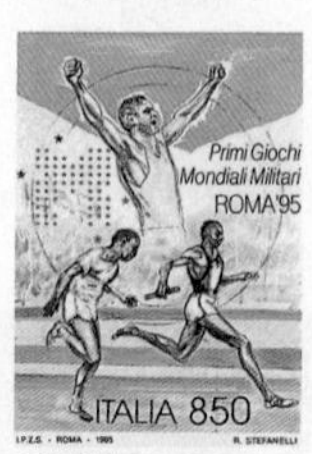

922 Athletes

1995. 1st World Military Games, Rome.
2338 **922** 850l. multicoloured 2·10 45

923 Globe and Means of Communication

1995. 50th Anniv of Ansa News Agency.
2339 **923** 750l. multicoloured 2·00 35

924 Crib (Stefano da Putignano), Polignano Cathedral

1995. Christmas. Multicoloured.

2340	750l. Type **924**	2·75	35
2341	850l. "Adoration of the Wise Men" (detail, Fra Angelico)	3·25	50

925 Renato Mondolfo (philatelist) and Trieste 1949 20l. Stamp

1995. Stamp Day.
2342 **925** 750l. multicoloured 1·60 35

1995. 1st Anniv of Incorporation of Italian Post. Size 26×17 mm.

2343	**897**	750l. red	1·50	15
2344	**897**	850l. black, green and red	1·80	30

926 Collage representing Marinetti's Works

1996. 120th Birth Anniv of Filippo Marinetti (writer and founder of Futurist movement).
2345 **926** 750l. multicoloured 2·00 35

1996. Treasures from State Archives and Museums (4th series). As T 871. Multicoloured.

2346	750l. Arms (Georgofili Academy, Florence)	1·90	35
2347	750l. Illuminated letter showing St. Luke and his ox from Constitution of 1372 (Lucca Archives) (vert)	1·90	35
2348	850l. Inkwells, pen and manuscript of Gabriele d'Annunzio (writer) (Il Vittoriale, Gardone Riviera)	2·20	50
2349	850l. "Life of King Modus and Queen Racio" from 1486 miniature (Turin Archives)	2·20	50

927 "Sarah and the Angel" (fresco, Archbishop's Palace, Udine)

1996. 300th Birth Anniv of Giambattista Tiepolo (painter).
2350 **927** 1000l. multicoloured 2·75 60

928 White Wine

1996. Italian Wine Production. Multicoloured.

2351	500l. Type **928**	1·40	50
2352	750l. Red wine	2·20	35

929 Marco Polo and Palace in the Forbidden City

1996. 700th Anniv (1995) of Marco Polo's Return from Asia and "China '96" International Stamp Exhibition, Peking.

2353 **929** 1250l. multicoloured 3·25 1·50

930 Milan Cathedral (left detail)

1996. "Italia 98" International Stamp Exhibition, Milan (1st issue). Multicoloured.

2354 750l. Type **930** 1·70 35

2355 750l. Cathedral (right detail) 1·70 35

Nos. 2354/5 were issued together, se-tenant, forming a composite design of the Cathedral.

See also Nos. **MS**2412, 2518, 2523, 2528/30 and 2531.

931 Quill pen and Satellite (50th Anniv of National Federation of Italian Press)

1996. Anniversaries.

2356 **931** 750l. multicoloured 2·00 50

2357 - 750l. blue, pink and black 2·00 50

DESIGN—HORIZ: No. 2357, Globe (centenary of "La Gazetta dello Sport" (newspaper)).

932 Postman and Emblem

1996. International Museum of Postal Images, Belvedere Ostrense.

2358 **932** 500l. multicoloured 1·30 60

933 Uniforms of Different Periods

1996. Centenary of Academy of Excise Guards.

2359 **933** 750l. multicoloured 2·00 35

934 Truck and Route Map

1996. Trans-continental Drive, Rome–New York.

2360 **934** 4650l. multicoloured 10·50 4·75

935 Carina Negrone (pilot) and Biplane

1996. Europa. Famous Women. Multicoloured.

2361 750l. Type **935** 2·20 60

2362 850l. Adelaide Ristori (actress) 2·50 60

936 Fishes, Sea and Coastline from St. Raphael to Genoa

1996. 20th Anniv of Ramoge Agreement on Environmental Protection of the Mediterranean.

2363 **936** 750l. multicoloured 2·00 45

937 Celestino V and Town of Fumone

1996. 700th Death Anniv of Pope Celestino V.

2364 **937** 750l. multicoloured 2·00 35

938 St Anthony's Church, Diano Marina

1996. Tourist Publicity (23rd series). Mult.

2365 750l. Type **938** 1·70 45

2366 750l. Pienza Cathedral 1·70 45

2367 750l. Belltower of St. Michael the Archangel's Church, Monte Sant'Angelo 1·70 45

2368 750l. Prehistoric stone dwelling, Lampedusa 1·70 45

939 Abbey and Relief from 12th-century Ivory Reliquary

1996. 500th Anniv of Reconsecration of Farfa Abbey.

2369 **939** 1000l. black, yell & orge 2·75 70

940 Fair Entrance and Mt. Pellegrino

1996. Mediterranean Fair, Palermo.

2370 **940** 750l. multicoloured 2·00 35

941 State Arms

1996. 50th Anniv of Italian Republic.

2371 **941** 750l. multicoloured 2·00 35

942 Rider and Emblem

1996. 50th Anniv of Production of Vespa Motor Scooters.

2372 **942** 750l. multicoloured 2·75 45

943 Views of Messina and Venice

1996. 40th Anniv of Founding Meetings of European Economic Community, Messina and Venice.

2373 **943** 750l. multicoloured 2·10 45

944 Athlete on Starting Block and 1896 Athletes

1996. Centenary of Modern Olympic Games and Olympic Games, Atlanta. Multicoloured.

2374 500l. Type **944** 1·10 50

2375 750l. Throwing the discus and view of Atlanta (vert) 1·60 65

2376 850l. Gymnast, stadium and basketball player 1·80 50

2377 1250l. 1896 stadium, Athens, and 1996 stadium, Atlanta (vert) 2·75 90

945 "Acanthobrahmaea europaea"

1996. Butterflies. Multicoloured.

2378 750l. Type **945** 2·00 35

2379 750l. "Melanargia arge" 2·00 35

2380 750l. "Papilio hospiton" 2·00 35

2381 750l. "Zygaena rubicundus" 2·00 35

946 "Prima Comunione"

1996. Italian Films (1st series).

2382 **946** 750l. black, red and blue 1·80 50

2383 - 750l. multicoloured 1·80 50

2384 - 750l. multicoloured 1·80 50

DESIGNS: No. 2383, Poster for "Cabiria"; 2384, "Scusate il Ritardo".

See also Nos. 2453/5 and 2528/30.

947 Santa Maria del Fiore

1996. 700th Anniv of Cathedral of Santa Maria del Fiore, Florence.

2385 **947** 750l. blue 2·00 35

948 Player, Shield and Club Badge

1996. Milan, National Football Champion, 1995–96.

2386 **948** 750l. multicoloured 2·75 45

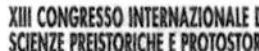

949 Choppy (congress mascot)

1996. 13th International Prehistoric and Protohistoric Sciences Congress.

2387 **949** 850l. multicoloured 2·20 45

950 Games Emblem and Pictograms

1996. Mediterranean Games, Bari (1997).

2388 **950** 750l. multicoloured 2·00 35

951 Fair Entrance

1996. Levant Fair, Bari.

2389 **951** 750l. multicoloured 2·00 35

952 Rejoicing Crowd and Club Badge

1996. Juventus, European Football Champion, 1995–96.

2390 **952** 750l. multicoloured 2·20 45

953 Pertini

1996. Birth Centenary of Alessandro Pertini (President 1978–85).
2391 **953** 750l. multicoloured 2·00 35

954 Montale and Hoopoe

1996. Birth Centenary of Eugenio Montale (poet).
2392 **954** 750l. brown and blue 2·00 35

955 "The Annunciation"

1996. 400th Birth Anniv of Pietro Berrettini da Cortona (artist).
2393 **955** 500l. multicoloured 2·00 60

956 Tex Willer (Galep)

1996. Stamp Collecting. Strip Cartoons. Mult.
2394 750l. Type **956** 2·20 35
2395 850l. Corto Maltese (Hugo Pratt) 2·50 50

957 Vortex and "Stamps"

1996. Stamp Day.
2396 **957** 750l. multicoloured 2·00 35

958 Bell Tower and Former Benedictine Abbey (seat of faculty)

1996. Universities.
2397 **958** 750l. brown 1·60 35
2398 - 750l. blue 1·60 35
2399 - 750l. green 1·60 35

DESIGNS—VERT: No. 2397. Type **958** (centenary of Faculty of Agriculture, Perugia University); 2398, Former St. Matthew's Cathedral (seat of Medical School), Salerno University. HORIZ: No. 2399, Athenaeum, Sassari University.

959 Emblem

1996. World Food Summit, Rome.
2400 **959** 850l. green and black 2·00 45

960 "Madonna of the Quail" (Antonio Pisanello)

1996. Christmas. Multicoloured.
2401 750l. Type **960** 2·30 35
2402 850l. Father Christmas and toys (horiz) 2·75 50

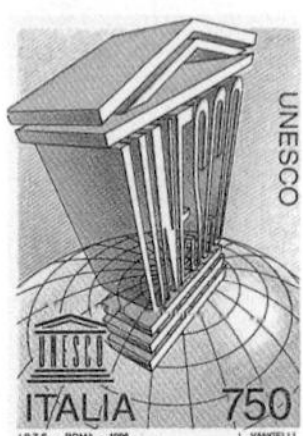

961 "UNESCO" and Globe

1996. 50th Anniversaries of UNESCO and UNICEF.
2403 750l. Type **961** 2·20 35
2404 850l. UNICEF emblem on kite, baby and globe 2·50 50

962 Headquarters, Rome

1996. 70th Anniv of National Statistics Institute.
2405 **962** 750l. multicoloured 2·00 35

963 Bookcase

1996. 50th Anniv of Strega Prize.
2406 **963** 3400l. multicoloured 8·00 2·75

964 Hall of the Tricolour, Reggio Emilia

1997. Bicentenary of First Tricolour (now national flag), Cisalpine Republic.
2407 **964** 750l. multicoloured 1·80 30

965 Tower Blocks and Skier

1997. World Alpine Skiing Championships, Sestriere. Multicoloured.
2408 750l. Type **965** 1·80 50
2409 850l. Olympic colours forming ski run and ski 1·80 50

966 Ferraris, Early Motor and Ferraris National Electrotechnology Institute, Turin

1997. Death Centenary of Galileo Ferraris (physicist).
2410 **966** 750l. multicoloured 1·80 45

967 Loi

1997. 5th Death Anniv of Emanuela Loi (bodyguard killed in Mafia car bombing).
2411 **967** 750l. multicoloured 2·20 45

968 1819 Letter and Handstamps of Italian States

1997. "Italia 98" International Stamp Exhibition, Milan (2nd issue). Sheet 150×80 mm containing T 968 and similar vert designs. Multicoloured.
MS2412 750l. Bologna 1910 cancellation aerogramme from Balboa flight and postcard with 1917 25c. airmail stamp (Aerophilately); 750l. Cancellations used for the signing of the Rome Treaty (forming European Economic Community), Rome Olympic Games and Holy Year, 1952 Leonardo da Vinci 80l. stamp and 1931 inauguration of Milan railway station postcard (Thematic Philately); 750l. Type **968** (Postal History); 750l. "Democratica", Italian stamp catalogue and L'Italia Filatelica (stamp review) (Philatelic Literature) 8·00 3·50

969 Statue of Marcus Aurelius

1997. 40th Anniv of Treaty of Rome (foundation of European Economic Community).
2413 **969** 750l. multicoloured 1·80 45

970 St. Germiniano (after Bartolomeo Schedoni) holding Modena Cathedral

1997. 1600th Death Anniv of St. Germiniano (patron saint of Modena).
2414 **970** 750l. multicoloured 1·80 45

971 "Baptism of St. Ambrose" and "Hand of God recalling him to City"

1997. 1600th Death Anniv of St. Ambrose, Bishop of Milan.
2415 **971** 1000l. multicoloured 2·30 50

The illustrations are taken from reliefs by Volvinio on the Golden Altar in St. Ambrose's Cathedral, Milan.

972 Statue of Minerva, Central Square, Rome University

1997. Universities.
2416 **972** 750l. red 1·80 35
2417 - 750l. blue 1·80 35

DESIGN: No. 2417, Palace of Bo, Padua University.

973 St. Peter's Cathedral and Colosseum within "Wolf suckling Romulus and Remus"

1997. 2750th Anniv of Foundation of Rome.
2418 **973** 850l. multicoloured 2·00 45

974 Pre-Roman Walls, Gela

1997
2419 **974** 750l. multicoloured 1·80 35

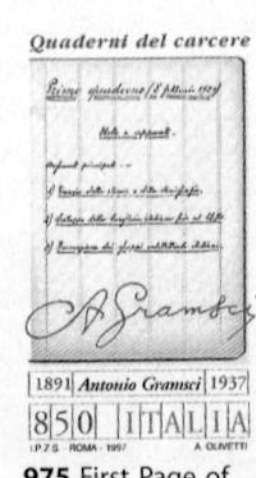

975 First Page of Prison Notebook and Signature

1997. 60th Death Anniv of Antonio Gramsci (politician).
2420 **975** 850l. multicoloured 2·75 45

976 Teracotta Relief and Cloisters

1997. 500th Anniv of Consecration of Pavia Church.
2421 **976** 1000l. multicoloured 2·20 50

977 Shoemaker's Workshop

1997. Europa. Tales and Legends. Mult.

2422	800l. Type **977** ("He who becomes the Property of Others works for his Soup")	1·80	35
2423	900l. Street singer (19th-century copper etching)	2·20	60

978 Detail of 1901 Poster for "Tosca" and Theatre

1997. Centenary of Teatro Massimo, Palermo.

2424	**978**	800l. multicoloured	2·20	30

979 St. Sebastian's Church, Acireale

1997. Tourist Publicity (24th series). Mult.

2425	800l. Type **979**	1·70	35
2426	800l. Cicero and his tomb, Formia	1·70	35
2427	800l. St. Mary of the Assumption, Positano	1·70	35
2428	800l. St. Vitale's Basilica, Ravenna	1·70	35

980 Books and Marble Floor

1997. 10th Book Salon, Turin.

2429	**980**	800l. multicoloured	2·00	35

981 Queen Paola and Castel Sant'Angelo, Rome

1997. 60th Birthday of Queen Paola of Belgium.

2430	**981**	750l. multicoloured	2·00	35

982 Palazzo della Civilta del Lavoro and Fair Pavilions

1997. Rome Fair.

2431	**982**	800l. multicoloured	2·20	35

983 Orvieto Cathedral

1997

2432	**983**	450l. violet	1·10	45

984 Morosini in Via Tasso Prison, 1944

1997. 53rd Death Anniv of Father Giuseppe Morosini.

2433	**984**	800l. multicoloured	2·00	35

985 Player, Club Emblem and Football

1997. Juventus, National Football Champion, 1996–97.

2434	**985**	800l. multicoloured	2·75	40

986 Chamois and "Iris marsica"

1997. 75th Anniv of Abruzzo National Park.

2435	**986**	800l. multicoloured	2·00	35

987 Towers and Fair Complex

1997. Bologna Fair.

2436	**987**	800l. multicoloured	2·00	35

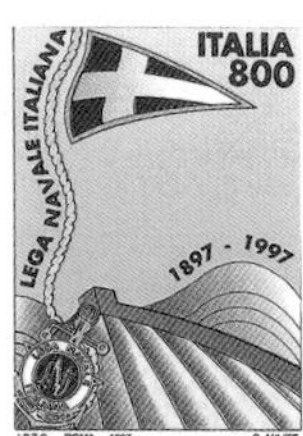
988 Pennant and Ships' Bows

1997. Centenary of Italian Naval League.

2437	**988**	800l. multicoloured	2·00	35

989 Runner, High Jumper and Gymnast

1997. 13th Mediterranean Games, Bari.

2438	**989**	900l. multicoloured	2·20	45

1997. Public Gardens (2nd series). As T 915. Multicoloured.

2439	800l. Orto Botanico, Palermo	1·70	35
2440	800l. Villa Sciarra, Rome	1·70	35
2441	800l. Cavour, Santena	1·70	35
2442	800l. Miramare, Trieste	1·70	35

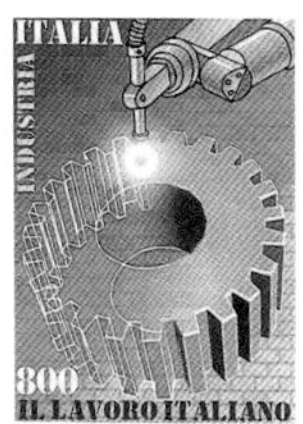
990 Cogwheel and Robot Arm (industry)

1997. Italian Work. Multicoloured.

2443	800l. Type **990**	1·70	35
2444	900l. Cereals, fruit trees, grapes and sun (agriculture) (horiz)	2·00	50

991 Globe and the "Matthew"

1997. 500th Anniv of John Cabot's Discovery of North America.

2445	**991**	1300l. multicoloured	3·25	2·40

992 Verri

1997. Death Bicentenary of Pietro Verri (illuminist).

2446	**992**	3600l. multicoloured	8·00	1·80

993 "Madonna of the Rosary" (Pomarancio il Vecchio)

1997. Painters' Anniversaries. Multicoloured.

2447	450l. Type **993** (400th death anniv)	1·10	35
2448	650l. "The Miracle of Ostia" ((detail, Paolo Uccello) (600th birth anniv)) (26×37 mm)	1·60	65

994 Procession

1997. Varia Festival, Palmi.

2449	**994**	800l. multicoloured	2·00	45

995 Basketball

1997. University Games, Sicily. Multicoloured.

2450	450l. Type **995**	1·10	45
2451	800l. High jumping	1·60	35

996 Rosmini

1997. Birth Bicentenary of Antonio Rosmini (philosopher).

2452	**996**	800l. multicoloured	2·00	30

1997. Italian Films (2nd series). As T 946.

2453	800l. multicoloured	1·80	45
2454	800l. black, blue and red	1·80	45
2455	800l. multicoloured	1·80	45

DESIGNS: No. 2453, Pietro Germi in "Il Ferroviere"; 2454, Anna Magnani in "Mamma Roma"; 2455, Ugo Tognazzi in "Amici Miei".

997 Open Book and Beach, Viareggio

1997. Viareggio-Repaci Prize.

2456	**997**	4000l. multicoloured	8·50	1·70

998 Venue and Bell Tower

1997. International Trade Fair, Bolzano.

2457	**998**	800l. multicoloured	2·00	35

999 Bronze Head (500 BC)

1997. Museum Exhibits. Multicoloured.

2458	450l. Type **999** (National Museum, Reggio Calabria)	1·10	35
2459	650l. "Madonna and Child with Two Vases of Roses" (Ercole de Roberti) (National Picture Gallery, Ferrara)	1·60	65
2460	800l. Miniature of poet Sordello da Goito (Arco Palace Museum, Mantua)	1·90	35
2461	900l. "St. George and the Dragon" (Vitale di Bologna) (National Picture Gallery, Bologna)	2·20	50

1000 Pope Paul VI and Door of Death, St. Peter's Cathedral, Rome

1997. Birth Centenary of Pope Paul VI.

2462	**1000**	4000l. blue	8·75	1·70

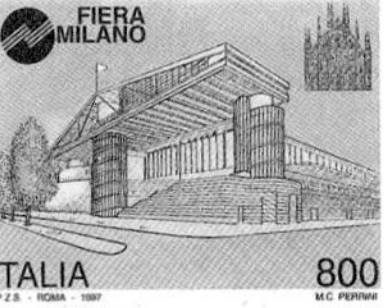
1001 Portello Pavilion (venue) and Milan Cathedral

1997. Milan Fair.

2463	**1001**	800l. multicoloured	2·00	45

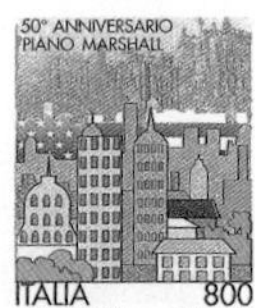

1002 War-ravaged and Reconstructed Cities

1997. 50th Anniv of European Recovery Programme ("Marshall Plan").
2464 **1002** 800l. multicoloured 2·00 30

1003 Nativity (crib, St Francis's Church, Leonessa)

1997. Christmas. Multicoloured.
2465 800l. Type **1003** 2·30 35
2466 900l. "Nativity" (painting, Sta. Maria Maggiore, Spelo) 2·75 50

1004 Production Plant and Merloni

1997. Birth Centenary of Aristide Merloni (entrepreneur).
2467 **1004** 800l. multicoloured 2·00 35

1005 Cavalcaselle and Drawings

1997. Death Centenary of Giovanni Battista Cavalcaselle (art historian).
2468 **1005** 800l. multicoloured 2·00 35

1006 Magnifying Glass and Fleur-de-lis

1997. Stamp Day.
2469 **1006** 800l. multicoloured 2·00 35

1007 Refugees aboard "Toscana" (steamer)

1997. 50th Anniv of Exodus of Italian Inhabitants from Istria, Fiume and Dalmatia.
2470 **1007** 800l. multicoloured 2·00 35

1008 Arms of State Police and Badge of Traffic Police

1997. 50th Anniv of Traffic Police.
2471 **1008** 800l. multicoloured 2·00 35

1009 Map of Italy in Column and Flag

1998. 50th Anniv of Constitution.
2472 **1009** 800l. black, red & green 2·00 35

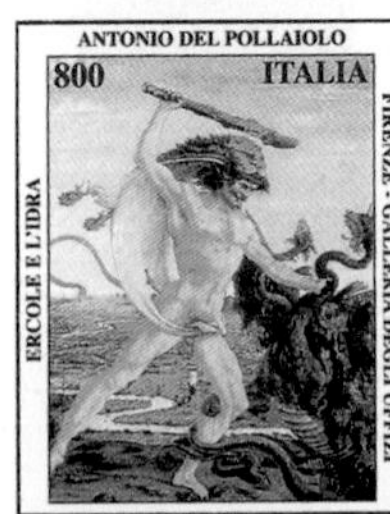

1010 "Hercules and the Hydra"

1998. 500th Death Anniv of Antonio del Pollaiolo (painter).
2473 **1010** 800l. multicoloured 2·10 35

1011 Bertolt Brecht

1998. Writers' Birth Centenaries.
2474 **1011** 450l. multicoloured 1·10 50
2475 - 650l. multicoloured 1·50 50
2476 - 800l. multicoloured 1·90 30
2477 - 900l. blue, green & black 2·20 30
DESIGNS—HORIZ: 650l. Federico Garcia Lorca (poet); 800l. Curzio Malaparte. VERT: 900l. Leonida Repaci.

1012 Fair Complex

1998. Verona Fair.
2478 **1012** 800l. multicoloured 2·10 45

1013 Memorial Tablet in Casale Montferrato Synagogue

1998. 150th Anniv of Granting of Full Citizen Rights to Italian Jews.
2479 **1013** 800l. multicoloured 2·10 45

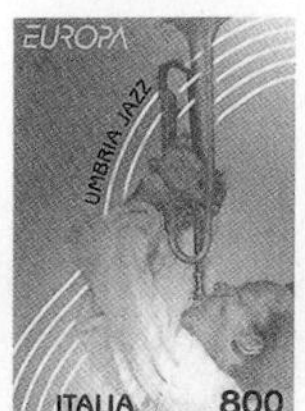

1014 Trombonist

1998. Europa. National Festivals. Mult.
2480 800l. Type **1014** (Umbria Jazz Festival) 1·80 35
2481 900l. Boy holding animal (Giffoni Film Festival) 2·20 50

1015 "The Last Supper"

1998. 500th Anniv of Completion of "The Last Supper" (mural) by Leonardo da Vinci.
2482 **1015** 800l. brown 2·40 45

1016 Costumes designed by Bernardo Buontalenti for First Opera in Florence

1998. Italian Theatre. Multicoloured.
2483 800l. Type **1016** (400th anniv of opera) 2·00 35
2484 800l. Gaetano Donizetti (composer, 150th death anniv) (horiz) 2·00 35

1017 Turin Cathedral and Holy Shroud

1998. 500th Anniv of Turin Cathedral. Display of the Holy Shroud.
2485 **1017** 800l. multicoloured 2·10 35

1018 Otranto Castle

1998. Tourist Publicity (25th series). Mult.
2486 800l. Type **1018** 1·90 35
2487 800l. Mori Fountain and Orsini Tower, Marino 1·90 35
2488 800l. Valfederia Chapel, Livigno 1·90 35
2489 800l. Marciana Marina, Elba 1·90 35

1019 Cagliari Cathedral, Drummer and Fair Building

1998. International Sardinia Fair, Cagliari.
2490 **1019** 800l. multicoloured 2·00 35

1020 "Charge of the Carabinieri at Pastrengo" (Sebastiano de Albertis)

1998. 150th Anniv of Battle of Pastrengo.
2491 **1020** 800l. multicoloured 2·00 35

1021 Flags

1998. Padua Fair.
2492 **1021** 800l. multicoloured 2·00 35

1022 Player and Club Badge

1998. Juventus, National Football Champion, 1997–98.
2493 **1022** 800l. multicoloured 2·20 45

1023 Turin Polytechnic

1998. Universities.
2494 **1023** 800l. blue 2·10 35

1024 Emblem

1998. World Food Programme.
2495 **1024** 900l. multicoloured 2·20 45

1025 Santa Maria de Pesio Carthusian Monastery

1998. Artistic Heritage.
2496 **1025** 800l. multicoloured 2·00 35

1026 Ammonites and Pergola

1998. 4th International "Fossils, Evolution, Ambience" Congress, Pergola.
2497 **1026** 800l. multicoloured 2·00 35

1027 Flag at Half-mast

1998. "The Forces of Order, the Fallen".
2498 **1027** 800l. multicoloured 2·10 35

1028 Endoscope and Globe

1998. 6th World General Endoscopic Surgery Congress, Rome.
2499 **1028** 900l. multicoloured 2·20 35

1029 First Parliamentary Chamber

1998. National Museums. Multicoloured.
2500 800l. Type **1029** (Italian Risorgimento Museum, Turin) 2·00 35
2501 800l. Statue of an ephebus (Athenian youth), Temple of Concord and column of Temple of Vulcan (Regional Archaeology Museum, Agrigento) (vert) 2·00 35
2502 800l. Sculpture by Umberto Boccioni and Palazzo Venier dei Leoni (venue) (Peggy Guggenheim Collection, Venice) 2·00 35

1030 Fair Complex and Basilica

1998. Vicenza Trade Fair.
2503 **1030** 800l. multicoloured 2·10 35

1031 Leopardi (after Luigi Lolli) and Palazzo Leopardi, Recanati

1998. Birth Bicentenary of Giacomo Leopardi (poet).
2504 **1031** 800l. brown and black 2·10 35

1032 Young Etruscan Girl (detail of tomb painting)

1998. Women in Art.
2505 **1032** 100l. black, green & sil 35 25
2506 - 450l. multicoloured 1·50 25
2507 - 650l. multicoloured 2·20 25
2508 - 800l. brown and black 2·75 15
2509 - 1000l. blue, brn & blk 3·50 25

DESIGNS: 450l. Detail of "Herod's Banquet and the Dance of Salome" (fresco by Filippo Lippi in Prato Cathedral); 650l. "Profile of a Woman" (Antonio del Pollaiuolo); 800l. "Lady with a Unicorn" (detail, Raphael); 1000l. "Constanza Buonarelli" (bust by Gian Lorenzo Bernini).

For these designs but with face values in euros added, see Nos. 2537/41.

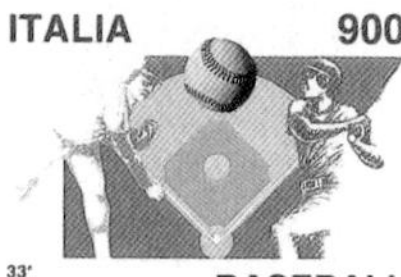

1033 Pitch, Pitcher and Batter

1998. 33rd World Cup Baseball Championship, Florence.
2510 **1033** 900l. multicoloured 2·20 45

1034 Columbus and Vespucci

1998. 500th Anniversaries of Landing of Christopher Columbus in Venezuela and of Amerigo Vespucci's Explorations.
2511 **1034** 1300l. multicoloured 3·25 1·20

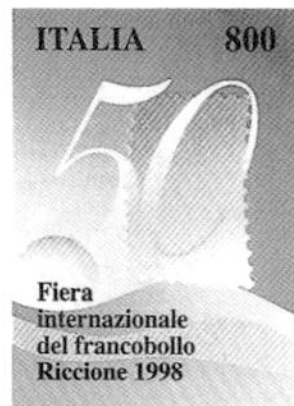

1035 Emblem

1998. 50th International Stamp Fair, Riccione.
2512 **1035** 800l. multicoloured 2·10 45

1036 Mother Teresa and Child

1998. 1st Death Anniv of Mother Teresa (founder of Missionaries of Charity). Multicoloured.
2513 800l. Type **1036** 1·80 35
2514 900l. Mother Teresa (vert) 2·10 45

1037 Father Pio and Monastery Church, San Giovanni Rotondo

1998. 30th Death Anniv of Father Pio da Pietrelcina (Capuchin friar who bore the stigmata).
2515 **1037** 800l. blue 2·20 35

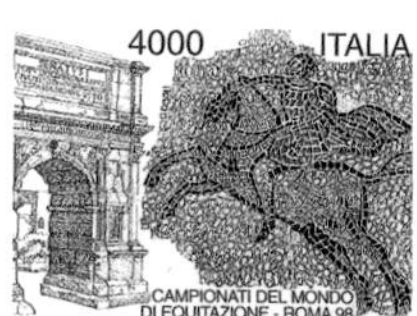

1038 Titus Arch, Rome, and Sicilian Mosaic of Rider

1998. World Equestrian Championships, Rome.
2516 **1038** 4000l. multicoloured 8·50 2·10

1039 Telecommunications College, Rome

1998. Universities.
2517 **1039** 800l. blue 2·00 35

1040 Pope John Paul II and his Message

1998. "Italia 98" International Stamp Exhibition, Milan (3rd issue). Stamp Day.
2518 **1040** 800l. multicoloured 2·75 35

1041 "Giuseppe Garibaldi" (aircraft carrier)

1998. Armed Forces Day. Multicoloured.
2519 800l. Type **1041** (Navy) 2·00 60
2520 800l. Eurofighter EF-2000 Typhoon (75th anniv of Air Force) 2·00 60
2521 800l. Carabiniere (vert) 2·00 45
2522 800l. Battle of El-Alamein at night (Army) (vert) 2·00 45

1042 "Dionysus" (bronze statue)

1998. "Italia 98" International Stamp Exhibition, Milan (4th issue). Art Day.
2523 **1042** 800l. multicoloured 2·00 45

1043 Ferrari competing in Race, 1931

1998. "Italia 98" International Stamp Exhibition, Milan (5th issue). Birth Centenary of Enzo Ferrari (car designer). Sheet 160×110 mm containing T 1043 and similar horiz designs. Multicoloured.
MS2524 800l. Type **1043**; 800l. Formula 1 Ferrari, 1952; 800l. Ferrari GTO, 1963; 800l. Formula 1 Ferrari, 1998 10·50 10·50

1044 Hand releasing Birds

1998. 50th Anniv of Universal Declaration of Human Rights.
2525 **1044** 1400l. multicoloured 4·00 60

1045 Cogwheels and "Proportions of Man" (Leonardo da Vinci)

1998. Europa Day. Ordinary or self-adhesive gum.
2526 **1045** 800l. multicoloured 2·75 30

1998. "Italia 98" International Stamp Exhibition, Milan (6th issue). Cinema Day. As T 946. Multicoloured.
2528 450l. "Ti Conosco Mascherino" (dir. Eduardo de Filippo) 1·80 80
2529 800l. "Fantasmia a Roma" (Antonio Pietrangeli) 3·00 60
2530 900l. "Il Signor Max" (Mario Camerini) 3·50 75

1046 Satellite Dish, Type, Book and "Internet"

1998. "Italia 98" International Stamp Exhibition, Milan (7th issue). Communications Day.
2531 **1046** 800l. multicoloured 2·20 35

1047 Arrows circling Letter

1998. "Italia 98" International Stamp Exhibition, Milan (8th issue). Post Day. Sheet 130×90 mm.
MS2532 **1047** 4000l. multicoloured 10·00 10·50

1048 "Epiphany" (sculpture, St. Mark's Church, Seminara)

1998. Christmas.
2533 **1048** 800l. blue 1·80 35
2534 - 900l. brown 2·20 45

DESIGN—HORIZ: 900l. "Adoration of the Shepherds" (drawing, Giulio Romano).

1049 "Ecstasy of St. Teresa"

1998. 400th Birth Anniv of Gian Lorenzo Bernini (sculptor).
2535 **1049** 900l. multicoloured 2·40 40

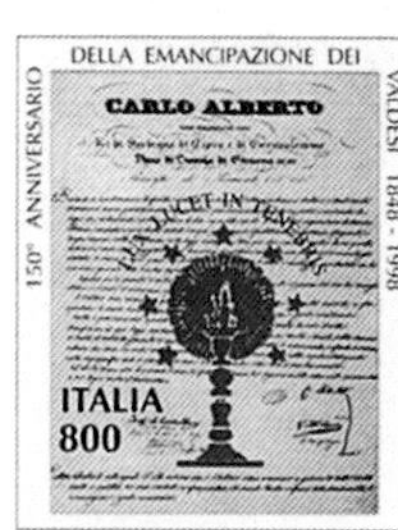

1050 Royal Decree and Waldensian Emblem

1998. 150th Anniv of Toleration of the Waldenses (religious sect).
2536 **1050** 800l. multicoloured 2·00 35

DENOMINATION. From No. 2537 Italian stamps are denominated both in lira and in euros. As no coins or notes for the latter were in circulation until 2002, the catalogue continues to use the lira value.

1999. As Nos. 2505/9, but with face value in euros added.
2537 100l. black, green and silver 25 25
2538 450l. multicoloured 1·10 25
2539 650l. multicoloured 1·60 35
2540 800l. brown and black 2·00 25
2541 1000l. blue, brown and black 2·50 25

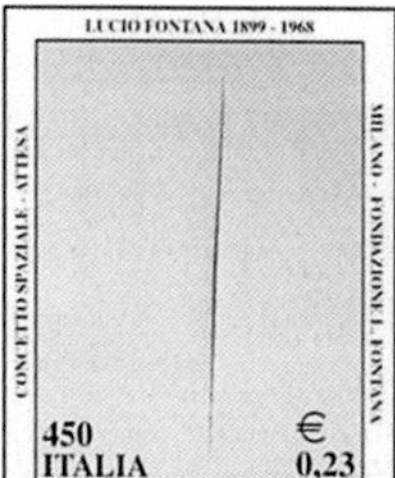

1051 "Space Concept–Wait"

1999. Birth Centenary of Lucio Fontana (artist).
2542 **1051** 450l. blue and black 1·30 45

1052 La Sila National Park, Calabria

1999. Europa. Parks and Gardens. Multicoloured.
2543 800l. Type **1052** 2·30 45
2544 900l. Tuscan Archipelago National Park (horiz) 2·75 45

1053 Holy Door, St. Peter's Cathedral

1999. Holy Year 2000.
2545 **1053** 1400l. multicoloured 3·75 70

1054 St. Egidius's Church, Cellere

1999. Artistic Heritage.
2546 **1054** 800l. brown 2·20 45

1055 Holy Year 2000 and 11th-century Bells

1999. Museums. Multicoloured.
2547 800l. Type **1055** (History of Campanology Museum, Agnone) 2·00 50
2548 800l. "Lake with Swan" (stained glass) (Casina delle Civette Museum, Rome) 2·00 45
2549 800l. Renaissance majolica dish (International Ceramics Museum, Faenza) (vert) 2·00 45

1056 Earth Pyramids, Segonzano

1999. Tourist Publicity (26th series). Multicoloured.
2550 800l. Type **1056** 2·00 45
2551 800l. Marmore Waterfall, Terni 2·00 45
2552 800l. Cathedral, Lecce 2·00 45
2553 800l. Lipari 2·00 45

1057 Audience Chamber

1999. Constitutional Court.
2554 **1057** 800l. multicoloured 2·20 45

1058 Fire Engine at Fire

1999. Fire Brigade.
2555 **1058** 800l. multicoloured 2·20 45

1059 Cadet and Academy

1999. Modena Military Academy.
2556 **1059** 800l. multicoloured 2·20 45

1060 Players and Airplane

1999. 50th Anniv of Death in Aircrash of Grand Turin Football Team. Multicoloured.
2557 800l. Type **1060** 2·00 35
2558 900l. Superga Basilica, club arms and names of victims 2·50 45

1061 Council Seat, Strasbourg

1999. 50th Anniv of Council of Europe.
2559 **1061** 800l. multicoloured 2·20 45

1062 Players and Club Emblem

1999. Milan, National Football Champion, 1998–99.
2560 **1062** 800l. multicoloured 2·40 45

1063 Ballot Box and Parliament Chamber, Strasbourg

1999. 20th Anniv of First Direct Elections to European Parliament.
2561 **1063** 800l. multicoloured 2·20 45

1064 Coppi

1999. 80th Birth Anniv of Fausto Coppi (racing cyclist).
2562 **1064** 800l. multicoloured 2·40 45

1065 "P"

1999. Priority Mail stamp. Self-adhesive.
2563 **1065** 1200l. black and gold 5·25 60
See also Nos. 2591 and 2660.

1066 First Fiat Car (advertising poster)

1999. Centenary of Fiat (motor manufacturer).
2564 **1066** 4800l. multicoloured 10·50 2·40

1067 "Our Lady of the Snow"

1999. Centenary of Erection of Statue of "Our Lady of the Snow" on Mt. Rocciamelone.
2565 **1067** 800l. multicoloured 2·20 45

1068 Pimentel and St. Elmo Castle, Naples

1999. Death Bicentenary of Eleonora de Fonseca Pimentel (writer and revolutionary).
2566 **1068** 800l. multicoloured 2·20 45

1069 Canoes

1999. 30th World Speed Canoeing Championships.
2567 **1069** 900l. multicoloured 2·40 40

1070 "Goethe in the Rome Countryside" (Johann Tischbein)

1999. 250th Birth Anniv of Johann Wolfgang Goethe (poet and playwright).
2568 **1070** 4000l. multicoloured 9·25 2·30

1071 Cyclist and Stopwatch

1999. World Cycling Championships, Treviso and Verona.
2569 **1071** 1400l. multicoloured 4·00 70

1072 Child with Rucksack

1999. Stamp Day.
2570 **1072** 800l. multicoloured 2·20 35

1073 Architectural Drawing of Basilica

1999. Re-opening of Upper Basilica of St. Francis of Assisi.
2571 **1073** 800l. multicoloured 2·20 45

1074 Parini (after Francesco Rosaspina)

1999. Death Bicentenary of Giuseppe Parini (poet).
2572 **1074** 800l. blue 2·20 45

1075 Volta (bust by Giovan Commolli) and Voltaic Pile

1999. Bicentenary of Invention of Electrochemical Battery by Alessandro Volta.
2573 **1075** 3000l. multicoloured 6·75 1·40

1076 Forms and U.P.U. Emblem

1999. 125th Anniv of Universal Postal Union.
2574 **1076** 900l. multicoloured 2·20 45

1077 Mameli with 1948 and 1949 100l. Stamps

1999. 150th Death Anniv of Goffredo Mameli (poet and patriot) and 150th Anniv of Roman Republic.
2575 **1077** 1500l. multicoloured 3·50 1·70

1078 Man and Town

1999. "The Stamp Our Friend". Multicoloured.

2576	450l. Type **1078**	1·10	40
2577	650l. Campaign emblem	1·60	50
2578	800l. Schoolchildren	2·00	60
2579	1000l. Windmill (toy)	2·50	70

1079 First World War Soldiers (after postcard)

1999. Centenary of Generation of '99.
2580 **1079** 900l. multicoloured 2·40 35

1080 Santa Claus

1999. Christmas. Multicoloured.

2581	800l. Type **1080**	2·20	45
2582	1000l. "Nativity" (Dosso Dossi)	2·75	60

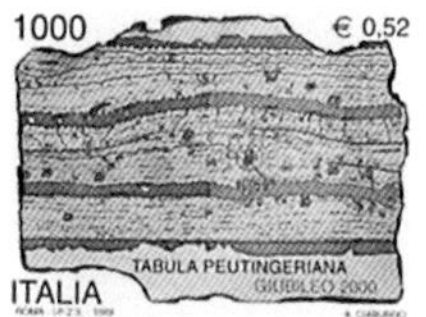
1081 Peutinger Tablet (medieval map showing pilgrim route by C. Celtes and Conrad Peutinger)

1999. Holy Year 2000. Multicoloured.

2583	1000l. Type **1081**	2·50	60
2584	1000l. 18th-century pilgrim's stamp	2·50	60
2585	1000l. 13th-century bas-relief of pilgrims (facade of Fidenza Cathedral)	2·50	60

1082 Urbino State Art Institute

1999. Schools and Universities.

2586	**1082**	450l. black	1·10	60
2587	-	650l. brown	1·60	45

DESIGN: 650l. Pisa High School.

1083 "Leopard bitten by Tarantula"

1999. Birth Centenary of Antonio Ligabue (artist).
2588 **1083** 1000l. multicoloured 2·75 60

1084 Robot's Hand meeting Man's Hand (after Michelangelo)

1999. Year 2000.
2589 **1084** 4800l. multicoloured 10·50 2·75

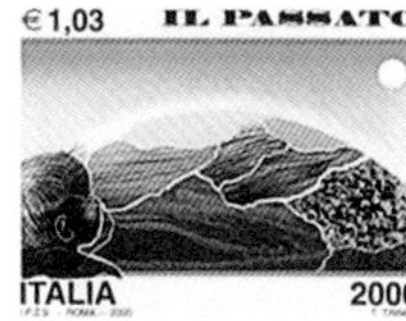
1085 Child looking at Aspects of Earth

2000. New Millennium. "The Past and the Future". Sheet 110×80 mm containing T 1085 and similar horiz design. Multicoloured.
MS2590 2000l. Type **1085**; 2000l. Astronaut looking at Moon 10·50 9·25

2000. Priority Mail Stamp. As T 1065 but different colour. Self-adhesive.
2591 1200l. black, yellow and gold 5·25 50

1086 Tosca and Scenery

2000. Centenary of the First Performance of Tosca (opera).
2592 **1086** 800l. multicoloured 2·75 45

1087 St. Paul (statue) and Holy Door, St. Peter's Basilica, Rome

2000. Holy Year 2000.
2593 **1087** 1000l. multicoloured 3·00 50

1088 Players

2000. Six Nations Rugby Championship.
2594 **1088** 800l. multicoloured 2·75 45

1089 Painting

2000. 5th Conference on Breast Diseases. Mult.

2595	800l. Type **1089**	2·00	35
2596	1000l. Painting (different)	2·75	60

1090 "Enigma of an Autumn Afternoon"

2000. New Millennium (1st issue). Art and Science. Sheet 111×80 mm containing T 1090 and similar horiz design showing paintings by Giorgio de Chirico. Multicoloured.
MS2597 800l. Type **1090** (art); 800l. "The Inevitable Temple" (science) 5·25 4·50

See also Nos. **MS**2613 and 2623.

1091 Skier and Trophy

2000. World Cup Skiing Championships.
2598 **1091** 4800l. multicoloured 10·50 2·75

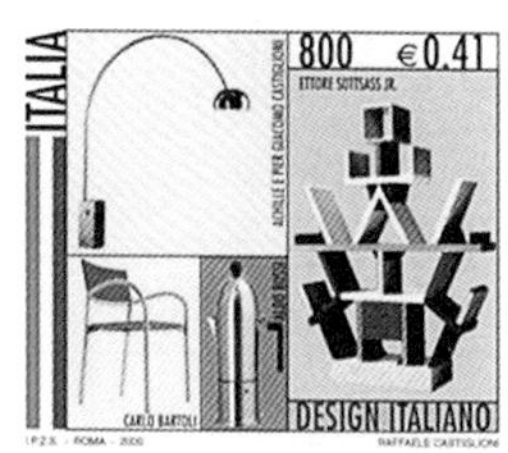
1092 Lamp (Achillle and Pier Giacomo Castiglioni), Chair (Carlo Batroli), Coffee Pot (Aldo Rossi) and Bookcase (Ettore Softsass Jr.)

2000. Italian Design. Sheet 154×138 mm containing T 1092 and similar horiz designs. Multicoloured.
MS2599 800l. Type **1092**; 800l. Armchair (Mario Bellini), corkscrew (Alessandro Mendini), table lamp (Vico Magistretti) and suspended lamp (Alberto Meda and Paolo Rizzatto); 800l. Chair (Gio Ponti), bean bag (Gatti Paolini Teodoro), pasta set (Massimo Morozzi) and standard uplighter (Tobia Scarpa); 800l. White standard uplighter (Pietro Chiesa), hostess trolley (Joe Columbo), chair (Cini Boeri and Tomu Katayanagi) and sideboard (Lodovico Acerbis and Giotto Stoppino); 800l. Easy chairs (Gaetano Pesce), chair (Enzo Mari), clothes horse (De Pas d'Urbino Lomazzi) and mobile filing cabinet (Antonio Citterio and Oliver Loew); 800l. Chair (Marco Zanuso), anglepoise lamp (Michele de Lucchi and Giancarlo Fassina), ice bucket (Bruno Munari) and stool (Anna Castelli Ferrieri) 10·50 9·25

1093 "Adoration of the Magi" (Domenico Ghirlandaio)

2000. Holy Year 2000. Multicoloured.

2600	450l. Type **1093**	1·10	35
2601	650l. "Baptism of Christ" (Paolo Caliari Veronese) (vert)	1·60	40
2602	800l. "The Last Supper" (Ghirlandaio) (vert)	1·90	35
2603	1000l. "Regret of Christ's Death" (Giotto di Bondone)	2·40	60
2604	1200l. "The Resurrection" (Piero della Francesca) (vert)	3·00	65

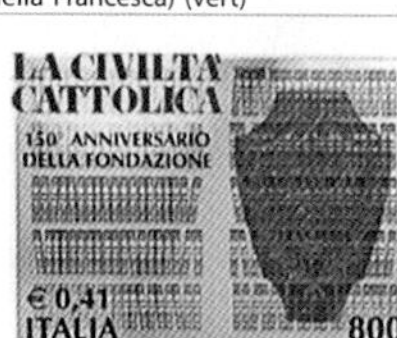
1094 Library and Emblem

2000. 150th Anniv of La Civilta Cattolica Foundation (collection of Church publications).
2605 **1094** 800l. multicoloured 2·75 45

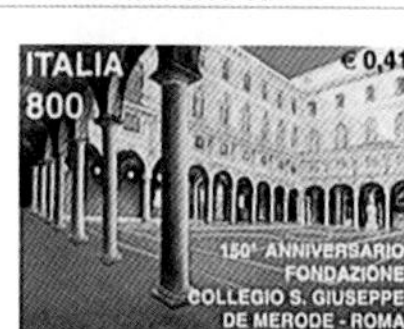
1095 Courtyard

2000. 150th Anniv of St. Joseph's College, Rome.
2606 **1095** 800l. multicoloured 2·75 45

1096 Terre di Franciacorta, Erbrusco

2000. Tourist Publicity (27th series). Multicoloured.

2607	800l. Type **1096**	2·00	45
2608	800l. Dunarobba fossil forest, Avigliano Umbro	2·00	45
2609	800l. View of Ercolano	2·00	45
2610	800l. Beauty Island, Taormina	2·00	45

1097 Cyclist

2000. Centenary of International Cycling Union.
2611 **1097** 1500l. multicoloured 4·00 80

1098 Christ carrying Cross

2000. Papier-mache Figurines, Caltanisetta.
2612 **1098** 800l. multicoloured 2·75 45

1099 Landscape (Gilorgione)

2000. New Millennium (2nd issue). Countryside and City. Sheet 110×80 mm containing T 1099 and similar horiz design. Multicoloured.
MS2613 800l. Type **1099**; 800l. "Perspective of an Ideal Town" (Piero della Francesca) 5·00 3·00

1100 Piccinni

2000. Death Bicentenary of Niccolo Piccinni (composer).
2614 **1100** 4000l. multicoloured 8·00 2·30

1101 "Building Europe"

2000. Europa.
2615 **1101** 800l. multicoloured 3·25 45

1102 Sardinia 1851 5, 20 and 40c. Stamps

2000. Museum of Posts and Telecommunications. Multicoloured.
2616 800l. Type **1102** 2·20 45

2617 800l. Reconstruction of radio and telegraph cabin aboard Elettra (Marconi's steam yacht) 2·20 45

1103 Footballer and Pitch

2000. Lazio, National Football Champion, 1999–2000.
2618 **1103** 800l. multicoloured 2·75 45

1104 Cathedral Facade

2000. 700th Anniv of Monza Cathedral.
2619 **1104** 800l. multicoloured 2·75 45

1105 Globe and Ears of Corn

2000. United Nations World Food Programme.
2620 **1105** 1000l. multicoloured 3·00 60

1106 Statue

2000. Centenary of the Jesus the Redeemer Monument, Nuoro.
2621 **1106** 800l. multicoloured 2·75 45

1107 Bridge, Parana River, Argentina

2000. 120th Anniv of Italian Water Board.
2622 **1107** 800l. multicoloured 2·75 45

€0,41 LE GENERAZIONI
ITALIA 800

1108 Profiles

2000. New Millennium (3rd issue). Technology and Space. Sheet 110×80 mm containing T 1108 and similar horiz design. Multicoloured.
MS2623 800l. Type **1108**; 800l. Symbolic man 4·75 3·00

1109 Child with Ladder to Moon (Giacomo Chiesa)

2000. "Stampin the Future". Winning Entry in Children's International Painting Competition.
2624 **1109** 1000l. multicoloured 3·00 60

1110 Archer

2000. World Archery Championship, Campagna.
2625 **1110** 1500l. multicoloured 3·50 80

1111 Cyclist and Globe

2000. World Junior Cycling Championships.
2626 **1111** 800l. multicoloured 2·75 45

1112 Fair Attractions

2000. Millenary of St. Orso.
2627 **1112** 1000l. multicoloured 3·00 60

1113 "Madonna and Child" (Crivelli)

2000. 570th Birth Anniv of Carlo Crivelli (artist).
2628 **1113** 800l. multicoloured 2·75 45

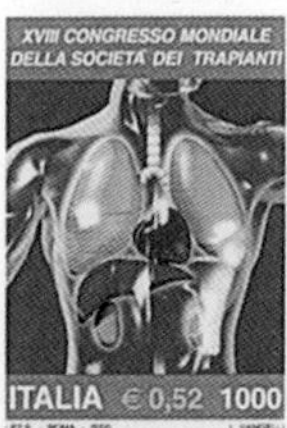

1114 Internal Organs

2000. 18th International Transplantation Society Congress, Rome.
2629 **1114** 1000l. multicoloured 3·00 60

1115 Athlete and Stadium

2000. Olympic Games, Sydney. Multicoloured.
2630 800l. Type **1115** 2·40 35
2631 1000l. "Discus Thrower" (statue) and Sydney Harbour 3·00 60

1116 "War"

2000. New Millennium (4th issue). War and Peace. Frescoes by Taddeo Zuccan. Sheet 110×80 mm containing T 1116 and similar vert design. Multicoloured.
MS2632 800l. Type **1116**; 800l. "Peace" 5·25 3·00

1117 Battle Scene (Jacques Debreville)

2000. Bicentenary of Marengo.
2633 **1117** 800l. multicoloured 2·75 45

1118 Figures in Evening Dress and City Skyline

2000. New Year.
2634 **1118** 800l. multicoloured 2·75 45

1119 Child holding Magnifying Glass

2000. Stamp Day.
2635 **1119** 800l. multicoloured 2·75 45

1120 Monti and Sick Child

2000. Death Centenary of Father Luigi Monti.
2636 **1120** 800l. multicoloured 2·75 45

1121 Salieri

2000. 250th Birth Anniv of Antonio Salieri (composer).
2637 **1121** 4800l. multicoloured 10·00 3·00

1122 Disabled Athletes

2000. Paralympic Games, Sydney.
2638 **1122** 1500l. multicoloured 4·00 80

1123 Emblem, Chaos Model and Globe in Container

2000. World Mathematics Year.
2639 **1123** 800l. multicoloured 2·75 45

1124 Couple and Globe

2000. Volunteers.
2640 **1124** 800l. multicoloured 2·75 45

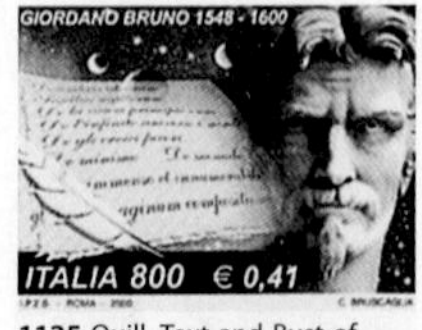

1125 Quill, Text and Bust of Bruno (Pietro Masulli)

2000. 400th Death Anniv of Giordano Bruno (writer and philosopher).
2641 **1125** 800l. multicoloured 2·75 45

1126 "Madonna of the Rose Garden"

2000. 600th Birth Anniv of Luca della Robbia (artist).
2642 **1126** 800l. multicoloured 2·75 45

1127 Arms of Academy

2000. 250th Anniv of Roveretana degli Agiati Academy.
2643 **1127** 800l. multicoloured 2·75 60

1128 Martino and Map of Europe

2000. Birth Centenary of Gaetano Martino (politician).
2644 **1128** 800l. multicoloured 2·50 60

1129 "Perseus with the Head of Medusa" (bronze statue)

2000. 500th Birth Anniv of Benvenuto Cellini (goldsmith and sculptor).
2645 **1129** 1200l. multicoloured 3·25 1·70

1130 Young Woman

2000. New Millennium (5th series). Meditation and Expression. Sheet 110×80 mm containing T 1130 and similar horiz design. Multicoloured.
MS2646 800l. Type **1130**; 800l. Dancing figures 5·00 3·00

1131 Camerino University

2000. Universities. Each blue.
2647 800l. Type **1131** 2·00 45
2648 1000l. Calabria University 2·75 60

1132 Snowflakes and Globe

2000. Christmas. Multicoloured.
2649 800l. Type **1132** 1·30 45
2650 1000l. Crib, Matera Cathedral 1·60 60

1133 Snowboarding

2001. World Snowboarding Championships, Madonna di Campiglio.
2651 **1133** 1000l. multicoloured 2·75 60

1134 "The Annunciation" (detail, Botticelli)

2001. "Italy in Japan 2001" (cultural and scientific event).
2652 **1134** 1000l. multicoloured 2·50 60

1135 Vincenzo Bellini (composer, birth bicentenary)

2001. Composers' Anniversaries. Sheet 87×180 mm containing T 1135 and similar vert designs. Multicoloured.
MS2653 800l. Type **1135**; 800l. Domenico Cimarosa (death bicentenary); 800l. Gasparo Luigi Pacifico Spontini (150th death anniv); 800l. Giuseppe Verdi (death centenary) 10·00 8·00

1136 St. Rose and Angels (Francesco Podesti di Ancona)

2001. 750th Death Anniv of St. Rose of Viterbo.
2654 **1136** 800l. multicoloured 2·50 35

1137 Racing Car

2001. Ferrari, Formula One Constructor's Championship Winner (2000). Sheet 110×81 mm.
MS2655 **1137** 5000l. multicoloured 11·50 9·25

1138 Abbey of Santa Maria in Sylvis, Sesto al Reghena

2001
2656 **1138** 800l. blue 2·10 45

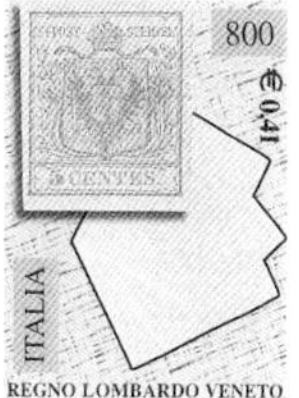

1139 Lombardy and Venetia 1850 5c. Stamp (151st anniv)

2001. Stamp Anniversaries. Multicoloured.
2657 800l. Type **1139** 2·30 45
2658 800l. Sardinia 1851 5c. stamp (150th anniv) 2·30 45
2659 800l. Tuscany 1851 1q. stamp (150th anniv) 2·30 45

2001. Priority Mail Stamp. As T 1065 but central "P" larger, 12×12 mm. Self-adhesive.
2660 1200l. black, yellow and gold 4·75 60

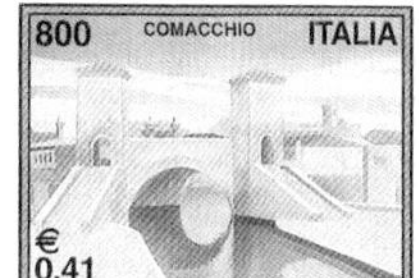

1140 Bridge, Comacchio

2001. Tourist Publicity (28th series). Multicoloured.
2661 800l. Type **1140** 1·70 45
2662 800l. Diamante 1·70 45
2663 800l. Pioraco 1·70 45
2664 800l. Stintino 1·70 45

1141 Campanula

2001. World Day to Combat Desertification and Drought. Multicoloured.
2665 450l. Type **1141** 95 60
2666 650l. Marmosets 1·40 60
2667 800l. White storks 1·60 45
2668 1000l. Desert and emblem 2·00 70

1142 Map of Italy and Tractors

2001. Confederation General of Italian Agriculture.
2669 **1142** 800l. multicoloured 2·10 45

1143 Castle and Emblem

2001. Millenary of Gorzia City.
2670 **1143** 800l. multicoloured 2·10 45

1144 Water pouring from Vase

2001. Europa. Water Resources.
2671 **1144** 800l. multicoloured 4·00 45

1145 Profiles

2001. European Union.
2672 **1145** 800l. multicoloured 2·00 45

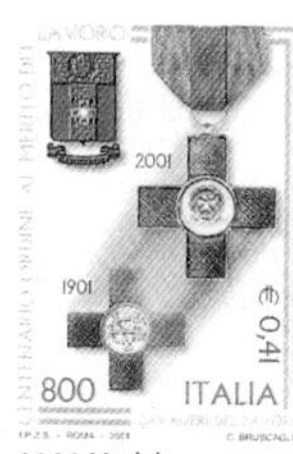

1146 Medals

2001. Centenary of Order of Merit for Labour.
2673 **1146** 800l. multicoloured 2·00 45

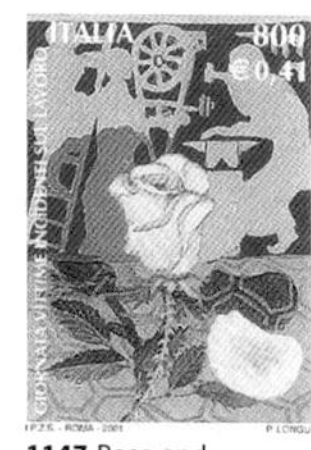

1147 Rose and Workers' Silhouettes

2001. National Day for Victims of Industrial Accidents.
2674 **1147** 800l. multicoloured 2·00 45

1148 Child with Stamp and Magnifying Glass (Rita Vergari)

2001. Day for Art and Student Creativity. Multicoloured.
2675 800l. Type **1148** 1·60 45
2676 800l. People standing on rainbow (Lucia Catena) 1·60 45
2677 800l. Painting with eye (Luigi di Cristo) 1·60 45
2678 800l. Colours and profile (Barbara Grilli) 1·60 45

1149 "St. Peter healing with his Shadow"

2001. 600th Birth Anniv of Tommaso de Giovanni di Simone Guidi "Masaccio " (painter).
2679 **1149** 800l. multicoloured 2·00 45

1150 "Madonna and Child" (Piero della Francesca)

2001. 500th Death Anniv of Giovanni della Rovere.
2680 **1150** 800l. multicoloured 2·00 45

1151 Emblem

2001. 50th Anniv of Panathlon International (sports organization).

2681	**1151**	800l. multicoloured	2·00	45

1152 Guaita Tower, Mt. Titano

2001. 1700th Anniv of San Marino.

2682	**1152**	800l. multicoloured	2·00	45

1153 Footballer and Net

2001. A S Roma, National Football Champion, 2000–1.

2683	**1153**	800l. multicoloured	2·75	45

1154 Motorboat and Bell UH1 Iroquois Helicopter

2001. Harbour Master's Office.

2684	**1154**	800l. multicoloured	2·50	45

1155 Quasimodo

2001. Birth Centenary of Salvatore Quasimodo (writer).

2685	**1155**	1500l. multicoloured	3·25	90

1156 Octagonal Hall, Domus Aurea, Rome

2001

2686	**1156**	1000l. brown	16·00	60

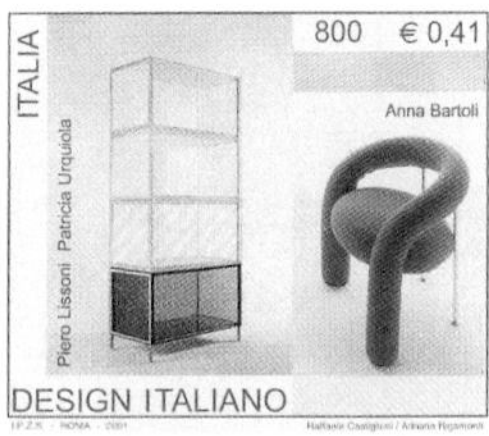
1157 Bookcase (Piero Lissoni and Patricia Urquiola) and Chair (Anna Bartolli)

2001. Italian Design. Sheet 155×137 mm containing T 1157 and similar horiz designs. Multicoloured.

MS2687 800l. Type **1157**; 800l. Chair (Monica Graffeo) and table lamp (Rodolfo Dordoni); 800l. Lamp (Ferruccio Laviani) and sofa (Massimo Iosa Ghini); 800l. Armchair (Anna Gili) and side table (Miki Astori); 800l. Vertical storage unit (Marco Ferreri) and double seat (M. Cananzi and R. Semprini); 800l. Stool (Stefano Giovannoni) and flexible-necked lamp (Massimiliano Datti) 10·00 7·00

1158 "The Fourth State" (detail, Guiseppe Pellizza da Volpedo)

2001

2688	**1158**	1000l. brown	2·75	60

1159 Stone Age Man and Pick

2001. Archaeological Museum, Alto Adige.

2689	**1159**	800l. multicoloured	2·00	45

1160 Schoolchildren

2001. Youth Philately.

2690	**1160**	800l. multicoloured	2·00	45

1161 Fermi

2001. Birth Centenary of Enrico Fermi (physicist).

2691	**1161**	800l. multicoloured	2·00	45

1162 Pavia University

2001. Universities.

2692	**1162**	800l. blue	1·80	45
2693	-	800l. brown	1·80	45
2694	-	800l. turquoise	1·80	45

DESIGNS—VERT: No. 2693 Bari, University. HORIZ: 2694, School of Science, Rome.

1163 Latinas and Messanger

2001. Unione Latina (Romance language speaking countries).

2695	**1163**	800l. black, yellow and blue	2·00	45

1164 Exhibits

2001. National Archaeological Museum, Taranto.

2696	**1164**	1000l. multicoloured	2·50	50

1165 International Fund for Agricultural Development Emblem

2001. World Food Day. Each stamp featuring "The Seed" (sculpture) by Roberto Joppolo. Multicoloured.

2697	800l. Type **1165**	2·20	40
2698	800l. Plants and woman hoeing (50th anniv of Food and Agriculture Organization Summit Conference, Rome) (50×29 mm)	2·20	40
2699	800l. World Food Programme emblem	2·20	40

1166 "Enthroned Christ with Angels" (painting on wood)

2001

2700	**1166**	800l. multicoloured	2·00	45

1167 "Madonna and Child" (painting from triptych)

2001. 500th Anniv of "Madonna and Child, Angels, St. Francis, St. Thomas Aquinas and two Donors" (triptych, Macrino d'Alba).

2701	**1167**	800l. multicoloured	2·00	45

1168 "Dawn of Peace" (collage, San Vito dei Normani Primary School)

2001. Christmas. Multicoloured.

2702	800l. Type **1168**	1·60	45
2703	1000l. "Nativity" (painting, St. Mary Major Basilica)	2·10	60

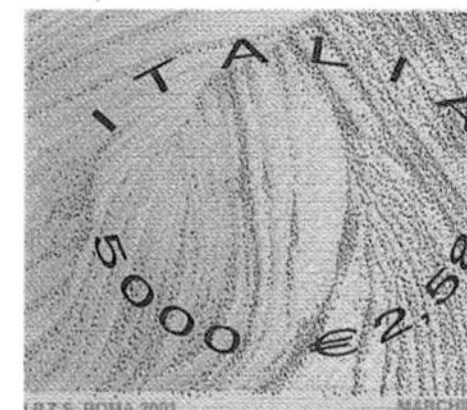
1169 Fabric

2001. Italian Silk Industry. Sheet 140×92 mm. Self-adhesive gum. Imperf.

MS2704 **1169** 5000l. multicoloured 13·50 9·25

No. **MS**2704 was printed on fabric mounted on silk jacquard. A peel-off plastic backing featured instructions for use. If required, the address could be written in the blank area at the bottom right of the sheet.

2002. Women in Art. As T 1032 but with values expressed in euros.

2705	1c. multicoloured	10	10
2706	2c. multicoloured	10	10
2707	3c. multicoloured	10	10
2708	5c. multicoloured	10	10
2709	10c. multicoloured	15	10
2710	20c. multicoloured	60	15
2711	23c. multicoloured	80	15
2715	41c. brown, grey and black	2·75	15
2716	45c. purple, blue and black	2·75	25
2716a	50c. turquoise, red and black	70	35
2716b	65c. blue and red	90	45
2716c	70c. violet and green	95	45
2717	77c. brown, green and black	2·75	35
2718	85c. purple and black	1·20	60
2719	90c. green and red	1·30	65

DESIGNS: 1c. "Ebe" (detail, painting, Antonia Canova); 2c. Profile (5th-century B.C. coin, Syracuse); 3c. Woman's head (detail from mural, Piero della Francesca); 5c. As No. 2505; 10c. Head (3rd-century B.C. sculpture, "G. Fiorelli" civic museum, Lucera); 20c. Portrait of a Lady (Correggio); 23c. As No. 2506; 41c. As No. 2508; 45c. "Venere di Urbino" (Tiziano Vecellio); 50c. "Portrait of a young girl" (detail, painting, Francesco Mazzola); 65c. "San Giorgio e la Principessa di Trebisonda" (detail by Antonis Pisano); 70c. "Wettuno a Venezia" (detail by Giambattista Foggini, sculpture); 77c. "Spring" (detail, painting, Botticelli); 85c. "Costigiana" (detail, by Vittore (arpaccio)), 90c. "Venere e Marte legati de Amore" (detail, by Paolo Calieri).

1170 "Ducato" (Venetian coin), 1285

2002. European Coins. Multicoloured.

2725	41c. Type **1170**	2·30	45
2726	41c. "Genovino" (Genoa) and "Fiorino" (Florence), 1252	2·30	45
2727	41c. Flags of E.U. forming Euro symbol	2·30	45
2728	41c. 1946 lira coin transforming into euro coin	2·30	45

2002. Priority Mail Stamps. Designs as No. 2660 but with face values in euros only. Multicoloured, background colour given. Self-adhesive gum.

2729	62c. yellow	4·00	35
2730	77c. blue	2·40	80
2731	€1 lavender	2·75	60
2732	€1.24 green	8·00	1·50
2733	€1.86 pink	13·00	2·30
2734	€4.13 lilac	15·00	5·25

1171 Woman's Head and State Arms

2002

2735	**1171**	€1 multicoloured	6·75	9·75
2736	**1171**	€1.24 multicoloured	8·00	90
2737	**1171**	€1.55 multicoloured	10·00	1·20
2738	**1171**	€2.17 multicoloured	13·50	1·40
2738a	**1171**	€2.35 multicoloured	3·25	1·50
2739	**1171**	€2.58 multicoloured	16·00	1·40
2739a	**1171**	€2.80 multicoloured	3·75	1·80
2739b	**1171**	€3 multicoloured	4·00	2·00
2740	**1171**	€3.62 multicoloured	20·00	3·75
2741	**1171**	€6.20 multicoloured	31·00	7·00

1172 Escriva

2002. Birth Centenary of Josemaria Escriva de Balaguer (founder of Opus Dei (religious organization)).
2745 1172 41c. multicoloured 2·00 45

1173 Luigi Bocconi and University Building

2002. Centenary of Bocconi University.
2746 1173 41c. brown and stone 2·00 45

The University was established with an endowment from Ferinando Bocconi in memory of his son Luigi.

1174 1852 5c. Stamp

2002. 150th Anniv of First Stamp of Parma. Fluorescent paper.
2747 1174 41c. multicoloured 2·00 45

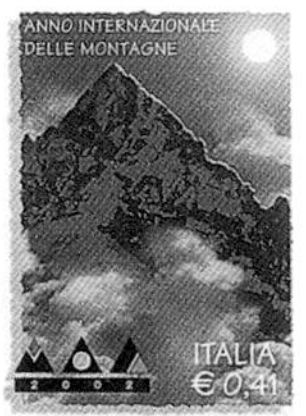
1175 Mountain Peak

2002. International Year of Mountains.
2748 1175 41c. multicoloured 2·00 45

1176 Emblem and Olympic Rings

2002. Winter Olympic Games, Turin (2006).
2749 1176 41c. multicoloured 2·00 35

1177 Queen Elena

2002. 50th Death Anniv of Queen Elena of Savoy.
2750 1177 41c.+21c. multicoloured 2·75 1·20

1178 Sculpture (Arnolfo di Cambio)

2002. 700th Death Anniv of Arnolfo di Cambio (sculptor).
2751 1178 41c. mauve 2·00 45

1179 Venaria Reale

2002. Tourist Publicity (29th series). Multicoloured.
2752 41c. Type 1179 1·90 45
2753 41c. Capo d'Orlando 1·90 45
2754 41c. San Gimignano 1·90 45
2755 41c. Sannicandro di Bari 1·90 45

1180 Santa Maria delle Grazie Sanctuary

2002
2756 1180 41c. brown 2·00 45

1181 Police Officers, Computer Screen and Patrol Car

2002. 150th Anniv of State Police Force.
2757 1181 41c. multicoloured 2·00 45

1182 Ricci and World Map

2002. 450th Birth Anniv of Matteo Rici (missionary).
2758 1182 41c. multicoloured 2·00 45

1183 Circus Performers

2002. Europa. Circus.
2759 1183 41c. multicoloured 2·75 45

1184 Sailing Ship and Student

2002. Francesco Morosini Naval Military School, Venice.
2760 1184 41c. multicoloured 2·00 45

1185 Vittorio de Sica (film director, birth centenary)

2002. Cinema Anniversaries. Multicoloured.
2761 41c. Type 1185 1·80 45
2762 41c. Text and clouds (birth centenary (1901) of Cesare Zavattini (screen writer)) 1·80 45

1186 Football Player and Emblem

2002. Juventus, National Football Champions, 2001–2002.
2763 1186 41c. multicoloured 2·00 45

1187 Falcone and Boresellino

2002. 10th Death Annivs of Giovanni Falcone and Paolo Borsellino (judges).
2764 1187 62c. multicoloured 3·25 70

1188 Emblems and Member Flags

2002. Russia's Membership of North Atlantic Treaty Organization (N.A.T.O.).
2765 1188 41c. multicoloured 2·00 60

1189 Kayaking

2002. World Kayaking Championship, Valsesia.
2766 1189 52c. multicoloured 2·75 45

1190 Modena 1853 1 lira Arms of Este Stamp

2002. 150th Anniv of Modena (Italian State) Stamps.
2767 1190 41c. multicoloured 2·00 45

1191 Arms

2002. Italian Military Involvement in Peace Missions.
2768 1191 41c. multicoloured 2·00 45

1192 Binda

2002. Birth Centenary of Alfrodo Binda (cyclist).
2769 1192 41c. multicoloured 2·00 45

1193 Santo

2002. Canonization of Father Padre Pio Santo.
2770 1193 41c. multicoloured 2·00 45

1194 Divisione Acqui (monument, Mario Salazzari)

2002. "Divisione Acqui" (World War II resistance group on Cephalonia).
2771 1194 41c. multicoloured 2·75 45

1195 Crucifixion (Arezzo Basilica)

2002
2772 1195 €2.58 multicoloured 11·50 2·75

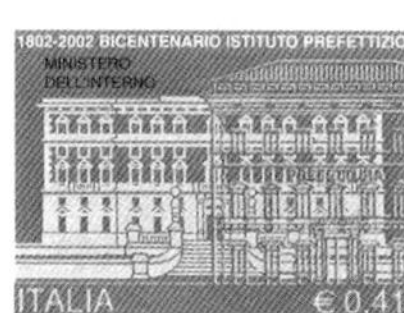
1196 Building Facade

2002. Bicentenary of Ministry of Interior.
2773 1196 41c. multicoloured 2·00 45

1197 Maria Goretti

2002. Death Centenary of Saint Maria Goretti.
2774 1197 41c. multicoloured 2·00 45

1198 Mazarin

2002. 400th Birth Anniv of Cardinal Jules Mazarin (minister to Louis XIV of France).
2775 1198 41c. multicoloured 2·00 45

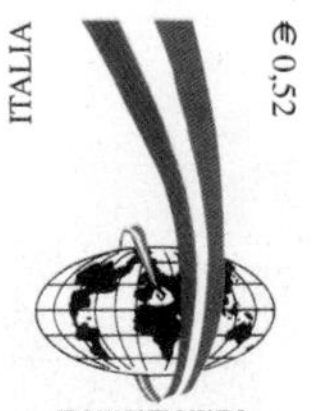

1199 National Colours encircling Globe

2002. "Italians in the World".
2776 **1199** 52c. multicoloured 2·75 60

1200 Monument (Vincenzo Gasperetti)

2002. Monument to the Victims of Massacre at Sant' Anna di Stazzema.
2777 **1200** 41c. multicoloured 2·00 45

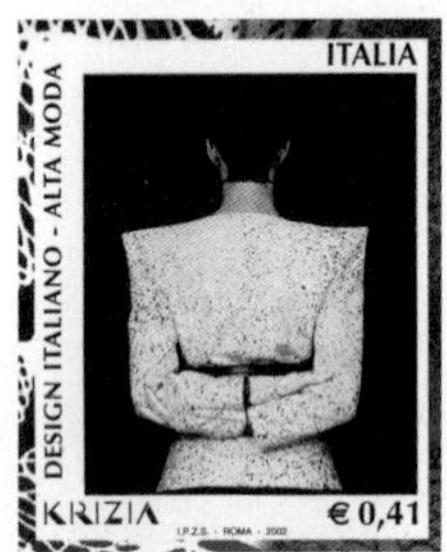

1201 Jacket (Krizia)

2002. Italian Design. Sheet 157×137 mm, containing T 1201 and similar vert designs. Multicoloured.
MS2778 41c. Type **1201**; 41c. Brassiere (Dolce & Gabbana); 41c. Drawing of dress (Gianfranco Ferre); 41c. Drawing of suit (Giorgio Armani); 41c. Dress (Laura Biagiotti); 41c. Shoes (Prada) 12·00 12·00

1202 Cathedral and Tower, Pisa

2002. UNESCO World Heritage Sites. Multicoloured.
2779 41c. Type **1202** 2·30 35
2780 52c. Aeolian Islands 3·00 40

Stamps of a similar design were issued by the United Nations.

1203 Dalla Chiesa

2002. 20th Anniv of Assassination of Carlo Alberto Dalla Chiesa (police chief and prefect of Palermo).
2781 **1203** 41c. multicoloured 2·00 45

1204 Teatro della Concordia, Monte Castello di Vibio, Perugia

2002
2782 **1204** 41c. multicoloured 2·00 45

1205 Yacht

2002. 12th Prada Classic Yacht Challenge, Imperia.
2783 **1205** 41c. multicoloured 2·00 45

1206 Papal States 1852 5b. Stamp

2002. 150th Anniv of First Papal States Stamp.
2784 **1206** 41c. multicoloured 2·00 45

1207 Cross, City Museum, Santa Giulia, Brescia

2002. Museum Exhibits. Multicoloured.
2785 41c. Type **1207** 1·90 45
2786 41c. Busts, Museo Nazionale, Palazzo Altemps, Rome (horiz) 1·90 45

1208 Orchid

2002. Flora and Fauna. Multicoloured.
2787 23c. Type **1208** 80 35
2788 52c. European lynx 1·80 50
2789 77c. Stag beetle 2·75 80

1209 Emblem

2002. World Food Day.
2790 **1209** 41c. multicoloured 2·00 45

1210 Corps Member and Emblem

2002. State Forestry Corps.
2791 **1210** 41c. multicoloured 2·00 45

1211 Gnocchi and Children

2002. Birth Centenary of Carlo Gnocchi (founder of rehabilitation centres for disabled children).
2792 **1211** 41c. multicoloured 2·00 45

1212 Microscope and Emblem

2002. "Telethon 2002" (campaign to combat muscular dystrophy and genetic disease).
2793 **1212** 41c. multicoloured 2·00 45

1213 The Holy Family

2002. Christmas. Multicoloured.
2794 41c. Type **1213** 7·25 40
2795 62c. Child and Christmas tree 2·00 65

1214 "Nike di Samotracia" (statue) and Athlete

2002. Women in Sport.
2796 **1214** 41c. multicoloured 2·00 45

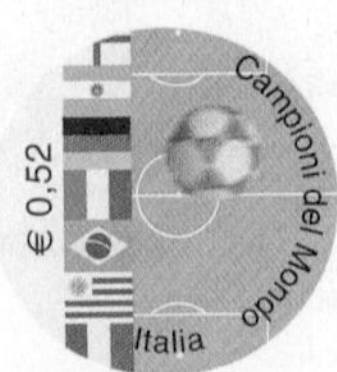

1215 Flags of Championship Winners and Football

2002. 20th-century World Cup Football Champions. Multicoloured.
2797 52c. Type **1215** 2·50 70
2798 52c. Italian footballer 2·50 70

1216 Magnifying Glass, Stamps and Children

2002. Stamp Day. Philately in Schools.
2799 **1216** 62c. multicoloured 2·00 65

1217 Vittorio Orlando

2002. 50th Death Anniv of Vittorio Emanuele Orlando (politician).
2800 **1217** 41c. multicoloured 2·00 45

1218 Event Emblem

2003. "Tarvisio 2003" (winter sports competition).
2801 **1218** 52c. multicoloured 2·75 50

1219 Family and Scales

2003. The Italian Republic on Stamps.
2802 **1219** 62c. multicoloured 2·75 65

1220 Cyclist carrying Cycle

2003. World Cyclo-cross Championship, Monopoli.
2803 **1220** 41c. multicoloured 1·80 45

1221 Building and Tandem

2003. 150th Anniv (2002) of Fratelli Alinari (photographic company).
2804 **1221** 77c. multicoloured 4·75 80

1222 Jigsaw Puzzle

2003. European Year of the Disabled.
2805 **1222** 41c. multicoloured 1·80 45

1223 Skiers

2003. World Nordic Skiing Championship, Val di Fiemme.
2806 **1223** 41c. multicoloured 1·80 45

1224 Couple, Flower and Emblem

2003. National Civil Service.
2807 **1224** 62c. multicoloured 2·75 65

1225 Knights on Horseback

2003. 500th Anniv of the Barletta Challenge (battle between 13 French and 13 Italian knights).
2808 **1225** 41c. multicoloured 1·80 70

1226 Building Facade

2003. Torquato Tasso Grammar School (gymnasium).
2809 **1226** 41c. multicoloured 1·80 70

1227 "Encounter by the Golden Door" (Giotto)

2003
2810 **1227** 41c. multicoloured 1·80 70

1228 Gian Rinaldo Carli and Building

2003. Gian Rinaldo Carli Grammar School (gymnasium).
2811 **1228** 41c. multicoloured 1·80 70

1229 Academy Emblem

2003. 400th Anniv of "Accademia dei Lincei" (academy of lynxes) (scientific society).
2812 **1229** 41c. multicoloured 1·80 70

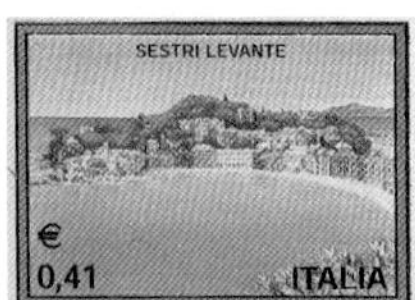

1230 Foils and Fencers

2003. World Junior Fencing Championships, Trapani.
2813 **1230** 41c. multicoloured 1·80 70

1231 Sestri Levante

2003. Tourist Publicity (30th series). Multicoloured.
2814 41c. Type **1231** 1·80 70
2815 41c. Lanciano 1·80 70
2816 41c. Procida 1·80 70

1232 Golfer

2003. Centenary of Roma Acquasanta Golf Course.
2817 **1232** 77c. multicoloured 3·50 1·60

1233 Minerva (statue) and Building Facade

2003. 700th Anniv of La Sapienza University, Rome.
2818 **1233** 41c. multicoloured 2·10 1·00

1234 Pasta

2003. National Pasta Museum, Rome.
2819 **1234** 41c. multicoloured 1·80 85

1235 Guido Carli and University Building

2003. Guido Carli-LUISS (international liberal social studies) University.
2820 **1235** €2.58 multicoloured 8·00 5·25

1236 Woman in Blue Dress

2003. Europa. Poster Art. Posters by Marcello Dudovich. Multicoloured.
2821 41c. Type **1236** 2·20 1·00
2822 52c. Woman in white dress 2·30 1·10

1237 Buildings and Text

2003. 50th Anniv of State Archives.
2823 **1237** 41c. multicoloured 1·70 90

1238 Logo and St. Peter of Verona

2003. Centenary of Veronafil Exhibition.
2824 **1238** 41c. multicoloured 1·70 90

1239 Aldo Moro

2003. 25th Death Anniv of Aldo Moro (politician).
2825 **1239** 62c. multicoloured 2·75 1·40

1240 Antonio Meucci

2003. Antonio Meucci (telephone pioneer) Commemoration. Sheet 90×70 mm.
MS2826 **1240** 52c. multicoloured 2·75 2·20

1241 Padre E. Barsanti and F. Matteucci (motor pioneers)

2003. 150th Anniv of Invention of Internal Combustion Engine.
2827 **1241** 52c. multicoloured 2·40 1·20

1242 Post and Telegraph Building (Angiolo Mazzoni)

2003
2828 **1242** 41c. blue 1·80 1·00

1243 Flags of Italy and European Union

2003. Italian Presidency of the European Union.
2829 **1243** 41c. multicoloured 1·80 1·00

1244 Ezio Vanoni

2003. Birth Centenary of Ezio Vanoni (politician).
2830 **1244** €2.58 multicoloured 11·00 6·50

1245 "The Ascension of Mary"

2003. 300th Birth Anniv of Corrado Giaquinto (artist).
2831 **1245** 77c. multicoloured 3·50 2·10

1246 Eugenio Balzan

2003. 50th Death Anniv of Eugenio Balzan (journalist).
2832 **1246** 41c. multicoloured 1·80 1·00

1247 "Diana and Atteone" (detail, fresco, Sanvitale Castle)

2003. 500th Birth Anniv of Francesco Mazzola (Parmigianino) (artist).
2833 **1247** 41c. multicoloured 1·80 1·00

1248 Player and Club Emblem

2003. Juventus, National Football Champions, 2002–3.
2834 **1248** 41c. multicoloured 1·80 1·00

1249 San Silvestro Abbey, Nonantola

2003
2835 **1249** 41c. multicoloured 1·80 1·00

1250 Mario Calderara

2003. Centenary of First Powered Flight. Italian Aviation. Multicoloured.
2836 52c. Type **1250** (first Italian pilot) 2·40 1·40
2837 52c. Mario Cobianchi (pilot) 2·40 1·40
2838 52c. Gianni Caproni (aircraft designer) 2·40 1·40
2839 52c. Alessandro Marchetti (aircraft designer) 2·40 1·40
MS2840 105×146 mm. Nos. 2836/9 9·75 5·75

1251 Giovanni Giolitti

2003. 75th Death Anniv of Giovanni Giolitti (prime minister 1892–3 and 1903–14).
2841 **1251** 41c. multicoloured 1·80 1·00

1252 "Still Life" (Giorgio Morandi)

2003. Europhalia 2003 Italy Festival. Italian Presidency of European Union. Multicoloured.
2842 41c. Type **1252** 1·80 1·00
2843 52c. Cistalia 202 (1947) 2·40 1·40
Stamps of the same design were issued by Belgium.

1253 Attilio Vallecchi (founder) and "Leonardo"

2003. Centenary of First Publication of "Leonardo". Centenary of Vallecchi Publishing House.
2844 **1253** 41c. multicoloured 1·80 1·00

1254 Family enclosed in Atom Model

2003. The Family.
2845 **1254** 77c. multicoloured 3·50 2·10

1255 "Maesta" (detail) (Duccio di Buoninsegna)

2003. Extension to Metropolitan Opera House, Sienna.
2846 **1255** 41c. multicoloured 1·80 1·00

1256 Vittorio Alfieri

2003. Death Bicentenary of Vittorio Alfieri (writer).
2847 **1256** 41c. multicoloured 1·80 1·00

1257 Ugo La Malfa and Chamber of Deputies Assembly Hall

2003. Birth Centenary of Ugo La Malfa (politician).
2848 **1257** 62c. multicoloured 3·00 1·70

1258 Bernardo Ramazzini and Frontispiece of "De morbis aertifcum diatriba"

2003. 370th Birth Anniv of Bernardo Ramazzini (medical pioneer).
2849 **1258** 41c. multicoloured 1·80 1·00

1259 Building Facade

2003. 120th Anniv of Confediliizia Institute, Rome.
2850 **1259** $2.58 multicoloured 11·50 6·75

1260 "Nativity" (Gian Paolo Cavagna)

2003. Christmas. Multicoloured.
2851 41c. Type **1260** 1·80 1·00
2852 62c. Poinsettia 3·00 1·70

1261 "Forme Grido Viva l'Italia"

2003. 40th Death Anniv of Giacomo Balla (artist). Multicoloured.
2853 41c. Type **1261** 1·80 1·00
2854 52c. "Linee—Forza del Pugno di Boccioni" 2·40 1·40

1262 Pencil and Sharpener

2003. Stamp Day.
2855 **1262** 41c. multicoloured 1·80 1·00

2004. Priority Mail Stamps. Designs as No. 2660. Multicoloured, background colour given. Self-adhesive gum.
2856 60c. orange 2·50 1·50
2856a 62c. yellow 3·00 1·80
2856b 80c. red 3·25 1·90
2856c £1 violet 10·50 6·50
2857 €1.40 green 5·25 3·25
2857a €1.50 grey 5·50 3·25
2858 €2 green 8·00 4·75
2859 €2.20 cannine 8·50 5·25
No. 2856/9 were issued with an attached label inscribed "postaprioritaria Priority Mail".

1263 "50" enclosing Test Screen

2004. 50th Anniv of Television.
2860 **1263** 41c. blue and grey 1·70 1·00
2861 - 62c. multicoloured 2·75 1·70
DESIGN: 62c. "50" enclosed in colour blocks.

1264 Giorgio La Pira and Script

2004. Birth Centenary of Giorgio La Pira (politician).
2862 **1264** 41c. cinnamon, blue and red 1·70 1·00

1265 Tower, Map and Compass

2004. Genoa–European Capital of Culture, 2004.
2863 **1265** 45c. multicoloured 1·90 1·20

1266 Santa Maria Assunta Church, Pragelato

2004. Winter Olympic Games, Turin (2006) (1st series). Multicoloured.
2864 23c. Type **1266** 90 60
2865 45c. San Pietro Apostolo church, Bardonecchia 1·80 1·20
2866 62c. 28th-century fountain, Sauze d'Oulx 2·40 1·50
2867 65c. Mole Antonelliana, Turin 2·50 1·70
See also Nos. 2926/9.

1267 Petrarch

2004. 700th Birth Anniv of Francesco Petrarca (Petrarch) (poet).
2868 **1267** 45c. multicoloured 1·80 1·20

1268 Mortar, Pestle, Museum Building and Liquorice Sticks

2004. Giorgio Amarelli Liquorice Museum.
2869 **1268** 45c. multicoloured 1·80 1·20

1269 Heart-shaped Seat Belt Buckle and Map covered with Traffic Signs

2004. Road Safety. Multicoloured.
2870 60c. Dashboard and traffic signs (horiz) 2·40 1·50
2871 62c. Type **1269** 2·50 1·70

1270 Vignola

2004. Tourist Publicity (31st series). Multicoloured.
2872 45c. Type **1270** 1·80 1·20
2873 45c. Viterbo 1·80 1·20
2874 45c. Egadi Islands 1·80 1·20

1271 Casa del Fascio

2004. Birth Centenary of Guiseppe Terragni (architect).
2875 **1271** 85c. multicoloured 3·25 2·20

1272 Sakate Temple, Bangkok

2004. Bangkok and Rome. Sheet 140×70 mm containing T 1272 and similar horiz design. Multicoloured.
MS2876 65c.×2, Type **1272**; Colosseum, Rome 5·00 3·25
Stamps of a similar design were issued by Thailand.

1273 St. George and Crowd

2004. 1700th Anniv of Martyrdom of St. George.
2877 **1273** €2.80 multicoloured 11·00 7·00

1274 Case

2004. Europa. Holidays. Multicoloured.
2878 45c. Type **1274** 1·80 1·20
2879 62c. Open case 2·50 1·70

1275 Sheep and Castle, Bologna

2004. Tratturo Magno (drovers' way). Sheet 90×70 mm.
MS2880 **1275** 45c. multicoloured 2·40 1·50

1276 Synagogue Facade

2004. Centenary of the Great Synagogue, Rome. Multicoloured.
2881 60c. Type **1276** 2·40 1·50
2882 62c. Candlestick, ornamental panel and synagogue (vert) 2·50 1·70
Stamps of the same design were issued by Israel.

1277 Football, Player and Emblem

2004. A. C. Milan, National Football Champions, 2004.
2883 **1277** 45c. multicoloured 1·80 1·20

1278 Giacomo Puccini

2004. 50th Anniv of Puccini Festival, Torre del Lago.
2884 **1278** 60c. multicoloured 2·40 1·50

1279 Courtyard and Emblem

2004. 600th Anniv of Turin University.
2885 **1279** 45c. brown 1·80 1·20

1280 Achille Varzi, Motorcycle and Racing Cars

2004. Birth Centenary of Achille Varzi (motorcyclist and racing driver).
2886 **1280** 45c. multicoloured 1·80 1·20

1281 Arms and Policemen

2004. Prison Police.
2887 **1281** 45c. multicoloured 1·80 1·20

1282 Ice Pick and Mountain Peak

2004. 50th Anniv of First Assent of K2 (mountain).
2888 **1282** 65c. blue, black and ultramarine 2·40 1·50

1283 Statuette and Map

2004. Regions. Multicoloured.
2889 45c. Type **1283** (Abruzzo) 1·80 1·20
2890 45c. Troglodyte settlement and map (Basilicata) 1·80 1·20
2891 45c. Medieval map (Liguria) 1·80 1·20
2892 45c. Roman mosaic (Emilia Romagna) 1·80 1·20

1284 Stained Glass Window

2004. 500th Anniv of the Apparition of Madonna di Tirano.
2893 **1284** 45c. multicoloured 1·80 1·20

1285 St. Nilo and Abbey Buildings

2004. Death Millenary Nilo di Rossano and Millenary of Foundation of Grottaferrata Abbey.
2894 **1285** 45c. multicoloured 1·80 1·20

1286 Map and Stylized Building Façade

2004. Florence State Archive.
2895 **1286** 45c. multicoloured 1·80 1·20

1287 Flower

2004. Lace Making. Self-adhesive. Textile. Imperf.
2896 **1287** €2.80 blue and cream 11·00 7·00

1288 Hands

2004. 40th Anniv of "Lega del Filo d'Oro" (humanitarian organization for deaf blind people).
2897 **1288** 45c. multicoloured 1·80 1·20

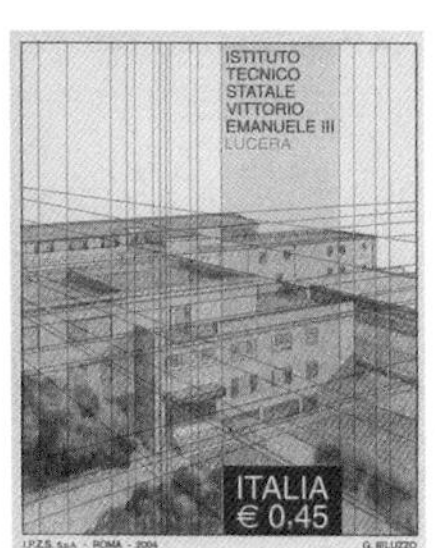

1289 Institute Buildings

2004. Vittorio Emanuele III Technical Institute.
2898 **1289** 45c. multicoloured 1·80 1·20

1290 Luigi Guanella

2004. Luigi Guanella Commemoration (priest and humanitarian).
2899 **1290** 45c. multicoloured 1·80 1·20

1291 Piazza dell'Unita, Trieste

2004. 50th Anniv of Return of Trieste to Italy.
2900 **1291** 45c. multicoloured 1·80 1·20

1292 Emblem

2004. Information and Military Emergency Service.
2901 **1292** 60c. multicoloured 2·40 1·50

1293 Stars and Map of Europe

2004. Constitution of Europe Treaty.
2902 **1293** 62c. multicoloured 2·50 1·70

1294 Nativity

2004. Christmas. Multicoloured.
2903 45c. Type **1294** 1·80 1·20
2904 62c. Decorated tree (vert) 2·50 1·70

1295 Map of Arsenal

2004. 900th Anniv of Venice Arsenal.
2905 **1295** €2.80 multicoloured 9·75 6·50

1296 St. Lucia

2004. 1700th Anniv of Martyrdom of St. Lucia.
2906 **1296** 45c. multicoloured 1·80 1·20

1297 Hands reading Braille

2004. Louis Braille System of Reading and Writing for the Blind.
2907 **1297** 45c. multicoloured 1·80 1·20
No. 2907 was embossed with Braille letters.

1298 Boy holding Stamp

2004. Stamp Day.
2908 **1298** 45c. multicoloured 1·80 1·20

1299 Emblem and Water

2004. 10th "Sport for All" Congress.
2909 **1299** 65c. multicoloured 2·50 1·70

1300 University Building

2004. Libera Universita Maria SS. Assunta (LUMSA) (university), Rome.
2910 **1300** 45c. multicoloured 1·80 1·20

1301 Woman's High-heeled Shoe

2004. Made in Italy. Shoes. Sheet 90×114 mm containing T 1301 and similar vert designs. Multicoloured.
2911- 45c.×4 Type **1301**; Man's laced
2914 shoe; Man's loafer; Trainers 7·50 2·40

1302 Club Emblem and Italy

2005. Centenary of Automobile Club d'Italia (ACI).
2915 **1302** 45c. multicoloured 1·80 1·20

2005
2916 **1171** €1 multicoloured 4·00 2·50

1303 Luigi Calabresi

2005. Luigi Calabresi (Milanese police officer) Commemoration.
2917 **1303** 45c. multicoloured 1·80 1·20

1304 Refugees

2005. Memorial Day for the Exodus from Istria, Fiume and Dalmazia.
2918 **1304** 45c. multicoloured 1·80 1·20

1305 Emblem

2005. Centenary of Rotary International (charitable organization).
2919 **1305** 65c. ultramarine and yellow 2·50 1·70

1306 Badge and Soldiers

2005. Sassari Brigade.
2920 **1306** 45c. multicoloured 1·80 1·20

1307 "Q"

2005. Quadrennial Exhibition, Rome.
2921 **1307** 45c. multicoloured 1·80 1·20

1308 "Bronzes of Riace" (Greek statues)

2005. Regions. Multicoloured.
2922 45c. Type **1308** (Calabria) 1·80 1·20
2923 45c. Ship (bas relief) and Miramare castle, Trieste (Fruili Venezia Guila) 1·80 1·20
2924 45c. Woman's head (fresco, Pompeii), (Campania) 1·80 1·20
2925 45c. Certosa, Pavia (Lombardy) 1·80 1·20

1309 San Maurizio Church, Pinerolo

2005. Winter Olympic Games, Turin (2006) (2nd series). Multicoloured.
2926 23c. Type **1309** 1·00 65
2927 45c. San Giovanni Battista church, Cesana Torinese, San Sicario 1·80 1·20
2928 60c. Neve and Gliz (Games' mascots) 2·40 1·50
2929 62c. Hotel, Sestriere 2·50 1·70

1310 Pavia (engraving by Gerolamo de Sanctis), Black Hole Diagram, Year Emblem and Feynman Diagram

2005. International Year of Physics.
2930 **1310** 85c. multicoloured 3·25 2·20

1311 Pavilions

2005. Inauguration of Milan International Fair Complex, Pero.
2931 **1311** 45c. multicoloured 1·80 1·20

1312 "100" and Steam

2005. Centenary of State Railways.
2932 **1312** 45c. multicoloured 1·80 1·20

1313 Early and Modern Soldiers

2005. National Army.
2933 **1313** 45c. multicoloured 1·80 1·20

1314 Stars and Grain

2005. Europa. Gastronomy. Multicoloured.
2934 45c. Type **1314** 1·80 1·20
2935 62c. Grapes, wine glass and stars 2·50 1·70

1315 Saint Ignazio

2005. Saint Ignazio of Laconi Commemoration.
2936 **1315** 45c. multicoloured 1·80 1·20

1316 Association Emblem

2005. 60th Anniv of Confcommercio (trade association).
2937 **1316** 60c. silver, steel blue and gold 2·40 1·50

1317 School Building

2005. Tommaso Campanella Grammar School, Reggio Calabria.
2938 **1317** 45c. multicoloured 1·80 1·20

1318 Building Facade

2005. Saint Giuseppe of Copertino Basilica, Osimo.
2939 **1318** 45c. indigo 1·80 1·20

1319 Asolo

2005. Tourist Publicity (32nd series). Multicoloured.
2940 45c. Type **1319** 1·80 1·20
2941 45c. Rocchetta a Volturno 1·80 1·20
2942 45c. Amalfi 1·80 1·20

1320 Gerardo Maiella and St. Gerardo Maiella Church, Materdomini

2005. 250th Death Anniv of Gerardo Maiella (priest).
2943 **1320** 45c. multicoloured 1·80 1·20

1321 Player and Club Emblem

2005. Juventus, National Football Champions, 2004–5.
2944 **1321** 45c. multicoloured 1·80 1·20

1322 Emblems and Map

2005. 20th Anniv of Ratification Italy–Vatican Concordat (abolishing Catholicism as state religion). Multicoloured.
2945 45c. Type **1322** 1·80 1·20
2946 €2.80 Emblems, manuscript and pen 11·00 7·25

Stamps of the same design were issued by Vatican City.

1323 Almerico da Schio and Dirigible

2005. Centenary of First Italian Dirigible.
2947 **1323** €3 multicoloured 12·00 7·75

1324 Mascot and Emblem

2005. European Youth Olympic Festival, Lignano.
2948 **1324** 62c. multicoloured 2·50 1·70

1325 Tunnel containing Flower

2005. International Day against Drugs.
2949 **1325** 45c. multicoloured 1·80 1·20

1326 Emblem

2005. Institute for Marine Security (I.P.SE.MA.).
2950 **1326** 45c. green, ultramarine and silver 1·80 1·20

1327 Leo Longanesi

2005. Birth Centenary of Leo Longanesi (writer and artist).

2951 **1327** 45c. blue 1·80 1·20

1328 Alberto Ascari and Race Car

2005. 50th Death Anniv of Alberto Ascari (World Champion race driver 1952–53).

2952 **1328** €2.80 multicoloured 11·00 7·00

1329 Emblem and Team Aermacchi MB-339 PAN

2005. Frecce Tricolori (Italian Air Force acrobatic display team). Multicoloured.

2953 45c. Type **1329** 1·80 1·20

2954 60c. Aermacchi MB-339 PAN (different) 2·40 1·50

1330 Pietro Savorgnan di Brazza

2005. Death Centenary of Pietro Paolo Savorgnan di Brazza (explorer).

2955 **1330** 45c. multicoloured 1·80 1·20

1331 Guido Gonella

2005. Birth Centenary of Guido Gonella (politician).

2956 **1331** 45c. multicoloured 1·80 1·20

1332 Space Craft and Mars

2005. Mars Exploration Programme. Self-adhesive.

2957 **1332** 80c. multicoloured 3·25 2·10

1333 Raised Arms

2005. 50th Anniv of Intercultura (voluntary service organization).

2958 **1333** 60c. multicoloured 2·40 1·50

1334 Yacht and Trapani Bay

2005. America's Cup Yacht Race, Trapani. Sheet 96×80 mm.

MS2959 **1334** €2.80 multicoloured 11·00 7·25

1335 "F"

2005. Stamp Day.

2960 **1335** 45c. multicoloured 1·80 1·20

1336 Heart as Flower

2005. Italian Organ Donors Association (AIDO).

2961 **1336** 60c. multicoloured 2·40 1·50

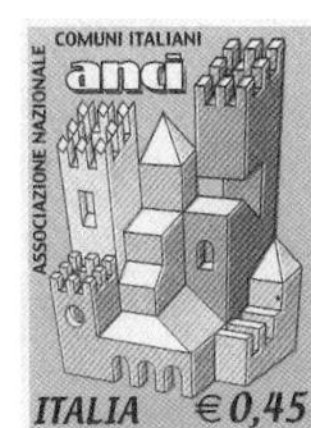

1337 Castle

2005. National Association (ANCI).

2962 **1337** 45c. multicoloured 1·80 1·20

1338 "Disputation in the Synagogue" (detail)

2005. Restoration of Frescoes by Filippo Lippi, Prato Cathedral. Multicoloured.

2963 45c. Type **1338** 1·80 1·20

2964 €1.50 "Saint's Funeral" (detail) 6·00 3·75

1339 "The Annunciation" (Beato Angelico)

2005. Christmas. Multicoloured.

2965 45c. Type **1339** 1·80 1·20

2966 62c. Family (vert) 2·50 1·70

1340 Alcide de Gasperi

2005. Alcide de Gasperi (politician) Commemoration.

2967 **1340** 62c. multicoloured 2·50 1·70

1341 "Humanity" Medal

2005. Birth Bicentenary of Giuseppe Mazzini (nationalist).

2968 **1341** 45c. multicoloured 1·80 1·20

1342 Civil Protection Department Emblem

2005. Civil Protection and Italian Red Cross. Multicoloured.

2969 45c. Type **1342** 1·80 1·20

2970 45c. Globe and Red Cross emblem 1·80 1·20

1343 "50" and UN Emblem

2005. 50th Anniv of United Nations Membership.

2971 **1343** 70c. multicoloured 2·75 1·80

1344 Pope John Paul II

2005. Pope John Paul II Commemoration and Election of Pope Benedict XVI. Multicoloured.

2972 45c. Type **1344** 1·80 1·20

2973 65c. Pope Benedict XVI 2·50 1·70

1345 Royal Palace

2005. 60th Anniv of Re-constitution of Caserta Province.

2974 **1345** 45c. multicoloured 1·80 1·20

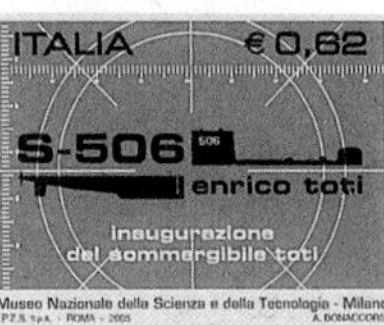

1346 Stylized Submarine

2005. Re-location of Submarine Enrico Toti to National Museum of Sciences and Technology, Milan.

2975 **1346** 62c. grey and deep grey 2·50 1·70

1347 Egg Timer

2006. Greetings Stamps. 18th Birthday Greetings. Multicoloured, background colour given.

2976 45c. Type **1347** (pink) 1·80 1·20

2977 45c. As No. 2976 (blue) 1·80 1·20

1348 Calciatori (footballers) Sticker Album Emblem

2006. Panini SpA (sticker manufacturer and publisher).

2978 **1348** €2.80 multicoloured 11·00 7·00

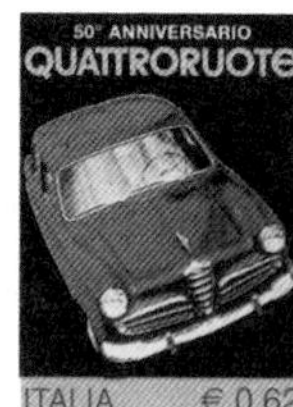

1349 First Magazine Cover

2006. 50th Anniv of *Quattroruote* (motoring magazine founded by G. Mazzochi).

2979 **1349** 62c. multicoloured 2·50 1·70

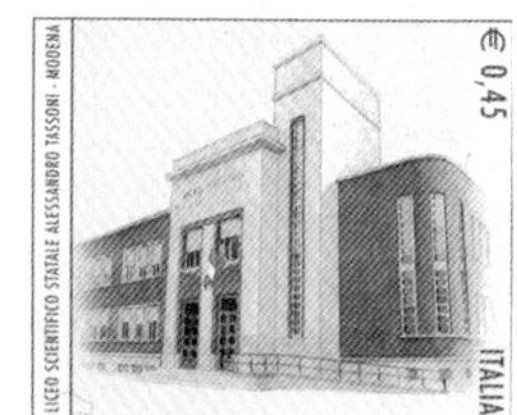

1350 Alessandro Tassoni State High School, Modena

2006. Schools and Universities.

2980 **1350** 45c. multicoloured 1·80 1·20

2981 - 45c. multicoloured 1·80 1·20

2982 - 45c. multicoloured 1·80 1·20

2983 - 45c. yellow, slate and ultramarine 1·80 1·20

DESIGNS: Type **1350**; No. 2981 Agostino Nifo State High School, Sessa Aurunca; 2982 Ernesto Cairoli State High School, Varese; 2983 Carlo Bo University, Urbino.

1351 Biathlon

2006. Winter Olympic Games, Turin. Each blue, new blue and light blue.

2984 23c. Type **1351** 1·00 65

2985 45c. Figure skating 1·80 1·20

2986 65c. Ice hockey 2·50 1·70

2987 70c. Curling 2·75 1·80

2988 85c. Bob sledding 3·25 2·20

2989 90c. Alpine skiing 3·50 2·30

2990 €1 Olympic flame (detail) 4·00 2·50

2991 €1.30 Luge 5·00 3·25

2992 $1.70 Three medals 6·75 4·25

MS2993 149×102 mm. Nos. 2984/92 29·00 19·00

The stamps and margins of **MS**2993 form a composite design.

1352 1879 5c., 1863 15c., 1901 10c. and 1930 20c. Stamps

2006. Il Regno d'Italia Philatelic Exhibition, Palazzo Montecitorio (chamber of deputies).

2994 **1352** 60c. multicoloured 2·40 1·50

1353 Society Emblem

2006. 80th Anniv of Society for the Preservation of Italian Culture in Dalmatia.

2995 **1353** 45c. blue and vermilion 1·80 1·20

1354 "Camera degli Sposi" (The Wedding Chamber) (Andrea Mantegna)

2006. 500th Death Anniv of Andrea Mantegna (artist).

2996 **1354** 45c. multicoloured 1·80 1·20

1355 Emblem

2006. Centenary of International Congress on Occupational Health. 28th Congress on Occupational Health, Milan.

2997 **1355** 60c.+30c. multicoloured 3·50 2·30

The premium was for the benefit of Breast Cancer charities.

1356 Emblem

2006. Winter Paralympic Games, Turin.

2998 **1356** 60c. multicoloured 2·40 1·50

1357 Ice Cream Seller

2006. Made in Italy. Multicoloured.

2999 60c. Type **1357** 2·40 1·50

3000 €2.80 Marble statue and quarry 11·00 7·00

1358 Football Team with Faces forming Notes

2006. 25th Anniv of National Association of Singers.

3001 **1358** 45c. multicoloured 1·80 1·20

1359 *Cavour* (aircraft carrier)

2006. Navy.

3002 **1359** 60c. multicoloured 2·40 1·50

1360 Swiss and Italian Flags and Tunnel

2006. Centenary of Simplon Tunnel.

3003 **1360** 62c. multicoloured 2·50 1·70

1361 Lake Como

2006. Tourist Publicity (33rd series). Multicoloured.

3004 45c. Type **1361** 1·80 1·20

3005 45c. Marina di Pietrasanta 1·80 1·20

3006 45c. Temple of Serapis, Pozzuoli 1·80 1·20

1362 Three Dimensional Diagram of Mountain Range

2006. Centenary of International Day of Mountains.

3007 **1362** 60c. multicoloured 2·40 1·50

1363 St. Mary Incaldana (icon), Basilica Minore, St. Mary Incaldana, Modragone.

2006. Cultural Heritage.

3008 **1363** 45c. multicoloured 1·80 1·20

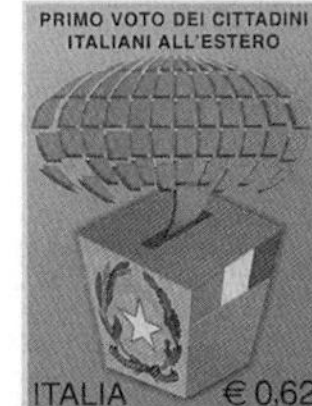

1364 Stylized Vote Papers and Ballot Box

2006. 1st Vote cast by Italian Citizens Resident Abroad.

3009 **1364** 62c. multicoloured 2·50 1·70

1365 Palazzo Mentcitorio, Rome and Palazzo Pubblico, San Marino

2006. Le Due Repubbliche (two republics) Philatelic Exhibition. Multicoloured.

3010 62c. Type **1365** 2·50 1·70

MS3011 121×90 mm. 62c.×2, Type **1365**; Type **584** of San Marino 5·00 3·25

No. **MS**3011 is identical to **MS**2084 of San Marino.

1366 Instructor and Pupils

2006. 70th Anniv of Ski School, Cervina.

3012 **1366** 45c. multicoloured 1·80 1·20

1367 "Madonna of Humility" (Gentile da Fabriano), Museo Nazionale di San Matteo, Pisa.

2006. Cultural Heritage.

3013 **1367** €2.80 multicoloured 11·00 7·00

1368 Man at Window (poster) (Raymond Savignac) (1956)

2006. 50th Anniv of *Il Giorno* Newspaper. Photo.

3014 **1368** 45c. multicoloured 1·80 1·20

1369 Court Chamber

2006. 50th Anniv of Constitutional Court.

3015 **1369** 45c. indigo 1·80 1·20

1370 Enrico Mattei

2006. Birth Centenary of Enrico Mattei (entrepreneur).

3016 **1370** 45c. multicoloured 1·80 1·20

1371 Statue (Emanuele Filiberto), Royal Castle, Racconigi (Piedmont)

2006. Regions. Multicoloured.

3017 45c. Type **1371** 1·80 1·20

3018 45c. David (statue) (Michelangelo) and landscape (Tuscany) 1·80 1·20

3019 45c. Sarcophagus of the bride and groom (Sarcofago degli Sposi) and Etruscan necropolis, Cerveteri (Lazio) 1·80 1·20

3020 45c. Basilica of St Nicholas, Bari, outline of Puglia and Tremiti Islands. (Puglia) 1·80 1·20

1372 "La Targa Florio" (Margaret Bradley)

2006. Centenary of Targa Florio (automobile endurance race), Palermo.

3021 **1372** 60c. multicoloured 2·40 1·50

1373 Christopher Columbus

2006. 500th Death Anniv of Christopher Columbus.

3022 **1373** 62c. multicoloured 2·50 1·70

1374 Young People of Many Nations

2006. Europa. Integration. Multicoloured.

3023 45c. Type **1374** 1·80 1·20

3024 62c. Backview 2·50 1·70

1375 Coliseum and Emblem

2006. International Military Sports Council General Meeting, Rome.

3025 **1375** 45c. multicoloured 1·80 1·20

1376 Emblem

2006. International Team Chess Championship, Turin.

3026	**1376**	62c. multicoloured	2·50	1·70

1377 Assembly Chamber and National Colours

2006. 60th Anniv of Elected Constituent Assembly.

3027	**1377**	60c. multicoloured	2·40	1·50

1378 Nilde Iotti (politician)

2006. 60th Anniv of Women's Suffrage.

3028	**1378**	60c. multicoloured	2·40	1·50

1379 Emblem

2006. World Bridge Championship.

3029	**1379**	65c. multicoloured	2·50	1·70

1380 Arms and Map

2006. Test Firing Range, Salto di Quirra (Poligono Interforze del Salto di Quirra (PISQ)), Sardinia.

3030	**1380**	60c. multicoloured	2·40	1·50

1381 Headquarters

2006. Centenary of Guardia di Finanza Cadets Corps and General Headquarters. Multicoloured.

3031	60c. Type **1381**	2·40	1·50
3032	60c. Cadet and building facade (horiz)	2·40	1·50

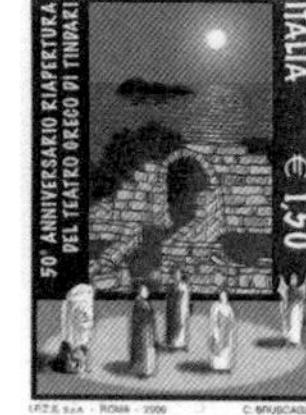
1382 Stage, Walls and Sea

2006. 50th Anniv of Greek Theatre, Tindari.

3033	**1382**	€1.50 multicoloured	6·00	3·75

1383 Bridge across Map of Italy

2006. 50th Anniv of Autostrada del Sole.

3034	**1383**	60c. multicoloured	2·40	1·50

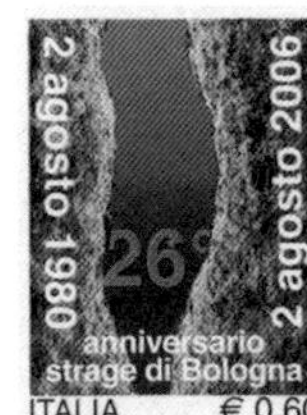
1384 Devastation

2006. 26th Anniv of Bombing of Bologna Railway Station.

3035	**1384**	60c. multicoloured	2·40	1·50

1385 Emblem

2006. 40th Anniv of Union of Italian Philatelic Journalists.

3036	**1385**	60c. multicoloured	2·50	1·70

1386 St Gregory

2006. St Gregory Commemoration.

3037	**1386**	60c. multicoloured	2·40	1·50

1387 Flag and Fans

2006. Italy—2006 World Cup Football Champions.

3038	**1387**	€1 multicoloured	4·00	2·50

1388 Face and Figure Outlines

2006. Victims of Terrorism.

3039	**1388**	60c. multicoloured	2·40	1·50

1389 Ettore Majorana and Atomic Symbol

2006. Birth Centenary of Ettore Majorana (physicist).

3040	**1389**	60c. multicoloured	2·40	1·50

1390 St Francis Xavier

2006. Saints' Anniversaries. Multicoloured.

3041	60c. Type **1390** (500th birth anniv)	2·40	1·50
3042	60c. St Ignatius Loyola (450th death anniv)	2·40	1·50

1391 Fencers

2006. World Fencing Championship, Turin.

3043	**1391**	65c. multicoloured	2·50	1·70

1392 Boy, Stamps and Globe

2006. Philately Day.

3044	**1392**	60c. multicoloured	2·40	1·50

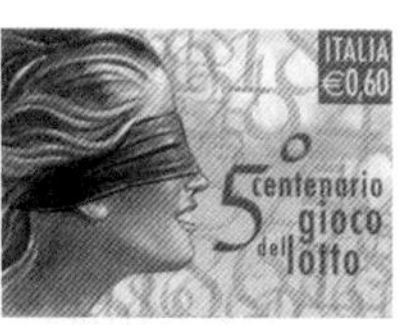
1393 Blind-folded Woman

2006. 500th Anniv of National Lottery.

3045	**1393**	60c. multicoloured	2·40	1·50

1394 Emblem

2006. National System of Environment Protection.

3046	**1394**	65c. multicoloured	2·50	1·70

1395 Luchino Visconti

2006. Birth Centenary of Luchino Visconti (film maker).

3047	**1395**	60c. multicoloured	2·40	1·50

1396 Dino Buzzati

2006. Birth Centenary of Dino Buzzati (writer).

3048	**1396**	60c. multicoloured	2·40	1·50

1397 "Adoration of the Magi" (Jacopo Bassano)

2006. Christmas.

3049	**1397**	60c. magenta	2·40	1·50
3050	–	65c. multicoloured (vert)	2·50	1·70

DESIGNS: 60c. Type **1397**; 65c. Decorated tree.

1398 Vittoriano Building, Rome and Tomb of the Unknown Warrior

2006. In Memory of the Fallen in Nassiriya.

3051	**1398**	60c. multicoloured	2·40	1·50

1399 St. Evasio Cathedral, Casale Monferrato

2007. Cultural Heritage.

3052	**1399**	60c. cerise	2·40	1·50

1400 Maria Montessori and Children

2007. Centenary of Montessori Nursery Schools.

3053	**1400**	60c. multicoloured	2·40	1·50

1401 Milvio Bridge, River Tiber and Building Facade

2007. 50th Anniv of National School for Public Administration.

3054	**1401**	65c. multicoloured	2·50	1·70

1402 Parma Cathedral and Baptistery

2007. Cultural Heritage.

3055	**1402**	60c. olive	2·40	1·50

1403 Arturo Toscanini

2007. 50th Death Anniv of Arturo Toscanini (conductor).
3056 **1403** 60c. multicoloured 2·40 1·50

1404 "St. Francis of Paola crossing Straits of Medina" (Benedetto Luti)

2007. 500th Death Anniv of St. Francis of Paola.
3057 **1404** 60c. multicoloured 2·40 1·50

1405 "Ferrante Gonzaga triumphing over Envy" (statue, Leone Leoni)

2007. 500th Birth Anniv of Ferrante Gonzaga (soldier).
3058 **1405** €1 multicoloured 4·00 2·50

1406 Foundation Office

2007. 20th Anniv of Fondazione Antonio Genovesi Salerno.
3059 **1406** 60c. multicoloured 2·40 1·50

1407 Refugees and Map of Sardinia

2007. 60th Anniv of Borgata Giuliana di Fertilia, Alghero (immigration of Italian speaking refugees from Istria and Dalmatia to Sardinia).
3060 **1407** 60c. multicoloured 2·40 1·50

1408 Father Lodovico Acernese

2007. Father Lodovico Acernese (founder of Congregation of the Franciscan Immaculatine Sisters) Commemoration.
3061 **1408** 23c. multicoloured 1·00 65

1409 Giosue Carducci

2007. Death Centenary of Giosue Carducci (1906—Nobel Prize for Literature winner).
3062 **1409** 60c. multicoloured 2·40 1·50

1410 Brescia University

2007
3063 **1410** 60c. multicoloured 2·40 1·50

1411 Stylized Woman and Child

2007. European Year of Equal Opportunities.
3064 **1411** 60c. multicoloured 2·40 1·50

1412 "Scipione Maffel" State High School

2007
3065 **1412** 60c. multicoloured 2·40 1·50

1413 Nicolo Carosio

2007. Birth Centenary of Nicolo Carosio (sports commentator).
3066 **1413** 65c. multicoloured 2·50 1·70

1414 Rialto Bridge and Gondola

2007. Venice–UNESCO World Heritage Site.
3067 **1414** 60c. black 2·40 1·50

1415 Mareccio Castle and Castell del Buonconsiglio (Trentino-Aldo Adige)

2007. Regions. Multicoloured.
3068 60c. Type **1415** 2·40 1·50
3069 60c. Asceli Piceno and "Bronzi Dorati da Cartoceto di Pergola" (statues) (Marche) 2·40 1·50
3070 60c. Orvieto Cathedral and "Annunciation" (mosaic) (Umbria) 2·40 1·50
3071 60c. Beach, flamingo and bronze statue (Sardinia) 2·40 1·50

1416 Circuit Board

2007. International Electro-technical Commission.
3072 **1416** €1.50 multicoloured 6·00 3·75

1417 '50', Stylized Piazza del Campidoglio and Stars

2007. 50th Anniv of Treaty of Rome. Sheet 120×96 mm containing T 1417 and similar vert design. Multicoloured.
MS3073 60c. Type **1417**; 65c. 'INSIEME', stylized Piazza del Campidoglio and stars 5·00 3·25

The stamps of **MS**3073 form a composite design.

1418 Bishop's Castle, Brunico-Bruneck

2007. Tourist Publicity (34th series). Multicoloured.
3074 60c. Type **1418** 2·40 1·50
3075 60c. Castle, Gaeta 2·40 1·50
3076 60c. Medieval Castle, Massafra 2·40 1·50
3077 60c. Eraclea Minoa Amphitheatre, Cattolica Eraclea 2·40 1·50

1419 Giuseppe di Lampedusa and Il Gattopardo

2007. 50th Death Anniv of Giuseppe Tomasi de Lampedusa (writer).
3078 **1419** 60c. multicoloured 2·40 1·50

1420 Forum

2007. Rome–Capital City.
3079 **1420** 60c. multicoloured 2·40 1·50

1421 Scouts and Canoe

2007. Europa. Centenary of Scouting. Multicoloured.
3080 60c. Type **1421** 2·40 1·50
3081 65c. Scouts and campfire 2·50 1·70
MS3082 97×120 mm. Nos. 3080/1 5·00 3·25

1422 Duccio Galimberti

2007. Birth Centenary of Duccio Galimberti (resistance organiser).
3083 **1422** 60c. multicoloured 2·40 1·50

1423 Statues and Building Facade

2007. 50th Anniv of National Higher School for Economics and Finance.
3084 **1423** €2.80 multicoloured 11·00 7·00

1424 Director, Camera and Building Facade

2007. 70th Anniv of Cinecitta Film Studios, Rome.
3085 **1424** 65c. multicoloured 2·50 1·70

1425 Polirone Monastery, Mantua

2007. Cultural Heritage.
3086 **1425** 60c. indigo 2·40 1·50

1426 Malatesta Castle, Montefiore

2007. Cultural Heritage.
3087 **1426** 60c. brown 2·40 1·50

1427 Stele enclosing Musical Score

2007. Folk Music Project.
3088 **1427** 60c. multicoloured 2·40 1·50

1428 Lamborghini Emblem

2007. Made in Italy. Lamborghini Miura.

3089	**1428**	85c. multicoloured	3·25	2·20

1429 Player, Ball and Emblem

2007. Inter Football Club, Italian Football Champions–Serie A 2007

3090	**1429**	60c. multicoloured	2·40	1·50

1430 Chianca Dolmen, Apulia

2007. Cultural Heritage.

3091	**1430**	60c. chestnut	2·40	1·50

1431 Luigi Ganna

2007. 50th Death Anniv of Luigi Ganna (cyclist, winner of first Giro d'Italia–1909).

3092	**1431**	60c. multicoloured	2·40	1·50

1432 Altiero Spinelli

2007. Birth Centenary of Altiero Spinelli (federalist).

3093	**1432**	60c. multicoloured	2·40	1·50

1433 Dancer and Rose Window, Spoleto Cathedral

2007. Festival dei Due Mondi (Festival of the Two Worlds) (annual music and opera festival), Spoleto.

3094	**1433**	60c. multicoloured	2·40	1·50

1434 Basilica, San Vincenzo in Galliano, Cantu

2007. Cultural Heritage. Birch wood. Self-adhesive.

3095	**1434**	€2.80 brown	11·00	7·00

No. 3095 was printed on wooden sheets.

1435 Fiat 500

2007. Made in Italy.

3096	**1435**	60c. multicoloured	2·40	1·50

1436 Giuseppe Garibaldi

2007. Birth Bicentenary of Giuseppe Garibaldi (soldier and nationalist).

3097	**1436**	65c. multicoloured	2·50	1·70

1437 Maurizio Poggiali and Tornado Fighter Airplane

2007. 10th Death Anniv of Maurizio Poggiali (poet and pilot).

3098	**1437**	60c. multicoloured	2·40	1·50

1438 Caver, Stalactites, Stalagmites and Bat (club emblem)

2007. Speleological Club of Rome.

3099	**1438**	€1.40 multicoloured	5·50	3·50

1439 Primo Carnera

2007. 40th Death Anniv of Primo Carnera (boxer).

3100	**1439**	60c. multicoloured	2·40	1·50

1440 Cloister, 'Marco Foscarini' Boarding School for Classical Studies

2007. Schools. Multicoloured.

3101	60c. Type **1440**	2·40	1·50
3102	60c. S.Pio V	2·40	1·50
3103	60c. Salerno Medical College	2·40	1·50

1441 Donkeys

2007. Italian Protected Donkey Breeds.

3104	**1441**	60c. multicoloured	2·40	1·50

1442 Player

2007. European Senior Women's Basketball Championship.

3105	**1442**	65c. multicoloured	2·50	1·70

1443 Sacra di San Michelle (abbey), Sant'Ambrogio di Torino

2007. Cultural Heritage.

3106	**1443**	60c. Indian red	2·40	1·50

1444 Concetto Marchesi

2007. 50th Death Anniv of Concetto Marchesi (Latin scholar, politician and writer).

3107	**1444**	60c. multicoloured	2·40	1·50

1445 Il Vignola and Scala Regia (royal stairs), Palazzo Farnese, Caprarola

2007. 400th Birth Anniv of Jacopo Barozzi da Vignola (Il Vignola) (architect).

3108	**1445**	€2.80 multicoloured	11·00	7·00

1446 Children and Grandparents

2007. Grandparents Day.

3109	**1446**	60c. multicoloured	2·40	1·50

1447 Stamps as Figure

2007. Stamp Day.

3110	**1447**	60c. multicoloured	2·40	1·50

1448 *Cupid and Pscyche* (sculpture)

2007. 250th Birth Anniv of Antonio Canova (artist).

3111	**1448**	€1.50 black	6·00	3·75

1449 Beniamino Gigli

2007. Entertainment Personalities' Anniversaries. Sheet 151×100 mm containing T 1449 and similar vert designs. Multicoloured.

MS3112 60c.×3, Type **1449** (tenor) (50th death anniv); Maria Callas (soprano) (30th death anniv); Amedeo Nazzari (actor) (birth centenary)	7·00	4·50

1450 Giuseppe di Vittorio

2007. 50th Death Anniv of Giuseppe di Vittorio (trade unionist and politician).

3113	**1450**	60c. multicoloured	2·40	1·50

1451 Anniversary Emblem

2007. Centenary of Mondadori (publishers).

3114	**1451**	60c. vermilion, black and gold	2·40	1·50

1452 *Madonna and Child* (Giovan Battista Cima Conegliano)

2007. Christmas (1st issue).

3115	**1452**	60c. olive	2·40	1·50

1453 Snow-covered House and Trees

2007. Christmas (2nd issue).
3116 **1453** 65c. multicoloured 2·50 1·70

1454 Soldier carrying Child

2007. Italy's Election as Temporary Member of UN Security Council.
3117 **1454** 85c. multicoloured 3·50 2·30

1455 Maritime and History Museum

2007. Fiume (now Croatian city of Rijeka).
3118 **1455** 65c. multicoloured 2·50 1·70

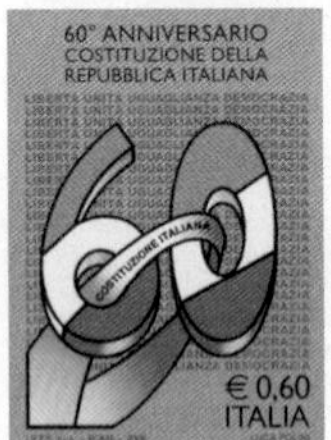

1456 '60'

2008. 60th Anniv of Constitution.
3119 **1456** 60c. multicoloured 2·50 1·60

1457 Nurses

2008. Centenary of Italian Red Cross Volunteer Nursing Corps.
3120 **1457** 60c. multicoloured 2·50 1·60

1458 Amintore Fanfani

2008. Birth Centenary of Amintore Fanfani (politician).
3121 **1458** €1 multicoloured 4·25 2·75

1459 Building Facade

2008. Bicentenary of Italian Stock Exchange.
3122 **1459** 65c. blue, light blue and brown 2·75 1·80

1460 Typewriter and Factory Building

2008. Centenary of Olivetti Typewriter Factory, Ivrea.
3123 **1460** 60c. multicoloured 2·50 1·60

1461 Viila Reale, Monza

2008. Death Bicentenary of Giuseppe Piermarini (architect).
3124 **1461** €1.40 blue and ultramarine 5·75 3·75

1462 Wheat, Cogwheels, Coin and Villa Lubin (headquarters), Rome

2008. 50th Anniv of National Council of Economics and Labour.
3125 **1462** €1.50 multicoloured 6·25 4·00

1463 Dorando Pietri winning Olympic Marathon, London, 1908

2008. Dorando Pietri (marathon runner) Commemoration.
3126 **1463** 60c. multicoloured 2·50 1·60

1464 Disc and Diver

2008. *Nel blu dipinto de blu* (song). Sheet 96×79 mm.
MS3127 **1464** 60c. multicoloured 2·75 1·80

1465 Anna Magnani

2008. Birth Centenary of Anna Magnani (actor).
3128 **1465** 60c. multicoloured 2·50 1·60

1466 Emblem and La Scala Opera House, Milan

2008. Bicentenary of Ricordi Publishing House.
3129 **1466** 60c. black and grey 2·50 1·60

1467 Congress Centre, Rome

2008. Italia 2009 International Festival of Philately. Multicoloured.
3130 60c. Type **1467** 2·50 1·60
3131 65c. Colosseum 2·75 1·80

1468 Building Facade

2008. Carlo Combi High School, Capodistria.
3132 **1468** 60c. multicoloured 2·50 1·60

1469 Edmundo de Amicis

2008. Death Centenary of Edmundo de Amicis (writer).
3133 **1469** 60c. green and black 2·50 1·60

1470 *Self Portrait*

2008. Artistic and Cultural Heritage. Bernadino di Betto (Pintoricchio) (artist) Commemoration.
3134 **1470** 60c. multicoloured 2·50 1·60

1471 Madonna supported by Members of Confraternita di Santa Maria di Loreto

2008. Folklore. Feast of 'La Madonna che scappa in piazza', Sulmona.
3135 **1471** 60c. multicoloured 2·50 1·60

1472 Early Rowers

2008. 120th Anniv of National Rowing Federation.
3136 **1472** 65c. multicoloured 2·75 1·80

1473 *La Conferma della Regola* (from *The Life of Saint Francis* series of paintings by Giotto di Bondone)

2008. 700th Anniv of the Franciscan Order.
3137 **1473** 60c. multicoloured 2·50 1·60

1474 Imperial Forum

2008. Rome–Capital City.
3138 **1474** 60c. multicoloured 2·50 1·60

1475 Newsletter No. 1

2008. Centenary of National Press Federation.
3139 **1475** 60c. grey and black 2·50 1·60

1476 *The Flight* (bronze statue) (Pasquale Basile) (campaign emblem)

2008. UNESCO International Decade of Education for Sustainable Development.
3140 **1476** €1.40 multicoloured 5·75 3·75

1477 *Giovannino Guareschi* (Arturo Coppola)

2008. Birth Centenary of Giovannino Guareschi (journalist, cartoonist and humorist).
3141 **1477** 60c. multicoloured 2·50 1·60

1478 Ludovico Geymonat

2008. Birth Centenary of Ludovico Geymonat (mathematician, historian and philosopher of science).
3142 **1478** 60c. multicoloured 2·50 1·60

1479 Post Box and Envelopes

2008. Europa. The Letter. Multicoloured.

3143	60c. Type **1479**	2·50	1·60
3144	65c. Brown post-box and envelopes	2·75	1·80

1480 Design for Bassano Bridge (Ponte Degli Alpini)

2008. 500th Birth Anniv of Andrea Palladio (architect).

3145	60c. brown, blue and black	2·50	1·60
3146	65c. chestnut and green	2·75	1·80

DESIGNS: 60c. Type **1480**; 65c. Palladian Basilica, Vincenza.

1480a Pope Sixtus V receiving Rule of Order from St Francis

2008. 400th Death Anniv of St Francis Caracciolo (Ascanio Pisquizio) (co-founder of Congregation of Minor Clerks Regular).

3146a	**1480a** 60c. multicoloured	2·75	1·80

1481 Savoy Castle, Gressoney Saint Jean and Mount Cervino (Aosta Valley)

2008. Regions. Multicoloured.

3147	60c. Type **1481**	2·75	1·80
3148	60c. *Salome with the Head of John the Baptist* (Titian) and Lagoon City (Veneto)	2·75	1·80
3149	60c. Romanesque Fraterna Fountain, Piazza Celestino V (Molise)	2·75	1·80
3150	60c. Baroque cathedral facade (Sicily)	2·75	1·80

1482 School Building

2008. Guastalla Boarding School.

3151	**1482** 60c. blue	2·75	1·80

1483 Motorcyclist riding Ducati Desmosedici GP7

2008. Ducatti Motorcycle.

3152	**1483** 60c. multicoloured	2·75	1·80

1484 Giacomo Puccini

2008. 150th Birth Anniv of Giacomo Puccini.

3153	**1484** €1.50 multicoloured	6·75	4·50

1485 Player wearing Centenary Shirt and Emblem of 16th Victory

2008. Inter Football Club, Italian Football Champions–Serie A 2008.

3154	**1485** 60c. multicoloured	2·75	1·80

1486 Torch Relay Runner on Globe

2008. Olympic Games, Beijing. Stylized ceramic plates. Multicoloured.

3155	60c. Type **1486**	2·75	1·80
3156	85c. Greek and Asian athletes	3·75	2·50

1487 Tommaso Landolfi

2008. Birth Centenary of Tommaso Landolfi (writer).

3157	**1487** 60c. multicoloured	2·75	1·80

1488 Dolomite Mountains, Tre Cime di Lavaredo

2008. Tourist Publicity (35th series). Multicoloured.

3158	60c. Type **1488**	2·75	1·80
3159	60c. Mt. Epomeo and port, Casamicciola Terme	2·75	1·80
3160	60c. Medieval tower and Introdacqua village	2·75	1·80
3161	60c. Mamuthones	2·75	1·80

1489 Stigmas and Flowers of *Crocus sativus*

2008. Made in Italy. Zafferano dell'Aquila (saffron from L'Aquila).

3162	**1489** 60c. multicoloured	2·75	1·80

1490 Ingredients

2008. Made in Italy. Spaghetti all'amatriciana Festival.

3163	**1490** 60c. multicoloured	2·75	1·80

1491 Bell Tower, Treviglio

2008. Cultural Heritage.

3164	**1491** 60c. indigo	2·75	1·80

1492 Dante Alighieri High School, Gorizia

2008. Universities and Schools. Multicoloured.

3165	60c. Type **1492**	2·75	1·80
3166	60c. Statue of San Ercolano and griffin (images from official seal), University of Perugia	2·75	1·80

1493 Cesare Pavese and Script

2008. Birth Centenary of Cesare Pavese (writer).

3167	**1493** 65c. black, vermilion and blue	3·00	2·00

1494 *Alberico Gentili* (sculpture by Giuseppe Guastalla)

2008. 400th Birth Anniv of Alberico Gentili (jurist; regius professor of civil law, University of Oxford and one of the first writers on public international law).

3168	**1494** 65c. multicoloured	3·00	2·00

1495 Malatestiana Library, Cesena

2008. Cultural Heritage.

3169	**1495** 60c. black	2·75	1·80

1496 Emblem

2008. Union Cycliste Internationale Road World Championships, Varese.

3170	**1496** 60c. multicoloured	2·75	1·70

1497 Stamps as Map of Italy

2008. Stamp Day.

3171	**1497** 60c. multicoloured	3·25	2·30

1498 Mouth of Truth (1st-century mask, Church of Santa Maria, Rome)

2008. Italia–2009 International Stamp Exhibition. Multicoloured. (a) Ordinary gum.

3172	85c. Type **1498**	4·75	3·25

(b) Self-adhesive.

3173	€2.80 Mouth of Truth	15·00	10·50

1499 Traffic Policeman

2008. Local Police Force.

3174	**1499** 60c. multicoloured	3·25	2·30

1500 *Les Gracques* (sculpture) (Eugene Guillaume)

2008. 2500th Anniv of Roman Republic's People's Tribune.

3175	**1500** 60c. multicoloured	3·25	2·30

1501 *Madonna and Child Enthroned with Two Angels* (Lorenzo di Credi)

2008. Christmas. Multicoloured. (a) Ordinary gum.

3176	60c. Type **1501**	3·25	2·30

(b) Self-adhesive.

3177	€2.80 Wreath	15·00	10·50

1502 Val d' Orcia

2008. World Heritage Sites.
3178 – 60c. green and mauve 3·25 1·70
3179 – €2.80 blue 4·50 2·25
DESIGNS: 60c. Type **1502**; €2.80 Historical Centre, Urbino.

1503 Epicentre

2008. Centenary of Messina Earthquake.
3180 **1503** 60c. multicoloured 3·25 1·70

1504 Cover of First Issue

2008. Centenary of Corriere dei Piccoli (weekly magazine for children).
3181 **1504** 60c. multicoloured 3·25 2·30

1505 Charles Darwin

2009. Birth Bicentenary of Charles Robert Darwin (naturalist and evolutionary theorist).
3182 **1505** 65c. multicoloured 3·50 2·40

1506 Moonlight

2009. *Tintarella di Luna* (song). Sheet 96×80 mm.
MS3183 **1506** 60c. multicoloured 3·25 2·30

1507 Father Oreste Benzi, Carlo Valenzi and Vincenzo Muccioli

2009. National Conference on Drugs, Trieste.
3184 **1507** 60c. multicoloured 3·00 2·20

1508 Stamps and Exhibition Visitors (pink background)

2009. Italia 2009–International Stamp Exhibition, Rome. Multicoloured.
3185 60c. Type **1508** 3·00 2·20
3186 €1 Stamps and exhibition visitors (blue-grey background) 5·25 2·50

1509 Rock Engraving, Camonica Valley

2009. Cultural Heritage.
3187 **1509** €2.80 brown 14·50 10·00

1510 Don Primo Mazzolari

2009. 50th Death Anniv of Don Primo Mazzolari (writer and partisan).
3188 **1510** 60c. multicoloured 3·00 2·20

1511 Soldiers

2009. 350th Anniv of Grenadier Corps of Sardinia.
3189 **1511** 60c. multicoooured 3·00 2·20

1512 Piazza di Spagna

2009. Rome–Capital City.
3190 **1512** 60c. multicoloured 3·00 2·20

1513 Indro Montanelli and Typewriter

2009. Birth Centenary of Indro Montanelli (journalist).
3191 **1513** 60c. multicoloured 3·00 2·20

1514 Necklace

2009. Made in Italy. 125th Anniv of Bvlgari (jewellery maker).
3192 **1514** 60c. multicoloured 3·00 2·20

1515 Swiss and Italian Flags

2009. Centenary of Italian Chamber of Commerce for Switzerland.
3193 **1515** 60c. multicoloured 3·00 2·20

1516 Division Arms

2009. 40th Anniv of Carabinieri Division for Protection of Cultural Heritage.
3194 **1516** 60c. multicoloured 3·00 2·20

1517 Map and Stylized Athletes

2009. Mediterranean Games.
3195 **1517** 60c. multicoloured 3·00 2·20

1518 European Parliament Headquarters, Strasbourg and Stars

2009. European Parliamentary Elections.
3196 **1518** 60c. multicoloured 3·00 2·20

1519 Italian Galileo Telescope, La Palma, Canary Islands

2009. Europa. Astronomy. Multicoloured.
3197 60c. Type **1519** 3·00 2·20
3198 65c. Satellite *AGILE* and Earth 3·25 2·30

1520 Early Cyclist

2009. Centenary of Giro d'Italia (cycle race).
3199 **1520** 60c. multicoloured 3·00 2·20

1521 Johann von Goethe and Dnate Alighieri (logo)

2009. 50th Anniv of Academy of Italian–German Studies, Merano.
3200 **1521** 60c. multicoloured 3·00 2·20

1522 Alfa Romeo 6C 1500 Gran Sport

2009. Mille Miglia (thousand miles (open-road endurance race which took place from 1927 to 1957)).
3201 **1522** 60c. multicoloured 3·00 2·20

1523 Carrying 'Ingegno' of Sant'Antonio Abate

2009. Festival of Mysteries, Campobasso.
3202 **1523** 60c. multicoloured 3·00 2·20

1524 Santa Maria Madre di Dio in Rieti Cathedral

2009. Cultural Heritage.
3203 **1524** 60c. black 2·75 2·10

1525 Giovanni Palatucci

2009. Birth Centenary of Giovanni Palatucci (police chief).
3204 **1525** 60c. multicoloured 2·75 2·10

1526 Gilera VT 317 (reconstruction of first motorbike made by Gilera)

2009. Centenary of Gilera (motorcycle manufacturer).
3205 **1526** 60c. multicoloured 2·75 2·10

1527 1859 ½g. Stamp of Sicily (As Type 1) and Handstamp

2009. 150th Anniv of First Stamps in Sicily.
3206 **1527** 60c. multicoloured 2·75 1·40

1528 Player

2009. Baseball World Cup. Sheet 80×60 mm.
MS3207 **1528** 60c. multicoloured 2·75 1·40

1529 Saint John Leonardi

2009. 400th Death Anniv of Saint John Leonardi (San Giovanni Leonardi) (founder of Clerks Regular of the Mother of God of Lucca).

3208 **1529** 60c. multicoloured 2·75 1·40

1530 Player

2009. Italian Football Championship (Inter 2009).

3209 **1530** 60c. multicoloured 2·75 1·40

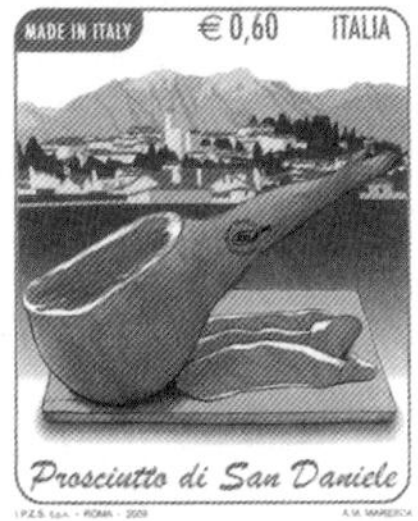

1531 Ham and San Daniele del Friuli

2009. Made in Italy. San Daniele Ham.

3210 **1531** 60c. multicoloured 2·75 1·40

1532 St. Marks Square

2009. St. Marks Square (SMS) Venice Project

3211 **1532** 60c. black and indigo 2·75 1·40

1533 Envelope

2009. Posta Italiana (Italian Mail). Self adhesive.

3212 **1533** 60c. multicoloured 2·75 1·40

3213 **1533** €1.40 multicoloured 5·75 2·75

3214 **1533** €1.50 multicoloured 5·75 2·75

3215 **1533** €2 multicoloured 8·50 4·00

1534 Women

2009. 65th Anniv of Insurrection of Women of Carrara.

3216 **1534** €1.50 multicoloured 6·75 3·50

1535 Summit Emblem

2009. G8 Summit, L'Aquila.

3217 **1535** 65c. multicoloured 3·25 1·60

1536 Piazza Sant'Agostino and Ligurian Coast, Verezzi

2009. Tourist Publicity (36th series). Multicoloured.

3218 60c. Type **1536** 75 40

3219 60c. Lighthouse and Port Giglio, Giglio Island 75 40

3220 60c. Headland and typical vegetation, Costa degli Dei–Capo Vaticano 75 40

3221 60c. Narrow lava walls, Alcantara Gorges 75 40

1537 Vintage Advertising Poster

2009. 150th Anniv of *La Nazione* Newspaper, Florence.

3222 **1537** 60c. multicoloured 3·00 1·50

1538 Freestyle Swimmer

2009. 13th World Aquatics Championships, Italy.

3223 **1538** €1.50 steel blue 6·75 3·50

1539 Living and Burnt Forest

2009. Measures to Prevent and Fight Fires.

3224 **1539** 60c. multicoloured 3·00 1·50

1540 '30' enclosing Dove

2009. 30th (2010) Meeting for Friendship Among Peoples, Rimini.

3225 **1540** 60c. bright emerald 3·00 1·50

1541 *Ufficiali e tromba dei Cavalleggeri di Montebello* (Antonio Cervi)

2009. 150th Anniv of Lancieri di Montebello Cavalry Regiment.

3226 **1541** 60c. multicoloured 3·00 1·50

1542 *San Gennaro* (Francesco Solimena)

2009. Artistic and Cultural Heritage. Museum of Treasure of San Gennaro, Naples.

3227 **1542** 60c. multicoloured 6·75 3·50

1543 Library and Picture Gallery Building, Milan and *Portrait of a Lady* (Giovanni Ambrogio de Predis)

2009. Artistic and Cultural Heritage. Ambrosian Academy Library and Picture Gallery, Milan.

3228 **1543** €1.40 black 6·75 3·50

1544 Emilio Alessandrini

2009. 30th Death Anniv of Emilio Alessandrini (magistrate).

3229 **1544** 60c. multicoloured 3·00 1·50

1545 Cross and Map of Europe

2009. Patron Saints of Europe. Sheet 126×126 mm containing T **1545** and similar horiz design. Multicoloured.

MS3230 60c. Type **1545**; 65c. As Type **1545** with colours reversed 5·50 5·50

1546 Early and Modern Front Page

2009. 120th Anniv of *L'Union Sarda* Newspaper.

3231 **1546** 60c. multicloured 3·00 1·50

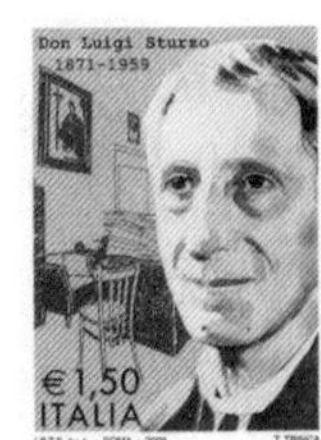

1547 Luigi Sturzo

2009. 50th Death Anniv of Luigi Sturzo (Catholic priest and politician).

3232 **1547** €1.50 salmon-pink and bistre-brown 7·00 3·50

1548 Norberto Bobbio

2009. Birth Centenary of Norberto Bobbio (philosopher of law and political sciences and historian of political thought).

3233 **1548** 65c. multicoloured 3·00 1·50

1549 Fathers Giovanni Minozzi and Giovanni Semeria

2009. Father Giovanni Semeria and Father Giovanni Minozzi (founders of Opera Nazionale per il Mezzogiorno d'Italia (poverty and war orphans charity)) Commemoration.

3234 **1549** 60c. multicoloured 3·00 1·50

1550 Envelopes surrounding School

2009. Stamp Day.

3235 **1550** 60c. multicoloured 3·00 1·50

1551 Dante and Virgil and Three Wild Beasts (from 15th-century Codex Urbinate Latino 365, Vatican Apostolic Library)

2009. Italia 2009 International Stamp Exhibition, Rome. Italian Language.

3236 **1551** 60c. multicoloured 3·00 1·50

A stamp of a similar design was issued by San Marino and Vatican City.

1552 Gino Bartali (cyclist, twice winner of Giro d'Italia)

2009. Italia 2009. Sports Day. Multicoloured.

3237 60c. Type **1552** 2·25 1·10
3238 65c. Valentino Mazzola (footballer, captain of Grande Torino) 2·25 1·10
3239 €1.40 Michele Alboreto beside a Ferrari F1 156/85 (1997–24 Hours of Le Mans and 2001–12 Hours of Sebring winner) 2·25 1·10

1553 Flags as Pen and Ink

2009. 130th Anniv of Italy–Bulgaria Diplomatic Relations. Sheet 101×71 mm.

MS3240 **1553** 65c. multicoloured 2·75 2·75

1554 *Coccobill* (Benito Franco Jacovitti)

2009. Italia 2009. Collectors' Day. Italian Comics. Sheet 80×120 mm containing T 1554 and similar horiz designs. Multicoloured.

MS3241 €1×3, Type **1554**; *Diabolik* (Angela and Luciana Giussani); *Lupo Alberto* (Guido Silvestri (Silver)) 5·25 5·25

1555 *The Adoration of the Shepherds* (Domenico Piola)

2009. Christmas (1st issue).

3242 **1555** 60c. multicoloured 3·00 1·50

1556 Bauble, Star and Moon

2009. Christmas (2nd issue). Self-adhesive.

3243 **1556** 60c. multicoloured 3·00 1·50

1557 Luciano Pavarotti (tenor)

2009. Italia 2009. Music Day. Multicoloured.

3244 65c. Type **1557** 3·00 1·50
3245 €1 Mino Reitano (singer and actor) 2·00 1·50
3246 €1.50 Nino Rota (musician and composer) 5·50 2·75

1558 Pont du Gard, France

2009. Italia 2009. Europe Day. Multicoloured. Self-adhesive.

3247 65c. Type **1558** 3·00 1·50
3248 65c. Hadrian's Wall, Great Britain 3·00 1·50
3249 65c. Odeon of Patras, Greece 3·00 1·50
3250 65c. Porta Nigra, Trier, Germany 3·00 1·50
3251 65c. Aqueduct of Segovia, Spain 3·00 1·50

1559 *Guantanamera* (sculpture) (Giacomo Manzù)

2009. Art. Italian Masters of the 20th Century. Multicoloured.

3252 60c. Type **1559** 3·00 1·50
3253 65c. *The Bear Dance* (Gino Severini) 3·25 1·70
3254 85c. *Donna e Ambiente* (Federico De Pistoris) 3·75 1·90

2009. Posta Italiana (Italian Mail). Self adhesive.

3255 **1533** €3.30 multicoloured 13·00 7·50

1560 Giorgio Perlasca

2010. Birth Centenary of Giorgio Perlasca (saviour of Jews during World War II and recipient of Righteous among the Nations)

3256 **1560** 60c. multicoloured 3·00 1·50

1561 Basilica Santa Maria di Collemaggio

2010. Artistic and Cultural Heritage

MS3257 **1561** 60c. multicoloured 3·00 1·50

1562 Corsa alla Stella and Componidori (Farmers' and Carpenters' Guilds) and Cathedral of Santa Maria Assunta (Sa Sartiglia, Oristano)

2010. Folklore Customs. Multicoloured.

3258 60c. Type **1562** 3·00 1·50
3259 60c. Float and Acireale Cathedral (Acireale carnival) 3·00 1·50

1563 Skier

2010. Winter Olympic Games, Vancouver

3260 **1563** 85c. multicoloured 4·00 2·00

1564 Basketball Players

2010. Youth Olympic Games, Singapore

3261 **1564** 85c. multicoloured 4·00 2·00

1565 Ennio Flaiano

2010. Birth Centenary of Ennio Flaiano

3262 **1565** 60c. multicoloured 3·00 1·50

1566 Mario Pannunzio

2010. Birth Centenary of Mario Pannunzio (writer and journalist)

3263 **1566** 60c. multicoloured 3·00 1·50

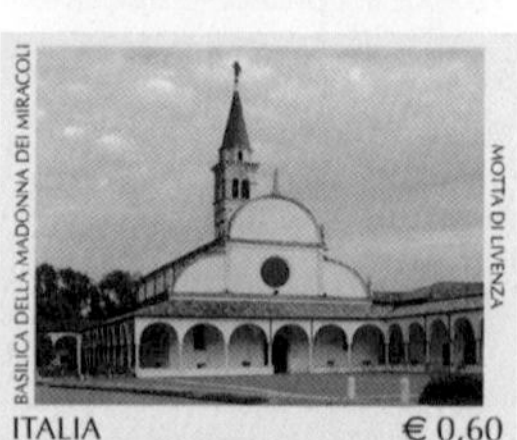
1567 Basilica of Madonna dei Miracoli, Motta di Livenza, Treviso

2010. Artistic and Cultural Heritage

3264 **1567** 60c. multicoloured 3·00 1·50

1568 Massimo D'Azeglio (first provincial president) and Palazzo Isimbardi

2010. 150th Anniv of Milan Province

3265 **1568** 60c. multicoloured 3·00 1·50

1569 24 HP (1910)

2010. Made in Italy. Multicoloured.

3266 60c. Type **1569** 2·25 1·10
3267 60c. Modern hatchback 2·25 1·10

Nos. 3266/7 were printed, *se-tenant*, forming a composite design

1570 Sepoltura del Cristo e tre angeli che reggono il Sudario(Burial of Christ with three angels holding up the Shroud) (Gerolamo della Rover)

2010. Ostension of Turin Shroud

3268 **1570** 60c. multicoloured 3·00 1·50

1571 L'imbarco di Garibaldi a Quarto (Garibaldi sets sail from Quarto) (V. Azzola)

2010. 150th Anniv of the Expedition of the Thousand. Multicoloured.

MS3269 60c. Type **1571**; 65c. *Lo sbarco a Marsala. 11 maggio 1860* (Landing at Marsala. 11th May 1860); 85c. *La Battaglia di Calatafimi* (Battle of Calatafimi) (Remigio Legat); €1 *L'incontro di Teano tra Giuseppe Garibaldi e Vittorio Emanuele II* (Meeting in Teano between Giuseppe Garibaldi and Vittorio Emanuele II) (Pietro Aldi) 6·25 6·25

1572 Centenary Emblem

2010. Centenary of Confindustria

3270 **1572** €1.40 multicoloured 6·25 3·00

1573 Viaduct

2010. Centenary of Rhaetian Railway

3271 **1573** 65c. multicoloured 3·00 1·50

1574 Pinocchio (Jacovitti after Carlo Collodi)

2010. Europa. Multicoloured.

3272 60c. Type **1574** 2·25 1·10
3273 65c. Geronimo Stilton (Elisabetta Dami) 2·25 1·10

No. 3274 and Type **1575** are vacant

1576 Sr. Maria Domenica Brun Barbantini (founder) and Sisters caring for the Sick

2010. 180th (2009) Anniv of Congregation of the Sister Servants of the Sick of St. Camillus

3275 **1576** 60c. multicoloured 2·75 1·40

1577 Gardens

2010. Hanbury Botanic Gardens, Ventimiglia
3276 **1577** 60c. multicoloured 2·75 1·40

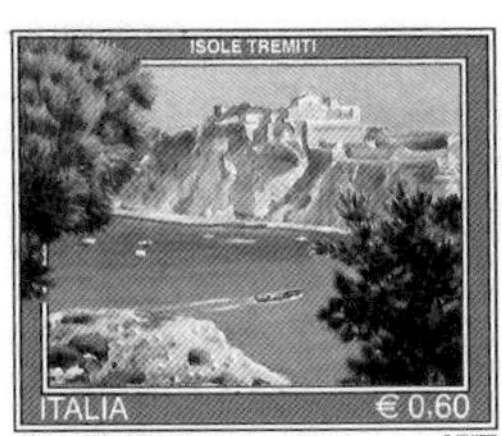

1578 Isole Tremiti

2010. Tourist Publicity (37th series). Multicoloured.
3277 60c. Type **1578** 2·75 1·40
3278 60c. Todi 2·75 1·40
3279 60c. Viggiano 2·75 1·40
3280 60c. Courmayeur 2·75 1·40

1579 ENIT (national tourist agency) Poster, 1955

2010. Tourism
3281 **1579** 60c. multicoloured 3·00 1·50

1580 Camillo Benso

2010. Birth Bicentenary of Camillo Benso, Count of Cavour.
3282 **1580** 60c. multicoloured 2·75 1·40

1581 Anniversary Emblem

2010. Centenary of Assonime (Association of Italian Joint Stock Companies)
3283 **1581** 60c. multicoloured 2·75 1·40

1582 Inter Milan Player, Number 18 (number of times Inter Milan has won championship) and the Club Crest

2010. Inter Milan, Italian Football Champions–Serie A 2010
3284 **1582** 60c. multicoloured 3·00 1·50

1583 Emblem

2010. Made in Italy. Centenary of Federacciai (iron and steel casting plant), Bagnoli
3285 **1583** €3.30 black 14·00 7·00

2010. Posta Italiana (Italian Mail)
3286 **1533** 5c. multicoloured 25 15
3287 10c. multicoloured 50 25
3288 20c. multicoloured 1·00 50
See also 3212/15

1584 Giovanni Schiaparelli, Map and Mars

2010. Death Centenary of Giovanni Virginio Schiaparelli (astronomer)
3289 **1584** 65c. multicoloured 3·00 1·50

1585 Pope Benedict XVI, Cathedral of San Panfilo of Sulmona and Pope Celestine V (statue)

2010. Celestian Jubilee Year
3290 **1585** 60c. multicoloured 2·75 1·40

1586 David with the Head of Goliath

2010. 400th Death Anniv of Michelangelo Merisi da Caravaggio (artist)
3291 **1586** 60c. multicoloured 3·00 1·50

1587 Ettore Paratore and 3rd-century Mosaic Trionfo di Dioniso (Triumph of Dionysius),

2010. 50th Anniv of Plautus Festival, Sarsina
3292 **1587** 65c. multicoloured 3·00 1·50

1588 Amphitheatre

2010. Artistic and Cultural Heritage
3293 **1588** 60c. reddish-brown 3·00 1·50

1589 Joe Petrosino, Brooklyn Bridge and Statue of Liberty

2010. 150th Birth Anniv of Giuseppe (Joe) Petrosino (New York City policeman who was a pioneer in the fight against organized crime)
3294 **1589** 85c. multicoloured 4·25 2·10

1590 17th Olympic Games Emblem, Torch Bearer and Tripod containing Olympic Flame

2010. 50th Anniv of Rome 1960, Olympic Games
3295 **1590** 60c. multicoloured 3·00 1·50

1591 Fire Brigade Members and Cortina d'Ampezzo (event venue)

2010. First National Gathering of Italian Fire Brigades
3296 **1591** 60c. multicoloured 3·00 1·50

1592 Italian Flag, National Acrobatic Team in Arrow Formation

2010. 50th Anniv National Air Force Acrobatic Team
3297 **1592** 60c. multicoloured 3·00 1·50

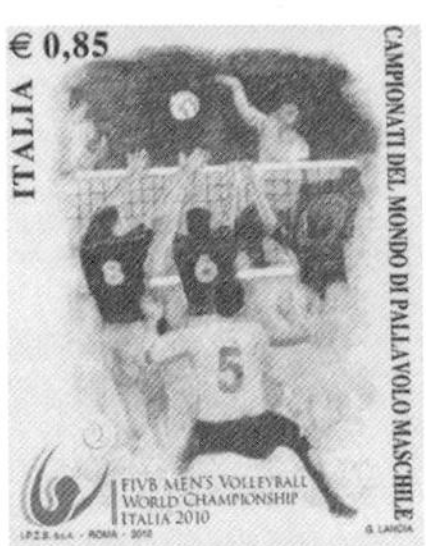

1593 Piazzale di Porta Pia, Monumento al Bersagliere and Porta Pia Gate in Aurelian Walls

2010. Rome as Capital City
3298 **1593** 60c. multicoloured 3·00 1·50

1594 Players

2010. Sport
3299 **1594** 85c. deep dull blue 4·25 2·10

1595 19th-century Coral Bracelet

2010. Made in Italy. Torre del Greco Coral Jewellery
3300 **1595** 60c. multicoloured 3·00 1·50

1596 Frecciarossa High Speed Train

2010. Turin–Salerno High Speed Rail Line
MS3301 multicoloured 3·00 1·50

1597 Front *Page of Corriere delle Marche* (previous title), 5 October 1860, Map of Area and *Corriere Adriatico* Front Page

2010. 150th Anniv of *Corriere Adriatico* Newspaper
3302 **1597** 60c. multicoloured 3·00 1·50

1598 People, Italian Flag and European Union Flag

2010. Anti-trust Authority
3303 **1598** €1.40 multicoloured 6·75 3·50

1599 Building Façade

2010. School of Oenology (study of wine and winemaking), Conegliano, Treviso
3304 **1599** 60c. multicoloured 3·00 1·50

1600 Leonardo Sciascia

2010. Leonardo Sciascia (writer) Commemoration
3305 **1600** 60c. black 3·00 1·50

1601 Players, Emblem and Anniversary Emblem

2010. Sport. Centenary of Italian Tennis Federation
3306 **1601** 60c. multicoloured 3·00 1·50

1602 Self Portrait

2010. Artistic and Cultural Heritage
3307 **1602** 60c. multicoloured 3·00 1·50

1603 Federico Fellini

2010. Italian Cinema 2010. Each black and green.
MS3308 60c.×3, Type **1603**; Vittorio Gassman; Alberto Sordi 8·25 8·25

1604 Adoration of the Magi (Sandro Botticelli)

2010. Christmas (1st issue)
3309 **1604** 60c. multicoloured 3·00 1·50

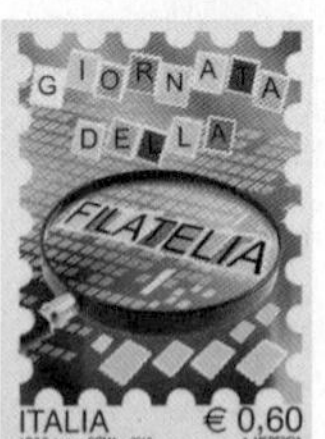
1605 Magnifying Glass and 'FILATELIA'

2010. Stamp Day
3310 **1605** 60c. multicoloured 3·00 1·50
Type **1606** is vacant.

1607 'NATALE' carried by Toy Train

2010. Christmas (2nd issue)
3311 **1607** 65c. multicoloured 3·00 1·50

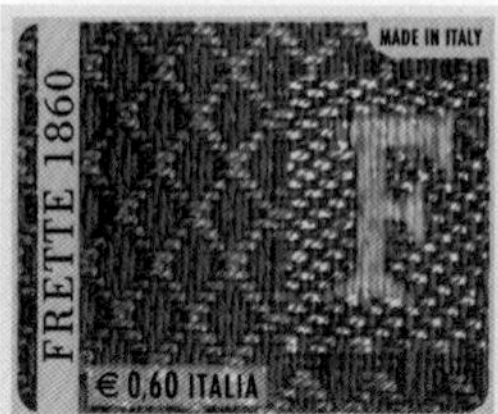
1608 19th-century Jaquard Fabric, featuring 'F' (company logo)

2010. Made in Italy
3312 **1608** 60c. multicoloured 3·00 1·50

1609 Mario Mazzuca and Rugby Players

2010. Sport
3313 **1609** 60c. multicoloured 3·00 1·50

1610 Biscuit Tin, Biscuits and Poster

2010. Made in Italy
3314 **1610** 60c. multicoloured 3·00 1·50

1611 Pinot di Franciacorta, 1961

2010. Made in Italy
3315 **1611** 60c. multicoloured 3·00 1·50

1612 Anniversary Emblem

2011. 150th Anniv of Re-unification of Italy. Multicoloured.

(a) Sheet stamp. Self-adhesive
3316 60c. Type **1612** 3·00 1·50

(b) Miniature sheet. Ordinary gum
MS3317 80×60 mm. 60c. Colours of Italian flag crossed through by two waving green and red ribbons (40×30 mm) 3·00 1·50

1613 Battle of the Oranges, Palazzo Comunale, Piazza Vittorio Emanuele. and Mugnaia, (heroic female figure, symbol of the Carnival)

2011
3318 **1613** 60c. multicoloured 3·00 1·50

1614 Antonio Fogazzaro

2011. Death Centenary of Antonio Fogazzaro (writer)
3319 **1614** 60c. multicoloured 3·00 1·50

1615 Three Women

2011. International Women's Day
3320 **1615** 75c. multicoloured 3·75 1·90

1616 'TERRITORIO' (land registry)

2011. Taxation Agencies. Multicoloured.
MS3321 60c.×4, Type **1616**;' DOGANE' (customs); 'DEMANIO' (state property); 'ENTRATE' (revenue) 11·25 11·25

1617 Palazzo Montecitorio, Rome, (current seat of the Italian Parliament) and Palazzo Carignano, Turin, (seat of the first Italian Parliament)

2011. 150th Anniv of Proclamation of Kingdom of Italy. Sheet 80×60 mm
MS3322 **1617** 60c. multicoloured 3·00 3·00

1618 Flaminio Obelisk, Santa Maria dei Miracoli Church and Santa Maria in Montesanto Church, Piazza del Popolo, Rome

2011. 150th Anniv of Unification of Italy. Sheet 96×80 mm
MS3323 **1618** €1.50 multicoloured 7·25 7·25

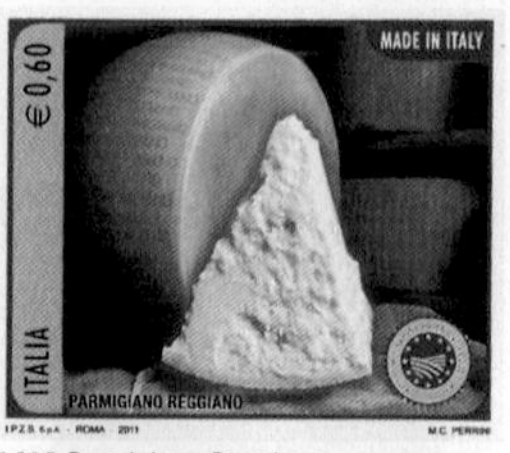
1619 Parmigiano Reggiano

2011. Made in Italy. Cheeses. Multicoloured.
3324 60c. Type **1619** 3·00 1·50
3325 60c. Gorgonzola 3·00 1·50
3326 60c. Mozzarella 3·00 1·50
3327 60c. Ragusano 3·00 1·50

1620 World Theatre Day Poster (Interaction) and '27 marzo 2011'

2011. World Theatre Day
3328 **1620** 60c. multicoloured 3·00 1·50

1621 1863 15c. Stamp (As No. 7)

2011. Philatelic Exhibition. 'Quel magnifico biennio 1859-1861'
3329 **1621** 60c. multicoloured 3·00 1·50

1622 Yuri Gagarin

2011. 50th Anniv of First Manned Space Flight
3330 **1622** 75c. multicoloured 3·75 1·90

1623 *Roma dalle Quadrighe del Vittoriano: dal Quirinale al Colosseo* (Marcella Morlacchi)

2011. Rome as Capital City
3331 **1623** 60c. multicoloured 3·00 1·50

1624 Emilio Salgari

2011. Death Centenary of Emilio Salgari (Journalist and writer)
3332 **1624** 60c. multicoloured 3·00 1·50

1625 Pope John Paul II

2011. Beatification of Pope John Paul II
3333 **1625** 60c. multicoloured 3·00 1·50

1626 Forest, Squirrel and Fungi

2011. Europa. Forests. Multicoloured.
3334 60c. Type **1626** 3·00 1·50
3335 75c. Trees, bird, flower and leaf 3·50 1·75

1627 Emblem

2011. 50th Anniv of Amnesty International
3336 **1627** 60c. multicoloured 3·00 1·50

1628 *Gli emigranti* (The Emigrants) (Angiolo Tommasi)

2011. Museum of Italian Emigration

3337	**1628**	60c. multicoloured	3·00	1·50

1629 *Count Camillo Benso di Cavour* and *Les Congres de Paris* (lithograph)

2011. 150th Anniv of Re-unification of Italy (3rd issue). Personalities. Multicoloured.

MS3338	60c. Type **1629**	2·75	2·75
MS3339	60c. *Carlo Cattaneo and I remember the days 5, 1848 in Port Victoria*	2·75	2·75
MS3340	60c. *Giuseppe Garibaldi and The Entry of Garibaldi into Naples September 7, 1860*	2·75	2·75
MS3341	60c. *Roscioni Vincenzo Vincenzo Gioberti and Event to Celebrate Joy of Neapolitan Pius IX and Gioberti*	2·75	2·75
MS3342	60c. *Clara Maffei, Cristina Trivulzio Belgiojoso and The Sharpshooter Lombard's Death and Spearmen carrying badly Wounded at Villa Luciano Manara*	2·75	2·75
MS3343	60c. *Giuseppe Mazzini,* frontispiece of *Young Italy* (magazine) and flag with 'Union, Strength and Freedom!'	2·75	2·75
MS3344	60c. Carlo Pisacane and *The Death of Carlo Pisacane*	2·75	2·75
MS3345	60c. *Vittorio Emanuele II* and Portrait of *Vittorio Emanuele II, King of Sardinia and Italy*	2·75	2·75

1630 Anita and Giuseppe Garibaldi, and Three Towers on Mount Titano

2011. 150th Anniv of Re-unification of Italy (4th issue). Sheet 80×60 mm

MS3346	**1630**	€1.50 multicoloured	7·25	7·25

1631 Arms of Savoia Family, with Royal Crown; Heraldic Emblem of Italian Navy, with Turreted Naval Crown, and Naval Pennant with Heraldic Emblem

2011. 150th Anniv of Re-unification of Italy (5th issue). 150th Anniv of Italian Navy. Multicoloured.

MS3347	60c.×4, Type **1631**; Naval Academy of Livorno; *Amerigo Vespucci* (training ship); Arms of Italian Sailors' Union and National Association of Italian Sailors	11·50	11·50

1632 Referee holding Yellow Card and Players

2011. Centenary of Italian Referees' Association

3348	**1632**	60c. multicoloured	3·00	1·50

1633 Carlo Dapporto

2011. Birth Centenary of Carlo Dapporto (actor)

3349	**1633**	60c. multicoloured	3·00	1·50

2011. Posta Italiana (Italian Mail)

3350	**1533**	75c. multicoloured	3·50	1·75

See also Nos. 3212/15 and 3286/8.

1634 Botanic Garden of Padua

2011. Gardens. Multicoloured.

3351	60c. Type **1634**	3·00	1·50
3352	60c. Giardino di Flora Appenninica (Garden of Apennine Flora of Capracotta)	3·00	1·50

1635 Benedictine Abbey of the Santissima Trinità

2011. Artistic and Cultural Heritage. Benedictine Abbey of the Santissima Trinità

3353	**1635**	60c. black	3·00	1·50

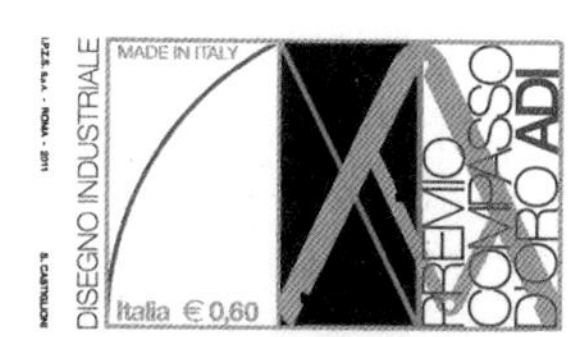

1636 Award Emblem

2011. Made in Italy. ADI Compasso d'Oro (Industrial Design Association Golden Compass) Award

3354	**1636**	60c. multicoloured	3·00	1·50

CONCESSIONAL LETTER POST

CL93 Arms of Savoy and Fasces

1928

CL227	**CL93**	10c. blue	3·25	20

CL109 Arms and Fasces

1930

CL267	**CL109**	10c. brown	10	15

1945. No. CL267, surch with Royal Arms (obliterating fasces) and new value.

CL647	40c. on 10c. brown	1·10	1·30

1945. As Type CL 109, but Arms redrawn without fasces.

CL648	10c. brown	55	55
CL649	1l. brown	7·50	3·25

CL201 Italia

1947

CL687	**CL201**	1l. green	1·30	40
CL688	**CL201**	8l. red	36·00	40

CL220 Italia

1948

CL734	**CL220**	15l. violet	£150	20
CL916	**CL220**	20l. violet	30	25
CL917	**CL220**	30l. green	30	25
CL918	**CL220**	35l. brown	30	25
CL919	**CL220**	110l. blue	30	25
CL920	**CL220**	270l. mauve	80	25
CL921	**CL220**	300l. green & pink	65	30
CL922	**CL220**	370l. brown & orge	80	35

CONCESSIONAL PARCEL POST

CP288

1953

CP918	**CP288**	40l. orange	20	55
CP919	**CP288**	50l. blue	20	55
CP920	**CP288**	60l. violet	1·10	3·50
CP921	**CP288**	70l. green	4·50	13·00
CP850	**CP288**	75l. sepia	6·50	50·00
CP923	**CP288**	80l. brown	10	10
CP924	**CP288**	90l. lilac	10	10
CP851	**CP288**	110l. red	6·50	65·00
CP926	**CP288**	110l. yellow	10	10
CP927	**CP288**	120l. green	10	10
CP928	**CP288**	140l. black	20	10
CP929	**CP288**	150l. red	30	35
CP930	**CP288**	180l. red	10	35
CP931	**CP288**	240l. slate	10	35
CP932	**CP288**	500l. brown	55	1·10
CP933	**CP288**	600l. turquoise	55	1·10
CP934	**CP288**	900l. blue	55	1·10

Unused prices are for the complete pair. Used prices are for the left half; right halves are worth more.

CP707

1984

CP1849	**CP707**	3000l. blue and red	4·00	4·00

EXPRESS LETTER STAMPS

E35

1903. For inland letters.

E73	**E35**	25c. red	48·00	1·60
E113	**E35**	50c. red	2·10	2·10
E129	**E35**	60c. red	5·25	1·10
E178	**E35**	70c. red	55	45
E179	**E35**	1l.25 blue	55	10

E41 King Victor Emmanuel III

1908. For foreign letters.

E80	**E41**	30c. blue and pink	1·10	4·25
E180	**E41**	2l. blue and pink	4·25	60·00
E181	**E41**	2l.50 blue and pink	3·25	5·25

E59

1917. Surch 25 and bars.

E112	**E59**	25c. on 40c. violet	37·00	90·00

1921. Surch with new value.

E118	**E41**	L.1.20 on 30c. blue and pink	1·10	19·00
E173	**E41**	L.1.60 on 1l.20 blue and pink	1·60	60·00

1922. Surch in words and figures.

E122	**E35**	60c. on 50c. red	35·00	2·40
E172	**E35**	70c. on 60c. red	1·10	1·10

E131 "Garibaldi" (statue), Savoia Marchetti S-55A Flying Boat and "Anita Garibaldi" (statue)

1932. Air. 50th Death Anniv of Garibaldi.

E348	**E131**	2l.25+1l. violet and red	10·50	60·00
E349	**E131**	4l.50+1l.50 brown and green	10·50	60·00

E132 King Victor Emmanuel III

1932

E350	**E132**	1l.25 green	20	25
E351	**E132**	2l.50 orange	30	4·50

1932. 10th Anniv of March on Rome. As T 132. (a) For inland letters. Inscribed "ESPRESSO".

E368	1l.25 green	2·10	2·10

(b) For foreign letters. Inscribed "EXPRES".

E369	2l.50 orange	6·50	£160

DESIGNS: 1l.25, Roman road; 2l.50, Flags and head of Mussolini.

E133 Savoia Marchetti S-55A Flying Boat

1933. Air.

E370	**E133**	2l. black	10	3·25
E371	**E133**	2l.25 black	4·75	£160

1934. Air. 10th Anniv of Annexation of Fiume. Inscr as in T 141.

E408	2l.+1l.25 blue	1·10	32·00
E409	2l.25+1l.25 green	2·10	27·00
E410	4l.50+2l. red	2·10	27·00

DESIGN: Foundation of Fiume.

1934. Air. Military Medal Centenary. Inscr as in T 146.

E442	2l.+1l.25 brown	6·50	43·00
E443	4l.50+2l. red	10·50	43·00

DESIGN—HORIZ: 2l., 4l.50, Caproni Ca 101 airplane over triumphal arch.

E192 Italia

1945

E647	**E192**	5l. red	30	1·30

E200 Winged Foot of Mercury

1945

E679	**E200**	5l. red	10	10
E680	-	10l. blue	50	55
E681	-	15l. red	5·25	15
E682	**E200**	25l. orange	60·00	10
E683	**E200**	30l. violet	4·25	2·10
E915	**E200**	50l. purple	10·00	30
E685	-	60l. red	80·00	15

DESIGN: 10, 15, 60l. Horse and torch bearer.

E209 Rising at Naples

1948. Centenary of 1848 Revolution.

E718	**E209**	35l. violet	£190	25·00

E341 Etruscan Horses

1958

E961	**E341**	75l. purple	30	10
E1220	**E341**	150l. green	20	10
E1221	**E341**	250l. blue & light blue	35	15
E1222	**E341**	300l. brown & lt brn	40	15

MILITARY POST STAMPS

1943. Stamps of Italy optd P.M. (a) Postage stamps of 1929 (Nos. 239/56).

M583	5c. brown	45	2·10
M584	10c. brown	45	2·10
M585	15c. green	45	2·10
M586	20c. red	45	2·10
M587	25c. green	45	2·10
M588	30c. brown	45	2·10
M589	50c. violet	45	2·10
M590	1l. violet	3·00	16·00
M591	1l.25 blue	45	3·25
M592	1l.75 orange	45	3·25
M593	2l. red	45	3·25
M594	5l. red	45	3·75
M595	10l. violet	45	21·00

(b) Air stamps of 1930 (Nos. 271/7).

M596	50c. brown	45	2·10
M597	1l. violet	45	2·40
M598	2l. blue	45	10·50
M599	5l. green	3·25	14·00
M600	10l. red	3·25	19·00

(c) Air Express stamp of 1933 (No. E370).

M601	2l. black	3·25	27·00

(d) Express Letter stamp of 1932 (No. E350).

M602	1l.25 green	45	16·00

NEWSPAPER STAMPS

N2

1862. Imperf.

N5	**N2**	2c. yellow	60·00	£130

For similar stamps in black, see Sardinia.

OFFICIAL STAMPS

O11

1875

O21	**O11**	2c. red	2·10	4·25
O22	**O11**	5c. red	2·10	4·25
O23	**O11**	20c. red	1·10	2·10
O24	**O11**	30c. red	1·10	3·25
O25	**O11**	1l. red	4·25	13·00
O26	**O11**	2l. red	21·00	37·00
O27	**O11**	5l. red	95·00	£160
O28	**O11**	10l. red	£170	£130

1934. Air. Optd SERVIZIO DI STATO.

O450	**148**	10l. grey	£900	£13000

PARCEL POST STAMPS

P13 King Umberto I

1884. Various frames.

P38	**P13**	10c. grey	£200	£100
P39	**P13**	20c. blue	£375	£180
P40	**P13**	50c. pink	21·00	15·00
P41	**P13**	75c. green	21·00	15·00
P42	**P13**	1l.25 orange	41·00	34·00
P43	**P13**	1l.75 brown	41·00	£140

The left-hand portion of the following parcel post stamps is affixed to the packet-card, the right-hand portion to the receipt. Unused prices are for the complete pair and used prices for the half-stamp. Unsevered stamps in used condition are usually from cancelled-to-order material and are worth more than the half-stamp.

P53

1914

P96	**P53**	5c. brown	1·10	6·50
P97	**P53**	10c. blue	1·10	6·50
P98	**P53**	20c. black	1·10	6·50
P99	**P53**	25c. red	2·10	6·50
P100	**P53**	50c. orange	2·10	19·00
P101	**P53**	1l. violet	2·10	6·50
P102	**P53**	2l. green	5·25	8·50
P103	**P53**	3l. yellow	7·50	21·00
P104	**P53**	4l. grey	16·00	27·00
P105	**P53**	10l. purple	43·00	27·00
P106	**P53**	12l. brown	£150	£300
P107	**P53**	15l. olive	£150	£300
P108	**P53**	20l. purple	£120	£300

1923. Surch with figures on left half and words and figures on right half.

P146	30c. on 5c. brown	1·10	16·00
P147	60c. on 5c. brown	1·10	16·00
P148	1l.50 on 5c. brown	4·25	£110
P149	3l. on 10l. purple	4·25	65·00

P92

1927

P217	**P92**	5c. brown	1·10	2·10
P218	**P92**	10c. blue	1·10	2·10
P219	**P92**	25c. red	1·10	2·10
P220	**P92**	30c. blue	1·10	3·25
P221	**P92**	50c. orange	1·10	2·10
P222	-	60c. red	1·10	3·25
P223	**P92**	1l. violet	1·10	3·25
P224	**P92**	2l. green	1·10	3·25
P225	**P92**	3l. bistre	1·10	7·50
P226	**P92**	4l. black	1·10	7·50
P227	**P92**	10l. purple	3·25	32·00
P228	**P92**	20l. purple	5·25	43·00

The value in the right-hand portion of the 60c. is in figures.

1945. Optd with ornamental device obliterating Fascist emblems in centre.

P647		5c. brown	2·75	2·75
P648		10c. blue	2·75	2·75
P649		25c. red	2·75	2·75
P650		30c. blue	27·00	8·00
P651		50c. orange	2·75	2·75
P652	-	60c. red	2·75	2·75
P653	**P92**	1l. violet	2·75	2·75
P654	**P92**	2l. green	2·75	2·75
P655	**P92**	3l. bistre	2·75	2·75
P656	**P92**	4l. black	2·75	2·75
P657	**P92**	10l. purple	27·00	27·00
P658	**P92**	20l. purple	55·00	55·00

1946. As Type P 92, but without fasces between stamps.

P679	1l. mauve	2·10	55
P680	2l. green	2·10	55
P681	3l. orange	3·25	1·60
P682	4l. black	4·25	1·60
P683	10l. purple	£110	27·00
P684	20l. purple	£160	70·00

P201

1946

P687a	**P201**	25c. blue	10	10
P688	**P201**	50c. brown	60	20
P689	**P201**	1l. brown	60	20
P690	**P201**	2l. blue	1·90	50
P691	**P201**	3l. orange	70	20
P692	**P201**	4l. grey	13·00	4·75
P910	**P201**	5l. purple	10	10
P911	**P201**	10l. violet	10	10
P912	**P201**	20l. purple	10	10
P914	**P201**	40l. violet	10	10
P915	**P201**	50l. red	10	10
P916	**P201**	60l. violet	10	10
P917	**P201**	100l. blue	10	10
P918	**P201**	140l. red	10	10
P919	**P201**	150l. brown	10	10
P920	**P201**	200l. green	10	10
P921	**P201**	280l. yellow	35	20
P922	**P201**	300l. purple	35	20
P923	**P201**	400l. black	55	30
P924	**P201**	500l. brown	1·60	45
P925	**P201**	600l. brown	1·30	55
P926	**P201**	700l. blue	2·20	30
P927	**P201**	800l. orange	2·75	30
P1348	**P201**	30l. purple	20	20

P298

1954

P928a	**P298**	1000l. blue	1·00	75
P929	**P298**	2000l. red and brown	5·00	55

PNEUMATIC POST LETTERS

PE53

1913

PE96	**PE53**	10c. brown	3·25	19·00
PE97	**PE53**	15c. lilac	3·25	24·00
PE191	**PE53**	15c. pink	4·25	13·00
PE192	**PE53**	15c. purple	4·25	13·00
PE193	**PE53**	20c. purple	16·00	37·00
PE98	**PE53**	30c. blue	13·00	£110
PE194	**PE53**	35c. red	19·00	£325
PE195	**PE53**	40c. red	27·00	£225

1924. Surch.

PE165	15c. on 10c. brown	4·25	24·00
PE166	15c. on 20c. purple	10·50	43·00
PE167	20c. on 10c. brown	8·50	40·00
PE168	20c. on 15c. lilac	10·50	24·00
PE169	35c. on 40c. red	21·00	£180
PE170	40c. on 30c. blue	10·50	£160

PE134 Galileo Galilei

1933

PE372	-	15c. purple	30	80
PE373	**PE134**	35c. red	30	80

DESIGN: 15c. Dante Alighieri.

1945. As Type PE 134, but inscr "ITALIA" instead of "REGNO D'ITALIA".

PE679	-	60c. brown (Dante)	55	1·60
PE680	**PE134**	1l.40 blue	55	1·60

PE204 Minerva

1947

PE694	**PE204**	3l. purple	9·00	8·75
PE695	**PE204**	5l. blue	55	15
PE961	**PE204**	10l. red	20	20
PE962	**PE204**	20l. blue	20	20

POSTAGE DUE STAMPS

D3

1863. Imperf.

D6B	**D3**	10c. yellow	£110	£250

FOOTNOTE: Our price for mint stamps is for stamps without gum. Stamps with gum are worth considerably more.

D11

1869. Perf.

D21	**D11**	10c. brown	£4750	65·00

D12

1870

D22	**D12**	1c. mauve and orange	6·50	16·00
D23	**D12**	2c. mauve and orange	17·00	30·00
D24	**D12**	5c. mauve and orange	1·60	1·10
D25	**D12**	10c. mauve and orange	1·60	1·10
D26	**D12**	20c. mauve and orange	16·00	1·10
D27	**D12**	30c. mauve and orange	4·75	1·30
D28	**D12**	40c. mauve and orange	4·75	3·75
D29	**D12**	50c. mauve and orange	4·75	1·10
D30		60c. mauve and orange	£200	4·25
D31		60c. brown and orange	32·00	15·00
D32		1l. brown and blue	£6500	27·00
D33		1l. mauve and blue	27·00	1·60
D34		2l. brown and blue	£6500	43·00
D35		2l. mauve and blue	65·00	6·50
D36		5l. brown and blue	£550	48·00
D37		5l. mauve and blue	£190	32·00
D38		10l. brown and blue	£9000	48·00
D39		10l. mauve and blue	£180	8·50

D13

1884

D40	**D13**	50l. green	95·00	55·00
D73	**D13**	50l. yellow	95·00	55·00
D41	**D13**	100l. red	75·00	21·00
D74	**D13**	100l. blue	75·00	21·00

(D 20)

1890. Surch over numeral as Type D 20.

D47	**D12**	10(c.) on 2c. (D23)	£130	37·00
D48	**D12**	20(c.) on 1c. (D22)	£550	27·00
D49	**D12**	30(c.) on 2c. (D23)	£1700	10·50

D141 **D142**

1934. With Fascist emblems.

D395	**D141**	5c. brown	55	60
D396	**D141**	10c. blue	55	60
D397	**D141**	20c. red	55	60
D398	**D141**	25c. green	55	60
D399	**D141**	30c. orange	55	60
D400	**D141**	40c. brown	55	3·25
D401	**D141**	50c. violet	55	60
D402	**D141**	60c. blue	55	7·50
D403	**D142**	1l. orange	55	60
D404	**D142**	2l. green	55	60
D405	**D142**	5l. violet	2·10	1·10
D406	**D142**	10l. blue	3·25	4·25
D407	**D142**	20l. red	5·25	15·00

D191 **D192**

1945. Fascist emblems removed.

D630	**D191**	5c. brown	2·75	2·10
D631	**D191**	10c. blue	75	1·10
D632	**D191**	20c. red	2·75	1·10
D633	**D191**	25c. green	75	1·10
D634	**D191**	30c. orange	75	1·10
D635	**D191**	40c. black	75	1·10
D636	**D191**	50c. violet	75	1·10
D637	**D191**	60c. blue	75	2·10
D685	**D192**	1l. orange	75	10
D639	**D192**	2l. green	75	1·10
D640	**D192**	5l. violet	75	1·10
D641	**D192**	10l. blue	75	1·10
D642	**D192**	20l. red	75	1·10

D201

1947

D690	**D201**	1l. orange	30	10
D691	**D201**	2l. green	65	10
D692	**D201**	3l. red	1·60	2·10
D693	**D201**	4l. brown	1·90	2·10
D924	**D201**	5l. violet	20	15
D695	**D201**	6l. blue	8·00	2·10
D696	**D201**	8l. mauve	30·00	3·25
D926	**D201**	10l. blue	20	15
D698	**D201**	12l. brown	10·50	2·10
D927	**D201**	20l. purple	20	15
D928	**D201**	25l. red	20	15
D929	**D201**	30l. purple	20	15
D930	**D201**	40l. brown	20	15
D931	**D201**	50l. green	20	15
D932	**D201**	100l. orange	20	15
D935	**D201**	500l. red and blue	1·70	55
D936	**D201**	500l. purple and blue	90	30
D937	**D201**	900l. mve, blk & grn	2·00	55
D938	**D201**	1500l. orange & brown	2·40	75

PUBLICITY ENVELOPE STAMPS

1921. Optd B.L.P.

B129	**37**	10c. red	£150	£110
B137	**37**	15c. grey	£130	80·00
B138	**41**	20c. orange	£400	£500
B132	**39**	25c. blue	£150	£120
B140	**39**	30c. brown	£275	£190
B115	**39**	40c. brown	£110	27·00
B134	**39**	50c. violet	£750	£750
B135	**39**	60c. red	£2750	£2250
B141	**39**	85c. brown	£350	£500
B136	**34**	1l. brown and green	£4250	£2750

ITALIAN SOCIAL REPUBLIC

Following the surrender of Italy on 3 September 1943, and his rescue from imprisonment on 12 September, Mussolini proclaimed the Italian Social Republic at Salo on 23 September 1943. From this town on Lake Garda the Republican government administered those parts of Italy, north of the Gustav Line, which were under German occupation.

1944. Stamps of Italy optd G. N. R. (a) Postage. (i) Nos. 239 and 241/59.

1	**98**	5c. brown	3·25	6·50
2	-	10c. brown	3·25	6·50
3	-	15c. green	3·25	6·50
4	**99**	20c. red	3·25	10·50
5	-	25c. green	3·25	6·50
6	**103**	30c. brown	3·25	6·50
7	-	35c. blue	£140	£225
8	**103**	50c. violet	3·25	10·50
9	-	75c. red	3·25	6·50
10	**99**	1l. violet	3·25	6·50
11	-	1l.25 blue	3·25	6·50
12	-	1l.75 red	6·50	37·00
13	-	2l. red	10·50	37·00
14	**98**	2l.55 green	55·00	£275
15	**98**	3l.70 violet	43·00	£190
16	**98**	5l. red	9·50	43·00
17	-	10l. violet	95·00	£350
18	**99**	20l. green	£275	£550
19	-	25l. black	£750	£1700
20	-	50l. violet	£600	£1700

(ii) War Propaganda issue. Nos. 563/74.

21	25c. green (Navy)	8·50	21·00
22	25c. green (Army)	8·50	21·00
23	25c. green (Air Force)	8·50	21·00
24	25c. green (Militia)	8·50	21·00
25	30c. brown (Navy)	8·50	43·00
26	30c. brown (Army)	8·50	43·00
27	30c. brown (Air Force)	8·50	43·00
28	30c. brown (Militia)	8·50	43·00
29	50c. violet (Navy)	8·50	21·00
30	50c. violet (Army)	8·50	21·00
31	50c. violet (Air Force)	8·50	21·00
32	50c. violet (Militia)	8·50	21·00

(b) Air. Nos. 270/7.

33	-	25c. green	16·00	55·00
34	**110**	50c. brown	4·25	10·50
35	-	75c. brown	21·00	75·00
36	-	80c. red	55·00	£160
37	-	1l. violet	4·25	10·50
38	**113**	2l. blue	95·00	£225
39	**110**	5l. green	90·00	£325
40	**110**	10l. red	£1200	£2750

(4) (5)

1944. Stamps of Italy. (a) Optd with T 4.

57	25c. green (No. 244)	45	2·20
60	75c. red (No. 248)	45	2·75

(b) Optd with T 5.

58	**103**	30c. brown	45	2·20
61	-	1l.25 blue (No. 250)	45	2·75
77	-	50l. violet (No. 259)	£300	£3000

(c) Optd REPUBBLICA SOCIALE ITALIANA.

59	**103**	50c. violet	45	2·10

1944. War Propaganda stamps. Nos. 563/74 optd with T 4 (25c.), T 5 (30c.) or REPUBBLICA SOCIALE ITALIANA (50c.).

64A	25c. green (Navy)	50	2·75
65A	25c. green (Army)	50	2·75
66A	25c. green (Air Force)	50	2·75
67A	25c. green (Militia)	50	2·75
68A	30c. brown (Navy)	50	5·50
69A	30c. brown (Army)	50	5·50
70A	30c. brown (Air Force)	50	5·50
71A	30c. brown (Militia)	50	5·50
72A	50c. violet (Navy)	50	1·70
73A	50c. violet (Army)	50	1·70
74A	50c. violet (Air Force)	50	1·70
75A	50c. violet (Militia)	70	1·70

Prices are for examples overprinted on the stamp part only; items overprinted twice (on stamp and label) are worth more.

10 Loggia dei Mercanti, Bologna

11 Loggia dei Mercanti, Bologna

12 Basilica de St. Lorenzo, Rome

13 Basilica de St. Lorenzo, Rome

1944. Inscr "REPUBBLICA SOCIALE ITALIANA".

106	-	5c. brown	20	30
107	-	10c. brown	20	25
102	**10**	20c. red	20	25
108	**11**	20c. red	20	25
103	**12**	25c. green	20	25
109	**13**	25c. green	20	25
110	-	30c. brown	20	25
111	-	50c. violet	20	25
112	-	75c. red	20	19·00
113	-	1l. violet	20	25
114	-	1l.25 blue	55	13·00
115	-	3l. green	55	55·00

DESIGN: 5c. St. Ciriaco's Church, Ancona; 10c., 1l. Montecassino Abbey; 30c., 75c. Drummer; 50c. Fascist allegory; 1l.25, 3l. St. Mary of Grace, Milan.

17 Bandiera Brothers

1944. Death Centenary of Attilio and Emilio Bandiera (revolutionaries).

117	**17**	25c. green	20	85
118	**17**	1l. violet	20	85
119	**17**	2l.50 red	20	7·00

CONCESSIONAL LETTER POST

Following the surrender of italy on 3 September 1943, and his rescue from imprisonment on 12 September, Mussolini proclaimed the Italian Social Republic at Salo on 23 September 1943. From this town on Lake Garda the Republican government administered those parts of Italy, north of Gustav Line, which were under German Ooccupation.

1944. Concessional Letter Post stamp of Italy optd as T 5 but smaller.

CL76	**CL109**	10c. brown	25	1·10

EXPRESS LETTER STAMPS

1944. Express stamps of Italy optd G. N. R.

E41	**E132**	1l.25 green (postage)	16·00	43·00
E42	**E132**	2l.50 red	£225	£650
E43	**E133**	2l. black (air)	£900	£1400

(E 7)

1944. Express stamps of Italy optd with Type E 7.

E62	**E132**	1l.25 green	45	85
E63	**E132**	2l.50 orange	45	13·00

E16 Palermo Cathedral

1944

E116	**E16**	1l.25 green	20	1·10

PARCEL POST STAMPS

1944. Parcel Post stamps of Italy optd REP. SOC. ITALIANA on left-hand side and Fascist Emblem on right.

P77	**P92**	5c. brown	3·25	37·00
P78	**P92**	10c. blue	3·25	37·00
P79	**P92**	25c. red	3·25	37·00
P80	**P92**	30c. blue	3·25	37·00
P81	**P92**	50c. orange	3·25	37·00
P82	**P92**	60c. red	3·25	£110
P83	**P92**	1l. violet	3·25	37·00
P84	**P92**	2l. green	£325	£1400
P85	**P92**	3l. bistre	6·50	£325
P86	**P92**	4l. black	16·00	£350
P87	**P92**	10l. purple	£140	£1700
P88	**P92**	20l. purple	£375	£2500

The unused and used prices are for unsevered stamps.

POSTAGE DUE STAMPS

1944. Postage Due stamps of Italy optd G. N. R.

D44	**D141**	5c. brown	21·00	60·00
D45	**D141**	10c. blue	21·00	60·00
D46	**D141**	20c. red	21·00	37·00
D47	**D141**	25c. green	21·00	37·00
D48	**D141**	30c. orange	21·00	60·00
D49	**D141**	40c. brown	21·00	37·00
D50	**D141**	50c. violet	75·00	£300
D51	**D141**	60c. blue	£425	£1200
D52	**D142**	1l. orange	32·00	43·00
D53	**D142**	2l. green	43·00	85·00
D54	**D142**	5l. violet	£225	£500
D55	**D142**	10l. blue	£130	£350
D56	**D142**	20l. red	£140	£350

1944. Postage Due stamps of Italy optd with small Fascist emblems.

D89	**D141**	5c. brown	2·10	5·50
D90	**D141**	10c. blue	2·10	5·50
D91	**D141**	20c. red	2·10	5·50
D92	**D141**	25c. green	2·10	5·50
D93	**D141**	30c. orange	2·10	9·50
D94	**D141**	40c. brown	2·10	10·50
D95	**D141**	50c. violet	2·10	4·25
D96	**D141**	60c. blue	10·50	21·00
D97	**D142**	1l. orange	2·10	4·25
D98	**D142**	2l. green	5·25	16·00
D99	**D142**	5l. violet	32·00	£120
D100	**D142**	10l. blue	90·00	£225
D101	**D142**	20l. red	90·00	£225

Pt. 8

LIECHTENSTEIN

A small independent principality lying between Austria and Switzerland.

1912. 100 heller = 1 krone.
1921. 100 rappen = 1 franc (Swiss).

1 Prince John II

1912

4	**1**	5h. green	14·50	22·00
2	**1**	10h. red	85·00	18·00
3	**1**	25h. blue	85·00	60·00

2

3

1917

7	**2**	3h. violet	2·20	2·20
8	**2**	5h. green	2·20	2·20
9	**3**	10h. purple	2·20	2·20
10	**3**	15h. brown	2·20	2·20
11	**3**	20h. green	2·20	2·20
12	**3**	25h. blue	2·20	2·20

1918. 60th Anniv of Prince John's Accession. As T 3 but dated "1858–1918" in upper corners.

13	20h. green	75	3·00

1920. Optd with a scroll pattern.

14	**2**	5h. green	3·00	9·00
15	**3**	10h. purple	3·00	9·75
16	**3**	25h. blue	3·00	9·75

1920. Surch.

17	**2**	40h. on 3h. violet	3·00	9·75
18	**3**	1k. on 15h. brown	3·00	9·75
19	**3**	2½k. on 20h. green	3·00	9·75

7

8 Castle of Vaduz

1920. Imperf.

20	**7**	5h. bistre	35	6·50
21	**7**	10h. orange	35	6·50
22	**7**	15h. blue	35	6·50
23	**7**	20h. brown	35	6·50
24	**7**	25h. green	35	6·50
25	**7**	30h. grey	35	6·50
26	**7**	40h. red	35	6·50
27	**8**	1k. blue	35	6·50

9 Prince John I

10 Arms

1920. Perf.

28	**7**	5h. bistre	35	75
29	**7**	10h. orange	35	75
30	**7**	15h. blue	35	75
31	**7**	20h. brown	35	75
32	-	25h. green	35	75
33	**7**	30h. grey	35	75
34	-	40h. purple	35	75
35	-	50h. green	35	75
36	-	60h. brown	35	75
37	-	80h. pink	35	75
38	**8**	1k. lilac	75	1·10
39	-	2k. blue	75	1·80
40	**9**	5k. black	75	2·50
41	-	7½k. grey	75	3·25
42	**10**	10k. brown	75	5·75

DESIGNS—As Type **8**: 25h. St. Mamertus Chapel; 40h. Gutenberg Castle; 50h. Courtyard, Vaduz Castle; 60h. Red House, Vaduz; 80h. Church Tower, Schaan; 2k. Bendern. As Type **9**: 7½k. Prince John II.

11 Madonna

1920. Prince John's 80th Birthday. Imperf or perf.

43A	**11**	50h. green	75	2·20
44A	**11**	80h. red	75	2·20
45A	**11**	2k. blue	75	3·00

1921. Surch 2 Rp. and bars.

47	**7**	2r. on 10h. orange (No. 21)	1·50	28·00

14 Arms

15 St. Mamertus Chapel

16 Vaduz

1921

47aB	**14**	2r. yellow	1·50	14·50
48A	**14**	2½r. brown	1·50	14·50
49A	**14**	3r. orange	1·50	14·50
50A	**14**	5r. green	14·50	2·20
51A	**14**	7½r. blue	7·25	20·00
53A	**14**	13r. brown	8·75	95·00
54B	**14**	15r. violet	28·00	25·00
55	**15**	20r. black and violet	75·00	2·20
56	-	25r. black and red	3·75	5·00
57	-	30r. black and green	85·00	22·00
58	-	35r. black and brown	7·25	17·00
59	-	40r. black and blue	11·00	6·50
60	-	50r. black and green	18·00	9·00
61	-	80r. black and grey	33·00	85·00
62	**16**	1f. black and red	60·00	60·00
65	**14**	10r. green	22·00	3·00
66	-	30r. black and blue	18·00	3·00

DESIGNS—As Type **15**: 25r. Vaduz Castle; 30r. Bendern; 35r. Prince John II; 40r. Church Tower at Schaan; 50r. Gutenberg Castle; 80r. Red House, Vaduz.

1924. Surch.

63A	**14**	5 on 7½r. blue	1·50	3·75
64B	**14**	10 on 13r. brown	1·50	3·75

19 Vine-dresser

21 Government Bldg. and Church, Vaduz

1924

67	**19**	2½r. mauve and green	1·50	7·25
68	**19**	5r. blue and brown	3·00	1·10
69	**19**	7½r. brown and green	2·20	7·25
70	-	10r. green	11·50	1·10
71	**19**	15r. green and purple	11·00	40·00
72	-	20r. red	44·00	1·50
73	**21**	1½f. blue	85·00	£120

DESIGN—As Type **19**: 10, 20r. Castle of Vaduz.

22 Prince John II

1925. 85th Birthday of Prince John.

74	**22**	10+5r. green	50·00	25·00
75	**22**	20+5r. red	29·00	25·00
76	**22**	30+5r. blue	7·25	7·25

23

1927. 87th Birthday of Prince. Arms multicoloured.

77	**23**	10+5r. green	11·00	29·00
78	**23**	20+5r. purple	11·00	29·00
79	**23**	30+5r. blue	7·25	22·00

24 Salvage Work by Austrian soldiers

1928. Flood Relief.

80	-	5r.+5r. brown and purple	18·00	29·00
81	-	10r.+10r. brown and green	25·00	36·00
82	**24**	20r.+10r. brown and red	25·00	40·00
83	-	30r.+10r. brown and blue	22·00	36·00

DESIGNS: 5r. Railway bridge between Buchs and Schaan; 10r. Village of Ruggell; 30r. Salvage work by Swiss soldiers.

26 Prince John II, 1858–1928

1928. 70th Anniv of Accession of Prince John II.

84		10r. green and brown	7·25	7·25
85		20r. green and red	11·00	14·50
86		30r. green and blue	36·00	25·00
87		60r. green and mauve	75·00	£110
88	**26**	1f.20 blue	60·00	£130
89	**26**	1f.50 brown	£110	£275
90	**26**	2f. red	£110	£275
91	**26**	5f. green	£110	£325

DESIGN—VERT: 10r. to 60r. Prince John II.

28 Prince Francis I

1929. Accession of Prince Francis I.

92	-	10r. green	60	4·25
93	**28**	20r. red	85	7·25
94	-	30r. blue	1·50	25·00
95	-	70r. brown	26·00	£150

PORTRAITS: 10r. Prince Francis I as a boy; 30r. Princess Elsa; 70r. Prince Francis and Princess Elsa.

31 Girl Vintager

32 Prince Francis I and Princess Elsa

1930

96A	**31**	3r. red	1·10	3·00
97B	-	5r. green	3·75	3·00
98B	-	10r. lilac	3·75	3·00
99B	-	20r. red	29·00	3·75
100A	-	25r. green	8·75	47·00
101B	-	30r. blue	8·75	5·00
102C	-	35r. green	11·00	22·00
103C	-	40r. brown	11·00	8·75
104C	-	50r. black	£110	21·00
105B	-	60r. green	£110	36·00
106B	-	90r. purple	£120	£150
107B	-	1f.20 brown	£160	£300
108B	-	1f.50 blue	60·00	75·00
109B	**32**	2f. brown and green	85·00	£150

DESIGNS—VERT: 5r. Mt. Three Sisters–Edelweiss; 10r. Alpine cattle-alpine roses; 20r. Courtyard of Vaduz Castle; 25r. Mt. Naafkopf; 30r. Valley of Samina; 35r. Rofenberg Chapel; 40r. St. Mamertus' Chapel; 50r. Kurhaus at Malbun; 60r. Gutenberg Castle; 90r. Schellenberg Monastery; 1f.20, Vaduz Castle; 1f.50, Pfaelzer club hut.

34 Monoplane over Vaduz Castle and Rhine Valley

1930. Air.

110	-	15r. brown	11·00	18·00
111	-	20r. green	25·00	25·00
112	-	25r. brown	14·50	47·00
113	-	35r. blue	22·00	44·00
114	**34**	45r. green	50·00	90·00
115	**34**	1f. purple	60·00	65·00

DESIGNS—VERT: 15, 20r. Biplane over snowy mountain peak. HORIZ: 25, 35r. Biplane over Vaduz Castle.

35 Airship LZ-127 "Graf Zeppelin" over Alps

1931. Air.

116	**35**	1f. green	75·00	£130
117	-	2f. blue	£150	£425

DESIGN: 2f. Airship "Graf Zeppelin" (different).

37 Princess Elsa

1932. Youth Charities.

118		10r.+5r. green	22·00	44·00
119	**37**	20r.+5r. red	22·00	44·00
120	-	30r.+10r. blue	29·00	60·00

DESIGNS—22×29 mm: 10r. Arms of Liechtenstein. As Type **37**: 30r. Prince Francis.

38 Mt. Naafkopf

1933

121	**38**	25r. orange	£275	90·00
122	-	90r. green	11·00	£110
123	-	1f.20 brown	£150	£375

DESIGNS: 90r. Gutenberg Castle; 1f.20, Vaduz Castle.

39 Prince Francis I

1933. Prince Francis's 80th Birthday.

124	**39**	10r. violet	29·00	50·00
125	**39**	20r. red	29·00	50·00
126	**39**	30r. blue	29·00	50·00

40

41 "Three Sisters"

42 Vaduz Castle

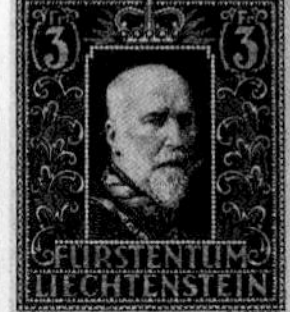
44 Prince Francis I

45 Arms of Liechtenstein

1933

127	**40**	3r. red	35	75
128	**41**	5r. green	5·75	2·20
129	-	10r. violet	3·00	1·50
130	-	15r. orange	35	1·50
131	-	20r. red	75	1·50
132	-	25r. brown	29·00	70·00
133	-	30r. blue	5·75	2·20
134	-	35r. green	8·75	18·00
135	-	40r. brown	1·80	7·25
136	**42**	50r. brown	25·00	22·00
137	-	60r. purple	2·20	9·50
138	-	90r. green	8·75	31·00
139	-	1f.20 blue	3·75	31·00
140	-	1f.50 brown	4·25	36·00
141	-	2f. brown	85·00	£250
142	**44**	3f. blue	£130	£250
143	**45**	5f. purple	£425	£1300

DESIGNS—As Type **41**: 10r. Schaan Church; 15r. Bendern am Rhein; 20r. Town Hall, Vaduz; 25r. Saminatal. As Type **44**: 2f. Princess Elsa. As Type **42**: 30r. Saminatal (different); 35r. Schellenberg ruins; 40r. Government Building, Vaduz; 60r. Vaduz Castle (different); 90r. Gutenberg Castle; 1f.20, Pfalzer Hut, Bettlerjoch; 1f.50, Valuna.

See also Nos. **MS**144, **MS**153, 174, 225/6 and 258.

1934. Vaduz First Liechtenstein Philatelic Exhibition. Sheet 105×125 mm.

MS144	**45** 5f. chocolate	£2000	£3000

46 Golden Eagle

1934. Air.

145a	**46**	10r. violet	7·25	25·00
146a	-	15r. orange	22·00	60·00
147a	-	20r. red	25·00	60·00
148a	-	30r. blue	25·00	60·00
149a	-	50r. green	22·00	44·00

DESIGNS: 10r. to 20r. Golden eagles in flight; 30r. Ospreys in nest; 50r. Golden eagle on rock.

1935. Air. No. 115 surch 60 Rp.

150	**34**	60r. on 1f. purple	44·00	75·00

49 LZ-129 "Hindenburg" and Schaan Church

1936. Air.

151	**49**	1f. red	55·00	£110
152	-	2f. violet	36·00	£110

DESIGN: 2f. LZ-127 "Graf Zeppelin" over Schaan Airport.

1936. 2nd Liechtenstein Philatelic Exhibition and Opening of Postal Museum, Vaduz. Sheet 165×119 mm containing two each of Nos. 131 and 133.

MS153	Sold at 2fr.	18·00	60·00

51 Masescha am Triesenberg

52 Schellenberg Castle

1937

154	-	3r. brown	35	75
155	**51**	5r. green and buff	35	35
156	-	10r. violet and buff	35	35
157	-	15r. black and buff	35	75
158	-	20r. red and buff	35	75
159	-	25r. brown and buff	75	3·75
160	-	30r. blue and buff	4·25	1·50
161	**52**	40r. green and buff	3·00	3·00
162	-	50c. brown and buff	3·75	7·25
163	-	60r. purple and buff	3·00	3·75
164	-	90r. violet and buff	22·00	44·00
165	-	1f. purple and buff	3·00	18·00
166	-	1f.20 brown and buff	11·00	33·00
167	-	1f.50 grey and buff	4·25	33·00

DESIGNS—As Type **51**: 3r. Schalun ruins; 10r. Knight and Vaduz Castle; 15r. Upper Saminatal; 20r. Church and Bridge at Bendern; 25r. Steg Chapel and girl. As Type **52**: 30r. Farmer and orchard, Triesenberg; 50r. Knight and Gutenberg Castle; 60r. Baron von Brandis and Vaduz Castle; 90r. "Three Sisters" mountain; 1f. Boundary-stone on Luziensteig; 1f.20, Minstrel and Gutenberg Castle; 1f.50, Lawena (Schwarzhorn).

53 Roadmakers at Triesenberg

1937. Workers' Issue.

168		10r. mauve	1·80	2·20
169	**53**	20r. red	1·80	3·00
170	-	30r. blue	1·80	3·75

171	-	50r. brown	1·80	4·25

DESIGNS: 10r. Bridge at Malbun; 30r. Binnen Canal Junction; 50r. Francis Bridge, near Planken.

1938. 3rd Liechtenstein Philatelic Exhibition, Vaduz. Sheet 100×135 mm containing stamps as No. 175 in different colour in a block of four.

MS173	**54**	50r. blue	29·00	29·00

1938. Death of Prince Francis I.

174	**44**	3f. black on yellow	14·50	£120

54 Josef Rheinberger

1939. Birth Centenary of Rheinberger (composer).

175	**54**	50r. grey	1·10	6·50

55 Black-headed Gulls

1939. Air.

176	-	10r. violet (Barn swallows)	1·50	1·80
177	**55**	15r. orange	75	3·75
178	-	20r. red (Herring gull)	3·00	1·50
179	-	30r. blue (Common buzzard)	1·80	3·00
180	-	50r. green (Northern goshawk)	4·25	5·00
181	-	1f. red (Lammergeier)	3·00	23·00
182	-	2f. violet Lammergeier	3·00	22·00

56 Offering Homage to First Prince

1939. Homage to Francis Joseph II.

183	**56**	20r. red	1·50	3·00
184	**56**	30r. blue	1·50	2·20
185	**56**	50r. green	1·50	3·00

57 Francis Joseph II

1939

186	-	2f. green on cream	11·00	55·00
187	-	3f. violet on cream	7·25	55·00
188	**57**	5f. brown on cream	22·00	£110

DESIGNS: 2f. Cantonal Arms; 3f. Arms of Principality.

58 Prince John when a Child

1940. Birth Centenary of Prince John II.

189	**58**	20r. red	75	3·00
190	-	30r. blue	75	4·25
191	-	50r. green	1·50	14·50
192	-	1f. violet	11·00	95·00
193	-	1f.50 black	21·00	85·00
194	-	3f. brown	5·00	29·00

DESIGNS—As Type **58**: Portraits of Prince John in early manhood (30r.), in middle age (50r.) and in later life (1f.), and Memorial tablet (1f.50). As Type **44**: 3f. Framed portrait of Prince John II.

60 Wine Press

1941. Agricultural Propaganda.

195		10r. brown	1·10	1·50
196	**60**	20r. purple	1·80	2·20
197	-	30r. blue	1·80	3·75
198	-	50r. green	3·00	22·00
199	-	90r. violet	3·25	25·00

DESIGNS: 10r. Harvesting maize; 30r. Sharpen-ing scythe; 50r. Milkmaid and cow; 90r. Girl wearing traditional headdress.

61 Madonna and Child

1941

200	**61**	10f. purple on stone	60·00	£150

62 Prince Hans Adam

1941. Princes (1st issue).

201	**62**	20r. red	75	2·20
202	-	30r. blue (Wenzel)	75	3·75
203	-	1f. grey (Anton Florian)	3·00	24·00
204	-	1f.50 green (Joseph)	75	25·00

See also Nos. 210/13 and 217/20.

63 St. Lucius preaching

1942. 600th Anniv of Separation from Estate of Montfort.

205	**63**	20r. red on pink	1·80	1·50
206	-	30r. blue on pink	1·10	3·75
207	-	50r. green on pink	3·25	11·00
208	-	1f. brown on pink	4·25	20·00
209	-	2f. violet on pink	4·75	20·00

DESIGNS: 30r. Count of Montfort replanning Vaduz; 50r. Counts of Montfort-Werdenberg and Sargans signing treaty; 1f. Battle of Gutenberg; 2f. Homage to Prince of Liechtenstein.

64 Prince John Charles

1942. Princes (2nd issue).

210	**64**	20r. pink	75	1·50
211	-	30r. blue (Francis Joseph I)	75	3·00
212	-	1f. purple (Alois I)	3·00	22·00
213	-	1f.50 brown (John I)	3·00	22·00

65 Princess Georgina

1943. Marriage of Prince Francis Joseph II and Countess Georgina von Wildczek.

214		10r. purple	75	1·80
215	**65**	20r. red	75	1·80
216	-	30r. blue	75	1·80

PORTRAITS—VERT: 10r. Prince Francis Joseph II. HORIZ (44×25 mm): 30r. Prince and Princess.

66 Alois II

1943. Princes (3rd issue).

217	**66**	20r. brown	75	1·50
218	-	30r. blue	1·50	2·20
219	-	1f. brown	2·20	11·00
220	-	1f.50 green	2·20	11·00

PORTRAITS: 30r. John II; 1f. Francis I; 1f.50, Francis Joseph II.

67 Marsh Land

1943. Completion of Irrigation Canal.

221	**67**	10r. violet	35	75
222	-	30r. blue	55	3·00
223	-	50r. green	2·00	12·50
224	-	2f. brown	3·75	20·00

DESIGNS: 30r. Draining the canal; 50r. Ploughing reclaimed land; 2f. Harvesting crops.

1943. Castles. As T 41.

225		10r. grey (Vaduz)	55	75
226		20r. brown (Gutenberg)	90	1·50

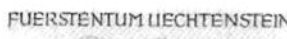

69 Planken

1944. Various designs. Buff backgrounds.

227	**69**	3r. brown	35	35
228	-	5r. green (Bendern)	35	35
228a	-	5r. brown (Bendern)	55	75
229	-	10r. grey (Triesen)	35	35
230	-	15r. grey (Ruggell)	45	1·10
231	-	20r. red (Vaduz)	45	75
232	-	25r. brown (Triesenberg)	45	1·50
233	-	30r. blue (Schaan)	45	75
234	-	40r. brown (Balzers)	90	1·80
235	-	50r. blue (Mauren)	1·10	3·00
236	-	60r. green (Schellenberg)	6·25	8·75
237	-	90r. green (Eschen)	6·25	8·75
238	-	1f. purple (Vaduz Castle)	3·75	8·75
239	-	1f.20 brown (Valunatal)	3·75	10·00
240	-	1f.50 blue (Lawena)	3·75	10·00

70 Prince Francis Joseph II

1944

241	**70**	2f. brown and buff	9·00	25·00
242	-	3f. green and buff	5·50	18·00

DESIGN: 3f. Princess Georgina.

See also Nos. 302/3.

72

1945. Birth of Crown Prince Johann Adam Pius (known as Prince Hans Adam).

243	**72**	20r. red, yellow and gold	1·50	75
244	**72**	30r. blue, yellow and gold	1·50	2·20
245	**72**	100r. grey, yellow and gold	4·25	8·75

73

1945

246	**73**	5f. blue on buff	33·00	50·00
247	**73**	5f. brown on buff	40·00	65·00

74 First Aid

1945. Red Cross. Cross in red.

248	-	10r.+10r. purple and buff	2·20	3·00
249	**74**	20r.+20r. purple and buff	2·20	4·25
250	-	1f.+1f.40 blue and buff	14·00	40·00

DESIGNS: 10r. Mother and children; 1f. Nurse and invalid.

75 St. Lucius

1946

251	**75**	10f. grey on buff	65·00	50·00

1946. 4th Liechtenstein Philatelic Exhibition, Vaduz and 25th Anniv of Postal Agreement with Switzerland. Sheet 84×60 mm.

MS251a		10r. (×2) Old Postal Coach (*horiz*), violet, brown and buff (sold at 3f.)	55·00	60·00

76 Red Deer Stag

1946. Wild Life.

252	**76**	20r. red	4·25	4·25
253	-	30r. blue (Arctic hare)	5·75	5·75
254	-	1f.50 green (Western capercaillie)	8·00	19·00
255	-	20r. red (Chamois)	7·25	7·25
256	-	30r. blue (Alpine marmot)	9·50	8·00
257	-	1f.50 brown (Golden eagle)	8·75	25·00
283	-	20r. red (Roebuck)	18·00	7·25
284	-	30r. green (Black grouse)	14·50	11·00
285	-	80r. brown (Eurasian badger)	60·00	75·00

1947. Death of Princess Elsa. As No. 141.

258		2f. black on yellow	7·25	22·00

79 Wilbur Wright

1948. Air. Pioneers of Flight.

259	-	10r. green	1·10	35
260	-	15r. violet	1·10	1·80
261	-	20r. brown	1·50	35
262	-	25r. red	2·20	3·00
263	-	40r. blue	2·50	3·00
264	-	50r. blue	3·00	3·00
265	-	1f. purple	4·75	6·25
266	-	2f. purple	7·25	8·00
267	**79**	5f. green	9·50	11·00
268	-	10f. black	60·00	31·00

PORTRAITS: 10r. Leonardo da Vinci; 15r. Joseph Montgolfier; 20r. Jakob Degen; 25r. Wilhelm Kress; 40r. Etienne Robertson; 50r. William Henson; 1f. Otto Lilienthal; 2f. Salomon Andree; 10f. Icarus.

80 "Ginevra de Benci" (Da Vinci)

1949. Paintings.

269	**80**	10r. green	1·50	55
270	-	20r. red	2·20	1·30
271	-	30r. brown	4·25	1·50
272	-	40r. blue	11·00	1·50
273	-	50r. violet	8·75	11·00
274	-	60r. grey	28·00	10·00

275	-	80r. brown	4·25	7·00
276	-	90r. green	20·00	9·50
277	-	120r. mauve	4·25	8·75

DESIGNS: 20r. "Portrait of a Young Girl" (Rubens); 30r. Self-portrait of Rembrandt in plumed hat; 40r. "Stephan Gardiner, Bishop of Winchester" (Quentin Massys); 50r. "Madonna and Child" (Hans Memling); 60r. "Franz Meister in 1456" (Jehan Fouquet); 80r. "Lute Player" (Orazio Gentleschi); 90r. "Portrait of a Man" (Bernhardin Strigel); 120r. "Portrait of a Man (Duke of Urbino)" (Raphael).

1949. No. 227 surch 5 Rp. and bars.

278	**69**	5r. on 3r. brown and buff	1·10	75

82 Posthorn and Map of World

1949. 75th Anniv of U.P.U.

279	**82**	40r. blue	5·75	7·25

1949. 5th Liechtenstein Philatelic Exhibition, Vaduz. Sheet 122×70 mm containing paintings as 1949 issue in new colours.

MS279a 10r. green (as 10r.); 20r. mauve (as 80r.); 40r. blue (as 120r.). Sold at 3f. £180 £180

83 Rossauer Castle

1949. 250th Anniv of Acquisition of Domain of Schellenberg.

280	**83**	20r. purple	3·75	3·75
281	-	40r. blue	12·50	11·00
282	-	1f.50 red	16·00	16·00

DESIGN—HORIZ: 40r. Bendern Church. VERT: 1f.50, Prince Johann Adam I.

1950. Surch 100 100.

286	**82**	100r. on 40r. blue	44·00	75·00

86 Boy cutting Loaf

1951. Agricultural scenes.

287	**86**	5r. mauve	75	50
288	-	10r. green	75	75
289	-	15r. brown	8·75	8·75
290	-	20r. brown	1·80	1·10
291	-	25r. purple	8·75	8·75
292	-	30r. green	5·00	90
293	-	40r. blue	16·00	11·00
294	-	50r. purple	13·00	5·50
295	-	60r. brown	13·00	5·00
296	-	80r. brown	16·00	11·50
297	-	90r. green	33·00	11·50
298	-	1f. blue	£100	11·50

DESIGNS: 10r. Man whetting scythe; 15r. Mowing; 20r. Girl and sweet corn; 25r. Haywain; 30r. Gathering grapes; 40r. Man with scythe; 50r. Herdsman with cows; 60r. Ploughing; 80r. Girl carrying basket of fruit; 90r. Woman gleaning; 1f. Tractor hauling corn.

87 "Lock on the Canal" (Aelbert Cuyp)

88 "Willem von Heythuysen, Burgomaster of Haarlem" (Frans Hals)

1951. Paintings.

299	**87**	10r.+10r. green	14·50	11·00
300	**88**	20r.+10r. brown	14·50	22·00
301	-	40r.+10r. blue	14·50	14·50

DESIGN—As Type **87**: 40r. "Landscape" (Jacob van Ruysdael).

90 Vaduz Castle

1951

302A	**70**	2f. blue	22·00	60·00
303B	-	3f. brown	£180	£325
304	**90**	5f. green	£225	£225

DESIGN: 3f. Princess Georgina.

1952. No. 281 surch 1.20.

308		1f.20 on 40r. blue	36·00	85·00

1952. Paintings from Prince's Collection. (a) As T 80 but size 25×30 mm.

309		10r. green	3·75	1·50
305		20r. purple	65·00	4·25
307		40r. blue	22·00	9·50
312		40r. blue	55·00	75·00

PAINTINGS: No. 309, "Portrait of a Young Man" (A. G.); 305, "Portrait" (Giovanni Salvoldo); 307, "St. John" (Andrea del Sarto); 312, "Leonhard, Count of Hag" (Hans von Kulmbach).

(b) As T 88 (22½×24 mm).

306		30r. green	44·00	11·50
310		20r. brown	28·00	4·00
311		30r. brown	47·00	12·50

PAINTINGS: No. 310, "St. Nicholas" (Bartholomaus Zeitblom); 306, "Madonna and Child" (Sandro Botticelli); 311, "St. Christopher" (Lucas Cranach the elder).

96 Lord Baden-Powell

1953. 14th International Scout Conference.

313	**96**	10r. green	3·75	1·50
314	**96**	20r. brown	23·00	3·75
315	**96**	25r. red	18·00	29·00
316	**96**	40r. blue	17·00	9·50

97 Alemannic Ornamental Disc, (c. A.D. 600)

98 Prehistoric Walled Settlement, Borscht

1953. Opening of National Museum, Vaduz.

317	**97**	10r. brown	14·50	18·00
318	**98**	20r. green	14·50	18·00
319	-	1f.20 blue	80·00	50·00

DESIGN—VERT: 1f.20, Rossen jug (3000 B.C.).

99 Footballers

1954. Football.

320	**99**	10r. brown and red	4·25	1·50
321	-	20r. deep green and green	12·50	2·20
322	-	25r. deep brown and brown	29·00	50·00
323	-	40r. violet and grey	25·00	14·50

DESIGNS: 20r. Footballer kicking ball; 25r. Goalkeeper; 40r. Two footballers.

For stamps in similar designs see Nos. 332/5, 340/3, 351/4 and 363/6.

1954. Nos. 299/301 surch in figures.

324	**87**	35r. on 10r.+10r. green	5·75	3·75
325	**88**	60r. on 20r.+10r. brown	29·00	17·00
326	-	65r. on 40r.+10r. blue	8·75	11·50

100 Madonna and Child

1954. Termination of Marian Year.

327	**100**	20r. brown	5·75	3·75
328	**100**	40r. black	29·00	17·00
329	**100**	1f. brown	29·00	11·50

101 Princess Georgina

1955

330	-	2f. brown	£130	75·00
331	**101**	3f. green	£130	75·00

PORTRAIT: 2f. Prince Francis Joseph II.

1955. Mountain Sports. As T 99.

332		10r. purple and blue	3·75	1·50
333		20r. green and bistre	9·50	1·50
334		25r. brown and blue	29·00	29·00
335		40r. green and red	29·00	11·00

DESIGNS: 10r. Slalom racer; 20r. Mountaineer hammering in piton; 25r. Skier; 40r. Mountaineer resting on summit.

102 Crown Prince John Adam Pius

1955. 10th Anniv of Liechtenstein Red Cross. Cross in red.

336	**102**	10r. violet	4·25	1·10
337	-	20r. green	8·75	2·50
338	-	40r. brown	11·00	11·50
339	-	60r. red	11·00	6·50

PORTRAITS: 20r. Prince Philip; 40r. Prince Nicholas; 60r. Princess Nora.

See also No. 350.

1956. Athletics. As T 99.

340		10r. green and brown	3·00	1·10
341		20r. purple and green	5·75	1·10
342		40r. brown and blue	8·75	7·25
343		1f. brown and red	20·00	25·00

DESIGNS: 10r. Throwing the javelin; 20r. Hurdling; 40r. Pole vaulting; 1f. Running.

103

1956. 150th Anniv of Sovereignty of Liechtenstein.

344	**103**	10r. purple and gold	5·75	1·50
345	**103**	1f.20 blue and gold	29·00	7·25

104 Prince Francis Joseph II

1956. 50th Birthday of Prince Francis Joseph II.

346	**104**	10r. green	3·00	75
347	**104**	15r. blue	19·00	4·75
348	**104**	25r. purple	19·00	4·75
349	**104**	60r. brown	17·00	4·25

1956. 6th Philatelic Exhibition, Vaduz. As T 102 but inscr "6. BRIEFMARKEN-AUSSTELLUNG".

350		20r. green	4·75	1·10

1956. Gymnastics. As T 99.

351		10r. green and pink	3·75	1·50
352		15r. purple and green	8·75	4·25
353		25r. green and drab	11·00	5·75
354		1f.50 brown and yellow	33·00	17·00

DESIGNS: 10r. Somersaulting; 15r. Vaulting; 25r. Exercising with rings; 1f.50, Somersaulting on parallel bars.

105 Norway Spruce

1957. Liechtenstein Trees and Bushes.

355	**105**	10r. purple	7·25	3·75
356	-	20r. red	7·25	1·50
357	-	1f. green	11·00	12·50

DESIGNS: 20r. Wild rose bush; 1f. Silver birch.

See also Nos. 369/71, 375/7 and 401/3.

106 Lord Baden-Powell

1957. 50th Anniv of Boy Scout Movement and Birth Centenary of Lord Baden-Powell (founder).

358		10r. blue	2·20	2·20
359	**106**	20r. brown	2·20	2·20

DESIGN: 10r. Torchlight procession.

107 St. Mamertus Chapel

1957. Christmas.

360	**107**	10r. brown	2·20	75
361	-	40r. blue	5·75	12·50
362	-	1f.50 purple	21·00	20·00

DESIGNS—(from St. Mamertus Chapel): 40r. Altar shrine; 1f.50, "Pieta" (sculpture).

See also Nos. 372/4 and 392/4.

1958. Sports. As T 99.

363		15r. violet and blue	1·50	2·20
364		30r. green and purple	9·50	14·50
365		40r. green and orange	14·50	14·50
366		90r. brown and green	3·75	7·25

DESIGNS: 15r. Swimmer; 30r. Fencers; 40r. Tennis player; 90r. Racing cyclists.

108 Relief Map of Liechtenstein

1958. Brussels International Exhibition.

367	**108**	25r. violet, stone and red	1·50	1·10
368	**108**	40r. purple, blue and red	2·20	1·10

1958. Liechtenstein Trees and Bushes. As T 105.

369		20r. brown (Sycamore)	5·50	1·50
370		50r. green (Holly)	22·00	9·50
371		90r. violet (Yew)	5·50	5·00

1958. Christmas. As T 107.

372		20r. green	4·25	3·75
373		35r. violet	4·25	5·75
374		80r. brown	5·75	4·25

DESIGNS: 20r. "St. Maurice and St. Agatha"; 35r. "St. Peter"; 80r. St. Peter's Chapel, Mals-Balzers.

1959. Liechtenstein Trees and Bushes. As T 105.

375		20r. lilac (Red-berried larch)	11·00	4·25
376		50r. red (Red-berried elder)	8·75	5·75
377		90r. green (Linden)	5·75	5·75

109

1959. Pope Pius XII Mourning.

378	**109**	30r. purple and gold	1·80	1·60

111 Harvester

110 Flags of Vaduz Castle and Rhine Valley

1959. Views.

379	-	5r. brown	35	35
380	**110**	10r. purple	35	35
381	-	20r. mauve	45	35
382	-	30r. red	60	45
383	-	40r. green	85	60
384	-	50r. blue	85	75
385	-	60r. blue	1·10	85
386	**111**	75r. brown	1·70	2·00
387	-	80r. green	1·50	1·10
388	-	90r. purple	1·60	1·20
389	-	1f. brown	1·80	1·30
390	-	1f.20 red	2·50	2·00
390a	-	1f.30 green	2·00	1·80
391	-	1f.50 blue	3·00	2·20

DESIGNS—HORIZ: 5r. Bendern Church; 20r. Rhine Dam; 30r. Gutenberg Castle; 40r. View from Schellenberg; 50r. Vaduz Castle; 60r. Naafkopf-Falknis Mountains (view from the Bettlerjoch); 1f.20, Harvesting apples; 1f.30, Farmer and wife; 1f.50, Saying grace at table. VERT: 80r. Alpine haymaker; 90r. Girl in vineyard; 1f. Mother in kitchen.

1959. Christmas. As T 107.

392	5r. green	75	35
393	60r. brown	10·00	8·00
394	1f. purple	8·75	5·50

DESIGNS: 5r. Bendern Church belfry; 60r. Relief on bell of St. Theodul's Church; 1f. Sculpture on tower of St. Lucius's Church.

112 Bell 47J Ranger Helicopter

1960. Air. 30th Anniv of 1st Liechtenstein Air Stamps.

395	**112**	30r. red	3·75	4·25
396	-	40r. blue	6·50	4·25
397	-	50r. purple	16·00	8·75
398	-	75r. green	3·00	4·25

DESIGNS: 40r. Boeing 707 jetliner; 50r. Convair 990A Coronado jetliner; 75r. Douglas DC-8 jetliner.

1960. World Refugee Year. Nos. 367/8 surch WELTFLUCHTLINGSJAHR 1960, uprooted tree and new value.

399	**108**	30+10r. on 40r. purple, blue and red	1·90	1·90
400	**108**	50+10r. on 25r. violet, stone and red	3·25	3·25

1960. Liechtenstein Trees and Bushes. As T 105.

401	20r. brown (Beech)	11·00	7·25
402	30r. purple (Juniper)	11·00	22·00
403	50r. turquoise (Mountain pines)	36·00	25·00

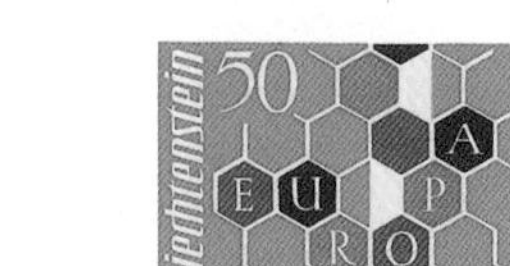

114 Europa "Honeycomb"

1960. Europa.

404	**114**	50r. multicoloured	£110	65·00

115 Princess Gina

1960

404a	-	1f.70 violet	2·50	1·50
405	**115**	2f. blue	3·75	2·20
406	-	3f. brown	4·25	2·20

PORTRAITS: 1f.70, Crown Prince Hans Adam; 3f. Prince Francis Joseph II.

116 Heinrich von Frauenberg

1961. Minnesingers (1st issue). Multicoloured. Reproduction from the Manessian Manuscript of Songs.

407	15r. Type **116**	25	55
408	25r. Ulrich von Liechtenstein	75	75
409	35r. Ulrich von Gutenberg	90	90
410	1f. Konrad von Altstatten	2·20	2·20
411	1f.50 Walther von der Vogelweide	11·50	18·00

See also Nos. 415/18 and 428/31.

117 "Power Transmission"

1961. Europa.

412	**117**	50r. multicoloured	55	55

117a Prince John II

1962. 50th Anniv of First Liechtenstein Postage Stamps. Sheet 133×118 mm. T 117a and similar horiz design.

MS412a 5r. green; 10r. red; 25r. blue. Sold at 2f.60	7·25	5·50

DESIGNS: 0r. Prince Francis I; 25r. Prince Francis Joseph I.

118 Clasped Hands

1962. Europa.

413	**118**	50r. red and blue	3·00	35

119 Campaign Emblem

1962. Malaria Eradication.

414	**119**	50r. blue	75	75

1962. Minnesingers (2nd issue). As T 116. Mult.

415	20r. King Konradin	75	75
416	30r. Kraft von Toggenburg	1·50	1·50
417	40r. Heinrich von Veldig	1·50	1·50
418	2f. Tannhauser	1·80	1·80

120 Pieta

1962. Christmas.

419	**120**	30r. mauve	75	75
420	-	50r. red	1·10	1·10
421	-	1f.20 blue	1·80	1·80

DESIGNS: 50r. Fresco with angel; 1f.20, View of Mauren.
See also Nos. 438/40.

121 Prince Francis Joseph II

1963. 25th Anniv of Reign of Prince Francis Joseph II.

422	**121**	5f. green	7·25	5·50

122 Milk and Bread

1963. Freedom from Hunger.

423	**122**	50r. brown, purple and red	1·00	75

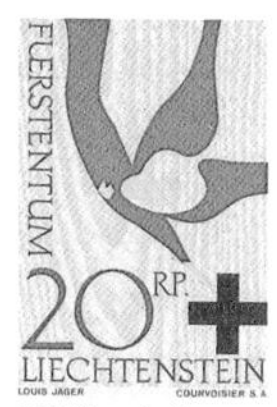

123 "Angel of Annunciation"

1963. Red Cross Cent. Cross in red; background grey.

424	**123**	20r. yellow and green	35	35
425	-	80r. violet and mauve	1·10	1·10
426	-	1f. blue and ultramarine	1·50	1·50

DESIGNS: 80r. "The Epiphany"; 1f. "Family".

124 "Europa"

1963. Europa.

427	**124**	50r. multicoloured	1·50	1·10

1963. Minnesingers (3rd issue). As T 116. Mult.

428	25r. Heinrich von Sax	35	35
429	30r. Kristan von Hamle	75	75
430	75r. Werner von Teufen	1·10	1·10
431	1f.70 Hartmann von Aue	2·20	2·20

125 Olympic Rings and Flags

1964. Olympic Games, Tokyo.

432	**125**	50r. red, black and blue	75	75

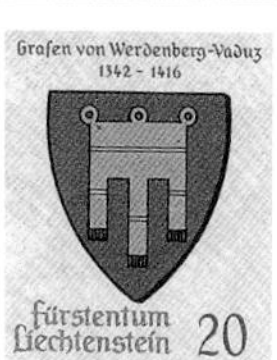

126 Arms of Counts of Werdenberg, Vaduz

1964. Arms (1st issue). Multicoloured.

433	20f. Type **126**	30	30
434	30f. Barons of Brandis	45	45
435	80r. Counts of Sulz	1·10	1·10
436	1f.50 Counts of Hohenems	1·80	1·80

See also Nos. 443/6.

127 Roman Castle, Schaan

1964. Europa.

437	**127**	50f. multicoloured	1·80	1·10

1964. Christmas. As T 120.

438	10r. purple	35	35
439	40r. blue	55	55
440	1f.30 purple	1·80	1·80

DESIGNS: 10r. Masescha Chapel; 40r. "Mary Magdalene" (altar painting); 1f.30, "St. Sebastian, Madonna and Child, and St. Rochus" (altar painting).

128 P. Kaiser

1964. Death Centenary of Peter Kaiser (historian).

441	**128**	1f. green on cream	1·50	1·50

129 "Madonna" (wood sculpture, c. 1700)

1965

442	**129**	10f. red	14·50	7·25

1965. Arms (2nd issue). As T 126. Multicoloured.

443	20r. Von Schellenberg	30	30
444	30r. Von Gutenberg	45	45
445	80r. Von Frauenberg	1·10	1·10
446	1f. Von Ramschwag	1·10	1·10

130 Europa "Links" (ancient belt-buckle)

1965. Europa.

447	**130**	50r. brown, grey and blue	75	75

131 "Jesus in the Temple"

1965. Birth Centenary of Ferdinand Nigg (painter).

448	-	10r. deep green and green	30	30
449	-	30r. brown and orange	35	35
450	**131**	1f.20 green and blue	1·20	1·30

DESIGNS—VERT: 10r. "The Annunciation"; 30r. "The Magi".

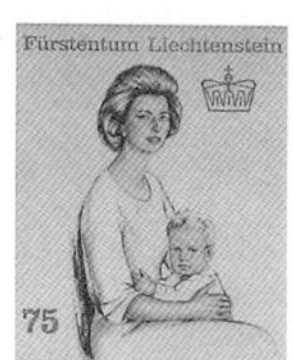

132 Princess Gina and Prince Franz (after painting by Pedro Leitao)

1965. Special Issue.

451	**132**	75r. multicoloured	90	90

See also No. 457.

133 Telecommunications Symbols

1965. Centenary of I.T.U.

452	**133**	25r. multicoloured	35	35

134 Tree ("Wholesome Earth")

1966. Nature Protection.

453	**134**	10r. green and yellow	20	20
454	-	20r. blue and light blue	20	20
455	-	30r. blue and green	20	20
456	-	1f.50 red and yellow	1·70	1·70

DESIGNS: 20r. Bird ("Pure Air"); 30r. Fish ("Clean Water"); 1f.50, Sun ("Protection of Nature").

1966. Prince Franz Joseph II's 60th Birthday. As T 132, but with portrait of Prince Franz and inscr "1906–1966".

457		1f. multicoloured	1·30	1·30

135 Arms of Herren von Richenstein

1966. Arms of Triesen Families. Multicoloured.

458	20r. Type **135**	35	35
459	30r. Jinker Vaistli	45	45
460	60r. Edle von Trisun	85	85
461	1f.20 Die von Schiel	1·30	1·30

136 Europa "Ship"

1966. Europa.

462	**136**	50r. multicoloured	75	75

137 Vaduz Parish Church

1966. Restoration of Vaduz Parish Church.

463	**137**	5r. green and red	20	20
464	-	20r. purple and bistre	35	35
465	-	30r. blue and red	45	45
466	-	1f.70 brown and green	2·00	2·00

DESIGNS: 20r. St. Florin; 30r. Madonna; 1f.70, God the Father.

138 Cogwheels

1967. Europa.

467	**138**	50r. multicoloured	75	60

139 "The Man from Malanser"

1967. Liechtenstein Sagas (1st series). Multicoloured.

468	20r. Type **139**	35	35
469	30r. "The Treasure of Gutenberg"	45	35
470	1f.20 "The Giant of Guflina"	1·50	1·20

See also Nos. 492/4 and 516/18.

140 Crown Prince Hans Adam

1967. Royal Wedding. Sheet 86×95 mm comprising T 140 and similar vert design.

MS471	1f.50 indigo and blue (T **140**); 1f.50 brown and light brown (Princess Marie)	4·25	3·75

141 "Alpha and Omega"

1967. Christian Symbols. Multicoloured.

472	20r. Type **141**	35	35
473	30r. "Tropaion" (Cross as victory symbol)	45	35
474	70r. Christ's monogram	1·10	85

142 Father J. B. Buchel (educator, historian and poet)

1967. Buchel Commemoration.

475	**142**	1f. red and green	1·50	1·10

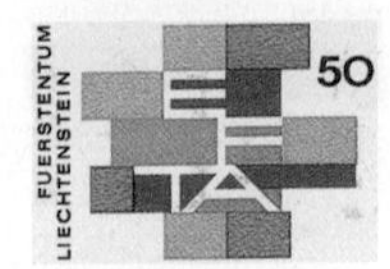

143 "E.F.T.A."

1967. European Free Trade Association.

476	**143**	50r. multicoloured	75	60

144 "Peter and Paul", Mauren

1967. "Patrons of the Church". Multicoloured.

477	5r. "St. Joseph", Planken	15	15
478	10r. "St. Lawrence", Schaan	30	30
479	20r. Type **144**	35	35
480	30r. "St. Nicholas", Balzers	45	35
480a	40r. "St. Sebastian", Nendeln	75	50
481	50r. "St. George", Schellenberg	75	55
482	60r. "St. Martin", Eschen	85	65
483	70r. "St. Fridolin", Ruggell	95	80
484	80r. "St. Gallus", Triesen	1·10	85
485	1f. "St. Theodolus", Triesenberg	1·50	1·10
486	1f.20 "St. Anna", Vaduz Castle	1·60	1·30
487	1f.50 "St. Marie", Bendern-Camprin	2·20	1·60
488	2f. "St. Lucius", (patron saint of Liechtenstein)	3·00	2·20

145 Campaign Emblem

1967. "Technical Assistance".

489	**145**	50r.+20r. multicoloured	1·10	1·10

146 Europa "Key"

1968. Europa.

490	**146**	50r. multicoloured	75	60

147 Arms of Liechtenstein and Wilczek

1968. Silver Wedding Anniv of Prince Francis Joseph II and Princess Gina.

491	**147**	75r. multicoloured	1·10	90

1968. Liechtenstein Sagas (2nd series). As T 139. Multicoloured.

492	30r. "The Treasure of St. Mamerten"	45	35
493	50r. "The Hobgoblin in the Bergerwald"	75	55
494	80r. "The Three Sisters"	1·00	90

148 Sir Rowland Hill

1968. "Pioneers of Philately" (1st series).

495	**148**	20r. green	35	35
496	-	30r. brown	45	35
497	-	1f. black	1·50	1·20

PORTRAITS: 30r. Philippe de Ferrary; 1f. Maurice Burrus.
See also Nos. 504/5 and 554/6.

150 Arms of Liechtenstein

1969

498	**150**	3f.50 brown	4·25	2·50

151 Colonnade

1969. Europa.

499	**151**	50r. multicoloured	75	60

152 "Biology"

1969. 250th Anniv of Liechtenstein. Multicoloured.

500	10r. Type **152**	35	35
501	30r. "Physics"	45	35
502	50r. "Astronomy"	80	60
503	80r. "Art"	1·20	1·10

1969. "Pioneers of Philately" (2nd series). As T 148.

504	80r. brown	1·20	1·10
505	1f.20 blue	1·70	1·50

PORTRAITS: 80r. Carl Lindenberg; 1f.20, Theodore Champion.

153 Arms of St. Luzi Monastery

1969. Arms of Church Patrons. Multicoloured.

506	20r. St. Johann's Abbey	35	35
507	30r. Type **153**	35	35
508	30r. Ladies' Priory, Schanis	45	35
509	30r. Knights Hospitallers, Feldkirch	45	45
510	50r. Pfafers Abbey	75	60
511	50r. Weingarten Abbey	75	65
512	75r. St. Gallen Abbey	1·10	85
513	1f.20 Ottobeuren Abbey	1·70	1·50
514	1f.50 Chur Episcopate	2·20	1·60

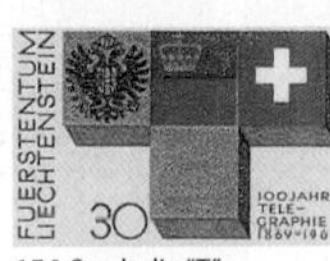

154 Symbolic "T"

1969. Centenary of Liechtenstein Telegraph System.

515	**154**	30r. multicoloured	45	35

1969. Liechtenstein Sagas (3rd series). As T 139. Multicoloured.

516	20r. "The Cheated Devil"	35	35
517	50r. "The Fiery Red Goat"	75	50
518	60r. "The Grafenberg Treasure"	80	65

155 Orange Lily

1970. Nature Conservation Year. Multicoloured.

519	20r. Type **155**	35	35
520	30r. Wild orchid	60	45
521	50r. Ranunculus	85	80
522	1f.20 Bog bean	1·80	1·70

See also Nos. 532/5 and 548/51.

156 "Flaming Sun"

1970. Europa.

523	**156**	50r. yellow, blue and green	75	60

157 Prince Wenzel

1970. 25th Anniv of Liechtenstein Red Cross.

524	**157**	1f. multicoloured	1·50	1·10

1970. 800th Anniv of Wolfram von Eschenbach. Sheet 73×96 mm containing vert designs similar to T 116 from the "Codex Manaesse". Multicoloured.

MS525	30r. Wolfram von Eschenbach; 50r. Reinmar the Fiddler; 80r. Hartmann von Starkenberg; 1f.20 Friedrich von Hausen. Sold for 3f.	4·25	4·25

158 Prince Francis Joseph II

1970

526	-	1f.70 green	2·50	1·80
526a	-	2f.50 blue	3·75	2·50
527	**158**	3f. black	4·25	3·00

DESIGNS: 1f.70, Prince Hans Adam; 2f.50, Princess Gina.

159 "Mother and Child" (R. Schadler)

1970. Christmas.

528	**159**	30r. multicoloured	45	35

160 Bronze Boar (La Tene period)

1971. National Museum Inauguration.

529	**160**	25r. black, blue & ultram	35	35
530	-	30r. green and brown	45	35
531	-	75r. multicoloured	1·00	80

DESIGNS: 30r. Ornamental peacock (Roman, 2nd-century); 75r. Engraved bowl (13th-century).

1971. Liechtenstein Flowers (2nd series). As T 155. Multicoloured.

532	10r. Cyclamen	35	35
533	20r. Moonwort	35	35
534	50r. Superb pink	75	65
535	1f.50 Alpine columbine	2·10	1·80

161 Europa Chain

1971. Europa.

536	**161**	50r. yellow, blue & black	75	60

162 Part of Text

1971. 50th Anniv of 1921 Constitution. Mult.

537		70r. Type **162**	1·00	85
538		80r. Princely crown	1·20	95

163 Cross-country Skiing

1971. Winter Olympic Games, Sapporo, Japan (1972). Multicoloured.

539	15r. Type **163**	35	35
540	40r. Ice hockey	60	55
541	65r. Downhill skiing	95	85
542	1f.50 Figure skating	2·20	2·00

164 "Madonna and Child" (sculpture, Andrea della Robbia)

1971. Christmas.

543	**164**	30r. multicoloured	45	35

165 Gymnastics

1972. Olympic Games, Munich. Multicoloured.

544	10r. Type **165**	20	20
545	20r. High jumping	35	35
546	40r. Running	60	50
547	60r. Throwing the discus	80	75

1972. Liechtenstein Flowers (3rd series). As T 155. Multicoloured.

548	20r. Sulphur anemone	35	35
549	30r. Turk's-cap lily	45	45
550	60r. Alpine centaury	85	75
551	1f.20 Reed-mace	1·70	1·50

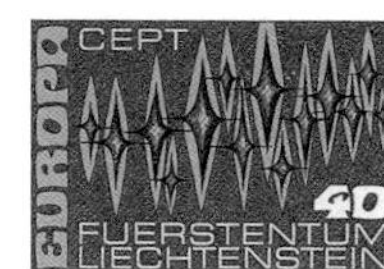

166 "Communications"

1972. Europa.

552	**166**	40r. multicoloured	75	50

167 Bendern

1972. "Liba '72" Stamp Exhibition, Vaduz. Sheet 101×65 mm containing T 167 and similar horiz design.

MS553	1f. violet; 2f. red	4·25	4·25

DESIGN: 2f. Vaduz castle.

1972. "Pioneers of Philately" (3rd series). As T 148.

554	30r. green	45	45
555	40r. purple	60	60
556	1f.30 blue	1·90	1·50

PORTRAITS: 30r. Emilio Diena; 40r. Andre de Cock; 1f.30, Theodore E. Steinway.

168 "Faun"

1972. "Natural Art". Motifs fashioned from roots and branches. Multicoloured.

557	20r. Type **168**	35	35
558	30r. "Dancer"	45	35
559	1f.10 "Owl"	1·50	1·30

169 "Madonna with Angels" (F. Nigg)

1972. Christmas.

560	**169**	30r. multicoloured	45	35

170 Lawena Springs

1972. Landscapes.

561	-	5r. purple and yellow	15	15
562	**170**	10r. green and light green	20	20
563	-	15r. brown and green	30	30
564	-	25r. purple and blue	35	35
565	-	30r. purple and brown	45	35
566	-	40r. purple and brown	60	45
567	-	50r. blue and lilac	75	55
568	-	60r. green and yellow	85	65
569	-	70r. blue and cobalt	1·00	80
570	-	80r. green and light green	1·20	85
571	-	1f. brown and green	1·50	1·10
572	-	1f.30 blue and green	1·90	1·50
573	-	1f.50 brown and blue	2·20	1·60
574	-	1f.80 brown & lt brown	2·50	2·00
575	-	2f. brown and blue	3·00	2·20

DESIGNS: 5r. Silum; 15r. Ruggeller Reed; 25r. Steg Kirchlispitz; 30r. Feld Schellenberg; 40r. Rennhof Mauren; 50r. Tidrufe; 60r. Eschner Riet; 70r. Mittagspitz; 80r. Schaan Forest; 1f. St. Peter's Chapel, Mals; 1f.30, Frommenhaus; 1f.50, Ochsenkopf; 1f.80, Hehlawangspitz; 2f. Saminasschlucht.

171 Europa "Posthorn"

1973. Europa.

576	**171**	30r. multicoloured	45	35
577	**171**	40r. multicoloured	60	50

172 Chambered Nautilus Goblet

1973. Treasures from Prince's Collection (1st issue). Drinking Vessels. Multicoloured.

578	30r. Type **172**	45	45
579	70r. Ivory tankard	1·00	80
580	1f.10 Silver cup	1·60	1·30

See also Nos. 589/92.

173 Arms of Liechtenstein

1973

581	**173**	5f. multicoloured	7·25	4·25

174 False Ringlet

1973. Small Fauna of Liechtenstein (1st series). Multicoloured.

582	30r. Type **174**	45	45
583	40r. Curlew	60	50
584	60r. Edible frog	80	75
585	80r. Grass snake	1·10	85

See also Nos. 596/9.

175 "Madonna" (Bartolomeo di Tommaso da Foligno)

1973. Christmas.

586	**175**	30r. multicoloured	45	35

176 "Shouting Horseman" (sculpture, Andrea Riccio)

1974. Europa. Multicoloured.

587	30r. Type **176**	45	35
588	40r. "Squatting Aphrodite" (sculpture, Antonio Susini)	60	50

1974. Treasures from Prince's Collection (2nd issue). Porcelain. As T 172. Multicoloured.

589	30r. Vase, 19th century	45	35
590	50r. Vase, 1740	75	55
591	60r. Vase, 1830	80	75
592	1f. Vase, c. 1700	1·30	1·30

177 Footballers

1974. World Cup Football Championship, West Germany.

593	**177**	80f. multicoloured	1·20	1·10

178 Posthorn and U.P.U. Emblem

1974. Centenary of Universal Postal Union.

594	**178**	40r. black, green and gold	60	50
595	**178**	60r. black, red and gold	85	75

1974. Small Fauna of Liechtenstein (2nd series). As T 174. Multicoloured.

596	15r. Mountain newt	30	30
597	25r. Adder	35	35
598	70r. Cynthia's fritillary (butterfly)	1·10	95
599	1f.10 Three-toed woodpecker	1·60	1·50

179 Bishop Marxer

1974. Death Centenary of Bishop Franz Marxer.

600	**179**	1f. multicoloured	1·50	1·10

180 Prince Francis Joseph II and Princess Gina

1974

601	**180**	10f. brown and gold	11·00	11·00

181 "St. Florian"

1974. Christmas. Glass Paintings. Multicoloured.

602	30r. Type **181**	45	35
603	50r. "St. Wendelin"	75	60
604	60r. "St. Mary, Anna and Joachim"	80	75
605	70r. "Jesus in Manger"	95	85

182 Prince Constantin

1975. Liechtenstein Princes.

606	**182**	70r. green and gold	1·00	95
607	-	80r. purple and gold	1·20	1·10
608	-	1f.20 blue and gold	1·70	1·60

PORTRAITS: 80r. Prince Maximilian; 1f.20, Prince Alois.

183 "Cold Sun" (M. Frommelt)

1975. Europa. Paintings. Multicoloured.

609	30r. Type **183**	45	35
610	60r. "Village" (L. Jager)	85	75

184 Imperial Cross

1975. Imperial Insignia (1st series). Multicoloured.

611	30r. Type **184**	45	35
612	60r. Imperial sword	85	75
613	1f. Imperial orb	1·50	1·30
614	1f.30 Imperial robe (50×32 mm)	3·00	3·00
615	2f. Imperial crown	3·00	2·75

See also Nos. 670/3.

185 "Red Cross Activities"

1975. 30th Anniv of Liechtenstein Red Cross.

616	**185**	60r. multicoloured	85	75

186 St. Mamerten, Triesen

1975. European Architectural Heritage Year. Multicoloured.

617	40r. Type **186**	60	55
618	50r. Red House, Vaduz	80	75
619	70r. Prebendary buildings, Eschen	1·00	90
620	1f. Gutenberg Castle, Balzers	1·60	1·50

187 Speed Skating

1975. Winter Olympic Games, Innsbruck (1976). Multicoloured.

621	20r. Type **187**	35	35
622	25r. Ice hockey	35	35
623	70r. Downhill skiing	1·10	95
624	1f.20 Slalom	1·80	95

188 "Daniel in the Lions' Den"

1975. Christmas and Holy Year. Capitals in Chur Cathedral.

625	**188**	30r. violet and gold	45	35
626	-	60r. green and gold	85	75
627	-	90r. red and gold	1·20	1·00

DESIGNS: 60r. "Madonna"; 90r. "St. Peter".

189 Mouflon

1976. Europa. Ceramics by Prince Hans von Liechtenstein. Multicoloured.

628	40r. Type **189**	60	45
629	80r. "Ring-necked Pheasant and Brood"	1·20	1·00

190 Crayfish

1976. World Wildlife Fund. Multicoloured.

630	25r. Type **190**	35	35
631	40r. Turtle	75	60
632	70r. European otter	1·10	1·00
633	80r. Northern lapwing	1·50	1·30

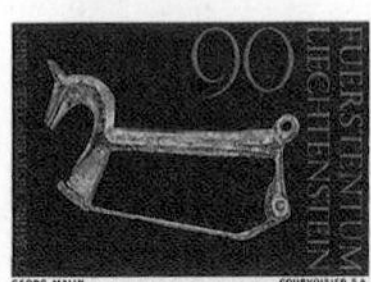

191 Roman Fibula

1976. 75th Anniv of National Historical Society.

634	**191**	90r. multicoloured	1·50	1·30

192 Obverse of 50f. Coin depicting portrait of Prince

1976. 70th Birthday of Prince Francis Joseph II. Sheet 102×65 mm containing T 192 and similar horiz design. Multicoloured.

MS635	1f. Type **192**; 1f. Reverse of 50f. coin depicting Arms of Liechtenstein	3·00	3·00

193 Judo

1976. Olympic Games, Montreal. Multicoloured.

636	35r. Type **193**	50	45
637	50r. Volleyball	75	65
638	80r. Relay	1·20	1·10
639	1f.10 Long jumping	1·60	1·50

194 "Singing Angels"

1976. 400th Birth Anniv (1977) of Peter Paul Rubens (painter). Multicoloured.

640	50r. Type **194**	75	75
641	70r. "Sons of the Artist"	1·10	1·10
642	1f. "Daughters of Cecrops" (49×39 mm)	5·50	5·50

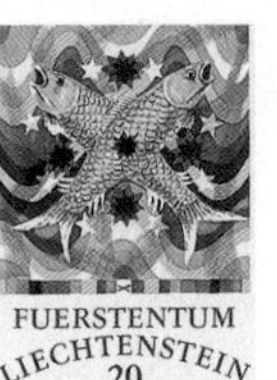

195 "Pisces"

1976. Signs of the Zodiac (1st series). Multicoloured.

643	20r. Type **195**	35	35
644	40r. "Aries"	50	50
645	80r. "Taurus"	1·20	1·00
646	90r. "Gemini"	1·30	1·10

See also Nos. 666/9 and 710/13.

196 "Child Jesus of Prague"

1976. Christmas. Monastic Wax Sculptures. Mult.

647	20r. Type **196**	35	35
648	50r. "The Flight into Egypt" (vert)	75	50
649	80r. "Holy Trinity" (vert)	1·20	1·00
650	1f.50 "Holy Family"	2·20	3·50

197 Sarcophagus Statue, Chur Cathedral

1976. Bishop Ortlieb von Brandis of Chur Commemoration.

651	**197**	1f.10 brown and gold	1·60	1·50

199 Map of Liechtenstein, 1721 (J. Heber)

1977. Europa. Multicoloured.

664	40r. Type **199**	60	50
665	80r. "View of Vaduz, 1815" (F. Bachmann)	1·20	95

1977. Signs of the Zodiac (2nd series). As T 195. Multicoloured.

666	40r. "Cancer"	60	50
667	70r. "Leo"	1·00	95
668	80r. "Virgo"	1·20	1·10
669	1f.10 "Libra"	1·60	1·50

1977. Imperial Insignia (2nd series). As T 184. Multicoloured.

670	40r. Holy Lance and Reliquary with Particle of the Cross	60	50
671	50r. "St. Matthew" (Imperial Book of Gospels)	75	60
672	80r. St. Stephen's Purse	1·10	1·00
673	90r. Tabard of Imperial Herald	1·20	1·20

200 Coin of Emperor Constantine II

1977. Coins (1st series). Multicoloured.

674	35r. Type **200**	60	50
675	70r. Lindau Brakteat	1·10	95
676	80r. Coin of Ortlieb von Brandis	1·20	1·10

See also Nos. 707/9.

201 Frauenthal Castle, Styria

1977. Castles.

677	**201**	20r. green and gold	35	35
678	-	50r. red and gold	75	75
679	-	80r. lilac and gold	1·20	1·20
680	-	90r. blue and gold	1·50	1·50

DESIGNS: 50r. Gross-Ullersdorf, Moravia; 80r. Liechtenstein Castle, near Modling, Austria; 90r. Palais Liechtenstein, Alserbachstrasse, Vienna.

202 Children in Costume

1977. National Costumes. Multicoloured.

681	40r. Type **202**	60	50
682	70r. Two girls in traditional costume	1·10	95
683	1f. Woman in festive costume	1·60	1·50

203 Princess Tatjana

1977. Princess Tatjana.

684	**203**	1f.10 lt brn, brn & gold	1·80	1·50

204 "Angel"

1977. Christmas. Sculptures by Erasmus Kern. Multicoloured.

685	20r. Type **204**	35	35
686	50r. "St. Rochus"	75	65
687	80r. "Madonna"	1·20	1·00
688	1f.50 "God the Father"	3·00	2·75

205 Palais Liechtenstein, Bankgasse, Vienna

1978. Europa.

689	**205**	40r. blue and gold	60	50
690	-	80r. red and gold	1·20	95

DESIGN: 80r. Feldsberg Castle.

206 Farmhouse, Triesen

1978. Buildings. Multicoloured.

691	10r. Type **206**	20	15
692	20r. Upper village of Triesen	35	30
693	35r. Barns at Balzers	50	35
694	40r. Monastery building, Bendern	60	45
695	50r. Rectory tower, Balzers-Mals	75	55

696	70r. Rectory, Mauren	95	80
697	80r. Farmhouse, Schellenberg	1·20	85
698	90r. Rectory, Balzers	1·30	1·00
699	1f. Rheinberger House, Vaduz	1·50	1·10
700	1f.10 Vaduz Mitteldorf	1·60	1·20
701	1f.50 Town Hall, Triesenberg	2·20	1·70
702	2f. National Museum and Administrator's residence, Vaduz	3·00	2·20

207 Vaduz Castle

1978. 40th Anniv of Prince Francis Joseph II's Accession. Royal Residence. Multicoloured.

703	40r. Type **207**	65	65
704	50r. Courtyard	75	75
705	70r. Hall	1·00	1·00
706	80r. High Altar, Castle Chapel	1·20	1·20

208 Coin of Prince Charles

1978. Coins (2nd series). Multicoloured.

707	40r. Type **208**	60	50
708	50r. Coin of Prince John Adam	75	65
709	80r. Coin of Prince Joseph Wenzel	1·20	1·00

1978. Signs of the Zodiac (3rd series). As T 195. Multicoloured.

710	40r. "Scorpio"	60	50
711	50r. "Sagittarius"	80	75
712	80r. "Capricorn"	1·20	1·10
713	1f.50 "Aquarius"	2·20	2·00

209 "Portrait of a Piebald" (J. G. von Hamilton and A. Faistenberger)

1978. Paintings. Multicoloured.

714	70r. Type **209**	95	95
715	80r. "Portrait of a Blackish-brown Stallion" (J. G. von Hamilton)	1·10	1·10
716	1f.10 "Golden Carriage of Prince Joseph Wenzel" (Martin von Meytens) (48½×38 mm)	1·60	1·60

210 "Adoration of the Shepherds"

1978. Christmas. Church Windows, Triesenberg. Multicoloured.

717	20r. Type **210**	35	35
718	50r. "Enthroned Madonna with St. Joseph"	75	65
719	80r. "Adoration of the Magi"	1·20	1·10

211 Comte AC-8 Mail Plane "St. Gallen" over Schaan

1979. Europa. Multicoloured.

720	40r. Type **211**	60	60
721	80r. Airship LZ-127 "Graf Zeppelin" over Vaduz Castle	1·20	1·20

212 Child Drinking

1979. International Year of the Child. Multicoloured.

722	80r. Type **212**	1·20	1·10
723	90r. Child eating	1·30	1·20
724	1f.10 Child reading	1·50	1·40

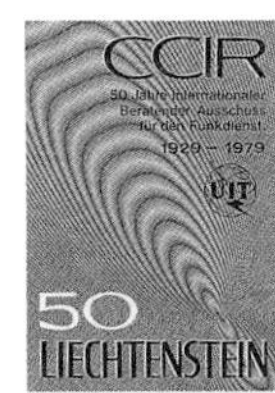
213 Ordered Wave-field

1979. 50th Anniv of International Radio Consultative Committee (CCIR).

725	213	50r. blue and black	75	65

214 Abstract Composition

1979. Liechtenstein's Entry into Council of Europe.

726	214	80r. multicoloured	1·20	1·00

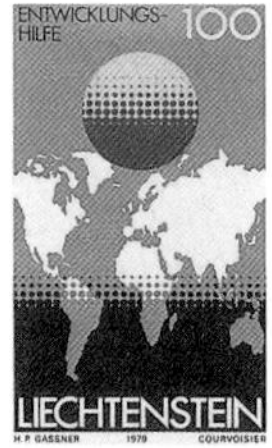
215 Sun rising over Continents

1979. Development Aid.

727	215	1f. multicoloured	1·40	1·20

216 Arms of Carl Ludwig von Sulz

1979. Heraldic Windows in the Liechtenstein National Museum. Multicoloured.

728	40r. Type **216**	60	50
729	70r. Arms of Barbara von Sulz	1·00	95
730	1f.10 Arms of Ulrich von Ramschwag and Barbara von Hallwil	1·70	1·50

217 Sts. Lucius and Florian (fresco, Waltensberg-Vuorz Church)

1979. Patron Saints.

731	217	20f. multicoloured	22·00	18·00

218 Base of Ski Slope, Valuna

1979. Winter Olympic Games, Lake Placid (1980). Multicoloured.

732	40r. Type **218**	60	50
733	70r. Malbun and Ochsenkopf	1·00	95
734	1f.50 Ski-lift, Sareis	2·00	1·80

219 "The Annunciation"

1979. Christmas. Embroideries by Ferdinand Nigg. Multicoloured.

735	20r. Type **219**	35	35
736	50r. "Christmas"	75	65
737	80r. "Blessed are the Peace-makers"	1·20	95

220 Maria Leopoldine von Esterhazy (bust by Canova)

1980. Europa.

738	220	40r. green, turq & gold	45	50
739	-	80r. brown, red and gold	1·20	95

DESIGN: 80r. Maria Theresia von Liechtenstein (after Martin von Meytens).

221 Arms of Andreas Buchel, 1690

1980. Arms of Bailiffs (1st series). Multicoloured.

740	40r. Type **221**	60	50
741	70r. Georg Marxer, 1745	1·00	95
742	80r. Luzius Frick, 1503	1·20	1·10
743	1f.10 Adam Oehri, 1634	1·60	1·50

See also Nos. 763/6, and 788/91.

222 3r. Stamp of 1930

1980. 50th Anniv of Postal Museum.

744	222	80r. red, green and grey	1·20	1·10

223 Milking Pail

1980. Alpine Dairy Farming Implements. Mult.

745	20r. Type **223**	35	35
746	50r. Wooden heart dairy herd descent marker	75	65
747	80r. Butter churn	1·20	1·00

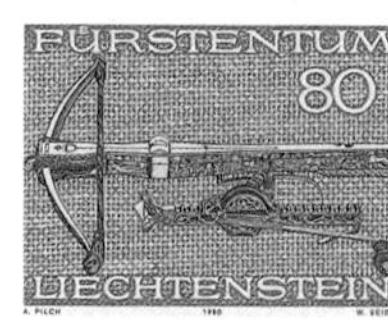
224 Crossbow

1980. Hunting Weapons.

748	224	80r. brown and lilac	1·20	1·10
749	-	90r. black and green	1·30	1·20
750	-	1f.10 black and stone	1·50	1·40

DESIGNS: 90r. Spear and knife; 1f.10, Rifle and powder-horn.

225 Triesenberg Costumes

1980. Costumes. Multicoloured.

751	40r. Type **225**	60	50
752	70r. Dancers, Schellenberg	1·10	95
753	80r. Brass band, Mauren	1·20	1·10

226 Beech Trees, Matrula (spring)

1980. The Forest in the Four Seasons. Multicoloured.

754	40r. Type **226**	60	50
755	50r. Firs in the Valorsch (summer)	80	75
756	80r. Beech tree, Schaan (autumn)	1·20	1·10
757	1f.50 Edge of forest at Oberplanken (winter)	2·20	2·00

227 Angel bringing Shepherds Good Tidings

1980. Christmas. Multicoloured.

758	20r. Type **227**	35	35
759	50r. Crib	75	65
760	80r. Epiphany	1·20	1·00

228 National Day Procession

1981. Europa. Multicoloured.

761	40r. Fireworks at Vaduz Castle	60	50
762	80r. Type **228**	1·20	95

1981. Arms of Bailiffs (2nd series). As T 221. Multicoloured.

763	40r. Anton Meier, 1748	60	50
764	70r. Kaspar Kindle, 1534	1·00	95
765	80r. Hans Adam Negele, 1600	1·20	1·10
766	1f.10 Peter Matt, 1693	1·60	1·50

229 Prince Alois and Princess Elisabeth with Francis Joseph

1981. 75th Birthday of Prince Francis Joseph II. Sheet 120×87 mm containing T 229 and similar vert designs. Multicoloured.

MS767	70r. Type **229**; 80r. Princes Alois and Francis Joseph; 150r. Prince Francis Joseph II	4·25	4·25

230 Scout Emblems

1981. 50th Anniv of Liechtenstein Boy Scout and Girl Guide Movements.

768	**230**	20r. multicoloured	45	40

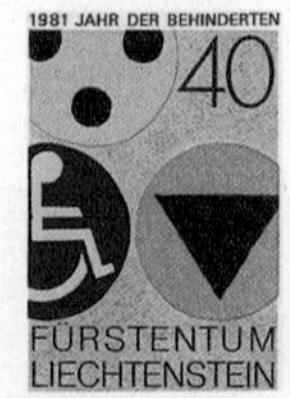

231 Symbols of Disability

1981. International Year of Disabled Persons.

769	**231**	40r. multicoloured	60	50

232 St. Theodul (sculpture)

1981. 1600th Birth Anniv of St. Theodul.

770	**232**	80r. multicoloured	1·20	1·00

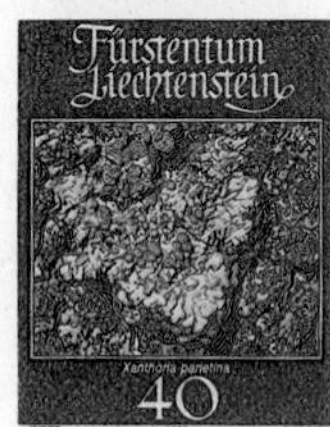

233 "Xanthoria parietina"

1981. Mosses and Lichens. Multicoloured.

771	40r. Type **233**	60	50
772	50r. "Parmelia physodes"	80	75
773	70r. "Sphagnum palustre"	1·00	95
774	80r. "Amblystegium serpens"	1·70	1·60

234 Gutenberg Castle

1981. Gutenberg Castle. Multicoloured.

775	20r. Type **234**	35	35
776	40r. Courtyard	65	65
777	50r. Parlour	75	75
778	1f.10 Great Hall	1·80	1·80

235 Cardinal Karl Borromaus von Mailand

1981. Famous Visitors to Liechtenstein (1st series). Multicoloured.

779	40r. Type **235**	60	60
780	70r. Johann Wolfgang von Goethe (writer)	1·00	95
781	80r. Alexander Dumas the younger (writer)	1·20	1·10
782	1f. Hermann Hesse (writer)	1·50	1·40

See also Nos. 804/7 and 832/5.

236 St. Nicholas blessing Children

1981. Christmas. Multicoloured.

783	20r. Type **236**	35	35
784	50r. Adoration of the Kings	75	65
785	80r. Holy Family	1·20	1·00

237 Peasant Revolt, 1525

1982. Europa. Multicoloured.

786	40r. Type **237**	60	50
787	80r. King Wenceslaus with Counts (Imperial direct rule, 1396)	1·20	95

1982. Arms of Bailiffs (3rd series). As T 221. Multicoloured.

788	40r. Johann Kaiser, 1664	60	50
789	70r. Joseph Anton Kaufmann, 1748	1·00	95
790	80r. Christoph Walser, 1690	1·20	1·10
791	1f.10 Stephan Banzer, 1658	1·60	1·50

238 Triesenberg Sports Ground

1982. World Cup Football Championship, Spain. Multicoloured.

792	15r. Type **238**	20	20
793	25r. Eschen/Mauren playing fields	35	35
794	1f.80 Rheinau playing fields, Balzers	2·50	2·30

239 Crown Prince Hans Adam

1982. "Liba 82" Stamp Exhibition. Multicoloured.

795	1f. Type **239**	1·50	1·50
796	1f. Princess Marie Aglae	1·50	1·50

240 Tractor (agriculture)

1982. Rural Industries. Multicoloured.

797	30r. Type **240**	45	45
798	50r. Cutting flowers (horticulture)	75	65
799	70r. Workers with logs (forestry)	1·00	95
800	150r. Worker and milk (dairy farming)	2·20	2·00

241 "Neu Schellenberg"

1982. 150th Birth Anniv of Mortiz Menzinger (artist). Multicoloured.

801	40r. Type **241**	60	50
802	50r. "Vaduz"	85	75
803	100r. "Bendern"	1·50	1·30

242 Angelika Kauffmann (artist, self-portrait)

1982. Famous Visitors to Liechtenstein (2nd series). Multicoloured.

804	40r. Emperor Maximilian I (after Benhard Strigel)	60	50
805	70f. Georg Jenatsch (liberator of Grisons)	1·00	95
806	80r. Type **242**	1·20	1·10
807	1f. St. Fidelis of Sigmaringen	1·60	1·50

243 Angel playing Lute

1982. Christmas. Details from High Altar by Jakob Russ, Chur Cathedral. Multicoloured.

808	20r. Type **243**	35	35
809	50r. Madonna and child	75	65
810	80r. Angel playing organ	1·20	1·00

244 Notker Balbulus of St. Gall

1983. Europa. Multicoloured.

811	40r. Type **244**	60	50
812	80r. Hildegard of Bingen	1·20	95

245 Shrove Thursday

1983. Shrovetide and Lent Customs. Mult.

813	40r. Type **245**	60	50
814	70r. Shrovetide carnival	1·10	95
815	1f.80 Lent Sunday bonfire	2·75	2·50

246 River Bank

1983. Anniversaries and Events. Multicoloured.

816	20r. Type **246**	50	35
817	40r. Montgolfier Brothers' balloon	60	50
818	50r. Airmail envelope	75	65
819	80r. Plant and hands holding spade	1·10	1·00

EVENTS: 20r. Council of Europe river and coasts protection campaign; 40r. Bicentenary of manned flight; 50r. World Communications Year; 80r. Overseas aid.

247 "Schaan"

1983. Landscape Paintings by Anton Ender. Mult.

820	40r. Type **247**	60	50
821	50r. "Gutenberg Castle"	85	75
822	200r. "Steg Reservoir"	3·00	2·75

248 Princess Gina

1983. Multicoloured.. Multicoloured..

823	2f.50 Type **248**	3·75	2·50
824	3f. Prince Francis Joseph II	4·25	3·00

249 Pope John Paul II

1983. Holy Year.

825	**249**	80r. multicoloured	1·20	1·10

250 Snowflakes and Stripes

1983. Winter Olympic Games, Sarajevo. Mult.

826	40r. Type **250**	60	50
827	80r. Snowflake	1·20	1·10
828	1f.80 Snowflake and rays	2·50	2·40

251 Seeking Shelter

1983. Christmas. Multicoloured.

829	20r. Type **251**	35	35
830	50r. Infant Jesus	75	65
831	80r. Three Kings	1·20	1·00

252 Aleksandr Vassilievich Suvorov (Russian general)

1984. Famous Visitors to Liechtenstein (3rd series). Multicoloured.

832	40r. Type **252**	65	60
833	70r. Karl Rudolf von Buol-Schauenstein, Bishop of Chur	1·00	95
834	80r. Carl Zuckmayer (dramatist)	1·20	1·10
835	1f. Curt Goetz (actor)	1·50	1·40

253 Bridge

1984. Europa. 25th Anniv of E.P.T. Conf.

836	**253**	50r. blue and deep blue	75	65
837	**253**	80r. pink and brown	1·10	1·00

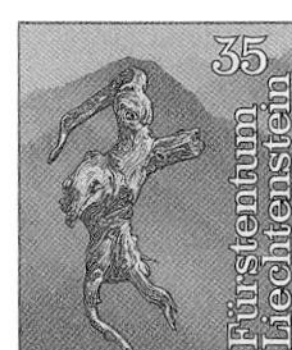

254 The Warning Messenger

1984. Liechtenstein Legends. The Destruction of Trisona. Each brown, grey and blue.

838	35r. Type **254**	50	45
839	50r. The buried town	80	65
840	80r. The spared family	1·20	1·10

255 Pole Vaulting

1984. Olympic Games, Los Angeles. Mult.

841	70r. Type **255**	1·00	85
842	80r. Throwing the discus	1·20	1·10
843	1f. Putting the shot	1·50	1·30

256 Currency (trade and banking)

1984. Occupations. Multicoloured.

844	5r. Type **256**	15	15
845	10r. Plumber adjusting pipe (building trade)	20	20
846	20r. Operating machinery (industry—production)	35	35
847	35r. Draughtswoman (building trade—planning)	60	45
848	45r. Office worker and world map (industry—sales)	85	65
849	50r. Cook (tourism)	95	60
850	60r. Carpenter (building trade—interior decoration)	1·10	75
851	70r. Doctor injecting patient (medical services)	1·20	1·00
852	80r. Scientist (industrial research)	1·30	1·20
853	100r. Bricklayer (building trade)	1·60	1·30
854	120r. Flow chart (industry—administration)	2·00	1·60
855	150r. Handstamping covers (post and communications)	2·75	2·00

257 Princess Marie

1984. Multicoloured.. Multicoloured..

856	1f.70 Type **257**	2·20	50
857	2f. Crown Prince Hans Adam	3·00	75

258 Annunciation

1984. Christmas. Multicoloured.

858	35r. Type **258**	50	50
859	50r. Holy Family	80	75
860	80r. The Three Kings	1·20	1·10

259 Apollo and the Muses playing Music (detail from 18th-century harpsichord lid)

1985. Europa. Music Year. Multicoloured.

861	50r. Type **259**	75	75
862	80r. Apollo and the Muses playing music (different)	1·10	1·10

260 St. Elisabeth Convent, Schaan

1985. Monasteries. Multicoloured.

863	50r. Type **260**	75	75
864	1f. Schellenberg Convent	1·50	1·50
865	1f.70 Gutenberg Mission, Balzers	2·50	2·50

261 Princess Gina and handing out of Rations

1985. 40th Anniv of Liechtenstein Red Cross. Multicoloured.

866	20r. Type **261**	45	45
867	50r. Princess Gina and Red Cross ambulance	1·10	1·10
868	120r. Princess Gina with refugee children	2·10	2·10

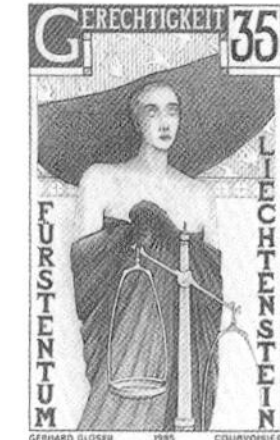

262 Justice

1985. Cardinal Virtues. Multicoloured.

869	35r. Type **262**	50	50
870	50r. Temperance	75	75
871	70r. Prudence	95	95
872	1f. Fortitude	1·50	1·50

263 Papal Arms

1985. Papal Visit. Sheet 100×67 mm containing T 263 and similar vert designs. Multicoloured.

MS873	50r. Type **263**; 80r. St. Maria zum Trost Chapel; 170r. Our Lady of Liechtenstein (statue) (29×43 mm)	4·25	4·25

264 "Portrait of a Canon" (Quentin Massys)

1985. Paintings in Metropolitan Museum, New York. Multicoloured.

874	50r. Type **264**	85	85
875	1f. "Clara Serena Rubens" (Rubens)	2·00	2·00
876	1f.20 "Duke of Urbino" (Raphael)	1·80	1·80

265 Halberd used by Charles I's Bodyguard

1985. Guards' Weapons and Armour. Mult.

877	35r. Type **265**	50	35
878	50r. Morion used by Charles I's bodyguard	85	85
879	80r. Halberd used by Carl Eusebius's bodyguard	1·20	1·20

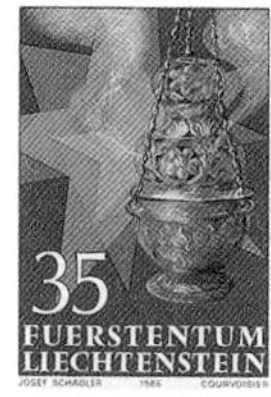

266 Frankincense

1985. Christmas. Multicoloured.

880	35r. Type **266**	60	60
881	50r. Gold	80	75
882	80r. Myrrh	1·20	1·20

267 Puppets performing Tragedy

1985. Theatre. Multicoloured.

883	50r. Type **267**	85	85
884	80r. Puppets performing comedy	1·20	1·20
885	1f.50 Opera	2·30	2·30

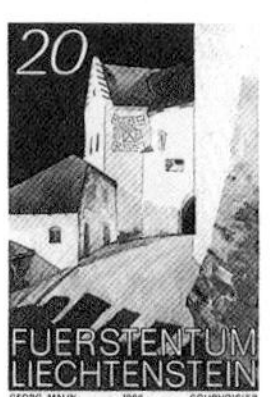

268 Courtyard

1986. Vaduz Castle. Multicoloured.

886	20r. Type **268**	30	20
887	25r. Keep	35	30
888	50r. Castle	75	60
889	90r. Inner gate	1·10	95
890	1f.10 Castle from gardens	1·50	1·30
891	1f.40 Courtyard (different)	1·80	1·60

269 Barn Swallows

1986. Europa. Birds. Multicoloured.

892	50r. Type **269**	75	75
893	90r. European robin	1·50	1·50

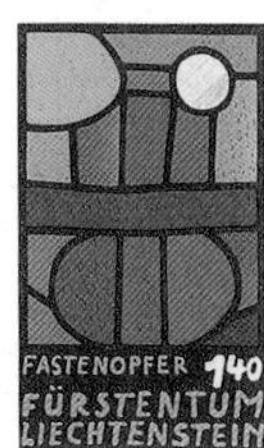

270 "Offerings"

1986. Lenten Fast.

894	**270**	1f.40 multicoloured	2·20	2·20

271 Palm Sunday

1986. Religious Festivals. Multicoloured.

895	35r. Type **271**	60	60
896	50r. Wedding	85	85
897	70r. Rogation Day procession	1·10	1·10

272 Karl Freiherr Haus von Hausen

1986. 125th Anniv of Liechtenstein Land Bank.

898	**272**	50r. brown, ochre and buff	75	75

273 Francis Joseph II

1986. 80th Birthday of Prince Francis Joseph II.

899	**273**	3f.50 multicoloured	4·25	3·75

274 Roebuck in Ruggeller Riet

1986. Hunting. Multicoloured.

900	35r. Type **274**	60	60
901	50r. Chamois at Rappenstein	85	85
902	1f.70 Stag in Lawena	3·00	3·00

275 Cabbage and Beetroot

1986. Field Crops. Multicoloured.

903	50r. Type **275**	85	85
904	80r. Red cabbages	1·30	1·30
905	90r. Potatoes, onions and garlic	1·50	1·50

276 Archangel Michael

1986. Christmas. Multicoloured.

906	35r. Type **276**	60	60
907	50r. Archangel Gabriel	85	85
908	90r. Archangel Raphael	1·50	1·50

277 Silver Fir

1986. Tree Bark. Multicoloured.

909	35r. Type **277**		45	45
910	90r. Norway spruce		1·60	1·60
911	1f.40 Pedunculate oak		2·30	2·30

278 Gamprin Primary School

1987. Europa. Multicoloured.

912	50r. Type **278**	80	80
913	90r. Schellenberg parish church	1·40	1·40

280 Niklaus von Flue

1987. 500th Death Anniv of Niklaus von Flue (martyr).

914	**280**	1f.10 multicoloured	1·80	1·60

281 Bullhead

1987. Fishes (1st series). Multicoloured.

915	50r. Type **281**	85	85
916	90r. Brown trout	1·50	1·50
917	1f.10 European grayling	2·00	2·00

See also Nos. 959/61.

282 Prince Alois (frame as in first stamps)

1987. 75th Anniv of First Liechtenstein Stamps.

918	**282**	2f. multicoloured	3·75	3·75

283 Staircase

1987. Liechtenstein City Palace, Vienna. Multicoloured.

919	35r. Type **283**	60	60
920	50r. Minoritenplatz doorway	85	85
921	90r. Staircase (different)	1·50	1·50

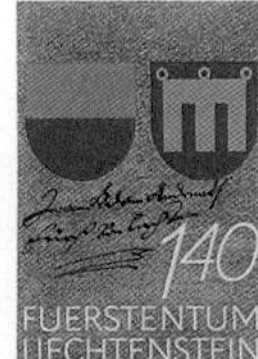

284 Arms

1987. 275th Anniv of Transfer of County of Vaduz to House of Liechtenstein.

922	**284**	1f.40 multicoloured	2·30	1·60

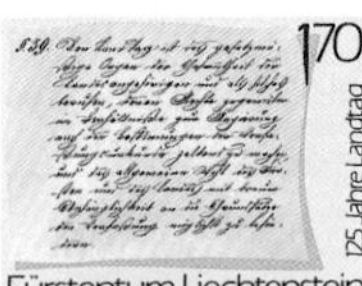

285 Constitution Charter, 1862

1987. 125th Anniv of Liechtenstein Parliament.

923	**285**	1f.70 multicoloured	2·75	2·75

286 St. Matthew

1987. Christmas. Illuminations from Golden Book of Pfafers Abbey. Multicoloured.

924	35r. Type **286**	60	60
925	50r. St. Mark	95	95
926	60r. St. Luke	1·10	1·10
927	90r. St. John	1·70	1·70

287 "The Toil of the Cross-country Skier"

1987. Winter Olympic Games, Calgary (1988). Multicoloured.

928	25r. Type **287**	45	45
929	90r. "The Courageous Pioneers of Skiing"	1·70	1·70
930	1f.10 "As our Grandfathers used to ride on a Bobsled"	2·20	2·20

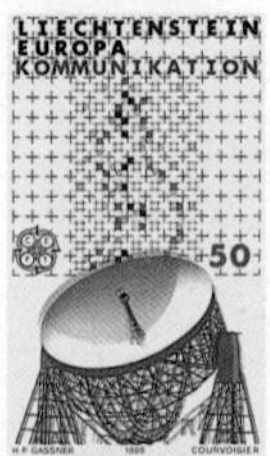

288 Dish Aerial

1988. Europa. Transport and Communications. Mult.

931	50r. Type **288**	75	75
932	90r. Maglev monorail	1·50	1·50

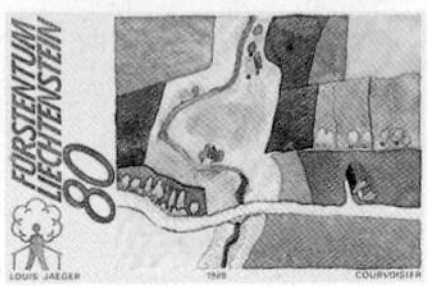

289 Agriculture

1988. European Campaign for Rural Areas. Multicoloured.

933	80r. Type **289**	1·50	1·50
934	90r. Village centre	1·80	1·80
935	1f.70 Road	2·50	2·50

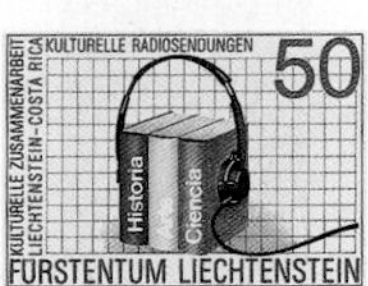

290 Headphones on Books (Radio Broadcasts)

1988. Costa Rica–Liechtenstein Cultural Co-operation.

936	**290**	50r. multicoloured	1·10	1·10
937	-	1f.40 red, brown and green	3·25	3·25

DESIGN: 1f.40, Man with pen and radio (Adult education).

291 Crown Prince Hans Adam

1988. 50th Anniv of Accesion of Prince Francis Joseph II. Sheet 100×68 mm containing T 291 and similar vert designs. Multicoloured.

MS938	50r. Type **291**; 50r. Prince Alois; 2f. Prince Francis Joseph II	6·50	6·50

292 St. Barbara's Shrine, Balzers

1988. Wayside Shrines. Multicoloured.

939	25r. Type **292**	50	50
940	35r. Shrine containing statues of Christ, St. Peter and St. Paul at Oberdorf, Vaduz	65	65
941	50r. St. Anthony of Egypt's shrine, Fallagass, Ruggel	1·00	1·00

293 Cycling

1988. Olympic Games, Seoul. Multicoloured.

942	50r. Type **293**	95	95
943	80r. Gymnastics	1·60	1·60
944	90r. Running	1·80	1·80
945	1f.40 Equestrian event	3·00	3·00

294 Joseph and Mary

1988. Christmas. Multicoloured.

946	35r. Type **294**	60	60
947	50r. Baby Jesus	85	85
948	90r. Wise Men presenting gifts to Jesus	1·50	1·50

295 Letter beside Footstool (detail)

1988. "The Letter" (portrait of Marie-Theresa, Princesse de Lamballe by Anton Hickel). Multicoloured.

949	50r. Type **295**	50	50
950	90r. Desk and writing materials (detail)	65	65
951	2f. "The Letter" (complete painting)	1·00	1·00

296 "Cat and Mouse"

1989. Europa. Children's Games. Multicoloured.

952	50r. Type **296**	1·10	75
953	90r. "Hide and Seek"	1·80	1·50

298 Rheinberger and Score

1989. 150th Birth Anniv of Josef Gabriel Rheinberger (composer).

954	**298**	2f.90 black, blue & purple	5·00	4·25

299 Little Ringed Plover

1989. Endangered Animals. Multicoloured.

955	25r. Type **299**	45	45
956	35r. Green tree frog	65	65
957	50r. "Libelloides coccajus" (lace-wing)	1·10	1·10
958	90r. Polecat	2·20	2·20

300 Northern Pike

1989. Fishes (2nd series). Multicoloured.

959	50r. Type **300**	75	75
960	1f.10 Brown trout	1·80	1·60
961	1f.40 Stone loach	2·50	2·00

301 Return of Cattle from Alpine Pastures

1989. Autumn Customs. Multicoloured.

962	35r. Type **301**	60	60
963	50r. Peeling corn cobs	85	80
964	80r. Cattle market	1·50	1·20

302 Falknis

1989. Mountains. Watercolours by Josef Schadler.

965	-	5r. multicoloured	10	10
966	-	10r. multicoloured	15	15
967	-	35r. multicoloured	50	50
968	-	40r. multicoloured	60	60
969	-	45r. multicoloured	65	65
970	**302**	50r. multicoloured	75	75
971	-	60r. multicoloured	85	85
972	-	70r. multicoloured	1·00	1·00
973	-	75r. multicoloured	1·10	1·10
974	-	80r. violet, brown & black	1·20	1·20
975	-	1f. multicoloured	1·50	1·50
976	-	1f.20 multicoloured	1·80	1·80

977	-	1f.50 multicoloured	2·20	2·20
978	-	1f.60 multicoloured	3·00	3·00
979	-	2f. multicoloured	3·00	3·00

DESIGNS: 5r. Augstenberg; 10r. Hahenespiel; 35r. Nospitz; 40r. Ochsenkopf; 45r. Three Sisters; 60r. Kuhgrat; 70r. Galinakopf; 75r. Plassteikopf; 80pf. Naafkopf; 1f. Schonberg; 1f.20, Bleikaturm; 1f.50, Garselliturm; 1f.60, Schwarzhorn; 2f. Scheienkopf.

303 "Melchior and Balthasar"

1989. Christmas. Details of triptych by Hugo van der Goes. Multicoloured.

981	35r. Type **303**	60	50
982	50r. "Kaspar and Holy Family" (27×34 mm)	85	75
983	90r. "St. Stephen"	1·50	1·30

304 Mace Quartz

1989. Minerals. Multicoloured.

984	50r. Type **304**	85	75
985	1f.10 Globe pyrite	1·80	1·50
986	1f.50 Calcite	2·40	2·20

305 Nendeln Forwarding Agency, 1864

1990. Europa. Post Office Buildings. Mult.

987	50r. Type **305**	75	75
988	90r. Vaduz post office, 1976	1·50	1·50

306 Penny Black

1990. 150th Anniv of the Penny Black.

989	**306**	1f.50 multicoloured	3·00	3·00

307 Footballers

1990. World Cup Football Championship, Italy.

990	**307**	2f. multicoloured	3·75	3·75

308 Tureen, Oranges and Grapes

1990. 9th Death Anniv of Benjamin Steck (painter). Multicoloured.

991	50r. Type **308**	1·10	85
992	80r. Apples and pewter bowl	1·50	1·30
993	1f.50 Basket, apples, cherries and pewter jug	3·00	3·00

309 Princess Gina

1990. Prince Francis Joseph II and Princess Gina Commemoration. Multicoloured.

994	2f. Type **309**	3·00	3·00
995	3f. Prince Francis Joseph II	4·25	4·25

310 Common Pheasant

1990. Game Birds. Multicoloured.

996	25r. Type **310**	50	50
997	50r. Black grouse	95	95
998	2f. Mallard	3·75	3·75

311 Annunciation

1990. Christmas. Paintings. Multicoloured.

999	35r. Type **311**	75	75
1000	50r. Nativity	85	85
1001	90r. Adoration of the Magi	1·30	1·30

312 St. Nicholas

1990. Winter Customs. Multicoloured.

1002	35r. Type **312**	50	50
1003	50r. Awakening on New Year's Eve	80	80
1004	1f.50 Giving New Year greetings	2·30	2·30

313 Mounted Courier

1990. 500th Anniv of Regular European Postal Services.

1005	**313**	90r. multicoloured	1·80	1·80

314 "Olympus 1" Satellite

1991. Europa. Europe in Space. Multicoloured.

1006	50r. Type **314**	75	75
1007	90r. "Meteosat" satellite	1·50	1·50

315 St. Ignatius de Loyola (founder of Society of Jesus)

1991. Anniversaries. Multicoloured.

1008	80r. Type **315** (500th birth anniv)	1·10	1·10
1009	90r. Wolfgang Amadeus Mozart (composer, death bicentenary)	1·50	1·50

316 U.N. Emblem and Dove

1991. Admission to U.N. Membership (1990).

1010	**316**	2f.50 multicoloured	3·75	3·75

317 Non-Commissioned Officer and Private

1991. 125th Anniv of Last Mobilization of Liechtenstein's Military Contingent (to the Tyrol). Multicoloured.

1011	50r. Type **317**	75	75
1012	70r. Tunic, chest and portrait	1·10	1·10
1013	1f. Officer and private	1·50	1·50

318 "Near Maloja" (Giovanni Giacometti)

1991. 700th Anniv of Swiss Confederation. Paintings by Swiss artists. Multicoloured.

1014	50r. Type **318**	75	75
1015	80r. "Rhine Valley" (Ferdinand Gehr)	1·10	1·10
1016	90r. "Bergell" (Augusto Giacometti)	1·50	1·50
1017	1f.10 "Hoher Kasten" (Hedwig Scherrer)	2·20	2·20

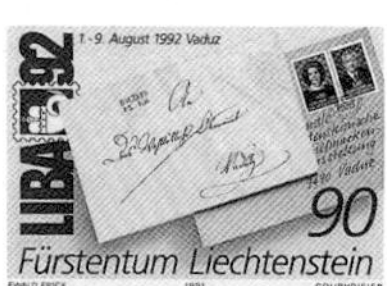

319 Stampless and Modern Covers

1991. "Liba 92" National Stamp Exhibition, Vaduz.

1018	**319**	90r. multicoloured	1·50	1·50

320 Princess Marie

1991. Multicoloured

1019	3f. Type **320**	3·75	3·25
1020	3f.40 Prince Hans Adam II	4·25	4·00

321 Virgin of the Annunciation (exterior of left wing)

1991. Christmas. Details of the altar from St. Mamertus Chapel, Triesen. Multicoloured.

1021	50r. Type **321**	80	80
1022	80r. Madonna and Child (wood-carving attr. Jorg Syrlin, inner shrine)	1·20	1·20
1023	90r. Angel Gabriel (exterior of right wing)	1·30	1·30

322 Cross-country Skiers and Testing for Drug Abuse

1991. Winter Olympic Games, Albertville. Mult.

1024	70r. Type **322**	1·50	1·50
1025	80r. Ice hockey player tackling opponent and helping him after fall	1·50	1·50
1026	1f.60 Downhill skier and fallen skier caught in safety net	2·50	2·50

323 Relay Race, Drugs and Shattered Medal

1992. Olympic Games, Barcelona. Multicoloured.

1027	50r. Type **323**	75	75
1028	70r. Cycling road race	1·50	1·50
1029	2f.50 Judo	4·25	4·25

324 Aztecs

1992. Europa. 500th Anniv of Discovery of America by Columbus. Multicoloured.

1030	80r. Type **324**	1·20	1·20
1031	90r. Statue of Liberty and New York skyline	1·40	1·40

325 Clown in Envelope ("Good Luck")

1992. Greetings Stamps. Multicoloured.

1032	50r. Type **325**	75	75
1033	50r. Wedding rings in envelope and harlequin violinist	75	75
1034	50r. Postman blowing horn (31×21 mm)	75	75
1035	50r. Flying postman carrying letter sealed with heart (31×21 mm)	75	75

326 Arms of Liechtenstein—Kinsky Alliance

1992. "Liba '92" National Stamp Exhibition. Silver Wedding Anniv of Prince Hans Adam and Princess Marie. Sheet 100×67 mm containing T 326 and similar vert design. Multicoloured.

MS1036	2f. Type **326**; 2f.50 Royal couple (photo by Anthony Buckley)	8·75	8·75

327 "Blechnum spicant"

1992. Ferns. Multicoloured.

1037	40r. Type **327**	60	60
1038	50r. Maidenhair spleenwort	75	75
1039	70r. Hart's-tongue	1·00	1·00
1040	2f.50 "Asplenium ruta-muraria"	4·25	4·25

328 Reading Edict

1992. 650th Anniv of County of Vaduz.

1041	**328** 1f.60 multicoloured	3·00	3·00

329 Chapel of St. Mamertus, Triesen

1992. Christmas. Multicoloured.

1042	50r. Type **329**	75	75
1043	90r. Crib, St. Gallus's Church, Triesen	1·30	1·30
1044	1f.60 St. Mary's Chapel, Triesen	2·30	2·30

330 Crown Prince Alois

1992

1045	**330** 2f.50 multicoloured	3·75	3·75

331 "Nafkopf and Huts, Steg"

1993. 1400th Birth Anniv of Hans Gantner (painter). Multicoloured.

1046	50r. Type **331**	75	75
1047	60r. "Hunting Lodge, Sass"	85	85
1048	1f.80 "Red House, Vaduz"	2·75	2·75

332 "910805" (Bruno Kaufmann)

1993. Europa. Contemporary Art. Multicoloured.

1049	80r. Type **332**	1·30	1·30
1050	1f. "The Little Blue" (Evi Kliemand)	1·50	1·50

333 "Tale of the Ferryman" (painting)

1993. Tibetan Collection in the National Museum. Multicoloured.

1051	60r. Type **333**	1·10	1·10
1052	80r. Religious dance mask	1·30	1·30
1053	1f. "Tale of the Fish" (painting)	1·60	1·60

334 "Tree of Life"

1993. Missionary Work.

1054	**334** 1f.80 multicoloured	3·00	3·00

335 "The Black Hatter"

1993. Homage to Liechtenstein.

1055	**335** 2f.80 multicoloured	4·25	4·25

336 Crown Prince Alois and Duchess Sophie of Bavaria

1993. Royal Wedding. Sheet 100×67 mm.

MS1056	**336** 4f. multicoloured	7·25	7·25

337 Origanum

1993. Flowers. Illustrations from "Hortus Botanicus Liechtensteinsis". Multicoloured.

1057	50r. Type **337**	90	90
1058	60r. Meadow sage	1·10	1·10
1059	1f. "Seseli annuum"	1·60	1·60
1060	2f.50 Large self-heal	3·75	3·75

338 Eurasian Badger

1993. Animals. Multicoloured.

1061	60r. Type **338**	1·10	1·10
1062	80r. Beech marten	1·50	1·50
1063	1f. Red fox	1·80	1·80

339 "Now that the Quiet Days are Coming ..." (Rainer Maria Rilke)

1993. Christmas. Multicoloured.

1064	60r. Type **339**	90	90
1065	80r. "Can You See the Light ..." (Th. Friedrich)	1·30	1·30
1066	1f. "Christmas, Christmas ..." (R. A. Schroder)	1·50	1·50

340 Ski Jump

1993. Winter Olympic Games, Lillehammer, Norway (1994). Multicoloured.

1067	60r. Type **340**	1·30	1·30
1068	80r. Slalom	1·60	1·60
1069	2f.40 Bobsleighing	3·75	3·75

341 Seal and Title Page

1994. Anniversaries. Multicoloured.

1070	60r. Type **341** (275th anniv of Principality)	1·10	1·10
1071	1f.80 State, Prince's and Olympic flags (centenary of International Olympic Committee)	3·00	3·00

342 Andean Condor

1994. Europa. Discoveries of Alexander von Humboldt. Multicoloured.

1072	80r. Type **342**	1·50	1·50
1073	1f. "Rhexia cardinalis" (plant)	1·80	1·80

343 Football Pitch and Hopi Indians playing Kickball

1994. World Cup Football Championship, U.S.A.

1074	**343** 2f.80 multicoloured	4·25	4·25

344 Elephant with Letter

1994. Greetings Stamps. Multicoloured.

1075	60r. Type **344**	1·10	1·10
1076	60r. Cherub with flower and hearts	1·10	1·10
1077	60r. Pig with four-leaf clover	1·10	1·10
1078	60r. Dog holding bunch of tulips	1·10	1·10

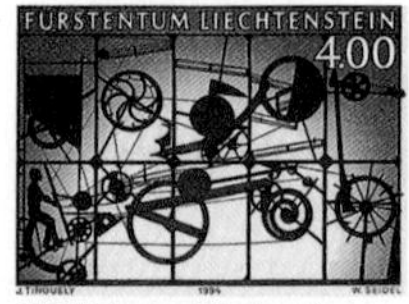

345 "Eulogy of Madness" (mobile, Jean Tinguely)

1994. Homage to Liechtenstein.

1079	**345** 4f. black, pink and violet	7·25	7·25

346 Spring

1994. Seasons of the Vine. Multicoloured.

1080	60r. Type **346**	1·10	1·10
1081	60r. Vine leaves (Summer)	1·10	1·10
1082	60r. Trunk in snowy landscape (Winter)	1·10	1·10
1083	60r. Grapes (Autumn)	1·10	1·10

Nos. 1080/3 were issued together, se-tenant, forming a composite design.

347 Strontium

1994. Minerals. Multicoloured.

1084	60r. Type **347**	1·10	1·10
1085	80r. Quartz	1·50	1·50
1086	3f.50 Iron dolomite	5·50	5·50

348 "The True Light"

1994. Christmas. Multicoloured.

1087	60r. Type **348**	1·10	1·10
1088	80r. "Peace on Earth"	1·50	1·50
1089	1f. "Behold, the House of God"	1·80	1·80

349 Earth

1994. The Four Elements. Multicoloured.

1090	60r. Type **349**	1·10	1·10
1091	80r. Water	1·50	1·50
1092	1f. Fire	1·80	1·80
1093	2f.50 Air	4·25	4·25

350 "The Theme of all our Affairs must be Peace"

1995. Europa. Peace and Freedom. Quotations of Franz Josef II. Multicoloured.

1094	80r. Type **350**	1·50	1·50
1095	1f. "Through Unity comes Strength and the Bearing of Sorrows"	1·80	1·80

351 U.N. Flag and Bouquet of Flowers

1995. Anniversaries and Event. Multicoloured.

1096	60r. Princess Marie with children (50th anniv of Liechtenstein Red Cross) (horiz)	1·10	1·10
1097	1f.80 Type **351** (50th anniv of U.N.O.)	1·50	1·50
1098	3f.50 Alps (European Nature Conservation Year)	1·80	1·80

352 "Falknis Mountains"

1995. Birth Centenary of Anton Frommelt (painter). Multicoloured.

1099	60r. Type **352**	1·50	1·50
1100	80r. "Three Oaks"	1·80	1·80
1101	4f.10 "The Rhine"	7·00	7·00

353 "One Heart and One Soul"

1995. Greetings Stamps. Multicoloured.

1102	60r. Type **353**	1·10	1·10
1103	60r. Bandage round sunflower ("Get Well")	1·10	1·10
1104	60r. Baby arriving over rainbow ("Hurrah! Here I am")	1·10	1·10
1105	60r. Delivering letter by hot-air balloon ("Write again")	1·10	1·10

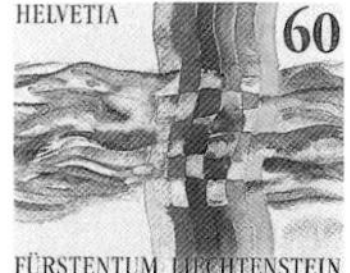

354 Coloured Ribbons woven through River

1995. Liechtenstein–Switzerland Co-operation.

1106	**354**	60r. multicoloured	1·10	1·10

No. 1106 was valid for use in both Liechtenstein and Switzerland (see No. 1308 of Switzerland).

355 Arnica

1995. Medicinal Plants. Multicoloured.

1107	60r. Type **355**	1·50	1·50
1108	80r. Giant nettle	1·80	1·80
1109	1f.80 Common valerian	3·25	3·25
1110	3f.50 Fig-wort	5·75	5·75

356 Angel (detail of painting)

1995. Christmas. Painting by Lorenzo Monaco. Multicoloured.

1111	60r. Type **356**	85	85
1112	80r. "Virgin Mary with Infant and Two Angels"	1·20	1·20
1113	1f. Angel facing left (detail of painting)	1·50	1·50

357 "Lady with Lap-dog" (Paul Wunderlich)

1995. Homage to Liechtenstein.

1114	**357**	4f. multicoloured	7·25	7·25

358 Eschen

1996. Scenes. Multicoloured.

1115	10r. Type **358**	20	20
1116	20r. Planken	30	30
1117	50r. Ruggell	85	85
1117a	60r. Balzers	1·10	1·10
1117b	70r. Schellenberg	1·70	1·70
1118	80r. Ruggell	1·20	1·20
1120	1f. Nendeln	1·50	1·50
1120a	1f.10 Eschen	2·00	1·50
1122	1f.20 Triesen	1·70	1·70
1123	1f.30 Triesen	1·90	1·90
1124	1f.40 Mauren	2·40	2·40
1125	1f.70 Schaanwald	2·50	2·50
1125a	1f.80 Malbun	3·25	3·25
1125b	1f.90 Schaan	3·50	3·50
1126	2f. Gamprin	3·00	3·00
1126a	2f.20 Balzers	6·00	6·00
1127	4f. Triesenberg	5·75	5·75
1127a	4f.50 Bendern	7·00	7·00
1128	5f. Vaduz Castle	7·25	7·25

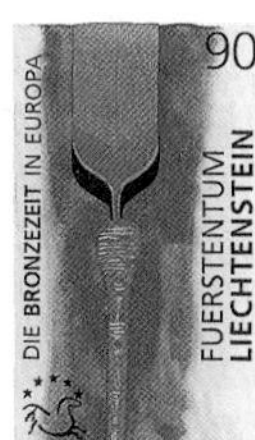

359 Crucible

1996. Bronze Age in Europe.

1130	**359**	90r. multicoloured	1·80	1·80

360 Kinsky and Diary Extract, 7 March 1917

1996. Europa. Famous Women. Nora, Countess Kinsky (mother of Princess Gina of Liechtenstein).

1131	**360**	90r. grey, purple and blue	1·80	1·80
1132	-	1f.10 grey, blue and purple	1·80	1·80

DESIGN: 1f.10, Kinsky and diary extract for 28 February 1917.

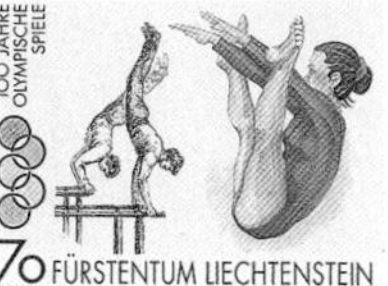

361 Gymnastics

1996. Centenary of Modern Olympic Games. Multicoloured.

1133	70r. Type **361**	1·50	1·50
1134	90r. Hurdling	1·90	1·90
1135	1f.10 Cycling	1·90	1·90

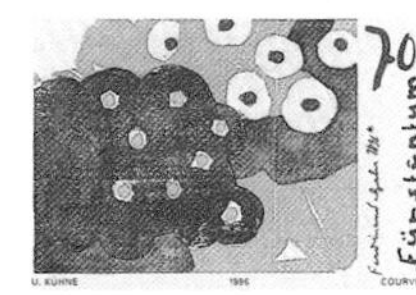

362 "Primroses"

1996. Birth Centenary of Ferdinand Gehr (painter). Multicoloured.

1136	70r. Type **362**	1·90	1·90
1137	90r. "Daisies"	1·90	1·90
1138	1f.10 "Poppy"	1·90	1·90
1139	1f.80 "Buttercups" (33×23 mm)	3·50	3·50

363 State Arms

1996

1140	**363**	10f. multicoloured	15·00	15·00

364 Veldkirch, 1550

1996. Millenary of Austria.

1141	**364**	90r. multicoloured	1·50	1·50

365 "Poltava"

1996. 43rd Death Anniv of Eugen Zotow (painter). Multicoloured.

1142	70r. Type **365**	1·50	1·50
1143	1f.10 "Three Bathers in a Berlin Park"	2·30	2·30
1144	1f.40 "Vaduz"	3·00	3·00

366 St. Matthew

1996. Christmas. Illustrations from Illuminated Manuscript "Liber Viventium Fabariensis". Multicoloured.

1145	70r. Type **366**	1·50	1·50
1146	90r. Emblems of St. Mark	1·70	1·70
1147	1f.10 Emblems of St. Luke	1·90	1·90
1148	1f.80 Emblems of St. John	3·50	3·50

367 Schubert

1997. Birth Bicent of Franz Schubert (composer).

1149	**367**	70r. multicoloured	1·50	1·50

368 The Wild Gnomes

1997. Europa. Tales and Legends. Multicoloured.

1150	90r. Type **368**	1·90	1·90
1151	1f.10 Man, pumpkin and rabbit (The Foal of Planken)	2·30	2·30

369 "Madonna and Child with St. Lucius and St. Florinus" (Gabriel Dreher)

1997. National Patron Saints.

1152	**369**	20f. multicoloured	43·00	43·00

370 "Phaeolepiota aurea"

1997. Fungi (1st series). Multicoloured.

1153	70r. Type **370**	1·50	1·50
1154	90r. "Helvella silvicola"	1·50	1·50
1155	1f.10 Orange peel fungus	2·30	2·30

See also Nos. 1238/40.

371 Steam Train, Schaanwald Halt

1997. 125th Anniv of Liechtenstein Railways. Mult.

1156	70r. Type **371**	1·50	1·50
1157	90r. Diesel-electric train, Nendeln station	2·30	2·30
1158	1f.80 Electric train, Schaan-Vaduz station	3·75	3·75

372 "Girl with Flower" (Enrico Baj)

1997. Homage to Liechtenstein.

1159	**372**	70r. multicoloured	1·50	1·50

373 Basket of Roses

1997. Christmas. Glass Tree Decorations. Multicoloured.

1160	70r. Type **373**	1·50	1·50
1161	90r. Bell	1·50	1·50
1162	1f.10 Bauble	2·30	2·30

374 Cross-country skiing

1997. Winter Olympic Games, Nagano, Japan (1998). Skiing. Multicoloured.

1163	70r. Type **374**	1·50	1·50
1164	90r. Slalom	1·90	1·90
1165	1f.80 Downhill	3·50	3·50

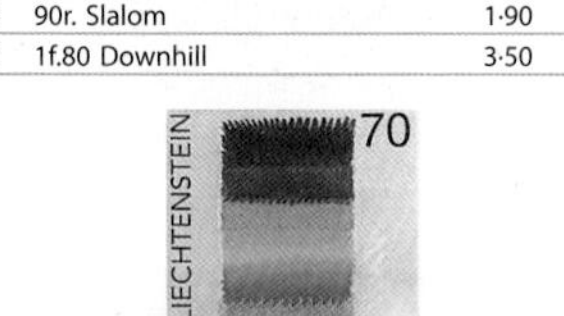
375 "Verano (The Summer)"

1998. Homage to Liechtenstein. Paintings by Heinz Mack. Multicoloured.

1166	70r. Type **375**	1·50	1·50
1167	70r. "Homage to Liechtenstein"	1·50	1·50
1168	70r. "Between Day and Dream"	1·50	1·50
1169	70r. "Salute Cirico!"	1·50	1·50

376 Prince's Festival Procession, Vaduz

1998. Europa. National Festivals. Multicoloured.

1170	90r. Type **376**	1·90	1·90
1171	1f.10 Music Societies Festival, Gutenberg Castle, Balzers	2·30	2·30

377 National Flags on Bridge

1998. 75th Anniv of Liechtenstein–Switzerland Customs Treaty.

1172	**377**	1f.70 multicoloured	3·00	3·00

378 Goalkeeper

1998. World Cup Football Championship, France.

1173	**378**	1f.80 multicoloured	3·00	3·00

379 Clown with Queen of Hearts

1998. Greeting Stamps. Clowns. Multicoloured.

1174	70r. Type **379**	1·50	1·50
1175	70r. Clown holding four-leaf clovers	1·50	1·50
1176	70r. Clown raising hat	1·50	1·50
1177	70r. Clown holding heart	1·50	1·50

380 Wooden Milk Vat

1998. Traditional Crafts (1st series). Multicoloured.

1178	90r. Type **380**	2·50	2·50
1179	2f.20 Clog	4·25	4·25
1180	3f.50 Wheel	6·00	6·00

See also Nos. 1257/9.

381 Expelling Johann Langer from Liechtenstein

1998. 150th Anniv of 1848 Revolutions in Europe.

1181	**381**	1f.80 multicoloured	3·75	3·75

382 Virgin Mary

1998. Christmas. Multicoloured.

1182	70r. Type **382**	1·50	1·50
1183	90r. "The Nativity" (35×26 mm)	1·90	1·90
1184	1f.10 Joseph	2·30	2·30

Nos. 1182 and 1184 show details of the complete relief depicted on No. 1183.

383 Zum Lowen Guest House

1998. Preservation of Historical Environment (1st series). Hinterschellenberg. Multicoloured.

1185	90r. Type **383**	1·90	1·90
1186	1f.70 St. George's Chapel (vert)	3·00	3·00
1187	1f.80 Houses	3·50	3·50

See also Nos. 1250/2, 1274/5, 1292/3, 1358/9, 1386/7, 1428/9, 1462/3 and 1498.

384 Automatic and Manual Switchboards

1998. Centenary of Telephone in Liechtenstein.

1188	**384**	2f.80 multicoloured	5·25	5·25

385 Eschen

1999. 300th Anniv of Purchase of Unterland by Prince Johann Adam. Sheet 107×68 mm containing T 385 and similar horiz design. Multicoloured.

MS1189	90r. ×5 plus label, Composite design of the Unterland showing the villages of Eschen, Gamprin, Mauren, Ruggell and Schellenberg	11·50	11·50

386 Smooth Snake and Schwabbrunnen-Aescher Nature Park

1999. Europa. Parks and Gardens. Multicoloured.

1190	90r. Type **386**	1·90	1·90
1191	1f.10 Corn crake and Ruggell marsh	2·30	2·30

387 Council Anniversary Emblem and Silhouettes

1999. Anniversaries and Event. Multicoloured.

1192	70r. Type **387** (50th anniv of Council of Europe and European Convention on Human Rights)	1·50	1·50
1193	70r. Bird with envelope in beak (125th anniv of U.P.U.)	1·50	1·50
1194	70r. Heart in hand (75th anniv of Caritas Liechtenstein (welfare organization))	1·50	1·50

388 Judo

1999. 8th European Small States Games, Liechtenstein. Multicoloured.

1195	70r. Type **388**	1·50	1·50
1196	70r. Swimming	1·50	1·50
1197	70r. Throwing the javelin	1·50	1·50
1198	90r. Cycling	1·90	1·90
1199	90r. Shooting	1·90	1·90
1200	90r. Tennis	1·90	1·90
1201	90r. Squash	1·90	1·90
1202	90r. Table tennis	1·90	1·90
1203	90r. Volleyball	1·90	1·90

389 "Herrengasse"

1999. Paintings by Eugen Verling. Multicoloured.

1204	70r. Type **389**	1·50	1·50
1205	2f. "Old Vaduz with Castle"	3·75	3·75
1206	4f. "House in Furst-Franz-Josef Street, Vaduz"	7·50	7·50

390 Scene from "Faust", Act I

1999. 250th Birth Anniv of Johann Wolfgang Goethe (poet and playwright). Multicoloured.

1207	1f.40 Type **390**	3·00	3·00
1208	1f.70 Faust and the Devil sealing wager	3·75	3·75

391 "The Annunciation"

1999. Christmas. Paintings by Joseph Walser from Chapel of Our Lady of Comfort, Dux. Mult.

1209	70r. Type **391**	1·50	1·50
1210	90r. "Nativity"	1·90	1·90
1211	1f.10 "Adoration"	2·30	2·30

392 Identification Mark on Door, Ubersaxen

1999. Walser Identification Marks. Multicoloured.

1212	70r. Type **392**	1·50	1·50
1213	90r. Mark on mural	1·90	1·90
1214	1f.80 Mark on axe	3·50	3·50

393 Gutenberg

1999. 600th Birth Anniv of Johannes Gutenberg (inventor of printing press).

1215	**393**	3f.60 multicoloured	7·50	7·50

394 "The Adoration of the Shepheards" (Matthia Stomer)

2000. 2000 Years of Christianity. Sheet 108×68 mm containing T 394 and similar square design. Multicoloured.

MS1216	70r. Type **394**; 1f.10 "Three Kings" (Ferdinand Gehr)	4·50	4·50

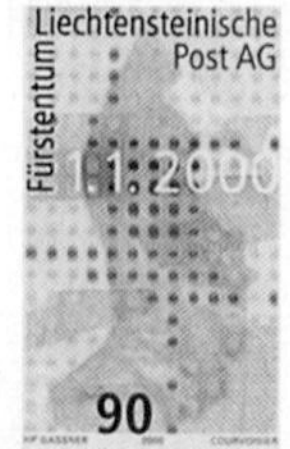
395 Emblem

2000. Provision of Postal Services by Liechtenstein Post in Partnership with Swiss Post.

1217	**395**	90r. multicoloured	1·70	1·70

396 "Mars and Rhea Silvia" (Peter Paul Rubens)

2000. Paintings. Multicoloured.

1218	70r. Type **396**	1·40	1·40
1219	1f.80 "Cupid with Soap-Bubble" (Rembrandt)	3·50	3·50

397 "Fragrance of Humus"

2000. "EXPO 2000" World's Fair, Hanover, Germany. Paintings by Friedensreich Hundertwasser. Multicoloured.

1220	70r. Type **397**	1·40	1·40
1221	90r. "Do Not Wait Houses-Move"	1·70	1·70
1222	1f.10 "The Car: a Drive Towards Nature and Creation"	2·00	2·10

398 "Building Europe"

2000. Europa.

1223	**398**	1f.10 multicoloured	2·10	2·10

399 "Dove of Peace" (Antonio Martini)

2000. "Peace 2000". Paintings by members of Association of Mouth and Foot Painting Artists. Mult.
1224 1f.40 Type **399** 2·75 2·75
1225 1f.70 "World Peace" (Alberto Alvarez) 3·25 3·25
1226 2f.20 "Rainbow" (Eiichi Minami) 4·25 4·25

400 Koalas on Rings (Gymnastics)

2000. Olympic Games, Sydney. Multicoloured.
1227 80r. Type **400** 1·50 1·50
1228 1f. Joey leaping over crossbar (High jump) 1·90 1·90
1229 1f.30 Emus approaching finish line (Athletics) 2·40 2·40
1230 1f.80 Duckbill platypuses in swimming race 3·50 3·50

401 "The Dreaming Bee" (Joan Miro)

2000. Inauguration of Art Museum. Multicoloured.
1231 80r. Type **401** 1·50 1·50
1232 1f.20 "Cube" (Sol LeWitt) 2·30 2·30
1233 2f. "Bouquet of Flowers" (Roelant Savery) (31×46 mm) 3·75 3·75

402 "Peace Doves"

2000. 25th Anniv of Organization for Security and Co-operation in Europe.
1234 **402** 1f.30 multicoloured 2·40 2·40

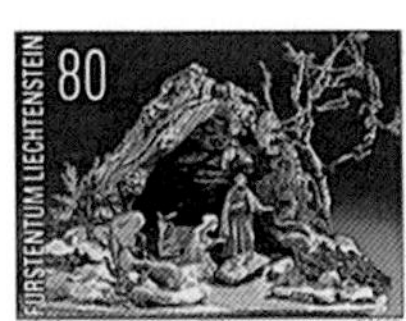

403 Root Crib

2000. Christmas. Cribs. Multicoloured.
1235 80r. Type **403** 1·50 1·50
1236 1f.30 Oriental crib 2·40 2·40
1237 1f.80 Crib with cloth figures 3·50 3·50

2000. Fungi (2nd series). As T 370. Multicoloured.
1238 90r. Mycena adonis 1·70 1·70
1239 1f.10 Chalciporus amarellus 2·10 2·10
1240 2f. Pink waxcap 3·75 3·75

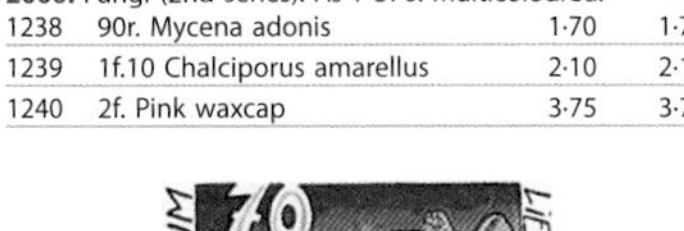

404 Postman delivering Parcel

2001. Greetings Stamps. Multicoloured.
1241 70r. Type **404** 1·40 1·40
1242 70r. Postman delivering flowers 1·40 1·40
Nos. 1241/2 are for the stamps with the parcel (1241) and flowers (1242) intact. The parcel and flowers can be scratched away to reveal a greetings message.

405 Silver Easter Egg

2001. Decorated Easter Eggs. Multicoloured.
1243 1f.20 Type **405** 2·30 2·30
1244 1f.80 Cloissonne egg 3·50 3·50
1245 2f. Porcelain egg 3·75 3·75

406 Mountain Spring

2001. Europa. Water Resources.
1246 **406** 1f.30 multicoloured 2·40 2·40

407 Emblem

2001. Liechtenstein Presidency of Council of Europe.
1247 **407** 1f.80 multicoloured 3·50 3·50

408 Carolingian Cruciform Fibula

2001. Centenary of Historical Association. Multicoloured.
1248 70r. Type **408** 1·40 1·40
1249 70r. "Mars of Gutenberg" (statue) 1·40 1·40

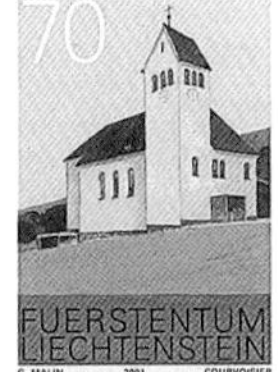

409 St. Theresa's Chapel, Schaanwald

2001. Preservation of Historical Environment (2nd series). Multicoloured.
1250 70r. Type **409** 1·40 1·40
1251 90r. St. Johann's Torkel (wine press), Mauren 1·70 1·70
1252 1f.10 Pirsch Transformer Station, Schaanwald 2·10 2·10

410 Mary and kneeling Votant (Chapel of Our Lady, Dux, Schann)

2001. Votive Paintings. Multicoloured.
1253 70r. Type **410** 1·50 1·50
1254 1f.20 Mary and Jesus, St. George among other Saints, and text of vow (St. George's Chapel, Schellenberg) 2·30 2·30
1255 1f.30 Mary, St. Joseph of Arimathea, St. Christopher, Johann Christoph Walser (votant) and text of vow (Chapel of Our Lady, Dux, Schann) 2·30 2·30

411 Rheinberger and Scene from *Zauberwort* (song cycle)

2001. Death Centenary of Josef Gabriel Rheinberger (composer).
1256 **411** 3f.50 multicoloured 6·75 6·75

2001. Traditional Crafts (2nd series). As T 380. Multicoloured.
1257 70r. Agricultural implements and horseshoe 1·40 1·40
1258 90r. Rake 1·70 1·70
1259 1f.20 Harness 2·30 2·30

412 "Annunciation"

2001. Christmas. Medallions from The Joyful, Sorrowful and Glorious Rosary Cycle. Multicoloured.
1260 70r. Type **412** 1·40 1·40
1261 90r. Nativity 1·70 1·70
1262 1f.30 Presentation of Jesus at the Temple 2·40 2·40

413 Square

2001. Paintings by Gottfried Honeggar. Mult.
1263 1f.80 Type **413** 3·50 3·50
1264 2f.20 Circle 4·25 4·25

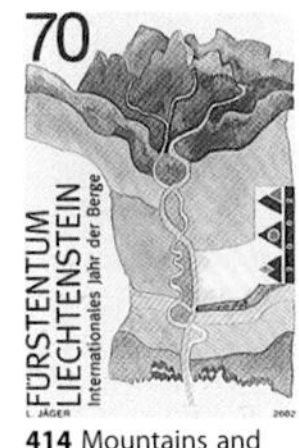

414 Mountains and River

2002. International Year of Mountains and 50th Anniv of the International Commission of Alpine Protection. Multicoloured.
1265 70r. Type **414** 90 90
1266 1f.20 Stylized mountains 2·30 2·30

415 "Schellenberg"

2002. 30th Death Anniv of Friedrich Kaufmann (artist). Multicoloured.
1267 70r. Type **415** 1·40 1·40
1268 1f.30 "Schaan" 2·40 2·40
1269 1f.80 "Steg" 3·50 3·50

416 Space Shuttle and Bee

2002. Liechtenstein's participation in N.A.S.A. Space Technology and Research Students Project.
1270 **416** 90r. multicoloured 1·70 1·70
The project submitted by the Liechtenstein Gymnasium concerned the study of the effects of space on carpenter bees.

417 Man on Tightrope

2002. Europa. Circus. Multicoloured.
1271 90r. Type **417** 1·70 1·70
1272 1f.30 Juggler 2·40 2·40

418 Emblem

2002. "Liba '02" National Stamp Exhibition, Vaduz (1st issue).
1273 **418** 1f.20 multicoloured 2·30 2·30
See also Nos. 1282/3 and 1318/20.

419 Houses, Popers

2002. Preservation of Historical Environment (2nd series). Multicoloured.
1274 70r. Type **419** 1·40 1·40
1275 1f.20 House, Weiherring 3·25 3·00

420 Footballers

2002. World Cup Football Championship, Japan and South Korea.
1276 **420** 1f.80 multicoloured 3·75 3·50

421 Princess Marie

2002. The Royal Couple. Multicoloured.
1277 3f. Type **421** 5·75 5·75
1278 3f.50 Prince Hans-Adam II 6·75 6·75

422 Ghost Orchid (*Epipogium aphyllum*)

2002. Orchids. Multicoloured.
1279 70r. Type **422** 1·40 1·40
1280 1f.20 Fly orchid (*Ophrys insectifera*) 2·30 2·30
1281 1f.30 Black vanilla orchid (*Nigritella nigra*) 2·40 2·40

423 Stamps and Emblem

2002. "Liba 02" National Stamp Exhibition, Vaduz (2nd issue). 90th Anniv of First Liechtenstein Stamps. Multicoloured.

1282	90r. Type **423**	1·70	1·70
1283	1f.30 Stamps showing royal family	2·40	2·40

424 Princess Sophie

2002. Prince Alois and Princess Sophie. Multicoloured.

1284	2f. Type **424**	3·75	3·75
1285	2f.50 Prince Alois	4·75	4·75

425 Mary and Joseph

2002. Christmas. Batik. Multicoloured.

1286	70r. Type **425**	1·40	1·40
1287	1f.20 Nativity	1·50	1·50
1288	1f.80 Flight into Egypt	3·50	3·50

426 The Eagle, Vaduz

2002. Inn Signs. Multicoloured.

1289	1f.20 Type **426**	2·30	2·30
1290	1f.80 The Angel, Balzers	3·50	3·50
1291	3f. The Eagle, Bendern	5·75	5·75

427 St. Fridolin Parish Church

2003. Preservation of Historical Environment (3rd series). Multicoloured.

1292	70r. Type **427**	1·40	1·40
1293	2f.50 House, Spidach (horiz)	4·75	4·75

428 Postal Emblem

2003. Europa. Poster Art.

1294	**428**	1f.20 multicoloured	2·30	2·30

429 Pruning Vines

2003. Viticulture (1st issue). Multicoloured.

1295	1f.30 Type **429**	2·30	2·30
1296	1f.80 Tying up vines	3·50	3·50
1297	2f.20 Hoeing	6·75	6·75

See also Nos. 1301/3, 1304/6 and 1312/14.

430 Bridge

2003. 50th Anniv of Liechtenstein Association for the Disabled.

1298	**430**	70r. multicoloured	1·70	1·70

431 Renovated Buildings and Ammonite

2003. Renovation of National Museum. Multicoloured.

1299	1f.20 Type **431**	2·75	2·75
1300	1f.30 Verweserhaus building and bailiff's shield	3·00	3·00

2003. Viticulture (2nd issue). As T 429. Multicoloured.

1301	1f.20 Looping the tendrils	2·75	2·75
1302	1f.80 Removing leaves from around grapes	4·25	4·25
1303	3f.50 Reducing top growth	8·50	8·50

2003. Viticulture (3rd issue). As T 429. Multicoloured.

1304	70r. Thinning out	1·70	1·70
1305	90r. Harvesting	2·00	2·00
1306	1f.10 Pressing the grapes	2·75	2·75

432 St. George

2003. Saints (1st series). Multicoloured.

1307	1f.20 Type **432**	2·75	2·75
1308	1f.20 St. Blaise	2·75	2·75
1309	1f.30 St. Vitus	3·00	3·00
1310	1f.30 St. Erasmus	3·00	3·00

See also Nos. 1323/8.

433 Parents and Young on Nest

2003. Conservation of White Storks in Rhine Valley.

1311	**433**	2f.20 multicoloured	5·00	5·00

2003. Viticulture (4th issue). As T 429. Multicoloured.

1312	70r. Tasting	1·70	1·70
1313	90r. Harvesting ice-wine grapes	2·00	2·00
1314	1f.20 Bottling	2·75	2·75

434 Archangel Gabriel appearing to Mary

2003. Christmas. Multicoloured.

1315	70r. Type **434**	1·70	1·70
1316	90r. Nativity	2·00	2·00
1317	1f.30 Three Kings	3·00	3·00

435 Cow (Laura Beck)

2003. "Liba 02" National Stamp Exhibition, Vaduz (3rd issue). Children's Drawing Competition Winners. Multicoloured.

1318	70r. Type **435**	1·70	1·70
1319	1f.80 Bee (Laura Lingg)	3·75	3·75
1320	1f.80 Apple tree (Patrick Marxer) (vert)	3·75	3·75

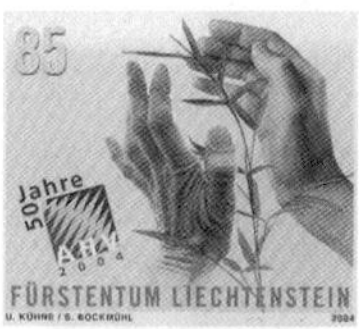

436 Hands enclosing Leaves

2004. 50th Anniv of AHV (retirement Insurance).

1321	**436**	85r. multicoloured	1·80	1·80

437 Hot Air Balloon

2004. Europa. Holidays.

1322	**437**	1f.30 multicoloured	2·75	2·75

2004. Saints (2nd series). As T 432. Multicoloured.

1323	1f. St. Achatius	2·10	2·10
1324	1f. St. Margaret	2·10	2·10
1325	1f.20 St. Christopher	2·75	2·75
1326	1f.20 St. Pantaleon	2·75	2·75
1327	2f.50 St. Cyriacus	5·00	5·00
1328	2f.50 St. Aegidius	5·00	5·00

438 Bendern

2004. Tourism. Aerial views of Liechtenstein. Multicoloured.

1329	15r. Type **438**	40	40
1330	85r. Gross-Teg	1·80	1·80
1331	1f. Tuass	2·00	2·00
1332	1f.50 Oberland	3·50	3·50
1333	1f.60 Ruggeller Riet	3·50	3·50
1334	2f.50 Canal	4·50	4·50
1335	3f. Naafkopf	5·50	5·50
1336	3f.50 Rhine Valley	6·50	6·50
1340	6f. Gutenberg	11·00	11·00

439 Olympic Torch

2004. Olympic Games, Athens 2004.

1350	**439**	85r. multicoloured	2·20	2·20

440 Bee Orchid (*Ophrys apifera*)

2004. Orchids. Multicoloured.

1351	85r. Type **440**	1·80	1·80
1352	1f. *Orchis ustulata*	2·00	2·00
1353	1f.20 *Epipactis purpurata*	2·40	2·40

441 Mathematical Symbols

2004. Science. Multicoloured.

1354	85r. Type **441**	1·80	1·80
1355	1f. Atomic diagram (physics)	2·00	2·00
1356	1f.30 Molecular structure (chemistry)	2·75	2·75
1357	1f.80 Star map and Saturn (astronomy)	3·75	3·75

442 Two-storied House on Unterdorfstrasse (street)

2004. Preservation of Historical Environment (4th series). Multicoloured.

1358	2f.20 Type **442**	4·25	4·25
1359	2f.50 Unterdorfstrasse (street)	4·50	4·50

443 The Annunciation

2004. Christmas. Multicoloured.

1360	85r. Type **443**	1·80	1·80
1361	1f. Nativity	2·10	2·10
1362	1f.80 Adoration of the Magi	4·25	4·25

444 Ammonite

2004. Fossils. Multicoloured.

1363	1f.20 Type **444**	2·75	2·75
1364	1f.30 Sea urchin	3·00	3·00
1365	2f.20 Shark's tooth	4·75	4·75

445 Map of Europe as Manuscript (emblem of Rinascimento Virtuale)

2004. Rinascimento Virtuale (Europe-wide co-operation in digital palimpsest (old manuscripts) research).

1366	**445**	2f.50 multicoloured	5·50	5·50

2005. Saints (2nd issue). As T 432. Multicoloured.

1367	85r. St. Eustachius	1·80	1·80
1368	85r. St. Dionysius	1·80	1·80
1369	1f.80 St. Barbara	3·75	3·75
1370	1f.80 St. Katharina	3·75	3·75

446 Female Customer, Waiters and Chef

2005. Europa. Gastronomy.

1371	**446**	1f.30 multicoloured	2·75	2·75

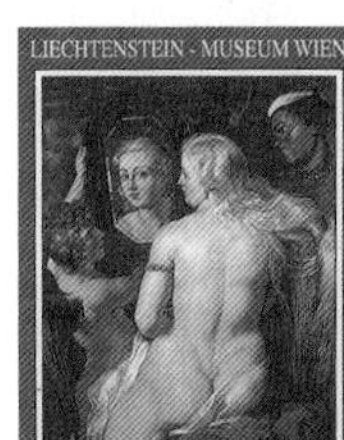
447 "Venus in Front of the Mirror" (Peter Paul Rubens)

2005. Liechtenstein Museum, Garden Palace, Vienna.

1372	**447**	2f.20 multicoloured	5·50	5·50

A stamp of the same design was issued by Austria.

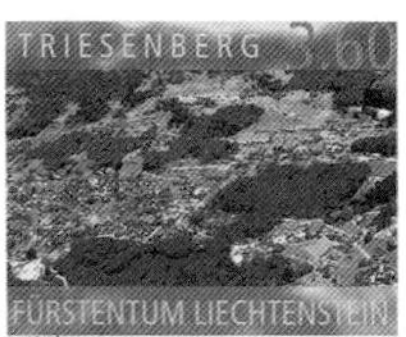
448 Triesenberg

2005. Tourism.

1373	**448**	3f.60 multicoloured	7·75	7·75

449 "Flower Vase in a Window Niche" (Ambrosius Bosschaert)

2005. Paintings. Multicoloured.

1374	85r. Type **449**	2·10	2·10
1375	85r. "Magnolias" (Chen Hongshou)	2·10	2·10

Stamps of a similar design were issued by People's Republic of China.

450 Rossle, Schaan

2005. Inn Signs. Multicoloured.

1376	1f. Type **450**	2·10	2·10
1377	1f.40 Edelweiss, Triesenberg	3·00	3·00
1378	2f.50 Lowen, Bendern	5·25	5·25

451 Herman Sieger (founder)

2005. 75th Anniv of Postal Museum. Multicoloured.

1379	1f.10 Type **451**	2·40	2·40
1380	1f.30 Stamps	2·75	2·75
1381	1f.80 Postcard sent by Zeppelin mail	3·75	3·75

452 Bargalla

2005. Alpine Pastures. Multicoloured.

1382	85r. Type **452**	1·80	1·80
1383	1f. Pradamee	2·10	2·10
1384	1f.30 Gritsch	2·75	2·75
1385	1f.80 Valuna	4·00	4·00

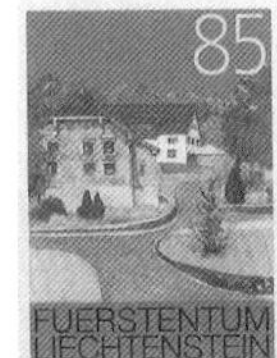
453 Oberbendern

2005. Preservation of Historical Environment (5th series). Multicoloured.

1386	85r. Type **453**	1·80	1·80
1387	2f.50 Schwurplatz	4·75	4·75

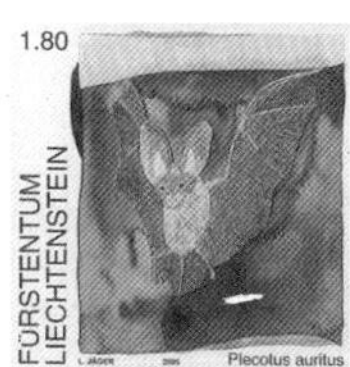
454 *Plecotus auritus*

2005. Bats. Multicoloured.

1388	1f.80 Type **454**	4·00	4·00
1389	2f. *Myotis myotis*	4·25	4·25

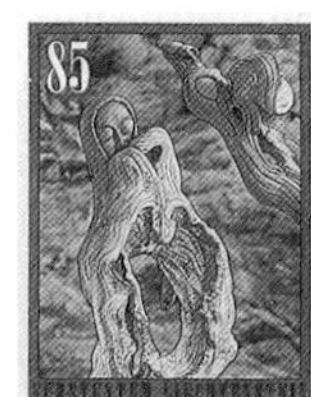
455 Virgin and Child

2005. Christmas. Wood Carvings by Toni Gstohl. Multicoloured.

1390	85r. Type **455**	1·80	1·80
1391	1f. Holy family	2·10	2·10
1392	1f.30 Three Kings	3·00	3·00

456 Skier and Angel

2005. Winter Olympic Games, Turin. Multicoloured.

1393	1f.20 Type **456**	2·75	2·75
1394	1f.30 Cross country skier and wild boar	3·00	3·00
1395	1f.40 Slalom skier	3·25	3·25

457 "Peat Cutters"

2006. Eugen Wilhelm Schüepp (artist) Commemoration. Paintings. Multicoloured.

1396	1f. Type **457**	2·10	2·10
1397	1f.80 "Neugut, Schaan"	4·00	4·00

458 Bridge (Nadja Beck)

2006. Europa. Integration. Winning Entries in Children's Painting Competition. Multicoloured.

1398	1f.20 Type **458**	3·00	2·75
1399	1f.30 Face (Elisabeth Mussner)	2·75	2·75

459 "Lost in her Dreams" (Friedrich von Amerling)

2006. Liechtenstein Museum, Garden Palace, Vienna.

1400	**459**	2f.20 multicoloured	4·75	4·75

A stamp of the same design was issued by Austria.

460 Prince Johann I

2006. Bicentenary of Sovereignty. Multicoloured.

1401	85r. Type **460**	1·80	1·80
1402	1f. National colours	2·10	2·10
1403	1f.20 Ruling house colours	2·75	2·75
1404	1f.80 State arms	4·00	4·00

461 Woman holding Base Clef (culture)

2006. Tourism. Multicoloured.

1405	85r. Type **461**	1·80	1·80
1406	1f. Hiker (summer)	2·10	2·10
1407	1f.20 Diner (hospitality)	2·75	2·75
1408	1f.80 Skier (winter)	4·00	4·00

462 Players on Field

2006. World Cup Football Championship, Germany.

1409	**462**	3f.30 multicoloured	7·25	7·25

2006. Alpine Pastures. As T 452. Multicoloured.

1410	85r. Lawena	1·80	1·80
1411	1f.30 Gapfahl	2·75	2·75
1412	2f.40 Gafadura	5·25	5·25

463 "The Magic Flute" (Wolfgang Amadeus Mozart)

2006. Composers and Works. Multicoloured.

1413	1f. Type **463**	2·10	2·10
1414	1f. "Radetzky March" (Johann Strauss Sr.)	2·10	2·10
1415	1f. "Rhapsody in Blue" (George Gershwin)	2·10	2·10
1416	1f. "Water Music" (George Frideric Handel)	2·10	2·10
1417	1f. "Pastoral Symphony" (Ludwig van Beethoven)	2·10	2·10
1418	1f. "Waltz of the Flowers" (Pytor Ilyich Tchaikovsky)	2·10	2·10
1419	1f. "The Swan" (Camille Saint-Saens)	2·10	2·10
1420	1f. "Midsummer Night's Dream" (Felix Mendelssohn)	2·10	2·10

464 Mozart

2006. 250th Birth Anniv of Wolfgang Amadeus Mozart.

1421	**464**	1f.20 multicoloured	2·75	2·75

465 The Annunciation

2006. Christmas. Paintings from Chapel of St. Mary, Dux. Multicoloured.

1422	85r. Type **465**	1·80	1·80
1423	1f. The Nativity	2·10	2·10
1424	1f.30 Presentation of Jesus	2·75	2·75

466 Curta Calculator

2006. Technical Innovations. Multicoloured.

1425	1f.30 Type **466**	2·75	2·75
1426	1f.40 Carrana narrow film camera	3·25	3·25
1427	2f.40 PVA sliding calliper	5·25	5·25

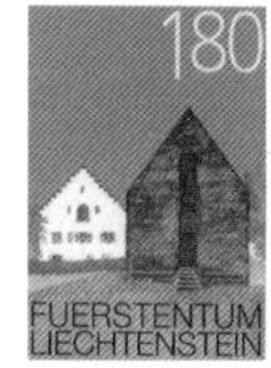
467 Governor's Residence and Liechtenstein Institute

2006. Preservation of Historical Environment (6th series). Multicoloured.

1428	1f.80 Type **467**	4·00	4·00
1429	3f.50 Buhl, Gamprin	7·50	7·50

468 Violinist (Allegro)

2007. Music. Tempo and Temperament. Mult.

1430	85r. Type **468**	1·80	1·80
1431	1f.80 Gramophone and flying music sheets (Capriccio)	3·75	3·75
1432	2f. Brass players (Crescendo)	4·25	4·25
1433	3f.50 Pianist and flaming piano (Con fuoco)	7·00	7·00

469 Trail Sign ("This Way")

2007. Europa. Centenary of Scouting.

1434	**469**	1f.30 multicoloured	2·75	2·75

470 "Portrait of a Lady" (Bernardino Zaganelli da Cottignola)

2007. Liechtenstein Museum, Garden Palace, Vienna.

1435	**470**	2f.40 multicoloured	5·00	5·00

A stamp of a similar design was issued by Austria.

471 Letter Post

2007. Greetings Cards. Multicoloured.

1436	85r. Type **471**	1·80	1·80
1437	1f. Boys carrying bier containing envelope (courier post)	2·10	2·10
1438	1f.30 Swallow holding envelope (airmail)	2·75	2·75

472 Castle and Vaduz

2007. Tourism. The Rhine. Paintings by Johann Ludwig Bleuler. Multicoloured.

1439	1f. Type **472**	2·10	2·10
1440	1f.30 Ratikon mountains	2·75	2·75
1441	2f.40 Confluence of Ill and Rhine	4·75	4·75

473 Nendeln

2007. Tourism. Liechtenstein from the Air. Mult.

1442	1f.10 Type **473**	2·40	2·40
1443	1f.80 Malbun	3·75	3·75
1444	2f.60 Arable land	5·50	5·50

474 *Trichodes apiarius* (bee beetle)

2007. Insects. Multicoloured.

1445	85r. Type **474**	2·20	2·20
1446	1f. *Cetonia aurata* (rose chafer)	2·50	2·50
1447	1f.30 *Dytiscus marginalis* (great diving beetle)	3·25	3·25

2007. Alpine Pastures. As T 452. Multicoloured.

1448	1f. Hintervalorsch	2·30	2·30
1449	1f.40 Sucka	3·00	3·00
1450	2f.20 Guschfiel	4·75	4·75

2007. Technical Innovations. As T 466. Mult.

1451	1f.30 Hilti hammer and drill	3·00	3·00
1452	1f.80 Kaiser walking excavator	4·00	4·00
1453	2f.40 aluFer heating surface	5·50	5·50

475 Liechtenstein from the Air

2007. SEPAC (small European mail services).

1454	**475**	1f.30 multicoloured	3·00	3·00

476 St Mary Chapel, Gamprin-Oberbuhl

2007. Christmas. Multicoloured.

1455	85r. Type **476**	2·00	2·00
1456	1f. Buel Chapel, Eschen	2·30	2·30
1457	1f.30 St Wolfgang Chapel, Triesen	3·00	3·00

477 Rainbow over Three Sisters Massif

2007. Natural Phenomena. Multicoloured.

1458	85r. Type **477**	2·00	2·00
1459	1f. Lightning over Bendern	2·30	2·30
1460	1f.80 Halo over Malbun	4·00	4·00

478 Landtagsgebaude (designed by Hansjorg Goritz)

2007. Architecture. New Parliament Building, Vaduz.

1461	**478**	1f.30 multicoloured	3·00	3·00

479 St Martin's Church

2007. Preservation of Historical Environment (7th series). Multicoloured.

1462	2f. Type **479**	4·50	4·50
1463	2f.70 Eschen Mill, St Martinsring (horiz)	6·00	6·00

480 Industrial Buildings, Spoerry-Areal, Vaduz (industry)

2008. National Identity. Liechtenstein as Brand (1st series). Multicoloured.

1464	85r. Type **480**	2·20	2·20
1465	1f. St Mamertus Chapel, Triesen (homeland)	2·50	2·50
1466	1f.30 Vaduz Castle (monarchy)	3·25	3·25

481 Firefighters

2008. Volunteer Civil Protection (1st issue). Volunteer Fire Service.

1467	**481**	1f. multicoloured	2·50	2·50

482 *Princess Marie Franziska von Liechtenstein* (Friedrich von Amerling)

2008. Liechtenstein Museum, Garden Palace, Vienna.

1468	**482**	2f.40 multicoloured	6·00	6·00

A stamp of a similar design was issued by Austria.

483 Script

2008. Europa. The Letter.

1469	**483**	1f.30 multicoloured	3·25	3·25

2008. Alpine Pastures. As T 452. Multicoloured.

1470	2f.60 Schaan, Guschg	6·25	6·25
1471	3f. Balzers, Guschgle	7·50	7·50

484 Huanhuan and Jingjing (martial arts)

2008. Olympic Games, Beijing. Multicoloured.

1472	85c. Type **484**	2·20	2·20
1473	1f. Huanhuan and Yingying (football and table tennis)	2·50	2·50

485 *Osmia brevicornis*

2008. Endangered Insects. Multicoloured.

1474	85c. Type **485**	2·20	2·20
1475	1f. *Epeoloides coecutiens*	2·50	2·50
1476	1f.30 *Odynerus spinipes*	3·25	3·25

486 Marathon

2008. Paralympics, Beijing. Stylized athletes. Multicoloured.

1477	1f.30 Type **486**	3·25	3·25
1478	1f. 80 Table tennis	4·75	4·75

487 St. Stephen's Cathedral (Austria)

2008. EURO 2008 Football Championships. Multicoloured.

1479	1f.30 Type **487**	3·25	3·25
1480	1f.30 Flag, dancer and musician (Liechtenstein)	3·25	3·25
1481	1f.30 Alphorn and Matterhorn (Switzerland)	3·25	3·25

488 *Mother and Queen of the Precious Blood*

2008. 150th Anniv of Schellenberg Convent.

1482	**488**	2f.20 multicoloured	6·00	6·00

489 *Schoolmaster Lampel*

2008. Death Centenary of Heinrich Christian William Busch (writer and cartoonist). Multicoloured.

1483	1f.30 Type **489**	3·25	3·25
1484	1f.30 *Hans Huckebein*	3·25	3·25
1485	1f.30 *Max and Moritz*	3·25	3·25
1486	1f.30 *Widow Bolte*	3·25	3·25
1487	1f.30 *Pious Helen*	3·25	3·25
1488	1f.30 *Fips the Monkey*	3·25	3·25
1489	1f.30 *Tailor Bock*	3·25	3·25
1490	1f.30 *Balduin Bahlamm*	3·25	3·25

490 Karl I of Liechtenstein

2008. 400th Anniv of Princes of Liechtenstein. Sheet 58×77 mm.

MS1491	**490**	5f. multicoloured	13·00	13·00

The stamp and margin of **MS**1491 form a composite design of painting.

491 Candle Wreath

2008. Christmas. Multicoloured.

1492	85r. Type **491**	2·40	2·40
1493	1f. Children carrying holly (horiz)	2·75	2·75
1494	1f.30 Decorated tree	3·75	3·75

2008. Technical Innovations. As T 466. Multicoloured.

1495	1f.20 Neutrik XLR cable connector NC3MX	3·25	3·25
1496	1f.40 Ivoclar Vivadent blue phase polymerisation unit	3·50	3·50
1497	2f.20 ThyssenKrupp Presta DeltaValve control	6·50	6·50

492 Schadler Ceramics Building, Nendeln

2008. Preservation of Historical Environment (8th series).

1498	**492**	3f.80 multicoloured	10·50	10·50

493 Postworker accepting Parcel

2009. Postal Service. Multicoloured.

1499	85c. Type **493**	2·75	2·75
1500	1f. Delivering	3·25	3·25
1501	1f.30 Sorting	4·25	4·25

494 First Aid

2009. Volunteer Civil Portection (2nd series). Association of Liechtenstein Samaritan Volunteers.

1502	**494**	1f. multicoloured	3·25	3·25

495 *Unfolding* (woman and butterfly)

2009. Artistic Techniques. Linocuts by Stephan Sude.

1503	1f. black and pink	3·25	3·25
1504	1f.30 black and olive	4·25	4·25
1505	2f.70 black and blue	8·00	8·00

DESIGNS: 1f. Type **495**; 1f.30 *Awareness* (man crying); 2f.70 *Fulfilment*(elderly man and mountains).

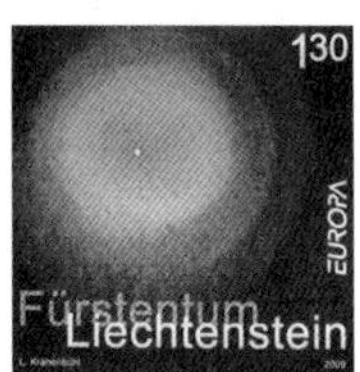

496 Super Nova (Leta Krahenbuhl)

2009. Europa. Astronomy.

1506	**496**	1f.30 multicoloured	4·25	4·25

497 Land Register

2009. Bicentenary of Land Register.

1507	**497**	3f.30 multicoloured	10·50	10·50

498 Ants and Forest

2009. Forest. Multicoloured.

1508	85c. Type **498**	2·75	1·90
1509	1f. Path through woods	3·25	2·50
1510	1f.40 Tree and rock	4·50	3·00
1511	1f.60 Mountain, lake and log pile	5·00	3·50

499 Summit Cross, Kuegrat

2009. Centenary of Alpine Association. Designs showing summit crosses. Multicoloured.

1512	1f. Type **499**	3·25	2·50
1513	1f.30 Langspitz (vert)	4·25	2·75
1514	2f.20 Rappastein (vert)	6·75	5·25
1515	2f.40 Jahn-Turm und Wolan	7·25	5·25

500 Vaduz Castle in Spring

2009. Vaduz Castle through the Seasons. Multicoloured.

1516	1f.30 Type **500**	4·25	2·75
1517	1f.80 In summer	5·50	3·75

501 *Pieris rapae*

2009. Butterflies. Multicoloured.

1518	85c. Type **501**	1·90	1·90
1519	1f. *Parnassius apollo*	2·50	2·50
1520	1f.30 *Melanargia galathea*	2·75	2·75
1521	2f. *Vanessa atlanta*	5·00	5·00

502 Emblem

2009. 75th Anniv of Liechtenstein Philatelic Society.

1522	**502**	1f.30 multicoloured	2·75	2·75

503 Badminton Cabinet (detail)

2009. Liechtenstein Museum, Garden Palace, Vienna. Designs showing details of Badminton Cabinet. Multicoloured.

1523	1f.30 Type **503**	2·75	2·75
1524	2f. Three birds and bouquet (detail centre) (34×49 mm)	4·50	4·50
1525	4f. Red-capped bird and lilies (detail left)	8·50	8·50

504 Chapel of St. Mamerta, Trisien

2009. SEPAC (small European mail services).

1526	**504**	1f.30 multicoloured	2·50	2·50

505 Lifestyle Museum, Schellenberg

2009. National Identity. Liechtenstein as Brand (2nd series). Multicoloured.

1527	20r. Type **505** (community)	70	70
1528	50r. Former Customs House, Vaduz (finance)	90	90
1529	60r. Parish House, Bendern (dialogue)	1·00	1·00

506 Annunciation

2009. Christmas. Advent Windows created by Pupils of Primary School, Gamprin. Multicoloured.

1530	85r. Type **506**	90	90
1531	1f. Journey to Bethlehem	1·50	1·50
1532	1f.30 The Nativity	1·70	1·70
1533	1f.80 The Three Magi	1·90	1·90

507 University of Applied Sciences (Karl+Probst), Vaduz

2009. Modern Architecture (1st issue). Multicoloured.

1534	85r. Type **507**	90	90
1535	2f.60 Art Museum (Morger, Degelo and Kerez), Vaduz	4·50	4·50
1536	3f.50 Ruggell–Nofels Border Crossing between Liechtenstein and Austria (EFFEFF)	5·50	5·50

508 Alpine Skier

2010. Winter Olympic Games, Vancouver. Multicoloured.

1537	1f. Type **508**	3·25	3·25
1538	1f.80 Nordic skier	3·75	3·75

509 Mountain Rescue (Liechtenstein Mountain Rescue (founded by Liechtenstein Alpine Association))

2010. Volunteer Civil Protection (3rd series). Volunteer Rescue Services. Multicoloured.

1539	85r. Type **509**	2·25	2·25
1540	1f.30 Water rescue (founded by 'Bubbles' diving club)	3·25	3·25

510 Hillside Farming

2010. Agriculture. Multicoloured.

1541	85r. Type **510**	1·50	1·50
1542	1f. Agriculture and the environment	2·50	2·50
1543	1f.10 Technology in farming	2·75	2·75
1544	1f.30 Farm animals	3·50	3·50

511 Natural Gas Filling Station (EFFEFF), Vaduz

2010. Modern Architecture (2nd issue). Multicoloured.

1545	2f.60 Type **511**	6·75	6·75
1546	3f.60 Liechtenstein Electric Power Authority Transformer Station (Marcel Ferrier)	8·25	8·25

512 Vaduz

2010. Expo 2010, Shanghai

MS1547	1f.60 Type **512**; 1f.90 Tidal bore on Qiantang river (32×60mm)	8·75	8·75

513 Ariadne giving Theseus the Thread

2011. Liechtenstein Museum, Garden Palace, Vienna. Multicoloured.

1548	1f. Type **513**	2·50	2·50
1549	1f.40 Surrender of Golden Fleece to Jason	3·50	3·50

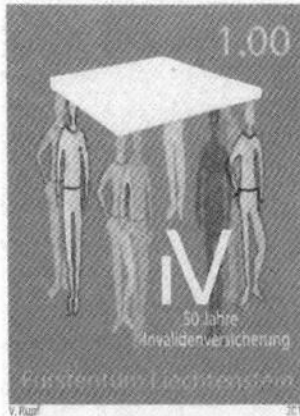

514 Figures supporting Roof

515 Flags of Members

516 Finger Print

2011. 50th Anniversaries

1550	**514**	1f. olive-bistre and black (Disability Insurance)	2·50	2·50
1551	**515**	1f.40 multicoloured (EFTA)	3·50	3·50
1552	**516**	1f.90 pale yellow-olive and slate grey (Interpol in Vaduz)	3·75	3·75

517 *Coenonympha oedippus* (false ringlet)

2011. Butterflies. Multicoloured.

1553	1f.40 Type **517**	2·75	2·75
1554	1f.60 *Gonepteryx rhamni* (brimstone)	3·00	3·00
1555	2f.60 *Papilio machaon* (Old World swallowtail)	7·25	7·25

518 Roadway and Eschnerberg

2011. Liechtenstein Panorama

1556	1f. Type **518**	2·30	2·30
1557	1f. Field and Alvier mountains	2·30	33·00

Nos. 1556/7 were printed, *se-tenant*, forming a composite design

519 Hydropower

2011. Renewable Energy. Multicoloured.

1558	1f. Type **519**	2·50	2·50
1559	1f.40 Wood	3·50	3·50
1560	2f.80 Near-surface geothermal power	8·00	8·00

520 Children and Symbols of Magic and Fantasy

2011. Europa

1561	**520**	1f.40 multicoloured	4·00	4·00

521 Autumn

2011. Vaduz Castle through the Seasons. Multicoloured.

1562	1f.40 Type **521**	4·00	4·00
1563	1f.90 Winter	4·75	4·75

OFFICIAL STAMPS

1932. Stamps of 1930 optd REGIERUNGS DIENSTSACHE under crown.

O118B	5r. green	11·00	16·00
O119B	10r. lilac	75·00	16·00
O120B	20r. red	85·00	16·00
O121B	30r. blue	18·00	22·00
O122C	35r. green	14·50	36·00
O123C	50r. black	80·00	20·00
O124A	60r. green	14·50	50·00
O125B	1f.20 brown	£150	£425

1933. Nos. 121 and 123 optd REGIERUNGS DIENSTSACHE in circle round crown.

O126	**38**	25r. orange	44·00	60·00
O127	-	1f.20 brown	£100	£400

1934. Nos. 128 etc. optd. REGIERUNGS DIENSTSACHE in circle round crown.

O150	**41**	5r. green	2·20	3·75
O151	-	10r. violet	4·25	3·75
O152	-	15r. orange	75	3·75
O153	-	20r. red	75	3·75
O155	-	25r. brown	3·75	22·00
O156	-	30r. blue	5·00	11·00
O157	**42**	50r. brown	1·50	5·00
O158	-	90r. green	11·00	60·00
O159	-	1f.50 brown	44·00	£300

1937. Stamps of 1937 optd REGIERUNGS DIENSTSACHE in circle round crown.

O174	**51**	5r. green and buff	35	75
O175	-	10r. violet and buff	75	2·20
O176	-	20r. red and buff	1·50	3·00
O177	-	25r. brown and buff	75	3·00
O178	-	30r. blue and buff	1·80	3·00
O179	-	50r. brown and buff	1·10	2·20
O180	-	1f. purple and buff	1·10	12·50
O181	-	1f.50 grey and buff	3·00	18·00

1947. Stamps of 1944 optd DIENSTMARKE and crown.

O255	5r. green	2·20	1·10
O256	10r. violet	2·20	1·50
O257	20r. red	3·00	1·50
O258	30r. blue	3·75	2·20
O259	50r. grey	3·75	4·25
O260	1f. red	14·50	16·00
O261	1f.50 blue	14·50	16·00

O86

1950. Buff paper.

O287	**O86**	5r. purple and grey	35	35
O288	**O86**	10r. green and mauve	35	35
O289	**O86**	20r. brown and blue	35	35
O290	**O86**	30r. purple and red	45	45
O291	**O86**	40r. blue and brown	60	60
O292	**O86**	55r. green and red	1·10	1·10
O293	**O86**	60r. grey and mauve	1·10	1·10
O294	**O86**	80r. orange and grey	1·20	1·20
O295	**O86**	90r. brown and blue	1·30	1·30
O296	**O86**	1f.20 turquoise and orange	1·80	1·80

1968. White paper.

O495	5r. brown and orange	15	15
O496	10r. violet and red	20	20
O497	20r. red and green	30	30
O498	30r. green and red	35	35
O499	50r. blue and red	60	60
O500	60r. orange and blue	75	75
O501	70r. purple and green	85	85
O502	80r. green and red	1·00	1·00
O503	95r. green and red	1·20	1·20
O504	1f. purple & turquoise	1·50	1·50
O505	1f.20 brown & turq	2·20	2·20
O506	2f. brown and orange	2·20	2·20

O198 Government Building, Vaduz

1976

O652	**O198**	10r. brown and violet	15	15
O653	**O198**	20r. red and blue	20	20
O654	**O198**	35r. blue and red	35	35
O655	**O198**	40r. violet and green	50	50
O656	**O198**	50r. green and mauve	55	55
O657	**O198**	70r. purple and green	75	75
O658	**O198**	80r. green and purple	85	85
O659	**O198**	90r. violet and blue	1·00	1·00
O660	**O198**	1f. grey and purple	1·10	1·10
O661	**O198**	1f.10 brown and blue	1·20	1·20
O662	**O198**	1f.50 green and red	1·60	1·60
O663	**O198**	2f. orange and blue	2·20	2·20
O664	**O198**	5f. purple and orange	14·50	11·00

POSTAGE DUE STAMPS

D11

1920

D43	**D11**	5h. red	35	45
D44	**D11**	10h. red	35	45
D45	**D11**	15h. red	35	45
D46	**D11**	20h. red	35	45
D47	**D11**	25h. red	35	60
D48	**D11**	30h. red	35	60
D49	**D11**	40h. red	35	60
D50	**D11**	50h. red	35	60
D51	**D11**	80h. red	35	60
D52	**D11**	1k. blue	45	1·50
D53	**D11**	2k. blue	45	1·50
D54	**D11**	5k. blue	45	1·50

D25

1928

D84	**D25**	5r. red and violet	1·50	3·75
D85	**D25**	10r. red and violet	1·80	3·75
D86	**D25**	15r. red and violet	3·00	16·00
D87	**D25**	20r. red and violet	3·00	3·75
D88	**D25**	25r. red and violet	3·00	11·00
D89	**D25**	30r. red and violet	9·50	17·00
D90	**D25**	40r. red and violet	10·00	18·00
D91	**D25**	50r. red and violet	12·00	22·00

D58

1940

D189	**D58**	5r. red and blue	1·80	4·25
D190	**D58**	10r. red and blue	75	1·50
D191	**D58**	15r. red and blue	1·10	7·25
D192	**D58**	20r. red and blue	1·10	2·20
D193	**D58**	25r. red and blue	2·20	4·75
D194	**D58**	30r. red and blue	4·75	8·00
D195	**D58**	40r. red and blue	4·75	7·25
D196	**D58**	50r. red and blue	5·50	8·25

Pt. 2

LOMBARDY AND VENETIA

Formerly known as Austrian Italy. Although these provinces used a different currency the following issues were valid throughout Austria. Lombardy was annexed by Sardinia in 1859 and Venetia by Italy in 1866.

1850. 100 centesimi = 1 lira.
1858. 100 soldi = 1 florin. 100 kreuzer = 1 gulden.

1 Arms of Austria

1850. Imperf.

1c	**1**	5c. orange	£1600	£120
2c	**1**	10c. black	£3000	£110
7	**1**	15c. red	£750	4·25
4c	**1**	30c. brown	£2750	8·50
5e	**1**	45c. blue	£7000	22·00

1859. As T 4 and 5 of Austria (Emperor Francis Joseph I) but value in soldi. Perf.

16B	**5**	2s. yellow	£600	£110
17A	**4**	3s. black	£2750	£300
18B	**4**	3s. green	£375	80·00
19B	**5**	5s. red	£300	5·50
20A	**5**	10s. brown	£450	60·00
21B	**5**	15s. blue	£1900	22·00

3 Emperor Francis Joseph I

1861

25	**3**	5s. red	£1600	2·75
26	**3**	10s. brown	£2750	27·00

4 Arms of Austria

1863

27	**4**	2s. yellow	£100	£190
33	**4**	3s. green	20·00	19·00
34	**4**	5s. red	3·25	1·60
35	**4**	10s. blue	19·00	6·00
36	**4**	15s. brown	80·00	60·00

JOURNAL STAMPS

J5

1858. Imperf.

J22	**J5**	1k. black	£1800	£4750
J23	**J5**	2k. red	£275	95·00
J24	**J5**	4k. red	£17000	£4250

Pt. 7

LUBECK

Formerly one of the free cities of the Hanseatic League. In 1868 joined the North German Confederation.

16 schilling = 1 mark.

1

1859. Imperf.

9	**1**	½s. lilac	55·00	£2000
10	**1**	1s. orange	£120	£2000
3	**1**	2s. brown	£150	£325
4	**1**	2½s. red	£275	£1100
6	**1**	4s. green	£120	£800

3

1863. Rouletted.

11	**3**	½s. green	65·00	£130
13	**3**	1s. orange	£170	£350
14	**3**	2s. red	37·00	85·00
16	**3**	2½s. blue	£170	£325
17	**3**	4s. bistre	75·00	£140

4

1864. Imperf.

18	**4**	1¼s. brown	42·00	£160

5

1865. Roul.

21	**5**	1½s. mauve	10·50	£120

Pt. 4

LUXEMBOURG

An independent Grand Duchy lying between Belgium and the Saar District. Under German Occupation from 1940 to 1944.

1852. 12½ centimes = 1 silver groschen.
100 centimes = 1 franc.
1940. 100 pfennig = 1 reichsmark.
1944. 100 centimes = 1 franc (Belgian).
2002. 100 cents = 1 euro.

1 Grand Duke William III

1852. Imperf.

2	**1**	10c. black	£3250	85·00
3	**1**	1s. red	£2000	£110

3

4

1859. Imperf or roul.

21	**3**	1c. orange	55·00	11·00
23	**3**	1c. brown	55·00	11·00
17	**3**	2c. black	28·00	22·00
8	**3**	4c. yellow	£275	£250
20	**3**	4c. green	55·00	33·00
10	**4**	10c. blue	£275	28·00
24	**4**	10c. purple	£170	5·50
25	**4**	10c. lilac	£200	5·50
28	**4**	12½c. red	£250	11·00
30	**4**	20c. brown	£200	11·00
12	**4**	25c. brown	£550	£400
32	**4**	25c. blue	£1100	17·00
13	**4**	30c. purple	£450	£325
14	**4**	37½c. green	£500	£275
35	**4**	37½c. bistre	£1100	£375
39	**4**	40c. orange	55·00	£110

1872. Surch UN FRANC. Roul.

37		1f. on 37½c. bistre	£1300	£110

1874. Perf.

57	**3**	1c. brown	5·50	2·75
58	**3**	2c. black	11·00	5·50
42	**3**	4c. green	5·50	14·00
43	**3**	5c. yellow	£250	39·00
60	**4**	10c. lilac	28·00	5·50
61a	**4**	12½c. red	17·00	17·00
62	**4**	20c. brown	8·25	5·50
63	**4**	25c. blue	28·00	2·75
64a	**4**	30c. red	8·25	22·00
55	**4**	40c. orange	5·50	14·00

1879. Surch Un Franc. Perf.

56		1f. on 37½c. bistre	11·00	39·00

7 Agriculture and Trade

1882

81c	**7**	1c. grey	1·10	85
82c	**7**	2c. brown	20	55
83c	**7**	4c. bistre	75	2·75
84c	**7**	5c. green	1·10	85
85c	**7**	10c. red	11·00	85
86a	**7**	12½c. blue	1·80	42·00
87c	**7**	20c. orange	4·50	3·25
88c	**7**	25c. blue	£250	2·75
89a	**7**	30c. green	33·00	20·00
90c	**7**	50c. brown	1·70	17·00
91	**7**	1f. lilac	2·20	£250
92	**7**	5f. orange	47·00	£250

8 Grand Duke Adolf

1891

125c	**8**	10c. red	1·10	45
126b	**8**	12½c. green	1·70	1·10
128b	**8**	20c. orange	11·00	1·70
129c	**8**	25c. blue	1·10	1·10
130b	**8**	30c. green	2·20	1·70
131b	**8**	37½c. green	4·50	4·50
132b	**8**	50c. brown	10·00	5·50
133b	**8**	1f. purple	20·00	9·00
134	**8**	2½f. black	2·20	31·00
135	**8**	5f. lake	40·00	£100

9

1895

152	**9**	1c. grey	8·25	1·10
153	**9**	2c. brown	2·20	55
154	**9**	4c. bistre	2·20	1·70
155	**9**	5c. green	17·00	55
156	**9**	10c. red	28·00	55

10

11 Grand Duke William IV

1906

157	**10**	1c. grey	20	30
158	**10**	2c. brown	20	30
159	**10**	4c. bistre	20	55
160	**10**	5c. green	35	30
231	**10**	5c. mauve	10	55
161	**10**	6c. lilac	20	85
161a	**10**	7½c. orange	20	4·50
162	**11**	10c. red	1·70	20
163	**11**	12½ slate	2·20	55
164	**11**	15c. brown	2·20	90
165	**11**	20c. orange	2·75	80
166	**11**	25c. blue	£100	55
166a	**11**	30c. olive	1·10	80
167	**11**	37½c. green	1·10	1·10
168	**11**	50c. brown	3·00	1·10
169	**11**	87½c. blue	2·20	17·00
170	**11**	1f. purple	4·50	2·20
171	**11**	2½f. red	£100	£110
172	**11**	5f. purple	13·50	90·00

1912. Surch 62½ cts.

173	**11**	62½c. on 87½c. blue	5·50	3·25
173a	**11**	62½c. on 2½f. red	5·50	6·75
173b	**11**	62½c. on 5f. purple	3·25	5·50

13 Grand Duchess Adelaide

1914

174	**13**	10c. purple	15	25
175	**13**	12½c. green	15	25
176	**13**	15c. brown	15	25
176a	**13**	17½c. brown	15	70
177	**13**	25c. blue	15	25
178	**13**	30c. brown	15	85
179	**13**	35c. blue	15	70
180	**13**	37½c. brown	15	70
181	**13**	40c. red	15	55
182	**13**	50c. grey	40	70
183	**13**	62½c. green	55	4·00
183a	**13**	87½c. orange	55	4·00
184	**13**	1f. brown	5·50	1·70
185	**13**	2½f. red	55	4·50
186	**13**	5f. violet	13·50	65·00

1916. Surch in figures and bars.

187	**10**	2½ on 5c. green	20	20
188	**10**	3 on 2c. brown	20	20
212	**10**	5 on 1c. grey	20	20
213	**10**	5 on 4c. bistre	20	55
214	**10**	5 on 7½c. orange	20	20
215	**10**	6 on 2c. brown	20	35
189	**13**	7½ on 10c. red	20	20
190	**13**	17½ on 30c. brown	20	55
191	**13**	20 on 17½c. brown	20	20
216	**13**	25 on 37½c. sepia	20	20
217	**13**	75 on 62½c. green	20	20
218	**13**	80 on 87½c. orange	20	20
192	**13**	87½ on 1f. brown	80	7·75

18 Vianden Castle

1921. Perf.

194	**17**	2c. brown	20	20
195	**17**	3c. green	20	20
196	**17**	6c. purple	20	20
197	**17**	10c. green	45	20
193a	**17**	15c. red*	15	20
198	**17**	15c. green	45	20
234	**17**	15c. orange	10	55
199	**17**	20c. orange	45	20
235	**17**	20c. green	10	55
200	**17**	25c. green	45	20
201	**17**	30c. red	45	20
202	**17**	40c. orange	45	20
203	**17**	50c. blue	1·10	65
236	**17**	50c. red	10	55
204	**17**	75c. red	65	1·70
237	**17**	75c. blue	10	55
205	**17**	80c. black	2·20	1·70
206a	**18**	1f. red	80	55
238	**18**	1f. blue	45	1·10
207	-	2f. blue	1·10	1·10
239	-	2f. brown	5·50	2·75
208	-	5f. violet	60·00	13·50

DESIGNS—As Type **18**: 2f. Factories at Esch; 5f. Railway viaduct over River Alzette.

*No. 193a was originally issued on the occasion of the birth of Crown Prince Jean.

See also Nos. 219/20.

21 Monastery at Clervaux

1921. War Monument Fund.

209	**21**	10c.+5c. green	55	8·25
210	-	15c.+10c. orange	55	11·00
211	-	25c.+10c. green	55	8·25

DESIGNS—HORIZ: 15c. Pfaffenthal; 25c. as Type **26**.

17 Grand Duchess Charlotte

1922. Philatelic Exhibition. Imperf.

219	**17**	25c. green	2·20	7·75
220	**17**	30c. red	2·20	7·75

26 Luxembourg

1923. Birth of Princess Elisabeth. Sheet 78×59 mm to 79×61 mm.

MS221	**26**	10f. green	£1700	£2750

1923

222a	**26**	10f. black	11·00	17·00

1923. Unveiling of War Memorial by Prince Leopold of Belgium. Nos. 209/11 surch 27 mai 1923 and additional values.

223	**21**	10+5+25c. green	2·20	22·00
224	-	15+10+25c. orange	2·20	28·00
225	-	25+10+25c. green	2·20	22·00

28 Echternach

1923

226	**28**	3f. blue	2·75	1·10

1924. Charity. Death of Grand Duchess Marie Adelaide. Surch CARITAS and new value.

227	**13**	12½c.+7½c. green	30	4·50
228	**13**	35c.+10c. blue	30	4·50
229	**13**	2½f.+1f. red	1·70	42·00
230	**13**	5f.+2f. violet	85	28·00

1925. Surch 5.

240	**17**	5 on 10c. green	45	45

31

1925. Anti-T.B. Fund.

241	**31**	5c.+5c. violet	40	1·10
242	**31**	30c.+5c. orange	40	4·50
243	**31**	50c.+5c. brown	65	8·25
244	**31**	1f.+10c. blue	1·10	21·00

32 Grand Duchess Charlotte

1926

245	**32**	5c. mauve	10	30
246	**32**	10c. olive	10	30
246a	**32**	15c. black	30	55
247	**32**	20c. orange	45	55
248	**32**	25c. green	45	55
248a	**32**	25c. brown	30	55
248b	**32**	30c. green	30	55
248c	**32**	30c. violet	55	55
248d	**32**	35c. violet	5·50	55
248e	**32**	35c. green	30	55
249	**32**	40c. brown	10	30
250	**32**	50c. brown	10	30
250a	**32**	60c. green	5·50	30
251	**32**	65c. brown	30	2·75
251a	**32**	70c. violet	55	55
252	**32**	75c. red	30	1·10
252a	**32**	75c. brown	10	55
253	**32**	80c. brown	30	2·75
253a	**32**	90c. red	2·20	2·75
254	**32**	1f. black	2·20	55
254a	**32**	1f. red	85	55
255	**32**	1¼f. blue	30	1·10
255a	**32**	1¼f. yellow	17·00	2·20
255b	**32**	1¼f. green	85	55
255c	**32**	1¼f. red	17·00	2·75
255d	**32**	1½f. blue	2·75	2·20
255e	**32**	1¾f. blue	1·70	55

33 Prince Jean

1926. Child Welfare.

256	**33**	5c.+5c. black and mauve	70	1·10
257	**33**	40c.+10c. black & green	70	1·70
258	**33**	50c.+15c. black & yellow	70	1·70
259	**33**	75c.+20c. black and red	70	17·00
260	**33**	1f.50+30c. black & bl	70	20·00

34 Grand Duchess and Prince Felix

1927. International Philatelic Exhibition.

261	**34**	25c. purple	1·70	16·00
262	**34**	50c. green	2·20	25·00
263	**34**	75c. red	1·70	16·00
264	**34**	1f. black	1·70	16·00
265	**34**	1½f. blue	1·70	16·00

35 Princess Elisabeth

1927. Child Welfare.

266	**35**	10c.+5c. black and blue	30	1·10
267	**35**	50c.+10 black and brown	30	1·70
268	**35**	75c.+20c. black & orange	30	2·75
269	**35**	1f.+30c. black and red	30	17·00
270	**35**	1½f.+50c. black and blue	30	17·00

1927. Stamps of 1921 and 1926 surch.

270a	**32**	10 on 30c. green	55	55
271	**17**	15 on 20c. green	30	30
272	**32**	15 on 25c. green	30	85
273	**17**	35 on 40c. orange	30	30
274	**32**	60 on 65c. brown	30	55
275	**17**	60 on 75c. blue	30	55
276	**32**	60 on 75c. red	30	55
277	**17**	60 on 80c. black	30	85
278	**32**	60 on 80c. brown	30	85
278a	**32**	70 on 75c. brown	11·00	55
278b	**32**	75 on 90c. red	3·25	1·10
278c	**32**	1¾ on 1½f. blue	5·50	3·25

1928. Perf.

279a	**37**	2f. black	2·75	1·10

See also No. 339.

38 Princess Marie Adelaide

1928. Child Welfare.

280	**38**	10c.+5c. purple & green	55	1·70
281	**38**	60c.+10c. olive & brown	1·10	4·50
282	**38**	75c.+15c. green and red	1·70	11·00
283	**38**	1f.+25c. brown & green	2·75	33·00
284	**38**	1½f.+50c. blue & yellow	2·75	33·00

39 Princess Marie Gabrielle

1928. Child Welfare.

285	**39**	10c.+10c. green & brown	55	2·20
286	**39**	35c.+15c. brown & green	2·20	11·00
287	**39**	75c.+30c. black and red	2·75	14·00
288	**39**	1¼f.+50c. green and red	3·25	33·00
289	**39**	1¾f.+75c. black and blue	4·50	42·00

40 Prince Charles

1930. Child Welfare.

290	**40**	10c.+5c. brown & green	55	1·70
291	**40**	75c.+10c. green & brown	2·75	7·25
292	**40**	1f.+25c. violet and red	5·50	28·00
293	**40**	1¼f.+75c. black & yellow	8·25	36·00
294	**40**	1¾f.+1f.50 brown & blue	11·00	36·00

41 Arms of Luxembourg

1930

295	**41**	5c. red	1·10	55
296	**41**	10c. green	2·20	55

42 Biplane over River Alzette

1931. Air.

296a	**42**	50c. green	1·10	1·70
297	**42**	75c. brown	1·10	2·20
298	**42**	1f. red	1·10	2·20
299	**42**	1¼f. purple	1·10	2·20
300	**42**	1¾f. blue	1·10	2·20
300a	**42**	3f. black	2·20	9·00

43 Luxembourg, Lower Town

1931

301	**43**	20f. green	5·50	28·00

44 Princess Alix

1931. Child Welfare.

302	**44**	10c.+5c. grey and brown	55	1·70
303	**44**	75c.+10c. green and red	5·50	22·00
304	**44**	1f.+25c. grey and green	17·00	45·00
305	**44**	1¼f.+75c. green and violet	11·00	45·00
306	**44**	1¾f.+1f.50 grey and blue	22·00	85·00

45 Countess Ermesinde

1932. Child Welfare.

307	**45**	10c.+5c. brown	55	1·70
308	**45**	75c.+10c. violet	5·50	22·00
309	**45**	1f.+25c. red	20·00	50·00
310	**45**	1¼f.+75c. lake	20·00	55·00
311	**45**	1¾f.+1f.50 blue	20·00	55·00

46 Emperor Henry VII

1933. Child Welfare.

312	**46**	10c.+5c. brown	55	1·70
313	**46**	75c.+10c. purple	8·25	22·00
314	**46**	1f.+25c. red	17·00	55·00
315	**46**	1¼f.+75c. brown	22·00	75·00
316	**46**	1¾f.+1f.50 blue	28·00	80·00

47 Gateway of the Three Towers

1934

317	**47**	5f. green	5·50	17·00

87 Date-stamp and Map

1949. 75th Anniv of U.P.U.

525	**87**	80c. green, lt green & black	95	95
526	**87**	2f.50 red, pink and black	4·00	2·50
527	**87**	4f. ultramarine, blue & black	7·75	8·25
528	**87**	8f. brown, buff and black	25·00	45·00

88 Michel Rodange

1949. National Welfare Fund.

529	**88**	60c.+40c. green and grey	95	95
530	**88**	2f.+1f. purple and claret	7·50	7·50
531	**88**	4f.+2f. blue and grey	13·00	15·00
532	**88**	10f.+5f. brown and buff	31·00	25·00

89 Young Girl

1950. War Orphans Relief Fund.

533	-	60c.+15c. turquoise	3·75	2·20
534	**89**	1f.+20c. red	8·25	2·20
535	-	2f.+30c. brown	6·25	2·20
536	**89**	4f.+75c. blue	22·00	25·00
537	-	8f.+3f. black	65·00	65·00
538	**89**	10f.+5f. purple	65·00	65·00

DESIGN: 60c., 2f., 8f. Mother and boy.

48 Arms of John the Blind

1934. Child Welfare.

318	**48**	10c.+5c. violet	1·10	2·75
319	**48**	35c.+10c. green	5·50	17·00
320	**48**	75c.+15c. red	5·50	17·00
321	**48**	1f.+25c. red	28·00	75·00
322	**48**	1¼f.+75c. orange	28·00	75·00
323	**48**	1¾f.+1½f. blue	28·00	75·00

50 Surgeon

1935. International Relief Fund for Intellectuals.

324	-	5c. violet	1·10	1·70
325	-	10c. red	1·10	1·70
326	-	15c. olive	1·10	2·75
327	-	20c. orange	2·75	4·00
328	-	35c. green	2·75	5·00
329	-	50c. black	3·25	7·25
330	-	70c. green	5·50	8·25
331	**50**	1f. red	5·50	11·00
332	-	1f.25 turquoise	22·00	80·00
333	-	1f.75 blue	22·00	80·00
334	-	2f. brown	55·00	£170
335	-	3f. brown	65·00	£225
336	-	5f. blue	£110	£425
337	-	10f. purple	£275	£700
338	**50**	20f. green	£300	£850

DESIGNS—HORIZ: 5c., 10f. Schoolteacher; 15c., 3f. Journalist; 20c., 1f.75, Engineer; 35c., 1f.25, Chemist. VERT: 10c., 2f. "The Arts"; 50c., 5f. Barrister; 70c. University.

This set was sold at the P.O. at double face value.

1935. Esch Philatelic Exhibition. Imperf.

339	**37**	2f.(+50c.) black	8·25	28·00

52 Vianden

1935

340	**52**	10f. green	5·50	22·00

53 Charles I

1935. Child Welfare.

341	**53**	10c.+5c. violet	30	55
342	**53**	35c.+10c. green	85	1·10
343	**53**	70c.+20c. brown	1·70	2·20
344	**53**	1f.+25c. red	28·00	55·00
345	**53**	1f.25+75c. brown	28·00	55·00
346	**53**	1f.75+1f.50 blue	28·00	75·00

54 Town Hall

1936. 11th Int Philatelic Federation Congress.

347	**54**	10c. brown	55	1·10
348	**54**	35c. green	55	1·70
349	**54**	70c. orange	85	2·20
350	**54**	1f. red	2·20	13·50
351	**54**	1f.25 violet	4·00	17·00
352	**54**	1f.75 blue	2·20	14·00

55 Wenceslas I

1936. Child Welfare.

353	**55**	10c.+5c. brown	55	55
354	**55**	35c.+10c. green	55	1·10
355	**55**	70c.+20c. slate	85	1·70
356	**55**	1f.+25c. red	4·50	25·00
357	**55**	1f.25+75c. violet	8·25	50·00
358	**55**	1f.75+1f.50 blue	8·25	31·00

1937. Dudelange Philatelic Exhibition. Sheet 125×85 mm. As No. 207 (pair) in new colour.

MS359	2f. (+3f.) brown	9·50	14·00

56 Wenceslas II

1937. Child Welfare.

360	**56**	10c.+5c. black and red	40	55
361	**56**	35c.+10c. green & purple	40	1·10
362	**56**	70c.+20c. red and blue	70	85
363	**56**	1f.+25c. red and green	4·25	25·00
364	**56**	1f.25+75c. purple & brn	5·50	25·00
365	**56**	1f.75+1f.50 blue & blk	8·25	28·00

57 St. Willibrord

1938. Echternach Abbey Restoration Fund (1st issue). 1200th Death Anniv of St. Willibrord.

366	57	35c.+10c. green	55	85
367	-	70c.+10c. black	1·10	85
368	-	1f.25+25c. red	2·75	4·00
369	-	1f.75+50c. blue	5·50	4·50
370	-	3f.+2f. red	11·00	14·00
371	-	5f.+5f. violet	11·00	32·00

DESIGNS—As Type **57**: 70c. Town Hall, Echternach; 1f.25, Pavilion, Echternach Municipal Park. 31×51 mm: 1f.75, St. Willibrord (from miniature). 42×38 mm: 3f. Echternach Basilica; 5f. Whitsuntide dancing procession.

See also Nos. 492/7 and 569/70.

61 Sigismond of Luxembourg

1938. Child Welfare.

372	61	10c.+5c. black & mauve	30	55
373	61	35c.+10c. black & green	30	85
374	61	70c.+20c. black & brown	55	85
375	61	1f.+25c. black and red	4·50	22·00
376	61	1f.25+75c. black & grey	4·50	22·00
377	61	1f.75+1f.50 black & bl	14·00	33·00

62 Arms of Luxembourg

63 William I

1939. Centenary of Independence.

378	62	35c. green	30	55
379	63	50c. orange	30	55
380	-	70c. green	30	55
381	-	75c. olive	85	1·70
382	-	1f. red	1·70	2·75
383	-	1f.25 violet	30	1·10
384	-	1f.75 blue	30	1·10
385	-	3f. brown	45	1·70
386	-	5f. black	45	11·00
387	-	10f. red	1·70	17·00

PORTRAITS—As Type **63**: 70c. William II; 75c. William III; 1f. Prince Henry; 1f.25 Grand Duke Adolphe; 1f.75 William IV; 3f. Marie-Anne, wife of William IV; 5f. Grand Duchess Marie Adelaide; 10f. Grand Duchess Charlotte.

1939. Surch in figures.

388	32	30c. on 60c. green	30	2·20

65 Allegory of Medicinal Spring

1939. Mondorf-les-Bains Propaganda.

389	65	2f. red	55	5·50

66 Prince Jean

1939. 20th Anniv of Reign and of Royal Wedding.

390	66	10c.+5c. brn on cream	30	55
391	-	35c.+10c. green on cream	55	1·70
392	-	70c.+20c. black on cream	1·70	2·20
393	66	1f.+25c. red on cream	5·50	50·00
394	-	1f.25+75c. violet on cream	8·25	80·00
395	-	1f.75+1f.50 blue on cream	11·00	£100

PORTRAITS: 35c., 1f.25, Prince Felix; 70c., 1f.75, Grand Duchess Charlotte.

1939. Twentieth Year of Reign of Grand Duchess Charlotte. Sheet 144×163 mm with designs as T 66 but without "CARITAS".

MS395a 2f. red (T **66**); 3f. green (Prince Felix); 5f. blue (Grand Duchess Charlotte)	80·00	£170

1940. Anti-T.B. Fund. Surch with Cross of Lorraine and premium.

396	65	2f.+50c. grey	2·75	31·00

1940–44. GERMAN OCCUPATION.

1940. T 94 of Germany optd Luxemburg.

397	94	3pf. brown	15	45
398	94	4pf. blue	15	55
399	94	5pf. green	15	55
400	94	6pf. green	15	45
401	94	8pf. red	15	45
402	94	10pf. brown	15	55
403	94	12pf. red	15	30
404	94	15pf. purple	45	85
405	94	20pf. blue	45	1·70
406	94	25pf. blue	55	1·70
407	94	30pf. green	55	1·10
408	94	40pf. mauve	55	1·70
409	94	50pf. black and green	55	2·20
410	94	60pf. black and purple	1·40	8·25
411	94	80pf. black and blue	5·50	31·00
412	94	100pf. black and yellow	2·00	8·25

1940. Types of Luxembourg surch.

413	32	3 Rpf. on 15c. black	15	85
414	32	4 Rpf. on 20c. orange	15	85
415	32	5 Rpf. on 35c. green	15	85
416	32	6 Rpf. on 10c. green	15	85
417	32	8 Rpf. on 25c. brown	15	85
418	32	10 Rpf. on 40c. brown	15	85
419	32	12 Rpf. on 60c. green	15	85
420	32	15 Rpf. on 1f. red	15	5·50
421	32	20 Rpf. on 50c. brown	15	1·70
422	32	25 Rpf. on 5c. mauve	1·40	5·50
423	32	30 Rpf. on 70c. violet	30	1·70
424	32	40 Rpf. on 75c. brown	30	1·70
425	32	50 Rpf. on 1¼f. green	30	1·70
426	65	60 Rpf. on 2f. red	4·25	35·00
427	47	80 Rpf. on 5f. green	85	5·50
428	52	100 Rpf. on 10f. green	85	5·50

1941. Nos. 739/47 of Germany optd Luxemburg.

429		3pf.+2pf. brown	55	1·10
430		4pf.+3pf. blue	55	1·10
431		5pf.+3pf. green	55	1·10
432		6pf.+4pf. green	55	1·10
433		8pf.+4pf. orange	55	1·10
434		12pf.+6pf. red	55	1·10
435		15pf.+10pf. purple	2·75	13·50
436		25pf.+15pf. blue	2·75	13·50
437		40pf.+35pf. purple	2·75	13·50

1944. INDEPENDENCE REGAINED.

70 Grand Duchess Charlotte

1944

438	70	5c. brown	15	30
439	70	10c. slate	15	30
440	70	20c. orange	30	30
441	70	25c. brown	15	55
442	70	30c. red	55	5·50
443	70	35c. green	15	45
444	70	40c. blue	55	55
445	70	50c. violet	15	30
445a	70	60c. orange	4·00	30
446	70	70c. red	15	30
447	70	70c. green	1·10	1·70
448	70	75c. brown	55	45
449	70	1f. olive	15	30
450	70	1¼f. orange	15	75
451	70	1½f. orange	55	55
452	70	1¾f. blue	30	55
453	70	2f. red	5·50	55
454	70	2½f. mauve	8·25	7·25
455	70	3f. green	1·10	85
456	70	3½f. blue	1·10	1·10
457	70	5f. green	30	55
458	70	10f. red	30	2·20
459	70	20f. blue	85	28·00

71 "Britannia"

1945. Liberation.

460	-	60c.+1f.40 green	45	30
461	-	1f.20+1f.80 red	45	30
462	71	2f.50+3f.50 blue	45	30
463	-	4f.20+4f.80 violet	45	30

DESIGNS: 60c. Ship symbol of Paris between Cross of Lorraine and Arms of Luxembourg; 1f.20, Man killing snake between Arms of Russia and Luxembourg; 4f.20, Eagle between Arms of U.S.A. and Luxembourg.

72 Statue of the Madonna in Procession

73 Altar and Shrine of the Madonna

1945. Our Lady of Luxembourg.

464	72	60c.+40c. green	40	3·75
465	-	1f.20+80c. red	45	3·75
466	-	2f.50+2f.50 blue	70	12·50
467	-	5f.50+6f.50 violet	2·00	£150
468	73	20f.+20f. brown	2·00	£150
MS468a 83×96 mm. 50f+50f. grey (as 1f.20)			2·50	55·00

DESIGNS: As Type **72**: 1f.20, The Madonna; 2f.50, The Madonna and Luxembourg; 5f.50, Portal of Notre Dame Cathedral.

74 Lion of Luxembourg

1945

469	74	20c. black	40	25
470	74	30c. green	40	40
470a	74	60c. violet	40	25
471	74	75c. brown	40	25
472	74	1f.20 red	40	25
473	74	1f.50 violet	40	25
474	74	2f.50 blue	60	50

75 Members of the Maquis

1945. National War Victims Fund.

475	75	20c.+30c. green and buff	40	1·70
476	-	1f.50+1f. red and buff	45	1·70
477	-	3f.50+3f.50 blue & buff	85	16·00
478	-	5f.+10f. brown and buff	85	16·00
MS478a 100×110 mm. Designs and colours as Nos. 475/8 but values changed; 2f.50+2f.50, 3f.50+6f.50, 5f.+15f., 20f.+20f.			36·00	£450

DESIGNS: 1f.50, Mother and children; 3f.50, Political prisoner; 5f. Executed civilian.

76

1946. Air.

479	-	1f. green and blue	45	25
480	76	2f. brown and yellow	45	35
481	-	3f. brown and yellow	45	35
482	-	4f. violet and grey	55	50
483	76	5f. purple and yellow	55	40
484	-	6f. purple and blue	55	65
485	-	10f. brown and yellow	2·10	65
486	76	20f. blue and grey	2·50	2·20
487	-	50f. green and light green	5·50	2·50

DESIGNS: 1, 4, 10f. Airplane wheel; 3, 6, 50f. Airplane engine and castle.

76a Old Rolling Mill, Dudelange

1946. National Stamp Exhibition, Dudelange. Sheet 100×80 mm.

MS487a **76a** 50f. (+5f.) blue on buff	22·00	55·00

77 John the Blind, King of Bohemia

1946. 600th Death Anniv of John the Blind.

488	77	60c.+40c. green and grey	65	2·75
489	77	1f.50+50c. red and buff	75	4·25
490	77	3f.50+3f.50 blue & grey	3·00	44·00
491	77	5f.+10f. brown and grey	2·00	36·00

78 Exterior Ruins of St. Willibrord Basilica

79 St. Willibrord

1947. Echternach Abbey Restoration (2nd issue). Inscr "ECHTERNACH".

492	78	20c.+10c. black	45	50
493	-	60c.+10c. green	80	1·00
494	-	75c.+25c. red	1·40	1·40
495	-	1f.50c.+50c. brown	1·70	1·40
496	-	3f.50c.+ 2f.50 blue	8·00	7·50
497	79	25f.+25f. purple	45·00	36·00

DESIGNS—As Type **78**: 60c. Statue of Abbot Bertels; 75c. Echternach Abbey emblem; 1f.50, Ruined interior of Basilica; 3f.50, St. Irmine and Pepin II carrying model of Abbey.

80 U.S. Military Cemetery, Hamm

1947. Honouring Gen. George S. Patton.

498	80	1f.50 red and buff	85	40
499	-	3f.50 blue and buff	4·25	3·75
500	80	5f. green and grey	4·25	4·25
501	-	10f. purple and grey	16·00	60·00

PORTRAIT: 3f.50, 10f. Gen. G. S. Patton.

82 Michel Lentz (national poet)

1947. National Welfare Fund.
502 **82** 60c.+40c. brown & buff 1·10 1·70
503 **82** 1f.50+50c. pur & buff 1·70 1·70
504 **82** 3f.50+3f.50 blue & grey 10·00 29·00
505 **82** 10f.+5f. green and grey 8·25 29·00

83 L'Oesling

1948. Tourist Propaganda.
505a - 2f.50 brown and chocolate 2·75 80
505b - 3f. violet 10·00 1·70
505c - 4f. blue 8·00 1·70
506 **83** 7f. brown 28·00 1·10
507 - 10f. green 4·50 40
508 - 15f. red 4·50 1·10
509 - 20f. blue 4·50 1·10
DESIGNS—HORIZ: 2f.50, Television transmitter, Dudelange; 3f. Radio Luxembourg; 4f. Victor Hugo's house, Vianden; 10f. River Moselle; 15f. Mining district. VERT: 20f. Luxembourg.

85 "Dicks" (Edmund de la Fontaine)

1948. National Welfare Fund.
510 **85** 60c.+40c. brown & bistre 85 1·40
511 **85** 1f.50+50c. red and pink 1·10 1·40
512 **85** 3f.50+3f.50 blue & grey 14·50 31·00
513 **85** 10f.+5f. green and grey 13·00 31·00

86 Grand Duchess Charlotte

1948
513a **86** 5c. orange 55 30
513b **86** 10c. blue 55 30
514 **86** 15c. olive 55 30
514a **86** 20c. purple 55 30
515 **86** 25c. grey 55 30
515a **86** 30c. olive 55 30
515b **86** 40c. red 55 85
515c **86** 50c. orange 85 30
516 **86** 60c. bistre 55 30
517 **86** 80c. green 55 30
518 **86** 1f. red 1·70 30
518a **86** 1f.20 black 1·70 45
518b **86** 1f.25 brown 1·70 55
519 **86** 1f.50 turquoise 1·70 30
520 **86** 1f.60 grey 2·20 2·20
521 **86** 2f. purple 1·70 30
521a **86** 2f.50 red 2·75 30
521b **86** 3f. blue 20·00 55
521c **86** 3f.50 red 6·75 85
522 **86** 4f. blue 6·75 85
522a **86** 5f. violet 16·00 1·10
523 **86** 6f. purple 14·00 1·10
524 **86** 8f. green 11·00 2·20

1949. 30th Year of Reign of Grand Duchess Charlotte. Sheet 110×75 mm.
MS524a **86** 8f.+3f. blue; 12f.+5f. green; 15f.+7f. brown £180 55·00

90 J. A. Zinnen (composer)

1950. National Welfare Week.
539 **90** 60c.+10c. violet and grey 1·00 55
540 **90** 2f.+15c. red and buff 1·00 70
541 **90** 4f.+15c. blue and grey 10·50 10·50
542 **90** 8f.+5f. brown and buff 33·00 42·00

91 Ploughman and Factories

1951. To Promote United Europe.
543 **91** 80c. green and light green 21·00 15·00
544 - 1f. violet and light violet 14·50 95
545 - 2f. brown and grey 50·00 95
546 **91** 2f.50 red and orange 50·00 28·00
547 - 3f. brown and yellow 80·00 37·00
548 - 4f. blue and light blue £120 60·00
DESIGNS: 1, 3f. Map, people and "Rights of Man" Charter; 2, 4f. Scales balancing "United Europe" and "Peace".

92 L. Menager (composer)

1951. National Welfare Fund.
549 **92** 60c.+10c. black and grey 85 55
550 **92** 2f.+15c. green and grey 85 55
551 **92** 4f.+15c. blue and grey 8·25 7·00
552 **92** 8f.+5f. purple and grey 39·00 50·00

92a T **1** and **86**

92b T **1**

1952. National Philatelic Exhibition ("CENTILUX") and Stamp Centenary.
552f **92b** 2f. blk & grn (postage) 55·00 50·00
552g **92b** 4f. red and green 55·00 50·00
552a **92a** 80c. black, pur & grn (air) 90 85
552b **92a** 2f.50 black, purple & red 2·30 2·20
552c **92a** 4f. black, purple and blue 5·50 5·50
552d **92a** 8f. black, purple and red 70·00 80·00
552e **92a** 10f. black, purple & brn 55·00 65·00

93 Hurdling

1952. 15th Olympic Games, Helsinki.
553 **93** 1f. black and green 95 85
554 - 2f. blk & lt brn (Football) 4·25 85
555 - 2f.50 blk & pink (Boxing) 5·50 2·20
556 - 3f. blk & drab (Water polo) 7·25 2·50
557 - 4f. black and blue (Cycling) 35·00 11·00
558 - 8f. black and lilac (Fencing) 22·00 5·00

94 J. B. Fresez (painter)

1952. National Welfare Fund.
559 **94** 60c.+15c. green and blue 85 55
560 **94** 2f.+25c. brown & orange 85 55
561 **94** 4f.+25c. violet and grey 6·25 5·50
562 **94** 8f.+4f.75 purple & lt pur 45·00 55·00

95 Prince Jean and Princess Josephine Charlotte

1953. Royal Wedding.
563 **95** 80c. violet and deep mauve 1·10 55
564 **95** 1f.20 deep brown & brown 1·10 55
565 **95** 2f. deep green and green 2·75 55
566 **95** 3f. deep purple and purple 2·75 95
567 **95** 4f. deep blue and blue 13·50 2·00
568 **95** 9f. brown and red 13·50 2·00

96 Echternach Basilica

1953. Echternach Abbey Restoration (3rd issue).
569 **96** 2f. red 5·50 55
570 - 2f.50 olive 8·25 8·25
DESIGN: 2f.50, Interior of Basilica.

97 Pierre D'Aspelt

1953. 7th Birth Centenary of Pierre D'Aspelt.
571 **97** 4f. black 13·00 7·25

98 "Candlemas Singing"

1953. National Welfare Fund.
572 **98** 25c.+15c. carmine and red 85 55
573 - 80c.+20c. blue and brown 85 55
574 - 1f.20+30c. green & turq 1·70 1·30
575 **98** 2f.+25c. brown and red 1·70 55
576 - 4f.+50c. blue & turquoise 12·50 12·50
577 - 7f.+3f.35 lilac and violet 29·00 31·00
DESIGNS: 80c., 4f. "The Rattles"; 1f.20, 7f. "The Eastereggs".

99 Foils, Mask and Gauntlet

1954. World Fencing Championships.
578 **99** 2f. deep brown and brown on cream 8·00 1·70

100 Fair Emblem

1954. Luxembourg International Fair.
579 **100** 4f. multicoloured 16·00 8·00

101 Earthenware Whistle

1954. National Welfare Fund.
580 **101** 25c.+5c. red and orange 95 75
581 - 80c.+20c. grey & black 95 75
582 - 1f.20+30c. green and cream 2·20 2·30
583 **101** 2f.+25c. brown and buff 1·10 85
584 - 4f.+50c. dp blue & blue 10·00 10·50
585 - 7f.+3f.45 violet & mve 32·00 39·00
DESIGNS: 80c., 4f. Sheep and drum; 1f.20, 7f. Merry-go-round horses.

102 Tulips

1955. Mondorf-les-Bains Flower Show.
586 **102** 80c. red, green and brown 40 40
587 - 2f. yellow, green and red 45 45
588 - 3f. purple, green & emer 5·25 5·00
589 - 4f. orange, green and blue 7·25 7·25
FLOWERS: 2f. Daffodils; 3f. Hyacinths; 4f. Parrot tulips.

103

1955. 1st National Crafts Exhibition.
590 **103** 2f. black and grey 2·20 55

104 "Charter"

1955. 10th Anniv of U.N.
591 **104** 80c. blue and black 1·00 1·00
592 - 2f. brown and red 7·75 55
593 - 4f. red and blue 6·50 5·50
594 - 9f. green and brown 3·00 1·50
SYMBOLIC DESIGNS: 2f. "Security"; 4f. "Justice"; 9f. "Assistance".

105 "Christmas Day"

1955. National Welfare Fund.
595 25c.+5c. red and pink 55 55
596 **105** 80c.+20c. black and grey 55 55
597 - 1f.20+30c. deep green and green 1·10 1·40
598 - 2f.+25c. deep brown and brown 85 55
599 **105** 4f.+50c. blue & lt blue 9·75 16·00
600 - 7f.+3f.45 purple & mve 22·00 23·00

ALLEGORICAL DESIGNS: 25c., 2f. "St. Nicholas's Day"; 1f.20, 7f. "Twelfth Night".

1956. Mondorf-les-Bains Flower Show. As T 102 but inscription at top in one line. Multicoloured.

601 2f. Anemones 1·10 55
602 3f. Crocuses 4·00 3·75

1956. Roses. As T 102 but inscr at top "LUXEMBOURG-VILLE DES ROSES". Multicoloured.

603 2f.50 Yellow roses 7·75 7·00
604 4f. Red roses 4·00 3·75

108 Steel Plant and Girder

1956. 50th Anniv of Esch-sur-Alzette.

605 **108** 2f. red, black & turquoise 4·50 90

109 Blast Furnaces and Map

1956. European Coal and Steel Community. Inscr as in T 109.

606 **109** 2f. red 39·00 55
607 - 3f. blue 39·00 32·00
608 - 4f. green 7·50 6·50

DESIGNS—VERT: 3f. Girder supporting City of Luxembourg. HORIZ: 4f. Chain and miner's lamp.

110

1956. Europa.

609 **110** 2f. black and brown £325 85
610 **110** 3f. red and orange £130 85·00
611 **110** 4f. deep blue and blue 11·00 7·00

111 Luxembourg Central Station

1956. Electrification of Luxembourg Railways.

612 **111** 2f. sepia and black 4·50 90

112 I. de la Fontaine

1956. Council of State Centenary. Inscr as in T 112.

613 **112** 2f. sepia 2·20 55
614 - 7f. purple 4·00 1·10

DESIGN: 7f. Grand Duchess Charlotte.

113 Arms of Echternach

1956. National Welfare Fund. Inscr "CARITAS 1956". Arms. Multicoloured.

615 25c.+5c. Type **113** 55 55
616 80c.+20c. Esch-sur-Alzette 55 55
617 1f.20+30c. Grevenmacher 85 1·10
618 2f.+25c. Type **113** 85 55
619 4f.+50c. Esch-sur-Alzette 7·00 7·25
620 7f.+3f.45 Grevenmacher 12·50 18·00

114 Lord Baden-Powell and Scout Emblems

1957. Birth Centenary of Lord Baden-Powell, and 50th Anniv of Scouting Movement.

621 **114** 2f. brown and green 1·80 50
622 - 2f.50 red and violet 3·75 3·00

DESIGN: 2f.50, as Type **114** but showing Girl Guide emblems.

115 Prince Henri

1957. "Prince Jean and Princess Josephine-Charlotte Foundation" Child Welfare Clinic.

623 **115** 2f. deep brown and brown 1·40 40
624 - 3f. deep green and green 6·00 6·00
625 - 4f. deep blue and blue 3·75 4·25

DESIGNS—HORIZ: 3f. Children's Clinic Project. VERT: 4f. Princess Marie-Astrid.

116 "Peace"

1957. Europa.

626 **116** 2f. brown 8·25 4·50
627 **116** 3f. red £120 29·00
628 **116** 4f. purple £110 28·00

1957. National Welfare Fund. Arms as T 113 inscr "CARITAS 1957". Multicoloured.

629 25c.+5c. Luxembourg 55 55
630 80c.+20c. Mersch 55 55
631 1f.20+30c. Vianden 85 95
632 2f.+25c. Luxembourg 55 55
633 4f.+50c. Mersch 7·00 7·75
634 7f.+3f.45 Vianden 8·25 11·50

117 Fair Entrance and Flags

1958. 10th Anniv of Luxembourg Int Fair.

635 **117** 2f. multicoloured 55 40

118 Luxembourg Pavilion

1958. Brussels Exhibition.

636 **118** 2f.50 blue and red 55 40

119 St. Willibrord holding Child (after Puseel)

1958. 1300th Birth Anniv of St. Willibrord.

637 - 1f. red 55 45
638 **119** 2f.50 sepia 55 30
639 - 5f. blue 1·50 1·00

DESIGNS: 1f. St. Willibrord and St. Irmina holding inscribed plaque; 5f. St. Willibrord and suppliant. (Miracle of the wine-cask).

119a Europa

1958. Europa.

640 **119a** 2f.50 blue and red 55 25
641 **119a** 3f.50 brown and green 1·10 55
642 **119a** 5f. red and blue 2·00 1·10

120 Open-air Theatre at Wiltz

1958. Wiltz Open-air Theatre Commemoration.

643 **120** 2f.50 sepia and grey 85 30

121 Vineyard

1958. Bimillenary of Moselle Wine Industry.

644 **121** 2f.50 brown and green 85 30

1958. National Welfare Fund. Arms as T 113 inscr "CARITAS 1958". Multicoloured.

645 30c.+10c. Capellen 55 55
646 1f.+25c. Diekirch 55 55
647 1f.50+25c. Redange 85 70
648 2f.50+50c. Capellen 55 55
649 5f.+50c. Diekirch 7·00 7·50
650 8f.50+4f.60 Redange 7·75 11·50

122 Grand Duchess Charlotte

1959. 40th Anniv of Accession of Grand Duchess Charlotte.

651 **122** 1f.50 deep green & green 1·40 70
652 **122** 2f.50 brown & lt brown 1·40 70
653 **122** 5f. lt blue and ultramarine 2·75 2·00

123 N.A.T.O. Emblem

1959. 10th Anniv of N.A.T.O.

654 **123** 2f.50 blue and olive 25 25
655 **123** 8f.50 blue and brown 75 70

1959. Mondorf-les-Bains Flower Show. As T 102 but inscr "1959".

656 1f. violet, yellow and turquoise 55 45
657 2f.50 red, green and blue 70 50
658 3f. blue, green and purple 1·00 95

FLOWERS: 1f. Iris; 2f.50, Peony; 3f. Hortensia.

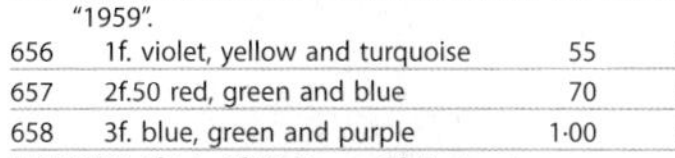

123a Europa

1959. Europa.

659 **123a** 2f.50 green 2·20 30
660 **123a** 5f. blue 4·00 1·70

124 Steam Locomotive and First Bars of Hymn "De Feierwon"

1959. Railways Centenary.

661 **124** 2f.50 blue and red 2·75 55

1959. National Welfare Fund. Arms as T 113 inscr "CARITAS 1959". Multicoloured.

662 30c.+10c. Clervaux 55 45
663 1f.+25c. Remich 55 45
664 1f.50+25c. Wiltz 85 85
665 2f.50+50c. Clervaux 55 45
666 5f.+50c. Remich 2·20 3·00
667 8f.50+4f.60 Wiltz 10·50 17·00

125 Refugees seeking Shelter

1960. World Refugee Year.

668 **125** 2f.50 blue and salmon 40 30
669 - 5f. blue and violet 55 55

DESIGN—HORIZ: 5f. "The Flight into Egypt" (Biblical scene).

126 Steel Worker

1960. 10th Anniv of Schuman Plan.

670 **126** 2f.50 lake 55 30

127 European School, Luxembourg

1960. European School Commemoration.

671 **127** 5f. black and blue 1·50 1·40

128 Grand Duchess Charlotte

1960

672 **128** 10c. red 40 25
673 **128** 20c. red 40 25
673a **128** 25c. orange 40 25
674 **128** 30c. drab 35 25
675 **128** 50c. green 90 25
676 **128** 1f. violet 90 25
677 **128** 1f.50 mauve 90 25
678 **128** 2f. turquoise 1·30 25
679 **128** 2f.50 purple 1·80 25
680 **128** 3f. dull purple 4·50 25
680a **128** 3f.50 turquoise 6·25 1·80
681 **128** 5f. brown 3·25 25
681a **128** 6f. turquoise 5·25 25

129 Heraldic Lion, and Tools

1960. 2nd National Crafts Exhibition.
682 **129** 2f.50 multicoloured 2·20 55

129a Conference Emblem

1960. Europa.
683 **129a** 2f.50 green and black 1·70 30
684 **129a** 5f. black and red 2·20 55

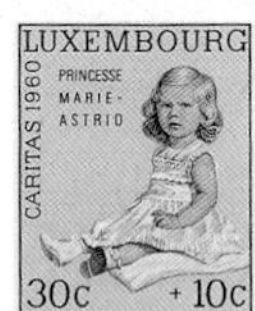

130 Princess Marie-Astrid

1960. National Welfare Fund. Inscr "CARITAS 1960". Centres and inscr in sepia.
685 **130** 30c.+10c. blue 45 40
686 - 1f.+25c. pink 45 40
687 - 1f.50+25c. turquoise 95 95
688 **130** 2f.50+50c. yellow 85 70
689 - 5f.+50c. lilac 1·50 4·25
690 - 8f.50+4f.60 sage 14·50 19·00
DESIGNS: Princess Marie-Astrid standing (1, 5f.), sitting with book on lap (1f.50, 8f.50).

131 Great Spotted Woodpecker

1961. Animal Protection Campaign. Inscr "PROTECTION DES ANIMAUX".
691 **131** 1f. multicoloured 40 30
692 - 1f.50 buff, blue and black 45 45
693 - 3f. brown, buff and violet 55 50
694 - 8f.50 multicoloured 1·10 1·00
DESIGNS—VERT: 8f.50, Dachshund. HORIZ: 1f.50, Cat; 3f. Horse.

132 Patton Monument, Ettelbruck

1961. Tourist Publicity.
695 **132** 2f.50 blue and black 95 35
696 - 2f.50 green 95 35
DESIGN—VERT: No. 696, Clervaux.

133 Doves

1961. Europa.
697 **133** 2f.50 red 55 30
698 **133** 5f. blue 85 35

134 Prince Henri

1961. National Welfare Fund. Inscr "CARITAS 1961". Centres and inscr in sepia.
699 **134** 30c.+10c. mauve 70 55
700 - 1f.+25c. lavender 70 55
701 - 1f.50+25c. salmon 1·00 85
702 **134** 2f.50+50c. green 1·00 55
703 - 5f.+50c. yellow 5·00 4·75
704 - 8f.50+4f.60 grey 7·50 12·00
DESIGNS: Prince Henri when young boy (1, 5f.); youth in formal dress (1f.50, 8f.50).

135 Cyclist carrying Cycle

1962. World Cross-country Cycling Championships, Esch-sur-Alzette.
705 **135** 2f.50 multicoloured 40 25
706 - 5f. multicoloured (Emblem) 50 55

136 Europa "Tree"

1962. Europa.
707 **136** 2f.50 multicoloured 85 30
708 **136** 5f. brown, green & purple 1·10 55

137 St. Laurent's Church, Diekirch

1962
709 **137** 2f.50 black and brown 75 35

138 Prince Jean and Princess Margaretha as Babies

1962. National Welfare Fund. inscr "CARITAS 1962". Centres and inscr in sepia.
710 **138** 30c.+10c. buff 40 40
711 - 1f.+25c. blue 40 40
712 - 1f.50+25c. olive 85 55
713 - 2f.50+50c. pink 85 40
714 - 5f.+50c. green 2·50 4·00
715 - 8f.50+4f.60 violet 6·50 7·50
PORTRAITS—VERT: 1f., 2f.50, Prince Jean and: 2f.50, 5f. Princess Margaretha, at various stages of childhood. HORIZ: 8f.50, The Royal Children.

139 Blackboard

1963. 10th Anniv of European Schools.
716 **139** 2f.50 green, red and grey 45 30

140 Benedictine Abbey, Munster

1963. Millenary of City of Luxembourg and International Philatelic Exhibition. (a) Horiz views.
717 - 1f. blue 60 30
718 **140** 1f.50 red 60 30
719 - 2f.50 green 60 30
720 - 3f. brown 60 30
721 - 5f. violet 1·00 65
722 - 11f. blue 2·75 2·40
VIEWS: 1f. Bock Rock; 2f.50, Rham Towers; 3f. Grand Ducal Palace; 5f. Castle Bridge; 11f. Millenary Buildings.

(b) Vert multicoloured designs.
723 1f. "Three Towers" Gate 60 40
724 1f.50 Great Seal 60 40
725 2f.50 "The Black Virgin" (statue), St. John's Church 60 40
726 3f. Citadel 75 40
727 5f. Town Hall 75 55

141 Colpach Castle

1963. Red Cross Centenary.
728 **141** 2f.50 red and slate 50 30

142 "Human Rights"

1963. 10th Anniv of European "Human Rights" Convention.
729 **142** 2f.50 blue on gold 40 30

143 "Co-operation"

1963. Europa.
730 **143** 3f. green, orange & turq 85 30
731 **143** 6f. orange, red and brown 1·70 65

144 Brown trout snapping Bait

1963. World Fishing Championships, Wormeldange.
732 **144** 3f. slate 45 30

145 Telephone Dial

1963. Inauguration of Automatic Telephone System.
733 **145** 3f. green, black and blue 45 30

146 St. Roch (patron saint of bakers)

1963. National Welfare Fund. Patron Saints of Crafts and Guilds. Inscr "CARITAS 1963". Multicoloured.
734 50c.+10c. Type **146** 35 25
735 1f.+25c. St. Anne (tailors) 35 25
736 2f.+25c. St. Eloi (smiths) 35 40
737 3f.+50c. St. Michel (haberdashers) 40 25
738 6f.+50c. St. Barthelemy (butchers) 1·70 2·50
739 10f.+5f.90 St. Thibaut (seven crafts) 2·50 4·50

147 Power House

1964. Inauguration of Vianden Reservoir.
740 **147** 2f. blue, brown and red 30 30
741 - 3f. blue, turq & red 30 30
742 - 6f. brown, blue and green 40 40
DESIGNS—HORIZ: 3f. Upper reservoir. VERT: 6f. Lohmuhle Dam.

148 Barge entering Canal

1964. Inauguration of Moselle Canal.
743 **148** 3f. indigo and blue 45 30

149 Europa "Flower"

1964. Europa.
744 **149** 3f. blue, brown and cream 85 30
745 **149** 6f. sepia, green and yellow 1·70 55

150 Students thronging "New Athenaeum"

1964. Opening of "New Athenaeum" (education centre).
746 **150** 3f. black and green 45 35

150a King Baudouin, Queen Juliana and Grand Duchess Charlotte

1964. 20th Anniv of "BENELUX".
747 **150a** 3f. brown, yellow & blue 45 30

151 Grand Duke Jean and Princess Josephine-Charlotte

1964. Accession of Grand Duke Jean.
748 **151** 3f. deep blue and light blue 40 25
749 **151** 6f. sepia and light brown 55 40

152 Three Towers

1964. National Welfare Fund. Inscr "CARITAS 1964". Multicoloured.

750		50c.+10c. Type **152**	25	25
751		1f.+25c. Grand Duke Adolphe Bridge	25	25
752		2f.+25c. Lower Town	25	25
753		3f.+50c. Type **152**	25	25
754		6f.+50c. Grand Duke Adolphe Bridge	1·50	2·50
755		10f.+5f.90 Lower Town	2·10	3·75

153 Rotary Emblem and Cogwheels

1965. 60th Anniv of Rotary International.

756	**153**	3f. multicoloured	45	30

154 Grand Duke Jean

1965

757	**154**	25c. brown	55	10
758	**154**	50c. red	55	10
759	**154**	1f. blue	85	10
760	**154**	1f.50 purple	85	10
761	**154**	2f. red	1·10	10
762	**154**	2f.50 orange	1·10	45
763	**154**	3f. green	1·10	10
763b	**154**	3f.50 brown	1·70	75
764a	**154**	4f. purple	1·70	15
764ba	**154**	5f. green	1·70	10
765	**154**	6f. lilac	1·70	10
765b	**154**	7f. orange	1·10	55
765c	**154**	8f. blue	2·20	30
766	**154**	9f. green	2·20	30
766a	**154**	10f. black	2·20	20
767	**154**	12f. red	2·75	30
767a	**154**	14f. blue	2·20	85
767b	**154**	16f. green	2·20	55
767c	**154**	18f. green	2·00	85
767d	**154**	20f. blue	2·75	30
767e	**154**	22f. brown	2·20	1·70

155 I.T.U. Emblem and Symbols

1965. Centenary of I.T.U.

768	**155**	3f. blue, lake and violet	45	30

156 Europa "Sprig"

1965. Europa.

769	**156**	3f. turquoise, red and black	85	30
770	**156**	6f. brown, blue and green	1·70	55

157 "The Roman Lady of the Titelberg"

1965. National Welfare Fund. Fairy Tales. Inscr "CARITAS 1965". Multicoloured.

771		50c.+10c. Type **157**	15	25
772		1f.+25c. "Schappchen, the Huntsman"	15	25
773		2f.+25c. "The Witch of Koerich"	25	25
774		3f.+50c. "The Goblins of Schoendels"	25	30
775		6f.+50c. "Tollchen, Watchman of Hesperange"	55	1·70
776		10f.+5f.90 "The Old Spinster of Heispelt"	1·80	4·25

158 "Flag" and Torch

1966. 50th Anniv of Luxembourg Workers' Union.

777	**158**	3f. red and grey	45	45

159 W.H.O. Building

1966. Inaug of W.H.O. Headquarters, Geneva.

778	**159**	3f. green	45	45

160 Golden Key

1966. Tercentenary of Solemn Promise to Our Lady of Luxembourg.

779	**160**	1f.50 green	30	25
780	-	2f. red	30	25
781	-	3f. blue	30	25
782	-	6f. brown	50	45

DESIGNS: 2f. Interior of Luxembourg Cathedral (after painting by J. Martin); 3f. Our Lady of Luxembourg (after engraving by R. Collin); 6f. Gallery pillar, Luxembourg Cathedral (after sculpture by D. Muller).

161 Europa "Ship"

1966. Europa.

783	**161**	3f. blue and grey	85	30
784	**161**	6f. green and brown	1·70	55

162 Class 1800 Diesel-electric Locomotive

1966. Luxembourg Railwaymen's Philatelic Exhibition. Multicoloured.

785		1f.50 Type **162**	90	25
786		3f. Class 3600 electric locomotive	90	40

163 Grand Duchess Charlotte Bridge

1966. Tourism.

787	**163**	3f. lake	30	30

See also Nos. 807/8, 828 and 844/5.

164 Kirchberg Building and Railway Viaduct

1966. "Luxembourg-European Centre".

788	**164**	1f.50 green	25	25
789	-	13f. blue (Robert Schuman monument)	85	40

165 "Mary, Veiled Matron of Wormeldange"

1966. National Welfare Fund. Luxembourg Fairy Tales. Multicoloured.

790		50c.+10c. Type **165**	20	25
791		1f.50+25c. "Jekel Warden of the Wark"	20	25
792		2f.+25c. "The Black Gentleman of Vianden"	20	40
793		3f.+50c. "The Gracious Fairy of Rosport"	30	25
794		6f.+1f. "The Friendly Shepherd of Donkolz"	85	1·40
795		13f.+6f.90 "The Little Sisters of Trois-Vierges"	1·10	3·50

166 City of Luxembourg, 1850 (after engraving by N. Liez)

1967. Centenary of Treaty of London.

796	**166**	3f. brown, blue and green	40	25
797	-	6f. red, brown and blue	60	40

DESIGN—VERT: 6f. Plan of Luxembourg fortress c. 1850 (after T. de Cederstolpe).

167 Cogwheels

1967. Europa.

798	**167**	3f. purple, grey and buff	2·20	30
799	**167**	6f. sepia, purple and blue	2·75	55

168 Lion on Globe

1967. 50th Anniv of Lions International.

800	**168**	3f. yellow, purple & black	35	30

169 European Institutions Building, Luxembourg

1967. N.A.T.O. Council Meeting, Luxembourg.

801	**169**	3f. turquoise and green	40	40
802	**169**	6f. red and pink	65	65

170 Hikers and Hostel

1967. Luxembourg Youth Hostels.

803	**170**	1f.50 multicoloured	35	35

171 Shaving-dish (after Degrotte)

1967. "200 Years of Luxembourg Pottery".

804	**171**	1f.50 multicoloured	35	35
805	-	3f. multicoloured	35	35

DESIGN—VERT: 3f. Vase, c. 1820.

172 "Gardener"

1967. "Family Gardens" Congress, Luxembourg.

806	**172**	1f.50 orange and green	35	35

1967. Tourism. As T 163.

807		3f. indigo and blue	75	30
808		3f. purple, green and blue	90	30

DESIGNS—HORIZ: No. 807, Moselle River and quayside, Mertert. VERT: No. 808, Moselle, Church and vines, Wormeldange.

173 Prince Guillaume

1967. National Welfare Fund. Royal Children and Residence.

809	**173**	50c.+10c. brown & buff	30	30
810	-	1f.50+25c. brown & bl	30	30
811	-	2f.+25c. brown and red	30	30
812	-	3f.+50c. brown & yell	1·30	30
813	-	6f.+1f. brown & lav	85	1·80
814	-	13f.+6f.90 brn, grn & bl	1·10	5·00

DESIGNS: 1f.50, Princess Margaretha; 2f. Prince Jean; 3f. Prince Henri; 6f. Princess Marie-Astrid; 13f. Berg Castle.

174 Football

1968. Olympic Games, Mexico.

815		50c. light blue and blue	45	30
816	**174**	1f.50 green and emerald	45	30
817	-	2f. yellow and green	65	30

818	-	3f. light orange and orange	45	30
819	-	6f. green and blue	65	55
820	-	13f. red and crimson	1·30	70

DESIGNS: 50c. Diving; 2f. Cycling; 3f. Running; 6f. Walking; 13f. Fencing.

175 Europa "Key"

1968. Europa.

821	**175**	3f. brown, black and green	2·00	35
822	**175**	6f. green, black and orange	2·75	65

176 Thermal Bath Pavilion, Mondorf-les-Bains

1968. Mondorf-les-Bains Thermal Baths.

823	**176**	3f. multicoloured	55	35

177 Fair Emblem

1968. 20th Anniv of Luxembourg Int Fair.

824	**177**	3f. multicoloured	55	35

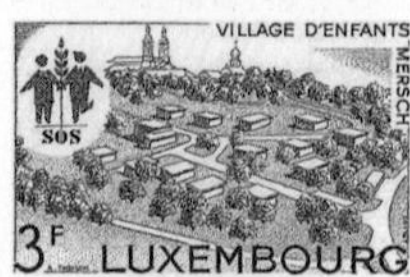

178 Village Project

1968. Luxembourg SOS Children's Village.

825	**178**	3f. purple and green	55	30
826	-	6f. black, blue and purple	65	45

DESIGN—VERT: 6f. Orphan with foster-mother.

179 "Blood Transfusion"

1968. Blood Donors of Luxembourg Red Cross.

827	**179**	3f. red and blue	65	35

180 Fokker F.27 Friendship over Luxembourg

1968. Tourism.

828	**180**	50f. dp blue, brown & blue	6·00	35

181 Cap Institute

1968. National Welfare Fund. Luxembourg Handicapped Children.

829	**181**	50c.+10c. brown and blue	30	30
830	-	1f.50+25c. brn & grn	30	30
831	-	2f.+25c. brown & yell	40	55
832	-	3f.+50c. brown and blue	40	30
833	-	6f.+1f. brown and buff	1·00	1·70
834	-	13f.+6f.90 brown and pink	2·75	5·75

DESIGNS: 1f.50, Deaf and dumb child; 2f. Blind child; 3f. Nurse supporting handicapped child; 6f. and 13f. Mentally handicapped children (different).

182

1969. "Juventus 1969" Junior International Philatelic Exhibition. Sheet 111×70 mm containing T 182 and similar vert designs. Multicoloured.

MS835	3f. Type **182**; 6f. "Sport"; 13f. Sun, open book and ball	6·00	7·00

183 Colonnade

1969. Europa.

836	**183**	3f. multicoloured	2·00	35
837	**183**	6f. multicoloured	2·75	65

184 "The Wooden Horse" (Kutter)

1969. 75th Birth Anniv of Joseph Kutter (painter). Multicoloured.

838	3f. Type **184**	90	30
839	6f. "Luxembourg" (Kutter)	90	65

185 ILO Emblem

1969. 50th Anniv of Int Labour Organization.

840	**185**	3f. gold, violet and green	45	35

186 National Colours

1969. 25th Anniv of "BENELUX" Customs Union.

841	**186**	3f. multicoloured	55	35

187 N.A.T.O. Emblem

1969. 20th Anniv of N.A.T.O.

842	**187**	3f. orange and brown	65	35

188 Ear of Wheat and Agrocentre, Mersch

1969. "Modern Agriculture".

843	**188**	3f. grey and green	45	35

189 Echternach

1969. Tourism.

844	**189**	3f. indigo and blue	60	35
845	-	3f. blue and green	60	35

DESIGN: No. 845, Wiltz.

190 Vianden Castle

1969. National Welfare Fund. Castles (1st series). Multicoloured.

846	50c.+10c. Type **190**	30	30
847	1f.50+25c. Lucilinburhuc	30	30
848	2f.+25c. Bourglinster	30	30
849	3f.+50c. Hollenfels	30	30
850	6f.+1f. Ansembourg	1·10	2·30
851	13f.+6f.90 Beaufort	1·70	5·75

See also Nos. 862/7.

191 Pasque Flower

1970. Nature Conservation Year. Multicoloured.

852	3f. Type **191**	45	30
853	6f. West European hedgehogs	65	65

192 Firecrest

1970. 50 Years of Bird Protection.

854	**192**	1f.50 green, black & orge	55	35

193 "Flaming Sun"

1970. Europa.

855	**193**	3f. multicoloured	2·00	35
856	**193**	6f. multicoloured	2·75	65

194 Road Safety Assoc. Emblem and Traffic

1970. Road Safety.

857	**194**	3f. black, red and lake	40	35

195 "Empress Kunegonde and Emperor Henry II" (stained-glass windows, Luxembourg Cathedral)

1970. Centenary of Luxembourg Diocese.

858	**195**	3f. multicoloured	40	40

196 Population Pictograph

1970. Population Census.

859	**196**	3f. red, blue and green	40	35

197 Facade of Town Hall, Luxembourg

1970. 50th Anniv of Union of Four Suburbs with Luxembourg City.

860	**197**	3f. brown, ochre and blue	40	35

199 Monks in the Scriptorium

1970. 25th Anniv of United Nations.

861	**198**	1f.50 violet and blue	40	35

1970. National Welfare Fund. Castles (2nd series). Designs as T 190.

862	50c.+10c. Clervaux	30	30
863	1f.50+25c. Septfontaines	30	30
864	2f.+25c. Bourschied	30	30
865	3f.+50c. Esch-sur-Sure	30	30
866	6f.+1f. Larochette	90	2·30
867	13f.+6f.90 Brandenbourg	1·70	5·75

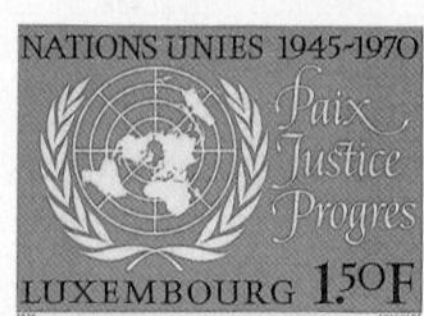

198 U.N. Emblem

1971. Medieval Miniatures produced at Echternach. Multicoloured.

868	1f.50 Type **199**	45	30
869	3f. Vine-growers going to work	45	30
870	6f. Vine-growers at work and returning home	55	30
871	13f. Workers with spades and hoe	1·50	90

200 Europa Chain

1971

872	**200**	3f. black, brown and red	2·00	35
873	**200**	6f. black, brown and green	2·75	1·00

201 Olympic Rings and Arms of Luxembourg

1971. Int Olympic Committee Meeting, Luxembourg.

874	**201**	3f. red, gold and blue	55	35

202 "50" and Emblem

1971. 50th Anniv of Luxembourg's Christian Workers' Union (L.C.G.B.).

875	**202**	3f. purple, orange & yell	55	35

203 Artificial Lake, Upper Sure Valley

1971. Man-made Landscapes.

876	**203**	3f. blue, grey and brown	85	35
877	-	3f. brown, green and blue	85	55
878	-	15f. black, blue and brown	1·70	35

DESIGNS: No. 877, Water-processing plant, Esch-sur-Sure; No. 878, ARBED (United Steelworks) Headquarters Building, Luxembourg.

204 Child with Coin

1971. Schoolchildren's Saving Campaign.

879	**204**	3f. multicoloured	55	35

205 "Bethlehem Children"

1971. National Welfare Fund. "The Nativity"–wood-carvings in Beaufort Church. Multicoloured.

880		1f.+25c. Type **205**	55	35
881		1f.50+25c. "Shepherds"	55	35
882		3f.+50c. "Virgin, Child Jesus and St. Joseph"	70	35
883		8f.+1f. "Herdsmen"	2·10	4·00
884		18f.+6f.50 "One of the Magi"	3·25	9·00

206 Coins of Belgium and Luxembourg

1972. 50th Anniv of Belgium–Luxembourg Economic Union.

885	**206**	1f.50 silver, black & green	55	35

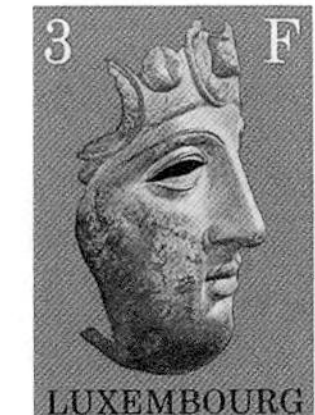

207 Bronze Mask (1st cent)

1972. Gallo-Roman Exhibits from Luxembourg State Museum. Multicoloured.

886		1f. Samian bowl (2nd century) (horiz)	65	25
887		3f. Type **207**	95	30
888		8f. Limestone head (2nd/3rd century)	2·00	1·30
889		15f. Glass "head" flagon (4th century)	1·90	1·00

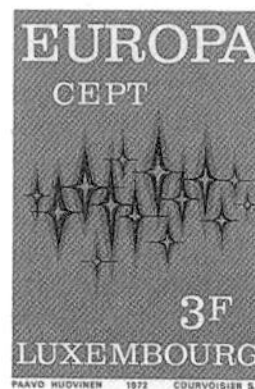

208 "Communications"

1972. Europa.

890	**208**	3f. multicoloured	2·00	35
891	**208**	8f. multicoloured	3·25	2·00

209 Archer

1972. 3rd European Archery Championships, Luxembourg.

892	**209**	3f. multicoloured	75	35

210 R. Schuman (after bronze by R. Zilli)

1972. 20th Anniv of Establishment of European Coal and Steel Community in Luxembourg.

893	**210**	3f. green and grey	85	35

211 National Monument

1972. Monuments and Buildings.

894	**211**	3f. brown, green and violet	1·00	35
895	-	3f. brown, green and blue	1·40	35

DESIGN: No. 895, European Communities' Court of Justice.

212 "Renert"

1972. Cent of Publication of Michel Rodange's "Renert" (satirical poem).

896	**212**	3f. multicoloured	60	35

213 "Angel"

1972. National Welfare Fund. Stained Glass Windows in Luxembourg Cathedral. Multicoloured.

897		1f.+25c. Type **213**	30	30
898		1f.50+25c. "St. Joseph"	30	30
899		3f.+50c. "Holy Virgin with Child Jesus"	30	30
900		8f.+1f. "People of Bethlehem"	1·70	4·00
901		18f.+6f.50 "Angel" (facing left)	5·00	11·50

214 "Epona on Horseback"

1973. Archaeological Relics. Multicoloured.

902		1f. Type **214**	65	30
903		4f. "Panther attacking swan" (horiz)	70	35
904		8f. Celtic gold coin	2·50	1·80
905		15f. Bronze boar (horiz)	1·90	1·00

215 Europa "Posthorn"

1973. Europa.

906	**215**	4f. orange, blue and violet	2·00	40
907	**215**	8f. green, yellow & purple	3·25	1·70

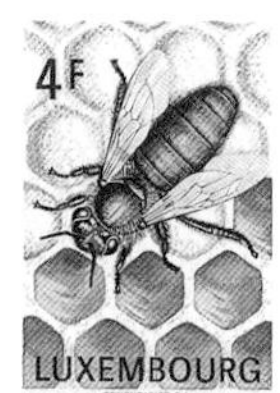

216 Bee on Honeycomb

1973. Bee-keeping.

908	**216**	4f. multicoloured	90	35

217 Nurse and Child

1973. Day Nurseries in Luxembourg.

909	**217**	4f. multicoloured	65	35

218 Capital, Vianden Castle

1973. Romanesque Architecture in Luxembourg.

910	**218**	4f. purple and green	55	35
911	-	8f. blue and brown	1·50	1·30

DESIGN: 8f. Detail of altar, St. Irmina's Chapel, Rosport.

219 Labour Emblem

1973. 50th Anniv of Luxembourg Board of Labour.

912	**219**	3f. multicoloured	55	35

220 J. de Busleyden

1973. 500th Anniv of Great Council of Malines.

913	**220**	4f. purple and brown	60	35

221 Monument, Wiltz

1973. National Strike Monument.

914	**221**	4f. green, brown and grey	85	35

222 Joachim and St. Anne

1973. National Welfare Fund. "The Nativity". Details from 16th-century reredos, Hachiville Hermitage. Multicoloured.

915		1f.+25c. Type **222**	30	35
916		3f.+25c. "Mary meets Elizabeth"	30	35
917		4f.+50c. "Magus presenting gift"	35	35
918		8f.+1f. "Shepherds at the manger"	1·80	4·25
919		15f.+7f. "St. Joseph with Candle"	5·25	11·50

223 Princess Marie-Astrid, Association President

1974. Luxembourg Red Cross Youth Association.

920	**223**	4f. multicoloured	2·75	65

224 Flame Emblem

1974. 50th Anniv of Luxembourg Mutual Insurance Federation.

921	**224**	4f. multicoloured	95	60

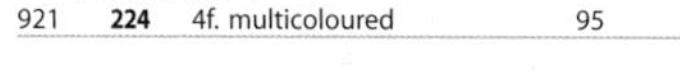

225 Seal of Henry VII, King of the Romans

1974. Seals in Luxembourg State Archives.

922	**225**	1f. brown, yellow & purple	45	30
923	-	3f. brown, yellow & green	55	45
924	-	4f. dk brown, yellow & brn	75	30
925	-	19f. brown, yellow & blue	2·00	1·30

DESIGNS: 3f. Equestrian seal of John the Blind, King of Bohemia; 4f. Municipal seal of Diekirch; 19f. Seal of Marienthal Convent.

226 "Hind" (A. Tremont)

1974. Europa. Sculptures. Multicoloured.
926 4f. Type **226** 4·00 35
927 8f. "Abstract" (L. Wercollier) 6·75 3·00

227 Churchill Memorial, Luxembourg

1974. Birth Centenary of Sir Winston Churchill.
928 **227** 4f. multicoloured 65 40

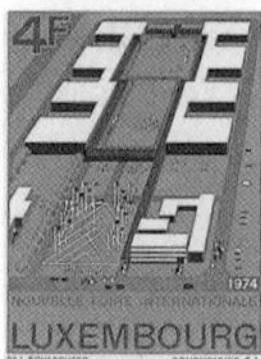

228 Diagram of Fair

1974. New International Fair, Luxembourg-Kirchberg.
929 **228** 4f. multicoloured 65 40

229 "Theis the Blind" (artist unknown)

1974. 150th Death Anniv of "Theis the Blind" (Mathias Schou, folk singer).
930 **229** 3f. multicoloured 65 65

230 "Crowning of St. Cecily and St. Valerien" (Hollenfels Church)

1974. Gothic Architecture.
931 **230** 4f. brown, green and violet 75 45
932 - 4f. black, brown and blue 75 45
DESIGN: No. 932, Interior of Septfontaines Church.

231 U.P.U. Emblem on "100"

1974. Centenary of Universal Postal Union.
933 **231** 4f. multicoloured 70 35
934 **231** 8f. multicoloured 1·70 1·20

232 "Benelux"

1974. 30th Anniv of Benelux (Customs Union).
935 **232** 4f. turquoise, green & blue 1·70 40

233 Differdange

1974. Tourism.
936 **233** 4f. purple 2·00 40

234 "Annunciation"

1974. National Welfare Fund. Illustrations from "Codex Aureus Epternacensis". Multicoloured.
937 1f.+25c. Type **234** 30 30
938 3f.+25c. "Visitation" 30 30
939 4f.+50c. "Nativity" 35 30
940 8f.+1f. "Adoration of the Magi" 2·00 4·25
941 15f.+7f. "Presentation at the Temple" 4·00 10·50

235 "Crucifixion"

1974. 50th Anniv of Christmas Charity Stamps. Detail of cover from "Codex Aureus Epternacensis". Sheet 80×90 mm.
MS942 **235** 20f.+10f. multicoloured 6·75 17·00

236 The Fish Market, Luxembourg

1975. European Architectural Heritage Year.
943 **236** 1f. green 95 35
944 - 3f. brown 2·30 65
945 - 4f. lilac 2·50 35
946 - 19f. red 2·75 1·70
DESIGNS—HORIZ: 3f. Bourglinster Castle; 4f. Market Square, Echternach. VERT: 19f. St. Michael's Square, Mersch.

237 "Joseph Kutter" (self-portrait)

1975. Luxembourg Culture, and Europa. Paintings. Multicoloured.
947 1f. Type **237** 65 30
948 4f. "Remich Bridge" (N. Klopp) (horiz) 2·75 55
949 8f. "Still Life" (J. Kutter) (horiz) 4·75 2·75
950 20f. "The Dam" (D. Lang) 3·00 85

238 Dr. Albert Schweitzer

1975. Birth Centenary of Dr. Albert Schweitzer (medical missionary).
951 **238** 4f. blue 1·10 40

239 Robert Schuman, G. Martino and P.-H. Spaak

1975. 25th Anniv of Robert Schuman Declaration for European Unity.
952 **239** 4f. black, gold and green 1·10 40

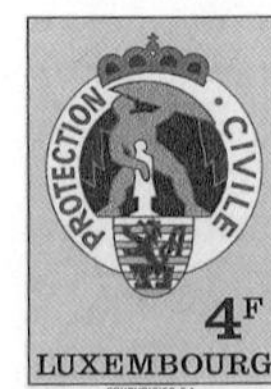

240 Civil Defence Emblem

1975. 15th Anniv of Civil Defence Reorganization.
953 **240** 4f. multicoloured 1·10 40

241 Ice Skating

1975. Sports. Multicoloured.
954 **241** 3f. purple, blue and green 1·00 55
955 - 4f. brown, green & dp brn 1·50 30
956 - 15f. blue, brown and green 2·75 95
DESIGNS—HORIZ: 4f. Water-skiing. VERT: 15f. Rock-climbing.

242 Fly Orchid

1975. National Welfare Fund. Protected Plants (1st series). Multicoloured.
957 1f.+25c. Type **242** 35 30
958 3f.+25c. Pyramid orchid 65 45
959 4f.+50c. Marsh helleborine 90 30
960 8f.+1f. Pasque flower 2·10 3·25
961 15f.+7f. Bee orchid 4·75 10·00
See also Nos. 976/80 and 997/1001.

243 Grand Duchess Charlotte (80th)

1976. Royal Birthdays. Multicoloured.
962 6f. Type **243** 2·75 60
963 6f. Prince Henri (21st) 2·75 60

244 7th-century Disc-shaped Brooch

1976. Luxembourg Culture. Ancient Treasures from Merovingian Tombs. Multicoloured.
964 2f. Type **244** 45 30
965 5f. 5th-6th century glass beaker (horiz) 55 55
966 6f. Ancient pot (horiz) 55 40
967 12f. 7th century gold coin 1·80 1·60

245 Soup Tureen

1976. Europa. 19th-century Pottery. Multicoloured.
968 6f. Type **245** 4·00 35
969 12f. Bowl 6·75 2·75

246 Independence Hall, Philadelphia

1976. Bicentenary of American Revolution.
970 **246** 6f. multicoloured 85 45

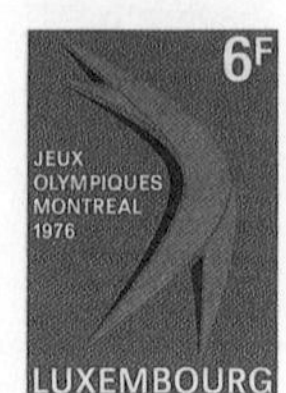

247 Symbol representing "Strength and Impetus"

1976. Olympic Games, Montreal.
971 **247** 6f. gold, magenta and mauve 85 45

249 "Virgin and Child"

1976. 30th Anniv of "Jeunesses Musicales" (Youth Music Association).
972 **248** 6f. multicoloured 85 45

248 Association Emblem and "Sound Vibrations"

1976. Renaissance Art. Multicoloured.
973 6f. Type **249** 85 40
974 12f. Bernard de Velbruck, Lord of Beaufort (funeral monument) 1·80 1·50

250 Alexander Graham Bell

1976. Telephone Centenary.

975	**250**	6f. green	85	45

1976. National Welfare Fund. Protected Plants (2nd series). As T 242. Multicoloured.

976	2f.+25c. Gentian	30	45
977	5f.+25c. Wild daffodil	30	45
978	6f.+50c. Red helleborine (orchid)	45	45
979	12f.+1f. Late spider orchid	1·80	4·25
980	20f.+8f. Twin leaved squill	5·00	12·00

251 Johann von Goethe (poet)

1977. Luxembourg Culture. Famous Visitors to Luxembourg.

981	**251**	2f. purple	55	30
982	-	5f. violet	65	40
983	-	6f. black	1·10	40
984	-	12f. violet	1·30	1·30

DESIGNS: 5f. Joseph Mallard William Turner (painter); 6f. Victor Hugo (writer); 12f. Franz Liszt (musician).

252 Fish Market, Luxembourg

1977. Europa. Multicoloured.

985	6f. Type **252**	3·25	65
986	12f. Grand Duke Adolphe railway bridge and European Investment Bank	5·25	2·75

253 Esch-sur-Sure

1977. Tourism.

987	**253**	5f. blue	90	40
988	-	6f. brown	85	40

DESIGNS 6f. Ehnen.

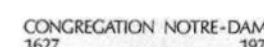

254 Marguerite de Busbach (founder)

1977. Anniversaries. Multicoloured.

989	6f. Type **254**	85	40
990	6f. Louis Braille (after Filippi)	85	40

ANNIVERSARIES: No. 989, 350th anniv of foundation of Notre Dame Congregation; No. 990, 125th death anniv.

LUXEMBOURG 40F

255 10c. and 1sgr. Stamps of 1852

1977. 125th Anniv of Luxembourg Stamps. Sheet 90×60 mm.

MS991	**255**	40f. black, chestnut and grey	9·50	9·50

256 St. Gregory the Great

1977. Baroque Art. Sculpture from Feulen Parish Church pulpit attributed to J.-G. Scholtus.

992	**256**	6f. purple	65	45
993	-	12f. grey	1·30	1·30

DESIGN: 12f. St. Augustine.

257 Head of Medusa

1977. Roman Mosaic at Diekirch.

994	**257**	6f. multicoloured	1·70	40

258 Scene from "Orpheus and Eurydice" (Gluck)

1977. 25th Wiltz International Festival.

995	**258**	6f. multicoloured	1·20	40

259 Map of E.E.C. and "Europa" (R. Zilli)

1977. 20th Anniv of Rome Treaties.

996	**259**	6f. multicoloured	1·10	40

1977. National Welfare Fund. Protected Plants (3rd series). As T 242. Multicoloured.

997	2f.+25c. Lily of the valley	35	45
998	5f.+25c. Columbine	55	55
999	6f.+50c. Mezereon	1·00	55
1000	12f.+1f. Early spider orchid	2·75	5·25
1001	20f.+8f. Spotted orchid	4·50	11·00

260 Grand Duke Jean and Duchess Josephine-Charlotte

1978. Royal Silver Wedding. Sheet 116×67 mm.

MS1002	**260**	6f., 12f. multicoloured	3·25	3·25

261 Fountain and Youth

1978. "Juphilux 78" Junior International Philatelic Exhibition. Sheet 103×72 mm containing T 261 and similar vert designs. Multicoloured.

MS1003	5f. Type **261**; 6f. Streamer; 20f. Dancing youths	5·25	6·25

MS1003 was on sale at 60f., including entrance fee of 29f., at the Exhibition, by postal application and at post offices.

262 Charles IV

1978. Europa.

1004	**262**	6f. lilac	1·70	45
1005	-	12f. red	4·00	2·00

DESIGN: 12f. Pierre d'Aspelt (funeral monument, Mainz Cathedral).

263 Head of Our Lady of Luxembourg

1978. Anniversaries. Multicoloured.

1006	6f. Type **263** (300th anniv of election as patron saint)	70	40
1007	6f. Trumpeters (135th anniv of Grand Ducal Military Band)	70	40

264 Emile Mayrisch (after T. van Rysselberghe)

1978. 50th Death Anniv of Emile Mayrisch (iron and steel magnate).

1008	**264**	6f. multicoloured	1·40	35

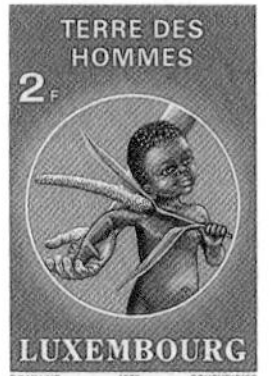

265 Child with Ear of Millet

1978. "Solidarity 1978". Multicoloured.

1009	2f. Type **265** (Terre des Hommes)	40	35
1010	5f. Flower and lungs (70th anniv of Luxembourg Anti-tuberculosis League)	50	35
1011	6f. Open cell (Amnesty International and 30th anniv of Declaration of Human Rights)	65	40

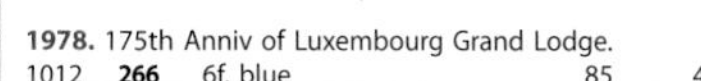

266 Perfect Ashlar

1978. 175th Anniv of Luxembourg Grand Lodge.

1012	**266**	6f. blue	85	40

267 "St. Matthew"

1978. National Welfare Fund. Glass Paintings (1st series). Multicoloured.

1013	2f.+25c. Type **267**	25	25
1014	5f.+25c. "St. Mark"	40	40
1015	6f.+50c. "Nativity"	55	45
1016	12f.+1f. "St. Luke"	2·00	1·50
1017	20f.+8f. "St. John"	2·75	6·25

See also Nos. 1035/9 and 1055/8.

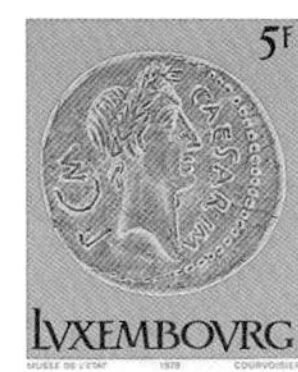

268 Denarius of Gaius Julius Caesar

1979. Luxembourg Culture. Roman Coins in the State Museum. Multicoloured.

1018	5f. Type **268**	45	35
1019	6f. Sestertius of Faustina 1	80	25
1020	9f. Follis of Helena	1·10	70
1021	26f. Solidus of Valens	2·20	1·70

See also Nos. 1040/3 and 1060/3.

269 Mondorf-les-Bains

1979. Tourism.

1022	**269**	5f. green, brown and blue	85	35
1023	-	6f. red	1·40	35

DESIGN: 6f. Luxembourg Central Station.

270 Stage Coach

1979. Europa. Multicoloured.

1024	6f. Type **270**	6·75	55
1025	12f. Old wall telephone (vert)	6·75	2·20

271 Antoine Meyer (poet)

1979. Anniversaries.

1026	-	2f. purple	75	35
1027	**271**	5f. red	60	35
1028	-	6f. turquoise	60	35
1029	-	9f. grey-black	2·30	60

DESIGNS—36×36 mm: 2f. Michel Pintz on trial (after L. Piedboeuf) and monument to rebels (180th anniv of peasant uprising against French). 22×36 mm: 5f. Type **271** (150th anniv of first publication in Luxembourg dialect); 6f. S. G. Thomas (cent of purchase of Thomas patent for steel production); 9f. "Abundance crowning Work and Saving" (ceiling painting by August Vinet) (50th anniv of Stock Exchange).

272 "European Assembly"

1979. First Direct Elections to European Assembly.

1030	**272**	6f. multicoloured	1·70	1·00

273 Blindfolded Cherub with Chalice

1979. Rococo Art. Details from altar of St. Michael's Church by Barthelemy Namur. Multicoloured.

1031	6f. Type **273**	55	40
1032	12f. Cherub with anchor	1·00	1·00

274 Child with Traffic Symbol Balloons jumping over Traffic

1979. International Year of the Child.

1033	**274**	2f. blue, brown and red	60	30

1979. 50th Anniv of Broadcasting in Luxembourg.

1034	**275**	6f. blue and red	90	35

275 Radio Waves, "RTL" and Dates

1979. National Welfare Fund. Glass Paintings (2nd series). As T 267. Multicoloured.

1035	2f.+25c. "Spring"	30	30
1036	5f.+25c. "Summer"	40	35
1037	6f.+50c. "Charity"	55	40
1038	12f.+1f. "Autumn"	1·10	2·10
1039	20f.+8f. "Winter"	2·10	7·00

1980. Luxembourg Culture. Medieval Coins in the State Museum. As T 268. Multicoloured.

1040	2f. Grosso of Emperor Henry VII	40	25
1041	5f. Grosso of John the Blind of Bohemia	40	40
1042	6f. "Mouton d'or" of Wenceslas I and Jeanne, Duke and Duchess of Brabant	1·10	25
1043	20f. Grosso of Wenceslas II, Duke of Luxembourg	2·50	1·10

276 State Archives Building

1980. Tourism.

1044	**276**	6f. purple, ultram & bl	1·20	30
1045	-	6f. red and brown	1·30	30

DESIGN—VERT: No. 1045, Ettelbruck Town Hall.

277 Jean Monnet (statesman)

1980. Europa.

1046	**277**	6f. black	2·75	30
1047	-	12f. olive	4·00	1·40

DESIGN: 12f. St. Benedict of Nursia (founder of Benedictine Order) (statue in Echternach Abbey).

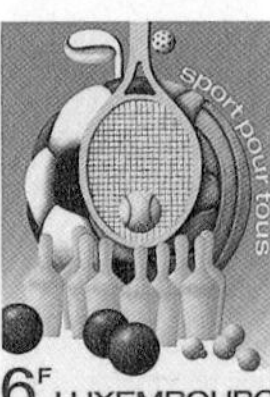

278 Sports Equipment

1980. "Sports for All".

1048	**278**	6f. black, orange & green	1·70	55

279 Gloved Hand protecting Worker from Machinery

1980. 9th World Congress on the Prevention of Accidents at Work and Occupational Diseases, Amsterdam.

1049	-	2f. multicoloured	55	25
1050	**279**	6f. brown, grey and red	70	40

DESIGN—VERT: 2f. Worker pouring molten iron.

280 "Mercury" (Jean Mich)

1980. Art Nouveau Sculpture. Statues beside entrance to State Savings Bank.

1051	**280**	8f. lilac	90	40
1052	-	12f. blue	1·10	1·00

DESIGN: 12f. "Ceres" (Jean Mich).

281 Postcoded Letter

1980. Postcode Publicity.

1053	**281**	4f. brown, ochre and red	95	40

282 Policemen and Patrol Car

1980. 50th Anniv of National Police Force.

1054	**282**	8f. multicoloured	95	40

1980. National Welfare Fund. Glass Paintings (3rd series). As T 267. Multicoloured.

1055	4f.+50c. "St. Martin"	55	30
1056	6f.+50c. "St. Nicholas"	55	35
1057	8f.+1f. "Virgin and child"	85	1·40
1058	30f.+10f. "St. George"	3·75	6·75

283 Grand Duke Jean

1981. Grand Duke Jean's 60th Birthday. Sheet 115×73 mm containing T 283 and similar vert design.

MS1059	8f. Type **283**; 12f. Grand Duke Jean's coat of arms; 30f. Type **283**	3·25	2·75

1981. Luxembourg Culture. Coins in the State Museum. As T 268.

1060	4f. Patagon of Philip IV of Spain, 1635	40	25
1061	6f. 12 sols coin of Maria Theresa, 1775	65	40
1062	8f. 12 sols coin of Emperor Joseph II, 1789	65	40
1063	30f. Siege crown of Emperor Francis II, 1795	2·20	1·50

284 European Parliament Building, Luxembourg

1981. Tourism.

1064	**284**	8f. brown and blue	70	45
1065	-	8f. red and blue	70	45

DESIGN: No. 1065, National Library.

285 Cock-shaped Whistle sold at Easter Monday Market

1981. Europa. Multicoloured.

1066	8f. Procession of beribboned sheep and town band to local fair	2·20	40
1067	12f. Type **285**	3·25	85

286 Staunton Knight on Chessboard

1981. Anniversaries.

1068	**286**	4f. multicoloured	85	40
1069	-	8f. ochre, brown & silver	85	40
1070	-	8f. multicoloured	85	40

DESIGNS—VERT: 4f. Type **286** (50th anniv of Luxembourg Chess Federation); 8f. (1070), Pass-book and State Savings Bank (125th anniv of State Savings Bank). HORIZ: 8f. (1069), First Luxembourg banknote (125th anniv of International Bank of Luxembourg's issuing rights).

287 Prince Henri and Princess Maria Teresa

1981. Royal Wedding.

1071	**287**	8f. multicoloured	75	55

288 Gliders over Useldange

1981. Aviation. Multicoloured.

1072	8f. Type **288**	85	45
1073	16f. Cessna 172F Skyhawk LX-AIZ and 182H Skylane sports planes	1·40	1·10
1074	35f. Boeing 747-200F over Luxembourg-Findel airport terminal	2·50	1·30

289 Flame

1981. Energy Conservation.

1075	**289**	8f. multicoloured	85	45

290 Arms of Petange

1981. National Welfare Fund. Arms of Local Authorities (1st series). Multicoloured.

1076	4f.+50c. Type **290**	30	30
1077	6f.+50c. Larochette	35	35
1078	8f.+1f. "Adoration of the Magi" (School of Rubens)	55	45
1079	16f.+2f. Stadtbredimus	1·10	2·50
1080	35f.+12f. Weiswampach	3·75	7·00

See also Nos. 1097/1101 and 1119/23.

291 "Apple Trees in Blossom" (Frantz Seimetz)

1982. Luxembourg Culture. Landscapes through the Four Seasons. Multicoloured.

1081	4f. Type **291**	40	35
1082	6f. "Landscape" (Pierre Blanc)	55	45
1083	8f. "The Larger Hallerbach" (Guido Oppenheim)	75	35
1084	16f. "Winter Evening" (Eugene Mousset)	1·50	1·00

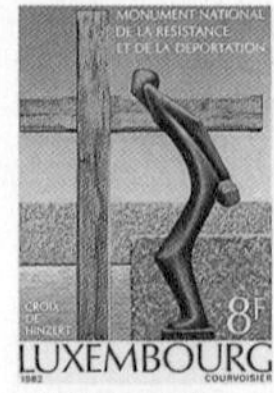

292 Cross of Hinzert and Statue "Political Prisoner" (Lucien Wercollier)

1982. National Monument of the Resistance and Deportation, Notre-Dame Cemetery.

1085	**292**	8f. multicoloured	70	40

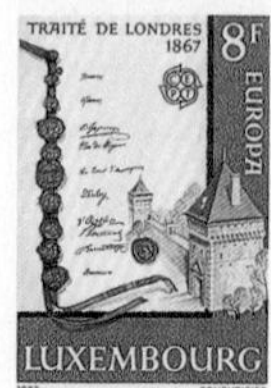

293 Treaty of London, 1867, and Luxembourg Fortress

1982. Europa. Multicoloured.

1086	8f. Type **293**	2·75	55
1087	16f. Treaty of Paris, 1951, and European Coal and Steel Community Building, Luxembourg	3·25	1·10

294 St. Theresa of Avila (wood statue, Carmel Monastery)

1982. Anniversaries. Multicoloured.

1088		4f. Type **294** (400th death anniv)	45	30
1089		8f. Raoul Follereau (social worker for lepers, 5th death anniv)	55	35

295 State Museum

1982. Tourism.

1090	**295**	8f. brown, blue and black	55	40
1091	-	8f. buff, black and blue	55	40

DESIGN: No. 1091, Luxembourg Synagogue.

296 Bourscheid Castle

1982. Classified Monuments (1st series).

1092	**296**	6f. blue	80	40
1093	-	8f. red	90	40

DESIGN—HORIZ: 8f. Vianden Castle.
See also Nos. 1142/3 and 1165/6.

297 Key in Lock

1982. Anniversaries. Multicoloured.

1094		4f. Type **297** (50th anniv of International Youth Hostel Federation)	90	40
1095		8f. Scouts holding hands around globe (75th anniv of Scouting Movement) (vert)	1·10	40

298 Monument to Civilian and Military Deportation

1982. Civilian and Military Deportation Monument, Hollerich Station.

1096	**298**	8f. multicoloured	85	45

1982. National Welfare Fund. Arms of Local Authorities (2nd series) and Stained Glass Window (8f.). As T 290. Multicoloured.

1097		4f.+50c. Bettembourg	30	20
1098		6f.+50c. Frisange	40	35
1099		8f.+1f. "Adoration of the Shepherds" (Gustav Zanter, Hoscheid parish church)	70	45
1100		16f.+2f. Mamer	1·40	2·50
1101		35f.+12f. Heinerscheid	3·75	7·00

300 "Mercury" (Auguste Tremont)

1983. Anniversaries and Events.

1104	**300**	4f. multicoloured	45	40
1105	-	6f. multicoloured	45	40
1106	-	8f. brown, black and blue	55	40
1107	-	8f. deep blue and blue	55	40

DESIGNS: No. 1104, Type **300** (25th Congress of International Association of Foreign Exchange Dealers); 1105, N.A.T.O. emblem surrounded by flags of member countries (25th anniv of N.A.T.O.); 1106, Echternach Cross of Justice (30th Congress of International Union of Barristers); 1107, Globe and customs emblem (30th anniv of Customs Co-operation Council).

301 Robbers attacking Traveller

1983. Europa. Miniatures from "Codex Aureus Escorialensis", illustrating Parable of the Good Samaritan. Multicoloured.

1108		8f. Type **301**	4·50	75
1109		16f. Good Samaritan helping traveller	6·75	2·20

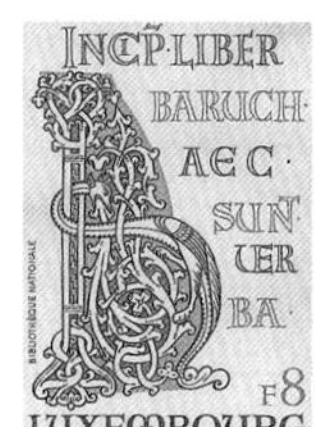

302 Initial "H" from "Book of Baruch"

1983. Luxembourg Culture. Echternach Abbey Giant Bible. Multicoloured.

1110		8f. Type **302**	75	45
1111		35f. Initial "B" from letter of St. Jerome to Pope Damasius I	2·20	1·50

303 Despatch Rider and Postcode

1983. World Communications Year. Mult.

1112		8f. Type **303**	1·50	35
1113		8f. European Communications Satellite (horiz)	3·00	40

304 St. Lawrence's Church, Diekirch

1983. Tourism.

1114	**304**	7f. orange, brown and blue	70	40
1115	-	10f. orange, brown & bl	80	40

DESIGN—HORIZ: 10f. Dudelange Town Hall.

305 Basketball

1983. Anniversaries and Events. Multicoloured.

1116		7f. Type **305** (50th anniv of Luxembourg basketball Federation)	90	50
1117		10f. Sheepdog (European Working Dog Championships)	1·10	50
1118		10f. City of Luxembourg ("The Green Heart of Europe")	1·80	50

1983. National Welfare Fund. Arms of Local Authorities (3rd series) and Painting. As T 290. Multicoloured.

1119		4f.+1f. Winseler	45	45
1120		7f.+1f. Beckerich	55	45
1121		10f.+1f. "Adoration of the Shepherds" (Lucas Bosch)	85	45
1122		16f.+2f. Feulen	1·50	2·75
1123		40f.+13f. Mertert	3·75	7·25

306 Lion and First Luxembourg Stamp

1984. Anniversaries. Each black, red and blue.

1124		10f. Type **306**	1·10	45
1125		10f. Lion and ministry buildings	1·10	45
1126		10f. Lion and postman's bag	1·10	45
1127		10f. Lion and diesel locomotive	1·10	45

ANNIVERSARIES: No. 1124, 50th anniv of Federation of Luxembourg Philatelic Societies; 1125, 75th anniv of Civil Service Trade Union Movement; 1126, 75th anniv of Luxembourg Postmen's Trade Union; 1127, 125th anniv of Luxembourg Railways.

307 Pedestrian Precinct

1984. Environmental Protection. Multicoloured.

1128		7f. Type **307**	1·00	55
1129		10f. City of Luxembourg sewage treatment plant	1·00	55

308 Hands supporting European Parliament Emblem

1984. 2nd Direct Elections to European Parliament.

1130	**308**	10f. multicoloured	1·10	45

309 Bridge

1984. Europa. 25th Anniv of European Post and Telecommunications Conference.

1131	**309**	10f. green, dp green & blk	5·50	55
1132	**309**	16f. orange, brown & blk	8·25	2·20

310 "The Smoker" (David Teniers the Younger)

1984. Paintings. Multicoloured.

1133		4f. Type **310**	85	40
1134		7f. "Young Turk caressing his Horse" (Eugene Delacroix) (horiz)	1·10	45
1135		10f. "Ephiphany" (Jan Steen) (horiz)	1·60	45
1136		50f. "The Lacemaker" (Pieter van Slingelandt)	5·50	4·00

311 "The Race" (Jean Jacoby)

1984. Olympic Games, Los Angeles.

1137	**311**	10f. orange, black & blue	1·00	55

312 "Pecten sp."

1984. Luxembourg Culture. Fossils in the Natural History Museum. Multicoloured.

1138		4f. Type **312**	70	35
1139		7f. Devil's toe-nail	80	50
1140		10f. "Coeloceras raquinianum" (ammonite)	1·40	40
1141		16f. Dapedium (fish)	1·70	1·30

1984. Classified Monuments (2nd series). As T 296.

1142		7f. turquoise	85	50
1143		10f. brown	85	50

DESIGNS: 7f. Hollenfels Castle; 10f. Larochette Castle.

313 "American Soldier" (statue by Michel Heitz at Clervaux)

1984. 40th Anniv of Liberation.

1144	**313**	10f. black, red and blue	2·50	50

314 Infant astounded by Surroundings

1984. National Welfare Fund. The Child. Mult.

1145		4f.+1f. Type **314**	55	55
1146		7f.+1f. Child dreaming	85	85
1147		10f.+1f. "Nativity (crib, Steinsel church)	1·40	85
1148		16f.+2f. Child sulking	3·25	4·25
1149		40f.+13f. Girl admiring flower	9·50	11·00

299 Modern Fire Engine

1983. Centenary of National Federation of Fire Brigades. Multicoloured.

1102		8f. Type **299**	1·40	55
1103		16f. Hand fire-pump (18th century)	1·70	1·10

315 Jean Bertels (abbot of Echternach Abbey)

1985. Luxembourg Culture. Portrait Medals in State Museum (1st series). Multicoloured.

No.	Description	Mint	Used
1150	4f. Type **315** (steatite medal, 1595)	55	35
1151	7f. Emperor Charles V (bronze medal, 1537)	70	50
1152	10f. King Philip II of Spain (silver medal, 1555)	90	40
1153	30f. Maurice of Orange-Nassau (silver medal, 1615)	2·75	1·50

See also Nos. 1173/6.

316 Fencing

1985. Anniversaries. Multicoloured.

No.	Description	Mint	Used
1154	10f. Type **316** (50th anniv of Luxembourg Fencing Federation)	1·00	50
1155	10f. Benz "Velo" (centenary of automobile)	1·00	50
1156	10f. Telephone within concentric circles (centenary of Luxembourg telephone service)	1·00	50

317 Papal Arms

1985. Visit of Pope John Paul II.

No.	Type	Description	Mint	Used
1157	317	10f. multicoloured	95	45

318 Treble Clef within Map of National Anthem

1965. Europa. Music Year. Multicoloured.

No.	Description	Mint	Used
1158	10f. Type **318** (Grand Duke Adolphe Union of choral, instrumental and folklore societies)	5·50	55
1159	16f. Neck of violin, music school and score of Beethoven's Violin Concerto opus 61	9·00	2·75

319 Maquisards Badge and "Wounded Soldiers" (sculpture, Rene Weyland)

1985. 40th Anniv of V.E. (Victory in Europe) Day. Sheet 120×72 mm containing T 319 and similar vert designs.

MS1160 10f. multicoloured (Type **319**); 10f. brown, black and blue (War medal); 10f. multicoloured (Union of Resistance Movements badge); 10f. black, red and blue (dove and barbed wire hands) (liberation of prison camps) 5·50 5·00

320 Little Owl

1985. Endangered Animals. Multicoloured.

No.	Description	Mint	Used
1161	4f. Type **320**	1·40	55
1162	7f. European wildcat (horiz)	2·50	85
1163	10f. Red admiral (horiz)	3·75	85
1164	50f. European tree frog	7·75	3·00

1985. Classified Monuments (3rd series). As T 296.

No.	Description	Mint	Used
1165	7f. red	70	40
1166	10f. green	70	40

DESIGNS—HORIZ: 7f. Echternach orangery. VERT: 10f. Mohr de Waldt house.

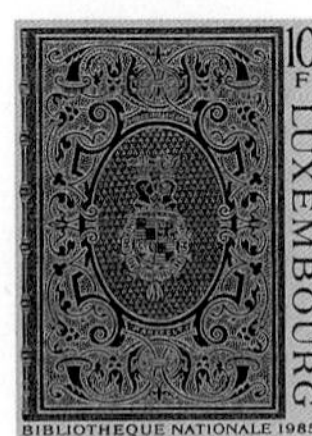

321 Mansfeld Arms (book binding)

1985. Luxembourg Culture.

No.	Type	Description	Mint	Used
1167	321	10f. multicoloured	95	45

322 Application

1985. National Welfare Fund. Multicoloured.

No.	Description	Mint	Used
1168	4f.+1f. Type **322**	55	55
1169	7f.+1f. Friendship	85	85
1170	10f.+1f. "Adoration of the Magi" (16th century alabaster sculpture)	1·50	85
1171	16f.+2f. Child identifying with his favourite characters	3·75	4·50
1172	40f.+13f. Shame	11·00	14·00

1986. Luxembourg Culture. Portrait Medals in State Museum (2nd series). As T 315.

No.	Description	Mint	Used
1173	10f. multicoloured	1·00	55
1174	12f. multicoloured	1·00	40
1175	18f. black, grey and blue	1·10	95
1176	20f. multicoloured	1·70	1·10

DESIGNS: 10f. Count of Monterey (silver medal, 1675); 12f. Louis XIV of France (silver medal, 1684); 18f. Pierre de Weyms (president of Provincial Council) (pewter medal, 1700); 20f. Duke of Marlborough (silver medal, 1706).

323 Bee on Flower

1986. Anniversaries. Multicoloured.

No.	Description	Mint	Used
1177	12f. Type **323** (centenary of Federation of Luxembourg Beekeeper's Associations)	1·30	55
1178	12f. Table tennis player (50th anniv of Luxembourg Table Tennis Federation)	1·30	55
1179	11f. Mosaic of woman with water jar (centenary of Mondorf State Spa)	1·30	55

324 Forest and City

1986. Europa. Multicoloured.

No.	Description	Mint	Used
1180	12f. Type **324**	4·00	55
1181	20f. Mankind, industry and countryside	5·00	2·00

325 Fort Thungen

1986. Luxembourg Town Fortifications. Mult.

No.	Description	Mint	Used
1182	15f. Type **325**	2·30	70
1183	18f. Invalids' Gate (vert)	2·30	70
1184	50f. Malakoff Tower (vert)	3·75	1·00

326 Schuman

1986. Birth Centenary of Robert Schuman (politician).

No.	Type	Description	Mint	Used
1185	326	2f. black and red	20	20
1186	326	10f. black and blue	55	45

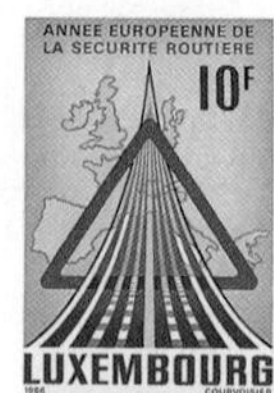

327 Road through Red Triangle on Map

1986. European Road Safety Year.

No.	Type	Description	Mint	Used
1187	327	10f. multicoloured	85	45

328 Ascent to Chapel of the Cross, Grevenmacher

1986. Tourism.

No.	Type	Description	Mint	Used
1188	328	12f. multicoloured	1·40	40
1189	-	12f. brown, stone and red	1·40	40

DESIGN: No. 1189, Relief from Town Hall facade, Esch-sur-Alzette.

329 Presentation of Letter of Freedom to Echternach (after P. H. Witkamp)

1986. 800th Birth Anniv of Countess Ermesinde of Luxembourg.

No.	Type	Description	Mint	Used
1190	329	12f. brown and stone	95	35
1191	-	30f. buff, black and grey	2·10	1·40

DESIGN: 30f. Seal, 1238.

330 Annunciation

1986. National Welfare Fund. Illustrations from 15th-century "Book of Hours". Multicoloured.

No.	Description	Mint	Used
1192	6f.+1f. Type **330**	1·40	55
1193	10f.+1f. Angel appearing to shepherds	85	55
1194	12f.+2f. Nativity	1·50	75
1195	18f.+2f. Adoration of the Magi	4·00	4·50
1196	20f.+8f. Flight into Egypt	7·00	8·75

331 Garden Dormouse

1987. Endangered Animals. Multicoloured.

No.	Description	Mint	Used
1197	6f. Type **331**	1·10	55
1198	10f. Banded agrion (vert)	1·70	70
1199	12f. White-throated dipper (vert)	2·50	55
1200	25f. Salamander	3·75	2·00

332 Network Emblem

1987. 50th Anniversaries. Multicoloured.

No.	Description	Mint	Used
1201	12f. Type **332** (Amateur Short Wave Network)	1·10	40
1202	12f. Anniversary Emblem (International Fair)	1·10	40

333 "St. Bernard of Siena and St. John the Baptist"

1987. Paintings by Giovanni Ambrogio Bevilacqua in State Museum. Multicoloured.

No.	Description	Mint	Used
1203	10f. Type **333**	1·00	55
1204	18f. "St. Jerome and St. Francis of Assisi"	1·60	1·10

334 National Swimming Centre (Roger Taillibert)

1987. Europa. Architecture. Multicoloured.

No.	Description	Mint	Used
1205	12f. Type **334**	4·50	75
1206	20f. European Communities' Court of Justice	6·75	2·20

335 "Consecration" (stained glass window by Gustav Zanter)

1987. Millenary of St. Michael's Church. Multicoloured.

No.	Description	Mint	Used
1207	12f. Type **335**	1·20	55
1208	20f. Baroque organ-chest	2·10	1·10

336 Charles Metz (first President) (after Jean-Baptiste Fresez)

1987. Chamber of Deputies.

No.	Type	Description	Mint	Used
1209	336	6f. brown	60	35
1210	-	12f. blue	95	55

DESIGN: 12f. Chamber of Deputies building.

337 Hennesbau, Niederfeulen

1987. Rural Architecture. Each ochre, brown and blue.

1211	10f. Type **337**	1·10	60
1212	12f. 18th-century dwelling house converted to health centre, Mersch	1·10	45
1213	100f. 18th-century house converted to Post Office, Bertrange	7·00	1·40

338 Annunciation

1987. National Welfare Fund. Illustrations from 15th-century Paris "Book of Hours". Multicoloured.

1214	6f.+1f. Type **338**	1·40	1·10
1215	10f.+1f. Visitation	1·80	1·70
1216	12f.+2f. Adoration of the Magi	2·50	1·70
1217	18f.+2f. Presentation in the Temple	4·50	4·00
1218	20f.+8f. Flight into Egypt	8·00	7·75

339 Lilies and Water-lily

1988. Luxembourg Culture. Flower Illustrations by Pierre-Joseph Redoute. Multicoloured.

1219	6f. Type **339**	1·10	55
1220	10f. Primulas and double narcissus	1·10	55
1221	12f. Tulips and chrysanthemums	2·50	75
1222	50f. Irises and gorterias	5·50	4·00

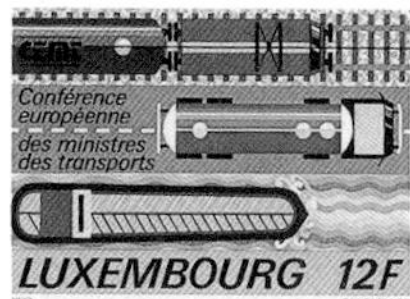
340 Rail, Road and Water Transport

1988. European Conference of Ministers of Transport, Luxembourg (1223) and 25th Anniv of Eurocontrol (air safety organization) (1224). Multicoloured.

1223	12f. Type **340**	1·40	55
1224	20f. Boeing 747 airplane	2·00	1·40

341 Princess Maria Teresa

1988. "Juvalux 88" Ninth Youth Philately Exhibition, Luxembourg. Sheet 11×72 mm containing T 341 and similar vert designs. Multicoloured.

MS1225	12f. Type **341**; 18f. Princes Guillaume, Felix and Louis; 50f. Crown Prince Henri	9·50	9·50

342 Wiltz Town Hall and Cross of Justice

1988. Tourism. Multicoloured.

1226	10f. Type **342**	1·50	45
1227	12f. Differdange Castle (vert)	1·50	65

See also Nos. 1254/5 and 1275/6.

343 Athletes

1988. 50th Anniv of League of Luxembourg Student Sports Associations.

1228	**343**	12f. multicoloured	1·40	65

344 Automated Mail Sorting

1988. Europa. Transport and Communications. Multicoloured.

1229	12f. Type **344**	8·25	55
1230	20f. Electronic communications	8·25	2·75

345 Jean Monnet (statesman, birth centenary)

1988. European Anniversaries.

1231	**345**	12f. pink, brn & lt brn	1·20	50
1232	-	12f. brown and green	1·60	50

DESIGN: No. 1232, European Investment Bank headquarters, Kirchberg (30th anniv).

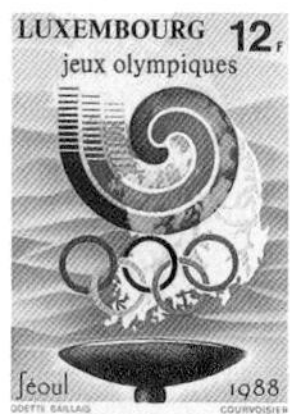
346 Emblem and Flame

1988. Olympic Games, Seoul.

1233	**346**	12f. multicoloured	1·10	55

347 Septfontaines Castle

1988. Doorways.

1234	**347**	12f. black and brown	90	45
1235	-	25f. black and green	1·80	1·40
1236	-	50f. black and brown	3·75	2·10

DESIGNS: 25f. National Library; 50f. Holy Trinity Church.

348 Annunciation to Shepherds

1988. National Welfare Fund. Illustrations from 16th-century "Book of Hours". Multicoloured.

1237	9f.+1f. Type **348**	65	55
1238	12f.+2f. Adoration of the Magi	70	55
1239	18f.+2f. Madonna and Child	3·75	3·75
1240	20f.+8f. Pentecost	4·25	4·25

349 C. M. Spoo (promoter of Luxembourgish)

1989. Anniversaries.

1241	**349**	12f. black, red and brown	85	45
1242	-	18f. multicoloured	1·40	90
1243	-	20f. red, black and grey	2·20	1·50

DESIGNS: 12f. Type **349** (75th death anniv); 18f. Stylized inking pad (125th anniv of Book Workers' Federation); 20f. Henri Dunant (founder of International Red Cross) (75th anniv of Luxembourg Red Cross).

350 Grand Ducal Family Vault Bronze (Auguste Tremont)

1989. 150th Anniv of Independence.

1244	**350**	12f. multicoloured	1·30	50

351 "Astra" Satellite and Map on T.V. Screens

1989. Launch of 16-channel T.V. Satellite.

1245	**351**	12f. multicoloured	1·30	55

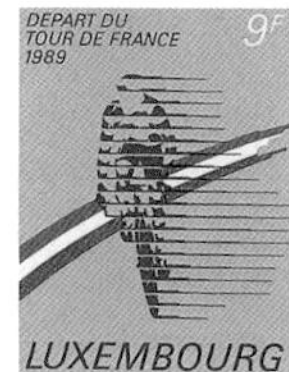
352 Cyclist

1989. Start in Luxembourg of Tour de France Cycling Race.

1246	**352**	9f. multicoloured	1·70	70

353 Assembly and Flag

1989. 40th Anniv of Council of Europe.

1247	**353**	12f. multicoloured	1·30	45

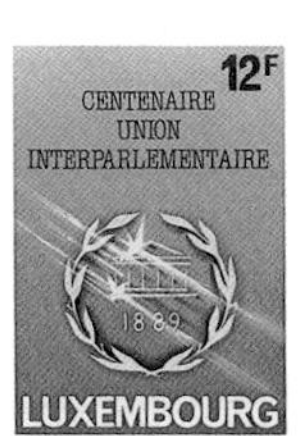
354 Emblem

1989. Centenary of Interparliamentary Union.

1248	**354**	12f. yellow, blue & indigo	1·30	45

355 Hands

1989. 3rd Direct Elections to European Parliament.

1249	**355**	12f. multicoloured	1·40	55

356 "Three Children in a Park" (anon)

1989. Europa. Children's Games and Toys. Multicoloured.

1250	12f. Type **356**	4·00	55
1251	20f. "Child with Drum" (anon)	5·00	1·70

357 Grand Duke Jean

1989. 25th Anniv of Accession of Grand Duke Jean.

1252	**357**	3f. black and orange	3·00	3·00
1253	**357**	9f. black and green	2·20	2·20

1989. Tourism. As T 342. Multicoloured.

1254	12f. Clervaux Castle	1·20	45
1255	18f. 1st-century bronze wild boar, Titelberg	1·70	1·00

358 Charles IV

1989. Luxembourg History. Stained Glass Windows by Joseph Oterberger, Luxembourg Cathedral. Multicoloured.

1256	12f. Type **358**	85	55
1257	20f. John the Blind	1·70	1·30
1258	25f. Wenceslas II	2·00	1·70

359 St. Lambert and St. Blase, Fennange

1989. National Welfare Fund. Restored Chapels (1st series). Multicoloured.

1259	9f.+1f. Type **359**	70	45
1260	12f.+2f. St. Quirinus, Luxembourg (horiz)	95	80
1261	18f.+3f. St. Anthony the Hermit, Reisdorf (horiz)	2·20	3·00
1262	25f.+8f. The Hermitage, Hachiville	4·75	4·50

See also Nos. 1280/3 and 1304/7.

360 Funfair (650th anniv of Schueberfouer)

1990. Anniversaries.

1263	**360**	9f. multicoloured	1·10	55
1264	-	12f. brown, pink & black	95	45
1265	-	18f. multicoloured	1·50	1·70

DESIGNS: 12f. Batty Weber (writer, 50th death anniv); 18f. Dish aerial (125th anniv of International Telecommunications Union).

361 Troops at Fortress

1990. Luxembourg Culture. Etchings of the Fortress by Christoph Wilhelm Selig. Multicoloured.

1266	9f. Type **361**	90	55
1267	12f. Soldiers by weir	95	55
1268	20f. Distant view of fortress	2·30	1·40
1269	25f. Walls	3·00	1·50

362 Paul Eyschen (75th anniv)

1990. Statesmen's Death Anniversaries.

1270	**362**	9f. brown and blue	75	55
1271	-	12f. blue and brown	95	55

DESIGN: 12f. Emmanuel Servais (centenary).

363 "Psallus pseudoplatini" (male and female) on Maple

1990. Centenary of Luxembourg Naturalists' Society.

1272	**363**	12f. multicoloured	1·00	50

364 General Post Office, Luxembourg City

1990. Europa. Post Office Buildings.

1273	**364**	12f. black and brown	5·50	55
1274	-	20f. black and blue	6·75	2·20

DESIGN—VERT: 20f. Esch-sur-Alzette Post Office.

1990. Tourism. As T 342. Multicoloured.

1275	12f. Mondercange administrative offices	1·60	40
1276	12f. Schifflange town hall and church	1·60	40

365 Hammelsmarsch Fountain (Will Lofy)

1990. Fountains. Multicoloured.

1277	12f. Type **365**	1·20	55
1278	25f. Doves Fountain	2·20	1·40
1279	50f. Maus Ketty Fountain, Mondorf-les-Bains (Will Lofy)	4·50	2·50

366 Congregation of the Blessed Virgin Mary, Vianden

1990. National Welfare Fund. Restored Chapels (2nd series). Multicoloured.

1280	9f.+1f. Type **366**	85	65
1281	12f.+2f. Notre Dame, Echternach (horiz)	1·40	85
1282	18f.+3f. Consoler of the Afflicted, Grentzingen (horiz)	2·50	2·30
1283	25f.+8f. St. Pirmin, Kaundorf	4·75	4·50

367 Grand Duke Adolf

1990. Centenary of Nassau-Weilbourg Dynasty. Sheet 115×160 mm containing T 367 and similar vert designs. Multicoloured.

MS1284	12f. Type **367**; 12f. Grand Duchess Marie Adelaide; 18f. Grand Ducal arms; 18f. Grand Duchess Charlotte; 20f. Grand Duke William IV; 20f. Grand Duke Jean	12·50	12·50

368 "Geastrum varians"

1991. Fungi. Illustrations by Pierre-Joseph Redoute. Multicoloured.

1285	14f. Type **368**	1·00	75
1286	14f. "Agaricus (Gymnopus) thiebautii"	1·00	75
1287	18f. "Agaricus (Lepiota) lepidocephalus"	1·80	1·30
1288	25f. "Morchella favosa"	2·10	1·40

369 "View from the Trier Road"

1991. Luxembourg Culture. 50th Death Anniv of Sosthene Weis (painter). Multicoloured.

1289	14f. Type **369**	1·40	65
1290	18f. "Vauban Street and the Viaduct"	1·40	1·00
1291	25f. "St. Ulric Street" (vert)	2·50	1·50

370 Dicks (after Jean Goedert)

1991. Death Centenary of Edmond de la Fontaine (pen-name Dicks) (poet).

1292	**370**	14f. multicoloured	1·40	70

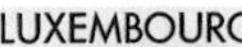

371 Claw grasping Piece of Metal (after Emile Kirscht)

1991. 75th Anniv of Trade Union Movement in Luxembourg.

1293	**371**	14f. multicoloured	1·40	70

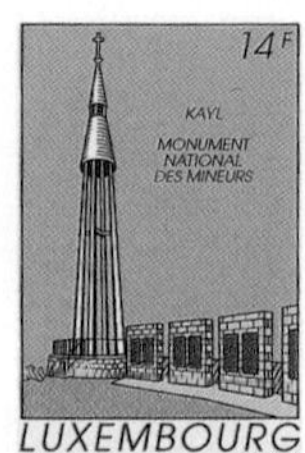

372 National Miners' Monument, Kayl

1991. Tourism. Multicoloured.

1294	14f. Type **372**	1·40	70
1295	14f. Magistrates' Court, Redange-sur-Attert (horiz)	1·40	70

373 Earth and Orbit of "Astra 1A" and "1B" Satellites

1991. Europa. Europe in Space. Multicoloured.

1296	14f. Type **373**	4·50	85
1297	18f. Betzdorf Earth Station	5·50	2·20

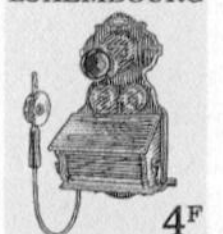

374 Telephone

1991. Posts and Telecommunications.

1298	**374**	4f. brown	4·00	2·50
1299	-	14f. blue	1·10	85

DESIGN: 14f. Postbox.

375 1936 International Philatelic Federation Congress Stamp

1991. 50th Stamp Day.

1300	**375**	14f. multicoloured	1·40	55

The stamp illustrated on No. 1300 incorrectly shows a face value of 10f.

376 Girl's Head

1991. Mascarons (stone faces on buildings) (1st series).

1301	**376**	14f. black, buff & brown	1·10	55
1302	-	25f. black, buff and pink	1·60	1·30
1303	-	50f. black, buff and blue	3·00	2·40

DESIGNS: 25f. Woman's head; 50f. Man's head.

See also Nos. 1320/22.

377 Chapel of St. Donatus, Arsdorf

1991. National Welfare Fund. Restored Chapels (3rd series). Multicoloured.

1304	14f.+2f. Type **377**	1·50	85
1305	14f.+2f. Chapel of Our Lady of Sorrows, Brandenbourg (horiz)	1·50	1·10
1306	18f.+3f. Chapel of Our Lady, Luxembourg (horiz)	2·40	2·50
1307	22f.+7f. Chapel of the Hermitage, Wolwelange	4·25	4·25

378 Jean-Pierre Pescatore Foundation

1992. Buildings. Multicoloured.

1308	14f. Type **378**	1·10	70
1309	14f. Higher Technology Institute, Kirchberg	1·10	70
1310	14f. New Fairs and Congress Centre, Kirchberg	1·10	70

379 Inner Courtyard, Bettembourg Castle

1992. Tourism. Multicoloured.

1311	18f. Type **379**	1·40	95
1312	25f. Walferdange railway station	2·00	1·30

380 Athlete (detail of mural, Armand Strainchamps)

1992. Olympic Games, Barcelona.

1313	**380**	14f. multicoloured	2·10	65

381 Luxembourg Pavilion

1992. "Expo '92" World's Fair, Seville.

1314	**381**	14f. multicoloured	1·10	65

382 Lions Emblem

1992. 75th Anniv of Lions International.

1315	**382**	14f. multicoloured	1·60	55

383 Memorial Tablet (Lucien Wercollier)

1992. 50th anniv of General Strike.

1316	**383**	18f. brown, grey and red	1·60	1·00

384 Nicholas Gonner (editor)

1992. Europa. 500th anniv of Discovery of America by Columbus. Luxembourg Emigrants to America.

1317	**384**	14f. brown, black & green	4·50	85
1318	-	22f. blue, black & orange	4·50	2·20

DESIGN: 22f. Nicolas Becker (writer).

385 Star and European Community Emblem

1992. Single European Market.

1319	**385**	14f. multicoloured	1·10	55

1992. Mascarons (2nd series). As T 376.

1320		14f. black, buff and green	1·20	55
1321		22f. black, buff and blue	1·80	1·40
1322		50f. black, buff and purple	3·00	2·40

DESIGNS: 14f. Ram's head; 22f. Lion's head; 50f. Goat's head.

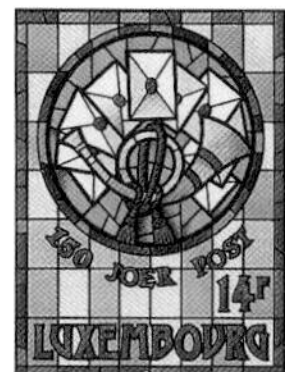

386 Posthorn and Letters

1992. 150th Anniv of Post and Telecommunications Office. Designs showing stained glass windows by Auguste Tremont. Mult.

1323		14f. Type **386**	95	70
1324		22f. Post rider	2·10	1·70
1325		50f. Telecommunications	3·00	4·50

387 Hazel Grouse

1992. National Welfare Fund. Birds (1st series). Multicoloured.

1326		14f.+2f. Type **387**	1·40	1·40
1327		14f.+2f. Golden oriole (vert)	1·40	1·40
1328		18f.+3f. Black stork	4·00	3·50
1329		22f.+7f. Red kite (vert)	7·00	6·25

See also Nos. 1364/7 and 1383/6.

388 Grand Duke Jean

1993

1330	**388**	1f. black and yellow	40	10
1331	**388**	2f. black and green	40	25
1332	**388**	5f. black and yellow	55	25
1333	**388**	7f. black and brown	55	25
1334	**388**	8f. black and green	1·10	45
1335	**388**	9f. black and mauve	70	45
1336	**388**	10f. black and blue	85	50
1337	**388**	14f. black and purple	2·00	55
1338	**388**	15f. black and green	1·30	75
1339	**388**	16f. black and orange	1·80	1·20
1340	**388**	18f. black and yellow	1·20	55
1341	**388**	20f. black and red	1·70	85
1342	**388**	22f. black and green	1·60	1·20
1343	**388**	25f. black and blue	1·70	1·30
1344	**388**	100f. black and brown	6·25	4·00

389 Old Ironworks Cultural Centre, Steinfort

1993. Tourism. Multicoloured.

1350		14f. Type **389**	1·30	55
1351		14f. "Children with Grapes" Fountain, Schwebsingen	1·30	55

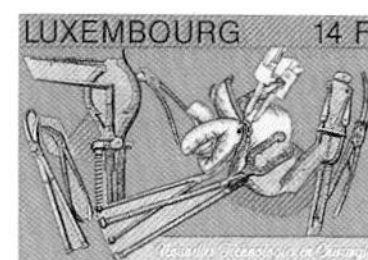

390 Collage by Maurice Esteve

1993. New Surgical Techniques.

1352	**390**	14f. multicoloured	1·20	65

391 Hotel de Bourgogne (Prime Minister's offices)

1993. Historic Houses. Multicoloured.

1353		14f. Type **391**	1·30	75
1354		20f. Simons House (now Ministry of Agriculture)	2·10	1·00
1355		50f. Cassal House	4·50	2·50

392 "Rezlop" (Fernand Roda)

1993. Europa. Contemporary Art. Multicoloured.

1356		14f. Type **392**	1·50	75
1357		22f. "So Close" (Sonja Roef)	4·00	1·70

393 Monument (detail, D. Donzelli), Tetange Cemetery

1993. 75th Death Anniv of Jean Schortgen (first worker elected to parliament).

1358	**393**	14f. multicoloured	1·30	60

394 Emblem

1993. Centenary of Artistic Circle of Luxembourg.

1359	**394**	14f. mauve and violet	1·30	60

395 European Community Ecological Label

1993. Protection of Environment.

1360	**395**	14f. blue, green & emerald	1·20	85

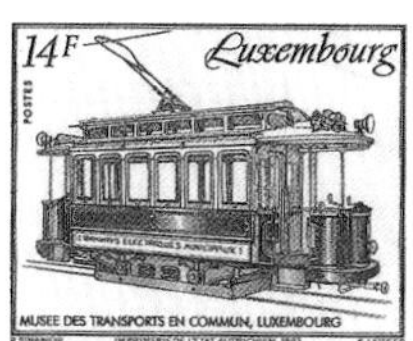

396 Tram No. 1 (Transport Museum, Luxembourg)

1993. Museum Exhibits (1st series). Multicoloured.

1361		14f. Type **396**	1·30	60
1362		22f. Iron ore tipper wagon (National Mining Museum, Rumelange)	1·90	1·60
1363		60f. Horse-drawn carriage (Arts and Ancient Crafts Museum, Wiltz)	4·75	3·75

See also Nos. 1404/6 and 1483/4.

1993. National Welfare Fund. Birds (2nd series). As T 387. Multicoloured.

1364		14f.+2f. Common snipe ("Becassine")	2·10	1·80
1365		14f.+2f. River kingfisher ("Martin-Pecheur") (vert)	2·10	1·80
1366		18f.+3f. Little ringed plover ("Petit Gravelot")	3·50	4·00
1367		22f.+7f. Sand martin ("Hirondelle de Rivage") (vert)	6·50	6·00

397 "Snow-covered Landscape" (Joseph Kutter)

1994. Artists' Birth Centenaries. Multicoloured.

1368		14f. Type **397**	1·60	70
1369		14f. "The Moselle" (Nico Klopp)	1·60	70

398 Members' Flags

1994. 4th Direct Elections to European Parliament.

1370	**398**	14f. multicoloured	1·40	1·30

399 17th-century Herald's Tabard

1994. Congresses. Multicoloured.

1371		14f. Type **399** (21st International Genealogy and Heraldry Congress)	2·30	90
1372		18f. International Police Association emblem on map (14th World Congress)	2·40	1·10

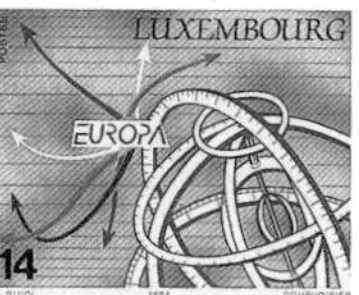

400 Arrows and Terrestrial Globe

1994. Europa. Discoveries. Multicoloured.

1373		14f. Type **400**	2·75	1·30
1374		22f. Chart, compass rose and sails	4·75	2·75

401 "Family" (Laura Lammar)

1994. International Year of the Family.

1375	**401**	25f. multicoloured	4·00	2·00

402 Crowds cheering American Soldiers

1994. 50th Anniv of Liberation.

1376	**402**	14f. multicoloured	1·40	1·10

403 Western European Union Emblem (40th anniv)

1994. Anniversaries and Campaign.

1377	**403**	14f. blue, lilac and ultramarine	2·10	90
1378	-	14f. multicoloured	2·10	90
1379	-	14f. multicoloured	5·25	2·10

DESIGNS—No. 1378, Emblem (25th anniv in Luxembourg of European Communities' Office for Official Publications); 1379, 10th-century B.C. ceramic bowl from cremation tomb, Bigelbach (European Bronze Age Campaign).

404 Munster Abbey (General Finance Inspectorate)

1994. Former Refuges now housing Government Offices. Multicoloured.

1380		15f. Type **404**	1·60	1·40
1381		25f. Holy Spirit Convent (Ministry of Finance)	2·30	1·80
1382		60f. St. Maximine Abbey of Trier (Ministry of Foreign Affairs)	5·00	3·50

1994. National Welfare Fund. Birds (3rd series). As T 387. Multicoloured.

1383		14f.+2f. Common stonechat ("Traquet Patre") (vert)	2·50	2·10
1384		14f.+2f. Grey partridge ("Perdix Grise")	2·50	2·10
1385		18f.+3f. Yellow wagtail ("Bergeronnette Printaniere")	4·25	4·25
1386		22f.+7f. Great grey shrike ("Pie-Grieche Grise") (vert)	7·25	5·00

405 "King of the Antipodes"

406/409 Panoramic View of City (image scaled to 43% of original size)

1995. Luxembourg, European City of Culture.

1387	**405**	16f. multicoloured	2·50	1·40
1388	-	16f. multicoloured	2·50	1·40
1389	-	16f. multicoloured	2·50	1·40

1390	406	16f. multicoloured	1·80	95
1391	407	16f. multicoloured	1·80	95
1392	408	16f. multicoloured	1·80	95
1393	409	16f. multicoloured	1·80	95
1394	-	16f. multicoloured	1·80	95

DESIGNS—As T **405**: No. 1388, "House with Arcades and Yellow Tower"; 1389, "Small Path" (maze). 35×26 mm: No. 1394, Emblem.

Nos. 1390/3 were issued together, se-tenant, forming the composite design illustrated.

410 Landscape and Slogan

1995. European Nature Conservation Year.

1395	410	16f. multicoloured	1·80	1·30

411 Colour Spectrum and Barbed Wire

1995. Europa. Peace and Freedom. 50th Anniv of Liberation of Concentration Camps. Mult.

1396	16f. Type **411**	2·75	1·40
1397	25f. Wire barbs breaking through symbolic sky and earth	3·50	2·75

412 Emblem

1995. Anniversaries and Event. Multicoloured.

1398	16f. Type **412** (6th Small European States Games, Luxembourg)	1·60	1·10
1399	32f. Diagram of section through Earth (27th anniv of underground Geodynamics Laboratory, Walferdange) (33×34 mm)	3·50	2·75
1400	80f. Anniversary emblem (50th anniv of U.N.O.)	7·25	5·75

413 Boeing 757

1995. 40th Anniv of Luxembourg–Iceland Air Link.

1401	413	16f. multicoloured	1·40	1·10

414 Erpeldange Castle

1995. Tourism. Multicoloured.

1402	16f. Type **414**	1·80	1·10
1403	16f. Schengen Castle	1·80	1·10

1995. Museum Exhibits (2nd series). Vert designs as T 396. Multicoloured.

1404	16f. Churn (Country Art Museum, Vianden)	1·60	90
1405	32f. Wine-press (Wine Museum, Ehnen)	3·50	2·10
1406	80f. Sculpture of potter (Leon Nosbusch) (Pottery Museum, Nospelt)	8·25	4·75

415 Stained Glass Window from Alzingen Church

1995. Christmas.

1407	415	16f.+2f. multicoloured	3·25	3·25

416 Broad-leaved Linden ("Tilia platyphyllos")

1995. National Welfare Fund. Trees (1st series). Multicoloured.

1408	16f.+2f. Type **416**	1·80	1·40
1409	16f.+2f. Horse chestnut ("Aesculus hippocastanum") (horiz)	1·80	1·40
1410	20f.+3f. Pedunculate oak (horiz)	2·75	2·50
1411	32f.+7f. Silver birch	5·25	5·00

See also Nos. 1432/5 and 1458/61.

417 Mayrisch (after Theo van Rysselberghe)

1996. 68th Death Anniv of Emile Mayrisch (engineer).

1412	417	A (16f.) multicoloured	1·80	1·10

418 Mounument, Place Clairefontaine (Jean Cardot)

1996. Birth Centenary of Grand Duchess Charlotte.

1413	418	16f. multicoloured	2·30	1·40

419 Electric Railcar

1996. 50th Anniv of Luxembourg National Railway Company. Multicoloured.

1414	16f. Type **419**	2·75	1·10
1415	16f. Linked cars	2·75	1·10
1416	16f. Train (right-hand detail)	2·75	1·10

Nos. 1414/16 were issued together, se-tenant, forming a composite design of a Series 2000 electric railcar set.

420 "Marie Munchen"

1996. 96th Death Anniv of Mihaly Munkacsy (painter). Multicoloured.

1417	16f. Type **420**	1·60	1·10
1418	16f. Munkacsy (after Edouard Charlemont) (horiz)	1·60	1·10

421 Workers and Emblem

1996. Anniversaries.

1419	421	16f. green, orge & blk	1·60	1·10
1420	-	20f. multicoloured	1·90	1·40
1421	-	25f. multicoloured	2·40	1·90
1422	-	32f. multicoloured	3·50	2·50

DESIGNS—HORIZ: 16f. Type **421** (75th anniv of Luxembourg Confederation of Christian Trade Unions); 32f. Film negative (centenary of motion pictures). VERT: 20f. Transmitter and radio waves (centenary of Guglielmo Marconi's patented wireless telegraph); 25f. Olympic flame and rings (centenary of modern Olympic Games).

422 Marie de Bourgogne

1996. Europa. Famous Women. Duchesses of Luxembourg. Multicoloured.

1423	16f. Type **422**	2·50	1·40
1424	25f. Maria-Theresa of Austria	4·00	2·75

423 Handstamp

1996. Bicentenary (1995) of Registration and Property Administration.

1425	423	16f. multicoloured	1·80	1·10

424 Children of different Cultures (Michele Dockendorf)

1996. "Let us Live Together". Multicoloured.

1426	16f. Type **424**	1·30	1·10
1427	16f. "L'Abbraccio" (statue, Marie-Josee Kerschen) (vert)	1·30	1·10

425 Eurasian Badger

1996. Mammals. Multicoloured.

1428	16f. Type **425**	1·80	90
1429	20f. Polecat	2·75	1·40
1430	80f. European otter	7·25	5·75

1996. Christmas.

1431	426	16f.+2f. multicoloured	5·00	5·00

426 "The Birth of Christ" (icon, Eva Mathes)

1996. National Welfare Fund. Trees (2nd series). As T 416. Multicoloured.

1432	16f.+2f. Willow ("Salix sp.") (horiz)	1·80	1·40
1433	16f.+2f. Ash ("Fraxinus excelsior")	1·80	1·40
1434	20f.+3f. Mountain ash (horiz)	3·50	3·25
1435	32f.+7f. Common beech	6·00	5·75

427 John the Blind

1996. 700th Birth Anniv of John the Blind (King of Bohemia and Count of Luxembourg).

1436	427	32f. multicoloured	3·25	2·10

428 Koerich Church

1997. Tourism. Multicoloured.

1437	16f. Type **428**	1·60	1·10
1438	16f. Servais House, Mersch (horiz)	1·60	1·10

429 Birthplace of Robert Schuman (politician), Luxembourg-Clausen

1997. Anniversaries. Multicoloured.

1439	16f. Type **429** (40th anniv of Treaties of Rome establishing European Economic Community and European Atomic Energy Community)	1·80	1·10
1440	20f. National colours forming wing of Mercury (75th anniv of Belgium–Luxembourg Economic Union)	2·10	1·40

430 "Grand Duchess Charlotte"

1997. 11th World Federation of Rose Societies Congress, Belgium, Mondorf (Luxembourg) and the Netherlands. Roses. Multicoloured.

1441	16f. Type **430**	2·75	1·10
1442	20f. "The Beautiful Sultana" (33×26 mm)	2·75	1·80
1443	80f. "In Memory of Jean Soupert" (33×26 mm)	8·50	6·00

431 Badge, Luxembourg Fortress, Shako and Sword

1997. Anniversaries.

1444	**431**	16f. multicoloured	1·80	1·10
1445	-	16f. black, blue and red	1·80	1·10
1446	-	16f. brown, green and pink	1·80	1·10

DESIGNS—As T **431**: No. 1444, Type **431** (bicentenary of Grand Ducal Gendarmerie Corps); 1445, Cock and rabbit (75th anniv of Luxembourg Union of Small Domestic Animals Farming Societies). 33×33 mm: No. 1446, Bather and attendant, early 1900s (150th anniv of Mondorf spa).

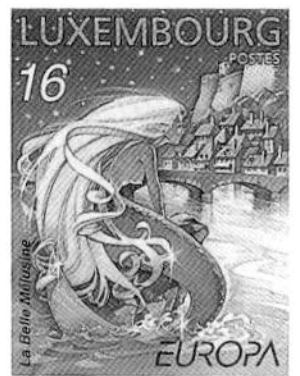

432 The Beautiful Melusina

1997. Europa. Tales and Legends. Multicoloured.

1447	16f. Type **432**	2·75	1·10
1448	25f. The Hunter of Hollenfels	4·25	2·75

433 Face on Globe

1997. "Juvalux 98" Youth Stamp Exhibition (1st issue). Multicoloured.

1449	16f. Type **433**	2·10	1·10
1450	80f. Postmen (painting, Michel Engels)	7·50	6·50

See also Nos. 1475/8.

434 Emblem

1997. Sar–Lor–Lux (Saarland–Lorraine–Luxembourg) European Region.

1451	**434**	16f. multicoloured	1·80	1·10

Stamps in similar designs were issued by France and Germany.

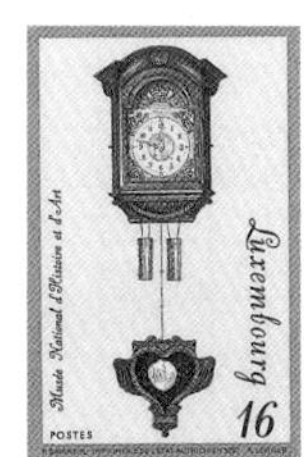

435 Wall Clock by Dominique Nauens, 1816

1997. Clocks. Multicoloured.

1452	16f. Type **435**	2·10	1·10
1453	32f. Astronomical clock by J. Lebrun, 1850 (26×44 mm)	4·75	2·30
1454	80f. Wall clock by Mathias Hebeler, 1815	8·25	5·25

436 "Kalborn Mill" (Jean-Pierre Gleis)

1997. Water Mills. Multicoloured.

1455	16f. Type **436**	2·10	95
1456	50f. Interior of Ramelli mill, 1588 (from book "The Water Wheel" by Wilhelm Wolfel) (vert)	5·00	3·50

437 Holy Family

1997. Christmas.

1457	**437**	16f.+2f. multicoloured	4·25	4·25

1997. National Welfare Fund. Trees (3rd series). As T 416. Multicoloured.

1458	16f.+2f. Wych elm ("Ulmus glabra")	1·80	1·80
1459	16f.+2f. Norway maple ("Acer platanoides")	1·80	1·80
1460	20f.+3f. Wild cherry	3·50	3·50
1461	32f.+7f. Walnut (horiz)	5·00	5·00

438 Count Henri V

1997. 750th Anniv of Accession of Henri V, Count of Luxembourg.

1462	**438**	32f. multicoloured	3·50	2·10

439 Rodange Church

1998. Tourism. Multicoloured.

1463	16f. Type **439**	1·80	1·10
1464	16f. Back of local authority building, Hesperange (horiz)	1·80	1·10

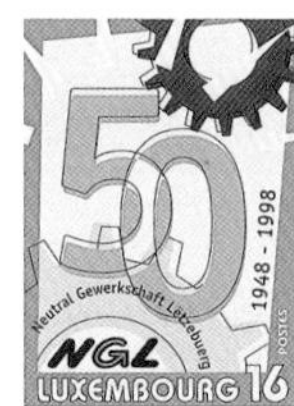

440 Cog and "50"

1998. Anniversaries.

1465	**440**	16f. multicoloured	2·30	1·10
1466	-	16f. multicoloured	2·30	1·10
1467	-	20f. multicoloured	2·30	1·30
1468	-	50f. black, red and stone	5·75	3·50

DESIGNS: No. 1465, Type **440** (50th anniv of Independent Luxembourg Trade Union); 1466, Festival poster (Rene Wismer) (50th anniv of Broom Festival, Wiltz); 1467, Memorial (death centenary of Jean Antoine Zinnen (composer of national anthem)); 1468, Typewriter keys and page from first issue of "Luxemburger Wort" (150th anniv of abolition of censorship).

441 Brown Trout

1998. Freshwater Fishes. Multicoloured.

1469	16f. Type **441**	2·75	1·30
1470	25f. Bullhead	5·00	2·75
1471	50f. Riffle minnow	6·50	4·00

442 Henri VII and Flags outside Fair Venue, Kirchberg

1998. 700th Anniv of Granting to Count Henri VII of Right to Hold a Fair. Value indicated by letter.

1472	**442**	A (16f.) multicoloured	2·10	1·10

443 Fireworks over Adolphe Bridge (National Day)

1998. Europa. National Festivals. Multicoloured.

1473	16f. Type **443**	3·50	1·10
1474	25f. Stained-glass window and flame (National Remembrance Day)	4·25	2·75

444 Town Postman, 1880

1998. "Juvalux '98" Youth Stamp Exhibition (2nd issue). Multicoloured.

1475	16f. Type **444**	2·10	1·10
1476	25f. Letter, 1590 (horiz)	2·75	2·10
1477	50f. Rural postman, 1880	4·25	3·25
MS1478	125×76 mm 16f., 80f. Railway viaduct and city (composite design)	13·50	13·50

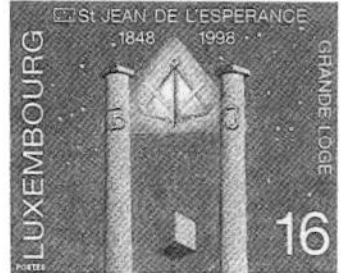

445 Masonic Symbols (Paul Moutschen)

1998. 150th Anniv of St. John of Hope Freemason Lodge.

1479	**445**	16f. multicoloured	2·10	1·30

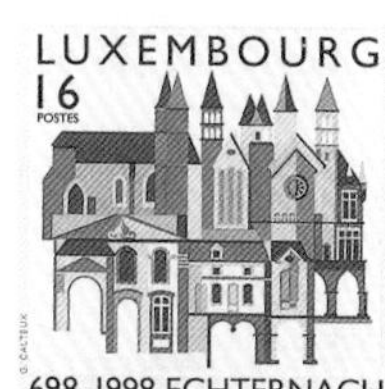

446 Echternach

1998. 1300th Anniv of Echternach Abbey. Multicoloured.

1480	16f. Type **446**	2·10	1·10
1481	48f. Buildings in Echternach	4·75	3·75
1482	60f. Echternach Abbey	5·00	4·00

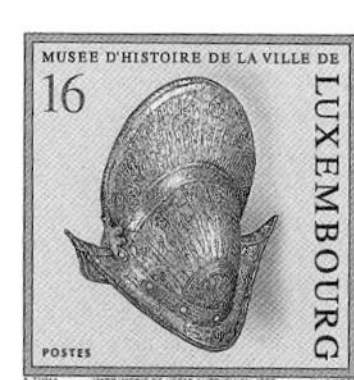

447 Spanish Morion (late 16th century)

1998. Museum Exhibits (3rd series). City of Luxembourg History Museum. Multicoloured.

1483	16f. Type **447**	2·50	1·10
1484	80f. Wayside Cross from Hollerich (1718)	5·75	5·50

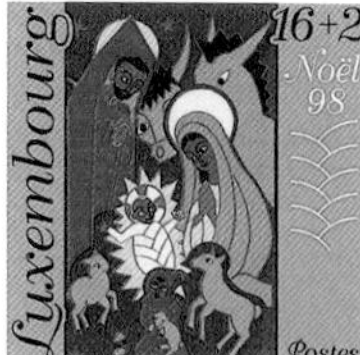

448 "Nativity" (altarpiece by Georges Saget, St. Mauritius Abbey, Clervaux)

1998. Christmas.

1485	**448**	16f.+2f. multicoloured	4·25	4·25

449 "Bech"

1998. National Welfare Fund (1st series). Villages. 16th-century drawings by Jean Bertels. Multicoloured.

1486	16f.+2f. Type **449**	2·50	1·90
1487	16f.+2f. "Ermes Turf" (now Ermsdorf)	2·50	1·90
1488	20f.+3f. "Itsich" (now Itzig)	3·25	2·30
1489	32f.+7f. "Stein Hem" (now Steinheim)	4·75	5·25

See also Nos. 1510/13 and 1550/3.

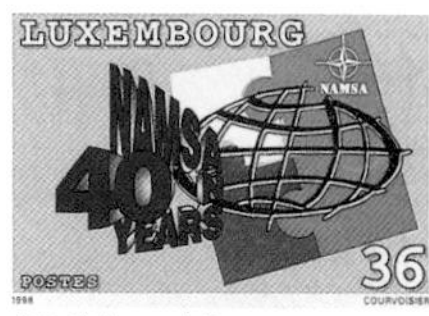

450 Globe and Jigsaw

1998. 40th Anniv of North Atlantic Maintenance and Supply Agency.

1490	**450**	36f. multicoloured	4·75	3·25

451 Council Building and Emblem

1999. 50th Anniv of Council of Europe.

1491	**451**	16f. multicoloured	2·10	1·40

452 Euro Coin and Map

1999. Introduction of the Euro (European currency). Value expressed by letter.

1492	**452**	A (16f.) multicoloured	2·10	1·10

453 Tawny Owl

1999. Owls. Multicoloured.

1493	A (16f.) Type **453**	2·10	1·30
1494	32f. Eagle owl (horiz)	3·25	3·00
1495	60f. Barn owl (horiz)	6·50	5·25

454 Globe and Emblem

1999. 50th Anniv of N.A.T.O.

1496	**454**	80f. multicoloured	7·25	5·75

455 Spectacles

1999. International Year of the Elderly.
1497 **455** 16f. multicoloured 1·80 1·10

456 Emblem and Envelopes

1999. 125th Anniv of Universal Postal Union.
1498 **456** 16f. multicoloured 1·80 1·10

457 Haute-Sure National Park

1999. Europa. Parks and Gardens. Multicoloured.
1499 16f. Type **457** 3·50 1·40
1500 25f. Ardennes-Eifel National Park 4·25 2·50

458 Emblem

1999. Anniversaries. Multicoloured.
1501 16f. Type **458** (75th anniv of National Federation of Mutual Socieites) 1·80 1·10
1502 32f. Camera and roll of film (50th anniv of Luxembourg Federation of Amateur Photographers) 2·75 2·75
1503 80f. Gymnasts (centenary of Luxembourg Gymnastics Federation) 7·25 5·75

460 Cars on Motorway

1999. 18th Birthday of Prince Guillaume.
1504 **459** 16f. multicoloured 1·40 1·10

459 Prince Guillaume

1999. Communications of the Future. Mult.
1505 16f. Type **460** 1·60 1·30
1506 20f. Earth and satellite 2·10 2·00
1507 80f. Planets and spacecraft 7·25 5·75

461 A. Mayrisch de Saint-Hubert

1999. 125th Birth Anniv of Aline Mayrisch de Saint-Hubert (President of Luxembourg Red Cross).
1508 **461** 20f. multicoloured 2·40 1·40

462 Decorated Church Tower

1999. Christmas.
1509 **462** 16f.+2f. multicoloured 3·25 2·75

1999. National Welfare Fund. Villages (2nd series). As T 449, showing 6th-century drawings by Jean Bertels. Multicoloured.
1510 16f.+2f. "Oswiler" (now Osweiler) 2·75 2·10
1511 16f.+2f. "Bettem Burch" (now Bettembourg) 2·75 2·10
1512 20f.+3f. "Cruchte auf der Alset" (now Cruchten) 3·25 3·25
1513 32f.+7f. "Berchem" 5·25 5·25

463 "Gateway" (sketch by Goethe)

1999. 250th Birth Anniv of Johann Wolfgang von Goethe (poet and playwright).
1514 **463** 20f. chestnut, cream & brn 2·40 1·40

464 "2000"

2000. New Millennium. Value expressed by letter. Multicoloured. Self-adhesive.
1515 A (16f.) Type **464** (blue streaks emanating from bottom right) 2·00 1·40
1516 A (16f.) Blue streaks emanating from bottom left 2·00 1·40
1517 A (16f.) Blue streaks emanating from top right 2·00 1·40
1518 A (16f.) Blue streaks emanating from top left 2·00 1·40

465 Charles V

2000. 500th Birth Anniv of Emperor Charles V. Value expressed by letter.
1519 **465** A (16f.) multicoloured 1·80 1·10

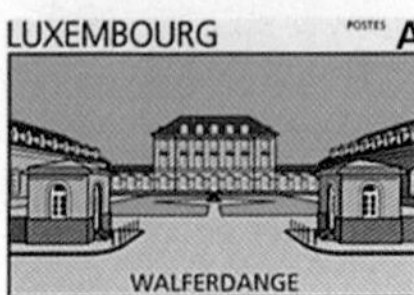

466 Walferdange Castle

2000. Tourism. Value expressed by letter. Multicoloured.
1520 A (16f.) Type **466** 1·30 1·10
1521 A (16f.) Local government offices, Wasserbillig (vert) 1·30 1·10

467 "2000" and Formulae

2000. World Mathematics Year.
1522 **467** 80f. multicoloured 6·25 4·50

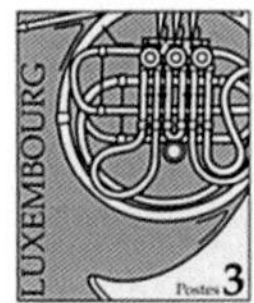

468 French Horn

2000. Musical Instruments.
1523 **468** 3f. black and violet 50 25
1524 - 9f. black and green 1·40 90
1525 - 12f. black and yellow 1·10 95
1526 - 21f. black and pink 1·90 1·40
1527 - 24f. black and blue 2·75 2·00
1528 - 30f. black and pink 2·50 2·00

DESIGNS: 9f. Electric guitar; 12f. Saxophone; 21f. Violin; 24f. Accordion; 30f. Grand piano.

469 Production and Storage Facilities, 1930s (Harry Rabinger)

2000. Centenary (1999) of Esch-sur-Alzette Gas Works.
1535 **469** 18f. multicoloured 2·50 1·60

470 Mallard

2000. Ducks. Multicoloured.
1536 18f. Type **470** 2·50 1·80
1537 24f. Common pochard (vert) 3·25 2·50
1538 30f. Tufted duck (vert) 4·25 3·25

471 "Building Europe"

2000. Europa.
1539 **471** 21f. multicoloured 2·50 1·80

472 Jean Monnet and Robert Schuman

2000. 50th Anniv of Schuman Plan (proposal for European Coal and Steel Community).
1540 **472** 21f. black, blue & yellow 2·50 2·00

473 Blast Furnace

2000. 20th Anniv of Blast Furnace "B", Esch-Belval.
1541 **473** A (18f.) multicoloured 2·50 1·10

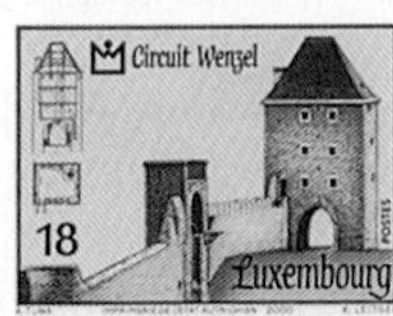

474 Castle Walls and Tower (Wenzel Walk)

2000. Circular City Walks. Multicoloured.
1542 18f. Type **474** 2·10 1·20
1543 42f. Bridge and tower (Vauban walk) 5·00 3·75

475 Will Kesseler

2000. Swearing in of Prince Henri as Head of State of Grand Duchy of Luxembourg. Multicoloured.
1544 18f. Type **475** 1·80 2·00
MS1545 125×90 mm. 100f. Prince Henri in civilian clothes and Princess Maria 19·00 6·50

476 Prince Henri in Uniform and Princess Maria

2000. Modern Art (1st series). Showing paintings by artist named. Multicoloured.
1546 21f. Type **476** 2·30 1·80
1547 24f. Joseph Probst (vert) 2·40 1·20
1548 36f. Mett Hoffmann 3·25 1·40

See also Nos. 1612/14.

477 Child before Christmas Tree

2000. Christmas.
1549 **477** 18f.+2f. multicoloured 2·75 2·75

2000. National Welfare Fund. Villages (3rd series). As T 449 showing 16th-century drawings by Jean Bertels. Multicoloured.
1550 18f.+2f. "Lorentzwiller" (now dorentzweiler) 2·10 2·00
1551 21f.+3f. "Coosturf" (now Consdorf) 2·75 2·75
1552 24f.+3f. "Elfingen" (now Elvange) 3·25 2·75
1553 36f.+7f. "Sprenckigen" (now Sprinkange) 4·75 4·75

478 Bestgensmillen Mill, Schifflange

2001. Tourism. Multicoloured.
1554 18f. Type **478** 1·80 1·40
1555 18f. Vineyard, Wormeldange (vert) 1·80 1·40

479 Nik Welter

2001. Writers' Death Anniversaries. Multicoloured.
1556 18f. Type **479** (50th anniv) 1·70 1·40
1557 24f. Andre Gide (50th anniv) 2·30 1·90
1558 30f. Michel Rodange (125th anniv) 2·75 2·50

480 Signatures and Seal

2001. 50th Anniv of Treaty of Paris.
1559 **480** 21f. multicoloured 2·50 1·80

481 Citroen 2CV Mini-Van

2001. Postal Vehicles. Mult. Self-adhesive.

No.	Description	Mint	Used
1560	3f. Type **481**	50	30
1561	18f. Volkswagen Beetle	2·10	1·30

482 Stream, Mullerthal

2001. Europa. Water Resources. Multicoloured. Value expressed by letter (No. 1562) or with face value (No. 1563).

No.	Description	Mint	Used
1562	A (18f.) Type **482**	2·10	1·40
1563	21f. Pond and Kaltreis water tower (vert)	2·75	1·80

483 "Mother and Child" (Ger Maas)

2001. Humanitarian Projects. Multicoloured.

No.	Description	Mint	Used
1564	18f. Type **483** (humanitarian aid)	2·10	1·40
1565	24f. International Organization for Migration emblem	3·25	2·50

484 MD Helicopters MD Explorer and Rescuer

2001. Rescue Services. Multicoloured.

No.	Description	Mint	Used
1566	18f. Type **484**	2·10	1·40
1567	30f. Divers and rubber dinghy	2·75	2·50
1568	45f. Fire engine and fireman wearing protective clothing	4·75	3·50

DENOMINATION. From No. 1569 Luxembourg stamps are denominated in euros only.

485 Five Cent Coin

2001. Euro Currency. Coins. Multicoloured.

No.	Description	Mint	Used
1569	5c. Type **485**	50	50
1570	10c. Ten cent coin	55	55
1571	20c. Twenty cent coin	1·10	70
1572	50c. Fifty cent coin	1·80	1·40
1573	€1 One euro coin	3·25	2·75
1574	€2 Two euro coin	6·50	5·75

486 Grand Duke Henri

2001. Grand Duke Henri.

No.	Type	Description	Mint	Used
1575		1c. indigo, blue and ultramarine	25	25
1576		3c. olive, green and ultramarine	30	30
1580	**486**	7c. dp blue, blue & red	25	25
1583	**486**	22c. sepia, brown & red	60	45
1584	**486**	25c. lilac and ultramarine	60	45
1585	**486**	30c. dp green, grn & red	70	60
1588	**486**	45c. dp violet, vio & red	1·10	70
1589	**486**	50c. black and ultramarine	1·20	1·00
1590	**486**	52c. brown, buff and red	1·30	1·20
1591	**486**	59c. deep blue, blue and red	1·40	1·20
1592	**486**	60c. black, green and blue	1·40	1·20
1592a	**486**	70c. lilac ultramarine	1·80	1·60
1593	**486**	74c. brown, stone and red	1·80	1·50
1594	**486**	80c. agate, green and blue	1·90	1·60
1595	**486**	89c. mauve, brown and red	2·20	1·70
1595a	**486**	90c. brown, ochre and ultramarine	2·30	1·90
1595b	**486**	€1 blue, azuree and ultramarine	2·75	2·40

487 Emblem

2001. European Year of Languages. Value expressed by letter.

No.	Type	Description	Mint	Used
1596	**487**	A (45c.) multicoloured	1·20	85

488 Sun, Wind-powered Generators and Houses (renewable energy)

2001. Environment and Medicine of the Future. Multicoloured.

No.	Description	Mint	Used
1597	45c. Type **488**	1·20	1·20
1598	59c. Tyre, tins, bottle and carton (recycling)	1·80	1·70
1599	74c. Microscope and test-tubes (biological research)	1·80	1·70

489 St. Nicholas

2001. Christmas.

No.	Type	Description	Mint	Used
1600	**489**	45c.+5c. multicoloured	1·80	1·70

490 Squirrel

2001. National Welfare Fund. Animals (1st issue). Multicoloured.

No.	Description	Mint	Used
1601	45c.+5c. Type **490**	1·60	1·40
1602	52c.+8c. Wild boar	1·80	1·60
1603	59c.+11c. Hare (vert)	2·10	1·90
1604	89c.+21c. Wood pigeon (vert)	3·00	2·75

See also Nos. 1632/5 and 1660/3.

491 Emblem

2001. Kiwanis International (community organization).

No.	Type	Description	Mint	Used
1605	**491**	52c. dp blue, bl & gold	1·80	1·50

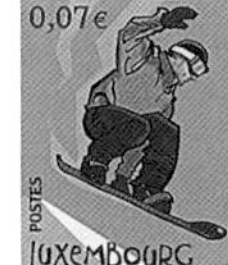

492 Snowboarding

2002. Sports. Self-adhesive. Multicoloured.

No.	Description	Mint	Used
1606	7c. Type **492**	25	25
1607	7c. Skateboarding	25	25
1608	7c. Inline skating	25	25
1609	45c. BMX biking	1·20	1·20
1610	45c. Beach volleyball	1·20	1·20
1611	45c. Street basketball	1·20	1·20

493 Mortiz Ney

2002. Modern Art (2nd series). Showing works by artist named. Multicoloured.

No.	Description	Mint	Used
1612	22c. Type **493**	60	60
1613	45c. Dany Prum (horiz)	1·20	1·20
1614	59c. Christiane Schmit	1·80	1·70

494 Map of Europe and "1977"

2002. Anniversaries. Multicoloured.

No.	Description	Mint	Used
1615	45c. Type **494** (25th anniv of European Court of Auditors)	1·20	1·20
1616	52c. Scales of Justice and map of Europe (50th anniv of European Communities Court of Justice)	1·80	1·70

495 Tightrope Walker

2002. Europa. The Circus. Multicoloured.

No.	Description	Mint	Used
1617	45c. Type **495**	1·20	1·20
1618	52c. Clown juggling	1·80	1·70

496 Emblem

2002. 2002 Tour de France (starting in Luxembourg). Multicoloured.

No.	Description	Mint	Used
1619	45c. Type **496**	1·20	60
1620	52c. Francois Faber (winner of 1909 Tour de France) (vert)	1·80	1·70
1621	€2.45 "The Champion" (Joseph Kutter) (vert)	6·75	6·50

497 Orchestra on Stage (50th Anniv of Festival of Wiltz)

2002. Cultural Anniversaries. Value expressed by letter (No. 1622) or face value (No. 1623). Multicoloured.

No.	Description	Mint	Used
1622	A (45c.) Type **497**	1·20	1·20
1623	€1.12 Victor Hugo and signature (birth bicentenary)	3·50	3·50

498 Grand Duke William III of Netherlands

2002. 150th Anniv of First Luxembourg Stamp (1st issue). Sheet 121×164 mm, containing T 498 and similar horiz designs. Multicoloured.

No.	Description	Mint	Used
MS1624	45c. Type **498**; 45c. Grand Duke Adolphe; 45c. Grand Duchess Charlotte; 45c. Grand Duke Henri	6·00	5·75

See also Nos. 1630/1.

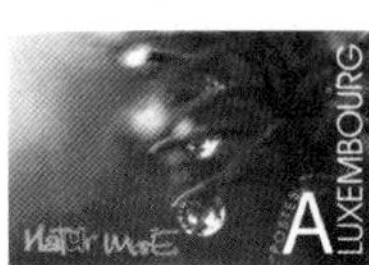

499 Water Droplet on Spruce

2002. Natural History Museum. Multicoloured. Value expressed by letter. Self-adhesive.

No.	Description	Mint	Used
1625	A (45c.) Type **499**	1·20	1·20
1626	A (45c.) Mocker swallowtail	1·20	1·20
1627	A (45c.) Houseleek	1·20	1·20
1628	A (45c.) Blackthorn berries	1·20	1·20

500 Emblem

2002. 750th Anniv of Grevenmacher City Charter.

No.	Type	Description	Mint	Used
1629	**500**	74c. multicoloured	1·80	1·70

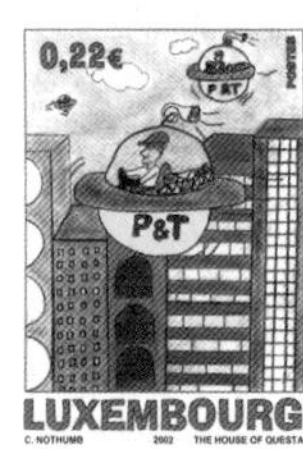

501 Postmen in Flying Vehicles (Clare Nothumb)

2002. 150th Anniv of First Luxembourg Stamp (2nd issue). Winning Entries in Stamp Design Competition. (a) With face value.

No.	Description	Mint	Used
1630	22c. Type **501**	60	60

(b) Value expressed by letter.

No.	Description	Mint	Used
1631	A (45c.) Symbols of communications and flying saucer orbiting planet (Christine Hengen) (horiz)	1·20	1·20

502 Fox

2002. National Welfare Fund. Animals (2nd series). Multicoloured.

No.	Description	Mint	Used
1632	45c.+5c. Type **502**	1·20	1·20
1633	52c.+8c. Hedgehog (vert)	1·40	1·40
1634	59c.+11c. Pheasant	1·70	1·60
1635	89c.+21c. Deer (vert)	3·00	2·75

503 Place d'Armes

2002. Christmas.

No.	Type	Description	Mint	Used
1636	**503**	45c.+5c. multicoloured	1·20	1·20

No. 1636 was issued in se-tenant sheetlets of 12 stamps, the margins of which were impregnated with the scent of cinnamon.

504 Grand Duke Jean and Grand Duchess Josephine-Charlotte

2003. Golden Wedding Anniversary of Grand Duke Jean and Grand Duchess Josephine-Charlotte.

1637	**504**	45c. multicoloured	1·20	1·20

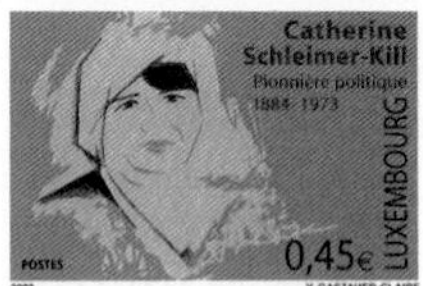

505 Catherine Schleimer-Kill

2003. 30th Death Anniversaries. Multicoloured.

1638	45c. Type **505** (political pioneer)	1·20	1·20
1639	45c. Lou Koster (composer)	1·20	1·20

506 Citeaux Abbey, Differdange

2003. Tourism. Multicoloured.

1640	50c. Type **506**	1·20	1·20
1641	€1 Mamer Castle	2·40	2·30
1642	€2.50 St. Joseph Church, Esch-sur-Alzette (vert)	6·00	5·75

507 Pamphlets and Compact Discs

2003. 50th Anniv of Official Journal of European Communities (daily publication of official reports).

1643	**507**	52c. multicoloured	1·80	1·70

508 Head and Symbols

2003. 400th Anniv of the Athenee (secondary school), Luxembourg.

1644	**508**	45c. multicoloured	1·20	1·00

509 1952 National Lottery Poster (Roger Gerson)

2003. Europa. Poster Art. Multicoloured.

1645	45c. Type **509**	1·20	1·00
1646	52c. Tiger (1924 Commercial Fair poster) (Auguste Tremont)	1·30	1·10

510 Adolphe Bridge

2003. Bridges and Viaducts. Multicoloured.

1647	45c. Type **510** (centenary)	1·20	1·00
1648	59c. Stierchen bridge (14th-century) (38×28 mm)	1·40	1·20
1649	89c. Victor Bodson bridge (Hesperange viaduct) (38×28 mm)	2·20	1·80

511 Woman Hoeing

2003. 75th Anniv of Gaart an Heem (gardening association). Multicoloured.

1650	25c. Type **511**	60	50
1651	A (45c.) Woman holding rake	1·20	1·00
1652	€2 Children	4·75	4·00

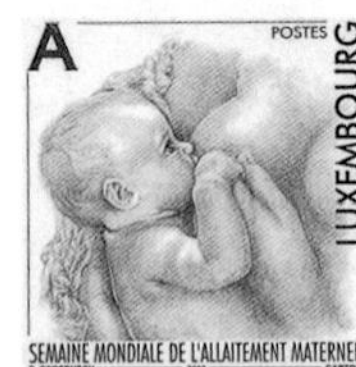

512 Baby at Breast

2003. Breastfeeding Campaign.

1653	**512**	A (45c.) brown, chestnut and black	1·20	1·00

513 Light Bulb

2003. 75th Anniv of Electricity.

1654	**513**	A (45c.) multicoloured	1·20	1·00

514 Engineering Steel Sheet Piles

2003. Made in Luxembourg. Multicoloured.

1655	60c. Type **514**	1·40	1·20
1656	70c. Medical valve	1·70	1·40
1657	80c. Technician and polyester film	1·90	1·60

515 Church and Cloud containing Buildings

2003. Christmas. Multicoloured.

1658	50c.+5c. Type **515**	1·90	1·50
1659	50c.+5c. Child, church and Christmas tree	1·90	1·50

516 Roe-deer

2003. Fauna (3rd series). Multicoloured.

1660	50c.+5c. Type **516**	1·40	1·10
1661	60c.+10c. Raccoon (horiz)	1·80	1·40
1662	70c.+10c. Weasel	2·00	1·60
1663	€1 +25c. Goshawk (horiz)	3·25	2·50

517 *Cantharellus tubaeformis*

2004. Fungi. Multicoloured. Self-adhesive.

1664	10c. Type **517**	30	25
1665	10c. *Ramaria flava*	30	25
1666	10c. *Stropharia cynea*	30	25
1667	50c. *Helvella lacunose*	1·60	1·30
1668	50c. *Anthurus archeri*	1·60	1·30
1669	50c. *Clitopilus prunulus*	1·60	1·30

518 Annual Street Market, Luxembourg-Ville

2004. Anniversaries. Multicoloured.

1670	50c. Type **518** (75th anniv)	1·60	1·30
1671	50c. Haberdashery (centenary of Esch-sur-Alzette Commercial Union)	1·60	1·30

519 Edward Steichen

2004. Birth Anniversaries. Multicoloured.

1672	**519**	50c. lilac, brown and black	1·60	1·30
1673	-	70c. blue, buff and black	2·20	1·80

DESIGNS: 50c. Type **519** (photographer) (125th); 70c. Hugo Gernsback (science fiction writer) (120th and centenary of his emigration to USA).

520 Stylized Figures

2004. European Elections.

1674	**520**	50c. multicoloured	1·60	1·30

521 Hikers on Bridge, Mullerthal

2004. Europa. Holidays. Multicoloured.

1675	50c. Type **521**	1·60	1·30
1676	60c. Camp site, Bourscheid-Beach	1·90	1·50

522 Runners carrying Olympic Flame (A. Bilska)

2004. Sport. Winning Entries in Children's Drawing Competition. Multicoloured.

1677	50c. Type **522** (Olympic Games, Athens, 2004)	1·60	1·30
1678	60c. Basketball (L. Eyschen) (European Year of Education through Sport)	1·90	1·50

523 Building and Anniversary Emblem

2004. 50th Anniv of European School, Luxembourg.

1679	**523**	70c. multicoloured	2·40	1·80

524 Breads and Beer

2004. Made in Luxembourg. Food. Multicoloured.

1680	35c. Type **524**	1·20	90
1681	60c. Meat products	2·00	1·60
1682	70c. Dairy products	2·40	1·80

525 Bull and Bear

2004. 75th Anniv of Luxembourg Stock Exchange.

1683	**525**	50c. multicoloured	1·70	1·30

526 Museum Building (Marc Angel)

2004. National Museum of History and Art. Multicoloured.

1684	50c. Type **526**	1·70	1·30
1685	€1.10 "Young Woman with a Fan" (Luigi Rubio)	3·75	2·75
1686	€3 "Charity" (Lucas Cranach)	10·00	7·75

527 Carol Singers

2004. Christmas.

1687	**527**	50c.+5c. multicoloured	2·00	1·60

528 Skiing

2004. Sport (1st series). Multicoloured.

1688	50c.+5c. Type **528**	1·90	1·40
1689	60c.+10c. Running (vert)	2·40	1·80
1690	70c.+10c. Swimming	2·75	2·10
1691	€1+25c. Football (vert)	4·25	3·25

See also Nos. 1729/32.

529 Tank, Soldiers and Liberation Monument, Schumannseck (Carlo Losch)

2004. Liberation of Luxembourg (1944–45).

1692	**529**	70c. multicoloured	2·50	1·90

530 Building

2005. Luxembourg's Presidency of European Parliament. Value expressed by letter. Multicoloured. Self-adhesive.

1693 A (50c.) Type **530** 1·70 1·30
1694 A (50c.) Roman arch, Echternach Basilica 1·70 1·30
1695 A (50c.) Moselle river, Remich 1·70 1·30
1696 A (50c.) Riveted iron plate 1·70 1·30

Nos. 1693/6 were for use on first class mail within Luxembourg.

531 Woman (painting) (A. Huberty)

2005. 150th Anniv of Ettelbruck Neuro-Psychiatric Medical Centre.

1697 **531** 50c. multicoloured 1·80 1·40

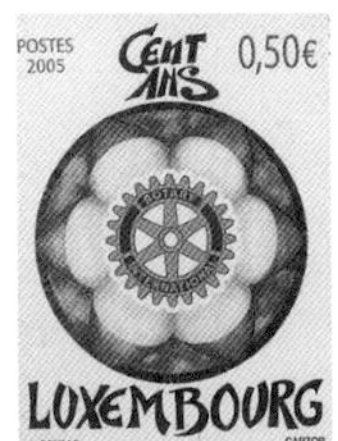

532 Emblem

2005. Centenary of Rotary International.

1698 **532** 50c. multicoloured 1·80 1·40

533 Shoe Factory, Kayl-Tetange

2005. Tourism (1st series). Multicoloured.

1699 50c. Type **533** 1·80 1·40
1700 60c. Rooftops (75th anniv of National Tourism Office) 2·10 1·70
1701 €1 St. Eloi (statue), Rodange 3·50 2·75

See also Nos. 1721/4 and 1737/8.

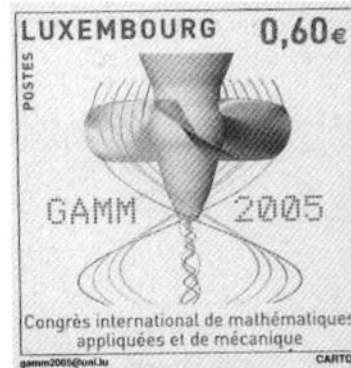

534 Turbine Air-stream Diagram

2005. GAMM 2005 International Congress of Applied Mathematics and Mechanics.

1702 **534** 60c. multicoloured 2·10 1·70

535 Parliament Building

2005. 50th Anniv of Benelux Parliament.

1703 **535** 60c. multicoloured 2·10 1·70

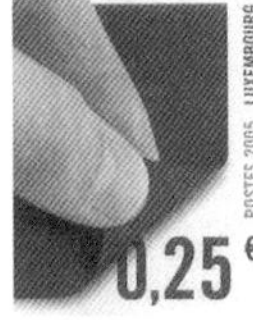

536 Fingers peeling back Label

2005. Business Stamps. Multicoloured, background colour given. Self-adhesive.

1704 **536** 25c. brown 90 70
1705 **536** 25c. red 90 70
1706 **536** 25c. salmon 90 70
1707 **536** 25c. yellow 90 70
1708 **536** 50c. bronze green 1·80 1·40
1709 **536** 50c. light green 1·80 1·40
1710 **536** 50c. bright green 1·80 1·40
1711 **536** 50c. apple green 1·80 1·40

537 Facade

2005. Opening of Grand Duchess Josephine-Charlotte Concert Hall (the Philharmonie).

1712 **537** 50c. multicoloured 1·80 1·40

538 "judd mat gaardebounen" (pork and beans)

2005. Europa. Gastronomy. Multicoloured.

1713 50c. Type **538** 1·80 1·40
1714 60c. "feierstengszalot" (diced beef and vinaigrette) 2·10 1·70

539 Rail Car CVE 357, De Jhangeli Narrow Guage Railway

2005. Railways. Multicoloured.

1715 50c. Type **539** 1·70 1·40
1716 60c. Locomotive AL-T3 2·10 1·70
1717 €2.50 Rail car PH 408 8·75 7·00

540 *Papilio machaon*

2005. Butterflies. Multicoloured.

1718 35c. Type **540** 1·20 95
1719 70c. *Argynnis paphia*(vert) 2·40 1·90
1720 €1.80 *Lysandra coridon* 6·25 5·00

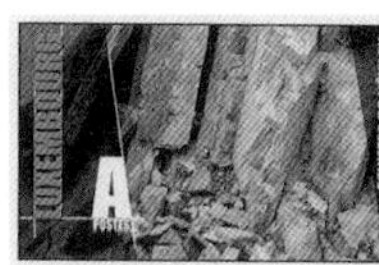

541 Schist, Eislek

2005. Tourism (2nd issue). Minerals. Value expressed by letter. Multicoloured. Self-adhesive.

1721 A (50c.) Type **541** 1·80 1·40
1722 A (50c.) Iron ore 1·80 1·40
1723 A (50c.) Sandstone 1·80 1·40
1724 A (50c.) Conglomerate, Folschette 1·80 1·40

Nos. 1721/4 were for use on first class mail within Luxembourg.

542 Jean Pierre Pescatore

2005. Anniversaries.

1725 **542** 50c. violet and grey 1·80 1·40
1726 - 90c. deep brown, brown and bistre brown 3·25 2·50
1727 - €1 bistre brown and deep brown (vert) 3·50 2·75

DESGNS: 50c. Type **542** (philanthropist) (150th death); 90c. Marcel Reuland (writer) (birth centenary); €1 Marie-Henriette Steil (writer) (75th death).

543 Shoppers

2005. Christmas.

1728 **543** 50c.+5c. multicoloured 2·00 1·50

544 Ice Skating

2005. Sport (2nd series). Multicoloured.

1729 50c.+5c. Type **544** 2·00 1·50
1730 60c.+10c. Basketball 2·75 2·20
1731 90c.+10c. Judo 3·50 2·75
1732 €1+25c. Tennis 4·50 3·50

545 Guide Dog

2005. Guide Dogs for the Blind.

1733 **545** 70c. ultramarine and yellow 2·50 1·90

No. 1733 was embossed with the value in Braille.

546 Grand Duke and Duchess

2006. 25th Wedding Anniv of Grand Duke Henri and Grand Duchess Maria Teresa. Multicoloured.

1734 50c. Type **546** 1·80 1·40
MS1735 74×102 mm. €2.50 As No. 1734 (30×40 mm.) 9·00 9·00

547 Hands

2006. Blood Donation Campaign.

1736 **547** 50c. multicoloured 1·80 1·40

548 Pigeon Tower, Birelerhaff, Sandweiler

2006. Tourism (3rd series). Multicoloured.

1737 50c. Type **548** 1·80 1·40
1738 50c. Parc Merveilleux, Bettembourg (50th anniv) (horiz) 1·80 1·40

549 Electric Locomotive

2006. 50th Anniv of Electrification of Luxembourg Rail Network. Multicoloured.

1739 50c. Type **549** 1·80 1·40
1740 70c. Train on viaduct 2·50 1·90
1741 €1 Repairs to overhead cables (vert) 3·50 2·75

550 "2006"

2006. Centenary of Esch-sur-Alzette (town).

1742 **550** 50c. multicoloured 1·80 1·40

551 Hands forming Heart-shape (Anne Marie Simon)

2006. Europa. Integration. Winning entries in MMS Photograph Competition. Multicoloured.

1743 50c. Type **551** 1·80 1·40
1744 70c. Hands holding globe (Tamara da Silva) 2·50 1·90

552 Early Match (centenary of first Luxembourg football club)

2006. Football. Multicoloured.

1745 50c. Type **552** 1·80 1·40
1746 90c. Emblem and football (World Cup Football Championship, Germany) 3·25 2·50

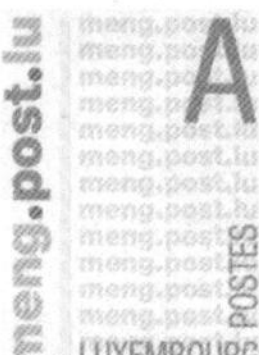

553 "meng.post.lu"

2006. Personal Stamp.

1747 **553 A** (50c.) multicoloured 1·80 1·40

No. 1747 was for use on standard first class mail within Luxembourg.

554 Building

2006. 150th Anniv of State Council.

1748	**554**	50c. grey, red and slate	1·80	1·40

555 Savings Bank Building

2006. 150th Anniv of Financial Centre.

1749	**555**	50c. grey, ultramarine and vermilion	1·80	1·40
1750	-	50c. ultramarine and vermilion	1·80	1·40

DESIGNS: Type **555**; No. 1750, Dexia-BIL building.

556 Figure holding Stop Drugs Sign (Victor Tesch)

2006. "Drugs are not for me" Campaign. Winning Designs in Children's Drawing Competition. Multicoloured.

1751		50c. Type **556**	1·80	1·40
1752		€1 Ashtray containing vegetables (Paul Hoffmann) (vert)	3·50	2·75

557 Chess Pieces

2006. 75th Anniv of National Chess Federation.

1753	**557**	90c. orange, light green and green	3·25	2·50

558 Yolande Tower, Marienthal

2006. Christmas. Marienthal Cultural Heritage.

1754	**558**	50c.+5c. multicoloured	1·90	1·50

559 Grand Auditorium, Luxembourg Music Conservatory

2006. Pipe Organs. Designs showing pipe organs. Multicoloured.

1755		50c.+5c. Type **559**	1·90	1·50
1756		70c.+10c. Bridel	2·75	2·20
1757		90c.+10c. Mondercange Parish Church	3·50	2·75
1758		€1+25c. Luxembourg Grund	4·50	3·50

560 Flowers

2006. 75th Anniv of Horticultural Association. Multicoloured.

1759		70c. Type **560**	2·50	1·90
1760		70c. Vegetables	2·50	1·90

Nos. 1759/60 were issued together, se-tenant, forming a composite design.

561 Men with Antlered Deer Heads

2007. Luxembourg European Capital of Culture—2007. Multicoloured. Self-adhesive.

1761		A (50c.) Type **561**	1·80	1·40
1762		A (50c.) Antlered man and deer	1·80	1·40
1763		A (50c.) Antlered men with arm raised	1·80	1·40
1764		A (50c.) Base of chair, legs and antlered man with raised arm	1·80	1·40

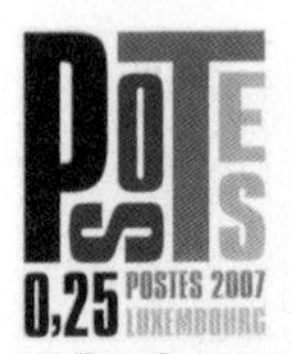

562 "Postes" **563** "€0,25"

2007. Self-adhesive.

1765	**562**	25c. multicoloured	90	70
1766	**562**	25c. multicoloured	90	70
1767	**563**	25c. multicoloured	90	70
1768	**563**	25c. multicoloured	90	70
1769	**562**	50c. multicoloured	1·80	1·40
1770	**562**	50c. multicoloured	1·80	1·40
1771	**563**	50c. multicoloured	1·80	1·40
1772	**563**	50c. multicoloured	1·80	1·40

564 Breakdown Truck

2007. 75th Anniv of Automobile Club du Luxembourg (ACL).

1773	**564**	50c. multicoloured	1·80	1·40

565 Girl holding Bubble

2007. 75th Anniv of Caritas Luxembourg Foundation.

1774	**565**	50c. multicoloured	1·80	1·40

566 Signatories

2007. 50th Anniv of Treaty of Rome. Multicoloured.

1775		70c. Type **566**	2·50	1·90
1776		€1 List of signatories	3·50	2·75

567 Early and Modern Buildings, Ettelbreck

2007. Centenary of "Law of 4 August 1907" conferring Town Status on Ettelbreck, Deifferdang, Diddeleng and Remeleng. Multicoloured.

1777		50c. Type **567**	1·80	1·40
1778		50c. Early buildings and gardens, Deifferdang	1·80	1·40
1779		50c. Early buildings and tower, Diddeleng	1·80	1·40
1780		50c. Early buildings, miner and modern machinery, Remeleng	1·80	1·40

568 Campsite (Jenny Spielmann)

2007. Europa. Centenary of Scouting. Winning designs in Children's Painting Competition. Multicoloured.

1781		50c. Type **568**	1·80	1·40
1782		70c. Children and globe (Jean Heuschling)	2·50	1·90

569 Musician (Rockhal)

2007. Cultural Centres. Multicoloured.

1783		50c. Type **569**	1·80	1·40
1784		70c. Grand Duke Jean Museum of Modern Art	2·50	1·90
1785		€1 Neumunster Abbey Meeting Centre	3·50	2·75

570 Letters (Stephanie Rausch)

2007. Luxembourg and Greater Regions Joint European Capital of Culture–2007. Winning Entry in Stamp Design Competition (1786).

1786		50c. Type **570**	1·80	1·40
1787		70c. Rotunda, Luxembourg Train Station	2·50	1·90

Stamps of a similar design were issued by Belgium.

571 Clio (history) and Urania (astronomy)

2007. Roman Mosaic, Vichten. Nine Muses. Sheet 111×111 mm containing T 571 and similar multicoloured designs showing muses.

MS1788	50c. Type **571**; 50c. Polyhymnia (choral singing) and Erato (lyrical poetry); 50c. Terpsichore (dance) and Melpomene (tragedy); 50c. Thalia (comedy) and Euterpe (music); €1 Calliope (epic poetry) and Homer (diamond shaped) (55×55 mm)	10·50	10·50

572 Luxembourg House, Sibiu

2007. Sibiu Joint European Capital of Culture–2007.

1789	**572**	70c. multicoloured	2·50	1·90

Stamps of a similar design were issued by Romania.

573 Soldier and Local Inhabitant

2007. Peace Keeping Missions of Luxembourg Army.

1790	**573**	70c. multicoloured	2·50	1·90

574 Robin

2007. Christmas.

1791		50c.+5c. multicoloured	1·90	1·50

575 Niederwilz Church

2007. Pipe Organs. Multicoloured.

1792		50c.+5c. Type **574**	1·90	1·50
1793		70c.+10c. Sandweiler (horiz)	2·75	2·20
1794		90c.+10c. St Joseph Church, Esch-sur-Alzette (horiz)	3·50	2·75
1795		€1+25c. Echternach Basilica	4·50	3·50

576 Dam and Reservoir (left)

2007. 50th Anniv of Esch-sur-Sure Dam. Self-adhesive. Multicoloured.

1796		70c. Type **575**	2·50	1·90
1797		70c. Reservoir (right)	2·50	1·90

Nos. 796/7 were issued together, se-tenant, a composite design of the reservoir and environs.

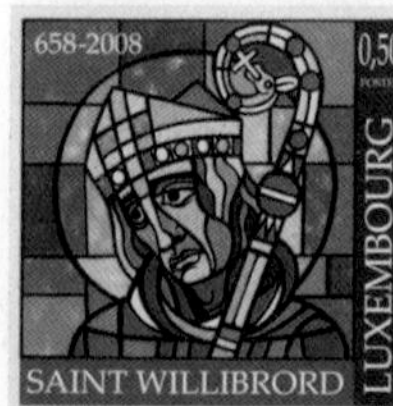

577 St. Willibrord

2008. 1350th Birth Anniv of St. Willibrord.

1798	**577**	50c. multicoloured	2·00	1·60

578 Orchestra

2008. 75th Anniv of Philharmonic Orchestra. 50th Death Anniv of Henri Pensis (composer). Multicoloured.

1799		50c. Type **578**	2·00	1·60
1800		70c. Henri Pensis	2·75	2·20

579 Emblem

2008. 50th Anniv of European Investment Bank.

1801	**579**	70c. ultramarine and silver	2·75	2·20

580 Stars and 'Eurotower' (New headquarters of ECB) (designed by COOP HIMMELB(L)AU)

2008. 10th Anniv of Eurosysteme (unitary system of European Central Bank and EU members using the euro).

1802	**580**	€1 multicoloured	4·00	3·25

581 Ball and Basket

2008. Sport 2008. Multicoloured.

1803	A (50c.) Type **581** (75th anniv of National Basketball Federation)	2·00	1·60
1804	A (50c.) Football and player's foot (centenary of National Football Federation)	2·00	1·60

582 10th-century Church, Rindschleiden

2008. Tourism. Multicoloured.

1805	A (50c.) Type **582**	2·00	1·60
1806	A (50c.) Leudelange (150th anniv) (horiz)	2·00	1·60
1807	A (50c.) Diekirch (125th anniv) (horiz)	2·00	1·60

583 Envelope containing Rainbow

2008. Europa. The Letter. Multicoloured.

1808	50c. Type **583**	2·00	1·60
1809	70c. Envelope with wings	2·75	2·20

584 Emblems

2008. Olympic Games, Beijing.

1810	**584**	70c. multicoloured	2·75	2·20

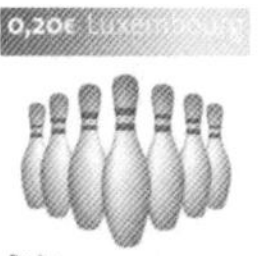

585 Skittles

2008. Happy. Multicoloured. Self-adhesive.

1811	20c. Type **585**	80	65
1811a	20c. As Type **585**	80	65
1812	20c. Parcel	80	65
1812a	20c. As No. 1812	80	65
1813	20c. Sweets	80	65
1813a	20c. As No. 1813	80	65
1814	A (50c.) Dice	2·00	1·60
1814a	A (50c.) As No. 1814	2·00	1·60
1815	A (50c.) Drum	2·00	1·60
1815a	A (50c.) As No. 1815	2·00	1·60
1816	A (50c.) Four leafed clover	2·00	1·60
1816a	A (50c.) As No. 1816	2·00	1·60

586 Symbols of Agriculture

2008. Anniversaries. Multicoloured.

1817	A (50c.) Type **586** (125th anniv of Agricultural College, Ettelbruck)	2·00	1·60
1818	A (50c.) Stylized flower (centenary of Ligue Medico-Sociale (medical and social league))	2·00	1·60

587 Symbols of Education and Culture

2008. Centenaries. Multicoloured.

1819	A (50c.) Type **587** (Volleksbildungsbewegung (cultural and educational association))	2·00	1·60
1820	A (50c.) Dog and cat (centenary of Letzebuerger Deiereschutz-liga (protection of animals association))	2·00	1·60

588 Flags as '50'

2008. 50th Anniv of NAMSA (NATO Maintenance and Supply Agency).

1821	**588**	70c. multicoloured	3·00	2·50

589 Town, River and Bridge (A. Wainer)

2008. Greetings from Luxembourg. Winning Designs in Children's Drawing Competition. Multicoloured.

1822	70c. Type **589**	3·00	2·50
1823	€1 Bridge and valley (S. Rauschenberger)	4·00	3·50

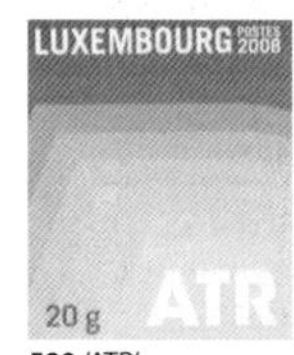

590 'ATR' **591** 'A'

2008. Self-adhesive. Multicoloured.

1824	(25c.) Type **590**	1·00	90
1825	(25c.) ATR at top left (purple)	1·00	90
1826	(25c.) ATR at bottom left (green)	1·00	90
1827	(25c.) ATR at top right (red)	1·00	90
1828	A (50c.) Type **591**	2·10	1·80
1829	A (50c.) A top left	2·10	1·80
1830	A (50c.) A bottom right	2·10	1·80
1831	A (50c.) A top right	2·10	1·80

592 Buck

2008. Christmas.

1832	**592**	50c.+5c. multicoloured	2·30	2·00

593 Junglinster

2008. Pipe Organs. Multicoloured.

1833	50c.+5c. Type **593**	2·30	2·00
1834	70c.+10c. Mondorf-les-Bains (horiz)	3·25	2·75
1835	90c.+10c. Vianden	4·00	3·50
1836	€1+25c. Cathedral	5·25	4·50

594 Building

2008. Court of Justice of the European Communities.

1837	**594**	70c. multicoloured	3·00	2·50

595 Coronation

2008. 700th Death Anniv (2009) of Henry VII.

1838	**595**	€1 multicoloured	4·25	3·75

596 Fire Appliance

2009. Firefighters. Multicoloured.

1839	20c. Type **596**	95	80
1840	A (50c.) Firefighter carrying child	2·30	2·00
1841	€2 Early fire appliance	9·25	7·75

597 Emblem

2009. 10th Anniv of the Euro.

1842	**597**	A (50c.) multicoloured	2·40	2·10

598 CGFP (General Confederation of Civil Service) Emblem

2009. Trade Union Centenaries. Multicoloured.

1843	A (50c.) Type **598**	2·50	2·10
1844	A (50c.) FNCTTFEL (National Federation of Railway Workers, Transport Workers and Employees) emblem	2·50	2·10
1845	50c. Postman (Postman's Federation)	2·50	2·10

599 Aircraft and Air Balloon

2009. Centenary of Areo-Club Luxembourgeois. Multicoloured.

1846	50c. Type **599**	2·50	2·10
1847	50c. Air balloon and aircraft (right)	2·50	2·10
1848	90c. Airport	4·50	3·75

Nos. 1846/7 were printed together, se-tenant, forming a composite design.

600 Emblem

2009. European Parliamentary Elections.

1849	**600**	50c. multicoloured	2·30	2·25

601 Researcher

2009. Tenth Anniv of National Research Fund.

1850	**601**	A (50c.) multicoloured	2·30	2·25

602 Children

2009. 125th Anniv of Children's Houses.

1851	**602**	A (50c.) multicoloured	2·30	2·25

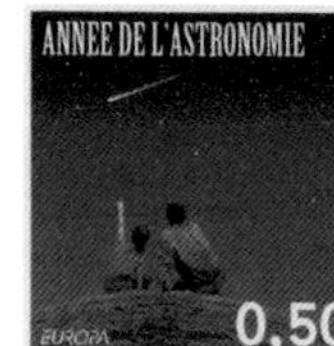

603 Shooting Star

2009. Europa. Astronomy. Multicoloured.

1852	50c. Type **603**	2·30	2·25
1853	70c. Galileo and satellite	2·75	2·75

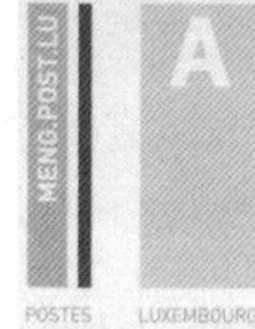

604 Red Line

2009. Personalised Stamps. New Designs for www.meng.post.lu.

1854	A (50c.) deep rose-red and grey	2·30	2·25
1855	A (70c.) bright blue and grey	2·75	2·75

DESIGNS: (50c.) Type **604**; (70c.) Blue line

No. 1854 was for use on domestic mail and No. 1855 was for use on mail within Europe.

605 Foni Tissen (artist) (birth centenary)

2009. Personalities. Multicoloured.

1856	70c. Type **605**	3·25	3·00
1857	90c. Charles Bernhoeft (photographer) (150th birth anniv)	4·25	3·75
1858	€1 Henri Tudor (electrical engineer) (150th birth anniv)	4·75	4·25

606 1934 5f. Stamp (As Type **47**)

2009. 75th Anniv of FSPL (federation of philatelic societies). Sheet 120×80 mm containing T 606 and similar horiz design. Multicoloured.

MS1859	50c. Type **606**; 70c. Gateway of the Three Towers	5·25	5·25

607 Modern Electric Locomotive

2009. 150th Anniv of Railways. Multicoloured.

1860	50c. Type **607**	2·25	2·25
1861	€1 Electric goods train	4·25	4·25
1862	€3 Early steam locomotive	12·50	12·50

608 Vanden Castle

2009. SEPAC (small European mail services).

1863	**608** 70c. multicoloured	3·00	3·00

609 Louis Braille and Fingerprint

2009. Birth Bicentenary of Louis Braille (inventor of Braille writing for the blind).

1864	**609** 90c. claret and new blue	4·00	4·00

No. 1864 is embossed with Braille letters.

610 Johannes Gutenberg (inventor of movable type printing)

2009. Communication–From Gutenberg to the Internet. Multicoloured.

1865	50c. Type **610**	2·25	2·25
1866	70c. @	3·00	3·00

611 Fox decorating Tree

2009. Christmas.

1867	**611** 50c.+5c. multicoloured	2·25	2·25

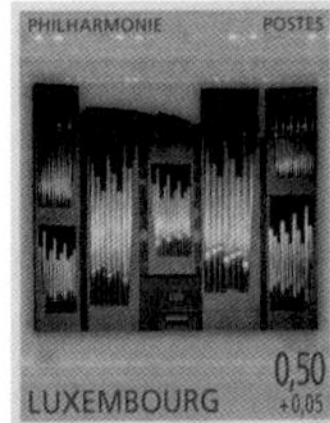

612 Philharmonie

2009. Pipe Organs. Designs showing pipe organs. Multicoloured.

1868	50c.+5c. Type **612**	2·25	2·25
1869	70c.+10c. Dudelange	3·00	3·00
1870	90c.+10c. Nommern	3·75	3·75
1871	€1+25c. Heiderscheid	4·50	4·50

613 Grand Duke Henri

2010. Tenth Anniv of Accession of Grand Duke Henri. 25th Death Anniv of Grand Duchess Charlotte. Multicoloured.

1872	50c. Type **613**	2·25	2·25
1873	€1 Grand Duchess Charlotte	4·25	4·25

614 Schengen Monument

2010. 25th Anniv of Schengen Accord (setting area of free movement between countries).

1874	**614** 70c. multicoloured	3·25	3·25

615 Septfontaines Castles

2010. Tourism. Eisch Valley. Value expressed by letter. Multicoloured. Self-adhesive.

1875	(70c.) Type **615**	3·25	3·25
1876	(70c.) Hollenfels	3·25	3·25

The two stamps and margins form a composite design

616 *Arnica montana*

2010. International Year of Biodiversity. Countdown 2010 (conservation and restoration project). Multicoloured.

1877	70c. Type **616**	3·00	3·00
1878	€1 Freshwater pearl mussel (inscr 'Moule perliere')	4·25	4·25

617 Luxembourg Pavillion

2010. World Expo 2010, Shanghai, China.

1879	**617** 90c. multicoloured	4·00	4·00

618 Grand Duke Henri and Grand Duchess Maria Teresa

2010. The Grand Ducal Family. Sheet 200×138 mm.

MS1880	**681** €3 multicoloured	13·00	13·00

619 Boy and Dragon reading

2010. Europa . Multicoloured.

1881	50c. Type **619**	2·25	2·25
1882	70c. Girl riding book lassoing horse as book	3·25	3·25

620

2010. Philalux 2011 International Stamp Exhibition. Multicoloured.

MS1883	50c. Type **620**; 70c. Red Bridge (Grand Duchess Charlotte Bridge) and skyscrapers; €3 New buildings (60×38 mm)	17·00	17·00

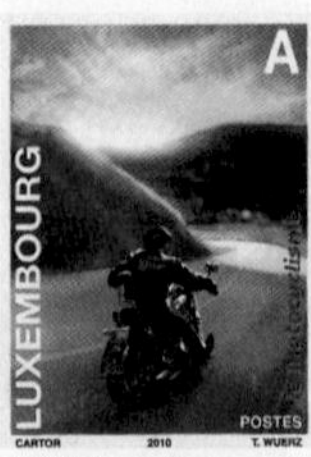

621 Motorcycling

2010. Leasure and Liberty. Multicoloured.

1884	A (60c.) Type **621**	2·25	2·25
1885	A (85c.) Camping	3·25	3·25

No. !884 was for use on mail within Luxembourg and No. 1885 was for use on mail within Europe

622 Bernie

2010. Cartoons. Multicoloured.

MS1886	A (60c.)×5, Type **622**; Police Chief Harespel; Leonie Lamesch (vert); Superjhemp; Leandre Schrobiltgen	12·50	12·50

623 John of Luxembourg and Elisabeth of Bohemia

2010. 700th Anniv of Accession of House of Luxembourg to Czech Throne

1887	**623** 70c. multicoloured	3·00	3·00

A stamp of a similar design was issued by Czech Republic

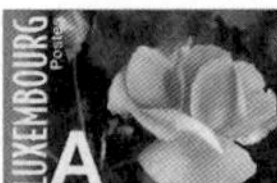

624 Grand-Duc Adolphe de Luxembourg

2010. Roses. Multicoloured.

1888	A (60c.) Type **624**	2·40	2·40
1889	A (60c.) Bagatelle (white single)	2·40	2·40
1890	A (60c.) Bordeaux (small pink double)	2·40	2·40
1891	A (60c.) Duc de Constantine (pink, three blooms)	2·40	2·40
1892	A (60c.) Prince Jean de Luxembourg (double white)	2·40	2·40
1893	A (60c.) Clothilde Soupert (double apricot)	2·40	2·40
1894	A (60c.) Mrs E G Hill (large bright pink)	2·40	2·40
1895	A (60c.) Pierre Watine (pale pink large bloom)	2·40	2·40
1896	A (60c.) Souvenir de Maria de Zayas (rich pink)	2·40	2·40
1897	A (60c.) Yvan Misson (pale pink two blooms)	2·40	2·40

625 Symbols of Education (fight against poverty in developing countries) (Timothy Clement)

2010. European Year of Fight against Poverty and Social Exclusion. Multicoloured.

1898	A (60c.) Type **625**	2·50	2·50
1899	A (85c.) Offering tools to work (fight against poverty in industrialised countries) (Cinthya Goncalves Guerriro)	3·50	3·50

626 Anne Beffort (educationalist and writer)

2010. Personalities. Multicoloured.

1900	70c. Type **626**	2·75	2·75
1901	90c. Duc de Constantine (rose) and Jean Soupert (rose breeder)	3·50	3·50
1902	€1 Nicolas Frantz (cyclist)	4·75	4·75

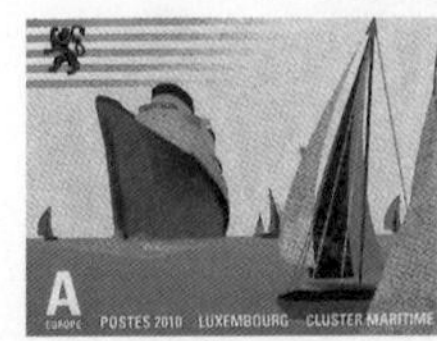

627 Liner and Yacht

2010. Ships and Navigation. Multicoloured.

1903	A (60c.) Type **627**	3·50	3·50
1904	A (60c.) Yacht and container ship	3·50	3·50

Nos. 1903/4 were printed, *se-tenant*, forming a composite design

628 Boy and Dog Sledding

2010. Christmas

1905	**628** 60c.+5c. multicoloured	3·00	3·00

629 Farrier

2010. Trades of Yesteryear. Multicoloured.
1906 60c.+5c. Type **629** 3·00 3·00
1907 85c.+10c. Basket weaver 3·75 3·75
1908 €1.10+10c. Knife grinder (horiz) 5·00 5·00
1909 €1.20+25c. Cooper (horiz) 6·25 6·25

630 Hands grasping Arms

2011. European Year of Volunteering
1910 **630** A(60c.) multicoloured 2·75 2·75

631 Bowlers, Pins and Alley

2011. 50th Anniv of Fédération luxembourgeoise des Quilleurs (nine pin bowlers)
1911 **631** 60c. multicoloured 2·75 2·75

632 Clock Tower and Perforated Edges

2011. 75th Anniv of 'Journée du Timbre' (Stamp Day)
1912 **632** 60c. multicoloured 2·75 2·75

633 Figures with Arms raised, Pen and 'sign'

2011. 50th Anniv of Amnesty International
1913 **633** 60c. multicoloured 2·75 2·75

634 Prince Guillaume

2011. House of Luxembourg Dynasty. Multicoloured.
1914 85c. Type **634** 3·25 3·25
1915 €1.10 Grand Duke Jean 5·25 5·25

635 Sun draped with Grapes holding Wine Glass and Bottle

2011. Centenary of Wënzerverband (wine growers federation) (60c.) or 20th Anniv of Appellation contrôlée Crémant de Luxembourg (85c.). Multicoloured.
1916 60c. Type **635** 2·75 2·75
1917 85c. Cork and wire 3·75 3·75

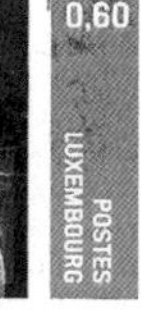

636 Girl blowing Bubbles

2011. Personalised Stamps. Multicoloured.
1918 60c. Type **636** 2·75 2·75
1919 85c. Boy dozing (vert) 3·75 3·75

637 Deciduous Forest

2011. Europa. Multicoloured.
1920 60c. Type **637** 2·75 2·75
1921 85c. Wooded valley 3·75 3·75

638 Maloo

2011. *De leschte Ritter* cartoon created by Lucien Czuga and illustrated by Andy "ND!" Genen. Multicoloured.
MS19222 A (60c.)×4, Type **638**; Jean, The Last Knight (horiz); Pedro (horiz); Pixel the Galago 10·50 10·50

OFFICIAL STAMPS

1875. Stamps of 1859–72 optd OFFICIEL. Roul.
O79 **3** 1c. brown 60·00 55·00
O80 **3** 2c. black 60·00 55·00
O81 **4** 10c. lilac £3250 £3250
O82 **4** 12½c. red £750 £850
O83 **4** 20c. brown 60·00 85·00
O84 **4** 25c. blue £400 £225
O85 **4** 30c. purple 60·00 £110
O88b **4** 40c. orange £325 £325
O87 **4** 1f. on 37½c. bistre (No. 37) £250 39·00

1875. Stamps of 1874–79 optd OFFICIEL. Perf.
O89 **3** 1c. brown 14·00 42·00
O90 **3** 2c. black 17·00 50·00
O91 **3** 4c. green £140 £225
O92 **3** 5c. yellow £110 £110
O93a **4** 10c. lilac £140 £170
O111 **4** 12½c. red £110 £170
O99a **4** 25c. blue 4·50 5·50
O96 **4** 1f. on 37½c. bistre (No. 56) 55·00 85·00

1881. Stamp of 1859 optd S. P. Roul.
O116 **3** 40c. orange 55·00 £110

1881. Stamps of 1874–79 optd S. P. Perf.
O121a **3** 1c. brown 17·00 14·00
O122a **3** 2c. black 17·00 14·00
O118 4c. green £250 £275
O123a **3** 5c. yellow £225 £275
O124a **4** 10c. lilac £225 £275
O125a **4** 12½c. red £250 £325
O126a **4** 20c. brown £100 £140
O127a **4** 25c. blue £110 £140
O128 **4** 30c. red £110 £170
O120 **4** 1f. on 37½c. bistre (No. 56) 55·00 85·00

7 Agriculture and Trade

1882. Stamps of 1882 optd S. P.
O141 **7** 1c. grey 55 55
O142 **7** 2c. brown 55 55
O143 **7** 4c. olive 55 75
O144 **7** 5c. green 55 85
O145 **7** 10c. red 20·00 22·00
O146 **7** 12½c. blue 2·20 7·25
O147 **7** 20c. orange 2·20 7·25
O148 **7** 25c. blue 33·00 35·00
O149 **7** 30c. olive 5·50 13·00
O150 **7** 50c. brown 1·70 4·25
O151 **7** 1f. lilac 1·70 4·25
O152 **7** 5f. orange 20·00 55·00

1891. Stamps of 1891 optd S. P.
O188 **8** 10c. red 30 85
O189 **8** 12½c. green 10·00 10·00
O190 **8** 20c. orange 17·00 13·00
O191a **8** 25c. blue 45 85
O192 **8** 30c. green 10·00 13·00
O193a **8** 37½c. green 10·00 13·00
O194 **8** 50c. brown 8·25 14·00
O195a **8** 1f. purple 8·25 17·00
O196 **8** 2½f. black 55·00 £110
O197 **8** 5f. lake 50·00 80·00

1898. Stamps of 1895 optd S. P.
O213 **9** 1c. grey 2·75 2·75
O214 **9** 2c. brown 2·20 2·75
O215 **9** 4c. bistre 2·20 2·20
O216 **9** 5c. green 11·00 5·50
O217 **9** 10c. red 39·00 50·00

1908. Stamps of 1906 optd Officiel.
O218 **10** 1c. grey 20 55
O219 **10** 2c. brown 20 55
O220 **10** 4c. bistre 20 55
O221 **10** 5c. green 20 55
O271 **10** 5c. mauve 15 55
O222 **10** 6c. lilac 20 55
O223 **10** 7½c. yellow 20 55
O224 **10** 10c. red 30 55
O225 **10** 12½c. slate 30 85
O226 **10** 15c. brown 45 85
O227 **10** 20c. orange 45 1·10
O228 **10** 25c. blue 45 1·10
O229 **10** 30c. olive 8·25 11·00
O230 **10** 37½c. green 1·10 1·10
O231 **10** 50c. brown 1·10 2·20
O232 **10** 87½c. blue 2·75 5·50
O233 **10** 1f. purple 4·50 5·50
O234 **10** 2½f. red £140 £110
O235 **10** 5f. purple 85·00 80·00

1915. Stamps of 1914 optd Officiel.
O236 **13** 10c. purple 30 85
O237 **13** 12½c. green 30 85
O238 **13** 15c. brown 30 85
O239 **13** 17½c. brown 30 85
O240 **13** 25c. blue 30 85
O241 **13** 30c. brown 2·20 8·25
O242 **13** 35c. blue 30 1·70
O243 **13** 37½c. brown 30 2·20
O244 **13** 40c. red 45 1·70
O245 **13** 50c. grey 45 1·70
O246 **13** 62½c. green 45 2·20
O247 **13** 87½c. orange 45 2·75
O248 **13** 1f. brown 45 2·20
O249 **13** 2½f. red 45 4·50
O250 **13** 5f. violet 45 5·50

1922. Stamps of 1921 optd Officiel.
O251 **17** 2c. brown 10 20
O252 **17** 3c. green 10 20
O253 **17** 6c. purple 20 55
O272 **17** 10c. green 15 55
O273 **17** 15c. green 15 55
O274 **17** 15c. orange 15 55
O256 **17** 20c. orange 20 55
O275 **17** 20c. green 15 55
O257 **17** 25c. green 20 55
O258 **17** 30c. red 20 55
O259 **17** 40c. orange 20 55
O260 **17** 50c. blue 35 80
O276 **17** 50c. red 30 85
O261 **17** 75c. red 35 80
O277 **17** 75c. blue 30 85
O266 **17** 80c. black 45 65
O263 **18** 1f. red 1·10 2·75
O278 **18** 1f. blue 45 2·20
O267 - 2f. blue 2·20 2·75
O279 - 2f. brown 2·10 7·75
O269 - 5f. violet 12·50 13·50

26 Luxembourg

28 Echternach

1922. Stamps of 1923 optd Officiel.
O268a **28** 3f. blue 1·70 2·00
O270 **26** 10f. black 40·00 33·00

1926. Stamps of 1926 optd Officiel.
O280 **32** 5c. mauve 10 30
O281 **32** 10c. green 10 30
O298 **32** 15c. black 45 1·70
O282 **32** 20c. orange 10 30
O283 **32** 25c. green 10 30
O300 **32** 25c. brown 40 1·10
O301 **32** 30c. green 65 2·75
O302 **32** 30c. violet 45 1·70
O303 **32** 35c. violet 45 1·70
O304 **32** 35c. green 45 1·70
O286 **32** 40c. brown 10 30
O287 **32** 50c. brown 10 30
O307 **32** 60c. green 45 1·10
O288 **32** 65c. brown 10 55
O308 **32** 70c. violet 4·25 9·50
O289 **32** 75c. red 10 55
O309 **32** 75c. brown 45 1·10
O291 **32** 80c. brown 15 55
O292 **32** 90c. red 30 1·10
O293 **32** 1f. black 30 85
O312 **32** 1f. red 55 3·25
O294 **32** 1¼f. blue 15 85
O313 **32** 1¼f. yellow 2·75 9·50
O314 **32** 1¼f. green 2·50 6·75
O315 **32** 1½f. blue 45 2·20
O316 **32** 1¾f. blue 55 2·20

1928. Stamp of 1928 optd Officiel.
O317 **37** 2f. black 1·10 2·75

43 Luxembourg, Lower Town

1931. Stamp of 1931 optd Officiel.
O318 **43** 20f. green 2·75 14·00

47 Gateway of the Three Towers

1934. Stamp of 1934 optd Officiel.
O319 **47** 5f. green 2·20 8·25

52 Vianden

1935. No. 340 optd Officiel.

O341	52	10f. green	2·20	11·00

POSTAGE DUE STAMPS

1907

D173	D12	5c. black and green	30	45
D174	D12	10c. black and green	1·70	45
D175	D12	12½c. black and green	55	1·40
D176	D12	20c. black and green	1·10	1·10
D177	D12	25c. black and green	22·00	1·70
D178	D12	50c. black and green	1·70	6·25
D179	D12	1f. black and green	55	5·50

D12 Arms of Luxembourg

1920. Surch.

D193	D 12	15 on 12½c. blk & grn	2·20	11·00
D194	D 12	30 on 25c. black & grn	2·20	14·00

1922

D221	D12	5c. red and green	30	55
D222	D12	10c. red and green	30	55
D223	D12	20c. red and green	30	55
D224	D12	25c. red and green	30	55
D225	D12	30c. red and green	55	1·10
D226	D12	35c. red and green	55	45
D227	D12	50c. red and green	55	1·10
D228	D12	60c. red and green	45	55
D229	D12	70c. red and green	55	45
D230	D12	75c. red and green	55	30
D231	D12	1f. red and green	55	2·75
D232	D12	2f. red and green	55	10·00
D233	D12	3f. red and green	2·20	20·00

D77

1946

D488	D77	5c. green	2·00	85
D489	D77	10c. green	2·00	70
D490	D77	20c. green	2·00	70
D491	D77	30c. green	2·00	70
D492	D77	50c. green	2·00	70
D493	D77	70c. green	2·00	1·10
D494	D77	75c. green	5·75	55
D495	D77	1f. red	2·00	55
D496	D77	1f.50 red	2·00	55
D497	D77	2f. red	2·00	55
D498	D77	3f. red	4·00	70
D499	D77	5f. red	4·00	70
D500	D77	10f. red	6·75	5·00
D501	D77	20f. red	11·50	42·00

Pt. 1

MALTA

An island in the Mediterranean Sea, south of Italy. After a period of self-government under various Constitutions, independence was attained on 21 September 1964. The island became a republic on 13 December 1974.

1860. 12 pence = 1 shilling; 20 shillings = 1 pound.
1972. 10 mils = 1 cent; 100 cents = M£1.
2008. 100 cents = 1 euro.

1

5

1860. Various frames.

18	1	½d. yellow	40·00	35·00
20	1	½d. green	4·00	50
22	-	1d. red	9·00	35
23	-	2d. grey	8·00	2·25
26	-	2½d. blue	50·00	1·00
27	-	4d. brown	11·00	3·00
28	-	1s. violet	48·00	12·00
30	5	5s. red	£110	80·00

6 Harbour of Valletta

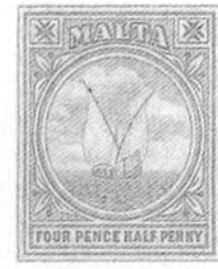

7 Gozo Fishing Boat

8 Galley of Knights of St. John

9 Emblematic Figure of Malta

10 Shipwreck of St. Paul

1899

31a	6	¼d. brown	1·50	40
79	6	4d. black	15·00	7·00
32	7	4½d. brown	22·00	16·00
58	7	4½d. orange	4·75	3·75
59	8	5d. red	35·00	6·50
60	8	5d. green	4·25	3·50
34	9	2s.6d. olive	45·00	14·00
35	10	10s. black	£100	65·00

1902. No. 26 surch One Penny.

37	10	1d. on 2½d. blue	1·00	2·00

12

1903

47b	12	½d. green	5·50	10
39	12	1d. black and red	15·00	40
49	12	1d. red	3·50	10
50	12	2d. purple and grey	12·00	3·00
51	12	2d. grey	4·25	5·50
52	12	2½d. purple and blue	30·00	60
53	12	2½d. blue	5·50	4·25
42	12	3d. grey and purple	1·75	50
54	12	4d. black and brown	11·00	7·50
55	12	4d. black and red on yellow	4·00	4·50
44	12	1s. grey and violet	26·00	7·00
62	12	1s. black on green	7·50	4·25
63	12	5s. green and red on yellow	65·00	75·00

13

15

17

1914

69	13	¼d. brown	1·00	10
71	13	½d. green	2·50	30
73	13	1d. red	1·50	10
75	13	2d. grey	11·00	6·00
77	13	2½d. blue	2·25	50
78	13	3d. purple on yellow	2·50	16·00
80	13	6d. purple	11·00	21·00
81a	13	1s. black on green	12·00	22·00
86	15	2s. purple and blue on blue	50·00	38·00
88	15	5s. green and red on yellow	£100	£110
104	17	10s. black	£350	£800

1918. Optd WAR TAX.

92	13	½d. green	2·00	15
93	12	3d. grey and purple	2·00	12·00

18

1921

100	18	2d. grey	7·50	1·75

1922. Optd SELF-GOVERNMENT.

114	13	¼d. brown	30	75
106	13	½d. green	1·00	2·50
116	13	1d. red	1·00	20
117	18	2d. grey	4·00	45
118	13	2½d. blue	1·10	1·75
108	13	3d. purple on yellow	4·50	26·00
109	13	6d. purple	4·25	23·00
110	13	1s. black on green	4·50	23·00
120	15	2s. purple and blue on blue	50·00	95·00
112	9	2s.6d. olive	30·00	50·00
113	15	5s. green and red on yellow	55·00	95·00
105	10	10s. black	£225	£400
121	17	10s. black	£140	£250

1922. Surch One Farthing.

122	18	¼d. on 2d. grey	85	30

22

23

1922

123	22	¼d. brown	2·50	60
124	22	½d. green	2·50	15
125	22	1d. orange and purple	4·50	20
126	22	1d. violet	4·25	80
127	22	1½d. red	5·50	15
128	22	2d. brown and blue	3·25	1·25
129	22	2½d. blue	4·50	13·00
130	22	3d. blue	6·00	2·50
131	22	3d. black on yellow	4·25	20·00
132	22	4d. yellow and blue	3·00	4·25
133	22	6d. green and violet	4·50	3·75
134	23	1s. blue and brown	10·00	3·50
135	23	2s. brown and blue	14·00	18·00
136	23	2s.6d. purple and black	11·00	15·00
137	23	5s. orange and blue	21·00	48·00
138	23	10s. grey and brown	65·00	£160
140	22	£1 black and red	£110	£325

1925. Surch Two pence halfpenny.

142		2½d. on 3d. blue	1·75	4·50

1926. Optd POSTAGE.

143		¼d. brown	70	5·50
144		½d. green	70	15
145		1d. violet	1·00	25
146		1½d. red	1·25	60
147		2d. brown and blue	75	2·00
148		2½d. blue	1·25	1·00
149		3d. black on yellow	75	80
150		4d. yellow and blue	17·00	28·00
151		6d. green and violet	2·75	5·50
152	23	1s. blue and brown	5·50	18·00
153	23	2s. brown and blue	55·00	£150
154	23	2s.6d. purple and black	17·00	48·00
155	23	5s. orange and blue	10·00	48·00
156	23	10s. grey and brown	7·00	20·00

26

27 Valletta Harbour

28 St. Publius

1926. Inscr "POSTAGE".

157	26	¼d. brown	80	15
158	26	½d. green	60	15
159	26	1d. red	3·00	1·00
160	26	1½d. brown	2·00	10
161	26	2d. grey	4·50	15·00
162	26	2½d. blue	4·00	1·50
162a	26	3d. violet	4·25	4·25
163	26	4d. black and red	3·25	16·00
164	26	4½d. violet and yellow	3·50	4·50
165	26	6d. violet and red	4·25	6·00
166	27	1s. black	6·50	8·50
167	28	1s.6d. black and green	7·50	18·00
168	-	2s. black and purple	7·50	23·00
169	-	2s.6d. black and red	19·00	55·00
170	-	3s. black and blue	19·00	35·00
171	-	5s. black and green	23·00	65·00
172	-	10s. black and red	65·00	£100

DESIGNS—As Type **27**: 2s. Mdina (Notabile); 5s. Neolithic temple, Mnajdra. As Type **28**: 2s.6d. Gozo boat; 3s. Neptune; 10s. St. Paul.

1928. Air. Optd AIR MAIL.

173	26	6d. violet and red	1·75	1·00

1928. Optd POSTAGE AND REVENUE.

174		¼d. brown	1·50	10
175		½d. green	1·50	10
176		1d. red	1·75	3·25
177		1d. brown	4·50	10
178		1½d. brown	2·00	85
179		1½d. red	4·25	10
180		2d. grey	4·25	9·00
181		2½d. blue	2·00	10
182		3d. violet	2·00	80
183		4d. black and red	2·00	1·75
184		4½d. violet and yellow	2·25	1·00
185		6d. violet and red	2·25	1·50
186	27	1s. black	5·50	2·50
187	28	1s.6d. black and green	11·00	9·50
188	-	2s. black and purple	26·00	70·00
189	-	2s.6d. black and red	17·00	21·00
190	-	3s. black and blue	21·00	24·00
191	-	5s. black and green	38·00	70·00
192	-	10s. black and red	70·00	£100

1930. As Nos. 157/72, but inscr "POSTAGE & REVENUE".

193	¼d. brown	60	10
194	½d. green	60	10
195	1d. brown	60	10
196	1½d. red	70	10
197	2d. grey	1·25	50
198	2½d. blue	2·00	10
199	3d. violet	1·50	20
200	4d. black and red	1·25	5·00
201	4½d. violet and yellow	3·25	1·25
202	6d. violet and red	2·75	1·25
203	1s. black	10·00	19·00
204	1s.6d. black and green	8·50	25·00
205	2s. black and purple	12·00	27·00
206	2s.6d. black and red	17·00	60·00
207	3s. black and blue	40·00	60·00
208	5s. black and green	48·00	75·00
209	10s. black and red	£100	£180

1935. Silver Jubilee. As Nos. 144/7 of Cyprus.

210	½d. black and green	50	70
211	2½d. brown and blue	2·50	4·50
212	6d. blue and olive	7·00	9·00
213	1s. grey and purple	17·00	24·00

1937. Coronation. As Nos. 148/50 of Cyprus.

214	½d. green	10	20
215	1½d. red	1·40	65
216	2½d. blue	1·40	80

37 Grand Harbour, Valletta

38 H.M.S. *St. Angelo*

39 Verdala Palace

1938. Various designs with medallion King George VI.

No.	Type	Description	Unused	Used
217	**37**	¼d. brown	10	10
218	**38**	½d. green	4·00	30
218a	**38**	½d. brown	55	30
219	**39**	1d. brown	5·50	40
219a	**39**	1d. green	60	10
220	-	1½d. red	2·50	30
220b	-	1½d. black	30	15
221	-	2d. black	2·50	2·00
221b	-	2d. red	40	30
222	-	2½d. blue	5·50	60
222a	-	2½d. violet	60	10
223	-	3d. violet	3·00	80
223a	-	3d. blue	30	20
224	-	4½d. olive and brown	50	30
225	-	6d. olive and red	2·50	30
226	-	1s. black	2·25	30
227	-	1s.6d. black and olive	8·00	4·00
228	-	2s. green and blue	4·50	7·00
229	-	2s.6d. black and red	9·00	6·00
230	-	5s. black and green	4·75	8·50
231	-	10s. black and red	19·00	17·00

DESIGNS—As Types **38/9**. VERT: 1½d. Hypogeum, Hal Saflieni; 3d. St. John's Co-Cathedral; 6d. Statue of Manoel de Vilhena; 1s. Maltese girl wearing faldetta; 5s. Palace Square, Valletta; 10s. St. Paul. HORIZ: 2d. Victoria and Citadel, Gozo; 2½d. De l'Isle Adam entering Mdina; 4½d. Ruins at Mnajdra; 1s.6d. St. Publius; 2s. Mdina Cathedral; 2s.6d. Statue of Neptune.

1946. Victory. As Nos. 164/5 of Cyprus.

No.	Description	Unused	Used
232	1d. green	15	10
233	3d. blue	50	2·00

1948. Self-government. As 1938 issue optd SELF-GOVERNMENT 1947.

No.	Description	Unused	Used
234	¼d. brown	30	20
235	½d. brown	30	10
236	1d. green	30	10
236a	1d. grey	75	10
237	1½d. black	1·25	10
237b	1½d. green	30	10
238	2d. red	1·25	10
238c	2d. yellow	30	10
239	2½d. violet	80	10
239a	2½d. red	75	1·50
240	3d. blue	3·00	15
240a	3d. violet	50	15
241	4½d. olive and brown	2·75	1·50
241a	4½d. olive and blue	50	90
242	6d. olive and red	3·25	15
243	1s. black	3·75	40
244	1s.6d. black and olive	2·50	50
245	2s. green and blue	5·00	2·50
246	2s.6d. black and red	12·00	2·50
247	5s. black and green	28·00	3·50
248	10s. black and red	28·00	23·00

1949. Silver Wedding. As 34a of Cyprus.

No.	Description	Unused	Used
249	1d. green	50	10
250	£1 blue	38·00	45·00

1949. U.P.U. As 38d/g of Cyprus.

No.	Description	Unused	Used
251	2½d. violet	30	10
252	3d. blue	3·00	1·00
253	6d. red	60	1·00
254	1s. black	60	2·50

53 Queen Elizabeth II when Princess

1950. Visit of Princess Elizabeth.

No.	Type	Description	Unused	Used
255	**53**	1d. green	10	15
256	**53**	3d. blue	20	20
257	**53**	1s. black	80	2·25

54 "Our Lady of Mount Carmel" (attrib Palladino)

1951. 7th Centenary of the Scapular.

No.	Type	Description	Unused	Used
258	**54**	1d. green	20	30
259	**54**	3d. violet	50	10
260	**54**	1s. black	1·75	1·60

1953. Coronation. As 38h of Cyprus.

No.	Description	Unused	Used
261	1½d. black and green	70	10

55 St. John's Co-Cathedral

1954. Royal Visit.

No.	Type	Description	Unused	Used
262	**55**	3d. violet	45	10

56 "Immaculate Conception" (Caruana) (altar-piece, Cospicua)

1954. Centenary of Dogma of the Immaculate Conception.

No.	Type	Description	Unused	Used
263	**56**	1½d. green	15	10
264	**56**	3d. blue	15	10
265	**56**	1s. grey	35	20

57 Monument of the Great Siege, 1565

1956

No.	Type	Description	Unused	Used
266	**57**	¼d. violet	20	10
267	-	½d. orange	50	10
314	-	1d. black	50	30
269	-	1½d. green	30	10
270	-	2d. sepia	1·50	10
271	-	2½d. brown	2·25	30
272	-	3d. red	1·50	10
273	-	4½d. blue	2·50	1·00
274	-	6d. indigo	75	10
275	-	8d. ochre	4·50	1·00
276	-	1s. violet	1·75	10
277	-	1s.6d. turquoise	15·00	35
278	-	2s. olive	13·00	4·50
279	-	2s.6d. brown	11·00	2·50
280	-	5s. green	17·00	3·25
281	-	10s. red	38·00	16·00
282	-	£1 brown	38·00	35·00

DESIGNS—VERT: ½d. Wignacourt aqueduct horsetrough; 1d. Victory church; 1½d. Second World War memorial; 2d. Mosta Church; 3d. The King's Scroll; 4½d. Roosevelt's Scroll; 8d. Vedette (tower); 1s. Mdina Gate; 1s.6d. "Les Gavroches" (statue); 2s. Monument of Christ the King; 2s.6d. Monument of Grand Master Cottoner; 5s. Grand Master Perellos's monument; 10s. St. Paul (statue); £1 Baptism of Christ (statue). HORIZ: 2½d. Auberge de Castile; 6d. Neolithic Temples at Tarxien.

74 "Defence of Malta"

1957. George Cross Commem. Cross in Silver.

No.	Type	Description	Unused	Used
283	**74**	1½d. green	15	10
284	-	3d. red	15	10
285	-	1s. brown	15	10

DESIGNS—HORIZ: 3d. Searchlights over Malta. VERT: 1s. Bombed buildings.

77 "Design"

1958. Technical Education in Malta. Inscr "TECHNICAL EDUCATION".

No.	Type	Description	Unused	Used
286	**77**	1½d. black and green	15	10
287	-	3d. black, red and grey	15	10
288	-	1s. grey, purple and black	15	10

DESIGNS—VERT: 3d. "Construction". HORIZ: 1s. Technical School, Paola.

81 Sea Raid on Grand Harbour, Valletta

1958. George Cross Commem. Cross in first colour outlined in silver.

No.	Type	Description	Unused	Used
289		1½d. green and black	15	10
290	**81**	3d. red and black	15	10
291	-	1s. mauve and black	25	10

DESIGNS—HORIZ: 1½d. Bombed-out family; 1s. Searchlight crew.

83 Air Raid Casualties

1959. George Cross Commemoration.

No.	Type	Description	Unused	Used
292	**83**	1½d. green, black and gold	25	10
293	-	3d. mauve, black and gold	25	10
294	-	1s. grey, black and gold	1·25	1·50

DESIGNS—HORIZ: 3d. "For Gallantry". VERT: 1s. Maltese under bombardment.

86 Shipwreck of St. Paul (after Palombi)

87 Statue of St. Paul, Rabat, Malta

1960. 19th Centenary of the Shipwreck of St. Paul. Inscr as in T 86/7.

No.	Type	Description	Unused	Used
295	**86**	1½d. blue, gold and brown	15	10
296	-	3d. purple, gold and blue	15	10
297	-	6d. red, gold and grey	25	10
298	**87**	8d. black and gold	30	60
299	-	1s. purple and gold	25	10
300	-	2s.6d. blue, green and gold	1·00	2·50

DESIGNS—As Type **88**: 3d. Consecration of St. Publius, First Bishop of Malta; 6d. Departure of St. Paul (after Palombi). As Type **87**: 1s. Angel with the "Acts of the Apostles"; 2s.6d. St. Paul with the "Second Epistle to the Corinthians".

92 Stamp of 1860

1960. Centenary of Malta Stamps. Stamp in buff and blue.

No.	Type	Description	Unused	Used
301	**92**	1½d. green	25	10
302	**92**	3d. red	30	10
303	**92**	6d. blue	60	1·00

93 George Cross

1961. George Cross Commemoration.

No.	Type	Description	Unused	Used
304	**93**	1½d. black, cream and bistre	15	10
305	-	3d. brown and blue	30	10
306	-	1s. green, lilac and violet	1·10	2·25

DESIGNS: 3d. and 1s. show George Cross as Type **93** over backgrounds with different patterns.

96 "Madonna Damascena"

1962. Great Siege Commemoration.

No.	Type	Description	Unused	Used
307	**96**	2d. blue	10	10
308	-	3d. red	10	10
309	-	6d. bronze	30	10
310	-	1s. purple	30	40

DESIGNS: 3d. Great Siege Monument; 6d. Grand Master La Valette; 1s. Assault on Fort St. Elmo.

1963. Freedom from Hunger. As T 41 of Gibraltar.

No.	Description	Unused	Used
311	1s.6d. sepia	1·75	2·50

1963. Cent of Red Cross. As T 42 of Gibraltar.

No.	Description	Unused	Used
312	2d. red on black	25	15
313	1s.6d. red and blue	1·75	4·50

100 Bruce, Zammit and Microscope

1964. Anti-brucellosis Congress.

316 **100** 2d. brown, black and green 10 10
317 - 1s.6d. black and purple 90 90

DESIGN: 1s.6d. Goat and laboratory equipment.

102 "Nicola Cotoner tending Sick Man" (M. Preti)

1964. 1st European Catholic Doctors' Congress, Valletta. Multicoloured.

318 2d. Type **102** 20 10
319 6d. St. Luke and hospital 50 15
320 1s.6d. Sacra Infermeria, Valletta 1·10 1·90

106 Dove and British Crown

1964. Independence.

321 **106** 2d. olive, red and gold 30 10
322 - 3d. brown, red and gold 30 10
323 - 6d. slate, red and gold 70 15
324 **106** 1s. blue, red and gold 70 15
325 - 1s.6d. blue, red and gold 1·50 1·00
326 - 2s.6d. blue, red and gold 1·50 2·75

DESIGNS: 3d., 1s.6d. Dove and Pope's tiara; 6d., 2s.6d. Dove and U.N. emblem.

109 "The Nativity"

1964. Christmas.

327 **109** 2d. purple and gold 10 10
328 **109** 4d. blue and gold 20 15
329 **109** 8d. green and gold 45 45

110 Neolithic Era

1965. Multicoloured.. Multicoloured..

330 ½d. Type **110** 10 10
331 1d. Punic era (vert) 10 10
332 1½d. Roman era (vert) 30 10
333 2d. Proto Christian era (vert) 10 10
334 2½d. Saracenic era (vert) 1·50 10
335 3d. Siculo Norman era (vert) 10 10
336 4d. Knights of Malta (vert) 1·50 10
337 4½d. Maltese Navy (vert) 1·50 75
337b 5d. Fortifications (vert) 30 20
338 6d. French occupation (vert) 30 10
339 8d. British rule 70 10
339c 10d. Naval Arsenal 50 1·90
340 1s. Maltese Corps of the British Army 30 10
341 1s.3d. International Eucharistic Congress, 1913 2·00 1·40
342 1s.6d. Self-government, 1921 60 20
343 2s. Gozo Civic Council 70 10
344 2s.6d. State of Malta 70 50
345 3s. Independence, 1964 1·75 75
346 5s. HAFMED (Allied Forces, Mediterranean) 6·00 1·00
347 10s. The Maltese Islands (map) 3·00 5·00
348 £1 Patron Saints 4·25 5·50

Nos. 339/48 are larger, 41×29 mm from perf to perf, and include portrait of Queen Elizabeth II.

129 "Dante" (Raphael)

1965. 700th Birth Anniv of Dante.

349 **129** 2d. blue 10 10
350 **129** 6d. green 25 10
351 **129** 2s. brown 1·10 1·50

131 Turkish Fleet

1965. 400th Anniv of Great Siege. Multicoloured.

352 2d. Turkish camp 30 10
353 3d. Battle scene 30 10
354 6d. Type **131** 40 10
355 8d. Arrival of relief force 80 90
356 1s. Grand Master J. de La Valette's arms 40 10
357 1s.6d. "Allegory of Victory" (from mural by M. Preti) 80 30
358 2s.6d. Victory medal 1·50 3·25

SIZES—As Type **131**: 1s. SQUARE (32½×32½ mm): others.

137 "The Three Kings"

1965. Christmas.

359 **137** 1d. purple and red 10 10
360 **137** 4d. purple and blue 30 30
361 **137** 1s.3d. slate and purple 30 30

138 Sir Winston Churchill

1966. Churchill Commemoration.

362 **138** 2d. black, red and gold 25 10
363 - 3d. green, olive and gold 25 10
364 **138** 1s. purple, red and gold 40 10
365 - 1s.6d. blue, ultram & gold 50 1·10

DESIGN : 3d., 1s.6d. Sir Winston Churchill and George Cross.

140 Grand Master La Valette

1966. 400th Anniv of Valletta. Multicoloured.

366 2d. Type **140** 10 10
367 3d. Pope Pius V 15 10
368 6d. Map of Valletta 20 10
369 1s. F. Laparelli (architect) 20 10
370 2s.6d. G. Cassar (architect) 50 60

145 President Kennedy and Memorial

1966. Pres. Kennedy Commemoration.

371 **145** 3d. olive, gold and black 10 10
372 **145** 1s.6d. blue, gold and black 10 10

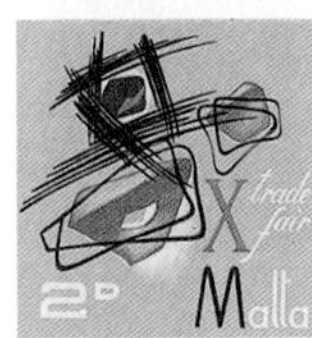

146 "Trade"

1966. 10th Malta Trade Fair.

373 **146** 2d. multicoloured 10 10
374 **146** 8d. multicoloured 30 95
375 **146** 2s.6d. multicoloured 30 1·00

147 "The Child in the Manger"

1966. Christmas.

376 **147** 1d. multicoloured 10 10
377 **147** 4d. multicoloured 10 10
378 **147** 1s.3d. multicoloured 10 10

148 George Cross

1967. 25th Anniv of George Cross Award to Malta.

379 **148** 2d. multicoloured 10 10
380 **148** 4d. multicoloured 10 10
381 **148** 3s. multicoloured 15 20

149 Crucifixion of St. Peter

1967. 1900th Anniv of Martyrdom of Saints Peter and Paul.

382 **149** 2d. brown, orange & black 10 10
383 - 8d. olive, gold and black 15 10
384 - 3s. blue and black 20 20

DESIGNS—As Type **149**: 3s. Beheading of St. Paul. HORIZ (47×25 mm): 8d. Open Bible and episcopal emblems.

152 "St. Catherine of Siena"

1967. 300th Death Anniv of Melchior Gafa (sculptor). Multicoloured.

385 2d. Type **152** 10 10
386 4d. "St. Thomas of Villanova" 10 10
387 1s.6d. "Baptism of Christ" (detail) 15 10
388 2s.6d. "St. John the Baptist" (from "Baptism of Christ") 15 20

156 Temple Ruins, Tarxien

1967. 15th International Historical Architecture Congress, Valletta. Multicoloured.

389 2d. Type **156** 10 10
390 6d. Facade of Palazzo Falzon, Notabile 10 10
391 1s. Parish Church, Birkirkara 10 10
392 3s. Portal, Auberge de Castille 25 25

160 "Angels"

1967. Christmas. Multicoloured.

393 1d. Type **160** 10 10
394 8d. "Crib" 20 10
395 1s.4d. "Angels" 20 10

163 Queen Elizabeth II and Arms of Malta

1967. Royal Visit.

396 **163** 2d. multicoloured 10 10
397 - 4d. black, purple and gold 10 10
398 - 3s. multicoloured 20 30

DESIGNS—VERT: 4d. Queen in Robes of Order of St. Michael and St. George. HORIZ: 3s. Queen and outline of Malta.

166 Human Rights Emblem and People

1968. Human Rights Year. Multicoloured.

399 2d. Type **166** 10 10
400 6d. Human Rights emblem and people (different) 10 10
401 2s. Type **166** (reversed) 10 15

169 Fair "Products"

1968. Malta International Trade Fair.

402 **169** 4d. multicoloured 10 10
403 **169** 8d. multicoloured 10 10
404 **169** 3s. multicoloured 15 15

170 Arms of the Order of St. John and La Valette

1968. 4th Death Cent of Grand Master La Valette. Multicoloured.

405 1d. Type **170** 10 10
406 8d. "La Valette" (A. de Favray) (vert) 15 10
407 1s.6d. La Valette's tomb (28×23 mm) 15 10
408 2s.6d. Angels and scroll bearing date of death (vert) 20 25

174 Star of Bethlehem and Angel waking Shepherds

1968. Christmas. Multicoloured.

409 1d. Type **174** 10 10
410 8d. Mary and Joseph with shepherd watching over Cradle 15 10
411 1s.4d. Three Wise Men and Star of Bethlehem 15 20

177 "Agriculture"

1968. 6th Food and Agricultural Organization Regional Conference for Europe. Mult.

412		4d. Type **177**	10	10
413		1s. F.A.O. emblem and coin	10	10
414		2s.6d. "Agriculture" sowing Seeds	10	15

180 Mahatma Gandhi

1969. Birth Centenary of Mahatma Gandhi.

415	**180**	1s.6d. brown, black & gold	50	10

181 ILO Emblem

1969. 50th Anniv of Int Labour Organization.

416	**181**	2d. blue, gold & turquoise	10	10
417	**181**	6d. sepia, gold and brown	10	10

182 Robert Samut

1969. Birth Centenary of Robert Samut (composer of Maltese National Anthem).

418	**182**	2d. multicoloured	10	10

183 Dove of Peace, U.N. Emblem and Sea-bed

1969. United Nations Resolution on Oceanic Resources.

419	**183**	5d. multicoloured	10	10

184 "Swallows" returning to Malta

1969. Maltese Migrants' Convention.

420	**184**	10d. black, gold and olive	10	10

185 University Arms and Grand Master de Fonseca (founder)

1969. Bicentenary of University of Malta.

421	**185**	2s. multicoloured	15	20

187 Flag of Malta and Birds

1969. 5th Anniv of Independence.

422	-	2d. multicoloured	10	10
423	**187**	5d. black, red and gold	10	10
424	-	10d. black, blue and gold	10	10
425	-	1s.6d. multicoloured	20	40
426	-	2s.6d. black, brown & gold	25	50

DESIGNS—SQUARE (31×31 mm): 2d. 1919 War Monument. VERT: 10d. "Tourism"; 1s.6d. U.N. and Council of Europe emblems; 2s.6d. "Trade and Industry".

191 Peasants playing Tambourine and Bagpipes

1969. Christmas. Children's Welfare Fund. Multicoloured.

427		1d.+1d. Type **191**	10	20
428		5d.+1d. Angels playing trumpet and harp	15	20
429		1s.6d.+3d. Choir boys singing	15	45

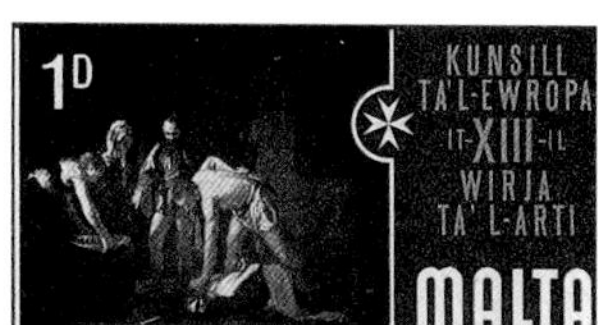

194 "The Beheading of St. John" (Caravaggio)

1970. 13th Council of Europe Art Exn. Mult.

430		1d. Type **194**	10	10
431		2d. "St. John the Baptist" (M. Preti)	10	10
432		5d. Interior of St. John's Co-Cathedral, Valletta	10	10
433		6d. "Allegory of the Order" (Neapolitan school)	15	10
434		8d. "St. Jerome" (Caravaggio)	15	50
435		10d. Articles from the Order of St. John in Malta	15	10
436		1s.6d. "The Blessed Gerard receiving Godfrey de Bouillon" (A. de Favray)	25	40
437		2s. Cape and Stolone (16th cent)	25	55

SIZES—HORIZ: 1d., 8d. 56×30 mm; 2d., 6d. 45×32 mm; 10d., 2s. 63×21 mm; 1s.6d. 45×34 mm. SQUARE: 5d. 39×39 mm.

202 Artist's Impression of Fujiyama

1970. World Fair, Osaka.

438	**202**	2d. multicoloured	10	10
439	**202**	5d. multicoloured	10	10
440	**202**	3s. multicoloured	15	15

203 "Peace and Justice"

1970. 25th Anniv of United Nations.

441	**203**	2d. multicoloured	10	10
442	**203**	5d. multicoloured	10	10
443	**203**	2s.6d. multicoloured	15	15

204 Carol-singers, Church and Star

1970. Christmas. Multicoloured.

444		1d.+½d. Type **204**	10	10
445		10d.+2d. Church, star and angels with Infant	15	20
446		1s.6d.+3d. Church, star and nativity scene	20	40

207 Books and Quill

1971. Literary Anniversaries. Multicoloured.

447		1s.6d. Type **207** (De Soldanis (historian) death bicent)	10	10
448		2s. Dun Karm (poet), books, pens and lamp (birth cent)	10	15

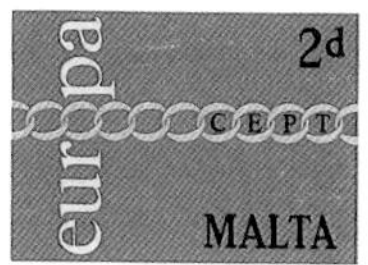

209 Europa "Chain"

1971. Europa.

449	**209**	2d. orange, black and olive	10	10
450	**209**	5d. orange, black and red	10	10
451	**209**	1s.6d. orange, blk & slate	60	90

210 "St. Joseph, Patron of the Universal Church" (G. Cali)

1971. Centenary of Proclamation of St. Joseph as Patron Saint of Catholic Church, and 50th Anniv of Coronation of the Statue of "Our Lady of Victories". Multicoloured.

452		2d. Type **210**	10	10
453		5d. Statue of "Our Lady of Victories" and galley	10	10
454		10d. Type **210**	15	10
455		1s.6d. As 5d.	30	40

211 "Centaurea spathulata"

1971. National Plant and Bird of Malta. Multicoloured.

456		2d. Type **211**	10	10
457		5d. Blue rock thrush (horiz)	20	10
458		10d. As 5d.	30	15
459		1s.6d. Type **211**	30	1·25

212 Angel

1971. Christmas. Multicoloured.

460		1d.+½d. Type **212**	10	10
461		10d.+2d. Mary and the Child Jesus	15	25
462		1s.6d.+3d. Joseph lying awake	20	40
MS463		131×113 mm. Nos. 460/2	75	2·50

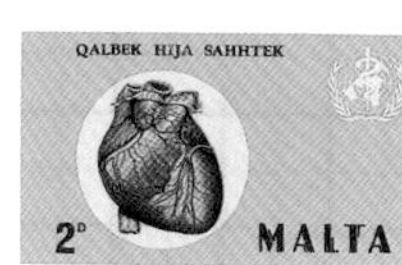

213 Heart and W.H.O. Emblem

1972. World Health Day.

464	**213**	2d. multicoloured	10	10
465	**213**	10d. multicoloured	15	10
466	**213**	2s.6d. multicoloured	40	80

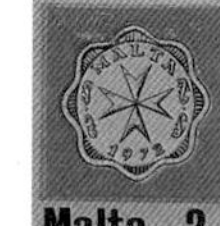

214 Maltese Cross

1972. Decimal Currency. Coins. Multicoloured.

467		2m. Type **214**	10	10
468		3m. Bee on honeycomb	10	10
469		5m. Earthen lampstand	10	10
470		1c. George Cross	10	10
471		2c. Classical head	10	10
472		5c. Ritual altar	10	10
473		10c. Grandmaster's galley	20	10
474		50c. Great Siege Monument	1·25	1·25

SIZES: 3m., 2c. As Type **214**: 5m., 1c., 5c. 25×30 mm; 10c., 50c. 31×38 mm.

1972. Nos. 337a, 339 and 341 surch.

475		1c.3 on 5d. multicoloured	10	10
476		3c. on 8d. multicoloured	15	10
477		5c. on 1s.3d. multicoloured	15	20

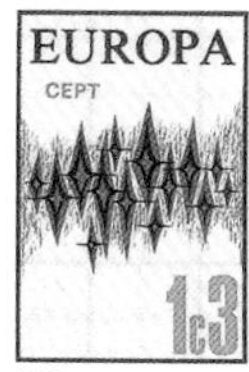

216 "Communications"

1972. Europa.

478	**216**	1c.3 multicoloured	10	10
479	**216**	3c. multicoloured	10	10
480	**216**	5c. multicoloured	15	35
481	**216**	7c.5 multicoloured	20	75

217 Angel

1972. Christmas.

482	**217**	8m.+2m. brown, grey and gold	10	10
483	-	3c.+1c. purple, violet and gold	15	40
484	-	7c.5+1c.5 indigo, blue and gold	20	50
MS485		137×113 mm. Nos. 482/4	1·75	4·25

DESIGNS: No. 483, Angel with tambourine; No. 484, Singing angel.

See also Nos. 507/9.

218 Archaeology

1973. Multicoloured.. Multicoloured..

486		2m. Type **218**	10	10
487		4m. History	10	10
488		5m. Folklore	10	10
489		8m. Industry	10	10
490		1c. Fishing industry	10	10
491		1c.3 Pottery	10	10
492		2c. Agriculture	10	10
493		3c. Sport	10	10
494		4c. Yacht marina	15	10
495		5c. Fiesta	15	10
496		7c.5 Regatta	25	10
497		10c. Voluntary service	25	10
498		50c. Education	2·00	50
499		£1 Religion	2·75	2·00
500		£2 Coat of arms (32×27 mm)	14·00	19·00
500b		£2 National Emblem (32×27 mm)	9·00	14·00

219 Europa "Posthorn"

1973. Europa.

501	**219**	3c. multicoloured	15	10
502	**219**	5c. multicoloured	15	35
503	**219**	7c.5 multicoloured	25	65

220 Emblem, and Woman holding Corn

1973. Anniversaries.

No.	Type	Description	Unused	Used
504	**220**	1c.3 multicoloured	10	10
505	-	7c.5 multicoloured	25	40
506	-	10c. multicoloured	30	50

ANNIVERSARIES: 1c.3, 10th anniv of World Food Programme; 7c.5, 25th anniv of W.H.O.; 10c. 25th anniv of Universal Declaration of Human Rights.

1973. Christmas. As T 217. Multicoloured.

No.	Description	Unused	Used
507	8m.+2m. Angels and organ pipes	15	10
508	3c.+1c. Madonna and Child	25	60
509	7c.5+1c.5 Buildings and Star	45	1·50
MS510	137×112 mm. Nos. 507/9	4·75	7·50

221 Girolamo Cassar (architect)

1973. Prominent Maltese.

No.	Type	Description	Unused	Used
511	**221**	1c.3 deep green, green and gold	10	10
512	-	3c. green, blue and gold	15	10
513	-	5c. brown, green and gold	20	15
514	-	7c.5 blue, lt blue & gold	20	30
515	-	10c. deep purple, purple and gold	20	40

DESIGNS: 3c. Giuseppe Barth (ophthalmologist); 5c. Nicolo' Isouard (composer); 7c.5, John Borg (botanist); 10c. Antonio Sciortino (sculptor).

222 "Air Malta" Emblem

1974. Air. Multicoloured.

No.	Description	Unused	Used
516	3c. Type **222**	15	10
517	4c. Boeing 720B	15	10
518	5c. Type **222**	15	10
519	7c.5 As 4c.	20	10
520	20c. Type **222**	35	60
521	25c. As 4c.	35	60
522	35c. Type **222**	45	1·40

223 Prehistoric Sculpture

1974. Europa.

No.	Type	Description	Unused	Used
523	**223**	1c.3 blue, black and gold	15	10
524	-	3c. brown, black and gold	20	15
525	-	5c. purple, black and gold	25	50
526	-	7c.5 green, black and gold	35	1·00

DESIGNS—VERT: 3c. Old Cathedral Door, Mdina; 7c.5, "Vetlina" (sculpture by A. Sciortino). HORIZ: 5c. Silver monstrance.

224 Heinrich von Stephan (founder) and Land Transport

1974. Centenary of U.P.U.

No.	Type	Description	Unused	Used
527	**224**	1c.3 green, blue & orange	30	10
528	-	5c. brown, red and green	30	10
529	-	7c.5 blue, violet and green	35	20
530	-	50c. purple, red and orange	1·00	1·25
MS531		126×91 mm. Nos. 527/30	4·75	7·50

DESIGNS (each containing portrait as Type **224**): 5c. "Washington" (paddle-steamer) and "Royal Viking Star" (liner); 7c.5, Balloon and Boeing 747-100; 50c. U.P.U. Buildings, 1874 and 1974.

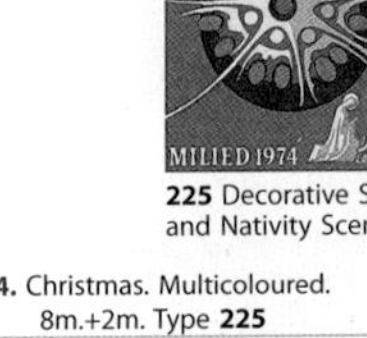

225 Decorative Star and Nativity Scene

1974. Christmas. Multicoloured.

No.	Description	Unused	Used
532	8m.+2m. Type **225**	10	10
533	3c.+1c. "Shepherds"	15	20
534	5c.+1c. "Shepherds with gifts"	20	35
535	7c.5+1c.5 "The Magi"	30	45

226 Swearing-in of Prime Minister

1975. Inauguration of Republic.

No.	Type	Description	Unused	Used
536	**226**	1c.3 multicoloured	10	10
537	-	5c. red and black	20	10
538	-	25c. multicoloured	60	1·00

DESIGNS: 5c. National flag; 25c. Minister of Justice, President and Prime Minister.

227 Mother and Child ("Family Life")

1975. International Women's Year.

No.	Type	Description	Unused	Used
539	**227**	1c.3 violet and gold	15	10
540	-	3c. blue and gold	15	10
541	**227**	5c. brown and gold	25	15
542	-	20c. brown and gold	80	2·50

DESIGN: 3c., 20c. Office secretary ("Public Life").

228 "Allegory of Malta" (Francesco de Mura)

1975. Europa. Multicoloured.

No.	Description	Unused	Used
543	5c. Type **228**	30	10
544	15c. "Judith and Holofernes" (Valentin de Boulogne)	50	75

The 15c. is smaller, 47×23 mm.

229 Plan of Ggantija Temple

1975. European Architectural Heritage Year.

No.	Type	Description	Unused	Used
545	**229**	1c.3 black and red	10	10
546	-	3c. purple, red and brown	20	10
547	-	5c. brown and red	30	25
548	-	25c. green, red and black	1·10	3·00

DESIGNS: 3c. Mdina skyline; 5c. View of Victoria, Gozo; 25c. Silhouette of Fort St. Angelo.

230 Farm Animals

1975. Christmas. Multicoloured.

No.	Description	Unused	Used
549	8m.+2m. Type **230**	25	25
550	3c.+1c. Nativity scene (50×23 mm)	40	75
551	7c.5+1c.5 Approach of the Magi	45	1·40

231 "The Right to Work"

1975. 1st Anniv of Republic.

No.	Type	Description	Unused	Used
552	**231**	1c.3 multicoloured	10	10
553	-	5c. multicoloured	20	10
554	-	25c. red, blue and black	70	1·10

DESIGNS: 5c. "Safeguarding the Environment"; 25c. National flag.

232 "Festa Tar-Rahal"

1976. Maltese Folklore. Multicoloured.

No.	Description	Unused	Used
555	1c.3 Type **232**	10	10
556	5c. "L-Imnarja" (horiz)	15	10
557	7c.5 "Il-Karnival" (horiz)	35	70
558	10c. "Il-Gimgha L-Kbira"	55	1·40

233 Water Polo

1976. Olympic Games, Montreal. Multicoloured.

No.	Description	Unused	Used
559	1c.7 Type **233**	10	10
560	5c. Sailing	25	10
561	30c. Athletics	85	1·50

234 Lace-making

1976. Europa. Multicoloured.

No.	Description	Unused	Used
562	7c. Type **234**	20	35
563	15c. Stone carving	25	60

235 Nicola Cotoner

1976. 300th Anniv of School of Anatomy and Surgery. Multicoloured.

No.	Description	Unused	Used
564	2c. Type **235**	10	10
565	5c. Arm	15	10
566	7c. Giuseppe Zammit	20	10
567	11c. Sacra Infermeria	35	65

236 St. John the Baptist and St. Michael

1976. Christmas. Multicoloured.

No.	Description	Unused	Used
568	1c.+5m. Type **236**	10	20
569	5c.+1c. Madonna and Child	15	60
570	7c.+1c.5 St. Christopher and St. Nicholas	20	80
571	10c.+2c. Complete painting (32×27 mm)	30	1·25

Nos. 568/71 show portions of "Madonna and Saints" by Domenico di Michelino.

237 Jean de la Valette's Armour

1977. Suits of Armour. Multicoloured.

No.	Description	Unused	Used
572	2c. Type **237**	10	10
573	7c. Aloph de Wignacourt's armour	20	10
574	11c. Jean Jacques de Verdelin's armour	25	50

1977. No. 336 surch 1c7.

No.	Description	Unused	Used
575	1c.7 on 4d. multicoloured	25	25

239 "Annunciation"

1977. 400th Birth Anniv of Rubens. Flemish Tapestries. Multicoloured.

No.	Description	Unused	Used
576	2c. Type **239**	10	10
577	7c. "Four Evangelists"	25	10
578	11c. "Nativity"	45	45
579	20c. "Adoration of the Magi"	80	1·00

See also Nos. 592/5, 615/18 and 638/9.

240 Map and Radio Aerial

1977. World Telecommunications Day.

No.	Type	Description	Unused	Used
580	**240**	1c. black, green and red	10	10
581	**240**	6c. black, blue and red	20	10
582	-	8c. black, brown and red	30	10
583	-	17c. black, mauve and red	60	40

DESIGN—HORIZ: 8, 17c. Map, aerial and airplane tail-fin.

241 Ta' L-Isperanza

1977. Europa. Multicoloured.

No.	Description	Unused	Used
584	7c. Type **241**	30	15
585	20c. Is-Salini	35	1·00

242 "Aid to Handicapped Workers" (detail from Workers' Monument)

1977. Maltese Worker Commemoration.

No.	Type	Description	Unused	Used
586	**242**	2c. orange and brown	10	10
587	-	7c. light brown and brown	15	10
588	-	20c. multicoloured	40	60

DESIGNS—VERT: 7c. "Stoneworker, modern industry and ship-building" (monument detail). HORIZ: 20c. "Mother with Dead Son" and Service Medal.

243 The Shepherds

1977. Christmas. Multicoloured.

No.	Description	Unused	Used
589	1c.+5m. Type **243**	10	35
590	7c.+1c. The Nativity	15	55
591	11c.+1c.5 The Flight into Egypt	20	70

1978. Flemish Tapestries. (2nd series). As T 239. Multicoloured.

No.	Description	Unused	Used
592	2c. "The Entry into Jerusalem"	10	10
593	7c. "The Last Supper" (after Poussin)	25	10
594	11c. "The Raising of the Cross" (after Rubens)	30	25
595	25c. "The Resurrection" (after Rubens)	70	80

244 "Young Lady on Horseback and Trooper"

1978. 450th Death Anniv of Albrecht Durer.

596	**244**	1c.7 black, red and blue	10	10
597	-	8c. black, red and grey	15	10
598	-	17c. black, red and grey	40	45

DESIGNS: 8c. "The Bagpiper"; 17c. "The Virgin and Child with a Monkey".

245 Monument to Grand Master Nicola Cotoner (Foggini)

1978. Europa. Monuments. Multicoloured.

599	7c. Type **245**	15	10
600	25c. Monument to Grand Master Ramon Perellos (Mazzuoli)	35	90

246 Goalkeeper

1978. World Cup Football Championship, Argentina. Multicoloured.

601	2c. Type **246**	10	10
602	11c. Players heading ball	15	10
603	15c. Tackling	25	35
MS604	125×90 mm. Nos. 601/3	2·00	3·25

247 Boeing 707 over Megalithic Temple

1978. Air. Multicoloured.

605	5c. Type **247**	20	10
606	7c. Air Malta Boeing 720B	20	10
607	11c. Boeing 747 taking off from Luqa Airport	35	10
608	17c. Type **247**	45	30
609	20c. As 7c.	40	40
610	75c. As 11c.	1·25	2·75

248 Folk Musicians and Village Church

1978. Christmas. Multicoloured.

611	1c.+5m. Type **248**	10	10
612	5c.+1c. Choir of Angels	15	20
613	7c.+1c.5 Carol singers	20	35
614	11c.+3c. Folk musicians, church, angels and carol singers (58×22 mm)	25	45

1979. Flemish Tapestries (3rd series) showing paintings by Rubens. As T 239. Multicoloured.

615	2c. "The Triumph of the Catholic Church"	10	10
616	7c. "The Triumph of Charity"	20	10
617	11c. "The Triumph of Faith"	30	25
618	25c. "The Triumph of Truth"	95	80

249 Fishing Boat and Aircraft Carrier

1979. End of Military Facilities Agreement. Multicoloured.

619	2c. Type **249**	10	10
620	5c. Raising the flag ceremony	10	10
621	7c. Departing soldier and olive sprig	15	10
622	8c. Type **249**	30	30
623	17c. As 5c.	40	45
624	20c. As 7c.	40	45

250 Speronara (fishing boat) and Tail of Air Malta Boeing 707

1979. Europa. Communications. Multicoloured.

625	7c. Type **250**	20	10
626	25c. Coastal watch tower and radio link towers	40	75

251 Children on Globe

1979. International Year of the Child. Multicoloured.

627	2c. Type **251**	10	10
628	7c. Children flying kites (27×33 mm)	15	10
629	11c. Children in circle (27×33 mm)	20	35

252 Shells

1979. Marine Life. Multicoloured.

630	2c. Type **252**	10	10
631	5c. Loggerhead turtle	20	10
632	7c. Dolphin (fish)	25	10
633	25c. Noble pen shell	90	1·25

253 "The Nativity" (detail)

1979. Christmas. Paintings by Giuseppe Cali. Multicoloured.

634	1c.+5m. Type **253**	10	10
635	5c.+1c. "The Flight into Egypt" (detail)	15	15
636	7c.+1c.5 "The Nativity"	20	20
637	11c.+3c. "The Flight into Egypt"	30	50

1980. Flemish Tapestries (4th series). As T 239. Multicoloured.

638	2c. "The Institution of Corpus Domini" (Rubens)	10	10
639	8c. "The Destruction of Idolatry" (Rubens)	20	20
MS640	114×86 mm. 50c. "Grand Master Perelles with St. Jude and St. Simon (unknown Maltese artist) (vert)	80	1·60

254 Hal Saflieni Hypogeum, Paola

1980. Int Restoration of Monuments Campaign. Multicoloured.

641	2c.5 Type **254**	10	15
642	6c. Vilhena Palace, Mdina	15	20
643	8c. Citadel of Victoria, Gozo (horiz)	20	40
644	12c. Fort St. Elmo, Valletta (horiz)	30	60

255 Dun Gorg Preca

1980. Birth Centenary of Dun Gorg Preca (founder of Society of Christian Doctrine).

645	**255**	2c. 5 grey and black	10	10

256 Ruzar Briffa (poet)

1980. Europa.

646	**256**	8c. yellow, brown & green	20	10
647	-	30c. green, brown and lake	55	1·25

DESIGN: 30c. Nikiol Anton Vassalli (scholar and patriot).

257 "Annunciation"

1980. Christmas. Paintings by A. Inglott. Multicoloured.

648	2c.+5m. Type **257**	10	10
649	6c.+1c. "Conception"	20	20
650	8c.+1c.5 "Nativity"	25	40
651	12c.+3c. "Annunciation", "Conception" and "Nativity" (47×38 mm)	30	70

258 Rook and Pawn

1980. 24th Chess Olympiad and International Chess Federation Congress. Multicoloured.

652	2c.5 Type **258**	20	20
653	8c. Bishop and pawn	45	20
654	30c. King, queen and pawn (vert)	70	1·50

259 Barn Owl

1981. Birds. Multicoloured.

655	3c. Type **259**	30	25

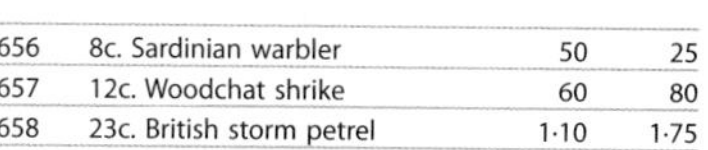

656	8c. Sardinian warbler	50	25
657	12c. Woodchat shrike	60	80
658	23c. British storm petrel	1·10	1·75

260 Traditional Horse Race

1981. Europa. Folklore. Multicoloured.

659	8c. Type **260**	20	10
660	30c. Attempting to retrieve flag from end of "gostra" (greasy pole)	40	65

261 Stylized "25"

1981. 25th Maltese International Trade Fair.

661	**261**	4c. multicoloured	15	15
662	**261**	25c. multicoloured	50	60

262 Disabled Artist at Work

1981. International Year for Disabled Persons. Multicoloured.

663	3c. Type **262**	20	10
664	35c. Disabled child playing football	90	75

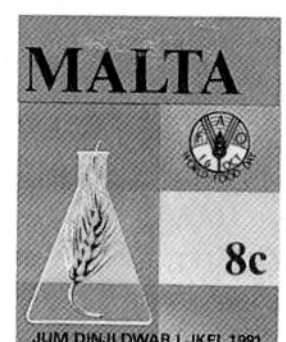

263 Wheat Ear in Conical Flask

1981. World Food Day.

665	**263**	8c. multicoloured	15	15
666	**263**	23c. multicoloured	60	50

264 Megalithic Building

1981. History of Maltese Industry. Multicoloured.

667	5m. Type **264**	10	85
668	1c. Cotton production	10	10
669	2c. Early ship-building	85	10
670	3c. Currency minting	30	10
671	5c. "Art"	30	25
672	6c. Fishing	1·25	25
673	7c. Agriculture	30	1·50
674	8c. Stone quarrying	1·00	35
675	10c. Grape pressing	35	50
676	12c. Modern ship-building	2·00	2·25
677	15c. Energy	70	2·00
678	20c. Telecommunications	70	75
679	25c. "Industry"	1·00	2·25
680	50c. Drilling for Water	2·50	2·75
681	£1 Sea transport	7·00	7·50
682	£3 Air transport	13·00	18·00

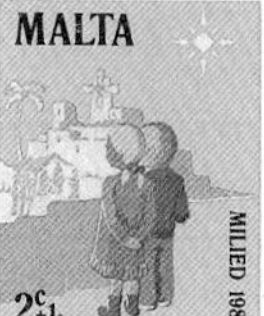

265 Children and Nativity Scene

1981. Christmas. Multicoloured.

No.	Description	Mint	Used
683	2c.+1c. Type **265**	25	10
684	8c.+2c. Christmas Eve procession (horiz)	35	20
685	20c.+3c. Preaching midnight sermon	50	1·10

266 Shipbuilding

1982. Shipbuilding Industry.

No.	Description	Mint	Used
686	**266** 3c. multicoloured	15	10
687	- 8c. multicoloured	30	30
688	- 13c. multicoloured	55	55
689	- 27c. multicoloured	1·25	1·25

DESIGNS: 8c. to 27c. Differing shipyard scenes.

267 Elderly Man and Has-Serh (home for elderly)

1982. Care of Elderly. Multicoloured.

No.	Description	Mint	Used
690	8c. Type **267**	30	20
691	30c. Elderly woman and Has-Zmien (hospital for elderly)	1·10	1·40

268 Redemption of Islands by Maltese, 1428

1982. Europa. Historical Events. Multicoloured.

No.	Description	Mint	Used
692	8c. Type **268**	40	20
693	30c. Declaration of rights by Maltese, 1802	70	1·40

269 Stylized Footballer

1982. World Cup Football Championship, Spain.

No.	Description	Mint	Used
694	**269** 3c. multicoloured	20	10
695	- 12c. multicoloured	60	55
696	- 15c. multicoloured	70	65
MS697	125×90 mm. Nos. 694/6	3·50	4·50

DESIGNS: 12c., 15c. Various stylized footballers.

270 Angel appearing to Shepherds

1982. Christmas. Multicoloured.

No.	Description	Mint	Used
698	2c.+1c. Type **270**	15	20
699	8c.+2c. Nativity and Three Wise Men bearing gifts	40	60
700	20c.+3c. Nativity scene (45×37 mm)	80	1·25

271 "Ta Salvo Serafino" (oared brigantine), 1531

1982. Maltese Ships (1st series). Multicoloured.

No.	Description	Mint	Used
701	3c. Type **271**	25	10
702	8c. "La Madonna del Rosaria" (tartane), 1740	50	30
703	12c. "San Paulo" (xebec), 1743	70	55
704	20c. "Ta' Pietro Saliba" (xprunara), 1798	90	90

See also Nos. 725/8, 772/5, 792/5 and 809/12.

272 Locomotive "Manning Wardle", 1883

1983. Centenary of Malta Railway. Multicoloured.

No.	Description	Mint	Used
705	3c. Type **272**	45	15
706	13c. Locomotive "Black Hawthorn", 1884	85	1·00
707	27c. Beyer Peacock locomotive, 1895	1·50	3·25

273 Peace Doves leaving Malta

1983. Commonwealth Day. Multicoloured.

No.	Description	Mint	Used
708	8c. Type **273**	20	30
709	12c. Tourist landmarks	30	60
710	15c. Holiday beach (vert)	35	75
711	23c. Ship-building (vert)	55	1·00

274 Ggantija Megalithic Temples, Gozo

1983. Europa. Multicoloured.

No.	Description	Mint	Used
712	8c. Type **274**	40	40
713	30c. Fort St. Angelo	70	2·40

275 Dish Aerials (World Communications Year)

1983. Anniversaries and Events. Multicoloured.

No.	Description	Mint	Used
714	3c. Type **275**	30	15
715	7c. Ships' prows and badge (25th anniv of I.M.O. Convention)	50	55
716	13c. Container lorries and badge (30th anniv of Customs Co-operation Council)	80	90
717	20c. Stadium and emblem (9th Mediterranean Games)	90	2·25

276 Monsignor Giuseppe de Piro

1983. 50th Death Anniv of Monsignor Giuseppe de Piro.

No.	Description	Mint	Used
718	**276** 3c. multicoloured	15	15

277 Annunciation

1983. Christmas. Multicoloured.

No.	Description	Mint	Used
719	2c.+1c. Type **277**	30	15
720	8c.+2c. The Nativity	70	60
721	20c.+3c. Adoration of the Magi	1·25	2·25

278 Workers at Meeting

1983. 40th Anniv of General Workers' Union. Multicoloured.

No.	Description	Mint	Used
722	3c. Type **278**	25	10
723	8c. Worker with family	45	40
724	27c. Union H.Q. Building	1·25	1·75

1983. Maltese Ships (2nd series). As T 271. Multicoloured.

No.	Description	Mint	Used
725	2c. "Strangier" (full-rigged ship), 1813	30	25
726	12c. "Tigre" (topsail schooner), 1839	80	1·25
727	13c. "La Speranza" (brig), 1844	80	1·25
728	20c. "Wignacourt" (barque), 1844	1·25	2·75

279 Boeing 737 9H-ABA

1984. Air. Multicoloured.

No.	Description	Mint	Used
729	7c. Type **279**	50	30
730	8c. Boeing 720B	60	35
731	16c. Vickers 953 Vanguard G-APED	1·25	70
732	23c. Vickers Viscount 700	1·50	70
733	27c. Douglas DC-3 G-AGHH	1·75	80
734	38c. Armstrong Whitworth A.W.15 Atalanta G-ABTJ "Artemis"	2·25	2·75
735	75c. Marina Fiat MF.5 flying boat I-AZDL	3·25	5·00

280 Bridge

1984. Europa. 25th Anniv of C.E.P.T.

No.	Description	Mint	Used
736	**280** 8c. green, black and yellow	35	35
737	**280** 30c. red, black and yellow	1·00	1·25

281 Early Policeman

1984. 170th Anniv of Malta Police Force. Multicoloured.

No.	Description	Mint	Used
738	3c. Type **281**	65	15
739	8c. Mounted police	1·25	65
740	11c. Motorcycle policeman	1·50	2·00
741	25c. Policeman and firemen	2·25	3·75

282 Running

1984. Olympic Games, Los Angeles. Multicoloured.

No.	Description	Mint	Used
742	7c. Type **282**	25	30
743	12c. Gymnastics	50	70
744	23c. Swimming	85	1·25

283 "The Visitation" (Pietru Caruana)

1984. Christmas. Paintings from Church of Our Lady of Porto Salvo, Valletta. Multicoloured.

No.	Description	Mint	Used
745	2c.+1c. Type **283**	55	65
746	8c.+2c. "The Epiphany" (Rafel Caruana) (horiz)	1·00	1·40
747	20c.+3c. "Jesus among the Doctors" (Rafel Caruana) (horiz)	2·00	4·00

284 Dove on Map

1984. 10th Anniv of Republic. Multicoloured.

No.	Description	Mint	Used
748	3c. Type **284**	30	20
749	8c. Fort St. Angelo	60	65
750	30c. Hands	2·10	4·75

285 1885 ½d. Green Stamp

1985. Centenary of Malta Post Office. Mult.

No.	Description	Mint	Used
751	3c. Type **285**	45	15
752	8c. 1885 1d. rose	65	45
753	12c. 1885 2½d. blue	90	1·40
754	20c. 1885 4d. brown	1·40	3·00
MS755	165×90 mm. Nos. 751/4	3·75	6·50

286 Boy, and Hands planting Vine

1985. International Youth Year. Multicoloured.

No.	Description	Mint	Used
756	2c. Type **286**	15	15
757	13c. Young people and flowers (vert)	70	60
758	27c. Girl holding flame in hand	1·40	1·40

287 Nicolo Baldacchino (tenor)

1985. Europa. European Music Year. Mult.

No.	Description	Mint	Used
759	8c. Type **287**	1·50	50
760	30c. Francesco Azopardi (composer)	2·75	5·00

288 Guzeppi Bajada and Manwel Attard (victims)

1985. 66th Anniv of 7 June 1919 Demonstrations. Multicoloured.

761	3c. Type **288**	30	15
762	7c. Karmnu Abela and Wenzu Dyer (victims)	60	40
763	35c. Model of projected Demonstration monument by Anton Agius (vert)	1·90	2·75

289 Stylized Birds

1985. 40th Anniv of United Nations Organization. Multicoloured.

764	4c. Type **289**	25	15
765	11c. Arrow-headed ribbons	60	1·25
766	31c. Stylized figures	1·40	3·25

290 Giorgio Mitrovich (nationalist) (death centenary)

1985. Celebrities' Anniversaries. Multicoloured.

767	8c. Type **290**	75	35
768	12c. Pietru Caxaru (poet and administrator) (400th death anniversary)	1·25	2·50

291 The Three Wise Men

1985. Christmas. Designs showing details of terracotta relief by Ganni Bonnici. Multicoloured.

769	2c.+1c. Type **291**	45	60
770	8c.+2c. Virgin and Child	1·00	1·50
771	20c.+3c. Angels	2·00	3·50

1985. Maltese Ships (3rd series). Steamships. As T 271. Multicoloured.

772	3c. "Scotia" (paddle-steamer), 1844	85	20
773	7c. "Tagliaferro" (screw-steamer), 1822	1·25	75
774	15c. "Gleneagles" (screw-steamer), 1885	1·75	2·75
775	23c. "L'Isle Adam" (screw-steamer), 1886	2·00	3·75

292 John XXIII Peace Laboratory and Statue of St. Francis of Assisi

1986. International Peace Year. Multicoloured.

776	8c. Type **292**	1·25	50
777	11c. Dove and hands holding olive branch (40×19 mm)	1·50	2·50
778	27c. Map of Africa, dove and two heads	3·25	4·75

293 Symbolic Plant and "Cynthia cardui", "Vanessa atalanta" and "Polyommatus icarus"

1986. Europa. Environmental Conservation. Multicoloured.

779	8c. Type **293**	1·25	50
780	35c. Island, Neolithic frieze, sea and sun	2·25	6·00

294 Heading the Ball

1986. World Cup Football Championship, Mexico. Multicoloured.

781	3c. Type **294**	50	20
782	7c. Saving a goal	1·00	1·00
783	23c. Controlling the ball	3·50	6·50
MS784	125×90 mm. Nos. 781/3	7·00	8·50

295 Father Diegu

1986. Maltese Philanthropists. Multicoloured.

785	2c. Type **295**	40	30
786	3c. Adelaide Cini	50	30
787	8c. Alfonso Maria Galea	1·25	60
788	27c. Vincenzo Bugeja	3·25	6·00

296 "Nativity"

1986. Christmas. Paintings by Giuseppe D'Arena. Multicoloured.

789	2c.+1c. Type **296**	1·25	1·75
790	8c.+2c. "Nativity" (detail) (vert)	2·75	3·50
791	20c.+3c. "Epiphany"	3·75	7·00

1986. Maltese Ships (4th series). As T 271. Multicoloured.

792	7c. "San Paul" (freighter), 1921	1·00	50
793	10c. "Knight of Malta" (mail steamer), 1930	1·25	1·75
794	12c. "Valetta City" (freighter), 1948	1·50	2·75
795	20c. "Saver" (freighter), 1959	2·25	4·50

297 European Robin

1987. 25th Anniv of Malta Ornithological Society. Multicoloured.

796	3c. Type **297**	1·25	50
797	8c. Peregrine falcon (vert)	2·50	1·00
798	13c. Hoopoe (vert)	3·25	4·00
799	23c. Cory's shearwater	3·75	6·00

298 Aquasun Lido

1987. Europa. Modern Architecture. Multicoloured.

800	8c. Type **298**	1·00	75
801	35c. Church of St. Joseph, Manikata	2·50	4·75

299 16th-century Pikeman

1987. Maltese Uniforms (1st series). Multicoloured.

802	3c. Type **299**	85	40
803	7c. 16th-century officer	1·60	90
804	10c. 18th-century standard bearer	1·75	2·25
805	27c. 18th-century General of the Galleys	3·75	4·75

See also Nos. 832/5, 851/4, 880/3 and 893/6.

300 Maltese Scenes, Wheat Ears and Sun

1987. Anniversaries and Events. Multicoloured.

806	5c. Type **300** (European Environment Year)	1·25	50
807	8c. Esperanto star as comet (Centenary of Esperanto)	2·00	60
808	23c. Family at house door (International Year of Shelter for the Homeless)	3·00	3·00

1987. Maltese Ships (5th series). As T 271. Multicoloured.

809	2c. "Medina" (freighter), 1969	70	60
810	11c. "Rabat" (container ship), 1974	2·50	2·50
811	13c. "Ghawdex" (passenger ferry), 1979	2·75	2·75
812	20c. "Pinto" (car ferry), 1987	3·75	4·00

301 "The Visitation"

1987. Christmas. Illuminated illustrations, score and text from 16th-century choral manuscript. Multicoloured.

813	2c.+1c. Type **301**	50	65
814	8c.+2c. "The Nativity"	1·75	2·50
815	20c.+3c. "The Adoration of the Magi"	3·25	4·50

302 Dr. Arvid Pardo (U.N. representative)

1987. 20th Anniv of United Nations Resolution on Peaceful Use of the Seabed. Multicoloured.

816	8c. Type **302**	1·00	75
817	12c. U.N. emblem and sea	1·75	3·00
MS818	125×90 mm. Nos. 816/17	3·00	4·50

303 Ven. Nazju Falzon (Catholic catechist)

1988. Maltese Personalities. Multicoloured.

819	2c. Type **303**	30	30
820	3c. Mgr. Sidor Formosa (philanthropist)	30	30
821	4c. Sir Luigi Preziosi (ophthalmologist)	60	30
822	10c. Fr. Anastasju Cuschieri (poet)	80	85
823	25c. Mgr. Pietru Pawl Saydon (Bible translator)	2·00	3·25

304 "St. John Bosco with Youth" (statue)

1988. Religious Anniversaries. Multicoloured.

824	10c. Type **304** (death centenary)	1·00	75
825	12c. "Assumption of Our Lady" (altarpiece by Perugino, Ta' Pinu, Gozo) (Marian Year)	1·25	1·25
826	14c. "Christ the King" (statue by Sciortino) (75th anniv of International Eucharistic Congress, Valletta)	1·50	2·00

305 Bus, Ferry and Airliner

1988. Europa. Transport and Communications. Multicoloured.

827	10c. Type **305**	1·25	75
828	35c. Control panel, dish aerial and pylons	2·00	3·75

306 Globe and Red Cross Emblems

1988. Anniversaries and Events. Multicoloured.

829	4c. Type **306** (125th anniv of Int Red Cross)	60	50
830	18c. Divided globe (Campaign for North–South Interdependence and Solidarity)	1·50	2·50
831	19c. Globe and symbol (40th anniv of W.H.O.)	1·50	2·50

1988. Maltese Uniforms (2nd series). As T 299. Multicoloured.

832	3c. Private, Maltese Light Infantry, 1800	50	30
833	4c. Gunner, Malta Coast Artillery, 1802	55	35
834	10c. Field Officer, 1st Maltese Provincial Battalion, 1805	1·40	1·25
835	25c. Subaltern, Royal Malta Regiment, 1809	2·75	4·25

307 Athletics

1988. Olympic Games, Seoul. Multicoloured.

836 4c. Type **307** 30 30
837 10c. Diving 70 80
838 35c. Basketball 2·00 3·00

308 Shepherd with Flock

1988. Christmas. Multicoloured.

839 3c.+1c. Type **308** 30 30
840 10c.+2c. The Nativity 75 1·00
841 25c.+3c. Three Wise Men 1·75 2·50

309 Commonwealth Emblem

1989. 25th Anniv of Independence. Multicoloured.

842 2c. Type **309** 25 35
843 3c. Council of Europe flag 25 35
844 4c. U.N. flag 30 35
845 10c. Workers, hands gripping ring and national flag 75 95
846 12c. Scales and allegorical figure of Justice 90 1·40
847 25c. Prime Minister Borg Olivier with Independence constitution (42×28 mm) 1·90 3·25

310 New State Arms

1989

848 **310** £1 multicoloured 4·00 4·50

311 Two Boys flying Kite

1989. Europa. Children's Games. Multicoloured.

849 10c. Type **311** 1·00 75
850 35c. Two girls with dolls 2·50 4·50

1989. Maltese Uniforms (3rd series). As T 299. Multicoloured.

851 3c. Officer, Maltese Veterans, 1815 45 45
852 4c. Subaltern, Royal Malta Fencibles, 1839 50 50
853 10c. Private, Malta Militia, 1856 1·50 1·50
854 25c. Colonel, Royal Malta Fencible Artillery, 1875 2·75 3·75

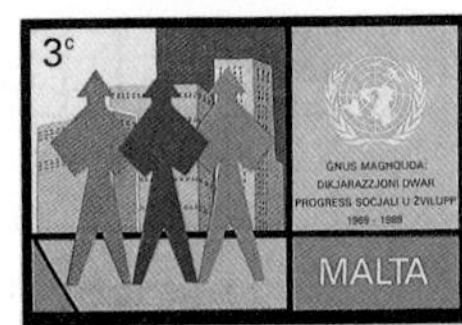

312 Human Figures and Buildings

1989. Anniversaries and Commemorations. Designs showing logo and stylized human figures. Multicoloured.

855 3c. Type **312** (20th anniv of U.N. Declaration on Social Progress and Development) 30 30
856 4c. Workers and figure in wheelchair (Malta's Ratification of European Social Charter) 35 35
857 10c. Family (40th anniv of Council of Europe) 80 1·25
858 14c. Teacher and children (70th anniv of Malta Union of Teachers) 1·00 1·75
859 25c. Symbolic knights (Knights of the Sovereign Military Order of Malta Assembly) 2·25 3·50

313 Angel and Cherub

1989. Christmas. Vault paintings by Mattia Preti from St. John's Co-Cathedral, Valletta.

860 3c.+1c. Type **313** 60 60
861 10c.+2c. Two angels 1·40 1·90
862 20c.+3c. Angel blowing trumpet 2·00 4·00

314 Presidents George H. Bush and Mikhail Gorbachev

1989. U.S.A.–U.S.S.R. Summit Meeting, Malta.

863 **314** 10c. multicoloured 1·00 1·25

315 General Post Office, Auberge d'Italie, Valletta

1990. Europa. Post Office Buildings. Multicoloured.

864 10c. Type **315** 1·00 50
865 35c. Branch Post Office, Zebbug (horiz) 2·00 3·75

316 Open Book and Letters from Different Alphabets (International Literacy Year)

1990. Anniversaries and Events. Multicoloured.

866 3c. Type **316** 25 25
867 4c. Count Roger of Sicily and Norman soldiers (900th anniv of Sicilian rule) (horiz) 60 30
868 19c. Communications satellite (25th anniv of I.T.U.) (horiz) 2·25 2·50
869 20c. Football and map of Malta (Union of European Football Association 20th Ordinary Congress, Malta) 2·25 2·50

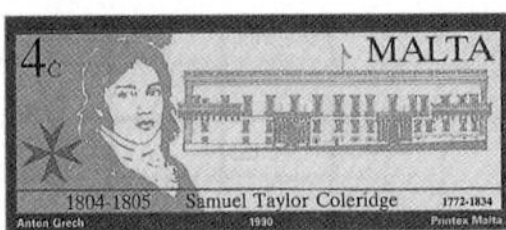

317 Samuel Taylor Coleridge (poet) and Government House

1990. British Authors. Multicoloured.

870 4c. Type **317** 50 30
871 10c. Lord Byron (poet) and map of Valletta 90 70
872 12c. Sir Walter Scott (novelist) and Great Siege 1·00 95
873 25c. William Makepeace Thackeray (novelist) and Naval Arsenal 2·00 2·25

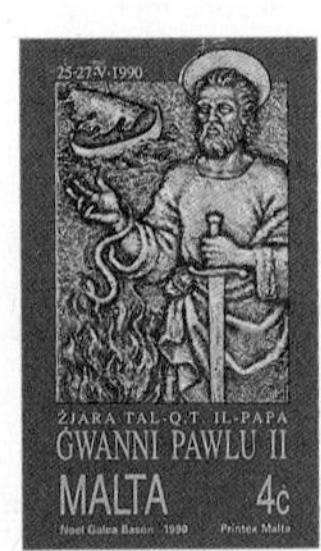

318 St. Paul

1990. Visit of Pope John Paul II. Bronze Bas-reliefs.

874 **318** 4c. black, flesh and red 50 1·50
875 - 25c. black, flesh and red 1·50 1·75

DESIGN: 25c. Pope John Paul II.

319 Flags and Football

1990. World Cup Football Championship, Italy. Multicoloured.

876 5c. Type **319** 35 30
877 10c. Football in net 65 1·00
878 14c. Scoreboard and football 1·00 1·75
MS879 123×90 mm. Nos. 876/8 3·00 4·25

1990. Maltese Uniforms (4th series). As T 299. Multicoloured.

880 3c. Captain, Royal Malta Militia, 1889 1·25 55
881 4c. Field officer, Royal Malta Artillery, 1905 1·40 60
882 10c. Labourer, Malta Labour Corps, 1915 2·50 1·50
883 25c. Lieutenant, King's Own Malta Regiment of Militia, 1918 3·75 4·50

320 Innkeeper

1990. Christmas. Figures from Crib by Austin Galea, Marco Bartolo and Rosario Zammit. Multicoloured.

884 3c.+1c. Type **320** 30 50
885 10c.+2c. Nativity (41×28 mm) 70 1·25
886 25c.+3c. Shepherd with sheep 1·60 2·50

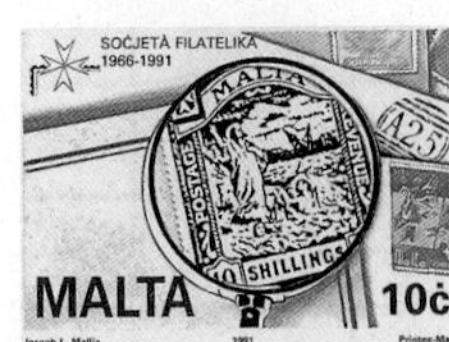

321 1919 10s. Stamp under Magnifying Glass

1991. 25th Anniv of Philatelic Society of Malta.

887 **321** 10c. multicoloured 60 70

322 "Eurostar" Satellite and V.D.U. Screen

1991. Europa. Europe in Space. Multicoloured.

888 10c. Type **322** 1·00 70
889 35c. "Ariane 4" rocket and projected HOTOL aerospace-plane 1·75 2·75

323 St. Ignatius Loyola (founder of Jesuits) (500th birth anniv)

1991. Religious Commemorations. Multicoloured.

890 3c. Type **323** 30 20
891 4c. Abbess Venerable Maria Adeodata Pisani (185th birth anniversary) (vert) 35 25
892 30c. St. John of the Cross (400th death anniversary) 2·00 2·75

1991. Maltese Uniforms (5th series). As T 299. Multicoloured.

893 3c. Officer with colour, Royal Malta Fencibles, 1860 50 25
894 10c. Officer with colour, Royal Malta Regiment of Militia, 1903 1·00 60
895 19c. Officer with Queen's colour, King's Own Malta Regiment, 1968 1·90 1·75
896 25c. Officer with colour, Malta Armed Forces, 1991 2·25 2·00

324 Interlocking Arrows

1991. 25th Anniv of Union Haddiema Maghqudin (public services union).

897 **324** 4c. multicoloured 30 30

325 Western Honey Buzzard

1991. Endangered Species. Birds. Multicoloured.

898 4c. Type **325** 2·50 2·50
899 4c. Marsh harrier 2·50 2·50
900 10c. Eleonora's falcon 2·50 2·50
901 10c. Lesser kestrel 2·50 2·50

326 Three Wise Men

1991. Christmas. Multicoloured.

902 3c.+1c. Type **326** 55 50
903 10c.+2c. Holy Family 1·25 1·40
904 25c.+3c. Two shepherds 2·25 3·25

327 Ta' Hagrat Neolithic Temple

1991. National Heritage of the Maltese Islands. Multicoloured.

905	1c. Type **327**	35	50
906	2c. Cottoner Gate	35	50
907	3c. St. Michael's Bastion, Valletta	35	50
908	4c. Spinola Palace, St. Julian's	40	15
909	5c. Birkirkara Church	50	20
910	10c. Mellieha Bay	90	35
911	12c. Wied iz-Zurrieq	1·25	40
912	14c. Mgarr harbour, Gozo	1·50	45
913	20c. Yacht marina	2·00	65
914	50c. Gozo Channel	3·25	1·60
915	£1 "Arab Horses" (sculpture by Antonio Sciortino)	5·50	3·25
916	£2 Independence Monument (Ganni Bonnici) (vert)	10·00	8·00

328 Aircraft Tailfins and Terminal

1992. Opening of Int Air Terminal. Mult.

917	4c. Type **328**	75	30
918	10c. National flags and terminal	1·25	70

329 Ships of Columbus

1992. Europa. 500th Anniv of Discovery of America by Columbus. Multicoloured.

919	10c. Type **329**	1·25	55
920	35c. Columbus and map of Americas	2·50	2·25

330 George Cross and Anti-aircraft Gun Crew

1992. 50th Anniv of Award of George Cross to Malta. Multicoloured.

921	4c. Type **330**	1·00	30
922	10c. George Cross and memorial bell	1·50	1·00
923	50c. Tanker "Ohio" entering Grand Harbour	7·00	8·50

331 Running

1992. Olympic Games, Barcelona. Multicoloured.

924	3c. Type **331**	65	20
925	10c. High jumping	1·25	1·00
926	30c. Swimming	2·50	4·50

332 Church of the Flight into Egypt

1992. Rehabilitation of Historical Buildings.

927	**332**	3c. black, stone and grey	55	30
928	-	4c. black, stone and pink	60	30
929	-	19c. black, stone and lilac	2·75	3·75
930	-	25c. black, stone and green	3·00	3·75

DESIGNS—HORIZ: 4c. St. John's Co-Cathedral; 25c. Auberge de Provence. VERT: 19c. Church of Madonna del Pillar.

333 "The Nativity" (Giuseppe Cali)

1992. Christmas. Religious Paintings by Giuseppe Cali from Mosta Church. Multicoloured.

931	3c.+1c. Type **333**	1·00	1·10
932	10c.+2c. "Adoration of the Magi"	2·25	2·50
933	25c.+3c. "Christ with the Elders in the Temple"	3·75	4·50

334 Malta College Building, Valletta

1992. 400th Anniv of University of Malta. Multicoloured.

934	4c. Type **334**	75	25
935	30c. Modern University complex, Tal-Qroqq (horiz)	2·75	4·25

335 Lions Club Emblem

1993. 75th Anniv of International Association of Lions Club. Multicoloured.

936	4c. Type **335**	50	25
937	50c. Eye (Sight First Campaign)	2·75	4·00

336 Untitled Painting by Paul Carbonaro

1993. Europa. Contemporary Art. Mult.

938	10c. Type **336**	1·25	50
939	35c. Untitled painting by Alfred Chircop (horiz)	3·00	5·00

337 Mascot holding Flame

1993. 5th Small States of Europe Games. Multicoloured.

940	3c. Type **337**	20	20
941	4c. Cycling	1·75	30
942	10c. Tennis	1·50	1·00
943	35c. Yachting	2·75	3·50
MS944	120×80 mm. Nos. 940/3	5·50	5·50

338 Learning First Aid

1993. 50th Anniv of Award of Bronze Cross to Maltese Scouts and Guides. Multicoloured.

945	3c. Type **338**	50	20
946	4c. Bronze Cross	50	20
947	10c. Scout building camp fire	1·10	90
948	35c. Governor Lord Gort presenting Bronze Cross, 1943	2·75	4·00

339 "Papilio machaon"

1993. European Year of the Elderly. Butterflies. Multicoloured.

949	5c. Type **339**	35	20
950	35c. "Vanessa atalanta"	1·75	2·25

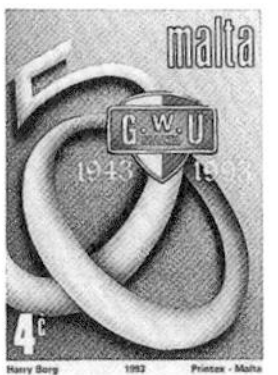

340 G.W.U. Badge and Interlocking "50"

1993. 50th Anniv of General Workers Union.

951	**340**	4c. multicoloured	35	40

341 Child Jesus and Star

1993. Christmas. Multicoloured.

952	3c.+1c. Type **341**	30	35
953	10c.+2c. Christmas tree	85	1·25
954	25c.+3c. Star in traditional window	1·60	2·75

342 Council Arms (face value top left)

1993. Inauguration of Local Community Councils. Sheet 110×93 mm, containing T 342 and similar horiz designs showing different Council Arms. Multicoloured.

MS955	5c. Type **342**; 5c. Face value top right; 5c. Face value bottom left; 5c. Face value bottom right	1·50	2·25

343 Symbolic Tooth and Probe

1994. 50th Anniv of Maltese Dental Association. Multicoloured.

956	5c. Type **343**	35	30
957	44c. Symbolic mouth and dental mirror	3·00	3·00

344 Sir Themistocles Zammit (discoverer of Brucella microbe)

1994. Europa. Discoveries. Multicoloured.

958	14c. Type **344**	50	30
959	30c. Bilingually inscribed candelabrum of 2nd century B.C. (deciphering of ancient Phoenician language)	1·90	3·25

345 Family in Silhouette (International Year of the Family)

1994. Anniversaries and Events. Multicoloured.

960	5c. Type **345**	30	20
961	9c. Stylized Red Cross (International recognition of Malta Red Cross Society)	60	50
962	14c. Animals and crops (150th anniv of Agrarian Society)	90	80
963	20c. Worker in silhouette (75th anniv of I.L.O.)	1·25	1·60
964	25c. St. Paul's Anglican Cathedral (155th anniv) (vert)	1·40	1·75

346 Football and Map

1994. World Cup Football Championship, U.S.A. Multicoloured.

965	5c. Type **346**	40	20
966	14c. Ball and goal	1·00	80
967	30c. Ball and pitch superimposed on map	2·00	4·25
MS968	123×88 mm. Nos. 965/7	3·75	4·50

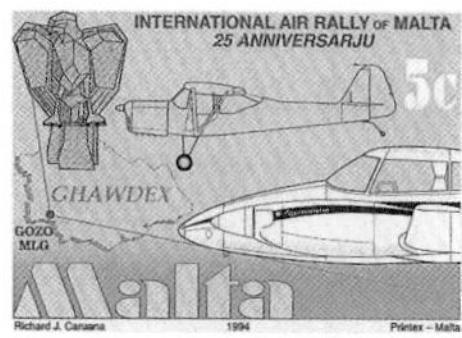

347 Falcon Trophy, Piper PA-30 Twin Commanche and Auster J-5 Autocar (25th anniv of Malta International Rally)

1994. Aviation Anniversaries and Events. Multicoloured.

969	5c. Type **347**	50	20
970	14c. Aerospatiale (Sud) Alouette helicopter, display teams and logo (Malta International Airshow)	1·75	85
971	20c. de Havilland DH.104 Dove "City of Valetta" and Avro Type 685 York aircraft with logo (50th anniv of I.C.A.O.)	1·90	1·75

972	25c. Airbus 320 "Nicolas Cottoner" and de Havilland DH.106 Comet aircraft with logo (50th anniv of I.C.A.O.)	1·90	1·90

348 National Flags and Astronaut on Moon

1994. 25th Anniv of First Manned Moon Landing.

973	**348**	14c. multicoloured	1·10	1·25

349 Virgin Mary and Child with Angels

1994. Christmas. Multicoloured.

974	5c. Type **349**	25	10
975	9c.+2c. Angel in pink (vert)	65	70
976	14c.+3c. Virgin Mary and Child (vert)	90	1·25
977	20c.+3c. Angel in green (vert)	1·60	2·50

Nos. 975/7 are larger, 28×41 mm, and depict details from Type **349**.

350 Helmet-shaped Ewer

1994. Maltese Antique Silver Exhibition. Multicoloured.

978	5c. Type **350**	50	20
979	14c. Balsamina	1·10	80
980	20c. Coffee pot	1·50	2·00
981	25c. Sugar box	1·75	2·75

351 "60 plus" and Hands touching

1995. Anniversaries and Events. Multicoloured.

982	2c. Type **351** (25th anniv of National Association of Pensioners)	15	15
983	5c. Child's drawing (10th anniv of National Youth Council)	25	20
984	14c. Conference emblem (4th World Conference on Women, Peking, China)	70	80
985	20c. Nurse and thermometer (50th anniv of Malta Memorial District Nursing Association)	1·25	1·40
986	25c. Louis Pasteur (biologist) (death centenary)	1·50	1·75

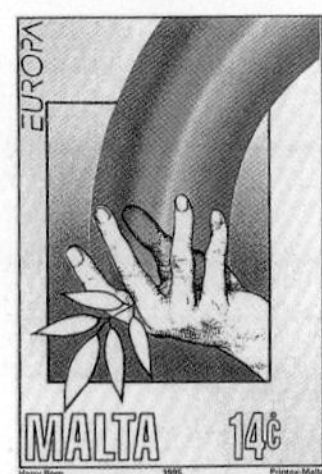

352 Hand holding Leaf and Rainbow

1995. Europa. Peace and Freedom. Multicoloured.

987	14c. Type **352**	1·00	55
988	30c. Peace doves (horiz)	1·50	2·50

353 Junkers Ju 87B Stuka Dive Bombers over Valletta and Anti-aircraft Gun

1995. Anniversaries. Multicoloured.

989	5c. Type **353** (50th anniv of end of Second World War)	25	25
990	14c. Silhouetted people holding hands (50th anniv of United Nations)	55	60
991	35c. Hands holding bowl of wheat (50th anniv of F.A.O.) (vert)	1·60	2·25

354 Light Bulb

1995. Maltese Electricity and Telecommunications. Multicoloured.

992	2c. Type **354**	15	15
993	5c. Symbolic owl and binary codes	25	25
994	9c. Dish aerial	45	50
995	14c. Sun and rainbow over trees	70	80
996	20c. Early telephone, satellite and Moon's surface	1·25	1·50

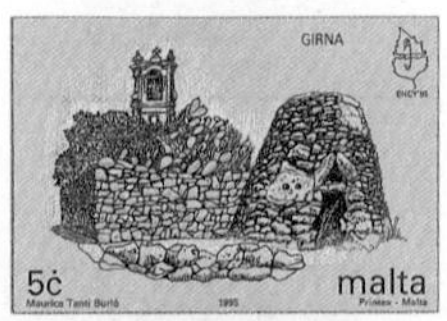

355 Rock Wall and Girna

1995. European Nature Conservation Year. Multicoloured.

997	5c. Type **355**	75	25
998	14c. Maltese wall lizards	2·25	80
999	44c. Aleppo pine	3·50	3·00

356 Pinto's Turret Clock

1995. Treasures of Malta. Antique Maltese Clocks. Multicoloured.

1000	1c. Type **356**	15	60
1001	5c. Michelangelo Sapiano (horologist) and clocks	50	25
1002	14c. Arlogg tal-lira clock	1·50	80
1003	25c. Sundials	2·50	3·50

357 Children's Christmas Eve Procession

1995. Christmas. Multicoloured.

1004	5c. Type **357**	25	10
1005	5c.+2c. Children with crib (vert)	30	50
1006	14c.+3c. Children with lanterns (vert)	1·00	1·25
1007	25c.+3c. Boy with lantern and balustrade (vert)	1·75	2·75

Nos. 1005/7 are 27×32 mm and depict details from Type **357**.

358 Silhouetted Children and President's Palace, San Anton

1996. Anniversaries. Multicoloured.

1008	5c. Type **358** (35th anniv of the President's Award)	25	25
1009	14c. Nazzareno Camilleri (priest) and St. Patrick's Church, Salesjani (90th birth anniv)	65	65
1010	20c. St. Mary Euphrasia and convent (birth bicentenary)	1·00	1·10
1011	25c. Silhouetted children and fountain (50th anniv of UNICEF)	1·25	1·40

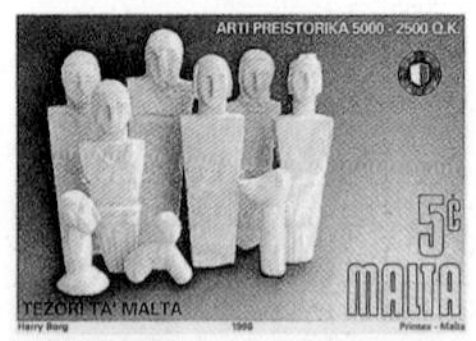

359 Carved Figures from Skorba

1996. Maltese Prehistoric Art Exhibition. Multicoloured.

1012	5c. Type **359**	30	20
1013	14c. Temple carving, Gozo	80	85
1014	20c. Carved figure of a woman, Skorba (vert)	1·10	1·25
1015	35c. Ghar Dalam pot (vert)	1·90	2·50

360 Mabel Strickland (politician and journalist)

1996. Europa. Famous Women. Multicoloured.

1016	14c. Type **360**	75	55
1017	30c. Inez Soler (artist, musician and writer)	2·00	2·00

361 Face and Emblem (United Nations Decade against Drug Abuse)

1996. Anniversaries and Events. Multicoloured.

1018	5c. Type **361**	25	25
1019	5c. "Fi" and emblem (50th anniv of Malta Federation of Industry)	25	25
1020	14c. Commemorative plaque and national flag (75th anniv of self-government)	80	80
1021	44c. Guglielmo Marconi and early radio equipment (centenary of radio)	2·25	2·50

362 Judo

1996. Olympic Games, Atlanta. Multicoloured.

1022	2c. Type **362**	10	10
1023	5c. Athletics	30	25
1024	14c. Diving	80	80
1025	25c. Rifle-shooting	1·40	1·60

363 "Harvest Time" (Cali)

1996. 150th Birth Anniv of Guiseppe Cali (painter). Multicoloured.

1026	5c. Type **363**	30	25
1027	14c. "Dog" (Cali)	70	70
1028	20c. "Countrywoman in a Field" (Cali) (vert)	90	1·10
1029	25c. "Cali at his Easel" (Edward Dingli) (vert)	1·00	1·25

364 Bus No. 1990 "Diamond Star", 1920s

1996. Buses. Multicoloured.

1030	2c. Type **364**	40	10
1031	5c. No. 434 "Tom Mix", 1930s	70	25
1032	14c. No. 1764 "Verdala", 1940s	1·40	80
1033	30c. No. 3495, 1960s	2·00	2·00

365 Stained Glass Window

1996. Christmas. Multicoloured.

1034	5c. Type **365**	35	10
1035	5c.+2c. Madonna and Child (29×35 mm)	40	60
1036	14c.+3c. Angel facing right (29×35 mm)	80	1·40
1037	25c.+3c. Angel facing left (29×35 mm)	1·25	2·50

Nos. 1035/7 show details from Type **365**.

366 Hompesch Arch and Arms, Zabbar

1997. Bicentenary of Maltese Cities. Multicoloured.

1038	6c. Type **366**	30	25
1039	16c. Statue, church and arms, Siggiewi	70	70
1040	26c. Seated statue and arms, Zejtun	1·10	1·25
MS1041	125×90 mm. Nos. 1038/40	5·50	4·50

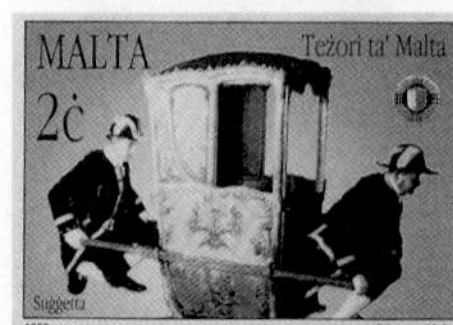

367 Captain-General of the Galleys' Sedan Chair

1997. Treasures of Malta. Sedan Chairs. Multicoloured.

1042	2c. Type **367**	15	15
1043	6c. Cotoner Grandmasters' chair	30	30
1044	16c. Chair from Cathedral Museum, Mdina (vert)	70	70
1045	27c. Chevalier D'Arezzo's chair (vert)	1·10	1·10

368 Gahan carrying Door

1997. Europa. Tales and Legends. Multicoloured.

1046	16c. Type **368**	1·00	75
1047	35c. St. Dimitrius appearing from painting	1·75	2·50

369 Modern Sculpture (Antonio Sciortino)

1997. Anniversaries. Multicoloured.

1048	1c. Type **369**	10	15
1049	6c. Joseph Calleia and film reel (horiz)	40	40
1050	6c. Gozo Cathedral (horiz)	40	40
1051	11c. City of Gozo (horiz)	60	50
1052	16c. Sculpture of head (Sciortino)	80	70
1053	22c. Joseph Calleia and film camera (horiz)	1·00	1·00

ANNIVERSARIES: 1, 16c. 50th death anniv of Antonio Sciortino (sculptor); 6 (No. 1049), 22c. Birth centenary of Joseph Calleia (actor); 6 (No. 1050), 11c. 300th anniv of construction of Gozo Cathedral.

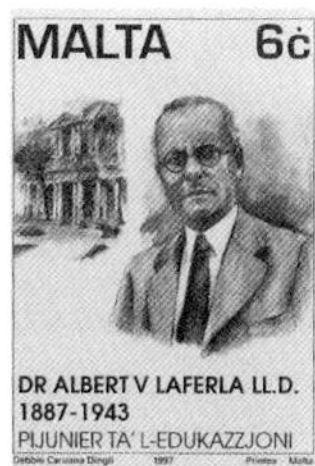

370 Dr. Albert Laferla

1997. Pioneers of Education. Multicoloured.

1054	6c. Type **370**	30	25
1055	16c. Sister Emilie de Vialar	70	70
1056	19c. Mgr. Paolo Pullicino	80	80
1057	26c. Mgr. Tommaso Gargallo	1·00	1·10

371 The Nativity

1997. Christmas. Multicoloured.

1058	6c. Type **371**	30	10
1059	6c.+2c. Mary and baby Jesus (vert)	35	50
1060	16c.+3c. Joseph with donkey (vert)	1·00	1·40
1061	26c.+3c. Shepherd with lamb (vert)	1·50	2·50

Nos. 1059/61 show details from Type **371**.

372 Plan of Fort and Soldiers in Victoria Lines

1997. Anniversaries. Multicoloured (except 6c.).

1062	2c. Type **372**	20	10
1063	6c. Sir Paul Boffa making speech (black and red)	30	25
1064	16c. Plan of fort and gun crew	90	65
1065	37c. Queue of voters	1·50	2·00

ANNIVERSARIES: 2, 16c. Centenary of Victoria Lines; 6, 37c. 50th anniv of 1947 Self-government Constitution.

373 "Maria Amelia Grognet" (Antonine de Favray)

1998. Treasures of Malta. Costumes and Paintings.

1066	6c. Type **373**	80	50
1067	6c. Gentleman's waistcoat, c.1790–1810	80	50
1068	16c. Lady's dinner dress, c.1880	1·10	90
1069	16c. "Veneranda, Baroness Abela, and her Grandson" (De Favray)	1·10	90
MS1070	123×88 mm. 26c. City of Valletta from old print (39×47 mm)	1·60	1·60

374 Grand Master Ferdinand von Hompesch

1998. Bicentenary of Napoleon's Capture of Malta. Multicoloured.

1071	6c. Type **374**	60	80
1072	6c. French fleet	60	80
1073	16c. French landing	1·10	1·60
1074	16c. General Napoleon Bonaparte	1·10	1·60

375 Racing Two-man Luzzus

1998. Europa. Sailing Regatta, Grand Harbour. Multicoloured.

1075	16c. Type **375**	1·10	55
1076	35c. Racing four-man luzzus	1·50	2·50

376 Dolphin and Diver

1998. International Year of the Ocean. Multicoloured.

1077	2c. Type **376**	40	25
1078	6c. Diver and sea-urchin	65	25
1079	16c. Jacques Cousteau and diver (horiz)	1·60	80
1080	27c. Two divers (horiz)	2·00	2·25

377 Goalkeeper saving Goal

1998. World Cup Football Championship, France. Players and flags. Multicoloured.

1081	6c. Type **377**	70	25
1082	16c. Two players and referee	1·40	70
1083	22c. Two footballers	1·60	2·00
MS1084	122×87 mm. Nos. 1081/3	3·50	3·25

378 Ships' Wheels (50th anniv of Int Maritime Organization)

1998. Anniversaries. Multicoloured.

1085	1c. Type **378**	10	30
1086	6c. Symbolic family (50th anniv of Universal Declaration of Human Rights)	40	25
1087	11c. "GRTU" and cogwheels (50th anniv of General Retailers and Traders Union)	70	40
1088	19c. Mercury (50th anniv of Chamber of Commerce)	1·10	1·40
1089	26c. Aircraft tailfins (25th anniv of Air Malta)	2·40	2·50

379 "Rest on the Flight to Egypt"

1998. Christmas. Paintings by Mattia Preti. Mult.

1090	6c. Type **379**	40	10
1091	6c.+2c. "Virgin and Child with Sts. Anthony and John the Baptist"	50	70
1092	16c.+3c. "Virgin and Child with Sts. Raphael, Nicholas and Gregory"	1·25	1·75
1093	26c.+3c. "Virgin and Child with Sts. John the Baptist and Nicholas"	1·75	3·00

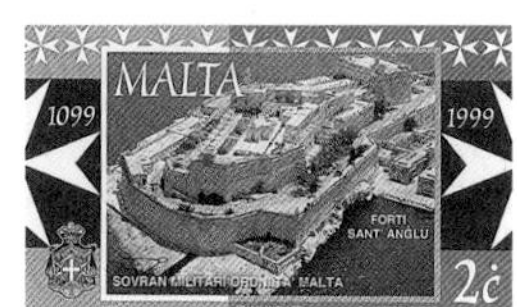

380 Fort St. Angelo

1999. 900th Anniv of the Sovereign Military Order of Malta. Multicoloured.

1094	2c. Type **380**	50	10
1095	6c. Grand Master De l'Isle Adam (vert)	80	25
1096	16c. Grand Master La Valette (vert)	1·50	65
1097	27c. Auberge de Castille et Leon	2·50	3·00

381 Little Ringed Plover, Ghadira Nature Reserve

1999. Europa. Parks and Gardens. Multicoloured.

1098	16c. Type **381**	2·00	55
1099	35c. River kingfisher, Simar Nature Reserve	2·50	3·00

382 Council of Europe Assembly

1999. 50th Anniv of Council of Europe. Mult.

1100	6c. Type **382**	60	25
1101	16c. Council of Europe Headquarters, Strasbourg	1·00	1·25

383 U.P.U. Emblem and Marsamxett Harbour, Valletta

1999. 125th Anniv of Universal Postal Union. Multicoloured.

1102	6c. Type **383**	1·25	1·50
1103	16c. Nuremberg and "iBRA '99" International Stamp Exhibition emblem	1·50	1·75
1104	22c. Paris and "Philexfrance '99" International Stamp Exhibition emblem	1·60	1·90
1105	27c. Peking and "China '99" International Stamp Exhibition emblem	1·75	2·00
1106	37c. Melbourne and "Australia '99" International Stamp Exhibition emblem	1·90	2·50

384 Couple in Luzzu

1999. Tourism. Multicoloured.

1107	6c. Type **384**	50	25
1108	16c. Tourist taking photograph	95	55
1109	22c. Man sunbathing (horiz)	1·25	1·00
1110	27c. Couple with horse-drawn carriage (horiz)	1·90	1·40
1111	37c. Caveman at Ta' Hagrat Neolithic temple (horiz)	2·50	3·25

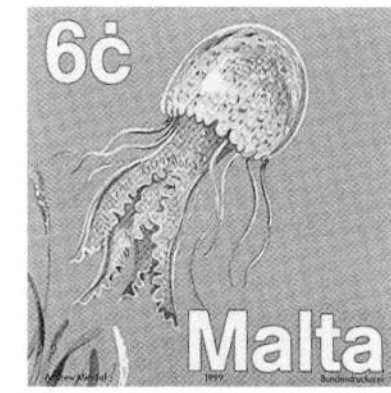

385 Common Jellyfish

1999. Marine Life of the Mediterranean. Mult.

1112	6c. Type **385**	70	75
1113	6c. Peacock wrasse	70	75
1114	6c. Common cuttlefish	70	75
1115	6c. Violet sea-urchin	70	75
1116	6c. Dusky grouper	70	75
1117	6c. Common two-banded seabream	70	75
1118	6c. Star-coral	70	75
1119	6c. Spiny spider crab	70	75
1120	6c. Rainbow wrasse	70	75
1121	6c. Octopus	70	75
1122	6c. Atlantic trumpet triton	70	75
1123	6c. Mediterranean parrotfish	70	75
1124	6c. Long-snouted seahorse	70	75
1125	6c. Deep-water hermit crab	70	75
1126	6c. Mediterranean moray	70	75
1127	6c. Common starfish	70	75

Nos. 1112/27 were printed together, se-tenant, forming a composite design.

386 Father Mikiel Scerri

1999. Bicentenary of Maltese Uprising against the French. Multicoloured.

1128	6c. Type **386**	90	90
1129	6c. "L-Eroj Maltin" (statue)	90	90
1130	16c. General Belgrand de Vaubois (French commander)	1·75	1·75
1131	16c. Captain Alexander Ball R.N.	1·75	1·75

387 "Wolfgang Philip Guttenberg interceding with The Virgin" (votive painting)

1999. Mellieha Sanctuary Commemoration. Mult.

1132	**387** 35c. multicoloured	2·25	2·75
MS1133	123×88 mm. 6c. "Mellieha Virgin and Child" (rock painting) (vert)	1·00	1·10

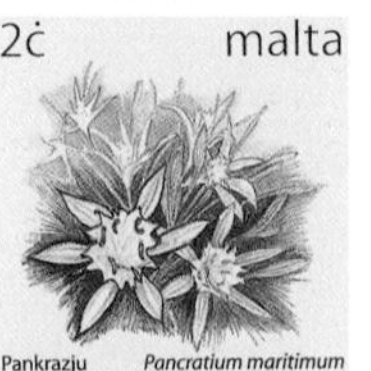

388 Sea Daffodil

1999. Maltese Flowers. Multicoloured.

1134	1c. *Helichrysum melitense*	10	10
1135	2c. Type **388**	10	10
1136	3c. *Cistus creticus*	10	15
1137	4c. Southern dwarf iris	15	20
1138	5c. *Papaver rhoeas*	30	25
1139	6c. French daffodil	25	25
1139a	7c. *Vitex angus-castus*	50	65
1140	10c. *Rosa sempervirens*	40	35
1141	11c. *Silene colorata*	60	40
1142	12c. *Cynara cardunculus*	50	45
1143	16c. Yellow-throated crocus	65	55
1144	19c. *Anthemis arvensis*	1·00	65
1145	20c. *Anacamptis pyramidalis*	1·00	70
1145a	22c. *Spartium junceum*	1·75	75
1146	25c. Large Star of Bethlehem	1·10	85
1147	27c. *Borago officinalis*	1·75	90
1147a	28c. *Crataegus azalorus*	1·75	95
1147b	37c. *Cercis siliquastrum*	2·00	1·40
1147c	45c. *Myrtus communis*	2·25	1·75
1148	46c. Wild tulip	2·25	1·75
1149	50c. *Chrysanthemum coronarium*	2·00	1·90
1149a	76c. *Pistacia lentiscus*	5·00	3·25
1150	£1 *Malva sylvestris*	4·50	4·25
1151	£2 *Adonis microcarpa*	8·00	8·50

389 Madonna and Child

1999. Christmas. Multicoloured.

1152	6c. Type **389**	60	10
1153	6c.+3c. Carol singers	65	80
1154	16c.+3c. Santa Claus	1·60	2·00
1155	26c.+3c. Christmas decorations	2·00	3·00

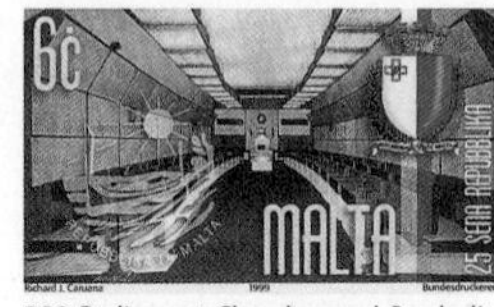

390 Parliament Chamber and Symbolic Luzzu

1999. 25th Anniv of Republic. Multicoloured.

1156	6c. Type **390**	40	25
1157	11c. Parliament in session and Council of Europe emblem	60	35
1158	16c. Church and Central Bank of Malta building	80	55
1159	19c. Aerial view of Gozo and emblems	1·10	1·00
1160	26c. Computer and shipyard	1·40	1·60

391 Gift and Flowers

2000. Greetings Stamps. Multicoloured.

1161	3c. Type **391**	30	15
1162	6c. Photograph, envelope and rose	50	25
1163	16c. Flowers and silver heart	1·00	55
1164	20c. Champagne and pocket watch	1·25	1·00
1165	22c. Wedding rings and roses	1·25	1·40

392 Luzzu and Cruise Liner

2000. Malta during the 20th Century. Multicoloured.

1166	6c. Type **392**	65	25
1167	16c. Street musicians and modern street carnival	90	65
1168	22c. Family in 1900 and illuminated quayside	1·25	1·25
1169	27c. Rural occupations and Citadel, Victoria	1·75	2·50

393 Footballers and Trophy (Centenary of Malta Football Association)

2000. Sporting Events. Multicoloured.

1170	6c. Type **393**	55	25
1171	16c. Swimming and sailing (Olympic Games, Sydney)	85	55
1172	26c. Judo, shooting and running (Olympic Games, Sydney)	1·40	1·10
1173	37c. Football (European Championship)	1·75	2·50

394 "Building Europe"

2000. Europa.

1174	**394** 16c. multicoloured	1·25	65
1175	**394** 46c. multicoloured	2·75	3·25

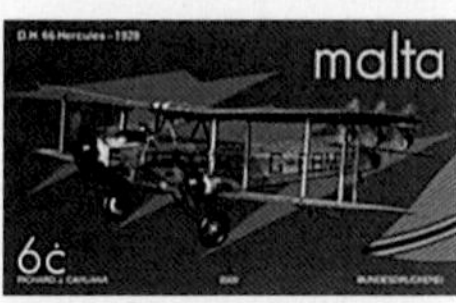

395 de Havilland DH.66 Hercules, 1928

2000. Century of Air Transport, 1900–2000. Mult.

1176	6c. Type **395**	85	1·10
1177	6c. LZ 127 *Graf Zeppelin*, 1933	85	1·10
1178	16c. Douglas DC-3 Dakota of Air Malta Ltd, 1949	1·60	1·90
1179	16c. Airbus Industries Airbus A320 of Air Malta	1·60	1·90
MS1180	122×87 mm. Nos. 1176/9	4·50	5·50

Nos. 1176/7 and 1178/9 were each printed together, se-tenant, with the backgrounds forming composite designs.

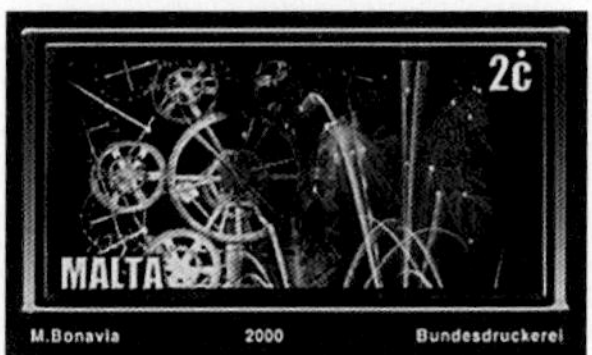

396 Catherine Wheel and Fireworks

2000. Fireworks. Multicoloured.

1181	2c. Type **396**	30	10
1182	6c. Exploding multicoloured fireworks	65	25
1183	16c. Catherine wheel	1·25	55
1184	20c. Exploding green fireworks	1·40	1·00
1185	50c. Numbered rockets in rack	3·00	5·00

397 "Boy walking Dog" (Jean Paul Zammit)

2000. "Stampin' the Future" (Children's stamp design competition winners). Multicoloured.

1186	6c. Type **397**	55	65
1187	6c. "Stars and Woman in Megalithic Temple" (Chiara Borg)	55	65
1188	6c. "Sunny Day" (Bettina Paris)	55	65
1189	6c. "Hands holding Heart" (Roxana Caruana)	55	65

398 Boy's Sermon, Nativity Play and Girl with Doll

2000. Christmas. Multicoloured.

1190	6c. Type **398**	65	10
1191	6c.+3c. Three Wise Men (23×27 mm)	75	75
1192	16c.+3c. Family with Father Christmas	1·75	2·00
1193	26c.+3c. Christmas tree, church and family	2·25	3·25
MS1194	174×45 mm. Nos. 1190/3	4·75	6·00

399 Crocodile Float

2001. Maltese Carnival. Multicoloured.

1195	6c. Type **399**	50	25
1196	11c. King Karnival in procession (vert)	75	40
1197	16c. Woman and children in costumes (vert)	90	55
1198	19c. Horseman carnival float (vert)	1·10	1·40
1199	27c. Carnival procession	1·50	2·00
MS1200	127×92 mm. 12c. Old-fashioned clowns; 37c. Women dressed as clowns (both 32×32 mm)	2·75	4·00

400 St. Elmo Lighthouse

2001. Maltese Lighthouses. Multicoloured.

1201	6c. Type **400**	65	25
1202	16c. Gurdan Lighthouse	1·25	70
1203	22c. Delimara Lighthouse	1·75	2·25

401 "The Chicken Seller" (E. Caruana Dingli)

2001. Edward Caruana Dingli (painter) Commemoration. Multicoloured.

1204	2c. Type **401**	20	30
1205	4c. "The Village Beau"	35	15
1206	6c. "The Faldetta"	50	25
1207	10c. "The Guitar Player"	80	60
1208	26c. "Wayside Orange Seller"	2·00	2·75

402 Nazju Falzon, Gorg Preca and Adeodata Pisani (candidates for Beatification)

2001. Visit of Pope John Paul II. Multicoloured.

1209	6c. Type **402**	1·00	25
1210	16c. Pope John Paul II and statue of St. Paul	1·75	1·50
MS1211	123×87 mm. 75c. Pope John Paul with Nazju Falzon, Gorg Preca and Adeodata Pisani	5·00	5·50

403 Painted Frog

2001. Europa. Pond Life. Multicoloured.

1212	16c. Type **403**	1·75	65
1213	46c. Red-veined darter (dragonfly)	3·25	3·75

404 Herring Gull ("Yellow-legged Gull") (*Larus cachinnans*)

2001. Maltese Birds. Multicoloured.

1214	6c. Type **404**	85	85
1215	6c. Common kestrel (*Falco tinnunculus*)	85	85
1216	6c. Golden oriole (*Oriolus oriolus*)	85	85
1217	6c. Chaffinch (*Fringilla coelebs*) and Eurasian goldfinch (*Carduelis carduelis*)	85	85
1218	6c. Blue rock thrush (*Monticola solitarius*)	85	85
1219	6c. European bee-eater (*Merops apiaster*)	85	85
1220	6c. House martin (*Delichon urbica*) and barn swallow (*Hirundo rustica*)	85	85
1221	6c. Spanish sparrow (*Passer hispaniolensis*)	85	85
1222	6c. Spectacled warbler (*Sylvia conspicillata*)	85	85
1223	6c. Turtle dove (*Streptopelia turtur*)	85	85
1224	6c. Northern pintail (*Anas acuta*)	85	85
1225	6c. Little bittern (*Ixobrychus minutus*)	85	85
1226	6c. Eurasian woodcock (*Scolopax rusticola*)	85	85
1227	6c. Short-eared owl (*Asio flammeus*)	85	85
1228	6c. Northern lapwing (*Vanellus vanellus*)	85	85
1229	6c. Moorhen (*Gallinula chloropus*)	85	85

Nos 1214/29 were printed together, se-tenant, with the backgrounds forming a composite design.

405 Whistle Flute

2001. Traditional Maltese Musical Instruments. Multicoloured.

1230	1c. Type **405**	15	50
1231	3c. Reed pipe	30	40
1232	14c. Maltese bagpipe	85	50
1233	20c. Friction drum	1·25	1·50
1234	25c. Frame drum	1·50	2·00

406 Kelb tal-Fenek (Pharaoh Hound)

2001. Maltese Dogs. Multicoloured.

1235 6c. Type **406** 75 25
1236 16c. Kelb tal-Kacca 1·50 55
1237 19c. Maltese 1·50 1·25
1238 35c. Kelb tal-But 2·25 3·50

407 Man with Net chasing Star

2001. Christmas. Multicoloured.

1239 6c.+2c. Type **407** 80 50
1240 15c.+2c. Father and children 1·50 1·75
1241 16c.+2c. Mother and daughter 1·50 1·75
1242 19c.+3c. Young woman with shopping bags 1·75 2·25

408 *Hippocampus guttulatus*

2002. Endangered Species. Mediterranean Seahorses. Multicoloured.

1243 6c. Type **408** 80 80
1244 6c. *Hippocampus hippocampus* 80 80
1245 16c. Close-up of *Hippocampus guttulatus* 1·60 1·75
1246 16c. *Hippocampus hippocampus* on seabed 1·60 1·75

409 Sideboard

2002. Antique Furniture. Multicoloured.

1247 2c. Type **409** 25 40
1248 4c. Bureau (vert) 45 30
1249 11c. Inlaid table (vert) 85 40
1250 26c. Cabinet (vert) 1·50 85
1251 60c. Carved chest 3·00 5·00

410 Child's Face painted as Clown

2002. Europa. Circus.

1252 **410** 16c. multicoloured 1·25 1·00

411 *Hyles sammuti*

2002. Moths and Butterflies. Multicoloured.

1253 6c. Type **411** 50 55
1254 6c. *Utetheisa pulchella* 50 55
1255 6c. *Ophiusa tirhaca* 50 55
1256 6c. *Phragmatobia fulginosa melitensis* 50 55
1257 6c. *Vanessa cardui* 50 55
1258 6c. *Polyommatus icarus* 50 55
1259 6c. *Gonepteryx cleopatra* 50 55
1260 6c. *Vanessa atlanta* 50 55
1261 6c. *Eucrostes indigenata* 50 55
1262 6c. *Macroglossum stellatarum* 50 55
1263 6c. *Lasiocampa quercus* 50 55
1264 6c. *Catocala electa* 50 55
1265 6c. *Maniola jurtina hyperhispulla* 50 55
1266 6c. *Pieris brassicaei* 50 55
1267 6c. *Papilio machaon melitensis* 50 55
1268 6c. *Dainaus chrysippus* 50 55

No. 1260 is inscribed "atalania" and 1264 "elocata", both in error.

412 "Kusksu Bil-ful" (bean stew)

2002. Maltese Cookery. Multicoloured.

1269 7c. Type **412** 70 25
1270 12c. "Qaqocc mimli" (stuffed artichoke) 1·25 50
1271 16c. "Lampuki" (dorada with aubergines) 1·40 75
1272 27c. "Qaghqd Tal-kavatelli" (chestnut dessert) 2·25 2·75
MS1273 125×90 mm. 75c. "Stuffat Tal-fenek" (rabbit stew) 4·50 5·50

413 *Yavia cryptocarpa* (cactus)

2002. Cacti and Succulents. Multicoloured.

1274 1c. Type **413** 15 50
1275 7c. *Aztekium hintonii* (cactus) (vert) 65 25
1276 28c. *Pseudolithos migiurtinus* (succulent) 1·75 70
1277 37c. *Pierrebraunia brauniorum* (cactus) (vert) 2·25 1·50
1278 76c. *Euphorbia turbiniformis* (succulent) 4·00 6·00

414 Chief Justice Adrian Dingli,

2002. Personalities.

1279 **414** 3c. green and black 30 40
1280 - 7c. green and black 60 25
1281 - 15c. brown and agate 1·00 60
1282 - 35c. brown and sepia 2·00 1·75
1283 - 50c. light blue and blue 2·50 4·00

DESIGNS: 7c. Oreste Kirkop (opera singer); 15c. Athanasius Kircher (Jesuit scholar); 35c. Archpriest Saverio Cassar; 50c. Emmanuele Vitali (notary).

415 Mary and Joseph in Donkey Cart

2002. Christmas. Multicoloured.

1284 7c. Type **415** 70 25
1285 16c. Shepherds and Kings on a bus 1·25 55
1286 22c. Holy Family and angels in luzzu (boat) 1·60 75
1287 37c. Holy Family in horse-drawn carriage 2·00 1·50
1288 75c. Nativity on Maltese fishing boat 3·75 6·00

416 Vanden Plas Princess Landaulette, 1965

2003. Vintage Cars. Multicoloured.

1289 2c. Type **416** 25 60
1290 7c. Allard "M" type, 1948 65 25
1291 10c. Cadillac Model "B", 1904 85 35
1292 26c. Fiat Cinquecento Model "A" Topolino, 1936 1·60 1·60
1293 35c. Ford Anglia Super, 1965 2·25 3·00

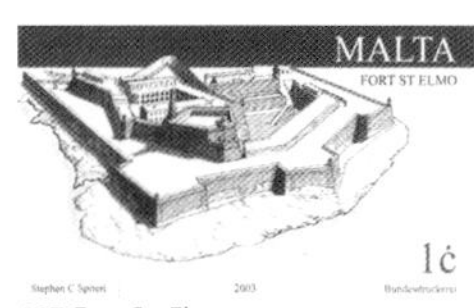

417 Fort St. Elmo

2003. Maltese Military Architecture. Multicoloured.

1294 1c. Type **417** 15 40
1295 4c. Rinella Battery 40 30
1296 11c. Fort St. Angelo 85 40
1297 16c. Section through Reserve Post R15 1·25 60
1298 44c. Fort Tigne 2·75 4·25

418 St. George on Horseback

2003. Paintings of St. George.

1299 **418** 3c. multicoloured 30 30
1300 - 7c. multicoloured 60 30
1301 - 14c. multicoloured 95 60
1302 - 19c. multicoloured 1·40 1·40
1303 - 27c. multicoloured 1·75 2·25

DESIGNS: 7c. to 27c. Various paintings of St. George.

419 "CISKBEER"

2003. Europa. Poster Art. Multicoloured.

1304 16c. Type **419** 1·10 55
1305 46c. "CARNIVAL 1939" 2·75 3·50

420 Games Mascot with Javelin

2003. Games of Small European States, Malta. Multicoloured.

1306 25c. Type **420** 1·25 85
1307 50c. Mascot with gun 2·25 1·75
1308 75c. Mascot with ball and net 3·75 2·75
1309 £3 Mascot with rubber ring at poolside 14·00 17·00

421 Princess Elizabeth in Malta, c. 1950

2003. 50th Anniv of Coronation. Multicoloured (except No. 1312).

1310 12c. black, grey and cinnamon 70 45
1311 15c. multicoloured 75 50
1312 22c. black, deep grey and grey 1·00 90
1313 60c. black, grey and deep ultramarine 2·50 3·50
MS1314 100×72 mm. £1 multicoloured 6·50 7·50

DESIGNS: 15c. Princess Elizabeth with crowd of children, Malta, c. 1950; 22c. Queen Elizabeth II in evening dress with Duke of Edinburgh, Malta; 60c. Queen Elizabeth II (receiving book) and Duke of Edinburgh, Malta; £1 Queen on walkabout with crowd.

422 Valletta Bastions at Night

2003. Elton John, The Granaries, Floriana. Sheet 125×90 mm.

MS1315 **422** £1.50 multicoloured 9·00 10·00

No. **MS**1315 also contains four labels showing different portraits of Elton John.

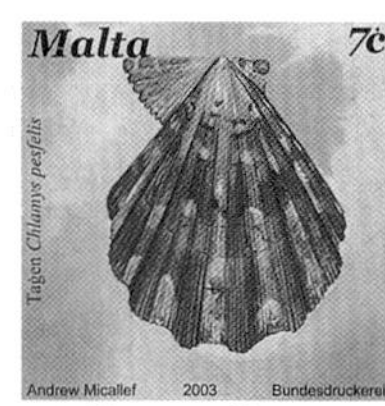

423 *Chlamys pesfelis*

2003. Sea Shells. Multicoloured.

1316 7c. Type **423** 50 55
1317 7c. *Gyroscala lamellose* 50 55
1318 7c. *Phalium granulatum* 50 55
1319 7c. *Fusiturris similes* 50 55
1320 7c. *uria lurida* 50 55
1321 7c. *Bolinus brandaris* 50 55
1322 7c. *Charonia tritonis variegate* 50 55
1323 7c. *Clanculus corallinus* 50 55
1324 7c. *Fusinus syracusanus* 50 55
1325 7c. *Pinna nobilis* 50 55
1326 7c. *Acanthocardia tuberculata* 50 55
1327 7c. *Aporrhais pespelecani* 50 55
1328 7c. *Haliotis tuberculata lamellose* 50 55
1329 7c. *Tonna galea* 50 55
1330 7c. *Spondylus gaederopus* 50 55
1331 7c. *Mitra zonata* 50 55

424 Racing Yachts, Malta–Syracuse Race

2003. Yachting. Multicoloured.

1332 8c. Type **424** 60 35
1333 22c. Yacht, Middle Sea Race (vert) 1·25 1·00
1334 35c. Racing yachts, Royal Malta Yacht Club (vert) 2·00 3·00

2003. As Nos. 1139a and 1143 but smaller, 23×23 mm. Self-adhesive.

1335 7c. *Vitex agnus-castus* 50 40
1336 16c. *Crocus longiflorus* 1·25 1·25

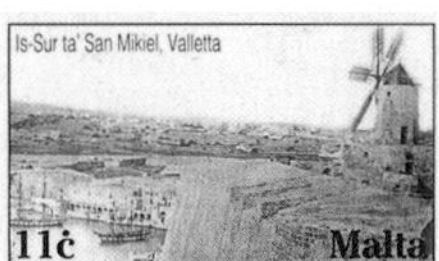

425 Is-Sur ta' San Mikiel, Valletta

2003. Windmills. Each black.

1337 11c. Type **425** 85 40
1338 27c. Ta' Kola, Xaghra (vert) 2·00 1·25
1339 45c. Tax-Xarolla, Zurrieq (vert) 2·75 4·50

426 The Annunciation

2003. Christmas. Multicoloured.
1340 7c. Type **426** 70 30
1341 16c. Holy Family 1·00 35
1342 22c. The Shepherds following the Star (horiz) 1·40 85
1343 50c. The Three Kings with gifts (horiz) 2·75 4·00

427 Pillar Box on Seafront

2004. Letter Boxes. Multicoloured.
1344 1c. Type **427** 10 30
1345 16c. Pillar box on pavement 1·50 55
1346 22c. Wall pillar boxes 1·75 90
1347 37c. Pillar box inside post office 2·50 1·75
1348 76c. Square pillar box and statue 6·00 8·00

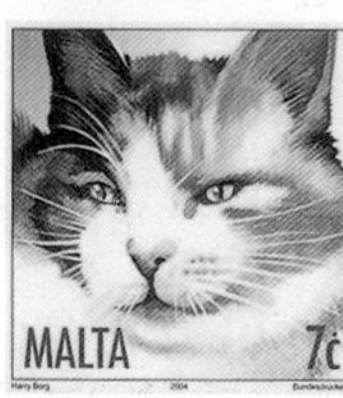

428 Tortoiseshell Cat

2004. Cats. Multicoloured.
1349 7c. Type **428** 70 30
1350 27c. Tabby 1·90 1·25
1351 28c. Silver tabby 1·90 1·25
1352 50c. Ginger tabby 3·50 4·00
1353 60c. Black and white cat 3·75 4·75

429 St. John Bosco

2004. Centenary of Salesians in Malta. Sheet 124×89 mm.
MS1354 75c. multicoloured 4·25 5·50

430 Pipistrelle (*Pipistrellus pygmaeus*)

2004. Mammals and Reptiles. Multicoloured.
1355 16c. Type **430** 85 90
1356 16c. Lesser mouse-eared bat (*Myotis blythi punicus*) 85 90
1357 16c. Weasel (*Mustela nivalis*) 85 90
1358 16c. Algerian hedgehog (*Atelerix algirus fallax*) 85 90
1359 16c. Mediterranean chameleon (*Chamaeleo chamaeleon*) 85 90
1360 16c. Sicilian shrew (*Crocidura sicula*) 85 90
1361 16c. Ocellated skink (*Chalcides ocellatus*) 85 90
1362 16c. Filfla Maltese wall lizard (*Podarcis filfolensis filfolensis*) 85 90
1363 16c. Moorish gecko (*Tarentola mauritanica*) 85 90
1364 16c. Turkish gecko (*Hemidactylus turcicus*) 85 90
1365 16c. Leopard snake (*Elaphe situla*) 85 90
1366 16c. Western whip snake (*Coluber viridiflavus*) 85 90
1367 16c. Common dolphin (*Delphinus delphis*) 85 90
1368 16c. Striped dolphin (*Stenella coeruleoalba*) 85 90
1369 16c. Mediterranean donk seal (*Monachus monachus*) 85 90
1370 16c. Green turtle (*Chelonia mydas*) 85 90

Nos. 1355/70 were printed together, se-tenant, in sheetlets of 16 with the background of each horizontal pair (1355/6, 1357/8, 1359/60, 1361/2, 1363/4, 1365/6, 1367/8 and 1369/70) forming a composite design.

431 New Members Flags inside E.U. Stars

2004. Accession to European Union. Multicoloured.
1371 16c. Type **431** 1·00 55
1372 28c. Former Prime Minister Eddie Fenech Adami and former Foreign Minister Joe Borg signing Accession Treaty 1·50 2·00

432 Children Jumping into Water

2004. Europa. Holidays. Multicoloured.
1373 16c. Type **432** 1·00 55
1374 51c. Hagar Qim prehistoric temples 2·75 3·50

433 Hal Millieri Chapel, Zurrieq

2004. Chapels. Multicoloured.
1375 3c. Type **433** 30 30
1376 7c. San Basilju, Mqabba 60 30
1377 39c. San Cir, Rabat 2·25 1·75
1378 48c. Santa Lucija, Mtarfa 2·50 2·75
1379 66c. Ta' Santa Marija, Kemmuna 4·25 6·00

434 Tram

2004. Trams.
1380 **434** 19c. green and black 1·25 65
1381 - 37c. orange and black (25×42 mm) 2·25 1·40
1382 - 50c. yellow and black (25×42 mm) 3·25 3·50
1383 - 75c. blue and black 4·50 6·00

DESIGNS: 19c. Type **434**; 37c. Tram driver; 50c. Ticket; 75c. Tram under bridge.

435 Discus Thrower

2004. Olympic Games, Athens. Multicoloured.
1384 11c. Type **435** 80 40
1385 16c. Greek column and laurel wreath 1·10 55
1386 76c. Javelin thrower 5·00 6·50

436 Children playing on Ascension Day (Luigi Brocktorff painting) (Lapsi)

2004. Festivals. Multicoloured.
1387 5c. Type **436** 45 30
1388 15c. Votive Penitentiary General Procession, Zejtun (San Girgor) 1·25 50
1389 27c. Pilgrimage in front of the Sanctuary of Our Lady of Graces, Zabbar (painting, Italo Horatio Serge) (Hadd In-Nies) 2·00 1·00
1390 51c. Children with St. Martin's Bags of nuts (Michele Bellanti lithograph) (San Martin) (vert) 3·50 3·75
1391 £1 Peasants in traditional costumes singing and dancing (painting, Antoine Favray) (Mnarja) (vert) 6·50 8·50

437 Church of St. Mary, Attard

2004. Art. Multicoloured.
1392 2c. Type **437** 30 35
1393 20c. Mdina Cathedral organ and music score (vert) 1·40 70
1394 57c. Statue of St. Agatha (vert) 4·25 5·00
1395 62c. Il-Gifen Tork (poem) and books (vert) 4·75 6·00
MS1396 93×100 mm. 72c. Medieval painting of St. Paul (vert) 4·50 6·00

438 Papier mache Bambino on rocks, Lecce

2004. Christmas. Bambino Models. Multicoloured.
1397 7c. Type **438** 55 25
1398 16c. Wax Bambino inside glass dome (vert) 1·10 55
1399 22c. Wax Bambino on back, Lija (vert) 1·50 75
1400 50c. Beeswax Bambino under tree (vert) 3·25 4·50

439 Quintinus Map

2005. Old Maps.
1401 **439** 1c. black and scarlet 15 40
1402 - 12c. multicoloured 90 50
1403 - 37c. multicoloured 2·75 2·00
1404 - £1 multicoloured 6·50 8·25

DESIGNS: 1c. Type **439**; 12c. Copper-engraved map; 37c. Fresco map; £1 Map of Gozo.

440 Dar il-Kaptan (Respite Home)

2005. Centenary of Rotary International (humanitarian organisation). Multicoloured.
1405 27c. Type **440** 1·50 90
1406 76c. Outline of Malta and Gozo and "CELEBRATE ROTARY" 4·75 6·00

441 Hans Christian Andersen

2005. Birth Bicentenary of Hans Christian Andersen (artist and children's writer).
1407 **441** 7c. black and silver 55 25
1408 - 22c. multicoloured 1·50 75
1409 - 60c. multicoloured 3·75 4·50
1410 - 75c. multicoloured 4·50 6·00

DESIGNS: 7c. Type **441**; 20×38 mm—22c. Scissors and paper cutting; 60c. Ugly Duckling, pen and inkwell; 75c. Moroccan travelling boots and drawing of Villa Borghese, Rome.

442 Pope John Paul II

2005. Pope John Paul II Commemoration.
1411 **442** 51c. multicoloured 4·25 4·00

443 *Coccinella septempunctata*

2005. Insects. Multicoloured.
1412 16c. Type **443** 1·10 1·25
1413 16c. *Chrysoperla carnea* 1·10 1·25
1414 16c. *Apis mellifera* 1·10 1·25
1415 16c. *Crocothemis erythraea* 1·10 1·25
1416 16c. *Anax imperator* 1·10 1·25
1417 16c. *Lampyris pallida* 1·10 1·25
1418 16c. *Henosepilachna elaterii* 1·10 1·25
1419 16c. *Forficula decipiens* 1·10 1·25
1420 16c. *Mantis religiosa* 1·10 1·25
1421 16c. *Eumenes lunulatus* 1·10 1·25
1422 16c. *Cerambyx cerdo* 1·10 1·25
1423 16c. *Gryllus bimaculatus* 1·10 1·25
1424 16c. *Xylocopa violacea* 1·10 1·25
1425 16c. *Cicada orni* 1·10 1·25
1426 16c. *Acrida ungarica* 1·10 1·25
1427 16c. *Oryctes nasicornis* 1·10 1·25

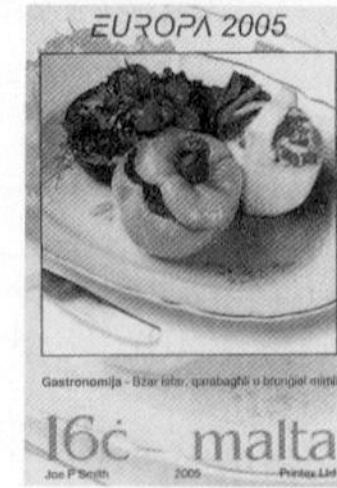

444 Cayenne Pepper, Baked, Stuffed Courgettes and Stuffed Eggplant

2005. Europa. Gastronomy. Multicoloured.
1428 16c. Type **444** 1·00 60
1429 51c. Roast rabbit 3·00 3·75

2005. Flowers. Personalised Stamps. As Nos. 1139a and 1143. Multicoloured.
1430 7c. *Vitex agnus-castus* 45 15
1431 16c. Yellow-throated crocus 80 55

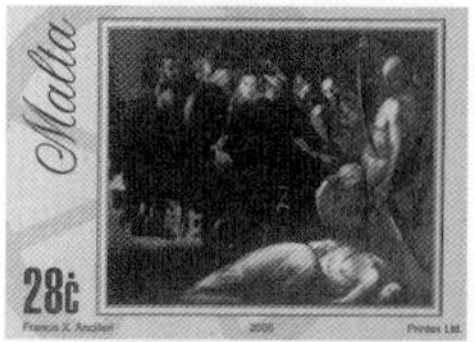

446 "The Beheading of St Catherine"

2005. St Catherine in Art. Multicoloured.
1432 28c. Type **446** 1·40 1·40
1433 28c. "Martyrdom of St Catherine" (Mattia Preti) (vert) 1·40 1·40
1434 45c. "Mystic Marriage" (Francesco Zahra) (vert) 2·00 2·75
1435 45c. "St Catherine Disputing the Philosophers" (Francesco Zahra) 2·00 2·75

447 Mons. Mikiel Azzopardi (philanthropist)

2005. Personalities. Multicoloured.

1436	3c. Type **447**	30	20
1437	19c. Egidio Lapira (professor of dental surgery)	1·25	1·00
1438	20c. Letter and shield of Order of the Knights (Guzeppi Callus, doctor)	1·25	1·00
1439	46c. Hand writing musical score (Geronimo Abos, composer)	2·50	2·75
1440	76c. Gann Frangisk Abela (historian)	4·00	5·50

448 Horse-drawn Hearse

2005. Equines in Malta. Multicoloured.

1441	11c. Type **448**	1·00	40
1442	15c. Mule pulling traditional wooden plough	1·25	50
1443	62c. Mule on treadmill grinding flour	3·75	4·50
1444	66c. Horse-drawn water sprinkler cart	3·75	4·50

449 Queue outside "Victory Kitchen" and Ruins of Royal Opera House, Valletta

2005. 60th Anniv of End of Second World War. Battle of Malta. All showing George Cross. Multicoloured.

1445	2c. Type **449**	50	30
1446	5c. Royal Navy convoy under air attack from Savoia Marchetti S-73 Sparviero	75	25
1447	25c. Anti aircraft guns and St. Publius Church, Floriana	2·00	95
1448	51c. Pilots scrambling, Hawker Hurricane, Supermarine Spitfire and Gloster Sea Gladiators	3·75	3·75
1449	£1 Tanker Ohio and unloading of supplies at Grand Harbour, August 1943	7·00	8·50

450 "The Nativity"

2005. Christmas. Paintings by Emvin Cremona from Sanctuary of Our Lady of Ta' Pinu, Gozo. Multicoloured.

1450	7c. Type **450**	60	25
1451	16c. "The Annunciation" (vert)	1·10	55
1452	22c. "The Adoration of the Magi"	1·50	75
1453	50c. "The Flight to Egypt" (69×30 mm)	3·50	4·50

451 Maltese, Commonwealth and CHOGM Flags

2005. Commonwealth Heads of Government Meeting (CHOGM), Valletta. Each showing Maltese and Commonwealth flags. Multicoloured.

MS1454	Four sheets, each 75×63 mm. (a) 14c. Type **451**. (b) 28c. Peace doves. (c) 37c. Maltese cross. (d) 75c. Silhouettes shaking hands	7·00	9·50

452 1986 8c. Butterflies Stamp

2006. 50th Anniv of Europa Stamps. Showing Maltese Europa stamps. Multicoloured.

MS1455	120×85 mm. 5c. Type **452**; 13c. 1983 30c. Fort St. Angelo stamp; 23c. 1977 20c. Is-Salini stamp; 24c. 1989 35c. Girls with dolls stamp	4·00	5·00

No. **MS**1455 has a composite background design.

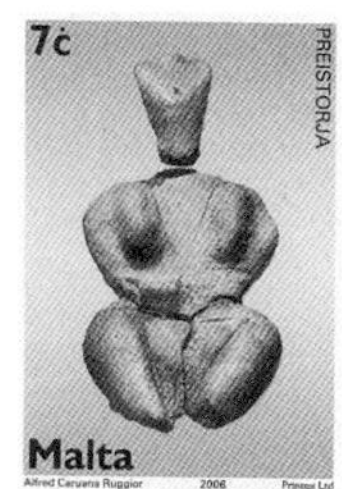

453 Female Terracotta Female Figurine, c. 4100 B.C.

2006. Ceramics in Maltese Collections. Mult.

1456	7c. Type **453**	50	25
1457	16c. Roman terracotta head, c. 1st-3rd century B.C	1·00	55
1458	28c. Terracotta oil lamp holder, 14th-15th century A.D	1·25	1·40
1459	37c. Sicilian maiolica display plate, 18th century	2·25	2·40
1460	60c. Modern stylized figure in Maltese costume (Ianni Bonniçi)	3·00	4·25

454 Shetland Pony

2006. Pets. Multicoloured.

1461	7c. Type **454**	85	90
1462	7c. Kelb tal-But (Maltese pocket dog)	85	90
1463	7c. Goldfish	85	90
1464	7c. Siamese cat	85	90
1465	7c. Siamese fighting fish	85	90
1466	7c. Ferret	85	90
1467	7c. Canary	85	90
1468	7c. Terrapin	85	90
1469	22c. Chinchilla	85	90
1470	22c. Budgerigar	85	90
1471	22c. Rabbit	85	90
1472	22c. Zebra finch	85	90
1473	22c. Kelb tal-Kacca (Maltese hunting dog)	85	90
1474	22c. Pigeon	85	90
1475	22c. Guinea pig	85	90
1476	22c. Cat	85	90

455 Penitents carrying Crosses

2006. Holy Week. Multicoloured.

1477	7c. Type **455**	50	15
1478	15c. Crucifixion tableau in procession	1·00	30
1479	22c. Burial of Christ tableau in procession	1·25	75
1480	27c. Statue of the Risen Christ paraded on Easter Sunday	1·50	1·10

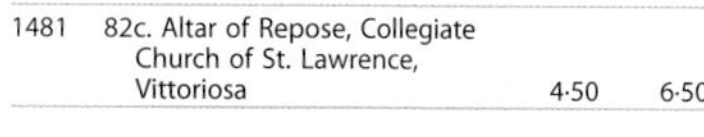

1481	82c. Altar of Repose, Collegiate Church of St. Lawrence, Vittoriosa	4·50	6·50

456 Circuit of Linked People

2006. Europa. Integration. Multicoloured.

1482	16c. Type **456**	1·00	50
1483	51c. Four rows of linked people (30×43 mm)	2·50	3·50

457 Bobby Charlton

2006. World Cup Football Championship, Germany. Multicoloured.

1484	7c. Type **457**	50	15
1485	16c. Pele	1·00	30
1486	27c. Franz Beckenbauer	1·60	1·10
1487	76c. Dino Zoff	4·25	6·00
MS1488	160×86 mm	6·50	7·50

2006. Sting Concert, Luxol Grounds. Sheet 121×86 mm containing design as No. 1188.

MS1489	£1.50 "Sunny Day" (Bettina Paris)	7·50	8·50

458 *Santa Anna* ("Gran Caracca di Rodi"), 1530

2006. Naval Vessels. Multicoloured.

1490	8c. Type **458**	80	20
1491	29c. *Guillaume Tell* (French) dismasted by HMS *Penelope*, *Lion* and *Foudroyant*, Malta, 1800 (Edwin Galea)	2·00	1·10
1492	51c. USS *Constitution*, 1837 (J. G. Evans)	3·25	3·00
1493	76c. HMS *Dreadnought* leaving Grand Harbour, November 1913	5·00	6·00
1494	£1 USS *Belknap* (frigate) and *Slava* (Soviet cruiser) providing communications support for Malta Summit, December 1989	6·00	7·50

459 Candles ("Happy Birthday")

2006. Occasions. Multicoloured.

1495	8c. Type **459**	55	15
1496	16c. Heart ("Happy Anniversary")	1·00	35
1497	27c. Stars holding parcel, balloon and candle ("Congratulations")	1·60	1·25
1498	37c. Balloons ("Best Wishes")	2·00	2·75

460 Wignacourt Tower

2006. Maltese Castles and Towers. Multicoloured.

1499	7c. Type **460**	65	15
1500	16c. Verdala Castle	1·25	35
1501	27c. San Lucjan Tower	1·90	1·10
1502	37c. Kemmuna Tower	2·50	1·75
1503	£1 Selmun Castle	6·00	8·50

461 Paolino Vassallo, "Inno per Natale" and Nativity

2006. Christmas Music. Showing composer and score. Multicoloured.

1504	8c. Type **461**	55	15
1505	16c. Carmelo Pace, "They Heard the Angels" and Three Magi	1·00	30
1506	22c. Paul Nani, "Maltese Christmas" and angels	1·40	1·25
1507	27c. Carlo Diacono, "Notte di Natale", shepherds and angel	1·60	1·60
MS1508	120×86 mm. 50c. Wolfgang Amadeus Mozart (250th birth anniv) and "Alma di Creatoris"	3·00	3·50

2006. Bob Geldof Concert for YMCA, Manoel Island. Sheet 121×86 mm containing design as No. 1189.

MS1509	£1.50 "Hands holding Heart" (Roxana Caruana)	7·50	8·50

462 Wrought Iron Work

2006. Crafts. Multicoloured.

1510	8c. Type **462**	55	15
1511	16c. Glass making	1·00	35
1512	22c. Filigree work	1·40	70
1513	37c. Pottery	2·00	1·75
1514	60c. Reed basketwork	3·75	5·00

463 Stone Head

2007. Prehistoric Sculptures, c. 3000–2500 BC. Multicoloured.

1515	15c. Type **463**	1·00	30
1516	29c. Stone bas-relief of animals (horiz)	1·75	1·10
1517	60c. Stone-carved spiral pattern (horiz)	3·75	4·25
1518	£1.50 Clay statuette of female figure	7·50	9·00

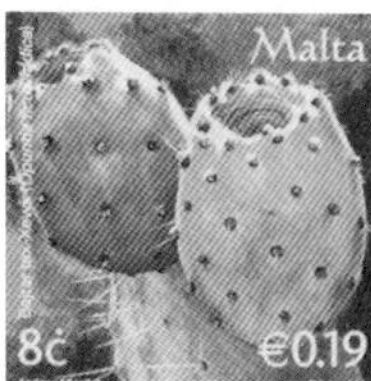

464 *Opuntia ficus-indica* (prickly pear)

2007. Maltese Fruits. Multicoloured.

1519	8c. Type **464**	45	50
1520	8c. *Vitis vinifera* (grapes)	45	50
1521	8c. *Eriobotrya japonica* (loquat)	45	50
1522	8c. *Morus nigra* (black mulberry)	45	50
1523	8c. *Ficus carica* (figs)	45	50
1524	8c. *Citrus limonum* (lemons)	45	50
1525	8c. *Pyrus communis* (pear)	45	50

1526 8c. *Prunus persica* (peaches) 45 50
1527 8c. *Punica granatum* (pomegranate) 45 50
1528 8c. *Prunus salicina* (Japanese plum) 45 50
1529 8c. *Citrullus vulgaris* (watermelon) 45 50
1530 8c. *Citrus sinensis* (orange) 45 50
1531 8c. *Olea europaea* (olives) 45 50
1532 8c. *Lycopersicon esculentum* (tomatoes) 45 50
1533 8c. *Malus domestica* (apples) 45 50
1534 8c. *Cucumis melo* (melon) 45 50

465 Wrought-iron Balcony

2007. Maltese Balconies. Multicoloured.
1535 8c. Type **465** 50 40
1536 22c. Ornate open stone balcony and recessed doorway, Gozo 1·25 1·10
1537 27c. Balustraded balcony, National Library of Malta 1·60 1·40
1538 29c. Carved stone balcony with glazed timber enclosure, Gozo 1·75 1·50
1539 46c. Two balconies on Art Deco 1930's building 2·75 3·50
MS1540 123×86 mm. 51c. Detail of balcony on Hostel de Verdelin, Valletta (horiz) 2·75 3·25

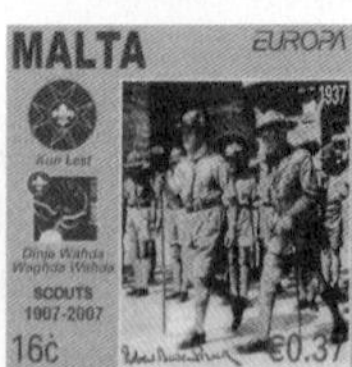

466 Lord Baden-Powell (founder) and District Commissioner Capt J. V. Abela, Malta, 1937

2007. Europa. Centenary of Scouting. Multicoloured.
1541 16c. Type **466** 1·00 60
1542 51c. Malta scouts marching, Golden Jubilee Jamboree, near Birmingham, 1957 3·00 3·50

467 St. Gorg Preca

2007. Canonization of Dun Gorg Preca. Mult.
1543 8c. Type **467** 50 50
1544 £1 As Type **467** but sun rising behind Basilica 5·00 6·00

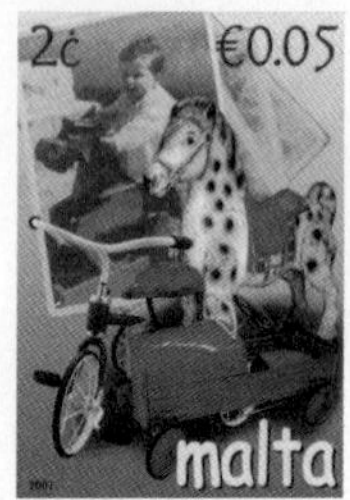

468 Rocking Horse, Tricycle and Car, all Triang (1950s)

2007. Toys from Days Gone By. Multicoloured.
1545 2c. Type **468** 10 10
1546 3c. Pedigree dolls pram (1950s), drums and skipping rope 15 15
1547 16c. Japanese tin cabin cruiser (1960s), sand pails, spade and Triang sailing boat 90 80
1548 22c. Lenci doll, Pedigree doll and 1930s Armand Marseille doll 1·25 1·10
1549 50c. Alps clockwork racing car (1950s), P.N. motorcycle (1950s) and Chad Valley delivery van (1930s) 3·25 4·00

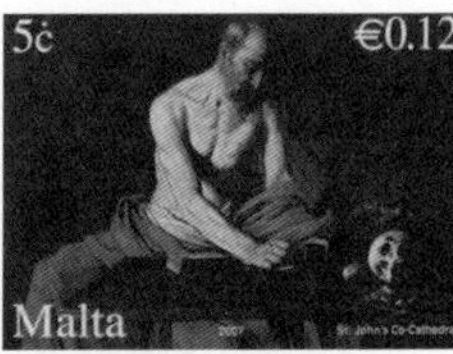

469 'St. Jerome' (Caravaggio)

2007. 400th Anniv of the Arrival of Michelangelo Merisi (Caravaggio) in Malta. Paintings. Multicoloured.
1550 5c. Type **469** 35 35
1551 29c. 'The Beheading of St. John the Baptist' (detail) 1·75 1·75
MS1552 130×86 mm. £2 'The Beheading of St. John the Baptist' (vert) 14·00 16·00

470 Malta GPO Royal Enfield Motorcycle, 1954

2007. Motorcycles. Multicoloured.
1553 1c. Type **470** 15 30
1554 16c. Malta Garrison Matchless G3/L, 1941 1·25 85
1555 27c. Civilian Minerva, 1903 2·00 1·40
1556 50c. Malta Police Triumph Speed Twin, 1965 4·00 4·50

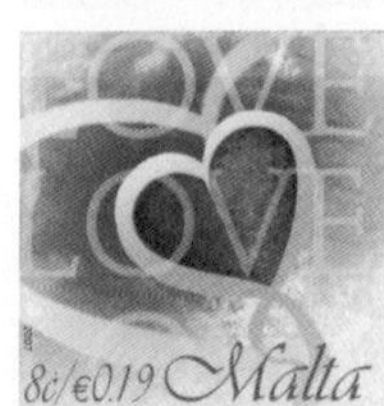

471 Heart and 'LOVE'

2007. Occasions Greetings Stamps. Multicoloured.
1557 8c. Type **471** 55 55
1558 8c. Teddy bears 55 55
1559 8c. Star decorations ('Congratulations!') 55 55
1560 8c. Pink roses ('GREETINGS') 55 55
1561 8c. Balloons 55 55
1562 8c. Champagne glasses 55 55

472 Mdina Skyline seen from Mtarfa

2007. Maltese Scenery. Designs showing watercolours by John Martin Borg.
1563 11c. Type **472** 90 65
1564 16c. Windmill, farmhouse and church, Qrendi 1·25 85
1565 37c. Vittoriosa waterfront 2·50 2·25
1566 46c. Mgarr Harbour, Gozo 3·00 3·00
1567 76c. Xlendi Bay, Gozo 4·75 6·00
No. 1564 is inscr 'sepac'.

2007. 34U (Tree for You) Campaign. Sheet 100×66 mm containing design as No. 1531.
MS1568 75c. *Olea europaea* (olives) 4·00 5·00

473 Military Band

2007. Maltese Bands. Multicoloured.
1569 4c. Type **473** 45 40
1570 15c. Police band 1·50 85
1571 21c. Band playing at carnival 1·75 1·25
1572 22c. Band playing at Christmas 1·75 1·25
1573 £1 Band and conductor 7·00 8·50

474 Madonna and Baby Jesus

2007. Christmas. Showing details from painting The Nativity by Giuseppe Cali in St. Andrew's parish church, Luqa. Multicoloured.
1574 8c. Type **474** 60 30
1575 16c. Holy Family with two countrywomen and young girl 1·25 85
1576 27c. Baby Jesus and young girl 2·00 2·25
Similar stamps were issued by the Vatican City.

475 Boys playing Football

2007. Anniversaries and Personalities. Multicoloured.
1577 4mils Type **475** (25th anniv of Youth Football Association) 10 10
1578 9c. Children receiving religious instruction (centenary of Society of Christian Doctrine) 65 30
1579 16c. Canon Monsignor Professor Francesco Bonnici (founder of St. Joseph Institute for orphan boys) 1·25 85
1580 43c. Father Manwel Magri (ethnographer, archaeologist and educator) 3·00 3·00
1581 86c. Carolina Cauchi (founder of Dominican order at Lunzjata Monastery, Gozo) 5·50 6·50
MS1582 100×70 mm. 76c. Signatories (50th anniv of Treaty of Rome) (horiz) 4·50 5·50

476 Malta £1 Coin

2007. Coins of Malta 1972–2007. Sheet 100×66 mm.
MS1583 **476** €2.33 multicoloured 6·00 7·00

2008. Adoption of the Euro Currency (1st issue). Sheet 100×66 mm containing square design as T 476. Multicoloured.
MS1584 €2.33 Obverse and reverse of one euro coin 3·50 4·00

477 'Aphrodite' State of Cyprus

2008. Adoption of the Euro Currency (2nd issue). Sheet 100×62 mm containing T 477 and similar square design. Multicoloured.
MS1585 €1 Type **477**; €1 'Sleeping Lady' statuette, Malta 5·50 7·00
A similar miniature sheet was issued by Cyprus.

478 Door Knocker from Ministry of Finance, Valletta

2008. Door Knockers. Multicoloured.
1586 26c. Type **478** 1·00 65
1587 51c. Fish door knocker from Museum of Fine Arts, Valletta 1·60 1·25
1588 63c. Door knocker from Department of Industrial & Employment Relations, Valletta 1·75 2·00
1589 €1.77 Door knocker from Museum of Archaeology, Valletta 5·00 6·00

479 Shooting

2008. Olympic Games, Beijing. Multicoloured.
1590 5c. Type **479** 15 10
1591 12c. Swimming 30 20
1592 €1.57 Running 4·75 5·50

480 Postman and Mail Room (in sepia)

2008. Europa. The Letter. Multicoloured.
1593 37c. Type **480** 1·25 85
1594 €1.19 As Type **480** (in monochrome) 4·00 4·25

481 Woodcarving by Xandru Farrugia, Conversion of St. Paul Church, Hal Safi

2008. Annus Paulinus 2008–2009 (2000th Birth Anniv of St. Paul). Showing statues of St. Paul. Multicoloured.
1595 19c. Type **481** 70 30
1596 68c. Papier mache statue by Agostino Camilleri, St. Paul's Shipwreck Church, Munxar, Gozo 2·25 2·25
1597 €1.08 Wooden statue by Giovanni Caruana, St. Paul's Shipwreck Church, Rabat 3·75 4·25
MS1598 120×86 mm. €3 Wooden statue by Melchiorre Gafà, St. Paul's Shipwreck Church, Valletta 8·50 9·50

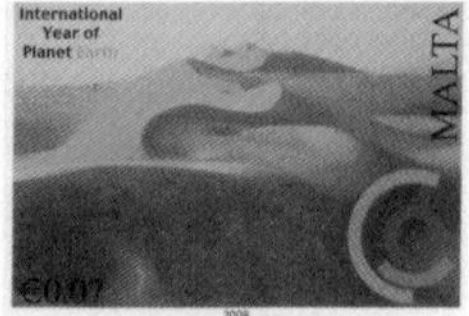

482 Sand Dunes

2008. International Year of Planet Earth. Multicoloured.
1599 7c. Type **482** 30 20
1600 86c. Single tree growing in field 3·00 3·00
1601 €1 Globe 3·50 3·75
1602 €1.77 Rocky coast 6·00 7·00

483 MSC *Musica*

2008. Cruise Liners. Multicoloured.

1603	63c. Type **483**	2·50	1·50
1604	€1.16 MS *Voyager of the Seas*	4·00	4·00
1605	€1.40 MS *Westerdam*	4·50	4·50
1606	€3 RMS *Queen Elizabeth II*	10·00	12·00

484 *Madonna and Child with Infant St. John the Baptist* (detail) (Francesco Trevisani)

2008. Christmas. Nativity Paintings from the National Museum of Fine Arts, Valletta. Multicoloured.

1607	19c. Type **484**	60	30
1608	26c. *Nativity* (detail of Virgin and Christ Child from panel by Maestro Alberto)	90	60
1609	37c. *Virgin and Child with Infant St. John the Baptist* (Carlo Maratta)	1·25	1·25

485 *Laetiorus sulphureus*

2009. Fungi. Multicoloured.

1610	5c. Type **485**	15	15
1611	12c. *Montagnea arenaria*	35	30
1612	19c. *Pleurotus eryngii*	65	40
1613	26c. *Inonotus indicus*	90	70
1614	€1.57 *Suillus collinitus*	5·25	5·75

486 Dornier Wal SANA Seaplane

2009. Vintage Postal Transport. Multicoloured.

1615	9c. Type **486**	40	25
1616	35c. Postmen on BSA motorcycles	1·75	1·00
1617	€2.50 Postmen with Raleigh bicycles	8·00	9·00
1618	€3 Gozo Mail Boat	9·00	10·00

487 Emblem

2009. 10th Anniv of the Euro.

1619	**487**	€2 multicoloured	6·00	7·00

488 Galileo Galilei, his Sketch of Moon and Apollo 11 Lunar Module *Eagle*

2009. Europa. Astronomy. Multicoloured.

1620	37c. Type **488**	1·50	1·10
1621	€1.19 William Lassell's telescope (set up in Malta 1861–5) and Nebula M42	3·00	3·50

489 Sailing

2009. 13th Games of the Small States of Europe, Nicosia and Limassol, Cyprus. Multicoloured.

1622	10c. Type **489**	35	25
1623	19c. Judo	65	40
1624	37c. Shooting	1·40	1·10
1625	67c. Swimming	2·50	2·50
1626	€1.77 Athletics	5·00	6·00

2009. Cruise Liners (2nd series). As T 483. Multicoloured.

1627	37c. *Seabourn Pride*	1·75	1·10
1628	68c. *Brilliance of the Seas*	2·50	1·90
1629	91c. *Costa Magica* and *Costa Atlantica*	3·25	3·25
1630	€2 MSC *Splendida*	6·00	7·00

490 Headland

2009. Scenery. Multicoloured.

1631	2c. Type **490**	15	25
1632	7c. Watchtower of Knights of the Sovereign Military Order of Malta	35	20
1633	37c. Stone salt pans, Qbajjar, Gozo	1·50	70
1634	€1.02 Segment of the Ggantija Temples, Gozo	3·50	4·50

No. 1633 is inscr 'sepac'.

491 *Mater Admirablis* (in the manner of Botticelli)

2009. Christmas. Multicoloured.

1635	19c. Type **491**	65	30
1636	37c. *Madonna and Child* (Corrado Giacquinto)	1·25	60
1637	63c. *The Madonna and Child* (follower of Simone Cantarini)	2·00	2·50

492 Skeleton of Prehistoric Animal (Pleistocene Period)

2009. History of Malta. Multicoloured.

1638	1c. Type **492**	15	30
1639	2c. Ruins of stone temple (Early Temple Period)	20	30
1640	5c. Carved stone pattern (Late Temple Period)	30	25
1641	7c. Pair of pots (Bronze Age)	35	25
1642	9c. Gold statue (Phoenician and Punic Period) (vert)	40	40
1643	10c. Mosaic (Roman Period)	40	40
1644	19c. Gold coin (Byzantine Period) (vert)	65	30
1645	26c. Fragment of carved stone (Arab Period)	90	60
1646	37c. Painting (Norman and Hohenstaufen Period) (vert)	1·25	75
1647	50c. Stone tablet carved with shield (Angevin and Aragonese) (vert)	1·75	1·75
1648	51c. Gold pattern with central Maltese Cross (Knights of St. John)	1·75	1·75
1649	63c. Painting of officers and crew disembarking in rowing boats from ships (French Period)	1·75	1·75
1650	68c. George Cross (British Period) (vert)	2·00	2·00
1651	86c. Independence (vert)	2·75	2·75
1652	€1 Republic (vert)	3·50	3·50
1653	€1.08 EU Accession (vert)	3·50	3·50
1654	€5 Arms of Malta (vert)	16·00	17·00

MS1655 is left for this miniature sheet, which has not yet been received.

493 100 Ton Gun, Fort Rinella, Malta, 2010

2010. 100 Ton Guns. Multicoloured.

MS1656	75c.×4 Type **493**; '100 ton' gun, Fort Rinella, Malta, 1882; '100 ton' gun, Napier of Magdala Battery, Gibraltar, 1880; '100 ton' gun, Napier of Magdala Battery, Gibraltar, 2010	7·00	8·00

A miniature sheet containing the same designs was issued by Gibraltar.

494 Balloons

2010. Occasions Greetings Stamps. Multicoloured.

1657	19c. Type **494**	65	65
1658	19c. Aerial view of coastline and offshore rocks	65	65
1659	19c. Mortarboard and scroll	65	65
1660	19c. Woman greeting man and crowd (painting)	65	65
1661	19c. Two glasses of champagne and bottle in ice bucket (vert)	65	65
1662	19c. St. John's Co-Cathedral, Valletta and fireworks (vert)	65	65
1663	19c. Hand holding trophy (vert)	65	65
1664	37c. Outline map of Malta and Gozo	1·10	1·10

495 Pope Benedict XVI

2010. Visit of Pope Benedict XVI to Malta

MS1665	**495**	€3 multicoloured	9·75	9·75

496 Puttinu u Toninu (Dr. Philip Farrugia Randon)

2010. Europa. Children's Books. Multicoloured.

1666	37c. Type **496**	1·50	1·10
1667	€1.19 *Meta l-Milied ma giex* (Clare Azzopardi)	3·00	3·25

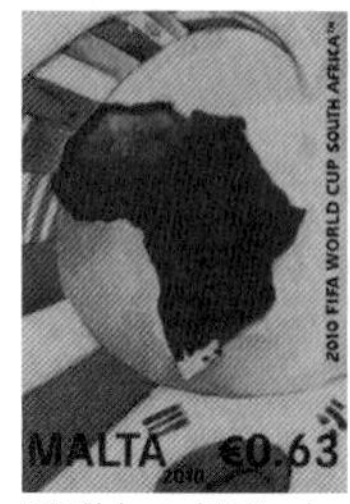

497 Globe and National Flags

2010. World Cup Football Championship, South Africa. Multicoloured.

1668	63c. Type **497**	1·75	1·75
1669	€2.50 Zakumi the leopard mascot	7·00	7·50
MS1669a	131×80 mm. As Nos. 1668/9	8·75	9·25

498 Maltese Wall Lizard

2010. Biodiversity. Multicoloured.

1670	19c. Type **498**	75	40
1671	68c. Storm petrel (vert)	2·50	2·00
1672	86c. Maltese pyramidal orchid (vert)	3·00	3·00
1673	€1.40 Freshwater crab	3·75	4·50

499 Azure Window, Gozo

2010. Natural Treasures. Multicoloured.

1674	37c. Type **499**	1·60	1·10
1675	51c. Blue Grotto, Zurrieq (vert)	2·25	2·00
1676	67c. Ta' Cenc, Gozo (vert)	2·50	2·50
1677	€1.16 Filfla	3·00	3·75

500 *The Adoration of the Magi* (Valerio Castello)

2010. Christmas. Multicoloured.

1678	19c. Type **500**	65	30
1679	37c. *The Flight into Egypt* (Filippo Paladini)	1·75	2·00
1680	63c. *Madonna di Maggio* (Pierre Guillemin) (vert)	3·50	3·00

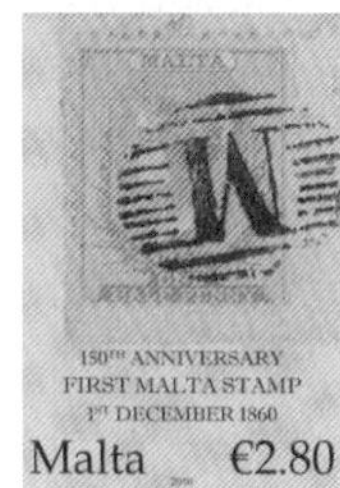

501 Cancelled 1860 ½d. Buff Stamp

2010. 150th Anniv of the First Malta Stamp

MS1681	**501**	€2.80 multicoloured	8·50	9·00

502 *Valletta*

2011. Treasures of Malta. Landscapes. Multicoloured.

1682	19c. Type **502**	65	30
1683	37c. *Manoel Island*	1·50	1·10
1684	€1.57 *Cittadella* (Gozo)	4·25	4·25

503 *Chimaera monstrosa* (Rabbit fish)

2011. 50th Anniv of WWF (Worldwide Fund for Nature). *Chimaera monstrosa* (Rabbit fish). Multicoloured.

MS1685	51c. Type **503**; 63c. Rabbit fish (swimming towards top right; 67c. Rabbit fish (seen from front); 97c. Rabbit fish (with fins outstretched)	8·50	8·50

504 Trees, Pine Cones, Flowers and Butterfly (Nicole Sciberras)

2011. Europa. Forests. Multicoloured.

1686	37c. Type **504**	1·50	1·10
1687	€1.19 Trees, fallen tree and fungi	3·25	4·00

505 Reo Bus, Birkirkara

2011. Malta Buses of the 1950s and 1960s. Make of Bus and Route given. Multicoloured.

1688	20c. Type **505**	70	45
1689	20c. Dodge T110L, Zabbar	70	45
1690	20c. Leyland Comet, Zurrieq	70	45
1691	20c. Ford V8, Zebbug-Siggiewi	70	45
1692	20c. Bedford SLD, Gudja-Ghaxaq	70	45
1693	20c. Gozo mail bus	70	45
1694	20c. Federal bus, Kalafrana	70	45
1695	20c. Dodge T110L, Siggiewi	70	45
1696	20c. Indiana bus, Rabat	70	45
1697	20c. Austin CXD, Zejtun	70	45
1698	69c. Ford V8, Sliema	2·00	2·40
1699	69c. Commer Q4, Lija	2·00	2·40
1700	69c. Fordson BB, Mosta - Naxxar	2·00	2·40
1701	69c. Thorneycroft Sturdy ZE, Mellieha	2·00	2·40
1702	69c. Bedford QL, Cospicua	2·00	2·40
1703	69c. Magirus Deutz, all routes	2·00	2·40
1704	69c. Commer Q4, Naxxar	2·00	2·40
1705	69c. Bedford SB8, Gozo	2·00	2·40
1706	69c. Thames ET7, Birkirkara - St. Julians	2·00	2·40
1707	69c. Bedford QL, private hire	2·00	2·40

POSTAGE DUE STAMPS

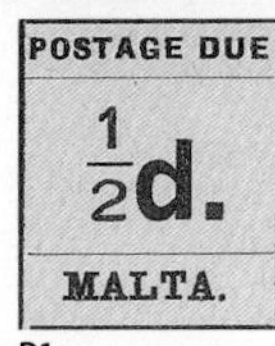

D1

1925. Imperf.

D1	**D1**	½d. black	1·25	7·50
D2	**D1**	1d. black	3·25	3·00
D3	**D1**	1½d. black	3·00	3·75
D4	**D1**	2d. black	12·00	21·00
D5	**D1**	2½d. black	2·75	2·75
D6	**D1**	3d. black on grey	9·00	15·00
D7	**D1**	4d. black on yellow	5·00	9·50
D8	**D1**	6d. black on yellow	5·00	23·00
D9	**D1**	1s. black on yellow	6·50	23·00
D10	**D1**	1s. 6d. black on yellow	16·00	60·00

D2

1925. Perf.

D11	**D2**	½d. green	1·25	60
D12	**D2**	1d. violet	1·25	45
D13	**D2**	1½d. brown	1·50	80
D14	**D2**	2d. grey	11·00	1·00
D35	**D2**	2d. brown	85	70
D36	**D2**	2½d. orange	60	70
D37	**D2**	3d. blue	60	60
D38	**D2**	4d. green	1·00	80
D39	**D2**	6d. purple	75	1·50
D40	**D2**	1s. black	90	1·50
D41	**D2**	1s.6d. red	2·75	7·00

D3 Maltese Lace

1973

D42	**D3**	2m. brown and red	10	10
D43	**D3**	3m. orange and red	10	15
D44	**D3**	5m. pink and red	15	20
D45	**D3**	1c. blue and green	30	35
D46	**D3**	2c. grey and black	40	35
D47	**D3**	3c. light brown & brown	40	35
D48	**D3**	5c. dull blue and blue	65	70
D49	**D3**	10c. lilac and plum	85	1·00

D4

1993

D50	**D4**	1c. magenta and mauve	20	30
D51	**D4**	2c. blue and light blue	25	40
D52	**D4**	5c. green and turquoise	35	45
D53	**D4**	10c. orange and yellow	55	55

Pt. 7

MECKLENBURG-SCHWERIN

In northern Germany. Formerly a Grand Duchy, Mecklenburg-Schwerin joined the North German Confederation in 1868.

48 schilling = 1 thaler.

1

2

1856. Imperf.

1	**1**	4/4s. red	£190	£160
1a	**1**	4/4s. red	†	£200
2	**2**	3s. yellow	£130	70·00
4	**2**	5s. blue	£300	£350

See note below No. 7.

1864. Roul.

5a	**1**	¼s. red	†	£2000
6a	**1**	¼s. red	†	£150
5	**1**	4/4s. red	£3750	£2250
6	**1**	4/4s. red	£550	95·00
11	**2**	2s. purple	£325	£325
9	**2**	3s. yellow	£200	£160
7	**2**	5s. bistre	£200	£325

Nos. 1, 1a, 5, 5a have a dotted background, Nos. 6 and 6a a plain background. Prices for Nos. 1a, 5a and 6a are for quarter stamps; prices for Nos. 1, 5 and 6 are for the complete on cover stamp (four quarters) as illustrated in Type **1**.

Pt. 7

MECKLENBURG-STRELITZ

In northern Germany. Formerly a Grand Duchy, Mecklenburg-Strelitz joined the North German Confederation in 1868.

30 silbergroschen = 1 thaler.

1

2

1864. Roul. Various frames.

2	**1**	¼sgr. orange	£225	£3250
3	**1**	⅓sgr. green	£110	£1800
6	**1**	1sch. mauve	£350	£4250
7	**2**	1sgr. red	£190	£250
9	**2**	2sgr. blue	55·00	£1100
11	**2**	3sgr. bistre	42·00	£1700

Pt. 8

MODENA

A state in Upper Italy, formerly a duchy and now part of Italy. Used stamps of Sardinia after the cessation of its own issues in 1860. Now uses Italian stamps.

100 centesimi = 1 lira.

1 Arms of Este

1852. Imperf.

9	**1**	5c. black on green	55·00	60·00
3	**1**	10c. black on pink	£600	£110
4	**1**	15c. black on yellow	80·00	38·00
5	**1**	25c. black on buff	£120	55·00
12	**1**	40c. black on blue	65·00	£150
13	**1**	1l. black on white	80·00	£2500

5 Cross of Savoy

1859. Imperf.

18a	**5**	5c. green	£900	£750
19	**5**	15c. brown	£2750	£4000
20	**5**	15c. grey	£375	
21	**5**	20c. black	£2250	£180
22	**5**	20c. lilac	70·00	£1400
23	**5**	40c. red	£225	£1500
24	**5**	80c. brown	£225	£24000

NEWSPAPER STAMPS

1853. As T 1 but in the value tablet inscr "B.G. CEN" and value. Imperf.

N15	**1**	9c. black on mauve	£900	95·00
N16	**1**	10c. black on lilac	90·00	£350

N4

1859. Imperf.

N17	**N4**	10c. black	£1300	£2750

Pt. 6

MONACO

A principality on the S. coast of France including the town of Monte Carlo.

1885. 100 centimes = 1 French franc.
2002. 100 cents = 1 euro.

1 Prince Charles III

1885

1	1	1c. olive	28·00	18·00
2	1	2c. lilac	65·00	32·00
3	1	5c. blue	80·00	41·00
4	1	10c. brown on yellow	£100	46·00
5	1	15c. red	£425	28·00
6	1	25c. green	£750	85·00
7	1	40c. blue on red	90·00	50·00
8	1	75c. black on red	£300	£140
9	1	1f. black on yellow	£1800	£600
10	1	5f. red on green	£3500	£2500

2 Prince Albert

1891

11	2	1c. green	90	65
12	2	2c. purple	90	65
13	2	5c. blue	60·00	7·25
22	2	5c. green	65	45
14	2	10c. brown on yellow	£130	20·00
23	2	10c. red	3·25	65
15	2	15c. pink	£225	12·00
24	2	15c. brown on yellow	4·25	90
25	2	15c. green	2·30	2·75
16	2	25c. green	£375	37·00
26	2	25c. blue	17·00	5·50
17	2	40c. black on pink	3·75	3·25
18	2	50c. brown on orange	9·25	5·50
23	2	75c. brown on buff	32·00	28·00
20	2	1f. black on yellow	23·00	11·00
21	2	5f. red on green	90·00	£100
28	2	5f. mauve	£225	£250
29	2	5f. green	37·00	34·00

1914. Surcharged +5c.

30	10c.+5c. red	10·00	9·25

4 War Widow and Monaco

1919. War Orphans Fund.

31	4	2c.+3c. mauve	41·00	46·00
32	4	5c.+5c. green	25·00	25·00
33	4	15c.+10c. red	26·00	26·00
34	4	25c.+15c. blue	55·00	46·00
35	4	50c.+50c. brown on orange	£225	£225
36	4	1f.+1f. black on yellow	£425	£450
37	4	5f.+5f. red	£1300	£1400

1920. Princess Charlotte's Marriage. Nos. 33/7 optd 20 mars 1920 or surch also.

38	2c.+3c. on 15c.+10c. red	70·00	75·00
39	2c.+3c. on 25c.+15c. blue	70·00	75·00
40	2c.+3c. on 50c.+50c. brown on orange	70·00	75·00
41	5c.+5c. on 1f.+1f. black on yellow	70·00	75·00
42	5c.+5c.on 5f.+5f. red	70·00	75·00
43	15c.+10c. red	32·00	37·00
44	25c.+15c. blue	28·00	12·00
45	50c.+50c. brown on orange	85·00	90·00
46	1f.+1f. black on yellow	£130	£140
47	5f.+5f. red	£9500	£9500

1921. Princess Antoinette's Baptism. Optd 28 DECEMBRE 1920 or surch also.

48	2	5c. green	1·00	1·00
49	2	75c. brown on buff	7·00	9·00
50	2	2f. on 5f. mauve	50·00	60·00

1922. Surch.

51	20c. on 15c. green	1·50	2·00
52	25c. on 10c. red	1·00	1·50
53	50c. on 1f. black on yellow	6·75	9·00

8 Prince Albert I

9 St. Devote Viaduct

1922

54	8	25c. brown	7·00	7·50
55	-	30c. green	1·50	2·50
56	-	30c. red	60	70
57	9	40c. brown	1·00	1·00
58	-	50c. blue	6·25	6·50
59	-	60c. grey	60	50
60	-	1f. black on yellow	50	30
61	-	2f. red	70	60
62	-	5f. brown	50·00	60·00
63	-	5f. green on blue	14·00	15·00
64	-	10f. red	22·00	25·00

DESIGNS:—As Type **9**: 30, 50c. Oceanographic Museum; 60c., 1, 2f. The Rock; 5, 10f. Prince's Palace, Monaco.

12 Prince Louis

13 Prince Louis and Palace

1923

65	12	10c. green	40	50
66	12	15c. red	60	1·00
67	12	20c. brown	40	50
68	12	25c. purple	20	30
69	13	50c. blue	40	50

1924. Surch with new value and bars.

70	2	45c. on 50c. brown on orange	60	1·00
71	2	75c. on 1f. black on yellow	60	1·00
72	2	85c. on 5f. green	60	1·00

14

15

16

17 St. Devote Viaduct

1924

73	14	1c. grey	10	20
74	14	2c. brown	10	20
75	14	3c. mauve	3·50	3·00
76	14	5c. orange	30	40
77	14	10c. blue	20	20
78	15	15c. green	20	20
79	15	15c. violet	4·00	2·30
80	15	20c. mauve	20	20
81	15	20c. pink	40	30
82	15	25c. pink	20	20
83	15	25c. red on yellow	20	20
84	15	30c. orange	20	20
85	15	40c. brown	20	20
86	15	40c. blue on blue	20	30
87	15	45c. black	1·30	90
88	16	50c. green	20	30
89	15	50c. brown on yellow	20	20
90	16	60c. brown	20	30
91	15	60c. green on green	20	30
92	15	75c. green on green	90	50
93	15	75c. red on yellow	30	20
94	15	75c. black	1·10	70
95	15	80c. red on yellow	50	30
96	15	90c. red on yellow	2·50	2·00
97	17	1f. black on yellow	30	50
98	17	1f.05 mauve	50	1·00
99	17	1f.10 green	15·00	7·50
100	15	1f.25 blue on blue	30	30
101	15	1f.50 blue on blue	4·75	3·00
102	-	2f. brown and mauve	2·50	1·50
103	-	3f. lilac and red on yellow	30·00	16·00
104	-	5f. red and green	10·00	8·00
105	-	10f. blue and brown	30·00	22·00

DESIGN—As Type **17**: 2f. to 10f. Monaco.

1926. Surch.

106	15	30c. on 25c. pink	35	40
107	15	50c. on 60c. green on green	1·80	50
108	17	50c. on 1f.05 mauve	1·30	80
109	17	50c. on 1f.10 green	16·00	11·00
110	15	50c. on 1f.25 blue on blue	1·80	80
111	15	1f.25 on 1f. blue on blue	1·00	70
112	-	1f.50 on 2f. brown and mauve (No. 102)	8·00	7·50

20 Prince Charles III, Louis II and Albert I

1928. International Philatelic Exn, Monte Carlo.

113	20	50c. red	3·00	6·00
114	20	1f.50 blue	3·00	6·00
115	20	3f. violet	3·00	6·00

20a

21 Palace Entrance

22 St. Devote's Church

23 Prince Louis II

1933

116	20a	1c. plum	20	30
117	20a	2c. green	20	30
118	20a	3c. purple	20	30
119	20a	5c. red	20	30
120	20a	10c. blue	20	30
121	20a	15c. violet	2·40	2·30
122	21	15c. red	1·00	30
123	21	20c. brown	1·00	30
124	A	25c. sepia	1·20	60
125	22	30c. green	1·50	60
126	23	40c. sepia	4·00	3·50
127	B	45c. brown	4·50	2·50
128	23	50c. violet	4·00	2·00
129	C	65c. green	4·50	1·40
130	D	75c. blue	5·00	2·50
131	23	90c. red	12·00	4·50
132	22	1f. brown	35·00	10·00
133	D	1f.25 red	8·50	6·00
134	23	1f.50 blue	50·00	15·00
135	A	1f.75 claret	45·00	14·00
136	A	1f.75 carmine	31·00	16·00
137	B	2f. blue	18·00	6·00
138	21	3f. violet	27·00	12·00
139	A	3f.50 orange	60·00	50·00
140	22	5f. purple	37·00	30·00
141	A	10f. blue	£150	£100
142	C	20f. black	£200	£180

DESIGNS—HORIZ (as Type **21**): A, The Prince's Residence; B, The Rock of Monaco; C, Palace Gardens; D, Fortifications nd Harbour.

For other stamps in Type **20a** see Nos. 249, etc.

1933. Air. Surch with Bleriot XI airplane and 1f50.

143	1f.50 on 5f. red & grn (No. 104)	35·00	35·00

28 Palace Gardens

1937. Charity.

144	28	50c.+50c. green	5·00	4·00
145	-	90c.+90c. red	5·00	4·00
146	-	1f.50+1f.50 blue	10·00	8·00
147	-	2f.+2f. violet	15·00	14·00
148	-	5f.+5f. red	£140	£150

DESIGNS—HORIZ: 90c. Exotic gardens; 1f.50, The Bay of Monaco. VERT: 2, 5f. Prince Louis II.

1937. Postage Due stamps optd POSTES or surch also.

149	D18	5 on 10c. violet	1·50	1·50
150	D18	10c. violet	1·50	1·50
151	D18	15 on 30c. bistre	1·50	1·50
152	D18	20 on 30c. bistre	1·50	1·50
153	D18	25 on 60c. red	2·30	2·50
154	D18	30c. bistre	3·00	3·50
155	D18	40 on 60c. red	2·75	3·00
156	D18	50 on 60c. red	3·00	5·00
157	D18	65 on 1f. blue	2·75	2·50
158	D18	85 on 1f. blue	6·50	6·25
159	D18	1f. blue	10·50	10·00
160	D18	2f.15 on 2f. red	10·50	15·00
161	D18	2f.25 on 2f. red	25·00	26·00
162	D18	2f.50 on 2f. red	35·00	35·00

30a Prince Louis II

1938. National Fete Day. Sheet 100×120 mm.

MS163	**30a** 10f. purple	£100	£130

31

1938

164	31	55c. brown	8·50	3·50
165	31	65c. violet	33·00	30·00
166	31	70c. brown	30	40
167	31	90c. violet	40	50
168	31	1f. red	20·00	12·50
169	31	1f.25 red	40	50
170	31	1f.75 blue	20·00	12·00
171	31	2f.25 blue	40	50

33 Monaco Hospital

1938. Anti-cancer Fund. 40th Anniv of Discovery of Radium.

172	-	65c.+25c. green	15·00	15·00
173	33	1f.75+50c. blue	17·00	20·00

DESIGN—VERT: 65c. Pierre and Marie Curie.

34 The Cathedral

38 Monaco Harbour

1939

174	34	20c. mauve	20	50
175	-	25c. brown	70	50
176	-	30c. green	60	50
177	-	40c. red	1·20	70
178	-	45c. purple	90	70
179	-	50c. green	60	50
180	-	60c. red	70	50
181	-	60c. green	2·00	1·20
182	38	70c. lilac	60	50
183	38	75c. green	60	50
184	-	1f. black	60	50
185	-	1f.30 brown	60	50
186	-	2f. purple	70	50
187	-	2f.50 red	30·00	30·00
188	-	2f.50 blue	2·50	2·10
189	38	3f. red	70	50
190	34	5f. blue	6·50	5·00
191	-	10f. green	1·80	2·00
192	-	20f. blue	1·80	2·00

DESIGNS—VERT: 25, 40c., 2f. Place St. Nicholas; 30, 60c., 20f. Palace Gateway; 50c., 1f., 1f.30, Palace of Monaco. HORIZ: 45c., 2f.50, 10f. Aerial view of Monaco.

40 Louis II Stadium

1939. Inauguration of Louis II Stadium, Monaco.

198	**40**	10f. green	£150	£150

41 Lucien

1939. National Relief. 16th–18th-century portrait designs and view.

199	**41**	5c.+5c. black	3·00	3·00
200	-	10c.+10c. purple	3·00	3·00
201	-	45c.+15c. green	9·00	9·00
202	-	70c.+30c. mauve	14·00	15·00
203	-	90c.+35c. violet	14·00	15·00
204	-	1f.+1f. blue	30·00	32·00
205	-	2f.+2f. red	39·00	35·00
206	-	2f.25+1f.25 blue	50·00	45·00
207	-	3f.+3f. red	55·00	65·00
208	-	5f.+5f. red	£100	£130

DESIGNS—VERT: 10c. Honore II; 45c. Louis I; 70c. Charlotte de Gramont; 90c. Antoine I; 1f. Marie de Lorraine; 2f. Jacques I; 2f.25, Louise-Hippolyte; 3f. Honore III. HORIZ: 5f. The Rock of Monaco.

1939. 8th International University Games. As T 40 but inscr "VIIIeme JEUX UNIVERSITAIRES INTERNATIONAUX 1939".

209	40c. green	1·50	1·50
210	70c. brown	3·75	2·00
211	90c. violet	2·75	2·75
212	1f.25 red	4·00	4·50
213	2f.25 blue	5·50	6·00

1940. Red Cross Ambulance Fund. As Nos. 174/92 in new colours surch with Red Cross and premium.

214	**34**	20c.+1f. violet	4·50	5·00
215	-	25c.+1f. green	4·50	5·00
216	-	30c.+1f. red	4·50	5·00
217	-	40c.+1f. blue	4·50	5·00
218	-	45c.+1f. red	4·50	5·00
219	-	50c.+1f. brown	4·50	5·00
220	-	60c.+1f. green	5·00	6·00
221	**38**	75c.+1f. black	5·00	6·00
222	-	1f.+1f. red	5·50	7·00
223	-	2f.+1f. slate	5·50	7·00
224	-	2f.50+1f. green	17·00	17·00
225	**38**	3f.+1f. blue	17·00	17·00
226	**34**	5f.+1f. black	25·00	25·00
227	-	10f.+5f. blue	40·00	45·00
228	-	20f.+5f. purple	40·00	45·00

44 Prince Louis II

1941

229	**44**	40c. red	50	70
230	**44**	80c. green	50	70
231	**44**	1f. violet	20	30
232	**44**	1f.20 green	20	30
233	**44**	1f.50 red	20	30
234	**44**	1f.50 violet	20	30
235	**44**	2f. green	80	60
236	**44**	2f.40 red	25	30
237	**44**	2f.50 blue	70	1·20
238	**44**	4f. blue	20	30

45

46

1941. National Relief Fund.

239	**45**	25c.+25c. purple	2·20	2·20
240	**46**	50c.+25c. brown	2·20	2·20
241	**46**	75c.+50c. purple	3·25	3·25
242	**45**	1f.+1f. blue	3·25	3·25
243	**46**	1f.50+1f.50 red	4·50	4·50
244	**45**	2f.+2f. green	4·50	4·50
245	**46**	2f.50+2f. blue	6·50	6·50
246	**45**	3f.+3f. brown	7·50	7·50
247	**46**	5f.+5f. green	10·00	10·00
248	**45**	10f.+8f. sepia	16·00	16·00

1941. New values and colours.

249	**20a**	10c. black	20	30
250	-	30c. red (as No. 176)	50	30
251	**20a**	30c. green	20	30
252	**20a**	40c. red	20	30
253	**20a**	50c. violet	20	30
362	**34**	50c. brown	40	30
254	**20a**	60c. blue	20	30
363	-	60c. pink (as No. 175)	40	30
255	**20a**	70c. brown	20	30
256	**34**	80c. green	20	30
257	-	1f. brown (as Nos. 178)	20	30
258	**38**	1f.20 blue	60	40
259	-	1f.50 blue (as Nos. 175)	80	35
260	**38**	2f. blue	20	30
261	-	2f. green (as No. 179)	90	40
262	-	3f. black (as No. 175)	30	30
364	-	3f. purple (as No. 176)	1·40	30
391	-	3f. green (as No. 175)	4·00	1·00
263	**34**	4f. purple	3·00	1·00
365	-	4f. green (as No. 175)	1·30	30
264	-	4f.50 violet (as No. 179)	20	30
265	-	5f. green (as No. 176)	20	30
392	-	5f. green (as No. 178)	1·00	50
393	-	5f. red (as No. 176)	1·50	1·50
266	-	6f. violet (as No. 179)	2·00	1·00
368	-	8f. brown (as No. 179)	3·50	1·60
267	**34**	10f. blue	40	50
370	-	10f. brown (as No. 179)	5·50	2·30
394	**38**	10f. yellow	2·00	80
268	**38**	15f. red	40	50
269	-	20f. brown (as No. 178)	40	50
373	-	20f. red (as No. 178)	2·00	80
270	**38**	25f. green	3·50	1·80
374	**38**	25f. black	36·00	20·00
397	-	25f. blue (as No. 176)	60·00	20·00
398	-	25f. red (as No. 179)	5·00	1·00
399	-	30f. blue (as No. 176)	13·00	5·00
400	-	35f. blue (as No. 179)	12·50	7·00
401	**34**	40f. red	10·50	7·50
402	**34**	50f. violet	6·50	1·50
403	-	65f. violet (as No. 178)	15·00	11·00
404	**34**	70f. yellow	12·00	10·00
405	-	75f. green (as No. 175)	30·00	12·00
406	-	85f. red (as No. 175)	20·00	10·00
407	-	100f. turquoise (as No. 178)	20·00	10·00

47 Caudron C-530 Rafale over Monaco **48** Propeller and Palace

49 Arms, Airplane and Globe

1942. Air.

271	**47**	5f. green	10	40
272	**47**	10f. blue	20	40
273	**48**	15f. brown	50	90
274	-	20f. brown	70	1·30
275	-	50f. purple	3·50	5·00
276	**49**	100f. red and purple	4·00	5·00

DESIGNS—VERT: 20f. Pegasus. HORIZ: 50f. Mew gull over Bay of Monaco.

50 Charles II

1942. National Relief Fund. Royal Personages.

277	-	2c.+3c. blue	30	50
278	**50**	5c.+5c. red	30	50
279	-	10c.+5c. black	30	50
280	-	20c.+10c. green	30	50
281	-	30c.+30c. purple	30	50
282	-	40c.+40c. red	30	50
283	-	50c.+50c. violet	30	50
284	-	75c.+75c. purple	30	50
285	-	1f.+1f. green	30	50
286	-	1f.50+1f. red	30	50
287	-	2f.50+2f.50 violet	3·50	6·00
288	-	3f.+3f. blue	3·50	6·00
289	-	5f.+5f. sepia	4·00	8·00
290	-	10f.+5f. purple	4·50	9·00
291	-	20f.+5f. blue	5·50	10·00

PORTRAITS: 2c. Rainier Grimaldi; 10c. Jeanne Grimaldi; 20c. Charles Auguste, Goyon de Matignon; 30c. Jacques I; 40c. Louise-Hippolyte; 50c. Charlotte Grimaldi; 75c. Marie Charles Grimaldi; 1f. Honore III; 1f.50, Honore IV; 2f.50, Honore V; 3f. Florestan I; 5f. Charles III; 10f. Albert I; 20f. Princess Marie-Victoire.

52 Prince Louis II

1943

292	**52**	50f. violet	1·10	1·60

53 St. Devote **54** Blessing the Sea

55 Arrival of St. Devote at Monaco

1944. Charity. Festival of St. Devote.

293	**53**	50c.+50c. brown	10	30
294	-	70c.+80c. blue	10	30
295	-	80c.+70c. green	10	30
296	-	1f.+1f. purple	10	30
297	-	1f.50+1f.50 red	50	50
298	**54**	2f.+2f. purple	80	80
299	-	5f.+2f. violet	80	80
300	-	10f.+40f. blue	80	80
301	**55**	20f.+60f. blue	4·00	6·00

DESIGNS—VERT: 70c., 1f. Various processional scenes; 1f.50, Burning the boat; 10f. Trial scene. HORIZ: 80c. Procession; 5f. St. Devote's Church.

1945. Air. For War Dead and Deported Workers. As Nos. 272/6 (colours changed) surch.

302	1f.+4f. on 10f. red	80	60
303	1f.+4f. on 15f. brown	80	60
304	1f.+4f. on 20f. brown	80	60
305	1f.+4f. on 50f. blue	80	60
306	1f.+4f. on 100f. purple	80	60

57 Prince Louis II **58** Prince Louis II

1946

361	**57**	30c. black	20	30
389	**57**	50c. olive	20	20
390	**57**	1f. violet	20	20
307	**57**	2f.50 green	80	40
308	**57**	3f. mauve	60	40
366	**57**	5f. brown	50	40
309	**57**	6f. red	60	40
367	**57**	6f. purple	5·75	3·25
310	**57**	10f. blue	60	40
369	**57**	10f. orange	50	30
371	**57**	12f. red	6·75	4·00
395	**57**	12f. slate	9·50	8·50
396	**57**	15f. lake	9·50	7·50
372	**57**	18f. blue	11·00	9·00
311	**58**	50f. grey	4·50	3·00
312	**58**	100f. red	6·25	4·00

59 Child Praying

1946. Child Welfare Fund.

313	**59**	1f.+3f. green	40	40
314	**59**	2f.+4f. red	40	40
315	**59**	4f.+6f. blue	40	40
316	**59**	5f.+40f. mauve	1·50	1·20
317	**59**	10f.+60f. red	1·50	1·20
318	**59**	15f.+100f. blue	2·10	1·70

60 Nurse and Baby

1946. Anti-tuberculosis Fund.

319	**60**	2f.+8f. blue	90	90

1946. Air. Optd POSTE AERIENNE over Sud Ouest SO.95 Corse II airplane.

320	**58**	50f. grey	6·00	5·50
321	**58**	100f. red	6·00	5·50

62 Steamship and Chart

1946. Stamp Day.

322	**62**	3f.+2f. blue	60	60

63

1946. Air.

323	**63**	40f. red	1·50	1·30
324	**63**	50f. brown	2·50	2·30
325	**63**	100f. green	3·75	3·00
326	**63**	200f. violet	4·25	5·00
326a	**63**	300f. blue and ultramarine	95·00	95·00
326b	**63**	500f. green and deep green	60·00	60·00
326c	**63**	1000f. violet and brown	£100	90·00

64 Pres. Roosevelt and Palace of Monaco

66 Pres. Roosevelt

1946. President Roosevelt Commemoration.

327	**66**	10c. mauve (postage)	60	50
328	-	30c. blue	60	50
329	**64**	60c. green	60	50
330	-	1f. sepia	1·50	1·50
331	-	2f.+3f. green	1·10	1·10
332	-	3f. violet	2·50	2·00
333	-	5f. red (air)	90	90
334	-	10f. black	1·10	90
335	**66**	15f.+10f. orange	3·00	2·20

DESIGNS—HORIZ: 30c., 5f. Rock of Monaco; 2f. Viaduct and St. Devote. VERT: 1, 3, 10f. Map of Monaco.

67 Prince Louis II

1947. Participation in the Centenary International Philatelic Exhibition, New York. (a) Postage.

336	**67**	10f. blue	5·00	5·00

68 Pres. Roosevelt as a Philatelist

69 Statue of Liberty, New York Harbour and Sud Ouest SO.95 Corse II

(b) Air. Dated "1847 1947".

337	**68**	50c. violet	1·50	1·50
338	-	1f.50 mauve	50	70
339	-	3f. orange	50	70
340	-	10f. blue	5·00	5·00
341	**69**	15f. red	9·50	9·50

DESIGNS—HORIZ: As Type **68**: 1f.50, G.P.O., New York; 3f. Oceanographic Museum, Monte Carlo. As Type **69**: 10f. Bay of Monaco and Sud Ouest SO.95 Corse II.

1947. Twenty-fifth Year of Reign of Prince Louis II. Sheet 85×98 mm.

MS341a	200f.+300f. brown	50·00	35·00

70 Prince Charles III

1948. Stamp Day.

342	**70**	6f.+4f. green on blue	50	50

71 Diving

72 Tennis

1948. Olympic Games, Wembley. Inscr "JEUX OLYMPIQUES 1948".

343	-	50c. green (postage)	20	30
344	-	1f. red	30	40
345	-	2f. blue	1·50	1·00
346	-	2f.50 red	4·50	3·25
347	**71**	4f. slate	5·00	4·00
348	-	5f.+5f. brown (air)	15·00	13·00
349	-	6f.+9f. violet	20·00	18·00
350	**72**	10f.+15f. red	30·00	25·00
351	-	15f.+25f. blue	40·00	35·00

DESIGNS—HORIZ: 50c. Hurdling; 15f. Yachting. VERT: 1f. Running; 2f. Throwing the discus; 2f.50, Basketball; 5f. Rowing; 6f. Skiing.

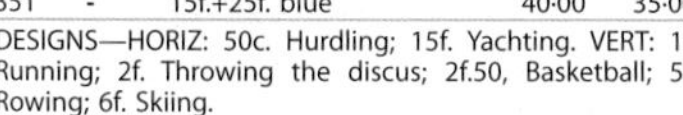

75 The Salmacis Nymph

77 F. J. Bosio (wrongly inscr "J. F.")

1948. Death Centenary of Francois Joseph Bosio (sculptor).

352	**75**	50c. green (postage)	80	50
353	-	1f. red	90	50
354	-	2f. blue	2·30	1·50
355	-	2f.50 violet	5·50	3·00
356	**77**	4f. mauve	4·50	3·00
357	-	5f.+5f. blue (air)	28·00	24·00
358	-	6f.+9f. green	28·00	24·00
359	-	10f.+15f. red	28·00	24·00
360	-	15f.+25f. brown	33·00	28·00

DESIGNS—VERT: 1, 5f. Hercules struggling with Achelous; 2, 6f. Aristaeus (Garden God); 15f. The Salmacis Nymph (36×48 mm). HORIZ: 2f.50, 10f. Hyacinthus awaiting his turn to throw a quoit.

79 Exotic Gardens

80 "Princess Alice II"

1949. Birth Centenary of Prince Albert I.

375		2f. blue (postage)	20	30
376	**79**	3f. green	20	20
377	-	4f. brown and blue	30	20
378	**80**	5f. red	1·00	1·00
379	-	6f. violet	1·20	1·00
380	-	10f. sepia	1·50	1·50
381	-	12f. pink	3·50	2·75
382	-	18f. orange and brown	5·00	4·25
383	-	20f. brown (air)	1·00	1·20
384	-	25f. blue	1·00	1·20
385	-	40f. green	2·30	2·30
386	-	50f. green, brown and black	3·25	3·25
387	-	100f. red	12·00	8·00
388	-	200f. orange	20·00	15·00

DESIGNS—HORIZ: 2f. Yacht "Hirondelle I" (1870); 4f. Oceanographic Museum, Monaco; 10f. "Hirondelle II" (1914); 12f. Albert harpooning whale; 18f. Buffalo (Palaeolithic mural); 20f. Constitution Day, 1911; 25f. Paris Institute of Palaeontology; 200f. Coin with effigy of Albert. VERT: 6f. Statue of Albert at tiller; 40f. Anthropological Museum; 50f. Prince Albert I; 100f. Oceanographic Institute, Paris.

82a Princess Charlotte

1949. Red Cross Fund. Sheet 150×172½ mm, containing vert portraits as T 82a.

MS408	10f.+5f. brown and red; 40f.+5f. green and red; 15f.+5f. red and 25f.+5f. blue and red. Each ×4	£500	£600
MS409	As **MS**408 but imperf	£500	£600

DESIGNS: 10, 40f. T **82a**; 15, 25f, Prince Rainier.

83 Palace of Monaco and Globe

1949. 75th Anniv of U.P.U.

410	**83**	5f. green (postage)	60	80
411	**83**	10f. orange	8·75	7·00
412	**83**	15f. red	80	70
413	**83**	25f. blue (air)	90	80
414	**83**	40f. sepia and brown	3·50	3·25
415	**83**	50f. blue and green	4·50	4·75
416	**83**	100f. blue and red	8·00	7·50

84 Prince Rainier III and Monaco Palace

1950. Accession of Prince Rainier III.

417	**84**	10c. purple & red (postage)	10	20
418	**84**	50c. brown, lt brn & orge	10	20
419	**84**	1f. violet	50	30
420	**84**	5f. deep green and green	4·25	2·50
421	**84**	15f. carmine and red	7·00	6·00
422	**84**	25f. blue, green & ultram	7·00	6·00
423	**84**	50f. brown and black (air)	10·00	8·00
424	**84**	100f. blue, dp brn & brn	15·00	13·00

85 Prince Rainier III

1950

425	**85**	50c. violet	20	20
426	**85**	1f. brown	20	20
434	**85**	5f. green	16·00	6·00
427	**85**	6f. green	2·50	1·00
428	**85**	8f. green	11·00	3·00
429	**85**	8f. orange	2·50	1·00
435	**85**	10f. orange	27·00	10·50
430	**85**	12f. blue	3·00	50
431	**85**	15f. red	5·00	80
432	**85**	15f. blue	3·00	50
433	**85**	18f. red	10·00	4·00

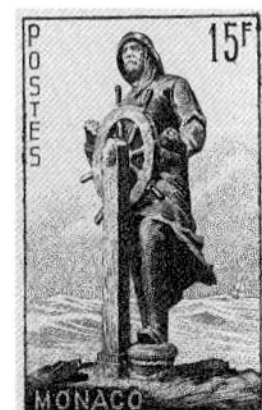

86 Prince Albert I

1951. Unveiling of Prince Albert Statue.

436	**86**	15f. blue	14·00	8·00

87 Edmond and Jules de Goncourt

1951. 50th Anniv of Goncourt Academy.

437	**87**	15f. purple	14·00	8·00

88 St. Vincent de Paul

89 Judgement of St. Devote

90 St. Peter's Keys and Papal Bull

1951. Holy Year.

438	**88**	10c. blue, ultramarine & red	20	30
439	-	50c. violet and red	20	30
440	**89**	1f. green and brown	20	30
441	**90**	2f. red and purple	30	50
442	-	5f. green	40	50
443	-	12f. violet	60	70
444	-	15f. red	6·75	6·50
445	-	20f. brown	10·50	9·00
446	-	25f. blue	13·00	12·00
447	-	40f. violet and mauve	15·00	14·00
448	-	50f. brown and olive	18·00	15·00
449	-	100f. brown	40·00	35·00

DESIGNS—TRIANGULAR: 50c. Pope Pius XII. HORIZ (as Type **90**): 5f. Mosaic. VERT (as Type **90**): 12f. Prince Rainier III in St. Peter's; 15f. St. Nicholas of Patara; 20f. St. Romain; 25f. St. Charles Borromeo; 40f. Coliseum; 50f. Chapel of St. Devote. VERT (as Type **89**): 100f. Rainier of Westphalia.

93 Wireless Mast and Monaco

1951. Monte Carlo Radio Station.

450	**93**	1f. orange, red and blue	1·00	60
451	**93**	15f. purple, red and violet	5·00	2·00
452	**93**	30f. brown and blue	30·00	10·00

94 Seal of Prince Rainier III

1951

453	**94**	1f. violet	1·00	70
454	**94**	5f. black	5·00	3·25
512	**94**	5f. violet	5·00	2·00
513	**94**	6f. red	9·00	3·50
455	**94**	8f. red	10·00	5·25
514	**94**	8f. brown	9·50	5·00
456	**94**	15f. green	20·00	10·00
515	**94**	15f. blue	22·00	8·50
457	**94**	30f. blue	30·00	25·00
516	**94**	30f. green	35·00	25·00

1951. Nos. MS408/9 surch 1f. on 10f.+5f., 3f. on 15f.+5f., 5f. on 25f. + 5f., 6f. on 40f.+5f.

MS458	As above	£550	£600
MS459	As above imperf	£550	£600

95 Gallery of Hercules

1952. Monaco Postal Museum.

460	**95**	5f. chestnut and brown	2·50	90
461	**95**	15f. violet and purple	3·25	1·00
462	**95**	30f. indigo and blue	4·50	1·40

96 Football

1953. 15th Olympic Games, Helsinki. Inscr "HELSINKI 1952".

463	-	1f. mauve & violet (postage)	20	30
464	**96**	2f. blue and green	20	30
465	-	3f. pale and deep blue	20	30
466	-	5f. green and brown	1·20	50
467	-	8f. red and lake	3·00	2·00
468	-	15f. brown, green and blue	1·50	1·20
469	-	40f. black (air)	15·00	13·00
470	-	50f. violet	20·00	13·00
471	-	100f. green	25·00	20·00
472	-	200f. red	35·00	25·00

DESIGNS: 1f. Basketball; 3f. Sailing; 5f. Cycling; 8f. Gymnastics; 15f. Louis II Stadium, Monaco; 40f. Running; 50f. Fencing; 100f. Rifle target and Arms of Monaco; 200f. Olympic torch.

97 "Journal Inedit"

1953. Centenary of Publication of Journal by E. and J. de Goncourt.

473	**97**	5f. green	1·00	50
474	**97**	15f. brown	5·00	1·30

98 Physalia, Yacht "Princess Alice", Prince Albert, Richet and Portier

1953. 50th Anniv of Discovery of Anaphylaxis.

475	**98**	2f. violet, green and brown	40	10
476	**98**	5f. red, lake and green	1·20	70
477	**98**	15f. lilac, blue and green	4·50	3·00

99 F. Ozanam

1954. Death Centenary of Ozanam (founder of St. Vincent de Paul Conferences).

478	**99**	1f. red	30	30
479	-	5f. blue	70	70
480	**99**	15f. black	2·50	2·50

DESIGN: 5f. Outline drawing of Sister of Charity.

100 St. Jean-Baptiste de la Salle

1954. St. J.-B. de la Salle (educationist).

481	**100**	1f. red	30	30
482	-	5f. sepia	70	70
483	**100**	15f. blue	2·50	2·50

DESIGN: 5f. Outline drawing of De la Salle and two children.

101 **102**

103

1954. Arms.

484	-	50c. red, black and mauve	10	20
485	-	70c. red, black and blue	10	20
486	**101**	80c. red, black and green	10	20
487	-	1f. red, black and blue	20	20
488	**102**	2f. red, black and orange	20	20
489	-	3f. red, black and green	20	20
490	**103**	5f. multicoloured	50	50

DESIGNS—HORIZ: 50c. as Type **101**. VERT: 70c., 1, 3f. as Type **102**.

104 Seal of Prince Rainier III

1954. Precancelled.

491	**104**	4f. red	2·00	1·00
492	**104**	5f. blue	50	40
493	**104**	8f. green	2·00	1·10
494	**104**	8f. purple	1·00	70
495	**104**	10f. green	50	40
496	**104**	12f. violet	7·00	2·75
497	**104**	15f. orange	1·50	1·00
498	**104**	20f. green	2·00	1·30
499	**104**	24f. brown	12·00	6·50
500	**104**	30f. blue	2·00	1·50
501	**104**	40f. brown	4·00	2·50
502	**104**	45f. red	3·00	2·30
503	**104**	55f. blue	9·00	4·50

See also Nos. 680/3.

105 Lambarene

106 Dr. Albert Schweitzer

1955. 80th Birthday of Dr. Schweitzer (humanitarian).

504	**105**	2f. grn, turq & bl (postage)	50	40
505	**106**	5f. blue and green	1·70	1·70
506	-	15f. purple, black and green	4·50	3·50
507	-	200f. slate, grn & bl (air)	60·00	45·00

DESIGNS—As Type **106**: 15f. Lambarene Hospital. HORIZ (48×27 mm): 200f. Schweitzer and jungle scene.

107 Great Cormorants

1955. Air.

508		100f. indigo and blue	35·00	17·00
509		200f. black and blue	36·00	18·00
510		500f. grey and green	60·00	40·00
511a	**107**	1,000f. black, turq & grn	£130	85·00

DESIGNS—As Type **107**: 100f. Roseate tern; 200f. Herring gull; 500f. Wandering albatrosses.

108 Eight Starting Points

1955. 25th Monte Carlo Car Rally.

517	**108**	100f. red and brown	£110	80·00

109 Prince Rainier III

1955

518	**109**	6f. purple and green	1·00	50
519	**109**	8f. violet and red	1·00	50
520	**109**	12f. green and red	1·00	50
521	**109**	15f. blue and purple	1·90	50
522	**109**	18f. blue and orange	7·00	90
523	**109**	20f. turquoise	3·75	1·00
524	**109**	25f. black and orange	1·50	80
525	**109**	30f. black and blue	21·00	9·00
526	**109**	30f. violet	6·50	3·00
527	**109**	35f. brown	6·00	3·75
528	**109**	50f. lake and green	9·00	4·00

See also Nos. 627/41.

110 "La Maison a Vapeur"

111 "The 500 Millions of the Begum"

113 U.S.S. "Nautilus"

112 "Round the World in Eighty Days"

1955. 50th Death Anniv of Jules Verne (author). Designs illustrating his works.

529	-	1f. blue & brown (postage)	10	20
530	-	2f. sepia, indigo and blue	10	20
531	**110**	3f. blue, black and brown	10	20
532	-	5f. sepia and red	20	30
533	**111**	6f. grey and sepia	60	50
534	-	8f. turquoise and olive	60	60
535	-	10f. sepia, turquoise & ind	1·60	1·20
536	**112**	15f. red and brown	1·20	1·00
537	-	25f. black and green	3·25	2·20
538	**113**	30f. black, purple & turq	8·00	7·00
539	-	200f. indigo and blue (air)	40·00	35·00

DESIGNS—VERT (as Type **111**): 1f. "Five Weeks in a Balloon". HORIZ (as Type **110**): 2f. "A Floating Island"; 10f. "Journey to the Centre of the Earth"; 25f. "20,000 Leagues under the Sea"; 200f. "From the Earth to the Moon". (as Type **111**): 5f. "Michael Strogoff"; 8f. "Le Superbe Orenoque".

114 "The Immaculate Virgin" (F. Brea)

1955. Marian Year.

540	**114**	5f. green, grey and brown	20	30
541	-	10f. green, grey and brown	30	40
542	-	15f. brown and sepia	1·00	1·00

DESIGNS—As Type **114**: 10f. "Madonna" (L. Brea). As Type **113**: 15f. Bienheureux Rainier.

115 Rotary Emblem

1955. 50th Anniv of Rotary International.

543	**115**	30f. blue and yellow	2·00	2·00

116 George Washington

118 President Eisenhower

117 Abraham Lincoln

1956. 5th International Stamp Exhibition, New York.

544	**116**	1f. violet and lilac	10	20
545	-	2f. lilac and purple	10	20
546	**117**	3f. blue and violet	10	20
547	**118**	5f. red	20	30
548	-	15f. brown and chocolate	1·00	80
549	-	30f. black, indigo and blue	5·25	4·00
550	-	40f. brown	7·75	5·00
551	-	50f. red	7·75	5·00
552	-	100f. green	7·75	5·00

DESIGNS—As Type **117**: 2f. F. D. Roosevelt. HORIZ (as Type **116**): 15f. Monaco Palace in the 18th century; 30f. Landing of Columbus. (48×36 mm): 50f. Aerial view of Monaco Palace in the 18th century; 100f. Louisiana landscape in 18th century. VERT (as Type **118**): 40f. Prince Rainier III.

120

1956. 7th Winter Olympic Games, Cortina d'Ampezzo and 16th Olympic Games, Melbourne.

553		15f. brown, green & pur	1·50	1·00
554	**120**	30f. red	3·50	2·20

DESIGN: 15f. "Italia" ski-jump.

1956. Nos. D482/95 with "TIMBRE TAXE" barred out and some surch also. (a) Postage.

555		2f. on 4f. slate and brown	60	60
556		2f. on 4f. brown and slate	60	60
557		3f. lake and green	60	60
558		3f. green and lake	60	60
559		5f. on 4f. slate and brown	1·00	1·00
560		5f. on 4f. brown and slate	1·00	1·00
561		10f. on 4f. slate and brown	1·80	1·80
562		10f. on 4f. brown and slate	1·80	1·80
563		15f. on 5f. violet and blue	2·50	2·50
564		15f. on 5f. blue and violet	2·50	2·50
565		20f. violet and blue	4·00	4·00
566		20f. blue and violet	4·00	4·00
567		25f. on 20f. violet and blue	6·50	6·50
568		25f. on 20f. blue and violet	6·50	6·50
569		30f. on 10f. indigo and blue	12·00	12·00
570		30f. on 10f. blue and indigo	12·00	12·00
571		40f. on 50f. brown and red	15·00	15·00
572		40f. on 50f. red and brown	15·00	15·00
573		50f. on 100f. green and purple	20·00	20·00
574		50f. on 100f. purple and green	20·00	20·00

(b) Air. Optd POSTE AERIENNE also.

575		100f. on 20f. violet and blue	14·00	14·00
576		100f. on 20f. blue and violet	14·00	14·00

121 Route Map from Glasgow

1956. 26th Monte Carlo Car Rally.

577	**121**	100f. brown and red	35·00	32·00

122 Princess Grace and Prince Rainier III

1956. Royal Wedding.

578	**122**	1f. black & grn (postage)	10	20
579	**122**	2f. black and red	25	30
580	**122**	3f. black and blue	45	50
581	**122**	5f. black and green	1·10	1·00
582	**122**	15f. black and brown	2·00	1·50
583	**122**	100f. brown & purple (air)	1·50	1·50
584	**122**	200f. brown and red	2·50	2·50
585	**122**	500f. brown and grey	5·00	5·00

123 Princess Grace

1957. Birth of Princess Caroline.

586	**123**	1f. grey	10	20
587	**123**	2f. olive	10	20
588	**123**	3f. brown	10	20
589	**123**	5f. red	30	30
590	**123**	15f. pink	30	30
591	**123**	25f. blue	1·20	1·00
592	**123**	30f. violet	1·30	1·00
593	**123**	50f. red	2·50	1·20
594	**123**	75f. orange	4·00	3·25

124 Princess Grace with Princess Caroline

1958. Birth of Prince Albert.

595	**124**	100f. black	12·00	8·00

125 Order of St. Charles

1958. Centenary of Creation of National Order of St. Charles.

596	**125**	100f. multicoloured	4·00	3·00

126 Route Map from Munich

1958. 27th Monte Carlo Rally.

597	**126**	100f. multicoloured	10·00	10·00

127 Statue of the Holy Virgin and Popes Pius IX and Pius XII

1958. Centenary of Apparition of Virgin Mary at Lourdes.

598	**127**	1f. grey & brown (postage)	10	20
599	-	2f. violet and blue	10	20
600	-	3f. sepia and green	10	20
601	-	5f. blue and sepia	10	20
602	-	8f. multicoloured	30	20
603	-	10f. multicoloured	30	30
604	-	12f. multicoloured	50	40
605	-	20f. myrtle and purple	60	50
606	-	35f. myrtle, bistre and brown	70	60
607	-	50f. blue, green and lake	1·20	1·00
608	-	65f. turquoise and blue	1·60	1·50
609	-	100f. grey, myrtle and blue (air)	2·50	2·00
610	-	200f. brown and chestnut	3·50	3·00

DESIGNS—VERT (26½×36 mm): 2f. St. Bernadette; 3f. St. Bernadette at Bartres; 5f. The Miracle of Bourriette; 20f. St. Bernadette at prayer; 35f. St. Bernadette's canonization. (22×36 mm): 8f. Stained-glass window. As Type **127**: 50f. St. Bernadette, Pope Pius XI, Mgr. Laurence and Abbe Peyramale. HORIZ (48×36 mm): 10f. Lourdes grotto; 12f. Interior of Lourdes grotto. (36×26½ mm): 65f. Shrine of St. Bernadette; (48×27 mm): 100f. Lourdes Basilica; 200f. Pope Pius X and subterranean interior of Basilica.

128 Princess Grace and Clinic

1959. Opening of new Hospital Block in "Princess Grace" Clinic, Monaco.

611	**128**	100f. grey, brown & green	6·25	3·50

129 UNESCO Headquarters, Paris, and Cultural Emblems

1959. Inaug of UNESCO Headquarters Building.

612	**129**	25f. multicoloured	25	30
613	-	50f. turquoise, black & ol	40	50

DESIGN: 50f. As Type **129** but with heads of children and letters of various alphabets in place of the emblems.

130 Route Map from Athens

1959. 28th Monte Carlo Rally.

614	**130**	100f. blue, red & grn on bl	10·00	8·00

131 Prince Rainier and Princess Grace

1959. Air.

615	**131**	300f. violet	22·00	14·00
616	**131**	500f. blue	30·00	25·00

See also Nos. 642/3.

132 "Princess Caroline" Carnation

1959. Flowers.

617	**132**	5f. mauve, green & brown	20	10
618	-	10f. on 3f. pink, green and brown	50	25
619	-	15f. on 1f. yellow & green	50	40
620	-	20f. purple and green	1·00	80
621	-	25f. on 6f. red, yellow and green	1·50	1·30
622	-	35f. pink and green	3·25	2·50
623	-	50f. green and sepia	4·75	3·25
624	-	85f. on 65f. lavender, bronze and green	5·00	4·00
625	-	100f. red and green	7·50	6·50

FLOWERS—As Type **132**: 10f. "Princess Grace" carnation; 100f. "Grace of Monaco" rose. VERT (22×36 mm): 15f. Mimosa; 25f. Geranium. HORIZ (36×22 mm): 20f. Bougainvillea; 35f. "Laurier" rose; 50f. Jasmine; 85f. Lavender.

133 "Uprooted Tree"

1960. World Refugee Year.

626	**133**	25c. green, blue and black	40	30

1960. Prince Rainier types with values in new currency.

627	**109**	25c. blk & orge (postage)	80	20
628	**109**	30c. violet	80	20
629	**109**	40c. red and brown	1·00	40
630	**109**	45c. brown and grey	1·00	40
631	**109**	50c. red and green	3·75	60
632	**109**	50c. red and brown	1·00	60
633	**109**	60c. brown and green	2·50	1·10
634	**109**	60c. brown and purple	3·50	2·00
635	**109**	65c. blue and brown	22·00	7·00
636	**109**	70c. blue and plum	2·00	1·00
637	**109**	85c. green and violet	3·00	2·20
638	**109**	95c. blue	1·00	1·20
639	**109**	1f.10 blue and brown	4·00	3·00
640	**109**	1f.30 brown and red	3·00	2·50
641	**109**	2f.30 purple and orange	4·00	1·70
642	**131**	3f. violet (air)	60·00	27·00
643	**131**	5f. blue	60·00	35·00

134 Oceanographic Museum

1960

644	-	5c. green, black and blue	10	20
645	**134**	10c. brown and blue	70	40
646	-	10c. blue, violet and green	70	30
647	-	40c. purple, grn & dp grn	1·00	50
648	-	45c. brown, green and blue	9·00	1·10
649	-	70c. brown, red and green	1·00	70
650	-	80c. red, green and blue	2·50	1·00
651	-	85c. black, brown and grey	13·50	4·50
652	-	90c. red, blue and black	4·00	2·00
653	-	1f. multicoloured	2·00	60
654	-	1f.15 black, red and blue	4·00	2·75
655	-	1f.30 brown, green & blue	1·50	1·00
656	-	1f.40 orange, green & vio	4·50	3·50

DESIGNS—HORIZ: 5c. Palace of Monaco; 10c. (No. 646), Aquatic Stadium; 40, 45, 80c., 1f.40, Aerial view of Palace; 70, 85, 90c., 1f.15, 1f.30, Court of Honour, Monaco Palace; 1f. Palace floodlit.

134a St. Devote

1960. Air.

No.	Type	Description	Mint	Used
668	**134a**	2f. violet, blue and green	2·00	1·50
669	**134a**	3f. brown, green and blue	3·00	2·00
670	**134a**	5f. red	5·50	4·00
671	**134a**	10f. brown, grey and green	9·00	6·00

135 Long-snouted Seahorse

1960. Marine Life and Plants. (a) Marine Life.

No.	Type	Description	Mint	Used
672	-	1c. red and turquoise	20	20
673	-	12c. brown and blue	30	20
674	**135**	15c. green and red	70	50
675	-	20c. multicoloured	90	50

DESIGNS—HORIZ: 1c. "Macrocheira kampferi" (crab); 20c. Lionfish. VERT: 12c. Trapezium horse conch.

(b) Plants.

No.	Description	Mint	Used
676	2c. multicoloured	20	20
677	15c. orange, brown and olive	70	50
678	18c. multicoloured	70	30
679	20c. red, olive and brown	90	50

PLANTS—VERT: 2c. "Selenicereus sp."; 15c. "Cereus sp."; 18c. "Aloe ciliaris"; 20c. "Nopalea dejecta".

1960. Prince Rainier Seal type with values in new currency. Precancelled.

No.	Type	Description	Mint	Used
680	**104**	8c. purple	2·00	1·40
681	**104**	20c. green	3·00	2·00
682	**104**	40c. brown	4·50	2·50
683	**104**	55c. blue	8·50	4·00

136 Route Map from Lisbon

1960. 29th Monte Carlo Rally.

No.	Type	Description	Mint	Used
684	**136**	25c. black, red & bl on bl	4·00	3·00

137 Stamps of Monaco 1885, France and Sardinia, 1860

1960. 75th Anniv of First Monaco Stamp.

No.	Type	Description	Mint	Used
685	**137**	25c. bistre, blue and violet	1·10	80

138 Aquarium

1960. 50th Anniv of Oceanographic Museum, Monaco.

No.	Type	Description	Mint	Used
686	-	5c. black, blue and purple	70	40
687	**138**	10c. grey, brown and green	80	45
688	-	15c. black, bistre and blue	80	50
689	-	20c. black, blue and mauve	1·50	80
690	-	25c. turquoise	3·00	2·00
691	-	50c. brown and blue	3·75	2·50

DESIGNS—VERT: 5c. Oceanographic Museum (similar to Type **134**). HORIZ: 15c. Conference Hall; 20c. Hauling-in catch; 25c. Museum, aquarium and underwater research equipment; 50c. Prince Albert, "Hirondelle I" (schooner) and "Princess Alice" (steam yacht).

139 Horse-jumping

1960. Olympic Games.

No.	Type	Description	Mint	Used
692	**139**	5c. brown, red and green	20	20
693	-	10c. brown, blue and green	30	30
694	-	15c. red, brown and purple	50	50
695	-	20c. black, blue and green	4·00	4·00
696	-	25c. purple, turq & grn	1·00	1·00
697	-	50c. purple, blue & turq	1·50	1·50

DESIGNS: 10c. Swimming; 15c. Long-jumping; 20c. Throwing the javelin; 25c. Free-skating; 50c. Skiing.

140 Rally Badge, Old and Modern Cars

1961. 50th Anniv of Monte Carlo Rally.

No.	Type	Description	Mint	Used
698	**140**	1f. violet, red and brown	2·50	2·50

141 Route Map from Stockholm

1961. 30th Monte Carlo Rally.

No.	Type	Description	Mint	Used
699	**141**	1f. multicoloured	2·00	2·00

142 Marine Life

1961. World Aquariological Congress. Orange network background.

No.	Type	Description	Mint	Used
700	**142**	25c. red, sepia and violet	30	30

143 Leper in Town of Middle Ages

1961. Sovereign Order of Malta.

No.	Type	Description	Mint	Used
701	**143**	25c. black, red and brown	30	30

144 Semi-submerged Sphinx of Ouadi-es-Saboua

1961. UNESCO Campaign for Preservation of Nubian Monuments.

No.	Type	Description	Mint	Used
702	**144**	50c. purple, blue & brown	1·40	1·20

145 Insect within Protective Hand

1962. Nature Preservation.

No.	Type	Description	Mint	Used
703	**145**	25c. mauve and purple	50	40

146 Chevrolet, 1912

1961. Veteran Motor Cars.

No.	Type	Description	Mint	Used
704	**146**	1c. brown, green and chestnut	10	20
705	-	2c. blue, purple and red	10	20
706	-	3c. purple, black and mauve	10	20
707	-	4c. blue, brown and violet	10	20
708	-	5c. green, red and olive	10	20
709	-	10c. brown, red and blue	10	20
710	-	15c. green and turquoise	20	30
711	-	20c. brown, red and violet	30	50
712	-	25c. violet, red and brown	50	50
713	-	30c. lilac and green	1·70	1·50
714	-	45c. green, purple and brown	3·00	3·00
715	-	50c. blue, red and brown	3·50	3·50
716	-	65c. brown, red and grey	4·50	4·00
717	-	1f. blue, red and violet	6·00	5·00

MOTOR CARS: 2c. Peugeot, 1898; 3c. Fiat, 1901; 4c. Mercedes, 1901; 5c. Rolls Royce, 1903;. 10c. Panhard-Lavassor, 1899; 15c. Renault, 1898; 20c. Ford "N", 1906 (wrongly inscr "FORD-S-1908"); 25c. Rochet-Schneider, 1894; 30c. FN-Herstal, 1901; 45c. De Dion Bouton, 1900; 50c. Buick, 1910; 65c. Delahaye, 1901; 1f. Cadillac, 1906.

147 Racing Car and Race Route

1962. 20th Monaco Motor Grand Prix.

No.	Type	Description	Mint	Used
718	**147**	1f. purple	2·50	2·20

148 Route Map from Oslo

1962. 31st Monte Carlo Rally.

No.	Type	Description	Mint	Used
719	**148**	1f. multicoloured	1·80	1·80

149 Louis XII and Lucien Grimaldi

1962. 450th Anniv of Recognition of Monegasque Sovereignty by Louis XII.

No.	Type	Description	Mint	Used
720	**149**	25c. black, red and blue	30	30
721	-	50c. brown, lake and blue	70	60
722	-	1f. red, green and brown	1·00	80

DESIGNS: 50c. Parchment bearing declaration of sovereignty; 1f. Seals of two Sovereigns.

150 Mosquito and Swamp

1962. Malaria Eradication.

No.	Type	Description	Mint	Used
723	**150**	1f. green and olive	70	70

151 Sun, Bouquet and "Hope Chest"

1962. National Multiple Sclerosis Society, New York.

No.	Type	Description	Mint	Used
724	**151**	20c. multicoloured	30	30

152 Harvest Scene

1962. Europa.

No.	Type	Description	Mint	Used
725	**152**	25c. brown, green and blue (postage)	1·00	50
726	**152**	50c. olive and turquoise	1·00	60
727	**152**	1f. olive and purple	1·50	1·00
728	-	2f. slate, brown & green (air)	2·00	2·00

DESIGN: 2f. Mercury in flight over Europe.

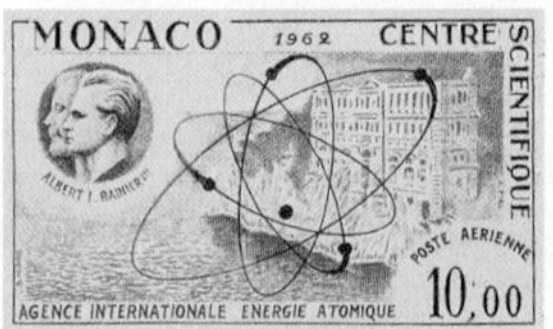

153 Atomic Symbol and Scientific Centre, Monaco

1962. Air. Scientific Centre, Monaco.

No.	Type	Description	Mint	Used
729	**153**	10f. violet, brown and blue	6·50	6·00

154 Yellow Wagtails

1962. Protection of Birds useful to Agriculture.

No.	Type	Description	Mint	Used
730	**154**	5c. yellow, brown & green	20	25
731	-	10c. red, bistre and purple	20	25
732	-	15c. multicoloured	30	30
733	-	20c. sepia, green & mauve	50	60
734	-	25c. multicoloured	80	80
735	-	30c. brown, blue & myrtle	1·10	90
736	-	45c. brown and violet	2·00	1·60
737	-	50c. black, olive & turq	3·00	2·20
738	-	85c. multicoloured	4·00	2·50
739	-	1f. sepia, red and green	4·50	3·25

BIRDS: 10c. European robins; 15c. Eurasian goldfinches; 20c. Blackcaps; 25c. Greater spotted woodpeckers; 30c. Nightingale; 45c. Barn owls; 50c. Common starlings; 85c. Red crossbills; 1f. White storks.

155 Galeazzi's Diving Turret

1962. Underwater Exploration.

740		5c. black, violet and blue	10	10
741	**155**	10c. blue, violet and brown	20	20
742	-	25c. bistre, green and blue	30	30
743	-	45c. black, blue and green	50	50
744	-	50c. green, bistre and blue	70	70
745	-	85c. blue and turquoise	1·50	1·40
746	-	1f. brown, green and blue	2·50	1·70

DESIGNS—HORIZ: 5c. Divers; 25c. Williamson's photo-sphere (1914) and bathyscaphe "Trieste"; 45c. Klingert's diving-suit (1797) and modern diving-suit; 50c. Diving saucer; 85c. Fulton's "Nautilus" (1800) and modern submarine; 1f. Alexander the Great's diving bell and Beebe's bathysphere.

156 Donor's Arm and Globe

1962. 3rd Int Blood Donors' Congress Monaco.

747	**156**	1f. red, sepia and orange	1·00	1·00

157 "Ring-a-ring o' Roses"

158 Feeding Chicks in Nest

1963. U.N. Children's Charter.

748	**157**	5c. red, blue and ochre	20	20
749	**158**	10c. green, sepia and blue	20	20
750	-	15c. blue, red and green	20	30
751	-	20c. multicoloured	20	30
752	-	25c. blue, purple & brown	30	30
753	-	50c. multicoloured	80	60
754	-	95c. multicoloured	2·00	1·00
755	-	1f. purple, red & turquoise	2·50	2·00

DESIGNS—As Type **157**: 1f. Prince Albert and Princess Caroline; Children's paintings as Type **158**: HORIZ: 15c. Children on scales; 50c. House and child. VERT: 20c. Sun's rays and children of three races; 25c. Mother and child; 95c. Negress and child.

159 Ship's Figurehead

1963. International Red Cross Centenary.

756	**159**	50c. red, brown & turquoise	50	60
757	-	1f. multicoloured	1·00	1·00

DESIGN—HORIZ: 1f. Moynier, Dunant and Dufour.

160 Racing Cars

1963. European Motor Grand Prix.

758	**160**	50c. multicoloured	80	70

161 Emblem and Charter

1963. Founding of Lions Club of Monaco.

759	**161**	50c. blue, bistre and violet	80	80

162 Hotel des Postes and U.P.U. Monument, Berne

1963. Paris Postal Conference Centenary.

760	**162**	50c. lake, green and yellow	60	60

163 "Telstar" Satellite and Globe

1963. 1st Link Trans-Atlantic T.V. Satellite.

761	**163**	50c. brown, green & purple	80	80

164 Route Map from Warsaw

1963. 32nd Monte Carlo Rally.

762	**164**	1f. multicoloured	1·50	1·50

165 Feeding Chicks

1963. Freedom from Hunger.

763	**165**	1f. multicoloured	80	80

166 Allegory

1963. 2nd Ecumenical Council, Vatican City.

764	**166**	1f. turquoise, green and red	80	80

167 Henry Ford and Ford "A" Car of 1903

1963. Birth Centenary of Henry Ford (motor pioneer).

765	**167**	20c. green and purple	40	40

168 H. Garin (winner of 1903 race) cycling through Village

1963. 50th "Tour de France" Cycle Race.

766	**168**	25c. green, brown and blue	50	50
767	-	50c. sepia, green and blue	70	70

DESIGN: 50c. Cyclist passing Desgrange Monument, Col du Galibier, 1963.

169 P. de Coubertin and Discus-thrower

1963. Birth Centenary of Pierre de Coubertin (reviver of Olympic Games).

768	**169**	1f. brown, red and lake	1·00	1·00

170 Roland Garros and Morane Saulnier Type I

1963. Air. 50th Anniv of 1st Aerial Crossing of Mediterranean Sea.

769	**170**	2f. sepia and blue	1·50	1·00

171 Route Map from Paris

1963. 33rd Monte Carlo Rally.

770	**171**	1f. red, turquoise and blue	1·50	1·50

172 Children with Stamp Album

1963. "Scolatex" International Stamp Exn, Monaco.

771	**172**	50c. blue, violet and red	40	40

173 "Europa"

1963. Europa.

772	**173**	25c. brown, red and green	1·00	50
773	**173**	50c. sepia, red and blue	1·80	1·00

174 Wembley Stadium

1963. Cent of (English) Football Association.

774	**174**	1c. violet, green and red	10	10
775	-	2c. red, black and green	10	10
776	-	3c. orange, olive and red	10	10
777	-	4c. multicoloured	10	10

Multicoloured horiz designs depicting (a) "Football through the Centuries".

778	10c. "Calcio", Florence (16th cent)	10	10
779	15c. "Soule", Brittany (19th cent)	10	10
780	20c. English military college (after Cruickshank, 1827)	20	20
781	25c. English game (after Overend, 1890)	20	20

(b) "Modern Football".

782	30c. Tackling	40	40
783	50c. Saving goal	80	80
784	95c. Heading ball	1·40	1·40
785	1f. Corner kick	1·90	1·70

DESIGNS—As Type **174**: 4c. Louis II Stadium, Monaco. This stamp is optd in commemoration of the Association Sportive de Monaco football teams in the French Championships and in the Coupe de France, 1962–63. HORIZ (36×22 mm): 2c. Footballer making return kick; 3c. Goal-keeper saving ball.

Nos. 778/81 and 782/5 were respectively issued together in sheets and arranged in blocks of 4 with a football in the centre of each block.

175 Communications in Ancient Egypt, and Rocket

1964. "PHILATEC 1964" Int Stamp Exn, Paris.

786	**175**	1f. brown, indigo and blue	70	70

176 Reproduction of Rally Postcard Design and Deperdussin Monocoque Racer

1964. 50th Anniv of 1st Aerial Rally, Monte Carlo.

787	**176**	1c. olive, blue & grn (postage)	10	20
788	-	2c. bistre, brown and blue	10	20
789	-	3c. brown, blue and green	10	20
790	-	4c. red, turquoise and blue	10	20
791	-	5c. brown, red and violet	10	20
792	-	10c. violet, brown and blue	20	20
793	-	15c. orange, brown and blue	30	30
794	-	20c. sepia, green and blue	35	35
795	-	25c. brown, blue and red	40	40
796	-	30c. myrtle, purple and blue	60	60
797	-	45c. sepia, turquoise and brown	1·00	90
798	-	50c. ochre, olive and violet	1·10	1·00
799	-	65c. red, slate and turquoise	2·00	1·50
800	-	95c. turquoise, red and bistre	2·50	2·20

801	-	1f. brown, blue and turquoise	3·50	2·75
802	-	5f. sepia, blue and brown (air)	5·00	7·00

DESIGNS: 48×27 mm—Rally planes: 2c. Renaux's Farman M.F.7 floatplane; 3c. Espanet's Nieuport 4 seaplane; 4c. Moineau's Breguet HU-3 seaplane; 5c. Roland Garros' Morane Saulnier Type I seaplane; 10c. Hirth's WDD Albatros seaplane; 15c. Prevost's Deperdussin Monocoque Racer. Famous planes and flights: 20c. Vickers-Vimy G-EAOU (Ross Smith: London–Port Darwin, 1919); 25c. Douglas World Cruiser seaplane (U.S. World Flight, 1924); 30c. Savoia Marchetti S-55M flying boat "Santa Maria" (De Pinedo's World Flight, 1925); 45c. Fokker F. VIIa/3m "Josephine Ford" (Flight over North Pole, Byrd and Bennett, 1925); 50c. Ryan NYP Special "Spirit of St. Louis" (1st solo crossing of N. Atlantic, Lindbergh, 1927); 65c. Breguet 19 Super Bidon TR "Point d'Interrogation" (Paris–New York, Coste and Bellonte, 1930); 95c. Latecoere 28-3 seaplane F-AJNQ "Comte de la Vaulx" (Dakar–Natal, first S. Atlantic airmail flight, Mermoz, 1930); 1f. Dornier Do-X flying boat (Germany–Rio de Janeiro, Christiansen, 1930); 5f. Convair B-58 Hustler (New York–Paris in 3 hours, 19'41' Major Payne, U.S.A.F., 1961).

177 Aquatic Stadium

1964. Precancelled.

803	**177**	10c. multicoloured	2·50	2·00
803a	**177**	15c. multicoloured	1·00	1·00
804	**177**	25c. turquoise, blue & blk	1·00	1·00
805	**177**	50c. violet, turq & blk	2·00	2·00

The "1962" date has been obliterated with two bars. See also Nos. 949/51a and 1227/30.

178 Europa "Flower"

1964. Europa.

806	**178**	25c. red, green and blue	1·00	50
807	**178**	50c. brown, bistre and blue	2·00	1·50

179 Weightlifting

1964. Olympic Games, Tokyo and Innsbruck.

808	**179**	1c. red, brown and blue (postage)	10	10
809	-	2c. red, green and olive	10	10
810	-	3c. blue, brown and red	10	10
811	-	4c. green, olive and red	10	10
812	-	5f. red, brown and blue (air)	3·00	3·00

DESIGNS: 2c. Judo; 3c. Pole vaulting; 4c. Archery; 5f. Bobsleighing.

180 Pres. Kennedy and Space Capsule

1964. Pres. Kennedy Commemoration.

813	**180**	50c. indigo and blue	70	70

181 Monaco and Television Set

1964. 5th Int Television Festival, Monte Carlo.

814	**181**	50c. brown, blue and red	60	60

182 F. Mistral and Statue

1964. 50th Death Anniv of Frederic Mistral (poet).

815	**182**	1f. brown and olive	70	70

183 Scales of Justice

1964. 15th Anniv of Declaration of Human Rights.

816	**183**	1f. green and brown	70	70

184 Route Map from Minsk

1964. 34th Monte Carlo Rally.

817	**184**	1f. brown, turq & ochre	1·70	1·70

185 FIFA Emblem

1964. 60th Anniv of Federation Internationale de Football Association (FIFA).

818	**185**	1f. bistre, blue and red	1·20	1·20

186 "Syncom 2" and Globe

1965. Centenary of I.T.U.

819	**186**	5c. grn & ultram (postage)	10	20
820	-	10c. chestnut, brown & bl	10	20
821	-	12c. purple, red and grey	10	20
822	-	18c. blue, red and purple	20	20
823	-	25c. violet, bistre & purple	30	30
824	-	30c. bistre, brown & sepia	35	35
825	-	50c. blue and green	40	40
826	-	60c. blue and brown	1·20	1·00
827	-	70c. sepia, orange and blue	1·30	1·10
828	-	95c. black, indigo and blue	1·60	1·30
829	-	1f. brown and blue	2·30	2·00
830	-	10f. green, bl & brn (air)	6·00	5·00

DESIGNS—HORIZ (as Type **186**): 10c. "Echo 2"; 18c. "Lunik 3"; 30c. A. G. Bell and telephone; 50c. S. Morse and telegraph; 60c. E. Belin and "belinograph". (48½×27 mm): 25c. "Telstar" and Pleumeur-Bodou Station; 70c. Roman beacon and Chappe's telegraph; 95c. Cable ships "Great Eastern" and "Alsace"; 1f. E. Branly, G. Marconi and English Channel. VERT (as Type **186**): 12c. "Relay"; 10f. Monte Carlo television transmitter.

187 Europa "Sprig"

1965. Europa.

831	**187**	30c. brown and green	2·50	1·00
832	**187**	60c. violet and red	3·50	1·50

188 Monaco Palace (18th cent)

1966. 750th Anniv of Monaco Palace.

833	**188**	10c. violet, green and blue	10	20
834	-	12c. bistre, blue and black	10	20
835	-	18c. green, black and blue	20	30
836	-	30c. brown, black and blue	30	30
837	-	60c. green, blue and bistre	1·00	1·00
838	-	1f.30 brown and green	2·00	1·90

DESIGNS (Different views of Palace): 12c. 17th century; 18c. 18th century; 30c. 19th century; 60c. 19th century; 1f.30, 20th century.

189 Dante

1966. 700th Anniv of Dante's Birth.

839	**189**	30c. green, deep green and red	40	40
840	-	60c. blue, turquoise & grn	70	70
841	-	70c. black, green and red	80	80
842	-	95c. blue, violet and purple	1·00	1·00
843	-	1f. turquoise, blue & dp bl	1·30	1·30

DESIGNS (Scenes from Dante's works): 60c. Dante harassed by the panther (envy); 70c. Crossing the 5th circle; 95c. Punishment of the arrogant; 1f. Invocation of St. Bernard.

190 "The Nativity"

1966. World Association of Children's Friends (A.M.A.D.E.).

844	**190**	30c. brown	35	35

191 Route Map from London

1966. 35th Monte Carlo Rally.

845	**191**	1f. blue, purple and red	1·70	1·70

192 Princess Grace with Children

1966. Air. Princess Stephanie's 1st Birthday.

846	**192**	3f. brown, blue and violet	2·75	2·20

193 Casino in 19th Century

1966. Centenary of Monte Carlo.

847	-	12c. black, red and blue (postage)	10	10
848	**193**	25c. multicoloured	15	20
849	-	30c. multicoloured	20	20
850	-	40c. multicoloured	20	35
851	-	60c. multicoloured	55	55
852	-	70c. blue and lake	55	55
853	-	95c. black and purple	1·50	1·50
854	-	1f.30 purple, brown and chestnut	1·70	1·70
855	-	5f. lake, ochre and blue (air)	3·25	3·25

DESIGNS—VERT: 12c. Prince Charles III. HORIZ (as Type **143**): 40c. Charles III Monument; 95c. Massenet and Saint-Saens; 1f.30, Faure and Ravel. (48×27 mm): 30c. F. Blanc, originator of Monte Carlo, and view of 1860; 60c. Prince Rainier III and projected esplanade; 70c. Rene Blum and Diaghilev, ballet character from "Petrouchka". (36×36 mm): 5f. Interior of Opera House, 1879.

194 Europa "Ship"

1966. Europa.

856	**194**	30c. orange	1·10	55
857	**194**	60c. green	2·20	1·70

195 Prince Rainier and Princess Grace

1966. Air.

858	**195**	2f. slate and red	1·70	1·10
859	**195**	3f. slate and green	3·25	2·00
860	**195**	5f. slate and blue	4·50	2·40
860a	**195**	10f. slate and bistre	7·75	4·50
860b	**195**	20f. brown and orange	70·00	50·00

196 Prince Albert I and Yachts "Hirondelle I" and "Princess Alice"

1966. 1st International Oceanographic History Congress, Monaco.

861	**196**	1f. lilac and blue	1·10	1·10

197 "Learning to Write"

1966. 20th Anniv of UNESCO.

862	**197**	30c. purple and mauve	20	20
863	**197**	60c. brown and blue	45	45

198 T.V. Screen, Cross and Monaco Harbour

1966. 10th Meeting of International Catholic Television Association (U.N.D.A.), Monaco.

864	**198**	60c. red, purple & crimson	45	35

199 "Precontinent III"

1966. 1st Anniv of Underwater Research Craft "Precontinent III".

865	**199**	1f. yellow, brown and blue	75	55

200 W.H.O. Building

1966. Inaug of W.H.O. Headquarters, Geneva.

866	**200**	30c. brown, green and blue	20	20
867	**200**	60c. brown, red and green	45	45

201 Bugatti, 1931

1967. 25th Motor Grand Prix, Monaco. Multicoloured. (a) Postage.

868	1c. Type **201**	10	20
869	2c. Alfa-Romeo, 1932	10	20
870	5c. Mercedes, 1936	10	20
871	10c. Maserati, 1948	10	20
872	18c. Ferrari, 1955	90	55
873	20c. Alfa-Romeo, 1950	20	20
874	25c. Maserati, 1957	35	35
875	30c. Cooper-Climax, 1958	55	35
876	40c. Lotus-Climax, 1960	90	65
877	50c. Lotus-Climax, 1961	1·10	90
878	60c. Cooper-Climax, 1962	1·70	1·20
879	70c. B.R.M., 1963–6	2·20	1·90
880	1f. Walter Christie, 1907	2·75	2·20
881	2f.30 Peugeot, 1910	4·50	3·50

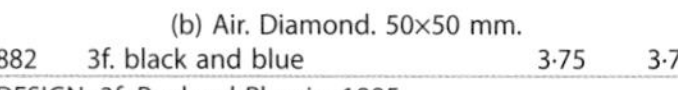

(b) Air. Diamond. 50×50 mm.

882	3f. black and blue	3·75	3·75

DESIGN: 3f. Panhard-Phenix, 1895.

202 Dog (Egyptian bronze)

1967. Int Cynological Federation Congress, Monaco.

883	**202**	30c. black, purple & green	55	55

203 View of Monte Carlo

1967. International Tourist Year.

884	**203**	30c. brown, green and blue	55	55

204 Pieces on Chessboard

1967. Int Chess Grand Prix, Monaco.

885	**204**	60c. black, plum and blue	1·10	1·10

205 Melvin Jones (founder), Lions Emblem and Monte Carlo

1967. 50th Anniv of Lions International.

886	**205**	60c. blue, ultramarine and brown	75	75

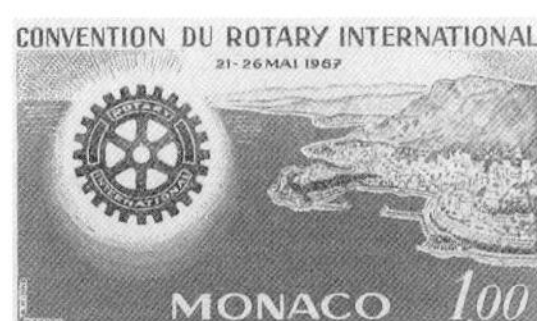

206 Rotary Emblem and Monte Carlo

1967. Rotary International Convention.

887	**206**	1f. bistre, blue and green	1·10	1·10

207 Fair Buildings

1967. World Fair, Montreal.

888	**207**	1f. red, slate and blue	75	75

208 Squiggle on Map of Europe

1967. European Migration Committee (C.I.M.E.).

889	**208**	1f. brown, bistre and blue	75	75

209 Cogwheels

1967. Europa.

890	**209**	30c. violet, purple and red	1·10	55
891	**209**	60c. green, turq & emer	2·20	1·10

210 Dredger and Coastal Chart

1967. 9th Int Hydrographic Congress, Monaco.

892	**210**	1f. brown, blue and green	75	75

211 Marie Curie and Scientific Equipment

1967. Birth Centenary of Marie Curie.

893	**211**	1f. blue, olive and brown	75	75

212 Skiing

1967. Winter Olympic Games, Grenoble.

894	**212**	2f.30 brown, blue & slate	2·10	1·70

213 "Prince Rainier I" (E. Charpentier)

1967. Paintings. "Princes and Princesses of Monaco". Multicoloured.

895	1f. Type **213**	90	90
896	1f. "Lucien Grimaldi" (A. di Predis)	90	90

See also Nos. 932/3, 958/9, 1005/6, 1023/4, 1070/1, 1108/9, 1213/14, 1271/2, 1325, 1380/1, 1405/6, 1460/1 and 1531/2.

214 Putting the Shot

1968. Olympic Games, Mexico.

897	**214**	20c. blue, brown and green (postage)	20	20

898	-	30c. brown, blue and plum	35	35
899	-	60c. blue, purple and red	45	45
900	-	70c. red, blue and ochre	55	55
901	-	1f. blue, brown and orange	90	90
902	-	2f.30 olive, blue and lake	2·30	2·30
903	-	3f. blue, violet & grn (air)	1·70	1·70

DESIGNS: 30c. High-jumping; 60c. Gymnastics; 70c. Water-polo; 1f. Greco-Roman wrestling; 2f.30, Gymnastics (different); 3f. Hockey.

215 "St. Martin"

1968. 20th Anniv of Monaco Red Cross.

904	**215**	2f.30 blue and brown	1·70	1·40

216 "Anemones" (after Raoul Dufy)

1968. Monte Carlo Floral Exhibitions.

905	**216**	1f. multicoloured	1·30	1·10

217 Insignia of Prince Charles III and Pope Pius IX

1968. Centenary of "Nullius Diocesis" Abbey.

906	**217**	10c. brown and red	10	20
907	-	20c. red, green and brown	20	20
908	-	30c. brown and blue	35	35
909	-	60c. brown, blue and green	45	45
910	-	1f. indigo, bistre and blue	75	75

DESIGNS—VERT: 20c. "St. Nicholas" (after Louis Brea); 30c. "St. Benedict" (after Simone Martini); 60c. Subiaco Abbey. HORIZ: 1f. Old St. Nicholas' Church (on site of present cathedral).

218 Europa "Key"

1968. Europa.

911	**218**	30c. red and orange	1·70	1·10
912	**218**	60c. blue and red	2·75	1·70
913	**218**	1f. brown and green	3·75	2·75

219 First Locomotive on Monaco Line, 1868

1968. Centenary of Nice–Monaco Railway.

914	**219**	20c. black, blue and purple	90	55

915	-	30c. black, blue and olive	1·10	90
916	-	60c. black, blue and ochre	1·90	1·70
917	-	70c. black, violet & brown	3·25	2·40
918	-	1f. black, blue and red	5·00	3·75
919	-	2f.30 blue, black and red	7·25	5·50

DESIGNS: 30c. Class 220-C steam locomotive, 1898; 60c. Class 230-C steam locomotive, 1910; 70c. Class 231-F steam locomotive, 1925; 1f. Class 241-A steam locomotive, 1932; 2f.30, Class BB 25200 electric locomotive, 1968.

220 Chateaubriand and Combourg Castle

1968. Birth Centenary of Chateaubriand (novelist).

920	**220**	10c. plum, green & myrtle	10	10
921	-	20c. violet, purple and blue	10	10
922	-	25c. brown, violet and blue	20	20
923	-	30c. violet, choc & brn	30	35
924	-	60c. brown, green and red	50	55
925	-	2f.30 brown, mauve & bl	2·10	1·90

Scenes from Chateaubriand's novels: 20c. "Le Genie du Christianisme"; 25c. "Rene"; 30c. "Le Dernier Abencerage"; 60c. "Les Martyrs"; 2f.30, "Atala".

221 Law Courts, Paris, and statues–"La France et la Fidelite"

1968. Birth Centenary of J. F. Bosio (Monegasque sculptor).

926	**221**	20c. brown and purple	20	20
927	-	25c. brown and red	35	30
928	-	30c. blue and green	35	35
929	-	60c. green and myrtle	75	55
930	-	2f.30 black and slate	1·70	1·10

DESIGNS—VERT (26×36 mm): 25c. "Henry IV as a Child"; 30c. "J. F. Bosio" (lithograph); 60c. "Louis XIV". HORIZ (as Type **221**): 2f.30, "Napoleon I, Louis XVIII and Charles X".

222 W.H.O. Emblem

1968. 20th Anniv of W.H.O.

931	**222**	60c. multicoloured	35	35

1968. Paintings. "Princes and Princesses of Monaco". As T 213. Multicoloured.

932	1f. "Prince Charles II" (Mimault)	1·00	90
933	2f.30 "Princess Jeanne Grimaldi" (Mimault)	1·90	1·80

223 The Hungarian March

1969. Death Centenary of Hector Berlioz (composer).

934	**223**	10c. brown, violet and green (postage)	10	20
935	-	20c. brown, olive & mauve	10	20
936	-	25c. brown, blue & mauve	20	20
937	-	30c. black, green and blue	30	35
938	-	40c. red, black and slate	35	35
939	-	50c. brown, slate & purple	45	45
940	-	70c. brown, slate and green	50	50
941	-	1f. black, mauve & brown	55	55
942	-	1f.15 black, blue & turq	1·10	90
943	-	2f. black, blue & grn (air)	1·70	1·70

DESIGNS—HORIZ: 20c. Mephistopheles appears to Faust; 25c. Auerbach's tavern; 30c. Sylphs' ballet; 40c. Minuet of the goblins; 50c. Marguerite's bedroom; 70c. "Forests and caverns"; 1f. The journey to Hell; 1f.15, Heaven; All scenes from Berlioz's "The Damnation of Faust". VERT: 2f. Bust of Berlioz.

224 "St. Elisabeth of Hungary"

1969. Monaco Red Cross.

944	**224**	3f. blue, brown and red	2·20	2·20

225 "Napoleon I" (P. Delaroche)

1969. Birth Bicentenary of Napoleon Bonaparte.

945	**225**	3f. multicoloured	2·20	2·20

226 Colonnade

1969. Europa.

946	**226**	40c. red and purple	1·70	1·10
947	**226**	70c. blue, brown and black	3·25	2·20
948	**226**	1f. ochre, brown and blue	5·50	3·25

1969. Precancelled. As T 177. No date.

949	22c. brown, blue and black	55	55
949a	26c. violet, blue and black	55	55
949b	30c. multicoloured	55	55
950	35c. multicoloured	55	55
950a	45c. multicoloured	1·10	1·10
951	70c. black and blue	1·10	1·10
951a	90c. green, blue and black	2·20	2·20

227 "Head of Woman" (Da Vinci)

1969. 450th Death Anniv of Leonardo da Vinci.

952	**227**	30c. brown	35	35
953	-	40c. red and brown	45	35
954	-	70c. green	50	35
955	-	80c. sepia	55	55
956	-	1f.15 brown	1·20	90
957	-	3f. brown	2·75	2·30

DRAWINGS: 40c. Self-portrait; 70c. "Head of an Old Man"; 80c. "Head of St. Madeleine"; 1f.15, "Man's Head"; 3f. "The Condottiere".

1969. Paintings. "Princes and Princesses of Monaco". As T 213. Multicoloured.

958	1f. "Prince Honore II" (Champaigne)	1·10	90
959	3f. "Princess Louise-Hippolyte" (Champaigne)	2·00	1·80

228 Marine Fauna, King Alfonso XIII of Spain and Prince Albert I of Monaco

1969. 50th Anniv of Int Commission for Scientific Exploration of the Mediterranean, Madrid.

960	**228**	40c. blue and black	55	55

229 I.L.O. Emblem

1969. 50th Anniv of I.L.O.

961	**229**	40c. multicoloured	55	55

230 Aerial View of Monaco and T.V. Camera

1969. 10th International Television Festival.

962	**230**	40c. purple, lake and blue	55	55

231 J.C.C. Emblem

1969. 25th Anniv of Junior Chamber of Commerce.

963	**231**	40c. violet, bistre and blue	55	55

232 Alphonse Daudet and Scenes from "Lettres"

1969. Centenary of Daudet's "Lettres de Mon Moulin".

964	**232**	30c. lake, violet and green	20	35
965	-	40c. green, brown and blue	35	45
966	-	70c. multicoloured	75	55
967	-	80c. violet, brown & green	90	65
968	-	1f.15 brown, orange & bl	1·10	1·10

DESIGNS (Scenes from the book): 40c. "Installation" (Daudet writing); 70c. "Mule, Goat and Wolf"; 80c. "Gaucher's Elixir" and "The Three Low Masses"; 1f.15, Daudet drinking, "The Old Man" and "The Country Sub-Prefect".

233 Conference Building, Albert I and Rainier III

1970. Interparliamentary Union's Spring Meeting, Monaco.

969	**233**	40c. black, red and purple	35	35

234 Baby Common Seal

1970. Protection of Baby Seals.

970	**234**	40c. drab, blue and purple	1·10	1·10

235 Japanese Print

1970. Expo 70.

971	**235**	20c. brown, green and red	20	20
972	-	30c. brown, buff and green	30	30
973	-	40c. bistre and violet	35	35
974	-	70c. grey and red	90	90
975	-	1f.15 red, green & purple	1·10	1·10

DESIGNS—VERT: 30c. Manchurian Cranes (birds); 40c. Shinto temple gateway. HORIZ: 70c. Cherry blossom; 1f.15, Monaco Palace and Osaka Castle.

236 Dobermann

1970. International Dog Show, Monte Carlo.

976	**236**	40c. black and brown	2·00	1·40

237 Apollo

1970. 20th Anniv of World Federation for Protection of Animals.

977	**237**	30c. black, red and blue	45	55
978	-	40c. brown, blue and green	90	65
979	-	50c. brown, ochre and blue	1·20	75
980	-	80c. brown, blue and green	2·75	2·20
981	-	1f. brown, bistre and slate	3·25	3·50
982	-	1f.15 brown, green & blue	4·50	3·75

DESIGNS—HORIZ: 40c. Basque ponies; 50c. Common seal. VERT: 80c. Chamois; 1f. White-tailed sea eagles; 1f.15, European otter.

238 "St. Louis" (King of France)

1970. Monaco Red Cross.

983	**238**	3f. green, brown and slate	2·20	2·75

See also Nos. 1022, 1041, 1114, 1189 and 1270.

239 "Roses and Anemones" (Van Gogh)

1970. Monte Carlo Flower Show.

984	**239**	3f. multicoloured	3·25	3·50

See also Nos. 1042 and 1073.

240 Moon Plaque, Presidents Kennedy and Nixon

1970. 1st Man on the Moon (1969). Multicoloured.

985	40c. Type **240**	65	75
986	80c. Astronauts on Moon	1·10	1·10

241 New U.P.U. Building and Monument

1970. New U.P.U. Headquarters Building.

987	**241**	40c. brown, black & green	35	35

242 "Flaming Sun"

1970. Europa.

988	**242**	40c. purple	1·70	1·10
989	**242**	80c. green	3·25	2·20
990	**242**	1f. blue	5·50	3·25

243 Camargue Horse

1970. Horses.

991	**243**	10c. slate, olive and blue (postage)	20	20
992	-	20c. brown, olive and blue	20	35
993	-	30c. brown, green and blue	75	90
994	-	40c. grey, brown and slate	1·90	1·30
995	-	50c. brown, olive and blue	2·75	1·70
996	-	70c. brown, orange & grn	4·25	3·25
997	-	85c. blue, green and olive	4·50	3·50
998	-	1f.15 black, green & blue	4·50	3·50
999	-	3f. multicoloured (air)	2·75	2·75

HORSES—HORIZ: 20c. Anglo-Arab; 30c. French saddle-horse; 40c. Lippizaner; 50c. Trotter; 70c. English thoroughbred; 85c. Arab; 1f.15, Barbary. DIAMOND (50×50 mm): 3f. Rock-drawings of horses in Lascaux grotto.

244 Dumas, D'Artagnan and the Three Musketeers

1970. Death Centenary of Alexandre Dumas (pere) (author).

1000	**244**	30c. slate, brown and blue	35	20

245 Henri Rougier and Voisin "Boxkite"

1970. 60th Anniv of First Mediterranean Flight.

1001	**245**	40c. brown, blue and slate	40	20

246 De Lamartine and scene from "Meditations Poetiques"

1970. 150th Anniv of "Meditations Poetiques" by Alphonse de Lamartine (writer).

1002	**246**	80c. brown, blue & turq	45	55

247 Beethoven

1970. Birth Bicentenary of Beethoven.

1003	**247**	1f.30 brown and red	3·25	2·20

1970. 50th Death Anniv of Modigliani. Vert Painting as T 213. Multicoloured.

1004	3f. "Portrait of Dedie"	4·50	3·25

1970. Paintings. "Princes and Princesses of Monaco". As T 213.

1005	1f. red and black	90	90
1006	3f. multicoloured	2·20	2·20

PORTRAITS: 1f. "Prince Louis I" (F. de Troy); 3f. "Princess Charlotte de Gramont" (S. Bourdon).

248 Cocker Spaniel

1971. International Dog Show, Monte Carlo.

1007	**248**	50c. multicoloured	3·75	3·00

See also Nos. 1036, 1082, 1119, 1218 and 1239.

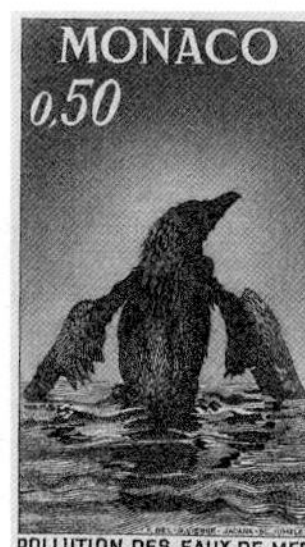

249 Razorbill

1971. Campaign Against Pollution of the Sea.

1008	**249**	50c. indigo and blue	75	75

250 Hand holding Emblem

1971. 7th Int Blood Donors Federation Congress.

1009	**250**	80c. red, violet and grey	55	55

251 Sextant, Scroll and Underwater Scene

1971. 50th Anniv of Int Hydrographic Bureau.

1010	**251**	80c. brown, green & slate	75	75

252 Detail of Michelangelo Painting ("The Arts")

1971. 25th Anniv of UNESCO.

1011	**252**	30c. brown, blue & violet	20	35
1012	-	50c. blue and brown	20	35
1013	-	80c. brown and green	35	45
1014	-	1f.30 green	1·10	75

DESIGNS—VERT: 50c. Alchemist and dish aerial ("Sciences"); 1f.30, Prince Pierre of Monaco (National UNESCO Commission). HORIZ: 80c. Ancient scribe, book and T.V. screen ("Culture").

253 Europa Chain

1971. Europa.

1015	**253**	50c. red	2·20	1·70
1016	**253**	80c. blue	3·75	2·20
1017	**253**	1f.30 green	7·25	3·75

254 Old Bridge, Sospel

1971. Protection of Historic Monuments.

1018	**254**	50c. brown, blue & green	35	40
1019	-	80c. brown, green & grey	55	45
1020	-	1f.30 red, green & brown	90	90
1021	-	3f. slate, blue and olive	2·20	1·70

DESIGNS—HORIZ: 80c. Roquebrune Chateau; 1f.30, Grimaldi Chateau, Cagnes-sur-Mer. VERT: 3f. Roman "Trophy of the Alps", La Turbie.

1971. Monaco Red Cross. As T 238.

1022	3f. brown, olive and green	2·20	2·30

DESIGN: 3f. St. Vincent de Paul.

1972. Paintings. "Princes and Princesses of Monaco". As T 213. Multicoloured.

1023	1f. "Prince Antoine I" (Rigaud)	90	90
1024	3f. "Princess Marie de Lorraine" (18th-century French School)	1·80	2·20

255 La Fontaine and Animal Fables (350th)

1972. Birth Anniversaries (1971).

1025	**255**	50c. brown, emer & grn	90	55
1026	-	1f.30 purple, black & red	1·30	1·10

DESIGN: 1f.30, Baudelaire, nudes and cats (150th).

256 Saint-Saens and scene from Opera, "Samson and Delilah"

1972. 50th Death Anniv (1971) of Camile Saint-Saens.

1027	**256**	90c. brown and sepia	75	65

257 Battle Scene

1972. 400th Anniv (1971) of Battle of Lepanto.

1028	**257**	1f. blue, brown and red	65	55

258 "Christ before Pilate" (engraving by Durer)

1972. 500th Birth Anniv (1971) of Albrecht Durer.

1029	**258**	2f. black and brown	2·20	2·00

259 "The Cradle" (B. Morisot)

1972. 25th Anniv (1971) of UNICEF.

1030	**259**	2f. multicoloured	2·30	1·80

260 "Gilles" (Watteau)

1972. 250th Death Anniv (1971) of Watteau.

1031	**260**	3f. multicoloured	3·75	2·75

261 Santa Claus

1972. Christmas (1971).
1032 **261** 30c. red, blue and brown 20 35
1033 **261** 50c. red, green & orange 20 35
1034 **261** 90c. red, blue and brown 65 65

262 Class 743 Steam Locomotive, Italy, and TGV 001 Turbotrain, France

1972. 50th Anniv of International Railway Union.
1035 **262** 50c. purple, lilac and red 1·40 1·10

1972. Int Dog Show, Monte Carlo. As T 248.
1036 60c. multicoloured 3·75 2·75
DESIGN: 60c. Great Dane.

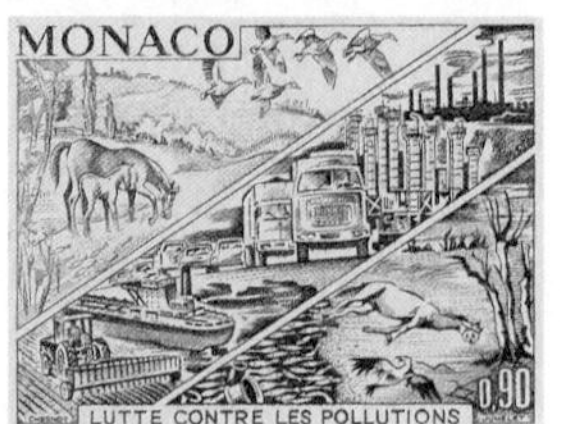

263 "Pollution Kills"

1972. Anti-pollution Campaign.
1037 **263** 90c. brown, green & black 1·00 65

264 Ski-jumping

1972. Winter Olympic Games, Sapporo, Japan.
1038 **264** 90c. black, red and green 1·00 75

1972. Europa.
1039 **265** 50c. blue and orange 3·75 1·70
1040 **265** 90c. blue and green 5·00 3·75

265 "Communications"

1972. Monaco Red Cross. As T 238.
1041 3f. brown and purple 2·00 2·20
DESIGN: 3f. St. Francis of Assisi.

1972. Monte Carlo Flower Show. As T 239.
1042 3f. multicoloured 6·00 4·50
DESIGN: 3f. "Vase of Flowers" (Cezanne).

266 "SS. Giovanni e Paolo" (detail, Canaletto)

1972. UNESCO "Save Venice" Campaign.
1043 **266** 30c. red 35 35
1044 - 60c. violet 65 65
1045 - 2f. blue 1·80 1·90

DESIGNS—27×48 mm: 60c. "S. Pietro di Castello" (F. Guradi). As Type **266**: 2f. "Piazetta S. Marco" (B. Bellotto).

267 Dressage

1972. Olympic Games, Munich. Equestrian Events.
1046 **267** 60c. brown, blue and lake 1·10 1·10
1047 - 90c. lake, brown and blue 1·40 1·40
1048 - 1f.10 blue, lake & brown 2·20 2·20
1049 - 1f.40 brown, lake & blue 3·50 3·50
DESIGNS: 90c. Cross country; 1f.10, Show jumping (wall); 1f.40, Show jumping (parallel bars).

268 Escoffier and Birthplace

1972. 125th Birth Anniv of Auguste Escoffier (master chef).
1050 **268** 45c. black and brown 45 55

269 Drug Addiction

1972. Campaign Against Drugs.
1051 **269** 50c. red, brown & orange 65 55
1052 **269** 90c. green, brown & blue 90 75
See also Nos. 1088/91 and 1280/1.

270 Globe, Birds and Animals

1972. 17th Int Congress of Zoology, Monaco.
1053 **270** 30c. green, brown and red 20 20
1054 - 50c. brown, purple and red 35 35
1055 - 90c. blue, brown and red 65 65
DESIGNS—HORIZ: 50c. VERT: 90c. Similar symbolic design.

271 Bouquet

1972. Monte Carlo Flower Show, 1973 (1st issue). Multicoloured.
1056 30c. Lilies in vase 1·10 55
1057 50c. Type **271** 1·40 1·10
1058 90c. Flowers in vase 2·75 2·00
See also Nos. 1073, 1105/7, 1143/4, 1225/6, 1244, 1282/3 and 1316/17.

272 "The Nativity" and Child's face

1972. Christmas.
1059 **272** 30c. grey, blue and purple 20 20
1060 **272** 50c. red, purple & brown 30 20
1061 **272** 90c. violet, plum & pur 65 65

273 Louis Bleriot and Bleriot XI (Birth cent)

1972. Birth Anniversaries.
1062 **273** 30c. blue and brown 20 35
1063 - 50c. blue, turq & new blue 1·40 1·20
1064 - 90c. brown and buff 1·10 1·10
DESIGNS AND ANNIVERSARIES: 50c. Amundsen and polar scene (birth centenary); 90c. Pasteur and laboratory scene (150th birth anniv).

274 "Gethsemane"

1972. Protection of Historical Monuments. Frescoes by J. Canavesio, Chapel of Notre-Dame des Fontaines, La Brigue.
1065 **274** 30c. red 20 20
1066 - 50c. grey 40 40
1067 - 90c. green 55 55
1068 - 1f.40 red 1·00 1·00
1069 - 2f. purple 1·70 1·70
DESIGNS: 50c. "Christ Outraged"; 90c. "Ascent to Calvary"; 1f.40, "The Resurrection"; 2f. "The Crucifixion".

1972. Paintings. "Princes and Princesses of Monaco". As T 213. Multicoloured.
1070 1f. "Prince Jacques 1" (N. Largilliere) 90 90
1071 3f. "Princess Louise-Hippolyte" (J. B. Vanloo) 2·00 2·20

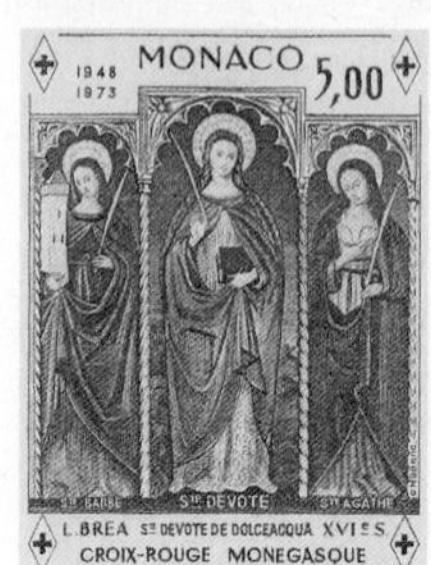

275 "St. Devote" (triptych by Louis Brea)

1973. 25th Anniv of Monaco Red Cross. Sheet 100×130 mm.
MS1072 **275** 5f. red 23·00 23·00

1973. Monte Carlo Flower Show (2nd issue). As T 239.
1073 3f.50 multicoloured 7·75 6·00
DESIGN: 3f.50, "Bouquet of Flowers".

276 Europa "Posthorn"

1973. Europa.
1074 **276** 50c. orange 5·50 3·75
1075 **276** 90c. green 8·25 6·50

277 Moliere and Characters from "Le Malade Imaginaire"

1973. 300th Death Anniv of Moliere.
1076 **277** 20c. red, brown and blue 50 55

278 Colette, Cat and Books

1973. Birth Anniversaries.
1077 **278** 30c. black, blue and red 1·10 90
1078 - 45c. multicoloured 2·75 2·40
1079 - 50c. lilac, purple and blue 45 45
1080 - 90c. multicoloured 65 65
DESIGNS AND ANNIVERSARIES—HORIZ: 30c., Type **278** (nature writer, birth cent); 45c. J.-H. Fabre and insects (entomologists, 150th birth anniv); 90c. Sir George Cayley and his "convertiplane" (aviation pioneer, birth bicent). VERT: 50c. Blaise Pascal (philosopher and writer, 350th birth anniv).

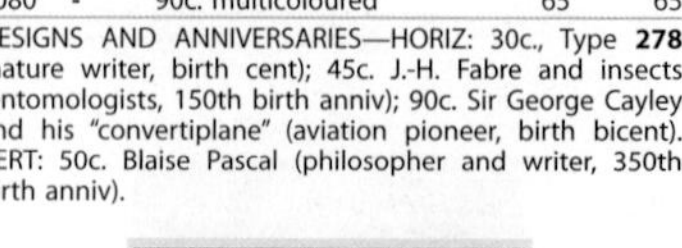

279 E. Ducretet, "Les Invalides" and Eiffel Tower

1973. 75th Anniv of Eugene Ducretet's First Hertzian Radio Link.
1081 **279** 30c. purple and brown 35 35

1973. International Dog Show, Monte Carlo. As T 248. Inscr "1973". Multicoloured.
1082 45c. Alsatian 15·00 10·50

280 C. Peguy and Chartres Cathedral

1973. Birth Bicentenary of Charles Peguy (writer).
1083 **280** 50c. brown, mauve & grey 35 35

281 Telecommunications Equipment

1973. 5th World Telecommunications Day.
1084 **281** 60c. violet, blue & brown 45 45

282 Stage Characters

1973. 5th World Amateur Theatre Festival.
1085 **282** 60c. lilac, blue and red 55 55

283 Ellis and Rugby Tackle

1973. 150th Anniv of Founding of Rugby Football by William Webb Ellis.

1086	**283**	90c. red, lake and brown	65	75

284 St. Theresa

1973. Birth Centenary of St. Theresa of Lisieux.

1087	**284**	1f.40 multicoloured	75	90

285 Drug Addiction

1973. Campaign Against Drugs.

1088	**285**	50c. red, green and blue	35	35
1089	-	50c. multicoloured	35	35
1090	**285**	90c. violet, green and red	75	75
1091	-	90c. multicoloured	75	75

DESIGN: Nos. 1089, 1091, Children, syringes and addicts.

286 "Institution of the Creche" (Giotto)

1973. 750th Anniv of St. Francis of Assisi Creche.

1092	**286**	30c. purple (postage)	50	55
1093	-	45c. red	90	90
1094	-	50c. brown	1·30	1·10
1095	-	1f. green	2·40	1·80
1096	-	2f. brown	5·00	5·00
1097	-	3f. blue (air)	3·25	3·25

DESIGN—HORIZ: 45c. "The Nativity" (School of F. Lippi); 50c. "The Birth of Jesus Christ" (Giotto). VERT: 1f. "The Nativity" (15th-century miniature); 2f. "The Birth of Jesus" (Fra Angelico); 3f. "The Nativity" (Flemish school).

287 Country Picnic

1973. 50th Anniv of National Committee for Monegasque Traditions.

1098	**287**	10c. blue, green & brown	10	15
1099	-	20c. violet, blue and green	20	20
1100	-	30c. sepia, brown & green	35	35
1101	-	45c. red, violet and purple	75	75
1102	-	50c. black, red and brown	1·00	1·00
1103	-	60c. red, violet and blue	1·10	1·10
1104	-	1f. violet, blue and brown	2·00	2·00

DESIGNS—VERT: 20c. Maypole dance. HORIZ: 30c. "U Bradi" (local dance); 45c. St. Jean fire-dance; 50c. Blessing the Christmas loaf; 60c. Blessing the sea, Festival of St. Devote; 1f. Corpus Christi procession.

1973. Monte Carlo Flower Show, 1974. As T 271. Multicoloured.

1105	45c. Roses and Strelitzia	2·20	1·40
1106	60c. Mimosa and myosotis	2·75	1·90
1107	1f. "Vase of Flowers" (Odilon Redon)	5·50	3·25

1973. Paintings. "Princes and Princesses of Monaco". As T 213. Multicoloured.

1108	2f. "Charlotte Grimaldi" (in day dress, P. Gobert)	2·75	2·30
1109	2f. "Charlotte Grimaldi" (in evening dress, P. Gobert)	2·75	2·30

288 Prince Rainier

1974. 25th Anniv of Prince Rainer's Accession. Sheet 100×130 mm.

MS1110	**288**	10f. black	11·00	11·00

289 U.P.U. Emblem and Symbolic Heads

1974. Centenary of Universal Postal Union.

1111	**289**	50c. purple and brown	35	35
1112	-	70c. multicoloured	55	55
1113	-	1f.10 multicoloured	1·10	1·10

DESIGNS: 70c. Hands holding letters; 1f.10, "Countries of the World" (famous buildings).

1974. Monaco Red Cross. As T 238.

1114	3f. blue, green and purple	2·20	1·90

DESIGN: 3f. St. Bernard of Menthon.

290 Farman, Farman F.60 Goliath and Farman H.F.III

1974. Birth Centenary of Henry Farman (aviation pioneer).

1115	**290**	30c. brown, purple & blue	35	35

291 Marconi, Circuit Plan and Destroyer

1974. Birth Centenary of Guglielmo Marconi (radio pioneer).

1116	**291**	40c. red, deep blue & blue	55	35

292 Duchesne and "Penicillium glaucum"

1974. Birth Centenary of Ernest Duchesne (microbiologist).

1117	**292**	45c. black, blue & purple	55	55

293 Forest and Engine

1974. 60th Death Anniv of Fernand Forest (motor engineer and inventor).

1118	**293**	50c. purple, red and black	55	35

1974. International Dog Show, Monte Carlo. As T 248, inscr "1974".

1119	60c. multicoloured	7·25	5·00

DESIGN: 60c. Schnauzer.

294 Ronsard and Characters from "Sonnet to Helene"

1974. 450th Birth Anniv of Pierre de Ronsard (poet).

1120	**294**	70c. brown and red	55	65

295 Sir Winston Churchill (after bust by O. Nemon)

1974. Birth Centenary of Sir Winston Churchill.

1121	**295**	1f. brown and grey	65	65

296 Interpol Emblem, and Views of Monaco and Vienna

1974. 60th Anniv of 1st International Police Judiciary Congress and 50th Anniv of International Criminal Police Organization (Interpol).

1122	**296**	2f. blue, brown and green	1·40	1·30

297 "The King of Rome" (Bosio)

1974. Europa. Sculptures by J. F. Bosio.

1123	**297**	45c. green and brown	2·20	1·80
1124	-	1f.10 bistre and brown	3·75	3·00
MS1125		170×140 mm. Nos. 1123/5 ×5	55·00	55·00

DESIGN: 1f.10, "Madame Elizabeth".

298 "The Box" (A. Renoir)

1974. "The Impressionists". Multicoloured.

1126	1f. Type **298**	2·75	2·75
1127	1f. "The Dance Class" (E. Degas)	2·75	2·75
1128	2f. "Impression-Sunrise" (C. Monet) (horiz)	6·00	6·00
1129	2f. "Entrance to Voisins Village" (C. Pissarro) (horiz)	6·00	6·00
1130	2f. "The Hanged Man's House" (P. Cezanne) (horiz)	6·00	6·00
1131	2f. "Floods at Port Marly" (A. Sisley) (horiz)	6·50	6·00

299 Tigers and Trainer

1974. 1st International Circus Festival, Monaco.

1132	**299**	2c. brown, green and blue	10	15
1133	-	3c. brown and purple	10	15
1134	-	5c. blue, brown and red	20	20
1135	-	45c. brown, black and red	65	75
1136	-	70c. multicoloured	1·20	1·00
1137	-	1f.10 brown, green and red	2·00	2·00
1138	-	5f. green, blue and brown	8·75	6·50

DESIGNS—VERT: 3c. Performing horse; 45c. Equestrian act; 1f.10, Acrobats; 5f. Trapeze act. HORIZ: 5c. Performing elephants; 70c. Clowns.

300 Honore II on Medal

1974. 350th Anniv of Monegasque Numismatic Art.

1139	**300**	60c. green and red	45	55

301 Marine Flora and Fauna

1974. 24th Congress of the International Commission for the Scientific Exploration of the Mediterranean. Multicoloured.

1140	45c. Type **301**	1·70	1·40
1141	70c. Sea-bed flora and fauna	2·75	1·90
1142	1f.10 Sea-bed flora and fauna (different)	3·75	3·25

Nos. 1141/2 are larger, size 52×31 mm.

1974. Monte Carlo Flower Show. As T 271. Multicoloured.

1143	70c. Honeysuckle and violets	1·70	1·10
1144	1f.10 Iris and chrysanthemums	2·75	1·80

302 Prince Rainier III (F. Messina)

303

1974

1145	**302**	60c. green (postage)	1·90	90
1146	**302**	80c. red	2·00	1·70
1147	**302**	80c. green	65	45
1148	**302**	1f. brown	3·75	1·90
1149	**302**	1f. red	1·00	65
1149a	**302**	1f. green	65	55
1149b	**302**	1f.10 green	1·00	75
1150	**302**	1f.20 violet	11·50	4·50
1150a	**302**	1f.20 red	1·00	65
1150b	**302**	1f.20 green	1·10	75
1151	**302**	1f.25 blue	2·40	1·30
1151a	**302**	1f.30 red	1·10	90
1152	**302**	1f.40 red	1·20	90
1152a	**302**	1f.50 black	1·30	90
1153	**302**	1f.60 grey	1·70	1·10
1153a	**302**	1f.70 blue	1·50	1·00
1153b	**302**	1f.80 blue	2·75	2·50
1154	**302**	2f. mauve	4·50	3·75
1154a	**302**	2f.10 brown	2·20	1·70
1155	**302**	2f.30 violet	3·75	2·30
1156	**302**	2f.50 black	3·50	2·75
1157	**302**	9f. violet	9·25	6·00
1158	**303**	10f. violet (air)	10·00	7·75
1159	**303**	15f. red	13·00	10·00
1160	**303**	20f. blue	19·00	13·00

304 Coastline, Monte Carlo

1974

1161	**304**	25c. blue, green & brown	3·75	1·10
1162	-	25c. brown, green & blue	35	45
1163	-	50c. brown and blue	3·75	1·70
1164	**304**	65c. blue, brown & green	45	55
1165	-	70c. multicoloured	90	75
1166	**304**	1f.10 brown, green & bl	3·25	2·20
1167	-	1f.10 black, brown & bl	1·10	90
1168	-	1f.30 brown, green & bl	1·20	75
1169	-	1f.40 green, grey & brn	3·75	2·20
1170	-	1f.50 green, blue & black	2·20	1·70
1171	-	1f.70 brown, green & bl	6·50	3·75
1172	-	1f.80 brown, green & bl	2·30	1·70
1173	-	2f.30 brown, grey & blue	3·75	2·20
1174	-	3f. brown, grey and green	9·25	6·50
1175	-	5f.50 brown, green & blue	15·00	13·00
1176	-	6f.50 brown, blue & grn	6·00	4·50

DESIGNS—VERT: 50c. Palace clock tower; 70c. Botanical gardens; 1f.30, Monaco Cathedral; 1f.40, 1f.50, Prince Albert I statue and Museum; 3f. Fort Antoine. HORIZ: 25c. (1162), 1f.70, "All Saints" Tower; 1f.10 (1167), Palais de Justice; 1f.80, 5f.50, La Condamine; 2f.30, North Galleries of Palace; 6f.50, Aerial view of hotels and harbour.

305 "Haagocereus chosicensis"

1975. Plants. Multicoloured.

1180	10c. Type **305**	20	20
1181	20c. "Matucana madisoniarum"	20	35
1182	30c. "Parodia scopaioides"	65	55
1183	85c. "Mediolobivia arachnacantha"	3·75	2·50
1184	1f.90 "Matucana yanganucensis"	6·00	4·50
1185	4f. "Echinocereus marksianus"	8·75	8·25

306 "Portrait of a Sailor" (P. Florence)

1975. Europa.

1186	**306**	80c. purple	3·25	2·20
1187	-	1f.20 blue	4·50	3·25
MS1188		170×130 mm. Nos. 1186/7 ×5	55·00	55·00

DESIGN: 1f.20, "St. Devote" (Ludovic Brea).

307 "St. Bernardin de Sienne"

1975. Monaco Red Cross.

1189	**307**	4f. blue and purple	3·25	2·75

308 "Prologue"

1975. Centenary of "Carmen" (opera by Georges Bizet).

1190	**308**	30c. violet, brown & blk	20	20
1191	-	60c. grey, green and red	35	45
1192	-	80c. green, brown & blk	90	75
1193	-	1f.40 purple, brn & ochre	1·10	1·30

DESIGNS—HORIZ: 60c. Lilla Pastia's tavern; 80c. "The Smuggler's Den"; 1f.40, "Confrontation at Seville".

309 Saint-Simon

1975. 300th Birth Anniv of Louis de Saint-Simon (writer).

1194	**309**	40c. blue	35	20

310 Dr. Albert Schweitzer

1975. Birth Centenary of Dr. Schweitzer (Nobel Peace Prize Winner).

1195	**310**	60c. red and brown	75	65

311 "Stamp" and Calligraphy

1975. "Arphila 75" International Stamp Exhibition, Paris.

1196	**311**	80c. brown and orange	90	65

312 Seagull and Sunrise

1975. International Exposition, Okinawa.

1197	**312**	85c. blue, green & orange	1·10	90

313 Pike smashing Crab

1975. Anti-cancer Campaign.

1198	**313**	1f. multicoloured	1·10	75

314 Christ with Crown of Thorns

1975. Holy Year.

1199	**314**	1f.15 black, brn & pur	1·10	90

315 Villa Sauber, Monte Carlo

1975. European Architectural Heritage Year.

1200	**315**	1f.20 green, brown & bl	1·10	1·10

316 Woman's Head and Globe

1975. International Women's Year.

1201	**316**	1f.20 multicoloured	1·10	90

317 Rolls-Royce "Silver Ghost" (1907)

1975. History of the Motor Car.

1202	**317**	5c. blue, green and brown	10	10
1203	-	10c. indigo and blue	15	15
1204	-	20c. blue, ultram & black	20	20
1205	-	30c. purple and mauve	35	35
1206	-	50c. blue, purple & mauve	1·10	1·10
1207	-	60c. red and green	1·70	1·70
1208	-	80c. indigo and blue	2·75	2·20
1209	-	85c. brown, orange & grn	3·75	3·25
1210	-	1f.20 blue, red and green	4·50	4·50
1211	-	1f.40 green and blue	6·50	4·75
1212	-	5f.50 blue, emerald and green	22·00	17·00

DESIGNS: 10c. Hispano-Suiza "H.6B" (1926); 20c. Isotta Fraschini "8A" (1928); 30c. Cord "L.29"; 50c. Voisin "V12" (1930); 60c. Duesenberg "SJ" (1933); 80c. Bugatti "57 C" (1938); 85c. Delahaye "135 M" (1940); 1f.20, Cisitalia "Pininfarina" (1945); 1f.40, Mercedes-Benz "300 SL" (1955); 5f.50, Lamborghini "Countach" (1974).

1975. Paintings. "Princes and Princesses of Monaco". As T 213. Multicoloured.

1213	2f. "Prince Honore III"	2·75	2·20
1214	4f. "Princess Catherine de Brignole"	5·00	3·75

318 Dog behind Bars

1975. 125th Birth Anniv of Gen. J. P. Delmas de Grammont (author of Animal Protection Code).

1215	**318**	60c. black and brown	1·70	1·10
1216	-	80c. black and brown	2·75	1·70
1217	-	1f.20 green and purple	3·75	3·25

DESIGNS—VERT: 80c. Cat chased up tree. HORIZ: 1f.20, Horse being ill-treated.

1975. International Dog Show, Monte Carlo. As T 248, but inscr "1975". Multicoloured.

1218	60c. black and purple	7·25	5·00

DESIGN: 60c. French poodle.

319 Maurice Ravel

1975. Birth Centenaries of Musicians.

1219	**319**	60c. brown and purple	1·10	65
1220	-	1f.20 black and purple	3·25	2·30

DESIGN: 1f.20, Johann Strauss (the younger).

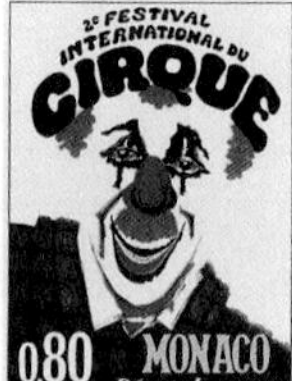

320 Circus Clown

1975. 2nd International Circus Festival.

1221	**320**	80c. multicoloured	1·70	1·30

321 Monaco Florin Coin, 1640

1975. Monaco Numismatics.

1222	**321**	80c. brown and blue	90	75

See also Nos. 1275, 1320 and 1448.

322 Andre Ampere with Electrical Meter

1975. Birth Centenary of Andre Ampere (physicist).

1223	**322**	85c. indigo and blue	1·10	90

323 "Lamentations for the Dead Christ"

1975. 500th Birth Anniv of Michelangelo.

1224	**323**	1f.40 olive and black	1·70	1·30

1975. Monte Carlo Flower Show (1976). As T 271. Multicoloured.

1225	60c. Bouquet of wild flowers	1·70	1·20
1226	80c. Ikebana flower arrangement	2·20	1·70

1975. Precancelled. Surch.

1227	42c. on 26c. violet, blue and black (No. 949a)	3·50	2·75
1228	48c. on 30c. multicoloured (No. 949b)	4·50	3·25
1229	70c. on 45c. multicoloured (No. 950a)	5·75	4·50
1230	1f.35 on 90c. green, blue and black (No. 951a)	7·25	6·00

325 Prince Pierre de Monaco

1976. 25th Anniv of Literary Council of Monaco.

1231	**325**	10c. black	20	20
1232	-	20c. blue and red	30	35
1233	-	25c. blue and red	35	45
1234	-	30c. brown	65	55
1235	-	50c. blue, red and purple	65	55
1236	-	60c. brown, grn & lt brn	90	55
1237	-	80c. purple and blue	1·70	1·10
1238	-	1f.20 violet, blue & mve	3·25	2·20

COUNCIL MEMBERS—HORIZ: 20c. A. Maurois and Colette; 25c. Jean and Jerome Tharaud; 30c. E. Henriot, M. Pagnol and G. Duhamel; 50c. Ph. Heriat, J. Supervielle and L. Pierard; 60c. R. Dorgeles, M. Achard and G. Bauer; 80c. F. Hellens, A. Billy and Mgr. Grente; 1f.20, J. Giono, L. Pasteur Vallery-Radot and M. Garcon.

326 Dachshunds

1976. International Dog Show, Monte Carlo.
1239 **326** 60c. multicoloured 10·00 6·50

327 Bridge Table and Monte Carlo Coast

1976. 5th Bridge Olympiad, Monte Carlo.
1240 **327** 60c. brown, green and red 65 65

328 Alexander Graham Bell and Early Telephone

1976. Telephone Centenary.
1241 **328** 80c. brown, light brown and grey 65 65

329 Federation Emblem on Globe

1976. 50th Anniv of International Philatelic Federation.
1242 **329** 1f.20 red, blue and green 90 75

330 U.S.A. 2c. Stamp, 1926

1976. Bicent of American Revolution.
1243 **330** 1f.70 black and purple 1·10 1·10

331 "The Fritillaries" (Van Gogh)

1976. Monte Carlo Flower Show.
1244 **331** 3f. multicoloured 17·00 11·00

332 Diving

1976. Olympic Games, Montreal.
1245 **332** 60c. brown and blue 45 55
1246 - 80c. blue, brown & green 55 65
1247 - 85c. blue, green & brown 65 75
1248 - 1f.20 brown, green & bl 1·10 90
1249 - 1f.70 brown, blue & grn 1·70 1·30
MS1250 150×145 mm. Nos. 1245/9 6·50 6·50

DESIGNS—VERT: 80c. Gymnastics; 85c. Hammer-throwing. HORIZ: 1f.20, Rowing; 1f.70, Boxing.

333 Decorative Plate

1976. Europa. Monegasque Ceramics. Multicoloured.
1251 80c. Type **333** 2·20 1·70
1252 1f.20 Grape-harvester (statuette) 3·75 2·75
MS1253 170×140 mm. Nos. 1251/2 ×5 55·00 55·00

334 Palace Clock Tower

1976. Precancelled.
1254 **334** 50c. red 65 65
1255 **334** 52c. orange 65 65
1256 **334** 54c. green 65 65
1257 **334** 60c. green 65 65
1258 **334** 62c. mauve 65 65
1259 **334** 68c. yellow 65 65
1260 **334** 90c. violet 1·70 1·70
1261 **334** 95c. red 1·70 1·70
1262 **334** 1f.05 brown 1·70 1·70
1263 **334** 1f.60 blue 2·50 2·50
1264 **334** 1f.70 turquoise 2·50 2·50
1265 **334** 1f.85 brown 2·50 2·50

335 "St. Louise de Marillac" (altar painting)

1976. Monaco Red Cross.
1270 **335** 4f. black, purple & green 3·25 3·25

1976. Paintings. "Princes and Princesses of Monaco". As T 213.
1271 2f. purple 3·25 2·75
1272 4f. multicoloured 6·00 4·50

DESIGNS: 2f. "Prince Honore IV"; 4f. "Princess Louise d'Aumont-Mazarin".

336 St. Vincent-de-Paul

1976. Centenary of St. Vincent-de-Paul Conference, Monaco.
1273 **336** 60c. black, brown & blue 55 45

337 Marie de Rabutin Chantal

1976. 350th Birth Anniv of Marquise de Sevigne (writer).
1274 **337** 80c. black, violet and red 65 65

338 Monaco 2g. "Honore II" Coin, 1640

1976. Monaco Numismatics.
1275 **338** 80c. blue and green 65 65

339 Richard Byrd, "Josephine Ford", Airship "Norge" and Roald Amundsen

1976. 50th Anniv of First Flights over North Pole.
1276 **339** 85c. black, blue and green 2·75 1·90

340 Gulliver and Lilliputians

1976. 250th Anniv of Jonathan Swift's "Gulliver's Travels".
1277 **340** 1f.20 multicoloured 1·30 75

341 Girl's Head and Christmas Decorations

1976. Christmas.
1278 **341** 60c. multicoloured 55 45
1279 **341** 1f.20 green, orge & pur 1·30 90

342 "Drug" Dagger piercing Man and Woman

1976. Campaign against Drug Abuse.
1280 **342** 80c. blue, orge & bronze 80 55
1281 **342** 1f.20 lilac, purple & brn 1·30 90

1976. Monte Carlo Flower Show (1977). As T 271. Multicoloured.
1282 80c. Flower arrangement 2·75 1·70
1283 1f. Bouquet of flowers 4·00 2·75

343 Circus Clown

1976. 3rd International Circus Festival, Monte Carlo.
1284 **343** 1f. multicoloured 3·25 1·90

344 Schooner "Hirondelle I"

1977. 75th Anniv of Publication of "Career of a Navigator" by Prince Albert I (1st issue). Illustrations by L. Tinayre.
1285 **344** 10c. brown, blue & turq 15 10
1286 - 20c. black, brown & lake 25 20
1287 - 30c. green, blue & orange 55 45
1288 - 80c. black, blue and red 80 65
1289 - 1f. black and brown 1·30 1·10
1290 - 1f.25 olive, green & violet 1·70 1·40
1291 - 1f.40 brown, olive & grn 2·75 2·20
1292 - 1f.90 blue, lt blue & red 5·25 3·25
1293 - 2f.50 brown, blue and turquoise 7·25 4·50

DESIGNS—VERT: 20c. Prince Albert I; 1f. Helmsman; 1f.90, Bringing in the trawl. HORIZ: 30c. Crew-members; 80c. "Hirondelle" in a gale; 1f.25, Securing the lifeboat; 1f.40, Shrimp fishing; 2f.50, Capture of an oceanic sunfish.

See also Nos. 1305/13.

345 Pyrenean Sheep and Mountain Dogs

1977. International Dog Show, Monte Carlo.
1294 **345** 80c. multicoloured 11·50 6·50

346 "Maternity" (M. Cassatt)

1977. World Association of the "Friends of Children".
1295 **346** 80c. deep brown, brown and black 2·00 1·70

347 Archers

1977. 10th International Archery Championships.
1296 **347** 1f.10 black, brown & bl 1·30 75

348 Charles Lindbergh and Ryan NYP "Spirit of St. Louis"

1977. 50th Anniv of Lindbergh's Transatlantic Flight.
1297 **348** 1f.90 light blue, blue and brown 2·75 1·90

349 "Harbour, Deauville"

1977. Birth Centenary of Raoul Dufy (painter).
1298 **349** 2f. multicoloured 8·00 5·00

350 "Portrait of a Young Girl"

1977. 400th Birth Anniv of Peter Paul Rubens (painter).

1299	**350**	80c. orange, brown & blk	1·30	1·10
1300	-	1f. red	1·70	1·40
1301	-	1f.40 orange and red	3·00	2·40

DESIGNS: 1f. "Duke of Buckingham"; 1f.40, "Portrait of a Child".

351 "L'Oreillon" Tower

1977. Europa. Views.

1302	**351**	1f. brown and blue	2·75	1·10
1303	-	1f.40 blue, brown and bistre	4·00	2·20
MS1304		169×130 mm. Nos. 1302/3 ×5	55·00	55·00

DESIGN: 1f.40, St. Michael's Church, Menton.

1977. 75th Anniv of Publication of "Career of a Navigator" by Prince Albert I (2nd issue). Illustrations by L. Tinayre. As T 344.

1305	10c. black and blue	15	20
1306	20c. blue	25	35
1307	30c. blue, light blue and green	40	45
1308	80c. brown, black and green	95	75
1309	1f. grey and green	1·20	1·10
1310	1f.25 black, brown and lilac	1·70	1·70
1311	1f.40 purple, blue and brown	3·00	2·75
1312	1f.90 black, blue and light blue	5·50	3·25
1313	3f. blue, brown and green	6·75	5·00

DESIGNS—HORIZ: 10c. "Princess Alice" (steam yacht) at Kiel; 20c. Ship's laboratory; 30c. "Princess Alice" in ice floes; 1f. Polar scene; 1f.25, Bridge of "Princess Alice" during snowstorm; 1f.40, Arctic camp; 1f.90, Ship's steam launch in floating ice; 3f. "Princess Alice" passing iceberg. VERT: 80c. Crewmen in Arctic dress.

352 Santa Claus & Sledge

1977. Christmas.

1314	**352**	80c. red, green and blue	95	55
1315	**352**	1f.40 multicoloured	1·30	90

1977. Monte Carlo Flower Show. As T 271. Mult.

1316	80c. Snapdragons and campanula	2·10	1·30
1317	1f. Ikebana	3·25	1·70

353 Face, Poppy and Syringe

1977. Campaign Against Drug Abuse.

1318	**353**	1f. black, red and violet	1·10	90

354 Clown and Flags

1977. 4th International Festival of Circus, Monaco.

1319	**354**	1f. multicoloured	3·25	2·20

355 Gold Coin of Honore II

1977. Monaco Numismatics.

1320	**355**	80c. brown and red	1·10	65

356 Mediterranean divided by Industry

1977. Protection of the Mediterranean Environment.

1321	**356**	1f. black, green and blue	1·10	90

357 Dr. Guglielminetti and Road Tarrers

1977. 75th Anniv of First Experiments at Road Tarring in Monaco.

1322	**357**	1f.10 black, bistre and brown	1·20	65

358 F.M.L.T. Badge and Monte Carlo

1977. 50th Anniv of Monaco Lawn Tennis Federation.

1323	**358**	1f. blue, red and brown	2·00	1·70

359 Wimbledon and First Championships

1977. Centenary of Wimbledon Lawn Tennis Championships.

1324	**359**	1f.40 grey, green & brown	2·75	2·20

1977. Paintings. "Princes and Princesses of Monaco". As T 213. Multicoloured.

1325	6f. "Prince Honore V"	6·75	5·50

360 St. Jean Bosco

1977. Monaco Red Cross. Monegasque Art.

1326	**360**	4f. green, brown and blue	4·00	2·75

1978. Precancelled. Surch.

1327	**334**	58c. on 54c. green	80	75
1328	**334**	73c. on 68c. yellow	1·20	1·20
1329	**334**	1f.15 on 1f.05 brown	2·75	2·40
1330	**334**	2f. on 1f.85 brown	3·00	2·75

362 Aerial Shipwreck from "L'Ile Mysterieuse"

1978. 150th Birth Anniv of Jules Verne.

1331	**362**	5c. brown, red and olive	15	20
1332	-	25c. turquoise, blue & red	20	20
1333	-	30c. blue, brown & lt blue	25	35
1334	-	80c. black, green & orge	65	65
1335	-	1f. brown, lake and blue	1·20	90
1336	-	1f.40 bistre, brown and green	1·30	1·10
1337	-	1f.70 brown, light blue and blue	2·50	1·70
1338	-	5f.50 violet and blue	7·00	4·50

DESIGNS: 25c. The abandoned ship from "L'Ile Mysterieuse"; 30c. The secret of the island from "L'Ile Mysterieuse"; 80c. "Robur the Conqueror"; 1f. "Master Zacharius"; 1f.40, "The Castle in the Carpathians"; 1f.70, "The Children of Captain Grant"; 5f.50, Jules Verne and allegories.

363 Aerial View of Congress Centre

1978. Inauguration of Monaco Congress Centre.

1339	**363**	1f. brown, blue and green	65	55
1340	-	1f.40 blue, brown & grn	1·00	90

DESIGN: 1f.40, View of Congress Centre from sea.

364 Footballers and Globe

1978. World Cup Football Championship, Argentina.

1341	**364**	1f. blue, slate and green	75	75

365 Antonio Vivaldi

1978. 300th Birth Anniv of Antonio Vivaldi (composer).

1342	**365**	1f. brown and red	1·00	1·00

366 "Ramoge" (research vessel) and Grimaldi Palace

1978. Environment Protection. "RAMOGE" Agreement.

1343	**366**	80c. multicoloured	65	65
1344	-	1f. red, blue and green	65	65

DESIGN—HORIZ (48×27 mm): 1f. Map of coastline between St. Raphael and Genes.

367 Monaco Cathedral

1978. Europa. Monaco Views.

1345	**367**	1f. green, brown and blue	1·90	1·10
1346	-	1f.40 brown, green & bl	2·50	2·20
MS1347		170×143 mm. Nos. 1345/6 ×5	50·00	50·00

DESIGN: 1f.40, View of Monaco from the east.

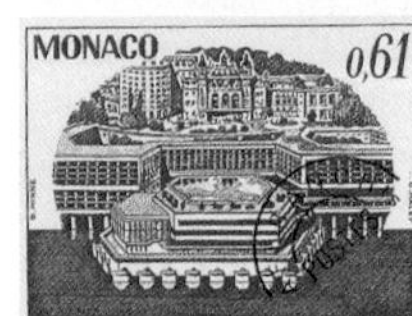

368 Monaco Congress Centre

1978. Precancelled.

1348	**368**	61c. orange	65	55
1349	**368**	64c. green	65	55
1350	**368**	68c. blue	65	55
1351	**368**	78c. purple	65	55
1352	**368**	83c. violet	65	55
1353	**368**	88c. orange	65	55
1354	**368**	1f.25 brown	1·50	1·30
1355	**368**	1f.30 red	1·50	1·30
1356	**368**	1f.40 green	1·50	1·30
1357	**368**	2f.10 blue	2·20	1·90
1358	**368**	2f.25 orange	2·20	1·90
1359	**368**	2f.35 mauve	2·20	1·90

369 "Cinderella"

1978. 350th Birth Anniv of Charles Perrault (writer).

1360	**369**	5c. red, olive and violet	25	20
1361	-	25c. black, brown & mve	25	20
1362	-	30c. green, lake & brown	25	20
1363	-	80c. multicoloured	75	65
1364	-	1f. red, brown and olive	1·00	90
1365	-	1f.40 mauve, ultramarine and blue	1·30	1·10
1366	-	1f.70 green, blue & grey	1·90	1·70
1367	-	1f.90 multicoloured	2·50	2·20
1368	-	2f.50 blue, orange & grn	3·75	3·25

DESIGNS: 25c. "Puss in Boots"; 30c. "The Sleeping Beauty"; 80c. "Donkey's Skin"; 1f. "Little Red Riding Hood"; 1f.40, "Bluebeard"; 1f.70, "Tom Thumb"; 1f.90, "Riquet with a Tuft"; 2f.50, "The Fairies".

370 "The Sunflowers" (Van Gogh)

1978. Monte Carlo Flower Show (1979) and 125th Birth Anniv of Vincent Van Gogh. Multicoloured.

1369	1f. Type **370**	5·75	3·25
1370	1f.70 "The Iris" (Van Gogh)	7·75	4·50

371 Afghan Hound

1978. International Dog Show, Monte Carlo. Multicoloured.

1371	1f. Type **371**	5·75	3·25
1372	1f.20 Borzoi	7·75	5·00

372 Girl with Letter

1978. Christmas.

1373	**372**	1f. brown, blue and red	90	75

373 Catherine and William Booth

1978. Centenary of Salvation Army.
1374 **373** 1f.70 multicoloured 1·80 1·50

374 Juggling Seals

1978. 5th International Circus Festival, Monaco.
1375 **374** 80c. orange, black & blue 75 65
1376 - 1f. multicoloured 1·30 1·10
1377 - 1f.40 brown, mauve and bistre 2·10 1·80
1378 - 1f.90 blue, lilac and mauve 2·50 2·75
1379 - 2f.40 multicoloured 4·50 3·25
DESIGNS—HORIZ: 1f.40, Horseback acrobatics; 1f.90, Musical monkeys; 2f.40, Trapeze. VERT: 1f. Lion tamer.

1978. Paintings. "Princes and Princesses of Monaco". As T 213. Multicoloured.
1380 2f. "Prince Florestan I" (G. Dauphin) 3·75 2·75
1381 4f. "Princess Caroline Gilbert de la Metz" (Marie Verroust) 6·50 5·00

375

1978. 150th Anniv of Henri Dunant (founder of Red Cross). Sheet 100×130 mm.
MS1382 **375** 5f. chocolate, crimson and red 7·00 7·25

376

1979. 21st Birthday of Prince Albert. Sheet 80×105 mm.
MS1383 **376** 10f. green and brown 11·50 11·50

377 "Jongleur de Notre-Dame" (Massenet)

1979. Centenary of "Salle Garnier" (Opera House) (1st issue).
1384 **377** 1f. blue, orange & mauve 75 65
1385 - 1f.20 violet, black & turq 1·30 1·10
1386 - 1f.50 maroon, grn & turq 1·90 1·70
1387 - 1f.70 multicoloured 2·10 1·80
1388 - 2f.10 turquoise and violet 3·25 2·75
1389 - 3f. multicoloured 3·75 3·25
DESIGNS—HORIZ: 1f.20, "Hans the Flute Player" (L. Ganne); 1f.50, "Don Quixote" (J. Massenet); 2f.10, "The Child and the Sorcerer" (M. Ravel); 3f. Charles Garnier (architect) and south facade of Opera House. VERT: 1f.70, "L'Aiglon" (A. Honegger and J. Ibert).
See also Nos. 1399/1404.

378 Flower, Bird and Butterfly

1979. International Year of the Child. Children's Paintings.
1390 **378** 50c. pink, green and black 25 35
1391 - 1f. slate, green and orange 75 65
1392 - 1f.20 slate, orange & mve 1·30 1·10
1393 - 1f.50 yellow, brown & bl 2·20 1·90
1394 - 1f.70 multicoloured 2·75 2·30
DESIGNS: 1f. Horse and Child; 1f.20, "The Gift of Love"; 1f.50, "Peace in the World"; 1f.70, "Down with Pollution".

379 Armed Foot Messenger

1979. Europa.
1395 **379** 1f.20 brown, green & bl 1·30 1·10
1396 - 1f.50 brown, turq & bl 1·90 1·70
1397 - 1f.70 brown, green & bl 2·50 2·20
MS1398 129×149 mm. Nos. 1395/7, each ×2 32·00 32·00
DESIGNS: 1f.50, 18th-cent felucca; 1f.70, Arrival of first train at Monaco.

380 "Instrumental Music" (G. Boulanger) (detail of Opera House interior)

1979. Centenary of "Salle Garnier" (Opera House) (2nd issue).
1399 1f. brown, orange & turq 90 75
1400 1f.20 multicoloured 1·30 1·10
1401 1f.50 multicoloured 1·70 1·40
1402 1f.70 blue, brown and red 2·30 2·00
1403 2f.10 red, violet & black 2·75 2·40
1404 **380** 3f. green, brown and light green 3·75 3·25
DESIGNS (as Type **377**)—HORIZ: 1f. "Les Biches" (F. Poulenc); 1f.20, "The Sailors" (G. Auric); 1f.70, "Gaiete Parisienne" (J. Offenbach). VERT: 1f.50, "La Spectre de la Rose" (C. M. Weber) (after poster by Jean Cocteau); 2f.10, "Salome" (R. Strauss).

1979. Paintings. "Princes and Princesses of Monaco". As T 213. Multicoloured.
1405 3f. "Prince Charles III" (B. Biard) 3·25 2·75
1406 4f. "Antoinette de Merode" 3·75 3·25

381 St. Pierre Claver

1979. Monaco Red Cross.
1407 **381** 5f. multicoloured 3·25 2·75

382 "Princess Grace" Orchid

1979. Monte Carlo Flora 1980.
1408 **382** 1f. multicoloured 3·25 2·75

383 "Princess Grace" Rose

1979. Monte Carlo Flower Show.
1409 **383** 1f.20 multicoloured 3·75 2·75

384 Clown balancing on Ball

1979. 6th International Circus Festival.
1410 **384** 1f.20 multicoloured 2·50 1·90

385 Sir Rowland Hill and Penny Black

1979. Death Centenary of Sir Rowland Hill.
1411 **385** 1f.70 brown, blue & blk 1·00 90

386 Albert Einstein

1979. Birth Centenary of Albert Einstein (physicist).
1412 **386** 1f.70 brown, grey and red 1·00 90

387 St. Patrick's Cathedral

1979. Centenary of St. Patrick's Cathedral, New York.
1413 **387** 2f.10 black, blue & brn 1·40 1·10

388 Nativity Scene

1979. Christmas.
1414 **388** 1f.20 blue, orange & mve 90 75

389 Early Racing Cars

1979. 50th Anniv of Grand Prix Motor Racing.
1415 **389** 1f. multicoloured 1·40 1·20

390 Arms of Charles V and Monaco

1979. 450th Anniv of Visit of Emperor Charles V.
1416 **390** 1f.50 brown, blue & blk 90 75

391 Setter and Pointer

1979. International Dog Show, Monte Carlo.
1417 **391** 1f.20 multicoloured 6·50 5·50

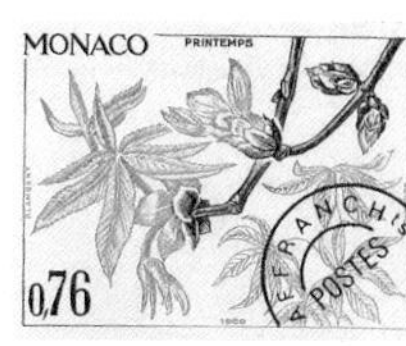

392 Spring

1980. Precancels. The Seasons.
1418 **392** 76c. brown and green 65 55
1419 **392** 88c. olive, emerald & grn 70 60
1420 - 99c. green and brown 90 75
1421 - 1f.14 green, emer & brn 95 85
1422 - 1f.60 brown, grey and deep brown 1·30 1·10
1423 - 1f.84 lake, grey & brown 1·40 1·20
1424 - 2f.65 brown, lt blue & bl 2·50 2·20
1425 - 3f.05 brown, bl & slate 2·75 2·30
DESIGNS: 99c., 1f.14, Summer; 1f.60, 1f.84, Autumn; 2f.65, 3f.05, Winter.

394 Paul P. Harris (founder) and View of Chicago

1980. 75th Anniv of Rotary International.
1434 **394** 1f.80 olive, blue & turq 1·00 90

395 Gymnastics

1980. Olympic Games, Moscow and Lake Placid.
1435 **395** 1f.10 blue, brown & grey 40 35
1436 - 1f.30 red, brown & blue 65 55
1437 - 1f.60 red, blue & brown 75 65
1438 - 1f.80 brown, bis & grn 1·00 90
1439 - 2f.30 grey, violet & mve 1·30 1·10
1440 - 4f. green, blue and brown 2·20 1·90
DESIGNS: 1f.30, Handball; 1f.60, Pistol-shooting; 1f.80, Volleyball; 2f.30, Ice hockey; 4f. Skiing.

396 Colette (novelist)

1980. Europa. Each black, green and red.

1441	1f.30 Type **396**	1·30	55
1442	1f.80 Marcel Pagnol (writer)	1·90	1·10
MS1443 171×143 mm. Nos. 1441/2, each ×5		19·00	17·00

397 "La Source"

1980. Birth Bicentenary of Jean Ingres (artist).

1444	**397**	4f. multicoloured	11·50	10·00

398 Montaigne

1980. 400th Anniv of Publication of Montaigne's "Essays".

1445	**398**	1f.30 black, red and blue	90	75

399 Guillaume Apollinaire (after G. Pieret)

1980. Birth Centenary of Guillaume Apollinaire (poet).

1446	**399**	1f.10 brown	75	65

400 Congress Centre

1980. Kiwanis International European Convention.

1447	**400**	1f.30 black, blue and red	90	75

401 Honore II Silver Ecu, 1649

1980. Numismatics.

1448	**401**	1f.50 black and blue	1·30	1·10

402 Lhassa Apso and Shih Tzu

1980. International Dog Show, Monte Carlo.

1449	**402**	1f.30 multicoloured	7·00	5·50

403 "The Princess and the Pea"

1980. 175th Birth Anniv of Hans Christian Andersen.

1450	**403**	70c. sepia, red and brown	40	35
1451	-	1f.30 blue, turq & red	90	75
1452	-	1f.50 black, blue & turq	1·30	1·10
1453	-	1f.60 red, black & brown	1·50	1·30
1454	-	1f.80 yellow, brn & turq	1·90	1·70
1455	-	2f.30 brown, pur & vio	2·30	2·00

DESIGNS: 1f.30, "The Little Mermaid"; 1f.50, "The Chimneysweep and Shepherdess"; 1f.60, "The Brave Little Lead Soldier"; 1f.80, "The Little Match Girl"; 2f.30, "The Nightingale".

404 "The Road" (M. Vlaminck)

1980. 75th Anniv of 1905 Autumn Art Exhibition. Multicoloured.

1456	2f. Type **404**	3·75	2·75
1457	3f. "Woman at Balustrade" (Van Dongen)	5·25	4·00
1458	4f. "The Reader" (Henri Matisse)	6·75	5·50
1459	5f. "Three Figures in a Meadow" (A. Derain)	7·75	6·00

1980. Paintings. "Princes and Princesses of Monaco". As T 213. Multicoloured.

1460	4f. "Prince Albert I" (L. Bonnat)	3·75	3·25
1461	4f. "Princess Marie Alice Heine" (L. Maeterlinck)	3·75	3·25

405 "Sunbirds"

1980. Monaco Red Cross.

1462	**405**	6f. red, bistre and brown	5·25	3·75

406 "MONACO" balanced on Tightrope

1980. 7th International Circus Festival, Monaco.

1463	**406**	1f.30 red, turquoise & blue	2·40	1·70

407 Children and Nativity

1980. Christmas.

1464	**407**	1f.10 blue, carmine and red	65	55
1465	**407**	2f.30 violet, orange and pink	1·30	1·10

1980. Monte Carlo Flower Show, 1981. As T 383. Multicoloured.

1466	1f.30 "Princess Stephanie" rose	1·50	90
1467	1f.80 Ikebana	2·30	1·70

408 "Alcyonium"

1980. Marine Fauna. Multicoloured.

1468	5c. "Spirographis spallanzanli"	15	20
1469	10c. "Anemonia sulcata"	15	20
1470	15c. "Leptopsammia pruvoit"	15	20
1471	20c. "Pteroides"	25	35
1472	30c. "Paramuricea clavata" (horiz)	25	35
1473	40c. Type **408**	40	45
1474	50c. "Corallium rubrum"	65	55
1475	60c. Trunculus murex ("Calliactis parasitica") (horiz)	1·30	1·10
1476	70c. "Cerianthus membranaceus" (horiz)	1·50	1·30
1477	1f. "Actinia equina" (horiz)	1·90	1·40
1478	2f. "Protula" (horiz)	3·75	2·20

409 Fish with Hand for Tail

1981. "Respect the Sea".

1479	**409**	1f.20 multicoloured	1·30	1·10

410 Prince Rainier and Princess Grace

1981. Royal Silver Wedding.

1480	**410**	1f.20 black and green	1·90	1·70
1481	**410**	1f.40 black and red	2·50	2·20
1482	**410**	1f.70 black and green	3·25	2·75
1483	**410**	1f.80 black and brown	3·75	3·25
1484	**410**	2f. black and blue	5·25	3·25

411 Mozart (after Lorenz Vogel)

1981. 225th Birth Anniv of Wolfgang Amadeus Mozart (composer).

1485	**411**	2f. brown, dp brown & bl	2·30	2·00
1486	-	2f.50 blue, brn & dp brn	3·25	2·75
1487	-	3f.50 dp brown, bl & brn	5·25	3·25

DESIGNS—HORIZ: 2f.50, "Mozart at 7 with his Father and Sister" (engraving by Delafoose after drawing by Carmontelle); 3f.50 "Mozart directing Requiem two Days before his Death" (painting by Baude).

412 Palm Cross

1981. Europa. Multicoloured.

1488	**412**	1f.40 green, brown & red	1·90	1·10
1489	-	2f. multicoloured	2·50	1·70
MS1490 171×143 mm. Nos. 1488/9, each ×5			24·00	17·00

DESIGN: 2f. Children carrying palm crosses.

413 Paris Football Stadium, Cup and Footballer

1981. 25th Anniv of European Football Cup.

1491	**413**	2f. black and blue	1·50	1·30

414 I.Y.D.P. Emblem and Girl in Wheelchair

1981. International Year of Disabled Persons.

1492	**414**	1f.40 blue and green	1·30	1·10

415 Palace flying Old Flag, National Flag and Monte Carlo

1981. Centenary of National Flag.

1493	**415**	2f. red, blue and brown	1·50	1·30

416 Oceanographic Institute, Paris and Oceanographic Museum, Monaco

1981. 75th Anniv of Oceanographic Institute.

1494	**416**	1f.20 blue, black & brn	1·00	90

417 Bureau Building and "Faddey Bellingshausen" (hydrographic research ship)

1981. 50th Anniv of Int Hydrographic Bureau.

1495	**417**	2f.50 sepia, brown and light brown	1·90	1·70

418 Rough Collies and Shetland Sheepdogs

1981. International Dog Show, Monte Carlo.

1496	**418**	1f.40 multicoloured	7·75	5·50

419 Rainier III and Prince Albert

1981. (a) 23×28 mm.

1497	**419**	1f.40 green (postage)	1·30	65
1498	**419**	1f.60 red	1·90	75
1499	**419**	1f.60 green	1·30	75
1500	**419**	1f.70 green	1·30	90
1501	**419**	1f.80 red	1·50	1·00
1502	**419**	1f.80 green	1·50	1·10
1503	**419**	1f.90 green	2·50	2·00
1504	**419**	2f. red	1·90	90
1505	**419**	2f. green	1·30	90
1506	**419**	2f.10 red	1·90	1·10
1507	**419**	2f.20 red	1·80	1·20
1508	**419**	2f.30 blue	5·75	3·75
1509	**419**	2f.50 brown	2·50	1·30
1510	**419**	2f.60 blue	3·75	2·75
1511	**419**	2f.80 blue	3·75	2·20
1512	**419**	3f. blue	3·75	2·40
1513	**419**	3f.20 blue	3·75	2·40
1514	**419**	3f.40 blue	5·75	3·00
1515	**419**	3f.60 blue	3·75	2·75
1516	**419**	4f. brown	3·25	2·20
1517	**419**	5f.50 black	3·75	2·75
1518	**419**	10f. purple	5·25	2·75
1519	**419**	15f. green	12·00	5·00
1520	**419**	20f. blue	13·00	5·50

(b) 36×27 mm.

1521	5f. violet (air)	2·50	1·10
1522	10f. red	6·50	2·75
1523	15f. green	7·75	3·25
1524	20f. blue	11·50	4·50
1525	30f. brown	15·00	8·75

DESIGN: Nos. 1521/5, Double portrait and monograms.

421 Arctic Scene and Map

1981. 1st International Congress on Discovery and History of Northern Polar Regions, Rome.

1530	**421**	1f.50 multicoloured	1·90	1·70

1981. Paintings. "Princes and Princesses of Monaco". Vert designs as T 213. Multicoloured.

1531	3f. "Prince Louis II" (P.-A. de Laszlo)	3·75	2·75
1532	5f. "Princess Charlotte" (P.-A. de Laszlo)	5·25	3·25

422 Hercules fighting the Nemean Lion

1981. Monaco Red Cross. The Twelve Labours of Hercules (1st series).

1533	**422**	2f.50+50c. green, brown and red	1·90	1·70
1534	-	3f.50+50c. blue, green and red	2·50	2·20

DESIGN: 3f.50, Slaying the Hydra of Lerna.

See also Nos. 1584/5, 1631/2, 1699/1700, 1761/2 and 1794/5.

423 Ettore Bugatti (racing car designer) (Cent)

1981. Birth Anniversaries.

1535	**423**	1f. indigo, blue and red	1·30	1·10
1536	-	2f. black, blue and brown	1·90	1·70
1537	-	2f.50 brown, black and red	2·50	2·20
1538	-	4f. multicoloured	4·50	3·75
1539	-	4f. multicoloured	4·50	3·75

DESIGNS: No. 1536, George Bernard Shaw (dramatist, 125th anniv); 1537, Fernand Leger (painter, centenary). LARGER: (37×48 mm): 1538, Pablo Picasso (self-portrait) (centenary); 1539, Rembrandt (self-portrait) (375th anniv).

424 Eglantines and Morning Glory

1981. Monte Carlo Flower Show (1982). Mult.

1540	1f.40 Type **424**	2·50	1·70
1541	2f. "Ikebana" (painting by Ikenobo)	3·75	2·20

425 "Catherine Deneuve"

1981. 1st International Rose Show, Monte Carlo.

1542	**425**	1f.80 multicoloured	5·25	3·75

426 Tiger, Clown, Acrobat and Elephants

1981. 8th International Circus Festival, Monaco.

1543	**426**	1f.40 violet, mauve & blk	3·75	2·20

427 Praying Children and Nativity

1981. Christmas.

1544	**427**	1f.20 blue, mauve & brn	90	75

428 "Lancia-Stratos" Rally Car

1981. 50th Monte Carlo Rally (1982).

1545	**428**	1f. blue, red & turquoise	2·50	1·30

429 Spring

1981. Seasons of the Persimmon Tree. Sheet 143×100 mm containing T 429 and similar horiz designs.

MS1546	1f. green, yellow and blue (T **429**); 2f. green and blue (Summer); 3f. red, brown and yellow (Autumn); 4f. brown and red (Winter)	11·00	9·25

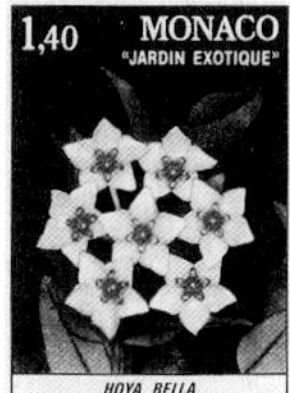

430 "Hoya bella"

1981. Plants in Exotic Garden. Multicoloured.

1547	1f.40 Type **430**	3·75	2·20
1548	1f.60 "Bolivicereus samaipatanus"	3·75	1·70
1549	1f.80 "Trichocereus grandiflorus" (horiz)	3·75	1·70
1550	2f. "Argyroderma roseum"	2·20	1·10
1551	2f.30 "Euphorbia milii"	4·25	2·75
1552	2f.60 "Echinocereus fitchii" (horiz)	4·25	3·25
1553	2f.90 "Rebutia heliosa" (horiz)	3·75	3·25
1554	4f.10 "Echinopsis multiplex cristata" (horiz)	5·25	4·50

431 Spring

1982. Precancels. The Seasons of the Peach Tree.

1555	**431**	97c. mauve and green	65	55
1556	-	1f.25 green, orge & mve	90	75
1557	-	2f.03 brown	1·40	1·20
1558	-	3f.36 brown and blue	2·50	2·20

DESIGNS: 1f.25, Summer; 2f.03, Autumn; 3f.36, Winter.

432 Common Nutcracker

1982. Birds from Mercantour National Park.

1559	**432**	60c. black, brown & grn	1·70	90
1560	-	70c. black and mauve	1·90	1·30
1561	-	80c. red, black & orange	2·10	1·40
1562	-	90c. black, red and blue	3·25	1·70
1563	-	1f.40 brown, black & red	3·50	2·75
1564	-	1f.60 brown, black & blue	4·50	3·25

DESIGNS—VERT: 70c. Black grouse; 80c. Rock partridge; 1f.60, Golden eagle. HORIZ: 90c. Wallcreeper; 1f.40, Rock ptarmigan.

433 Capture of Monaco Fortress, 1297

1982. Europa.

1565	**433**	1f.60 blue, brown and red	1·50	90
1566	-	2f.30 blue, brown and red	1·90	1·10

MS1567	173×143 mm. Nos. 1565/6, each ×5	26·00	22·00

DESIGN: 2f.30, Signing the Treaty of Peronne, 1641.

434 Old Quarter

1982. Fontvieille.

1568	**434**	1f.40 blue, brown & grn	1·30	90
1569	-	1f.60 light brown, brown and red	1·50	65
1570	-	2f.30 purple	1·90	1·10

DESIGNS: 1f.60, Land reclamation; 2f.30, Urban development.

435 Stadium

1982. Fontvieille Sports Stadium (1st series).

1571	**435**	2f.30 green, brown & blue	1·90	1·10

See also No. 1616.

436 Arms of Paris

1982. "Philexfrance" International Stamp Exhibition, Paris.

1572	**436**	1f.40 red, grey and deep red	1·20	1·00

437 Old English Sheepdog

1982. International Dog Show, Monte Carlo. Multicoloured.

1573	60c. Type **437**	3·75	2·75
1574	1f. Briard	5·25	3·25

438 Monaco Cathedral and Arms

1982. Creation of Archbishopric of Monaco (1981).

1575	**438**	1f.60 black, blue and red	1·20	1·00

439 St. Francis of Assisi

1982. 800th Birth Anniv of St. Francis of Assisi.

1576	**439**	1f.40 grey and light grey	1·00	90

440 Dr. Robert Koch

1982. Centenary of Discovery of Tubercle Bacillus.

1577	**440**	1f.40 purple and lilac	1·50	1·30

441 Lord Baden-Powell

1982. 125th Birth Anniv of Lord Baden-Powell (founder of Boy Scout Movement).

1578	**441**	1f.60 brown and black	1·50	1·30

442 Running for Ball

1982. World Cup Football Championship, Spain. Sheet 143×120 mm containing T 442 and similar square designs, each brown, blue and green.

MS1579		1f. Type **442**; 2f. Kicking ball; 3f. Heading ball; 4f. Goalkeeper	11·00	10·00

443 St. Hubert (18th-century medallion)

1982. 29th Meeting of International Hunting Council, Monte Carlo.

1580	**443**	1f.60 multicoloured	1·40	1·20

444 Books, Reader and Globe

1982. International Bibliophile Association General Assembly, Monte Carlo.

1581	**444**	1f.60 blue, purple & red	1·20	1·00

445 "Casino, 1870"

1982. Monaco in the "Belle Epoque" (1st series). Paintings by Hubert Clerissi. Multicoloured.

1582		3f. Type **445**	3·25	2·20
1583		5f. "Porte d'Honneur, Royal Palace, 1893"	4·75	2·75

See also Nos. 1629/30, 1701/2, 1763/4, 1801/2, 1851/2, 1889/90 and 1965/6.

1982. Monaco Red Cross. The Twelve Labours of Hercules (2nd series). As T 422.

1584		2f.50+50c. green, red and bright red	1·90	1·70
1585		3f.50+50c. brown, blue and red	2·50	2·20

DESIGNS: 2f.50, Capturing the Erymanthine Boar; 3f.50, Shooting the Stymphalian Birds.

446 Nicolo Paganini (violinist and composer, bicent)

1982. Birth Anniversaries.

1586	**446**	1f.60 brown and purple	1·50	1·30
1587	-	1f.80 red, mauve & brn	2·30	1·70
1588	-	2f.60 green and red	3·00	2·75
1589	-	4f. multicoloured	5·25	4·50
1590	-	4f. multicoloured	5·25	4·50

DESIGNS—VERT: No. 1587, Anna Pavlova (ballerina, centenary); 1588, Igor Stravinsky (composer, centenary). HORIZ (47×36 mm): 1589, "In a Boat" (Edouard Manet, 150th anniv); 1590, "The Black Fish" (Georges Braque, centenary).

447 Vase of Flowers

1982. Monte Carlo Flower Show (1983). Mult.

1591		1f.60 Type **447**	2·50	1·70
1592		2f.60 Ikebana arrangement	3·25	2·20

448 Bowl of Flowers

1982

1593	**448**	1f.60 multicoloured	2·50	1·70

449 The Three Kings

1982. Christmas.

1594	**449**	1f.60 green, blue & orge	1·00	45
1595	-	1f.80 green, blue & orge	1·20	55
1596	-	2f.60 green, blue & orge	2·10	90
MS1597		143×105 mm. Nos. 1594/6	4·50	4·50

DESIGNS: 1f.80, The Holy Family; 2f.60, Shepherds and angels.

450 Prince Albert I and Polar Scene

1982. Centenary of First International Polar Year.

1598	**450**	1f.60 brown, green & bl	3·25	2·20

451 Viking Longships off Greenland

1982. Millenary of Discovery of Greenland by Erik the Red.

1599	**451**	1f.60 blue, brown & blk	3·25	2·20

452 Julius Caesar in the Port of Monaco ("Aeneid", Book VI)

1982. 2000th Death Anniv of Virgil (poet).

1600	**452**	1f.80 deep blue, blue and brown	3·25	2·20

453 Spring

1983. Precancels. The Seasons of the Apple Tree.

1601	**453**	1f.05 purple, green and yellow	1·00	90
1602	-	1f.35 light green, deep green and turquoise	1·20	1·00
1603	-	2f.19 red, brown & grey	2·10	1·80
1604	-	3f.63 yellow and brown	1·90	2·40

DESIGNS: 1f.35, Summer; 2f.19, Autumn; 3f.63, Winter.

454 Tourism

1983. 50th Anniv of Exotic Garden. Mult.

1605		1f.80 Type **454**	1·90	1·70
1606		2f. Cactus plants (botanical collections)	2·40	1·90
1607		2f.30 Cactus plants (international flower shows)	2·75	2·20
1608		2f.60 Observatory grotto (horiz)	3·25	2·40
1609		3f.30 Museum of Prehistoric Anthropology (horiz)	3·75	2·75

455 Alaskan Malamute

1983. International Dog Show, Monte Carlo.

1610	**455**	1f.80 multicoloured	9·75	5·50

456 Princess Grace

1983. Princess Grace Commemoration. Sheet 105×143 mm.

MS1611	**456**	10f. black	13·00	13·00

457 St. Charles Borromee and Church

1983. Centenary of St. Charles Church, Monte Carlo.

1612	**457**	2f.60 deep blue, blue and green	1·30	1·10

458 Montgolfier Balloon, 1783

1983. Europa.

1613	**458**	1f.80 blue, brown & grey	1·90	75
1614	-	2f.60 grey, blue & brown	1·90	1·10
MS1615		170×143 mm. Nos. 1613/14, each ×5	32·00	28·00

DESIGN: 2f.60, Space shuttle.

459 Franciscan College

1983. Centenary of Franciscan College, Monte Carlo.

1616	**459**	2f. grey, brown and red	1·30	1·10

460 Stadium

1983. Fontvieille Sports Stadium (2nd series).

1617	**460**	2f. green, blue and brown	1·30	1·10

461 Early and Modern Cars

1983. Centenary of Petrol-driven Motor Car.

1618	**461**	2f.90 blue, brown & green	3·75	2·75

462 Blue Whale

1983. International Commission for the Protection of Whales.

1619	**462**	3f.30 blue, light blue and grey	4·50	4·00

463 Dish Aerial, Pigeon, W.C.Y. Emblem and Satellite

1983. World Communications Year.

1620	**463**	4f. lilac and mauve	1·90	1·70

464 Smoking Moor

1983. Nineteenth Century Automata from the Galea Collection. Multicoloured.

1621		50c. Type **464**	40	35
1622		60c. Clown with diabolo	40	35
1623		70c. Smoking monkey	40	35
1624		80c. Peasant with pig	50	45
1625		90c. Buffalo Bill smoking	65	55
1626		1f. Snake charmer	75	65
1627		1f.50 Pianist	1·50	1·00
1628		2f. Young girl powdering herself	1·90	1·10

1983. Monaco in the "Belle Epoque" (2nd series). As T 445. Multicoloured.

1629		3f. "The Beach, 1902"	4·00	3·25
1630		5f. "Cafe de Paris, 1905"	5·25	4·50

1983. Monaco Red Cross. The Twelve Labours of Hercules (3rd series). As T 422.

1631		2f.50+50c. brn, bl & red	2·00	1·70
1632		3f.50+50c. violet, mve & red	2·75	2·20

DESIGNS: 2f.50, Capturing the Hind of Ceryneia; 3f.50, Cleaning the Augean stables.

465 Johannes Brahms (composer)

1983. Birth Anniversaries.

1633	**465**	3f. deep brown, brown and green	2·00	1·70
1634	-	3f. black, brown and red	2·00	1·70
1635	-	4f. multicoloured	4·00	2·75
1636	-	4f. multicoloured	4·00	2·75

DESIGNS—HORIZ: No. 1633, Type **465** (150th anniv); 1634, Giacomo Puccini (composer) and scene from "Madame Butterfly" (125th anniv). VERT (37×48 mm): 1635, "Portrait of a Young Man" (Raphael (artist), 500th anniv); 1636, "Cottin Passage" (Utrillo (artist), centenary).

466 Circus Performers

1983. 9th International Circus Festival, Monaco.

1637	**466**	2f. blue, red and green	2·00	1·70

467 Bouquet

1983. Monte Carlo Flower Show (1984). Mult.

1638	1f.60 Type **467**	1·90	1·10
1639	2f.60 Arrangement of poppies	3·00	2·40

468 Provencale Creche

1983. Christmas.

1640	**468**	2f. multicoloured	2·00	1·10

469 Nobel Literature Prize Medal

1983. 150th Birth Anniv of Alfred Nobel (inventor of dynamite and founder of Nobel Prizes).

1641	**469**	2f. black, grey and red	1·30	1·10

470 O. F. Ozanam (founder) and Paris Headquarters

1983. 150th Anniv of Society of St. Vincent de Paul.

1642	**470**	1f.80 violet and purple	1·30	1·10

471 "Tazerka" (oil rig)

1983. Oil Industry.

1643	**471**	5f. blue, brown & turq	3·00	1·70

472 Spring

1983. Seasons of the Fig. Sheet 143×100 mm containing T 472 and similar horiz designs.

MS1644 1f. green (Type **472**); 2f. green, yellow and red (Summer); 3f. green and (Autumn); 4f. green and red (Winter)	12·00	12·00

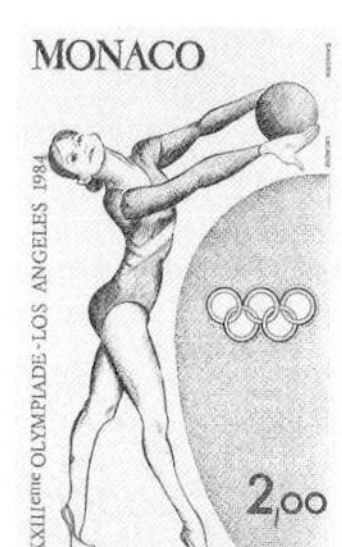

473 Gymnast with Ball

1984. Olympic Games, Los Angeles. Sheet 161×143 mm containing T 473 and similar vert designs, each brown, slate and red.

MS1645 2f. Type **473**; 3f. Gymnast with clubs; 4f. Gymnast with ribbon; 5f. Gymnast with hoop	11·00	11·00

474 Skater and Stadium

1984. Winter Olympic Games, Sarajevo.

1646	**474**	2f. blue, green and turquoise	1·30	1·10
1647	-	4f. blue, violet and purple	2·40	2·00

DESIGN: 4f. Skater and snowflake.

475 Bridge

1984. Europa. 25th Anniv of European Post and Telecommunications Conference.

1648	**475**	2f. blue	2·00	1·70
1649	**475**	3f. green	2·75	2·20

MS1650 143×170 mm. Nos. 1648/9, each ×4	33·00	28·00

476 Balkan Fritillary

1984. Butterflies and Moths in Mercantour National Park. Multicoloured.

1651	1f.60 Type **476**	2·75	1·70
1652	2f. "Zygaena vesubiana"	3·50	1·90
1653	2f.80 False mnestra ringlet	4·25	2·40
1654	3f. Small apollo (horiz)	4·75	2·75
1655	3f.60 Southern swallowtail (horiz)	5·25	3·25

477 Auvergne Pointer

1984. International Dog Show, Monte Carlo.

1656	**477**	1f.60 multicoloured	5·25	3·25

478 Sanctuary and Statue of Virgin

1984. Our Lady of Laghet Sanctuary.

1657	**478**	2f. blue, brown and green	1·30	55

479 Piccard's Stratosphere Balloon "F.N.R.S."

1984. Birth Centenary of Auguste Piccard (physicist).

1658	**479**	2f.80 black, green & blue	1·30	90
1659	-	4f. blue, green & turq	2·00	1·10

DESIGN: 4f. Bathyscaphe.

480 Concert

1984. 25th Anniv of Palace Concerts.

1660	**480**	3f.60 blue and deep blue	2·00	1·10

481 Place de la Visitation

1984. Bygone Monaco (1st series). Paintings by Hubert Clerissi.

1661	**481**	5c. brown	15	20
1662	-	10c. red	15	20
1663	-	15c. violet	25	20
1664	-	20c. blue	15	20
1665	-	30c. blue	25	20
1666	-	40c. green	1·10	35
1667	-	50c. red	25	10
1668	-	60c. blue	25	15
1669	-	70c. orange	65	45
1670	-	80c. green	65	35
1671	-	90c. mauve	65	35
1672	-	1f. blue	65	20
1673	-	2f. black	1·30	50
1674	-	3f. red	3·25	1·50
1675	-	4f. blue	2·00	1·10
1676	-	5f. green	2·75	1·50
1677	-	6f. green	4·00	2·20

DESIGNS: 10c. Town Hall; 15c. Rue Basse; 20c. Place Saint-Nicolas; 30c. Quai du Commerce; 40c. Rue des Iris; 50c. Ships in harbour; 60c. St. Charles's Church; 70c. Religious procession; 80c. Olive tree overlooking harbour; 90c. Quayside; 1f. Palace Square; 2f. Fishing boats in harbour; 3f. Bandstand; 4f. Railway station; 5f. Mail coach; 6f. Monte Carlo Opera House.

See also Nos. 2015/27.

482 Spring

1984. Precancels. The Seasons of the Quince.

1678	**482**	1f.14 red and green	80	80
1679	-	1f.47 deep green & green	85	90
1680	-	2f.38 olive, turquoise and green	1·60	1·50
1681	-	3f.95 green	2·10	2·00

DESIGNS: 1f.47, Summer; 2f.38, Autumn; 3f.95, Winter.

483 Shepherd

1984. Christmas. Crib Figures from Provence. Multicoloured.

1682	70c. Type **483**	65	45
1683	1f. Blind man	80	55
1684	1f.70 Happy man	1·60	1·10
1685	2f. Spinner	2·00	1·40
1686	2f.10 Angel playing trumpet	2·10	1·50
1687	2f.40 Garlic seller	2·30	1·60
1688	3f. Drummer	2·75	1·80
1689	3f.70 Knife grinder	3·25	2·30
1690	4f. Elderly couple	4·00	2·75

484 Gargantua and Cattle

1984. 450th Anniv of First Edition of "Gargantua" by Francois Rabelais.

1691	**484**	2f. black, red and brown	2·00	1·40
1692	-	2f. black, red and blue	2·00	1·40
1693	-	4f. green	3·25	2·30

DESIGNS—As T **484**: No. 1692, Panurge's sheep. 36×48 mm: 1693, Francois Rabelais.

485 Bowl of Mixed Flowers

1984. Monte Carlo Flower Show (1985). Mult.

1694	2f.10 Type **485**	2·00	1·40
1695	3f. Ikebana arrangement	3·25	2·30

486 Television Lights and Emblem

1984. 25th Int Television Festival, Monte Carlo.

1696	**486**	2f.10 blue, grey and mauve	1·30	90
1697	-	3f. grey, blue and red	2·10	1·50

DESIGN: 3f. "Golden Nymph" (Grand Prix).

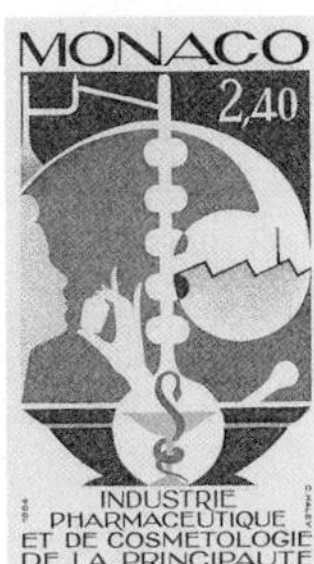

487 Chemical Equipment

1984. Pharmaceutical and Cosmetics Industry.
1698 **487** 2f.40 blue, deep blue and green 1·30 90

1984. Monaco Red Cross. The Twelve Labours of Hercules (4th series). As T 422.
1699 3f.+50c. brown, light brown and red 2·00 1·80
1700 4f.+50c. green, brown and red 2·75 2·30
DESIGNS: 3f. Killing the Cretan bull; 4f. Capturing the Mares of Diomedes.

1984. Monaco in the "Belle Epoque" (3rd series). Paintings by Hubert Clerissi. As T 445. Mult.
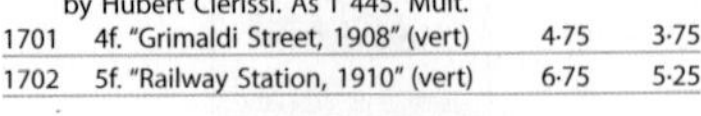
1701 4f. "Grimaldi Street, 1908" (vert) 4·75 3·75
1702 5f. "Railway Station, 1910" (vert) 6·75 5·25

488 Clown

1984. Tenth International Circus Festival, Monaco. Sheet 88 x 72 mm.
MS1703 **488** 5f. multicoloured 8·00 7·50

489 "Woman with Chinese Vase"

1984. 150th Birth Anniv of Edgar Degas (artist).
1704 **489** 6f. multicoloured 6·75 4·75

490 Spring

1985. Precancels. Seasons of the Cherry.
1705 **490** 1f.22 olive, green and blue 1·10 85
1706 - 1f.57 red, green and yellow 1·20 95
1707 - 2f.55 orange and brown 1·50 1·70
1708 - 4f.23 purple, green and blue 2·10 2·30
DESIGNS: 1f.57, Summer; 2f.55, Autumn; 4f.23, Winter.

491 First Stamp

1985. Centenary of First Monaco Stamps.
1709 **491** 1f.70 green 95 75
1710 **491** 2f.10 red 1·20 95
1711 **491** 3f. blue 1·90 1·50

493 "Berardia subacaulis"

1985. Flowers in Mercantour National Park. Mult.
1724 1f.70 Type **493** 1·30 90
1725 2f.10 "Saxifraga florulenta" (vert) 1·60 1·10
1726 2f.40 "Fritillaria moggridgei" (vert) 1·90 1·30
1727 3f. "Sempervivum allionii" (vert) 2·40 1·70
1728 3f.60 "Silene cordifolia" (vert) 3·00 2·00
1729 4f. "Primula allionii" 3·25 2·30

494 Spring

1985. Seasons of the Japanese Medlar. Sheet 144×100 mm containing T 494 and similar horiz designs.
MS1730 1f. olive and deep olive (Type **494**); 2f. olive, yellow and deep olive (Summer); 3f. olive and deep olive (Autumn); 4f. orange, yellow and olive (Winter) 9·50 8·25

495 Nadia Boulanger (composer)

1985. 25th Anniv of First Musical Composition Competition.
1731 **495** 1f.70 brown 1·20 85
1732 - 2f.10 blue 1·70 1·20
DESIGN: 2f.10, Georges Auric (composer).

496 Stadium and Runners

1985. Inauguration of Louis II Stadium, Fontvieille, and Athletics and Swimming Championships.
1733 **496** 1f.70 brown, red and violet 1·20 85
1734 - 2f.10 blue, brown and green 1·70 1·20
DESIGN: 2f.10, Stadium and swimmers.

497 Prince Antoine I

1985. Europa.
1735 **497** 2f.10 blue 2·00 1·40
1736 - 3f. red 2·75 1·80
MS1737 170×143 mm. Nos. 1735/6, each ×5 40·00 37·00
DESIGN: 3f. John-Baptiste Lully (composer).

498 Museum, "Hirondelle I" (schooner) and "Denise" (midget submarine)

1985. 75th Anniv of Oceanographic Museum.
1738 **498** 2f.10 black, green and blue 1·40 1·00

499 Boxer

1985. International Dog Show, Monte Carlo.
1739 **499** 2f.10 multicoloured 3·00 2·30

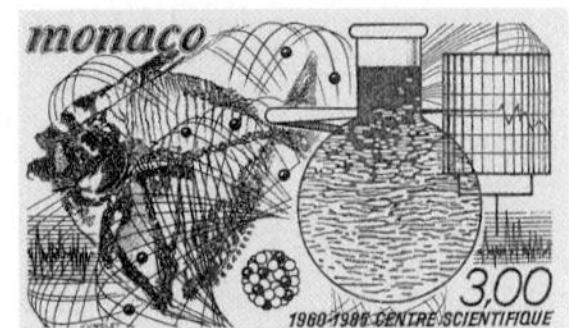

500 Scientific Motifs

1985. 25th Anniv of Scientific Centre.
1740 **500** 3f. blue, black and violet 1·90 1·10

501 Children and Hands holding Seedling and Emblem

1985. International Youth Year.
1741 **501** 3f. brown, green and light brown 1·90 1·10

502 Regal Angelfish

1985. Fishes in Oceanographic Museum Aquarium (1st series). Multicoloured.
1742 1f.80 Type **502** 2·00 1·50
1743 1f.90 Type **502** 3·00 1·80
1744 2f.20 Powder blue surgeonfish 2·10 1·60
1745 3f.20 Red-tailed butterflyfish 2·75 2·00
1746 3f.40 As No. 1745 4·75 2·75
1747 3f.90 Clown triggerfish 3·25 2·40
1748 7f. Fishes in aquarium (36×48 mm) 5·00 3·75
See also Nos. 1857/62.

503 Catamaran

1985. Monaco–New York Sailing Race. Sheet 143×105 mm containing T 503 and similar vert designs. Each black, blue and turquoise.
MS1749 4f. Type **503**; 4f. Single hull yacht; 4f. Trimaran 7·50 7·50

504 Rome Buildings and Emblem

1985. "Italia '85" International Stamp Exhibition, Rome.
1750 **504** 4f. black, green and red 2·00 1·50

505 Clown

1985. 11th International Circus Festival, Monaco.
1751 **505** 1f.80 multicoloured 1·90 1·40

506 Decorations

1985. Christmas.
1752 **506** 2f.20 multicoloured 1·50 1·10

507 Ship and Marine Life

1985. Fish Processing Industry.
1753 **507** 2f.20 blue, turquoise and brown 1·10 85

508 Arrangement of Roses, Tulips and Jonquil

1985. Monte Carlo Flower Show (1986). Mult.
1754 2f.20 Type **508** 1·90 1·40
1755 3f.20 Arrangement of chrysanthemums and heather 2·75 2·00

509 Globe and Satellite

1985. European Telecommunications Satellite Organization.
1756 **509** 3f. black, blue and violet 1·90 1·40

510 Sacha Guitry (actor, centenary)

1985. Birth Anniversaries.
1757 **510** 3f. orange and brown 1·90 1·40
1758 - 4f. blue, brown and mauve 2·50 1·80
1759 - 5f. turquoise, blue and grey 3·00 2·30
1760 - 6f. blue, brown and black 3·75 2·75

DESIGNS: 4f. Wilhelm and Jacob Grimm (folklorists, bicentenaries); 5f. Frederic Chopin and Robert Schumann (composers, 175th annivs); 6f. Johann Sebastian Bach and Georg Friedrich Handel (composers, 300th annivs).

1985. Monaco Red Cross. The Twelve Labours of Hercules (5th series). As T 422.

1761 3f.+70c. green, deep red and red 1·90 1·40
1762 4f.+80c. brown, blue & red 2·10 1·60

DESIGNS: 3f. The Cattle of Geryon; 4f. The Girdle of Hippolyte.

1985. Monaco in the "Belle Epoque" (4th series). As T 445, showing paintings by Hubert Clerissi. Multicoloured.

1763 4f. "Port of Monaco, 1912" 3·75 2·75
1764 6f. "Avenue de la Gare 1920" 5·00 3·75

511 Prince Charles III

1985. Centenary of First Monaco Stamps (2nd issue). Sheet 142×71 mm containing T 511 and similar vert designs. Each blue and black.

MS1765 5f. Type **511**; 5f. Prince Albert I; 5f. Prince Louis II; 5f. Prince Rainier III 10·00 10·00

512 Spring

1986. Precancels. Seasons of the Hazel Tree.

1766 **512** 1f.28 brown, green & bl 75 75
1767 - 1f.65 green, brown & yell 80 85
1768 - 2f.67 grey, brown and deep brown 1·50 1·50
1769 - 4f.44 green and brown 2·00 2·00

DESIGNS: 1f.65, Summer; 2f.67, Autumn; 4f.44, Winter.

513 Ancient Monaco

1986. 10th Anniv of "Annales Monegasques" (historical review).

1770 **513** 2f.20 grey, blue and brown 1·20 90

514 Scotch Terriers

1986. International Dog Show, Monte Carlo.

1771 **514** 1f.80 multicoloured 6·25 4·25

515 Mouflon

1986. Mammals in Mercantour National Park. Multicoloured.

1772 2f.20 Type **515** 1·40 1·00
1773 2f.50 Ibex 1·90 1·40
1774 3f.20 Chamois 2·50 1·80
1775 3f.90 Alpine marmot (vert) 3·00 2·30
1776 5f. Arctic hare (vert) 3·75 2·75
1777 7f.20 Stoat (vert) 5·00 3·75

516 Research Vessel "Ramoge"

1986. Europa. Each green, blue and red.

1778 2f.20 Type **516** 2·50 1·20
1779 3f.20 Underwater nature reserve, Larvotto beach 3·00 1·60

MS1780 171×144 mm. Nos. 1778/79, each ×5 37·00 32·00

517 Prince Albert I and National Council Building

1986. Anniversaries and Events.

1781 **517** 2f.50 brown and green 1·20 90
1782 - 3f.20 brown, red and black 2·20 1·70
1783 - 3f.90 purple and red 3·00 2·30
1784 - 5f. green, red and blue 3·75 1·40

DESIGNS—HORIZ: 2f.50, Type **517** (75th anniv of First Constitution); 3f.20, Serge Diaghilev and dancers (creation of new Monte Carlo ballet company); 3f.90, Henri Rougier and Turcat-Mery car (75th Anniv of first Monte Carlo Rally). VERT: 5f. Flags and Statue of Liberty (centenary).

518 Chicago and Flags

1986. "Ameripex '86" International Stamp Exhibition, Chicago.

1785 **518** 5f. black, red and blue 2·50 1·80

519 Player and Mayan Figure

1986. World Cup Football Championship, Mexico. Sheet 100×143 mm containing T 519 and similar vert design. Each black, red and blue.

MS1786 5f. Type **519**; 7f. Goalkeeper and Mayan figures 8·75 8·25

520 Comet, Telescopes and 1532 Chart by Apian

1986. Appearance of Halley's Comet.

1787 **520** 10f. blue, brown & green 5·00 3·25

521 Monte Carlo and Congress Centre

1986. 30th International Insurance Congress.

1788 **521** 3f.20 blue, brown & grn 1·70 1·30

522 Christmas Tree Branch and Holly

1986. Christmas. Multicoloured.

1789 1f.80 Type **522** 1·00 45
1790 2f.50 Christmas tree branch and poinsettia 1·50 75

523 Clown's Face and Elephant on Ball

1986. 12th International Circus Festival, Monaco.

1791 **523** 2f.20 multicoloured 2·20 1·70

524 Posy of Roses and Acidanthera

1986. Monte Carlo Flower Show (1987). Mult.

1792 2f.20 Type **524** 2·00 1·30
1793 3f.90 Lilies and beech in vase 3·00 2·00

1986. Monaco Red Cross. The Twelve Labours of Hercules (6th series). As T 422.

1794 3f.+70c. green, yell & red 1·90 1·40
1795 4f.+80c. blue, brown & red 2·50 1·80

DESIGNS: 3f. The Golden Apples of the Hesperides; 4f. Capturing Cerberus.

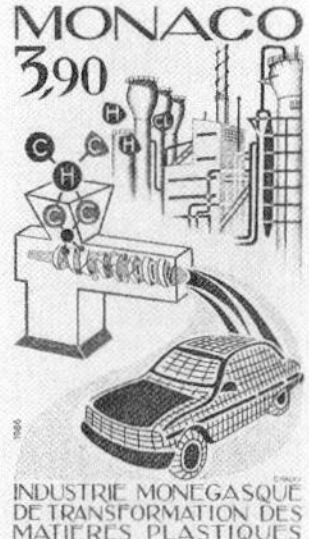

525 Making Plastic Mouldings for Car Bodies

1986. Plastics Industry.

1796 **525** 3f.90 turquoise, red and grey 2·00 1·50

526 Scenes from "Le Cid" (Pierre Corneille)

1986. Anniversaries.

1797 **526** 4f. deep brown & brown 2·00 1·50
1798 - 5f. brown and blue 2·50 1·80

DESIGNS: 4f. Type **526** (350th anniv of first performance); 5f. Franz Liszt (composer) and bible (175th birth anniv).

527 Horace de Saussure, Mont Blanc and Climbers

1986. Bicentenary of First Ascent of Mont Blanc by Dr. Paccard and Jacques Balmat.

1799 **527** 5f.80 blue, red and black 3·00 2·20

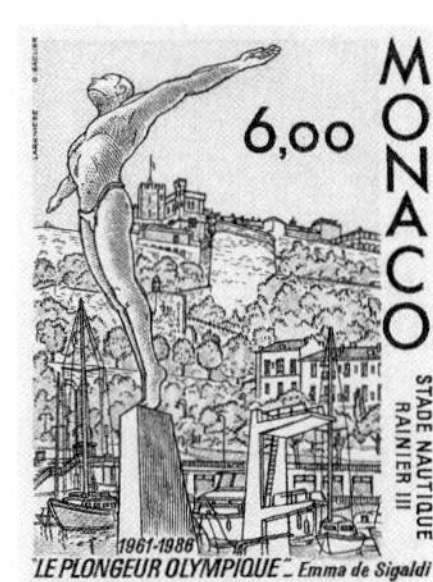

528 "The Olympic Diver" (Emma de Sigaldi)

1986. 25th Anniv of Unveiling of "The Olympic Diver" (statue).

1800 **528** 6f. multicoloured 3·00 2·30

1986. Monaco in the "Belle Epoque" (5th series). Paintings by Hubert Clerissi. As T 445. Mult.

1801 6f. "Bandstand and Casino, 1920" (vert) 5·00 3·75
1802 7f. "Avenue du Beau Rivage, 1925" (vert) 6·25 4·50

1986. Seasons of the Strawberry Tree. Sheet 143×100 mm containing T 529 and similar horiz designs.

MS1803 3f. red and olive (T **529**); 4f. olive, lake and red (Summer); 5f. lake, olive and brown-red (Autumn); 6f. olive and red (Winter) 12·50 12·00

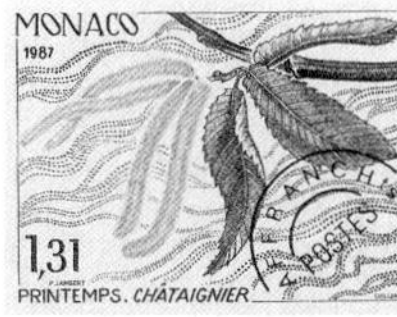

530 Spring

1987. Precancels. Seasons of the Chestnut.

1804 **530** 1f.31 green, yellow & brn 75 75
1805 - 1f.69 green and brown 80 85
1806 - 2f.74 brown, yellow & bl 1·20 1·50
1807 - 4f.56 brown, grn & grey 1·90 2·00

DESIGNS: 1f.69, Summer; 2f.74, Autumn; 4f.56, Winter.

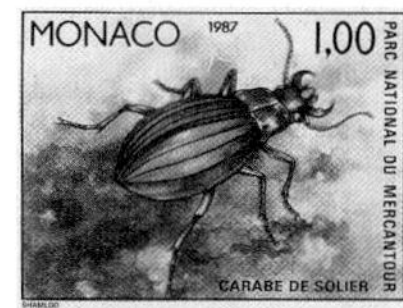

531 Golden Hunter

1987. Insects in Mercantour National Park. Multicoloured.

1808 1f. Type **531** 60 55
1809 1f.90 Golden wasp (vert) 1·20 90
1810 2f. Green tiger beetle 1·40 1·00
1811 2f.20 Brown aeshna (vert) 1·60 1·20
1812 3f. Leaf beetle 3·00 1·80
1813 3f.40 Grasshopper (vert) 4·00 2·75

532 St. Devote Church

1987. Centenary of St. Devote Parish Church.

1814 **532** 1f.90 brown 1·00 75

533 Dogs

1987. International Dog Show, Monte Carlo.

1815 **533** 1f.90 grey, black & brn 2·50 1·80
1816 - 2f.70 black and green 4·00 2·75

DESIGN: 2f.70, Poodle.

534 Stamp Album

1987. Stamp Day.
1817 **534** 2f.20 red, purple and mauve 1·20 65

535 Louis II Stadium, Fontvieille

1987. Europa. Each blue, green and red.
1818 2f.20 Type **535** 2·50 1·40
1819 3f.40 Crown Prince Albert Olympic swimming pool 3·00 1·80
MS1820 143×71 mm. Nos. 1818/19, each ×5 37·00 32·00

536 Cathedral

1987. Centenary of Monaco Diocese.
1821 **536** 2f.50 green 1·50 90

537 Spring

1987. Seasons of the Vine. Sheet 142×100 mm containing T 537 and similar horiz designs.
MS1822 3f. green and brown (Type **537**); 4f. green and brown (Summer); 5f. violet, brown and green (Autumn); 6f. orange-brown (Winter) 19·00 17·00

538 Lawn Tennis

1987. 2nd European Small States Games, Monaco.
1823 **538** 3f. black, red and purple 2·75 2·00
1824 - 5f. blue and black 3·50 2·50
DESIGN: 5f. Sailing dinghies and windsurfer.

539 "Red Curly Tail" (Alexander Calder)

1987. "Monte Carlo Sculpture 1987" Exhibition.
1825 **539** 3f.70 multicoloured 2·00 1·50

540 Prince Rainier III

1987. 50th Anniv of Monaco Stamp Issuing Office.
1826 **540** 4f. blue 2·20 2·30
1827 - 4f. red 2·20 2·30
1828 - 8f. black 4·50 3·75
DESIGNS: No. 1827, Prince Louis II. (47×37 mm): 1828, Villa Miraflores.

541 Swallowtail on Stamp

1987. International Stamp Exhibition.
1829 **541** 1f.90 deep green and green 85 65
1830 **541** 2f.20 purple and red 1·20 90
1831 **541** 2f.50 purple and mauve 1·40 1·00
1832 **541** 3f.40 deep blue and blue 2·00 1·50

542 Festival Poster (J. Ramel)

1987. 13th International Circus Festival, Monaco (1988).
1833 **542** 2f.20 multicoloured 2·50 1·80

543 Christmas Scenes

1987. Christmas.
1834 **543** 2f.20 red 1·20 90

544 Strawberry Plants and Campanulas in Bowl

1987. Monte Carlo Flower Show (1988). Mult.
1835 2f.20 Type **544** 1·90 1·20
1836 3f.40 Ikebana arrangement of water lilies and dog roses (horiz) 2·10 1·60

545 Obverse and Reverse of Honore V 5f. Silver Coin

1987. 150th Anniv of Revival of Monaco Coinage.
1837 **545** 2f.50 black and red 1·20 90

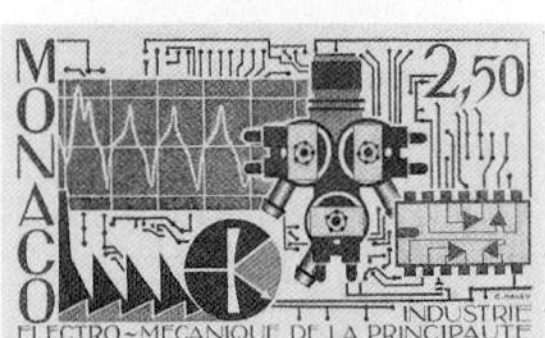

546 Graph, Factory, Electron Microscope and Printed Circuit

1987. Electro-Mechanical Industry.
1838 **546** 2f.50 blue, green and red 1·20 90

547 St. Devote

1987. Monaco Red Cross. St. Devote, Patron Saint of Monaco (1st series). Multicoloured.
1839 4f. Type **547** 2·20 1·40
1840 5f. St. Devote and her nurse 2·75 2·00
See also Nos. 1898/9, 1956/7, 1980/1, 2062/3 and 2101/2.

1987. 50th Anniv of Monaco Stamp Issuing Office (2nd issue). Sheet 140×70 mm containing T 540 and other designs. Each purple.
MS1841 4f. Type **540**; 4f. As No. 1827; 8f. As No. 1828 8·75 8·25

548 Oceanographic Museum and I.A.E.A. Headquarters, Vienna

1987. 25th Anniv of International Marine Radioactivity Laboratory, Monaco.
1842 **548** 5f. black, brown and blue 2·50 1·80

549 Jouvet

1987. Birth Centenary of Louis Jouvet (actor).
1843 **549** 3f. black 1·50 1·10

550 River Crossing

1987. Bicentenary of First Edition of "Paul and Virginia" by Bernardin de Saint-Pierre.
1844 **550** 3f. green, orange and blue 1·50 1·10

551 Marc Chagall (painter)

1987. Anniversaries.
1845 **551** 4f. black and red 2·10 1·60
1846 - 4f. purple, red and brown 2·10 1·60
1847 - 4f. red, blue and brown 2·10 1·60
1848 - 4f. green, brown & purple 2·10 1·60
1849 - 5f. blue, brown and green 3·00 2·30
1850 - 5f. brown, green and blue 3·00 2·30
DESIGNS: No. 1845, Type **551** (birth centenary); 1846, Chapel of Ronchamp and Charles Edouard Jeanneret (Le Corbusier) (architect, birth centenary); 1847, Sir Isaac Newton (mathematician) and diagram (300th anniv of publication of "Principia Mathematica"); 1848, Key and Samuel Morse (inventor, 150th Anniv of Morse telegraph); 1849, Wolfgang Amadeus Mozart and scene from "Don Juan" (opera, bicentenary of composition); 1850, Hector Berlioz (composer) and scene from "Mass for the Dead" (150th anniv of composition).

1987. Monaco in the "Belle Epoque" (6th series). As T 445 showing paintings by Hubert Clerissi. Multicoloured.
1851 6f. "Main Ramp to Palace Square, 1925" (vert) 5·00 3·75
1852 7f. "Monte Carlo Railway Station, 1925" (vert) 5·50 4·25

552 Coat of Arms

1987
1853 **552** 2f. multicoloured 1·10 85
1854 **552** 2f.20 multicoloured 1·00 75

553 Spanish Hogfish

1988. Fishes in Oceanographic Museum Aquarium (2nd series). Multicoloured.
1857 2f. Type **553** 1·20 90
1858 2f.20 Copper-banded butterflyfish 1·50 1·10
1859 2f.50 Harlequin filefish 2·00 1·50
1860 3f. Blue boxfish 2·20 1·70
1861 3f.70 Lionfish 3·00 2·30
1862 7f. Moon wrasse (horiz) 5·00 3·75

554 Spring

1988. Precancels. Seasons of the Pear Tree. Multicoloured.
1863 1f.36 Type **554** 75 75
1864 1f.75 Summer 80 85
1865 2f.83 Autumn 1·20 1·50
1866 4f.72 Winter 1·90 2·00
See also Nos. 1952/5.

555 Cross-country Skiing

1988. Winter Olympic Games, Calgary. Sheet 143×93 mm containing T 555 and similar horiz design. Each black, lilac and blue.
MS1867 4f. Type **555**; 6f. Shooting 25·00 18·00

556 Dachshunds

1988. European Dachshunds Show, Monte Carlo.
1868 **556** 3f. multicoloured 3·00 2·30

557 Children of different Races around Globe

1988. 25th Anniv of World Association of Friends of Children.
1869 **557** 5f. green, brown and blue 3·00 2·30

558 Satellite Camera above Man with World as Brain

1988. Europa. Transport and Communications. Each black, brown and red.

1870		2f.20 Type **558**	2·50	1·80
1871		3f.60 Atlantique high speed mail train and aircraft propeller	3·75	2·75
MS1872		170×143 mm. Nos. 1870/1, each ×5	37·00	32·00

559 Coxless Four

1988. Centenary of Monaco Nautical Society (formerly Regatta Society).

1873	**559**	2f. blue, green and red	1·50	1·10

560 Jean Monnet (statesman)

1988. Birth Centenaries.

1874	**560**	2f. black, brown and blue	3·75	2·75
1875	-	2f. black and blue	3·75	2·75

DESIGN: No. 1875, Maurice Chevalier (entertainer).

561 "Leccinum rotundifoliae"

1988. Fungi in Mercantour National Park. Multicoloured.

1876		2f. Type **561**	1·50	1·10
1877		2f.20 Crimson wax cap	1·90	1·40
1878		2f.50 "Pholiota flammans"	2·20	1·70
1879		2f.70 "Lactarius lignyotus"	2·75	2·00
1880		3f. Goaty smell (vert)	3·00	2·30
1881		7f. "Russula olivacea" (vert)	5·25	3·75

562 Nansen

1988. Centenary of First Crossing of Greenland by Fridtjof Nansen (Norwegian explorer).

1882	**562**	4f. violet	3·00	2·20

563 Church and "Miraculous Virgin"

1988. Restoration of Sanctuary of Our Lady of Laghet.

1883	**563**	5f. multicoloured	2·50	1·80

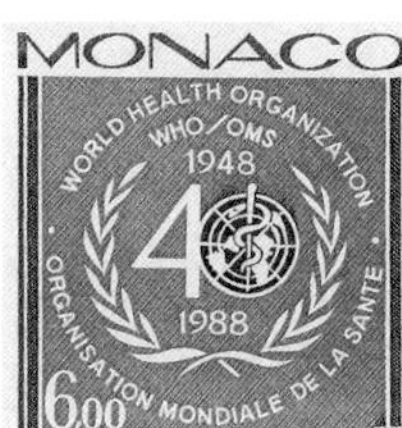

564 Anniversary Emblem

1988. 40th Anniv of W.H.O.

1884	**564**	6f. red and blue	3·25	2·40

565 Anniversary Emblem

1988. 125th Anniv of Red Cross.

1885	**565**	6f. red, grey and black	3·25	2·40

566 Congress Centre

1988. 10th Anniv of Monte Carlo Congress Centre.

1886	**566**	2f. green	1·20	90
1887	-	3f. red	1·50	1·10

DESIGN: 3f. Auditorium.

567 Tennis

1988. Olympic Games, Seoul. New Women's Disciplines. Sheet 143×100 mm containing T 567 and similar horiz designs. Each brown, black and blue.

MS1888		2f. Type **567**; 3f. Table tennis; 5f. "470" dinghy; 7f. Cycling	12·50	12·00

1988. Monaco in the "Belle Epoque" (7th series). Paintings by Hubert Clerissi. As T 445. Mult.

1889		6f. "Steam packet in Monte Carlo Harbour, 1910"	5·00	3·25
1890		7f. "Place de la Gare, 1910"	6·25	4·25

568 Festival Poster (J. Ramel)

1988. 14th International Circus Festival, Monaco (1989).

1891	**568**	2f. multicoloured	1·90	1·40

569 Star Decoration

1988. Christmas.

1892	**569**	2f. multicoloured	1·40	1·00

570 Arrangement of Fuchsias, Irises, Roses and Petunias

1988. Monte Carlo Flower Show (1989).

1893	**570**	3f. multicoloured	2·20	1·70

571 Models

1988. Ready-to-Wear Clothing Industry.

1894	**571**	3f. green, orange & black	1·90	1·40

572 Lord Byron (bicentenary)

1988. Writers' Birth Anniversaries.

1895	**572**	3f. black, brown and blue	1·90	1·40
1896	-	3f. purple and blue	1·90	1·40

DESIGN: No. 1896, Pierre de Marivaux (300th anniv).

573 Spring

1988. Seasons of the Olive Tree. Sheet 143×100 mm containing T 573 and similar horiz designs.

MS1897		3f. deep olive, yellow and olive (Type **573**); 4f. deep olive and olive (Summer); 5f. deep olive and olive (Autumn); 6f. deep olive and olive (Winter)	17·00	17·00

1988. Monaco Red Cross. St. Devote, Patron Saint of Monaco (2nd series). As T 547. Multicoloured.

1898		4f. Roman governor Barbarus arriving at Corsica	2·40	1·70
1899		5f. St. Devote at the Roman senator Eutychius's house	3·00	2·30

574 "Le Nain and his Brothers" (Antoine Le Nain)

1988. Artists' Birth Anniversaries.

1900	**574**	5f. brown, olive and red	3·50	2·50
1901	-	5f. black, green and blue	3·50	2·50

DESIGNS: No. 1900, Type **574** (400th anniv): 1901, "The Great Archaeologists" (bronze statue, Giorgio de Chirico) (centenary).

575 Sorcerer

1989. Rock Carvings in Mercantour National Park. Multicoloured.

1902		2f. Type **575**	1·20	90
1903		2f.20 Oxen in yoke	1·20	90
1904		3f. Hunting implements	1·90	1·40
1905		3f.60 Tribal chief	2·50	1·80
1906		4f. Puppet (vert)	3·00	2·30
1907		5f. Jesus Christ (vert)	3·75	2·75

576 Rue des Spelugues

1989. Old Monaco (1st series). Multicoloured.

1908		2f. Type **576**	1·10	85
1909		2f.20 Place Saint Nicolas	1·40	1·00

See also Nos. 1969/70 and 2090/1.

577 Prince Rainier

1989

1910	**577**	2f. blue and azure	1·00	65
1911	**577**	2f.10 blue and azure	1·10	45
1912	**577**	2f.20 brown and pink	1·20	75
1913	**577**	2f.20 blue and azure	1·20	65
1914	**577**	2f.30 brown and pink	1·20	65
1915	**577**	2f.40 blue and azure	1·20	65
1916	**577**	2f.50 brown and pink	1·20	90
1917	**577**	2f.70 blue	1·00	55
1918	**577**	2f.80 brown and pink	1·50	75
1919	**577**	3f. brown and pink	1·10	85
1920	**577**	3f.20 blue and cobalt	1·90	1·40
1922	**577**	3f.40 blue and cobalt	2·00	1·50
1923	**577**	3f.60 blue and cobalt	2·10	1·60
1924	**577**	3f.70 blue and cobalt	2·50	1·00
1925	**577**	3f.80 purple and lilac	2·50	1·80
1926	**577**	3f.80 blue and cobalt	1·40	90
1927	**577**	4f. purple and lilac	2·50	1·80
1930	**577**	5f. brown and pink	2·50	1·70
1932	**577**	10f. deep green and green	4·00	2·30
1934	**577**	15f. blue and grey	7·50	5·00
1936	**577**	20f. red and pink	8·00	5·00
1938	**577**	25f. black and grey	10·00	6·50
1940	**577**	40f. brown and pink	15·00	9·25

See also Nos. 2388/90.

578 Yorkshire Terrier

1989. International Dog Show, Monte Carlo.

1941	**578**	2f.20 multicoloured	1·90	1·30

579 Magician, Dove and Cards

1989. 5th Grand Prix of Magic, Monte Carlo.

1942	**579**	2f.20 black, blue and red	1·50	1·10

580 Nuns and Monks around "Our Lady of Misericorde"

1989. 350th Anniv of Archiconfrerie de la Misericorde.

1943	**580**	3f. brown, black and red	1·70	1·30

581 Charlie Chaplin (actor) and Film Scenes

1989. Birth Centenaries.

1944	-	3f. green, blue and mauve	1·70	1·30
1945	**581**	4f. purple, green and red	2·50	1·80

DESIGN: 3f. Jean Cocteau (writer and painter), scene from "The Double-headed Eagle" and frescoes in Villefranche-sur-Mer chapel.

582 Spring

1989. Seasons of the Pomegranate. Sheet 144×100 mm containing T 582 and similar horiz designs.

MS1946 3f. red, green and (Type **582**); 4f. brown, green and red (Summer); 5f. green, red and brown (Autumn); 6f. brown and green (Winter) 12·00 12·00

583 Boys playing Marbles

1989. Europa. Children's Games. Each mauve, brown and grey.

1947	2f.20 Type **583**	1·90	1·40
1948	3f.60 Girls skipping	3·00	2·30
MS1949	171×143 mm. Nos. 1947/8, each ×5	31·00	31·00

584 Prince Rainier

1989. 40th Anniv of Reign of Prince Rainier. Sheet 100×130 mm.

MS1950	**584**	20f. lilac	12·50	12·00

585 "Lliberty"

1989. "Philexfrance 89" International Stamp Exhibition, Paris. Sheet 143×105 mm containing T 585 and similar vert designs.

MS1951 5f. blue (Type **585**); 5f. black ("Equality"); 5f. red ("Fraternity") 8·25 8·25

1989. Precancels. As Nos. 1863/6 but values changed. Multicoloured.

1952	1f.39 Type **554**	75	75
1953	1f.79 Summer	80	85
1954	2f.90 Autumn	1·20	1·50
1955	4f.84 Winter	1·90	2·00

1989. Monaco Red Cross. St. Devote, Patron Saint of Monaco (3rd series). As T 547. Multicoloured.

1956	4f. St. Devote beside the dying Eutychius	2·10	1·60
1957	5f. Barbarus condemns St. Devote to torture for refusing to make a sacrifice to the gods	3·00	2·30

586 "Artist's Mother" (Philibert Florence)

1989. Artists' 150th Birth Anniversaries.

1958	**586**	4f. brown	3·00	2·30
1959	-	6f. multicoloured	3·75	2·75
1960	-	8f. multicoloured	5·00	3·75

DESIGNS—HORIZ: 6f. "Molesey Regatta" (Alfred Sisley). VERT: 8f. "Farmyard at Auvers" (Paul Cezanne).

587 Poinsettia, Christmas Roses and Holly

1989. Christmas.

1961	**587**	2f. multicoloured	2·75	2·00

588 Map and Emblem

1989. Centenary of Interparliamentary Union.

1962	**588**	4f. black, green and red	2·50	1·80

589 Princess Grace (founder)

1989. 25th Anniv of Princess Grace Foundation. Sheet 133×104 mm containing T 589 and similar vert design. Each blue.

MS1963 5f. Type **589**; 5f. Princess Caroline (Foundation president) 10·00 10·00

590 Monaco Palace, White House, Washington, and Emblem

1989. 20th U.P.U. Congress, Washington D.C.

1964	**590**	6f. blue, brown and black	3·00	2·30

1989. Monaco in the "Belle Epoque" (8th series). Paintings by Hubert Clerissi. As T 445. Mult.

1965	7f. "Barque in Monte Carlo Harbour, 1915" (vert)	4·25	3·00
1966	8f. "Gaming Tables, Casino, 1915" (vert)	5·25	3·75

591 World Map

1989. 10th Anniv of Monaco Aide et Presence (welfare organization).

1967	**591**	2f.20 brown and red	3·00	2·30

592 Clown and Horses

1989. 15th International Circus Festival, Monte Carlo.

1968	**592**	2f.20 multicoloured	3·75	2·75

1990. Old Monaco (2nd series). Paintings by Claude Rosticher. As T 576. Multicoloured.

1969	2f.10 La Rampe Major	1·00	75
1970	2f.30 Town Hall Courtyard	1·10	85

593 Phalaenopsis "Princess Grace"

1990. International Garden and Greenery Exposition, Osaka, Japan. Multicoloured.

1971	2f. Type **593**	1·20	90
1972	3f. Iris "Grace Patricia"	1·90	1·40
1973	3f. "Paphiopedilum" "Prince Rainier III"	1·90	1·40
1974	4f. "Cattleya" "Principessa Grace"	2·50	1·80
1975	5f. Rose "Caroline of Monaco"	3·50	2·30

594 Bearded Collie

1990. International Dog Show, Monte Carlo.

1976	**594**	2f.30 multicoloured	2·30	1·70

595 Noghes and Racing Car

1990. Birth Centenary of Antony Noghes (founder of Monaco Grand Prix and Monte Carlo Rally).

1977	**595**	3f. red, lilac and black	1·70	1·20

596 Cyclist and Lancia Rally Car

1990. Centenary of Automobile Club of Monaco (founded as Cycling Racing Club).

1978	**596**	4f. blue, brown & purple	2·30	1·70

597 Telephone, Satellite and Dish Aerial

1990. 125th Anniv of I.T.U.

1979	**597**	4f. lilac, mauve and blue	2·30	1·70

1990. Monaco Red Cross. St. Devote, Patron Saint of Monaco (4th series). As T 547. Multicoloured.

1980	4f. St. Devote being flogged	2·30	1·70
1981	5f. Placing body of St. Devote in fishing boat	3·00	2·20

598 Sir Rowland Hill and Penny Black

1990. 150th Anniv of Penny Black.

1982	**598**	5f. blue and black	3·25	2·30

599 "Post Office, Place de la Mairie"

1990. Europa. Post Office Buildings. Paintings by Hubert Clerissi. Multicoloured.

1983	2f.30 Type **599**	1·90	1·40
1984	3f.70 "Post Office, Avenue d'Ostende"	3·25	2·30
MS1985	170×145 mm. Nos. 1983/4, each ×4	39·00	32·00

600 Ball, Player and Trophy

1990. World Cup Football Championship, Italy. Sheet 142×100 mm containing T 600 and similar horiz designs.

MS1986 5f. green, black and red; (Type **600**); 5f. black, red and green (Players); 5f. black and green (Pitch, ball and map of Italy); 5f. red, green and black (Pitch, players and stadium)	17·00	17·00

601 Anatase

1990. Minerals in Mercantour National Park. Mult.

1987	2f.10 Type **601**	1·30	90
1988	2f.30 Albite	1·40	1·00
1989	3f.20 Rutile	1·90	1·40
1990	3f.80 Chlorite	2·50	1·80
1991	4f. Brookite (vert)	2·75	2·00
1992	6f. Quartz (vert)	4·50	3·25

602 Powerboat

1990. World Offshore Powerboat Racing Championship.

1993	**602**	2f.30 brown, red & blue	1·50	1·10

603 Pierrot writing (mechanical toy)

1990. Philatelic Round Table.

1994	**603**	3f. blue	1·80	1·30

604 Christian Samuel Hahnemann (founding of homeopathy)

1990. Bicentenaries.

1995	**604**	3f. purple, green & black	1·80	1·30
1996	-	5f. chestnut, brown & bl	2·75	2·00

DESIGN: 5f. Jean-Francois Champollion (Egypt-ologist) and hieroglyphics (birth bicentenary).

605 Bell 206B Jet-Ranger III Helicopters at Monaco Heliport, Fontvieille

1990. 30th International Civil Airports Association Congress, Monte Carlo.

1997	**605**	3f. black, red and brown	1·90	1·40
1998	-	5f. black, blue and brown	3·25	1·80

DESIGN: 5f. Aerospatiale AS-350 Ecureuil helicopters over Monte Carlo Congress Centre.

606 Petanque Player

1990. 26th World Petanque Championship.

1999	**606**	6f. blue, brown & orange	3·75	2·75

607 Spring

1990. Precancels. Seasons of the Plum Tree. Multicoloured.

2000	1f.46 Type **607**	75	75
2001	1f.89 Summer	85	85
2002	3f.06 Autumn	1·30	1·50
2003	5f.10 Winter	1·90	2·00

608 Miller on Donkey

1990. Christmas. Crib figures from Provence. Multicoloured.

2004	2f.30 Type **608**	1·30	90
2005	3f.20 Woman carrying faggots	1·90	1·40
2006	3f.80 Baker	2·50	1·80

See also Nos. 2052/4, 2097/9, 2146/8 and 2191/3.

609 Spring

1990. Seasons of the Lemon Tree. Sheet 143×100 mm containing T 609 and similar horiz designs. Multicoloured.

MS2007 3f. Type **609**; 4f. Summer; 5f. Autumn; 6f. Winter	13·00	12·00

610 Pyotr Ilich Tchaikovsky (composer)

1990. 150th Birth Anniversaries.

2008	**610**	5f. blue and green	2·75	2·00
2009	-	5f. bistre and blue	2·75	2·00
2010	-	7f. multicoloured	6·50	5·50

DESIGNS—As T **610**: No. 2009, "Cathedral" (Auguste Rodin, sculptor). 48×37 mm: "The Magpie" (Claude Monet, painter).

611 Clown playing Concertina

1991. 16th International Circus Festival, Monte Carlo.

2011	**611**	2f.30 multicoloured	1·90	1·30

See also No. 2069.

1991. Bygone Monaco (2nd series). Paintings by Hubert Clerissi. As T 481.

2015	20c. purple	25	20
2017	40c. green	25	20
2018	50c. red	25	20
2019	60c. blue	25	20
2020	70c. green	40	30
2021	80c. blue	40	30
2022	90c. lilac	40	30
2023	1f. blue	55	35
2024	2f. red	80	55
2025	3f. black	1·30	90
2027	7f. grey and black	3·25	2·30

DESIGNS: 20c. Rock of Monaco and Fontvieille; 40c. Place du Casino; 50c. Place de la Cremaillere and railway station; 60c. National Council building; 70c. Palace and Rampe Major; 80c. Avenue du Beau Rivage; 90c. Fishing boats, Fontvieille; 1f. Place d'Armes; 2f. Marche de la Condamine; 3f. Yacht; 7f. Oceanographic Museum.

612 Abdim's Stork

1991. International Symposium on Bird Migration. Multicoloured.

2029	2f. Type **612**	1·30	90
2030	3f. Broad-tailed hummingbirds	2·00	1·40
2031	4f. Garganeys	2·75	1·80
2032	5f. Eastern broad-billed roller	3·25	2·30
2033	6f. European bee eaters	4·00	2·75

613 Phytoplankton

1991. Oceanographic Museum (1st series).

2034	**613**	2f.10 multicoloured	1·60	1·10

See also Nos. 2095/6.

614 Schnauzer

1991. International Dog Show, Monte Carlo.

2035	**614**	2f.50 multicoloured	2·75	1·80

615 Cyclamen, Lily-of-the-Valley and Pine Twig in Fir-cone

1991. Monte Carlo Flower Show.

2036	**615**	3f. multicoloured	1·90	1·30

616 Corals

1991. "Joys of the Sea" Exhibition. Multicoloured.

2037	2f.20 Type **616**	1·30	90
2038	2f.40 Coral necklace	2·00	1·40

617 Control Room, "Eutelsat" Satellite and Globe

1991. Europa. Europe in Space. Each blue, black and green.

2039	2f.30 Type **617**	2·75	1·80
2040	3f.20 Computer terminal, "Inmarsat" satellite, research ship transmitting signal and man with receiving equipment	4·00	2·75
MS2041	143×171 mm. Nos. 2039/40, each ×5	37·00	32·00

618 Cross-country Skiers and Statue of Skiers by Emma de Sigaldi

1991. 1992 Olympic Games. (a) Winter Olympics, Albertville.

2042	**618**	3f. green, blue and olive	1·90	1·30
2043	-	4f. green, blue and olive	2·40	1·70

(b) Olympic Games, Barcelona.

2044		3f. green, lt brown & brown	1·90	1·30
2045		5f. black, brown and green	3·25	2·20

DESIGNS: No. 2043, Right-hand part of statue and cross-country skiers; 2044, Track, relay runners and left part of statue of relay runners by Emma de Sigaldi; 2045, Right part of statue, view of Barcelona and track.

619 Head of "David" (Michelangelo), Computer Image and Artist at Work

1991. 25th International Contemporary Art Prize.

2046	**619**	4f. green, dp green & lilac	2·75	1·80

620 Prince Pierre, Open Book and Lyre

1991. 25th Anniv of Prince Pierre Foundation.

2047	**620**	5f. black, blue and brown	3·25	2·30

621 Tortoises

1991. Endangered Species. Hermann's Tortoise. Multicoloured.

2048	1f.25 Type **621**	1·60	1·10
2049	1f.25 Head of tortoise	1·60	1·10
2050	1f.25 Tortoise in grass	1·60	1·10
2051	1f.25 Tortoise emerging from among plants	1·60	1·10

1991. Christmas. As T 608 showing crib figures from Provence. Multicoloured.

2052	2f.50 Consul	1·70	1·20
2053	3f.50 Arlesian woman	2·75	1·80
2054	4f. Mayor	3·00	2·00

622 Norway Spruce

1991. Conifers in Mercantour National Park. Multicoloured.

2055	2f.50 Type **622**	1·30	90
2056	3f.50 Silver fir	2·00	1·40
2057	4f. "Pinus uncinata"	2·30	1·60
2058	5f. Scots pine (vert)	2·75	1·80
2059	6f. Arolla pine	3·25	2·30
2060	7f. European larch (vert)	4·00	2·75

623 Spring

1991. Seasons of the Orange Tree. Sheet 142×101 mm containing T 623 and similar horiz designs.

MS2061 3f. orange, green and brown (Type **623**); 4d. green and brown (Summer); 5f. green, orange and brown (Autumn); 6f. green and olive-brown (Winter) 13·50 13·00

1991. Monaco Red Cross. St. Devote, Patron Saint of Monaco (5th series). As T 547. Multicoloured.

2062	4f.50 Fishing boat carrying body caught in storm	2·75	1·80
2063	5f.50 Dove guiding boatman to port of Monaco	3·00	2·00

624 "Portrait of Claude Monet"

1991. 150th Birth Anniv of Auguste Renoir (painter).

2064	**624**	5f. multicoloured	3·25	2·30

625 Prince Honore II of Monaco

1991. 350th Anniv of Treaty of Peronne (giving French recognition of sovereignty of Monaco). Paintings by Philippe de Champaigne. Mult.

2065	6f. Type **625**	4·00	2·75
2066	7f. King Louis XIII of France	5·25	3·75

626 Princess Grace (after R. Samini)

1991. 10th Anniv of Princess Grace Theatre.

2067	**626**	8f. multicoloured	5·50	3·75

627 1891 Stamp Design

1991. Centenary of Prince Albert Stamps. Sheet 114×72 mm.

MS2068 **627** 10f. red; 10f. green; 10f. lilac 17·00 18·00

1992. 16th International Circus Festival, Monte Carlo. As No. 2011 but value and dates changed.

2069	**611**	2f.50 multicoloured	1·70	1·20

The 1991 Festival was cancelled.

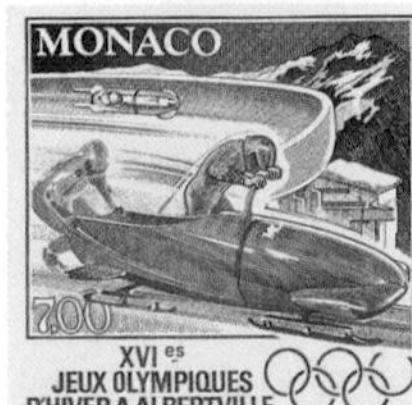
628 Two-man Bobsleighs

1992. Winter Olympic Games, Albertville (7f.), and Summer Games, Barcelona (8f.).

2070	**628**	7f. blue, turquoise & blk	4·00	2·75
2071	-	8f. purple, blue and green	4·25	3·00

DESIGN: 8f. Football.

629 Spring

1992. Exotic Gardens. Seasons of the Prickly Pear. Sheet 142×100 mm containing T 629 and similar horiz designs. Multicoloured.

MS2072 3f. Type **629**; 4f. Summer; 5f. Autumn; 6f. Winter 13·50 12·00

630 Spring

1992. Precancels. Seasons of the Walnut Tree. Mult.

2073	1f.60 Type **630**	80	85
2074	2f.08 Summer	85	90
2075	2f.98 Autumn	1·30	1·50
2076	5f.28 Winter	2·00	2·00

631 Golden Labrador

1992. International Dog Show, Monte Carlo.

2077	**631**	2f.20 multicoloured	3·00	1·50

632 Racing along Seafront

1992. 50th Monaco Grand Prix.

2078	**632**	2f.50 black, purple & bl	1·60	1·10

633 Mixed Bouquet

1992. 25th Monte Carlo Flower Show.

2079	**633**	3f.40 multicoloured	2·75	1·80

634 Ford Sierra Rally Car

1992. 60th Monte Carlo Car Rally.

2080	**634**	4f. black, green and red	3·00	2·00

635 Rough-toothed Dolphin (*Steno bredanensis*)

1992. Mediterranean Dolphins. Sheet 142×100 mm containing T 635 and similar horiz designs. Multicoloured.

MS2081 4f. Type **635** 5f. Common dolphin (*Delphinus delphis*); 6f. Bottle-nosed dolphin (*Tursiops truncates*); 7f. Striped dolphin (*Stenella coeruleoalba*) 16·00 16·00

636 "Pinta" off Palos

1992. Europa. 500th Anniv of Discovery of America by Columbus. Multicoloured.

2082	2f.50 Type **636**	2·00	1·40
2083	3f.40 "Santa Maria" in the Antilles	3·25	2·30
2084	4f. "Nina" off Lisbon	4·25	3·00
MS2085	140×170 mm. Nos. 2082/4, each ×2	33·00	28·00

637 Produce

1992. "Ameriflora" Horticultural Show, Columbus, Ohio. Multicoloured.

2086	4f. Type **637**	2·75	1·80
2087	5f. Vase of mixed flowers	3·25	2·30

638 Prince Rainier I and Fleet (detail of fresco by E. Charpentier, Spinola Palace, Genoa)

1992. Columbus Exhibition, Genoa (6f.), and "Expo '92" World's Fair, Seville (7f.).

2088	**638**	6f. brown, red and blue	3·25	2·30
2089	-	7f. brown, red and blue	4·00	2·75

DESIGN: 7f. Monaco pavilion.

1992. Old Monaco (3rd series). Paintings by Claude Rosticher. As T 576. Multicoloured.

2090	2f.20 La Porte Neuve (horiz)	1·30	90
2091	2f.50 La Placette Bosio (horiz)	1·30	90

639 "Christopher Columbus"

1992. "Genova '92" International Thematic Stamp Exhibition. Roses. Multicoloured.

2092	3f. Type **639**	2·40	1·70
2093	4f. "Prince of Monaco"	3·00	2·00

640 Lammergeier

1992

2094	**640**	2f.20 orange, blk & grn	2·00	1·40

1992. Oceanographic Museum (2nd series). As T 613. Multicoloured.

2095	2f.20 "Ceratium ranipes"	2·00	1·40
2096	2f.50 "Ceratium hexacanthum"	2·00	1·40

1992. Christmas. As T 608 showing crib figures from Provence. Multicoloured.

2097	2f.50 Basket-maker	2·00	1·40
2098	3f.40 Fishwife	2·40	1·70
2099	5f. Rural constable	3·00	2·00

641 "Seabus" (projected tourist submarine)

1992

2100	**641**	4f. blue, red and brown	2·40	1·70

642 Burning Boat Ceremony, St. Devote's Eve

1992. Monaco Red Cross. St. Devote, Patron Saint of Monaco (6th series).

2101	**642**	6f. red, blue and brown	3·25	2·30
2102	-	8f. purple, orange and red	4·00	2·75

DESIGN: 8f. Procession of reliquary, St. Devote's Day.

643 Athletes, Sorbonne University and Coubertin

1992. Centenary of Pierre de Coubertin's Proposal for Revival of Olympic Games.

2103	**643**	10f. blue	5·50	3·75

644 Baux de Provence and St. Catherine's Chapel

1992. Titles of Princes of Monaco. Marquis of Baux de Provence.

2104 **644** 15f. multicoloured 7·25 5·00

645 1856 40c. Sardinian Stamp

1992. Stamp Museum. Sheet 115×72 mm containing T 645 and similar vert design.

MS2105 10f. red and black (Type **645**); 10f. green and black (1860 1c. French stamp) 12·00 12·00

646 Clown and Tiger

1993. 17th Int Circus Festival, Monte Carlo.

2106 **646** 2f.50 multicoloured 1·60 1·10

647 Short-toed Eagles

1993. Birds of Prey in Mercantour National Park.

2107 **647** 2f. chestnut, brown and orange 1·30 90
2108 - 3f. indigo, orange & blue 2·00 1·40
2109 - 4f. brown, ochre and blue 2·75 1·80
2110 - 5f. brown, chestnut and green 3·00 2·00
2111 - 6f. brown, mauve & grn 4·00 2·75

DESIGNS—HORIZ: 3f. Peregrine falcon. VERT: 4f. Eagle owl; 5f. Western honey buzzard; 6f. Tengmalm's owl.

648 Fin Whale (*Balaenoptera physalus*)

1993. Mediterranean Whales. Sheet 143×100 mm containing T 648 and similar horiz designs. Multicoloured.

MS2112 4f. Type **648**; 5f. Minke whale (*Balaenoptera acutorostrata*); 6f. Sperm whale (Physeter catodon); 7f. Cuvier's beaked whale (Ziphius cavirostris) 16·00 18·00

649 Spring

1993. Seasons of the Almond. Sheet 142×100 mm containing T 649 and similar horiz designs.

MS2113 5f. Type **649**; 5f. Summer; 5f. Autumn; 5f. Winter 13·50 13·00

650 Mixed Bouquet

1993. Monte Carlo Flower Show.

2114 **650** 3f.40 multicoloured 1·90 1·30

651 Pennants, Auditorium and Masks

1993. 10th International Amateur Theatre Festival.

2115 **651** 4f.20 multicoloured 2·40 1·70

652 Fire Fighting and Rescue

1993. World Civil Protection Day.

2116 **652** 6f. black, red and green 4·00 2·75

653 Newfoundland

1993. International Dog Show, Monte Carlo.

2117 **653** 2f.20 multicoloured 1·70 1·20

654 Golfer

1993. 10th Monte Carlo Open Golf Tournament.

2118 **654** 2f.20 multicoloured 1·30 90

655 Princess Grace

1993. 10th Death Anniv (1992) of Princess Grace.

2119 **655** 5f. blue 2·30 1·60

656 Mirror and Candelabra

1993. 10th Antiques Biennale.

2120 **656** 7f. multicoloured 3·50 2·40

657 "Echinopsis multiplex"

1993. Cacti.

2121 **657** 2f.50 green, purple & yell 1·20 85
2122 - 2f.50 green and purple 1·20 85
2123 - 2f.50 green, purple & yell 1·20 85
2124 - 2f.50 green and yellow 1·20 85

DESIGNS: No. 2122, "Zygocactus truncatus"; 2123, "Echinocereus procumbens"; 2124, "Euphorbia virosa".

See also Nos. 2154/66.

658 Monte Carlo Ballets

1993. Europa. Contemporary Art.

2125 **658** 2f.50 black, brn & pink 2·00 1·40
2126 - 4f.20 grey and brown 2·75 1·80
MS2127 143×172 mm. Nos. 2125/6, each ×3 14·50 14·50

DESIGN: 4f.20, "Evolution" (sculpture, Emma de Sigaldi).

659

1993. Admission to United Nations Organization. Sheet 115×72 mm.

MS2128 10f. blue (T **659**); 10f. brown (T **577**); 10f. red and brown (State Arms) 16·00 14·50

660 State Arms and Olympic Rings

1993. 110th International Olympic Committee Session, Monaco.

2129 **660** 2f.80 red, brown & blue 1·10 90
2130 - 2f.80 blue, lt blue & red 1·10 90
2131 - 2f.80 brown, blue & red 1·10 90
2132 - 2f.80 blue, lt blue & red 1·10 90
2133 - 2f.80 brown, blue & red 1·10 90
2134 - 2f.80 blue, lt blue & red 1·10 90
2135 - 2f.80 brown, blue & red 1·10 90
2136 **660** 2f.80 blue, lt blue & red 1·10 90
2137 - 4f.50 multicoloured 2·00 1·40
2138 - 4f.50 black, yellow & bl 2·00 1·60
2139 - 4f.50 red, yellow & blue 2·00 1·60
2140 - 4f.50 black, yellow & bl 2·00 1·60
2141 - 4f.50 red, yellow & blue 2·00 1·60
2142 - 4f.50 black, yellow & bl 2·00 1·60
2143 - 4f.50 red, yellow & blue 2·00 1·60
2144 - 4f.50 red, yellow & blue 2·00 1·60

DESIGNS: 2130, Bobsleighing; 2131, Skiing; 2132, Yachting; 2133, Rowing; 2134, Swimming; 2135, Cycling; 2136, 2144, Commemorative inscription; 2138, Gymnastics (rings exercise); 2139, Judo; 2140, Fencing; 2141, Hurdling; 2142, Archery; 2143, Weightlifting.

661 Examining 1891 1c. Stamp

1993. Centenary of Monaco Philatelic Union.

2145 **661** 2f.40 multicoloured 1·30 90

1993. Christmas. Crib figures from Provence. As T 608. Multicoloured.

2146 2f.80 Donkey 1·30 90
2147 3f.70 Shepherd holding lamb 2·00 1·40
2148 4f.40 Ox lying down in barn 2·40 1·70

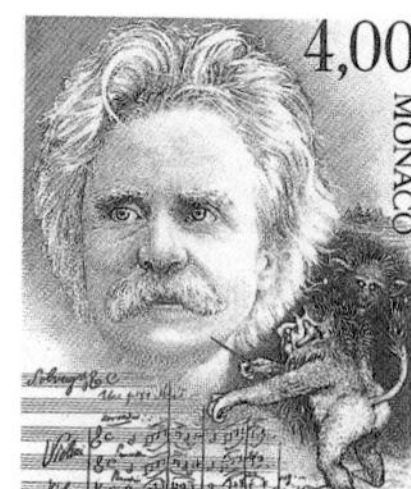

662 Grieg, Music and Trolls

1993. 150th Birth Anniv of Edvard Grieg (composer).

2149 **662** 4f. blue 3·25 2·30

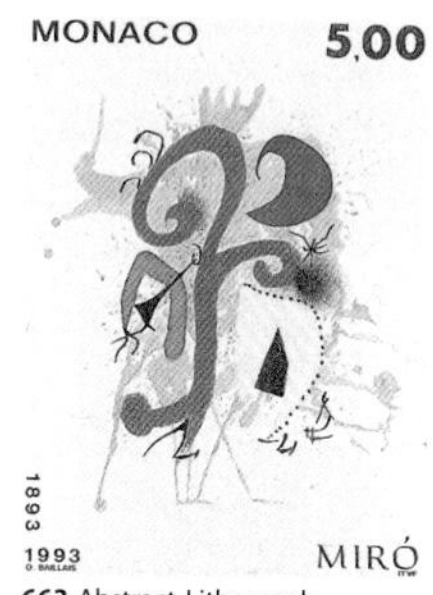

663 Abstract Lithograph

1993. Birth Centenary of Joan Miro (painter and sculptor).

2150 **663** 5f. multicoloured 3·25 2·30

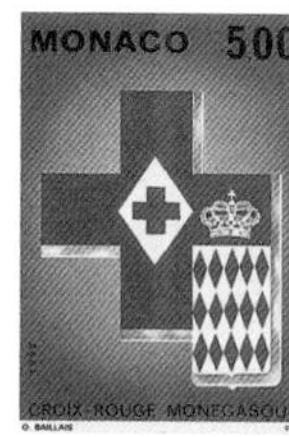

664 Monaco Red Cross Emblem

1993. Monaco Red Cross.

2151 **664** 5f. red, yellow and black 2·75 1·80
2152 - 6f. red and black 3·00 2·00

DESIGN: 6f. Crosses inscribed with fundamental principles of the International Red Cross.

665 "St. Joseph the Carpenter"

1993. 400th Birth Anniv of Georges de la Tour (painter).

2153 **665** 6f. multicoloured 3·25 2·30

1994. Cacti. As Nos. 2121/4 but values changed and additional designs.

2153a - 10c. green, orange and red 15 20
2154 **657** 20c. green, purple and yellow 25 20
2155 - 30c. green and purple 25 20
2156 - 40c. green and yellow 25 20
2157 - 50c. green, red and olive 25 20
2158 - 60c. green, red and yellow 35 25
2159 - 70c. green, red and blue 40 30
2160 - 80c. green, orange and red 40 30
2161 - 1f. green, brown and yellow 40 30
2162 - 2f. green, red and yellow 80 55
2163 - 2f.70 green, red and yellow 1·10 75
2164 - 4f. green, purple and yellow 1·50 1·00
2165 - 4f. green, red and yellow 2·00 1·40
2166 - 5f. green, mauve and brown 2·10 1·50
2167 - 6f. brown, green and red 2·40 1·70
2167a - 7f. green, brown and red 2·75 1·80

DESIGNS: 10c. "Bromelia brevifolia"; 30c. "Zygocactus truncatus"; 40c. "Euphorbia virosa"; 50c. "Selenicereus grandiflorus"; 60c. "Opuntia basilaris"; 70c. "Aloe plicatilis"; 80c. "Opuntia hybride"; 1f. "Stapelia flavirostris"; 2f. "Aporocactus flagelliformis"; 2f.70, "Opuntia dejecta"; 4f. (2164), "Echinocereus procumbens"; 4f. (2165), "Echinocereus blanckii"; 5f. "Cereus peruvianus"; 6f. "Euphorbia milii; 7f. "Stapelia variegata.

666 Festival Poster

1994. 18th Int Circus Festival, Monte Carlo.
2168 **666** 2f.80 multicoloured 1·60 1·10

667 Artist/Poet

1994. Mechanical Toys.

2169	**667**	2f.80 blue	1·20	95
2170	-	2f.80 red	1·20	95
2171	-	2f.80 purple	1·20	95
2172	-	2f.80 green	1·20	95

DESIGNS: No. 2170, Bust of Japanese woman; 2171, Shepherdess with sheep; 2172, Young Parisienne.

1994. Mediterranean Whales and Dolphins. Sheet 143×100 mm containing horiz designs as T 648. Multicoloured.
MS2173 4f. Killer whale (*Orcimus orca*); 5f. Risso's dolphin (*Grampus griseus*); 6f. False killer whale (*Pseudorca crassidens*); 7f. Long-finned pilot whale (*Globicephala melas*) 16·00 16·00

668

1994. Winter Olympic Games, Lillehammer, Norway. Sheet 123×80 mm containing T 668 and similar horiz design. Each blue and red.
MS2174 10f. Type **668**; 10f. Bobsleighing 12·00 12·00

669 King Charles Spaniels

1994. International Dog Show, Monte Carlo.
2175 **669** 2f.40 multicoloured 1·90 1·30

670 Couple, Leaves and Pollution

1994. Monaco Committee of Anti-tuberculosis and Respiratory Diseases Campaign.
2176 **670** 2f.40+60c. mult 1·60 1·10

671 Iris

1994. Monte Carlo Flower Show.
2177 **671** 4f.40 multicoloured 2·75 1·80

672 Levitation Trick

1994. 10th Monte Carlo Magic Grand Prix.
2178 **672** 5f. blue, black and red 2·75 1·80

673 Ingredients and Dining Table overlooking Harbour

1994. 35th Anniv of Brotherhood of Cordon d'Or French Chefs.
2179 **673** 6f. multicoloured 3·25 2·30

674 Isfjord, Prince Albert I, Map of Spitzbergen and "Princess Alice II"

1994. Europa. Discoveries made by Prince Albert I. Each black, blue and red.

2180 2f.80 Type **674** 2·00 1·40
2181 4f.50 Oceanographic Museum, Grimaldi's spookfish and "Eryoneicus alberti" (crustacean) 2·75 1·80
MS2182 155×130 mm. Nos. 2180/1, each ×3 16·00 14·50

675 Olympic Flag and Sorbonne University

1994. Centenary of International Olympic Committee.
2183 **675** 3f. multicoloured 1·60 1·10

676 Dolphins through Porthole

1994. Economic Institute of the Rights of the Sea Conference, Monaco.
2184 **676** 6f. multicoloured 3·25 2·30

677 Family around Tree of Hearts

1994. International Year of the Family.
2185 **677** 7f. green, orange and blue 3·50 2·40

678 Footballer's Legs and Ball

1994. World Cup Football Championship, U.S.A.
2186 **678** 8f. red and black 4·00 2·75

679 Athletes and Villa Miraflores

1994. Inauguration of New Seat of International Amateur Athletics Federation.
2187 **679** 8f. blue, purple and bistre 4·00 2·75

680 De Dion Bouton, 1903

1994. Vintage Car Collection of Prince Rainier III.
2188 **680** 2f.80 black, brown and mauve 1·60 1·10

681 Emblem and Monte Carlo

1994. 1st Association of Postage Stamp Catalogue Editors and Philatelic Publications Grand Prix.
2189 **681** 3f. multicoloured 1·70 1·20

682 Emblem and Korean Scene

1994. 21st Universal Postal Union Congress, Seoul.
2190 **682** 4f.40 black, blue and red 3·00 2·00

1994. Christmas. As T 608 showing crib figures from Provence. Multicoloured.
2191 2f.80 Virgin Mary 1·50 1·00
2192 4f.50 Baby Jesus 2·30 1·60
2193 6f. Joseph 3·00 2·00

683 Prince Albert I

1994. Inaug of Stamp and Coin Museum (1st issue). Coins.

2194	**683**	3f. stone, brown and red	1·30	90
2195	-	4f. grey, brown and red	2·00	1·40
2196	-	7f. stone, brown and red	4·00	2·75

MS2197 115×73 mm. 10f. ×3, As Nos. 2194/6 17·00 17·00

DESIGNS: 4f. Arms of House of Grimaldi; 7f. Prince Rainier III.

See also Nos. **MS**2225; 2265/7 and 2283/**MS**6.

684 Three Ages of Voltaire (writer, 300th anniv)

1994. Birth Anniversaries.
2198 **684** 5f. green 2·75 1·80
2199 - 6f. brown and purple 3·25 2·30

DESIGN—HORIZ: 6f. Sarah Bernhardt (actress, 150th anniv).

685 Heliport and Bell 206 Helicopter

1994. 50th Anniv of International Civil Aviation Organization.
2200 **685** 5f. green, black and blue 2·75 1·80
2201 - 7f. brown, black and red 3·50 2·40

DESIGN: 7f. Harbour and Eurocopter AS365 Dauphin 2 helicopter.

686 Spring

1994. 1st European Stamp Salon, Flower Gardens, Paris. Seasons of the Apricot. Sheet 142×100 mm containing T 686 and similar horiz designs. Multicoloured.
MS2202 6f. Type **686**; 7f. Summer; 8f. Autumn; 9f. Winter 17·00 17·00

687 Blood Vessels on Woman (anti-cancer)

1994. Monaco Red Cross. Health Campaigns.
2203 **687** 6f. blue, black and red 2·75 1·80
2204 - 8f. green, black and red 4·00 2·75

DESIGN: 8f. Tree and woman (anti-AIDS).

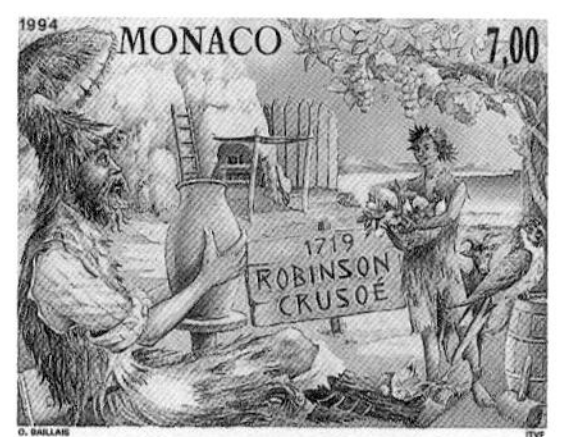

688 Robinson Crusoe and Friday

1994. Anniversaries. Multicoloured.
2205 7f. Type **688** (275th anniv of publication of "Robinson Crusoe" by Daniel Defoe) 4·00 2·75
2206 9f. "The Snake Charmer" (150th birth anniv of Henri Rousseau, painter) 4·75 3·25

689 Clown playing Trombone

1995. 19th Int Circus Festival, Monte Carlo.
2207 **689** 2f.80 multicoloured 1·60 1·10

690 Crown Prince Albert

1995. 35th Television Festival, Monte Carlo.
2208 **690** 8f. brown 4·00 2·75

691 Fontvieille

1995. European Nature Conservation Year.
2209 **691** 2f.40 multicoloured 1·50 1·00

692 American Cocker Spaniel

1995. International Dog Show, Monte Carlo.
2210 **692** 4f. multicoloured 2·10 1·40

693 Parrot Tulips

1995. Monte Carlo Flower Show.
2211 **693** 5f. multicoloured 2·50 1·70

694 "Acer palmatum"

1995. European Bonsai Congress.
2212 **694** 6f. multicoloured 3·00 2·00

695 Alfred Nobel (founder of Nobel Prizes) and Dove

1995. Europa. Peace and Freedom. Multicoloured.
2213 2f.80 Type **695** 2·75 1·80
2214 5f. Roses, broken chain and watchtower 3·50 2·30

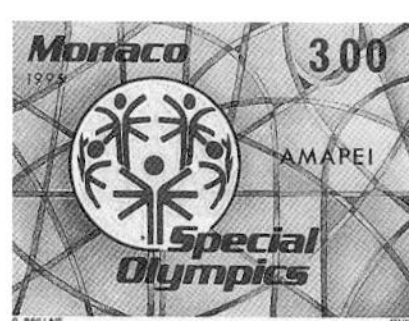

696 Emblem of Monagasque Disabled Children Association

1995. Int Special Olympics, New Haven, U.S.A.
2215 **696** 3f. multicoloured 1·20 85

697 Emblem

1995. Rotary International Convention, Nice.
2216 **697** 4f. blue 1·90 1·30

699 Jean Giono

1995. Writers' Birth Centenaries.
2218 **699** 5f. lilac, brown and green 2·50 1·70
2219 - 6f. brown, violet and green 3·00 2·00
DESIGN: 6f. Marcel Pagnol.

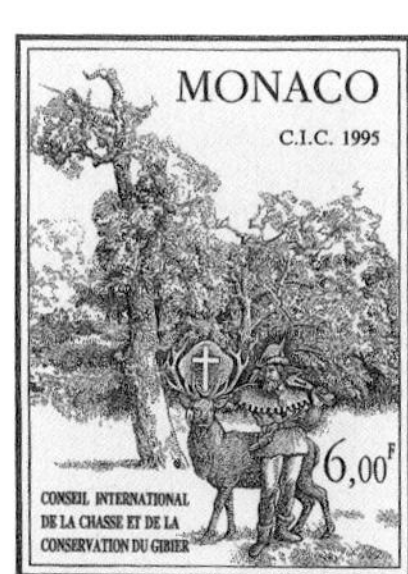

700 Saint Hubert (patron saint of hunting)

1995. General Assembly of International Council for Hunting and Conservation of Game.
2220 **700** 6f. blue 3·00 2·00

701 Princess Caroline (President)

1995. World Association of Friends of Children General Assembly, Monaco.
2221 **701** 7f. blue 3·50 2·40

702 Athletes and Medal

1995. International Amateur Athletics Federation Grand Prix, Monaco.
2222 **702** 7f. mauve, purple and grey 3·50 2·40

703 "Trophee des Alpes" (Hubert Clerissi)

1995. 2000th Anniv of Emperor Augustus Monument, La Turbie.
2223 **703** 8f. multicoloured 4·25 2·75

704 Prince Pierre (after Philip Laszlo de Lombos)

1995. Birth Centenary of Prince Pierre of Monaco.
2224 **704** 10f. purple 5·00 3·25

705 1974 60c. Honore II Stamp

1995. Inauguration of Stamp and Coin Museum (2nd issue). Sheet 135×89 mm containing T **705** and similar designs.
MS2225 10f. red, brown and blue (T **706**); 10f. blue and brown (entrance of museum) (*vert*); 10f. blue (1051 30f. first museum stamp) 15·00 16·00

706 St. Antony (wooden statue)

1995. 800th Birth Anniv of St. Antony of Padua.
2226 **706** 2f.80 multicoloured 1·10 75

707 United Nations Charter and Peacekeeping Soldiers

1995. 50th Anniv of U.N.O.
2227 **707** 2f.50 multicoloured 1·40 90
2228 - 2f.50 multicoloured 1·40 90
2229 - 2f.50 multicoloured 1·40 90
2230 - 2f.50 blue, black and brown 1·40 90
2231 - 3f. black, brown and blue 1·70 1·10
2232 - 3f. multicoloured 1·70 1·10
2233 - 3f. multicoloured 1·70 1·10
2234 - 3f. multicoloured 1·70 1·10
MS2235 112×151 mm. 3f. As No. 2227; 3f. As No. 2228; 3f. As No. 2229; 3f. As No. 2230; 4f.50, As No. 2231; 4f.50, As No. 2232; 4f.50, As No. 2233; 4f.50, As No. 2234 17·00 17·00

DESIGNS: No. 2228, Wheat ears, boy and arid ground; 2229, Children from different nationalities; 2230, Head of Colossus, Abu Simbel Temple; 2231, United Nations meeting; 2232, Growing crops and hand holding seeds; 2233, Figures and alphabetic characters; 2234, Lute and UNESCO head-quarters, Paris.

Nos. 2228 and 2232 commemorate the F.A.O., Nos. 2229 and 2233 International Year of Tolerance, Nos. 2230 and 2234 UNESCO.

708 Rose "Grace de Monaco"

1995. Flowers. Multicoloured.
2236 3f. Type **708** 1·50 1·00
2237 3f. Fuchsia "Lakeland Princess" 1·50 1·00
2238 3f. Carnation "Centenaire de Monte-Carlo" 1·50 1·00
2239 3f. Fuchsia "Grace" 1·50 1·00
2240 3f. Rose "Princesse de Monaco" 1·50 1·00
2241 3f. Alstroemeria "Gracia" 1·50 1·00
2242 3f. Lily "Princess Gracia" 1·50 1·00
2243 3f. Carnation "Princesse Caroline" 1·50 1·00
2244 3f. Rose "Stephanie de Monaco" 1·50 1·00
2245 3f. Carnation "Prince Albert" 1·50 1·00
2246 3f. Sweet pea "Grace de Monaco" 1·50 1·00
2247 3f. Gerbera "Gracia" 1·50 1·00

709 Balthazar

1995. Christmas. Crib Figures from Provence of the Three Wise Men. Multicoloured.
2248 3f. Type **709** 1·20 75
2249 5f. Gaspard 2·10 1·30
2250 6f. Melchior 2·75 1·70

710 Tree, Bird, Seahorse and Association Emblem

1995. 20th Anniv of Monaco Association for Nature Protection.
2251 **710** 4f. green, black and red 2·10 1·30

711 Rontgen and X-Ray of Hand

1995. Centenary of Discovery of X-Rays by Wilhelm Rontgen.
2252 **711** 6f. black, yellow and green 3·25 2·00

712 First Screening to Paying Public, Paris, December 1895

1995. Centenary of Motion Pictures.
2253 **712** 7f. blue 3·75 2·40

713 Allegory of Anti-leprosy Campaign

1995. Monaco Red Cross. Multicoloured.
2254 7f. Type **713** 3·75 2·30
2255 8f. Doctors Prakash and Mandakini Amte (anti-leprosy campaign in India) 4·50 2·75

714 First Car with Tyres

1995. Centenary of Invention of Inflatable Tyres.
2256 **714** 8f. purple and claret 4·50 2·75

715 "Spring"

1995. 550th Birth Anniv of Sandro Botticelli (artist).
2257 **715** 15f. blue 10·50 7·75

716 Poster

1996. 20th International Circus Festival, Monte Carlo.
2258 **716** 2f.40 multicoloured 1·50 90

717 Illusion

1996. Magic Festival, Monte Carlo.
2259 **717** 2f.80 black 1·60 1·00

718 Rhododendron

1996. Monte Carlo Flower Show.
2260 **718** 3f. multicoloured 1·80 1·10

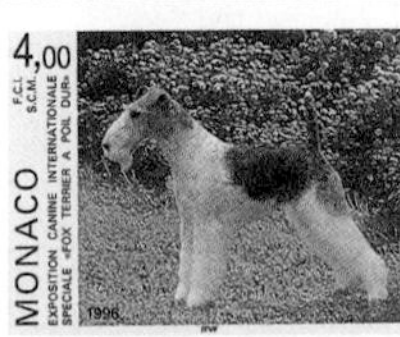

719 Wire-haired Fox Terrier

1996. International Dog Show, Monte Carlo.
2261 **719** 4f. multicoloured 2·30 1·50

720 "Chapel" (Hubert Clerissi)

1996. 300th Anniv of Chapel of Our Lady of Mercy.
2262 **720** 6f. multicoloured 3·25 2·00

721 Prince Albert I of Monaco (image scaled to 61% of original size)

1996. Centenary of Oceanographic Expeditions. Multicoloured.
2263 3f. Type **721** 1·80 1·10
2264 4f.50 King Carlos I of Portugal 2·75 1·70

722 Prince Rainier III (after F. Messina)

1996. Inauguration of Stamp and Coin Museum (2nd issue). 1974 Prince Rainier design.
2265 **722** 10f. violet 4·50 3·00
2266 **722** 15f. brown 6·50 4·50
2267 **722** 20f. blue 8·75 6·00

723 Princess Grace

1996. Europa. Famous Women.
2268 **723** 3f. brown and red 4·50 2·50

724 Fishes, Sea and Coastline

1996. 20th Anniv of Ramoge Agreement on Environmental Protection of Mediterranean.
2269 **724** 3f. multicoloured 1·80 1·20

725 Saint Nicolas (detail of altarpiece by Louis Brea)

1996. 20th Anniv of Annales Monegasques (historical review). Sheet 180×100 mm containing T 725. and similar vert designs. Each brown.
MS2270 3f. Type **725**; 3f. hector Berlioz (composer); 4f. Guillaume Apollinare (poet and art critic); 4f. Niccolo Machiavelli (statesman); 5f. Jean-Baptiste Bosio (painter); 5f. Sidonie Colette (writer); 6f. Francois-Joseph Bosio (sculptor); 6f. Michel Eyqüem de Montaigne (writer and philosopher) 26·00 25·00

726 Chinese Acrobatics Group in Monaco

1996. Monaco–Chinese Diplomatic Relations. Sheet 100×60 mm containing T 726 and similar horiz design. Multicoloured.
MS2271 5f. Type **726**; 5f. Fuling Tomg, Peking 6·00 6·00

727 Code and Monaco

1996. Introduction of International Dialling Code "377".
2272 **727** 3f. blue 1·80 1·20
2273 **727** 3f.80 red 2·10 1·40

728 Throwing the Javelin

1996. Olympic Games, Atlanta. Multicoloured.
2274 3f. Type **728** 1·60 1·20
2275 3f. Baseball 1·60 1·20
2276 4f.50 Running 2·50 1·90
2277 4f.50 Cycling 2·50 1·90

729 Children of Different Races with Balloon

1996. 50th Anniv of UNICEF.
2278 **729** 3f. brown, blue and lilac 1·60 1·20

730 Angel and Star

1996. Christmas. Multicoloured.
2279 3f. Type **730** 1·50 1·10
2280 6f. Angels heralding 3·25 2·40

731 Planet and Neptune, God of the Sea (after Roman mosaic, Sousse)

1996. Anniversaries.
2281 **731** 4f. red, blue and black 2·10 1·50
2282 - 5f. blue and red 2·75 2·00

DESIGNS—4f. Type **731** (150th anniv of discovery of planet Neptune by Johann Galle); 5f. Rene Descartes (after Franz Hals) (philosopher and scientist, 400th birth anniv).

732 Coins and Press

1996. Inauguaration of Stamp and Coin Museum (3rd issue).
2283 **732** 5f. brown and blue 2·75 2·00
2284 - 5f. brown and purple 2·75 2·00
2285 - 10f. blue and brown 5·25 3·75
MS2286 130×80 mm. Nos. 2283/5 10·50 11·00

DESIGNS—As T **733**: 5f. Stamp press and engraver. 48×37 mm: 10f. Museum entrance.

733 Camille Corot (bicentenary)

1996. Artists' Birth Anniversaries. Self-portraits. Multicoloured.
2287 6f. Type **733** 3·25 2·40
2288 7f. Francisco Goya (250th anniv) 3·75 2·75

734 Allegory

1996. Monaco Red Cross. Anti-tuberculosis Campaign. Multicoloured.
2289 7f. Type **734** 3·75 2·75
2290 8f. Camille Guerin and Albert Calmette (developers of vaccine) 4·50 3·25

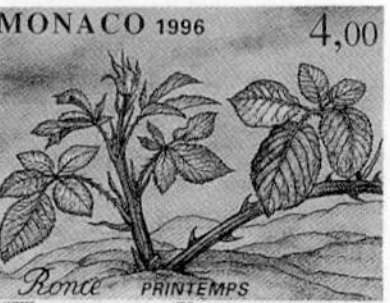

735 Spring

1996. Seasons of the Blackberry. Sheet 143×100 mm containing T 735 and similar horiz designs. Multicoloured.

MS2291 4f. Type **735**; 5f. Summer; 6f. Autumn; 7f. Winter 13·00 13·00

736 "Gloria" (cadet barque), Club, Motorboat and "Tuiga" (royal yacht)

1996. Monaco Yacht Club.

2292 **736** 3f. multicoloured 1·80 1·30

737 Seal of Prince Rainier III

1996. 700th Anniv of Grimaldi Dynasty (1st issue).

2293 **737** 2f.70 red, brown and blue 1·50 1·10

See also Nos. 2302/14 and 2326/38.

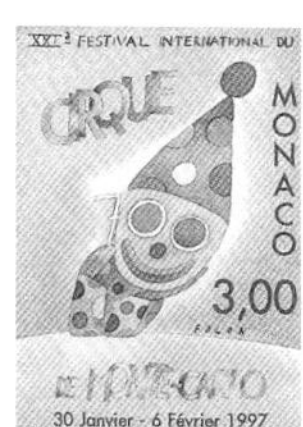

738 Clown

1996. 21st International Circus Festival, Monte Carlo (1997).

2294 **738** 3f. multicoloured 1·60 1·20

739 Old and New Racing and Rally Cars

1996. Motor Sport.

2295 **739** 3f. multicoloured 1·90 1·40

740 Pictures, Engraving Tools and "Stamps"

1996. 60th Anniv of Stamp Issuing Office (2296) and "Monaco 97" International Stamp Exhibition, Monte Carlo (2297). Each brown, mauve and blue.

2296 3f. Type **740** 3·00 2·20

2297 3f. Stamp, magnifying glass and letters 3·00 2·20

Nos. 2296/7 were issued together, se-tenant, forming a composite design featuring the Grand Staircase of the Prince's Palace.

741 Double Red Camellia

1996. Monte Carlo Flower Show (1997).

2298 **741** 3f.80 multicoloured 2·20 1·70

742 Afghan Hound

1996. International Dog Show, Monte Carlo.

2299 **742** 4f.40 multicoloured 3·50 2·75

743 Award

1996. 37th Television Festival, Monte Carlo (1997).

2300 **743** 4f.90 multicoloured 2·75 2·00

744 Giant Bellflower and Carob Pods and Leaves

1996

2301 **744** 5f. multicoloured 2·75 2·00

745 Rainier I, Battle of Zerikzee, Arms of his wife Andriola Grillo and Chateau de Cagnes

1997. 700th Anniv of Grimaldi Dynasty (2nd issue). The Seigneurs. Multicoloured.

2302 1f. Type **745** 45 35

2303 1f. Seal of Charles I, Battle of Crecy, Chateau de Roquebrune and Rocher fortifications 45 35

2304 1f. Siege of Rocher by Boccanegra, seal of Rainier II, arms of his two wives Ilaria del Caretto and Isabelle Asinari, Vatican and Papal Palace, Avignon 45 35

2305 2f. Defeat of combined fleets of Venice and Florence and Jean I on horseback and with his wife Pomelline Fregoso 1·00 75

2306 2f. Claudine, acclamation by crowd of her husband Lambert, seals of Lambert and his father Nicolas and strengthening of Monaco Castle 1·00 75

2307 7f. Statue of Francois Grimaldi disguised as Franciscan monk and clashes between Ghibellines and Guelphs at Genoa 3·75 2·75

2308 7f. Honore I flanked by Pope Paul III and Duke of Savoy and Battle of Lepanto 3·75 2·75

2309 7f. Charles II, flags of Genoa and Savoy and attack on Rocher by Capt. Cartier 3·75 2·75

2310 7f. Hercule I, flags of Savoy, Nice and Provence, assassination of Hercule and acclamation of his infant son Honore II 3·75 2·75

2311 9f. Catalan aiding Doge of Venice in war against Aragon, exercising "Right of the Sea" and entrusting education of his heiress Claudine to his wife Pomelline 4·75 3·50

2312 9f. Jean II with his wife Antoinette of Savoy, retable in Chapel of St. Nicholas and assassination of Jean by his brother Lucien 4·75 3·50

2313 9f. Lucien and siege of Monaco by Genoa 4·75 3·50

2314 9f. Seal of Augustin, Treaty of Tordesillas, visit by King Charles V and Augustin as bishop with his nephew and heir Honore 4·75 3·50

MS2315 **737** 150×80 mm. 2 ×2f.70 red; 2 ×2f.70 brown; 2 ×2f.70 blue; 2 ×2f.70 red, brown and blue 13·00 13·00

746 Tennis Match and Players

1997. Centenary of Monaco Tennis Championships.

2316 **746** 4f.60 multicoloured 2·75 2·00

747 Prince Rainier, Trophy and Stamp and Coin Museum

1997. Award to Prince Rainier of International Philately Grand Prix (made to "Person who has Contributed Most to Philately") by Association of Catalogue Editors.

2317 **747** 4f.60 multicoloured 2·75 2·00

748 Images of St.Devote (patron saint)

1997. Europa. Tales and Legends.

2318 **748** 3f. orange and brown 3·00 2·20

2319 - 3f. blue 3·00 2·20

DESIGN: No. 2319, Hercules.

749 Syringe and Drug Addicts

1997. Monaco Red Cross. Anti-drugs Campaign.

2320 **749** 7f. black, blue and red 3·75 2·75

750 First Stamps of United States and Monaco 1996 15f. Stamp

1997. "Pacific 97" International Stamp Exhibiton, San Francisco. 150th Anniv of First United States Stamps.

2321 **750** 4f.90 multicoloured 2·75 2·00

751 Winter and Summer Uniforms, 1997

1997. The Palace Guard. Multicoloured.

2322 3f. Type **751** 1·80 1·30

2323 3f.50 Uniforms of 1750, 1815, 1818, 1830 and 1853 2·20 1·70

2324 5f.20 Uniforms of 1865, 1870, 1904, 1916 and 1935 2·75 2·00

1997. Victory of Marcelo M. Rios at Monaco Tennis Championships. No. 2316 optd M. RIOS.

2325 **746** 4f.60 multicoloured 2·75 2·00

1997. 700th Anniv of Grimaldi Dynasty (3rd issue). The Princes. As T 745. Multicoloured.

2326 1f. Honore II 45 35

2327 1f. Louis I 45 35

2328 1f. Antoine I 45 35

2329 2f. Jacques I 1·00 75

2330 7f. Charles III 3·25 2·40

2331 7f. Albert I 3·25 2·40

2332 7f. Louis II 3·25 2·40

2333 7f. Rainier III 3·25 2·40

2334 9f. Louise-Hippolyte 4·50 3·25

2335 9f. Honore IV (wrongly inscr "Honore III") 4·50 3·25

2336 9f. Honore III (wrongly inscr "Honore IV") 4·50 3·25

2337 9f. Honore V 4·50 3·25

2338 9f. Florestan I 4·50 3·25

753 Club Badge, Ball as Globe and Stadium

1997. Monaco, Football Champion of France, 1996–97.

2339 **753** 3f. multicoloured 1·30 1·00

754 Magic Wand, Hands and Stars

1997. 13th Magic Grand Prix, Monte Carlo.

2340 **754** 4f.40 black and gold 1·90 1·40

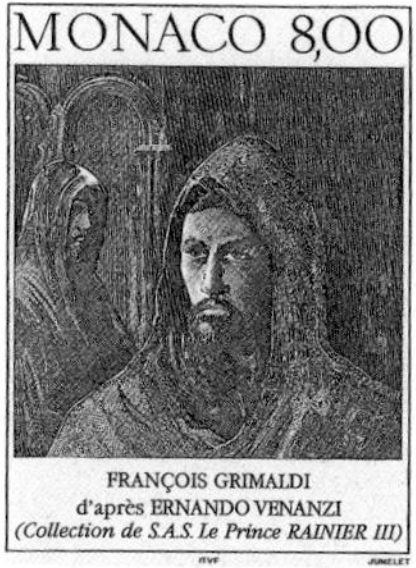

755 "Francois Grimaldi" (Ernando Venanzi)

1997. Paintings. Multicoloured.

2341 8f. Type **755** 3·50 2·75

2342 9f. "St. Peter and St. Paul" (Peter Paul Rubens) 3·75 2·75

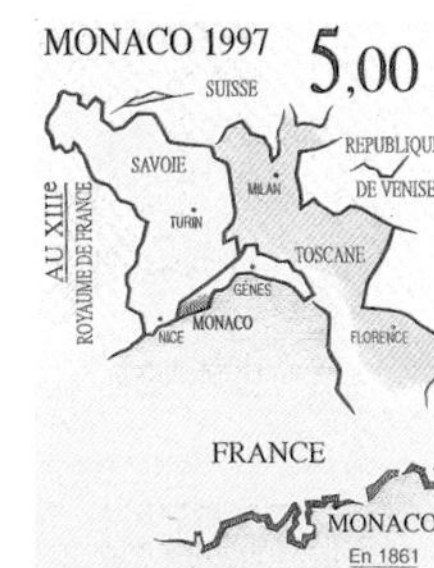

756 Monaco in 13th Century and 1861

1997. 700th Anniv of Grimaldi Dynasty (4th issue). Geographical Evolution of Monaco. Sheet 120×145 mm containing T 756 and similar vert designs. Multicoloured.

MS2343 5f. Type **756**; 5f. Monaco from 15th–19th centuries; 5f. Left half of Monaco; 5f. Right half of Monaco 8·75 8·75

The bottom two stamps of the miniature sheet form a composite design of present-day Monaco with a map showing dates at which the territory was expanded.

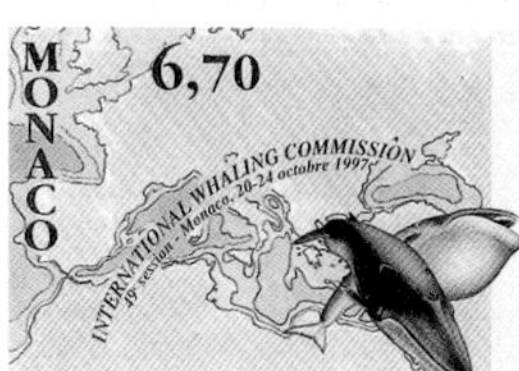

757 Map of Europe and Blue Whales

1997. 49th Session of International Whaling Commission, Monaco.

2344 **757** 6f.70 multicoloured 3·00 2·20

1997. Election of 1995 Botticelli Stamp as Most Beautiful Stamp in the World. Sheet 115×100 mm.
MS2345 **715** 15f. blue 7·25 7·25

758 Princess Charlotte

1997. 20th Death Anniv of Princess Charlotte.
2346 **758** 3f.80 brown 1·60 1·20

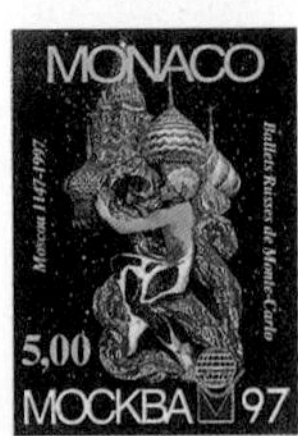

759 Dancer of Russian Ballet and Kremlin, Moscow

1997. "Moskva 97" International Stamp Exhibition, Moscow.
2347 **759** 5f. multicoloured 2·20 1·70

760 Trees in Monaco

1997. 10th Anniv of Marcel Korenlein Arboretum.
2348 **760** 9f. multicoloured 3·75 2·75

761 Diamond-Man (Ribeiro)

1997. Winning Entries in Schoolchildren's Drawing Competition.
2349 **761** 4f. multicoloured 1·80 1·30
2350 - 4f.50 blue, ultramarine and red 1·90 1·40
DESIGN—HORIZ: 4f.50, Flying diamonds (Testa).

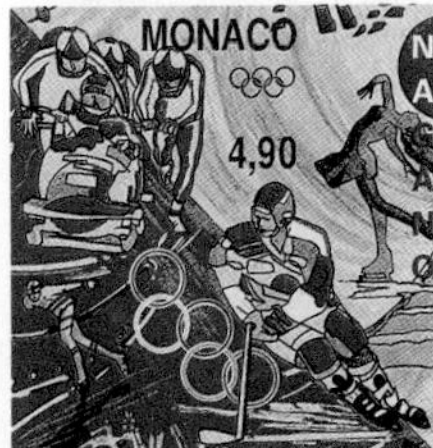

762 Four-man Bobsleighing, Speed and Figure Skating and Ice Hockey

1997. Winter Olympic Games, Nagano, Japan (1998). Multicoloured.
2351 4f.90 Type **762** 2·20 1·70
2352 4f.90 Alpine skiing, biathlon, two-man bobsleighing and ski-jumping 2·20 1·70
Nos. 2351/2 were issued together, se-tenant, forming a composite design.

763 Albert I (statue) (image scaled to 63% of original size)

1997. 150th Birth Anniv of Prince Albert I (1st issue).
2353 **763** 8f. multicoloured 3·50 2·75
See also No. 2368.

764 Clown and Horse

1997. 22nd International Circus Festival, Monte Carlo (1998).
2354 **764** 3f. multicoloured 1·30 1·10

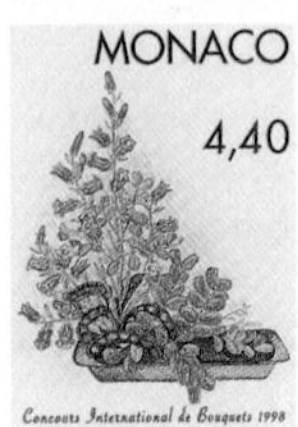

765 Pink Campanula and Carob Plant

1997. Monte Carlo Flower Show (1998).
2355 **765** 4f.40 multicoloured 1·90 1·60

766 "The Departure of Marcus Attilius Regulus for Carthage"

1997. 250th Birth Anniv of Louis David (painter).
2356 **766** 5f.20 green and red 2·20 1·80

767 Pope Innocent IV

1997. 750th Anniv of Creation of Parish of Monaco by Papal Bull.
2357 **767** 7f.50 brown and blue 3·25 2·50

768 Baseball Hat, Television Controller, Ballet Shoe and Football Boot

1998. 38th Television Festival.
2358 **768** 4f.50 multicoloured 1·90 1·60

769 Past and Present Presidents

1998. 50th Anniv of Monaco Red Cross.
2359 **769** 5f. brown and red 2·20 1·80

770 Boxer and Dobermann

1998. International Dog Show, Monte Carlo.
2360 **770** 2f.70 multicoloured 1·20 95

771 White Doves and Laurel Wreath

1998. 30th Meeting of Academy of Peace and International Security.
2361 **771** 3f. green and blue 1·30 1·10

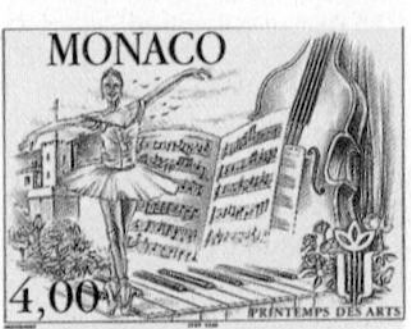

772 Ballet Dancer, Piano Keys, Music Score and Violin

1998. 15th Spring Arts Festival.
2362 **772** 4f. multicoloured 1·80 1·40

773 Pierre and Marie Curie

1998. Centenary of Discovery of Radium.
2363 **773** 6f. blue and mauve 2·75 2·10

774 Caravel and Globe

1998. "Expo '98" World's Fair, Lisbon. International Year of the Ocean.
2364 **774** 2f.70 multicoloured 1·20 95

775 St. Devote (stained glass window, Palace Chapel) (image scaled to 64% of original size)

1998. Europa (1st issue). National Festivals.
2365 **775** 3f. multicoloured 2·20 1·80
See also No. 2372.

776 Monte Carlo

1998. Junior Chamber of Commerce European Conference, Monte Carlo.
2366 **776** 3f. multicoloured 1·30 1·10

777 Kessel

1998. Birth Centenary of Joseph Kessel (writer).
2367 **777** 3f.90 multicoloured 1·60 1·30

778 Prince Albert I at different Ages (image scaled to 62% of original size)

1998. 150th Birth Anniv of Prince Albert I (2nd issue).
2368 **778** 7f. brown 3·00 2·40

779 Garnier and Monte Carlo Casino

1998. Death Centenary of Charles Garnier (architect).
2369 **779** 10f. multicoloured 4·50 3·50

780 Trophy and Monte Carlo

1998. 10th World Music Awards, Monte Carlo.
2370 **780** 10f. multicoloured 4·50 3·50

781 Racing Cars

1998. 1st Formula 3000 Grand Prix, Monte Carlo.
2371 **781** 3f. red and black 1·30 1·10

782x Prince Rainier III, Prince Albert and Royal Palace (image scaled to 63% of original size)

1998. Europa (2nd issue). National Festivals.
2372 **782** 3f. multicoloured 2·20 1·80

783 Porcelain Teapot and Figure of Francois Grimaldi

1998. Fine Arts. Multicoloured.
2373 8f. Type **783** 3·50 2·75
2374 9f. Fine-bound books and illustration 3·75 3·00

784 Player on Map of France

1998. World Cup Football Championship, France.
2375 **784** 15f. multicoloured 6·50 5·25

785 Modern and Old Motor Cars and Ferrari

1998. Birth Centenary of Enzio Ferrari (motor manufacturer).
2376 **785** 7f. multicoloured 3·00 2·40

786 Gershwin, Trumpeter, Dancers and Opening Bars of "Rhapsody in Blue"

1998. Birth Cent of George Gershwin (composer).
2377 **786** 7f.50 ultramarine, blue and black 3·25 2·50

787 Int Marine Pollution College and Marine Environment Laboratory

1998. Int Marine Pollution Conference, Monaco.
2378 **787** 4f.50 multicoloured 1·90 1·60

788 Venue

1998. Post Europ (successor to C.E.P.T.) Plenary Assembly, Monaco.
2379 **788** 5f. multicoloured 2·20 1·80

789 Belem Tower, Lisbon, and Palace, Monaco

1998. "Expo '98" World's Fair and Stamp Exhibition, Lisbon.
2380 **789** 6f.70 multicoloured 3·00 2·40

790 Sportsmen

1998. 30th Anniv of International Association against Violence in Sport.
2381 **790** 4f.20 multicoloured 1·80 1·40

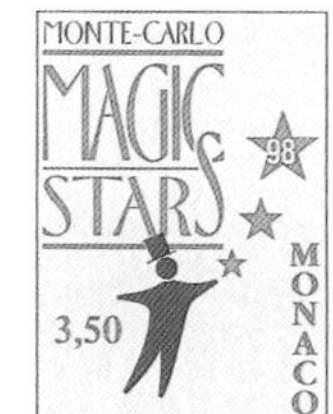
791 Magician

1998. "Magic Stars" Magic Festival, Monte Carlo.
2382 **791** 3f.50 gold and red 1·50 1·20

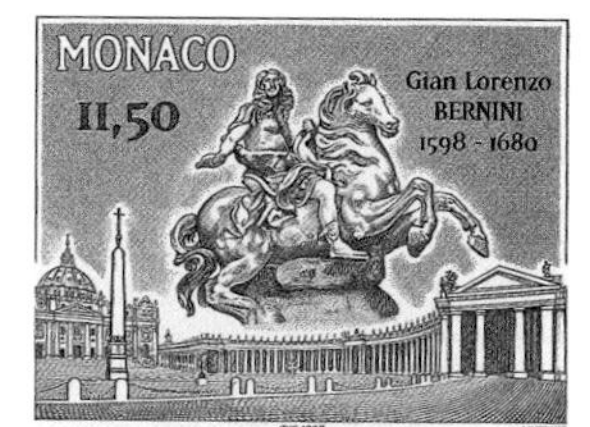
792 Statue and Vatican Colonnade

1998. 400th Birth Anniv of Giovanni Lorenzo Bernini (architect and sculptor).
2383 **792** 11f.50 blue and brown 5·25 4·25

793 Milan Cathedral

1998. "Italia 98" Int Stamp Exhibition, Milan.
2384 **793** 4f.90 green and red 2·20 1·80

794 Christmas Tree Decoration

1998. Christmas. Multicoloured.
2385 3f. Type **794** 1·30 1·10
2386 6f.70 "The Nativity" (detail of icon) (horiz) 3·00 2·40
MS2387 86×95 mm. 15f. "Virgin and Child" (detail of icon) (36×49 mm) 6·50 6·50

1998. As Nos. 1910 etc but no value expressed.
2388 **577** (2f.70) turquoise & blue 1·20 25
2389 **577** (3f.) red and pink 1·30 35
2390 **577** (3f.80) blue and cobalt 1·60 70

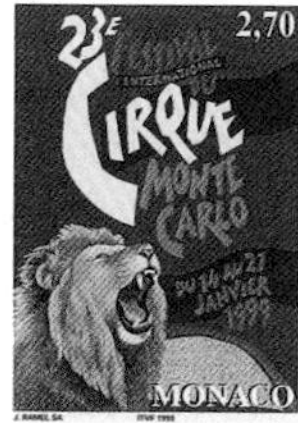
795 Lion

1998. 23rd International Circus Festival, Monte Carlo (1999).
2391 **795** 2f.70 multicoloured 1·20 95

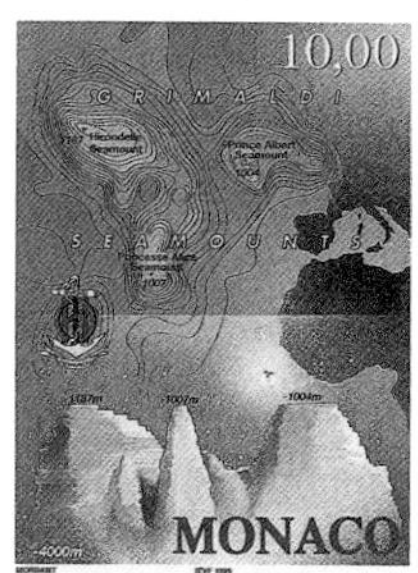
796 Map and Elevation of Seamounts

1998. Grimaldi Seamounts.
2392 **796** 10f. multicoloured 4·50 3·50

797 Prince's Arms and Monogram

1998. 50th Anniv (1999) of Accession of Prince Rainier III (1st issue). Sheet 100×130 mm.
MS2393 **797** 25f. gold and red 14·50 14·50
See also No. **MS**2417.

798 1860 Cover and Stamp and Coin Museum

1999. "Monaco 99" International Stamp Exhibition.
2394 **798** 3f. multicoloured 1·30 1·00
MS2395 160×111 mm. No. 2394 ×4 6·00 6·00

799 Festival Poster

1999. 39th Television Festival.
2396 **799** 3f.80 multicoloured 2·20 1·40

800 Cocker Spaniel and American Cocker

1999. International Dog Show, Fontvieille.
2397 **800** 4f. multicoloured 2·20 1·40

801 World Map

1999. 50th Anniv of Geneva Conventions.
2398 **801** 4f.40 red, brown and black 2·20 1·40

802 Arrangement of Flowers named after Grimaldi Family Members

1999. Monte Carlo Flower Show.
2399 **802** 4f.50 multicoloured 2·20 1·40

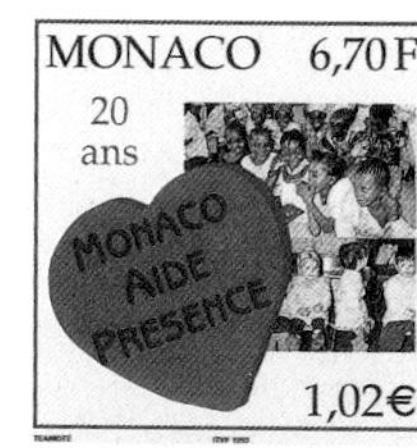
803 Children and Heart

1999. 20th Anniv of Monaco Aid and Presence.
2400 **803** 6f.70 multicoloured 4·50 2·75
No. 2400 is also denominated in euros.

804 Palace and Centre

1999. 20th Anniv of Congress Centre Auditorium.
2401 **804** 2f.70 multicoloured 1·50 90

DENOMINATION. From No. 2402 Monaco stamps are denominated both in francs and in euros. As no cash for the latter was in circulation until 2002, the catalogue continues to use the franc value.

805 Globe and Piano Keys

1999. 10th Piano Masters, Monte Carlo.
2402 **805** 4f.60 multicoloured 2·20 1·40

806 Rose "Jubile du Prince de Monaco"

1999. Flowers. Multicoloured.
2403 4f.90 Type **806** 2·40 1·40
2404 6f. Rose "Prince de Monaco", rose "Grimaldi" and orchid "Prince Rainier III" 3·25 1·80

807 Williams's Bugatti (winner of first race) and Michael Schumacher's Car (winner of 1999 race)

1999. 70th Anniv of Monaco Motor Racing Grand Prix.

2405	**807**	3f. multicoloured	1·60	90

808 Olympic Rings and Trophy

1999. 3rd Association of Postage Stamp Catalogue Editors and Philatelic Publications Grand Prix.

2406	**808**	4f.40 multicoloured	2·40	1·40

809 Riders jumping over Monte Carlo (image scaled to 63% of original size)

1999. 5th International Show Jumping Competition, Monte Carlo.

2407	**809**	5f.20 red, black and blue	3·00	1·70

810 Footballer, Runner and Palace (image scaled to 63% of original size)

1999. 75th Anniv of Monaco Sports Association. Multicoloured.

2408	7f. Type **810**	3·25	1·80
2409	7f. Boxer, footballer, harbour, runner and handballer	3·25	1·80

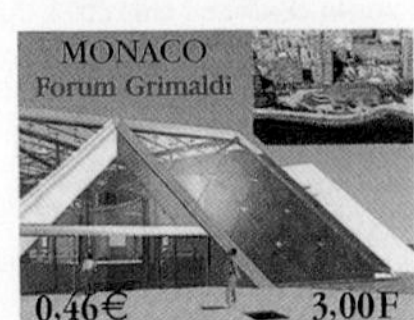

811 Architect's Drawing of Forum

1999. Construction of Grimaldi Forum (congress and exhibition centre).

2410	**811**	3f. multicoloured	1·60	90

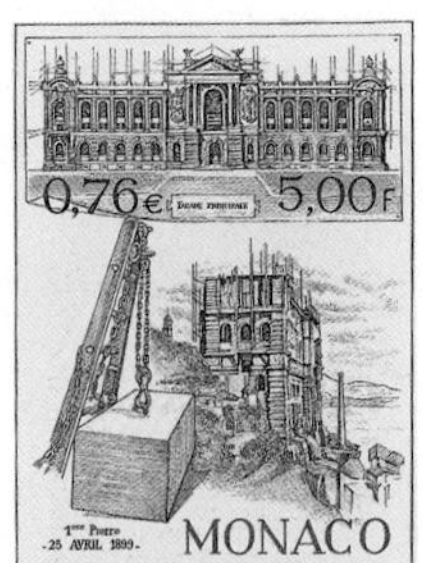

812 Facade and Construction

1999. Centenary of Laying of First Stone of Oceanographic Museum.

2411	**812**	5f. multicoloured	3·00	1·70

813 Eiffel Tower on Map of France, 1849 20c. "Ceres" Stamp and Emblem

1999. "Philexfrance 99" International Stamp Exhibition, Paris (1st issue). 150th Anniv of First French Stamps.

2412	**813**	2f.70 multicoloured	1·60	90

See also No. 2423.

814 Casino and Rock

1999. Europa. Parks and Gardens. Multicoloured.

2413	3f. Type **814**	1·90	1·10
2414	3f. Fontvieille (48×27 mm)	1·90	1·10

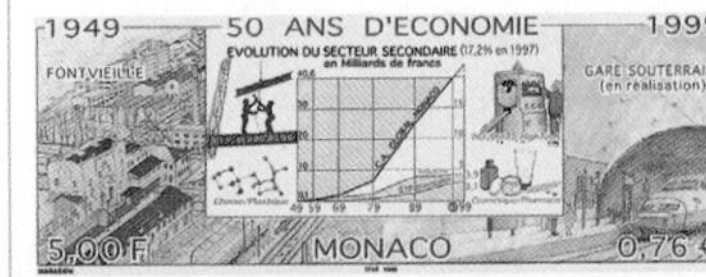

815x Fontvieille in 1949, Line Graph and Underground Station in 1999 (image scaled to 63% of original size)

1999. 50 Years of the Economy. Multicoloured.

2415	5f. Type **815** (second sector)	2·40	1·70
2416	5f. Le Larvotto in 1949, line graph and Grimaldi Forum in 1999 (third sector)	2·40	1·70

816 Definitive Stamps, 1950–89 (image scaled to 61% of original size)

1999. 50th Anniv of Accession of Prince Rainier III (2nd issue). Two sheets, 100×130 mm (a) or 119×145 mm (b).

MS2417 Two sheets. (a) 20f. blue and gold (as Type **584** but with monogram superimposed); (b) 30f. multicoloured (Type **816**)	24·00	24·00

817 Honore de Balzac

1999. Writers' Birth Bicentenaries.

2418	**817**	4f.50 blue and scarlet	2·40	1·70
2419	-	5f.20 brown, blue and red	3·00	2·20

DESIGN: 5f.20, Sophie Rostopchine, Comtesse de Segur.

818 Emblem and Chinese Drawing

1999. 125th Anniv of Universal Postal Union.

2420	**818**	3f. blue, red and yellow	1·60	1·20

819 Iris "Rainier III" and Rose "Rainier III"

1999. Flowers.

2421	**819**	4f. multicoloured	2·10	1·50

820 Anniversary Emblem

1999. 50th Anniv of Monaco's Admission to United Nations Educational, Scientific and Educational Organization.

2422	**820**	4f.20 multicoloured	2·20	1·70

821 Emblem and Monaco 1885 and French 1878 Stamps

1999. "Philexfrance 99" International Stamp Exhibition, Paris (2nd issue).

2423	**821**	7f. black, blue and mauve	3·25	2·40

822 Athletes

1999. 10th Sportel (sport and television) Congress, Fontvieille.

2424	**822**	10f. multicoloured	5·25	3·75

823 Maltese Cross, Knights and Valletta

1999. 900th Anniv of Sovereign Military Order of Malta and 25th Anniv of National Association of the Order.

2425	**823**	11f.50 red, brown and blue	5·75	4·50

824 1999 Postcard of Monaco, 1989 Definitive Design and Obverse of Jubilee Coin

1999. Postcard, Coin and Stamp Exhibition, Fontvieille (1st issue).

2426	**824**	3f. multicoloured	1·50	1·10

See also No. 2429.

1999. "Magic Stars" Magic Festival, Monte Carlo. As No. 2382 but face value and date changed.

2427	**791**	4f.50 gold and red	2·20	1·70

825 Fontvielle Project, Stage 2

1999. Achievements and Projects. Sheet 150×100 mm containing T **825** and similar multicoloured designs.

MS2428 4f. Type **825**; 9f. New harbour mole; 9f. Grimaldi Forum (congress centre); 19f. Underground train, harbour and station (76×36 mm)	20·00	20·00

826 1949 Postcard of Monaco, Reverse of Jubilee Coin and 1950 Definitive

1999. Postcard, Coin and Stamp Exhibition, Fontvieille (2nd issue).

2429	**826**	6f.50 multicoloured	3·25	2·40

827 Pierrot juggling "2000"

1999. 24th International Circus Festival, Monte Carlo (2000).

2430	**827**	2f.70 multicoloured	1·80	1·30

828 "Madonna and Child" (Simone Cantarini)

1999. Christmas.

2431	**828**	3f. multicoloured	1·60	1·20

829 Blessing and Holy Door, St. Peter's Cathedral, Rome

1999. Holy Year 2000.

2432	**829**	3f.50 multicoloured	1·90	1·40

830 Mixed Arrangement

1999. 33rd Monte Carlo Flower Show.
2433 **830** 4f.50 multicoloured 2·30 1·80

831 Emblem

1999. "Monaco 2000" International Stamp Exhibitions.
2434 **831** 3f. multicoloured 1·60 1·20

832 Bust of Napoleon (Antonio Canova)

2000. 30th Anniv of Napoleonic Museum.
2435 **832** 4f.20 multicoloured 2·30 1·80

833 Festival Emblem

2000. 40th Television Festival, Monte Carlo.
2436 **833** 4f.90 multicoloured 2·75 2·10

834 St. Peter and St. James the Major

2000. The Twelve Apostles. Multicoloured.

2437	**834**	4f. blue, orange and gold	1·60	1·20
2438	-	5f. red and gold	2·30	1·80
2439	-	6f. violet and gold	3·00	2·40
2440	-	7f. brown and gold	4·00	3·00
2441	-	8f. green and gold	4·75	3·50
2442	-	9f. red, orange and gold	5·50	4·25

DESIGNS: 5f. St. John and St. Andrew; 6f. St. Philip and St. Bartholomew; 7f. St. Matthew and St. Thomas; 8f. St. James the Minor and St. Jude; 9f. St. Simon and St. Mathias.

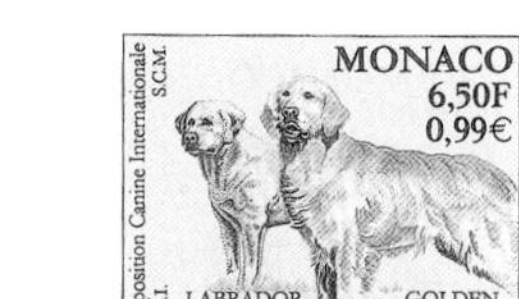

835 Golden Labrador and Golden Retriever

2000. International Dog Show, Monte Carlo.
2443 **835** 6f.50 multicoloured 3·50 2·50

836 Man's Head, Drawings and Key (Adami)

2000. Monaco and the Sea. Multicoloured.

2444		6f.55 Type **836**	3·50	2·50
2445		6f.55 "Monaco" above sea (Arman)	3·50	2·50
2446		6f.55 Abstract designs (Cane)	3·50	2·50
2447		6f.55 Hand touching sun in sky (Folon)	3·50	2·50
2448		6f.55 Angel sleeping and boats (Fuchs)	3·50	2·50
2449		6f.55 Harbour (E. de Sigaldi)	3·50	2·50
2450		6f.55 Views of harbour on silhouettes of yachts (Sosno)	3·50	2·50
2451		6f.55 Waves and floating ball (Verkade)	3·50	2·50

837 Olympic Rings on Globe and Flags

2000. Olympic Games, Sydney, Australia.
2452 **837** 7f. multicoloured 3·50 2·50

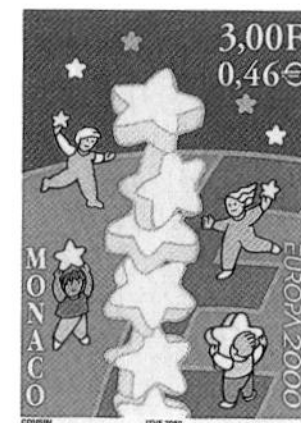

838 "Building Europe"

2000. Europa. Multicoloured.

2453		3f. Type **838**	3·00	2·40
2454		3f. Map of Europe and Post Europ member countries' flags (56×37 mm)	3·00	2·40

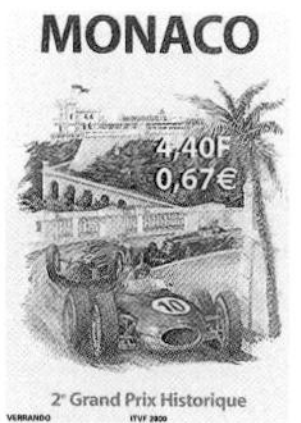

839 Racing Cars

2000. 2nd Historic Vehicles Grand Prix.
2455 **839** 4f.40 multicoloured 2·30 1·80

840 Monaco Pavilion and Emblem

2000. "EXPO 2000" World's Fair, Hanover.
2456 **840** 5f. multicoloured 2·75 2·10

841 Sts. Mark, Matthew, John and Luke

2000. The Four Evangelists.
2457 **841** 20f. black, flesh and green 11·00 11·00

842 St. Stephen and Emblem

2000. "WIPA 2000" International Stamp Exhibition, Vienna.
2458 **842** 4f.50 black, blue and red 2·30 1·80

843 Golfer

2000. Pro-celebrity Golf Tournament, Monte Carlo.
2459 **843** 4f.40 multicoloured 2·30 1·80

844 Fencing

2000. Olympic Games, Sydney. Multicoloured.

2460		2f.70 Type **844**	1·60	1·20
2461		4f.50 Rowing	2·30	1·80

845 Humber Beeston and Woman with Parasol, 1911

2000. Motor Cars and Fashion. Motor cars from the Royal Collection. Multicoloured.

2462		3f. Type **845**	2·30	1·80
2463		6f.70 Jaguar 4-cylinder and woman, 1947	4·00	3·00
2464		10f. Rolls Royce Silver Cloud and woman wearing swing coat, 1956	5·50	4·25
2465		15f. Lamborghini Countach and woman wearing large hat, 1986	8·50	6·50

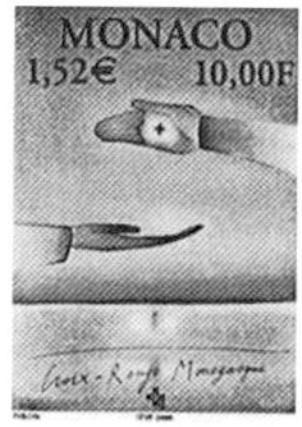

846 Entrance to Museum

2000. Philatelic Rarities Exhibition (1999), Stamp and Coin Museum, Monte Carlo.
2466 **846** 3f.50 multicoloured 2·00 1·60

847 Open Hands and Emblem

2000. Monaco Red Cross.
2467 **847** 10f. multicoloured 5·50 4·25

848 Magnifying Glass, Stamps and Exhibition Hall

2000. "WORLD STAMP USA" International Exhibition, Anaheim, California.
2468 **848** 4f.40 multicoloured 2·30 1·80

849 Magician

2000. "Magic Stars" Magic Festival, Monte Carlo.
2469 **849** 4f.60 multicoloured 2·30 1·80

850 Da Vinci's "Man" and Mathematical Symbols

2000. World Mathematics Year.
2470 **850** 6f.50 brown 3·50 2·50

851 Right-hand Section of Screen

2000. Holy Year. Restoration of Altar Screen, Monaco Cathedral. Sheet 120×100 mm containing T 851 and similar design.

MS2471	10f. Type **851**; 20f. Left-hand and central sections (53×52 mm)	16·00	16·00

852 Shark and Museum Facade

2000. Opening of New Aquarium, Oceanographical Museum.

2472	**852**	3f. multicoloured	1·60	1·20

853 Cathedral and Statue of Bear

2000. "ESPANA 2000" International Stamp Exhibition, Madrid.

2473	**853**	3f.80 multicoloured	2·30	1·80

854 Fishes and Corals

2000. 5th International Congress on Aquaria (5f.) and 25th Anniv of Monaco Nature Protection Association (9f.). Multicoloured.

2474	5f. Type **854**	2·75	2·10
2475	9f. Starfish, water plant and fish	4·75	3·50

855 Museum Facade and Plants

2000. 50th Anniv of Observatory Cave and 40th Anniv of Anthropological Museum.

2476	**855**	5f.20 purple, green and brown	3·00	2·40

856x Fresco, Oceanography Museum (image scaled to 63% of original size)

2000. International Aquariological Congress.

2477	**856**	7f. multicoloured	3·50	2·50

857 18th-century Crib

2000. Christmas.

2478	**857**	3f. multicoloured	1·60	1·20

2000. Motor Cars and Fashion. Motor cars from the Royal Collection. As T 845. Multicoloured.

2479	5f. Ferrari Formula 1 racing car and woman in racing clothes, 1989	3·00	2·40
2480	6f. Fiat 600 "Jolly" and woman wearing swimming costume, 1955	4·00	3·00
2481	8f. Citroen C4F "Autochenille" and woman wearing coat and hat, 1929	4·75	3·50

858 Princess Stephanie (President)

2000. Association for Help and Protection of Disabled Children (A.M.A.P.E.I.).

2482	**858**	11f.50 blue and red	6·25	4·75

859 Exhibition Poster

2000. "Monaco 2000" Stamp Exhibition, Sheet 150×90 mm containing two examples of T 859.

MS2483	20f. ×2 multicoloured	23·00	24·00

860 Warrior kneeling

2000. Terracotta Warrior Exhibition, Grimaldi Forum (2001).

2484	**860**	2f.70 black and red	1·60	1·20

861 Museum Building

2000. 50th Anniv of Postal Museum.

2485	**861**	3f. multicoloured	1·70	1·30

862 Arms

2000. Self-adhesive.

2486	**862**	(3f.) black and red	1·70	1·30

863 Iris "Princess Caroline of Monaco"

2000. 34th Monte Carlo Flower Show.

2487	**863**	3f.80 multicoloured	2·00	1·60

864 Sardinian 1851 5c., 20c. and 40c. Stamps

2000. 150th Anniv (2001) of First Sardinian Stamp.

2488	**864**	6f.50 blue, red and black	3·50	2·50

865 Seahorse, Marine Life and Life Belt

2000. 25th Anniv (2001) of the Ramoge Agreement on Environmental Protection of Mediterranean.

2489	**865**	6f.70 multicoloured	3·50	2·50

866 Breitling Orbiter and 1984 2f.80 Stamp

2000. 1st Non-Stop Balloon Circumnavigation of Globe (1999). Award to Bertrand Picard of International Philately Grand Prix by Association of Catalogue Editors.

2490	**866**	9f. multicoloured	4·75	3·50

867 Clown with Seal balancing Ball

2000. 25th International Circus Festival, Monte Carlo (2001). Different poster designs by artist named. Multicoloured (except No. 2492).

2491	2f.70 Type **867**	1·90	1·40
2492	6f. Clown playing guitar (Hodge) (black, red and blue)	3·00	2·40
2493	6f. Clown resting head (Knie)	3·00	2·40
2494	6f. Tiger and circus tent (P. Merot)	3·00	2·40
2495	6f. Lions, horses and trapeze artists (Poulet)	3·00	2·40
2496	6f. Monkey and circus tents (T. Mordant)	3·00	2·40

868 Player kicking Ball

2000. Monaco, Football Champion of France, 1999–2000.

2497	**868**	4f.50 multicoloured	2·30	1·80

869 Sea Mammals and Mediterranean Sea

2000. Mediterranean Sea Marine Mammals Sanctuary.

2498	**869**	5f.20 multicoloured	3·00	2·40

870 Nativity Scene (image scaled to 63% of original size)

2000. Christmas.

2499	**870**	10f. multicoloured	5·50	4·25

871 Poster

2001. 41st Television Festival, Monte Carlo.

2500	**871**	3f.50 multicoloured	1·90	1·40

872 Leonberger and Newfoundland Dogs

2001. International Dog Show, Monte Carlo.

2501	**872**	6f.50 multicoloured	3·50	2·50

873 Flower Arrangement

2001. Flower Show, Genoa.

2502	**873**	6f.70 multicoloured	3·50	2·50

874 Monaco Palace

2001. Europa. Water Resources. Multicoloured.

2503	3f. Type **874**	2·75	2·10
2504	3f. Undercover washing area	2·75	2·10

875 Princess Caroline and Portrait of Prince Pierre of Monaco (founder)

2001. 50th Anniv of Literary Council of Monaco.

2505	**875**	2f.70 black, brown and green	1·60	1·20

876 Malraux

2001. Birth Centenary of Andre Malraux (writer).
2506 **876** 10f. black and red 5·50 4·25

877 Town Hall

2001. "BELGICA 2001" International Stamp Exhibition, Brussels.
2507 **877** 4f. blue and red 2·30 1·80

878 Coins, Stamp and Book

2001. Postcard, Coin and Stamp Exhibition, Fontvielle.
2508 **878** 2f.70 multicoloured 1·60 1·20

879 Princess Grace and Ballet Dancer

2001. 25th Anniv of Princess Grace Dance Academy.
2509 **879** 4f.40 multicoloured 2·30 1·80

880 Model

2001. Naval Museum, Fontvielle.
2510 **880** 4f.50 multicoloured 2·30 1·80

881 Petanque Balls

2001. World Petanque Championships.
2511 **881** 5f. multicoloured 2·75 2·10

882 Fireplace, Throne Room

2001. Royal Palace (1st series). Multicoloured.
2512 3f. Type **882** 1·60 1·20
2513 4f.50 Blue Room 2·30 1·80
2514 6f.70 York Chamber 4·00 3·00
2515 15f. Throne room ceiling fresco 7·75 6·00
See also Nos. 2541/3.

883 Littre and Diderot

2001. 250th Anniv of Encyclopaedia or Critical Dictionary of Sciences, Arts and Trades (Denis Diderot) and Birth Bicentenary of Emile Littre (compiler of Dictionary of the French Language).
2516 **883** 4f.20 black, blue and green 2·30 1·80

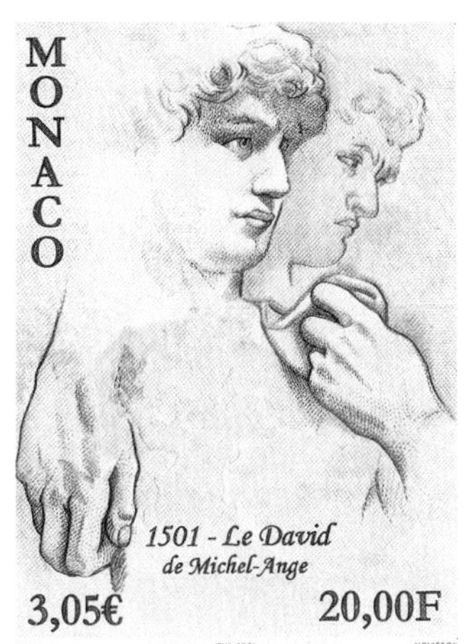

884 Medal and Steam Yacht

2001. 30th Anniv of Prince Albert Oceanography Prize.
2517 **884** 9f. blue 4·75 3·50

885 Drawings

2001. 500th Anniv of David (sculpture, Michaelangelo).
2518 **885** 20f. multicoloured 11·00 9·50

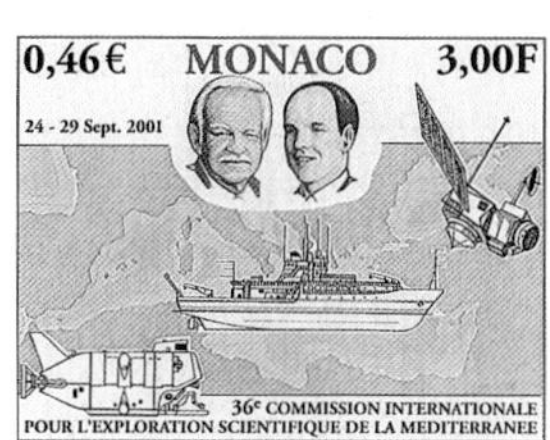

886 Alfred Nobel (prize fund founder)

2001. Centenary of the Nobel Prize. Multicoloured.
2519 5f. Type **886** 3·00 2·40
2520 8f. Henri Dunant (founder of Red Cross and winner of Peace Prize, 1901) 4·75 3·50
2521 11f.50 Enrico Fermi (physicist and winner of Physics Prize, 1938) 6·25 4·75

887 Prince Rainier, Prince Albert, Map, Satellite, Ship, and Submarine

2001. 36th International Commission for Scientific Exploration of the Mediterranean Meeting.
2522 **887** 3f. multicoloured 1·90 1·40

888 Virgin and Child

2001. Christmas.
2523 **888** 3f. multicoloured 1·90 1·40

889 Garden Tiger Moth (*Artica caja*)

2002. Flora and Fauna.
2524 **889** 1c. black, red and sepia 15 10
2525 - 2c. multicoloured 15 10
2526 - 5c. multicoloured 25 20
2527 - 10c. black, green and yellow 30 25
2528 - 20c. red, yellow and black 60 50
2529 - 41c. multicoloured 1·20 95
2530 - 50c. multicoloured 1·70 1·10
2531 - €1 multicoloured 3·00 1·80
2532 - €2 multicoloured 6·25 3·00
2533 - €5 brown, green and black 16·00 7·25
2534 - €10 green, red and black 31·00 12·00
DESIGNS—VERT: 5c. Blue trumpet vine (*Thunbergia grandiflora*); 41c. *Helix aspera*; 50c. Foxy charaxes (*Charaxes jasius*); €2 Red thorn apple (*Datura sanguinea*); €5 Crested tit (*Parus crisatus*). HORIZ: 2c. *Luria lurida*; 10c. Great tit (*Parus major*); 20c. Common barberfish (*Anthias anthias*); €1 Zoned mitre (*Mitra zonata*); €10 Common snipefish (*Macroramphosus scolopax*).

890 Lion and Ringmaster

2002. 26th International Circus Festival, Monte Carlo.
2540 **890** 41c. multicoloured 1·40 95

891 Crystal Gallery

2002. Royal Palace (2nd series). Multicoloured.
2541 41c. Type **891** 1·20 95
2542 46c. Throne room (horiz) 1·60 1·20
2543 58c. Landscape painting in Crystal Gallery (horiz) 1·90 1·40

892 Rocking Horse of Flowers

2002. 35th Monte Carlo Flower Show.
2544 **892** 53c. multicoloured 1·70 1·30

893 Old and Modern Rally Cars

2002. Motoring Events in Monaco. Sheet 124×95 mm, containing T 893 and similar vert design. Multicoloured.
MS2545 €1.07, Type **893** (70th Monte Carlo car rally); €1.22, Old racing car (Historic Vehicles third Grand Prix) and modern Formula 1 racing car (60th Monaco Grand Prix) 7·25 7·25

894 Skiers, Ice Skater and Ice Hockey Player

2002. Winter Olympic Games, Salt Lake City, U.S.A. Multicoloured.
2546 23c. Type **894** 80 60
2547 23c. Bobsleigh, luge and skiers (face value, emblem and country inscription at right) 80 60
Nos. 2446/7 were issued together, se-tenant, forming a composite design.

895 Exhibition Cases and Prince Albert I

2002. Anniversaries. Multicoloured.
2548 64c. Type **895** (centenary of Prehistoric Anthropology Museum) 2·00 1·40
2549 67c. Title page, Prince Albert I and ship (centenary of publication of "La Carriere d'un Navigateur" (memoirs) by Prince Albert I) 2·20 1·50

896 Mazarin (painting, Phillippe de Champaigne)

2002. 400th Birth Anniv of Jules Mazarin (cardinal to Louis XIV).
2550 **896** 69c. multicoloured 2·20 1·50

897 Bust of Napoleon Bonaparte and Medal

2002. Bicentenary of Legion d'Honneur.
2551 **897** 70c. multicoloured 2·20 1·50

898 Whales and Dolphins

2002. 1st Meeting of Signatories to Agreement on the Conservation of Cetaceans of the Black Sea, Mediterranean Sea and Contiguous Atlantic Area (ACCOBAMS), Monaco.
2552 **898** 75c. multicoloured 2·30 1·70

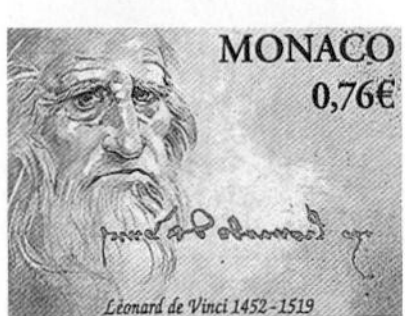

899 Da Vinci

2002. 550th Birth Anniv of Leonardo da Vinci (artist).
2553 **899** 76c. multicoloured 2·30 1·70

900 St. Bernard and Bouvier

2002. International Dog Show, Monte Carlo.
2554 **900** 99c. multicoloured 3·00 2·20

901 Police Officers and Badge

2002. Centenary of Police Force.
2555 **901** 53c. multicoloured 1·70 1·20

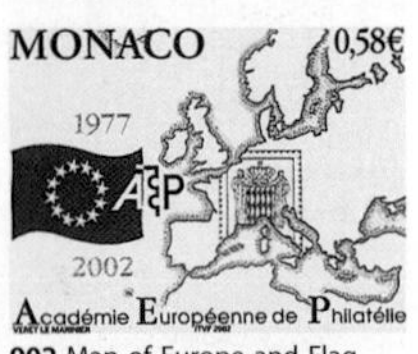

902 Map of Europe and Flag

2002. 25th Anniv of European Academy of Postal Studies.
2556 **902** 58c. multicoloured 1·90 1·30

903 Circus and Globe

2002. Europa. Circus. Multicoloured.
2557 46c. Type **903** 2·00 1·40
2558 46c. "JOURS DE CIRQUE" and performers 2·00 1·40

904 Emblem

2002. 20th International Swimming Competition.
2559 **904** 64c. multicoloured 2·00 1·40

905 Tarmac Roads

2002. Centenary of First Tarmac Roads.
2560 **905** 41c. red, black and brown 1·40 1·00

906 Exhibition Hall and Displays

2002. "Monacophil 2002" International Stamp Exhibition.
2561 **906** 46c. green, violet and red 1·60 1·10

907 Emblem

2002. 42nd Television Festival, Monte Carlo.
2562 **907** 70c. multicoloured 2·20 1·50

908 Footballers and Globe

2002. World Cup Football Championship, Japan and South Korea.
2563 **908** 75c. green, blue and red 2·30 1·70

909 Obverse of 1, 2 and 5 cent Coins and Reverse

2002. Coins.
2564 **909** 46c. copper, red and black 1·60 1·10
2565 - 46c. gold, red and black 1·60 1·10
2566 - €1.50 multicoloured 4·75 3·25
2567 - €1.50 multicoloured 4·75 3·25

DESIGNS: Type **909**; 46c. Obverse of 10, 20 and 50 cent coins and reverse; €1.50, Obverse and reverse of 1 euro coin; €1.50, Obverse and reverse of 2 euro coin.

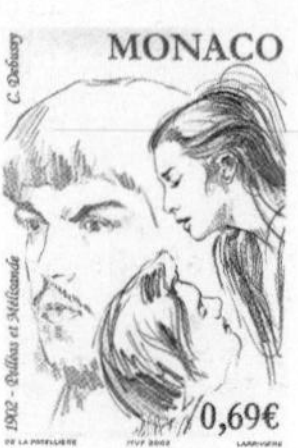

910 Debussy, Pelleas and Melisande

2002. Centenary of First Performance of Claude Debussy's Opera "Pelleas and Melisande".
2568 **910** 69c. green, blue and red 2·20 1·50

911 Saint Devote, Boat and Dove

2002. Monaco Red Cross.
2569 **911** €1.02 red, greenish blue and black 3·00 2·20

912 Aerial View of Monaco

2002. International Year of Mountains.
2570 **912** €1.37 multicoloured 4·25 3·00

913 Hugo

2002. Birth Bicentenary of Victor Hugo (writer). Each blue, brown and red.
2571 50c. Type **913** 1·60 1·10
2572 57c. Scenes from his books 1·90 1·30

Nos. 2571/2 were issued together, se-tenant, forming a composite design.

914 Dumas

2002. Birth Bicentenary of Alexandre Dumas (writer). Multicoloured.
2573 61c. Type **914** 2·00 1·40
2574 61c. Scenes from his books 2·00 1·40

Nos. 2573/4 were issued together, se-tenant, forming a composite design.

915 Princess Grace

2002. 26th Publication of "Annales Monegasques" (archives).
2575 **915** €1.75 multicoloured 5·50 3·75

916 Star-shaped Flower

2002. Christmas.
2576 **916** 50c. multicoloured 1·60 1·10

917 Frame from Film and Melies

2002. Centenary of "Le Voyage dans la Lune" (film by Georges Melies).
2577 **917** 76c. multicoloured 2·30 1·70

918 Magician

2002. "Magic Stars" Magic Festival, Monte Carlo.
2578 **918** €1.52 multicoloured 4·75 3·25

919 1949 Mercedes 220A Cabriolet

2002. Motor Cars from the Royal Collection. Multicoloured.
2579 46c. Type **919** 1·40 1·00
2580 69c. 1956 Rolls Royce Silver Cloud 2·20 1·50
2581 €1.40 1974 Citroen DS 21 4·25 3·00

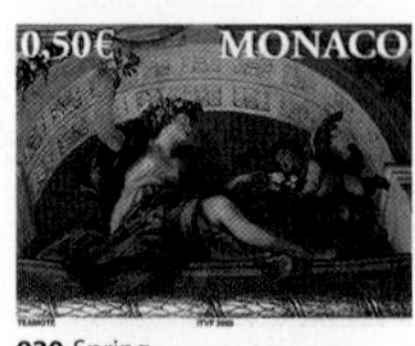

920 Spring

2002. Royal Palace (3rd series). Frescoes. Sheet 120×100 mm containing T 920 and similar horiz designs showing the Four Seasons. Multicoloured.
MS2582 50c. Type **920**; €1 Summer; €1.50, Autumn; €2 Winter 16·00 16·00

921 Footballer and Golden Ball

2002. Award of International Philatelic Grand Prix to Luis Figo (footballer and 2001 Golden Ball winner). Centenary of Real Madrid Football Club.
2583 **921** 91c. multicoloured 2·75 2·00

922 Exhibition Poster

2002. "MonacoPhil 2002" Stamp Exhibition (2nd issue). Sheet 120×82 mm, containing T 922 and similar vert design. Multicoloured. Imperf.
MS2584 €3 Type **922**; €3 Exhibition emblem 19·00 19·00

923 Flower Arrangement

2002. 36th Monte Carlo Flower Show.
2585 **923** 67c. multicoloured 2·20 1·50

924 Princesses Caroline and Stephanie (presidents)

2002. 40th Anniv of "Association Mondiale des Amis de l'Enfance" (children's society).

2586 **924** €1.25 multicoloured 4·00 2·75

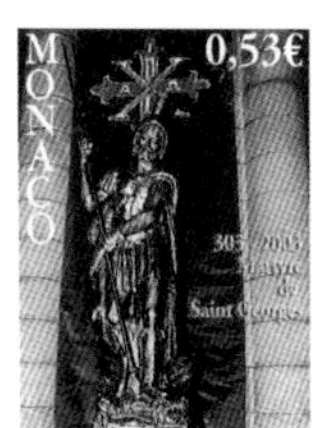

925 St. George (statue)

2002. 1700th Anniv of St. George's Martyrdom.

2587 **925** 53c. multicoloured 1·70 1·20

926 Prince Louis II, Flag, Arch and Building

2002. Bicentenary of Saint-Cyr Imperial Military School.

2588 **926** 61c. multicoloured 1·90 1·30

927 Clown

2003. 27th International Circus Festival, Monte Carlo.

2589 **927** 59c. multicoloured 1·90 1·30

928 Crossed Pennants and Part of Yacht and Crew

2003. 50th Anniv of Monaco Yacht Club.

2590 **928** 46c. multicoloured 1·60 1·10

929 Children

2003. 15th Premiere Rampe (children's circus) Festival.

2591 **929** €2.82 multicoloured 9·00 6·50

930 Team Members pushing Bobsleigh

2003. 10th World Bobsleigh Pushing Championship.

2592 **930** 80c. multicoloured 2·50 1·80

931 Dove, Globe and Prince Albert I

2003. Centenary of Monaco International Peace Institute.

2593 **931** €1.19 multicoloured 3·75 2·75

932 Leaves, Spectator, Tennis Court and Player

2003. Tennis Masters Championship, Monte Carlo.

2594 **932** €1.30 multicoloured 4·00 2·75

933 Rough Collie

2003. International Dog Show, Monte Carlo.

2595 **933** 79c. multicoloured 2·75 2·00

934 Anniversary Emblem

2003. 40th Anniv of Monaco Junior Chamber of Commerce.

2596 **934** 41c. multicoloured 1·20 90

935 Club Grounds

2003. 75th Anniv of Monte Carlo Country Club.

2597 **935** 46c. multicoloured 1·40 1·00

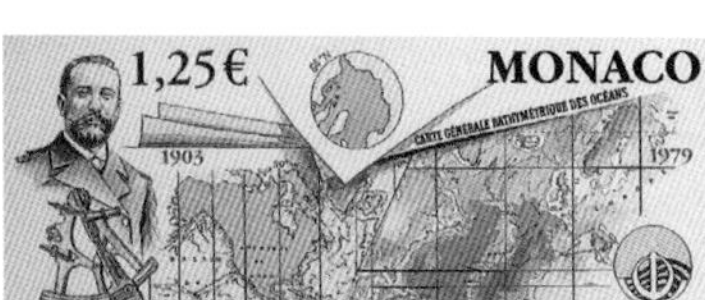

936 Prince Albert I, Sextant, Maps and Emblem (image scaled to 62% of original size)

2003. Centenary of First General Bathymetric Chart of the Oceans. Multicoloured.

2598 €1.25 Type **936** 4·00 2·75

2599 €1.25, Buildings and maps 4·00 2·75

Nos. 2598/9 were issued together, se-tenant, forming a composite design.

937 Girl on Diving Board (Jean-Gabriel Domergue)

2003. Europa. Poster Art. Multicoloured.

2600 50c. Type **937** 2·00 1·40

2601 50c. Monte-Carlo (Alphonse Mucha) 2·00 1·40

938 Castle, Coin and Ship

2003. Postcard Coin and Stamp Exhibition, Fontvielle.

2602 **938** 45c. multicoloured 1·60 1·10

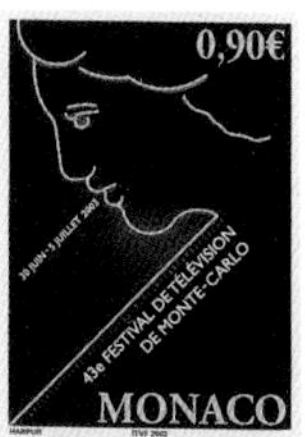

939 Face

2003. 43rd International Television Festival.

2603 **939** 90c. multicoloured 2·75 2·00

940 Bronze Statuette

2003. 15th Biannual Antique Dealers Meeting.

2604 **940** €1.80 multicoloured 5·50 4·00

941 Roald Amundsen and Polar Scene

2003. Centenaries. Multicoloured.

2605 90c. Type **941** (1st crossing of North Pole) 2·75 2·00

2606 €1.80 Wright brothers and *Flyer 1* 5·50 4·00

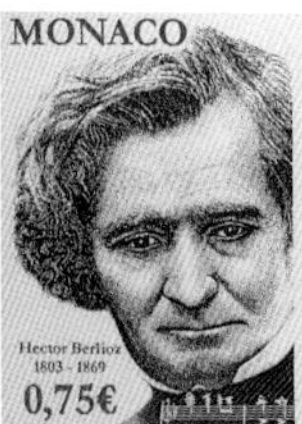

942 Hector Berlioz

2003. Composers Birth Anniversaries.

2607 **942** 75c. black and red 2·30 1·70

2608 - €1.60 blue, sepia and red 5·00 3·50

DESIGNS—VERT: Type **942** (bicentenary). HORIZ: €1.60 Aram Khatchaturian (centenary).

943 Woman's Head (Francois Boucher) (300th anniv)

2003. Artists' Birth Anniversaries.

2609 **943** €1.30 multicoloured 4·00 2·75

2610 - €3 mauve and black 9·25 6·50

2611 - €3.60 brown and black 11·00 7·75

DESIGNS: €1.30, Type **943**; €3 Vincent Van Gogh (150th anniv); €3.60, Girolamo Francesco Maria Mazzola (Le Parmigianino) (500th anniv).

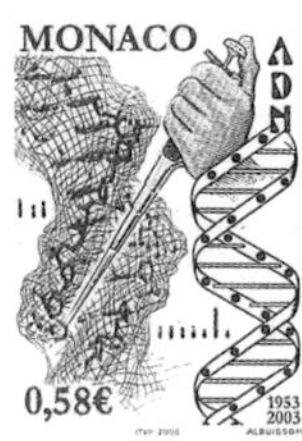

944 Hand holding Pipette and DNA Double Helix (50th anniv of discovery)

2003. Scientific Anniversaries.

2612 **944** 58c. black, blue and red 1·90 1·30

2613 - €1.11 chestnut, blue and red 3·50 2·40

DESIGNS: Type **944**; Alexander Fleming (75th anniv of discovery of penicillin).

945 Nostradamus

2003. 500th Birth Anniv of Michel de Nostre-Dame (Nostradamus) (astrologer).

2614 **945** 70c. multicoloured 2·20 1·50

946 Magician

2003. "Magic Stars" Magic Festival, Monte Carlo.

2615 **946** 75c. multicoloured 2·30 1·70

947 Marie and Pierre Curie

2003. Centenary of Award of Nobel Prize for Physics to Antoine Henri Becquerel and Pierre and Marie Curie.

2616 **947** €1.20 multicoloured 3·75 2·75

948 St. Devote kneeling before Cross

2003. 1700th (2004) Anniv of Arrival of St. Devote (patron saint) in Monaco (1st series). Each blue, black and red.

2617		45c. Type **948**	1·40	1·00
2618		45c. St. Devote facing Barbarus	1·40	1·00
2619		45c. Boat carrying St. Devote's body	1·40	1·00
2620		45c. St. Devote (statue)	1·40	1·00

See also No. 2626/30.

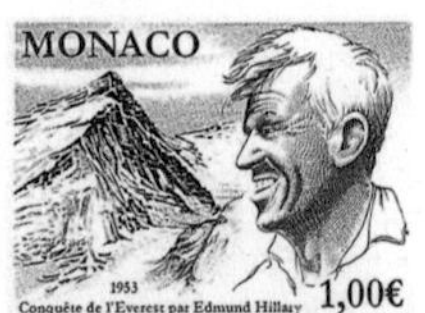

949 Edmund Hilary and Mount Everest

2003. 50th Anniv of First Ascent of Mount Everest.

2621	**949**	€1 multicoloured	3·25	2·20

950 Star-shaped Flower

2003. Christmas.

2622	**950**	50c. multicoloured	1·60	1·10

951 Lion and Lion Tamer

2003. MonacoPhil 2004 Stamp Exhibition (December 2004).

2623	**951**	50c. multicoloured	1·60	1·10

952 Exhibition Poster

2003. 28th International Circus Festival (January 2004), Monte Carlo.

2624	**952**	70c. multicoloured	2·20	1·50

953 Tram and Buildings

2004. Centenary of Beausoleil Municipality.

2625	**953**	75c. multicoloured	2·40	1·70

954 St. Devote kneeling before Alta

2004. 1700th Anniv of St. Devote's Arrival (2nd series).

2626	**954**	50c. red and brown	1·60	1·10
2627	-	75c. orange and brown (horiz)	2·40	1·70
2628	-	90c. brown and deep brown (horiz)	3·00	2·00
2629	-	€1 brown and deep brown	3·25	2·20
2630	-	€4 purple and brown (horiz)	13·00	8·75

DESIGNS: 75c. Before Barbarus; 90c. Martyrdom; €1 Boat carrying St. Devote's body; €4 Arrival in Monaco.

955 Princesses Grace and Caroline

2004. 40th Anniv of Princess Grace Foundation.

2640	**955**	50c. multicoloured	1·60	1·10

956 *Hyla meridionalis*

2004. Amphibians.

2641	**956**	75c. green, yellow and black	2·40	1·70
2642	-	€4.50 green, blue and black	14·50	10·00

DESIGN: Type **956**; €4.50, *Lacerte viridis*.

957 Princess Grace and Shamrock Leaf

2004. 20th Anniv of Princess Grace Irish Library.

2643	**957**	€1.11 green and brown	3·50	2·40

958 Hands

2004. 6th Biennial Oncological Meeting.

2644	**958**	€1.11 multicoloured	3·50	2·40

959 Princess Grace (statue) (Daphne du Barry)

2004

2645	**959**	€1.45 multicoloured	4·75	3·25

960 Garden

2004. 20th Anniv of Princess Grace Rose Garden.

2646	**960**	€1.90 multicoloured	6·25	4·25

961 Mask, Musical Instruments, Dancer and Actor

2004. Spring Arts Festival.

2647	**961**	€1 brown, scarlet and green	3·25	2·20

962 Cathedral Facade, Choirboy and Emblem

2004. Centenary of Cathedral Choir.

2648	**962**	45c. multicoloured	1·50	1·00

963 Flower Arrangement

2004. 37th Monte Carlo Flower Show.

2649	**963**	58c. multicoloured	2·00	1·30

964 Cavalier King Charles Spaniels

2004. International Dog Show, Monte Carlo.

2650	**964**	90c. multicoloured	3·00	2·00

965 Antony Noghes, King Louis II and Bugatti 35B Race Car driven by William Grover-Williams

2004. 75th Anniv of First Monaco Motor Racing Grand Prix.

2651	**965**	€1.20 multicoloured	4·00	2·75

966 Hands enclosing Children

2004. Monaco International School.

2652	**966**	50c. multicoloured	1·70	1·10

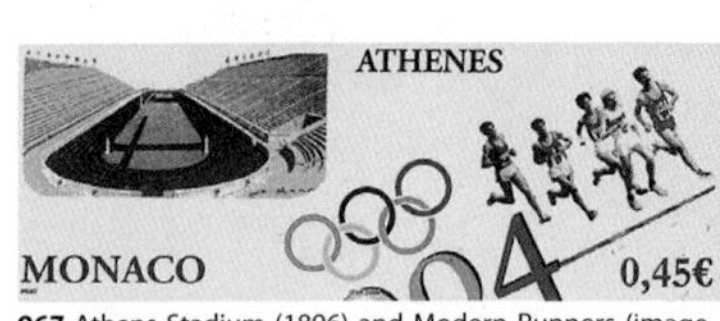

967 Athens Stadium (1896) and Modern Runners (image scaled to 62% of original size)

2004. Olympic Games, Athens. Multicoloured.

2653		45c. Type **967**	1·40	1·00
2654		45c. Classical Greek runners and Athens stadium (2004)	1·40	1·00

Nos. 2653/4 were issued together, se-tenant, forming a composite design.

968 Women wearing Swimsuits ("What Joy to Live the Summer in Monte Carlo") (poster, 1948)

2004. Europa. Holidays. Multicoloured.

2655		50c. Type **968**	1·60	1·10
2656		50c. Frontier sign ("The border of your dreams") (poster, 1951)	1·60	1·10

969 Medal

2004. 50th Anniv of Order of Grimaldi (medal).

2657	**969**	90c. multicoloured	2·75	2·00

970 Napoleon, Crown Prince Honore-Gabriel and Prince Joseph (officers in Napoleon's army)

2004. Bicentenary of Coronation of Emperor Napoleon I. Multicoloured.

2658		58c. Type **970**	1·90	1·30
2659		75c. Eagle and bees (imperial insignia) (horiz)	2·30	1·70
2660		€1.90 Stephanie de Beauharnais (Napoleon's niece and adopted daughter)	6·00	4·25
2661		€2.40 Napoleon I wearing coronation robes	7·75	5·50

971 George Balanchine (choreographer) and Serge Diaghilev (ballet impresario)

2004. First Production of Russian Ballet in Monaco.

2662	**971**	€1.60 multicoloured	5·25	3·50

972 Eye enclosing Globe

2004. 44th International Television Festival.
2663 **972** €1.80 multicoloured 6·00 4·00

973 Frederic Mistral

2004. Centenary of Frederic Mistral's Nobel Prize for Literature.
2664 **973** 45c. vermilion, brown and green 1·50 1·00

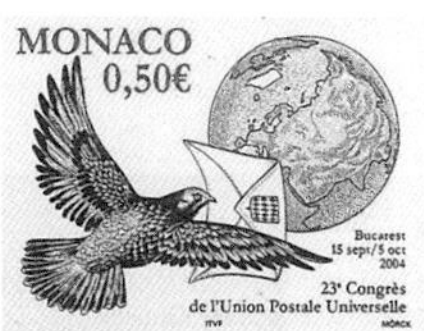
974 Bird holding Envelope and Globe

2004. 23rd UPU Conference, Bucharest.
2665 **974** 50c. multicoloured 1·70 1·10

975 Chinese Landscape and Marco Polo

2004. 750th Birth Anniv of Marco Polo (traveller).
2666 **975** 50c. multicoloured 1·70 1·10

976 Stamps and Park

2004. Salon de Timbre International Stamp Exhibition, Paris.
2667 **976** 75c. brown, green and vermilion 2·50 1·70

977 Scenes from the Stories

2004. 300th Anniv of French Translation of "One Thousand and One Nights" (collection of stories).
2668 **977** €1 indigo 3·25 2·20

978 Hotel Complex

2004. 75th Anniv of Monte Carlo Beach Hotel.
2669 **978** 45c. multicoloured 1·50 1·00

979 Anniversary Emblem

2004. Centenary of FIFA (Federation Internationale de Football Association).
2670 **979** €1.60 multicoloured 5·25 3·50

980 Female Magician

2004. "Magic Stars" Magic Festival.
2671 **980** 45c. multicoloured 1·50 1·00

981 Cacti and Presents

2004. Christmas.
2672 **981** 50c. multicoloured 1·70 1·10

982 Princess Grace

2004. 75th Birth Anniv of Princess Grace (MS2673a). MonacoPhil 2004 (MS2673b). Two sheets, each 141×75 mm containing T 982 and similar vert designs. Each ultramarine and green.
MS2673 (a) 75c. Type **982**; €1.75 Wearing tiara; €3.50 Wearing earrings. (b) As No. **MS**2673a but with colours reversed. Imperf Set of 2 sheets 20·00 20·00

983 Monte Carlo and Emblem

2004. Monaco's Accession to the Council of Europe.
2674 **983** 50c. blue and vermilion 1·70 1·10

984 Equestrian Performer

2004. 29th International Circus Festival (January 2005), Monte Carlo.
2675 **984** 70c. multicoloured 1·50 1·00

985 Stadium Building, Pool and Court

2004. 20th Anniv of Louis II Stadium, Monte Carlo.
2676 **985** 50c. ultramarine, brown and vermilion 1·70 1·10

986 Prince Rainier III

2004. Monaco Prince's Palace. Each salmon, deep green and green.
2677 50c. Type **986** 1·70 1·10
2678 50c. Palace facade (60×27 mm) 1·70 1·10
2679 50c. Prince Albert 1·70 1·10
Nos. 2677/9 were issued together, se-tenant, forming a composite design.

987 Entrance

2004. 70th Anniv of Foundation of Monaco Hall of Residence, Cité University, Paris.
2680 **987** 58c. brown, black and vermilion 2·00 1·30

988 Building Facade

2004. 75th Anniv of Law Courts.
2681 **988** 75c. multicoloured 2·50 1·70

989 Artistic and Cultural Symbols

2004. 25th Anniv of "Alliance Francaise" (French language and culture promotion organization).
2682 **989** 75c. multicoloured 2·50 1·70

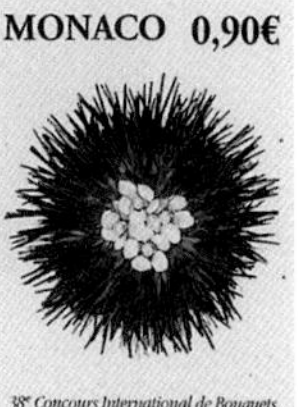
990 Flower Arrangement

2004. 38th Monte Carlo Flower Show (2005).
2683 **990** 90c. multicoloured 3·00 2·00

991 Luigi Valentino Brugnatelli (inventor)

2004. Bicentenary of Electroplating.
2684 **991** €1 brown and black 3·25 2·20

992 Goalkeeper's Hands holding Ball

2004. 75th Anniv of First Football World Cup Championship. Multicoloured.
2685 €1 Type **992** 3·25 2·20
2686 €1 Players' legs and ball 3·25 2·20

993 Jean-Paul Sartre

2004. Birth Centenary of Jean-Paul Sartre (writer).
2687 **993** €1.11 multicoloured 3·75 2·40

994 Johan Edvard Lundstrom (Swedish inventor)

2004. 150th Anniv of Safety Matches.
2688 **994** €1.20 multicoloured 4·00 2·75

995 Don Quixote and Sancho Panza

2004. 400th Anniv of "Don Quixote de la Mancha" (novel by Miguel de Cervantes Saavedra).
2689 **995** €1.20 black, brown and vermilion 4·00 2·75

996 Leo Ferre

2004. Leo Ferre (songwriter, singer and poet) Commemoration.
2690 **996** €1.40 multicoloured 4·50 3·00

997 Hand holding Hypodermic

2004. 150th Anniv of Invention of Hypodermic Syringe by Alexander Wood.
2691 **997** €1.60 purple, black and vermilion 5·25 3·50

998 Frank Libby

2004. 25th Death Anniv of Frank Willard Libby (inventor of Carbon 14 dating and winner of Nobel Prize for Chemistry, 1960).

2692	**998**	€1.80 multicoloured	6·00	4·00

999 Emblem and Founder Members (Rotary Club, Chicago)

2005. Centenary of Rotary International (charitable organization). Multicoloured.

2693	55c. Type **999**	1·80	1·20
2694	70c. Emblem and "100 ans" (vert)	2·30	1·50

1000 Artist and Castle

2005. 50th Anniv of Fine Arts Committee Exhibition.

2695	**1000**	48c. multicoloured	1·70	1·10

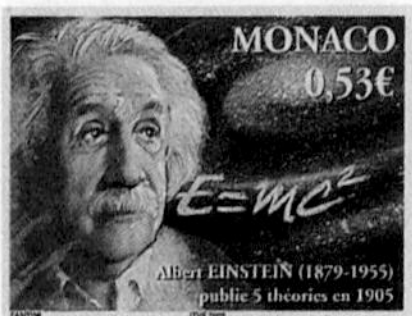
1001 Albert Einstein

2005. Centenary of Publication of Five Papers by Albert Einstein.

2696	**1001**	53c. multicoloured	1·80	1·20

1002 Emblem

2005. Granting of University Diploma to Bosio Pavilion Fine Arts School.

2697	**1002**	64c. vermilion and black	2·10	1·40

1003 Dachshund

2005. International Dog Show, Monte Carlo.

2698	**1003**	82c. multicoloured	2·75	1·90

1004 Centenary Emblem and Race Cars

2005. Centenary of FIA (Federation Internationale de L'Automobile).

2699	**1004**	55c. multicoloured	1·80	1·20

1005 Venturi Fetish

2005. 21st Electric Car Congress (EVS 21), Monaco. Multicoloured.

2700	75c. Type **1005**	2·50	1·70
2701	€1.30 Car enclosing exhibition centre	4·25	2·75

1006 Show Jumper

2005. 10th International Show Jumping Competition, Monaco.

2702	**1006**	90c. green and vermilion	3·00	2·00

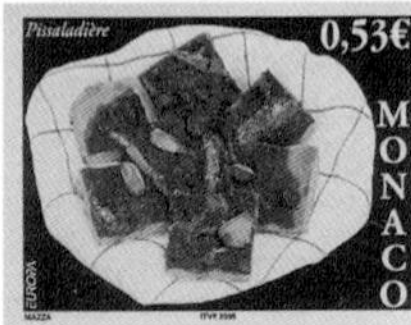
1007 Pissaladiere (pizza)

2005. Europa. Gastronomy. Multicoloured.

2703	53c. Type **1007**	1·80	1·20
2704	53c. Barbagiuans	1·80	1·20
2705	55c. Pastries	1·80	1·20
2706	55c. Chard pie	1·80	1·20

1008 Louis II Stadium and Emblem

2005. 25th Anniv of Monaco Special Olympics.

2707	**1008**	€1.20 multicoloured	4·00	2·75

1009 Poster

2005. Centenary of First Industries. Advertising posters. Multicoloured.

2708	77c. Type **1009** (tourism)	2·75	1·80
2709	€2.50 Woman and bath (sanitary ware)	8·25	5·50
2710	€3.10 Harlequin and biscuits (biscuit making)	10·00	6·75

1010 Yachts in Berth

2005. Yacht Show.

2711	**1010**	82c. multicoloured	2·75	1·90

1011 Edmond Halley (predicted the continuing return of Halley's comet)

2005. Astronomers.

2712	**1011**	€1.22 violet, vermilion and green	4·25	2·75
2713	-	€1.98 deep green, vermilion and green	6·50	4·50
2714	-	€3.80 brown, vermilion and green	12·50	8·25

DESIGNS: €1.22 Type **1011**; €1.98 Gerald Kuiper (discovered Kuiper's belt) (birth centenary); €3.80 Clyde Tombaugh (75th anniv of discovery of Pluto).

1012 Emblem

2005. 50th Anniv of Universal Postal Union Membership.

2715	**1012**	€3.03 ultramarine, purple and vermilion	10·00	6·50

1013 Arms

2005. Self-adhesive.

2716	**1013**	(48c.) emerald, black and vermilion	1·70	1·10

No. 2716 was for use on mail up to 20 grammes within Monaco and France.

1014 Emblem

2005. 10th "Journee du Patrimoine" (culture day).

2717	**1014**	48c. multicoloured	1·70	1·10

1015 Emblem

2005. "Magic Stars" Magic Festival.

2718	**1015**	€1.45 scarlet and gold	5·00	3·25

1016 Virgin and Child

2005. Christmas.

2719	**1016**	53c. black and vermilion	1·80	1·20

1017 Monte-Carlo Bay Hotel

2005

2720	**1017**	55c. multicoloured	1·80	1·20

1018 Nadia and Lili Boulanger

2005. 25th Anniv of Nadia and Lili Boulanger Music Competition.

2721	**1018**	90c. indigo, vermilion and green	2·75	2·00

1019 Singer (Le Chant)

2005. 180th Birth Anniv of Charles Garnier (architect).

2722	**1019**	82c. claret and vermilion	2·50	1·80
2723	-	82c. claret and vermilion	2·50	1·80
2724	-	82c. claret and vermilion	2·50	1·80
2725	-	82c. claret and vermilion	2·50	1·80
2726	-	82c. green and vermilion	2·50	1·80
2727	-	82c. claret and vermilion	2·50	1·80

DESIGNS: 82c.×6, Type **1019**; Casino (Salle Garnier); Three figures (La Comedie); Two figures (La Danse); Charles Garnier; Musicians (La Musique).

1020 Prince Albert II

2005. No value expressed.

2728	**1020**	(48c.) green	1·60	1·10
2729	**1020**	(53c.) carmine	1·70	1·20
2730	**1020**	(75c.) blue	2·30	1·70

1021 Monte Carlo

2005. National Day. Multicoloured.

2731	€1.01 Type **1021**	3·00	2·20
2732	€1.01 Palace facade (60×32 mm)	3·00	2·20
2733	€1.01 Fontvielle	3·00	2·20

Nos. 2731/3 were issued together, se-tenant, forming a composite design.

1022 Prince Rainier III

2005. Prince Rainier III Commemoration. Sheet 101×130 mm.

MS2734	**1022**	€4 black	12·50	12·50

1023 Stamp Museum

2005. MonacoPhil 2006 International Stamp Exhibition.
2735 **1023** 55c. multicoloured 1·70 1·20

1024 Clown

2005. 30th International Circus Festival (January 2006), Monte Carlo. Multicoloured.
2736 64c. Type **1024** 2·00 1·40
2737 75c. Charlie Rivel — Clown d'Or 1974 2·30 1·70
2738 75c. Fredy Knie — Clown d'Or 1977 2·30 1·70
2739 75c. Alexis Gruss Senior — Clown d'Or 1975 2·30 1·70
2740 75c. Clown d'Or statue 2·30 1·70
2741 75c. Georges Carl — Clown d'Or 19791 2·30 1·70

1025 Neve (mascot)

2006. Winter Olympic Games, Turin. Multicoloured.
2742 55c. Type **1025** 1·70 1·20
2743 55c. Gliz 1·70 1·20
2744 82c. Bobsleigh and skier (40×30 mm) 2·75 1·90
Nos. 2742/3 were issued together, se-tenant, forming a composite design.

1026 Stamps, Coins and Printing Press

2006. Centenary of Stamp and Coin Museum.
2745 **1026** 53c. black, vermilion and brown 1·70 1·20

1027 Book as Clapperboard

2006. Cinema and Literature Forum.
2746 **1027** 82c. multicoloured 2·75 1·90

1028 Leopold Senghor

2006. Birth Centenary of Leopold Sedar Senghor (writer and politician). Organisation Internationale de la Francophonie.
2747 **1028** €1.45 multicoloured 4·50 3·25

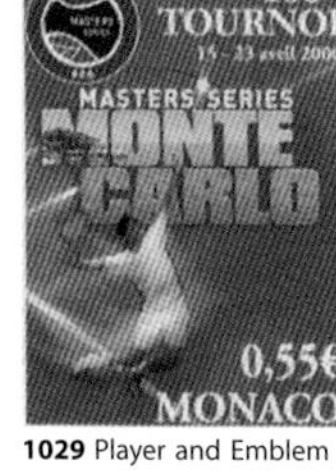

1029 Player and Emblem

2006. Centenary of Masters Tennis Tournament.
2748 **1029** 55c. multicoloured 1·80 1·20

1030 Grimaldi Arms

2006. Self-adhesive.
2749 **1030** A (55c.) black and vermilion 1·80 1·20

1031 Conductors and Musical Instruments

2006. 150th Anniv of Philharmonic Orchestra.
2750 **1031** 64c. multicoloured 2·10 1·40

1032 Map and Ship

2006. Centenary of Prince Albert I's Arctic Expeditions.
2751 **1032** €1.60 multicoloured 5·00 3·50

1033 Schnauzer

2006. International Dog Show, Monte Carlo.
2752 **1033** 64c. multicoloured 2·00 1·40

1034 Blooms

2006. 39th Monte Carlo Flower Show.
2753 **1034** 77c. multicoloured 2·50 1·80

1035x 1035 Trophy and Stadium

2006. World Cup Football Championship, Germany. Multicoloured.
2754 90c. Type **1035** 2·75 2·00

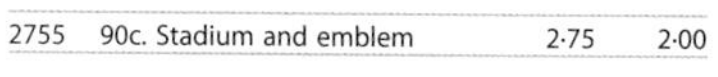
2755 90c. Stadium and emblem 2·75 2·00

1036 Boxes enclosing Shapes

2006. Europa. Integration. Multicoloured.
2756 53c. Type **1036** 1·70 1·20
2757 55c. Globe containing face, and microchip (horiz) 1·70 1·20

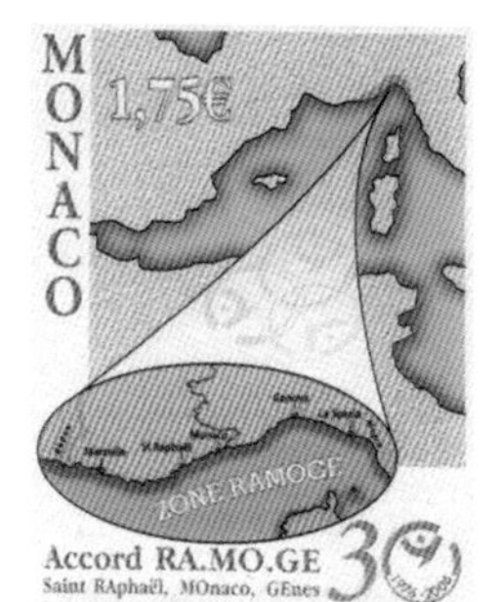

1037 Mediterranean Coastline

2006. 30th Anniv of RAMOGE (Monaco, France and Italy accord to combat coastal and maritime pollution).
2758 **1037** €1.75 multicoloured 5·50 3·75

1038 Capitol

2006. Washington 2006 International Stamp Exhibition.
2759 **1038** 90c. ultramarine and vermilion 2·75 2·00

1039 John Huston

2006. Birth Centenary of John Huston (actor and director).
2760 **1039** 90c. slate and red 5·50 4·00

1040 Prince Albert and Fencers

2006. 20th Prince Albert Challenge Fencing Competition.
2761 **1040** 48c. multicoloured 1·60 1·10

1041 Pierre Corneille

2006. 400th Birth Anniv of Pierre Corneille (dramatist).
2762 **1041** 53c. multicoloured 1·70 1·20

1042 Hand and TV Screen

2006. 46th International Television Festival.
2763 **1042** 82c. multicoloured 2·75 1·90

1043 Mozart and Scenes from his Operas

2006. 250th Birth Anniv of Wolfgang Amadeus Mozart.
2764 **1043** €1.22 blue and vermilion 4·00 2·75

1044 Prince Pierre and Cultural Symbols

2006. 40th Anniv of Prince Pierre Foundation (art and culture).

2765 **1044** €2.50 lilac, blue and vermilion 7·75 5·50

1045 Dino Buzzati

2006. Birth Centenary of Dino Buzzati (writer).
2766 **1045** 55c. multicoloured 1·70 1·20

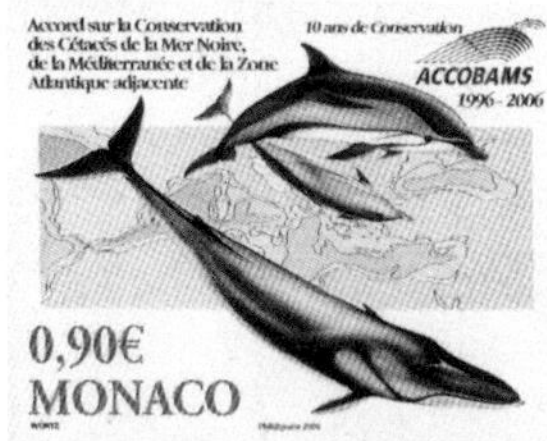

1046 Cetaceans

2006. 10th Anniv of ACCOBAMS.
2767 90c. multicoloured 2·75 2·00

1047 Luchino Visconti

2006. Birth Centenary of Luchino Visconti (film director).
2768 **1047** €1.75 Indian red 5·50 3·75

1048 Rolls Royce Motor Car

2006. Centenary of Rolls Royce (car manufacturer).
2769 **1048** 64c. multicoloured 2·00 1·40

1049 Hand and Cards

2006. "Magic Stars" Magic Festival.
2770 **1049** 77c. multicoloured 2·50 1·80

1050 Heads

2006. Red Cross.
2771 **1050** 48c. multicoloured 1·60 1·10

1051 Virgin and Child

2006. Christmas.
2772 **1051** 53c. multicoloured 1·70 1·20

1052 Josephine Baker

2006. Birth Centenary of Josephine Baker (entertainer). 25th Anniv of Princess Grace Theatre.
2773 **1052** 49c. multicoloured 1·60 1·10

1053 Emblems

2006. 10th Anniv of AIDS Awareness Campaign.
2774 **1053** 49c. multicoloured 1·60 1·10

1054 Prince Albert II

2006. No value expressed.
2775 **1054** (49c.) green 1·60 1·10
2776 **1054** (54c.) scarlet 1·70 1·20
2777 **1054** (85c.) blue 2·75 1·90

1055 Emblems, Envelopes and Stamps

2006. 70th Anniv of Stamp Issuing Office. 20th Anniv of Consultative Committee to the Prince of Monaco's Philatelic Collection.
2778 **1055** 54c. multicoloured 1·70 1·20

1056 Clown and Elephant

2006. 31st International Circus Festival (January 2007), Monte Carlo. Multicoloured.
2779 60c. Type **1056** 1·90 1·30
2780 84c. Poster 2·75 1·90

1057 Prince Albert II

2006. Official Photographic Portrait.
2781 **1057** 60c. multicoloured 1·90 1·30

1058 Formula 1 Race Car

2006. 65th Anniv of Monte Carlo Formula 1 Grand Prix (2782). 75th Anniv of Monte Carlo Rally (2783). Multicoloured.
2782 60c. Type **1058** 1·90 1·30
2783 60c. Rally race car 1·90 1·30

1059 Face

2006. 10th Anniv of Les Enfants de Frankie (children's charitable association).
2784 **1059** 70c. multicoloured 2·20 1·50

1060 Albert Camus

2006. 50th Anniv of Albert Camus's Nobel Prize for Literature.
2785 **1060** 84c. black, blue and vermilion 2·75 1·90

1061 Auguste Escoffier

2006. 160th Birth Anniv of Auguste Escoffier (chef).
2786 **1061** 85c. chestnut, vermilion and ultramarine 2·75 1·90

1062 Daniel Bovet and Alfred Nobel

2006. Red Cross. Birth Centenary (2007) of Daniel Bovet—Winner of 1957 Nobel Prize for Medicine.
2787 **1062** 86c. lilac and vermilion 2·75 1·90

1063 Blue and Pink Bouquet

2006. 40th Anniv of International Flower Competition. Multicoloured.
2788 €1.30 Type **1063** 4·00 2·75
2789 €1.30 Two orange flowers and thin leaves 4·00 2·75
2790 €1.30 Tall arrangement 4·00 2·75
2791 €1.30 Gerberas 4·00 2·75

1064 Cardio-Thoracic Centre Building

2006. 20th Anniv of Cardio Thoracic Centre (2792). Opening of Institute of Medicine and Sports Surgery (2793).
2792 **1064** €1.15 ultramarine, vermilion and black 3·50 2·50
2793 - €1.70 vermilion, black and cinnamon 5·00 3·75
DESIGNS: €1.15 Type **1064**; €1.70 Institute building.

1065 Frontispiece and Rudyard Kipling

2006. Centenary of Rudyard Kipling's Nobel Prize for Literature.
2794 **1065** €1.57 green, vermilion and black 4·75 3·50

1066 Prince Albert II and Pope Benedict XVI

2006. Prince Albert II's Official Visit to the Vatican.
2795 **1066** €1.70 multicoloured 5·00 3·75

1067 "Sunrise"

2006. Grimaldi Forum. Paintings by Nall. Multicoloured.
2796 €1.70 Type **1067** 5·00 3·75
2797 €1.70 "Sunset" 5·00 3·75

1068 Paul-Emile Victor and dog

2006. Birth Centenary of Paul-Emile Victor (explorer).
2798 **1068** €2.11 blue, black and vermilion 6·25 4·50

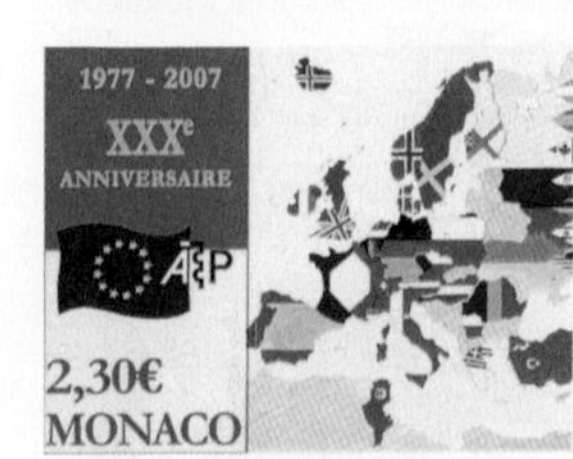
1069 Flags as Map of Europe

2006. 30th Anniv of European Academy of Philately.
2799 **1069** €2.30 multicoloured 6·75 5·00

1070 Trophy

2006. Alexander Kroo—ASCAT 2006 Philatelic Grand Prix Winner.
2800 **1070** €3 multicoloured 8·75 6·50

1071 Prince Albert II

2006. MonacoPhil (2006). Sheet 101×126 mm.
MS2801 **1071** €6 multicoloured 16·00 16·00

1072 *Stenella coeruleoalba*

2007. Pre-cancelled. No value expressed.
2802 **1072** (36c.) multicoloured 1·30 90

No. 2802 was for mass mailing within France weighing less than 35g.

1073 Guiseppe Garibaldi

2007. Birth Bicentenary of Guiseppe Garibaldi (soldier).
2803 **1073** €1.40 sepia and vermilion 4·50 3·00

1074 Carlo Goldoni

2007. 300th Birth Anniv of Carlo Goldoni (playwright).
2804 **1074** €4.54 multicoloured 12·50 10·00

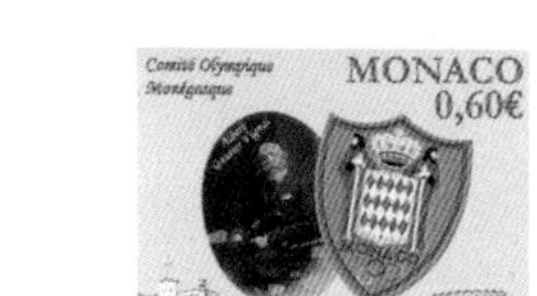

1075 Albert Gautier-Vignal and Committee Emblem

2007. Centenary of Monaco Olympic Committee.
2805 **1075** 60c. multicoloured 1·90 1·30

1076 Dalmatian

2007. International Dog Show, Monte Carlo.
2806 **1076** 70c. multicoloured 2·20 1·50

1077 Members' Flags and Emblem

2007. Small European States' Games.
2807 **1077** 86c. multicoloured 2·75 2·00

1078 Grace Kelly

2007. 25th Death Anniv of Princess Grace. "The Grace Kelly Years" Exhibition, Grimaldi Forum.
2808 **1078** 85c. black and vermilion 2·75 1·90

1079 Leger and Modern Helicopter

2007. Centenary of First Flight of Leger Helicopter (created by Maurice Stanislas Leger).
2809 **1079** €1.15 violet, ultramarine and vermilion 3·75 2·75

1080 Scouts and Campfire

2007. Europa. Centenary of Scouting. Multicoloured.
2810 60c. Type **1080** 1·90 1·40
2811 60c. Robert Baden Powell (founder) 1·90 1·40

Nos. 2810/11 were issued together, *se-tenant*, forming a composite design.

1081 Lights

2007. 47th International Television Festival.
2812 **1081** €2.90 multicoloured 8·75 7·00

1082 Postcard, Coin and Stamp

2007. Postcard Coin and Stamp Exhibition.
2813 **1082** 49c. multicoloured 1·80 1·30

1083 Magician

2007. 'Magic Stars' Magic Festival.
2814 **1083** €1.30 vermilion and black 4·25 3·00

1084 Virgin Mary

2007. Christmas (Visions of Virgin Mary by Bernadette Soubirous at Lourdes, 1858).
2815 **1084** 54c. multicoloured 1·90 1·40

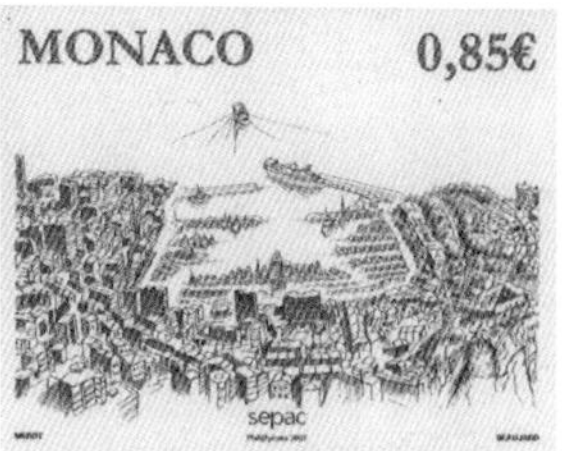

1085 Bay

2007. SEPAC (small European mail services).
2816 **1085** 85c. brown, blue and red 3·00 2·20

1086 Ringmaster

2007. 32nd International Circus Festival (January 2008), Monte Carlo.
2817 **1086** 60c. multicoloured 2·10 1·50

1087 Giacomo Puccini

2007. 140th Birth Anniv of Giacomo Puccini (composer).
2818 **1087** €1.40 blue and vermilion 5·00 3·50

1088 Church Building

2008. 50th Anniv of Reformed Church.
2819 **1088** 49c brown and blue 1·90 1·40

1089 Flower Arrangement

2008. 41st International Flower Competition.
2820 **1089** 49c. multicoloured 1·90 1·40

1090 Church Building

2008. 125th Anniv of Consecration of St Charles Church.
2821 **1090** 54c. slate and vermilion 2·00 1·50

1091 Quadriga and Arc de Triomphe du Carrousel

2008. Bicentenary of Francois Bosio's Quadriga (statue of chariot drawn by four horses).
2822 **1091** 54c. brown, vermilion and carmine 2·00 1·50

1092 Andrea Palladio

2008. 500th Birth Anniv of Andrea Palladio (architect).
2823 **1092** 60c. multicoloured 2·20 1·70

1093 Monte Carlo Country Club

2008. Posters of 1932 by Raymond Gid. Multicoloured.
2824 70c. Type **1093** 2·50 1·90
2825 85c. Monte Carlo Beach Hotel 3·00 2·30
2826 €1.15 Monte Carlo Golf Club 4·25 3·25

1094 Hands enclosing Emblem

2008. 10th Special Session of United Nations Environment Programme Forum.
2827 **1094** 85c. multicoloured 3·00 2·30

1095 Johannes Brahms

2008. 175th Birth Anniv of Johannes Brahms (composer and pianist).
2828 **1095** €1.15 green and vermilion 4·25 3·25

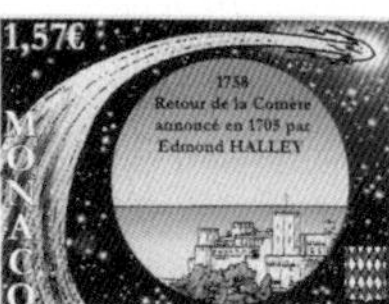

1096 Comet and Castle

2008. 250th Anniv of First Recorded Appearance of Halley's Comet.
2829 **1096** €1.57 multicoloured 5·75 4·50

1097 Leaves and Cones

2008. 20th Anniv of Marcel Kronenlein's Arboretum.
2830 **1097** €2.11 olive, ultramarine and vermilion 7·25 5·75

1098 'Monte Carlo, Pole d'Attraction' (1948)

2008. Poster by Louis Rue.
2831 **1098** €2.90 multicoloured 10·00 8·00

1099 Andre Massena

2008. 250th Birth Anniv of Andre Massena (Marshal of France).
2832 **1099** 86c. green and brown 3·00 2·30

1100 Bernadette Soubirous

2008. 150th Anniv of Apparition at Lourdes.
2833 **1100** €1.30 ultramarine and blue 4·75 3·50

1101 Henry Ford and Model 'T' Ford Car

2008. Anniversaries.
2834 **1101** €1.70 brown, green and vermilion 6·25 4·75
2835 - €2.30 indigo, vermilion and ultramarine 8·50 6·25
2836 - €4 brown and red 14·00 11·00

DESIGNS: €1.70 Type **1101** (centenary); €2.30 *Apollo*, *Atlantis* and *Mercury* spacecraft (50th anniv of NASA); €4 Alfred Nobel and nitroglycerine (175th birth anniv).

1102 Van Gogh (greyhound)

2008. International Dog Show, Monte Carlo.
2837 **1102** 88c. multicoloured 3·25 2·50

1103 Water Droplet

2008. Zaragoza 2008 International Water and Sustainable Development Exhibition.
2838 **1103** 65c. multicoloured 2·50 2·00

1104 Arms and Map

2008. Centenary of Cap d'Ail.
2839 **1104** 55c. black, brown and vermilion 2·10 1·60

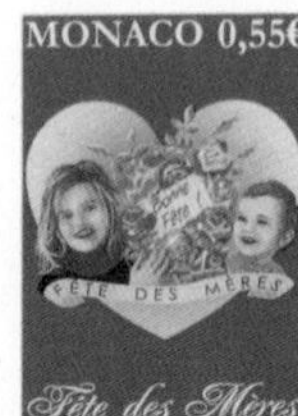

1105 Heart enclosing Children and Flowers

2008. Mothers' Day.
2840 **1105** 55c. multicoloured 2·10 1·60

1106 Pagoda and Stylized Athletes

2008. Olympic Games, Beijing. Each vermilion and black.
2841 55c. Type **1106** 2·10 1·60
2842 85c. Athletes and games emblem 3·25 2·40

1107 Stendhal and Scenes from his Novels

2008. 225th Birth Anniv of Henri Beyle (Stendhal) (writer).
2843 **1107** €1.33 blue, lilac and vermilion 5·25 3·75

1108 Boris Pasternak and Scene from *Dr. Zhivago*

2008. 50th Anniv of Boris Pasternak's Nobel Prize for Literature.
2844 **1108** €2.18 vermilion and green 8·50 6·25

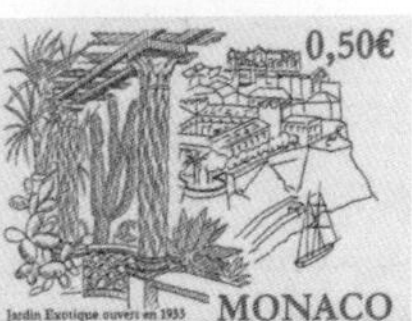

1109 Plants and Monaco

2008. 75th Anniv of Jardin Exotique (garden created by Prince Albert I).
2845 **1109** 50c. olive, purple and vermilion 2·00 1·40

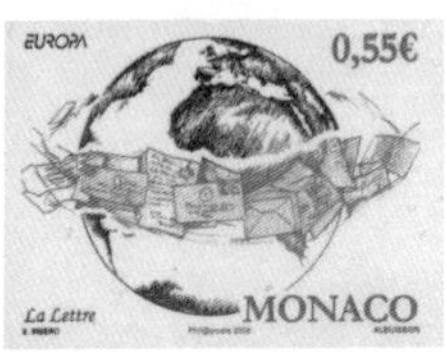

1110 Globe circled by Mail

2008. Europa. The Letter.
2846 55c. brown, orange and vermilion 2·20 1·60
2847 65c. light brown, brown and vermilion 2·50 1·80

DESIGNS: 55c. Type **1110**; 65c. Symbols of transport.

1111 Magician

2008. Magic Stars Festival, Monte-Carlo.
2848 **1111** 72c. multicoloured 3·00 2·10

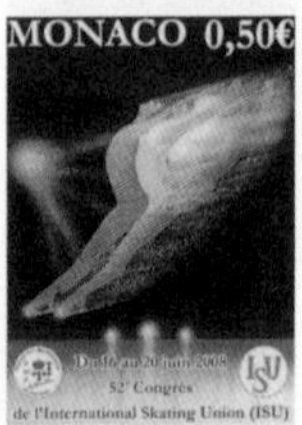

1112 Skater

2008. International Skating Union Congress.
2849 **1112** 50c. multicoloured 2·00 1·40

1113 *Gypaetus barbatus* (bearded vulture), Emblem and *Hieraaetus fasciatus* (Bonelli's eagle)

2008. Prince Albert II Foundation.
2850 **1113** 88c. multicoloured 3·50 2·50

1114 Face, Hand and Colours

2008. 48th International Television Festival.
2851 **1114** €2.80 multicoloured 10·50 7·75

1115 School Children

2008. International Co-operation.
2852 65c. black and vermilion 2·50 1·80
2853 €1 agate and vermilion 4·00 2·75
2854 €1.25 blue and vermilion 5·00 3·50
2855 €1.70 green and vermilion 6·75 4·75

DESIGNS: 65c. Type **1115** (campaign for education); €1 Health worker (health—Monegasque Red Cross); €1.25 Women (campaign against poverty); €1.70 Oasis and desert dwellers (campaign against desertification).

1116 Honore II Pistole (1648) and Monegasque Euro

2008. Monaco Numismatique 2008 Exhibition.
2856 **1116** 65c. multicoloured 2·75 2·00

1117 Franc 'Germinal', 1837

2008. Coins. Multicoloured.
2857 50c. Type **1117** 2·10 1·60
2858 55c. Franc, 1943 2·30 1·70
2859 72c. Franc 'Rainier III', 1950 3·00 2·30
2860 €1.25 Franc 'Rainier III', 1960 5·25 4·00
2861 €1.64 Euro coins, 1999 6·75 5·25
2862 €1.72 Euro coins, 2006 7·00 5·25

1118 Schonbrunn Palace

2008. WIPA 2008 International Stamp Exhibition, Vienna.
2863 **1118** 65c. multicoloured 2·75 2·00

1119 Order

2008. 150th Anniv of Order of St Charles
2864 **1119** €1.50 multicoloured 6·25 4·75

1120 Sleigh and Globe

2008. Christmas.
2865 **1120** 55c. multicoloured 2·30 1·70

1121 Symbols of Festival

2008. 33rd International Circus Festival.
2866 **1121** 85c. multicoloured 4·00 3·00

1122 Prince Albert I

2008. International Polar Year. Multicoloured.

2867 85c. Type **1122** 4·00 3·00
2868 85c. Flag of Monaco (41×41 mm) 4·00 3·00
2869 85c. Prince Albert II 4·00 3·00

1123 Robert Peary

2008. Centenary of Robert Peary's Expedition to North Pole. Multicoloured.

2870 87c. Type **1123** 4·25 3·25
2871 87c. USA flag and North Pole (41×41 mm) 4·25 3·25
2872 87c. Matthew Henson and *Theodore Roosevelt* (expedition ship) 4·25 3·25

1124 Railway and Road Emergency Vehicle

2009. Centenary of Monaco Firefighters. Multicoloured.

2873 50c. Type **1124** 2·30 1·70
2874 72c. Emergency vehicle, 1909 3·50 2·50
2875 87c. Long ladder emergency vehicle 4·25 3·25

1125 Rose Garden

2009. 25th Anniv of Princess Grace Rose Garden.

2876 **1125** €1.25 multicoloured 5·50 4·25

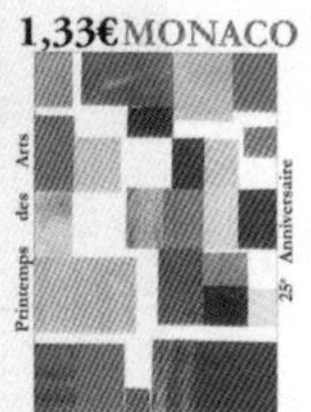

1126 Abstract

2009. 25th Anniv of Spring Arts Festival.

2877 **1126** €1.33 multicoloured 6·00 4·75

1127 Louis Bleriot and *Bleriot XI*

2009. Centenary of First Flight over English Channel.

2878 **1127** 87c. multicoloured 4·00 3·25

1128 Felix Mendelssohn

2009. Birth Bicentenary of Jakob Ludwig Felix Mendelssohn Bartholdy (composer).

2879 **1128** €1.50 indigo and olive 6·75 5·25

1129 Joan of Arc

2009. Centenary of Beatification of Joan of Arc.

2880 **1129** €2.22 scarlet, black and green 9·75 7·75

1130 Stamps and Building

2009. MonacoPhil 2009 International Stamp Exhibition.

2881 **1130** 56c. multicoloured 2·50 2·10

1131 Chihuahua and Cavalier King Charles Spaniel

2009. International Dog Show, Monte Carlo.

2882 **1131** 72c. multicoloured 3·50 2·50

1132 Blue-point Birman

2009. 2nd International Cat Show.

2883 **1132** 88c. multicoloured 4·25 3·25

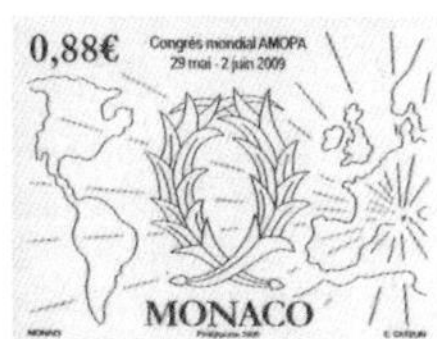

1133 Palms and Map

2009. World Conference of Order of Academic Palms Association Members.

2884 **1133** 88c. violet, brown and scarlet 4·25 3·25

1134 Barbie

2009. 50th Anniv of Barbie Doll.

2885 **1134** 88c. multicoloured 4·25 3·25

1135 Flowers

2009. 42nd International Flower Exhibition.

2886 **1135** 89c. multicoloured 4·25 3·25

1136 Fencer and Arms

2009. Centenary of Monaco Fencing and Handgun Club.

2887 **1136** 55c. black, scarlet and lemon 3·00 2·00

1137 Race Winner and Map of Italy

2009. Centenary of Tour of Italy (Giro) Cycle Race.

2888 **1137** 70c. multicoloured 3·75 2·50

1138 Arthur Conan Doyle and Outline of Sherlock Holmes (character)

2009. 150th Birth Anniv of Arthur Conan Doyle (writer).

2889 **1138** 85c. purple, scarlet and vermilion 4·50 3·00

1139 Edgar Allen Poe and Death

2009. Birth Bicentenary of Edgar Allen Poe (writer).

2890 **1139** €1.70 green and scarlet 9·00 6·25

1140 Arms

2009. Booklet Stamp. Self-adhesive.

2891 **1140** (70c.) multicoloured 3·00 2·40

No. 2891 was issued in single sided booklets of ten stamps for use on mail up to 20g. within Zone 1 (EU and Switzerland).

1141 Louis Notari and Script

2009. Centenary of Louis Notari Library.

2892 **1141** 51c. scarlet vermilion and bright violet 2·40 1·90

1142 Early and Modern Race Cars

2009. Centenary of First Formula I Grand Prix.

2893 **1142** 70c. multicoloured 3·00 2·40

1143 Flags of Members

2009. 60th Anniv of Monaco's Membership of UNESCO.

2894 **1143** €1.70 multicoloured 7·75 7·75

1144 Louis Braille

2009. Birth Bicentenary of Louis Braille (inventor of Braille writing for the blind).

2895 **1144** €3.80 indigo, scarlet and bistre 16·00 13·00

1145 Orchestra

2009. 50th Anniv of Princes's Palace Summer Concerts.

2896 **1145** 51c. bright violet and black 2·40 1·00

1146 Francesco Maria Grimaldi

2009. Europa. Astronomy.

2897 56c. deep brown, deep blue and scarlet 2·50 1·90

2898 70c. deep brown, turquoise blue and scarlet 3·00 2·40

DESIGNS: 56c. Type **1146**; 70c. Galileo.

1147 Dancer

2009. Ballet. Multicoloured.

2899 73c. Type **1147** (Ballet de Monte-Carlo) 3·25 2·50

2900 89c. Early dancers and audience (centenary of Ballets Russe) 4·00 3·25

2901 €1.35 Modern dancers (centenary of Ballets Russe) 6·00 4·75

1148 Georges Seurat

2009. 150th Birth Anniv of Georges Seurat (artist)

2902 **1148** 73c. multicoloured 3·25 2·50

1149 Pope Innocent III and Francis of Assisi

2009. 800th Anniv of Franciscan Order.

2903 **1149** 90c. new blue and black 4·00 3·25

1150 John Calvin

2009. 500th Birth Anniv of John Calvin (religious reformer).

2904 **1150** €1.67 black, scarlet and pale orange 7·25 5·75

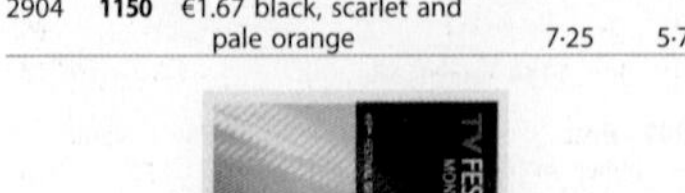

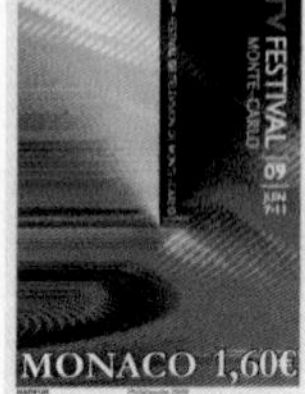

1151 'Waves'

2009. 49th International Television Festival.

2905 **1151** €1.60 multicoloured 7·25 5·50

1152 Niccolo Machiavelli

2009. 30th Anniv of Dante Alighieri Society (for the promulgation of Italian language and culture).

2906 70c. slate grey, scarlet and orange-brown 3·00 2·40

2907 85c. orange, scarlet and yellow-brown 3·75 3·00

2908 €1.30 new blue, scarlet and bright orange-brown 5·75 4·50

DESIGNS: 70c. Type 1152; 85c. Giovanni Boccaccio; €1.30 Francesco Petrarca.

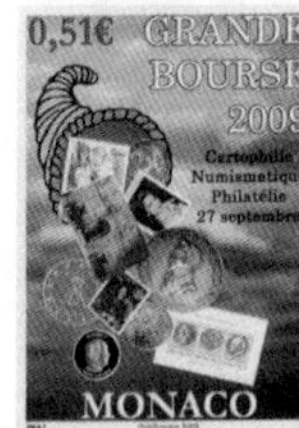

1153 Cornucopia

2009. Postcard, Coin and Stamp Exhibition.

2909 **1153** 51c. multicoloured 2·20 1·70

1154 Emblem and Young People

2009. Centenary of Youth Hostels.

2910 **1154** 90c. multicoloured 4·00 3·25

1155 *Tuiga*

2009. Centenary of Tuiga (racing yacht).

2911 **1155** 70c. multicoloured 3·00 2·40

1156 Cyclist

2009. Start of Tour de France Cycle Race in Monaco.

2912 **1156** 56c. multicoloured 2·50 2·25

1157 Pig as Magician

2009. Magic Stars Festival.

2913 **1157** 73c. multicoloured 3·00 2·40

1158 Place de la Marie

2009. SEPAC (small European mail services).

2914 **1158** 85c. multicoloured 3·25 4·75

1159 Big Ben

2009. 150th Anniv of Big Ben Clock, Palace of Westminster.

2915 **1159** €1 black, lemon and scarlet-vermilion 4·50 4·00

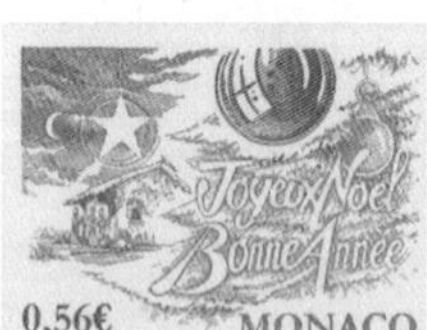

1160 Symbols of Christmas

2009. Christmas.

2916 **1160** 56c. new blue, light green and scarlet-vermilion 2·50 2·25

1161 Inscr 'Bengal' (name–Junglewhisper Elia)

2009. International Cat Show, 2010, Rainer III Auditorium.

2917 **1161** 56c. multicoloured 5·75 4·50

1162 Ayrton Senna

2009. 50th Birth Anniv of Ayrton Senna da Silva (racing driver).

2918 **1162** 73c. purple-brown, green and scarlet-vermilion 5·00 2·40

No. 2919 and Type **1163** are left for Birth Centenary of Jean Anouilth, issued on 4 December 2009, not yet received.

1164 Auguste Rodin and *Le Baiser* (sculpture)

2009. 170th (2010) Birth Anniv of Auguste Rodin (sculptor).

2920 **1164** 85c. blue-black and scarlet-vermilion 3·75 3·00

1165 Grace Kelly receiving Oscar for Best Actress, 1955

2009. 80th Birth Anniv of Grace Kelly (actress and Princess Grace of Monaco).

2921 **1165** 89c. black and scarlet-vermilion 4·00 3·25

1166 Gustav Mahler

2009. 150th (2010) Birth Anniv of Gustav Mahler (composer).

2922 **1166** 90c. deep dull purple and new blue 4·00 3·25

1167 Skier

2009. Winter Olympic Games, Vancouver.

2923 90c. turquoise-green, scarlet-vermilion and deep blue 4·00 3·25

2924 90c. deep blue, scarlet-vermilion and dull orange 4·00 3·25

DESIGNS: Type **1167**; 2924 Snowboarder.

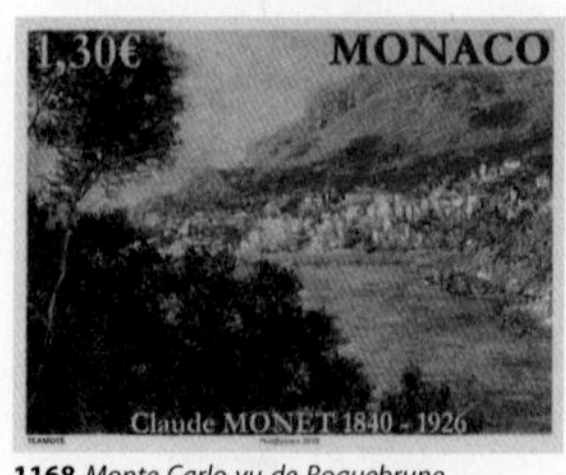

1168 *Monte Carlo vu de Roquebrune*

2009. 170th (2010) Birth Anniv of Oscar Claude Monet (Claude Monet) (artist).

2925 **1168** €1.30 multicoloured 5·75 4·50

1169 USA 1868 1c. (Z grill) Stamp and Association Emblem

2009. 2009 ASCAT Grand Prix to William H. Gross (for complete 19th-century USA collection).

2926 **1169** €1.35 multicoloured 6·00 4·75

1170 *La Naissance de Venus* (William Bouguereau)

2009. Art.
2927 **1170** €1.60 multicoloured 7·25 5·75

1171 Anton Chekov and Scenes from *Three Sisters, The Cherry Orchard* and *The Seagull*

2009. 150th (2010) Birth Anniv of Anton Pavlovich Chekhov (dramatist).
2928 **1171** €1.67 indigo, brown-olive and scarlet-vermilion 7·50 6·00

1172 Rally Race Car

2009. 120th Anniv of Automobile Club de Monaco. Sheet 123×94 mm containing T 1172 and similar horiz design. Multicoloured.
MS2929 €1.30 Type **1172**; €1.70 Formula I race car 14·00 14·00

1173 Prince Albert II

2009. MonacoPhil 2009 International Stamp Exhibition. Sheet 120×100 mm.
MS2930 **1173** €4 black and scarlet-vermilion 21·00 21·00

The margins of No. **MS**2930 were printed in multicoloured offset.

1174 Big Top and Performers

2009. 34th International Circus Festival.
2931 **1174** 70c. multicoloured 3·00 2·40

1175 Crystal Blue Velvet (Australian shepherd dog)

2010. International Dog Show, Monte Carlo
2952 **1175** 51c. multicoloured 2·50 2·25

1176 Scenes from *Seven Samurai*

2010. Birth Centenary of Akira Kurosawa (film director, producer, screenwriter and editor)
2933 **1176** 51c. blackish purple and greenish yellow 2·50 2·25

1177 Players

2010. Centenary of First Five Nations Rugby Championship
2934 **1177** 70c. multicoloured 3·00 2·40

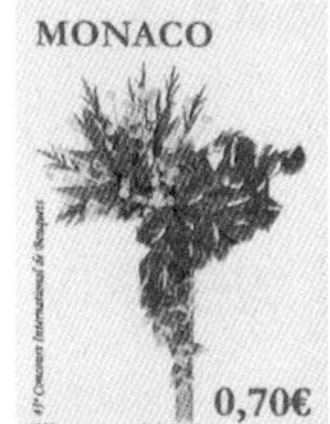
1178 Firebird

2010. 43rd International Flower Exhibition
2935 **1178** 70c. multicoloured 3·00 2·40

1179 Centre Court

2010. Monte-Carlo Rolex Masters Tennis Tournament
2936 **1179** 85c. multicoloured 3·75 2·75

1180 Albert II

2010. Expo 2010, Shanghai. Sheet 114×95 mm
MS2937 **1180** €1 multicoloured 5·25 5·25

1181 Player and Ball

2010. World Cup Football Championships, South Africa. Multicoloured.
2938 89c. Type **1181** 3·75 3·00
2939 89c. Player wearing red 3·75 3·00

Nos. 2938/9 were printed, *se-tenant*, each pair forming a composite design of the South African flag, stadium, two players and ball.

1182 Prince Albert I

2010. Centenary of Oceanographic Museum. Multicoloured.
MS2940 51c. Type **1182**; 56c. *Ursus maritimus* (polar bear); 73c. *Pterapogon kauderni* (Banggai cardinalfish) (horiz); 90c. Hands and starfish (horiz) 12·00 12·00

1183 Comte de Thann

2010. Former Grimaldi Family Fiefdoms. Multicoloured.
MS2941 €1×4, Type **1183**; Barony of Altkirch; Comte de Rosemont; Comte de Ferrette 21·00 21·00

1184 *Pinna nobilis*

2010. Larvotto Submarine Reserve
2942 **1184** 2c. multicoloured 1·00 60

1185 Mother Teresa carrying Child

2010. Birth Centenary of Mother Teresa (founder of Missionaries of Charity)
2943 **1185** multicoloured 3·75 3·00

1186 Lilium martagon (inscr 'Lis martagon')

2010. Mercantour National Park
2944 **1186** €2 multicoloured 12·00 12·00

1187 Children and Books

2010. Europa. Multicoloured.
2945 56c. Type **1187** 2·00 1·50
2946 70c. Boy reading, open book and pages 3·00 2·40

1188 Anniversary Emblem

2010. 15th Anniv of United Nations AIDS Programme
2947 **1188** 89c. multicoloured 3·75 3·00

1189 London Bridge

2010. London 2010 Festival of Stamps. London 2010 International Stamp Exhibition
2948 **1189** €1.30 scarlet vermilion and indigo 5·25 2·75

POSTAGE DUE STAMPS

D3

1906

D29a	**D3**	1c. green	45	55
D30	**D3**	5c. green	65	90
D31	**D3**	10c. red	65	90
D32	**D3**	10c. brown	£475	£150
D33	**D3**	15c. purple on cream	3·25	1·80
D113	**D3**	20c. bistre on buff	50	40
D34	**D3**	30c. blue	65	90
D114	**D3**	40c. mauve	50	40
D35	**D3**	50c. brown on buff	6·00	5·25
D115	**D3**	50c. green	50	40
D116	**D3**	60c. black	50	70
D117	**D3**	60c. mauve	26·00	35·00
D118	**D3**	1f. purple on cream	70	50
D119	**D3**	2f. red	1·50	1·80
D120	**D3**	3f. red	1·50	1·80
D121	**D3**	5f. blue	1·80	2·00

D4

1910

D36	**D4**	1c. olive	30	45
D37	**D4**	10c. lilac	65	90
D38	**D4**	30c. bistre	£225	£225

1919. Surch.

D39	20c. on 10c. lilac	4·50	9·25
D40	40c. on 30c. bistre	5·50	11·00

D18

1925

D106	**D18**	1c. olive	40	60
D107	**D18**	10c. violet	40	60
D108	**D18**	30c. bistre	60	1·00
D109	**D18**	60c. red	60	1·30
D110	**D18**	1f. blue	£110	£120
D111	**D18**	2f. red	£140	£150

1925. Surch 1 franc a percevoir.
D112 **D3** 1f. on 50c. brown on buff 1·00 1·20

D64 **D65**

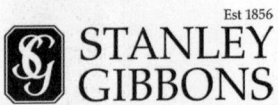

1946

D327	**D64**	10c. black	10	20
D328	**D64**	30c. violet	10	20
D329	**D64**	50c. blue	10	20
D330	**D64**	1f. green	10	30
D331	**D64**	2f. brown	10	30
D332	**D64**	3f. mauve	10	30
D333	**D64**	4f. red	50	70
D334	**D65**	5f. brown	50	70
D335	**D65**	10f. blue	70	70
D336	**D65**	20f. turquoise	1·00	1·20
D337	**D65**	50f. red and mauve	60·00	65·00
D338	**D65**	100f. red and green	15·00	15·00

D99 Buddicom Locomotive, 1843

1953

D478	-	1f. red and green	10	20
D479	-	1f. green and red	10	20
D480	-	2f. turquoise and blue	10	20
D481	-	2f. blue and turquoise	10	20
D482	**D 99**	3f. lake and green	10	30
D483	-	3f. green and lake	10	30
D484	-	4f. slate and brown	10	30
D485	-	4f. brown and slate	10	30
D486	-	5f. violet and blue	60	70
D487	-	5f. blue and violet	60	70
D488	-	10f. indigo and blue	10·00	10·00
D489	-	10f. blue and indigo	10·00	10·00
D490	-	20f. violet and blue	7·00	7·00
D491	-	20f. blue and violet	7·00	7·00
D492	-	50f. brown and red	15·00	15·00
D493	-	50f. red and brown	15·00	15·00
D494	-	100f. green and purple	24·00	24·00
D495	-	100f. purple and green	24·00	24·00

TRIANGULAR DESIGNS: Nos. D478, Pigeons released from mobile loft; D479, Sikorsky S-51 helicopter; D480, Brig; D481, "United States" (liner); D483, Streamlined steam locomotive; D484, Santos-Dumont's monoplane No. 20 "Demoiselle"; D485, De Havilland Comet 1 airliner; D486, Old motor car; D487, "Sabre" racing-car; D488, Leonardo da Vinci's drawing of "flying machine"; D489, Postal rocket; D490, Mail balloon, Paris, 1870; D491, Airship LZ-127 "Graf Zeppelin"; D492, Postilion; D493, Motor cycle messenger; D494, Mail coach; D495, Railway mail van.

D140 18th-century Felucca

1960

D698	**D140**	1c. brown, green & bl	10	20
D699	-	2c. sepia, blue & grn	10	20
D700	-	5c. purple, blk & turq	10	25
D701	-	10c. black, green & bl	20	40
D702	-	20c. purple, grn & bl	1·20	1·20
D703	-	30c. brown, bl & grn	2·00	2·00
D704	-	50c. blue, brn & myrtle	2·50	2·50
D705	-	1f. brown, myrtle & bl	3·00	3·00

DESIGNS: 2c. Paddle-steamer "La Palmaria"; 5c. Arrival of first railway train at Monaco; 10c. 15th–16th-century armed messenger; 20c. 18th-century postman; 30c. "Charles III" (paddle-steamer); 50c. 17th-century courier; 1f. Mail coach (19th-century).

D393 Prince's Seal

1980

D1426	**D393**	5c. red and brown	15	20
D1427	**D393**	10c. orange and red	15	20
D1428	**D393**	15c. violet and red	15	20
D1429	**D393**	20c. green and red	15	30
D1430	**D393**	30c. blue and red	15	35
D1431	**D393**	40c. bistre and red	30	35
D1432	**D393**	50c. violet and red	40	45
D1433	**D393**	1f. grey and blue	75	75
D1434	**D393**	2f. brown and black	1·00	1·20
D1435	**D393**	3f. red and green	2·30	2·30
D1436	**D393**	4f. green and red	3·25	3·00
D1437	**D393**	5f. brown and mauve	3·50	3·25

D492 Coat of Arms

1985

D1712	**D492**	5c. multicoloured	15	20
D1713	**D492**	10c. multicoloured	15	20
D1714	**D492**	15c. multicoloured	15	20
D1715	**D492**	20c. multicoloured	15	20
D1716	**D492**	30c. multicoloured	15	20
D1717	**D492**	40c. multicoloured	15	25
D1718	**D492**	50c. multicoloured	15	25
D1719	**D492**	1f. multicoloured	55	55
D1720	**D492**	2f. multicoloured	1·10	95
D1721	**D492**	3f. multicoloured	2·00	1·70
D1722	**D492**	4f. multicoloured	2·40	2·00
D1723	**D492**	5f. multicoloured	2·75	2·75

Pt. 8

NAPLES

A state on the S.W. coast of Central Italy, formerly part of the Kingdom of Sicily, but now part of Italy.

200 tornesi = 100 grano = 1 ducato.

1 Arms under Bourbon Dynasty

1858. The frames differ in each value. Imperf.

8	**1**	½t. blue	£203000	£13000
1A	**1**	½g. red	£2250	£375
2	**1**	1g. red	£600	60·00
3	**1**	2g. red	£425	20·00
4A	**1**	5g. red	£3000	80·00
5A	**1**	10g. red	£7000	£325
6A	**1**	20g. red	£6000	£1500
7A	**1**	50g. red	£12000	£3500

4 Cross of Savoy

1860. Imperf.

9	**4**	½t. blue	£45000	£4250

Pt. 8

NEAPOLITAN PROVINCES

Temporary issues for Naples and other parts of S. Italy which adhered to the new Kingdom of Italy in 1860.

200 tornesi = 100 grano = 1 ducato.

1

1861. Embossed. Imperf.

2	**1**	½t. green	19·00	£275
5	**1**	½g. brown	£200	£275
9	**1**	1g. black	£425	40·00
10	**1**	2g. blue	£130	17·00
15	**1**	5g. red	£150	90·00
18	**1**	10g. orange	£130	£190
19	**1**	20g. yellow	£600	£2500
23	**1**	50g. slate	75·00	£9000

Pt. 4

NETHERLANDS

A kingdom in the N.W. of Europe on the North Sea.

1852. 100 cents = 1 gulden (florin).
2002. 100 cents = 1 euro.

1

1852. Imperf.

1	**1**	5c. blue	£550	50·00
2	**1**	10c. red	£600	39·00
3b	**1**	15c. orange	£1100	£190

3 King William III

1864. Perf.

8	**3**	5c. blue	£425	22·00
9	**3**	10c. red	£600	11·00
10	**3**	15c. orange	£1500	£130

4

1867

17b	**4**	5c. blue	£130	4·00
18c	**4**	10c. red	£250	4·50
19c	**4**	15c. brown	£950	45·00
20	**4**	20c. green	£900	33·00
15	**4**	25c. purple	£3000	£140
16	**4**	50c. gold	£3750	£225

5

1869

58	**5**	½c. brown	33·00	4·50
53	**5**	1c. black	£300	£100
59	**5**	1c. green	22·00	3·25
55a	**5**	1½c. red	£225	£110
56	**5**	2c. yellow	85·00	20·00
62	**5**	2½c. mauve	£650	£100

6

1872

80	**6**	5c. blue	20·00	1·80
81	**6**	7½c. brown	50·00	25·00
100	**6**	10c. red	85·00	2·20
83	**6**	12½c. grey	90·00	3·25
102	**6**	15c. brown	£500	11·00
85	**6**	20c. green	£600	7·75
86	**6**	22½c. green	£110	60·00
87	**6**	25c. lilac	£750	5·50
97	**6**	50c. bistre	£950	17·00
90	**6**	1g. violet	£700	55·00
75	-	2g.50 blue and red	£1200	£150

No. 75 is similar to Type **6** but larger and with value and country scrolls transposed.

8

1876

133	**8**	½c. red	4·50	35
134	**8**	1c. green	15·00	45
137	**8**	2c. yellow	45·00	4·00
139	**8**	2½c. mauve	20·00	45

9 Queen Wilhelmina

1891

147a	**9**	3c. orange	11·00	3·25
148a	**9**	5c. blue	5·50	35
149b	**9**	7½c. brown	22·00	11·00
150b	**9**	10c. red	33·00	2·20
151b	**9**	12½c. grey	33·00	2·20
152a	**9**	15c. brown	80·00	7·25
153b	**9**	20c. green	90·00	4·50
154a	**9**	22½c. green	45·00	20·00
155	**9**	25c. mauve	£160	8·50
156a	**9**	50c. bistre	£800	28·00
159	-	50c. brown and green	£120	22·00
157	**9**	1g. violet	£900	£110
160	-	1g. green and brown	£275	33·00
161	-	2g.50 blue and red	£600	£200
165	-	5g. red and green	£1100	£650

Nos. 159, 160, 161 and 165 are as Type **9** but larger and with value and country scrolls transposed.

11

12

13

1898. Nos. 174 and 176 also exist imperf.

167	**12**	½c. lilac	65	35
168	**12**	1c. red	1·30	15
170	**12**	1½c. blue	4·00	45
171	**12**	2c. brown	5·50	35
172	**12**	2½c. green	4·50	35
173	**13**	3c. orange	25·00	5·00
174	**13**	3c. green	1·70	35
175	**13**	4c. purple	2·20	1·70
176	**13**	4½c. mauve	5·00	5·00
177	**13**	5c. red	2·20	35
178	**13**	7½c. brown	1·10	35
179	**13**	10c. grey	9·00	3·25
180	**13**	12½c. blue	5·00	45
181	**13**	15c. brown	£160	5·00
182	**13**	15c. red and blue	9·00	35
183	**13**	17½c. mauve	75·00	18·00
184	**13**	17½c. brown and blue	22·00	1·30
185	**13**	20c. green	£225	1·10
186	**13**	20c. grey and green	15·00	80
187	**13**	22½c. green and brown	14·00	90
188	**13**	25c. blue and pink	14·00	65
189	**13**	30c. purple and mauve	36·00	80
190	**13**	40c. orange and green	50·00	1·70
191	**13**	50c. red and green	£170	1·70
192	**13**	50c. violet and grey	90·00	1·70
193	**13**	60c. green and olive	50·00	1·70
194b	**11**	1g. green	75·00	1·10
195c	**11**	2½g. lilac	£130	4·00
196b	**11**	5g. red	£300	9·00
197	**11**	10g. red	£1200	£1000

14

1906. Society for the Prevention of Tuberculosis.

208	**14**	1c. (+1c.) red	28·00	17·00
209	**14**	3c. (+3c.) green	45·00	39·00
210	**14**	5c. (+5c.) violet	45·00	22·00

15 Admiral M. A. de Ruyter

1907. Birth Tercentenary of Admiral de Ruyter.

211	**15**	½c. blue	2·75	1·70
212	**15**	1c. red	4·50	3·25
213	**15**	2½c. red	9·00	3·25

16 William I

1913. Independence Centenary.

214	**16**	2½c. green on green	1·70	1·10
215	-	3c. yellow on cream	2·75	2·20
216	-	5c. red on buff	2·20	1·10
217	-	10c. grey	5·50	4·00
218	**16**	12½c. blue on blue	4·50	3·25
219	-	20c. brown	17·00	17·00
220	-	25c. blue	22·00	11·00
221	-	50c. green	45·00	45·00
222	**16**	1g. red	90·00	28·00
223	-	2½g. lilac	£170	60·00
224	-	5g. yellow on cream	£325	50·00
225	-	10g. orange	£1200	£1100

DESIGNS: 3c., 20c., 2½g. William II; 5c., 25c., 5g. William III; 10c., 50c., 10g. Queen Wilhelmina.

1919. Surch Veertig Cent (40c.) or Zestig Cent (60c.).

234	**13**	40c. on 30c. purple & mve	39·00	7·75
235	**13**	60c. on 30c. purple & mve	39·00	7·75

1920. Surch in figures.

236	**11**	2.50 on 10g. red	£225	£170
237	-	2.50 on 10g. red (No. 225)	£225	£170
238	**13**	4c. on 4½c. mauve	5·50	2·20

23

1921. Air.

239	**23**	10c. red	2·20	1·70
240	**23**	15c. green	9·00	2·75
241	**23**	60c. blue	28·00	55

24

1921

242	**24**	5c. green	17·00	35
243	**24**	12½c. red	28·00	2·75
244	**24**	20c. blue	39·00	35

25 Lion in Dutch Garden and Orange Tree (emblematic of Netherlands)

26

27

1923

248	**25**	1c. violet	80	80
249	**25**	2c. orange	7·50	35
250	**26**	2½c. green	2·20	90
251	**27**	4c. blue	1·80	80

1923. Surch.

252	**12**	2c. on 1c. red	70	35
253	**12**	2c. on 1½c. blue	70	45
254	**13**	10c. on 3c. green	6·50	35
255	**13**	10c. on 5c. red	12·50	80
256	**13**	10c. on 12½c. blue	10·50	1·20
257a	**13**	10c. on 17½c. brown & blue	4·25	4·75
258a	**13**	10c. on 22½c. olive & brown	4·25	4·75

30

31

1923. 25th Anniv of Queen's Accession.

259b	**31**	2c. green	30	35
260a	**30**	5c. green	60	45
261b	**31**	7½c. red	85	45
262b	**31**	10c. red	60	35
263	**31**	20c. blue	5·75	1·50
264a	**31**	25c. yellow	11·50	2·30
265	**31**	35c. orange	8·25	4·75
266a	**31**	50c. black	23·00	1·70
267	**30**	1g. red	35·00	7·25
268	**30**	2½g. black	£325	£350
269	**30**	5g. blue	£300	£300

1923. Surch DIENST ZEGEL PORTEN AAN TEEKEN RECHT and value.

270	**13**	10c. on 3c. green	1·70	1·70
271	**13**	1g. on 17½c. brown & blue	£100	29·00

33

1923. Culture Fund.

272	**33**	2c. (+5c.) blue on pink	26·00	26·00
273	-	10c. (+5c.) red on pink	26·00	26·00

DESIGN: 10c. Two women.

35 Carrier Pigeon

36 Queen Wilhelmina

1924

304C	**35**	½c. grey	60	60
305A	**35**	1c. red	35	10
306C	**35**	1½c. mauve	60	60
424a	**35**	1½c. grey	35	10
425	**35**	2c. orange	35	10
426a	**35**	2½c. green	1·20	60
427	**35**	3c. green	35	10
427a	**35**	4c. blue	35	10
428	**36**	5c. green	35	25
429	**36**	6c. brown	35	10
279A	**36**	7½c. yellow	60	10
313A	**36**	7½c. violet	4·75	10
314A	**36**	7½c. red	45	10
279cA	**36**	9c. red and black	2·30	1·70
281A	**36**	10c. red	2·30	10
317A	**36**	10c. blue	4·00	10
282A	**36**	12½c. red	2·30	60
319A	**36**	12½c. blue	60	10
320A	**36**	15c. blue	10·50	35
321C	**36**	15c. yellow	1·20	95
322C	**36**	20c. blue	7·50	4·00
434	**36**	21c. brown	35·00	1·20
324B	**36**	22½c. brown	9·25	3·50
434a	**36**	22½c. orange	23·00	26·00
435	**36**	25c. green	5·75	35
326A	**36**	27½c. grey	5·75	1·20
286cA	**36**	35c. brown	50·00	14·00
437	**36**	30c. violet	8·25	60
437a	**36**	40c. brown	17·00	35
330A	**36**	50c. green	8·25	35
289A	**36**	60c. violet	46·00	1·20
331A	**36**	60c. black	41·00	1·50
301	**36**	1g. blue (23×29 mm)	11·50	1·20
302	**36**	2½g. red (23×29 mm)	£140	8·25
303	**36**	5g. black (23×29 mm)	£275	4·00

For further stamps in Type **35**, see Nos. 546/57.

1924. International Philatelic Exn, The Hague.

290	10c. green	60·00	60·00
291	15c. black	70·00	70·00
292	35c. red	60·00	60·00

37

38

1924. Dutch Lifeboat Centenary.

293	**37**	2c. brown	5·25	3·75
294	**38**	10c. brown on yellow	9·25	3·25

39

1924. Child Welfare.

295	**39**	2c. (+2c.) green	3·00	3·00
296	**39**	7½c. (+3½c.) brown	10·50	13·00
297	**39**	10c. (+2½c.) red	6·50	3·00

40 Arms of South Holland

1925. Child Welfare. Arms as T **40**.

298A	-	2c. (+2c.) green and yellow	1·20	1·20
299A	-	7½c. (+3½c.) violet and blue	6·50	7·00
300A	**40**	10c. (+2½c.) red and yellow	4·75	60

ARMS: 2c. North Brabant; 7½c. Gelderland.
See also Nos. 350/3A and 359/62A.

1926. Child Welfare. Arms as T **40**.

350A	2c. (+2c.) red and silver	1·20	60
351A	5c. (+3c.) green and blue	2·30	2·30
352A	10c. (+3c.) red and green	3·50	60
353A	15c. (+3c.) yellow and blue	10·50	9·25

ARMS: 2c. Utrecht; 5c. Zeeland; 10c. North Holland; 15c. Friesland.

46 Queen Wilhelmina

47 Red Cross Allegory

1927. 60th Anniv of Dutch Red Cross Society.

354	**46**	2c. (+2c.) red	5·75	5·25
355	-	3c. (+2c.) green	11·50	14·00
356	-	5c. (+3c.) blue	2·30	2·30
357	-	7½c. (+3½c.) blue	7·50	3·00
358	**47**	15c. (+5c.) red and blue	16·00	16·00

PORTRAITS: 2c. King William III; 3c. Queen Emma; 5c. Henry, Prince Consort.

1927. Child Welfare. Arms as T **40**.

359A	2c. (+2c.) red and lilac	1·20	1·20
360A	5c. (+3c.) green and yellow	2·30	2·30
361A	7½c. (+3½c.) red and black	5·75	60
362A	15c. (+3c.) blue and brown	8·25	7·50

ARMS: 2c. Drente; 5c. Groningen; 7½c. Limburg; 15c. Overyssel.

48 Sculler

49 Footballer

1928. Olympic Games, Amsterdam.

363	**48**	1½c.+1c. green	4·75	4·75
364	-	2c.+1c. purple	4·75	5·75
365	**49**	3c.+1c. green	7·00	7·00
366	-	5c.+1c. blue	5·75	3·50
367	-	7½c.+2½c. orange	5·75	3·50
368	-	10c.+2c. red	10·50	8·25
369	-	15c.+2c. blue	14·00	8·25
370	-	30c.+3c. sepia	28·00	29·00

DESIGNS—HORIZ: 2c. Fencing. VERT: 5c. Sailing; 7½c. Putting the shot; 10c. Running; 15c. Show-jumping; 30c. Boxing.

50 Lieut. Koppen

1928. Air.

371	**50**	40c. red	85	70
372	-	75c. green	85	70

DESIGN: 75c. Van der Hoop.

52 J. P. Minckelers

1928. Child Welfare.

373	**52**	1½c.+1½c. violet	80	70
374	-	5c.+3c. green	2·75	1·20
375a	-	7½c.+2½c. red	5·25	45
376a	-	12½c.+3½c. blue	14·50	13·00

PORTRAITS: 5c. Boerhaave; 7½c. H. A. Lorentz; 12½c. G. Huygens.

53 Mercury

1929. Air.

377	**53**	1½g. black	3·50	2·30
378	**53**	4½g. red	3·50	7·00
379	**53**	7½g. green	39·00	7·00

1929. Surch 21.

380	**36**	21c. on 22½c. brown	29·00	2·30

55 "Friendship and Security"

1929. Child Welfare.

381A	**55**	1½c. (+1½c.) grey	3·25	80
382A	**55**	5c. (+3c.) green	5·25	1·30
383A	**55**	6c. (+4c.) red	3·25	60
384A	**55**	12½c. (+3½c.) blue	17·00	18·00

56 Rembrandt and "De Staalmeesters"

1930. Rembrandt Society.

385	**56**	5c. (+5c.) green	10·50	10·50
386	**56**	6c. (+5c.) black	8·25	8·25
387	**56**	12½c. (+5c.) blue	16·00	16·00

57 Spring

1930. Child Welfare.

388A	**57**	1½c. (+1½c.) red	2·30	80
389A	-	5c. (+3c.) green	3·50	1·20
390A	-	6c. (+4c.) purple	3·00	95
391A	-	12½c. (+3½c.) blue	23·00	17·00

DESIGNS (allegorical): 5c. Summer; 6c. Autumn; 12½c. Winter.

58

1931. Gouda Church Restoration Fund.

392	**58**	1½c.+1½c. green	27·00	26·00
393	-	6c.+4c. red	31·00	29·00

DESIGN: No. 393, Church facade.

59 Queen Wilhelmina and Fokker F.XII Monoplanes

1931

394	**59**	36c. red and blue (air)	20·00	1·20
395	-	70c. blue and red (postage)	44·00	1·20
395b	-	80c. green and red	£160	4·75

DESIGNS: 70c. Portrait and factory; 80c. Portrait and shipyard.

61 Mentally Deficient Child

1931. Child Welfare.

396A		1½c. (+1½c.) red and blue	2·30	2·30
397A	**61**	5c. (+3c.) green and purple	8·25	2·30
398A	-	6c. (+4c.) purple and green	9·25	2·30
399D	-	12½c. (+3½c.) blue and red	41·00	29·00

DESIGNS: 1½c. Deaf mute; 6c. Blind girl; 12½c. Sick child.

62 Windmill and Dykes, Kinderdijk

1932. Tourist Propaganda.

400	**62**	2½c.+1½c. green and black	11·50	9·25
401	-	6c.+4c. grey and black	16·00	9·25
402	-	7½c.+3½c. red and black	45·00	26·00
403	-	12½c.+2½c. blue and black	49·00	31·00

DESIGNS: 6c. Aerial view of Town Hall, Zierikzee; 7½c. Bridges at Schipluiden and Moerdijk; 12½c. Tulips.

63 Gorse (Spring)

1932. Child Welfare.

404A	**63**	1½c. (+1½c.) brown & yell	3·25	80
405A	-	5c. (+3c.) blue and red	4·25	1·40
406A	-	6c. (+4c.) green and orange	3·25	70
407A	-	12½c. (+3½c.) blue & orange	42·00	35·00

DESIGNS: Child and: 5c. Cornflower (Summer); 6c. Sunflower (Autumn); 12½c. Christmas rose (Winter).

64 Arms of House of Orange

65 Portrait by Goltzius

1933. 4th Birth Centenary of William I of Orange. T 64 and portraits of William I inscr "1533", as T 65.

408	**64**	1½c. black	80	60
409	**65**	5c. green	2·75	60
410	-	6c. purple	4·00	60
411	-	12½c. blue	24·00	5·25

DESIGNS: 6c. Portrait by Key; 12½c. Portrait attributed to Moro.

68 Dove of Peace

1933. Peace Propaganda.

412	**68**	12½c. blue	13·50	60

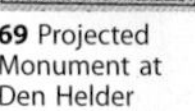

69 Projected Monument at Den Helder

70 "De Hoop" (hospital ship)

1933. Seamen's Fund.

413	**69**	1½c. (+1½c.) red	5·75	5·25
414	**70**	5c. (+3c.) green and red	17·00	8·75
415	-	6c. (+4c.) green	26·00	6·50
416	-	12½c. (+3½c.) blue	38·00	32·00

DESIGNS: 6c. Lifeboat; 12½c. Seaman and Seamen's Home.

73 Pander S.4 Postjager

1933. Air. Special Flights.

417	**73**	30c. green	1·20	1·20

74 Child and Star of Epiphany

1933. Child Welfare.

418A	**74**	1½c. (+1½c.) orange and grey	2·30	95
419A	**74**	5c. (+3c.) yellow and brown	3·25	1·00
420A	**74**	6c. (+4c.) gold and green	3·75	95
421A	**74**	12½c. (+3½c.) silver and blue	37·00	32·00

75 Princess Juliana

1934. Crisis stamps.

438	-	5c. (+4c.) purple	19·00	5·25
439	**75**	6c. (+5c.) blue	16·00	6·50

DESIGN: 5c. Queen Wilhelmina.

76 Dutch Warship

1934. Tercentenary of Curacao.

440	-	6c. black	5·25	30
441	**76**	12½c. blue	31·00	4·25

DESIGN: 6c. Willemstad Harbour.

77 Dowager Queen Emma

1934. Anti-T.B. Fund.

442	**77**	6c. (+2c.) blue	19·00	2·30

78 Destitute child

1934. Child Welfare.

443	**78**	1½c. (+1½c.) brown	2·30	1·20
444	**78**	5c. (+3c.) red	4·00	5·25
445	**78**	6c. (+4c.) green	4·00	60
446	**78**	12½c. (+3½c.) blue	36·00	26·00

79 H. D. Guyot

1935. Cultural and Social Relief Fund.

447	**79**	1½c. (+1½c.) red	3·00	3·00
448	-	5c. (+3c.) brown	7·00	7·50
449	-	6c. (+4c.) green	8·25	1·20
450	-	12½c. (+3½c.) blue	40·00	11·50

PORTRAITS: 5c. A. J. M. Diepenbrock; 6c. F. C. Donders; 12½c. J. P. Sweelinck.

See also Nos. 456/9, 469/72, 478/82 and 492/6.

80 Aerial Map of Netherlands

1935. Air Fund.

451	**80**	6c. (+4c.) brown	42·00	15·00

81 Child picking Fruit

1935. Child Welfare.

452	**81**	1½c. (+1½c.) red	85	60
453	**81**	5c. (+3c.) green	2·30	1·70
454	**81**	6c. (+4c.) brown	2·00	60
455	**81**	12½c. (+3½c.) blue	33·00	14·50

1936. Cultural and Social Relief Fund. As T 79.

456		1½c. (+1½c.) sepia	1·20	1·20
457		5c. (+3c.) green	7·00	5·25
458		6c. (+4c.) red	5·75	1·20
459		12½c. (+3½c.) blue	21·00	4·00

PORTRAITS: 1½c. H. Kamerlingh Onnes; 5c. Dr. A. S. Talma; 6c. Mgr. Dr. H. J. A. M. Schaepman; 12½c. Desiderius Erasmus.

83 Pallas Athene

1936. Tercentenary of Utrecht University Foundation.

460	**83**	6c. red	2·30	60
461	-	12½c. blue	8·25	7·50

DESIGN: 12½c. Gisbertus Voetius.

84 Child Herald

1936. Child Welfare.

462	**84**	1½c. (+1½c.) slate	60	60
463	**84**	5c. (+3c.) green	3·50	1·20
464	**84**	6c. (+4c.) brown	3·00	60
465	**84**	12½c. (+3½c.) blue	22·00	7·00

85 Scout Movement

1937. Scout Jamboree.

466	-	1½c. black and green	60	35
467	**85**	6c. brown and black	1·70	35
468	-	12½c. black and blue	5·75	2·20

DESIGNS: 1½c. Scout Tenderfoot Badge; 12½c. Hermes.

1937. Cultural and Social Relief Fund. Portraits as T 79.

469		1½c.+1½c. sepia	60	60
470		5c.+3c. green	6·50	5·25
471		6c.+4c. purple	1·70	60
472		12½c.+3½c. blue	11·50	3·50

PORTRAITS: 1½c. Jacob Maris; 5c. F. de la B. Sylvius; 6c. J. van den Vondel; 12½c. A. van Leeuwenhoek.

86 "Laughing Child" by Frans Hals

1937. Child Welfare.

473	**86**	1½c. (+1½c.) black	30	30
474	**86**	3c. (+2c.) green	2·30	1·70
475	**86**	4c. (+2c.) red	95	60
476	**86**	5c. (+3c.) green	80	30
477	**86**	12½c. (+3½c.) blue	10·00	3·00

1938. Cultural and Social Relief Fund. As T 79.

478		1½c.+1½c. sepia	50	85
479		3c.+2c. green	95	60
480		4c.+2c. red	3·00	3·25
481		5c.+3c. green	3·75	60
482		12½c.+3½c. blue	13·00	1·70

PORTRAITS: 1½c. M. van St. Aldegonde; 3c. O. G. Heldring; 4c. Maria Tesselschade; 5c. Rembrandt; 12½c. H. Boerhaave.

87 Queen Wilhelmina

1938. 40th Anniv of Coronation.

483	**87**	1½c. black	30	30
484	**87**	5c. red	40	30
485	**87**	12½c. blue	5·00	2·30

88 Carrion Crow

1938. Air. Special Flights.

486	**88**	12½c. blue and grey	80	60
790a	**88**	25c. blue and grey	4·75	2·30

89 Boy with Flute

1938. Child Welfare.

487	**89**	1½c.+1½c. black	30	30
488	**89**	3c.+2c. brown	70	60
489	**89**	4c.+2c. green	1·40	1·20
490	**89**	5c.+3c. red	50	30
491	**89**	12½c.+3½c. blue	13·00	3·00

1939. Cultural and Social Relief Fund. As T 79.

492		1½c.+1½c. brown	1·20	60
493		2½c.+2½c. green	5·25	3·50
494		3c.+3c. red	1·20	1·70
495		5c.+3c. green	4·00	60
496		12½c.+3½c. blue	9·25	1·70

PORTRAITS: 1½c. M. Maris; 2½c. Anton Mauve; 3c. Gerardus van Swieten; 5c. Nicolas Beets; 12½c. Pieter Stuyvesant.

91 St. Willibrord's landing in the Netherlands

1939. 12th Death Centenary of St. Willibrord.

497	**91**	5c. green	85	30
498	-	12½c. blue	7·75	4·00

DESIGN: 12½c. St. Willibrord as Bishop of Utrecht.

92 Replica of Locomotive "De Arend"

1939. Centenary of Netherlands Railway.

499	**92**	5c. green	1·20	30
500	-	12½c. blue	11·50	5·75

DESIGN: 12½c. Electric railcar.

93 Child and Cornucopia

1939. Child Welfare.

501	**93**	1½c.+1½c. black	35	60
502	**93**	2½c.+2½c. green	7·00	3·50
503	**93**	3c.+3c. red	80	60
504	**93**	5c.+3c. green	1·70	60
505	**93**	12½c.+3½c. blue	5·75	2·30

94 Queen Wilhelmina

1940

506	**94**	5c. green	40	10
506a	**94**	6c. brown	80	30
507	**94**	7½c. red	40	10
508	**94**	10c. purple	40	10
509	**94**	12½c. blue	40	30
510	**94**	15c. blue	40	30
510a	**94**	17½c. blue	1·90	1·20
511	**94**	20c. violet	95	30
512	**94**	22½c. olive	3·25	3·00
513	**94**	25c. red	70	30
514	**94**	30c. ochre	1·60	60
515	**94**	40c. green	3·00	1·20
515a	**94**	50c. orange	12·00	1·20
515b	**94**	60c. purple	12·00	3·75

95 Vincent Van Gogh

1940. Cultural and Social Relief Fund.

516	**95**	1½c.+1½c. brown	3·50	80
517	-	2½c.+2½c. green	5·75	1·60
518	-	3c.+3c. red	3·50	1·60
519	-	5c.+3c. green	8·75	70
520	-	12½c.+3½c. blue	7·00	2·75

PORTRAITS: 1½c. E. J. Potgieter; 3c. Petrus Camper; 5c. Jan Steen; 12½c. Joseph Scaliger.

See also Nos. 558/62 and 656/60.

1940. As No. 519, colour changed. Surch.

521		7½c.+2½c. on 5c.+3c. red	60	60

1940. Surch with large figures and network.

522	**35**	2½ on 3c. red	7·00	35
523	**35**	5 on 3c. green	35	35
524	**35**	7½ on 3c. red	35	10
525	**35**	10 on 3c. green	35	35
526	**35**	12½ on 3c. blue	60	60
527	**35**	17½ on 3c. green	1·70	60
528	**35**	20 on 3c. green	1·20	35
529	**35**	22½ on 3c. green	5·75	7·00
530	**35**	25 on 3c. green	2·10	60
531	**35**	30 on 3c. green	1·70	70
532	**35**	40 on 3c. green	4·75	3·25
533	**35**	50 on 3c. green	2·10	95
534	**35**	60 on 3c. green	3·50	1·90
535	**35**	70 on 3c. green	15·00	5·75
536	**35**	80 on 3c. green	19·00	9·25
537	**35**	100 on 3c. green	55·00	50·00
538	**35**	250 on 3c. green	65·00	65·00
539	**35**	500 on 3c. green	60·00	60·00

98 Girl with Dandelion

1940. Child Welfare.

540	**98**	1½c.+1½c. violet	1·40	35
541	**98**	2½c.+2½c. olive	4·75	1·40
542	**98**	4c.+3c. blue	5·75	1·40
543	**98**	5c.+3c. green	6·00	35
544	**98**	7½c.+3½c. red	1·70	35

1941

546	**35**	5c. green	10	10
547	**35**	7½c. red	10	10
548	**35**	10c. violet	1·50	35
549	**35**	12½c. blue	60	45
550	**35**	15c. blue	1·50	60
551	**35**	17½c. red	35	35
552	**35**	20c. violet	1·50	35
553	**35**	22½c. olive	35	60
554	**35**	25c. lake	60	45
555	**35**	30c. brown	5·25	45
556	**35**	40c. green	35	45
557	**35**	50c. brown	35	35

1941. Cultural and Social Relief Fund. As T 95 but inscr "ZOMERZEGEL 31.12.46".

558		1½c.+1½c. brown	1·40	45
559		2½c.+2½c. green	1·40	45
560		4c.+3c. red	1·40	45
561		5c.+3c. green	1·40	45
562		7½c.+3½c. purple	1·40	45

PORTRAITS: 1½c. Dr. A. Mathijsen; 2½c. J. Ingenhousz; 4c. Aagje Deken; 5c. Johan Bosboom; 7½c. A. C. W. Staring.

100 "Titus Rembrandt"

1941. Child Welfare.

563	**100**	1½c.+1½c. black	70	45
564	**100**	2½c.+2½c. olive	70	45
565	**100**	4c.+3c. blue	70	45
566	**100**	5c.+3c. green	70	45
567	**100**	7½c.+3½c. red	70	45

101 Legionary

1942. Netherlands Legion Fund.

568	**101**	7½c.+2½c. red	1·70	1·00
569	-	12½c.+87½c. blue	13·50	13·00
MS569a		155×110 mm. No. 568 (block of ten)	£190	£130
MS569b		96×97 mm. No. 569 (block of ten)	£150	£150

DESIGN—HORIZ: 12½c. Legionary with similar inscription.

1943. 1st European Postal Congress. As T 26 but larger (21×27½ mm) surch EUROPEESCHE P T T VEREENIGING 19 OCTOBER 1942 10 CENT.

570	**26**	10c. on 2½c. yellow	1·00	45

103 Seahorse

1943. Old Germanic Symbols.

571	**103**	1c. black	10	10
572	-	1½c. red	10	10
573	-	2c. blue	10	10
574	-	2½c. green	10	10
575	-	3c. red	10	10
576	-	4c. brown	10	10
577	-	5c. olive	10	10

DESIGNS—VERT: 1½c. Triple crowned tree; 2½c. Birds in ornamental tree; 4c. Horse and rider. HORIZ: 2c. Swans; 3c. Trees and serpentine roots; 5c. Prancing horses.

104 Michiel A. de Ruyter

1943. Dutch Naval Heroes.

578	**104**	7½c. red	15	10
579	-	10c. green	15	10
580	-	12½c. blue	15	15
581	-	15c. violet	35	15
582	-	17½c. grey	15	15
583	-	20c. brown	15	15
584	-	22½c. red	15	15
585	-	25c. purple	70	80
586	-	30c. blue	15	35
587	-	40c. grey	15	45

PORTRAITS: 10c. Johan Evertsen; 12½c. Maarten H. Tromp; 15c. Piet Hein; 17½c. Wilhelm Joseph van Gent; 20c. Witte de With; 22½c. Cornelis Evertsen; 25c. Tjerk Hiddes de Fries; 30c. Cornelis Tromp; 40c. Cornelis Evertsen the younger.

105 Mail Cart

1943. Stamp Day.

589	**105**	7½c.+7½c. red	25	35

106 Child and Doll's House

1944. Child Welfare and Winter Help Funds. Inscr "WINTERHULP" (1½c. and 7½c.) or "VOLKSDIENST" (others).

590	**106**	1½c.+3½c. black	35	45
591	-	4c.+3½c. brown	35	45
592	-	5c.+5c. green	35	45
593	-	7½c.+7½c. red	35	45
594	-	10c.+40c. blue	35	45

DESIGNS: 4c. Mother and child; 5c., 10c. Mother and children; 7½c. Child and wheatsheaf.

107 Infantryman

111 Queen Wilhelmina

1944

595	**107**	1½c. black	15	10
596	-	2½c. green	15	10
597	-	3c. brown	15	10
598	-	5c. blue	15	10
599	**111**	7½c. red	15	10
600	**111**	10c. orange	15	10
601	**111**	12½c. blue	15	10
602	**111**	15c. red	2·30	2·30
603	**111**	17½c. green	1·60	1·60
604	**111**	20c. violet	70	45
605	**111**	22½c. red	1·70	1·70
606	**111**	25c. brown	2·75	2·10
607	**111**	30c. green	45	45
608	**111**	40c. purple	3·50	3·50
609	**111**	50c. mauve	2·40	1·60

The above set was originally for use on Netherlands warships serving with the Allied Fleet, and was used after liberation in the Netherlands.

112 Lion and Dragon

1945. Liberation.

610	**112**	7½c. orange	25	15

113

1945. Child Welfare.

611	**113**	1½c.+2½c. grey	45	45
612	**113**	2½c.+3½c. green	45	45
613	**113**	5c.+5c. brown	45	45
614	**113**	7½c.+4½c. red	45	45
615	**113**	12½c.+5½c. blue	45	45

114 Queen Wilhelmina

1946

616	**114**	1g. blue	4·75	1·50
617	**114**	2½g. red	£225	23·00
618	**114**	5g. green	£225	50·00
619	**114**	10g. violet	£225	50·00

115 Emblem of Abundance

1946. War Victims' Relief Fund.

620	**115**	1½c.+3½c. black	70	45
621	**115**	2½c.+5c. green	80	80
622	**115**	5c.+10c. violet	80	80
623	**115**	7½c.+15c. red	70	45
624	**115**	12½c.+37½c. blue	1·40	95

116 Princess Irene

1946. Child Welfare.

625	**116**	1½c.+1½c. brown	80	80
626	-	2½c.+1½c. green	80	80
627	**116**	4c.+2c. red	1·00	80
628	-	5c.+2c. brown	1·00	80
629	-	7½c.+2½c. red	80	35
630	-	12½c.+7½c. blue	80	1·20

PORTRAITS: 2½c., 5c. Princess Margriet; 7½c., 12½c. Princess Beatrix.

117 Boy on Roundabout

1946. Child Welfare.

631	**117**	2c.+2c. violet	80	70
632	**117**	4c.+2c. green	80	70
633	**117**	7½c.+2½c. red	80	70
634	**117**	10c.+5c. purple	1·00	35
635	**117**	20c.+5c. blue	1·40	95

118 Numeral

1946

636	**118**	1c. red	10	10
637	**118**	2c. blue	10	10
638	**118**	2½c. orange	7·75	2·30

638a	**118**	3c. brown	10	10
639	**118**	4c. green	45	10
639a	**118**	5c. orange	10	10
639c	**118**	6c. grey	60	35
639d	**118**	7c. red	35	10
639f	**118**	8c. mauve	35	10

119 Queen Wilhelmina

1947

640	**119**	5c. green	1·60	10
641	**119**	6c. black	45	10
642	**119**	6c. blue	80	10
643	**119**	7½c. red	60	10
644	**119**	10c. purple	1·20	10
645	**119**	12½c. red	1·20	60
646	**119**	15c. violet	13·50	10
647	**119**	20c. blue	14·50	10
648	**119**	22½c. green	1·20	1·20
649	**119**	25c. blue	27·00	10
650	**119**	30c. orange	27·00	45
651	**119**	35c. blue	26·00	80
652	**119**	40c. brown	30·00	80
653	-	45c. blue	33·00	17·00
654	-	50c. brown	21·00	60
655	-	60c. red	27·00	3·50

Nos. 653/5 are as Type **119** but have the inscriptions in colour on white ground.

1947. Cultural and Social Relief Fund. As T 95 but inscr "ZOMERZEGEL ... 13.12.48".

656		2c.+2c. red	1·40	70
657		4c.+2c. green	1·90	95
658		7½c.+2½c. violet	3·00	1·20
659		10c.+5c. brown	2·75	60
660		20c.+5c. blue	2·20	95

PORTRAITS: 2c. H. van Deventer; 4c. P. C. Hooft; 7½c. Johan de Witt; 10c. J. F. van Royen; 20c. Hugo Grotius.

122 Children

1947. Child Welfare.

661	**122**	2c.+2c. brown	35	35
662	-	4c.+2c. green	1·60	1·00
663	-	7½c.+2½c. brown	1·60	1·30
664	-	10c.+5c. lake	1·90	35
665	**122**	20c.+5c. blue	2·10	1·60

DESIGN: 4c. to 10c. Baby.

124 Ridderzaal, The Hague

1948. Cultural and Social Relief Fund.

666	**124**	2c.+2c. brown	2·75	95
667	-	6c.+4c. green	3·00	95
668	-	10c.+5c. red	2·10	60
669	-	20c.+5c. blue	3·00	1·60

BUILDINGS: 6c. Palace on the Dam; 10c. Kneuterdijk Palace; 20c. Nieuwe Kerk, Amsterdam.

125 Queen Wilhelmina

1948. Queen Wilhelmina's Golden Jubilee.

670	**125**	10c. red	35	25
671	**125**	20c. blue	3·25	2·75

126 Queen Juliana

1948. Coronation.

672	**126**	10c. brown	2·50	25
673	**126**	20c. blue	3·25	70

127 Boy in Canoe

1948. Child Welfare.

674	**127**	2c.+2c. green	35	25
675	-	5c.+3c. green	3·50	1·00
676	-	6c.+4c. grey	1·90	45
677	-	10c.+5c. red	70	25
678	-	20c.+8c. blue	3·50	1·90

DESIGNS: 5c. Girl swimming; 6c. Boy on toboggan; 10c. Girl on swing; 20c. Boy skating.

128 Terrace near Beach

1949. Cultural and Social Relief Fund.

679	**128**	2c.+2c. yellow and blue	3·00	25
680	-	5c.+3c. yellow and blue	5·25	3·00
681	-	6c.+4c. green	4·25	70
682	-	10c.+5c. yellow and blue	5·00	25
683	-	20c.+5c. blue	5·25	3·00

DESIGNS: 5c. Hikers in cornfield; 6c. Campers by fire; 10c. Gathering wheat; 20c. Yachts.

129 Queen Juliana

130 Queen Juliana

1949

684	**129**	5c. green	1·20	10
685	**129**	6c. blue	60	10
686	**129**	10c. orange	60	10
687	**129**	12c. red	3·50	4·75
688	**129**	15c. green	7·00	10
689	**129**	20c. blue	5·75	10
690	**129**	25c. brown	21·00	10
691	**129**	30c. violet	14·50	10
692	**129**	35c. blue	39·00	35
693	**129**	40c. purple	65·00	45
694	**129**	45c. orange	3·00	1·40
695	**129**	45c. violet	80·00	80
696	**129**	50c. green	19·00	45
697	**129**	60c. brown	29·00	45
697a	**129**	75c. red	£120	3·00
698	**130**	1g. red	5·75	60
699	**130**	2½g. brown	£325	5·75
700a	**130**	5g. brown	£700	8·25
701	**130**	10g. violet	£475	26·00

131 Hands reaching for Sunflower

1949. Red Cross and Indonesian Relief Fund.

702	**131**	2c.+3c. yellow and grey	1·70	45
703	**131**	6c.+4c. yellow and red	3·00	60
704	**131**	10c.+5c. yellow and blue	5·75	35
705	**131**	30c.+10c. yellow & brn	14·00	5·00

132 Posthorns and Globe

1949. 75th Anniv of U.P.U.

706	**132**	10c. lake	1·20	10
707	**132**	20c. blue	13·00	3·75

133 "Autumn"

1949. Child Welfare Fund. Inscr "VOOR HET KIND".

708	**133**	2c.+3c. brown	60	25
709	-	5c.+3c. red	11·50	3·00
710	-	6c.+4c. green	7·00	60
711	-	10c.+5c. grey	60	25
712	-	20c.+7c. blue	10·50	3·00

DESIGNS: 5c. "Summer"; 6c. "Spring"; 10c. "Winter"; 20c. "New Year".

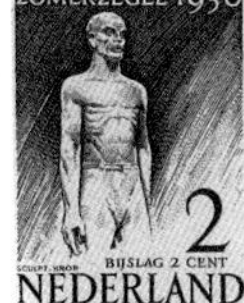

134 Resistance Monument

135 Section of Moerdijk Bridge

1950. Cultural and Social Relief Fund. Inscr "ZOMERZEGEL 1950".

713	**134**	2c.+2c. brown	4·75	1·70
714	-	4c.+2c. green	19·00	17·00
715	-	5c.+3c. grey	15·00	8·25
716	-	6c.+4c. violet	8·25	1·20
717	**135**	10c.+5c. slate	9·25	60
718	-	20c.+5c. blue	24·00	23·00

DESIGNS—VERT: 4c. Sealing dykes; 5c. Rotterdam skyscraper. HORIZ: 6c. Harvesting; 20c. "Overijssel" (canal freighter).

1950. Surch with bold figure 6.

719	**119**	6c. on 7½c. red	2·30	35

137 Good Samaritan and Bombed Church

1950. Bombed Churches Rebuilding Fund.

720	**137**	2c.+2c. olive	15·00	4·75
721	**137**	5c.+3c. brown	20·00	17·00
722	**137**	6c.+4c. green	13·00	7·00
723	**137**	10c.+5c. red	37·00	1·20
724	**137**	20c.+5c. blue	49·00	42·00

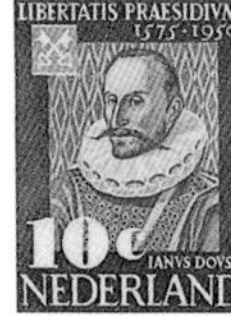

138 Janus Dousa

1950. 375th Anniv of Leyden University.

725	**138**	10c. olive	7·00	35
726	-	20c. blue	7·00	2·30

PORTRAIT: 20c. Jan van Hout.

139 Baby and Bees

1950. Child Welfare. Inscr "VOOR HET KIND".

727	**139**	2c.+3c. red	60	35

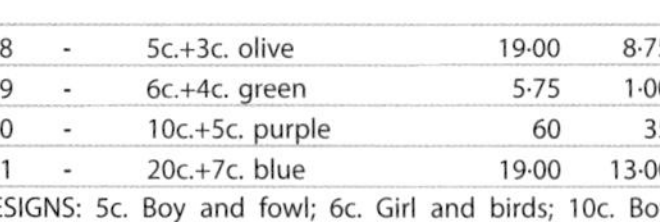

728	-	5c.+3c. olive	19·00	8·75
729	-	6c.+4c. green	5·75	1·00
730	-	10c.+5c. purple	60	35
731	-	20c.+7c. blue	19·00	13·00

DESIGNS: 5c. Boy and fowl; 6c. Girl and birds; 10c. Boy and fish; 20c. Girl, butterfly and frog.

140 Bergh Castle

1951. Cultural and Social Relief Fund. Castles.

732		2c.+2c. violet	5·75	1·90
733	**140**	5c.+3c. red	16·00	11·50
734	-	6c.+4c. sepia	7·00	1·70
735	-	10c.+5c. green	10·50	45
736	-	20c.+5c. blue	16·00	12·00

DESIGNS—HORIZ: 2c. Hillenraad; 6c. Hernen. VERT: 10c. Rechteren; 20c. Moermond.

141 Girl and Windmill

1951. Child Welfare.

737	**141**	2c.+3c. green	1·20	35
738	-	5c.+3c. blue	13·00	6·50
739	-	6c.+4c. brown	8·25	1·00
740	-	10c.+5c. lake	60	35
741	-	20c.+7c. blue	13·00	11·50

DESIGNS: Each shows boy or girl: 5c. Crane; 6c. Fishing nets; 10c. Factory chimneys; 20c. Flats.

142 Gull

1951. Air.

742	**142**	15g. brown	£400	£170
743	**142**	25g. black	£400	£170

143 Jan van Riebeeck

1952. Tercentenary of Landing in South Africa and Van Riebeeck Monument Fund.

744	**143**	2c.+3c. violet	7·50	5·75
745	**143**	6c.+4c. green	9·25	7·00
746	**143**	10c.+5c. red	10·50	5·75
747	**143**	20c.+5c. blue	7·50	7·00

144 Miner

1952. 50th Anniv of State Mines, Limburg.

748	**144**	10c. blue	3·00	25

145 Wild Rose

1952. Cultural and Social Relief Fund. Floral designs inscr "ZOMERZEGEL 1952".

749	**145**	2c.+2c. green and red	1·40	80
750	-	5c.+3c. yellow and green	6·75	5·75

751	-	6c.+4c. green and red	3·50	1·60
752	-	10c.+5c. green & orange	3·00	45
753	-	20c.+5c. green and blue	16·00	11·50

FLOWERS: 5c. Marsh marigold; 6c. Tulip; 10c. Marguerite; 20c. Cornflower.

146 Radio Masts

1952. Netherlands Stamp Centenary and Centenary of Telegraph Service.

754		2c. violet	70	10
755	**146**	6c. red	80	25
756	-	10c. green	80	10
757	-	20c. slate	11·50	2·75

DESIGNS: 2c. Telegraph poles and steam train; 10c. Postman delivering letters, 1852; 20c. Postman delivering letters, 1952.

1952. International Postage Stamp Exn, Utrecht ("ITEP"). Nos. 754/7 but colours changed.

757a		2c. brown	37·00	20·00
757b	**146**	6c. blue	37·00	20·00
757c	-	10c. lake	37·00	20·00
757d	-	20c. blue	37·00	20·00

Nos. 757a/d were sold only in sets at the Exhibition at face plus 1g. entrance fee.

147 Boy feeding Goat

1952. Child Welfare.

758	**147**	2c.+3c. black and olive	25	35
759	-	5c.+3c. black and pink	4·75	2·75
760	-	6c.+4c. black and green	3·75	70
761	-	10c.+5c. black & orange	25	35
762	-	20c.+7c. black and blue	11·00	8·75

DESIGNS: 5c. Girl riding donkey; 6c. Girl playing with dog; 10c. Boy and cat; 20c. Boy and rabbit.

1953. Flood Relief Fund. Surch 19 53 10c +10 WATERSNOOD.

763	**129**	10c.+10c. orange	95	15

149 Hyacinth

1953. Cultural and Social Relief Fund.

764	**149**	2c.+2c. green and violet	1·20	60
765	-	5c.+3c. green & orange	7·00	6·50
766	-	6c.+4c. yellow and green	3·50	1·20
767	-	10c.+5c. green and red	5·75	60
768	-	20c.+5c. green and blue	21·00	17·00

FLOWERS: 5c. African marigold; 6c. Daffodil; 10c. Anemone; 20c. Dutch iris.

150 Red Cross

1953. Red Cross Fund. Inscr "RODE KRUIS".

769	**150**	2c.+3c. red and sepia	1·50	80
770	-	6c.+4c. red and brown	7·50	5·25
771	-	7c.+5c. red and olive	1·70	80
772	-	10c.+5c. red	1·20	35
773	-	25c.+8c. red and blue	12·50	8·00

DESIGNS: 6c. Man with lamp; 7c. Rescue worker in flooded area; 10c. Nurse giving blood transfusion; 25c. Red Cross flags.

151 Queen Juliana

152 Queen Juliana

1953

775	**151**	10c. brown	15	10
776	**151**	12c. turquoise	15	10
777	**151**	15c. red	15	10
777b	**151**	18c. turquoise	15	10
778	**151**	20c. purple	15	10
778b	**151**	24c. olive	45	25
779	**151**	25c. blue	1·90	10
780	**151**	30c. orange	60	10
781	**151**	35c. brown	1·20	10
781a	**151**	37c. turquoise	60	25
782	**151**	40c. slate	60	10
783	**151**	45c. red	45	10
784	**151**	50c. green	95	10
785	**151**	60c. brown	1·20	10
785a	**151**	62c. red	3·50	3·50
785b	**151**	70c. blue	1·40	10
786	**151**	75c. purple	1·40	10
786a	**151**	80c. violet	1·40	10
786b	**151**	85c. green	1·90	10
786c	**151**	95c. brown	1·90	45
787	**152**	1g. red	3·00	10
788	**152**	2½g. green	13·50	25
789	**152**	5g. black	5·25	45
790	**152**	10g. blue	25·00	2·75

153 Girl with Pigeon

1953. Child Welfare. Inscr "VOOR HET KIND".

791	-	2c.+3c. blue and yellow	35	35
792	-	5c.+3c. lake and green	8·25	5·75
793	**153**	7c.+5c. brown and blue	5·00	1·60
794	-	10c.+5c. lilac and bistre	35	35
795	-	25c.+8c. turq & pink	16·00	14·00

DESIGNS: 2c. Girl, bucket and spade; 5c. Boy and apple; 10c. Boy and tjalk (sailing boat); 25c. Girl and tulip.

154 M. Nijhoff (poet)

1954. Cultural and Social Relief Fund.

796	**154**	2c.+3c. blue	3·50	2·75
797	-	5c.+3c. brown	7·00	7·00
798	-	7c.+5c. red	7·00	2·10
799	-	10c.+5c. green	11·50	1·00
800	-	25c.+8c. purple	17·00	16·00

PORTRAITS: 5c. W. Pijper (composer); 7c. H. P. Berlage (architect); 10c. J. Huizinga (historian); 25c. Vincent van Gogh (painter).

155 St. Boniface

1954. 1200th Anniv of Martyrdom of St. Boniface.

801	**155**	10c. blue	3·00	35

156 Boy and Model Glider

1954. National Aviation Fund.

802	**156**	2c.+2c. green	1·70	1·20
803	-	10c.+4c. blue	4·00	1·20

PORTRAIT: 10c. Dr. A. Plesman (aeronautical pioneer).

157 Making Paperchains

1954. Child Welfare.

804	**157**	2c.+3c. brown	25	25
805	-	5c.+3c. olive	6·50	6·25
806	-	7c.+5c. blue	3·00	80
807	-	10c.+5c. red	35	25
808	-	25c.+8c. blue	14·50	9·25

DESIGNS—VERT: 5c. Girl brushing her teeth; 7c. Boy and toy boat; 10c. Nurse and child. HORIZ: 25c. Invalid boy drawing in bed.

158 Queen Juliana

1954. Ratification of Statute for the Kingdom.

809	**158**	10c. red	1·20	25

159 Factory, Rotterdam

1955. Cultural and Social Relief Fund.

810	**159**	2c.+3c. brown	2·30	1·90
811	-	5c.+3c. green	5·25	4·75
812	-	7c.+5c. red	2·30	1·60
813	-	10c.+5c. blue	4·00	35
814	-	25c.+8c. brown	19·00	14·50

DESIGNS—HORIZ: 5c. Post Office, The Hague; 10c. Town Hall, Hilversum; 25c. Office Building, The Hague. VERT: 7c. Stock Exchange, Amsterdam.

160 "The Victory of Peace"

1955. 10th Anniv of Liberation.

815	**160**	10c. red	1·70	35

161 Microscope and Emblem of Cancer

1955. Queen Wilhelmina Anti-cancer Fund.

816	**161**	2c.+3c. black and red	1·40	80
817	**161**	5c.+3c. green and red	4·75	3·50
818	**161**	7c.+5c. purple and red	2·75	1·00
819	**161**	10c.+5c. blue and red	2·10	35
820	**161**	25c.+8c. olive and red	10·00	8·25

162 "Willem van Loon" (D. Dircks)

1955. Child Welfare Fund.

821	**162**	2c.+3c. green	60	35
822	-	5c.+3c. red	5·75	4·00
823	-	7c.+5c. brown	5·75	1·20
824	-	10c.+5c. blue	60	35
825	-	25c.+8c. lilac	14·00	12·50

PORTRAITS: 5c. "Portrait of a Boy" (J. A. Backer); 7c. "Portrait of a Girl" (unknown); 10c. "Philips Huygens" (A. Hanneman); 25c. "Constantin Huygens" (A. Hanneman).

163 "Farmer"

1956. Cultural and Social Relief Fund and 350th Birth Anniv of Rembrandt. Details from Rembrandt's paintings.

826	**163**	2c.+3c. slate	4·75	4·00
827	-	5c.+3c. olive	4·75	4·00
828	-	7c.+5c. brown	7·00	7·00
829	-	10c.+5c. green	17·00	60
830	-	25c.+8c. brown	24·00	22·00

PAINTINGS: 5c. "Young Tobias with Angel"; 7c. "Persian wearing Fur Cap"; 10c. "Old Blind Tobias"; 25c. Self-portrait, 1639.

164 Yacht

165 Amphora

1956. 16th Olympic Games, Melbourne.

831	**164**	2c.+3c. black and blue	1·40	1·30
832	-	5c.+3c. black and yellow	2·10	2·00
833	**165**	7c.+5c. black and brown	2·30	2·00
834	-	10c.+5c. black and grey	3·50	1·00
835	-	25c.+8c. black and green	7·00	7·00

DESIGNS: As Type **164**: 5c. Runner; 10c. Hockey player; 25c. Water polo player.

1956. Europa. As T 110 of Luxembourg.

836	10c. black and lake	5·75	35
837	25c. black and blue	70·00	2·30

167 "Portrait of a Boy" (Van Scorel)

1956. Child Welfare Fund. 16th-century Dutch Paintings.

838	**167**	2c.+3c. grey and cream	60	35
839	-	5c.+3c. olive and cream	1·90	1·70
840	-	7c.+5c. purple & cream	5·25	2·30
841	-	10c.+5c. red and cream	45	35
842	-	25c.+8c. blue and cream	9·25	6·75

PAINTINGS: 5c. "Portrait of a Boy"; 7c. "Portrait of a Girl"; 10c. "Portrait of a Girl"; 25c. "Portrait of Eechie Pieters".

168 "Curacao" (trawler) and Fish Barrels

1957. Cultural and Social Relief Fund. Ships.

843		4c.+3c. blue	2·10	1·70
844		6c.+4c. lilac	5·50	5·25
845		7c.+5c. red	3·25	2·10
846	**168**	10c.+8c. green	6·00	60
847	-	30c.+8c. brown	7·75	6·50

DESIGNS: 4c. "Gaasterland" (freighter); 6c. Coaster; 7c. "Willem Barendsz" (whale factory ship) and whale; 30c. "Nieuw Amsterdam" (liner).

169 Admiral M. A. de Ruyter

1957. 350th Birth Anniv of M. A. de Ruyter.

848	**169**	10c. orange	1·00	35
849	-	30c. blue	6·00	1·70

DESIGN: 30c. De Ruyter's flagship, "De Zeven Provincien".

170 Blood Donors' Emblem

1957. 90th Anniv of Netherlands Red Cross Society and Red Cross Fund.

850	**170**	4c.+3c. blue and red	1·60	1·60
851	-	6c.+4c. green and red	2·10	1·90
852	-	7c.+5c. red and green	2·10	1·90
853	-	10c.+8c. red and ochre	1·90	35
854	-	30c.+8c. red and blue	4·00	3·50

DESIGNS: 6c. "J. Henry Dunant" (hospital ship); 7c. Red Cross; 10c. Red Cross emblem; 30c. Red Cross on globe.

171 "Europa" Star

1957. Europa.
855 **171** 10c. black and blue 2·30 35
856 **171** 30c. green and blue 9·25 2·30

172 Portrait by B. J. Blommers

1957. Child Fund Welfare. 19th- and 20th-Century Paintings by Dutch Masters.
857 **172** 4c.+4c. red 60 35
858 - 6c.+4c. green 5·50 5·25
859 - 8c.+4c. sepia 5·00 3·00
860 - 12c.+9c. purple 45 35
861 - 30c.+9c. blue 11·50 9·25

PORTRAITS: Child paintings by: W. B. Tholen (6c.); J. Sluyters (8c.); M. Maris (12c.); C. Kruseman (30c.).

173 Walcheren Costume

1958. Cultural and Social Relief Fund. Provincial Costumes.
862 **173** 4c.+4c. blue 2·30 80
863 - 6c.+4c. ochre 5·25 4·00
864 - 8c.+4c. red 8·25 2·75
865 - 12c.+9c. brown 3·50 35
866 - 30c.+9c. lilac 13·00 10·50

COSTUMES: 6c. Marken; 8c. Scheveningen; 12c. Friesland; 30c. Volendam.

1958. Surch 12 C.
867 **151** 12c. on 10c. brown 1·60 10

1958. Europa. As T 119a of Luxembourg.
868 12c. blue and red 60 35
869 30c. red and blue 2·30 1·00

176 Girl on Stilts and Boy on Tricycle

1958. Child Welfare Fund. Children's Games.
870 **176** 4c.+4c. blue 35 35
871 - 6c.+4c. red 4·75 4·00
872 - 8c.+4c. green 3·00 1·60
873 - 12c.+9c. red 25 35
874 - 30c.+9c. blue 9·25 7·00

DESIGNS: 6c. Boy and girl on scooter; 8c. Boys playing leap-frog; 12c. Boys on roller-skates; 30c. Girl skipping and boy in toy car.

1959. 10th Anniv of N.A.T.O. As T 123 of Luxembourg (N.A.T.O. emblem).
875 12c. blue and yellow 35 35
876 30c. blue and red 1·40 80

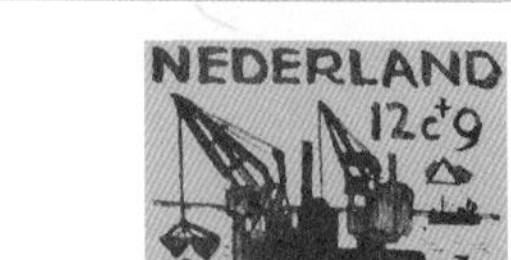

177 Cranes

1959. Cultural and Social Relief Fund. Prevention of Sea Encroachment.
877 - 4c.+4c. blue on green 2·30 2·10
878 - 6c.+4c. brown on grey 3·50 3·00
879 - 8c.+4c. violet on blue 3·50 2·30
880 **177** 12c.+9c. green on yell 5·75 35
881 - 30c.+9c. black on red 9·25 8·50

DESIGNS: 4c. Tugs and caisson; 6c. Dredger; 8c. Labourers making fascine mattresses; 30c. Sand-spouter and scoop.

1959. Europa. As T 123a of Luxembourg.
882 12c. red 1·70 35
883 30c. green 5·75 2·30

178 Silhouette of Douglas DC-8 Airliner and World Map

1959. 40th Anniv of K.L.M. (Royal Dutch Airlines).
884 **178** 12c. blue and red 35 35
885 - 30c. blue and green 2·30 1·70

DESIGN: 30c. Silhouette of Douglas DC-8 airliner.

179 Child in Play-pen

1959. Child Welfare Fund.
886 **179** 4c.+4c. blue and brown 35 35
887 - 6c.+4c. brown and green 2·75 2·10
888 - 8c.+4c. blue and red 4·25 2·75
889 - 12c.+9c. red, black and blue 35 35
890 - 30c.+9c. turquoise and yellow 6·50 6·50

DESIGNS: 6c. Boy as "Red Indian" with bow and arrow; 8c. Boy feeding geese; 12c. Traffic warden escorting children; 30c. Girl doing homework.

180 Refugee Woman

1960. World Refugee Year.
891 **180** 12c.+8c. purple 60 35
892 **180** 30c.+10c. green 5·25 3·50

181 White Water-lily

1960. Cultural and Social Relief Fund. Flowers.
893 - 4c.+4c. red, green and grey 2·30 95
894 - 6c.+4c. yellow, green and salmon 3·50 3·50
895 **181** 8c.+4c. multicoloured 5·75 3·50
896 - 12c.+8c. red, green and buff 4·75 35
897 - 30c.+10c. blue, green and yellow 9·25 7·00

FLOWERS—VERT: 4c. "The Princess" tulip; 6c. Gorse; 12c. Poppy; 30c. Blue sea-holly.

182 J. van der Kolk

1960. World Mental Health Year.
898 **182** 12c. red 1·20 35
899 - 30c. blue (J. Wier) 8·25 2·30

1960. Europa. As T 113a of Norway.
900 12c. yellow and red 60 35
901 30c. yellow and blue 4·75 2·30

183 Marken Costume

1960. Child Welfare Fund. Costumes. Mult portraits.
902 **183** 4c.+4c. slate 60 35
903 - 6c.+4c. ochre 4·75 3·25
904 - 8c.+4c. turquoise 8·25 3·25
905 - 12c.+9c. violet 60 35
906 - 30c.+9c. grey 9·25 8·00

DESIGNS: Costumes of: 6c. Volendam; 8c. Bunschoten; 12c. Hindeloopen; 30c. Huizen.

184 Herring Gull

1961. Cultural and Social Relief Fund. Beach and Meadow Birds.
907 **184** 4c.+4c. slate and yellow 2·10 1·90
908 - 6c.+4c. sepia and brown 3·25 3·00
909 - 8c.+4c. brown and olive 1·90 1·60
910 - 12c.+8c. black and blue 3·75 60
911 - 30c.+10c. black & green 4·25 4·25

BIRDS—HORIZ: 6c. Oystercatcher; 12c. Pied avocet. VERT: 8c. Curlew; 30c. Northern lapwing.

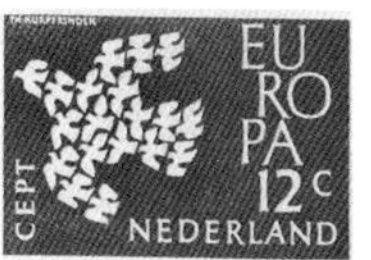

185 Doves

1961. Europa.
912 **185** 12c. brown 25 25
913 **185** 30c. turquoise 35 35

186 St. Nicholas

1961. Child Welfare.
914 **186** 4c.+4c. red 35 35
915 - 6c.+4c. blue 1·90 1·30
916 - 8c.+4c. bistre 1·60 1·50
917 - 12c.+9c. green 35 35
918 - 30c.+9c. orange 5·00 4·75

DESIGNS: 6c. Epiphany; 8c. Palm Sunday; 12c. Whitsuntide; 30c. Martinmas.

187 Queen Juliana and Prince Bernhard

1962. Silver Wedding.
919 **187** 12c. red 35 35
920 **187** 30c. green 2·00 1·20

188 Detail of "The Repast of the Officers of the St. Jorisdoelen" after Frans Hals

1962. Cultural, Health and Social Welfare Funds.
921 - 4c.+4c. green 1·90 1·40
922 - 6c.+4c. black 1·60 1·40
923 - 8c.+4c. purple 2·30 2·10
924 - 12c.+8c. bistre 2·30 60
925 **188** 30c.+10c. blue 2·30 2·30

DESIGNS—HORIZ: 4c. Roman cat (sculpture). VERT: 6c. "Pleuroceras spinatus" (ammonite); 8c. Pendulum clock (after principle of Huygens); 12c. Ship's figurehead.

189 Telephone Dial

1962. Completion of Netherlands Automatic Telephone System. Inscr "1962".
926 **189** 4c. red and black 35 35
927 - 12c. drab and black 1·20 35
928 - 30c. ochre, blue and black 3·25 2·20

DESIGNS—VERT: 12c. Diagram of telephone network. HORIZ: 30c. Arch and telephone dial.

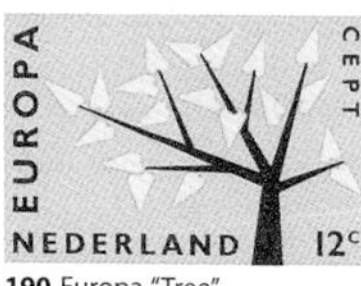

190 Europa "Tree"

1962. Europa.
929 **190** 12c. black, yellow & bistre 45 25
930 **190** 30c. black, yellow and blue 1·90 1·00

191 "Polder" Landscape (reclaimed area)

1962
935 - 4c. deep blue and blue 10 10
937 **191** 6c. deep green and green 45 10
938 - 10c. deep purple and purple 10 10

DESIGNS: 4c. Cooling towers, State mines, Limburg; 10c. Delta excavation works.

192 Children cooking Meal

1962. Child Welfare.
940 **192** 4c.+4c. red 35 35
941 - 6c.+4c. bistre 1·50 80
942 - 8c.+4c. blue 2·30 2·10
943 - 12c.+9c. green 35 35
944 - 30c.+9c. lake 4·25 4·00

DESIGNS—Children: 6c. Cycling; 8c. Watering flowers; 12c. Feeding poultry; 30c. Making music.

193 Ears of Wheat

1963. Freedom from Hunger.
945 **193** 12c. ochre and blue 35 35
946 **193** 30c. ochre and red 1·60 1·60

194 "Gallery" Windmill

1963. Cultural, Health and Social Welfare Funds. Windmill types.
947 **194** 4c.+4c. blue 1·90 1·60
948 - 6c.+4c. violet 1·90 1·60
949 - 8c.+4c. green 2·30 2·10
950 - 12c.+8c. brown 2·30 45
951 - 30c.+10c. red 3·25 3·25

WINDMILLS—VERT: 6c. North Holland polder; 12c. "Post"; 30c. "Wip". HORIZ: 8c. South Holland polder.

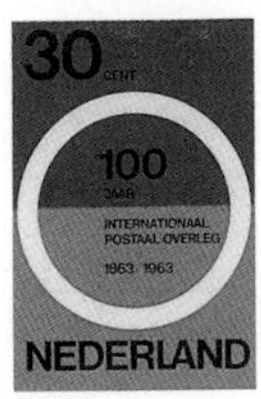

195

1963. Paris Postal Conference Centenary.
952 **195** 30c. blue, green & blk 2·10 1·90

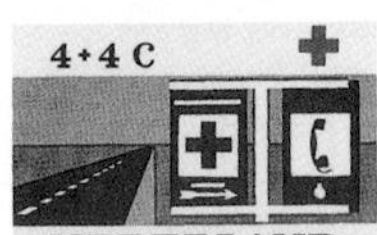

196 Wayside First Aid Post

1963. Red Cross Fund and Centenary (8c.).
953 **196** 4c.+4c. blue and red 60 60
954 - 6c.+4c. violet and red 95 95
955 - 8c.+4c. red and black 1·60 1·20
956 - 12c.+9c. brown and red 35 35
957 - 30c.+9c. green and red 2·30 2·30
DESIGNS: 6c. "Books" collection-box; 8c. Crosses; 12c. "International Aid" (Negro children at meal); 30c. First aid party tending casualty.

197 "Co-operation"

1963. Europa.
958 **197** 12c. orange and brown 60 35
959 **197** 30c. orange and green 2·30 1·40

198 "Auntie Luce sat on a goose ..."

1963. Child Welfare.
960 **198** 4c.+4c. ultramarine & bl 25 35
961 - 6c.+4c. green and red 1·70 1·20
962 - 8c.+4c. brown & green 2·30 95
963 - 12c.+9c. violet & yellow 25 35
964 - 30c.+8c. blue and pink 2·40 2·30
DESIGNS (Nursery rhymes): 6c. "In the Hague there lives a count ..."; 8c. "One day I passed a puppet's fair ..."; 12c. "Storky, storky, Billy Spoon ..."; 30c. "Ride on a little pram ...".

199 William, Prince of Orange, landing at Scheveningen

1963. 150th Anniv of Kingdom of the Netherlands.
965 **199** 4c. black, bistre and blue 25 10
966 **199** 5c. black, red and green 25 10
967 - 12c. bistre, blue and black 25 10
968 - 30c. red and black 1·00 1·00
DESIGNS: 12c. Triumvirate: Van Hogendorp, Van Limburg, and Van der Duyn van Maasdam; 30c. William I taking oath of allegiance.

200 Knights' Hall, The Hague

1964. 500th Anniv of 1st States-General Meeting.
969 **200** 12c. black and olive 35 10

201 Guide Dog for the Blind

1964. Cultural, Health and Social Welfare Funds. Animals.
970 **201** 5c.+5c. red, black and olive 80 70
971 - 8c.+5c. brown, black and red 60 45
972 - 12c.+9c. black, grey and bistre 80 35
973 - 30c.+9c. multicoloured 1·00 95
DESIGNS: 8c. Three red deer; 12c. Three kittens; 30c. European bison and calf.

202 University Arms

1964. 350th Anniv of Groningen University.
974 **202** 12c. slate 35 25
975 - 30c. brown 45 45
DESIGN: 30c. "AG" monogram.

203 Signal No. 144, Amersfoort Station

1964. 125th Anniv of Netherlands Railways.
976 **203** 15c. black and green 35 25
977 - 40c. black and yellow 1·20 1·20
DESIGN: 40c. Class ELD-4 electric train.

204 Bible and Dove

1964. 150th Anniv of Netherlands Bible Society.
978 **204** 15c. brown 35 25

205 Europa "Flower"

1964. Europa.
979 **205** 15c. green 45 25
980 **205** 20c. brown 1·30 60

1964. 20th Anniv of "BENELUX". As T 150a of Luxembourg, but smaller 35×22 mm.
981 15c. violet and flesh 35 25

206 Young Artist

1964. Child Welfare.
982 **206** 7c.+3c. blue and green 70 60
983 - 10c.+5c. red, pink and green 60 60
984 - 15c.+10c. yellow, black and bistre 35 35
985 - 20c.+10c. red, sepia and mauve 1·20 80
986 - 40c.+15c. green & blue 1·50 1·20
DESIGNS: 10c. Ballet-dancing; 15c. Playing the recorder; 20c. Masquerading; 40c. Toy-making.

207 Queen Juliana

1964. 10th Anniv of Statute for the Kingdom.
987 **207** 15c. green 35 25

208 "Killed in Action" (Waalwijk) and "Destroyed Town" (Rotterdam) (monuments)

1965. "Resistance" Commemoration.
988 **208** 7c. black and red 35 35
989 - 15c. black and olive 35 35
990 - 40c. black and red 1·40 1·30
MONUMENTS: 15c. "Docker" (Amsterdam) and "Killed in Action" (Waalwijk); 40c. "Destroyed Town" (Rotterdam) and "Docker" (Amsterdam).

209 Medal of Knight (Class IV)

1965. 150th Anniv of Military William Order.
991 **209** 1g. grey 1·90 1·80

210 I.T.U. Emblem and "Lines of Communication"

1965. Centenary of I.T.U.
992 **210** 20c. blue and drab 25 25
993 **210** 40c. brown and blue 65 55

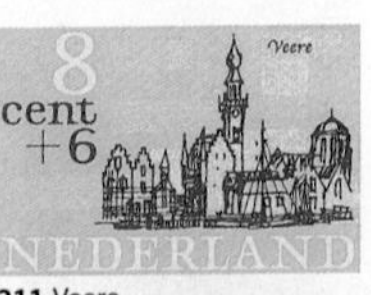

211 Veere

1965. Cultural, Health and Social Welfare Funds.
994 **211** 8c.+6c. black and yellow 35 25
995 - 10c.+6c. black & turq 55 45
996 - 18c.+12c. black & brn 45 25
997 - 20c.+10c. black & blue 55 45
998 - 40c.+10c. black & green 65 55
DESIGNS: (Dutch towns): 10c. Thorn; 18c. Dordrecht; 20c. Staveren; 40c. Medemblik.

212 Europa "Sprig"

1965. Europa.
999 **212** 18c. black, red and brown 25 20
1000 **212** 20c. black, red and blue 45 35

213 Girl's Head

1965. Child Welfare. Multicoloured.
1001 8c.+6c. Type **213** 25 25
1002 10c.+6c. Ship 1·00 70
1003 18c.+12c. Boy (vert) 20 25
1004 20c.+10c. Duck-pond 1·30 70
1005 40c.+10c. Tractor 1·70 1·10
MS1006 143×124 mm. Nos. 1001 (5) and 1003 (6) 31·00 29·00

214 Marines of 1665 and 1965

1965. Tercentenary of Marine Corps.
1007 **214** 18c. blue and red 25 20

215 "Help them to a safe Haven" (Queen Juliana)

1966. Intergovernmental Committee for European Migration (I.C.E.M.) Fund.
1008 **215** 10c.+7c. yellow & blk 65 35
1009 **215** 40c.+20c. red & black 35 25
MS1010 117×44 mm. Nos. 1008 and 1009 (2) 3·25 1·30

216 Writing Materials

1966. Cultural, Health and Social Welfare Funds. Gysbert Japicx Commem and 200th Anniv of Netherlands Literary Society. Multicoloured.
1011 10c.+5c. Type **216** 45 45
1012 12c.+8c. Part of MS, Japicx's poem "Wobbelke" 45 45
1013 20c.+10c. Part of miniature, "Knight Walewein" 65 45
1014 25c.+10c. Initial "D" and part of MS, novel, "Ferguut" 80 65
1015 40c.+20c. 16th-century printery (woodcut) 65 65

217 Aircraft in Flight

1966. Air (Special Flights).
1016 **217** 25c. multicoloured 20 45

218 Europa "Ship"

1966. Europa.
1017 **218** 20c. green and yellow 25 20
1018 **218** 40c. deep blue and blue 1·10 25

219 Infant

1966. Child Welfare.
1019 **219** 10c.+5c. red and blue 25 25
1020 - 12c.+8c. green and red 25 25
1021 - 20c.+10c. blue and red 25 25
1022 - 25c.+10c. purple & bl 1·00 1·00
1023 - 40c.+20c. red & green 90 90
MS1024 132×125 mm. Nos. 1019×4, 1020 ×5, 1021 ×3 3·25 3·25
DESIGNS: 12c. Young girl; 20c. Boy in water; 25c. Girl with moped; 40c. Young man with horse.

220 Assembly Hall

1967. 125th Anniv of Delft Technological University.

1025	**220**	20c. sepia and yellow	25	20

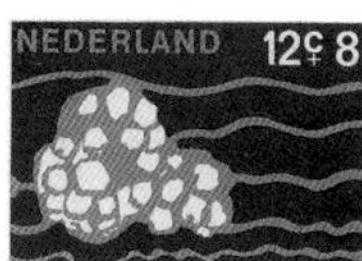

221 Common Northern Whelk Eggs

1967. Cultural, Health and Social Welfare Funds. Marine Fauna.

1026	**221**	12c.+8c. brown & grn	35	35
1027	-	15c.+10c. blue, light blue and deep blue	35	35
1028	-	20c.+10c. mult	35	25
1029	-	25c.+10c. brown, purple and bistre	65	65
1030	-	45c.+20c. mult	90	70

DESIGNS: 15c. Common northern whelk; 20c. Common blue mussel; 25c. Jellyfish; 45c. Crab.

222 Cogwheels

1967. Europa.

1031	**222**	20c. blue and light blue	70	25
1032	**222**	45c. purple & light purple	1·50	90

223 Netherlands 5c. Stamp of 1852

1967. "Amphilex 67" Stamp Exn, Amsterdam.

1035	**223**	20c. blue and black	3·50	2·75
1036	-	25c. red and black	3·50	2·75
1037	-	75c. green and black	3·50	2·75

DESIGNS: 25c. Netherlands 10c. stamp of 1864; 75c. Netherlands 20c. stamp of 1867.

Nos. 1035/7 were sold at the exhibition and at post offices at 3g.70, which included entrance fee to the exhibition.

224 "1867–1967"

1967. Centenary of Dutch Red Cross.

1038	12c.+8c. blue and red	35	30
1039	15c.+10c. red	45	45
1040	20c.+10c. olive and red	35	25
1041	25c.+10c. green and red	55	55
1042	45c.+20c. grey and red	80	80

DESIGNS: 12c. Type **224**; 15c. Red crosses; 20c. "NRK" ("Nederlandsche Rood Kruis") in the form of a cross; 25c. Maltese cross and "red" crosses; 45c. "100" in the form of a cross.

225 "Porcupine Lullaby"

1967. Child Welfare. Multicoloured.

1043	12c.+8c. Type **225**	25	25
1044	15c.+10c. "The Whistling Kettle"	25	25
1045	20c.+10c. "Dikkertje Dap" (giraffe)	25	25
1046	25c.+10c. "The Flower-seller"	1·50	90
1047	45c.+20c. "Pippeloentje" (bear)	1·50	1·00
MS1048	150×108 mm. Nos. 1043 (3), 1044 (4), 1045 (3)	6·25	6·25

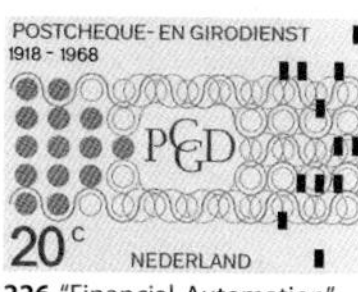

226 "Financial Automation"

1968. 50th Anniv of Netherlands Postal Cheque and Clearing Service.

1049	**226**	20c. red, black and yellow	25	20

227 St. Servatius' Bridge, Maastricht

1968. Cultural, Health and Social Welfare Funds. Dutch Bridges.

1050	**227**	12c.+8c. green	65	65
1051	-	15c.+10c. brown	80	80
1052	-	20c.+10c. red	55	25
1053	-	25c.+10c. blue	65	65
1054	-	45c.+20c. blue	1·00	1·00

BRIDGES: 15c. Magere ("Narrow"), Amsterdam; 20c. Railway, Culemborg; 25c. Van Brienenoord, Rotterdam; 45c. Oosterschelde, Zeeland.

228 Europa "Key"

1968. Europa.

1055	**228**	20c. blue	65	65
1056	**228**	45c. red	1·30	90

229 "Wilhelmus van Nassouwe"

1968. 400th Anniv of Dutch National Anthem, "Wilhelmus".

1057	**229**	20c. multicoloured	25	20

230 Wright Type A and Cessna 150F

1968. Dutch Aviation Anniversaries.

1058	12c. black, red and mauve	25	20
1059	20c. black, emerald and green	25	20
1060	45c. black, blue and green	1·40	1·30

DESIGNS AND EVENTS: 12c. T **230** (60th anniv (1967) of Royal Netherlands Aeronautical Assn); 20c. Fokker F.II H-NABC and Fokker F.28 Fellowship aircraft (50th anniv (1969) of Royal Netherlands Aircraft Factories "Fokker"); 45c. Airco de Havilland D.H.9B biplane H-NABE and Douglas DC-9 airliner (50th anniv (1969) of Royal Dutch Airlines "KLM").

231 "Goblin"

1968. Child Welfare.

1061	**231**	12c.+8c. pink, black and green	25	25
1062	-	15c.+10c. pink, blue and black	25	25
1063	-	20c.+10c. blue, green and black	25	25
1064	-	25c.+10c. red, yellow and black	2·20	1·90
1065	-	45c.+20c. yellow, orange and black	2·20	1·90
MS1066		106½×151 mm. Nos. 1061 (3), 1062 (2), 1063 (3)	8·50	8·50

DESIGNS: 15c. "Giant"; 20c. "Witch"; 25c. "Dragon"; 45c. "Sorcerer".

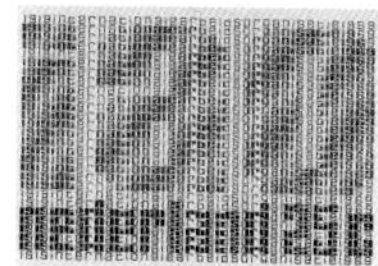

232 "I A O" (Internationale Arbeidsorganisatie)

1969. 50th Anniv of I.L.O.

1067	**232**	25c. red and black	65	20
1068	**232**	45c. blue and black	1·20	1·00

233 Queen Juliana

1969. (a) Type 233.

1069	**233**	25c. red	55	10
1069b	**233**	30c. brown	25	10
1070	**233**	35c. blue	25	10
1071	**233**	40c. red	35	10
1072	**233**	45c. blue	35	10
1073	**233**	50c. purple	45	10
1073bc	**233**	55c. red	20	10
1074a	**233**	60c. blue	55	20
1075	**233**	70c. brown	65	10
1076	**233**	75c. green	65	10
1077	**233**	80c. red	70	10
1077a	**233**	90c. grey	70	10

(b) Size 22×33 mm.

1078	1g. green	80	10
1079	1g.25 lake	1·00	10
1080	1g.50 brown	1·30	10
1081	2g. mauve	1·60	20
1082	2g.50 blue	2·10	20
1083	5g. grey	4·00	20
1084	10g. blue	8·00	90

DESIGN: 1g.to 10g. similar to Type **233**.

234 Villa, Huis ter Heide (1915)

1969. Cultural, Health and Social Welfare Funds. 20th-century Dutch Architecture.

1085	**234**	12c.+8c. black & brn	90	90
1086	-	15c.+10c. black, red and blue	90	90
1087	-	20c.+10c. black & vio	90	90
1088	-	25c.+10c. brown & grn	90	35
1089	-	45c.+20c. black, blue and yellow	90	90

DESIGNS: 15c. Private House, Utrecht (1924); 20c. Open-air School, Amsterdam (1930); 25c. Orphanage, Amsterdam (1960); 45c. Congress Building, The Hague (1969).

235 Colonnade

1969. Europa.

1090	**235**	25c. blue	45	20
1091	**235**	45c. red	1·80	1·30

236 Stylized "Crab" (of Cancer)

1969. 20th Anniv of Queen Wilhelmina Cancer Fund.

1092	**236**	12c.+8c. violet	70	70
1093	**236**	25c.+10c. orange	1·10	45
1094	**236**	45c.+20c. green	1·80	1·80

1969. 25th Anniv of "BENELUX" Customs Union. As T 186 of Luxembourg.

1095	25c. multicoloured	30	10

238 Erasmus

1969. 500th Birth Anniv of Desiderius Erasmus.

1096	**238**	25c. purple on green	25	10

239 Child with Violin

1969. Child Welfare.

1097	-	12c.+8c. black, yellow and blue	25	25
1098	**239**	15c.+10c. black and red	25	25
1099	-	20c.+10c. black, yellow and red	2·75	2·30
1100	-	25c.+10c. black, red and yellow	25	25
1101	-	45c.+20c. black, red and green	2·75	2·40
MS1102		150×99 mm. Nos. 1097 (4), 1098 (4), 1100 (2)	9·75	9·75

DESIGNS—VERT: 12c. Child with recorder; 20c. Child with drum. HORIZ: 25c. Three choristers; 45c. Two dancers.

240 Queen Juliana and "Sunlit Road"

1969. 25th Anniv of Statute for the Kingdom.

1103	**240**	25c. multicoloured	25	10

241 Prof. E. M. Meijers (author of "Burgerlijk Wetboek")

1970. Introduction of New Netherlands Civil Code ("Burgerlijk Wetboek").

1104	**241**	25c. ultramarine, green and blue	35	10

242 Netherlands Pavilion

1970. Expo 70 World Fair, Osaka, Japan.

1105	**242**	25c. grey, blue and red	35	10

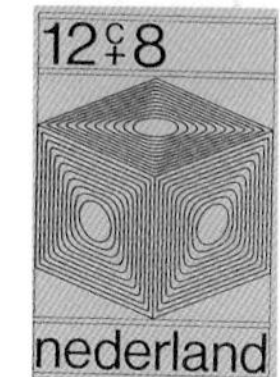

243 "Circle to Square"

1970. Cultural, Health and Social Welfare Funds.

1106	**243**	12c.+8c. black on yell	1·30	1·30
1107	-	15c.+10c. black on silver	1·30	1·30
1108	-	20c.+10c. black	1·30	1·30
1109	-	25c.+10c. black on bl	1·30	70
1110	-	45c.+20c. white on grey	1·30	1·30

DESIGNS: 15c. Parallel planes in cube; 20c. Overlapping scales; 25c. Concentric circles in transition; 45c. Spirals.

244 "V" Symbol

1970. 25th Anniv of Liberation.

1111	**244**	12c. red, blue and brown	35	10

245 "Flaming Sun"

1970. Europa.

1112	**245**	25c. red	70	20
1113	**245**	45c. blue	1·50	1·30

246 "Work and Co-operation"

1970. Inter-Parliamentary Union Conference.

1114	**246**	25c. green, black and grey	65	10

247 Globe on Plinth

1970. 25th Anniv of United Nations.

1115	**247**	45c. black, violet & blue	1·20	1·00

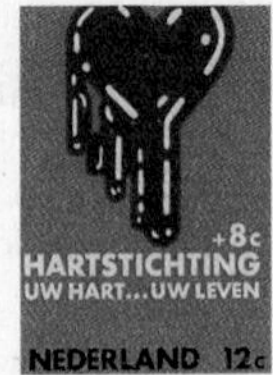

248 Human Heart

1970. Netherlands Heart Foundation.

1116	**248**	12c.+8c. red, black and yellow	80	80
1117	**248**	25c.+10c. red, black and mauve	80	65
1118	**248**	45c.+20c. red, black and green	80	80

249 Toy Block

1970. Child Welfare. "The Child and the Cube".

1119	**249**	12c.+8c. blue, violet and green	20	15
1120	-	15c.+10c. green, blue and yellow	1·90	1·50
1121	**249**	20c.+10c. mauve, red and violet	1·90	1·50
1122	-	25c.+10c. red, yellow and mauve	25	25
1123	**249**	45c.+20c. grey, cream and black	2·20	1·80
MS1124		126×145 mm. Nos. 1119 (9), 1122 (2)	18·00	16·00

DESIGN: 15c., 25c. As Type **249**, but showing underside of block.

250 "Fourteenth Census 1971"

1971. 14th Netherlands Census.

1125	**250**	15c. purple	25	10

251 "50 years of Adult University Education"

1971. Cultural, Health and Social Welfare Funds. Other designs show 15th-century wooden statues by unknown artists.

1126	**251**	15c.+10c. black, red and yellow	1·40	1·30
1127	-	20c.+10c. black and green on green	1·40	1·30
1128	-	25c.+10c. black and orange on orange	1·40	55
1129	-	30c.+15c. black and blue on blue	1·40	1·30
1130	-	45c.+20c. black and red on pink	1·40	1·30

STATUES: 20c. "Apostle Paul"; 25c. "Joachim and Ann"; 30c. "John the Baptist and Scribes"; 45c. "Ann, Mary and Christ-Child" (detail).

252 Europa Chain

1971. Europa.

1131	**252**	25c. yellow, red and black	70	20
1132	**252**	45c. yellow, blue & black	1·80	1·30

253 Carnation Symbol of Prince Bernhard Fund

1971. Prince Bernhard's 60th Birthday.

1133	**253**	15c. yellow, grey & black	25	20
1134	-	20c. multicoloured	90	35
1135	-	25c. multicoloured	35	20
1136	-	45c.+20c. black, purple and yellow	2·50	2·50

DESIGNS—HORIZ: 20c. Panda symbol of World Wildlife Fund. VERT: 25c. Prince Bernhard, Boeing 747 and Fokker F.27 Friendship; 45c. Statue, Borobudur Temple, Indonesia.

254 "The Good Earth"

1971. Child Welfare.

1137	**254**	15c.+10c. red, purple and black	25	25
1138	-	20c.+10c. mult	45	45
1139	-	25c.+10c. mult	25	25
1140	-	30c.+15c. blue, violet and black	1·30	80
1141	-	45c.+20c. blue, green and black	2·10	1·80
MS1142		100×145 mm. Nos. 1137 (6), 1138 and 1139 (2)	11·50	11·00

DESIGNS—VERT: 20c. Butterfly; 45c. Reflecting water. HORIZ: 25c. Sun waving; 30c. Moon winking.

255 Delta Map

1972. Delta Sea-Defences Plan.

1143	**255**	20c. multicoloured	25	10

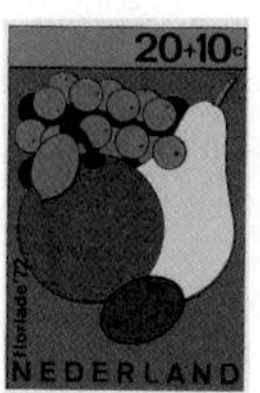

256 "Fruits"

1972. Cultural, Health and Social Welfare Funds. "Floriade Flower Show" (20c., 25c.) and "Holland Arts Festival" (30c., 45c.). Multicoloured.

1144	20c.+10c. Type **256**	1·30	1·20
1145	25c.+10c. "Flower"	1·30	1·20
1146	30c.+15c. "Sunlit Landscape"	1·30	70
1147	45c.+25c. "Music"	1·30	1·20

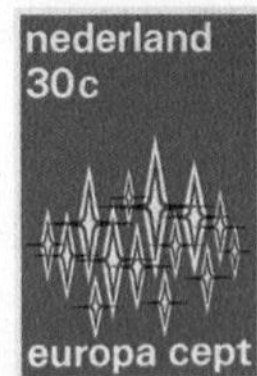

257 "Communications"

1972. Europa.

1148	**257**	30c. brown and blue	90	20
1149	**257**	45c. brown and orange	1·30	1·20

258 "There is more to be done in the world than ever before" (Thorbecke)

1972. Death Centenary of J. R. Thorbecke (statesman).

1150	**258**	30c. black and blue	90	25

259 Netherlands Flag

1972. 400th Anniv of Netherlands Flag.

1151	**259**	20c. multicoloured	55	20
1152	**259**	25c. multicoloured	1·30	20

260 Hurdling

1972. Olympic Games, Munich. Multicoloured.

1153	20c. Type **260**	35	25
1154	30c. Diving	35	25
1155	45c. Cycling	1·10	1·10

261 Red Cross

1972. Netherlands Red Cross.

1156	**261**	5c. red	40	30
1157	-	20c.+10c. red and pink	65	65
1158	-	25c.+10c. red & orange	1·10	1·20
1159	-	30c.+15c. red & black	80	55
1160	-	45c.+25c. red and blue	1·20	1·10

DESIGNS: 20c. Accident services; 25c. Blood transfusion; 30c. Refugee relief; 45c. Child care.

262 Prince Willem-Alexander

1972. Child Welfare. Multicoloured.

1161	25c.+15c. Type **262**	25	25
1162	30c.+10c. Prince Johan Friso (horiz)	1·00	80
1163	35c.+15c. Prince Constantin (horiz)	1·00	25
1164	50c.+20c. The Three Princes (horiz)	3·00	2·50
MS1165	126×109 mm. Nos. 1161 ×4 and 1163 ×3	9·00	9·00

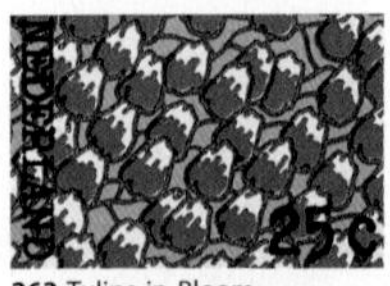

263 Tulips in Bloom

1973. Tulip Exports.

1166	**263**	25c. multicoloured	70	10

264 "De Zeven Provincien" (De Ruyter's flagship)

1973. Cultural, Health and Social Welfare Funds. Dutch Ships. Multicoloured.

1167	25c.+15c. Type **264**	1·10	1·10
1168	30c.+10c. "W.A. Scholten" (steamship) (horiz)	1·10	1·10
1169	35c.+15c. "Veendam" (liner) (horiz)	1·30	80
1170	50c.+20c. Fishing boat (from etching by R. Nooms)	1·30	1·30

265 Europa "Posthorn"

1973. Europa.

1171	**265**	35c. light blue and blue	90	20
1172	**265**	50c. blue and violet	1·80	90

266 Hockey-players

1973. Events and Anniversaries. Multicoloured.

1173	25c. Type **266**	65	20
1174	30c. Gymnastics	1·30	70
1175	35c. Dish aerial (vert)	90	25
1176	50c. Rainbow	1·30	90

EVENTS—VERT: 25c. 75th anniv of Royal Netherlands Hockey Association; 30c. World Gymnastics Championships, Rotterdam. HORIZ: 35c. Opening of Satellite Station, Burum; 50c. Centenary of World Meteorological Organization.

267 Queen Juliana

1973. Silver Jubilee of Queen Juliana's Accession.

1177	**267**	40c. multicoloured	55	25

268 "Co-operation"

1973. International Development Co-operation.

1178	**268**	40c. multicoloured	70	25

269 "Chess"

1973. Child Welfare.

1179	**269**	25c.+15c. red, yellow and black	35	25
1180	-	30c.+10c. green, mauve and black	90	70
1181	-	40c.+20c. yellow, green and black	35	25
1182	-	50c.+20c. blue, yellow and black	2·75	2·30
MS1183 74×144 mm. Nos. 1179 ×2, 1180 and 1181 ×3			10·50	10·50

DESIGNS: 30c. "Noughts and crosses"; 40c. "Maze"; 50c. "Dominoes".

270 Northern Goshawk

1974. "Nature and Environment". Multicoloured.

1184	25c. Type **270**	90	45
1185	25c. Tree	90	45
1186	25c. Fisherman and frog	90	45

Nos. 1184/6 were issued together, se-tenant, forming a composite design.

271 Bandsmen (World Band Contest, Kerkrade)

1974. Cultural, Health and Social Welfare Funds.

1187	**271**	25c.+15c. mult	1·10	1·10
1188	-	30c.+10c. mult	1·10	1·10
1189	-	40c.+20c. brown, black and red	1·20	80
1190	-	50c.+20c. purple, black and red	1·20	1·10

DESIGNS: 30c. Dancers and traffic-lights ("Modern Ballet"); 40c. Herman Heijermans; 50c. "Kniertje" (character from Heijermans' play "Op hoop van zegan"). The 40c. and 50c. commemorate the 50th death anniv of the playwright.

272 Football on Pitch

1974. Sporting Events.

1191	**272**	25c. multicoloured	80	25
1192	-	40c. yellow, red & mauve	80	25

DESIGNS AND EVENTS—HORIZ: 25c. (World Cup Football Championship, West Germany). VERT: 40c. Hand holding tennis ball (75th anniv of Royal Dutch Lawn Tennis Association).

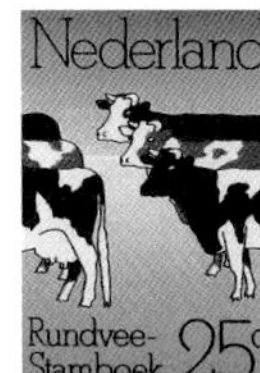

273 Netherlands Cattle

1974. Anniversaries. Multicoloured.

1193	25c. Type **273**	9·75	2·20
1194	25c. "Cancer"	1·80	25
1195	40c. "Suzanna" (lifeboat) seen through binoculars	1·80	25

EVENTS AND ANNIVERSARIES: No. 1193, Cent of Netherlands Cattle Herdbook Society; 1194, 25th anniv of Queen Wilhelmina Cancer Research Fund; 1195, 150th anniv of Dutch Lifeboat Service.

274 "BENELUX" (30th Anniv of Benelux (Customs Union))

1974. International Anniversaries.

1196	**274**	30c. green, turquoise & blue	90	25
1197	-	45c. deep blue, silver & blue	90	25
1198	-	45c. yellow, blue & black	90	25

DESIGNS—VERT: No. 1197, NATO emblem (25th anniv); 1198, Council of Europe emblem (25th anniv).

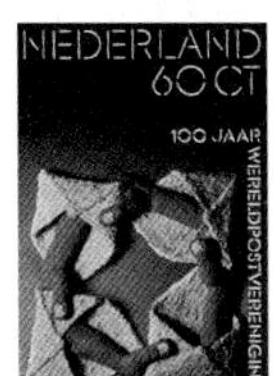

275 Hands with Letters

1974. Centenary of Universal Postal Union.

1199	**275**	60c. multicoloured	70	35

276 Boy with Hoop

1974. 50th Anniv of Child Welfare Issues. Early Photographs.

1200	**276**	30c.+15c. brown & blk	35	25
1201	-	35c.+20c. brown	90	65
1202	-	45c.+20c. black	90	25
1203	-	60c.+20c. black	2·10	1·70
MS1204 75×145 mm. Nos. 1200 ×4 and 1201/2			4·75	4·50

DESIGNS: 35c. Child and baby; 45c. Two young girls; 60c. Girl sitting on balustrade.

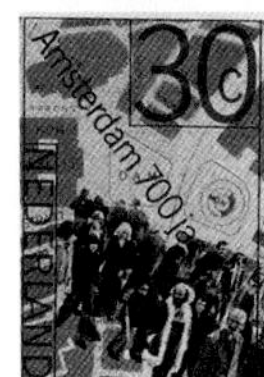

277 Amsterdam

1975. Anniversaries. Multicoloured.

1205	30c. Type **277**	45	25
1206	30c. Synagogue and map	45	35
1207	35c. Type **277**	45	25
1208	45c. "Window" in human brain	55	25

ANNIVERSARIES: Nos. 1205, 1207, Amsterdam (700th anniv); 1206, Portuguese-Israelite Synagogue, Amsterdam (300th anniv); 1208, Leyden University and university education (400th anniv).

278 St. Hubertus Hunting Lodge, De Hoge Veluwe National Park

1975. Cultural, Health and Social Welfare Funds. National Monument Year. Preserved Monuments. Multicoloured.

1209	35c.+20c. Type **278**	65	65
1210	40c.+15c. Bergijnhof (Beguinage), Amsterdam (vert)	65	65
1211	50c.+20c. "Kuiperspoort" (Cooper's gate), Middelburg (vert)	80	65
1212	60c.+20c. Orvelte village, Drenthe	1·10	1·10

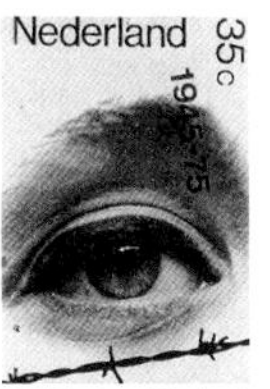

279 Eye and Barbed Wire

1975. 30th Anniv of Liberation.

1213	**279**	35c. black and red	45	25

280 Company Emblem and "Stad Middelburg" (schooner)

1975. Centenary of Zeeland Shipping Company.

1214	**280**	35c. multicoloured	55	25

281 Dr. Albert Schweitzer crossing Lambarene River

1975. Birth Centenary of Dr. Schweitzer (medical missionary).

1215	**281**	50c. multicoloured	55	25

282 Man and Woman on "Playing-card"

1975. International Events. Multicoloured.

1216	35c. Type **282** (Int Women's Year)	55	25
1217	50c. Metric scale (Metre Convention cent) (horiz)	55	25

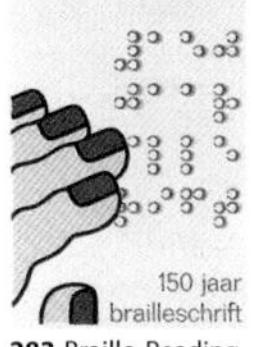

283 Braille Reading

1975. 150th Anniv of Invention of Braille.

1218	**283**	35c. multicoloured	55	25

284 Dutch 25c. Coins

1975. Savings Campaign.

1219	**284**	50c. grey, green and blue	55	25

285 "Four Orphans" (C. Simons), Torenstraat Orphanage, Medemblik

1975. Child Welfare. Historic Ornamental Stones. Multicoloured.

1220	35c.+15c. Type **285**	25	25
1221	40c.+15c. "Milkmaid" Kooltuin Alkmaar	90	55
1222	50c.+25c. "Four Sons of Aymon seated on Beyaert", Herengracht	45	25
1223	60c.+25c. "Life at the Orphanage", Molenstraat Orphanage, Gorinchem	1·30	1·00
MS1224 145×75 mm. Nos. 1220 ×3 and 1222 ×2		3·50	3·50

286 18th-century Lottery Ticket

1976. 250th Anniv of National Lottery.

1225	**286**	35c. multicoloured	35	25

287 Numeral

1976. (a) Ordinary gum.

1226	**287**	5c. grey	10	10
1227	**287**	10c. blue	20	10
1228	**287**	25c. violet	25	10
1229	**287**	40c. brown	45	10
1230	**287**	45c. blue	45	10
1231	**287**	50c. mauve	55	10
1232	**287**	55c. green	70	10
1233	**287**	60c. yellow	80	10
1234	**287**	65c. brown	1·30	10
1235	**287**	70c. violet	1·30	10
1236	**287**	80c. mauve	1·80	20

(b) Self-adhesive gum.

1237	5c. grey	20	10
1238	10c. blue	25	10
1239	25c. violet	35	10

288 West European Hedgehog

1976. Cultural, Health and Social Welfare Funds. Nature Protection (40, 75c.) and Anniversaries. Multicoloured.

1241	40c.+20c. Type **288**	90	65
1242	45c.+20c. Open book (vert)	80	65
1243	55c.+20c. People and organization initials	80	25
1244	75c.+25c. Frog and spawn (vert)	1·10	90

ANNIVERSARIES: No. 1242, 175th anniv of Primary education and centenary of Agricultural education; 1243, 75th anniv of Social Security Bank and legislation.

289 Admiral Michiel de Ruyter (statue)

1976. 300th Death Anniv of Admiral Michiel de Ruyter.

1245	**289**	55c. multicoloured	45	15

290 Guillaume Groen van Prinsterer

1976. Death Centenary of Guillaume Groen van Prinsterer (statesman).

1246	**290**	55c. multicoloured	45	15

291 Detail of 18th-century Calendar

1976. Bicentenary of American Revolution.
1247 **291** 75c. multicoloured 65 35

292 Long-distance Marchers

1976. Sport and Recreation Anniversaries. Mult.
1248 40c. Type **292** 45 25
1249 55c. Runners "photo-finish" 90 25
ANNIVERSARIES: 40c. 60th Nijmegen Long-distance March; 55c. Royal Dutch Athletics Society (75th anniv).

293 The Art of Printing

1976. Anniversaries.
1250 **293** 45c. red and blue 65 25
1251 - 55c.+25c. mult 70 55
DESIGNS AND EVENTS: 45c. Type **293** (75th anniv of Netherlands Printers' organization); 55c. Rheumatic patient "Within Care" (50th anniv of Dutch Anti-Rheumatism Association).

294 Dutch Tjalk and Reclaimed Land

1976. Zuider Zee Project—Reclamation and Urbanization. Multicoloured.
1252 **294** 40c. blue, olive and red 65 25
1253 - 75c. yellow, red and blue 90 55
DESIGN: 75c. Duck flying over reclaimed land.

295 Queen Wilhelmina 4½c. Stamp, 1919

1976. "Amphilex '77" International Stamp Exhibition, Amsterdam (1977) (1st series). Stamp Portraits of Queen Wilhelmina. Multicoloured.
1254 55c.+55c. blue, deep grey and grey 1·00 90
1255 **295** 55c.+55c. purple, deep grey and grey 1·00 90
1256 - 55c.+55c. brown, deep grey and grey 1·00 90
1257 - 75c.+75c. turquoise, deep grey and grey 1·00 90
1258 - 75c.+75c. blue, deep grey and grey 1·00 90
DESIGNS: No. 1254, 5c. stamp, 1891; 1256, 25c. stamp, 1924; 1257, 15c. stamp, 1940; 1258, 25c. stamp, 1947.
See also Nos. 1273/6.

296 "Football" (J. Raats)

1976. Child Welfare. Children's Paintings. Mult.
1259 40c.+20c. Type **296** 45 25
1260 45c.+20c. "Boat" (L. Jacobs) 55 25
1261 55c.+20c. "Elephant" (M. Lugtenburg) 65 25
1262 75c.+25c. "Caravan" (A. Seeleman) 2·00 90
MS1263 145×75 mm. Nos. 1259/61 ×2 3·50 2·20

297 Ballot-paper and Pencil

1977. National Events. Multicoloured.
1264 40c. "Energy" (vert) 45 25
1265 45c. Type **297** 45 25
EVENTS: 40c. "Be wise with energy" campaign; 45c. Elections to Lower House of States-General.
See also No. 1268.

298 Spinoza

1977. 300th Death Anniv of Barach (Benedictus) de Spinoza (philosopher).
1266 **298** 75c. multicoloured 80 35

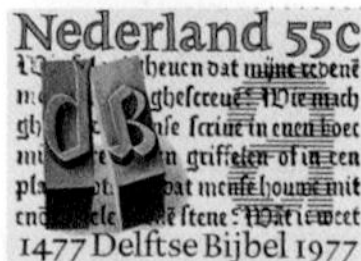

299 Early Type Faces and "a" on Bible Script

1977. 500th Anniv of Printing of "Delft Bible".
1267 **299** 55c. multicoloured 55 45

1977. Elections to Lower House of States-General. As T 297 but also inscribed "25 MEI '77".
1268 45c. multicoloured 45 25

300 Altar of Goddess Nehalennia

1977. Cultural, Health and Social Welfare Funds. Roman Archaeological Discoveries.
1269 - 40c.+20c. mult 65 35
1270 **300** 45c.+20c. black, stone and green 70 35
1271 - 55c.+20c. black, blue and red 70 35
1272 - 75c.+25c. black, grey and yellow 90 65
DESIGNS: 40c. Baths, Heerlen; 55c. Remains of Zwammerdam ship; 75c. Parade helmet.

1977. "Amphilex 1977" International Stamp Exhibition, Amsterdam (2nd series). As T 295.
1273 55c.+45c. grn, brn & grey 95 45
1274 55c.+45c. blue, brn & grey 95 70
1275 55c.+45c. blue, brn & grey 95 70
1276 55c.+45c. red, brn & grey 95 45
MS1277 100×72 mm. Nos. 1273 and 1276 2·20 1·20
DESIGNS: No. 1273, Queen Wilhelmina 1g. stamp, 1898; 1274, Queen Wilhelmina 20c. stamp, 1923; 1275, Queen Wilhelmina 12½c. stamp, 1938; 1276, Queen Wilhelmina 10c. stamp, 1948.

301 "Kaleidoscope"

1977. Bicentenary of Netherlands Society for Industry and Commerce.
1278 **301** 55c. multicoloured 70 10

302 Man in Wheelchair and Maze of Steps

1977. Anniversaries.
1279 **302** 40c. brown, green & blue 60 35
1280 - 45c. multicoloured 60 35
1281 - 55c. multicoloured 60 35
DESIGNS—HORIZ: 40c. Type **302** (50th anniv of A.V.O. Nederland); 45c. Diagram of water current (50th anniv of Delft Hydraulic Laboratory). VERT: 55c. Teeth (centenary of dentists' training in Netherlands).

303 Risk of Drowning

1977. Child Welfare. Dangers to Children. Mult.
1282 40c.+20c. Type **303** 60 35
1283 45c.+20c. Medicine cabinet (poisons) 70 35
1284 55c.+20c. Balls in road (traffic) 70 35
1285 75c.+25c. Matches (fire) 1·70 95
MS1286 75×144 mm. Nos. 1282/4 ×2 4·75 3·00

304 "Postcode"

1978. Introduction of Postcodes.
1287 **304** 40c. red and blue 60 10
1288 **304** 45c. red and blue 70 10

305 Makkum Dish

1978. Cultural, Health and Social Welfare Funds. Multicoloured.
1289 40c.+20c. Anna Maria van Schurman (writer) 70 45
1290 45c.+20c. Passage from letter by Belle de Zuylen (Mme. de Charriere) 80 45
1291 55c.+20c. Delft dish 95 45
1292 75c.+25c. Type **305** 1·00 70

306 "Human Rights" Treaty

1978. European Series.
1293 **306** 45c. grey, black and blue 60 35
1294 - 55c. black, stone and orange 60 35
DESIGN: 55c. Haarlem Town Hall (Europa).

307 Chess

1978. Sports.
1295 **307** 40c. multicoloured 60 35
1296 - 45c. red and blue 70 35
DESIGN: 45c. The word "Korfbal".

308 Kidney Donor

1978. Health Care. Multicoloured.
1297 **308** 40c. black, blue and red 60 35
1298 - 45c. multicoloured 70 35
1299 - 55c.+25c. red, grey and black 70 45
MS1300 144×50 mm. No. 1299 ×3 2·30 2·10
DESIGNS—VERT: 45c. Heart and torch. HORIZ: 55c. Red crosses on world map.

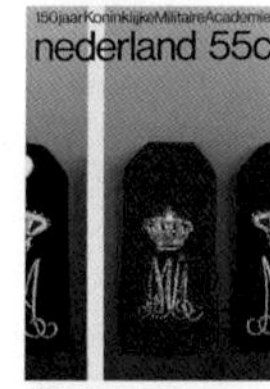

309 Epaulettes

1978. 150th Anniv of Royal Military Academy, Breda.
1301 **309** 55c. multicoloured 60 35

310 Verkade as Hamlet

1978. Birth Centenary of Eduard Rutger Verkade (actor and producer).
1302 **310** 45c. multicoloured 60 35

311 Boy ringing Doorbell

1978. Child Welfare. Multicoloured.
1303 40c.+20c. Type **311** 60 35
1304 45c.+20c. Child reading 70 35
1305 55c.+20c. Boy writing (vert) 70 35
1306 75c.+25c. Girl and blackboard 1·60 95
MS1307 144×75 mm. Nos. 1303/5 ×2 4·75 3·00

312 Clasped Hands and Arrows

1979. 400th Anniv of Treaty of Utrecht.
1308 **312** 55c. blue 70 35

313 Names of European Community Members

1979. First Direct Elections to European Assembly.
1309 **313** 45c. red, blue and black 60 35

314 Queen Juliana

1979. Queen Juliana's 70th Birthday.
1310 **314** 55c. multicoloured 70 35

315 Fragment of "Psalmen Trilogie" (J. Andriessen)

1979. Cultural, Health and Social Welfare Funds.

1311	**315**	40c.+20c. grey and red	70	45
1312	-	45c.+20c. grey and red	80	45
1313	-	55c.+20c. mult	95	35
1314	-	75c.+25c. mult	1·00	70

DESIGNS AND EVENTS: 150th anniv of Musical Society; 45c. Choir. Restoration of St. John's Church, Gouda (stained glass windows); 55c. Mary (detail, "Birth of Christ"); 75c. William of Orange (detail, "Relief of Leyden").

316 Netherlands Stamps and Magnifying Glass

1979. Europa and 75th Anniv of Scheveningen Radio. Multicoloured.

1315	55c. Type **316**	60	15
1316	75c. Liner and Morse Key	95	45

317 Map of Chambers of Commerce

1979. 175th Anniv of First Dutch Chamber of Commerce, Maastricht.

1317	**317**	45c. multicoloured	60	35

318 Action Shot of Football Match

1979. Anniversaries. Multicoloured.

1318	45c. Type **318** (centenary of organized football)	60	20
1319	55c. Women's suffrage meeting (60th anniv of Women's suffrage) (vert)	70	20

319 Porch of Old Amsterdam Theatre

1979. 300th Death Annivs of Joost van den Vondel (poet) and Jan Steen (painter). Multicoloured.

1320	40c. Type **319**	60	25
1321	45c. "Gay Company" (detail) (Jan Steen)	60	25

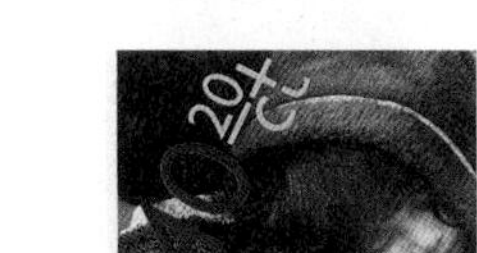

320 Hindustani Girl on Father's Shoulder (The Right to Love)

1979. Child Welfare. International Year of the Child.

1322	**320**	40c.+20c. grey, red and yellow	60	35
1323	-	45c.+20c. grey, red and black	70	35
1324	-	55c.+20c. grey, black and yellow	70	35
1325	-	75c.+25c. black, blue and red	1·50	70
MS1326		144×75 mm. Nos. 1322/4, each ×2	4·75	3·00

DESIGNS—HORIZ: 45c. Chilean child from refugee camp (The Right to Medical Care). VERT: 55c. Senegalese boy from Sahel area (The Right to Food); 75c. Class from Albert Cuyp School, Amsterdam (The Right to Education).

321 A. F. de Savornin Lohman

1980. Dutch Politicians. Multicoloured.

1327	45c. Type **321** (Christian Historical Union)	60	20
1328	50c. P. J. Troelstra (Socialist Party)	70	20
1329	60c. P. J. Oud (Liberal Party)	80	20

322 Dunes

1980. Cultural, Health and Social Welfare Funds. Multicoloured.

1330	45c.+20c. Type **322**	95	45
1331	50c.+20c. Country estate (vert)	95	45
1332	60c.+25c. Lake District	1·00	45
1333	80c.+35c. Moorland	1·30	70

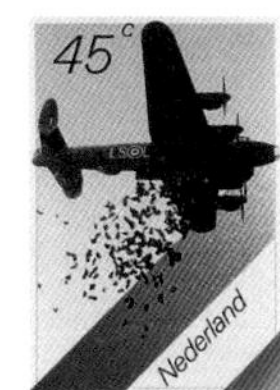

323 Avro Type 683 Lancaster dropping Food Parcels

1980. 35th Anniv of Liberation. Multicoloured.

1334	45c. Type **323**	80	25
1335	60c. Anne Frank (horiz)	95	25

324 Queen Beatrix and New Church, Amsterdam

1980. Installation of Queen Beatrix.

1336	**324**	60c. blue, red and yellow	70	10
1337	**324**	65c. blue, red and yellow	80	10

325 Young Stamp Collectors

1980. "Jupostex 1980" Stamp Exhibition, Eindhoven, and Dutch Society of Stamp Dealers Show, The Hague.

1338	**325**	50c. multicoloured	60	35

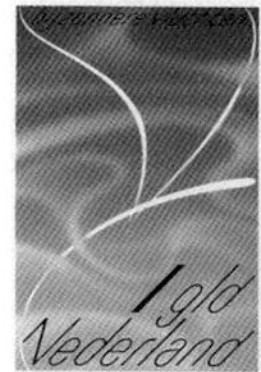

326 "Flight"

1980. Air. (Special Flights).

1339	**326**	1g. blue and black	1·20	1·20

327 Bridge Players and Cards

1980. Sports Events. Multicoloured.

1340	50c. Type **327** (Bridge Olympiad, Valkenburg)	70	20
1341	60c.+25c. Sportswoman in wheelchair (Olympics for the Disabled, Arnhem and Veenendaal)	95	45

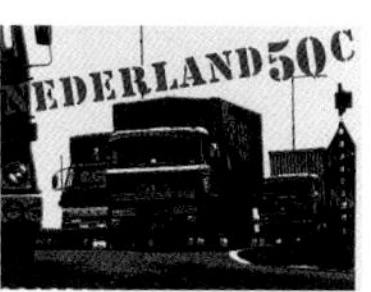

328 Road Haulage

1980. Transport.

1342	**328**	50c. multicoloured	60	25
1343	-	60c. blue, brown & black	70	25
1344	-	80c. multicoloured	95	35

DESIGNS: 60c. Rail transport; 80c. Motorized canal barge.

329 Queen Wilhelmina

1980. Europa.

1345	**329**	60c. black, red and blue	80	10
1346	-	80c. black, red and blue	1·00	35

DESIGN: 80c. Sir Winston Churchill.

330 Abraham Kuyper (first rector) and University Seal

1980. Centenary of Amsterdam Free University.

1347	**330**	50c. multicoloured	60	20

331 "Pop-up" Book

1980. Child Welfare. Multicoloured.

1348	45c.+20c. Type **331**	60	35
1349	50c.+20c. Child flying on a book (vert)	1·30	45
1350	60c.+30c. Boy reading "Kikkerkoning" (vert)	80	35
1351	80c.+30c. Dreaming in a book	1·50	95
MS1352	144×75 mm. Nos. 1348 ×2 and 1350 ×3	5·00	2·75

332 Saltmarsh

1981. Cultural, Health and Social Welfare Funds. Multicoloured.

1353	45c.+20c. Type **332**	70	35
1354	55c.+25c. Dyke	80	35
1355	60c.+25c. Drain	95	35
1356	65c.+30c. Cultivated land	1·00	35

333 Parcel (Parcel Post)

1981. P.T.T. Centenaries. Multicoloured.

1357	45c. Type **333**	60	15
1358	55c. Telephone, dish aerial and telephone directory page (public telephone service)	70	15
1359	65c. Savings bank books, deposit transfer card and savings bank stamps (National Savings Bank)	80	15
MS1360	145×75 mm. Nos. 1357/9	1·70	1·40

334 Huis ten Bosch Royal Palace, The Hague

1981

1361	**334**	55c. multicoloured	70	35

335 Carillon

1981. Europa. Multicoloured.

1362	45c. Type **335**	70	25
1363	65c. Barrel organ	1·00	25

336 Council of State Emblem and Maps of 1531 and 1981

1981. 450th Anniv of Council of State.

1364	**336**	65c. orange, deep orange and red	80	10

337 Marshalling Yard, Excavator and Ship's Screw

1981. Industrial and Agricultural Exports. Mult.

1365	45c. Type **337**	60	25
1366	55c. Inner port, cast-iron component and weighing machine	70	25
1367	60c. Airport, tomato and lettuce	80	45
1368	65c. Motorway interchange, egg and cheese	95	25

338 "Integration in Society"

1981. Child Welfare. Integration of Handicapped Children. Multicoloured.

1369	45c.+25c. Type **338**	60	25
1370	55c.+20c. "Integration in the Family" (vert)	70	60
1371	60c.+25c. Child vaccinated against polio (Upper Volta project) (vert)	80	60
1372	65c.+30c. "Integration among Friends"	95	25
MS1373	144×76 mm. Nos. 1369 ×3 and 1372 ×2	4·00	2·30

339 Queen Beatrix

1981

1374	**339**	65c. brown and black	80	10
1375	**339**	70c. lilac and black	1·00	10
1376	**339**	75c. pink and black	1·00	10
1377	**339**	90c. green and black	1·00	10
1378	**339**	1g. lilac and black	1·70	20
1379	**339**	1g.20 bistre and black	1·70	25
1380	**339**	1g.40 green and black	1·70	35

1381	**339**	1g.50 lilac and black	1·60	35
1382	**339**	2g. bistre and black	2·10	15
1383	**339**	2g.50 orange and black	2·75	35
1384	**339**	3g. blue and black	3·25	35
1385	**339**	4g. green and black	4·25	35
1386	**339**	5g. blue and black	5·25	35
1387	**339**	6g.50 lilac and black	7·00	45
1388	**339**	7g. blue and black	8·25	60
1389	**339**	7g.50 green and black	11·50	3·00

For this design but on uncoloured background see Nos. 1594/1605.

340 Agnieten Chapel and Banners

1982. 350th Anniv of University of Amsterdam.

1395	**340**	65c. multicoloured	70	10

341 Skater

1982. Centenary of Royal Dutch Skating Association.

1396	**341**	45c. multicoloured	60	25

342 Apple Blossom

1982. Cultural, Health and Social Welfare Funds. Multicoloured.

1397	50c.+20c. Type **342**	1·20	45
1398	60c.+25c. Anemones	1·20	45
1399	65c.+25c. Roses	1·20	45
1400	70c.+30c. African violets	1·20	70

343 Stripes in National Colours

1982. Bicentenary of Netherlands–United States Diplomatic Relations.

1401	**343**	50c. red, blue and black	60	25
1402	**343**	65c. red, blue and black	80	25

344 Sandwich Tern and Eider

1982. Waddenzee. Multicoloured.

1403	50c. Type **344**	70	25
1404	70c. Barnacle Geese	95	25

345 Zebra Crossing

1982. 50th Anniv of Dutch Road Safety Organization.

1405	**345**	60c. multicoloured	60	25

346 Ground Plan of Enkhuizen Fortifications

1982. Europa. Multicoloured.

1406	50c. Type **346**	70	25
1407	70c. Part of ground plan of Coevorden fortifications	95	25

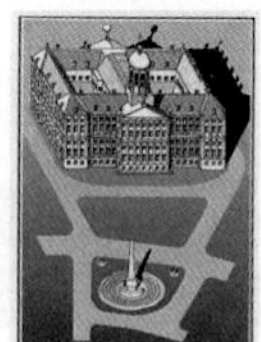

347 Aerial view of Palace and Liberation Monument

1982. Royal Palace, Dam Square, Amsterdam. Mult.

1408	50c. Facade, ground plan and cross-section of palace	60	25
1409	60c. Type **347**	70	25

348 Great Tits and Child

1982. Child Welfare. Child and Animal. Mult.

1410	50c.+30c. Type **348**	60	35
1411	60c.+20c. Child arm-in-arm with cat	80	35
1412	65c.+20c. Child with drawing of rabbit	1·30	95
1413	70c.+30c. Child with palm cockatoo	1·50	95
MS1414	75×144 mm. Nos. 1410 ×4 and 1411	4·00	2·50

349 Touring Club Activities

1983. Centenary of Royal Dutch Touring Club.

1415	**349**	70c. multicoloured	80	25

350 Johan van Oldenbarnevelt (statesman) (after J. Houbraken)

1983. Cultural, Health and Social Welfare Funds.

1416	**350**	50c.+20c. pink, blue and black	95	60
1417	-	60c.+25c. mult	95	60
1418	-	65c.+25c. mult	95	80
1419	-	70c.+30c. grey, black and gold	95	80

DESIGNS: 60c. Willem Jansz Blaeu (cartographer) (after Thomas de Keijser); 65c. Hugo de Groot (statesman) (after J. van Ravesteyn); 70c. "Saskia van Uylenburch" (portrait of his wife by Rembrandt).

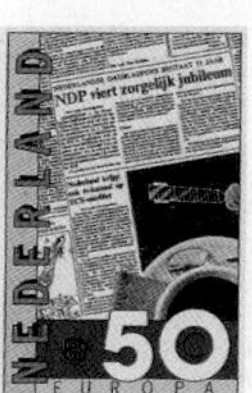

351 Newspaper

1983. Europa. Multicoloured.

1420	50c. Type **351** (75th anniv of Netherlands Newspaper Publishers Association)	60	25
1421	70c. European Communications Satellite and European Telecommunication Satellites Organization members' flags	80	25

352 "Composition 1922" (P. Mondriaan)

1983. De Stijl Art Movement. Multicoloured.

1422	50c. Type **352**	60	25
1423	65c. Contra construction from "Maison Particuliere" (C. van Eesteren and T. van Doesburg)	80	35

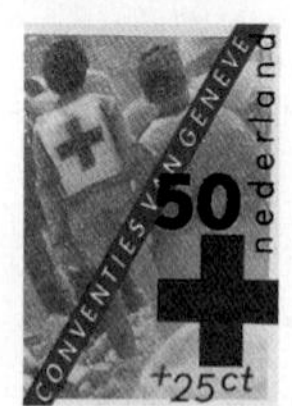

353 "Geneva Conventions"

1983. Red Cross.

1424	**353**	50c.+25c. mult	95	60
1425	-	60c.+20c. mult	95	70
1426	-	65c.+25c. mult	95	70
1427	-	70c.+30c. grey, black and red	95	70

DESIGNS: 60c. Red Cross and text "charity, independence, impartiality"; 65c. "Socio-medical work"; 70c. Red Cross and text "For Peace".

354 Luther's Signature

1983. 500th Birth Anniv of Martin Luther (Protestant Reformer).

1428	**354**	70c. multicoloured	80	10

355 Child looking at Donkey and Ox through Window

1983. Child Welfare. Child and Christmas. Mult.

1429	50c.+10c. Type **355**	1·20	70
1430	50c.+25c. Child riding flying snowman	70	35
1431	60c.+30c. Child in bed and star	1·30	95
1432	70c.+30c. Children dressed as the three kings	1·00	35
MS1433	144×75 mm. Nos. 1430 ×4 and 1432 ×2	5·00	4·50

356 Parliament

1984. Second Elections to European Parliament.

1434	**356**	70c. multicoloured	80	10

357 Northern Lapwings

1984. Cultural, Health and Social Welfare Funds. Pasture Birds. Multicoloured.

1435	50c.+20c. Type **357**	45	35
1436	60c.+25c. Ruffs	1·30	45
1437	65c.+25c. Redshanks (vert)	1·30	70
1438	70c.+30c. Black-tailed godwits (vert)	1·30	70

358 St. Servaas

1984. 1600th Death Anniv of St. Servaas (Bishop of Tongeren and Maastricht).

1439	**358**	60c. multicoloured	70	15

359 Bridge

1984. Europa. 25th Anniv of European Post and Telecommunications Conference.

1440	**359**	50c. deep blue and blue	60	25
1441	**359**	70c. green and light green	80	25

360 Eye and Magnifying Glass

1984. Centenary of Organized Philately in the Netherlands and "Filacento" International Stamp Exhibition, The Hague. Multicoloured.

1442	50c.+20c. Type **360**	1·00	80
1443	60c.+25c. 1909 cover	1·20	95
1444	70c.+30c. Stamp club meeting, 1949	1·30	1·20
MS1445	144×50 mm. Nos. 1442/4	4·25	3·25

361 William of Orange (after Adriaen Thomaszoon Key)

1984. 400th Death Anniv of William of Orange.

1446	**361**	70c. multicoloured	80	15

362 Giant Pandas and Globe

1984. World Wildlife Fund.

1447	**362**	70c. multicoloured	1·20	20

363 Graph and Leaf

1984. 11th International Small Business Congress, Amsterdam.

1448	**363**	60c. multicoloured	70	20

364 Violin Lesson

1984. Child Welfare. Strip Cartoons. Mult.

1449	50c.+25c. Type **364**	60	35
1450	60c.+20c. At the dentist	1·50	80
1451	65c.+20c. The plumber	1·60	1·00
1452	70c.+30c. The king and money chest	95	35
MS1453	75×144 mm. Nos. 1449 ×4 and 1452 ×2	4·75	4·00

365 Sunny, First Dutch Guide-Dog

1985. 50th Anniv of Royal Dutch Guide-Dog Fund.

1454	**365**	60c. black, ochre and red	70	20

366 Plates and Cutlery on Place-mat

1985. Tourism. Multicoloured.

1455	50c. Type **366** (centenary of Travel and Holidays Association)	60	20
1456	70c. Kroller-Muller museum emblem, antlers and landscape (50th anniv of De Hoge Veluwe National Park)	80	20

367 Saint Martin's Church, Zaltbommel

1985. Cultural, Health and Social Welfare Funds. Religious Buildings. Multicoloured.

1457a	50c.+20c. Type **367**	45	25
1458	60c.+25c. Winterswijk synagogue and Holy Ark (horiz)	1·40	80
1459	65c.+25c. Bolsward Baptist church	1·40	80
1460	70c.+30c. Saint John's Cathedral, 's-Hertogen-bosch (horiz)	1·40	60

368 Star of David, Illegal Newspapers and Rifle Practice (Resistance Movement)

1985. 40th Anniv of Liberation.

1461	**368**	50c. black, stone and red	60	25
1462	-	60c. black, stone and blue	70	25
1463	-	65c. black, stone & orge	80	60
1464	-	70c. black, stone & green	95	25

DESIGNS: 60c. Fighters over houses, "De Vliegende Hollander" (newspaper) and soldier (Allied Forces); 65c. Soldiers and civilians, "Parool" (newspaper) and American war cemetery, Margraten (Liberation); 70c. Women prisoners, prison money and Burma Railway (Dutch East Indies).

369 Piano Keyboard

1985. Europa. Music Year. Multicoloured.

1465	50c. Type **369**	60	25
1466	70c. Organ	80	35

370 National Museum, Amsterdam (centenary)

1985. Anniversaries and Events. Multicoloured.

1467	50c. Type **370**	60	25
1468	60c. Teacher with students (bicentenary of Amsterdam Nautical College)	60	25
1469	70c. Ship's mast and rigging ("Sail '85", Amsterdam)	80	25

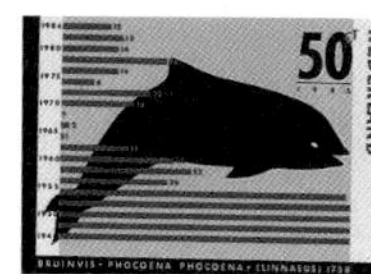

371 Porpoise and Graph

1985. Endangered Animals.

1470	**371**	50c. black, blue and red	70	35
1471	-	70c. black, blue and red	95	35

DESIGN: 70c. Seal and PCB molecule structure.

372 Ignition Key and Framed Photograph ("Think of Me")

1985. Child Welfare. Road Safety. Multicoloured.

1472	50c.+25c. Type **372**	60	35
1473	60c.+20c. Child holding target showing speeds	1·50	1·00
1474	65c.+20c. Girl holding red warning triangle	1·50	1·20
1475	70c.+30c. Boy holding "Children Crossing" sign	1·00	35
MS1476	132×80 mm. Nos. 1472 ×4 and 1475 ×2	5·00	4·25

373 Penal Code Extract

1986. Centenary of Penal Code.

1477	**373**	50c. black, yellow & purple	60	35

374 Surveyor with Pole and N.A.P. Water Gauge

1986. 300th Anniv of Height Gauging Marks at Amsterdam.

1478	**374**	60c. multicoloured	70	25

375 Windmill, Graph and Cloudy Sky

1986. Inaug of Windmill Test Station, Sexbierum.

1479	**375**	70c. multicoloured	80	10

376 Scales

1986. Cultural, Health and Social Welfare Funds. Antique Measuring Instruments. Multicoloured.

1480a	50c.+20c. Type **376**	45	35
1481	60c.+25c. Clock (vert)	1·30	45
1482	65c.+25c. Barometer (vert)	1·30	95
1483	70c.+30c. Jacob's staff	1·30	95

377 Het Loo Palace Garden, Apeldoorn

1986. Europa. Multicoloured.

1484	50c. Type **377**	60	35
1485	70c. Tree with discoloured crown	80	25

378 Cathedral

1986. Utrecht Events.

1486	**378**	50c. multicoloured	95	35
1487	-	60c. blue, pink and black	1·00	35
1488	-	70c. multicoloured	1·20	35

DESIGNS—VERT: 50c. Type **378** (completion of interior restoration); 60c. German House (75th anniv of Heemschut Conservation Society). HORIZ: 70c. Extract from foundation document (350th anniv of Utrecht University).

379 Drees at Binnenhof, 1947

1986. Birth Centenary of Dr. Willem Drees (politician).

1489	**379**	55c. multicoloured	60	20

380 Draughts as Biscuits in Saucer

1986. 75th Anniversary of Royal Dutch Draughts Association (1490) and Royal Dutch Billiards Association (1491). Multicoloured.

1490	75c. Type **380**	95	25
1491	75c. Player in ball preparing to play	95	35

381 Map of Flood Barrier

1986. Delta Project Completion. Multicoloured.

1492	65c. Type **381**	80	35
1493	75c. Flood barrier	95	25

382 Children listening to Music (experiencing)

1986. Child Welfare. Child and Culture.

1494	55c.+25c. Type **382**	1·50	95
1495	65c.+35c. Boy drawing (achieving)	1·30	45
1496	75c.+35c. Children at theatre (understanding)	1·30	35
MS1497	150×72 mm. Nos. 1494, 1495 ×2 and 1496 ×2	5·75	3·75

383 Engagement Picture

1987. Golden Wedding of Princess Juliana and Prince Bernhard.

1498	**383**	75c. orange, black and gold	1·00	20

384 Block of Flats and Hut

1987. International Year of Shelter for the Homeless (65c.) and Centenary of Netherlands Salvation Army (75c.). Multicoloured.

1499	65c. Type **384**	80	35
1500	75c. Army officer, meeting and tramp	95	25

385 Eduard Douwes Dekker (Multatuli) and De Harmonie Club

1987. Writers' Death Annivs. Multicoloured.

1501	55c. Type **385** (centenary)	80	25
1502	75c. Constantijn Huygens and Scheveningseweg, The Hague (300th anniv)	95	25

386 Steam Pumping Station, Nijerk

1987. Cultural Health and Social Welfare Funds. Industrial Buildings.

1503a	**386**	55c.+30c. red, grey and black	45	35
1504	-	65c.+35c. grey, black and blue	1·40	1·20
1505	-	75c.+35c. grey, yellow and black	1·50	95

DESIGNS: 65c. Water tower, Deventer; 75c. Brass foundry, Joure.

387 Dance Theatre, Scheveningen (Rem Koolhaas)

1987. Europa. Architecture. Multicoloured.

1506	55c. Type **387**	60	25
1507	75c. Montessori School, Amsterdam (Herman Hertzberger)	80	25

388 Auction at Broek op Langedijk

1987. Centenary of Auction Sales (55, 75c.) and 150th Anniv of Groningen Agricultural Society (65c.). Multicoloured.

1508	55c. Type **388**	60	25
1509	65c. Groningen landscape and founders' signatures	70	25
1510	75c. Auction sale and clock	80	25

389 Telephone Care Circles

1987. Dutch Red Cross. Multicoloured.

1511a		55c.+30c. Type **389**	45	35
1512		65c.+35c. Red cross and hands (Welfare work)	1·40	1·00
1513		75c.+35c. Red cross and drip (Blood transfusion)	1·50	70

390 Map of Holland

1987. 75th Anniv of Netherlands Municipalities Union.

1514	**390**	75c. multicoloured	95	20

391 Noordeinde Palace, The Hague

1987

1515	**391**	65c. multicoloured	80	10

392 Woodcutter

1987. Child Welfare. Child and Profession. Mult.

1516		55c.+25c. Type **392**	1·20	60
1517		65c.+35c. Woman sailor	1·20	45
1518		75c.+35c. Woman pilot	1·20	25
MS1519		150×72 mm. Nos. 1516, 1517 ×2 and 1518 ×2	5·75	4·25

393 Star

1987. Christmas.

1520	**393**	50c. red, blue and green	80	35
1521	**393**	50c. yellow, red and blue	80	35
1522	**393**	50c. red, blue and yellow	80	35
1523	**393**	50c. yellow, red and green	80	35
1524	**393**	50c. blue, green and red	80	35

The first colour described is that of the St. George's Cross.

394 "Narcissus cyclamineus" "Peeping Tom" and Extract from "I Call You Flowers" (Jan Hanlo)

1988. "Filacept" European Stamp Exhibition, The Hague (1st issue). Flowers. Multicoloured.

1525		55c.+55c. Type **394**	1·40	1·20
1526		75c.+70c. "Rosa gallica" "Versicolor" and "Roses" (Daan van Golden)	1·40	1·20
1527		75c.+70c. Sea holly and 1270 map of The Hague	1·40	1·20

See also No. **MS**1542.

395 Quagga

1988. Cultural, Health and Social Welfare Funds. 150th Anniv of Natura Artis Magistra Zoological Society. Multicoloured.

1528a		55c.+30c. Type **395**	45	35
1529		65c.+35c. American manatee	1·70	1·20
1530		75c.+35c. Orang-utan (vert)	1·70	95

396 Man's Shoulder

1988. 75th Anniv of Netherlands Cancer Institute.

1531	**396**	75c. multicoloured	95	20

397 Traffic Scene with Lead Symbol crossed Through

1988. Europa. Transport. Multicoloured.

1532		55c. Type **397** (lead-free petrol)	80	35
1533		75c. Cyclists reflected in car wing mirror (horiz)	1·00	25

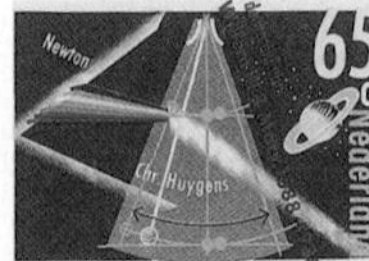

398 Pendulum, Prism and Saturn

1988. 300th Anniv of England's Glorious Revolution. Multicoloured.

1534		65c. Type **398**	85	25
1535		75c. Queen Mary, King William III and 17th-century warship	95	25

399 "Cobra Cat" (Appel)

1988. 40th Anniv of Founding of Cobra Painters Group. Multicoloured.

1536		55c. Type **399**	1·30	95
1537		65c. "Kite" (Corneille)	1·30	95
1538		75c. "Stumbling Horse" (Constant)	1·30	50

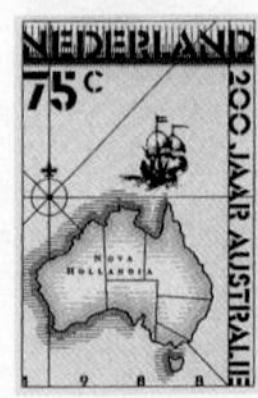

400 Sailing Ship and Map of Australia

1988. Bicentenary of Australian Settlement.

1539	**400**	75c. multicoloured	1·10	20

401 Statue of Erasmus, Rotterdam

1988. 75th Anniv of Erasmus University, Rotterdam (1540) and Centenary of Concertgebouw Concert Hall and Orchestra (1541).

1540	**401**	75c. deep green and green	1·10	20
1541	-	75c. violet	1·10	20

DESIGN: No. 1541, Violin and Concertgebouw concert hall.

1988. "Filacept" European Stamp Exhibition, The Hague (2nd issue). Flowers. Sheet 144×62 mm.

MS1542		Nos. 1525/7	5·00	4·75

402 "Rain"

1988. Child Welfare. Centenary of Royal Netherlands Swimming Federation. Children's drawings. Multicoloured.

1543		55c.+25c. Type **402**	1·60	85
1544		65c.+35c. "Getting Ready for the Race"	1·30	70
1545		75c.+35c. "Swimming Test"	1·30	35
MS1546		150×72 mm. Nos. 1543, 1544 ×2 and 1545 ×2	7·50	5·50

403 Stars

1988. Christmas.

1547	**403**	50c. multicoloured	60	10

404 Postal and Telecommunications Services

1989. Privatization of Netherlands PTT.

1548	**404**	75c. multicoloured	1·10	25

405 "Solidarity"

1989. Trade Unions. Multicoloured.

1549		55c. Type **405**	70	35
1550		75c. Talking mouths on hands	95	20

406 Members' Flags

1989. 40th Anniv of NATO.

1551	**406**	75c. multicoloured	95	25

407 Boier

1989. Cultural, Health and Social Welfare Funds. Old Sailing Vessels.

1552a	**407**	55c.+30c. green & blk	1·20	85
1553	-	65c.+35c. blue & black	1·70	1·10
1554	-	75c.+35c. brown & blk	1·70	1·10

DESIGNS: 65c. Fishing smack; 75c. Clipper.

408 Boy with Homemade Telephone

1989. Europa. Children's Games. Multicoloured.

1555		55c. Type **408**	60	20
1556		75c. Girl with homemade telephone	85	20

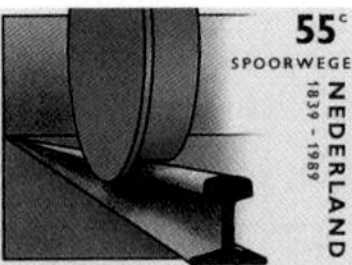

409 Wheel on Rail

1989. 150th Anniv of Netherlands' Railways. Mult.

1557		55c. Type **409**	70	25
1558		65c. Steam, electric and diesel locomotives	85	25
1559		75c. Diesel train, station clock and "The Kiss" (sculpture by Rodin)	1·10	25

410 Boy with Ball and Diagram of Goal Scored in European Championship

1989. Centenary of Royal Dutch Football Assn.

1560	**410**	75c. multicoloured	85	20

411 Map

1989. 150th Anniv of Division of Limburg between Netherlands and Belgium.

1561	**411**	75c. multicoloured	85	20

412 Right to Housing

1989. Child Welfare. 30th Anniv of Declaration of Rights of the Child. Multicoloured.

1562		55c.+25c. Type **412**	1·20	95
1563		65c.+35c. Right to food	1·20	60
1564		75c.+35c. Right to education	1·20	50
MS1565		150×72 mm. Nos. 1562, 1563 ×2 and 1564 ×2	6·00	4·75

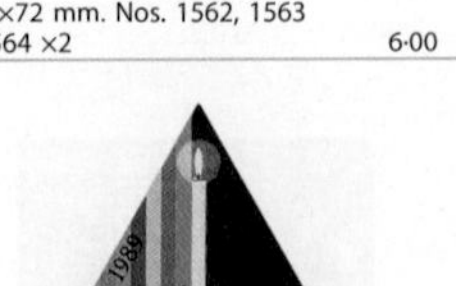

413 Candle

1989. Christmas.

1566	**413**	50c. multicoloured	60	10

414 "Arms of Leiden" (tulip) and Plan of Gardens in 1601

1990. 400th Anniv of Hortus Botanicus (botanical gardens), Leiden.

1567	**414**	65c. multicoloured	85	25

415 Pointer on Graduated Scale

1990. Centenary of Labour Inspectorate.
1568 **415** 75c. multicoloured 95 25

416 "Self-portrait" (detail)

1990. Death Centenary of Vincent van Gogh (painter). Multicoloured.
1569 55c. Type **416** 85 20
1570 75c. "Green Vineyard" (detail) 1·10 20

417 Summer's Day

1990. Cultural, Health and Social Welfare Funds. The Weather. Multicoloured.
1571a 55c.+30c. Type **417** 1·20 85
1572 65c.+35c. Clouds and isobars (vert) 1·70 1·10
1573a 75c.+35c. Satellite weather picture (vert) 1·20 85

418 Zuiderkerk Ruins

1990. 50th Anniv of German Bombing of Rotterdam.
1574 **418** 55c. deep brown, brown and black 70 25
1575 - 65c. multicoloured 85 25
1576 - 75c. multicoloured 95 25
DESIGNS: 65c. City plan as stage; 75c. Girder and plans for future construction.

419 Postal Headquarters, Groningen, and Veere Post Office

1990. Europa. Post Office Buildings.
1577 55c. grey, mauve & brn 70 25
1578 **419** 75c. blue, green and grey 95 25
DESIGN: 55c. As Type **419** but inscr "Postkantoor Veere".

420 Construction of Indiaman and Wreck of "Amsterdam"

1990. 3rd Anniv of Dutch East India Company Ships Association (replica ship project) (1579) and "Sail 90", Amsterdam (1580). Multicoloured.
1579 65c. Type **420** 85 25
1580 75c. Crew manning yards on sailing ship 95 25

421 Queens Emma, Wilhelmina, Juliana and Beatrix

1990. Netherlands Queens of the House of Orange.
1581 **421** 150c. multicoloured 2·20 1·10

422 Flames, Telephone Handset and Number

1990. Introduction of National Emergency Number.
1582 **422** 65c. multicoloured 85 25

423 Girl riding Horse

1990. Child Welfare. Hobbies. Multicoloured.
1583 55c.+25c. Type **423** 1·60 85
1584 65c.+35c. Girl at computer 1·30 60
1585 75c.+35c. Young philatelist 1·40 35
MS1586 150×71 mm. Nos. 1583, 1584 ×2 and 1585 ×2 7·75 5·50

424 Falling Snow

1990. Christmas.
1587 **424** 50c. multicoloured 60 10

425 Industrial Chimneys, Exhaust Pipes and Aerosol Can (Air Pollution)

1991. Environmental Protection. Multicoloured.
1588 55c. Type **425** 70 25
1589 65c. Outfall pipes and chemicals (sea pollution) 85 25
1590 75c. Agricultural chemicals, leaking drums and household landfill waste (soil pollution) 95 25

426 German Raid on Amsterdam Jewish Quarter and Open Hand

1991. 50th Anniv of Amsterdam General Strike.
1591 **426** 75c. multicoloured 95 25

427 Princess Beatrix and Prince Claus on Wedding Day

1991. Royal Silver Wedding Anniversary. Mult.
1592 75c. Type **427** 1·10 35
1593 75c. Queen Beatrix and Prince Claus on horseback 1·10 35

428 Queen Beatrix

1991. (a) Ordinary gum.
1594 **428** 75c. deep green & green 1·20 25
1595 **428** 80c. brown & lt brown 1·20 10
1597 **428** 90c. blue 2·40 1·80
1598 **428** 1g. violet 2·40 60
1599 **428** 1g.10 blue 3·50 3·50
1600 **428** 1g.30 blue and violet 1·80 35
1601 **428** 1g.40 green and olive 1·80 35
1601a **428** 1g.50 green 3·50 2·40
1602 **428** 1g.60 purple and mauve 2·40 25
1603 **428** 2g. brown 3·50 60
1603a **428** 2g.50 purple 4·75 2·40
1604 **428** 3g. blue 3·50 1·80
1605 **428** 5g. red 6·00 1·80
1706 **428** 7g.50 violet 14·50 6·00
1708 **428** 10g. green 7·25 1·20

(b) Self-adhesive gum.
1606 1g. violet 1·80 1·20
1607 1g.10 blue 2·10 2·10
1608 1g.45 green 2·20 2·20
1609 2g.50 purple 4·25 3·50
1609a 5g. red 8·50 6·75

429 "Meadow" Farm, Wartena, Friesland

1991. Cultural, Health and Social Welfare Funds. Traditional Farmhouses. Multicoloured.
1611 65c.+35c. "T-house" farm, Kesteren, Gelderland 1·60 1·10
1613 55c.+30c. Type **429** 85 35
1614 75c.+35c. "Courtyard" farm, Nuth, Limburg 85 35

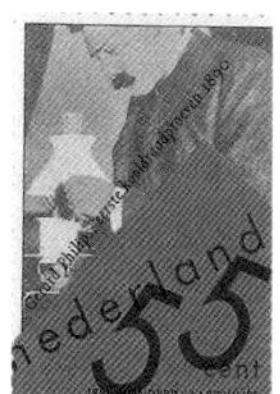

430 Gerard Philips's Experiments with Carbon Filaments

1991. 75th Anniv of Netherlands Standards Institute (65c.) and Centenary of Philips Organization (others). Multicoloured.
1615 55c. Type **430** 70 50
1616 65c. Wiring to Standard NEN 1010 (horiz) 85 20
1617 75c. Laser beams reading video disc 95 20

431 Man raising Hat to Space

1991. Europa. Europe in Space. Multicoloured.
1618 55c. Type **431** 85 35
1619 75c. Ladders stretching into space 1·10 25

432 Sticking Plaster over Medal

1991. 75th Anniv of Nijmegen International Four Day Marches.
1620 **432** 80c. multicoloured 95 20

433 Jacobus Hendericus van't Hoff

1991. Dutch Nobel Prize Winners (1st series). Multicoloured.
1621 60c. Type **433** (chemistry, 1901) 70 25
1622 70c. Pieter Zeeman (physics, 1902) 85 25
1623 80c. Tobias Michael Carel Asser (peace, 1911) 95 25
See also Nos. 1690/2 and 1773/5.

434 Children and Open Book

1991. Centenary (1992) of Public Libraries in the Netherlands.
1624 **434** 70c. drab, black & mauve 95 25
1625 - 80c. multicoloured 1·10 25
DESIGN: 80c. Books on shelf.

435 Girls with Doll and Robot

1991. Child Welfare. Outdoor Play. Multicoloured.
1626 60c.+30c. Type **435** 1·10 35
1627 70c.+35c. Bicycle race 1·80 1·30
1628 80c.+40c. Hide and seek 1·40 1·70
MS1629 144×75 mm. Nos. 1626 ×4 and 1638 ×2 8·50 6·75

436 "Greetings Cards keep People in Touch"

1991. Christmas.
1630 **436** 55c. multicoloured 60 10

437 Artificial Lightning, Microchip and Oscilloscope

1992. 150th Anniv of Delft University of Technology.
1631 **437** 60c. multicoloured 85 25

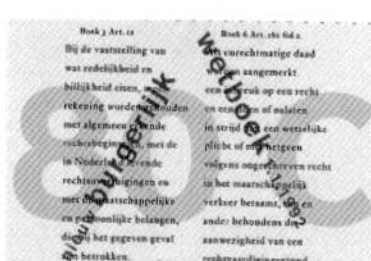

438 Extract from Code

1992. Implementation of Property Provisions of New Civil Code.
1632 **438** 80c. multicoloured 1·10 25

439 Volleyball

1992. Winter Olympic Games, Albertville and Summer Games, Barcelona. Sheet 125×72 mm containing T 439 and similar vert designs. Multicoloured.
MS1633 80c. Type **439**; 80c. Putting the shot and rowing; 80c. Speed skating and rowing; 80c. Hockey 4·75 4·00

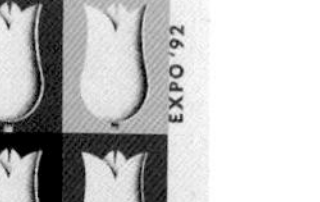

440 Tulips ("Mondrian does not like Green")

1992. "Expo '92" World's Fair, Seville. Mult.
1634 70c. Type **440** 95 25
1635 80c. "Netherland Expo '92" 1·10 25

441 Tasman's Map of Staete Landt (New Zealand)

1992. 350th Anniv of Discovery of Tasmania and New Zealand by Abel Tasman.
1636 **441** 70c. multicoloured 95 25

442 Yellow and Purple Flowers

1992. Cultural, Health and Social Welfare Funds. "Floriade" Flower Show, Zoetermeer. Mult.
1639 80c.+40c. Type **442** 1·40 1·20
1640 60c.+30c. Water lilies 85 50
1641 70c.+35c. Orange and purple flowers 95 85

443 Geometric Planes

1992. 150th Anniv of Royal Association of Netherlands Architects (60c.) and Inauguration of New States General Lower House (80c.). Mult.
1643 60c. Type **443** 85 35
1644 80c. Atrium and blue sky (symbolizing sending of information into society) 95 35

444 Globe and Columbus

1992. Europa. 500th Anniv of Discovery of America by Columbus.
1645 **444** 60c. multicoloured 85 35
1646 - 80c. black, mauve & yellow 1·20 35
DESIGN—VERT: 80c. Galleon.

445 Moneta (Goddess of Money)

1992. Centenary of Royal Netherlands Numismatics Society.
1647 **445** 70c. multicoloured 95 25

446 Teddy Bear wearing Stethoscope

1992. Centenary of Netherlands Paediatrics Society.
1648 **446** 80c. multicoloured 1·20 25

447 List of Relatives and Friends

1992. 50th Anniv of Departure of First Deportation Train from Westerbork Concentration Camp.
1649 **447** 70c. multicoloured 95 25

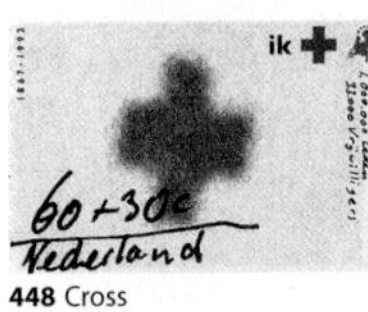

448 Cross

1992. 125th Anniv of Netherlands Red Cross. Multicoloured.
1652 80c.+40c. Red cross on dirty bandage 1·40 1·20
1653 60c.+30c. Type **448** 85 50
1654 70c.+35c. Supporting injured person 95 85

449 "United Europe" and European Community Flag

1992. European Single Market.
1656 **449** 80c. multicoloured 95 25

450 Queen Beatrix on Official Birthday, 1992, and at Investiture

1992. 12½ Years since Accession to the Throne of Queen Beatrix.
1657 **450** 80c. multicoloured 95 25

451 Saxophone Player

1992. Child Welfare. Child and Music. Mult.
1658 60c.+30c. Type **451** 1·10 50
1659 70c.+35c. Piano player 1·30 70
1660 80c.+40c. Double bass player 1·80 1·10
MS1661 104×75 mm. Nos. 1658 ×3, 1659 ×2 and 1660 7·75 6·00

452 Poinsettia

1992. Christmas.
1662 **452** 55c. multicoloured (centre of flower silver) 70 10
1663 **452** 55c. multicoloured (centre red) 70 10

453 Cycling

1993. Centenary of Netherlands Cycle and Motor Industry Association.
1664 **453** 70c. multicoloured 1·10 25
1665 - 80c. brown, grey & yell 1·20 25
DESIGN: 80c. Car.

454 Collages

1993. Greetings Stamps. Multicoloured.
1666 70c. Type **454** 85 25
1667 70c. Collages (different) 85 25

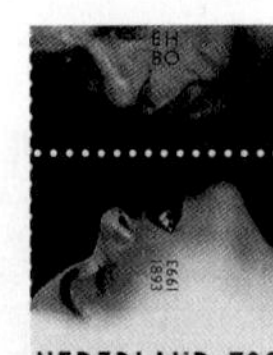

455 Mouth to Mouth Resuscitation

1993. Anniversaries. Multicoloured.
1668 70c. Type **455** (centenary of Royal Netherlands First Aid Association) 95 25
1669 80c. Pests on leaf (75th anniv of Wageningen University of Agriculture) 95 25
1670 80c. Lead driver and horses (bicentenary of Royal Horse Artillery) 95 25

456 Emblems

1993. 150th Anniv of Royal Dutch Notaries Association. Each red and violet.
1671 80c. Type **456** ("150 Jaar" reading up) 1·20 25
1672 80c. As Type **456** but emblems inverted and "150 Jaar" reading down 1·20 25
Nos. 1671/2 were issued together in horizontal tete-beche pairs, each pair forming a composite design.

457 Large White

1993. Butterflies. Multicoloured.
1673 70c. Pearl-bordered fritillary 1·20 60
1674 80c. Large tortoiseshell 1·20 35
1675 90c. Type **457** 1·20 1·20
MS1676 104×71 mm. 160c. Common blue 3·50 3·25

458 Elderly Couple

1993. Cultural, Health and Social Welfare Funds. Senior Citizens' Independence.
1677 70c.+35c. Type **458** 1·40 1·30
1681 70c.+35c. Elderly man 1·10 85
1682 80c.+40c. Elderly woman with dog 95 70

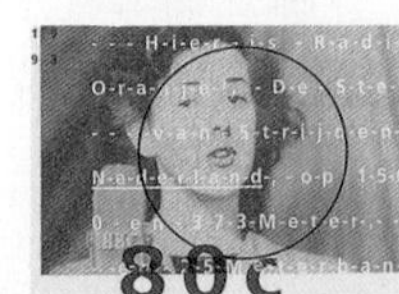

459 Broadcaster

1993. Radio Orange (Dutch broadcasts from London during Second World War). Mult.
1683 80c. Type **459** 1·20 25
1684 80c. Man listening to radio in secret 1·20 25

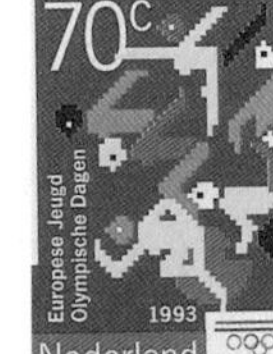

460 Sports Pictograms

1993. 2nd European Youth Olympic Days. Mult.
1685 70c. Type **460** 85 25
1686 80c. Sports pictograms (different) 95 25

461 "The Embodiment of Unity" (Wessel Couzijn)

1993. Europa. Contemporary Art. Multicoloured.
1687 70c. Type **461** 1·20 50
1688 80c. Architectonic sculpture (Per Kirkeby) 1·20 35
1689 160c. Sculpture (Naum Gabo) (vert) 2·40 2·20

462 Johannes Diderik van der Waals (Physics, 1910)

1993. Dutch Nobel Prize Winners (2nd series).
1690 **462** 70c. blue, black and red 85 50
1691 - 80c. mauve, black & red 95 35
1692 - 90c. multicoloured 1·10 1·40
DESIGNS: 80c. Willem Einthoven (medicine, 1924); 90c. Christiaan Eijkman (medicine, 1929).

463 Pen and Pencils

1993. Letter Writing Campaign. Multicoloured.
1693 80c. Type **463** 95 25
1694 80c. Envelope 95 25

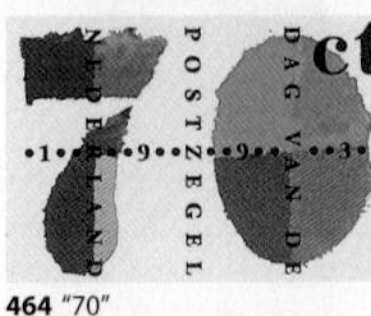

464 "70"

1993. Stamp Day (70c.) and Netherlands PTT (80c.). Multicoloured.
1695 70c. Type **464** 85 25
1696 80c. Dish aerial and dove carrying letter 95 25

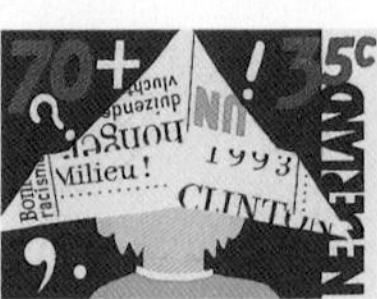

465 Child in Newspaper Hat

1993. Child Welfare. Child and the Media. Mult.
1697 70c.+35c. Type **465** 1·20 60
1698 70c.+35c. Elephant using headphones 1·20 60
1699 80c.+40c. Television 1·20 60
MS1700 143×75 mm. Nos. 1697/99, each ×2 7·75 6·75

466 Candle

1993. Christmas. Multicoloured.
1711 55c. Type **466** 60 25
1712 55c. Fireworks 60 25
Both designs have a number of punched holes.

467 "Composition"

1994. 50th Death Anniv of Piet Mondriaan (artist). Multicoloured.
1713 70c. "The Red Mill" (detail) 95 50
1714 80c. Type **467** 1·10 35
1715 90c. "Broadway Boogie Woogie" (detail) 1·20 1·20

468 Barnacle Goose

1994. "Fepapost 94" European Stamp Exhibition, The Hague. Multicoloured.
1716 70c.+60c. Type **468** 1·80 1·40
1717 80c.+70c. Bluethroat 1·80 1·40
1718 90c.+80c. Garganey 1·80 1·40

469 Downy Rose

1994. Wild Flowers. Multicoloured.
1719 70c. Type **469** 95 50
1720 80c. Daisies 1·10 35
1721 90c. Wood forgetmenot 1·20 1·40
MS1722 71×50 mm. 160c. Orange lily 3·50 3·50

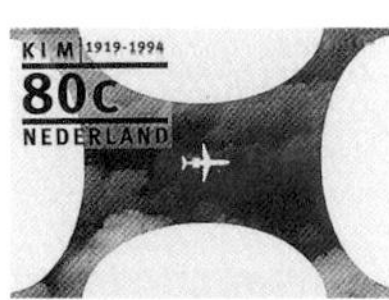

470 Fokker F.28 Airliner

1994. 75th Aircraft Industry Anniversaries.
1723 **470** 80c. blue and black 1·10 25
1724 - 80c. grey, red and black 1·10 25
1725 - 80c. multicoloured 1·10 25
DESIGNS: No. 1723, Type **470** (KLM (Royal Dutch Airlines)); 1724, Plan and outline of aircraft and clouds (Royal Netherlands Fokker Aircraft Industries); 1725, Airplane and clouds (National Aerospace Laboratory).

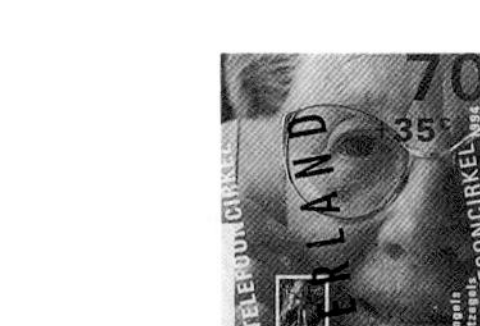

471 Woman using Telephone

1994. Cultural, Health and Social Welfare Funds. Senior Citizens' Security. Multicoloured.
1727 80c.+40c. Man using telephone 1·10 85
1728 90c.+35c. Man using telephone (different) 1·40 1·40
1729 70c.+35c. Type **471** 95 85

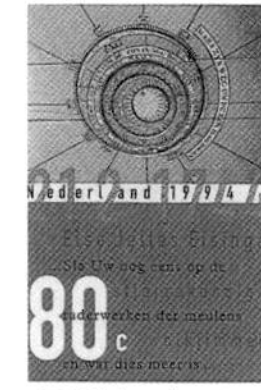

472 Eisinga's Planetarium

1994. Anniversaries. Multicoloured.
1732 80c. Type **472** (250th birth anniv of Eise Eisinga) 95 25
1733 90c. Astronaut and boot print on Moon surface (25th anniv of first manned Moon landing) 1·20 95

473 Players Celebrating

1994. World Cup Football Championship, U.S.A.
1734 **473** 80c. multicoloured 1·20 70

474 Stock Exchange

1994. Quotation of Netherlands PTT (KPN) on Stock Exchange.
1735 **474** 80c. multicoloured 1·10 25

475 Road Sign, Car and Bicycle

1994. Anniversaries and Events. Multicoloured.
1736 70c. Type **475** (centenary of provision of road signs by Netherlands Motoring Association) 1·10 25
1737 80c. Equestrian sports (World Equestrian Games, The Hague) 1·20 25

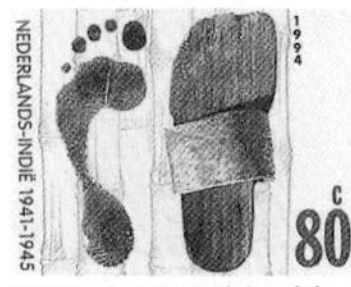

476 Footprint and Sandal

1994. Second World War. Multicoloured.
1738 80c. Type **476** (war in Netherlands Indies, 1941–45) 95 25
1739 90c. Soldier, children and Douglas C-47 dropping paratroops (50th anniv of Operation Market Garden (Battle of Arnhem)) (vert) 1·20 1·20

477 Brandaris Lighthouse, Terschelling

1994. Lighthouses. Multicoloured.
1740 70c. Type **477** 1·70 60
1741 80c. Ameland (vert) 1·70 25
1742 90c. Vlieland (vert) 1·70 1·40

1994. "Fepapost '94" European Stamp Exhibition, The Hague (2nd issue). Sheet 144×62 mm.
MS1743 Nos. 1716/18 plus 3 labels 7·25 6·00

478 Decorating

1994. Child Welfare. "Together". Multicoloured.
1744 70c.+35c. Type **478** 1·20 60
1745 80c.+40c. Girl on swing knocking fruit off tree (vert) 1·20 60
1746 90c.+35c. Girl helping boy onto playhouse roof (vert) 1·20 1·80
MS1747 144×75 mm. No. 1744×2, 1745×3 and 1746 8·25 7·25

479 Star and Christmas Tree

1994. Christmas. Multicoloured.
1748 55c. Type **479** 60 10
1749 55c. Candle and star 60 10

480 Flying Cow

1995
1750 **480** 100c. multicoloured 2·20 35

481 "Prayer" (detail)

1995. Anniversary and Events.
1751 **481** 80c. multicoloured 1·20 50
1752 - 80c. multicoloured 1·20 50
1753 - 80c. black and red 1·20 50
DESIGNS—VERT: No. 1751, Type **481** (50th death anniv of Hendrik Werkman (graphic designer); 1752, "Mesdag Panorama" (detail) (re-opening of Mesdag Museum). HORIZ: No. 1753, Mauritius 1847 2d. "POST OFFICE" stamp (purchase of remaining mint example in private hands by PTT Museum).

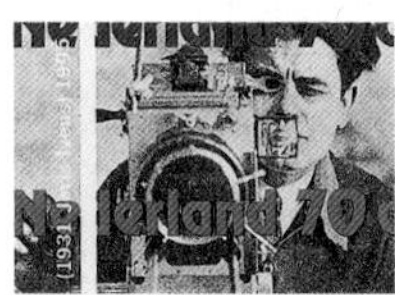
482 Joriz Ivens (documentary maker)

1995. Year of the Film (centenary of motion pictures). Multicoloured.
1754 70c. Type **482** 1·10 25
1755 80c. Scene from "Turkish Delight" 1·20 25

483 Mahler and Score of 7th Symphony

1995. Mahler Festival, Amsterdam.
1756 **483** 80c. black and blue 1·10 25

484 Dates and Acronym

1995. Centenaries. Multicoloured.
1757 80c. Type **484** (Netherlands Institute of Chartered Accountants) 1·30 40
1758 80c. Builders, bricklayer's trowel and saw (Netherlands Association of Building Contractors) 1·30 40

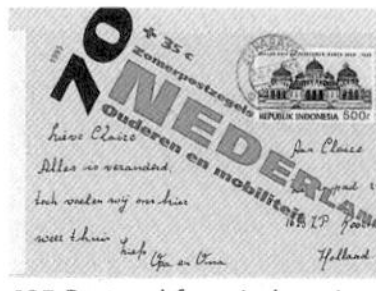

485 Postcard from Indonesia

1995. Cultural, Health and Social Welfare Funds. Mobility of the Elderly. Multicoloured.
1759 70c.+35c. Type **485** 1·50 1·90
1760 80c.+40c. Couple reflected in mirror 1·60 65
1761 100c.+45c. Couple with granddaughter at zoo 1·90 1·90
MS1762 144×75 mm. Nos. 1759 ×2, 1760 ×3 and 1761 10·50 9·00

486 "40 45"

1995. 50th Anniversaries. Multicoloured.
1763 80c. Type **486** (end of Second World War) 1·30 40
1764 80c. "45 95" (liberation) 1·30 40
1765 80c. "50" (U.N.O.) 1·30 40

487 Birthday Cake and Signs of the Zodiac

1995. Birthday Greetings.
1766 **487** 70c. multicoloured 1·30 40

488 Scout

1995. Events. Multicoloured.
1767 70c. Type **488** (World Scout Jamboree, Dronten) 1·30 50
1768 80c. Amsterdam harbour ("Sail '95" and finish of Tall Ships Race) (horiz) 1·30 40

489 Common Kestrel

1995. Birds of Prey. Multicoloured.
1769 70c. Type **489** 1·30 40
1770 80c. Face of hen harrier (horiz) 1·30 25
1771 100c. Red kite (horiz) 1·90 1·90
MS1772 72×50 mm. 160c. Honey buzzard 3·75 3·75

490 Petrus Debye (Chemistry, 1936)

1995. Dutch Nobel Prize Winners (3rd series). Multicoloured.
1773 80c. Type **490** 1·30 40

1774	80c. Frederik Zernike (Physics, 1953)	1·30	40
1775	80c. Jan Tinbergen (Economics, 1969)	1·30	40

491 Eduard Jacobs and Jean-Louis Pisuisse

1995. Centenary of Dutch Cabaret. Multicoloured.

1776	70c. Type **491**	90	40
1777	80c. Wim Kan and Freek de Jonge	1·00	40

492 "The Schoolteacher" (Leonie Ensing)

1995. Child Welfare. "Children and Fantasy". Children's Computer Drawings. Multicoloured.

1778	70c.+35c. "Dino" (Sjoerd Stegeman) (horiz)	1·30	65
1779	80c.+40c. Type **492**	1·30	65
1780	100c.+50c. "Children and Colours" (Marcel Jansen) (horiz)	2·50	1·90
MS1781	144×74 mm. Nos. 1778 ×2, 1779 ×3 and 1780	9·00	8·50

493 Children with Stars

1995. Christmas. Self-adhesive.

1782	**493**	55c. red, yellow and black	90	15
1783	-	55c. blue, yellow and black	90	15

DESIGN: No. 1783, Children looking at star through window.

494 "Woman in Blue reading a Letter"

1996. Johannes Vermeer Exhibition, Washington and The Hague. Details of his Paintings. Mult.

1784	70c. "Lady writing a Letter with her Maid"	1·50	65
1785	80c. "The Love Letter"	1·60	40
1786	100c. Type **494**	1·90	1·80
MS1787	144×75 mm. Nos. 1784/6	5·75	5·00

495 Trowel, Daffodil Bulb and Glove

1996. Spring Flowers. Multicoloured.

1788	70c. Type **495**	1·50	50
1789	80c. Tulips "kissing" woman	1·60	40
1790	100c. Snake's-head fritillary (detail of painting, Charles Mackintosh)	1·90	1·80
MS1791	72×50 mm. 160c. Crocuses	3·75	3·75

496 Putting up "MOVED" sign

1996. Change of Address Stamp.

1792	**496**	70c. multicoloured	90	50

For 80c. self-adhesive version of this design see No. 1826.

497 Swimming

1996. Cultural, Health and Social Welfare Funds. The Elderly in the Community. Multicoloured.

1793	70c.+35c. Type **497**	1·30	90
1794	80c.+40c. Grandad bottle-feeding baby	1·30	90
1795	100c.+50c. Playing piano	2·50	2·00
MS1796	144×75 mm. Nos. 1793 ×2, 1794 ×3 and 1795	10·00	10·00

498 Beside Car

1996. Heer Bommel (cartoon character). Sheet 108×50 mm containing T 498 and similar horiz design. Multicoloured.

MS1797	70c. Type **498**; 80c. Reading letter	3·75	3·75

499 Cycling

1996. Tourism. Multicoloured.

1798	70c. Type **499**	1·40	40
1799	70c. Paddling in sea	1·50	65
1800	80c. Traditional architecture, Amsterdam	1·50	40
1801	100c. Windmills, Zaanse Schand Open-Air Museum	1·50	65

500 Parade in Traditional Costumes

1996. Bicentenary of Province of North Brabant.

1802	**500**	80c. multicoloured	1·10	40

501 Lighting Olympic Torch

1996. Sporting Events. Multicoloured.

1803	70c. Type **501** (Olympic Games, Atlanta)	1·30	50
1804	80c. Flag and cyclists (Tour de France cycling championship)	1·30	40
1805	100c. Player, ball and Wembley Stadium (European Football Championship, England)	1·50	1·40
1806	160c. Olympic rings and athlete on starting block (Olympic Games, Atlanta)	2·30	1·50

502 Erasmus Bridge

1996. Bridges and Tunnels. Multicoloured.

1807	80c. Type **502**	1·30	40
1808	80c. Wijker Tunnel (horiz)	1·30	40
1809	80c. Martinus Nijhoff Bridge (horiz)	1·30	40

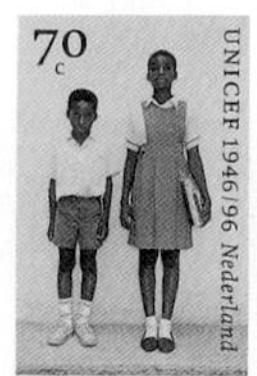

503 Children in School Uniforms

1996. 50th Anniv of UNICEF. Multicoloured.

1810	70c. Type **503**	1·10	25
1811	80c. Girl carrying platter on head	1·10	25

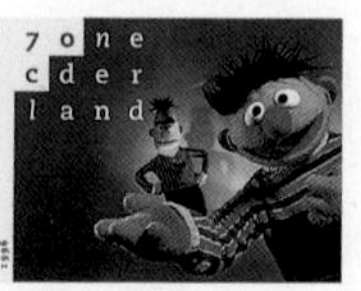

504 Bert and Ernie

1996. Sesame Street (children's television programme). Multicoloured.

1812	70c. Type **504**	1·10	40
1813	80c. Bears holding Big Bird's foot	1·00	40

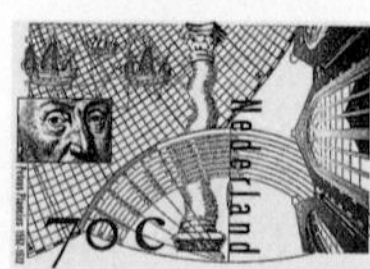

505 Petrus Plancius

1996. 16th-century Voyages of Discovery.

1814	**505**	70c. black, yellow and red	1·40	50
1815	-	80c. multicoloured	1·40	40
1816	-	80c. multicoloured	1·40	40
1817	-	100c. multicoloured	2·10	1·50

DESIGNS: No. 1815, Cornelis de Houtman; 1816, Willem Barentsz; 1817, Mahu en De Cordes.

506 Books and Baby

1996. Child Welfare. Multicoloured.

1818	70c.+35c. Type **506**	1·30	65
1819	80c.+40c. Animals and boy	1·30	65
1820	80c.+40c. Tools and girl	1·30	65
MS1821	75×144 mm. Nos. 1818/20, each ×2	8·25	8·25

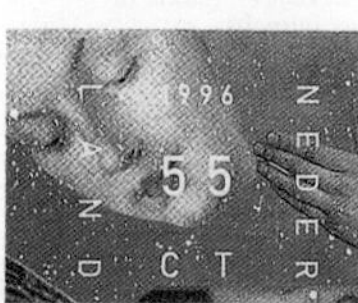

507 Woman's Face and Hand

1996. Christmas. Multicoloured. Self-adhesive.

1822	55c. Type **507**	65	25
1823	55c. Woman's eyes and man shouting	65	25
1824	55c. Bird's wing, hands and detail of man's face	65	25
1825	55c. Men's faces and bird's wing	65	25

Nos. 1822/5 were issued together, se-tenant, forming a composite design.

1997. Change of Address Stamp. Self-adhesive.

1826	**496**	80c. multicoloured	1·00	65

No. 1826 was intended for use by people moving house.

508 Numeral on Envelope with Top Flap

1997. Business Stamps. Multicoloured. Self-adhesive.

1827	80c. Type **508**	90	20
1828	160c. Numeral on envelope with side flap	1·80	20

509 Skaters

1997. 15th Eleven Cities Skating Race.

1829	**509**	80c. multicoloured	1·10	40

510 Heart

1997. Greetings Stamps.

1830	**510**	80c. multicoloured	90	65

The price quoted for No. 1830 is for an example with the heart intact. The heart can be scratched away to reveal different messages.

511 Pony

1997. Nature and the Environment. Multicoloured.

1831	80c. Type **511**	1·40	40
1832	100c. Cow	1·80	1·40
MS1833	72×50 mm. 160c. Sheep	3·75	3·75

512 Suske, Wiske, Lambik and Aunt Sidonia

1997. Suske and Wiske (cartoon by Willy Vandersteen). Multicoloured.

1834	80c. Type **512**	1·00	25
MS1835	108×50 mm. 80c. Wilbur; 80c. Type **512**	5·00	4·50

513 Rosebud

1997. Cultural, Health and Social Welfare Funds. The Elderly and their Image. Multicoloured.

1836	80c.+40c. Type **513**	1·50	1·50
1837	80c.+40c. Rose stem	1·50	1·50
1838	80c.+40c. Rose	1·50	1·50
MS1839	144×75 mm. Nos. 1836/8, each ×2	9·00	9·00

514 Birthday Cake

1997. Greetings Stamps. Multicoloured.

1840	80c. Type **514**	1·00	25
1841	80c. Cup of coffee, glasses of wine, candles, writing letter, and amaryllis	1·00	25

See also No. 1959.

515 "REKENKAMER ..." (550th anniv of Court of Audit)

1997. Anniversaries.
1842 **515** 80c. multicoloured 1·40 40
1843 - 80c. red, yellow and black 1·40 40
1844 - 80c. red, black and blue 1·40 40
DESIGNS—50th anniv of Marshall Plan (post-war American aid for Europe): No. 1843, Map of Europe; 1844, Star and stripes.

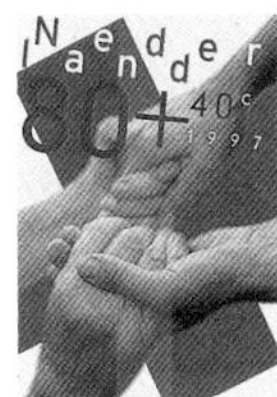
516 Clasped Hands over Red Cross

1997. Red Cross.
1845 **516** 80c.+40c. mult 1·70 1·40

517 "eu" and Globe

1997. European Council of Ministers' Summit, Amsterdam.
1846 **517** 100c. multicoloured 1·60 1·10

518 Children playing in Boat

1997. Water Activities. Multicoloured.
1847 80c. Type **518** 1·10 40
1848 1g. Skutsje (sailing barges) race, Friesland 1·50 1·00

519 "vernuft"

1997. Anniversaries. Multicoloured.
1849 **519** 80c. ultramarine and blue 1·30 45
1850 - 80c. ultramarine and blue 1·30 45
1851 - 80c. multicoloured 1·30 45
1852 - 80c. multicoloured 1·30 45
DESIGNS: No. 1849, Type **519** (150th anniv of Royal Institute of Engineers); 1850, "adem" (centenary of Netherlands Asthma Centre, Davos, Switzerland); 1851, Flower (centenary of Florens College (horticultural college) and 125th anniv of Royal Botanical and Horticultural Society); 1852, Pianist accompanying singer (birth bicentenary of Franz Schubert (composer)).

520 "Nederland80"

1997. Youth. Multicoloured.
1853 **520** 80c. red and blue 1·00 40
1854 - 80c. multicoloured 1·00 40
DESIGN: No. 1854, "NEDERLAND80" in style of computer games giving appearance of three-dimensional block on race track.

521 Stork with Bundle

1997. New Baby Stamp. Self-adhesive gum.
1855 **521** 80c. multicoloured 1·10 30
See also Nos. 1960, 2120 amd 2189.

522 "Little Red Riding Hood"

1997. Child Welfare. Fairy Tales. Multicoloured.
1856 80c.+40c. Type **522** 1·50 65
1857 80c.+40c. Man laying loaves on ground ("Tom Thumb") 1·50 65
1858 80c.+40c. Woodman with bottle ("Genie in the Bottle") 1·50 65
MS1859 144×75 mm. Nos. 1856/8, each ×2 9·25 9·00

523 Heads and Star

1997. Christmas. Multicoloured, colour of background given.
1860 **523** 55c. yellow 75 25
1861 **523** 55c. blue 75 25
1862 - 55c. orange 75 25
1863 - 55c. red 75 25
1864 - 55c. green 75 25
1865 **523** 55c. green 75 25
DESIGN: Nos. 1862/4, Heads and heart.

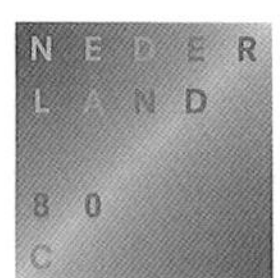

524 Light across Darkness

1998. Bereavement Stamp.
1866 **524** 80c. blue 1·10 25

525 Cow and "Ship" Tiles

1998. Delft Faience.
1867 **525** 100c. multicoloured 1·30 65
1868 - 160c. blue 2·00 1·30
DESIGN: 160c. Ceramic tile showing boy standing on head.

526 Strawberries in Bloom (Spring)

1998. The Four Seasons. Multicoloured.
1869 80c. Type **526** 1·30 1·30
1870 80c. Strawberry, flan and strawberry plants (Summer) 1·30 1·30
1871 80c. Bare trees and pruning diagram (Winter) 1·30 1·30
1872 80c. Orchard and apple (Autumn) 1·30 1·30

527 Handshake

1998. Anniversaries. Multicoloured.
1873 80c. Type **527** (350th anniv of Treaty of Munster) 1·00 45
1874 80c. Statue of Johan Thorbecke (politician) (150th anniv of Constitution) 1·00 45
1875 80c. Child on swing (50th anniv of Declaration of Human Rights) 1·00 45

528 Bride and Groom

1998. Wedding Stamp. Self-adhesive gum.
1876 **528** 80c. multicoloured 1·10 25
See also No. 1961.

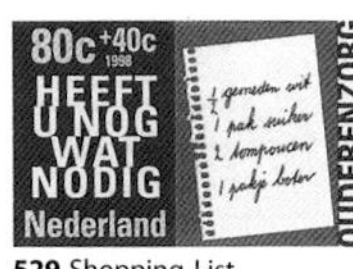

529 Shopping List

1998. Cultural, Health and Social Welfare Funds. Care and the Elderly.
1877 80c.+40c. Type **529** 1·50 1·40
1878 80c.+40c. Sweet 1·50 1·40
1879 80c.+40c. Training shoe 1·50 1·40
MS1880 144×75 mm. Nos. 1877/9, each ×2 9·00 9·00

530 Letters blowing in Wind

1998. Letters to the Future.
1881 **530** 80c. multicoloured 1·10 35

531 Customers

1998. Centenary of Rabobank.
1882 **531** 80c. yellow, green and blue 1·10 35

532 Goalkeeper catching Boot

1998. Sport. Multicoloured.
1883 80c. Type **532** (World Cup Football Championship, France) 1·10 35
1884 80c. Family hockey team (centenary of Royal Netherlands Hockey Federation) (35×24 mm) 1·10 35

533 Map of Friesland, c. 1600

1998. 500th Anniv of Central Administration of Friesland.
1885 **533** 80c. multicoloured 1·10 35

534 River Defences

1998. Bicentenary of Directorate-General of Public Works and Water Management. Multicoloured.
1886 80c. Type **534** 1·00 35
1887 1g. Sea defences 1·30 95

535 "tnt post groep"

1998. Separation of Royal Netherlands PTT into TNT Post Groep and KPN NV (telecommunications).
1888 **535** 80c. black, blue and red 1·00 55
1889 - 80c. black, blue and green 1·00 55
DESIGN: No. 1889, "kpn nv".
Nos. 1888/9 were issued together, se-tenant, forming a composite design of the complete "160".

536 Books and Keyboard

1998. Cultural Anniversaries. Multicoloured.
1890 80c. Type **536** (bicentenary of National Library) 1·10 40
1891 80c. Maurits Escher (graphic artist, birth centenary) looking at his mural "Metamorphose" in The Hague Post Office (vert) 1·10 50
1892 80c. Simon Vestdijk (writer, birth centenary) and page from "Fantoches" (vert) 1·10 50

537 Queen Wilhelmina

1998. Royal Centenaries. Sheet 144×75 mm containing T 537 and similar vert design. Multicoloured.
MS1893 80c. Type **537** (coronation); 80c. Gilded Coach 4·50 3·75

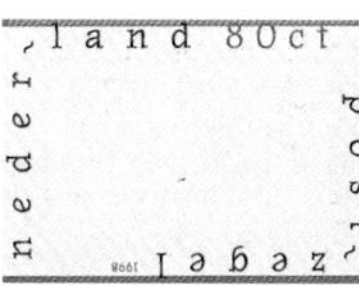

538 "land 80 ct"

1998. Greetings Stamps. Multicoloured. Self-adhesive.
1894 80c. Type **538** (top of frame red) 1·30 65
1895 80c. "80 ct post" (top of frame mauve) 1·30 65
1896 80c. Type **538** (top of frame orange) 1·30 65
1897 80c. "80 ct post" (top of frame orange) 1·30 65
1898 80c. Type **538** (top of frame yellow) 1·30 65
The part of the frame used for identification purposes is above the face value.
Nos. 1894/8 were only available in sheetlets of ten stamps and 20 labels (five stamps and ten labels on each side of the card). It was intended that the sender should insert the appropriate greetings label into the rectangular space on each stamp before use.

539 Rabbits

1998. Domestic Pets. Multicoloured.
1899 80c. Type **539** 1·30 50
1900 80c. Drent partridge dog 1·30 50
1901 80c. Kittens 1·30 50

540 Cathy and Jeremy writing a Letter

1998. 25th Anniv of Jack, Jacky and the Juniors (comic strip characters).
1902 80c. Type **540** 1·10 40
MS1903 108×50 mm. 80c. Type **540**; 80c. Posting letter 4·50 3·75

541 St. Nicholas on Horseback

1998. Child Welfare. Celebrations. Multicoloured.

1904	80c.+40c. Type **541**	1·90	65
1905	80c.+40c. Making birthday cake	1·90	65
1906	80c.+40c. Carnival parade	1·90	65
MS1907	144×75 mm. Nos. 1904/6, each ×2	11·50	9·50

542 Hare and Snowball

1998. Christmas. Self-adhesive.

1908	**542**	55c. blue, red and black	75	40
1909	-	55c. multicoloured	75	40
1910	-	55c. blue, red and black	75	40
1911	-	55c. multicoloured	75	40
1912	-	55c. blue, red and black	75	40
1913	-	55c. green, blue and red	75	40
1914	-	55c. green, blue and red	75	40
1915	-	55c. green, blue and red	75	40
1916	-	55c. green, blue and red	75	40
1917	-	55c. green, blue and red	75	40
1918	-	55c. blue, green and red	75	40
1919	-	55c. red, green and black	75	40
1920	-	55c. blue, green and red	75	40
1921	-	55c. green, red and black	75	40
1922	-	55c. blue, green and red	75	40
1923	-	55c. blue, green and red	75	40
1924	-	55c. blue, green and red	75	40
1925	-	55c. blue, green and red	75	40
1926	-	55c. blue, green and red	75	40
1927	-	55c. blue, green and red	75	40

DESIGNS: No. 1909, House and snowball; 1910, Dove and snowball; 1911, Christmas tree and snowball; 1912, Reindeer and snowball; 1913, Hare; 1914, House; 1915, Dove; 1916, Christmas tree; 1917, Reindeer; 1918, House and hare; 1919, House and heart; 1920, Dove and house; 1921, Christmas tree and house; 1922, House and reindeer; 1923, Christmas tree and hare; 1924, Christmas tree and house; 1925, Christmas tree and dove; 1926, Christmas tree and heart; 1927, Christmas tree and reindeer.

543 House and Tree on Snowball

1999. Make-up Rate Stamp.

1928	**543**	25c. red and black	40	25

544 Euro Coin

1999. Introduction of the Euro (European currency).

1929	**544**	80c. multicoloured	1·10	80

545 Pillar Box, 1850

1999. Bicentenary of Netherlands Postal Service.

1930	**545**	80c. multicoloured	1·30	1·00

546 Richard Krajicek serving

1999. Centenary of Royal Dutch Lawn Tennis Federation.

1931	**546**	80c. multicoloured	1·00	40

547 White Spoonbill

1999. Protection of Bird and Migrating Waterfowl. Multicoloured.

1932	80c. Type **547** (centenary of Dutch Bird Protection Society)	1·00	40
1933	80c. Section of globe and arctic terns (African–Eurasian Waterbird Agreement)	1·00	40

548 Haarlemmerhout in Autumn

1999. Parks during the Seasons. Multicoloured.

1934	80c. Type **548**	1·30	1·40
1935	80c. Sonsbeek in winter	1·30	1·40
1936	80c. Weerribben in summer	1·30	1·40
1937	80c. Keukenhof in spring	1·30	1·40

549 Woman

1999. Cultural, Health and Social Welfare Funds. International Year of the Elderly. Multicoloured.

1938	80c.+40c. Type **549**	1·90	1·90
1939	80c.+40c. Man (green background)	1·90	1·90
1940	80c.+40c. Man (blue background)	1·90	1·90
MS1941	144×75 mm. Nos. 1938/40, each ×2	11·50	11·50

550 Lifeboats on Rough Sea

1999. Water Anniversaries. Multicoloured.

1942	80c. Type **550** (175th Anniv of Royal Netherlands Lifeboat Association)	1·00	40
1943	80c. Freighters in canal (150th Anniv of Royal Association of Ships' Masters "Schuttevaer")	1·00	40

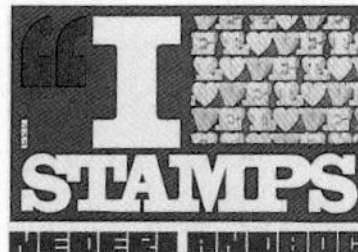

551 "I Love Stamps"

1999

1944	**551**	80c. blue and red	1·00	25
1945	-	80c. red and blue	1·50	1·30

DESIGN: No. 1945, "Stamps love Me".

552 "The Goldfinch" (Carel Fabritius)

1999. 17th-century Dutch Art. Multicoloured. Self-adhesive gum (1g.).

1946	80c. Type **552**	1·30	1·20
1947	80c. "Self-portrait" (Rembrandt)	1·30	1·20
1948	80c. "Self-portrait" (Judith Leyster)	1·30	1·20
1949	80c. "St. Sebastian" (Hendrick ter Brugghen)	1·30	1·20
1950	80c. "Beware of Luxury" (Jan Steen)	1·30	1·20
1951	80c. "The Sick Child" (Gabriel Metsu)	1·30	1·20
1952	80c. "Gooseberries" (Adriaen Coorte)	1·30	1·20
1953	80c. "View of Haarlem" (Jacob van Ruisdael)	1·30	1·20
1954	80c. "Mariaplaats, Utrecht" (Pieter Saenredam)	1·30	1·20
1955	80c. "Danae" (Rembrandt)	1·30	1·20
1956	1g. "The Jewish Bride" (Rembrandt)	1·30	1·20

553 "80" on Computer Screen

1999. Ordinary or self-adhesive gum.

1957	**553**	80c. multicoloured	1·10	30

554 Amaryllis, Coffee Cup, Candles, Letter Writing and Wine Glasses

1999. Greetings Stamp. Self-adhesive.

1959	**554**	80c. multicoloured	1·10	30

1999. New Baby Stamp. As No. 1855 but ordinary gum.

1960	**521**	80c. multicoloured	1·30	40

1999. Wedding Stamp. As No. 1876 but ordinary gum.

1961	**528**	80c. multicoloured	1·30	40

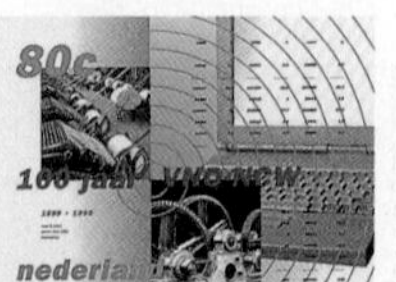
555 Victorian Heavy Machinery and Modern Computer

1999. Centenary of Confederation of Netherlands Industry and Employers.

1962	**555**	80c. multicoloured	1·10	35

556 Tintin and Snowy wearing Space Suits

1999. 70th Anniv of Tintin (comic strip character by Herge). Scenes from "Explorers on the Moon". Multicoloured.

1963	80c. Type **556**	1·30	30
MS1964	108×50 mm. 80c. Tintin, Snowy and Captain Haddock in moon buggy; 80c. Type **556**	5·25	5·00

557 Pillar Box, 1850

1999. Bicentenary of Netherlands Postal Service (2nd issue). Sheet 144×75 mm.

MS1965	**557**	5g. red, black and blue	6·50	6·50

558 Digger (completion of Afsluitdijk, 1932)

1999. The Twentieth Century. Multicoloured.

1966	80c. Type **558**	1·70	1·40
1967	80c. Space satellite	1·70	1·40
1968	80c. Berlage Commodity Exchange, Amsterdam (inauguration, 1903)	1·70	1·40
1969	80c. Empty motorway (car-free Sundays during oil crisis, 1973–74)	1·70	1·40
1970	80c. Old man (Old Age Pensions Act, 1947)	1·70	1·40
1971	80c. Delta Flood Project, 1953–97	1·70	1·40
1972	80c. Players celebrating (victory of Netherlands in European Cup Football Championship, 1998)	1·70	1·40
1973	80c. Four riders on one motor cycle (liberation and end of Second World War, 1945)	1·70	1·40
1974	80c. Woman posting vote (Women's Franchise, 1919)	1·70	1·40
1975	80c. Ice skaters (eleven cities race)	1·70	1·40

559 Pluk van de Pettevlet on Fire Engine

1999. Child Welfare. Characters created by Fiep Westendorp. Multicoloured.

1976	80c.+40c. Type **559**	1·90	75
1977	80c.+40c. Otje drinking through straw	1·90	75
1978	80c.+40c. Jip and Janneke with cat	1·90	75
MS1979	144×75 mm. Nos. 1976/8, each ×2	11·50	9·50

560 Father Christmas (Robin Knegt)

1999. Christmas. Winning entries in design competition. Multicoloured.

1980	55c. Type **560**	75	30
1981	55c. Angel singing (Davinia Bovenlander) (vert)	75	30
1982	55c. Dutch doughnuts in box (Henk Drenth)	75	30
1983	55c. Moon wearing Christmas hat (Lizet van den Berg) (vert)	75	30
1984	55c. Father Christmas carrying sacks (Noortje Kruse)	75	30
1985	55c. Clock striking midnight (Hucky de Haas) (vert)	75	30
1986	55c. Ice skater (Marleen Bos)	75	30
1987	55c. Human Christmas tree (Mariette Strik) (vert)	75	30
1988	55c. Woman wearing Christmas tree earrings (Saskia van Oversteeg)	75	30
1989	55c. Woman vacuuming pine needles (Frans Koenis) (vert)	75	30
1990	55c. Angel with harp and music score (Evelyn de Zeeuw)	75	30
1991	55c. Hand balancing candle, star, hot drink, hat and Christmas tree on fingers (Aafke van Ewijk) (vert)	75	30
1992	55c. Christmas tree (Daan Roepman) (vert)	75	30
1993	55c. Cat wearing crown (Sjoerd van der Zee) (vert)	75	30
1994	55c. Bird flying over house (Barbara Vollers)	75	30
1995	55c. Baby with angel wings (Rosmarijn Schmink) (vert)	75	30
1996	55c. Dog wearing Christmas hat (Casper Heijstek and Mirjam Crosser)	75	30
1997	55c. Angel flying (Patricia van der Neut) (vert)	75	30
1998	55c. Nativity (Marco Cockx)	75	30
1999	55c. Christmas tree with decorations (Matthias Meiling) (vert)	75	30

561 "25"

2000. Make-up Rate Stamp.
2000 **561** 25c. red, blue and yellow 30 25

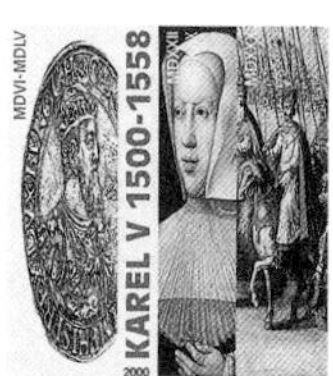

562 1 Guilder Coin, Margaret of Austria (Regent of Netherlands) (after Bernard van Orley) and "Coronation of Charles V" (Juan de la Coate)

2000. 500th Birth Anniv of Charles V, Holy Roman Emperor. Multicoloured.
2001 80c. Type **562** 1·40 1·20
2002 80c. Map of the Seventeen Provinces, "Charles V after the Battle of Muehlberg" (Titian) and Margaret of Parma (Regent of Netherlands) (after Antonius Mohr) 1·40 1·20

563 "Gefeliciteerd" ("Congratulations")

2000. Greetings stamps. Showing greetings messages on hands. Multicoloured.
2003 80c. Type **563** 1·20 1·10
2004 80c. "Succes met je nieuwe baan" ("Good luck with your new job") 1·20 1·10
2005 80c. "gefeliciteerd met je huis" ("Congratulations on your new home") 1·20 1·10
2006 80c. "PROFICIAT" ("Congratulations") 1·20 1·10
2007 80c. "Succes" ("Hope you have success") 1·20 1·10
2008 80c. "Veel geluk samen" ("Good luck together") 1·20 1·10
2009 80c. "Proficiat met je diploma" ("Congratulations on passing your exam") 1·20 1·10
2010 80c. "Geluk" ("Good luck") 1·20 1·10
2011 80c. "Van Harte" ("Cordially") 1·20 1·10
2012 80c. "GEFELICITEERD MET JE RUBEWIJS!" ("Congratulations on passing your driving test!") 1·20 1·10

564 Players celebrating

2000. European Football Championship, Netherlands and Belgium. Multicoloured.
2013 80c. Type **564** 95 40
2014 80c. Football 1·20 95

565 Man and Woman passing Ball

2000. Cultural, Health and Social Welfare Funds. Senior Citizens. Multicoloured.
2015 80c.+40c. Type **565** 1·90 1·60
2016 80c.+40c. Woman picking apples 1·90 1·60
2017 80c.+40c. Woman wearing swimming costume 1·90 1·60
MS2018 144×74 mm. Nos. 2015/17, each ×2 11·50 9·50

566 "Feigned Sadness" (C. Troost)

2000. Bicentenary of the Rijksmuseum, Amsterdam. Multicoloured. (a) Ordinary gum.
2019 80c. Type **566** 1·40 1·30
2020 80c. "Harlequin and Columbine" (porcelain figurine) (J. J. Kandler) 1·40 1·30
2021 80c. "Ichikawa Ebizo IV" (woodcut) (T. Sharaku) 1·40 1·30
2022 80c. "Heavenly Beauty" (sandstone sculpture) 1·40 1·30
2023 80c. "St. Vitus" (wood sculpture) 1·40 1·30
2024 80c. "Woman in Turkish Costume" (J. E. Liotard) 1·40 1·30
2025 80c. "J. van Speyk" (J. Schoemaker Doyer) 1·40 1·30
2026 80c. "King Saul" (engraving) (L. van Leyden) 1·40 1·30
2027 80c. "L'Amour Menacant" (marble sculpture) (E. M. Falconet) 1·40 1·30
2028 80c. "Sunday" (photograph) (C. Ariens) 1·40 1·30

(b) Self-adhesive.
2029 100c. "The Nightwatch" (Rembrandt) 1·70 1·30

567 "80" and "Doe Maar" Record Cover

2000. Doe Maar (Dutch pop group). Multicoloured.
2030 80c. Type **567** 1·00 40
2031 80c. "80" and song titles 1·50 1·30

568 "Dutch Landscape" (Jeroen Krabb)

2000. Priority Mail. Contemporary Art. Self-adhesive.
2033 **568** 110c. multicoloured 1·90 1·60

569 "The Nightwatch" (Rembrandt)

2000. Priority Mail. Self-adhesive.
2034 **569** 110c. multicoloured 1·90 1·60

570 *Libertad* (full-rigged cadet ship)

2000. "Sail Amsterdam 2000". Sailing Ships. Multicoloured.
2036 80c. Type **570** 1·40 1·30
2037 80c. *Amerigo Vespucci* (cadet ship) and figurehead 1·40 1·30
2038 80c. *Dar Mlodziezy* (full-rigged cadet ship) and sail 1·40 1·30
2039 80c. *Europa* (cadet ship) and wheel 1·40 1·30
2040 80c. *Kruzenshtern* (cadet barque) and bell 1·40 1·30
2041 80c. *Sagres II* (cadet barque) and sail 1·40 1·30
2042 80c. *Alexander von Humboldt* (barque) and sail 1·40 1·30
2043 80c. *Sedov* (cadet barque) and sailors dropping sail 1·40 1·30
2044 80c. *Mir* (square-rigged training ship) 1·40 1·30
2045 80c. *Oosterschelde* (schooner) and rope 1·40 1·30

571 Roller Skating

2000. Sjors and Sjimmie (comic strip characters by Frans Piet). Multicoloured.
2046 80c. Type **571** 1·40 1·10
2047 80c. In car 1·40 1·10
MS2048 108×50 mm. 80c. As No. 2049; 80c. As No. 2047 4·50 3·75
2049 80c. Listening to radio 1·40 1·10
2050 80c. Swinging on rope 1·40 1·10

2000. Bereavement Stamp. As No. 1866 but self-adhesive.
2051 **524** 80c. blue 1·30 65

572 Green Dragonfly

2000. Endangered Species. Multicoloured.
2052 80c. Type **572** 1·10 30
2053 80c. Weather loach 1·30 95

573 Canal Boat

2000. 150th Anniv (2002) of Netherlands Stamps (1st issue). Sheet 108×50 mm containing T 573 and similar horiz design. Multicoloured.
MS2054 80c. Type **573**; 80c. Mail carriage 3·25 2·50
See also Nos. **MS**2138 and **MS**2250.

574 Children wearing Monster Hats

2000. Child Welfare. Multicoloured. (a) Self-adhesive gum.
2055 80c.+40c. Type **574** 2·20 2·20
2056 80c.+40c. Boy sailing bath-tub 2·20 2·20
2057 80c.+40c. Children brewing magical stew 2·20 2·20

(b) Ordinary gum.
MS2058 80c.+40c. Type **574**; 80c.+40c. Ghostly games; 80c.+40c. Girl riding crocodile; 80c.+40c. As No. 2056; 80c.+40c. As No. 2057; 80c.+40c. Children playing dragon 9·75 8·75

575 Couple with Christmas Tree

2000. Christmas. Multicoloured.
2059 60c. Type **575** 95 30
2060 60c. Children making snow balls 95 30
2061 60c. Couple dancing 95 30
2062 60c. Man playing French horn 95 30
2063 60c. Man carrying Christmas tree 95 30
2064 60c. Man carrying young child 95 30
2065 60c. Woman reading book 95 30
2066 60c. Couple kissing 95 30
2067 60c. Man playing piano 95 30
2068 60c. Woman watching from window 95 30
2069 60c. Woman sitting in chair 95 30
2070 60c. Man sitting beside fire 95 30
2071 60c. Snowman flying 95 30
2072 60c. Couple in street 95 30
2073 60c. Child playing violin 95 30
2074 60c. Children on sledge 95 30
2075 60c. Man writing letter 95 30
2076 60c. Woman carrying plate of food 95 30
2077 60c. Family 95 30
2078 60c. Woman sleeping 95 30

576 Moon

2001. Make-up Rate Stamp.
2079 **576** 20c. multicoloured 30 25

577 Whinchat

2001. Centenary of Royal Dutch Nature Society. Multicoloured.
2080 80c. Type **577** 1·20 1·10
2081 80c. Family in rowing boat 1·60 1·10
2082 80c. Fox 1·20 1·10
2083 80c. Couple bird watching 1·60 1·10
2084 80c. Flowers 1·20 1·10

578 Poem (by E. du Perron)

2001. "Between Two Cultures". National Book Week. Multicoloured.
2085 80c. Type **578** 1·20 1·20
2086 80c. Men in street 1·20 1·20
2087 80c. Poem (by Hafid Bouazza) 1·20 1·20
2088 80c. Woman and young men 1·20 1·20
2089 80c. Poem (by Adriaan van Dis) 1·20 1·20
2090 80c. Profiles of two women 1·20 1·20
2091 80c. Poem (by Kader Abdolah) 1·20 1·20
2092 80c. Two young girls 1·20 1·20
2093 80c. Poem (by Ellen Ombre) 1·20 1·20
2094 80c. Boy carrying map 1·20 1·20

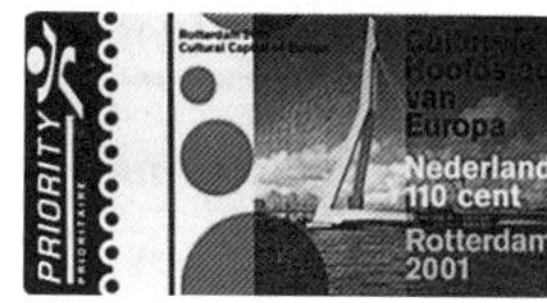

579 Rotterdam Bridge

2001. Priority Mail. Rotterdam, European City of Culture. Self-adhesive gum.
2095 **579** 110c. multicoloured 1·80 1·30

580 Emergency Rescuers

2001. International Year of Volunteers. Sheet 108×50 mm. containing Type 580 and similar horiz design. Multicoloured.
MS2096 80c. Type 508, 80c. Animal rescuers 3·25 3·25

581 Chess Board

2001. Birth Centenary of Machgielis "Professor Max" Euwe (chess player). Sheet 108×50 mm containing T 581 and similar horiz design. Multicoloured.
MS2097 80c. Type **581**; 80c. Euwe and chess pieces 3·25 3·25

582 Helen's Flower (*Helenium rubinzwerg*)

2001. Flowers. Multicoloured. (a) Self-adhesive gum.
2098 80c.+40c. Type **582** 2·75 2·75

2099	80c.+40c. Russian hollyhock (*Alcea rugosa*)	2·75	2·75
2100	80c.+40c. Persian cornflower (*Centaurea dealbata*)	2·75	2·75

(b) Ordinary gum.

MS2101	144×75 mm. 80c.+40c. *Caryopteris* "Heavenly Blue"; 80c.+40c. Type **582**; 80c.+40c. As No. 2099; 80c.+40c. Spurge (*Euphorbia schillingii*); 80c.+40c. As No. 2100; 80c.+40c. Hooker inula (*Inula hookeri*)	11·50	9·50

583 "Autumn" (detail) (L. Gestel)

2001. Art Nouveau. Multicoloured.

2102	80c. Type **583**	1·30	1·30
2103	80c. Book cover by C. Lebeau for *De Stille Kracht*	1·30	1·30
2104	80c. Burcht Federal Council Hall, Amsterdam (R. N. Roland Holst and H. P. Berlage)	1·30	1·30
2105	80c. "O Grave Where is Thy Victory" (painting) (J. Throop)	1·30	1·30
2106	80c. Vases by C. J. van der Hoef from Amphora factory	1·30	1·30
2107	80c. Capital from staircase of Utrecht building (J. Mendes da Costa)	1·30	1·30
2108	80c. Illustration of common peafowl from *The Happy Owls* (T. van Hoytema)	1·30	1·30
2109	80c. "The Bride" (detail) (painting) (J. Thorn Prikker)	1·30	1·30
2110	80c. Factory-printed cotton fabric (M. Duco Crop)	1·30	1·30
2111	80c. Dentz van Schaik room (L. Zyl)	1·30	1·30

2001. As T 428 but with face value expressed in euros and cents. Self-adhesive gum.

2112	85c. blue	1·40	25

584 Sky and Landscape

2001. Self-adhesive gum.

2113	**584**	85c. multicoloured	1·40	45

585 Arrows

2001. Business Coil Stamp. Self-adhesive gum.

2114	**585**	85c. purple and silver	1·10	25

586 Reclaimed Land

2001. Multicoloured. Self-adhesive gum.

2115	85c. Type **586** (postage)	1·40	40
2116	1g.20 Beach (priority mail)	1·90	1·40
2117	1g.65 Town and canal	2·50	2·10

587 House carrying Suitcase

2001. Greetings Stamps. Self-adhesive gum.

2118	**587**	85c. black and yellow	1·30	1·10
2119	-	85c. red, yellow and gold	1·30	95
2120	-	85c. multicoloured	1·40	1·10
2121	-	85c. multicoloured	2·10	1·30

DESIGNS: No. 2118, Type **587** (change of address stamp); 2119, Couple (wedding stamp); 2120, As Type **521** (new baby); 2121, As Type **524** (bereavement stamp).

588 Tom and Jerry

2001. Cartoon Characters. Multicoloured.

2122	85c. Type **588**	1·30	1·30
2123	85c. Fred Flintstone and Barney Rubble	1·30	1·30
2124	85c. Johnny Bravo	1·30	1·30
2125	85c. Dexter posting letter	1·30	1·30
2126	85c. Powerpuff Girls	1·30	1·30

589 "Veel Geluk" ("Good Luck")

2001. Greetings Stamps. Multicoloured. Self-adhesive gum.

2127	85c. Type **589**	1·40	1·30
2128	85c. "Gefeliciteerd!" ("Congratulations!")	1·40	1·30
2129	85c. "Veel Geluk" with envelope flap (horiz)	1·40	1·30
2130	85c. "Gefeliciteerd!" with envelope flap (horiz)	1·40	1·30
2131	85c. "Proficiat" ("Congratulations")	1·40	1·30
2132	85c. "Succes !" ("Success")	1·40	1·30
2133	85c. "Van Harte ..." ("Cordially ...")	1·40	1·30
2134	85c. "Proficiat" with envelope flap (horiz)	1·40	1·30
2135	85c. "Succes !" with envelope flap (horiz)	1·40	1·30
2136	85c. "Van Harte ..." with envelope flap (horiz)	1·40	1·30

590 Guilder Coins

2001. Replacement of the Guilder. Self-adhesive.

2137	**590**	12g.75 silver	18·00	14·50

591 Waaigat Canal and Williamstad, Curacao (J. E. Heemskerk after G. C. W. Voorduin)

2001. 150th Annivs of Netherlands Stamps (2002) (2nd issue) and of Royal Institute foe Linguistics and Anthropology. Sheet 108×50 mm containing T 591 and similar horiz design. Multicoloured.

MS2138	39c. Type **591**; 39c. Pangka sugar refinery, Java (J.C. Grieve after A. Salm)	3·25	2·50

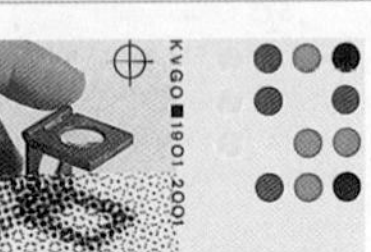

592 Magnifier, Target Mark and Dots

2001. Centenary of Royal Dutch Printers' Association. Sheet 108×50 mm containing T 592 and similar horiz design. Multicoloured.

MS2139	39c. Type **592**; 39c. Magnifier, computer zoom symbol and colour palette	3·25	2·50

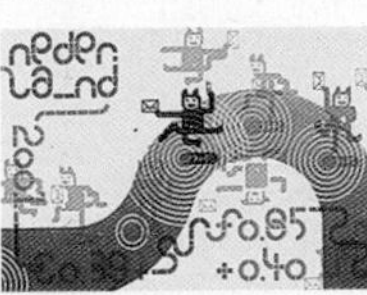

593 Computer Figure and River

2001. Child Welfare. Multicoloured. (a) Self-adhesive gum.

2140	85c.+40c. Type **593**	3·25	2·75

(b) Ordinary gum.

MS2141	146×76 mm. 85c.+40c. Figure and printer; 85c.+40c. Road, car and figure; 85c.+40c. Post box, blocks and droplets; 85c.+40c. Post box, figure and stairs; 85c.+40c. Type **593**; 85c.+40c. Figure swinging on rope and log in river	11·50	9·50

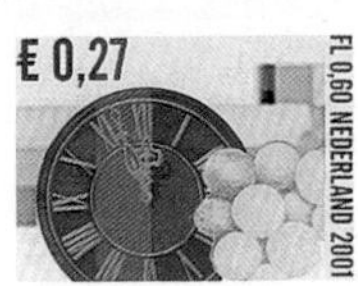

594 Clock and Grapes

2001. Christmas. Multicoloured. Self-adhesive gum.

2142	27c. Type **594**	75	25
2143	27c. Stars and bun	75	25
2144	27c. Steeple and buns	75	25
2145	27c. Cherub and coins	75	25
2146	27c. Champagne bottle	75	25
2147	27c. Wreath around chimney	75	25
2148	27c. Tower	75	25
2149	27c. Christmas tree bauble	75	25
2150	27c. Playing card with Christmas tree as sign	75	25
2151	27c. Cake seen through window	75	25
2152	27c. Decorated Christmas tree	75	25
2153	27c. Father Christmas	75	25
2154	27c. Sign displaying hot drink	75	25
2155	27c. Candles seen through window	75	25
2156	27c. Illuminated roof-tops	75	25
2157	27c. Reindeer	75	25
2158	27c. Snowman	75	25
2159	27c. Parcel	75	25
2160	27c. Bonfire	75	25
2161	27c. Children on toboggan	75	25

595 "12"

2002. Make-up Rate Stamp. (a) Self-adhesive gum.

2162	**595**	2c. red	5·00	15
2166	**595**	12c. green	40	25

(b) Ordinary gum.

2169	2c. red	15	15
2170	3c. agate	15	15
2171	5c. mauve	15	15
2172	10c. blue	15	15

596 Queen Beatrix

2002. Queen Beatrix. Self-adhesive gum

2175	**596**	25c. brown and green	65	30
2176	**596**	39c. blue and pink	1·10	25
2177	**596**	40c. blue and brown	1·10	65
2177b	**596**	44c. rose and olive	1·10	75
2177c		1 (46c.) blue and red-dish lilac	1·20	60
2178	**596**	50c. pink and green	1·30	65
2179	**596**	55c. mauve and brown	2·50	1·40
2180	**596**	57c. blue and purple	2·50	1·90
2180b	**596**	61c. violet and brown	2·75	1·90
2181	**596**	65c. green and violet	2·75	1·40
2181b	**596**	67c. rose and olive	2·75	2·20
2181b	**596**	88c. violet and green	2·10	1·30
2182	**596**	70c. deep green and green	2·75	2·10
2183	**596**	72c. ochre and blue	3·00	2·20
2183a	**596**	76c. ochre and green	16·00	90
2184	**596**	78c. blue and brown	1·90	30
2184a	**596**	80c. blue and purple	10·00	40
2184b		2 (92c.) gold and dull green	2·20	1·10
2185	**596**	€1 green and blue	2·50	65
2187	**596**	€3 mauve and green	7·50	1·30

597 Arrows

2002. Business Coil Stamps. Self-adhesive gum.

2195	**597**	39c. purple and silver	95	25
2196	**597**	78c. blue and gold	1·90	45

598 Prince Willem-Alexander and Máxima Zorreguieta

2002. Marriage of Prince Willem-Alexander and Maxima Zorreguieta. Sheet 145×75 mm, containing T 598 and similar horiz design.

MS2197	**598** 39c. black, silver and orange; 39c. multicoloured	3·25	3·25

DESIGN: 39c. "Willem-Alexander Maxima" and "222".

599 Sky and Landscape

2002. Self-adhesive gum.

2198	**599**	39c. multicoloured	95	25

600 Couple

2002. Greetings Stamps. Face values in euros. Self-adhesive gum.

2199	-	39c. black and yellow	1·10	30
2200	**600**	39c. red, yelow and gold	1·00	30
2201	-	39c. multicoloured	1·00	30
2202	-	39c. blue	1·00	30

DESIGNS: No. 2199, As Type **587** (change of address stamp); 2200, Type **600** (wedding stamp); 2201, As Type **521** (new baby); 2202, As Type **524** (bereavement stamp).

601 "Veel Geluk" ("Good Luck")

2001. Greetings Stamps. Face values in euros. Multicoloured. Self-adhesive gum.

2203	39c. Type **601**	1·30	95
2204	39c. "Gefeliciteerd!" ("Congratulations!")	1·30	95
2205	39c. "Veel Geluk" ("Good Luck") (horiz)	1·30	95
2206	39c. "Gefeliciteerd!" with envelope flap (horiz)	1·30	95
2207	39c. "Proficiat" ("Congratulations")	1·30	95
2208	39c. "Succes !" ("Success")	1·30	95
2209	39c. "Van Harte..." ("Cordially ...")	1·30	95
2210	39c. "Proficiat" with envelope flap (horiz)	1·30	95
2211	39c. "Succes !" with envelope flap (horiz)	1·30	95
2212	39c. "Van Harte..." with envelope flap (horiz)	1·30	95

602 Reclaimed Land

2002. Landscapes. Face values in euros. Multicoloured. Self-adhesive gum.

2213	39c. Type **603** (postage)	95	25
2214	54c. Beach (priority mail)	1·40	90
2215	75c. Town and canal	1·80	1·30

603 Water Lily

2002. "Floriade 2002" International Horticultural Exhibition, Harlemmermeer. Flowers. Multicoloured.
2216 39c. + 19c. Type **603** 1·40 1·10
2217 39c. + 19c. Dahlia 1·40 1·10
2218 39c. + 19c. Japanese cherry blossom 1·40 1·10
2219 39c. + 19c. Rose 1·40 1·10
2220 39c. + 19c. Orchid 1·40 1·10
2221 39c. + 19c. Tulip 1·40 1·10

Nos. 2216/21 were printed on paper impregnated with perfume which was released when the stamps were scratched.

604 Flowers and Red Crosses

2002. Red Cross. 10th Annual Blossom Walk.
2222 **604** 39c. + 19c. multicoloured 1·50 1·40

605 Langnek

2002. 50th Anniv of Efteling Theme Park. Multicoloured. Self-adhesive gum.
2223 39c. Type **605** 1·10 55
2224 39c. Pardoes de Tovernar 1·10 55
2225 39c. Droomvlucht Elfje 1·10 55
2226 39c. Kleine Boodschap 1·10 55
2227 39c. Holle Bolle Gijs 1·10 55

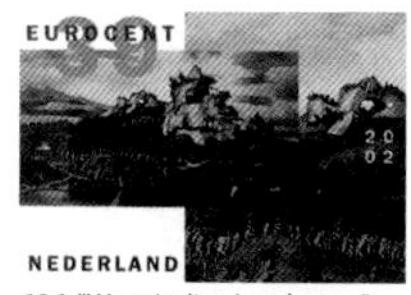

606 "West Indies Landscape" (Jan Mostaert)

2002. Landscape Paintings. Showing paintings and enlarged detail in foreground. Multicoloured.
2228 39c. Type **606** 1·10 1·00
2229 39c. "Riverbank with Cows" (Aelbert Cuyp) 1·10 1·00
2230 39c. "Cornfield" (Jacob van Ruisdael) 1·10 1·00
2231 39c. "Avenue at Middelharnis" (Meindert Hobbema) 1·10 1·00
2232 39c. "Italian Landscape with Umbrella Pines" (Hendrik Voogd) 1·10 1·00
2233 39c. "Landscape in Normandy" (Andreas Schelfhout) 1·10 1·00
2234 39c. "Landscape with Waterway" (Jan Toorop) 1·10 1·00
2235 39c. "Landscape" (Jan Sluijters) 1·10 1·00
2236 39c. "Kismet" (Michael Raedecker) 1·10 1·00
2237 39c. "Untitled" (Robert Zandvliet) 1·10 1·00

607 Circus Performers

2002. Priority Mail. Europa. Circus. Multicoloured.
2238 54c. Type **607** 1·90 1·30
2239 54c. Lions and Big Top 1·90 1·30

608 Circles

2002. Business Coil Stamp. Self-adhesive gum.
2240 **608** 39c. deep blue, blue and red 1·00 25
2241 **608** 78c. green, light green and red 2·00 25

609 Dutch East Indiaman and 1852 Stamps

2002. 150th Anniv of Netherlands Stamps. 400th Anniv of Dutch East India Company (V. O. C.). Sheet 108×50 mm, containing T 609 and similar horiz design. Multicoloured.
MS2250 39c. Type **609**; 39c. Two Dutch East Indiamen and stamps of 1852 3·25 3·25

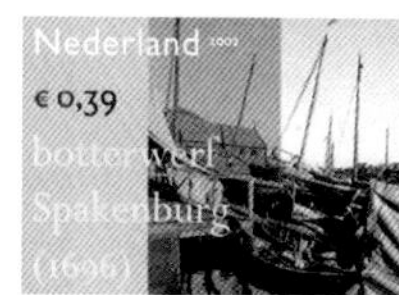

610 Boatyard, Spakenburg

2002. Industrial Heritage. Multicoloured.
2251 39c. Type **610** 1·10 1·10
2252 39c. Limekiln, Dedemsvaart 1·10 1·10
2253 39c. Steam-driven pumping station, Cruquius 1·10 1·10
2254 39c. Mine-shaft winding gear, Heerlen 1·10 1·10
2255 39c. Salt drilling tower, Hengelo 1·10 1·10
2256 39c. Windmill, Weidum 1·10 1·10
2257 39c. Brick-works, Zevenaar 1·10 1·10
2258 39c. "Drie Hoefijzers" brewery, Breda 1·10 1·10
2259 39c. Water-treatment plant, Tilburg 1·10 1·10
2260 39c. "Nodding-donkey" oil pump, Schoonebeck 1·10 1·10

611 Cat and Child

2002. Child Welfare. Sheet 147×76 mm, containing T 611 and similar horiz designs. Multicoloured.
MS2261 Type **611**, 39c.+19c. Blue figure and upper part of child with green head; 39c.+19c. Child and ball; 39c.+19c. Child with yellow head and raised arms; 39c.+19c. Child with brown head and left arm raised; 39c.+19c. Dog and child 10·00 8·75

612 Woman and Child

2002. Christmas. Multicoloured. Self-adhesive gum.
2262 29c. Type **612** 75 55
2263 29c. Seated man facing left 75 55
2264 29c. Profile with raised collar 75 55
2265 29c. Stream and figure wearing scarf 75 55
2266 29c. Woman, tree and snowflakes 75 55
2267 29c. Snowflakes and man wearing knee-length coat beside grasses 75 55
2268 29c. Snowflakes, man, and gate and stream 75 55
2269 29c. Snowflakes, windmill, stream and woman 75 55
2270 29c. Seated man facing right 75 55
2271 29c. Willow tree and profile of child facing left 75 55
2272 29c. Man leaning against tree 75 55
2273 29c. Man with hands in pockets 75 55
2274 29c. Seated couple 75 55
2275 29c. Fir tree and man's profile facing left 75 55
2276 29c. Man carrying child on shoulders 75 55
2277 29c. Profile of boy facing right 75 55
2278 29c. Standing child facing left 75 55
2279 29c. Snowflakes, sea and upper part of man with raised collar 75 55
2280 29c. Sea behind man wearing hat and glasses 75 55
2281 29c. Figure with out-stretched arms 75 55

Nos. 2262/81 were issued together, se-tenant, the stamps arranged in strips of five, each strip forming a composite design.

613 "Landscape with Four Trees"

614 "Self-portrait with Straw Hat"

2003. 150th Birth Anniv of Vincent Van Gogh (artist). Multicoloured. (a) Ordinary gum.
2282 39c. Type **613** 1·20 1·10
2283 39c. "The Potato Eaters" 1·20 1·10
2284 39c. "Four Cut Sunflowers" 1·20 1·10
2285 39c. "Self-portrait with Grey Felt Hat" 1·20 1·10
2286 39c. "The Zouave" 1·20 1·10
2287 39c. "Place Du Forum Cafe Terrace by Night, Arles" 1·20 1·10
2288 39c. "Tree Trunks in Long Grass" 1·20 1·10
2289 39c. "Almond Blossom" 1·20 1·10
2290 39c. "Auvers-sur-Oise" 1·20 1·10
2291 39c. "Wheatfield with Crows, Auvers-sur-Oise" 1·20 1·10

(b) Self-adhesive gum.
2292 39c. Type **614** 1·10 75
2293 59c. "Vase with Sunflowers" 1·40 1·10
2294 75c. "The Sower" 2·10 1·60

615 North Pier, Ijmuiden

2003. 50th Anniv of Floods in Zeeland, North Brabant and South Holland. Designs showing photographs from national archives. Each grey and black.
2295 39c. Type **615** 1·10 1·10
2296 39c. Hanswert Lock 1·10 1·10
2297 39c. Building dam, Wieringermeer 1·10 1·10
2298 39c. Ijsselmeer Dam 1·10 1·10
2299 39c. Breached dyke, Willemstad 1·10 1·10
2300 39c. Repairing dyke, Stavenisse 1·10 1·10
2301 39c. Building dam, Zandkreek 1·10 1·10
2302 39c. Building dam, Grevelingen 1·10 1·10
2303 39c. Flood barrier, Oosterschelde 1·10 1·10
2304 39c. Floods, Roermond 1·10 1·10

616 See-through Register (security feature)

2003. 300th Anniv of Joh. Enschede (printers). Multicoloured.
2305 39c. Type **616** 1·00 70
2306 39c. Fleischman's musical notation 1·00 70

No. 2305 has the remaining symbols of the see-through register printed on the back over the gum. This forms a complete design when held up to the light.

No. 2305 was embossed with a notional barcode and No. 2306 with a security device.

617 Alstroemeria

2003. Flower Paintings. Multicoloured.
2307 39c.+19c. Type **617** 1·20 95
2308 39c.+19c. Sweet pea 1·20 95
2309 39c.+19c. Pansies 1·20 95
2310 39c.+19c. Trumpet vine 1·20 95
2311 39c.+19c. Lychnis 1·20 95
2312 39c.+19c. Irises 1·20 95

618 Oystercatcher

2003. Fauna of the Dutch Shallows. Winning Entry in Stamp Design Competition. Multicoloured.
MS2313 Two sheets, each 140×82 mm. (a) 39c. ×4, Type **618**; Spoonbill (horiz); Eider duck: Grey seal (horiz) (b) 59c. ×4, Herring gull; Curlew (horiz); Seals and gull; Crab (horiz) 4·75 4·75

MS2313 (b) were issued with "PRIORITY/Prioritaire" label attached at either upper or lower edge.

619 "39"

2003. Greetings Stamps. Two sheets, each 122×170 mm, containing T 619 and similar vert designs. Multicoloured.
MS2314 (a) 39c. ×10, Type **619** (blue) (green) (purple) (pink) (orange) (yellow) (olive) (turquoise) (red) (brown); (b) 39c. ×10, Flowers; Flag; Present; Champagne glass; Medal; Guitar; Balloons; Cut-out figures; Slice of cake; Garland 6·00 6·00

Nos. **MS**2314a/b were each issued with a se-tenant label attached at left showing either Marjolein Bastin (artist); Paint tubes and splashes (painting, Marjolein Bastin); Humberto Tan (television presenter); Figures symbolising Red Cross; Daphne Deckers (presenter and actress); Fanmail; Prime Minister Jan Balkenende; Palm top computer; Sien Diels (Sesame Street presenter); Tommie (character from Sesame Street) (**MS**2314a) or a girl (**MS**2314b). The labels could be personalised by the addition of a photograph for an inclusive fee of €12 for the first sheet and €5.95 for subsequent sheets bearing the same design.

620 Coffee Cup

2003. 250th Anniv of Douwe Egberts (coffee and tea retailers). Multicoloured.
2315 39c. Type **620** 95 35
2316 39c. As No. 2315 but with colours reversed 95 35

Nos. 2315/16 were impregnated with the scent of coffee which was released when the stamps were rubbed.

621 Airplane, Ship and Trucks

2003. Land, Air and Water. Winning Entry in Stamp Design Competition. Multicoloured.
2317 39c. Type **621** 95 35
2318 39c. Cat, bird, fish and envelope 95 35

622 Nelson Mandela and Child

2003. 85th Birth Anniv of Nelson Mandela (President of South Africa). Multicoloured.
2319 39c. Type **622** 95 35
2320 39c. Children (Nelson Mandela's Children's Fund) 95 35

623 "For You from Me"

2003. Self-adhesive gum.
2321 **623** 39c. multicoloured 95 35

624 Children Kissing

2003. Winning Entries in Stamp Design Competition. Sheet 108×151 mm containing T 624 and similar horiz designs. Multicoloured.

MS2322 39c. ×10, Type **624**; Traditional costume; Cat; Puppies; Child; Bride and groom; 2CV cars; Motorcycle; Peacock butterfly; Flowers 13·50 12·00

625 "39"

2003. Company Stamp. Self-adhesive.

2323	**625**	39c. multicoloured	1·20	1·20

626 Coloured Squares

2003. Stamp Day. 75th Anniv of Netherlands Association of Stamp Dealers (NVPH).

2324	**626**	39c. multicoloured	95	60

627 Notepad, Radio and Ballet Shoes

2003. Child Welfare. Sheet 147×76 mm containing T 627 and similar horiz designs. Multicoloured.

MS2325 39c.+19c. ×6, Type **627**; Masks and open book; Microphone, music notation and paint brush; Violin, pencil, football and television; Drum and light bulbs; Trumpet, light bulbs, hat and earphones 8·50 8·50

628 Star

2003. Greetings Stamp.

2326	**628**	29c. multicoloured	75	65

629 Family

2003. Christmas. Multicoloured. Self-adhesive.

2327	29c. Type **629**	75	40
2328	29c. Parcel	75	40
2329	29c. Cat and dog	75	40
2330	29c. Tree	75	40
2331	29c. Hands holding glasses	75	40
2332	29c. Bell	75	40
2333	29c. Hand holding pen	75	40
2334	29c. Stag's head	75	40
2335	29c. Hand holding toy windmill	75	40
2336	29c. Holly leaf	75	40
2337	29c. Candle flame	75	40
2338	29c. Star	75	40
2339	29c. Couple	75	40
2340	29c. Snowman	75	40
2341	29c. Fireplace and fire	75	40
2342	29c. Angel	75	40
2343	29c. Couple dancing	75	40
2344	29c. Round bauble	75	40
2345	29c. Mother and child	75	40
2346	29c. Pointed bauble	75	40

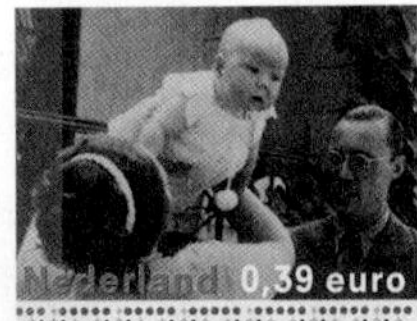

630 Queen Beatrix as Baby

2003. The Royal Family. Queen Beatrix. Sheet 123×168 mm containing T 630 and similar horiz designs. Multicoloured.

MS2347 39c.×10, Type **630**; Sitting on swing as small child; As young girl leading pony; Reading magazine; With Claus von Amsberg on their engagement; Holding baby Prince Willem-Alexander; Royal family when young; Queen Beatrix and Prince Claus dancing; Prince Willem-Alexander, Prince Johan Friso, Prince Claus, Queen Beatrix and Prince Constantijn, Queen Beatrix viewing painting in art gallery 9·00 9·00

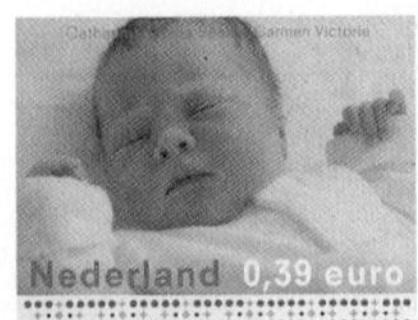

631 Princess Amalia

2003. Birth of Princess Amalia of Netherlands. Sheet 104×71 mm.

MS2348 39c. multicoloured 90 90

632 "Woman Reading a Letter" (Gabriel Metsu) (detail)

2004. Art. Multicoloured. Self-adhesive.

2349	61c. Type **632**	1·50	55
2350	77c. "The Love Letter" (Jan Vermeer) (detail)	1·80	1·00

633 Water, Buildings and Rainbow

2004. 150th Anniv of Royal Netherlands Meteorological Institute (KNMI). Multicoloured.

2351	39c. Type **633**	90	55
2352	39c. Water, buildings and rainbow (different)	90	55

Nos. 2351/2 were issued together, se-tenant, forming a composite design.

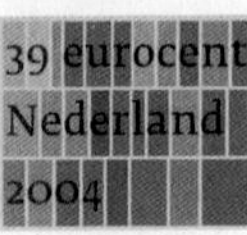

634 Patchwork

2004. Business Stamp. Self-adhesive.

2353	**634**	39c. multicoloured	1·00	25
2354	**634**	78c. multicoloured	2·00	40

635 Iris

2004. Flower Paintings. Multicoloured.

2355	39c.+19c. Type **635**	1·30	90
2356	39c.+19c. Lily	1·30	90
2357	39c.+19c. Poppy	1·30	90
2358	39c.+19c. Tulips	1·30	90
2359	39c.+19c. Orange flower	1·30	90
2360	39c.+19c. Thistle	1·30	90

636 Spiker C4 (1922)

2004. 50th Anniv of Dutch Youth Philately Association.

2361	**636**	39c. multicoloured	1·00	75
2362	-	39c. orange and black	1·00	75

DESIGNS: No. 2361, Type **636**; 2362, Spiker C8 Double12 R (2003).

637 Czech Republic Flag, Stamp, Map and Country Identification Code

2004. Enlargement of European Union. Sheet 108×150 mm containing T 637 and similar horiz designs showing the flag, stamp, map and country identification code of the new member states. Multicoloured.

MS2363 39c. ×10, Type **637**; Lithuania; Estonia; Poland; Malta; Hungary. Latvia; Slovakia; Cyprus; Slovenia 10·00 10·00

638 "39" and Rays

2004. Greetings Stamp.

2364	**638**	39c. multicoloured	1·00	90

2004. Company Stamp. Self-adhesive.

2365	**625**	39c. multicoloured	1·50	1·50

639 Prince Willem-Alexander and Máxima Zorreguieta on their Engagement

2004. The Royal Family. Prince Willem-Alexander. Sheet 123×168 mm containing T 639 and similar horiz designs. Multicoloured.

MS2366 39c. ×10, Type **639**; Máxima Zorreguieta showing engagement ring; Facing each other on their wedding day; Facing left; Kissing; Princess Maxima leaning towards Prince Willem-Alexander; Royal couple with Princess Amalia; With Princess Amalia and reading book; Princess Maxima holding Princess Amalia at christening font; At font Princess Amalia looking upwards 9·25 9·25

640 Red Squirrel

2004. Veluwe Nature Reserve. Two sheets, each 144×81 mm containing T 640 and similar horiz designs. Multicoloured.

MS2367 (a) 39c. ×4, Type **640**; Hoopoe; Deer; Wild boar (b) 61c. ×4, Fox; Woodpecker; Stag and hind; Mouflon sheep 13·00 13·00

641 Pen Nib

2004. Greetings Stamps. Sheet 144×75 mm containing T 641 and similar square designs.

MS2368 39c. light orange and orange; 39c. multicoloured; 39c. blue and red 3·00 3·00

DESIGNS: 39c.Type **641**; 39c. Hand; 39c. Profiles.

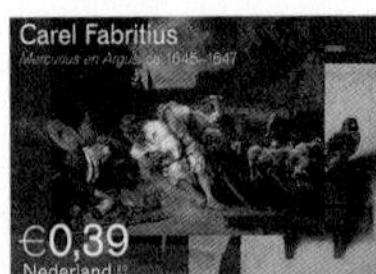

642 "Mercury and Argus"

2004. 350th Death Anniv of Carel Fabritius (artist). Paintings. Multicoloured.

2369	39c. Type **642**	1·00	90
2370	39c. "Self Portrait" (wearing large hat)	1·00	90
2371	39c. "Mercury and Aglauros"	1·00	90
2372	39c. "Abraham de Potter"	1·00	90
2373	39c. "Hagar and the Angel"	1·00	90
2374	39c. "The Sentry"	1·00	90
2375	78c. "Hera"	1·60	1·40
2376	78c. "Self Portrait" (wearing small-brimmed hat)	1·60	1·40
2377	78c. "Self Portrait" (hatless)	1·60	1·40
2378	78c. "The Goldfinch"	1·60	1·40

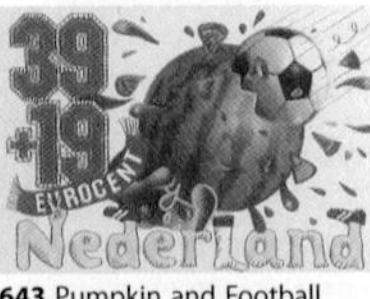

643 Pumpkin and Football

2004. Child Welfare. 80th Anniv of Foundation for Children's Welfare Stamps. Sheet 144×75 mm containing T 643 and similar horiz designs. Multicoloured.

MS2379 39c.+19c.×6, Type **643**; Lemon skipping; Orange cycling; Pear skateboarding; Banana doing sit-ups; Strawberry weightlifting 8·25 8·25

644 Snowman

2004. Greetings Stamp.

2380	**644**	29c. multicoloured	90	70

645 Family as Shadows

2004. Christmas. Multicoloured.

2381	29c. Type **645**	90	70
2382	29c. Girls holding parcels	90	70
2383	29c. Girl and dog	90	70
2384	29c. Two children	90	70
2385	29c. Sheep	90	70
2386	29c. Two polar bears	90	70
2387	29c. Children making snowman	90	70
2388	29c. Couple pulling tree	90	70
2389	29c. Couple swimming	90	70
2390	29c. Three people wearing fur hats	90	70

646 Woman (NOVIB)

2004. Christmas. Charity Stamps. Multicoloured. Self-adhesive.

2401	29c.+10c. Type **646**	1·30	1·10
2402	29c.+10c. Children (Stop AIDS Now)	1·30	1·10
2403	29c.+10c. Deer (Natuurmonumenten)	1·30	1·10
2404	29c.+10c. Two boys (KWF Kankerbestrijding)	1·30	1·10
2405	29c.+10c. Girl holding baby (UNICEF)	1·30	1·10
2406	29c.+10c. Two boys writing (Plan Nederland)	1·30	1·10
2407	29c.+10c. Bauble containing mother and child (Tros Helpt)	1·30	1·10
2408	29c.+10c. Canoeist and snow covered mountains (Greenpeace)	1·30	1·10

2409 29c.+10c. Woman and child (Artsen Zonder Grenzen) 1·30 1·10
2410 29c.+10c. Girl feeding toddler (World Food Programme) 1·30 1·10

647 Two Hearts

2005. Greetings Stamp. Self-adhesive.
2411 **647** 39c. multicoloured 1·10 90

648 Traditional and Modern Windmills

2005. Dutch Buildings. Multicoloured. Self-adhesive gum.
2412 39c. Type **648** 1·10 90
2413 65c. Canal-side house and modern housing 1·70 1·50
2414 81c. Farmhouse and green-house 2·10 1·80

651 "Trying" (Liza May Post)

2005. Art. Multicoloured.
2415 39c. Type **651** 1·00 85
2416 39c. "Emilie" (Sidi el Karchi) 1·00 85
2417 39c. "ZT" (Koen Vermeule) 1·00 85
2418 39c. "Het Bedrijf" (Atelier van Lieshout) 1·00 85
2419 39c. "Me kissing Vinoodh" (Inez van Lamsweerde) 1·00 85
2420 39c. "Lena" (Carla van de Puttelaar) 1·00 85
2421 39c. "NR. 13" (Tom Claassen) 1·00 85
2422 39c. "Zonder Titel" (Pieter Kusters) 1·00 85
2423 39c. "Witte Roos" (Ed van der Kooy) 1·00 85
2424 39c. "Portrait of a Boy" (Tiong Ang) 1·00 85

652 Symbols of Industry

2005. Business Stamps. Entrepreneur Week. Self-adhesive.
2425 **652** 39c. multicoloured 1·50 1·30

653 Cormorant

2005. Centenary of Vereniging Natuurmonumenten (Nature preservation society). Multicoloured.
2426 39c. Type **653** 1·90 1·60
2427 39c. Pike 1·90 1·60
2428 39c. Blue-tailed damsel fly 1·90 1·60
2429 39c. Water lily 1·90 1·60
2430 65c. Hawfinch 3·00 2·50
2431 65c. Sconebeeker sheep 3·00 2·50
2432 65c. Sand lizard 3·00 2·50
2433 65c. Common blue butterfly 3·00 2·50
MS2434 Two sheets, each 144×81 mm. (a) 39c.×4, As Nos. 2426/9 (b) 65c.×4, As Nos. 2430/3 11·00 11·00

Nos. 2430/3 and the stamps of **MS**2434b, each have a Priority label attached at left.

654 "Who is the Wisest"

2005. Birth Centenary of Cornelis Jetses (children's reading book illustrator). Showing illustrations from "Ot en Sien". Multicoloured.
2435 39c.+19c. Type **654** 1·50 1·30
2436 39c.+19c. "Two old chums" 1·50 1·30
2437 39c.+19c. "His own fault" 1·50 1·30
2438 39c.+19c. "What does Puss think?" 1·50 1·30
2439 39c.+19c. "Nothing forgotten" 1·50 1·30
2440 39c.+19c. "Two bright things" 1·50 1·30

Nos. 2435/7 and 2438/40, each had a se-tenant label at head and foot, the upper inscribed with text from the book, the lower showing a modern photograph on the same theme.

655 Queen Beatrix and Prince Claus (Coronation, 1980)

2005. 25th Anniv of Coronation of Queen Beatrix. Multicoloured.
2441 39c. Type **655** 1·00 85
2442 78c. Seated (Queen's speech, 1991) 2·10 1·70
2443 117c. With Nelson Mandela (state visit, 1999) 3·00 2·50
2444 156c. Wearing glasses (visit to Netherlands Antilles, 1999) 4·00 3·50
2445 225c. Wearing hat (speech to European Parliament, 2004) 5·75 5·00
MS2446 144×75 mm. 39c. Type **655**; 78c. As No. 2442; 117c. As No. 2443; 156c. As No. 2444; 225c. As No. 2445 16·00 16·00

656 Circles

2005. Business Coil Stamps.
2447 **656** 39c. copper 1·00 85
2448 **656** 78c. silver 2·10 1·70

657 Thought Bubble

2005. Greetings Stamps. Sheet 144×75 mm containing T 657 and similar square designs. Two phosphor bands. Multicoloured background colour given.
MS2451 39c.×3, Type **657**; Thought bubble (yellow); Thought bubble (blue) 3·00 3·00

658 Windmill, Netherlands

2005. Waterwheels and Windmills. Multicoloured.
2452 81c. Type **658** 2·10 1·70
2453 81c. Waterwheel, China 2·10 1·70

Stamps of the same design were issued by China.

659 Dorothy Counts (black student) (Douglas Martin, 1957)

2005. 50th Anniv of World Press Photo (photojournalism competition). Multicoloured.
2454 39c. Type **659** 1·00 85
2455 39c. Chaplin Luis Padillo with wounded soldier (Hector Rondon Lovera, 1962) 1·00 85
2456 39c. Tank commander, Vietnam (Co Rentmeester, 1967) 1·00 85
2457 39c. Catholic graffiti (Hans-Jorg Anders, 1969) 1·00 85
2458 39c. Niger drought victims (Ovie Cartor, 1974) 1·00 85
2459 39c. Cambodian famine victim (Devid Burnett, 1979) 1·00 85
2460 39c. South Korea soldiers and mother (Anthony Suau, 1987) 1·00 85
2461 39c. Mourners at deathbed of Elshani Nashim (Georges Merillon, 1990) 1·00 85
2462 39c. Wounded man, Kukes (Claus Bjorn Larsen, 1999) 1·00 85
2463 39c. Woman mourns tsunami victims (Arko Datta, 2004) 1·00 85

660 Nijmegen

2005. Tourism. Multicoloured.
2464 39c. Type **660** 1·00 85
2465 39c. Rotterdam 1·00 85
2466 39c. Amsterdam 1·00 85
2467 39c. Roermond 1·00 85
2468 39c. Goer 1·00 85
2469 39c. Boalsert 1·00 85
2470 39c. Monnickendam 1·00 85
2471 39c. Netherland 1·00 85
2472 39c. Weesp 1·00 85
2473 39c. Papendrecht 1·00 85

661 *Blauwe Engel*

2005. Trains. Multicoloured.
2474 39c. Type **661** 1·10 90
2475 39c. Steam locomotive 3737 1·10 90
2476 39c. Intercity Express (ICE) 1·60 1·30
2477 39c. *Koploper* 1·60 1·30

662 Miffy and Snuffy

2005. Child Welfare. Miffy created by Dick Bruna. Sheet 144×75 mm containing T 662 and similar horiz designs. Multicoloured.
MS2478 39c.+19c.×6, Type **662**; Miffy and friends; Miffy and bear, Miffy writing; Miffy and Nina; Miffy at school 9·50 9·50

663 Bells

2005. Personal Stamps.
2479 **663** 29c. multicoloured 1·00 80

664 Flames

2005. Christmas. Multicoloured. Self-adhesive.
2480 29c. Type **664** 1·00 80
2481 29c. Parcel 1·00 80
2482 29c. Stars 1·00 80
2483 29c. Bells 1·00 80
2484 29c. Doves 1·00 80
2485 29c. Snowmen hugging 1·00 80
2486 29c. Balloons 1·00 80
2487 29c. Ice skates 1·00 80
2488 29c. Trees 1·00 80
2489 29c. Glasses 1·00 80

665 The Annunciation

2005. Christmas. Charity Stamps. Multicoloured. Self-adhesive.
2490 29c.+10c. Type **665** 1·10 95
2491 29c.+10c. Mary and Jesus 1·10 95
2492 29c.+10c. Adoration of the shepherds 1·10 95
2493 29c.+10c. Adoration of the Magi 1·10 95
2494 29c.+10c. Journey to Bethlehem 1·10 95
2495 29c.+10c. The Annunciation (different) 1·10 95
2496 29c.+10c. Mary and Jesus (different) 1·10 95
2497 29c.+10c. Adoration of the shepherds (different) 1·10 95
2498 29c.+10c. Adoration of the Magi (different) 1·10 95
2499 29c.+10c. Journey to Bethlehem (different) 1·10 95

666 "Koe in optrekkende avondmist" (Ed van der Elsken)

2006. Contemporary Art. Multicoloured. Self-adhesive.
2500 39c. Type **666** 1·10 95
2501 39c. "Double Dutch" (Berend Strik) 1·10 95
2502 39c. "Hollandese Velden" (Hans van der Meer) 1·10 95
2503 39c. "Tomorrow" (Marijke van Warmerdam) 1·10 95
2504 39c. "A Day in Holland/Holland in a Day" (Barbara Visser) 1·10 95
2505 39c. "Compositie met rode ruit" (Daan van Golden) 1·10 95
2506 39c. "Untitled" (JCJ Vander-heyden) 1·10 95
2507 39c. "De Goene Kathedraal" (Marinus Boezem) 1·10 95
2508 39c. "Hollandpan" (John Kormeling) 1·10 95
2509 39c. "Drijftbeeld" (Atelier Van Lieshout) 1·10 95
2510 69c. "Study for the horizon" (Sigurdur Gudmundsson) 2·00 1·60
2511 69c. "Lost luggage depot" (Jeff Wall) 2·00 1·60
2512 69c. "11000 Tulips" (Daniel Buren) 2·00 1·60
2513 69c. "Fiets & Stal" (FAT) 2·00 1·60
2514 69c. "Double sunset" (Olafur Eliasson) 2·00 1·60
2515 85c. "Untitled" (Dustin Larson) 2·40 2·00
2516 85c. "Working Progress" (Tadshi Kawamata) 2·40 2·00
2517 85c. "Boerderligezichten" (Sean Snyder) 2·40 2·00
2518 85c. "Toc Toc" (Amalie Pica) 2·40 2·00
2519 85c. "Freude" (Rosemarie Trockel) 2·40 2·00

Nos. 2500/9 were for use on mail within Netherlands, Nos. 2510/14 were for use within Europe and Nos. 2515/19 were for use worldwide.

667 Ard Schenk (10000 metres, Sapporo (1972))

2006. Winter Olympic Gold Medal Winners. Sheet 141×102 mm containing T 667 and similar horiz design. Multicoloured.
MS2520 39c.×2, Type **667**; Yvonne van Gennip (3000 metres, Calgary (1988)) 5·75 5·75

668 Monkey

2006. Summer Charity Stamps. Designs showing traditional reading boards. Multicoloured.

2521 39c.+19c. Type **668** 1·70 1·40
2522 39c.+19c. Nut 1·70 1·40
2523 39c.+19c. Cat 1·70 1·40
2524 39c.+19c. Boy and puzzle 1·70 1·40
2525 39c.+19c. Toddler 1·70 1·40
2526 39c.+19c. Girl and doll 1·70 1·40

The premium was for the benefit of Nationaal Fonds Ouderenhulp (for the assistance of vulnerable seniors).

669 Dirk Kuyt

2006. Personal Stamp.

2527 **669** 39c. multicoloured 1·10 95

670 Elvis Presley (50th anniv of "Heartbreak Hotel" (record))

2006. The Dutch Choice. Winning Designs in Stamp of your Choice Competition. Multicoloured.

2528 39c. Type **670** 1·10 95
2529 39c. Square and compass (250th anniv of Masons in Netherlands) 1·10 95
2530 39c. Purk and Pino (30th anniv of "Sesame Street" (children's TV programme)) 1·10 95
2531 39c. Sampler (regional languages) 1·10 95
2532 39c. Multatuli (creator of Max Havelaar (Dutch fictional character)) 1·10 95

671 "Bearded Man in Oriental Cap"

2006. 400th Birth Anniv of Rembrandt Harmenszoon van Rijn (artist). Multicoloured.

2533 39c. Type **671** 1·10 95
2534 39c. "Old Woman seated at a Table" 1·10 95
2535 39c. "Saskia" 1·10 95
2536 39c. "Titus" 1·10 95
2537 39c. "Woman at Window" 1·10 95
MS2538 104×71 mm. €6.45 "Self-portrait with Saskia" 17·00 17·00

672 Figure

2006. Greetings Stamp.

2539 **672** 39c. multicoloured 1·10 95

673 Reticulated Giraffe

2006. World Animal Day. Endangered Species. Sheet 135×170 mm containing T 673 and similar square designs. Multicoloured.

MS2540 39c×12, Type **673**; Tropical butterfly; Manchurian crane; Francois's leaf monkey; Blue poison dart frog; Red panda; Lowland gorilla; Sumatran tiger; Asiatic lion; Indian rhinoceros; Asian elephant; Pygmy hippopotamus 13·00 13·00

The stamps and margins of No. **MS**2540 form a composite design of a forest.

2006. Tourism. As T 660. Multicoloured.

2541 39c. Sittard 1·10 95
2542 39c. Leiden 1·10 95
2543 39c. Woudrichem 1·10 95
2544 39c. Vlieland 1·10 95
2545 39c. Enkhuizen 1·10 95
2546 39c. Zutphen 1·10 95
2547 39c. Schoonhoven 1·10 95
2548 39c. Deventer 1·10 95
2549 39c. Zwolle 1·10 95
2550 39c. Kampen 1·10 95

674 Bands

2006. Change of Postal Service Name from TPG Post to Royal TNT Post.

2551 **674** 39c. multicoloured 1·10 95

675 Children

2006. Child Welfare. Sheet 144×75 mm containing T 675 and similar horiz designs. Multicoloured.

MS2552 39c.+19c.×6, Type **675**; Children, boy wearing green jumper looking up; Children, boy riding bicycle facing right; Children, boy wearing orange jumper with football; Children, girl wearing purple jumper nursing baby; Children, girl seated holding teddy bear 10·00 10·00

The stamps of No. **MS**2552 were laid in two strips of three, each strip forming a composite design.

676 Snowflakes

2006. Christmas. Sheet 143×80 mm containing T 676 and similar vert designs showing snowflakes, colours given. Multicoloured. Self-adhesive.

MS2553 29c.×10, Type **676**; Small orange and large magenta; Large brown and small orange; Large blue and small orange; Large brown and small blue; Large blue and brown; Small blue and large magenta; Small brown and large orange; Large blue and small magenta 8·50 8·50

677 Boy as Angel

2006. Christmas. Charity Stamps. Designs showing children as angels. Multicoloured. Self-adhesive.

2554 29c.+10c. Type **677** 11·50 95
2555 29c.+10c. Girl with dark hair 1·10 95
2556 29c.+10c. Girl lying 1·10 95
2557 29c.+10c. Boy with blonde hair standing 1·10 95
2558 29c.+10c. Boy with blonde hair facing right 1·10 95
2559 29c.+10c. Child with brown hair facing left 1·10 95
2560 29c.+10c. Girl with long hair seated 1·10 95
2561 29c.+10c. Boy with curly hair facing left 1·10 95
2562 29c.+10c. Angel wearing blue 1·10 95
2563 29c.+10c. Girl with blonde hair standing 1·10 95

2006. Greetings Stamps. As T 521, 524 and 647. Self-adhesive gum.

2564 44c. multicoloured 1·50 1·20
2565 44c. multicoloured 1·50 1·20
2566 44c. multicoloured 1·50 1·20

DESIGNS: 2564, As Type **521** (new baby); 2565 As Type **524** (bereavement stamp); 2566 As Type **647** (Valentine's Day).

678 Glass ('Glidglas')

2006. Dutch Manufacture. Multicoloured. Self-adhesive.

2567 44c. Type **678** 1·50 1·20
2568 44c. Chair ('Revolt Stoel') 1·50 1·20
2569 44c. Beer bottle ('Heineken Longneck') 1·50 1·20
2570 44c. Child's buggy ('Bugaboo') 1·50 1·20
2571 44c. Kettle ('Fluitketel') 1·50 1·20
2572 44c. Lamp ('Flessenlamp') 1·50 1·20
2573 44c. Cargo bicycle ('Bakfiets') 1·50 1·20
2574 44c. Light bulb ('Spaarlamp') 1·50 1·20
2575 44c. Sausage ('Unox Rookworst') 1·50 1·20
2576 44c. Tulip ('Tulp') 1·50 1·20
2577 72c. Ice skate ('Klapschaats') 2·50 1·90
2578 89c. Cheese slice ('Kaasschaaf') 3·00 2·30

2006. Business Stamps. Self-adhesive.

2579 **634** 44c. multicoloured 1·50 1·20
2580 **634** 88c. multicoloured 3·00 2·30

679 '44' **680** '88'

2006. Business Stamps.

2581 **679** 44c. multicoloured 1·50 1·20
2582 **680** 88c. multicoloured 3·00 2·30

2007. As Type 679. Self-adhesive gum.

2583 **679** 44c. multicoloured 1·50 1·20

681 Royal Dutch Mint, Utrecht

2007. Personal Stamp. Bicentenary of Royal Dutch Mint.

2584 **681** 44c. multicoloured 1·50 1·20

2007. Tourism. As T 660. Multicoloured.

2585 44c. Groningen 1·50 1·20
2586 44c. Gouda 1·50 1·20

682 Lime Tree

2007. Trees (1st issue). Spring. 50th Anniv of National Tree Planting Committee. Multicoloured. Self-adhesive.

2587 44c. Type **682** 1·50 1·20
2588 44c. Chestnut flower bud 1·50 1·20

See also Nos. 2594/5, 2607/8 and 2611/12.

2007. Tourism. As T 660. Multicoloured.

2589 44c. Hoorn 1·50 1·20
2590 44c. Vissingen 1·50 1·20

683 Children (c. 2000) playing and Group (c. 1920)

2007. Summer Charity Stamps. Two sheets, each 145×76 mm containing T 683 and similar horiz designs showing beach holiday photographs. Multicoloured.

MS2591 (a) 44c.+22c. Type **683**; 44c.+22c. Three women in cane seat; 44c.+22c. Sand yacht. (b) 44c.+22c. Woman wearing traditional dress paddling; 44c.+22c. Woman (c. 1910) in sea and children (c. 1950) riding donkeys; 44c.+22c. Children riding donkeys and children (c. 2000) playing 9·25 9·25

The stamps and margins of **MS**2591a/b each form a composite design. The premium was for the benefit of Nationaal Fonds Ouderenhulp (for the assistance of vulnerable seniors).

Nos. 2592 has been left for 'Tourism. Schone (as T **660**), issued on 13 April 2007, respectively, not yet received.

684 Snapdragons

2007. Flowers. Sheet 107×150 mm containing T 684 and similar horiz designs. Multicoloured.

MS2593 44c.×8, Type **684**; Blue lobelia; Snapdragons and red dianthus; White petunias; Arabis; Red and white petunias; Arabis and sweet peas; Pink flox and red and white petunias; 88c.×2, Red and white dianthus and sweet peas; Pink flox 15·00 15·00

The stamps of **MS**2593 form a composite design and each contain a small amount of seeds placed centrally.

2007. Trees. Summer. 50th Anniv of National Tree Planting Committee (2nd issue). As T 682. Multicoloured.

2594 44c. Plane tree bark (detail) 1·50 1·20
2595 44c. Oak 1·50 1·20

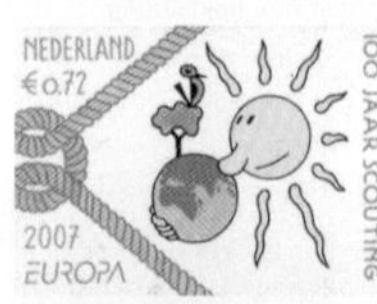

685 'JIJ' (you)

2007. 140th Anniv of Dutch Red Cross.

2596 **685** 44c.+22c. multicoloured 2·20 1·70

2007. Tourism. As T 660. Multicoloured.

2597 44c. Den Helder 1·50 1·20

686 Knot, Globe and Sun

2007. Centenary of Scouting. Multicoloured.

2598 72c. Type **686** 2·00 1·60
2599 72c. Moon, globe and knot 2·00 1·60

2007. Tourism. As T 660. Multicoloured.

2600 44c. Lelystad 1·50 1·20
2601 44c. The Hague 1·50 1·20

687 'De zee schuimt/Al seen?' and *Snow* (detail, paintings) (Jan Wolkers)

2007. Greetings Stamp.

2602 **687** 44c. multicoloured 1·50 1·20

688 Crown

2007. Bicentenary of Dutch Monarchy and Royal Designation of Products. Sheet 104×71 mm.

MS2603 **688** €6.45 multicoloured 17·00 17·00

The stamp and margins of **MS**2603 form a composite design.

689 L. E. J. Brouwer

2007. Personal Stamp. Centenary of Publication of Mathematic Dissertation by L. E. J. Brouwer. Self-adhesive.

2604 **689** 44c. multicoloured 1·50 1·20

2007. Trees. Autumn. 50th Anniv of National Tree Planting Committee (3rd issue). As T 682. Multicoloured.

2605 44c. Norway maple seeds 1·50 1·20
2606 44c. Purple beech trunk and branches 1·50 1·20

2007. Tourism. As T 660. Multicoloured.

2607 44c. Utrecht 1·50 1·20
2608 44c. Edam 1·50 1·20

2007. Tourism. Two sheets each 144×75 mm containing vert designs as T 660 Multicoloured.

MS2609 (a) 44c.×5, Den Helder; Lelystad; Hoorn; The Hague; Vissingen. (b) 44c.×5, Gouda; Edam; Leerdam; Groningen; Utrecht 10·00 10·00

The stamps and margins of **MS**2609a/b, respectively, each form a composite design.

690 Child watching Television

2007. Child Welfare. Sheet 144×75 mm containing T 690 and similar horiz designs. Multicoloured.

MS2610 44c.+22c.×6, Type **690**; Girl looking through window at tall building; Child in bed playing with flashlight; Girl using computer; Boy holding cat; Girl reading 10·00 10·00

The stamps of No. **MS**2610 share a common background.

2007. Trees. Winter. 50th Anniv of National Tree Planting Committee (4th issue). As T 682. Multicoloured.

2611 44c. Black alder 1·50 1·20
2612 44c. Willows in water 1·50 1·20

691 Firework

2007. December Lottery Stamps (scratch stamps). Sheet 141×79 mm containing T 691 and similar vert designs showing fireworks, colours given. Multicoloured. Self-adhesive.

2613 29c. Type **691** 1·00 80
2614 29c. Pink with green edges 1·00 80
2615 29c. Green with pink tips 1·00 80
2616 29c. Orange with pale centre 1·00 80
2617 29c. Pink with multicoloured centre 1·00 80
2618 29c. Orange with lavender centre 1·00 80
2619 29c. Green with pink and yellow centre 1·00 80
2620 29c. Purplish blue with multicoloured centre 1·00 80
2621 29c. Blue with pink centre 1·00 80
2622 29c. Large pink with dark centre 1·00 80

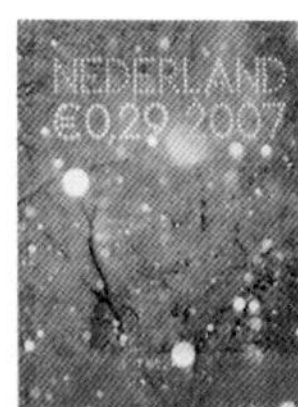

692 Tree and Snow

2007. Christmas. Sheet 143×79 mm containing T 692 and similar vert designs showing trees in snow. Multicoloured. Self-adhesive.

2623 29c. Type **692** 1·00 80
2624 29c. Branches to left and falling snow 1·00 80
2625 29c. Outline of snow covered tree 1·00 80
2626 29c. Large central snow flake and falling snow 1·00 80
2627 29c. Falling snow and outline of buildings 1·00 80
2628 29c. Falling snow 1·00 80
2629 29c. Trunk, branches and falling snow 1·00 80
2630 29c. Conifer 1·00 80
2631 29c. Copse 1·00 80
2632 29c. Snow covered trunk and branches 1·00 80

693 Heart, '80' and Stamps

2008. Personal Stamps. Multicoloured.

2633 44c. Type **693** (80th anniv of NVPH (Netherlands Association of Stamp Dealers)) 1·50 1·20
2634 44c. Pigeons in flight (centenary of NBFV (Netherlands Federation of Philatelic Associations)) 1·50 1·20

694 Hybrid Fuel Car

2008. Think Green, Act Green. Multicoloured. Self-adhesive.

2635 44c. Type **694** 1·50 1·20
2636 44c. House and sun (solar power) 1·50 1·20
2637 44c. Cow (methane—bio-fuel) 1·50 1·20
2638 44c. Wind turbines 1·50 1·20
2639 44c. Trees (CO^2 offsetting) 1·50 1·20
2640 44c. Car sharing 1·50 1·20
2641 44c. Plug with leaves (green energy) 1·50 1·20
2642 44c. Lorry with soot filter (pollution control) 1·50 1·20
2643 44c. Envelope (greener postal service) 1·50 1·20
2644 44c. House enclosed (home insulation) 1·50 1·20
2645 75c. Cycle with globes as wheels (25×30 mm) 2·50 1·90
2646 92c. Globe as heart (25×30 mm) 3·25 2·50

Nos. 2645/6 each include a label inscribed 'PRIORITY' attached at top.

Nos. 2635/44 were for use on domestic mail.

No. 2645 was for use on mail within Europe, No. 2646 was for use on mail for rest of the world.

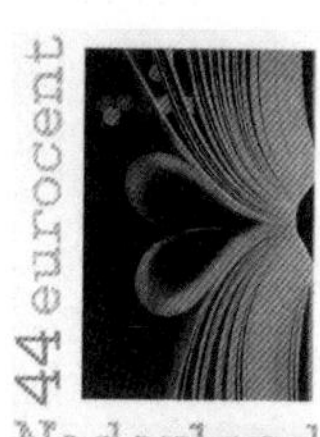

695 Book Pages as Heart (Bart Kuipers)

2008. Winning Designs in Design a Stamp Competition. Multicoloured.

2647 44c. Type **695** 1·50 1·20
2648 44c. Man, woman and 'heart' tree (Ramona) 1·50 1·20
2649 44c. Love 1·50 1·20
2650 44c. Stylized red heart (Palle van der Lijke) 1·50 1·20
2651 44c. Heart in checkerboard (Jasper) 1·50 1·20

2008. Tourism. As T 660. Multicoloured.

2652 44c. Cow, rowing boat and Coevorden Castle enclosed in goose silhouette (Coevorden) 1·50 1·20
2653 44c. Sküsje boat, Water Gate and peppermints enclosed in silhouette of Pieter Gerbrandy (prime minister during WW II) (Sneek) 1·50 1·20

696 Stylized Forget-me-not

2008. Summer Charity Stamps. Two sheets, each 144×75 mm containing T 696 and similar horiz designs. Multicoloured.

MS2654 (a) 44c.+22c.×3, Type **696**; Blue flower (crane's bill); Pink flower (larkspur). (b) 44c.+22c.×3, Japanese anemone; Globe thistle; Stylized forget-me-not (different) 10·00 10·00

The stamps and margins of **MS**2654a/b each form a composite design and, if the sheets are laid horizontally together, they also form a continuous composite design.

The premium was for the benefit of Nationaal Fonds Ouderenhulp (for the assistance of vulnerable seniors).

2008. Tourism. As T 660. Multicoloured.

2655 44c. Heiligenbergbeek, blue butterfly, Amersfoort boulder and Tower of Our Lady enclosed in silhouette of Piet Mondriaan (artist) (Amersfoort) 1·50 1·20
2656 44c. Windmill, St George and dragon enclosed in silhouette of Gisbertus Voetius (theologian) (Heusden) 1·50 1·20

697 Book, Cells, Tweezers, Moon and Ladder

2008. Anniversaries. Multicoloured.

2657 44c. Type **697** (bicentenary of KNAW (Royal Netherlands Academy of Arts and Science)) 1·50 1·20
2658 44c. Bridge, map, currency symbols and De Nederlandsche Bank building (tenth anniv of European Central Bank) 1·50 1·20
2659 44c. Amsterdam skyline, Beurs van Berlage tower, share price graph, trader and market (25th anniv of AEX (Amsterdam Exchanges)) 1·50 1·20
2660 44c. Girl reading, book piles, bookshelves and elderly man reading (140th anniv of Bruna (bookshop)) 1·50 1·20
2661 44c. Tent and symbols of tourism (125th anniv of ANWB (Royal Dutch Tourist Board)) 1·50 1·20

698 Envelope and Smiley

2008. Europa. The Letter.

2662 **698** 75c. multicoloured 2·50 1·90

No. 2657 was issued with a se-tenant label inscribed 'PRIORITY'.

2008. Tourism. As T 660. Multicoloured.

2663 44c. De Nieuwe Polder pumping station, Old Church, snow boarder and snow crystal enclosed in silhouette of Dappere Dirk (Zoetermeer) 1·50 1·20

2008. Tourism. Sheet 144×75 mm containing vert designs as T 660. Multicoloured.

MS2664 44c.×5, Sneek; Zoetermeer; Heusden; Amersfoort; Coevorden 6·50 6·50

The stamps and margins of **MS**2664 form a composite design.

699 Artists' Signatures and Coils

2008. 125th Anniv of Vereniging Rembrandt (Rembrandt Association). Sheet 104×71 mm.

MS2665 **699** €6.65 multicoloured 17·00 17·00

700 Chillies and Cheese (food)

2008. Netherlands and Beyond. Sheet 145×75 mm containing T 700 and similar multicoloured.

MS2666 92c.×3, Type **700**; Peas, condensed milk and papaya (vert); Ham, plantain and Ponche Pistachio (vert) 6·50 6·50

No. **MS**2666 also includes Netherlands Antilles 5c. stamp (Houses (architecture)) and Aruba 240c. stamp (Script (poem by Frederico Oduber)).

The 'foreign' stamps could only be used in their country of origin.

701 Heart and Pen Nib

2008. Greetings Stamp.

2667 **701** 44c. multicoloured 1·50 1·20

702 Aries

2008. Constellations. Signs of the Zodiac. Multicoloured.

2668 44c. Type **702** 1·50 1·20
2669 44c. Taurus 1·50 1·20
2670 44c. Gemini 1·50 1·20
2671 44c. Cancer 1·50 1·20
2672 44c. Leo 1·50 1·20
2673 44c. Virgo 1·50 1·20
2674 44c. Libra 1·50 1·20
2675 44c. Scorpio 1·50 1·20
2676 44c. Sagittarius 1·50 1·20
2677 44c. Capricorn 1·50 1·20
2678 44c. Pisces 1·50 1·20
2679 44c. Aquarius 1·50 1·20

703 Squid-shaped Fungi

2008. Centenary of Mycological Society. Showing fungi. Multicoloured.

2680 44c. Type **703** 1·50 1·20
2681 44c. Star-shaped 1·50 1·20
2682 44c. Fly agaric 1·50 1·20
2683 44c. Nest-shaped 1·50 1·20
2684 44c. Ink cap 1·50 1·20
2685 44c. Squid-shaped decaying 1·50 1·20
2686 44c. Star-shaped decaying 1·50 1·20
2687 44c. Fly agaric (different) 1·50 1·20
2688 44c. Nest-shaped decaying 1·50 1·20
2689 44c. Ink cap decaying 1·50 1·20

704 Pinkeltje (Dick Laan)

2008. Gnomes from Dutch Literature. Multicoloured.

2690 75c. blue, orange and bright violet 2·20 1·70
2691 75c. bistre, new blue and blue 2·20 1·70
2692 75c. orange, blue and new blue 2·20 1·70
2693 75c. blue, violet and bistre 2·20 1·70
2694 75c. violet, bistre and orange 2·20 1·70

DESIGNS: 2690 Type **704**; 2691 Wipneus en Pim (Leonardus van der Made); 2692 Piggelmee (L. C. Steenhuizen); 2693 Paulus de boskabouter (Jean Dulieu); 2694 de Kabouter (Rien Poorlvliet).

Nos. 2690/4 were issued each with a label inscribed 'Priority' attached at left.

705 'O'

2008. Child Welfare. Sheet 144×75 mm containing T 705 and similar horiz designs. Multicoloured.
MS2695 44c.+22c.×6,Type **705**; 'N' and 'D'; 'E' and 'R'; 'W'; 'I' and 'J'; 'S' 11·50 11·50

The stamps of **MS**2695 share a common background, and spell out 'ONDERWIJS' (education).

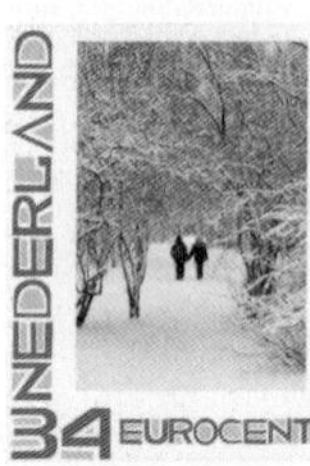

706 Walkers in Snowy Landscape

2008. Personal Stamp. Self-adhesive.
2696 **706** 34c. multicoloured 1·20 90

707 Clock Tower and Present

2008. Christmas. Sheet 144×75 mm containing vert designs as T 707. Multicoloured. Self-adhesive.
MS2697 34c.×10, Type **707**; Envelopes and Christmas tree in glass box; Christmas tree in glass box and rockets; Bell, Christmas tree and three-storied building; Three-storied building and pile of presents; Christmas tree and three-storied building with narrow windows; Three-storied building with narrow windows and candle; Snow-covered house; Envelope and left-side of fireplace; Fireplace as building 12·00 12·00

The stamps and margins of **MS**2697 form a composite design of a stylized townscape.

2009. Think Green, Act Green. As T 694. Self-adhesive gum.
2698 77c. Cycle with globes as wheels (As No. 2645) (25×30 mm) 2·75 2·10
2699 95c. Globe as heart (As No. 2646) (25×30 mm) 3·25 2·50

Nos. 2698/9 each include a label inscribed 'PRIORITY' attached at top.

Designs as Nos. 2635/44 were re-issued on the same date.

No. 2698 was for use on mail within Europe, No. 2699 was for use on mail for rest of the world.

708 'H LD OE MY H

2009. Birth Bicentenary of Louis Braille (inventor of Braille writing for the blind). Sheet 135×170 mm containing T 708 and similar vert designs. Multicoloured.
MS2700 44c.×12, Type **708**; 'DR K MS T UI'; 'NI K Z LF AN'; 'S PE O R AD U'; 'EV G DW S N IE'; 'M D XTR KA S'; ' EG N M RG XA T'; ' FI N B AF K S'; 'GE U W S RAV'; 'F BE CR O L FS'; 'Q A I N TS PHE'; 'RI F VU G H RT' 17·00 17·00

The letters missing from the front of the stamps of No. **MS**2700 are printed on the back.

The stamps are also embossed with Braille letters.

709 Golfer

2009. Personal Stamps. 125th Anniv of NVPV (philatelic society) (2702). Multicoloured. Self-adhesive.
2701 44c. Type **709** 1·50 1·20
2702 44c. Young stamp collector 1·50 1·20

2009. Tourism. As T 660. Multicoloured.
2703 44c. Spinner, ferris wheel and buildings (Tilburg) 1·50 1·20
2704 44c. Barje (character created by Anne de Vries) (statue), Pedal cars and motorcycles (Assen) 1·50 1·20

710 Couple ('DANSJE?)

2009. Summer Charity Stamps. Multicoloured.
2705 44c.+22c. Type **710** 2·00 1·60
2706 44c.+22c. Woman ('ER-OP-UIT!') 2·00 1·60
2707 44c.+22c. Ballet dancer ('JONG GELLEERD OUD GEDAN') 2·00 1·60
2708 44c.+22c. Woman and dog ('VERGEET ME NIET') 2·00 1·60
2709 44c.+22c. Trumpeter ('LET'S TWIST AGAIN!') 2·00 1·60
2710 44c.+22c. Woman holding diploma ('CHATTEN?') 2·00 1·60

The premium was for the benefit of Nationaal Fonds Ouderenhulp (for the assistance of vulnerable seniors).

711 Christian Huygens' Lens and Sketch of Saturn and Titan

2009. Europa. Astronomy. Multicoloured.
2711 77c. Type **711** 2·50 1·90
2712 77c. Locations of LOFAR (Low frequency Array) radio telescope antennae 2·50 1·90

Nos. 2711/12, respectively, have a label inscribed 'PRIORITY' attached at left, with the face value of the stamps leaching into the label.

2009. Tourism. As T 660. Multicoloured.
2713 44c. Pheasant, locomotive and stylized roses (Roosendaal) 1·50 1·20
2714 44c. Antenna, entertainers and St. Driehoek Church (Oosterhout) 1·50 1·20

712 Queens Wilhelmina Heleana Pauline Maria, Juliana Louise Emma Marie Wilhelmina and Beatrix Wilhelmina Armgard

2009. Three Queens. Sheet 104×71 mm.
MS2715 **712** €7 multicoloured 20·00 20·00

713 Books, Wooden Figure and Bottles

2009. Charities' Anniversaries. Multicoloured.
2716 44c. Type **713** (60th anniv of Cancer Support Fund) 1·50 1·20
2717 44c. Swallow, binoculars and egg (110th anniv of Bird Protection League) 1·50 1·20
2718 44c. Figures sheltered by book (95th anniv of Cordaid–People in need charity) 1·50 1·20
2719 44c. Pouring coffee (60th anniv of The Sunflower Care Association) 1·50 1·20
2720 44c. Children's building blocks as house (60th anniv of SOS Childrens' Villages) 1·50 1·20

2009. Tourism. As T 660. Multicoloured.
2721 44c. Sail ship, Maigret and container ship (Delfzijl) 1·50 1·20

MS2722 144×75 mm. As Nos. 2703/4; 2713/14; 2721 7·50 7·50

714 Tubas in Brass Band

2009. Music. World Music and Europa Cantat 2009 Competitions, Netherlands. Multicoloured.
2723 77c. Type **714** 2·50 1·90
2724 77c. WHEN YOU SING YOU BEGIN WITH DO RE MI 2·50 1·90
2725 77c. Drum majorettes 2·50 1·90
2726 77c. JAUCHZET FROH-LOCKET 2·50 1·90
2727 77c. Tubas in military band 2·50 1·90
2728 77c. para bailar la bamba 2·50 1·90

Nos. 2723/4×2, 2725/6×2 and 2727/8 were printed, each stamp having a label inscribed 'PRIORITY', attached at left or right.

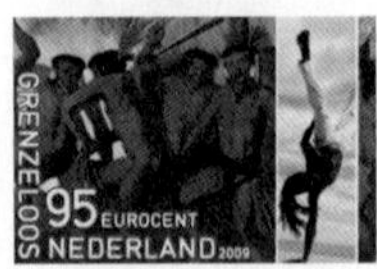

715 Aboriginal Dancers (detail of painting by Albert Eckhout)

2009. Netherlands and Beyond. Netherlands and Brazil. Sheet 108×150 mm containing T 715 and similar horiz designs. Multicoloured.
MS2729 95c.×6, Type **915**; Capoeira dancers and aboriginal warrior; Passion fruit (extract from *Historia Naturalis Brasiliae*); Cashew nut (extract from *Historia Naturalis Brasiliae*); Farmer and sugar plantation (detail of painting by Frans Post); Church ruins, Olinda (detail of painting by Frans Post) 9·50 9·50

The stamps of **MS**2729 were laid in pairs within the sheet, each stamp having a label inscribed 'PRIORITY', attached at either left or right.

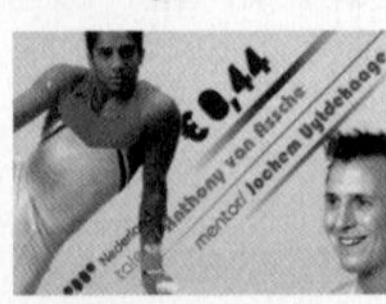

716 Anthony van Assiche (gymnast) and Jochem Uyldehaage (mentor)

2009. Sport. Stichting Sporttop–Mentoring for Olympic Athletes. Multicoloured.
2730 44c. Type **716** 1·50 1·20
2731 44c. Leon Commandeur (cyclist) and Johan Kenkhuis (mentor) 1·50 1·20
2732 44c. Mike Marissen (swimmer) and Bas van de Goor (mentor) 1·50 1·20
2733 44c. Maureen Groefsema (judo) and Lobke Berkhout (mentor) 1·50 1·20
2734 44c. Aniek van Koot (wheelchair tennis player) and Marko Koers (mentor) 1·50 1·20

717 Parcel Ribbon and Bow

2009. Greetings Stamp.
2735 **717** 44c. multicoloured 1·50 1·20

718 '88' and 'GEFELICITEERD!'

719 '88' and 'VAN HARTE!'

2009. Greetings Stamps. Birthdays. (a) Ordinary gum.
2736 44c. bright ultramarine and black 1·50 1·20
2737 44c. bright scarlet and black 1·50 1·20
2738 44c. bright emerald and black 1·50 1·20
2739 44c. bright ultramarine and black 1·50 1·20
2740 44c. bright scarlet and black 1·50 1·20

(b) Size 21×26 mm. Self-adhesive.
2741 44c. bright scarlet and black 1·50 1·20
2742 44c. bright emerald and black 1·50 1·20
2743 44c. bright ultramarine and black 1·50 1·20
2744 44c. bright ultramarine and black 1·50 1·20
2745 44c. bright scarlet and black 1·50 1·20

DESIGNS: 2736 Type **718**; 2737 '88' and 'HOERA!'; 2738 '88' and 'PROFICIAT!'; 2739 '88' and 'NOG VELE JAREN!'; 2740 '88' and 'VAN HARTE!'; 2741 Type **719**; 2742 As No. 2737; 2743 As No. 2738; 2744 As No. 2739; 2745 As Type **718**.

The phosphor bands were laid at right-angles along the left and bottom edge of the stamps.

The numerals on the stamps could be altered with a ballpoint pen to show the age of the recipient.

720 1905 10g. Stamp (As Type **11**)

2009. Stamp Day. Personal Stamp.
2746 **720** 44c. multicoloured 1·50 1·20

721 Trauma Helicopter, 1995

2009. Centenary of Powered Flight in the Netherlands. Sheet 108×150 mm containing T 721 and similar horiz designs. Multicoloured.
MS2747 44c.×10, Type **721**; Boeing 747, 1971; Apache helicopter, 1998; Schipol airport (opened 1967); Fokker F-27 Friendship, 1955; Lockheed Super Constellation, 1953; Fokker F-18 Pelican and crew (flew Christmas post to Jakarta in record time of four days); Douglas DC-2 Univer (handicap class winner and second overall in London to Melbourne air race, 1934); Wright Flyer, 1909; Anthony Fokker piloting *Spin*, 1911 15·00 15·00

722 Blue Stripe as Figure holding Pencil

2009. Child Welfare. Sheet 145×75 mm containing T 722 and similar horiz designs showing stripes as figures. Multicoloured.
MS2748 44c.+22c.×6,Type **722**; Turquoise stripe holding magnifying glass; Six stripe figures watching falling star;Blue stripe curved around red stripe; Eight stripe figures reading; Three stripe figures leaning to right watching pegasus figure 12·00 12·00

723 Parcel

2009. Christmas. Christmas rate stamps. Multicoloured. Self-adhesive.
2749 34c. Type **723** 90 80
2750 34c. Candlestick in window 90 80
2751 34c. Christmas tree on parcel (green background) 90 80
2752 34c. Pink parcel 90 80
2753 34c. Woman holding glass in window 90 80
2754 34c. Man holding glass in window 90 80
2755 34c. Christmas tree on parcel (pink background) 90 80
2756 34c. Tall magenta parcel 90 80
2757 34c. Christmas tree on parcel (blue background) 90 80
2758 34c. Blue parcel with white ribbon and Christmas tree 90 80

724 Silhouettes of Wildlife

2010. Personal Stamp

2759	**724**	44c. rosine, blue-black and indigo	1·50	1·20

2010. Tourism. Multicoloured.

2760	44c. Silhouette of Vleeshal, Frans Hals, De Adriaan windmill, St. Bavo church, Toneelschuur and city seal (Haarlem)		
2761	44c. City Hall, Abbey, Veerse-poort district building and Hans Lipperhey (Middelburg)	1·50	1·20

Vert designs as T **660**.

725 Submarine (invented by Cornelis Drebbel (1620))

2010. Centenary of Patents Act. Multicoloured.
MS2762 44c.×10, Type **725**; LED light (Philips (2007)); Artificial kidney (Willem Kolff (1943)); Wine bottle vacuum valve (Bernd Schneider (1987)); Milking machine robot (Van der Lely (1987)); Bicycle chain casing (Wilhelmine J. van der Woerd (1974)); TNT Post's automated handwriting recognition (1980); Solar vehicle (Solar Team Twente (University of Twente and Saxion University of Applied Sciences, Twente) (2009)); Dyneema fibre, world's strongest fibre (DSM (1979); Telescope (Hans Lipperhey (1608)) 15·00 15·00

726 'BOEKENWEEK'

2010. 75th Anniv of Book Week

2763	**726**	€2.20 multicoloured	6·50	5·25

727 VVV (Tourist Information Office of the Netherlands (125th anniv))

2010. Tourism and Environmental Anniversaries. Multicoloured.

2764	44c. Type **727**	1·50	1·20
2765	44c. Silhouettes of Africa (Royal Tropical Institute (centenary))	1·50	1·20
2766	44c. Duinrell, Wassenaar (holiday and amusement park) (75th anniv)	1·50	1·20
2767	44c. Euromast Tower, Rotterdam (50th anniv)	1·50	1·20
2768	44c. Pyramids of Giza, Sphinx and camels (Djoser (tour organization) (25th anniv))	1·50	1·20

728 Four-leafed Clover

2010. Greetings Stamp

2769	**728**	44c. multicoloured	1·50	1·20

2010. Tourism. Multicoloured.

2770	44c. Basilica of Saint Servatius, Helspoort gate, St Servatius Bridge, Church of St John, Bonnefanten Museum, fool's cap (reference to the Carnival festivities held annually in Maastricht) and André Rieu playing violin (Maastricht)	1·50	1·20
2771	44c. St Eusebius Church tower, City Hall, John Frost Bridge, the Rhine, ArtEZ Institute of Arts, sculpture by French artist François Pompon, Le grand cerf (big deer), Sonsbeek Park and Dutch singer-songwriter Ilse DeLange (Arnhem)	1·50	1·20

Vert designs as T **660**.

729 Ramses Shaffy

2010. 75th Anniv of Summer Stamps
MS2772 44c.+22c.×6, olive-bistre and black; orange and black; reddish purple and black; grey-blue and black; deep yellow-brown and black; dull yellow-green and black 14·00 14·00

Designs-: Type **729** (songwriter); Fanny Blankers-Koen (female athlete); Mies Bouwman (children's author and TV personality); Willy Alberti (singer); Dick Bruna (children's author); Annie M. G. Schmidt (children's author).

The premium was for the benefit of Nationaal Ouderenfonds (senior aid foundation).

730 Breskens Lighthouse

2010. Lighthouses
MS2773 **730** €7 multicoloured 10·50 10·50

No. **MS**2773 was for use on domestic registered mail.

2010. Tourism. Multicoloured.

2774	44c. Oldehove Tower, the Chancellery, Church of St Boniface, Achmea Tower, Harmonie Municipal Theatre, golden skate (reference to Elfstedentocht) and Jan Jacob Slauerhoff (poet) (Leeuwarden)	1·50	1·20

Vert designs as T **660**

731 Two Hearts

2010. Greetings Stamp

2775	**731**	1 (46c.) multicoloured	1·60	1·30

See also No. 2411.

732 Stork carrying Bundle

2010. Greetings Stamp

2776	**732**	1 (46c.) multicoloured	1·60	1·30

See also No. 1855.

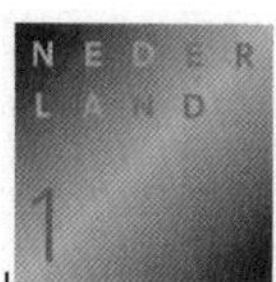

733 Light across Darkness

2010. Beareavement Stamp

2777	**733**	1 (46c.) deep turquoise	1·60	1·30

See also No. 1866.

734 Hybrid Car

2010. Think Green, Act Green. Multicoloured.

2778	1 (46c.) Type **734**	1·60	1·30
2779	1 (46c.) House and sun (solar power)	1·60	1·30
2780	1 (46c.) Cow (methane—bio-fuel)	1·60	1·30
2781	1 (46c.) Wind turbines	1·60	1·30
2782	1 (46c.) Trees (CO^2 offsetting)	1·60	1·30
2783	1 (46c.) Car sharing	1·60	1·30
2784	1 (46c.) Plug with leaves (green energy)	1·60	1·30
2785	1 (46c.) Lorry with soot filter (pollution control)	1·60	1·30
2786	1 (46c.) Envelope (greener postal service)	1·60	1·30
2787	1 (46c.) House enclosed (home insulation)	1·60	1·30
2788	1 EUROPA (79c.) Cycle with globes as wheels (25×30 mm)	2·50	1·90
2789	1 WERELD (95c.) Globe as heart (25×30 mm)	3·25	2·50

Nos. 2788/9 each include a label inscribed 'PRIORITY' attached at top, separated from the design by a line of rouletting.

See also Nos. 2635/46.

735 Children (painting)

2010. Personal Stamp

2790	**735**	1 (46c.) multicoloured	1·60	1·30

736 Patchwork

2010. Business Stamp

2791	**736**	1 (46c.) multicoloured	1·60	1·30

See also Nos. 2353/4.

737 '1'

2010. Business Stamps

2792	1 (46c.) Type **737**	1·60	1·30
2793	2 (92c.) As Type **737**	3·25	2·50

See also Nos. 2581/2.

2010. Horiz design as Type **737**

2794	1 (46c.) multicoloured	1·60	1·30

See also No. 2583.

738 'GRAND DEPART ROTTERDAM'

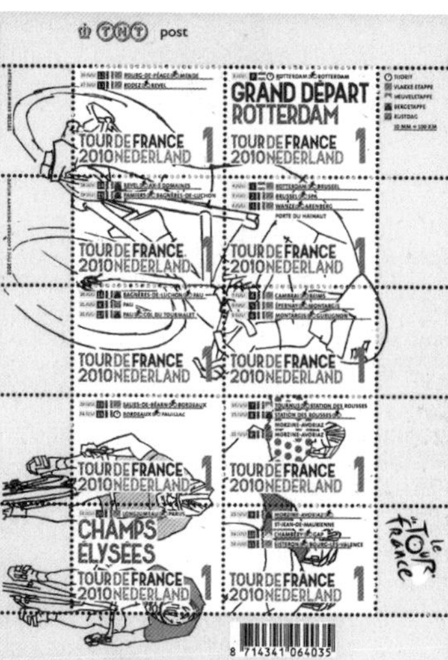

739 Tour de France (image scaled to 45% of original size)

2010. Tour de France. Multicoloured.
MS2795 1 (46c.)×10, Type **738**; Stages 1-3; Stages 4-6; Stages 7-R; Stages 9-11; Stages 12-13; Stages 14-15; Stages 16-17; 18-19; Stage 20, 'CHAMPS ELYSEES' 17·00 17·00

740 Maple Leaves

741 Forests

2010. Centenary of Royal Dutch Forestry Association. Multicoloured.
MS2796 1 (46c.)×10, Type **740**; Maple leaf (different); Jay; Pine trees; Rose hips; Rose leaves; Rose hips and fern; Ferns and logs; Tree roots; Fungi 16·00 16·00

742 Plantation House and Lamp

2010. Netherlands and Beyond. Multicoloured.
MS2797 1 WERELD (95c.) ×6, Type **742**; Handrail and building; Surinam and Dutch costume; Surinam and Dutch caps; Coloured feathers; Fruit 3·25 2·50

The stamps of **MS**2797 have a label inscribed 'PRIORITY', attached at either left or right.

743 1923 10c. Stamp

2010. Stamp Day

2798	**743**	1 (46c.) multicoloured	1·60	1·30

744 Carice van Houten and Windmill (scene from *Kleinste Kortste Film* (Tiniest, shortest film) directed by Anton Corbijn)

2010. 30th Anniv of Netherlands Film Festival

2799	**744**	5 (€2.30) mulutícoloured	8·00	6·50

745 Poster on Woman's Head

2010. AIDS Awareness Campaign. Each scarlet, black and bright lemon.

2800	1 (46c.) Type **745**	1·60	1·30
2801	1 (46c.) AIDS emblem as woman's skirt	1·60	1·30
2802	1 (46c.) Hand holding pill	1·60	1·30
2803	1 (46c.) Woman wearing sari teaching	1·60	1·30
2804	1 (46c.) Mother and child	1·60	1·30
2805	1 (46c.) Woman with eyes downcast	1·60	1·30

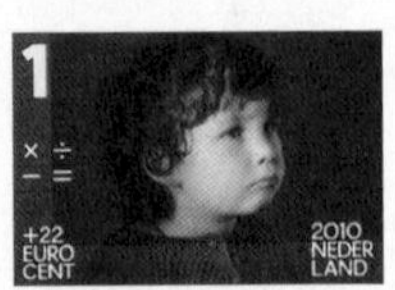

746 Child

2010. Child Welfare. Multicoloured.

MS2806 1 (46c.)+22c.×6, Type **746**; Boy with hand to his head; Boy with dark curly hair; Girl looking up, facing right; Child with hands behind head; Child with left hand raised	13·00	13·00

Nos. 2807/8 are vacant.

747 Snoopy

2010. 60th Anniv of *Peanuts* (comic strip)

2809	**747**	'DECEMBER' (32c.) muulticoloured	1·20	95

748 Child carrying Christmas Tree

2010. Christmas. Multicoloured.

2810	'DECEMBER' (32c.) Type **748**	1·20	95
2811	'DECEMBER' (32c.) Bell	1·20	95
2812	'DECEMBER' (32c.) Rocking horse	1·20	95
2813	'DECEMBER' (32c.) Embroidered heart-shaped cushion	1·20	95
2814	'DECEMBER' (32c.) Candle	1·20	95
2815	'DECEMBER' (32c.) Deer wearing ribbon	1·20	95
2816	'DECEMBER' (32c.) Santa enclosed in roundel	1·20	95
2817	'DECEMBER' (32c.) Clasped hands and roses (old-style Christmas card)	1·20	95
2818	'DECEMBER' (32c.) Angel kneeling	1·20	95
2819	'DECEMBER' (32c.) Gingerbread house	1·20	95

MARINE INSURANCE STAMPS

M22

1921

M238	**M22**	15c. green	17·00	£110
M239	**M22**	60c. red	22·00	£110
M240	**M22**	75c. brown	28·00	£110
M241	-	1g.50 blue	£100	£950
M242	-	2g.25 brown	£160	£1300
M243	-	4½g. black	£250	£1600
M244	-	7½g. red	£375	£2250

DESIGNS (inscr "DRIJVENDE BRANDKAST"): 1g.50, 2g.25, "Explosion"; 4½g., 7½g. Lifebelt.

OFFICIAL STAMPS

1913. Stamps of 1898 optd ARMENWET.

O214	**12**	1c. red	5·00	4·00
O215	**12**	1½c. blue	1·10	3·25
O216	**12**	2c. brown	9·00	10·00
O217	**12**	2½c. green	22·00	18·00
O218	**13**	3c. green	5·00	2·20
O219	**13**	5c. red	5·00	7·25
O220	**13**	10c. grey	50·00	55·00

POSTAGE DUE STAMPS

D8

1870

D76	**D8**	5c. brown on yellow	£100	17·00
D77	**D8**	10c. purple on blue	£225	22·00

For same stamps in other colours, see Netherlands Indies, Nos. D1/5.

D9

1881

D174	**D9**	½c. black and blue	55	55
D175	**D9**	1c. black and blue	1·70	55
D176	**D9**	1½c. black and blue	1·10	55
D177	**D9**	2½c. black and blue	2·20	1·10
D178	**D9**	3c. black and blue	2·20	1·70
D179	**D9**	4c. black and blue	2·20	2·20
D180	**D9**	5c. black and blue	14·00	55
D181	**D9**	6½c. black and blue	45·00	46·00
D182	**D9**	7½c. black and blue	2·75	85
D183	**D9**	10c. black and blue	39·00	85
D184	**D9**	12½c. black and blue	33·00	1·70
D185	**D9**	15c. black and blue	39·00	1·10
D186	**D9**	20c. black and blue	22·00	9·00
D187	**D9**	25c. black and blue	47·00	55
D173b	**D9**	1g. red and blue	£120	33·00

No. D188 is inscribed "EEN GULDEN".

1906. Surch.

D213b	3c. on 1g. red and blue	39·00	39·00
D215	4 on 6½c. black and blue	5·50	7·75
D216	6½ on 20c. black & blue	5·50	6·75
D214b	50c. on 1g. red & blue	£180	£180

1907. De Ruyter Commemoration. stamps surch PORTZEGEL and value.

D217A	**15**	½c. on 1c. red	1·70	2·20
D218A	**15**	1c. on 1c. red	1·10	1·10
D219A	**15**	1½c. on 1c. red	1·10	1·10
D220A	**15**	2½c. on 1c. red	3·25	3·25
D221A	**15**	5c. on 2½c. red	2·20	1·10
D222A	**15**	6½c. on 2½c. red	4·00	4·50
D223A	**15**	7½c. on ½c. blue	2·75	2·20
D224A	**15**	10c. on ½c. blue	2·75	1·70
D225A	**15**	12½c. on ½c. blue	5·50	6·25
D226A	**15**	15c. on 2½c. red	9·00	5·50
D227A	**15**	25c. on ½c. blue	11·00	10·00
D228A	**15**	50c. on ½c. blue	65·00	55·00
D229A	**15**	1g. on ½c. blue	90·00	75·00

1912. Re-issue of Type D 9 in one colour.

D230	**D 9**	½c. blue	55	55
D231	**D 9**	1c. blue	55	55
D232	**D 9**	1½c. blue	2·75	2·20
D233	**D 9**	2½c. blue	90	55
D234	**D 9**	3c. blue	1·70	1·10
D235	**D 9**	4c. blue	90	90
D236	**D 9**	4½c. blue	7·25	7·25
D237	**D 9**	5c. blue	55	55
D238	**D 9**	5½c. blue	7·75	6·75
D239	**D 9**	7c. blue	3·25	3·25
D240	**D 9**	7½c. blue	4·50	2·20
D241	**D 9**	10c. blue	90	90
D242	**D 9**	12½c. blue	90	90
D453	**D 9**	15c. blue	95	95
D244	**D 9**	20c. blue	90	55
D245	**D 9**	25c. blue	£100	1·10
D246	**D 9**	50c. blue	90	55

D25

1921

D442	**D25**	3c. blue	45	45
D445	**D25**	6c. blue	45	45
D446	**D25**	7c. blue	95	95
D447	**D25**	7½c. blue	95	95
D448	**D25**	8c. blue	95	95
D449	**D25**	9c. blue	1·00	95
D247	**D25**	11c. blue	14·00	4·50
D451	**D25**	12c. blue	95	60
D455	**D25**	25c. blue	95	60
D456	**D25**	30c. blue	95	60
D458	**D25**	1g. red	1·20	60

1923. Surch in white figures in black circle.

D272	**D9**	1c. on 3c. blue	1·20	1·00
D273	**D9**	2½c. on 7c. blue	1·70	95
D274	**D9**	25c. on 1½c. blue	11·50	1·00
D275	**D9**	25c. on 7½c. blue	14·50	95

1924. Stamps of 1898 surch TE BETALEN PORT and value in white figures in black circle.

D295	**13**	4c. on 3c. green	2·30	1·60
D296	**12**	5c. on 1c. red	1·20	60
D297	**12**	10c. on 1½c. blue	1·70	95
D298	**13**	12½c. on 5c. red	1·70	95

D121

1947

D656	**D121**	1c. blue	30	30
D657	**D121**	3c. blue	30	40
D658	**D121**	4c. blue	14·50	1·30
D659	**D121**	5c. blue	30	30
D660	**D121**	6c. blue	50	50
D661	**D121**	7c. blue	40	40
D662	**D121**	8c. blue	40	40
D663	**D121**	10c. blue	40	30
D664	**D121**	11c. blue	70	70
D665	**D121**	12c. blue	1·30	1·30
D666	**D121**	14c. blue	1·30	1·00
D667	**D121**	15c. blue	50	30
D668	**D121**	16c. blue	1·20	1·30
D669	**D121**	20c. blue	50	40
D670	**D121**	24c. blue	1·60	1·90
D671	**D121**	25c. blue	50	40
D672	**D121**	26c. blue	2·30	3·50
D673	**D121**	30c. blue	80	30
D674	**D121**	35c. blue	1·00	30
D675	**D121**	40c. blue	1·00	30
D676	**D121**	50c. blue	1·30	40
D677	**D121**	60c. blue	1·50	70
D678	**D121**	85c. blue	23·00	80
D679	**D121**	90c. blue	4·00	1·00
D680	**D121**	95c. blue	4·00	95
D681	**D121**	1g. red	3·25	30
D682	**D121**	1g.75 red	8·00	50

For stamps as Types D **121**, but in violet, see under Surinam.

INTERNATIONAL COURT OF JUSTICE

Stamps specially issued for use by the Headquarters of the Court of International Justice.

1934. Optd COUR PER- MANENTE DE JUSTICE INTERNATIONALE.

J1	**35**	1½c. mauve	2·30
J2	**35**	2½c. green	2·30
J3	**36**	7½c. red	3·50
J4	**68**	12½c. blue	41·00
J5	**36**	15c. yellow	3·00
J7	**36**	12½c. blue	23·00
J6	**36**	30c. purple	£575

1940. Optd COUR PER- MANANTE DE JUSTICE INTERNATIONALE.

J9	**94**	7½c. red	13·00
J10	**94**	12½c. blue	13·00
J11	**94**	15c. blue	13·00
J12	**94**	30c. bistre	13·00

1947. Optd COUR INTERNATIONALE DE JUSTICE.

J13	7½c. red	1·60
J14	10c. purple	1·60
J15	12½c. blue	1·60
J16	20c. violet	1·60
J17	25c. red	1·60

J3

1950

J18	**J3**	2c. blue	11·50
J19	**J3**	4c. green	11·50

J4 Peace Palace, The Hague

J5 Queen Juliana

1951

J20	**J4**	2c. lake		95
J21	**J4**	3c. blue		95
J22	**J4**	4c. green		95
J23	**J4**	5c. brown		95
J24	**J5**	6c. mauve		3·50
J25	**J4**	6c. green	1·30	1·30
J26	**J4**	7c. red	1·30	1·30
J27	**J5**	10c. green		35
J28	**J5**	12c. red		2·75
J29	**J5**	15c. red		60
J30	**J5**	20c. blue		60
J31	**J5**	25c. brown		60
J32	**J5**	30c. purple		60
J33	**J4**	40c. blue		60
J34	**J4**	45c. red		60
J35	**J4**	50c. mauve		85
J36	**J5**	1g. grey		1·20

J6 Olive Branch and Peace Palace, The Hague

1989

J37	**J 6**	5c. black and yellow	30	30
J38	**J 6**	10c. black and blue	30	30
J39	**J 6**	25c. black and red	35	35
J41	**J 6**	50c. black and green	60	60
J42	**J 6**	55c. black and mauve	60	60
J43	**J 6**	60c. black and bistre	60	60
J44	**J 6**	65c. black and green	60	60
J45	**J 6**	70c. black and blue	65	65
J46	**J 6**	75c. black and yellow	60	60
J47	**J 6**	80c. black and green	75	75
J49	**J 6**	1g. black and orange	90	90
J50	**J 6**	1g.50 black and blue	1·20	1·20
J51	**J 6**	1g.60 black and brown	3·00	3·00
J54	-	5g. multicoloured	5·00	5·00
J56	-	7g. multicoloured	6·75	6·50

DESIGNS: 5, 7g. Olive branch and column.

J7 Peace Palace, The Haag

2004

J57	**J7**	39c. blue, green and black	90	95
J58	-	61c. blue, azure and black	1·30	1·40

DESIGNS: 39c. Type J **7**; 61c. Seal.

PROVINCIAL STAMPS

The following stamps, although valid for postage throughout Netherlands, were only available from Post Offices within the province depicted and from the Philatelic Bureau.

V1 Freisland

2002. Multicoloured.

V1	39c. Type V **1**	90	50
V2	39c. Drenthe	90	50
V3	39c. North Holland	90	50
V4	39c. Gelderland	90	50

V5	39c. North Brabant	90	50
V6	39c. Groningen	90	50
V7	39c. South Holland	90	50
V8	39c. Utrecht	90	50
V9	39c. Limburg	90	50
V10	39c. Zeeland	90	50
V11	39c. Flevoland	90	50
V12	39c. Overijssel	90	50

The following stamps, although valid for postage throughout Netherlands, were only available from Post Offices within the province depicted and from the Philatelic Bureau.

V2 Nijmegen

2005. Multicoloured.

V13	39c. Type V **2**	65	55
V14	39c. Nederland, Overjissel	65	55
V15	39c. Rotterdam	65	55
V16	39c. Weesp	65	55
V17	39c. Monnickendam	65	55
V18	39c. Goes	65	55

Pt. 7

NORTH GERMAN CONFEDERATION

The North German Confederation was set up on 1 January 1868, and comprised the postal services of Bremen, Brunswick, Hamburg Lubeck, Mecklenburg (both), Oldenburg, Prussia (including Hanover, Schleswig-Holstein with Bergedorf and Thurn and Taxis) and Saxony.

The North German Confederation joined the German Reichspost on 4 May 1871, and the stamps of Germany were brought into use on 1 January 1872.

Northern District: 30 groschen = 1 thaler.
Southern District: 60 kreuzer = 1 gulden.

1

1868. Roul or perf. (a) Northern District.

19	**1**	¼g. mauve	19·00	21·00
22	**1**	⅓g. green	6·75	3·75
23	**1**	½g. orange	6·75	4·75
25	**1**	1g. red	5·25	2·10
27	**1**	2g. blue	9·50	2·75
29	**1**	5g. bistre	11·50	13·50

(b) Southern District.

30	1k. green	17·00	13·50
13	2k. orange	75·00	75·00
33	3k. red	9·50	4·25
36	7k. blue	15·00	16·00
18	18k. bistre	48·00	85·00

The 1k. to 18k. have the figures in an oval.

3

1869. Perf.

38	**3**	10g. grey	£425	85·00
39	-	30g. blue	£325	£180

The frame of the 30g. is rectangular.

OFFICIAL STAMPS

O5

1870. (a) Northern District.

O40	**O 5**	¼g. black and brown	37·00	60·00
O41	**O 5**	⅓g. black and brown	12·50	26·00
O42	**O 5**	½g. black and brown	3·75	5·25
O43	**O 5**	1g. black and brown	3·75	2·75
O44	**O 5**	2g. black and brown	9·50	6·25

(b) Southern District.

O45	1k. black and grey	42·00	£350
O46	2k. black and grey	£110	£1200
O47	3k. black and grey	32·00	65·00
O48	7k. black and grey	60·00	£375

Pt. 11

NORWAY

In 1814 Denmark ceded Norway to Sweden, from 1814 to 1905 the King of Sweden was also King of Norway after which Norway was an independent Kingdom.

1855. 120 skilling = 1 speciedaler.
1877. 100 ore = 1 krone.

1

1855. Imperf.

1	**1**	4s. blue	£5000	80·00

3 King Oscar I

1856. Perf.

4	**3**	2s. yellow	£550	95·00
6	**3**	3s. lilac	£300	60·00
7	**3**	4s. blue	£275	9·50
11	**3**	8s. red	£950	28·00

4

1863

12	**4**	2s. yellow	£550	£130
13	**4**	3s. lilac	£425	£275
21	**4**	4s. blue	£180	9·75
17	**4**	8s. pink	£600	36·00
18	**4**	24s. brown	34·00	85·00

5

1867

22	**5**	1s. black	60·00	37·00
23	**5**	2s. buff	20·00	37·00
26	**5**	3s. lilac	£275	80·00
27	**5**	4s. blue	85·00	8·00
29	**5**	8s. red	£400	34·00

6

1872. Value in "Skilling".

33	**6**	1s. green	11·50	21·00
36	**6**	2s. blue	12·50	44·00
39	**6**	3s. red	50·00	7·50
42	**6**	4s. mauve	30·00	40·00
44	**6**	6s. brown	£350	39·00
45	**6**	7s. brown	41·00	48·00

10 With background shading

A

1877. Letters without serifs as Type A. Value in "ore".

47	**10**	1ore brown	6·00	5·25
83	**10**	2ore brown	3·50	4·75
84c	**10**	3ore orange	46·00	4·50
52	**10**	5ore blue	60·00	11·50
85d	**10**	5ore green	39·00	1·40
86a	**10**	10ore red	38·00	1·60
55	**10**	12ore green	80·00	14·00
75b	**10**	12ore brown	21·00	16·00
76	**10**	20ore brown	£110	13·00
87	**10**	20ore blue	70·00	2·20
88	**10**	25ore mauve	13·00	11·00
61	**10**	35ore green	17·00	9·50
62	**10**	50ore purple	39·00	7·75

63	**10**	60ore blue	38·00	7·50

9 King Oscar II

1878

68	**9**	1k. green and light green	25·00	8·50
69	**9**	1k.50 blue and ultramarine	55·00	32·00
70	**9**	2k. brown and pink	35·00	19·00

1888. Surch 2 ore.

89a	**6**	2ore on 12ore brown	2·00	1·90

D

1893. Letters with serifs as Type D.

133	**10**	1ore drab	75	45
134	**10**	2ore brown	50	30
135	**10**	3ore orange	65	30
136	**10**	5ore green	3·75	25
529	**10**	5ore purple	50	20
138	**10**	7ore green	1·10	25
139	**10**	10ore red	5·00	20
140	**10**	10ore green	16·00	45
529a	**10**	10ore grey	50	20
141	**10**	12ore violet	85	1·10
143	**10**	15ore blue	12·50	30
530	**10**	15ore brown	50	20
144	**10**	20ore blue	5·75	25
530a	**10**	20ore green	2·20	20
146	**10**	25ore mauve	35·00	35
147	**10**	25ore red	10·50	65
531	**10**	25ore blue	20	20
148	**10**	30ore grey	7·25	40
149	**10**	30ore blue	16·00	4·25
119	**10**	35ore green	11·00	6·25
150	**10**	35ore brown	13·00	30
151	**10**	40ore green	7·50	40
152	**10**	40ore blue	55·00	25
531b	**10**	50ore purple	20	20
154	**10**	60ore blue	34·00	55
531c	**10**	60ore orange	30	20
531d	**10**	70ore orange	30	25
531e	**10**	80ore brown	30	20
531f	**10**	90ore brown	30	25

See also Nos. 279 etc and 1100/3.

1905. Surch.

122	**5**	1k. on 2s. buff	28·00	32·00
123	**5**	1k.50 on 2s. buff	55·00	75·00
124	**5**	2k. on 2s. buff	60·00	65·00

1906. Surch.

162	**10**	5ore on 25ore mauve	85	60
125	**6**	15ore on 4s. mauve	5·00	4·25
126	**6**	30ore on 7s. brown	8·25	7·50

15 King Haakon VII

1907

127	**15**	1k. green	28·00	27·00
128	**15**	1½k. blue	75·00	75·00
129	**15**	2k. red	£110	95·00

16 King Haakon VII

1910

155a	**16**	1k. green	60	20
156	**16**	1½k. blue	2·40	75
157	**16**	2k. red	3·00	95
158	**16**	5k. violet	5·00	4·75

17 Constitutional Assembly (after O. Wergeland)

1914. Centenary of Independence.

159	**17**	5ore green	1·10	40
160	**17**	10ore red	3·00	40
161	**17**	20ore blue	8·25	5·50

19

1922

163	**19**	10ore green	24·00	45
164	**19**	20ore purple	43·00	20
165	**19**	25ore red	44·00	55
166	**19**	45ore blue	4·75	85

20

1925. Air. Amundsen's Polar Flight.

167	**20**	2ore brown	3·00	3·00
168	**20**	3ore orange	6·00	4·00
169	**20**	5ore mauve	12·50	11·50
170	**20**	10ore green	15·00	14·50
171	**20**	15ore blue	16·00	19·00
172	**20**	20ore mauve	18·00	21·00
173	**20**	25ore red	7·25	5·00

21

1925. Annexation of Spitzbergen.

183	**21**	10ore green	8·50	7·75
184	**21**	15ore blue	8·50	4·25
185	**21**	20ore purple	8·50	1·20
186	**21**	45ore blue	8·50	5·50

22

1926. Size 16×19½ mm.

187	**22**	10ore green	90	20
187a	**22**	14ore orange	1·50	2·20
188	**22**	15ore brown	1·10	20
189	**22**	20ore purple	60·00	20
189a	**22**	20ore red	1·80	20
190	**22**	25ore red	19·00	1·90
190a	**22**	25ore brown	1·90	20
190b	**22**	30ore blue	2·10	25
191	**22**	35ore brown	£120	20
191a	**22**	35ore violet	3·25	30
192	**22**	40ore blue	7·75	95
193	**22**	40ore grey	2·75	20
194	**22**	50ore pink	3·00	20
195	**22**	60ore blue	3·00	20

For stamps as Type **22** but size 17×21 mm, see Nos. 284, etc.

1927. Surcharged with new value and bar.

196		20ore on 25ore red	6·00	1·20
197	**19**	30ore on 45ore blue	21·00	1·20
198	**21**	30ore on 45ore blue	5·50	4·75

24 Akershus Castle

1927. Air.

199a	**24**	45ore blue (with frame-lines)	8·75	2·75
323	**24**	45ore blue (without frame-lines)	1·10	30

25 Ibsen

1928. Ibsen Centenary.

200	**25**	10ore green	10·50	1·70
201	**25**	15ore brown	4·50	2·50
202	**25**	20ore red	5·75	45
203	**25**	30ore blue	6·50	3·00

1929. Postage Due stamps optd Post Frimerke (204/6 and 211) or POSTand thick bar (others).

204	**D12**	1ore brown	40	80
205	**D12**	4ore mauve (No. D96a)	40	45
206	**D12**	10ore green	2·10	2·10
207	**D12**	15ore brown	3·25	3·50
208	**D12**	20ore purple	1·40	55
209	**D12**	40ore blue	3·75	80
210	**D12**	50ore purple	12·50	6·75
211	**D12**	100ore yellow	3·50	2·50
212	**D12**	200ore violet	5·50	3·00

28 Abel

1929. Death Cent of N. H. Abel (mathematician).

213	**28**	10ore green	4·50	65
214	**28**	15ore brown	4·00	1·30
215	**28**	20ore red	1·70	35
216	**28**	30ore blue	2·50	1·60

1929. Surch 14 ORE 14.

217	**5**	14ore on 2s. buff	3·00	3·25

30 St. Olaf (sculpture, Brunlanes Church)

31 Nidaros Trondhjem Cathedral

32 Death of St. Olaf (after P. N. Arbo)

1930. 9th Death Centenary of St. Olaf.

219	**30**	10ore green	16·00	45
220	**31**	15ore sepia and brown	1·20	45
221	**30**	20ore red	1·60	35
222	**32**	30ore blue	6·75	2·75

33 North Cape and "Bergensfjord" (liner)

1930. Norwegian Tourist Association Fund. Size 35½×21½ mm.

223	**33**	15ore+25ore brown	2·30	2·75
224	**33**	20ore+25ore red	42·00	33·00
225	**33**	30ore+25ore blue	95·00	75·00

For smaller stamps in this design see Nos. 349/51, 442/66 and 464/6.

34 Radium Hospital

1931. Radium Hospital Fund.

226	**34**	20ore+10ore red	17·00	5·00

35 Bjornson

1932. Birth Cent of Bjornstjerne Bjornson (writer).

227	**35**	10ore green	14·00	45
228	**35**	15ore brown	1·60	1·10
229	**35**	20ore red	1·90	30
230	**35**	30ore blue	3·50	2·40

36 L. Holberg

1934. 250th Birth Anniv of Holberg (writer).

231	**36**	10ore green	3·50	45
232	**36**	15ore brown	85	65
233	**36**	20ore red	19·00	30
234	**36**	30ore blue	4·00	2·20

37 Dr. Nansen

1935. Nansen Refugee Fund.

235	**37**	10ore+10ore green	3·75	3·50
236	**37**	15ore+10ore brown	8·25	9·00
237	**37**	20ore+10ore red	4·00	1·90
238	**37**	30ore+10ore blue	8·75	8·50

See also Nos. 275/8.

38 No background shading

1937

279	**38**	1ore green	25	20
280	**38**	2ore brown	25	20
281	**38**	3ore orange	25	20
282	**38**	5ore mauve	30	20
283	**38**	7ore green	35	20
413	**38**	10ore grey	70	20
285	**38**	12ore violet	75	1·40
414	**38**	15ore green	1·70	55
415	**38**	15ore brown	60	20
416	**38**	20ore brown	3·75	1·80
417	**38**	20ore green	35	20
531a	**38**	40ore brown	20	20

1937. As T 22, but size 17×21 mm.

284	**22**	10ore green	45	20
286	**22**	14ore orange	2·30	3·25
287	**22**	15ore green	1·40	20
288a	**22**	20ore red	50	20
289	**22**	25ore brown	2·00	20
289a	**22**	25ore red	70	20
290	**22**	30ore blue	2·50	20
290a	**22**	30ore grey	8·75	20
291	**22**	35ore violet	3·25	20
292	**22**	40ore grey	2·75	20
292a	**22**	40ore blue	4·75	20
293	**22**	50ore purple	2·20	20
293a	**22**	55ore orange	29·00	20
294	**22**	60ore blue	3·00	20
294a	**22**	80ore brown	28·00	25

38b King Haakon VII

1937

255	**38b**	1k. green	30	20
256	**38b**	1k.50 blue	1·20	2·75
257	**38b**	2k. red	75	8·25
258	**38b**	5k. purple	6·50	42·00

39 Reindeer

41 Joelster in Sunnfjord

1938. Tourist Propaganda.

262	**39**	15ore brown	60	55
263	-	20ore red	60	30
264	**41**	30ore blue	60	35

DESIGN—As T **39** but VERT: 20ore, Stave Church, Borgund.

42 Queen Maud

1939. Queen Maud Children's Fund.

267	**42**	10ore+5ore green	65	9·25
268	**42**	15ore+5ore brown	65	9·25
269	**42**	20ore+5ore red	65	7·25
270	**42**	30ore+5ore blue	65	11·00

43 Lion Rampant

1940

271	**43**	1k. green	1·30	20
272	**43**	1½k. blue	2·50	45
273	**43**	2k. red	3·75	1·10
274	**43**	5k. purple	4·25	4·25

See also Nos. 318/21.

44 Dr. Nansen

1940. National Relief Fund.

275	**44**	10ore+10ore green	2·50	3·25
276	**44**	15ore+10ore brown	3·50	4·25
277	**44**	20ore+10ore red	75	1·10
278	**44**	30ore+10ore blue	1·80	2·50

46 Femboring (fishing boat) and Iceberg

1941. Haalogaland Exhibition and Fishermen's Families Relief Fund.

295	**46**	15ore+10ore blue	1·60	4·75

47 Colin Archer (founder) and Lifeboat "Colin Archer"

1941. 50th Anniv of National Lifeboat Institution.

296	**47**	10ore+10ore green	1·30	1·90
297	**47**	15ore+10ore brown	1·60	2·40
298	-	20ore+10ore red	55	65
299	-	30ore+10ore blue	4·00	5·75

DESIGN—VERT: 20ore, 30ore, "Osloskoyta" (lifeboat).

48 Soldier and Flags

1941. Norwegian Legion Support Fund.

300	**48**	20ore+80ore red	50·00	70·00

1941. Stamps of 1937 optd V (= Victory).

301B	**38**	1ore green	35	3·75
302B	**38**	2ore brown	35	6·25
303B	**38**	3ore orange	35	3·75
304B	**38**	5ore mauve	35	40
305A	**38**	7ore green	70	3·50
306B	**22**	10ore green	35	25
307B	**38**	12ore violet	1·10	14·00
308A	**22**	14ore orange	1·70	13·00
309A	**22**	15ore green	85	1·00
310B	**22**	20ore red	30	25
311B	**22**	25ore brown	60	50
312B	**22**	30ore blue	1·20	2·20
313A	**22**	35ore violet	1·70	85
314B	**22**	40ore grey	90	60
315B	**22**	50ore purple	1·70	2·40
316A	**22**	60ore blue	1·80	1·60
317B	**43**	1k. green	1·60	55
318B	**43**	1½k. blue	6·00	13·50
319B	**43**	2k. red	17·00	42·00
320B	**43**	5k. purple	30·00	£100

1941. As No. 413, but with "V" incorporated in the design.

321	10ore green	1·20	10·00

51 Oslo University

1941. Centenary of Foundation of Oslo University Building.

322	**51**	1k. green	33·00	44·00

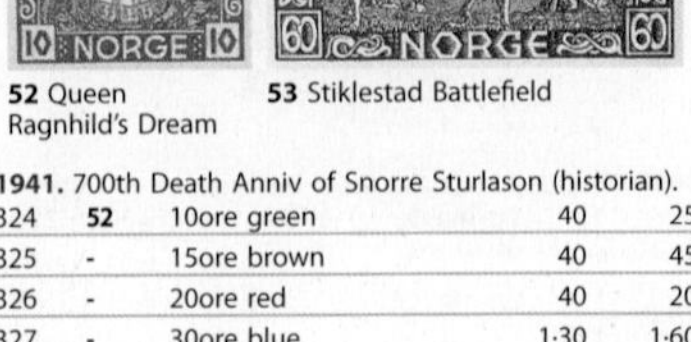

52 Queen Ragnhild's Dream

53 Stiklestad Battlefield

1941. 700th Death Anniv of Snorre Sturlason (historian).

324	**52**	10ore green	40	25
325	-	15ore brown	40	45
326	-	20ore red	40	20
327	-	30ore blue	1·30	1·60
328	-	50ore violet	95	1·30
329	**53**	60ore blue	1·40	1·40

DESIGNS (illustrations from "Sagas of Kings")—As T **53**: 15ore Einar Tambarskjelve at Battle of Svolder; 30ore King Olav II sails to his wedding; 50ore Svipdag's men enter Hall of the Seven Kings. As T **52**: 20ore Snorre Sturlason.

55 Vidkun Quisling

1942. (a) Without opt.

330	**55**	20ore+30ore red	4·50	19·00

(b) Optd 1-2-1942.

331	20ore+30ore red	4·50	19·00

See also No. 336.

56 Rikard Nordraak

57 Embarkation of the Viking Fleet

1942. Birth Centenary of Rikard Nordraak (composer).

332	**56**	10ore green	1·10	1·70
333	**57**	15ore brown	1·10	1·70
334	**56**	20ore red	1·10	1·70
335	-	30ore blue	1·10	1·70

DESIGN—As Type **57**: 30ore Mountains across sea and two lines of the National Anthem.

1942. War Orphans' Relief Fund. As T 55 but inscr "RIKSTINGET 1942".

336	20ore+30ore red	45	4·75

58 J. H. Wessel

1942. Birth Bicentenary of Wessel (poet).

337	**58**	15ore brown	25	30
338	**58**	20ore red	25	30

59 Reproduction of Types **55** and **1**

1942. Inaug of European Postal Union, Vienna.

339	**59**	20ore red	25	95
340	**59**	30ore blue	40	1·90

60 "Sleipner" (Destroyer)

1943

341	**60**	5ore purple	25	20
342	-	7ore green	35	30
343	**60**	10ore green	25	20
344	-	15ore green	95	95
345	-	20ore red	25	20
346	-	30ore blue	1·10	1·10
347	-	40ore green	1·10	1·10
348	-	60ore blue	1·10	1·10

DESIGNS: 7ore, 30ore Merchant ships in convoy; 15ore Airman; 20ore "Vi Vil Vinne" (We will win) written on the highway; 40ore Soldiers on skis; 60ore King Haakon VII.

For use on correspondence posted at sea on Norwegian merchant ships and (in certain circumstances) from Norwegian camps in Gt. Britain during the German Occupation of Norway. After liberation all values were put on sale in Norway.

1943. Norwegian Tourist Association Fund. As T 33, but reduced to 27×21 mm.

349	**33**	15ore+25ore brown	75	1·20
350	**33**	20ore+25ore red	1·40	2·20
351	**33**	30ore+25ore blue	1·40	2·20

61 Edvard Grieg

1943. Birth Centenary of Grieg (composer).

352	**61**	10ore green	30	25
353	**61**	20ore red	30	25
354	**61**	40ore green	30	30
355	**61**	60ore blue	30	30

62 Soldier's Emblem

1943. Soldiers' Relief Fund.

356	**62**	20ore+30ore red	50	5·00

63 Fishing Station

1943. Winter Relief Fund.

357	**63**	10ore+10ore green	90	5·75
358	-	20ore+10ore red	90	5·75
359	-	40ore+10ore grey	90	5·75

DESIGNS: 20ore Mountain scenery; 40ore Winter landscape.

64 Sinking of "Baroy" (freighter)

1944. Shipwrecked Mariners' Relief Fund.

360	**64**	10ore+10ore green	70	5·75
361	-	15ore+10ore brown	70	5·75
362	-	20ore+10ore red	70	5·75

DESIGNS—HORIZ: 15ore "Sanct Svithun" (cargo liner) attacked by Bristol Type 142 Blenheim Mk IV airplane. VERT: 20ore Sinking of "Irma" (freighter).

65 Gran's Bleriot XI "Nordsjoen"

1944. 30th Anniv of First North Sea Flight, by Tryggve Gran.

363	**65**	40ore blue	50	3·00

66 Girl Spinning

1944. Winter Relief Fund. Inscr as in T 66.

364	**66**	5ore+10ore mauve	55	5·25
365	-	10ore+10ore green	55	5·25
366	-	15ore+10ore purple	55	5·25
367	-	20ore+10ore red	55	5·25

DESIGNS: 10ore Ploughing; 15ore Tree felling; 20ore Mother and children.

67 Arms

1945

368	**67**	1½k. blue	2·00	55

68 Henrik Wergeland

1945. Death Centenary of Wergeland (poet).

369	**68**	10ore green	25	25
370	**68**	15ore brown	85	90
371	**68**	20ore red	25	25

69 Red Cross Sister

1945. Red Cross Relief Fund and Norwegian Red Cross Jubilee.

372	**69**	20ore+10ore red	60	60

70 Folklore Museum Emblem

1945. 50th Anniv of National Folklore Museum.

373	**70**	10ore green	65	40
374	**70**	20ore red	1·00	40

71 Crown Prince Olav

1946. National Relief Fund.

375	**71**	10ore+10ore green	55	45
376	**71**	15ore+10ore brown	55	45
377	**71**	20ore+10ore red	65	45
378	**71**	30ore+10ore blue	1·80	1·40

72 "R.N.A.F."

1946. Honouring Norwegian Air Force trained in Canada.

379	**72**	15ore red	60	80

73 King Haakon VII

1946

380	**73**	1k. green	1·90	20
381	**73**	1½k. blue	4·00	20
382	**73**	2k. brown	32·00	20
383	**73**	5k. violet	22·00	65

74 Fridtjof Nansen, Roald Amundsen and "Fram"

1947. Tercentenary of Norwegian Post Office.

384	-	5ore mauve	50	20
385	-	10ore green	50	20
386	-	15ore brown	90	20
387	-	25ore red	65	20
388	-	30ore grey	1·20	20
389	-	40ore blue	3·00	20
390	-	45ore violet	2·50	60
391	-	50ore brown	3·75	45
392	**74**	55ore orange	6·00	30
393	-	60ore grey	4·75	1·20
394	-	80ore brown	5·50	55

DESIGNS: 5ore Hannibal Sehested (founder of postal service) and Akershus Castle; 10ore "Postal-peasant"; 15ore Admiral Tordenskiold and 18th-century warship; 25ore Christian M. Falsen; 30ore Cleng Peerson and "Restaurationen" (emigrant sloop), 1825; 40ore "Constitutionen" (paddle-steamer), 1827; 45ore First Norwegian locomotive "Caroline"; 50ore Svend Foyn and "Spes et Fides" (whale catcher); 60ore Coronation of King Haakon and Queen Maud in Nidaros Cathedral; 80ore King Haakon and Oslo Town Hall.

75 Petter Dass

1947. Birth Tercentenary of Petter Dass (poet).

395	**75**	25ore red	80	65

76 King Haakon VII

1947. 75th Birthday of King Haakon VII.

396	**76**	25ore orange	55	55

77 Axel Heiberg

1948. 50th Anniv of Norwegian Forestry Society and Birth Centenary of Axel Heiberg (founder).

397	**77**	25ore red	85	50
398	**77**	80ore brown	1·80	30

1948. Red Cross. Surch 25+5 and bars.

399	**69**	25+5 ore on 20+10 ore red	80	75

1949. Nos. 288a and 292a surch.

400	**22**	25ore on 20ore red	40	20
401	**22**	45ore on 40ore blue	3·00	55

80 A. L. Kielland

1949. Birth Centenary of Alexander L. Kielland (author).

402	**80**	25ore red	1·50	30
403	**80**	40ore blue	1·50	55
404	**80**	80ore brown	2·00	85

81 Symbolising Universe

82 Pigeons and Globe

1949. 75th Anniv of U.P.U.

405	**81**	10ore green and purple	50	45
406	**82**	25ore red	50	30
407	-	40ore blue	50	45

DESIGN—37×21 mm: 40ore Dove, globe and signpost.

84 King Harald Haardraade and Oslo Town Hall

1950. 900th Anniv of Founding of Oslo.

408	**84**	15ore green	60	55
409	**84**	25ore red	60	30
410	**84**	45ore blue	65	55

85 Child with Flowers

1950. Infantile Paralysis Fund.

411	**85**	25ore+5ore red	1·70	1·50
412	**85**	45ore+5ore blue	6·25	6·00

87 King Haakon VII

1950

418	**87**	25ore red	60	20
419	**87**	25ore grey	17·00	20
419a	**87**	25ore green	1·10	20
420	**87**	30ore grey	7·75	65
421	**87**	30ore red	60	20
422a	**87**	35ore red	4·25	20
422b	**87**	40ore purple	1·70	1·80
423	**87**	45ore blue	1·70	1·80

424	87	50ore brown	3·75	20
425	87	55ore orange	1·70	1·10
426	87	55ore blue	1·30	50
427	87	60ore blue	13·50	20
427a	87	65ore blue	1·10	30
427b	87	70ore brown	11·00	25
428	87	75ore purple	2·20	25
429	87	80ore brown	3·00	30
430	87	90ore orange	1·30	25

"NOREG" on the stamps was the spelling advocated by Arne Garborg.

88 Arne Garborg (after O. Rusti)

1951. Birth Centenary of Garborg (author).

431	88	25ore red	55	30
432	88	45ore blue	2·20	2·20
433	88	80ore brown	2·20	1·70

89 Ice Skater

1951. 6th Winter Olympic Games. Inscr "OSLO 1952".

434	89	15ore+5ore green	2·75	2·75
435	-	30ore+10ore red	2·75	2·75
436	-	55ore+20ore blue	10·00	9·75

DESIGNS—As T **89**: 30ore Ski jumping. 38×21 mm: 55ore Winter landscape.

1951. Surch in figures.

437	87	30ore on 25ore red	55	20
440	38	20ore on 15ore green	50	20

92 King Haakon VII

1952. 80th Birthday of King Haakon.

438	92	30ore scarlet and red	35	30
439	92	55ore blue and grey	85	75

94 "Supplication"

1953. Anti-cancer Fund.

441	94	30ore+10ore red and cream	2·00	1·90

1953. Norwegian Tourist Association Fund. As T 33 but smaller 27½×21 mm.

442	33	20ore+10ore green	9·50	9·25
464	33	25ore+10ore green	5·00	5·00
443	33	30ore+15ore red	9·50	9·25
465	33	35ore+15ore red	6·50	6·25
444	33	55ore+25ore blue	14·50	13·50
466	33	65ore+25ore blue	3·75	3·50

95 Medieval Sculpture

1953. 8th Cent of Archbishopric of Nidaros.

445	95	30ore red	85	50

96 Stephenson Locomotive on Hoved Railway, 1854, and Horse-drawn Sledge

1954. Centenary of Norwegian Railways.

446	96	20ore green	80	40
447	-	30ore red	80	30
448	-	55ore blue	1·60	1·00

DESIGNS: 30ore Diesel-hydraulic express train; 55ore Alfred Andersen (engine driver) in locomotive cab.

97 C. T. Nielsen (first Director)

1954. Centenary of Telegraph Service.

449	97	20ore black and green	35	35
450	-	30ore red	35	30
451	-	55ore blue	80	75

DESIGNS: 30ore Radio masts at Tryvannshogda; 55ore Telegraph lineman on skis.

98 "Posthorn" Type Stamp

1955. Norwegian Stamp Centenary.

452		20ore blue and green	45	45
453	98	30ore deep red and red	35	25
454	-	55ore blue and grey	75	60

DESIGNS: 20ore Norway's first stamp; 55ore "Lion" type stamp.

1955. Stamp Cent and Int Stamp Exn, Oslo. Nos. 452/4 with circular opt OSLO NORWEX.

455		20ore blue and green	10·00	9·75
456	98	30ore deep red and red	10·00	9·75
457	-	55ore blue and grey	10·00	9·75

Nos. 455/7 were only on sale at the Exhibition P.O. at face plus 1k. entrance fee.

100 King Haakon and Queen Maud

1955. Golden Jubilee of King Haakon.

458	100	30ore red	35	25
459	100	55ore blue	50	45

101 Crown Princess Martha

1956. Crown Princess Martha Memorial Fund.

460	101	35ore+10ore red	1·20	1·20
461	101	65ore+10ore blue	3·00	3·00

101a Whooper Swans

1956. Northern Countries' Day.

462	101a	35ore red	60	55
463	101a	65ore blue	60	60

102 Jan Mayen Island (after aquarell, H. Mohn)

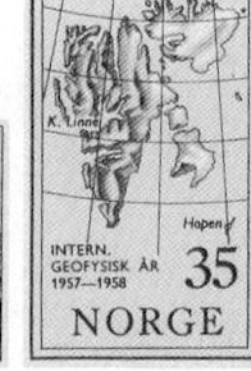

103 Map of Spitzbergen

1957. Int Geophysical Year. Inscr "INTERN. GEOFYSISK AR 1957–1958".

467	102	25ore green	45	40
468	103	35ore red and grey	45	25
469	-	65ore green and blue	45	40

DESIGN—VERT: 65ore Map of Antarctica showing Queen Maud Land.

104 King Haakon VII

1957. 85th Birthday of King Haakon.

470	104	35ore red	35	25
471	104	65ore blue	70	75

105 King Olav V

106 King Olav V

1958

472	105	25ore green	1·00	20
473	105	30ore violet	1·70	20
474	105	35ore red	65	25
474a	105	35ore green	4·00	20
475	105	40ore red	85	20
475a	105	40ore grey	3·25	1·20
476	105	45ore red	1·00	20
477	105	50ore brown	5·25	20
478	105	50ore red	6·75	20
479	105	55ore grey	1·70	95
480	105	60ore violet	4·00	85
481	105	65ore blue	2·00	40
482	105	80ore brown	11·00	55
483	105	85ore brown	1·70	25
484	105	90ore orange	1·00	20
485	106	1k. green	1·10	30
486	106	1k.50 blue	2·50	20
487	106	2k. red	9·75	30
488	106	5k. purple	37·00	20
489	106	10k. orange	5·50	20

107 Asbjorn Kloster (founder)

1959. Cent of Norwegian Temperance Movement.

490	107	45ore brown	55	30

108 Society's Centenary Medal

1959. 150th Anniv of Royal Norwegian Agricultural Society.

491	108	45ore brown and red	45	40
492	108	90ore grey and blue	1·50	1·60

109 Sower

1959. Centenary of Norwegian Royal College of Agriculture.

493	109	45ore black and brown	65	40
494	-	90ore black and blue	1·20	1·10

DESIGN—VERT: 90ore Ears of corn.

110 White Anemone

1960. Tuberculosis Relief Funds.

495	110	45ore+10ore yellow, green and red	2·50	2·40
496	-	90ore+10ore mult	6·50	6·25

DESIGN: 90ore Blue anemone.

111 Society's Original Seal

1960. Bicentenary of Royal Norwegian Society of Scientists.

497	111	45ore red on grey	55	45
498	111	90ore blue on grey	1·40	1·40

112 Refugee Mother and Child

1960. World Refugee Year.

499	112	45ore+25ore black and pink	4·25	4·00
500	112	90ore+25ore blk & bl	7·50	7·25

113 Viking Longship

1960. Norwegian Ships.

501	113	20ore black and grey	1·20	90
502	-	25ore black and green	85	85
503	-	45ore black and red	85	55
504	-	55ore black and brown	2·20	2·20
505	-	90ore black and blue	2·75	1·90

SHIPS: 25ore Hanse kogge; 45ore "Skomvaer" (barque); 55ore "Dalfon" (tanker); 90ore "Bergensfjord" (liner).

113a Conference Emblem

1960. Europa.

506	113a	90ore blue	70	65

113b Douglas DC-8

1961. 10th Anniv of Scandinavian Airlines System (SAS).

507	113b	90ore blue	75	60

114 Throwing the Javelin

1961. Centenary of Norwegian Sport.

508 **114** 20ore brown 55 55
509 - 25ore green 55 55
510 - 45ore red 55 45
511 - 90ore mauve 1·00 95

DESIGNS: 25ore Ice skating; 45ore Ski jumping; 90ore Yachting.

115 Haakonshallen Barracks and Rosencrantz Tower

1961. 700th Anniv of Haakonshallen, Bergen.

512 **115** 45ore black and red 45 30
513 **115** 1k. black and green 65 30

116 Oslo University

1961. 150th Anniv of Oslo University.

514 **116** 45ore red 45 30
515 **116** 1k.50 blue 75 30

117 Nansen

1961. Birth Centenary of Fridtjof Nansen (polar explorer).

516 **117** 45ore black and red 50 35
517 **117** 90ore black and blue 95 90

118 Amundsen, "Fram" and Dog-team

1961. 50th Anniv of Amundsen's Arrival at South Pole.

518 **118** 45ore red and grey 60 45
519 - 90ore deep blue and blue 1·10 95

DESIGN: 90ore Amundsen's party and tent at South Pole.

119 Frederic Passy and Henri Dunant (winners in 1901)

1961. Nobel Peace Prize.

520 **119** 45ore red 35 30
521 **119** 1k. green 1·30 40

120 Prof. V. Bjerknes

1962. Birth Centenary of Prof. Vilhelm Bjerknes (physicist).

522 **120** 45ore black and red 35 30
523 **120** 1k.50 black and blue 90 35

121 Etrich/Rumpler Taube Monoplane "Start"

1962. 50th Anniv of Norwegian Aviation.

524 **121** 1k.50 brown and blue 2·30 50

122 Branch of Fir, and Cone

1962. Cent of State Forestry Administration.

525 **122** 45ore grey, black and red 50 50
526 **122** 1k. grey, black and green 5·25 35

123 Europa "Tree"

1962. Europa.

527 **123** 50ore red 55 55
528 **123** 90ore blue 1·40 1·30

125 Reef Knot

1962

531g - 25ore green 30 25
532 - 30ore drab 3·50 3·25
532a - 30ore green 40 25
533 **125** 35ore green 20 20
533a - 40ore red 3·50 20
534 - 40ore green 20 20
534a - 45ore green 55 55
535 **125** 50ore red 3·25 20
535a **125** 50ore grey 25 20
536 - 55ore brown 55 55
536a **125** 60ore green 9·25 25
537a **125** 60ore red 1·30 30
537b - 65ore violet 2·50 20
538 **125** 65ore red 25 15
538a **125** 70ore brown 25 20
539 - 75ore green 25 15
539a - 80ore purple 8·50 2·20
539b - 80ore brown 20 15
540 - 85ore brown 40 25
540a - 85ore buff 30 25
540b - 90ore blue 30 20
541 - 100ore violet 60 25
541a - 100ore red 35 15
542 - 110ore red 30 20
542a - 115ore brown 85 35
543 - 120ore blue 35 30
543a - 125ore red 40 20
544 - 140ore blue 50 30
544a - 750ore brown 2·10 25

DESIGNS: 25, 40, 90, 100 (2), 110, 120, 125ore, Runic drawings; 30, 45, 55, 75, 85ore, Ear of wheat and Atlantic cod; 65 (537b), 80, 140ore, "Stave" (wooden) church and "Aurora Borealis"; 115ore Fragment of Urnes stave-church; 750ore Sigurd Farnesbane (the Dragon killer) and Regin (the blacksmith), portal from Hylestad stave-church.

126 Camilla Collett

1963. 150th Birth Anniv of Camilla Collett (author).

545 **126** 50ore red 50 30
546 **126** 90ore blue 1·10 1·30

127 Boatload of Wheat

1963. Freedom from Hunger.

547 **127** 25ore bistre 35 30
548 **127** 35ore green 65 60
549 - 50ore red 55 45
550 - 90ore blue 1·10 1·10

DESIGN—37½×21 mm: 50, 90ore Birds carrying food on cloth.

128 River Mail Boat

1963. Tercentenary of Southern-Northern Norwegian Postal Services.

551 **128** 50ore red 80 75
552 - 90ore blue 2·20 2·20

DESIGN: 90ore Femboring (Northern sailing vessel).

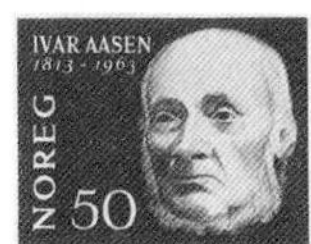

129 Ivar Aasen

1963. 150th Birth Anniv of Ivar Aasen (philologist).

553 **129** 50ore red and grey 35 30
554 **129** 90ore blue and grey 1·20 1·20

The note after No. 433 re "NOREG" also applies here.

130 "Co-operation"

1963. Europa.

555 **130** 50ore orange and purple 75 55
556 **130** 90ore green and blue 2·30 1·80

131 "Herringbone" Pattern

1963. 150th Anniv of Norwegian Textile Industry.

557 **131** 25ore green and bistre 55 55
558 **131** 35ore ultramarine and blue 1·00 95
559 **131** 50ore purple and red 55 45

132 Edvard Munch (self-portrait)

1963. Birth Centenary of Edvard Munch (painter and engraver).

560 **132** 25ore black 25 25
561 - 35ore green 30 30
562 - 50ore brown 45 25
563 - 90ore blue and indigo 60 60

DESIGNS (woodcuts)—HORIZ: 35ore "Fecundity"; 50ore "The Solitaries". VERT: 90ore "The Girls on the Bridge".

133 Eilert Sundt (founder)

1964. Centenary of Oslo Workers' Society.

564 **133** 25ore green 50 40
565 - 50ore purple 50 20

DESIGN: 50ore Beehive emblem of O.W.S.

134 C. M. Guldberg and P. Waage (chemists)

1964. Centenary of Law of Mass Action.

566 **134** 35ore green 55 45
567 **134** 55ore stone 1·40 1·30

135 Eidsvoll Manor

1964. 150th Anniv of Norwegian Constitution.

568 **135** 50ore grey and red 60 40
569 - 90ore black and blue 1·50 1·40

DESIGN: 90ore Storting (Parliament House), Oslo.

On 1 June 1964 a stamp depicting the U.N. refugee emblem and inscr "PORTO BETALT ... LYKKEBREVET 1964" was put on sale. It had a franking value of 50ore but was sold for 2k.50, the balance being for the Refugee Fund. In addition, each stamp bore a serial number representing participation in a lottery which took place in September. The stamp was on sale until 15 July and had validity until 10 August.

136 Harbour Scene

1964. Cent of Norwegian Seamen's Mission.

570 **136** 25ore green and yellow 55 45
571 **136** 90ore blue and cream 1·50 1·40

137 Europa "Flower"

1964. Europa.

572 **137** 90ore deep blue and blue 3·25 2·75

138 H. Anker and O. Arvesen (founders)

1964. Cent of Norwegian Folk High Schools.

573 **138** 50ore pink 55 40
574 **138** 90ore blue 2·00 1·90

The note after No. 433 re "NOREG" also applies here.

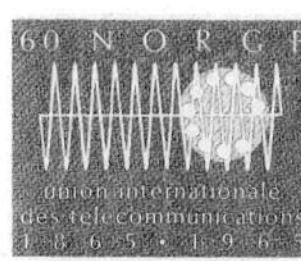

139 "Radio-telephone"

1965. Centenary of I.T.U.

575 **139** 60ore purple 55 25
576 - 90ore grey 1·00 1·00

DESIGN: 90ore "T.V. transmission".

140 Dove of Peace and Broken Chain

1965. 20th Anniv of Liberation.

577 **140** 30ore+10ore brown, green and sepia 35 30
578 - 60ore+10ore blue and red 45 40

DESIGN: 60ore Norwegian flags.

141 Mountain Landscapes

1965. Centenary of Norwegian Red Cross.

579 **141** 60ore brown and red 55 45
580 - 90ore blue and red 3·25 3·00

DESIGN: 90ore Coastal view.

142 Europa "Sprig"

1965. Europa.

581	**142**	60ore red	80	35
582	**142**	90ore blue	1·80	1·60

143 St. Sunniva and Bergen Buildings

1965. Bicentenary of Harmonien Philharmonic Society.

583	-	30ore black and green	45	30
584	**143**	90ore black and blue	1·10	1·10

DESIGN—VERT: 30ore St. Sunniva.

144 Rondane Mountains (after H. Sohlberg)

1965. Rondane National Park.

585	**144**	1k.50 blue	1·80	30

145 "Rodoy Skier" (rock carving)

1966. World Skiing Championships, Oslo. Inscr "VM OSLO 1966".

586	**145**	40ore brown	90	75
587	-	55ore green	1·30	1·30
588	-	60ore brown	50	35
589	-	90ore blue	1·30	1·30

DESIGNS—HORIZ: 55ore Ski jumper; 60ore Cross-country skier. VERT: 90ore Holmenkollen ski jumping tower, Oslo.

146 "The Bible"

1966. 150th Anniv of Norwegian Bible Society.

590	**146**	60ore red	45	30
591	**146**	90ore blue	90	1·10

147 Guilloche Pattern

1966. 150th Anniv of Bank of Norway.

592	**147**	30ore green	50	45
593	-	60ore red (Bank building)	25	25

No. 593 is size 27½×21 mm.

148 J. Sverdrup (after C. Krohg)

1966. 150th Birth Anniv of Johan Sverdrup (statesman).

594	**148**	30ore green	50	45
595	**148**	60ore purple	30	25

149 Europa "Ship"

1966. Europa.

596	**149**	60ore red	55	35
597	**149**	90ore blue	1·60	1·20

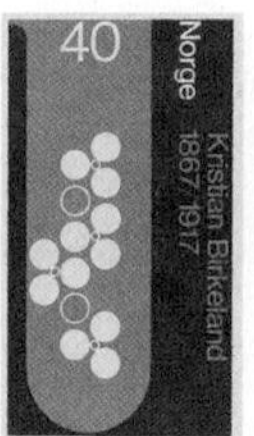

150 Molecules in Test-tube

1966. Birth Centenaries of S. Eyde (industrialist) (1966) and K. Birkeland (scientist) (1967), founders of Norwegian Nitrogen Industry.

598	**150**	40ore blue and light blue	1·40	1·10
599	-	55ore mauve and red	1·70	1·40

DESIGN: 55ore Ear of wheat and conical flask.

151 E.F.T.A. Emblem

1967. European Free Trade Association.

600	**151**	60ore red	45	30
601	**151**	90ore blue	1·70	1·40

152 "Owl" and Three Swords

1967. 150th Anniv of Higher Military Training.

602	**152**	60ore brown	55	55
603	**152**	90ore green	2·00	1·90

153 Cogwheels

1967. Europa.

604	**153**	60ore deep plum, plum and purple	80	30
605	**153**	90ore deep violet, violet and blue	1·30	1·30

154 Johanne Dybwad

1967. Birth Centenary of J. Dybwad (actress).

606	**154**	40ore blue	45	30
607	**154**	60ore red	45	30

155 I. Skrefsrud (missionary and founder)

1967. Centenary of Norwegian Santal Mission.

608	**155**	60ore brown	40	20
609	-	90ore blue	90	85

DESIGN—HORIZ: 90ore Ebenezer Church, Benagaria, Santal, India.

156 Climbers on Mountain-top

1968. Centenary of Norwegian Mountain Touring Association.

610	**156**	40ore brown	90	85
611	-	60ore red	70	20
612	-	90ore blue	1·10	1·10

DESIGNS: 60ore Mountain cairn and scenery; 90ore Glitretind peak.

157 "The Blacksmiths"

1968. Norwegian Handicrafts.

613	**157**	65ore brown, black & red	45	30
614	**157**	90ore brown, black & blue	1·10	1·10

158 Vinje

1968. 150th Birth Anniv of Aasmund Vinje (poet).

615	**158**	50ore brown	50	45
616	**158**	65ore red	30	20

See note below No. 433.

159 Cross and Heart

1968. Centenary of Norwegian Lutheran Home Mission Society.

617	**159**	40ore red and green	2·30	2·20
618	**159**	65ore red and violet	45	20

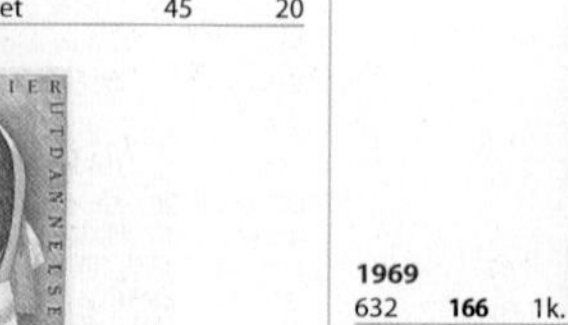

160 Cathinka Guldberg (first deaconess)

1968. Centenary of Deaconess House, Oslo.

619	**160**	50ore blue	45	40
620	**160**	65ore red	45	20

161 K. P. Arnoldson and F. Bajer

1968. Nobel Peace Prize Winners of 1908.

621	**161**	65ore brown	45	40
622	**161**	90ore blue	95	90

161a Viking Ships (from old Swedish coin)

1969. 50th Anniv of Northern Countries' Union.

623	**161a**	65ore red	45	35
624	**161a**	90ore blue	1·00	95

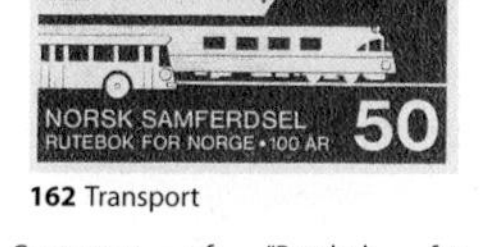

162 Transport

1969. Centenary of "Rutebok for Norge" ("Communications of Norway") and Road Safety Campaign.

625	**162**	50ore green	70	60
626	-	65ore red and green	40	20

DESIGN: 65ore Pedestrian-crossing.

163 Colonnade

1969. Europa.

627	**163**	65ore black and red	80	25
628	**163**	90ore black and blue	1·80	1·10

164 J. Hjort and Atlantic Cod Eggs

1969. Birth Centenary of Professor Johan Hjort (fisheries pioneer).

629	**164**	40ore brown and blue	75	70
630	-	90ore blue and green	2·00	1·80

DESIGN: 90ore Hjort and polyp.

165 Traena Islands

1969

631	**165**	3k.50 black	1·20	20

166 King Olav V

1969

632	**166**	1k. green	50	20
633	**166**	1k.50 blue	55	20
634	**166**	2k. red	70	20
635	**166**	5k. blue	1·70	20
636	**166**	10k. brown	4·50	20
637	**166**	20k. brown	7·75	30
637a	**166**	50k. green	12·50	35

167 "Mother and Child"

1969. Birth Centenary of Gustav Vigeland (sculptor).

638	**167**	65ore black and red	40	25
639	-	90ore black and blue	80	80

DESIGN: 90ore "Family" (sculpture).

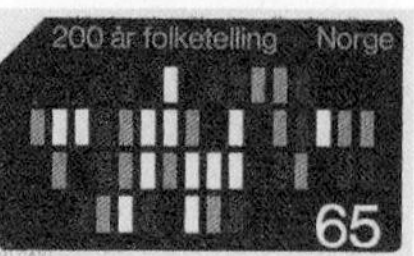

168 Punched Cards

1969. Bicentenary of 1st National Census. Mult.

640	65ore Type **168**	45	30
641	90ore "People" (diagram)	90	85

169 Queen Maud

1969. Birth Centenary of Queen Maud.

642	**169**	65ore purple	45	25
643	**169**	90ore blue	80	80

170 Wolf ("Canis lupus")

1970. Nature Conservation Year.

644	**170**	40ore brown and blue	1·00	95
645	-	60ore grey and brown	1·80	1·30
646	-	70ore brown and blue	1·00	65
647	-	100ore brown and blue	1·50	1·40

DESIGNS—VERT: 60ore Pale pasque flower ("Pulsatilla vernalis"); 70ore Voringsfossen Falls. HORIZ: 100ore White-tailed sea eagle ("Haliaeetus albicilla").

171 "V" Symbol

1970. 25th Anniv of Liberation.

648	**171**	70ore red and violet	1·30	55
649	-	100ore blue and green	1·60	1·30

DESIGN—HORIZ: 100ore Merchant ships in convoy.

172 "Citizens"

1970. 900th Anniv of Bergen.

650	**172**	40ore green	1·20	80
651	-	70ore purple	1·80	45
652	-	1k. blue	1·50	1·50

DESIGNS: 70ore "City between the Mountains"; 1k. "Ships".

173 Hands reaching for Globe

1970. 25th Anniv of United Nations.

653	**173**	70ore red	2·00	60
654	**173**	100ore green	1·40	1·30

174 G. O. Sars

1970. Norwegian Zoologists.

655	**174**	40ore brown	1·00	95
656	-	50ore lilac	1·00	75
657	-	70ore brown	1·00	45
658	-	100ore blue	1·00	95

ZOOLOGISTS: 50ore Hans Strom; 70ore J. E. Gunnerus; 100ore Michael Sars.

175 Ball-game

1970. Centenary of Central School of Gymnastics, Oslo.

659	**175**	50ore brown and blue	50	40
660	-	70ore brown and red	80	20

DESIGN—HORIZ: 70ore "Leapfrog" exercise.

176 Tonsberg's Seal c. 1340

1971. 1100th Anniv of Tonsberg.

661	**176**	70ore red	45	30
662	**176**	100ore blue	1·00	70

177 Parliament House, Oslo

1971. Centenary of Introduction of Annual Parliamentary Sessions.

663	**177**	70ore lilac and red	40	30
664	**177**	100ore green and blue	1·00	75

178 "Helping Hand"

1971. "Help for Refugees".

665	**178**	50ore green and black	45	45
666	**178**	70ore red and black	35	20

179 "Hauge addressing Followers" (A. Tidemand)

1971. Birth Centenary of Hans Nielson Hauge (church reformer).

667	**179**	60ore black	45	45
668	**179**	70ore brown	35	20

180 Bishop welcoming Worshippers

1971. 900th Anniv of Oslo Bishopric.

669	-	70ore black and red	40	35
670	**180**	1k. black and blue	1·10	95

DESIGN—VERT: 70ore Masons building first church.

181 Roald Amundsen and Treaty Emblem

1971. 10th Anniv of Antarctic Treaty.

671	**181**	100ore red and blue	2·50	1·80

182 "The Preacher and the King"

1971. Norwegian Folk Tales. Drawings by Erik Werenskiold.

672	-	40ore black and green	50	35
673	**182**	50ore black and blue	50	25
674	-	70ore black and purple	45	25

DESIGNS—VERT: 40ore "The Farmer and the Woman"; 70ore "The Troll and the Girl".

183 Anniversary Symbol

1972. 150th Anniv of Norwegian Savings Banks.

675	**183**	80ore gold and red	40	25
676	**183**	1k.20 gold and blue	95	75

184 3s. "Posthorn" Stamp

1972. Centenary of Norwegian "Posthorn" Stamps.

677	**184**	80ore red and brown	55	30
678	**184**	1k. blue and violet	55	45
MS679		120×71 mm. Nos. 677/8 (sold at 2k.50)	5·00	5·50

185 Alstad "Picture" Stone (detail)

1972. 1100th Anniv of Norway's Unification. Relics.

680	**185**	50ore green	55	55
681	-	60ore brown	1·10	85
682	-	80ore red	1·10	40
683	-	1k.20 blue	1·20	1·20

DESIGNS: 60ore Portal, Hemsedal Church (detail); 80ore Figurehead of Oseberg Viking ship; 1k.20, Sword-hilt (Lodingen).

186 King Haakon VII

1972. Birth Centenary of King Haakon VII.

684	**186**	80ore red	2·20	45
685	**186**	1k.20 blue	1·10	95

187 "Joy" (Ingrid Ekrem)

1972. "Youth and Leisure".

686	**187**	80ore mauve	60	20
687	-	1k.20 blue	1·10	1·10

DESIGN: 1k.20, "Solidarity" (Ole Instefjord).

1972. "Interjunex 1972" Stamp Exhibition, Oslo. Nos. 686/7 optd INTERJUNEX 72.

688	**187**	80ore mauve	2·40	2·30
689	-	1k.20 blue	2·40	2·30

189 "Maud"

1972. Norwegian Polar Ships.

690	**189**	60ore olive and green	1·10	95
691	-	80ore red and black	1·50	45
692	-	1k.20 blue and red	1·50	1·20

DESIGNS: 80ore "Fram" (Amundsen and Nansen's ship); 1k.20, "Gjoa".

190 "Little Man"

1972. Norwegian Folk Tales. Drawings of Trolls by Th. Kittelsen.

693	**190**	50ore black and green	55	20
694	-	60ore black and blue	60	45
695	-	80ore black and pink	60	20

TROLLS: 60ore "The troll who wonders how old he is"; 80ore "Princess riding on a bear".

191 Dr. Hansen and Bacillus Diagram

1973. Centenary of Hansen's Identification of Leprosy Bacillus.

696	**191**	1k. red and blue	45	25
697	-	1k.40 blue and red	1·10	95

DESIGN: 1k.40, As Type **191** but bacillus as seen in modern microscope.

192 Europa "Posthorn"

1973. Europa.

698	**192**	1k. red, scarlet and carmine	1·50	35
699	**192**	1k.40 emerald, green and blue	3·00	1·10

192a "The Nordic House", Reykjavik

1973. Nordic Countries' Postal Co-operation.

700	**192a**	1k. multicoloured	80	50
701	**192a**	1k.40 multicoloured	90	85

193 King Olav V

1973. King Olav's 70th Birthday.

702	**193**	1k. brown and purple	90	25
703	**193**	1k.40 brown and blue	90	80

194 J. Aall

1973. Birth Centenary of Jacob Aall (industrialist).

704	**194**	1k. purple	50	30
705	**194**	1k.40 blue	85	80

195 Bone Carving

1973. Lapp Handicrafts.

706	**195**	75ore brown and cream	50	35
707	-	1k. red and cream	60	25

708 - 1k.40 black and blue 80 70
DESIGNS: 1k. Detail of weaving; 1k.40, Detail of tin-ware.

196 Yellow Wood Violet

1973. Mountain Flowers. Multicoloured.
709 65ore Type **196** 35 30
710 70ore Rock speedwell 50 55
711 1k. Mountain heath 50 25

197 Land Surveying

1973. Bicent of Norwegian Geographical Society.
712 **197** 1k. red 40 30
713 - 1k.40 blue 90 85
DESIGN: 1k.40, Old map of Hestbraepiggene (mountain range).

198 Lindesnes

1974. Norwegian Capes.
714 **198** 1k. green 70 50
715 - 1k.40 blue 2·00 1·90
DESIGN: 1k.40, North Cape.

199 "Bridal Procession on Hardanger Fjord" (A. Tidemand and H. Gude)

1974. Norwegian Paintings. Multicoloured.
716 1k. Type **199** 50 30
717 1k.40 "Stugunoset from Filefjell" (J. Dahl) 70 65

200 Gulating Law Manuscript, 1325

1974. 700th Anniv of King Magnus Lagaboter National Legislation.
718 **200** 1k. red and brown 50 25
719 - 1k.40 blue and brown 90 85
DESIGN: 1k.40, King Magnus Lagaboter (sculpture in Stavanger Cathedral).

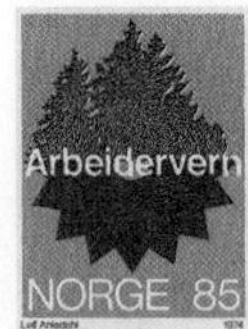

201 Trees and Saw Blade

1974. Industrial Accident Prevention.
720 **201** 85ore green, deep green and emerald 1·90 1·80
721 - 1k. carmine, red and orange 1·00 40
DESIGN: 1k. Flower and cogwheel.

202 J. H. L. Vogt

1974. Norwegian Geologists.
722 **202** 65ore brown and green 35 30
723 - 85ore brown and purple 1·30 1·20
724 - 1k. brown and orange 40 25
725 - 1k.40 brown and blue 1·00 95
DESIGNS: 85ore V. M. Goldschmidt; 1k. Th. Kjerulf; 1k.40, W. C. Brogger.

203 Buildings of the World

1974. Centenary of Universal Postal Union.
726 **203** 1k. brown and green 35 20
727 - 1k.40 blue and brown 90 85
DESIGN: 1k.40, People of the World.

204 Detail of Chest of Drawers

1974. Norwegian Folk Art. Rose Painting. Mult.
728 85ore Type **204** 50 50
729 1k. Detail of cupboard 50 35

205 Woman Skier, 1900

1975. Norwegian Skiing.
730 **205** 1k. red and green 55 25
731 - 1k.40 blue and brown 75 65
DESIGN: 1k.40, Skier making telemark turn.

206 "Three Women with Ivies" Gate, Vigeland Park, Oslo

1975. International Women's Year.
732 **206** 1k.25 violet and purple 35 20
733 **206** 1k.40 ultramarine and blue 75 65

207 Nusfjord Fishing Harbour, Lofoten Islands

1975. European Architectural Heritage Year.
734 **207** 1k. green 55 55
735 - 1k.25 red 50 30
736 - 1k.40 blue 85 65
DESIGNS: 1k.25, Old Stavanger; 1k.40, Roros.

208 Norwegian 1k. Coin, 1875 (Monetary Convention)

1975. Cent of Monetary and Metre Conventions.
737 **208** 1k.25 red 50 20
738 - 1k.40 blue 70 65
DESIGN: 1k.40, O. J. Broch (original Director of the International Bureau of Weights and Measures) (Metre Convention).

209 Camping and Emblem

1975. World Scout Jamboree, Lillehammer. Mult.
739 1k.25 Type **209** 50 20
740 1k.40 Skiing and emblem 1·00 85

210 Colonist's Peat House

1975. 150th Anniv of First Emigrations to America.
741 **210** 1k.25 brown 50 20
742 - 1k.40 blue 80 65
DESIGNS: 1k.40, C. Peerson and extract from letter to America, 1874.

211 "Templet" (Temple Mountain), Tempelfjord, Spitzbergen

1975. 50th Anniv of Norwegian Administration of Spitzbergen.
743 **211** 1k. grey 60 45
744 - 1k.25 purple 60 20
745 - 1k.40 blue 1·20 1·20
DESIGNS: 1k.25, Miners leaving pit; 1k.40, Polar bear.

212 "Television Screen" (T. E. Johnsen)

1975. 50th Anniv of Norwegian Broadcasting System. Multicoloured.
746 1k.25 Type **212** 35 20
747 1k.40 Telecommunications antenna (N. Davidsen) (vert) 75 65

213 "The Annunciation"

1975. Paintings from "Altaket" (wooden vault) of "Al" Stave Church, Hallingdal.
748 80ore Type **213** 30 30
749 1k. "The Visitation" 45 35
750 1k.25 "The Nativity" (30×38 mm) 35 20
751 1k.40 "The Adoration" (30×38 mm) 55 55

214 "Halling" (folk dance)

1976. Norwegian Folk Dances. Multicoloured.
752 80ore Type **214** 55 55
753 1k. "Springar" 55 30
754 1k.25 "Gangar" 55 20

215 Silver Sugar Caster, Stavanger, 1770

1976. Centenary of Oslo Museum of Applied Art.
755 **215** 1k.25 brown, red and pink 40 30
756 - 1k.40 lilac, blue and azure 65 65
DESIGN: 1k.40, Goblet, Nostetangen Glass-works, 1770.

216 Bishop's "Mitre" Bowl, 1760

1976. Europa. Early Products of Herrebo Potteries, Halden.
757 **216** 1k.25 red and mauve 55 25
758 - 1k.40 ultramarine & blue 1·10 95
DESIGN: 1k.40, Decorative plate, 1760.

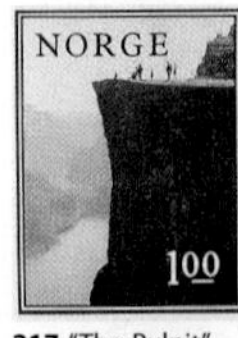

217 "The Pulpit", Lyse Fjord

1976. Norwegian Scenery. Multicoloured.
759 1k. Type **217** 55 55
760 1k.25 Peak of Gulleplet ("The Golden Apple"), Balestrand, Sognefjord 75 25

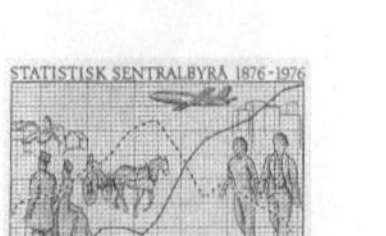

218 Social Development Graph

1976. Cent of Norwegian Central Bureau of Statistics.
761 **218** 1k.25 red 35 20
762 - 2k. blue 70 35
DESIGN: 2k. National productivity graph.

219 Olav Duun and Cairn, Dun Mountain, Joa Island, Namsen Fjord

1976. Birth Centenary of Olav Duun (novelist).
763 **219** 1k.25 multicoloured 40 25
764 **219** 1k.40 multicoloured 75 75

220 "Slindebirkin" (T. Fearnley)

1976. Norwegian Paintings. Multicoloured.
765 1k.25 Type **220** 45 20
766 1k.40 "Gamle Furutraer" (L. Hertervig) 80 75

221 Details of "April"

1976. Tapestry from Baldishol Stave Church. Mult.
767 80ore Type **221** 35 30
768 1k. Detail of "May" 40 30
769 1k.25 "April" and "May" section of tapestry (48×30 mm) 45 20

222 Five Water-lilies

1977. Nordic Countries Co-operation in Nature Conservation and Environment Protection.

770	**222**	1k.25 multicoloured	45	30
771	**222**	1k.40 multicoloured	65	65

223 Akershus Castle, Oslo

1977

772	-	1k. green	25	20
773	-	1k.10 purple	40	20
774	**223**	1k.25 red	30	15
775	-	1k.30 brown	35	20
776	-	1k.40 lilac	45	25
777	-	1k.50 red	40	15
778	-	1k.70 green	50	45
779	-	1k.75 green	45	20
780	-	1k.80 blue	45	35
781	-	2k. red	45	20
782	-	2k.20 blue	60	45
783	-	2k.25 violet	65	35
784	-	2k.50 red	55	15
785	-	2k.75 red	80	65
786	-	3k. blue	65	25
787	-	3k.50 violet	90	35

DESIGNS—HORIZ: 1k. Austraat Manor; 1k.10, Trondenes Church, Harstad; 1k.30, Steinviksholm Fortress, Asen Fjord; 1k.40, Ruins of Hamar Cathedral; 2k.20, Tromsdalen Church; 2k.50, Loghouse, Breiland; 2k.75, Damsgard Palace, Laksevag, near Bergen; 3k. Ruins of Selje Monastery; 3k.50, Lindesnes lighthouse. VERT: 1k.50, Stavanger Cathedral; 1k.70, Rosenkrantz Tower, Bergen; 1k.75, Seamen's commemoration hall, Stavern; 1k.80, Torungen lighthouses, Arendal; 2k. Tofte royal estate, Dovre; 2k.25, Oscarshall (royal residence), Oslofjord.

224 Hamnoy, Lofoten Islands

1977. Europa. Multicoloured.

795	1k.25 Type **224**	65	30
796	1k.80 Huldrefossen, Nordfjord (vert)	1·00	85

225 Spruce

1977. Norwegian Trees.

797	**225**	1k. green	40	30
798	-	1k.25 brown	50	30
799	-	1k.80 black	55	55

DESIGNS: 1k.25, Fir; 1k.80, Birch.
See note below No. 433.

226 "Constitutionen" (paddle-steamer) at Arendal

1977. Norwegian Coastal Routes.

800	**226**	1k. brown	35	25
801	-	1k.25 red	65	25
802	-	1k.30 green	1·30	1·10
803	-	1k.80 blue	75	60

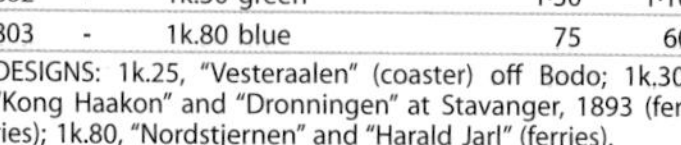
DESIGNS: 1k.25, "Vesteraalen" (coaster) off Bodo; 1k.30, "Kong Haakon" and "Dronningen" at Stavanger, 1893 (ferries); 1k.80, "Nordstjernen" and "Harald Jarl" (ferries).

227 "From the Herring Fishery" (after photo by S. A. Borretzen)

1977. Fishing Industry.

804	**227**	1k.25 brown on orange	50	20
805	-	1k.80 blue on blue	65	60

DESIGN: 1k.80, Saithe and fish hooks.
See note below No. 433.

228 "Saturday Evening" (H. Egedius)

1977. Norwegian Paintings. Multicoloured.

806	1k.25 Type **228**	35	30
807	1k.80 "Forest Lake in Lower Telemark" (A. Cappelen)	75	70

229 "David with the Bells"

1977. Miniatures from the Bible of Aslak Bolt. Mult.

808	80ore Type **229**	30	20
809	1k. "Singing Friars"	35	20
810	1k.25 "The Holy Virgin with the Child" (34×27 mm)	40	20

230 "Peer and the Buck Reindeer" (after drawing by P. Krohg for "Peer Gynt")

1978. 150th Birth Anniv of Henrik Ibsen (dramatist).

811	**230**	1k.25 black and stone	35	25
812	-	1k.80 multicoloured	70	65

DESIGN: 1k.80, Ibsen (after E. Werenskiold).

231 Heddal Stave Church, Telemark

1978. Europa.

813	**231**	1k.25 brown and orange	85	35
814	-	1k.80 green and blue	1·40	90

DESIGN: 1k.80, Borgund stave church, Sogn.

232 Lenangstindene and Jaegervasstindene, Troms

1978. Norwegian Scenery. Multicoloured.

815	1k. Type **232**	55	25
816	1k.25 Gaustatoppen, Telemark	60	20

233 King Olav in Sailing-boat

1978. 75th Birthday of King Olav V.

817	**233**	1k.25 brown	45	20
818	-	1k.80 violet	75	65

DESIGN—VERT: 1k.80, King Olav delivering royal speech at opening of Parliament.

234 Amundsen's Polar Flight Stamp of 1925

1978. "Norwex 80" International Stamp Exhibition (1st issue).

819	**234**	1k.25 green and grey	65	65
820	**234**	1k.25 blue and grey	65	65
821	-	1k.25 green and grey	65	65
822	-	1k.25 blue and grey	65	65
823	**234**	1k.25 purple and grey	65	65
824	**234**	1k.25 red and grey	65	65
825	-	1k.25 purple and grey	65	65
826	-	1k.25 blue and grey	65	65

DESIGNS: Nos. 821/2, 825/6, Annexation of Spitzbergen stamp of 1925.

On Nos. 819/26 each design incorporates a different value of the 1925 issues.

See also Nos. **MS**847 and **MS**862.

235 Willow Pipe Player

1978. Musical Instruments.

827	**235**	1k. green	30	20
828	-	1k.25 red	35	20
829	-	1k.80 blue	60	50
830	-	7k.50 grey	2·75	30
831	-	15k. brown	3·75	30

DESIGNS: 1k.25, Norwegian violin; 1k.80, Norwegian zither; 7k.50, Ram's horn; 15k. Jew's harp.
See note below No. 433.

236 Wooden Doll, c. 1830

1978. Christmas. Antique Toys from Norwegian Folk Museum. Multicoloured.

835	80ore Type **236**	30	25
836	1k. Toy town, 1896/7	40	25
837	1k.25 Wooden horse from Torpo, Hallingdal	35	20

237 Ski Jumping at Huseby, 1879

1979. Centenary of Skiing Competitions at Huseby and Holmenkollen.

838	**237**	1k. green	40	30
839	-	1k.25 red	45	20
840	-	1k.80 blue	70	60

DESIGNS: 1k.25, Crown Prince Olav ski jumping at Holmenkollen, 1922; 1k.80, Cross-country skiing at Holmenkollen, 1976.

238 "Portrait of Girl" (M. Stoltenberg)

1979. International Year of the Child. Mult.

841	1k.25 Type **238**	40	25
842	1k.80 "Portrait of Boy" (H. C. F. Hosenfelder)	70	65

239 Road to Briksdal Glacier

1979. Norwegian Scenery. Multicoloured.

843	1k. Type **239**	45	25
844	1k.25 Skjernoysund, near Mandal	55	25

240 Falkberget (after Harald Dal)

1979. Birth Centenary of Johan Falkberget (novelist).

845	**240**	1k.25 brown	45	25
846	-	1k.80 blue	60	60

DESIGN: 1k.80, "Ann-Magritt and the Hovi Bullock" (statue by Kristofer Leirdal).

241 Dornier Do-J Wal Flying Boat N-25

1979. "Norwex 80" International Stamp Exhibition, Oslo (2nd issue). Arctic Aviation. Sheet 113×91 mm containing T 241 and similar horiz designs, each black, yellow and ultramarine.

MS847 1k.25 Type **241** (Amundsen and Ellsworth, 1925); 2k. Airship N.1 *Norge* (Amundsen, Ellsworth and Nobile, 1926); 2k.80, Loening OA-2 amphibian *Live Eriksson* (Thor Solberg, 1935); 4k. Douglas DC-7C *Reider Viking* (first scheduled flight over North Pole, 1957) (sold at 15k.)	4·75	4·50

242 Steam Train on Kylling Bridge, Verma, Romsdal

1979. Norwegian Engineering.

848	**242**	1k.25 black and brown	40	15
849	-	2k. black and blue	60	25
850	-	10k. brown and bistre	2·75	45

DESIGNS: 2k. Vessingsjo Dam, Nea, Sor- Trondelag; 10k. Statfjord A offshore oil drilling and production platform.

243 Glacier Buttercup ("Ranunculus glacialis")

1979. Flowers. Multicoloured.

851	80ore Type **243**	35	20
852	1k. Alpine cinquefoil ("Potentilla crantzii")	35	20
853	1k.25 Purple saxifrage ("Saxifraga oppositifolia")	45	20

See also Nos. 867/8.

244 Leaf and Emblems

1980. Centenary of Norwegian Christian Youth Association. Multicoloured.

854	1k. Type **244**	30	25
855	1k.80 Plant and emblems	65	60

245 Oystercatcher Chick ("Haematopus ostralegus")

1980. Birds (1st series). Multicoloured.

No.	Type	Description	Unused	Used
856		1k. Type **245**	30	20
857		1k. Mallard chick ("Anas platyrhynchos")	30	20
858		1k.25 White-throated dipper ("Cinclus cinclus")	40	20
859		1k.25 Great tit ("Parus major")	40	20

See also Nos. 869/72, 894/5 and 914/15.

246 Telephone and Dish Aerial

1980. Centenary of Norwegian Telephone Service.

No.	Type	Description	Unused	Used
860	**246**	1k.25 brown, purple & bl	35	25
861	-	1k.80 multicoloured	75	70

DESIGN: 1k.80, Erecting a telephone pole.

247 *Bergen* (paddle-steamer)

1980. "Norwex 80" International Stamp Exhibition, Oslo (3rd issue). Sheet 113×90 mm containing T 247 and similar horiz designs.

No.	Description	Unused	Used
MS862	1k.25, red and black; 2k. yellow and black; 2k.80, yellow, green and black; 4k. dull blue and black (sold at 15k.)	4·75	4·50

DESIGNS: 2k. Steam locomotive and carriages, 1900; 2k.80, Motor coach, 1940; 4k. Boeing 737 and Douglas DC-9 aircraft.

248 "Vulcan as an Armourer" (Hassel Jerverk after Bech)

1980. Nordic Countries' Postal Co-operation. Cast-iron Stove Ornaments.

No.	Type	Description	Unused	Used
863	**248**	1k.25 brown	35	25
864	-	1k.80 violet	70	65

DESIGN: 1k.80, "Hercules at a burning Altar" (Moss Jerverk after Henrich Bech).

249 "Jonsokbal" (Nikolai Astrup)

1980. Norwegian Paintings. Multicoloured.

No.	Type	Description	Unused	Used
865		1k.25 Type **249**	35	25
866		1k.80 "Seljefloyten" (Christian Skredsvig)	70	65

1980. Flowers. As T 243. Multicoloured.

No.	Type	Description	Unused	Used
867		80ore Rowan berries ("Sorbus aucparia")	30	25
868		1k. Dog rose hips ("Rosa canina")	30	25

1981. Birds (2nd series). As T 245. Multicoloured.

No.	Type	Description	Unused	Used
869		1k.30 Lesser white-fronted goose ("Anser erythropus")	40	30
870		1k.30 Peregrine falcon ("Falco peregrinus")	40	30
871		1k.50 Atlantic puffin ("Fratercula arctica")	50	25
872		1k.50 Black guillemot ("Cepphus grylle")	50	25

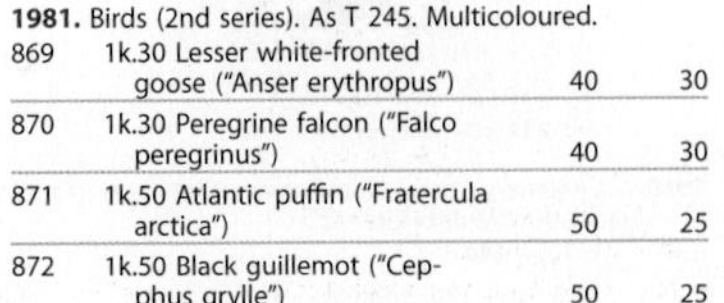

250 Cow

1981. Centenary of Norwegian Milk Producers' National Association. Multicoloured.

No.	Type	Description	Unused	Used
873		1k.10 Type **250**	40	20
874		1k.50 Goat	45	20

See note below No. 433.

251 "The Mermaid" (painting by Kristen Aanstad on wooden dish from Hol)

1981. Europa. Multicoloured.

No.	Type	Description	Unused	Used
875		1k.50 Type **251**	65	30
876		2k.20 "The Proposal" (painting by Ola Hansson on box from Nes)	1·00	85

See note below No. 433.

252 Weighing Anchor

1981. Sailing Ship Era.

No.	Type	Description	Unused	Used
877	**252**	1k.30 green	40	30
878	-	1k.50 red	45	25
879	-	2k.20 blue	65	55

DESIGNS—VERT: 1k.50, Climbing the rigging. HORIZ: 2k.20, "Christian Radich" (cadet ship).

253 "Skibladner" (paddle-steamer)

1981. Norwegian Lake Shipping.

No.	Type	Description	Unused	Used
880	**253**	1k.10 brown	45	20
881	-	1k.30 green	55	45
882	-	1k.50 red	55	25
883	-	2k.30 blue	80	45

DESIGNS: 1k.30, "Victoria" (ferry); 1k.50, "Faemund II" (ferry); 2k.30, "Storegut" (train ferry).

254 Handicapped People as Part of Community

1981. International Year of Disabled Persons.

No.	Type	Description	Unused	Used
884	**254**	1k.50 pink, red and blue	50	25
885	-	2k.20 blue, deep blue and red	60	50

DESIGN: 2k.20, Handicapped and non-handicapped people walking together.

255 "Interior in Blue" (Harriet Backer)

1981. Norwegian Paintings. Multicoloured.

No.	Type	Description	Unused	Used
886		1k.50 Type **255**	35	25
887		1k.70 "Peat Moor on Jaeren" (Kitty Lange Kielland)	65	60

256 Hajalmar Branting and Christian Lange

1981. Nobel Peace Prize Winners of 1921.

No.	Type	Description	Unused	Used
888	**256**	5k. black	1·40	30

257 "One of the Magi" (detail from Skjak tapestry, 1625)

1981. Tapestries. Multicoloured.

No.	Type	Description	Unused	Used
889		1k.10 Type **257**	30	25
890		1k.30 "Adoration of Christ" (detail, Skjak tapestry, 1625)	30	30
891		1k.50 "Marriage in Cana" (pillow slip from Storen, 18th century) (29×36 mm)	45	20

258 Ski Sticks

1982. World Ski Championships, Oslo.

No.	Type	Description	Unused	Used
892	**258**	2k. red and blue	45	25
893	-	3k. blue and red	70	45

DESIGN: 3k. Skis.

1982. Birds (3rd series). As T 245. Multicoloured.

No.	Type	Description	Unused	Used
894		2k. Bluethroat ("Luscinia svecica")	50	25
895		2k. European robin ("Erithacus rubecula")	50	25

259 Nurse

1982. Anti-tuberculosis Campaign. Mult.

No.	Type	Description	Unused	Used
896		2k. Type **259**	45	20
897		3k. Microscope	70	60

See note below No. 433.

260 King Haakon VII disembarking from "Heimdal" after Election, 1905

1982. Europa.

No.	Type	Description	Unused	Used
898	**260**	2k. brown	1·70	30
899	-	3k. blue	1·90	45

DESIGN: 3k. Crown Prince Olav greeting King Haakon VII after liberation, 1945.

261 "Girls from Telemark" (Erik Werenskiold)

1982. Norwegian Paintings. Multicoloured.

No.	Type	Description	Unused	Used
900		1k.75 Type **261**	50	40
901		2k. "Tone Veli by Fence" (Henrik Sorenson) (vert)	50	25

See note below No. 433.

262 Consecration Ceremony, Nidaros Cathedral, Trondheim

1982. 25th Anniv of King Olav V's Reign.

No.	Type	Description	Unused	Used
902	**262**	3k. violet	1·00	75

263 "Bjornstjerne Bjornson on Balcony at Aulestad" (Erik Werenskiold)

1982. Writers' Birth Anniversaries. Multicoloured.

No.	Type	Description	Unused	Used
903		1k.75 Type **263** (150th anniv)	60	30
904		2k. "Sigrid Undset" (after A. C. Svarstad) (birth centenary)	60	20

264 Construction of Letter "A"

1982. Centenary of Graphical Union of Norway.

No.	Type	Description	Unused	Used
905	**264**	2k. yellow, green and black	50	30
906	-	3k. multicoloured	75	50

DESIGN: 3k. Offset litho printing rollers.

265 Fridtjof Nansen

1982. 1922 Nobel Peace Prize Winner.

No.	Type	Description	Unused	Used
907	**265**	3k. blue	1·00	40

See note below No. 433.

266 "Christmas Tradition" (Adolf Tidemand)

1982. Christmas.

No.	Type	Description	Unused	Used
908	**266**	1k.75 multicoloured	45	25

267 Buhund (farm dog)

1983. Norwegian Dogs. Multicoloured.

No.	Type	Description	Unused	Used
909		2k. Type **267**	70	40
910		2k.50 Elkhound	80	20
911		3k.50 Lundehund (puffin hunter)	1·10	60

See note below No. 433.

268 Mountain Scenery

1983. Nordic Countries' Postal Co-operation. "Visit the North". Multicoloured.

912	2k.50 Type **268**		60	25
913	3k.50 Fjord scenery		1·20	65

1983. Birds (4th series). As T 245. Mult.

914	2k.50 Barnacle goose ("Branta leucopsis")	85	25
915	2k.50 Little auk ("Alle alle")	85	25

269 Edvard Grieg with Concerto in A minor

1983. Europa.

916	**269**	2k.50 red	1·70	30
917	-	3k.50 blue and green	2·40	75

DESIGN—VERT: 3k.50, Statue of Niels Henrik Abel (mathematician) by Gustav Vigeland.

270 Arrows forming Posthorn

1983. World Communications Year. Multicoloured.

918	2k.50 Type **270**	60	25
919	3k.50 Arrows circling globe	1·00	60

271 King Olav V and Royal Birch, Molde

1983. 80th Birthday of King Olav V.

920	**271**	5k. green	1·70	35

272 Lie

1983. 150th Birth Anniv of Jonas Lie (author).

921	**272**	2k.50 red	70	25

273 Northern Femboring

1983. North Norwegian Ships.

922	**273**	2k. blue and brown	75	40
923	-	3k. brown and blue	1·10	60

DESIGNS: 3k. Northern jekt.

See note below No. 433.

274 "The Sleigh Ride" (Axel Ender)

1983. Christmas. Multicoloured.

924	2k. Type **274**	75	30
925	2k.50 "The Guests are arriving" (Gustav Wendel)	80	30

275 Post Office Counter

1984. Postal Work. Multicoloured.

926	2k. Type **275**	65	30
927	2k.50 Postal sorting	65	20
928	3k.50 Postal delivery	1·10	55

276 Freshwater Fishing

1984. Sport Fishing.

929	**276**	2k.50 red	60	20
930	-	3k. green	65	45
931	-	3k.50 blue	1·00	45

DESIGNS: 3k. Atlantic salmon fishing; 3k.50, Sea fishing.

277 Magnetic Meridians and Parallels

1984. Birth Bicentenary of Christopher Hansteen (astronomer and geophysicist).

932	**277**	3k.50 blue	1·00	45
933	-	5k. red	1·30	30

DESIGN—VERT: 5k. Portrait of Hansteen by Johan Gorbitz.

278 Bridge

1984. Europa. 25th Anniv of European Post and Telecommunications Conference.

934	**278**	2k.50 multicoloured	1·10	30
935	**278**	3k.50 multicoloured	2·50	75

279 Vegetables, Fruit and Herbs

1984. Centenary of Norwegian Horticultural Society. Multicoloured.

936	2k. Type **279**	65	30
937	2k.50 Rose and garland of flowers	70	25

280 Honey Bees

1984. Centenaries of Norwegian Beekeeping Society and Norwegian Poultry-breeding Society. Mult.

938	2k.50 Type **280**	70	25
939	2k.50 Leghorn cock	70	25

See note below No. 433.

281 Holberg (after J. M. Bernigeroth)

1984. 300th Birth Anniv of Ludvig Holberg (writer).

940	**281**	2k.50 red	75	25

282 Children reading

1984. 150th Anniv of "Norsk Penning-Magazin" (1st weekly magazine in Norway).

941	**282**	2k.50 purple, blue and red	60	25
942	-	3k.50 orange and violet	80	45

DESIGN: 3k.50, 1st edition of "Norsk Penning-Magazin".

283 Entering Parliamentary Chamber, 2 July 1884

1984. Cent of Norwegian Parliament.

943	**283**	7k.50 brown	3·00	85

284 Karius and Baktus (tooth decay bacteria)

1984. Characters from Stories by Thorbjorn Egner. Multicoloured.

944	2k. Type **284**	1·10	25
945	2k. The tree shrew playing guitar	1·10	25
946	2k.50 Kasper, Jesper and Jonatan (Rovers) in Kardemomme Town	1·20	20
947	2k.50 Chief Constable Bastian	1·20	20

285 Mount Sagbladet (Saw Blade)

1985. Antarctic Mountains. Multicoloured.

948	2k.50 Type **285**	1·00	25
949	3k.50 Mount Hoggestabben (Chopping Block)	1·30	65

286 Return of Crown Prince Olav, 1945

1985. 40th Anniv of Liberation.

950	**286**	3k.50 red and blue	1·30	55

287 Kongsten Fort

1985. 300th Anniv of Kongsten Fort.

951	**287**	2k.50 multicoloured	1·10	25

288 Bronze Cannon, 1596

1985. Artillery Anniversaries. Multicoloured.

952	3k. Type **288** (300th anniv of Artillery)	1·00	55
953	4k. Cannon on sledge carriage, 1758 (bicentenary of Artillery Officers Training School)	1·30	45

289 "Boy and Girl" (detail)

1985. International Youth Year. Sculptures in Vigeland Park, Oslo. Multicoloured.

954	2k. Type **289**	65	30
955	3k.50 Bronze fountain (detail)	1·10	60

See note below No. 433.

290 Torgeir Augundsson (fiddler)

1985. Europa. Music Year.

956	**290**	2k.50 red	1·10	30
957	-	3k.50 blue	3·00	65

DESIGN: 3k.50, Ole Bull (composer and violinist).

291 Workers at Glomfjord

1985. Centenary of Electricity in Norway.

958	**291**	2k.50 red and scarlet	80	20
959	-	4k. blue and green	1·20	40

DESIGN: 4k. Men working on overhead cable.

292 Ekofisk Centre

1985. Stamp Day. Norwegian Working Life (1st series). Offshore Oil Industry. Sheet 112×91 mm containing T 292 and similar horiz designs. Multicoloured.

MS960	2k.+1k. Type **292**; 2k.+1k. Drilling rig *Treasure Scout* and supply ship *Odin Viking*; 2k.+1k. Towing *Statfjord C* platform to oil field, 1984; 2k.+1k. Drilling team on rig *Neptuno Nordraug*	5·25	6·50

See also Nos. **MS**989 and **MS**1012.

293 Carl Deichman on Book Cover

1985. Bicentenary of Public Libraries.

961	**293**	2k.50 sepia and brown	95	25
962	-	10k. green	3·75	55

DESIGN—HORIZ: 10k. Library interior.

294 Wreath

1985. Christmas. Multicoloured.

963	2k. Type **294**	1·50	25
964	2k.50 Northern bullfinches	1·40	25

295 "Berghavn" (dredger)

1985. 250th Anniv of Port Authorities and Bicentenary of Hydrography in Norway.

965 **295** 2k.50 purple, orange & bl 1·40 25
966 - 5k. blue, green and brown 65 25

DESIGN: 5k. Sextant and detail of chart No. 1 of Lt. F.C. Grove showing Trondheim sealane, 1791.

296 Sun

1986

967 **296** 2k.10 orange and brown 1·50 10
968 - 2k.30 green and blue 75 25
970 - 2k.70 pink and red 80 25
971 - 4k. blue and green 1·10 30

DESIGNS: 2k.30, Atlantic cod and herring; 2k.70, Flowers; 4k. Star ornaments.

297 Marksman in Prone Position

1986. World Biathlon Championships. Mult.

977 2k.50 Type **297** 70 25
978 3k.50 Marksman standing to take aim 1·00 65

298 Industry and Countryside

1986. Europa. Multicoloured.

979 2k.50 Type **298** 1·10 25
980 3k.50 Dead and living forest, mountains and butterflies 2·30 80

299 Stone Cutter

1986. Centenary of Norwegian Craftsmen's Federation.

981 **299** 2k.50 lake and red 85 25
982 - 7k. blue and red 2·75 65

DESIGN: 7k. Carpenter.

300 Moss

1986. Nordic Countries' Postal Co-operation. Twinned Towns. Multicoloured.

983 2k.50 Type **300** 85 25
984 4k. Alesund 1·30 50

See note below No. 433.

301 Hans Polson Egede (missionary) and Map

1986. Birth Anniversaries.

985 **301** 2k.10 brown and red 60 55
986 - 2k.50 red, green and blue 65 25
987 - 3k. brown and red 90 40
988 - 4k. purple and lilac 1·10 40

DESIGNS: 2k.10, Type **301** (300th anniv); 2k.50, Herman Wildenvey (poet) and poem carved in wall at Stavern (centenary); 3k. Tore Ojasaeter (poet) and old cupboard from Skjak (centenary); 4k. Engebret Soot (engineer) and lock gates, Orje (centenary).

See note below No. 433.

302 Timber being debarked and cut

1986. Stamp Day. Norwegian Working Life (2nd series). Paper Industry. Sheet 113×91 mm containing T 302 and similar horiz designs. Multicoloured.

MS989 2k.50+1k. Type **302**; 2k.50+1k. Boiling plant; 2k.50+1k. Paper factory; 2k.50+1k. Paper being dried and rolled into bales 7·25 7·00

303 "Olav Kyrre founds Diocese in Nidaros"

1986. Christmas. Stained Glass Windows by Gabriel Kielland in Nidaros Cathedral, Trondheim. Multicoloured.

990 2k.10 Type **303** 90 35
991 2k.50 "The King and the Peasant at Sul" 1·00 25

304 Doves

1986. International Peace Year.

992 **304** 15k. red, blue and green 6·25 65

305 Numeral

1987

993 **305** 3k.50 yellow, red and blue 1·00 60
994 **305** 4k.50 blue, yellow & green 1·30 45

306 Wooden Building

1987. Europa. Multicoloured.

1000 2k.70 Type **306** 1·60 30
1001 4k.50 Building of glass and stone 1·90 45

307 The Final Vote

1987. 150th Anniv of Laws on Local Councils (granting local autonomy).

1002 **307** 12k. green 4·50 60

308 Rehabilitation Centre, Mogadishu

1987. Norwegian Red Cross in Somalia. Sheet 113×92 mm.

MS1003 **308** 4k.50 multicoloured 1·80 1·70

309 Funnel-shaped Chanterelle ("Cantharellus tubaeformis")

1987. Fungi (1st series). Multicoloured.

1004 2k.70 Type **309** 1·00 25
1005 2k.70 The gypsy ("Rozites caperata") 1·00 25

See also Nos. 1040/1 and 1052/3.

310 Bjornstad Farm from Vaga

1987. Centenary of Sandvig Collections, Maihaugen.

1006 **310** 2k.70 sepia and brown 80 25
1007 - 3k.50 purple and blue 1·20 60

DESIGN: 3k.50, "Horse and Rider" (wooden carving, Christen Erlandsen Listad).

311 Valevag Churchyard

1987. Birth Centenary of Fartein Valen (composer).

1008 **311** 2k.30 blue and green 75 60
1009 - 4k.50 brown 1·30 35

DESIGN—VERT: 4k.50, Fartein Valen.

See note below No. 433.

312 "Storm at Sea" (Christian Krohg)

1987. Paintings. Multicoloured.

1010 2k.70 Type **312** 85 25
1011 5k. "The Farm" (Gerhard Munthe) 1·70 40

313 Eggs and Alevin

1987. Stamp Day. Norwegian Working Life (3rd series). Atlantic Salmon Farming. Sheet 113×91 mm containing T 313 and similar horiz designs. Multicoloured.

MS1012 2k.30+50ore Type **313**; 2k.70+50ore Hatching tanks and parr; 3k.50+50ore Marine stage; 4k.50+50ore Harvested salmon 7·00 6·75

314 Cat with Children making Decorations

1987. Christmas. Multicoloured.

1013 2k.30 Type **314** 1·00 40
1014 2k.70 Dog with children making gingersnaps 1·10 25

315 Dales Pony

1987. Native Ponies.

1015 **315** 2k.30 deep brown, green and brown 80 60
1016 - 2k.70 buff, brown & blue 80 25
1017 - 4k.50 brown, red and blue 1·30 45

DESIGNS: 2k.70, Fjord pony; 4k.50, Nordland pony.

See note below No. 433.

316 Western Capercaillie

1988. Wildlife.

1018 2k.60 deep brown, brown and green 80 25
1019 **316** 2k.90 black, brn & grn 1·00 20
1020 - 3k. brown, grey and green 1·00 20
1021 - 3k.20 ultramarine, green and blue 1·00 20
1022 - 3k.80 brown, blue & blk 1·30 25
1023 - 4k. brown, red and green 1·30 25
1024 - 4k.50 brown, green & bl 1·20 25
1025 - 5k.50 brown, grey & grn 1·40 30
1026 - 6k.40 brown, blk & grn 1·80 50

DESIGNS: 2k.60, Fox; 3k. Stoat; 3k.20, Mute swan; 3k.80, Reindeer; 4k. Eurasian red squirrel; 4k.50, Beaver; 5k.50, Lynx; 6k.40, Tengmalm's owl.

317 Band

1988. Centenary of Salvation Army in Norway. Multicoloured.

1035 2k.90 Type **317** 85 25
1036 4k.80 Othilie Tonning (early social worker) and Army nurse 1·70 65

318 Building Fortress

1988. Military Anniversaries.

1037 **318** 2k.50 green 85 30
1038 - 2k.90 brown 1·00 20
1039 - 4k.60 blue 1·50 60

DESIGNS: 2k.50, Type **318** (300th anniv of Defence Construction Service); 2k.90, Corps members in action (centenary of Army Signals corps); 4k.60, Making pontoon bridge (centenary of Engineer Corps).

1988. Fungi (2nd series). As T 309. Mult.

1040 2k.90 Wood blewits ("Lepista nuda") 95 20
1041 2k.90 "Lactarius deterrimus" 95 20

319 Globe

1988. European Campaign for Interdependence and Solidarity of North and South.

1042 **319** 25k. multicoloured 7·75 1·00

320 King Olav V

1988. 85th Birthday of King Olav V. Multicoloured.

1043	2k.90 Type **320**	1·00	25

MS1044 121×91 mm. 2k.90 King Olav arriving as baby; 2k.90 Type **320**; 2k.90 King Olav at Holmenkollen 3·75 3·50

321 "Prinds Gustav" (paddle-steamer)

1988. Europa. Transport and Communications.

1045	**321**	2k.90 black, red and blue	1·10	30
1046	-	3k.80 blue, red & yellow	3·25	1·10

DESIGN: 3k.80, Heroybrua Bridge.

322 King Christian IV

1988. 400th Anniv of Christian IV's Accession to Danish and Norwegian Thrones.

1047	**322**	2k.50 black, stone & vio	1·10	25
1048	-	10k. multicoloured	3·50	45

DESIGN: 10k. 1628 silver coin and extract from decree on mining in Norway.

323 Handball

1988. Stamp Day. Sport. Sheet 113×91 mm containing T 323 and similar horiz designs. Multicoloured.

MS1049 2k.90 Type **323**; 2k.90 Football; 2k.90 Basketball; 2k.90 Volleyball (sold at 15k.) 7·00 7·25

324 Ludvig with Ski Stick

1988. Christmas. Multicoloured.

1050	2k.90 Type **324**	1·00	20
1051	2k.90 Ludvig reading letter	1·00	20

1989. Fungi (3rd series). As T 309. Multicoloured.

1052	3k. Chanterelle ("Cantharellus cibarius")	95	20
1053	3k. Butter mushroom ("Suillus luteus")	95	20

325 Start and Finish of Race

1989. World Cross-country Championship, Stavanger.

1054	**325**	5k. multicoloured	1·60	40

326 Vardo

1989. Town Bicentenaries.

1055	**326**	3k. blue, red & light blue	90	20
1056	-	4k. purple, blue & orange	1·10	55

DESIGN: 4k. Hammerfest.

327 Setesdal Woman

1989. Nordic Countries' Postal Co-operation. Traditional Costumes. Multicoloured.

1057	3k. Type **327**	1·00	25
1058	4k. Kautokeino man	1·50	85

328 Children making Snowman

1989. Europa. Children's Games. Multicoloured.

1059	3k.70 Type **328**	1·50	80
1060	5k. Cat's cradle	2·75	80

See note below No. 433.

329 Rooster and Cover of 1804 First Reader

1989. 250th Anniv of Primary Schools.

1061	**329**	2k.60 multicoloured	1·00	40
1062	-	3k. brown	95	20

DESIGN: 3k. Pocket calculator and child writing.

330 "Impressions of the Countryside" (detail)

1989. Stamp Day. Sheet 107×85 mm. containing T 330 and similar horiz designs, forming a composite design of the painting by Jakob Weidemann.

MS1063 3k.×4 multicoloured (sold at 15k.) 6·75 6·50

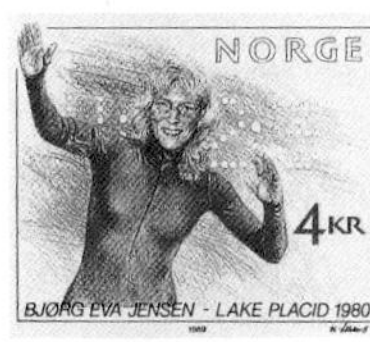

331 Bjorg Eva Jensen (300m. speed skating 1980)

1989. Winter Olympic Games, Lillehammer (1994) (1st issue). Norwegian Gold Medallists. Sheet 113×91 mm containing T 331 and similar horiz designs. Multicoloured.

MS1064 4k. Type **331**; 4k. Eirik Kvalfoss (biathlon, 1984); 4k. Tom Sandberg (combined cross-country and ski-jumping, 1984); 4k. Women's team (10km cross-country relay, 1984) (sold at 20k.) 7·00 6·75

See also Nos. **MS**1083, **MS**1097, **MS**1143, 1150/1, **MS**1157, 1169/70 and 1175/80.

332 Arnulf Overland (poet, centenary)

1989. Writers' Birth Anniversaries.

1065	**332**	3k. red and blue	1·00	20
1066	-	25k. blue, orange & green	6·75	95

DESIGN: 25k. Hanna Winsnes (pseudonym Hugo Schwartz) (bicentenary).

333 Star Decoration

1989. Christmas. Tree Decorations. Mult.

1067	3k. Type **333**	1·00	20
1068	3k. Bauble	1·00	20

334 Larvik Manor

1989. Manor Houses.

1069	**334**	3k. brown	90	20
1070	-	3k. green	90	20

DESIGN: No. 1070, Rosendal Barony.

335 Emblem

1990. Winter Cities Events, Tromso.

1071	**335**	5k. multicoloured	1·60	40

336 Common Spotted Orchid ("Dactylorhiza fuchsii")

1990. Orchids (1st series). Multicoloured.

1072	3k.20 Type **336**	75	20
1073	3k.20 Dark red helleborine ("Epipactis atrorubens")	75	20

See also Nos. 1141/2.

337 Merchant Navy, Airforce, Home Guard, "Moses" (coastal gun) and Haakon VII's Monogram

1990. 50th Anniv of Norway's Entry into Second World War. Multicoloured.

1074	3k.20 Type **337**	1·10	25
1075	4k. Second Battle of Narvik, 1940	1·40	60

338 Penny Black

1990. 150th Anniv of the Penny Black. Sheet 113×91 mm containing T 338 and similar vert design.

MS1076 5k. Type **338**; 5k. First Norwegian stamp (sold at 15k.) 5·50 5·25

339 Trondheim Post Office

1990. Europa. Post Office Buildings. Mult.

1077	3k.20 Type **339**	1·50	30
1078	4k. Longyearbyen Post Office	3·25	80

340 "Tordenskiold" (from print by J. W. Tegner after Balthazar Denner)

1990. 300th Birth Anniv of Admiral Tordenskiold (Peter Wessel). Multicoloured.

1079	3k.20 Type **340**	95	25
1080	5k. Tordenskiold's coat-of-arms	1·40	50

341 Svendsen

1990. 150th Birth Anniv of Johan Svendsen (composer and conductor).

1081	**341**	2k.70 black and red	90	60
1082	-	15k. brown and yellow	4·75	85

DESIGN: 15k. Svendsen Monument (Stinius Fredriksen), Oslo.

342 Thoreleif Haug (cross-country skiing, 1924)

1990. Winter Olympic Games, Lillehammer (1994) (2nd issue). Norwegian Gold Medallists. Sheet 113×91 mm containing T 342 and similar horiz designs. Multicoloured.

MS1083 4k. Type **342**; 4k. Sonja Henie (figure skating, 1928, 1932, 1936); 4k. Ivar Ballangrud (speed skating, 1928, 1936); 4k. Hjalmar Andersen (speed skating, 1952) (sold at 20k.) 6·75 6·50

343 "Children and Snowman" (Ragni Engstrom Nilsen)

1990. Christmas. Children's Prize-winning Drawings. Multicoloured.

1084	3k.20 Type **343**	85	20
1085	3k.20 "Christmas Church" (Jorgen Ingier)	85	20

344 Nobel Medal and Soderblom

1990. 60th Anniv of Award of Nobel Peace Prize to Nathan Soderblom, Archbishop of Uppsala.

1086	**344**	30k. brown, blue and red	7·25	90

345 Plan and Elevation of Container Ship and Propeller

1991. Centenaries of Federation of Engineering Industries (1989) and Union of Iron and Metal Workers.

1087	**345**	5k. multicoloured	1·30	45

346 Satellite transmitting to Tromso

1991. Europa. Europe in Space. Mult.
1088 3k.20 Type **346** 1·90 30
1089 4k. Rocket leaving Andoya rocket range 5·25 75
See note below No. 433.

347 Christiansholm Fortress (late 17th- century)

1991. 350th Anniv of Kristiansand. Each black, blue and red.
1090 3k.20 Type **347** 1·10 25
1091 5k.50 Present day view of Christiansholm Fortress 1·50 35

348 Fountain, Vigeland Park, Oslo

1991. Nordic Countries' Postal Co-operation. Tourism. Multicoloured.
1092 3k.20 Type **348** 1·10 25
1093 4k. Globe, North Cape Plateau 1·80 1·10

349 "Skomvaer III" (lifeboat)

1991. Centenary of Norwegian Society for Sea Rescue.
1094 **349** 3k.20 brown, black & grn 1·10 35
1095 - 27k. brown, grey & purple 6·75 1·50
DESIGN—VERT: 27k. "Colin Archer" (first lifeboat).

350 Engraving on Steel

1991. Stamp Day. Stamp Engraving. Sheet 113×91 mm containing T 350 and similar horiz designs.
MS1096 2k.70 Type **350**; 3k.20 Engraver using magnifying glass; 4k. Engraver's hands seen through magnifying glass; 5k. Positive impression of engraving and burin (sold at 20k.) 5·75 6·00

351 Birger Ruud (ski jumping, 1932, 1936; downhill, 1936)

1991. Winter Olympic Games, Lillehammer (1994) (3rd issue). Norwegian Gold Medallists. Sheet 113×91 mm containing T 351 and similar horiz designs. Multicoloured.
MS1097 4k. Type **351**; 4k. Johann Grottumsbraten (cross-country skiing, 1928, 1932); 4k. Knut Johannesen (speed skaing, 1960, 1964); 4k. Magnar Solberg (biathlon, 1960, 1968, 1972) (sold at 20k.) 6·50 6·25

352 Posthorn

1991
1098 **352** 1k. black and orange 25 20
1099 **352** 2k. red and green 45 20
1100 **352** 3k. green and blue 65 20
1101 **352** 4k. red and orange 85 20
1102 **352** 5k. blue and green 1·10 25
1103 **352** 6k. red and green 1·30 20
1104 **352** 7k. blue and brown 1·50 25
1105 **352** 8k. green and purple 1·70 30
1106 **352** 9k. brown and blue 1·90 40

353 Guisers with Goat Head

1991. Christmas. Guising. Multicoloured.
1120 3k.20 Type **353** 80 20
1121 3k.20 Guisers with lantern 80 20

354 Queen Sonja **355** King Harald **356** King Harald

1992
1122 **354** 2k.80 lake, purple & red 85 20
1123 **354** 3k. green, deep green and turquoise 85 40
1124 **355** 3k.30 blue, ultramarine and light blue 1·00 20
1125 **355** 3k.50 black and grey 95 45
1127 **355** 4k.50 deep red and red 1·00 55
1128 **355** 5k.50 brown, sepia & blk 1·30 65
1129 **355** 5k.60 orange, red and vermilion 1·50 35
1131 **355** 6k.50 emerald, green and turquoise 1·70 45
1132 **355** 6k.60 maroon, purple and brown 2·00 35
1133 **355** 7k.50 violet, lilac and purple 1·60 1·00
1134 **355** 8k.50 chestnut, deep brown and brown 1·90 1·30
1135 **356** 10k. green 2·50 40
1438 **356** 20k. violet 4·25 50
1138 **356** 30k. blue 6·50 60
1139 **356** 50k. green 10·00 1·30

1992. Orchids (2nd series). As T 336. Mult.
1141 3k.30 Lady's slipper orchid ("Cypripedium calceolus") 85 20
1142 3k.30 Fly orchid ("Ophrys insectifera") 85 20

357 Hallgeir Brenden (cross-country skiing, 1952, 1956)

1992. Winter Olympic Games, Lillehammer (4th issue). Norwegian Gold Medallists. Sheet 113×91 mm containing T 357 and similar horiz designs. Multicoloured.
MS1143 4k. Type **357**; 4k. Arnfinn Bergmann (ski jumping, 1952); 4k. Stein Eriksen (super slalom, 1952); 4k. Simon Slattvik (combined, 1952) (sold at 20k.) 6·50 6·25

358 "Restaurationen" (emigrant sloop)

1992. Europa. 500th Anniv of Discovery of America by Columbus. Transatlantic Ships. Multicoloured.
1144 3k.30 Type **358** 1·50 50
1145 4k.20 "Stavangerfjord" (liner) and American skyline 2·10 75
See note below No. 433.

359 Norwegian Pavilion, Rainbow and Ship

1992. "Expo '92" World's Fair, Seville. Mult.
1146 3k.30 Type **359** 90 25
1147 5k.20 Mountains, rainbow, fish and oil rig 1·50 55

360 Molde

1992. 250th Anniversaries of Molde and Kristiansund.
1148 **360** 3k.30 blue, green & brn 1·00 25
1149 - 3k.30 blue, brown & lt bl 1·00 25
DESIGN: No. 1149, Kristiansund.

361 Banners and Lillehammer Buildings

1992. Winter Olympic Games, Lillehammer (1994) (5th issue). Multicoloured.
1150 3k.30 Type **361** 80 25
1151 4k.20 Flags 1·20 55

362 Flask with Etched Figures (Serre Petersen)

1992. Stamp Day. Sheet 113×91 mm containing T 362 and similar horiz designs. Multicoloured.
MS1152 2k.80 Type **362**; 3k.30 Monogrammed carafe; 4k.20 Cut-glass salad bowl; 5k.20 Engraved goblet (Heinrich Gottlieb Kohler) (sold at 20k.) 5·75 5·50

363 Gnomes below Pillar Box

1992. Christmas. Christmas card designs by Otto Moe. Multicoloured.
1153 3k.30 Type **363** 80 20
1154 3k.30 Gnome posting letter 80 20

364 Orange-tip ("Anthocaris cardamines")

1993. Butterflies (1st series). Multicoloured.
1155 3k.50 Type **364** 80 20
1156 3k.50 Small tortoiseshell ("Aglais urticae") 80 20
See also Nos. 1173/4.

365 Finn Chr. Jagge (slalom)

1993. Winter Olympic Games, Lillehammer (1994) (6th issue). Norwegian Gold Medallists at 1992 Games. Sheet 113×91 mm containing T 365 and similar horiz designs. Multicoloured.
MS1157 4k.50 Type **365**; 4k.50 Bjorn Daehlie (cross-country skiing); 4k.50 Geir Karlstad (speed skating); 4k.50 Vegard Ulvang (cross-country skiing) 6·75 6·25

366 Grieg

1993. 150th Birth Anniv of Edvard Grieg (composer). Multicoloured.
1158 3k.50 Type **366** 90 25
1159 5k.50 "Spring" 2·00 45

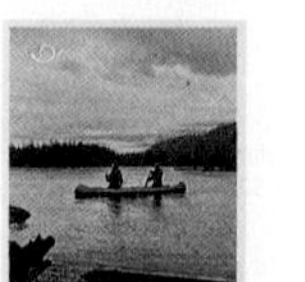

367 Two-man Kayak on Lake

1993. Nordic Countries' Postal Co-operation. Tourist Activities. Multicoloured.
1160 4k. Type **367** 1·10 50
1161 4k.50 White-water rafting 1·70 55

368 Richard With (founder) and "Vesteraalen"

1993. Centenary of Express Coaster Service.
1162 **368** 3k.50 blue, violet and red 90 25
1163 - 4k.50 multicoloured 1·20 45
DESIGN: 4k.50, "Kong Harald".

369 Handball

1993. Sports Events. Multicoloured.
1164 3k.50 Type **369** (Women's World Championship, Norway) 90 25
1165 5k.50 Cycling (World Championships, Oslo and Hamar) 1·30 45

370 Johann Castberg (politician)

1993. Centenary of Workforce Protection Legislation.
1166 **370** 3k.50 brown and blue 90 25
1167 - 12k. blue and brown 3·25 55
DESIGN: 12k. Betzy Kjelsberg (first woman factory inspector).

371 Deail of Altarpiece (Jakob Klukstad), Lesja Church

1993. Stamp Day. Wood Carvings of Acanthus Leaves. Sheet 113×91 mm containing T 371 and similar horiz designs. Multicoloured.

MS1168 3k. Type **371**; 3k.50 Detail of dresser (Ola Teigeroen); 4k.50 Detail of Fliksaker chest (Jens Strammerud); 5k.50 Detail of pulpit, Our Saviour's Church, Oslo (sold at 21k.) 5·75 5·50

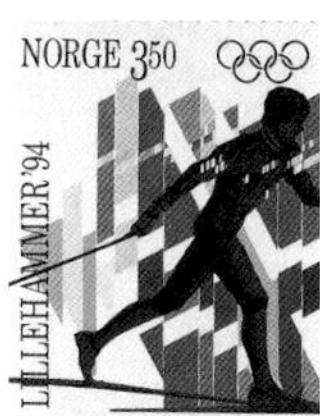

372 Torch Bearer on Skis

1993. Winter Olympic Games, Lillehammer (1994) (7th issue). Morgedal–Lillehammer Torch Relay. Multicoloured.

1169	3k.50 Type **372**	85	30
1170	3k.50 Lillehammer	85	30

Nos. 1169/70 were issued together, se-tenant, forming a composite design.

373 Store Mangen Chapel

1993. Christmas. Multicoloured.

1171	3k.50 Type **373**	75	20
1172	3k.50 Stamnes church, Sandnessjoen	80	15

1994. Butterflies (2nd series). As T 364. Mult.

1173	3k.50 Northern clouded yellow ("Colias hecla")	80	20
1174	3k.50 Freya's fritillary ("Clossiana freija")	80	20

374 Flags

1994. Winter Olympic Games, Lillehammer (8th issue). Multicoloured.

1175	3k.50 Type **374**	85	20
1176	3k.50 Flags (different)	85	20
1177	3k.50 Lillehammer (church) and rings	85	20
1178	3k.50 Lillehammer (ski jump) and rings	85	20
1179	4k.50 Flags of European countries	1·10	45
1180	5k.50 Flags of non-European countries	1·30	55

Nos. 1175/8 were issued together, se-tenant, forming a composite design.

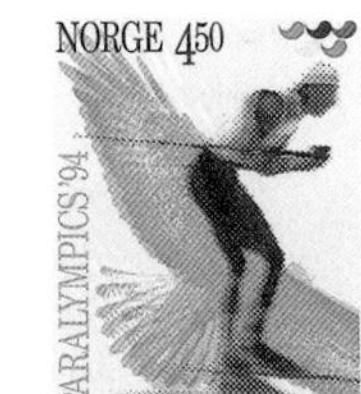

375 Cross-country Skiing

1994. Paralympic Games, Lillehammer. Mult.

1181	4k.50 Type **375**	1·10	60
1182	5k.50 Downhill skiing	1·10	50

376 King Christian VII's Signature and Seal

1994. Bicentenary of Tromso.

1183	**376**	3k.50 red, bistre & brn	95	20
1184	-	4k.50 blue, yellow and light blue	1·30	55

DESIGN: 4k.50, Tromsdalen church.

377 Mount Floy Incline Railway Cars, Bergen

1994. Tourism. Multicoloured.

1185	4k. Type **377**	95	45
1186	4k.50 "Svolvaer Goat" (rock formation), Lofoten	1·20	55
1187	5k.50 Beacon, World's End, Tjome	1·30	50

378 Osterdal Farm Buildings

1994. Cent of Norwegian Folk Museum, Bygdoy.

1188	**378**	3k. multicoloured	75	30
1189	-	3k.50 blue, yellow and purple	1·00	30

DESIGN: 3k.50, Horse-drawn sleigh, 1750 (Torsten Hoff).

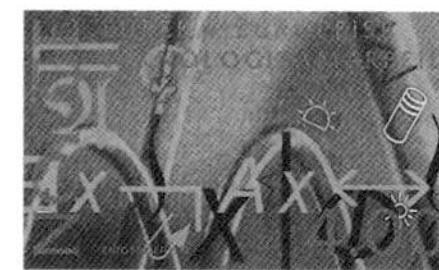

379 Technological Symbols and Formula ("Glass Flasks")

1994. EUREKA (European technology co-operation organization) Conference of Ministers, Lillehammer. Multicoloured.

1190	4k. Type **379**	1·10	55
1191	4k.50 Technological symbols ("Electronic Chips")	1·70	60

380 Electric Tram and Street Plan of Oslo, 1894

1994. Centenary of Electric Trams. Multicoloured.

1192	3k.50 Type **380**	1·00	25
1193	12k. Articulated tram and Oslo route map	3·25	1·00

381 Engraved Brooch

1994. Stamp Day. Jewellery. Sheet 113×91 mm containing T 381 and similar horiz designs. Multicoloured.

MS1194 3k. Type **381**; 3k.50 Silver and gem studded brooch; 4k.50 "Rings" brooch; 5k.50 Brooch with medallions and central stone (sold at 21k.) 6·25 6·00

382 Sledge

1994. Christmas.

1195	**382**	3k.50 red and black	75	25
1196	-	3k.50 ultramarine, blue and black	75	25

DESIGN: No. 1196, Kick-sledge.

383 Cowberry ("Vaccinium vitis-idaea")

1995. Wild Berries (1st Series). Multicoloured.

1197	3k.50 Type **383**	75	35
1198	3k.50 Bilberry ("Vaccinium myrtillus")	75	35

See also Nos. 1224/5.

384 Swan Pharmacy, Bergen

1995. 400th Anniv of Norwegian Pharmacies. Multicoloured.

1199	3k.50 Type **384**	1·00	30
1200	25k. Scales, pestle and mortar and ingredients	6·50	1·40

385 German Commander saluting Terje Rollem (Home Guard commander)

1995. 50th Anniv of Liberation of Norway.

1201	**385**	3k.50 silver, green and black	90	30
1202	-	4k.50 silver, blue and black	1·20	80
1203	-	5k.50 silver, red and black	1·40	65

DESIGNS: 4k.50, King Haakon VII and family returning to Norway; 5k.50, Children waving Norwegian flags.

386 Old Moster Church

1995. Millenary of Christianity in Norway. Multicoloured.

1204	3k.50 Type **386**	95	30
1205	15k. Slettebakken Church, Bergen	3·75	1·50

387 Skudeneshavn

1995. Nordic Countries' Postal Co-operation. Tourism. Multicoloured.

1206	4k. Type **387**	85	60
1207	4k.50 Hole in the Hat (coastal rock formation)	1·00	75

388 Flagstad as Isolde

1995. Birth Centenary of Kirsten Flagstad (opera singer). Multicoloured.

1208	3k.50 Type **388**	95	30
1209	5k.50 Flagstad in scene from "Lohengrin" (Wagner)	1·40	50

389 Disputants in Conflict

1995. Bicentenary of Conciliation Boards. Multicoloured.

1210	7k. Type **389**	1·80	80
1211	12k. Disputants in conciliation with mediator	3·00	1·20

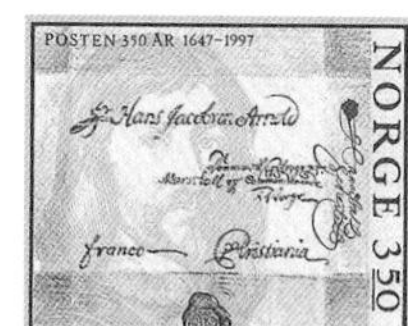

390 Letter and Vice-regent Hannibal Sehested (founder)

1995. 350th Anniv (1997) of Norwegian Postal Service (1st issue). Multicoloured.

1212	3k.50 Type **390** (letter post, 1647)	85	50
1213	3k.50 Wax seal (registered post, 1745)	85	50
1214	3k.50 Postmarks (1845)	85	50
1215	3k.50 Banknotes, coins and money orders (transfer of funds, 1883)	85	50
1216	3k.50 Editions of "Norska Intelligenz-Sedler" and "Arkiv" (newspapers and magazines, 1660)	85	50
1217	3k.50 Address label, cancellations and "Constitutionen" (paddle-steamer) (parcel post, 1827)	85	50
1218	3k.50 Stamps (1855)	85	50
1219	3k.50 Savings book (Post Office Savings Bank, 1950)	85	50

The dates are those of the introduction of the various services.

See also Nos. 1237/44 and 1283/90.

391 Trygve Lie (first Secretary-General) and Emblem

1995. 50th Anniv of U.N.O. Multicoloured.

1220	3k.50 Type **391**	95	25
1221	5k.50 Relief worker, water pump and emblem	1·40	50

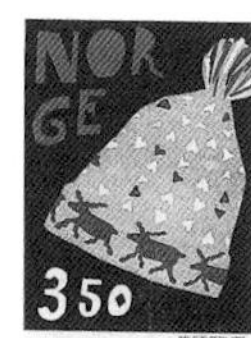

392 Woolly Hat

1995. Christmas. Multicoloured.

1222	3k.50 Type **392**	75	30
1223	3k.50 Mitten	75	30

1996. Wild Berries (2nd series). As T 383. Multicoloured.

1224	3k.50 Wild strawberries ("Fragaria vesca")	75	30
1225	3k.50 Cloudberries ("Rubus chamaemorus")	75	30

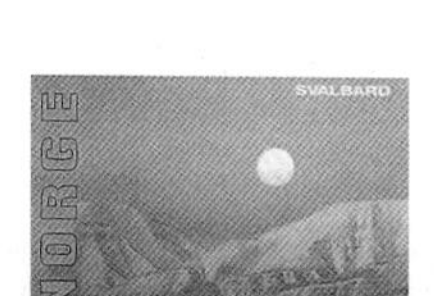

393 Advent Bay

1996. Svalbard Islands. Multicoloured.

1226	10k. Type **393**	2·50	80
1227	20k. Polar bear	5·00	1·60

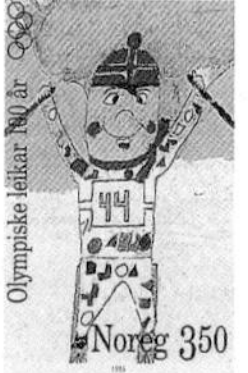

394 Cross-country Skier (Hakon Paulsen)

1996. Centenary of Modern Olympic Games. Children's Drawings. Multicoloured.

1228	3k.50 Type **394**	95	30
1229	5k.50 Athlete (Emil Tanem)	1·40	55

395 Besseggen

1996. Tourism. UNESCO World Heritage Sites. Multicoloured.

1230 4k. Type **395** 80 60
1231 4k.50 Stave church, Urnes 95 1·00
1232 5k.50 Rock carvings, Alta 1·20 45

See also Nos. 1291/3.

396 Steam Train, Urskog-Holand Line

1996. Railway Centenaries. Multicoloured.

1233 3k. Type **396** 70 45
1234 4k.50 Steam train, Setesdal line 1·00 70

397 Location Map and Height Indicator

1996. Natural Gas Production at Troll, near Bergen. Multicoloured.

1235 3k.50 Type **397** 80 35
1236 25k. Planned route map of pipelines to Europe for next 200 years 6·00 2·75

398 Postal Courier crossing Mountains

1996. 350th Anniv (1997) of Postal Service (2nd issue). Multicoloured.

1237 3k.50 Type **398** 95 65
1238 3k.50 "Framnaes" (fjord steamer) 95 65
1239 3k.50 Postal truck in Oslo 95 65
1240 3k.50 Taking mail on board Junkers W-34 "Ternen" (seaplane) on Jonsvatn Lake, Trondheim 95 65
1241 3k.50 Loading mail train at East Station, Oslo 95 65
1242 3k.50 Rural postman at Mago farm, Nittedal 95 65
1243 3k.50 Serving customer, Elverum post office 95 65
1244 3k.50 Computer, letters and globe 95 65

399 Leif Juster, Sean Connery, Liv Ullmann and Olsen Gang

1996. Centenary of Motion Pictures. Multicoloured.

1245 3k.50 Type **399** 80 40
1246 5k.50 Wenche Foss, Jack Fjeldstad, Marilyn Monroe, blood and gun 1·30 55
1247 7k. Charlie Chaplin in "Modern Times", Ottar Gladvedt, Laurel and Hardy and Marlene Dietrich 1·70 80

400 Left Detail of Embroidery

1996. Christmas. Embroidery Details from Telemark Folk Costume. Multicoloured.

1248 3k.50 Type **400** 75 40
1249 3k.50 Right detail 75 40

Nos. 1248/9 were issued together, se-tenant, forming a composite design.

401 Skram

1996. 150th Birth Anniv of Amalie Skram (writer).

1250 **401** 3k.50 red 95 35
1251 - 15k. violet and red 3·75 1·40

DESIGN: 15k. Scene from dramatisation of "People of Hellemyr".

402 Posthorn

1997. Multicoloured, colour of oval given.

1252 **402** 10ore red 25 20
1253 **402** 20ore blue 25 20
1254 **402** 30ore orange 25 20
1255 **402** 40ore black 25 20
1256 **402** 50ore green 25 20

403 Coltsfoot

1997. Flowers. Multicoloured.

1259 3k.20 Red clover 75 30
1260 3k.40 Marsh marigold 75 25
1261 3k.60 Red campion 75 40
1262 3k.70 Type **403** 85 30
1263 3k.80 Wild pansy 85 35
1264 4k. Wood anemone 85 35
1265 4k.30 Lily of the valley 1·10 50
1266 4k.50 White clover 1·00 60
1267 5k. Harebell 1·10 65
1268 5k.40 Oeder's lousewort 1·20 70
1269 5k.50 Hepatica 1·20 50
1270 6k. Ox-eye daisy 1·30 45
1271 7k. Yellow wood violet 1·50 75
1272 7k.50 Pale pasque flower 1·70 85
1273 8k. White water-lily 1·70 55
1274 13k. Purple saxifrage 3·00 95
1275 14k. Globe flower 3·00 1·50
1276 25k. Melancholy thistle 5·25 2·20

404 Bumble Bee

1997. Insects (1st series). Multicoloured.

1277 3k.70 Type **404** 75 30
1278 3k.70 Ladybird 75 30

See also Nos. 1306/7.

405 Ski Jumping

1997. World Nordic Skiing Championships, Trondheim. Multicoloured.

1279 3k.70 Type **405** 90 40
1280 5k. Speed skiing 1·20 60

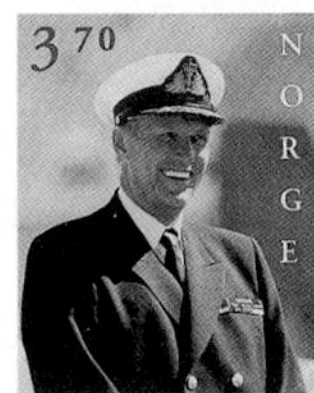

406 King Harald (photo by Erik Johansen)

1997. 60th Birthdays of King Harald and Queen Sonja. Multicoloured.

1281 3k.70 Type **406** 85 30
1282 3k.70 Queen Sonja and King Harald (photo by Knut Falch) (horiz) 85 30

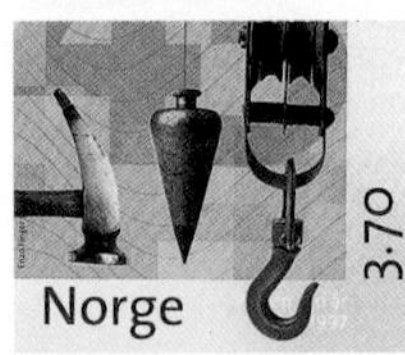

407 Hammer, Plumb Line and Hook (post-war reconstruction)

1997. 350th Anniv of Postal Service (3rd issue). Post-war History. Multicoloured.

1283 3k.70 Type **407** 85 65
1284 3k.70 "Kon Tiki" (replica of balsa raft) (Thor Heyerdahl's expedition from Peru to Polynesia, 1947) 85 65
1285 3k.70 Grouse feather (official bird of Rondane National Park (first National Park, 1962)) 85 65
1286 3k.70 Hands of man and woman (Welfare State (introduction of National Insurance, 1967)) 85 65
1287 3k.70 Drilling platform, Ekofisk oil field (discovery of oil in Norwegian sector of North Sea, 1969) 85 65
1288 3k.70 Grete Waitz (first women's world Marathon champion, 1983) 85 65
1289 3k.70 Askoy Bridge, 1992 (communications) 85 65
1290 3k.70 Crown Prince Haakon Magnus lighting Olympic flame (Winter Olympic Games, Lillehammer, 1994) 85 65

1997. Tourism. As T 395. Multicoloured.

1291 4k.30 Roros 85 85
1292 5k. Faerder Lighthouse 1·10 95
1293 6k. Nusfjord 1·30 65

408 University, Cathedral, Statue of King Olav, City Gate and Broadcasting Tower

1997. Millenary of Trondheim. Multicoloured.

1294 3k.70 Type **408** 1·00 30
1295 12k. Trees, mine, King Olav, pilgrims, burning buildings and harbour 3·00 1·50

409 Gerhardsen and Storting (Parliament House)

1997. Birth Centenary of Einar Gerhardsen (Prime Minister 1945–51, 1955–63 and 1963–65).

1296 **409** 3k.70 black, stone and red 1·00 35
1297 - 25k. black, flesh and green 6·00 3·00

DESIGN: 25k. Gerhardsen, mountain, factory and electricity pylon.

410 Thematic Subjects

1997. Inauguration of National Junior Stamp Club. Multicoloured.

1298 3k.70 Type **410** 85 35
1299 3k.70 Thematic subjects including fish and tiger 85 35

411 Harald Saeverud (composer)

1997. Birth Centenaries.

1300 **411** 10k. blue 2·75 1·20
1301 - 15k. green 3·75 1·40

DESIGN: 15k. Tarjei Vesaas (writer).

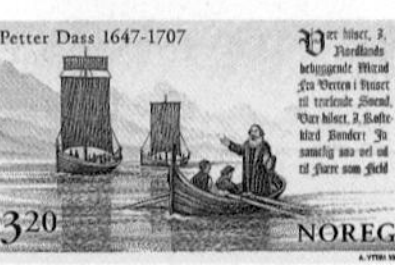

412 Dass in Rowing Boat

1997. 350th Birth Anniv of Petter Dass (priest and poet). Multicoloured.

1302 **412** 3k.20 blue and brown 80 45
1303 - 3k.70 green, blue and brown 95 50

DESIGN: 3k.70, Dass and Alstahaug Church.

413 Golden Calendar Stick Symbols against Candle Flames

1997. Christmas. Multicoloured. Self-adhesive.

1304 3k.70 Type **413** 80 45
1305 3k.70 Silver calendar stick symbols against night sky 80 45

1998. Insects (2nd series). As T 404. Multicoloured.

1306 3k.80 Dragonfly 85 40
1307 3k.80 Grasshopper 85 40

414 Roses

1998. St. Valentine's Day. Self-adhesive.

1308 **414** 3k.80 multicoloured 1·00 40

415 "Hornelen" (passenger and mail steamer)

1998. Nordic Countries' Postal Co-operation. Ships.

1309 **415** 3k.80 blue and green 1·00 55
1310 - 4k.50 green and blue 1·50 1·10

DESIGN: No. 1310, "Kommandoren" (passenger catamaran).

416 Holmenkollen Ski Jump, Oslo

1998. Tourist Sights. Multicoloured.

1311	3k.80 Type **416**	80	55
1312	4k.50 Fisherman, Alesund Harbour	1·00	65
1313	5k.50 Mt Hamaroyskaftet	1·30	1·00

417 Egersund Harbour

1998. Bicentenary of Egersund.

1314	**417**	3k.80 blue and pink	1·00	50
1315	-	6k. blue and mauve	1·50	75

DESIGN: No. 1315, Egersund ceramics.

418 Silver

1998. Minerals. Multicoloured.

1316	3k.40 Type **418**	90	55
1317	5k.20 Cobalt	1·30	65

419 "Water Rider" (Frans Widerberg)

1998. Contemporary Art. Multicoloured.

1318	6k. Type **419**	1·50	75
1319	7k.50 "Red Moon" (carpet, Synnove Anker Aurdal)	1·80	95
1320	13k. "King Haakon VII" (sculpture, Nils Aas)	3·00	1·40

420 Hopscotch

1998. Children's Games (1st series). Multicoloured.

1321	3k.80 Type **420**	95	50
1322	5k.50 Throwing coins at a stick	1·40	95

See also Nos 1355/6.

421 Boeing 747, Douglas DC-3 and Junkers Ju 52/3m Airliners

1998. Inauguration of Oslo Airport, Gardermoen. Multicoloured.

1323	3k.80 Type **421**	1·00	50
1324	6k. Boeing 737 airliner and map of former approaches to Gardermoen Airport	1·50	70
1325	24k. Terminal building, control tower and wings drawn by Leonardo da Vinci	5·75	2·75

422 Main Entrance and Guard

1998. 150th Anniv of Royal Palace, Oslo.

1326	**422**	3k.40 purple	85	65
1327	-	3k.80 blue, pink and yellow	95	50

DESIGN: 3k.80, Main front of palace.

423 Music Score

1998. Christmas. Multicoloured. Self-adhesive.

1328	3k.80 Type **423** (red background)	85	45
1329	3k.80 Music score (blue background)	85	45

424 Cheese Slicer (Thor Bjorklund)

1999. Norwegian Inventions. Self-adhesive.

1330	**424**	3k.60 black and blue	80	35
1331	-	4k. black and red	90	40
1332	-	4k.20 black and green	85	65

DESIGNS: 4k. Paper clip (Johan Vaaler); 4k.20 Aerosol can (Erik Rotheim).

425 Salmon and Fly

1999. Fishes and Fishing Flies. Multicoloured. Self-adhesive.

1333	4k. Type **425**	85	40
1334	4k. Cod and fly	85	40

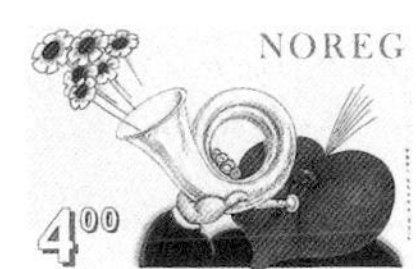

426 Heart blowing Flowers out of Posthorn

1999. St. Valentine's Day.

1335	**426**	4k. multicoloured	85	40

427 "The Pioneer" (statue, Per Palle Storm)

1999. Centenary of Norwegian Confederation of Trade Unions.

1336	**427**	4k. multicoloured	85	45

428 Poland v Norway, Class B Championship, 1998

1999. World Ice Hockey Championships, Norway. Multicoloured.

1337	4k. Type **428**	85	50
1338	7k. Switzerland v Sweden, Class A Championship, 1998	1·50	90

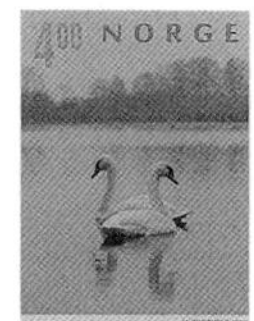

429 Mute Swans

1999. Tourism. Multicoloured.

1339	4k. Type **429**	85	70
1340	5k. Hamar Cathedral	1·10	85
1341	6k. Sami man from Troms	1·30	1·00

430 Emigration

1999. "Norway 2000" (1st issue). Norwegian History. Multicoloured.

1342	4k. Type **430**	85	60
1343	6k. King Olav and Bible (conversion to Christianity, 11th century)	1·30	85
1344	14k. Medal of King Christian IV and quarry workers (union of Norway and Denmark)	3·00	1·60
1345	26k. Oslo at Beier Bridge, 1850s (industrialization)	5·25	2·75

431 Horse Ferry, Amli, East Agder, 1900

1999. "Norway 2000" (2nd issue). Photographs of Everyday Life. Multicoloured.

1346	4k. Type **431**	85	50
1347	4k. Men hewing rock during construction of Valdres railway line, 1900	85	50
1348	4k. Taxi driver Aarseth Odd filling up car with petrol, Kleive, 1930	85	50
1349	4k. Dairymaid Mathea Isaksen milking cow, Karmoy, 1930	85	50
1350	4k. Haymakers, Hemsedal, 1943	85	50
1351	4k. Cross-country skier Dagfinn Knutsen, 1932	85	50
1352	4k. "Bolgen" (coastal fishing boat), Varanger Fjord, 1977	85	50
1353	4k. Boy Jon Andre Koch holding football, 1981	85	50
MS1354	136×148 mm. Nos. 1346/53	6·75	6·50

432 Skateboarding

1999. Children's Games (2nd series). Multicoloured.

1355	4k. Type **432**	85	45
1356	6k. Inline skating	1·20	1·00

433 Wenche Foss and Per Haugen in "An Ideal Husband" (Oscar Wilde)

1999. Centenary of National Theatre.

1357	**433**	3k.60 purple and orange	90	85
1358	-	4k. ultramarine and blue	85	65

DESIGN: 4k. Toralv Maurstad and Tore Segelcke in "Per Gynt" (Henrik Ibsen).

434 Family bringing in Logs

1999. Christmas. Multicoloured. Self-adhesive.

1359	4k. Type **434**	85	45
1360	4k. Family sitting by window	85	45

435 "Sunset" (Sverre Simonsen)

1999. Year 2000. Winning entries in photographic competition. Multicoloured. Self-adhesive.

1361	4k. Type **435**	1·00	60
1362	4k. "Winter Nights" (Poul Christensen)	1·00	60

436 Eye within Heart

2000. St. Valentine's Day.

1363	**436**	4k. multicoloured	85	55

437 "Angry Child" (statue, Gustav Vigeland)

2000. Millenary of Oslo City. Multicoloured.

1364	4k. Type **437**	85	60
1365	6k. Christian IV statue	1·30	95
1366	8k. City Hall and clock face	1·70	1·10
1367	27k. Oslo Stock Exchange and Mercury (statue)	5·75	3·00

438 Golden Eagle

2000. Endangered Species. Multicoloured.

1368	5k. Type **438**	1·10	70
1369	6k. European moose	1·30	90
1370	7k. Sperm whale	1·50	1·00

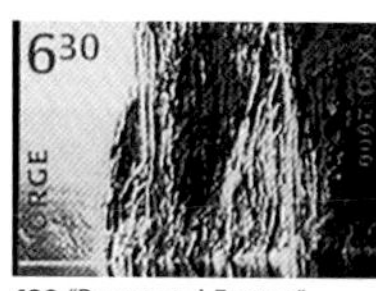

439 "Power and Energy"

2000. "EXPO 2000" World's Fair, Hanover, Germany. Paintings by Marianne Heske. Mult.

1371	4k.20 "The Quiet Room"	1·10	65
1372	6k.30 Type **439**	1·50	80

440 Cadets, 1750

2000. 250th Anniv of Royal Norwegian Military Academy.

1373	**440**	3k.60 multicoloured	90	85
1374	-	8k. blue, yellow and red	1·70	1·20

DESIGN: 8k. Cadets, 2000.

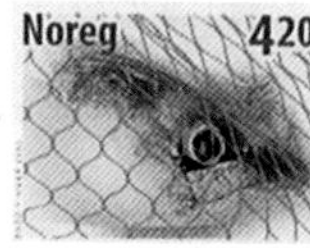

441 Mackerel

2000. Fishes. Multicoloured. Self-adhesive.

1375	4k.20 Type **441**	85	40
1376	4k.20 Herring	85	40

442 Spaceman (May-Therese Vorland)

2000. "Stampin the Future". Winning Entries in Children's International Painting Competition. Multicoloured.

1377	4k.20 Type **442**	85	55
1378	6k.30 Rocket and Earth (Jann Fredrik Ronning)	1·30	85

443 "Monument to Log Drivers" (sculpture, Trygve M. Barstad)

2000. Millennium of Skien City. Multicoloured.

1379	4k.20 Type **443**	85	55
1380	15k. Skien Church	3·25	2·00

444 Laestadius, Lifelong Saxifrage and Laestadius Poppy

2000. Birth Bicentenary of Lars Levi Laestadius (clergyman and botanist).

1381	**444**	5k. multicoloured	1·10	85

445 Nils og Blamann with Goat and Cart

2000. Cartoon Characters. Multicoloured. Self-adhesive.

1382	4k.20 Type **445**	85	60
1383	4k.20 Soldier No. 91 Stomperud and birds	85	60

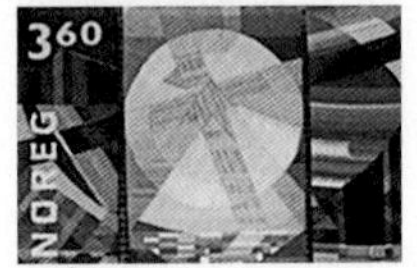

446 Woven Altar Piece, Hamaroy Church

2000. Altar Pieces. Multicoloured.

1384	3k.60 Type **446**	85	65
1385	4k.20 Ski Church	85	65

2000

1388	**352**	1k. multicoloured	25	25
1389	**352**	2k. multicoloured	45	35
1389a	**352**	3k. multicoloured	65	85
1389b	**352**	5k. multicoloured	1·10	70
1390	**352**	6k. multicoloured	1·30	75
1391	**352**	7k. multicoloured	1·50	1·60
1392	**352**	9k. multicoloured	1·90	1·00

447 Sekel Rose

2001. Roses (1st series). Multicoloured. Self-adhesive.

1395	4k.50 Type **447**	95	55
1396	4k.50 Namdal rose	95	55

See also Nos 1418/19 and 1491/2.

448 Place Mat

2001. Crafts (1st series). Multicoloured. Self-adhesive.

1397	4k. Type **448**	80	50
1398	4k.50 Pot with lid	95	55
1399	7k. Bunad (woven cloth)	1·50	85

See also Nos. 1415/17.

449 Aase Bye

2001. Thespians (1st series).

1400	**449**	4k. black and brown	80	65
1401	-	4k.50 black and blue	95	55
1402	-	5k.50 black and brown	1·20	65
1403	-	7k. black and purple	1·50	1·00
1404	-	8k. black and grey	1·70	1·00

DESIGNS: 4k.50, Per Aabel; 5k.50, Alfred Maurstad; 7k. Lillebil Ibsen; 8k. Tore Segelcke.

See also Nos 1410/14 and 1450/4.

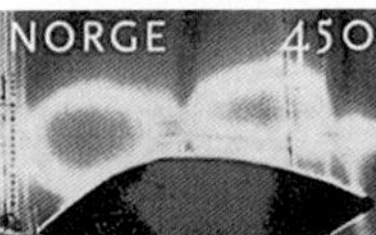

450 "Ties that Bind" (Magne Furuholmen)

2001. St. Valentine's Day.

1405	**450**	4k.50 multicoloured	95	60

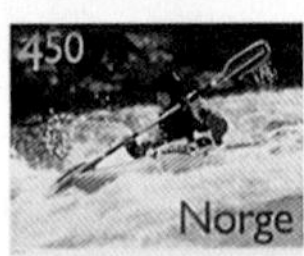

451 Whitewater Kayaking

2001. Sports. Multicoloured. Self-adhesive.

1406	4k.50 Type **451**	95	60
1407	7k. Rock climbing	1·50	65

452 Tuba Player

2001. Centenary of School Bands. Multicoloured.

1408	4k.50 Type **452**	95	60
1409	9k. Majorette	1·90	1·20

453 Lalla Carlsen

2001. Thespians (2nd series). Multicoloured.

1410	5k. Type **453**	1·10	80
1411	5k.50 Leif Juster	1·20	80
1412	7k. Kari Diesen	1·50	1·00
1413	9k. Arvid Nilssen	1·90	1·20
1414	10k. Einar Rose	2·20	1·40

2001. Crafts (2nd series). As T 449. Multicoloured.

1415	5k. Wooden drinking vessel	1·20	65
1416	6k.50 Crocheted doll's clothing	1·40	65
1417	8k.50 Knitted woollen hat	2·00	1·30

454 Rose "Heidekonigin"

2001. Roses (2nd series). Multicoloured. Self-adhesive.

1418	5k.50 Type **454**	1·40	65
1419	5k.50 Rose "Old Master"	1·40	65

Nos. 1418/19 are impregnated with the scent of roses.

455 Old Bank of Norway

2001. Norwegian Architecture. Multicoloured.

1420	5k.50 Type **455**	1·20	55
1421	8k.50 Ivar Aasen Centre	1·90	1·00

456 Kittens

2001. Pets. Multicoloured.

1422	5k.50 Type **456**	1·20	75
1423	7k.50 Goat	1·60	1·00

457 Aung San Suu Kyi (Burmese opposition leader), 1991

2001. Centenary of Nobel Prizes. Peace Prize Winners (Nos. 1424/5 and 1427). Multicoloured.

1424	5k.50 Type **457**	1·30	65
1425	5k.50 Nelson Mandela (South African President), 1993	1·30	65
1426	7k. Alfred Nobel (Prize Fund founder)	1·50	85
1427	7k. Henry Dunant (founder of Red Cross), 1901	1·50	85
1428	9k. Fridtjof Nansen (Norwegian organizer for League of Nations refugee relief), 1922	2·00	1·30
1429	9k. Mikhail Gorbachev (Soviet President), 1990	2·00	1·30
1430	10k. Martin Luther King (Civil Rights leader), 1964	2·20	1·40
1431	10k. Rigoberta Menchu Tum (Guatemalan Civil Rights leader), 1992	2·20	1·40
MS1432	170×64 mm. No. 1426	2·30	1·90

Dates are those on which the Prize was awarded.

458 Snow-covered Trees and Lights

2001. Northern Lights. Multicoloured.

1433	5k. Type **458**	1·10	80
1434	5k.50 Lights and reindeer	1·20	85

459 Gingerbread Man

2001. Christmas. Multicoloured. Self-adhesive.

1435	5k.50 Type **459**	1·20	55
1436	5k.50 Gingerbread house	1·20	55

460 Tordis Maurstad

2002. Thespians (3rd series). Showing caricatures by Arne Roar Lund.

1450	**460**	5k. black and lilac	1·10	80
1451	-	5k.50 black and grey	1·20	80
1452	-	7k. black and green	1·50	1·00
1453	-	9k. black and green	1·90	1·30
1454	-	10k. black and brown	2·20	1·50

DESIGNS: 5k.50 Rolf Just Nilsen; 7k. Lars Tvinde; 9k. Henry Gleditsch; 10k. Norma Balean.

461 Boys tackling

2002. Centenary of Norwegian Football Association (1st issue). Multicoloured. Self-adhesive.

1455	5k.50 Type **461**	1·40	75
1456	5k.50 German referee Peter Hertel and player	1·40	75
1457	5k.50 Girls tackling	1·40	75
1458	5k.50 Boy kicking ball	1·40	75

See also Nos. 1469/**MS**1475.

462 Scene from "Askeladden and the Good Helpers" (animated film by Ivo Caprino)

2002. Fairytale Characters. Multicoloured. Self-adhesive.

1459	5k.50 Type **462**	1·20	75
1460	9k. Giant troll (drawing by Theodor Kittelsen)	2·10	1·30

463 "Monument to Whaling" (Sivert Donali)

2002. Nordic Countries' Postal Co-operation. Modern Art. Sculptures. Multicoloured.

1461	7k.50 Type **463**	1·60	1·20
1462	8k.50 "Throw" (Kåre Groven)	1·80	1·30

464 Holmestrand

2002. City Charter Anniversaries. Multicoloured.

1463	5k.50 Type **464** (300th anniv)	1·20	85
1464	5k.50 Kongsberg (200th anniv)	1·30	85

465 Abel

2002. Birth Bicentenary of Niels Henrik Abel (mathematician). Multicoloured.

1465	5k.50 Type **465**	1·80	1·80
1466	22k. Mathematical rosette	7·00	6·25

466 Johan Borgen

2002. Writers' Birth Centenaries. Portraits by Nils Aas.

1467	**466**	11k. yellow and green	2·50	1·60
1468	-	20k. green and blue	4·50	2·75

DESIGN: 20k. Nordahl Grieg.

467 Norwegian Team (Olympic Games, Berlin, 1936)

2002. Centenary of Norwegian Football Association (2nd issue). Multicoloured.

1469	5k. Type **467**	1·10	80
1470	5k.50 No. 9 player and Brazil No. 4 player (World Cup, France, 1998)	1·20	80
1471	5k.50 Norway and U.S.A. women players (Olympic Games, Sydney, 2000)	1·20	80
1472	7k. Player capturing ball from Sweden No. 11 player (Norway–Sweden, 1960)	1·50	1·30
1473	9k. Player with chevron sleeves (Norway–England, 1981)	2·00	1·50
1474	10k. Winning team members (Rosenborg–Milan (Champions League, 1996))	2·20	1·60
MS1475	140×127 mm. Nos. 1469/74	10·00	9·75

468 Clown on Tightrope

2002. Europa. Circus. Multicoloured.

1476	5k.50 Type **468**	1·30	85
1477	8k.50 Elephant, horse and chimpanzee	2·10	1·40

2002. "Nordia 2002" Nordic Stamp Exhibition, Kristiansand. Nos. 1465/6 surch NORDIC 2002.

1478	5k.50 multicoloured	2·00	2·00
1479	22k. multicoloured	7·00	6·50

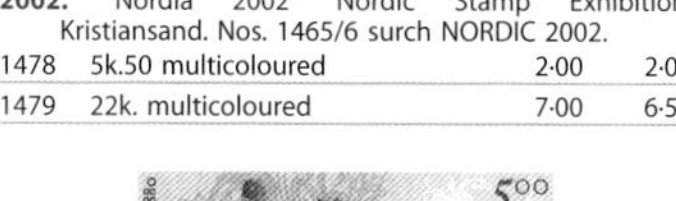

470 Landstad on Horseback and Frontispiece of "Norske Folkeviser"

2002. Birth Bicentenary of Magnus Brostrup Landstad (folk-song collector and hymn writer). Multicoloured.

1480	5k. Type **470**	1·20	85
1481	5k.50 Landstad and frontispiece of Kirkefalmebog	1·30	85

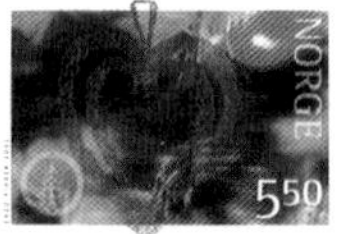

471 Straw Heart-shaped Decoration

2002. Christmas. Multicoloured. Self-adhesive.

1482	5k.50 Type **471**	1·20	75
1483	5k.50 Paper star-shaped decoration	1·20	75

472 "Nordmandens Krone" (Kare Espolin Johnson)

2003. Graphic Art (1st series). Multicoloured.

1484	5k. Type **472**	1·20	80
1485	8k.50 "Bla Hester" (Else Hagen)	2·00	1·60
1486	9k. "Dirigent og Solist" (Niclas Gulbrandsen)	2·10	1·60
1487	11k. "Olympia" (Svein Strand)	2·50	2·00
1488	22k. "Still Life XVII" (Rigmor Hansen)	5·00	4·25

See also Nos. 1515/16.

473 Heart

2003. St. Valentine.

1489	**473** 5k.50 multicoloured	1·50	85

474 Doudji Knife Handle (Havard Larsen)

2003. Crafts. Coil stamp. Self-adhesive.

1490	**474** 5k.50 multicoloured	1·50	75

475 Rose "Grand Prix"

2003. Roses (3rd series). Multicoloured. Self-adhesive.

1491	5k.50 Type **475**	1·30	75
1492	5k.50 Rose "Champagne"	1·30	75

476 Operating Theatre

2003. 400th Anniv of Public Health Service. Multicoloured.

1493	5k.50 Type **476**	1·30	75
1494	7k. Doctor examining baby	1·70	1·20

477 Forest Troll

2003. Fairytale Characters (2nd series). Showing drawings by Theodor Kittelsen. Self-adhesive. Multicoloured.

1495	5k.50 Type **477**	1·50	75
1496	9k. Water sprite (horiz)	2·10	1·40

478 Hand and Violin

2003. Bergen International Festival. Multicoloured.

1497	5k.50 Type **478**	1·30	75
1498	10k. Children's faces	2·50	1·50

479 Child holding Bread

2003. World Refugee Day. Multicoloured.

1499	5k.50 Type **479**	1·30	75
1500	10k. Refugees	2·50	1·50

480 Crown Prince Olav as a Child

2003. Birth Centenary of King Olav V (1903–1991). Multicoloured.

1501	5k.50 Type **480**	1·30	85
1502	8k.50 Crown Prince Olav and Crown Princess Martha	2·10	1·20
1503	11k. King Olav V	2·50	1·50
MS1504	170×101 mm. Nos. 1501/3	6·25	6·00

481 Baby

2003. Greetings Stamps. Multicoloured. Self-adhesive.

1505	5k.50 Type **481**	1·20	85
1506	5k.50 Hand wearing ring	1·20	85
1507	5k.50 Lily	1·20	85
1508	5k.50 Couple	1·20	85
1509	5k.50 Children and cake	1·20	85

482 Dagbladet (Per Krohg)

2003. Europa. Poster Art. Multicoloured.

1510	8k.50 Type **482**	1·50	1·30
1511	9k. Winter Olympics, Oslo (Knut Yran)	2·00	1·50
1512	10k. Music festival (Willibald Storn)	2·20	1·80

483 Bjornstjerne Bjornson (literature, 1903)

2003. Norwegian Nobel Prize Winners (1st series). Multicoloured.

1513	11k. Type **483**	2·40	2·00
1514	22k. Lars Onsager (chemistry, 1968)	5·00	4·50

See also Nos. 1549/50.

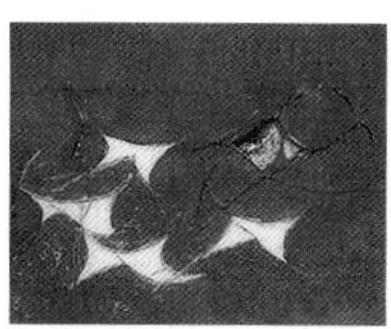

484 "Goatherd and Goats" (Rolf Nesch)

2003. Graphic Art (2nd series). Multicoloured.

1515	5k. Type **484**	1·30	95
1516	5k.50 "Winter Landscape 1980" (Terje Grostad)	1·30	1·00

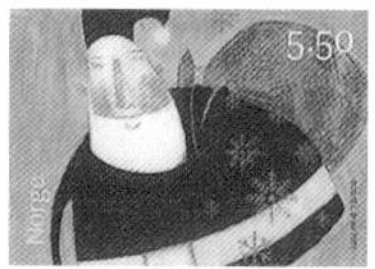

485 Santa Claus

2003. Christmas. Self-adhesive gum. Multicoloured.

1517	5k.50 Type **485**	1·20	80
1518	5k.50 Present	1·20	80

486 Coronet Medusa (*Periphylla periphylla*)

2004. Marine Life (1st series). Multicoloured. Self-adhesive.

1519	5k.50 Type **486**	1·50	1·10
1520	6k. Catfish (*Anarhichas lupus*)	1·60	1·10
1521	9k. Little cuttlefish (*Sepiola atlantica*)	2·75	2·10

See also Nos. 1576/7, 1608, 1621/2, 1649 and 1658/61.

487 Couple

2004. Greetings Stamps. Self-adhesive gum. Each green and grey.

1522	6k. Type **487**	1·80	1·20
1523	6k. Globe	1·80	1·20

488 "Idyll" (Christian Skredsbvig)

2004. Painters' Birth Anniversaries. Multicoloured.

1524	6k. Type **488** (150th anniv)	1·70	1·20
1525	9k.50 "Stetind in Fog" (Peder Balke) (bicentenary)	2·75	2·00
1526	10k.50 "Workers' Protest" (Reidar Aulie) (centenary)	3·00	2·20

489 Heart

2004. St. Valentine's Day.

1527	**489** 6k. multicoloured	1·50	1·30

490 Cyclist

2004. Europa. Holidays. Multicoloured.

1528	6k. Type **490**	1·70	1·30
1529	7k.50 Canoeist	2·00	1·60
1530	9k.50 Skiers	2·50	2·00

491 Otto Sverdrup

2004. 150th Birth Anniv of Otto Sverdrup (polar explorer). Each purple and buff.

1531	6k. Type **491**	1·60	1·30
1532	9k.50 *Fram* (polar research ship)	2·50	2·10
MS1533	166×60 mm. Nos. 1541/2 plus 1 label	4·00	3·75

No. **MS**1533 was issued with a stamp-sized label showing design of Greenland stamp.

Stamps of similar designs were issued by Greenland and Canada.

492 Sea God Njord

2004. Nordic Mythology. Multicoloured.

1534	7k.50 Type **492**	1·90	1·60
1535	10k.50 Balder's funeral	2·75	2·50
MS1536	106×70 mm. Nos. 1544/5	4·75	4·50

Stamps of a similar theme were issued by Aland Islands, Denmark, Faeroe Islands, Finland, Greenland, Iceland and Sweden.

493 Princess Ingrid Alexandra

2004. Birth of Princess Ingrid Alexandra of Norway. Sheet 94×61 mm.

MS1537	6k. multicoloured	1·80	1·80

494 Steam Locomotive, Koppang Station

2004. 150th Anniv of Norwegian Railways. Multicoloured.

1538	6k. Type **494**	1·70	1·60
1539	7k.50 Passengers and staff, Dovre station	2·10	2·00
1540	9k.50 Early diesel locomotive, Flatmark halt	2·75	2·50
1541	10k.50 Airport Express locomotive	3·25	3·00

495 Hakon Hakonsson

2004. 800th Birth Anniv of Hakon Hakonsson (Viking leader). Multicoloured.

1542 12k. Type **495** 3·25 3·00

1543 22k. Outline of Hakon's hall and sword 6·00 5·75

496 Smiley (emblem)

2004. Youth Stamps. Multicoloured.

1544 6k. Type **496** 1·60 1·50

1545 9k. Badges 2·50 2·10

497 Ship's Prow and Barrels

2004. Centenary of Archaeological Discovery, Oseberg. Multicoloured.

1546 7k.50 Type **497** 2·30 2·00

1547 9k.50 Sled 3·00 2·75

1548 12k. Bed 3·50 3·25

2004. Norwegian Nobel Prize Winners (2nd series). As T 483. Multicoloured.

1549 5k.50 Odd Hassel (chemistry, 1969) 1·60 1·40

1550 6k. Christian Lous Lange (peace, 1921) 1·70 1·60

498 "Friends" (Hanne Soteland)

2004. Christmas. Winning Designs in UNICEF Painting Competition. Multicoloured. Self-adhesive.

1551 6k. Type **498** 1·70 1·60

1552 6k. "Caring" (Synne Amalie Lund Kallak) 1·70 1·60

499 Princesses and Guard

2005. 150th Birth Anniv of Erik Werenskiold (artist). Illustrations from "The Three Princesses in the Blue Hill" fairytale by Peter Christen Asbjornsen and Jorgen Moe. Multicoloured.

1553 7k.50 Type **499** 2·20 1·80

1554 9k.50 Royal cradle 2·50 2·30

500 Soup Kitchen, Møllergata (1953)

2005. 150th Anniv of Church City Missions (humanitarian organization). Multicoloured.

1555 5k.50 Type **500** 1·60 1·40

1556 6k. Ministers giving communion at street service, Oslo 1·60 1·50

501 Heart and "Nar du er Borte" (poem by Tor Jonsson)

2005. St. Valentine's Day.

1557 **501** 6k. carmine and silver 1·70 1·50

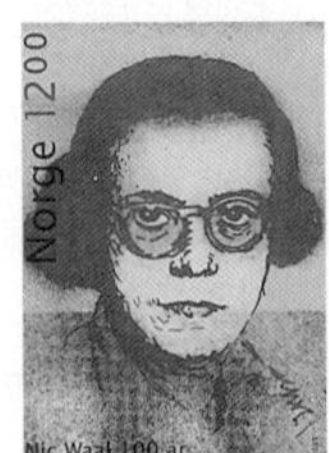

502 Caroline (Nic) Waal

2005. Birth Centenaries. Multicoloured.

1558 12k. Type **502** (first child psychiatrist) 3·50 3·00

1559 22k. Aase Gruda Skard (first child psychologist) 6·25 5·50

503 "City of the Future" (Maja Anna Marszalek)

2005. Winning Entries in Children's Drawing Competition. Multicoloured.

1560 6k. Type **503** 1·70 1·50

1561 7k.50 "The Modern Classroom" (Tobias Abrahamsen) 2·20 1·90

504 Fjord, Geiranger

2005. Tourism. Self-adhesive. Multicoloured.

1562 6k. Type **504** 1·70 1·50

1563 9k.50 Kjosfossen, Flam 2·50 2·30

1564 10k.50 Polar bear, Svalbard 3·00 2·75

505 Prime Minister Christian Michelsen (Norway)

2005. Centenary of Dissolution of Union with Sweden. Multicoloured.

1565 6k. Type **505** 1·70 1·50

1566 7k.50 King Haakon VII (Sweden) 2·20 1·90

MS1567 162×94 mm. Nos. 1565/56 4·00 3·50

506 King Haakon VII taking Oath (1905)

2005. 20th-century Events. Multicoloured.

1568 6k. Type **506** 2·10 1·70

1569 6k. Crown Prince Olav riding through Oslo (1945) 2·10 1·70

1570 6k. King Olav V appearing on first Norwegian television broadcast (1960) 2·10 1·70

1571 6k. Prime Minister Trygve Bratteli opening Ekofisk oilfield (1971) 2·10 1·70

1572 9k. Kjetil Rekdal scoring winning goal in World Cup match against Brazil (1998) 2·10 1·70

507 *Christian Radich*

2005. Ships. Multicoloured.

1573 6k. Type **507** 2·00 1·80

1574 9k.50 *Sorlandet* 3·00 2·75

1575 10k.50 *Statsraad Lehmkuhl* 3·25 3·00

508 Killer Whale (*Orcinus orca*)

2005. Marine Life (2nd series). Multicoloured. Self-adhesive.

1576 B (5k.50) Type **508** 1·80 2·00

1577 A (6k.) Sea anemone (*Urticina eques*) 2·00 1·80

509 Jomfruland Lighthouse

2005. Lighthouses. Self-adhesive. Multicoloured.

1578 (6k.) Type **509** 2·00 1·80

1579 (6k.) Tranoy 2·00 1·80

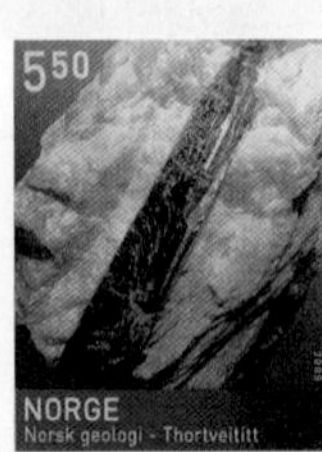

510 Thortveitite (rare mineral)

2005. Centenary of Geological Society. Mult.

1580 5k.50 Type **510** 1·80 1·60

1581 6k. Drilling rig, ship, continental shelf, stylized rock section and *Lamprocyclas maritalis* 2·00 1·80

511 Transmitting Apparatus

2005. 150th Anniv of Telegraph in Norway. Multicoloured.

1582 6k. Type **511** 2·10 1·80

1583 10k.50 Girl using mobile phone 3·25 3·00

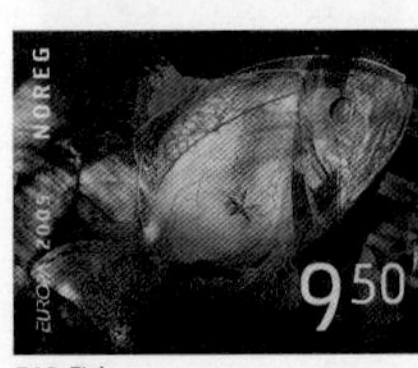

512 Fish

2005. Europa. Gastronomy. Multicoloured.

1584 9k.50 Type **512** 3·00 2·75

1585 10k.50 Decorated table 3·25 3·00

513 Eye and "150th Anniversary" (image scaled to 71% of original size)

2005. 150th Anniv of Norwegian Stamps. Mult.

1586 (6k.) Type **513** 1·80 1·60

MS1587 170×60 mm. (6k.) Type **513**; 12k. First stamp and woman writing letter 5·50 4·75

514 King Haakon holding Crown Prince Olav and Prime Minister Christian Michelsen

2005. Centenary of Norwegian Royal House. Multicoloured.

1588 6k. Type **514** 1·80 1·60

1589 6k. King Harald VII and Crown Prince Haakon holding Princess Ingrid Alexandra 1·80 1·60

515 Gingerbread Christmas Tree

2005. Christmas. Multicoloured. Self-adhesive.

1590 (6k.) Type **515** 1·80 1·60

1591 (6k.) Spiced oranges 1·80 1·60

516 Comet and "Tanke og draum er himmelske køyrety" (Olav Hauge)

2006. Centenary of Language Society.

1592 **516** 6k. multicoloured 1·80 1·60

517 Kari Traa performing Iron Cross

2006. Winter Olympic Games, Turin. Multicoloured.

1593 6k. Type **517** 1·80 1·60

1594 22k. Elinar Bjørndalen (biathlete) 6·25 5·75

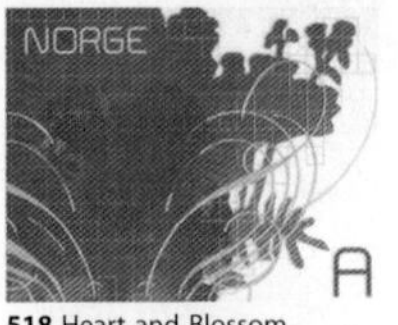

518 Heart and Blossom

2006. St. Valentine's Day.

1595 **518** A (6k.) multicoloured 1·80 1·60

519 Flower

2006. Greetings Stamps. Multicoloured. Self-adhesive.

1596 A (6k.) Type **519** 1·90 1·70

1597 A (6k.) Baby 1·90 1·70

1598 A (6k.) Heart and rings 1·90 1·70

1599 A (6k.) Cake 1·90 1·70

520 Lifeguard carrying Victim

2006. Centenary of Lifesaving Society. Mult.

1600 10k. Type **520** 2·75 2·50
1601 10k.50 Baby swimming 3·00 2·50

521 Shaman's Drum (detail)

2006. Nordic Mythology. Sheet 105×70 mm containing T 521 and similar horiz design. Multicoloured.

MS1602 A (6k.) Type **521**; 10k.50 Fafnir (dragon) (carved door panel) 4·75 4·50

Stamps of a similar theme were issued by Aland Islands, Denmark, Faroe Islands, Finland, Greenland, Iceland and Sweden.

522 Lynx

2006. Wildlife. Multicoloured.

1603 6k.50 Type **522** 1·90 1·80
1604 8k.50 Capercaillie 2·50 2·30
1605 10k. Golden eagle 3·00 2·75
1606 10k.50 Artic fox 3·25 3·00
1607 13k. Mountain hare 3·75 3·50

523 *Polycera quadrilineata*

2006. Marine Life. (3rd series). Self-adhesive.

1608 **523** 10k. multicoloured 3·00 2·75

524 Shopper c. 1947

2006. Centenary of Cooperative Movement.

1609 **524** 6k.50 multicoloured 1·90 1·80

525 *Skibladner*

2006. Tourism. Multicoloured. Self-adhesive.

1610 6k.50 Type **525** 1·90 1·80
1611 6k.50 Maihaugen, Lillehammer 1·90 1·80
1612 8k.50 Kirkenporten, Nordkapp 2·50 2·10
1613 8k.50 Nordkapp 2·50 2·40
1614 10k.50 Bryggen, Bergen 3·25 3·00
1615 10k.50 Atlanterhavsveien 3·25 3·00

526 Surveying c. 1906

2006. Centenary of Prince Albert I of Monaco's Expedition to Svalbard, Arctic Circle and Establishment of Longyearbyen and Stoke Norske Coal Mining Company. Multicoloured.

1616 6k.50 Type **526** 2·00 1·80
1617 8k.50 Coal transport terminal 1·80 2·50
1618 22k. Longyearbyen today 6·50 6·25
MS1619 171×100 mm. Nos. 1616/18 10·50 10·00

527 Dove

2006. Personalised Stamp. Self-adhesive.

1620 **527** A (6k.50) multicoloured 1·75 85

528 Sea urchin (*Strongylocentrotus droebachiensis*)

2006. Marine Life. (4th series). Multicoloured. Self-adhesive.

1621 B (6k.) Type **528** 1·70 1·50
1622 A (6k.50) Cuckoo wrasse (*Labrus bimaculatus*) 1·80 1·60

529 On Parade

2006. 150th Anniv of King's Guard. Multicoloured.

1623 6k.50 Type **529** 1·80 1·60
1624 13k. Field training 3·50 3·25
MS1625 178×65 mm. Nos. 1623/4 5·25 5·00

530 Lantern

2006. Personalised Stamp. Self-adhesive.

1626 **530** A (6k.50) multicoloured 1·80 1·60

531 Children and Tree

2006. Christmas. Multicoloured. Self-adhesive.

1627 A (6k.50) Type **531** 1·80 1·60
1628 A (6k.50) Snowman 1·80 1·60

532 Circle of Children

2006. Europa. Integration. Multicoloured.

1629 8k.50 Type **532** 2·40 3·50
1630 13k. Children and ball 2·10 3·25

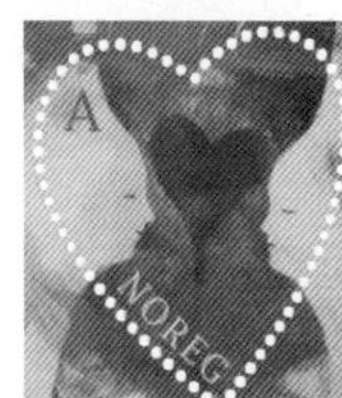

533 Heart

2007. St. Valentine's Day.

1631 **533** A (6k.50) multicoloured 1·80 1·60

534 Petter Solberg driving Subaru Impreza

2007. Motor Sport. Norway Winter Rally. Multicoloured.

1632 A (6k.50) "Innland" Type **534** 1·80 1·60
1633 A (8k.50) "Europa" Henning Solberg driving Peugeot 307 2·50 2·20
1634 A (10k.50) "Verden" Thomas Schie driving Ford Focus 3·00 2·75
MS1635 170×100 mm. Nos. 1632/4 7·00 6·75

No. 1632 was for use on priority domestic mail, 1633 was for use on priority mail within Europe and 1634 was for use on worldwide priority mail.

535 King Harald V

2007. 70th Birthday of King Harald V.

1636 **535** 6k.50 multicoloured 1·80 1·60

536 Water Samples and CTD Machine

2007. International Polar Year. Sheet 170×100 mm containing T 536 and similar horiz design. Multicoloured.

MS1637 170×100 mm. 10k.50 Type **536**; 13k. *Svalbard* (research ship) and antenna 6·50 6·25

537 Hedgehog

2007. Wildlife. Multicoloured.

1638 12k. Type **537** 3·25 3·00
1639 22k. Red squirrel 6·00 5·75

538 Arms, *Dionne* (barque), Customs House and Perfume Bottle

2007. Bicentenary of Porgrunn. Value expressed by letter.

1640 **538** A "Innland" (7k.) mult 1·90 1·70

No. 1640 was for use on Priority mail within Norway.

539 Free Fall over Voss

2007. Tourism. Multicoloured. Self-adhesive.

1641 A "Innland" (7k.) Type **539** 2·00 1·80
1642 A "Innland" (7k.) Cyclists on Old Navvy Road, Finse 2·00 1·80
1643 A "Europa" (9k.) Houses, Roros 2·50 2·30
1644 A "Europa" (9k.) River, Fredrikstad 2·50 2·30
1645 A "Verden" (11k.) House and bay, Portor 3·00 2·75
1646 A "Verden" (11k.) View from sea, Reine 3·00 2·75

Nos. 1641/2 was for use on priority domestic mail, 1643/4 was for use on priority mail within Europe and 1645/6 was for use on priority mail worldwide.

540 "Et Overfall" (An Attack)

2007. 150th Birth Anniv of Theodor Kittelsen (artist). Multicoloured.

1647 A "Europa" (9k.) Type **540** 2·50 2·20
1648 A "Verden" (11k.) "For tidlig Nedkomst" (Premature Delivery) 3·00 2·50

Nos. 1647 was for use on priority mail within Europe and 1648 was for use on priority mail worldwide.

541 Mackerel (*Scomber scombrus*)

2007. Marine Life (5th series). Multicoloured. Self-adhesive.

1649 **541** 11k. multicoloured 3·00 2·50

542 Scouts and Knots

2007. Europa. Centenary of Scouting. Multicoloured.

1650 9k. Type **542** 2·50 2·20
1651 11k. Camp 3·00 2·50

543 Church of Our Lady, Trondheim

2007. Architectural Anniversaries. Multicoloured.

1652 14k. Type **543** (800th anniv) 3·50 3·25
1653 23k. Vardohus Fortress (700th anniv) 6·50 6·25

544 Ona Lighthouse

2007. Lighthouses. Multicoloured. Self-adhesive.

1654 (7k.) Type **544** 2·00 1·80
1655 (7k.) Tungeneset 2·00 1·80

See also Nos. 1578/9.

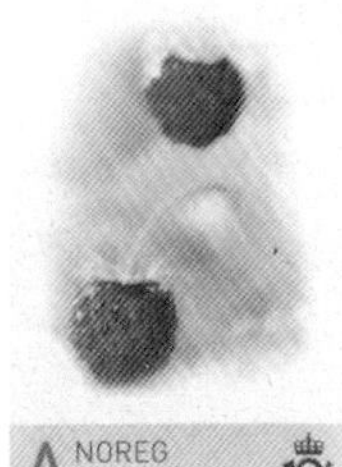

545 Strawberries

2007. Personalised Stamp. Self-adhesive.

1656 **545** (7k.) multicoloured 2·00 1·80

546 'Ingen tanke er tenkt fo den er stot i ord' (Inge Loning)

2007. Centenary of Riksmaal (language) Society.

1657	**546**	7k. multicoloured	2·00	1·80

547 *Pandalus montagui*

2007. Marine Life (6th series). Mlticoloured. Self-adhesive.

1658	(7k.) Type **547**	2·30	2·00
1659	(7k.) *Homarus gammarus*	2·30	2·00
1660	(7k.) *Cancer pagurus*	2·30	2·00
1661	(7k.) *Galathea strigosa*	2·30	2·00

548 Halldis Moren

2007. Birth Centenary of Halldis Moren Vesaas (poet and translator).

1662	**548**	23k. bronze, black and gold	6·50	6·25

549 Reindeer

2007. Personal Stamp. Self-adhesive A-Priority Domestic Stamp.

1663	**549**	(7k.) blue and vermilion	2·30	2·00

No. 1663 was inscr 'A INNLAND'.

550 Star

2007. Christmas. A-Priority Domestic Stamps. Multicoloured. Self-adhesive.

1664	(7k.) Type **550**	2·30	2·00
1665	(7k.) Three Wise Men	2·30	2·00

Nos. 1664/5 were inscr 'A INNLAND'.

551 Academy Building and Machinery

2007. Scientific Anniversaries. Multicoloured.

1666	14k. Type **551** (250th anniv of Kongsberg Mining Academy)	4·25	4·00
1667	14k. Molecule and microscope (150th anniv of Academy of Science and Letters)	4·25	4·00

552 'Love'

2008. St Valentine's Day. Multicoloured. (a) Inscr 'INNLAND A'.

1668	(7k.) Type **552**	2·30	2·00

(b) Inscr 'EUROPA A'.

1669	(9k.) Letter, roses and doves	3·00	2·75

No. 1668 was for use on domestic mail and No. 1669 for use on mail within Europe.

553 Elk

2008. Wildlife. Multicoloured.

1670	11k. Type **553**	2·75	2·75
1671	14k. Brown bear	4·25	4·25
1672	23k. Wolf	7·00	7·00

554 Thorleif Haug

2008. Centenary of Norwegian Ski Federation. Multicoloured. Self adhesive.

1673	A (7k.) Type **554** (Olympic cross country and Nordic gold medallist–1924)	2·00	2·00
1674	A (7k.) Espen Bredesen (Olympic hill gold medallist–1994)	2·00	2·00
1675	A (7k.) Children skiing	2·00	2·00
1676	A (7k.) Kjetil Andre Aamodt (four times Olympic alpine gold medallist)	2·00	2·00

555 Harald Fairhair and Snofrid

2008. Norse Mythology. Mythological Places. Sheet 105×70 mm containing T 555 and similar horiz design. Multicoloured.

MS1677	A (70k.)×2, Type **555**; Snøhetta (home of giants) in Dovre mountains	25·00	25·00

The stamps and margins of **MS**1677 form a composite design.

556 Building Facade

2008. Inauguration of New Opera House, Oslo.

1678	**556**	A (7k.) multicoloured	2·00	2·00

557 Frederick Stang

2008. Birth Bicentenaries. Multicoloured.

1679	A (7k.) Type **557** (politician)	2·00	2·00
1680	A (7k.) Henrick Wergland (lyricist)	2·00	2·20

558 Oslo Harbour

2008. Tourism. Multicoloured. Self-adhesive. (a) Inscr 'INNLAND A'.

1681	A (7k.) Type **558**	2·00	2·00
1682	A (7k.) *Divers* (sculpture) (Ola Enstad)	2·00	2·00

(b) Inscr 'EUROPA A'.

1683	A (9k.) The Blade, Molladalen (Sunnmore alps)	2·20	2·20
1684	A (9k.) Wedged boulder, Kjerag plateau, Lyse Fjord	2·20	2·20

556 Building Facade

(c) Inscr 'VERDEN A'.

1685	A (11k.) Yacht and Lyngør lighthouse	2·75	2·75
1686	A (11k.) Houses, Lyngor	2·75	2·75

Nos. 1681/2 was for use on priority domestic mail, 1683/4 was for use on priority mail within Europe and 1685/6 was for use on priority mail worldwide.

559 *Boroysund*

2008. Transportation Centenaries.

1687	7k. olive and brown	2·00	2·00
1688	9k. indigo and crimson	2·20	2·20
1689	25k. brown and blue	6·25	6·25
1690	30k. lilac and green	9·50	9·50

DESIGNS: 7k. Type **559**; 9k. *Oster* (ice breaker and transport ship); 25k. French Unic 1907 bus and driver; 30k. Thamshavn electric railway locomotive and train.

560 *Dancer in a Cultural Landscape* (composed photograph by Marcel Lelienhof)

2008. Stavanger–European Capital of Culture, 2008. Multicoloured.

1691	7k. Type **560**	2·00	2·00
1692	14k. *Swords in Rock* (sculpture by Fritz Roed)	4·00	4·00
1693	23k. 'Eye' (character from *The Thousandth Heart* (musical)) (vert)	7·50	7·50

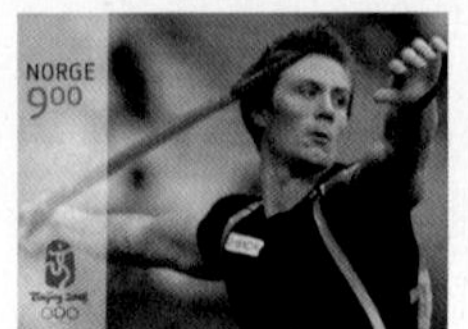

561 Andreas Thorkildsen (javelin)

2008. Olympic Games, Beijing. Multicoloured.

1694	9k. Type **561**	3·00	7·50
1695	23k. Gro Hammerseng (handball)	7·50	7·50

562 New Post Logo

2008. Personalised Stamp.

1696	**562**	A (7k.) multicoloured	2·25	2·25

No. 1696 was for use on priority domestic mail, and originally sold for 7k.

2008. Stavanger–European Capital of Culture, 2008. As T 560. Multicoloured.

MS1697	170×65 mm. Nos. 1691/3	14·00	14·00

563 *I revolusjonens forgard* (Arne Ekeland)

2008. Norwegian Art. Multicoloured. Self-adhesive.

1698	A (7k.) Type **563**	2·25	2·25
1699	A (7k.) *Svalbardmotiv* (Kare Tveter)	2·25	2·25
1700	A (7k.) *Komposisjon i rodt* (Inge Sitter)	2·25	2·25
1701	A (7k.) *Fra Sagorsk ca 1985* (Terje Bergstad)	2·25	2·25

No. 1698/701 were for use on priority domestic mail, and originally sold for 7k.

564 Gnomes and Amperhaugen Farm

2008. Christmas. Multicoloured. Self-adhesive.

1702	A (7k.) Type **564**	2·25	2·25
1703	A (7k.) Gnome looking down on Nordre Lien farm	2·25	2·25

Nos. 1702/3 were for use on priority domestic mail, and originally sold for 7k.

2009. Norwegian Art (2nd series). Self-adhesive Coil Stamps. As T 563. Multicoloured.

1704	B (7k.50) *Sommernatt til E.M.* (Kjell Nupen)	2·25	2·25
1705	12k. *Lyset ved pinsetider* (Irmo Salo Jæger)	3·00	3·00

No. 1704 were for use on economy domestic mail, and originally sold for 7k.50.

565 Roe Deer

2009. Wildlife. Multicoloured.

1706	11k.50 Type **565**	3·00	3·00
1707	15k.50 Reindeer	4·25	4·25
1708	25k. Willow grouse	6·25	6·25

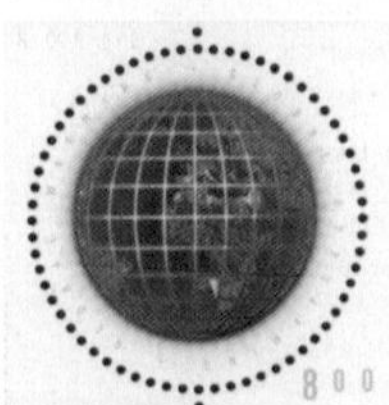
566 Over-heated Globe

2009. Preserve Polar Regions and Glaciers. Sheet 120×80 mm containing T 566 and similar circular design. Multicoloured.

MS1709	8k.×2, Type **566**; Polar ice	5·00	5·00

567 Hepatica

2009. Personal Stamp. Self-adhesive.

1710	**567**	A (8k.) multicoloured	2·50	2·50

No. 1710 was for use on priority domestic mail, and originally sold for 8k.

568 Bergen Railway Line

2009. Tourism. Self-adhesive Booklet Stamps. Multicoloured.

1711	A (8k.) Type **568**	2·75	2·75
1712	A (8k.) Locomotive in snow	2·75	2·75
1713	A (10k.) Stottafjorden, Meloy, Nordland	3·25	3·25
1714	A (10k.) Revtangen, Kiepp, Rogaland	3·25	3·25
1715	A (12k.) Bleik, Andoya, Nordland	4·00	4·00
1716	A (12k.) Kennesteinen, Vagsoy, Sogh og Fjordane	4·00	4·00

Nos. 1711/12 were for use on priority domestic mail, and originally sold for 8k. Nos. 1713/14 were for use on priority mail within Europe, and originally sold for 10k. Nos. 1715/16 were for use on priority worldwided mail, and originally sold for 12k.

569 Procession

2009. 150th Anniv of National Anthem.

1717	**569**	12k. multicoloured	4·00	4·00

570 Telephone Kiosk (designed by Georg Fasting, 1932)

2009. Norwegian Year of Cultural Heritage. Coil stamps. Multicoloured. Self-adhesive.

1718	(8k.) Type **570**	2·75	2·75
1719	(8k.) Kurer radio (1950)	2·75	2·75

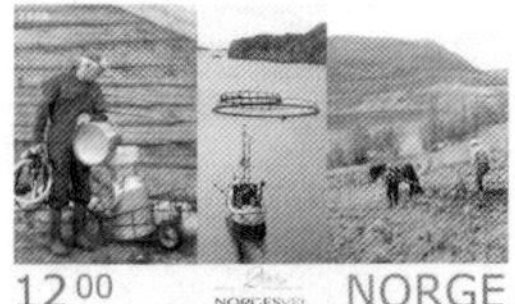

571 Explosion on Sun's Surface

2009. Europa. Astronomy. Multicoloured.

1720	10k. Type **571**	3·00	3·00
1721	12k. Moon	4·00	4·00
MS1722	156×108 mm. Nos. 1720/1	7·00	7·00

572 Symbols of Development

2009. Bicentenary of Royal Norwegian Society for Development.

1723	**572**	12k. multicoloured	4·50	4·50

573 *Kobben* (1909)

2009. Centenary of Naval Submarines. Multicoloured.

1724	14k.50 Type **573**	5·00	5·00
1725	15k.50 Modern Ula class submarine	6·00	6·00

574 Knut Hamsun

2009. 150th Birth Anniv of Knut Hamsun (writer and winner of 1920 Nobel Prize for Literature).

1726	**574**	25k. deep claret, silver and gold	8·50	8·50

575 Roald Stensby

2009. Norwegian Rock Pioneers. Multicoloured. Self-adhesive.

1727	A (8k.) Type **575**	3·00	3·00
1728	A (8k.) Rocke-Pelle (Per Hartvig)	3·00	3·00
1729	A (8k.) Jan Rhode	3·00	3·00
1730	A (8k.) Per 'Elvis' Granberg	3·00	3·00

576 Cruise Ship

2009. Centenary of Shipowners' Association.

1731	**576**	15k.50 multicoloured	4·50	4·50

577 Man with Guide Dog and White Stick

2009. Centenary of Norwegian Association of the Blind and Partially Sighted.

1732	**577**	8k. vermilion	3·25	3·25

No. 1732 is embossed with Braille letters.

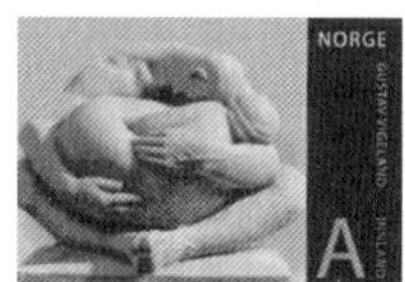

578 Apple

2009. Christmas. Booklet Stamps. Multicoloured. Self-adhesive.

1733	A (8k.) Type **578**	3·00	3·00
1734	A (8k.) Star	3·00	3·00

Nos. 1733/4 were for use on priority domestic mail, and originally sold for 8k.

579 *Woman on a Man's Lap* (Gustav Vigeland)

2009. Modern Art. Multicoloured. Self-adhesive.

1735	A (8k.) Type **579**	3·00	3·00
1736	A (8k.) *Crow* (Nils Aas)	3·00	3·00
1737	A (8k.) *Birds in Flight* (Arnold Haukeland)	3·00	3·00
1738	A (8k.) *Granite Head on Side* (Kristian Blystad)	3·00	3·00

No. 1735/8 were for use on priority domestic mail, and originally sold for 8k.

580 *Mann som drikker* (Per Salle Storm)

2010. Modern Art. Self-adhesive.

1739	**580**	13k. multicoloured	4·75	4·75

581 Otter

2010. Fauna. Multicoloured.

1740	15k. Type **581**	3·50	3·50
1741	16k. Lemming	4·75	4·75
1742	26k. Wolverine	13·00	13·00

582 Ole Bull (violinist)

2010. Birth Bicentenaries. Multicoloured. Self-adhesive.

1743	A (8k.) Type **582**	3·00	3·00
1744	A (8k.) Peter Andreas Munch (historian)	3·00	3·00

No. 1743/4 were for use on priority domestic mail, and originally sold for 8k.

583 Fish on Drying Rack, Lofoten

2010. Norden. Life at the Coast

MS1745	**583** A (11k.) multicoloured	4·00	4·00

Stamps of a similar theme were issued by Denmark, Greenland, Faröe Islands, Finland, Iceland, Aland Islands and Sweden.

584 Valdresflya

2010. Tourism. Multicoloured.

1746	A INNLAND (8k.50) Type **584**	3·00	3·00
1747	A INNLAND (8k.50) Gamle Strynefjellsveien	3·00	3·00
1748	A EUROPA (11k.) Sognfjellet	3·75	3·75
1749	A EUROPA (11k.) Trollstigen	3·75	3·75
1750	A VERDA (13k.) Helgelandsky-sten Nord	4·75	4·75
1751	A VERDA (13k.) Lofoten	4·75	4·75

Nos. 1746/7 were for use on priority domestic mail, and originally sold for 8k.50

Nos. 1748/9 were for use on priority mail within Europe, and originally sold for 11k

Nos. 1750/1 were for use on priority worldwide mail, and originally sold for 13k.

585 Heather

2010. Personal Stamp

1752	A INNLAND (8k.50) multicoloured	4·00	4·00

586 Jahn Teigen

2010. Eurovision Song Contest Performers.. Multicoloured.

1753	A INNLAND (8k.50) Type **586**	3·25	3·25
1754	A INNLAND (8k.50) Alexander Rybak	3·25	3·25
1755	A INNLAND (8k.50) Secret Garden	3·25	3·25
1756	A INNLAND (8k.50) Bobbysocks	3·25	3·25

587 Nils Petter Molvær (trumpeter)

2010. 50th (2011) Anniv of Molde Jazz Festival

1757	**587**	13k. black and turquoise-blue	4·50	4·50

588 Hands, Feet and Microscope

2010. Centenary of Norwegian National Health Association

1758	**588**	26k. multicoloured	9·25	9·25

589 Bjørnen Teodor, Komekameratene,Pompel & Piltand Titten Tei (children's television)

2010. 50th Anniv of Norwegian Television. Multicoloured.

(a) Coil stamps. Self-adhesive

1759	A INNLAND (8k.50) Type **489**	3·00	3·00
1760	A INNLAND (8k.50) Trond Kirkvåg as *Skremmer'n*, Robert Stolenberg as *Narvestad*, Rolv Wesenlund as *Fleksnes* and Trond-Viggo Torgesen as *Vaktmester'n* (comedy)	3·00	3·00
1761	A INNLAND (8k.50) Erik Diesen, Dan Børge Åkerø, Ivar Dyrhaug and Anne Grosvald (entertainment)	3·00	3·00
1762	A INNLAND (8k.50) Arne Schele, Ingrid Espelid Høvig, Erik Bye and Ragnhild Sælthun Fjørtoft (personalities)	3·00	3·00

(b) Miniature sheet. Ordinary gum

MS1763	120×80 mm. A INNLAND (8k.50)×2, As Type **589** and As No. 1762	6·00	6·00

590 Norwegian University of Technology and Science, Gloshaugen (centenary)

2010. Anniversaries. Multicoloured.

1764	8k.50 Type **590**	3·25	3·25
1765	13k. Society seal and building, Klalvskinnet, Trondheim (Royal Norwegian Society of Science and Letters (250th anniv))	4·50	4·50

591 'YTRINGSFRIHET' (freedom of speech)

2010. Centenary of Norwegian Press Association and Norwegian Media Businesses' Association

1766	**591**	11k. multicoloured	4·00	4·00

592 Boatswain Mikel Våge aboard Stavanger (1973)

2010. Centenary of Norwegian Seafarers' Union

1767	**592**	16k. multicoloured	5·75	5·75

Nos. 1768/9 and Type **593** are left for DKNVS and NTNU Anniversaries issue on 15 September 2010, not yet received.

2010. Posthorn. Multicoloured, colour of oval given.

1770	4k. royal blue	1·75	1·75
1771	8k. deep carmine-red	2·75	2·75
1772	30k. reddish lilac	11·00	11·00

594 Christmas Goat

2010. Christmas. Multicoloured.

1773	A (8k.50) Type **594**	3·25	3·25
1774	A (8k.50) Candlestick with candles	3·25	3·25

Nos. 1773/4 were both inscribed 'INNLAND' and were for use on priority domestic mail, and originally sold for 8k.60.

595 In the Sledge

2010. Europa. Multicoloured.

1176	A(11k.) Father, Mother, Grandmother and children approaching cottage	4·50	4·50
1775	A(8k.50) Type **595**	2·75	2·75

Nos. 1775 was inscribed 'INNLAND' and was for use on priority domestic mail, and originally sold for 8k.60 No. 1776 was inscribed 'EUROPA' and were for use on priority European mail, and originally sold for 11k.

596 Athletes

2011. 150th Anniv of Norwegian Confederation of Sports

1777	**596**	14k. multicoloured	7·75	7·75

597 Polar Bear

2011. Fauna. Multicoloured.

1778	17k. Type **597**	12·00	12·00
1779	27k. Musk ox	16·00	16·00

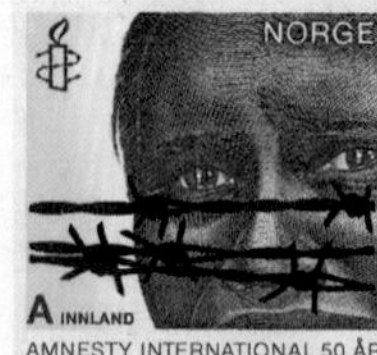

598 Barbed Wire and Face

2011. 50th Anniv of Amnesty International

1780	**598**	A(9k.) multicoloured	3·50	3·50

599 Svalbard Global Seed Vault

2011. Tourism. Modern Architecture. Multicoloured.

1781	A INNLAND (9k.) Type **599**	2·75	2·75
1782	A EUROPA (12k.) Borgund Visitor Centre	4·25	4·25
1783	A VERDEN (14k.) Preikestolen Mountain Lodge	7·00	7·00

No. 1781 as for use on priority domestic mail, and originally sold for 9k.

No. 1782 was for use on priority mail within Europe, and originally sold for 12k.

No. 1783 was for use on priority worldwide mail, and originally sold for 13k.

600 Fridtjof Nansen

2011. 150th Birth Anniv of Fridtjof Nansen (first High Commissioner for Refugees at League of Nation and winner of 1922 Nobel Peace Prize)

1784	**600**	12k. multicoloured	4·75	4·75

601 Roald Amudsen (expedition leader), Olav Bjaaland, Helmer Hanssen, Sverre Hassel and Oscar Wisting

2011. Centenary of First Men at South Pole. Multicoloured.

1785	14k. Type **601**	5·25	5·25
1786	17k. Sled dogs and *Fram* (expedition ship)	6·75	6·75

OFFICIAL STAMPS

O22

1925

O187	**O22**	5ore mauve	1·20	1·10
O188	**O22**	10ore green	45	25
O189	**O22**	15ore blue	2·50	2·40
O190	**O22**	20ore purple	40	25
O191	**O22**	30ore grey	4·25	4·50
O192	**O22**	40ore blue	3·00	1·20
O193	**O22**	60ore blue	5·00	4·75

1929. Surch 2 2.

O219	2ore on 5ore mauve	85	85

O36

1933

O231	**O36**	2ore brown	60	1·60
O243	**O36**	5ore purple	2·10	1·60
O233	**O36**	7ore orange	5·75	4·75
O245	**O36**	10ore green	85	40
O235	**O36**	15ore green	65	55
O247	**O36**	20ore red	1·10	35
O237	**O36**	25ore brown	65	60
O238	**O36**	30ore blue	85	65
O248	**O36**	35ore violet	80	45
O249	**O36**	40ore grey	1·20	50
O250	**O36**	60ore blue	1·30	80
O241	**O36**	70ore brown	1·70	2·40
O242	**O36**	100ore blue	3·00	2·10

O39

1937

O267	**O39**	5ore mauve	40	25
O268	**O39**	7ore orange	60	55
O269	**O39**	10ore green	25	25
O270	**O39**	15ore brown	40	25
O271	**O39**	20ore red	25	25
O260	**O39**	25ore brown	1·40	65
O273	**O39**	25ore red	25	20
O261	**O39**	30ore blue	90	75
O275	**O39**	30ore grey	95	40
O276	**O39**	35ore purple	60	25
O277	**O39**	40ore grey	65	25
O278	**O39**	40ore blue	4·25	30
O279	**O39**	50ore lilac	95	30
O280	**O39**	60ore blue	65	25
O281	**O39**	100ore blue	1·30	25
O282	**O39**	200ore orange	2·40	30

O58 Quisling Emblem

1942

O336	**O58**	5ore mauve	40	1·80
O337	**O58**	7ore orange	40	1·80
O338	**O58**	10ore green	15	30
O339	**O58**	15ore brown	2·50	13·00
O340	**O58**	20ore red	15	30
O341	**O58**	25ore brown	5·00	19·00
O342	**O58**	30ore blue	3·25	19·00
O343	**O58**	35ore purple	3·25	10·00
O344	**O58**	40ore grey	20	30
O345	**O58**	60ore blue	3·00	11·00
O346	**O58**	1k. blue	3·00	15·00

1949. Surch 25 and bar.

O402	**O39**	25ore on 20ore red	35	30

O89

1951

O434	**O89**	5ore mauve	1·20	15
O435	**O89**	10ore grey	1·00	15
O436	**O89**	15ore brown	1·20	65
O437	**O89**	30ore red	75	15
O438	**O89**	35ore brown	1·10	50
O439	**O89**	60ore blue	1·30	20
O440	**O89**	100ore violet	1·90	40

O99

1955

O458	**O99**	5ore purple	20	20
O459	**O99**	10ore grey	20	15
O460	**O99**	15ore brown	55	1·80
O461	**O99**	20ore green	40	20
O736	**O99**	25ore green	20	20
O463	**O99**	30ore red	2·10	70
O464	**O99**	30ore green	2·20	20
O465	**O99**	35ore red	45	15
O466	**O99**	40ore lilac	85	15
O467	**O99**	40ore green	45	40
O468	**O99**	45ore red	1·50	15
O469	**O99**	50ore brown	2·50	20
O470	**O99**	50ore red	1·80	30
O471	**O99**	50ore blue	50	20
O738	**O99**	50ore grey	20	15
O473	**O99**	60ore red	65	20
O739	**O99**	60ore blue	1·10	3·50
O475	**O99**	65ore red	1·40	25
O476	**O99**	70ore brown	4·75	85
O477	**O99**	70ore red	30	20
O478	**O99**	75ore purple	13·00	11·50
O479	**O99**	75ore green	75	45
O481	**O99**	80ore brown	60	15
O741	**O99**	80ore red	35	15
O482	**O99**	85ore brown	55	1·60
O483	**O99**	90ore orange	1·30	20
O484	**O99**	1k. violet	1·30	15
O485	**O99**	1k. red	30	20
O486	**O99**	1k.10 red	60	80
O744	**O99**	1k.25 red	85	20
O745	**O99**	1k.30 purple	1·10	1·50
O746	**O99**	1k.50 red	50	30
O747	**O99**	1k.75 green	1·50	1·40
O748	**O99**	2k. green	1·20	25
O749	**O99**	2k. red	1·20	25
O750	**O99**	3k. violet	1·50	55
O488	**O99**	5k. violet	5·50	70
O752	**O99**	5k. blue	1·30	25

POSTAGE DUE STAMPS

D12

1889. Inscr "at betale" and "PORTOMAERKE".

D95	**D12**	1ore green	65	80
D96a	**D12**	4ore mauve	85	45
D97	**D12**	10ore red	2·75	45
D98	**D12**	15ore brown	1·30	80
D99	**D12**	20ore blue	1·70	45
D94	**D12**	50ore purple	3·75	1·50

1922. Inscr "a betale" and "PORTOMERKE".

D162	4ore purple	6·75	10·00
D163	10ore green	4·25	1·40
D164	20ore purple	5·00	2·75
D165	40ore blue	8·50	85
D166	100ore yellow	34·00	7·50
D167	200ore violet	43·00	18·00

Pt. 7

OLDENBURG

A former Grand Duchy in North Germany. In 1867 it joined the North German Federation.

72 grote = 1 thaler

1

1852. Imperf.

2	**1**	1/30th. black on blue	£475	37·00
5	**1**	1/15th. black on red	£1100	£110
8	**1**	1/10th. black on yellow	£1100	£130
1	**1**	1/3sgr. black on green	£1700	£1300

2

1859. Imperf.

17	**2**	1/4g. yellow	£400	£4750
10	**2**	1/3g. black on green	£3250	£3750
19	**2**	1/3g. green	£650	£1200
21	**2**	1/2g. brown	£550	£700
11	**2**	1g. black on blue	£950	60·00
23	**2**	1g. blue	£325	£200
15	**2**	2g. black on red	£1300	£800
26	**2**	2g. red	£600	£600
16	**2**	3g. black on yellow	£1300	£800
28	**2**	3g. yellow	£600	£600

3

1862. Roul.

30	**3**	1/3g. green	£275	£250
32	**3**	1/2g. orange	£275	£130
42	**3**	1g. red	25·00	75·00
36	**3**	2g. blue	£275	65·00
39	**3**	3g. bistre	£275	70·00

Pt. 8

PAPAL STATES

Parts of Italy under Papal rule till 1870 when they became part of the Kingdom of Italy.

1852. 100 bajoochi = 1 scudo.
1866. 100 centesimi = 1 lira.

1

2

1852. Papal insignia as in T 1 and 2 in various shapes and frames. Imperf.

2	1/2b. black on grey	£750	70·00
5	1/2b. black on lilac	80·00	£160
10	1b. black on green	£110	£110
11	2b. black on green	£275	21·00
14	2b. black on white	20·00	95·00
15	3b. black on brown	£225	80·00
16	3b. black on yellow	21·00	£140
17	4b. black on brown	£8000	95·00
19	4b. black on yellow	£300	95·00
20	5b. black on pink	£300	21·00
22	6b. black on lilac	£1600	£275
23	6b. black on grey	£1100	90·00
25	7b. black on blue	£1800	90·00
26	8b. black on white	£700	55·00
27	50b. blue	£18000	£2000
29	1s. pink	£4500	£3750

1867. Same types. Imperf.

30	2c. black on green	£140	£325
32	3c. black on grey	£1800	£2250
33	5c. black on blue	£225	£300

34	10c. black on red	£1900	£110
35	20c. black on red	£225	£140
36	40c. black on yellow	£225	£225
37	80c. black on pink	£225	£600

1868. Same types. Perf.

42	2c. black on green	16·00	95·00
43	3c. black on grey	65·00	£4000
45	5c. black on blue	37·00	85·00
46	10c. black on orange	5·25	19·00
49	20c. black on mauve	6·50	43·00
50	20c. black on red	3·75	18·00
52	40c. black on yellow	13·00	£120
55	80c. black on pink	65·00	£450

Pt. 8

PARMA

A former Grand Duchy of N. Italy, united with Sardinia in 1860 and now part of Italy.

100 centesimi = 1 lira.

1 Bourbon "fleur-de-lis"

1852. Imperf.

2	1	5c. black on yellow	£150	£170
11	1	5c. yellow	£9000	£850
4	1	10c. black	£150	£170
5	1	15c. black on pink	£4250	80·00
13	1	15c. red	£12000	£250
7	1	25c. black on purple	£18000	£275
14	1	25c. brown	£12000	£475
9	1	40c. black on blue	£2750	£450

2

1857. Imperf.

17	2	15c. red	£425	£425
19	2	25c. purple	£700	£225
20	2	40c. blue	£120	£650

3

1859. Imperf.

28	3	5c. green	£3250	£4500
29	3	10c. brown	£1400	£850
32	3	20c. blue	£1400	£250
33	3	40c. red	£800	£9500
35	3	80c. yellow	£8500	

NEWSPAPER STAMPS

1853. As T 3. Imperf.

N1	6c. black on pink	£2250	£475
N3	9c. black on blue	£1300	£28000

Pt. 9

PORTUGAL

A country on the S.W. coast of Europe, a kingdom until 1910, when it became a republic.

1853. 1000 reis = 1 milreis.
1912. 100 centavos = 1 escudo.
2002. 100 cents = 1 euro.

1 Queen Maria II

1853. Various frames. Imperf.

1	1	5r. brown	£4500	£1300
4	1	25r. blue	£1400	29·00
6	1	50r. green	£5500	£1500
8	1	100r. lilac	£47000	£3000

5 King Pedro V

1855. Various frames. Imperf.

18a	5	5r. brown	£650	£120
21	5	25r. blue	£600	22·00
22	5	25r. pink	£450	8·75
13	5	50r. green	£750	£110
15	5	100r. lilac	£1200	£150

9 King Luis

1862. Various frames. Imperf.

24	9	5r. brown	£200	39·00
28	9	10r. yellow	£225	70·00
30	9	25r. pink	£160	7·00
32	9	50r. green	£1100	£120
34	9	100r. lilac	£1300	£140

14 King Luis

1866. With curved value labels. Imperf.

35	14	5r. black	£170	14·50
36	14	10r. yellow	£350	£225
38	14	20r. bistre	£275	£100
39	14	25r. pink	£350	12·00
41	14	50r. green	£375	£110
43	14	80r. orange	£375	£110
45	14	100r. purple	£450	£170
46	14	120r. blue	£475	£110

1867. With curved value labels. Perf.

52	5r. black	£180	65·00
54	10r. yellow	£375	£160
56	20r. bistre	£450	£170
57	25r. pink	£100	11·50
60	50r. green	£375	£160
61	80r. orange	£550	£160
62	100r. lilac	£375	£160
64	120r. blue	£450	£110
67	240r. lilac	£1500	£700

15

1870. With straight value labels. Perf.

69	15	5r. black	80·00	8·25
70	15	10r. yellow	£110	43·00
158	15	10r. green	£200	55·00
74	15	15r. brown	£150	43·00
76	15	20r. bistre	£110	38·00
143	15	20r. red	£500	85·00
80	15	25r. red	43·00	5·50
115	15	50r. green	£225	60·00
117	15	50r. blue	£475	80·00
148	15	80r. orange	£180	28·00
153	15	100r. mauve	£100	16·00
93	15	120r. blue	£425	£110
95	15	150r. blue	£500	£180
155	15	150r. yellow	£190	22·00
99	15	240r. lilac	£2250	£1600
156	15	300r. mauve	£180	45·00
128	15	1000r. black	£450	£140

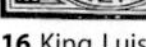

16 King Luis 17

1880. Various frames for T 16.

185	16	5r. black	43·00	6·00
180	17	25r. grey	£475	44·00
188	16	25r. grey	44·00	5·50
190	16	25r. brown	44·00	5·50
184	16	50r. blue	£475	22·00

19 King Luis

1882. Various frames.

229	19	5r. black	19·00	1·70
231	19	10r. green	55·00	6·00
232	19	20r. red	65·00	26·00
212	19	25r. brown	42·00	3·75
234	19	25r. mauve	44·00	4·50
236	19	50r. blue	65·00	4·50
216	19	500r. black	£650	£425
217	19	500r. mauve	£400	85·00

26 King Carlos

1892

271	26	5r. orange	18·00	3·00
239	26	10r. mauve	42·00	8·25
256	26	15r. brown	42·00	6·00
242	26	20r. lilac	50·00	13·50
275	26	25r. green	60·00	4·25
244	26	50r. blue	50·00	14·50
245	26	75r. red	£100	12·00
262	26	80r. green	£130	80·00
248	26	100r. brown on buff	95·00	9·50
265	26	150r. red on pink	£250	80·00
252	26	200r. blue on blue	£250	65·00
267	26	300r. blue on brown	£275	£110

1892. Optd PROVISORIO.

284	19	5r. black	21·00	10·50
283	19	10r. green	24·00	13·50
297	15	15r. brown	27·00	24·00
290	19	20r. red	60·00	34·00
291	19	25r. mauve	21·00	8·25
292	19	50r. blue	£120	95·00
293	15	80r. orange	£150	£140

1893. Optd 1893 PROVISORIO or surch also.

302	19	5r. black	35·00	32·00
303	19	10r. green	33·00	29·00
304	19	20r. red	55·00	47·00
309	19	20r. on 25r. mauve	75·00	65·00
305	19	25r. mauve	£150	£150
306	19	50r. blue	£150	£150
310	15	50r. on 80r. orange	£180	£150
312	15	75r. on 80r. orange	£100	£100
308	15	80r. orange	£150	£140

32 Prince Henry in his Caravel and Family Motto

1894. 500th Birth Anniv of Prince Henry the Navigator.

314	32	5r. orange	5·50	1·20
315	32	10r. red	5·50	1·20
316	32	15r. brown	14·50	4·50
317	32	20r. lilac	14·50	5·25
318	-	25r. green	13·50	1·70
319	-	50r. blue	43·00	9·00
320	-	75r. red	85·00	19·00
321	-	80r. green	85·00	22·00
322	-	100r. brown on buff	65·00	18·00
323	-	150r. red	£190	44·00
324	-	300r. blue on buff	£225	60·00
325	-	500r. purple	£500	£120
326	-	1000r. black on buff	£850	£180

DESIGNS: 25r. to 100r. Prince Henry directing movements of his fleet; 150r. to 1000r. Prince Henry's studies.

35 St. Anthony's Vision 37 St. Anthony ascending into Heaven

1895. 700th Birth Anniv of St. Anthony (Patron Saint). With a prayer in Latin printed on back.

327	35	2½r. black	6·00	2·00
328	-	5r. orange	6·00	2·00
329	-	10r. mauve	17·00	11·00
330	-	15r. brown	20·00	11·00
331	-	20r. lilac	20·00	12·00
332	-	25r. purple and green	17·00	2·00
333	37	50r. brown and blue	42·00	31·00
334	37	75r. brown and red	70·00	55·00
335	37	80r. brown and green	85·00	80·00
336	37	100r. black and brown	75·00	43·00
337	-	150r. red and bistre	£250	£150
338	-	200r. blue and bistre	£225	£160
339	-	300r. grey and bistre	£325	£225
340	-	500r. brown and green	£650	£475
341	-	1000r. lilac and green	£1100	£600

DESIGNS—HORIZ: 5r. to 25r. St. Anthony preaching to fishes. VERT: 150r. to 1000r. St. Anthony from picture in Academy of Fine Arts, Paris.

39 King Carlos

1895. Numerals of value in red (Nos. 354 and 363) or black (others).

342	39	2½r. grey	50	20
343	39	5r. orange	50	20
344	39	10r. green	70	25
345	39	15r. green	70·00	4·00
346	39	15r. brown	£140	5·50
347	39	20r. lilac	90	55
348	39	25r. green	£100	35
349	39	25r. red	55	20
351	39	50r. blue	75	35
352	39	65r. blue	80	45
353	39	75r. red	£170	6·75
354	39	75r. brown on yellow	2·20	1·00
355	39	80r. mauve	2·75	1·60
356	39	100r. blue on blue	1·30	60
357	39	115r. brown on pink	6·50	4·50
358	39	130r. brown on cream	4·50	2·20
359	39	150r. brown on yellow	£225	34·00
360	39	180r. grey on pink	29·00	13·50
361	39	200r. puple on pink	27·00	3·75
362	39	300r. blue on pink	5·00	3·00
363	39	500r. black on blue	12·50	6·75

40 Departure of Fleet

43 Muse of History

44 Da Gama and Camoens and "Sao Gabriel" (flagship)

1898. 4th Centenary of Discovery of Route to India by Vasco da Gama.

378	40	2½r. green	1·90	55
379	-	5r. red	1·90	55
380	-	10r. purple	12·00	2·30
381	43	25r. green	8·25	65
382	44	50r. blue	17·00	4·25
383	-	75r. brown	65·00	17·00
384	-	100r. brown	50·00	17·00
385	-	150r. brown	£110	44·00

DESIGNS—HORIZ: 5r. Arrival at Calicut; 10r. Embarkation at Rastello; 100r. Flagship "Sao Gabriel"; 150r. Vasco da Gama. VERT: 75r. Archangel Gabriel, Patron Saint of the Expedition.

48 King Manoel II

49

1910

390	48	2½r. lilac	40	35
391	48	5r. black	40	35
392	48	10r. green	70	40
393	48	15r. brown	3·75	2·50

394	**48**	20r. red	1·40	1·10
395	**48**	25r. brown	85	25
396	**48**	50r. blue	2·30	95
397	**48**	75r. brown	14·00	7·75
398	**48**	80r. grey	4·25	3·25
399	**48**	100r. brown on green	16·00	4·00
400	**48**	200r. green on orange	9·00	6·50
401	**48**	300r. black on blue	11·50	7·25
402	**49**	500r. brown and green	21·00	18·00
403	**49**	1000r. black and blue	48·00	38·00

1910. Optd REPUBLICA.

404	**48**	2½r. lilac	45	30
405	**48**	5r. black	45	30
406	**48**	10r. green	4·50	1·50
407	**48**	15r. brown	1·60	1·20
408	**48**	20r. red	6·25	2·75
409	**48**	25r. brown	1·20	45
410	**48**	50r. blue	8·75	3·25
411	**48**	75r. brown	15·00	6·75
412	**48**	80r. grey	4·50	3·50
413	**48**	100r. brown on green	2·75	1·40
414	**48**	200r. green on orange	3·25	3·00
415	**48**	300r. black on blue	5·75	5·00
416	**49**	500r. brown and green	16·00	13·50
417	**49**	1000r. black and blue	40·00	30·00

1911. Optd REPUBLICA or surch also.

441	**40**	2½r. green	75	30
442	**D48**	5r. black	1·70	75
443	**D48**	10r. mauve	2·10	1·20
444	-	15r. on 5r. red (No. 379)	1·30	60
445	**D48**	20r. orange	7·75	5·00
446	**43**	25r. green	90	45
447	**44**	50r. blue	4·50	2·10
448	-	75r. brown (No. 383)	65·00	47·00
449	-	80r. on 150r. (No. 385)	8·00	6·25
450	-	100r. brown (No. 384)	8·00	3·75
451	**D48**	200r. brown on buff	£180	£110
452	**D48**	300r. on 50r. grey	£130	65·00
453	**D48**	500r. on 100r. red on pink	70·00	36·00
454	-	1000r. on 10r. (No. 380)	90·00	55·00

1911. Vasco da Gama stamps of Madeira optd REPUBLICA or surch also.

455	2½r. green	17·00	13·50
456	15r. on 5r. red	3·75	3·75
457	25r. green	7·50	7·25
458	50r. blue	17·00	13·50
459	75r. brown	17·00	8·25
460	80r. on 150r. brown	18·00	16·00
461	100r. brown	60·00	13·50
462	1000r. on 10r. purple	60·00	38·00

56 Ceres

1912

484	**56**	¼c. brown	95	30
485	**56**	½c. black	1·00	30
486	**56**	1c. green	1·90	55
515	**56**	1c. brown	35	30
488	**56**	1½c. brown	10·50	4·50
516	**56**	1½c. green	45	30
490	**56**	2c. red	10·50	3·75
517	**56**	2c. yellow	1·80	40
702	**56**	2c. brown	20	20
492	**56**	2½c. lilac	90	30
521	**56**	3c. red	55	40
703	**56**	3c. blue	20	20
495	**56**	3½c. green	55	30
523	**56**	4c. green	35	30
704	**56**	4c. orange	20	20
497	**56**	5c. blue	10·50	1·00
705	**56**	5c. brown	20	20
527	**56**	6c. purple	1·40	65
706	**56**	6c. brown	20	20
815	**56**	6c. red	50	40
500	**56**	7½c. brown	19·00	3·75
529	**56**	7½c. blue	55	30
530	**56**	8c. grey	65	65
531	**56**	8c. green	1·10	70
532	**56**	8c. orange	1·20	65
503	**56**	10c. brown	25·00	1·60
707	**56**	10c. red	20	20
504	**56**	12c. blue	2·20	1·20
534	**56**	12c. green	85	55
535	**56**	13½c. blue	2·20	1·60
481	**56**	14c. blue on yellow	3·50	2·40
536	**56**	14c. purple	1·00	85
505	**56**	15c. brown	3·25	1·30
708	**56**	15c. black	45	20
709	**56**	16c. blue	45	20
474	**56**	20c. brown on green	26·00	2·75
475	**56**	20c. brown on buff	27·00	7·25
539	**56**	20c. brown	1·00	70
540	**56**	20c. green	85	55
541	**56**	20c. grey	1·20	65
542	**56**	24c. blue	1·00	65
543	**56**	25c. pink	85	45
710	**56**	25c. grey	45	20
819	**56**	25c. green	95	45
476	**56**	30c. brown on pink	£190	18·00
477	**56**	30c. brown on yellow	18·00	3·50
545	**56**	30c. brown	85	50
820	**56**	32c. green	95	45
548	**56**	36c. red	3·00	65
549	**56**	40c. blue	2·10	1·10
550	**56**	40c. brown	1·40	55
478	**56**	50c. orange on orange	26·00	2·20
712	**56**	40c. green	80	20
713	**56**	48c. pink	2·00	1·40
553	**56**	50c. yellow	3·00	1·10
824	**56**	50c. red	3·50	1·20
554	**56**	60c. blue	2·75	1·10
715	**56**	64c. blue	3·25	3·00
826	**56**	75c. red	3·00	1·30
510	**56**	80c. pink	2·75	1·70
558	**56**	80c. lilac	2·40	90
827	**56**	80c. green	3·00	1·30
559	**56**	90c. blue	3·00	1·10
717	**56**	96c. red	4·25	1·90
480	**56**	1e. green on blue	29·00	2·20
561	**56**	1e. lilac	6·75	3·50
565	**56**	1e. blue	7·50	2·20
566	**56**	1e. purple	7·00	2·50
829	**56**	1e. red	8·25	1·30
562	**56**	1e.10 brown	6·75	3·25
563	**56**	1e.20 green	3·75	2·10
830	**56**	1e.20 brown	6·00	1·40
831	**56**	1e.25 blue	5·50	1·40
568	**56**	1e.50 lilac	30·00	7·75
720	**56**	1e.60 blue	4·50	75
721	**56**	2e. green	28·00	1·60
833	**56**	2e. mauve	36·00	10·50
572	**56**	2e.40 green	£425	£250
573	**56**	3e. pink	£425	£225
722	**56**	3e.20 green	12·00	1·60
723	**56**	4e.50 yellow	12·00	1·60
575	**56**	5e. green	90·00	16·00
724	**56**	5e. brown	£150	5·75
725	**56**	10e. red	17·00	3·25
577	**56**	20e. blue	£700	£300

60 Presidents of Portugal and Brazil and Admiral Gago Coutinho, Sacadura Cabral and Fairey IIID

1923. Portugal–Brazil Trans-Atlantic Flight.

578	**60**	1c. brown	20	1·10
579	**60**	2c. orange	20	1·10
580	**60**	3c. blue	20	1·10
581	**60**	4c. green	20	1·10
582	**60**	5c. brown	20	1·10
583	**60**	10c. brown	20	1·10
584	**60**	15c. black	20	1·10
585	**60**	20c. green	20	1·10
586	**60**	25c. red	20	1·10
587	**60**	30c. brown	1·00	2·75
588	**60**	40c. brown	70	1·10
589	**60**	50c. yellow	60	1·30
590	**60**	75c. purple	60	1·40
591	**60**	1e. blue	60	2·75
592	**60**	1e.50 grey	1·10	3·50
593	**60**	2e. green	1·30	8·75

62 Camoens at Ceuta

63 Saving the "Lusiad"

1924. 400th Birth Anniv of Camoens (poet). Value in black.

600	**62**	2c. blue	35	35
601	**62**	3c. orange	35	35
602	**62**	4c. grey	35	35
603	**62**	5c. green	35	35
604	**62**	6c. red	35	35
605	**63**	8c. brown	35	35
606	**63**	10c. violet	35	35
607	**63**	15c. green	35	35
608	**63**	16c. purple	40	40
609	**63**	20c. orange	50	40
610	-	25c. violet	50	40
611	-	30c. brown	50	40
612	-	32c. green	1·40	1·40
613	-	40c. blue	50	45
614	-	48c. red	2·10	2·30
615	-	50c. red	2·50	1·50
616	-	64c. green	2·50	1·50
617	-	75c. lilac	2·75	1·50
618	-	80c. brown	1·90	1·50
619	-	96c. red	1·90	1·50
620	-	1e. turquoise	1·60	1·20
621	-	1e.20 brown	9·25	6·75
622	-	1e.50 red	2·50	1·50
623	-	1e.60 blue	2·50	1·50
624	-	2e. green	9·25	6·25
625	-	2e.40 green on green	8·00	4·25
626	-	3e. blue on blue	2·75	1·40
627	-	3e.20 black on turquoise	2·75	1·30
628	-	4e.50 black on yellow	8·50	5·50
629	-	10e. brown on pink	15·00	11·00
630	-	20e. violet on mauve	18·00	11·00

DESIGNS—VERT: 25c. to 48c. Luis de Camoens; 50c. to 96c. 1st Edition of "Lusiad"; 20e. Monument to Camoens. HORIZ: 1e. to 2e. Death of Camoens; 2e.40 to 10e. Tomb of Camoens.

65 Branco's House at S. Miguel de Seide

67 Camilo Castelo Branco

1925. Birth Centenary of Camilo Castelo Branco (novelist). Value in black.

631	**65**	2c. orange	40	25
632	**65**	3c. green	40	25
633	**65**	4c. blue	40	25
634	**65**	5c. red	40	25
635	**65**	6c. purple	40	25
636	**65**	8c. brown	40	25
637	**A**	10c. blue	40	25
638	**67**	15c. green	45	35
639	**A**	16c. orange	55	50
640	**A**	20c. violet	55	50
641	**67**	25c. red	55	50
642	**A**	30c. bistre	55	50
643	**A**	32c. green	1·70	1·50
644	**67**	40c. black and green	1·20	95
645	**A**	48c. red	4·50	5·00
646	**B**	50c. green	1·20	95
647	**B**	64c. brown	4·75	5·00
648	**B**	75c. grey	1·40	1·00
649	**67**	80c. brown	1·40	1·10
650	**B**	96c. red	2·40	2·30
651	**B**	1e. lilac	2·20	2·30
652	**B**	1e.20 green	2·50	2·30
653	**C**	1e.50 blue on blue	46·00	22·00
654	**67**	1e.60 blue	9·00	5·75
655	**C**	2e. green on green	10·50	6·25
656	**C**	2e.40 red on orange	£100	50·00
657	**C**	3e. red on blue	£130	65·00
658	**C**	3e.20 black on green	60·00	50·00
659	**67**	4e.50 black and red	25·00	5·75
660	**C**	10e. brown on buff	26·00	6·00
661	**D**	20e. black on orange	27·00	6·00

DESIGNS—HORIZ: A, Branco's study. VERT: B, Teresa de Albuquerque; C, Mariana and Joao da Cruz; D, Simao de Botelho. Types B/D shows characters from Branco's "Amor de Peredicao".

76 Afonso I, first King of Portugal, 1140

77 Battle of Aljubarrota

1926. 1st Independence issue. Dated 1926. Centres in black.

671	**76**	2c. orange	40	40
672	-	3c. blue	40	40
673	**76**	4c. green	40	40
674	-	5c. brown	40	40
675	**76**	6c. orange	40	40
676	-	15c. green	40	40
677	**76**	16c. blue	1·40	1·10
678	**77**	20c. violet	1·40	1·10
679	-	25c. red	1·40	1·10
680	**77**	32c. green	1·50	1·30
681	-	40c. brown	1·00	75
682	-	46c. red	6·50	5·00
683	-	50c. bistre	6·50	5·00
684	-	64c. green	9·00	6·50
685	-	75c. brown	9·00	6·25
686	-	96c. red	13·50	10·50
687	-	1e. violet	13·50	11·00
688	**77**	1e.60 blue	18·00	15·00
689	-	3e. purple	50·00	43·00
690	-	4e.50 green	70·00	55·00
691	**77**	10e. red	£110	85·00

DESIGNS—VERT: 25, 40, 50, 75c. Philippa de Vilhena arms her sons; 64c., 1e. Don Joao IV, 1640; 96c., 3e., 4e.50, Independence Monument, Lisbon. HORIZ: 3, 5, 15, 46c. Monastery of D. Joao I.

1926. 1st Independence issue surch. Centres in black.

692	2c. on 5c. brown	2·00	1·80
693	2c. on 46c. red	2·00	1·80
694	2c. on 64c. green	2·30	2·10
695	3c. on 75c. brown	2·30	2·10
696	3c. on 96c. red	3·50	2·75
697	3c. on 1e. violet	3·00	2·50
698	4c. on 1e.60 blue	23·00	17·00
699	4c. on 3e. purple	8·50	7·00
700	6c. on 4e.50 green	8·50	7·00
701	6c. on 10e. red	8·75	7·00

80 Goncalo Mendes da Maia

1927. 2nd Independence issue. Dated 1927. Centres in black.

726	**80**	2c. brown	40	20
727	-	3c. blue	40	20
728	**80**	4c. orange	40	20
729	-	5c. brown	40	20
730	-	6c. brown	40	20
731	-	15c. brown	90	65
732	-	16c. blue	1·90	80
733	**80**	25c. grey	2·10	1·50
734	-	32c. green	4·75	2·40
735	-	40c. green	1·30	95
736	**80**	48c. red	20·00	16·00
737	-	80c. violet	14·50	11·00
738	-	96c. red	30·00	22·00
739	-	1e.60 blue	31·00	23·00
740	-	4e.50 brown	44·00	34·00

DESIGNS—HORIZ: 3, 15, 80c. Gulmaraes Castle; 6, 32c. Battle of Montijo. VERT: 5, 16c., 1e.50, Joao das Regras; 40, 96c. Brites de Aimelda; 4e.50, J. P. Ribeiro.

1928. Surch.

742	**56**	4c. on 8c. orange	85	50
743	**56**	4c. on 30c. brown	85	50
744	**56**	10c. on ¼c. brown	85	50
745	**56**	10c. on ½c. black	1·10	65
746	**56**	10c. on 1c. brown	1·10	65
747	**56**	10c. on 4c. green	85	55
748	**56**	10c. on 4c. orange	85	55
749	**56**	10c. on 5c. brown	85	55
751	**56**	15c. on 16c. blue	2·10	1·20
752	**56**	15c. on 20c. brown	65·00	50·00
753	**56**	15c. on 20c. grey	85	50
754	**56**	15c. on 24c. blue	4·00	2·50
755	**56**	15c. on 25c. pink	85	50
756	**56**	15c. on 25c. grey	85	50
757	**56**	16c. on 32c. green	1·60	1·20
758	**56**	40c. on 2c. yellow	85	50
760	**56**	40c. on 2c. brown	85	50
761	**56**	40c. on 3c. blue	85	55
762	**56**	40c. on 50c. yellow	85	50
763	**56**	40c. on 60c. blue	1·60	1·10
764	**56**	40c. on 64c. blue	1·60	1·20
765	**56**	40c. on 75c. pink	1·70	1·40
766	**56**	40c. on 80c. lilac	1·20	80
767	**56**	40c. on 90c. blue	8·25	5·00
768	**56**	40c. on 1e. grey	1·60	1·20
769	**56**	40c. on 1e.10 brown	1·60	1·20
770	**56**	80c. on 6c. purple	1·60	1·10
771	**56**	80c. on 6c. brown	1·60	1·10

772	56	80c. on 48c. pink	2·30	1·70
773	56	80c. on 1e.50 lilac	3·50	1·90
774	56	96c. on 1e.20 green	7·00	4·00
775	56	96c. on 1e.20 buff	6·75	4·50
777	56	1e.60 on 2e. green	75·00	50·00
778	56	1e.60 on 3e.20 green	19·00	11·50
779	56	1e.60 on 20e. blue	27·00	15·00

84 Storming of Santarem

1928. 3rd Independence issue. Dated 1928. Centres in black.

780	-	2c. blue	60	35
781	84	3c. green	60	35
782	-	4c. red	60	35
783	-	5c. green	60	35
784	-	6c. brown	60	35
785	84	15c. grey	1·20	1·10
786	-	16c. purple	1·20	1·10
787	-	25c. blue	1·20	1·10
788	-	32c. green	6·25	5·75
789	-	40c. brown	1·20	1·10
790	-	50c. red	18·00	8·50
791	84	80c. grey	18·00	11·00
792	-	96c. red	35·00	23·00
793	-	1e. mauve	60·00	44·00
794	-	1e.60 blue	23·00	17·00
795	-	4e.50 yellow	24·00	22·00

DESIGNS—VERT: 2, 25c., 1e.60, G. Paes; 6, 32, 96c. Joana de Gouveia; 4e.50, Matias de Albuquerque. HORIZ: 4, 16, 50c. Battle of Rolica; 5, 40c., 1e. Battle of Atoleiros.

1929. Optd Revalidado.

805	56	10c. red	85	50
806	56	15c. black	85	50
807	56	40c. brown	1·20	90
808	56	40c. green	1·10	65
810	56	96c. red	10·50	6·75
811	56	1e.60 blue	43·00	27·00

1929. Telegraph stamp surch CORREIO 1$60 and bars.

812	1e.60 on 5c. brown	27·00	17·00

88 Camoens' Poem "Lusiad"

1931

835	88	4c. brown	45	20
836	88	5c. brown	45	20
837	88	6c. grey	45	20
838	88	10c. mauve	45	30
839	88	15c. black	45	30
840	88	16c. blue	2·30	1·00
841	88	25c. green	5·75	55
841a	88	25c. blue	6·75	65
841b	88	30c. green	3·50	65
842	88	40c. red	11·50	20
843	88	48c. brown	2·30	1·60
844	88	50c. brown	55	20
845	88	75c. red	9·75	1·80
846	88	80c. green	80	25
846a	88	95c. red	31·00	10·00
847	88	1e. purple	60·00	25
848	88	1e.20 green	4·00	1·60
849	88	1e.25 blue	3·75	35
849a	88	1e.60 blue	60·00	6·75
849b	88	1e.75 blue	1·20	35
850	88	2e. mauve	1·40	35
851	88	4e.50 orange	3·00	40
852	88	5e. green	3·00	40

89 St. Anthony's Birthplace

1931. 700th Death Anniv of St. Anthony.

853	89	15c. purple	1·60	45
854	-	25c. myrtle and green	1·80	45
855	-	40c. brown and buff	1·60	45
856	-	75c. pink	55·00	22·00
857	-	1e.25 grey and blue	£100	46·00
858	-	4e.50 purple and mauve	55·00	5·50

DESIGNS—VERT: 25c. Saint's baptismal font; 40c. Lisbon Cathedral; 75c. St. Anthony; 1e.25, Santa Cruz Cathedral, Coimbra. HORIZ: 4e.50, Saint's tomb, Padua.

90 Don Nuno Alvares Pereira

1931. 5th Death Centenary of Pereira.

859	90	15c. black	1·90	1·70
860	90	25c. green and black	10·00	1·70
861	90	40c. orange	5·25	95
862	90	75c. red	44·00	38·00
863	90	1e.25 light blue and blue	50·00	33·00
864	90	4e.50 green and brown	£275	85·00

1933. Pereira issue of 1931 surch.

865	15c. on 40c. orange	1·30	75
866	40c. on 15c. black	6·25	3·50
867	40c. on 25c. green & black	1·60	1·20
868	40c. on 75c. red	13·50	8·00
869	40c. on 1e.25 light blue and blue	13·50	6·00
870	40c. on 4e.50 green and brown	13·50	6·00

1933. St. Anthony issue of 1931 surch.

871	-	15c. on 40c. brown and buff	1·70	75
872	89	40c. on 15c. purple	3·50	1·60
873	-	40c. on 25c. myrtle and green	3·00	75
874	-	40c. on 75c. pink	13·50	8·00
875	-	40c. on 1e.25 grey and blue	13·50	8·00
876	-	40c. on 4e.50 purple and mauve	13·50	8·00

94 President Carmona

1934

877	94	40c. violet	35·00	50

95

1934. Colonial Exhibition.

878	95	25c. brown	7·50	1·90
879	95	40c. red	36·00	60
880	95	1e.60 blue	75·00	20·00

96 Queen Maria

1935. 1st Portuguese Philatelic Exhibition.

881	96	40c. red	2·40	40

97 Temple of Diana at Evora

98 Prince Henry the Navigator

99 "All for the Nation"

100 Coimbra Cathedral

1935

882	97	4c. black	85	30
883	97	5c. blue	90	30
884	97	6c. brown	1·40	50
885	98	10c. green	13·50	30
886	98	15c. red	55	30
887	99	25c. blue	12·50	65
888	99	40c. brown	4·25	20
889	99	1e. red	20·00	75
890	100	1e.75 blue	£140	1·90
890a	99	10e. grey	46·00	4·50
890b	99	20e. blue	60·00	3·25

102 Shield and Propeller

1937. Air.

891	102	1e.50 blue	1·40	45
892	102	1e.75 red	2·10	50
893	102	2e.50 red	2·20	50
893a	102	3e. blue	31·00	17·00
893b	102	4e. green	40·00	25·00
894	102	5e. red	3·50	1·70
895	102	10e. purple	6·50	1·80
895a	102	15e. orange	30·00	11·00
896	102	20e. brown	17·00	4·00
896a	102	50e. purple	£325	£120

103 Symbol of Medicine

1937. Centenary of Medical and Surgical Colleges at Lisbon and Oporto.

897	103	25c. blue	19·00	1·40

104 Gil Vicente

1937. 400th Death Anniv of Gil Vicente (poet).

898	104	40c. brown	36·00	30
899	104	1e. red	4·50	30

106 Grapes

1938. Wine and Raisin Congress.

900	106	15c. violet	2·50	95
901	106	25c. brown	5·00	2·40
902	106	40c. mauve	17·00	50
903	106	1e.75 blue	55·00	40·00

107 Cross of Avis

1940. Portuguese Legion.

904	107	5c. buff	80	35
905	107	10c. violet	80	35
906	107	15c. blue	80	35
907	107	25c. brown	44·00	1·50
908	107	40c. green	70·00	60
909	107	80c. green	3·75	1·00
910	107	1e. red	£100	5·75
911	107	1e.75 blue	17·00	4·00
MS911a 155×170 mm. Nos. 904/11 (sold at 5e.50)			£700	£1200

109 Portuguese World Exhibition

1940. Portuguese Centenaries.

912	109	10c. purple	45	35
913	-	15c. blue	45	35
914	-	25c. green	2·20	45
915	-	35c. green	2·00	60
916	-	40c. brown	4·75	30
917	109	80c. purple	9·75	55
918	-	1e. red	23·00	2·40
919	-	1e.75 blue	13·50	4·00
MS919a 160×229 mm. Nos. 912/9 (sold at 10e.)			£325	£500

DESIGNS—VERT: 15, 35c. Statue of King Joao IV; 25c., 1e. Monument of Discoveries, Belem; 40c., 1e.75, King Afonso Henriques.

113 Sir Rowland Hill

1940. Centenary of First Adhesive Postage Stamps.

920	113	15c. purple	50	25
921	113	25c. red	50	25
922	113	35c. green	50	25
923	113	40c. purple	90	25
924	113	50c. green	36·00	6·25
925	113	80c. blue	3·50	1·80
926	113	1e. red	43·00	5·75
927	113	1e.75 blue	9·75	5·50
MS928 160×152 mm. Nos. 920/7 (sold at 10e.)			£150	£300

114 Fish-woman of Nazare

1941. Costumes.

932	114	4c. green	40	30
933	-	5c. brown	40	30
934	-	10c. purple	5·50	1·70
935	-	15c. green	40	40
936	-	25c. purple	4·50	90
937	-	40c. green	40	30
938	-	80c. blue	7·25	3·25
939	-	1e. red	21·00	2·50
940	-	1e.75 blue	22·00	7·25
941	-	2e. orange	85·00	38·00
MS941a 163×146 mm. Nos. 932/41 (sold at 10e.)			£250	£250

DESIGNS: 5c. Woman from Coimbra; 10c. Vine-grower of Saloio; 15c. Fish-woman of Lisbon; 25c. Woman of Olhao; 40c. Woman of Aveiro; 80c. Shepherdess of Madeira; 1e. Spinner of Viana do Castelo; 1e.75, Horsebreeder of Ribatejo; 2e. Reaper of Alentejo.

115 Caravel

1943

942	115	5c. black	35	20
943	115	10c. brown	35	20
944	115	15c. grey	35	20
945	115	20c. violet	35	20
946	115	30c. purple	35	20
947	115	35c. green	40	20

948	115	50c. purple	40	20
948a	115	80c. green	6·75	60
949	115	1e. red	14·00	20
949a	115	1e. lilac	4·25	35
949b	115	1e.20 red	6·75	45
949c	115	1e.50 green	55·00	55
950	115	1e.75 blue	40·00	20
950a	115	1e.80 orange	60·00	5·25
951	115	2e. brown	3·00	20
951a	115	2e. blue	8·75	65
952	115	2e.50 red	4·75	20
953	115	3e.50 blue	20·00	70
953a	115	4e. orange	90·00	3·75
954	115	5e. red	2·75	35
954a	115	6e. green	£170	6·00
954b	115	7e.50 green	60·00	5·50
955	115	10e. grey	5·00	35
956	115	15e. green	55·00	1·60
957	115	20e. green	£200	95
958	115	50e. red	£550	1·50

116 Labourer

1943. 1st Agricultural Science Congress.

959	116	10c. blue	1·50	50
960	116	50c. red	2·40	55

117 Mounted Postal Courier

1944. 3rd National Philatelic Exhibition, Lisbon.

961	117	10c. brown	50	25
962	117	50c. violet	50	25
963	117	1e. red	6·00	1·10
964	117	1e.75 blue	6·00	2·50
MS964a 82×121 mm. Nos. 961/4 (sold at 7e.50)			70·00	£350

118 Felix Avellar Brotero

1944. Birth Bicentenary of Avellar Brotero (botanist).

965	118	10c. brown	45	25
966	-	50c. green	2·20	25
967	-	1e. red	14·50	2·20
968	118	1e.75 blue	11·00	4·50
MS968a 144×195 mm. Nos. 965/8 (sold at 7e.50)			85·00	£200

DESIGN: 50c., 1e. Brotero's statue, Coimbra.

120 Vasco da Gama

1945. Portuguese Navigators.

969	-	10c. brown	45	25
970	-	30c. orange	45	25
971	-	35c. green	95	40
972	120	50c. green	2·75	45
973	-	1e. red	7·25	1·10
974	-	1e.75 blue	9·25	3·25
975	-	2e. black	11·00	3·75
976	-	3e.50 red	22·00	6·50
MS976a 167×173 mm. Nos. 969/76 (sold at 15e.)			75·00	£200

PORTRAITS: 10c. Gil Eanes; 30c. Joao Goncalves Zarco; 35c. Bartolomeu Dias; 1e. Pedro Alvares Cabral; 1e.75, Fernao de Magalhaes (Magellan); 2e. Frey Goncalo Velho; 3e.50, Diogo Cao.

121 President Carmona

1945

977	121	10c. violet	60	35
978	121	30c. brown	60	35
979	121	35c. green	55	35
980	121	50c. green	1·20	35
981	121	1e. red	24·00	2·20
982	121	1e.75 blue	20·00	6·00
983	121	2e. purple	£120	8·00
984	121	3e.50 grey	80·00	12·00
MS984a 136×98 mm. Nos. 977/84 (sold at 15e.)			£325	£350

122

1945. Naval School Centenary.

985	122	10c. brown	65	25
986	122	50c. green	85	25
987	122	1e. red	7·25	1·40
988	122	1e.75 blue	7·75	4·00
MS988a 115×134 mm. Nos. 985/8 (sold at 7e.50)			75·00	£200

123 Almourol Castle

1946. Portuguese Castles.

989	-	10c. purple	40	35
990	-	30c. brown	65	35
991	-	35c. green	90	35
992	-	50c. grey	1·50	35
993	123	1e. red	50·00	1·90
994	-	1e.75 blue	32·00	3·75
995	-	2e. green	£100	6·50
996	-	3e.50 brown	46·00	8·50
MS996a 135×102 mm. 1e.75 grey-blue on buff (block of 4) (sold at 12e.50)			£275	£450

DESIGNS: Castles at Silves (10c.); Leiria (30c.); Feira (35c.); Guimaraes (50c.); Lisbon (1e.75); Braganza (2e.) and Ourem (3e.50).

124 "Decree Founding National Bank"

1946. Centenary of Bank of Portugal.

997	124	50c. blue	1·20	40
MS997a 156×144 mm. No. 997 (block of four) (sold at 7e.50)			£250	£350

125 Madonna and Child

1946. Tercentenary of Proclamation of St. Mary of Castile as Patron Saint of Portugal.

998	125	30c. grey	75	35
999	125	50c. green	50	35
1000	125	1e. red	5·00	1·70
1001	125	1e.75 blue	8·00	3·25
MS1001a 108×158 mm. Nos. 998/1001 on grey paper (sold at 7e.50)			90·00	£200

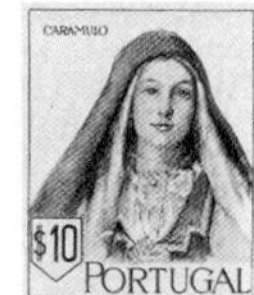

126 Caramulo Shepherdess

1947. Regional Costumes.

1002	126	10c. mauve	40	25
1003	-	30c. red	40	25
1004	-	35c. green	80	25
1005	-	50c. brown	1·30	25
1006	-	1e. red	29·00	1·00
1007	-	1e.75 blue	31·00	6·25
1008	-	2e. blue	£110	7·25
1009	-	3e.50 green	75·00	12·00
MS1009a 135×98 mm. Nos. 1002/9 (sold at 15e.)			£325	£400

COSTUMES: 30c. Malpique timbrel player; 35c. Monsanto flautist; 50c. Woman of Avintes; 1e. Maia field labourer; 1e.75, Woman of Algarve; 2e. Miranda do Douro bastonet player; 3e.50, Woman of the Azores.

127 Surrender of the Keys of Lisbon

1947. 800th Anniv of Recapture of Lisbon from the Moors.

1010	127	5c. green	40	30
1011	127	20c. red	65	30
1012	127	50c. violet	95	30
1013	127	1e.75 blue	11·50	7·50
1014	127	2e.50 brown	16·00	9·50
1015	127	3e.50 black	31·00	20·00

128 St. Joao de Brito

1948. Birth Tercentenary of St. Joao de Brito.

1016	128	30c. green	40	35
1017	-	50c. brown	40	35
1018	128	1e. red	16·00	2·50
1019	-	1e.75 blue	20·00	4·25

DESIGN: 50c., 1e.75, St. Joao de Brito (different).

130 "Architecture and Engineering"

1948. Exhibition of Public Works and National Congress of Engineering and Architecture.

1020	130	50c. purple	1·60	45

131 King Joao I

1949. Portraits.

1021	131	10c. violet and buff	75	35
1022	-	30c. green and buff	75	35
1023	-	35c. green and olive	1·50	35
1024	-	50c. blue and light blue	2·40	35
1025	-	1e. lake and red	2·50	35
1026	-	1e.75 black and grey	45·00	18·00
1027	-	2e. blue and light blue	28·00	3·00
1028	-	3e.50 chocolate & brown	90·00	33·00
MS1028a 136×98 mm. Nos. 1021/8 (sold for 15e.)			£100	£120

PORTRAITS: 30c. Queen Philippa; 35c. Prince Fernando; 50c. Prince Henry the Navigator; 1e. Nun Alvares; 1e.75, Joao da Regras; 2e. Fernao Lopes; 3e.50, Afonso Domingues.

132 Statue of Angel

1949. 16th Congress of the History of Art.

1029	132	1e. red	18·00	30
1030	132	5e. brown	4·75	55

133 Hands and Letter

1949. 75th Anniv of U.P.U.

1031	133	1e. lilac	55	25
1032	133	2e. blue	1·60	35
1033	133	2e.50 green	9·25	1·60
1034	133	4e. brown	25·00	6·00

134 Our Lady of Fatima

1950. Holy Year.

1035	134	50c. green	1·10	40
1036	134	1e. brown	5·00	45
1037	134	2e. blue	10·50	3·25
1038	134	5e. lilac	£160	44·00

135 Saint and Invalid

1950. 400th Death Anniv of San Juan de Dios.

1039	135	20c. violet	75	35
1040	135	50c. red	1·20	45
1041	135	1e. green	2·75	60
1042	135	1e.50 orange	35·00	5·25
1043	135	2e. blue	28·00	4·00
1044	135	4e. brown	80·00	12·50

136 G. Junqueiro

1951. Birth Centenary of Junqueiro (poet).

1045	136	50c. brown	9·00	55
1046	136	1e. blue	2·75	50

137 Fisherman with Meagre

1951. Fisheries Congress.

1047	137	50c. green on buff	8·50	85
1048	137	1e. purple on buff	2·00	20

138 Dove and Olive Branch

1951. Termination of Holy Year.

1049	**138**	20c. brown and buff	85	40
1050	**138**	90c. green and yellow	20·00	2·75
1051	-	1e. purple and pink	18·00	45
1052	-	2e.30 green and blue	22·00	3·25

PORTRAIT: 1e., 2e.30, Pope Pius XII.

139 15th century Colonists

1951. 500th Anniv of Colonization of Terceira, Azores.

1053	**139**	50c. blue on flesh	5·50	75
1054	**139**	1e. brown on buff	2·75	70

140 Revolutionaries

1951. 25th Anniv of National Revolution.

1055	**140**	1e. brown	15·00	40
1056	**140**	2e.30 blue	11·50	2·00

141 Coach of King Joao VI

1952. National Coach Museum.

1057	-	10c. purple	40	30
1058	**141**	20c. green	40	30
1059	-	50c. green	1·20	30
1060	-	90c. green	4·75	2·40
1061	-	1e. orange	2·10	35
1062	-	1e.40 pink	11·00	6·50
1063	**141**	1e.50 brown	9·75	3·50
1064	-	2e.30 blue	6·25	3·25

DESIGNS (coaches of): 10, 90c. King Felippe II; 50c., 1e.40, Papal Nuncio to Joao V; 1e., 2e.30, King Jose.

142 "N.A.T.O."

1952. 3rd Anniv of N.A.T.O.

1065	**142**	1e. green and deep green	16·00	65
1066	**142**	3e.50 grey and blue	£500	34·00

143 Hockey Players

1952. 8th World Roller-skating Hockey Championship.

1067	**143**	1e. black and blue	6·00	35
1068	**143**	3e.50 black and brown	10·50	3·50

144 Teixeira

1952. Birth Centenary of Prof. Gomes Teixeira (mathematician).

1069	**144**	1e. mauve and pink	1·50	35
1070	**144**	2e.30 deep blue and blue	11·50	6·50

145 Marshal Carmona Bridge

1952. Centenary of Ministry of Public Works.

1071	**145**	1e. brown on stone	1·20	40
1072	-	1e.40 lilac on stone	20·00	7·25
1073	-	2e. green on stone	12·50	4·50
1074	-	3e.50 blue on stone	21·00	6·25

DESIGNS: 1e.40, 28th May Stadium, Braga; 2e. Coimbra University; 3e.50, Salazar Barrage.

146 St. Francis Xavier

1952. 4th Death Centenary of St. Francis Xavier.

1075	**146**	1e. blue	1·00	40
1076	**146**	2e. purple	2·75	80
1077	**146**	3e.50 blue	38·00	18·00
1078	**146**	5e. lilac	75·00	6·50

147 Medieval Knight

1953

1079	**147**	5c. green on yellow	40	20
1080	**147**	10c. grey on pink	40	20
1081	**147**	20c. orange on yellow	40	20
1081a	**147**	30c. purple on buff	50	20
1082	**147**	50c. black	40	20
1083	**147**	90c. green on yellow	29·00	1·10
1084	**147**	1e. brown on pink	70	20
1085	**147**	1e.40 red	29·00	1·60
1086	**147**	1e.50 red on yellow	90	20
1087	**147**	2e. black	1·40	20
1088	**147**	2e.30 blue	45·00	1·30
1089	**147**	2e.50 black on pink	2·50	25
1089a	**147**	2e.50 green on yellow	2·50	25
1090	**147**	5e. purple on yellow	2·50	25
1091	**147**	10e. blue on yellow	11·00	35
1092	**147**	20e. brown on yellow	22·00	50
1093	**147**	50e. lilac	15·00	70

148 St. Martin of Dume

1953. 14th Centenary of Landing of St. Martin of Dume on Iberian Peninsula.

1094	**148**	1e. black and grey	2·50	35
1095	**148**	3e.50 brown and yellow	20·00	8·25

149 G. Gomes Fernandes

1953. Birth Centenary of Fernandes (fire-brigade chief).

1096	**149**	1e. purple and cream	1·50	35
1097	**149**	2e.30 blue and cream	20·00	8·75

150 Club Emblems, 1903 and 1953

1953. 50th Anniv of Portuguese Automobile Club.

1098	**150**	1e. deep green and green	1·20	40
1099	**150**	3e.50 brown and buff	21·00	8·50

151 Princess St. Joan

1953. 5th Centenary of Birth of Princess St. Joan.

1100	**151**	1e. black and green	2·75	35
1101	**151**	3e.50 deep blue and blue	21·00	10·00

152 Queen Maria II

1953. Centenary of First Portuguese Stamps. Bottom panel in gold.

1102	**152**	50c. red	40	35
1103	**152**	1e. brown	40	35
1104	**152**	1e.40 purple	4·00	1·40
1105	**152**	2e.30 blue	7·50	3·25
1106	**152**	3e.50 blue	7·50	3·25
1107	**152**	4e.50 green	13·00	2·40
1108	**152**	5e. green	15·00	2·10
1109	**152**	20e. violet	£110	12·50

153

1954. 150th Anniv of Trade Secretariat.

1110	**153**	1e. blue and light blue	1·10	25
1111	**153**	1e.50 brown and buff	4·75	1·00

154

1954. People's Education Plan.

1112	**154**	50c. blue and light blue	60	25
1113	**154**	1e. red and pink	60	25
1114	**154**	2e. deep green and green	55·00	1·70
1115	**154**	2e.50 brown and light brown	47·00	2·40

155 Cadet and College Banner

1954. 150th Anniv of Military College.

1116	**155**	1e. brown and green	2·50	35
1117	**155**	3e.50 blue and green	11·00	4·25

156 Father Manuel da Nobrega

1954. 400th Anniv of Sao Paulo.

1118	**156**	1e. brown	1·20	40
1119	**156**	2e.30 blue	95·00	37·00
1120	**156**	3e.50 green	25·00	4·50
1121	**156**	5e. green	80·00	7·25

157 King Sancho I, 1154–1211

1955. Portuguese Kings.

1122	-	10c. purple	45	35
1123	**157**	20c. green	45	35
1124	-	50c. blue	55	35
1125	-	90c. green	8·00	2·20
1126	-	1e. brown	2·10	40
1127	-	1e.40 red	16·00	5·50
1128	-	1e.50 green	5·25	1·70
1129	-	2e. red	18·00	4·50
1130	-	2e.30 blue	14·50	4·25

KINGS: 10c. Afonso I; 50c. Afonso II; 90c. Sancho II; 1e. Afonso III; 1e.40, Diniz; 1e.50, Afonso IV; 2e. Pedro I; 2e.30, Fernando.

158 Telegraph Poles

1955. Centenary of Electric Telegraph System in Portugal.

1131	**158**	1e. red and brown	1·10	35
1132	**158**	2e.30 blue and green	42·00	6·25
1133	**158**	3e.50 green and yellow	41·00	4·75

159 A. J. Ferreira da Silva

1956. Birth Centenary of Ferreira da Silva (teacher).

1134	**159**	1e. deep blue, blue and azure	95	35
1135	**159**	2e.30 deep green, emerald and green	25·00	7·75

160 Steam Locomotive, 1856

1956. Centenary of Portuguese Railways.

1136	**160**	1e. olive and green	85	35
1137	-	1e.50 blue and green	19·00	80
1138	-	2e. brown and bistre	50·00	2·20
1139	**160**	2e.50 brown and deep brown	70·00	3·00

DESIGN: 1e.50, 2e. Class 2500 electric locomotive, 1956.

161 Madonna and Child

1956. Mothers' Day.

1140	**161**	1e. sage and green	85	20
1141	**161**	1e.50 lt brown and brown	2·10	40

162 Almeida Garrett (after Barata Feyo)

1957. Almeida Garrett (writer) Commem.

1142	**162**	1e. brown	1·20	35
1143	**162**	2e.30 lilac	70·00	17·00
1144	**162**	3e.50 green	24·00	1·80
1145	**162**	5e. red	£130	16·00

163 Cesario Verde

1957. Cesario Verde (poet) Commem.

1146	**163**	1e. brown, buff and green	65	25
1147	**163**	3e.30 black, olive and green	3·25	1·80

164 Exhibition Emblem

1958. Brussels International Exhibition.

1148	**164**	1e. multicoloured	55	25
1149	**164**	3e.30 multicoloured	2·75	2·00

165 St. Elizabeth

1958. St. Elizabeth and St. Teotonio Commem.

1150	**165**	1e. red and cream	45	30
1151	-	2e. green and cream	85	60
1152	**165**	2e.50 violet and cream	7·25	1·30
1153	-	5e. brown and cream	12·00	1·60

PORTRAIT: 2, 5e. St. Teotonio.

166 Institute of Tropical Medicine, Lisbon

1958. 6th Int Congress of Tropical Medicine.

1154	**166**	1e. green and grey	3·25	40
1155	**166**	2e.50 blue and grey	13·00	2·20

167 Liner

1958. 2nd National Merchant Navy Congress.

1156	**167**	1e. brown, ochre & sepia	7·50	40
1157	**167**	4e.50 violet, lilac and blue	10·50	3·50

168 Queen Leonora

1958. 500th Birth Anniv of Queen Leonora. Frames and ornaments in bistre, inscriptions and value tablet in black.

1158	**168**	1e. blue and brown	45	25
1159	**168**	1e.50 turquoise and blue	6·50	1·00
1160	**168**	2e.30 blue and green	5·75	2·10
1161	**168**	4e.10 blue and grey	5·75	2·10

169 Arms of Aveiro

1959. Millenary of Aveiro.

1162	**169**	1e. multicoloured	2·10	40
1163	**169**	5e. multicoloured	22·00	3·00

170

1960. 10th Anniv of N.A.T.O.

1164	**170**	1e. black and lilac	55	35
1165	**170**	3e.50 green and grey	5·25	2·75

171 "Doorway to Peace"

1960. World Refugee Year. Symbol in black.

1166	**171**	20c. yellow, lemon & brn	25	20
1167	**171**	1e. yellow, green and blue	80	20
1168	**171**	1e.80 yellow and green	1·70	1·40

172 Glider

1960. 50th Anniv of Portuguese Aero Club. Multicoloured.

1169	1e. Type **172**	40	35
1170	1e.50 Light monoplane	1·30	45
1171	2e. Airplane and parachutes	2·10	1·10
1172	2e.50 Model glider	3·75	1·60

173 Padre Cruz (after M. Barata)

1960. Death Centenary of Padre Cruz.

1173	**173**	1e. brown	70	35
1174	**173**	4e.30 blue	13·50	10·00

174 University Seal

1960. 400th Anniv of Evora University.

1175	**174**	50c. blue	40	25
1176	**174**	1e. brown and yellow	60	25
1177	**174**	1e.40 purple	4·25	2·40

175 Prince Henry's Arms

1960. 5th Death Centenary of Prince Henry the Navigator. Multicoloured.

1178	1e. Type **175**	55	35
1179	2e.50 Caravel	4·75	55
1180	3e.50 Prince Henry the Navigator	6·00	2·10
1181	5e. Motto	15·00	1·20
1182	8e. Barketta	6·25	1·20
1183	10e. Map showing Sagres	21·00	3·00

175a Conference Emblem

1960. Europa.

1184	**175a**	1e. light blue and blue	45	35
1185	**175a**	3e.50 red and lake	5·25	3·00

176 Emblems of Prince Henry and Lisbon

1960. 5th National Philatelic Exhibition, Lisbon.

1186	**176**	1e. blue, black and green	60	35
1187	**176**	3e.30 blue, black and light blue	8·75	5·50

177 Portuguese Flag

1960. 50th Anniv of Republic.

1188	**177**	1e. multicoloured	50	15

178 King Pedro V

1961. Cent of Lisbon University Faculty of Letters.

1189	**178**	1e. green and brown	75	30
1190	**178**	6e.50 brown and blue	5·00	1·40

179 Arms of Setubal

1961. Centenary of Setubal City.

1191	**179**	1e. multicoloured	80	30
1192	**179**	4e.30 multicoloured	29·00	9·00

180

1961. Europa.

1193	**180**	1e. light blue, blue and deep blue	35	35
1194	**180**	1e.50 light green, green and deep green	2·00	1·80
1195	**180**	3e.50 pink, red and lake	2·30	2·10

181 Tomar Gateway

1961. 800th Anniv of Tomar.

1196	-	1e. multicoloured	35	25
1197	**181**	3e.50 multicoloured	2·10	1·70

DESIGN: 1e. As Type **181** but without ornamental background.

182 National Guardsman

1962. 50th Anniv of National Republican Guard.

1198	**182**	1e. multicoloured	35	25
1199	**182**	2e. multicoloured	3·50	1·20
1200	**182**	2e.50 multicoloured	3·25	1·00

183 St. Gabriel (Patron Saint of Telecommunications)

1962. St. Gabriel Commemoration.

1201	**183**	1e. brown, green and olive	1·00	30
1202	**183**	3e.50 green, brown & ol	1·10	60

184 Scout Badge and Tents

1962. 18th International Scout Conference (1961).

1203	**184**	20c. multicoloured	35	25
1204	**184**	50c. multicoloured	40	25
1205	**184**	1e. multicoloured	85	30
1206	**184**	2e.50 multicoloured	5·75	75
1207	**184**	3e.50 mulitcoloured	2·75	75
1208	**184**	6e.50 multicoloured	1·70	1·30

185 Children with Ball

1962. 10th International Paediatrics Congress, Lisbon. Centres in black.

1209	-	50c. yellow and green	35	25
1210	-	1e. yellow and grey	1·30	25
1211	**185**	2e.80 yellow and brown	4·25	2·10
1212	-	3e.50 yellow and purple	7·75	2·75

DESIGNS: 50c. Children with book; 1e. Inoculating child; 3e.50, Weighing baby.

186 Europa "Honeycomb"

1962. Europa. "EUROPA" in gold.

1213	**186**	1e. ultramarine, light blue and blue	40	35
1214	**186**	1e.50 deep green, light green and green	2·00	1·30
1215	**186**	3e.50 purple, pink and claret	2·30	2·00

187 St. Zenon (the Courier)

1962. Stamp Day. Saint in yellow and pink.

1216	**187**	1e. black and purple	35	30
1217	**187**	2e. black and green	1·60	1·10
1218	**187**	2e.80 black and bistre	2·75	2·75

188 Benfica Emblem and European Cup

1963. Benfica Club's Double Victory in European Football Cup Championship (1961–62).

1219	**188**	1e. multicoloured	1·20	30
1220	**188**	4e.30 multicoloured	2·10	1·90

189 Campaign Emblem

1963. Freedom from Hunger.

1221	**189**	1e. multicoloured	35	30
1222	**189**	3e.30 multicoloured	2·00	1·60
1223	**189**	3e.50 multicoloured	2·20	1·60

190 Mail Coach

1963. Centenary of Paris Postal Conference.

1224	**190**	1e. blue, light blue and grey	35	20
1225	**190**	1e.50 multicoloured	3·00	75
1226	**190**	5e. brown, lilac & lt brown	1·30	60

191 St. Vincent de Paul

1963. 300th Death Anniv of St. Vincent de Paul. Inscr in gold.

1227	**191**	20c. ultramarine and blue	35	35
1228	**191**	1e. blue and grey	55	35
1229	**191**	2e.80 black and green	6·50	2·75
1230	**191**	5e. grey and mauve	5·75	2·00

192 Medieval Knight

1963. 800th Anniv of Military Order of Avis.

1231	**192**	1e. multicoloured	35	25
1232	**192**	1e.50 multicoloured	1·00	40
1233	**192**	2e.50 mulitcoloured	2·00	1·40

193 Europa "Dove"

1963. Europa.

1234	**193**	1e. grey, blue and black	50	35
1235	**193**	1e.50 grey, green & black	4·25	2·00
1236	**193**	3e.50 grey, red and black	6·25	3·00

194 Supersonic Flight

1963. 10th Anniv of T.A.P. Airline.

1237	**194**	1e. blue and deep blue	30	25
1238	**194**	2e.50 light green & green	2·10	1·00
1239	**194**	3e.50 orange and red	2·50	1·80

195 Pharmacist's Jar

1964. 400th Anniv of Publication of "Coloquios dos Simples" (Dissertation on Indian herbs and drugs) by Dr. G. d'Orta.

1240	**195**	50c. brown, black & bis	80	35
1241	**195**	1e. purple, black and red	55	35
1242	**195**	4e.30 blue, black & grey	7·00	5·75

196 Bank Emblem

1964. Centenary of National Overseas Bank.

1243	**196**	1e. yellow, green and blue	35	30
1244	**196**	2e.50 yellow, olive & grn	4·00	1·60
1245	**196**	3e.50 yellow, green & brn	3·50	1·70

197 Sameiro Shrine (Braga)

1964. Centenary of Sameiro Shrine.

1246	**197**	1e. yellow, brown and red	35	25
1247	**197**	2e. yellow, light brown and brown	3·00	1·10
1248	**197**	5e. yellow, green and blue	3·50	1·70

198 Europa "Flower"

1964. Europa.

1249	**198**	1e. deep blue, light blue and blue	1·00	35
1250	**198**	3e.50 brown, light brown and purple	8·00	2·50
1251	**198**	4e.30 deep green, light green and green	9·50	4·75

199 Sun and Globe

1964. International Quiet Sun Years.

1252	**199**	1e. mulitcoloured	45	25
1253	**199**	8e. multicoloured	2·20	1·60

200 Olympic "Rings"

1964. Olympic Games, Tokyo.

1254	**200**	20c. multicoloured	35	30
1255	**200**	1e. multicoloured	45	35
1256	**200**	1e.50 multicoloured	2·50	1·60
1257	**200**	6e.50 multicoloured	4·50	3·00

201 E. Coelho (founder)

1964. Centenary of "Diario de Noticias" (newspaper).

1258	**201**	1e. multicoloured	95	20
1259	**201**	5e. multicoloured	11·50	1·60

202 Traffic Signals

1965. 1st National Traffic Congress Lisbon.

1260	**202**	1e. yellow, red and green	40	35
1261	**202**	3e.30 green, red & yellow	10·00	5·25
1262	**202**	3e.50 red, yellow & green	6·50	2·50

203 Dom Fernando (second Duke of Braganza)

1965. 500th Anniv of Braganza.

1263	**203**	1e. red and black	40	25
1264	**203**	10e. green and black	4·50	1·20

204 Angel and Gateway

1965. 900th Anniv of Capture of Coimbra from the Moors.

1265	**204**	1e. multicoloured	35	35
1266	**204**	2e.50 multicoloured	3·00	2·40
1267	**204**	5e. multicoloured	3·75	3·00

205 I.T.U. Emblem

1965. Centenary of I.T.U.

1268	**205**	1e. green and brown	35	35
1269	**205**	3e.50 purple and green	2·40	2·00
1270	**205**	6e.50 blue and green	2·75	1·80

206 C. Gulbenkian

1965. 10th Death Anniv of Calouste Gulbenkian (oil industry pioneer and philanthropist).

1271	**206**	1e. multicoloured	1·00	20
1272	**206**	8e. multicoloured	1·10	75

207 Red Cross Emblem

1965. Centenary of Portuguese Red Cross.

1273	**207**	1e. red, green and black	40	35
1274	**207**	4e. red, green and black	6·50	3·25
1275	**207**	4e.30 red, light red & black	18·00	11·50

208 Europa "Sprig"

1965. Europa.

1276	**208**	1e. lt blue, black and blue	55	35
1277	**208**	3e.50 flesh, brown & red	13·50	2·40
1278	**208**	4e.30 light green, black and green	24·00	11·50

209 North American F-86 Sabre Jet Fighter

1965. 50th Anniv of Portuguese Air Force.

1279	**209**	1e. red, green and olive	45	25
1280	**209**	2e. red, green and brown	2·20	1·00
1281	**209**	5e. red, green and blue	4·50	2·75

210

1965. 500th Birth Anniv of Gil Vicente (poet and dramatist). Designs depicting characters from Vicente's poems.

1282	210	20c. multicoloured	25	20
1283	-	1e. multicoloured	70	20
1284	-	2e.50 multicoloured	4·75	80
1285	-	6e.50 multicoloured	2·30	1·10

211 Monogram of Christ

1966. International Committee for the Defence of Christian Civilisation Congress, Lisbon.

1286	211	1e. violet, gold and bistre	40	20
1287	211	3e.30 black, gold & pur	10·00	5·50
1288	211	5e. black, gold and red	7·50	3·00

212 Emblems of Agriculture, Construction and Industry

1966. 40th Anniv of National Revolution.

1289	212	1e. black, blue and grey	45	35
1290	212	3e.50 brown, light brown and bistre	4·50	2·10
1291	212	4e. purple, red and pink	4·50	1·70

213 Giraldo the "Fearless"

1966. 800th Anniv of Reconquest of Evora.

1292	213	1e. multicoloured	55	25
1293	213	8e. multicoloured	1·80	1·00

214 Salazar Bridge

1966. Inauguration of Salazar Bridge, Lisbon.

1294	214	1e. red and gold	45	25
1295	214	2e.50 blue and gold	2·50	1·40
1296	-	2e.80 blue and silver	3·25	2·50
1297	-	4e.30 green and silver	3·50	2·50

DESIGN—VERT: 2e.80, 4e.30, Salazar Bridge (different view).

215 Europa "Ship"

1966. Europa.

1298	215	1e. multicoloured	60	35
1299	215	3e.50 multicoloured	19·00	3·00
1300	215	4e.50 multicoloured	19·00	4·75

216 C. Pestana (bacteriologist)

1966. Portuguese Scientists. Portraits in brown and bistre; background colours given.

1301	216	20c. green	25	15
1302	-	50c. orange	25	15
1303	-	1e. yellow	35	15
1304	-	1e.50 brown	50	15
1305	-	2e. brown	2·75	25
1306	-	2e.50 green	3·00	70
1307	-	2e.80 orange	4·75	2·50
1308	-	4e.30 blue	6·25	4·75

SCIENTISTS: 50c. E. Moniz (neurologist); 1e. E. A. P. Coutinho (botanist); 1e.50, J. C. da Serra (botanist); 2e. R. Jorge (hygienist and anthropologist); 2e.50, J. L. de Vasconcelos (ethnologist); 2e.80, M. Lemos (medical historian); 4e.30, J. A. Serrano (anatomist).

217 Bocage

1966. Birth Bicentenary (1965) of Manuel M. B. du Bocage (poet).

1309	217	1e. black, green and bistre	25	15
1310	217	2e. black, green & brown	1·60	70
1311	217	6e. black, green and grey	2·10	1·30

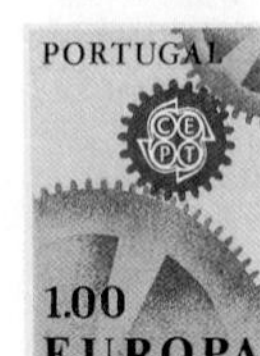

218 Cogwheels

1967. Europa.

1312	218	1e. blue, black & lt blue	60	35
1313	218	3e.50 brown, black and orange	15·00	1·90
1314	218	4e.30 green, black and light green	21·00	3·75

219 Adoration of the Virgin

1967. 50th Anniv of Fatima Apparitions. Mult.

1315	1e. Type **219**	20	15
1316	2e.80 Fatima Church	95	90
1317	3e.50 Virgin of Fatima	60	45
1318	4e. Chapel of the Apparitions	70	55

220 Roman Senators

1967. New Civil Law Code.

1319	220	1e. red and gold	20	15
1320	220	2e.50 blue and gold	3·25	1·80
1321	220	4e.30 green and gold	2·75	1·80

221 Lisnave Shipyard

1967. Inauguration of Lisnave Shipyard, Lisbon.

1322	221	1e. multicoloured	20	20
1323	-	2e.80 multicoloured	4·00	1·90
1324	221	3e.50 multicoloured	3·00	1·80
1325	-	4e.30 multicoloured	3·75	2·00

DESIGN: 2e.80, 4e.30, Section of ship's hull and location map.

222 Serpent Symbol

1967. 6th European Rheumatological Congress, Lisbon.

1326	222	1e. multicoloured	20	20
1327	222	2e. multicoloured	1·90	1·00
1328	222	5e. multicoloured	3·00	2·00

223 Flags of EFTA Countries

1967. European Free Trade Association.

1329	223	1e. multicoloured	35	35
1330	223	3e.50 multicoloured	2·40	2·00
1331	223	4e.30 multicoloured	4·75	4·50

224 Tombstones

1967. Centenary of Abolition of Death Penalty in Portugal.

1332	224	1e. green	20	20
1333	224	2e. brown	2·10	1·30
1334	224	5e. green	3·75	3·00

225 Bento de Goes

1968. Bento de Goes Commemoration.

1335	225	1e. blue, brown and green	95	20
1336	225	8e. purple, green & brown	2·50	1·00

226 Europa "Key"

1968. Europa.

1337	226	1e. multicoloured	60	35
1338	226	3e.50 multicoloured	16·00	2·75
1339	226	4e.30 multicoloured	24·00	5·00

227 "Maternal Love"

1968. 30th Anniv of Organization of Mothers for National Education (O.M.E.N.).

1340	227	1e. black, orange and grey	35	25
1341	227	2e. black, orange and pink	2·75	1·00
1342	227	5e. black, orange and blue	5·25	2·75

228 "Victory over Disease"

1968. 20th Anniv of W.H.O.

1343	228	1e. multicoloured	35	35
1344	228	3e.50 multicoloured	2·20	1·10
1345	228	4e.30 multicoloured	12·00	8·50

229 Vineyard, Girao

1968. "Lubrapex 1968" Stamp Exhibition. Madeira—"Pearl of the Atlantic". Multicoloured.

1346	50c. Type **229**	25	20
1347	1e. Firework display	30	15
1348	1e.50 Landscape	60	20
1349	2e.80 J. Fernandes Vieira (liberator of Pernambuco) (vert)	3·50	2·50
1350	3e.50 Embroidery (vert)	2·75	1·60
1351	4e.30 J. Goncalves Zarco (navigator) (vert)	12·00	11·50
1352	20e. "Muschia aurea" (vert)	7·75	2·20

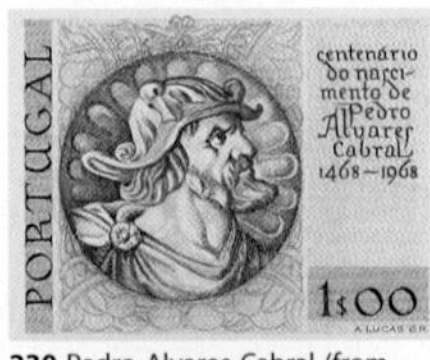

230 Pedro Alvares Cabral (from medallion)

1969. 500th Birth Anniv of Pedro Alvares Cabral (explorer).

1353	230	1e. blue	40	20
1354	-	3e.50 purple	6·25	3·50
1355	-	6e.50 multicoloured	4·50	3·50

DESIGNS—VERT: 3e.50, Cabral's arms. HORIZ: 6e.50, Cabral's fleet (from contemporary docu-ments).

231 Colonnade

1969. Europa.

1356	231	1e. multicoloured	60	35
1357	231	3e.50 multicoloured	17·00	3·50
1358	231	4e.30 multicoloured	26·00	5·75

232 King Joseph I

1969. Centenary of National Press.

1359	232	1e. multicoloured	20	20
1360	232	2e. multicoloured	1·70	95
1361	232	8e. multicoloured	1·60	1·30

233 I.L.O. Emblem

1969. 50th Anniv of I.L.O.

1362	233	1e. multicoloured	25	20
1363	233	3e.50 multicoloured	3·00	1·00
1364	233	4e.30 multicoloured	4·00	3·25

234 J. R. Cabrilho (navigator and colonizer)

1969. Bicentenary of San Diego, California.

No.	Type	Description	Mint	Used
1365	**234**	1e. dp green, yellow & grn	20	20
1366	**234**	2e.50 brown, light brown and blue	2·50	1·00
1367	**234**	6e.50 deep brown, green and brown	3·25	1·90

235 Vianna da Motta (from painting by C. B. Pinheiro)

1969. Birth Centenary (1968) of Jose Vianna da Motta (concert pianist).

No.	Type	Description	Mint	Used
1368	**235**	1e. multicoloured	1·20	20
1369	**235**	9e. multicoloured	1·70	1·30

236 Coutinho and Fairey IIID Seaplane

1969. Birth Centenary of Gago Coutinho (aviator). Multicoloured.

No.	Description	Mint	Used
1370	1e. Type **236**	35	15
1371	2e.80 Coutinho and sextant	3·75	2·10
1372	3e.30 Type **236**	3·50	3·00
1373	4e.30 As No. 1371	3·50	3·00

237 Vasco da Gama

1969. 500th Birth Anniv of Vasco da Gama. Multicoloured.

No.	Description	Mint	Used
1374	1e. Type **237**	35	25
1375	2e.50 Arms of Vasco da Gama	4·75	3·75
1376	3e.50 Route map (horiz)	3·50	1·70
1377	4e. Vasca da Gama's fleet (horiz)	3·25	1·40

238 "Flaming Sun"

1970. Europa.

No.	Type	Description	Mint	Used
1378	**238**	1e. cream and blue	60	25
1379	**238**	3e.50 cream and brown	16·00	2·10
1380	**238**	4e.30 cream and green	23·00	6·25

239 Distillation Plant and Pipelines

1970. Inauguration of Porto Oil Refinery.

No.	Type	Description	Mint	Used
1381	**239**	1e. blue and light blue	25	20
1382	-	2e.80 black and green	3·50	2·75
1383	**239**	3e.30 green and olive	2·75	2·20
1384	-	6e. brown and light brown	2·50	1·90

DESIGN: 2e.80, 6e. Catalytic cracking plant and pipelines.

240 Marshal Carmona (from sculpture by L. de Almeida)

1970. Birth Centenary of Marshal Carmona.

No.	Type	Description	Mint	Used
1385	**240**	1e. green and black	25	10
1386	**240**	2e.50 blue, red and black	2·20	90
1387	**240**	7e. blue and black	2·50	1·70

241 Station Badge

1970. 25th Anniv of Plant-breeding Station.

No.	Type	Description	Mint	Used
1388	**241**	1e. multicoloured	30	10
1389	**241**	2e.50 multicoloured	1·80	70
1390	**241**	5e. multicoloured	2·20	90

242 Emblem within Cultural Symbol

1970. Expo 70. Multicoloured.

No.	Description	Mint	Used
1391	1e. Compass (postage)	25	15
1392	5e. Christian symbol	2·00	1·70
1393	6e.50 Symbolic initials	4·75	4·00
1394	3e.50 Type **242** (air)	90	45

243 Wheel and Star

1970. Centenaries of Covilha (Nos. 1395/6) and Santarem (Nos. 1397/8). Multicoloured.

No.	Description	Mint	Used
1395	1e. Type **243**	30	20
1396	2e.80 Ram and weaving frame	3·50	3·00
1397	1e. Castle	20	15
1398	4e. Two knights	2·30	1·30

244 "Great Eastern" laying Cable

1970. Centenary of Portugal–England Submarine Telegraph Cable.

No.	Type	Description	Mint	Used
1399	**244**	1e. black, blue and green	30	15
1400	**244**	2e.50 black, green & buff	2·50	70
1401	-	2e.80 multicoloured	4·00	3·25
1402	-	4e. multicoloured	2·50	1·30

DESIGN: 2e.80, 4e. Cable cross-section.

245 Harvesting Grapes

1970. Port Wine Industry. Multicoloured.

No.	Description	Mint	Used
1403	50c. Type **245**	15	10
1404	1e. Harvester and jug	25	10
1405	3e.50 Wine-glass and wine barge	95	25
1406	7e. Wine-bottle and casks	1·60	80

246 Mountain Windmill, Bussaco Hills

1971. Portuguese Windmills.

No.	Type	Description	Mint	Used
1407	**246**	20c. brown, black & sepia	15	10
1408	-	50c. brown, black & blue	20	10
1409	-	1e. purple, black and grey	30	10
1410	-	2e. red, black and mauve	1·00	35
1411	-	3e.30 chocolate, black and brown	3·50	2·50
1412	-	5e. brown, black & green	3·25	1·20

WINDMILLS: 50c. Beira Litoral Province; 1e. "Saloio" type Estremadura Province; 2e. St. Miguel Azores; 3e.30, Porto Santo, Madeira; 5e. Pico, Azores.

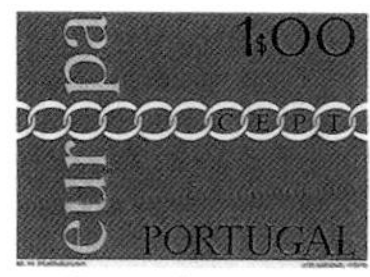
247 Europa Chain

1971. Europa.

No.	Type	Description	Mint	Used
1413	**247**	1e. green, blue and black	45	30
1414	**247**	3e.50 yellow, brn & blk	12·00	1·10
1415	**247**	7e.50 brown, green & blk	17·00	2·75

248 F. Franco

1971. Portuguese Sculptors.

No.	Type	Description	Mint	Used
1416	**248**	20c. black	15	10
1417	-	1e. red	35	10
1418	-	1e.50 brown	85	60
1419a	-	2e.50 blue	1·20	55
1420	-	3e.50 mauve	1·50	90
1421	-	4e. green	4·00	2·50

DESIGNS: 1e. A. Lopes; 1e.50, A. de Costa Mota; 2e.50, R. Gameiro; 3e.50, J. Simoes de Almeida (the Younger); 4e. F. dos Santos.

249 Pres. Salazar

1971. Pres. Antonio Salazar Commemoration.

No.	Type	Description	Mint	Used
1422	**249**	1e. brown, green & orge	25	10
1423	**249**	5e. brown, purple & orge	2·30	80
1424	**249**	10e. brown, blue & orge	3·50	1·60

250 Wolframite

1971. 1st Spanish–Portuguese–American Congress of Economic Geology. Multicoloured.

No.	Description	Mint	Used
1425	1e. Type **250**	15	10
1426	2e.50 Arsenopyrite	2·50	60
1427	3e.50 Beryllium	90	55
1428	6e.50 Chalcopyrite	1·70	80

251 Town Gate

1971. Bicentenary of Castelo Branco. Mult.

No.	Description	Mint	Used
1429	1e. Type **251**	15	15
1430	3e. Town square and monument	1·80	90
1431	12e.50 Arms of Castelo Branco (horiz)	1·60	90

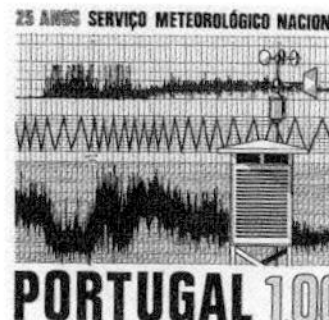
252 Weather Equipment

1971. 25th Anniv of Portuguese Meteorological Service. Multicoloured.

No.	Description	Mint	Used
1432	1e. Type **252**	20	10
1433	4e. Weather balloon	3·00	1·40
1434	6e.50 Weather satellite	2·00	1·00

253 Drowning Missionaries

1971. 400th Anniv of Martyrdom of Brazil Missionaries.

No.	Type	Description	Mint	Used
1435	**253**	1e. black, blue and grey	15	10
1436	**253**	3e.30 black, purple & brn	2·75	1·90
1437	**253**	4e.80 black, grn & olive	2·75	1·90

254 Man and his Habitat

1971. Nature Conservation. Multicoloured.

No.	Description	Mint	Used
1438	1e. Type **254**	15	10
1439	3e.30 Horses and trees ("Earth")	90	60
1440	3e.50 Birds ("The Atmosphere")	90	55
1441	4e.50 Fishes ("Water")	3·50	2·10

255 Clerigos Tower, Oporto

1972. Buildings and Views.

No.	Type	Description	Mint	Used
1442	-	5c. grey, black and green	30	15
1443	-	10c. black, green & blue	20	15
1444	-	30c. sepia, brown & yell	20	15
1445p	-	50c. blue, orange & blk	55	10
1446	**255**	1e. black, brown & grn	1·20	10
1447a	-	1e.50 brown, blue & blk	75	10
1448	-	2e. black, brown & pur	3·25	10
1449p	-	2e.50 brown, light brown and grey	55	10
1450p	-	3e. yellow, black & brn	90	10
1451p	-	3e.50 green, orge & brn	55	10
1452	-	4e. black, yellow & blue	1·00	10
1453	-	4e.50 black, brn & grn	1·50	10
1454	-	5e. green, brown & black	9·25	10
1455	-	6e. bistre, green & black	3·75	25
1456	-	7e.50 black, orge & grn	2·10	20
1457	-	8e. bistre, black & green	2·75	15
1458	-	10e. multicoloured	1·30	15
1459	-	20e. multicoloured	8·75	55
1460	-	50e. multicoloured	9·25	40
1461	-	100e. multicoloured	10·00	95

DESIGNS—As T **255**: 5c. Aguas Livres aqueduct, Lisbon; 10c. Lima Bridge; 30c. Monastery interior, Alcobaca; 50c. Coimbra University; 1e.50, Belem Tower, Lisbon; 2e. Domus Municipalis, Braganza; 2e.50, Castle, Vila de Feira; 3e. Misericord House, Viana do Castelo; 3e.50, Window, Tomar Convent; 4e. Gateway, Braga; 4e.50, Dolmen of Carrazeda; 5e. Roman Temple, Evora; 6e. Monastery, Leca do Balio; 7e.50, Almourol Castle; 8e. Ducal Palace, Guimaraes. 31×22 mm: 10e. Cape Girao, Madeira; 20e. Episcopal Garden, Castelo Branco; 50e. Town Hall, Sintra; 100e. Seven Cities' Lake, Sao Miguel, Azores.

256 Arms of Pinhel

1972. Bicentenary of Pinhel's Status as a City. Multicoloured.

No.	Type	Description	Mint	Used
1464		1e. Type **256**	25	10
1465		2e.50 Balustrade (vert)	2·30	55
1466		7e.50 Lantern on pedestal (vert)	1·80	80

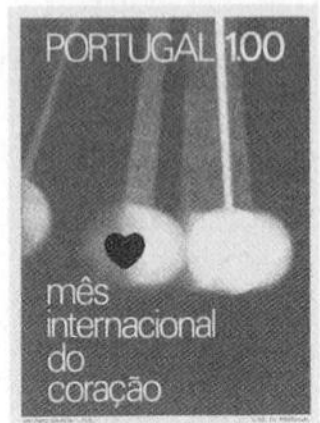

257 Heart and Pendulum

1972. World Heart Month.

No.	Type	Description	Mint	Used
1467	**257**	1e. red and lilac	25	15
1468	-	4e. red and green	3·50	1·60
1469	-	9e. red and brown	2·40	1·00

DESIGNS: 4e. Heart in spiral; 9e. Heart and cardiogram trace.

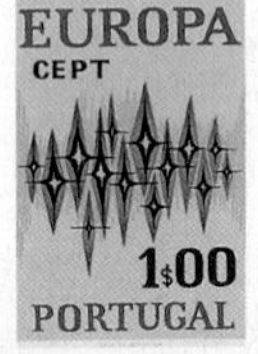

258 "Communications"

1972. Europa.

No.	Type	Description	Mint	Used
1470	**258**	1e. multicoloured	50	20
1471	**258**	3e.50 multicoloured	9·75	65
1472	**258**	6e. multicoloured	16·00	2·30

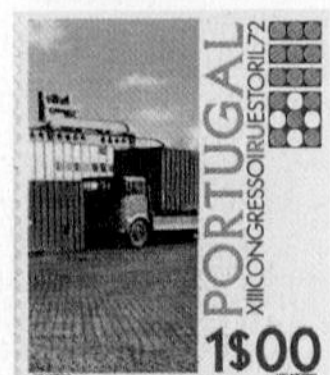

259 Container Truck

1972. 13th International Road Transport Union Congress, Estoril. Multicoloured.

No.	Type	Description	Mint	Used
1473		1e. Type **259**	25	20
1474		4e.50 Roof of taxi-cab	2·50	1·50
1475		8e. Motor-coach	2·30	1·30

260 Football

1972. Olympic Games, Munich. Multicoloured.

No.	Type	Description	Mint	Used
1476		50c. Type **260**	15	10
1477		1e. Running	20	10
1478		1e.50 Show jumping	55	25
1479		3e.50 Swimming	1·20	50
1480		4e.50 Yachting	1·80	1·40
1481		5e. Gymnastics	3·50	1·50

261 Marquis de Pombal

1972. Pombaline University Reforms. Multicoloured.

No.	Type	Description	Mint	Used
1482		1e. Type **261**	20	10
1483		2e.50 "The Sciences" (emblems)	2·10	1·20
1484		8e. Arms of Coimbra University.	2·20	1·60

262 Tome de Sousa

1972. 150th Anniv of Brazilian Independence. Mult.

No.	Type	Description	Mint	Used
1485		1e. Type **262**	20	15
1486		2e.50 Jose Bonifacio	1·10	40
1487		3e.50 Dom Pedro IV	1·10	45
1488		6e. Dove and globe	2·10	1·00

263 Sacadura, Cabral, Gago, Coutinho and Fairey III D Seaplane

1972. 50th Anniv of 1st Lisbon–Rio de Janeiro Flight. Multicoloured.

No.	Type	Description	Mint	Used
1489		1e. Type **263**	15	10
1490		2e.50 Route map	1·20	70
1491		2e.80 Type **263**	1·50	1·10
1492		3e.80 As 2e.50	1·90	1·60

264 Camoens

1972. 400th Anniv of Camoens' "Lusiads" (epic poem).

No.	Type	Description	Mint	Used
1493	**264**	1e. yellow, brown & black	25	15
1494	-	3e. blue, green and black	1·60	95
1495	-	10e. brown, purple & blk	2·30	1·10

DESIGNS: 3e. "Saved from the Sea"; 10e. "Encounter with Adamastor".

265 Graph and Computer Tapes

1973. Portuguese Productivity Conference, Lisbon. Multicoloured.

No.	Type	Description	Mint	Used
1496		1e. Type **265**	20	10
1497		4e. Computer scale	1·60	85
1498		9e. Graphs	1·60	80

266 Europa "Posthorn"

1973. Europa.

No.	Type	Description	Mint	Used
1499	**266**	1e. multicoloured	75	30
1500	**266**	4e. multicoloured	18·00	1·40
1501	**266**	6e. multicoloured	20·00	2·40

267 Pres. Medici and Arms

1973. Visit of Pres. Medici of Brazil. Mult.

No.	Type	Description	Mint	Used
1502		1e. Type **267**	20	15
1503		2e.80 Pres. Medici and globe	1·00	85
1504		3e.50 Type **267**	1·10	80
1505		4e.80 As No. 1503	1·10	85

268 Child Running

1973. "For the Child".

No.	Type	Description	Mint	Used
1506	**268**	1e. dp blue, blue & brown	20	10
1507	-	4e. purple, mauve & brn	1·90	85
1508	-	7e.50 orange, ochre and brown	2·30	1·50

DESIGNS: 4e. Child running (to right); 7e.50, Child jumping.

269 Transport and Weather Map

1973. 25th Anniv of Ministry of Communications. Multicoloured.

No.	Type	Description	Mint	Used
1509		1e. Type **269**	15	10
1510		3e.80 "Telecommunications"	65	40
1511		6e. "Postal Services"	1·50	90

270 Child and Written Text

1973. Bicentenary of Primary State School Education. Multicoloured.

No.	Type	Description	Mint	Used
1512		1e. Type **270**	25	10
1513		4e.50 Page of children's primer	2·10	65
1514		5e.30 "Schooldays" (child's drawing) (horiz)	1·80	95
1515		8e. "Teacher and children" (horiz)	4·75	2·00

271 Electric Tramcar

1973. Centenary of Oporto's Public Transport System. Multicoloured.

No.	Type	Description	Mint	Used
1516		1e. Horse tram	30	10
1517		3e.50 Modern bus	2·75	1·90
1518		7e.50 Type **271**	3·00	1·60

Nos. 1516/17 are 31½×31½ mm.

272 League Badge

1973. 50th Anniv of Servicemen's League. Multicoloured.

No.	Type	Description	Mint	Used
1519		1e. Type **272**	20	15
1520		2e.50 Servicemen	3·00	85
1521		11e. Awards and medals	2·10	90

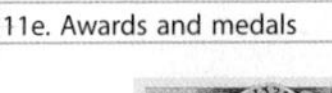

273 Death of Nuno Goncalves

1973. 600th Anniv of Defence of Faria Castle by the Alcaide, Nuno Goncalves.

No.	Type	Description	Mint	Used
1522	**273**	1e. green and yellow	30	15
1523	**273**	10e. purple and yellow	2·75	1·50

274 Damiao de Gois (after Durer)

1974. 400th Death Anniv of Damiao de Gois (scholar and diplomat). Multicoloured.

No.	Type	Description	Mint	Used
1524		1e. Type **274**	20	10
1525		4e.50 Title-page of "Chronicles of Prince Dom Joao"	3·00	80
1526		7e.50 Lute and "Dodecahordon" score	1·80	80

275 "The Exile" (A. Soares dos Reis)

1974. Europa.

No.	Type	Description	Mint	Used
1527	**275**	1e. green, blue and olive	90	30
1528	**275**	4e. green, red and yellow	21·00	1·40
1529	**275**	6e. dp green, green & blue	25·00	1·80

276 Light Emission

1974. Inauguration of Satellite Communications Station Network.

No.	Type	Description	Mint	Used
1530	**276**	1e.50 green	25	20
1531	-	4e.50 blue	1·80	90
1532	-	5e.30 purple	2·50	1·30

DESIGNS: 4e.50, Spiral Waves; 5e.30, Satellite and Earth.

277 "Diffusion of Hertzian Radio Waves"

1974. Birth Centenary of Guglielmo Marconi (radio pioneer). Multicoloured.

No.	Type	Description	Mint	Used
1533		1e.50 Type **277**	20	10
1534		3e.30 "Radio waves across Space"	2·50	1·10
1535		10e. "Radio waves for Navigation"	1·90	80

278 Early Post-boy and Modern Mail Van

1974. Centenary of U.P.U. Multicoloured.

No.	Type	Description	Mint	Used
1536		1e.50 Type **278**	15	10

1537	2e. Hand with letters	90	15
1538	3e.30 Sailing packet and modern liner	70	25
1539	4e.50 Dove and airliner	1·40	65
1540	5e.30 Hand with letter	1·40	75
1541	20e. Steam and electric locomotives	3·00	1·60
MS1542	106×147 mm. Nos. 1536/41 (sold at 50e.)	8·75	7·50

279 Luisa Todi

1974. Portuguese Musicians.

1543	**279**	1e.50 purple	20	15
1544	-	2e. red	1·40	35
1545	-	2e.50 brown	1·00	25
1546	-	3e. blue	1·50	50
1547	-	5e.30 green	1·20	80
1548	-	11e. red	1·30	80

PORTRAITS: 2e. Joao Domingos Bomtempo; 2e.50,Carlos Seixas; 3e. Duarte Lobo; 5e.30, Joaode Sousa Carvalho; 11e. Marcos Portugal.

280 Arms of Beja

1974. Bimillenary of Beja. Multicoloured.

1549	1e.50 Type **280**	25	10
1550	3e.50 Beja's inhabitants through the ages	3·00	1·50
1551	7e. Moorish arches	3·25	1·70

281 "The Annunciation"

1974. Christmas. Multicoloured.

1552	1e.50 Type **281**	20	10
1553	4e.50 "The Nativity"	4·00	80
1554	10e. "The Flight into Egypt"	3·50	1·10

282 Rainbow and Dove

1974. Portuguese Armed Forces Movement of 25 April.

1555	**282**	1e.50 multicoloured	15	15
1556	**282**	3e.50 multicoloured	4·00	1·90
1557	**282**	5e. multicoloured	3·00	1·10

283 Egas Moniz

1974. Birth Centenary of Professor Egas Moniz (brain surgeon).

1558	**283**	1e.50 brown and orange	35	15
1559	-	3e.30 orange and brown	3·00	80
1560	-	10e. grey and blue	6·00	1·00

DESIGNS: 3e.30, Nobel Medicine and Physiology Prize medal, 1949; 10e. Cerebral angiograph, 1927.

284 Farmer and Soldier

1975. Portuguese Cultural Progress and Citizens' Guidance Campaign.

1561	**284**	1e.50 multicoloured	25	10
1562	**284**	3e. multicoloured	2·50	85
1563	**284**	4e.50 multicoloured	3·50	1·40

285 Hands and Dove of Peace

1975. 1st Anniv of Portuguese Revolution. Multicoloured.

1564	1e.50 Type **285**	20	10
1565	4e.50 Hands and peace dove	3·50	90
1566	10e. Peace dove and emblem	4·25	1·50

286 "The Hand of God"

1975. Holy Year. Multicoloured.

1567	1e.50 Type **286**	20	15
1568	4e.50 Hand with cross	4·25	1·30
1569	10e. Peace dove	5·75	1·50

287 "The Horseman of the Apocalypse" (detail of 12th-cent manuscript)

1975. Europa. Multicoloured.

1570	1e.50 Type **287**	1·20	15
1571	10e. "Fernando Pessoa" (poet) (A. Negreiros)	55·00	1·90

288 Assembly Building

1975. Opening of Portuguese Constituent Assembly.

1572	**288**	2e. black, red and yellow	45	10
1573	**288**	20e. black, green & yellow	7·50	1·80

289 Hiking

1975. 36th International Camping and Caravanning Federation Rally. Multicoloured.

1574	2e. Type **289**	1·10	15
1575	4e.50 Boating and swimming	3·25	1·40
1576	5e.30 Caravanning	2·40	1·40

290 Planting Tree

1975. 30th Anniv of U.N.O. Multicoloured.

1577	2e. Type **290**	55	10
1578	4e.50 Releasing peace dove	1·80	80
1579	20c. Harvesting corn	4·75	1·60

291 Lilienthal Glider and Modern Space Rocket

1975. 26th International Astronautical Federation Congress, Lisbon. Multicoloured.

1580	2e. Type **291**	70	15
1581	4e.50 "Apollo"–"Soyuz" space link	2·30	1·10
1582	5e.30 R. H. Goddard, R. E. Pelterie, H. Oberth and K. E. Tsiolkovsky (space pioneers)	1·50	1·10
1583	10e. Astronaut and spaceships (70×32 mm)	5·75	1·60

292 Surveying the Land

1975. Centenary of National Geographical Society, Lisbon. Multicoloured.

1584	2e. Type **292**	35	10
1585	8e. Surveying the sea	2·30	90
1586	10e. Globe and people	3·50	1·50

293 Symbolic Arch

1975. European Architectural Heritage Year.

1587	**293**	2e. grey, blue & deep blue	35	25
1588	-	8e. grey and red	4·00	1·10
1589	-	10e. multicoloured	4·50	1·40

DESIGNS: 8e. Stylized building plan; 10e. Historical building being protected from development.

294 Nurse in Hospital Ward

1975. International Women's Year. Multicoloured.

1590	50c. Type **294**	30	15
1591	2e. Woman farm worker	1·10	40
1592	3e.50 Woman office worker	1·40	90
1593	8e. Woman factory worker	2·10	1·50
MS1594	104×115 mm. Nos. 1590/3 (sold at 25e.)	5·50	4·50

295 Pen-nib as Plough Blade

1976. 50th Anniv of National Writers Society.

1595	**295**	3e. blue and red	50	10
1596	**295**	20e. red and blue	5·25	1·60

296 First Telephone Set

1976. Telephone Centenary.

1597	**296**	3e. black, green & dp grn	1·10	15
1598	-	10e.50 black, red and pink	4·25	1·20

DESIGNS: 10e.50, Alexander Graham Bell.

297 "Industrial Progress"

1976. National Production Campaign.

1599	**297**	50c. red	35	10
1600	-	1e. green	55	20

DESIGN: 1e. Consumer goods.

298 Carved Olive-wood Spoons

1976. Europa. Multicoloured.

1601	3e. Type **298**	3·75	50
1602	20e. Gold ornaments	75·00	7·25

299 Stamp Designing

1976. "Interphil 76" International Stamp Exhibition, Philadelphia. Multicoloured.

1603	3e. Type **299**	35	10
1604	7e.50 Stamp being hand-cancelled	1·30	85
1605	10e. Stamp printing	2·20	90

300 King Fernando promulgating Law

1976. 600th Anniv of Law of "Sesmarias" (uncultivated land). Multicoloured.

1606	3e. Type **300**	25	15
1607	5e. Plough and farmers repelling hunters	1·90	60
1608	10e. Corn harvesting	2·75	1·00
MS1609	230×150 mm. Nos. 1606/8 (sold at 30e.)	6·00	£100

301 Athlete with Olympic Torch

1976. Olympic Games, Montreal. Multicoloured.

1610	3e. Type **301**	35	15
1611	7e. Women's relay	1·90	1·50
1612	10e.50 Olympic flame	2·50	1·40

302 "Speaking in the Country"

1976. Literacy Campaign. Multicoloured.

1613	3e. Type **302**	65	15
1614	3e. "Speaking at Sea"	65	15
1615	3e. "Speaking in Town"	65	15
1616a	3e. "Speaking at Work"	85	25

MS1617	145×104 mm. Nos. 1613/16 (sold at 25e.)	18·00	16·00

303 Azure-winged Magpie

1976. "Portucale 77" Thematic Stamp Exhibition, Oporto (1st issue). Flora and Fauna. Mult.

1618	3e. Type **303**	35	10
1619	5e. Lynx	1·50	50
1620	7e. Portuguese laurel cherry and blue tit	1·60	1·10
1621	10e.50 Little wild carnation and lizard	1·80	1·30

See also Nos 1673/8.

304 "Lubrapex" Emblem and Exhibition Hall

1976. "Lubrapex 1976" Luso-Brazilian Stamp Exhibition. Multicoloured.

1622	3e. Type **304**	45	15
1623	20e. "Lubrapex" emblem and "stamp"	3·00	2·00
MS1624	180×142 mm. Nos. 1622/3 (sold at 30e.)	5·00	5·00

305 Bank Emblem

1976. Centenary of National Trust Fund Bank.

1625	**305**	3e. multicoloured	15	10
1626	**305**	7e. multicoloured	2·75	1·20
1627	**305**	15e. multicoloured	4·00	1·40

306 Sheep Grazing

1976. Water Conservation. Protection of Humid Zones. Multicoloured.

1628	1e. Type **306**	55	10
1629	3e. Marshland	1·10	40
1630	5e. Sea trout	3·00	55
1631	10e. Mallards	4·25	1·10

307 "Liberty"

1976. Consolidation of Democratic Institutions.

1632	**307**	3e. grey, green and red	90	25

308 Examining Child's Eyes

1976. World Health Day. Detection and Prevention of Blindness. Multicoloured.

1633	3e. Type **308**	35	15
1634	5e. Welder wearing protective goggles	2·40	35
1635	10e.50 Blind person reading Braille	2·50	1·50

309 Hydro-electric Power

1976. Uses of Natural Energy. Multicoloured.

1636	1e. Type **309**	30	20
1637	4e. Fossil fuel (oil)	60	25
1638	5e. Geo-thermic sources	1·00	35
1639	10e. Wind power	1·70	1·00
1640	15e. Solar energy	3·75	1·70

310 Map of Member Countries

1977. Admission of Portugal to the Council of Europe.

1641	**310**	8e.50 multicoloured	1·60	1·60
1642	**310**	10e. multicoloured	1·80	1·70

311 Bottle inside Human Body

1977. 10th Anniv of Portuguese Anti-Alcoholic Society. Multicoloured.

1643	3e. Type **311**	30	10
1644	5e. Broken body and bottle	1·10	55
1645	15e. Sun behind prison bars and bottle	3·00	1·60

312 Forest

1977. Natural Resources. Forests. Multicoloured.

1646	1e. Type **312**	30	20
1647	4e. Cork oaks	95	35
1648	7e. Logs and trees	2·00	1·60
1649	15e. Trees by the sea	2·00	1·70

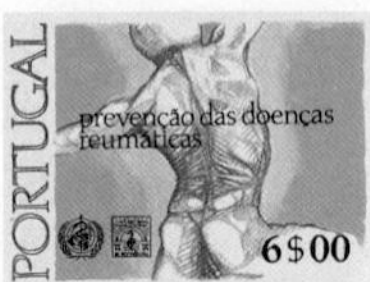

313 Exercising

1977. International Rheumatism Year.

1650	-	4e. orange, brown & blk	35	15
1651	**313**	6e. ultramarine, blue and black	1·50	1·10
1652	-	10e. red, mauve and black	1·40	95

DESIGNS: 4e. Rheumatism victim; 10e. Group exercising.

314 Southern Plains

1977. Europa. Multicoloured.

1653	4e. Type **314**	70	15
1654	8e.50 Northern terraced mountains	4·50	1·00
MS1655	148×95 mm. Nos. 1653/4 each ×3	55·00	33·00

315 John XXI Enthroned

1977. 7th Death Centenary of Pope John XXI. Multicoloured.

1656	4e. Type **315**	30	20
1657	15e. Pope as doctor	80	65

316 Compass

1977. Camoes Day.

1658	**316**	4e. multicoloured	35	20
1659	**316**	8e.50 multicoloured	1·50	1·40

317 Child and Computer

1977. Permanent Education. Multicoloured.

1660	4e. Type **317**	55	20
1661	4e. Flautist and dancers	55	20
1662	4e. Farmer and tractor	55	20
1663	4e. Students and atomic construction	55	20
MS1664	148×96 mm. Nos. 1660/3 (sold at 20e.)	7·50	8·25

318 Pyrite

1977. Natural Resources. The Subsoil. Mult.

1665	4e. Type **318**	35	15
1666	5e. Marble	1·10	45
1667	10e. Iron ore	1·20	60
1668	20e. Uranium	3·25	1·60

319 Alexandre Herculano

1977. Death Centenary of Alexandre Herculano (writer and politician).

1669	**319**	4e. multicoloured	40	15
1670	**319**	15e. multicoloured	2·00	70

320 Early Steam Locomotive and Peasant Cart (ceramic panel, J. Colaco)

1977. Centenary of Railway Bridge over River Douro. Multicoloured.

1671	4e. Type **320**	40	20
1672	10e. Maria Pia bridge (Eiffel)	3·00	2·20

321 Poviero (Northern coast)

1977. "Portucale 77" Thematic Stamp Exhibition, Oporto (2nd issue). Coastal Fishing Boats. Multicoloured.

1673	2e. Type **321**	55	15
1674	3e. Sea-going rowing boat, Furadouro	40	15
1675	4e. Rowing boat from Nazare	40	20
1676	7e. Caicque from Algarve	60	35
1677	10e. Tunny fishing boat, Algarve	1·20	75
1678	15e. Boat from Buarcos	1·60	1·10
MS1679	148×104 mm. Nos. 1673/8 (sold at 60e.)	6·00	5·00

322 "The Adoration" (Maria do Sameiro A. Santos)

1977. Christmas. Children's Paintings. Mult.

1680	4e. Type **322**	40	15
1681	7e. "Star over Bethlehem" (Paula Maria L. David)	1·40	50
1682	10e. "The Holy Family" (Carla Maria M. Cruz) (vert)	1·60	75
1683	20e. "Children following the Star" (Rosa Maria M. Cardoso) (vert)	3·50	1·60

323 Medical Equipment and Operating Theatre

1978. (a) Size 22×17 mm.

1684	**323**	50c. green, black and red	15	10
1685	-	1e. blue, orange and black	15	10
1686	-	2e. blue, green & brown	15	10
1687	-	3e. brown, green and black	15	10
1688	-	4e. green, blue & brown	20	15
1689	-	5e. blue, green & brown	20	15
1690	-	5e.50 brown, buff and green	25	15
1691	-	6e. brown, yellow & grn	25	15
1692	-	6e.50 blue, deep blue and green	25	15
1693	-	7e. black, grey and blue	25	15
1694	-	8e. ochre, brown and grey	25	15
1694a	-	8e.50 brn, blk & lt brn	40	15
1695	-	9e. yellow, brown & blk	35	15
1696	-	10e. brown, black & grn	35	15
1697	-	12e.50 blue, red and black	45	15
1698	-	16e. brown, black and violet	2·75	45

(b) Size 30×21 mm.

1699	20e. multicoloured	70	15
1700a	30e. multicoloured	1·00	50
1701	40e. multicoloured	90	40
1702	50e. multicoloured	1·30	30
1703	100e. multicoloured	2·20	65
1703a	250e. multicoloured	5·75	1·00

DESIGNS: 1e. Old and modern kitchen equipment; 2e. Telegraph key and masts, microwaves and dish aerial; 3e. Dressmaking and ready-to-wear clothes; 4e. Writing desk and computer; 5e. Tunny fishing boats and modern trawler; 5e.50, Manual and mechanical weaver's looms; 6e. Plough and tractor; 6e.50, Monoplane and B.A.C. One Eleven airliner; 7e. Hand press and modern printing press; 8e. Carpenter's hand tools and mechanical tool; 8e.50, Potter's wheel and modern ceramic machinery; 9e. Old cameras and modern cine and photo cameras; 10e. Axe, saw and mechanical saw; 12e.50, Navigation and radar instruments; 16e. Manual and automatic mail sorting; 20e. Hand tools and building site; 30e. Hammer, anvil, bellows and industrial complex; 40e. Peasant cart and lorry; 50e. Alembic, retorts and modern chemical plant; 100e. Carpenter's shipyard, modern shipyard and tanker; 250e. Survey instruments.

324 Mediterranean Soil

1978. Natural Resources. The Soil. Mult.

1704	4e. Type **324**	40	20
1705	5e. Rock formation	60	25
1706	10e. Alluvial soil	1·60	90
1707	20e. Black soil	3·25	1·30

325 Pedestrian on Zebra Crossing

1978. Road Safety.

1708	**325**	1e. blue, black and orange	20	20
1709	-	2e. blue, black and green	45	20
1710	-	2e.50 blue, black & lt bl	75	20
1711	-	5e. blue, black and red	1·60	25
1712	-	9e. blue, black & ultram	3·75	85
1713	-	12e.50 blue and black	4·50	2·20

DESIGNS: 2e. Motor cyclist; 2e.50, Children in back of car; 5e. Driver in car; 9e. View of road from driver's seat; 12e.50, Road victim ("Don't drink and drive").

326 Roman Tower of Centum Cellas, Belmonte

1978. Europa. Multicoloured.

1714	10e. Type **326**	1·50	35
1715	40e. Belem Monastery, Lisbon	6·00	1·80
MS1716	111×96 mm. Nos. 1714/15 each ×2 (sold at 120e.)	27·00	16·00

327 Roman Bridge, Chaves

1978. 19th Century of Chaves (Aquae Flaviae). Multicoloured.

1717	5e. Type **327**	55	20
1718	20e. Inscribed tablet from bridge	3·25	1·40

328 Running

1978. Sport for All. Multicoloured.

1719	5e. Type **328**	25	15
1720	10e. Cycling	55	35
1721	12e.50 Swimming	1·10	95
1722	15e. Football	1·10	1·10

329 Pedro Nunes

1978. 400th Death Anniv of Pedro Nunes (cosmographer). Multicoloured.

1723	5e. Type **329**	30	10
1724	20e. Nonio (navigation instrument) and diagram	1·70	55

330 Trawler, Crates of Fish and Lorry

1978. Natural Resources. Fishes. Multicoloured.

1725	5e. Type **330**	35	15
1726	9e. Trawler and dockside cranes	90	25
1727	12e.50 Trawler, radar and lecture	1·40	1·10
1728	15e. Trawler with echo-sounding equipment and laboratory	2·50	1·60

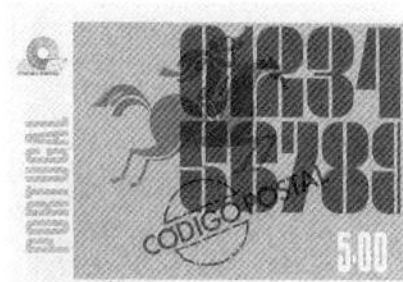

331 Post Rider

1978. Introduction of Post Code. Multicoloured.

1729	5e. Type **331**	45	20
1730	5e. Pigeon with letter	45	20
1731	5e. Sorting letters	45	20
1732	5e. Pen nib and post codes	45	20

332 Symbolic Figure

1978. 30th Anniv of Declaration of Human Rights. Multicoloured.

1733	14e. Type **332**	70	50
1734	40e. Similar symbolic figure, but facing right	2·50	1·40
MS1735	120×100 mm. Nos. 1733/4 each ×2	7·75	5·25

333 Sebastiao Magalhaes Lima

1978. 50th Death Anniv of Magalhaes Lima (journalist and pacifist).

1736	**333**	5e. multicoloured	45	20

334 Portable Post Boxes and Letter Balance

1978. Centenary of Post Museum. Multicoloured.

1737	4e. Type **334**	65	15
1738	5e. Morse equipment	45	20
1739	10e. Printing press and Portuguese stamps of 1853 (125th anniv)	1·60	30
1740	14e. Books, bookcase and entrance to Postal Library (centenary)	2·75	1·90
MS1741	120×99 mm. Nos. 1737/40 (sold at 40e.)	7·00	5·75

335 Emigrant at Railway Station

1979. Portuguese Emigrants. Multicoloured.

1742	5e. Type **335**	25	10
1743	14e. Emigrants at airport	85	65
1744	17e. Man greeting child at railway station	1·60	1·40

336 Traffic

1979. Fight Against Noise. Multicoloured.

1745	4e. Type **336**	60	25
1746	5e. Pneumatic drill	90	20
1747	14e. Loud hailer	1·70	75

337 N.A.T.O. Emblem

1979. 30th Anniv of N.A.T.O.

1748	**337**	5e. blue, red and brown	45	10
1749	**337**	50e. blue, yellow and red	3·75	3·00
MS1750		120×100 mm. Nos. 1748/9 each ×2	8·25	5·25

338 Door-to-door Delivery

1979. Europa. Multicoloured.

1751	14e. Postal messenger delivering letter in cleft stick	1·10	50
1752	40e. Type **338**	2·20	1·10
MS1753	119×103 mm. Nos. 1751/2 each ×2	16·00	8·25

339 Children playing Ball

1979. International Year of the Child. Multicoloured.

1754	5e.50 Type **339**	45	35
1755	6e.50 Mother, baby and dove	45	10
1756	10e. Child eating	55	50
1757	14e. Children of different races	1·10	1·00
MS1758	110×104 mm. Nos. 1754/7 (sold at 40e.)	5·00	4·00

340 Saluting the Flag

1979. Camoes Day.

1759	**340**	6e.50 multicoloured	50	20
MS1760		148×125 mm. No. 1759 ×9	5·50	4·00

341 Pregnant Woman

1979. The Mentally Handicapped. Multicoloured.

1761	6e.50 Type **341**	45	10
1762	17e. Boy sitting in cage	1·00	65
1763	20e. Face, and hands holding hammer and chisel	1·50	1·00

342 Children reading Book

1979. 50th Anniv of International Bureau of Education. Multicoloured.

1764	6e.50 Type **342**	45	10
1765	17e. Teaching a deaf child	2·40	1·30

343 Water Cart, Caldas de Monchique

1979. "Brasiliana 79" International Stamp Exhibition. Portuguese Country Carts. Mult.

1766	2e.50 Type **343**	25	25
1767	5e.50 Wine sledge, Madeira	25	25
1768	6e.50 Wine cart, Upper Douro	40	20
1769	16e. Covered cart, Alentejo	1·10	95
1770	19e. Cart, Mogadouro	1·60	1·30
1771	20e. Sand cart, Murtosa	1·70	55

344 Aircraft flying through Storm Cloud

1979. 35th Anniv of TAP National Airline. Multicoloured.

1772	16e. Type **344**	1·40	65
1773	19e. Aircraft and sunset	1·60	1·10

345 Antonio Jose de Almeida

1979. Republican Personalities (1st series).

1774	**345**	5e.50 mauve, grey and red	45	15
1775	-	6e.50 red, grey and carmine	45	10
1776	-	10e. brown, grey and red	65	10
1777	-	16e. blue, grey and red	1·40	75
1778	-	19e.50 green, grey and red	1·80	1·30
1779	-	20e. purple, grey and red	2·00	65

DESIGNS: 6e. Afonso Costa; 10e. Teofilo Braga; 16e. Bernardino Machado; 19e.50, Joao Chagas; 20e. Elias Garcia.

See also Nos. 1787/92.

346 Family Group

1979. Towards a National Health Service. Mult.

1780	6e.50 Type **346**	45	10
1781	20e. Doctor examining patient	1·80	65

347 "The Holy Family"

1979. Christmas. Tile Pictures. Multicoloured.

1782	5e.50 Type **347**	50	35

1783	6e.50 "Adoration of the Shepherds"	50	30
1784	16e. "Flight into Egypt"	1·50	1·10

348 Rotary Emblem and Globe

1980. 75th Anniv of Rotary International. Mult.

1785	16e. Type **348**	1·60	90
1786	50e. Rotary emblem and torch	3·50	2·40

349 Jaime Cortesao

1980. Republican Personalities (2nd series).

1787	-	3e.50 orange and brown	35	15
1788	-	5e.50 green, olive and deep olive	45	25
1789	-	6e.50 lilac and violet	45	25
1790	**349**	11e. multicoloured	2·20	1·30
1791	-	16e. ochre and brown	1·20	80
1792	-	20e. green, blue & lt blue	1·20	55

DESIGNS: 3e.50, Alvaro de Castro; 5e.50, Antonio Sergio; 6e.50, Norton de Matos; 16e. Teixeira Gomes; 20e. Jose Domingues dos Santos.

350 Serpa Pinto

1980. Europa. Multicoloured.

1793	16e. Type **350**	1·10	55
1794	60e. Vasco da Gama	2·75	1·30
MS1795	107×110 mm. Nos. 1793/4 each ×2	9·25	3·25

351 Barn Owl

1980. Protection of Species. Animals in Lisbon Zoo. Multicoloured.

1796	6e.50 Type **351**	30	10
1797	16e. Red fox	1·20	80
1798	19e.50 Wolf	1·50	85
1799	20e. Golden eagle	1·50	80
MS1800	109×107 mm. Nos. 1796/9	5·00	4·00

352 Luis Vaz de Camoes

1980. 400th Death Anniv of Luis Vaz de Camoes (poet).

1801	**352**	6e.50 multicoloured	55	15
1802	**352**	20e. multicoloured	1·40	65

353 Pinto in Japan

1980. 400th Anniv of Fernao Mendes Pinto's "A Peregrinacao" (The Pilgrimage). Multicoloured.

1803	6e.50 Type **353**	45	10
1804	10e. Sea battle	1·30	75

354 Lisbon and Statue of St. Vincent (Jeronimos Monastery)

1980. World Tourism Conference, Manila, Philippines. Multicoloured.

1805	6e.50 Type **354**	45	20
1806	8e. Lantern Tower, Evora Cathedral	65	35
1807	11e. Mountain village and "Jesus with Top-hat" (Mirando do Douro Cathedral)	1·40	75
1808	16e. Canicada dam and "Lady of the Milk" (Braga Cathedral)	1·90	1·00
1809	19e.50 Aveiro River and pulpit from Santa Cruz Monastery, Coimbra	2·20	1·10
1810	20e. Rocha beach and ornamental chimney, Algarve	1·70	80

355 Caravel

1980. "Lubrapex 80" Portuguese–Brazilian Stamp Exhibition, Lisbon. Multicoloured.

1811	6e.50 Type **355**	45	10
1812	8e. Nau	1·20	60
1813	16e. Galleon	1·70	80
1814	19e.50 Early paddle-steamer with sails	2·20	85
MS1815	132×88 mm. Nos. 1811/14 (sold at 60e.)	8·75	7·50

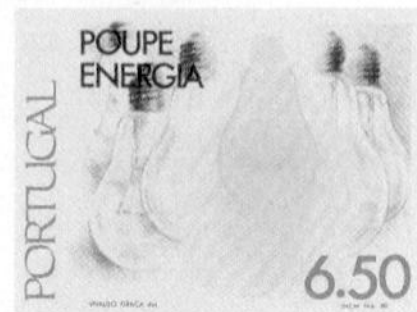

356 Lightbulbs

1980. Energy Conservation. Multicoloured.

1816	6e.50 Type **356**	45	10
1817	16e. Speeding car	2·50	90

357 Duke of Braganza and Open Book

1980. Bicentenary of Academy of Sciences, Lisbon. Multicoloured.

1818	6e.50 Type **357**	40	10
1819	19e.50 Uniformed academician, Academy and sextant	1·90	90

358 Cigarette contaminating Lungs

1980. Anti-Smoking Campaign. Multicoloured.

1820	6e.50 Type **358**	40	10
1821	19e.50 Healthy figure pushing away hand with cigarette	2·40	1·40

359 Head and Computer Punch-card

1981. National Census. Multicoloured.

1822	6e.50 Type **359**	45	25
1823	16e. Houses and punch-card	1·70	1·30

360 Fragata, River Tejo

1981. River Boats. Multicoloured.

1824	8e. Type **360**	40	30
1825	8e.50 Rabelo, River Douro	40	25
1826	10e. Moliceiro, Aveiro River	55	30
1827	16e. Barco, River Lima	95	60
1828	19e.50 Carocho, River Minho	1·00	60
1829	20e. Varino, River Tejo	1·00	55

361 "Rajola" Tile from Setubal Peninsula (15th century)

1981. Tiles (1st series).

1830	**361**	8e.50 multicoloured	95	15
MS1831		146×102 mm. No. 1830 ×6	6·50	80

See also Nos. 1483/**MS**1844, 1847/**MS**1848, 1862/**MS**1864, 1871/**MS**1872, 1885/**MS**1886, 1893/**MS**1894, 1902/**MS**1904, 1914/**MS**1915, 1926/**MS**1927, 1935/**MS**1936, 1941/**MS**1943, 1952/**MS**1953, 1970/**MS**1971, 1972/**MS**1973, 1976/**MS**1978, 1983/**MS**1984, 1993/**MS**1994, 2020/**MS**2021 and 2031/**MS**2033.

362 Agua Dog

1981. 50th Anniv of Kennel Club of Portugal. Multicoloured.

1832	7e. Type **362**	55	30
1833	8e.50 Serra de Aires	55	30
1834	15e. Perdigueiro	1·00	30
1835	22e. Podengo	1·90	80
1836	25e.50 Castro Laboreiro	2·40	1·40
1837	33e.50 Serra de Estrela	2·75	1·00

363 "Agriculture"

1981. May Day. Multicoloured.

1838	8e.50 Type **363**	45	10
1839	25e.50 "Industry"	1·80	1·20

364 Dancer and Tapestry

1981. Europa. Multicoloured.

1840	22e. Type **364**	1·60	65
1841	48e. Painted boat prow, painted plate and shipwright with model boat	3·25	1·70
MS1842	108×109 mm. Nos. 1840/1 each ×2	13·00	6·50

1981. Tiles (2nd series). Horiz design as T 361.

1843	8e.50 multicoloured	95	15
MS1844	146×102 mm. No. 1843 ×6	6·25	5·00

DESIGN: 8e.50, Tracery-pattern tile from Seville (16th century).

365 St. Anthony Writing

1981. 750th Death Anniv of St. Anthony of Lisbon. Multicoloured.

1845	8e.50 Type **365**	55	15
1846	70e. St. Anthony giving blessing	4·75	2·50

1981. Tiles (3rd series). As T 361. Mult.

1847	8e.50 Arms of Jaime, Duke of Braganca (Seville, 1510)	95	15
MS1848	146×102 mm. No. 1847 ×6	6·00	5·00

366 King Joao II and Caravels

1981. 500th Anniv of King Joao II's Accession. Multicoloured.

1849	8e.50 Type **366**	55	15
1850	27e. King Joao II on horseback	3·25	1·10

367 "Dom Luiz", 1862

1981. 125th Anniv of Portuguese Railways. Multicoloured.

1851	8e.50 Type **367**	90	25
1852	19e. Pacific steam locomotive, 1925	2·75	1·30
1853	27e. Alco 1500 diesel locomotive, 1948	2·75	1·40
1854	33e.50 Alsthom BB 2600 electric locomotive, 1974	3·25	1·20

368 "Perrier" Pump, 1856

1981. Portuguese Fire Engines. Multicoloured.

1855	7e. Type **368**	95	25
1856	8e.50 Ford fire engine, 1927	85	25
1857	27e. Renault fire pump, 1914	2·40	1·30
1858	33e.50 Ford "Snorkel" combined hoist and pump, 1978	3·75	1·40

369 "Virgin and Child"

1981. Christmas. Crib Figures. Multicoloured.

1859	7e. Type **369**	1·20	40
1860	8e.50 "Nativity"	95	40
1861	27e. "Flight into Egypt"	2·50	1·50

1981. Tiles (4th series). As T 361. Multicoloured.

1862	8e.50 "Pisana" tile, Lisbon (16th century)	95	20
MS1863	146×102 mm. No. 1862 ×6	6·00	5·00
MS1864	120×102 mm. Nos. 1830, 1843, 1847 and 1862	6·75	5·75

370 St. Francis with Animals

1982. 800th Birth Anniv of St. Francis of Assisi. Multicoloured.
1865 8e.50 Type **370** 50 30
1866 27e. St. Francis helping to build church 2·75 1·90

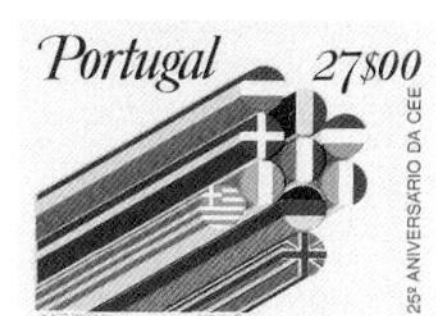

371 Flags of E.E.C. Members

1982. 25th Anniv of European Economic Community.
1867 **371** 27e. multicoloured 1·70 1·00
MS1868 155×88 mm. No. 1867 ×4 6·75 5·75

372 Fort St. Catherina, Lighthouse and Memorial Column

1982. Centenary of Figueira da Foz City. Mult.
1869 10e. Type **372** 60 10
1870 19e. Tagus Bridge, shipbuilding yard and trawler 2·30 1·20

1982. Tiles (5th series). As T 361. Multicoloured.
1871 10e. Italo-Flemish pattern tile (17th century) 95 20
MS1872 146×102 mm. No. 1871 ×6 6·75 5·00

373 "Sagres I" (cadet barque)

1982. Sporting Events. Multicoloured.
1873 27e. Type **373** (Lisbon sailing races) 2·00 1·10
1874 33e.50 Roller hockey (25th World Championship) 2·75 1·80
1875 50e. "470" dinghies (World Championships) 4·00 1·90
1876 75e. Football (World Cup Football Championship, Spain) 6·25 2·20

374 Edison Gower Bell Telephone, 1883

1982. Centenary of Public Telephone Service. Multicoloured.
1877 10e. Type **374** 55 10
1878 27e. Consolidated telephone, 1887 1·80 1·40

375 Embassy of King Manuel to Pope Leo X

1982. Europa.
1879 **375** 33e.50 multicoloured 2·75 1·10
MS1880 140×114 mm. No. 1879 ×4 13·00 6·50

376 Pope John Paul II and Shrine of Fatima

1982. Papal Visit. Multicoloured.
1881 10e. Type **376** 55 10
1882 27e. Pope and Sameiro Sanctuary 2·50 1·50
1883 33e.50 Pope and Lisbon Cathedral 3·00 1·50
MS1884 138×78 mm. Nos. 1881/3 each ×2 12·00 5·75

1982. Tiles (6th series). As T 361. Multicoloured.
1885 10e. Altar front panel depicting oriental tapestry (17th century) 95 20
MS1886 146×102 mm. No. 1885 ×6 6·00 5·00

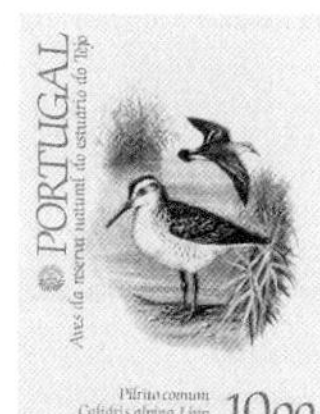

377 Dunlin

1982. "Philexfrance 82" International Stamp Exhibition, Paris. Birds. Multicoloured.
1887 10e. Type **377** 55 15
1888 19e. Red-crested pochard 2·20 80
1889 27e. Greater flamingo 2·50 1·10
1890 33e.50 Black-winged stilt 2·75 1·60

378 Dr. Robert Koch

1982. Centenary of Discovery of Tubercle Bacillus. Multicoloured.
1891 27e. Type **378** 2·00 1·50
1892 33e.50 Lungs 2·30 1·60

1982. Tiles (7th series). As T 361. Multicoloured.
1893 10e. Polychromatic quadrilobate pattern, 1630–40 95 15
MS1894 146×102 mm. No. 1893 ×6 6·00 5·00

379 Wine Glass and Stop Sign

1982. "Don't Drink and Drive".
1895 **379** 10e. multicoloured 70 15

380 Fairey IIID Seaplane "Lusitania"

1982. "Lubrapex 82" Brazilian–Portuguese Stamp Exhibition, Curitiba. Multicoloured.
1896 10e. Type **380** 45 30
1897 19e. Dornier Do-J Wal flying boat "Argus" 2·10 1·00
1898 33e.50 Douglas DC-7C "Seven Seas" airliner 2·50 1·00
1899 50e. Boeing 747-282B jetliner 2·75 1·30
MS1900 155×98 mm. Nos. 1896/9 8·00 6·50

381 Marquis de Pombal

1982. Death Bicentenary of Marquis de Pombal (statesman and reformer).
1901 **381** 10e. multicoloured 70 15

1982. Tiles (8th series). As T 361. Multicoloured.
1902 10e. Monochrome quadrilobate pattern, 1670–90 95 15
MS1903 146×102 mm. No. 1902 ×6 6·00 5·00
MS1904 101×121 mm. Nos. 1871, 1885, 1893 and 1902 6·00 5·00

382 Gallic Cock and Tricolour

1983. Centenary of French Alliance (French language teaching association).
1905 **382** 27e. multicoloured 2·00 1·00

383 Lisnave Shipyard

1983. 75th Anniv of Port of Lisbon Administration.
1906 **383** 10e. multicoloured 70 15

384 Export Campaign Emblem

1983. Export Promotion.
1907 **384** 10e. multicoloured 70 15

385 Midshipman, 1782, and Frigate "Vasco da Gama"

1983. Naval Uniforms. Multicoloured.
1908 12e.50 Type **385** 1·00 15
1909 25e. Seaman and steam corvette "Estefania", 1845 1·70 40
1910 30e. Marine sergeant and cruiser "Adamastor", 1900 2·30 75
1911 37e.50 Midshipman and frigate "Joao Belo", 1982 2·50 90

386 W.C.Y. Emblem

1983. World Cummunications Year. Mult.
1912 10e. Type **386** 55 25
1913 33e.50 W.C.Y. emblem (diff) 2·30 1·40

1983. Tiles (9th series). As T 361. Multicoloured.
1914 12e.50 Hunter killing white bull (tile from Saldanha Palace, Lisbon, 17/18th century) 1·10 20
MS1915 146×102 mm. No. 1914 ×6 7·25 6·25

387 Portuguese Helmet (16th century)

1983. "Expo XVII" Council of Europe Exhibition. Multicoloured.
1916 11e. Type **387** 1·20 35
1917 12e.50 Astrolabe (16th century) 95 35
1918 25e. Portuguese caravels (from 16th-century Flemish tapestry) 2·00 65
1919 30e. Carved capital (12th century) 2·30 70
1920 37e.50 Hour glass (16th century) 2·10 1·20
1921 40e. Detail from Chinese panel painting (16th–17th century) 2·50 1·10
MS1922 115×120 mm. Nos. 1916/21 16·00 9·75

388 Egas Moniz (Nobel Prize winner and brain surgeon)

1983. Europa.
1923 **388** 37e.50 multicoloured 2·75 1·00
MS1924 140×114 mm. No. 1923 ×4 14·50 8·25

389 Passenger in Train

1983. European Ministers of Transport Conference.
1925 **389** 30e. blue, deep blue and silver 3·00 1·00

1983. Tiles (10th series). As T 361. Multicoloured.
1926 12e.50 Tiles depicting birds (18th century) 1·10 20
MS1927 146×102 mm. No. 1926 ×6 7·25 6·25

390 Mediterranean Monk Seal

1983. "Brasiliana 83" International Stamp Exhibition, Rio de Janeiro. Marine Mammals. Multicoloured.
1928 12e.50 Type **390** 1·00 35
1929 30e. Common dolphin 3·75 60
1930 37e.50 Killer whale 3·25 1·60
1931 80e. Humpback whale 5·75 1·50
MS1932 133×81 mm. Nos. 1928/31 14·50 12·50

391 Assassination of Spanish Administrator by Prince John

1983. 600th Anniv of Independence. Mult.
1933 12e.50 Type **391** 1·00 25
1934 30e. Prince John proclaimed King of Portugal 3·50 1·60

1983. Tiles (11th series). As T 361. Multicoloured.
1935 12e.50 Flower pot by Gabriel del Barco (18th century) 1·10 20
MS1936 146×102 mm. No. 1935 ×6 7·00 5·75

392 Bartolomeu de Gusmao and Model Balloon, 1709

1983. Bicentenary of Manned Flight. Mult.
1937 16e. Type **392** 75 15
1938 51e. Montgolflier balloon, 1783 2·75 1·20

393 "Adoration of the Magi"

1983. Christmas. Stained Glass Windows from Monastery of Our Lady of Victory, Batalha. Multicoloured.
1939 12e.50 Type **393** 70 25

1940 30e. "The Flight into Egypt" 3·00 1·20

1983. Tiles (12th series). As T 361. Multicoloured.
1941 12e.50 Turkish horseman (18th century) 1·10 20
MS1942 146×102 mm. No. 1941 ×6 7·00 5·75
MS1943 120×102 mm. Nos. 1914, 1926, 1935 and 1941 6·00 5·00

394 Siberian Tiger

1983. Centenary of Lisbon Zoo. Multicoloured.
1944 16e. Type **394** 1·80 25
1945 16e. Cheetah 1·80 25
1946 16e. Blesbok 1·80 25
1947 16e. White rhino 1·80 25

395 Fighter Pilot and Hawker Hurricane Mk II, 1954

1983. Air Force Uniforms. Multicoloured.
1948 16e. Type **395** 80 10
1949 35e. Pilot in summer uniform and Republic F-84G Thunder-jet, 1960 2·50 80
1950 40e. Paratrooper in walking-out uniform and Nord 250ID Noratlas military transport plane, 1966 2·50 85
1951 51e. Pilot in normal uniform and Vought A-70 Corsair II bomber, 1966 3·00 1·20

1984. Tiles (13th series). As T 361. Multicoloured.
1952 16e. Coat of arms of King Jose I (late 18th century) 1·10 20
MS1953 146×102 mm. No. 1952 ×6 7·25 6·25

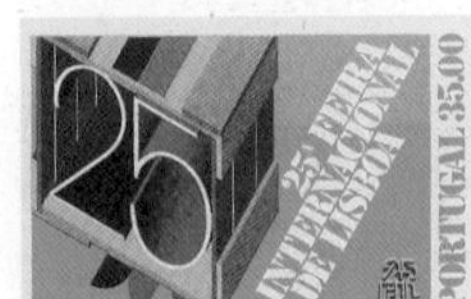

396 "25" on Crate (25th Lisbon International Fair)

1984. Events.
1954 35e. Type **396** 2·50 85
1955 40e. Wheat rainbow and globe (World Food Day) 2·20 85
1956 51e. Hand holding stylized flower (15th World Congress of International Rehabilitation) (vert) 3·00 1·20

397 National Flag

1984. 10th Anniv of Revolution.
1957 **397** 16e. multicoloured 1·40 20

398 Bridge

1984. Europa.
1958 **398** 51e. multicoloured 3·00 1·50
MS1959 140×114 mm. No. 1958 ×4 14·00 8·25

399 "Panel of St. Vincent"

1984. "Lubrapex 84" Portuguese–Brazilian Stamp Exhibition. Multicoloured.
1960 16e. Type **399** 70 25
1961 40e. "St. James" (altar panel) 3·25 90
1962 51e. "View of Lisbon" (painting) 4·00 1·20
1963 66e. "Head of Youth" (Domingos Sequeira) 4·25 1·60
MS1964 110×111 mm. Nos. 1960/3 12·50 9·75

400 Fencing

1984. Olympic Games, Los Angeles, and 75th Anniv of Portuguese Olympic Committee. Multicoloured.
1965 35e. Type **400** 2·40 70
1966 40e. Gymnastics 2·75 90
1967 51e. Running 3·25 1·30
1968 80e. Pole vaulting 3·50 1·30
MS1969 90×92 mm. 100e. Hurdling 9·75 8·25

1984. Tiles (14th series). As T 361. Multicoloured.
1970 16e. Pictorial tile from Pombal Palace, Lisbon (late 18th century) 1·10 20
MS1971 146×102 mm. No. 1970 ×6 7·25 6·25

1984. Tiles (15th series). As T 361. Multicoloured.
1972 16e. Four art nouveau tiles (late 19th century) 1·10 20
MS1973 146×102 mm. No. 1972 ×6 7·25 6·25

401 Gil Eanes

1984. Anniversaries. Multicoloured.
1974 16e. Type **401** (550th anniv of rounding of Cape Bojador) 55 10
1975 51e. King Pedro IV of Portugal and I of Brazil (150th death anniv) 3·25 1·30

1984. Tiles (16th series). As T 361. Multicoloured.
1976 16e. Grasshoppers and wheat (R. Bordalo Pinheiro, 19th century) 1·10 20
MS1977 146×102 mm. No. 1976 ×6 7·25 6·25
MS1978 120×102 mm. Nos. 1952, 1970, 1972 and 1976 6·00 5·00

402 Infantry Grenadier, 1740, and Regiment in Formation

1985. Army Uniforms. Multicoloured.
1979 20e. Type **402** 80 25
1980 46e. Officer, Fifth Cavalry, 1810, and cavalry charge 3·25 85
1981 60e. Artillery corporal, 1891, and Krupp 9 mm gun and crew 3·25 1·00
1982 100e. Engineer in chemical protection suit, 1985, and bridge-laying armoured car 3·75 1·50

1985. Tiles (17th series). As T 361. Multicoloured.
1983 20e. Detail of panel by Jorge Barrados in Lisbon Faculty of Letters (20th century) 1·10 20
MS1984 146×102 mm. No. 1983 ×6 6·75 5·75

403 Calcada R. dos Santos Kiosk

1985. Lisbon Kiosks. Multicoloured.
1985 20e. Type **403** 1·20 25
1986 20e. Tivoli kiosk, Avenida da Liberdade 1·20 25
1987 20e. Porto de Lisboa kiosk 1·20 25
1988 20e. Rua de Artilharia Um kiosk 1·20 25

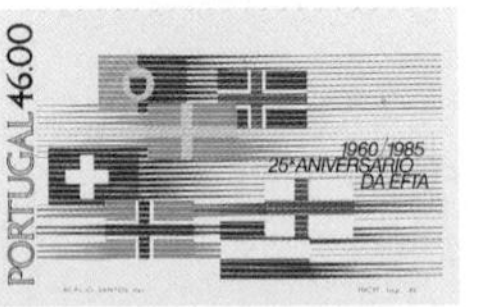

404 Flags of Member Countries

1985. 25th Anniv of European Free Trade Assn.
1989 **404** 46e. multicoloured 1·90 80

405 Profiles

1985. International Youth Year.
1990 **405** 60e. multicoloured 2·40 1·10

406 Woman holding Adufe (tambourine)

1985. Europa.
1991 **406** 60e. multicoloured 4·25 1·70
MS1992 140×114 mm. No. 1991 ×4 18·00 8·25

1985. Tiles (18th series). As T 361. Multicoloured.
1993 20e. Detail of panel by Maria Keil on Avenida Infante Santo (20th century) 1·10 20
MS1994 146×102 mm. No. 1993 ×6 6·75 5·75

407 Knight on Horseback

1985. Anniversaries. Multicoloured.
1995 20e. Type **407** (600th anniv of Battle of Aljubarrota) 90 15
1996 46e. Queen Leonor and hospital (500th anniv of Caldas da Rainha thermal hospital) 2·75 90
1997 60e. Pedro Reinel (500th anniversary of first Portuguese sea-chart) 3·00 1·50

408 Farmhouse, Minho

1985. Architecture.
1998 - 50c. black, bistre and blue 15 15
1999 - 1e. black, yellow & green 15 15
2000 - 1e.50 black, green and emerald 15 15
2001 - 2e.50 brown, orange & bl 15 15
2002 - 10e. black, purple & pink 25 20
2003 **408** 20e. brn, yell & dp yell 40 15
2004 - 22e.50 brown, blue and ochre 40 20
2005 - 25e. brown, yellow & grn 45 15
2006 - 27e. black, grn & yell 65 15
2007 - 29e. black, yellow & orge 65 15
2008 - 30e. black, blue & brown 65 15
2009 - 40e. black, yellow & grn 90 25
2010 - 50e. black, blue & brown 1·00 20
2011 - 55e. black, yellow & grn 1·00 20
2012 - 60e. black, orange & blue 1·30 40
2013 - 70e. black, yellow & orge 1·30 40
2014 - 80e. brown, green and red 1·50 45
2015 - 90e. brown, yellow & grn 1·70 45
2016 - 100e. brown, yellow & bl 2·00 50
2017 - 500e. black, grey and blue 8·50 3·00

DESIGNS: 50e. Saloia house, Estremadura; 1e. Beira inland house; 1e.50, Ribatejo house; 2e.50, Tras-os-montes houses; 10e. Minho and Douro coast house; 22e.50, Alentejo houses; 25e. Sitio house, Algarve; 27e. Beira inland house (different); 29e. Tras-os-montes house; 30e. Algarve house; 40e. Beira inland house (different); 50e. Beira coasthouse; 55e. Tras-os-montes house (different); 60e. Beira coast house (different); 70e. South Estramadura and Alentejo house; 80e. Estremadura house; 90e. Minho house; 100e. Monte house, Alentejo; 500e. Terraced houses, East Algarve.

1985. Tiles (19th series). As T 361. Multicoloured.
2020 20e. Head of woman by Querubim Lapa (20th century) 1·10 20
MS2021 147×101 mm. No. 2020 ×6 6·75 5·75

409 Aquilino Ribeiro (writer)

1985. Anniversaries. Multicoloured.
2022 20e. Type **409** (birth centenary) 95 10
2023 46e. Fernando Pessoa (poet 50th death anniv) 2·40 85

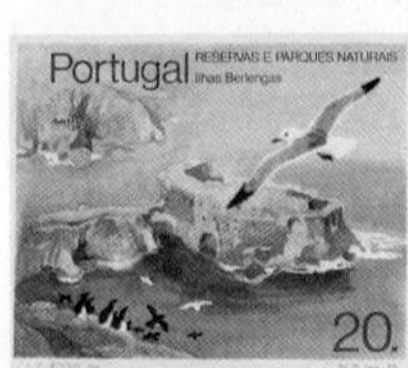

410 Berlenga National Reserve

1985. National Parks and Reserves. Multicoloured.
2024 20e. Type **410** 55 10
2025 40e. Estrela Mountains National Park 2·40 90
2026 46e. Boquilobo Marsh National Reserve 3·00 1·10
2027 80e. Formosa Lagoon National Reserve 3·25 1·20
MS2028 100×68 mm. 100e. Jacinto Dunes National Reserve 7·75 6·50

411 "Nativity"

1985. Christmas. Illustrations from "Book of Hours of King Manoel I". Multicoloured.
2029 20e. Type **411** 60 10
2030 46e. "Adoration of the Three Wise Men" 2·40 90

1985. Tiles (20th series). As T 361. Multicoloured.
2031 20e. Detail of panel by Manuel Cargaleiro (20th century) 1·10 20
MS2032 146×102 mm. No. 2031 ×6 10·50 6·25
MS2033 120×102 mm. Nos. 1983, 1993, 2020 and 2031 6·75 5·75

412 Post Rider

1985. No value expressed.
2034 **412** (-) green and deep green 1·10 15

413 Map and Flags of Member Countries

1985. Admission of Portugal and Spain to European Economic Community. Multicoloured.
2035 20e. Flags of Portugal and Spain uniting with flags of other members 80 25
2036 57e.50 Type **413** 3·00 1·30
See also No. **MS**2056.

414 Feira Castle

1986. Castles (1st series). Multicoloured.
2037 22e.50 Type **414** 1·20 20
2038 22e.50 Beja Castle 1·20 20
See also Nos. 2040/1, 2054/5, 2065/6, 2073/4, 2086/7 2093/4, 2102/3 and 2108/9.

415 Globe and Dove

1986. International Peace Year.
2039 **415** 75e. multicoloured 3·25 1·40

1986. Castles (2nd series). As T 414. Multicoloured.
2040 22e.50 Braganca Castle 1·20 20
2041 22e.50 Guimaraes Castle 1·20 20

416 Benz Motor Tricycle, 1886

1986. Centenary of Motor Car. Multicoloured.
2042 22e.50 Type **416** 1·50 15
2043 22e.50 Daimler motor car, 1886 1·50 15

417 Allis Shad

1986. Europa.
2044 **417** 68e.50 multicoloured 3·75 1·60
MS2045 140×114 mm. No. 2044 ×4 19·00 9·75

418 Alter

1986. "Ameripex 86" International Stamp Exn, Chicago. Thoroughbred Horses. Multicoloured.
2046 22e.50 Type **418** 80 25
2047 47e.50 Lusitano 2·75 95
2048 52e.50 Garrano 3·00 1·30
2049 68e.50 Sorraia 3·25 1·50

419 Comet

1986. Appearance of Halley's Comet. Sheet 100×68 mm.
MS2050 **419** 100e. multicoloured 15·00 12·50

420 Diogo Cao (navigator) and Monument

1986. Anniversaries. Multicoloured.
2051 22e.50 Type **420** (500th anniv of 2nd expedition to Africa) 80 15
2052 52e.50 Passos Manuel (Director) and capital (150th anniv of National Academy of Fine Arts, Lisbon) 2·10 95
2053 52e.50 Joao Baptista Ribeiro (painter and Oporto Academy Director) and drawing (150th anniv of Portuguese Academy of Fine Arts, Oporto) 2·10 95

1986. Castles (3rd series). As T 414. Multicoloured.
2054 22e.50 Belmonte Castle 1·20 25
2055 22e.50 Montemor-o-Velho Castle 1·20 25

1986. "Europex 86" Stamp Exhibition, Lisbon. Sheet 127×91 mm.
MS2056 Nos. 2035/6 each ×2 8·00 6·50

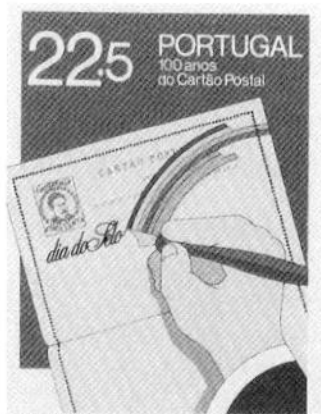

421 Hand writing on Postcard

1986. Anniversaries. Multicoloured.
2057 22e.50 Type **421** (centenary of first Portuguese postcards) 1·10 20
2058 47e.50 Guardsman and houses (75th anniv of National Republican Guard) 2·00 95
2059 52e.50 Calipers, globe and banner (50th anniv of Order of Engineers) 2·20 1·00

422 Seasonal Mill, Douro

1986. "Luprapex 86" Portuguese–Brazilian Stamp Exhibition, Rio de Janeiro. Multicoloured.
2060 22e.50 Type **422** 80 30
2061 47e.50 Seasonal mill, Coimbra 1·80 1·10
2062 52e.50 Overshot bucket mill, Gerez 2·40 1·20
2063 90e. Permanent stream mill, Braga 3·00 1·10
MS2064 140×114 mm. Nos. 2060/3 12·00 8·25

1987. Castles (4th series). As T 414. Mult.
2065 25e. Silves Castle 1·20 20
2066 25e. Evora-Monte Castle 1·20 20

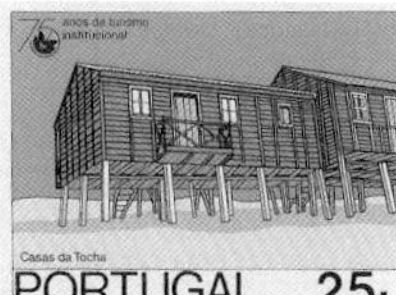

423 Houses on Stilts, Tocha

1987. 75th Anniv (1986) of Organized Tourism. Multicoloured.
2067 25e. Type **423** 80 25
2068 57e. Fishing boats, Espinho 2·75 1·20
2069 98e. Fountain, Arraiolos 3·50 2·00

424 Hand, Sun and Trees

1987. European Environment Year. Multicoloured.
2070 25e. Type **424** 80 30
2071 57e. Hands and flower on map of Europe 2·00 1·10
2072 74e.50 Hand, sea, purple dye murex shell, moon and rainbow 3·25 1·40

1987. Castles (5th series). As T 414. Multicoloured.
2073 25e. Leiria Castle 1·20 20
2074 25e. Trancoso Castle 1·20 20

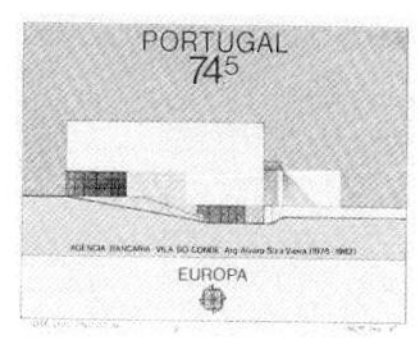

425 Bank Borges and Irmao Agency, Vila do Conde (Alvaro Siza)

1987. Europa. Architecture.
2075 **425** 74e.50 multicoloured 3·00 1·60
MS2076 140×114 mm. No. 2075 ×4 15·00 8·25

426 Cape Mondego

1987. "Capex '87" International Stamp Exhibition Toronto. Portuguese Lighthouses. Multicoloured.
2077 25e. Type **426** 1·00 35
2078 25e. Berlenga 1·00 35
2079 25e. Aveiro 1·00 35
2080 25e. Cape St. Vincent 1·00 35

427 Souza-Cardoso (self-portrait)

1987. Birth Centenary of Amadeo de Souza-Cardoso (painter).
2081 **427** 74e.50 multicoloured 2·40 1·10

428 Clipped 400 Reis Silver Coin

1987. 300th Anniv of Portuguese Paper Currency.
2082 **428** 100e. multicoloured 3·25 1·00

429 Dias's Fleet leaving Lisbon

1987. 500th Anniv of Bartolomeu Dias's Voyages (1st issue). Multicoloured.
2083 25e. Type **429** 1·20 20
2084 25e. Ships off coast of Africa 1·20 20

Nos. 2083/4 were printed together, se-tenant, each pair forming a composite design.
See also Nos. 2099/2100.

430 Library

1987. 150th Anniv of Portuguese Royal Library, Rio de Janeiro.
2085 **430** 125e. multicoloured 3·75 1·60

1987. Castles (6th series). As T 414. Multicoloured.
2086 25e. Marvao Castle 1·20 20
2087 25e. St. George's Castle, Lisbon 1·20 20

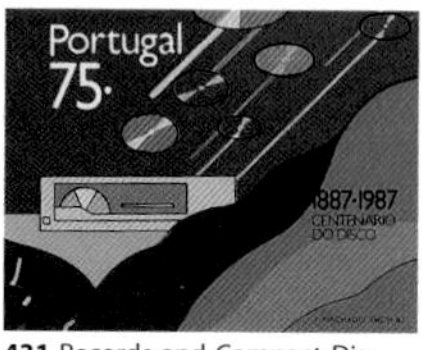

431 Records and Compact Disc Player

1987. Centenary of Gramophone Record. Sheet 140×114 mm containing T 431 and similar horiz design. Multicoloured.
MS2088 75e. Type **431**; 125e. Early gramophone 12·00 9·75

432 Angels around Baby Jesus, Tree and Kings (Jose Manuel Coutinho)

1987. Christmas. Children's Paintings. Mult.
2089 25e. Type **432** 1·10 25
2090 57e. Children dancing around sunburst (Rosa J. Leitao) 2·10 1·00
2091 74e.50 Santa Claus flying on dove (Sonya Alexandra Hilario) 2·30 1·30
MS2092 140×114 mm. Nos. 2089/91 6·75 5·25

1988. Castles (7th series). As T 414. Multicoloured.
2093 27e. Fernandine Walls, Oporto 1·10 20
2094 27e. Almourol Castle 1·10 20

433 Lynx

1988. Iberian Lynx. Multicoloured.
2095 27e. Type **433** 1·40 35
2096 27e. Lynx carrying rabbit 1·40 35
2097 27e. Pair of lynxes 1·40 35
2098 27e. Mother with young 1·40 35

434 King Joao II sending Pero da Covilha on Expedition

1988. 500th Anniv of Voyages of Bartolomeu Dias (2nd issue) (2099/2100) and Pero da Covilha (2101). Multicoloured.
2099 27e. Dias's ships in storm off Cape of Good Hope 1·00 25
2100 27e. Contemporary map 1·00 55
2101 105e. Type **434** 3·25 1·50
Nos. 2099/2100 are as T **429**.

1988. Castles (8th series). As T 414. Multicoloured.
2102 27e. Palmela Castle 1·10 20
2103 27e. Vila Nova da Cerveira Castle 1·10 20

435 19th-century Mail Coach

1988. Europa. Transport and Communications.

2104	**435**	80e. multicoloured	4·25	1·70
MS2105		139×112 mm. As No. 2104 ×4 but with cream background	16·00	9·75

436 Map of Europe and Monnet

1988. Birth Centenary of Jean Monnet (statesman). "Europex 88" Stamp Exhibition.

2106	**436**	60e. multicoloured	1·90	1·10

437 Window reflecting Cordovil House and Fountain

1988. UNESCO World Heritage Site, Evora. "Lubrapex 88" Stamp Exhibition. Sheet 112×139 mm.

MS2107	**437**	150e. multicoloured	10·50	9·25

1988. Castles (9th series). As T 414. Multicoloured.

2108	27e. Chaves Castle	1·10	25
2109	27e. Penedono Castle	1·10	25

438 "Part of a Viola" (Amadeo de Souza-Cardoso)

1988. 20th-century Portuguese Paintings (1st series). Multicoloured.

2110	27e. Type **438**	80	30
2111	60e. "Acrobats" (Almada Negreiros)	2·00	1·00
2112	80e. "Still Life with Viola" (Eduardo Viana)	2·30	1·20
MS2113	138×112 mm. Nos. 2110/12	7·50	6·25

See also Nos. 2121/**MS**2125, 2131/**MS**2134, 2148/**MS**2152, 2166/**MS**2169 and 2206/**MS**2210.

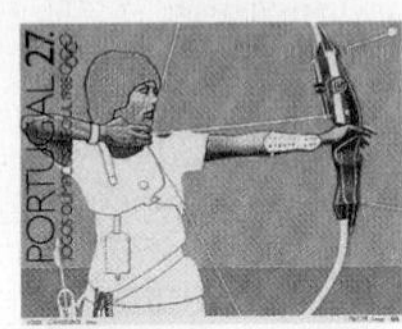

439 Archery

1988. Olympic Games, Seoul. Multicoloured.

2114	27e. Type **439**	1·00	30
2115	55e. Weightlifting	1·90	1·10
2116	60e. Judo	2·00	1·10
2117	80e. Tennis	2·50	1·10
MS2118	114×67 mm. 200e. Yachting (39×30 mm)	12·50	11·50

440 "Winter" (House of the Fountains, Coimbra)

1988. Roman Mosaics of 3rd Century. Mult.

2119	27e. Type **440**	70	30
2120	80e. "Fish" (Baths, Faro)	2·40	1·10

1988. 20th Century Portuguese Paintings (2nd series). As T 438. Multicoloured.

2121	27e. "Internment" (Mario Eloy)	80	20
2122	60e. "Lisbon Houses" (Carlos Botelho)	1·90	80
2123	80e. "Avejao Lirico" (Antonio Pedro)	2·20	1·10
MS2124	140×114 mm. Nos. 2121/3	7·50	6·25
MS2125	139×144 mm. Nos. 2110/12 and 2121/3	13·00	10·50

441 Braga Cathedral

1989. Anniversaries. Multicoloured.

2126	30e. Type **441** (900th anniv)	1·00	40
2127	55e. Caravel, Fischer's lovebird and S. Jorge da Mina Castle (505th anniv)	1·70	80
2128	60e. Sailor using astrolabe (500th anniv of South Atlantic voyages)	2·40	1·30

Nos. 2127/8 also have the "India 89" Stamp Exhibition, New Delhi, emblem.

442 "Greetings"

1989. Greetings Stamps. Multicoloured.

2129	29e. Type **442**	80	20
2130	60e. Airplane distributing envelopes inscribed "with Love"	1·30	70

1989. 20th-Century Portuguese Paintings (3rd series). As T 438. Multicoloured.

2131	29e. "Antithesis of Calm" (Antonio Dacosta)	80	15
2132	60e. "Unskilled Mason's Lunch" (Julio Pomar)	1·90	90
2133	87e. "Simumis" (Vespeira)	2·20	1·20
MS2134	139×111 mm. Nos. 2131/3	7·50	6·25

443 Flags in Ballot Box

1989. 3rd Direct Elections to European Parliament.

2135	**443**	60e. multicoloured	1·90	1·10

444 Boy with Spinning Top

1989. Europa. Children's Games and Toys. Multicoloured.

2136	80e. Type **444**	2·50	1·50
MS2137	138×112 mm. 80e. ×2 Type **444**; 80e. ×2 Spinning tops	8·75	7·25

445 Cable Railway

1989. Lisbon Transport. Multicoloured.

2138	29e. Type **445**	80	25
2139	65e. Electric tramcar	2·30	95
2140	87e. Santa Justa lift	2·40	1·30
2141	100e. Bus	2·75	1·30
MS2142	100×50 mm. 250e. River ferry (39×29 mm)	11·00	10·00

446 Gyratory Mill, Ansiao

1989. Windmills. Multicoloured.

2143	29e. Type **446**	80	25
2144	60e. Stone mill, Santiago do Cacem	2·30	95
2145	87e. Post mill, Afife	2·40	1·20
2146	100e. Wooden mill, Caldas da Rainha	2·75	1·40

447 Drummer Boy

1989. Bicentenary of French Revolution and "Philexfrance 89" International Stamp Exhibition, Paris. Sheet 111×139 mm.

MS2147	**447**	250e. multicoloured	11·00	10·00

1989. 20th-Century Portuguese Paintings (4th series). As T 438.

2148	29e. blue, green and black	75	30
2149	60e. multicoloured	1·90	1·10
2150	87e. multicoloured	2·30	1·40
MS2151	139×111 mm. Nos. 2148/50	7·50	6·25
MS2152	138×144 mm. Nos. 231/3 and 2148/50	13·00	10·50

DESIGNS: 29e. "046-72" (Fernando Lanhas); 60e. "Spirals" (Nadir Afonso); 87e. "Sim" (Carlos Calvet).

448 Luis I (death centenary) and Ajuda Palace, Lisbon

1989. National Palaces (1st series). Multicoloured.

2153	29e. Type **448**	45	20
2154	60e. Queluz Palace	1·80	1·10

See also Nos. 2211/14.

449 "Armeria pseudarmeria"

1989. Wild Flowers. Multicoloured.

2155	29e. Type **449**	70	20
2156	60e. "Santolina impressa"	1·70	80
2157	87e. "Linaria lamarckii"	2·10	1·20
2158	100e. "Limonium multiflorum"	2·50	1·60

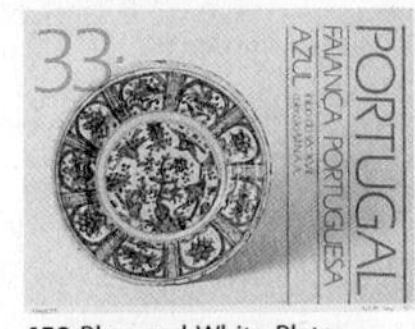

450 Blue and White Plate

1990. Portuguese Faience (1st series). Mult.

2159	33e. Type **450**	80	30
2160	33e. Blue and white plate with man in centre	80	30
2161	35e. Vase decorated with flowers	95	35
2162	60e. Fish-shaped jug	1·50	95
2163	60e. Blue and white plate with arms in centre	1·50	95
2164	60e. Blue and white dish with lid	1·50	95
MS2165	112×140 mm. 250e. Plate with crown in centre	7·75	7·00

See also Nos. 2221/**MS**2227 and 2262/**MS**2268.

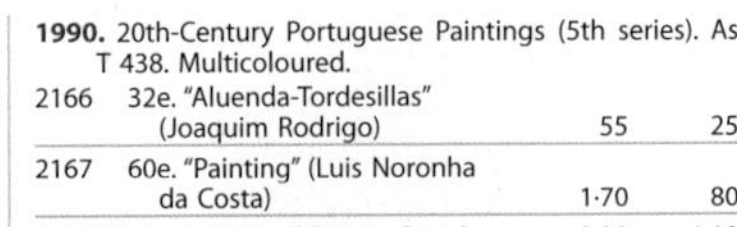

1990. 20th-Century Portuguese Paintings (5th series). As T 438. Multicoloured.

2166	32e. "Aluenda-Tordesillas" (Joaquim Rodrigo)	55	25
2167	60e. "Painting" (Luis Noronha da Costa)	1·70	80
2168	95e. "Painting" (Vasco Costa)	2·30	1·10
MS2169	138×111 mm. Nos. 2166/8	7·50	6·25

451 Joao Goncalves Zarco

1990. Portuguese Navigators.

2170	**451**	2e. red, pink and black	15	15
2171	-	3e. green, blue and black	10	10
2172	-	4e. purple, red and black	10	10
2173	-	5e. brown, grey & black	20	15
2174	-	6e. deep green, green and black	20	15
2175	-	10e. dp red, red & black	15	10
2176	-	32e. green, brown & blk	75	15
2177	-	35e. red, pink and black	70	15
2178	-	38e. blue, lt blue & black	75	25
2179	-	42e. green, grey & black	75	20
2180	-	45e. green, yellow & blk	55	30
2181	-	60e. yellow, purple & blk	1·40	50
2182	-	65e. brown, green & blk	1·30	40
2183	-	70e. violet, mauve & blk	1·20	40
2184	-	75e. olive, green & black	1·00	65
2185	-	80e. orange, brn & blk	1·80	70
2186	-	100e. red, orange & blk	2·40	85
2187	-	200e. green, yellow & blk	3·00	90
2188	-	250e. blue, green & black	4·75	1·90
2189	-	350e. red, pink and black	5·75	2·20

DESIGNS: 3e. Pedro Lopes de Sousa; 4e. Duarto Pacheco Pereira; 5e. Tristao Vaz Teixeira; 6e. Pedro Alvares Cabral; 10e. Joao de Castro; 32e. Bartolomeu Perestrelo; 35e. Gil Eanes: 38e. Vasco da Gama; 42e. Joao de Lisboa; 45e. Joao Rodrigues Cabrilho; 60e. Nuno Tristao; 65e. Joaoda Nova; 70e. Fernao de Magalhaes (Magellan); 75e. Pedro Fernandes de Queiros; 80e. Diogo Gomes; 100e. Diogo de Silves; 200e. Estevao Gomes; 250e. Diogo Cao; 350e. Bartolomeu Dias.

452 Score and Singers

1990. Anniversaries. Multicoloured.

2191	32e. Type **452** (centenary of "A Portuguesa" (national anthem))	60	20
2192	70e. Students and teacher (700th anniv of granting of charter to Lisbon University) (vert)	2·20	1·10

453 Santo Tirso Post Office

1990. Europa. Post Office Buildings. Multicoloured.

2193	80e. Type **453**	2·10	1·10
MS2194	139×111 mm. 80e. ×2 Type **453**; 80e. ×2 19th-century Mail Coach Office	8·25	5·25

454 Stamping Letter

1990. "Stamp World London 90" International Stamp Exhibition and 150th Anniv of the Penny Black. Sheet 111×140 mm.

MS2195	**454**	250e. multicoloured	11·00	9·75

455 Street with Chairs under Trees

1990. Greetings Stamps. Multicoloured.

2196	60e. Type **455**	1·70	90
2197	60e. Hand holding bouquet out of car window	1·70	90
2198	60e. Man with bouquet crossing street	1·70	90
2199	60e. Women with bouquet behind pillar box	1·70	90

456 Camilo Castelo Branco (writer)

1990. Death Anniversaries. Multicoloured.

2200	65e. Type **456** (centenary)	1·30	90
2201	70e. Brother Bartolomeu dos Martires (Bishop of Braga, 400th anniv)	1·90	1·10

457 Barketta

1990. 15th-Century Explorers' Ships. Mult.

2202	32e. Type **457**	55	25
2203	60e. Carvel-built fishing boat	1·60	80
2204	70e. Nau	1·80	1·10
2205	95e. Caravel	2·20	1·40

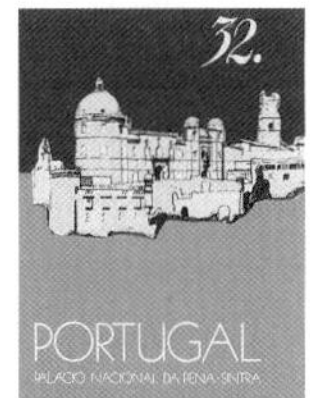

458 Pena Palace

1990. 20th-Century Portuguese Paintings (6th series). As T 438. Multicoloured.

2206	32e. "Dom Sebastiao" (Costa Pinheiro)	55	30
2207	60e. "Domestic Scene with Green Dog" (Paula Rego)	1·80	1·10
2208	95e. "Homage to Magritte" (Jose de Guimaraes)	2·75	1·30
MS2209	138×112 mm. Nos. 2206/8	4·50	2·40
MS2210	138×145 mm. Nos. 2166/8 and 2206/8	13·00	10·50

1990. National Palaces (2nd series). Mult.

2211	32e. Type **458**	75	25
2212	60e. Vila Palace	1·60	80
2213	70e. Mafra Palace	1·70	1·10
2214	120e. Guimaraes Palace	2·10	1·40

459 Carneiro

1990. 10th Death Anniv of Francisco Sa Carneiro (founder of Popular Democratic Party and Prime Minister, 1980).

2215	**459** 32e. black and brown	70	25

460 Steam Locomotive No. 02, 1887

1990. Centenary of Rossio Railway Station, Lisbon. Multicoloured.

2216	32e. Type **460**	75	25
2217	60e. Steam locomotive No. 010, 1891	1·60	80
2218	70e. Steam locomotive No. 071, 1916	1·70	1·10
2219	95e. Electric train, 1956	2·10	1·40
MS2220	112×80 mm. 200e. Station clock (39×29 mm)	7·50	7·25

1991. Portuguese Faience (2nd series). As T 450. Multicoloured.

2221	35e. Barrel of fish and plate (Rato factory Lisbon)	70	25
2222	35e. Floral vase (Bica do Sapato factory)	70	25
2223	35e. Gargoyle (Costa Briozo factory, Coimbra)	70	25
2224	60e. Dish with leaf pattern (Juncal factory)	1·30	70
2225	60e. Coffee pot (Cavaquinho factory, Oporto)	1·30	70
2226	60e. Mug (Massarelos factory, Oporto)	1·30	70
MS2227	114×140 mm. 250e. Plate with portrait in centre (Miragaia factory, Oporto)	8·25	8·00

461 Greater Flamingoes

1991. European Tourism Year. Multicoloured.

2228	60e. Type **461**	1·20	90
2229	110e. European chameleon	2·30	1·70
MS2230	112×104 mm. 250e. Red deer (39×31 mm)	7·25	7·00

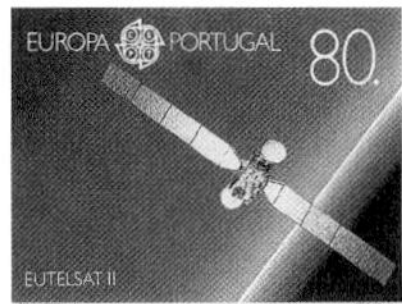

462 "Eutelsat II" Satellite

1991. Europa. Europe in Space. Multicoloured.

2231	80e. Type **462**	2·50	2·00
MS2232	140×112 mm. 80e. ×2, Type **462**; 80e. ×2, "Olympus I" satellite	8·50	5·75

463 Caravel

1991. 16th-Century Explorers' Ships. Mult.

2233	35e. Type **463**	55	30
2234	75e. Port view of nau	1·80	85
2235	80e. Stern view of nau	1·90	1·00
2236	110e. Galleon	2·20	1·10

464 "Isabella of Portugal and Philip the Good" (anon)

1991. "Europhalia 91 Portugal" Festival, Belgium. Sheet 140×112 mm.

MS2237	**464** 300e. multicoloured	10·50	9·50

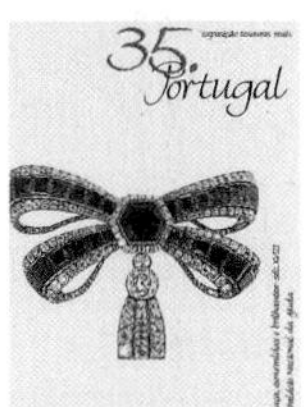

465 Emerald and Diamond Bow

1991. "Royal Treasures" Exhibition, Ajuda Palace (1st issue). Multicoloured.

2238	35e. Type **465**	55	35
2239	60e. Royal sceptre	1·60	70
2240	70e. Sash of the Grand Cross	1·80	95
2241	80e. Hilt of sabre	1·90	1·00
2242	140e. Crown	2·40	1·20

See also Nos. 2270/4.

466 Antero de Quental (writer)

1991. Anniversaries. Multicoloured.

2243	35e. Type **466** (death centenary)	60	20
2244	110e. Arrival of expedition and baptism of Sonyo prince (500th anniv of first Portuguese missionary expedition to the Congo)	2·40	1·20

467 Faculty of Architecture, Oporto University (Siza Vieira)

1991. Architecture. Multicoloured.

2245	35e. Type **467**	55	20
2246	60e. Torre do Tombo (Arsenio Cordeiro Associates)	1·40	50
2247	80e. Maria Pia bridge over River Douro (Edgar Cardoso) and Donna Maria bridge	1·70	1·00
2248	110e. Setubal–Braga highway	2·10	1·10

468 King Manoel I creating Public Post, 1520

1991. History of Communications in Portugal. Mult.

2249	35e. Type **468**	60	25
2250	60e. Woman posting letter and telegraph operator (merging of posts and telegraph operations, 1881)	1·20	65
2251	80e. Postman, mail van and switchboard operator (creation of Posts and Telecommunications administration, 1911)	1·50	85
MS2252	140×111 mm. 110e. Modern means of communications (introduction of priority mail service, 1991)	2·75	2·30

469 Show Jumping

1991. Olympic Games, Barcelona (1992) (1st issue). Multicoloured.

2253	35e. Type **469**	60	25
2254	60e. Fencing	1·30	55
2255	80e. Shooting	1·60	90
2256	110e. Yachting	2·10	1·10

See also Nos. 2295/8.

470 Peugeot "19", 1899

1991. Caramulo Automobile Museum. Mult.

2257	35e. Type **470**	55	25
2258	60e. Rolls Royce "Silver Ghost", 1911	1·30	55
2259	80e. Bugatti "35B", 1930	1·60	95
2260	110e. Ferrari "1965 Inter", 1950	2·10	1·10
MS2261	140×111 mm. 70e. ×2 Mercedes Benz 380K (1934); 70e ×2 Hispano-Suiza H6b (1924)	6·00	4·50

See also Nos. 2275/**MS**2279.

1992. Portuguese Faience (3rd series). As T 450. Multicoloured.

2262	40e. Jug (Viana do Castelo factory)	65	35
2263	40e. Plate with flower design ("Ratinho" faience, Coimbra)	65	35
2264	40e. Dish with lid (Estremoz factory)	65	35
2265	65e. Decorated violin by Wescislau Cifka (Constancia factory, Lisbon)	1·30	65
2266	65e. Figure of man seated on barrel (Calvaquinho factory, Oporto)	1·30	65
2267	65e. Figure of woman (Fervenca factory, Oporto)	1·30	65
MS2268	112×140 mm. 260e. Political figures by Rafael Bordalo Pinheiro (Caldas da Rainha factory) (44×38 mm)	5·25	5·00

471 Astrolabe (Presidency emblem)

1992. Portuguese Presidency of European Community.

2269	**471** 65e. multicoloured	1·50	1·00

1992. "Royal Treasures" Exhibition, Ajuda Palace (2nd issue). As T 465. Multicoloured.

2270	38e. Coral diadem	55	35
2271	65e. Faberge clock	1·40	75
2272	70e. Gold tobacco box studded with diamonds and emeralds by Jacqumin	1·30	65
2273	85e. Royal sceptre with dragon supporting crown	1·40	90
2274	125e. Necklace of diamond stars by Estevao de Sousa	1·80	1·10

1992. Oeiras Automobile Museum. As T 470. Multicoloured.

2275	38e. Citroen "Torpedo", 1922	55	25
2276	65e. Robert Schneider, 1914	1·40	65
2277	85e. Austin "Seven", 1933	1·60	85
2278	120e. Mercedes Benz armoured "770", 1938	2·00	1·10
MS2279	140×111 mm. 70e. ×2 Renault 10/14 (1911); 70e. ×2 Ford Model T (1927)	6·00	4·50

472 Portuguese Traders

1992. 450th Anniv of First Portuguese Contacts with Japan (1st issue). Details of painting attributed to Kano Domi. Multicoloured.

2280	38e. Type **472**	60	30
2281	120e. Portuguese visitors with gifts	1·90	1·30

See also Nos. 2342/4.

473 Portuguese Pavilion

1992. "Expo '92" World's Fair, Seville.

2282	**473** 65e. multicoloured	1·00	75

474 Cross-staff

1992. Nautical Instruments (1st series). Mult.

2283	60e. Type **474**	95	45
2284	70e. Quadrant	1·30	70
2285	100e. Astrolabe	1·50	90
2286	120e. Compass	1·80	1·10
MS2287	140×112 mm. Nos. 2283/6	6·00	5·00

See also Nos. 2318/21.

475 Royal All Saints Hospital, Lisbon

1992. Anniversaries. Multicoloured.

2288 38e. Type **475** (500th anniv of foundation) 70 40
2289 70e. Lucia, Francisco and Jacinta (75th anniv of apparition of Our Lady at Fatima) 1·20 90
2290 120e. Crane and docks (centenary of Port of Leixoes) 2·00 1·20

476 Columbus with King Joao II

1992. Europa. 500th Anniv of Discovery of America. Multicoloured.

2291 85e. Type **476** 2·40 1·80
MS2292 Six sheets (a) 260e. brown and black (Type **479**); (b) 260e. blue and black (Columbus sighting land); (c) 260e. purple and black (Landing of Columbus); (d) 260e. lilac and black (Columbus welcomed at Barcelona); (e) 260e. black (Columbus presenting natives); (f) 260e. black ("America", Columbus and "Liberty") 41·00 29·00

478 Black-headed Gull flying over contaminated River

1992. 2nd United Nations Conference on Environment and Development, Rio de Janeiro. Multicoloured.

2293 70e. Type **478** 1·10 55
2294 120e. River kingfisher and butterfly beside clean river 1·90 1·10

Nos. 2293/4 were issued together, se-tenant, forming a composite design.

479 Running

1992. Olympic Games, Barcelona (2nd issue). Mult.

2295 38e. Type **479** 55 35
2296 70e. Football 1·30 65
2297 85e. Hurdling 1·50 75
2298 120e. Roller hockey 1·70 1·00
MS2299 140×112 mm. 250e. Basketball 4·50 4·25

480 Bullfighter on Horse

1992. Centenary of Campo Pequeno Bull Ring, Lisbon. Multicoloured.

2300 38e. Type **480** 55 30
2301 65e. Bull charging at horse 1·30 60
2302 70e. Bullfighter attacking bull 1·40 85
2303 155e. Bullfighter flourishing hat 1·90 1·30
MS2304 140×113 mm. 250e. Entrance to ring (35×50 mm) 4·50 4·25

482 Star

1992. European Single Market.

2313 **482** 65e. multicoloured 1·10 75

483 Industrial Safety Equipment

1992. European Year of Health, Hygiene and Safety in the Workplace.

2314 **483** 120e. multicoloured 2·00 1·50

484 Post Office Emblem

1993. No value expressed.

2315 **484** (–) red and black 75 35

No. 2315 was sold at the current first class inland letter rate. This was 42e. at time of issue.

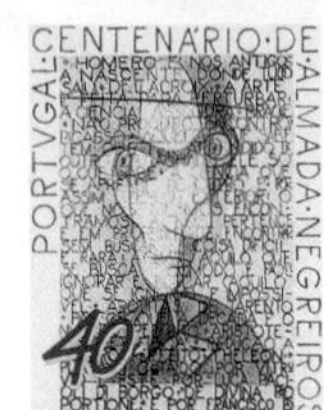

485 Graphic Poem

1993. Birth Centenary of Jose de Almada Negreiros (artist and poet). Multicoloured.

2316 40e. Type **485** 70 35
2317 65e. Trawlers (painting) 1·10 85

486 Sand Clock

1993. Nautical Instruments (2nd series). Mult.

2318 42e. Type **486** 55 25
2319 70e. Nocturlabio 1·10 65
2320 90e. Kamal 1·70 90
2321 130e. Back-staff 2·10 1·00

487 View from Window

1993. Europa. Contemporary Art. Untitled paintings by Jose Escada. Multicoloured.

2322 90e. Type **487** 2·00 1·40
MS2323 140×112 mm. 90e. ×2 Type **487**; 90e. × 2 Body parts 10·00 6·50

488 Rossini and "The Barber of Seville"

1993. Bicentenary of San Carlos National Theatre, Lisbon. Multicoloured.

2324 42e. Type **488** 55 35
2325 70e. Verdi and "Rigoletto" 1·20 65
2326 90e. Wagner and "Tristan and Isolde" 1·50 90
2327 130e. Mozart and "The Magic Flute" 2·30 1·00
MS2328 140×112 mm. 300e. Exterior of theatre (39×29 mm) 5·25 5·00

489 Fireman's Helmet

1993. 125th Anniv of Association of Volunteer Firemen of Lisbon.

2329 **489** 70e. multicoloured 1·30 80

490 Santos-o-Velho, Lisbon

1993. Union of Portuguese-speaking Capital Cities.

2330 **490** 130e. multicoloured 2·10 1·30
MS2331 140×112 mm. No. 2330 ×4 8·50 7·00

491 "Angel of the Annunciation" (from Oporto Cathedral)

1993. Sculptures (1st series). Multicoloured.

2332 42e. Type **491** 55 25
2333 70e. "St Mark" (Cornelius de Holanda) (horiz) 1·30 65
2334 75e. "Madonna and Child" 1·60 70
2335 90e. "Archangel St. Michael" 1·70 75
2336 130e. "Count of Ferreira" (Soares dos Reis) 2·10 1·10
2337 170e. "Construction" (Heldar Batista) 2·40 1·30
MS2338 112×140 mm. 75e. Marble bust of Agrippina the Elder; 75e. "Virgin of the Annunciation" (Master of the Royal Tombs); 75e. "The Widow" (Teixeira Lopes); 75e. "Love Ode" (Canto da Maya) 5·25 4·25

See also Nos. 2380/**MS**2386 and 2466/**MS**2472.

492 Road Tanker and Electric Tanker Train

1993. Int Railways Congress, Lisbon. Mult.

2339 90e. Type **492** 1·20 70
2340 130e. Electric train and traffic jam 2·00 1·10
MS2341 140×112 mm. 300e. Train 4·75 4·50

493 Japanese Man with Musket

1993. 450th Anniv of First Portuguese Visit to Japan (2nd issue). Multicoloured.

2342 42e. Type **493** 55 40
2343 130e. Portuguese missionaries 2·75 1·50
2344 350e. Traders carrying goods 4·50 2·40

494 Peniche Trawler

1993. Trawlers (1st series). Multicoloured.

2345 42e. Type **494** 55 25
2346 70e. Peniche type trawler 1·00 55
2347 90e. "Germano 3" (steam trawler) 1·60 75
2348 130e. "Estrela 1" (steam trawler) 2·00 1·00

See also Nos. 2392/5.

495 Rural Post Bag, 1800

1993. Post Boxes. Multicoloured.

2349 42e. Type **495** 55 30
2350 70e. 19th-century wall-mounted box for railway travelling post office 1·00 55
2351 90e. 19th-century pillar box 1·60 70
2352 130e. Modern multi-function post box 2·00 1·00
MS2353 140×112 mm. 300e. 19th-century box for animal-drawn post wagons 4·75 4·50

496 Imperial Eagle

1993. Endangered Birds of Prey. Multicoloured.

2354 42e. Type **496** 55 30
2355 70e. Eagle owl 1·20 70
2356 130e. Peregrine falcon 2·75 1·10
2357 350e. Hen harrier 4·50 2·40

497 Knot

1993. 40th Anniv of Brazil–Portugal Consultation and Friendship Treaty.

2358 **497** 130e. multicoloured 2·00 1·20

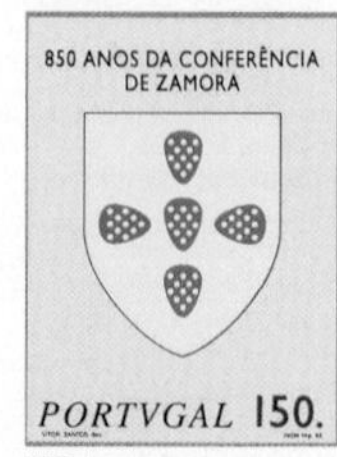

498 Arms

1993. 850th Anniv of Zamora Conference (recognizing Afonso I as King of Portugal). Sheet 106×114 mm.

MS2359 **498** 150e. multicoloured 2·75 2·75

499 Stylized Map of Member Nations

1994. 40th Anniv of Western European Union.

2360 **499** 85e. multicoloured 1·30 85

500 Olympic Rings as Torch Flame

1994. Centenary of Int Olympic Committee. Mult.

2361 100e. Type **500** 2·30 1·10
2362 100e. "100" and rings 2·30 1·10

501 Oliveira Martins (historian)

1994. Centenaries. Multicoloured.

2363 45e. Type **501** (death) 70 30

2364 100e. Florbela Espanca (poet, birth) 1·30 80

502 Map and Prince Henry (image scaled to 65% of original size)

1994. 600th Birth Anniv of Prince Henry the Navigator.

2365 **502** 140e. multicoloured 2·00 1·10

503 Dove

1994. 20th Anniv of Revolution.

2366 **503** 75e. multicoloured 1·00 60

504 Mounted Knight and Explorer with Model Caravel

1994. Europa. Discoveries. Multicoloured.

2367 100e. Type **MS**504 1·60 1·10

MS2368 140×112 mm. 100e. ×2 Type **504**; 100e. ×2 Millet and explorer with model caravel 8·75 6·50

505 Emblem

1994. International Year of the Family.

2369 **505** 45e. red, black and lake 65 25

2370 **505** 140e. red, black and green 1·90 1·10

506 Footballer kicking Ball and World Map

1994. World Cup Football Championship, U.S.A. Multicoloured.

2371 100e. Type **506** 1·40 70

2372 140e. Ball and footballers' legs 2·00 1·00

507 King Joao II of Portugal and King Fernando of Spain (image scaled to 65% of original size)

1994. 500th Anniv of Treaty of Tordesillas (defining Portuguese and Spanish spheres of influence).

2373 **507** 140e. multicoloured 2·00 1·10

508 Music

1994. Lisbon, European Capital of Culture. Multicoloured.

2374 45e. Type **508** 50 35

2375 75e. Photography and cinema 1·20 70

2376 100e. Theatre and dance 1·50 1·10

2377 140e. Art 1·90 1·50

MS2378 140×112 mm. Nos. 2374/7 5·75 5·75

509 Emblem

1994. Portuguese Road Safety Year.

2379 **509** 45e. red, green and black 65 30

1994. Sculptures (2nd series). As T 491. Mult.

2380 45e. Carved stonework from Citania de Briteiros (1st century) (horiz) 60 25

2381 75e. Visigothic pilaster (7th century) 80 45

2382 80e. Capital from Amorim Church (horiz) 1·00 60

2383 100e. Laying Christ's body in tomb (attr Joao de Ruao) (Monastery Church of Santa Cruz de Coimbra) (horiz) 1·20 70

2384 140e. Carved wood reliquary (Santa Maria Monastery, Alcobaca) (horiz) 1·80 1·00

2385 180e. Relief of Writers (Leopoldo de Almeida) (Lisbon National Library) (horiz) 2·40 1·20

MS2386 112×140 mm. 75e. Queen Urraca's tomb (Santa Maria Monastery, Alcobaca); 75e. Count of Ourem tomb (Colegiada de Ourem Church); 75e. Joao de Noronha and Isabel de Sousa's tomb (Santa Maria Church, Obidos); 75e. Mausoleum of Admiral Machado dos Santos (Alto de Sao Joao Cemetery, Lisbon) 4·75 4·00

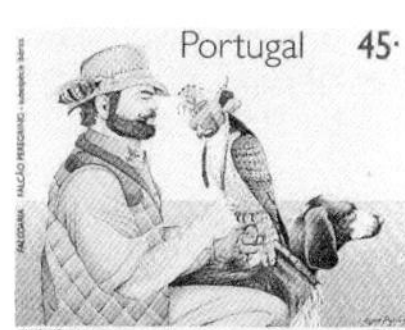

510 Falconer, Peregrine Falcon and Dog

1994. Falconry. Designs showing a peregrine falcon in various hunting scenes. Multicoloured.

2387 45e. Type **510** 50 25

2388 75e. Falcon chasing duck 90 50

2389 100e. Falconer approaching falcon with dead duck 1·20 70

2390 140e. Falcons 1·60 1·00

MS2391 97×121 mm. 250e. Hooded falcon on falconer's arm 3·75 3·75

511 "Maria Arminda"

1994. Trawlers (2nd series). Multicoloured.

2392 45e. Type **511** 50 25

2393 75e. "Bom Pastor" 1·20 50

2394 100e. Aladores trawler with triplex haulers 1·30 70

2395 140e. "Sueste" 1·70 1·00

512 19th-century Horse-drawn Wagon

1994. Postal Transport. Multicoloured.

2396 45e. Type **512** 60 25

2397 75e. Travelling Post Office sorting carriage No. C7, 1910 1·00 50

2398 100e. Mercedes mail van, 1910 1·20 70

2399 140e. Volkswagen mail van, 1950 1·60 95

MS2400 140×112 mm. 250e. Daf truck, 1983A 3·50 3·00

513 Multiple Unit Set, Sintra Suburban Railway (image scaled to 65% of original size)

1994. Modern Electric Locomotives (1st series). Multicoloured.

2401 45e. Type **513** 50 25

2402 75e. Locomotive No. 5611-7 (national network) 95 55

2403 140e. Lisbon Underground train 1·70 95

See also No. 2465.

514 Medal

1994. 150th Anniv of Montepio Geral Savings Bank (45e.) and World Savings Day (100e.). Mult.

2404 45e. Type **514** 65 30

2405 100e. Coins and bee 1·20 65

515 St. Philip's Fort, Setubal

1994. Pousadas (hotels) in Historic Buildings. Multicoloured.

2406 45e. Type **515** 50 25

2407 75e. Obidos Castle 1·20 50

2408 100e. Convent of Loios, Evora 1·30 70

2409 140e. Santa Marinha Monastery, Guimaraes 1·60 95

516 Businessman and Tourist

1994. American Society of Travel Agents World Congress, Lisbon.

2410 **516** 140e. multicoloured 1·80 95

517 Statuette of Missionary, Mozambique

1994. Evangelization by Portuguese Missionaries. Multicoloured.

2411 45e. Type **517** 50 25

2412 75e. "Child Jesus the Good Shepherd" (carving), India 1·20 50

2413 100e. Chalice, Macao 1·30 70

2414 140e. Carving of man in frame, Angola (horiz) 1·60 95

518 Africans greeting Portuguese

1994. 550th Anniv of First Portuguese Landing in Senegal.

2415 **518** 140e. multicoloured 1·80 95

519 Battle Scene (detail of the panel, Hall of Battles, Fronteira Palace, Lisbon)

1994. 350th Anniv of Battle of Montijo. Sheet 63× 83 mm.

MS2416 **519** 150e. multicoloured 2·20 2·20

520 Adoration of the Wise Men

1994. Christmas. Sheet 140×111 mm.

MS2417 **520** 150e. multicoloured 2·20 2·20

521 Great Bustard

1995. European Nature Conservation Year. Multicoloured.

2418 42e. Type **521** 90 55

2419 90e. Osprey 1·50 1·10

2420 130e. Schreiber's green lizard 1·70 1·40

MS2421 140×112 mm. Nos. 2418/20 4·50 5·00

522 St. John and Sick Man

1995. 500th Birth Anniv of St. John of God (founder of Order of Hospitallers).

2422 **522** 45e. multicoloured 65 30

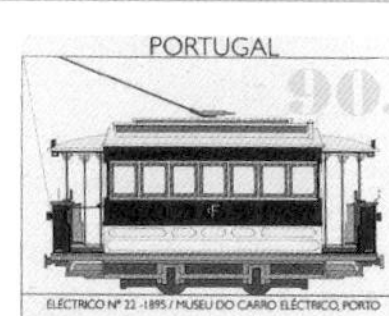

523 Electric Tramcar No. 22, 1895

1995. Centenaries of Trams and Motor Cars in Portugal. Multicoloured.

2423 90e. Type **523** 1·20 55

2424 130e. Panhard and Levassor motor car 1·50 95

524 Bread Seller

1995. 19th-century Itinerant Trades. Multicoloured.

2425 1e. Type **524** 10 10

2426 2e. Laundrywoman 10 10

2427 3e. Broker 10 10

2428 5e. Broom seller 10 10

2429 10e. Fish seller 10 10

2431 20e. Spinning-wheel and spoon seller 20 10

2432 30e. Olive oil and vinegar seller 30 20

2433 40e. Seller of indulgences 40 30

2434 45e. General street trader 50 30

2435 47e. Hot chestnut seller 40 25

2436	49e. Clothes mender	55	40
2437	50e. Fruit seller	70	40
2437a	50e. Pottery seller	65	45
2438	51e. Knife grinder	45	30
2439	75e. Whitewasher	90	60
2440	78e. Cloth seller	90	45
2440b	80e. Carrier/messenger boy	95	55
2440c	85e. Goose seller	1·00	70
2440d	86e. Bread seller	80	55
2440e	95e. Coachman	90	65
2441	100e. Mussels seller	1·30	65
2441a	100e. Milk seller	1·00	70
2442	210e. Basket seller	2·10	1·40
2443	250e. Water seller	2·75	1·60
2444	250e. Pastry seller	2·75	1·60

526 Emblem

1995. 50th Anniv of U.N.O. Multicoloured.

2449	75e. Type **526**	90	55
2450	135e. Clouds and emblem	1·60	1·00
MS2451	140×111 mm. No. 2449/50 each ×2	5·50	5·00

527 Evacuees from Gibraltar arriving at Madeira (image scaled to 64% of original size)

1995. Europa. Peace and Freedom. Portuguese Neutrality during Second World War. Mult.

2452	95e. Type **527**	2·00	1·20
2453	95e. Refugees waiting at Lisbon for transatlantic liner and Aristides de Sousa Mendes (Portuguese Consul in Bordeaux)	2·00	1·20

528 "St. Antony holding Child Jesus" (painting)

1995. 800th Birth Anniv of St. Antony of Padua (Franciscan preacher). Multicoloured.

2454	45e. Type **528**	1·40	35
2455	75e. St. Antony with flowers (vert)	2·50	85
2456	135e. "St. Antony holding Child Jesus" (statue)	4·00	1·60
MS2457	96×110 mm. 250e. "St. Anthony holding Baby Jesus" (18th-century Madeiran statue)	17·00	10·00

529 Carpenters with Axes and Women with Water, 1395

1995. 600th Anniv of Fire Service in Portugal. Multicoloured.

2458	45e. Type **529**	50	25
2459	80e. Fire cart and men carrying barrels of water, 1834	1·00	55
2460	95e. Merryweather steam-powered fire engine, 1867	1·10	70
2461	135e. Zoost fire engine No. 1, 1908	1·50	1·00
MS2462	Two sheets, each 120×100 mm. (a) 4 ×45e. Dutch fire engine, 1701; (b) 4 ×75e. Picota fire engine, 1780 and Portuguese fire cart, 1782	5·25	5·75

530 Coronation

1995. 500th Anniv of Accession of King Manoel I.

2463	**530** 45e. brown, yellow and red	55	30
MS2464	112×140 mm. No. 2463 ×4	2·50	2·50

1995. Modern Electric Locomotives (2nd series). As T 513.

2465	80e. multicoloured	95	55

DESIGN: 80e. Articulated trams.

1995. Sculptures (3rd series). As T 491. Multicoloured.

2466	45e. "Warrior" (castle statue)	45	25
2467	75e. Double-headed fountain	95	55
2468	80e. "Truth" (monument to Eca de Queiros by Antonio Teixeira Lopes)	95	55
2469	95e. First World War memorial, Abrantes (Ruy Gameiro)	1·10	65
2470	135e. "Fernao Lopes" (Martins Correia)	1·60	1·00
2471	190e. "Fernando Pessoa" (Lagoa Henriques)	2·10	1·30
MS2472	112×140 mm. 75e. "Knight" (from Chapel of the Ferreiros); 75e. "King Jose I" (J. Machado de Castro), Commerce Square, Lisbon; 75e. "King Joao IV" (Francisco Franco), Vila Vicosa; 75e. "Vimara Peres" (Barata Feyo), Oporto Cathedral Square	3·75	3·25

531 "Portugal's Guardian Angel" (sculpture, Diogo Pires)

1995. Art of the Period of Discoveries (15th–16th centuries). Multicoloured.

2473	45e. Type **531**	45	25
2474	75e. Reliquary of Queen Leonor (Master Joao)	95	55
2475	80e. "Don Manuel" (sculpture, Nicolas Chanterenne)	95	55
2476	95e. "St. Anthony" (painting, Nuno Goncalves)	1·10	65
2477	135e. "Adoration of the Three Wise Men" (painting, Grao Vasco)	1·90	1·00
2478	190e. "Christ on the Way to Calvary" (painting, Jorge Afonso)	2·10	1·30
MS2479	140×112 mm. 200e. "St. Vincent" (polyptych, Nuno Goncalves)	2·50	2·00

532 Queiroz

1995. 150th Birth Anniv of Eca de Queiroz (writer).

2480	**532** 135e. multicoloured	1·50	1·00

533 Archangel Gabriel

1995. Christmas. Multicoloured. (a) With country name at foot.

2481	80e. Type **533**	1·40	1·00
MS2482	112×140 mm. No. 2481×4	6·50	5·00

(b) With country name omitted.

2483	80e. Type **533**	1·30	1·00
MS2484	112×140 mm. No. 2483 ×4	6·25	6·25

534 Airbus Industrie A340/300

1995. 50th Anniv of TAP Air Portugal.

2485	**534** 135e. multicoloured	1·50	1·00

535 King Carlos I of Portugal (image scaled to 63% of original size)

1996. Centenary of Oceanographic Expeditions. Multicoloured.

2486	95e. Type **535**	1·10	65
2487	135e. Prince Albert I of Monaco	1·60	1·20

536 Books

1996. Anniversaries. Multicoloured.

2488	80e. Type **536** (bicentenary of National Library)	95	55
2489	200e. Hand writing with quill pen (700th anniv of adoption of Portuguese as official language)	2·20	1·40

537 Joao de Deus (poet and author of reading primer)

1996. Writers' Anniversaries. Multicoloured.

2490	78e. Type **537** (death centenary)	95	55
2491	140e. Joao de Barros (historian, philosopher and grammarian, 500th birth)	1·50	1·00

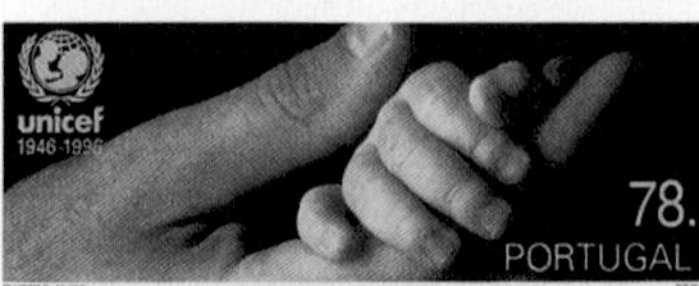

538 Holding Child's Hand (image scaled to 66% of original size)

1996. 50th Anniv of UNICEF. Multicoloured.

2492	78e. Type **538**	1·00	55
2493	140e. Children of different races	1·60	95

539 Helena Vieira da Silva (artist, self-portrait)

1996. Europa. Famous Women.

2494	**539** 98e. multicoloured	1·70	1·20
MS2495	140×112 mm. No. 2494 ×3	5·50	6·50

540 Match Scene

1996. European Football Championship, England. Multicoloured.

2496	78e. Type **540**	1·00	55
2497	140e. Match scene (different)	1·70	95
MS2498	140×112 mm. Nos. 2496/7	2·75	2·50

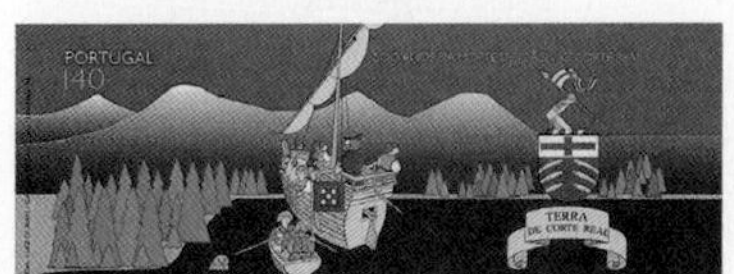

541 Caravel and Arms (image scaled to 56% of original size)

1996. 500th Death Anniv of Joao Vaz Corte-Real (explorer). Multicoloured.

2499	140e. Type **541**	1·70	1·00
MS2500	90×127 mm. 315e. Close-up of caravel in Type **541** (39×30 mm)	4·25	4·25

542 Wrestling

1996. Olympic Games, Atlanta. Multicoloured.

2501	47e. Type **542**	50	25
2502	78e. Show jumping	95	55
2503	98e. Boxing	1·10	65
2504	140e. Running	1·50	95
MS2505	96×110 mm. 300e. Athletes at starting blocks	4·00	4·00

543 Hilario and Guitar

1996. Death Centenary of Augusto Hilario (fado singer).

2506	**543** 80e. multicoloured	95	55

544 Antonio Silva (actor)

1996. Centenary of Motion Pictures. Multicoloured.

2507	47e. Type **544**	50	25
2508	78e. Vasco Santana (actor)	90	55
2509	80e. Laura Alves (actress)	90	55
2510	98e. Auelio Pais dos Reis (director)	1·10	55
2511	100e. Leitao de Barros (director)	1·10	65
2512	140e. Antonio Lopes Ribeiro (director)	1·60	90
MS2513	Two sheets, each 112×140 mm. (a) Nos. 2507/9; (b) Nos. 2510/12	6·50	5·50
MS2514	141×111 mm. Nos. 2507/12	6·50	5·75

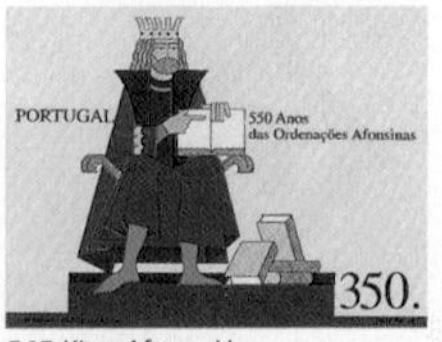

545 King Afonso V

1996. 550th Anniv of Alphonsine Collection of Statutes.

2515	**545** 350e. multicoloured	3·75	2·20

546 Perdigao

1996. Birth Centenary of Jose de Azeredo Perdigao (lawyer and Council of State member).

2516	**546** 47e. multicoloured	65	40

547 Aveiro

1996. District Arms (1st series). Multicoloured.

2517	47e. Type **547**	55	25
2518	78e. Beja	90	60
2519	80e. Braga	90	60
2520	98e. Braganca	1·10	65
2521	100e. Castelo Branco	1·10	75
2522	140e. Coimbra	1·60	1·00

MS2523	Two sheets, each 140×112 mm. (a) Nos. 2517/19; (b) Nos. 2520/2	7·00	6·50

See also Nos. 2579/**MS**85 and 2648/**MS**54.

548 Henry of Burgundy (governor of Portucale) and his Wife Theresa

1996. 900th Anniv of Foundation of County of Portucale by King Afonso VI of Leon and Castille.

2524	**548**	47e. multicoloured	65	40

549 Rojoes (Pork dish)

1996. Traditional Portuguese Dishes (1st series). Multicoloured.

2525	47e. Type **549**	60	35
2526	78e. Boticas trout	90	50
2527	80e. Oporto tripe	90	50
2528	98e. Baked cod with jacket potatoes	1·10	55
2529	100e. Aveiro eel	1·10	70
2530	140e. Peniche lobster	1·70	90

See also Nos. 2569/74.

550 Lisbon Postman, 1821

1996. 175th Anniv of Home Delivery Postal Service. Multicoloured.

2531	47e. Type **550**	55	25
2532	78e. Postman, 1854	90	65
2533	98e. Rural postman, 1893	1·10	70
2534	100e. Postman, 1939	1·10	80
2535	140e. Modern postman, 1992	1·60	1·00

551 King Manoel I in Shipyard

1996. 500th Anniv (1997) of Discovery of Sea-route to India by Vasco da Gama (1st issue). Multicoloured.

2536	47e. Type **551**	70	35
2537	78e. Departure from Lisbon	1·30	70
2538	98e. Fleet in Atlantic Ocean	1·50	85
2539	140e. Sailing around Cape of Good Hope	1·70	1·00
MS2540	141×113 mm. 315e. "Dream of King Manuel I" (illustration from Poem IV of *The Lusiads* by Luis de Camoes)	4·25	4·25

See also Nos. 2592/**MS**96 and 2665/**MS**80.

552 "Banknote"

1996. 150th Anniv of Bank of Portugal.

2541	**552**	78e. multicoloured	90	55

553 East Timorese Couple

1996. Rights of People of East Timor. Award of 1996 Nobel Peace Prize to Don Carlos Ximenes Belo and Jose Ramos Horton.

2542	**553**	140e. multicoloured	1·50	1·10

554 Clouds forming Map of Europe

1996. Organization for Security and Co-operation in Europe Summit Meeting, Lisbon. Sheet 95×110 mm.

MS2543	**554**	200e. multicoloured	3·00	3·00

555 Portuguese Galleon

1997. Sailing Ships of the India Shipping Line. Multicoloured.

2544	49e. Type **555**	50	35
2545	80e. "Principe da Beira" (nau)	1·20	75
2546	100e. Bow view of "Don Fernando II e Gloria" (sail frigate)	1·20	95
2547	140e. Stern view of "Don Fernando II e Gloria"	1·50	1·10

556 Youth with Flower

1997. "No to Drugs – Yes to Life" (anti-drugs campaign).

2548	**556**	80e. multicoloured	90	60

557 Arms

1997. Bicent of Managing Institute of Public Credit.

2549	**557**	49e. multicoloured	65	40

558 Desman eating Worm

1997. The Pyrenean Desman. Multicoloured.

2550	49e. Type **558**	70	40
2551	49e. Diving	70	40
2552	49e. With wet fur	70	40
2553	49e. Cleaning snout	70	40

559 Moorish Girl guarding Hidden Treasure

1997. Europa. Tales and Legends.

2554	**559**	100e. multicoloured	1·70	1·40
MS2555		140×107 mm. No. 2554 ×3	6·50	6·25

560 Surfing

1997. Adventure Sports. Multicoloured.

2556	49e. Type **560**	55	35
2557	80e. Skateboarding	95	65
2558	100e. In-line skating	1·10	85
2559	140e. Paragliding	1·50	1·10
MS2560	134×113 mm. 150e. B.M.X. cycling; 150e. Hang-gliding	4·00	3·00

561 Night Attack on Santarem Fortress

1997. 850th Anniv of Capture from the Moors of Santarem and Lisbon. Multicoloured.

2561	80e. Type **561**	85	65
2562	80e. Victorious King Afonso riding past Lisbon city walls	85	65
MS2563	140×113 mm. Nos. 2561/2 each ×2	4·25	4·00

562 Frois with Japanese Man

1997. 400th Death Anniv of Father Luis Frois (author of "The History of Japan"). Multicoloured.

2564	80e. Type **562**	1·20	75
2565	140e. Father Frois and church (vert)	1·60	1·10
2566	140e. Father Frois and flowers (vert)	1·60	1·10

563 Indian Children and Jose de Anchieta

1997. Death Anniversaries of Missionaries to Brazil. Multicoloured.

2567	140e. Type **563** (400th)	1·50	1·00
2568	350e. Antonio Vieira in pulpit (300th)	4·00	2·75

1997. Traditional Portuguese Dishes (2nd series). As T 549. Multicoloured.

2569	10e. Scalded kid, Beira Baixa	10	10
2570	49e. Fried shad with bread-pap, Ribatejo	55	35
2571	80e. Lamb stew, Alentejo	90	60
2572	100e. Rich fish chowder, Algarve	1·10	80
2573	140e. Black scabbardfish fillets with maize, Madeira	1·60	1·10
2574	200e. Stewed octopus, Azores	2·20	1·60

564 Centre of Oporto

1997. "Lubrapex 97" Portuguese–Brazilian Stamp Exhibition, Oporto. UNESCO World Heritage Site. Sheet 121×85 mm.

MS2575	**564**	350e. multicoloured	4·25	4·25

565 Couple before Clerk

1997. 700th Anniv of Mutual Assurance in Portugal.

2576	**565**	100e. multicoloured	1·20	80

566 Laboratory, Lisbon

1997. 50th Anniv of National Laboratory of Civil Engineering.

2577	**566**	80e. multicoloured	90	50

567 King Dinis and Arms of Portugal and King Fernando IV and Arms of Castile and Leon

1997. 700th Anniv of Treaty of Alcanices (defining national frontiers).

2578	**567**	80e. multicoloured	90	50

568 Evora

1997. District Arms (2nd series). Multicoloured.

2579	10e. Type **568**	10	10
2580	49e. Faro	55	30
2581	80e. Guarda	80	55
2582	100e. Leiria	1·20	65
2583	140e. Lisbon	1·40	1·00
2584	200e. Portalegre	2·10	1·30
MS2585	Two sheets, each 140×112 mm. (a) Nos. 2579, 2581 and 2583; (b) Nos. 2480, 2582 and 2584	5·00	2·75

569 Chart by Lopo Homem-Reineis, 1519

1997. Portuguese Charts. Multicoloured.

2586	49e. Type **569**	45	25
2587	80e. Chart by Joao Freire, 1546	95	70
2588	100e. Planisphere by Diogo Ribeiro, 1529	1·10	75
2589	140e. Chart showing Tropic of Capricorn (anon), 1630	1·40	95
MS2590	139×112 mm. Nos. 2586/9	4·50	4·50

570 Queen Maria I and Mail Coach

1997. Bicentenary of State Postal Service.

2591	**570**	80e. multicoloured	90	50

571 Erecting Landmark Monument, Quelimane

1997. 500th Anniv of Discovery of Portugal–India Sea Route (2nd issue). Multicoloured.

2592	49e. Type **571**	50	35
2593	80e. Arrival of fleet at Mozambique	90	50
2594	100e. Arrival of fleet in Mombasa	1·10	80
2595	140e. King of Melinde greeting Vasco da Gama	1·50	1·00
MS2596	140×113 mm. 315e. Vasco da Gama on beach at Natal	4·00	4·00

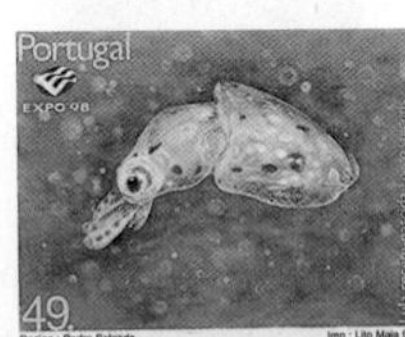

572 Squid

1997. "Expo'98" World Fair, Lisbon. Ocean Life (1st issue). Multicoloured.

2597	49e. Type **572**	50	35
2598	80e. Rock lobster larva	95	65
2599	100e. Adult "Pontellina plumata" (crustacean)	1·10	80
2600	140e. Senegal sole (pastlarva)	1·40	1·20
MS2601	110×150 mm. 100e. *Calcidiscus leptoporus*; 100e. *Tabellaria sp.* colonies	2·50	2·50

See also Nos. 2611/**MS**2615, 2621/**MS**2629 and 2630/41.

573 Sintra

1997. UNESCO World Heritage Site, Sintra. "Indepex 97" International Stamp Exhibition, New Delhi. Sheet 112×140 mm.

MS2602	**573** 350e. multicoloured	4·25	4·25

574 Officer and Plan of Almeida Fortress, 1848

1998. 350th Anniv of Portuguese Military Engineering. Multicoloured.

2603	50e. Type **574**	50	30
2604	80e. Officer and plan of Miranda do Oduro Fortress, 1834	1·10	65
2605	100e. Officer and plan of Moncao Fortress, 1797	1·30	70
2606	140e. Officer and plan of Elvas Fortress, 1806	1·50	1·10

575 Ivens and African Scene

1998. Death Centenary of Roberto Ivens (explorer).

2607	**575**	140e. multicoloured	1·50	1·00

576 Adoration of the Madonna (carving)

1998. 500th Anniv of Holy Houses Misericordia (religious social relief order).

2608	80e. Type **576**	90	50
2609	100e. Attending patient (tile mural)	1·00	85

577 Aqueduct ocer Alcantra

1998. 250th Anniv of Aqueduct of the Free Waters (from Sintra to Lisbon). Sheet 155×110 mm.

MS2610	**577** 350e. multicoloured	4·25	4·25

1998. "Expo '98" World's Fair, Lisbon (2nd issue). Ocean Life. As T 572. Multicoloured.

2611	50e. Crab ("Pilumnus" sp.) larva	50	25
2612	85e. Monkfish ("Lophius piscatonis") larva	1·10	55
2613	100e. Gilthead sea bream ("Sparus aurata") larva	1·20	70
2614	140e. Medusa ("Cladonema radiatum")	1·40	1·00
MS2615	112×140 mm. 110e. Bioluminescent protozoan (*Noctiluca miliaris*); 110e. Dinoflagellate (*Dinophysis acuta*)	2·50	2·50

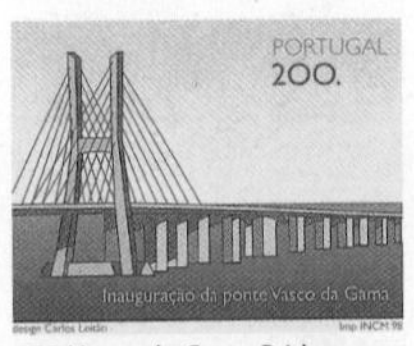

578 Vasco da Gama Bridge

1998. Opening of Vasco da Gama Bridge (from Sacavem to Montijo).

2616	**578**	200e. multicoloured	2·00	1·60
MS2617		125×85 mm. As No. 2616 but with background extended to edges	2·30	2·20

579 Coloured Balls

1998. 150th Anniv of Oporto Industrial Association.

2618	**579**	80e. multicoloured	90	50

580 Seahorse

1998. International Year of the Ocean. Centenary of Vasco da Gama Aquarium. Multicoloured.

2619	50e. Type **580**	70	35
2620	80e. Angelfish and shoal	95	75

581 Diver and Astrolabe

1998. "Expo '98" World's Fair, Lisbon (3rd issue). (a) The Ocean. Multicoloured.

2621	50e. Type **581**	50	25
2622	50e. Caravel	50	25
2623	85e. Fishes and coral reef (inscr "oceanario")	90	55
2624	85e. Underwater exploration equipment observing fishes	90	55
2625	140e. Mermaid and sea anemones	1·70	1·00
2626	140e. Children with hands on globe	1·70	1·00

(b) Miniature Sheets. Designs as T 581.

MS2627	154×116 mm. 50e. Portuguese Pavilion; 85e. Pavilion of the Future; 85e. Oceanarium; 140e. Knowledge of the Seas Pavilion; 140e. Pavilion of Utopia	6·25	6·25
MS2628	Two sheets, each 147×90 mm. (a) Nos. 2621/6; (b) 80e. Postal mascot; stamps as in No. **MS**2627	7·25	†
MS2629	148×151 mm. Nos. 2597/**MS**2601 and 2611/**MS**2615	14·50	†

(c) As Nos. 2611/14 (but with Latin names removed) and 2621/6. Size 29×23 mm. Self-adhesive.

2630	50e. As No. 2612	85	55
2631	50e. Bioluminescent protozoan	85	55
2632	50e. As No. 2611	85	55
2633	50e. As No. 2613	85	55
2634	50e. Dinoflagellate	85	55
2635	50e. As No. 2614	85	55
2636	85e. Type **581**	1·50	90
2637	85e. As No. 2624	1·50	90
2638	85e. As No. 2626	1·50	90
2639	85e. As No. 2622	1·50	90
2640	85e. As No. 2623 but inscr "Portugal e os Oceanos"	1·50	90
2641	85e. As No. 2625	1·50	90

The designers' names and printer's imprints have been removed from Nos. 2630/41.

582 Revellers before Statues of St. Antony of Padua, St. John and St. Peter

1998. Europa. National Festivals.

2642	**582**	100e. multicoloured	1·50	1·20
MS2643		140×108 mm. No. 2642 ×3	5·00	5·75

583 Marie Curie

1998. Centenary of Discovery of Radium.

2644	**583**	140e. multicoloured	1·40	90

584 Ferreira de Castro and Illustration to "The Jungle"

1998. Birth Centenary of Jose Ferreira de Castro (writer).

2645	**584**	50e. multicoloured	60	35

585 Untitled Painting

1998. Death Centenary of Bernardo Marques (artist).

2646	**585**	85e. multicoloured	90	65

586 Adam (Michelangelo) (detail from Sistine Chapel ceiling)

1998. "Juvalex '98" Stamp Exhibition. 50th Anniv of Universal Declaration of Human Rights. Sheet 90×55 mm.

MS2647	**586** 315e. multicoloured	3·50	3·50

1998. District Arms (3rd series). As T 568. Multicoloured.

2648	50e. Vila Real	50	35
2649	85e. Setubal	1·30	80
2650	85e. Viana do Castelo (150th anniv of elevation to city)	1·30	80
2651	100e. Santarem	1·40	80
2652	100e. Viseu	1·40	80
2653	200e. Oporto	2·00	1·20
MS2654	Two sheets, each 140×113 mm. (a) Nos. 2648, 2650 and 2653; (b) Nos. 2649 and 2651/2	8·25	9·00

587 Glass Production

1998. 250th Anniv of Glass Production in Marinha Grande. Multicoloured.

2655	50e. Type **587**	50	25
2656	80e. Heating glass and finished product	95	65
2657	100e. Bottles and factory	1·00	70
2658	140e. Blue bottles and glass-maker	1·90	1·00

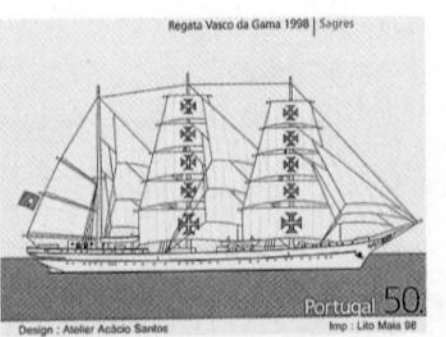

588 "Sagres II" (cadet barque), Portugal

1998. Vasco da Gama Regatta. Multicoloured.

2659	50e. Type **588**	50	30
2660	85e. "Asgard II" (Irish cadet brigantine)	1·20	60
2661	85e. "Rose" (American replica)	1·20	60
2662	100e. "Amerigo Vespucci" (Italian cadet ship)	1·30	80
2663	100e. "Kruzenshtern" (Russian cadet barque)	1·30	80
2664	140e. "Creoula" (Portuguese cadet schooner)	2·00	1·10

589 Da Gama with Pilot Ibn Madjid

1998. 500th Anniv (1997) of Discovery of Sea-route to India by Vasco da Gama (3rd issue). Mult.

2665	50e. Type **551**	75	45
2666	50e. As No. 2537	75	45
2667	50e. As No. 2538	75	45
2668	50e. As No. 2539	75	45
2669	50e. Type **571**	75	45
2670	50e. As No. 2593	75	45
2671	50e. As No. 2594	75	45
2672	50e. As No. 2595	75	45

2673 50e. Type **589** 95 60
2674 50e. "Sao Gabriel" (flagship) in storm 75 45
2675 50e. Fleet arriving at Calicut 75 45
2676 50e. Audience with the Samorin of Calicut 75 45
2677 80e. As No. 2674 1·00 70
2678 100e. As No. 2675 1·10 75
2679 140e. As No. 2676 1·40 90
MS2680 140×112 mm. 315e. King of Melinde listening to Vasco da Gama 4·00 4·00

590 Modern Mail Van

1998. Bicentenaries of Inauguration of Lisbon–Coimbra Mail Coach Service and of Re-organ-ization of Maritime Mail Service to Brazil. Mult.
2681 50e. Type **590** 50 35
2682 140e. Mail coach and "Postilhao da America" (brigantine) 1·80 1·10

591 Globe and Flags of participating Countries

1998. 8th Iberian-American Summit of State Leaders and Govenors, Oporto. Sheet 90×55 mm.
MS2683 **591** 140e. multicoloured 1·70 1·60

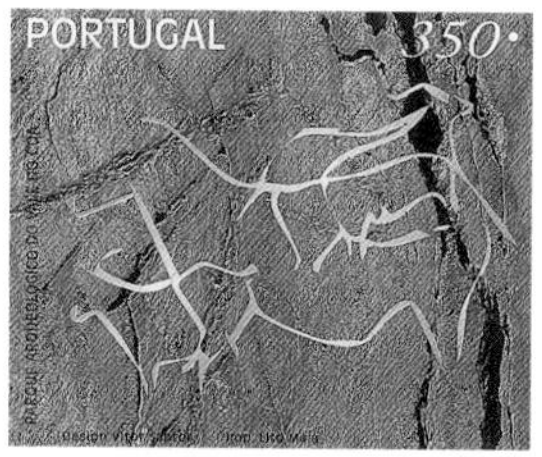

592 Cave paintings

1998. Archeological Park, Coa Valley. Sheet 140×113 mm.
MS2684 **592** 350e. multicoloured 4·25 4·25

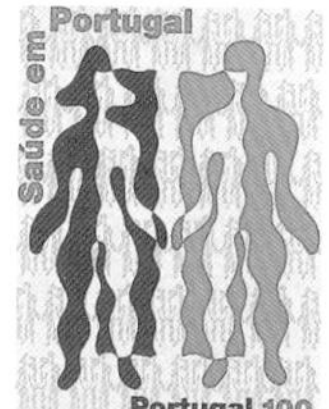

593 Male and Female Figures

1998. Health Awareness.
2685 **593** 100e. multicoloured 1·20 80

594 Saramago

1998. Jose Saramago (winner of Nobel prize for Literature, 1998). Sheet 140×114 mm.
MS2686 **594** 200e. multicoloured 2·40 2·40

DENOMINATION. From No. 2687 Portugal stamps are denominated both in escudos and in euros. As no cash for this latter is in circulation, the catalogue continues to use the escudo value.

595 Knife Grinder

1999. 19th-Century Itinerant Trades. Multicoloured. Self-adhesive.
2687 51e. Type **595** 50 35
2688 95e. Coachman 1·20 80

596 Flags of European Union Members and Euro Emblem

1999. Introduction of the Euro (European currency).
2696 **596** 95e. multicoloured 1·20 95

597 Galleon and Aborigines

1999. "Australia 99" International Stamp Exhibition, Melbourne. The Portuguese in Australia. Multicoloured.
2697 140e. Kangaroos and galleon 1·40 90
2698 140e. Type **597** 1·40 90
MS2699 137×104 mm. 350e. Motifs of Nos. 2697/8 (79×30 mm) 4·25 4·00
Nos. 2697/8 were issued together, se-tenant, forming a composite design.

598 Norton de Matos

1999. 50th Anniv of Candidature of General Jose Norton de Matos to Presidency of the Republic.
2700 **598** 80e. multicoloured 1·10 70

599 Almeida Garrett

1999. Birth Bicentenary of Joao Bapista Almeida Garrett (writer).
2701 **599** 95e. multicoloured 1·20 75
MS2702 130×105 mm. **599** 210e. multicoloured 2·50 2·40

600 Breguet Bre 16 Bri 2 *Patria*

1999. 25th Anniv of Sarmento de Beires and Brito Pais's Portugal–Macao Flight. Multicoloured.
2703 140e. Type **600** 1·60 1·00
2704 140e. Airco de Havilland D.H.9 biplane 1·60 1·00
MS2705 137×104 mm. Nos. 2703/4 3·25 3·25

601 Carnation

1999. 25th Anniv of Revolution. Multicoloured.
2706 51e. Type **601** 50 30
2707 80e. National Assembly building (78×29 mm) 90 60
MS2708 140×108 mm. Nos. 2706/7 1·60 1·60

602 Council Emblem

1999. 50th Anniv of Council of Europe.
2709 **602** 100e. multicoloured 1·40 1·10

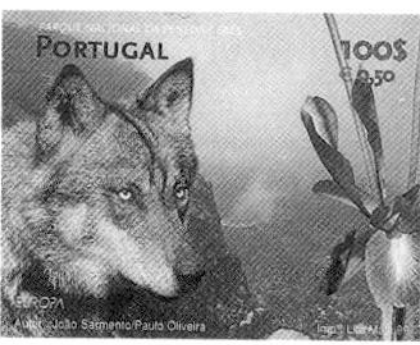

603 Wolf and Iris (Peneda-Geres National Park)

1999. Europa. Parks and Gardens.
2710 **603** 100e. multicoloured 1·40 1·20
MS2711 154×109 mm. No. 2710×3 5·25 6·50

604 Marquis de Pombal

1993. 300th Birth Anniv of Marquis de Pombal (statesman and reformer). Multicoloured.
2712 80e. Type **604** 90 70
MS2713 170×135 mm. 80e. Head of Marquis and part of statue; 210e. Hand holding quill 3·50 2·75

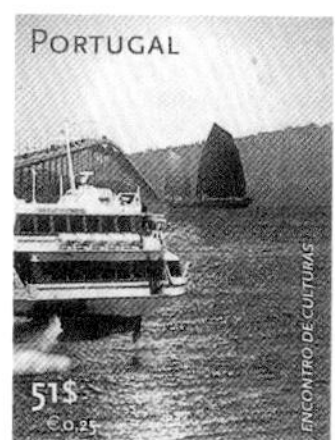

605 Harbour

1999. "Meeting of Cultures". Return of Macao to China. Multicoloured.
2714 51e. Type **605** 50 30
2715 80e. Dancers 90 55
2716 95e. Procession of the Madonna 95 80
2717 100e. Ruins of St. Paul's Basilica 1·20 80
2718 140e. Garden with bust of Luis Camoes (horiz) 1·60 95

606 de Havilland D.H.82A Tiger Moth

1999. 75th Anniv of Military Aeronautics. Multicoloured.
2719 51e. Type **606** 50 30
2720 51e. Supermarine Spitfire V6 fighter 50 30
2721 85e. Breguet Bre XIV-A2 1·20 65
2722 85e. SPAD VII-C1 1·20 65
2723 95e. Caudron G-3 1·40 75
2724 95e. Junkers Ju 52/3m 1·40 75
MS2725 150×117 mm. Nos. 2719/24 6·25 6·50

607 Portion by Antonio Pedro

1999. 50th Anniv of Surrealism (modern art movement) in Portugal. Designs showing details by artist named of collective painting "Cadavre Exquis". Multicoloured.
2726 51e. Type **607** 45 30
2727 80e. Vespeira 90 65
2728 95e. Moniz Pereira 95 70
2729 100e. Fernando de Azevedo 1·00 70
2730 140e. Antonio Domingues 1·50 1·00
MS2731 175×153 mm. Nos. 2726/30 forming a composite design of complete picture 4·75 5·25

608 Passenger Train on Bridge

1999. Inauguration of Railway Section of the 25th of April Bridge over River Tagus, Lisbon. Mult.
2732 51e. Type **608** 50 30
2733 95e. Passenger train on bridge (different) 1·20 75
MS2734 Two sheets, each 140×110 mm. (a) 350e. Close-up of part of Type **608** (79×30 mm); (b) 350e. Close-up of part of No. 2733 (79×30 mm) 8·25 8·00

609 Heinrich von Stephan (founder)

1999. 125th Anniv of Universal Postal Union. Multicoloured.
2735 95e. Type **609** 95 70
2736 140e. Globe, letter and keyboard 1·40 90
MS2737 140×98 mm. 315e. Combination of motifs in Nos. 2735/6 (79×29 mm) 3·75 3·50

610 Egg Packs

1999. Convent Sweets (1st series). Multicoloured.
2738 51e. Type **610** 50 30
2739 80e. Egg pudding 85 50
2740 95e. Angel's purses 95 65
2741 100e. Abrantes straw 1·60 70
2742 140e. Viseu chestnuts 1·80 1·10
2743 210e. Honey cake 2·20 1·60
See also Nos. 2785/90.

611 Portuguese Troops and Moslem Ships

1999. 750th Anniv of King Afonso III's Conquest of the Algarve.
2744 **611** 100e. multicoloured 1·20 75

612 Camara Pestana (bacteriologist)

1999. Medical Anniversaries. Multicoloured.
2745 51e. Type **612** (death centenary) 50 30
2746 51e. Ricardo Jorge (founder of National Health Institute, 60th death anniv) 50 30
2747 80e. Francisco Gentil (oncologist, 35th death anniv) 85 65
2748 80e. Egas Moniz (neurosurgeon, 125th birth anniv) 85 65

2749 95e. Joao Cid dos Santos (surgeon, 23rd death anniv) 1·00 70
2750 95e. Reynaldo dos Santos (arteriography researcher, 30th death anniv (2000)) 1·00 70

613 Jose Diogo de Mascarenhas Neto (first General Mail Lieutenant)

1999. Bicentenary of the Provisional Mail Rules (reorganization of postal system).
2751 **613** 80e. multicoloured 90 55

614 Barata, Stamps and Mural

1999. Birth Centenary of Jaime Martins Barata (artist and stamp designer).
2752 **614** 80e. multicoloured 90 55

615 Wise Men following Star (Maria Goncalves)

1999. Christmas. National Association of Art and Creativity for and by Handicapped Persons. Designs with artists name in brackets. Multicoloured.
2753 51e. Type **615** 45 30
2754 95e. Father Christmas delivering presents (Marta Silva) 95 65
2755 140e. Father Christmas (Luis Farinha) 2·00 95
2756 210e. The Nativity (Maria Goncalves) 2·40 1·30

616 Macanese Architecture

1999. Portuguese–Chinese Cultural Mix in Macao. Sheet 138×90 mm.
MS2757 **616** 140e. black and red 1·80 1·80

618 "Madonna and Child" (Alvaro Pires of Evora) Maia, Oporto)

2000. 2000th Birth Anniv of Jesus Christ.
2759 **618** 52e. multicoloured 80 40

619 Astronaut and Space Craft

2000. The Twentieth Century. Conquest of Space.
2760 **619** 86e. multicoloured 1·10 65

620 Golden Eagle

2000. Birds. (1st series). Multicoloured. (a) Ordinary gum. Size 30×27 mm.
2761 52e. Type **620** 50 35
2762 85e. Great crested grebe 90 65
2763 90e. Greater flamingo 90 70
2764 100e. Northern gannet 1·60 80
2765 215e. Green-winged teal 2·75 1·60

(b) Self-adhesive gum. Size 28×25 mm.
2766 52e. As No. 2761 55 35
2767 100e. As No. 2764 1·00 80
See also Nos. 2832/9.

621 Crowd and Suffragetts

2000. The Twentieth Century (2nd issue). Three sheets, each 190×220 mm, containing T 621 and similar multicoloured designs.
MS2768 (a) 52e. Type **621** (human Rights); 52e. Fashion through the century (59×29 mm); 52e. Windmills, electricity pylon and birds (ecology) (59×39 mm); 52e. Early airplanes, car, stylised steamlined high speed train and ship (transport); 52e. As No. 2760; 52e. Space shuttle on launch pad (conquest of Space). (b) 52e. Marcel Proust and Thomas Marin (novelists), James Joyce (writer), Franz Kafka (novelist), Fernando Pessoa (poet), Jorge Luis Borges and Samuel Beckett (writers) (literature) (49×29 mm); 52e. Achille-Claude Debussy, Igor Stravinsky, Arnold Schoenberg, Bela Bartok, George Gershwin (composers), Charlie Parker (saxophonist) and William (Bill) Evans (pianist) (music) (49×29 mm); 52e. Performers (theatre); 52e. Auditorium and performers (theatre) (59×29 mm); 52e. Sculptures and paintings (art) (49×29 mm); 52e. Abstract art (29×29 mm); 52e. Charlie Chaplin on left (cinema) (49×29 mm); 52e. Woody Allen on left (cinema and television) (29×29 mm); 52e. Old and modern buildings (architecture); 52e. Modern buildings (architecture); 52e. Front and aerial views of modern buildings (architecture). (c) 52e. Edmund Husser, Ludwig Wittgenstein and Martin Heidegger (philosophy); 52e. Jules Poincare, Kurt Godel and Andrei Kolmogorov (mathematics); 52e. Max Planck, Albert Einstein and Niels Bohr (physics) (49×29 mm); 52e. Franz Boas (anthropologist), Levi Strauss (clothing manufacturer) and Margaret Mead (anthropologist) (social science and medicine); 52e. Sigmund Freud (neurologist) and Alexander Fleming (bacteriologist) (social science and medicine) (29×29 mm); 52e. Christiaan Barnard performing operation (organ transplant surgeon) (medicine); 52e. Office workers, Joseph Schumpeter and John Keynes (economics); 52e. Circuit boards (technology); 52e. Fibre optics (technology) (29×29 mm); 52e. Binary code, Alan Tuning (mathematician) and John von Neuman (mathematician) (information technology and telecommunications); 52e. Guglielmo Marconi (physicist) and satellite aerials (information technology and telecommunications); 52e. Binary code and satellite (information technology and telecommunications) (29×29 mm) 22·00 20·00

622 Members' Flags forming Stars

2000. Portuguese Presidency of European Union Council.
2769 **622** 100e. multicoloured 1·50 1·20

623 Native Indians

2000. 500th Anniv of Discovery of Brazil. Multicoloured.
2770 52e. Type **623** 60 40
2771 85e. Native Indians watching Pedro Alvares Cabral's fleet 1·10 75
2772 100e. Ship's crew and sails 1·60 95
2773 140e. Native Indians and Portuguese sailors meeting 1·80 1·30
MS2774 140×140 mm. Nos. 2770/3 5·00 3·50

624 "Building Europe"

2000. Europa.
2775 **624** 100e. multicoloured 2·00 1·70
MS2776 154×109 mm. No. 2775 ×3 6·25 7·75

625 Pope John Paul II and Children

2000. Papal Visit to Portugal. Beatification of Jacinta and Francisco Marto (Children of Fatima).
2777 **625** 52e. multicoloured 75 45

626 Draisienne Bicycle, 1817

2000. "The Stamp Show 2000" International Stamp Exhibition, London. Centenary of International Cycling Union. Bicycles. Mult.
2778 52e. Type **626** 55 40
2779 85e. Michaux, 1868 1·60 75
2780 100e. Ariel, 1871 1·20 95
2781 140e. Rover, 1888 1·90 1·30
2782 215e. BTX, 2000 3·00 1·90
2783 350e. GT, 2000 4·50 3·25
MS2784 140×112 mm. Nos. 2778/83 12·50 12·00

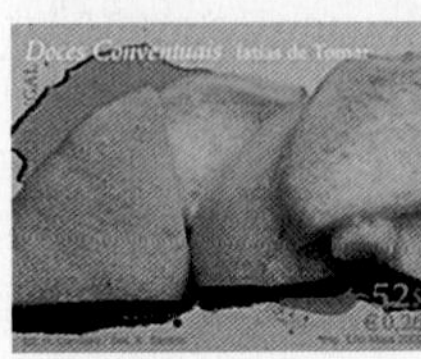

627 Slices of Tomar

2000. Convent Sweets (2nd series). Multicoloured.
2785 52e. Type **627** 55 40
2786 85e. Rodrigo's present 1·60 75
2787 100e. Sericaia 1·20 95
2788 140e. Lo bread 1·90 1·30
2789 215e. Grated bread 3·00 1·90
2790 350e. Royal paraiso cake 4·50 3·25

628 Fishing Boat and Fishes

2000. Fishermen's Day.
2791 **628** 52e. multicoloured 75 45

629 Portuguese Landscapes (image scaled to 55% of original size)

2000. "EXPO 2000" World's Fair, Hanover, Germany. Humanity–Nature–Technology. Mult.
2792 100e. Type **629** 1·20 90
MS2793 140×113 mm. 350e. Portuguese Pavilion, Hanover (39×30 mm) 4·00 4·00

630 Statue and Assembly Hall

2000. 25th Anniv of Constituent Assembly.
2794 **630** 85e. multicoloured 1·10 75

631 Fishermen and Boat

2000. Cod Fishing. Multicoloured.
2795 52e. Type **631** 55 40
2796 85e. Fishing barquentine and fisherman at ship's wheel 1·10 75
2797 100e. Three fishermen and boat 1·20 90
2798 100e. Fisherman and dories on fishing schooner 1·20 90
2799 140e. Fisherman rowing and fishing barquentine 1·90 1·20
2800 215e. Fisherman and fishing schooner 2·75 1·90
MS2801 140×112 mm. Nos. 2795/2800 9·50 9·75

632 De Queiroz

2000. Death Centenary of Eca de Queiroz (author).
2802 **632** 85e. multicoloured 1·10 75

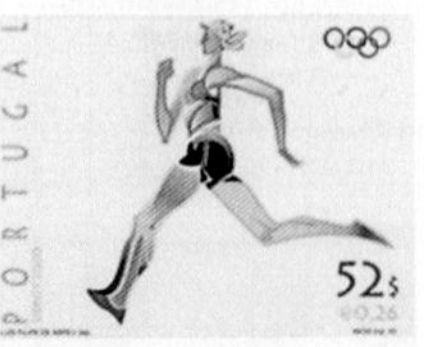

633 Running

2000. Olympic Games, Sydney. Multicoloured.
2803 52e. Type **633** 55 40
2804 85e. Show jumping 1·10 75
2805 100e. Dinghy racing 1·20 90
2806 140e. Diving 1·70 1·20
MS2807 140×112 mm. 85e. Fencing; 215e. Beach volleyball 4·50 4·25
Nos. 2803/6 are wrongly inscribed "Sidney".

634 Airbus A310 and Runway

2000. Inauguration of Madeira Airport Second Runway Extension.
2808 **634** 140e. multicoloured 1·90 1·30
MS2809 110×80 mm. 140e. multicoloured 1·90 2·00

635 Writing Letter on Computer

2000. 50th Anniv of Snoopy (cartoon character created by Charles Schulz). Postal Service. Mult.

2810	52e. Type **635**	55	40
2811	52e. Posting letter	55	40
2812	85e. Driving post van	1·10	75
2813	100e. Sorting post	1·40	90
2814	140e. Delivering post	1·90	1·20
2815	215e. Reading letter	2·40	1·90
MS2816	140×112 mm. Nos. 2810/15	9·25	9·75

636 Drawing, Telescope and Sextant

2000. 125th Anniv of Lisbon Geographic Society. Multicoloured.

2817	85e. Type **636**	1·10	75
2818	100e. Sextant and drawing	1·40	1·00

Nos. 2817/18 were issued together, se-tenant, forming a composite design.

637 Carolina Michaelis de Vasconcellos (teacher)

2001. The Twentieth Century. History and Culture. Multicoloured.

2819	85e. Type **637**	1·00	80
2820	85e. Miguel Bombarda (doctor and politician)	1·00	80
2821	85e. Bernardino Machado (politician)	1·00	80
2822	85e. Tomas Alcaide (lyricist)	1·00	80
2823	85e. Jose Regio (writer)	1·00	80
2824	85e. Jose Rodrigues Migueis (writer)	1·00	80
2825	85e. Vitorino Nemesio (scholar)	1·00	80
2826	85e. Bento de Jesus Caraca (scholar)	1·00	80

638 Athletics

2001. World Indoor Athletics Championship, Lisbon. Multicoloured.

2827	85e. Type **638**	1·10	85
2828	90e. Pole vault	1·10	90
2829	105e. Shot put	1·40	95
2830	250e. High jump	3·25	2·20
MS2831	122×100 mm. 350e. hurdles	4·75	4·75

2001. Birds (2nd series). As T 620. Multicoloured. (a) Ordinary gum. Size 27×25 mm.

2832	53e. Little bustard	60	45
2833	85e. Purple swamphen	95	75
2834	105e. Collared Pratincole	1·20	90
2835	140e. Black-shouldered kite	1·60	1·30
2836	225e. Egyptian vulture	2·75	2·10

(b) Self-adhesive gum. (i) Size 25×21 mm.

2837	53e. As No. 2832	75	45
2838	105e. As No. 2834	1·30	1·00

(ii) Size 48×22 mm.

2839	85e. Purple swamphen	1·30	85

No. 2839 is inscribed "CorreioAzul".

639 Decorated Dish

2001. Arab Artefacts. Multicoloured.

2840	53e. Type **639**	60	40
2841	90e. Painted tile	1·10	80
2842	105e. Carved stone tablet and fortress	1·40	95
2843	140e. Coin	2·40	1·30
2844	225e. Carved container	3·00	2·00
2845	350e. Jug	4·25	3·25

640 Coastal Environment (Angela M. Lopes)

2001. "Stampin' the Future". Winning Entries in Children's International Painting Competition. Multicoloured.

2846	85e. Type **640**	1·00	75
2847	90e. Earth, Sun and watering can (Maria G. Silva) (vert)	1·10	80
2848	105e. Marine life (Joao A. Ferreira)	1·20	95

641 Statue, Building Facade and Stained Glass Window

2001. Centenary of National Fine Arts Society. Multicoloured.

2849	85e. Type **641**	1·00	75
2850	105e. Painting and woman holding palette and brush	1·20	1·00
MS2851	105×80 mm. 350e. "Hen with Chicks" (detail) (Girao)	4·75	4·75

642 Congress in Session

2001. 25th Anniv of Portuguese Republic Constitution.

2852	642	85e. multicoloured	1·10	80

643 Fishes

2001. Europa. Water Resources.

2853	643	105e. multicoloured	1·70	1·40
MS2854		140×110 mm. No. 2853 ×3	5·50	6·50

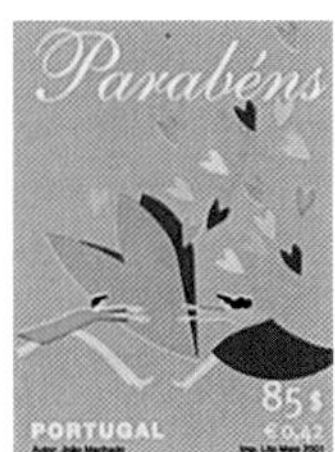

644 Couple and Heart

2001. Greetings Stamps. Multicoloured.

2855	85e. Type **644**	1·10	85
2856	85e. Birthday cake	1·10	85
2857	85e. Glasses	1·10	85
2858	85e. Bunch of flowers	1·10	85
MS2859	91×110 mm. Nos. 2855/8	4·25	4·00

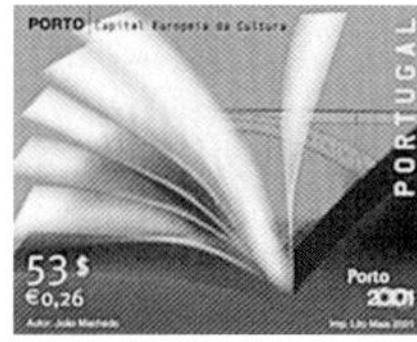

645 Open Book

2001. Porto, European City of Culture. Multicoloured.

2860	53e. Type **645**	60	45
2861	85e. Bridge and Globe	1·10	70
2862	105e. Grand piano	1·20	95
2863	140e. Stage curtain	1·60	1·30
2864	225e. Picture frame	2·75	2·10
2865	350e. Firework display	4·00	3·25
MS2866	140×110 mm. Nos. 2861/6	12·00	11·00

646 Campaign Cannon, 1773

2001. 150th Anniv of Military Museum, Lisbon. Multicoloured.

2867	85e. Type **646**	1·10	80
2868	105e. 16th-century armour	1·40	1·10
MS2869	140×112 mm. 53e. Pistol of King Jose I, 1757; 53e. Cannon on carriage, 1797; 140e. Cannon "Tigre", 1533; 140e. 15th-century helmet	5·00	4·50

647 Brown Bear

2001. Lisbon Zoo. Multicoloured.

2870	53e. Type **647**	55	40
2871	85e. Emperor tamarin	1·00	75
2872	90e. Green iguana	1·00	85
2873	105e. Humboldt penguin	1·30	1·00
2874	225e. Toco toucan	2·75	2·10
2875	350e. Giraffe	4·00	3·25
MS2876	140×112 mm. 85e. Indian elephant (29×38 mm); 85e. Grevy's zebra (29×39 mm); Lion (29×38 mm); White rhinoceros (29×38 mm)	8·00	6·50

648 Emblem

2001. 47th Lion's European Forum, Oporto.

2877	648	85e. multicoloured	1·10	75

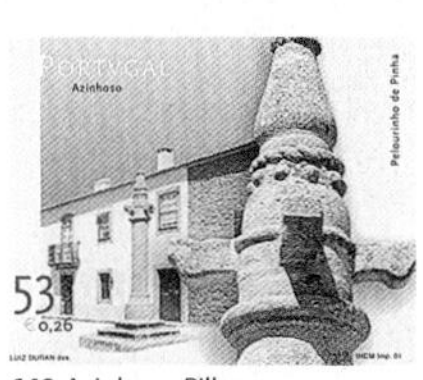

649 Azinhoso Pillory

2001. Pillories. Multicoloured.

2878	53e. Type **649**	60	45
2879	53e. Soajo	60	45
2880	53e. Braganca	60	45
2881	53e. Linhares	60	45
2882	53e. Arcos de Valdevez	60	45
2883	53e. Vila de Rua	60	45
2884	53e. Sernancelhe	60	45
2885	53e. Frechas	60	45

650 Faces

2001. United Nations Year of Dialogue among Civilizations.

2886	650	140e. multicoloured	1·60	1·20

651 Disney

2001. Birth Centenary of Walt Disney (artist and film producer).

2887	53e. Type **651**	65	50
MS2888	160×132 mm. 53e. Huey, Dewey and Louie, and 15th-century Mudejares tiles; 53e. Mickey Mouse and 16th-century tiles forming coat of arms; 53e. Minnie Mouse and 17th-century religious allegory tiles; 53e. Goofy and 18th-century tiles of birds; 53e. Type **651**; 53e. Pluto and 19th-century tile design by Rafael Bordalo Pinheiro; 53e. Donald Duck and 19th-century tiles; 53e. Scrooge McDuck and 20th-century "Querubim Lapa" tiles; 53e. Daisy Duck and 20th-century tile designs by Manuel Cargaleiro	8·00	7·00

652 Royal Police Guard, 1801

2001. Bicentenary of National Guard. Multicoloured.

2889	53e. Type **652**	60	50
2890	85e. Lisbon Municipal Guard bandsman, 1834	1·00	75
2891	90e. Infantry helmet, 1911 and modern guardsman	1·00	80
2892	105e. Mounted division helmet of 1911 and modern guardsmen	1·20	95
2893	140e. Guardsmen with motor-cycle and car	1·60	1·20
2894	350e. Customs and Excise officer and boat	4·25	3·00
MS2895	117×90 mm. 225e. Mounted division helmet and guardsman of 1911	3·00	3·00

653 Chinese Junk

2001. Ships. Multicoloured.

2896	53e. Type **653**	65	50
2897	53e. Portuguese caravel	65	50

654 1c. Coin

2002. New Currency. Multicoloured.

2898	1c. Type **654**	10	10
2899	2c. 2c. coin	10	10
2900	5c. 5c. coin	15	10
2901	10c. 10c. coin	20	15
2902	20c. 20c. coin	45	35
2903	50c. 50c. coin	1·10	90
2904	€1 €1 coin	2·50	1·80
2905	€2 €2 coin	4·75	3·50

655 Horse-rider

2002. No value expressed.

2906	655	A (28c.) multicoloured	65	50

No. 2906 was sold at the current first class inland letter rate.

657 European Bee-eater

2002. Birds (1st series). Multicoloured. (i) Ordinary gum. Size 30×26 mm.

2914	2c. Type **657**	10	10
2915	28c. Little tern	70	50
2916	43c. Eagle owl	1·00	80
2917	54c. Pin-tailed sandgrouse	1·30	95
2918	60c. Red-necked nightjar	1·40	1·10
2919	70c. Greater spotted cuckoo	1·70	1·30

(ii) Self-adhesive gum. Size 49×23 mm.

2920	43c. Little tern (different)	1·30	85

(iii) Self-adhesive gum. Size 29×24 mm.

2921	28c. As No. 2919	75	55
2922	54c. As No. 2916	1·30	1·00

(iiii) Self-adhesive gum. Size 27×23 mm.

2923	28c. As No. 2919	1·00	70
2924	54c. As No. 2916	1·70	1·10

See also Nos. 2988/92.

658 De Gois (image scaled to 61% of original size)

2002. 500th Birth Anniv of Damiao de Gois (writer).

2925	**658** 45c. multicoloured	1·10	80

659 Loxodromic Curve, Ship and Globe

2002. 500th Birth Anniv of Pedro Nunes (mathematician). Multicoloured.

2926	28c. Type **659**	65	50
2927	28c. Nonius (navigational instrument)	65	50
2928	€1.15 Portrait of Nunes	2·75	2·10
MS2929	140×105 mm Nos. 2926/8	4·25	4·00

660 Children and Flower

2002. America. Youth, Education and Literacy. Multicoloured.

2930	70c. Type **660**	1·60	1·30
2931	70c. Children, book and letters	1·60	1·30
2932	70c. Children and pencil	1·60	1·30

661 Refracting Telescope and Polytechnic School Observatory, Lisbon

2002. Astronomy. Multicoloured.

2933	28c. Type **661**	65	50
2934	28c. 16th-century astrolabe and Colegio dos Nobres, Lisbon	65	50
2935	43c. Quadrant and Solar Observatory, Coimbra	1·00	80
2936	45c. Terrestrial telescope and King Pedro V	1·00	80
2937	45c. Cassegrain telescope and King Luis	1·00	80
2938	54c. Earth, refracting telescope and Observatory, Ajuda	1·30	1·00
2939	€1.15 Cassegrain telescope and Saturn	2·75	2·10
2940	€1.75 Zeiss projector and planets	4·00	3·25
MS2941	140×111 mm. 70c. 18th-century armillary sphere; 70c. 19th-century theodolite	3·75	3·75

662 Square and Compass

2002. Bicentenary of Grande Oriente Lusitano (Masonic Grand Lodge).

2942	**662** 43c. multicoloured	1·10	80

663 Clown

2002. Europa. Circus.

2943	**663** 54c. multicoloured	2·00	1·60
MS2944	140×110 mm No. 2943×3	6·25	7·75

664 *Scabiosa nitens*

2002. Flowers of Azores. Multicoloured.

2945	28c. Type **664**	65	50
2946	45c. *Viburnum tinus subcordatum*	1·00	75
2947	54c. *Euphorbia azorica*	1·20	95
2948	70c. *Lysimachia nemorum azorica*	1·60	1·30
2949	€1.15 *Bellis azorica*	2·75	2·10
2950	€1.75 *Spergularia azorica*	4·00	3·25
MS2951	120×121 mm €1.15 *Azorina vidalli*; €1.75 *Senecio malvifolius*	6·75	6·50

665 Lockheed Martin (General Dynamics) F-16 Fighting Falcon

2002. 50th Anniv of Portuguese Air Force. Multicoloured.

2952	28c. Type **665**	65	50
2953	43c. Sud Aviation SA300 Puma helicopter	1·00	80
2954	54c. Dassault Dornier Alphajet A	1·20	95
2955	70c. Lockheed C-130 Hercules transport aircraft	1·60	1·30
2956	€1.25 Lockheed P-3P Orion reconnaissance aircraft	2·75	2·20
2957	€1.75 Fiat G-91 fighter aircraft	4·00	3·00
MS2958	140×112 mm €1.15 Four Cessna T-37; €1.75 Aerospatiale TB30 Epsilon and Cessna T-37	7·25	7·00

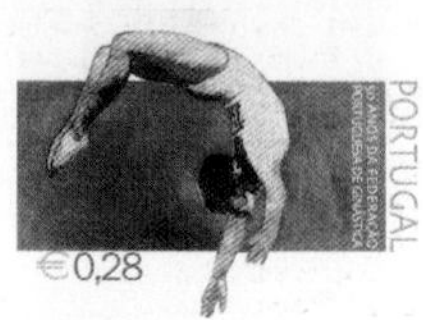

666 Gymnastics

2002. Sports and Sports Anniversaries. Multicoloured.

2959	28c. Type **666** (50th anniv of Portuguese Gymnastic Federation)	60	50
2960	28c. Walking race	60	50
2961	45c. Basketball	1·00	80
2962	45c. Handball	1·00	80
2963	54c. Roller hockey (sixth Women's World Roller Hockey Championship, Pacos de Ferriera)	1·20	95
2964	54c. Fencing (World Fencing Championship, Lisbon)	1·20	95
2965	€1.75 Footballers (World Cup Football Championship, Japan and South Korea)	3·75	3·00
2966	€1.75 Golf	3·75	3·00
MS2967	140×110 mm. €1 Footballer and part of football; €2 Torsos and legs of two players	7·00	5·75

Nos. **MS**2967 was inscribed for "PHILAKOREA 2002" International Stamp Exhibition, Seoul, in the margin.

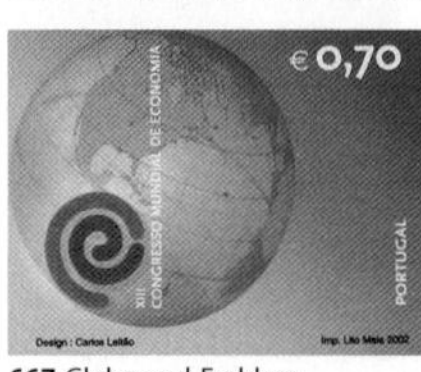

667 Globe and Emblem

2002. 13th World International Economic Association Congress.

2968	**667** 70c. multicoloured	1·60	1·20

668 Anniversary Emblem

2002. 150th Anniv of Ministry of Public Works, Transport and Housing. Multicoloured.

2969	43c. Type **668**	1·00	75
MS2970	144×123 mm. 43c. ×6, Ship and oil terminal; Locomotive; Stylised Boeing 737; Bridge and city skyline; Factories; Houses	6·50	5·00

669 Portrait and Symbols of Industry and Agriculture

2002. 150th Anniv of Technical Education.

2971	**669** 43c. multicoloured	1·00	75

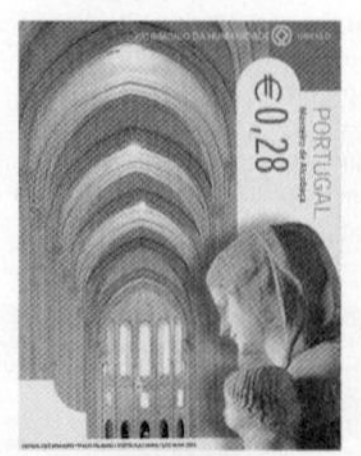

670 Virgin and Child (statue) and Window, Alcobaca Monastery

2002. UNESCO World Heritage Sites. Multicoloured.

2972	28c. Type **670**	60	50
2973	28c. Lion (statue) and embossed ceiling, Jeronimos Monastery	60	50
2974	43c. Column capitals, Guimaraes	95	75
2975	43c. Cherub (statue) and vineyards, Alto Douro	95	75
2976	54c. Corbel, lake and vineyards, Alto Douro (horiz) (80×30 mm)	1·20	95
2977	54c. Houses and statues, Guimaraes (horiz) (80×30 mm)	1·20	95
2978	70c. Carved arch and statue, Jeronimos Monastery (horiz) (80×30 mm)	1·60	1·20
2979	70c. Nave and tomb, Alcobaca Monastery (horiz) (80×30 mm)	1·60	1·20
MS2980	Four sheets, each 141×114 mm. (a) €1.25 Door and statue, Alcobaca Monastery; (b) €1.25 Double doors, Jeronimos Monastery; (c) €1.25 Arches, Guimaraes; (d) €1.25 Grapes, Alto Douro	12·00	9·75

671 1870 Dress Uniform

2003. Bicentenary of Military College, Luz. Multicoloured.

2981	20c. Type **671**	40	35
2982	30c. 1806 uniform	65	50
2983	43c. 1837 parade uniform	95	75
2984	55c. 1861 uniform (rear view)	1·20	95
2985	70c. 1866 dress uniform	1·60	1·30
2986	€2 1912 cavalry cadet uniform	4·50	3·50
MS2987	141×114 mm. €1 1802 uniform; €1 1948 Porta Guiao dress uniform	4·75	4·00

2003. Birds (2nd series). As T 657. Multicoloured. (a) Ordinary gum.

2988	1c. Green woodpecker	10	10
2989	30c. Rock dove	70	50
2990	43c. Blue thrush	1·00	75
2991	55c. Sub-alpine warbler	1·30	95
2992	70c. Black-eared wheatear	1·60	1·20

(b) Self-adhesive gum. Size 27×23 mm.

2992a	30c. No. 2989	75	50
2992b	43c. No. 2990 (50×23 mm)	1·00	80
2992c	55c. No. 2991	1·80	1·20

No. 2992b is inscribed "CorreioAzul".

672 People forming Mobility Symbol

2003. European Year of the Disabled. Multicoloured.

2993	30c. Type **672**	75	50
2994	55c. People forming head shape	1·30	95
2995	70c. As No. 2994 but with eyes, ears and mouth pink	1·60	1·20

673 1853 5r. Stamp and Queen Donna Maria II

2003. 150th Anniv of First Postage Stamp (1st issue). Designs showing 1853 stamps. Multicoloured.

2996	30c. Type **673**	65	50
2997	43c. 25r. stamp and coin	95	75
2998	55c. 50r. stamp and portrait	1·20	95
2999	70c. 100r. stamp and arms	1·60	1·20

See also Nos. 3011 and **MS**3047.

674 *Orchis italica*

2003. Orchids. Multicoloured.

3000	46c. *Aceras anthropophorum*	1·00	80
3001	46c. *Dactylorhiza maculate*	1·00	80
MS3002	Two sheets, each 113×140 mm. (a) 30c. Type **674**; 30c. *Ophrys tenthredinifera*; 30c. *Ophrys fusca fusca*; 30c. *Orchis papilionacea*; 30c. *Barlia robertiana*; 30c. *Ophrys lutea*; 30c. *Ophrys fusca*; 30c. *Ophrys apifera*; 30c. *Dactylorhiza ericetorum*. (b) 30c. *Orchis champagneuxii*; 30c. *Orchis morio*; 30c. *Serapias cordigera*; 30c. *Orchis coriophora*; 30c. *Ophrys bombyliflora*; 30c. *Ophrys vernixia*; 30c. *Ophrys speculum*; 30c. *Ophrys scoplopax*; 30c. *Anacamptis pyramidalis*	14·00	11·00

675 Jazz Festival (Joao Machado)

2003. Europa. Poster Art. Multicoloured.

3003 55c. Type **675** 1·60 1·20

3004 55c. Woman wearing swimsuit ("Espimho") (Fred Kradolfer) 1·60 1·20

MS3005 140×113 mm. Nos. 3004/5 3·25 3·50

676 Lawyer and Union Seal

2003. International Lawyer's Congress, Lisbon. Multicoloured.

3006 30c. Type **676** 65 50

3007 43c. Lawyers, arms and Court building 95 75

3008 55c. Medieval lawyer, Bishop and legal document 1·20 95

3009 70c. Lawyer's union presidential medal and female lawyer 1·60 1·20

MS3010 140×113 mm. €1 Lawyer wearing red robe and seal; €2 Seal, painted plaque and bishop 7·00 5·50

677 "150" and Stamp (Viseu)

2003. 150th Anniv of Portuguese First Stamp (2nd issue). Itinerant Exhibition.

3011 **677** 30c. multicoloured 80 50

3012 **677** 30c. multicoloured 80 50

3013 **677** 30c. multicoloured 80 50

678 Championship Emblem

2003. Euro 2004 Football Championship, Portugal (1st issue).

3014 **678** 30c. multicoloured 70 50

3015 **678** 43c. multicoloured 1·00 75

3016 **678** 47c. multicoloured 1·10 85

3017 **678** 55c. multicoloured 1·30 95

3018 **678** 70c. multicoloured 1·60 1·20

MS3019 (a) 140×109 mm. 55c. ×4, Parts of championship emblem. (b) 190×200 mm. Nos. 3014/18 and **MS**3019a 5·25 4·25

See also Nos. **MS**3072, 3073/4, 3084/**MS**88, 3110/17, 3119/28 and **MS**3147.

679 Open-topped Car

2003. Centenary of Portuguese Automobile Club. Multicoloured.

3020 30c. Type **679** 65 50

3021 43c. Club engineer riding motorcycle 95 75

3022 €2 Racing cars 4·50 3·50

680 Ricardo do Espirito Santo Silva

2003. 50th Anniv of Ricardo do Espirito Santo Silva Foundation. Multicoloured.

3023 30c. Type **680** 60 50

3024 30c. 18th-century inlaid chess table 60 50

3025 43c. Cutlery box, 1720–1750 95 75

3026 43c. 15th-century silver tray 95 75

3027 55c. 18th-century wooden container 1·20 95

3028 55c. Ming dynasty ceramic box 1·20 95

MS3029 140×112 mm. €1 17th-century cupboard; €1 18th-century tapestry 7·00 5·50

681 "Bay of Funchal" (W. G. James) (1839)

2003. Museums of Madeira. Black (No. MS3034) or multicoloured (others).

3030 30c. Type **681** 60 50

3031 43c. Nativity (straw sculpture, Manuel Orlando Noronha Gois) 1·00 75

3032 55c. "O Largo da Fonte" (Andrew Picken) (1840) 1·30 95

3033 70c. "Le Depart" (Martha Teles) (1983) 1·50 1·20

MS3034 140×112 mm. €1 Vicente Gomes da Silva (photograph); €2 Jorge Bettencourt (photograph) 6·75 5·25

682 Curved Shape containing "EXD"

2003. ExperimentaDesign2003 (design exhibition). Sheet containing T 682 and similar curved designs. Either black (30c.) or black and red (others). Self-adhesive.

3035 30c. Type **682** 65 50

3036 30c. "EXD" centrally 65 50

3037 30c. "EXD" bottom 65 50

3038 30c. "EXD" left 65 50

3039 43c. As No. 3038 but design reversed 95 75

3040 43c. As No. 3037 but design reversed 95 75

3041 43c. As No. 3036 but design reversed 95 75

3042 43c. As No. 3035 but design reversed 95 75

3043 55c. As No. 3035 1·20 90

3044 55c. As No. 3036 1·20 90

3045 55c. As No. 3037 1·20 90

3046 55c. As No. 3038 1·20 90

683 Queen Maria II

2003. 150th Anniv of First Portuguese Stamp (3rd issue). Four sheets, each 140×112 mm containing T 683 and similar multicoloured designs.

MS3047 (a) 30c. Type **683**; 30c. ×4 No. 2996 ×4 (25.9); (b) €1 Queen Maria II and euro coins (90×40 mm) (12.12); (c) €2.50 Seal and postal marks (80×30 mm) (23.9); (d) €3 King Pedro V, 1853 25r. stamp and Queen Maria II (80×30 mm) 18·00 15·00

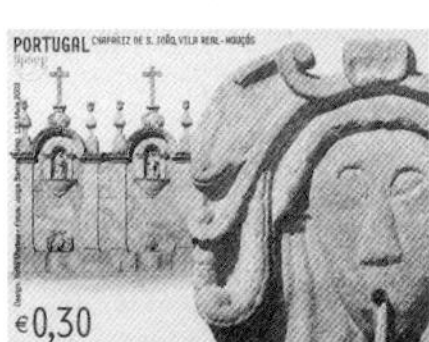

684 St. John's Well, Vila Real

2003. America. Fountains. Multicoloured.

3048 30c. Type **684** 60 50

3049 43c. Fountain of Virtues, Porto 95 75

3050 55c. Fountain, Giraldo Square, Evora 1·20 95

3051 70c. Senora da Saude fountain, St. Marcos de Tavira 1·50 1·20

3052 €1 Town fountain, Castelo de Vide 2·20 1·70

3053 €2 St. Andreas fountain, Guarda 4·25 2·40

685 Jose I engraved Glass Tumbler (18th-century)

2003. Glass Production. Multicoloured.

3054 30c. Type **685** 60 50

3055 55c. Maria II engraved tumbler (19th-century) 1·20 95

3056 70c. Blue glass vase (Carmo Valente) (20th-century) 1·50 1·20

3057 €2 Bulbous vase (Helena Matos) (20th-century) 4·25 3·50

MS3058 140×112 mm. €1.50 Stained glass window (detail) (Fernando Santos) (19th-century) 3·50 2·75

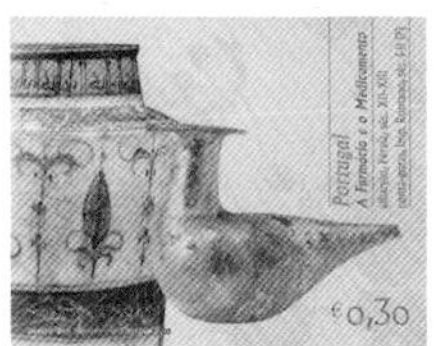

686 Persian Medicine Jar and Roman Dropper

2003. Medicine and Pharmacy. Multicoloured.

3059 30c. Type **686** 60 50

3060 43c. Ceramic bottle and jar 95 75

3061 55c. Pestle and mortar 1·20 95

3062 70c. Still and glass bottle 1·50 1·20

687 Drawing Board and Chair (Jose Epinho)

2003. Contemporary Design. Multicoloured.

3063 43c. Type **687** 95 75

3064 43c. Telephone point (Pedro Silva Dias) (vert) 95 75

3065 43c. Tea trolley (Cruz de Carvlho) 95 75

3066 43c. Tap (Carlos Aguiar) 95 75

3067 43c. Desk (Daciano da Costa) 95 75

3068 43c. Knives (Eduardo Afonso Dias) 95 75

3069 43c. Stacking chairs (Leonor and Antonio Sena da Silva) 95 75

3070 43c. Flask (Carlos Rocha) (vert) 95 75

3071 43c. Chair (Antonio Garcia) (vert) 95 75

688 Championship Emblem

2003. Euro 2004 Football Championship, Portugal (2nd issue). Stadiums (2nd issue). Sheet 150×165 mm containing T 688 and similar horiz designs. Multicoloured.

MS3072 30c.×10 Type **688**; Municipal stadium, Aveiro; Dr. Magalhaes Pessoa stadium, Leiria; Luz stadium, Lisbon; D. Afonso Henriques stadium, Guimaraes; Municipal stadium, Coimbra; Bessa stadium, Porto; Dragao stadium, Porto; Algarve stadium, Faro-Loule; Jose Alvalade stadium, Lisbon 12·00 6·00

689 Kinas

2004. European Football Championship 2004, Portugal (3rd series). Mascot. Multicoloured. Self-adhesive.

3073 45c. Type **689** (postage) 95 80

3074 €1.75 Kinas and football (air) 3·75 3·00

No. 3073 was inscribed "CorreioAzul". No. 3074 was inscribed "Airmail Priority".

690 King Joao IV and Vila Vicosa

2004. 400th Birth Anniv of King Joao IV. Multicoloured.

3075 45c. Type **690** 95 80

3076 €1 King Joao standing 2·20 1·80

Nos. 3075/6 were issued together, se-tenant, forming a composite design.

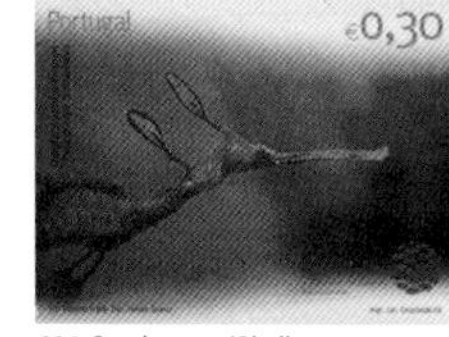

691 Seadragon (*Phyllopteryx taeniolatus*)

2004. Lisbon Oceanarium. Multicoloured.

3077 30c. Type **691** 60 50

3078 45c. Magellanic penguin (*Spheniscus magellanicus*) 95 75

3079 56c. *Hypsypops rubicundus* 1·20 95

3080 72c. Sea otter (*Enhydra lutris*) 1·60 1·30

3081 €1 Grey nurse shark (*Carcharias Taurus*) 2·10 1·70

3082 €2 Atlantic puffin (*Fratercula artica*) 4·25 3·50

MS3083 140×112 mm. €1.50 Macaroni penguin (*Eudyptes Chrysolophus*) (80×30 mm) 3·50 2·75

692 Foot kicking Ball

2004. European Football Championship 2004, Portugal (4th series). Official Match Ball. Multicoloured. Self-adhesive.

3084 10c. Type **692** 25 15

3085 20c. Ball right 45 35

3086 30c. Ball and line 70 50

3087 50c. Ball and goal post 1·10 85

MS3088 105×105 mm. Nos. 3084/7. 4·25 2·30

MS3088 is ordinary gum.

693 Portugal

2004. European Football Championship 2004, Portugal (5th series). Participating Teams. Designs showing Kinas (mascot) and country flags. Multicoloured.

3089 30c. Type **693** 70 55

3090 30c. France 70 55

3091 30c. Sweden 70 55

3092 30c. Czech Republic 70 55

3093 30c. Greece 70 55

3094 30c. UK 70 55

3095 30c. Bulgaria 70 55

3096 30c. Latvia 70 55

3097 30c. Spain 70 55

3098 30c. Switzerland 70 55

3099 30c. Denmark 70 55

3100 30c. Germany 70 55

3101 30c. Russia 70 55

3102 30c. Croatia 70 55

3103 30c. Italy 70 55

3104 30c. Netherlands 70 55

2004. Birds (3rd series). As T 657. Multicoloured.

3105 30c. Red crossbill 60 50

3106 45c. Red-rumped swallow 95 75

3107 55c. Golden oriole 1·20 95

3108 58c. Crested lark 1·30 1·00

3109 72c. Crested tit 1·60 1·30

3109a 30c. As No. 3105 (28×23 mm) 60 50

3109b 45c. As No. 3106 (50×23 mm) 95 75

3109c 56c. As No. 3107 (28×23 mm) 1·20 95

Nos. 3105a/7a all self-adhesive.

694 "Moliceiros" Boat (Aveiro)

2004. European Football Championship 2004, Portugal (6th series). Host Cities. Multicoloured.

3110	30c. Type **694**	65	55
3111	30c. University tower (Coimbra)	65	55
3112	30c. Don Afonso Henriques (statue) (Guimaraes)	65	55
3113	30c. Castle (Leiria)	65	55
3114	30c. Tower (Faro/Loule)	65	55
3115	30c. Bom Jesus (Braga)	65	55
3116	30c. Torre di Belem (Lisbon)	65	55
3117	30c. D. Luís I Bridge (Porto)	65	55

695 Carnations

2004. 30th Anniv of 25 April (Carnation revolution).

3118	**695**	45c. multicoloured	1·00	80

696 Dr. Magalhaes Pessoa Stadium, Leiria

2004. European Football Championship 2004, Portugal (7th series). Stadiums (2nd issue). Multicoloured.

3119	30c. Type **696**	65	55
3120	30c. Municipal stadium, Coimbra	65	55
3121	30c. Municipal stadium, Braga	65	55
3122	30c. Bessa stadium, Porto	65	55
3123	30c. Luz stadium, Lisbon	65	55
3124	30c. D. Afonso Henriques stadium, Guimaraes	65	55
3125	30c. Algarve stadium, Faro-Loule	65	55
3126	30c. Jose Alvalade stadium, Lisbon	65	55
3127	30c. Dragao stadium, Porto	65	55
3128	30c. Municipal stadium, Aveiro	65	55

697 Stylized Figures

2004. European Union. Multicoloured.

3129	30c. Type **697** (EU parliamentary elections)	70	50
3130	56c. EU emblem and new members' flags (80×30 mm) (new members)	1·20	90
MS3131	140×111 mm×2 Original members' flags (80 30 mm)	4·75	4·00

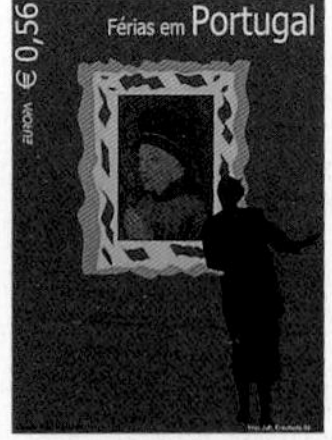

698 Picture Gallery

2004. Europa. Holidays. Multicoloured.

3132	56c. Type **698**	1·50	1·20
3133	56c. Beach	1·50	1·20
MS3134	141×112 mm. Nos. 3132/3	4·50	3·50

699 Bells of Early Telephone

2004. Centenary of Telephone Line from Porto to Lisbon. Multicoloured.

3135	30c. Type **699**	60	50
3136	45c. Insulator	95	75
3137	56c. Fibre optic cable	1·20	95
3138	72c. Video telephone	1·60	1·30
MS3139	140×112 mm. €1. ×2, No. 3135; No. 3138	6·75	4·00

700 Flower (illustration, Maimonides' Mishneh Torah)

2004. Jewish Heritage. Multicoloured.

3140	30c. Type **700**	60	50
3141	45c. Star of David (illustration, Cervera Bible)	95	75
3142	56c. Menorah (illustration, Cervera Bible)	1·20	95
3143	72c. Menorah (carved tablet)	1·60	1·30
3144	€1 Illustration, Abravanel Bible	2·10	1·70
3145	€2 Prophet (statue, de Cristo Convent, Tomar)	4·25	3·50
MS3146	140×112 mm. €1.50 Shaare Tikva Synagogue (centenary)	3·50	2·75

701 Henri Delaunay Trophy

2004. European Football Championship 2004, Portugal (8th series). Sheet 140×112 mm. Multicoloured.

MS3147	**701** €1 multicoloured	2·40	2·00

702 Stamps

2004. 50th Anniv of Portuguese Philatelic Federation. Multicoloured.

3148	30c. Type **702**	75	50
MS3149	111×79 mm €1.50 Seal	3·50	2·75

703 Footballers Past and Present (image scaled to 55% of original size)

2004. 50th Anniv of Union of European Football Associations (UEFA). Sheet 141×85 mm.

MS3150	€1 multicoloured	2·40	1·90

704 Hurdler

2004. Olympic Games, Athens 2004. Multicoloured.

3151	30c. Type **704**	65	50
3152	45c. High jump	1·10	75

705 Swimmer

2004. Paralymic Games, Athens 2004. Multicoloured.

3153	30c. Type **705**	60	50
3154	45c. Wheelchair racer	95	75
3155	56c. Cyclist	1·20	95
3156	72c. Runner	1·50	1·30

706 Pedro Homem de Melo

2004. Birth Centenary of Pedro Homem de Melo (folklorist). Sheet 140×112 mm.

MS3157	€2 multicoloured	4·75	4·00

707 Museum Facade (image scaled to 55% of original size)

2004. Inauguration of Belem Palace Museum (President of the Republic's Museum). Multicoloured.

3158	45c. Type **708**	1·00	75
MS3159	140×112 mm. €1 Museum interior	2·40	1·90

708 Quim and Manecas (Jose Stuart Carvalhais)

2004. Comic Strips. Multicoloured.

3160	30c. Type **708**	60	50
3161	45c. Guarda Abila (Julio Pinto and Nuno Saraiva)	95	75
3162	56c. Simao Infante (Raul Correia and Eduardo Teixeira Coelho)	1·20	95
3163	72c. APior Banda du Mondo (Jose Carlos Fernandes)	1·50	1·30
MS3164	141×111 mm. 50c.×4, Oespiao Acacio (Relvas); Jim del Monaco (Louro and Simoes); Tomahawk Tom (Vitor Peon); Pitanga (Arlndo Fagundes)	4·75	4·00

709 Third-century Sarcophagus and Mosaic

2004. Viticulture. Multicoloured.

3165	30c. Type **709**	70	50
3166	45c. Mosaic and 12th-century tapestry	1·10	75
3167	56c. Man carrying grapes (14th-century mirror) and grape harvesting (15th-century Book of Hours)	1·30	95
3168	72c. Grape harvesting and "Grupo de Leao" (Columbano Bordalo Pine)	1·70	1·30
3169	€1 "Grupo de Leo" and 20th-century stained glass window	2·30	1·70
MS3170	140×115 mm. 50c. ×4, Fields, grapes and mechanical harvester; Harvester and amphora; Barrels in cellar, steel vats and barrels; Barrels, bottling and glass of wine	4·50	4·00

Nos. 3165/6 were issued together, se-tenant, forming a composite design.

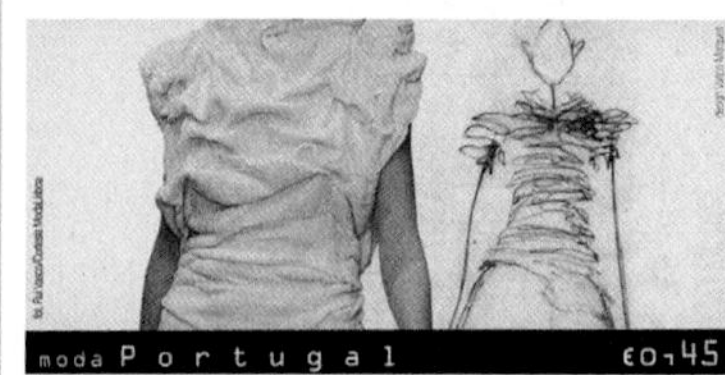

710 Ruched Dress (Alexandra Moura) (image scaled to 61% of original size)

2004. Fashion. Sheet 190×200 mm containing T 710 and similar horiz designs. Multicoloured.

MS3171	45c. ×10, Type **710**; Poncho (Ana Salazar); Boned and laced dress (Filipe Faisca); Ribboned skirt (J. Branco and L. Sanchez); Wrap-over dress Antonio Tenente); Frilled front (Luis Buchinho); White top and skirted pants (Osvaldo Martins); Magenta dress with red attachments (Dino Alves); Silk-edged coat (Alves and Goncalves); Sequinned halter necked dress (Fatima Lopes)	11·00	8·50

711 "Adoration of the Magi" (Jorge Afonso)

2004. Christmas. Multicoloured.

3172	30c. Type **711**	60	50
3173	45c. "Adoration of the Magi" (16th-century Flamenga school)	95	75
3174	56c. "Escape into Egypt" (Francisco Vieira)	1·20	95
3175	72c. "Nativity" (Portuguese school)	1·50	1·30
MS3176	140×112 mm. €3 "Nativity" (detail) (Josefa de Obidos) (50×35 mm)	6·75	5·50

712 "Entrudo", Lazarim, Lamego

2005. Masks. Multicoloured. (a) Ordinary gum.

3177	10c. Type **712**	20	15
3178	30c. "Festa dos Rapazes", Salsas, Braganca	60	50
3179	45c. "Festa do Chocalheiro" Mougadouro, Braganca	90	75
3180	57c. "Cardador", Vale de Ilhavo	1·20	1·00
3181	74c. "Festa dos Rapazes", Avelada, Braganca	1·60	1·30

(b) Self-adhesive gum.

3182	30c. As No. 3178 (29×24 mm)	1·10	50
3183	45c. As No. 3179 (48×23 mm)	1·60	80
3184	57c. As No. 3180 (29×24 mm)	2·10	1·00

No. 3183 is inscribed "Correio Azul".
See also No. 3319/21.

713 Subway Train and Tram

2005. Public Transport. Multicoloured.

3185	30c. Type **713**	60	50
3186	50c. Locomotive and tram	1·00	85
3187	57c. Hovercraft	1·20	1·00
3188	€1 Coach	2·10	1·70
3189	€2 Train	4·25	3·50

Nos. 3185/9 were issued together, se-tenant, forming a composite design.

714 Sortelha

2005. Historic Villages (1st issue). Multicoloured.

3190 30c. Type **714** 65 50
3191 30c. Idanha-a-Velha 65 50
3192 30c. Castelo Novo 65 50
3193 30c. Castelo Rodrigo 65 50
3194 30c. Piodao 65 50
3195 30c. Linhares 65 50
3196 30c. Transcoso 65 50
3197 30c. Monsanto 65 50
3198 30c. Almeida 65 50
3199 30c. Belmonte 65 50
3200 30c. Marialva 65 50
3201 30c. Castelo Mendo 65 50
3202 30c. Buildings and coast, Linhares 65 50
3203 30c. Roof tops, Transcoso 65 50
3204 30c. Church, Marialva 65 50
3205 30c. Castle and houses, Castelo Rodrigo 65 50
3206 30c. Buildings and terrace, Almeida 65 50
3207 30c. Houses, Castelo Mendo 65 50
3208 30c. Rooftops, Sortelha 65 50
3209 30c. Balcony, Belmonte 65 50
3210 30c. Rooftops, Monsanto 65 50
3211 30c. Ruins, Idanha-a-Velha 65 50
3212 30c. Tower, Castelo Novo 65 50
3213 30c. Rooftops, Piodao 65 50
3214 57c. Castle, Linhares 1·30 1·00
3215 57c. Castle walls, Transcoso 1·30 1·00
3216 57c. Bells, Mariavla 1·30 1·00
3217 57c. Church, Castelo Rodrigo 1·30 1·00
3218 57c. Walls, Almeida 1·30 1·00
3219 57c. Rooftops, Castelo Mendo 1·30 1·00
3220 57c. Column, Sortelha 1·30 1·00
3221 57c. Castle walls, Belmonte 1·30 1·00
3222 57c. Tower, Monsanto 1·30 1·00
3223 57c. Doorway, Idanha-a-Velha 1·30 1·00
3224 57c. Rooftops, Castelo Novo 1·30 1·00
3225 57c. Building facade, Piodao 1·30 1·00

See also No. **MS**3247.

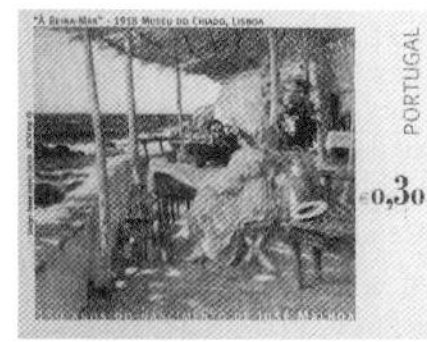

715 "A Beira-Mar"

2005. 150th Birth Anniv of Jose Malhoa (artist). Multicoloured.

3226 30c. Type **715** 60 50
3227 45c. "As Promessas" 95 80
MS3228 93×117 mm. €1.77 "Conversa com o Vizinho" 3·75 2·75

716 Cozido a Portuguesa (stew)

2005. Europa. Gastronomy. Multicoloured.

3229 57c. Type **716** 1·50 1·20
MS3230 125×95 mm. 57c.×2, Bacalhau assado com batatas a murro (cod and potatoes)×2 6·50 5·25

717 Paul Harris (founder)

2005. Centenary of Rotary International.

3231 **717** 74c. Multicoloured 1·50 1·30
MS3232 125×95 mm. **717** €1.75 multicoloured 3·75 3·00

718 19th-century Open Carriage (Carrinho de Passeio)

2005. Centenary of National Coach Museum, Lisbon. Multicoloured.

3233 30c. Type **718** 60 50
3234 30c. 19th-century closed carriage (Carruagem de Porto Covo) 60 50
3235 45c. 17th-century carriage (Coche Francisca Saboia) 95 80
3236 45c. 18th-century small carriage ("Das Plumas") 95 80
3237 57c. 18th-century sedan chair 1·20 1·00
3238 74c. 18th-century coach (Coches dos oceanos) 1·60 1·30
MS3239 125×100 mm. €1.75 Queen Amelia 3·75 3·00

719 Pegoes Aqueduct, Tomar

2005. Cultural Heritage. Multicoloured.

3240 5c. Type **719** 10 10
3241 30c. Chalice (1581) 60 50
3242 45c. Stained glass, De Christo convent, Tomar 95 80
3243 57c. Turret, Angra, Azores 1·20 1·00
3244 €1 Ship 2·10 1·70
3245 €2 St. Vincente de Fora church, Lisbon 4·25 3·50
MS3246 112×140 mm. €1.20 Crucifix, Tesauro da Se, Lisbon 3·00 2·75

2005. Historic Villages (2nd issue). 12 sheets, each 60×150 mm containing horiz designs as T 714.

MS3247 (a) Nos. 3202 and 3214 (b) Nos. 3203 and 3215 (c) Nos. 3204 and 3216 (d) Nos. 3205 and 3217 (e) Nos. 3206 and 3218 (f) Nos. 3207 and 3219 (g) Nos. 3208 and 3220 (h) Nos. 3209 and 3221 (i) Nos. 3210 and 3222 (j) Nos. 3211 and 3223 (k) Nos. 3212 and 3224 (l) Nos. 3213 and 3225 19·00 14·00

720 Man and Cat (Raphael Bordallo Pinheiro)

2005. Caricaturists. Multicoloured.

3248 30c. Type **720** 75 50
3249 30c. Bearded man (Sebastiao Sanhudo) 75 50
3250 30c. Soldier (Celso Herminio) 75 50
3251 30c. Man wearing glasses (Leal da Camara) 75 50
3252 30c. Man holding broken pencil (Francisco Valenca) 75 50
3253 30c. Man smoking (Stuart Carvalhais) 75 50
3254 30c. Guarda Ricardo (Sam (Samuel Torres de Carvalho)) 75 50
3255 30c. Almada Negreios (Joao Abel Manta) 75 50
3256 30c. Man tie (Augusto Cid) 75 50
3257 30c. Head and pencil (Antonio Atunes) 75 50
3258 30c. Ze Povinho (Raphael Bordallo Pinheiro) 75 50

721 Conductor's Hands

2005. Faro—National Cultural Capital 2005. Multicoloured.

3259 30c. Type **721** 60 50
3260 45c. Ancient pot 95 80
3261 57c. Shell 1·20 1·00
3262 74c. Hands 1·60 1·30

722 Coastline and Bell

2005. Tourism. Multicoloured. (a) Lisbon.

3263 45c. Type **722** 95 75
3264 48c. Monument and tram 1·00 85
3265 57c. Tram, rooftops and cupola 1·40 1·00

(b) Porto e Norte.

3266 45c. Ceramic rooster, valley and church 95 75
3267 48c. Church, bay and wine glass 1·00 85
3268 57c. Wine glass, seafront and yachts 1·40 1·00

Nos. 3263/5 and 3266/8, respectively were printed together, se-tenant, each forming a composite design.

723 Harvesting Bark from protected Cork Trees

2005. Environmental Protection. Multicoloured.

3269 30c. Type **723** 60 50
3270 45c. Fire prevention officers 90 75
3271 57c. Bucaco Forest 1·20 1·00
MS3272 95×95 mm. €2 Chestnut trees (Serra de S. Mamede) 4·00 3·25

724 "50" and UN Emblem

2005. 50th Anniv of United Nations Membership. Multicoloured.

3273 30c. Type **724** 60 50
3274 45c. Dove (International Day of Peace) 90 75
3275 57c. Child (UNESCO—Children at Risk) 1·20 1·00
3276 74c. Albert Einstein (International Year of Physics) 1·50 1·30

725 Sundial, St John the Baptist Church, Sao Joao das Lampas

2005. Annular Solar Eclipse—3rd October. Multicoloured.

3277 45c. Type **725** 95 75
3278 €1 Portable sundial, 1770 2·00 1·70
MS3279 125×135 mm. €1.20×3, Partial eclipse, Lisbon; Annulus, Braganca; Partial eclipse, Faro 7·50 6·00

726 Pen Nib

2005. Communications. Multicoloured.

3280 30c. Type **726** 60 50
3281 45c. Radio microphone 90 75
3282 57c. Television camera 1·20 1·00
3283 74c. Globe and @ (internet) 1·50 1·30
MS3284 Two sheets, each 125×90 mm. (a) €1.10 Newspaper; €1.55 Radio studio. (b) €1.10 Television studio; €1.55 "http://www" (internet) 10·50 10·00

727 Fisherman and Boats, Aldeia da Carrasqueira

2005. Fishing Villages. Multicoloured.

3285 30c. Type **727** 60 50
3286 30c. Moorings and pier, Aldeia da Carrasqueira 60 50
3287 30c. Boat, Tai O, Hong Kong 60 50
3288 30c. Wrapped fish, Tai O 60 50

Nos. 3285/6 and 3287/8 respectively were issued together, se-tenant, forming a composite design.

Stamps of the same design were issued by Hong Kong.

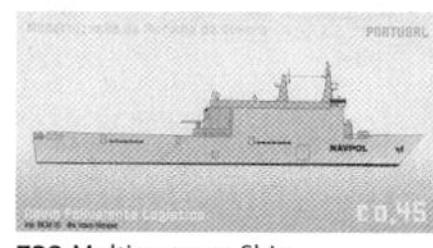

728 Multipurpose Ship

2005. Modernisation of the Navy. Black.

3289 45c. Type **728** 90 75
3290 57c. Hydro-oceanographic ship 1·20 1·00
3291 74c. Patrol vessel 1·50 1·30
3292 €2 Submarine 4·00 3·25

729 Alvaro Cunhal, Women and Children

2005. Alvaro Barreirinhas Cunhal (politician and writer) Commemoration. Multicoloured.

3293 30c. Type **729** 1·00 50
MS3294 112×104 mm. €1 Alvaro Cunhal and girl 1·80 1·80

730 Building

2005. Serralves Foundation. Multicoloured.

3295 30c. Type **730** 60 50
3296 45c. "Projected Shadow of Adami" (Lourdes de Castro) 90 75
3297 48c. Building facade 1·00 85
3298 57c. Trowel (Claes Oldenburg Cooseje van Bruggen) 1·20 95
3299 74c. Hand and painting 1·50 1·30
3300 €1 Path, hedges and lawn 2·00 1·70
MS3301 Two sheets, each 125×150 mm. (a) 30c. As No. 3297 (horiz); 45c. Path; 45c. Columns and balustrade; 45c. Tower; 45c. Canal and evergreens (b) €1 Museum building (80×30 mm); €1 Museum displays (80×30 mm); €1 Parkland 10·50 8·25

731 Futebol Clube do Porto Emblem and Player (1993)

2005. Football Clubs' Centenaries. Showing emblem and player. Multicoloured.

3302 N (30c.) Type **731** 60 50
3303 N (30c.) Sport Lisboa e Benefica (2004) 60 50
3304 N (30c.) Sporting Clube de Portugal (2006) 60 50
MS3305 Three sheets, each 125×96 mm. (a) €1 Porto Football Club emblem and trophy; (b) €1 Sport Lisboa e Benefica emblem, player, stadium and trophy; (c) €1 Anniversary emblem 6·75 1·70

Nos. 3302/4 were for use on letters weighing 20 grams or less.

732 Scenes of Devastation (image scaled to 55% of original size)

2005. 250th Anniv of Earthquake—31 October 1755. Multicoloured.

3306	45c. Type **732**	90	75
3307	€2 Aftermath	4·00	3·25
MS3308	80×80 mm. €2.65 Survivors (40×30 mm)	5·25	4·25

733 Children's Party

2006. Greetings Stamps. Multicoloured. (a) Sheet stamps.

3309	N. Type **733**	60	50
3310	N. Girl and couples	60	50
3311	N. Mother, father and baby	60	50
3312	N. Conductor	60	50
3313	N. Couple about to kiss	60	50

(b) Size 40×29 mm.

3314	N. As No. 3309	60	50
3315	N. As No. 3310	60	50
3316	N. As No. 3311	60	50
3317	N. As No. 3312	60	50
3318	N. As No. 3313	60	50

Nos. 3314/18 were issued together, se-tenant, forming a composite design.

2006. Masks (2nd series). As T 712. Multicoloured. Self-adhesive gum.

3319	N. "Festa dos Rapazes", Salsas, Bragança (29×24 mm)	60	50
3320	A. Lazarim carnival, Bragança (29×24 mm)	90	75
3321	E. "Dia de Ano Novo", Mogadouro, Bragança (29×24 mm)	1·20	1·00

No. 3320 is inscribed "Correio Azul".

No. 3319 was for use on normal domestic mail, up to 20 grams, 3320 was for domestic first class (blue) mail and 3321 was for European mail.

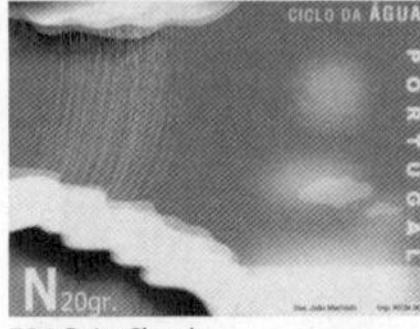

734 Rain Clouds

2006. Water. Multicoloured.

3322	N. Type **734**	60	50
3323	N. Glass of water	60	50
3324	A. Water from tap	90	75
3325	A. Water turbines	90	75
3326	E. Yacht	1·20	1·00
3327	E. Flower	1·20	1·00

Nos. 3322/3 was for use on normal domestic mail, up to 20 grams, 3324/5 was for domestic first class (blue) mail and, 3326/7 was for European mail.

735 Baptising

2006. 500th Birth Anniv of Saint Francis Xavier. Multicoloured.

3328	45c. Type **735**	95	75
3329	€1 Preaching	2·00	1·70
MS3330	85×125 mm. €2.75 Saint Francis Xavier (painting)	4·50	3·25

736 Enclosed Figure (Bento Luz)

2006. Europa. Integration. Winning Entries in ANACED (association for art and creativity by and for people with disabilities) Painting Competition. Multicoloured.

3331	60c. Type **736**	1·30	1·00
MS3332	125×95 mm. 60c.×2, Figure in wheelchair (David Fernandes); Aliens and humans from many nations (Ana Sofia, Renarto, Jose Luis and Alcidia)	2·50	2·00

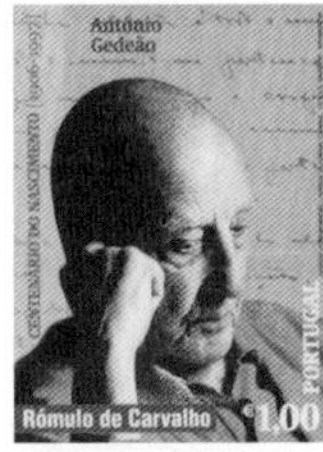

737 Romulo de Carvalho (science writer)

2006. Birth Centenaries. Multicoloured.

3333	€1 Type **737**	2·00	1·70
3334	€1 Agostinho da Silva (philosopher)	2·00	1·70
3335	€1 Thomaz de Mello (artist)	2·00	1·70
3336	€1 Humberto Delgado (politician)	2·00	1·70
3337	€1 Lopes-Graca (composer and musician)	2·00	1·70

738 Players' Legs

2006. UEFA Under-21 Football Championship, Portugal. Sheet 125×65 mm.

MS3338	**738** €2.75 multicoloured	5·50	4·50

739 Players

2006. World Cup Football Championship, Germany. Multicoloured.

3339	45c. Type **739**	90	4·75
3340	€1 Players (different)	2·00	1·70
MS3341	125×85 mm. €2.40 Emblem and trophy	5·00	4·00

739a Mozart (etching)

2006. 250th Birth Anniv of Wolfgang Amadeus Mozart (composer). Etchings by Giovanni Antonio Sasso. Multicoloured.

3341a	60c. Type **739a**	1·20	1·00
MS3341b	90×115 mm. €2.75 Mozart facing right	5·50	4·50

740 Dunes

2006. International Year of Deserts and Desertification. Multicoloured.

3342	30c. Type **740**	60	50
3343	60c. Dead and live trees	1·20	1·00

741 Oceanus (mosaic)

2006. Roman Heritage. Multicoloured.

3344	30c. Type **741**	60	50
3345	45c. Temple, Evora	90	75
3346	50c. Patera de Lameira Larga	1·00	85
3347	60c. Two headed statue ("Herma Bifronte")	1·20	1·00
MS3348	125×95 mm. €2.40 Seahorse (mosaic)	5·00	4·00

2006. Masks (3rd series). As T 712. Multicoloured. Ordinary gum.

3349	3c. Owl (Lazarim carnival, Bragança)	10	10
3350	5c. Scarecrow, "Festa dos Rapazes", Bacal, Braganca	10	10
3351	30c. As No. 3319 ("Festa dos Rapazes", Salsas, Braganca)	60	50
3352	45c. As No. 3320 (Lazarim carnival, Bragança)	90	75
3353	60c. As No. 3321 ("Dia de Ano Novo", Mogadouro, Braganca)	1·20	1·00
3354	75c. Devil ("Dia dos Diabos", Vinhais, Braganca)	1·50	1·30

743 Flags

2006. 10th Anniv of Community of Portuguese Speaking Countries (CPLP). Sheet 125×65 mm.

MS3357	**743** €2.85 multicoloured	6·00	4·75

744 "Picture of a Young Woman" (Domenico Ghirlandaio)

2006. 50th Anniv of Calouste Gulbenkian Foundation. Multicoloured.

3358	30c. Type **744**	60	50
3359	45c. Brooch (Rene Lalique)	90	75
3360	60c. Tiles (Turkish c.1573)	1·20	1·00
3361	75c. "Flora" (sculpture) (Jean Baptiste Carpeaux) and Roman medallion	1·50	1·30
3362	€1 Jade jar	2·00	1·70
3363	€2 "Calouste Gulbenkian" (C. J. Watelet)	4·00	3·25
MS3364	125×95 mm. 30c.×4, Statues (art); Books (education); Spectroscope (science); Mother and child (charity)	2·50	2·00

Nos. 3358/63 when laid together form a composite design. The stamps of **MS**3364 form a composite design.

745 Jose Gomes Ferreira School, Lisbon (Raul Hestnes Ferreira)

2006. Contemporary Architecture. Multicoloured.

3365	30c. Type **745**	60	50
3366	30c. Borges & Irmao Bank, Vila do Conde (Alvaro Siza)	60	50
3367	30c. Matosinhos City Council (Alcino Soutinho)	60	50
3368	30c. Casa das Artes, Porto (Eduardo Souto Moura)	60	50
3369	30c. University campus, Santiago (Nuno Portas/CEFAUP)	60	50
3370	30c. Escola Superior de Comunicao Social (ESCS), Lisbon (Carrilho da Graca)	60	50
3371	30c. Plan for Alto do Restelo, Lisbon (Teotonio Pereira, Nuno Portas, Pedro Botelho and Joao Paciencia)	60	50
3372	30c. Order of architects, Lisbon (Manuel Graca Dias and Egas JoseVieira)	60	50
3373	30c. St. Mary's church, Forno, Marco de Canaveses (Alvaro Siza)	60	50
3374	30c. Bairro da Bouca, SAAL, Porto (Alvaro Siza)	60	50

746 Early Camera and Crew

2006. 50th Anniv of First Television Broadcast in Portugal. Multicoloured.

3375	30c. Type **746**	60	50
3376	60c. Modern camera	1·20	1·00

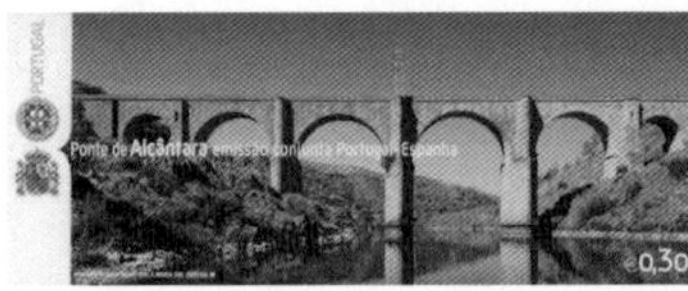

747 Ponte de Alcantara (image scaled to 61% of original size)

2006. Bridges. Multicoloured.

3377	30c. Type **747**	60	50
3378	52c. Ponte de Vila Real de Sto. Antonio	1·10	90

Stamps of similar design were issued by Spain.

748 Grapes and Terraces (image scaled to 56% of original size)

2006. 250th Anniv of Douro Wine Demarcated Region. Sheet 125×95 mm.

MS3379	**748** €2.40 multicoloured	5·00	4·00

749 *Capros aper*

2006. Fish. Multicoloured.

3380	30c. Type **749**	60	50
3381	45c. *Anthias anthias*	90	75
3382	60c. *Lepadogaster lepadogaster*	1·20	1·00
3383	75c. *Gobiusculus flavescens*	1·50	1·30
3384	€1 *Coris julis*	2·00	1·70
3385	€2 *Calliomymus lyra*	4·00	3·25
MS3386	Two sheets, each 125×115 mm. (a) 80c.×2, *Macroramphosus scolopax*; *Echiichthys vipera*. (b) 80c.×2, *Thalassoma pavo*; *Blennius ocellaris*	7·00	5·50

750 "a"

2006. School Correspondence. Multicoloured.

3387	N Type **750**	60	50
3388	N "c, g, d"	60	50

751 Flecha de Prata (Silver Arrow)

2006. 150th Anniv of National Railways. Multicoloured.

3389	30c. Type **751**	60	50
3390	45c. Sud-Express	90	75
3391	60c. Foguette	1·20	1·00
3392	€2 Alfa Pendular	4·00	3·25
MS3393	125×95 mm. €1.60 Blessing first train (80×30 mm)	3·25	2·50

752 "A Cidade de Gale"

2006. 500th Anniv of Portuguese in Ceylon. Multicoloured.

3394	30c. Type **752**	60	50

3395 75c. "O Livro das Plantas e Todas as Fortalezas" 1·50 1·30
MS3396 125×95 mm. €2.40 As No. 3394 5·00 4·00

753 16th-century Tiles

2007. In Search of Arab Lisbon. Multicoloured.
3397 30c. Type **753** 60 50
3398 45c. 9th-century limestone carving 90 75
3399 52c. Neo-Arab door 1·00 90
3400 61c. Neo-Arab interior, National Film Library 1·20 1·00
3401 75c. Casa Alentejo 1·50 1·20
3402 €1 Palacete Ribeiro da Cunha 2·00 1·60
MS3403 130×95 mm. €2.95 11th-century Islamic jug 6·00 4·75

754 Laundress wearing Scarves ("Lavadeira") (Minho)

2007. Regional Costume. Multicoloured.
3404 30c. Type **754** 60 50
3405 30c. Bride wearing gold chains ("Noiva") (Minho) 30 50
3406 30c. Cape ("Capa de Honras") (Tras-os-Montes) 60 50
3407 30c. Embroidered tunic ("Pauliteiro") (Tras-os-Montes) 60 50
3408 30c. Fisherman's jersey ("Camisola de Pescador") (Douro Litoral) 60 50
3409 30c. Straw cape ("Coroça") (Beiras/Tras-os-Montes) 60 50
3410 30c. Embroidered apron and skirts ("Saias de Nazare") (Estremadura) 60 50
3411 30c. Horseman wearing red waistcoat ("Campino") (Ribatejo) 60 50
3412 30c. Floral apron and skirt ("Camponesa") (Algarve) 60 50
3413 30c. Cape with fur collar ("Capote") (Alentejo) 60 50
3414 30c. Hooded cloak ("Capote e Capelo") (Azores) 60 50
3415 30c. Short jacket, white shirt and red sash ("Campones") (Beira Litoral) 60 50
3416 30c. Striped dress and red cape ("Viloa") (Madeira) 60 50
3417 30c. Smoked blouse, apron and embroidered cloak ("Camponesa") (Ribatejo) 60 50

755 "Carreaux Diamants"

2007. Manuel Cargaleiro (artist and ceramist). Multicoloured.
3418 30c. Type **755** 60 50
3419 45c. "Composizione Floreale" 90 75
3420 52c. "Decorcao Mural" 1·20 1·00

756 "D. Joao i Reforca a Casa dos Contos" (painting by Jaime Martins Barata)

2007. Bicentenary of European Court of Auditors. Multicoloured.
3421 30c. Type **756** 60 50
3422 61c. Creation of Court of Auditors (painting by Almada Negreiros) 1·20 1·20
3423 €2 Headquarters of the Court, 1954–1989 4·00 3·25

MS3424 95×125 mm. €2.95 "The Auditor" (tapestry) 6·00 4·75

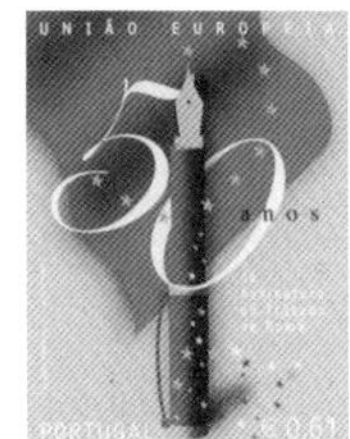

757 Pen, Flag and Stars

2007. 50th Anniv of Treaty of Rome.
3425 **757** 61c. multicoloured 1·20 1·00

758 Ox-drawn Carriage

2007. Public Transport. Multicoloured. (a) Ordinary gum.
3425a 1c. Articulated bus (8.3.10) 10 10
3425b 6c. Electric car (1927) 10 30
3425c 20c. Bus (1957) 40 30
3426 30c. Type **758** 65 35
3426a 31c. Oldsmobile taxi (1928) 60 45
3426b 32c. Triple unit electric car (1957) 65 50
3426c 32c. Articulated electric car (1995) (8.3.10) 65 50
3427 45c. Horse-drawn tram facing right ("Americano") (1872) 90 70
3427a 47c. Tram (1926) 1·00 60
3427b 47c. Carruagem ML7 (1959) 1·10 35
3427c 47c. Carruagem ML7 (1959) 1·10 35
3427d 47c. Comboio ML79 (1984) (Lisbon metro) (8.3.10) 1·00 60
3428 50c. Horse-drawn tram facing left ("Americano") (1873) 1·00 80
3429 61c. Electric tram (Eletrico No. 22) (1895) 1·20 95
3429a 67c. Coach (1944) 1·40 70
3429b 68c. Bus No. 207 (1960) 1·70 85
3429c 68c. Bus No. 207 (1960) 1·30 1·30
3429d 68c. *Madragoa* (1981) (ferry) (8.3.10) 1·30 1·30
3430 75c. Electric tram (Eletrico No. 283) (1901) 1·50 1·20
3430a 80c. Electric car (1911) 1·60 75
3430b 80c. Trolley bus (1961) 1·60 1·20
3430c 80c. Trolley bus (1961) 1·80 90
3430d 80c. Quadruple unit electric car (1992) (8.3.10) 1·60 70

(b) Size 30×22 mm. Self-adhesive gum.
3436 N As No. 3427 60 50
3436a N Oldsmobile taxi (1928) 60 45
3436b N (32c.) Triple electric car (1957) (As. No. 3426b) 65 50
3436c N (32c.) Articulated electric car (1995) (inscribed Crreio Azul) (As No. 3426c) (8.3.10) 60 45
3437 A Tram with driver (Eletrico No. 22) (1895) 90 75
3437a A Tram (1928) inaugeration of electrical tractors company, Estopil 90 70
3437b A (47c.) Carruagem ML7 (1959) (As. No. 3427b) 1·00 75
3437c A (47c.) Comboio ML79 (1984) (Lisbon metro) (As No. 3427c) (8.3.10) 90 70
3438 E Tram with driver (Eletrico No. 283) (1901) 1·40 70
3438a E Coach (1944) ingeration of coach company, Carris 1·40 70
3438b E (67c.) Bus No. 207 (1960) (As No. 3429b) 1·40 70
3438c E (67c.) *Madragoa* (1981) (ferry) (As No. 3429c) (8.3.10) 1·40 70

No. 3436/b was for use on normal domestic mail, up to 20 grams, No. 3437/b was for domestic first class (blue) mail and No. 3438/b was for European mail.

759 Castelo do Bode Dam

2007. Dams. Multicoloured. (a) Size 40×30 mm.
3445 30c. Type **759** 60 50

(b) Size 80×30 mm.
3446 30c. Aguieira 60 50
3447 61c. Valeira 1·20 1·00
3448 75c. Alto Lindoso 1·50 1·20
3449 €1 Castelo do Bode extended 2·00 1·60

760 Robert Baden Powell (founder)

2007. Europa. Centenary of Scouting Multicoloured.
3450 61c. Type **760** 1·30 1·00
MS3451 125×95 mm. 61c.×2, Compass; Scouts reading map 2·50 2·00

The stamps of **MS**3451 form a composite design.

2007. Contemporary Architecture. As T 745. Multicoloured.
3452 30c. ESAD, Caldas da Rainha (Vitor Figueiredo) 60 50
3453 30c. Pavilion, Lisbon (Alvaro Siza) 60 50
3454 30c. VTS Tower, Lisbon Port (Goncalo Byrne) 60 50
3455 30c. Casa dos 24, Porto (Fernando Tavora) 60 50
3456 30c. Jose Saramago Library, Loures (Fernando Martins) 60 50
3457 30c. Documentation and Information Centre of President of the Republic, Lisbon (Carrilho da Graca) 60 50
3458 30c. Art Centre, Sines (Aires Mateus) 60 50
3459 30c. Municipal building, Braga (Eduardo Souto Moura) 60 50
3460 30c. Centre for Visual Arts, Coimbra (Joao Mendes Ribeiro) 60 50
3461 30c. Maritime Museum, Ilhavo (ARX Portugal) 60 50
MS3462 125×95 mm. €1.85 Pavilion, Lisbon (Alvaro Siza) (different) (Lisbon Architecture Triennale 2007) 3·75 3·00

The stamps and margins of **MS**3462 form a composite design.

761 Catamarans

2007. ISAF World Sailing Championships. Showing stylized craft. Multicoloured.
3463 61c. Type **761** 1·20 1·00
3464 61c. Two yachts, sail nos. '23' and '105' 1·20 1·00
3465 75c. Yacht, sail no. '75' 1·30 1·10
3466 75c. Two yachts, sail nos. '34' and '16' 1·30 1·10
MS3467 125×95 mm. €2.95 As No. 3465 6·00 4·75

The stamp and margin of **MS**3467 form a composite design.

762 Castelo de Guimaraes

2007. Seven Marvels of Portugal. Multicoloured.
3468 30c. Type **762** 60 50
3469 30c. Palacio de Mateus, Vila Real 60 50
3470 30c. Sao Francisco church, Porto 60 50
3471 30c. Torre dos Clerigos church, Porto 60 50
3472 30c. Clock tower, University of Coimbra 60 50
3473 30c. Ruins, Conimbriga, Condeixa-a-Nova 60 50
3474 30c. Batalha monastery 60 50
3475 30c. Convent of Christ, Tomar 60 50
3476 30c. Almourol castle, Vila Nova da Barquinha 60 50
3477 30c. Alcobaca monastery 60 50
3478 30c. Obidos castle 60 50
3479 30c. Basilica and convent of Mafra 60 50
3480 30c. Marvao castle 60 50
3481 30c. Blockhouses, Monsaraz 60 50
3482 30c. Vila Vicosa Ducal palace 60 50
3483 30c. Roman temple, Evora 60 50
3484 30c. Palacio Nacional da Pena, Sintra 60 50
3485 30c. Palacio Nacional da Queluz, Sintra 60 50
3486 30c. Mosteiro dos Jeronimos, Lisbon 60 50
3487 30c. Torre de Belem, Lisbon 60 50
3488 30c. Sagres fortress, Vila do Bispo 60 50

763 *Ponte* (Amadeo de Souza Cardoso)

2007. Exhibits from Berado Museum Collection. Multicoloured.
3489 45c. Type **763** 90 75
3490 61c. *Les Baigneuses* (Niki de Saint Phalle) (vert) 1·20 1·00
3491 61c. *Interior with Restful Paintings* (Roy Lichtenstein) (vert) 1·20 1·00
3492 61c. *Femme dans un Fauteuil* (Pablo Picasso) (vert) 1·20 1·00
3493 61c. *Le Couple* (Oacar Dominguez) (vert) 1·20 1·00
3494 61c. *Cafe Man Ray* (Man Ray) (vert) 1·20 1·00
3495 61c. *Nectar* (Joana Vasconcelos) (vert) 2·00 1·60
3496 61c. *Head* (Jackson Pollack) (vert) 4·00 3·25

764 Building and Stars

2007. Portugal–Presidency of European Union. Multicoloured.
3497 61c. Type **764** 1·20 1·00
MS3498 125×95 mm. €2.45 As No. 3497 but direction of stars reversed 4·50 4·50

765 SMC Nacional 500cc., 1935

2007. Motorcycles. Multicoloured.
3499 30c. Type **765** 60 50
3500 52c. Famel Fougete, 1959 1·00 90
3501 61c. Vilar Cucciolo, 1955 1·20 1·00
3502 €1 Casal Carina, 1969 2·00 1·60
MS3503 125×95 mm. 61c.×4, Qimera Alma, 1952; Cinal Pachancho, 1958; SIS Sachs V5, 1965; Casal K287, 1985 5·00 4·00

The stamps of **MS**3467 form a composite background design.

766 Globe

2007. Declaration of Winning Entries in New Seven Wonders of the World Competition–Lisbon 2007. Sheet 125×95 mm.
MS3504 **766** €2.95 multicoloured 6·00 4·75

The stamp and margin of **MS**3467 form a composite design.

767 Raul Maria Pereira and Postal Building, Peru

2007. 130th Birth Anniv of Raul Maria Pereira (artist and architect).

3505	**767**	75c. multicoloured	1·50	1·20

Stamp of a similar design was issued by Peru.

768 Jose Valentim Fialho de Almeida

2007. Personalities. Multicoloured.

3506	45c. Type **768** (writer) (150th birth anniv)	90	75
3507	45c. Columbano Bordalo Pinheiro (Columbano) (artist) (150th birth anniv)	90	75
3508	45c. Adolfo Correia da Rocha (Miguel Torga) (writer) (birth centenary)	90	75

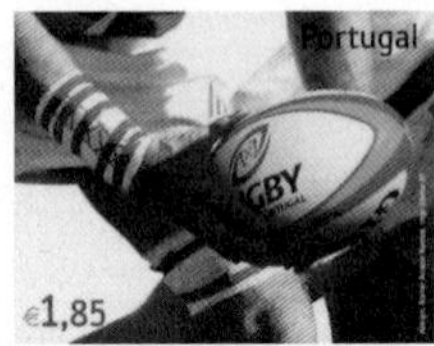

769 Hands clasping Ball

2007. Rugby World Cup, France. Sheet 125×95 mm.

MS3509 **769**	€1.85 multicoloured	3·75	3·00

The stamp and margin of **MS**3509 form a composite design.

770 *Horus,* 1953

2007. Portuguese Artists. Nadir Afonso. Mult.

3510	30c. Type **770**	60	50
3511	45c. *Veneza,* 1956	90	75
3512	61c. *Processao em Veneza,* 2002	1·20	1·00

771 Jacaranda

2007. Plants and Animals from the Americas. Multicoloured.

3513	30c. Type **771**	60	50
3514	30c. Potatoes	60	50
3515	30c. Maize	60	50
3516	45c. Cocoa	90	75
3517	61c. Turkeys (inscr 'Peru')	1·20	1·00
3518	75c. Passion fruit	1·50	1·20
MS3519	125×95 mm. €1.85 Humming bird and passion fruit (horiz)	3·75	3·00

The stamp and margin of **MS**3519 form a composite design.

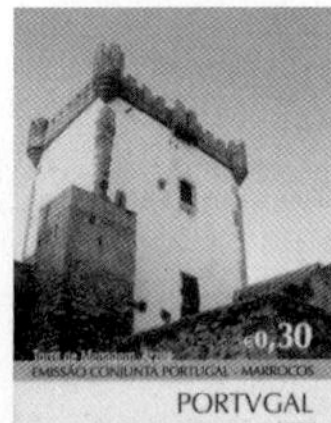

772 Torre de Menagem, Arzila

2007. Architecture. Multicoloured.

3520	30c. Type **772**	60	50
3521	75c. Castelo de Silves, Portugal	1·50	1·20

Stamps of a similar design were issued by Morocco.

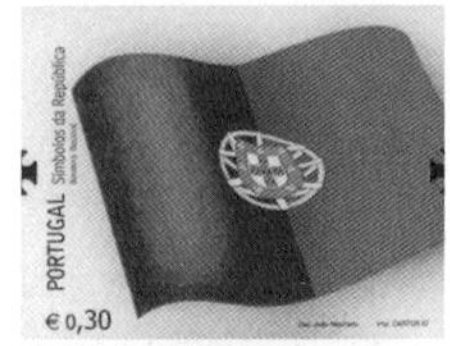

773 National Flag

2007. Symbols of the Republic. Flags. Mult.

3522	30c. Type **773**	60	50
MS3523	95×125 mm. 30c.×5, As Type **773**; President of the Republic; National Assembly; Azores; Madeira	3·00	2·50

The stamps and margins of **MS**3523 form a composite background design.

774 Children and Globe (Sofia Fiteire Passeira)

2007. School Correspondence. Children's Paintings. Multicoloured.

3524	N Type **774**	60	50
3525	N Girls and flowers (Ines Filipa Navrat)	60	50
3526	N Globe enclosed in hands (Maria Correira Borges)	60	50

Nos. 3524/6 were for use on domestic mail weighing 20 grams or less.

775 Fallow Deer (*Cervus dama*)

2007. Mafra National Park. Multicoloured.

3527	30c. Type **775**	60	50
3528	45c. Wild boar (*Sus scrofa*)	90	75
3529	61c. Fox (*Vulpes vulpes*)	1·20	1·00
3530	75c. Red deer (*Cervus elaphus*)	1·50	1·20
3531	€1 Eurasian eagle owl (*Bubo bubo*)	2·00	1·25
3532	€2 Bonelli's eagle (*Hieraaetus fasciatus*)	4·00	2·50

776 Courtyard, Centro Ismali, Lisbon

2007. 50th Anniv of Ismaili Community in Portugal. Multicoloured.

3533	N Type **776**	60	50
3534	I Aerial view of courtyard	1·50	1·20

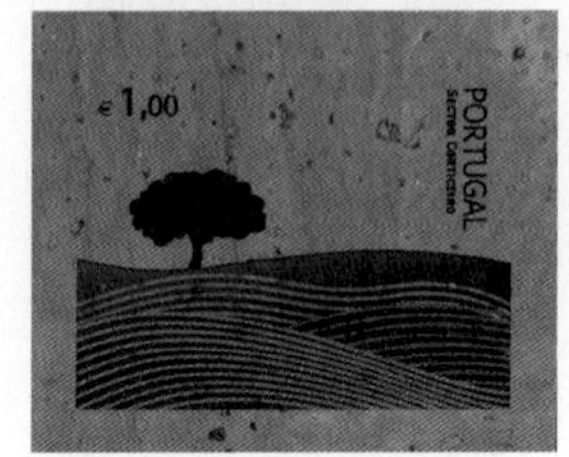

777 Cork Tree

2007. Cork Production. Self-adhesive.

3535	**777**	€1 multicoloured	2·00	1·25

No. 3535 was made of cork applied to a paper backing.

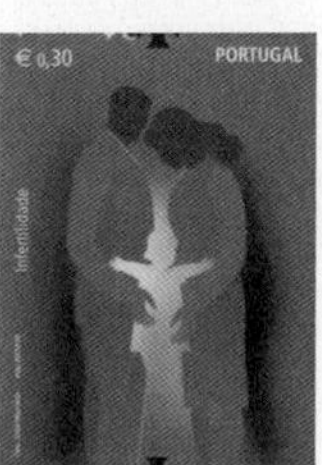

780 Family

2008. Infertility Awareness Campaign.

3539	**780**	30c. multicoloured	60	45

781 Woodland

2008. International Year of Planet Earth. Multicoloured. each vert side).

3540	30c. Type **781**	60	45
3541	45c. Clouds	90	70
3542	61c. Volcano erupting	1·20	95
3543	75c. Under water	1·50	1·20

782 Throw

2008. Sporting Events (1st issue). European Judo Championships. Multicoloured.

3544	30c. Type **782**	60	45
3545	61c. Throw (different)	1·20	95
MS3546	125×95 mm. 45c. As Type **782** but including competition emblem; €2 As No. 3545 but including competition emblem	3·00	2·00

See also Nos. 353/6 and 3559.

783 Father Antonio Vieira

2008. Personalities. Multicoloured.

3547	30c. Type **783** (Jesuit and writer) (400th birth anniv)	60	45
3548	30c. Jose Maria Mascarenhas Relvas (politician) (150th birth anniv)	60	45
3549	30c. Aureliano de Mira Fernandes (mathematician) (50th death anniv)	60	45
3550	30c Ricardo Jorge (physician and humanist) (150th birth anniv)	60	45
3551	30c. Maria Elena Vieira da Silva (artist) (birth centenary)	60	45
3552	30c. Manoel Candido Pinto de Oliveira (film director) (birth centenary)	60	45

784 Runners

2008. Sporting Events (2nd issue). Olympic Games, Beijing. Multicoloured.

3553	30c. Type **784**	60	45
3554	30c. Cyclists	60	45
3555	75c. Long jumper	1·50	1·20
MS3556	125×95 mm. 75c.×4, Show jumper; Rower; Marksman; Gymnast	6·00	4·50

The stamps and margins of **MS**3556 form a composite design.

785 Envelope Rider

2008. Europa. The Letter. Multicoloured.

3557	61c. Type **785**	1·20	95
MS3558	125×95 mm. 61c.×2, As Type **785**; Postvan, envelope and bull	2·40	1·90

The stamps of **MS**3558 form a composite design.

786 Athletes (image scaled to 56% of original size)

2008. Sporting Events (3rd issue). European Triathlon Championship, Lisbon.

3559	**786**	€2 multicoloured	4·00	3·00

787 Mother, Child and Teacher

2008. The Rights of the Child. Right to Education. Multicoloured.

3560	30c. Type **787**	60	45
3561	45c. Teacher and pupils	90	70
3562	61c. Children reading	1·20	95
3563	75c. Child reading with parents	1·50	1·20
MS3564	95×125 mm. €2.95 Boy hugging '4'	6·00	4·50

788 Players

2008. Euro 2008–European Football Championships, Austria and Switzerland. Multicoloured.

3565	30c. Type **788**	60	45
3566	61c. Goal keeper catching ball and player	1·20	95
MS3567	125×95 mm. €1.20 Players heading ball; €1.66 Players tackling	5·75	4·50

789 Esposende

2008. Lighthouses. Multicoloured.

3568	30c. Type **789**	60	50
3569	30c. Penedo da Saudade	60	50
3570	30c. Cabo Sardao (horiz)	60	50
3571	30c. Cabo da Roca (horiz)	60	50
3572	30c. Torre do Bugio (horiz)	60	50
3573	30c. Leca	60	50
3574	30c. Montedor	60	50
3575	30c. Santa Marta	60	50
3576	30c. Cabo de Sao Vincente (horiz)	60	50
3577	30c. Cabo Espichel	60	50

790 *Calidris alba* (sanderling)

2008. International Polar Year. Multicoloured.

3578	30c. Type **790**	60	45
3579	52c. *Alca torda* (razorbill)	1·00	85
3580	61c. *Oceanites oceanicus* (Wilson's storm-petrel)	1·20	95
3581	€1 *Sterna paradisea* (arctic tern)	2·00	1·60
MS3582	125×95 mm. €2.95 *Phoca hispida* (ringed seal) and *Ursus maritimus* (polar bear) (80×30 mm)	6·00	4·50

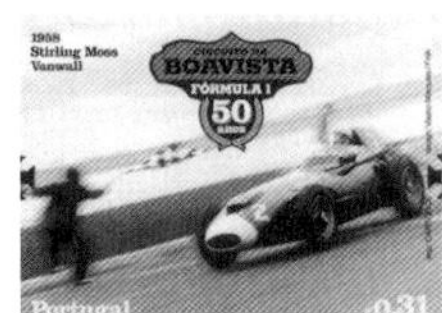

791 Vanwall 57 VW5 driven by Stirling Moss, 1958

2008. 50th Anniv of Formula I Grand Prix in Portugal. Multicoloured.

3583 31c. Type **791** 60 45
3584 67c. Cooper T53 driven by Jack Brabham, 1960 1·40 1·10
3585 80c. Cooper driven by Mark Haywood, 2005 1·60 1·20
3586 €2 McLaren M26 driven by Bobby Vernon Roe 4·00 3·00
MS3587 125×95 mm. €2.45 FI Grand Prix, 1960 (80×30 mm) 5·00 3·75

792 Symbols of Information Technology (image scaled to 61% of original size)

2008. Information Technology 'E-School' Programme. Sheet 125×95 mm.

MS3588 multicoloured 6·00 4·75

793 Metal Work

2008. Centenary of Group CUF. Multicoloured.

3589 31c. Type **793** 60 45
3590 67c. Textiles 1·40 1·10
3591 €1 Naval construction 2·00 1·60
3592 €2 Chemicals 4·00 3·00
MS3593 125×95 mm. €2.45 Alfredo da Silva (founder) (vert) 5·00 4·00

794 Vases (17th century)

2008. Pharmaceutical Ceramics. Multicoloured.

3594 31c. Type **794** 60 45
3595 47c. Bottle (18th century) 1·00 80
3596 67c. Vases (17th–18th century) 1·40 1·10
3597 80c. Vases (19th century) 1·60 1·20
MS3598 125×95 mm. €2.45 Pharmacy (17th–18th century) 5·00 4·00

795 Vineyard, Dao Region

2008. Centenary of Demarcated Wine Regions. Multicoloured.

3599 31c. Type **795** 60 45
3600 31c. Barrels, Dao 60 45
3601 31c. Vineyard, Vinhos Verdes 60 45
3602 31c. Terraces, Vinhos Verdes 60 45
3603 31c. Vines, Colares 60 45
3604 31c. Barrels, Colares 60 45
3605 31c. Vineyard, Bucelas 60 45
3606 31c. Barrels, Bucelas 60 45
3607 31c. Barrels, Moscatel de Setubal 60 45
3608 31c. Vineyard, Moscatel de Setubal 60 45

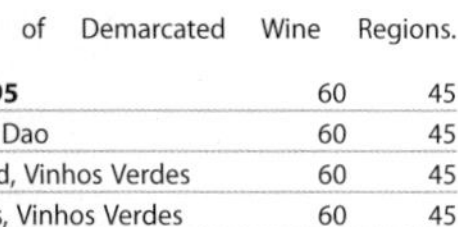

Nos. 3599/600, 3601/2, 3605/6 were printed together, se-tenant, forming a composite design.

796 Centenary of First 'Executivo Republicano Camarario', Lisbon

2008. Republican Ideas. Multicoloured.

3609 31c. Type **796** 60 45
3610 31c. Republican school 60 45
3611 47c. Industrialization 1·00 80
3612 47c. Housing 1·00 80
3613 57c. State modernization 1·20 95
3614 67c. Civil register 1·30 1·00
3615 67c. Public health 1·40 1·10
3616 80c. Civic participation 1·50 1·20
MS3617 125×95 mm. €2.95 Rail–road link project over River Tejo (80×30 mm) 6·00 4·75

797 Olive Grove

2008. Olive Oil Production. Multicoloured.

3618 31c. Type **797** 60 45
3619 47c. Early harvesters 1·00 80
3620 57c. Early milling 1·20 95
3621 67c. Mill stones 1·40 1·10
3622 80c. Oil storage 1·60 1·20
3623 €2 Ready for consumption 4·00 3·00
MS3624 125×95 mm. €1.85 Hands holding olives 3·75 3·00

798 Rainbow and Symbols of Communication (Erica Bluemel Potocarrero)

2008. School Correspondence. Childrens Drawings. Multicoloured.

3625 31c. Type **798** 60 45
3626 47c. Girl and symbols of communication (Eloisa Pereira) 1·00 80
3627 67c. Postman (Joao Mario Martins Branco) 1·40 1·10

799 Ponte 25 de Abril, Lisbon

2008. Bridges. Multicoloured.

3628 31c. Type **799** 60 45
3629 47c. Arrabida, Porto 1·00 80
3630 57c. Arade, Portimao 1·20 95
3631 67c. Mosteiro, Cinfaes 1·40 1·10
3632 80c. Amizade, Vila Nova de Cerveira 1·60 1·20
3633 €1 St Clara, Coimbra 2·00 1·60
MS3634 125×95 mm. €1.85 Ponte 25 de Abril (80×30 mm) 3·75 3·00

800 Mesoamerican Bas Relief and Ceramic Plate

2008. European Year of Intercultural Dialogue. Multicoloured.

3635 31c. Type **800** 60 45
3636 47c. Asian mask and Greek head 1·00 80
3637 67c. Moorish window and feathered headdress 1·40 1·10
3638 80c. African mask and Chinese lion headdress 1·60 1·20

801 *Waiting for Success* (Henrique Cesar de Araujo Pousao)

2009. Personalities. Multicoloured.

3639 32c. Type **801** (artist) (150th birth anniv) 65 50
3640 32c. Soeiro Pereira Gomes (writer) (birth centenary) (horiz) 65 50

802 Euro Coins

2009. Tenth Anniv of Euro. Multicoloured.

3641 47c. Type **802** 1·00 75
3642 €1 € 2·00 1·50

803 Finches

2009. Birth Bicentenary of Charles Darwin (naturalist and evolutionary theorist). Multicoloured.

3643 32c. Type **803** 65 50
3644 32c. Iguana 65 50
3645 68c. Orchid 1·40 1·00
3646 68c. Diana monkey 1·40 1·00
3647 80c. Platypus 1·60 1·20
3648 80c. Skull and fossils 1·60 1·20
MS3649 125×95 mm. €2.50 *Charles Darwin* (George Richmond) (vert) 5·50 3·75

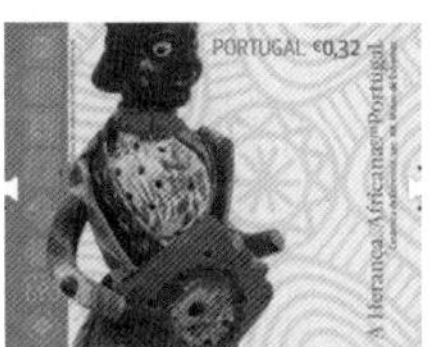

803b Guitarist (ceramic statue)

2009. African Heritage in Portugal. Multicoloured.

3649a 32c. Type **803b** 65 50
3649b 47c. Trumpeter (altarpiece, St Auta (detail)) 1·00 75
3649c 57c. Three children (Conrado Roza) 1·10 75
3649d 68c. Woman 1·40 1·00
3649e 80c. Woman's head (ceramic) 1·60 1·20
3649f €2 Three musicians (painted wood) 4·25 3·00
MS3649g 125×95 mm. €2.50 Musicians (Joaquim Marques) 4·50 3·00

Type **803a** is vacant.

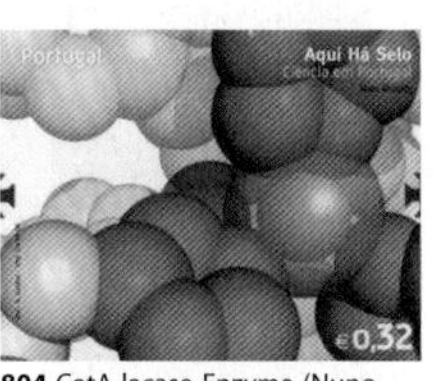

804 CotA-lacase Enzyme (Nuno Micaêlo)

2009. Aquihaselo. Winning Designs in Painting Competition. Multicoloured.

3650 32c. Type **804** 65 50
3651 32c. Multiplication (Sa de Miranda School pupils) 65 50

805 St. Francis and Dog

2009. 800th Anniv of Franciscan Order. Multicoloured.

3652 32c. Type **805** 65 50
MS3653 125×95 mm. Size 31×40 mm. 50c. St. Francis kneeling; €2 Pope Innocent III giving blessing (vert) 5·50 4·00

806 Álvares Pereira

2009. Canonization of Nuno De Santa Maria (Álvares Pereira).

3654 **806** 32c. multicoloured 65 50

807 Eclipse of the Moon (3rd March 2007) Sequence

2009. Europa. Astronomy. Multicoloured.

3655 68c. Type **807** 1·40 1·00
MS3656 125×95 mm. 68c.×2, European Southern Observatory's 'Very Large Telescope', Chile; As Type **807** 2·75 2·10

The stamps and margins of **MS**3656 form a composite design.

808 Iznik Mosque Lamp (Turkey)

2009. Ceramics. Multicoloured.

3657 32c. Type **808** 65 50
3658 68c. Ceramic Jar (Portugal) 1·40 1·00

Stamps of a similar design were issued by Turkey.

809 Sanctuary

2009. 50th Anniv of Cristo Rei Sanctuary, South Bank of the River Tagus, near Lisbon. Multicoloured.

3659 32c. Type **809** 65 50
3660 68c. Christ (statue) 1·40 1·00
MS3661 125×95 mm. €2.48 Head of Christ, bridge and Lisbon (80×31 mm) 5·00 3·75

810 Bebinca das Sete Colinas (layered pudding) (India)

2009. Flavours of Lusophone (Portuguese speaking countries). Multicoloured.

3662 32c. Type **810** 65 50
3663 32c. Leitoa num ar de Sarapatel (meat dish) (Brazil) 65 50
3664 68c. Caldeirada de cabrito (goat stew) (Angola) 1·40 1·00
3665 68c. Balcalhau, pao, vinho e azeite (cooked dried cod, bread, wine and olive oil) 1·40 1·00

3666 80c. No caldeiro a tempura (stew and tempura) (Asia) 1·60 1·20

3667 80c. Do cozido a Cachupa (slow boiled stew of corn, beans, vegetables, spices and marinated pork or tuna) (Cape Verde Islands) 1·60 1·20

MS3668 125×95 mm. €1.85 Balcalhau, pao, vinho e azeite (detail) (vert) 3·75 2·75

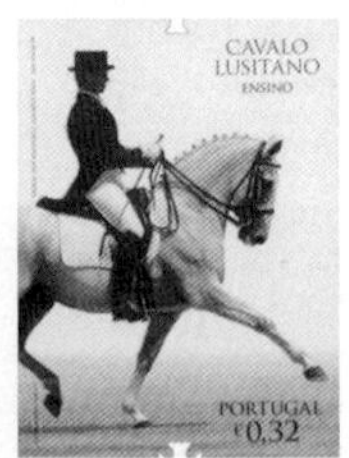

811 'Ensino' (training)

2009. The Lusitanian Horse. Multicoloured.

3669 32c. Type **811** 65 50

3670 32c. Equitacao de Trabalho 65 50

3671 57c. Toureio 1·20 90

3672 68c. Alta Escola 1·40 1·00

3673 80c. Atrelagem de Competicao 1·60 1·20

MS3674 125×95 mm. €2.50 'Alter-Real' 5·00 3·75

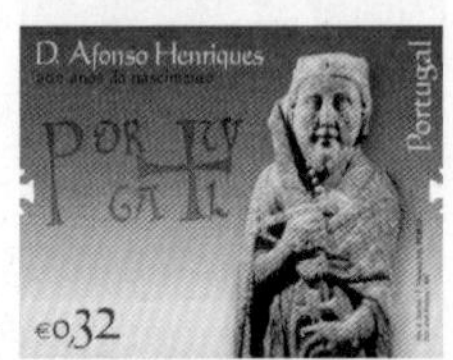

812 Alfonso Henriques (statue)

2009. 900th Birth Anniv of Alfonso Henriques (Afonso I, first king of Portugal). Multicoloured.

3675 32c. Type **812** 65 50

MS3676 95×125 mm. €3.07 On horseback 6·00 4·50

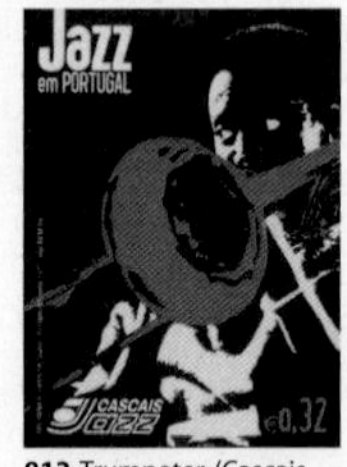

813 Trumpeter (Cascais Jazz)

2009. Jazz in Portugal. Multicoloured.

3677 32c. Type **813** 65 50

3678 47c. Trees and musicians as keyboard (Estoril Jazz Festival–Jazz On A Summer Day) 1·00 75

3679 57c. Saxophonist walking in street on instruments (Jazz in August, Calouste Gulbenkian Foundation) 1·20 90

3680 68c. Saxophonist (European Jazz Festival, Oporto) 1·40 1·00

3681 80c. Trumpeter (different) (Guimaraes Jazz Festival) 1·60 1·20

3682 €1 Fish playing saxophone (Seixal Jazz Festival) 2·00 1·50

MS3683 125×95 mm. €3.16 Hot Club of Portugal quartet 6·25 4·75

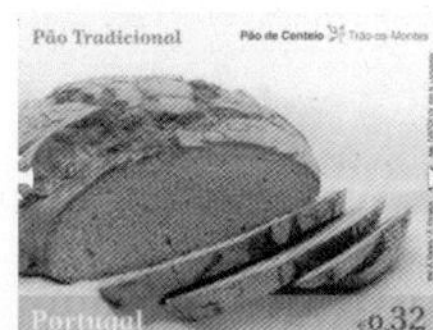

814 Pao de Centeio (rye bread)

2009. Bread. Showing loaves of bread. Multicoloured.

3684 32c. Type **814** 65 50

3685 32c. Quartos (quartered) 65 50

3686 47c. Regueifa (Arabic bread) 1·00 75

3687 68c. Chouriço (bread with sausage) 1·40 1·00

3688 68c. Testa ('brow' bread) 1·40 1·00

3689 80c. Mealhada (bread from Mealhada) 1·60 1·20

Nos. 3690/1 are vacant.

815 Antonio Pedro

2009. Birth Centenary of António Pedro da Costa (actor, writer and painter). Multicoloured.

3692 32c. Type **815** 65 50

MS3693 125×95 mm. €3.16 Facing right 6·25 4·75

816 Building Façade, 1841

2009. Belem Palace. Multicoloured.

3694 32c. Type **816** 65 50

3695 47c. Pintura das Sobreporta (painting over doorway) 1·00 75

3696 57c. Copper and silver writing equipment 1·20 90

3697 68c. Satyrs (bas relief) 1·40 1·00

3698 80c. Gold Room, detail of the ceiling molding 1·60 1·20

3699 €1 Floral allegory 2·00 1·50

MS3700 125×95 mm. €2.50 Salas das Bicas (fountain room) 5·50 3·75

817 *Pandion haliaetus* (osprey)

2009. Raptors. Multicoloured.

3701 32c. Type **817** 65 50

3702 80c. *Haliaeetus albicilla* (white-tailed eagle) 1·60 1·20

Stamps of a similar design were issued by Iran.

818 Coffee (smell)

2009. Stamps and the Senses. Birth Bicentenary of Louis Braille (inventor of Braille writing for the blind). Multicoloured.

3703 32c. Type **818** 65 50

3704 68c. Ice lolly (taste) 1·40 1·00

3705 80c. Glasses (vision) 1·60 1·20

3706 €1 Paint (touch) 2·00 1·50

3707 €2 File (Hearing) 4·00 3·00

MS3708 135×105 mm. €2.50 Louis Braille 5·00 3·75

No. **MS**3708 is embossed with Braille letters.

819 Adelaide Cabete

2009. Women of the Republic. Multicoloured.

3709 32c. Type **819** 65 50

3710 32c. Maria Veleda 65 50

3711 57c. Ana de Castro Osorio 1·20 90

3712 68c. Angelina Vidal 1·40 1·00

3713 80c. Carolina Beatriz Angelo 1·60 1·20

3714 €1 Carolina Michaelis 2·00 1·50

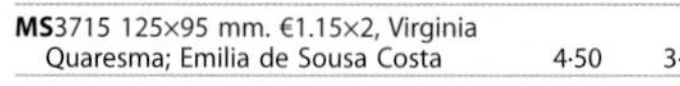
MS3715 125×95 mm. €1.15×2, Virginia Quaresma; Emilia de Sousa Costa 4·50 3·50

820 Children (Martina Marques Teixeira Santos)

2009. School Correspondence. Children's Drawings. Multicoloured.

3716 32c. Type **820** 65 50

3717 47c. Lets recycle to improve the world 1·00 75

3718 68c. Post boxes and recycle bins (Manuel Pedro A. B. Paiva Martins) 1·40 1·00

821 Santa and Hearts

2009. Christmas. Multicoloured.

3719 32c. Type **821** 65 50

3720 47c. Santa delivering letter through window 1·00 75

3721 68c. Christmas tree and Santa 1·30 1·00

3722 80c. Santa and reindeer 1·60 1·20

MS3723 125×95 mm. 50c. Santa riding reindeer on rocker; €1 Stocking containing Santa and parcels 3·00 2·20

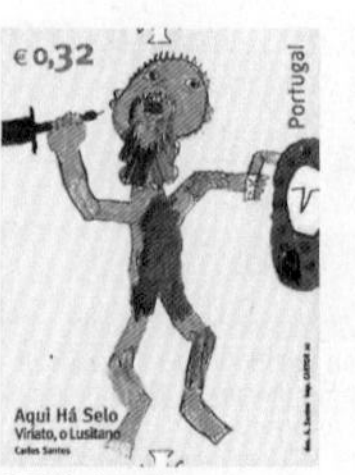

822 Variato, the Lusitanian (Carlos Santos)

2010. Aqui Há Selo (your own stamp). Multicoloured.

3724 32c. Type **822** 90 70

3725 32c. Dog in a cage (animal abandonment awareness campaign) (Pedro Trindade) 90 70

823 Frédéric François Chopin

2010. Composers Birth Bicentenaries. Multicoloured.

3726 Type **823** 2·00 1·40

3727 68c. Robert Alexander Schumann 2·00 1·40

MS3728 126×95 mm. €2 Frédéric Chopin 6·00 4·50

MS3729 126×95 mm. €2 Robert Schumann 6·00 4·50

No. 3730 is vacant.

824 Thunnus thynnus (Atlantic bluefin tuna)

2010. International Year of Biodiversity. Multicoloured.

3731 32c. Type **824** 95 70

3732 47c. *Centrophorus granulosus* (gulper shark) 1·30 95

3733 68c. *Ailuropoda melanoleuca* (panda) 2·10 1·60

3734 80c. Hummingbird (Atlantic forest) 2·40 1·80

MS3735 126×95 mm. €2.50 Golden lion tamarin (Atlantic forest) 7·50 7·50

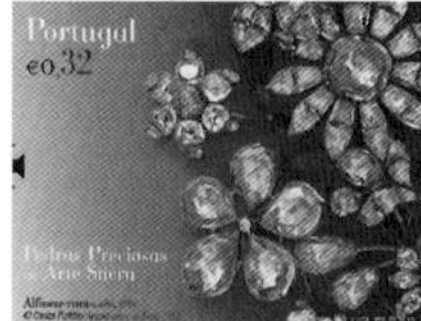

825 Floral Pin

2010. Precious Stones in Portuguese Sacred Art. Multicoloured.

3736 32c. Type **825** 95 70

3737 68c. 18th-century bodice trim 2·10 1·60

3738 €1 Processional cross of Sancho I (detail) 3·00 2·20

MS3739 126×95 mm. €2.50 Crown of Sr. de Fatima (detail) 6·75 5·00

826 Broa

2010. Bread. Multicoloured.

3740 32c. Type **826** 95 70

3741 47c. Padas 1·30 95

3742 68c. Broa de Avintes (bread from Avintes) 2·10 1·60

3743 80c. Pão Alentejano (bread from Alentejano) 2·40 1·80

MS3744 126×95 mm. 80c. Caraça; €1 Pão de Mafra (bread from Mafra) 5·50 4·00

827 Francisco Keli do Amaral (architect) (birth centenary)

2010. Historical and Cultural Personalities. Multicoloured.

3745 32c. Type **827** 95 70

3746 32c. Gomez Eanes de Azuara (writer) (600th birth anniv) 95 70

3747 32c. Fernão Mendes Pinto (explorer) (500th birth anniv) 95 70

3748 32 Alexandre Herculano (novelist and historian) (birth bicentenary) 95 70

828 Monkey

2010. Europa. Multicoloured.

3749 68c. Type **828** 2·00 1·50

MS3750 125×95 mm. 68c.×2, As Type **828**; Man with razor and monkey's tail 4·00 3·00

The stamps and margins of **MS**3750 form a composite design.

829 Pope Benedict XVI

2010. Visit of Pope Benedict XVI to Portugal. Multicoloured.

3751 68c. Type **829** 2·00 1·50

MS3752 125×95 mm. 80c.×3, Pope Paul VI; Pope John Paul II; Pope Benedict XVI 7·00 5·25

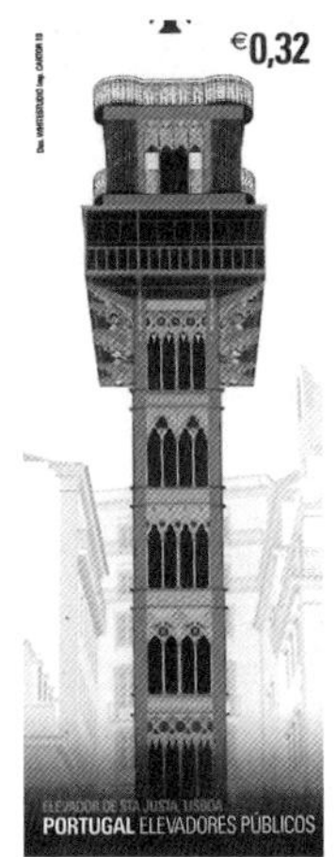

830 Santa Justa, Lisbon

2010. Public Elevators. Multicoloured.

3753	32c. Type **830**	90	70
3754	47c. Gloria, Lisbon	1·10	80
3755	57c. Guindos funicular, Porto	1·20	90
3756	68c. Bom Jesús do Monte Sanctuary, Braga	1·70	1·30
3757	80c. Santa Luzia, Viana do Castello	2·20	1·70
3758	€1 Nazare	3·50	2·50
MS3759	95×125 mm. €1.25×2, Bica, Lisbon; Lavra, Lisbon	7·00	5·25

831 Exotic Football

2010. World Cup Football Championships, South Africa. Multicoloured.

(a) Self-adhesive.

3760	80c. Type **831**	2·30	1·70

(b) Ordinary gum

MS3761	105×105 mm (circular). €2.50 Player and cheetah (80×30 mm)	7·25	5·50

832 Estrangeiros e Vilhalpandos

2010. Theatre. Multicoloured.

3762	32c. Type **832**	95	70
3763	32c. Auto da Barca do Inferno	95	70
3764	57c. A Castro	1·20	90
3765	68c. O Fidalgo Aprendiz	1·80	1·40
3766	668c. El-Rei Seleuco	1·80	1·40
3767	80c. Guerras de Alecrim e Manjerona	2·75	2·10

833 'Republic' (Júlio Pomar)

2010. Portugal 2010–World Philatelic Exhibition. Multicoloured.

MS3768	32c. Type **833**; 32c. Francisco dos Santos; 32c. Costa Pinheiro; 32c. Bento Condado; 32c. Luis Maciera; 68c. João Abel Manta; 68c. João Machado; 80c. André Carrilho	10·00	10·00

834 Rabaçal

2010. Cheese. Multicoloured.

3769	32c. Type **834**	95	70
3770	32c. Sierra de Estrela	95	70
3771	47c. Azeitão	1·30	1·00
3772	68c. Cabra Transmontana	2·10	1·60
3773	80c. São Jorge	2·40	1·80
MS3774	95×125 mm. €2.50 Sierra de Estrela (different)	7·00	5·50

835 AzulejoTile with Seated Musician (National Museum, Lisbon)

2010. 130th Anniv of Portugal–Romania Diplomatic Relations. Multicoloured.

3775	68c. Type **835**	1·90	1·40
3776	80c. Blue tile (Peasant Life Museum, Bucharest)	2·10	1·60

Stamps of a similar design were issued by Romania.

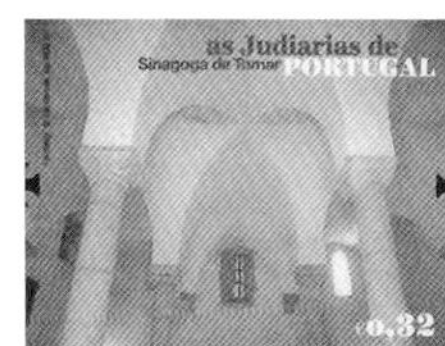

836 Synagogue of Tomar

2010. Jewish Quarters in Portugal. Multicoloured.

3777	32c. Type **836**	90	70
3778	57c. Rua Nova de Lamego	1·30	95
3779	68c. Jewish quarter, Castelo de Vide	2·10	1·60
MS3780	125×95 mm. €2.50 Jewish construction (medieval manuscript)	7·00	5·50

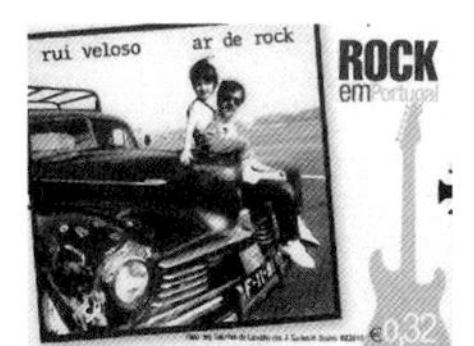

837 Rui Veluso (ar de rock)

2010. Portuguese Rock Bands. Multicoloured.

3781	32c. Type **837**	85	65
3782	47c. Herois do Mar (*Herois do Mar*)	1·10	80
3783	57c. GNR (*Pscicopatria*)	1·30	95
3784	68c. UHF (*À flor da pele*)	2·00	1·50
3785	80c. Xutos & Pontapés (*88*)	2·20	1·60
3786	€1 Moonspell (*Wolfheart*)	3·00	2·20
MS3787	125×95 mm. €2.50 Quarteto 1111 (*A Lenda de El-Rei D. Sebastião*)	7·00	5·25

838 Battle of Vimeiro

2010. Bicentenary of Peninsular War. Multicoloured.

3788	32c. Type **838**	95	70
3789	68c. Battle of Buçaco	2·10	1·60
MS3790	125×95 mm. €2.50 Battle of Pombal (80×30 mm)	7·25	5·50

839 Chamber

2010. Centenary of the Republic. Multicoloured.

3791	32c. Type **839**	1·70	1·30
3792	68c. Senate Chamber	3·50	2·75
MS3793	125×95 mm. €2 Assembly Building, Lisbon	5·75	4·25

840 Research Ship

2010. 50th Anniv of Hydrographic Institute. Multicoloured.

3794	32c. Type **840**	1·10	70
3795	68c. Research ship, Scientist and equipment array	1·90	1·40

Nos. 3794/5 were printed, *se-tenant*, forming a composite design.

841 Clown

2010. Chapito Circus School, Lisbon. Multicoloured.

3796	32c. Type **841**	1·10	70
3797	47c. Clown riding unicycle	1·20	90
3798	68c. Female juggler with hoops	1·90	1·40
3799	80c. Clown wearing stilts and juggling clubs	2·40	1·80
MS3800	125×95 mm. €2.50 Acrobats (30×80 mm)	7·25	5·50

842 Ceres

2010. Centenary of the Republic

3801	**842** 80c. reddish brown and yellow-ochre	2·25	1·70

843 Establishment of Republic, 1910

2010. History of Freedom. Multicoloured.

3802	32c. Type **843**	90	70
3803	32c. Female figure, symbolizing the Republic	90	70
3804	47c. Soldier with machine gun and civilian with rifle	1·20	90
3805	68c. Female symbol of French revolution and revolutionary	1·90	1·50
3806	80c. Male symbol of American revolution driving off British soldiers	2·40	1·80
3807	€1 Medieval cleric, king and peasant ('in the middle ages nobility, clergy and people had different rights and duties and the king's decisions were obeyed without question')	3·25	2·50

CHARITY TAX STAMPS

Used on certain days of the year as an additional postal tax on internal letters. Other values in some of the types were for use on telegrams only. The proceeds were devoted to public charities. If one was not affixed in addition to the ordinary postage, postage due stamps were used to collect the deficiency and the fine.

1911. Optd ASSISTENCIA.

C455	**48**	10r. green (No. 406)	13·00	3·50
C484	**56**	1c. green (No. 486)	9·50	3·00

C57 "Lisbon"

1913. Lisbon Festival.

C485	**C57**	1c. green	1·80	1·30

C58 "Charity"

1915. For the Poor.

C486	**C58**	1c. red	50	45
C669	**C58**	15c. red	95	95

1924. Surch 15 ctvs.

C594	15c. on 1c. red	2·50	1·10

C71 Muse of History

1925. Portuguese Army in Flanders, 1484 and 1918.

C662	**C71**	10c. red	1·80	1·60
C663	**C71**	10c. green	1·80	1·60
C664	**C71**	10c. blue	1·80	1·60
C665	**C71**	10c. brown	1·80	1·60

C73 Monument to De Pombal

C75 Marquis de Pombal

1925. Marquis de Pombal Commemoration.

C666	**C73**	15c. blue and black	1·80	1·10
C667	-	15c. blue and black	1·80	1·10
C668	**C 75**	15c. blue and black	65	55

DESIGN: No. C677, Planning reconstruction of Lisbon.

C81 Hurdler

1928. Olympic Games.

C741	**C81**	15c. black and red	6·00	3·50

NEWSPAPER STAMPS

N16

N17

1876

N180	**N16**	2r. black	33·00	21·00
N178	**N 17**	2½r. green	22·00	2·00
N187	**N 17**	2½r. brown	19·00	1·70

OFFICIAL STAMPS

1938. Optd OFICIAL.

O900	**99**	40c. brown	90	20

O144

1952. No value.

O1069	**O144**	(1e.) black and stone	90	15
O1070	**O144**	(1e.) black and stone	1·00	35

On No. O1069 "CORREIO DE PORTUGAL" is in stone on a black background, on No. O1070 it is in black on the stone background.

PARCEL POST STAMPS

P59

1920

P578	**P59**	1c. brown	55	45
P579	**P59**	2c. orange	55	45
P580	**P59**	5c. brown	55	45
P581	**P59**	10c. brown	55	45
P582	**P59**	20c. blue	75	45
P583	**P59**	40c. red	75	45
P584	**P59**	50c. black	1·10	80
P585	**P59**	60c. blue	1·00	80
P586	**P59**	70c. brown	6·25	3·00
P587	**P59**	80c. blue	6·50	4·75
P588	**P59**	90c. violet	6·75	3·50
P589	**P59**	1e. green	7·00	4·25
P591	**P59**	2e. lilac	20·00	5·25
P592	**P59**	3e. green	37·00	6·00
P593	**P59**	4e. blue	80·00	10·50
P594	**P59**	5e. lilac	£110	7·00
P595	**P59**	10e. brown	£170	12·50

P101

1936

P891	**P101**	50c. grey	1·10	95
P892	**P101**	1e. brown	1·10	95
P893	**P101**	1e.50 violet	1·10	95
P894	**P101**	2e. purple	4·75	1·00
P895	**P101**	2e.50 green	4·75	1·00
P896	**P101**	4e.50 purple	12·50	1·00
P897	**P101**	5e. violet	18·00	1·20
P898	**P101**	10e. orange	23·00	2·50

POSTAGE DUE STAMPS

D48 Da Gama received by the Zamorin of Calicut

1898

D386	**D48**	5r. black	5·00	3·50
D387	**D48**	10r. mauve	6·25	4·00
D388	**D48**	20r. orange	10·50	4·50
D389	**D48**	50r. grey	80·00	9·00
D390	**D48**	100r. red on pink	£120	65·00
D391	**D48**	200r. brown on buff	£130	90·00

D49

1904

D392	**D49**	5r. brown	85	80
D393	**D49**	10r. orange	4·25	1·30
D394	**D49**	20r. mauve	12·00	5·75
D395	**D49**	30r. green	8·50	4·25
D396	**D49**	40r. lilac	9·75	4·25
D397	**D49**	50r. red	65·00	7·25
D398	**D49**	100r. blue	14·50	9·50

1911. Optd REPUBLICA.

D418	5r. brown	80	70
D419	10r. orange	80	70
D420	20r. mauve	2·10	1·80
D421	30r. green	2·00	70
D422	40r. lilac	2·10	70
D423	50r. red	8·75	6·75
D424	100r. blue	9·25	7·25

1915. As Type D 49 but value in centavos.

D491	½c. brown	90	85
D498	1c. orange	1·10	1·00
D493	2c. purple	90	85
D499	3c. green	1·10	1·00
D500	4c. lilac	1·10	1·00
D501	5c. red	1·10	1·00
D497	10c. blue	1·10	1·00

1921

D578	½c. green	80	55
D579	4c. green	80	55
D580	8c. green	80	55
D581	10c. green	80	55
D582	12c. green	90	65
D583	16c. green	90	65
D584	20c. green	90	65
D585	24c. green	90	65
D586	32c. green	1·40	90
D587	36c. green	2·50	1·80
D588	40c. green	2·50	1·80
D589	48c. green	1·60	1·00
D590	50c. green	1·60	1·00
D591	60c. green	1·60	1·00
D592	72c. green	1·60	1·00
D593	80c. green	12·00	10·50
D594	1e.20 green	5·50	5·50

D72

1925. Portuguese Army in Flanders, 1484 and 1918.

D662	**D72**	20c. brown	95	75

1925. De Pombal types optd MULTA.

D663	**C73**	30c. blue	1·90	1·60
D664	-	30c. blue	1·90	1·60
D665	**C75**	30c. blue	1·90	1·60

D82

1928. Olympic Games.

D741	**D82**	30e. black and red	3·00	2·75

D91

1932

D865	**D91**	5e. buff	1·20	90
D866	**D91**	10e. blue	1·20	90
D867	**D91**	20e. pink	2·50	1·30
D868	**D91**	30e. blue	2·75	1·30
D869	**D91**	40e. green	2·75	1·30
D870	**D91**	50e. grey	3·75	1·30
D871	**D91**	60e. pink	7·50	3·50
D872	**D91**	80e. purple	14·00	7·25
D873	**D91**	1e.20 green	23·00	18·00

D108

1940

D912	**D108**	5c. brown	95	60
D922	**D108**	5e. orange	20·00	14·00
D923	**D108**	10c. lilac	50	25
D924	**D108**	20c. red	50	25
D925	**D108**	30c. violet	50	25
D926	**D108**	40c. mauve	50	25
D927	**D108**	50c. blue	50	25
D928	**D108**	60c. green	50	25
D929	**D108**	80c. red	50	25
D930	**D108**	1e. brown	50	25
D931	**D108**	2e. mauve	70	60

D218

1967

D1312	**D218**	10c. brown, yellow and orange	15	10
D1313	**D218**	20e. purple, yellow and brown	15	10
D1314	**D218**	30e. brown, light yellow and yellow	15	10
D1315	**D218**	40e. purple, yellow and bistre	15	10
D1316	**D218**	50e. indigo, blue and light blue	20	10
D1317	**D218**	60e. olive, blue and turquoise	20	10
D1318	**D218**	80e. indigo, blue and light blue	20	10
D1319	**D218**	1e. indigo, bl & ultram	20	10
D1320	**D218**	2e. olive, light green and green	20	15
D1321	**D218**	3e. deep green, light green and green	45	15
D1322	**D218**	4e. deep green, green and turquoise	45	20
D1323	**D218**	5e. brown, mauve and purple	35	20
D1324	**D218**	9e. deep lilac, lilac and violet	45	25
D1325	**D218**	10e. deep purple, grey and purple	45	25
D1326	**D218**	20e. maroon, grey and purple	1·30	35
D1327	**D218**	40e. lilac, grey and mauve	3·00	1·40
D1328	**D218**	50e. maroon, grey and purple	3·75	1·60

D481

1992. Inscr "CORREIOS DE PORTUGAL".

D2305	**D481**	1e. blue, deep blue and black	10	10
D2306	**D481**	2e. light green, green and black	10	10
D2307	**D481**	5e. yellow, brown and black	10	10
D2308	**D481**	10e. red, orange and black	20	10
D2309	**D481**	20e. green, violet and black	35	10
D2310	**D481**	50e. yellow, green and black	80	45
D2311	**D481**	100e. orange, red and black	1·50	1·00
D2312	**D481**	200e. mauve, violet and black	3·00	1·90

1995. Inscr "CTT CORREIOS".

D2445	3e. multicoloured	20	10
D2446	4e. multicoloured	20	10
D2446a	5e. multicoloured	10	10
D2447	9e. multicoloured	45	10
D2447a	10e. red, orange and black	15	10
D2447b	20e. multicoloured	25	20
D2448	40e. multicoloured	80	65
D2449	50e. multicoloured	90	60
D2450	100e. orange, red and black	1·30	90

D656 "0.01"

2002. Multicoloured

D2907	1c. Type D **656**	10	10
D2908	2c. "0.02"	10	10
D2909	5c. "0.05"	15	10
D2910	10c. "0.10"	30	25
D2911	25c. "0.25"	60	50
D2912	50c. "0.50"	1·30	95
D2913	€1 "1"	2·50	2·00

Pt. 7

PRUSSIA

Formerly a kingdom in the N. of Germany. In 1867 it became part of the North German Confederation.

1850. 12 pfennig = 1 silbergroschen;
30 silbergroschen = 1 thaler.
1867. 60 kreuzer = 1 gulden.

1 Friedrich Wilhelm IV

1850. Imperf.

14	**1**	4pf. green	95·00	48·00
4	**1**	6pf. red	£120	70·00
22	**1**	½sgr. (=6pf.) red	£250	£200
5	**1**	1sgr. black on pink	£110	16·00
16	**1**	1sgr. pink	42·00	5·25
6	**1**	2sgr. black on blue	£150	21·00
18	**1**	2sgr. blue	£150	23·00
8	**1**	3sgr. black on yellow	£150	21·00
21	**1**	3sgr. yellow	£130	21·00

3

4

1861. Roul.

24	**3**	3pf. lilac	36·00	60·00
26	**3**	4pf. green	16·00	16·00
28	**3**	6pf. orange	16·00	19·00
31	**4**	1sgr. pink	4·25	2·10
35	**4**	2sgr. blue	16·00	2·10
36	**4**	3sgr. yellow	11·50	2·75

5

1866. Printed in reverse on back of specially treated transparent paper. Roul.

38	**5**	10sgr. pink	£130	£140
39	-	30sgr. blue	£150	£300

The 30 sgr. has the value in a square.

7

1867. Roul.

40	**7**	1k. green	32·00	60·00
42	**7**	2k. orange	55·00	£130
43	**7**	3k. pink	26·00	37·00
45	**7**	6k. blue	26·00	60·00
46	**7**	9k. bistre	32·00	65·00

Pt. 8

ROMAGNA

One of the Papal states, now part of Italy. Stamps issued prior to union with Sardinia in 1860.

100 bajocchi = 1 scudo.

1

1859. Imperf.

2	**1**	½b. black on buff	43·00	£375
3	**1**	1b. black on grey	43·00	£190
4	**1**	2b. black on buff	60·00	£200
5	**1**	3b. black on green	70·00	£375
6	**1**	4b. black on brown	£800	£190
7	**1**	5b. black on lilac	85·00	£450
8	**1**	6b. black on green	£475	£9500
9	**1**	8b. black on pink	£275	£2250
10	**1**	20b. black on green	£275	£3250

Pt. 7

SAAR

A German territory South-east of Luxembourg. Occupied by France under League of Nations control from 1920 to 1935. Following a plebiscite, Saar returned to Germany in 1935 from when German stamps were used until the French occupation in 1945, after which Nos. F1/13 of Germany followed by Nos. 203 etc of Saar were used. The territory was autonomous under French protection until it again returned to Germany at the end of 1956 following a national referendum. Issues from 1957 were authorised by the German Federal Republic pending the adoption of German currency on 6 July 1959, after which West German stamps were used.

1920–May 1921. 100 pfennig = 1 mark.
May 1921–March 1935. 100 centimes = 1 franc.
1935–47. 100 pfennig = 1 reichsmark.
1947. 100 pfennig = 1 Saarmark.
November 1947–July 1959. 100 centimes =1 franc.
From 1959. 100 pfennig = 1 Deutsche mark.

LEAGUE OF NATIONS COMMISSION

1920. German stamps inscr "DEUTSCHES REICH" optd Sarre and bar.

No.	Type	Description	Mint	Used
1	24	2pf. grey	1·90	5·75
2c	24	2½pf. grey	2·10	7·50
3	10	3pf. brown	1·40	3·75
4c	10	5pf. green	65	1·30
5	24	7½pf. orange	85	2·30
6	10	10pf. red	75	1·70
7	24	15pf. violet	65	1·40
8	10	20pf. blue	65	1·40
9	10	25pf. black & red on yellow	12·50	26·00
10	10	30pf. black & orange on buff	23·00	48·00
11	24	35pf. brown	75	1·70
12	10	40pf. black and red	75	1·70
13	10	50pf. black & pur on cream	75	1·40
14	10	60pf. purple	75	1·70
15	10	75pf. black and green	65	1·60
16	10	80pf. black and red on red	£250	£350
17b	12	1m. red	37·00	60·00

1920. Bavarian stamps optd Sarre or SARRE (Nos. 30/1) and bars.

No.	Type	Description	Mint	Used
18	15	5pf. green	95	2·10
19	15	10pf. red	95	2·10
19a	15	15pf. red	1·30	2·50
21	15	20pf. blue	85	2·10
22	15	25pf. grey	15·00	21·00
23	15	30pf. orange	8·50	15·00
24	15	40pf. green	13·50	21·00
25	15	50pf. brown	2·10	3·75
26	15	60pf. green	4·25	10·50
27	16	1m. brown	21·00	42·00
28	16	2m. violet	80·00	£180
29	16	3m. red	£160	£200
30	-	5m. blue (No. 192)	£1000	£1200
31	-	10m. green (No. 193)	£180	£350

1920. German stamps inscr "DEUTSCHES REICH" optd SAARGEBIET.

No.	Type	Description	Mint	Used
32	10	5pf. green	30	65
33	10	5pf. brown	65	1·10
34	10	10pf. red	30	65
35	10	10pf. orange	60	65
36	24	15pf. violet	30	65
37	10	20pf. blue	30	65
38	10	20pf. green	95	65
39	10	30pf. black & orange on buff	55	65
40	10	30pf. blue	75	95
41	10	40pf. black and red	40	65
42	10	40pf. red	1·40	95
43	10	50pf. black & purple on buff	55	65
44	10	60pf. purple	85	65
45	10	75pf. black and green	95	65
46	12	1m.25 green	3·00	1·60
47	12	1m.50 brown	2·75	1·60
48	13	2m.50 purple	5·25	17·00
49	10	4m. red and black	11·50	30·00

1920. No. 45 of Saar surch 20 and No. 102 of Germany surch SAARGEBIET, arms and value.

No.	Type	Description	Mint	Used
50		20 on 75pf. black and green	55	1·60
51	24	5m. on 15pf. purple	6·50	21·00
52	24	10m. on 15pf. purple	7·50	25·00

9 Miner

11 Colliery Shafthead

12 Burbach Steelworks

1921

No.	Type	Description	Mint	Used
53	-	5pf. violet and green	40	65
54	9	10pf. orange and blue	40	65
55	-	20pf. grey and green	40	1·40
56	-	25pf. blue and brown	55	1·10
57	-	30pf. brown and green	55	95
58	-	40pf. red	55	65
59	-	50pf. black and grey	1·30	5·25
60	-	60pf. brown and red	2·10	4·75
61	-	80pf. blue	95	1·60
62	-	1m. black and red	1·10	2·10
63	11	1m.25 green and brown	1·30	2·75
64	-	2m. black and orange	3·25	5·25
65	-	3m. sepia and brown	4·25	12·50
66	-	5m. violet and yellow	12·50	30·00
67	-	10m. brown and green	16·00	32·00
68	12	25m. blue, black and red	42·00	95·00

DESIGNS—As Type **11**. HORIZ: 5pf. Mill above Mettlach; 20pf. Pit head at Reden; 25pf. River traffic, Saarbrucken; 30pf. River Saar at Mettlach; 40pf. Slag-heap, Volklingen; 50pf. Signal gantry, Saarbrucken; 80pf. "Old Bridge", Saarbrucken; 1m. Wire-rope Railway; 2m. Town Hall, Saarbrucken; 3m. Pottery, Mettlach; 5m. St. Ludwig's Church; 10m. Chief Magistrate's and Saar Commissioner's Offices. VERT: 60pf. Gothic Chapel, Mettlach.

See also Nos. 84/97.

1921. Nos. 55/68 surch in French currency.

No.	Type	Description	Mint	Used
70		3c. on 20pf. grey and green	55	65
71		5c. on 25pf. blue and brown	55	65
72		10c. on 30pf. brown and green	55	65
73		15c. on 40pf. red	65	65
74		20c. on 50pf. black and grey	55	65
75		25c. on 60pf. brown and red	65	65
76		30c. on 80pf. blue	2·10	1·40
77		40c. on 1m. black and red	2·75	65
78		50c. on 1m.25 green & brown	4·25	1·40
79		75c. on 2m. black and orange	5·25	2·75
80		1f. on 3m. black and brown	6·25	3·25
81		2f. on 5m. violet and yellow	16·00	8·50
82		3f. on 10m. brown and green	21·00	34·00
83		5f. on 25m. blue, black and red	23·00	48·00

1922. Larger designs (except 5f.) and value in French currency.

No.	Type	Description	Mint	Used
84		3c. green (as No. 62)	55	85
85		5c. black & orange (as No. 54)	55	55
86		10c. green (as No. 61)	55	55
87		15c. brown (as No. 62)	1·60	55
98		15c. orange (as No. 62)	3·25	55
88		20c. blue & yellow (as No. 64)	18·00	55
100		25c. red and yellow (as No. 64)	3·25	55
90		30c. red and yellow (as No. 58)	2·75	2·75
91		40c. brown & yell (as No. 65)	1·30	55
92		50c. blue & yellow (as No. 56)	1·30	55
93		75c. green & yellow (as No. 65)	18·00	32·00
94		1f. brown (as No. 66)	3·25	1·10
95		2f. violet (as No. 63)	4·75	4·25
96		3f. green & orange (as No. 60)	32·00	8·50
97		5f. brown & choc (as No. 68)	32·00	60·00

14 Madonna of Blieskastel

1925

No.	Type	Description	Mint	Used
102	14	45c. purple	3·75	6·75
103	14	10f. brown (31×36 mm)	21·00	32·00

15 Army Medical Service

1926. Welfare Fund.

No.	Type	Description	Mint	Used
104	15	20c.+20c. green	10·50	26·00
105	-	40c.+40c. brown	10·50	26·00
106	-	50c.+50c. orange	10·50	26·00
107	-	1f.50+1f.50 blue	25·00	65·00

DESIGNS: 40c. Hospital work (nurse and patient); 50c. Child welfare (children at a spring); 1f.50, Maternity nursing service.

18 Tholey Abbey

1926

No.	Type	Description	Mint	Used
108		10c. brown	95	65
109		15c. green	55	1·40
110		20c. brown	55	65
111	18	25c. blue	95	65
112	-	30c. green	1·30	65
113	-	40c. brown	95	65
114	18	50c. red	1·30	65
114a	-	60c. orange	5·25	75
115	-	75c. purple	95	65
116	-	80c. orange	3·25	11·50
116a	-	90c. red	16·00	23·00
117	-	1f. violet	3·25	65
118	-	1f.50 blue	6·25	65
119	-	2f. red	7·50	65
120	-	3f. green	15·00	1·70
121	-	5f. brown	16·00	9·50

DESIGNS—VERT: 10, 30c. Fountain, St. Johann, Saarbrucken. HORIZ: 15, 75c. Saar Valley near Gudingen; 20, 40, 90c. View from Saarlouis fortifications; 60, 80c., 1f. Colliery shafthead; 1f.50, 2, 3, 5f. Burbach Steelworks.

1927. Welfare Fund. Optd 1927–28.

No.	Type	Description	Mint	Used
122	15	20c.+20c. green	17·00	37·00
123	15	40c.+40c. brown	17·00	37·00
124	15	50c.+50c. orange	15·00	26·00
125	15	1f.50+1f.50 blue	23·00	85·00

19 Breguet 14 Biplane over Saarbrucken

1928. Air.

No.	Type	Description	Mint	Used
126	19	50c. red	5·25	5·25
127	19	1f. violet	8·50	6·25

20 "The Blind Beggar" by Dyckmanns

1928. Christmas Charity.

No.	Type	Description	Mint	Used
128	20	40c.(+40c.) brown	16·00	95·00
129	20	50c.(+50c.) purple	16·00	95·00
130	20	1f.(+1f.) violet	16·00	95·00
131	-	1f.50(+1f.50) blue	16·00	95·00
132	-	2f.(+2f.) red	19·00	£140
133	-	3f.(+3f.) green	19·00	£180
134	-	10f.(+10f.) brown	£475	£5500

DESIGNS: 1f.50, 2, 3f. "Almsgiving" by Schiestl; 10f. "Charity" by Raphael (picture in circle).

1929. Christmas Charity. Paintings. As T 20.

No.	Type	Description	Mint	Used
135		40c.(+15c.) green	2·75	7·50
136		50c.(+20c.) red	5·25	12·50
137		1f.(+50c.) purple	5·25	15·00
138		1f.50(+75c.) blue	5·25	15·00
139		2f.(+1f.) red	5·25	15·00
140		3f.(+2f.) green	10·50	34·00
141		10f.(+8f.) brown	65·00	£180

DESIGNS: 40c. to 1f. "Orphaned" by H. Kaulbach; 1f.50, 2, 3f. "St. Ottilia" by M. Feuerstein; 10f. "The Little Madonna" by Ferruzzio.

1930. Nos. 114 and 116 surch.

No.	Type	Description	Mint	Used
141a	18	40c. on 50c. red	2·10	2·10
142	-	60c. on 80c. orange	2·75	3·25

1931. Christmas Charity (1930 issue). Paintings. As T 20.

No.	Type	Description	Mint	Used
143		40c.(+15c.) brown	10·50	32·00
144		60c.(+20c.) orange	10·50	32·00
145		1f.(+50c.) red	10·50	65·00
146		1f.50(+75c.) blue	16·00	65·00
147		2f.(+1f.) brown	16·00	65·00
148		3f.(+2f.) green	26·00	65·00
149		10f.(+10f.) brown	£130	£375

DESIGNS: 40, 60c., 1f.50, "The Safetyman" (miner and lamp) by F. Zolnhofer; 1, 2, 3f. "The Good Samaritan" by J. Heinemann; 10f. "At the Window" by F. G. Waldmuller.

1931. Christmas Charity. Paintings. As T 20.

No.	Type	Description	Mint	Used
150		40c.(+15c.) brown	17·00	48·00
151		60c.(+20c.) red	17·00	48·00
152		1f.(+50c.) purple	21·00	75·00
153		1f.50(+75c.) blue	25·00	75·00
154		2f.(+1f.) red	30·00	75·00
155		3f.(+2f.) green	37·00	£130
156		5f.(+5f.) brown	£130	£425

DESIGNS: 40c. to 1f. "St. Martin" by F. Boehle; 1f.50, 2f. "Charity" by Ridgeway-Knight; 5f. "The Widow's Mite" by Dubufe.

29 Focke Wulf A-17 Mowe over Saarbrucken Airport

1932. Air.

No.	Type	Description	Mint	Used
157	29	60c. red	8·50	6·25
158	29	5f. brown	60·00	£130

30 Kirkel Castle Ruins

1932. Christmas Charity.

No.	Type	Description	Mint	Used
159	30	40c.(+15c.) brown	12·50	30·00
160	-	60c.(+20c.) red	12·50	30·00
161	-	1f.(+50c.) purple	19·00	55·00
162	-	1f.50(+75c.) blue	26·00	65·00
163	-	2f.(+1f.) red	26·00	75·00
164	-	3f.(+2f.) green	75·00	£225
165	-	5f.(+5f.) brown	£160	£375

DESIGNS—VERT: 60c. Blieskastel Church; 1f. Ottweiler Church; 1f.50, St. Michael's Church, Saarbrucken; 2f. Cathedral and fountain, St. Wendel; 3f. St. John's Church, Saarbrucken. HORIZ: 5f. Kerpen Castle, Illingen.

32 Scene of the Disaster

1933. Neunkirchen Explosion Disaster.

No.	Type	Description	Mint	Used
166	32	60c.(+60c.) orange	22·00	26·00
167	32	3f.(+3f.) green	48·00	95·00
168	32	5f.(+5f.) brown	48·00	95·00

33 "Love"

1934. Christmas Charity.

No.	Type	Description	Mint	Used
169	33	40c.(+15c.) brown	7·50	21·00
170	-	60c.(+20c.) red	7·50	21·00
171	-	1f.(+50c.) mauve	9·50	26·00
172	-	1f.50(+75c.) blue	19·00	48·00
173	-	2f.(+1f.) red	17·00	48·00
174	-	3f.(+2f.) green	19·00	48·00
175	-	5f.(+5f.) brown	42·00	£120

DESIGNS: 60c. "Solicitude". 1f. "Peace". 1f.50, "Consolation". 2f. "Welfare". 3f. "Truth". 5f. Countess Elizabeth von Nassau.

Nos. 169/74 show statues by C. L. Pozzi in church of St. Louis, Saarbrucken.

1934. Saar Plebiscite. Optd VOLKSABSTIMMUNG 1935. (a) Postage. On Nos. 108/15, 116a/21 and 103.

No.	Type	Description	Mint	Used
176		10c. brown	55	75
177		15c. green	55	75
178		20c. brown	85	1·80
179	18	25c. blue	85	1·80
180	-	30c. green	55	75
181	-	40c. brown	55	95
182	18	50c. red	95	1·80
183	-	60c. orange	55	75
184	-	75c. purple	95	1·80
185	-	90c. red	95	1·90

186	-	1f. violet	95	2·10
187	-	1f.50 blue	1·70	4·25
188	-	2f. red	2·75	6·25
189	-	3f. green	6·25	12·50
190	-	5f. brown	26·00	42·00
191	14	10f. brown	32·00	80·00

(b) Air. On Nos. 126/7 and 157/8.

192	19	50c. red	5·25	9·50
193	29	60c. red	4·25	3·75
194	19	1r. violet	9·50	12·50
195	29	5f. brown	12·50	19·00

1934. Christmas Charity. Nos. 169/75 optd VOLKSABSTIMMUNG 1935.

196	33	40c.(+15c.) brown	4·75	19·00
197	-	60c.(+20c.) red	4·75	19·00
198	-	1f.(+50c.) mauve	15·00	34·00
199	-	1f.50(+75c.) blue	9·50	34·00
200	-	2f.(+1f.) red	15·00	48·00
201	-	3f.(+2f.) green	13·50	42·00
202	-	5f.(+5f.) brown	20·00	55·00

FRENCH OCCUPATION

36 Coal-miner **37** Loop of the Saar

1947. Inscr "SAAR".

203	36	2pf. grey	30	55
204	36	3pf. orange	30	65
205	36	6pf. green	30	55
206	36	8pf. red	30	40
207	36	10pf. mauve	30	55
208	36	12pf. green	30	65
209	-	15pf. brown	30	8·50
210	-	16pf. blue	30	55
211	-	20pf. red	30	55
212	-	24pf. brown	30	55
213	-	25pf. mauve	65	30·00
214	-	30pf. green	30	1·10
215	-	40pf. brown	30	1·60
216	-	45pf. red	75	21·00
217	-	50pf. violet	75	30·00
218	-	60pf. violet	65	30·00
219	-	75pf. blue	30	55
220	-	80pf. orange	30	55
221	-	84pf. brown	30	55
222	37	1m. green	30	65

DESIGNS—As T **36**: 15pf. to 24pf. Steel workers; 25pf. to 50pf. Sugar beet harvesters; 60pf. to 80pf. Mettlach Abbey. As T **37**—VERT: 84pf. Marshal Ney.

1947. As last surch in French currency.

223B	36	10c. on 2pf. grey	30	75
224B	36	60c. on 3pf. orange	30	1·50
225B	36	1f. on 10pf. mauve	30	75
226B	36	2f. on 12pf. green	40	1·90
227B	-	3f. on 15pf. brown	40	1·90
228B	-	4f. on 16pf. blue	40	10·50
229B	-	5f. on 20pf. red	40	1·40
230B	-	6f. on 24pf. brown	40	85
231B	-	9f. on 30pf. green	55	18·00
232B	-	10f. on 50pf. violet	55	26·00
233B	-	14f. on 60pf. violet	85	18·00
234B	-	20f. on 84pf. brown	1·40	27·00
235B	37	50f. on 1m. green	1·90	27·00

42 Clasped Hands **43** Builders

44 Saar Valley

1948. Inscr "SAARPOST".

236	42	10c. red (postage)	95	2·75
237	42	60c. blue	95	2·75
238	42	1f. black	40	40
239	-	2f. red	55	40
240	-	3f. brown	55	40
241	-	4f. red	55	40
242	-	5f. violet	55	40
243	-	6f. red	95	40
244	-	9f. blue	6·25	65
245	-	10f. blue	3·75	1·10
246	-	14f. purple	5·25	1·50
247	43	20f. red	10·50	1·50
248	-	50f. blue	18·00	3·75
249	44	25f. red (air)	6·25	4·25
250	44	50f. blue	3·75	3·25
251	44	200f. red	37·00	48·00

DESIGNS—As Type **42**: 2, 3f. Man's head;. 4, 5f. Woman's head; 6, 9f. Miner's head. As Type **43**: 10f. Blast furnace chimney; 14f. Foundry; 50f. Facade of Mettlach Abbey.

46 Floods in St. Johann, Sarbrucken

1948. Flood Disaster Relief Fund. Flood Scenes.

252	-	5f.+5f. green (postage)	5·75	44·00
253	46	6f.+4f. purple	5·75	42·00
254	-	12f.+8f. red	8·50	55·00
255	-	18f.+12f. blue	10·50	65·00
MS255a 147×104 mm. Nos. 252/5. Imperf			£750	£3500
256	-	25f.+25f. brown (air)	32·00	£300
MS256a 90×60 mm. No. 256			£650	£2500

DESIGNS—VERT: 18f. Flooded street, Saarbrucken. HORIZ: 5f. Flooded industrial area; 12f. Landtag building, Saarbrucken; 25f. Floods at Ensdorf, Saarlouis.

47 Map of Saarland

1948. 1st Anniv of Constitution.

257	47	10f. red	2·75	5·25
258	47	25f. blue	3·75	10·50

48 Hikers and Ludweiler Hostel

1949. Youth Hostels Fund.

259	48	8f.+5f. brown	4·75	£140
260	-	10f.+7f. green	5·75	£140

DESIGN: 10f. Hikers and Weisskirchen hostel.

49 Chemical Research

1949. Saar University.

261	49	15f. red	9·50	65

50 Mare and Foal

1949. Horse Day.

262	50	15f.+5f. red	16·00	42·00
263	-	25f.+15f. blue	21·00	48·00

DESIGN: 25f. Two horses in steeple-chase.

51 Symbolic of Typography **52** Labourer and Foundry

1949

264		10c. purple	40	2·75
265		60c. black	40	2·75
266		1f. red	1·60	40
267		3f. brown	10·50	55
268		5f. violet	2·75	40
269		6f. green	13·50	55
270		8f. green	1·60	85
271	51	10f. orange	6·25	40
272	-	12f. green	19·00	40
273	-	15f. red	9·50	40
274	-	18f. mauve	3·75	6·75
275	52	20f. grey	2·75	40
276	-	25f. blue	26·00	40
277	-	30f. red	23·00	65
278	-	45f. purple	6·25	75
279	-	60f. green	10·50	2·75
280	-	100f. brown	13·50	3·25

DESIGNS—As Type **51**: 10c. Building trade; 60c. Beethoven; 1f. and 3f. Heavy industries; 5f. Slag heap; 6f. and 15f. Colliery; 8f. Posthorn and telephone; 12f. and 18f. Pottery. As Type **52**—VERT: 25f. Blast furnace worker; 60f. Landsweiler; 100f. Wiebelskirchen. HORIZ: 30f. St. Arnual; 45f. "Giant's Boot", Rentrisch.

53 Detail from "Moses Striking the Rock" (Murillo)

1949. National Relief Fund.

281	53	8f.+2f. blue	10·50	55·00
282	-	12f.+3f. green	12·50	65·00
283	-	15f.+5f. purple	19·00	£110
284	-	25f.+10f. blue	32·00	£170
285	-	50f.+20f. purple	48·00	£300

DESIGNS: 12f. "Our Lord healing the Paralytic" (Murillo); 15f. "The Sick Child" (Metsu); 25f. "St. Thomas of Villanueva" (Murillo); 50f. "Madonna of Blieskastel".

54 A. Kolping

1950. Honouring Adolf Kolping (miners' padre).

286	54	15f.+5f. red	34·00	£110

55 P. Wust

1950. 10th Death Anniv of Peter Wust (philosopher).

287	55	15f. red	17·00	9·50

56 Mail Coach

1950. Stamp Day.

288	56	15f.+5f. brown and red	90·00	£150

57 "Food for the Hungry"

1950. Red Cross Fund.

289	57	25f.+10f. lake and red	36·00	85·00

58 St. Peter

1950. Holy Year.

290	58	12f. green	4·25	13·50
291	58	15f. red	6·25	12·50
292	58	25f. blue	10·50	27·00

59 Town Hall, Ottweiler

1950. 400th Anniv of Ottweiler.

293	59	10f. brown	8·00	10·50

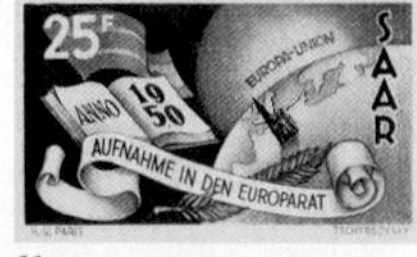

61

1950. Saar's Admission to Council of Europe.

294	61	25f. blue (postage)	48·00	16·00
295	-	200f. red (air)	£190	£325

DESIGN: 200f. As T **61** but with dove in flight over book.

62 St. Lutwinus enters Monastery

1950. National Relief Fund. Inscr "VOLKSHILFE".

296	62	8f.+2f. brown	12·50	42·00
297	-	12f.+3f. green	11·50	42·00
298	-	15f.+5f. brown	16·00	70·00
299	-	25f.+10f. blue	17·00	95·00
300	-	50f.+20f. purple	25·00	£160

DESIGNS: 12f. Lutwinus builds Mettlach Abbey; 15f. Lutwinus as Abbot; 25f. Bishop Lutwinus confirming children at Rheims; 50f. Lutwinus helping needy.

63 Orphans

1951. Red Cross Fund.

301	63	25f.+10f. green and red	25·00	85·00

64 Mail-carriers, 1760

1951. Stamp Day.

302	**64**	15f. purple	11·50	25·00

65 Allegory

1951. Trade Fair.

303	**65**	15f. green	3·75	8·50

66 Flowers and Building

1951. Horticultural Show, Bexbach.

304	**66**	15f. green	3·75	2·30

67 Calvin and Luther

1951. 375th Anniv of Reformation in Saar.

305	**67**	15f.+5f. brown	4·75	9·50

68 "The Good Mother" (Lepicie)

1951. National Relief Fund. Inscr "VOLKSHILFE 1951".

306	**68**	12f.+3f. green	8·50	25·00
307	-	15f.+5f. violet	10·50	25·00
308	-	18f.+7f. red	9·50	25·00
309	-	30f.+10f. blue	16·00	48·00
310	-	50f.+20f. brown	26·00	95·00

PAINTINGS: 18f. "Outside the Theatre" (Kampf); 18f. "Sisters of Charity" (Browne); 30f. "The Good Samaritan" (Bassano); 50f. "St. Martin and the Poor" (Van Dyck).

69 Mounted Postman

1952. Stamp Day.

311	**69**	30f.+10f. blue	16·00	37·00

70 Athlete bearing Olympic Flame

1952. 15th Olympic Games, Helsinki. Inscr "OLYMPISCHE SPIELE 1952".

312	**70**	15f.+5f. green	8·00	16·00
313	-	30f.+5f. blue	8·00	18·00

DESIGN: 30f. Hand, laurels and globe.

71 Globe and Emblem

1952. Saar Fair.

314	**71**	15f. red	3·25	1·80

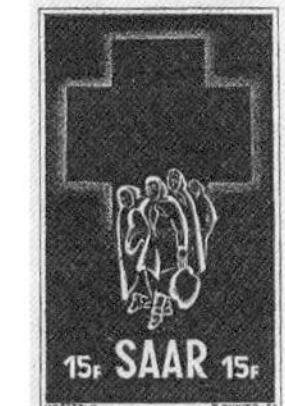

72 Red Cross and Refugees

1952. Red Cross Week.

315	**72**	15f. red	4·75	1·80

73 G.P.O., Saarbrucken

1952. (A) Without inscr in or below design. (B) With inscr.

316	-	1f. green (B)	30	30
317	-	2f. violet	30	30
318	-	3f. red	30	30
319	**73**	5f. green (A)	6·25	30
320	**73**	5f. green (B)	30	30
321	-	6f. purple	55	30
322	-	10f. brown	55	30
323	**73**	12f. green (B)	95	30
324	-	15f. brown (A)	10·50	30
325	-	15f. brown (B)	4·75	30
326	-	15f. red (B)	40	30
327	-	18f. purple	3·75	6·25
329	-	30f. blue	1·30	1·30
334	-	500f. red	21·00	85·00

DESIGNS—HORIZ: 1, 15f. (3) Colliery shafthead; 2, 10f. Ludwigs High School, Saarbrucken; 3, 18f. Gersweiler Bridge; 6f. Mettlach Bridge; 30f. University Library, Saarbrucken. VERT: 500f. St. Ludwig's Church, Saarbrucken.

74 "Count Stroganov as a Boy" (Greuze)

1952. National Relief Fund. Paintings inscr "VOLKSHILFE 1952".

335	**74**	15f.+5f. brown	4·25	15·00
336	-	18f.+7f. red	6·25	19·00
337	-	30f.+10f. blue	8·50	21·00

PORTRAITS: 18f. "The Holy Shepherd" (Murillo); 30f. "Portrait of a Boy" (Kraus).

75 Fair Symbol

1953. Saar Fair.

338	**75**	15f. blue	2·75	2·10

76 Postilions

1953. Stamp Day.

339	**76**	15f. blue	9·00	17·00

77 Henri Dunant

1953. Red Cross Week and 125th Anniv of Birth of Dunant (founder).

340	**77**	15f.+5f. brown and red	3·75	9·50

79 St. Benedict blessing St. Maurus

1953. Tholey Abbey Fund.

344	**79**	30f.+10f. black	3·50	10·50

80 Saar Fair

1954. Saar Fair.

345	**80**	15f. green	2·75	1·30

81 Postal Motor Coach

1954. Stamp Day.

346	**81**	15f. red	12·50	18·00

82 Red Cross and Child

1954. Red Cross Week.

347	**82**	15f.+5f. brown	4·25	9·50

83 Madonna and Child (Holbein)

1954. Marian Year.

348	**83**	5f. red	3·25	4·25
349	-	10f. green	3·25	4·25
350	-	15f. blue	4·25	7·50

DESIGNS: 10f. "Sistine Madonna" (Raphael); 15f. "Madonna and Child with Pear" (Durer).

84 "Street Urchin with a Melon" (Murillo)

1954. National Relief Fund. Paintings inscr "VOLKSHILFE 1954".

351	**84**	5f.+3f. red	1·30	1·90
352	-	10f.+5f. green	1·30	1·90
353	-	15f.+7f. violet	1·30	2·75

DESIGNS: 10f. "Maria de Medici" (A. Bronzino); 15f. "Baron Emil von Maucler" (J. F. Dietrich).

85 Cyclist and Flag

1955. World Cross-Country Cycle Race.

354	**85**	15f. blue, red and black	55	95

86 Rotary Emblem and Industrial Plant

1955. 50th Anniv of Rotary International.

355	**86**	15f. brown	55	1·10

87 Exhibitors' Flags

1955. Saar Fair.
356 **87** 15f. multicoloured 55 95

88 Nurse and Baby

1955. Red Cross Week.
357 **88** 15f.+5f. black and red 75 1·40

89 Postman

1955. Stamp Day.
358 **89** 15f. purple 2·75 3·25

1955. Referendum. Optd VOLKSBEFRAGUNG 1955.
359 15f. red (No. 326) 65 95
360 18f. purple (No. 327) 65 75
361 30f. blue (No. 329) 85 95

91 "Mother" (Durer)

1955. National Relief Fund. Durer paintings inscr as in T 91.
362 **91** 5f.+3f. green 65 1·70
363 - 10f.+5f. green 1·10 2·10
364 - 15f.+7f. bistre 1·50 2·50
PAINTINGS: 10f. "The Praying Hands"; 15f. "The Old Man from Antwerp".

92

1956. Saar Fair.
365 **92** 15f. green and red 55 1·30

93 Radio Tower

1956. Stamp Day.
366 **93** 15f. green and turquoise 55 1·30

94 Casualty Station

1956. Red Cross Week.
367 **94** 15f.+5f. brown 55 1·30

95

1956. Olympic Games.
368 **95** 12f.+3f. blue and green 75 95
369 **95** 15f.+5f. brown & purple 75 95

96 Winterberg Memorial

1956. Winterberg Memorial Reconstruction Fund.
370 **96** 5f.+2f. green 40 65
371 **96** 12f.+3f. purple 40 65
372 **96** 15f.+5f. brown 40 85

97 "Portrait of Lucrezia Crivelli" (da Vinci)

1956. National Relief Fund. Inscr as in T 97.
373 **97** 5f.+3f. blue 40 40
374 - 10f.+5f. red 40 65
375 - 15f.+7f. green 40 1·10
PAINTINGS: 10f. "Saskia" (Rembrandt); 15f. "Lady Playing Spinet" (Floris).

RETURN TO GERMANY

98 Arms of the Saar

1957. Return of the Saar to Germany.
376 **98** 15f. blue and red 30 55

99 President Heuse

1957. (a) Without "F" after figure of value.
377 **99** 1f. green 30 20
378 **99** 2f. violet 30 20
379 **99** 3f. brown 30 20
380 **99** 4f. mauve 40 1·10
381 **99** 5f. green 30 20
382 **99** 6f. red 30 65
383 **99** 10f. grey 30 40
384 **99** 12f. orange 30 20
385 **99** 15f. green 30 20
386 **99** 18f. red 85 3·25
387 **99** 25f. lilac 65 1·10
388 **99** 30f. purple 65 1·10
389 **99** 45f. green 1·50 3·75
390 **99** 50f. brown 1·50 1·70
391 **99** 60f. red 2·10 4·25
392 **99** 70f. orange 3·75 6·25
393 **99** 80f. green 1·30 4·75
394 **99** 90f. grey 3·75 8·50
395 **99** 100f. red (24×29½ mm) 3·25 10·50
396 **99** 200f. lilac (24×29½ mm) 8·50 34·00

78 "Painter's Young Son" (Rubens)

1953. National Relief Fund. Paintings inscr "VOLKSHILFE 1953".
341 - 15f.+5f. violet 4·25 7·50
342 - 18f.+7f. red 4·25 8·00
343 **78** 30f.+10f. green 6·25 12·50
DESIGNS—VERT: 15f. "Clarice Strozzi" (Titian). HORIZ: 18f. "Painter's Children" (Rubens).

(b) With "F" after figure of value.
406 1f. grey 30 30
407 3f. blue 30 30
408 5f. green 30 30
409 6f. brown 30 65
410 10f. violet 30 30
411 12f. orange 30 30
412 15f. green 55 30
413 18f. grey 2·75 6·25
414 20f. green 1·60 4·25
415 25f. brown 55 55
416 30f. mauve 1·30 55
417 35f. brown 3·25 4·25
418 45f. green 2·75 5·25
419 50f. brown 1·30 2·75
420 70f. green 6·25 7·50
421 80f. blue 3·25 6·75
422 90f. red 7·50 8·50
423 100f. orange (24×29½ mm) 6·25 9·50
424 200f. green (24×29½ mm) 11·50 34·00
425 300f. blue (24 ×29½ mm) 12·50 38·00

100 Iron Foundry

1957. Saar Fair.
397 **100** 15f. red and black 30 55

101 Arms of Merzig and St. Pierre Church

1957. Centenary of Merzig.
398 **101** 15f. blue 30 55

101a "Europa" Tree

1957. Europa.
399 **101a** 20f. orange and yellow 85 1·40
400 **101a** 35f. violet and pink 1·30 1·90

101b Young Miner

1957. Humanitarian Relief Fund.
401 **101b** 6f.+4f. black & brown 30 30
402 - 12f.+6f. black & green 30 40
403 - 15f.+7f. black and red 40 55
404 - 30f.+10f. black & blue 55 95
DESIGNS: 12f. Miner drilling at coalface; 15f. Miner with coal-cutting machine; 30f. Operator at mine lift-shaft.

101c Carrier Pigeons

1957. International Correspondence Week.
405 **101c** 15f. black and red 30 55

101d Max and Moritz (cartoon characters)

1958. 150th Death Anniv of Wilhelm Busch (writer and illustrator).
426 **101d** 12f. green and black 30 30
427 - 15f. red and black 30 55
DESIGN: 15f. Wilhelm Busch.

101e "Prevent Forest Fires"

1958. Forest Fires Prevention Campaign.
428 **101e** 15f. black and red 30 55

101f Diesel and First Oil Engine

1958. Birth Centenary of Rudolf Diesel (engineer).
429 **101f** 12f. green 30 55

101g "The Fox who stole the Goose"

1958. Berlin Students' Fund.
430 **101g** 12f.+6f. red, black and green 20 40
431 - 15f.+7f. brown, green and red 30 55
DESIGN: 15f. "A Hunter from the Palatinate".

102 Saarbrucken Town Hall and Fair Emblem

1958. Saar Fair.
432 **102** 15f. purple 30 55

103 Homburg

1958. 400th Anniv of Homburg.
433 **103** 15f. green 30 55

103a Emblem

1958. 150th Anniv of German Gymnastics.

434	**103a**	12f. black, green and grey	30	55

103b Schulze-Delitzsch

1958. 150th Birth of Schulze-Delitzsch (pioneer of German Co-operative Movement).

435	**103b**	12f. green	30	55

103c "Europa"

1958. Europa.

436	**103c**	12f. blue and green	75	1·30
437	-	30f. red and blue	95	1·90

103d Friedrich Raiffeisen (philanthropist)

1958. Humanitarian Relief and Welfare Funds.

438	**103d**	6f.+4f. brn, lt brn & chest	30	30
439	-	12f.+6f. red, yell & grn	30	30
440	-	15f.+7f. blue, grn & red	65	65
441	-	30f.+10f. yellow, grn & bl	65	85

DESIGNS—Inscr "WOHLFAHRTSMARKE": 12f. Dairymaid; 15f. Vine-dresser 30f. Farm labourer.

103e Fugger

1959. 500th Birth Anniv of Jakob Fugger (merchant prince).

442	**103e**	15f. black and red	30	55

104 Hands holding Crates

1959. Saar Fair.

443	**104**	15f. red	30	55

105 Saarbrucken

1959. 50th Anniv of Greater Saarbrucken.

444	**105**	15f. blue	30	55

105a Humboldt

1959. Death Centenary of Alexander von Humboldt (naturalist).

445	**105a**	15f. blue	55	65

OFFICIAL STAMPS

1922. Nos. 84 to 94 optd DIENSTMARKE.

O98	3c. green	1·30	42·00
O99	5c. black and orange	55	55
O100	10c. green	55	40
O109	15c. orange	3·25	65
O101	15c. brown	55	40
O102	20c. blue and yellow	55	40
O111	25c. red and yellow	3·25	65
O104	30c. red and yellow	55	40
O105	40c. brown and yellow	75	40
O106	50c. blue and yellow	75	40
O112	75c. green and yellow	6·25	3·25
O108a	1f. brown	16·00	3·25

1927. Nos. 108/15, 117 and 119 optd DIENSTMARKE.

O128	10c. brown	2·75	3·25
O129	15c. green	2·75	8·50
O130	20c. brown	2·75	2·10
O131	25c. blue	3·25	8·50
O122	30c. green	7·50	1·10
O133	40c. brown	2·75	40
O134	50c. red	5·25	55
O135	60c. orange	1·60	40
O136	75c. purple	3·25	1·10
O137	1f. violet	3·25	55
O138	2f. red	3·25	55

O51 Arms

1949

O264	**O51**	10c. red	55	25·00
O265	**O51**	30c. black	40	30·00
O266	**O51**	1f. green	40	1·40
O267	**O51**	2f. red	2·10	1·60
O268	**O51**	5f. blue	2·75	1·40
O269	**O51**	10f. black	1·10	1·40
O270	**O51**	12f. mauve	10·50	15·00
O271	**O51**	15f. blue	1·10	1·40
O272	**O51**	20f. green	2·75	1·60
O273	**O51**	30f. mauve	7·50	6·25
O274	**O51**	50f. purple	2·75	5·25
O275	**O51**	100f. brown	95·00	£400

Pt. 8

SAN MARINO

An independent republic lying near the east coast of the Italian peninsula.

1877. 100 centesimi = 1 lira.
2002. 100 cents = 1 euro.

1

1877

1	**1**	2c. green	21·00	6·50
18	**1**	2c. blue	12·00	6·50
32	**1**	2c. purple	9·00	6·50
2	**2**	5c. yellow	£170	14·00
33	**2**	5c. green	6·75	4·25
3	**2**	10c. blue	£200	14·00
20	**2**	10c. green	6·75	3·25
34	**2**	10c. red	6·75	4·25
21	**2**	15c. red	£180	55·00
4	**2**	20c. red	28·00	7·50
35	**2**	20c. lilac	6·75	4·25
5	**2**	25c. purple	£170	21·00
36	**2**	25c. blue	6·75	5·25
6	**2**	30c. brown	£1000	70·00
22	**2**	30c. yellow	7·75	7·50
7	**2**	40c. mauve	£1000	70·00
23	**2**	40c. brown	7·75	7·50
24	**2**	45c. green	7·75	7·50
25	**2**	65c. brown	7·75	7·50
26	**2**	1l. red and yellow	£2000	£650
37	**2**	1l. blue	£1900	£550
27	**2**	2l. brown and buff	90·00	£225
28	**2**	5l. red and blue	£200	£200

2

1892. Surch Cmi. and figure of value.

10c	5c. on 10c. blue	85·00	15·00
12	5c. on 30c. brown	£300	50·00
16	10c. on 20c. red	75·00	8·50

1892. Surch 10 10.

17	10(c.) on 20c. red	£375	13·00

13 Government Palace

14 Government Palace

15 Interior of Government Palace

1894. Opening of Government Palace and Installation of Captains-Regent.

29	**13**	25c. purple and blue	5·50	2·10
30	**14**	50c. purple and red	55·00	5·25
31	**15**	1l. purple and green	33·00	8·50

17 Statue of Liberty

1899

38	**17**	2c. brown	1·70	1·40
39	**17**	5c. orange	4·50	3·00

See also Nos. 86/91.

18

19 Mt. Titano

1903

40	**18**	2c. lilac	14·50	5·25
73	**18**	2c. brown	45	75
74	**19**	5c. green	45	75
111	**19**	5c. purple	40	25
42	**19**	10c. pink	6·75	2·10
75	**19**	10c. orange	45	75
112	**19**	10c. green	40	25
76	**19**	15c. green	45	75
113	**19**	15c. purple	40	25
43	**19**	20c. orange	£130	32·00
77	**19**	20c. brown	45	75
114	**19**	20c. green	40	25
44	**19**	25c. blue	18·00	5·25
78	**19**	25c. grey	45	75
115	**19**	25c. violet	40	25
45	**19**	30c. red	6·75	10·50
79	**19**	30c. mauve	45	75
116	**19**	30c. orange	18·00	1·30
46	**19**	40c. red	12·00	13·00
80	**19**	40c. pink	1·30	1·10
117	**19**	40c. brown	65	25
47	**19**	45c. yellow	9·00	12·00
81	**19**	50c. purple	1·80	1·60
118	**19**	50c. grey	65	25
119	**19**	60c. red	65	25
48	**19**	65c. brown	9·00	12·00
82	**19**	80c. blue	2·20	2·75
83	**19**	90c. brown	2·20	2·75
49	**19**	1l. green	28·00	17·00
120	**19**	1l. blue	65	65
50	**19**	2l. violet	£850	£225
85	**19**	2l. red	34·00	21·00
121	**19**	2l. green	6·75	4·75
122	**19**	5l. blue	18·00	18·00

1905. Surch 1905 15.

52	15c. on 20c. orange	11·00	6·50

22

23

1907

53a	**22**	1c. brown	5·50	2·10
54	**23**	15c. grey	18·00	5·25

1917. For Combatants. Surch 1917 Pro combattenti and value.

55	**18**	25c. on 2c. lilac	4·50	4·25
56	**19**	50c. on 2l. violet	50·00	38·00

1918. Surch Cent. 20 1918.

57	**23**	20c. on 15c. grey	3·50	2·75

26 Statue of Liberty

1918. War Casualties Fund. Inscr as in T 26.

58	**26**	2c.(+5c.) black and lilac	70	1·10
59	**26**	5c.(+5c.) black and green	70	1·10
60	**26**	10c.(+5c.) black and red	70	1·10
61	**26**	20c.(+5c.) black and orange	70	1·10
62	**26**	25c.(+5c.) black and blue	70	1·10
63	**26**	45c.(+5c.) black and brown	70	1·10
64	-	1l.(+5c.) black and green	20·00	21·00
65	-	2l.(+5c.) black and lilac	20·00	19·00
66	-	3l.(+5c.) black and red	20·00	18·00

DESIGN—HORIZ: 1, 2, 3l. San Marino.

1918. Italian Victory over Austria and Premium for War Casualties Fund. Optd 3 Novembre 1918.

67	**26**	20c.(+5c.) black and orange	2·20	3·75
68	**26**	25c.(+5c.) black and blue	2·20	3·75
69	**26**	45c.(+5c.) black and brown	2·20	3·75
70	-	1l.(+5c.) black and green	9·00	6·50
71	-	2l.(+5c.) black and lilac	18·00	13·00
72	-	3l.(+5c.) black and red	22·00	15·00

DESIGN—HORIZ: 1, 2, 3l. As Nos. 64/66.

1922. Re-issue of T 17. Colours changed.

86	**17**	2c. purple	20	30
87	**17**	5c. green	20	30
88	**17**	10c. brown	40	30
89	**17**	20c. brown	40	30
90	**17**	25c. blue	40	30
91	**17**	45c. red	4·00	2·10

30 Arbe (Rab)

1923. Delivery to San Marino of Italian Flag flown on Arbe, after the island returned to Yugoslavia.

92	**30**	50c. green	55	55

31 St. Marinus

1923. San Marino Mutual Aid Society.

93	**31**	30c. brown	55	55

32 Mt. Titano

33 "Liberty"

1923. Red Cross Fund.

94	**32**	5c.+5c. green	40	30
95	**32**	10c.+5c. orange	75	30
96	**32**	15c.+5c. green	3·25	30
97	**32**	25c.+5c. red	2·20	85
98	**32**	40c.+5c. purple	7·75	3·25
99	**32**	50c.+5c. grey	14·50	45
100	**33**	1l.+5c. blue and black	5·00	7·50

34

1923. San Marino Volunteers in the Great War.

101	**34**	1l. brown	14·50	10·50

35 Garibaldi

36

1924. 75th Anniv of Garibaldi's Refuge in San Marino.

102	**35**	30c. purple	2·75	1·80
103	**35**	50c. brown	3·00	2·50
104	**35**	60c. red	4·50	3·75
105	**36**	1l. blue	10·00	6·00
106	**36**	2l. green	13·50	7·50

1924. Red Cross stamps of 1918 surch.

107	**26**	30c. on 45c. black & brown	2·00	1·10
108	-	60c. on 1l. black and green	7·00	5·25
109	-	1l. on 2l. black and lilac	20·00	15·00
110	-	2l. on 3l. black and red	18·00	13·00

1926. Surch.

123	**19**	75c. on 80c. blue	1·90	85
124	**19**	1l.20 on 90c. brown	1·90	85
125	**19**	1l.25 on 90c. brown	4·00	3·25
126	**19**	2l.50 on 80c. blue	7·75	8·50

40 Onofri

1926. Death Centenary of Antonio Onofri, "Father of the Country".

127	**40**	10c. black and blue	90	25
128	**40**	20c. black and green	90	65
129	**40**	45c. black and violet	90	85
130	**40**	65c. black and green	90	85
131	**40**	1l. black and orange	5·50	5·25
132	**40**	2l. black and mauve	5·50	5·25

1926. No. E92 surch Lire 1,85.

133	**19**	1l.85 on 60c. violet	55	75

1927. Surch.

134	**40**	"1,25" on 1l. black & orge	5·00	3·25
135	**40**	"2,50" on 2l. black & mauve	13·00	9·50
136	**40**	"5" on 2l. black and mauve	55·00	50·00

1927. Unissued Express stamp (No. 115 surch ESPRESSO 50) surch L. 1,75.

137	**19**	1l.75 on 50c. on 25c. violet	85	80

44 San Marino War Memorial

1927. War Cenotaph Commemoration.

138	**44**	50c. purple	1·30	2·10
139	**44**	1l.25 blue	4·00	2·10
140	**44**	10l. violet	23·00	22·00

45 Franciscan Convent and Capuchin Church

1928. 700th Death Anniv of St. Francis of Assisi.

141	**45**	50c. red	34·00	6·50
142	**45**	1l.25 blue	8·00	7·50
143	-	2l.50 brown	8·00	7·50
144	-	5l. violet	39·00	32·00

DESIGN: 2l.50, 5l. Death of St. Francis.

46 La Rocca Fortress

47 Government Palace

48 Statue of Liberty

1929

145	**46**	5c. blue and purple	1·00	65
146	**46**	10c. mauve and blue	1·00	65
147	**46**	15c. green and orange	1·00	65
148	**46**	20c. red and blue	1·00	65
149	**46**	25c. black and green	1·00	65
150	**46**	30c. red and grey	1·00	65
151	**46**	50c. green and purple	1·00	65
152	**46**	75c. grey and red	1·00	65
153	**47**	1l. green and brown	1·00	65
154	**47**	1l.25 black and blue	1·30	65
155	**47**	1l.75 orange and green	8·75	1·60
156	**47**	2l. red and blue	2·00	1·60
157	**47**	2l.50 blue and red	2·00	1·60
158	**47**	3l. blue and orange	2·00	1·60
159	**47**	3l.70 purple and green	2·00	2·75
160	**48**	5l. green and violet	10·00	2·75
161	**48**	10l. blue and brown	20·00	10·50
162	**48**	15l. purple and green	90·00	85·00
163	**48**	20l. red and blue	£350	£375

50 Mt. Titano

1931. Air.

164	**50**	50c. green	9·00	7·50
165	**50**	80c. red	9·00	7·50
166	**50**	1l. brown	6·75	4·25
167	**50**	2l. purple	6·75	4·25
168	**50**	2l.60 blue	49·00	55·00
169	**50**	3l. grey	49·00	55·00
170	**50**	5l. green	16·00	4·25
171	**50**	7l.70 brown	16·00	8·50
172	**50**	9l. orange	18·00	10·50
173	**50**	10l. blue	£425	£400

51 G.P.O., San Marino

1932. Inauguration of New G.P.O.

174	**51**	20c. green	9·00	8·50
175	**51**	50c. red	13·50	13·00
176	**51**	1l.25 blue	£250	£130
177	**51**	1l.75 brown	£250	85·00
178	**51**	2l.75 violet	44·00	32·00

52 San Marino Railway Station

1932. Opening of San Marino Electric Railway, Rimini.

179	**52**	20c. green	3·00	2·10
180	**52**	50c. red	4·25	3·25
181	**52**	1l.25 blue	14·50	10·50
182	**52**	5l. brown	80·00	70·00

53 Garibaldi

1932. 50th Death Anniv of Garibaldi.

183	**53**	10c. brown	7·50	3·25
184	**53**	20c. violet	7·50	3·25
185	**53**	25c. green	7·50	3·25
186	**53**	50c. brown	12·00	7·50
187	-	75c. red	20·00	10·50
188	-	1l.25 blue	36·00	15·00
189	-	2l.75 orange	85·00	43·00
190	-	5l. green	£350	£350

DESIGN: 75c. to 5l. Garibaldi's arrival at San Marino.

1933. Air. LZ-127 "Graf Zeppelin". Surch ZEPPELIN 1933 under airship and new value.

191	**50**	3l. on 50c. orange	8·25	£110
192	**50**	5l. on 80c. green	44·00	£110
193	**50**	10l. on 1l. blue	44·00	£160
194	**50**	12l. on 2l. brown	44·00	£160
195	**50**	15l. on 2l.60 red	48·00	£160
196	**50**	20l. on 3l. green	48·00	£275

1933. 20th Italian Philatelic Congress. Surch 28 MAGGIO 1933 CONVEGNO FILATELICO and new value.

197	**51**	25c. on 2l.75 violet	13·50	10·50
198	**51**	50c. on 1l.75 brown	26·00	21·00
199	**51**	75c. on 2l.75 violet	65·00	43·00
200	**51**	1l.25 on 1l.75 brown	£400	£400

1934. Philatelic Exn. Surch 12-27 APRILE 1934 MOSTRA FILATELICA and value with wheel.

201	25c. on 1l.25 blue	1·80	2·10
202	50c. on 1l.75 brown	3·50	3·25
203	75c. on 50c. red	7·00	6·50
204	1l.25 on 20c. green	32·00	42·00

1934. Surch with value and wheel.

205	3l.70 on 1l.25 blue	90·00	75·00
206	3l.70 on 2l.75 violet	90·00	95·00

58 Ascent to Mt. Titano

1935. 12th Anniv of San Marino Fascist Party.

207	**58**	5c. black and brown	40	25
208	**58**	10c. black and violet	40	25
209	**58**	20c. black and orange	40	25
210	**58**	25c. black and green	40	25
211	**58**	50c. black and bistre	40	25
212	**58**	75c. black and red	1·20	2·75
213	**58**	1l.25 black and blue	4·75	6·00

59 Delfico

1935. Death Centenary of Melchiorre Delfico (historian of San Marino).

214	**59**	5c. black and purple	95	1·10
215	**59**	7½c. black and brown	95	1·10
216	**59**	10c. black and green	95	1·10
217	**59**	15c. black and red	24·00	7·50
218	**59**	20c. black and orange	1·90	2·10
219	**59**	25c. black and green	1·90	2·10
220	-	30c. black and violet	1·90	2·10
221	-	50c. black and green	4·75	6·50
222	-	75c. black and red	12·00	12·00
223	-	1l.25 black and blue	3·25	4·25
224	-	1l.50 black and brown	55·00	48·00
225	-	1l.75 black and orange	85·00	85·00

DESIGN—25×35 mm: 30c. to 1l.75, Statue of Delfico.

1936. Surch. (a) Postage.

226	**40**	80c. on 45c. black & violet	4·00	3·75
227	**40**	80c. on 65c. black & green	4·00	3·75
228	**45**	2l.05 on 1l.25 blue	6·50	6·50
229	-	2l.75 on 2l.50 brown (No. 143)	24·00	26·00

(b) Air.

230	**50**	75c. on 50c. green	2·20	3·75
231	**50**	75c. on 80c. red	13·50	12·50

63 St. Marinus and St. Leo

1937. Independence Monument. Sheet 125×105 mm.

MS232 **63** 5l.	16·00	21·00

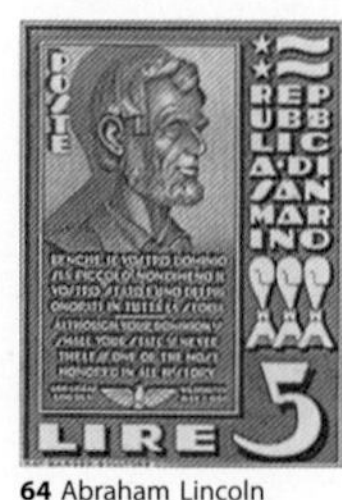
64 Abraham Lincoln

1938. Dedication of Bust of Abraham Lincoln. Sheets (each 125×105 mm).

MS232a **64** 3l. blue	3·50	3·25
MS232b 5l. red	24·00	13·00

1941. Surch 10.

233	**19**	10c. on 15c. purple	20	25
234	**19**	10c. on 30c. orange	1·30	1·10

1942. Air. Surch Lire 10 and bars.

235	**50**	10l. on 2l.60 blue	£140	£130
236	**50**	10l. on 3l. grey	30·00	32·00

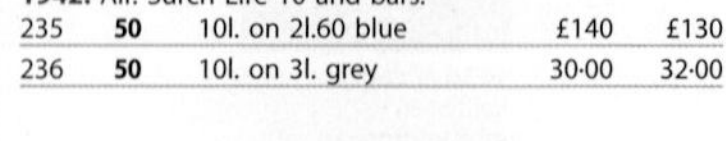

67 Gajarda Tower, Arbe, and Flags of Italy and San Marino

1942. Restoration of Italian Flag to Arbe (Rab) annexed by Italy in 1941.

237	**67**	10c. red and bistre (postage)	15	10
238	**67**	15c. red and brown	15	10
239	**67**	20c. grey and green	15	10
240	**67**	25c. blue and green	20	10
241	**67**	50c. brown and red	20	10
242	**67**	75c. grey and red	20	10
243	-	1l.25 light blue and blue	20	10
244	-	1l.75 grey and brown	45	25
245	-	2l.75 blue and bistre	65	55
246	-	5l. brown and green	4·50	4·25
247	-	25c. grey and brown (air)	30	10
248	-	50c. brown and green	30	10
249	-	75c. brown and blue	30	10
250	-	1l. brown and bistre	85	75
251	-	5l. blue and bistre	8·25	6·25

DESIGNS—HORIZ: Nos. 243/6, Galleon in Arbe Harbour. VERT: Nos. 247/51, Granda Belfry, Arbe.

1942. Italian Philatelic Congress. Surch GIORNATA FILATELICA RIMINI - SAN MARINO 3 AGOSTO 1942 (1641 d. F. R.) C. – 30.

252	**67**	30c. on 10c. red and bistre	20	25

1942. Surch.

253		30c. on 20c. grey and green	20	30
254	-	20l. on 75c. black and red (No. 222)	17·00	16·00

71 Printing Press

1943. Press Propaganda.

255	**71**	10c. green	15	15
256	**71**	15c. brown	15	15
257	**71**	20c. brown	15	15
258	**71**	30c. purple	15	15
259	**71**	50c. blue	15	15
260	**71**	75c. red	15	15
261	**72**	1l.25 blue	15	15
262	**72**	1l.75 violet	30	20
263	**72**	5l. blue	1·00	1·20
264	**72**	10l. brown	5·75	4·75

72 Newspapers

1943. Philatelic Exhibition. Optd GIORNATA FILATELICA RIMINI - SAN MARINO 5 LUGLIO 1943 (1642 d. F. R.).

265	**71**	30c. purple	10	15
266	**71**	50c. blue	10	15

74 Gateway **75** War Memorial

1943. Fall of Fascism. Unissued series for 20th Anniv of Fascism optd 28 LVGLIO 1943 1642 d. F.R. (the "d." is omitted on T 74) and bars cancelling commemorative inscription.

267	**74**	5c. brown (postage)	20	25
268	**74**	10c. orange	20	25
269	**74**	20c. blue	20	25
270	**74**	25c. green	20	25
271	**74**	30c. purple	20	25
272	**74**	50c. violet	20	25
273	**74**	75c. red	20	25
274	**75**	1l.25 blue	20	25
275	**75**	1l.75 orange	20	25
276	**75**	2l.75 brown	45	60
277	**75**	5l. green	1·00	1·20
278	**75**	10l. violet	1·70	2·10
279	**75**	20l. blue	6·00	4·75
280	-	25c. brown (air)	20	25
281	-	50c. purple	20	25
282	-	75c. brown	20	25
283	-	1l. purple	20	25
284	-	2l. blue	20	25
285	-	5l. orange	1·10	25
286	-	10l. green	1·80	1·40
287	-	20l. black	7·00	7·00

DESIGN—Air: Nos. 280/7, Map of San Marino.

1943. Provisional Govt. Optd GOVERNO PROVVISORIO over ornamentation.

288	**74**	5c. brown (postage)	20	20
289	**74**	10c. orange	20	20
290	**74**	20c. blue	20	20
291	**74**	25c. green	20	20
292	**74**	30c. purple	20	20
293	**74**	50c. violet	20	20
294	**74**	75c. red	20	20
295	**75**	1l.25 blue	20	20
296	**75**	1l.75 orange	25	20
297	**75**	5l. green	80	65
298	**75**	20l. blue	3·25	2·40
299	-	25c. brown (air)	20	25
300	-	50c. red	20	25
301	-	75c. brown	20	25
302	-	1l. purple	20	25
303	-	5l. orange	65	1·20
304	-	20l. black	4·00	3·25

78 St. Marinus

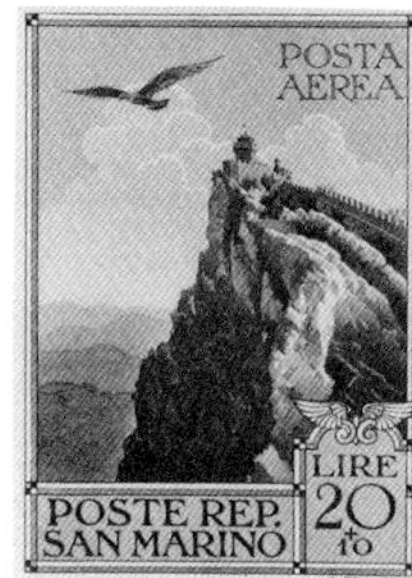
79 Mt. Titano

1944

305	**78**	20l.+10l. brown (postage)	2·75	2·75
306	**79**	20l.+10l. green (air)	2·20	2·75

80 Govt Palace **81** Govt Palace

1945. 50th Anniv of Government Palace.

307	**80**	25l. purple (postage)	27·00	8·50
308	**81**	25l. brown (air)	39·00	7·50
MS308a		180×120 mm comprising 10l. blue and15l. green (angels and crowd scene, horiz); 25l. red (Palace, vert). Perf or imperf	£375	£225

82 Arms of Montegiardino **83** Arms of San Marino

1945. Arms Types.

309	-	10c. blue	30	25
310	**82**	20c. red	30	25
311	-	40c. orange	30	25
312	**82**	60c. grey	30	25
313	-	80c. green	30	25
314	-	1l. red	55	25
315	-	1l.20 violet	55	25
316	-	2l. brown	55	25
317	-	3l. blue	55	25
317a	-	4l. orange	55	25
318	-	5l. brown	55	25
319	-	10l. red and brown	4·25	3·25
318a	-	15l. blue	5·00	3·25
320	-	20l. red and blue	9·50	4·25
321	-	20l. brown and blue	22·00	4·25
322	**82**	25l. blue and brown	21·00	7·50
323	**83**	50l. blue and green	33·00	19·00

DESIGNS (Arms of San Marino and villages in the Republic): 10c., 1l., 1l.20, 15l. Faetano; 40c., 5l. San Marino; 80c., 2, 3, 4l. Fiorentino; 10l. Borgomaggiore; 20l. (2) Serravalle.

84 U.N.R.R.A. Aid for San Marino

1946. U.N.R.R.A.

324	**84**	100l. red, purple and orange	22·00	10·50

85 Airplane and Mt. Titano

1946. Air.

325	-	25c. grey	30	25
326	**85**	75c. red	30	25
327	-	1l. brown	30	25
328	**85**	2l. green	30	25
329	**85**	3l. violet	30	25
330	-	5l. blue	55	25
331	-	10l. red	55	25
334	-	20l. purple	2·50	2·75
332	-	35l. red	13·00	7·00
335	-	50l. green	20·00	10·50
333	-	100l. brown	3·25	1·50

DESIGNS—HORIZ: 25c., 1, 10l. Wings over Mt. Titano; 100l. Airplane over globe. VERT: 5, 20, 35, 50l. Four aircraft over Mt. Titano.

1946. Stamp Day. Surch L.10.

336	**83**	50l.+10l. blue and green	33·00	15·00

1946. National Philatelic Convention. Nos. 329/31 but colours changed and without "POSTA AEREA" surch CONVEGNO FILATELICO 30 NOVEMBRE 1946 and premium.

336a	**85**	3l.+25l. brown	2·20	1·10
336b	-	5l.+25l. orange	2·20	1·10
336c	-	10l.+50l. blue	18·00	9·00

87 Quotation from F.D.R. on Liberty

88 Franklin D. Roosevelt

1947. In Memory of President Franklin D. Roosevelt.

336d	**87**	1l. brn & ochre (postage)	30	25
336e	**88**	2l. brown and blue	30	25
336f	-	5l. multicoloured	30	25
336g	-	15l. multicoloured	30	25
336h	**87**	50l. brown and red	2·20	30
336i	**88**	100l. brown and violet	4·50	1·30

DESIGN—HORIZ: 5l., 15l. Roosevelt and flags of San Marino and U.S.A.

336j	1l. brown and blue (air)	30	25
336k	2l. brown and red	30	25
336l	5l. multicoloured	30	25
336m	20l. brown and purple	85	25
336n	31l. brown and orange	1·70	25
336o	50l. brown and red	4·50	1·10
336p	100l. brown and blue	6·75	2·10
336q	200l. multicoloured	44·00	22·00

DESIGNS—HORIZ: 1, 3, 50l. Roosevelt and eagle; 2, 20, 100l. Roosevelt and San Marino arms. VERT: 5, 200l. Roosevelt and flags of San Marino and U.S.A.

1947. Surch in figures.

336r	**87**	3 on 1l. brown and ochre (postage)	55	30
336s	**88**	4 on 2l. brown and blue	65	30
336t	-	6 on 5l. mult (No. 336f)	65	45
336u	-	3 on 1l. brown and blue (No. 336j) (air)	55	30
336v	-	4 on 2l. brown and red (No. 336k)	70	30
336w	-	6 on 5l. mult (No. 336l)	70	45

1947. No. 317a surch.

337	6l. on 4l. orange	35	25
338	21l. on 4l. orange	1·90	85

91 St. Marinus founding Republic

1947. Reconstruction.

339	**91**	1l. mauve & green (postage)	30	25
340	**91**	2l. green and mauve	30	25
341	**91**	4l. green and brown	30	25
342	**91**	10l. blue and orange	55	25
343	**91**	25l. mauve and red	3·50	2·10
344	**91**	50l. brown and green	48·00	20·00
345	**91**	25l. blue and orange (air)	2·20	2·40
346	**91**	50l. blue and brown	5·50	5·00

Nos. 343/6 are larger (24½×32 mm) and have two rows of ornaments forming the frame.

1947. Air. Rimini Philatelic Exhibition. No. 333 optd Giornata Filatelica Rimini - San Marino 8 Luglio 1947.

347	100l. brown	3·25	1·40

1947. Reconstruction. Surch + and value in figures.

348	1l.+1 mauve and green	20	20
349	1l.+2 mauve and green	20	20
350	1l.+3 mauve and green	20	20
351	1l.+4 mauve and green	20	20
352	1l.+5 mauve and green	20	20
353	2l.+1 green and mauve	20	20
354	2l.+2 green and mauve	20	20
355	2l.+3 green and mauve	20	20
356	2l.+4 green and mauve	20	20
357	2l.+5 green and mauve	20	20
358	4l.+1 green and brown	11·00	5·25
359	4l.+2 green and brown	11·00	5·25

94 Mt. Titano, Statue of Liberty and 1847 U.S.A. Stamp

95 Mt. Titano and 1847 U.S.A. Stamp

1947. Centenary of First U.S.A. Postage Stamp.

360	**94**	2l. brown & pur (postage)	30	25
361	-	3l. grey, red and blue	30	25
362	**94**	6l. green and blue	30	25
363	-	15l. violet, red and blue	1·10	55
364	-	35l. brown, red and blue	4·25	1·60
365	-	50l. green, red and blue	5·00	1·60
366	**95**	100l. brown and violet (air)	26·00	16·00

DESIGNS: 3, 35l. U.S.A. stamps, 5c. and 10c. of 1847 and 90c. of 1869 and flags of U.S.A. and San Marino; 15, 50l. Similar but differently arranged.

96 Worker and San Marino Flag

1948. Workers' Issue.

367	**96**	5l. brown	4·50	55
368	**96**	8l. green	4·50	55
369	**96**	30l. red	7·75	1·10
370	**96**	50l. brown and mauve	17·00	3·25
371	**96**	100l. blue and violet	55·00	48·00

See also Nos. 506/7.

1948. Surch L.100 between circular ornaments.

372	**59**	100l. on 15c. black and red	£110	32·00

1948. Air. Surch POSTA AEREA 200.

373	**91**	200l. on 25l. mauve and red (No. 343)	70·00	29·00

99 Faetano **100** Mt. Titano

1949

374	-	1l. blue and black	55	25
375	-	2l. red and purple	55	25
376	**99**	3l. blue and violet	55	25
377	-	4l. violet and black	55	25
378	-	5l. brown and purple	55	25
379	**99**	6l. black and blue	1·70	80
380	**100**	8l. brown and deep brown	1·70	25
381	-	10l. blue and black	1·10	25
382	-	12l. violet and red	4·00	1·30
383	-	15l. red and violet	9·00	1·90
383a	**99**	20l. brown and blue	39·00	2·75
384	-	35l. violet and green	17·00	5·25
385	-	50l. brown and red	10·00	2·10
385a	-	55l. green and blue	£130	50·00
386	**100**	100l. green and brown	£140	75·00
387	-	200l. brown and blue	£140	£110

DESIGNS—HORIZ: 1, 5, 35l. Guaita Tower and walls; 2, 12, 50l. Serravalle and Mt. Titano; 4, 15, 55l. Franciscan Convent and Capuchin Church. VERT: 10, 200l. Guaita Tower.
For similar stamps see Nos. 491/5, 522a/7a and 794/9.

1949. Stamp Day. Optd Giornata Filatelica San Marino-Riccione 28-6-1949.

388	**91**	1l. mauve and green	55	25
389	**91**	2l. green and mauve	85	25

104 Garibaldi

1949. Centenary of Garibaldi's Retreat from Rome. (a) Postage. Portraits as T 104. (i) Size 22×28 mm.

390	-	1l. red and black	30	25
391	-	2l. blue and brown	30	25
392	**104**	3l. green and red	30	25
393	-	4l. brown and blue	30	25

(ii) Size 27×37 mm.

394		5l. brown and mauve	45	25
395		15l. blue and red	2·20	1·20
396		20l. red and violet	4·00	1·90
397	**104**	50l. violet and purple	40·00	15·00

105 Garibaldi in San Marino

(b) Air. (i) Size 28×22 mm.

398	**105**	2l. blue and purple	55	25
399	**105**	3l. black and green	55	25
400	**105**	5l. green and blue	55	25

(ii) Size 37×27 mm.

401		25l. violet and green	6·00	2·40
402		65l. black and green	17·00	9·50

PORTRAITS—VERT: 1, 20l. Francesco Nullo; 2, 5l. Anita Garibaldi; 4, 15l. Ugo Bassi.
See also Nos. 538/44.

106 Mail Coach and Mt. Titano

1949. 75th Anniv of U.P.U.

403	**106**	100l. purple & blue (postage)	28·00	12·00
404	**106**	200l. blue (air)	4·50	2·10
405	**106**	300l. brown, light brown and purple	9·00	4·75

107 Mt. Titano from Serravalle **108** Second and Guaita Towers

109 Guaita Tower

1950. Air. Views.

406	**107**	2l. green and violet	55	55
407	-	3l. brown and blue	55	55
408	**108**	5l. red and brown (22×28 mm)	55	55
409	-	10l. blue and green	4·50	1·10
410	-	15l. violet and black	6·00	1·30
411	-	55l. green and blue	55·00	18·00
412	**107**	100l. black and red (37×27 mm)	44·00	14·00
413	**108**	250l. brown and violet	£225	48·00
414	**109**	500l. brown and green (37×27 mm)	£110	£100
415	**109**	500l. purple, green and blue	£325	£150

DESIGNS—As Type **107**: 3l. Distant view of Domagnano; 10l. Domagnano; 15l. San Marino from St. Mustiola. 27×37 mm: 55l. Borgo Maggiore.

1950. Air. 28th Milan Fair. As Nos. 408, 410 and 411 but in different colours, optd XXVIII FIERA INTERNAZIONALE DI MILANO APRILE 1950.

416	5l. green and blue	55	25
417	15l. black and red	1·10	55
418	55l. brown and violet	8·25	4·75

111 Government Palace

1951. Red Cross.

419	**111**	25l. purple, red and brown	14·50	7·50
420	-	75l. brown, red & lt brown	22·00	10·50
421	-	100l. black, red and brown	30·00	14·00

DESIGNS—HORIZ: 75l. Archway of Murata Nuova. VERT: 100l. Guaita Tower.

1951. Air. Stamp Day. No. 415 surch Giornata Filatelica San Marino - Riccione 20-8-1951 L. 300.

422	**109**	300l. on 500l. purple, green and blue	£100	43·00

113 Flag, Douglas DC-6 Airliner and Mt. Titano

1951. Air.

423	**113**	1000l. blue and brown	£850	£550

108 Second and Guaita Towers

1951. Air. Italian Flood Relief Fund. Surch Pro-alluvionati italiani 1951 L. 100 and bars.

424	**108**	100l. on 250l. brown and violet	13·00	6·00

115 "Columbus at the Council of Salamanca" (after Barabino)

1952. 500th Birth Anniv (1951) of Christopher Columbus.

425	**115**	1l. orange & grn (postage)	55	25
426	-	2l. brown and violet	55	25
427	-	3l. violet and brown	55	25
428	-	4l. blue and brown	55	25
429	-	5l. green and turquoise	55	60
430	-	10l. brown and black	1·70	85
431	-	15l. red and black	2·20	1·40
432	-	20l. blue and green	3·25	1·70
433	-	25l. purple and brown	18·00	5·25
434	**115**	60l. brown and violet	28·00	10·50
435	-	80l. grey and black	60·00	27·00
436	-	200l. green and blue	£120	60·00
437	-	200l. blue and black (air)	55·00	32·00

DESIGNS—HORIZ: 2, 25l. Columbus and fleet; 3, 10, 20l. Landing in America; 4, 15, 80l. Red Indians and American settlers; 5, 200l. (No. 436) Columbus and Map of America; 200l. (No. 437) Columbus, Statue of Liberty (New York) and skyscrapers.

1952. Trieste Fair. As Columbus issue of 1952, but colours changed, optd FIERA DI TRIESTE 1952.

438	1l. violet and brown (postage)	30	25
439	2l. red and black	30	25
440	3l. green and turquoise	30	25
441	4l. brown and black	55	25
442	5l. mauve and violet	85	55
443	10l. blue and brown	2·20	1·10
444	15l. brown and blue	6·75	2·75
445	200l. brown and black (air)	90·00	43·00

117 Rose

118 Cyclamen, Douglas DC-6 Airliner, Rose, San Marino and Riccione

1952. Air. Stamp Day and Philatelic Exhibition.

446	-	1l. purple and violet	55	25
447	-	2l. green and blue	55	25
448	**117**	3l. red and brown	55	25
449	**118**	5l. brown and purple	1·70	25
450	**118**	25l. green and violet	4·50	1·70
451	**118**	200l. multicoloured	£100	45·00

DESIGNS—As Type **117**: 1l. Cyclamen; 2l. San Marino and Riccione.

119 Airplane over San Marino

1952. Air. Aerial Survey of San Marino.

452	**119**	25l. green and yellow	4·00	1·60
453	-	75l. violet and brown	10·00	4·75

DESIGN: 75l. Airplane over Mt. Titano.

120 "The Discus Thrower"

121 Tennis

1953. Sports.

454	**120**	1l. black & brn (postage)	15	25
455	**121**	2l. brown and black	15	25
456	-	3l. blue and black	15	25
457	-	4l. blue and green	15	25
458	-	5l. green and brown	15	25
459	-	10l. red and blue	1·40	25
460	-	25l. brown and black	6·00	1·70
461	-	100l. black and brown	19·00	7·50
462	-	200l. turquoise & grn (air)	25·00	9·75

DESIGNS—As Type **120**: 3l. Running. As Type **121**: HORIZ: 4l. Cycling; 5l. Football; 100l. Roller skating; 200l. Skiing. VERT: 10l. Model glider flying; 25l. Shooting.
See also No. 584.

1953. Stamp Day and Philatelic Exn. As No. 461 but colour changed, optd GIORNATA FILATELICA S. MARINO - RICCIONE 24 AGOSTO 1953.

463	100l. green and turquoise	40·00	16·00

123 Narcissus

1953. Flowers.

464	**123**	1l. blue, green and yellow	15	25
465	-	2l. blue, green and yellow	15	25
466	-	3l. blue, green and yellow	15	25
467	-	4l. blue, green and yellow	15	25
468	-	5l. green and red	15	25
469	-	10l. blue, green and yellow	1·40	60
470	-	25l. blue, green and pink	5·50	2·75
471	-	80l. blue, green and red	28·00	16·00
472	-	100l. blue, green and pink	47·00	22·00

FLOWERS: 2l. "Parrot" tulip; 3l. Oleander; 4l. Cornflower; 5l. Carnation; 10l. Iris; 25 l; Cyclamen; 80l. Geranium; 100l. Rose.

124 Douglas DC-6 Airliner over Mt. Titano and Arms

1954. Air.

473	**124**	1000l. brown and blue	75·00	38·00

125 Walking

1954. Sports.

474	**125**	1l. mauve and violet	10	15
475	-	2l. violet and green	10	15
476	-	3l. chestnut and brown	10	15
477	-	4l. blue and turquoise	10	15
478	-	5l. brown and green	10	15
479	-	8l. lilac and purple	10	15
480	-	12l. red and black	55	25
481	-	25l. green and blue	3·25	30
482	**125**	80l. green and blue	4·50	1·10
483	-	200l. brown and lilac	12·00	4·25
484	-	250l. multicoloured	90·00	43·00

DESIGNS—HORIZ: 2l. Fencing; 3l. Boxing; 5l. Motor-cycle racing; 8l. Throwing the javelin; 12l. Car racing. VERT: 4, 200, 250l. Gymnastics; 25l. Wrestling.
The 200l. measures 27×37 mm and the 250l. 28×37½ mm.

126 Statue of Liberty

1954
485 **126** 20 1. blue & brn (postage) 1·10 30
486 **126** 60l. green and red 4·00 80
487 **126** 120l. brown and blue (air) 2·20 1·30

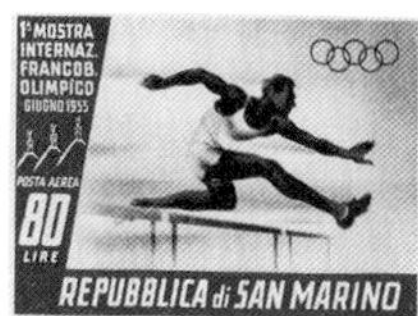

127 Hurdling

1955. Air. 1st Int Exhibition of Olympic Stamps.
488 **127** 80l. black and red 3·25 1·20
489 - 120l. red and green 5·50 2·20
DESIGN—HORIZ: 120l. Relay racing.

128 Yacht

1955. 7th International Philatelic Exhibition.
490 **128** 100l. black and blue 8·25 3·25
See also No. 518.

1955. Views as T 99.
491 5l. brown and blue 10 15
492 10l. green and orange 10 15
493 15l. red and green 10 15
494 25l. violet and brown 20 20
495 35l. red and lilac 20 20
DESIGNS—HORIZ: 5, 25l. Archway of Murata Nuova. VERT: 10, 35l. Guaita Tower; 15l. Government Palace.
See also Nos. 519/21 and 797/9.

129 Ice Skating

1955. Winter Olympic Games, Cortina D'Ampezzo.
496 **129** 1l. brown & yell (postage) 15 15
497 - 2l. blue and red 15 15
498 - 3l. black and brown 15 15
499 - 4l. brown and green 15 15
500 - 5l. blue and red 15 15
501 - 10l. blue and pink 15 20
502 - 25l. black and red 1·70 75
503 - 50l. brown and blue 4·00 1·30
504 - 100l. black and green 11·50 4·50
505 - 200l. black and orange (air) 55·00 21·00
DESIGNS—HORIZ: 2, 25l. Skiing; 3, 50l. Bobsleighing; 5, 100l. Ice hockey; 200l. Ski jumping. VERT: 4l. Slalom racing; 10l. Figure skating.

1956. Winter Relief Fund. As T 96 but additionally inscr "ASSISTENZA INVERNALE".
506 50l. green 14·50 8·00

1956. 50th Anniv of "Arengo" (San Marino Parliament). As T 96 but additionally inscr "50° ANNIVERSARIO ARENGO 25 MARZO 1906".
507 50l. blue 14·50 8·00

130 Pointer

1956. Dogs. 25l. to 100l. have multicoloured centres.
508 **130** 1l. brown and blue 10 25
509 - 2l. grey and red 10 25
510 - 3l. brown and blue 10 25
511 - 4l. grey and blue 10 25
512 - 5l. brown and red 10 25
513 - 10l. brown and blue 10 25
514 - 25l. blue 4·00 1·10
515 - 60l. red 13·00 4·75
516 - 80l. blue 17·00 6·50
517 - 100l. red 26·00 12·00
DOGS: 2l. Borzoi; 3l. Sheepdog; 4l. Greyhound; 5l. Boxer; 10l. Great Dane; 25l. Irish setter; 60l. Alsatian; 80l. Rough collie; 100l. Foxhound.

1956. Philatelic Exn. As T 128 but inscr "1956".
518 **128** 100l. brown and green 3·25 1·70

1956. International Philatelic Congress. Designs as Nos. 491/5 but larger and new values inscr "CONGRESSO INTERNAZ. PERITI FILATELICI SAN MARINO SALSOMAGGIORE 6–8 OTTOBRE 1956".
519 20l. brown and blue 2·20 55
520 80l. red and violet 4·50 2·10
521 100l. green and orange 7·00 3·75
SIZES—26½×37 mm: 20l. Guaita Tower; 100l. Government Palace. (36½×27 mm): 8l. Archway of Murata Nuova.

1956. Air. No. 504 optd with an airplane and POSTA AEREA.
522 100l. black and green 5·00 2·75

1957. Views as I 99.
522a 1l. green and deep green 10 10
523 2l. red and green 10 15
524 3l. brown and blue 15 15
524a 4l. blue and brown 20 15
525 20l. green and deep green 30 15
525a 30l. violet and brown 65 30
526 60l. violet and brown 3·25 1·20
526a 115l. brown and blue 1·10 65
527 125l. blue and black 85 55
527a 500l. black and green £170 80·00
DESIGNS—VERT: 2l. Borgo Maggiore Church; 3, 30l. Town gate, San Marino; 4, 125l. View of San Marino from southern wall; 20, 115l. Borgo Maggiore market place. HORIZ: 1, 60l. View of San Marino from Hospital Avenue. 37½×28 mm: 500l. Panorama of San Marino.
See also Nos. 794/6.

132 Marguerites

1957. Flowers. Multicoloured.
528 1l. Type **132** 10 15
529 2l. Polyanthuses 10 15
530 3l. Lilies 10 15
531 4l. Orchid 10 15
532 5l. Lilies of the valley 10 15
533 10l. Poppies 10 15
534 25l. Pansies 45 20
535 60l. Gladiolus 1·10 60
536 80l. Wild roses 2·10 90
537 100l. Anemones 3·25 1·70

104 Garibaldi

1957. 150th Birth Anniv of Garibaldi. As T 104 but inscr "COMMEMORAZIONE 150° NASCITA G. GARIBALDI 1807 1957. (a) Size 22×28 mm.
538 - 2l. blue and violet (as No. 391) 15 15
539 - 3l. green and red (as No. 390) 15 15
540 **104** 5l. drab and brown 15 15

(b) Size 26½×37 mm.
541 - 15l. violet and blue (as No. 395) 20 20
542 - 25l. black and green (as No. 396) 55 45
543 - 50l. brown and violet (as No. 394) 1·70 1·30
544 **104** 100l. violet and brown 3·25 1·60

134 St. Marinus and Fair Entrance

1958. 36th Milan Fair.
545 **134** 15l. yellow & bl (postage) 30 25
546 - 60l. green and red 55 55
547 - 125l. blue and brown (air) 4·25 3·00
DESIGNS—HORIZ: 60l. Italian pavilion and giant arch. VERT: 125l. Bristol 173 Rotocoach helicopter and airplane over fair.

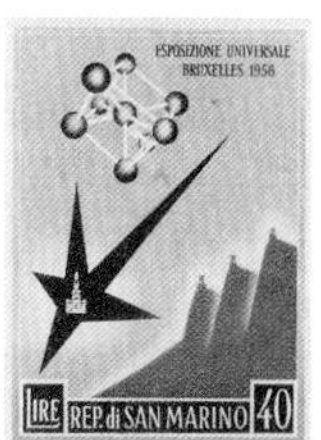

135 Exhibition Emblem, Atomium and Mt. Titano

1958. Brussels International Exhibition.
548 **135** 40l. sepia and green 30 25
549 **135** 60l. lake and blue 70 45

136 View of San Marino

1958. Air.
550 **136** 200l. blue and brown 8·00 2·75
551 - 300l. violet and red 8·00 2·75
DESIGN: 300l. Mt. Titano.

137 Wheat

1958. Fruit and Agricultural Products.
552 **137** 1l. yellow and blue 10 10
553 - 2l. red and green 10 10
554 - 3l. orange and blue 10 10
555 - 4l. red and green 10 10
556 - 5l. yellow, green and blue 10 10
557 **137** 15l. yellow, brown & blue 10 10
558 - 25l. multicoloured 55 10
559 - 40l. multicoloured 1·30 45
560 - 80l. multicoloured 2·20 1·40
561 - 125l. multicoloured 6·00 3·25
DESIGNS: 2, 125l. Maize; 3, 80l. Grapes; 4, 25l. Peaches; 5, 40l. Plums.

138 Naples 10 grana stamp of 1858 and Bay of Naples

1958. Centenary of First Naples Postage Stamps.
562 **138** 25l. brown & blue (postage) 30 25
563 **138** 125l. brown and bistre (air) 4·25 2·00
The Naples stamp on No. 563 is the 50gr.

139 Mediterranean Gull

1959. Air. Native Birds.
564 **139** 5l. black and green 30 20
565 - 10l. brown, black and blue 30 20
566 - 15l. multicoloured 55 25
567 - 120l. multicoloured 2·20 75
568 - 250l. black, yellow & green 4·50 2·20
BIRDS: 10l. Common kestrel; 15l. Mallard; 120l. Feral rock dove; 250l. Barn swallow.

140 P. de Coubertin (founder)

1959. Pre-Olympic Games Issue.
569 **140** 2l. black & brn (postage) 10 10
570 - 3l. sepia and mauve 10 10
571 - 5l. green and blue 10 10
572 - 30l. black and violet 10 10
573 - 60l. sepia and green 35 20
574 - 80l. green and lake 45 20
575 - 120l. brown (air) 7·75 2·50
PORTRAITS—As Type **140**: 3l. A. Bonacossa; 5l. A. Brundage; 30l. C. Montu; 60l. J. S. Edstrom; 80l. De Baillet-Latour. HORIZ: (36×21½ mm): 120l. De Coubertin and Olympic Flame. All, except the founder, De Coubertin are executives of the Olympic Games Committee.

141 Vickers Viscount 700 Airliner over Mt. Titano

1959. Air. Alitalia Inaugural Flight, Rimini–London.
576 **141** 120l. violet 3·00 1·70

142 Abraham Lincoln and Scroll

1959. Abraham Lincoln's 150th Birth Anniv. Inscr "ABRAMO LINCOLN 1809–1959".
577 **142** 5l. brn & sepia (postage) 10 10
578 - 10l. green and blue 10 10
579 - 15k. grey and green 10 10
580 - 70k. violet 20 50
581 - 200l. blue (air) 10·50 3·75
DESIGNS—Portraits of Lincoln with: HORIZ: 10l. Map of San Marino; 15l. Govt Palace, San Marino; 200l. Mt. Titano. VERT: 70l. Mt. Titano.

143 1859 Romagna ½b. stamp and Arch of Augustus, Rimini

1959. Romagna Stamp Centenary. Inscr "1859–1959".
582 **143** 30l. brown & sepia (postage) 30 25
583 - 120l. green and black (air) 3·00 2·00
DESIGN: 120 1. 1989 Romagna 3l. stamp and view of Bologna.

1959. World University Games, Turin. Inscr "UNIVERSITY TORINO 1959".
584 **120** 30l. red 90 65

144 Portal of Messina Cathedral and ½gr. Sicily stamp

1959. Centenary of First Sicilian Postage Stamp.

585	**144**	1l. brown & yell (postage)	10	10
586	-	2l. red and green	10	10
587	-	3l. slate and blue	10	10
588	-	4l. brown and red	10	10
589	-	5l. purple and blue	10	10
590	-	25l. multicoloured	15	20
591	-	60l. multicoloured	20	25
592	-	200l. multicoloured (air)	3·50	1·40

DESIGNS—VERT: 2l. Selinunte Temple (1gr.); 3l. Erice Church (2gr.); 4l. "Concordia" Temple, Agrigento (5gr.); 5l. "Castor and Pollux" Temple, Agrigento (10gr.); 25l. "St. John of the Hermits" Church, Palermo (20gr.). HORIZ: 60l. Taormina (50gr.); 200l. Bay of Palermo (50gr.).

145 Golden Oriole

1960. Birds.

593	**145**	1l. yellow, olive and blue	20	20
594	-	2l. brown, red and green	20	20
595	-	3l. red, brown and green	20	20
596	-	4l. black, brown and green	20	20
597	-	5l. red, brown and green	20	25
598	-	10l. multicoloured	30	25
599	-	25l. multicoloured	1·10	50
600	-	60l. multicoloured	2·20	1·40
601	-	80l. multicoloured	3·50	2·75
602	-	110l. multicoloured	6·75	4·75

DESIGNS—VERT: 2l. Nightingale; 4l. Hoopoe; 10l. Eurasian goldfinch; 25l. River kingfisher; 80l. Green woodpecker; 110l. Red-breasted flycatcher. HORIZ: 3l. Eurasian woodcock; 5l. Red-legged partridge; 60l. Common pheasant.

146 Putting the Shot

1960. Olympic Games.

603	**146**	1l. violet and red (postage)	10	10
604	-	2l. orange and black	10	10
605	-	3l. violet and brown	10	10
606	-	4l. brown and red	10	10
607	-	5l. blue and brown	10	10
608	-	10l. blue and brown	10	10
609	-	15l. violet and green	10	15
610	-	25l. orange and green	10	15
611	-	60l. brown and green	45	20
612	-	110l. red, black and green	65	30
613	-	20l. violet (air)	10	30
614	-	40l. red and brown	30	25
615	-	80l. yellow and blue	30	25
616	-	125l. brown and red	55	55
MS616a 90×125 mm. 1, 2, 3, 60l. brown, green and light green			3·25	3·25
MS616b 90×127 mm. 4, 10, 20, 40l. brown, red and light red			3·25	3·25
MS616c 145×100 mm. 5, 15, 25, 80, 110, 125l. brown, deep brown and light green			5·75	5·75

DESIGNS—VERT: 2l. Gymnastics; 3l. Long-distance walking; 4l. Boxing; 10l. Cycling; 20l. Handball; 40l. Breasting the tape; 60l. Football. HORIZ: 5l. Fencing; 15l. Hockey; 25l. Rowing; 80l. Diving; 110l. Horse-jumping; 125l. Rifle shooting.

147 Melvin Jones (founder) and Lions International H.Q.

1960. Lions International Commemoration.

617		30l. brown and violet (postage)	30	30
618	**147**	45l. brown and violet	55	30
619	-	60l. red and blue	30	30
620	-	115l. green and black	55	60
621	-	150l. brown and violet	4·00	2·50
622	-	200l. blue and green (air)	21·00	8·00

DESIGNS—VERT: 30l. Mt. Titano; 60l. San Marino Government Palace. HORIZ: 115l. Pres. Clarence Sturm; 150l. Vice-Pres. Finis E. Davis; 200l. Globe. All designs except Type **147** bear the Lions emblem.

148 Riccione

1960. 12th Riccione–San Marino Stamp Day. Centres multicoloured.

623	**148**	30l. red (postage)	20	20
624	**148**	125l. blue (air)	3·00	1·40

149 "Youth with Basket of Fruit"

1960. 350th Death Anniv of Caravaggio (painter).

625	**149**	200l. multicoloured	18·00	8·00

150 Hunting Roe Deer

1961. Hunting (1st issue). Historical Scenes.

626	**150**	1l. blue and mauve	10	10
627	-	2l. red and brown	10	10
628	-	3l. black and red	10	10
629	-	4l. red and blue	10	10
630	-	5l. brown and green	10	10
631	-	10l. violet and orange	10	10
632	-	30l. blue and yellow	15	15
633	-	60l. brown, orange & black	20	20
634	-	70l. red, purple and green	30	20
635	-	115l. blue, purple & black	85	35

DESIGNS—VERT: 2l. 16th-cent falconer; 10l. 16th-cent falconer (mounted); 60l. 17th-century hunter with rifle and dog. HORIZ: 3l. 16th-cent wild boar hunt; 4l. Duck-shooting with crossbow (16th-cent); 5l. 16th-cent stag hunt with bow and arrow; 30l. 17th-cent huntsman with horn and dogs; 70l. 18th-cent hunter and beater; 115l. Duck-shooting with bow and arrow (18th-cent).

See also Nos. 679/88.

151 Bell 47J Ranger Helicopter near Mt. Titano

1961. Air.

636	**151**	1000l. red	60·00	44·00

152 Guaita Tower, Mt. Titano and 1858 Sardinian Stamp

1961. Centenary of Italian Independence Philatelic Exhibition, Turin.

637	**152**	30l. multicoloured	35	50
638	**152**	70l. multicoloured	55	70
639	**152**	200l. multicoloured	1·80	1·20

153 Mt. Titano

1961. Europe.

640	**153**	500l. green and brown	50·00	22·00

155 King Enzo's Palace, Bologna

1961. Bologna Stamp Exn. Inscr "BOLOGNA".

641	**155**	30l. black and blue	15	15
642	-	70l. black and myrtle	20	20
643	-	100l. black and brown	20	30

DESIGNS: 70l. Gateway of Merchant's Palace; 100l. Towers of Garisenda and Asinelli, Bologna.

156 Duryea, 1892

1962. Veteran Motor Cars.

644	**156**	1l. blue and brown	10	15
645	-	2l. orange and blue	10	15
646	-	3l. orange and black	10	15
647	-	4l. red and black	10	15
648	-	5l. orange and violet	10	15
649	-	10l. orange and black	10	15
650	-	15l. red and black	10	15
651	-	20l. blue and black	10	30
652	-	25l. orange and black	10	30
653	-	30l. buff and black	10	30
654	-	50l. mauve and black	15	30
655	-	70l. green and black	20	30
656	-	100l. red, yellow and black	55	50
657	-	115l. green, orange & black	80	60
658	-	150l. yellow, orange & black	1·00	90

MOTOR CARS—HORIZ: 2l. Panhard and Levassor, 1895; 3l. Peugeot "Vis-a-vis", 1895; 4l. Daimler, 1899; 10l. Decauville, 1900; 15l. Wolseley, 1901; 20l. Benz, 1902; 25l. Napier, 1903; 50l. Oldsmobile, 1904; 100l. Isotta Fraschini, 1908; 115l. Bianchi, 1910; 150l. Alfa, 1910. VERT: 5l. F.I.A.T., 1899; 30l. White, 1903; 70l. Renault, 1904.

157 Wright Type A Biplane

1962. Vintage Aircraft.

659	**157**	1l. black and yellow	10	20
660	-	2l. brown and green	10	20
661	-	3l. brown and green	10	20
662	-	4l. black and bistre	10	20
663	-	5l. red and blue	10	20
664	-	10l. brown and green	10	30
665	-	30l. bistre and blue	10	35
666	-	60l. bistre and violet	35	35
667	-	70l. black and orange	35	50
668	-	115l. bistre, black & green	1·70	1·00

DESIGNS: 2l. Archdeacon-Voisin "Boxkite" float glider; 3l. Albert and Emile Bonnet-Labranche biplane; 4l. Glenn Curtiss "June Bug"; 5l. Henri Farman H.F.III biplane; 10l. Bleriot XI, 30l. Hubert Latham's Antoinette IV; 60l. Alberto Santos-Dumont's biplane "14 bis"; 70l. Alliott Verdon Roe's Triplane II; 115l. Faccioli's airplane.

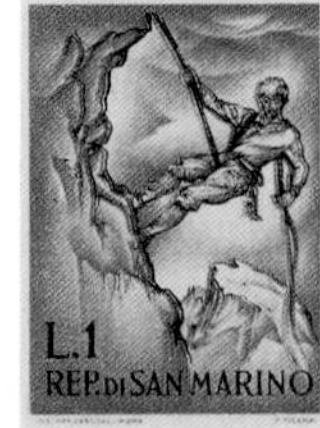

158 Roping Down

1962. Mountaineering.

669	**158**	1l. bistre and black	10	15
670	-	2l. turquoise and black	10	15
671	-	3l. purple and black	10	15
672	-	4l. blue and black	10	15
673	-	5l. orange and black	10	15
674	-	15l. yellow and black	10	15
675	-	30l. red and black	10	15
676	-	40l. blue and black	10	15
677	-	85l. green and black	20	20
678	-	115l. blue and black	65	65

DESIGNS: 2l. Sassolungo; 3l. Mt. Titano; 4l. Three Lavaredo peaks; 5l. The Matterhorn; 15l. Skier; 30l. Climber negotiating overhang; 40l. Step-cutting in ice; 85l. Aiguille du Geant; 115l. Citadel on Mt. Titano.

159 Hunter and Retriever

1962. Hunting (2nd issue). Modern scenes.

679	**159**	1l. deep purple and green	10	15
680	-	2l. blue and orange	10	15
681	-	3l. black and blue	10	15
682	-	4l. sepia and brown	10	15
683	-	5l. brown and green	10	15
684	-	15l. black and green	10	15
685	-	50l. sepia and green	30	30
686	-	70l. turquoise and red	30	30
687	-	100l. black and red	30	30
688	-	150l. green and lilac	90	55

DESIGNS—HORIZ: 3l. Marsh ducks (with decoys); 4l. Roe deer; 5l. Grey partridge; 15l. Northern lapwing; 50l. Partridge; 70l. Marsh geese; 100l. Wild boar. VERT: 2l. Huntsman and hounds; 150l. Hunter shooting pheasant.

160 Arrows encircling "Europa"

1962. Europa.

689	**160**	200l. red and black	3·25	1·40

161 Egyptian Merchant Ship, 2000 B.C.

1963. Historical Ships.

690	**161**	1l. blue and orange	10	15
691	-	2l. sepia and purple	10	15
692	-	3l. sepia and mauve	10	15
693	-	4l. dull purple and grey	10	15
694	-	5l. sepia and yellow	10	15
695	-	10l. brown and green	10	15
696	-	30l. sepia and blue	55	55
697	-	60l. blue and green	55	60
698	-	70l. red and deep grey	55	70
699	-	115l. brown and blue	3·75	2·00

DESIGNS—HORIZ: 2l. Greek trier, 5th-cent, B.C.; 3l. Roman trireme, 1st-cent, B.C.; 4l. Viking longship, 10th-cent; 5l. The "Santa Maria"; 30l. Gallery, c. 1600; 115l. "Duncan Dunbar" (full-rigged merchantman), 1550. VERT: 10l. Carrack, c. 1550; 60l. "Sovereign of the Seas" (English galleon), 1637; 70l. "Fyn" (Danish ship of the line), c. 1750.

162 "The Fornarina" (or "The Veiled Woman")

1963. Paintings by Raphael. Multicoloured.

700	30l. Type **162**	10	20
701	70l. Self portrait	15	20
702	100l. Sistine Madonna (detail of woman praying)	20	30
703	200l. "Portrait of a Young Woman" (Maddalena Strozzi)	55	80

The 200l. is larger, 27×44 mm.

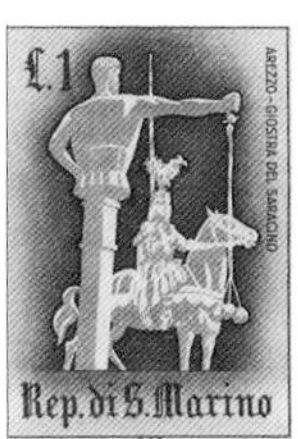

163 Saracen Game, Arezzo

1963. Ancient Tournaments.

704	**163**	1l. mauve	10	15
705	-	2l. black	10	15
706	-	3l. black	10	15
707	-	4l. violet	10	15
708	-	5l. violet	10	15
709	-	10l. green	10	15
710	-	30l. red	10	15
711	-	60l. blue	15	15
712	-	70l. brown	20	20
713	-	115l. black	55	30

TOURNAMENTS—HORIZ: 2l. 14th-century, French cavaliers; 4l. 15th-century, Presenting arms to an English cavalier; 30l. Quintana game, Foligno; 70l. 15th-century, Cavaliers (from castle mural, Malpaga). VERT: 3l. Crossbow Champion-ships, Gubbio; 5l. 16th-century, Cavaliers, Florence; 10l. Quintana game, Ascoli Piceno; 60l. Palio (horse-race), Siena; 115l. 13th-century, The Crusades: cavaliers' challenge.

164 Peacock

1963. Butterflies. Multicoloured.

714	25l. Type **164**	20	20
715	30l. "Nessaea obrinus"	20	20
716	60l. Large tortoiseshell	20	20
717	70l. Peacock (horiz)	35	45
718	115l. "Papilio blumei" (horiz)	65	55

165 Corner of Government Palace, San Marino

1963. San Marino–Riccione Stamp Fair.

719	**165**	100l. black and blue	20	20
720	-	100l. blue and sepia	20	20

DESIGN: No. 720, Fountain, Riccione.

166 Pole Vaulting

1963. Olympic Games, Tokyo (1964) (1st issue).

721		1l. purple and orange	10	10
722	**166**	2l. sepia and green	10	10
723	-	3l. sepia and blue	10	10
724	-	4l. sepia and blue	10	10
725	-	5l. sepia and red	10	10
726	-	10l. mauve and purple	10	10
727	-	30l. purple and grey	10	10
728	-	60l. sepia and yellow	10	10
729	-	70l. sepia and blue	35	10
730	-	115l. sepia and green	45	10

SPORTS—HORIZ: 1l. Hurdling; 3l. Relay-racing; 4l. High jumping (men); 5l. Football; 10l. High jumping (women); 60l. Throwing the javelin; 70l. Water polo; 115l. Throwing the hammer. VERT: 30l. Throwing the discus.

See also Nos. 743/52.

167 "E" and Flag of San Marino

1963. Europa.

731	**167**	200l. blue and brown	1·00	45

168 Tupolev Tu-104A Jetliner

1963. Air. Contemporary Aircraft.

732	**168**	5l. purple, brown and blue	15	15
733	-	10l. blue and red	15	15
734	-	15l. red, mauve and violet	15	15
735	-	25l. red, mauve and violet	15	15
736	-	50l. red and blue	20	15
737	-	75l. orange and green	20	15
738	-	120l. red and blue	35	30
739	-	200l. black and yellow	65	20
740	-	300l. black and orange	90	45
741	-	500l. multicoloured	7·25	5·50
742	-	1000l. multicoloured	4·00	2·75

DESIGNS—HORIZ: 15l. Douglas DC-8 jetliner; 25, 1000l. Boeing 707 jetliner (different views); 50l. Vickers Viscount 837 airliner; 120l. Vickers VC-10; 200l. Hawker Siddley Comet 4C jetliner; 300l. Boeing 727-100 jetliner. VERT: 10l. Boeing 707 jetliner; 75l. Sud Aviation SE 210 Caravelle jetliner; 500l. Rolls Royce Dart 527 turboprop engine.

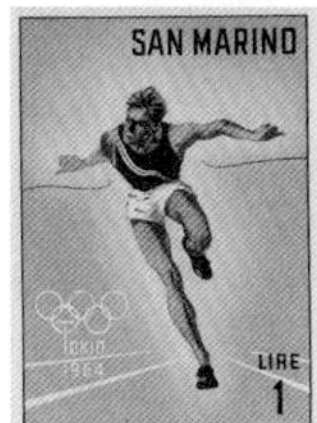

169 Running

1964. Olympic Games, Tokyo (2nd issue).

743	**169**	1l. brown and green	15	10
744	-	2l. brown and sepia	15	10
745	-	3l. brown and black	15	10
746	-	4l. blue and red	15	10
747	-	5l. brown and blue	15	10
748	-	15l. purple and orange	15	10
749	-	30l. blue and light blue	15	10
750	-	70l. brown and green	15	10
751	-	120l. brown and blue	30	10
752	-	150l. purple and red	45	30

DESIGNS—VERT: 2l. Gymnastics; 3l. Basketball; 120l. Cycling; 150l. Fencing. HORIZ: 4l. Pistol-shooting; 5l. Rowing; 15l. Long jumping; 30l. Diving; 70l. Sprinting.

1964. "Towards Tokyo" Sports Stamp Exn, Rimini. As Nos. 749/50, but inscr "VERSO TOKIO" and colours changed.

753	30l. blue and violet	20	15
754	70l. brown and turquoise	20	15

170 Murray Blenkinsop Rack Locomotive (1812)

1964. "Story of the Locomotive".

755	**170**	1l. black and buff	10	10
756	-	2l. black and green	10	10
757	-	3l. black and violet	10	10
758	-	4l. black and yellow	10	10
759	-	5l. black and salmon	10	10
760	-	15l. black and green	15	10
761	-	20l. black and pink	15	15
762	-	50l. black and blue	20	15
763	-	90l. black and orange	30	15
764	-	110l. black and blue	45	30

LOCOMOTIVES: 2l. "Puffing Billy" (1813–14); 3l. "Locomotion" (1825); 4l. "Rocket" (1829); 5l. "Lion" (1838); 15l. "Bayard" (1839); 20l. Crampton type No. 125, France (1849); 50l. "Little England" (1851); 90l. "Spitfire", Canada (1855); 110l. Rogers, U.S.A. (c. 1865).

171 Baseball Players

1964. 7th European Baseball Championships, Milan.

765	**171**	30l. sepia and green	20	15
766	-	70l. black and red	35	30

DESIGN: 70l. Player pitching ball.

172 "E" and Part of Globe

1964. Europa.

767	**172**	200l. red, blue & light blue	3·00	55

173 Pres. Kennedy giving Inaugural Address

1964. 1st Death Anniv of John F. Kennedy (President of U.S.A.). Multicoloured.

768	70l. Type **173**	20	15
769	130l. Pres. Kennedy and U.S. flag (vert)	20	30

174 Cyclists at Government Palace

1965. Cycle Tour of Italy.

770	**174**	30l. sepia	15	15
771	-	70l. purple	15	15
772	-	200l. red	30	30

DESIGNS—Cyclists passing: 70l. "The Rock"; 200l. Mt. Titano.

175 Brontosaurus

1965. Prehistoric Animals.

773	**175**	1l. purple and green	10	15
774	-	2l. black and blue	10	15
775	-	3l. yellow and green	10	15
776	-	4l. brown and blue	10	15
777	-	5l. purple and green	10	15
778	-	10l. purple and green	10	15
779	-	75l. blue and turquoise	30	20
780	-	100l. purple and green	40	55
781	-	200l. purple and green	80	60

ANIMALS—VERT: 2l. Brachyosaurus. HORIZ: 3l. Pteranodon; 4l. Elasmosaurus; 5l. Tyrannosaurus; 10l. Stegosaurus; 75l. Thamatosaurus Victor; 100l. Iguanodon; 200l. Triceratops.

176 Rooks on Chessboard

1965. Europa.

782	**176**	200l. multicoloured	50	40

177 Dante

1965. 700th Anniv of Dante's Birth.

783	**177**	40l. sepia and blue	20	15
784	-	90l. sepia and red	20	15
785	-	130l. sepia and brown	35	15
786	-	140l. sepia and blue	35	30

DESIGNS: 90l. "Hell"; 130l. "Purgatory"; 140l. "Paradise".

178 Mt. Titano and Flags

1965. Visit of Pres. Saragat of Italy.

787	**178**	115l. multicoloured	30	30

179 Trotting

1966. Equestrian Sports. Multicoloured.

788	10l. Type **179**	20	15
789	20l. Cross-country racing (vert)	20	15
790	40l. Horse-jumping	20	15
791	70l. Horse-racing	20	15
792	90l. Steeple-chasing	20	15
793	170l. Polo (vert)	35	20

1966. New values in previous designs.

794	5l. brown and blue (as No. 522a)	15	10
795	10l. green and black (as No. 524)	15	10
796	15l. violet and brown (as No. 524a)	15	10
797	40l. red and lilac (as No. 491)	15	10
798	90l. blue and black (as No. 492)	15	10
799	140l. orange and violet (as No. 493)	35	10

180 "La Bella"

1966. Paintings by Titian. Multicoloured.

800	40l. Type **180**	20	15
801	90l. "The Three Graces"	20	15
802	100l. "The Three Graces"	20	20
803	170l. "Sacred and Profane Love"	45	45

The 90 and 100l. show different details from the picture.

181 Stone Bass

1966. Sea Animals. Multicoloured.

804	1l. Type **181**	15	15
805	2l. Cuckoo wrasse	15	15
806	3l. Common dolphin	15	15
807	4l. John Dory	15	15
808	5l. Octopus (vert)	15	15
809	10l. Red scorpionfish	15	15
810	40l. Eyed electric ray (vert)	15	15
811	90l. Medusa (vert)	15	15
812	115l. Long-snouted seahorse (vert)	35	20
813	130l. Dentex seabream	35	20

182 Our Lady of Europe

1966. Europa.

814	**182**	200l. multicoloured	45	35

183 Peony

1967. Flowers. Multicoloured.

815	5l. Type **183**	10	15
816	10l. Campanula	10	15
817	15l. Pyrenean poppy	10	15
818	20l. Purple deadnettle	10	15
819	40l. Hemerocallis	10	15
820	140l. Gentian	10	15
821	170l. Thistle	35	15

Each flower has a different background view of Mt. Titano.

184 St. Marinus

1967. Paintings by Francesco Barbieri (Guercino). Multicoloured.

822	40l. Type **184**	10	20
823	170l. "St. Francis"	45	45

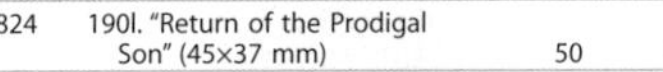

824	190l. "Return of the Prodigal Son" (45×37 mm)	50	45

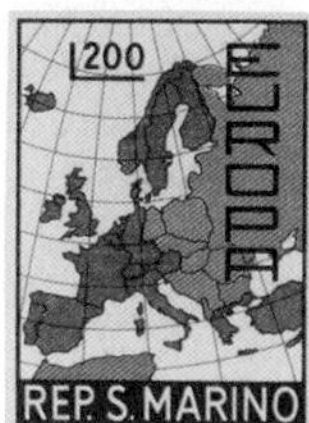

185 Map of Europe

1967. Europa.

825	**185**	200l. green and orange	65	35

186 Caesar's Mushroom

1967. Fungi. Multicoloured.

826	5l. Type **186**	15	10
827	15l. The Miller	15	10
828	20l. Parasol mushroom	15	10
829	40l. Cep	15	10
830	50l. "Russula paludosa"	15	10
831	170l. St. George's mushroom	35	30

187 Salisbury Cathedral

1967. Gothic Cathedrals.

832	-	20l. violet on cream	15	15
833	-	40l. green on cream	15	15
834	-	80l. blue on cream	15	15
835	**187**	90l. sepia on cream	15	15
836	-	170l. red on cream	40	35

DESIGNS: 20l. Amiens; 40l. Siena; 80l. Toledo; 170l. Cologne.

188 Cimabue Crucifix, Florence

1967. Christmas.

837	**188**	300l. brown and violet	80	50

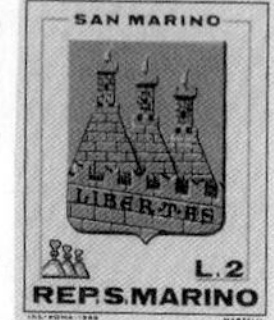

189 Arms of San Marino

1968. Arms of San Marino Villages. Mult.

838	2l. Type **189**	10	15
839	3l. Penna Rossa	10	15
840	5l. Fiorentino	10	15
841	10l. Montecerreto	10	15
842	25l. Serravalle	10	15
843	35l. Montegiardino	10	15
844	50l. Faetano	10	15
845	90l. Borgo Maggiore	10	15
846	180l. Montelupo	30	15
847	500l. State crest	55	35

190 Europa "Key"

1968. Europa.

848	**190**	250l. brown	65	45

191 "The Battle of San Romano" (detail, P. Uccello)

1968. 671st Birth Anniv of Paolo Uccello (painter).

849	**191**	50l. black on lilac	10	15
850	-	90l. black on lilac (vert)	10	15
851	-	130l. black on lilac	10	15
852	-	230l. black on pink	55	35

All stamps show details of "The Battle of San Romano".

192 "The Nativity" (detail, Botticelli)

1968. Christmas.

853	**192**	50l. blue	15	15
854	**192**	90l. red	20	15
855	**192**	180l. sepia	35	30

193 "Peace"

1969. "The Good Government" (frescoes) by Ambrogio Lorenzetti.

856	**193**	50l. blue	10	10
857	-	80l. sepia	15	10
858	-	90l. violet	20	10
859	-	180l. red	35	20

DESIGNS—VERT: 80l. "Justice"; 90l. "Temper- ance". HORIZ: 180l. View of Siena.

194 "Young Soldier" (Bramante)

1969. 525th Birth Anniv of Donato Bramante (architect and painter). Multicoloured.

860	50l. Type **194**	20	15
861	90l. "Old Soldier" (Bramante)	35	15

195 Colonnade

1969. Europa.

862	**195**	50l. green	35	20
863	**195**	180l. purple	1·00	20

196 Benched Carriage ("Char-a-banc")

1969. Horses and Carriages. Multicoloured.

864	5l. Type **196**	10	15
865	10l. Barouche	10	15
866	25l. Private drag	10	15
867	40l. Hansom cab	10	15
868	50l. Curricle	10	15
869	90l. Wagonette	10	20
870	180l. Spider phaeton	35	30

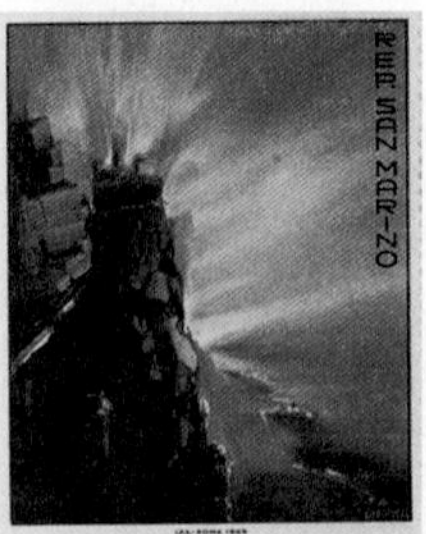

197 Mt. Titano

1969. Paintings by R. Viola. Multicoloured.

871	20l. Type **197**	20	15
872	180l. "Pier at Rimini"	45	30
873	200l. "Pier at Riccione" (horiz)	45	45

198 "Faith"

1969. Christmas. "The Theological Virtues" by Raphael.

874	**198**	20l. violet and orange	20	15
875	-	180l. violet and green	35	30
876	-	200l. violet and buff	45	45

DESIGNS: 180l. "Hope"; 200l. "Charity".

199 "Aries"

1970. Signs of the Zodiac. Multicoloured.

877	1l. Type **199**	10	10
878	2l. "Taurus"	10	10
879	3l. "Gemini"	10	10
880	4l. "Cancer"	10	10
881	5l. "Leo"	10	10
882	10l. "Virgo"	10	10
883	15l. "Libra"	10	10
884	20l. "Scorpio"	10	10
885	70l. "Sagittarius"	10	30
886	90l. "Capricorn"	10	30
887	100l. "Aquarius"	30	35
888	180l. "Pisces"	45	55

200 "Flaming Sun"

1970. Europa.

889	**200**	90l. red and green	35	20
890	**200**	180l. red and yellow	55	45

201 "The Fleet in the Bay of Naples" (Pieter Brueghel the Elder)

1970. 10th "Europa" Stamp Exhibition, Naples.

891	**201**	230l. multicoloured	45	40

202 St. Francis' Gate

1970. 65th Anniv of Rotary International and 10th Anniv of San Marino Rotary Club. Multicoloured.

892	180l. Type **202**	35	35
893	220l. "Rocco" Fort, Mt. Titano	55	55

203 "Girl with Mandolin"

1970. Death Bicentenary of Giambattista Tiepolo (painter).

894	50l. Type **203**	20	15
895	180l. "Girl with Parrot"	20	45
896	220l. "Rinaldo and Armida Surprised"	20	60

SIZES: 180l. As Type **203**; 220l. 57×37 mm.

204 Black Pete

1970. 4th Death Anniv of Walt Disney (film producer). Cartoon Characters. Multicoloured.

897	1l. Type **204**	15	15
898	2l. Gyro Gearloose	15	15
899	3l. Pluto	15	15
900	4l. Minnie Mouse	15	15
901	5l. Donald Duck	15	15
902	10l. Goofy	15	15
903	15l. Scrooge McDuck	15	15
904	50l. Hewey, Dewey and Louie	80	35
905	90l. Mickey Mouse	1·30	1·10
906	220l. Walt Disney and scene from "The Jungle Book" (horiz)	7·25	5·50

205 "Customs House, Venice"

1971. "Save Venice" Campaign. Paintings by Canaletto. Multicoloured.

907	20l. Type **205**	20	20
908	180l. "Grand Canal, Balbi Palace and Rialto Bridge, Venice"	80	55
909	200l. "St. Mark's and Doge's Palace"	90	60

206 Congress Building and San Marino Flag

1971. Italian Philatelic Press Union Congress, San Marino. Multicoloured.

910	20l. Type **206**	10	10
911	90l. Government Palace door and emblems (vert)	10	10
912	180l. Type **206**	35	20

207 Europa Chain

1971. Europa.

913	**207**	50l. blue and yellow	35	15
914	**207**	90l. orange and blue	55	20

208 "Duck" Jug with "Lasa" Decoration

1971. Etruscan Art (1st series).

915	**208**	50l. black and orange	10	15
916	-	80l. black and green	10	15
917	-	90l. black and green	10	20
918	-	180l. black and orange	55	30

DESIGNS—VERT: 80l. Head of Hermes (bust); 90l. Man and Wife (relief on sarcophagus). HORIZ: 180l. Chimera (bronze).

See also Nos. 1018/21.

209 Day Lily

1971. Flowers. Multicoloured.

919	1l. Type **209**	10	10
920	2l. "Phlox paniculata"	10	10
921	3l. Wild pink	10	10
922	4l. Globe flower	10	10
923	5l. "Centaurea dealbata"	10	10
924	10l. Peony	10	10
925	15l. Christmas rose	10	10
926	50l. Pasque flower	10	10
927	90l. "Gaillardia aristata"	10	10
928	220l. "Aster dumosus"	45	30

210 "Allegory of Spring" (detail, Botticelli)

1972. "Allegory of Spring" by Sandro Botticelli. Multicoloured.

929	50l. Type **210**	20	20
930	190l. The Three Graces (27×37 mm)	55	35
931	220l. Flora	65	50

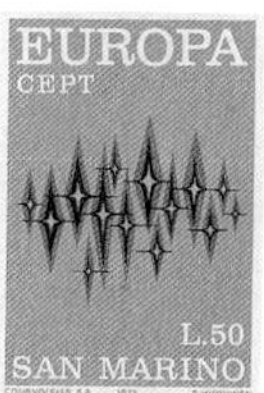
211 "Communications"

1972. Europa.

932	**211**	50l. multicoloured	65	15
933	**211**	90l. multicoloured	55	20

212 "Taming the Bear"

1972. "Life of St. Marinus". 16th-century paintings from former Government Palace.

934	**212**	25l. black and buff	10	10
935	-	55l. black and orange	15	10
936	-	100l. black and blue	20	10
937	-	130l. black and yellow	30	20

DESIGNS: 55l. "The Conversion of Donna Felicissima"; 100l. "Hostile archers turned to stone"; 130l. "Mount Titano given to St. Marinus".

213 House Sparrow

1972. Birds. Multicoloured.

938	1l. Type **213**	20	15
939	2l. Firecrest	20	15
940	3l. Blue tit	20	15
941	4l. Ortulan bunting	20	15
942	5l. Bluethroat	20	15
943	10l. Northern bullfinch	20	15
944	25l. Linnet	20	15
945	50l. Black-eared wheatear	20	15
946	90l. Sardinian warbler	35	15
947	220l. Western greenfinch	45	15

214 "Healthy Man"

1972. World Heart Month. Multicoloured.

948	50l. Type **214**	20	10
949	90l. "Sick Man" (horiz)	20	10

215 Veterans Emblem

1972. "Veterans of Philately" Award of Italian Philatelic Federation.

950	**215**	25l. gold and blue	35	30

216 Plane over Mt. Titano

1972. Air.

951	**216**	1000l. multicoloured	2·00	1·60

217 Five-Cent Coin of 1864

1972. San Marino Coinage.

952	**217**	5l. bronze, black and grey	20	10
953	-	10l. bronze, black & orge	20	10
954	-	15l. silver, black and red	20	10
955	-	20l. silver, black and purple	20	10
956	-	25l. silver, black and blue	20	10
957	-	50l. silver, black and blue	20	10
958	-	55l. silver, black and ochre	20	10
959	-	220l. gold, black and green	45	20

COINS (obverse and reverse on each stamp): 10l. 10c. of 1935; 15l. 1l. of 1906; 20l. 5l. of 1898; 25l. 5l. of 1937; 50l. 10l. of 1932; 55l. 20l. of 1938; 220l. 20l. of 1925.

218 New York, 1673

1973. "Interpex" Stamp Exhibition and Important Cities of the World (1st series). New York.

960	**218**	200l. brown, grey & black	35	35
961	-	300l. blue, lilac & deep lilac	45	55

DESIGN: 300l. New York, 1973.

See also Nos. 1032/3, 1075/6, 1144/5, 1160/1, 1197/8, 1215/16, 1230/1, 1259/60, 1271/2, 1306/7, 1331/2, 1358/9 and 1524/5.

219 Printing Press

1973. Tourist Press Congress.

962	**219**	50l. multicoloured	35	30

220 "Sportsmen"

1973. Youth Games.

963	**220**	100l. multicoloured	35	30

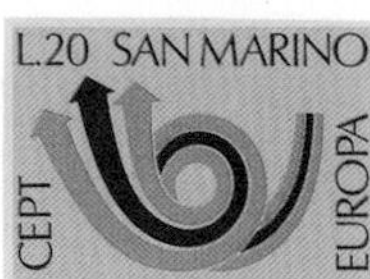

221 Europa "Posthorn"

1973. Europa.

964	221	20l. green, blue and flesh	30	20
965	221	180l. mauve, red and blue	85	35

222 Grapes

1973. Fruits. Multicoloured.

966	1l. Type 222	10	10
967	2l. Mandarines	10	10
968	3l. Apples	10	10
969	4l. Plums	10	10
970	5l. Strawberries	10	10
971	10l. Pears	10	10
972	25l. Cherries	10	10
973	50l. Pomegranate	10	10
974	90l. Apricots	10	10
975	200l. Peaches	45	20

223 Couzinet 70 F-AMBV "Arc en Ciel"

1973. Aircraft.

976	223	25l. blue, yellow and gold	10	10
977	-	55l. blue, grey and gold	10	10
978	-	60l. blue, pink and gold	10	10
979	-	90l. blue, bistre and gold	10	10
980	-	220l. blue, orange and gold	45	35

AIRCRAFT: 55l. Macchi Castoldi MC-72-181 seaplane; 60l. Tupolev ANT-9; 90l. Ryan NYP "Spirit of St. Louis" (Charles Lindburgh's plane); 220l. Handley Page H.P.42.

224 Crossbowman, Serravalle Castle

1973. San Marino's Victory in Crossbow Tournament, Masa Marittima. Multicoloured.

981	5l. Type 224	10	10
982	10l. Crossbowman, Pennarossa Castle	10	10
983	15l. Drummer, Montegiardino Castle	10	10
984	20l. Trumpeter, Fiorentino Castle	10	10
985	30l. Crossbowman, Montecerreto Castle	10	10
986	40l. Crossbowman, Borgo Maggiore Castle	10	10
987	50l. Trumpeter, Guaita Castle	10	10
988	80l. Crossbowman, Faetano Castle	10	10
989	200l. Crossbowman, Montelupo Castle	55	30

225 "Adoration of the Magi" (detail)

1973. Christmas. 600th Birth Anniv of Gentile da Fabriano. Details of Gentile's altarpiece "Adoration of the Magi".

990	225	5l. multicoloured	10	10
991	-	30l. multicoloured	10	10
992	-	115l. multicoloured	20	15
993	-	250l. multicoloured	45	35

226 Combat Shield (16th-century)

1974. Ancient Weapons from "Cesta" Museum, San Marino.

994	226	5l. black brown and green	10	10
995	-	10l. black, blue & brown	10	10
996	-	15l. black, blue & lt blue	10	10
997	-	20l. black, blue & brown	10	10
998	-	30l. black, brown & blue	10	10
999	-	50l. black, blue and pink	10	10
1000	-	80l. black, blue and lilac	10	10
1001	-	250l. black and yellow	45	30

DESIGNS: 10l. German armour (16th-century); 15l. Crested morion (16th-century); 20l. Horse head-armour (15th–16th century); 30l. Italian morion with crest (16th–17th century); 50l. Gauntlets and sword pommel (16th-century); 80l. Sallet helmet (16th-century); 250l. Sforza shield (16th-century).

227 "The Joy of Living" (Emilio Greco)

1974. Europa. Sculpture.

1002	227	100l. black and brown	45	30
1003	-	200l. black and green	90	40

DESIGN: 200l. "The Joy of Living" (complete sculpture).

228 "Sea and Mountains"

1974. San Marino–Riccione Stamp Fair.

1004	228	50l. multicoloured	35	30

229 Arms of Sansepolcro

1974. 9th Crossbow Tournament, San Marino. Arms. Multicoloured.

1005	15l. Type 229	55	20
1006	20l. Massa Marittima	55	20
1007	50l. San Marino	55	30
1008	115l. Gubbio	55	60
1009	300l. Lucca	55	90

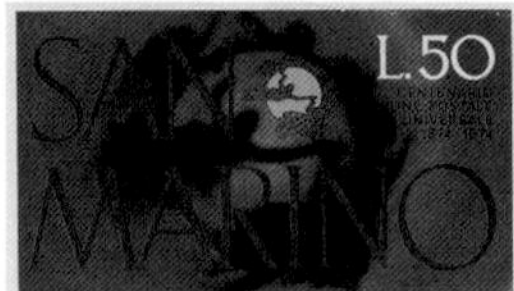

230 U.P.U. Emblem and Shadow

1974. Centenary of Universal Postal Union.

1010	230	50l. multicoloured	20	15
1011	230	90l. multicoloured	35	15

231 Glider

1974. Air. 50th Anniv of Gliding in Italy.

1012	231	40l. blue, green and brown	20	15
1013	-	120l. blue, lt blue & pur	20	20
1014	-	500l. violet, mauve & purple	65	60

DESIGNS: 120, 500l. Gliders in "air currents" (both different).

232 Mt. Titano and Verses of Hymn

1974. Death Centenary of Niccolo Tommaseo (writer).

1015	232	50l. black, green and red	20	15
1016	-	150l. black, yellow & blue	35	20

DESIGN: 150l. Portrait of Tommaseo.

233 "Madonna and Child" (4th-century painting)

1974. Christmas.

1017	233	250l. multicoloured	85	45

234 "Dancing Scene", Tomb of the Leopards, Tarquinia

1975. Etruscan Art (2nd series). Tomb Paintings. Multicoloured.

1018	20l. Type 234	10	10
1019	30l. "Chariot Race", Tomb of the Hill, Chiusi	10	10
1020	180l. "Achilles and Troillus", Tomb of the Bulls, Tarquinia	35	30
1021	220l. "Dancers", Tomb of the Triclinium, Tarquinia	45	45

235 "Escape Tunnel"

1975. 30th Anniv of Escape of 100,000 Italian War Refugees to San Marino.

1022	235	50l. multicoloured	35	30

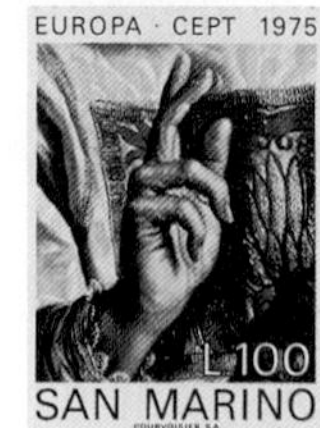

236 "The Blessing"

1975. Europa. Details from "St. Marinus" by Guercino. Multicoloured.

1023	100l. Type 236	55	30
1024	200l. "St. Marinus"	1·10	40

237 "The Virgin Mary"

1975. Holy Year. Details from Frescoes by Giotto from Scrovegni Chapel, Padua. Multicoloured.

1025	10l. Type 237	10	15
1026	40l. "Virgin and Child"	10	15
1027	50l. "Heads of Angels"	10	15
1028	100l. "Mary Magdalene" (horiz)	10	15
1029	500l. "Heads of Saints" (horiz)	55	55

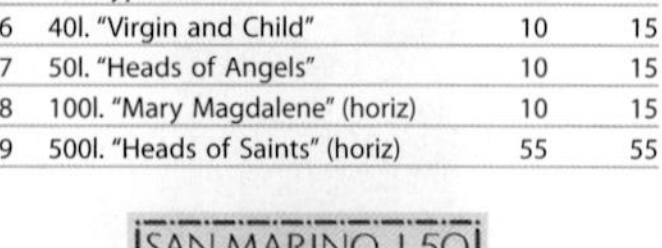

238 "Aphrodite" (sculpture)

1975. 15th Europa Stamp Exhibition, Naples.

1030	238	50l. black, grey and violet	35	30

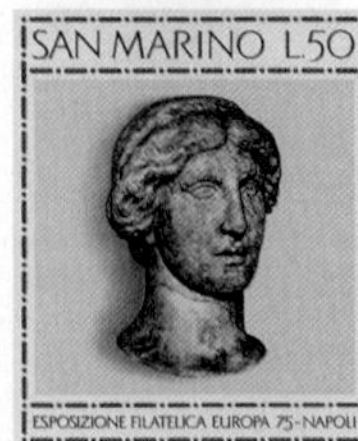

239 Congress Emblem

1975. "Eurocophar" International Pharmaceutical Congress, San Marino.

1031	239	100l. multicoloured	35	30

240 Tokyo, 1835

1975. Important Cities of the World (2nd series). Tokyo. Multicoloured.

1032	200l. Type 240	35	50
1033	300l. Tokyo, 1975	45	70

241 "Woman on Balcony"

1975. International Women's Year. Paintings by Gentilini. Multicoloured.

1034		50l. Type **241**	20	10
1035		150l. "Heads of Two Women" (horiz)	40	20
1036		230l. "Profile of Girl"	50	50

242 "Head of the Child" (detail)

1975. Christmas. 500th Birth Anniv of Michelangelo. Painting "Doni Madonna" and details. Multicoloured.

1037		50l. Type **242**	10	15
1038		100l. "Head of Virgin" (detail)	20	20
1039		250l. "Doni Madonna"	35	50

243 "Modesty"

1976. "The Civil Virtues". Sketches by Emilio Greco.

1039a	-	5l. black and lilac	10	10
1040	**243**	10l. black and stone	10	10
1041	-	20l. black and lilac	10	10
1041a	-	35l. black and stone	10	10
1042	-	50l. black and green	10	10
1043	-	70l. black and pink	10	10
1044	-	90l. black and pink	10	10
1045	-	100l. black and pink	10	10
1046	-	120l. black and blue	20	10
1047	-	150l. black and lilac	20	10
1048	-	160l. black and green	30	15
1049	-	170l. black and flesh	30	20
1050	-	220l. black and grey	30	20
1051	-	250l. black and yellow	30	30
1052	-	300l. black and grey	55	35
1053	-	320l. black and mauve	55	45
1054	-	500l. black and stone	55	35
1055	-	1000l. black and blue	1·10	1·10
1055a	-	2000l. black and cream	3·25	2·50

DESIGNS: 5l. "Wisdom"; 20, 160l. "Temperance"; 35l. "Love"; 50, 70l. "Fortitude"; 90, 220l. "Prudence"; 100, 120l. "Altruism"; 150, 170l. "Hope"; 250l. "Justice"; 300, 320l. "Faith"; 500l. "Honesty"; 1000l. "Industry"; 2000l. "Faithfulness".

244 Capitol, Washington

1976. Bicentenary of American Revolution and "Interphil 1976" International Stamp Exhibition, Philadelphia. Multicoloured.

1056		70l. Type **244**	20	15
1057		150l. Statue of Liberty, New York	20	20
1058		180l. Independence Hall, Philadelphia	35	35

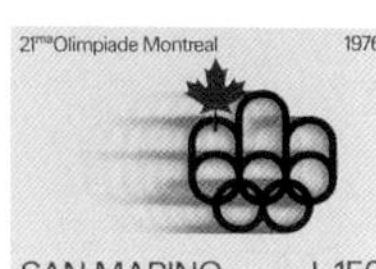

245 Emblem and Maple Leaf

1976. Olympic Games, Montreal.

1059	**245**	150l. black and red	35	65

246 Polychrome Plate (U. Bruno)

1976. Europa. Handicrafts. Multicoloured.

1060		150l. Type **246**	65	30
1061		180l. Silver plate (A. Ruscelli)	80	45

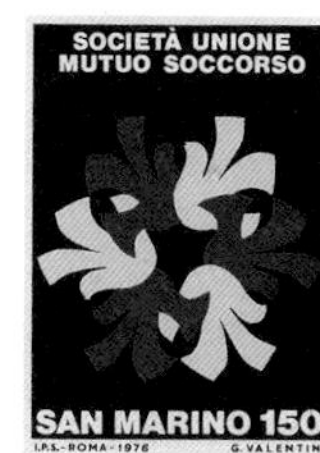

247 S.U.M.S. Emblem

1976. Centenary of San Marino Social Welfare Union.

1062	**247**	150l. red, yellow and lilac	35	35

248 Children of Different Races

1976. 30th Anniv of UNESCO.

1063	**248**	180l. brown, orange & blue	30	25
1064	**248**	220l. brown, buff & sepia	40	50

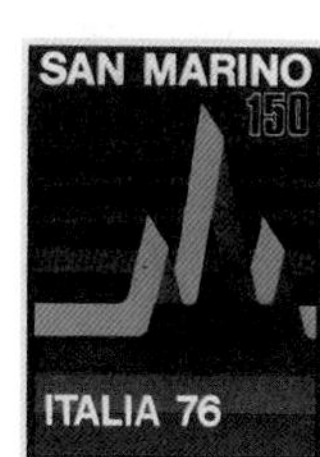

249 "San Marino"

1976. "Italia '76" International Stamp Exhibition, Milan.

1065	**249**	150l. multicoloured	35	35

250 "The Annunciation"

1976. Christmas. 400th Death Anniv of Titian. Multicoloured.

1066		150l. Type **250**	35	45
1067		300l. "The Nativity"	55	80

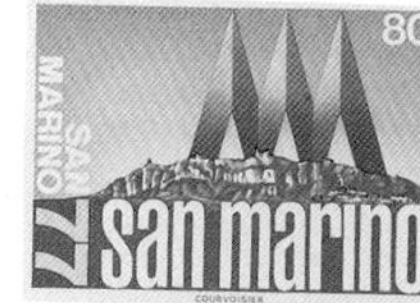

251 Mount Titano and Emblem

1977. "San Marino 77" International Stamp Exhibition (1st issue).

1068	**251**	80l. red, green and olive (postage)	10	10
1069	**251**	170l. yellow, violet & blue	20	20
1070	**251**	200l. orange, ultram & blue	35	35
1071	**251**	200l. ochre, green and blue (air)	45	35

See also No. 1082.

252 "San Marino" (Ghirlandaio)

1977. Europa. Landscapes. Multicoloured.

1072		170l. Type **252**	90	35
1073		200l. "San Marino" (Guercino)	1·10	55

253 Leonardo da Vinci's Drawing of "Helicopter"

1977. Centenary of Enrico Forlanini's First Vertical Flight Experiment.

1074	**253**	120l. multicoloured	35	30

254 University Square, 1877

1977. Centenary of Rumanian Independence. Important Cities of the World (3rd series). Bucharest.

1075	**254**	200l. green and blue	35	45
1076	-	400l. brown and stone	55	80

DESIGN: 400l. City centre, 1977.

255 Design of First San Marino Stamp

1977. Centenary of San Marino Postage Stamps.

1077	**255**	40l. green	10	10
1078	**255**	70l. blue	10	10
1079	**255**	170l. red	10	15
1080	**255**	500l. brown	40	45
1081	**255**	1000l. lilac	55	85

256 "St. Marinus Blessing" (Retrosi)

1977. "San Marino 1977" International Stamp Exhibition (2nd issue).

1082	**256**	1000l. multicoloured	2·75	2·00

257 Medicinal Plants

1977. Italian Pharmacists' Union Congress.

1083	**257**	170l. multicoloured	35	35

258 Woman gripped by Octopus

1977. World Rheumatism Year.

1084	**258**	200l. multicoloured	35	40

259 Angel

1977. Christmas.

1085	**259**	170l. black, grey & silver	20	20
1086	-	230l. black, grey & silver	35	30
1087	-	300l. black, grey & silver	45	35

DESIGNS: 230l. Palm tree and olive; 300l. The Virgin.

260 Baseball Player

1978. World Baseball Championships.

1088	**260**	90l. black, blue and ultramarine	10	15
1089	**260**	120l. black, light green and green	10	20

261 San Francesco Gate

1978. Europa. Architecture.

1090	**261**	170l. blue and light blue	1·20	35
1091	-	200l. brown and stone	1·60	55

DESIGN: 200l. Ripa Gate.

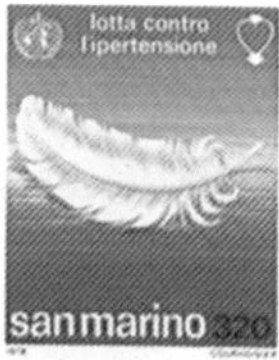

262 Feather

1978. World Hypertension Month.

1092	**262**	320l. black, blue and red	55	55

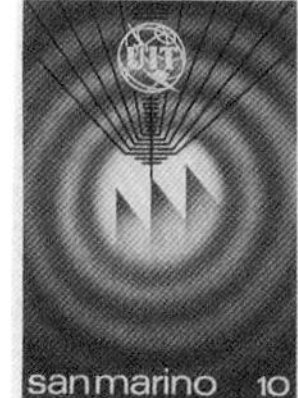

263 Mt. Titano and Antenna

1978. San Marino's Admission to the I.T.U.

1093	**263**	10l. yellow and red	10	10
1094	**263**	200l. blue and violet	20	20

264 Hawk and Slender-billed Gull

1978. 30th San Marino–Riccione Stamp Fair.

1095	**264**	120l. multicoloured	20	20
1096	**264**	170l. multicoloured	35	35

265 Wright "Flyer I"

1978. Air. 75th Anniv of First Powered Flight.

1097	**265**	10l. multicoloured	20	10
1098	**265**	50l. multicoloured	20	10
1099	**265**	200l. multicoloured	35	20

266 Allegory of Human Rights

1978. 30th Anniv of Declaration of Human Rights.

1100	**266**	200l. multicoloured	35	35

267 Holly

1978. Christmas. Multicoloured.

1101	10l. Type **267**	10	10
1102	120l. Star	20	10
1103	170l. Snowflakes	35	20

268 Albert Einstein

1979. Birth Cent of Albert Einstein (physicist).

1104	**268**	120l. brown, sepia and grey	35	30

269 Motor-coach, 1915

1979. Europa. Multicoloured.

1105	170l. Type **269**	2·40	60
1106	220l. Horse-drawn stage-coach	3·00	80

270 San Marino Crossbowmen Federation Emblem

1979. 14th Crossbow Tournament.

1107	**270**	120l. multicoloured	35	30

271 Maigret (G. Simenon)

1979. Fictional Detectives. Multicoloured.

1108	10l. Type **271**	10	15
1109	80l. Perry Mason (S. Gardner)	10	15
1110	150l. Nero Wolfe (R. Stout)	10	15
1111	170l. Ellery Queen (F. Dannay and M. B. Lee)	10	15
1112	220l. Sherlock Holmes (A. Conan Doyle)	45	35

272 Water Skiing

1979. Water Skiing Championships, Castelgandolfo.

1113	**272**	150l. green, blue & black	35	35

273 St. Apollonia

1979. 13th International Stomatology Congress.

1114	**273**	170l. multicoloured	35	35

274 "Knowledge"

1979. International Year of the Child. Mult.

1115	20l. Type **274**	15	10
1116	120l. "Friendship"	20	10
1117	170l. "Equality"	20	15
1118	220l. "Love"	35	35
1119	350l. "Existence"	65	50

275 Horse Chestnut and Red Deer

1979. Environment Protection. Trees and Animals. Multicoloured.

1120	5l. Type **275**	20	10
1121	10l. Cedar of Lebanon and golden eagle	20	10
1122	35l. Flowering dogwood and common racoon	20	10
1123	50l. Banyan and tiger	20	10
1124	70l. Stone pine and hoopoe	20	10
1125	90l. Larch and yellow-throated marten	20	10
1126	100l. Tasmanian blue gum and koala	20	10
1127	120l. Date palm and dromedary	20	10
1128	150l. Silver maple and American beaver	30	20
1129	170l. Baobab and African elephant	35	30

276 "Disturbing Muses"

1979. 1st Death Anniv of Giorgio de Chirico (painter). Multicoloured.

1130	40l. Type **276**	10	10
1131	150l. "Ancient Horses"	35	20
1132	170l. "Self-portrait"	35	30

277 St. Joseph

1979. Christmas. "The Holy Family" (fresco) by Antonio Alberti or details from it.

1133	80l. Type **277**	20	15
1134	170l. Infant Jesus	30	15
1135	220l. Magus	40	35
1136	320l. "The Holy Family"	65	60

278 St. Benedict of Nursia

1980. 1500th Birth Anniv of Saint Benedict of Nursia (founder of Benedictine Order).

1137	**278**	170l. multicoloured	35	35

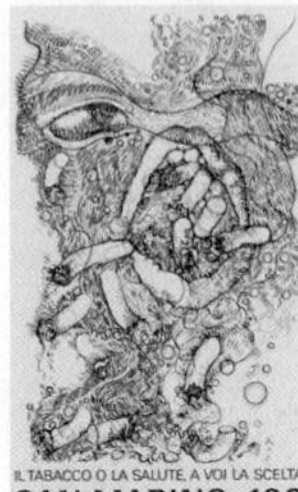

279 Cigarette Ends

1980. Anti-smoking Campaign. Multicoloured.

1138	120l. Type **279**	20	20
1139	220l. Face hidden by cigarettes	35	35
1140	520l. Face wreathed in smoke	65	65

280 Naples

1980. "Europa" Stamp Exhibition, Naples.

1141	**280**	170l. multicoloured	35	35

281 Giovanbattista Belluzzi (military architect)

1980. Europa. Multicoloured.

1142	170l. Type **281**	1·80	45
1143	220l. Antonio Orafo (silver and goldsmith)	2·75	50

282 London, 1850

1980. "London 1980" International Stamp Exhibition and Important Cities of the World (4th series). London.

1144	**282**	200l. brown and green	35	45
1145	-	400l. blue and lilac	55	80

DESIGN: 400l. London, 1980.

283 Cycling

1980. Olympic Games, Moscow.

1146	**283**	70l. black, emerald & green	10	10
1147	-	90l. black, orange & brown	10	10
1148	-	170l. black, red & mauve	20	20
1149	-	350l. black, blue & dp blue	55	55
1150	-	450l. black, violet & blue	80	65

DESIGNS: 90l. Basketball; 170l. Running; 350l. Gymnastics; 450l. High jumping.

284 Stolz and Score of "Philatelic Waltz"

1980. Birth Centenary of Robert Stolz (composer).

1151	**284**	120l. blue and black	35	30

285 Weightlifting

1980. European Junior Weightlifting Championship.

1152	**285**	170l. red, black and green	35	35

286 City Fortifications

1980. World Tourism Conference, Manila.

1153	**286**	220l. multicoloured	40	40

287 "The Annunciation" (detail)

1980. Christmas. Details of Paintings by Andrea del Sarto. Multicoloured.

1154		180l. "Madonna of the Harpies" (detail)	35	30
1155		250l. "Annunciation" (Mary)	55	45
1156		500l. Type **287**	1·10	85

288 St. Joseph's Eve Bonfire

1981. Europa. Multicoloured.

1157		200l. Type **288**	2·10	35
1158		300l. National Day fireworks	3·00	55

289 Hands holding Broken Branch

1981. International Year of Disabled Persons.

1159	**289**	300l. yellow, green and light green	45	55

290 "St. Charles' Square, 1817" (Jakob Alt)

1981. "WIPA 1981" International Stamp Exn and Important Cities of the World (5th series). Vienna. Multicoloured.

1160		200l. Type **290**	35	25
1161		300l. St. Charles' Square, 1981	55	50

291 Motor Cyclist

1981. San Marino Motor Cycle Grand Prix.

1162	**291**	200l. multicoloured	35	30

292 Girl playing Pipes

1981. Birth Bimillenary of Virgil (poet).

1163	**292**	300l. grey and silver	35	35
1164	-	550l. grey and silver	65	65
1165	-	1500l. grey and silver	2·20	1·90

DESIGNS: 550l. Soldier; 1500l. Shepherd.

293 House

1981. Urban Development Scheme. Multicoloured.

1167		20l. Type **293**	10	15
1168		80l. Tree (provision of green belts)	10	15
1169		400l. Gas flame (power plants)	55	55

294 Judo

1981. European Junior Judo Championships, San Marino.

1170	**294**	300l. multicoloured	50	45

295 "Girl with Dove" (Picasso)

1981. Birth Centenary of Pablo Picasso (artist). Multicoloured.

1171		150l. Type **295**	20	20
1172		200l. "Homage to Picasso" (detail, Renato Guttuso)	55	50

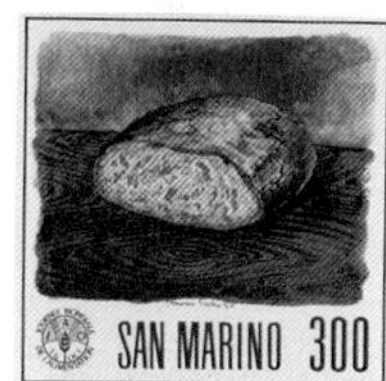

296 Bread

1981. World Food Day.

1173	**296**	300l. multicoloured	50	45

297 King presenting Gift

1981. Christmas. 500th Birth Anniv of Benvenuto Tisi da Garofalo (artist). Details from "Adoration of the Magi and St. Bartholomew". Multicoloured.

1174		200l. Type **297**	30	30
1175		300l. Kneeling King	50	45
1176		600l. Virgin and Child	1·00	95

298 Cancellation and "San Marino 82" Emblem

1982. Centenary of Postal Stationery.

1177	**298**	200l. multicoloured	35	35

299 "The Cicada and the Ant" (Aesop fable)

1982. Centenary of Savings Bank.

1178	**299**	300l. multicoloured	50	45

300 Assembly of Heads of Families, 1906

1982. Europa. Multicoloured.

1179		300l. Type **300**	4·50	90
1180		450l. Napoleon at the border of San Marino, 1797	6·75	1·30

301 Archimedes

1982. Pioneers of Science.

1181	**301**	20l. red and black	10	10
1182	-	30l. blue and black	10	10
1183	-	40l. brown and black	10	10
1184	-	50l. green and black	10	10
1185	-	60l. red and black	10	10
1186	-	100l. brown and black	10	10
1187	-	150l. brown and black	10	10
1188	-	200l. brown and black	35	30
1189	-	250l. red and black	35	30
1190	-	300l. green and black	45	45
1191	-	350l. green and black	55	35
1192	-	400l. red and black	65	50
1193	-	450l. red and black	65	60
1194	-	1000l. red and black	1·80	1·00
1195	-	1400l. red and black	2·50	2·00
1196	-	5000l. black and blue	6·75	5·25

DESIGNS: 30l. Copernicus; 40l. Isaac Newton; 50l. Antoine Lavoisier; 60l. Marie Curie; 100l. Robert Koch; 150l. Alexander Fleming; 200l. Thomas Edison; 250l. Alessandro Volta; 300l. Guglielmo Marconi; 350l. Evangelista Torricelli; 400l. Carl Linnaeus; 450l. Hippocrates; 1000l. Pythagoras; 1400l. Leonardo da Vinci; 5000l. Galileo.

302 "Notre Dame", 1806 (J. Hill)

1982. "Philexfrance 82" International Stamp Exhibition and Important Cities of the World (6th series). Paris.

1197	**302**	300l. buff and black	45	55
1198	-	450l. multicoloured	65	80

DESIGN: 450l. Notre Dame and Ile de Cite, 1982.

303 Hands and Birds

1982. 800th Birth Anniv of St. Francis of Assisi.

1199	**303**	200l. multicoloured	35	35

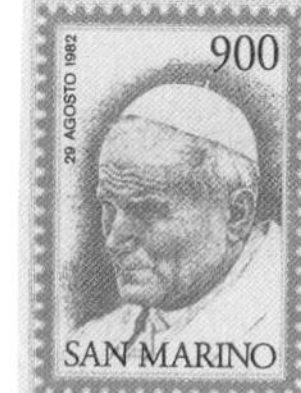

304 Pope John Paul II

1982. Visit of Pope John Paul II to San Marino.

1200	**304**	900l. purple, deep green and green	1·40	1·30

305 Globe encircled by Flag Stamps

1982. 5th Anniv of International Association of Stamp Philatelic Catalogue Editors (ASCAT).

1201	**305**	300l. multicoloured	50	45

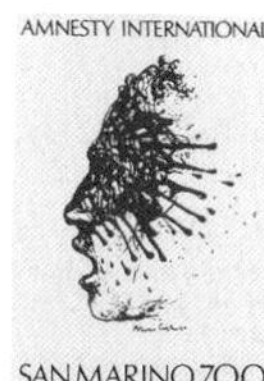

306 Face besplattered with Blood

1982. 15th International Congress of Amnesty International, Rimini.

1202	**306**	700l. red and black	1·00	90

307 "Accipe Lampadam Ardentem" (detail)

1982. Christmas. Paintings by Gregorio Sciltian. Multicoloured.

1203		200l. Type **307**	40	35
1204		300l. "Madonna della Citta" (detail)	60	55
1205		450l. Angel (detail, "Accipe Sal Sapientiae")	1·00	80

308 Refugee

1982. "For Refugees".

1206	**308**	300l.+100l. mult	50	45

309 Begni Building and Quill

1983. Centenary of Secondary School.

1207	**309**	300l. multicoloured	50	45

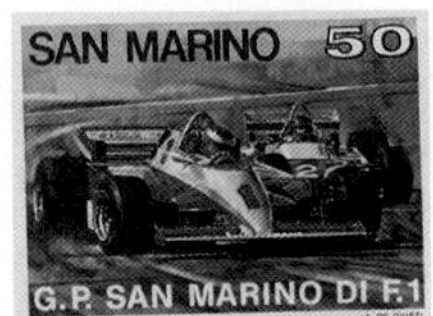

310 Formula One Racing Cars

1983. San Marino Formula One Grand Prix.
1208 **310** 50l. multicoloured 10 10
1209 **310** 350l. multicoloured 45 80

311 Auguste Piccard and Stratosphere Balloon "F.N.R.S."

1983. Europa. Multicoloured.
1210 400l. Type **311** 3·25 1·50
1211 500l. Piccard and bathyscaphe 4·00 1·90

312 Amateur Radio Operator

1983. World Communications Year.
1212 **312** 400l. black, blue and red 55 55
1213 - 500l. black, brown & red 85 85
DESIGN: 500l. Postman on bicycle.

313 Montgolfier Balloon

1983. Bicentenary of Manned Flight.
1214 **313** 500l. multicoloured 80 65

314 "Rio de Janeiro, 1845" (Richard Bate)

1983. "Brasiliana 83" International Stamp Exhibition and Important Cities of the World (7th series). Rio de Janeiro. Multicoloured.
1215 400l. Type **314** 55 60
1216 1400l. Rio de Janeiro, 1983 1·90 1·70

315 Feeding Colt

1983. World Food Programme.
1217 **315** 500l. multicoloured 85 70

316 "Madonna of the Grand Duke"

1983. Christmas. 500th Birth Anniv of Raphael. Multicoloured.
1218 300l. Type **316** 45 55
1219 400l. "Madonna of the Goldfinch" (detail) 55 80
1220 500l. "Madonna of the Chair" (detail) 80 1·10

317 Demetrius Vikelas

1984. 90th Anniv of International Olympic Committee. I.O.C. Presidents.
1221 **317** 300l. black and green 80 70
1222 - 400l. purple and blue 1·00 90
1223 - 550l. lilac and green 1·40 1·10
DESIGNS: 400l. Lord Killanin; 550l. Juan Samaranch.

318 Bridge

1984. Europa. 25th Anniv of C.E.P.T.
1224 **318** 400l. yellow, violet & black 3·25 1·30
1225 **318** 550l. yellow, red & black 4·50 1·70

319 Flag Waver

1984. Flag Wavers. Multicoloured.
1226 300l. Type **319** 45 45
1227 400l. Waver with two flags 65 65

320 Male Athlete

1984. Olympic Games, Los Angeles. Sheet 151×110 mm containing T 320 and similar vert designs. Multicoloured.
MS1228 550l. Type **320**; 1000l. Female athlete 25·00 2·75

321 Motocross

1984. World Motocross Championship.
1229 **321** 450l. multicoloured 65 65

322 Collins Street, 1839

1984. "Ausipex 84" International Stamp Exhibition, and Important Cities of the World (8th series). Melbourne. Multicoloured.
1230 1500l. Type **322** 2·20 2·30
1231 2000l. Collins Street, 1984 2·75 3·00

323 Pres. Pertini and San Marino City

1984. Visit of President Sandro Pertini of Italy.
1232 **323** 1950l. multicoloured 3·00 3·00

324 "Universe"

1984. Youth Philately. Multicoloured.
1233 50l. Type **324** 10 15
1234 100l. Caveman and modern man framed by television ("The Evolution of Life") 20 20
1235 150l. Pipe smoker driving car ("The World in which we Live") 20 20
1236 200l. Man with fig leaf and snake with apple ("Mankind") 30 30
1237 450l. Scientist with H-bomb ("Science") 60 60
1238 550l. Man in barrel with books and candle ("Philosophy") 90 85

325 Angel with Book

1984. Christmas. Designs showing details of "Madonna of San Girolamo" by Correggio. Mult.
1239 400l. Type **325** 65 80
1240 450l. Virgin and Child 90 65
1241 550l. Attendant 1·00 1·10

326 Johann Sebastian Bach and Score

1985. Europa.
1242 **326** 450l. black and brown 3·25 1·60
1243 - 600l. black and green 4·50 2·30
DESIGN: 600l. Vincenzo Bellini and score.

327 State Flags, Stadium and Swimming Pictogram

1985. 1st Small States Games. Multicoloured.
1244 50l. Type **327** 20 15
1245 350l. Flags, stadium and running pictogram 45 45
1246 400l. Flags, stadium and shooting pictogram 55 55
1247 450l. Flags, stadium and cycling pictogram 65 60
1248 600l. Flags, stadium and handball pictogram 1·00 90

328 Sunset and Birds

1985. Emigration.
1249 **328** 600l. multicoloured 1·00 90

329 Face and Hand holding Dove

1985. International Youth Year.
1250 **329** 400l. yellow, blue and gold 55 55
1251 - 600l. gold, blue and yellow 1·00 90
DESIGN: 600l. Girl's face, dove and horse's head.

330 Camera and San Marino

1985. 18th Int Federation of Photographic Art Congress.
1252 **330** 450l. multicoloured 80 80

331 Sun breaking through Clouds and Sapling

1985. 10th Anniv of Helsinki European Security and Co-operation Conference.
1253 **331** 600l. multicoloured 1·00 1·00

332 Don Abbondio and Don Rodrigo's Henchmen

1985. Birth Bicentenary of Alessandro Manzoni (writer). Scenes from "I Promessi Sposi".
1254 **332** 400l. green 55 55
1255 - 450l. brown 65 65
1256 - 600l. blue 90 90
DESIGNS: 450l. Forcing curate to bless wedding; 600l. Plague in Milan.

333 Common Carp caught on Hook

1985. World Angling Championships, River Arno, Florence.
1257 **333** 600l. multicoloured 1·00 1·00

334 Cat (after Pompeian mosaic)

1985. International Feline Federation Congress.
1258 **334** 600l. multicoloured 1·00 1·00

335 Colosseum, 85 A.D.

1985. "Italia 85" International Stamp Exhibition, and Important Cities of the World (9th series). Rome. Multicoloured.
1259 1000l. Type **335** 1·40 1·30
1260 1500l. Colosseum, 1985 2·10 1·80

336 Flying Angel

1985. Christmas. Multicoloured.
1261 400l. Type **336** 80 80
1262 450l. Madonna and Child 90 90
1263 600l. Angel resting 1·10 1·30

337 Aerial View of Cailungo Hospital

1986. 30th Anniv of Social Security Institute (450l.) and World Health Day (650l.). Mult.
1264 450l. Type **337** 65 65
1265 650l. Front view of Cailungo hospital 90 90

338 "Giotto" Space Probe

1986. Appearance of Halley's Comet. Mult.
1266 550l. Type **338** 1·00 90
1267 1000l. "Adoration of the Magi" (Giotto) 1·70 1·70

339 Player and Emblem

1986. World Table Tennis Championships, Rimini.
1268 **339** 450l. blue, ultram & red 80 80

340 Deer

1986. Europa. Multicoloured.
1269 550l. Type **340** 13·00 5·50
1270 650l. Common kestrel 15·00 7·75

341 Water Tower, 1870 (lithograph, Charles Shober)

1986. "Ameripex" International Stamp Exhibition, and Important Cities of the World (10th series). Chicago. Multicoloured.
1271 2000l. Type **341** 2·75 2·30
1272 3000l. Water tower, 1986 4·00 3·50

342 Swallows

1986. International Peace Year.
1273 **342** 550l. multicoloured 1·00 95

343 Head of Soldier

1986. 15th Anniv of Establishment of Diplomatic Relations with Chinese People's Republic. Terracotta Figures from Qin Shi Huang's Tomb. Sheet 153×95 mm, containing T 343 and similar designs.
MS1274 550l. black and blue; 650l. black and brown; 2000l. black and magenta 5·50 5·50
DESIGNS—VERT: 650l. Head of horse. VERT: 2000l. Head of soldier (different).

344 "Apollo dancing with the Muses" (detail, Giulio Romano)

1986. 25th Anniv of San Marino Choral Society.
1275 **344** 450l. multicoloured 80 70

345 Boules Player

1986. European Boules Championships, San Marino.
1276 **345** 550l. multicoloured 90 85

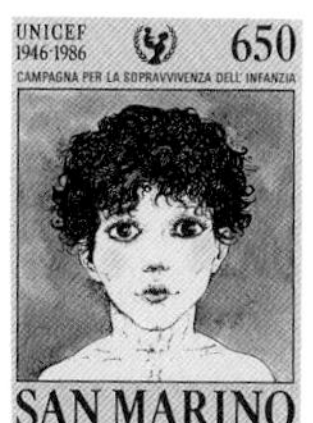

346 Boy

1986. 40th Anniv of UNICEF. Child Survival Campaign.
1277 **346** 650l. multicoloured 1·10 1·00

347 "St. John the Baptist"

1986. Christmas. Triptych by Hans Memling. Mult.
1278 450l. Type **347** 1·10 85
1279 550l. "Madonna and Child" 1·30 70
1280 650l. "St. John the Evangelist" 1·40 1·20

348 Motor Car and Route Map (Paris–Peking Rally, 1907)

1987. Motor Rallies. Multicoloured.
1281 500l. Type **348** 65 65
1282 600l. Peugeot "205" (15th San Marino Rally) 80 80
1283 700l. Motor car and crowds (60th anniv of Mille Miglia) 1·10 1·10

349 Sketch of Church

1987. Europa. Architecture. Our Lady of Consolation Church, Borgomaggiore (Giovanni Michelucci).
1284 **349** 600l. black and red 14·00 6·75
1285 - 700l. black and yellow 16·00 7·75
DESIGN: 700l. Church interior.

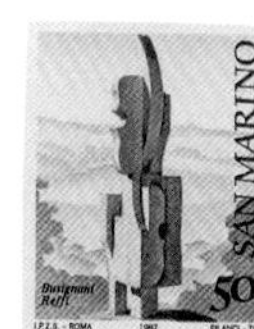

350 Modern Sculpture (Reffi Busignani)

1987. Modern Sculptures in San Marino. Designs showing works by artists named. Multicoloured.
1286 50l. Type **350** 10 15
1287 100l. Bini 10 15
1288 200l. Guguianu 35 30
1289 300l. Berti 45 45
1290 400l. Crocetti 55 55

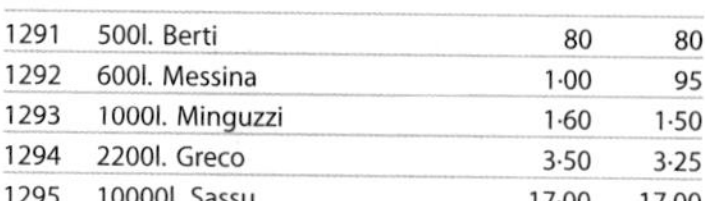
1291 500l. Berti 80 80
1292 600l. Messina 1·00 95
1293 1000l. Minguzzi 1·60 1·50
1294 2200l. Greco 3·50 3·25
1295 10000l. Sassu 17·00 17·00

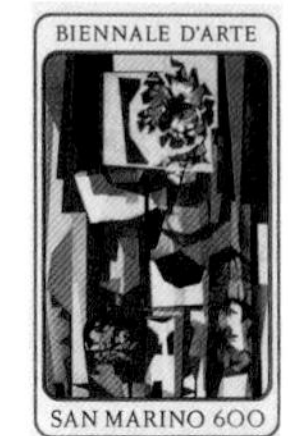

351 "Chromatic Invention" (Corrado Cagli)

1987. Art Biennale.
1300 - 500l. blue, black and red 80 80
1301 **351** 600l. multicoloured 95 90
DESIGN: 500l. "From My Brazilian Diary—Virgin Forest" (Emilio Vedova).

352 Baroudeur Microlight, San Marino Air Club

1987
1302 **352** 600l. multicoloured 1·00 1·00

353 Bust of Mahatma Gandhi in Gandhi Square, San Marino

1987. "A Society based on Non-violence".
1303 **353** 500l. multicoloured 85 85

354 Olympic Rings and Hurdler in "Stamp"

1987. "Olymphilex" Olympic Stamp Exhibition and World Light Athletics Championships, Rome.
1304 **354** 600l. multicoloured 1·00 1·00

355 Sports Pictograms

1987. Mediterranean Games, Syria.
1305 **355** 700l. red, blue and black 1·10 1·10

356 "View from Round Tower, 1836" (anon)

1987. "Hafnia 87" International Stamp Exhibition, and Important Cities of the World (11th series). Copenhagen. Multicoloured.
1306 1200l. Type **356** 2·20 2·00
1307 2200l. View from Round Tower, 1987 4·00 3·75

357 "The Annunciation" (detail)

1987. Christmas. 600th Birth Anniv of Fra Giovanni of Florence (Beato Angelico). Mult.

1308	600l. Type **357**	1·30	1·20
1309	600l. Madonna and Child (detail, Triptych of Cortona)	1·30	1·20
1310	600l. Saint (detail, "The Annunciation")	1·30	1·20

358 1923 30c., 1944 20l.+10l. and 1975 200l. Stamps of St. Marinus

1988. Thematic Collecting. Multicoloured.

1311	50l. Type **358**	10	15
1312	150l. Aerogramme and 1933 3l. LZ-127 "Graf Zeppelin" stamp (transport)	20	20
1313	300l. 1954 5l. and 1981 200l. motor cycle racing stamps and 1986 meter mark showing motor cycle (sport)	50	50
1314	350l. 1978 200l. human rights stamp on cover and 1982 200l. St. Francis of Assisi stamp (art)	60	60
1315	1000l. 1949 50l. Garibaldi stamp, 1985 450l. Europa stamp and 1952 1l. Columbus stamp (famous people)	1·60	1·60

See also Nos. 1340/4 and 1393/7.

359 Maglev Monorail Train and Globe

1988. Europa. Transport and Communications. Multicoloured.

1316	600l. Type **359**	7·75	3·25
1317	700l. Optical fibres and globe	11·00	4·50

360 Carlo Malagola and Palazzo della Mercanzia

1988. 900th Anniv of Bologna University. Mult.

1318	550l. Type **360**	80	80
1319	650l. Pietro Ellero and Palazzo del Podesta	90	90
1320	1300l. Giosue Carducci and Pala dei Mercanti	1·80	1·80
1321	1700l. Giovanni Pascoli and Atheneum	2·30	2·30

361 "La Strada"

1988. Award of Celebrities of Show Business Prize to Federico Fellini (film director). Film posters. Multicoloured.

1322	300l. Type **361**	45	45
1323	900l. "La Dolce Vita"	1·30	1·30
1324	1200l. "Amarcord"	1·90	1·90

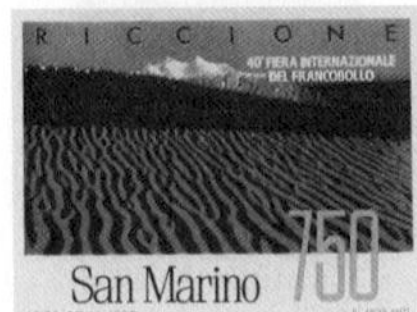

362 Mt. Titano from Beach

1988. 40th Riccione Stamp Fair.

1325	**362**	750l. blue, green and mauve	1·10	1·10

363 Healthy Tree with Diseased Roots

1988. Present Day Problems. International AIDS Congress, San Marino.

1326	**363**	250l. multicoloured	40	40
1327	-	350l. red and black	55	55
1328	-	650l. multicoloured	95	95
1329	-	1000l. multicoloured	1·70	1·70

DESIGNS: 350l. "AIDS" crumbling; 650l. Knotted cord and emblem of virus; 1000l. Printed information.

364 Man Running

1988. Olympic Games, Seoul. Sheet 118×103 mm containing T 364 and similar vert designs, each black, magenta and yellow.

MS1330	650l. Type **364**; 750l. Hurdling; 1300l. Woman running	4·25	4·25

365 "Kurhaus, Scheveningen, 1885" (anon)

1988. "Filacept" International Stamp Exhibition, and Important Cities of the World (12th series). The Hague. Multicoloured.

1331	1600l. Type **365**	2·20	1·70
1332	3000l. Kurhaus, Scheveningen, 1988	4·50	3·50

366 "Angel with Violin"

1988. Christmas. 550th Birth Anniv of Melozzo da Forli. Multicoloured.

1333	650l. Type **366**	1·10	90
1334	650l. "Angel of the Annunciation" (20×37 mm)	1·10	90

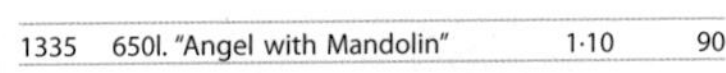

1335	650l. "Angel with Mandolin"	1·10	90

367 Bird in Tree (Federica Sparagna)

1989. "Nature is Beautiful. Nature is Useful. Nature is ...". Multicoloured.

1336	200l. Type **367**	40	30
1337	500l. Birds beneath tree (Giovanni Monteduro)	95	80
1338	650l. Landscape (Rosa Mannarino)	1·20	1·00

Nos. 1336/8 depict the first three winning entries in a children's drawing competition.

368 Sledging

1989. Europa. Children's Games. Sheet 115×80 mm containing T 368 and similar vert design. Multicoloured.

MS1339	60l. Type **368**; 750l. Hopscotch	28·00	14·50

1989. Postal History. As T 358. Multicoloured.

1340	100l. "San Marino 1977" Exhibition 1000l. stamp on cover (postal tariffs)	10	10
1341	200l. 1988 350l. stamp on cover (cancellations)	35	20
1342	400l. Parcel receipt (parcel post)	65	65
1343	500l. Essay by Martin Riester, 1865	90	80
1344	1000l. 1862 handstamp on cover (pre-stamp period)	1·70	1·60

369 Emblem

1989. Sport. Multicoloured.

1345	650l. Type **369** (30th anniv of San Marino Olympic Committee)	1·00	95
1346	750l. Emblems (admission of San Marino Football Federation to UEFA and FIFA)	1·20	1·10
1347	850l. Tennis racquet and ball (San Marino championships)	1·30	1·30
1348	1300l. Formula 1 racing car (San Marino Grand Prix, Imola)	1·80	1·80

370 Oath of the Tennis Court

1989. Bicentenary of French Revolution. Mult.

1349	700l. Type **370**	1·10	1·10
1350	1000l. Arrest of Louis XVI	1·60	1·40
1351	1800l. Napoleon's army	3·00	2·50

371 "Marguerite and Armand"

1989. Award of Celebrities of Show Business Prize to Rudolph Nureyev (ballet dancer). Mult.

1352	1200l. Type **371**	2·10	2·10
1353	1500l. "Apollo Musagete"	2·50	2·40
1354	1700l. Ken Russell's film "Valentino"	3·00	2·75

372 "Angel of the Annunciation"

1989. Christmas. Details of the polyptych in Church of Servants of Mary. Multicoloured.

1355	650l. Type **372**	1·10	90
1356	650l. "Nativity" (50×40 mm)	1·10	90
1357	650l. Mary ("Annunciation")	1·10	90

373 Capitol, 1850

1989. "World Stamp Expo '89" Int Stamp Exhibition, and Important Cities of the World (13th series). Washington D.C. Multicoloured.

1358	2000l. Type **373**	2·75	2·30
1359	2500l. Capitol, 1989	3·25	3·00

374 Old Post Office

1990. Europa. Post Office Buildings. Mult.

1360	700l. Type **374**	3·25	1·40
1361	800l. Dogana Post Office	4·00	1·60

375 "Martyrdom of St. Agatha" (Tiepolo) and Cardinal Alberoni leaving City

1990. 250th Anniv of End of Cardinal Alberoni's Occupation of San Marino.

1362	**375**	3500l. multicoloured	6·00	4·25

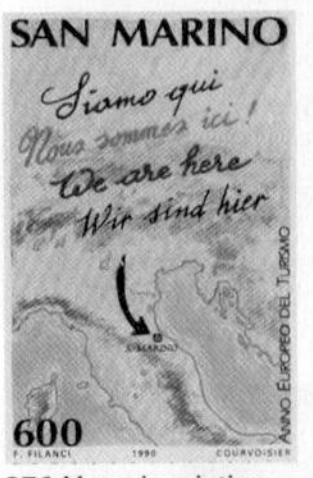

376 Map pinpointing San Marino **377** Statue, Government Palace

1990. European Tourism Year. Multicoloured.

1366	50l. Type **377**	10	10
1367	50l. Liberty Statue and English inscription	10	10
1368	50l. Government Palace and German inscription	10	10
1369	50l. Man with flag and French inscription	10	10
1370	600l. Type **376**	85	55
1371	600l. Aerial view showing villages	85	55
1372	600l. First Tower	85	55

See also Nos. 1424/7.

378 West Germany (winners 1954, 1974)

1990. World Cup Football Championship, Italy. Previous Winners. Sheet 120×114 mm containing T 378 and similar vert designs. Multicoloured.

MS1373	700l Type **378**; 700l. Italy (1934, 1938, 1982); 700l. England (1966); 700l. Uruguay (1930, 1950); 700l. Brazil (1958, 1962, 1970); 700l. Argentina (1978, 1986)	7·25	7·00

379 Olivier in "Hamlet"

1990. Award of Celebrities of Show Business Prize to Laurence Olivier (actor). Multicoloured.

1374	600l. Type **379**	1·20	1·20
1375	700l. "Richard III"	1·40	1·40
1376	1500l. "The Runner"	3·25	2·75

Nos. 1374/6 are wrongly inscribed "Lawrence".

380 Mt. Titano and State Flags

1990. Visit of President Francesco Cossiga of Italy.

1377	**380**	600l. multicoloured	1·00	85

381 Pinocchio

1990. Death Centenary of Carlo Collodi (writer). Characters from "Pinocchio". Multicoloured.

1378	250l. Type **381**	45	45
1379	400l. Geppetto	65	65
1380	450l. Blue fairy	85	85
1381	600l. Cat and wolf	1·10	1·10

382 Pre-Columbian Civilizations

1990. 500th Anniv (1992) of Discovery of America by Columbus (1st issue). Multicoloured.

1382	1500l. Type **382**	2·20	2·20
1383	2000l. Produce of the New World	3·00	3·00

See also Nos. 1401/2 and 1417/18.

383 Mary and Two Kings

1990. Christmas. Details of Cuciniello Crib. Mult.

1384	750l. Type **383**	1·30	1·20
1385	750l. Baby Jesus in manger and third King	1·30	1·20

Nos. 1384/5 were issued together, se-tenant, forming a composite design.

384 Swallowtail on "Ephedra major"

1990. Flora and Fauna. Multicoloured.

1386	200l. Type **384**	30	30
1387	300l. "Apoderus coryli" (weevil) and hazelnut	55	55
1388	500l. Garden dormouse and acorns of holm oak	85	85
1389	1000l. Green lizard and "Ophrys bertolonii" (orchid)	1·70	1·70
1390	2000l. Firecrest on black pine	3·25	3·25

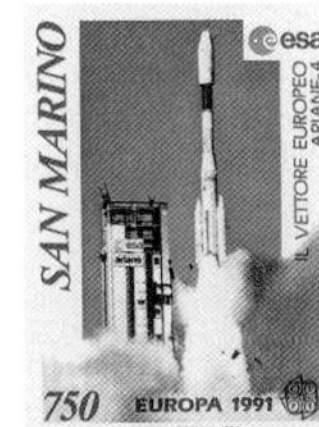

385 Launch of "Ariane-4"

1991. Europa. Europe in Space. Multicoloured.

1391	750l. Type **385**	3·25	3·25
1392	800l. "E.R.S.-1." survey satellite	4·00	4·00

1991. World of Stamps. As T 358. Multicoloured.

1393	100l. Stamp shop	20	15
1394	150l. Stamp club	30	20
1395	200l. Exhibition	40	35
1396	450l. Stamp album and catalogues	80	70
1397	1500l. Philatelic publications (25th anniv of Italian Philatelic Press Union)	2·75	2·40

386 Torch Bearer leaving Athens

1991. Olympic Games, Barcelona (1992) (1st issue). Multicoloured.

1398	400l. Type **386**	70	70
1399	600l. Torch bearer passing through San Marino	1·10	1·10
1400	2000l. Torch bearer arriving in Barcelona	3·50	3·00

See also No. **MS**1434.

1991. 500th Anniv (1992) of Discovery of America by Columbus (2nd issue). As T 382. Mult.

1401	750l. Navigational dividers, quadrant, hour-glass, compass and route map	1·10	1·10
1402	3000l. "Santa Maria", "Nina" and "Pinta"	5·00	4·50

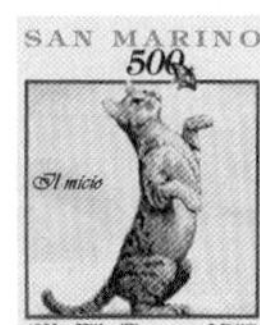

387 Cat

1991. Pets. Multicoloured.

1403	500l. Type **387**	80	65
1404	550l. Hamster on wheel	90	80
1405	750l. Great Dane and Pomeranian	1·20	1·10
1406	1000l. Aquarium fishes	1·60	1·50
1407	1200l. Canaries in cage	2·00	1·80

388 Players, Balls and Baskets

1991. Centenary of Basketball. Multicoloured.

1408	650l. Type **388**	1·10	1·00
1409	750l. James Naismith (inventor) and players	1·40	1·30

389 James Clerk-Maxwell (physicist)

1991. 100 Years of Radio (1st issue).

1410	**389**	750l. multicoloured	1·10	1·10

Clerk-Maxwell formulated the theory of electromagnetic radiation.

See also Nos. 1431, 1452, 1479 and 1521/2.

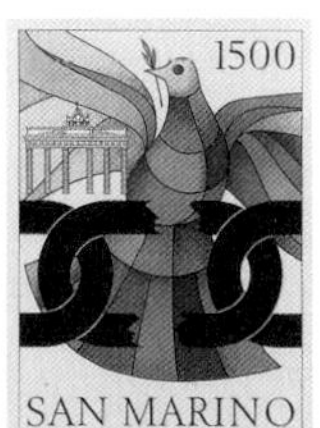

390 Dove and Broken Chain (unification of Germany)

1991. "Birth of a New Europe". Sheet 120×72 mm containing T 390 and similar vert designs. Multicoloured.

MS1411	1500l. Type **390**; 1500l. Pres. Gorbachev of Soviet Union, Pres. Bush of United States and rainbow (stategic arms talks); 1500l. Flower breaking through barbed wire (Eastern European democracy)	7·25	7·25

391 Keep

1991. Christmas. La Rocca Fortress. Multicoloured.

1412	600l. Type **391** (postage)	1·00	90
1413	750l. Inland view of fortress	1·30	1·10
1414	1200l. Fortress on crag (air)	2·10	1·80

392 "Bianca and Falliero" (Pesaro production)

1992. Birth Bicentenary of Gioachino Rossini (composer). Scenes from productions of his operas. Multicoloured.

1415	750l. Type **392**	1·30	1·30
1416	1200l. "The Barber of Seville" (La Scala Theatre, Milan)	2·30	2·20

1992. 500th Anniv of Discovery of America by Columbus (3rd issue). As T 382. Multicoloured.

1417	1500l. Amerindians watching fleet	2·20	2·20
1418	2000l. Route map of the four voyages	3·00	3·00

393 Roses

1992. Plants. Multicoloured.

1419	50l. Type **393**	20	20
1420	200l. Ficus as house plant	20	20
1421	300l. Orchid in conservatory	40	40
1422	450l. Cacti in pots	60	60
1423	5000l. Pelargoniums in trough	7·50	7·00

1992. Tourism. Multicoloured. (a) As T 377.

1424	50l. Man with crossbow and Italian inscription	10	15
1425	50l. Tennis player and English inscription	10	15
1426	50l. Motor cycle rider and French inscription	10	15
1427	50l. Ferrari racing car and German inscription	10	15

394 Courting Couple

(b) As T 394.

1428	600l. Type **394**	80	55
1429	600l. Man in restaurant	80	55
1430	600l. Woman reading on veranda	80	55

1992. 100 Years of Radio (2nd issue). As T 389. Multicoloured.

1431	750l. Heinrich Rudolf Hertz (physicist)	1·20	1·20

Hertz proved Clerk-Maxwell's theory.

395 Egg-shaped Globe and Caravel

1992. Europa. 500th Anniv of Discovery of America. Multicoloured.

1432	750l. Type **395**	1·20	1·20
1433	850l. Caravel and island inside broken egg	1·40	1·40

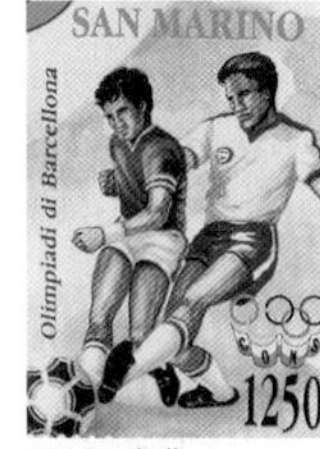

396 Football

1992. Olympic Games, Barcelona (2nd Issue). Sheet 137×105 mm containing T 396 and similar multicoloured designs.

MS1434	1250l. Type **396**; 1250l. Shooting (horiz); 1250l. Swimming; 1250l. Running	7·25	7·25

397 Inedible Mushrooms

1992. 3rd Titano Mycological Exhibition, Borgo Maggiore. Multicoloured.

1435	250l. Type **397**	55	50

1436 250l. Inedible mushrooms (different) 55 50
1437 350l. Edible mushrooms in bowl 65 70
1438 350l. Edible mushrooms on cloth 65 70

Stamps of the same value were issued together, se-tenant, each pair forming a composite design.

398 View and Arms of San Marino

1992. Admission of San Marino to United Nations Organization. Multicoloured.
1439 1000l. Type **398** 1·40 1·40
1440 1000l. View of San Marino (different) and United Nations emblem 1·40 1·40

399 "La Sacra Conversazione"

1992. Christmas. 500th Death Anniv of Piero della Francesca (artist). Multicoloured.
1441 750l. Type **399** 1·10 90
1442 750l. Close-up of Madonna 1·10 90
1443 750l. Close-up of shell decoration 1·10 90

400 Tennis Player

1993. Sporting Events. Multicoloured.
1444 300l. Type **400** (Italian and San Marino Youth Games) 35 35
1445 400l. Cross-country skiers (European Youth Olympic Days (winter), Aosta, Italy) 50 50
1446 550l. Runners (European Youth Olympic Days (summer), Eindhoven, Netherlands) 65 65
1447 600l. Fisherman (Freshwater Angling Clubs World Championship, Ostellato, Italy) 70 70
1448 700l. Runners breasting tape (Small States Games, Malta) 90 90
1449 1300l. Sprinters (Mediterranean Games, Rousillon, France) 2·75 1·70

401 Stars

1993. Europa. Contemporary Art.
1450 **401** 750l. multicoloured 1·10 1·10
1451 - 850l. blue and orange 1·30 1·30

DESIGN: 850l. Silhouette.

1993. 100 Years of Radio (3rd issue). As T 389. Multicoloured.
1452 750l. Edouard Branly (physicist) and his "radioconductor" 1·10 1·10

Branly developed a method of revealing Hertzian waves.

402 Finish of World Championship 100 Metres Race, Tokyo, 1991

1993. Inauguration of State Television. Sheet 140×70 mm containing T 402 and similar horiz designs. Multicoloured.
MS1453 2000l. Type **402**; 2000l. Hologram of satellite over San Marino by night; 2000l. Neil Armstrong on the Moon, 1969 7·25 7·25

404 Scarce Swallowtail ("Iphidides podalirius") on Wild Apple

1993. Butterflies. Multicoloured.
1454 250l. Type **404** 40 35
1455 250l. Clouded yellow ("Colias crocea") on wild vetch 40 35
1456 250l. Glanville's fritillary ("Melitaea anxia") 40 35
1457 250l. Camberwell beauty ("Nymphalis antiopa") on white willow 40 35

405 Denmark

1993. "The European Village". Sheet 145×170 mm containing T 405 and similar vert designs, each representing a European Community member. Multicoloured.
MS1458 750l. Type **405**; 750l. England; 750l. Eire; 750l. Luxembourg; 750l. Germany; 750l. Netherlands; 750l. Belgium; 750l. Portugal; 750l. Italy; 750l. Spain; 750l. France; 750l. Greece 10·50 10·50

406 Carlo Goldoni

1993. Death Anniversaries. Multicoloured.
1459 550l. Type **406** (dramatist, bicentenary) 55 55
1460 650l. Horace (Quintus Horatius Flaccus) (poet) (2000th anniv) 80 80
1461 850l. Scene from opera "Orpheus" by Claudio Monteverdi (composer, 350th anniv) (horiz) 1·00 1·00
1462 1850l. Guy de Maupassant (writer, centenary) (horiz) 2·30 2·30

407 San Marino

1993. Christmas. Multicoloured.
1463 600l. Type **407** 65 65
1464 750l. "Adoration of the Child" (Gerrit van Honthorst) (horiz) 90 90
1465 850l. "Adoration of the Shepherds" (Van Honthorst) 1·20 1·20

408 Long-haired Dachshund

1994. 10th International Dog Show. Multicoloured.
1466 350l. Type **408** 45 45
1467 400l. Afghan hound 50 50
1468 450l. Belgian tervuren shepherd dog 55 55
1469 500l. Boston terrier 60 60
1470 550l. Mastiff 65 65
1471 600l. Malamute 80 80

409 Ernst Vettori (90 metre ski jumping)

1994. Winter Olympic Games, Lillehammer, Norway. 1992 Gold Medal Winners. Sheet 164×112 mm containing T 409 and similar square designs. Multicoloured.
MS1472 750l. ×2, Type **409**; 750l. ×2, Patrick Ortlieb (downhill skiing); 750l. ×2, Alberto Tomba (giant slalom); 750l. Natalia Mishkutionok and Arthur Dmitriev (pairs figure skating) 7·25 7·25

410 Gate

1994. Gardens. Multicoloured.
1473 100l. Type **410** 20 20
1474 200l. Pergola 20 20
1475 300l. Well 45 45
1476 450l. Gazebo 55 55
1477 1850l. Pond 2·10 2·10

411 Olympic Flags

1994. Centenary of International Olympic Committee.
1478 **411** 600l. multicoloured 1·20 1·10

1994. 100 Years of Radio (4th issue). As T 389. Multicoloured.
1479 750l. Aleksandr Stepanovich Popov 1·10 1·10

Popov was the first to use a suspended wire as an aerial.

412 Players

1994. World Cup Football Championship, U.S.A. Multicoloured.
1480 600l. Type **412** 70 70
1481 600l. Player kicking ball 70 70
1482 600l. Player heading ball 70 70
1483 600l. Players tackling 70 70
1484 600l. Goalkeeper saving goal 70 70

413 Route Map

1994. Europa. Discoveries. Exploration of Sun by "Ulysses" Space Probe. Multicoloured.
1485 750l. Type **413** 1·10 1·10
1486 850l. "Ulysses" approaching Sun 1·30 1·30

414 Government Palace

1994. Centenary of Government Palace. Mult.
1487 150l. Type **414** 20 20
1488 600l. Tower and San Marino from ramparts 65 65
1489 650l. Clock-tower 80 80
1490 1000l. Government chamber (horiz) 1·10 1·10

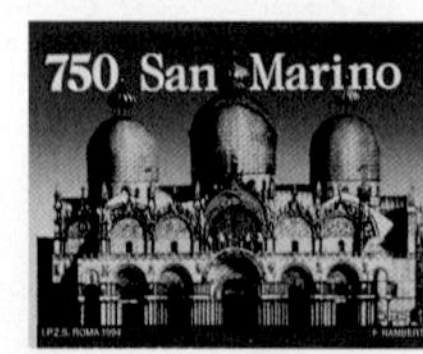

415 St. Mark's Basilica

1994. 900th Anniv of Dedication of St. Mark's Basilica, Venice.
1491 **415** 750l. multicoloured 6·00 6·00
MS1492 80×115 mm. No. 1491 together with No. 2276 of Italy 4·00 3·50

416 Angels playing Musical Instruments

1994. Christmas. 500th Death Anniv of Giovanni Santi (painter). Details of "The Enthroned Madonna and Child with Saints". Multicoloured.
1493 600l. Type **416** 70 70
1494 750l. Madonna and Child 90 90
1495 850l. Angel playing harp 1·10 1·10

417/420 "Italy on the Road in a Sea of Flowering Greenery"

1994. Centenary of Italian Touring Club.

1496	**417**	1000l. multicoloured	1·10	90
1497	**418**	1000l. multicoloured	1·10	90
1498	**419**	1000l. multicoloured	1·10	90
1499	**420**	1000l. multicoloured	1·10	90

Nos. 1496/9 were issued together, se-tenant, forming the composite design illustrated.

421 Cyclist

1995. Sporting Events. Multicoloured.

1500	100l. Type **421** (Junior World Cycling Championships, Italy and San Marino)	20	20
1501	500l. Volleyball (centenary)	55	55
1502	650l. Skater (Men's Speed-skating Championships, Baselga di Pine, Italy)	90	80
1503	850l. Sprinter (World Athletics Championships, Gothenburg, Sweden)	1·20	1·10

422 Flora and Fauna

1995. European Nature Conservation Year. Mult.

1504	600l. Type **422**	65	60
1505	600l. Frog, lizard and water lily	65	60
1506	600l. Water lily, bird and ladybirds	65	60
1507	600l. Butterfly, white-headed duckling and frog	65	60
1508	600l. Mallard and duckling	65	60

Nos. 1504/8 were issued together, se-tenant, forming a composite design of river life.

423 U.N. Emblem

1995. 50th Anniv of U.N.O. Multicoloured.

1509	550l. Type **423**	65	65
1510	600l. Rose with emblem	80	80
1511	650l. Hourglass	90	90
1512	1200l. Rainbow and emblem forming "50"	1·20	1·20

424 Mute Swans over Coastline

1995. Europa. Peace and Freedom. Multicoloured.

1513	750l. Type **424**	1·00	1·00
1514	850l. Landscape	1·20	1·20

425 Basilica and "Legend of the True Cross" (detail of fresco, Agnolo Gaddi)

1995. 700th Anniv of Santa Croce Basilica, Florence. Multicoloured.

1515	1200l. Type **425**	1·30	1·30
1516	1250l. Pazzi Chapel and "Madonna and Child with Saints" (Andrea della Robbia)	1·60	1·60

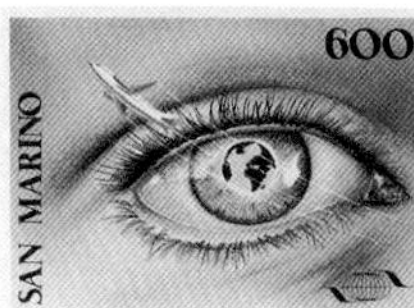

426 Eye and Airplane

1995. 20th Anniv of World Tourism Organization. Multicoloured.

1517	600l. Type **426**	55	55
1518	750l. Five ribbons (continents) around La Rocca fortress	85	85
1519	850l. Airplane and postcards circling globe	95	95
1520	1200l. Five ribbons around globe	1·30	1·30

427 Guglielmo Marconi and Transmitter

1995. 100 Years of Radio (5th issue). Centenary of First Radio Transmission. Multicoloured.

1521	850l. Type **427**	1·10	90
1522	850l. Radio frequency dial	1·10	90

428 *The General*, 1928 (1)

1995. Centenary of Motion Pictures. Sheet 187×120 mm containing T 428 and similar horiz designs. Black "The General" or multicoloured (others).

MS1523	250l. ×4, Buster Keaton in *The General*; 250l. ×4, Burt Lancaster and Claudia Cardinale in *The Leopard*; 250l. ×4, Bruno Bozzetto's *Allegro non Troppo* (animated film); 250l. ×4, Mel Gibson in *Braveheart*	5·00	5·00

Each film is represented by four different frames, numbered from 1 to 4.

429 Qianmen Complex, 1914

1995. "Beijing 1995" International Stamp and Coin Exhibition, Peking, and Important Cities of the World (14th series). Multicoloured.

1524	1500l. Type **429**	1·90	1·10
1525	1500l. Qianmen complex, 1995	1·90	1·10

430 "The Anunciation" (detail of illuminated MS)

1995. "Neri of Rimini" Art and Literature Exn.

1526	**430**	650l. multicoloured	1·20	1·00

431 Reindeer pulling Sleigh

1995. Christmas. Multicoloured.

1527	750l. Type **431**	1·40	1·10
1528	750l. Children dancing around Christmas tree	1·40	1·10
1529	750l. Wise Men approaching stable with crib	1·40	1·10

Nos. 1527/9 were issued together, se-tenant, forming a composite design.

432 Cheetah

1995. Inaug of San Marino Express Mail Service.

1530	**432**	6000l. multicoloured	8·00	8·00

433 Throwing the Discus

1996. Centenary of Modern Olympic Games. Mult.

1531	100l. Type **433**	15	15
1532	500l. Wrestling	65	60
1533	650l. Long jumping	90	85
1534	1500l. Throwing the javelin	2·10	1·80
1535	2500l. Running	3·50	3·00

434 Dolphin swimming

1996. 3rd "Nature World" Exhibition, Rimini. Mult.

1536	50l. Type **434**	10	10
1537	100l. Frog on leaf	15	15
1538	150l. Emperor penguins in snow	20	20
1539	1000l. Butterfly on flower	1·20	1·20
1540	3000l. Mallards flying over water	3·25	3·25

435 Mother Teresa of Calcutta

1996. Europa. Famous Women.

1541	**435**	750l. multicoloured	2·30	1·60

436 Marco Polo and Palace in the Forbidden City

1996. 700th Anniv (1995) of Marco Polo's Return from Asia and "China '96" International Stamp Exhibition, Peking.

1542	**436**	1250l. multicoloured	3·25	2·20

437 Great Wall of China

1996. 25th Anniv of San Marino–China Diplomatic Relations. Multicoloured.

1543	750l. Type **437**	1·40	85
1544	750l. Walled rampart, San Marino	1·40	85
MS1545	110×75 mm. Nos. 1543/4	2·75	2·75

Nos. 1543/4 were issued together, se-tenant, forming a composite design.

438 Traditional Weaving

1996. "Medieval Days" Traditional Festival. Mult.

1546	750l. Type **438**	90	65
1547	750l. Potter	90	65
1548	750l. Traditional craftswoman	90	65
1549	750l. Playing traditional game	90	65
1550	750l. Trumpeters (horiz)	90	65
1551	750l. Flag display (horiz)	90	65
1552	750l. Crossbow tournament (horiz)	90	65
1553	750l. Dancing and playing musical instruments (horiz)	90	65

439 Front Page

1996. Centenary of "La Gazzetta dello Sport" (newspaper).

1554	**439**	1850l. multicoloured	3·00	2·30

440 Applauding Crowd

1996. 33rd "Festivalbar" Song Festival.

1555	**440**	2000l. multicoloured	3·00	2·40

441 Enrico Caruso and "O Sole Mio"

1996. Italian Music. Singers and Their Songs. Multicoloured.

1556	750l. Type **441**	1·00	90
1557	750l. Armando Gill and "Come Pioveva"	1·00	90
1558	750l. Ettore Petrolini and "Gastone"	1·00	90
1559	750l. Vittorio de Sica and "Parlami d'Amore Mariu"	1·00	90
1560	750l. Odoardo Spadaro and "La porti un bacione a Firenze"	1·00	90
1561	750l. Alberto Rabagliati and "O mia bela Madonina"	1·00	90
1562	750l. Beniamino Gigli and "Mamma"	1·00	90
1563	750l. Claudio Villa and "Luna rossa"	1·00	90
1564	750l. Secondo Casadei and "Romagna Mia"	1·00	90
1565	750l. Renato Rascel and "Arrivederci Roma"	1·00	90
1566	750l. Fred Buscaglione and "Guarda che luna"	1·00	90
1567	750l. Domenico Modugno and "Nel blu, dipinto di blu"	1·00	90

442 Yellowstone National Park, United States

1996. 50th Anniv of UNESCO. World Heritage Sites. Multicoloured.

1568	450l. Type **442**	55	55
1569	500l. Prehistoric cave paintings, Vezere Valley, France	65	65
1570	650l. San Gimignano, Italy	90	80

1571	1450l. Wies Pilgrimage Church, Germany	2·20	1·90

443 Hen and Chicks

1996. 50th Anniv of UNICEF. Multicoloured.

1572	550l. Type **443**	80	65
1573	1000l. Chicks in nest	1·40	1·30

444 Playing Lotto

1996. Christmas. Multicoloured.

1574	750l. Type **444**	85	65
1575	750l. Hanging decoration	85	65
1576	750l. Father Christmas on sleigh and child reading book	85	65
1577	750l. Christmas tree	85	65
1578	750l. Bowls of fruit and nuts	85	65
1579	750l. Snowflakes and shooting star	85	65
1580	750l. Children's toys	85	65
1581	750l. Presents	85	65
1582	750l. Hanging Father Christmas decoration	85	65
1583	750l. Nativity scene	85	65
1584	750l. Mistletoe	85	65
1585	750l. Stocking hanging on mantelpiece	85	65
1586	750l. Family celebrating	85	65
1587	750l. Christmas tree outside window and party	85	65
1588	750l. Snowman outside window and party	85	65
1589	750l. Calendar pages and bottle of champagne (New Year's celebrations)	85	65

Nos. 1574/89 were issued together, se-tenant, forming a composite design.

445 Hong Kong, 1897

1997. Important Cities of the World (15th series). Sheet 84×94 mm containing T 445 and similar horiz design. Multicoloured.

MS1590	750l. Type **445**; 750l. Hong Kong, 1997	2·10	2·10

446/449 Championship Races

1997. World Skiing Championships, Sestriere.

1591	**446**	1000l. multicoloured	1·10	1·10
1592	**447**	1000l. multicoloured	1·10	1·10
1593	**448**	1000l. multicoloured	1·10	1·10
1594	**449**	1000l. multicoloured	1·10	1·10

Nos. 1591/4 were issued together, se-tenant, forming the composite design illustrated.

450 Acquaviva

1997. Communes. Multicoloured.

1595	100l. Type **450**	15	15
1596	200l. Borgomaggiore	20	20
1597	250l. Chiesanuova	35	30
1598	400l. Domagnano	55	50
1599	500l. Faetano	65	60
1600	550l. Fiorentino	80	65
1601	650l. Montegiardino	90	80
1602	750l. Serravalle	1·10	90
1603	5000l. San Marino	6·50	5·75

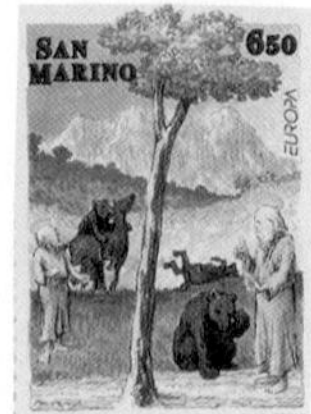

451 St. Marinus tames the Bear

1997. Europa. Tales and Legends. Multicoloured.

1604	650l. Type **451**	90	90
1605	750l. Felicissima begs St. Marinus to cure her son Verissimus	1·20	1·20

452 Bicycle and Stopwatch

1997. Sporting Events in San Marino. Each with Mt. Titano in the background. Multicoloured.

1606	500l. Type **452** (80th Giro d'Italia cycle race)	60	60
1607	550l. Tennis racket and ball (men's tennis championships)	65	65
1608	750l. Ferrari Formula One racing car (17th San Marino Grand Prix)	90	90
1609	850l. Juventus badge, football and trophy (Republic of San Marino Trophy football championship)	1·00	1·00
1610	1000l. Boules (World Petanque Championship)	1·20	1·20
1611	1250l. Motor cycle (World 250cc Motocross Championship)	1·50	1·40
1612	1500l. Car dashboard (Mille Miglia (classic car rally))	1·90	1·70

453 Scanning the Heavens

1997. 5th International Symposium on Unidentified Flying Objects and Associated Phenomena, San Marino.

1613	**453**	750l. multicoloured	1·00	85

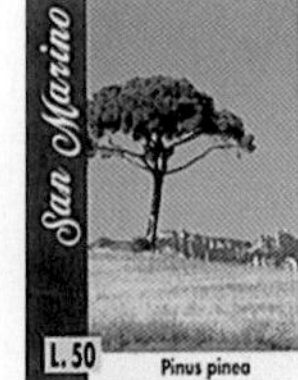

454 Stone Pine

1997. Trees. Multicoloured.

1614	50l. Type **454**	15	15
1615	800l. White oak	85	95
1616	1800l. Walnut	2·50	2·20
1617	2000l. Pear	3·00	2·50

455 Count Giovanni Barbavera di Grevellona

1997. 120th Anniv of First San Marino Postage Stamp.

1618	**455**	800l. brown and green	90	90
1619	-	800l. brown and blue	90	90
1620	-	800l. brown and mauve	90	90
1621	-	800l. brown and red	90	90

DESIGNS: No. 1618, Type **455** (Director-General of Italian Post Office and co-signatory of postal convention between Italy and San Marino); 1619, Italian Government Printing Works, Turin, and Enrico Repettati (chief engraver); 1620, "San Marino-Philatelist" (monthly magazine) and Otto Bickel (collectables dealer) holding illustrated envelopes; 1621, Alfredo Reffi (stamp dealer and postcard publisher) and postcard.

456 First Tower and Dal Monte

1997. Beatification of Father Bartolomeo Maria dal Monte.

1622	**456**	800l. multicoloured	1·10	90

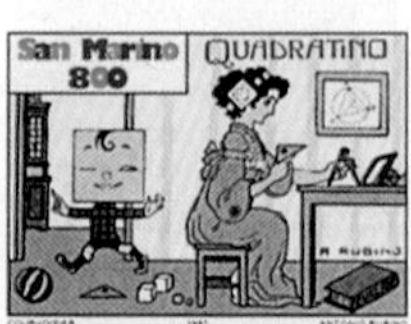

457 Quadratino (Antonio Rubino)

1997. Italian Comic Strips. Multicoloured.

1623	800l. Type **457**	1·10	1·10
1624	800l. Signor Bonaventura (Sergio Tofano)	1·10	1·10
1625	800l. Kit Carson (Rino Albertarelli)	1·10	1·10
1626	800l. Cocco Bill (Benito Jacovitti)	1·10	1·10
1627	800l. Tex Willer (Gian Bonelli and Aurelio Galleppini)	1·10	1·10
1628	800l. Diabolik (Angela and Luciana Giussani and Franco Paludetti)	1·10	1·10
1629	800l. Valentina (Guido Crepax)	1·10	1·10
1630	800l. Corto Maltese (Hugo Pratt)	1·10	1·10
1631	800l. Sturmtruppen (Franco Bonvicini)	1·10	1·10
1632	800l. Alan Ford (Max Bunker)	1·10	1·10
1633	800l. Lupo Alberto (Guido Silvestri)	1·10	1·10
1634	800l. Pimpa (Francesco Tullio Altan)	1·10	1·10
1635	800l. Bobo (Sergio Staino)	1·10	1·10
1636	800l. Zanardi (Andrea Pazienza)	1·10	1·10
1637	800l. Martin Mystere (Alfredo Castelli and Giancarlo Alessandrini)	1·10	1·10
1638	800l. Dylan Dog (Tiziano Sclavi and Angelo Stano)	1·10	1·10

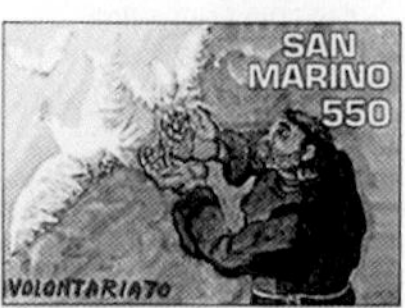

458 St. Francis of Assisi and Dove

1997. Voluntary and Charitable Service. Mult.

1639	550l. Type **458** (voluntary aid after Assisi earthquake)	65	65
1640	650l. Mariele Ventre (organizer of Zecchino d'Oro) and children (40th anniv of Antoniano in Bologna (charitable organization))	80	80
1641	800l. Children around globe (40th anniv of Zecchino d'Oro (children's song festival))	1·10	1·00

459 "Adoration of the Magi" (detail of altarpiece by Giorgio Vasari, San Fortunato Abbey, Rimini)

1997. Christmas.

1642	**459**	800l. multicoloured	1·30	1·10

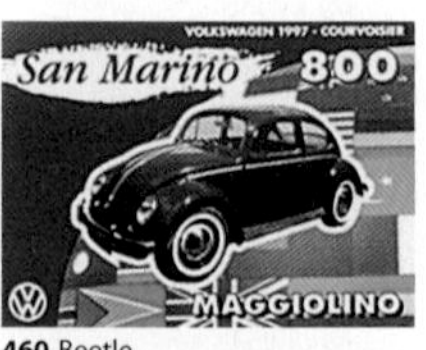

460 Beetle

1997. 60th Anniv of Volkswagen (motor manufacturer). Sheet 154×115 mm containing T 460 and similar horiz designs. Multicoloured.

MS1643	800l. Type **460**; 800l. Golf Mk I; 800l. New Beetle; 800l. Golf Mk IV	3·50	3·50

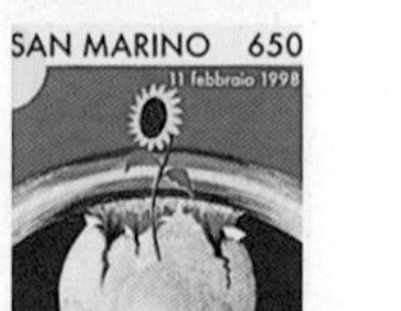

461 Rainbow over Grass and Sunflower erupting from Globe

1998. World Day of the Sick. Multicoloured.

1644	650l. Type **461**	85	80
1645	1500l. Dove and rainbow over waves and globe	1·90	1·80

462 125S Racing Car, 1947

1998. Birth Centenary of Enzo Ferrari (motor manufacturer). Racing Cars. Multicoloured.

1646	800l. Type **462**	1·20	1·20
1647	880l. Model 375, 1950 (wrongly inscr "500 F2, 1952")	1·20	1·20
1648	800l. Lancia D50, 1956 (wrongly inscr "801")	1·20	1·20
1649	800l. Racing car (wrongly inscr "246 Dino")	1·20	1·20
1650	800l. Model 156, 1961	1·20	1·20
1651	800l. John Surtees' 158, 1964	1·20	1·20
1652	800l. Niki Lauda's 312T, 1975	1·20	1·20
1653	800l. Jody Scheckter's 312T4, 1979	1·20	1·20
1654	800l. Model 126C, 1981	1·20	1·20
1655	800l. Michelo Alboreto's 156/85, 1985	1·20	1·20
1656	800l. Model 639, 1989	1·20	1·20
1657	800l. Michael Schumacher's F310, 1996	1·20	1·20

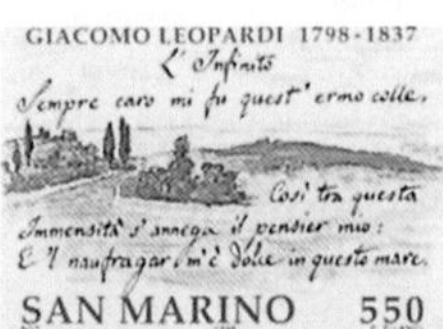

463 Verse of "Infinity", 1819

1998. Birth Bicentenary of Giacomo Leopardi (poet). Multicoloured.

1658	550l. Type **463**	80	65
1659	650l. "A Village Saturday", 1829	95	80
1660	900l. "Nocturne of a Wandering Asian Shepherd", 1822–30	1·30	1·10
1661	2000l. "To Sylvia", 1828	2·75	2·40

464 Installation of Captains Regent

1998. Europa. National Festivals. Multicoloured.

1662	650l. Type **464**	1·10	90
1663	1200l. Religious procession (Feast Day of Patron Saint)	2·20	1·90

465 Emigrants on Ship, Passport and Ticket

1998. Museum of the Emigrant. Multicoloured.

1664	800l. Type **465**	1·20	95
1665	1500l. Emigrants working, restaurant, work permit, pay slip, money and residency permit	2·40	1·70

466 Goalkeeper reaching for Ball

1998. World Cup Football Championship, France. Multicoloured.

1666	650l. Type **466**	1·40	1·70
1667	800l. Two players challenging for ball	1·90	1·90
1668	900l. Three players challenging for ball	2·20	1·90

467 Launch of Space Shuttle, Cape Canaveral

1998. San Marino Flag in Space. Sheet 140×70 mm containing T 467 and similar horiz designs. Multicoloured.

MS1669 2000l. Type **467**; 2000l, Space capsule in orbit and San Marino flag; 2000l. Space shuttle returning to Earth — 7·75 — 7·75

468 "20,000 Leagues Under the Sea" (Jules Verne)

1998. Science Fiction Novels. Multicoloured.

1670	800l. Type **468**	1·00	80
1671	800l. "War of the Worlds" (H. G. Wells) (centenary of publication)	1·00	80
1672	800l. "Brave New World" (Aldous Huxley)	1·00	80
1673	800l. "1984" (George Orwell)	1·00	80
1674	800l. "Foundation Trilogy" (Isaac Asimov)	1·00	80
1675	800l. "City" (Clifford D. Simak)	1·00	80
1676	800l. "Fahrenheit 451" (Ray Bradbury)	1·00	80
1677	800l. "The Seventh Victim" (Robert Sheckley)	1·00	80
1678	800l. "The Space Merchants" (Frederik Pohl and Cyril Kornbluth)	1·00	80
1679	800l. "The Coming Dark Age" (Roberto Vacca)	1·00	80
1680	800l. "Stranger in a Strange Land" (Robert Heinlein)	1·00	80
1681	800l. "A Clockwork Orange" (Anthony Burgess)	1·00	80
1682	800l. "The Drowned World" (James Ballard)	1·00	80
1683	800l. "Dune" (Frank Herbert)	1·00	80
1684	800l. "2001 A Space Odyssey" (Arthur Clarke)	1·00	80
1685	800l. "Do Androids Dream of Electric Sheep?" (Philip K. Dick)	1·00	80

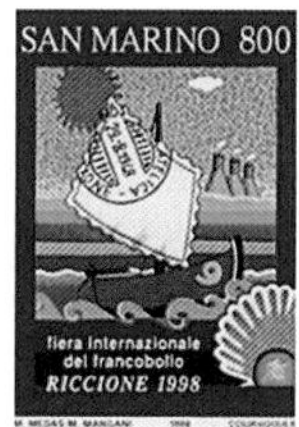

469 Sailing Dinghy and Factory Chimneys

1998. International Stamp Fair, Riccione. Mult.

1686	800l. Type **469**	1·00	95
1687	1500l. Dolphin jumping through stamp and factory chimneys	1·80	1·80

470 Pope John Paul II

1998. "Italia 98" International Stamp Exhibition, Milan (1st issue).

1688	470	800l. multicoloured	2·20	1·10

See also No. 1695.

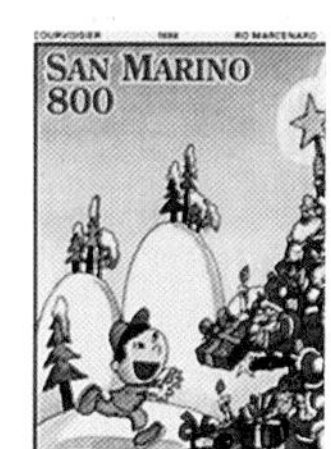

471 Boy and Tree of Santa Clauses

1998. Christmas. Multicoloured.

1689	800l. Type **471**	1·10	90
1690	800l. Pacific Island child	1·10	90
1691	800l. Boy in clogs and rabbit	1·10	90
1692	800l. Girl and dog	1·10	90

Nos. 1689/92 were issued together, se-tenant, forming a composite design of a tree of Santa Clauses bearing gifts.

472 Woman

1998. 50th Anniv of Universal Declaration of Human Rights. Multicoloured.

1693	900l. Type **472**	1·00	1·10
1694	900l. Man	1·00	1·10

Nos. 1693/4 were issued together, se-tenant, forming a composite design.

473 "The Joy of Living" (Emilio Greco)

1998. "Italia 98" International Stamp Exhibition (2nd issue). Art Day.

1695	473	1800l. multicoloured	2·50	2·20

DENOMINATION. From No. 1696 to No. 1890 San Marino stamps are denominated both in lire and in euros. As no cash for the latter is in circulation, the catalogue continues to use the lira value.

474 "The Coronation of Poppea" (Claudio Monteverdi)

1999. 400 Years of Opera. Multicoloured.

1696	800l. Type **474**	1·10	90
1697	800l. "Dido and Aeneas" (Henry Purcell)	1·10	90
1698	800l. "Orpheus and Eurydice" (Christoph Willibald Gluck)	1·10	90
1699	800l. "Don Juan" (Wolfgang Amadeus Mozart)	1·10	90
1700	800l. "The Barber of Seville" (Gioacchino Rossini)	1·10	90
1701	800l. "Norma" (Vincenzo Bellini)	1·10	90
1702	800l. "Lucia di Lammermoor" (Gaetano Donizetti)	1·10	90
1703	800l. "Aida" (Giuseppe Verdi)	1·10	90
1704	800l. "Faust" (Charles Gounod)	1·10	90
1705	800l. "Carmen" (Georges Bizet)	1·10	90
1706	800l. "The Ring of the Nibelung" (Richard Wagner)	1·10	90
1707	800l. "Boris Godunov" (Modest Musorgsky)	1·10	90
1708	800l. "Tosca" (Giacomo Puccini)	1·10	90
1709	800l. "The Love for Three Oranges" (Sergei Prokofiev)	1·10	90
1710	800l. "Porgy and Bess" (George Gershwin)	1·10	90
1711	800l. "West Side Story" (Leonard Bernstein)	1·10	90

475 Hand writing with Quill Pen

1999. 12th World Hang-gliding Championship, Montecucco, Italy. Multicoloured.

1712	800l. Type **475**	1·10	95
1713	1800l. Hang-glider with balloon	2·50	2·10

476 Mountain Pine

1999. San Marino Bonsai Exhibition. Mult.

1714	50l. Type **476**	15	15
1715	300l. Olive	40	35
1716	350l. Scots pine	45	45
1717	500l. Pedunculate oak	65	60

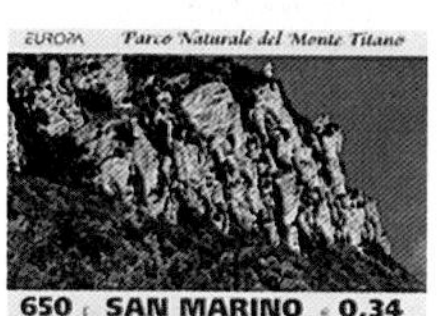

477 Eastern Slopes of Mount Titano

1999. Europa. Parks and Gardens. Multicoloured.

1718	650l. Type **477**	95	80
1719	1250l. Cesta Tower, Mount Titano	1·80	1·40

478 Emblem and Town Hall, Treviso

1999. World Cycling Championships, Treviso and Verona, Italy. Multicoloured.

1720	900l. Type **478**	1·20	1·10
1721	3000l. Emblem and amphitheatre, Verona	4·00	3·50

479 Article 1 of First Treaty (1874) and Swiss Parliament Building

1999. 125th Anniv of Universal Postal Union. Multicoloured.

1722	800l. Type **479**	1·10	95
1723	3000l. World map highlighting original U.P.U. signatories, 1875	4·00	3·50

480 Garibaldi (after Lorusso) and Crowds in front of the Quirinale, Rome

1999. 150th Anniv of Garibaldi's Refuge in San Marino after Fall of the Roman Republic.

1724	480	1250l. multicoloured	1·80	1·60

481 "50" and People climbing Ladder to Council Emblem

1999. 50th Anniv of Council of Europe.

1725	481	1300l. multicoloured	1·90	1·70

482 European Brown Hare

1999. Animals. Multicoloured.

1726	500l. Type **482**	60	60
1727	650l. Eurasian red squirrel	85	80
1728	1100l. Eurasian badger	1·30	1·30
1729	1250l. Red fox	1·60	1·40
1730	1850l. North African crested porcupine	2·50	2·20

483 Pilgrimage Route Map and Canterbury Cathedral

1999. Holy Year 2000. Multicoloured.

1731	650l. Type **483**	90	80
1732	800l. Priest blessing pilgrim (fresco, Novalesa Abbey) and Rheims Cathedral	1·10	1·00
1733	900l. Hospice welcoming pilgrims (fresco, St. James's Chapel, Briancon) and Pavia Cathedral	1·20	1·10
1734	1250l. Pilgrims on the road (bas-relief, Fidenza Cathedral) and Fidenza Cathedral	1·70	1·40
1735	1500l. "Mount of Joy" (Sir Charles Eastlake) and St. Peter's Cathedral, Rome	2·10	1·90

SAN MARINO
SANT'AGATA FELTRIA
50 €0,03

484 Fregoso Castle, Sant'Agata Feltria

1999. Architecture of Montefeltro. Multicoloured.

1736	50l. Type **484**	15	15
1737	250l. Feltresca Castle, San Leo	20	30
1738	650l. Ducal Palace, Urbino	85	80
1739	1300l. Ubaldinesca Castle, Sassocorvaro	1·80	1·60
1740	6000l. Il Montale and La Rocca fortress, San Marino	8·00	7·25

485 St. Martin tearing Cloak in Half

1999. 50th Anniv of San Marino Red Cross.

1741	**485** 800l. multicoloured	1·40	1·10

486 Team Photograph (Italian championship, 1901)

1999. Centenary of A. C. Milan Football Club. Sheet 155×115 mm containing T 486 and similar horiz designs. Multicoloured.

MS1742	800l. Type **486**; 800l. Players Gren, Nordahl and Liedholm, 1950s; 800l. Team photograph, Wembley (goalkeeper in front row) (European Championship, 1963); 800l. Team photograph, Vienna (goalkeeper in back row), 1990; 800l. Team and children celebrating Italian Championship, 1994; 800l. Team with trophy (Italian Championship, 1999)	7·25	7·25

487 Nativity

1999. Christmas.

1743	**487** 800l. multicoloured	1·40	1·10

488 18/50 h.p. Horch

1999. Centenary of Audi (car manufacturer). Sheet 155×115 mm containing T 488 and similar horiz designs. Multicoloured.

MS1744	1500l. Type **488**; 1500l. Audi TT; 1500l. Audi A8; 1500l. Auto Union racing car	7·75	7·75

489 Tank, Soldiers and Civilians (First and Second World Wars)

2000. The Twentieth Century. Multicoloured.

1745	650l. Type **489**	70	70
1746	650l. Syringe being filled, scanner and DNA molecular structure (science and medicine)	70	70
1747	650l. Washing machine, underground train and lamp (electricity)	70	70
1748	650l. Switchboard operators, radio and computer (telecommunications)	70	70
1749	650l. Wright *Flyer*, Boeing 727 airship and astronaut on Moon (conquest of space)	70	70
1750	650l. Factory chimneys and rubbish (pollution)	70	70
1751	650l. Sports car, lorry and traffic jam (development of motor vehicles)	70	70
1752	650l. Submarine and mushroom cloud (atomic energy)	70	70
1753	650l. Charlie Chaplin in *Modern Times*, comic strip and chair (cinema, comics and design)	70	70
1754	650l. Crossword puzzle, art gallery and car towing caravan (leisure activities)	70	70
1755	650l. Advertising posters (publicity)	70	70
1756	650l. Cyclist, stadium and footballers (sport)	70	70

490 St. John Lateran Basilica, Rome, Pilgrim (detail of engraving by G. Perugino) and Mt. Titano

2000. Holy Year 2000. Sheet 155×115 mm containing T 490 and similar horiz designs. Multicoloured.

MS1757	1000l. Type **490**; 1000l. St. Paul without the Walls Basilica, Rome, St. Marinus (statue) and La Rocca fortress; 1000l. St. Mary Major Basilica, Rome, with Madonna and Child; 1000l. St. Peter's Basilica, Rome, and St. Marinus (detail of painting by Pompeo Batoni)	5·50	5·50

491 Emblem and La Rocca Fortress

2000. 40th Anniv of San Marino Rotary Club. Mult.

1758	650l. Type **491**	1·00	80
1759	800l. Government Palace, Arms and Statue of Liberty, San Marino	1·20	1·00

492 I.I.S.A. Emblem, Government Palace, Fiera di Bologna Towers and Statue of Liberty, San Marino

2000. International Institute of Administrative Science Conference, Bologna (1760) and European City of Culture (others). Multicoloured.

1760	650l. Type **492**	85	80
1761	800l. Guglielmo Marconi's workbench, radio aerial, San Pietro Cathedral, clock tower, Tubertini dome and St. Petronius Basilica	1·10	95
1762	1200l. Microchip, musical instruments, St. Petronius Basilica, Santa Maria della Vita Church and Asinelli and Garisenda Towers	1·60	1·40
1763	1500l. Books, detail of still life by Giorgio Morandi, campanile and apse of St. Giacomo Maggiore and St. Francis Churches and Arengo Tower	2·10	1·90

493 Vincenzo Muccioli (founder of San Patrignano Community) and Drug Addict

2000. 5th Anniv of Rainbow International Association Against Drugs. Multicoloured.

1764	650l. Type **493**	90	80
1765	1200l. Blocks spelling "rainbow" in sky	1·70	1·40
1766	2400l. Muccioli and reformed addicts	3·50	3·00

494 "Building Europe"

2000. Europa.

1767	**494** 800l. multicoloured	1·40	1·10

495 "2000"

2000. "Stampin' the Future". Winning Entries in Children's International Painting Competition.

1768	**495** 800l. multicoloured	1·10	95

496 Dog and Butterfly

2000. Olympic Games, Sydney. Multicoloured.

1769	1000l. Type **496**	1·10	1·10
1770	1000l. Hippopotamus and penguin	1·10	1·10
1771	1000l. Elephant and ladybird	1·10	1·10
1772	1000l. Rabbit and snail	1·10	1·10

497 Bicycles

2000. Centenary of International Cycling Union.

1773	**497** 1200l. multicoloured	1·70	1·30

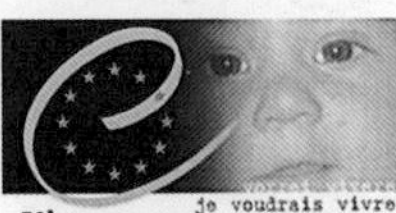

498 Child hiding beneath Soldier's Helmet

2000. 10th Anniv of International Convention on Children's Rights. Multicoloured.

1774	650l. Type **498**	90	80
1775	800l. Child cowering away from frightening shadow	1·10	95
1776	1200l. Child in flower	1·60	1·40
1777	1500l. Childhood fantasies tumbling from book	2·00	1·80

499 Council Emblem and child's face

2000. 50th Anniv of the European Convention on Human Rights.

1778	**499** 800l. multicoloured	1·10	90

500 Basilica of the Saint

2000. Churches of Montefeltro. Multicoloured.

1779	650l. Type **500**	90	80
1780	800l. Church of St. Mary of Antico, Maiolo	1·10	95
1781	1000l. St. Lawrence's Church, Talamello	1·30	1·20
1782	1500l. Parish Church, San Leo	2·00	1·70
1783	1800l. Sanctuary of Our Lady of Graces, Pennabilli	2·40	2·10

501 "Virgin and Child" (Ludovico Carracci)

2000. Christmas.

1784	**501** 800l. multicoloured	4·50	2·20

502 Melchiorre Delfico (author of *History of the Republic of San Marino*) and Title Page

2000. 1700th Anniv of San Marino (1st issue). Multicoloured.

1785	800l. Type **502**	1·00	1·00
1786	800l. Guiseppe Garibaldi (painting)	1·00	1·00
1787	800l. Abraham Lincoln and passage from his letter to the Captains Regent, 1861	1·00	1·00
1788	800l. Refugees arriving in San Marino, 1943–45	1·00	1·00
1789	800l. Roman jewels	1·00	1·00
1790	800l. 1463 map of San Marino	1·00	1·00
1791	800l. Napoleon Bonaparte	1·00	1·00
1792	800l. "L'Arengo" (detail) (postcard, 1906)	1·00	1·00
1793	800l. Child, class and swimming pool	1·00	1·00
1794	800l. Young man, construction site and computers	1·00	1·00
1795	800l. Woman, street scene and church	1·00	1·00
1796	800l. Man, dancers and building	1·00	1·00
1797	1200l. St. Marinus (detail) (Francesco Manzocchi di Forl)	1·40	1·40
1798	1200l.15 th-century painting of St. Marinus	1·40	1·40
1799	1200l. St. Marinus (painting, School of Guercino)	1·40	1·40
1800	1200l. "St. Marinus in glory" (anon)	1·40	1·40
1801	1200l. Double throne of Captains Regent	1·40	1·40
1802	1200l. Title page of 17th-century edition of Republican Statutes	1·40	1·40
1803	1200l. Parade of Palace guards	1·40	1·40
1804	1200l. Flags	1·40	1·40

See also Nos. 1846/9.

503 Michael Schumacher and Ferrari Racing Car

2001. Michael Schumacher Drivers' Champion and Ferrari. Constructors' Champion (2000). Sheet 110×75 mm containing T 503 and similar horiz designs. Multicoloured.

MS1805	1500l. Type **503**; 1500l. Schumacher, racing car and engineers	5·00	5·00

504 Verdi and Scene from *Nabucco*

2001. Death Centenary of Guiseppe Verdi (composer). Scenes from named operas. Multicoloured.

1806	800l. Type **504**	80	80
1807	800l. *Ernani*	80	80

1808	800l. *Rigoletto*	80	80
1809	800l. *Il Trovatore*	80	80
1810	800l. *La Traviata*	80	80
1811	800l. *I Vespri Siciliani*	80	80
1812	800l. *Un Ballo in Maschera*	80	80
1813	800l. *La Forza del Destino*	80	80
1814	800l. *Don Carlos*	80	80
1815	800l. *Aida*	80	80
1816	800l. *Otello*	80	80
1817	800l. *Falstaff*	80	80

505 Malatestian Temple (by Leon Battista Alberti), Rimini

2001. Commemoration of Malatesta Family (Lords of Rimini). Multicoloured.

1818	800l. Type **505**	1·10	95
1819	1200l. "Christ's Devotion" (Giovanni Bellini)	1·70	1·40

506 Yacht

2001. 10th Anniv of "San Marino 24 Hour Yacht Race". Multicoloured.

1820	1200l. Type **506**	1·40	1·40
1821	1200l. Yacht with green and purple spinnaker	1·40	1·40
1822	1200l. Yacht with brown and white sails	1·40	1·40
1823	1200l. Yacht with white spinnaker	1·40	1·40

507 Bowls and Athletics

2001. 9th European Small States Games. Multicoloured.

1824	800l. Type **507**	95	95
1825	800l. Swimming	95	95
1826	800l. Cycling	95	95
1827	800l. Target and skeet shooting	95	95
1828	800l. Judo	95	95
1829	800l. Tennis and table tennis	95	95
1830	800l. Basketball and volleyball	95	95
1831	800l. RASTA (mascot)	95	95

508 Safe containing Water and Forest

2001. Europa. Water Resources. Multicoloured.

1832	800l. Type **508**	1·40	1·10
1833	1200l. Mountain, tap and running water	2·20	1·70

509 *Santa Maria* and *Dahlia variablis*

2001. "Euroflora 2001" International Flower Show, Genoa. Multicoloured.

1834	800l. Type **509**	1·10	95
1835	1200l. *Santa Maria* and *Zantedeschia aethiopica*	2·00	1·40
1836	1500l. *Santa Maria* and rose "Helen Troubel"	1·90	1·90
1837	2400l. Faro Tower, Genoa and *Amaryllis hippeastrum*	3·00	3·00

510 Ellis Island Immigration Museum, New York

2001. "Emigration of the Sammarinese" Exhibition, New York and 25th Anniv of San Marino Social Club, Detroit. Multicoloured.

1838	1200l. Type **510**	1·70	1·40
1839	2400l. San Marino Social Club, Detroit	4·00	3·00

511 Early Stringed Instrument and Ceramics

2001. Inauguration of State Museum. Multicoloured.

1840	550l. Type **511**	55	55
1841	800l. Painting and gallery	90	90
1842	1500l. Ancient ceramics	1·70	1·70
1843	2000l. European artifacts	2·20	2·20

512 Figure reaching Downwards

2001. 50th Anniv of United Nations High Commissioner for Refugees. Multicoloured.

1844	1200l. Type **512**	1·40	1·40
1845	1200l. Figure reaching upwards	1·40	1·40

Nos. 1844/5 were issued together, se-tenant, forming a composite design.

513 Mount Titan

2001. 1700th Anniv of San Marino (2nd issue). Scenes of Mount Titan. Multicoloured.

1846	1200l. Type **513**	1·40	1·40
1847	1200l. Three Towers, Mount Titan	1·40	1·40
1848	1200l. Fields below Mount Titan	1·40	1·40
1849	1200l. Urban infrastructure below Mount Titan	1·40	1·40

514 Old Bakery Mill Silo and Woman surrounded by People

2001. 125th Anniv of San Marino Social Welfare Union (S.U.M.S.). Multicoloured.

1850	1200l. Type **514**	1·40	1·30
1851	1200l. New Bakery Mill Silo headquarters and woman giving sheaves of corn to crowd	1·40	1·30

515 Banner

2001. "Defence of Nature" Exhibition of Works by Joseph Beuys (artist), San Marino.

1852	**515**	2400l. multicoloured	4·00	2·50

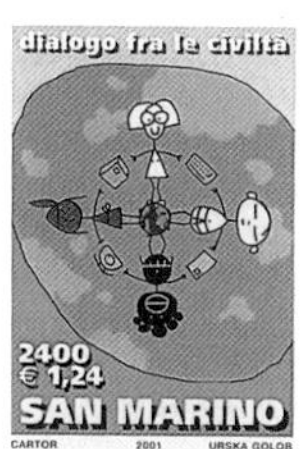

516 Children encircling Globe

2001. United Nations Year of Dialogue among Civilizations.

1853	**516**	2400l. multicoloured	4·00	2·50

517 Angel playing Lute

2001. Christmas. Multicoloured.

1854	800l. Type **517**	1·20	1·00
1855	800l. Woman with basket and king riding on camel	1·20	1·00
1856	800l. King riding camel, woman leading sheep, and woman with parcel	1·20	1·00
1857	800l. Man with parcel and Holy Family on Mount Titano	1·20	1·00
1858	800l. Sheep, birds and man with lantern	1·20	1·00
1859	800l. Ascending angel with trumpet	1·20	1·00
1860	800l. Angel with lyre	1·20	1·00
1861	800l. King with blue crown riding camel	1·20	1·00
1862	800l. Women with parcel, basket and dog	1·20	1·00
1863	800l. Shepherd and sheep	1·20	1·00
1864	800l. Descending angel with trumpet	1·20	1·00
1865	800l. Woman with parcel and angel with trumpet	1·20	1·00
1866	800l. Angel playing violin	1·20	1·00
1867	800l. Man with parcels on sledge	1·20	1·00
1868	800l. Woman with parcel in right hand	1·20	1·00
1869	800l. Angel playing drum	1·20	1·00

Nos. 1854/69 were issued together, se-tenant, forming a composite design.

518 Coins and Map of Euro Zone

2001. Introduction of Euro Coins and Banknotes (2002). Multicoloured.

1870	1200l. Type **518**	1·70	1·30
1871	2400l. Banknotes and map of Euro Zone	3·50	2·50

519 Rabbits

2002. New Currency. Multicoloured.

1872	1c. Type **519**	10	10
1873	2c. Sunset	10	10
1874	5c. Cactus flower	10	10
1875	10c. Field of grain	30	15
1876	25c. Alpine landscape	70	50
1877	50c. Olive leaves	1·40	1·10

1878	€1 Sparrows	2·75	2·20
1879	€5 Baby	13·50	10·50

520 Hippopotamus Ice Skating

2002. Winter Olympic Games, Salt Lake City. Multicoloured.

1885	41c. Type **520**	1·00	1·00
1886	41c. Dog skiing	1·00	1·00
1887	41c. Elephant playing ice hockey	1·00	1·00
1888	41c. Rabbit cross-country skiing	1·00	1·00

521 Poggiali racing

2002. Manuel Poggiali—2001 125cc. Motorcycle World Champion. Multicoloured.

1889	62c. Type **521**	1·50	1·30
1890	62c. Side view of Poggiali racing	1·50	1·30

522 Trapeze Artist

2002. Europa. Circus. Multicoloured.

1891	36c. Type **522**	8·00	4·50
1892	62c. Equestrienne performer	14·00	7·00

523 Players and Ball (finals, 1934)

2002. World Cup Football Championship, Japan and South Korea. Winning Italian Teams. Sheet 155×116 mm, containing T 523 and similar horiz designs. Multicoloured.

MS1893	41c. Type **523** (score wrongly inscr as 4-2); 41c. Player heading ball (finals, 1938) (score wrongly inscr as 1-0); 41c. Players jumping (semi-finals, 1970); 41c. Italy and Brazil players at goal mouth (finals, 1982); 41c. Player tackling (third-place playoff, 1990); 41c. Italy and Nigeria (No 10 players at goal (second round, 1994))	7·00	7·00

524 Cyclist

2002. Priority Mail Stamps. Multicoloured.

1894	62c. Type **524**	2·10	1·30
1895	€1.24 Hurdler	4·00	2·75

525 Three Towers, Mount Titano

2002. International Year of Mountains. Mult.

1896	41c. Type **525**	1·00	85
1897	41c. Tower and wall on Mount Titano	1·00	85
1898	41c. Tower on peak	1·00	85

526 Map of Europe as Tree

2002. 10th Anniv of Maastricht Treaty.

1899	**526**	€1.24 multicoloured	3·50	2·75

€1,24
125° anniversario del 1° francobollo di
SAN MARINO

527 1877 2c. and 10c. Stamps

2002. 125th Anniv of First San Marino Stamps. Sheet 140×71 mm, containing T 527 and similar square designs depicting stamps (issued in 1877). Multicoloured.

MS1900 €1.24, Type **527**; €1.24, 10c. and 20c. stamps; €1.24, 20c. and 30c. stamps; €1.24, 30c. and 40c. stamps 13·50 13·50

528 Blacksmith working at Anvil

2002. Traditional Crafts. Multicoloured.

1901	26c. Type **528**	70	60
1902	36c. Broom-maker tying grass bundle	90	80
1903	41c. Chair-mender repairing chair seat	1·00	90
1904	77c. Scribe writing at table	2·20	1·70
1905	€1.24 Knife-grinder sharpening knife at wheel	3·75	3·00
1906	€1.55 Charcoal burner and wood clamp	5·25	3·50

529 Emblems, World Map, Aerial and Morse Code Notation

2002. International Amateur Radio Union Region 1 Conference. Multicoloured.

1907	36c. Type **529**	1·00	80
1908	62c. Emblems, national flag, world map, aerial and Morse code notation	2·10	1·50

530 Government Palace

2002. Tourism. Sheet 150×116 mm, containing T 530 and similar multicoloured designs showing places of interest.

MS1909 62c. Type **530**; 62c. Guaita (First Tower), Mount Titan (44×30 mm); 62c. Cesta (Second Tower) and Montale (Third Tower), Mount Titan (44×30 mm); 62c. Basilicia del Santo and San Pietro Church; 62c. Capuchin Church; 62c. St. Francis gate (39×39 mm) 11·00 9·25

531 Woman's Mouth

2002. Greetings Stamps. Multicoloured.

1910	41c. Type **531**	1·30	90
1911	41c. Child's face and "Hello"	1·30	90
1912	41c. Man's face and "best wishes"	1·30	90
1913	41c. Baby's face and "Ehi"	1·30	90
1914	41c. Man's perplexed face	1·30	90
1915	41c. Hand covering smiling face and "sorry"	1·30	90

532 Child's and Adults Hands

2002. Christmas. Sheet 185×144 mm, containing T 532 and similar vert designs. Multicoloured.

MS1916 41c. Type **532**; 41c. Mother wearing earrings and baby; 41c. Baby at breast; 41c. Mother and baby sleeping; 41c. Adult hands holding baby; 41c. Mother and baby wrapped in shawl; 41c. Wakeful baby against mother's left shoulder; 41c. Baby with finger in mouth laughing with mother; 41c. Baby asleep against mother's left shoulder; 41c. Baby looking away from smiling mother; 41c. Baby with arm extended towards mother's face; 41c. Two babies 15·00 12·50

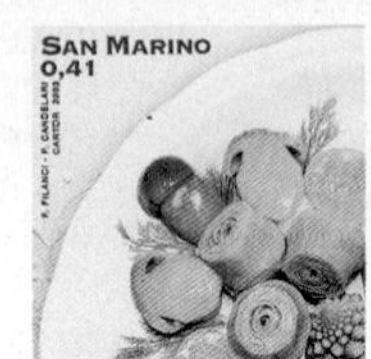

533 Mushrooms and Artichokes

2003. Italian Cuisine. Multicoloured.

1917	41c. Type **533**	1·20	90
1918	41c. Cooked meats	1·20	90
1919	41c. Spaghetti	1·20	90
1920	41c. Cappelletti	1·20	90
1921	41c. Prawns	1·20	90
1922	41c. Mixed seafood	1·20	90
1923	41c. Ravioli	1·20	90
1924	41c. Tagliatelle	1·20	90
1925	41c. Chicken and potatoes	1·20	90
1926	41c. Fish	1·20	90
1927	41c. Fruit tart	1·20	90
1928	41c. Chocolate pudding	1·20	90
1929	41c. Scrambled eggs	1·20	90
1930	41c. Pancetta	1·20	90
1931	41c. Pastries	1·20	90
1932	41c. Brandy snap basket	1·20	90

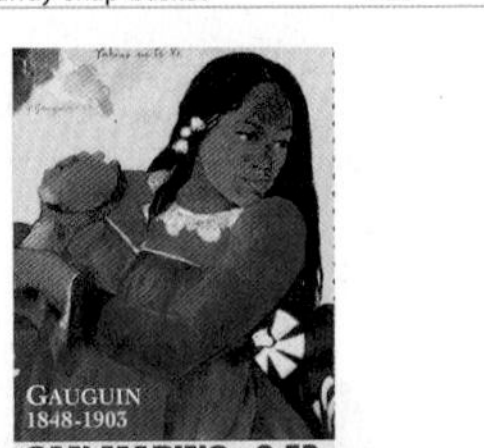

534 "Woman with Mango" (Paul Gauguin)

2003. Artists' Anniversaries. Multicoloured.

1933	52c. Type **534** (death centenary)	1·40	1·40
1934	62c. "Wheat-field with flight of crows" (Vincent Van Gogh) (150th birth anniv)	1·60	1·50
1935	€1.55 "Portrait of a young woman" (Parmigianino) (500th birth anniv)	4·25	4·00

535 Combination Skiing

2003. World Nordic Skiing Championship, Val di Femme. Sheet 156×116 mm containing T 535 and similar vert designs. Multicoloured.

MS1936 Type **535**; 77c. Ski jumping; 77c. Cross-country skiing 6·50 6·00

536 Molvedo (horse)

2003. Horse Racing. Showing champion race horses. Multicoloured.

1937	11c. Type **536**	25	25
1938	15c. Tornese	40	40
1939	26c. Ribot	65	65
1940	€1.55 Varenne	4·25	4·25

537 Partially submerged Woman's Head (Armando Testa)

2003. Europa. Poster Art. Multicoloured.

1941	28c. Type **537**	4·00	4·00
1942	77c. "Jane Avril" (Toulouse Latrec)	10·50	10·50

538 Girolamo Fracastoro

2003. 550th Death Anniv of Girolamo Fracastoro (writer and scientist) Centenary of Veronafil Exhibition.

1943	**538**	77c. multicoloured	2·10	2·10

539 Bridge over Winter Canal

2003. 300th Anniv of St. Petersburg. Multicoloured.

1944	15c. Type **539**	40	40
1945	26c. Bartolomeo Francesco Rastrelli (architect)	65	65
1946	36c. Trinity bridge over River Neva	95	95
1947	41c. Aleksander Sergeyevich Pushkin (writer)	1·10	1·10
1948	77c. Queen Catherine II	2·10	2·10
1949	€1.55 Tsar Peter I	4·00	4·00

540 Wright *Flyer I*

2003. Centenary of Powered Flight. Multicoloured.

1950	36c. Type **540**	95	95
1951	41c. Bleriot XI	1·10	1·10
1952	62c. Aermacchi MB339	1·70	1·70
1953	77c. Aermacchi MB339s of Frecce Tricolori (Italian acrobatic flying team)	2·10	2·10

541 Stagecoach on Road

2003. 120th Anniv of First Daily Mail Coach between Rimini and San Marino. Multicoloured.

1954	41c. Type **541**	1·10	1·10
1955	77c. Stagecoach in town	2·10	2·10

542 Chain Wheel (Tour de France)

2003. Centenary of Tour de France Cycle Race. Hamilton 2003 World Championship Road Race, Hamilton, Canada. Sheet 155×115 mm containing T 542 and similar circular design. Multicoloured.

MS1956 77c. Type **542**; 77c. Front wheel (Hamilton 2003) 4·25 4·25

543 Go-Carting

2003. Children's Games. Multicoloured.

1957	36c. Type **543**	95	95
1958	41c. Blind man's buff	1·10	1·10
1959	62c. Hoops	1·70	1·70
1960	77c. Marbles	2·10	2·10
1961	€1.24 Dance	3·25	3·25
1962	€1.55 Tug-of-war	4·00	4·00

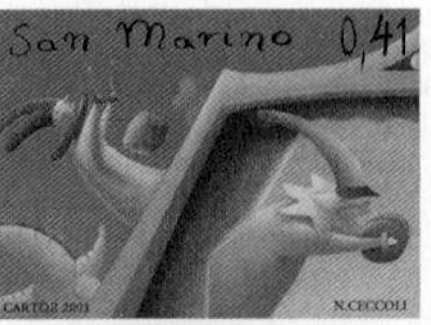

544 Masked Puppet

2003. Puppetry. Multicoloured.

1963	41c. Type **544**	1·10	1·10
1964	41c. Blowing trumpet	1·10	1·10
1965	41c. Male puppet offering flower to female	1·10	1·10
1966	41c. Two puppets with sticks	1·10	1·10

Nos. 1963/6 were issued together, se-tenant, forming a composite design of a puppet theatre.

545 Two Players and Ball

2003. Rugby World Cup Championship, Australia. Multicoloured.

1967	41c. Type **545**	1·10	1·10
1968	62c. Player about to throw ball	1·70	1·70
1969	77c. Two players fighting for possession	2·10	2·10
1970	€1.55 Player with ball	4·00	4·00

546 Angel

2003. Christmas. Sheet 186×143 mm containing T **546** and similar horiz designs. Multicoloured.

MS1971 41c. ×16, Type **546** (1/2); Shepherds and three kings (3/4); Holy family (5/6); Christmas cards (7/8); Decorated tree (9); Filled stocking (10); Wreath (11/12); Child and snowman (13/14); Father Christmas (15/16); Children and toys (17/18); Toys (19); Angels singing (20/21); Children and cake (22); Girl and games (23); Cornucopia (24); San Marino arms (25) 17·00 17·00

MS1971 was arranged in the shape of a snakes and ladders board, with seven stamps (1/2; 3/4; 5/6; 7/8; 20/21; 22; 23) reversed and two (9; 10) at right angles. The numbers on the board are given in brackets.

547 Theatre Emblem

2003. Reopening of La Fenice Theatre, Venice.

1972	**547**	$3.72 multicoloured	10·00	10·00

548 "Ballet" (Edgar Degas) and Tango Dancers

2004. 50th Anniv of Latin Union (inter-government organization). Multicoloured.

1973	41c. Type **548**	1·10	1·10
1974	77c. "Don Quixote" (Miguel De Cervantes) and "Donna Flor and her Two Husbands" (Jorge Amado)	2·10	2·10
1975	€1.55 "Susanna and the Elders" (Tintoretto) and "Sunday Afternoon" (Fernando Botero)	4·00	4·00

549 Building Facade and Coloured Spheres

2004. Venice Carnival. Multicoloured.

1976	77c. Type **549**	2·10	2·10
1977	€1.55 Masked woman	4·00	4·00

550 Manuel Poggiali

2004. Manuel Poggiali—2003 250cc. Motorcycle World Champion.

1978	**550**	€1.55 multicoloured	4·00	4·00

See also 1889/90.

551 Bonsai Tree

2004. 20th European Bonsai Association Convention, San Marino.

1979	45c. Type **551**	1·20	1·20
1980	60c. Bonsai (different)	1·60	1·60

552 Government Palace, San Marino and Tian-An-Men Palace, China

2004. 55th Anniv of People's Republic of China. Sheet 180×166 mm containing T **552** and similar horiz designs. Multicoloured.

MS1981 80c. ×3, Type **552**; San Marino mountain and Great Wall, China; Temple of Heaven Pagoda, China and San Marino Tower 6·25 6·25

553 Emblem

2004. Centenary of FIFA (Federation Internationale de Football Association).

1982	**553**	€2.80 multicoloured	7·25	7·25

554 "Autoshipplane"

2004. Europa. Tourism. Multicoloured.

1983	45c. Type **554**	1·30	1·30
1984	80c. "Boatcampertrainbus" (horiz)	2·75	2·75

555 Chariot Racing, Boxers and Javelin Thrower

2004. Olympic Games 2004, Athens. Multicoloured.

1985	90c. Type **555**	2·40	2·40
1986	90c. Runner, discus thrower and wrestlers	2·40	2·40
1987	90c. Relay runner, cyclist and golfer	2·40	2·40
1988	90c. Racquet player, weightlifter and gymnasts	2·40	2·40

Nos. 1985/8 were issued together, se-tenant, forming a composite design.

556 Volkswagen Golf

2004. 50th Anniv of Volkswagen (car manufacturers). Multicoloured.

1989	€1.50 Type **556** (30th anniv of Golf)	4·00	4·00
1990	€1.50 Early and modern Beetles ("50" upright)	4·00	4·00
1991	€1.50 Early and modern Beetles ("50" diagonal)	4·00	4·00
1992	€1.50 Golf (different)	4·00	4·00

557 *Hansel and Gretel* (Jakob and Wilhelm Grimm)

2004. Fairytales.

1993	45c. Type **557**	1·20	1·20
1994	60c. *Little Red Riding Hood* (Jakob and Wilhelm Grimm)	1·60	1·60
1995	80c. *Pinocchio* (Carlo Collodi)	2·10	2·10
1996	€1 *Puss in Boots* (Charles Perrault)	2·75	2·75

558 Francesco Petrarca (Petrarch)

2004. Writers' Anniversaries. Multicoloured.

1997	45c. Type **558** (700th birth anniv)	1·20	1·20
1998	€1.50 Oscar Wilde (150th birth anniv)	4·00	4·00
1999	€2.20 Anton Chekov (death centenary)	5·75	5·75

559 Manuel de Nobrega and Josa Anchieta (founders)

2004. 450th Anniv of Founding of San Paulo, Brazil. Multicoloured.

2000	60c. Type **559**	1·60	1·60
2001	80c. Mario Andrade and Antonio Machado (writers)	2·10	2·10
2002	€1.40 Modern San Paulo and Imaculada Conceicao da Luz monastery	3·75	3·75

560 Three Men

2004. 25th Meeting for Friendship Among Peoples, Rimini, Italy (Meeting Rimini). Sheet 155×115 mm containing T **560** and similar horiz designs. Multicoloured.

MS2003 €1 ×4 Type **560**; Two women and child; Family; Priests 10·50 10·50

The stamps and margin of No.**MS**2003 form a composite design.

561 "Rebecca at the Well" (Giovanni Battista Piazzetta)

2004. Artists' Anniversaries. Multicoloured.

2004	45c. Type **561** (250th death anniv)	1·20	1·20
2005	€1.40 "Piazza Navona" (Scipione Gino Bonichi) (birth centenary)	3·75	3·75
2006	€1.70 "The Persistence of Memory" (Salvador Dali) (birth centenary)	4·50	4·50

562 Cherubs and Musical Instruments

2004. Christmas. Designs showing cherubs. Multicoloured.

2007	60c. Type **562**	1·60	1·60
2008	60c. Holding bag of presents	1·60	1·60
2009	60c. Carrying Christmas tree	1·60	1·60
2010	60c. Holding cornucopia	1·60	1·60

563 Antonio Salieri and 18th-century Auditorium

2004. Re-opening of La Scala Theatre, Milan. Sheet 132×172 mm containing T **563** and similar horiz designs. Multicoloured.

MS2011 $1.50×3, Type **563**; 19th-century and modern theatre building facade; Ricardo Muti and modern auditorium 12·00 12·00

The stamps of No.**MS**2011 merge with the score of "Europa riconosciuta" (opera by Antonio Salieri) in the margin to form a composite design.

564 Manuel Fangio (1956)

2005. Ferrari—World Champion Racing Team. Showing World Champions and their cars. Multicoloured.

2012	1c. Type **564**	15	15
2013	4c. Niki Lauda (1975–77)	15	15
2014	5c. John Surtees (1964)	15	15
2015	45c. Michael Schumacher (2000–04)	1·20	1·20
2016	62c. Race car	1·70	1·70
2017	€1.50 Alberto Ascari (1952–3)	4·00	4·00

565 Carrying wounded Man

2005. Beatification of Alberto Marvelli. Multicoloured.

2018	90c. Type **565**	2·40	2·40
2019	€1.80 Pope John Paul II and Alberto Marvelli	4·75	4·75

566 "In the Hollow of a Wave off the Coast at Kanagawa" (Hokusai Katsushika) and Faces of Victims

2005. Support For Victims of the Tsunami Disaster.

2020	**566**	€1.50 multicoloured	4·00	4·00

567 Weightlifter

2005. Centenary of International Weightlifting Federation.

2021	**567**	€2.20 multicoloured	5·75	5·75

568 Soldier scaling Cliff

2005. Alpine Troops. Multicoloured.

2022	36c. Type **568**	1·10	1·10
2023	45c. Soldier picking flower	1·20	1·20
2024	62c. Soldier, mother and child	1·70	1·70
2025	€1 Map of faces	2·75	2·75

569 NCO and Third Tower

2005. Militia. Showing militia men. Multicoloured.

2026	36c. Type **569**	1·10	1·10
2027	45c. Dress uniform and Second Tower	1·20	1·20
2028	62c. Standard bearer and Palazzo Pubblico	1·70	1·70
2029	€1.50 Two militia men and First Tower	4·00	4·00

570 Bread

2005. Europa. Gastronomy. Multicoloured.

2030	62c. Type **570**	1·70	1·70
2031	€1.20 Wine	3·25	3·25

571 Ship, Courier, Letter and Train

2005. History of the Letter. Multicoloured.

2032	36c. Type **571**	1·10	1·10
2033	45c. Man reading letter	1·20	1·20
2034	60c. Three men	1·60	1·60
2035	62c. Man and woman	1·70	1·70

572 1864 5 cent Coin

2005. Coins. Multicoloured.

2036	36c. Type **572**	1·10	1·10
2037	45c. 1898 5 lira coin	1·20	1·20
2038	€1.10 and 20 lira gold coins	2·75	2·75
2039	€2.20 Modern euro coins	5·75	5·75

573 Erminio Macario

2005. Variety Performers. Multicoloured.

2040	45c. Type **573**	1·20	1·20
2041	45c. Wanda Osiris	1·20	1·20
2042	45c. Toto	1·20	1·20
2043	45c. Anna Magnani	1·20	1·20
2044	45c. Aldo Fabrizi	1·20	1·20
2045	45c. Renato Rascel	1·20	1·20
2046	45c. Nino Taranto	1·20	1·20
2047	45c. Delia Scala	1·20	1·20
2048	45c. Tino Scotti	1·20	1·20
2049	45c. Carlo Dapporto	1·20	1·20

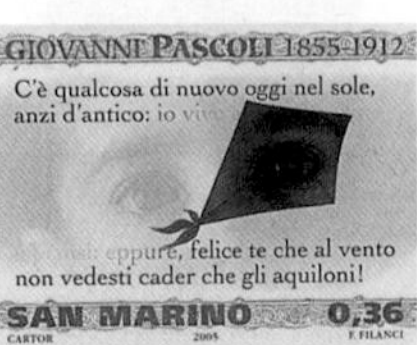

574 Face and Kite

2005. 150th Birth Anniv of Giovanni Pascoli (writer). Multicoloured.

2050	36c. Type **574**	1·10	1·10
2051	45c. Mount Titan	1·20	1·20
2052	€1 Family home and horse	2·75	2·75
2053	€2 Tower and Giovanni Pascoli	5·25	5·25

575 Ferrari Wine Label

2005. Wine. Designs showing wine labels. Multicoloured.

2054	45c. Type **575**	1·20	1·20
2055	45c. Amarone della Valpolicella	1·20	1·20
2056	45c. Canevel	1·20	1·20
2057	45c. Biondi-Santi	1·20	1·20
2058	45c. Vecchioflorio	1·20	1·20
2059	45c. Verdicchio dei Castellidijesi	1·20	1·20
2060	45c. Sassicaia (vert)	1·20	1·20
2061	45c. Piano di Monte Vergine dei Feudi di San Gregorio (vert)	1·20	1·20
2062	45c. Tocai Friulano (vert)	1·20	1·20
2063	45c. Barolo (vert)	1·20	1·20

576 Devil and Angel as Gondoliers

2005. Venice Regatta. Multicoloured.

2064	€1.40 Type **576**	3·75	3·75
2065	€2 Gondolier wearing traditional costume (vert)	5·25	5·25

577 Dahlia

2005. Self-adhesive.

2066	**577**	(20g.) multicoloured	1·20	1·20

578 Panel, St. John the Baptist (Lorenzo Ghiberti) (550th death anniv)

2005. Anniversaries. Multicoloured.

2067	36c. Type **578**	95	95
2068	62c. "The Annunciation" (Beato Angelico) (550th death anniv)	1·70	1·70
2069	€1 Jules Verne and illustrations (writer) (death centenary)	2·75	2·75
2070	€2 Hans Christian Andersen and illustrations (writer) (birth bicentenary)	3·50	3·50

579 The Annunciation

2005. Christmas. Multicoloured.

2071	62c. Type **579**	1·70	1·70
2072	€1.55 The Nativity	4·25	4·25
2073	€2.20 Three Wise Men	6·00	6·00

580 Pope Clement XIV

2005. 300th Birth Anniv of Pope Clement XIV. Multicoloured.

2074	80c. Type **580**	2·10	2·10
2075	€1 Pope Clement XIV facing left	2·75	2·75

581 Ski Jump, Snow Board and Flags

2006. Winter Olympic Games, Turin. Multicoloured.

2076	45c. Type **581**	1·20	1·20
2077	45c. Ski run, village and flags	1·20	1·20
2078	45c. Cross-country skiing, bob-sleigh, ice hockey and finish line	1·20	1·20
2079	45c. Ice skating, cross-country skiing and chair lift	1·20	1·20

Nos. 2076/9 were issued together, se-tenant, forming a composite design.

582 Palazzo Pubblico

2006. Centenary of Arengo of Patriarchs (first governing body). Multicoloured.

2080	45c. Type **582**	1·20	1·20
2081	62c. Statue of Liberty, Piazza della Liberta	1·70	1·70
2082	€1.50 Basilica Del Santo Marino	4·00	4·00

583 Christopher Columbus and Native American

2006. 500th Death Anniv of Christopher Columbus (explorer). Multicoloured.

2083	90c. Type **583**	2·40	2·40
2084	€1.80 Holding globe and compasses	4·75	4·75

584 Palazzo Mentcitorio, Rome and Palazzo Pubblico, San Marino

2006. Le Due Repubbliche (two republics) Philatelic Exhibition. Sheet 121×90 mm containing T 584 and similar horiz design. Multicoloured.

MS2085	62c.×2, Type **584**; Type **1365** of Italy	33·00	33·00

No. **MS**2085 is identical to **MS**3011 of Italy. Nos. **MS**2085 of San Marino and Nos. 3010/**MS**3011 of Italy were all issued on the same day.

585 "Bathers" (Paul Cezanne)

2006. Art. Multicoloured.

2086	36c. Type **585**	1·10	1·10
2087	45c. "Bathsheba with Letter from David" (Rembrandt)	1·20	1·20
2088	60c. "Coronation of the Virgin" (Gentile da Fabriano)	1·60	1·60
2089	€1.80 "The Room of Spouses" (Andrea Mantegna)	4·75	4·75

586 Emblem, Flag and Ball

2006. World Cup Football Championship, Germany.

2090	**586**	€2.20 multicoloured	5·75	5·75

587 Flag Throwers

2006. 50th Anniv of Crossbow Federation. Multicoloured.

2091	36c. Type **587**	95	95
2092	45c. Standard bearers	1·20	1·20
2093	62c. Archer preparing to shoot	1·70	1·70
2094	€1 Two archers positioning arrows	2·75	2·75
2095	€1.50 Three flag throwers	4·00	4·00
2096	€2.80 Arms master holding target full of arrows	7·50	7·50

588 Butterfly (Sara Santolini)

2006. Europa. Integration. Multicoloured.
2097 45c. Type **588** 1·20 1·20
2098 62c. Vitruvian man (after Leonardo da Vinci) (Marco Moliari and Clementina Casadei) 1·70 1·70

589 Doctor and Child

2006. Military Order of Malta.
2099 €2.20 multicoloured 5·75 5·75

590 Hand in Ring

2006. 125th Anniv of International Gymnastic Federation. Multicoloured.
2100 15c. Type **590** 40 40
2101 €2.80 Gymnast 7·50 7·50

591 Second Tower

2006. 40th Anniv of Italian Philatelic Press Union. Multicoloured.
2102 90c. Type **591** 2·40 2·40
2103 €2.20 Archway, Palazzo Strozzi and "Gli Amanti" (sculpture) (Giacomo Maria Cavina) 5·75 5·75

592 Grandmother's Face

2006. Italy—2006 Football World Cup Champions.
2104 **592** €1 multicoloured 2·75 2·75

593 Scene from "Rome Open City" (film)

2006. Anniversaries. Multicoloured.
2105 5c. Type **593** (Roberto Rosellini (director) (birth centenary)) 25 25
2106 65c. Top hat (Luchino Visconti (director) (birth centenary)) 1·70 1·70
2107 85c. Friar (Iacopone da Todi (writer) (700th death anniv)) 2·30 2·30
2108 €1.40 "K 551" (Wolfgang Amadeus Mozart (composer) (250th birth anniv)) 3·75 3·75

594 Joseph (detail)

2006. Christmas. Showing details from "La Natività" by Giovan Battista Tiepolo. Multicoloured.
2109 60c. Type **594** 1·60 1·60
2110 60c. Angel 1·60 1·60
2111 65c. Infant Jesus 1·70 1·70
2112 65c. Virgin Mary 1·70 1·70
2113 €2.80 "La Nativita" (29×40 mm) 7·25 7·25

595 Duke Guidubaldo de Montefeltro (founder), "Ideal City" (painting) and Carlo Bo (rector, 1947–2001)

2006. 500th Anniv of Urbino University.
2119 **595** €2.20 multicoloured 5·75 5·75

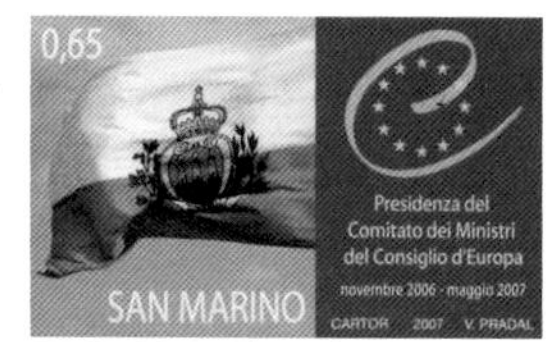

596 San Marino Flag and EU Emblem

2007. San Merino's Presidency of Council of Europe Council of Ministers.
2120 **596** 65c. multicoloured 1·70 1·70

597 "Self Portrait" (painting)

2006. Gina Lollobrigida, Artist. Designs showing Gina Lollobrigida's work. Multicoloured.
2121 65c. Type **597** 1·70 1·70
2122 85c. "Potato Seller" (photograph) 2·30 2·30
2123 €1 "Esmeralda" (sculpture) 2·75 2·75
2124 €3.20 Gina Lollobrigida with Mother Teresa (as ambassador for FAO) 8·50 8·50

598 Alessandro Glaray and Philatelic Material

2007. Alessandro Glaray (philatelic expert) Commemoration.
2125 **598** €1.80 multicoloured 4·75 4·75

599 Arriving in San Marino with Anita and the Thousand

2007. Birth Bicentenary of Giuseppe Garibaldi (soldier and nationalist). Multicoloured.
2126 65c. Type **599** 1·70 1·70
2127 €1.40 Arriving in Marsala (the Kingdom of Two Sicilies war) and fighting in Uruguayan War of Independence 3·75 3·75
2128 €2 Handshake at Teano ending Italian War of Independence 5·25 5·25

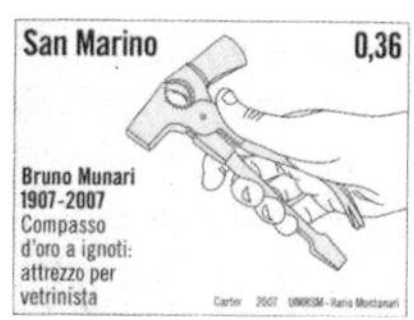

600 Window Dresser's Tool

2007. Birth Centenary of Bruno Munari (artist, designer, writer, and educator).
2129 **600** 36c. yellow and black 95 95
2130 - 65c. blue and black 1·70 1·70
2131 - €1.40 magenta and black 3·75 3·75
2132 - €2 green and black 5·25 5·25

DESIGNS: 36c. Type **600**; 65c. Milk carton; €1.40 Roll-up shutter lock; €2 Garage lamp.

601 Cherubs, Church of the Immaculate Conception, Palermo

2007. San Gabriel International Philatelic Art Award, Legnago.
2133 **601** €1.50 multicoloured 4·00 4·00

602 Scouts, Globe, Compass and Brownsea Island

2007. Europa. Centenary of Scouting. Multicoloured.
2134 60c. Type **602** 1·60 1·60
2135 65c. Scout master, scout and Three Towers 1·70 1·70

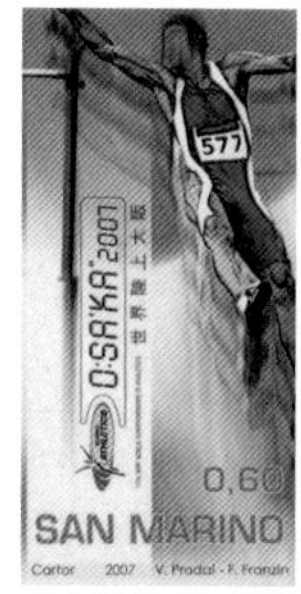

603 High Jump

2007. World Athletics Championships, Osaka. Multicoloured.
2136 60c. Type **603** 1·60 1·60
2137 85c. Long jump (horiz) 2·30 2·30
2138 €1.50 Runner (horiz) 4·00 4·00

603a Striker

2007. European Baseball Cup, San Marino. Multicoloured.
2139 65c. Type **603a** 1·70 1·70
2140 €1 Pitcher 2·75 2·75

604 Cliffs and Postilion (detail from 'Theatrum civitatum et admirandorum Italiae' by Joan (Johannes) Blaeu)

2007. 400th Anniv of Mail Services. Sheet 110×83 mm.
MS2141 **604** €4.50 multicoloured 12·00 12·00

The stamp and margin of **MS**2141 form a composite design.

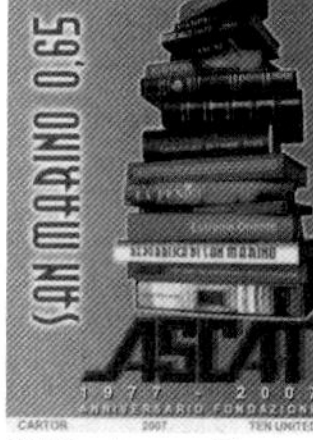

605 Catalogues, Albums and Magazines

2007. 30th Anniv of Constitution of ASCAT (association of philatelic editors). Riccione International Stamp Fair.
2142 **605** 65c. multicoloured 1·70 1·70

606 La Guaita (Rocca) Tower, San Marino

2007. The Oldest (San Marino–301) and Newest (Slovakia–1993) Republics of Europe. Mult.
2143 65c. Type **606** 1·70 1·70
2144 65c. Orava Castle, Slovakia 1·70 1·70

Stamps of a similar design were issued by Slovakia.

607 Port (Quinta do Estanho, Portugal)

2007. European Wines. Sheet 185×143 mm. T 607 and similar multicoloured designs.
MS2145 65c.×8, Type **607**; Champagne (Tarlant, France) (horiz); Champagne (Bauget-Jouette, France) (horiz); Zlahtina white wine (Katunar, Croatia); Reisling (Petri, Germany); Tokaji (Chateau Pajzos, Hungary) (horiz); Ribera del Duero (Carmelo Rodero, Spain) (horiz); Teodor Belo (Simcic, Slovenia) 14·00 14·00

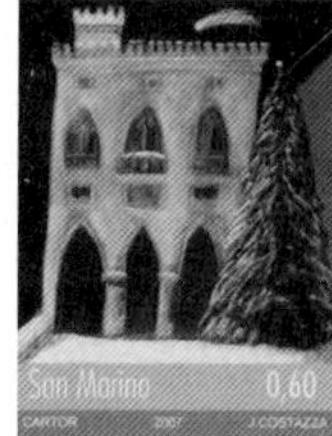

608 Palazzo del Governo

2007. Christmas. Multicoloured.
2146 60c. Type **608** 1·60 1·60
2147 65c. Santa Claus 1·70 1·70
2148 85c. Holy Family and Three Towers, San Marino 2·30 2·30

609 Arturo Toscanni (conductor)

2007. Artistes' Anniversaries. Multicoloured.

2149	60c. Type **609** (50th death anniv)	1·60	1·60
2150	65c. *Paolina Borghese* (sculpture) (Antonio Canova) (250th birth anniv)	1·70	1·70
2151	€1 Harlequin (Carlos Goldoni) (comedic playwright) (300th birth anniv)	2·75	2·75
2152	€1.80 *Via Toscanella* (painting) (Ottone Rosai) (50th death anniv)	4·75	4·75

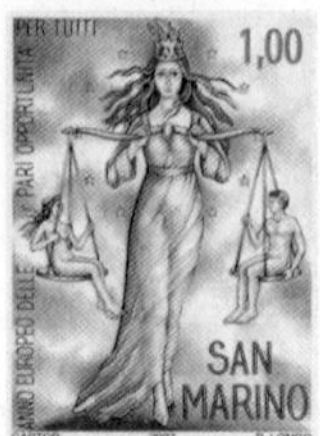

610 Woman holding Scales

2007. Equal Opportunities for All.

2153	**610**	€1 multicoloured	3·25	3·25

611 *Crocefissione* (Crucifixion) (Giovanni Bellini)

2008. Capolavori che ritornano. Multicoloured.

2154	36c. Type **611**	1·10	1·10
2155	60c. *Madonna con bambino e San Giovannino* (Madonna with Child and Saint John) (Jacopo Bassano)	1·60	1·60
2156	65c. *Venere e Amore* (Venus and Love) (Gian Antonio Pellegrini)	1·70	1·70
2157	85c. *Testa di vecchio* (Old Man's Face) (Giandomenico Tiepolo)	2·30	2·30

612 'Aria' (air) (Andrea Lisi)

2008. International Year of Planet Earth. Drawings by Faculty of Industrial Design Students, University of San Marino. Multicoloured.

2158	60c. Type **612**	1·60	1·60
2159	85c. Uomo	2·30	2·30
2160	€1.40 Aqua	3·75	3·75
2161	€2 Terra	5·25	5·25

613 Emblem

2008. Centenary of Inter Football Club.

2162	**613**	€1 multicoloured	2·75	2·75

614 Pianello, Old Public Palace, First Post Office and 'Affrancata' (cancellation)

2008. 175th Anniv of Post Office in San Marino.

2163	**614**	€1.80 multicoloured	4·75	4·75

615 Bernadette Soubirous and First Miracle

2008. 150th Anniv of Apparition at Lourdes. Multicoloured.

2164	36c. Type **615**	1·10	1·10
2165	60c. Pilgrims and Basilica	1·60	1·60
2166	€2 Bernadette Soubirous and Madonna	5·25	5·25

616 Globe as Pangea

2008. European Year of Intercultural Dialogue.

2167	**616**	65c. multicoloured	1·70	1·70

617 Concetto Marchesi

2008. 130th Birth Anniv of Concetto Marchesi (academic and politician).

2168	**617**	€1 multicoloured	2·75	2·75

618 Table Tennis

2008. Olympic Games, Beijing. Sheet 137×105 mm containing T 618 and similar horiz design. Multicoloured.

MS2169	36c. Type **618**; 65c. Fencing; 85c. Swimming	5·00	5·00

619 Envelopes as Ships

2008. Europa. The Letter. Multicoloured.

2170	60c. Type **619**	1·60	1·60
2171	65c. Couple on globe releasing envelopes as doves	1·70	1·70

620 *Our Lady of Mercy*

2008. Art for Basilica of the Annunciation, Nazareth.

2172	**620**	€1 multicoloured	2·75	2·75

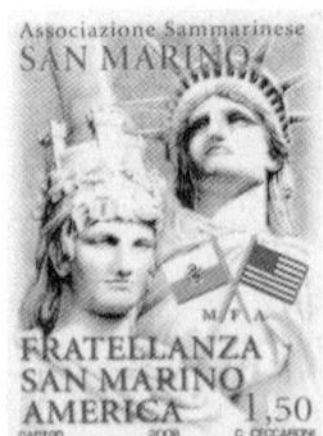

621 Statues of Liberty of San Marino and USA

2008. 30th Anniv of San Marino–USA Friendship Association.

2173	**621**	€1.50 multicoloured	4·00	4·00

622 Posters for *La Boheme* and *Madame Butterfly*

2008. Anniversaries. Multicoloured.

2174	60c. Type **622** (Giacomo Puccini) (composer) (150th birth anniv)	1·60	1·60
2175	€1 *Rotonda di Palmieri* and *Vita Militare* (Giovanni Fattori) (artist) (death centenary)	2·75	2·75
2176	€1.40 Book covers for *Don Camillo* and *Diario Clandestino* (Giovannino Guareschi) (writer) (birth centenary)	3·75	3·75
2177	€1.70 *The Print Collectors* and ceramic bust (Honoré Daumier) (artist) (birth bicentenary)	4·50	4·50

623 Chronometer and Cyclist

2008. World Road Cycling Championships, Varese. Multicoloured.

2178	85c. Type **623**	2·30	2·30
2179	€3.85 Rider and cycle	8·50	8·50

624 Andrea Palladio and Villa Pojana

2008. 500th Birth Anniv of Andrea Palladio (architect).

2180	**624**	€1 multicoloured	2·75	2·75

625 Angel

2008. Christmas. Multicoloured.

2181	36c. Type **625**	1·30	1·30
2182	60c. Holy Family	1·90	1·90
2183	€1 Angel carrying gift	3·25	3·25

626 Polar Landscape

2008. International Polar Year. Multicoloured.

2184	60c. Type **626**	1·90	1·90
2185	€1 Penguins	3·25	3·25
2186	€1.20 Research helicopter	4·00	4·00

627 Tamburino (character from *Cuore*)

2008. Writers. Multicoloured.

2187	60c. Type **627** (Edmondo de Amicis) (death centenary)	1·90	1·90
2188	€2.20 Scene from *La Lune e i falo* (Cesare Pavese) (birth centenary)	7·25	7·25

628 Second Tower (Cesta Fortress)

2008. Inclusion of Historic Centre and Mount Titano in UNESCO World Heritage Lists. Sheet 185×143 mm containing T 628 and similar vert designs. Multicoloured.

MS2189	€1×6, Type **628**; San Marino Basilica; Piazza della Liberta, Il Palazzo Pubblico; Contrada Omerelli; Contrada delle Mura; First Tower (Guaita)	19·00	19·00

629 Two-handled Amphora (Libero Cellarosi)

2009. Sammarinese Ceramists. Multicoloured.

2190	36c. Type **629**	1·30	1·30
2191	60c. Amphora (Umberto Masi)	1·90	1·90
2192	85c. Vase (Giorgio Monti)	2·75	2·75

630 *Dinamismo di un cane al guinzaglio* (Giacomo Balla)

2009. Centenary of Futurist Manifesto. Sheet 185×143 mm containing T 630 and similar multicoloured designs.

MS2193 60c.×10, Type **630**; *Treno armato* (Gino Severini) (vert); *Studio per centrale electtrica* (Antonio Sant'elia) (vert); *Zang Tumb Tumb* (Filippo Tommaso Marinetti); *Cavaliere rosso* (Carlo Carra); *Risveglio di una città* (Luigi Russolo); *Dinamismo di un ciclista* (Umberto Boccioni); *Natura morta con uvovo rosso* (Ardengo Soffici) (vert); *Forme uniche nella continuità dello spazio* (Umberto Boccioni) (vert); *Serata futurista* (Umberto Boccioni); 19·00 19·00

631 Emblem

2009. 50th Anniv of Comitato Olimpico Nazionale di San Marino (CONS) (Olympic committee).

2194	**631**	€1.80 multicoloured	5·75	5·75

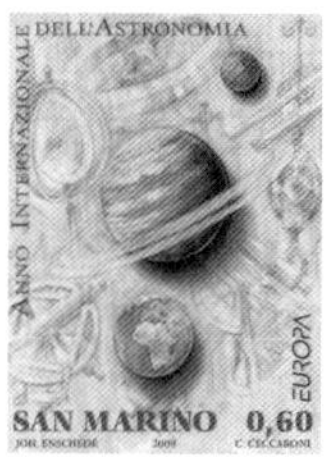

632 Saturn and Astronomical Instruments

2009. Europa. Astronomy. Multicoloured.

2195	60c. Type **632**	1·90	1·90
2196	65c. Solar system	2·10	2·10

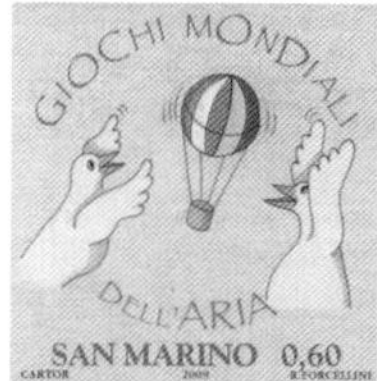

633 Hot Air Balloon and Doves

2009. World Air Games, Turin. Multicoloured.

2197	60c. Type **633**	1·90	1·90
2198	85c. Glider with a dove on each wing	2·75	2·75
2199	€1.50 Dove swinging below helicopter	4·75	4·75
2200	€1.80 Dove surfing on aircraft trail	6·00	6·00

634 Emblem

2009. ICPO–Interpol European Regional Conference, San Marino.

2201	**634**	€2 multicoloured	6·50	6·50

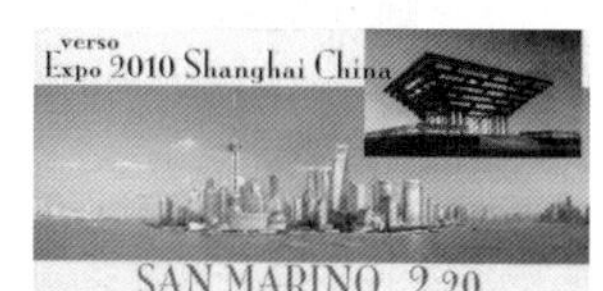

635 Shanghai Financial Centre and China Pavilion

2009. Expo 2010, Shanghai, China.

2202	**635**	€2.20 multicoloured	6·75	6·75

636 August Dauphin (Edgar Allan Poe)

2009. Writers' Anniversaries. Designs showing symbols of characters. Multicoloured.

2203	36c. Type **636** (birth bicentenary)	1·30	1·30
2204	85c. Sherlock Holmes (Arthur Conan Doyle) (150th birth anniv)	2·75	2·75
2205	€1.40 Philip Marlowe (Raymond Chandler) (50th death anniv)	4·50	4·50

637 Tessano

2009. Wines of San Marino. Sheet 137×105 mm containing T 637 and similar horiz designs showing wine bottles. Multicoloured.

MS2206 60c.×6, Type **637**; Brugneto; Riserva Titano; Caldese; Roncale; Moscato Spumante 9·50 9·50

638 Athletics

2009. Mediterranean Games, Pescara. Multicoloured.

2207	60c. Type **638**	1·90	1·90
2208	€1.40 Cycling	4·50	4·50
2209	€1.70 Wrestling	5·25	5·25

639 'Braille'

2009. Birth Bicentenary of Louis Braille (inventor of Braille writing for the blind).

2210	**639**	€1.50 multicoloured	4·75	4·75

No. 2210 is embossed with Braille writing.

640 '30' enclosing Dove

2009. 30th (2010) Meeting for Friendship Among Peoples, Rimini.

2211	**640**	€1.80 multicoloured	6·00	6·00

641 Centenary Emblem, Club Colours and Player

2009. Centenary of Bologna Football Club.

2212	**641**	€1 multicoloured	3·25	3·25

642 Statue of Liberty

2009. European Year of Creativity and Innovation. Stereoscopic Stamps. Three sheets, each 150×43 mm containing T 642 and similar horiz designs. Multicoloured.

MS2213 €1×2, Type **642**×2 6·50 6·50

MS2214 €1×2, Palazzo Pubblico interior×2 6·50 6·50

MS2215 €1×2, Statue of St. Marinus×2 6·50 6·50

The stamps of Nos. **MS**2213/**MS**2215, whilst showing the same image, differ slightly.

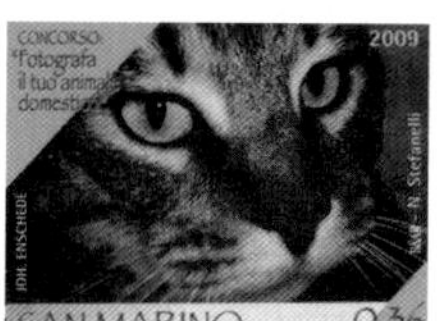

643 Cat (Natascia Stefanelli)

2009. Pet Photograph Competition Winners. Multicoloured.

2216	36c. Type **643**	1·30	1·30
2217	60c. Cocker spaniel (Tina Woodcock)	1·90	1·90
2218	65c. Duck (Ettore Zonzini)	2·10	2·10
2219	75c. Goat, foal and dog (Anna Rosa Francioni)	2·50	2·50
2220	85c. Tiny tortoise (Maria Eleonora Vaglio)	2·75	2·75
2221	€1.20 Basset hound (Lorenzo Zamagni)	3·75	3·75

644 Dante and Virgil and Three Wild Beasts (from 15th-century Codex Urbinate Latino 365, Vatican Apostolic Library)

2009. Italia 2009 International Stamp Exhibition, Rome. Italian Language.

2222	**644**	60c. multicoloured	1·90	1·90

A stamp of a similar design was issued by Italy and Vatican City.

645 Joseph

2009. Christmas. Rest on the Flight into Egypt (Caravaggio). Sheet 137×105 mm containing T 645 and similar multicoloured design.

MS2223 €1.50 Type **645**; €2 Virgin and Child (vert) 4·75 4·75

646 Narcissi

2010. Flowers. Multicoloured.

2224	10c. Type **646**	20	20
2225	85c. Hyacinth	2·50	2·50
2226	€1 Muscari	3·50	3·50
2227	€1.50 Tulips	3·75	3·75

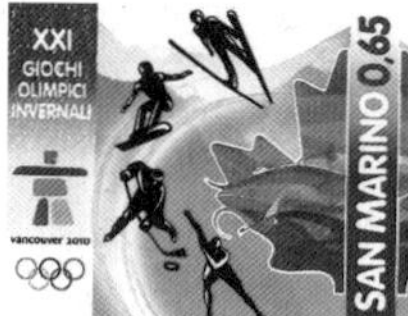

647 Ski Jump, Snowboarding, Ice Hockey and Speed Skating

2010. Winter Olympic Games, Vancouver. Multicoloured.

MS2228 65c. Type **647**; 85c. Downhill skiing, Nordic skiing, Curling and Bob sleigh; €1 Speed skating (different), Ice dance and Grand Slalom 7·50 7·50

648 Third Tower

2010. Expo 2010, Shanghai. Multicoloured.

MS2229 65c. Type **648**; €1 Second tower; €1.50 First Tower; €1.80 Government Building and the Statue of Liberty (36×51 mm) 15·00 15·00

649 La Republica (V. Pochini) and First Tower (Guaita)

2010. 50th Anniv of Association of Blood and Organ Donors (AVSSO)

2230	**649**	€1.80 multicoloured	5·25	5·25

650 Flying Girl with Open Book as Wings

2010. Europa. Multicoloured.

2231	60c Type **650**	3·50	3·50
2232	65c. Girl sleeping on open book, amongst clouds containing characters and planets	3·75	3·74

651 Gino Bartali (10th death anniv)

2010. Cyclists' Anniversaries. Multicoloured.

2233	€1.40 Type **651**	4·25	4·25
2234	€1.50 Fausto Coppi (50th death anniv)	4·25	2·25

Nos. 2233/4 were printed, *se-tenant*, forming a composite design

652 Player and Net

2010. World Men's Volleyball Championship, Italy

2235	**652**	€1 multicoloured	3·00	3·00

653 Emblem and Players

2010. World Cup Football Championships, South Africa

2236	**653**	€1.50 multicoloured	8·50	8·50

654 La Republica (V. Pochini) and First Tower (Guaita)

2010. San Marino–Japan. Multicoloured.

MS2237 €1.50×4, Type **654**; Himej Castle; *Apparizione di San Marino al suo popolo* (E. Retrosi) (mural); *Tokaido-Gojyusantugi* (Nihonbashi in the Morning) 18·00 18·00

Stamps of a similar design were issued by Japan

655 San Marino from East

2010. 50th Anniv of San Marino Lions Club. Multicoloured.

2238	36c. Type **655**	90	90
2239	60c. San Marino, aerial view	1·90	1·90

656 'inter', Italian Flag and Football

2010. Inter Football Club, winners of Italian Football League, Italian Cup and European Champions League. Multicoloured.

2240	€1 Type **656**	3·00	3·00
2241	€1 '3 volte', Italian shield enclosing '18'	3·00	3·00
2242	€1 'campione' and 'Campione d'Europa'	3·00	3·00

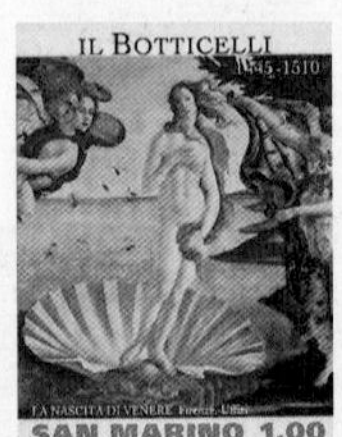

657 *The Birth of Venus* (Sandro Botticelli)

2010. Art. Multicoloured.

2243	€1 Type **657**	3·00	3·00
2244	€1.40 *The Tempest* (Giorgione da Castelfranco Veneto)	3·75	3·75
2245	€1.45 *Supper at Emmaus* (Michelangelo Merisi da Caravaggio)	4·25	4·25
2246	€1.50 *The Football Players* (Henri Rousseau)	5·00	5·00

658 Second Tower

2010. San Marino–Gibraltar. Multicoloured.

MS2247 €1.50×4, Type **658**; Moresco Castle, Gibraltar; Mount Titano; Rock of Gibraltar 16·00 16·00

Stamps of a similar design were issued by Gibraltar

EXPRESS LETTER STAMPS

E22 Mt. Titano and "Liberty"

1907

E53	**E22**	25c. pink	27·00	10·50

1923. Optd ESPRESSO.

E92	**19**	60c. violet	55	55

1923. Surch Cent. 60.

E93	**E22**	60c. on 25c. pink	55	55

E34

1923. Red Cross.

E101	**E34**	60c.+5c. red	2·20	2·10

1926. No. E92 surch Lire 1,25.

E134	**E19**	1l.25 on 60c. violet	1·10	1·10

1927. No. E93 surch L. 1,25 and bars over old surch.

E138	**E22**	1l.25 on 60c. on 25c. pink	80	85

E50 Statue of Liberty and View of San Marino

1929. As Type E 50 but without "UNION POSTALE UNIVERSELLE" and inscr "ESPRESSO".

E164	**E50**	1l.25 green	30	20

1929. Optd UNION POSTALE UNIVERSELLE as in Type E 50.

E165	2l.50 blue	70	80

E78

1943

E305	**E78**	1l.25 green	15	15
E306	**E78**	2l.50 orange	15	15

E79 Mt. Titano

1945

E307	**E79**	2l.50 green	20	15
E308	**E79**	5l. orange	20	15
E309	**E79**	5l. red	1·40	60
E310	**E79**	10l. blue	3·25	1·90
E419	**E79**	60l. red	15·00	5·50

E87 Pegasus and Mt. Titano

1946

E337	**E87**	30l. blue	7·25	4·25
E420	**E87**	80l. blue	24·00	9·50

1947. Surch.

E339	**E79**	15l. on 5l. red	60	25
E340	**E79**	15l. on 10l. blue	60	25
E374	**E 87**	35l. on 30l. blue	46·00	31·00
E341	**E 87**	60l. on 30l. blue	5·50	5·50
E545	**E 79**	75l. on 60l. red	4·25	2·50
E375	**E 87**	80l. on 30l. blue	49·00	22·00
E546	**E 87**	100l. on 80l. blue	4·25	2·50
E783	**E 180**	120l. on 75l. black and yellow	15	15
E784	**E 180**	135l. on 100l. black and orange	15	15

E180 Crossbow and Three "Castles"

1966

E800	**E180**	75l. black and yellow	15	15
E801	**E180**	80l. black and purple	15	15
E802	**E180**	100l. black and orange	15	15

No. E800 has crossbow in white without "shadows".

PARCEL POST STAMPS Unused and used prices are for complete pairs

P46

1928

P145	**P46**	5c. purple and blue	30	25
P146	**P46**	10c. blue and light blue	30	25
P147	**P46**	20c. black and blue	30	25
P148	**P46**	25c. red and blue	30	25
P149	**P46**	30c. ultramarine & blue	40	25
P150	**P46**	30c. orange and blue	40	25
P151	**P46**	60c. red and blue	40	25
P152	**P46**	1l. violet and red	40	25
P153	**P46**	2l. green and red	80	1·30
P154	**P46**	3l. bistre and red	1·30	2·10
P155	**P46**	4l. grey and red	1·60	2·75
P156	**P46**	10l. mauve and red	4·75	4·25
P157	**P46**	12l. lake and red	13·50	12·00
P158	**P46**	15l. green and red	21·00	21·00
P159	**P46**	20l. purple and red	34·00	34·00

1945

P309	5c. purple and red	20	15
P310	10c. brown and black	20	15
P311	20c. red and green	20	15
P312	25c. yellow and black	20	15
P313	30c. mauve and red	20	15
P314	50c. violet and black	20	15
P315	60c. red and black	20	15
P316	1l. brown and blue	35	15
P317	2l. brown and blue	35	15
P318	3l. grey and brown	35	15
P319	4l. green and brown	35	15
P320	10l. grey and violet	80	15
P770	10l. green and red	15	15
P321	12l. green and blue	4·25	4·75
P322	15l. green and violet	3·00	2·40
P323	20l. violet and brown	3·00	2·40
P324	25l. red and blue	80·00	37·00
P771	50l. yellow and red	15	15
P455	300l. violet and red	£275	£170
P773	300l. violet and brown	35	35
P526	500l. brown and red	3·25	5·25
P775	1000l. green and brown	1·10	1·10

1948. Nos. P324 and P771 surch in figures and wavy lines on each half of design.

P524	100l. on 50l. yellow and red	85	1·70
P375	200l. on 25l. red & blue	£350	£180

POSTAGE DUE STAMPS

D18

1897

D38	**D18**	5c. brown and green	1·10	55
D39	**D18**	10c. brown and green	1·10	55
D40	**D18**	30c. brown and green	2·75	1·10
D41	**D18**	50c. brown and green	7·25	2·10
D42	**D18**	60c. brown and green	29·00	7·50
D43	**D18**	1l. brown and pink	13·50	6·50
D44	**D18**	3l. brown and pink	40·00	20·00
D45	**D18**	5l. brown and pink	£250	65·00
D46	**D18**	10l. brown and pink	80·00	36·00

1924

D102	5c. brown and red	80	1·10
D103	10c. brown and red	80	1·10
D104	30c. brown and red	1·30	1·10
D105	50c. brown and red	1·90	1·30
D106	60c. brown and red	10·00	7·25
D107	1l. brown and green	16·00	12·00
D108	3l. brown and green	50·00	37·00
D109	5l. brown and green	70·00	55·00
D110	10l. brown and green	£400	£350

1925

D112	5c. brown and red	40	25
D113	10c. brown and blue	85	60
D114	15c. brown and blue	40	25
D115	20c. brown and blue	40	25
D116	25c. brown and blue	65	60
D117	30c. brown and blue	85	55
D118	40c. brown and blue	4·00	3·75
D119	50c. brown and blue	1·90	2·10
D120	60c. brown and blue	4·00	1·10
D121	1l. brown and orange	7·75	1·60
D122	2l. brown and orange	2·30	2·10
D123	3l. brown and orange	£110	46·00
D124	5l. brown and orange	28·00	7·50
D125	10l. brown and orange	44·00	16·00
D126	15l. brown and orange	3·50	2·10
D127	25l. brown and orange	55·00	34·00
D128	30l. brown and orange	10·50	14·00
D129	50l. brown and orange	14·00	14·00

1931. As Type D 18 but with centre obliterated in black and new value superimposed in silver.

D164	15c. on 5c. blue	55	55
D165	15c. on 10c. blue	55	55
D166	15c. on 30c. blue	55	55
D167	20c. on 5c. blue	55	55
D168	20c. on 10c. blue	65	55
D169	20c. on 30c. blue	65	55
D170	25c. on 5c. blue	2·40	1·60
D171	25c. on 10c. blue	2·40	1·60
D172	25c. on 30c. blue	21·00	13·00
D173	40c. on 10c. blue	2·50	1·10
D174	40c. on 10c. blue	3·00	1·60
D175	40c. on 30c. blue	3·00	1·60
D176	2l. on 5c. blue	80·00	46·00
D177	2l. on 10c. blue	£150	85·00
D178	2l. on 30c. blue	£110	70·00

1936. Surch in figures and words and bars. Nos. D233/8 and D242 are brown and blue; the rest brown and orange.

D233	10c. on 5c.	55	55
D234	25c. on 30c.	16·00	16·00
D235	50c. on 5c.	4·00	1·60
D237	1l. on 30c.	60·00	9·50
D238	1l. on 40c.	12·00	9·50
D239	1l. on 3l.	60·00	2·25
D240	1l. on 25l.	£120	28·00
D241	2l. on 15l.	55·00	33·00
D242	3l. on 20c.	42·00	28·00
D243	25l. on 50l.	3·00	3·00

D82

1945

D309	**D82**	5c. green	30	15
D310	**D82**	10c. brown	30	15
D311	**D82**	15c. red	30	15
D312	**D82**	20c. blue	30	15
D313	**D82**	25c. violet	30	15
D314	**D82**	30c. mauve	30	15
D315	**D82**	40c. yellow	30	15
D316	**D82**	50c. grey	30	15
D317	**D82**	60c. brown	30	15
D318	**D82**	1l. orange	30	15
D319	**D82**	2l. red	30	15
D320	**D82**	5l. violet	30	15
D321	**D82**	10l. blue	1·10	80
D322	**D82**	20l. green	18·00	12·00
D323	**D82**	25l. brown	18·00	12·00
D324	**D82**	50l. brown	18·00	12·00

Pt. 8

SARDINIA

A former Italian kingdom, including the island of Sardinia, a large part of the mainland and parts of what is now south-east France. The kingdom of Italy was formed by the adhesion of other Italian states to Sardinia, whose king became the first ruler of united Italy.

100 centesimi = 1 lira.

1 Victor Emmanuel II

1851. Imperf.

1	**1**	5c. black	£12000	£2250
3	**1**	20c. blue	£11000	£275
7	**1**	40c. pink	£20000	£5000

1853. Embossed on coloured paper. Imperf.

9	5c. on green	£20000	£1400
10	20c. on blue	£18000	£225
11	40c. on pink	£13000	£1200

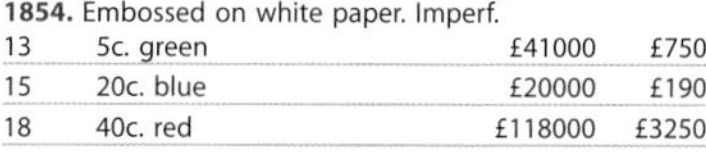

1854. Embossed on white paper. Imperf.

13	5c. green	£41000	£750
15	20c. blue	£20000	£190
18	40c. red	£118000	£3250

2 Victor Emmanuel II

1855. Head embossed. Imperf.

28	2	5c. green	8·50	21·00
35	2	10c. grey	32·00	£130
39	2	10c. brown	£120	£110
40	2	10c. bistre	8·50	21·00
47	2	20c. blue	£225	29·00
55	2	40c. red	32·00	65·00
59	2	80c. yellow	32·00	£400
61	2	3l. bronze	£550	£3500

For Type **2** perf, see Italy Nos. 1/4.

NEWSPAPER STAMPS

N3

1861. Numerals embossed. Imperf.

N62	N3	1c. black	10·50	19·00
N63	N3	2c. black	£225	£140

For 2c. stamps of similar types in yellow see Italy No. N5.

Pt. 7

SAXONY

A former kingdom in S. Germany. Stamps superseded in 1868 by those of the North German Federation.

10 pfennige = 1 neugroschen;
30 neugroschen = 1 thaler.

1

1850. Imperf.

1	1	3pf. red	£8500	£8500

2

1851. Imperf.

7	2	3pf. green	£170	£130

3 Friedrich August II

1851. Imperf.

10	3	½ngr. black on grey	95·00	16·00
12	3	1ngr. black on pink	£130	12·50
13	3	2ngr. black on blue	£350	85·00
14	3	3ngr. black on yellow	£200	32·00

4 King Johann I

1855. Imperf.

16	4	½ngr. black on grey	12·50	5·25
18	4	1ngr. black on pink	12·50	5·25
20	4	2ngr. black on blue	25·00	21·00
23	4	3ngr. black on yellow	27·00	16·00
24	4	5ngr. red	£120	75·00
28	4	10ngr. blue	£325	£325

5

6

1863. Perf.

31	5	3pf. green	2·75	55·00
36	5	½ngr. orange	2·75	3·75
39	6	1ngr. pink	1·60	3·25
40	6	2ngr. blue	3·75	8·50
42	6	3ngr. brown	5·25	16·00
45	6	5ngr. blue	26·00	65·00
46	6	5ngr. purple	42·00	65·00
47	6	5ngr. grey	32·00	£375

Pt. 7

SCHLESWIG-HOLSTEIN

Two former Duchies of the King of Denmark which, following a revolt, established a Provisional Government in 1848. Danish stamps were in use from 1851 in Schleswig and 1853 in Holstein.

The Duchies were invaded by Prussia and Audtria in 1864 and, by the Convention of Gastein in 1865, were placed under joint sovereignty of those countries, with Holstein administered by Austria.

The Duchies were annexed by Prussia in 1867 adn from 1868 used the stamps of the North German Confederation.

96 skilling = 1 Rigsbankdaler (Danish).
16 schilling = 1 mark.

SCHLESWIG-HOLSTEIN

1

2

1850. Imperf.

2a	1	1s. blue	£425	£7500
4	1	2s. pink	£750	£9500

1865. Inscr "SCHLESWIG-HOLSTEIN". Roul.

6	2	½s. pink	48·00	60·00
7	2	1¼s. green	23·00	26·00
8	2	1⅓s. mauve	60·00	£160
9	2	2s. blue	65·00	£325
10	2	4s. bistre	85·00	£1700

SCHLESWIG

1864. Inscr "HERZOGTH. SCHLESWIG". Roul.

24		½s. green	42·00	75·00
21		1¼s. green	60·00	26·00
25		1¼s. lilac	75·00	32·00
27		1⅓s. pink	38·00	85·00
28		2s. blue	38·00	65·00
22		4s. red	£130	£650
29		4s. bistre	42·00	£110

HOLSTEIN

6

1864. Imperf.

51	6	1¼s. blue	70·00	75·00

9

1864. Roul.

59	9	1¼s. blue	55·00	26·00

10

1865. Roul.

61	10	½s. green	85·00	£130
62	10	1¼s. mauve	65·00	32·00
63	10	1⅓s. pink	80·00	60·00
64	10	2s. blue	70·00	65·00
65	10	4s. bistre	75·00	£110

On the 1⅓s. and 4s. the word "SCHILLING" is inside the central oval.

1868. Inscr "HERZOGTH. HOLSTEIN". Roul.

66	2	1¼s. purple	95·00	32·00
67	2	2s. blue	£190	£200

Pt. 8

SICILY

An island to the south of Italy, which, with Naples, formed the Kingdom of the Two Sicilies, until incorporated in the Kingdom of Italy.

100 grano = 1 ducato.

1 King "Bomba"

1859. Imperf.

1c	1	½g. yellow	£650	£1300
2b	1	1g. olive	£850	£180
3	1	2g. blue	£225	£160
4	1	5g. red	£800	£600
5	1	10g. blue	£800	£300
6	1	20g. grey	£950	£750
7	1	50g. brown	£950	£5500

Pt. 11

SLESVIG

Stamps issued during the plebiscite of 1920.

100 pfennig = 1 German mark. 100 ore = 1 Danish Krone.

1 Arms

3 Rural View

1920

1	1	2½pf. grey	20	25
2	1	5pf. green	20	25
3	1	7½pf. brown	20	25
4	1	10pf. red	20	25
5	1	15pf. purple	20	25
6	1	20pf. blue	20	25
7	1	25pf. orange	35	25
8	1	35pf. brown	45	35
9	1	40pf. violet	35	20
10	1	75pf. green	45	35
11	3	1m. brown	45	35
12	3	2m. blue	60	55
13	3	5m. green	1·30	90
14	3	10m. red	2·75	1·80

1920. Values in Danish currency and optd 1. ZONE.

29	1	1ore grey	20	1·80
30	1	5ore green	20	90
31	1	7ore brown	20	1·10
32	1	10ore red	20	1·10
33	1	15ore purple	20	1·80
34	1	20ore blue	20	2·10
35	1	25ore orange	20	5·75
36	1	35ore brown	90	10·50
37	1	40ore violet	25	3·50
38	1	75ore green	45	5·75
39	3	1k. brown	60	9·75
40	3	2k. blue	7·00	35·00
41	3	5k. green	3·50	35·00
42	3	10k. red	8·00	65·00

OFFICIAL STAMPS

1920. Nos. 1/14 optd C.I.S. (= "Comission Interalliee Slesvig").

O15	1	2½pf. grey	65·00	95·00
O16	1	5pf. green	65·00	£110
O17	1	7½pf. brown	65·00	95·00
O18	1	10pf. red	65·00	£120
O19	1	15pf. red	44·00	60·00
O20	1	20pf. blue	65·00	70·00
O21	1	25pf. orange	£130	£180
O22	1	35pf. brown	£130	£180
O23	1	40pf. violet	£110	£110
O24	1	75pf. green	£130	£275
O25	3	1m. brown	£130	£275
O26	3	2m. blue	£190	£275
O27	3	5m. green	£275	£450
O28	3	10m. red	£550	£650

Pt. 9

SPAIN

A kingdom in south-west Europe; a republic between 1873 and 1874, and from 1931 until 1939.

1850. 8½ (later 8) cuartos = 1 real.
1866. 80 cuartos = 100 centimos de escudo = 1 escudo.
1867. 1000 milesimas = 100 centimos de escudo = 80 cuartos = 1 escudo.
1872. 100 centimos = 1 peseta.
2002. 100 cents = 1 euro.

1 Queen Isabella II

2 Queen Isabella II

1850. Imperf.

2	1	6c. black	£475	18·00
3	2	12c. lilac	£2750	£325
4	2	5r. red	£2750	£325
5	2	6r. blue	£3750	£900
6	2	10r. green	£5000	£2500

3 Queen Isabella II

1851. Imperf.

9	3	6c. black	£300	3·50
10	3	12c. lilac	£4750	£200
11	3	2r. red	£22000	£13000
12	3	5r. pink	£2750	£300
13	3	6r. blue	£4250	£1200
14	3	10r. green	£3250	£550

4

1852. Imperf.

16	4	6c. pink	£425	3·00
17	4	12c. purple	£2250	£160
18	4	2r. red	£18000	£6000
19	4	5r. green	£2500	£140
20	4	6r. blue	£3750	£550

5

1853. Imperf.

22	5	6c. red	£550	2·75
23	5	12c. purple	£2250	£130
24	5	2r. red	£13000	£2250
25	5	5r. green	£2500	£130
26	5	6r. blue	£3500	£475

7 Arms of Castile and Leon

1854. Imperf.

32	7	2c. green	£2250	£550
33	7	4c. red	£450	2·50
34	7	6c. red	£375	1·80
35	7	1r. blue	£3750	£375
36	7	2r. red	£1700	£120
37	7	5r. green	£1700	£110
38	7	6r. blue	£2750	£350

9

1855. Imperf.

54	**9**	2c. green	£600	45·00
55a	**9**	4c. red	4·75	45
61	**9**	1r. blue	20·00	25·00
57	**9**	2r. purple	75·00	27·00

12

1860. Imperf.

63	**12**	2c. green on green	£375	22·00
64	**12**	4c. orange on green	44·00	80
65	**12**	12c. red on buff	£375	14·00
66	**12**	19c. brown on brown	£3000	£1600
67	**12**	1r. blue on green	£350	12·50
68	**12**	2r. lilac on lilac	£400	12·50

13

1862. Imperf.

69a	**13**	2c. blue on yellow	35·00	9·50
70	**13**	4c. brown on brown	5·75	65
70b	**13**	4c. brown on white	19·00	4·75
71	**13**	12c. blue on pink	49·00	9·25
72	**13**	19c. red on lilac	£200	£275
72a	**13**	19c. red on white	£275	£190
73a	**13**	1r. brown on yellow	75·00	25·00
74	**13**	2r. green on pink	41·00	14·00

14

1864. Imperf.

75	**14**	2c. blue on lilac	60·00	21·00
75b	**14**	2c. blue on white	60·00	28·00
76b	**14**	4c. red on red	2·50	1·00
76c	**14**	4c. pink on white	19·00	9·50
77a	**14**	12c. green on pink	42·00	12·00
78	**14**	19c. lilac on lilac	£225	£225
79	**14**	1r. brown on green	£200	95·00
80	**14**	2r. blue on pink	49·00	15·00
80b	**14**	2r. blue on white	65·00	24·00

15

1865. Imperf.

81a	**15**	2c. red	£375	41·00
82	**15**	12c. pink and blue	£450	22·00
83	**15**	19c. pink and brown	£1600	£850
84	**15**	1r. green	£450	75·00
85	**15**	2r. mauve	£450	37·00
85c	**15**	2r. red	£500	60·00
85e	**15**	2r. yellow	£500	75·00

1865. Perf.

86	2c. red	£500	£140
87	4c. blue	40·00	95
88	12c. pink and blue	£650	65·00
89	19c. pink and brown	£4000	£2750
90	1r. green	£1900	£550
91	2r. lilac	£1300	£275
91b	2r. orange	£1500	£350

16

1866. Perf.

92	**16**	2c. pink	£300	34·00
93a	**16**	4c. blue	37·00	65
94a	**16**	12c. orange	£275	13·50
95	**16**	19c. brown	£1200	£475
96	**16**	10c. de e. green	£325	30·00
97	**16**	20c. de e. lilac	£225	22·00

1866. As T 14, but dated "1866", and perf.

98	20c. de e. lilac	£1200	80·00

19

1867. Inscr "CORREOS DE ESPANA". Various frames.

99a	**19**	2c. brown	£425	42·00
100	**19**	4c. blue	26·00	1·10
101a	**19**	12c. orange	£225	8·25
102	**19**	19c. pink	£1500	£450
150	**19**	19c. brown	£2500	£600
103	**19**	10c. de e. green	£275	25·00
104	**19**	20c. de e. lilac	£130	11·00

25

26

1867. Various frames.

105	**25**	5m. green	48·00	19·00
106	**25**	10m. brown	48·00	19·00
107	**26**	25m. pink and blue	£275	27·00
145	**26**	25m. blue	£300	17·00
108	**26**	50m. brown	22·00	80
146a	**19**	50m. purple	25·00	1·00
147	**19**	100m. brown	£600	80·00
148	**19**	200m. green	£200	13·50

1868. Various stamps optd HABILITADO POR LA NACION.

109	**25**	5m. green	19·00	5·75
110	**25**	10m. brown	14·00	4·75
111	**26**	25m. pink and blue	38·00	14·00
151	**26**	25m. blue	38·00	11·50
112	**26**	50m. brown	7·50	4·75
152	**19**	50m. purple	7·50	3·75
153	**19**	100m. brown	75·00	28·00
154	**19**	200m. green	26·00	9·50
115	**19**	12c. orange	38·00	9·50
116	**19**	19c. pink	£375	£140
156	**19**	19c. brown	£750	£190
113	**19**	10c. de e. green	28·00	14·00
114	**19**	20c. de e. lilac	24·00	9·50

36

1870

172	**36**	1m. brown on buff	8·50	8·25
173	**36**	2m. black on buff	11·00	10·00
174	**36**	4m. brown	22·00	17·00
175	**36**	10m. red	23·00	8·00
176a	**36**	25m. mauve	85·00	9·75
177a	**36**	50m. blue	13·50	45
178b	**36**	100m. brown	40·00	8·00
179	**36**	200m. brown	45·00	8·75
180	**36**	400m. green	£350	33·00
181	**36**	12c. red	£275	8·50
182	**36**	19c. green	£450	£275
183a	**36**	1e.60m. lilac	£1800	£1200
184	**36**	2e. blue	£1800	£750

38a

38

1872. Imperf.

185	**38a**	¼c. blue	2·50	2·50
186	**38**	¼c. green	2·10	1·60
187	**38a**	¼c. green	25	15

1872. As T 25, but currency in centavos de peseta and bottom panel inscr "COMUNICS".

192	**25**	2c. lilac	26·00	19·00
193	**25**	5c. green	£190	90·00

40 King Amadeo

41

1872

194	**40**	5c. pink	26·00	8·25
195b	**40**	6c. blue	£180	70·00
196	**40**	10c. lilac	£375	£325
197	**40**	10c. blue	7·25	45
199	**40**	12c. lilac	17·00	2·20
200	**40**	20c. lilac	£160	85·00
201	**40**	25c. brown	60·00	10·00
202	**40**	40c. brown	85·00	11·00
203	**40**	50c. green	£110	10·00
204	**41**	1p. lilac	£110	55·00
205	**41**	4p. brown	£650	£600
206	**41**	10p. green	£2500	£2500

42 Allegorical Figure of Peace

1873

207	**42**	2c. orange	14·00	5·75
208	**42**	5c. pink	43·00	8·00
209	**42**	10c. green	9·00	45
210	**42**	20c. black	£120	38·00
211	**42**	25c. brown	42·00	8·00
212	**42**	40c. purple	45·00	8·00
213	**42**	50c. blue	17·00	8·00
214a	**42**	1p. lilac	60·00	42·00
215	**42**	4p. brown	£750	£600
216	**42**	10p. purple	£2500	£2500

43 Allegorical Figure of Justice

1874

217	**43**	2c. yellow	27·00	11·50
218a	**43**	5c. mauve	42·00	9·00
219	**43**	10c. blue	17·00	45
220	**43**	20c. green	£200	60·00
221	**43**	25c. brown	42·00	9·00
222a	**43**	40c. mauve	£475	11·00
223	**43**	50c. orange	£150	11·00
224	**43**	1p. green	£110	55·00
225	**43**	4p. red	£850	£600
226	**43**	10p. black	£3500	£2500

44

1874

227	**44**	10c. brown	27·00	85

45 King Alfonso XII

1875

228	**45**	2c. brown	22·00	11·00
229	**45**	5c. lilac	80·00	13·00
230	**45**	10c. blue	9·00	45
231	**45**	20c. brown	£325	£160
232	**45**	25c. pink	70·00	8·25
233	**45**	40c. brown	£130	43·00
234	**45**	50c. mauve	£200	38·00
235	**45**	1p. black	£225	95·00
236	**45**	4p. green	£550	£550
237	**45**	10p. blue	£1800	£1900

46 King Alfonso XII

1876

238	**46**	5c. brown	13·50	3·75
239	**46**	10c. blue	3·75	45
240	**46**	20c. green	23·00	17·00
241	**46**	25c. brown	8·75	5·50
242	**46**	40c. brown	90·00	£100
250	**46**	50c. green	15·50	8·75
244	**46**	1p. blue	23·00	10·50
245	**46**	4p. purple	65·00	75·00
246	**46**	10p. red	£150	£160

48

1878

253	**48**	2c. mauve	42·00	13·00
254a	**48**	5c. yellow	60·00	15·00
255	**48**	10c. brown	8·50	50
256	**48**	20c. black	£200	£150
257	**48**	25c. green	25·00	2·75
258	**48**	40c. brown	£190	£170
259	**48**	50c. green	£110	11·00
260	**48**	1p. grey	85·00	22·00
261	**48**	4p. violet	£250	£150
262a	**48**	10p. blue	£375	£375

49

1879

263	**49**	2c. black	9·25	4·25
264	**49**	5c. green	13·50	1·10
265	**49**	10c. pink	12·50	45
266	**49**	20c. brown	£130	17·00
267	**49**	25c. grey	17·00	45
268	**49**	40c. brown	31·00	5·50
269b	**49**	50c. yellow	£100	4·50
270	**49**	1p. red	£150	2·20
271	**49**	4p. grey	£800	42·00
272	**49**	10p. bistre	£2000	£275

50 King Alfonso XII

1882

273	**50**	15c. pink	10·50	20
273b	**50**	15c. yellow	65·00	1·50
274	**50**	30c. mauve	£375	6·00
275	**50**	75c. lilac	£325	6·00

51 King Alfonso XIII

1889

276	**51**	2c. green	5·50	45
289	**51**	2c. black	33·00	6·50
277	**51**	5c. blue	9·25	20
290	**51**	5c. green	£110	1·20
278	**51**	10c. brown	16·00	20
291	**51**	10c. red	£325	4·00
279	**51**	15c. brown	4·00	20
280	**51**	20c. green	42·00	4·00
281	**51**	25c. blue	16·00	20
282	**51**	30c. grey	65·00	3·75
283	**51**	40c. brown	65·00	2·50
284	**51**	50c. red	65·00	1·50
285	**51**	75c. orange	£225	4·00
286	**51**	1p. purple	49·00	40
287	**51**	4p. red	£700	46·00
288	**51**	10p. red	£1100	£120

For 15c. yellow see No. O289.

52

1900

292a	**52**	2c. brown	3·75	30
293b	**52**	5c. green	6·50	30
294	**52**	10c. red	10·50	25
295	**52**	15c. black	19·00	25
296	**52**	15c. mauve	12·50	25
297	**52**	15c. violet	7·00	25
298	**52**	20c. black	43·00	2·50
299	**52**	25c. blue	6·50	25
300	**52**	30c. green	43·00	50
301	**52**	40c. bistre	£150	4·75

302	**52**	40c. pink	£325	5·00
303	**52**	50c. blue	43·00	60
304	**52**	1p. purple	39·00	60
305	**52**	4p. purple	£325	22·00
306	**52**	10p. orange	£300	85·00

54 Quixote setting out

1905. Tercentenary of Publication of Cervantes' "Don Quixote".

307	**54**	5c. green	1·30	1·20
308	-	10c. red	3·00	2·00
309	-	15c. violet	3·00	2·00
310	-	25c. blue	10·00	3·75
311	-	30c. green	50·00	10·50
312	-	40c. red	£110	36·00
313	-	50c. grey	24·00	8·00
314	-	1p. red	£350	£100
315	-	4p. purple	£180	£100
316	-	10p. orange	£225	£190

DESIGNS: 10c. Quixote attacking windmill; 15c. Meeting country girls; 25c. Sancho Panza tossed in a blanket; 30c. Don Quixote knighted by innkeeper; 40c. Tilting at the flock of sheep; 50c. On the wooden horse; 1p. Adventure with lions; 4p. In the bullock-cart; 10p. The enchanted lady.

64

1909

344	**64**	2c. brown	65	65
330	**64**	5c. green	2·00	20
331	**64**	10c. red	2·50	20
332	**64**	15c. violet	12·50	20
343	**64**	15c. yellow	6·00	20
334	**64**	20c. green	65·00	75
335	**64**	20c. violet	49·00	20
336	**64**	25c. blue	4·75	20
337	**64**	30c. green	12·50	20
338	**64**	40c. pink	18·00	95
339a	**64**	50c. blue	17·00	45
340	**64**	1p. red	41·00	35
341	**64**	4p. purple	£110	13·50
342	**64**	10p. orange	£140	25·00

1920. Air. Optd CORREO AEREO.

353	5c. green	1·70	1·10
354	10c. red	2·75	1·60
355	25c. blue	4·25	3·00
356	50c. blue	18·00	9·00
357	1p. red	65·00	37·00

66

1920. Imperf.

358	**66**	1c. green	40	15

67 G.P.O., Madrid

1920. U.P.U. Congress, Madrid.

361	**67**	1c. black and green	60	25
362	**67**	2c. black and brown	60	20
363	**67**	5c. black and green	2·30	1·20
364	**67**	10c. black and red	2·30	1·10
365	**67**	15c. black and yellow	3·25	1·70
366	**67**	20c. black and violet	5·00	1·80
367	**67**	25c. black and blue	5·50	3·50
368	**67**	30c. black and green	18·00	6·75
369	**67**	40c. black and red	65·00	9·50
370	**67**	50c. black and blue	80·00	26·00
371	**67**	1p. black and pink	80·00	21·00
372	**67**	4p. black and brown	£225	£110
373	**67**	10p. black and orange	£500	£225

68

69

1922

374	**68**	2c. green	1·30	15
375	**68**	5c. purple	7·75	15
376	**68**	5c. red	3·50	15
377	**68**	10c. red	3·25	1·20
378a	**68**	10c. green	8·00	10
380	**68**	15c. blue	13·50	15
382	**68**	20c. violet	7·75	15
383a	**68**	25c. red	9·50	10
387	**68**	30c. brown	27·00	20
388	**68**	40c. blue	8·25	20
389	**68**	50c. orange	35·00	20
391	**69**	1p. grey	44·00	15
392	**69**	4p. red	£170	5·00
393	**69**	10p. brown	75·00	18·00

70 Princesses Maria Cristina and Beatriz

71 King Alfonso XIII

1926. Red Cross.

394	**70**	1c. black	3·25	2·40
395	-	2c. blue	3·25	2·40
396	-	5c. purple	8·00	5·25
397	-	10c. green	6·50	4·75
398	**70**	15c. blue	2·50	2·00
399	-	20c. violet	3·50	2·75
400	**71**	25c. red	1·10	50
401	**70**	30c. green	70·00	48·00
402	-	40c. blue	43·00	29·00
403	-	50c. red	42·00	28·00
404	-	1p. grey	2·50	1·70
405	-	4p. red	3·50	2·75
406	**71**	10p. brown	3·50	2·75

DESIGNS—VERT: 2, 50c. Queen Victoria Eugenie as nurse; 5, 40c., 4p. Queen Victoria Eugenie; 10, 20c., 1p. Prince of the Asturias.

75 CASA-built Dornier Do-J Wal Flying Boat M-MWAL "Plus Ultra"

76 Route Map and Gallarza and Loriga's Breguet 19A2 Biplane

1926. Air. Red Cross and Trans-Atlantic and Madrid-Manila Flights.

407	**75**	5c. violet and black	4·00	2·20
408	**75**	10c. black and blue	5·00	2·50
409	**76**	15c. blue and red	70	45
410	**76**	20c. red and green	70	45
411	**75**	25c. black and red	70	45
412	**76**	30c. brown and blue	70	45
413	**76**	40c. green and brown	70	45
414	**75**	50c. black and red	70	45
415	**75**	1p. green and black	4·75	3·25
416	**76**	4p. red and yellow	£170	£120

1927. 25th Anniv of Coronation. Red Cross stamps of 1926 variously optd or surch 17-V 1902 17-V 1927 A XIII or 17-V-1902 17-V-1927 ALFONSO XIII or 17 MAYO 17 1902 1927 ALFONSO XIII with ornaments.
(a) Postage stamps of Spain optd only.

417	**70**	1c. black	8·75	6·50
418	-	2c. blue	16·00	13·00
419	-	5c. purple	4·75	3·50
420	-	10c. green	£110	80·00
421	**70**	15c. blue	3·00	2·50
422	-	20c. violet	5·50	4·25
423	**71**	25c. red	95	80
424	**70**	30c. green	1·50	1·20
425	-	40c. blue	1·40	1·10
426	-	50c. red	1·40	1·10
427	-	1p. grey	3·25	2·20
428	-	4p. red	17·00	13·00
429	**71**	10p. brown	65·00	50·00

(b) Postage stamps of Spain also surch with new value.

430	-	3c. on 2c. blue	16·00	13·00
431	-	4c. on 2c. blue	15·00	12·00
432	**71**	10c. on 25c. red	80	55
433	**71**	25c. on 25c. red	80	55
434	-	55c. on 2c. blue	1·30	1·20
435	-	55c. on 10c. green	85·00	65·00
436	-	55c. on 20c. violet	85·00	65·00
437	**70**	75c. on 15c. blue	1·20	80
438	**70**	75c. on 30c. green	£300	£225
439	-	80c. on 5c. purple	80·00	60·00
440	-	2p. on 40c. blue	1·50	1·10
441	-	2p. on 1p. grey	1·50	1·10
442	-	5p. on 50c. red	3·25	2·10
443	-	5p. on 4p. red	5·00	3·25
444	**71**	10p. on 10p. brown	36·00	25·00

(c) Air stamps of Spain optd only.

445	**75**	5c. violet and black	3·50	1·90
446	**75**	10c. black and blue	7·75	3·75
447	**76**	15c. blue and red	70	45
448	**76**	20c. red and green	70	45
449	**75**	25c. black and red	70	45
450	**76**	30c. brown and blue	70	45
451	**76**	40c. green and brown	70	45
452	**75**	50c. black and red	70	45
453	**75**	1p. green and black	4·75	4·25
454	**76**	4p. red and yellow	£200	£140

(d) Air stamps of Spain also surch with new value.

455	**75**	75c. on 5c. violet and black	8·50	6·75
456	**75**	75c. on 10c. black and blue	46·00	29·00
457	**75**	75c. on 25c. black and red	85·00	60·00
458	**75**	75c. on 50c. black and red	33·00	25·00

(e) Nos. 24/5 of Spanish Post Offices in Tangier.

460	1p. on 10p. violet	£200	£200
461	4p. bistre	80·00	80·00

(f) Nos. 122/3 of Spanish Morocco.

462	55c. on 4p. bistre	40·00	40·00
463	80c. on 10p. violet	40·00	40·00

(g) Nos. 34 and 35 of Cape Juby.

464	5p. on 4p. bistre	£100	£100
465	10p. on 10p. violet	80·00	80·00

(h) Nos. 231/2 of Spanish Guinea.

466	1p. on 10p. violet	40·00	40·00
467	2p. on 4p. bistre	40·00	40·00

(i) Nos. 23/4 of Spanish Sahara.

468	80c. on 10p. violet	60·00	60·00
469	2p. on 4p. bistre	40·00	40·00

82 Pope Pius XI and King Alfonso XIII

1928. Rome Catacombs Restoration Fund.

470	**82**	2c. black and violet	55	30
471	**82**	2c. black and purple	60	50
486	**82**	2c. red and black	55	30
487	**82**	2c. red and blue	60	50
472	**82**	3c. violet and black	55	30
473	**82**	3c. violet and blue	60	50
488	**82**	3c. blue and bistre	55	30
489	**82**	3c. blue and green	60	50
474	**82**	5c. violet and green	1·10	80
490	**82**	5c. red and purple	1·10	80
475	**82**	10c. black and green	1·80	1·50
491	**82**	10c. blue and green	1·80	1·50
476	**82**	15c. violet and green	8·00	5·75
492	**82**	15c. red and blue	8·00	5·75
477	**82**	25c. violet and red	8·00	5·75
493	**82**	25c. blue and brown	8·00	5·75
478	**82**	40c. black and blue	55	30
494	**82**	40c. red and blue	55	30
479	**82**	55c. violet and brown	55	30
495	**82**	55c. blue and brown	55	30
480	**82**	80c. black and red	55	30
496	**82**	80c. red and black	55	30
481	**82**	1p. violet and grey	55	30
497	**82**	1p. red and yellow	55	30
482	**82**	2p. black and brown	9·50	7·25
498	**82**	2p. blue and grey	9·50	7·25
483	**82**	3p. violet and pink	9·50	7·25
499	**82**	3p. red and violet	9·50	7·25
484	**82**	4p. black and purple	9·50	7·25
500	**82**	4p. red and purple	9·50	7·25
485	**82**	5p. violet and black	9·50	7·25
501	**82**	5p. blue and yellow	9·50	7·25

83 A Spanish Caravel, Seville in background

84 Miniature of Exhibition Poster

1929. Seville and Barcelona Exhibitions. Inscr "EXPOSICION GENERAL (or GRAL.) ESPANOLA".

502	**83**	1c. green	2·50	2·10
503	**84**	2c. green	40	25
504	-	5c. red	65	45
505	-	10c. green	70	45
506	**83**	15c. blue	2·30	2·10
507	**84**	20c. violet	80	55
508	**83**	25c. red	80	45
509	-	30c. brown	7·50	5·00
510	-	40c. blue	12·50	9·25
511	**84**	50c. orange	7·50	5·00
512	-	1p. grey	17·00	10·00
513	-	4p. purple	46·00	37·00
514	-	10p. brown	£110	80·00

DESIGNS—VERT: 5, 30c., 1p. View of exhibition. HORIZ: 10, 40c., 4, 10p. Alfonso XIII and Barcelona.

87 Ryan NYP "Spirit of St. Louis" over Coast

1929. Air. Seville and Barcelona Exhibitions.

515	**87**	5c. brown	8·50	6·00
516	**87**	10c. red	9·00	6·50
517	**87**	25c. blue	17·00	13·50
518	**87**	50c. violet	13·00	9·00
519	**87**	1p. green	65·00	46·00
520	**87**	4p. black	44·00	32·00

1929. Meeting of Council of League of Nations at Madrid. Optd Sociedad de las Naciones LV reunion del Consejo Madrid.

521	**66**	1c. green	90	75
522	**68**	2c. green	90	75
523	**68**	5c. red	90	75
524	**68**	10c. green	90	75
525	**68**	15c. blue	90	75
526	**68**	20c. violet	90	75
527	**68**	25c. red	90	75
528	**68**	30c. brown	4·00	3·50
529	**68**	40c. blue	4·00	3·50
530	**68**	50c. orange	4·00	3·50
531	**69**	1p. grey	19·00	17·00
532	**69**	4p. red	19·00	17·00
533	**69**	10p. brown	70·00	60·00

89 Class 4601 Steam Locomotive, 1924

1930. 11th Int Railway Congress, Madrid.

534	**89**	1c. green (postage)	1·20	80
535	**89**	2c. green	1·20	80
536	**89**	5c. purple	1·20	80
537	**89**	10c. green	1·20	80
538	**89**	15c. blue	1·20	80
539	**89**	20c. violet	1·20	80
540	**89**	25c. red	1·20	75

541	**89**	30c. brown	3·50	2·75
542	**89**	40c. blue	3·50	2·50
543	**89**	50c. orange	10·50	5·75
544	-	1p. grey	10·50	6·25
545	-	4p. red	£200	£120
546	-	10p. brown	£800	£600

DESIGN: 1p. to 10p. Class 1301 steam locomotive (1914) at points.

90 Stinson Junior over Congress Emblem

547	**90**	5c. brown (air)	10·00	7·75
548	**90**	10c. red	10·00	7·75
549	**90**	25c. blue	10·00	7·75
550	**90**	50c. violet	29·00	19·00
551	**90**	1p. green	60·00	41·00
552	**90**	4p. black	65·00	43·00

91 Francisco Goya (after Lopez) **92**

93 "The Naked Maja"

1930. Death Cent of Goya (painter). (a) Postage.

553	**91**	1c. yellow	20	15
554	**91**	2c. brown	20	15
555	**92**	2c. green	20	15
556	**91**	5c. mauve	20	15
557	**92**	5c. violet	20	15
558	**91**	10c. green	25	15
559	**91**	15c. blue	25	15
560	**91**	20c. purple	25	15
561	**91**	25c. red	25	15
562	**92**	25c. red	35	35
563	**91**	30c. brown	7·00	5·75
564	**91**	40c. blue	7·00	5·75
565	**91**	50c. red	7·00	5·75
566	**91**	1p. black	8·25	7·75
567	**93**	1p. purple	1·10	1·10
568	**93**	4p. black	80	75
569	**93**	10p. brown	17·00	17·00

94 "Flight"

(b) Air. Designs show works by Goya, all with curious flying figures.

570	**94**	5c. yellow and red	20	20
571	-	5c. blue and green	20	20
572	-	10c. green and turquoise	20	20
573	-	15c. red and black	55	40
574	-	20c. red and blue	20	20
575	**94**	25c. red and purple	25	25
576	-	30c. violet and brown	40	40
577	-	40c. blue and ultramarine	75	60
578	-	50c. green and red	75	60
579	-	1p. violet and purple	1·90	1·20
580	-	4p. black and purple	2·50	2·30
581	-	4p. blue and light blue	3·75	3·00
582	-	10p. brown and sepia	16·00	13·00

DESIGNS—VERT: 5, 10, 20, 40c. Asmodeus and Cleofas; 1, 4 (581), 10p. Woman and dwarfs in flight. HORIZ: 30, 50c., 4p. (580), Weird flying methods.

97 King Alfonso XIII

1930

583	**97**	2c. brown	15	15
584	**97**	5c. brown	1·20	15
585	**97**	10c. green	6·25	15
586	**97**	15c. green	28·00	15
587	**97**	20c. violet	12·00	90
588	**97**	25c. red	1·20	15
589	**97**	30c. red	31·00	2·20
590	**97**	40c. blue	55·00	1·50
592	**97**	50c. orange	41·00	2·50

98 The *Santa Maria* **99**

100 *Santa Maria, Pinta* and *Nina* (image scaled to 69% of original size)

101 The Departure from Palos

1930. Columbus issue.

593	**98**	1c. brown	55	20
594	**98**	2c. green	55	20
595	**99**	2c. green	55	20
596	**98**	5c. purple	55	20
597	**99**	5c. purple	55	20
598	**99**	10c. green	1·60	1·00
599	**98**	15c. blue	1·60	1·00
600	**99**	20c. violet	2·20	1·50
601	**100**	25c. red	2·20	1·50
602	**101**	30c. brown, blue and sepia	12·00	8·00
603	**100**	40c. blue	11·00	7·50
604	**101**	50c. violet, blue and purple	13·50	11·00
605	**100**	1p. black	13·50	11·00
606	-	4p. black and blue	14·50	12·00
607	-	10p. brown and purple	60·00	55·00

DESIGNS—As Type **101**: 4, 10p. Arrival in America.

103 Monastery of La Rabida

104 Martin Pinzon

106 Columbus

1930. "Columbus" Air stamps (for Europe and Africa).

608	**103**	5c. red	25	15
609	**103**	5c. brown	25	15
610	**103**	10c. green	40	30
611	**103**	15c. violet	40	30
612	**103**	20c. blue	40	30
613	**104**	25c. red	40	30
614	-	30c. brown	2·75	2·40
615	**104**	40c. blue	2·75	2·40
616	-	50c. orange	2·75	2·40
617	**104**	1p. violet	2·75	2·40
618	**106**	4p. green	2·75	2·40
619	**106**	10p. brown	18·00	16·00

DESIGNS—As Type **104**: 30, 50c. Vincent Pinzon.

107 Monastery of La Rabida

108 Columbus

109 Columbus and the brothers Pinzon

1930. "Columbus" Air stamps (for America and Philippines).

620	**107**	5c. red	25	15
621	**107**	10c. green	25	15
622	**108**	25c. red	30	25
623	**108**	50c. grey	3·25	2·75
624	**108**	1p. brown	3·25	2·75
625	**109**	4p. blue	3·25	2·75
626	**109**	10p. purple	19·00	14·50

110 Arms of Bolivia and Paraguay

1930. Spanish-American Exhibition. Views of pavilions of various countries.

627	**110**	1c. green (postage)	30	15
628	-	2c. brown (C. America)	30	15
629	-	5c. brown (Venezuela)	30	15
630	-	10c. green (Colombia)	65	40
631	-	15c. blue (Dominican Republic)	65	40
632	-	20c. violet (Uruguay)	65	40
633	-	25c. red (Argentina)	65	40
634	-	25c. red (Chile)	65	40
635	-	30c. purple (Brazil)	3·50	2·30
636	-	40c. blue (Mexico)	1·80	1·30
637	-	40c. blue (Cuba)	1·80	1·30
638	-	50c. orange (Peru)	3·50	2·50
639	-	1p. blue (U.S.A.)	5·00	3·50
640	-	4p. purple (Portugal)	65·00	46·00
641	-	10p. brown	4·25	3·00

The 10p. shows King Alfonso and Queen Victoria, maps of S. America and Spain, and the Giralda, Seville. The 2, 5c., 4, 10p. are vert.

113 Sidar and Douglas 0-2-M Biplane

114 Breguet 19GR "Jesus del Gran Poder" over "Santa Maria"

643		5c. black (air)	1·80	95
644		10c. green	1·80	95
645		25c. blue	1·80	95
646		50c. blue	3·25	2·00
647	**113**	50c. black	3·25	2·00
648	-	1p. red	7·25	4·75
649	-	1p. purple	£160	85·00
650	-	1p. green	6·25	4·75
651	**114**	4p. blue	21·00	10·00

DESIGNS—HORIZ: 5c. Alberto Santos Dumont and Wright Flyer I over Rio de Janeiro; 10c. Teodoro Fels and Douglas 0-2-M biplane; 25c. Dagoberto Godoy and Nieuport 17 biplane; 50c. Admiral Gago Coutinha, Sacadura Cabral and Fairey IIID seaplane; 1p. (650) Charles Lindbergh and Ryan NYP Special "Spirirt of St. Louis". VERT: 1p. (648/9) Jimenez Iglesias and Breguet 19GR "Jesus de Gran Poder".

115

1930

652	**115**	5c. black	10·50	15

1931. Optd REPUBLICA. (a) Postage.

660	**66**	1c. green	20	20
673	**97**	2c. brown	30	30
662	**97**	5c. brown	20	20
671	**115**	5c. black	1·90	1·90
675	**97**	10c. green	30	30
664	**97**	15c. green	65	65
677	**97**	20c. violet	45	45
678	**97**	25c. red	45	45
667	**97**	30c. red	5·25	5·25
668	**97**	40c. blue	1·60	1·60
669	**97**	50c. orange	1·60	1·60
670	**69**	1p. grey	9·50	9·50

(b) Air. On Nos. 353/6.

683	**64**	5c. green	11·50	11·50
684	**64**	10c. red	11·50	11·50
685	**64**	25c. blue	16·00	16·00
686	**64**	50c. blue	33·00	33·00

1931. Optd Republica Espanola in two lines continuously.

687	**97**	2c. brown	15	15
688	**97**	5c. brown	45	15
689	**97**	10c. green	65	15
690	**97**	15c. green	6·25	20
691	**97**	20c. violet	2·20	1·40
692	**97**	25c. red	60	15
693	**97**	30c. red	10·00	1·60
694	**97**	40c. blue	8·25	80
695	**97**	50c. orange	16·00	95
696	**69**	1p. grey	£100	1·20

121 The Fountain of the Lions

1931. 3rd Pan-American Postal Union Congress. (a) Postage.

697	**121**	5c. purple	25	15
698	-	10c. green	75	55

699	-	15c. violet	75	55
700	-	25c. red	75	55
701	-	30c. green	75	55
702	**121**	40c. blue	2·00	1·30
703	-	50c. red	2·00	1·30
704	-	1p. black	4·00	2·75
705	-	4p. purple	21·00	14·50
706	-	10p. brown	65·00	46·00

DESIGNS—VERT: 10, 25, 50c. Cordoba Cathedral. HORIZ: 15c., 1p. Alcantara Bridge, Toledo; 30c. Dr. F. Garcia y Santos; 4, 10p. Revolutionaries hoisting Republican flag, 14 April, 1931.

123 Royal Palace and San Francisco el Grande

(b) Air.

707	**123**	5c. purple	20	15
708	**123**	10c. green	20	15
709	**123**	25c. red	20	15
710	-	50c. blue	60	60
711	-	1p. violet	1·10	90
712	-	4p. black	14·50	12·50

DESIGNS—HORIZ: 50c., 1p. G.P.O. and Cibeles Fountain; 4p. Calle de Alcala.

125a Montserrat Arms

1931. 900th Anniv of Montserrat Monastery.

713	**125a**	1c. green (postage)	2·20	1·90
714	**125a**	2c. brown	1·20	85
715	**125a**	5c. brown	1·50	1·00
716	**125a**	10c. green	1·50	1·00
717	-	15c. green	2·10	1·30
718	-	20c. purple	4·50	3·25
719	-	25c. purple	6·00	4·50
720	-	30c. red	70·00	50·00
721	-	40c. blue	40·00	22·00
722	-	50c. orange	95·00	60·00
723	-	1p. blue	95·00	60·00
724	-	4p. mauve	£850	£550
725	-	10p. brown	£700	£475

DESIGNS: 15, 50c. Monks planning Monastery; 20, 30c. "Black Virgin" (full length); 25c., 1, 10p. "Black Virgin" (profile); 40c., 4p. Monastery.

125b Airplane above Montserrat

726	**125b**	5c. brown (air)	70	60
727	**125b**	10c. green	3·75	3·50
728	**125b**	25c. purple	14·00	13·00
729	**125b**	50c. orange	49·00	43·00
730	**125b**	1p. blue	33·00	29·00

126 Blasco Ibanez

127 Pi y Margall

128 Joaquin Costa

129 Mariana Pineda

130 Nicolas Salmeron

131 Concepcion Arenal

132 Ruiz Zorilla

133 Pablo Iglesias

134 Ramon y Cajal

135 Azcarate

136 Jovellanos

137 Pablo Iglesias

138 Emilio Castelar

139 Pablo Iglesias

140 Velazquez

141 F. Salvoechea

142 Cuenca

1931

738	**126**	2c. brown	20	15
731	**127**	5c. brown	5·25	40
740	**126**	5c. brown	15	15
741	**128**	10c. green	8·75	15
742	**129**	10c. green	20	15
744	**130**	15c. green	1·30	15
745	**131**	15c. green	40	15
747	**131**	15c. black	40	10
748	**127**	20c. violet	50	15
734	**133**	25c. red	47·00	1·10
750	**132**	25c. red	1·00	15
751	**133**	30c. red	3·50	15
752	**134**	30c. brown	16·00	2·40
753	**135**	30c. red	17·00	30
755	**136**	30c. red	15	15
756	**137**	30c. red	20	10
757	**139**	30c. red	3·50	45
758	**138**	40c. blue	20	15
759	**138**	40c. red	3·25	45
760	**139**	45c. red	30	10
761	**130**	50c. orange	65·00	1·10
762	**130**	50c. blue	2·75	1·10
763	**140**	50c. blue	20	10
764	**138**	60c. green	20	15
765	**141**	60c. blue	1·90	1·20
766	**141**	60c. orange	17·00	11·50
767c	**142**	1p. black	30	20
768c	-	4p. mauve	95	30
769c	-	10p. brown	1·10	1·10

DESIGNS—As Type **142**: 4p. Castle of Segovia; 10p. Sun Gate, Toledo.

143

144

1933. Imperf (1c.), perf (others).

770	**143**	1c. green	20	20
771	**143**	2c. brown	55	10
772	**144**	2c. brown	†	†
773	**143**	5c. brown	†	†
774	**143**	10c. green	†	†
775	**143**	15c. green	20	20
776a	**143**	20c. violet	1·50	1·50
777a	**143**	25c. mauve	20	20
778	**143**	30c. red	†	†

145 Cierva C.30A Autogyro over Seville

1935

780	**145**	2p. blue	30	20

146 Lope De Vega's Book-plate

148 Scene from "Peribanez"

1935. 300th Death Anniv of Lope de Vega (author).

781	**146**	15c. green	12·00	30
782	-	30c. red	5·25	25
783	-	50c. blue	29·00	3·50
784	**148**	1p. black	47·00	2·30

DESIGN—As Type **146**: 30, 50c. Lope de Vega (after Tristan).

149 Old-time Map of the Amazon

1935. Iglesias' Amazon Expedition.

785	**149**	30c. red	4·75	1·20

150 M. Moya

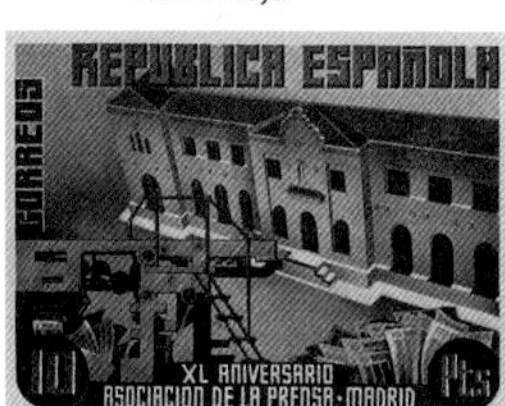

151 House of Nazareth and Rotary Press

1936. 40th Anniv of Madrid Press Association.

786	**150**	1c. red (postage)	15	15
787	-	2c. brown	15	15
788	-	5c. brown	15	15
789	-	10c. green	15	15
790	**150**	15c. green	20	15
791	-	20c. violet	20	15
792	-	25c. mauve	20	15
793	-	30c. red	15	15
794	**150**	40c. orange	70	25
795	-	50c. blue	40	15
796	-	60c. green	90	30
797	-	1p. black	90	30
798	**151**	2p. blue	12·50	4·50
799	**151**	4p. purple	12·50	7·50
800	**151**	10p. red	29·00	18·00

SIZES: 1c. to 10c. 22×27 mm; 15c. to 30c. 24×30 mm; 40c. to 1p. 26×31½ mm.

152 Pyrenean Eagle and Newspapers

153 Airplane over Press Association Building

801	**152**	1c. red (air)	15	15
802	**153**	2c. brown	15	15
803	**152**	5c. brown	15	15
804	**153**	10c. green	15	15
805	-	15c. blue	35	15
806	**152**	20c. violet	35	15
807	**153**	25c. mauve	35	15
808	-	30c. red	15	15
809	**152**	40c. orange	75	35
810	**152**	50c. blue	50	35
811	**153**	60c. green	1·20	35
812	-	1p. black	1·20	35
813	-	2p. blue (45×34 mm)	7·50	4·25
814	-	4p. purple (45×34 mm)	8·25	6·75
815	-	10p. red (45×34 mm)	25·00	16·00

DESIGNS—VERT: 15, 30, 50c., 1p. Cierva C.30A autogyro over House of Nazareth. HORIZ: 2, 4, 10p. Don Quixote on wooden horse.

155 Gregorio Fernandez

1936. 300th Birth Anniv of Gregorio Fernandez (sculptor).

816	**155**	30c. red	2·20	1·00

156

1936. 1st National Philatelic Exhibition, Madrid. Imperf. (a) Postage.

817	**156**	10c. brown	65·00	55·00
818	**156**	15c. green	65·00	55·00

(b) Air. Optd CORREO AEREO.

819	10c. red	£225	£190
820	15c. blue	£225	£190

1936. Manila–Madrid Flight of Arnaiz and Calvo. Optd VUELO MANILA MADRID 1936 ARNAIZ CALVO.

821	**137**	30c. red	8·50	6·25

159

1937. Fiscal stamp of Austrias and Leon surch.

822	**159**	25c. on 5c. red	16·00	8·00
823	**159**	45c. on 5c. red	8·50	4·75
824	**159**	60c. on 5c. red	45	95
825	**159**	1p. on 5c. red	45	65

1938. Surch 45 centimos.

826	**143**	45c. on 1c. green (imperf)	6·00	3·75
827	**143**	45c. on 1c. green (perf)	65	30
830	**143**	45c. on 2c. brown	47·00	45·00
831	**144**	45c. on 2c. brown	20	15
832	**126**	45c. on 2c. brown	36·00	16·00

160a Republican Symbol

1938

833	**160a**	40c. pink	15	15
834	**160a**	45c. red	15	15
835	**160a**	50c. blue	15	15
836	**160a**	60c. blue	80	40

1938. 7th Anniv of Republic. Nos. 308/9 surch 14 ABRIL 1938 VII Aniversario de la Republica and values. (a) Postage.

837	45c. on 15c. violet	19·00	18·00

(b) Air. Additionally optd CORREO AEREO.

838	2p.50 on 10c. red	£140	£130

163 Defence of Madrid

1938. Defence of Madrid Relief Fund. (a) Postage.

839	**163**	45c.+2p. blue & lt blue	95	85
MS840		120×105 mm. No. 839	40·00	48·00

(b) Air. Surch AEREO + 5 Pts.

841	45c.+2p.+5p. blue and light blue	£550	£425
MS842	120×105 mm. No. 841	£7500	£9500

1938. Labour Day. Surch FIESTA DEL TRABAJO 1 MAYO 1938 and values.

843	**54**	45c. on 15c. violet	4·25	4·25
844	**54**	1p. on 15c. violet	7·75	7·25

167 Statue of Liberty and Flags

1938. 150th Anniv of U.S. Constitution. (a) Postage.

845	**167**	1p. multicoloured	29·00	26·00
MS846		120×105 mm. No. 845	45·00	41·00

(b) Air. Surch AEREO + 5 Pts.

847	1p.+5p. multicoloured	£450	£375
MS848	120×105 mm. No. 847	£1700	£1700

169

1938. Red Cross. (a) Postage.

849	**169**	45c.+5p. red	85	65

(b) Air. Surch +3 Pts. Aereo.

850	45c.+5p.+3p. red	17·00	13·00

1938. Air. No. 719 surch with two airplanes, CORREO AEREO twice and value.

851	50c. on 25c. purple	50·00	44·00
852	1p. on 25c. purple	1·90	1·40
853	1p.25 on 25c. purple	1·90	1·40
854	1p.50 on 25c. purple	2·00	1·50
855	2p. on 25c. purple	55·00	44·00

172 Steelworks

1938. Workers of Sagunto.

856	**172**	45c. black	20	15
857	-	1p.25 blue	20	15

DESIGN: 1p.25, Blast furnace and air raid victims.

173 "Isaac Peral"

1938. Submarine Service.

857a	**173**	1p. blue	6·75	6·75
857b	-	2p. brown	12·50	12·50
857c	-	4p. orange	14·50	14·50
857d	-	6p. blue	43·00	29·00
857e	-	10p. purple	55·00	50·00
857f	-	15p. green	£550	£500
MS857g		150×118 mm. 4p. black and red; 6p. black and blue; 15p. black and green	£650	£550

DESIGNS: 2, 6p. "Narciso Monturiol". 4, 10p. "B-2".

174 Troops on the Alert

1938. In Honour of 43rd Division. Perf or imperf.

858	**174**	25c. green	20·00	13·00
859	-	45c. brown	20·00	13·00

DESIGN—VERT: 45c. Two soldiers on guard.

1938. 2nd Anniv of Defence of Madrid. Optd SEGUNDO ANIVERSARIO DE LA HEROICA DEFENSA DE MADRID 7 NOV. 1938.

860	**163**	45c.+2p. blue and light blue	4·25	4·75

1938. No. 719 surch 2'50 PTAS., bars and ornaments.

861	2p.50 on 25c. purple	30	30

176a Man and Woman in Firing Position

1938. In honour of the Militia.

861b	**176a**	5c. brown	4·75	4·25
861c	**176a**	10c. purple	4·75	4·25
861d	**176a**	25c. green	4·75	4·25
861e	-	45c. red	4·75	4·25
861f	-	60c. blue	10·00	7·25
861g	-	1p.20 black	£200	£160
861h	-	2p. orange	60·00	47·00
861i	-	5p. brown	£375	£300
861j	-	10p. green	65·00	55·00

DESIGNS—HORIZ: 45, 60c., 1p.20, Militia with machine gun. VERT: 2, 5, 10p. Grenade-thrower.

NATIONAL STATE

The Civil War began on 17 July 1936. Until it ended on 1 April 1939, the stamps listed below were current only in areas held by the forces of General Franco.

177 Seville Cathedral

178 Xavier Castle, Navarre

1936. Junta of National Defence.

862		5c. brown	95	80
863		15c. green	95	80
864	**177**	25c. red	95	80
865	**178**	30c. red	95	80
867	-	1p. black	8·25	5·25

DESIGNS—VERT: 5c. Burgos Cathedral. HORIZ: 15c. Zaragoza Cathedral; 1p. Alcantara Bridge and Alcazar, Toledo.

179

180 Cordoba Cathedral

1936

868	**179**	1c. green (imperf)	8·25	6·25
869	**179**	2c. brown	95	70
870	-	10c. green	95	70
871	-	50c. blue	24·00	13·50
872	**180**	60c. green	1·60	90
873	-	4p. lilac, red and yellow	95·00	41·00
874	-	10p. brown	85·00	41·00

DESIGNS (As T **180**)—HORIZ: 10c. Salamanca University; 50c. Court of Lions, Granada; 10p. Troops disembarking at Algeciras. VERT: 4p. National flag at Malaga.

181

182

183 "El Cid"

184 Isabella the Catholic

1937

875	**181**	1c. green (imperf)	20	15
876	**182**	2c. brown	20	15
902	**183**	5c. brown	25	15
879	**183**	10c. green	20	15
903	**183**	10c. red	20	15
880	**184**	15c. black	35	20
896	**183**	15c. green	25	15
881	**184**	20c. violet	75	20
882	**184**	25c. red	65	20
883	**184**	30c. red	1·00	20
885	**184**	40c. orange	3·75	20
886	**184**	50c. blue	3·75	20
887	**184**	60c. yellow	65	20
897	**184**	70c. blue	1·20	20
888	**184**	1p. blue	29·00	75
889	**184**	4p. mauve	35·00	7·25
891	**183**	10p. blue	70·00	20·00

See also No. 1113.

186 Santiago Cathedral

1937. Holy Year of Compostela.

905	-	15c. brown	3·50	80
906	**186**	30c. red	12·00	70
908	-	1p. orange and blue	41·00	4·25

DESIGNS—VERT: 15c. St. James of Compostela. HORIZ: 1p. Portico de la Gloria.

188 Alcazar, Toledo (before Siege)

1937. 1st Anniv of National Uprising. Sheets 140×110 mm containing T 909 and similar designs.

MS909 **188**	2p. (+2p.) orange	42·00	30·00
MS910	Imperf	£600	£500
MS911 –	2p. (+2p.) green	42·00	30·00
MS912 –	Imperf	£600	£500

DESIGN: No. **MS**911/12 Alcazar in ruins.

189

1937. Anti-tuberculosis Fund. Cross in red.

913	**189**	10c. blue and black	15·00	6·00

189a Covadonga Monastery

1938. Historic Monuments. Sheet 140×100 mm containing T 189a and similar designs.

MS914	20c. violet, 30c. red, 50c. blue, 1p. green (sold at 4p.)	75·00	65·00
MS915	Imperf	£130	£100

DESIGNS—VERT: 30c. Cathedral, Palma de Mallorca; 50c. Alcazar, Segovia. VERT 1p. Leon Cathedral.

190 Ferdinand the Catholic

1938

917	**190**	15c. green	4·00	15
918	**190**	20c. violet	17·00	2·50
919	**190**	25c. red	1·20	15
921	**190**	30c. red	11·50	15

1938. Air. Optd correo aereo.

922	50c. blue	1·70	80
923	1p. blue	4·75	80

191a Soldier with Flag

1938. Honouring Army and Navy. Sheet 175×132 mm containing designs as T 191a (various frames).

MS924	2c. violet (Type **191a**), 2c. violet (a), 3c. blue (b), 3c. blue (c), 5c. sepia (a), 5c. sepia (Type **191a**), 10c. green (b), 10c. green (c), 30c. orange (b), 30c. orange (c). Two of each stamp (sold at 4p.)	50·00	48·00
MS925	Imperf	£250	£190

DESIGNS: (a) Cruiser *Almirante Cervera*; (b) Trenches near Teruel; (c) General Franco's Moorish bodyguard.

192

1938. 2nd Anniv of National Uprising.

926	**192**	15c. green and light green	7·25	5·50
927	**192**	25c. red and pink	7·25	5·50
928	**192**	30c. blue and light blue	3·75	3·00
929	**192**	1p. brown and yellow	£160	£110

193 Isabella the Catholic

1938

930	**193**	20c. violet	2·75	20
931	**193**	25c. red	14·50	80
932	**193**	30c. red	40	20
933	**193**	40c. mauve	40	15
934	**193**	50c. blue	55·00	3·25
935	**193**	1p. blue	19·00	1·30

193a Don Juan of Austria

1938. Battle of Lepanto. Sheets each 90×75 mm containing T 193a and another design.

MS936 **193a**	30c. carmine (perf)	24·00	†
MS937 –	50c. blue	24·00	†
MS938 **193a**	30c. violet (imperf)	£500	†
MS939 –	50c. green	£500	†

DESIGN—(36½×23 mm): 50c. Naval Battle of Lepanto.

194

1938. Anti-tuberculosis Fund. Cross in red.

940	194	10c. blue and black	9·25	2·40

195 Juan de la Cierva and Cierva C.30A Autogyro

1939. Air.

1010	195	20c. orange	25	15
1011	195	25c. red	25	15
943	195	35c. mauve	80	40
1013	195	50c. brown	55	15
945	195	1p. blue	1·20	25
1015	195	2p. green	2·40	20
1016	195	4p. blue	8·25	30
1017	195	10p. violet	6·50	80

196 General Franco

1939

960	196	5c. brown	50	20
961	196	10c. red	2·50	1·00
962	196	15c. green	70	20
1114	196	20c. violet	25	15
1115	196	25c. purple	30	15
950	196	30c. red	40	20
1116	196	30c. blue	35	15
1117	196	35c. blue	55	20
951	196	40c. green	40	20
966	196	40c. grey	60	15
952	196	45c. red	3·25	2·50
1119	196	45c. blue	25	15
1120	196	50c. grey	45	15
1121	196	60c. orange	25	15
955	196	70c. blue	50	20
956	196	1Pts. black	19·00	20
974	196	1PTA. black	8·50	15
975	196	1PTS. grey	90·00	95
957	196	2Pts. brown	28·00	1·60
1124	196	2PTAS. brown	7·00	15
958	196	4Pts. purple	£170	19·00
1125	196	4PTAS. red	16·00	20
959	196	10Pts. brown	80·00	45·00
978	196	10PTS. brown	£250	4·75
1126	196	10PTAS. brown	3·75	60

For 10c. brown imperf, see No. 981.

197 "Spain" and Wreath of Peace

1939. Homage to the Army.

980	197	10c. blue	35	15

1939. Anti-tuberculosis Fund. Imperf.

981	196	10c. brown	35	15

198 Ruins of Belchite

1940. Zaragoza Cathedral Restoration Fund and 19th Centenary of Apparition of Virgin of El Pilar at Zaragoza. (a) Postage.

982	198	10c.+5c. brown and blue	20	15
983	-	15c.+10c. green and lilac	20	15
984	-	20c.+10c. blue & violet	20	15
985	-	25c.+10c. brown & red	20	15
986	-	40c.+10c. purple & grn	20	15
987	-	45c.+15c. red and blue	40	30
988	198	70c.+20c. black & brn	40	30
989	-	80c.+20c. violet and red	50	40
990	-	1p.+30c. purple & black	50	40
991	-	1p.40+40c. black & vio	60·00	48·00
992	-	1p.50+50c. purple & bl	70	60
993	-	2p.50+50c. blue & pur	70	60
994	-	4p.+1p. grey and lilac	21·00	16·00
995	-	10p.+4p. brown & blue	£300	£225

DESIGNS—HORIZ: 15, 80c. Procession of the Rosary; 20c., 1p.50, El Pilar; 25c., 1p. Mother Rafols praying; 40c., 2p.50, Sanctuary of the Virgin; 45c., 1p.40, Oath of the besieged; 4p. Miracle of Calanda; 10p. Virgin appearing to St. James.

(b) Air.

996	25c.+5c. grey and purple	30	30
997	50c.+5c. violet and red	30	30
998	65c.+15c. blue and violet	30	30
999	70c.+15c. violet and grey	30	30
1000	90c.+20c. red and brown	30	30
1001	1p.20+30c. purple & violet	30	30
1002	1p.40+40c. brown & blue	70	35
1003	2p.+50c. violet and purple	1·10	70
1004	4p.+1p. purple and green	16·00	11·00
1005	10p.+4p. blue and brown	£400	£300

DESIGNS—VERT: 25, 70c. Prayer during bombardment; 50c., 1p.40, Caravel and Image of the Virgin; 65, 90c. The Assumption; 1p.20, 2p. Coronation of the Virgin; 4p. "The Cave", after Goya; 10p. Bombing of Zaragoza Cathedral.

199 Gen. Franco

1940. Anti-tuberculosis Fund.

1006	199	10c. violet and red (post)	25	20
1007	199	20c.+5c. green and red	1·20	80
1008	199	40c.+10c. blue and red	1·90	50
1009	199	10c. pink and red (air)	1·80	1·10

200 Knight and Cross of Lorraine

1941. Anti-tuberculosis Fund.

1018	200	10c. black and red (post)	35	20
1019	200	20c.+5c. violet and red	90	40
1020	200	40c.+10c. grey and red	90	40
1021	200	10c. blue and red (air)	65	30

201 Gen. Franco

1942

1022	201	40c. brown	45	20
1023	201	75c. blue	5·25	70
1024a	201	90c. green	40	20
1025b	201	1p.35 violet	45	20

202 St. John of the Cross

1942. 400th Birth Anniv of St. John of the Cross.

1026	202	20c. violet	1·00	20
1027	202	40c. orange	2·40	40
1028	202	75c. blue	2·50	2·10

203 Arms and Lorraine Cross

1942. Anti-T.B. Fund. Inscr "1942–43".

1029	203	10c. orange and red (postage)	20	20
1030	203	20c.+5c. brown and red	2·10	1·90
1031	203	40c.+10c. green and red	1·70	30
1032	-	10c. orange and red (air)	1·40	65

DESIGN—HORIZ: No. 1032, Lorraine Cross and two doves in flight.

204 St. James of Compostela

205

1943. Holy Year. Inscr "ANO SANTO 1943".

1033	204	20c. blue	30	20
1034	-	20c. red	30	20
1035	-	20c. lilac	30	20
1036	-	40c. brown	85	20
1037	205	40c. green	70	20
1038	-	40c. brown	85	20
1039	-	75c. blue	4·00	2·30
1040	-	75c. blue	4·50	2·50
1041	-	75c. blue	65·00	47·00

DESIGNS—VERT: Nos. 1034 and 1040. Details of pillars in Santiago Cathedral; No. 1036, St. James enthroned; No. 1038, Portal of Santiago Cathedral; No. 1039, Censer; No. 1041, Santiago Cathedral. HORIZ: No. 1035, Tomb of St. James.

206

1943. Anti-Tuberculosis Fund. Inscr "1943–1944".

1042	206	10c. violet & red (postage)	45	30
1043	206	20c.+5c. green and red	6·00	1·90
1044	206	40c.+10c. blue and red	3·75	1·30
1045	-	10c. violet and red (air)	1·80	1·30

DESIGN: No. 1045. Lorraine Cross and outline of bird.

207 10th-cent Tower

208 Arms of Soria

1944. Millenary of Castile. Arms designs as T 208 inscr "MILENARIO DE CASTILLA".

1046	207	20c. lilac	40	25
1047	208	20c. lilac	30	25
1048	-	20c. lilac	30	25
1049	-	40c. brown	5·00	80
1050	-	40c. brown	5·00	80
1051	-	40c. brown	3·75	85
1052	-	75c. blue	5·25	4·50
1053	-	75c. blue	4·50	4·50
1054	-	75c. blue	6·25	5·00

DESIGNS: No. 1048, Avila (Shield at left); No. 1049, Castile (Arms in centre); No. 1050, Segovia (Shield at left); No. 1051, Burgos (Shield at right); No. 1052, Avila (Shield at left); No. 1053, Fernan Gonzalez, founder of Castile (Helmet, bow and arrows at left); No. 1054, Santander (Shield at right).

209 "Dr. Thebussem" (M. P. de Figueroa, author and postal historian) and Douglas DC-2

1944. Air. Stamp Day.

1055	209	5p. blue	27·00	20·00

210

1944. Anti-tuberculosis Fund. Inscr "1944 1945". (a) Postage.

1056	210	10c. orange and red	20	15
1057	210	20c.+5c. black and red	40	40
1058	210	40c.+10c. violet & red	90	70
1059	210	80c.+10c. blue and red	15·00	13·00

(b) Air. Inscr "CORRESPONDENCIA AEREA".

1060	25c. orange and red	7·00	5·75

DESIGN—HORIZ: No. 1060, Hospital.

211 Quevedo

1945. 300th Death Anniv of Francisco de Quevedo (author).

1061	211	40c. brown	1·20	80

212 Conde de San Luis, Mail Vehicle of 1850 and Airplane

1945. Air. Stamp Day.

1062	212	10p. green	35·00	21·00

213 Carlos de Haya Gonzalez

214 J. Garcia Morato and Fiat CR-32 biplane

1945. Air. Civil War Air Aces.

1063	213	4p. red	18·00	9·50
1064	214	10p. purple	48·00	9·75

215 St. George and Dragon

216 Lorraine Cross and Eagle

1945. Anti-T.B. Fund.

1065	215	10c. orge & red (postage)	25	15
1066	215	20c.+5c. green and red	40	35
1067	215	40c.+10c. violet and red	70	20
1068	215	80c.+10c. blue and red	17·00	11·50
1069	216	25c. red (air)	2·75	1·70

217 E. A. de Nebrija (compiler of first Spanish Grammar)

219 Statue of Fray Bartolome de las Casas and native Indian

1946. Stamp Day and Day of the Race.

1070	217	50c. red (postage)	85	25
1071	-	75c. blue	1·00	70
1072	219	5p.50 green (air)	5·50	3·50

DESIGN—As Type 217: 75c. Salamanca University and signature of F. F. de Vitoria (founder of International Law).

220 Self-portrait of Goya

1946. Birth Bicentenary of Goya (painter).

1073	220	25c. red	20	15
1074	220	50c. green	25	15
1075	220	75c. blue	1·20	85

221 Woman and Child

1946. Anti-tuberculosis Fund. Dated "1946 1947".
1076 **221** 5c. violet and red (postage) 30 15
1077 **221** 10c. green and red 30 15
1078 - 25c. orange and red (air) 55 25
DESIGN—HORIZ: 25c. Eagle.

222 B. J. Feijoo y Montenegro

1947
1079 **222** 50c. green 1·40 70

223 Don Quixote in Library **224** Don Quixote

1947. Stamp Day and 400th Birth Anniv of Cervantes.
1080 **223** 50c. brown (postage) 50 20
1081 **224** 75c. blue 1·10 50
1082 - 5p.50 violet (air) 10·00 6·25
DESIGN—HORIZ: 5p.50, Quixote on Wooden Horse (after Gustav Dore).

226 Manuel de Falla (composer)

1947. Air.
1083 **226** 25p. purple 75·00 27·00
1084 - 50p. red £275 60·00
PORTRAIT: 50p. Ignacio Zuloaga (painter).

228 Lorraine Cross

1947. Anti-tuberculosis Fund. Dated "1947 1948".
1085 **228** 5c. brown & red (postage) 25 15
1086 - 10c. blue and red 25 20
1087 - 25c. mauve and red (air) 55 25
DESIGNS—VERT: 10c. Deckchair in garden. HORIZ: 25c. Sanatorium.

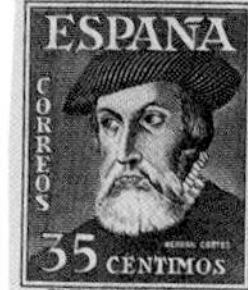

229 General Franco

1948
1088 **229** 5c. brown 25 20
1088a **229** 5c. green 20 20
1089 **229** 15c. green 25 20
1090 **229** 50c. brown 4·50 20
1091 **229** 80c. red 6·50 20

230 Hernando Cortes

1948
1092 **230** 35c. black 25 20
1093 - 70c. purple 4·25 2·50
PORTRAIT: 70c. M. Aleman (writer).

232 Gen. Franco and Castillo de la Mota

1948
1094 **232** 25c. orange 30 20
1095 **232** 30c. green 40 15
1096 **232** 35c. green 30 20
1097 **232** 40c. brown 1·70 20
1099 **232** 45c. red 1·20 20
1100 **232** 50c. purple 2·40 20
1101 **232** 70c. violet 3·50 20
1102 **232** 75c. blue 3·25 20
1103 **232** 1p. red 9·75 20

233 Ferdinand III of Castile

1948. 700th Anniv of Institution of Castilian Navy.
1104 **233** 25c. violet 55 20
1105 - 30c. red (Admiral R. de Bonifaz) 35 20

235 Marquis of Salamanca **236** Series ABJ Diesel Railcar (1936) and Lockheed Constellation Airliner

1948. Stamp Day and Spanish Railway Centenary Inscr "F.F.C.C. ESPANOLES 1848 1948".
1106 **235** 50c. brown (postage) 90 20
1107 - 5p. green 3·75 20
1108 **236** 2p. red (air) 4·25 2·20
DESIGN—HORIZ: 5p. Garganta de Pancorbo Viaduct.

238 Aesculapius

1948. Anti-tuberculosis Fund. Dated "1948 1949".
1109 **238** 5c. brown & red (postage) 25 15
1110 **238** 10c. green and red 25 20
1111 **238** 50c.+10c. brown & red 1·70 1·00
1112 - 25c. blue and red (air) 70 40
DESIGN: 25c. Lockheed Constellation airliner over sanatorium.

1949. Relief of War Victims. As T 183, but larger and inscr "AUXILIO A LAS VICTIMAS DE LA GUERRA 1946".
1113 5c. violet 40 25

240 Globe and Buildings

1949. 75th Anniv of U.P.U.
1127 **240** 50c. brown (postage) 1·40 25
1128 **240** 75c. blue 1·00 50
1129 **240** 4p. green (air) 75 45

241 Galleon

1949. Anti-tuberculosis Fund. Inscr "1949 1950".
1130 **241** 5c. violet & red (postage) 15 15
1131 **241** 10c. green and red 15 15
1132 **241** 50c.+10c. brown & red 1·00 40
1133 - 25c. brown and red (air) 30 25
DESIGN: 25c. Bell.

242 San Juan de Dios and Leper

1950. 400th Death Anniv of San Juan de Dios.
1134 **242** 1p. violet 23·00 7·00

243 Calderon de la Barca (dramatist)

1950. Portraits.
1135 **243** 5c. brown 25 20
1136 - 10c. purple 25 25
1137 - 15c. green 50 20
1138 - 20c. violet 1·10 20
1139 - 2p. blue 35·00 35
1140 - 4p.50 purple 1·70 1·40
PORTRAITS—VERT: 10c. Lope de Vega (author); 15c. Tirso de Molina (poet); 20c. Ruiz de Alarcon (author); 2p. Dr. Ramon y Cajal (physician); 4p.50, Dr. Ferran y Clua (bacteriologist).

244 Isabella II

1950. Stamp Centenary. Imperf. (a) Postage. Reproduction of T 1.
1141 **244** 50c. violet 16·00 8·25
1142 **244** 75c. blue 16·00 8·25
1143 **244** 10p. green £170 £120
1144 **244** 15p. red £170 £120

(b) Air. Reproduction of T 2.
1145 1p. purple 16·00 8·25
1146 2p.50 brown 16·00 8·25
1147 20p. blue £170 £120
1148 25p. green £170 £120

1950. Gen. Franco's Canary Is Visit. Nos. 1100 and 1103 surch VISITA DEL CAUDILLO A CANARIAS OCTUBRE 1950 SOBRETASA: DIEZ CTS and No. 1083 with Correspondencia por avion also.
1149B **232** 10c. on 50c. purple (postage) £100 60·00
1150B **232** 10c. on 1p. red £100 60·00
1151 **226** 10c. on 25p. purple (air) £750 £350

246 Candle and Conifer

1950. Anti-T.B. Fund. Cross in red. Inscr "1950 1951".
1152 **246** 5c. violet (postage) 20 20
1153 **246** 10c. green 20 20
1154 **246** 50c.+10c. brown 3·00 1·40
1155 - 25c. blue (air) 90 40

DESIGN: 25c. Dove and flowers.

247 Map

1951. Air. 6th Conference of Spanish-American Postal Union.
1156 **247** 1p. blue 9·50 3·50

248 Isabella the Catholic

1951. 5th Centenary of Birth of Isabella.
1157 **248** 50c. brown 1·40 50
1158 **248** 75c. blue 1·80 45
1159 **248** 90c. purple 70 25
1160 **248** 1p.50 orange 19·00 10·00
1161 **248** 2p.80 olive 43·00 28·00

248a St. Antonio Claret

1951. Stamp Day.
1162 **248a** 50c. blue 6·50 4·25

249 Children on Beach

1951. Anti-tuberculosis Fund. Cross in red.
1163 **249** 5c. red (postage) 20 15
1164 **249** 10c. green 90 20
1165 - 25c. brown (air) 1·20 20
DESIGN: 25c. Nurse and child.

250 Isabella the Catholic

1951. Air. Stamp Day and 500th Birth Anniv of Isabella the Catholic.
1166 **250** 60c. green 10·00 55
1167 **250** 90c. yellow 1·30 70
1168 **250** 1p.30 red 13·50 6·25
1169 **250** 1p.90 sepia 10·00 7·75
1170 **250** 2p.30 blue 6·00 4·00

251 Ferdinand the Catholic

1952. 500th Birth Anniv of Ferdinand the Catholic.
1171 **251** 50c. green 1·10 25
1172 **251** 75c. blue 10·50 2·00
1173 **251** 90c. purple 75 25
1174 **251** 1p.50 orange 20·00 10·50
1175 **251** 2p.80 brown 32·00 22·00

252 St. Maria Micaela

1952. 35th International Eucharistic Congress, Barcelona.

1176	**252**	90c. red (postage)	35	20
1177	-	1p. green (air)	5·50	60

DESIGN: 1p. "The Eucharist" (Tiepolo).

252a St. Francis Xavier

1952. Air. 400th Death Anniv of St. Francis Xavier.

1178	**252a**	2p. blue	85·00	30·00

1952. Air. Stamp Day and 500th Anniv of Birth of Ferdinand the Catholic. As T 250 but interior scene and portrait of Ferdinand the Catholic.

1179	60c. green	25	20
1180	90c. orange	25	20
1181	1p.30 red	1·10	1·10
1182	1p.90 brown	4·00	2·75
1183	2p.30 blue	19·00	12·00

254 Nurse and Baby

1953. Anti-tuberculosis Fund. Cross in red.

1184	**254**	5c. lake (postage)	90	15
1185	**254**	10c. green	2·30	20
1186	-	25c. brown (air)	8·75	6·75

DESIGN: 25c. Girl and angel.

255 J. Sorolla (painter)

1953. Air.

1187	**255**	50p. violet	£850	31·00

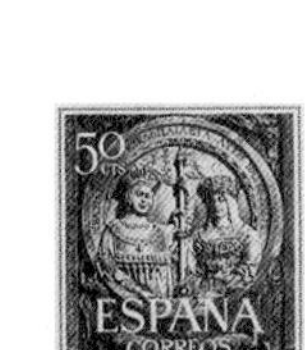

256 Bas-relief

257 Fray Luis de Leon

1953. Stamp Day and 700th Anniv of Salamanca University. Inscr "UNIVDAD DE SALAMANCA".

1188	**256**	50c. red	55	25
1189	**257**	90c. green	3·25	3·00
1190	-	2p. brown	24·00	6·25

DESIGN—As Type **185**—HORIZ: 2p. Salamanca University.

258 M. L. de Legazpi (founder of Manila)

1953. Air. Signing of Filipino–Spanish Postal Convention.

1191	**258**	25p. black	£190	45·00

259 "St. Mary Magdalene"

1954. Death Tercentenary of Ribera (painter).

1192	**259**	1p.25 lake	35	20

260 St. James of Compostela

1954. Holy Year.

1193	**260**	50c. brown	65	25
1194	-	3p. blue	80·00	5·75

DESIGN: 3p. Santiago Cathedral.

261 "Purity" (after Cano)

1954. Marian Year.

1195	**261**	10c. red	35	15
1196	-	15c. green	35	15
1197	-	25c. violet	35	15
1198	-	30c. brown	35	15
1199	-	50c. green	1·20	15
1200	-	60c. black	35	15
1201	-	80c. green	4·75	15
1202	-	1p. violet	4·75	15
1203	-	2p. brown	1·40	20
1204	-	3p. blue	2·00	1·30

DESIGNS: 15c. Virgin of Begona, Bilbao; 25c. Virgin of the Abandoned, Valencia Cathedral; 30c. The "Black Virgin" of Montserrat; 50c. El Pilar Virgin, Zaragoza; 60c. Covadonga Virgin; 80c. Virgin of the Kings, Seville Cathedral; 1p. Almudena Virgin, Madrid; 2p. Virgin of Africa; 3p. Guadalupe Virgin.

262 M. Menendez Pelayo (historian)

1954. Stamp Day.

1205	**262**	80c. green	10·50	20

263 Gen. Franco

1955

1206	**263**	10c. red	15	15
1207	**263**	15c. ochre	15	15
1208	**263**	20c. green	15	15
1209	**263**	25c. violet	15	15
1210	**263**	30c. brown	15	15
1211	**263**	40c. purple	15	15
1212	**263**	50c. brown	15	15
1213	**263**	60c. purple	20	15
1214	**263**	70c. green	20	15
1215	**263**	80c. turquoise	20	15
1216	**263**	1p. orange	15	15
1217	**263**	1p.40 mauve	25	20
1218	**263**	1p.50 turquoise	25	20
1219	**263**	1p.80 green	25	20
1220	**263**	2p. red	23·00	1·00
1221	**263**	2p. mauve	25	20
1222	**263**	3p. blue	20	15
1222a	**263**	4p. red	15	15
1223	**263**	5p. brown	25	15
1224	**263**	6p. black	25	15
1224a	**263**	7p. blue	20	15
1225	**263**	8p. violet	25	20
1226	**263**	10p. green	25	15
1226a	**263**	12p. green	20	15
1226b	**263**	20p. red	20	15

264 Torres Quevedo (engineer and inventor)

1955. Air.

1229	-	25p. black	34·00	90
1230	**264**	50p. violet	13·00	2·20

PORTRAIT: 25p. Fortuny (painter).

265 St. Ignatius of Loyola

1955. Stamp Day and 4th Centenary of Death of St. Ignatius of Loyola.

1231	**265**	25c. slate	20	20
1232	-	60c. ochre	1·00	45
1233	**265**	80c. green	4·50	45

DESIGN—HORIZ: 60c. St. Ignatius and Loyola Castle.

266 Lockheed L.1049 Super Constellation and Caravel

1955. Air.

1234	**266**	20c. green	20	20
1235	**266**	25c. violet	15	15
1236	**266**	50c. brown	20	20
1237	**266**	1p. red	15	15
1238	**266**	1p.10 green	35	20
1239	**266**	1p.40 mauve	20	15
1240	**266**	3p. blue	35	20
1241	**266**	4p.80 yellow	20	15
1242	**266**	5p. brown	2·00	15
1243	**266**	7p. mauve	1·00	20
1244	**266**	10p. green	90	35

267 "Telecommunications"

1955. Centenary of Telegraphs in Spain.

1245	**267**	15c. brown	55	25
1246	**267**	80c. green	13·00	25
1247	**267**	3p. blue	23·00	1·40

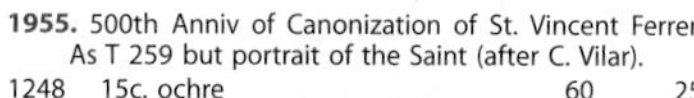

1955. 500th Anniv of Canonization of St. Vincent Ferrer. As T 259 but portrait of the Saint (after C. Vilar).

1248	15c. ochre	60	25

269 "The Holy Family" (after El Greco)

1955. Christmas.

1249	**269**	80c. myrtle	7·00	70

270

1956. 20th Anniv of Civil War.

1250	**270**	15c. brown and bistre	20	20
1251	**270**	50c. olive and green	90	50
1252	**270**	80c. grey and mauve	9·25	25
1253	**270**	3p. blue and ultramarine	13·00	2·50

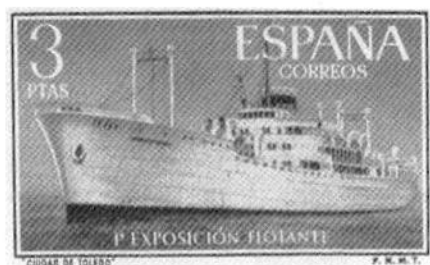

271 "Ciudad de Toledo" (cargo liner)

1956. 1st Floating Exhibition of National Products.

1254	**271**	3p. blue	6·50	2·75

272 The "Black Virgin"

1956. 75th Anniv of "Black Virgin" of Montserrat.

1255	**272**	15c. brown	35	20
1256	-	60c. purple	40	25
1257	**272**	80c. green	45	45

DESIGN—VERT: 60c. Montserrat Monastery.

273 Archangel Gabriel

1956. Stamp Day.

1258	**273**	80c. green	70	40

274 "Statistics"

1956. Centenary of Statistics in Spain.

1259	**274**	15c. ochre	45	30
1260	**274**	80c. green	5·50	65
1261	**274**	1p. red	5·50	65

275 Hermitage and Monument

1956. 20th Anniv of Gen. Franco's Assumption of Office as Head of State.

1262	**275**	80c. green	6·50	40

276 Refugee Children

1956. Hungarian Children's Relief.

1263	**276**	10c. lake	20	20
1264	**276**	15c. brown	20	20
1265	**276**	50c. sepia	55	20
1266	**276**	80c. green	5·00	25
1267	**276**	1p. red	5·00	25
1268	**276**	3p. blue	19·00	2·75

277 Apparition of the Sacred Heart

1957. Stamp Day and Centenary Feast of the Sacred Heart.

1269	**277**	15c. brown	20	15
1270	**277**	60c. purple	25	20
1271	**277**	80c. green	25	20

278 "The Great Captain"

1958. 5th Birth Cent of Gonzalves de Cordoba.

1272	**278**	1p.80 green	20	15

279 Francisco Goya after Lopez

1958. Stamp Day and Goya (painter) Commem. Frames in gold.

1273	-	15c. ochre	20	15
1274	-	40c. purple	20	15
1275	-	50c. green	20	15
1276	-	60c. purple	20	15
1277	-	70c. green	20	15
1278	**279**	80c. green	20	15
1279	-	1p. red	20	15
1280	-	1p.80 green	20	15
1281	-	2p. purple	45	25
1282	-	3p. blue	1·10	50

PAINTINGS—HORIZ: 15c. "The Sunshade"; 3p. "The Drinker". VERT: 40c. "The Bookseller's Wife"; 50c. "The Count of Fernan-Nunez"; 60c. "The Crockery Vendor"; 70c. "Dona Isabel Cobos de Porcel"; 1p. "The Carnival Doll"; 1p.80, "Marianito Goya"; 2p. "The Vintage".

For similar designs see Nos. 1301/10, 1333/42, 1391/1400, 1479/88, 1495/8, 1559/68, 1627/36, 1718/27, 1770/9, 1837/46, 1912/21, 1968/77, 2021/30, 2077/84, 2135/42 and 2204/11.

280 Exhibition Emblem

1958. Brussels International Exhibition.

1283	**280**	80c. brown, red and deep brown	20	15
1284	**280**	3p. blue, red and black	95	90

1958. Brussels Exhibition, Madrid. Sheets each 49×83 mm containing Nos. 1283/4 in new colours.

MS1285	80c. green, red and brown (sold at 2p.)	37·00	27·00
MS1286	3p. violet, orange and brown (sold at 5p.)	37·00	27·00

281 Emperor Charles V (after Strigell)

1958. 4th Death Cent of Emperor Charles V.

1287	**281**	15c. brown and ochre	15	15
1288	-	50c. olive and green	15	15
1289	-	70c. green and drab	20	15
1290	-	80c. green and brown	20	15
1291	**281**	1p. red and buff	25	15
1292	-	1p.80 emerald and green	20	15
1293	-	2p. purple and grey	65	50
1294	-	3p. blue and brown	1·70	1·30

PORTRAITS of Charles V: 50c., 1p.80, At Battle of Muhlberg (after Titian); 70c., 2p. (after Leoni); 80c., 3p. (after Titian).

282 Talgo II Articulated Train and Escorial

1958. 17th Int Railway Congress, Madrid. Inscr "XVII CONGRESO", etc.

1295	**282**	15c. ochre	15	15
1296	-	60c. plum	15	15
1297	-	80c. green	20	15
1298	**282**	1p. orange	60	20
1299	-	2p. purple	60	25
1300	-	3p. blue	2·75	1·20

DESIGNS—VERT: 60c., 2p. Class 1600 diesel-electric locomotive on viaduct, Despenaperros Gorge. HORIZ: 80c., 3p. Class 242F steam locomotive and Castillo de La Mota.

1959. Stamp Day and Velazquez Commem. Designs as T 279. Frames in gold.

1301	15c. sepia	20	20
1302	40c. purple	20	20
1303	50c. olive	20	20
1304	60c. sepia	20	20
1305	70c. green	20	20
1306	80c. myrtle	20	20
1307	1p. brown	20	20
1308	1p.80 green	20	20
1309	2p. purple	50	30
1310	3p. blue	1·00	50

PAINTINGS—HORIZ: 15c. "The Drunkards". VERT: 40c. "The Spinners" (detail); 50c. "The Surrender of Breda"; 60c. "Las Meninas"; 70c. "Balthasar Don Carlos"; 80c. Self-portrait; 1p. "The Coronation of the Virgin"; 1p.80, "Aesop"; 2p. "The Forge of Vulcan"; 3p. "Menippus".

284 The Holy Cross of the Valley of the Fallen

1959. Completion of Monastery of the Holy Cross of the Valley of the Fallen.

1311	**284**	80c. green and brown	20	15

285 Mazarin and Luis de Haro (after tapestry by Lebrun)

1959. 300th Anniv of Treaty of the Pyrenees.

1312	**285**	1p. brown and gold	20	20

286 Monastery from Courtyard

1959. 50th Anniv of Entry of Franciscan Community into Guadeloupe Monastery.

1313	**286**	15c. brown	25	15
1314	-	80c. myrtle	30	15
1315	-	1p. red	30	20

DESIGNS: 80c. Exterior view of monastery; 1p. Entrance doors of church.

287 "The Holy Family" (after Goya)

1959. Christmas.

1316	**287**	1p. brown	35	15

288 Pass with Muleta

1960. Bullfighting.

1317	-	15c. brown and ochre (postage)	20	20
1318	-	20c. violet and blue	20	20
1319	-	25c. black	20	20
1320	-	30c. brown and bistre	20	20
1321	-	50c. brown and violet	20	20
1322	-	70c. green and brown	20	20
1323	**288**	80c. emerald and green	20	20
1324	-	1p. brown and red	25	20
1325	-	1p.40 purple and brown	20	20
1326	-	1p.50 green and blue	20	20
1327	-	1p.80 blue and green	20	20
1328	-	5p. red and brown	70	55
1329	-	25c. dp pur & pur (air)	20	20
1330	-	50c. blue and turquoise	20	20
1331	-	1p. red and vermilion	25	20
1332	-	5p. violet and purple	65	45

DESIGNS—HORIZ: No. 1317, Fighting bull; No. 1318, Rounding-up bull; No. 1327, Placing darts from horseback; No. 1330, Pass with cape; No. 1332, Bull-ring. VERT: No. 1319, Corralling bulls at Pamplona; No. 1320, Bull entering ring; No. 1321, As No. 1330 (different pass); No. 1322, Banderillero placing darts; No. 1323/6, As Type **288** (different passes with muleta); No. 1328, Old-time bullfighter; No. 1329, Village bull-ring; No. 1331, Dedicating the bull.

1960. Stamp Day and Murillo Commemoration. (painter). Designs as T 279. Frames in gold.

1333	25c. violet	15	15
1334	40c. purple	15	15
1335	50c. olive	15	15
1336	70c. green	15	15
1337	80c. turquoise	15	15
1338	1p. brown	20	15
1339	1p.50 turquoise	20	15
1340	2p.50 red	20	15
1341	3p. blue	1·90	80
1342	5p. brown	45	25

PAINTINGS—VERT: 25c. "The Good Shepherd"; 40c. "Rebecca and Elizer"; 50c. "The Virgin of the Rosary"; 70c. "The Immaculate Conception"; 80c. "Children with Shells"; 1p. Self-portrait; 2p.50, "The Dice Game"; 3p. "Children Eating"; 5p. "Children with Coins". HORIZ: 1p.50, "The Holy Family with Bird".

289 "Christ of Lepanto"

290 Pelota Player

1960. International Philatelic Congress and Exhibition, Barcelona. Inscr "CIF".

1343	**289**	70c. lake & green (postage)	1·80	1·50
1344	-	80c. black and sage	1·80	1·50
1345	**289**	1p. purple and red	1·80	1·50
1346	-	2p.50 slate and violet	1·80	1·50
1347	**289**	5p. sepia and bistre	1·80	1·50
1348	-	10p. sepia and ochre	1·80	1·50
1349	**290**	1p. black and red (air)	5·00	3·25
1350	**290**	5p. red and brown	5·00	3·25
1351	**290**	6p. red and purple	5·00	3·25
1352	**290**	10p. red and green	5·00	3·25

DESIGN—VERT: Nos. 1344, 1346, 1348, Church of the Holy Family, Barcelona.

291 St. John of Ribera

1960. Canonization of St. John of Ribera.

1353	**291**	1p. brown	20	15
1354	**291**	2p.50 mauve	25	20

1960. Europa. 1st Anniv of European Postal and Telecommunications Conference. As T 144a of Switzerland but size 38½×22 mm.

1355	1p. drab and green	65	35
1356	5p. red and brown	1·20	1·10

292 St. Vincent de Paul

1960. 300th Death Anniv of St. Vincent de Paul.

1357	**292**	25c. violet	20	15
1358	**292**	1p. brown	25	15

293 Menendez de Aviles

1960. 400th Anniv of Discovery and Colonization of Florida.

1359	**293**	25c. blue and light blue	20	15
1360	-	70c. green and orange	20	15
1361	-	80c. green and stone	20	15
1362	-	1p. brown and yellow	20	15
1363	**293**	2p. red and pink	40	20
1364	-	2p.50 mauve and green	60	25
1365	-	3p. blue and green	4·00	85
1366	-	5p. brown and bistre	2·75	1·40

PORTRAITS: 70c., 2p.50, Hernando de Soto; 80c., 3p. Ponce de Leon; 1, 5p. Cabeza de Vaca.

294 Running

1960. Sports.

1367	**294**	25c. brn and bl (postage)	15	15
1368	-	40c. orange and violet	15	15
1369	-	70c. red and green	35	20
1370	-	80c. red and green	25	15
1371	-	1p. green and red	80	15
1372	**294**	1p.50 sepia and turquoise	35	20
1373	-	2p. green and purple	2·00	15
1374	-	2p.50 green and mauve	40	20
1375	-	3p. red and blue	90	40
1376	-	5p. blue and brown	75	70
1377	-	1p.25 red and brown (air)	20	20
1378	-	1p.50 brown and violet	35	25
1379	-	6p. red and violet	1·10	85
1380	-	10p. red and olive	1·70	1·10

DESIGNS—HORIZ: 40c., 2p. Cycling; 70c., 2p.50, Football; 1, 5p. Hockey; 1p.25, 6p. Horse-jumping. VERT: 80c., 3p. Gymnastics; 1p.50 (air), 10p. Pelota.

295 Albeniz

1960. Birth Cent of Isaac Albeniz (composer).

1381	**295**	25c. violet	15	15
1382	**295**	1p. brown	25	15

296 Cloisters

1960. Samos Monastery.

1383	**296**	80c. turquoise and green	20	15
1384	-	1p. lake and brown	1·30	20
1385	-	5p. sepia and bistre	1·50	1·10

DESIGNS—VERT: 1p. Fountain; 5p. Portico and facade.

297 "The Nativity" (Velazquez)

1960. Christmas.

1386	**297**	1p. brown	40	15

298 "The Flight to Egypt" (after Bayeu)

1961. World Refugee Year.

1387	**298**	1p. brown	25	20
1388	**298**	5p. brown	55	35

299 L. F. Moratin (after Goya)

1961. Birth Bicentenary of Moratin (poet and dramatist).

1389	**299**	1p. red	20	15
1390	**299**	1p.50 turquoise	20	15

1961. Stamp Day and El Greco (painter) Commem. Designs as T 279. Frames in gold.

1391	25c. purple	20	15
1392	40c. purple	20	15
1393	70c. green	25	20
1394	80c. turquoise	25	15
1395	1p. purple	2·75	15
1396	1p.50 turquoise	25	15
1397	2p.50 lake	45	25
1398	3p. blue	2·10	1·20
1399	5p. sepia	4·50	2·50
1400	10p. violet	90	50

PAINTINGS: 25c. "St. Peter"; 40c. Madonna (detail, "The Holy Family" ("Madonna of the Good Milk")); 70c. Detail of "The Agony in the Garden"; 80c. "Man with Hand on Breast"; 1p. Self-portrait; 1p.50, "The Baptism of Christ"; 2p.50, "The Holy Trinity"; 3p. "Burial of the Count of Orgaz"; 5p. "The Spoliation"; 10p. "The Martyrdom of St. Maurice".

301 Velazquez (Prado Memorial)

1961. 300th Death Anniv of Velazquez.

1401	**301**	80c. green and blue	1·40	20
1402	-	1p. brown and red	6·75	20
1403	-	2p.50 violet and blue	1·00	55
1404	-	10p. green and light green	9·25	2·10

PAINTINGS—VERT: 1p. "The Duke of Olivares"; 2p.50, "Princess Margarita". HORIZ: Part of "The Spinners".

Sheets each 71×86 mm. Colours changed. Imperf.

MS1405	80c. slate and brown	8·50	8·75
MS1406	1p. violet and blue	8·50	8·75
MS1407	2p.50 blue and green	8·50	8·75
MS1408	10p. blue and slate	8·50	8·75

Sold at 1p.10, 1p.40, 3p.50 and 14p. respectively.

302 "Stamp" and "Postmark"

1961. World Stamp Day.

1409	**302**	25c. black and red	20	15
1410	**302**	1p. red and black	1·20	20
1411	**302**	10p. green and purple	1·30	65

303 Vazquez de Mella

1961. Birth Centenary of Juan Vazquez de Mella (politician and writer).

1412	**303**	1p. red	45	20
1413	**303**	2p.30 purple	20	20

304 Gen. Franco

1961. 25th Anniv of National Uprising. Mult.

1414	70c. Angel and flag	15	15
1415	80c. Straits of Gibraltar	15	15
1416	1p. Knight and Alcazar, Toledo	20	15
1417	1p.50 Victory Arch	15	15
1418	2p. Knight crossing River Ebro	15	15
1419	2p.30 Soldier, flag and troops	25	15
1420	2p.50 Shipbuilding	25	15
1421	3p. Steelworks	30	25
1422	5p. Map of Spain showing electric power stations (horiz)	2·40	1·60
1423	6p. Irrigation (woman beside dam)	1·80	1·80
1424	8p. Mine	95	75
1425	10p. Type **304**	80	65

305 "Portico de la Gloria" (Cathedral of Santiago de Compostela)

1961. Council of Europe's Romanesque Art Exhibition. Inscr as in T 305.

1426	**305**	25c. violet and gold	15	15
1427	-	1p. brown and gold	25	15
1428	-	2p. purple and gold	60	20
1429	-	3p. multicoloured	60	65

DESIGNS: 1p. Courtyard of Dominican Monastery, Santo Domingo de Silos; 2p. Madonna of Irache; 3p. "Christos Pantocrator" (from Tahull Church fresco).

306 L. de Gongora (after Velazquez)

1961. 400th Birth Anniv of De Gongora (poet).

1430	**306**	25c. violet	15	15
1431	**306**	1p. brown	30	15

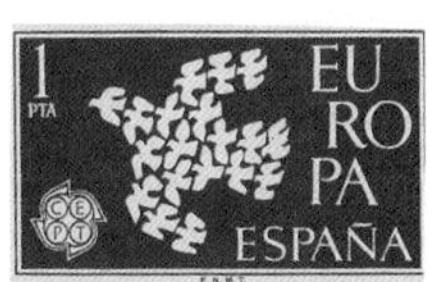

307 Doves and C.E.P.T. Emblem

1961. Europa.

1432	**307**	1p. red	20	20
1433	**307**	5p. brown	50	45

308 Burgos Cathedral

1961. 25th Anniv of Gen. Franco as Head of State.

1434	**308**	1p. green and gold	20	20

309 S. de Belalcazar

1961. Explorers and Colonizers of America (1st series).

1435	**309**	25c. violet and green	15	15
1436	-	70c. green and buff	15	15
1437	-	80c. green and pink	15	15
1438	-	1p. blue and flesh	45	15
1439	**309**	2p. red and blue	3·75	40
1440	-	2p.50 purple and mauve	95	45
1441	-	3p. blue and grey	2·30	90
1442	-	5p. brown and yellow	2·30	1·30

PORTRAITS: 70c., 2p.50, B de Lezo; 80c., 3p. R. de Bastidas; 1, 5p. N. de Chaves.

See also Nos. 1515/22, 1587/94, 1683/90, 1738/45, 1810/17, 1877/84, 1947/51, 1997/2001 and 2054/8.

310 Courtyard

1961. Escorial.

1443		70c. green and turquoise	30	20
1444	**310**	80c. slate and green	25	15
1445	-	1p. red and brown	60	20
1446	-	2p.50 purple and violet	40	20
1447	-	5p. sepia and ochre	1·80	95
1448	-	6p. purple and blue	3·00	2·40

DESIGNS—VERT: 70c. Patio of the Kings; 2p.50, Grand Staircase; 6p. High Altar. HORIZ: 1p. Monks' Garden; 5p. View of Escorial.

311 King Alfonso XII Monument

1961. 400th Anniv of Madrid as Capital of Spain.

1449	**311**	25c. purple and green	20	15
1450	-	1p. brown and bistre	35	15
1451	-	2p. purple and grey	40	15
1452	-	2p.50 violet and red	25	15
1453	-	3p. black and blue	80	55
1454	-	5p. blue and brown	1·70	1·10

DESIGNS—VERT: 1p. King Philip II (after Pantoja); 5p. Plaza, Madrid. HORIZ: 2p. Town Hall, Madrid; 2p.50, Fountain of Cybele; 3p. Portals of Alcala Palace.

312 Santa Maria del Naranco Church

1961. 1200th Anniv of Oviedo.

1455	**312**	25c. violet and green	15	15
1456	-	1p. brown and bistre	45	15
1457	-	2p. sepia and purple	1·20	15
1458	-	2p.50 violet and purple	20	15
1459	-	3p. black and blue	95	55
1460	-	5p. brown and green	95	1·10

DESIGNS: 1p. Fruela (portrait); 2p. Cross of the Angels; 2p.50, Alfonso II; 3p. Alfonso III; 5p. Apostles of the Holy Hall, Oviedo Cathedral.

313 "The Nativity" (after Gines)

1961. Christmas.

1461	**313**	1p. plum	30	15

314 Cierva C.30A Autogyro

1961. 50th Anniv of Spanish Aviation.

1462	**314**	1p. violet and blue	20	15
1463	-	2p. green and lilac	40	15
1464	-	3p. black and green	1·40	70
1465	-	5p. purple and slate	3·75	1·60
1466	-	10p. brown and blue	1·50	60

DESIGNS—HORIZ: 2p. CASA-built Dornier Do-J Wal flying boat M-MWAL "Plus Ultra"; 3p. Breguet Bre. 19GR airplane "Jesus del Gran Poder" (Madrid-Manila Flight). VERT: 5p. Avro 504K biplane hunting great bustard; 10p. Madonna of Loreto (patron saint) and North American F-86F Sabre jet fighters.

315 Arms of Alava

1962. Arms of Provincial Capitals. Multicoloured.

1467	5p. Type **315**	20	20
1468	5p. Albacete	20	20
1469	5p. Alicante	25	25
1470	5p. Almeria	25	25
1471	5p. Avila	25	25
1472	5p. Badajoz	25	25
1473	5p. Baleares	25	20
1474	5p. Barcelona	25	20
1475	5p. Burgos	1·00	50
1476	5p. Caceres	70	45
1477	5p. Cadiz	75	45
1478	5p. Castellon de la Plana	5·00	2·30

See also Nos. 1542/53, 1612/23, 1692/1703 and 1756/64.

1962. Stamp Day and Zurbaran (painter) Commem. As T 279. Frames in gold.

1479	25c. olive	20	15
1480	40c. purple	25	20
1481	70c. green	30	20
1482	80c. turquoise	25	20
1483	1p. sepia	8·00	35
1484	1p.50 turquoise	80	20
1485	2p.50 lake	80	30
1486	3p. blue	1·50	1·00
1487	5p. brown	3·50	1·90
1488	10p. olive	3·50	1·70

PAINTINGS—HORIZ: 25c. "Martyr". VERT: 40c. "Burial of St. Catalina"; 70c. "St. Casilda"; 80c. "Jesus crowning St. Joseph"; 1p. Self-portrait; 1p.50, "St. Hieronymus"; 2p.50, "Madonna of the Grace"; 3p. Detail from "Apotheosis of St. Thomas Aquinas"; 5p. "Madonna as a Child"; 10p. "The Immaculate Madonna".

316 "Ecstasy of St. Teresa" (Bernini)

1962. 4th Centenary of Teresian Reformation.

1489	-	25c. violet	15	15
1490	**316**	1p. brown	20	15
1491	-	3p. blue	1·40	60

DESIGNS—As Type **316**: 25c. St. Joseph's Monastery, Avila. (22×38½ mm): 3p. "St. Teresa of Avila" (Velazquez).

317 Mercury

1962. World Stamp Day.

1492	**317**	25c. pink, purple & violet	20	15
1493	**317**	1p. yellow, brown and bistre	25	20
1494	**317**	10p. green and turquoise	1·90	1·10

1962. Rubens Paintings. As T 279. Frames in gold.

1495	25c. violet	25	20
1496	1p. brown	3·75	25
1497	3p. turquoise	5·75	2·50
1498	10p. green	7·00	2·40

PAINTINGS—As Type **279**: 25c. Ferdinand of Austria; 1p. Self-portrait; 3p. Philip II. (26×39 mm): 10p. Duke of Lerma.

318 St. Benedict

1962. 400th Death Anniv of Alonso Berruguete (sculptor). Sculptures by Berruguete.

1499	**318**	25c. mauve and blue	20	15
1500	-	80c. green and brown	20	15
1501	-	1p. red and stone	45	15
1502	-	2p. mauve and stone	4·00	15
1503	-	3p. blue and mauve	1·40	1·20
1504	-	10p. brown and pink	1·90	1·40

SCULPTURES: 80c. "The Apostle"; 1p. "St. Peter"; 2p. "St. Christopher and Child Jesus"; 3p. "Ecce Homo"; 10p. "St. Sebastian".

319 El Cid (R. Diaz de Vivar), after statue by J. Cristobal

1962. El Cid Campeador Commem. Inscr "EL CID".

1505	**319**	1p. drab and green	20	20
1506	-	2p. violet and sepia	1·70	20
1507	-	3p. green and blue	4·75	2·40
1508	-	10p. green and yellow	2·75	1·60

DESIGNS—VERT: 2p. El Cid (equestrian statue by A. Huntington). HORIZ: 3p. El Cid's treasure chest; 10p. Oath-taking ceremony of Santa Gadea.

320 Honey Bee and Honeycomb

1962. Europa.

1509	**320**	1p. red	35	20
1510	**320**	5p. green	1·30	70

321 Throwing the Discus

1962. 2nd Spanish-American Athletic Games, Madrid.

1511	**321**	25c. blue and pink	25	20
1512	-	80c. green and yellow	25	20
1513	-	1p. brown and pink	25	20
1514	-	3p. blue and light blue	30	25

DESIGNS: 80c. Running; 1p. Hurdling; 3p. Start of sprint.

1962. Explorers and Colonizers of America (2nd series). As T 309.

1515	25c. mauve and grey	25	20
1516	70c. green and pink	80	20
1517	80c. green and yellow	55	20
1518	1p. brown and green	1·20	20
1519	2p. red and blue	3·25	40
1520	2p.50 violet and brown	75	25
1521	3p. blue and pink	8·00	1·90
1522	5p. brown and yellow	3·75	2·75

PORTRAITS: 25c., 2p. A. de Mendoza; 70c., 2p.50, J. de Quesada; 80c., 3p. J. de Garay; 1, 5p. P. de la Gasca.

322 U.P.A.E. Emblem

1962. 50th Anniv of Postal Union of the Americas and Spain.

1523	**322**	1p. brown, grn & dp grn	20	15

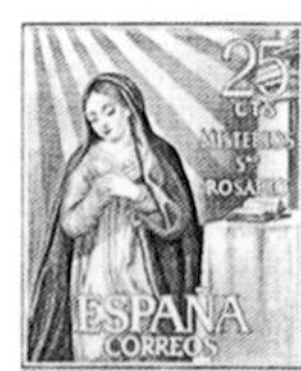

323 "The Annunciation" (after Murillo)

1962. Mysteries of the Rosary.

1524	**323**	25c. brn & vio (postage)	15	15
1525	-	70c. turquoise and green	15	15
1526	-	80c. turquoise and olive	15	15
1527	-	1p. sepia and green	5·75	75
1528	-	1p.50 blue and green	20	15
1529	-	2p. sepia and violet	1·30	55
1530	-	2p.50 red and purple	20	20
1531	-	3p. black and violet	20	20
1532	-	5p. lake and brown	90	85
1533	-	8p. black and purple	75	85
1534	-	10p. green and myrtle	75	45
1535	-	25c. violet and slate (air)	15	15
1536	-	1p. olive and purple	20	20
1537	-	5p. lake and purple	65	40
1538	-	10p. yellow, green & grey	1·70	1·00

PAINTINGS—"Joyful Mysteries": No. 1525, "Visit of Elizabeth" (Correa); 1526, "The Birth of Christ" (Murillo); 1527, "Christ shown to the Elders" (Campana); 1528, "Jesus lost and found in the Temple" (unknown artist). "Sorrowful Mysteries": 1529, "Prayer on the Mount of Olives" (Giaquinto); 1530, "Scourging" (Cano); 1531, "The Crown of Thorns" (Tiepolo); 1532, "Carrying the Cross" (El Greco); 1533, "The Crucifixion" (Murillo). "Glorious Mysteries": 1534, "The Resurrection" (Murillo); 1535, "The Ascension" (Bayeu); 1536, "The Sending-forth of the Holy Ghost" (El Greco); 1537, "The Assumption of the Virgin" (Cerezo); 1538, "The Coronation of the Virgin" (El Greco).

324 "The Nativity" (after Pedro de Mena)

1962. Christmas.

1539	**324**	1p. olive	40	20

325 Campaign Emblem and Swamp

1962. Malaria Eradication.

1540	**325**	1p. black, yellow & green	20	15

326 Pope John and Dome of St. Peter's

1962. Ecumenical Council. Vatican City (1st issue).

1541	**326**	1p. slate and purple	30	20

See also Nos. 1601 and 1755.

1963. Arms of Provincial Capitals. As T 315. Multicoloured.

1542	5p. Ciudad Real	60	60
1543	5p. Cordoba	5·00	2·20
1544	5p. Coruna	70	65
1545	5p. Cuenca	75	60
1546	5p. Fernando Poo	1·10	1·30
1547	5p. Gerona	20	20
1548	5p. Gran Canaria	25	25
1549	5p. Granada	45	40
1550	5p. Guadalajara	75	40
1551	5p. Guipuzcoa	20	20
1552	5p. Huelva	20	20
1553	5p. Huesca	20	20

327 "St. Paul" (after El Greco)

1963. 1900th Anniv of Arrival of St. Paul in Spain.

1554	**327**	1p. sepia, olive and brown	30	20

328 Poblet Monastery

1963. Poblet Monastery.

1555	**328**	25c. purple, sepia & green	20	20
1556	-	1p. orange and red	45	20
1557	-	3p. blue and violet	1·20	35
1558	-	5p. ochre and brown	2·30	1·80

DESIGNS—VERT: 1p. Tomb; 5p. Arch. HORIZ: 3p. Aerial view of monastery.

1963. Stamp Day and Ribera (painter) Commem. As T 279. Frames in gold.

1559	25c. violet	20	15
1560	40c. purple	20	15
1561	70c. green	45	20
1562	80c. turquoise	45	20
1563	1p. brown	55	15
1564	1p.50 turquoise	60	20
1565	2p.50 red	2·50	20
1566	3p. blue	4·50	1·10
1567	5p. brown	13·50	3·75
1568	10p. brown and purple	4·50	1·70

PAINTINGS: 25c. "Archimedes"; 40c. "Jacob's Flock"; 70c. "Triumph of Bacchus"; 80c. "St. Christopher"; 1p. Self-portrait; 1p.50, "St. Andrew"; 2p.50, "St. John the Baptist"; 3p. "St. Onofrius"; 5p. "St. Peter"; 10p. "The Madonna".

329 Mail Coach

1963. Centenary of Paris Postal Conference.

1569	**329**	1p. multicoloured	20	15

330 Globe

1963. World Stamp Day.

1570	**330**	25c. multicoloured	20	15
1571	**330**	1p. multicoloured	25	15
1572	**330**	10p. multicoloured	1·20	70

331 "Give us this day our daily bread"

1963. Freedom from Hunger.

1573	**331**	1p. multicoloured	20	15

332 Pillars and Globes

1963. Spanish Cultural Institutions Congress. Multicoloured.

1574		25c. Type **332**	20	15
1575		80c. "Santa Maria", "Pinta" and "Nina"	50	20
1576		1p. Columbus	50	20

333 Civic Seals

1963. 150th Anniv of San Sebastian.

1577	**333**	25c. blue and green	15	15
1578	-	80c. red and purple	20	15
1579	-	1p. green and bistre	20	15

DESIGNS: 80c. City aflame; 1p. View of San Sebastian, 1836.

334 "St. Maria of Europe"

1963. Europa.

1580	**334**	1p. brown and bistre	20	20
1581	**334**	5p. sepia and green	65	60

335 Arms of the Order of Mercy

1963. 75th Anniv of the Order of Mercy.

1582	**335**	25c. red, gold and black	20	15
1583	-	80c. sepia and green	20	15
1584	-	1p. purple and blue	20	15
1585	-	1p.50 brown and blue	20	15
1586	-	3p. black and violet	20	20

DESIGNS: 80c. King Jaime I; 1p. Our Lady of Mercy; 1p.50, St. Pedro Nolasco; 3p. St. Raimundo de Penafort.

1963. Explorers and Colonizers of America (3rd series). As T 309.

1587		25c. deep blue and blue	20	15
1588		70c. green and salmon	20	15
1589		80c. green and cream	45	15
1590		1p. blue and salmon	60	15
1591		2p. red and blue	1·80	15
1592		2p.50 violet and flesh	1·40	15
1593		3p. blue and pink	2·75	1·60
1594		5p. brown and cream	3·75	3·00

PORTRAITS: 25c., 2p. Brother J. Serra; 70c., 2p.50, Vasco Nunez de Balboa; 80c., 3p. J. de Galvez; 1, 5p. D. Garcia de Paredes.

336 Scenes from Parable of the Good Samaritan

1963. Red Cross Centenary.

1595	**336**	1p. violet, red and gold	15	15

337 "The Nativity" (after sculpture by Berruguete)

1963. Christmas.

1596	**337**	1p. green	20	15

338 Fr. Raimundo Lulio

1963. Famous Spaniards (1st series).

1597	**338**	1p. black & vio (postage)	25	15
1598	-	1p.50 violet and sepia	20	15
1599	-	25p. purple and red (air)	1·40	35
1600	-	50p. black and green	1·80	55

PORTRAITS: 1p.50, Cardinal Belluga; 25p. King Recaredo; 50p. Cardinal Cisneros.

See also Nos. 1714/17.

339 Pope Paul and Dome of St. Peter's

1963. Ecumenical Council, Vatican City (2nd issue).

1601	**339**	1p. black and turquoise	15	15

340 Alcazar de Segovia

1964. Tourist Series.

1602	-	40c. brown, blue & green	25	20
1603	-	50c. sepia and blue	25	20
1604	-	70c. blue and green	25	20
1605	-	70c. brown and lilac	20	15
1606	-	80c. black and blue	25	20
1607	**340**	1p. lilac and violet	20	15
1608	-	1p. red and purple	20	15
1609	-	1p. black and green	20	15
1610	-	1p. red and purple	20	15
1611	-	1p.50 brown, green and blue	25	20

DESIGNS—HORIZ: No. 1602, Potes; 1604, Crypt of St. Isidore (Leon); 1608, Lion Court of the Alhambra (Granada); 1611, Gerona. VERT: 1603, Leon Cathedral; 1605, Costa Brava; 1606, "Christ of the Lanterns" (Cordoba); 1609, Drach Caves (Majorca); 1610, Mosque (Cordoba).

See also Nos. 1704/13, 1786/95, 1798/1805, 1860/6, 1867/74, 1933/42, 1985/9, 1993/6, 2035/9, 2040/5, 2311/6, 2379/84, 2466/7, 2575/8, 2696/2700, 2744/8, 2858/9, 2870/1 and 2915/18.

1964. Arms of Provincial Capitals. As T 315. Multicoloured.

1612		5p. Ifni	20	20
1613		5p. Jaen	20	20
1614		5p. Leon	20	15
1615		5p. Lerida	20	15
1616		5p. Logrono	20	15
1617		5p. Lugo	20	15
1618		5p. Madrid	20	15
1619		5p. Malaga	20	15
1620		5p. Murcia	20	15
1621		5p. Navarra	20	15
1622		5p. Orense	20	15
1623		5p. Oviedo	20	15

341 Santa Maria Monastery

1964. Monastery of Santa Maria, Huerta.

1624	-	1p. bronze and green	20	15
1625	-	2p. sepia, black & turq	25	20
1626	**341**	5p. slate and violet	1·50	80

DESIGNS—VERT: 1p. Great Hall; 2p. Cloisters.

1964. Stamp Day and Sorolla (painter) Commem. As T 279. Frames in gold.

1627		25c. violet	15	15
1628		40c. purple	15	15
1629		70c. green	15	15
1630		80c. turquoise	15	15
1631		1p. brown	15	15
1632		1p.50 turquoise	15	15
1633		2p.50 mauve	15	15
1634		3p. blue	45	40
1635		5p. brown	1·90	1·20
1636		10p. green	1·30	35

PAINTINGS—VERT: 25c. "The Earthen Jar"; 70c. "La Mancha Types"; 80c. "Valencian Fisherwoman"; 1p. Self-portrait; 5p. "Pulling the Boat"; 10p. "Valencian Couple on Horse". HORIZ: 40c. "Castillan Oxherd"; 1p.50, "The Catllepen"; 2p.50, "And people say fish is dear" (fish market); 3p. "Children on the Beach".

342 "25 Years of Peace"

1964. 25th Anniv of End of Spanish Civil War.

1637	**342**	25c. gold, green and black	15	15
1638	-	30c. red, blue and green	15	15
1639	-	40c. black and gold	15	15
1640	-	50c. multicoloured	15	15
1641	-	70c. multicoloured	15	15
1642	-	80c. multicoloured	15	15
1643	-	1p. multicoloured	30	15
1644	-	1p.50 olive, red and blue	20	15
1645	-	2p. multicoloured	20	15
1646	-	2p.50 multicoloured	20	15
1647	-	3p. multicoloured	1·10	1·20
1648	-	5p. red, green and gold	35	35
1649	-	6p. multicoloured	50	50
1650	-	10p. multicoloured	60	65

DESIGNS—VERT: 30c. Athletes ("Sport"); 50c. Apartment-houses ("National Housing Plan"); 1p. Graph and symbols ("Economic Development"); 1p.50, Rocks and tower ("Construction"); 2p.50, Wheatear and dam ("Irrigation"); 5p. "Tree of Learning" ("Scientific Research"); 10p. Gen. Franco. HORIZ: 40c. T.V. screen and symbols ("Radio and T.V."); 70c. Wheatears, tractor and landscape ("Agriculture"); 80c. Tree and forests ("Reafforestation"); 2p. Forms of transport ("Transport and Communications"); 3p. Pylon and part of dial ("Electrification"); 6p. Ancient buildings ("Tourism").

343 Spanish Pavilion at Fair

1964. New York World's Fair.

1651	**343**	1p. green and turquoise	20	15
1652	-	1p.50 brown and red	25	15
1653	-	2p.50 green and blue	25	15
1654	-	5p. red	25	35
1655	-	50p. blue and grey	1·10	40

DESIGNS—VERT: 1p.50, Bullfighting; 2p.50, Castillo de la Mota; 5p. Spanish dancing; 50p. Pelota.

344 6c. Stamp of 1850 and Globe

1964. World Stamp Day.

1656	**344**	25c. red and purple	20	15
1657	**344**	1p. green and blue	20	20
1658	**344**	10p. orange and red	35	30

345 Macarena Virgin

1964. Canonical Coronation of Macarena Virgin.

1659	**345**	1p. green and yellow	15	15

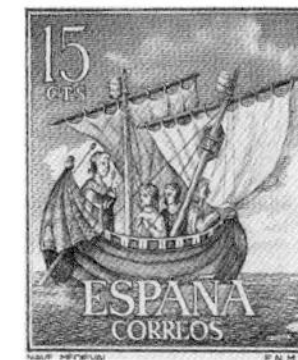

346 Medieval Ship

1964. Spanish Navy Commemoration.

1660	**346**	15c. slate and purple	15	15
1661	-	25c. green and orange	15	15
1662	-	40c. grey and blue	15	15
1663	-	50c. green and slate	15	15
1664	-	70c. violet and blue	15	15
1665	-	80c. blue and green	15	15
1666	-	1p. purple and brown	15	15
1667	-	1p.50 sepia and red	15	15
1668	-	2p. black and green	1·30	30
1669	-	2p.50 red and violet	15	15
1670	-	3p. blue and brown	15	15
1671	-	5p. blue and green	90	90
1672	-	6p. violet and turquoise	70	70
1673	-	10p. red and orange	25	25

SHIPS—VERT: 25c. Carrack; 1p. Ship of the line "Santissima Trinidad"; 1p.50, Corvette "Atrevida". HORIZ: 40c. "Santa Maria"; 50c. Galley; 70c. Galleon; 80c. Xebec; 2p. Steam frigate "Isabel II"; 2p.50, Frigate "Numancia"; 3p. Destroyer "Destructor"; 5p. Isaac Peral's submarine; 6p. Cruiser "Baleares"; 10p. Cadet schooner "Juan Sebastian de Elcano".

347 Europa "Flower"

1964. Europa.

1674	**347**	1p. ochre, red and green	40	30
1675	**347**	5p. blue, purple and green	95	90

348 "The Virgin of the Castle"

1964. 700th Anniv of Reconquest of Jerez.

1676	**348**	25c. brown and buff	15	15
1677	**348**	1p. blue and grey	20	15

349 Putting the Shot

1965. Olympic Games, Tokyo and Innsbruck. Olympic rings in gold.

1678	**349**	25c. blue and orange	15	15
1679	-	80c. blue and green	15	15
1680	-	1p. blue and light blue	15	15
1681	-	3p. blue and buff	20	20
1682	-	5p. blue and violet	20	20

DESIGNS: 80c. Long jumping; 1p. Skiing (slalom); 3p. Judo; 5p. Throwing the discus.

1964. Explorers and Colonizers of America (4th series). As T 309. Inscr "1964" at foot.

1683		25c. violet and blue	15	15
1684		70c. olive and pink	15	15
1685		80c. green and buff	30	25
1686		1p. violet and buff	30	15
1687		2p. olive and blue	30	15
1688		2p.50 purple and turquoise	25	15
1689		3p. blue and grey	3·50	1·20
1690		5p. brown and cream	2·30	1·60

PORTRAITS: 25c., 2p. D. de Almagro; 70c., 2p.50, F. de Toledo; 80c., 3p. T. de Mogrovejo; 1, 5p. F. Pizarro.

350 "Adoration of the Shepherds" (after Zurbaran)

1964. Christmas.

1691	**350**	1p. brown	25	20

1965. Arms of Provincial Capitals. As T 315. Multicoloured.

1692		5p. Palencia	20	15
1693		5p. Pontevedra	20	15
1694		5p. Rio Muni	20	15
1695		5p. Sahara	20	15
1696		5p. Salamanca	20	15
1697		5p. Santander	20	15
1698		5p. Segovia	20	15
1699		5p. Seville	20	15
1700		5p. Soria	20	15
1701		5p. Tarragona	20	15
1702		5p. Tenerife	20	15
1703		5p. Teruel	20	15

1965. Tourist Series. As T 340.

1704		25c. black and blue	20	15
1705		30c. brown and turquoise	20	15
1706		50c. purple and red	20	15
1707		70c. indigo and blue	20	15
1708		80c. purple and mauve	20	15
1709		1p. mauve, red and sepia	20	15
1710		2p.50 purple and brown	20	15
1711		2p.50 olive and blue	20	15
1712		3p. purple and purple	20	15
1713		6p. violet and slate	20	15

DESIGNS—VERT: 25c. Columbus Monument, Barcelona; 30c. Santa Maria Church, Burgos; 50c. Synagogue, Toledo; 80c. Seville Cathedral; 1p. Cudillero Port; 2p.50, (No. 1710), Burgos Cathedral (interior); 3p. Bridge at Cambados (Pontevedra); 6p. Ceiling, Lonja (Valencia). HORIZ: 70c. Zamora; 2p.50, (No. 1711), Mogrovejo (Santander).

1965. Famous Spaniards (2nd series). As T 338.

1714		25c. sepia and turquoise	15	15
1715		70c. deep blue and blue	20	20
1716		2p.50 sepia and bronze	20	20
1717		5p. bronze and green	35	35

PORTRAITS: 25c. Donoso Cortes; 70c. King Alfonso X (the Saint); 2p.50, G. M. de Jovellanos; 5p. St. Dominic de Guzman.

1965. Stamp Day and J. Romero de Torres Commem. As T 279. Frames in gold.

1718		25c. purple	20	15
1719		40c. purple	20	15
1720		70c. green	20	15
1721		80c. turquoise	20	15
1722		1p. brown	20	15
1723		1p.50 turquoise	20	15
1724		2p.50 mauve	30	20
1725		3p. blue	40	35
1726		5p. brown	40	35
1727		10p. green	75	35

PAINTINGS (by J. Romero de Torres): 25c. "Girl with Jar"; 40c. "The Song"; 70c. "The Virgin of the Lanterns"; 80c. "Girl with Guitar"; 1p. Self-portrait; 1p.50, "Poem of Cordoba"; 2p.50, "Marta and Maria"; 3p. "Poem of Cordoba" (different); 5p. "A Little Charcoal-maker"; 10p. "Long Live the Hair!".

351 Bull and Stamps

1965. World Stamp Day.

1728	**351**	25c. multicoloured	15	15
1729	**351**	1p. multicoloured	15	15
1730	**351**	10p. multicoloured	45	40

352 I.T.U. Emblem and Symbols

1965. Centenary of I.T.U.

1731	**352**	1p. red, black and pink	15	15

353 Pilgrim

1965. Holy Year of Santiago de Compostela. Multicoloured.

1732		1p. Type **353**	15	15
1733		2p. Pilgrim (profile)	15	15

354 Spanish Knight and Banners

1965. 400th Anniv of Florida Settlement.

1734	**354**	3p. black, red and yellow	20	15

355 St. Benedict (after sculpture by Pereira)

1965. Europa.

1735	**355**	1p. green and emerald	25	25
1736	**355**	5p. violet and purple	55	35

356 Sports Palace, Madrid

1965. Int Olympic Committee Meeting, Madrid.

1737	**356**	1p. brown, gold and grey	15	15

1965. Explorers and Colonizers of America (5th series). As T 309. Inscr "1965" at foot.

1738		25c. violet and green	15	15
1739		70c. brown and pink	15	15
1740		80c. green and cream	15	15
1741		1p. violet and buff	15	15
1742		2p. brown and blue	20	15
1743		2p.50 purple and turquoise	20	20
1744		3p. blue and grey	1·20	50
1745		5p. brown and yellow	1·20	45

PORTRAITS: 25c., 2p. Don Fadrique de Toledo; 70c., 2p.50, Padre Jose de Anchieta; 80c., 3p. Francisco de Orellana; 1p., 5p. St. Luis Beltran.

357 Cloisters

1965. Yuste Monastery.

1746	**357**	1p. blue and sepia	15	15
1747	-	2p. sepia and brown	20	15
1748	-	5p. green and blue	25	25

DESIGNS—VERT: 2p. Charles V room. HORIZ: 5p. Courtyard.

358 Spanish 1r. Stamp of 1865

1965. Centenary of Spanish Perforated Stamps.

1749	**358**	80c. green and bronze	15	15
1750	-	1p. brown and purple	15	15
1751	-	5p. brown and sepia	15	15

DESIGNS: 1p. 1865 19c. stamp; 5p. 1865 2r. stamp.

359 "The Nativity" (after Mayno)

1965. Christmas.

1752	**359**	1p. green and blue	15	15

360 Madonna of Antipolo

1965. 400th Anniv of Christianity in the Philippines.

1753	**360**	1p. brown, black and buff	20	15
1754	-	3p. blue and grey	20	20

DESIGN: 3p. Father Urdaneta.

361 Globe

1965. 21st Ecumenical Council, Vatican City (3rd issue).

1755	**361**	1p. multicoloured	15	15

1966. Arms of Provincial Capitals. As T 315. Multicoloured.

1756		5p. Toledo	20	15
1757		5p. Valencia	20	15
1758		5p. Valladolid	20	15
1759		5p. Vizcaya	20	15
1760		5p. Zamora	20	15
1761		5p. Zaragoza	20	15
1762		5p. Ceuta	20	15
1763		5p. Melilla	20	15
1764		10p. Spain (26×38½ mm)	25	20

362 Admiral Alvaro de Bazan

1966. Celebrities (1st series).

1765	**362**	25c. black and blue (postage)	20	15
1766	-	2p. violet and purple	25	20
1767	-	25p. bronze & green (air)	1·30	25
1768	-	50p. grey and blue	2·00	75

PORTRAITS: 2p. Benito Daza de Valdes (doctor); 25p. Seneca; 50p. St. Damaso.

See also Nos. 1849/52.

363 Exhibition Emblem

1966. Graphic Arts Exn, "Graphispack", Barcelona.

1769	**363**	1p. green, blue and red	15	15

1966. Stamp Day and J. M. Sert Commem. Designs as T 279. Frames in gold.

1770		25c. violet	20	15
1771		40c. purple	20	15
1772		70c. green	20	15
1773		80c. bronze	20	15
1774		1p. brown	20	15
1775		1p.50 blue	20	15
1776		2p.50 red	20	15
1777		3p. blue	20	15
1778		5p. sepia	20	15
1779		10p. green	20	15

PAINTINGS (by J. M. Sert)—VERT: 25c. "The Magic Ball"; 70c. "Christ Addressing the Disciples"; 80c. "The Balloonists"; 1p. Self-portrait; 1p.50, "Audacity"; 2p.50, "Justice"; 3p. "Jacob's Struggle with the Angel"; 5p. "The Five Parts of the World"; 10p. "St. Peter and St. Paul". HORIZ: 40c. "Memories of Toledo".

364 Luno Church

1966. 600th Anniv of Guernica. Multicoloured.

1780		80c. Type **364**	15	15
1781		1p. Arms of Guernica	15	15
1782		3p. "Tree of Guernica"	15	15

365 Postmarked 6 cuartos Stamp of 1850

1966. World Stamp Day.

1783	**365**	25c. multicoloured	15	15
1784	-	1p. multicoloured	15	15
1785	-	10p. multicoloured	20	20

DESIGNS—POSTMARKED STAMPS: 1p. 5r. stamp of 1850; 10p. 10r. stamp of 1850.

1966. Tourist Series. As T 340.

1786		10c. emerald and green	15	15
1787		15c. bistre and green	15	15
1788		40c. brown and chestnut	15	15
1789		50c. purple and red	15	15
1790		80c. purple and mauve	15	15
1791		1p. turquoise and blue	15	15
1792		1p.50 black and blue	15	15
1793		2p. brown and blue	15	15
1794		3p. brown and blue	15	15
1795		10p. blue and turquoise	15	15

DESIGNS—VERT: 10c. Bohi waterfalls (Lerida); 40c. Sigena monastery (Huesca); 50c. Santo Domingo Church (Soria); 80c. Golden Tower (Seville); 1p. El Teide (Canaries); 10p. Church of St. Gregory (Valladolid). HORIZ: 15c. Torla (Huesca); 1p.50, Cathedral, Guadalupe; 2p. University, Alcala de Henares; 3p. La Seo Cathedral (Lerida).

366 Tree and Globe

1966. World Forestry Congress.

1796	**366**	1p. green, brown and deep brown	15	15

367 Crown and Anchor

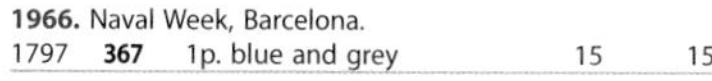

1966. Naval Week, Barcelona.

1797	**367**	1p. blue and grey	15	15

368 Butron Castle (Vizcaya)

1966. Spanish Castles (1st series).

1798	-	10c. sepia and blue	15	15
1799	-	25c. purple and violet	15	15
1800	-	40c. green and turquoise	15	15
1801	-	50c. blue and indigo	15	15
1802	-	70c. blue and ultramarine	15	15
1803	**368**	80c. green and violet	15	15
1804	-	1p. olive and brown	15	15
1805	-	3p. purple and red	15	15

CASTLES—HORIZ: 10c. Guadamur (Toledo); 25c. Alcazar (Segovia); 40c. La Mota (Medina del Campo); 50c. Olite (Navarra); 70c. Monteagudo (Murcia); 1p. Manzanares (Madrid). VERT: 3p. Almansa (Albacete).

369 Don Quixote, Dulcinea and Aldonza Lorenzo

1966. 4th World Psychiatric Congress, Madrid.

1806	**369**	1p.50 multicoloured	15	15

370 "Europa and the Bull"

1966. Europa.

1807	**370**	1p. multicoloured	20	20
1808	**370**	5p. multicoloured	40	40

371 Horseman in the Sky

1966. 17th Int Astronautics Federation Congress, Madrid.

1809	**371**	1p.50 red, black and blue	15	15

1966. Explorers and Colonizers of America (6th series). As T 309. Inscr "1966" at foot.

1810	30c. bistre and brown	15	15
1811	50c. red and green	15	15
1812	1p. violet and blue	15	15
1813	1p.20 slate and grey	15	15
1814	1p.50 myrtle and green	15	15
1815	3p. blue	15	15
1816	3p.50 violet and lilac	20	20
1817	6p. brown and buff	20	15

DESIGNS: 30c. A. de Mendoza; 50c. Title page of Dominican Fathers' "Christian Doctrine"; 1p. J. A. Manso de Velasco; 1p.20, Coins of Lima Mint (1699); 1p.50, M. de Castro y Padilla; 3p. Oruro Convent; 3p.50, M. de Amat; 6p. Inca postal runner.

372 R. del Valle Inclan

1966. Spanish Writers.

1818	**372**	1p.50 green and black	15	15
1819	-	3p. violet and black	15	15
1820	-	6p. blue and black	15	15

WRITERS: 3p. Carlos Arniches; 6p. J. Benavente y Martinez.

See also Nos. 1888/91.

373 Monastery Facade

1966. St. Mary's Carthusian Monastery, Jerez.

1821	**373**	1p. indigo and blue	15	15
1822	-	2p. light green and green	20	15
1823	-	5p. plum and purple	20	15

DESIGNS—HORIZ: 2p. Cloisters; 5p. Gateway.

374 "The Nativity" (after P. Duque Cornejo)

1966. Christmas.

1824	**374**	1p.50 multicoloured	15	15

375 Alava Costume

1967. Provincial Costumes. Multicoloured.

1825	6p. Type **375**	20	15
1826	6p. Albacete	15	15
1827	6p. Alicante	15	15
1828	6p. Almeria	20	15
1829	6p. Avila	15	15
1830	6p. Badajoz	15	15
1831	6p. Baleares	15	15
1832	6p. Barcelona	15	15
1833	6p. Burgos	15	15
1834	6p. Caceres	20	15
1835	6p. Cadiz	15	15
1836	6p. Castellon de la Plana	15	15

See also Nos. 1897/1908, 1956/67, 2007/18 and 2072/6.

376 Archers

1967. Stamp Day. Cave Paintings. Multicoloured.

1837	40c. Type **376**	15	15
1838	50c. Boar-hunting	15	15
1839	1p. Trees (vert)	15	15
1840	1p.20 Bison	15	10
1841	1p.50 Hands	15	15
1842	2p. Hunter (vert)	15	15
1843	2p.50 Deer (vert)	15	15
1844	3p.50 Hunters	15	15
1845	4p. Chamois-hunters (vert)	15	15
1846	6p. Deer-hunter (vert)	15	15

377 Cathedral, Palma de Mallorca, and Union Emblem

1967. Interparliamentary Union Congress, Palma de Mallorca.

1847	**377**	1p.50 green	20	20

378 Wilhelm Rontgen (physicist)

1967. Radiology Congress, Barcelona.

1848	**378**	1p.50 green	20	20

1967. Celebrities (2nd series). As T 362.

1849	1p.20 violet and purple	15	15
1850	3p.50 purple	20	20
1851	4p. sepia and brown	15	20
1852	25p. grey and blue	25	20

PORTRAITS: 1p.20, Averroes (physician and philosopher); 3p.50, Acosta (poet); 4p. Maimonides (physician and philosopher); 25p. Andres Laguna (physician).

379 Cogwheels

1967. Europa.

1853	**379**	1p.50 green, brown & red	20	20
1854	**379**	6p. violet, blue & purple	25	25

380 Fair Building

1967. 50th Anniv of Valencia Int Samples Fair.

1855	**380**	1p.50 green	15	15

381 Spanish 5r. Stamp of 1850 with Numeral Postmark

1967. World Stamp Day.

1856	**381**	40c. brown, blue & black	15	15
1857	-	1p.50 lake, black and green	15	15
1858	-	6p. blue, red and black	15	15

See also Nos. 1927/8, 1980/1, 2032, 2091, 2150 and 2185.

382 Sleeping Vagrant and "Guardian Angel"

1967. National Day for Caritas Welfare Organization.

1859	**382**	1p.50 multicoloured	15	15

383 I.T.Y. Emblem

1967. Tourist Series and Int Tourist Year.

1860	-	10c. black and blue	20	15
1861	-	1p. black and blue	20	15
1862	-	1p.50 black and brown	20	15
1863	-	2p.50 blue and turquoise	25	15
1864	**383**	3p.50 blue and purple	25	20
1865	-	5p. bronze and green	25	15
1866	-	6p. purple and mauve	25	15

DESIGNS: 10c. Betanzos Church (Corunna); 1p. St. Miguel's Tower (Palencia); 1p.50, Castellers (acrobats); 2p.50, Columbus Monument (Huelva); 5p. "Enchanted City" (Cuenca); 6p. Church of our Lady, Sanlucar (Cadiz).

1967. Spanish Castles (2nd series). As T 368.

1867	50c. brown and grey	20	15
1868	1p. violet and grey	20	15
1869	1p.50 green and blue	20	15
1870	2p. brown and red	20	15
1871	2p.50 brown and green	20	15
1872	5p. blue and purple	20	15
1873	6p. sepia and brown	20	15
1874	10p. green and blue	20	15

CASTLES—HORIZ: 50c. Balsareny (Barcelona); 1p. Jarandilla (Caceres); 1p.50, Almodovar (Cordoba); 2p.50, Peniscola (Castellon); 5p. Coca (Segovia); 6p. Loarre (Huesca); 10p. Belmonte (Cuenca). VERT: 2p. Ponferrada (Leon).

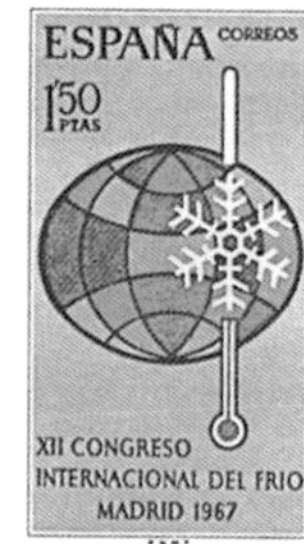

384 Globe and Snow Crystal

1967. 12th Int Refrigeration Congress, Madrid.

1875	**384**	1p.50 blue	15	15

385 Map of the Americas, Spain and the Philippines

1967. 4th Spanish, Portuguese, American and Philippine Municipalities Congress, Barcelona.

1876	**385**	1p.50 violet	15	15

1967. Explorers and Colonizers of America (7th series). As T 309. Inscr "1967" at foot.

1877	40c. olive and orange	15	15
1878	50c. agate and grey	15	15
1879	1p. mauve and blue	15	15
1880	1p.20 green and cream	15	15
1881	1p.50 green and flesh	15	15
1882	3p. violet and buff	20	15
1883	3p.50 blue and pink	25	20
1884	6p. brown	20	15

DESIGNS—VERT: 40c. J. Francisco de la Bodega y Quadra; 50c. Map of Nutka coast; 1p. F. A. Mourelle; 1p.50, E. J. Martinez; 3p.50, Cayetano Valdes y Florez. HORIZ: 1p.20, View of Nutka; 3p. Map of Californian coast; 6p. San Elias, Alaska.

387 Ploughing with Oxen

1967. 2000th Anniv of Caceres. Multicoloured.

1885	1p.50 Statue and archway	15	15
1886	3p.50 Type **387**	15	15
1887	6p. Roman coins	20	20

Nos. 1885 and 1887 are vert.

1967. Anniversaries. Portraits as T 372.

1888	1p.20 brown and black	15	15
1889	1p.50 green and black	15	15
1890	3p.50 violet and black	15	15
1891	6p. blue and black	15	15

DESIGNS: 1p.20, P. de S. Jose Bethencourt (founder of Bethlehemite Order, 300th death anniv); 1p.50, Enrique Granados (composer, birth cent); 3p.50, Ruben Dario (poet, birth centenary); 6p. San Ildefonso, Archbishop of Toledo (after El Greco) (1900th death anniv).

388 Main Portal, Veruela Monastery

1967. Veruela Monastery.

1892	**388**	1p.50 blue & ultramarine	15	15
1893	-	3p.50 grey and green	15	15
1894	-	6p. purple and brown	20	20

DESIGNS—HORIZ: 3p.50, Aerial view of monastery; 6p. Cloisters.

389 "The Canonization of San Jose de Calasanz" (from painting by Goya)

1967. Bicentenary of Canonization of San Jose de Calasanz.

1895	**389**	1p.50 multicoloured	15	15

390 "The Nativity" (Salzillo)

1967. Christmas.

1896	**390**	1p.50 multicoloured	15	15

1968. Provincial Costumes. As T 375. Mult.

1897	6p. Ciudad Real	25	20
1898	6p. Cordoba	25	20
1899	6p. Coruna	25	20
1900	6p. Cuenca	20	15
1901	6p. Fernando Poo	25	20
1902	6p. Gerona	25	20
1903	6p. Las Palmas (Gran Canaria)	25	20
1904	6p. Granada	20	15
1905	6p. Guadalajara	20	15
1906	6p. Guipuzcoa	20	15
1907	6p. Huelva	25	20
1908	6p. Huesca	25	20

391 Slalom

1968. Winter Olympic Games, Grenoble. Multicoloured.

1909	1p.50 Type **391**	20	20
1910	3p.50 Bobsleighing (vert)	20	20
1911	6p. Ice hockey	20	20

1968. Stamp Day and Fortuny Commemoration As T 279. Frames in gold.

1912	40c. purple	20	15
1913	50c. green	20	15
1914	1p. brown	20	15
1915	1p.20 violet	20	15
1916	1p.50 green	20	15
1917	2p. brown	20	15
1918	2p.50 red	20	15
1919	3p.50 brown	20	15
1920	4p. olive	20	15
1921	6p. blue	20	15

Fortuny Paintings—HORIZ: 40c. "The Vicarage"; 1p.20, "The Print Collector"; 6p. "Queen Christina". VERT: 50c. "Fantasia"; 1p. "Idyll"; 1p.50, Self-portrait; 2p. "Old Man Naked to the Sun"; 2p.50, "Typical Calabrian"; 3p.50, "Portrait of Lady"; 4p. "Battle of Tetuan".

392 Beatriz Galindo

1968. Famous Spanish Women. With background scenes.

1922	**392**	1p.20 brown and bistre	15	15
1923	-	1p.50 blue and turquoise	15	15
1924	-	3p.50 violet	15	15
1925	-	6p. black and blue	20	20

WOMEN: 1p.50, Agustina de Aragon; 3p.50, Maria Pacheco; 6p. Rosalia de Castro.

393 Europa "Key"

1968. Europa.

1926	**393**	3p.50 gold, brn & blue	25	25

1968. World Stamp Day. As T 381, but stamps and postmarks changed. Inscr "1968".

1927	1p.50 black, brown and blue	15	15
1928	3p.50 blue, black and green	15	15

DESIGNS: 1p.50, Spanish 6c. stamp of 1850 with Puebla (Galicia) postmark; 3p.50, Spanish 6r. stamp of 1850 with Serena postmark.

394 Emperor Galba's Coin

1968. 1900th Anniv of Foundation of Leon by VIIth Roman Legion.

1929	-	1p. brown and purple	20	20
1930	-	1p.50 brown and yellow	20	20
1931	**394**	3p.50 green and ochre	20	20

DESIGNS—VERT: 1p. Inscribed tile and town map of Leon (26×47 mm); 1p.50, Legionary with standard (statue).

395 Human Rights Emblem

1968. Human Rights Year.

1932	**395**	3p.50 red, green and blue	25	20

1968. Tourist Series. As T 340.

1933	50c. brown	20	15
1934	1p.20 green	20	15
1935	1p.50 blue and green	20	15
1936	2p. purple	20	15
1937	3p.50 purple	20	15

DESIGNS—VERT: 50c. Count Benavente's Palace, Baeza; 1p.50, Sepulchre, St. Vincent's Church, Avila; 3p.50, Main portal, Church of Santa Maria, Sanguesa (Navarra). HORIZ: 1p.20, View of Salamanca; 2p. "The King's Page" (statue), Siguenza Cathedral.

1968. Spanish Castles (3rd series). As T 368.

1938	40c. sepia and blue	20	15
1939	1p.20 purple	20	15
1940	1p.50 black and bistre	20	15
1941	2p.50 bronze and green	20	15
1942	6p. turquoise and blue	20	15

DESIGNS—HORIZ: 40c. Escalona; 1p.20, Fuensaldana; 1p.50, Penafiel; 2p.50, Villas and obroso. VERT: 6p. Frias.

396 Rifle-shooting

1968. Olympic Games, Mexico. Multicoloured.

1943	1p0. Type **396**	25	15
1944	1p.50 Horse-jumping	25	15
1945	3p.50 Cycling	25	20
1946	6p. Yachting (vert)	25	20

1968. Explorers and Colonisers of America (8th series). As T 309 but inscr "1968" at foot.

1947	40c. blue and light blue	15	15
1948	1p. purple and blue	15	15
1949	1p.50 green and flesh	15	15
1950	3p.50 blue and mauve	30	1·50
1951	6p. brown and yellow	30	25

DESIGNS—VERT: 40c. Map of Orinoco missions; 1p. Diego de Losada (founder of Caracas); 1p.50, Arms of the Losadas; 3p.50, Diego de Henares (builder of Caracas). HORIZ: 6p. Old plan of Santiago de Leon de Caracas.

397 Monastery Building

1968. Santa Maria del Parral Monastery.

1952	**397**	1p.50 lilac and blue	20	15
1953	-	3p.50 brown & chocolate	25	20
1954	-	6p. brown and red	25	20

DESIGNS—VERT: 3p.50, Cloisters; 6p. "Santa Maria del Parral".

398 "The Nativity" (Barocci)

1968. Christmas.

1955	**398**	1p.50 multicoloured	25	20

1969. Provincial Costumes. As T 375. Mult.

1956	6p. Ifni	20	15
1957	6p. Jaen	20	15
1958	6p. Leon	20	15
1959	6p. Lerida	20	15
1960	6p. Logrono	25	20
1961	6p. Lugo	25	20
1962	6p. Madrid	25	20
1963	6p. Malaga	20	15
1964	6p. Murcia	20	15
1965	6p. Navarra	20	15
1966	6p. Orense	20	15
1967	6p. Oviedo	20	15

1969. Stamp Day and Alonso Cano Commem. Various paintings as T 279. Frames gold: centre colours below.

1968	40c. red	15	15
1969	50c. green	15	15
1970	1p. sepia	15	15
1971	1p.50 green	15	15
1972	2p. brown	15	15
1973	2p.50 mauve	15	15
1974	3p. blue	15	15
1975	3p.50 purple	15	15
1976	4p. purple	15	15
1977	6p. blue	15	15

Alonso Cano paintings—VERT: 40c. "St. Agnes"; 50c. "St. Joseph"; 1p. "Christ supported by an Angel"; 1p.50, "Alonso Cano" (Velazquez); 2p. "The Holy Family"; 2p.50, "The Circumcision"; 3p. "Jesus and the Samaritan"; 3p.50, "Madonna and Child"; 6p. "The Vision of St. John the Baptist". HORIZ: 4p. "St. John Capistrano and St. Bernardin".

399 Molecules and Diagram

1969. 6th European Biochemical Congress.

1978	**399**	1p.50 multicoloured	20	20

400 Colonnade

1969. Europa.

1979	**400**	3p.50 multicoloured	25	25

1969. World Stamp Day. As T 381.

1980	1p.50 black, red and green	15	15
1981	3p.50 green, red and blue	15	15

DESIGNS: 1p.50, Spanish 6c. stamp of 1851 with "A 3 1851" postmark; 3p.50, Spanish 10r. stamp of 1851 with "CORVERA" postmark.

401 Spectrum

1969. 15th Int Spectroscopical Conf, Madrid.

1982	**401**	1p.50 multicoloured	25	20

402 Red Cross Symbols and Globe

1969. 50th Anniv of League of Red Cross Societies.

1983	**402**	1p.50 multicoloured	25	20

403 Capital, Lugo Cathedral

1969. 300th Anniv of Dedication of Galicia to Jesus Christ.

1984	**403**	1p.50 brown, blk & grn	15	15

1969. Spanish Castles (4th series). As T 368.

1985	1p. purple and green	15	15
1986	1p.50 blue and violet	15	15
1987	2p.50 lilac and blue	15	15
1988	3p.50 brown and green	35	25
1989	6p. drab and green	15	15

CASTLES—HORIZ: 1p. Turegano; 1p.50, Villalonso; 2p.50, Velez Blanco; 3p.50, Castilnovo; 6p. Torrelobaton.

404 Franciscan Friar and Child

1969. Bicentenary of San Diego (California).

1990	**404**	1p.50 multicoloured	25	20

405 Rock of Gibraltar

1969. Aid for Spanish "ex-Gibraltar" Workers.

1991	**405**	1p.50 blue	20	15
1992	-	2p. purple	20	15

DESIGN: 2p. Aerial view of Rock.

1969. Tourist Series. As T 340.

1993	1p.50 green and turquoise	20	15
1994	3p. turquoise and green	15	15
1995	3p.50 blue and green	20	15
1996	6p. violet and green	20	15

DESIGNS—HORIZ: 1p.50, Alcaniz (Teruel). VERT: 3p. Murcia Cathedral; 3p.50, "The Lady of Elche" (sculpture); 6p. Church of Our Lady of the Redonda, Logrono.

1969. Explorers and Colonizers of America (9th series). Chile. As T 309. Inscr "1969" at foot.

1997	40c. brown on blue	15	15
1998	1p.50 violet on flesh	25	15
1999	2p. green on mauve	25	15
2000	3p.50 green on cream	45	40
2001	6p. brown on cream	30	20

DESIGNS—VERT: 40c. Convent of Santo Domingo, Santiago de Chile; 2p. Ambrosio O'Higgins; 3p.50, Pedro de Valdivia (founder of Santiago de Chile). HORIZ: 1p.50, Chilean Mint; 6p. Cal y Canto Bridge.

406 "Adoration of the Three Kings" (Maino)

1969. Christmas. Multicoloured.

2002	1p.50 Type **406**		15	15
2003	2p. "The Nativity" (Gerona Cathedral)		15	15

407 Las Huelgas Monastery

1969. Las Huelgas Monastery, Burgos.

2004	**407**	1p.50 slate and green	25	15
2005	-	3p.50 blue	45	45
2006	-	6p. olive and green	25	45

DESIGNS—HORIZ: 3p.50, Tombs. VERT: 6p. Cloisters.

1970. Provincial Costumes. As T 375. Multicoloured.

2007	6p. Palencia	20	15
2008	6p. Pontevedra	20	15
2009	6p. Sahara	20	15
2010	6p. Salamanca	20	15
2011	6p. Santa Cruz de Tenerife	20	15
2012	6p. Santander	20	15
2013	6p. Segovia	20	15
2014	6p. Seville	20	15
2015	6p. Soria	20	15
2016	6p. Tarragona	20	15
2017	6p. Teruel	20	15
2018	6p. Toledo	20	15

408 Blessed Juan of Avila (after El Greco)

1970. Spanish Celebrities.

2019	**408**	25p. blue and lilac	4·75	35
2020	-	50p. brown and orange	2·10	40

DESIGN: 25p. Type **408** (400th death anniv); 50p. Cardinal Rodrigo Ximenes de Rada (after J. de Borgena) (800th birth anniv).

See also Nos. 2129/31.

409 "St. Stephen"

1970. Stamp Day and Luis de Morales Commem. Various paintings. Multicoloured.

2021	50c. Type **409**	20	15
2022	1p. "The Annunciation"	20	15
2023	1p.50 "Virgin and Child with St. John"	20	15
2024	2p. "Virgin and Child"	20	15
2025	3p. "The Presentation of the Infant Christ"	20	15
2026	3p.50 "St. Jerome"	20	15
2027	4p. "St. John of Ribera"	20	15
2028	5p. "Ecce Homo"	20	15
2029	6p. "Pieta"	20	20
2030	10p. "St. Francis of Assisi"	20	20

See also Nos. 2077/84, 2135/42, 2204/11, 2261/8, 2420/7, 2478/85, 2529/36 and 2585/90.

410 "Flaming Sun"

1970. Europa.

2031	**410**	3p.50 gold & ultramarine	25	25

1970. World Stamp Day. As T 381 but stamp and postmark changed.

2032	2p. red, black and green	15	15

DESIGN: 2p. Spanish 12c. stamp of 1860 with railway cachet.

411 Fair Building

1970. 50th Anniv of Barcelona Fair.

2033	**411**	15p. multicoloured	25	15

412 Gen. Primo de Rivera

1970. Birth Cent of General Primo de Rivera.

2034	**412**	2p. green, brown and buff	15	15

1970. Spanish Castles (5th series). As T 368.

2035	1p. black and blue	45	25
2036	1p.20 blue and turquoise	20	15
2037	3p.50 brown and green	20	15
2038	6p. violet and brown	20	15
2039	10p. brown and chestnut	1·00	20

CASTLES—HORIZ: 1p. Valencia de Don Juan; 1p.20, Monterrey; 3p.50, Mombeltran; 6p. Sadaba; 10p. Bellver.

1970. Tourist Series. As T 340.

2040	50c. lilac and blue	15	15
2041	1p. brown and ochre	20	15
2042	1p.50 green and blue	20	15
2043	2p. blue and deep blue	50	15
2044	3p.50 blue and violet	25	20
2045	5p. brown and blue	90	20

DESIGNS—HORIZ: 50c. Alcazaba, Almeria; 1p. Malaga Cathedral; 2p. St. Francis' Convent, Orense. VERT: 1p.50, Our Lady of the Assumption, Lequeitio; 3p.50, The Lonja, Zaragoza; 5p. The Portalon, Vitoria.

413 17th-century Tailor

1970. International Tailoring Congress.

2046	**413**	2p. violet, red and brown	15	15

414 Diver on Map

1970. 12th European Swimming, Diving and Water-polo Championships, Barcelona.

2047	**414**	2p. brown, blue and green	15	15

415 Concha Espina

1970. Spanish Writers.

2048	**415**	50c. blue, brown and buff	15	15
2049	-	1p. violet, green and drab	15	15
2050	-	1p.50 green, blue & drab	15	15
2051	-	2p. olive, green and buff	20	15
2052	-	2p.50 pur, vio & ochre	20	15
2053	-	3p.50 red, brown & lilac	20	15

WRITERS: 1p. Guillen de Castro; 1p.50, J. R. Jimenez; 2p. G. A. Becquer; 2p.50, Miguel de Unamuno; 3p.50, J. M. Gabriel y Galan.

1970. Explorers and Colonizers of America (10th series). Mexico. As T 309.

2054	40c. green on light green	20	15
2055	1p.50 brown on blue	20	15
2056	2p. violet on cream	70	20
2057	3p.50 green on light green	20	15
2058	6p. blue on pink	30	15

DESIGNS—VERT: 40c. House in Queretaro; 2p. Vasco de Quiroga; 3p.50, F. Juan de Zumarraga; 6p. Morelia Cathedral. HORIZ: 1p.50, Cathedral, Mexico City.

416 Survey Map of Southern Spain and North Africa

1970. Centenary of Spanish Geographical and Survey Institute.

2059	**416**	2p. multicoloured	20	15

417 "The Adoration of the Shepherds" (El Greco)

1970. Christmas. Multicoloured.

2060	1p.50 Type **417**	15	15
2061	2p. "The Adoration of the Shepherds" (Murillo)	15	15

418 U.N. Emblem and New York Headquarters

1970. 25th Anniv of United Nations.

2062	**418**	8p. multicoloured	20	15

419 Ripoll Monastery

1970. Ripoll Monastery.

2063	-	2p. purple and violet	50	20
2064	**419**	3p.50 purple and orange	20	15
2065	-	5p. green and slate	1·10	20

DESIGNS: 2p. Entrance; 5p. Cloisters.

420 Pilgrims' Route Map

1971. Holy Year of Compostela (1st issue). "St. James in Europe".

2066	**420**	50c. brown and blue	15	15
2067	-	1p. black and brown	15	15
2068	-	1p.50 purple and green	25	20
2069	-	2p. brown and purple	30	15
2070	-	3p. deep blue and blue	25	20
2071	-	4p. olive	45	20

DESIGNS—VERT: 1p. Statue of St. Brigid, Vadstena (Sweden); 1p.50, St. Jacques' Church tower, Paris; 2p. "St. James" (carving from altar, Pistoia, Italy). HORIZ: 3p. St. David's Cathedral, Wales; 4p. Carving from Ark of Charlemagne (Aachen, West Germany).

See also Nos. 2105/11 and 2121/8.

1971. Provincial Costumes. As T 375. Mult.

2072	6p. Valencia	25	20
2073	8p. Valladolid	45	20
2074	8p. Vizcaya	45	20
2075	8p. Zamora	45	20
2076	8p. Zaragoza	45	20

1971. Stamp Day and Ignacio Zuloaga Commem. Paintings as T 409. Multicoloured.

2077	50c. "My Uncle Daniel"	20	15
2078	1p. "Segovia" (horiz)	20	15
2079	1p.50 "The Duchess of Alba"	20	15
2080	2p. "Ignacio Zuloaga" (self-portrait)	20	15
2081	3p. "Juan Belmonte"	25	15
2082	4p. "The Countess of Noailles"	20	15
2083	5p. "Pablo Uranga"	30	20
2084	8p. "Boatmen's Houses, Lerma" (horiz)	30	25

421 Amadeo Vives (composer)

1971. Spanish Celebrities. Multicoloured.

2085	1p. Type **421**	20	15
2086	2p. St. Teresa of Avila (mystic)	25	20
2087	8p. B. Perez Galdos (writer)	25	20
2088	15p. R. Menendez Pidal (writer)	20	20

422 Europa Chain

1971. Europa.

2089	**422**	2p. brown, violet and blue	70	30
2090	**422**	8p. brown, light green and green	45	45

1971. World Stamp Day. As T 381, but with different stamp and postmark.

2091	2p. black, blue and green	20	15

DESIGN: 2p. Spanish 6c. stamp of 1850 with "A.s." postmark.

423 Gymnast on Vaulting-horse

1971. 9th European Male Gymnastics Cup Championships, Madrid. Multicoloured.

2092	1p. Type **423**	20	15
2093	2p. Gymnast on bar	20	15

424 Great Bustard

1971. Spanish Fauna (1st series). Mult.

2094	1p. Type **424**	35	20
2095	2p. Lynx	30	15
2096	3p. Brown bear	30	15
2097	5p. Red-legged partridge (vert)	45	25
2098	8p. Spanish ibex (vert)	65	45

See also Nos. 2160/4, 2192/6, 2250/4, 2317/21, 2452/6 and 2579/83.

426 Legionaries in Battle

1971. 50th Anniv of Spanish Foreign Legion. Multicoloured.

2101	1p. Type **426**	20	20
2102	2p. Ceremonial parade	25	20
2103	5p. Memorial service	30	20
2104	8p. Officer and mobile column	30	25

1971. Holy Year of Compostela (2nd issue). "En Route to Santiago". As T 420.

2105	50c. purple and blue	20	15
2106	6p. blue	20	15
2107	7p. purple and deep purple	45	20
2108	7p.50 red and purple	20	20
2109	8p. purple and green	20	20
2110	9p. violet and green	20	20
2111	10p. brown and green	25	20

DESIGNS—HORIZ: 50c. Pilgrims' route map of northern Spain; 7p.50, Cloisters, Najera Monastery; 9p. Eunate Monastery. VERT: 6p. "Pilgrims" (sculpture, Royal Hospital, Burgos); 7p. Gateway, St. Domingo de la Calzada Monastery; 8p. Statue of Christ, Puente de la Reina; 10p. Cross of Roncesvalles.

427 "Children of the World"

1971. 25th Anniv of UNICEF.

2112	**427**	8p. multicoloured	25	20

428 "Battle of Lepanto" (after L. Valdes)

1971. 400th Anniv of Battle of Lepanto.

2113	-	2p. green & brown (vert)	45	15
2114	**428**	5p. chocolate and brown	90	20
2115	-	8p. blue and red (vert)	75	75

DESIGNS: 2p. "Don John of Austria" (S. Coello); 8p. Standard of the Holy League.

429 Hockey Players

1971. World Hockey Cup Championships, Barcelona.

2116	**429**	5p. multicoloured	65	15

430 Airco (de Havilland) D.H.9B over Seville

1971. 50th Anniv of Spanish Airmail Services. Multicoloured.

2117	2p. Type **430**	30	20
2118	15p. Boeing 747-100 airliner over Madrid	30	20

431 "The Nativity" (detail from altar, Avia)

1971. Christmas. Multicoloured.

2119	2p. Type **431**	20	15
2120	8p. "The Birth" (detail from altar, Saga)	20	15

1971. Holy Year of Compostela (3rd issue). As T 420.

2121	1p. black and green	20	15
2122	1p.50 violet and purple	25	25
2123	2p. blue and green	90	20
2124	2p.50 violet and red	15	15
2125	3p. purple and red	50	20
2126	3p.50 green and pink	20	15
2127	4p. brown and blue	20	15
2128	5p. black and green	40	15

DESIGNS—VERT: 1p. Santiago Cathedral; 2p. Lugo Cathedral; 3p. Astorga Cathedral; 4p. San Tirso, Sahagun. HORIZ: 1p.50, Pilgrim approaching Santiago de Compostela; 2p.50, Villafranca del Bierzo; 3p.50, San Marcos, Leon; 5p. San Martin, Fromista.

1972. Spanish Celebrities. As T 408.

2129	15p. green and brown	30	15
2130	25p. black and green	30	20
2131	50p. brown and red	55	20

CELEBRITIES: 15p. Emilia Pardo Bazan (novelist); 25p. Jose de Espronceda (poet); 50p. Fernan Gonzalez (first King of Castile).

432 Ski Jumping

1972. Winter Olympic Games, Sapporo, Japan. Multicoloured.

2132	2p. Type **432**	45	20
2133	15p. Figure skating (vert)	25	25

433 Title-page of "Don Quixote" (1605)

1972. International Book Year.

2134	**433**	2p. red and brown	15	15

1972. Stamp Day and Solana Commem. Paintings by Solana. As T 409. Multicoloured.

2135	1p. "Clowns" (horiz)	20	20
2136	2p. "Solana and Family" (self-portrait)	35	15
2137	3p. "Blind Musician"	45	15
2138	4p. "Return of the Fishermen"	25	15
2139	5p. "Decorating Masks"	1·30	30
2140	7p. "The Bibliophile"	60	20
2141	10p. "Merchant Navy Captain"	60	20
2142	15p. "Pombo Reunion" (vert)	55	25

434 "Abies pinsapo"

1972. Spanish Flora (1st series). Multicoloured.

2143	1p. Type **434**	25	15
2144	2p. Strawberry tree	40	15
2145	3p. Maritime pine	45	15
2146	5p. Holm oak	70	25
2147	8p. "Juniperus thurifera"	40	25

See also Nos. 2178/82, 2278/82 and 2299/303.

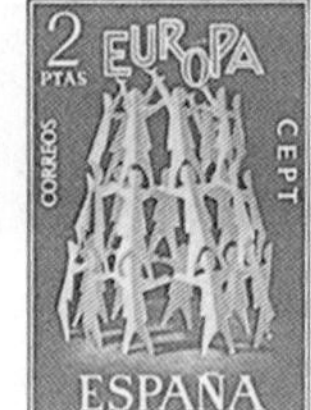

435 "Europeans"

1972. Europa. Multicoloured.

2148	2p. Type **435**	1·30	30
2149	8p. "Communications"	75	45

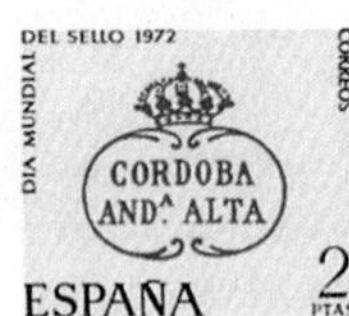

436 Cordoba Pre-stamp Postmark

1972. World Stamp Day.

2150	**436**	2p. red, black and brown	15	15

1972. Spanish Castles (6th series). As T 368.

2151	1p. brown and green	50	40
2152	2p. brown and green	85	20
2153	3p. brown and red	90	20
2154	5p. green and blue	90	20
2155	10p. violet and blue	2·75	20

CASTLES—VERT: 1p. Sajazarra. HORIZ: 2p. Santa Catalina; 3p. Biar; 5p. San Servando; 10p. Pedraza.

437 Fencing

1972. Olympic Games, Munich. Multicoloured.

2156	1p. Type **437**	25	15
2157	2p. Weightlifting (vert)	30	15
2158	5p. Rowing (vert)	25	20
2159	8p. Pole vaulting (vert)	25	20

438 Chamois

1972. Spanish Fauna (2nd series). Mult.

2160	1p. Pyrenean desman	25	20
2161	2p. Type **438**	25	20
2162	3p. Wolf	30	20
2163	5p. Egyptian mongoose (horiz)	70	20
2164	7p. Small-spotted genet (horiz)	65	20

439 Brigadier M. A. de Ustariz

1972. "Spain in the New World" (1st series). 450th Anniv of Puerto Rico. Multicoloured.

2165	1p. Type **439**	20	15
2166	2p. View of San Juan, 1870 (horiz)	30	15
2167	5p. View of San Juan, 1625 (horiz)	50	20
2168	8p. Map of Plaza de Bahia, 1792 (horiz)	40	40

See also Nos. 2212/5, 2271/4, 2338/41 and 2430/3.

440 Facade of Monastery

1972. Monastery of St.Thomas, Avila.

2169	**440**	2p. green and blue	95	20
2170	-	8p. purple and brown	80	30
2171	-	15p. blue and purple	45	20

DESIGNS—VERT: 8p. Interior of monastery. HORIZ: 15p. Cloisters.

441 Grand Lyceum Theatre

1972. 125th Anniv of Grand Lyceum Theatre, Barcelona.

2172	**441**	8p. brown and blue	30	20

442 "The Nativity"

1972. Christmas. Murals in Royal Collegiate Basilica of San Isidoro, Leon. Multicoloured.

2173	2p. Type **442**	20	15
2174	8p. "The Annunciation"	20	15

443 J. de Herrera and Escorial

1973. Spanish Architects (1st series).

2175	**443**	8p. green and sepia	50	15
2176	-	10p. blue and brown	1·80	20
2177	-	15p. blue and green	35	20

DESIGNS: 10p. J. de Villanueva and Prado; 15p. V. Rodriguez and Apollo Fountain, Madrid.

See also Nos. 2295/7.

444 "Apollonias canariensis"

1973. Spanish Flora (2nd series). Canary Islands. Multicoloured.

2178	1p. Type **444**	20	20
2179	2p. "Myrica faya"	65	20
2180	4p. "Phoenix canariensis"	20	20
2181	5p. "Ilex canariensis"	80	25
2182	15p. "Dracaena draco"	40	20

Nos. 2179/82 are vert.

445 Roman Mosaic

1973. Europa.

2183	**445**	2p. multicoloured	70	25
2184	-	8p. blue, red and black	65	25

DESIGN—HORIZ (37×26 mm): 8p. Europa "Posthorn".

1973. World Stamp Day. As T 381, but with different stamp and postmark.

2185	2p. red, blue and black	20	15

DESIGN: 2p. Spanish 6r. stamp of 1853 with Madrid postmark.

446 Iznajar Dam

1973. 11th Congress of Int High Dams Commission, Madrid.

2186	**446**	8p. multicoloured	20	15

1973. Tourist Series. As T 340.

2187	1p. brown and green	25	15
2188	2p. green and dark green	60	15
2189	3p. brown and light brown	60	15
2190	5p. violet and blue	1·50	20
2191	8p. red and green	70	20

DESIGNS—HORIZ: 1p. Gateway, Onate University, Guipuzcoa; 2p. Town Square, Lugo; 5p. Columbus' House, Las Palmas; 8p. Windmills, La Mancha. VERT: 3p. Llerena Square, Badajoz.

447 Black-bellied Sandgrouse

1973. Spanish Fauna (3rd series). Birds. Mult.

2192	1p. Type **447**	30	20
2193	2p. Black stork	40	20
2194	5p. Azure-winged magpie (vert)	70	50
2195	7p. Imperial eagle	75	20
2196	15p. Red-crested pochard (vert)	35	25

448 Hermandad Standard-bearer, Castile, 1488

1973. Spanish Military Uniforms (1st series). Multicoloured.

2197	1p. Type **448**	20	20
2198	2p. Mounted knight, Castile, 1493 (horiz)	55	15
2199	3p. Arquebusier, 1534	60	15
2200	7p. Mounted arquebusier, 1560	40	20
2201	8p. Infantry sergeant, 1567	40	20

See also Nos. 2225/7, 2255/9, 2290/4, 2322/6, 2410/14, 2441/5, 2472/6 and 2499/503.

449 Fishes in Net and Trawler

1973. World Fishing Fair and Congress, Vigo.

2202	**449**	2p. multicoloured	15	15

450 Conference Building

1973. I.T.U. Conference, Torremolinos.

2203	**450**	8p. multicoloured	20	15

1973. Stamp Day and Vicente Lopez Commem. Paintings. As T 409. Multicoloured.

2204	1p. "Ferdinand VII"	25	15
2205	2p. Self-portrait	25	15
2206	3p. "La Senora de Carvallo"	25	15
2207	4p. "M. de Castelldosrrius"	25	15
2208	5p. "Isabella II"	40	20
2209	7p. "Goya"	25	20
2210	10p. "Maria Amalia of Saxony"	25	20
2211	15p. "Felix Lopez, the Organist"	25	20

451 Leon Cathedral, Nicaragua

1973. "Spain in the New World" (2nd series). Nicaragua. Multicoloured.

2212	1p. Type **451**	20	15
2213	2p. Subtiava Church	35	20
2214	5p. Colonial-style house (vert)	60	25
2215	8p. Rio San Juan Castle	35	20

452 Pope Gregory XI receiving St. Jerome's Petition

1973. 600th Anniv of Order of St. Jerome.

2216	**452**	2p. multicoloured	15	15

453 Courtyard

1973. Monaster of Santo Domingo de Silos, Burgos.

2217	**453**	2p. purple and brown	55	15
2218	-	8p. purple and blue	20	15
2219	-	15p. blue and green	25	20

DESIGNS—HORIZ: 8p. Cloisters. VERT: 15p. "Three Saints" (statue).

454 "The Nativity" (pillar capital, Silos)

1973. Christmas. Multicoloured.

2220	2p. Type **454**	20	15
2221	8p. "Adoration of the Kings" (bas-relief, Butrera) (horiz)	15	15

455 Map of Spain and the Americas

1973. 500th Anniv of Spanish Printing.

2222	**455**	1p. blue and green	40	15
2223	-	7p. violet and blue	25	20
2224	-	15p. green and purple	30	25

DESIGNS—VERT: 7p. "Teacher and pupils" (ancient woodcut); 15p. "Los Sinodales" (manuscript).

1974. Spanish Military Uniforms (2nd series). As T 448. Multicoloured.

2225	1p. Mounted arquebusier, 1603	20	15
2226	2p. Arquebusier, 1632	65	20
2227	3p. Mounted cuirassier, 1635	80	20
2228	5p. Mounted drummer, 1677	1·20	35
2229	9p. Musketeers, "Viejos Morados" Regiment, 1694	35	25

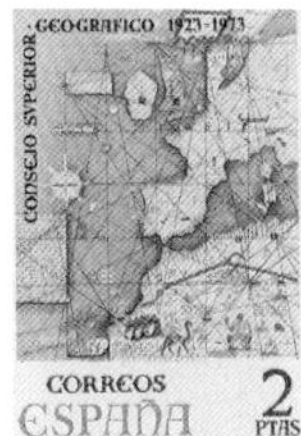

456 14th-century Nautical Chart

1974. 50th Anniv of Spanish Higher Geographical Council.

2230	**456**	2p. multicoloured	15	15

457 Miguel Biada (construction engineer) and Locomotive "Mataro"

1974. 125th Anniv of Barcelona–Mataro Railway.

2231	**457**	2p. multicoloured	15	15

458 Stamp Collector, Album and Magnifier

1974. "ESPANA 75" Int Stamp Exhibition, Madrid.

2232	**458**	2p. multicoloured	20	20
2233	-	5p. blue, black and brown	45	35
2234	-	8p. multicoloured	35	30

DESIGNS—DIAMOND (43×43 mm): 5p. Exhibition emblem; 8p. Globe and arrows.

459 "Woman with Offering"

1974. Europa. Stone Sculptures. Multicoloured.

2235	2p. Type **459**	75	20
2236	8p. "Woman from Baza"	35	30

460 2r. Stamp of 1854 with Seville Postmark

1974. World Stamp Day.

2237	**460**	2p. multicoloured	15	15

461 Jaime Balmes (philosopher) and Monastery

1974. Spanish Celebrities.

2238	**461**	8p. brown and blue	20	20
2239	-	10p. brown and red	65	35
2240	-	15p. blue and brown	25	20

DESIGNS: 10p. Pedro Poveda (educationalist) and mountain village; 15p. Jorge Juan (cosmographer and mariner) and shipyard.

462 Bramante's "Little Temple", Rome

1974. Centenary of Spanish Fine Arts Academy, Rome.

2241	**462**	5p. multicoloured	20	20

463 Roman Aqueduct, Segovia

1974. Spain as a Province of the Roman Empire.

2242	**463**	1p. black and brown	10	10
2243	-	2p. brown and green	35	10
2244	-	3p. brown & light brown	10	10
2245	-	4p. blue and green	10	10
2246	-	5p. purple and blue	10	10
2247	-	7p. purple and green	10	10
2248	-	8p. green and red	20	15
2249	-	9p. brown and purple	20	20

DESIGNS—HORIZ: 2p. Roman Bridge, Alcantara; 3p. Martial (poet) giving public reading; 5p. Theatre, Merida; 7p. Ossio, 1st Bishop of Cordoba, addressing the Synod. VERT: 4p. Triumphal Arch, Bara; 8p. Ruins of Curia, Talavera la Vieja; 9p. Statue of Emperor Trajan.

464 Tortoise

1974. Spanish Fauna (4th series). Reptiles. Mult.

2250	1p. Type **464**	20	15
2251	2p. Chameleon	35	15
2252	5p. Gecko	55	55
2253	7p. Green lizard	45	25
2254	15p. Adder	20	15

1974. Spanish Military Uniforms (3rd series). As T 448. Multicoloured.

2255	1p. Dismounted trooper, Hussars de la Muerte, 1705	15	10
2256	2p. Officer, Royal Regiment of Artillery, 1710	40	10
2257	3p. Drummer and fifer, Granada Regiment, 1734	45	15
2258	7p. Guidon-bearer, Numancia Dragoons, 1737	35	15
2259	8p. Ensign with standard, Zamora Regiment, 1739	15	15

465 Swimmer making Rescue

1974. 18th World Life-saving Championships. Barcelona.

2260	**465**	2p. multicoloured	20	15

1974. Stamp Day and Eduardo Rosales. Commemoration. Various paintings as T 409. Multicoloured.

2261	1p. "Tobias and the Angel"	15	10
2262	2p. Self-portrait	15	15
2263	3p. "Testament of Isabella the Catholic" (horiz)	15	10
2264	4p. "Nena"	15	15
2265	5p. "Presentation of Don Juan of Austria" (horiz)	15	10
2266	7p. "The First Steps" (horiz)	15	15
2267	10p. "St. John the Evangelist"	30	15
2268	15p. "St. Matthew the Evangelist"	15	15

466 Figure with Letter and Posthorns

1974. Centenary of U.P.U. Multicoloured.

2269	2p. Type **466**	15	10
2270	8p. U.P.U. Monument, Berne	20	15

467 Sobremonte's House, Cordoba

1974. "Spain in the New World" (3rd series). Argentina. Multicoloured.

2271	1p. Type **467**	15	10
2272	2p. Town Hall, Buenos Aires (1929)	35	15
2273	5p. Ruins of St. Ignacio de Mini (vert)	30	15
2274	10p. "The Gaucho" (M. Fierro) (vert)	20	15

468 "Nativity" (detail, Valdavia Church)

1974. Christmas. Church Fonts. Multicoloured.

2275	2p. Type **468**	10	10
2276	3p. "Adoration of the Kings", Valcobero Church (vert)	15	10
2277	8p. As No. 2276	15	10

469 "Teucrium lanigerum"

1974. Spanish Flora (3rd series). Multicoloured.

2278	1p. Type **469**	15	10
2279	2p. "Hypericum ericoides"	20	10
2280	4p. "Thymus longiflorus"	15	10
2281	5p. "Anthyllis onobrychioides"	25	20
2282	8p. "Helianthemum paniculatum"	15	15

The 1p. and 8p. are wrongly inscribed "Teucriun" and "Helianthemum" respectively.

470 Leyre Monastery

1974. Leyre Monastery.

2283	**470**	2p. grey and green	50	10
2284	-	8p. red and brown	15	10
2285	-	15p. deep green and green	35	10

DESIGNS—VERT: 8p. Pillars and bas-relief. HORIZ: 15p. Crypt.

471 Spanish 6c. and 5p. Stamps of 1850 and 1975

1975. 125th Anniv of Spanish Postage Stamps.

2286	**471**	2p. blue	35	35
2287	-	3p. brown and green	45	40
2288	-	8p. mauve and violet	1·00	45
2289	-	10p. green and purple	50	40

DESIGNS—HORIZ: 3p. Mail coach, 1850; 8p. Sail packet of West Indian service. VERT: 10p. St. Mark's Chapel.

1975. Spanish Military Uniforms (4th series). As T 448. Multicoloured.

2290	1p. Toledo Regiment, 1750	15	10
2291	2p. Royal Corps of Artillery, 1762	35	15
2292	3p. Queen's Regt of the Line, 1763	1·70	25
2293	5p. Vitoria Regt of Fusiliers, 1766	50	15
2294	10p. Dragoon of Sagunto Regt, 1775	1·50	20

1975. Spanish Architects (2nd series). As T 443.

2295	8p. olive and green	15	15
2296	10p. brown and red	45	10
2297	15p. black and brown	20	15

ARCHITECTS: 8p. Antonio Gaudi and apartment building; 10p. Antonio Palacios and palace; 15p. Secundino Zuazo and block of flats.

472 Agate Casket

1975. "Espana 75" International Stamp Exhibition, Madrid (2nd issue). Two sheets, 124×88 mm or 88×124 mm, containing T 472 and similar designs.

MS2298 (a) 2p. blue and brown; 8p. brown and blue; 15p. red and brown; 50p. red, brown and deep brown. (b) 3p. green and brown; 10p. green, brown and deep brown; 12p. blue and brown; 25p. blue, brown and deep brown 14·00 16·00

473 Almonds

1975. Spanish Flora (4th series). Multicoloured.

2299	1p. Type **473**	10	10
2300	2p. Pomegranates (vert)	25	15
2301	3p. Oranges (vert)	25	10
2302	4p. Chestnuts (vert)	20	10
2303	5p. Apples (vert)	20	15

474 Woman and Pitcher, La Aranya

1975. Europa. Primitive Cave Paintings.

2304	**474**	3p. red, brown and stone	35	15
2305	-	12p. mauve, black & brn	70	25

DESIGN—HORIZ: 12p. Horse, Tito Bustillo.

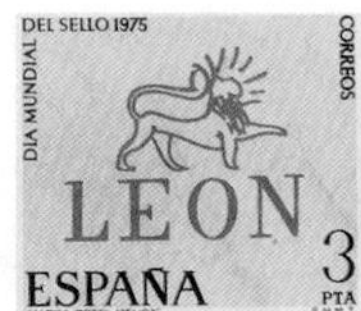

475 Early Leon Postmark

1975. World Stamp Day.

2306	**475**	3p. multicoloured	10	10

476 Emblem and Inscription

1975. 1st General Assembly of World Tourism Organization, Madrid.

2307	**476**	3p. blue	10	10

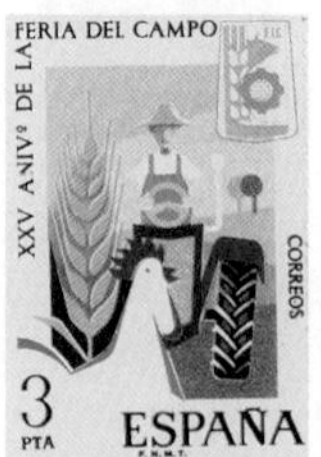

477 Farm Scene

1975. 25th Anniv of "Feria del Campo".

2308	**477**	3p. multicoloured	10	10

478 Heads of Different Races

1975. International Women's Year.

2309	**478**	3p. multicoloured	10	10

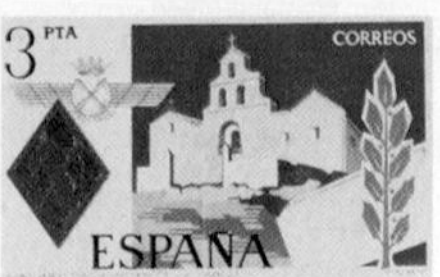

479 Virgin of Cabeza Sanctuary and Forces Emblems

1975. Defence of Virgin of Cabeza Sanctuary during Civil War Commemoration.

2310	**479**	3p. multicoloured	10	10

1975. Tourist Series. As T 340.

2311	1p. lilac and purple	15	10
2312	2p. deep brown and brown	15	10
2313	3p. black and blue	20	10
2314	4p. mauve and orange	20	10
2315	5p. black and green	30	15
2316	7p. indigo and blue	35	15

DESIGNS—HORIZ: 1p. Cervantes' cell, Argamasilla de Alba; 2p. St. Martin's Bridge, Toledo; 3p. St. Peter's Church, Tarrasa. VERT: 4p. Alhambra archway, Granada; 5p. Mijas village, Malaga; 7p. St. Mary's Chapel, Tarrasa.

480 Salamander Lizard

1975. Spanish Fauna (5th series). Reptiles and Amphibians. Multicoloured.

2317	1p. Type **480**	10	10
2318	2p. Triton lizard	25	10
2319	3p. Tree-frog	25	10
2320	6p. Toad	20	15
2321	7p. Frog	20	15

1975. Spanish Military Uniforms (5th series). As T 448. Multicoloured.

2322	1p. Montesa Regt. 1788	15	10
2323	2p. Asturias Regt of Fusiliers, 1789	55	20
2324	3p. Infantry of the Line, 1802	15	10
2325	4p. Royal Corps of Artillery, 1803	15	15
2326	7p. Royal Engineers Regt, 1809	15	15

481 Child

1975. Child Welfare.

2327	**481**	3p. multicoloured	10	10

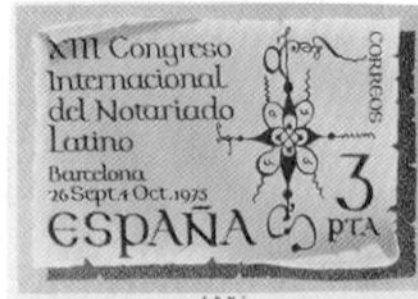

482 Scroll

1975. Latin Notaries' Congress, Barcelona.

2328	**482**	3p. multicoloured	10	10

483 "Blessing the Birds"

1975. Stamp Day and Millenary of Gerona Cathedral. Beatitude Miniatures. Multicoloured.

2329	1p. Type **483**	15	10
2330	2p. "Angel and River of Life" (vert)	15	10
2331	3p. "Angel at Gates of Paradise" (vert)	15	10
2332	4p. "Fox seizing Cockerel"	15	10
2333	6p. "Daniel with the Lions"	15	10
2334	7p. "Blessing the Multitude" (vert)	25	25
2335	10p. "The Four Horsemen of the Apocalypse" (vert)	15	15
2336	12p. "Peacock and Snake" (vert)	20	15

484 Industry Emblems

1975. Spanish Industry.

2337	**484**	3p. violet and purple	10	10

485 El Cabildo, Montevideo

1975. "Spain in the New World" (4th series). 150th Anniv of Uruguayan Independence. Multicoloured.

2338	1p. Type **485**	10	10
2339	2p. Ox wagon	20	10
2340	3p. Fortress, St. Teresa	25	10
2341	8p. Cathedral, Montevideo (vert)	20	15

486 San Juan de la Pena Monastery

1975. San Juan de la Pena Monastery Commem.

2342	**486**	3p. brown and green	30	10
2343	-	8p. violet and mauve	15	10
2344	-	10p. red and mauve	25	15

DESIGNS—HORIZ: 8p. Cloisters. VERT: 10p. Pillars.

487 "Virgin and Child"

1975. Christmas. Navarra Art. Multicoloured.

2345		3p. Type **487**	15	10
2346		12p. "The Flight into Egypt" (horiz)	15	10

488 King Juan Carlos I

1975. Proclamation of King Juan Carlos I. Multicoloured.

2347		3p. Type **488**	15	10
2348		3p. Queen Sophia	15	10
2349		3p. King Juan Carlos and Queen Sophia (33×33 mm)	15	10
2350		12p. As No. 2349	15	15

489 Virgin of Pontevedra

1975. Holy Year of Compostela.

2351	**489**	3p. brown and orange	15	10

490 Mountain Scene and Emblems

1976. Centenary of Catalunya Excursion Centre.

2352	**490**	6p. multicoloured	15	10

491 Cosme Damian Churruca and "San Juan Nepomucendo"

1976. Spanish Navigators.

2353	**491**	7p. black and brown	1·50	25
2354	-	12p. violet	30	20
2355	-	50p. brown and green	55	15

NAVIGATORS—VERT: 12p. Luis de Requesens. HORIZ: 50p. Juan Sebastian del Cano and "Vitoria".

492 Alexander Graham Bell and Telephone Equipment

1976. Telephone Centenary.

2356	**492**	3p. multicoloured	1·10	30

493 Crossing the Road

1976. Road Safety. Multicoloured.

2357		1p. Type **493**	10	10
2358		3p. Dangerous driving (vert)	30	10
2359		5p. Wearing of seat-belts	20	15

494 St. George on Horseback

1976. 700th Anniv of St. George's Guardianship of Alcoy.

2360	**494**	3p. multicoloured	15	10

495 Talavera Pottery

1976. Europa. Spanish Handicrafts. Multicoloured.

2361		3p. Type **495**	70	15
2362		12p. Camarinas lace-making	80	45

496 Spanish 1851 6r. Stamp with Coruna Postmark

1976. World Stamp Day.

2363	**496**	3p. red, blue and black	15	10

497 Coins

1976. Bimillenary of Zaragoza. Roman Antiquities.

2364	**497**	3p. brown and black	2·10	15
2365	-	7p. blue and black	95	35
2366	-	25p. brown and black	55	10

DESIGNS—HORIZ: 7p. Plan of site and coin. VERT: 25p. Mosaic.

498 Rifle, 1757

1976. Bicentenary of American Revolution.

2367	**498**	1p. blue and brown	15	10
2368	-	3p. brown and green	95	10
2369	-	5p. green and brown	45	15
2370	-	12p. brown and green	45	25

DESIGNS: 3p. Bernado de Galvez and emblem; 5p. Richmond $1 banknote of 1861; 12p. Battle of Pensacola.

499 Customs-house, Cadiz

1976. Spanish Customs Buildings.

2371	**499**	1p. brown and black	15	10
2372	-	3p. brown and green	65	15
2373	-	7p. purple and brown	1·10	35

BUILDINGS: 3p. Madrid; 7p. Barcelona.

500 Savings Jar and "Industry"

1976. Spanish Post Office. Multicoloured.

2374		1p. Type **500**	10	10
2375		3p. Railway mail-sorting van	35	10
2376		6p. Mounted postman (horiz)	15	15
2377		10p. Automatic letter sorting equipment (horiz)	25	15

501 King Juan Carlos I, Queen Sophia and Map of the Americas

1976. Royal Visit to America (1st issue).

2378	**501**	12p. multicoloured	25	15

See also No. 2434.

1976. Tourist Series. As T 340.

2379		1p. brown and blue	15	10
2380		2p. green and blue	70	10
2381		3p. chocolate and brown	50	10
2382		4p. blue and brown	30	10
2383		7p. brown and blue	85	40
2384		12p. purple and red	1·30	25

DESIGNS—HORIZ: 1p. Cloisters, San Marcos, Leon; 2p. Las Canadas, Tenerife; 4p. Cruz de Tejeda, Las Palmas; 7p. Gredos, Avila; 12p. La Arruzafa, Cordoba. VERT: 3p. Hospice of the Catholic Kings, Santiago de Compostela.

502 Rowing

1976. Olympic Games, Montreal. Multicoloured.

2385		1p. Type **502**	15	10
2386		2p. Boxing	45	15
2387		3p. Wrestling (vert)	40	15
2388		12p. Basketball (vert)	25	15

503 King Juan Carlos I

1976

2389	**503**	10c. orange	10	10
2390	**503**	25c. yellow	10	10
2391	**503**	30c. blue	10	10
2392	**503**	50c. purple	10	10
2393	**503**	1p. green	10	10
2394	**503**	1p.50 red	10	10
2395	**503**	2p. blue	10	10
2396	**503**	3p. green	10	10
2397	**503**	4p. turquoise	10	10
2398	**503**	5p. red	10	10
2399	**503**	6p. turquoise	10	10
2400	**503**	7p. olive	15	10
2401	**503**	8p. blue	15	10
2402	**503**	10p. red	15	10
2403	**503**	12p. brown	20	10
2403a	**503**	13p. brown	25	10
2403b	**503**	14p. orange	20	10
2404	**503**	15p. violet	30	10
2405	**503**	16p. brown	25	10
2405a	**503**	17p. blue	35	10
2406	**503**	19p. orange	30	10
2407	**503**	20p. red	30	10
2408	**503**	30p. green	40	10
2409	**503**	50p. red	70	10
2409a	**503**	60p. blue	80	10
2409b	**503**	75p. green	1·00	25
2409c	**503**	85p. grey	1·20	40
2409d	-	100p. brown	1·40	10
2409e	-	200p. green	2·75	10
2409f	-	500p. blue	6·75	85

Nos. 2409d/f are as Type **503**, but larger, 25×30 mm.

1976. Spanish Military Uniforms (6th series). As T 448. Multicoloured.

2410		1p. Alcantara Regiment, 1815	15	15
2411		2p. Regiment of the line, 1821	85	15
2412		3p. Gala Engineers, 1825	30	15
2413		7p. Artillery Regiment, 1828	25	25
2414		25p. Light Infantry Regiment, 1830	30	20

504 "Giving Blood"

1976. Blood Donors Publicity.

2415	**504**	3p. red and black	20	15

505 Batitales Mosaic

1976. Bimillenary of Lugo.

2416	**505**	1p. purple and black	15	15
2417	-	3p. brown and black	20	15
2418	-	7p. red and green	50	25

DESIGNS: 3p. Old City Wall; 7p. Roman coins.

506 Parliament House, Madrid

1976. 63rd Inter-Parliamentary Union Congress, Madrid.

2419	**506**	12p. brown and green	20	15

1976. Stamp Day and Luis Menendez Commemoration. Paintings as T 409. Mult.

2420		1p. "Jug, Cherries, Plums and Cheese"	10	10
2421		2p. "Jar, Melon, Oranges and Savouries"	10	10
2422		3p. "Barrel, Pears and Melon"	10	10
2423		4p. "Pigeons, Basket and Bowl"	15	10
2424		6p. "Fish and Oranges" (horiz)	20	10
2425		7p. "Melon and Bread" (horiz)	25	25
2426		10p. "Jug, Plums and Bread" (horiz)	25	15
2427		12p. "Pomegranates, Apples and Grapes" (horiz)	25	15

507 "The Nativity"

1976. Christmas. Statuettes. Multicoloured.

2428		3p. Type **507**	80	10
2429		12p. St. Christopher carrying Holy Child (vert)	1·50	55

508 Nicoya Church

1976. "Spain in the New World" (5th series). Costa Rica. Multicoloured.

2430		1p. Type **508**	15	10
2431		2p. Juan Vazquez de Coronado	25	15
2432		3p. Orosi Mission (horiz)	20	15

2433 12p. Tomas de Acosta 25 20

1976. Royal Visit to America (2nd issue). As T 501. Multicoloured.
2434 12p. "Santa Maria" and South America 20 15

510 San Pedro de Alcantara Monastery

1976. Monastery of San Pedro de Alcantara.
2435 **510** 3p. brown and purple 35 15
2436 - 7p. purple and blue 15 15
2437 - 20p. chocolate. and brown 35 15
DESIGNS—VERT: 7p. High Altar; 20p. San Pedro de Alcantara.

511 Hand releasing Doves

1976. Civil War Invalids' Association Commem.
2438 **511** 3p. multicoloured 20 15

512 Pablo Casals and Cello

1976. Birth Centenaries.
2439 **512** 3p. black and blue 15 10
2440 - 5p. green and red 20 10
DESIGN: 5p. Manuel de Falla and "Fire Dance".

1977. Spanish Military Uniforms (7th series). Vert designs as T 448. Multicoloured.
2441 1p. Calatrava Regiment of Lancers, 1844 15 10
2442 2p. Engineers' Regiment, 1850 35 10
2443 3p. Light Infantry Regiment, 1861 20 10
2444 4p. Infantry of the Line, 1861 20 15
2445 20p. Horse Artillery, 1862 25 15

513 King James I and Arms of Aragon

1977. 700th Death Anniv of King James I.
2446 **513** 4p. brown and violet 20 15

514 Jacinto Verdaguer (poet)

1977. Spanish Celebrities.
2447 **514** 5p. red and purple 25 10
2448 - 7p. green and brown 15 15
2449 - 12p. green and blue 20 15
2450 - 50p. brown and green 75 15
DESIGNS: 7p. Miguel Servet (theologian and physician); 12p. Pablo Sarasate (violinist); 50p. Francisco Tarrega (guitarist).

515 King Charles III

1977. Bicentenary of Economic Society of the Friends of the Land.
2451 **515** 4p. brown and green 20 15

516 Atlantic Salmon

1977. Spanish Fauna (6th series). Freshwater Fish. Multicoloured.
2452 1p. Type **516** 20 10
2453 2p. Brown trout (horiz) 20 10
2454 3p. European eel (horiz) 20 10
2455 4p. Common carp (horiz) 20 10
2456 6p. Barbel (horiz) 20 10

517 Skiing

1977. World Ski Championships, Granada.
2457 **517** 5p. multicoloured 20 15

518 La Cuadra, 1902

1977. Vintage Cars. Multicoloured.
2458 2p. Type **518** 10 10
2459 4p. Hispano Suiza, 1916 10 10
2460 5p. Elizade, 1915 15 15
2461 7p. Abadal, 1914 15 15

519 Donana

1977. Europa. Landscapes, National Parks. Multicoloured.
2462 3p. Type **519** 15 15
2463 12p. Ordesa 25 25

520 Plaza Mayor, Madrid and Stamps

1977. 50th Anniv of Philatelic Bourse on Plaza Mayor, Madrid.
2464 **520** 3p. green, red and violet 20 15

521 Enrique de Osso (founder)

1977. Centenary of Society of St. Theresa of Jesus.
2465 **521** 8p. multicoloured 20 15

1977. Tourist Series. As T 340.
2466 1p. brown and orange 10 10
2467 2p. grey and brown 10 10
2468 3p. purple and blue 10 10
2469 4p. green and blue 10 10
2470 7p. grey and brown 10 10
2471 12p. brown and violet 15 10
DESIGNS—HORIZ: 1p. Toledo Gate, Ciudad Real; 2p. Roman Aqueduct, Almunecar; 7p. Ampudia Castle, Palencia; 12p. Bisagra Gate, Toledo. VERT: 3p. Jaen Cathedral; 4p. Bridge and Gate, Ronda Gorge, Malaga.

1977. Spanish Military Uniforms (8th series). As T 448. Multicoloured.
2472 1p. Administration officer, 1875 20 10
2473 2p. Lancer, 1883 20 10
2474 3p. General Staff commander, 1884 20 10
2475 7p. Trumpeter, Divisional Artillery, 1887 20 15
2476 25p. Medical Corps officer, 1895 25 15

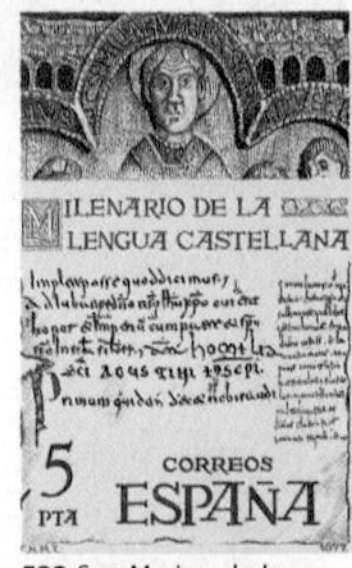

522 San Marino de la Cogalla (carving) and Early Castilian Manuscript

1977. Millenary of Castilian Language.
2477 **522** 5p. brown, green & pur 20 15

1977. Stamp Day and F. Madrazo (painter) Commemoration. Portraits. As T 409. Mult.
2478 1p. "The Youth of Florez" 10 10
2479 2p. "Duke of San Miguel" 10 10
2480 3p. "C. Coronado" 10 10
2481 4p. "Campoamor" 10 10
2482 6p. "Marquesa de Montelo" 10 10
2483 7p. "Rivadeneyra" 15 10
2484 10p. "Countess of Vilches" 15 10
2485 15p. "Gomez de Avellaneda" 20 10

523 West Indies Sailing Packet and Map of Mail Routes to America

1977. Bicentenary of Mail to the Indies, and "Espamer 77" Stamp Exhibition, Barcelona.
2486 **523** 15p. green and brown 25 25

524 St. Francis's Church

1977. Spanish–Guatemalan Relations. Guatemala City Buildings. Multicoloured.
2487 1p. Type **524** 10 10
2488 3p. High-rise flats 10 10
2489 7p. Government Palace 10 10
2490 12p. Monument, Columbus Square 15 15

525 Monastery Building

1977. St. Peter's Monastery, Cardena Commem.
2491 **525** 3p. grey and blue 10 10
2492 - 7p. red and brown 15 10
2493 - 20p. grey and green 25 15
DESIGNS: 7p. Cloisters; 20p. El Cid (effigy).

526 Adoration of the Kings

1977. Christmas. Miniatures from Manuscript "Romanico de Huesca". Multicoloured.
2494 5p. Type **526** 15 10
2495 12p. Flight into Egypt (vert) 20 10

527 Rohrbach RO.VII Roland M-CBBB, 1927, and Douglas DC-10 EC-CPN

1977. 50th Anniv of Iberia (State Airline).
2496 **527** 12p. multicoloured 20 15

528 Crown Prince Felipe

1977. Felipe de Borbon, Prince of Asturias.
2497 **528** 5p. multicoloured 20 15

529 Judo

1977. 10th World Judo Championships.
2498 **529** 3p. black, red and brown 20 15

1977. Spanish Military Uniforms (9th series). Multicoloured. Vert designs as T 448.
2499 1p. Standard bearer, Royal Infantry Regiment, 1908 10 10
2500 2p. Lieutenant-Colonel, Pavia Hussars, 1909 10 10
2501 3p. Lieutenant, Horse Artillery, 1912 10 10
2502 5p. Engineers' Captain, 1921 10 10
2503 12p. Captain-General of the Armed Forces, 1925 10 10

530 Hilarion Eslava (composer)

1977. Spanish Celebrities.
2504 **530** 5p. black and purple 10 10
2505 - 8p. black and green 15 10
2506 - 25p. black and green 30 10
2507 - 50p. purple and brown 65 20
DESIGNS: 8p. Jose Clara (sculptor); 25p. Pio Baroja (writer); 50p. Antonio Machado (writer).

531 "The Deposition of Christ" (detail Juan de Juni)

1978. Anniversaries of Artists.

2508	**531**	3p. multicoloured	10	10
2509	-	3p. multicoloured	10	10
2510	-	3p. mauve and violet	10	10
2511	-	5p. multicoloured	10	10
2512	-	5p. multicoloured	10	10
2513	-	5p. brown and black	10	10
2514	-	8p. multicoloured	10	10
2515	-	8p. multicoloured	10	10
2516	-	8p. pink and green	10	10

DESIGNS—As T **531**. No. 2510, Portrait of Juan de Juni (sculptor, 400th death anniv); No. 2511, Detail of "Rape of the Sabines" (Rubens); No. 2513, Artist's palette and Ruben's signature; No. 2514, Detail of "Bacchanal" (Titian); No. 2516, Artist's palette and Titian's initial. 46×25 mm: No. 2509, Different detail of "Deposition of Christ" and sculptor's tools; No. 2512, Different detail of "Rape of the Sabines" and portrait of Rubens (400th birth anniv); No. 2515, Different detail of "Bacchanal" and portrait of Titian (500th birth anniv).

532 Edelweiss in the Pyrenees

1978. Protection of the Environment. Mult.

2517	3p. Type **532**	10	10
2518	5p. Brown trout and red-breasted merganser	10	10
2519	7p. Forest (fire prevention)	15	10
2520	12p. Tanker, oil rig and industrial complex (protection of the sea)	15	10
2521	20p. Audouin's gull and Mediterranean monk seal (vert)	25	10

533 Palace of Charles V, Granada

1978. Europa.

2522	**533**	5p. green and light green	20	15
2523	-	12p. red and green	30	20

DESIGN: 12p. Exchange building, Seville.

534 Council Emblem and Map of Spain

1978. Membership of the Council of Europe.

2524	**534**	12p. multicoloured	15	15

535 Columbus Hermitage

1978. 500th Anniv of Las Palmas, Gran Canaria. Multicoloured.

2525	3p. 16th-century plan of city (horiz)	10	10
2526	5p. Type **535**	15	10
2527	12p. View of Las Palmas (16th century) (horiz)	15	10

536 Post Box, Stamp, U.P.U. Emblem and Postal Transport

1978. World Stamp Day.

2528	**536**	5p. green and deep green	20	15

1978. Stamp Day and Picasso Commemoration. As T 409. Multicoloured.

2529	3p. "Portrait of Senora Canals"	15	10
2530	5p. Self-portrait	15	10
2531	8p. "Portrait of Jaime Sabartes"	15	10
2532	10p. "The End of the Number"	15	10
2533	12p. "Science and Charity" (horiz)	15	10
2534	15p. "Las Meninas" (horiz)	15	10
2535	20p. "The Pigeons"	20	15
2536	25p. "The Painter and Model" (horiz)	25	15

537 Jose de San Martin

1978. Latin-American Heroes.

2537	**537**	7p. brown and red	10	10
2538	-	12p. violet and red	15	10

DESIGNS: 12p. Simon Bolivar.

538 Flight into Egypt

1978. Christmas. Capitals from Santa Maria de Nieva. Multicoloured.

2539	5p. Type **538**	10	10
2540	12p. The Annunciation	15	10

539 Aztec Calendar

1978. Royal Visits to Mexico, Peru and Argentina. Multicoloured.

2541	5p. Type **539**	10	10
2542	5p. Macchu Piccu, Peru	10	10
2543	5p. Pre-Columbian pots, Argentina	10	10

540 Philip V

1978. Spanish Kings and Queens of the House of Bourbon.

2544	**540**	5p. red and blue	10	10
2545	-	5p. deep green and green	10	10
2546	-	8p. lake and blue	20	15
2547	-	10p. black and green	20	15
2548	-	12p. lake and brown	20	15
2549	-	15p. blue and green	25	15
2550	-	20p. blue and olive	25	15
2551	-	25p. violet and blue	30	20
2552	-	50p. brown and red	55	25
2553	-	100p. violet and blue	1·40	55

DESIGNS: 5p. (No. 2545), Luis I; 8p. Ferdinand VI; 10p. Charles III; 12p. Charles IV; 15p. Ferdinand VII; 20p. Isabel II; 25p. Alfonso XII; 50p. Alfonso XIII; 100p. Juan Carlos I.

541 Miniatures from Bible

1978. Millenary of Consecration of Third Basilica of Santa Maria, Ripoll.

2554	**541**	5p. multicoloured	25	20

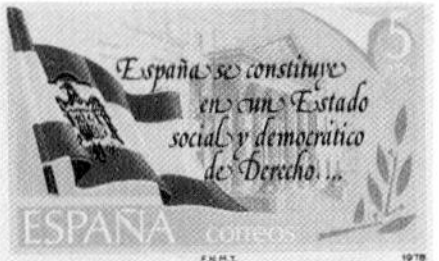

542 Flag, First Lines of Constitution and Cortes Building

1978. New Constitution.

2555	**542**	5p. multicoloured	25	20

543 Car and Oil Drop

1979. Energy Conservation. Multicoloured.

2556	5p. Type **543**	15	15
2557	8p. Insulated house and thermometer	20	15
2558	10p. Hand removing electric plug	20	15

544 St. Jean Baptiste de la Salle (founder)

1979. Centenary of Brothers of the Christian Schools in Spain.

2559	**544**	5p. brown, blue & mauve	15	15

545 Jorge Manrique (poet)

1979. Spanish Celebrities.

2560	**545**	5p. brown and green	15	15
2561	-	8p. blue and red	15	15
2562	-	10p. violet and brown	15	15
2563	-	20p. green and bistre	30	15

DESIGNS: 8p. Fernan Caballero (novelist); 10p. Francisco Villaespesa (poet); 20p. Gregorio Maranon (writer).

546 Running and Jumping

1979. Sport for All.

2564	**546**	5p. red, green and black	15	15
2565	-	8p. blue, ochre and black	20	15
2566	-	10p. brown, blue & black	20	15

DESIGNS: 8p. Football, running, skipping and cycling; 10p. Running.

547 School Library (child's drawing)

1979. International Year of the Child.

2567	**547**	5p. multicoloured	15	15

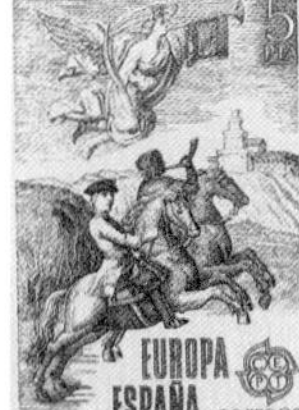

548 Cabinet Messenger and Postilion, 1761

1979. Europa.

2568	**548**	5p. deep brown and brown on yellow	35	20
2569	-	12p. green and brown on yellow	35	20

DESIGN—HORIZ: 12p. Manuel de Ysasi (postal reformer).

549 Wave Pattern and Television Screen

1979. World Telecommunications Day. Mult.

2570	5p. Type **549**	15	15
2571	8p. Satellite and receiving aerial (horiz)	15	15

550 First Bulgarian Stamp and Exhibition Hall

1979. "Philaserdica 79" Stamp Exhibition, Sofia.

2572	**550**	12p. multicoloured	15	10

551 Tank, "Roger de Lauria" (destroyer) and Hawker Siddeley Matador

1979. Armed Forces Day.

2573	**551**	5p. multicoloured	10	10

1979. Stamp Day.

2574	**552**	5p. multicoloured	10	10

552 King receiving Messenger

1979. Tourist Series. As T 340.

2575	5p. lilac and blue	15	10
2576	8p. brown and blue	15	10
2577	10p. green and myrtle	15	15
2578	20p. sepia and brown	25	15

DESIGNS—VERT: 5p. Daroca Gate, Zaragoza; 8p. Gerona Cathedral; 10p. Interior of Carthusian Monastery Church, Granada; 20p. Portal of Marques de Dos Aguas Palace, Valencia.

553 Turkey Sponge

1979. Spanish Fauna (7th series). Invertebrates. Multicoloured.

2579	5p. Type **553**	10	10
2580	7p. Crayfish	15	10
2581	8p. Scorpion	15	10

2582 20p. Starfish 20 10
2583 25p. Sea anemone 25 15

554 Antonio Gutierrez

1979. Defence of Tenerife, 1797.
2584 **554** 5p. multicoloured 15 10

1979. Stamp Day and J. de Juanes (painter) Commemoration. Religious Paintings as T 409. Multicoloured.
2585 8p. "Immaculate Conception" 15 10
2586 10p. "Holy Family" 15 10
2587 15p. "Ecce Homo" 15 10
2588 20p. "St. Stephen in the Synagogue" 25 10
2589 25p. "The Last Supper" (horiz) 30 15
2590 50p. "Adoration of the Mystic Lamb" (horiz) 55 20

555 Cathedral and Statue of Virgin and Child, Zaragoza

1979. 8th Mariological Congress, Zaragoza.
2591 **555** 5p. multicoloured 15 10

556 St. Bartholomew's College, Bogota

1979. Latin-American Architecture.
2592 **556** 7p. green, blue and brown 15 10
2593 - 12p. indigo, purple & brn 15 15
DESIGN: 12p. University of San Marcos, Lima.

557 Hands and Governor's Palace, Barcelona

1979. Catalonian Autonomy.
2594 **557** 8p. multicoloured 20 15

558 Autonomy Statute

1979. Basque Autonomy.
2595 **558** 8p. multicoloured 20 15

559 Prince of Asturias and Hospital

1979. Centenary of Hospital of the Child Jesus, Madrid.
2596 **559** 5p. multicoloured 20 15

560 Barcelona Tax Stamp, 1929

1979. 50th Anniv of Barcelona Exhibition Tax Stamps.
2597 **560** 5p. multicoloured 20 15

561 The Nativity

1979. Christmas. Capitals from San Pedro el Viejo, Huesca. Multicoloured.
2598 8p. Type **561** 10 10
2599 19p. Flight into Egypt 25 10

562 Charles I

1979. Spanish Kings of the House of Hapsburg.
2600 **562** 15p. green and blue 30 10
2601 - 20p. blue and mauve 30 10
2602 - 25p. violet and brown 35 10
2603 - 50p. brown and green 65 15
2604 - 100p. mauve and brown 1·10 35
DESIGNS: 20p. Philip II; 25p. Philip III; 50p. Philip IV; 100p. Charles II.

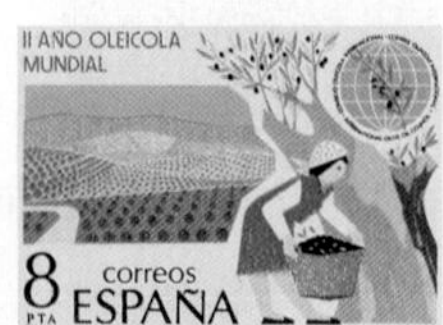

563 Olive Plantation and Harvester

1979. International Olive Oil Year.
2605 **563** 8p. multicoloured 20 15

564 Electric Train

1980. Public Transport.
2606 **564** 3p. lake and brown 10 10
2607 - 4p. blue and brown 10 10
2608 - 5p. green and brown 10 10
DESIGNS: 4p. Motorbus; 5p. Underground train.

565 Steel Products

1980. Spanish Exports (1st series). Multicoloured.
2609 5p. Type **565** 10 10
2610 8p. Tankers 15 10
2611 13p. Footwear 15 10
2612 19p. Industrial machinery 25 10
2613 25p. Factory buildings, bridge and symbols of technology 35 20
See also Nos. 2653/5.

566 Federico Garcia Lorca

1980. Europa. Writers.
2614 **566** 8p. violet and green 20 15
2615 - 19p. brown and green 25 20
DESIGN: 19p. J. Ortega y Gasset.

567 Footballers

1980. World Cup Football Championship, Spain (1982) (1st issue). Multicoloured.
2616 8p. Type **567** 15 10
2617 19p. Football and flags 25 10
See also Nos. 2640/1, 2668/9 and 2683/**MS**2685.

568 Armed Forces

1980. Armed Forces Day.
2618 **568** 8p. multicoloured 15 10

569 Bourbon Arms, Ministry of Finance, Madrid

1980. Public Finances under the Bourbons.
2619 **569** 8p. deep brown & brown 15 10

570 Helen Keller

1980. Birth Centenary of Helen Keller.
2620 **570** 19p. red and green 25 10

571 Postal Courier (14th century)

1980. Stamp Day.
2621 **571** 8p. brown, stone and red 15 10

572 King Alfonso XIII and Count of Maceda at Exhibition

1980. 50th Anniv of First National Stamp Exhibition.
2622 **572** 8p. multicoloured 15 10

573 Altar of the Virgin, La Palma Cathedral

1980. 300th Anniv of Appearance of the Holy Virgin at La Palma.
2623 **573** 8p. brown and black 15 10

574 Ramon Perez de Ayala

1980. Birth Centenary of Ramon Perez de Ayala (writer).
2624 **574** 100p. green and brown 1·30 15

575 Manuel Falla, Ruins of Atlantis and Bonampak Musicians

1980. "Espamer `80" International Stamp Exhibition, Madrid. Sheet 150×100 mm containing T 575 and similar horiz designs.
MS2625 25p. ×2, 50p., 100p. each brown, green and blue (sold at 250p.) 2·30 2·10
DESIGNS: 25p. Type **575**; 25p. Sun Gate, Tiahuanaco and Roman arch, Medinaceli; 50p. Alonos de Ercilla, Garcilaso de la Vega and title pages from *La Araucana* and *Commentarios Reales*; 100p. Virgin of Quito and Virgin of Seafarers.

576 Juan de Garay and Founding of Buenos Aires (after Moreno Carbonero)

1980. 400th Anniv of Buenos Aires.
2626 **576** 19p. blue, green and red 25 10

577 Tapestry Detail

1980. The Creation Tapestry, Gerona. Sheet 132×106 mm containing T 577 and similar designs showing tapestry details.
MS2627 25p. ×3 (each 33×26 mm), 50p. ×3, multicoloured 2·40 2·30

578 Palace of Congresses, Madrid

1980. European Security and Co-operation Conference, Madrid.
2628 **578** 22p. multicoloured 25 15

579 "Nativity" (mural from Church of Santa Maria de Cuina, Oza de los Rios)

1980. Christmas. Multicoloured.
2629 10p. Type **579** 15 10
2630 22p. "Adoration of the Kings" (doorway of Church of St. Nicholas of Cines, Oza de los Rios) (horiz) 25 10

580 Pedro Vives and Farman M.F.7 Biplane

1980. Aviation Pioneers. Multicoloured.
2631 5p. Type **580** 15 10
2632 10p. Benito Loygorri and Farman H.F.20 type biplane 15 10
2633 15p. Alfonso de Orleans and Caudron G-3 20 10
2634 22p. Alfredo Kindelan and biplane 25 15

581 Games Emblem and Skier

1981. Winter University Games.
2635 **581** 30p. multicoloured 30 15

582 "Homage to Picasso" (Joan Miro)

1981. Birth Centenary of Pablo Picasso (artist).
2636 **582** 100p. multicoloured 1·50 20

583 Newspaper, Camera, Notepaper and Pen

1981. The Press.
2637 **583** 12p. multicoloured 15 10

584 Map of Galicia, Arms and National Anthem

1981. Galician Autonomy.
2638 **584** 12p. multicoloured 15 10

585 Mosaic forming Human Figure

1981. International Year of Disabled Persons.
2639 **585** 30p. multicoloured 35 10

586 Heading Ball

1981. World Cup Football Championship (1982) (2nd issue). Multicoloured.
2640 12p. Type **586** 15 10
2641 30p. Kicking ball (horiz) 30 10

587 La Jota (folk dance)

1981. Europa.
2642 **587** 12p. black and brown 25 15
2643 - 30p. deep lilac and lilac 40 20
DESIGN: 30p. Procession of the Virgin of Rocio.

588 King Juan Carlos reviewing Army

1981. Armed Forces Day.
2644 **588** 12p. multicoloured 15 10

589 Gabriel Miro (writer)

1981. Spanish Celebrities.
2645 **589** 6p. violet and green 15 15
2646 - 12p. brown and violet 15 15
2647 - 30p. green and brown 40 15
DESIGNS: 12p. Francisco de Quevedo (writer); 30p. St. Benedict.

590 Messenger (14th-century woodcut)

1981. Stamp Day.
2648 **590** 12p. pink, brown & green 15 10

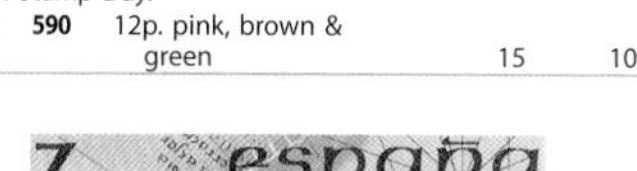
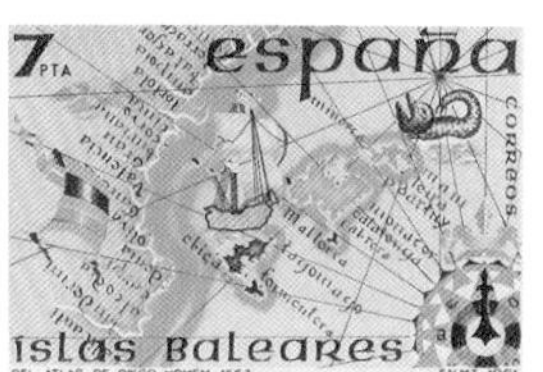

591 Map of the Balearic Islands (from Atlas of Diego Homem, 1563)

1981. Spanish Islands. Multicoloured.
2649 7p. Type **591** 15 10
2650 12p. Map of the Canary Islands (from map of Mateo Prunes, 1563) 15 10

592 Alfonso XII, Juan Carlos and Arms

1981. Century of Public Prosecutor's Office.
2651 **592** 50p. brown, green & blue 55 10

593 King Sancho VI of Navarre with Foundation Charter

1981. 800th Anniv of Vitoria.
2652 **593** 12p. multicoloured 15 10

594 Citrus Fruit

1981. Spanish Exports (2nd series). Multicoloured.
2653 6p. Type **594** 10 10
2654 12p. Wine 15 10
2655 30p. CASA C-212 Aviocar airplane, car and lorry 35 10

595 Foodstuffs

1981. World Food Day.
2656 **595** 30p. multicoloured 35 10

596 "Guernica" (image scaled to 60% of original size)

1981. Birth Centenary of Pablo Picasso (2nd issue) and Return of "Guernica" to Spain. Sheet 163×105 mm.
MS2657 **596** 200p. black, grey and green 2·40 2·40

597 Congress Palace, Buenos Aires

1981. "Espamer 81" International Stamp Exhibition, Buenos Aires.
2658 **597** 12p. red and blue 15 10

598 "Adoration of the Kings" (from Cervera de Pisuerga)

1981. Christmas. Multicoloured.
2659 12p. Type **598** 15 10
2660 30p. "Nativity" (from Paredes de Nava) 30 10

599 Plaza de Espana, Seville

1981. Air.
2661 **599** 13p. green and blue 15 10
2662 - 20p. blue and brown 25 10
DESIGN: 20p. Rande Bridge, Ria de Vigo.

600 Telegraph Operator

1981. Postal and Telecommunications Museum, Madrid.
2663 **600** 7p. green and brown 30 10
2664 - 12p. brown and violet 30 10
MS2665 135×100 mm. Nos. 2663/4; 50p. violet and green; 100p. green and brown 2·20 2·20
DESIGNS: 12p. Post wagon; 50p. Emblem of Spanish American and Philippines Postal Academy; 100p. Cap, pouch, posthorn, books and cancellation.

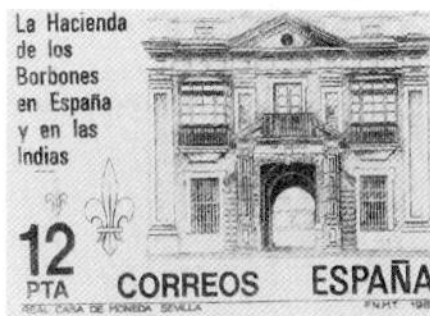

601 Royal Mint, Seville

1981. Financial Administration by the Bourbons in Spain and the Indies.
2666 **601** 12p. brown and grey 15 10

602 Iparraguirre

1981. Death Centenary of Jose Maria Iparraguirre.
2667 **602** 12p. blue and black 15 10

603 Publicity Poster by Joan Miro

1982. World Cup Football Championship, Spain (3rd issue). Multicoloured.

2668 14p. Type **603** 20 10

2669 33p. World Cup trophy and championship emblem 35 10

604 Andres Bello (author and philosopher) (birth bicent)

1982. Anniversaries (1981).

2670 **604** 30p. deep green and green 35 10

2671 - 30p. green and blue 35 15

2672 - 50p. violet and black 65 15

DESIGNS: No. 2671, J. R. Jimenez (author, birth centenary); 2672, P. Calderon (playwright, 300th death anniv).

605 St. James of Compostela (Codex illustration)

1982. Holy Year of Compostela.

2673 **605** 14p. multicoloured 15 10

606 Manuel Fernandez Caballero

1982. Masters of Operetta (1st series). As T 606 (2674, 2676, 2678) or T 625 (others). Multicoloured.

2674 3p. Type **606** 10 10

2675 3p. Scene from "Gigantes y Cabezudos" (horiz) 10 10

2676 6p. Amadeo Vives Roig 10 10

2677 6p. Scene from "Maruxa" (horiz) 10 10

2678 8p. Tomas Breton y Hernandez 10 10

2679 8p. Scene from "La Verbena de la Paloma" (horiz) 10 10

See also Nos. 2713/8 and 2772/7.

607 Arms, Seals and Signatures (Unification of Spain, 1479)

1982. Europa. Multicoloured.

2680 14p. Type **607** 25 20

2681 33p. Symbolic ship, Columbus map of "La Spanola" and signature (Discovery of America) 40 30

608 Swords, Arms and Flag

1982. Armed Forces Day and Centenary of General Military Academy.

2682 **608** 14p. multicoloured 15 10

609 Tackling

1982. World Cup Football Championship, Spain (4th issue). Multicoloured.

2683 14p. Type **609** 25 10

2684 33p. Goal 45 25

MS2685 163×105 mm. 9p. Handshake; 14p. Type **609**; 33p. As No. 2684; 100p. Players with cup 3·00 3·00

610 "St. Andrew and St. Francis"

1982. Air. Paintings by El Greco. Multicoloured.

2686 13p. Type **610** 15 10

2687 20p. "St. Thomas" 30 15

611 Map of Tenerife and Letter

1982. Stamp Day.

2688 **611** 14p. multicoloured 20 10

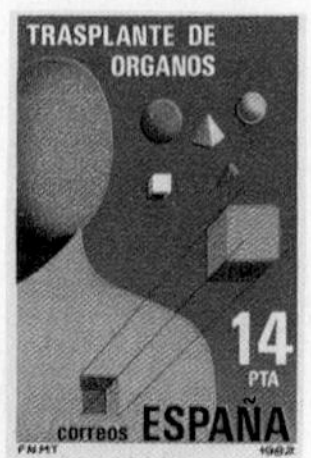

612 "Transplants"

1982. Organ Transplants.

2689 **612** 14p. multicoloured 20 10

613 White Storks and Diesel Locomotive

1982. 23rd International Railway Congress, Malaga. Multicoloured.

2690 9p. Type **613** 20 10

2691 14p. Steam locomotive "Antigua" (37×26 mm) 30 15

2692 33p. Steam locomotive "Montana" (wrongly inscr "Santa Fe") (37×26 mm) 45 15

614 La Fortaleza, San Juan

1982. "Espamer 82" Stamp Exhibition, San Juan, Puerto Rico.

2693 **614** 33p. blue and lilac 45 15

615 St. Theresa of Avila (sculpture by Gregorio Hernandez)

1982. 400th Death Anniv of St. Theresa of Avila.

2694 **615** 33p. brown, blue and green 45 15

616 Pope John Paul II

1982. Papal Visit.

2695 **616** 14p. blue and brown 20 15

1982. Tourist Series. As T 340.

2696 4p. blue and grey 15 15

2697 6p. grey and blue 15 15

2698 9p. lilac and blue 15 15

2699 14p. lilac and blue 15 15

2700 33p. brown and red 35 15

DESIGNS—VERT: 4p. Arab water-wheel, Alcantarilla; 9p. Dying Christ, Seville; 14p. St. Martin's Tower, Teruel; 33p. St. Andrew's Gate, Villalpando. HORIZ: 6p. Bank of Spain, Madrid.

617 "Adoration of The Kings" (sculpture, Covarrubias Collegiate Church)

1982. Christmas. Multicoloured.

2701 14p. Type **617** 15 10

2702 33p. "The Flight into Egypt" (painting) 40 15

618 "The Prophet"

1982. Birth Centenary of Pablo Gargallo (sculptor).

2703 **618** 14p. green and blue 15 10

619 St. John Bosco (founder) and Children

1982. Centenary of Salesian Schools in Spain.

2704 **619** 14p. multicoloured 15 10

620 Arms of Spain

1983

2705 **620** 14p. multicoloured 20 10

621 Sunrise over Andalusia

1983. Andalusian Autonomy.

2706 **621** 14p. multicoloured 25 10

622 Arms of Cantabria, Mountains and Monuments

1983. Cantabrian Autonomy.

2707 **622** 14p. multicoloured 25 10

623 National Police

1983. State Security Forces. Multicoloured.

2708 9p. Type **623** 15 10

2709 14p. Civil Guard 20 15

2710 33p. Superior Police Corps 35 25

624 Cycling

1983. Air. Sports. Multicoloured.

2711 13p. Type **624** 20 10

2712 20p. Bowling (horiz) 30 10

625 Scene from "La Parranda"

1983. Masters of Operetta (2nd series). As T 625 (2714, 2716, 2718) or T 606 (others). Multicoloured.

2713	4p. Francisco Alonso (vert)	10	10
2714	4p. Type **625**	10	10
2715	6p. Jacinto Guerrero (vert)	10	10
2716	6p. Scene from "La Rosa del Azafran"	10	10
2717	9p. Jesus Guridi (vert)	15	15
2718	9p. Scene from "El Caserio"	15	15

626 Cervantes and Scene from "Don Quixote"

1983. Europa.

2719	**626**	16p. red and green	30	20
2720	-	38p. sepia and brown	60	35

DESIGN: 38p. Torres Quevedo and Niagara cable-car.

627 Francisco Salzillo (artist)

1983. Spanish Celebrities.

2721	**627**	16p. purple and green	20	15
2722	-	38p. blue and brown	50	25
2723	-	50p. blue and brown	65	25
2724	-	100p. brown and violet	1·30	50

DESIGNS: 38p. Antonio Soler (composer); 50p. Joaquin Turina (composer); 100p. St. Isidro Labrador (patron saint of Madrid).

628 W.C.Y. Emblem

1983. World Communications Year.

2725	**628**	38p. multicoloured	45	15

629 Leaves

1983. Riojan Autonomy.

2726	**629**	16p. multicoloured	25	15

630 Army Monument, Burgos

1983. Armed Forces Day.

2727	**630**	16p. multicoloured	25	15

631 Burgos Setter

1983. Spanish Dogs.

2728	**631**	10p. blue, brown and red	20	15
2729	-	16p. multicoloured	30	15
2730	-	26p. multicoloured	45	25
2731	-	38p. multicoloured	65	20

DESIGNS: 16p. Spanish mastiff; 26p. Ibiza spaniel; 38p. Navarrese basset.

632 Juan-Jose and Fausto Elhuyar y de Suvisa

1983. Anniversaries. Multicoloured.

2732	16p. Type **632** (bicentenary of discovery of wolfram)	25	20
2733	38p. Scout camp (75th anniv of Boy Scout Movement)	60	20
2734	50p. University of Zaragoza (400th anniv)	80	20

633 Arms of Murcia

1983. Murcian Autonomy.

2735	**633**	16p. multicoloured	25	15

634 Covadonga Basilica and Victory Cross

1983. Autonomy of Asturias.

2736	**634**	14p. multicoloured	25	15

635 National Statistical Institute, Madrid

1983. 44th International Institute of Statistics Congress.

2737	**635**	38p. multicoloured	50	20

636 Roman Horse-drawn Mail Cart

1983. Stamp Day.

2738	**636**	16p. pink and brown	30	30

637 Palace and Arms of Valencia

1983. Valencian Autonomy.

2739	**637**	16p. multicoloured	30	15

638 Seville (Illustration from "Floods of Guadalquivir" by Francisco Palomo)

1983. America–Spain.

2740	**638**	38p. violet and blue	50	25

639 "Biblical King" (Leon Cathedral)

1983. Stained Glass Windows. Multicoloured.

2741	10p. Type **639**	20	15
2742	16p. "Epiphany" and Gerona Cathedral	30	20
2743	38p. "St. James" and Santiago de Compostela Hospital	55	20

1983. Tourist Series. As T 340.

2744	3p. blue and green	20	15
2745	6p. indigo	20	15
2746	16p. violet and red	25	15
2747	38p. red and brown	45	25
2748	50p. red and brown	65	20

DESIGNS: 3p. Church and tower, Llivia, Gerona; 6p. Santa Maria del Mar, Barcelona; 16p. Ceuta Cathedral; 38p. Bridge gateway, Melilla; 50p. Charity Hospital, Seville.

640 "Nativity" (altarpiece, Tortosa)

1983. Christmas. Multicoloured.

2749	16p. Type **640**	25	15
2750	38p. "Adoration of the Kings" (altarpiece, Vich)	55	20

641 Indalecio Prieto

1983. Birth Centenary of Indalecio Prieto (politician).

2751	**641**	16p. brown and black	25	15

642 Worker falling from Scaffolding

1984. Safety at Work. Multicoloured.

2752	7p. Type **642**	10	10
2753	10p. Burning factory and extinguisher	15	10
2754	16p. Electric plug and wiring, cutters, gloved hands and warning sign	20	10

643 Tree

1984. Extremaduran Autonomy.

2755	**643**	16p. multicoloured	25	10

644 Burgos Cathedral and Coat of Arms

1984. 1500th Anniv of Burgos City.

2756	**644**	16p. brown and blue	20	10

645 Carnival Dancer, Santa Cruz, Tenerife

1984. Festivals. Multicoloured.

2757	16p. Type **645**	25	10
2758	16p. Carnival figure and fireworks, Valencia	25	10

646 "Man" (Leonardo da Vinci)

1984. Man and Biosphere.

2759	**646**	38p. multicoloured	45	15

647 Map and Flag of Aragon and "Justice"

1984. Aragon Autonomy.

2760	**647**	16p. multicoloured	25	10

648 King Juan Carlos I

1984. "Espana 84" International Stamp Exhibition, Madrid. Sheet 146×102 mm containing T 648 and similar vert designs, each maroon.

MS2761	38p. Type **648**; 38p. Queen Sophia; 38p. Princess Cristina; 38p. Prince of Asturias; 38p. Princess Elena	3·50	3·50

649 F.I.P. Emblem

1984. 53rd International Philatelic Federation Congress, Madrid.

2762	**649**	38p. red and violet	45	15

650 Bridge

1984. Europa.

2763	**650**	16p. red	50	15
2764	**650**	38p. blue	60	45

651 Monument to the Alcantara Cazadores Regiment, Valladolid (Mariano Benlliure)

1984. Armed Forces Day.

2765	**651**	17p. multicoloured	20	10

652 Arms of Canary Islands

1984. Autonomy of Canary Islands.

2766	**652**	16p. multicoloured	25	10

653 Arms of Castilla- La Mancha

1984. Autonomy of Castilla-La Mancha.

2767	**653**	17p. multicoloured	25	10

654 King Alfonso X, the Wise, of Castile and Leon (700th death anniv)

1984. Anniversaries.

2768	**654**	16p. red, blue and black	25	10
2769	-	38p. blue, red and black	50	25

DESIGN: 38p. Ignacio Barraquer (opthalmologist, birth centenary).

655 "James III confirming Grants"

1984. Autonomy of Balearic Islands.

2770	**655**	17p. multicoloured	25	10

656 Running before Bulls

1984. Pamplona Festival, San Fermin.

2771	**656**	17p. multicoloured	25	10

1984. Masters of Operetta (3rd series). Horiz designs as T 625 (2772, 2775/6) or vert designs as T 606 (others). Multicoloured.

2772	6p. Scene from "El Nino Judio"	15	10
2773	6p. Pablo Luna	15	10
2774	7p. Ruperto Chapi	15	10
2775	7p. Scene from "La Revoltosa"	15	10
2776	10p. Scene from "La Reina Mora"	15	10
2777	10p. Jose Serrano	15	10

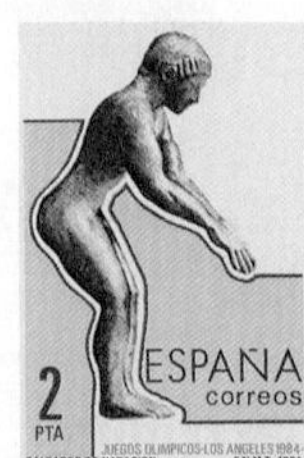

657 Bronze of Swimmer ready to Dive

1984. Olympic Games, Los Angeles. Mult.

2778	1p. Roman quadriga (horiz)	10	10
2779	2p. Type **657**	10	10
2780	5p. Bronze of two wrestlers (horiz)	10	10
2781	8p. "The Discus-thrower" (statue, Miron)	15	10

658 Arms and Map of Navarra

1984. Autonomy of Navarra.

2782	**658**	17p. multicoloured	25	10

659 Cyclist

1984. International Cycling Championship, Barcelona.

2783	**659**	17p. multicoloured	20	10

660 Arms (Levante Building Salamanca University)

1984. Autonomy of Castilla y Leon.

2784	**660**	17p. multicoloured	25	10

661 Women gathering Grapes

1984. Vintage Festival, Jerez.

2785	**661**	17p. multicoloured	25	10

662 Egeria on Donkey and Map of Middle East

1984. 1600th Anniv of Nun Egeria's Visit to Middle East.

2786	**662**	40p. multicoloured	45	25

663 Arab Courier

1984. Stamp Day.

2787	**663**	17p. multicoloured	20	10

664 Father Junipero Serra

1984. Death Bicentenary of Father Junipero Serra (missionary).

2788	**664**	40p. red and blue	45	20

665 "Adoration of the Kings" (Miguel Moguer) (Campos altarpiece)

1984. Christmas. Multicoloured.

2789	17p. "Nativity" (15th-century retable) (horiz)	20	10
2790	40p. Type **665**	55	25

666 Arms, Buildings and Trees

1984. Autonomy of Madrid.

2791	**666**	17p. multicoloured	25	10

667 Flags and Andean Condor

1985. 15th Anniv (1984) of Andes Pact.

2792	**667**	17p. multicoloured	20	10

668 "Virgin of Louvain" (attr Jan Gossaert)

1985. "Europalia 85 Espana" Festival.

2793	**668**	40p. multicoloured	55	30

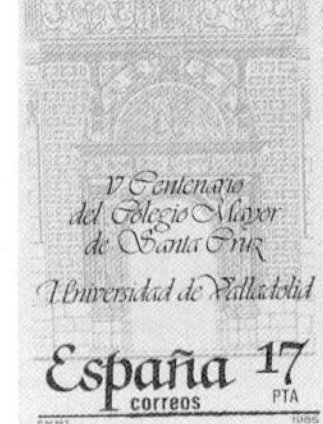

669 College Porch and Tympanum

1985. 500th Anniv of Santa Cruz College, Valladolid University.

2794	**669**	17p. yellow, brown & red	20	10

670 Flames and "Olymphilex '85"

1985. "Olymphilex 85" International Olympic Stamps Exhibition, Lausanne.

2795	**670**	40p. red, yellow & black	55	20

671 Havana Cathedral

1985. "Espamer '85" International Stamp Exhibition, Havana, Cuba.

2796	**671**	40p. blue and purple	55	25

672 Couple in Traditional Dress on Horseback

1985. April Fair, Seville.

2797	**672**	17p. multicoloured	25	10

673 Heads as Holder for Flames

1985. International Youth Year.

2798	**673**	17p. green, black and red	20	10

674 Moors and Christians fighting

1985. Festival of Moors and Christians, Alcoy.

2799	**674**	17p. multicoloured	25	10

675 Don Antonio de Cabezon (organist)

1985. Europa.

2800	**675**	18p. red, black and blue on yellow	30	15
2801	-	45p. red, black and green on yellow	85	50

DESIGN: 45p. Musicians of National Youth Orchestra.

676 Capitania General Headquarters, La Coruna

1985. Armed Forces Day.

2802	**676**	18p. multicoloured	25	10

677 Carlos III's Arms, 1785 Decree and "Santissima Trinidad" (ship of the line)

1985. Bicentenary of National Flag. Mult.

2803	18p. Type **677**	25	15
2804	18p. State arms, 1978 constitution and lion (detail from House of Deputies)	25	15

678 Sunflower and Bird

1985. World Environment Day.

2805	**678**	17p. multicoloured	20	15

679 Monstrance in Decorated Street

1985. Corpus Christi Festival, Toledo.

2806	**679**	18p. multicoloured	25	15

680 King Juan Carlos I

1985

2807	**680**	10c. blue	15	10
2808	**680**	50c. green	15	10
2809	**680**	1p. blue	15	15
2810	**680**	2p. green	10	10
2811	**680**	3p. brown	10	10
2812	**680**	4p. bistre	15	10
2813	**680**	5p. purple	2·50	90
2814	**680**	6p. brown	15	10
2815	**680**	7p. violet	15	10
2816	**680**	7p. green	10	10
2817	**680**	8p. grey	1·00	50
2818	**680**	10p. red	15	10
2819	**680**	12p. red	15	15
2820	**680**	13p. blue	20	10
2821	**680**	15p. green	20	10
2822	**680**	17p. orange	25	10
2823	**680**	18p. green	25	15
2824	**680**	19p. brown	30	10
2825	**680**	20p. mauve	30	10
2825a	**680**	25p. green	30	10
2825b	**680**	27p. mauve	30	10
2826	**680**	30p. blue	45	10
2827	**680**	45p. green	55	15
2828	**680**	50p. blue	65	10
2828a	**680**	55p. brown	70	10
2829	**680**	60p. red	90	15
2830	**680**	75p. mauve	1·00	15

681 Planetary System

1985. Inauguration of Astrophysical Observatories, Canary Islands.

2831	**681**	45p. multicoloured	55	20

682 Ataulfo Argenta (conductor)

1985. European Music Year. Multicoloured.

2832	12p. Type **682**	15	15
2833	17p. Tomas Luis de Victoria (composer)	25	15
2834	45p. Fernando Sor (guitarist and composer)	65	35

683 Bernal Diaz del Castillo (conquistador)

1985. Celebrities.

2835	**683**	7p. red, black and green on yellow	15	10
2836	-	12p. red, black and blue on yellow	20	10
2837	-	17p. green, red and black on yellow	30	15
2838	-	45p. green, black and brown on yellow	65	25

DESIGNS: 12p. Esteban Terradas (mathematician); 17p. Vicente Aleixandre (poet); 45p. Leon Felipe Camino (poet).

684 Canoeist

1985. "Descent down the Sella" Canoe Festival, Asturias.

2839	**684**	17p. multicoloured	25	10

685 Monk returning with Rotulet to Savigni Abbey, 1122

1985. Stamp Day.

2840	**685**	17p. multicoloured	25	10

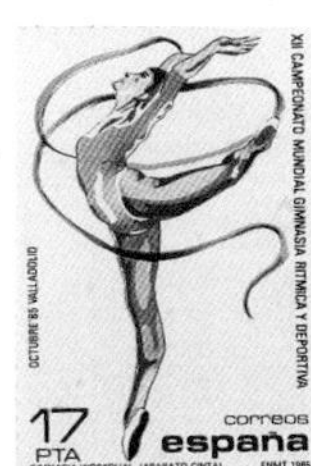

686 Ribbon Exercise

1985. 12th World Rhythmic Gymnastics Championship, Valladolid. Multicoloured.

2841	17p. Type **686**	20	10
2842	45p. Hoop exercise	60	25

687 Prado Museum and "la Alcacofa" Fountain

1985. "Exfilna '85" National Stamp Exhibition, Madrid. Sheet 120×80 mm.

MS2843	17p. multicoloured	70	70

688 "Virgin and Child" (Escalas Chapel, Seville Cathedral)

1985. Stained Glass Windows. Multicoloured.

2844	7p. Type **688**	10	10
2845	12p. Monk (Toledo Cathedral)	15	10
2846	17p. King Enrique II of Castile and Leon (Alcazar of Segovia)	25	15

689 "Nativity" (detail of altarpiece by Ramon de Mur)

1985. Christmas. Multicoloured.

2847	17p. Type **689**	15	10
2848	45p. "Adoration of the Magi" (embroidered frontal, after Jaume Huguet)	60	25

690 Subalpine Warbler

1985. Birds. Multicoloured.

2849	6p. Type **690**	20	10
2850	7p. Rock thrush	20	10
2851	12p. Spotless starling	25	10
2852	17p. Bearded reedling	55	15

691 Count of Penaflorida

1985. Death Bicentenary of Count of Penaflorida (founder of Economic Society of Friends of the Land).

2853	**691**	17p. blue	20	10

692 Royal Palace, Madrid

1986. Admission of Spain and Portugal to European Economic Community. Multicoloured.

2854	7p. Type **692**	15	15
2855	17p. Map and flags of member countries	15	15
2856	30p. Hall of Columns, Royal Palace	35	15
2857	45p. Flags of Portugal and Spain uniting with flags of other members	65	35

1986. Tourist Series. As T 340.

2858	12p. black and red	15	10
2859	35p. brown and blue	45	15

DESIGNS: 12p. Lupiana Monastery, Guadalajara; 35p. Balcony of Europe, Nerja.

693 Merino

1986. 2nd World Conference on Merinos.

2860	**693**	45p. multicoloured	45	15

694 "Revellers" (detail, F. Hohenleiter)

1986. Cadiz Carnival.

2861	**694**	17p. multicoloured	25	10

695 Helmets and Flower

1986. International Peace Year.

2862	**695**	45p. multicoloured	45	15

696 Organ Pipes

1986. Religious Music Week, Cuenca.

2863	**696**	17p. multicoloured	25	10

697 "Swearing in of Regent, Queen Maria Cristina" (detail, Joaquin Sorolla y Bastida)

1986. Centenary of Chambers of Commerce, Industry and Navigation.

2864	**697**	17p. black and green	20	10

698 Man with Suitcase

1986. Emigration.

2865	**698**	45p. multicoloured	45	15

699 Boy and Birds

1986. Europa. Multicoloured.

2866	17p. Type **699**	30	15
2867	45p. Woman watering young tree	65	45

700 Our Lady of the Dew

1986. Our Lady of the Dew Festival, Rocio, near Almonte.
2868 **700** 17p. multicoloured 25 10

701 Capitania General Building, Tenerife

1986. Armed Forces Day.
2869 **701** 17p. multicoloured 20 10

1986. Tourist Series. As T 340. Multicoloured.
2870 12p. black and blue 15 15
2871 35p. brown and blue 45 15
DESIGNS: 12p. Ciudad Rodrigo Cathedral, Salamanca; 35p. Calella lighthouse, Barcelona.

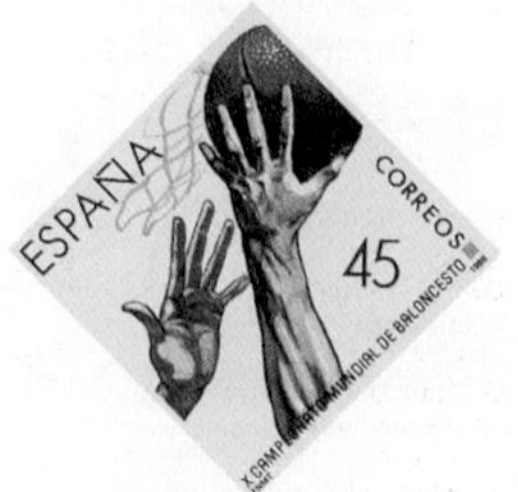

702 Hands and Ball

1986. 10th World Basketball Championship.
2872 **702** 45p. multicoloured 45 15

703 Francisco Loscos (botanist)

1986. Celebrities.
2873 **703** 7p. green and black 10 10
2874 - 11p. red and black 15 10
2875 - 17p. brown and black 20 10
2876 - 45p. purple, orange and black 70 35
DESIGNS: 11p. Salvador Espriu (writer); 17p. Azorin (Jose Martinez Ruiz) (writer); 45p. Juan Gris (artist).

704 Apostles awaiting Angels carrying Virgin's Soul

1986. Elche Mystery Play.
2877 **704** 17p. multicoloured 25 10

705 Swimmer

1986. 5th World Swimming, Water Polo, Leap and Synchronous Swimming Championships.
2878 **705** 45p. multicoloured 45 15

706 Pelota Player

1986. 10th World Pelota Championship.
2879 **706** 17p. multicoloured 25 10

707 King's Messenger with Letter summoning Nobleman to Court

1986. Stamp Day.
2880 **707** 17p. multicoloured 20 10

708 Man releasing Dove and Cordoba Mosque

1986. "Exfilna '86" National Stamp Exhibition, Corosba. Sheet 120×80 mm.
MS2881 **708** 17p. multicoloured 30 30

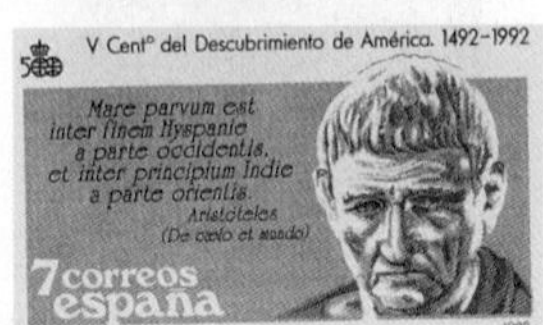

709 Aristotle

1986. 500th Anniv (1992) of Discovery of America by Columbus (1st issue). Designs showing historic figures and prophecies of discovery of New World.
2882 **709** 7p. black and mauve 10 10
2883 - 12p. black and lilac 15 10
2884 - 17p. black and yellow 20 15
2885 - 30p. black and mauve 40 15
2886 - 35p. black and green 50 15
2887 - 45p. black and orange 65 15
DESIGNS: 12p. Seneca and quote from "Medea"; 17p. St. Isidoro of Seville and quote from "Etymologies"; 30p. Cardinal Pierre d'Ailly and quote from "Imago Mundi"; 35p. Mayan and quote from "Chilam Balam" books; 45p. Conquistador and quote from "Chilam Balam" books.
See also Nos. 2932/7, 2983/8, 3035/40, 3079/82, 3126/9, **MS**3147, 3175/6, **MS**3177 and 3190.

710 Gaspar de Portola

1986. Death Bicentenary of Gaspar de Portola (first Governor of California).
2888 **710** 22p. blue, red and black 30 10

711 "Holy Family" (detail, Diego de Siloe)

1986. Christmas. Wood Carvings. Multicoloured.
2889 19p. Type **711** 25 10
2890 48p. "Nativity" (detail, Toledo Cathedral altarpiece, Felipe de Borgona) (horiz) 65 15

712 Abd-er Rahman II and Cordoba Mosque

1986. Hispanic Islamic Culture.
2891 **712** 7p. brown and red 10 10
2892 - 12p. brown and red 15 10
2893 - 17p. blue and black 20 10
2894 - 45p. green and black 70 15
DESIGNS: 12p. Ibn Hazm (writer) and burning book; 17p. Al-Zarqali (astronomer) and azophea (astrolabe); 45p. King Alfonso VII of Castile and Leon and scholars of Toledo School of Translators.

713 "The Good Curate"

1986. Birth Centenary of Alfonso Castelao (artist and writer).
2895 **713** 32p. multicoloured 40 15

714 Chateau de la Muette (headquarters)

1987. 25th Anniv of Organization for Economic Co-operation and Development.
2896 **714** 48p. multicoloured 55 15

715 Abstract Shapes

1987. "Expo 92" World's Fair, Seville (1st issue). Multicoloured.
2897 19p. Type **715** 35 10
2898 48p. Moon surface, Earth and symbol 90 10
See also Nos. 2941/2, 2951/2, 3004/7, 3052/5, 3094/7, 3143 and 3148/**MS**3172.

716 Francisco de Vitoria

1987. 500th Birth Anniv of Francisco de Vitoria (jurist).
2899 **716** 48p. brown 55 15

717 18th-century Warship and Standard Bearer

1987. 450th Anniv of Marine Corps.
2900 **717** 19p. multicoloured 25 10

718 University

1987. Centenary of Deusto University.
2901 **718** 19p. red, green and black 25 10

719 Breastfeeding Baby

1987. UNICEF Child Survival Campaign.
2902 **719** 19p. brown and deep brown 25 10

720 Crowd

1987. 175th Anniv of Constitution of Cadiz. Multicoloured.
2903 25p. Type **720** 35 15
2904 25p. Crowd and herald on steps 35 15
2905 25p. Dignitaries on dais 35 15
2906 25p. Crown and Constitution 35 15
Nos. 2903/6 were printed together, se-tenant, the first three stamps forming a composite design showing "The Promulgation of the Constitution of 1812" by Salvador Viniegra.

721 15th-century Pharmacy Jar, Manises

1987. Ceramics. Multicoloured.
2907 7p. Type **721** 10 10
2908 14p. 20th-century glazed figure, Sargadelos 15 15
2909 19p. 18th-century vase, Buen Retiro 25 15
2910 32p. 20th-century pot, Salvatierra de los Barros 45 20
2911 40p. 18th-century jar, Talavera 55 20
2912 48p. 18–19th century jug, Granada 70 20

722 "Procession at Dawn, Zamora" (Gallego Marquina)

1987. Holy Week Festivals. Multicoloured.
2913 19p. Type **722** 30 10
2914 48p. Gate of Pardon, Seville Cathedral and "Passion" (statue by Martinez Montanes) 65 15

1987. Tourist Series. As T 340.
2915 14p. green and blue 20 10
2916 19p. deep green and green 20 10
2917 40p. brown 50 15
2918 48p. black 90 15
DESIGNS—HORIZ: 14p. Ifach Rock, Calpe, Alicante; 19p. Ruins of Church of Santa Maria d'Ozo, Pontevedra; 40p. Palace of Sonanes, Villacarriedo, Santander. VERT: 48p. 11th-century monastery of Sant Joan de les Abadesses, Gerona.

723 Bilbao Bank, Madrid (Saenz de Oiza)

1987. Europa. Architecture.

2919	**723**	19p. multicoloured	60	35
2920	-	48p. brown, bistre & grn	75	35

DESIGN—HORIZ: 14p. National Museum of Roman Art, Merida (Rafael Moneo).

724 Horse's Head and Harnessed Pair

1987. Jerez Horse Fair.

2921	**724**	19p. multicoloured	35	15

725 Carande

1987. Birth Centenary of Ramon Carande (historian and Honorary Postman).

2922	**725**	40p. black and brown	55	20

726 Numbers on Pen Nib

1987. Postal Coding.

2923	**726**	19p. multicoloured	25	15

727 Arms and School

1987. 75th Anniv of Eibar Armoury School.

2924	**727**	20p. multicoloured	25	15

728 Batllo House Chimneys (Antonio Gaudi)

1987. Nomination of Barcelona as 1992 Olympic Games Host City. Multicoloured.

2925		32p. Type **728**	55	20
2926		65p. Athletes	95	20

729 Festival Poster (Fabri)

1987. 25th Pyrenees Folklore Festival, Jaca.

2927	**729**	50p. multicoloured	75	15

730 Monturiol (after Marti Alsina) and Diagrams of Submarine "Ictineo"

1987. Death Cent of Narcis Monturiol (scientist).

2928	**730**	20p. black and brown	25	15

731 Detail from Jaime II of Majorca's Law appointing Couriers

1987. Stamp Day.

2929	**731**	20p. multicoloured	25	15

732 18th-century Pre-stamp Letter

1987. "Espamer '87" Stamp Exhibition, La Coruna. Maritime Post to America. Sheet 149×83 mm containing T 732 and similar horiz designs.

MS2930	8p. Type **732**; 12p. 19th-century engraving of La Coruna harbour; 20p. 18th-century view of Havana harbour; 50p. 18th-century sailing packets running between La Coruna and Havana (sold at 180p.)	4·50	4·25

No. **MS**2930 included an entrance coupon divided from the sheet by a line of rouletting. Price quoted is for the sheet with coupon attached.

733 "Aesculapius" and Olympic Torch Bearer

1987. "Exfilna '87" National Stamp Exhibition, Gerona. Sheet 120×80 mm.

MS2931	**733**	20p. multicoloured	60	35

734 Amerigo Vespucci

1987. 500th Anniv (1992) of Discovery of America by Columbus (2nd issue). Explorers. Multicoloured.

2932	14p. Type **734**	20	20
2933	20p. King Ferdinand and Queen Isabella the Catholic and arms on ships	25	20
2934	32p. Juan Perez and departing ships	40	20
2935	40p. Juan de la Cosa and ships	55	20
2936	50p. Map, ship and Christopher Columbus	65	30
2937	65p. Native on shore, approaching ships and Martin Alonzo and Vincente Yanez Pinzon	90	30

735 Star and Baubles

1987. Christmas. Multicoloured.

2938	20p. Type **735**	35	15
2939	50p. Zambomba and tambourine	75	30

736 Macho (self-sculpture)

1987. Birth Centenary of Victorio Macho (sculptor).

2940	**736**	50p. brown and black	65	20

1987. "Expo '92" World's Fair, Seville (2nd issue). As Nos. 2897/8 but values changed. Multicoloured.

2941	20p. Type **715**	35	15
2942	50p. As No. 2898	75	15

737 Queen Sofia

1988. 50th Birthdays of King Juan Carlos I and Queen Sofia. Each brown, yellow and violet.

2943	20p. Type **737**	20	15
2944	20p. King Juan Carlos I	20	15

738 Campoamor

1988. Birth Centenary of Clara Campoamor (politician and women's suffrage campaigner).

2945	**738**	20p. multicoloured	25	15

739 Speed Skating

1988. Winter Olympic Games, Calgary.

2946	**739**	45p. multicoloured	75	15

740 "Christ tied to the Pillar" (statue) and Valladolid Cathedral

1988. Holy Week Festivals. Multicoloured.

2947	20p. Type **740**	30	10
2948	50p. Float depicting Christ carrying the Cross, Malaga	65	15

741 Ingredients for and Dish of Paella

1988. Tourist Series. Multicoloured.

2949	18p. Type **741**	30	10
2950	45p. Covadonga National Park (70th anniv of National Parks)	65	15

742 Globe and Stylized Roads

1988. "Expo '92" World's Fair, Seville (3rd issue).

2951		8p. Type **742**	15	10
2952		45p. Compass rose and globe (horiz)	55	10

743 18th-Century Valencian Chalice

1988. Glassware. Multicoloured.

2953	20p. Type **743**	25	10
2954	20p. 18th-century pitcher, Cadalso de los Vidrios, Madrid	25	10
2955	20p. 18th-century crystal sweet jar, La Granja de San Ildefonso	25	10
2956	20p. 18th-century Andalusian two-handled jug, Castril	25	10
2957	20p. 17th-century Catalan four-spouted jug	25	10
2958	20p. 20th-century bottle, Balearic Islands	25	10

744 Francis of Taxis (organiser of European postal service, 1505)

1988. Stamp Day.

2959	**744**	20p. violet and brown	25	10

745 Pablo Iglesias (first President)

1988. Centenary of General Workers' Union.

2960	**745**	20p. multicoloured	20	10

746 Steam Locomotive, 1837, Cuba

1988. Europa. Transport and Communications.

2961	**746**	20p. red and black	30	30
2962	-	50p. green and black	95	50

DESIGN: 50p. Light telegraph, Philippines, 1818.

747 Monnet

1988. Birth Cent of Jean Monnet (statesman).

2963	**747**	45p. blue	65	30

748 Emblem

1988. Centenary of 1888 Universal Exhibition, Barcelona.

2964	**748**	50p. multicoloured	65	10

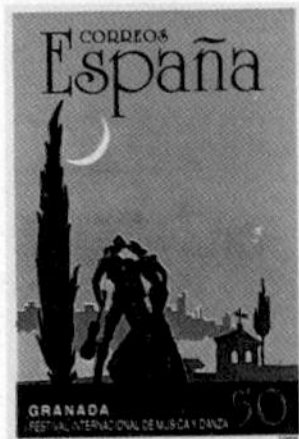

749 Couple in Granada

1988. International Festival of Music and Dance, Granada.

2965	**749**	50p. multicoloured	65	10

750 Bull

1988. "Expo 88" World's Fair, Brisbane.

2966	**750**	50p. multicoloured	65	10

751 "Virgin of Hope"

1988. Coronation of "Virgin of Hope", Malaga.

2967	**751**	20p. multicoloured	25	10

752 Plan of Pamplona Palace

1988. "Exfilna '87" National Stamp Exhibition, Pamplona. Sheet 120×81 mm.

MS2968	**752**	20p. multicoloured	30	25

753 Orreo (agricultural store), Cantabria

1988. Tourist Series.

2969	**753**	18p. green, brown & blue	25	10
2970	-	45p. black, brn & ochre	60	15

DESIGN: 45p. Dulzaina (wind instrument), Castilla y Leon.

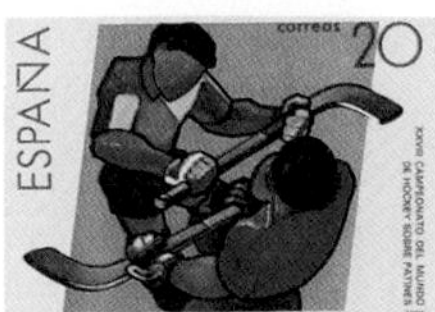

754 Players

1988. 28th World Roller Skate Hockey Championship, La Coruna.

2971	**754**	20p. multicoloured	25	10

755 Congress Emblem

1988. 1st Spanish Regional Homes and Centres World Congress, Madrid.

2972	**755**	20p. multicoloured	25	10

756 "Olympic" Class Yacht

1988. Olympic Games, Seoul.

2973	**756**	50p. multicoloured	65	15

757 Borrell II, Count of Barcelona

1988. Millenary of Catalonia.

2974	**757**	20p. multicoloured	25	10

758 King Alfonso IX of Leon (detail of Codex of "Toxos Outos")

1988. 800th Anniv of 1st Leon Parliament.

2975	**758**	20p. multicoloured	25	10

759 Emblem on Band around Peace Year Stamps

1988. 25th Anniv of Spanish Philatelic Associations Federation.

2976	**759**	20p. multicoloured	25	10

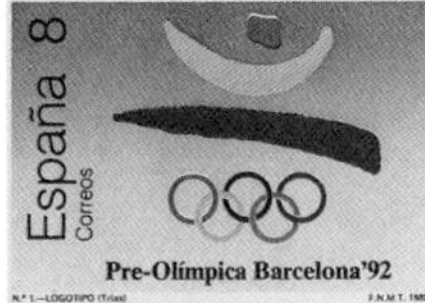

760 Games Emblem

1988. Olympic Games, Barcelona (1992) (1st issue). Designs showing stylized representations of sports. Multicoloured.

2977		8p. Type **760**	10	10
2978		20p.+5p. Athletics	35	35
2979		45p.+5p. Badminton	70	70
2980		50p.+5p. Basketball	85	75

See also Nos. 3008/11, 3031/3, 3056/8, 3076/8, 3098/3100, 3123/5, 3144/6, 3180/2 and 3183/5.

761 Palace of the Generality, Valencia, and Seal of Jaime I

1988. 750th Anniv of Re-conquest of Valencia by King Jaime I of Aragon.

2981	**761**	20p. multicoloured	25	10

762 Manuel Alonso Martinez (statesman)

1988. Centenary of Civil Code.

2982	**762**	20p. multicoloured	25	10

763 Hernan Cortes and Quetzalcoatl Serpent

1988. 500th Anniv (1992) of Discovery of America by Columbus (3rd issue). Each red, blue and orange.

2983		10p. Type **763**	20	10
2984		10p. Vasco Nunez de Balboa and waves	20	10
2985		20p. Francisco Pizarro and guanaco	30	10
2986		20p. Ferdinand Magellan, Juan Sebastian del Cano and globe	30	10
2987		50p. Alvar Nunez Cabeza de Vaca and river	65	15
2988		50p. Andres de Urdaneta and maritime currents	65	15

764 Enrique III of Castile and Leon (first Prince of Asturias)

1988. 600th Anniv of Title of Prince of Asturias.

2989	**764**	20p. multicoloured	25	10

765 Snowflakes

1988. Christmas. Multicoloured.

2990		20p. Type **765**	30	10
2991		50p. Shepherd carrying sheep (vert)	65	25

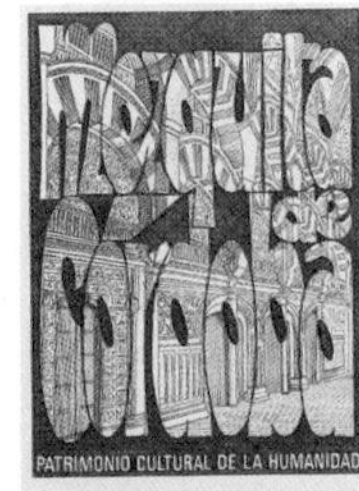

766 Cordoba Mosque

1988. UNESCO World Heritage Sites.

2992	**766**	18p. brown	25	10
2993	-	20p. blue	30	15
2994	-	45p. brown	65	15
2995	-	50p. green	80	15

DESIGNS—VERT: 20p. Burgos Cathedral. HORIZ: 45p. San Lorenzo Monastery, El Escorial; 50p. Alhambra, Granada.

767 Representation of Political Parties

1988. 10th Anniv of Constitution.

2996	**767**	20p. multicoloured	30	15

768 Courtiers in Palace Grounds

1988. Death Bicentenary of King Charles III. Sheet 100×80 mm.

MS2997	**768**	45p. green and black	65	35

769 Blind Person

1988. 50th Anniv of National Organization for the Blind.

2998	**769**	20p. multicoloured	30	15

770 Luis de Granada

1988. 400th Death Anniv of Brother Luis de Granada (mystic).

2999	**770**	20p. multicoloured	30	15

771 Olympic Rings and Sails (Natalia Barrio Fernandez)

1989. Children's Stamp Designs. Multicoloured.

3000		20p. Type **771**	30	10
3001		20p. Magnifying glass on stamp (Jose Luis Villegas Lopez) (vert)	30	10

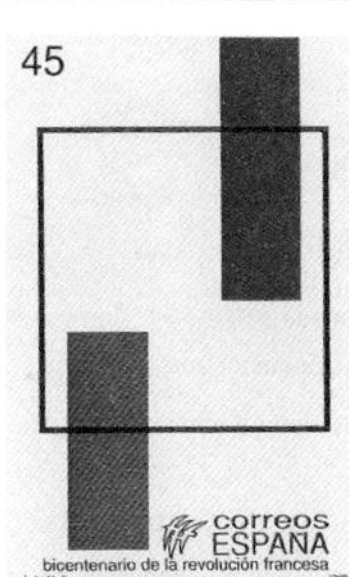

772 Abstract

1989. Bicentenary of French Revolution.

3002	**772**	45p. red, blue and black	65	15

773 Maria de Maeztu

1989. 107th Birth Anniv of Maria de Maeztu (educationist).

3003	**773**	20p. multicoloured	25	10

774 London, 1851

1989. "Expo '92" World's Fair, Seville (4th issue). Great Exhibitions. Multicoloured.

3004	8p.+5p. Type **774**	15	15
3005	8p.+5p. Paris, 1889	15	15
3006	20p.+5p. Brussels, 1958	35	30
3007	20p.+5p. Osaka, 1970	35	30

1989. Olympic Games, Barcelona (1992) (2nd issue). As T 760. Multicoloured.

3008	8p.+5p. Handball	30	15
3009	18p.+5p. Boxing	35	25
3010	20p.+5p. Cycling	35	35
3011	45p.+5p. Show jumping	90	70

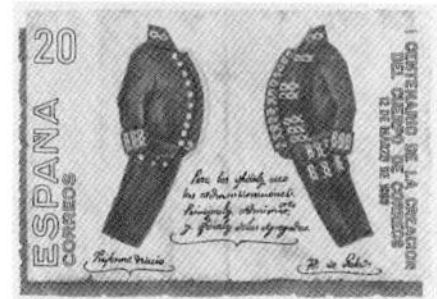

775 Uniforms, 1889

1989. Centenary of Post Office.

3012	**775**	20p. multicoloured	25	10

776 International Postal Service Treaty, 1601

1989. Stamp Day.

3013	**776**	20p. black	25	10

777 Entrance Door

1989. Cordon House, Burgos.

3014	**777**	20p. black	25	10

778 Skittles

1989. Europa. Children's Toys. Multicoloured.

3015	40p. Type **778**	60	35
3016	50p. Spinning top	85	60

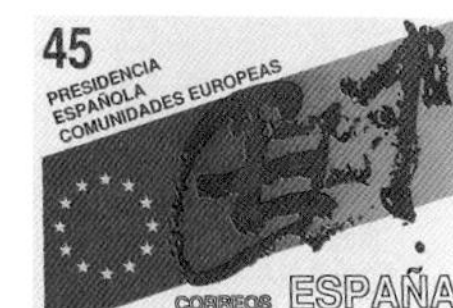

779 European Flag

1989. Spanish Presidency of European Economic Community.

3017	**779**	45p. multicoloured	65	35

780 "Holy Family with St. Anne" (El Greco)

1989. "Exfilna '89" National Stamp Exhibition, Toledo. Sheet 105×78 mm.

MS3018	**780** 20p. multicoloured	45	45

781 Manuscript and Portrait

1989. Birth Centenary of Gabriela Mistral (poet).

3019	**781**	50p. multicoloured	70	15

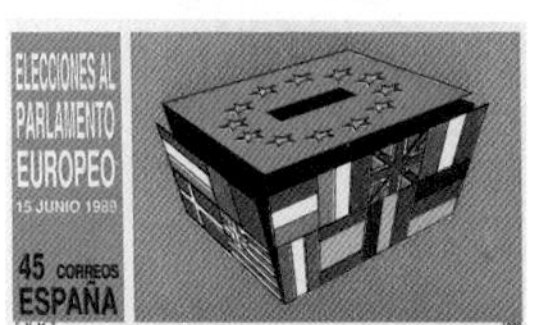

782 Flags forming Ballot Box

1989. European Parliament Elections.

3020	**782**	45p. multicoloured	65	35

783 Catalonia

1989. Lace. Typical designs from named region.

3021	**783**	20p. blue and brown	25	15
3022	-	20p. blue and brown	25	15
3023	-	20p. blue	25	15
3024	-	20p. blue	25	15
3025	-	20p. blue and brown	25	15
3026	-	20p. blue and brown	25	15

DESIGNS: No. 3022, Andalucia; 3023, Extremadura; 3024, Canary Islands; 3025, Castilla-La Mancha; 3026, Galicia.

784 Pope John Paul II and Youths

1989. 3rd Papal Visit.

3027	**784**	50p. green, brown & blk	65	15

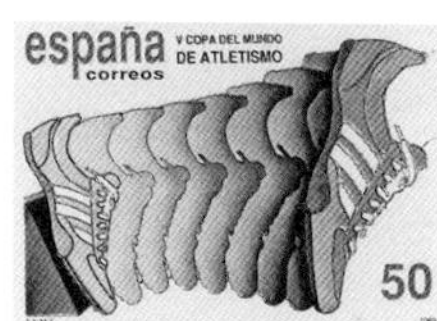

785 Foot leaving Starting Block

1989. World Cup Athletics Championships, Barcelona.

3028	**785**	50p. multicoloured	55	15

786 Chaplin

1989. Birth Centenary of Charlie Chaplin (actor).

3029	**786**	50p. multicoloured	65	15

787 1p. Stamp

1989. Centenary of First King Alfonso XIII Stamps.

3030	**787**	50p. brown, grey and red	65	15

1989. Olympic Games, Barcelona (1992) (3rd issue). As T 760.

3031	18p.+5p. Fencing	70	55
3032	20p.+5p. Football	70	60
3033	45p.+5p. Gymnastics	1·00	95

788 Fr. Andres Manjon (founder)

1989. Centenary of Ave Maria Schools.

3034	**788**	20p. multicoloured	25	10

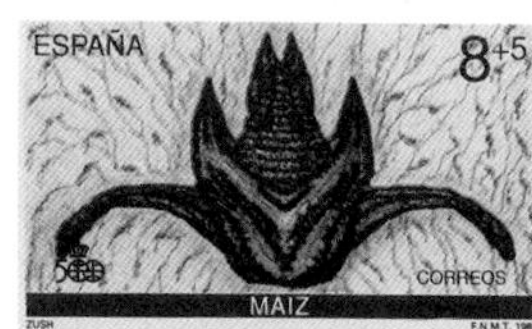

789 Maize

1989. 500th Anniv (1992) of Discovery of America by Columbus (4th issue). Multicoloured.

3035	8p.+5p. Type **789**	15	15
3036	8p.+5p. Cacao nut	15	15
3037	20p.+5p. Tomato	30	25
3038	20p.+5p. Horse	30	25
3039	50p.+5p. Potato	70	55
3040	50p.+5p. Turkey	70	55

790 Inca irrigating Corn (from "New Chronicle" by Waman Puma)

1989. America. Pre-Columbian Life.

3041	**790**	50p. multicoloured	55	10

791 "Navidad 89"

1989. Christmas. Multicoloured.

3042	20p. Type **791**	25	[illegible]
3043	45p. Girl with Christmas present (horiz)	60	15

792 Altamira Caves

1989. World Heritage Sites. Multicoloured.

3044	20p. Type **792**	30	10
3045	20p. Segovia Aqueduct	30	10
3046	20p. Santiago de Compostela	30	10
3047	20p. Guell Park and Palace and Mila House	30	10

793 San Lorenzo Monastery, El Escorial

1989. National Heritage. Royal Palaces. Sheet 162×92 mm containing T 793 and similar horiz designs. Multicoloured.

MS3048	45p. Type **793**; 45p. Aranjuez; 45p. La Granja de San Ildefonso; 45p. Madrid	2·20	2·20

794 Olympic Rings, Compass Rose, Church of Holy Family, Barcelona, and Seville

1990. Children's Stamp Design.

3049	**794**	20p. multicoloured	25	10

795 Getxo City Hall and Competitor

1990. World Cyclo-cross Championship, Getxo.

3050	**795**	20p. multicoloured	25	10

796 Victoria Kent

1990. 3rd Death Anniv of Victoria Kent (prison reformer).

3051	**796**	20p. lilac	25	10

797 Curro (mascot) flying over Path of Discoveries

1990. "Expo '92" World's Fair, Seville (5th issue). Multicoloured.

3052	8p.+5p. Type **797**	15	15
3053	20p.+5p. Curro and Exhibition building	30	30
3054	45p.+5p. Curro and view of Project Cartuja '93	65	65
3055	50p.+5p. Curro crossing bridge in Project Cartuja '93	80	80

1990. Olympic Games, Barcelona (1992) (4th issue). As T 760. Multicoloured.

3056	18p.+5p. Weightlifting	45	35
3057	20p.+5p. Hockey	45	35
3058	45p.+5p. Judo	90	60

798 Rafael Alvarez Sereix (Honorary Postman)

1990. Stamp Day.

3059	**798**	20p. flesh, brown & green	25	10

799 Vitoria Post Office

1990. Europa. Post Office Buildings.

3060	20p. Type **799**	55	30
3061	50p. Malaga Post Office (vert)	95	55

800 "Hispasat" Communications Satellite

1990. 125th Anniv of I.T.U.

3062	**800**	8p. multicoloured	20	10

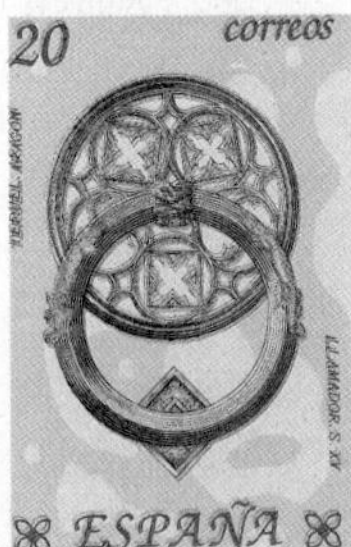

801 Door Knocker, Aragon

1990. Wrought Ironwork. Each black, grey and red.

3063	20p. Type **801**	30	15
3064	20p. Door knocker, Andalucia	30	15
3065	20p. Pistol, Catalonia	30	15
3066	20p. Door knocker, Castilla-La Mancha	30	15
3067	20p. Mirror with lock, Galicia	30	15
3068	20p. Basque fireback	30	15

802 Infanta's Patio, Zaragoza

1990. "Exfilna '90" National Stamp Exhibition, Zaragoza. Sheet 105×78 mm.

MS3069	**802** 20p. chestnut	35	35

803 "Charity" (Lopez Alonso)

1990. Anniversaries.

3070	**803**	8p. multicoloured	15	10
3071	-	20p. multicoloured	25	10
3072	-	45p. orange and brown	60	15
3073	-	50p. red and blue	65	15

DESIGNS—VERT: 8p. Type **803** (bicent of arrival in Spain of Daughters of Charity); 50p. Page of book (500th anniv of publication of "Tirant lo Blanch" by Joanot Martorell and Marti Joan de Galba). HORIZ: 20p. Score of "Leilah" and Jose Padilla (composer, birth centenary (1989)); 45p. Palace of Kings of Navarre (900th anniv of grant of privileges to Estella).

804 St. Antolin's Crypt, Palencia Cathedral

1990. "Filatem '90" Third National Thematic Stamps Exhibition, Palencia. Sheet 105×77 mm.

MS3074	**804** 20p. brown	35	35

805 Poster

1990. 17th International Historical Sciences Congress, Madrid.

3075	**805**	50p. multicoloured	70	15

1990. Olympic Games, Barcelona (1992) (5th issue). As T 760. Multicoloured.

3076	8p.+5p. Wrestling	20	15
3077	18p.+5p. Swimming	35	30
3078	20p.+5p. Baseball	45	35

806 Caravel and Compass Rose

1990. 500th Anniv of Discovery of America by Columbus (5th issue). Multicoloured.

3079	8p.+5p. Type **806**	20	15
3080	8p.+5p. Caravels	20	15
3081	20p.+5p. Caravel	35	30
3082	20p.+5p. Galleons	35	30

807 Puerto Rican Todys

1990. America. The Natural World.

3083	**807**	50p. multicoloured	70	15

808 Sun

1990. Christmas. Details of "Cosmic Poem" by Jose Antonio Sistiaga. Multicoloured.

3084	25p. Type **808**	35	10
3085	45p. Moon (horiz)	65	15

809 "Flemish Soldiers" (after Philips Wouvermans)

1990. Tapestries. Sheet 105×151 mm containing T 809 and similar vert designs. Multicoloured.

MS3086	20p. ×4: "Calvary" (Peter Pannemaker, after Jan van Roome and Bernard van Orley); Type **809**; "Wreck of the Telemach" (Urbano Leyniers after Miguel Houasse); "Flower Sellers" (Antonio Morena and Eusebio de Candano, after Goya)	1·40	1·20

810 Tourism Logo (Joan Miro)

1990. European Tourism Year.

3087	**810**	45p. multicoloured	65	40

811 Church of St. Miguel de Lillo, Oviedo

1990. World Heritage Sites. Multicoloured.

3088	20p. Type **811**	25	10
3089	20p. St. Peter's Tower, Teruel	25	10
3090	20p. Bujaco Tower, Caceres (horiz)	25	10
3091	20p. St. Vincent's Church, Avila (horiz)	25	10

812 Conductor and Orchestra

1990. Spanish National Orchestra.

3092	**812**	25p. green, turq & blk	35	10

813 Maria Moliner

1991. 10th Death Anniv of Maria Moliner (philologist).

3093	**813**	25p. multicoloured	35	10

814 La Cartuja (Santa Maria de las Cuevas Monastery)

1991. "Expo 92" World's Fair, Seville (6th issue). Views of Seville. Multicoloured.

3094	15p.+5p. Type **814**	25	25
3095	25p.+5p. The Auditorium	45	35
3096	45p.+5p. La Cartuja bridge	65	65
3097	55p.+5p. La Barqueta bridge	80	75

1991. Olympic Games, Barcelona (1992) (6th series). As T 760.

3098	15p.+5p. grey, black and red	35	30
3099	25p.+5p. multicoloured	40	40
3100	45p.+5p. multicoloured	75	65

DESIGNS: 15p. Modern pentathlon; 25p. Canoeing; 45p. Rowing.

815 Olympic Rings and Yachts

1991. Children's Stamp Design.

3101	**815**	25p. multicoloured	35	10

816 Loja Gate

1991. "Granada '92" International Thematic Stamp Exhibition (1st issue) and 500th Anniv of Santa Fe. Sheet 106×78 mm.

MS3102	**816** 25p. purple and gold	40	40

See also No. **MS**3174.

817 Juan de Tassis y Peralta (Chief Courier to Kings Philip III and IV)

1991. Stamp Day.

3103	**817**	25p. black	35	15

818 Talavera Apothecary Jar

1991. Porcelain and Ceramics. Sheet 106×150 mm containing T 818 and similar vert designs. Multicoloured.

MS3104 25p. Type **818**; 25p. Buen Retiro figurine; 25p. Pickman bottle; 25p. La Moncloa plate 1·60 1·60

819 Dish Aerials, INTA-NASA Earth Station, Robledo de Chavela

1991. Europa. Europe in Space. Multicoloured.

3105		25p. Type **819**	55	30
3106		45p. "Olympus I" telecommunications satellite	1·10	55

820 Brother Luis Ponce de Leon (translator and poet, 400th death anniv)

1991. Anniversaries.

3107	-	15p. multicoloured	25	15
3108	**820**	15p. orange, red & black	25	15
3109	-	25p. multicoloured	40	15
3110	-	25p. multicoloured	40	15

DESIGNS—HORIZ: No. 3107, Table and chair (400th death anniv of St. John of the Cross). VERT: No. 3109, Banner and cap (500th birth anniv of St. Ignatius de Loyola (founder of Society of Jesus)); 3110, Abd-er Rahman III, Emir of Cordoba (1100th birth anniv).

821 Apollo Fountain

1991. Madrid. European City of Culture (1st issue). Multicoloured.

3111		15p.+5p. Type **821**	45	45
3112		25p.+5p. "Don Alvaro de Bazan" (statue, Mariano Benlliure)	50	50
3113		45p.+5p. Bank of Spain	80	80
3114		55p.+5p. Cloisters, St. Isidro Institute	90	90

See also Nos. 3195/8.

822 Choir (after mural mosaic, Palau de la Musica)

1991. Centenary of Orfeo Catala (Barcelona choral group).

3115	**822**	25p. multicoloured	30	10

823 Basque Drug Cupboard

1991. Furniture. Multicoloured.

3116		25p. Type **823**	30	10
3117		25p. Kitchen dresser, Castilla y Leon	30	10
3118		25p. Chair, Murcia	30	10
3119		25p. Cradle, Andalucia	30	10
3120		25p. Travelling chest, Castilla-La Mancha	30	10
3121		25p. Bridal chest, Catalonia	30	10

824 Hands holding Net

1991. World Fishing Exhibition, Vigo.

3122	**824**	55p. multicoloured	85	15

1991. Olympic Games, Barcelona (1992) (7th series). As T 760. Multicoloured.

3123		15p.+5p. Tennis	45	40
3124		25p.+5p. Table tennis	65	60
3125		55p.+5p. Shooting	1·30	1·20

825 Garcilaso de la Vega (Spanish-Inca poet)

1991. 500th Anniv of Discovery of America by Columbus (6th issue). Multicoloured.

3126		15p.+5p. Type **825**	25	25
3127		25p.+5p. Pope Alexander VI	45	40
3128		45p.+5p. Luis de Santangel (banker)	70	70
3129		55p.+5p. Brother Toribio Motolinia (missionary)	90	80

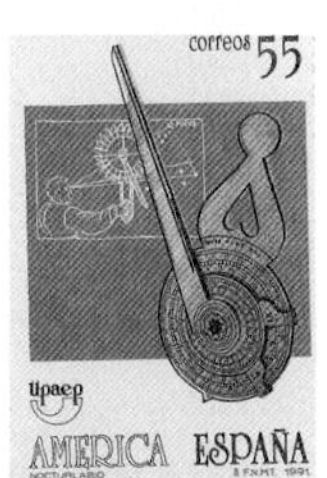

826 Nocturlabe

1991. America. Voyages of Discovery.

3130	**826**	55p. brown and purple	80	20

827 "Nativity" (from "New Chronicle" by Guaman Poma de Ayala)

1991. Christmas.

3131	**827**	25p. buff and brown	40	15
3132	-	45p. multicoloured	80	20

DESIGN: 45p. "Nativity" (16th-century Russian icon).

828 "The Meadow of San Isidro" (Francisco Goya)

1991. "Exfilna '91" National Stamp Exhibition, Madrid. Sheet 106×78 mm.

MS3133 **828** 25p. multicoloured 45 45

829 Alcantara Gate, Toledo

1991. World Heritage Sites.

3134	**829**	25p. agate and brown	45	15
3135	-	25p. black and brown	45	15
3136	-	25p. brown and blue	45	15
3137	-	25p. violet and green	45	15

DESIGNS—VERT: No. 3135, Casa de las Conchas, Salamanca. HORIZ: No. 3136, Seville Cathedral; 3137, Aeonio (flower) and Garajonay National Park, Gomera.

830 Gen. Carlos Ibanez de Ibero (cartographer)

1991. Anniversaries and Events. Multicoloured.

3138		25p. Type **830** (death centenary)	50	15
3139		55p. "Las Palmas" (Antarctic survey ship) (signing of Antarctic Treaty protocol of Madrid declaring the Antarctic a nature reserve)	95	20

831 Margarita Xirgu

1992. 23rd Death Anniv of Margarita Xirgu (actress).

3140	**831**	25p. brown and red	35	15

832 "Expo 92, Seville"

1992. Children's Stamp Design.

3141	**832**	25p. multicoloured	35	15

833 Pedro Rodriguez, Count of Campomanes (administrator and postal consultant)

1992. Stamp Day.

3142	**833**	27p. multicoloured	40	15

834 Spanish Pavilion

1992. "Expo '92" World's Fair, Seville (7th issue).

3143	**834**	27p. grey, black & brown	40	15

1992. Olympic Games, Barcelona (8th issue). As T 760. Multicoloured.

3144		15p.+5p. Archery	50	50
3145		25p.+5p. Sailing	70	70
3146		55p.+5p. Volleyball	1·20	1·10

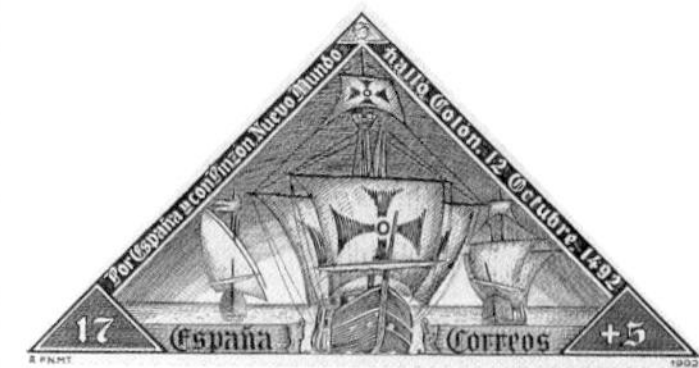

835 Columbus's Fleet (image scaled to 73% of original size)

1992. 500th Anniv of Discovery of America by Columbus (7th issue). Sheet 164×94 mm reproducing 1930 Columbus design.

MS3147 **835** 17p.+5p. red; 17p.+5p. blue; 17p.+5p. black 1·50 1·50

836 Cable-cars

1992. "Expo '92" World's Fair, Seville (8th issue). Multicoloured.

3148		17p. Exhibition World Trade Centre	30	25
3149		17p. Type **836**	30	25
3150		17p. Fourth Avenue	30	25
3151		17p. Barqueta entrance	30	25
3152		17p. Nature pavilion	30	25
3153		17p. Bioclimatic sphere	30	25
3154		17p. Alamillo bridge	30	25
3155		17p. Press centre	30	25
3156		17p. Pavilion of the 15th century	30	25
3157		17p. Expo harbour	30	25
3158		17p. Tourist train	30	25
3159		17p. One-day entrance ticket showing bridge	30	25
3160		27p. Santa Maria de las Cuevas Carthusian monastery	50	40
3161		27p. Palisade	50	40
3162		27p. Monorail	50	40
3163		27p. Avenue of Europe	50	40
3164		27p. Pavilion of Discovery	50	40
3165		27p. Auditorium	50	40
3166		27p. First Avenue	50	40
3167		27p. Square of the Future	50	40
3168		27p. Italica entrance	50	40
3169		27p. Last avenue	50	40
3170		27p. Theatre	50	40
3171		27p. Curro (official mascot)	50	40

MS3172 105×77 mm. 17p.+5p. View of 16th-century Seville (after A. Sanchez Coello) 40 40

837 Wheelchair Sports

1992. Paralympic (Physically Handicapped) Games, Barcelona.

3173	**837**	27p. multicoloured	45	20

838 Arrival in America

1992. "Granada '92" International Thematic Stamp Exhibition (2nd issue). Sheet 114×105 mm reproducing 1930 Columbus stamps.

MS3174	**835** 250p. black; **838** 250p. brown	7·75	7·75

839 "Preparation before leaving Palos" (R. Espejo)

1992. Europa. 500th Anniv of Discovery of America by Columbus (7th issue).

3175	**839**	17p. multicoloured	65	45
3176	-	45p. grey and brown	70	45

DESIGN: 45p. Map of the Americas, Columbus's fleet and Monastery of Santa Maria de La Rabida.

840 Columbus soliciting Aid of Isabella

1992. 500th Anniv of Discovery of America by Columbus (9th issue). Six sheets, each 107×91 mm, containing horiz designs as T 840 reproducing scenes from United States 1893 Columbian Exposition issue.

MS3177	Six sheets. (a) 60p. brown (Type **840**); (b) 60p. blue (Columbus sighting land); (c) 60p. brown (Landing of Columbus); (d) 60p. violet (Columbus welcomed at Barcelona); (e) 60p. black (Columbus presenting natives); (f) 60p. black ("America", Columbus and "Liberty") Set of 6 sheets	7·75	7·75

841 "Water and the Environment"

1992. World Environment Day.

3178	**841**	27p. blue and yellow	40	15

842 "Albertville", Olympic Rings and "Barcelona"

1992. Winter Olympic Games, Albertville, and Summer Games, Barcelona.

3179	**842**	45p. multicoloured	65	20

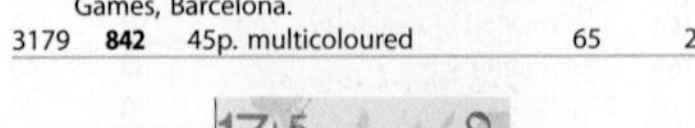

843 Victorious Athlete

1992. Olympic Games, Barcelona (9th issue). Multicoloured.

3180	17p.+5p. Type **843**	40	40
3181	17p.+5p. Cobi (official mascot)	40	40
3182	17p.+5p. Olympic torch (horiz)	40	40

844 Olympic Stadium

1992. Olympic Games, Barcelona (10th issue). Multicoloured.

3183	27p.+5p. Type **844**	40	40
3184	27p.+5p. San Jordi sports arena	40	40
3185	27p.+5p. I.N.E.F. sports university	40	40

845 Cobi holding Magnifying Glass and Stamp Album

1992. "Olymphilex 92" International Stamp Exhibition, Barcelona. Multicoloured.

3186	17p.+5p. Type **845**	35	30
3187	17p.+5p. Church of the Holy Family, Barcelona, and exhibition emblem	35	30

846 Athletes

1992. Paralympic (Mentally Handicapped) Games, Madrid.

3188	**846**	27p. blue and red	40	20

847 St. Paul's Church

1992. "Exfilna '92" National Stamp Exhibition, Valladolid. Sheet 105×78 mm.

MS3189	**814** 27p. brown	45	45

848 Quarterdeck of "Santa Maria"

1992. America. 500th Anniv of Discovery of America by Columbus (8th issue).

3190	**848**	60p. brown, cinnamon and ochre	90	35

849 Luis Vives (philosopher)

1992. Anniversaries. Multicoloured.

3191	17p. Type **849** (500th birth anniv)	20	15
3192	27p. Pamplona Choir (centenary) (horiz)	45	20

850 Helmet of Mercury and European Community Emblem

1992. European Single Market.

3193	**850**	45p. blue and yellow	70	40

851 "Nativity" (Obdulia Acevedo)

1992. Christmas.

3194	**851**	27p. multicoloured	35	15

852 Municipal Museum

1992. Madrid, European City of Culture (2nd issue). Multicoloured.

3195	17p.+5p. Type **852**	40	30
3196	17p.+5p. Queen Sofia Art Museum	40	30
3197	17p.+5p. Prado Museum	40	30
3198	17p.+5p. Royal Theatre	40	30

853 Huitzilopochtli, Mexican God of War

1992. Codices. Sheet 106×151 mm containing T 853 and similar vert designs. Multicoloured.

MS3199	27p. Type **853** (Codex Veitia); 27p. "Mounted Spaniard" (Bishop Baltasar Jaime's *History of the Diocese of El Trujillo del Peru*); 27p. 13th-century miniature from King Alfonso X's *Book of Chess, Dice and Tablings*; 27p. "Of the Months and the Festivals" from Bernardino de Sahagun's *General History of the Matters of New Spain*	1·60	1·60

854 Bird, Sun, Leaves and Silhouettes

1993. Public Services. Protection of the Environment.

3200	**854**	28p. blue and green	40	15

855 Maria Zambrano

1993. 2nd Death Anniv of Maria Zambrano (writer).

3201	**855**	45p. multicoloured	70	25

856 Figures and Blue Cross

1993. Public Services. Health and Sanitation.

3202	**856**	65p. blue and green	95	25

857 Segovia

1993. Birth Centenary of Andres Segovia (guitarist).

3203	**857**	65p. black and brown	1·00	25

858 Post-box, Cadiz, 1908

1993. Stamp Day.

3204	**858**	28p. multicoloured	50	15

859 Parasol Mushroom ("Lepiota procera")

1993. Fungi (1st series). Multicoloured.

3205	17p. Type **859**	40	15
3206	17p. Caesar's mushroom ("Amanita caesarea")	40	15
3207	28p. "Lactarius sanguifluus"	55	20
3208	28p. The charcoal burner ("Russula cyanoxantha")	55	20

See also Nos. 3256/9 and 3312/13.

860 Holy Week Procession

1993. "Exfilna '93" National Stamp Exhibition, Alcaniz. Sheet 105×78 mm.

MS3209	**860** 100p. multicoloured	1·50	1·50

861 Road Safety

1993. Public Services.

3210	**861**	17p. green and red	30	15

863 "Fusees"

1993. Europa. Contemporary Art. Paintings by Joan Miro.

3212	**863**	45p. black and blue	85	35
3213	-	65p. multicoloured	1·50	55

DESIGN—VERT: 65p. "La Bague d'Aurore".

864 "Translation of Body from Palestine to Galicia" (detail of altarpiece, Santiago de Compostela Cathedral)

1993. St. James's Holy Year (1st issue). Mult.

3214	17p. Type **864**	30	20

3215 28p. "Discovery of St. James's tomb by Bishop Teodomiro" (miniature from "Tumbo A" (codex)) 40 20

3216 45p. "St. James" (illuminated initial letter from Bull issued by Pope Alexander III declaring Holy Years of St. James) 70 20

See also No. 3218/**MS**3219.

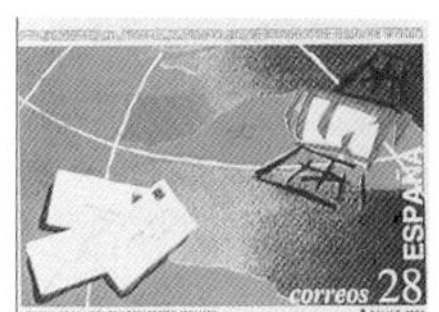

865 Letters, Map and Satellite

1993. World Telecommunications Day.

3217 **865** 28p. multicoloured 40 15

866 Bagpipe Player (Isaac Diaz Pardo)

1993. St. James's Holy Year (2nd issue). Multicoloured.

3218 28p. Type **866** 40 15

MS3219 106×82 mm. 100p. Pilgrim under the star tree (Eugenio Granel) (vert) 2·00 1·80

867 King Juan Carlos I

1993

No.	Type	Description	Mint	Used
3220	**867**	1p. blue and gold	20	15
3221	**867**	2p. green and gold	15	15
3222	**867**	10p. red and gold	20	20
3222b	**867**	15p. green and gold	20	20
3223	**867**	16p. brown and gold	20	15
3224	**867**	17p. orange and gold	20	15
3225	**867**	18p. turquoise and gold	30	15
3226	**867**	19p. brown and gold	40	20
3226a	**867**	20p. mauve and gold	60	25
3227	**867**	21p. green and gold	25	15
3229	**867**	28p. brown and gold	35	15
3230	**867**	29p. green and gold	70	20
3231	**867**	30p. blue and gold	45	25
3232	**867**	32p. green and gold	40	15
3233	**867**	35p. red and gold	40	20
3234	**867**	45p. green and gold	65	15
3235	**867**	55p. brown and gold	80	20
3236	**867**	60p. red and gold	90	25
3237	**867**	65p. orange and gold	90	15
3238	**867**	70p. red and gold	85	20

Nos. 3228 and 3239 are vacant.

868 "Water and the Environment"

1993. World Environment Day.

3240 **868** 28p. multicoloured 40 15

869 Count of Barcelona (after Ricardo Macarrion)

1993. Juan de Borbon, Count of Barcelona (King Juan Carlos's father) Commemoration.

3241 **869** 28p. multicoloured 40 15

870 Tank Locomotive

1993. Centenary of Igualada–Martorell Railway.

3242 **870** 45p. green and black 70 20

871 "The Mint" (lithograph, Pic de Leopold, 1866)

1993. Cent of National Coin and Stamp Mint.

3243 **871** 65p. blue 95 30

872 Alejandro Malaspina (navigator)

1993. Explorers. Multicoloured.

3244 45p. Type **872** 65 20

3245 65p. Jose Celestino Mutis (naturalist) (vert) 1·00 40

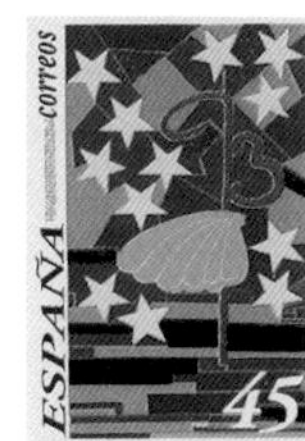

873 "Road to Santiago"

1993. Children's Stamp Design.

3246 **873** 45p. multicoloured 70 20

874 Black Stork

1993. America. Endangered Animals.

3247 **874** 65p. black and orange 95 35

3248 - 65p. black and red 95 35

DESIGN: No. 3248, Lammergeier.

875 Old and Young Hands

1993. European Year of Senior Citizens and Solidarity between Generations.

3249 **875** 45p. multicoloured 70 30

876 Star and Three Wise Men

1993. Christmas. Multicoloured.

3250 17p. Type **876** 30 15

3251 28p. Holy Family (vert) 45 25

877 Guillen

1993. Birth Centenary of Jorge Guillen (poet).

3252 **877** 28p. green 45 20

878 Santa Maria de Poblet Monastery, Tarragona

1993. World Heritage Sites.

3253 **878** 50p. brown, blue & green 85 30

879 Luis Bunuel and Camera

1994. Spanish Cinema (1st series). Multicoloured.

3254 29p. Type **879** 55 20

3255 55p. Segundo de Chomon and scene from "Goblin House" 90 30

See also Nos. 3308/9 and 3419/20.

1994. Fungi (2nd series). As T 859. Multicoloured.

3256 18p. Cep ("Boletus edulis") 30 15

3257 18p. Satan's mushroom ("Boletus satanas") 30 15

3258 29p. Death cap ("Amanita phalloides") 60 25

3259 29p. Saffron milk cap ("Lactarius deliciosus") 60 25

880 Cinnabar

1994. Minerals (1st series).

3260 **880** 29p. multicoloured 50 20

3261 - 29p. multicoloured 50 20

3262 - 29p. multicoloured 50 20

3263 - 29p. black and blue 50 20

DESIGNS: 3261, Blende (inscr "Esfalerita"); 3262, Pyrites; 3263, Galena.

See also Nos. 3314/16 and 3366/7.

881 Barristers' Mailbox, Barcelona

1994. Stamp Day.

3264 **881** 29p. brown and cinnamon 50 20

882 Worker (detail of sculpture), I.L.O. Building, Geneva.

1994. 75th Anniv of I.L.O., Geneva.

3265 **882** 65p. multicoloured 1·00 35

883 *Poetry of America*

1994. 90th Birth Anniv of Salvador Dali (painter). Multicoloured.

3266 18p. Type **883** 30 15

3267 18p. "Portrait of Gala" (horiz) 30 15

3268 29p. "Port Alguer" 45 20

3269 29p. "The Great Masturbator" (horiz) 45 20

3270 55p. "The Bread Basket" 85 30

3271 55p. "Soft Self-portrait" 85 30

3272 65p. "Galatea of the Spheres" 1·00 30

3273 65p. "The Enigma without End" (horiz) 1·00 30

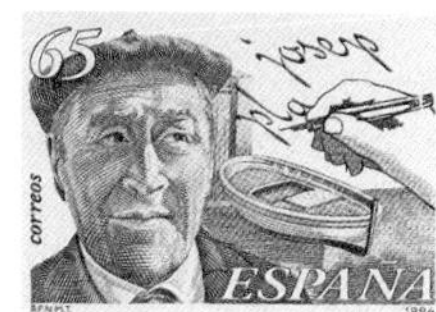

884 Pla

1994. 13th Death Anniv of Josep Pla (writer).

3274 **884** 65p. green and red 1·00 30

885 "Martyrdom of St. Andrew" (Peter Paul Rubens)

1994. 400th Anniv of Carlos de Amberes Foundation (philanthropic organization).

3275 **885** 55p. multicoloured 90 30

886 "Foundation of Santa Cruz de Tenerife" (Gonzalez Mendez)

1994. Anniversaries. Multicoloured.

3276 18p. Type **886** (500th anniv of city) 30 15

3277 29p. Sancho IV's Foundation Charter at Alcala, 1293 (700th anniv of Complutense University, Madrid) (horiz) 55 20

887 Severo Ochoa (biochemist)

1994. Europa. Discoveries. Multicoloured.

3278 55p. Type **887** (research into DNA) 1·50 55

3279 65p. Miguel Catalan (spectrochemist) (research into atomic structures) 1·60 55

888 "Family of Pascual Duarte"

1994. Spanish Literature. Works of Camilo Jose Cela. Multicoloured.
3280 18p. Type **888** 30 15
3281 29p. Walker and horse rider ("Journey to Alcarria") 55 25

889 Sancho I Ramirez

1994. 900th Death Anniv of King Sancho I Ramirez of Aragon (3282) and 500th Anniv of Treaty of Tordesillas (defining Portuguese and Spanish spheres of influence) (others).
3282 **889** 18p. red, yellow and blue 25 15
3283 - 29p. multicoloured 50 20
3284 - 55p. green, orange and brown 85 35
DESIGN—HORIZ: 29p Compass rose and arms of Tordesillas; 55p. Treaty House, Tordesillas.

890 St. Anne's Cathedral

1994. "Exfilna '94" National Stamp exhibition, Las Palmas, Gran Canaria. Sheet 105×78 mm.
MS3285 **890** 100p. multicoloured 1·50 1·50

891 "Giralda" (yacht)

1994. Ships sailed by Count of Barcelona. Multicoloured.
3286 16p. Type **891** 25 15
3287 29p. "Saltillo" (schooner) 50 20

892 Forum Caryatid and Tablet bearing Roman Name of Merida

1994. World Heritage Site. Merida.
3288 **892** 55p. brn, cinnamon & red 85 30

893 Knight of Swords (14th-century Catalan deck)

1994. Playing Card Museum, Vitoria. Multicoloured.
3289 18p. Type **893** 25 20
3290 29p. Jack of Clubs (Catalan Tarot deck, 1900) 40 20
3291 55p. King of Cups (Spanish deck by Juan Barbot, 1750) 80 30
3292 65p. "Mars", Jack of Diamonds (English deck by Stopforth, 1828) 1·10 30

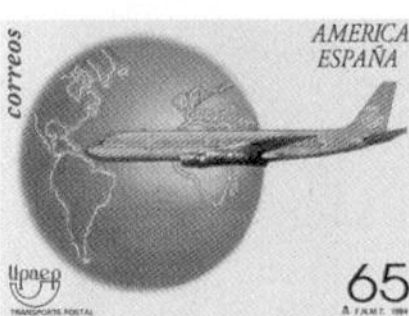

894 Globe and Douglas DC-8

1994. America. Postal Transport.
3293 **894** 65p. multicoloured 95 30

895 Civil Guard (150th anniv)

1994. Public Services.
3294 - 18p. red and blue 30 20
3295 **895** 29p. multicoloured 50 25
DESIGN—As T **854**: 18p. Underground train (75th anniv of Madrid Metro).

896 Map of Member Countries

1994. 40th Anniv of Western European Union.
3296 **896** 55p. multicoloured 85 30

897 Running

1994. Centenary of International Olympic Committee. Spanish Olympic Gold Medal Sports. Multicoloured.
3297 29p. Type **897** 40 30
3298 29p. Cycling 40 30
3299 29p. Skiing 40 30
3300 29p. Football 40 30
3301 29p. Show jumping 40 30
3302 29p. Hockey 40 30
3303 29p. Judo 40 30
3304 29p. Swimming 40 30
3305 29p. Archery 40 30
3306 29p. Yachting 40 30
See also Nos. 3332/45 and 3373/81.

898 "Adoration of the Kings" (detail of Ripoll altarpiece, Esteve Bover)

1994. Christmas.
3307 **898** 29p. multicoloured 50 20

899 "Belle Epoque" (dir. Fernando Trueba)

1995. Spanish Cinema (2nd series). Film posters. Multicoloured.
3308 30p. Type **899** 45 20
3309 60p. "Volver a Empezar" (dir. Jose Luis Garci) 90 40

900 Logrono

1995. 900th Anniv of Logrono Law Code.
3310 **900** 30p. multicoloured 50 20

901 Snow Star

1995. "Filatem '95" National Thematic Stamp Exhibition, Granada, and Worl Alpine Skiing Championships, Sierra Nevasa. Sheet 105×78 mm.
MS3311 **901** 130p. multicoloured 2·00 2·30

902 Shaggy Ink Cap

1995. Fungi (3rd series). Multicoloured.
3312 19p. Type **902** 30 15
3313 30p. "Dermocybe cinnamomea" 50 25

1995. Minerals (2nd series). As T 880. Mult.
3314 30p. Aragonite 45 20
3315 30p. Advanced Mining Engineering Technical School and Mining Museum, Madrid 45 20
3316 30p. Dolomite 45 20

903 19th-century Lion's Head Letter Box

1995. Stamp Day.
3317 **903** 30p. brown and green 50 20

904 Goicoechea and Talgo Train

1995. Birth Centenary of Alejandro Goicoechea (inventor of Talgo articulated train).
3318 **904** 30p. multicoloured 45 20
3319 - 60p. blue and brown 95 35
DESIGN: 60p. Goicoechea and "Virgen del Pilar" articulated train.

905 Globe as Tree on Hand

1995. European Nature Conservation Year.
3320 **905** 60p. multicoloured 1·20 65

906 *"San Juan Nepomuceno"*

1995. Ships Paintings by AlejoBerlinquero de la y Gallego. Two sheets, each 87×164 mm, containing vert designs as T 906. Multicoloured.
MS3321 Two sheets. (a) 19p. ×4, Type **906**; (b) 30p. ×4, *"San Telmo"* 3·00 3·00

907 Angel (from illuminated manuscript)

1995. 900th Anniv of Monastery of Liebana. Multicoloured.
3322 30p. Type **907** 45 20
3323 60p. Liebana landscape 90 40

908 Miguel Hernandez and part of "El Nino Yuntero"

1995. Literature.
3324 **908** 19p. multicoloured 35 20
3325 - 30p. blue, green and black 50 20
DESIGN—VERT: 30p. Juan Valera and scene from "Juanita la Larga".

909 Marti

1995. Death Centenary of Jose Marti (Cuban poet).
3326 **909** 60p. multicoloured 95 35

910 Captain Trueno

1995. Comic Strip Characters. Multicoloured.
3327 30p. Type **910** 50 20
3328 60p. Carpanta (vert) 95 40

911 Chain and Laurel Twig

1995. Europa. Peace and Freedom.
3329 **911** 60p. multicoloured 1·60 85

912 Lumiere Brothers

1995. Centenary of Motion Pictures.
3330 **912** 19p. brown 35 15

913 Typewriter, Pen and Camera

1995. Centenary of Madrid Press Association.
3331 **913** 30p. multicoloured 50 25

1995. Spanish Olympic Silver Medal Sports. As T 897. Multicoloured.

3332	30p. Type **897**	45	40
3333	30p. Basketball	45	40
3334	30p. Boxing	45	40
3335	30p. As No. 3300	45	40
3336	30p. Gymnastics	45	40
3337	30p. As No. 3301	45	40
3338	30p. As No. 3302	45	40
3339	30p. Canoeing	45	40
3340	30p. Polo	45	40
3341	30p. Rowing	45	40
3342	30p. Tennis	45	40
3343	30p. Shooting	45	40
3344	30p. As No. 3306	45	40
3345	30p. Water polo	45	40

914 King Juan Carlos I at National Assembly, 1986

1995. Anniversaries. Multicoloured.
3346 60p. Type **914** (50th anniv of U.N.O.) 90 40
3347 60p. Anniversary emblem, globes and wheat ears (50th anniv of F.A.O.) (vert) 90 40
3348 60p. Emblem and coloured bands (20th anniv of World Tourism Organization) 90 40

915 Presidency Emblem

1995. Spanish Presidency of the European Union.
3349 **915** 60p. red, yellow and blue 1·20 65

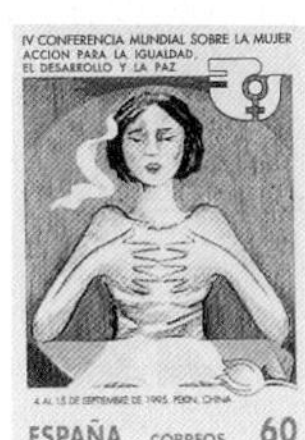

916 Spotlight on Woman

1995. 4th U.N. Conference on Women, Peking.
3350 **916** 60p. multicoloured 95 40

917 Cover Illustration of National Atlas of Spain

1995. 17th International Cartography Conference, Barcelona. Sheet 105×78 mm.
MS3351 **917** 130 p. multicoloured 2·00 2·00

918 Entrance to Hospital de la Azabacheria

1995. 500th Anniv of University of Santiago de Compostela.
3352 **918** 30p. multicoloured 50 25

919 Royal Monastery of Santa Maria, Guadalupe

1995. World Heritage Sites.
3353 **919** 60p. brown 90 40
3354 - 60p. multicoloured 90 40
DESIGN—HORIZ: No. 3354, Route map of Spanish section of road to Santiago de Compostela and statue of pilgrim.

920 The Peddler" (sculpture, Jamie Pimentel)

1994. "Exfilna '95" National Stamp Exhibition, Malaga. Sheet 105×78 mm.
MS3355 **920** 130p. green 2·00 2·00

921 Red-crested pochard, Mallard and Lagoon of La Mancha

1995. America. Environmental Protection.
3356 **921** 60p. multicoloured 85 40

922 La Cueva de Menga, Malaga (Bronze Age)

1995. Archaeology. Multicoloured.
3357 30p. Type **922** 45 25
3358 30p. La Taula de Torralba (c. 700 B.C.) 45 25

923 Reciation

1995. Art. Sheet 145×95 mm containing details of "The Contemporary Poets" by Antonio Wsquivel. Multicoloured.
MS3359 19p.; 30p.; 60p.; 60p. Composite design of painting 2·50 2·75

924 "Adoration of the Kings" (capital, Collegiate Church, San Martin de Elines)

1995. Christmas.
3360 **924** 30p. multicoloured 55 20

925 King Juan Carlos

1995. 20th Anniv of Accession of King Juan Carlos I.
3361 **925** 1000p. violet 47·00 8·25
See also Nos. 3408/11.

926 Cordoba Station, Plaza de Armas, Seville (venue)

1995. "Espamer" Spanish–Latin American and "Aviation and Space" Stamp Exhibitions, Seville. Multicoloured.
3362 60p. Type **926** 95 35
3363 60p. Dr. Lorenzo Galindez de Carvajal (Master Courier of the Indies and Terra Firma of the Ocean Sea, 1514) 95 35
See also No. **MS**3382.

927 "Leaving Mass at Pilar de Zaragoza" (first Spanish film, 1896)

1996. Centenary of Motion Pictures.
3364 **927** 30p. brown, mauve and black 40 20
3365 - 60p. multicoloured 65 40
DESIGN: 60p. "Bienvenido, Mister Marshall!" (poster).

928 Miner's Lamp

1996. Minerals (3rd series). Multicoloured.
3366 30p. Type **928** 60 20
3367 60p. Amber fluorite 1·00 40

929 Jose Mathe Aragua (General Director) and Telegraph Tower

1996. Stamp Day. 150th Anniv of Madrid–Irun Telegraph Signal Line.
3368 **929** 60p. green and red 80 40

930 Columbus (statue), "B" and Arch of Triumph

1996. 10th Anniv (1995) of Start of Barcelona Urbanization Programme.
3369 **930** 30p. multicoloured 35 20

931 Brown Bear with Cubs

1996. Endangered Species.
3370 **931** 30p. multicoloured 4·00 20

932 *Real Phelipe* (ship of the line)

1996. 18th-century Ships. Two sheets each 87×165 mm containing vert designs as T 932. Multicoloured.
MS3371 Two sheets. (a) 30p. ×4, Type **932**; (b) 60p. ×4, *El Catalan* (after Rafael Moleon) 5·50 5·50

933 Scales

1996. 400th Anniv of Madrid Bar Assocation.
3372 **933** 19p. multicoloured 30 20

1996. Spanish Olympic Bronze Medal Sports. As T 897. Multicoloured. Dated "1996".

3373	30p. Type **897**	35	25
3374	30p. As No. 3334	35	25
3375	30p. As No. 3299	40	30
3376	30p. As No. 3302	40	30
3377	30p. As No. 3304	40	30
3378	30p. As No. 3339	40	30
3379	30p. As No. 3342	40	30
3380	30p. As No. 3343	40	30
3381	30p. As No. 3306	40	30

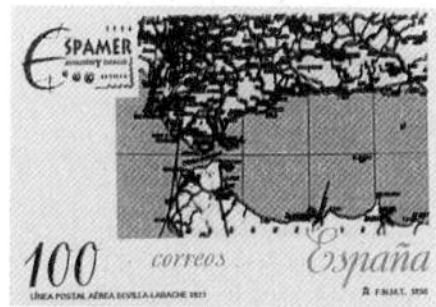

934 Map of Seville—Larache Postal Route

1996. "Espamer" Spanish-Latin American and "Aviation and Space" Stamp Exhibitions, Seville (2nd issue). Two sheets, each 164×87 mm containing T 934 and similar horiz designs (sheet a) or single stamp (b). Multicoloured.
MS3382 Two sheets. (a) 100p. Type **934**; 100p. Cover flown by airship LZ-127 *Graf Zeppelin*, 1930; 100p. Rocket launch, El Arenosillo, Huelva; 100 p. Hispano HA200 Saeta jet fighter. (b) 400p. The Royal Family (78×54 mm) 8·25 8·25

935 Carmen Amaya (flamenco dancer)

1996. Europa. Famous Women.
3383 **935** 60p. multicoloured 1·60 85

936 El Jabato (Victor Mora and Francisco Darnis)

1996. Comic Strip Characters. Multicoloured.
3384 19p. Type **936** 30 20
3385 30p. Reporter Tribulete (Guillermo Cifre) (horiz) 50 20

937 "General Don Antonio Ricardos"

1996. 250th Birth Anniv of Francisco de Goya (artist). Multicoloured.
3386 19p. Type **937** 40 20
3387 30p. "The Milkmaid of Bordeaux" 45 25
3388 60p. "Boys with Mastiffs" (horiz) 1·00 40
3389 130p. "3rd of May 1808 in Madrid" (horiz) 2·20 85

938 Magnifying Glass and Stamp Album

1996. 50th Anniv of Philatelic Service.
3390 **938** 30p. multicoloured 45 25

939 Jose Monge Cruz (Camaron de la Isla)

1996. Flamenco Artistes.
3391 **939** 19p. multicoloured 25 20
3392 - 30p. purple and red 40 25
DESIGN—HORIZ: 30p. Lola Flores.

940 Lanuza Market, Zaragoza (Felix Navarro Perez)

1996. 19th International Architects Congress, Barcelona. Metallic Buildings.
3393 **940** 30p. multicoloured 45 20

941 Gerardo Diego and Pen (poet, birth centenary)

1996. Anniversaries.
3394 **941** 19p. violet and red 25 20
3395 - 30p. multicoloured 40 25
3396 - 60p. black, red and blue 85 40
DESIGNS—HORIZ: 30p. Joaquin Costa and birthplace (politician and historian, 150th birth anniv). VERT: 60p. The five senses (50th anniv of UNICEF.).

942 Naveta (tomb) des Tudons, Minorca

1996. Archaeology. Multicoloured.
3397 30p. Type **942** 50 20
3398 30p. Cabezo de Alcala de Azila, Teruel 50 20

944 Salamancan Costumes

1996. America. Traditional Costumes.
3400 **944** 60p. multicoloured 80 40

945 Albaicin Quarter, Granada

1996. World Heritage Sites.
3401 **945** 19p. blue 30 20
3402 - 30p. purple 50 25
3403 - 60p. blue 1·00 40
DESIGNS—HORIZ: 30p. Tiberiades Square and statue of Maimonides (centre of Cordova). VERT: 60p. Deer, Donana National Park.

946 Oviedo Cathedral, Leopoldo Alas and Quotation from "La Regenta"

1996. Literature.
3404 **946** 30p. blue and purple 35 25
3405 - 60p. blue and purple 80 45
DESIGN—HORIZ: 60p. Scene from "Don Juan Tenorio" by Jose Zorrilla.

947 "Nativity" (Fernando Gallego)

1996. Christmas.
3406 **947** 30p. multicoloured 45 20

948 Map (image scaled to 61% of original size)

1996. Autonomous Communities of Spain. Sheet 164×87 mm.
MS3407 **948** 130p. multicoloured 1·90 1·90

1996. King Juan Carlos I.
3408 **925** 100p. brown 2·75 35
3409 **925** 200p. green 6·50 70
3410 **925** 300p. purple 13·50 2·40
3411 **925** 500p. blue 24·00 5·25

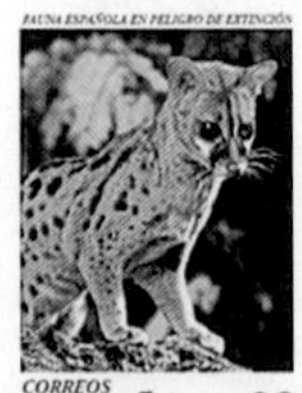

949 Genet

1997. Endangered Species.
3416 **949** 32p. multicoloured 40 20

950 Exhibition Poster (Jose Sanchez)

1997. "Juvenia '97" National Youth Stamp Exhibition, El Puerto de Santa Maria.
3417 **950** 32p. multicoloured 40 25

951 Stone Post Box, Madrid

1997. Stamp Day.
3418 **951** 65p. blue and red 85 45

952 "The Journey to Nowhere" (dir. Fernando Fernan)

1997. Spanish Cinema (3rd series). Posters. Multicoloured.
3419 21p. Type **952** 25 20
3420 32p. "The South" (dir. Victor Erice) 45 25

953 La Caprichosa and Bano de Diana Waterfalls, Monastery of Piedra Park

1997. World Water Day.
3421 **953** 65p. multicoloured 80 40

954 *Asturias* (frigate)

1997. 19th-century Ships. Two sheets each 87×164 mm containing similar vert designs as T 954. Multicoloured.
MS3422 Two sheets (a) 21p. ×4, Type **954**; (b) 32p. ×4, 16-gun brigantine (after Rodriguez and Gasco) 3·75 3·75

955 Vizcaya Bridge

1997. Anniversaries. Metal Structures. Mult.
3423 32p. Type **955** (centenary of Engineering School, Bilbao) 40 20
3424 194p. Atocha railway station and AVE locomotive (fifth anniv of AVE high speed train) 2·50 1·20

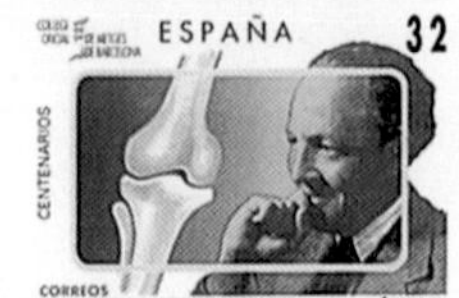

956 Joint and Trueta

1997. Birth Centenary of Josep Trueta i Raspall (orthopaedic surgeon).
3425 **956** 32p. multicoloured 40 25

957 Prince and Princess, Castle and Forest

1997. Europa. Tales and Legends.
3426 **957** 65p. multicoloured 1·60 90

958 Lazaro with Blind Beggar

1997. Spanish Literature.
3427 **958** 21p. black and green 25 15
3428 - 32p. brown and blue 45 25
DESIGNS—VERT: 21p. Type **958** ("Life of Lazarillo de Tormes and his Fortunes and Setbacks"). HORIZ: 32p. Jose Maria Peman and character El Seneca.

959 Anxel Fole (writer) (after Siro Lopez Lorenzo)

1997. Galician Literature Day.

3429	**959**	65p. multicoloured	85	40

960 The Ulysses Family (Mariano Benejam)

1997. Comic Strip Characters. Multicoloured.

3430	21p. Type **960**	25	15
3431	32p. The Masked Warrior (Manuel Gago)	45	25

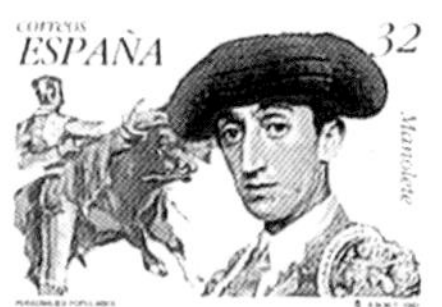

961 Manolete (Manuel Rodriguez Sanchez) (matador)

1997. Anniversaries. Multicoloured.

3432	32p. Type **961** (50th death anniv)	45	25
3433	65p. Charlie Rivel (Josep Andreu i Lasserre) (clown, birth centenary (1996))	90	40

962 "The Annunciation" (from Church of Our Lady of Sorrow, Agreda)

1997. Sixth "The Ages of Man" Exhibition. El Burgo de Osma. Sheet 92×148 mm containing T 962 and similar vert designs. Multicoloured.

MS3434	21p. Type **962**; 32p. El Burgo de Osma Cathedral; 65p. Illustration from Codex, 1086; 140p. Santo Domingo de Silos (17-century statue)	3·75	3·75

963 Championship Poster (Manel Esclusa)

1997. 30th Men's European Basketball Championship, Barcelona, Girona and Badalona.

3435	**963**	65p. multicoloured	1·10	40

964 Cibeles Fountain, Madrid

1997. North Atlantic Co-operation Council Summit, Madrid.

3436	**964**	65p. multicoloured	1·10	40

965 Grape Harvest Monument (Jose Esteve Edo)

1997. 50th Anniv of Grape Harvest Festival, Requena.

3437	**965**	32p. multicoloured	50	20

966 Antonio Canovas del Castillo (author of 1876 Constitution)

1997. Anniversaries. Multicoloured.

3438	21p. Type **966** (death centenary)	35	15
3439	32p. Roman coin and arrival of "Virgin of the Assumption" (statue) (2000th anniv of Elche)	55	25
3440	65p. Ships attacking city (after contemporary painting) (bicentenary of defence of Tenerife) (horiz)	95	40

967 Blue Ribbon

1997. Campaign for Peaceful Co-existence.

3441	**967**	32p. blue and black	40	20

968 Mariano Benlliure and "Breath of Life"

1997. Spanish Art.

3442	**968**	32p. multicoloured	45	20
3443	-	65p. black and stone	90	40

DESIGNS: 32c. Type **968** (sculptor, 50th death anniv); 65c. "Basque Rower" (photograph by Jose Ortiz Echague).

969 Net and Boat

1997. 4th World Fishing Fair, Vigo.

3444	**969**	32p. blue, deep blue and gold	40	20

970 City

1997. Anniversaries.

3445	**970**	21p. multicoloured	25	15
3446	-	32p. multicoloured	45	25
3447	-	65p. violet and red	85	40

DESIGNS—VERT: 21p. Type **970** (500th anniv of Spanish administration of Melilla); 32p. St. Pascual Baylon (after Vincente Carducho) (centenary of proclamation as World Patron of Eucharistic Congresses). HORIZ: 65p. Ausias March (after Jacomart) (poet, 600th birth anniv).

971 San Julian de los Prados Church, Oviedo

1997. World Heritage Sites.

3448	**971**	21p. brown, blue and green	40	15
3449	-	32p. brown, blue and green	65	25

DESIGN: 32p. Santa Cristina de Lena.

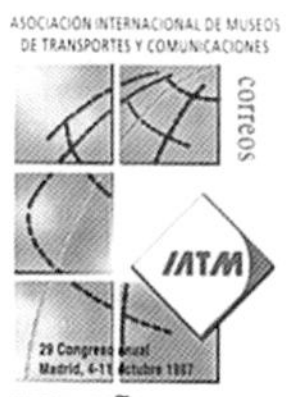

972 Emblem

1997. 29th Annual Congress of International Transport and Communications Museums Association, Madrid.

3450	**972**	140p. multicoloured	1·80	85

973 Statue of Don Palayo (Jose Maria Lopez)

1997. "Exfilna '97" National Stamp Exhibition, Gijon. Sheet 105×78 mm.

MS3451	**973**	140p. multicoloured	2·00	2·00

974 Postman

1997. America. Postal Delivery.

3452	**974**	65p. multicoloured	85	40

975 Miguel Fleta (tenor)

1997. Re-opening of Royal Theatre, Madrid.

3453	**975**	21p. brown	25	15
3454	-	32p. brown	45	25

DESIGNS: 21p. Type **975** (birth centenary); 32p. Theatre facade.

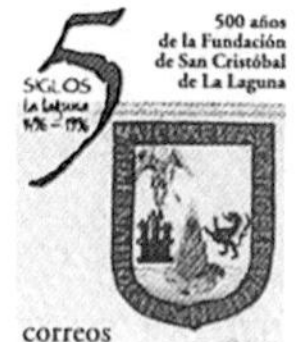

976 Town Arms

1997. 500th Anniv of San Cristobal de la Laguna, Tenerife.

3455	**976**	32p. multicoloured	40	20

977 Emblem

1997. 6th World Downs Syndrome Congress, Madrid.

3456	**977**	65p. blue and yellow	85	40

978 School

1997. 150th Anniv of Cordoba Veterinary School.

3457	**978**	21p. green and blue	30	15

979 "Adoration of the Kings" (detail, Pedro Berruguete)

1997. Christmas.

3458	**979**	32p. multicoloured	40	20

980 New Gate, Ribadavia

1997. Jewish Quarters.

3459	**980**	21p. brown and black	25	25
3460	-	32p. violet and black	45	40
3461	-	32p. brown and black	45	40
3462	-	65p. violet and black	80	70

DESIGNS: No. 3460, Women's Gallery, Cordoba Synagogue; 3461, Facade of 15th-century building, St. Anthony's Quarter, Caceres; 3462, Street, El Call, Girona.

981 Ball in Net

1997. Spanish Sporting Success. Zarra's Winning Goal in Spain v England Match, World Cup Football Championship, Brazil, 1950.

3463	**981**	32p. multicoloured	1·30	70

982 Emblem

1998. St. James's Holy Year (1999).

3464	**982**	35p. orange, grey and black	40	20

983 Lynx

1998. Endangered Species.
3465 **983** 35p. multicoloured 40 20

984 Club Flag and Emblem

1998. Centenary of Athletic Bilbao Football Club.
3466 **984** 35p. multicoloured 40 20

985 Clever and Smart (Francisco Ibanez)

1998. Comic Strip Characters. Multicoloured.
3467 35p. Type **985** 45 20
3468 70p. Zipi and Zape (Josep Escobar) (horiz) 90 55

986 Gredos Parador

1998. 70th Anniv of Paradores (state hotels).
3469 **986** 35p. multicoloured 40 20

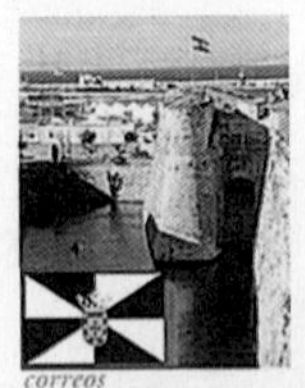

987 St. Philip's Fort and Harbour, Ceuta

1998. 3rd Anniv of Autonomy of Ceuta and Melilla. Multicoloured.
3470 150p. Type **987** 1·90 90
3471 150p. Plaza de Menendez Pelayo, Melilla (horiz) 1·90 90

988 1898 Generation

1998. 1898 Generation of Spanish Writers.
3472 **988** 70p. multicoloured 90 45

The writers depicted are Azorin, Pio Baroja, Miguel de Unamuno, Ramiro de Maeztu, Antonio Machado and Valle Inclan.

989 Pedro Abarca de Bolea, Count of Aranda

1998. Death Bicentenary of Pedro Abarca de Bolea, Count of Aranda (politician).
3473 **989** 35p. multicoloured 40 20

990 "The Celestine" (Fernando de Rojas)

1998. Spanish Literature.
3474 **990** 35p. deep green and green 45 20
3475 - 70p. green and red 90 45

DESIGN: 70p. "Fortunata and Jecinta" (Benito Perez Galdos).

991 Royal Barge

1998. Ship Paintings by Carlos Broschi from "Royal Celebrations in Reign of Fernando VI". Multicoloured.
3476 35p. Type **991** 45 20
3477 70p. Tajo xebec (for court officials) 90 45

992 St. John's Bonfires, Alicante

1998. Europa. National Festivals.
3478 **992** 70p. multicoloured 1·60 90

993 Jimenez Diaz

1998. Centenary of Professional Institute of Doctors of Madrid and Birth Centenary of Carlos Jimenez Diaz (physician).
3479 **993** 35p. black and blue 40 20

994 Felix Rodriguez de la Fuente (naturalist, 70th anniv)

1998. Birth Anniversaries.
3480 **994** 35p. multicoloured 45 20
3481 - 70p. orange and red 90 45

DESIGN—VERT: 70p. Fofo (Alfonso Aragon) (clown, 75th anniv).

995 Philip II (after Antonio Moro)

1998. 400th Death Anniv of King Philip II.
3482 **995** 35p. multicoloured 40 20

996 Lorca

1998. Birth Centenary of Federico Garcia Lorca (writer).
3483 **996** 35p. multicoloured 60 20

997 Antonio Manso Fernandez and 1978 Queen Isabel II Stamp

1998. Spanish Engravers.
3484 **997** 35p. brown, blue and deep blue 50 20
3485 - 70p. purple, blue and black 95 45

DESIGN: 70p. Jose Luis Sanchez Toda and 1935 Mariana Pineda stamp.

998 Spanish and Philippine Flags, Cebu Basilica (after M. Miguel) and "Holy Child" (statuette)

1998. Centenary of Philippine Independence.
3486 **998** 70p. multicoloured 85 45

999 "Foster Brothers" (sculpture, Aniceto Marinas)

1998. Spanish Art.
3487 **999** 35p. multicoloured 40 20

1000 "Union of the Oceans"

1998. "Expo '98" World's Fair, Lisbon.
3488 **1000** 70p. multicoloured 85 45

1001 Computer, Computer Disk and Letter

1998. 20th International Data Protection Conference, Santiago de Compostela.
3489 **1001** 70p. multicoloured 85 45

1002 Barcelona Cathedral

1998. "Exfilna '98" National Stamp Exhibition, Barcelona. Sheet 106×88 mm.
MS3490 **1002** 150p. black and blue 2·30 2·30

1003 Fortified City, Cuenca

1998. World Heritage Sites.
3491 **1003** 35p. brown and blue 55 20
3492 - 70p. brown and red 1·10 45

DESIGN: 70p. Silk Exchange, Valencia.

1004 Man writing with Quill

1998. School Correspondence Programme. Scenes from "Don Quixote" (novel by Cervantes). Multicoloured.
3493 20p. Type **1004** 35 25
3494 20p. Man reading book 35 25
3495 20p. Priest dubbing Quixote 35 25
3496 20p. Quixote riding off at dawn (angel blowing trumpet) 35 25
3497 20p. Man beating Quixote with stick 35 25
3498 20p. Investigator burning books 35 25
3499 20p. Quixote and Sancho on horseback 35 25
3500 20p. Quixote and horse on sail of windmill 35 25
3501 20p. Quixote watching Sancho fly through air 35 25
3502 20p. Quixote charging through flock of sheep 35 25
3503 20p. Quixote and galley slaves 35 25
3504 20p. Quixote piercing goat-skins of wine 35 25
3505 20p. Quixote in cage 35 25
3506 20p. Quixote and Sancho on knees and woman on donkey 35 25
3507 20p. Quixote on foot holding sword to Knight of the Mirrors 35 25
3508 20p. Lion escaping cage 35 25
3509 20p. Quixote attacking birds 35 25
3510 20p. Quixote on wooden horse 35 25
3511 20p. Sancho as governor at meal 35 25
3512 20p. Quixote surprised in bed by Dona Rodriguez 35 25
3513 20p. Sancho and donkey 35 25
3514 20p. Quixote and Sancho looking over lake 35 25
3515 20p. Quixote on horse holding sword to Knight of the White Moon 35 25
3516 20p. Quixote and Sancho returning home at night 35 25

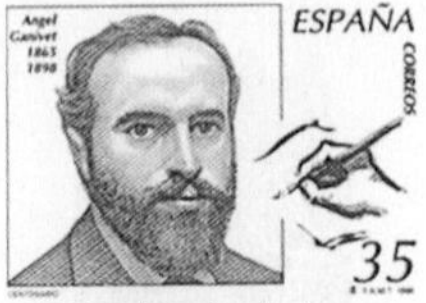

1005 Angel Ganivet (writer, death centenary)

1998. Anniversaries.
3517 **1005** 35p. brown and violet 45 20
3518 - 70p. brown and blue 85 45

DESIGN—VERT: 70p. Giralda Tower, Seville (800th anniv).

1006 Ladies' Tower and El Partal Gardens, Alhambra, Granada

1998. Aga Khan 1998 Architecture Award.
3519 **1006** 35p. brown and green 40 20

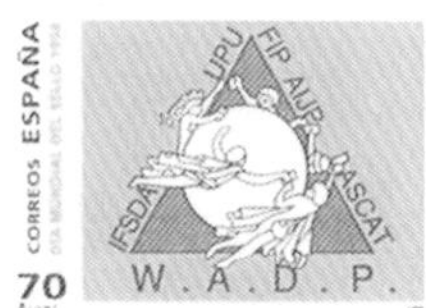

1007 U.P.U. Emblem

1998. World Stamp Day.

3520	**1007**	70p. blue and green	85	45

1008 Maria Guerrero (actress) and Scene from "The Lioness of Castille" by Francisco Villaespesa

1998. America. Famous Women.

3521	**1008**	70p. multicoloured	85	45

1009 Steam Locomotive "Mataro" (1848) and Euromed Electric Train (1998)

1998. 150th Anniv of Spanish Railways.

3522	**1009**	35p. blue and black	40	20

1010 Antarctic Base

1998. 10th Anniv of Juan Carlos I Antarctic Base.

3523	**1010**	35p. multicoloured	40	20

1011 Altarpiece (detail)

1998. Restoration of San Salavador's Cathedral, Zaragoza. Details of Altarpiece by Hans of Swabia. Sheet 105×122 mm containing T 1011 and similar vert design. Multicoloured.

MS3524 35p. Type **1011**; 35p. Adoration of the Wise Men (detail) 1·40 1·40

1012 Chestnut Seller

1998. Christmas. Multicoloured.

3525	35p. Type **1012**	45	20
3526	70p. "Wedding of Virgin Mary and Joseph" (detail of capital from Oviedo Cathedral)	85	45

1013 Juan de Onate (expedition leader)

1998. 400th Anniv of Foundation of Spanish Province of New Mexico. Multicoloured.

3527	35p. Type **1013**	45	20
3528	70p. Map and arms of New Mexico	85	45

1014 House, Hervas

1998. Jewish Quarters.

3529	**1014**	35p. purple and blue	45	25
3530	-	35p. green and blue	45	25
3531	-	70p. purple and blue	65	40
3532	-	70p. green and blue	65	40

DESIGNS: No. 3530, Bust of Benjamin Tudela (travel writer); 3531, Corpus Christi Church (former synagogue), Segovia; 3532, Santa Maria la Blanca synagogue, Toledo.

1015 Alaior and Mt. Toro

1998. UNESCO Biosphere Reserve, Minorca.

3533	**1015**	35p. multicoloured	40	20

1016 Bust of Plato and Ancient Greek Amphora

1998. 30th Anniv of Spanish Olympic Academy.

3534	**1016**	70p. multicoloured	85	45

1017 Angel Sanz Briz (diplomat)

1998. 50th Anniv of Universal Declaration of Human Rights. Multicoloured.

3535	35p. Type **1017**	45	20
3536	70p. Fingerprints forming heart (painting, Javier Valmaseda Calvo)	85	45

1018 Mare and Foal

1998. "Espana 2000" International Stamp Exhibition (1st issue). La Cartuja-Hierro del Bocado Horses. Multicoloured.

3537	20p. Type **1018** (emblem bottom right)	55	55
3538	20p. Type **1018** (emblems top left and top right)	55	55
3539	35p. Brown horse (emblem top right)	90	90
3540	35p. As No. 3538 (emblem bottom left)	90	90
3541	70p. Horse's head (emblems bottom left and bottom right)	1·90	1·90
3542	70p. As No. 3541 (emblem top left)	1·90	1·90
3543	100p. Mare and foal (different) (emblems top left and top right)	3·00	3·00
3544	100p. As No. 3543 (emblem bottom right)	3·00	3·00
3545	150p. Grey (emblem bottom left)	4·00	4·00
3546	150p. As No. 3545 (emblem top right)	4·00	4·00
3547	185p. Two white horses (emblem top left)	5·00	5·00
3548	185p. As No. 3547 (emblems bottom left and bottom right)	5·00	5·00

See also Nos. 3612/23, 3662/73 and MS3701.

1019 Giant Lizard, El Hierro Island

1999. Endangered Species. Multicoloured.

3549	35p. Type **1019**	50	20
3550	70p. Osprey (vert)	1·00	30
3551	100p. Manx shearwater	1·50	55

1020 Stone Cross, Perelada, Galicia

1999. St. James's Holy Year. Multicoloured.

3552	35p. Type **1020**	40	20
3553	70p. Figure of St. James on tympanum, St. James's Church, Sanguesa, Navarra (horiz)	1·00	40
3554	100p. Stone cross and Cizur bridge, Pamplona, Navarra	1·30	55
3555	185p. Jurisdictional stone pillar, Boadilla del Camino, Palencia	2·50	55

1021 Poster (Antoni Tapies)

1999. Centenary of Barcelona Football Club.

3556	**1021**	35p. multicoloured	50	20

1022 "Alaior" (Aroa Vidal)

1999. "Juvenia'99" National Youth Stamp Exhibition, Alaior, Minorca.

3557	**1022**	35p. black, red and yellow	50	20

1023 Police Moped, Bolkow (MBB/Eurocopter) BO 105 and Men in Protective Suits

1999. 175th Anniv of Spanish Police Force.

3558	**1023**	35p. multicoloured	50	20

1024 Aljaferia Palace, Zaragoza

1999. "Exfilna '99" National Stamp Exhibition, Zaragoza. Sheet 106×79 mm.

MS3559 **1024** 185p. green and chestnut 2·75 2·75

1025 Radio Transmitter and Receiver

1999. 50th Anniv of Spanish Amateur Radio Union.

3560	**1025**	70p. multicoloured	90	40

1026 Emblem and Athletes

1999. 7th World Athletics Championship, Seville.

3561	**1026**	70p. multicoloured	90	40

1027 Monfrague Nature Park, Caceres, and Wild Cat

1999. Europa. Parks and Gardens.

3562	**1027**	70p. multicoloured	1·50	90

1028 Underground Train

1999. 75th Anniv of Barcelona Metro.

3563	**1028**	70p. multicoloured	90	40

1029 "King Solomon" (detail of reredos from Becerril de Campos Church)

1999. "The Ages of Man" Exhibition, Palencia. Multicoloured.

3564	35p. Type **1029**	45	20
3565	70p. Detail of choir railing, Palencia Cathedral	90	40

1030 European Community Flag

1999. The Euro (European single currency). Showing maps of the participating countries and the appropriate exchange rate. Multicoloured.

3566	166p. Type **1030**	2·75	1·70
3567	166p. Germany	2·75	1·70
3568	166p. Austria	2·75	1·70
3569	166p. Belgium	2·75	1·70
3570	166p. Spain	2·75	1·70
3571	166p. Finland	2·75	1·70
3572	166p. France	2·75	1·70
3573	166p. Netherlands	2·75	1·70
3574	166p. Republic of Ireland	2·75	1·70
3575	166p. Italy	2·75	1·70
3576	166p. Luxembourg	2·75	1·70
3577	166p. Portugal	2·75	1·70

1031 Footballers and Club Badge

1999. Real Club Recreativo (Royal Recreation Club) of Huelva.

3578	**1031**	35p. multicoloured	50	20

1032 Dona Urraca (Jorge (Miguel Bernet Toledano))

1999. Comic Strip Characters. Multicoloured.

3579	35p. Type **1032**	45	20
3580	70p. El Coyote (Jose Mallorqui and Francisco Batet)	90	40

1033 Games Emblem

1999. World University Summer Games and Fifth National Thematic Stamps Exhibition, Palma de Mallorca. Sheet 105×78 mm.

MS3581	**1033**	185p. multicoloured	2·50	2·50

1034 Attack of Dutch Navy (after De Bry) and Arms of Las Palmas

1999. 400th Anniv of Defence of Las Palmas, Gran Canaria.

3582	**1034**	70p. black and yellow	90	40

1035 Cangas de Onis Parador (former Monastery of San Pedro de Villanueva)

1999. Paradores (state hotels).

3583	**1035**	35p. multicoloured	50	20

1036 Old Bridge

1999. 800th Anniv of Granting of Township Rights to Balmaseda.

3584	**1036**	35p. multicoloured	45	20

1037 Society and Anniversary Emblems

1999. Centenary of Society of Authors and Publishers.

3585	**1037**	70p. multicoloured	90	40

1038 Illuminated Fountain

1999. Birth Centenary of Carles Buigas (engineer).

3586	**1038**	70p. multicoloured	90	40

1039 Queen Isabel II, Geological Map of Spain and Founding Decree

1999. 150th Anniv of Spanish Technical Institute of Geology and Mining.

3587	**1039**	150p. multicoloured	2·10	90

1040 El Cid (after Vela Zanetti)

1999. 900th Death Anniv of El Cid (Rodrigo Diaz de Vivar).

3588	**1040**	35p. multicoloured	45	35

1041 "Winter"

1999. Spanish Art. Paintings by Vela Zanetti. Multicoloured.

3589	70p. Type **1041**	85	40
3590	150p. "The Harvest" (vert)	1·90	85

1042 "The Jester Don Sebastian de Morra"

1999. 400th Birth Anniv of Diego de Silva Velazquez (artist). Multicoloured.

3591	35p. Type **1042**	45	20
3592	70p. "A Sibyl"	90	40

1043 Emblem, Couple, Man and Baby

1999. International Year of the Elderly.

3593	**1043**	35p. multicoloured	50	20

1044 Oix Castle

1999. Catalan Lower Pyrenees Region.

3594	**1044**	70p. brown and blue	90	40

1045 St. Millan of Yuso Monastery, La Rioja

1999. World Heritage Sites.

3595	**1045**	35p. brown, green and blue	60	20
3596	-	70p. brown, green and blue	1·30	40

DESIGN: 70p. St. Millan of Suso Monastery, La Rioja.

1046 U.P.U. Monument, Berne

1999. Stamp Day. 125th Anniv of Universal Postal Union.

3597	**1046**	70p. multicoloured	90	40

1047 First Spanish Stamp, 1850

1999. School Correspondence Programme. Designs showing a stamp performing various activities. Multicoloured.

3598	20p. Type **1047**	25	20
3599	20p. Watching Boeing 747 taking off over city	25	20
3600	20p. As postman delivering letter	25	20
3601	20p. Writing letter	25	20
3602	20p. Reading book	25	20
3603	20p. With bird, butterfly and fish (nature)	25	20
3604	20p. Viewing historical buildings (heritage)	25	20
3605	20p. Painting portrait	25	20
3606	20p. With football, tennis racquet and sailboard	25	20
3607	20p. With baton, cello and saxophone	25	20
3608	20p. Holding magnifying glass over 40c. stamp	25	20
3609	20p. On horseback	25	20

1048 Dove on Hand

1999. America. A New Millennium without Arms.

3610	**1048**	70p. multicoloured	90	40

1049 "The Money Changer and his Wife" (Marinus Reymerswaele)

1999. National Money Museums Congress, Madrid.

3611	**1049**	70p. brown and blue	90	40

1050 Horse and Rider

1999. "Espana 2000" International Stamp Exhibition, Madrid (2nd issue). La Cartuja-Hierro del Bocado Horses. Paintings by Jose Manuel Gomez. Multicoloured.

3612	20p. Type **1050** (emblem bottom right)	85	85
3613	20p. Type **1050** (emblem top left)	85	85
3614	35p. Exhibition emblem and horses (emblems top left and right)	1·30	1·30
3615	35p. As No. 3614 (emblems top left and right but transposed)	1·30	1·30
3616	70p. Exhibition emblem (emblems bottom left and right)	2·20	2·20
3617	70p. As No. 3616 (emblems bottom left and right but transposed)	2·20	2·20
3618	100p. White horses (emblem top right)	3·75	3·75
3619	100p. As No. 3618 (emblem bottom left)	3·75	3·75
3620	150p. Heads of two white horses (emblem bottom left)	5·00	5·00
3621	150p. As No. 3620 (emblem top right)	5·00	5·00
3622	185p. Men inspecting horse (emblem top left)	6·75	6·75
3623	185p. As No. 3622 (emblem bottom right)	6·75	6·75

1051 "The Epiphany" (altarpiece, Toledo Cathedral)

1999. Christmas. Multicoloured.

3624	35p. Type **1051**	45	20
3625	70p. "Christmas" (Isabel Guerra) (horiz)	90	40

1052 King Juan Carlos and 1850 12c. Stamp

2000. 150th Anniv of First Spanish Stamp. Mult.

3626	35p. Type **1052**	45	35
3627	35p. King Juan Carlos and 6c. stamp	45	35
3628	35p. King Juan Carlos and 5r. stamp	45	35
3629	35p. King Juan Carlos and 6r. stamp	45	35
3630	35p. Anniversary emblem and 6c. stamp	45	35
3631	35p. King Juan Carlos and 10r. stamp	45	35
3632	35p. King Juan Carlos and State arms	45	35

1053 Apollo

2000. Endangered Butterflies. Multicoloured.

3633	35p. Type **1053**	45	20
3634	70p. *Agriades zullichi*	90	45

1054 Virgin Mary and Baby Jesus (xylographic engraving, Juan Luschner)

2000. 500th Anniv of the Monastery of Santa Maria of Montserrat Printing House.

3635	**1054**	35p. multicoloured	45	20

1055 "Charles V as Sovereign Master of the Order of the Golden Fleece" (anon)

2000. 500th Birth Anniv of King Charles V, Holy Roman Emperor. Multicoloured.

3636	35p. Type **1055**	45	25
3637	70p. "Charles V" (Corneille da la Haye)	90	45
MS3638	126×91 mm. 150p. "Charles V on Horseback" (40×49 mm)	2·10	2·10

1056 The Virgin de al Majestad (12th-century statue), Astorga Cathedral

2000. "The Age of Man" Exhibition, Astorga, Leon. Multicoloured.

3639	70p. Type **1056**	90	45
3640	100p. 12th-century Lignum Crucis and 10th-century Arab perfume bottle	1·40	75

1057 Sos del Rey Catolico, Saragossa

2000. Paradores (state hotels).

3641	**1057**	35p. multicoloured	45	25

1058 Lleida University

2000. University Anniversaries.

3642	**1058**	35p. brown and mauve	45	25
3643	-	70p. brown and blue	90	45

DESIGNS: 35p. Type **1058** (700th anniv); 70p. Valencia (500th anniv (1999)).

1059 Emblem

2000. Centenary of Reial Club Deportiu Espanyol Football Club, Barcelona.

3644	**1059**	35p. multicoloured	45	25

1060 Maria de las Mercedes (painting, Ricardo Macarron)

2000. Maria de las Mercedes de Borbon y Orleans (mother of King Juan Carlos I) Commemoration.

3645	**1060**	35p. multicoloured	45	25

1061 "Building Europe"

2000. Europa.

3646	**1061**	70p. multicoloured	1·60	1·20

1062 Emblem

2000. World Mathematics Year (3648) and Science (others). Multicoloured.

3647	35p. Type **1062** (300th anniv of Royal Academy of Medicine, Seville)	45	25
3648	70p. Julio Rey Pastor (mathematician) (painting, Pedro Piug Adam) and mathematical equation	90	45
3649	100p. School of Pharmacy, Granada (150th anniv) (vert)	1·30	75
3650	185p. Prince Felipe Science Museum, Valencia	2·50	1·20

1063 Hermenegilda and Leovigilda (Manuel Vazquez Gallego)

2000. Comic Strip Characters. Multicoloured.

3651	35p. Type **1063**	45	25
3652	70p. Roberto Alcazar and Pedrin (Eduardo Vano and Juan Bautista Puerto Belda) (vert)	90	45

1064 Guggenheim Museum

2000. 700th Anniv of Bilbao.

3653	**1064**	70p. multicoloured	90	45

1065 "Prayer in the Garden" (detail, Francisco Salzillo)

2000. Spanish Art.

3654	**1065**	70p. multicoloured	90	45

1066 Water Fountain

2000. "Exfilna '2000" National Philatelic Exhibition, Aviles. Sheet 105×78 mm.

MS3655	**1066**	185p. brown and blue	2·40	2·40

1067 Wild Pine (*Pinus silvestris*)

2000. Trees (1st series). Multicoloured.

3656	70p. Type **1067**	90	45
3657	150p. Holm oak (*Quercus ilex*)	1·90	1·00

See also Nos. 3757/8, 3837/8, 3994/5, 4021, 4095 and 4155.

1068 Fire Walking, San Pedro Manrique, Soria

2000. Festivals (1st series). Multicoloured.

3658	35p. Type **1068**	45	25
3659	70p. Rearing horse, crowd and flag (700th anniv of Chivalry Festival of San Juan, Ciudadela, Menorca)	90	45

See also Nos 3760/1.

1069 Escriva

2000. 25th Death Anniv of Josemaria Escriva de Balaguer (founder of Opus Dei (religious organization)).

3660	**1069**	70p. black and orange	90	40

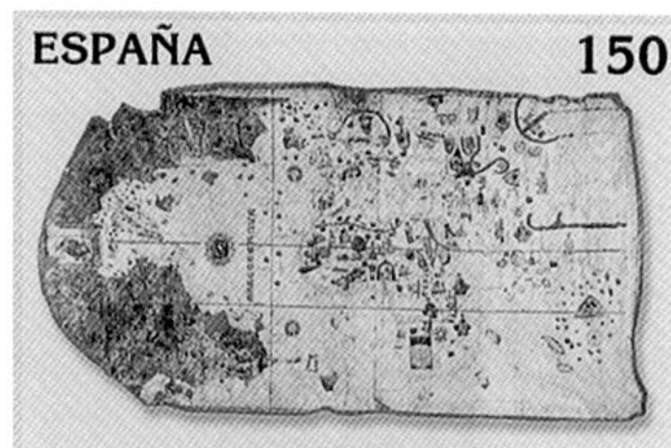

1070 Detail of Chart (image scaled to 54% of original size)

2000. 500th Anniv of Chart by Juan de la Cosa (sailor and cartographer) (first chart showing the Americas). Sheet 164×87 mm.

MS3661	**1070**	150p. multicoloured	2·30	2·30

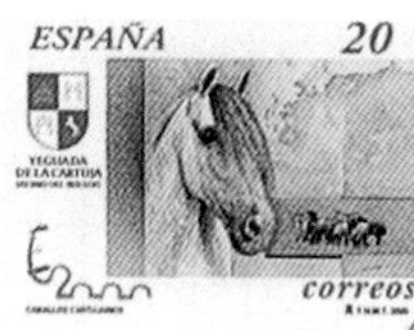

1071 Horse and Emblem

2000. "Espana 2000" International Stamp Exhibition, Madrid (3rd issue). La Carbija-Hierro de Bocado Horses. Multicoloured.

3662	20p. Type **1071** (emblem bottom right)	1·00	1·00
3663	20p. Type **1071** (emblems top right)	1·00	1·00
3664	35p. Horse on beach (emblem top right)	1·70	1·70
3665	35p. As No. 3664 (emblem bottom left)	1·70	1·70
3666	70p. Galloping horses and horse's head (emblems bottom left and right)	3·50	3·50
3667	70p. As No. 3666 (emblem top left)	3·50	3·50
3668	100p. Two horses' heads (emblems top left and right)	4·75	4·75
3669	100p. As No. 3668 (emblem bottom right)	4·75	4·75
3670	150p. Horse and horse's head (emblem bottom left)	7·50	7·50
3671	150p. As No. 3671 (emblem top right)	7·50	7·50
3672	185p. Horse outside stable (emblem top left)	8·75	8·75
3673	185p. As No. 3672 (emblems bottom left and right)	8·75	8·75

Nos. 3662/73 were issued together in se-tenant sheetlets of 12 stamps. Two different emblems were each printed twice in orange within the sheet, occurring in each case at the intersection of four stamps so that each stamp carries only part of one or two emblems as described in brackets.

1072 Las Medulas, Leon

2000. UNESCO World Heritage Sites.

3674	**1072**	35p. multicoloured	50	25
3675	-	70p. brown and blue (vert)	95	45
3676	-	150p. red and brown	2·10	1·00

DESIGNS: 70p. Mount Perdido, Pyrenees; 150p. Catalan Music Palace, Barcelona.

1073 Atapuercan Man wearing Football Scarf

2000. School Correspondence Programme (1st series). Spanish History. Multicoloured.

3677	20p. Type **1073**	30	25
3678	20p. Cave artists, Altamira	30	25
3679	20p. Phoenician ship	30	25
3680	20p. Question marks in Roman helmets (Tartessos)	30	25
3681	20p. Celtic and Iberian men	30	25
3682	20p. "The Lady of Elche" listening to music	30	25
3683	20p. Elephant on low-loader (Carthage) (first Punic war)	30	25
3684	20p. Romans	30	25
3685	20p. Viriathus (leader) attacking Roman (uprising in northern Spain)	30	25
3686	20p. Roman preparing to kick football into net full of Numanians (fall of the city of Numantia)	30	25
3687	20p. Aqueduct of Segova	30	25
3688	20p. Roman facing Vandal, Suevian and Alani (invasion, 409)	30	25
3689	20p. Visigoth kings Teodoredo I, Wallia, Sigerico and Ataulfo	30	25
3690	20p. King Recaredo I (conversion to Christianity, 589)	30	25
3691	20p. Map showing extent of Arab rule (conquest by Arab forces, 711)	30	25
3692	20p. Pelayo (Visigoth soldier), Covadonga, 722 (victory over the Moors)	30	25
3693	20p. Horseman (discovery of Tomb of the Apostle, 813)	30	25

3694	20p. Kings (union of Castille and Navarre)	30	25
3695	20p. Death of El Cid (soldier), 1099	30	25
3696	20p. Battle of Las Navas de Tolosa represented by chess game	30	25
3697	20p. Accession of Alfonso X (1252)	30	25
3698	20p. Enrique II and slain Pedro I foundation of House of Trastamara (Kingdom of Castille and Leon), 1396	30	25
3699	20p. Monk with magnifying glass (The Inquisition, established 1478)	30	25
3700	20p. Two crowns (unification of Kingdoms of Castile and Aragon 1479)	30	25

See also Nos. 3775/86 and 3882/93.

1074 Record and Hand (Julio Iglesias, singer)

2000. "Espana 2000" International Stamp Exhibition, Madrid (4th issue). Eleven sheets 105×78 mm containing T 1074 and similar multicoloured designs.

MS3701	Eleven sheets (a) 200p. Type **1074**; (b) 200p. Record and signature (Alejandro Sanz, singer-songwriter); (c) 200p. Film projector (Antonio Banderas, actor); (d) 200p. Designers mannequin (Jesus de Pozo, designer and couturier); (e) 200p. Football (Raul Gonzalez Blanco, footballer); (f) 200p. Cycle wheel (Miguel Indurain, cyclist); (g) 200p. Hands (Joquin Cortes, dancer and choreographer); (h) 200p. Dancing feet (Sara Baras, Flamenco dancer); (i) 200p Emblem (televisin); (j) 200p. Radio mast; (k) 200p. Newspaper titles (the press)	32·00	32·00

1075 Boy putting up Poster

2000. America. A.I.D.S. Awareness.

3702	**1075**	70p. multicoloured	90	45

1076 Portrait and Treble Clef

2000. 1st Death Anniv of Alfred Kraus (tenor).

3703	**1076**	70p. multicoloured	90	45

1077 The Adoration of Jesus (triptych) (Cristiane Hemmerich)

2000. Christmas. Multicoloured.

3704	35p. Type **1077**	45	25
3705	70p. "Birth of Christ" (Conrad von Soest)	90	45

1078 Building Facade

2000. Millenary of Santa María la Real Church, Aranda de Duero.

3706	**1078**	35p. brown	45	25

1079 Couple in Orange Grove (*Etre Naranjos*, Vicente Blasco Ibanez)

2000. Literature.

3707	35p. Type **1079**	50	25
3708	70p. Troubadour with lute, figures and castle (*La Venganza de Don Mendo*, Pedro Munzo Seca)	90	45
3709	100p. Soldiers (*El Alcalde Zalamea*, Pedro Calaeron de la Barca)	1·40	75

1080 "Tribute to Broker" (sculpture) (Francisco Lopez Hernandez) and Emblem

2001. 75th Anniv of Brokers' Schools.

3710	**1080**	40p. multicoloured	50	20

1081 Firefighters

2001

3711	**1081**	75p. multicoloured	90	50

1082 Soldier, Building and Emblem

2001. 150th Anniv of Infantry College, Toledo.

3712	**1082**	120p. multicoloured	1·50	80

1083 Emblem

2001. Campaign Against Domestic Violence.

3713	**1083**	155p. multicoloured	1·90	1·00

1084 First Post Box in Spain, Mayorga (1793)

2001. Stamp Day.

3714	**1084**	155p. black	1·90	1·00

1085 Young Couple and Yacht

2001. "Juvenia 2001" Youth Stamp Exhibition, Cadiz.

3715	**1085**	12p. multicoloured	1·50	85

1086 Plasencia Hotel (former monastery of San Vicente Ferrer)

2001. Paradores (state hotels).

3716	**1086**	40p. multicoloured	50	30

1087 Joaquin Rodrigo (composer, birth centenary)

2001. Personalities.

3717	**1087**	40p. violet	50	30
3718	-	75p. brown and blue	90	50

DESIGNS: 75p. Rafael Alberti (poet and dramatist, first death anniv).

1088 Zuda Castle, Tortosa

2001. Castles. Multicoloured.

3719	40p. Type **1088**	50	30
3720	75p. Castle of El Cid, Jadraque (horiz)	90	45
3721	155p. San Fernando Castle, Figueres (horiz)	1·90	1·10
3722	260p. Montesquiu Castle (horiz)	3·25	1·90

1089 Books forming Flower

2001. World Book Day.

3723	**1089**	40p. multicoloured	50	30

1090 Dornier Do-J Wal Flying Boat, *Plus Ultra* and Map of South America

2001. 75th Anniv of Spanish Aviation. Multicoloured.

3724	40p. Type **1090** (flight from Palos de Fontera, Spain to Buenos Aires, 1926)	50	50
3725	75p. Breguet 19A2 and map of Europe (flight by Gallariza and Loruga from Madrid to Manilla, 1926)	90	90
3726	155p. Dornier flying boat and map of Africa (flight from Melilla to Santa Isabel, Equatorial Guinea, 1926)	1·90	1·90
3727	260p. C-295 (transport) (commemorative flight)	3·25	3·25

Nos. 3724/7 were issued together, se-tenant, the backgrounds forming the composite design of a map.

1091 Decorated Ceiling and Emblem

2001. 154th Anniv of Liceu Theatre.

3728	**1091**	120p. multicoloured	1·50	80

1092 King Juan Carlos I

2001

3729		5p. red and silver	15	15
3730	**1092**	40p. green and silver	50	20
3731	**1092**	75p. violet and silver	90	35
3732		100p. brown and silver	1·20	40

Nos. 3733/49 are vacant.

1093 Garden

2001. Europa. Water Resources.

3750	**1093**	75p. multicoloured	1·20	1·00

1094 Church Facade (church of San Martino, Noia)

2001. Architecture.

3751	**1094**	40p. brown and blue	50	30
3752	-	75p. multicoloured	90	50
3753	-	155p. blue and brown	1·90	1·00

DESIGNS: 75p. Tui Cathedral, Pontevedra; 155p. Dovecote, Villaconcha, Frechilla.

1095 Peninsula, Marina and Bay

2001. Luarca.
3754 **1095** 40p. multicoloured 50 30

1096 De Castro (statue, Juan de Bologna) and School of Our Lady of Antigua

2001. 400th Death Anniv of Cardinal Rodrigo de Castro (Supreme Counsellor of The Inquisition).
3755 **1096** 40p. multicoloured 50 30

1097 Children and Calf (*Adios Corderia*, Leopoldo Alas ("Clarin"))

2001. Literature.
3756 **1097** 75p. multicoloured 90 50

2001. Trees (2nd series). As T 1067. Multicoloured.
3757 40p. Olive 50 30
3758 75p. Beech 90 50

1098 Emblem and Shield

2001. 25th Anniv of Copa del Rey Football Championship.
3759 **1098** 40p. multicoloured 50 30

1099 Hooded Dancer being pelted with Tomatoes, Zaragoza

2001. Festivals (2nd series). Multicoloured.
3760 40p. Type **1099** 50 30
3761 70p. Giants, Barcelona (vert) 1·50 85

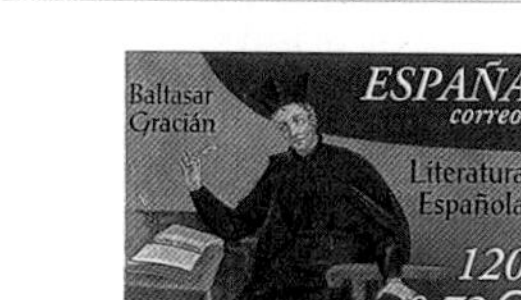

1100 Gracian

2001. 400th Birth Anniv of Baltasar Gracian (philosopher and writer).
3762 **1100** 120p. multicoloured 1·50 50

1101 Our Lady of Calva (statue), Zamora Cathedral

2001. "Ages of Man Exhibition", Zamora.
3763 **1101** 120p. mauve and red 1·50 85
3764 - 155p. red and black 1·90 1·10
DESIGN: 155p. Cupola and cathedral.

1102 Boy looking up (Grandmothers' Day)

2001. Social Activities. Multicoloured.
3765 40p. Type **1102** 50 30
3766 75p. Nun and building (Servants of Jesus for Charity (social relief organization)) 90 50

1103x View of City (image scaled to 68% of original size)

2001. Salamanca, European City of Culture, 2002.
3767 **1103** 75p. multicoloured 1·00 75

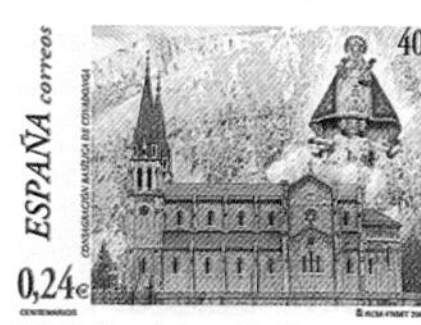

1104 Covadonga Basilica

2001. Centenary of Consecration of Basilica of Covadonga.
3768 **1104** 40p. multicoloured 50 30

1105 Emblem

2001. Formation of State Post and Telegraph Company.
3769 **1105** 40p. multicoloured 50 25

1106 View of Vigo

2001. "EXFILNA 2001" National Philatelic Exhibition, Vigo. Sheet 105×78 mm.
MS3770 **1106** 260p. ultramarine and deep ultramarine 3·25 3·25

1107 Musicians

2001. Birth Millenary of St. Dominic of Silos (Benedictine monk and abbot).
3771 **1107** 40p. multicoloured 50 30
MS3772 106×79 mm. No. 3771 6·50 6·50

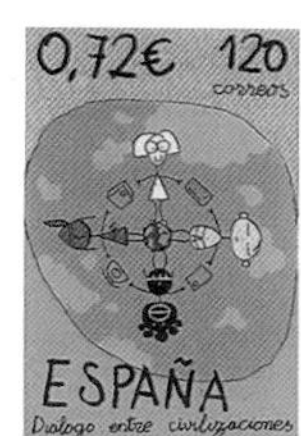

1108 Children encircling Globe

2001. United Nations Year of Dialogue among Civilizations.
3773 **1108** 120p. multicoloured 1·50 85

1109 Grasses, Ses Salines Nature Reserve

2001. America. UNESCO World Heritage Sites.
3774 **1109** 155p. multicoloured 1·90 1·10

2001. School Correspondence Programme. Spanish History (2nd series). As T 1073 but with currency inscribed in both euros and pesetas. Multicoloured.
3775 25p. Christopher Columbus juggling eggs (discovery of America, 1492) 35 30
3776 25p. Spanish and Portuguese boys each holding balloons showing maps (Treaty of Tordesillas, 1494) 35 30
3777 25p. King Carlos I of Spain (elected Emperor Charles V, 1519) 35 30
3778 25p. Hernan Cortes and Mexican musicians (conquest of Mexico, 1519) 35 30
3779 25p. Juan Sebastian Elcano (first circumnavigation of globe, 1522) 35 30
3780 25p. Inca city and bull on mountain (Francisco Pizarro's conquest of Peru, 1532) 35 30
3781 25p. King Felipe II with globe shaped as map of Spain (accession, 1556) 35 30
3782 25p. King Felipe II drawing plans (commencement of Monastery San Lorenzo de El Escorial, 1563) 35 30
3783 25p. Severed arm attacking Turk (Battle of Lepanto, 1571) 35 30
3784 25p. St John of the Cross, St. Teresa of Avila and El Greco being drawn up into spacecraft 35 30
3785 25p. Lope de Vega Carpio using his open skull as inkwell (Spanish playwright, died 1593) 35 30
3786 25p. King Felipe III surrounded by buckets collecting water (accession, 1598) 35 30

1110 Cape and Bull's Head

2001. Retirement of Francisco Romero Lopez (Curro Romero) (bullfighter).
MS3787 104×78 mm. **1110** 260p. multicoloured 3·25 3·25

1111 "Virgin and Child" (Alfredo Roldan)

2001. Christmas. Religious Paintings. Mult.
3788 40p. Type **1111** 50 30
3789 75p. "The Shepherd's Adoration" (Jusepe de Ribera) 95 50
MS3790 106×133 mm. Nos. 3788/9 together with Nos. 3082/3 of Germany 4·75 4·75

1112 Music Score

2001. 125th Birth Anniv of Manuel de Falla (composer).
3791 **1112** 75p. multicoloured 90 50

1113 Man driving Car

2001. 75th Birth Anniv of Josep Coll (cartoonist). Multicoloured.
3792 40p. Type **1113** 50 30
3793 75p. Man and dog 90 50

1114 Cano

2001. 55th Birth Anniv of Carlos Cano (singer).
3794 **1114** 40p. black 50 30

1115 Woman and Flowers

2001. International Volunteers' Day.
3795 **1115** 120p. multicoloured 1·50 85

1116 12th-century Church of San Climent, Taull (Lleida)

2001. UNESCO. World Heritage Sites. Multicoloured.
3796 40p. Type **1116** 50 40
3797 40p. El Misteri d'Elx (religious festival at Elche cathedral) 50 40
3798 40p. Sant Pau Hospital, Barcelona 50 40
3799 40p. Map of St. Cristobal, La Laguna 50 40
3800 40p. Archeological excavations, Atapuerca 50 40
3801 40p. Protected palm trees, Elche 50 40
3802 40p. La Foncalada (medieval monument), Oviedo 50 40
3803 40p. Roman walls, Lugo 50 40
3804 40p. Cave painting, Cueva de los Caballos, Albocacer, Castellon 50 40
3805 40p. Dalt Villa, Eivissa, Ibiza 50 40
3806 40p. Roman amphitheatre, Tarraco 50 40
3807 40p. Renaissance university building, Alcala de Henares 50 40

1117 Map and Postal Emblem (Postal Service)

2001. 150th Anniv of Ministry of Public Works.
3808 **1117** 40p. multicoloured 50 50
3809 - 75p. lilac, black and blue 90 90
3810 - 120p. blue, green and black 1·50 1·50
3811 - 155p. multicoloured 1·90 1·90
3812 - 260p. multicoloured 3·25 3·25
DESIGNS: Maps showing—75p. Ports; 120p. Railways; 155p. Airports; 260p. Motorways.

1118 Crown Prince Felipe de Borbon

2001. Silver Jubilee of King Juan Carlos I. Sheet 125×80 mm. containing T 1118 and similar multicoloured designs.

MS3813	40p. Type **1118**; 40p. Infanta Elena; 40p. Arms; 40p. Infanta Cristina; 75p. King Juan Carlos; 75p. Queen Sofia; 260p. Palace (49×28 mm)	7·75	7·75

1119 King Juan Carlos I

2002. King Juan Carlos I

3814	**1119**	1c. black and silver	15	15
3815	**1119**	2c. magenta and silver	15	15
3818	**1119**	5c. blue and silver	15	15
3823	**1119**	10c. green and silver	20	20
3826	**1119**	25c. red and silver	35	20
3827	**1119**	27c. blue and silver	50	20
3827a	**1119**	28c. yellow	55	25
3827aa	**1119**	29c. sepia and silver	55	20
3827b	**1119**	35c. orange	65	25
3827c	**1119**	40c. blue	60	20
3828	**1119**	50c. green and silver	95	25
3829	**1119**	52c. cinnamon and silver	1·00	25
3829a	**1119**	53c. purple	1·00	25
3829b	**1119**	57c. orange and silver	1·10	25
3830	**1119**	75c. purple and silver	1·40	30
3831	**1119**	77c. green and silver	1·60	30
3831a	**1119**	78c. rosine	1·50	30
3832	**1119**	€1 green and silver	1·90	40
3832a	**1119**	€1.95 ochre	3·75	80
3833	**1119**	€2 red and silver	3·75	55
3833a	**1119**	€2.21 bistre	4·25	1·20
3833b	**1119**	€2.26 lilac and silver	4·00	1·00
3833c	**1119**	€2.33 carmine and silver	4·50	1·30
3833d	**1119**	€2.39 green and silver	4·50	1·50
MS3834		100×87 mm. No. 3827 ×4	2·40	2·40

1120 Emblem

2002. Spanish Presidency of European Union.

3835	**1120**	25c. red, black and yellow	55	30
3836	**1120**	50c. red, yellow and black	1·10	50

1121 Sabina

2002. Trees (3rd series). Multicoloured.

3837	50c. Type **1121**	1·00	50
3838	75c. Elm	1·50	85

1122 Orchids

2002. Flowers.Depicting paintings by Eduardo Naranjo. Multicoloured. Self-adhesive.

3839	25c. Type **1122**	50	30
3840	25c. Gardenia in vase	50	30
3841	25c. Hands holding white rose	50	30
3842	25c. Iris	50	30
3843	25c. Two white orchid blooms	50	30
3844	25c. Pink-tinged rose in vase	50	30
3845	25c. Two pink orchid blooms	50	30
3846	25c. Three pink orchid blooms on one stem	50	30

1123 Emblem

2002. "Espana 2002" International Youth Stamp Exhibition, Salamanca (1st issue). Multicoloured.

3847	50c. Type **1123**	1·00	45
MS3848	80×105 mm. £1.80 Salamanca Cathedral	4·25	3·75

See also Nos. 2913/22.

1124 Father Francisco Piquer (founder)

2002. 300th Anniv of Caja Madrid Savings Bank.

3849	**1124**	25c. multicoloured	50	30

1125 Anniversary Emblem

2002. Centenary of Real Madrid Football Club.

3850	**1125**	75c. yellow and grey	1·50	95

1126 Town Hall Portico, Tarazona

2002. "PHILAIBERIA '02" Spanish-Portuguese Stamp Exhibition, Tarazona. Sheet 106×80 mm.

MS3851	€2.10 multicoloured	4·50	4·50

1127 Mon

2002. Birth Centenary (2001) of Alejandro Mon (politician).

3852	**1127**	25c. multicoloured	50	30

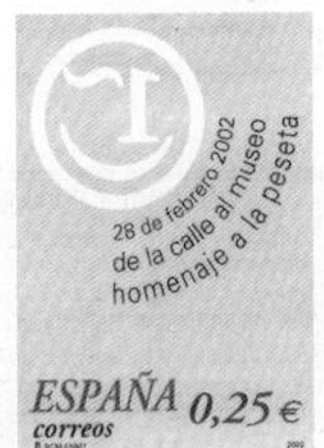

1128 Stylized Coin

2002. "Homage to the Peseta".

3853	**1128**	25c. multicoloured	50	35

1129 Canon do Sil, Ribeira Sacra

2002. Nature. Multicoloured.

3854	75c. Type **1129**	1·50	95
3855	€2.10 Cabo de Gata, Nijer Park, Almeria (horiz)	4·25	2·40

1130 Cadets on Parade, 1886

2002. 75th Anniv of Military Academy, Zaragoza.

3856	**1130**	25c. multicoloured	50	30

1131 Emblem

2002. Centenary of Real Union Irun Football Club.

3857	**1131**	50c. multicoloured	1·00	45

1132 Tweezers, Stamp and Magnifying Glass

2002. Stamp Day.

3858	**1132**	25c. multicoloured	50	30

1133 Banyeres de Mariola Castle, Alicante

2002. Castles.

3859	**1133**	25c. brown and blue	50	35
3860	-	50c. black	1·00	55
3861	-	75c. black	1·50	95

DESIGNS: 50c. Soutomaior Castle, Pontevedra; 75c. Calatorao Castle, Zaragoza.

1134 View across River

2002. Anniversaries. Multicoloured.

3862	75c. Type **1134** (1200th anniv of Tuleda)	1·50	95
3863	€1.80 View through pillars (millennium of St. Cugat Monastery)	3·75	1·90

1135 Luis Cernuda

2002. Birth Anniversaries. Multicoloured.

3864	50c. Type **1135** (poet, centenary)	1·00	50
3865	50c. Dr. Federico Rubio and nurses (175th anniv)	1·00	50

1136 Clown (Sara Blanco Quintas)

2002. Europa. The Circus.

3866	**1136**	50c. multicoloured	1·20	95

1137 Soldiers on Horseback

2002. Bicentenary of Inclusion of Menorca under Spanish Rule.

3867	**1137**	50c. multicoloured	1·00	50

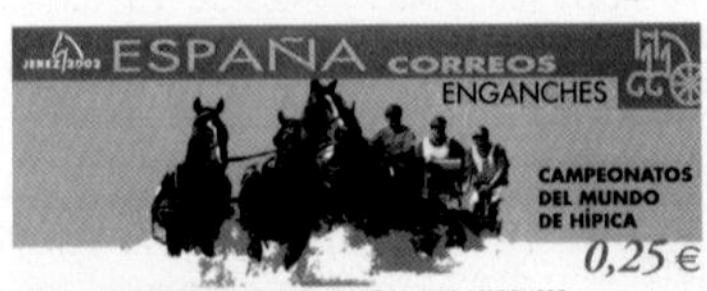

1138 Driving

2002. World Equestrian Games, Jerez. Mult.

3868	25c. Type **1138**	50	35
3869	25c. Hunting	50	35
3870	25c. Dressage	50	35
3871	25c. Reining	50	35
3872	25c. Acrobats	50	35
3873	75c. Racing	1·50	95
3874	€1.80 Show jumping	3·75	1·90

1139 Maria de las Dolores

2002. 108th Death Anniv of Maria "La Dolores" de las Dolores.

3875	**1139**	50c. multicoloured	1·00	50

1140 Plaza Mayor, Salamanca

2002. "EXFILNA 2002" National Stamp Exhibition, Salamanca. European City of Culture. Sheet 155×94 mm, containing T 1140 and similar horiz design. Multicoloured (€1.80) or orange and blue (others).

MS3876	25c. Type **1140**; 25c. Centre view of Plaza; 25c. Right side of Plaza; €1.80 Aerial view of Plaza	5·50	5·50

1141 Rohrbach R-VIII Aircraft, 1927

2002. 75th Anniv of IBERIA Airlines. Multicoloured.

3877	25c. Type **1141**	50	35
3878	50c. Boeing 747	1·00	55

1142 Grapes (Rias Baixas)

2002. Wine Regions (1st series).
3879 **1142** 25c. multicoloured 50 35

1143 Grapes and Glass of Red Wine (Rioja)

2002. Wine Regions (2nd series). Multicoloured.
3880 50c. Type **1143** 1·00 45
3881 75c. Grapes, wine bottle and glass of sherry (Manzanilla) 1·50 95

2002. School Correspondence Programme. Spanish History (3rd series). As T 1073 but with currency inscribed in euros. Multicoloured.
3882 10c. Man being knighted with pen (*Don Quixote* by Miguel de Cervantes) 25 20
3883 10c. Felipe IV and the Count-Duke of Olivares (accession, 1621) 25 20
3884 10c. Quevedo and Gongora pulling on rope of words (literary rivalry) 25 20
3885 10c. Velazquez (artist) sitting at easel 25 20
3886 10c. Carlos II and witch holding apple 25 20
3887 10c. Man rolling out carpet and Felipe V (start of War of the Spanish Succession) 25 20
3888 10c. Fernando VI (accession, 1746) 25 20
3889 10c. Carlos III holding architectural drawings (accession, 1759) 25 20
3890 10c. Bull and toreador (Riot of Esquilanche) 25 20
3891 10c. Book escaping from bird cage 25 20
3892 10c. Carlos IV (accession, 1788) and Napoleon 25 20
3893 10c. Manuel de Godoy (politician) and open door 25 20

1144 Temple Expiatori de la Sagrada Famíla, Barcelona

2002. 150th Birth Anniv of Antonio Gaudi (architect).
3894 **1144** 50c. blue and black 1·00 50

1145 Musicians

2002. Music. Designs depicting paintings by G. Dominguez. Multicoloured. Self-adhesive.
3895 25c. Type **1145** 50 30
3896 25c. Vase of flowers and lute 2·50 2·40
3897 25c. Woman holding lute 50 30
3898 25c. Flowers and open book of music 50 30
3899 25c. Vase of flowers, clock and violin 50 30
3900 25c. Man holding lute with woman 50 30
3901 25c. Flowers, violin, compass and sheet music 50 30
3902 25c. Woman wearing blue dress holding lute 50 30

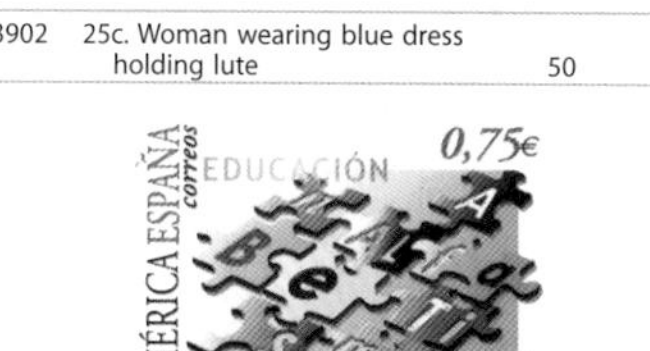

1146 Alphabet Jigsaw Puzzle

2002. America. Education and Literacy Campaign.
3903 **1146** 75c. multicoloured 1·50 95

1147 Cordoba Mosque and Silhouette of Almanzor

2002. Death Millenary of Abu Amir Muhammad al-Ma'afiri (Almanzor) (Arab ruler).
3904 **1147** 75c. multicoloured 1·50 95

1148 Basket

2002. Dijous Bo Fair, Inca, Mallorca.
3905 **1148** 75c. multicoloured 1·50 95

1149 Cupola, Aranjuez

2002. UNESCO. World Heritage Sites. Multicoloured.
3906 25c. Type **1149** 50 35
3907 25c. Santa Maria church, Calatayud, Aragon 50 35
3908 50c. San Martin church, Teruel, Aragon 1·00 55
3909 75c. Santa Maria church, Tobed, Aragon 1·50 1·10
3910 €1.80 Santa Tecla church, Cervera de la Canada, Aragon 3·75 2·00
3911 €2.10 San Pablo church, Zaragoza, Aragon 4·25 2·50

1150 Alcaniz (former Monastery of Calatrava)

2002. Paradores (state hotels).
3912 **1150** 25c. multicoloured 50 35

1151 Capitan Alatriste (Arturo Perez-Reverte)

2002. "Espana 2002" International Youth Stamp Exhibition, Salamanca (2nd issue). Multicoloured. (a) Self-adhesive gum.
3913 50c. As No. 3847 1·00 55
3914 75c. Type **1151** (comic strip character) 1·50 95
3915 75c. Television screen and emblem (television) 1·50 95
3916 75c. Hand and record (music) 1·50 95
3917 75c. Radio and music score (radio) 1·50 95
3918 75c. Cyclist, skier and football (sport) 1·50 95
3919 75c. Person holding camera (the press) 1·50 95
3920 75c. Film clapper board (film) 1·50 95
3921 €1.80 Salamanca Cathedral (vert) 3·75 2·30

(b) Ordinary gum.
MS3922 Seven sheets 79×106 mm (g) or 106×79 mm (others) (a) 75c. As No. 3920; (b) 75c. As 3915; (c) 75c. As 3919; (d) 75c. As 3917; (e) 75c. As 3918; (f) 75c. As 3916; (g) 75c. As 3914 Set of 7 sheets 12·50 12·50

1152 San Jorge Church, Alicante

2002
3923 **1152** 75c. multicoloured 1·50 95

1153 Cruceiro do Hio (crucifix) (Jose Cervino) Hio, Galicia

2002. Historical Monuments. Multicoloured.
3924 50c. Type **1153** 50 35
3925 50c. Herreria de Compludo (smithy), Leon (horiz) 1·00 50

1154 Mary (detail, stained glass window)

2002. 140th Anniv of St. Mary's Cathedral, Vitoria-Gasteiz. Sheet 106×79 mm.
MS3926 50c. multicoloured 1·00 95

1155 "Adoration of Kings" (Carlos Munoz de Pablos) (alterpiece, Calzadilla de Barros Church)

2002. Christmas. Multicoloured.
3927 25c. Type **1155** 50 30
3928 50c. "Maternity" (Goyo Dominguez) 1·00 50

1156 Somport Tunnel Entrance

2003. Spain–France Tunnel through Pyrenees.
3929 **1156** 51c. multicoloured 1·00 50

1157 Costumes from Anso (Huesca)

2003. Traditional Costumes.
3930 **1157** 76c. multicoloured 1·60 95

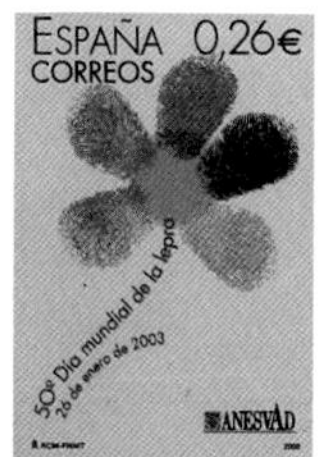

1158 Fingerprints forming Flower

2003. 50th World Leprosy Awareness Day.
3931 **1158** 26c. multicoloured 55 30

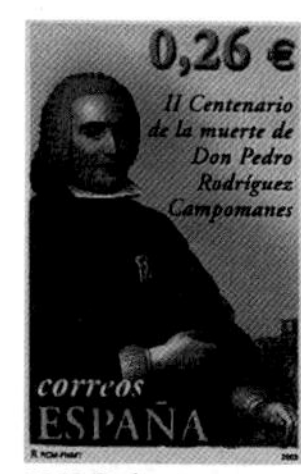

1159 Pedro Campomanes

2003. Death Bicentenary of Pedro Rodriguez Campomanes (statesman and writer).
3932 **1159** 26c. multicoloured 55 30

1160 Benissa Cathedral

2003. Juvenia 2003 National Youth Stamp, Benissa, Alicante.
3933 **1160** 51c. Multicoloured 1·00 50

1161 Praxedes Sagasta

2003. Death Centenary of Praxedes Mateo Sagasta (politician).
3934 **1161** 26c. brown and blue 55 30

1162 "ABC"

2003. Centenary of "ABC" (newspaper).
3935 **1162** €2.15 multicoloured 4·50 **2·20**

1163 Santiago Ramon y Cajal (1906)

2003. Nobel Prize Winners for Medicine. Multicoloured.
3936 51c. Type **1163** 1·00 50
3937 76c. Severo Ochoa (1959) 1·50 95

Stamps of the same design were issued by Sweden.

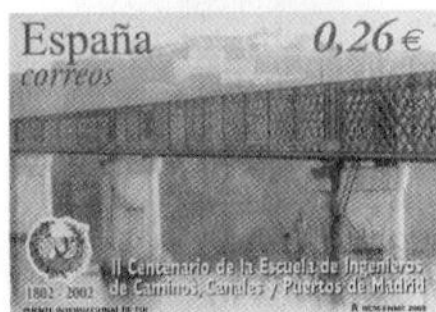

1164 Tui Bridge to Valenca do Minho (Portugal)

2003. Bicentenary of School of Civil Engineers, Madrid. Multicoloured.
3938 26c. Type **1164** 55 30
MS3939 106×78 mm. 26c. Type **1164**; 51c. Murcia valley; 76c. Gigon 3·50 3·25

1165 Anniversary Emblem

2003. Centenary of "La Laverdad" (Catholic newspaper).
3940 **1165** 26c. multicoloured 55 30

1166 "La Hoz de Priego"

2003. Paintings. Designs depicting paintings by Chico Montilla. Multicoloured. Self-adhesive.
3941 26c. Type **1166** 55 30
3942 26c. "Fields of Gold" 55 30
3943 26c. "Los Tornos Gorge" 55 30
3944 26c. "Armilla Countryside" 55 30
3945 26c. "Nenufar" 55 30
3946 26c. "What Colour is the Wind?" 55 30
3947 51c. "Pastrana Countryside" 1·00 50
3948 76c. "Early Flowers" 1·60 90

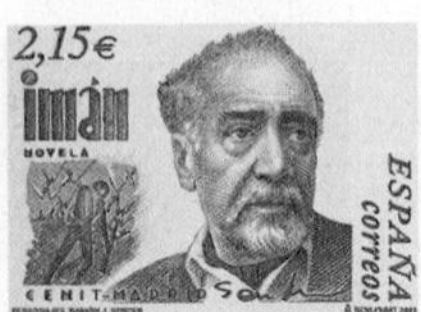

1167 Ramon Sender and Book Cover

2003. Ramon Jose Sender (writer) Commemoration.
3949 **1167** €2.15 brown, yellow and deep brown 4·50 1·90

1168 Blackboard and Pupil

2003. Rural Schools.
3950 **1168** 26c. multicoloured 55 30

1169 Pillar Capital, Lron Patio, Alhambra, Granada

2003. Exfilna 2003 National Stamp Exhibition, Granada. Sheet 79×106 mm.
MS3951 **1169** €2.15 brown and green 4·50 4·50

1170 Valdecarzana Palace, Aviles, Asturias

2003. Avilés Villa Millenary.
3952 **1170** 51c. multicoloured 1·00 50

1171 Anniversary Emblem

2003. Stamp Day. 25th Anniv of Spanish Philatelic Academy.
3953 **1171** €1.85 multicoloured 3·75 1·30

1172 Toy Cars (Jimenez Carrero)

2003. Europa. Poster Art.
3954 **1172** 76c. multicoloured 1·80 1·30

1173 Centenary Emblem

2003. Centenary of Athletic Club of Madrid.
3955 **1173** 26c. red and blue 55 30

1174 Roman Amphitheatre, Zaragoza

2003
3956 **1174** €1.85 multicoloured 3·75 1·30

1175 Map of Europe, Faces and Wheelchair User

2003. European Year of the Disabled.
3957 **1175** 76c. multicoloured 1·60 80
No. 3957 has "correos" written in Braille across it.

1176 San Felipe Castle, Ferrol, Coruna

2003. Castles.
3958 **1176** 26c. maroon and blue 55 30
3959 - 51c. brown and green 1·00 55
3960 - 76c. orange and black 1·50 80
DESIGNS: 21c. Type **1176**; 51c. Cuellar Castle, Segovia; 76c. Montilla Castle, Cordoba (500th Anniv of Battles of Cerinola and Garellano).

1177 Swimmer

2003. Barcelona '03 International Swimming Championship. Multicoloured.
3961 26c. Type **1177** 55 30
3962 51c. Diver 1·00 50

MS3963 115×106 mm. 26c. Type **1177**; 51c. No. 3962; 76c. Synchronised swimmers; €1.85 Freestyle swimmer; €2.15 Water polo 12·50 12·50

1178 Max Aub

2003. Birth Centenary of Max Aub (writer).
3964 **1178** 76c. black and red 1·60 85

1179 Football and Club Emblem

2003. Centenary of Centre D'Esports Sabadell Football Club.
3965 **1179** 76c. multicoloured 1·60 85

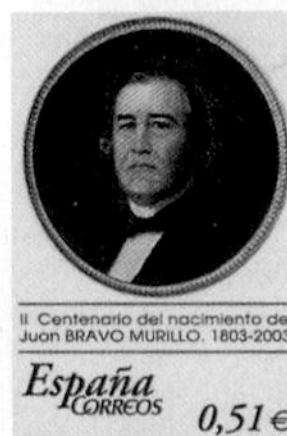

1180 Juan Murillo

2003. Birth Bicentenary of Juan Bravo Murillo (politician).
3966 **1180** 51c. multicoloured 1·30 75

1181 Newspaper Vendor

2003. 135th Anniv of "Diario de Cadiz" Newspaper.
3967 **1181** 26c. multicoloured 55 30

1182 Dodge Dart Barreiros (1967)

2003. Centenary of Royal Automobile Club (RACE). Sheet 106×80 mm containing T 1182 and similar horiz designs. Multicoloured.
MS3968 26c. Type **1182**; 51c.Seat 600 (1967–73); 76c. Hispano Suiza 20/30 HP (1907); €1.85 Pegaso Z102 Touring Berlinetta (1953) 7·25 7·25

1183 5c. Chile Stamp of 1853

2003. 150th Anniv of First Chilean Stamp.
3969 **1183** 76c. brown and black 1·60 85

1184 "El Diario Montanes"

2003. Centenary of "El Diario Montanes" Newspaper.
3970 **1184** 26c. multicoloured 55 30

1185 Santa Catalina Castle

2003. Paradores (state hotels).
3971 **1185** 25c. multicoloured 1·40 85

1186 Front Page

2003. Centenary of "Diario de Navarra" Newspaper.
3972 **1186** 26c. multicoloured 55 30

1187 Doorway

2003. 800th Anniv of Seu Vella Old Cathedral, Lleida, Segria.
3973 **1187** €1.85 sepia, violet and brown 4·00 1·90

1188 Stylized Hat and Newspaper

2003. 120th Anniv of "El Adelanto de Salamanca" Newspaper.
3974 **1188** 26c. multicoloured 55 30

1189 Woman attaching Flowers to Hat

2003. Paintings. No value expressed. Designs depicting portraits of women and flowers by Alfredo Roldan. Multicoloured. Self-adhesive.
3975 A (26c.) Type **1189** 55 30
3976 A (26c.) With bouquet 55 30
3977 A (26c.) Stood behind lilies 55 30
3978 A (26c.) With raised arms arranging flowers in hair 55 30
3979 A (26c.) Wearing flowers in hair 55 30
3980 A (26c.) Woman lying with fruit and flowers 55 30
3981 A (26c.) Wearing dark dress putting flowers in hair 55 30
3982 A (26c.) With vase of flowers 55 30

1190 Building Interior, Ferrol

2003. 25th Anniv of "El Correo Gallego" Newspaper.

3983	**1190**	26c. multicoloured	55	30

1191 Masthead

2003. 125th Anniv of "El Comercio" Newspaper.

3984	**1191**	26c. multicoloured	55	30

1192 Reliquary, Chapel of La Vera Cruz

2003. Granting of Perpetual Jubilee to Caravaca de la Cruz.

3985	**1192**	76c. multicoloured	1·60	65

1193 49er Dinghy, Map and Statue

2003. ISAF World Sailing Championship, Cadiz.

3986	**1193**	76c. multicoloured	1·60	65

1194 Wine Glass (Penedes)

2003. Wine. Multicoloured.

3987	26c. Type **1194**	55	30
3988	51c. Angel holding wine dipper (Montilla-Moriles)	1·00	55
3989	76c. Grapes and hands holding wine glass (Valdepenas)	1·60	85
3990	$1.85 Bottles (Bierzo)	3·75	1·90

1195 College Building and Emblem

2003. Bicentenary of Military Engineering College, Madrid.

3991	**1195**	51c. multicoloured	4·25	2·10

1196 Stained Glass Window (detail)

2003. 700th Anniv of Leon Cathedral. Sheet 105×78 mm.

MS3992	**1196**	76c. multicoloured	1·60	1·60

1197 Society Emblem and Map (detail)

2003. Centenary of Real Geographic Society. Sheet 105×78 mm.

MS3993	**1197**	€1.85 multicoloured	4·00	4·00

1198 *Ficus Macrophylla*

2003. Trees (4th issue). Multicoloured.

3994	26c. Type **1198**	55	30
3995	51c. Pedunculate oak (*Quercus robur*)	1·00	55

1199 College Building

2003. 75th Anniv of Aircraft Engineering Technical College, Madrid.

3996	**1199**	51c. multicoloured	1·00	55

1200 Type 1-2-0 Engine Madrilena (1851)

2003. America. Railways.

3997	**1200**	76c. multicoloured	1·60	85

1201 "El Virjo y el Pajaro"

2003. 93rd Birth Anniv of Luis Seoane (artist).

3998	**1201**	€1.85 multicoloured	4·00	1·90

1202 "La Voz de Galicia"

2003. Newspaper Anniversaries.

3999	**1202**	26c. red and black	55	30
4000	-	26c. red, orange and black	55	30
4001	-	26c. multicoloured	55	30

DESIGNS: Type **1202** (120th anniv (2002); "El Correo de Andalucia" (centenary (1999)); "Faro de Vigo" (150th anniv).

1203 Camilo Jose Cela

2003. 1st Death Anniv of Camilo Jose Cela Trulock (writer (winner of 1989 Nobel Prize for Literature)).

4002	**1203**	26c. multicoloured	55	30

1204 Donkey and Child (Los Reyes Magos festival, Alcoy)

2003. Christmas. Multicoloured.

4003	26c. Type **1204**	55	25
4004	51c. "Christmas" (Raquel Farinas)	1·00	55

1205 Exhibition Emblem

2003. Espana 2004 International Stamp Exhibition, Valencia. Multicoloured.

4005	76c. Type **1205**	1·60	85
MS4006	78×106 mm. €1.85 City of Arts and Sciences Building, Valencia	4·75	4·25

1206 Organos de Montoro, Teruel Mountains

2003

4007	**1206**	51c. multicoloured	1·00	55

1207 Geological Map

2003. New National Geological Survey. Sheet 106×79 mm.

MS4008	**1207**	26c. multicoloured	55	55

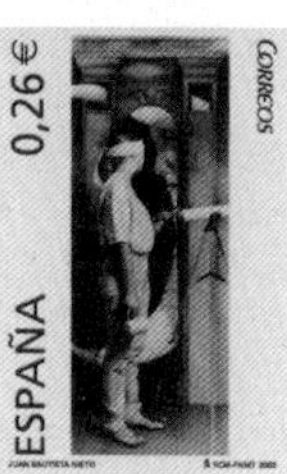

1208 Blindfolded Woman

2003. 25th Anniv of Constitution. Ten sheets, each 78×105 mm containing T 1208 and similar multicoloured designs.

MS4009	(a) 26c. Type **1208** (Juan Bautista Nieto) (judicial power); (b) 26c. Dove and doors (J. Carrero) (general courts); (c) 26c. Ship (Araceli Alarcon) (state territorial organization) (horiz); (d) 26c. Families (R. Seco) (economy and property) (horiz); (e) 26c. King Juan Carlos (horiz); (f) 26c. Boy writing (fundamental rights and duties) (horiz); (g) 26c. Woman and bird (Goyo Dominguez) (relations between government and courts); (h) 26c. Flower and window (Galicia) (constitutional reform) (horiz); (i) 26c. Scales containing child and couple (J. Carrero) (Constitutional Court) (horiz); (j) 26c. Seated woman holding Arms (Fesanpe) (government and administration) (horiz)	6·25	6·25

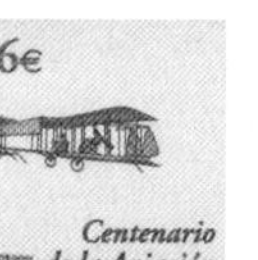

1209 Control Tower, Four Winds Aerodrome, Madrid and Wright *Flyer*

2003. Centenary of Powered Flight.

4010	**1209**	76c. brown and blue	1·60	85

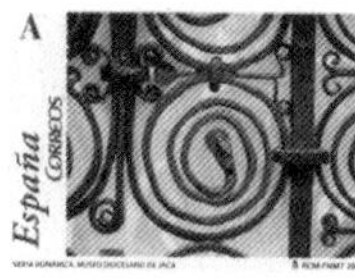

1210 Ironwork, Santa Maria de Iguacel, Jaca

2004. Romanic Architecture, Aragon. No value expressed. Multicoloured. Self-adhesive.

4011	A (26c.) Type **1210**	55	30
4012	A (26c.) Bible (detail), Huesca	55	30
4013	A (26c.) Apostles (fresco)	55	30
4014	A (26c.) Cloister, San Juan Bautista de Ruesta	55	30
4015	A (26c.) Jacobean dinars	55	30
4016	A (26c.) Column capital, La Iglesia de Santiago	55	30
4017	A (26c.) Sarcophagus of Dona Sancha	55	30
4018	A (26c.) Crucifix, Jaca Cathedral	55	30

1211 Woman Reading whilst Boating

2004. Women and Reading. Two sheets, each 106×79 mm containing T 1211 and similar horiz designs showing women reading. Multicoloured.

MS4019	(a) 27c. Type **1211**; 52c. With head resting in hand; 77c. Reading newspaper; (b) 27c. Lying facing left; 52c. Lying facing right; 77c. Looking over top of book Set of 2 sheets	6·75	6·75

1212 Hand and Damaged Leaf

2004. 50th (2003) Anniv of Spanish Cancer Association.

4020	**1212**	27c. multicoloured	55	30

1213 "La Terrona" (oak tree), Zarza de Montánchez

2004. Trees (5th series).

4021	**1213**	52c. multicoloured	1·00	50

1214 Stylized Canoe

2004. World Rowing Championship, Banyoles.
4022 **1214** 77c. multicoloured 1·60 85

1215 Woman standing on Cliff

2004. School Correspondence Programme. Trazo y Tiza (graphic novel by Miguelanxo Prado). Sheet 183×145 mm containing T 1215 and similar horiz designs. Multicoloured.
MS4023 27c. × 4, Type **1215**; Yacht and lighthouse; Seagull, yacht, lighthouse and woman; Lighthouse 2·40 2·40

1216 Stairs and Arches

2004. Saint Maria de Carracedo Monastery. Sheet 80×105 mm.
MS4024 **1216** €1.90 multicoloured 4·00 4·00

1217 Emblem

2004. 36th Chess Olympiad, Calvia, Mallorca.
4025 **1217** 77c. multicoloured 1·60 85

1218 19th-century Bronze Clock (La Almudaina Palace, Palma De Mallorca)

2004. Cultural Heritage. Clocks. Sheet 106×151 mm containing T 1218 and similar vert designs. Each brown, blue and gold.
MS4026 27c. Type **1218**; 52c. 18th-century bronze (La Granja Palace, Segovia); 77c. 19th-century bronze clock (La Granja Palace, Segovia); €1.90 18th-century bronze clock (El Pardo Palace, Madrid) 7·00 7·00

1219 Newspaper Vendor (statue)

2004. Centenary (2001) of "Diario de Burgos" Newspaper.
4027 **1219** 27c. multicoloured 60 35

1220 Ribbon

2004. European Day (11 March) for Victims of Terrorism.
(a) Ordinary gum.
4028 **1220** 27c. black 60 35

(b) No value expressed. Self-adhesive gum.
4029 A (27c.) black 60 30

1221 Eggs

2004. Painted Eggs Festival.
4030 **1221** 27c. multicoloured 60 35

1222 Floral Shawl and Shell

2004. Shawls. Sheet 80×105 mm containing T 1222 and similar vert designs showing details of paintings by Soledad Fernandez. Multicoloured.
MS4031 27c. Type **1222**; 52c. Hands across dark shawl; 77c. Gladioli and part of shawl; €1.90 Shawl draped over chair 7·00 7·00

1223 Saint Domingo de la Calzada

2004. 150th Anniv of Public Technical Engineering Works.
4032 **1223** 52c. multicoloured 1·00 50

1224 Cable Ingles Bridge, Almeria

2004. Centenary of Cable Ingles Bridge, Almeria.
4033 **1224** 52c. multicoloured 1·00 50

1225 Historical Buildings (Sagrada Familia, Barcelona, Antoni Gaudi's Church, Fuente de Cibeles, Madrid, Giralda and Torre del Oro, Seville) and Parasols on Beach

2004. Europa. Holidays.
4034 **1225** 77c. multicoloured 1·80 1·30

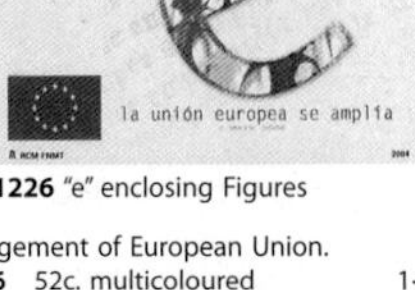

1226 "e" enclosing Figures

2004. Enlargement of European Union.
4035 **1226** 52c. multicoloured 1·10 60

1227 "Self Portrait with Neck of Raphael"

2004. Birth Centenary of Salvador Dali (artist).
4036 **1227** 77c. multicoloured 1·60 85

1228 "100" containing Football and FIFA Emblem

2004. Centenary of FIFA (Federation Internationale de Football Association).
4037 **1228** 77c. multicoloured 1·60 85

1229 Bourbon Royal Arms

2004. Wedding of Crown Prince Felipe de Bourbon and Letizia Ortiz.
4038 **1229** 27c. multicoloured 60 40

1230 Vincente Martin y Soler

2004. Espana 2004 International Stamp Exhibition, Madrid (1st issue). 350th Birth Anniv of Vincente Martin y Soler (musician).
4039 27c. Type **1230** 60 35
4040 52c. Saxophone and drum 1·10 65

See also Nos. **MS**4041, 4042/3, **MS**4044 and 4045/6.

1231 Crown Prince Felipe and Princess Letizia

2004. Espana 2004 International Stamp Exhibition, Madrid (2nd issue). The Royal Family. Sheet 151×86 mm containing T 1231 and similar horiz designs.
MS4041 27c. multicoloured; 77c. multicoloured; €6 blue and deep blue 14·00 14·00
DESIGNS: 27c. Type **1231**; 77c. Prince Felipe; €6 King Juan Carlos and Queen Sophia.

1232 Entry of the Bulls

2004. Espana 2004 International Stamp Exhibition, Madrid (3rd issue). Festivals.
4042 27c. Type **1232** 60 35
4043 52c. Lance taurino (bullfighter's cape pass) 1·60 85

1233 Tennis Player (image scaled to 56% of original size)

2004. Espana 2004 International Stamp Exhibition, Madrid (4th issue). Sport. Sheet 232×86 mm containing T 1233 and similar horiz designs.
MS4044 35c. Type **1233**; 52c. Ricardo Tormo (motorcyclist) and Valencia circuit; €1.90 Golf course 5·75 5·75

1234 *Bravo Espana* (yacht)

2004. Espana 2004 International Stamp Exhibition (5th issue), Valencia.
4045 27c. Type **1234** 1·00 55
4046 52c. Architectural heritage 1·60 95

1235 Newsboy and Masthead

2004. 214th Anniv of "Diario de Valencia" Newspaper.
4047 **1235** 27c. multicoloured 60 35

1236 Portico de la Gloria and Nave, Santiago Cathedral

2004. Xacobeo 2004 Holy Year (St. James jubilee year).
4048 **1236** 52c. multicoloured 1·00 50

1237 Lerma (former Ducal palace)

2004. Paradores (state hotels).
4049 **1237** 52c. multicoloured 1·00 50

1238 Aguas Mansas, Agoncillo

2004. Castles.
4050 - 27c. orange and red 60 30
4051 **1238** 52c. brown 1·10 45
4052 - 77c. green 1·60 1·10
4053 - €1.90 black (vert) 4·00 1·90
DESIGNS: 27c. Granadilla Castle, Caceres; 52c. Type **1238**; 77c. Mota, Alcala la Real, Jaen; €1.90 Villafuerte de Esgueva, Valladolid.

1239 Danforth Anchor

2004. Salinas Anchor Museum, Castrillon, Asturias.
4054 **1239** €1.90 multicoloured 3·75 2·10

1240 Pot with Handles and Lid

2004. Paintings. Designs depicting paintings of ceramics by Antonio Miguel Gonzalez. Multicoloured. Self-adhesive.

4055	A (27c.) Type **1240**	60	30
4056	A (27c.) Tall pot with handles, wide-necked pot and pot containing brushes	60	30
4057	A (27c.) Pot with central handle, bread and figs	60	30
4058	A (27c.) Pot with long neck and decorated body	60	30
4059	A (27c.) Broken bread, onions, tall pot and pentagon	60	30
4060	A (27c.) Decorated vase	60	30
4061	A (27c.) Fruit and jug	60	30
4062	A (27c.) Decorated storage jar	60	30

1241 Building Facade

2004. Centenary of the Circulo Oscense Building, Huesca.
4063 **1241** 52c. multicoloured 1·00 50

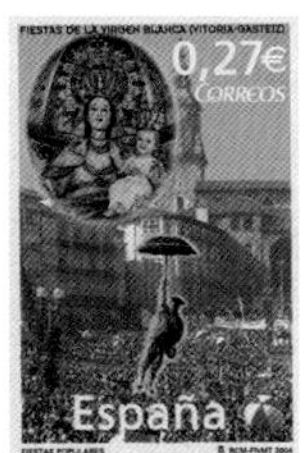
1242 Virgin and Celebrating Crowds

2004. White Virgin Festival, Vitoria-Gasteiz.
4064 **1242** 27c. multicoloured 60 35

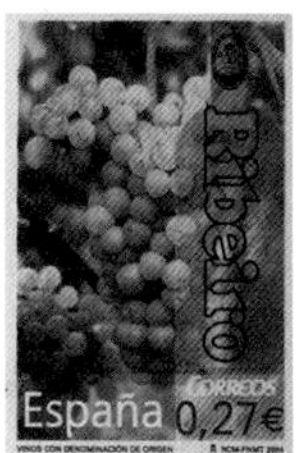
1243 Grapes and Bottle (Ribeiro)

2004. Wine. Multicoloured.

4065	27c. Type **1243**	60	30
4066	52c. Glass and bottle (Malaga)	1·10	50

1244 1854 Philippine Stamp and Postmark

2004. 150th Anniv of First Philippine Stamp.
4067 **1244** 77c. multicoloured 1·60 85

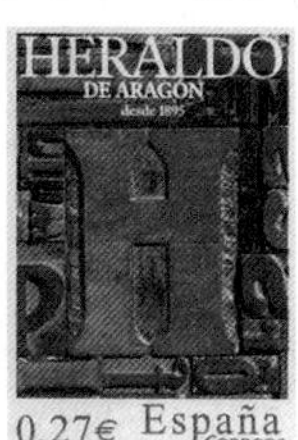
1245 Mural (detail)

2004. 109th Anniv of "Heraldo de Aragon" Newspaper.
4068 **1245** 27c. multicoloured 60 35

1246 Jorge Juan (sailor and scientist)

2004. 250th Anniv of Nautical Astronomy.
4069 **1246** €1.90 multicoloured 4·00 1·90

1247 Columbus Monument

2004. Exfilna 2004 National Stamp Exhibition, Valladolid. Sheet 78×106 mm.
MS4070 **1247** €1.90 brown and green 4·25 4·25

1248 Parc Guell, Barcelona

2004. Urban Architecture. Multicoloured.

4071	52c. Type **1248**	1·10	50
4072	77c. Jinmao Tower, Shanghai	1·60	85

Stamps of the same design were issued by China.

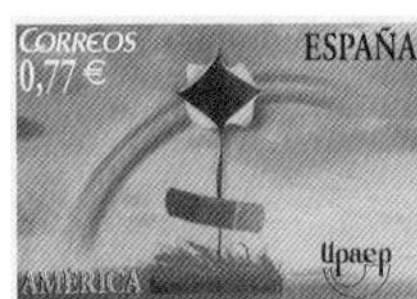
1249 Rainbow, Torn Sky and Fire (J. Carrero)

2004. America. Environmental Protection.
4073 **1249** 77c. multicoloured 1·60 85

1250 Accelerator

2004. 50th Anniv of European Organization for Nuclear Research (CERN).
4074 **1250** €1.90 multicoloured 4·00 1·90

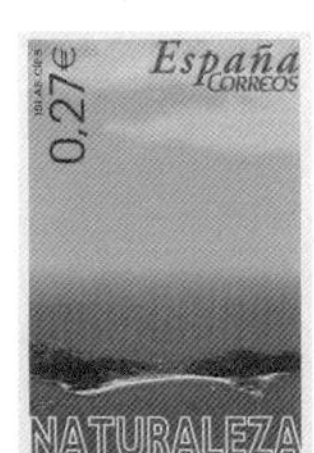
1251 Cies Archipelago

2004. Nature. Multicoloured.

4075	27c. Type **1251**	60	30
4076	52c. Ebro Delta National Park (horiz)	1·10	50
4077	77c. La Palm National Park (horiz)	1·60	85

1252 Letter

2004. Stamp Day. 400th Anniv of First Registered Letter.
4078 **1252** 77c. multicoloured 1·60 85

1253 Observatory

2004. Centenary of Erbe Observatory.
4079 **1253** €1.90 multicoloured 3·75 1·90

1254 Alfonso I (statue) (Jose Bueno)

2004. 900th Anniv of Coronation of Alfonso I (king of Aragon and Navarre).
4080 **1254** €1.90 multicoloured 3·75 1·90

1255 The Nativity (18th-century)

2004. Christmas. Multicoloured.

4081	27c. Type **1255**	60	30
4082	52c. The Nativity (Juan Manuel Cossio)	1·10	60

1256 Queen Isabel and Castle

2004. 500th Death Anniv of Queen Isabel the Catholic.
4083 **1256** €2.19 multicoloured 4·50 2·20

1257 Ship leaving Port

2004. 200th Anniv of Royal Expedition to take Anti-Smallpox Vaccine to America and Asia.
4084 **1257** 77c. brown 1·60 85

1258 Santiago el Mayor (stained glass window)

2004. Toledo Cathedral. Sheet 105×79 mm.
MS4085 **1258** €1.90 multicoloured 4·25 4·25

1259 Jugglers at Rest

2005. Circus. Designs depicting paintings by Manola Elices. Self-adhesive. Multicoloured.

4086	A (28c.) Type **1259**	55	35
4087	A (28c.) Performing dogs	55	35
4088	A (28c.) Unicyclist and juggler	55	35
4089	A (28c.) Balancing act	55	35
4090	A (28c.) Women with hoops	55	35
4091	A (28c.) Tightrope walker	55	35
4092	A (28c.) Two women and man balancing	55	35
4093	A (28c.) Fire-eating	55	35

Nos. 4086/93 were for standard mail within Spain weighing up to 20grams.

1260 Emblem

2005. European Constitution.
4094 **1260** 28c. multicoloured 55 35

1261 Ahuehuete Tree, Retiro Park, Madrid

2005. Trees (6th series).
4095 **1261** 78c. multicoloured 1·50 85

1262 Stylized Car and Pedestrians

2005. Civic Responsibility. Multicoloured.

4096	28c. Type **1262** (road safety campaign)	55	35
4097	53c. Stylized blood transfusion (blood donation campaign)	1·00	60

1263 Seville University

2005. Anniversaries.
4098 **1263** 28c. brown and lake 55 35

4099 - 28c. ochre, lake and green 55 35

DESIGNS: Type **1263** (500th anniv); No. 4099 Frontispiece *Royal Pharmacopoeia* (400th anniv of publication).

1264 Woman watering Flowers ("Al levanter una lancha")

2005. Children's Songs. Paintings by Raquel Farinas. Sheet 144×124 mm containing T 1264 and similar vert designs. Multicoloured.

MS4100 28c. Type **1264**; 28c. "Aqui te espero"; 28c. "Estaba la pajara pinta"; 53c. "Cuatro esquinitas"; 53c. "El patio de mi casa"; 53c. "Pero mira como beben"; 78c. "Los pollitos cantan"; 78c. "Para entraer en clase" 7·75 7·75

1265 Belfry, Sant Esteve Church, Tordera

2005. Juvenia 2005 National Youth Stamp Exhibition, Tordera.

4101 **1265** 28c. multicoloured 55 35

1266 Emblem

2005. Centenary of Seville Football Club.

4102 **1266** 35c. carmine 65 40

1267 Footballer

2005. Centenary of Real Sporting de Gijon Football Club.

4103 **1267** 40c. multicoloured 75 45

1268 Emblem

2005. 15th Mediterranean Games, Almería.

4104 **1268** 78c. multicoloured 1·50 85

1269 Ham, Bread and Wine

2005. Europa. Gastronomy.

4105 **1269** 53c. multicoloured 1·10 55

1270 Juan Valera

2005. Death Centenary of Juan Valera (writer).

4106 **1270** €2.21 chocolate and blue 4·25 2·50

1271 Don Quixote and Sancho Panza

2005. 400th Anniv of Publication of "El Ingenioso Hidalgo Don Quixote de la Mancha" (novel) by Miguel de Cervantes. Sheet 80×107 mm containing T 1271 and similar vert designs. Each black.

MS4107 28c. Type **1271**; 53c. Tilting at windmill; 78c. With sheep; €2.21 In cage 7·25 7·25

1272 Telegraph Machine

2005. 150th Anniv of Telegraph System.

4108 **1272** 28c. multicoloured 55 35

1273 Emblem and "$E=mc^2$"

2005. International Year of Physics. Self-adhesive.

4109 **1273** 28c. multicoloured 55 35

1274 Fan (image scaled to 72% of original size)

2005. National Heritage. Fans. Sheet 164×92 mm containing T 1274 and similar triangular designs. Multicoloured.

MS4110 28c. Type **1274**; 53c. 18th-century Madrid; 78c. Nymphs and cherubs 3·25 3·25

1275 "Diario Palentino"

2005. Newspaper Anniversaries. Multicoloured.

4111 78c. Type **1275** (120th anniv (2001)) 1·50 85

4112 €1.95 "Ultima Hora" (110th anniv (2003)) (horiz) 3·75 2·00

4113 €2.21 "Diario de Ibiza" (110th anniv (2003)) (horiz) 4·25 2·50

1276 Oropesa (former palace)

2005. Paradores (state hotels).

4114 **1276** €1.95 chocolate 3·75 2·20

1277 Santa Barbara Castle, Alicante

2005. Exfilna 2005 National Stamp Exhibition, Alicante. Sheet 80×107 mm.

MS4115 **1277** €2.21 multicoloured 4·25 4·25

1278 Alcaudete Castle, Jaen

2005. Castles.

4116 **1278** 78c. black 1·50 85

4117 - €1.95 brown and green 3·75 2·00

4118 - €2.21 black 4·25 2·50

DESIGNS: 78c. Type **1278**; €1.95 Valderrobres, Teruel; €2.21 Molina de Aragon, Guadalajara.

1279 Baby and Fingerprint

2005. 76th Anniv of Spanish Interpol.

4119 **1279** 28c. multicoloured 55 35

1280 Postal Delivery

2005. Stamp Day. Self-adhesive.

4120 **1280** 28c. multicoloured 55 35

1281 Our Lady of Asuncion Church, Pont de Suert

2005

4121 **1281** 28c. multicoloured 55 35

1282 Lunnispark

2005. For Children. Los Lunnis (children's television programme). Self-adhesive. Multicoloured.

4122 28c. Type **1282** 55 35

4123 28c. Lucho 55 35

4124 28c. Lunnispark (green house) 55 35

4125 28c. Lulila 55 35

4126 28c. Lupita 55 35

4127 28c. Lupita in bed 55 35

4128 28c. Lublu 55 35

4129 28c. Lunnispark (orange house) 55 35

1283 Championship Emblem

2005. World Cycling Championship, Madrid.

4130 **1283** 78c. multicoloured 1·50 85

1284 Emblem

2005. Espana 2006 International Stamp Exhibition, Malaga.

4131 **1284** 53c. black, blue and orange 1·00 60

1285 La Granja de San Ildefonso Garden, Segovia

2005. Gardens. Multicoloured.

4132 78c. Type **1285** 1·50 85

4133 €2.21 Bagh-e-Shahzadeh, Kerman 4·25 2·50

Stamps of a similar design were issued by Iran.

1286 Salamanca University

2005. IberoAmerican Summit Conference, Salamanca.

4134 **1286** 78c. multicoloured 1·50 85

1287 Hands

2005. America. Struggle against Poverty.

4135 **1287** 78c. multicoloured 1·50 85

1288 Foundation Emblem and Trophy

2005. 25th Anniv of Prince of Asturias Awards.

4136 **1288** 28c. multicoloured 55 30

1289 Arms and Town Hall, La Orotava (500th anniv)

2005. Anniversaries. Multicoloured.

4137 €2.21 Type **1289** 4·25 2·50
4138 €2.21 Envelope and stamp (150th anniv of Cuba and Puerto Rico post) (horiz) 4·25 2·50

1290 Diver

2005. For the Young. Al filo de lo Imposible (On the edge of Impossible (television programme)) Sheet 145×164 mm containing T 1290 and similar vert designs (1st issue). Multicoloured.

MS4139 28c.×6, Type **1290**; Ballooning; Traversing polar ice; White water canoeing; Mountaineering; Rock climbing 3·25 3·25

The stamps of No. **MS**4139 are arranged amongst stamp size labels to construct composite designs of six scenes from the programme.

See also No. **MS**4159.

1291 "Adoration of the Kings" (Francisco Ribalta)

2005. Christmas. Multicoloured.

4140 28c. Type **1291** 60 35
4141 53c. Three kings 1·10 60

1292 St. Paul (stained glass window)

2005. Avila Cathedral. Sheet 78×105 mm.

MS4142 **1292** €2.21 multicoloured 4·75 4·75

1293 Barcelona

2005. Euromediterranean (Euromed) Summit, Barcelona.

4143 **1293** 53c. multicoloured 1·00 60

1294 Juana I of Castille

2005. 500th Anniv of Parliament of Toro.

4144 **1294** 28c. multicoloured 55 35

1295 Puppets

2006. Toys. Self-adhesive. Multicoloured.

4145 A Type **1295** 55 40
4146 A Spinning tops 55 40
4147 A Car 55 40
4148 A Lorry 55 40
4149 A Doll 55 40
4150 A Marbles 55 40
4151 A Horse and cart 55 40
4152 A Motorcycle 55 40

Nos. 4145/52 were for use on letters up to 20 grams within Spain.

1296 Dianthus

2006. Flora and Fauna (1st issue). Self-adhesive.

4153 **1296** 28c. multicoloured 55 30

See also No. 4156, 4187/8 and 4207/8.

1297 Building Facade

2006. 150th Anniv of National Bank.

4154 **1297** 78c. chestnut and black 1·50 1·20

1298 "La Anunciada" Cypress, Villafranca del Bierzo, Léon

2006. Trees (7th series).

4155 **1298** 53c. multicoloured 1·00 80

1299 Sparrow

2006. Flora and Fauna (2nd issue). Self-adhesive.

4156 **1299** A multicoloured 55 45

No. 4156 was for use on letters up to 20 grams.

1300 Desert overlaying Green Hills

2006. International Day against Desertification.

4157 **1300** 29c. multicoloured 55 45

1301 Women voting

2006. 75th Anniv of Votes for Women.

4158 **1301** 29c. brown and blue 55 35

2006. For the Young. "Al filo de lo Imposible" (On the Edge of Impossible (television programme)) (2nd issue). Sheet 145×164 mm containing vert designs as T 1290. Multicoloured.

MS4159 29c. Cycling; 38c. Traversing sand dunes; 41c. Paragliding; 57c. Sea canoeing; 78c. White water rafting; £2.39 Abseiling waterfall 9·25 7·25

The stamps of No. **MS**4159 are arranged amongst stamp size labels to construct composite designs of six scenes from the programme.

1302 Goldfinch

2006. Flora and Fauna. Multicoloured. Self-adhesive.

4160 29c. Type **1302** 55 40
4161 38c. Strelitzia flower 75 60

1303 Stylized Figure and Tap (water conservation campaign)

2006. Civic Responsibility. Multicoloured.

4162 29c. Type **1303** 55 35
4163 29c. Figure holding balloons ("Say no to Drugs" campaign) 55 35
4164 38c. Workers and factories (centenary of Social Security and Labour Inspectorate) (horiz) 75 45
4165 57c. Legs (Campaign against people trafficking) (horiz) 1·10 65

1304 "Diario de Leon" (centenary)

2006. Newspapers' Anniversaries.

4166 **1304** 41c. multicoloured 80 45
4167 - 41c. multicoloured 80 45
4168 - 41c. multicoloured 80 45
4169 - 41c. scarlet and black 80 45
4170 - 41c. multicoloured 80 45

DESIGNS: Type **1304**; "Diario de Pontevedra" (115th (2003) anniv) (horiz); "Levante-El Mercantil Valenciano" (135th (2007) anniv) (horiz); "El Norte de Castilla" (150th anniv); Diario de Avila (120th (2008) anniv).

1305 Christopher Columbus

2006. 500th Death Anniv of Christopher Columbus. Sheet 105×78 mm.

MS4171 **1305** £2.39 multicoloured 4·50 4·50

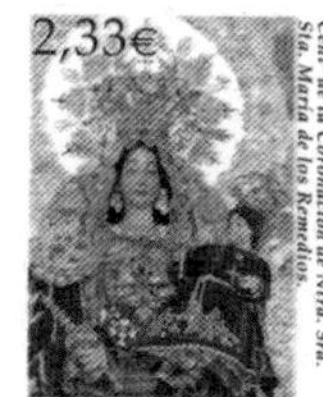

1306 Santa Maria de los Remedios

2006. Centenary of Coronation of Santa Maria de los Remedios.

4172 **1306** £2.33 multicoloured 4·50 2·75

1307 City Council Building Facade

2006. Exfilna 2006 National Stamp Exhibition. Sheet 106×78 mm.

MS4173 **1307** £2.39 multicoloured 4·50 4·50

1308 Horseman

2006. 500th Anniv of the Tasso Family (postal service suppliers) in Spain.

4174 **1308** 29c. multicoloured 55 35

1309 Emblem

2006. Science. Internet Day (29c.) and International Mathematicians' Congress, Madrid (57c.). Multicoloured. Self-adhesive.

4175 29c. Type **1309** 45 35
4176 57c. Emblem and numerals (vert) 1·10 60

1310 Faces and Star

2006. Centenary of Socialist Youth Organization.

4177 **1310** 78c. multicoloured 1·50 80

1311 Posy as Parasol

2006. Espana 2006 International Stamp Exhibition, Malaga. Sheet 78×105 mm.

MS4178	**1311**	78c. multicoloured	1·50	1·50

1313 Casa Batllo, Barcelona

2006. Architecture.

4180	**1313**	29c. grey	55	35
4181	-	38c. green	75	50
4182	-	41c. multicoloured	80	50
4183	-	57c. brown	1·10	70
4184	-	78c. multicoloured	1·50	80
4185	-	£2.33 multicoloured	4·50	2·50

DESIGNS: 29c. Type **1313**; 38c. Vapor Aymerich, Terrassa; 41c. Depósitos del Sol Library, Albacete; 57c. Campos Eliseos Theatre, Bilbao; 78c. Alfredo Kraus auditorium, Las Palmas de Gran Canaria (horiz); £2.33 Bus Station, Casar de Caceres (horiz).

1314 Faces and Star

2006. Abu Abdallah Mohamed Ben Idrisi (Al Idrisi) (geographer and cartographer) Commemoration.

4186	**1314**	78c. multicoloured	1·50	80

2006. Flora and Fauna (3rd issue). As T 1296. Multicoloured. Self-adhesive.

4187	29c. Greenfinch	55	25
4188	41c. Iris	80	35

1315 Walls, Los Millares

2006. Archaeology. Multicoloured.

4189	29c. Type **1315**	55	35
4190	57c. Fresco, L'Alcudia (horiz)	1·10	60
4191	78c. Guerrer de Moixent (3rd–4th century Iberian statue)	1·50	80

1316 Horses and Riders

2006. Festivals. Carreras de Caballos de Sanuucar de Barrameda (horse race).

4192	**1316**	£2.33 multicoloured	4·50	2·75

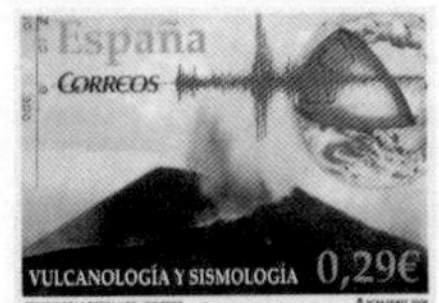

1317 Teneguia Volcano erupting and Seismograph (vulcanology)

2006. Earth and Universe Sciences. Multicoloured.

4193	29c. Type **1317**	55	35
4194	29c. Magnifier and map (cartography)	55	35

1318 Anniversary Emblem

2006. Anniversaries.

4195	**1318**	38c. light blue and blue (700th anniv)	†	†
4196	-	38c. multicoloured (centenary)	†	†

DESIGNS: 4195, Type **1318**; 4196, Aqueduct.

1319 13th-century Capital, Misericordia Convent, Palma and Shrine of the Book, Jerusalem

2006. 20th Anniv of Spain–Israel Diplomatic Relations.

4197	**1319**	78c. multicoloured	1·50	85

1320 Banos de la Encina Castle, Jaen

2006. Castles.

4198	**1320**	29c. black	55	35
4199	-	£2.39 brown and blue	4·50	3·00

DESIGNS: 29c. Type **1320**; £2.39 Torroella de Montgri castle, Girona.

1321 Hand and Braille Numerals

2006. Europa. Integration.

4200	29c. Type **1321**	55	35
4201	57c. Hands	1·10	60

1322 Peunte Internacional de Ayamonte (image scaled to 66% of original size)

2006. Bridges. Multicoloured.

4202	29c. Type **1322**	55	45
4203	57c. Peunte de Alcantara	1·10	85

Stamps of similar design were issued by Portugal.

1323 Grape Treading

2006. 50th Anniv of Rioja Wine Harvest Festival.

4204	**1323**	29c. multicoloured	55	35

1324 Emblem

2006. Centenary of Real Club Deportivo de La Coruna.

4205	**1324**	57c. ultramarine and blue	1·10	60

1325 Hand, Ball and Hoop

2006. Spain–2006 World Basketball Champions. Sheet 107×80 mm.

MS4206	**1325**	29c. multicoloured	55	55

1326 Swallow

2006. Flora and Fauna (4th issue). Multicoloured. Self-adhesive.

4207	29c. Type **1326**	55	45
4208	29c. Poinsettia	55	45

1327 "Victorio & Luchino"

2006. Espana 2006 International Stamp Exhibition, Malaga. Seven sheets, each 105×78 mm containing T 1327 and similar designs.

MS4209 (a) £2.33 red, orange and black; (b) £2.33 multicoloured; (c) £2.33 multicoloured; (d) £2.33 multicoloured; (e) £2.33 multicoloured; (f) £2.33 multicoloured; (g) £2.33 multicoloured 31·00 31·00

DESIGNS: **MS**4209a Type **1327** (fashion); **MS**4209b Hat, "Alfredo Landa" "Concha Velasco" and "Belen Rueda" (cinema) (vert); **MS**4209c Music annotation and "El canto del loco" (music); **MS**4209d Stylized guitarist, "Ana Belen" "Victor Manuel" and "Miguel Rios" (music) (vert); **MS**4209e Hand, "Cristina Hoyos" and "José Merce" (flamenco); **MS**4209f Ball, "Pau Gasol" and "Rafael Nadal" (sport) (vert); **MS**4209g Pablo Picasso (art). A different miniature sheet was issued on each day of the exhibition.

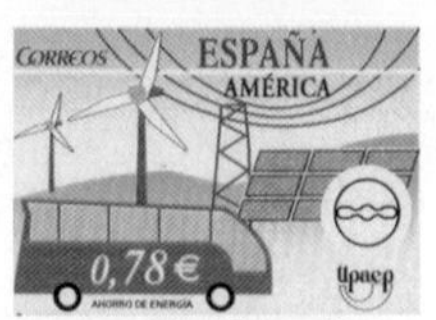

1328 Symbols of Energy Use

2006. America. Energy Conservation.

4210	**1328**	78c. multicoloured	1·50	80

1329 Stylized Early and Modern Postmen

2006. 250th Anniv of First Postman. Self-adhesive.

4211	**1329**	29c. multicoloured	55	35

1330 Ramon Rubal

2006. Birth Centenary of Ramon Rubal (politician).

4212	**1330**	57c. black and vermilion	1·10	70

1331 "Adoracion de los Pastores" (sculpture), Cuenca Cathedral

2006. Christmas. Multicoloured.

4213	29c. Type **1331**	55	35
4214	57c. "Entranable Navidad" (painting) (Belén Elorrieta) (vert)	1·10	60

1332 Construction (stained glass window)

2006. Higher Architecture School of Madrid. Sheet 106×80 mm.

MS4215	**1332**	£2.39 multicoloured	4·50	4·50

1333 Francis Xavier

2006. 500th Birth Anniv of Saint Francis Xavier.

4216	**1333**	29c. multicoloured	55	35

1334 Symbols of Television

2006. 50th Anniv of Spanish Television.

4217	**1334**	29c. multicoloured	55	35

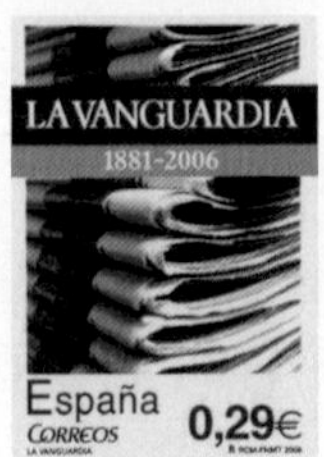

1335 Piles of Newspaper

2006. 125th Anniv of La Vanguardia Newspaper.

4218	**1335**	29c. multicoloured	55	35

1336 Pio Baroja

2006. 50th Death Anniv of Pio Baroja (writer).

4219	**1336**	29c. multicoloured	55	35

1337 Arms

2006. 25th Anniv of Arms of Spain.

4220	**1337**	29c. multicoloured	55	35

1338 Dove and Flag

2006. International Year of Historical Memory.

4221	**1338**	29c. vermilion and lemon	55	35
4222	-	29c. multicoloured	55	35

DESIGNS: 4221, Type **1338**; 4222, Adult and child.

1339 Early Tricycle

2007. Toys. Multicoloured. Self-adhesive.

4223	A (30c.) Type **1339**		55	45
4224	A (30c.) Bus		55	45
4225	A (30c.) Train		55	45
4226	A (30c.) Skittles		55	45
4227	A (30c.) Wooden pram		55	45
4228	A (30c.) Aeroplane		55	45
4229	A (30c.) Printing set		55	45
4230	A (30c.) Fire truck		55	45

Nos. 4223/30 were for standard mail within Spain weighing up to 20 grams.

1340 Hoopoe

2007. Flora and Fauna. Multicoloured. Self-adhesive.

4231	30c. Type **1340**	55	45
4232	39c. Rose	75	60

1341 Teacher and Pupils

2007. Teacher Awareness. Self-adhesive.

4233	**1341**	58c. multicoloured	1·10	85

1342 Masthead

2007. 140th Anniv (2006) of La Provincias Newspaper.

4234	**1342**	42c. multicoloured	80	65

1343 Stylized Table of Elements

2007. Science. Multicoloured. Self-adhesive.

4235	30c. Type **1343** (birth centenary of Dimtri Mendeleyiev (first classification))	55	45
4236	42c. Astrolabe (425th anniv of Gregorian calendar) (vert)	80	65

1344 Emblem and Courtyard

2007. Centenary of Institut d'Estudis Catalans (Institute of Catalan Studies).

4237	**1344**	30c. multicoloured	55	45

1345 Yacht

2007. Desafio Espanol 2007 (Spanish entry in 32nd America's Cup Challenge Yacht Race, Valencia).

4238	**1345**	30c. multicoloured	55	45

1346 Map

2007. Earth and Universe Sciences. Multicoloured. Self-adhesive.

4239	30c. Type **1346** (basic cartography)	55	45
4240	78c. Radio telescope (Astronomy centre, Yebes)	1·50	1·20

See also Nos. 4193/4.

Nos. 4241 and Type **1347** have been left for 'Tree' issued on 5 March 2007, not yet received.

1348 Mosaic, Roman Villa, La Olmeda

2007. Archaeology. Multicoloured.

4242	30c. Type **1348**	55	45
4243	30c. Roman baths, Campo Valdes	55	45

1349 Map of Europe

2007. 50th Anniv of Treaty of Rome.

4244	**1349**	58c. multicoloured	1·30	85

1350 Canary

2007. Flora and Fauna. Multicoloured. Self-adhesive.

4245	30c. Type **1350**	55	45
4246	42c. Violet	80	65

1351 'Movida Madrilena'

2007. 25th Anniv of Movida Madrilena (Madrid movement). Sheet 79×106 mm.

MS4247	**1351**	30c. multicoloured	1·10	1·10

1352 Palma Cathedral

2007. EXFILNA 2007 National Philatelic Exhibition, Palma. Sheet 79×106 mm.

MS4248	**1352**	€2.43 blue	4·75	4·75

1353 Emblem and Doves

2007. Europa. Centenary of Scouting.

4249	**1353**	58c. multicoloured	1·10	85

1354 Chapel of Valleaceron, Almadenejos

2007. Architecture.

4250	**1354**	30c. multicoloured	55	45
4251	-	39c. red	75	60
4252	-	42c. multicoloured	80	65
4253	-	58c. multicoloured	1·10	85
4254	-	78c. black	1·50	1·20
4255	-	€2.49 multicoloured	4·75	3·50

DESIGNS: 30c. Type **1354**; 39c. El Capricho, Comilla; 42c. Santa Caterina market; 58c. Vizcaya Bridge, Las Arenas (horiz); 78c. Terminal 4, Barajas Airport, Madrid; €2.49 Casa Lis Museum, Salamanca (horiz).

1355 Calahorra

2007. JUVENIA 2007 Youth Stamp Exhibition, Calahorra.

4256	**1355**	30c. multicoloured	55	45

1356 Stylized Figures and Stamp

2007. Stamp Day. Spanish Philatelic Associations. Self-adhesive.

4257	**1356**	30c. multicoloured	55	45

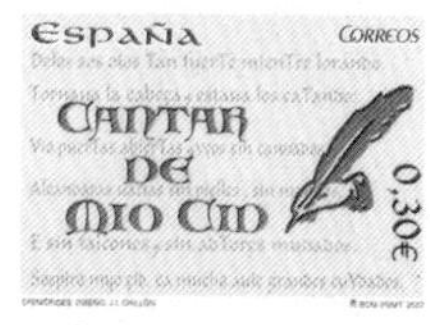

1357 Script

2007. 800th Anniv of Cantar de Mio Cid (epic poem). Self-adhesive.

4258	**1357**	30c. multicoloured	55	45

1358 Court of Auditors Building

2007. 25th Anniv of Court of Auditors.

4259	**1358**	30c. multicoloured	55	45

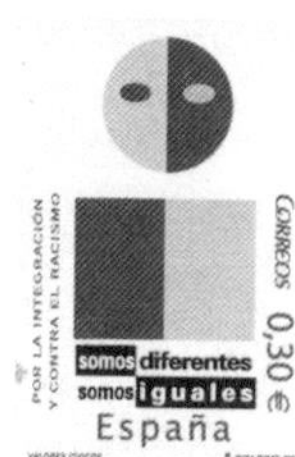

1359 'somos differntes somos iguales' (we are different we are the same)

2007. Civic Values. Multicoloured.

4260	30c. Type **1359**	55	45
4261	39c. Stylized students and open book (we are all classmates, against school violence)	75	60
4262	58c. Stylized couple (organ donation)	1·10	85
4263	78c. Multicoloured figure (sexual equality)	1·50	1·20

1360 *Tricholoma equestre*

2007. Fungi. Multicoloured.

4264	30c. Type **1360**	55	45
4265	78c. *Amanita muscaria*	1·50	1·20

1361 Carmen Conde (birth centenary)

2007. Women Writers.

4266	**1361**	€2.49 black and vermilion	4·75	3·50
4267	-	€2.49 black and salmon	4·75	3·50

DESIGNS: 4266, Type **1361**; 4267, Rosa Chacal (birth centenary) (1998).

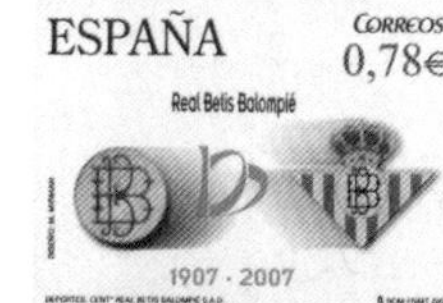

1362 Emblem and Colours

2007. Centenary of Real Betis Balompie Football Club.

4268	**1362**	78c. multicoloured	1·50	1·20

1363 Virgin Mary (wooden sculpture by Antonio Castillo Lastrucci)

2007. Coronation of Maria Santisima de la O, Triana, Seville.

4269	**1363**	30c. multicoloured	55	45

España

1364 Nightingale

2007. Flora and Fauna. Multicoloured. Self-adhesive.

4270	30c. Type **1364**	55	45

4271 30c. Hyacinth 55 45

1365 Soldiers and Globe (image scaled to 65% of original size)

2007. Armed Forces Peace Missions.
4272 **1365** 30c. multicoloured 55 50

1366 Expo Emblem and Fluvi (Expo mascot)

2007. Expo 2008, Zaragoza. International Warter and Substainable Development Exhibition (1st issue). Self-adhesive.
4273 **1366** 58c. multicoloured 85 60
See also Nos. 4337, **MS**4370 and **MS** 4373.

2007. For the Young. Al filo de lo Imposible (On the edge of Impossible) (television programme) (3rd issue). Sheet 145×164 mm containing vert designs as T 1290. Multicoloured.
MS4274 30c. Antarctic diving; 39c. Traversing mountain approach; 42c. Crossing snowfield with sleds; 58c. On board *Le Sourire*; 78c. Canoeing; €2.43 With dog sled during Iditarod race, Alaska 9·50 7·50
The stamps of No. **MS**4274 are arranged amongst stamp size labels to construct composite designs of six scenes from the programme.

1367 Dehesa de Saler, L'Albufera Park

2007. Parks. Multicoloured.
4275 30c. Type **1367** 55 45
4276 30c. Waterfall, Las Lagunas de Ruidera 55 45

1368 Punta del Hidalgo Lighthouse, Tenerife

2007. Lighthouses. Sheet 116×106 mm containing T 1368 and similar vert designs showing lighthouses. Multicoloured.
MS4277 30c. Type **1368**; 39c. Cabo Mayor, Cantabria; 42c. Punta Almina, Ceuta; 58c. Melilla; 78c. Cabo de Palos, Murcia; €2.43 Gorliz, Vizcaya 9·25 9·25

1369 Almenar Castle, Soria

2007. Castles.
4278 **1369** €2.49 agate and green 4·75 3·50
4279 - €2.49 black and green 4·75 3·50
DESIGNS: No. 4278, Type **1369**; No. 4279, Villena Castle, Alicante.

1370 Dupont's Lark

2007. Flora and Fauna. Multicoloured. Self-adhesive.
4280 30c. Type **1370** 55 45
4281 30c. Daisy 55 45

1371 Masthead

2007. Centenary (1901) of El Adelanto de Segovia.
4282 **1371** 78c. multicoloured 1·50 1·20

1372 'education para todos'

2007. America. Education for All.
4283 **1372** 78c. multicoloured 1·50 1·20

1373 Ivory Chantilly Lace over Taffeta, Empire Line Dress (1948–50)

2007. Fashion. Cristobal Balenciaga (designer). Sheet 105×150 mm containing T 1373 and similar vert designs showing his designs. Multicoloured.
MS4284 39c.Type **1373**; 42c. Red embroidered jacket and long dress (1960); 58c. Red coat and dress (c.1960); 78c.Yellow linen button through dress with belt 4·25 4·25

1374 'The Nativity' (sculpture) (Damian Forment)

2007. Christmas. Multicoloured. Self-adhesive.
4285 30c. Type **1374** 55 45
4286 58c. Children in envelope 1·10 85

1375 *Self Portrait* (Pedro Berruguete)

2007. Art. Multicoloured.
4287 39c. Type **1375** 75 60
4288 42c. *Self Portrait* (Mariano Salvador Maella) 80 65

1376 Construction (stained glass window)

2007. Operations Courtyard of the Bank of Spain. Sheet 106×80 mm.
MS4289 **1376** €2.43 multicoloured 4·75 4·75

1377 King Juan Carlos

2008. King Juan Carlos I

No.	Type	Description	Unused	Used
4290	**1377**	1c. black and orange	15	15
4291	**1377**	2c. magenta and orange	15	15
4292	**1377**	5c. blue and orange	15	15
4293	**1377**	10c. green and orange	20	20
4293a	**1377**	30c. blue and pale orange (P 13×13½)	1·00	1·00
4294	**1377**	31c. brown and orange	60	40
4294a	**1377**	32c. scarlet and orange	65	40
4294b	**1377**	34c. blue and pale orange (P 13×13½)	2·00	2·00
4294ba		34c. violet and pale orange (P 13×13½)	2·00	2·00
4294c		45c. yellow-olive and pale orange (P 13×13½)	2·10	2·10
4294d		58c. dull yellow-green and pale orange (P 13×13½)		
4295	**1377**	60c. ultramarine and orange	1·10	70
4295a	**1377**	62c. slate and orange	1·20	80
4295b		64c. olive-bistre and pale orange (P 13×13½)	1·50	1·50
4296	**1377**	78c. carmine and orange (P 13×13½)	1·50	95
4296a		80c. emerald and pale orange (P 13×13½)	1·50	1·50
4296b		€2.43 Indian red and pale orange	3·75	3·75
4296c	**1377**	€2.47 yellow-olive and orange	4·75	3·00
4296d		€2.49 bright purple and pale orange (P 13×13½)	4·75	3·00
4297	**1377**	€2.60 deep dull green and pale orange	5·00	3·00
4298	**1377**	€2.70 ultramarine and pale orange	5·25	3·50
4299		€2.75 deep purple and pale orange (P 13×13½)	5·25	3·75
4300		€2.84 deep blue and pale orange (P 13×13½)	5·25	3·00

Numbers have been left for additions to this series.

1378 Ship

2008. Toys. Multicoloured. Self-adhesive.
4320 A (30c.) Type **1378** 60 45
4321 A (30c.) Clown shaped ball catcher 60 45
4322 A (30c.) Buckets for bean bag catch 60 45
4323 A (30c.) Stage coach 60 45
4324 A (30c.) Barquillero (rolled wafer container) 60 45
4325 A (30c.) Diablo 60 45
4326 A (30c.) Architecture bricks 60 45
4327 A (30c.) Submarine 60 45
Nos. 4320/7 were for use on standard mail within Spain weighing up to 20 grams.

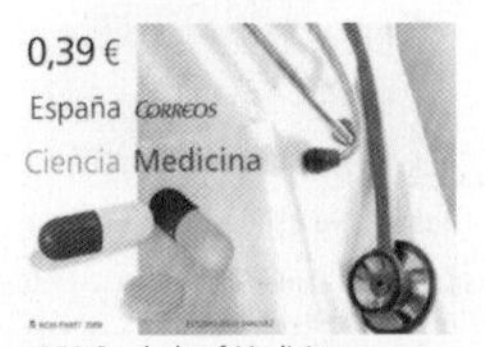

1379 Green Woodpecker

2008. Flora and Fauna. Multicoloured. Self-adhesive.
4328 31c. Type **1379** 60 45
4329 60c. Camellia 1·10 85

1380 Symbols of Medicine

2008. Science. Multicoloured. Self-adhesive.
4330 39c. Type **1380** 75 60
4331 43c. Symbols of meteorology 85 65

1381 Masthead

2008. Centenary of La Voz de Aviles.
4332 **1381** 31c. multicoloured 60 45

1382 Globe

2008. Science. Multicoloured. Self-adhesive.
4333 78c. Type **1382** (International Polar Year) 1·50 1·20
4334 €2.60 Leaves growing from rock (International Year of Planet Earth) 5·00 3·75

1383 Hand and '016' (help line telephone number)

2008. Stop Violence against Women Campaign. Self-adhesive.
4335 **1383** 31c. multicoloured 60 45

1384 Black Poplar, Horcajjuelo (Alamo negro de Horajuelo)

2008. Trees (9th series).
4336 **1384** €2.44 multcoloured 4·75 3·50

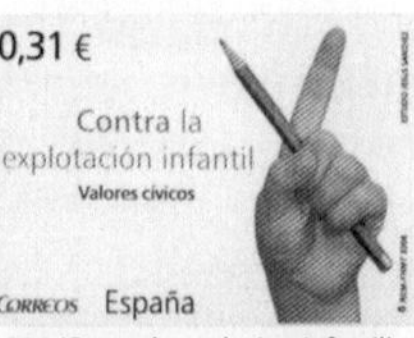

1385 Pabellon Puente and Torre del Agua (bridge pavillion and water tower), Zaragoza

2008. Zaragoza 2008 International Water and Sustainable Development Exhibition (2nd issue). Self- adhesive.
4337 **1385** 31c. multicoloured 60 45

1386 'Contra la explocion infantil' (fight against child exploitation)

2008. Civic Values. Multicoloured.
4338 31c. Type **1386** 60 45
4339 39c. Two hands (intergenerational solidarity) 75 60
4340 43c. Multicoloured fingers (cultural diversity) 80 65

1387 Bicha of Balzote (6th century BC sculpture)

2008. Archaeology. Multicoloured.
4341 31c. Type **1387** 60 45
4342 31c. Apep I funerary vase ('Vaso cinerario Apofis I') 60 45

1388 Toledo Mountains

2008. Nature. Multicoloured.
4343 31c. Type **1388** 60 45
4344 31c. Hoces del Rio Duration park 60 45

1389 Helicopters and Boats

2008. Maritime Rescue.
4345 **1389** 31c. multicoloured 60 45

1390 University Building

2008. 400th Anniv of Oviedo University.
4346 **1390** 31c. multicoloured 60 45

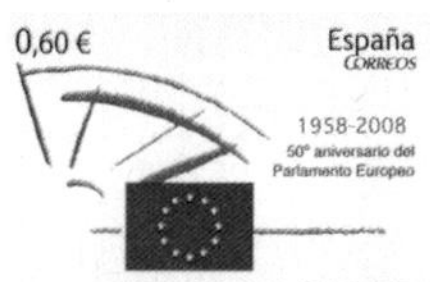

1391 Emblem

2008. 50th Anniv of European Parliament.
4347 **1391** 60c. multicoloured 1·10 85

1392 Palacio de Longoria, Madrid (Josep Grases Riera)

2008. Architecture.
4348 31c. deep brown 60 45
4349 31c. reddish brown 60 45
4350 31c. multicoloured 60 45
4351 31c. multicoloured 60 45
4352 31c. multicoloured 60 45
4353 31c. multicoloured 60 45

DESIGNS: 4348 Type **1392**; 4349 Casa Vicens, Barcelona (Antoni Gaudí) (vert); 4350 Auditorio de Tenerife (Tenerife Auditorium) (Santiago Calatrava); 4351 Torre Agbar, Barcelona (Agbar Tower) (Jean Nouvel) (vert); 4352 Torrespana (television tower) (28×74 mm); 4353 Torre de Comunicaciones de Montjuic, Barcelona (Montjuic Comunications Tower) (Santiago Calatrava) (28×74 mm).

1393 Kestrel

2008. Flora and Fauna. Multicoloured. Self-adhesive.
4354 31c. Type **1393** 60 45
4355 43c. Tulip 85 65

1394 Pelota Valencia

2008. Traditional Sports. Multicoloured.
4356 43c. Type **1394** 85 65
4357 43c. Pelota Vasca (Basque) (vert) 85 65

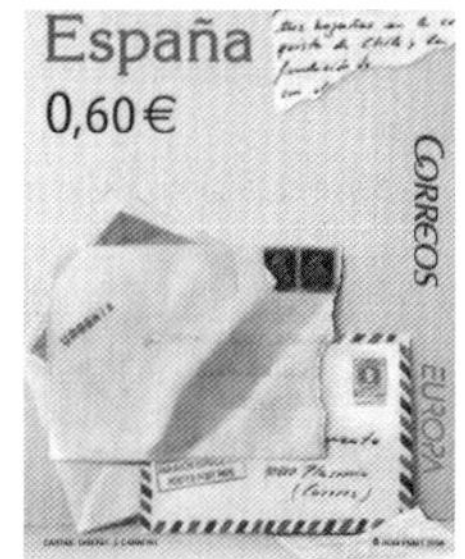

1395 Envelopes

2008. Europa. The Letter. Sheet 80×105 mm.
MS4358 **1395** 60c. multicoloured 1·10 1·10

1396 Cross of Victory, Oviedo Cathedral

2008. Exfilna 2008 Philatelic Exhibition. Sheet 80×105 mm.
MS4359 **1396** €2.44 multicoloured 4·75 4·75

1397 Arms from Maritime Post Royal Decree

2008. Stamp Day. Self-adhesive.
4360 **1397** 39c. brown, blue and black 75 60

1398 'El Progreso' and Tree (painting by Garcia Gesto)

2008. Centenary of El Progreso Newspaper.
4361 **1398** 31c. multicoloured 60 45

2008. Traditional Sports. Vert designs as T 1394. Multicoloured.
4362 43c. Levantamiento de Piedras (stone lifting) 85 65
4363 43c. Tira con Honda (sling shot) 85 65
4364 43c. Lanzamiento de Barra (pitching the bar) 85 65

1399 Joan Oro

2008. Personalities.
4365 31c. black 55 45
4366 31c. black and vermilion 55 45
4367 31c. black and vermilion 55 45
4368 31c. black and vermilion 55 45

DESIGNS: 4365, Type **1399** (biochemist); 4366, Maria Lejarraga (Maria Martinez Sierra) (writer) (horiz); 4367, Carmen Martin Gaite (writer) (horiz); 4368, Zenobia Camprubi (writer and translator).

1400 Goya Monument, Zaragoza

2008. Zaragoza 2008 International Water and Sustainable Development Exhibition (3rd issue). Sheet 105×80 mm.
MS4370 **1400** €2.60 green 5·00 5·00

1401 European Bee-eater

2008. Flora and Fauna. Multicoloured. Self-adhesive.
4371 31c. Type **1401** 60 45
4372 60c. Dahlia 1·10 80

1402 Water Plaza

2008. Zaragoza 2008 International Water and Sustainable Development Exhibition (4th issue). Sheet 106×80 mm containing T 1402 and similar horiz designs. Multicoloured.
MS4373 31c. Type **1402**; 78c. Exhibition compound; €2.60 Pabellon-Puente 7·00 7·00

The stamps and margins of **MS**4373 form a composite design of the exhibition site.

1403 Hurdler

2008. Olympic Games, Beijing.
4374 **1403** 31c. multicoloured 60 45

2008. Traditional Sports. As T 1394. Multicoloured.
MS4376 144×115 mm. 43c.×2, Palo Canario (stick fighting); Lucha Leonesa (wrestling) 3·00 2·75

No. **MS**4376 includes six stamp size labels which, with the stamps, form composite designs of the sport.

1404 Ball and Foot

2008. Spain–Euro 2008 Championship Winners. Sheet 106×79 mm.
MS4377 **1404** €1 multicoloured 1·90 1·90

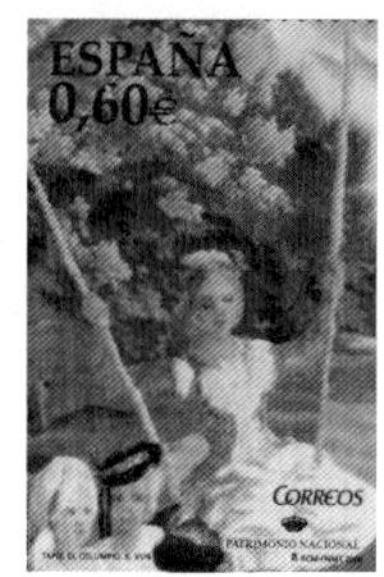

1405 *The Swing*

2008. National Heritage. Tapestries. Two sheets containing T 1405 and similar vert design. Multicoloured.
MS4378 79×106 mm. 60c. Type **1405** 1·10 1·10
MS4379 106×79 mm. €2.60 *The Blind Man and the Guitar* 5·00 5·00

1406 Barbaria, Formentera

2008. Lighthouses. Multicoloured.
4380 60c. Type **1406** 1·10 1·10
4381 60c. Irta, Castellon 1·10 1·10
4382 60c. Pechiguera, Lanzarote 1·10 1·10
4383 60c. Silleiro, Pontevedra 1·10 1·10
4384 60c. Torredembarra, Tarragona 1·10 1·10
4385 60c. Punta Orchilla, El Hierro 1·10 1·10

1407 *Self-Portrait* (Antonio Maria Esquivel)

2008. Spanish Artists. Multicoloured.
4386 31c. Type **1407** 60 45
4387 43c. *Self-Portrait* (Dario de Regoyos) 85 65

1408 Emblem

2008. Centenary of Royal Spanish Tennis Federation.
4388 **1408** 31c. vermilion and yellow 60 45

1409 Jay

2008. Flora and Fauna. Multicoloured. Self-adhesive.
4389 31c. Type **1409** 60 45
4390 31c. Narcissi 60 45

2008. Traditional Sports. As T 1394. Multicoloured.
4391 43c. Castillos humanos (human tower) 85 65

1410 *Lepista nuda*

2008. Fungi. Multicoloured.

4392	31c. Type **1410**	60	45
4393	31c. *Boletus regius*	60	45

1411 Emblem

2008. America. Festivals. 12 October 1492 Festival (National Day).

4394	**1411** 78c. scarlet, yellow and black	1·50	1·10

1412 Maqueda Castle, Toledo

2008. Castles.

4395	€2.60 olive and magenta	5·00	3·75
4396	€2.60 black and violet	5·00	3·75

DESIGNS: No. 4395, Type **1412**; No. 4396, La Calahorra Castle, Granada.

1413 Evening Dress

2008. Fashion. Pedro Rodriguez (designer). Multicoloured.

4397	31c. Type **1413**	60	60
4398	31c. Strapless embroidered evening gown	60	60
4399	31c. Multicoloured halter-neck dress	60	60
4400	31c. Pink evening coat	60	60

2008. Traditional Sports. As T 1394. Multicoloured.

MS4401	106×115 mm. 43c.×3, Chito (throwing at wooden cylinder); Chave (throwing at post); La calva (throwing at curved piece of wood (morillo))	2·50	2·50

No. **MS**4401 includes three stamp size labels which, with the stamps, form composite designs of the sport.

1414 Belen del Príncipe (18th-century crib)

2008. Christmas. Multicoloured. Self-adhesive.

4402	31c. Type **1414**	60	45
4403	60c. *Maternidad* (J. Carrero) (vert)	1·10	85

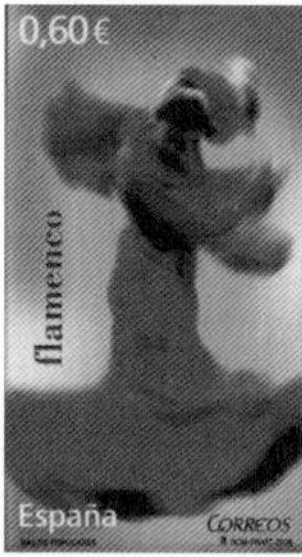

1415 Flamenco Dancer

2008. Traditional Dances. Sheet 120×76 mm containing T 1415 and similar vert design. Multicoloured.

MS4404	60c. Type **1415**; 78c. Irish dancer	2·75	2·75

Stamps of a similar design were issued by Ireland.

1416 *Elocuencia* (eloquence) (stained glass window)

2008. Real Academia Espanola (Royal Spanish Academy). Sheet 106×80 mm.

MS4405	**1416** €2.60 multicoloured	3·75	5·00

1417 National Flag

2008. Autonomous Communities within Spain. Self-adhesive Booklet Stamps. Designs showing the community's flag and area outline. Multicoloured.

4406	A Type **1417**	65	50
4407	A Asturias	65	50
4408	A Galicia	65	50
4409	A Cantabria	65	50
4410	A National arms	65	50
4411	A Cataluna	65	50
4412	A Basque Country	65	50
4413	A Andalucia	65	50

Nos. 4402/13 were for use on mail within Spain up to 20g.

1418 Fan and Manila Shawl

2009. Cultural Heritage. Self-adhesive.

4414	**1418** B multicoloured	1·20	90

No. 4414 was for use on mail within Europe up to 20g.

1419 Leaf

2009. Science. Multicoloured. Self-adhesive.

4415	39c. Type **1419** (Botany)	75	60
4416	€2.60 DNA strand (Genetics)	85	65

1420 Emblems

2009. 120th Anniv of La Rioja. .

4417	**1420** 32c. multicoloured	65	50

1421 Great Tit

2009. Flora and Fauna. Multicoloured. Self-adhesive.

4418	32c. Type **1421**	65	50
4419	62c. Hydrangea	1·20	90

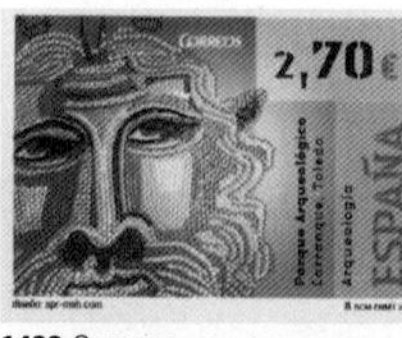

1422 Oceanus

2009. Archaeology. Mosaics, Casa sel Mitreo, Merida. Multicoloured.

4420	€2.70 Type **1422**	5·25	4·00
4421	€2.70 Oriens	5·25	4·00

1423 'Plantemos para el Planeta' (plant for the planet)

2009. Civic Values. Multicoloured.

4422	32c. Type **1423**	65	50
4423	62c. Key board (reconciliation of work and family life)	1·20	90
4424	78c. DESCO2ECTA	1·50	1·10

1424 Dam (hydro electricity)

2009. Renewable Energy. Multicoloured.

4425	32c. Type **1424**	65	50
4426	62c. Wind turbines	85	65
4427	62c. Solar energy	1·20	90
4428	78c. Geothermal energy	1·50	1·10

1425 Globe enclosing Face

2009. Millenium Development Goals.

4429	**1425** 32c. multicoloured	65	50

1426 Izki Nature Park, Alava

2009. Nature. Multicoloured.

4430	43c. Type **1426**	85	65
4431	43c. Canon del Río Lobos Nature Park, Segovia	85	65

1427 Gladioli

2009. Flora and Fauna. Multicoloured. Self-adhesive.

4432	32c. Type **1427**	65	50
4433	43c. Capercaillie	85	65

1428 Emblem

2009. 60th Anniv of Council of Europe.

4434	**1428** 62c. multicoloured	1·20	90

1429 Porto Colom, Mallorca

2009. Lighthouses. Multicoloured.

4435	62c. Type **1429**	1·20	90
4436	62c. La Higuera, Huelva	1·20	90
4437	62c. Igueldo, Guipuzcoa	1·20	90
4438	62c. Arinaga, Gran Canaria	1·20	90
4439	62c. Torre del Hercules, La Coruña	1·20	90
4440	62c. Torrox, Málaga	1·20	90

1430 Globe and Space

2009. Europa. Astronomy.

4441	**1430** 62c. multicoloured	1·20	90

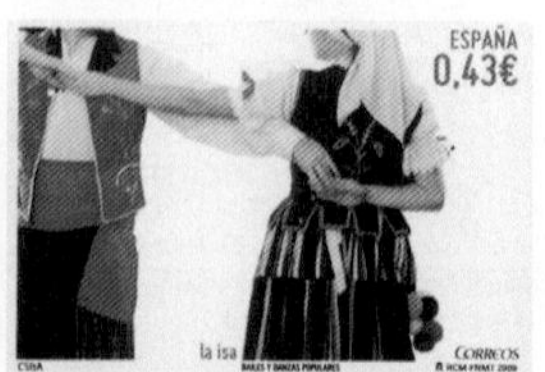

1431 La Isa

2009. Popular Dances (1st series). Multicoloured.

4442	43c. Type **1431**	85	65
MS4443	106×79 mm. 43c. Las Sevillanas (vert)	1·50	1·30

1432 King Alfonso VI of Leon and Castilla (Alfonso the Brave)

2009. 900th Death Anniversaries. Multicoloured.

4444	39c. Type **1432**	75	60
4445	62c. Domingo García (Santo Domingo de La Calzada) (Bishop of Ostia)	1·20	90

2009. Popular Dances (2nd series). As T 1431. Multicoloured.

4446	43c. La Mateixa	85	65
4447	43c. El Bolero	85	65

No. 4447 was issued with a stamp size label, which with the stamp, forms a composite design of a dancer.

1433 Paper Making (stained glass window)

2009. Spanish National Mint (main stairway, Paper Factory). Sheet 80×106 mm.
MS4448 **1433** €2.70 multicoloured 5·00 5·00

2009. Popular Dances (3rd series). As T 1431. Multicoloured.
4449 43c. La Rueda (74×28 mm) 85 65
4450 43c. El Aurresku (28×74 mm) 85 65

1434 Sleeveless Top and Hat

2009. Fashion. Manuel Pina (designer). Sheet 106×150 mm containing T 1434 and similar vert designs. Multicoloured.
MS4451 32c.×4, Type **1434**; Dress and jacket; Multicoloured evening gown; White evening gown 2·50 2·50

1435 *Graellsia isabelae*

2009. Flora and Fauna. Multicoloured. Self-adhesive.
4452 32c. Type **1435** 65 50
4453 62c. Geranium 1·20 90

1436 *El Juego de la pelota a pala* (Francisco de Goya)

2009. National Heritage. Tapestries. Sheet 144×115 mm containing T 1436 and similar horiz design. Multicoloured.
MS4454 78c. Type **1436**; €2.70 *Juego de bolos* (Antonio González Velazquez) 6·50 6·50

1437 Euro

2009. 10nth Anniv of Euro. Sheet 115×105 mm.
MS4455 **1437** €1 multicoloured 1·90 1·90

1438 Wine Bottle and Crashed Car

2009. Road Safety Campaign. Perils of Drink Driving.
4456 **1438** 32c. light bright carmine, black and grey 65 17·00

1439 Charles Darwin (naturalist and evolutionary theorist)

2009. Birth Bicentenaries.
4457 32c. black and reddish lilac 60 35
4458 32c. black and carmine-vermilion 60 35
4459 32c. black and carmine 60 35

DESIGNS:Type **1439**; Claudio Moyano Samaniego (politician); Louis Braille (inventor of Braille writing for the blind).

No. 4459 has raised Braille letters on the surface of the stamp.

2009. Popular Dances (4th series). As T 1431. Multicoloured.
4460 43c. La Muneira (33×50 mm) 85 65
4461 43c. El Fandango (33×50 mm) 85 65

Nos. 4460/1 each have a stamp size label attached at right, which with the stamp, creates a composite design.

1440 Bi-plane (designed by Gaspar Brunet)

2009. Centenary of First Spanish Powered Flight by Juan Olivert Serra.
4462 **1440** 32c. multicoloured 65 50

1441 Footballer and Emblem

2009. Centenary of Real Sociedad de Futbol.
4463 **1441** 32c. multicoloured 65 50

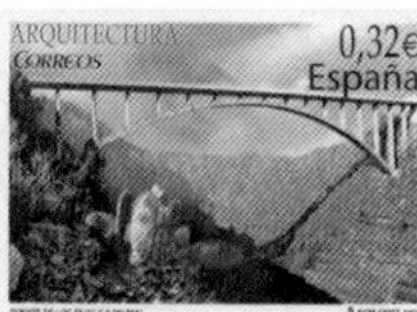

1442 Puente de los Tilos (built by Santiago Perez-Fadon Martinez and Jose Emilio Herrero Beneitez), Las Palmas

2009. Architecture. Multicoloured.
4464 32c. Type **1442** 65 50
4465 32c. Canal de Castilla, Valldolid 65 50
MS4466 150×105 mm. 32c.×4, Torre de Cristal (Cesar Pelli); Torre Espacio (Pei, Cobb Freed & Partners); Torre Sacyr Vallehermoso (Carlos Rubio Carvajal and Enrique Alvarez-Sala Walter); Torre Torre Caja Madrid (Norman Foster) 2·50 2·50

2009. Popular Dances (5th series). As T 1431. Multicoloured.
4467 43c. El Candil (33×50 mm) 85 65
4468 43c. Las Seguidillas (33×50 mm) 85 65

Nos. 4467/8 each have a stamp size label attached at right, which with the stamp, creates a composite design.

1443 Javier Castle, Navarra

2009. Castles.
4469 €2.70 black 5·00 3·75
4470 €2.70 black and orange-brown 5·00 3·75

DESIGNS: No. 4469, Type **1443**; No. 4470, Arevalo Castle, Avila.

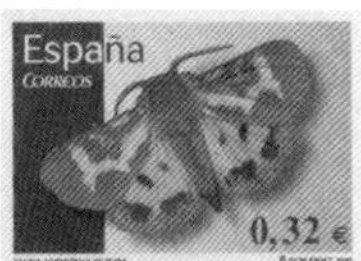

1444 *Hyphoraia dejeani*

2009. Flora and Fauna. Multicoloured. Self-adhesive.
4471 32c. Type **1444** 65 65
4472 32c. Pansy (vert) 65 65

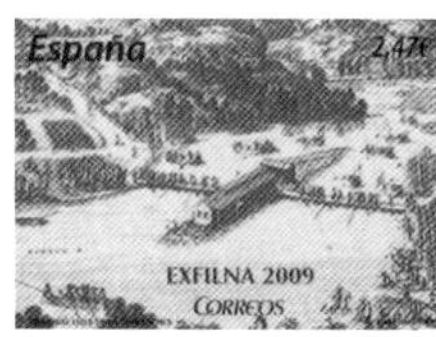

1445 *Lisle de la Conference* (engraving by Adam Perelle) (showing Isla de los Faisanes, Bidosa river (neutral territory used in Royal marriages negotiations))

2009. EXFILNA 2009, the National Philatelic Exhibition, Irun. Sheet 106×80 mm.
MS4473 **1445** €2.47 multicoloured 4·75 4·75

1446 Spanish Baraja Cards

2009. America. Games.
4474 **1446** 78c. multicoloured 1·50 1·50

1447 Player and Emblem

2009. Centenary of Royal Spanish Football Federation.
4475 **1447** 32c. multicoloured 65 65

2009. Popular Dances (6th series). As T 1431. Multicoloured.
4476 43c. La Sardana 85 85
MS4477 106×80 mm. 43c. La Jota (29×41 mm) 85 85

No. 4476 has a stamp size label attached at left, which with the stamp, creates a composite design.

1448 *Cantharellus cibarius*

2009. Fungi. Multicoloured.
4478 32c. Type **1448** 65 65
4479 32c. *Boletus pinophilus* 65 65

1449 *Las Meninas (The Royal Family of Felipe IV)*

2009. Diego Rodriguez de Silva y Velazquez (artist) Commemoration. Sheet 106×151 mm containing T 1449 and similar horiz design. Multicoloured.
MS4480 62c. Type **1449**; 78c. *The Infanta Margarita Teresa in a Blue Dress* 2·75 2·75

Stamps of the same design were issued by Austria.

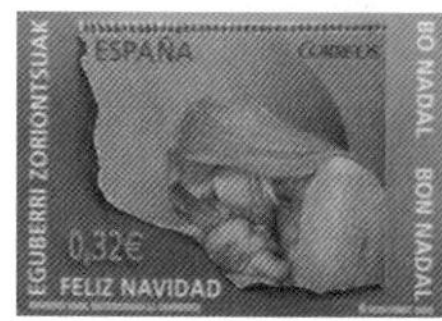

1450 *Maternity*

2009. Christmas. Multicoloured designs showing paintings by J. Carrero. (a) Self-adhesive.
4481 32c. Type **1450** 65 65
4482 62c. *The arrival of the Magi* 1·20 1·20

(b) Miniature sheet. Ordinary gum.
MS4483 115×105 mm. €2.47×2, *Adoracion al nino a y paisaje con mujer en rojo* (detail); *Adoracion al nino a y paisaje con mujer en rojo* (detail, different) (old wood carving from the Italian school and a painting by J.Carrero) 9·50 9·50

1451 Cartoon Airplane over Plaza de Requejo, Mieres

2009. Juvenia 2009–Youth Stamp Exhibition, Mieres
4484 **1451** 39c. multicoloured 75 75

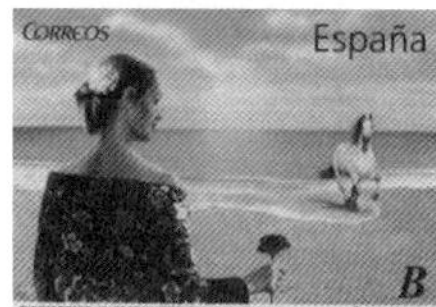

1452 Mujer con Manton de Manila (J. Carrero)

2010. Tourism
4485 **1452** B multicoloured 1·20 1·20

1453 Congress Building

2010. Autonomous Communities. Multicoloured.
4486 A Type **1453** 65 50
4487 A La Rioja, map and flag 65 50
4488 A Castilla la Mancha, map and flag 65 50
4489 A Valencia, map and flag 65 50
4490 A Senate building 65 50
4491 A Canary Islands, map and flag 65 50
4492 A Murcia, map and flag 65 50
4493 A Aragon, map and flag 65 50

1454 Artimelia latreillei

2010. Fauna. Multicoloured.
4494 34c. Type **1454** 65 65
4495 64c. *Zygaena rhadamanthus* 1·20 1·20

1455 Hand holding Paper (recycling)

2010. Civic Values. Multicoloured.

4496	€1 Type **1455**	2·75	2·75
4497	€2 Locked jar (responsible consumerism)	5·75	5·75

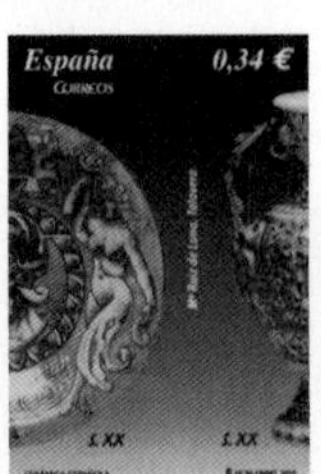

1456 20th-Century Plate (right) and Amphora (left)

2010. Spanish Ceramics. Multicoloured.

4498	34c. Type **1456**	65	65
4499	34c. Amphora (right) and 18th-century inkwell (left)	65	65
4500	34c. Inkwell (right) and 18th-century Pitcher (left)	65	65
4501	34c. Pitcher (right) and plate (left)	65	65

Nos. 4498/501 were printed, *se-tenant*, in horizontal strips of four stamps within the sheet, each strip forming a composite design.

1457 'Presidencia de la Unión Europea'

2010. Spain's Presidency of European Union

4502	**1457**	34c. multicoloured	65	65
4503	**1457**	64c. multicoloured	1·20	1·20

1458 Saxaphone

2010. Musical Instruments

4504	**1458**	45c. multicoloured	80	80

1459 Hand Print on Page

2010. Bicentenary of Constituent Assembly

4505	**1459**	34c. multicoloured	65	65

1460 Old Chapter House (Sala Capitular), Plasencia Cathedral

2010. Cathedrals

MS4506	**1460**	€2.75 chocolate and light blue	4·75	4·75

1461 Trophy and Poster for Celda 211

2010. Spanish Cinema (1st issue)

4507	**1461**	34c. multicoloured	65	65

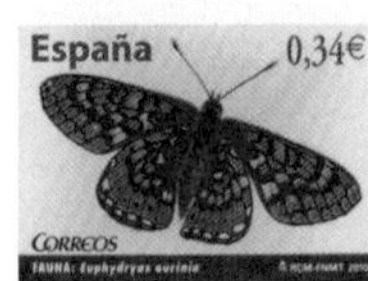

1462 *Zerynthia rumina*

2010. Fauna. Multicoloured.

4508	34c. Type **1462**	65	65
4509	64c. *Euphydryas aurinia*	1·20	1·20

1463 Trophy and Film Poster

2010. Spanish Cinema (2nd issue)

4510	**1463**	34c. multicoloured	65	65

1464 Stylized figures

2010. Bicentenary of Independence of Latin American Republics

4511	**1464**	€2.49 multicoloured	4·50	4·50

1466 Casa de las Torres, Ubeda

2010. World Heritage. Multicoloured.

4513	45c. Type **1466**	80	80
4514	45c. Jabalquinto Palace, Baeza	80	80

1467 Carlos María de Castro and Map of Expansion of Madrid

2010. Town Planning

4515	**1467**	34c. multicoloured	65	65

1468 Anniversary Emblem

2010. Centenary of Gran Via, Madrid

4516	**1468**	34c. multicoloured	65	65

1469 Stylized Spain and Madrid Pavillions

2010. Expo 2010, Shanghai

MS4517	**1469**	€2.49 multicoloured	4·50	4·50

1470 Club and Anniversary Emblems

2010. Centenary of Levante U D Football Club

4518	**1470**	34c. multicoloured	65	65

1471 Newspapers

2010. Centenary of *El Corro* Newspaper

4519	**1471**	34c. multicoloured	65	65

1472 Infant with Book

2010. Europa. Children's Books

4520	**1472**	64c. multicoloured	1·10	1·10

1473 Early Banner of León with Lion Passant (image scaled to 52% of original size)

2010. 1100th Anniv of Kingdom of Leon

MS4521	**1473**	€2.49 scarlet and gold	4·50	4·50

1474 Pilgrim and Cathedral of Santiago de Compostela

2010. Compostelian Jubilee Year (Ano Santo Xacobeo in Galician) (when St James's Day (July 25) falls on a Sunday)

4522	**1474**	34c. multicoloured	65	65

1475 Sierra de Cazorla, Segura y Las Villas Natural Park

2010. Nature Reserves. Multicoloured.

4523	45c. Type **1475**	1·10	1·10
4524	45c. Garajonay National Park	1·10	1·10
4525	45c. Doñana National Park	1·10	1·10

1476 Athlete (Ibero-American Athletics Championship, San Fernando, Cádiz)

2010. Sporting Events in 2010. Multicoloured.

4526	34c. Type **1476**	65	65
4527	64c. Barni (official mascot) (European Athletics Championships, Barcelona)	1·10	1·10
4528	78c. Championship emblem (World Cup Football Championships, South Africa)	1·25	1·25

1477 Gregorio Marañón and Microscope

2010. Personalities

4529	34c. black, deep ultramarine and dull orange	65	65
4530	34c. dull violet and dull orange (vert)	65	65

Designs:- 4529 Type **1477** (doctor and writer) (50th death anniv); 4530 Julián Gabino Arcas Lacal (Julián Arcas) (guitarist) Commemoration

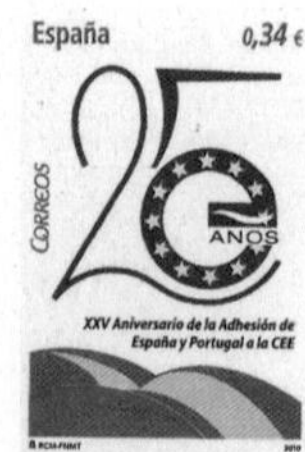

1478 '25' and European 'Stars'

2010. 25th Anniv of Spain and Portugal's Accession to European Economic Community (EEC)

4531	**1478**	34c. multicoloured	65	65

1479 Oscar Niemeyer International Cultural Centre, Asturias

2010. FILATEM 2010 Thematic Philatelic Exhibition, Avilés

MS4532	**1479**	€2.49 multicoloured	4·50	4·50

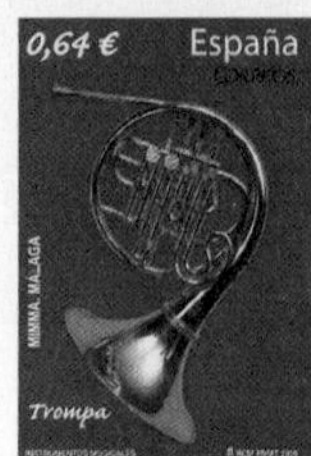

1480 Horn

2010. Musical Instruments

4532a	**1480**	64c. multicoloured	1·10	1·10

1481 José Luis López Vázquez

2010. Spanish Cinema (3rd issue)

4533	**1481**	45c. multicoloured	80	80

1482 Julia Aurelia (Septimia Zenobia) captured by Emperor Aurelian

2010. Cultural Heritage

4534	**1482**	78c. multicoloured	1·25	1·25

1483 Cathedral Façade

2010. Cathedrals

MS4535 **1483**	€2.75 reddish brown and deep turquoise-blue	5·00	5·00

1484 Cantabrian Brown Bear, Picos de Europa National Park

Nature Reserves. Multicoloured.

4536	45c. Type **1484**	65	65
4537	45c. Egyptian vulture, Monfragüe National Park	65	65
4538	45c. Ibex, Sierra Nevada National Park	65	65

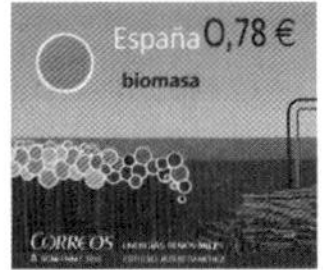

1485 Biomass

2010. Renewable Energy. Multicoloured.

4539	78c. Type **1485**	1·25	1·25
4540	78c. Wave energy ('undimotriz')	1·25	1·25
4541	78c. Tidal energy ('mareomotriz')	1·25	1·25

1486 Older Person

2010. Alzheimers Awareness Campaign

4542	**1486**	34c. multicoloured	65	65

1487 Football and Emblem

2010. Centenary of Cádiz Club de Fútbol

4543	**1487**	34c. multicoloured	65	65

1488 Teide National Park

2010. Nature Reserves. Multicoloured.

4544	45c. Type **1488**	1·10	1·10
4545	45c. Chamois, Ordesa and Monteperdido National Park	1·10	1·10
4546	45c. Wolf, Sanabria Lake Nature Reserve	1·10	1·10

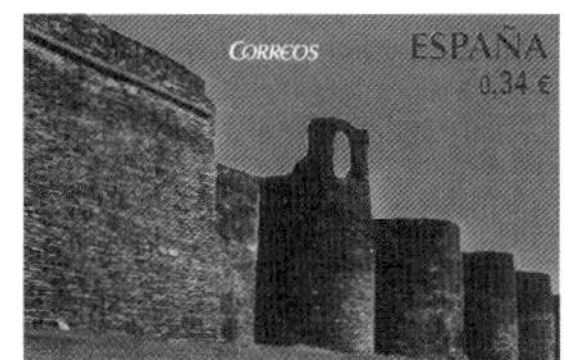

1489 Roman Walls of Lugo

2010. World Heritage Sites

4547	34c. Type **1489**	65	65
MS4548	105×150 mm. €2 Alhama Mosque, Cordoba (circular)	4·25	4·25

1490 Alviles

2010. Lighthouses. Multicoloured.

4549	64c. Type **1490**	1·10	1·10
4550	64c. Ciutadella de Menorca	1·10	1·10
4551	664c. Cabo de Huertas	1·10	1·10
4552	64c. Punta La Polacra	1·10	1·10
4553	64c. San Cibrao	1·10	1·10
4554	64c. Punta Cumplida	1·10	1·10

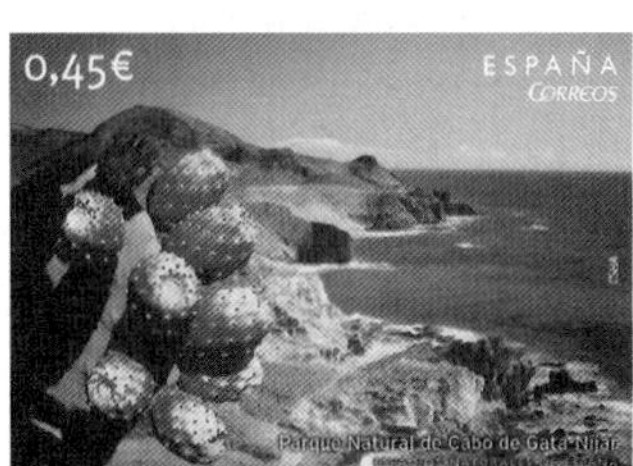

1491 Parque Natural de Gata

2010. Nature Reserves. Multicoloured.

4555	45c. Type **1491**	80	80
4556	45c. Archipiélago de Cabrera National Park	80	80
4557	45c. Aigüestortes y Lago de San Mauricio National Park	80	80

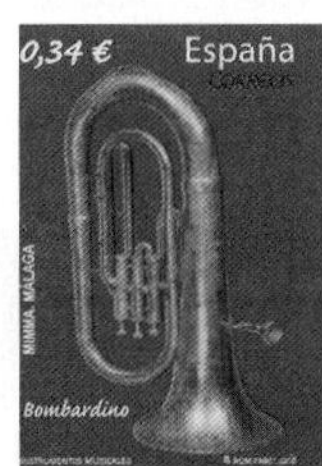

1492 Euphonium

2010. Musical Instruments

4558	**1492**	34c. multicoloured	65	65

1493 Gonzalo Torrente Ballester (writer and journalist)

2010. Personalities. Each black and new blue.

4559	34c. Type **1493**	65	65
4560	34c. Francisco Ayala (writer)	65	65
4561	34c. Vicente Ferrer (missionary and aid worker)	65	65

1494 Flag as Map Outline and Arms

2010. America

4562	**1494**	78c. multicoloured	1·25	1·25

1495 Outline Figures, Flags and Bicentennial Group Emblem

2010. Bicentenary of Latin-American Independence

4563	**1495**	78c. multicoloured	1·25	1·25

1496 Ildefonso Cerdá

2010. Town Planning

4564	**1496**	34c. multicoloured	65	65

1497 *La Prensa* (previous name) and *El Dia* Mast Heads

2010. Centenary of *El Dia* Newspaper

4565	**1497**	34c. multicoloured	65	65

1498 Evening Gown

2010. Spanish Fashion. Multicoloured.

MS4566	34c.×4, Type **1498**; Suit; Floral dress with frilled skirt; Strapless cocktail dress with black lace overlay	2·75	2·75

1499 Collegiate Church of Santa María la Mayor, Toro, Spain

2010. Alliance of Civilizations. Multicoloured.

MS4567	64c.×2, Type **1499**; Grand Imperial Mosque, Ortakoy, Turkey	2·25	2·25

Stamps of a similar design were issued by Turkey.

1500 Printing Plates

2010. EXFILNA 2009, the National Philatelic Exhibition, Madrid

MS4568 **1500**	€2.49 multicoloured	4·50	4·50

The margins of **MS**4568 are inscribed for:140th anniversary of the Midwife; 80th anniversary of Goya's Naked Maja; 70th anniversary of El Cid and 35th anniversary of King Juan Carlos.

1501 Trophy

2010. Spain, World Cup Football Champions—2010

MS4569 **1501**	€2 multicoloured	3·75	3·75

1502 Mother and Child

2010. Christmas. Multicoloured.

4570	34c. Type **1502**	65	65
4571	64c. Arms cradling child	1·10	1·10

1503 Holy Family (sculpture)

2010. Millenary of Monastery of San Salvador de Oña

MS4572 **1503**	78c. multicoloured	1·25	1·25

1504 Bilbao Cathedral

2010. Cathedrals. Sheet 80×106 mm

MS4573 **1504**	€2.75 reddish brown and steel blue	5·50	5·50

1505 Constitutional Court

2011. Autonomous Communities. Multicoloured.

4574	A Type **1505**	65	50
4575	A Ciudad Autónoma de Ceuta, map and flag	65	50
4576	A Extremadura, map and flag	65	50
4577	A Ciudad Autónoma de Melilla, map and flag	65	50
4578	A Balearic Islands, map and flag	65	50
4579	A Comunidad de Madrid, map and flag	65	50
4580	A Comunidad de Castilla y León, map and flag	65	50
4581	A Comunidad Foral de Navarra, map and flag	65	50

1506 Symbols of Tourism (painting by J. Carrero)

2011. Spanish Tourism

4582	**1506**	B multicoloured	1·20	1·20

1507 *Charaxes jasius*

2011. Fauna. Multicoloured.

4583	65c. Type **1507**	1·10	1·10
4584	65c. *Melanargia ines*	1·10	1·10
4585	65c. *Argynnis adippe*	1·10	1·10
4586	65c. *Papilio machaon*	1·10	1·10

1508 Hand holding Apple (symbolizing hand-over to new priors)

2011. Festivals

4587	**1508**	35c. multicoloured	65	65

1509 *Hespérides* (research ship) with *Atrevida* (1st scientific expedition) as its Reflection and Specimen Jar

2011. International Year of Biodiversity

4588	**1509**	50c. multicoloured	90	90

1510 Guitar

2011. Musical Instruments. Multicoloured.

4589	35c. Type **1510**	65	65
4590	35c. Lute	65	65
4591	35c. Mandolin	65	65
4592	35c. Violin	65	65

1511 Almería Railway Station

2011. Architecture

4593	**1511**	35c. multicoloured	65	65

1512 Marie Curie (winner of Nobel Prize in Chemistry, 1903)

2011. International Year of Chemistry

4594	**1512**	35c. multicoloured	65	65

1513 Hands, Pen and Book

2011. 150th Anniv of Property Act

4595	**1513**	65c. multicoloured	1·10	1·10

1514 Safety Belt and Teddy (Use of Safety Belt)

2011. Civic Values. Multicoloured.

4596	35c. Type **1514**	65	65
4597	35c. Dog waste disposal (Keep your City Clean)	65	65
4598	35c. Disabled symbol and hand using computer mouse (Protection of Persons with Disabilities)	65	65
4599	35c. Stylized figures (Respect on the Net)	65	65

No. 4600 and Type **1515** are left for Cathedrals issued on 4 March 2011, not yet received.

No. 4601 and Type **1516** are are left for Women's Day issued on 8 March 2011, not yet received.

1517 *Autumn in Hayedo de la Pedrosa* (Juan A. González)

2011. Europa

4602	**1517**	65c. multicoloured	1·10	1·10

1518 Holy Cross del Voto

2011. Jubilee Year to Mark 400th Anniv of Santa Cruz del Voto, Parish Church of Santa Cruz de Canjáyar

4603	**1518**	65c. multicoloured	1·10	1·10

1519 Calella (Barcelona)

2011. Lighthouses. Multicoloured.

4604	65c. Type **1519**	1·10	1·10
4605	65c. Chipiona (Cádiz)	1·10	1·10
4606	65c. La Entallada (Fuerteventura)	1·10	1·10
4607	65c. Cap de Sant Sebastiá (Girona)	1·10	1·10
4608	65c. Castell de Ferro (Granada)	1·10	1·10
4609	65c. Valencia lighthouse	1·10	1·10

1520 Centre of Santa Fe and Boy wearing 15th-century (1491, year of the Capitulations) Dress

2011. Juvenia 2011–National Youth Philatelic Exhibition, Pósito Building, Granada

4610	**1520**	65c. multicoloured	1·10	1·10

1521 Scene from Pa negre (best film of 2010) (directed by Agusti Villaronga)

2011. Spanish Cinema (4th issue). Multicoloured.

4611	35c. Type **1521**	65	65
MS4612	105×80 mm. €2.84 Trophy (bust of Francisco José de Goya y Lucientes)	5·25	3·00

1522 €2 Coin containing Image of Patio de los Leones

2011. World Heritage Site. Alhambra. Sheet 104×150 mm

MS4613	**1522** €2 multicoloured	9·50	9·50

1523 Dido bids farewell to Aeneas (detail from Dido and Aeneas), Palacio Real de Madrid

2011. Cultural Heritage. Sheet 144×115 mm

MS4614	**1523** €2.84 multicoloured	13·50	13·50

1524 Super Puma Aerospatiale SA-332

2011. Centenary of Military Aviation. Multicoloured.

MS4615	65c.×4, Type **1524**; CASA-101 *Aviojet*; C/KC-130 Lockheed Hercules; EF-2000 Eurofighter *Typhoon* (123×106 mm)	13·50	13·50

EXPRESS LETTER STAMPS

E53 Pegasus and Arms

1905

E308	**E53**	20c. red	42·00	1·10

E77 Spanish Royal Family

1926. Red Cross.

E417	**E77**	20c. purple and deep purple	15·00	9·00

1927. 25th Anniv of Coronation. No. E417 optd 17-V-1902 17-V-1927 ALFONSO XIII.

E459	20c. purple and deep purple	14·50	8·25

E88 Gazelle

1929. Seville and Barcelona Exhibitions.

E521	**E88**	20c. brown	28·00	19·00

E89

1929

E522	**E89**	20c. red	28·00	4·00

1929. Optd Sociedad de las Naciones LV reunion del Consejo Madrid.

E534	20c. red	20·00	19·00

1930. Optd URGENCIA.

E535	20c. red	33·00	4·00

E91 Class 7201 Electric Locomotive

1930. 11th Int Railway Congress, Madrid.

E553	**E91**	20c. red	95·00	75·00

1930. "Goya" types optd URGENTE.

E570	**91**	20c. mauve (postage)	50	25
E583	-	20c. brown and blue (as No. 574) (air)	40	40

1930. "Columbus" type optd URGENTE.

E608	**99**	20c. purple	3·50	2·50

E113 Seville Exhibition

1930. Spanish–American Exhibition.

E643	**E113**	20c. orange	1·90	1·70

1931. Optd REPUBLICA.

E660	**E89**	20c. red (No. E535)	4·25	4·25
E672	**E89**	20c. red (No. E522)	4·75	4·75

1931. Optd Republica Espanola in two lines continuously.

E697	29c. red (No. E522)	19·00	3·00

E126

1931. 900th Anniv of Montserrat Monastery.

E731	**E126**	20c. red	38·00	33·00

E145

1934

E779	**E145**	20c. red	30	20

E152 Newspaper Boy

1936. 40th Anniv of Madrid Press Association.

E801	**E152**	20c. red	40	35

E185 Pegasus

1937

E906	**E185**	20c. brown	2·40	50

E198 Pegasus

1942

E1022	**E198**	25c. red	35	20

E199

1940. 19th Centenary of Apparition of Virgin of El Pilar at Zaragoza.

E1006	**E199**	25c.+5c. red & buff	40	30

E270 "Speed"

E271 Centaur

1956

E1250	**E270**	2p. red	20	15
E1251	**E270**	3p. red	20	15
E1252	**E 271**	4p. mauve and black	20	15
E1253	**E 270**	5p. red	15	15
E1254	**E 271**	6p.50 red and violet	20	15

E425 Roman Chariot

1971

E2099	**E425**	10p. green, blk & red	20	15
E2100	-	15p. blue, black & red	20	15

DESIGN—VERT: 15p. Letter encircling globe.

E862 Communications

1993. Public Services.

E3211	**E862**	180p. red and yellow	2·75	65

FRANK STAMPS

F36

1869. For use on "Cartilla Postal de Espana" (book) by Senor Castell.

F172	**F 36**	(-) blue	65·00	60·00

F50

1881. For use on book by A. F. Duro.

F273	**F 50**	(-) black on buff	47·00	21·00

F163

1938. For use by Agencia Filatelica Oficial, Barcelona.

F839	**F 163**	(-) blue	60·00	4·75
F840	**F 163**	(-) lilac	60·00	4·75
F841	**F 163**	(-) green	60·00	4·75
F842	**F 163**	(-) brown	60·00	4·75
F843	**F 163**	(-) black	60·00	4·75

OFFICIAL STAMPS

O9

1854. Imperf.

O46	**O 9**	½ onza black on orange	2·75	1·90
O47	**O 9**	1 onza black on pink	4·75	4·75
O48	**O 9**	4 onza black on green	11·50	9·50
O49	**O 9**	1 libra black on blue	70·00	65·00

The face values of Nos. O46/53 are expressed in onzas (ounces) and libra (pound) which refer to the maximum weight for which each value could prepay postage.

O10

1855. Imperf.

O50	**O10**	½ onza black on yellow	2·50	2·50
O52	**O10**	4 onza black on green	5·50	5·00
O53	**O10**	1 libra black on blue	18·00	25·00
O55	**O10**	1 onza black on pink	5·75	3·25

O52

1895. For use by Members of Chamber of Deputies.

O289	**51**	15c. yellow	11·00	4·25
O290	**O 52**	(-) pink	8·25	17·00
O291	**O 52**	(-) blue	27·00	8·50

O66 National Library

O67 Cervantes (from painting by J. de Jauregui)

O68 Statue of Cervantes by A. Sola

1916. Death Tercentenary of Cervantes. (a) For use by Members of the Chamber of Deputies.

O353	-	(-) black and violet	1·70	1·30
O354	**O 66**	(-) black and green	1·70	1·30
O355	**O 67**	(-) black and violet	1·70	1·30
O356	**O 68**	(-) black and red	1·70	1·30

(b) For use by Members of the Senate.

O357	-	(-) black and green	1·70	1·30
O358	**O 66**	(-) black and red	1·70	1·30
O359	**O 67**	(-) black and brown	1·70	1·30
O360	**O 68**	(-) black and brown	1·70	1·30

DESIGN—As Type O **66**: Chamber of Deputies.

1931. 3rd Pan-American Postal Union Congress. T 121 etc optd Oficial.

O707	5c. purple	40	30
O708	10c. green	40	30
O709	15c. violet	40	30
O710	25c. red	40	30
O711	30c. green	40	30
O712	40c. blue	95	65
O713	50c. orange	95	65
O714	1p. grey	95	65
O715	4p. mauve	17·00	15·00
O716	10p. brown	43·00	34·00

Air. T 123 etc optd OFICIAL.

O717	5c. brown	20	15
O718	10c. green	20	15
O719	25c. red	20	15
O720	50c. blue	20	15
O721	1p. lilac	20	15
O722	4p. grey	7·75	5·75

WAR TAX STAMPS

W42

1874. The 5c. perf or imperf.

W217	**W42**	5c. de p. black	12·50	1·30
W218	**W42**	10c. de p. blue	16·00	2·50

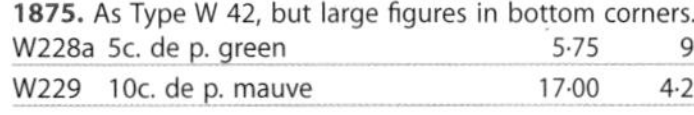

1875. As Type W 42, but large figures in bottom corners.

W228a	5c. de p. green	5·75	95
W229	10c. de p. mauve	17·00	4·25

W48

1876. 2nd Carlist War (1873–76) and Cuban War (1868–78).

W253	**W48**	5c. de p. green	5·50	85
W254	**W48**	10c. de p. blue	5·50	85
W255	**W48**	25c. de p. black	42·00	15·00
W256	**W48**	1p. lilac	£500	£110
W257	**W48**	5p. pink	£800	£325

W49

1877. Cuban War (1868–78).

W258	**W49**	15c. de p. purple	25·00	80
W259	**W49**	50c. de p. yellow	£850	£120

1897. Cuban War of Independence (1895–98). Inscr "1897–1898" (15c.) or "1897 A 1898" (others).

W289	5c. green	4·50	1·90
W290	10c. green	4·50	1·90
W291	15c. green	£550	£325
W292	20c. green	10·00	3·25

W52

1898. Cuban War of Independence (1895–98) and Spanish-American War (1898). Inscr "1898–99".

W293	**W 52**	5c. black	3·50	1·90
W294	**W 52**	10c. black	3·50	1·90
W295	**W 52**	15c. black	65·00	19·00
W296	**W 52**	20c. black	5·25	3·25

W53

1898. Cuban War of Independence (1895–98) and Spanish-American War (1898).

W297	**W 53**	5c. black	10·50	80

W163

1938

W839	**W 163**	10c. red	95	1·40
W840	**W 163**	20c. blue	95	95
W841	**W 163**	60c. pink	3·25	3·75
W842	**W 163**	1p. blue	95	1·10
W843	**W 163**	2p. green	95	1·10
W844	**W 163**	10p. blue	4·75	5·75

Nos. W842/3 have coloured figures of value on white backgrounds.

Pt. 11

SWEDEN

A kingdom of N. Europe, united to Norway till 1905.

1855. 48 skilling banco = 1 riksdaler.
1858. 100 ore = 1 riksdaler.
1875. 100 ore = 1 krona.

1

1855

1	**1**	3s. green	£6500	£2500
2	**1**	4s. blue	£1100	55·00
3	**1**	6s. grey	£7500	£850
4	**1**	8s. orange	£4000	£475
5	**1**	24s. red	£6000	£1400

1858

6b	5ore green	£160	16·00
7a	9ore purple	£350	£190
8a	12ore blue	£170	1·80
9a	24ore orange	£400	19·00
10a	30ore brown	£400	22·00
11b	50ore red	£550	70·00

2

3

1862

12bc	2	3ore brown	£110	9·75
13	3	17ore purple	£600	£110
14	3	17ore grey	£750	£600
15b	3	20ore red	£190	14·00

4

5

6 King Oscar II

1872

29	4	2ore orange	1·80	4·75
30	4	3ore brown	10·50	15·00
31	4	4ore grey	27·00	1·20
32	4	5ore green	65·00	65
20	4	6ore green	£800	50·00
33	4	6ore mauve	28·00	46·00
34	6	10ore pink	65·00	35
21a	4	12ore blue	23·00	65
35	4	20ore red	£110	60
23a	4	24ore yellow	47·00	21·00
36	4	30ore brown	£180	1·00
37	4	50ore red	£140	3·00
26	5	1r. blue and bistre	£750	65·00
38	5	1k. blue and bistre	95·00	2·00

No. 26 has the value expressed as one riksdaler and No. 38 one krona.

1889. Surch 10 10 TIO ORE and Arms.

39	4	10ore on 12ore blue	2·40	3·75
40	4	10ore on 24ore yellow	8·25	23·00

9

10 Oscar II

11

1891

41	9	1ore blue and brown	1·20	45
42a	9	2ore yellow and blue	4·00	40
43	9	3ore orange and brown	55	95
44	9	4ore blue and red	4·50	30
45c	10	5ore green	2·75	25
46	10	8ore purple	3·00	90
47	10	10ore red	3·75	25
48	10	15ore brown	23·00	25
49	10	20ore blue	21·00	25
56	10	25ore orange	35·00	3·00
51a	10	30ore brown	60·00	25
53	10	50ore grey	95·00	40
54	11	1k. grey and red	£130	1·40

13 G.P.O., Stockholm

1903. Opening of new Post Office.

57	13	5k. blue	£190	24·00

14

15 Gustav V

1910

65	14	1ore black	20	20
66	14	2ore orange	20	20
67	14	3ore brown	20	20
68	14	4ore mauve	20	20
69	15	5ore green	1·70	20
70	15	7ore green	30	20
71	15	8ore purple	30	30
72	15	10ore red	2·20	20
73	15	12ore purple	30	20
74	15	15ore brown	4·75	20
75	15	20ore blue	7·75	20
76	15	25ore orange	30	20
77	15	27ore blue	45	60
78	15	30ore brown	18·00	20
79	15	35ore violet	17·00	20
80	15	40ore green	22·00	20
81	15	50ore grey	55·00	20
82	15	55ore blue	£1300	£3500
83	15	65ore green	60	1·40
84	15	80ore black	£1300	£3500
85	15	90ore green	55	45
63	15	1k. black on yellow	65·00	45
64	15	5k. purple on yellow	2·00	2·10

1916. Clothing Fund for Mobilized Reservists ("Landstorm"). (a) Postage stamps surch FRIMARKE LANDSTORMEN and value in figures and words round Arms.

86a	4	5+5 on 2ore orange	3·50	5·50
86b	4	5+5 on 3ore brown	3·50	5·50
86c	4	5+5 on 4ore grey	3·50	5·50
86d	4	5+5 on 5ore green	3·50	5·50
86e	4	5+5 on 6ore mauve	3·50	5·50
86f	4	10+10 on 12ore blue	3·50	5·50
86g	4	10+10 on 20ore red	3·50	5·50
86h	4	10+10 on 24ore yellow	3·50	5·50
86i	4	10+10 on 30ore brown	3·50	5·50
86j	4	10+10 on 50ore brown	3·50	5·50

(b) Postage Due stamps surch FRIMARKE SVERIGE in frame round Arms, LANDSTORMEN and value in figures and words.

86k	D6	5+5 on 1ore black	28·00	7·75
86l	D6	5+5 on 3ore red	5·75	3·75
86m	D6	5+5 on 5ore brown	7·50	4·50
86n	D6	5+10 on 6ore orange	4·50	4·75
86o	D6	5+15 on 12ore red	43·00	20·00
86p	D6	10+20 on 20ore blue	12·50	17·00
86q	D6	10+40 on 24ore mauve	50·00	70·00
86r	D6	10+20 on 30ore green	4·75	5·75
86s	D6	10+40 on 50ore brown	20·00	27·00
86t	D6	10+90 on 1k. blue and brown	£120	£275

(c) No. 57 surch FRIMARKE ORE 10 ORE FRIMARKE LANDSTORMEN KR. 4,90 and Arms.

86u	13	10 ore+4k.90 on 5k. blue	£110	£275

1917. Surch in figures only.

87	15	7 on 10ore red	20	20
88	15	12 on 25ore orange	1·70	25
89	15	12 on 65ore green	75	85
90	15	27 on 55ore blue	60	1·10
91	15	27 on 65ore green	1·10	2·75
92	15	27 on 80ore black	65	1·10
93	15	1.98k. on 5k. purple on yell	1·00	4·50
94	15	2.12k. on 5k. purple on yell	1·20	4·50

1918. Landstorm Fund. Nos. 86a/j surch.

94a	4	7+3 on 5ore on 2ore	7·25	8·00
94b	4	7+3 on 5ore on 3ore	2·20	1·00
94c	4	7+3 on 5ore on 4ore	2·20	1·00
94d	4	7+3 on 5ore on 5ore	2·20	1·00
94e	4	7+3 on 5ore on 6ore	2·20	1·00
94f	4	12+8 on 10ore on 12ore	2·20	1·00
94g	4	12+8 on 10ore on 20ore	2·20	1·00
94h	4	12+8 on 10ore on 24ore	2·20	1·00
94i	4	12+8 on 10ore on 30ore	2·20	1·00
94j	4	12+8 on 10ore on 50ore	2·20	1·00

19 Arms

20 Lion (after sculpture by B. Foucquet)

21 Gustav V

22 Emblem of Swedish Post

1920

95A	19	3ore red	20	30
96Bb	20	5ore green	1·10	1·50
97A	20	5ore brown	5·00	20
98B	20	10ore green	2·20	55
99A	20	10ore violet	4·25	30
102a	21	10ore red	8·25	5·50
103	21	15ore purple	30	30
104a	21	20ore blue	39·00	2·10
100A	20	25ore orange	12·50	35
101A	20	30ore brown	35	30
105A	22	35ore yellow	46·00	45
106A	22	40ore green	37·00	1·20
107A	22	45ore brown	1·00	45
108A	22	60ore purple	18·00	25
109A	22	70ore brown	55	1·80
110A	22	80ore green	35	25
111A	22	85ore green	3·75	30
112A	22	90ore blue	60·00	25
113A	22	1k. orange	6·50	25
114A	22	110ore blue	55	20
115A	22	115ore brown	8·75	30
116A	22	120ore black	60·00	40
117A	22	120ore mauve	12·50	40
118A	22	140ore black	65	20
119A	22	145ore green	7·00	60

23 Gustavus II Adolphus

1920. Tercentenary of Swedish Post between Stockholm and Hamburg.

120A	23	20ore blue	3·25	30

1920. Air. Official stamps surch LUFTPOST and value.

120a	O 17	10 on 3ore brown	2·40	4·75
120b	O 17	20 on 2ore yellow	4·00	6·75
120c	O 17	50 on 4ore lilac	16·00	18·00

24 Gustav V (after portrait by E. Osterman)

1921

121	24	15ore violet	17·00	20
122	24	15ore red	9·00	30
123	24	15ore brown	4·00	30
124	24	20ore violet	30	20
125	24	20ore red	18·00	35
126	24	20ore orange	25	40
128	24	25ore red	55	1·00
129	24	25ore blue	13·00	30
131	24	25ore orange	30·00	30
133	24	30ore brown	18·00	20
134	24	30ore blue	5·50	30
135	24	35ore purple	15·00	30
136	24	40ore blue	35	45
137	24	40ore green	36·00	80
138	24	45ore brown	3·75	60
139a	24	50ore black	1·30	45
140	24	85ore green	11·00	80
141	24	115ore brown	10·50	1·20
142	24	145ore green	7·25	1·10

25 Gustavus Vasa

1921. 400th Anniv of Liberation of Sweden.

143	25	20ore violet	8·50	20·00
144	25	110ore blue	48·00	5·00
145	25	140ore black	24·00	5·00

26 Old City, Stockholm

27 Gustav V

1924. 8th Congress of U.P.U.

146	26	5ore brown	1·60	1·90
147	26	10ore green	1·60	1·90
148	26	15ore violet	1·90	1·60
149	26	20ore red	10·50	8·75
150	26	25ore orange	15·00	14·50
151	26	30ore blue	13·50	14·50
152	26	35ore black	18·00	19·00
153	26	40ore green	25·00	20·00
154	26	45ore brown	30·00	26·00
155	26	50ore grey	26·00	21·00
156	26	60ore purple	39·00	36·00
157	26	80ore green	33·00	31·00
158	27	1k. green	60·00	60·00
159	27	2k. red	£140	£170
160	27	5k. blue	£275	£325

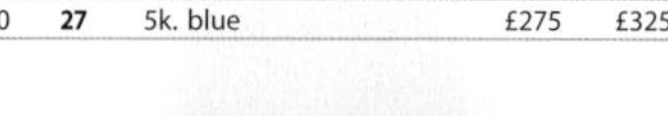

28 Post Rider and Friedrichsafen FF-49 Seaplane

29 Carrier-pigeon

1924. 50th Anniv of U.P.U.

161	28	5ore brown	2·75	2·75
162	28	10ore green	2·75	3·50
163	28	15ore violet	2·50	2·10
164	28	20ore red	18·00	17·00
165	28	25ore orange	25·00	19·00
166	28	30ore blue	22·00	19·00
167	28	35ore black	28·00	33·00
168	28	40ore green	27·00	21·00
169	28	45ore brown	36·00	23·00
170	28	50ore grey	43·00	35·00
171	28	60ore purple	47·00	47·00
172	28	80ore green	36·00	22·00
173	29	1k. green	70·00	65·00
174	29	2k. red	£150	55·00
175	29	5k. blue	£275	£180

29a King Gustav V

1928. 70th Birthday of King Gustav V and Cancer Research Fund.

175a	29a	5(+5)ore green	2·20	4·00
175b	29a	10(+5)ore violet	2·20	4·00
175c	29a	15(+5)ore red	2·20	3·50
175d	29a	20(+5)ore orange	3·75	2·50
175e	29a	25(+5)ore blue	3·75	2·75

29c Night Flight by Junkers F-13 (with skis) over Stockholm

1930. Air.

175f	29c	10ore blue	20	35
175g	29c	50ore violet	90	1·00

30 Royal Palace, Stockholm

1931

176	30	5k. green	95·00	7·50

31 Death of Gustavus Adolphus at Lutzen

1932. Death Tercentenary of Gustavus Adolphus.

177	31	10ore violet	1·80	25
178	31	15ore red	2·00	50
179	31	25ore blue	5·25	55
180	31	90ore green	29·00	1·40

32 Allegory of Thrift

1933. 50th Anniv of Swedish Postal Savings Bank.

181a	**32**	5ore green	2·00	20

33 Stockholm Cathedral

1935. 500th Anniv of First Swedish Parliament. Stockholm Buildings.

182	-	5ore green	2·00	20
183	-	10ore violet	4·75	20
184	**33**	15ore red	2·40	20
185	-	25ore blue	7·25	50
186	-	35ore purple	11·00	1·60
187	-	60ore purple	17·00	1·00

DESIGNS: 5ore Old City Hall; 10ore Exchange; 25ore House of the Nobility; 35ore Houses of Parliament; 60ore Arms of Engelbrekt and representatives of the Four Estates.

35 A. Oxenstierna (after D. Dumonstier)

1936. Tercentenary of Swedish Post.

188	**35**	5ore green	1·30	30
189	-	10ore violet	1·60	50
190	-	15ore red	2·50	30
191	-	20ore blue	8·50	3·25
192	-	25ore blue	5·50	35
193	-	30ore brown	18·00	2·30
194	-	35ore mauve	5·25	1·00
195	-	40ore green	5·25	1·80
196	-	45ore green	7·50	1·00
197	-	50ore grey	25·00	2·00
198	-	60ore purple	32·00	50
199	-	1k. blue	8·50	6·50

DESIGNS: 10ore Early courier; 15ore Post rider; 20ore Sailing packet "Hiorten"; 25ore Paddle-steamer "Constitutionen"; 30ore Mail coach; 35ore Arms; 40ore Class F steam locomotive and mail train; 45ore A. W. Roos (Postmaster General 1867–89); 50ore Motor bus and trailer; 60ore Liner "Gripsholm"; 1k. Junkers Ju 52/3m seaplane.

For similar designs, but dated "1972" at foot, see Nos. 700/4.

38 Junkers W.34 over Scandinavia

1936. Inauguration of Bromma Aerodrome.

200	**38**	50ore blue	4·25	6·25

39 E. Swedenborg (after P. Krafft)

1938. 250th Birth Anniv of Swedenborg.

201	**39**	10ore violet	1·40	20
202	**39**	100ore green	4·75	1·10

40 Governor Printz and Red Indian

1938. 300th Anniv of Founding of New Sweden, U.S.A.

203	**40**	5ore green	70	30
204	-	15ore brown	85	40
205	-	20ore red	1·60	60
206	-	30ore blue	4·25	75
207	-	60ore purple	7·25	35

DESIGNS: 15ore Emigrant ships "Calmare Nyckel" and "Fagel Grip"; 20ore Swedish landing in America; 30ore First Swedish church, Wilmington; 60ore Queen Christina (after S. Bourdon).

41 King Gustav V

1938. 80th Birthday of King Gustav V.

208	**41**	5ore green	90	25
209	**41**	15ore brown	90	25
210	**41**	30ore blue	12·50	70

42 King Gustav V

43 Small Arms of Sweden

1939

234	**42**	5ore green	25	20
299	**42**	5ore orange	20	20
235	**42**	10ore violet	30	20
300	**42**	10ore green	30	20
236b	**42**	15ore brown	30	20
237	**42**	20ore red	25	20
238	**42**	25ore orange	85	20
301	**42**	25ore violet	85	20
239	**42**	30ore blue	30	20
240	**42**	35ore purple	45	20
241	**42**	40ore green	45	20
242	**42**	45ore brown	45	20
243	**42**	50ore grey	2·30	20
301a	**43**	50ore grey	1·50	20
302	**43**	55ore brown	85	30
221	**43**	60ore red	90	20
302a	**43**	65ore green	45	20
302b	**43**	70ore blue	2·50	1·00
302c	**43**	75ore brown	1·80	55
303	**43**	80ore green	45	20
222	**43**	85ore green	35	20
303a	**43**	85ore brown	4·25	1·20
223	**43**	90ore blue	50	20
224	**43**	1k. orange	50	20
303b	**43**	1k.05 blue	95	25
304	**43**	1k.10 violet	3·75	20
225	**43**	1k.15 brown	50	20
226	**43**	1k.20 purple	1·80	20
304a	**43**	1k.20 blue	3·25	2·00
305	**43**	1k.40 green	60	20
227	**43**	1k.45 green	2·20	50
305a	**43**	1k.50 purple	1·10	90
305b	**43**	1k.50 brown	60	25
305c	**43**	1k.70 red	85	20
306	**43**	1k.75 blue	7·75	5·75
306a	**43**	1k.80 blue	1·50	40
306b	**43**	1k.85 blue	3·50	75
306c	**43**	2k. purple	60	20
306ca	**43**	2k. mauve	50	20
306d	**43**	2k.10 blue	5·50	20
306e	**43**	2k.15 green	3·25	40
306f	**43**	2k.30 brown	4·00	30
306g	**43**	2k.50 green	85	20
306h	**43**	2k.55 red	2·30	1·70
306i	**43**	2k.80 red	1·00	20
306j	**43**	2k.85 orange	2·40	2·50
306k	**43**	3k. blue	85	20

44 P. H. Ling (after J. G. Sandberg)

1939. Death Centenary of P. H. Ling (creator of "Swedish Drill").

228	**44**	5ore green	30	20
229	**44**	25ore brown	90	25

45 Carl von Linne (Linnaeus) (after A. Roslin)

1939. Bicent of Swedish Academy of Sciences.

230a	-	10ore violet	1·70	50
231	**45**	15ore brown	35	20
232	-	30ore blue	8·75	35
233	**45**	50ore grey	11·00	80

PORTRAIT: 10ore, 30ore J. J. Berzelius (after O. J. Sodermark).

47 Carl Michael Bellman

1940. Birth Bicent of C. M. Bellman (poet).

244	**47**	5ore green	20	20
245	**47**	35ore red	55	45

48 Johan Tobias Sergel (self-portrait bust)

1940. Birth Bicent of J. T. Sergel (sculptor).

246	**48**	15ore brown	3·25	25
247	**48**	50ore grey	14·50	90

49 Reformers presenting Bible to Gustavus Vasa

1941. 400th Anniv of First Authorized Version of Bible in Swedish.

248	**49**	15ore brown	20	20
249	**49**	90ore blue	16·00	75

50 Hasjo Belfry

1941. 50th Anniv of Foundation of Skansen Open-air Museum.

250a	**50**	10ore violet	1·80	20
251	**50**	60ore purple	7·25	55

50a Royal Palace, Stockholm

1941

252	**50a**	5k. blue	1·30	25

51 A. Hazelius

1941. Artur Hazelius (founder of Skansen Museum).

253	**51**	5ore green	30	20
254	**51**	1k. orange	5·50	2·30

52 St. Bridget (from altar painting, Vasteras Cathedral)

1941. 550th Anniv of Canonization of St. Bridget (Foundress of Brigittine Order of Our Saviour).

255	**52**	15ore brown	25	20
256	**52**	120ore purple	20·00	9·00

53 Mute Swans

1942

257a	**53**	20k. blue	3·00	30

54 King Gustavus III (after A. Roslin)

1942. 150th Anniv of National Museum, Stockholm.

258	**54**	20ore red	55	20
259	-	40ore green	15·00	90

PORTRAIT: 40ore Carl Gustaf Tessin (architect and chancery president) (after Gustav Lundberg).

55 Count Rudenschold and Nils Mansson

1942. Centenary of Institution of National Elementary Education.

260a	**55**	10ore red	25	30
261	**55**	90ore blue	2·30	4·50

56 Carl Wilhelm Scheele

1942. Birth Bicent of C. W. Scheele (chemist).

262	**56**	5ore green	20	20
263	**56**	60ore red	5·75	30

57 King Gustav V

1943. 85th Birthday of King Gustav V.

264	**57**	20ore red	50	30
265	**57**	30ore blue	90	2·10
266	**57**	60ore purple	1·00	2·50

58 Rifle Assn Badge

1943. 50th Anniv of National Voluntary Rifle Association.

267	**58**	10ore purple	20	15
268	**58**	90ore blue	3·00	40

59 O. Montelius (after E. Stenberg)

1943. Birth Centenary of Oscar Montelius (archaeologist).

269	**59**	5ore green	20	15
270	**59**	120ore purple	5·25	2·10

60 First Swedish Navigators' Chart

1944. Tercent of First Swedish Marine Chart.

271	**60**	5ore green	20	15
272	**60**	60ore red	3·25	45

61 "Smalands Lejon" (ship of the line)

1944. Swedish Fleet (Tercentenary of Battle of Femern).

273	**61**	10ore violet	20	25
274	-	20ore red	35	15
275	-	30ore blue	45	80
276	-	40ore green	80	90
277	-	90ore grey	7·00	1·60

DESIGNS—27×22½ mm: 30ore "Kung Karl" (ship of the line); 40ore Stern of "Amphion" (royal yacht); 90ore "Gustav V" (cruiser). 18½×20½ mm: 20ore Admiral C. Fleming (after L. Pasch).

See also Nos. 517/22.

62 Red Cross

1945. 80th Anniv of Swedish Red Cross and Birthday of Prince Carl.

278	**62**	20ore red	65	15

63 Press Symbols

1945. Tercentenary of Swedish Press.

279	**63**	5ore green	30	15
280	**63**	60ore red	5·25	35

64 Viktor Rydberg (after A. Edelfelt)

1945. 50th Death Anniv of Viktor Rydberg (author).

281	**64**	20ore red	35	15
282	**64**	90ore blue	5·25	40

65 Oak Tree, Savings Banks' Symbol

1945. 125th Anniv of Swedish Savings Banks.

283	**65**	10ore violet	25	20
284	**65**	40ore green	1·10	90

66 Cathedral Model **67** Lund Cathedral

1946. 800th Anniv of Lund Cathedral.

285	**66**	15ore brown	75	30
286	**67**	20ore red	30	15
287	**66**	90ore blue	6·75	60

68 Mare and Foal

1946. Centenary of Swedish Agricultural Show.

288	**68**	5ore green	30	15
289	**68**	60ore red	4·00	35

69 Tegner (after bust by J. N. Bystrom)

1946. Death Centenary of Esaias Tegner (poet).

290	**69**	10ore violet	30	15
291	**69**	40ore green	1·30	45

70 A. Nobel

1946. 50th Death Anniv of Alfred Nobel (scientist and creator of Nobel Foundation).

292	**70**	20ore red	65	15
293	**70**	30ore blue	2·20	35

71 E. G. Geijer (after J. G. Sandberg)

1947. Death Centenary of Erik Gustav Geijer (historian, philosopher, poet and composer).

294	**71**	5ore green	25	15
295	**71**	90ore blue	3·25	30

72 King Gustav V

1947. Forty Years Reign of King Gustav V.

296	**72**	10ore violet	25	20
297	**72**	20ore red	25	20
298	**72**	60ore purple	1·10	1·00

73 Ploughman and Skyscraper

1948. Centenary of Swedish Pioneers in U.S.A.

307	**73**	15ore brown	25	15
308	**73**	30ore blue	55	40
309	**73**	1k. orange	1·10	70

73a King Gustav V

1948. King Gustav V's 90th Birthday, and Youth Fund.

309a	**73a**	10ore+10ore green	45	50
309b	**73a**	20ore+10ore red	55	60
309c	**73a**	30ore+10ore blue	50	50

74 J. A. Strindberg (after R. Bergh)

1949. Birth Centenary of Strindberg (dramatist).

310	**74**	20ore red	35	20
311	**74**	30ore blue	65	55
312	**74**	80ore green	2·40	40

75 Gymnasts

1949. 2nd Lingiad, Stockholm.

313	**75**	5ore blue	25	30
314	**75**	15ore brown	25	20

76 Globe and Hand Writing **77**

1949. 75th Anniv of U.P.U.

315	**76**	10ore green	25	20
316	**76**	20ore red	25	20
317	**77**	30ore blue	35	40

78 King Gustav VI Adolf

1951. (a) Coloured lettering and figures.

318	**78**	10ore green	15	15
318b	**78**	10ore brown	20	20
319	**78**	15ore brown	25	20
388	**78**	15ore red	20	20
320	**78**	20ore red	30	20
391	**78**	20ore black	25	20
322a	**78**	25ore black	40	30
323	**78**	25ore red	75	25
324a	**78**	25ore blue	15	15
392	**78**	25ore brown	75	20
326	**78**	30ore brown	35	30
326a	**78**	30ore red	5·25	20
393	**78**	30ore blue	30	15
327	**78**	40ore blue	55	20
328	**78**	40ore green	60	20

(b) White lettering and figures.

429	15ore red	15	15
430	20ore black	25	15
431	25ore brown	15	15
432a	30ore blue	55	20
433	30ore violet	40	20
433b	30ore red	70	60
434	35ore violet	50	15
435a	35ore blue	30	15
436	35ore black	50	20
437	40ore green	40	15
438a	40ore blue	30	15
439a	45ore orange	50	15
439b	45ore blue	50	15
440	50ore green	65	20
440a	50ore green	50	20
440c	55ore red	45	15
441	60ore red	65	55
441a	65ore blue	85	20
441c	70ore mauve	65	20
441d	85ore purple	70	35

79 Christopher Polhem (after G. E. Schroder)

1951. Death Bicentenary of Polhem (engineer).

329a	**79**	25ore black	35	30
330	**79**	45ore brown	45	40

80

1951

383	**80**	5ore red	20	15
386	**80**	10ore blue	20	15
387a	**80**	10ore brown	20	20

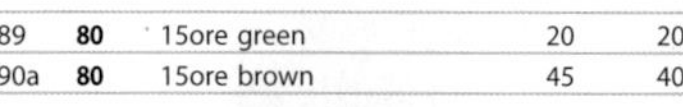

389	**80**	15ore green	20	20
390a	**80**	15ore brown	45	40

81 Olavus Petri Preaching

1952. 400th Death Anniv of Petri (reformer).

332	**81**	25ore black	30	20
333	**81**	1k.40 brown	3·25	65

81a King Gustav VI Adolf

1952. 70th Birthday of King Gustav VI Adolf and Culture Fund.

333a	**81a**	10ore+10ore green	35	30
333bba	**81a**	25ore+10ore red	40	40
333c	**81a**	40ore+10ore blue	40	35

82 Ski Jumping

1953. 50th Anniv of Swedish Athletic Assn.

334	**82**	10ore green	40	20
335	-	15ore brown	55	50
336	-	40ore blue	1·10	1·30
337	-	1k.40 mauve	3·50	80

DESIGNS—HORIZ: 1k.40, Wrestling. VERT: 15ore Ice hockey; 40ore Slingball.

83 Stockholm, 1650

1953. 700th Anniv of Stockholm.

338	**83**	25ore blue	25	20
339	-	1k.70 red	2·20	50

DESIGN: 1k.70, Seal of Stockholm, 1296 (obverse and reverse).

84 "Radio"

1953. Cent of Telecommunications in Sweden.

340		25ore blue ("Telephones")	25	20
341	**84**	40ore green	95	1·10
342	-	60ore red ("Telegraphs")	2·00	1·90

85 Skier

1954. World Skiing Championships.

343	**85**	20ore grey	35	25
344	-	1k. blue (Woman skier)	6·50	90

86 Anna Maria Lenngren (after medallion, J. T. Sergel)

1954. Birth Bicentenary of Anna Maria Lenngren (poetess).

345	**86**	20ore grey	25	20
346	**86**	65ore brown	3·25	2·30

87 Rock-carvings

1954

347	**87**	50ore grey	25	20
348	**87**	55ore red	95	20
349	**87**	60ore red	40	20
350	**87**	65ore green	1·10	20
351	**87**	70ore orange	55	20
352	**87**	75ore brown	1·90	20
353	**87**	80ore green	45	20
355	**87**	90ore blue	45	20
356	**87**	95ore violet	2·50	3·00

88

1955. Centenary of First Swedish Postage Stamps.

362	**88**	25ore blue	20	20
363	**88**	40ore green	85	30

89 Swedish Flag

1955. National Flag Day.

364	**89**	10ore yellow, blue & green	20	20
365	**89**	15ore yellow, blue and red	30	20

1955. Cent of First Swedish Postage Stamps and "Stockholmia" Philatelic Exn. As T 1 but with two rules through bottom panel.

366	**1**	3ore green	1·80	3·50
367	**1**	4ore blue	1·80	3·50
368	**1**	6ore grey	1·80	3·50
369	**1**	8ore yellow	1·80	3·50
370	**1**	24ore orange	1·80	3·50

Nos. 366/70 were sold only at the exhibition in single sets, at 2k.45 (45ore face + 2k. entrance fee).

91 P. D. A. Atterbom (after Fogelberg)

1955. Death Centenary of Atterbom (poet).

371	**91**	20ore blue	20	20
372	**91**	1k.40 brown	3·25	45

92 Greek Horseman, (from Parthenon frieze)

1956. 16th Olympic Games Equestrian Competitions, Stockholm.

373	**92**	20ore red	25	20
374	**92**	25ore blue	40	20
375	**92**	40ore green	1·80	1·50

92a Whooper Swans

1956. Northern Countries' Day.

376	**92a**	25ore red	35	20
377	**92a**	40ore blue	80	55

93 Railway Construction

1956. Centenary of Swedish Railways.

378	**93**	10ore green	35	20
379	-	25ore blue	30	20
380	-	40ore orange	2·50	2·40

DESIGNS: 25ore Steam locomotive, "Fryckstad" and passenger carriage; 40ore Type XOa5 electric train on Arsta Bridge, Stockholm.

94 Trawler in Distress and Lifeboat

1957. 50th Anniv of Swedish Life Saving Service.

381	**94**	30ore blue	2·40	20
382	**94**	1k.40 red	4·25	1·00

95 Galleon and "Gripsholm II" **96** Bell 47G Helicopter with Floats

1958. Postal Services Commemoration.

395	**95**	15ore red	25	20
396	**96**	30ore blue	20	20
397	**95**	40ore green	3·25	2·40
398	**96**	1k.40 brown	3·50	70

97 Footballer

1958. World Cup Football Championship.

399	**97**	15ore red	40	20
400	**97**	20ore green	40	20
401	**97**	1k.20 blue	1·20	60

98 Bessemer Tilting-furnace

1958. Centenary of Swedish Steel Industry.

402	**98**	30ore blue	20	20
403	**98**	170ore brown	3·00	75

99 Selma Lagerlof (after bust by G. Malmquist)

1958. Birth Centenary of Selma Lagerlof (writer).

404	**99**	20ore red	20	20
405	**99**	30ore blue	20	20
406	**99**	80ore green	70	70

100 Overhead Power Lines

1959. 50th Anniv of Swedish State Power Board.

407	**100**	30ore blue	30	20
408	-	90ore red	2·75	1·80

DESIGN—HORIZ: 90ore Dam sluice-gates.

101 Henri Dunant (founder)

1959. Red Cross Centenary.

409	**101**	30ore+10ore red	45	45

102 Heidenstam

1959. Birth Centenary of Verner von Heidenstam (poet).

410	**102**	15ore red	55	35
411	**102**	1k. black	2·50	70

103 Forest Trees

1959. Centenary of Crown Lands and Forests Administration.

412	**103**	30ore green	95	20
413	-	1k.40 red	2·75	50

DESIGN: 1k.40, Forester felling tree.

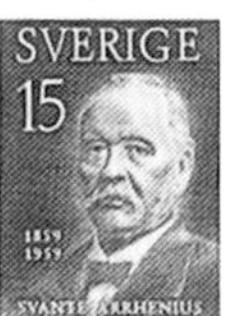

104 S. Arrhenius

1959. Birth Centenary of Arrhenius (chemist).

414	**104**	15ore brown	20	20
415	**104**	1k.70 blue	3·25	40

105 Anders Zorn (self-portrait)

1960. Birth Cent of Zorn (painter and etcher).

416	**105**	30ore grey	20	20
417	**105**	80ore brown	2·50	1·20

106 "Uprooted Tree"

1960. World Refugee Year.

418	**106**	20ore brown	20	20
419	-	40ore violet	35	25

DESIGN—VERT: 40ore Refugees.

107 Target-shooting

1960. Centenary of Voluntary Shooting Organization.

420	**107**	15ore red	20	20
421	-	90ore blue	2·20	1·20

DESIGN: 90ore Organization members marching, 1860.

108 G. Froding

1960. Birth Centenary of Gustav Froding (poet).

422	**108**	30ore brown	20	20
423	**108**	1k.40 green	2·30	35

1960. Europa. As T 144a of Switzerland.

424	40ore blue	35	30
425	1k. red	65	40

109 H. Branting

1960. Birth Centenary of Hjalmar Branting (statesman).

426	**109**	15ore red	20	20
427	**109**	1k.70 blue	2·50	45

109a Douglas DC-8

1961. 10th Anniv of Scandinavian Airlines System.

428	**109a**	40ore blue	35	20

111 "Coronation of Gustav III" (after Pilo)

1961. 250th Birth Anniv of Carl Gustav Pilo (painter).

442	**111**	30ore brown	25	20
443	**111**	1k.40 blue	2·75	80

112 J. Alstromer (after bust by P. H. l'Archeveque)

1961. Death Bicentenary of Jonas Alstromer (industrial reformer).

444	**112**	15ore purple	20	20
445	**112**	90ore blue	1·00	1·20

113 Printing Works and Library

1961. Tercentenary of Royal Library Regulation.

446	**113**	20ore red	20	20
447	**113**	1k. blue	4·25	70

114 Motif on Runic Stone at Oland

1961

448	**114**	10k. purple	17·00	50

115 Nobel Prize Winners of 1901

1961. Nobel Prize Winners of 1901.

449	**115**	20ore red	20	20
450	**115**	40ore blue	20	20
451	**115**	50ore green	20	20

See also Nos. 458/9, 471/2, 477/8, 488/9, 523/4, 546/7 and 573/4.

116 Postman's Footprints

1962. Cent of Swedish Local Mail Delivery Service.

452	**116**	30ore violet	20	20
453	**116**	1k.70 red	3·00	35

117 Code, Voting Instrument and Mallet

1962. Centenary of Municipal Laws.

454	**117**	30ore blue	25	20
455	**117**	2k. red	3·25	35

118 St. George and Dragon, Storkyrkan ("Great Church"), Stockholm

1962. Swedish Monuments (1st series).

456	**118**	20ore purple	20	20
457	-	50ore green	25	20

DESIGN—HORIZ: 50ore Skokloster Castle.

See also Nos. 469/70 and 479/80.

118a King Gustav VI Adolf and Cultural Themes

1962. King Gustav's 80th Birthday and Swedish Culture Fund.

457b	**118a**	20ore+10ore brown	20	20
457c	**118a**	35ore+10ore blue	20	20

1962. Nobel Prize Winners of 1902. As T 115 but inscr "NOBELPRIS 1902".

458	25ore red	20	20
459	50ore blue	35	20

PORTRAITS: 25ore Theodor Mommsen (literature) and Sir Ronald Ross (medicine); 50ore Emil Hermann Fischer (chemistry) and Pieter Zeeman and Hendrik Lorentz (physics).

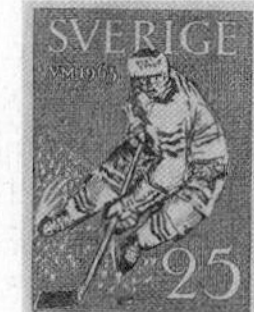

119 Ice Hockey Player

1963. World Ice Hockey Championships.

460	**119**	25ore green	20	20
461	**119**	1k.70 blue	2·75	30

120 Hands reaching for Wheat

1963. Freedom from Hunger.

462	**120**	35ore mauve	20	20
463	**120**	50ore violet	20	20

121 Engineering and Industrial Symbols

1963. "Engineering and Industry".

464	**121**	50ore black	20	20
465	**121**	1k.05 orange	2·30	2·20

122 Dr. G. F. Du Rietz (after D. K. Ehrenstrahl)

1963. 300th Anniv of Swedish Board of Health.

466	**122**	25ore brown	25	25
467	**122**	35ore blue	25	20
468	**122**	2k. red	3·00	40

123 Linne's Hammarby (country house)

1963. Swedish Monuments (2nd series).

469	**123**	20ore red	20	20
470	**123**	50ore green	20	20

1963. Nobel Prize Winners of 1903. As T 115 but inscr "NOBELPRIS 1903".

471	25ore green	40	40
472	50ore brown	40	20

PORTRAITS: 25ore Svante Arrhenius (chemistry), Niels Ryberg Finsen (medicine) and Bjornstjerne Bjornson (literature); 50ore Antoine Henri Becquerel and Pierre and Marie Curie (physics).

124 Motif from Poem "Elie Himmelsfard"

1964. Birth Centenary of E. A. Karlfeldt (poet).

473	**124**	35ore blue	45	20
474	**124**	1k.05 red	3·00	3·00

125 Seal of Archbishop Stefan

1964. 800th Anniv of Archbishopric of Uppsala.

475	**125**	40ore green	20	20
476	**125**	60ore brown	25	20

1964. Nobel Prize Winners of 1904. As T 115 but inscr "NOBELPRIS 1904".

477	30ore blue	30	40
478	40ore red	50	20

PORTRAITS: 30ore Jose Echegaray y Eizaguirre and Frederic Mistral (literature) and J. W. Strutt (Lord Rayleigh) (physics); 40ore Sir William Ramsay (chemistry) and Ivan Petrovich Pavlov (medicine).

126 Visby Town Wall

1965. Swedish Monuments (3rd series).

479	**126**	30ore mauve	20	20
480	**126**	2k. blue	3·00	20

127 Posthorns

1965

481	**127**	20ore blue and yellow	20	20

128 Telecommunications

1965. Centenary of I.T.U.

482	**128**	60ore violet	30	20
483	**128**	1k.40 blue	1·80	95

129 Prince Eugen (after D. Tagtstrom)

1965. Birth Centenary of Prince Eugen (painter).

484	**129**	40ore black	20	20
485	**129**	1k. brown	1·80	30

130 F. Bremer (after O. J. Sodermark)

1965. Death Centenary of Fredrika Bremer (novelist).

486	**130**	25ore violet	20	20
487	**130**	3k. green	3·75	35

1965. Nobel Prize Winners of 1905. As T 115 but inscr "NOBELPRIS 1905".

488	30ore blue	30	25
489	40ore red	30	20

PORTRAITS: 30ore Philipp von Lenard (physics) and Johann von Baeyer (chemistry); 40ore Robert Koch (medicine) and Henryk Sienkiewicz (literature).

131 N. Soderblom

1966. Birth Centenary of Nathan Soderblom, Archbishop of Uppsala.

490	**131**	60ore brown	30	20
491	**131**	80ore green	85	20

132 Skating

1966. World Men's Speed Skating Championships, Gothenburg.

492	**132**	5ore red	20	20
493	**132**	25ore green	20	20
494	**132**	40ore blue	45	40

133 Entrance Hall, National Museum

1966. Centenary of Opening of National Museum Building.

495	**133**	30ore violet	20	20
496	**133**	2k.30 green	90	85

134 Ale's Stones, Ship Grave, Kaseberga

1966

498	-	35ore brown and blue	20	20
499	**134**	3k.50 grey	1·00	20
500	-	3k.70 violet	1·20	20
501	-	4k.50 red	1·50	20
502	-	7k. red and blue	2·10	40

DESIGNS—HORIZ: 35ore Fjeld (mountains); 7k. Gripsholm Castle. VERT: 3k.70, Lion Fortress, Gothenburg; 4k.50, Uppsala Cathedral (interior).

135 Louis de Geer (advocate of reform)

1966. Cent of Representative Assembly Reform.

510	**135**	40ore blue	25	20
511	**135**	3k. red	3·25	45

136 Theatre Stage

1966. Bicentenary of Drottningholm Theatre.

512	**136**	5ore red on pink	20	20
513	**136**	25ore bistre on pink	20	20
514	**136**	40ore purple on pink	45	45

137 Almqvist (after C. P. Mazer)

1966. Death Centenary of Carl Almqvist (writer).

515	**137**	25ore mauve	20	20
516	**137**	1k. green	1·80	20

1966. National Cancer Fund. Swedish Ships. Designs as T 61, but with imprint "1966" at foot.

517	10ore red	20	30
518	15ore red	20	30
519	20ore green	20	30
520	25ore blue	20	30
521	30ore red	20	30
522	40ore red	20	30

SHIPS—HORIZ: 10ore "Smalands Lejon"; 15ore "Calmare Nyckel" and "Fagel Grip"; 20ore "Hiorten"; 25ore "Constitutionen"; 30ore "Kung Karl"; 40ore Stern of "Amphion".

1966. Nobel Prize Winners of 1906. As T 115 but inscr "NOBELPRIS 1906".

523	30ore red	40	20
524	40ore green	35	20

PORTRAITS: 30ore Sir Joseph John Thomson (physics) and Giosue Carducci (literature); 40ore Henri Moissan (chemistry) and Camillo Golgi and Santiago Ramon y Cajal (medicine).

138 Handball

1967. World Handball Championships.

525	**138**	45ore blue	20	20
526	**138**	2k.70 mauve	2·50	1·10

139 "E.F.T.A."

1967. European Free Trade Assn (E.F.T.A.).

527	**139**	70ore orange	35	20

140 Table Tennis Player

1967. World Table Tennis Championships, Stockholm.

528	**140**	35ore mauve	20	20
529	**140**	90ore blue	95	40

141 Axeman and Beast

1967. Iron Age Helmet Decorations, Oland.

530	**141**	10ore blue and brown	20	20
531	-	15ore brown and blue	20	20
532	-	30ore mauve and brown	20	20
533	-	35ore brown and mauve	20	20

DESIGNS: 15ore Man between two bears; 30ore "Lion man" putting enemy to flight; 35ore Two warriors.

142 "Solidarity"

1967. Finnish Settlers in Sweden.

534	**142**	10ore multicoloured	20	20
535	**142**	35ore multicoloured	20	20

143 "Keep to the Right"

1967. Adoption of Changed Rule of the Road.

536	**143**	35ore black, yellow & blue	20	25
537	**143**	45ore black, yellow & grn	20	20

144 18th-century Post-rider

1967

538	**144**	5ore black and red	15	15
539	-	10ore black and blue	15	15
539b	-	20ore black on flesh	20	20
540	-	30ore red and blue	20	15
541	-	40ore blue, green & black	20	20
541b	-	45ore black and blue	20	20
542	-	90ore brown and blue	30	20
543	-	1k. green	35	20

DESIGNS—As T **144**. VERT: 10ore "Svent Skepp" (warship); 20ore "St. Stephen" (ceiling painting, Dadesjo Church, Smaland); 30ore Angelica plant on coast. HORIZ: 40ore Haverud Aqueduct, Dalsland Canal. 27½×22½ mm: 45ore Floating logs; 90ore Elk; 1k. Dancing cranes.

145 King Gustav VI Adolf

1967. 85th Birthday of King Gustav VI Adolf.

544	**145**	45ore blue	20	20
545	**145**	70ore green	25	20

1967. Nobel Prize Winners 1907. As T 115, but inscr "NOBELPRIS 1907".

546	35ore red	55	35
547	45ore blue	25	20

PORTRAITS: 35ore Eduard Buchner (chemistry) and Albert Abraham Michelson (physics); 45ore Charles Louis Alphonse Laveran (medicine) and Rudyard Kipling (literature).

146 Berwald, Violin and Music

1968. Death Centenary of Franz Berwald (composer).

548	**146**	35ore black and red	20	20
549	**146**	2k. black, blue and yellow	2·50	50

147 Bank Seal

1968. 300th Anniv of Bank of Sweden.

550	**147**	45ore blue	20	20
551	**147**	70ore black on orange	25	20

148 Butterfly Orchids

1968. Wild Flowers.

552	**148**	45ore green	80	30
553	-	45ore green	80	30
554	-	45ore red and green	80	30
555	-	45ore green	80	30
556	-	45ore green	80	30

DESIGNS: No. 553, Wood anemone; 554, Wild rose; 555, Wild cherry; 556, Lily of the valley.

149 University Seal

1968. 300th Anniv of Lund University.

557	**149**	10ore blue	15	20
558	**149**	35ore red	30	35

150 Ecumenical Emblem

1968. 4th General Assembly of World Council of Churches, Uppsala.

559	**150**	70ore purple	30	25
560	**150**	90ore blue	75	30

151 "The Universe"

1968. Centenary of the People's College.

561	**151**	45ore red	20	20
562	**151**	2k. blue	2·75	20

152 "Orienteer" crossing Forest

1968. World Orienteering Championships, Linkoping.

563	**152**	40ore red and violet	20	20
564	**152**	2k.80 violet and green	2·30	2·20

153 "The Tug of War" (wood-carving by Axel Petersson)

1968. Birth Centenary of Axel Petersson ("Doderhultarn").

565	**153**	5ore green	15	15
566	**153**	25ore brown	85	80
567	**153**	45ore brown and sepia	15	15

154 Red Fox

1968. Bruno Liljefors' Fauna Sketches.

568	-	30ore blue	65	55
569	-	30ore black	65	55
570	**154**	30ore brown	65	55
571	-	30ore brown	65	55
572	-	30ore blue	65	55

DESIGNS: No. 568, Arctic hare; 569, Greater black-backed gull; 571, Golden eagle and carrion crows; 572, Stoat.

1968. Nobel Prize Winner of 1908. As T 115, but inscr "NOBELPRIS 1908".

573	35ore red	40	35
574	45ore green	40	20

PORTRAITS: 35ore Ilya Mechnikov and Paul Ehrlich (medicine) and Lord Rutherford (chemistry); 45ore Gabriel Lippman (physics) and Rudolf Eucken (literature).

154a Viking Ships

1969. 50th Anniv of Northern Countries Union.

575	**154a**	45ore brown	30	20
576	**154a**	70ore blue	75	80

155 "The Worker" (A. Amelin)

1969. 50th Anniv of I.L.O.

577	**155**	55ore red	20	20
578	**155**	70ore blue	65	35

156 Colonnade

1969. Europa.

579	**156**	70ore multicoloured	1·80	45
580	**156**	1k. multicoloured	1·60	20

157 A. Engstrom with Eagle Owl (self-portrait)

1969. Birth Centenary of Albert Engstrom (painter and writer).

581	**157**	35ore black	25	20
582	**157**	55ore blue	25	20

158 "Still Life"

1969. Birth Centenary of Ivan Agueli (painter) Sheet 135×90 mm containing multicoloured designs as T 158.

MS583	45ore "Landscape" (35×28 mm); 45ore Type **158**; 45ore "Arab town" (35×28 mm); 55ore "Egyptian Girl" (28×43 mm); 55ore "Street Scene" (48×43 mm); 55ore "Landscape" (28×43 mm) (sold at 3k.)	2·40	2·75

159 Tjorn Bridges

1969. Tjorn Bridges.

584	**159**	15ore blue on blue	1·00	40
585	-	30ore green and black on blue	1·00	40
586	-	55ore black and blue on blue	1·00	45

DESIGNS—As T **159**: 30ore Tjorn Bridges (different). 41×19 mm: 55ore Tjorn Bridges (different).

160 Helmeted Figure (carving)

1969. Warship "Wasa" Commemoration.

587	**160**	55ore red	35	20
588	-	55ore brown	35	20
589	-	55ore blue	35	20
590	-	55ore brown	35	20
591	-	55ore red	35	20
592	-	55ore blue	35	25

DESIGNS—As T **160**: No. 588, Crowned lion's head (carving); 590, Lion's head (carving); 591, Carved support. 46×28 mm: No. 589, Ship's coat-of-arms; 592, Ship of the line "Wasa", 1628.

161 H. Soderberg (writer)

1969. Birth Centenaries of Hjalmar Soderberg and Bo Bergman.

593	**161**	45ore brown on cream	20	20
594	-	55ore green on green	25	20

DESIGN—HORIZ: 55ore Bo Bergman (poet).

162 Lighthouses and Lightship "Cyklop"

1969. 300th Anniv of Swedish Lighthouse Service.

595	**162**	30ore black, red and grey	30	25
596	**162**	55ore black, orange & blue	30	20

163 "The Adventures of Nils" by S. Lagerlof (illus by J. Bauer)

1969. Swedish Fairy Tales.

597	-	35ore brown, red & orange	1·40	1·20
598	**163**	35ore brown	1·40	1·20
599	-	35ore brown, red & orange	1·40	1·20
600	-	35ore brown	1·40	1·20
601	-	35ore red and orange	1·40	1·20

DESIGNS: No. 597, "Pelle's New Suit" written and illus by Elsa Beskow; 599, "Pippi Longstocking" by A. Lindgren (illus by I. Vang Nyman); 600, "Vill-Vallareman, the Shepherd" (from "With Pucks and Elves" illus by J. Bauer); 601, "The Cat's Journey" written and illus by I. Arosenius.

164 Emil Kocher (medicine) and Wilhelm Ostwald (chemistry)

1969. Nobel Prize Winners of 1909.

602a	**164**	45ore green	45	40
603	-	55ore black on flesh	45	20
604	-	70ore black	55	60

DESIGNS: 55ore Selma Lagerlof (literature); 70ore Guglielmo Marconi and Ferdinand Braun (physics).

165 Weathervane, Soderala Church

1970. Swedish Forgings.

605	**165**	5ore green and brown	30	20
606	-	10 green and brown	30	20
607	-	30 ore black and green	35	20
608	-	55 ore brown and green	35	20

DESIGNS—As T **165**: 10ore As Type **165**, but design and country name/figures of value in reverse order; 30ore Memorial Cross, Ekshärad Churchyard. 24×44 mm: 55ore 14th-century door, Bjorksta Church.

166 Seal of King Magnus Ladulas

1970

609	**166**	2k.55 blue on cream	65	40
610	-	3k. blue on cream	80	15
611	-	5k. green on cream	1·50	20

DESIGNS: 3k. Seal of Duke Erik Magnusson; 5k. Great Seal of Erik IX.

167 River Ljungan

1970. Nature Conservation Year.

612	**167**	55ore multicoloured	25	20
613	**167**	70ore multicoloured	60	40

168 View of Kiruna

1970. Sweden within the Arctic Circle.

614	**168**	45ore brown	45	50
615	-	45ore blue	45	50
616	-	45ore green	45	50
617	-	45ore brown	45	50
618	-	45ore blue	45	50

DESIGNS: No. 615, Winter landscape and skiers; 616, Lake and Lapp hut, Stora National Park; 617, Reindeer herd; 618, Rocket-launching.

170 Chinese Palace, Drottningholm

1970. Historic Buildings.

619		55ore green	20	20
620	**170**	2k. multicoloured	1·20	20

DESIGN—21×27½ mm: 55ore Glimmingehus (15th-century castle).

171 Lumber Trucks

1970. Swedish Trade and Industry.

621	**171**	70ore brown and blue	2·20	2·10
622	-	70ore blue, brown & pur	2·20	2·10
623	-	70ore purple and blue	2·20	2·10
624	-	70ore blue and purple	2·20	2·10
625	-	70ore blue and purple	2·20	2·10
626	-	70ore brown and purple	2·20	2·10
627a	-	1k. black on cream	35	20

DESIGNS—As Type **171**: No. 623, Ship's propeller; 624, Dam and Class Dm3 electric locomotive; 626, Technician and machinery. 44×20 mm: No. 622, Loading freighter at quayside; 625, Mine and electric ore train. 26×20 mm: No. 627a, Miners at coal face.

173 Three Hearts

1970. 25th Anniv of United Nations.

628	**173**	55ore red, yellow and black	25	20
629	-	70ore green, yellow & blk	45	20

DESIGN: 70ore Three four-leaved clovers.

174 Blackbird

1970. Christmas. Birds. Multicoloured.

630		30ore Type **174**	70	65
631		30ore Great tit	70	65
632		30ore Northern bullfinch	95	65
633		30ore Western greenfinch	70	65
634		30ore Blue tit	70	65

175 Paul Heyse (literature)

1970. Nobel Prize Winners of 1910.

635	**175**	45ore violet	80	40
636	-	55ore blue	55	20
637	-	70ore black	85	75

PORTRAITS: 55ore Otto Wallach (chemistry) and Johannes van der Waals (physics); 70ore Albrecht Kossel (medicine).

176 Ferry "Storskar" and Royal Palace, Stockholm

1971

638	**176**	80ore black and blue	35	20
639	-	4k. black	95	20
639a	-	6k. blue	1·60	20

DESIGN: 4k. 16th-century "Blood Money" coins; 6k. Gustav Vasa's dollar.

178 Kerstin Hesselgren (suffragette)

1971. 50th Anniv of Swedish Women's Suffrage.

640	**178**	45ore violet on green	25	20
641	**178**	1k. brown on yellow	45	20

179 Arctic Terns

1971. Nordic Help for Refugees Campaign.

642	**179**	40ore red	25	30
643	**179**	55ore blue	60	20

180 "The Prodigal Son" (painting, Sodra Rada Church)

1971

644	**180**	15ore green on green	20	20
645	-	25ore blue and brown	25	20
646	-	25ore blue and brown	25	20

DESIGNS—HORIZ (Panels from Grodinge Tapestry, Swedish Natural History Museum): No. 645, Griffin; 646, Lion.

182 Container Port, Gothenburg

1971

647	**182**	55ore violet and blue	20	20
648	-	60ore brown on cream	20	20
649	-	75ore green on green	30	20

DESIGNS—28×23 mm: 60ore Timber-sledge; 75ore Windmills, Oland.

184 Musical Score

1971. Bicent of Swedish Royal Academy of Music.

650	**184**	55ore purple	20	20
651	**184**	85ore green	35	30

185 "The Mail Coach" (E. Schwab)

1971

652	**185**	1k.20 multicoloured	35	20

186 "The Three Wise Men"

1971. Gotland Stone-masons' Art.

653	**186**	5ore violet and brown	45	25
654	-	10ore violet and green	45	25
655	-	55ore green and brown	55	20
656	-	65ore brown and violet	40	20

DESIGNS—As T **186**: 10ore "Adam and Eve". 40×21 mm: 55ore "Winged Knight" and "Samson and the Lion"; 65ore "The Flight into Egypt".

187 Child beside Lorry Wheel

1971. Road Safety.

657	**187**	35ore black and red	25	20
658	**187**	65ore blue and red	30	20

188 State Sword of Gustavus Vasa, c. 1500

1971. Swedish Crown Regalia. Multicoloured.

659		65ore Type **188**	45	30
660		65ore Sceptre of Erik XIV, 1561	45	30
661		65ore Crown of Erik XIV, 1561	45	30
662		65ore Orb of Erik XIV, 1561	45	30
663		65ore Anointing horn of Karl IX, 1606	45	30

189 Santa Claus and Gifts

1971. Christmas. Traditional Prints.

664	**189**	35ore red	1·30	1·10
665	-	35ore blue	1·30	1·10
666	-	35ore purple	1·30	1·10
667	-	35ore blue	1·30	1·10
668	-	35ore green	1·30	1·10

DESIGNS: No. 665, Market scene; 666, Musical evening; 667, Skating; 668, Arriving for Christmas service.

190 "Nils Holgersson on Goose" (from "The Wonderful Adventures of Nils" by Selma Lagerlof)

1971

669	**190**	65ore blue on cream	25	20

191 Maurice Maeterlinck (literature)

1971. Nobel Prize Winners of 1911.

670	**191**	55ore orange	50	30
671	-	65ore green	60	20
672	-	85ore red	65	50

DESIGNS: 65ore Allvar Gullstrand (medicine) and Wilhelm Wien (physics); 85ore Marie Curie (chemistry).

192 Fencing

1972. Sportswomen.

673	**192**	55ore purple	55	55
674	-	55ore blue	55	55
675	-	55ore green	55	55
676	-	55ore purple	55	55
677	-	55ore blue	55	55

DESIGNS: No. 674, Diving; 675, Gymnastics; 676, Tennis; 677, Figure-skating.

193 L. J. Hierta (newspaper editor, statue by C. Eriksson)

1972. Anniversaries of Swedish Cultural Celebrities.

678	**193**	35ore multicoloured	20	20
679	-	50ore violet	20	20
680	-	65ore blue	30	20
681	-	85ore multicoloured	40	30

DESIGNS AND ANNIVERSARIES—VERT: 35ore (death cent); 85ore G. Stiernhielm (poet 300th death anniv) (portrait by D. K. Ehrenstrahl). HORIZ: 50ore F. M. Franzen (poet and hymn-writer, birth bicent) (after K. Hultstrom); 65ore Hugo Alfven (composer, birth cent) (granite bust by C. Milles).

195 Roe Deer

1972

682	**195**	95ore brown on cream	30	20

196 Glass-blowing

1972. Swedish Glass Industry.

683	**196**	65ore black	85	40
684	-	65ore blue	85	40
685	-	65ore red	85	40
686	-	65ore black	85	40
687	-	65ore blue	85	40

DESIGNS: No. 684, Glass-blowing (close-up); 685, Shaping glass; 686, Handling glass vase; 687, Bevelling glass vase.

197 Horses, Borgholm Castle (after N. Kreuger)

1972. Tourism in South-east Sweden.

688	**197**	55ore brown on cream	40	40
689	-	55ore blue on cream	40	40
690	-	55ore brown on cream	40	40
691	-	55ore green on cream	40	40
692	-	55ore blue on cream	40	40

DESIGNS: No. 689, Oland Bridge and sailing barque "Meta"; 690, Kalmar Castle; 691, Salmon-fishing, Morrumsan; 692, Cadet schooner "Falken", Karlskrona Naval Base.

198 Conference Emblem and Motto, "Only One Earth"

1972. U.N. Environment Conservation Conference, Stockholm.

693	**198**	65ore blue and red on cream	30	20
694	-	85ore mult on cream	50	35

DESIGN—28×45 mm: 85ore "Spring" (wooden relief by B. Hjorth).

199 Junkers F-13 SA-GAA

1972. Swedish Mailplanes.

695	**199**	5ore lilac	20	20
696	-	15ore blue	30	20
697	-	25ore blue	30	20
698	-	75ore green	30	20

DESIGNS—45×19 mm: 15ore Junkers Ju 52/3m; 25ore Friedrichshafen FF-49 seaplane; 75ore Douglas DC-3 SE-BAB Hoken.

200 Reindeer and Sledge (woodcut from "Lapponia")

1972. Centenary of "Lapponia" (book by J. Schefferus).

699	**200**	1k.40 red and blue	40	20

201 Early Courier

1972. "Stockholmia 74" Stamp Exhibition (1st issue) and Birth Centenary of Olle Hjortzberg (stamp designer).

700	**201**	10ore red	35	30
701	-	15ore green	35	30
702	-	40ore blue	35	30
703	-	50ore brown	35	30
704	-	60ore blue	35	30

DESIGNS: 15ore Post-rider; 40ore Steam train; 50ore Motor bus and trailer; 60ore Liner "Gripsholm".

See also Nos. 779/82.

202 Figurehead of Royal Yacht "Amphion" (Per Ljung)

1972. Swedish 18th-century Art.

705		75ore green	35	20
706		75ore brown	35	20
707	**202**	75ore red	35	20
708	-	75ore red	35	20
709	-	75ore black, brown and red	35	20
710	-	75ore black, blue & purple	35	20

DESIGNS—59×24 mm: No. 705, "Stockholm" (F. Martin); 706, "The Forge" (P. Hillestrom). As T **202**: No. 708, "Quadriga" (Sergel). 28×37 mm: No. 709, "Lady with a Veil" (A. Roslin); 710, "Sophia Magdalena" (C. G. Pilo).

203 Christmas Candles (J. Wikstrom)

1972. Christmas. Multicoloured.

711	45ore Type **203**	25	20
712	45ore Father Christmas (E. Flygh)	25	20
713	75ore Carol singers (S. Hagg) (40×23 mm)	50	20

204 King Gustav VI Adolf

1972

714	**204**	75ore blue	25	15
715	**204**	1k. red	40	20

205 King Gustav with Book

1972. King Gustav VI Adolf's 90th Birthday.

716	**205**	75ore blue	1·60	2·00
717	-	75ore green	1·60	2·00
718	-	75ore red	1·60	2·00
719	-	75ore blue	1·60	2·00
720	-	75ore green	1·60	2·00

DESIGNS: No. 717, Chinese objets d'art; 718, Opening Parliament; 719, Greek objets d'art; 720, King Gustav tending flowers.

206 Alexis Carrel (medicine)

1972. Nobel Prize Winners of 1912.

721		60ore brown	45	30
722	**206**	65ore blue	55	30
723	-	75ore violet	85	20
724	-	1k. brown	85	20

DESIGNS—HORIZ: 60ore Paul Sabatier and Victor Grignard (chemistry). VERT: 75ore Nils Gustav Dalen (physics); 1k. Gerhart Hauptmann (literature).

207 "Tintomara" Stage Set (B-R. Hedwall)

1973. Bicentenary of Swedish Royal Theatre.

725	**207**	75ore green	20	15
726	-	1k. purple	30	25

DESIGN—41×23 mm: 1k. "Orpheus" (P. Hillestrom).

208 Modern Mail Coach, Vietas

1973

727		60ore black on yellow	20	20
728	**208**	70ore orange, blue & green	30	20

DESIGN: 60ore Mail bus, 1923.

209 Vasa Ski Race

1973. Tourism in Dalecarlia.

729	**209**	65ore green	35	30
730	-	65ore green	35	30
731	-	65ore black	35	30
732	-	65ore green	35	30
733	-	65ore red	35	30

DESIGNS: No. 730, "Going to the Church in Mora" (A. Zorn); 731, Church stables in Rattvik; 732, "The Great Pit"; 733, "Mid-summer Dance" (B. Nordenberg).

210 Horse (bas relief)

1973. Gottland Picture Stones.

734	**210**	5ore purple	15	15
735	-	10 blue	15	15

DESIGN: 10ore Viking longship (bas relief).

211 "Row of Willows" (P. Persson)

1973. Swedish Landscapes.

736	**211**	40ore brown	25	15
737	-	50ore black and brown	25	20
738	-	55ore green on cream	30	20

DESIGNS—20×28 mm: 50ore "View of Trosa" (R. Ljunggren). 27×23 mm: 55ore "Spring Birches" (O. Bergman).

212 Lumberman

1973. 75th Anniv of Swedish Confederation of Trade Unions.

739	**212**	75ore red	20	20
740	**212**	1k.40 blue	35	20

213 Observer reading Thermometer

1973. Centenary of I.M.O./W.M.O. and Swedish Meteorological Organizations.

741	**213**	65ore green	90	30
742	-	65ore blue and black	90	30

DESIGN: No. 742, U.S. satellite weather picture.

214 Nordic House, Reykjavik

1973. Nordic Countries' Postal Co-operation.

743	**214**	75ore multicoloured	40	20
744	**214**	1k. multicoloured	45	20

215 C. P. Thunberg, Japanese Flora and Scene

1973. Swedish Explorers.

745	**215**	1k. brown, green and blue	75	80
746	-	1k. multicoloured	75	80
747	-	1k. brown, green and blue	75	80
748	-	1k. multicoloured	75	80
749	-	1k. multicoloured	75	80

DESIGNS: No. 746, Anders Sparrman and Tahiti; 747, Adolf Erik Nordenskiold and the "Vega"; 748, Salomon Andree and wreckage of balloon "Ornen"; 749, Sven Hedin and camels.

216 Team of Oxen

1973. Centenary of Nordic Museum.

750	**216**	75ore black	1·10	30
751	-	75ore brown	1·10	30
752	-	75ore black	1·10	30
753	-	75ore purple	1·10	30
754	-	75ore brown	1·10	30

DESIGNS: No. 751, Braking flax; 752, Potato-planting; 753, Baking bread; 754, Spring sowing.

217 Grey Seal

1973. "Save Our Animals".

755	**217**	10ore green	20	20
756	-	20ore violet	20	20
757	-	25ore blue	20	20
758	-	55ore blue	25	20
759	-	65ore violet	25	20
760	-	75ore green	25	20

DESIGNS: 20ore Peregrine falcon; 25ore Lynx; 55ore European otter; 65ore Wolf; 75ore White-tailed sea eagle.

218 King Gustav VI Adolf

1973. King Gustav VI Adolf Memorial Issue.

761	**218**	75ore blue	20	20
762	**218**	1k. purple	30	20

219 "Country Dance" (J. Nilsson)

1973. Christmas. Peasant Paintings. Mult.

763		45ore Type **219**	45	25
764		45ore "The Three Wise Men" (A. Clemetson)	45	25
765		75ore "Gourd Plant" (B. A. Hansson) (23×28 mm)	1·30	20
766		75ore "The Rider" (K. E. Jonsson) (23×28 mm)	1·30	20

220 "Goosegirl" (E. Josephson)

1973. Ernst Josephson Commemoration.

767	**220**	10k. multicoloured	2·75	20

221 A. Werner (chemistry) and H. Kamerlingh-Onnes (physics)

1973. Nobel Prize Winners 1913.

768	**221**	75ore violet	40	20
769	-	1k. brown	45	20
770	-	1k.40 green	60	20

DESIGNS—VERT: 1k. Charles Robert Richet (medicine); 1k.40, Rabindranath Tagore (literature).

222 Ski Jumping

1974. "Winter Sports on Skis".

771	**222**	65ore green	45	40
772	-	65ore blue	45	40
773	-	65ore green	45	40
774	-	65ore red	45	40
775	-	65ore blue	45	40

DESIGNS: No 772, Cross-country (man); 773, Relay-racing; 774, Downhill-racing; 775, Cross-country (woman).

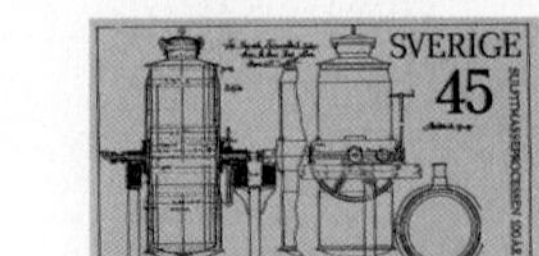

223 Ekman's Sulphite Pulping Machine

1974. Swedish Anniversaries.

776	**223**	45ore brown on grey	20	20
777	-	60ore green	20	30
778	-	75ore red	30	20

DESIGNS AND EVENTS: 45ore Type **223** (centenary of first sulphite pulp plant, Bergvik); 60ore Hans Jarta and part of Government Act (birth bicent); 75ore Samuel Owen and engineers (birth bicent).

224 U.P.U. Congress Stamp of 1924

1974. "Stockholmia '74" Stamp Exn (2nd issue).

779	**224**	20ore green	25	25
780	**224**	25ore blue	25	25
781	**224**	30ore brown	25	25
782	**224**	35ore red	25	25

MS783 Four sheets, 120×80 mm. containing stamps as Nos. 779/82, each in separate block of four. Colours changed. 20ore yellow; 25ore lilac; 30ore red; 35ore green. Set of 4 sheets 2·50 4·00

225 Great Falls

1974

784	**225**	35ore black and blue	20	20
785	-	75ore brown	20	20

DESIGN—HORIZ: 75ore Ystad (town).

226 "Figure in a Storm" (B. Marklund)

1974. Europa. Sculptures.

786	**226**	75ore purple	90	25
787	-	1k. green	1·30	25

DESIGN: 1k. Picasso statue (from "Les Dames de Mougins"), Kristinehamn.

227 King Carl XVI Gustav

1974

788	**227**	75ore green	25	20
789	**227**	90ore blue	35	20
790	**227**	1k. purple	40	20
791	**227**	1k.10 red	35	20
792	**227**	1k.30 green	35	20
793	**227**	1k.40 blue	40	20
794	**227**	1k.50 mauve	45	20
795	**227**	1k.70 orange	45	20
796	**227**	2k. brown	50	20

228 Central Post Office, Stockholm

1974. Centenary of Universal Postal Union.

800	**228**	75ore purple	80	20
801	-	75ore purple	80	20
802	-	1k. green	35	20

DESIGNS—As Type **228**: No. 801, Interior of Central Post Office, Stockholm. 40×24 mm: No. 802, Rural postman.

229 Regatta

1974. Tourism on Sweden's West Coast.

803	**229**	65ore red	30	30
804	-	65ore blue	30	30
805	-	65ore green	30	30
806	-	65ore green	30	30
807	-	65ore brown	30	30

DESIGNS: No. 804, Vinga Lighthouse; 805, Varberg Fortress; 806, Seine fishing; 807, Mollosund.

230 "Mr. Simmons" (A. Fridell)

1974. Centenary of Publicists' Club (Swedish press, radio and television association).

808	**230**	45ore black	20	20
809	**230**	1k.40 purple	30	20

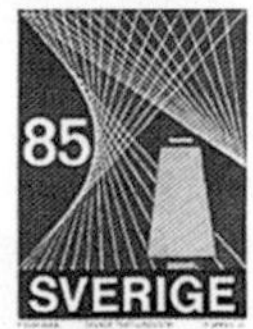

231 Thread and Spool

1974. Swedish Textile and Clothing Industry.

810	**231**	85ore violet	25	20
811	-	85ore black and orange	25	20

DESIGN: No. 811, Stylized sewing-machine.

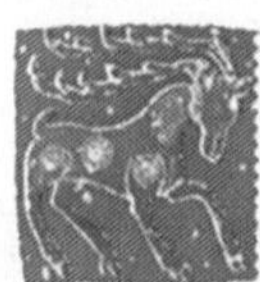
232 Deer

1974. Christmas. Mosaic Embroideries of Mythical Creatures. Each blue, red and green (45ore) or multicoloured (75ore).

812		45ore Type **232**	85	80
813		45ore Griffin	85	80
814		45ore Lion	85	80
815		45ore Griffin	85	80
816		45ore Unicorn	85	80
817		45ore Horse	85	80
818		45ore Lion	85	80
819		45ore Griffin	85	80
820		45ore Lion	85	80
821		45ore Lion-like creature	85	80
822		75ore Deer-like creature	25	20

No. 813 is facing right and has inscr at top, No. 815 faces left with similar inscr and No. 819 has inscr at bottom.

No. 814 has the inscr at top, No. 818 has it at the foot of the design, the lion having blue claws, No. 820 has similar inscr, but white claws.

Nos. 812/22 were issued together, se-tenant, forming a complete design.

233 Tanker "Bill"

1974. Swedish Shipping. Each blue.

823		1k. Type **233**	45	50
824		1k. "Snow Storm" (liner)	45	50
825		1k. "Tor" and "Atle" (ice-breakers)	45	50
826		1k. "Skanes" (train ferry)	45	50
827		1k. Tugs "Bill", "Bull" and "Starkodder"	45	50

234 Max von Laue (physics)

1974. Nobel Prize Winners of 1914.

828	**234**	65ore red	35	20
829	-	70ore green	35	20
830	-	1k. blue	55	20

DESIGNS:—70ore Theodore William Richards (chemistry); 1k. Richard Barany (medicine).

235 Sven Jerring (first announcer), Children and Microphone

1974. 50th Anniv of Swedish Broadcasting Corporation.

831	**235**	75ore blue and brown	65	20
832	-	75ore blue and brown	65	20

DESIGN: No. 832, Television camera at Parliamentary debate.

236 Giro Envelope

1975. 50th Anniv of Swedish Postal Giro Office.

833	**236**	1k.40 black and brown	35	20

237 Male and Female Engineers

1975. International Women's Year.

834	**237**	75ore green	20	20
835	-	1k. purple	40	20

DESIGN—VERT: 1k. Jenny Lind (singer) (portrait by O. J. Sodermark).

238 Bronze Helmet Decoration, Vendel

1975. Archaeological Discoveries.

836	**238**	10ore red	15	15
837	-	15ore green	15	15
838	-	20ore violet	15	15
839	-	25ore yellow	15	15
840	-	55ore brown	15	15

DESIGNS: 15ore Iron sword hilt and chapel, Vendel; 20ore Iron shield buckle, Vendel; 25ore Embossed gold plates (Gold Men), Eketorp Fortress, Oland; 55ore Iron helmet, Vendel.

239 "New Year's Eve at Skansen" (Eric Hallstrom)

1975. Europa. Paintings. Multicoloured.

841		90ore Type **239**	85	25
842		1k.10 "Inferno" (August Strindberg) (vert)	1·00	30

240 Metric Tape-measure (centenary of Metre Convention)

1975. Anniversaries.

843	**240**	55ore blue	25	20
844	-	70ore sepia and brown	25	25
845	-	75ore violet	30	25

DESIGNS AND EVENTS—44×27 mm: 70ore Peter Hernqvist (founder) and title-page of his book "Comprehensive Thesis on Glanders in Horses" (bicent of Swedish Veterinary Service). 24×31 mm: 75ore "Folke Filbyter" (birth centenary of Carl Milles (sculptor)).

241 Western European Hedgehog

1975

846	**241**	55ore black	20	20
847	-	75ore red	25	20
848	-	1k.70 blue	40	20
849	-	2k. purple	60	20
850	-	7k. green	1·80	30

DESIGNS—HORIZ: 75ore Key-fiddler; 1k.70, Western capercaillie ("cock of the woods"). VERT: 2k. Rok stone (ancient inscribed rock), Ostergotland; 7k. Ballet dancers (from "Romeo and Juliet").

242 Village Buildings, Skelleftea

1975. European Architectural Heritage Year.

851	**242**	75ore black	30	30
852	-	75ore red	30	30
853	-	75ore black	30	30
854	-	75ore red	30	30
855	-	75ore blue	30	30

DESIGNS: No. 852, Engelsberg iron-works, Vastmanland; 853, Gunpowder tower, Visby, Gotland; 854, Iron-mine, Falun; 855, Rommehed military barracks, Dalecarlia.

243 Fire Brigade

1975. "Watch, Guard and Help". Public Services.

856	**243**	90ore red	30	25
857	-	90ore blue	30	25
858	-	90ore red	30	25
859	-	90ore blue	30	25
860	-	90ore green	30	25

DESIGNS: No. 857, Customs service; 858, Police service; 859, Ambulance and hospital service; 860, Shipwreck of "Merkur" (Sea rescue service).

244 "Fryckstad"

1975. Swedish Steam Locomotives.

861	**244**	5ore green	20	15
862	-	5ore blue	20	15
863	-	90ore green	60	20

DESIGNS—As Type **244**: No. 862, "Gotland". 49×22 mm: 90ore "Prins August".

245 Canoeing

1975. Scouting. Multicoloured.

864	90ore Type **245**	60	20
865	90ore Camping	60	20

246 "Madonna" (sculpture), Vikiau church, Gotland

1975. Christmas. Religious Art.

866	**246**	55ore multicoloured	20	20
867	-	55ore multicoloured	35	25
868	-	55ore multicoloured	35	30
869	-	90ore brown	40	20
870	-	90ore red	55	20
871	-	90ore blue	55	20

DESIGNS—VERT: No. 867, "Birth of Christ" (embossed copper), Broddetorp church, Vastergotland; 868, "The Sun" (embossed copper), Broddetorp church, Vastergotland; 869, "Mourning Mary" (sculpture), Oja church, Gotland. HORIZ: Noore 870, 871, "Jesse at Foot of Christ's genealogical tree" (retable), Lofta church, Smaland.

247 W. H. and W. L. Bragg (physics)

1975. Nobel Prize Winners of 1915.

872	**247**	75ore purple	20	20
873	-	90ore blue	35	20
874	-	1k.10 green	40	20

DESIGNS: 90ore Richard Willstatter (chemistry); 1k.10, Romain Rolland (literature).

248 Bronze Coiled Snake Brooch, Vendel

1976

875	**248**	15ore bistre	15	15
876	-	20ore green	15	15
877	-	30ore purple	20	15
878	-	85ore blue	35	20
879	-	90ore blue	20	15
880	-	1k. purple	25	20
881	-	1k.90 green	50	20
882	-	9k. deep green and green	2·20	20

DESIGNS—21×19 mm: 20ore Pilgrim badge. 28×21 mm: 30ore Drinking horn; 85ore Common guillemot and razorbills. 28×23 mm: 1k.90, "Cave of the Winds" (sculpture) (Eric Grate). 21×28 mm: 90ore Chimney sweep; 1k. Bobbin lace-making; 9k. "Girl's Head" (wood-carving) (Bror Hjorth).

249 Early and Modern Telephones

1976. Telephone Centenary.

883	**249**	1k.30 mauve	35	20
884	**249**	3k.40 red	85	45

250 Wheat and Cornflower Seed

1976. Swedish Seed-testing Centenary.

885	**250**	65ore brown	25	20
886	-	65ore green and brown	25	20

DESIGN: No. 886, Viable and non-viable plants.

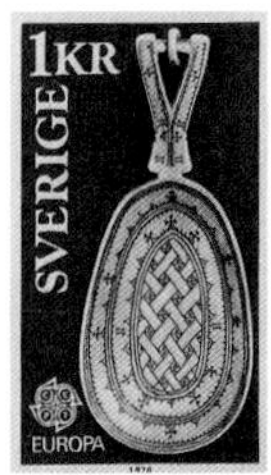
251 Lapp Spoon

1976. Europa. Handicrafts.

887	**251**	1k. black, pink and blue	75	25
888	-	1k.30 multicoloured	75	40

DESIGN: 1k.30, Tile stove (from aquarelle by C. Slania).

252 "View from Ringkallen" (H. Osslund)

1976. Tourism. Angermanland.

889	**252**	85ore green	30	30
890	-	85ore blue	30	30
891	-	85ore brown	30	30
892	-	85ore blue	30	30
893	-	85ore red	30	30

DESIGNS: No. 890, Tug towing timber; 891, Hay-drying racks; 892, Granvagsnipan; 893, Seine-net fishing.

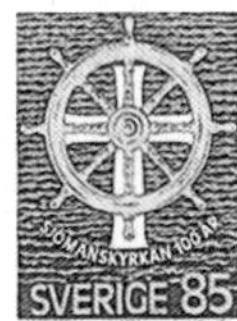
253 Ship's Wheel and Cross

1976. Centenary of Swedish Seamen's Church.

894	**253**	85ore blue	25	20

254 Torgny Segerstedt and "Goteborg Handels-och Sjofarts-tidning"

1976. Birth Centenary of Torgny Segerstedt (newspaper editor).

895	**254**	1k.90 black and brown	55	30

255 King Carl XVI Gustav and Queen Silvia

1976. Royal Wedding.

896	**255**	1k. red	30	20
897	**255**	1k.30 green	35	20

256 John Ericsson (marine propeller)

1976. Swedish Technological Pioneers. Mult.

898	1k.30 Type **256**	50	60
899	1k.30 Helge Palmcrantz (hay maker)	50	60
900	1k.30 Lars Magnus Ericsson (telephone improvements)	50	60
901	1k.30 Sven Wingquist (ball bearing)	50	60
902	1k.30 Gustaf de Laval (milk separator and reaction turbine)	50	60

257 Hands and Cogwheels

1976. Industrial Safety.

903	**257**	85ore orange and violet	25	20
904	**257**	1k. green and brown	30	20

258 Verner von Heidenstam

1976. Literature Nobel Prize Winner of 1916.

905	**258**	1k. green	35	20
906	**258**	1k.30 blue	45	30

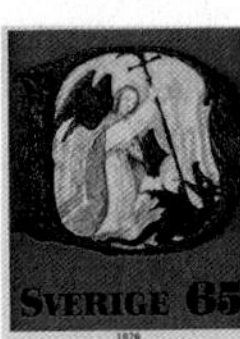
259 "Archangel Michael Destroying Lucifer" (Flemish prayer book)

1976. Christmas. Mediaeval Book Illustrations. Multicoloured.

907	65ore Type **259**	20	20
908	65ore "St. Nicholas awakening Children from Dead" (Flemish prayer book)	20	20
909	1k. "Mary visiting Elizabeth" (Austrian prayer book)	30	20
910	1k. "Prayer to the Virgin" (Austrian prayer book)	30	80

Nos. 909/10 are vert, 26×44 mm.

260 Water-lilies

1977. Nordic Countries Co-operation in Nature Conservation and Environment Protection.

911	**260**	1k. multicoloured	40	25
912	**260**	1k.30 multicoloured	35	35

261 Tawny Owl

1977

913	**261**	45ore green	20	20
914	-	70ore blue	25	20
915	-	1k.40 brown	40	40
916	-	2k.10 brown	55	20

DESIGNS—23×29 mm: 70ore Norwegian cast-iron stove decoration. 41×21 mm: 1k.40, Gotland ponies. 28×22 mm: 2k.10, Tailor.

262 "Politeness"

1977. Birth Centenary of Oskar Andersson (cartoonist).

917	**262**	75ore black	20	20
918	**262**	3k.80 red	1·00	30

263 Skating

1977. Keep-fit Activities.

919	**263**	95ore blue	30	30
920	-	95ore green	30	30
921	-	95ore red	30	30
922	-	95ore green	30	30
923	-	95ore blue	30	30

DESIGNS: No. 920, Swimming; 921, Cycling; 922, Jogging; 923, Badminton.

264 Gustavianum Building

1977. 500th Anniv of Uppsala University.

924	**264**	1k.10 black, yellow & blue	25	20

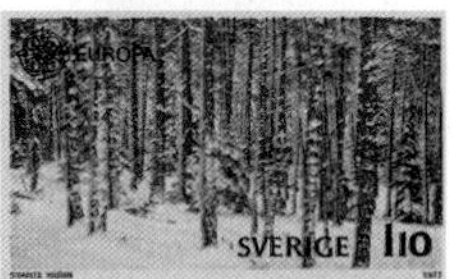
265 Winter Forest Scene

1977. Europa. Landscapes. Multicoloured.

925	1k.10 Type **265**	75	30
926	1k.40 Rapadalen valley, Sarek	80	50

266 Calle Schewen at Breakfast

1977. Tourism. Roslagen. Poem "Calle Schewen Waltz" by E. Taube.

927	**266**	95ore green	30	35
928	-	95ore violet	30	35

929	-	95ore black and red	30	35
930	-	95ore blue	30	35
931	-	95ore red	30	35

DESIGNS: No. 928, Black-headed gull; 929, Calle Schewen dancing; 930, Fishing; 931, Sunset.

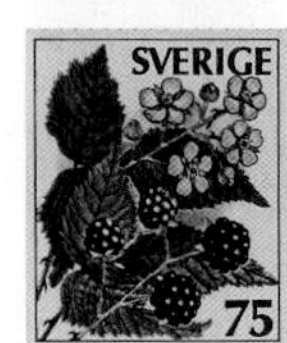

267 Blackberries

1977. Wild Berries. Multicoloured.

932		75ore Type **267**	20	20
933		75ore Cowberries	20	20
934		75ore Cloudberries	20	20
935		75ore Bilberries	20	20
936		75ore Strawberries	20	20

268 Horse-drawn Tram

1977. Public Transport.

937	**268**	1k.10 green	30	30
938	-	1k.10 blue	30	30
939	-	1k.10 blue	30	30
940	-	1k.10 blue	30	30
941	-	1k.10 green	30	30

DESIGN: No. 938, Electric tram; 939, Ferry "Djurgarden 6"; 940, Articulated bus; 941, Underground train, Stockholm.

269 H. Pontoppidan and K. A. Gjellerup (literature)

1977. Nobel Prize Winners of 1917.

942	**269**	1k.10 brown	30	30
943	-	1k.40 green	45	45

DESIGN: 1k.40, Charles Glover Barkla (physics).

270 Erecting Sheaf for Birds

1977. Christmas. Seasonal Customs.

944	**270**	75ore violet	25	20
945	-	75ore orange	25	20
946	-	75ore green	25	20
947	-	1k.10 green	40	20
948	-	1k.10 red	40	20
949	-	1k.10 blue	40	20

DESIGNS: No. 945, Making gingersnaps; 946, Bringing in the Christmas tree; 947, Preparing the traditional fish dish; 948, Making straw goats for the pantomime; 949, Candle-making.

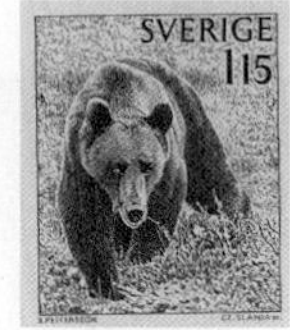

271 Brown Bear

1978

950	**271**	1k.15 brown	35	20
951	-	2k.50 blue	65	20

DESIGN: 2k.50, "Space without Affiliation" (sculpture by Arne Jones).

272 Orebro Castle

1978. Europa.

952	**272**	1k.30 green	80	25
953	-	1k.70 red	1·00	55

DESIGN—VERT: 1k.70, Doorway, Orebro Castle.

273 Pentecostal Meeting

1978. Independent Christian Associations.

954	**273**	90ore purple	30	30
955	-	90ore black	30	30
956	-	90ore violet	30	30
957	-	90ore green	30	30
958	-	90ore purple	30	30

DESIGNS: No. 955, Minister with children (Swedish Missionary Society); 956, Communion Service, Ethopia (Evangelical National Missionary Society); 957, Baptism (Baptist Society); 958, Salvation Army band.

274 Brosarp Hills

1978. Travels of Carl Linne (botanist).

959	**274**	1k.30 black	30	30
960	-	1k.30 blue	30	30
961	-	1k.30 purple	30	30
962	-	1k.30 red	30	30
963	-	1k.30 blue	30	30
964	-	1k.30 purple	30	30

DESIGNS—58×23 mm: No. 960, Pied avocets. 27×23 mm: No. 961, Grindstone production (after J. W. Wallander); 962, "Linnaea borealis". 27×36 mm: No. 963, Red limestone cliff; 964, Linnaeus wearing Lapp dress and Dutch doctor's hat, and carrying Lapp drum (H. Kingsbury).

275 Glider over Alleberg Plateau

1978. Tourism. Vastergotland.

965	**275**	1k.15 green	30	30
966	-	1k.15 red	30	30
967	-	1k.15 blue	30	30
968	-	1k.15 grey	30	30
969	-	1k.15 black and purple	30	30

DESIGNS: No. 966, Common cranes; 967, Fortress on Lacko Island Skara; 968, Rock tomb, Luttra; 969, "Traders of South Vastergotland" (sculpture, N. Sjogren).

276 Diploma and Laurel Wreath

1978. Centenary of Stockholm University.

970	**276**	2k.50 green on brown	75	30

277 "The Homecoming" (Carl Kylberg)

1978. Paintings by Swedish Artists. Mult.

971		90ore Type **277**	35	20
972		1k.15 "Standing Model seen from Behind" (Karl Isakson)	40	20
973		4k.50 "Self-portrait with a Floral Wreath" (Ivar Arosenius)	1·10	40

278 Northern Arrow

1978

974	**278**	10k. mauve	2·00	25

279 Coronation Carriage, 1699

1978

975	**279**	1k.70 red on buff	45	45

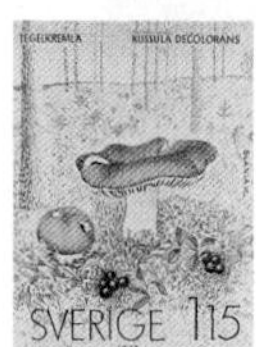

280 "Russula decolorans"

1978. Edible Mushrooms. Multicoloured.

976		1k.15 Type **280**	40	40
977		1k.15 Common puff-ball ("Lycoperdon perlatum")	40	40
978		1k.15 Parasol mushroom ("Macrolepiota procera")	40	40
979		1k.15 Chanterelle ("Cantharellus cibarius")	40	40
980		1k.15 Cep ("Boletus edulis")	40	40
981		1k.15 Cauliflower clavaria ("Ramaria botrytis")	40	40

281 Dalecarlian Horse

1978. Christmas. Old Toys.

982	**281**	90ore multicoloured	30	20
983	-	90ore multicoloured	30	20
984	-	90ore green and red	30	20
985	-	1k.30 multicoloured	40	20
986	-	1k.30 multicoloured	40	20
987	-	1k.30 blue	40	20

DESIGNS—VERT: No. 983, Swedish Court doll; 984, Meccano; 987, Teddy bear. HORIZ: No. 985, Tops; 986, Equipage with water barrel (metal toy).

282 Fritz Haber (chemistry)

1978. Nobel Prize Winners of 1918.

988	**282**	1k.30 brown	45	20
989	-	1k.70 black	55	50

DESIGN: 1k.70, Max Planck (physics).

283 Bandy Players fighting for Ball

1979. Bandy.

990	**283**	1k.05 blue	40	20
991	**283**	2k.50 orange	55	20

284 Child in Gas-mask

1979. International Year of the Child.

992	**284**	1k.70 blue	55	50

285 Wall Hanging

1979

993	**285**	4k. blue and red	95	20

286 Carrier Pigeon and Hand with Quill

1979. Rebate Stamp.

994	**286**	(1k.) yellow, black and blue	95	20

No. 994 was only issued in booklets of 20 sold at 20k. in exchange for tokens distributed to all households in Sweden. Valid for inland postage only, they represented a rebate of 30ore on the normal rate of 1k.30.

287 Sledge-boat

1979. Europa.

995	**287**	1k.30 black and green	1·70	30
996	-	1k.70 black and brown	1·90	65

DESIGN: 1k.70, Hand using telegraph key.

288 Felling Tree

1979. Farming.

997	**288**	1k.30 black, red & green	30	30
998	-	1k.30 green and black	30	30
999	-	1k.30 green and black	30	30
1000	-	1k.30 brown and green	30	30
1001	-	1k.30 red, black & green	30	30

DESIGNS: No. 998, Sowing; 999, Cows; 1000, Harvesting; 1001, Ploughing.

289 Tourist Launch "Juno"

1979. Tourism. Gota Canal.

1002	**289**	1k.15 violet	40	40
1003	-	1k.15 green	40	40
1004	-	1k.15 purple	40	40
1005	-	1k.15 red	40	40
1006	-	1k.15 violet	40	40
1007	-	1k.15 green	40	40

DESIGNS—As T **289**: No. 1003, Borenshult lock. 27×23½ mm: No. 1004, Hajstorp roller bridge; 1005, Opening lock gateore 27×36½ mm: No. 1006, Motor barge "Wilhelm Tham" in lock; 1007, Kayak in lock.

290 "Aeshna cyanea" (dragonfly)

1979. Wildlife.

1008	**290**	60ore violet	40	20
1009	-	65ore green	45	20
1010	-	80ore green	45	30

DESIGNS—41×21 mm: 65ore Northern pike. 27×22 mm: 80ore Green spotted toad.

291 Workers leaving Sawmills

1979. Centenary of Sundsvall Strike.

1011	**291**	90ore brown and red	30	20

292 Banner

1979. Cent of Swedish Temperance Movement.

1012	**292**	1k.30 multicoloured	35	20

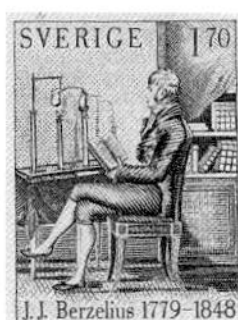
293 J. J. Berzelius

1979. Birth Bicentenaries of J. J. Berzelius (chemist) and J. O. Wallin (poet and hymn-writer).

1013	**293**	1k.70 brown and green	45	45
1014	-	4k.50 blue	1·40	40

DESIGN: 4k.50, J. O. Wallin and hymn numbers.

294 Pot-pourri Jar

1979. Swedish Rococo. Sheet 143×63 mm containing T 294 and similar vert designs.

MS1015 90ore multicoloured; 1k.15 multicoloured; 1k.30 blue, black and pink; 1k.15 multicoloured; 1k.30 blue, black and pink; 1k.70 buff and black (sold at 6k.) 2·00 1·90

295 Atlantic Herrings and Growth Marks

1979. Marine Research.

1016	**295**	1k.70 green and blue	50	55
1017	-	1k.70 brown	50	55
1018	-	1k.70 green and blue	50	55
1019	-	1k.70 brown	50	55
1020	-	1k.70 green and blue	50	55

DESIGNS: No. 1017, Acoustic survey of sea-bed; 1018, Plankton bloom; 1019, Echo-sounding chart of Baltic Sea, October 1978; 1020, Fishery research ship "Argos".

296 Ljusdal Costume

1979. Peasant Costumes and Jewellery.

1021	**296**	90ore multicoloured	30	20
1022	-	90ore multicoloured	30	20
1023	-	90ore blue	30	20
1024	-	1k.30 multicoloured	40	20
1025	-	1k.30 multicoloured	40	20
1026	-	1k.30 red	40	20

DESIGNS: As T **296**: No. 1022, Osteraker costume. 21×27 mm: No. 1023, Brooch from Jamtland; 1026, Brooch from Smaland. 23×40 mm: No. 1024, Goinge church dress; 1025, Mora church dress.

297 Jules Bordet (chemistry)

1979. Nobel Prize Winners of 1919.

1027	**297**	1k.30 mauve	35	20
1028	-	1k.70 blue	40	60
1029	-	2k.50 green	60	30

DESIGNS: 1k.70, Johannes Stark (physics); 2k.50, Carl Spitteler (literature).

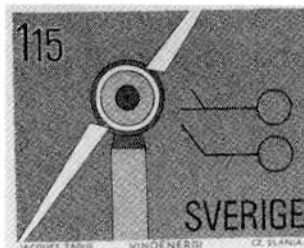
298 Wind Power

1980. Renewable Energy Sources.

1030	**298**	1k.15 blue	40	40
1031	-	1k.15 buff and green	40	40
1032	-	1k.15 orange	40	40
1033	-	1k.15 green	40	40
1034	-	1k.15 green and blue	40	40

DESIGNS: No. 1031, Biological energy; 1032, Solar energy; 1033, Geothermal energy; 1034, Wave energy.

299 King Carl XVI Gustav and Crown Princess Victoria

1980. New Order of Succession to Throne.

1035	**299**	1k.30 blue	35	20
1036	**299**	1k.70 red	55	45

300 Child's Hand in Adult's

1980. Care.

1037	**300**	1k.40 brown	35	20
1038	-	1k.60 green	40	20

DESIGN: 1k.60, Aged hand clasping stick.

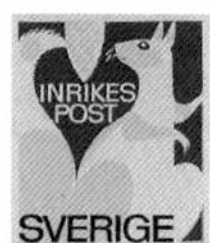
301 Squirrel

1980. Rebate Stamp.

1039	**301**	(1k.) yellow, blue & black	1·00	20

No. 1039 was only issued in booklets of 20 sold at 20k. on production of tokens distributed to all households in Sweden.

302 Elise Ottesen-Jensen (pioneer of birth control)

1980. Europa.

1040	**302**	1k.30 green	95	25
1041	-	1k.70 red	1·30	70

DESIGN: 1k.70, Joe Hill (member of workers' movement).

303 Tybling Farm, Tyby

1980. Tourism. Halsingland.

1042	**303**	1k.15 red	30	35
1043	-	1k.15 blue and purple	30	35
1044	-	1k.15 green	30	35
1045	-	1k.15 purple	30	35
1046	-	1k.15 blue	30	35

DESIGNS: No. 1043, Old iron works, Iggesund; 1044, Blaxas ridge, Forsa; 1045, Banga farm, Alfta; 1046, Sunds Canal, Hudiksvall.

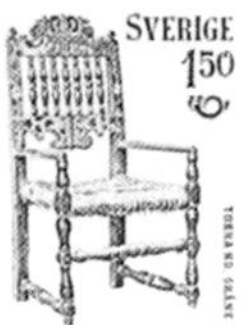
304 Chair from Scania (1831)

1980. Nordic Countries' Postal Co-operation.

1047	**304**	1k.50 green	45	20
1048	-	2k. brown	65	40

DESIGN: 2k. Cradle from North Bothnia (19th century).

305 Motif from film "Diagonal Symphony"

1980. Birth Bicentenary of Viking Eggeling (film-maker).

1049	**305**	3k. blue	90	20

306 Gustaf Erikson's Paraffin-driven Car, 1898

1980. Swedish Motor Vehicles. Sheet 120×67 mm containing T 306 and similar horiz designs.

MS1050 90ore black and blue; 1k.15 black and ochre; 1k.30 black and blue; 1k.40 black and blue; 1k.50 black and ochre; 1k.70, black and blue (sold at 9k.) 2·50 2·75

307 Bamse

1980. Christmas. Swedish Comic Strips.

1051	**307**	1k.15 blue and red	25	20
1052	-	1k.15 multicoloured	25	20
1053	-	1k.50 black	45	25
1054	-	1k.50 multicoloured	45	25

DESIGNS—As T **307** but VERT: No. 1052, Karlsson; 1053, Adamson. 40×23 mm: No. 1054, Kronblom.

308 "Necken" (Ernst Josephson)

1980

1055	**308**	8k. brown, black and blue	2·10	20

309 Knut Hamsun (literature)

1980. Nobel Prize Winners of 1920.

1056	**309**	1k.40 blue	40	30
1057	-	1k.40 red	40	30
1058	-	2k. green	50	40
1059	-	2k. brown	50	40

DESIGNS: No. 1057, August Krogh (medicine); 1058, Charles-Edouard Guillaume (physics); 1059, Walther Nernst (chemistry).

310 Angel blowing Horn

1980. Christmas.

1060	**310**	1k.25 brown and blue	35	20

311 Ernst Wigforss

1981. Birth Centenary of Ernst Wigforss (politician).

1061	**311**	5k. red	1·20	35

312 Thor catching Midgard Serpent

1981. Norse Mythology.

1062	**312**	10ore black	15	20
1063	-	15ore red	15	20
1064	-	50ore red	20	20
1065	-	75ore green	25	25
1066	-	1k. black	35	25

DESIGNS: 15ore Heimdall blowing horn; 50ore Freya riding boar; 75ore Freya in carriage drawn by cats; 1k. Odin on eight-footed steed.

313 Gyr Falcon

1981

1067	**313**	50k. brown, black & blue	11·00	1·10

314 Troll

1981. Europa.

1068	**314**	1k.50 blue and red	1·10	25
1069	-	2k. red and green	1·30	30

DESIGN: 2k. The Lady of the Woods.

315 Blind Boy feeling Globe

1981. International Year of Disabled Persons.

1070	**315**	1k.50 green	35	20
1071	**315**	3k.50 violet	80	40

316 Arms of Bohuslan

1981. Rebate stamps. Arms of Swedish Provinces (1st series). Multicoloured.

1072	1k.40 Ostergotland	95	20
1073	1k.40 Jamtland	95	20
1074	1k.40 Dalarna	95	20
1075	1k.40 Type **316**	95	20

See also Nos. 1112/15, 1153/6, 1189/92, 1246/9 and 1302/5.

317 King Carl XVI Gustav

1981				
1076	**317**	1k.65 green	35	20
1077	-	1k.75 blue	40	25
1077a	**317**	1k.80 blue	45	20
1077b	**317**	1k.90 red	50	20
1078	**317**	2k.40 purple	65	25
1078a	-	2k.40 green	80	45
1078b	**317**	2k.70 purple	65	30
1078c	-	3k.20 red	85	30

DESIGN: 1k.75, 2k.40 (1078a), 3k.20, Queen Silvia.

318 Boat from Bohuslan

1981. Provincial Sailing Boats.

1079	**318**	1k.65 blue	45	30
1080	-	1k.65 blue	45	30
1081	-	1k.65 blue	45	30
1082	-	1k.65 blue	45	30
1083	-	1k.65 blue	45	30
1084	-	1k.65 blue	45	30

DESIGNS: No. 1080, Boat from Blekinge; 1081, Boat from Norrbotten; 1082, Boat from Halsingland; 1083, Boat from Gotland; 1084, Boat from West Skane.

319 "Night and Day"

1981				
1085	**319**	1k.65 violet	40	20

320 Par Lagerkvist riding Railway Trolley with Father (illustration from "Guest of Reality")

1981				
1086	**320**	1k.50 green	40	20

321 Electric Locomotive

1981. "Sweden in the World".

1087	**321**	2k.40 red	55	50
1088	-	2k.40 red	55	50
1089	-	2k.40 purple	55	50
1090	-	2k.40 violet	55	50
1091	-	2k.40 blue	60	60
1092	-	2k.40 blue	60	60

DESIGNS—As T **321**: No. 1088, Scania trucks with rock drilling equipment; 1089, Birgit Nilsson (opera singer) and Sixten Ehrling (conductor); 1090, North Sea gas rig. 19×23 mm: No. 1091, Bjorn Borg (tennis player); 1092, Ingemar Stenmark (skier).

322 Baker's Sign

1981. Business Mail.

1093	**322**	2k.30 brown	85	25
1094	-	2k.30 brown	85	25

DESIGN: No. 1094, Pewterer's sign.

323 Olof As in *The Coachman*

1981. Swedish Film History. Sheet 135×69 mm containing T 323 and similar horiz designs.

MS1095 1k.50 black and yellow; 1k.50 black and blue; 1k.65 black and yellow; 1k.65 black and blue; 2k.40 multicoloured (sold at 10k.) 2·75 3·25

324 Wooden Bird

1981. Christmas.

1096	**324**	1k.40 red	35	20
1097	-	1k.40 green	35	20

DESIGN: No. 1097, Wooden bird (different).

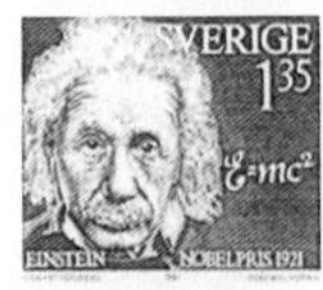

325 Albert Einstein (physics)

1981. Nobel Prize Winners of 1921.

1098	**325**	1k.35 red	35	35
1099	-	1k.65 green	40	20
1100	-	2k.70 blue	55	50

DESIGNS: 1k.65, Anatole France (literature); 2k.70, Frederick Soddy (chemistry).

326 Knight on Horseback

1982. Birth Centenary of John Bauer (illustrator of fairy tales).

1101	**326**	1k.65 blue, yellow & lilac	40	30
1102	-	1k.65 multicoloured	40	30
1103	-	1k.65 black and yellow	40	30
1104	-	1k.65 yellow and lilac	40	30

DESIGNS: No. 1102, "What a wretched pale creature, said the Troll Woman"; 1103, "The Princess beside the Forest Lake"; 1104, "Now it is already twilight Night".

327 Impossible Triangle

1982				
1105	**327**	25ore brown	15	15
1106	-	50ore brown	15	15
1107	-	75ore blue	20	20
1108	-	1k.35 blue	35	25
1109	-	5k. purple	1·30	20

DESIGNS: 50, 75ore, Impossible figures (different); 1k.35, Newspaper distributor; 5k. "Graziella wonders if she could be a Model" (etching, Carl Larsson).

328 Villages before and after Land Reform

1982. Europa.

1110	**328**	1k.65 green and black	1·70	30
1111	-	2k.40 green	80	65

DESIGN—26×22 mm: 2k.40, Anders Celsius.

1982. Rebate Stamps. Arms of Swedish Provinces (2nd series). As T 316. Multicoloured.

1112	1k.40 Dalsland	95	20
1113	1k.40 Oland	95	20
1114	1k.40 Vastmanland	95	20
1115	1k.40 Halsingland	95	20

329 Elin Wagner

1982. Birth Centenary of Elin Wagner (novelist).

1116	**329**	1k.35 brown on grey	45	40

330 Burgher House

1982. Centenary of Museum of Cultural History, Lund.

1117	**330**	1k.65 brown	45	20
1118	-	2k.70 brown	65	45

DESIGN: 2k.70, Embroidered lace.

331 Lateral Mark

1982. New International Buoyage System.

1119	**331**	1k.65 blue and green	35	20
1120	-	1k.65 green and blue	35	20
1121	-	1k.65 deep blue and blue	35	20
1122	-	1k.65 blue and green	35	20
1123	-	1k.65 deep blue and blue	35	20

DESIGNS: No. 1120, Cardinal mark and Sweden–Finland ferry "Sally"; 1121, Racing yachts and special mark; 1122, Safe-water mark; 1123, Pilot boat, isolated danger mark and lighthouse.

332 Scene from "The Emigrants" (film)

1982. Living Together.

1124	**332**	1k.65 green	45	25
1125	-	1k.65 purple	45	25
1126	-	1k.65 blue	45	25
1127	-	1k.65 red	45	25

DESIGNS: No. 1125, Vietnamese boat people in factory; 1126, Immigrants examining local election literature; 1127, Three girls arm-in-arm.

333 Lady's Slipper (*Cypropedium calceolus*)

1982. Wild Orchids. Sheet 144×63 mm containing T 333 and similar vert design.

MS1128 1k.65 Early purple orchid (*Orchis mascula*); 1k.65 Type **333**; 2 k.40 Marsh helleborine (*Epipactris*); 2k.70 Elderflowered orchid (*Dactylorhiza sambucia*) (sold at 10k.) 3·50 3·50

334 Angel

1982. Christmas. Medieval Glass Paintings from Lye Church. Multicoloured.

1129	1k.40 Type **334**	40	35
1130	1k.40 "The Child in the Temple"	40	35
1131	1k.40 "Adoration of the Magi"	40	35
1132	1k.40 "Tidings to the Shepherds"	40	35
1133	1k.40 "The Birth of Christ"	40	35

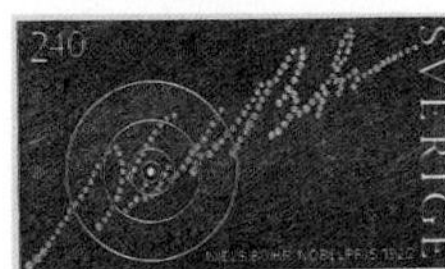

335 Quantum Mechanics (Niels Bohr, 1922)

1982. Nobel Prize Winners for Physics.

1134	**335**	2k.40 blue	60	55
1135	-	2k.40 red	60	55
1136	-	2k.40 green	60	55
1137	-	2k.40 lilac	60	55
1138	-	2k.40 red	60	55

DESIGNS: No. 1135, Fuse distribution (Erwin Schrodinger, 1933); 1136, Wave pattern (Louis de Broglie, 1929); 1137, Electrons (Paul Dirac, 1933); 1138, Atomic model (Werner Heisenberg, 1932).

336 Horse Chestnut

1983. Fruits.

1139	**336**	5ore brown	15	15
1140	-	10ore green	15	15
1141	-	15ore red	15	15
1142	-	20ore blue	25	20

DESIGNS: 10ore Norway maple; 15ore Dog rose; 20ore Blackthorn.

337 Ferlin (statue by K. Bejemark)

1983. 85th Birth Anniv of Nils Ferlin (poet).

1143	**337**	6k. green	1·40	25

338 Peace March

1983. Centenary of Swedish Peace Movement.

1144	**338**	1k.35 blue	40	40

339 Lead Type

1983. 500th Anniv of Printing in Sweden.

1145	**339**	1k.65 black and brown on stone	40	20
1146	-	1k.65 black, green and red on stone	40	20
1147	-	1k.65 brown and black on stone	40	20
1148	**339**	1k.65 black and brown on stone	40	20
1149	-	1k.65 brown, green and black on stone	40	20

DESIGNS: No. 1146, Ox plough (illustration from "Dialogus creaturarum" by Johan Snell, 1483); 1147, Title page of Karl XII's Bible, 1703; 1148, 18th-century alphabet books; 1149, Laser photocomposition.

340 Family Cycling in Countryside

1983. Nordic Countries' Postal Co-operation. "Visit the North".

1150	**340**	1k.65 green	40	20
1151	-	2k.40 blue and brown	65	50

DESIGN: 2k.40, Yachts at Stockholm.

341 Benjamin Franklin and Great Seal of Sweden

1983. Bicentenary of Sweden–U.S.A. Treaty of Amity and Commerce.

1152	**341**	2k.70 blue, brown & blk	75	50

1983. Rebate Stamps. Arms of Swedish Provinces (3rd series). As T 316. Multicoloured.

1153	1k.60 Vastergotland	95	20
1154	1k.60 Medelpad	95	20
1155	1k.60 Gotland	95	20
1156	1k.60 Gastrikland	95	20

342 Costume Sketch by Fernand Leger for "Creation du Monde"

1983. Europa.

1157	1k.65 chocolate and brown	1·10	30
1158	2k.70 blue	1·70	90

DESIGNS: 1k.65, Type **342** (Swedish Ballet); 2k.70, J. P. Johansson's adjustable spanner.

343 Essay for Unissued Stamp, 1885

1983. "Stockholmia 86" International Exhibition (1st issue). Oscar II stamp designs by Max Mirowsky.

1159	**343**	1k. blue	40	40
1160	-	2k. red	50	50
1161	-	3k. blue	65	60
1162	-	4k. green	75	70

DESIGNS: 2k. Issued stamp of 1885; 3k. Essay for unissued stamp, 1891; 4k. Issued stamp of 1891.

See also Nos. 1199/1202, 1252/5, 1285/8 and 1310/13.

344 Greater Karlso

345 Freshwater Snail

1983

1163	**344**	1k.60 blue	45	20
1164	**345**	1k.80 green	50	20
1165	-	2k.10 green	55	20

DESIGN—22×27 mm: 2k.10, Arctic fox.

346 Bergman

1983. Birth Centenary of Hjalmar Bergman (novelist and dramatist).

1166	**346**	1k.80 blue	45	20
1167	-	1k.80 multicoloured	45	20

DESIGN: No. 1167, Jac the Clown (novel character).

347 Helgeandsholmen, 1580 (after Franz Hogenberg) and Riksdag

1983. Return of Riksdag (Parliament) to Helgeandsholmen Island, Stockholm.

1168	**347**	2k.70 purple and blue	75	45

348 Red Cross

1983. Swedish Red Cross.

1169	**348**	1k.50 red	30	20

349 Wilhelm Stenhammer (after R. Thegerstrom) (classical music)

1983. Music in Sweden. Sheet 135×69 mm containing T 349 and similar designs.

MS1170 1k.80 green and black (Type **349**); 1k.80 yellow and black (*Aniara*) (opera)); 1k.80 pink and black (Abba (pop)); 2k.70, multicoloured ("Fiddler" (Anders Zorn) (folk music)) (44×48 mm) (sold at 11k. 50) 3·00 3·25

350 Dancing round the Christmas Tree

1983. Christmas. Early Christmas Cards. Multicoloured.

1171	1k.60 Type **350**	40	30
1172	1k.60 Straw goats	40	30
1173	1k.60 The Christmas table	40	30
1174	1k.60 Carrying Christmas presents on pole	40	30

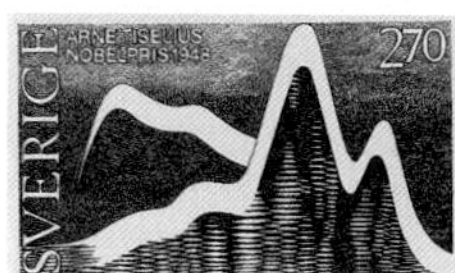
351 Electrophoresis (Arne Tiselius, 1948)

1983. Nobel Prize Winners for Chemistry.

1175	**351**	2k.70 black	65	60
1176	-	2k.70 violet	65	60
1177	-	2k.70 mauve	65	60
1178	-	2k.70 violet	65	60
1179	-	2k.70 black	65	60

DESIGNS: No. 1176, Radioactive isotopes (George de Hevesy, 1943); 1177, Electrolytic dissociation (Svante Arrhenius, 1903); 1178, Colloids (Theodor Svedberg, 1926); 1179, Fermentation of sugar (Hans von Euler-Chelpin, 1929).

352 Three Crowns (detail from Postal Savings Receipt)

1984. Centenary of Postal Savings.

1180	**352**	100ore orange	30	15
1181	-	1k.60 violet	40	30
1182	-	1k.80 mauve	55	15

DESIGNS: 1k.60, 1k.80, Postal Savings badge.

353 Bridge

1984. Europa. 25th Anniv of European Post and Telecommunications Conference.

1183	**353**	1k.80 red	60	20
1184	**353**	2k.70 blue	2·20	80

354 Norway Lemming

1984. Swedish Mountain World.

1185	**354**	1k.90 brown	45	20
1186	-	1k.90 blue	45	30
1187	-	2k. green	40	20
1188	-	2k.25 black	65	45

DESIGNS: No. 1186, Musk ox; 1187, Garden angelica; 1188, Tolpagorni mountain.

1984. Rebate Stamps. Arms of Swedish Provinces (4th series). As T 316. Multicoloured.

1189	1k.60 Sodermanland	95	20
1190	1k.60 Blekinge	95	20
1191	1k.60 Vasterbotten	95	20
1192	1k.60 Skane	95	20

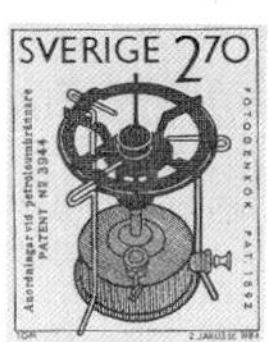
355 Paraffin Stove (F. W. Lindqvist)

1984. "Made in Sweden". Centenary of Patent Office. Patented Swedish Inventions.

1193	**355**	2k.70 red	70	65
1194	-	2k.70 lilac	70	65
1195	-	2k.70 green	70	65
1196	-	2k.70 green	70	65
1197	-	2k.70 lilac	70	65
1198	-	2k.70 blue	70	65

DESIGNS: No. 1194, "ASEA IRB 6" industrial robot for arc welding; 1195, Vacuum cleaner (Axel Wennergren); 1196, "AQ 200" inboard/outboard engine; 1197, Integrated circuit; 1198, Tetrahedron container.

356 King Erik XIV (after S. van der Meulen) and Letter to Queen Elizabeth I of England

1984. "Stockholmia 86" International Stamp Exhibition (2nd issue).

1199	**356**	1k. brown, blue and ultramarine	40	35
1200	-	2k. multicoloured	55	45
1201	-	3k. multicoloured	70	55
1202	-	4k. multicoloured	90	65

DESIGNS: 2k. Erik Dahlbergh (architect) (after J. H. Stromer) and letter to Sten Bielke (Paymaster General), 1674; 3k. Feather letter, 1843; 4k. Harriet Bosse and letter from her husband, August Strindberg, 1905.

357 Jonkoping

1984. Old Towns. 17th-century views by M. Karl (1207) or Erik Dahlberg (others).

1203	**357**	1k.90 blue	50	45
1204	-	1k.90 brown	50	45
1205	-	1k.90 blue	50	45
1206	-	1k.90 brown	50	45
1207	-	1k.90 blue	50	45
1208	-	1k.90 brown	50	45

DESIGNS: No. 1204, Karlstad; 1205, Gavle; 1206, Sigtuna; 1207, Norrkoping; 1208. Vadstena.

358 Genetic Symbols forming "100"

1984. Centenary of Fredrika Bremer Association (for promotion of male/female equal rights).

1209	**358**	1k.50 purple	40	20
1210	**358**	6k.50 red	1·80	45

359 "Viking" in Orbit

1984. Launch of Swedish "Viking" Satellite.

1211	**359**	1k.90 ultramarine, blue and deep blue	40	20
1212	-	3k.20 green, yellow and black	85	65

DESIGN: 3k.20, Dish aerial and rocket pad at Esrange space station.

360 Thulin Type D Biplane, 1915

1984. Swedish Aviation History. Sheet 132×73 mm containing T 360 and similar designs.

MS1213 1k.90 ultramarine and red (Type **360**); 1k.90 ultramarine and orange (SAAB 90 Scandia, 1946); 1k.90 orange, ultramarine and red (Carl Gustaf Cedarstrom ("The Flying Baron") and Bleriot X1 monoplane, 1910); 1k.90 multicoloured (Ahrenberg's Junkers F-13 S-AAAB airplane *The Gnome* 1927); 2k.70 brown, red and dull ultramarine (Carl Nyberg and *The Tiny Fly*, 1900) (43×46 mm) (sold at 12k.) 3·25 3·00

361 Hawfinch ("Coccothraustes coccothraustes")

1984. Christmas. Birds. Multicoloured.

1214	1k.60 Type **361**	45	35
1215	1k.60 Bohemian waxwing ("Bombycilla garrulus")	45	35
1216	1k.60 Great-spotted woodpecker ("Dendrocopos major")	45	35
1217	1k.60 Eurasian nuthatch ("Sitta europaea")	45	35

362 Inner Ear (Georg von Bekesy, 1961)

1984. Nobel Prize Winners for Medicine.

1218	**362**	2k.70 blue, black and red	70	65
1219	-	2k.70 blue and black	70	65
1220	-	2k.70 red, black and blue	70	65
1221	-	2k.70 blue and black	70	65
1222	-	2k.70 red, black and blue	70	65

DESIGNS: No. 1219, Nerve cell activation (John Eccles, Alan Hodgkin and Andrew Huxley, 1963); 1220, Nerve cell signals (Bernard Katz, Ulf von Euler and Julius Axelrod, 1970); 1221, Functions of the brain (Roger Sperry, 1981); 1222, Eye (David Hubel and Torsten Wiesel, 1981).

363 Post Office Emblem

1985

1223	**363**	1k.60 blue	45	20
1224	**363**	1k.70 violet	40	20
1326	**363**	1k.80 purple	45	20
1225	**363**	2k.50 yellow	60	20
1226	**363**	2k.80 green	75	45
1327	**363**	3k.20 brown	75	55
1227	**363**	4k. red	95	25
1328	**363**	6k. turquoise	1·40	45

364 King Carl XVI Gustav

1985

1228	**364**	2k. black	40	20
1229	**364**	2k.10 blue	65	20
1230	**364**	2k.20 blue	60	20
1230a	**364**	2k.30 green	70	30
1230b	**364**	2k.50 purple	60	30
1231	**364**	2k.70 brown	65	45
1232	**364**	2k.90 green	80	40
1233	**364**	3k.10 brown	85	30
1234	-	3k.20 blue	80	60
1235	**364**	3k.30 purple	90	40
1236	-	3k.40 red	95	50
1237	-	3k.60 green	90	55
1238	-	3k.90 blue	1·10	65
1239	-	4k.60 orange	1·10	80

DESIGNS: 3k.20 and 3k.40 to 4k.60, Queen Silvia.

365 Hazel Dormouse ("Muscardinus avellanarius")

1985. Nature.

1240	**365**	2k. brown and black	45	20
1241	-	2k. orange and black	45	20
1242	-	2k.20 red	45	25
1243	-	3k.50 red and green	85	25

DESIGNS: No. 1241, Char ("Salvelinus salvelinus"); 1242, Black vanilla orchid ("Nigritella nigra"); 1243, White water-lily ("Nymphaea alba frosea").

366 Jan-Ove Waldner

1985. World Table Tennis Championships, Gothenburg.

1244	**366**	2k.70 blue	90	50
1245	-	3k.20 mauve	95	60

DESIGN: 3k.20, Cai Zhenhua (Chinese player).

1985. Rebate Stamps. Arms of Swedish Provinces (5th series). As T 316. Multicoloured.

1246	1k.80 Narke	95	20
1247	1k.80 Angermanland	95	20
1248	1k.80 Varmland	95	20
1249	1k.80 Smaland	95	20

367 Clavichord

1985. Europa. Music Year.

1250	**367**	2k. purple on buff	3·75	20
1251	-	2k.70 brown on buff	90	75

DESIGN—28×24 mm: 2k.70, Keyed fiddle.

368 "View of Slussen" (Sigrid Hjerten)

1985. "Stockholmia 86" International Stamp Exhibition (3rd issue). Multicoloured.

1252	2k. Type **368**	55	50
1253	2k. "Skeppsholmen, Winter" (Gosta Adrian-Nilsson)	55	50
1254	3k. "A Summer's Night by Riddarholmen Canal" (Hilding Linnqvist)	85	70
1255	4k. "Klara Church Tower" (Otte Skold)	1·10	90

369 Syl Hostel, 1920

1985. Centenary of Swedish Touring Club.

1256	**369**	2k. blue and black	50	20
1257	-	2k. black and blue	50	20

DESIGN—58×24 mm: No. 1257, "Af Chapman" (youth hostel in Stockholm).

370 Canute and Helsingborg

1985. 900th Anniv of Saint Canute's Deed of Gift to Lund.

1258		2k. blue and black	50	20
1259	**370**	2k. red and black	50	20

DESIGN: No. 1258, Canute and Lund Cathedral.

371 Nilsson's Music Shop Sign

1985. Trade Signs.

1260	**371**	10ore blue	15	15
1261	-	20ore brown	15	15
1262	-	20ore brown	15	15
1263	-	50ore blue	15	15
1264	-	2k. green	45	25

DESIGNS: No. 1261, Erik Johansson's furrier's sign; 1262, O. L. Sjowals's coppersmith's sign; 1263, Bodecker's hatter's sign; 1264, Berggren's shoemaker's sign.

372 "Otryades" (Johan Tobias Sergel)

1985. 250th Anniv of Royal Academy of Fine Arts.

1265	**372**	2k. blue	45	25
1266	-	7k. brown	1·80	60

DESIGN—20×28 mm: 7k. "Baron Carl Fredrik Adelcrantz" (former Academy president) (Alexander Roslin).

373 Fox and Geese

1985. Board Games.

1267	**373**	50ore blue	20	20
1268	-	60ore green	20	20
1269	-	70ore yellow	20	20
1270	-	80ore red	25	20
1271	-	90ore mauve	25	20
1272	-	3k. purple	60	20

DESIGNS—As T **373**: 60k. Dominoes; 70k. Ludo; 80k. Chinese checkers; 90k. Backgammon. 23×28 mm: 3k. Chess.

374 Birger Sjoberg (writer)

1985. Birth Centenaries.

1273		1k.60 red and black	40	35
1274	**374**	4k. green	1·10	25

DESIGN—40×24 mm: 1k.60, Per Albin Hansson (politician).

375 Boy helping Old Lady collect Leaves (Marina Karlsson)

1985. International Youth Year. Sheet 134×64 mm containing T 375 and similar vert designs showing children's drawings. Multicoloured.

MS1275	2k. Type **375**; 2k. Silhouettes and light (Madeleine Andersson); 3k.20 Children on swing (Charlotte Ankar) (sold at 10k)	2·75	3·25

376 "Annunciation"

1985. Christmas. Medieval Church Frescoes by Albertus Pictor.

1276	**376**	1k.80 blue, brown and red	40	25
1277	-	1k.80 brown, blue and red	40	25
1278	-	1k.80 brown, blue and red	40	25
1279	-	1k.80 blue, brown and red	40	25

DESIGNS: No. 1277, "Birth of Christ"; 1278, "Adoration of the Magi"; 1279, "Mary as the Apocalyptic Virgin".

377 American Deep South Scene (William Faulkner, 1949)

1985. Nobel Prize Winners for Literature.

1280	**377**	2k.70 green	75	70
1281	-	2k.70 brown, blue and green	75	70
1282	-	2k.70 green and brown	75	70
1283	-	2k.70 green and blue	75	70
1284	-	2k.70 brown and blue	75	70

DESIGNS: No. 1281, Icelandic scene (Halldor Kiljan Laxness, 1955); 1282, Guatemalan scene (Miguel Angel Asturias, 1967); 1283, Japanese scene (Yasunari Kawabata, 1968); 1284, Australian scene (Patrick White, 1973).

378 1879 "20 TRETIO" Error

1986. "Stockholmia 86" International Stamp Exhibition (4th issue).

1285	**378**	2k. orange, purple & grn	70	55
1286	-	2k. multicoloured	70	55
1287	-	3k. purple, blue and green	85	60
1288	-	4k. multicoloured	95	70

DESIGNS: No. 1286, Sven Ewert (engraver); 1287, Magnifying glass and United States 1938 Scandinavian Settlement 3c. stamp; 1288, Boy soaking stamps.

379 Eiders ("Somaterna mollissima")

1986. Water Birds.

1289	**379**	2k.10 blue and brown	55	20
1290	-	2k.10 brown	55	20
1291	-	2k.30 blue	60	25

DESIGNS: No. 1290, Whimbrel ("Numenius phaeopus"); 1291, Black-throated diver ("Gavia arctica").

380 Swedish Academy Emblem

1986. Bicentenaries of Swedish Academy and Royal Swedish Academy of Letters, History and Antiquities.

1292	**380**	1k.70 green and red on grey	40	40
1293	-	1k.70 blue and purple on grey	40	40

DESIGN: No. 1293, Royal Swedish Academy emblem.

381 Jubilee Emblem

1986. 350th Anniv of Post Office.

1294	**381**	2k.10 blue and yellow	50	20

382 Palme

1986. Olof Palme (Prime Minister) Commemoration.

1295	**382**	2k.10 purple	85	80
1296	**382**	2k.90 black	85	80

383 Carl Gustav Birdwatching

1986. 40th Birthday of King Carl XVI Gustav.

1297	**383**	2k.10 black and green	50	25
1298	-	2k.10 gold, mauve and blue	50	25
1299	-	2k.10 deep blue and blue	50	25
1300	-	2k.10 gold, blue and deep blue	50	25
1301	-	2k.10 black and mauve	50	25

DESIGNS: Nos. 1298, 1300, Crowned cypher; 1299, King presenting Nobel Prize for Literature to Czeslaw Milosz; 1301, King and family during summer holiday at Solliden Palace.

1986. Rebate Stamps. Arms of Swedish Provinces (6th series). As T 316. Multicoloured.

1302	1k.90 Harjedalen	95	20
1303	1k.90 Uppland	95	20
1304	1k.90 Halland	95	20
1305	1k.90 Lappland	95	20

384 Uppsala

1986. Nordic Countries' Postal Co-operation. Twinned Towns.

1306	**384**	2k.10 green, chestnut and brown	45	20
1307	-	2k.90 green, red & brown	75	55

DESIGN: 2k.90, Eskilstuna.

385 Forest and Car Fumes

1986. Europa. Each black, green and red.

1308	2k.10 Type **385**	1·60	30

1309 2k.90 Forest and industrial pollution 80 70

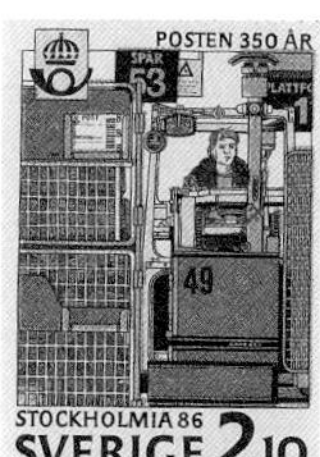

386 Tomteboda Sorting Office (20th-century)

1986. "Stockholmia 86" International Stamp Exhibition (5th issue). Multicoloured.

1310 2k.10 19th-century railway sorting carriage 3·25 3·50
1311 2k.10 Type **386** 3·25 3·50
1312 2k.90 17th-century farmhand postal messenger 3·25 3·50
1313 2k.90 18th-century post office 3·25 3·50

387 Ann-Louise Skoglund (400 m. hurdles European Champion, 1982)

1986. Athletics. Sheet 93×72 mm containing T 387 and similar horiz designs.

MS1314 2k.10 brown, blue and green (Type **387**); 2k.10 brown and green (Eric Lemming, early Olympic Medal winner, and Dag Wennlund (javelin throwers)); 2k.10 blue and brown (Patrik Sjoberg (high jumper)); 2k.10 green and brown (Anders Garderud, 3000 m. steeplechase world record holder) (sold at 11k.) 3·00 3·50

388 Olive Branch sweeping away Weapons

1986. International Peace Year (1315) and 25th Anniv of Amnesty International (1316).

1315 **388** 3k.40 green and black 90 85
1316 - 3k.40 red and black 90 85

DESIGN: No. 1316, Emblem above broken manacles.

389 Bertha von Suttner (founder of Austrian Society of Peace Lovers, 1905)

1986. Nobel Prize Winners for Peace.

1317 **389** 2k.90 black, red and blue 80 75
1318 - 2k.90 black and red 80 75
1319 - 2k.90 black, brown and blue 80 75
1320 - 2k.90 brown and black 80 75
1321 - 2k.90 red, black and blue 80 75

DESIGNS: No. 1318, Carl von Ossietzky (anti-Nazi fighter and concentration camp victim, 1935); 1319, Albert Luthuli (South African anti-apartheid leader, 1960); 1320, Martin Luther King (American civil rights leader, 1964); 1321, Mother Teresa (worker amongst poor of Calcutta, 1979).

390 Mail Van

1986. Christmas. Designs showing a village at Christmas. Multicoloured.

1322 1k.90 Type **390** 40 25
1323 1k.90 Postman on cycle delivering mail 40 25
1324 1k.90 Children and sledge loaded with parcels 40 25
1325 1k.90 Christmas tree, man carrying parcel and child posting letter 40 25

Nos. 1322/5 were printed together, se-tenant, forming a composite design.

391 Clouded Apollo ("Parnassius mnemosyne")

1987. Threatened Species of Meadows and Pastures.

1331 **391** 2k.10 black, green and purple 45 20
1332 - 2k.10 black, green and purple 45 20
1333 - 2k.50 brown 55 20
1334 - 4k.20 green and yellow 90 20

DESIGNS: 2k.10 (1332), Field gentian ("Gentianella campestris"); 2k.50, Leather beetle ("Osmoderma eremita"); 4k.20, Arnica ("Arnica montana").

392 SAAB-Fairchild SF-340 SE-ISS

1987. Swedish Aircraft.

1335 **392** 25k. purple 5·75 60

393 Boys flying over Rooftops ("Karlsson")

1987. Rebate Stamps. Characters from Children's Books by Astrid Lindgren. Multicoloured.

1336 1k.90 Type **393** 1·10 20
1337 1k.90 Girl holding doll ("Bullerby Children") 1·10 20
1338 1k.90 Girls dancing ("Madicken") 1·10 20
1339 1k.90 Boys on horse ("Mio, Min Mio") 1·10 20
1340 1k. Boy doing handstand ("Nils Karlsson-Pyssling") 1·10 20
1341 1k.90 Emil picking cherries ("Emil") 1·10 20
1342 1k.90 "Ronja the Robber's Daughter" 1·10 20
1343 1k.90 "Pippi Longstocking" 1·10 20
1344 1k.90 Dragon ("Brothers Lionheart") 1·10 20
1345 1k.90 "Lotta" 1·10 20

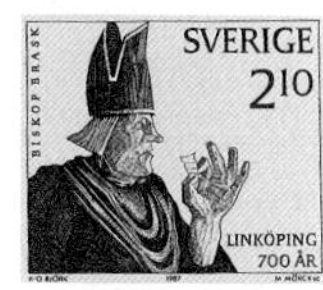

394 Hans Brask, Bishop of Linkoping (sculpture, Karl-Olav Bjork)

1987. Town Anniversaries. Each brown, blue and black.

1346 2k.10 Type **394** (700th anniv) 60 30
1347 2k.10 Nykoping Castle (800th anniv) 60 30

395 Stockholm City Library (Gunnar Asplund)

1987. Europa. Architecture.

1348 **395** 2k.10 brown and blue 2·20 35
1349 **395** 3k.10 brown and green 90 80
1350 - 3k.10 purple and green 90 80

DESIGN: No. 1350, Marcus Church (Sigurd Lewerentz).

396 "King Gustavus Vasa" (anon)

1987. 450th Anniv of Gripsholm Castle.

1351 **396** 2k.10 multicoloured 55 30
1352 - 2k.10 multicoloured 55 30
1353 - 2k.10 multicoloured 55 30
1354 - 2k.10 brown, black and blue 55 30

DESIGNS: No. 1352, "Blue Tiger" (David Klocker Ehrenstrahl); 1353, "Hedvig Charlotta Nordenflycht" (after Johan Henrik Scheffel); 1354, "Gripsholm Castle" (lithograph, Carl Johan Billmark).

397 Raoul Wallenberg (rescuer of Hungarian Jews) and Prisoners

1987. "In the Service of Humanity".

1355 **397** 3k.10 blue 85 65
1356 - 3k.10 green 85 65
1357 - 3k.10 brown 85 65

DESIGNS: No. 1356, Dag Hammarskjold (U.N. Secretary-General, 1953–1961); 1357, Folke Bernadotte (leader of "white bus" relief action to rescue prisoners, 1945).

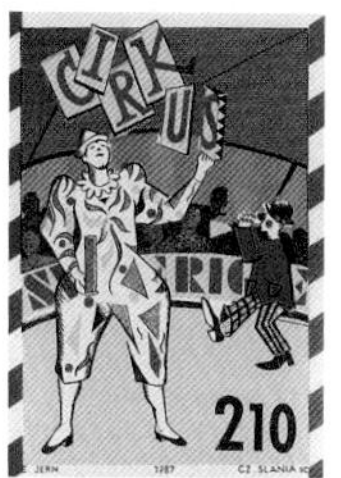

398 Clowns

1987. Stamp Day. Bicentenary of Circus in Sweden. Multicoloured.

1358 2k.10 Type **398** 60 60
1359 2k.10 Reino riding one-wheel cycle on wire 60 60
1360 2k.10 Acrobat on horseback 60 60

399 "Victoria cruziana" at Bergian Garden, Stockholm University

1987. Bicentenary of Swedish Botanical Gardens.

1361 **399** 2k.10 green, deep green and blue 45 25
1362 - 2k.10 green and brown 45 25
1363 - 2k.10 deep green, green and blue 45 25
1364 - 2k.10 yellow, brown and green 45 25

DESIGNS: No. 1362, Uppsala University Baroque Garden plan and Carl Harleman (architect); 1363, Rock garden, Gothenburg Botanical Garden; 1364, "Liriodendron tulipifera", Lund Botanical Garden.

400 Porridge left for the Grey Christmas Elf

1987. Christmas. Folk Customs. Multicoloured.

1365 2k. Type **400** 45 30
1366 2k. Staffan ride (watering horses in North-running spring on Boxing Day) 45 30

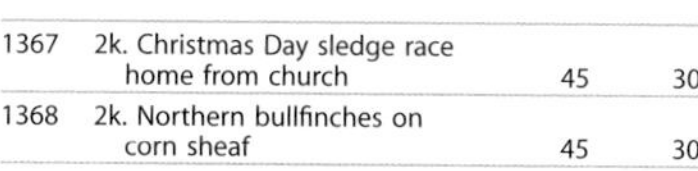

1367 2k. Christmas Day sledge race home from church 45 30
1368 2k. Northern bullfinches on corn sheaf 45 30

401 Pulsars (Antony Hewish, 1974)

1987. Nobel Prize Winners for Physics.

1369 **401** 2k.90 blue 65 65
1370 - 2k.90 black 65 65
1371 - 2k.90 blue 65 65
1372 - 2k.90 blue 65 65
1373 - 2k.90 black 65 65

DESIGNS: No. 1370, Formula of maximum white dwarf star mass (S. Chandrasekhar, 1983); 1371, Heavy atom nuclei construction (William Fowler, 1983); 1372, Temperature of cosmic background radiation (A. Penzias and R. Wilson, 1978); 1373, Radio telescopes receiving radio waves from galaxy (Martin Ryle, 1974).

402 Lake Hjalmaren Fishing Skiff

1988. Inland Boats. Each purple on buff.

1374 3k.10 Type **402** 70 65
1375 3k.10 Lake Vattern market boat 70 65
1376 3k.10 River Byske logging boat 70 65
1377 3k.10 Lake Asnen rowing boat 70 65
1378 3k.10 Lake Vanern ice boat 70 65
1379 3k.10 Lake Lockne church longboat 70 65

403 Bishop Hill and Erik Jansson (founder)

1988. 350th Anniv of New Sweden (settlement in America).

1380 - 3k.60 multicoloured 95 80
1381 **403** 3k.60 multicoloured 95 80
1382 - 3k.60 brown 95 80
1383 - 3k.60 blue and brown 95 80
1384 - 3k.60 blue, yellow and red 95 80
1385 - 3k.60 black, blue and red 95 80

DESIGNS—As T **403**: No. 1380, Map, settlers, Indians, "Calmare Nyckel" and "Fagel Grip". 27×23 mm: No. 1382, Carl Sandburg (American poet) and Jenny Lind (Swedish soprano); 1383, Charles Lindbergh (aviator) and Ryan NYP Special "Spirit of St. Louis". 27×37 mm: No. 1384, Alan Bean (astronaut) on Moon with Hasselblad camera; 1385, Ice hockey.

404 White-tailed Sea Eagle ("Haliaetus albicilla")

1988. Coastal Wildlife.

1386 **404** 2k.20 brown and red 55 25
1387 - 2k.20 brown and blue 45 25
1388 - 4k. black, brown and green 1·10 25

DESIGNS: No. 1387, Grey seal ("Halichoerus gryphus"); 1388, European eel ("Anguilla anguilla").

405 Daisies and Bluebells

1988. Rebate stamps. Midsummer Festival. Multicoloured.

1389 2k. Type **405** 1·10 20
1390 2k. Garlanded longboat 1·10 20
1391 2k. Children making garlands 1·10 20
1392 2k. Raising the maypole 1·10 20
1393 2k. Fiddlers 1·10 20

1394		2k. "Norrskar" (tourist launch)	1·10	20
1395		2k. Couples dancing	1·10	20
1396		2k. Accordianist	1·10	20
1397		2k. Archipelago with decorated landing stage	1·10	20
1398		2k. Bouquet of seven wild flowers	1·10	20

406 Detail of "Creation" Stained Glass Window (Bo Beskow), Skara Cathedral

1988. Anniversaries.

1399	**406**	2k.20 multicoloured	55	20
1400	-	4k.40 red on brown	95	30
1401	-	8k. red, green and black	1·90	85

DESIGNS: 2k.20, Type **406** (millenary of Skara). 23×41 mm: 4k.40, "Falun Copper Mine" (Pehr Hillestrom) (700th anniv of Stora Kopparberg (mining company)); 8k. Scene from play "The Queen's Diamond Ornament" (bicentenary of Royal Dramatic Theatre, Stockholm).

407 "Self-portrait" (Nils Dardel)

1968. Swedish Artists in Paris. Multicoloured.

1402	2k.20 Type **407**	55	50
1403	2k.20 "Autumn, Gubbhuset" (Vera Nilsson) (40×43 mm)	55	50
1404	2k.20 "Self-Portrait" (Isaac Grunewald)	55	50
1405	2k.20 "Visit to an Eccentric Lady" (Nils Dardel)	55	50
1406	2k.20 "Soap Bubbles" (Vera Nilsson) (40×43 mm)	55	50
1407	2k.20 "The Singing Tree" (Isaac Grunewald)	55	50

408 X2 High-speed Train

1988. Europa. Transport and Communications.

1408	**408**	2k.20 blue, orange and brown	1·90	40
1409	**408**	3k.10 blue, black and purple	85	75
1410	-	3k.10 black and purple	85	75

DESIGN: No. 1410, Narrow-gauge steam locomotive.

409 Common Swift

1988

1411	**409**	20k. purple and mauve	4·25	40

410 Andersson

1988. Birth Centenary of Dan Andersson (poet). Each violet, green and blue.

1412	2k.20 Type **410**	50	20
1413	2k.20 Lake, Finnmarken (58×24 mm)	50	20

411 Players

1988. Swedish Football. Multicoloured.

1414	2k.20 Type **411**	70	65
1415	2k.20 Three players	70	65
1416	2k.20 Women players	70	65

412 Angel and Shepherds

1988. Christmas. Multicoloured.

1417	2k. Type **412**	40	25
1418	2k. Horse and angel	40	25
1419	2k. Birds singing in trees	40	25
1420	2k. Three wise men	40	25
1421	2k. Holy Family	40	25
1422	2k. Shepherds and sheep	40	25

Nos. 1417/22 were printed together, se-tenant, forming a composite design.

413 Archaeologist, Carbon 14 Dating Graph and Tutankhamun

1988. Nobel Prize Winners for Chemistry. Mult.

1423	3k.10 Type **413** (Willard Frank Libby, 1960)	75	60
1424	3k.10 Plastics molecules (Karl Ziegler and Giulio Natta, 1963)	75	60
1425	3k.10 Electron microscope (Aaron Klug, 1982)	75	60
1426	3k.10 Landscape and symbols (Ilya Prigogine, 1977)	75	60

414 Nidingen 1946 Concrete and 1832 Twin Lighthouses

1989. Lighthouses.

1427	**414**	1k.90 green, brown and black	40	20
1428	-	2k.70 blue, red and deep blue	60	50
1429	-	3k.80 brown, deep blue and blue	85	60
1430	-	3k.90 black, red & brown	85	65

DESIGNS: 2k.70, Soderarm stone lighthouse; 3k.80, Sydostbrotten caisson lighthouse; 3k.90, Sandhammaren iron lighthouse.

415 Wolverine ("Gulo gulo")

1989. Animals in Threatened Habitats.

1431	**415**	2k.30 brown, orange and green	50	20
1432	-	2k.30 brown, green and orange	50	20
1433	-	2k.40 brown, chocolate and red	50	20
1434	-	2k.60 agate, brown and orange	65	35
1435	-	3k.30 deep green, green and brown	80	45
1436	-	4k.60 black, green and orange	1·10	45

DESIGNS: 2k.30 (1432), Ural owl ("Strix uralensis"): 2k.40, Lesser spotted woodpecker ("Dendrocopos minor"); 2k.60, Dunlin ("Calidris alpina schinzii"); 3k.30, Common tree frog ("Hyla arborea"); 4k.60, Red-breasted flycatcher ("Ficedula parva").

416 Globe Arena

1989. Opening of Globe Arena, Stockholm. Mult.

1437	2k.30 Type **416**	55	25
1438	2k.30 Ice hockey	55	25
1439	2k.30 Gymnastics	55	25
1440	2k.30 Pop concert	55	25

417 Woman's Woollen Bib Front

1989. Nordic Countries' Postal Co-operation. Traditional Lapp Costumes.

1441	2k.30 Type **417**	80	35
1442	3k.30 Man's belt pouch	1·10	75

418 Sailing

1989. Rebate stamps. Summer Activities. Mult.

1443	2k.10 Type **418**	1·10	25
1444	2k.10 Beach ball	1·10	25
1445	2k.10 Cycling	1·10	25
1446	2k.10 Canoeing	1·10	25
1447	2k.10 Fishing	1·10	25
1448	2k.10 Camping	1·10	25
1449	2k.10 Croquet	1·10	25
1450	2k.10 Badminton	1·10	25
1451	2k.10 Gardening	1·10	25
1452	2k.10 Sand castle, bucket and spade	1·10	25

419 "Protest March" (Nils Kreuger)

1989. Centenary of Swedish Labour Movement.

1453	**419**	2k.30 black and red	65	25

420 Playing with Boats

1989. Europa. Children's Games and Toys.

1454	**420**	2k.30 brown	2·20	50
1455	**420**	3k.30 mauve	80	80
1456	-	3k.30 green	80	80

DESIGN: No. 1456, Girl riding kick-sled.

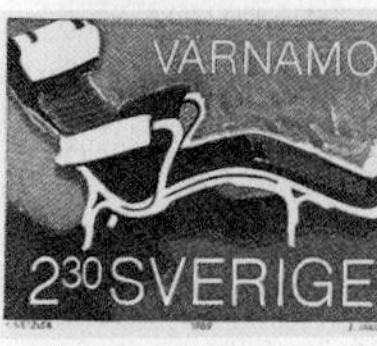

421 Lounger (Varnamo)

1989. Industries of Smaland Towns. Each mauve, orange and red.

1457	2k.30 Type **421**	55	50
1458	2k.30 Tools for self-assembly furniture (Almhult)	55	50
1459	2k.30 Sewing machine and embroidery (Huskvarna)	55	50
1460	2k.30 Blowing glass (Afors)	55	50
1461	2k.30 Coathanger hook and clothes-peg spring (Gnosjo)	55	50
1462	2k.30 Match (Jonkoping)	55	50

422 Researcher in Greenland, Lockheed C-130 Hercules and Temperature Curve

1989. 250th Anniv of Swedish Academy of Sciences. Polar Research. Multicoloured.

1463	3k.30 Type **422**	80	70
1464	3k.30 Abisko Natural Science Station, Lapland (40×43 mm)	80	70
1465	3k.30 "Oden" (ice research ship) and researchers	80	70
1466	3k.30 Otto Nordenskiold 1901–03 expedition's "Antarctic" and Emperor penguin with chick	80	70
1467	3k.30 1988 Antarctic expedition's vehicles and Hughes Model 500 helicopter (40×43 mm)	80	70
1468	3k.30 Geodimeter and South polar skua	80	70

423 Eagle Owl

1989

1469	**423**	30k. brown, black & mve	6·25	95

424 Arctic Rhododendron ("Rhododendron lapponicum")

1989. National Parks (1st series).

1470	**424**	2k.40 mauve, green & bl	55	25
1471	-	2k.40 mauve and green	55	25
1472	-	4k.30 red, black and blue	95	80

DESIGNS—HORIZ: No. 1471, Calypso ("Calypso bulbosa"). VERT: No. 1472, Black guillemots at Bla Jungfrun.

See also Nos. 1486/90.

425 Jamthund

1989. Centenary of Swedish Kennel Club. Mult.

1473	2k.40 Type **425**	75	75
1474	2k.40 Hamilton foxhound	75	75
1475	2k.40 Vastgota sheep dog	75	75

426 Decorated Tree

1989. Christmas. Multicoloured.

1476	2k.10 Type **426**	50	25
1477	2k.10 Candelabra and food	50	25
1478	2k.10 Star, poinsettia and tureen	50	25
1479	2k.10 Decorated tree and straw goat	50	25
1480	2k.10 Girl watching television	50	25
1481	2k.10 Family with present	50	25

Nos. 1476/81 were issued together, se-tenant, forming a composite design.

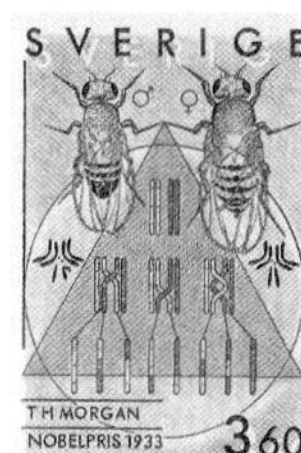

427 Vinegar Flies (T. H. Morgan, 1933)

1989. Nobel Prize Winners for Medicine.

1482	**427**	3k.60 brown, yellow & bl	90	75
1483	-	3k.60 yellow, blue & red	90	75
1484	-	3k.60 multicoloured	90	75
1485	-	3k.60 multicoloured	90	75

DESIGNS: No. 1483 X-ray diffractogram and D.N.A. molecule (Francis Crick, James Watson and Maurice Wilkins, 1962); 1484, D.N.A. molecule cut by restriction enzyme (W. Arber, D. Nathans and H. O. Smith, 1978); 1485, Maize kernels (Barbara McClintock, 1983).

428 Angso

1990. National Parks (2nd series).

1486	**428**	2k.50 blue, green and red	50	35
1487	-	2k.50 red, green and blue	50	35
1488	-	3k.70 blue, brown & grn	95	60
1489	-	4k.10 blue, green & brn	1·10	75
1490	-	4k.80 green, brown & bl	1·20	80

DESIGNS: No. 1487, Pieljekaise; 1488, Muddus; 1489, Padjelanta; 1490, Sanfjallet.

429 Lumberjack

1990. Centenary of Industrial Safety Inspectorate.

1491	**429**	2k.50 blue and brown	55	25

430 Postal Museum, Stockholm

1990. Europa. Post Office Buildings.

1492	**430**	2k.50 brown, orange & bl	2·40	55
1493	-	3k.80 blue, yellow and brown	1·10	85
1494	-	3k.80 brown, blue and yellow	1·10	85

DESIGNS: No. 1493, Sollebrunn Post Office; 1494, Vasteras Post Office.

431 Carved Bone Head and Cast Dragon Head

1990. Vikings. Multicoloured.

1495	2k.50 Type **431**	55	45
1496	2k.50 Returning Viking long-ships (34×29 mm)	55	45
1497	2k.50 Wooden houses (34×29 mm)	55	45
1498	2k.50 Bronze figurine of God of Fertility and silver cross	55	45
1499	2k.50 Crosier and gold embroidered deer	55	45
1500	2k.50 Vikings in roundship (34×29 mm)	55	45
1501	2k.50 Viking disembarking (34×29 mm)	55	45
1502	2k.50 Viking swords	55	45

Nos. 1496/7 and 1500/1 form a composite design.

432 Worker collecting Pollen

1990. Rebate stamps. Honey Bees. Multicoloured.

1503	2k.30 Type **432**	1·10	25
1504	2k.30 Worker on bilberry	1·10	25
1505	2k.30 Worker flying back to hive	1·10	25
1506	2k.30 Beehive	1·10	25
1507	2k.30 Bees building honey-combs	1·10	25
1508	2k.30 Drone	1·10	25
1509	2k.30 Queen	1·10	25
1510	2k.30 Swarm on branch	1·10	25
1511	2k.30 Beekeeper collecting frame	1·10	25
1512	2k.30 Pot of honey	1·10	25

433 Prow of "Wasa" and Museum

1990. Opening of New "Wasa" (17th-century ship of the line) Museum.

1513	**433**	2k.50 black and red	85	30
1514	-	4k.60 blue and red	1·40	90

DESIGNS: 4k.60, Stern of "Wasa" and museum.

434 Endurance Event

1990. World Equestrian Games, Stockholm. Mult.

1515	3k.80 Type **434**	85	80
1516	3k.80 Mark Todd on Carisma jumping wall (3-day event)	85	80
1517	3k.80 John Whitaker on Next Milton jumping fence (show jumping)	85	80
1518	3k.80 Louise Nathorst (dressage)	85	80
1519	3k.80 Team vaulting	85	80
1520	3k.80 Pahlsson brothers driving four-in-hand	85	80

435 Papermaking, 1600

1990. Centenary of Swedish Pulp and Paper Industry. Multicoloured.

1521	2k.50 Type **435**	50	40
1522	2k.50 Crown watermark	50	40
1523	2k.50 Foreign newspapers using Swedish newsprint	50	40
1524	2k.50 Rolls of paper	50	40

436 "Dearest Brothers, Sisters and Friends"

1990. 250th Birth Anniv of Carl Michael Bellman (poet) (1525/7) and Birth Centenary of Evert Taube (poet) (1528/30). Designs showing illustrations of their poems.

1525	**436**	2k.50 brown and black	70	55
1526	-	2k.50 multicoloured	70	55
1527	-	2k.50 black, blue and red	70	55
1528	-	2k.50 multicoloured	70	55
1529	-	2k.50 multicoloured	70	55
1530	-	2k.50 multicoloured	70	55

DESIGNS—As Type **436**: No. 1527, "Fredman in the Gutter"; 1528, "Happy Baker of San Remo"; 1530, "Violava". 40×43 mm: 1526, "Proud City"; 1529, "At Sea".

437 Oved Castle

1990

1531	**437**	40k. brown, black and red	9·00	80

438 Moa Martinson

1990. Birth Centenary of Moa Martinson (novelist).

1532	**438**	2k.50 black and red	60	25
1533	-	2k.50 black and violet	60	25

DESIGN: No. 1533, Fredrika and Sofi bathing (from "Women and Apple Trees").

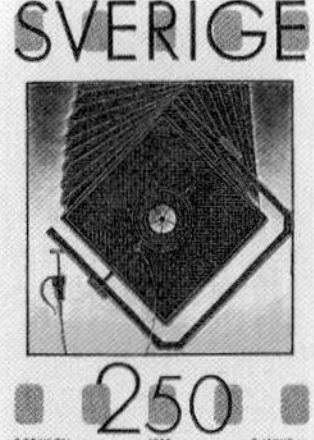

439 Box Camera with Bellows

1990. Photography. Multicoloured.

1534	2k.50 Type **439**	75	75
1535	2k.50 August Strindberg (self-photograph)	75	75
1536	2k.50 Modern 35 mm camera	75	75

440 Cumulus Clouds

1990. Clouds.

1537	**440**	4k.50 multicoloured	1·10	25
1538	-	4k.70 black and blue	1·10	70
1539	-	4k.90 blue, green & brn	1·30	80
1540	-	5k.20 blue & ultramarine	1·40	85

DESIGNS: 4k.70, Cumulonimbus; 4k.90, Cirus uncinus; 5k.20, Altocumulus lenticularis.

441 Christmas Cactus ("Schlumbergera x buckleyi")

1990. Christmas. Flowers. Multicoloured.

1541	2k.30 Type **441**	60	30
1542	2k.30 Christmas rose ("Helleborus niger")	60	30
1543	2k.30 Azalea ("Rhododenron simsii")	60	30
1544	2k.30 Amaryllis ("Hippeastrum × hortorum")	60	30
1545	2k.30 Hyacinth ("Hyacinthus orientalis")	60	30
1546	2k.30 Poinsettia ("Euphorbia pulcherrima")	60	30

442 Par Lagerkvist (1951)

1990. Nobel Prize Winners for Literature.

1547	**442**	3k.80 blue	1·10	85
1548	-	3k.80 red	1·10	85
1549	-	3k.80 green	1·10	85
1550	-	3k.80 violet	1·10	85

DESIGNS: No. 1548, Ernest Hemingway (1954); 1549, Albert Camus (1957); 1550, Boris Pasternak (1958).

443 Heath of Wels ("Silurus glanis") and Young

1991. Freshwater Fishes.

1551	**443**	2k.50 black, green & brn	60	25
1552	-	2k.50 black, green & brn	60	25
1553	-	5k. black, blue and brown	1·00	25
1554	-	5k.40 black, violet & red	1·30	95
1555	-	5k.50 brown and green	1·30	30
1556	-	5k.60 black, blue & orge	1·30	85

DESIGNS: No. 1552, Wels (different); 1553, Spined loach ("Cobitis taeina"); 1554, Gudgeon ("Gobio gobio"); 1555, Stone loach ("Noemacheilus barbataulus"); 1556, Sunbleak ("Leucaspius delineatus").

Nos. 1551/2 form a composite design of two catfish.

444 "Carta Marina", 1572 (Olaus Magnus)

1991. Maps. Multicoloured.

1557	5k. Type **444**	1·10	1·00
1558	5k. Sweden, Denmark and Norway, 1662 (A. Bureus and J. Blaeu) (40×43 mm)	1·10	1·00
1559	5k. Star globe, 1759 (Anders Akerman)	1·10	1·00
1560	5k. Relief map of Areskutan, 1938	1·10	1·00
1561	5k. Stockholm old town, 1989 (40×43 mm)	1·10	1·00
1562	5k. Bed-rock map of Areskutan, 1984	1·10	1·00

445 Queen Silvia

1991

1564	-	2k.80 blue	60	25
1565	-	2k.90 green	70	25

1566	-	3k.20 violet	65	25
1568	**445**	5k. purple	1·10	35
1569	**445**	6k. red	1·40	35
1570	**445**	6k.50 violet	1·40	50

DESIGN: 2k.80 to 3k.20, King Carl XVI Gustav.

446 Drottningholm Palace (after Erik Dahlbergh)

1991. Royal Residence at Drottningholm Palace.

1576	**446**	25k. brown, black & grn	5·50	1·20

447 Seglora Church

1991. Rebate stamps. Centenary of Skansen Park, Stockholm. Multicoloured.

1577	2k.40 Type **447**	70	25
1578	2k.40 Celebration of Swedish Flag and National Days at Skansen	70	25
1579	2k.40 Wedding at Skansen	70	25
1580	2k.40 Animals, Skansen Zoo	70	25

448 Park Entrance

1991. Centenary of Public Amusement Parks. Each blue.

1581	2k.50 Type **448**	65	25
1582	2k.50 Dancers and violinist	65	25

449 Polar Bears

1991. Nordic Countries' Postal Co-operation. Tourism. Animals in Kolmarden Zoo.

1583	**449**	2k.50 black, brown & bl	80	35
1584	-	4k. red and purple	1·10	60

DESIGN: 4k. Dolphins and trainer.

450 "Hermes" Rocket

1991. Europa. Europe in Space. Multicoloured.

1585	4k. Type **450**	1·20	85
1586	4k. "Freja" Northern Lights research satellite	1·20	85
1587	4k. "Tele-X" television satellite	1·20	85

451 Magda Julin (figure skating, Antwerp, 1920)

1991. Olympic Games Gold Medallists (1st issue). Multicoloured.

1588	2k.50 Type **451**	55	40
1589	2k.50 Toini Gustafsson (cross-country skiing, Grenoble, 1968)	55	40
1590	2k.50 Agneta Andersson and Anna Olsson (canoeing, Los Angeles, 1984)	55	40
1591	2k.50 Ulrika Knape (high diving, Munich, 1972)	55	40

See also Nos. 1619/22 and 1635/8.

452 Spetal Mine, Norberg (after Carl David af Uhr)

1991. Bergslagen Iron Industry. Multicoloured.

1592	2k.50 Type **452**	55	50
1593	2k.50 Walloon smithy, Forsmark Mill (after J. Wilhem Wallender)	55	50
1594	2k.50 Forge (27×24 mm)	55	50
1595	2k.50 Foundry (after Johann Ahlback) (27×24 mm)	55	50
1596	2k.50 Dannemora Mine (after Elias Martin) (27×37 mm)	55	50
1597	2k.50 Pershyttan Mill (27×37 mm)	55	50

453 Stromsholm Castle

1991

1598	**453**	10k. green and black	2·00	35

454 Lena Philipsson

1991. Rock and Pop Music. Multicoloured.

1599	2k.50 Type **454**	70	50
1600	2k.50 Roxette (duo)	70	50
1601	2k.50 Jerry Williams	70	50

455 Close-up of Gustav III

1991. 70th Birthday of Czeslaw Slania (engraver). Designs showing "Coronation of King Gustav III" by Carl Gustav Pilo.

1602	**455**	10k. blue	2·50	2·75
1603	-	10k. violet	2·50	2·75
1604	-	10k. black	2·50	2·75

DESIGNS—As T **455**: No. 1603, Close-up of lowering of crown onto King's head. 76×44 mm: 1604, Complete picture.

456 "Mans and Mari from Spring to Winter" (Kaj Beckman)

1991. Christmas. Illustrations from children's books. Multicoloured.

1605	2k.30 Type **456**	50	30
1606	2k.30 Family dancing round Christmas tree ("Peter and Lottas's Christmas", Elsa Beskow)	50	30
1607	2k.30 Dressed cat by Christmas tree ("Pettersson gets a Christmas Visit", Sven Nordqvist)	50	30
1608	2k.30 Girl by bed ("Little Anna's Christmas Present", Lasse Sandberg)	50	30

457 Henri Dunant (founder of Red Cross), 1901

1991. Nobel Prize Winners for Peace.

1609	**457**	4k. red	90	70
1610	-	4k. green	90	70
1611	-	4k. blue	90	70
1612	-	4k. lilac	90	70

DESIGNS: No. 1610, Albert Schweitzer (medical missionary), 1953; 1611, Alva Myrdal (disarmament negotiator), 1982; 1612, Andrei Sakharov (human rights activist), 1975.

458 Mulle, the Forest Elf, with Children

1992. Centenary of Outdoor Life Association.

1613	**458**	2k.30 brown, red & grn	55	20

459 Roe Buck

1992. Wildlife.

1614	**459**	2k.80 brown, agate & grn	70	20
1615	-	2k.80 agate, brn & grn	70	20
1617	-	6k. brown and agate	1·40	60
1618	-	7k. brown and green	1·70	55

DESIGNS—As T **459**: No. 1615, Roe deer ("Capreolus capreolus") with fawn. 20×28 mm: No. 1617, Eurasian red squirrel ("Sciurus vulgaris"); 1618, Elk ("Alces alces").

1992. Olympic Games Gold medallists (2nd issue). As T 451. Multicoloured.

1619	2k.80 Gunde Svan (cross-country skiing, Sarajevo, 1984, and Calgary, 1988)	60	40
1620	2k.80 Thomas Wassberg (cross-country skiing, Lake Placid, 1980, and Sarajevo, 1984)	60	40
1621	2k.80 Tomas Gustafson (speed skating, Sarajevo, 1984, and Calgary, 1988)	60	40
1622	2k.80 Ingemar Stenmark (slalom, Lake Placid, 1980)	60	40

460 Gunnar Nordahl (Sweden)

1992. European Football Championship, Sweden. Each blue and green.

1623	2k.80 Type **460**	80	25
1624	2k.80 Lothar Matthaus (Germany) and Tomas Brolin (Sweden)	80	25

461 1855 3s. Green

1992. Stamp Year.

1625	**461**	2k.80 green, yellow & blk	1·30	1·50
1626	**461**	4k.50 green, yellow & blk	1·50	1·70
1627	-	5k.50 yellow, grey & blk	1·60	1·60

DESIGN: 5k.50, 1857 3s. yellow error.

462 "Sprengtporten" (frigate), 1785

1992. Europa. 500th Anniv of Discovery of America by Columbus. Multicoloured.

1628	4k.50 Type **462**	1·40	1·00
1629	4k.50 "Superb" (brig), 1855	1·40	1·00
1630	4k.50 "Big T" (yacht) (competitor in Discovery Race)	1·40	1·00

463 Rabbit (Emma Westerberg)

1992. Rebate stamps. Centenary of "Kamratposten" (children's magazine) showing children's drawings. Multicoloured.

1631	2k.50 Type **463**	70	25
1632	2k.50 Horses (Helena Johansson)	70	25
1633	2k.50 Kitten (Sabina Ostermark)	70	25
1634	2k.50 Elephant (Hanna Bengtsson)	70	25

1992. Olympic Games Gold Medallists (3rd series). As T 451. Multicoloured.

1635	5k.50 Gunnar Larsson (swimming, Munich, 1972)	1·10	95
1636	5k.50 Bernt Johansson (cycling, Montreal, 1976)	1·10	95
1637	5k.50 Anders Garderud (steeplechase, Montreal, 1976)	1·10	95
1638	5k.50 Gert Fredriksson (canoeing, London, 1948)	1·10	95

464 Karlberg Castle

1992

1639	**464**	20k. black, green and blue	3·75	70

465 Hand holding Flower

1992. Greetings Stamps. Multicoloured.

1640	2k.80 Type **465**	55	30
1641	2k.80 Wedge of cheese ("Lyckans ost")	55	30
1642	2k.80 New-born baby ("Lev val!")	55	30
1643	2k.80 Writing with feather ("Gratulerar")	55	30

466 Gustaf Dalen's Sun Valve and First Automated Lighthouse, Gasfeten

1992. Centenary of Patent and Registration Office.

1644	**466**	2k.80 black and blue	55	25

467 Riksdag (Parliament), Helgeandsholmen Island

1992. 88th Interparliamentary Union Conference, Stockholm.

1645	467	2k.80 violet on buff	55	25

468 "Kitchen Maid" (Rembrandt)

1992. Bicentenary of National Museum of Fine Arts. Multicoloured.

1646	5k.50 Type 468	1·30	1·10
1647	5k.50 "Triumph of Venus" (Francois Boucher) (40×44 mm)	1·30	1·10
1648	5k.50 "Portrait of a Girl" (Albrecht Durer)	1·30	1·10
1649	5k.50 Rorstrand vase decorated by Erik Wahlberg	1·30	1·10
1650	5k.50 "Seine Motif" (Carl Fredrik Hill) (40×44 mm)	1·30	1·10
1651	5k.50 "Sergel in his Studio" (Carl Larsson)	1·30	1·10

469 Plateosaurus

1992. Prehistoric Animals. Mult.

1652	2k.80 Type 469	85	75
1653	2k.80 Crocodile ("Thoracosaurus scanicus")	85	75
1654	2k.80 Woolly-haired rhino ("Coelodonta antiquitatis")	85	75
1655	2k.80 Mammoth ("Mammuthus primigenius")	85	75

470 Volvo "PV831", 1950

1992. Swedish Cars.

1656	470	4k. blue	95	55
1657	-	4k. green and blue	95	55

DESIGN: No. 1657 Saab "92", 1950.

471 Osprey ("Pandion haliaetus")

1992. Birds of the Baltic.

1658	471	4k.50 black and blue	1·00	90
1659	-	4k.50 brown, black & bl	1·00	90
1660	-	4k.50 deep brown, brown and blue	1·00	90
1661	-	4k.50 black, brown & bl	1·00	90

DESIGNS: No. 1659, Black-tailed godwit ("Limosa limosa"); 1660, Goosander ("Mergus merganser"); 1661, Common shelducks ("Tadorna tadorna").

472 "Meeting of Joachim and Anna"

1992. Christmas. Icons. Multicoloured.

1662	2k.30 Type 472	50	30
1663	2k.30 "Madonna and Child"	50	30
1664	2k.30 "Archangel Gabriel" (head)	50	30
1665	2k.30 "Saint Nicholas" (½-length portrait)	50	30

473 Walcott

1992. Award of Nobel Literature Prize to Derek Walcott.

1666	473	5k.50 purple, blue & brn	1·30	80
1667	-	5k.50 purple, brown & bl	1·30	80

DESIGN: No. 1667, Palm trees, ocean and text.

474 Brown Bear Cubs

1993. Wildlife.

1668	474	2k.90 brown and black	60	25
1669	-	2k.90 brown and black	60	25
1671	-	3k. multicoloured	65	40
1672	-	5k.80 black, grey & brn	1·50	40
1673	-	12k. brown, blue and red	2·10	1·00

DESIGNS—As T 474: No. 1669, Brown bear. 27×21 mm: No. 1671, Polecat; 1672, Wolf. 21×27 mm: No. 1673, Lynx.

475 "Big Bird" Glider (World Gliding Championships, Borlange)

1993. Int Sports Championships in Sweden. Mult.

1674	6k. Type 475	1·40	1·20
1675	6k. Martin Kornbakk (World Wrestling Championships, Stockholm)	1·40	1·20
1676	6k. Jorgen Persson (World Table Tennis Championships, Gothenburg)	1·40	1·20
1677	6k. Lars Erik Andersson (European Bowling Championships, Malmo)	1·40	1·20
1678	6k. Per Carlen (World Handball Championships, Gothenburg)	1·40	1·20
1679	6k. Marie Helene Westin (World Cross-country Skiing Championships, Falun)	1·40	1·20

Nos. 1675/9 show Swedish competitors.

476 Gooseberries ("Ribes uva-crispa")

1993. Fruits.

1680	476	2k.40 green	55	20
1681	-	2k.40 green	55	25
1682	-	2k.40 red	55	25

DESIGNS: No. 1681, Pears ("Pryus communis"); 1682, Cherries ("Prunus avium").

477 The Creation (relief, Uppsala Cathedral)

1993. 400th Anniv of Uppsala Convocation.

1683	477	2k.90 violet and buff	70	35
1684	-	2k.90 red and buff	70	35

DESIGN: No. 1684, Uppsala Cathedral before fire of 1702.

478 "Poseidon" (Carl Milles)

1993. Nordic Countries' Postal Co-operation. Tourism. Tourist Attractions in Gothenburg.

1685	478	3k.50 green, yellow & bl	85	60
1686	-	3k.50 indigo, yellow and blue	85	60

DESIGN: No. 1686, Liseberg Loop (fairground ride).

479 Ox-eye Daisies

1993. Rebate stamps. Flowers. Multicoloured.

1687	2k.60 Type 479	60	25
1688	2k.60 Poppies	60	25
1689	2k.60 Buttercups	60	25
1690	2k.60 Harebells	60	25

480 "Oguasark" (Olle Baertling)

1993. Europa. Contemporary Art. Multicoloured.

1691	5k. Type 480	1·00	95
1692	5k. "Ade-Ledic-Nander II" (Oyvind Fahlstrom) (horiz)	1·00	95
1693	5k. "The Cubist Chair" (Otto Carlsund)	1·00	95

481 Swallowtail ("Papilio machaon")

1993. Butterflies. Multicoloured.

1694	6k. Type 481	1·40	1·00
1695	6k. Camberwell beauty ("Nymphalis antiopa")	1·40	1·00
1696	6k. Moorland clouded yellow ("Colias palaeno")	1·40	1·00
1697	6k. Scarce fritillary ("Euphydryas maturna")	1·40	1·00

482 Fireworks ("Hurray")

1993. Greetings Stamps. Multicoloured.

1698	2k.90 Type 482	65	25
1699	2k.90 "Hor av Dig" ("Get in touch")	65	30
1700	2k.90 "Tycker om Dig" ("I like you")	65	25
1701	2k.90 "Lycka Till" ("Good luck")	65	30

483 Red-breasted Merganser ("Mergus serrator")

1993. Sea Birds. Multicoloured.

1702	5k. Type 483	1·20	95
1703	5k. Velvet scoter ("Melanitta fusca")	1·20	95
1704	5k. Tufted duck ("Aythya fuligula")	1·20	95
1705	5k. Eider ("Somateria mollissima")	1·20	95

484 Surveyor, 1643 (cover of Johan Mansson's nautical book)

1993. 350th Anniv of Hydrographic Service.

1706	484	2k.90 brown, blue & blk	70	25
1707	-	2k.90 brown, blue & blk	70	25

DESIGN: No. 1707, Survey ship "Nils Stromcrona", 1993.

485 King Carl Gustav

1993. 20th Anniv of Accession of King Carl XVI Gustav and Queen Silvia's 50th Birthday.

1708	8k. Type 485	1·60	1·70
1709	10k. King Carl Gustav wearing medals	2·50	1·90
1710	10k. Queen Silvia	2·50	1·90
1711	12k. Family group and Stockholm and Drottningholm Palaces (75×44 mm)	3·00	2·50

486 Plaited Heart

1993. Christmas.

1712	486	2k.40 green	55	30
1713	-	2k.40 red	55	30

DESIGN: No. 1713, Straw goat.

487 Stockholm City Hall

1993. Award of Nobel Literature Prize to Toni Morrison.

1714	487	6k. red and blue	1·40	90
1715	-	6k. brown and red	1·40	90

DESIGN: No. 1715, Toni Morrison.

488 Victoria Plums

1994. Fruits.

1716	488	2k.80 multicoloured	70	20
1717	-	2k.80 multicoloured	70	35
1718	-	2k.80 light green & green	70	35

DESIGNS: No. 1717, Opal plums; 1718, "James Grieve" apples.

489 North Sweden Horse's Head

1994. Domestic Animals (1st series).

1719	489	3k.20 brown, agate and red	75	30
1720	-	3k.20 brown, agate and red	75	30
1721	-	3k.20 black, brown & bl	75	30
1722	-	6k.40 black and green	1·40	55

DESIGNS—VERT: No. 1720, North Sweden horses in harness. HORIZ: 1721, Gotland sheep; 1722, Mountain cow.
See also Nos. 1787/91 and 1802/3.

490 Mother Svea and European Union Emblem

1994. Single European Market.

1723	**490**	5k. blue	1·30	60

491 Siamese

1994. Cats. Multicoloured.

1724	4k.50 Type **491**	1·20	90
1725	4k.50 Persian	1·20	90
1726	4k.50 European	1·20	90
1727	4k.50 Abyssinian	1·20	90

492 Illustration from "Le Roman de la Rose"

1994. Franco-Swedish Cultural Relations. Multicoloured.

1728	5k. Type **492**	1·20	1·10
1729	5k. Swedish and French flags	1·20	1·10
1730	5k. Sketch by De la Vallee of Knight's House (40×43 mm)	1·20	1·10
1731	5k. "Household Chores" (Pehr Hillestrom)	1·20	1·10
1732	5k. "Banquet for Gustav III at the Trianon, 1784" (Niclas Lafrensen the younger) (40×43 mm)	1·20	1·10
1733	5k. "Carl XIV Johan" (Francois Gerard)	1·20	1·10

493 Martin Dahlin during Match

1994. World Cup Football Championship, U.S.A.

1734	**493**	3k.20 blue and red	95	30

494 Wild Rose ("Rosa dumalis")

1994. Roses. Multicoloured.

1735	3k.20 Type **494**	85	25
1736	3k.20 "Rosa alba maxima"	85	25
1737	3k.20 "Tuscany Superb"	85	25
1738	3k.20 "Peace"	85	25
1739	3k.20 "Four Seasons"	85	25

495 Lunar Module "Eagle" and Astronauts

1994. 25th Anniv of First Manned Moon Landing.

1740	**495**	6k.50 orange, black & bl	1·50	1·00

496 Iris Vase (Gunnar Wennerberg), 1897

1994. 150th Annivs of Stockholm College of Arts, Crafts and Design and of Swedish Society of Crafts and Design. Multicoloured.

1741	6k.50 Type **496**	1·40	1·20
1742	6k.50 Wallpaper (Uno Ahren) and Chair (Carl Malmsten), 1917	1·40	1·20
1743	6k.50 Aralia cloth, 1920, and cabinet, 1940 (Josef Frank)	1·40	1·20
1744	6k.50 Crystal bowl engraved with fireworks design (Edward Hald), 1921	1·40	1·20
1745	6k.50 Silver water jug, 1941, and sketch of coffee pot, 1970s (Wiwen Nilsson)	1·40	1·20
1746	6k.50 Linen towel (Astrid Sampe), plate (Stig Lindberg) and cutlery (Sigurd Persson), 1955	1·40	1·20

497 Cat ("Love and Kisses")

1994. Greetings Stamps. Multicoloured.

1747	3k.20 Type **497**	75	35
1748	3k.20 Snail ("You've got time")	75	35
1749	3k.20 Frog ("You're lovely just as you are")	80	40
1750	3k.20 Dog ("Hi there!")	80	40

498 Musicians (sketch, Johan Silvius) and Opening Bars of "Drottningholm Music"

1994. 300th Birth Anniv of Johan Helmich Roman (composer) (1751) and Inauguration of Gothenburg Opera House (1752).

1751	**498**	3k.20 brown and blue	75	30
1752	-	3k.20 multicoloured	75	30

DESIGN: No. 1752, Opera House (designed Jan Izikowitz) and opening bars of opera "Aniara" by Karl Birger (inaugural programme).

499 Sepo Raty (javelin)

1994. Sweden-Finland Athletics Meeting, Stockholm. Multicoloured.

1753	4k.50 Type **499**	1·10	85
1754	4k.50 Patrik Sjoberg (high jump)	1·10	85

500 Erland Nordenskiold (South America)

1994. Europa. Swedish Explorers. Multicoloured.

1755	5k.50 Type **500**	1·40	1·20
1756	5k.50 Eric von Rosen (Africa)	1·40	1·20
1757	5k.50 Sten Bergman (Asia and Australasia)	1·40	1·20

501 Caspian Tern ("Sterna caspia")

1994. Endangered Birds. Multicoloured.

1758	5k.50 Type **501**	1·30	1·20
1759	5k.50 White-tailed sea eagle ("Haliaeetus albicilla")	1·30	1·20
1760	5k.50 White-backed woodpecker ("Dendrocopos leucotos")	1·30	1·20
1761	5k.50 Lesser white-fronted goose ("Anser erythropus")	1·30	1·20

502 Bengtsson and Illustration from "The Longships" (novel)

1994. Birth Centenary of Frans Bengtsson (writer).

1762	**502**	6k.40 violet, red and black	1·50	1·10

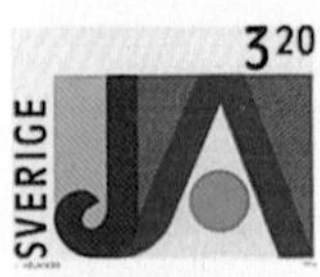

503 "Ja" ("Yes")

1994. European Union Membership Referendum (1st issue). Multicoloured.

1763	3k.20 Type **503**	80	30
1764	3k.20 "Nej" ("No")	80	30

See also Nos. 1785/6.

504 "The Annunciation"

1994. Christmas. Details from Askeby altarpiece. Multicoloured.

1765	2k.80 Type **504**	65	30
1766	2k.80 "Flight into Egypt"	65	30

505 Erik Axel Karlfeldt (1931)

1994. Swedish Winners of the Nobel Literature Prize.

1767	**505**	4k.50 brown, dp bl & bl	1·00	65
1768	-	5k.50 deep brn, bl & brn	1·30	90
1769	-	6k.50 brn, dp grn & grn	1·50	1·10

DESIGNS: 5k.50, Eyvind Johnson (1974); 6k.50, Harry Martinsson (1974).

506 King Carl XVI Gustav

1995

1772	**506**	3k.70 red	80	30
1773	**506**	3k.85 black	80	40
1775	-	6k. green	1·20	65
1776	-	7k.50 purple	1·50	1·20
1777	-	8k. red	1·60	90

DESIGN: 6k., 7k.50, 8k. Queen Silvia.

1995. European Union Membership Referendum (2nd issue). Designs as Nos. 1763/4 but colours and values changed. Multicoloured.

1785	3k.70 Type **503**	80	40
1786	3k.70 "Nej" ("No")	80	40

507 Swedish Dwarf Cock

1995. Domestic Animals (2nd series).

1787	**507**	3k.10 brown, chocolate and red	75	35
1788	-	3k.70 chestnut, brown and red	80	35
1789	-	3k.70 chestnut, brown and red	80	35

DESIGNS—VERT: No. 1788, Red poll cow; 1789, Goat.

508 Strawberries

1995. Berries.

1790	**508**	3k.35 red, green and black on cream	70	30
1791	-	3k.35 black, green and purple on cream	70	30
1792	-	3k.35 red, green and black on cream	70	30

DESIGNS: No. 1791, Blackberries; 1792, Raspberries.

509 Cottage with Allotment, Sodermanland

1995. Traditional Buildings (1st series). Rural Houses. Multicoloured.

1793	3k.70 Type **509**	80	40
1794	3k.70 Soldier's smallholding, Skanegard	80	40
1795	3k.70 17th-century farmhouse, Scania	80	40
1796	3k.70 19th-century farmhouse, Jamtland	80	40
1797	3k.70 18th-century manor house, Dalarna	80	40

See also Nos. 1856/64, 1905/10 and 1961/5.

510 Jesus, Walt Whitman and Socrates

1995. Europa. Peace and Freedom. "Love, Peace and Labour" (wooden relief, Bror Hjorth). Multicoloured.

1798	5k. Type **510**	1·10	1·00
1799	5k. Lumumba, Albert Schweitzer and people of different races	1·10	1·00
1800	6k. Type **510**	1·30	1·20
1801	6k. As No. 1799	1·30	1·20

511 Scanian Geese

1995. Domestic Animals.

1802	**511**	7k.40 deep brown, brown and green	1·70	65
1803	-	7k.50 brown, green and blue	1·70	1·00

DESIGN: 7k.50, Swedish yellow duck.

512 Members' Flags forming "EU"

1995. Admission of Sweden to European Union.

1804	**512**	6k. multicoloured	1·40	75

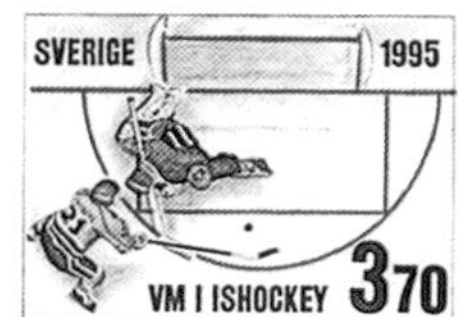

513 Ice Hockey

1995. World Ice Hockey Championship, Stockholm and Gavle (1805) and World Athletics Championships, Gothenburg (1806). Mult.

1805	3k.70 Type **513**	1·60	50
1806	3k.70 Erica Johansson (1992 junior long jump champion) (27½×28 mm)	90	40

514 Rock Speedwell

1995. Mountain Flowers. Multicoloured.

1807	3k.70 Type **514**	85	35
1808	3k.70 Cloudberry (white flowers)	85	35
1809	3k.70 Mountain heath (pink flowers) and black bearberry	85	35
1810	3k.70 Alpine arnica (yellow flowers) and crowberry	85	35

515 "Wilhelm Tham" (motor barge) on Gota Canal

1995. Nordic Countries' Postal Co-operation. Tourism.

1811	**515**	5k. green	1·10	85
1812	-	5k. violet	1·10	85

DESIGN: No. 1812, Moored yacht, Lake Vattern.

516 English Horse-drawn Tram, Gothenburg

1995. Trams.

1813	**516**	7k.50 red	1·60	1·40
1814	-	7k.50 purple	1·60	1·40
1815	-	7k.50 green	1·60	1·40
1816	-	7k.50 lilac	1·60	1·40
1817	-	7k.50 blue	1·60	1·40

DESIGNS: No. 1814, Electric tram, Norrkoping; 1815, Commuter tram, Helsingborg; 1816, Narrow gauge tram, Kiruna; 1817, Mustang tram, Stockholm.

517 "Non-Violence" (sculpture, Carl Frederik Reutersward) (U.N. Building, New York)

1995. 50th Anniv of U.N.O.

1818	**517**	3k.70 deep blue and blue	85	40

518 "The Ball is Yours!" (Mikael Angesjo)

1995. Greetings Stamps. Winning Entries in Children's Drawing Competition. Multicoloured.

1819	3k.70 Type **518**	85	35
1820	3k.70 Happy man saying "Hello" (Erica Sandstrom)	85	35
1821	3k.70 Teddy bear saying "I miss you" (Linda Nordenhem)	85	35
1822	3k.70 Shy mussel saying "Hello" (Christoffer Stenbom)	85	35

519 Maria Akraka

1995. World Athletics Championships, Gothenburg.

1823	**519**	7k.50 multicoloured	1·50	1·20

520 "Soldier Bom" (1948)

1995. Centenary of Motion Pictures. Scenes from Swedish Films. Multicoloured.

1824	6k. Type **520**	1·40	1·50
1825	6k. "Sir Arne's Treasure" (1919)	1·40	1·50
1826	6k. "Wild Strawberries" (1957)	1·40	1·50
1827	6k. "House of Angels" (1992)	1·40	1·50
1828	6k. "One Summer of Happiness" (1951)	1·40	1·50
1829	6k. "The Apple War" (1971)	1·40	1·50

521 Nilsson

1995. Birth Centenary of Fritiof Nilsson (writer).

1830	**521**	3k.70 blue and red	85	50

522 Bronze Figures (Bronze Age)

1995. Ancient Treasures from Museum of National Antiquities, Stockholm. Multicoloured.

1831	3k.70 Type **522**	85	60
1832	3k.70 Gold collar (400–550 A.D.)	85	60
1833	3k.70 Pendant (400–550 A.D.)	85	60
1834	3k.70 Bronze drum (Bronze Age)	85	60

523 Uraniborg Observatory

1995. 450th Birth Anniv of Tycho Brahe (astronomer). Multicoloured.

1835	5k. Type **523**	1·20	65
1836	6k. Instrument for measuring positions in Space	1·30	1·00

524 Santa Candlestick, Varmland

1995. Christmas. Candlesticks. Multicoloured.

1837	3k.35 Type **524**	80	45
1838	3k.35 Apple candlestick, Smaland	80	45
1839	3k.35 Wrought iron candlestick, Dalarna	80	45
1840	3k.35 Three-armed candlestick, Bergslagen	80	45

525 Nobel and Will

1995. Centenary of Nobel Prize Trust Fund. Multicoloured.

1841	6k. Type **525**	1·50	1·30
1842	6k. Nobel's home in Paris	1·50	1·30
1843	6k. Laboratory, Bjorkborn Manor, Karlskoga	1·50	1·30
1844	6k. Medal and award ceremony for Wilhelm Rontgen, 1901	1·50	1·30

526 Rose Hips and Juniper

1996. Winter Berries. Multicoloured.

1845	3k.50 Type **526**	85	40
1846	3k.50 Cowberries and sloes	85	40
1847	3k.50 Holly	85	40
1848	7k.50 Rowan	1·50	1·10

527 West European Hedgehog ("Erinaceus europaeus")

1996. Wildlife.

1849	**527**	1k. sepia, brown and green	25	20
1850	-	3k.20 multicoloured	70	60
1851	-	3k.85 multicoloured	75	35
1852	-	7k.70 brown, deep brown and chocolate	1·60	65
1854	-	3k.85 green, olive and black	85	35

DESIGNS—VERT: No. 1850, Eurasian beaver ("Castor fiber"). HORIZ: No. 1851, Stoat ("Mustela erminea"); 1852, Red fox ("Vulpes vulpes"); 1854, European otter ("Lutra lutra").

528 Postal Sorters and Modern Mail Carriage

1996. Discontinuation of Mail Sorting on Train Travelling Post Offices.

1855	**528**	6k. black, blue and red	1·40	95

529 Post Office and Railway Station, Halsingland

1996. Traditional Buildings (2nd series). Business and Commercial Premises. Multicoloured.

1856	3k.85 Type **529**	85	55
1857	3k.85 Motala Assembly Hall, Ostergotland	85	55
1858	3k.85 Parish storehouse, Smaland (27×23 mm)	85	55
1859	3k.85 Octagonal log barn, Vasterbotten (27×23 mm)	85	55
1860	3k.85 Sheep shelter, Gotland (27×36 mm)	85	55
1861	3k.85 Old Town Hall, Lidkoping (27×36 mm)	85	55

530 King Carl Gustav opening Tyresta National Park, 1993

1996. 50th Birthday of King Carl XVI Gustaf. Multicoloured.

1862	10k. Type **530**	2·20	2·50
1863	10k. In Bernadotte Gallery with painting of King Karl XIV Johan	2·20	2·50
1864	10k. With King Albert of Belgium, 1994	2·20	2·50
1865	20k. With royal family, 1995 (76×43 mm)	4·25	4·00

531 Karin Kock (politician)

1996. Europa. Famous Women.

1866	**531**	6k. brown and red	1·30	1·10
1867	-	6k. blue and red	1·30	1·10

DESIGN: No. 1867, Astrid Lindgren (children's writer).

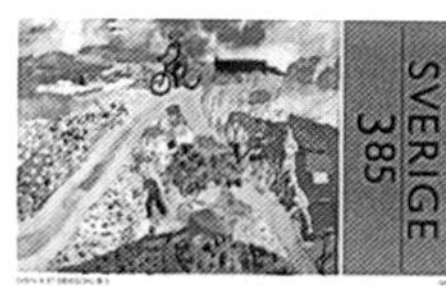

532 "Summer" (Sven X:et Erixson)

1996. Summer Paintings. Multicoloured.

1868	3k.85 Type **532**	85	35
1869	3k.85 "Summer Evening in Stora Nassa" (Roland Svensson)	85	35
1870	3k.85 "On The Island" (Eric Hallstrom)	85	35
1871	3k.85 "Rallarros" (Thage Nordholm)	85	35
1872	3k.85 "On the Bridge" (Ragnar Sandberg)	85	35

533 Annika Sorenstam

1996. Golf.

1873	**533**	3k.50 green on cream	1·10	55

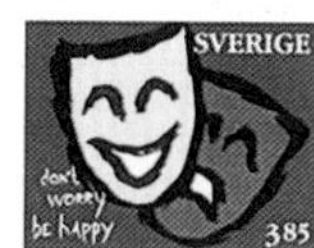

534 Theatre Masks

1996. Greetings Stamps.

1874	**534**	3k.85 multicoloured	90	40
1875	-	3k.85 blue, yellow and black	90	40
1876	-	3k.85 violet, yellow and black	90	40
1877	-	3k.85 red, black and pink	90	40

DESIGNS: No. 1875, Hearts forming four-leaved clover ("Be Happy!"); 1876, Heart within posthorn; 1877, Girl and hearts ("Do you remember me?").

535 Cep ("Boletus edulis")

1996. Fungi. Multicoloured.

1878	3k.85 Type **535**	90	40
1879	5k. "Russula integra"	1·00	70
1880	5k. Chanterelle ("Cantherellus cibarius")	1·00	70
1881	5k. Death trumpets ("Craterellus cornucopioides")	1·00	70
1882	5k. Shaggy ink caps ("Coprinus comatus")	1·00	70

536 Grass Slopes, Haga Park

1996. The Ecopark, Stockholm. Multicoloured.

1883	7k.50 Type **536**	1·50	1·40
1884	7k.50 Copper tents, Haga Park	1·50	1·40
1885	7k.50 Rosendal Palace	1·50	1·40
1886	7k.50 Herons, Isbladskarret Swamp	1·50	1·40

537 Errand Boy, 1930s

1996. Four Decades of Youth. Multicoloured.

1887	3k.85 Type **537**	95	85
1888	3k.85 Hippy, 1960s	95	85
1889	3k.85 Zoot-suiter, 1940s	95	85
1890	3k.85 Biker, 1950s	95	85

538 "Baroque Chair" (Endre Nemes)

1996. Art.

1891	**538**	6k. multicoloured	1·30	1·00

539 The Annunciation

1996. Christmas. Illustrations from 15th-century Book of Hours. Multicoloured.

1892	3k.50 Type **539**	80	50
1893	3k.50 Nativity	80	50
1894	3k.50 Adoration of the Wise Men	80	50

540 Sune Bergstrom (1982)

1996. Swedish Winners of the Nobel Physiology and Medicine Prize.

1895	**540**	5k. black, blue and green	1·30	90
1896	-	5k. black and green	1·30	90
1897	-	5k. black, blue and green	1·30	90
1898	-	5k. blue, green and black	1·30	90

DESIGNS: No. 1896, Bengt Samuelsson (1982); 1897, Hugo Theorell (1955); 1898, Ragnar Granit (1967).

541 Wolverine ("Gulo gulo")

1997. Wildlife.

1899	**541**	3k.20 black, green and blue	80	65
1900	-	3k.50 black, green and red	90	60
1901	-	7k.70 black, red and green	1·70	1·30

DESIGNS—HORIZ: 3k.50, Snowy owl ("Nyctea scandiaca"). VERT: 7k.70, White stork ("Ciconia ciconia").

542 Queen Margareta, Coronation Document and Erik of Pommern

1997. 600th Anniv of Kalmar Union (of Sweden, Denmark and Norway).

1902	**542**	3k.85 blue	85	55

543 Roses forming Heart

1997. Greetings Stamps.

1903	**543**	3k.85 multicoloured (red roses)	90	45
1904	**543**	3k.85 multicoloured (pink roses)	90	45

544 Dalby Church

1997. Traditional Buildings (3rd series). Churches. Multicoloured.

1905	3k.85 Type **544**	85	65
1906	3k.85 Vendel	85	65
1907	3k.85 Hagby (27×23 mm)	85	65
1908	3k.85 Overtornea (27×23 mm)	85	65
1909	3k.85 Varnhem (27×37 mm)	85	65
1910	3k.85 Ostra Amtervik (27×23 mm)	85	65

545 Cockerel

1997. Easter. Inscr "INRIKES BREV". Mult.

1911	(5k.) Type **545**	1·20	50
1912	(5k.) Daffodils	1·20	50

Nos. 1911/12 were for use on domestic first class mail.

546 King Carl XVI Gustav

1997. Inscr "INRIKES BREV".

1913	**546**	(5k.) blue	1·20	45

No. 1913 was for use on domestic first class mail.

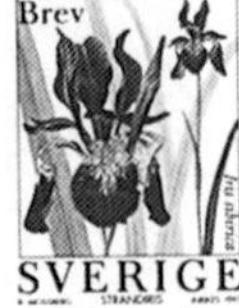

547 Arctic Fox ("Alopex lagopus")

1997. Wildlife (2nd series). (a) Inscr "EKONOMIBREV".

1914	**547**	(4k.50) black, brn & bl	95	45

(b) Inscr "BREV INRIKES" (1915/16) or "INRIKES BREV" (1917).

1915	(5k.) brown, black & grn	1·20	55
1916	(5k.) black and blue	1·20	55
1917	(5k.) black and red	1·20	55

DESIGNS: No. 1915, Przewalski's horses; 1916, Snow leopard; 1917, Snow leopard cubs.

No. 1914 was for use on domestic second class mail and Nos. 1915/17 on domestic first class mail.

548 Siberian Iris ("Iris sibirica")

1997. Garden Flowers. Inscr "INRIKES BREV". Multicoloured.

1918	(5k.) Type **548**	1·10	65
1919	(5k.) Honeysuckle ("Lonicera periclymenum")	1·10	65
1920	(5k.) Columbine ("Aquilegia vulgaris")	1·10	65
1921	(5k.) Day lily ("Hemerocallis flava")	1·10	65
1922	(5k.) Pansy ("Viola wittrockiana")	1·10	65

Nos. 1918/22 were for use on domestic first class mail.

549 Common Pheasant ("Phasianus colchicus")

1997. Pheasants. Multicoloured.

1923	2k. Type **549**	45	35
1924	2k. Lady Amherst's pheasants ("Chrysolophus amherstiae")	45	35

550 Figurehead from "Carl XIII" (ship of the line)

1997. Inauguration of Naval Museum, Karlskrona.

1925	**550**	6k. blue, brown and red	1·30	90

551 Troll with Treasure Chest ("The Troll and the Gnome Boy")

1997. Europa. Tales and Legends. Illustrations by John Bauer. Multicoloured.

1926	7k. Type **551**	1·50	1·20
1927	7k. Trolls gazing at fairy ("The Boy and the Trolls or the Adventure")	1·50	1·20
1928	7k. Boy before troll ("The Fearless Boy")	1·50	1·20

552 18th-century Compass Rose (Sven Billing)

1997. 18th International Cartographic Conference, Stockholm. Multicoloured.

1929	7k. Type **552**	1·50	85
1930	8k. Compass rose, 1568 (from atlas by Diego Homem)	1·80	1·00

553 Lesser Panda

1997. Inscr "FORENINGSBREV".

1931	**553**	(3k.50) choc, brn & red	85	55

No. 1931 was for use on bulk rate mail from societies.

554 Bridge

1997. Inauguration of High Coast Suspension Bridge. Inscr "INRIKES Brev".

1932	**554**	(5k.) blue, green & dp bl	1·20	45

No. 1932 was for use on domestic first class mail.

555 Elk and Mountains

1997. Greeting Stamps. Elk. Inscr "INRIKES BREV".

1933	**555**	(5k.) multicoloured	1·10	65
1934	-	(5k.) multicoloured	1·10	65
1935	-	(5k.) multicoloured	1·10	65
1936	-	(5k.) multicoloured	1·10	65
1937	-	(5k.) black, yellow and red	1·10	65
1938	-	(5k.) black and red	1·10	65

DESIGNS: No. 1934, Elk-shaped bar code; 1935, Striped elk; 1936, Running elk; 1937, Running elk (different); 1938, Elk and young.

Nos. 1933/8 were for use on domestic first class mail.

556 "Gallery of the Muses" (Peter Hillerstrom)

1997. Gustav III's Museum of Antiquities, Stockholm. Multicoloured.

1939	8k. Type **556**	1·70	1·40
1940	8k. "Endymion"	1·70	1·40

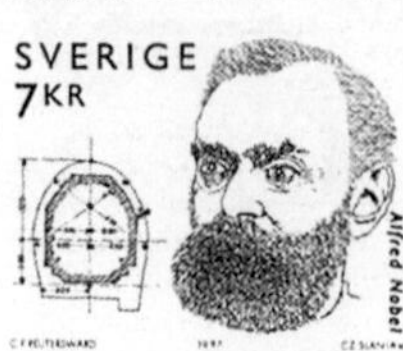

557 Volvo "Duett", 1958

1997. Cars. Inscr "INRIKES BREV". Mult.

1941	(5k.) Type **557**	1·10	95
1942	(5k.) Chevrolet "Bel Air", 1955	1·10	95
1943	(5k.) Porsche "356", 1959	1·10	95
1944	(5k.) Citroen "B11", 1952	1·10	95
1945	(5k.) Saab "Monte Carlo" (Erik Carlsson's rally car)	1·10	95
1946	(5k.) Jaguar "E-type", 1961	1·10	95

Nos. 1941/6 were for use on domestic first class mail.

558 Alfred Nobel (founder of Prize Fund)

1997. The Nobel Prize.

1947	**558**	7k. black and pink	1·60	1·40
1948	-	7k. black and grey	1·60	1·40

DESIGN: No. 1948, Paul Karrer and molecular structure of Vitamin A (Chemistry Prize, 1937).

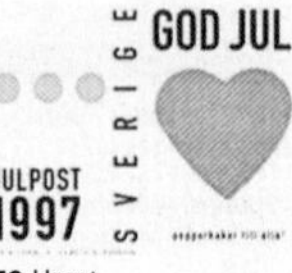

559 Heart

1997. Christmas Gingerbread Biscuits. Each brown, ochre and silver on yellow. Inscr "JULPOST".

1949	(3k.50) Type **559**	85	65
1950	(3k.50) Pigs	85	65
1951	(3k.50) Gingerbread men	85	65

560 Angels with Pipe and Lute

1997. Christmas. Angels from altarpiece, Litslena Church. Multicoloured.

1952	6k. Type **560**	1·30	1·20
1953	6k. Angels with pipes and harp	1·30	1·20

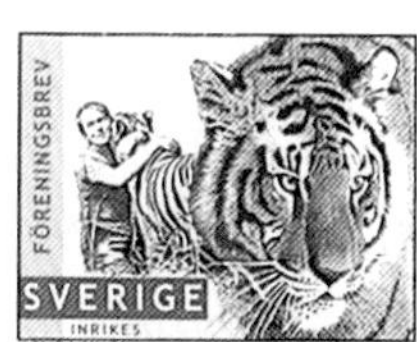

561 Tiger's Head

1998. Wildlife Photographs by Jan Lindblad. Inscr "FORENINGSBREV". Multicoloured.

1954	(3k.50) Type **561**	85	60
1955	(3k.50) Two tigers on rock	85	60

Nos. 1954/5 were for use on bulk rate mail from societies.

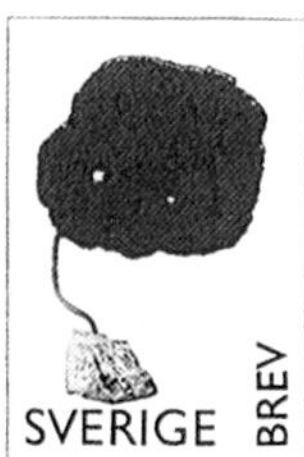

562 "Sponge Sculpture" (Yves Klein)

1998. Modern Art. Inscr "INRIKES BREV". Multicoloured.

1956	(5k.) Type **562**	1·10	70
1957	(5k.) "Skeppsholmen" (Goran Gidenstam)	1·10	70
1958	(5k.) "Monogram" (Robert Rauschenberg)	1·10	70

Nos. 1956/8 were for use on domestic first class mail.

563 Heart with Love Birds

1998. St. Valentine's Day. Inscr "INRIKES Brev".

1959	**563**	(5k.) red and green	1·10	55
1960	**563**	(5k.) mauve and blue	1·10	55

Nos. 1959/60 were for use on domestic first class mail.

564 Fire Station, Gavle

1998. Traditional Buildings (4th series). Town Houses. Inscr "INRIKES BREV". Multicoloured.

1961	(5k.) Type **564**	1·10	55
1962	(5k.) Shoe shop, Askersund	1·10	55
1963	(5k.) Fish and delicatessen market hall, Goteborg	1·10	55
1964	(5k.) Red Mill Cinema, Halmstad	1·10	55
1965	(5k.) Stads Hotel, Eksjo	1·10	55

Nos 1961/5 were for use on domestic first class mail.

565 Apron, Dalarna

1998. Handicrafts. (a) Inscr "EKONOMI BREV INRIKES".

1966	**565**	(4k.50) scarlet, blk & red	1·00	55

(b) Inscr "INRIKES BREV".

1967	(5k.) black and brown	1·10	60

(c) With face value.

1968	8k. orange, violet and red	1·60	1·50
1969	8k. violet and red	1·60	1·50

DESIGNS: No. 1967, Iron candlestick, Skane; 1968, Lumberjack's woollen glove; 1969, Decorative wooden box.

No. 1966 was for use on domestic second class mail and No. 1967 on domestic first class mail.

566 Confederation Building, Stockholm (after Birger Lundquist)

1998. Centenary of Swedish Confederation of Trade Unions. Inscr "Inrikes BREV".

1970	**566**	(5k.) black, stone & red	1·10	45

No. 1970 was for use on domestic first class mail.

567 Queen Kristina and Memorial Medal

1998. 350th Anniv of Peace of Westphalia.

1971	**567**	7k. green and red	1·50	1·10

568 Marsh Violet

1998. Wetland Flowers. Inscr "BREV INRIKES". Multicoloured.

1972	(5k.) Type **568**	1·10	50
1973	(5k.) Great willow herb	1·10	50

Nos. 1972/3 were for use on domestic first class mail.

569 The Royal Palace

1998. Stockholm, Cultural Capital of Europe. Multicoloured. (a) Inscr "INRIKES BREV".

1974	(5k.) Type **569**	1·10	50
1975	(5k.) Archipelago ferries	1·10	80
1976	(5k.) Fisherman in front of Opera House (31×26 mm)	1·10	80
1977	(5k.) Yachts (31×26 mm)	1·10	80
1978	(5k.) Open-air swimming (31×39 mm)	1·10	80
1979	(5k.) City Hall (31×39 mm)	1·10	80

(b) With face value.

1980	7k. Type **569**	1·60	1·30
1981	7k. As No. 1975	1·60	1·30

Nos. 1974/9 were for use on domestic first class mail.

570 "Albatros" (cruise ship) in Stadsgard Harbour

1998. Nordic Countries, Postal Co-operation. Shipping.

1982	**570**	6k. multicoloured	1·50	85

571 Paper Moon and Plate of Crayfish ("Crayfish Party")

1998. Europa. National Festivals. Multicoloured.

1983	7k. Type **571**	1·60	1·30
1984	7k. Children dancing around midsummer pole	1·60	1·30

572 King Carl XVI Gustav and Coat of Arms

1998. 25th Anniv of Accession of King Carl XVI Gustav. Inscr "INRIKES BREV".

1985	**572**	(5k.) purple, green and red	1·10	55

No. 1985 was for use on domestic first class mail.

573 Moberg and Characters from "The Emigrants" (novel)

1998. Birth Centenary of Vilhelm Moberg (writer). Inscr "BREV INRIKES".

1986	**573**	(5k.) multicoloured	1·20	60

No. 1986 was for use on domestic first class mail.

574 Princess Cake

1998. Greetings Stamps. Pastries. Inscr "BREV". Multicoloured.

1987	(5k.) Type **574**	1·10	65
1988	(5k.) Gustav Adolf pastry	1·10	65
1989	(5k.) Napoleon pastry	1·10	65
1990	(5k.) Mocha cake	1·10	65
1991	(5k.) National pastry	1·10	65
1992	(5k.) Lent bun	1·10	65

Nos. 1987/92 were for use on domestic first class mail.

575 "Flowers in the window" (Carl Larsson)

1998. The Twentieth Century (1st series). 1900–1938. Inscr "INRIKES BREV". Multicoloured.

1993	(5k.) Type **575**	1·40	1·00
1994	(5k.) Stockholm Stadium and poster (Olympic Games, 1912)	1·40	1·00
1995	(5k.) Porjus hydro-electric power station and electric iron-ore. train on Lulea (Sweden)–Narvik (Norway) railway line	1·40	1·00
1996	(5k.) Zip, ball-bearing, vacuum cleaner and refrigerator (Swedish inventions)	1·40	1·00
1997	(5k.) Map of trans-ocean shipping routes and liner	1·40	1·00
1998	(5k.) Sven Jerring (first Swedish radio reporter)	1·40	1·00
1999	(5k.) Jazz musicians and Charleston dancers	1·40	1·00
2000	(5k.) Ellen Key (writer and suffragist) and Kerstin Hesselgren (first woman member of parliament)	1·40	1·00
2001	(5k.) Arne Borg (swimmer) and Gillis Grafstrom (figure skater) (Olympic and world champions)	1·40	1·00
2002	(5k.) Ernst Rolf (entertainer)	1·40	1·00

Nos. 1993/2002 were for use on domestic first class mail.

See also Nos. 2026/35 and 2083/92.

576 Nadine Gordimer (1991)

1998. The Nobel Literature Prize.

2003	**576**	6k. violet and blue	1·20	1·20
2004	-	6k. violet and red	1·20	1·20

DESIGN: No. 2004, Sigrid Undset (1928).

577 "King Sigismund of Sweden and Poland" (Studio of Rubens)

1998. 400th Anniv of Battle of Stangebro.

2005	**577**	7k. multicoloured	1·40	1·10

578 Hyacinths

1998. Christmas. Flowers. (a) No value expressed. Inscr "Julpost". Size 21×28 mm. Multicoloured.

2006	(4k.) Type **578**	85	55
2007	(4k.) Mistletoe	85	55
2008	(4k.) Amaryllis	85	55

(b) With face value. Size 23×27½ mm.

2009	6k. Lingonberry wreath	1·20	85
2010	6k. Azaleas	1·20	85

579 King Gustav Vasa 1 Daler, 1540

1999. Coins. (a) Inscr "Ekonomibrev".

2011	**579**	(4k.50) green	85	55

(b) Inscr "Brev inrikes".

2012	(5k.) blue	1·00	55

DESIGN: No. 2012, King Carl XIV John 1 riksdaler, 1831–43.

No. 2011 was for use on domestic second class mail and No. 2012 on domestic first class mail.

580 Harbour and Katarina Lift, Stockholm

1999. Centenary of Co-operative Union. Inscr "INRIKES BREV".

2013	**580**	(5k.) multicoloured	1·00	90

No. 2013 was for use on domestic first class mail.

581 Easter Egg and Rabbit

1999. Easter. Inscr "INRIKES Brev". Mult.

2014	(5k.) Type **581**	1·00	90
2015	(5k.) Easter eggs and chicks	1·00	90

Nos. 2014/15 were for use on domestic first class mail.

582 Rabbit cooking

1999. Rabbits. Drawings by Eva Eriksson from "Little Sister Rabbit" by Ulf Nilsson. Inscr "INRIKES BREV". Multicoloured.

2016	(5k.) Type **582**	1·00	90
2017	(5k.) Rabbit feeding baby rabbit	1·00	90
2018	(5k.) Rabbits dancing	1·00	90
2019	(5k.) Rabbits running through grass	1·00	90

Nos. 2016/19 were for use on domestic first class mail.

583 "East Indies" (anon)

1999. "Australia 99" International Stamp Exhibition, Melbourne. Paintings of Ships. Multicoloured.

2020	8k. Type **583**	1·60	1·40
2021	8k. "Mary Anne" (brigantine) (Folke Sjogren)	1·60	1·40
2022	8k. "Beatrice" (barque) (A. V. Gregory)	1·60	1·40
2023	8k. "Australic" (steamship) (T. G. Purvis)	1·60	1·40

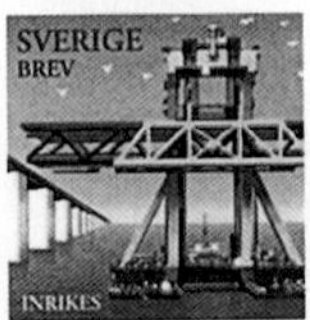

584 Pontoon "Swan" at Dresund Bridge

1999. Construction of Oresund Bridge between Sweden and Denmark. (a) Inscr "INRIKES BREV". Multicoloured.

2024	(5k.) Type **584**	1·00	55

(b) With face value.

2025	6k. Bridge under construction (different)	1·20	1·20

No. 2024 was for use on domestic first class mail.

585 Eva Dahlbeck and Gunnar Bjornstrand in "Smiles of a Summer Night" (director Ingmar Bergman), 1955

1999. The Twentieth Century (2nd series). 1939–1969. Inscr "INRIKES BREV". Multicoloured.

2026	(5k.) Type **585**	1·00	75
2027	(5k.) Vallingby (first satellite town of Stockholm)	95	75
2028	(5k.) Ulla Billquist and scene from "My Soldier somewhere in Sweden" (song) (emergency military service, 1939–45)	95	75
2029	(5k.) Cobra telephone (L.M. Ericsson), three-point seat belt (Nils Bohlins), high voltage cables and Tetra Pak milk carton (Swedish inventions)	95	75
2030	(5k.) Douglas DC-4 airliner (first scheduled flight of state airline SAS)	95	75
2031	(5k.) Jester, Carl-Gustaf Lindstedt, host of "Hyland's Corner", and Prime Minister Tage Erlander (television)	95	75
2032	(5k.) Demonstrators, girl wearing optical-patterned dress and pop group Hep Stars (the 60s)	95	75
2033	(5k.) Volvo Amazon Car and family camping (leisure time)	95	75
2034	(5k.) Ingemar Johansson (world heavy-weight boxing champion), Mora-Nisse Karlsson (skier) and Gunder Hagg (athlete)	95	75
2035	(5k.) Alice Babs (jazz singer) and Jussi Bjorling (opera tenor)	95	75

Nos. 2026/35 were for use on domestic first class mail.

586 Postman's Bicycle

1999. Bicycles. (a) Inscr "FORENINGSBREV".

2036	**586**	(3k.50) bl, ultram & yell	90	65

(b) Inscr "INRIKES BREV".

2037	(5k.) multicoloured	1·00	55

(c) With face value.

2038	6k. blue, purple and black	1·00	80
2039	8k. green, lt green & red	1·60	1·20

DESIGNS: No. 2037, Racing cyclist; 2038, City bike; 2039, Bike messenger.

No. 2036 was for use on bulk rate mail from societies; No. 2037 for use on domestic first class mail.

587 Pyramidal Orchid ("Salepsrot")

1999. Orchids. Inscr "INRIKES BREV". Multicoloured.

2040	(5k.) Type **587**	1·10	65
2041	(5k.) Lady's slipper ("Guckusko")	1·10	65
2042	(5k.) Marsh helleborine ("Karrknipprot")	1·10	65
2043	(5k.) Green-winged orchid ("Goknycklar")	1·10	65

Nos. 2040/3 were for use on domestic first class mail.

588 Plant Shoot

1999. 50th Anniv of Council of Europe.

2044	**588**	7k. multicoloured	1·60	1·20

589 Eurasian Pygmy Owl and Tyresta National Park

1999. Europa. Parks and Gardens. Multicoloured.

2045	7k. Type **589**	1·50	1·40
2046	7k. Pink helleborine and Gotska Sandon National Park	1·50	1·40

590 Peacock ("Inachis io")

1999. Butterflies. Multicoloured.

2047	6k. Type **590**	1·30	1·10
2048	6k. Blue argus ("Junonia orithya")	1·30	1·10
2049	6k. Common eggfly ("Hypolimnas bolina")	1·30	1·10
2050	6k. Red admiral ("Vanessa atalanta")	1·30	1·10

591 "Pisces"

1999. Signs of the Zodiac. Inscr "INRIKES Brev".

2051	**591**	(5k.) blue, ultram and orge	1·10	75
2052	-	(5k.) multicoloured	1·10	75
2053	-	(5k.) blue, ultram and orge	1·10	75
2054	-	(5k.) multicoloured	1·10	75
2055	-	(5k.) blue, ultram and orge	1·10	75
2056	-	(5k.) multicoloured	1·10	75
2057	-	(5k.) multicoloured	1·10	75
2058	-	(5k.) blue, ultram and orge	1·10	75
2059	-	(5k.) orange, ultram and bl	1·10	75
2060	-	(5k.) blue, ultram and orge	1·10	75
2061	-	(5k.) orange, ultram and bl	1·10	75
2062	-	(5k.) blue, ultram and orge	1·10	75

DESIGNS: No. 2052, "Aries"; 2053, "Taurus"; 2054, "Gemini"; 2055, "Cancer"; 2056, "Aquarius"; 2057, "Virgo"; 2058, "Libra"; 2059, "Scorpio"; 2060, "Sagittarius"; 2061, "Capricorn"; 2062, "Leo".

Nos. 2051/62 were for use on domestic first class mail.

592 Auguste Beernaert (Prime Minister of Belgium 1884–94), 1909

1999. Belgian Winners of Nobel Peace Prize.

2063	**592**	7k. blue and gold	1·40	1·30
2064	-	7k. red and gold	1·40	1·30

DESIGN: No. 2064, Henri la Fontaine (President of International Peace Bureau), 1913.

593 Thorleifs

1999. Swedish Dance Bands. Inscr "INRIKES BREV". Multicoloured.

2065	(5k.) Type **593**	1·10	75
2066	(5k.) Arvingara	1·10	75
2067	(5k.) Lotta Engbergs	1·10	75
2068	(5k.) Sten and Stanley	1·10	75

Nos. 2065/8 were for use on domestic first class mail.

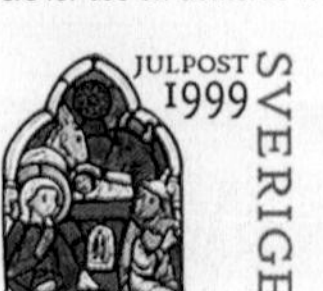

594 "Nativity"

1999. Christmas. Stained-glass Windows (2069/71) and Wood Sculptures (2072/3). Multicoloured. (a) Inscr "JULPOST".

2069	(4k.) Type **594**	95	55
2070	(4k.) "Nativity" (different)	95	55
2071	(4k.) "Adoration of the Wise Men"	95	55

(b) With face value. Size 27½×30 mm.

2072	6k. Crowned Madonna with child	1·30	90
2073	6k. Madonna (in white cloak) and child	1·30	90

Nos. 2069/71 were for use on domestic first class mail.

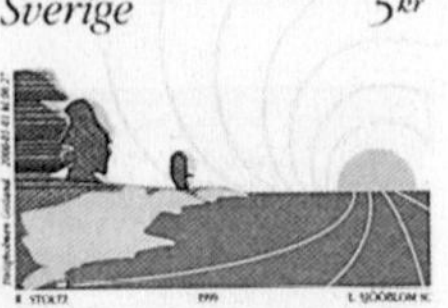

595 Sun rising over Heligholmen

1999. Dawning of New Millennium. Multicoloured.

2074	5k. Type **595**	1·40	1·10
2075	5k. Sun rising over coast at Gotland	1·40	1·10

596 Watch Mechanism

2000. Recovery of King Karl XII's Pocket Watch. (a) Inscr "EKONOMIBREV".

2076	**596**	(4k.50) blue	90	50

(b) Inscr "INRIKES BREV".

2077	(5k.) brown	1·00	45

DESIGN: 5k. Watch face.

No. 2076 was for use on domestic second class mail and No. 2077 on domestic first class mail.

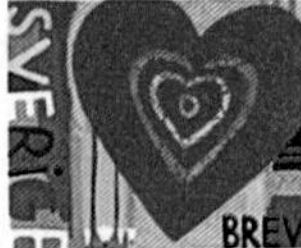

597 Heart

2000. Valentine's Day. Inscr "INRIKES BREV". Multicoloured.

2078	(5k.) Type **597**	1·00	65
2079	(5k.) Scribbled line in heart	1·00	65

Nos. 2078/9 were for use on domestic first class mail.

598 Dragon

2000. Chinese New Year. Year of the Dragon. Illustrations from "The Little Dragon with Red Eyes" by Astrid Lindgren. Inscr "INRIKES BREV". Multicoloured.

2080	(5k.) Type **598**	1·00	70
2081	(5k.) Dragon with basket	1·00	70
2082	(5k.) Dragon flying	1·00	70

Nos. 2080/2 were for use on domestic first class mail.

599 Modern Art, Stockholm Underground Railway

2000. The Twentieth Century (3rd series). 1970–1999. Inscr "INRIKES BREV". Multicoloured.

2083	(5k.) Type **599**	1·00	85
2084	(5k.) Swedish soldiers in United Nations peace- keeping force	1·00	85
2085	(5k.) Computer screen, mouse and voice-activated mobile phone (Swedish inventions)	1·00	85
2086	(5k.) Cullberg Ballet dancer and Hans Alfredson and Tage Danielsson (sketch writers)	1·00	85
2087	(5k.) Jonkoping Railway Station and high-speed train	1·00	85
2088	(5k.) Punk and Abba (pop group)	1·00	85
2089	(5k.) European flag and map of Europe (European Union membership, 1994)	1·00	85
2090	(5k.) Couple in orchard (film "The Apple War, 1971")	1·00	85
2091	(5k.) Pernilla Wiberg (slalom skier), Ingemar Stenmark (downhill skier) and Björn Borg (tennis player)	1·00	85
2092	(5k.) Child in womb (photograph, Lennart Nilsson)	1·00	85

Nos. 2083/92 were for use on domestic first class mail.

600 Parent and Child walking through Forest (public access)

2000. Swedish Forests. Multicoloured. (a) Inscr "Foreningsbrev".

2093	(3k.80) Type **600**	95	60

(b) Inscr "INRIKES BREV".

2094	(5k.) Felled trees and elk (forestry)	1·10	65
2095	(5k.) Western capercaillie in fir forest	1·10	65

(c) With face value.

2096	6k. Birch trees	1·10	1·00

No. 2093 was for use on bulk rate mail from societies. Nos. 2094/5 were for use on domestic first class mail.

601 "Great deeds by Swedish Kings" (David Klocker Ehrenstrahl) (image scaled to 63% of original size)

2000. 1000th Stamp Engraving by Czeslew Slanis. Sheet 94×126 mm.

MS2097 **601** 50k. multicoloured 9·75 9·75

602 Oresund Bridge

2000. Inauguration of Oresund Link (Sweden–Denmark road and rail system). (a) Inscr "INRIKES BREV".

2098 **602** (5k.) black, bl & ultram 1·00 55

(b) Size 58×24 mm.

2099 6k. multicoloured 1·20 1·10

2100 6k. ultramarine and green 1·20 1·10

DESIGNS: No. 2099, Oresund Bridge; 2100, Map of Oresund Region.

No. 2098 was for use on domestic first class mail.

603 " A Peck of Apples"

2000. Modern Paintings by Philip von Schantz. Inscr "INRIKES BREV". Multicoloured.

2101 (5k.) Type **603** 1·00 65

2102 (5k.) "A Bowl of Blueberries" 1·00 65

Nos. 2101/2 were for use on domestic first class mail.

604 " Building Europe"

2000. Europa.

2103 **604** 7k. multicoloured 1·80 1·20

605 Hurdling

2000. Olympic Games, Sydney. Multicoloured.

2104 8k. Type **605** 1·60 1·50

2105 8k. Archery 1·60 1·50

2106 8k. Wind surfing 1·60 1·50

2107 8k. Beach volleyball 1·60 1·50

606 Red Sun and Clouds

2000. Weather. Inscr "INRIKES BREV". Multicoloured. Self-adhesive.

2108 (5k.) Type **606** 1·00 60

2109 (5k.) Lightning 1·00 60

2110 (5k.) Black clouds 1·00 60

2111 (5k.) Northern lights 1·00 60

2112 (5k.) Rainbow 1·00 60

2113 (5k.) Blue sky and white clouds 1·00 60

Nos. 2108/13 were for use on domestic first class mail.

607 King Carl Gustaf XVI

2000. (a) Inscr "INRIKES Brev".

2114 **607** (5k.) blue 1·00 60

2115 **607** (5k.50) lake 1·10 1·00

(b) With face values.

2118 8k. red 1·60 1·30

2119 10k. mauve 2·00 1·90

DESIGN: 8k. Queen Silvia.

No. 2114/15 were for use on domestic first class mail.

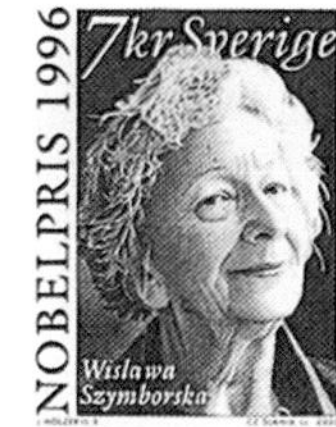

608 Wislawa Szymborska (poet), 1996

2000. Nobel Prize Winners for Literature.

2120 **608** 7k. purple and green 1·50 1·20

2121 - 7k. green and purple 1·50 1·20

DESIGN: No. 2121, Nelly Sachs (author), 1966.

609 Teddy Bear and Doll

2000. Children's Toys. Booklet stamps. Inscr "BREV". Multicoloured.

2122 (5k.) Type **609** 1·10 1·20

2123 (5k.) Skipping rope, marbles and tin soldier 1·10 1·20

2124 (5k.) Toy horses pulling cart, doll and flag 1·10 1·20

2125 (5k.) Toy cars and policeman 1·10 1·20

2126 (5k.) Railway carriages and porter 1·10 1·20

2127 (5k.) Modern toys 1·10 1·20

Nos. 2122/27 were for use on domestic first class mail.

610 Elves drinking

2000. Christmas. Traditional Songs (2128/32) or Snowflakes (2133/4) (others). (a) No value expressed. Inscr "JULPOST".

2128 (4k.30) Type **610** 85 65

2129 (4k.30) Children dancing around tree (vert) 85 65

2130 (4k.30) Three gingerbread men (vert) 85 65

2131 (4k.30) Fox running (vert) 85 65

2132 (4k.30) Children dancing around candles (vert) 85 65

(b) With face value. Size 28×29 mm.

2133 6k. silver and blue (face value in blue) 1·20 1·00

2134 6k. silver and blue (face value in white) 1·20 1·00

DESIGNS: Nos. 2133/34 Snowflakes.

Nos. 2128/32 were for use on domestic first class mail.

611 Farming

2001. UNESCO World Heritage Sites. Rock Carvings, Tanum. (a) Inscr "EKONOMIBREV".

2135 **611** (4k.50) blue on grey 95 70

(b) Inscr "INRIKES BREV".

2136 (5k.) red on grey 1·00 50

612 Gammelstad Church Village

(c) With face value 35×28 mm.

2137 6k. Type **612** 1·10 1·10

2138 6k. Karlskrona Naval Base 1·10 1·10

2139 6k. Interior of Drottningholm Palace Theatre 1·10 1·10

2140 6k. Ironworks, Engelsberg 1·10 1·10

DESIGN: No. 2136, Men in ships.

No. 2135 was for use on domestic second class mail and No. 2136 on domestic first class mail.

613 Rosa

2001. Chinese New Year. Year of the Snake. Depicting scenes from Nelson the Snake (book) by Ulf Stark. Multicoloured. Inscr "INRIKES BREV".

2141 (5k.) Type **613** 1·10 85

2142 (5k.) Nelson coiled on rock 1·10 85

Nos. 2141/2 were for use on domestic first class mail.

614 Children with Golden Retriever

2001. Working Dogs. Multicoloured. Inscr "INRIKES BREV".

2143 (5k.) Type **614** 1·00 95

2144 (5k.) German shepherds hunting in snow 1·00 95

2145 (5k.) Labrador guide dog with blind woman 1·00 95

2146 (5k.) Dachshunds and man 1·00 95

615 Northern Lapwing (*Vanellus vanellus*)

2001. Birds. (a) Inscr "FORENINGSBREV".

2147 **615** (3k.80) blue, green and brown 90 70

(b) Inscr "INRIKES Brev".

2148 (5k.) blue and black 1·00 85

(c) With face value.

2149 6k. green, black and orange 1·20 1·10

2150 7k. purple, brown and green 1·40 1·20

DESIGNS: No. 2148, Black-billed magpie (*Pica pica*); 2149, Herring gull (*Larus argentatus*); 2150, Long-tailed tit (*Aegithalos caudatus*).

No. 2147 was for use on bulk rate mail from societies and No. 2148 for use on domestic first class mail.

616 Yellow Egg

2001. Easter. Multicoloured. Self-adhesive. Inscr "INRIKES Brev".

2151 (5k.) Type **616** 1·00 85

2152 (5k.) Purple egg 1·00 85

2153 (5k.) Chick 1·00 85

Nos. 2151/3 were for use on domestic first class mail.

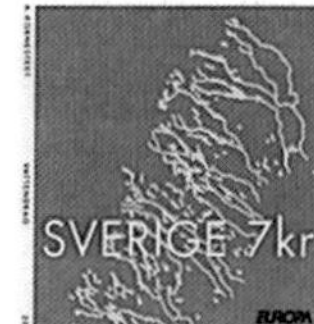

617 Waterways of Northern Sweden

2001. Europa. Water Resources.

2154 **617** 7k. blue, green and black 1·60 1·40

2155 - 7k. blue, green and black 1·60 1·40

2156 - 7k. multicoloured 1·60 1·40

2157 - 7k. multicoloured 1·60 1·40

DESIGNS: No. 2155, Waterways of Southern Sweden; 2156, Freighter entering lock, Trollhatte Canal; 2157 *Juno* (canal boat) leaving lock, Trollhatte Canal.

618 Obverse of Medals and Alfred Nobel (founder)

2001. Centenary of Nobel Prizes (1st issue). Each yellow and brown.

2158 8k. Type **618** 1·60 1·50

2159 8k. Reverse of medal for Medicine 1·60 1·50

2160 8k. Reverse of medal for Physics and Chemistry 1·60 1·50

2161 8k. Reverse of medal for Literature 1·60 1·50

See also Nos. 2172/3.

619 Lo-Johansson

2001. Birth Centenary of Ivar Lo-Johansson (writer). Each indigo, red and blue. Inscr "INRIKES BREV".

2162 (5k.) Type **619** 1·10 75

2163 (5k.) "The Last Vanload of Furniture of the Agricultural Labourers, 1945" (Svenolov Ehren) 1·10 75

Nos. 2162/3 were for use on domestic first class mail.

620 Fern Leaf Peony

2001. Peonies. Multicoloured. Inscr "INRIKES brev".

2164 (5k.) Type **620** 1·10 60

2165 (5k.) Garden peony "Monsieur Jules Elie" 1·10 60

2166 (5k.) Herbaceous peony 1·10 60

2167 (5k.) Common peony 1·10 60

2168 (5k.) Tree peony 1·10 60

Nos. 2164/8 were for use on domestic first class mail.

621 Eurasian Perch (*Perca fluviatilis*)

2001. Fish. Illustrations by Wilhelm von Wright from The Fishes of Scandinavia. Inscr "INRIKES Brev". Multicoloured. Self-adhesive.

2169 (5k.) Type **621** 1·10 75

2170 (5k.) Bream (*Abramis brama*) 1·10 75

2171 (5k.) Four-horned sculpin (*Triglopsis quadricornis*) 1·10 75

Nos. 2169/71 were for use on domestic first class mail.

622 Doctors (Medicins sans Frontiers (1999))

2001. Centenary of Nobel Prize (2nd issue). Organizations. Peace Prize Winners. Multicoloured.

2172	8k. Type **622**	1·60	1·40
2173	8k. Relief workers distributing food (Red Cross (1901, 1917, 1944 and 1963))	1·60	1·40

623 Solander

2001. 230th Anniv of Daniel Solander's (botanist) Voyage on H.M.S. Endeavour. Multicoloured.

2174	8k. Type **623**	1·60	1·50
2175	8k. Plant and H.M.S. *Endeavour*	1·60	1·50

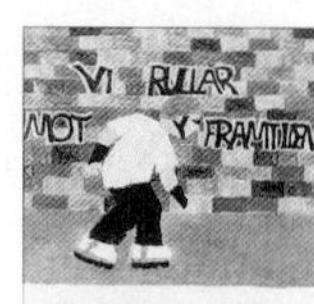

624 Inline Skater and Wall with Graffiti (Emelie Kilstrom)

2001. Design a Stamp Prize Winners. Inscr "BREV INRIKES". Multicoloured.

2176	(5k.) Type **624**	1·10	85
2177	(5k.) Letter dropping through letter-box (Thomas Frohling)	1·10	85

Nos. 2176/7 were for use on domestic first class mail.

625 Otto Lilienthal and Biplane Glider, 1895

2001. Aviation. Multicoloured.

2178	5k. Type **625**	1·10	1·00
2179	5k. DFS Weihl glider and emblem of Royal Swedish Flying Club	1·10	1·00
2180	5k. SAAB J29, 1962	1·10	1·00
2181	5k. Friedrichshafen FF-49, 1920	1·10	1·00
2182	5k. Nyberg Flugan, 1999	1·10	1·00
2183	5k. Douglas DC-3, 1938	1·10	1·00

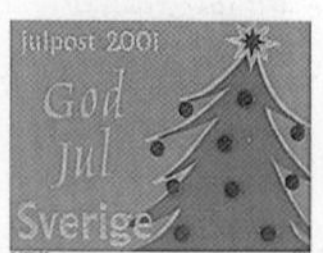

626 Christmas Tree

2001. Christmas. Decorations (2184/9) or Presents (2190/1). Multicoloured. (a) Inscr "julpost" (i) Ordinary gum.

2184	(4k.50) Type **626**	90	80

(ii) Size 26×20 mm. Self-adhesive.

2185	(4k.50) Star	90	80
2186	(4k.50) Home-made candy	90	80
2187	(4k.50) Angel	90	80
2188	(4k.50) Heart-shaped decoration	90	80
2189	(4k.50) Cone filled with sweets	90	80

(b) With face value. Size 26×29 mm. Ordinary gum.

2190	6k. Goat-shaped parcel	1·40	1·00
2191	6k. Christmas tree-shaped parcel	1·40	1·00

Nos. 2184/9 were for domestic first class mail.

627 Hockey Players

2002. World Ice Hockey Championship, Sweden. Inscr "INRIKES BREV".

2192	**627**	(5k.) multicoloured	1·10	8·00

No. 2192 was for use on domestic first class mail.

628 Children riding Horse

2002. Year of the Horse. Showing illustrations from Fairhair the Horse (cartoon character) by Bertil Almquist. Multicoloured. Inscr "INRIKES BREV".

2193	(5k.) Type **628**	1·10	80
2194	(5k.) Child leading Fairhair	1·10	80

Nos. 2193/4 were for use on domestic first class mail.

629 Couple in Bed

2002. Illustrations from Love and Miss Terrified by Joanna Dranger (book). Self-adhesive.

2195	**629**	(5k.) pink, mauve and orange	1·10	80
2196	**629**	(5k.) mauve, pink and orange	1·10	80
2197	**629**	(5k.) orange, mauve and pink	1·10	80

Nos. 2195/7 were for use on domestic first class mail.

630 Osprey (*Pandion haliaetus*)

2002

2198	**630**	10k. brown and blue	2·50	1·00

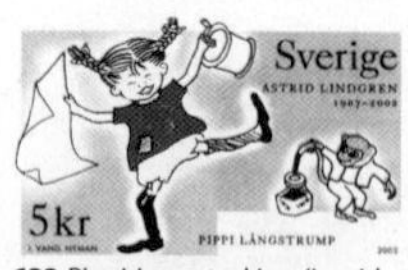

631 Scientists, Ship and Seabird

2002. Swedish Antarctic Expedition (1901–03). Multicoloured.

2199	10k. Type **631**	2·40	1·90
2200	10k. Icebergs, ship and Gentoo penguin	2·40	1·90

632 Pippi Longstocking (Ingrid Vang Nyman)

2002. Astrid Lindgren (children's writer) Commemoration. Depicting book illustrations by named artists.

2201	**632**	5k. multicoloured	1·30	1·00
2202	-	5k. multicoloured	1·30	1·00
2203	-	5k. multicoloured	1·30	1·00
2204	-	5k. brown and black	1·30	1·00
2205	-	5k. multicoloured	1·30	1·00
2206	-	5k. multicoloured	1·30	1·00
2207	-	5k. multicoloured	1·30	1·00

DESIGNS: No. 2202, Karlsson Pa Taket (Ilon Wikland); 2206, Lotta Pa Brakmakargatan (I. Wikland); 2207, Madicken (I. Wikland). 24×31 mm-No. 2203, Broderna Lejonhjarta (I. Wikland); 2205, Emil I Lonneberga (Bjorn Berg). 27×31 mm—No. 2204, Astrid Lindgren.

633 Cross (pendant, Birka)

2002. World Heritage Sites. (a) Birka and Hovgarden. (i) Inscr "FORENINGS BREV".

2208	**633**	(3k.80) lilac	1·00	70

(ii) Inscr "EKONOMI BREV".

2209	(4k.50) blue	1·10	80

(iii) Inscr "INRIKES BREV".

2210	(5k.) brown and mauve	1·30	85

DESIGNS: No. 2209, Runic stone, Hovgarden; 2210, Face-shaped pendant, Birka.

634 Visby

(b) Visby. Multicoloured. Inscr "INRIKES BREV".

2211	(5k.) Type **634**	1·20	85
2212	(5k.) Part of town wall	1·20	85
2213	(5k.) Burmeister building	1·20	85
2214	(5k.) Ruins of St. Catherine's Church	1·20	85

No. 2208 was for use on bulk rate mail from societies, No. 2209 was for domestic second class mail and Nos. 2210/14 were for domestic first class mail.

635 "Vadersolstavlan"

2002. 750th Anniv of Stockholm. (a) Inscr "INRIKES BREV".

2215	**635**	(5k.) green and mauve	1·30	85

(b) With face value. Size 30×31 mm.

2216	10k. mauve	2·20	1·70

DESIGN: 10k. Stadsholmen Island ("Vadersolstavlan" (detail)).

636 "Structure" (Takashi Naraha)

2002. Nordic Countries' Postal Co-operation. Modern Art. Sculptures. Multicoloured.

2217	8k. Type **636**	1·90	1·40
2218	8k. "Sprung From" (Pal Svensson)	1·90	1·40

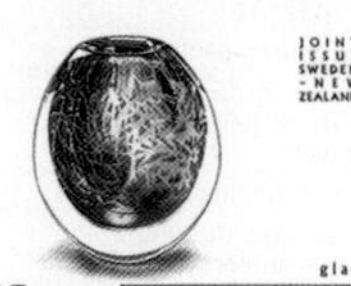

637 Charlie Rivel (clown)

2002. Europa. Circus. Multicoloured.

2219	8k. Type **637**	1·90	1·40
2220	8k. Clown with child (Clowns without Borders)	1·90	1·40
2221	8k. Man in balloon (Cirkus Cirkor)	1·90	1·40
2222	8k. Elephant and rider (Cirkus Scott)	1·90	1·40

638 "Rain Forest" (glass vase) (Marie and Ola Hoglund)

2002. Artistic Crafts. Joint Issue with New Zealand. Multicoloured.

2223	10k. Type **638**	2·40	1·90
2224	10k. Flax basket (Willa Rogers)	2·40	1·90

Nos. 2223/4 are additionally inscr "JOINT ISSUE SWEDEN–NEW ZEALAND".

639 Haro Warehouse

2002. Bohuslan Province. Inscr "INRIKES BREV". (a) Ordinary gum.

2225	**639**	(5k.) multicoloured	1·30	85

640 Lighthouse and Cliffs

(b) Multicoloured. Self-adhesive.

2226	(5k.) Type **640**	1·30	85
2227	(5k.) Lighthouse, rocks and birds	1·30	85
2228	(5k.) Yacht and waterfront houses	1·30	85
2229	(5k.) Dinghy with outboard engine	1·30	85

Nos. 2225/9 were for use on domestic first class mail.

641 Police Chief

2002. Centenary of Gronkopings Veckoblad (satirical newspaper). Inscr "INRIKES Brev". Each blue, buff and red.

2230	(5k.) Type **641**	1·30	95
2231	(5k.) Postman	1·30	95

Nos. 2230/1 were for use on domestic first class mail.

642 Charles Emil Hagdahl and Cajsa Warg

2002. Swedish Gastronomy. Chefs. Inscr "INRIKES BREV". Multicoloured.

2232	(5 k.) Type **642**	1·30	95
2233	(5k.) Marit "Hiram" Huldt	1·30	95
2234	(5k.) Tore Wretman	1·30	95
2235	(5k.) Leif Mannerstrom	1·30	95
2236	(5k.) Gert Klotzke	1·30	95
2237	(5k.) Christer Lingstrom	1·30	95

Nos. 2232/7 were for use on domestic first class mail.

643 The Royal Palace, Stockholm

2002. Palaces. Joint Issue with Thailand. Multicoloured.

2238	5k. Type **643**	1·60	1·30
2239	5k. Dusit Maha Prasat Throne Hall	1·60	1·30

644 Hakan Carlqvist (motocross)

2002. Motorcycle Sports. Multicoloured.

2240	5k. Type **644**	1·30	1·30
2241	5k. Sten Lundin (motocross)	1·30	1·30
2242	5k. Anders Eriksson (enduro)	1·30	1·30
2243	5k. Ulf Karlsson (trial)	1·30	1·30
2244	5k. Ove Fundin (speedway)	1·30	1·30
2245	5k. Tony Rickardsson (speedway)	1·30	1·30
2246	5k. Peter Linden (road racing)	1·30	1·30
2247	5k. Varg-Olle Nygren (road racing)	1·30	1·30

645 Karl-Bertil Jonsson and Father

2002. Christmas. Karl-Bertil Jonsson's Christmas (animated film by Per Ahlin). Scenes from the film. Inscr "julpost" Multicoloured. (a) Ordinary gum.

2248	(4k. 50) Type **645**	1·10	85

(b) Self-adhesive gum.

2249 (4k.50) With sack of presents 1·10 85
2250 (4k.50) Asleep wearing cap with feather 1·10 85
2251 (4k.50) Shaking hands with man 1·10 85
2252 (4k.50) Surrounded by family 1·10 85

Nos. 2248/52 were for domestic first class mail.

646 Kiruna Church

2002. Christmas. Churches. Multicoloured.

2253 8k. Type **646** 2·10 1·50
2254 8k. Habo 2·10 1·50
2255 8k. Sundborns 2·10 1·50
2256 8k. Tensta 2·10 1·50

647 Bowline

2003. Knots. Coil stamps. (a) Inscr "Forenings brev".

2257 **647** (4k.80) green 1·10 85

(b) Inscr "Ekonomibrev".

2258 - (5k.) blue 1·20 95

(c) Inscr "Brev inrikes".

2259 - (5k.50) redon 1·30 1·00

DESIGNS: (5k.) Sheet bend; (5k.50) Reef knot.

No. 2257 was for use on bulk rate mail from societies, No. 2258 was for domestic second-class mail and No. 2259 were for domestic first class mail.

648 Boy and Teacher

2003. Centenary of Swedish Sports Federation. Multicoloured. Self-adhesive.

2260 (5k.50) Type **648** 1·30 1·00
2261 (5k.50) Wheelchair racing 1·30 1·00
2262 (5k.50) Snowboarding and deaf sign for sport 1·30 1·00
2263 (5k.50) Girl running 1·30 1·00

Nos. 2260/3 were for use on domestic first class mail.

649 St. Birgitta (Bridget) (sculpture) (Johannes Stanrat)

2003. 700th Birth Anniv of St. Birgitta (1st issue). Inscr "INRIKES BREV".

2264 **649** (5k.50) sepia and scarlet 1·30 1·00

Nos. 2264 was for use on domestic first class mail.

650 "Kaos" (Georg Magnusson)

2003. Europa. Poster Art. Multicoloured.

2265 10k. Type **650** 2·40 1·90
2266 10k. "Biologika Museum" (Carina Lank) 2·40 1·90
2267 10k. "Aerotransport" (Anders Beckman) 2·40 1·90
2268 10k. "Levande Lantbruk" (Owe Gustafson) 2·40 1·90

651 Cottage, Narke

2003. Provincial Houses (1st series). Designs from watercolour paintings by Laila Reppen.

2269 **651** 2k. lake, chestnut and green 50 40
2270 - 4k. green, lake and indigo 1·10 85
2271 - 5k. sepia, blue and emerald 1·30 1·00

DESIGNS: 4k. Double cottage, Bohuslan; 5k. Hall house, Medelpad.

See also Nos. 2338/40 and 2357/60.

652 Hepatica (*Hepatica nobilis*)

2003. Flowers. Inscr "INRIKES BREV". Multicoloured. Self-adhesive.

2272 (5k.50) Type **652** 1·30 1·00
2273 (5k.50) Cowslip (*Primula veris*) 1·30 1·00
2274 (5k.50) Coltsfoot (*Tussilago farfara*) 1·30 1·00

Nos. 2272/4 were for use on domestic first class mail.

653 Windmills

2003. World Heritage Sites. Oland. Inscr "INRIKES BREV".

2275 (5k.50) Type **653** 1·30 1·00
2276 (5k.50) Stone circle, Stora Alvar 1·30 1·00
2277 (5k.50) Village 1·30 1·00
2278 (5k.50) Sheep grazing coastal wetlands 1·30 1·00

Nos. 2275/8 were for use on domestic first class mail.

654 Santiago Ramon y Cajal (1906)

2003. Nobel Prize Winners for Medicine. Joint Issue with Spain. Multicoloured.

2279 10k. Type **654** 2·40 1·90
2280 10k. Severo Ochoa (1959) 2·40 1·90

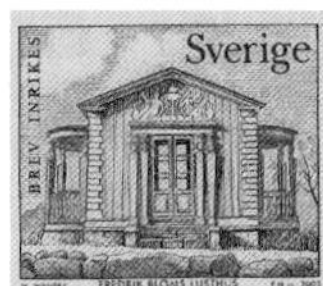

655 Frederik Blom's 19th-century Folly

2003. Garden Follies. Multicoloured. (a) Ordinary gum.

2281 (5k.50) Type **655** 1·30 1·00

(b) Self-adhesive gum.

2282 (5k.50) Emanuel Swedenborg's 18th-century folly 1·30 1·00
2283 (5k.50) Ebba Brahe's folly 1·30 1·00
2284 (5k.50) Raised folly 1·30 1·00
2285 (5k.50) Godegard manor folly, Ostergotland 1·30 1·00

656 St. Bridget

2003. 700th Birth Anniv of St. Bridget. Sheet 94×128 mm.

MS2286 **656** 40k. multicoloured 10·00 9·25

657 Red Cabbage, Parsnip, Cucumber, Beetroot and Onion

2003. Harvest. Multicoloured. Self-adhesive.

2287 (5k.50) Type **657** 1·30 1·00
2288 (5k.50) Melon, apple, raspberries and pumpkin 1·30 1·00
2289 (5k.50) Cabbage, potatoes, carrots and tomato 1·30 1·00
2290 (5k.50) Cherries, strawberries, plums and pear 1·30 1·00

Nos. 2287/90 form a composite design of a basket of fruit and vegetables.

658 Lion (figurehead)

2003. 250th Anniv of Sinking of Gotheborg (East Indiaman). Reconstruction of Gotheborg. Multicoloured.

2291 5k.50 Type **658** 1·30 1·00
2292 5k.50 Interior of hull (44×26 mm) 1·30 1·00
2293 10k. Side elevation (43×53 mm) 2·40 1·90
2294 30k. "Under Sail" (Marc Grieves) 7·75 6·25

659 Pied Avocet (*Recurvirostra avosetta*)

2003. Water Birds. Multicoloured.

2295 10k. Type **659** 2·40 1·90
2296 10k. Slavonian grebe (*Podiceps auritus*) 2·40 1·90
2297 10k. Black-throated diver (*Gavia artica*) 2·40 1·90
2298 10k. Great crested grebe (*Podiceps cristatus*) 2·40 1·90

Stamps of the same design were issued by Hong Kong.

660 "Evening Meal"

2003. Christmas. Birth Centenary of Carl Larsson (artist). Paintings. Multicoloured. (a) Inscr "Julpost". (i) Coil stamp. Ordinary gum.

2299 (5k.) Type **660** 1·20 95

(ii) Size 23×27 mm. Self-adhesive.

2300 (5k.) "Esbjorn on Skis" 1·20 95
2301 (5k.) "Brita as Idun" 1·20 95
2302 (5k.) "Esbjorn" 1·20 95
2303 (5k.) "Front-yard and Wash-house" (detail) 1·20 95

(b) With face value. Size 27×30 mm. Ordinary gum.

2304 9k. "Martina with Breakfast Tray" 2·10 1·70
2305 9k. "Kersti's Sleigh Ride" 2·10 1·70

661 Anna Lindh

2003. Anna Lindh (foreign minister) Commemoration.

2306 **661** (5k.50) purple 1·40 1·10
2307 **661** 10k. indigo 2·50 2·00

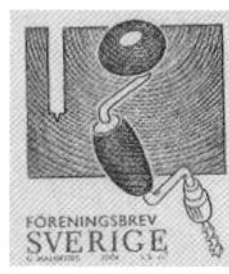

662 Brace and Bit

2004. Woodworking Tools. Coil stamps. (a) Inscr "Forenings brev".

2308 **662** (4k.80) green 1·30 1·10

(b) Inscr "Ekonomibrev".

2309 (5k.) blue 1·30 1·10

(c) Inscr "Brev inrikes".

2310 (5k.50) red 1·50 1·20

DESIGNS: Saw (5k.); Plane (5k.50).

No. 2308 was for use on bulk rate mail from societies, No. 2309 was for domestic second-class mail and No. 2310 was for domestic first class mail.

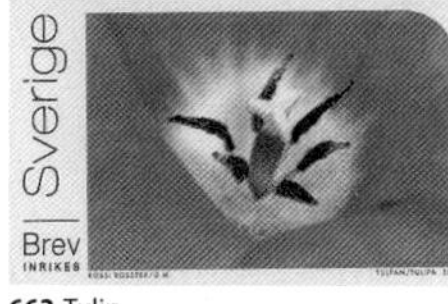

663 Tulip

2004. Flowers. Multicoloured.

2311 (5k.50) Type **663** 1·50 1·20
2312 (5k.50) Lily 1·50 1·20
2313 (5k.50) Hibiscus 1·50 1·20
2314 (5k.50) Amaryllis 1·50 1·20
2315 (5k.50) Zantedeschia 1·50 1·20

664 Lake and Mountain

2004. World Heritage Sites. Lapona. Multicoloured.

2316 10k. Type **664** 2·75 2·20
2317 10k. Tents 2·75 2·20

665 Mine Head

2004. World Heritage Sites. Falun. Multicoloured.

2318 (5k.50) Type **665** 1·50 1·20
2319 (5k.50) Water tower and buildings 1·50 1·20
2320 (5k.50) Doorway 1·50 1·20
2321 (5k.50) Miners 1·50 1·20

666 Two Footballers (Nils Liedholm)

2004. Centenary of Swedish Football Association. Multicoloured. Self-adhesive.

2322 (5k.50) Type **666** 1·50 1·20
2323 (5k.50) Women players (Hanna Ljungberg) 1·50 1·20
2324 (5k.50) Two players chasing ball (Fredrik Ljungberg) 1·50 1·20
2325 (5k.50) Player with raised arm (Henrik Larsson) 1·50 1·20

2326 (5k.50) Women players tackling (Victoria Svensson) 1·50 1·20
2327 (5k.50) Goalkeeper (Thomas Ravelli) 1·50 1·20

667 Returning Warrior

2004. Nordic Mythology. Sheet 104×70 mm containing T 667 and similar multicoloured design.
MS2328 10k. ×2, Type **667**; Welcoming Valkyrie 5·25 4·75

Stamps of a similar theme were issued by Aland Islands, Denmark, Faroe Islands, Finland, Greenland, Iceland and Norway.

668 Night Fishing

2004. "Northern Light".
2329 **668** (5k.50) blue 1·50 1·20
2330 - (5k.50) brown 1·50 1·20
DESIGN: No. 2330 Lighthouse.

669 Yacht and Hut (Gilloga)

2004. Stockholm Archipelago. Multicoloured.
2331 (5k.50) Type **669** 1·50 1·20
2332 (5k.50) Rowing boat (Langviksskar) 1·50 1·20
2333 (5k.50) Saltsjon (steam boat) (Stora Nassa) 1·50 1·20
2334 (5k.50) Yacht and lighthouse (Namdofjarden) 1·50 1·20

670 Collared Dove (*Streptopelia decaocto*)

2004. Centenary of Swedish Pigeon Society. (a) Inscr "EKONOMIBREV".
2335 **670** (5k.) blue and agate 1·30 1·10

(b) Inscr "Brev inrikes".
2336 (5k.50) multicoloured 1·50 1·20

(c) With face value.
2337 10k. multicoloured 2·75 2·20
DESIGNS: (5k.50) Swedish tumbler; 10k Wood pigeon (*Columba palumbus*).

No. 2335 was for use on bulk rate mail from societies and No. 2336 was for domestic second-class mail.

2004. Provincial Houses (2nd series). As T 651 showing watercolour paintings by Laila Reppen.
2338 3k. yellow, red and brown 85 70
2339 6k. red, brown and green 1·70 1·40
2340 8k. deep green, brown and green 2·20 1·80
DESIGNS: 3k. Blacksmith's cottage, Uppland; 6k. Dalstand cottage; 8k. Gotland cottage.

671 Tree, Berries, Fungi and Flowers

2004. Forest Food. Multicoloured. Self-adhesive.
2341 (5k.50) Type **671** 1·50 1·20
2342 (5k.50) Tree stump, butterfly and berries 1·50 1·20
2343 (5k.50) Basket of fungi 1·50 1·20
2344 (5k.50) Flowers, pond, berries and tree 1·50 1·20

Nos. 2341/2 and 2343/4, respectively, form composite designs.

672 William Butler Yeats

2004. Irish Winners of Nobel Prize for Literature. Multicoloured.
2345 10k. Type **672** 2·75 2·20
2346 10k. George Bernard Shaw 2·75 2·20
2347 10k. Samuel Beckett 2·75 2·20
2348 10k. Seamus Heaney 2·75 2·20

Stamps of similar designs were issued by Ireland.

673 Jerry Williams

2004. Rock 54–04. 50th Anniv of "That's alright Mama" (record by Elvis Presley). Multicoloured.
2349 5k.50 Type **673** 1·50 1·20
2350 5k.50 Elvis Presley 1·50 1·20
2351 5k.50 Eve Dahlgren 1·50 1·20
2352 5k.50 Ulf Lundell 1·50 1·20
2353 5k.50 Tomas Leon 1·50 1·20
2354 5k.50 Pugh Rogefeldt 1·50 1·20
2355 5k.50 Maria Anderson (Sahara Hotnights) 1·50 1·20
2356 5k.50 Louise Hoffsten 1·50 1·20

2004. Provincial Houses (3rd series). Designs as T 651 showing watercolour paintings by Laila Reppen.
2357 50ore. blue and black (21×24 mm) 10 10
2358 1k. brown, green and black (31×24 mm) 35 30
2359 7k. black, brown and green 1·90 1·60
2360 9k. black, green and grey 2·40 2·00
DESIGNS: 50ore. Log cabin, Lapland; 1k. Miner's house, Västmanland; 7k. Scanian farm house; 9k. Blekinge cottage.

674 Gnomes playing Leap-frog

2004. Christmas. Designs showing gnomes. Multicoloured. Inscr "Julpost". (a) Ordinary gum.
2361 (5k.) Type **674** 1·30 1·10

(b) Self-adhesive gum.
2362 (5k.) Talking on cell phone 1·30 1·10
2363 (5k.) Carrying tree 1·30 1·10
2364 (5k.) Sledding 1·30 1·10
2365 (5k.) Collecting post 1·30 1·10

675 Great Tit (*Parus major*)

2004. Winter Birds. Multicoloured.
2366 10k. Type **675** 2·75 2·20
2367 10k. Yellowhammer (*Emberiza citronella*) 2·75 2·20
2368 10k. Pine grosbeak (*Pinicola enucleator*) 2·75 2·20
2369 10k. Bullfinch (*Pyrrhula pyrrhula*) 2·75 2·20

676 Glassware (Ingegerd Raman)

2005. Swedish Design. Self-adhesive. Inscr "INRIKES BREV".
2370 **676** (5k.50) indigo and azure 1·50 1·20
2371 - (5k.50) multicoloured 1·50 1·20
2372 - (5k.50) azure, black and magenta 1·50 1·20
2373 - (5k.50) azure, black and vermilion 1·50 1·20
2374 - (5k.50) green and black 1·50 1·20
2375 - (5k.50) multicoloured 1·50 1·20
DESIGNS: (5k.50)×6, Type **676**; Turn-o-matic ticket machine (Tom Ahlstrom and Hans Ehrich); Welding helmet (Carl-Goran Crafoord); Chair and shelves (John Kandell); Watch (Vivianna Torun Bulow-Hube); Streamliner toy car (Ulf Hanes).

677 King Carl XVI Gustaf

2005. Coil stamps. (a) Inscr "Brev".
2376 **677** (5k.50) violet and magenta 1·50 1·20

(b) With face value.
2377 10k. agate and brown 2·75 2·20
DESIGNS: Type **677**; 10k. Queen Silvia.

No. 2376 was for use on domestic mail and No. 2377 was for use on international mail.

678 Hogbonden Lighthouse

2005. World Heritage Sites. High Coast. Multicoloured.
2378 10k. Type **678** 2·75 2·20
2379 10k. Eagles and cliffs, Storon Nature Reserve 2·75 2·20
2380 10k. Fishing village, Ulvon 2·75 2·20
2381 10k. Lakes, Haggvik 2·75 2·20

679 Dag Hammarskjold

2005. Birth Centenary of Dag Hammarskjold (Secretary-General of the United Nations, 1953–61). Inscr "INRIKES BREV".
2382 **679** (5k.50) red-brown 1·50 1·20
2383 - (5k.50) blue 1·50 1·20
DESIGNS: Type **679**; No. 2383 United Nations emblem.

No. 2382/3 were for use on domestic mail.

680 Lily of the Valley (*Convallaria majalis*)

2005. Spring Flowers. Self-adhesive. Inscr "INRIKES BREV". Multicoloured.
2384 (5k.50) Type **680** 1·50 1·20
2385 (5k.50) Yellow Star of Bethlehem (*Gagea lutea*) 1·50 1·20
2386 (5k.50) Pasque Flower (*Pulsatilla vulgaris*) 1·50 1·20
2387 (5k.50) Wood Anemone (*Anemone nemorosa*) 1·50 1·20

Nos. 2384/7 were for use on domestic first class mail.

681 Lemon, Star Anise and Elderberry Marmalade

2005. Europa. Gastronomy. Multicoloured.
2388 10k. Type **681** 1·50 1·20
2389 10k. Katja apples, rosemary and Jerusalem artichoke 1·50 1·20
2390 10k. Chives, cheese and beets 1·50 1·20

682 Golden Oriole (*Oriolus oriolus*) (Magnus Von Wright)

2005. Birds
2391 **682** 11k. multicoloured 3·00 2·40

683 "Lady with a Veil" (A. Roslin) (As No. 709)

2005. 150th Anniv of First Swedish Stamp. Inscr "INRIKES BREV". Designs showing details of earlier stamps (Nos. 2392/5). Multicoloured.
2392 (5k.50) Type **683** 1·50 1·20
2393 (5k.50) Numeral (As No. 331) 1·50 1·20
2394 (5k.50) Post rider (As. No. 190) 1·50 1·20
2395 (5k.50) Angelica (As No. 1187) 1·50 1·20
2396 (5k.50) Pehr Ambjorn Sparre (creator of first stamps) 1·50 1·20
2397 (5k.50) Woman reading letter 1·50 1·20
2398 (5k.50) Airplane and train 1·50 1·20
2399 (5k.50) Modern postman 1·50 1·20

684 Woman digging

2005. Allotments. Inscr "INRIKES BREV". Multicoloured. (a) Ordinary gum.
2400 (4k.50) Type **684** 1·50 1·20

(b) Size 23×26 mm. Self-adhesive.
2401 (5k.50) Man weeding 1·50 1·20
2402 (5k.50) Woman sat at table 1·50 1·20
2403 (5k.50) Woman, basket of vegetables and onions 1·50 1·20
2404 (5k.50) Man watering 1·50 1·20

Nos. 2400/4 were for use on domestic first class mail.

685 Mother Svea

2005. 250th Anniv of Tumba Bruk Bank.
2405 **685** 15k. black, silver and lavender 4·00 3·25

686 Svinesund Bridge

2005. Inauguration of Svinesund Bridge over Ides Fjord (joining Sweden and Norway). Sheet 162×94 mm containing T 686 and similar horiz design. Multicoloured.
MS2406 10k.×2 Type **686**; Bridge from side 5·25 5·00

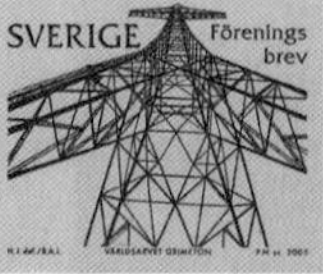

687 Varberg Radio Station, Grimeton

2005. World Heritage Sites. Coil stamps. (a) Inscr "Ekonomibrev".
2407 **687** (4k.80) violet and green 1·20 1·00

(b) Inscr "Forenings brev".
2408 (5k.) multicoloured (40×23 mm) 1·30 1·10
DESIGNS: Type **687**; (5k.) Skogskyrkogarden cemetery.

688 Lynx

2005. Animal Cubs. Self-adhesive. Inscr "INRIKES BREV". Multicoloured.
2409 (5k.50) Type **688** 1·50 1·20

2410 (5k.50) Bear 1·50 1·20
2411 (5k.50) Wolf 1·50 1·20
2412 (5k.50) Fox 1·50 1·20
Nos. 2409/12 were for use on domestic first class mail.

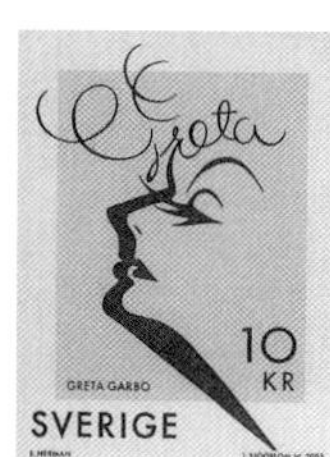

689 Profile and Signature

2005. Birth Centenary of Greta Garbo (actress).
2413 **689** 10k. azure and sepia 2·75 2·20
2414 - 10k. sepia 2·75 2·20
DESIGNS: Type **689**; 10k. Greta Garbo.
Stamps of similar designs were issued by USA.

690 Fram-King Moped

2005. Mopeds. Multicoloured.
2415 5k.50 Type **690** 1·50 1·20
2416 5k.50 Husqvarna 1·50 1·20
2417 5k.50 Kuli rear-wheel and engine 1·50 1·20
2418 5k.50 Two mopeds and riders 1·50 1·20
2419 5k.50 Mechanic and moped 1·50 1·20
2420 5k.50 Three-wheel delivery moped 1·50 1·20
2421 5k.50 Frame-hung Zundapp engine 1·50 1·20
2422 5k.50 Modern Peugeot 1·50 1·20

691 Kerstin's Skiing Tour

2005. Christmas. Illustrations by Ilon Wikland from Christmas in Noisy Village by Astrid Lindgren. Inscr "Julpost". Designs showing children. Multicoloured. (a) Ordinary gum.
2423 (5k.) Type **691** 1·30 1·10

(b) Self-adhesive.
2424 (5k.) Opening gate and feeding birds 1·30 1·10
2425 (5k.) Fetching tree on sled 1·30 1·10
2426 (5k.) Wrapping presents 1·30 1·10
2427 (5k.) Children and decorated tree 1·30 1·10

692 Angel

2005. Angel Sculptures by Carl Milles. Each deep blue, blue and red.
2428 10k. Type **692** 2·75 2·20
2429 10k. Playing horn facing left 2·75 2·20
2430 10k. Playing flute 2·75 2·20
2431 10k. Playing crooked horn 2·75 2·20

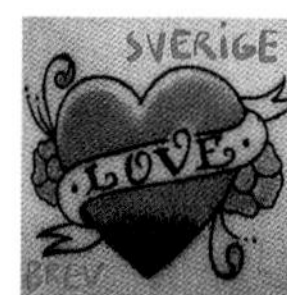

693 Tattooed Heart

2006. St. Valentine's Day. Multicoloured. Self-adhesive. Inscr "INRIKES BREV".
2432 (5k.50) Type **693** 1·50 1·20
2433 (5k.50) Painted heart 1·50 1·20
2434 (5k.50) Heart-shaped leaf 1·50 1·20
2435 (5k.50) Graffiti 1·50 1·20

694 Steam Locomotive *A. Mallet*

2006. 150th Anniv of Swedish Railways. Inscr "INRIKES BREV". Multicoloured.
2436 (5k.50) Type **694** 1·50 1·20
2437 (5k.50) Rail bus 1·50 1·20
2438 (5k.50) D electric locomotive 1·50 1·20
2439 (5k.50) R steam locomotive 1·50 1·20
2440 (5k.50) Electric locomotive 1281 1·50 1·20
2441 10k. Train on viaduct 2·75 2·20

695 Coffee Cups

2006. Coffee Drinking. Multicoloured. Self-adhesive. Inscr "BREV".
2442 (5k.50) Type **695** 1·50 1·20
2443 (5k.50) Cafe latte and menu 1·50 1·20
2444 (5k.50) Coffee machine and cup 1·50 1·20
2445 (5k.50) Steam machine 1·50 1·20

696 Skogsraet

2006. Nordic Mythology. Sheet 105×70 mm containing T 696 and similar vert design. Multicoloured.
MS2446 10k.×2, Type **696**; Nacken 5·25 5·00
Stamps of a similar theme were issued by Aland Islands, Denmark, Faröe Islands, Finland, Greenland, Iceland and Norway.

697 King Carl XVI Gustaf

2006. 60th Birthday of King Carl XVI Gustaf. Sheet 126×126 mm containing T 697 and similar vert design.
MS2447 10kr.×2, slate black; 10kr. slate black 7·75 7·50
DESIGNS: Type **697**×2; As Type **697**.

698 Stefan Holm

2006. Swedish Track and Field Athletes. Multicoloured. (i) Inscr "FORENINGS BREV".
2448 (4k.80) Type **698** 1·20 1·00

(ii) Inscr "BREV".
2449 (5k.50) Carolina Kluft 1·50 1·20
2450 (5k.50) Kaja Bergqvist 1·50 1·20

(iii) With face value.
2451 10k. Christian Olsson 2·75 2·20

699 Mother and Children paddling

2006. Summer by the Lake. Inscr "INRIKES BREV". Multicoloured. (a) Ordinary gum.
2452 (5k.50) Type **699** 1·50 1·20

(b) Self-adhesive.
2453 (5k.50) Women picnicking 1·50 1·20
2454 (5k.50) Man and girl fishing 1·50 1·20
2455 (5k.50) Dog watching swimmers 1·50 1·20
2456 (5k.50) Frog and couple in boat 1·50 1·20

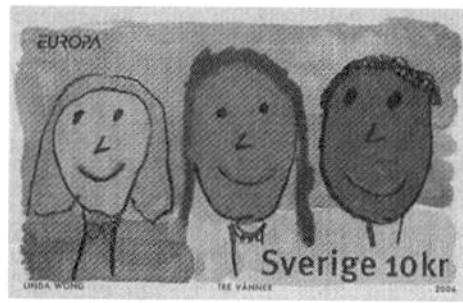

700 Faces (Linda Wong)

2006. Europa. Integration. Winning Designs in Children's Design a Stamp Competition. Multicoloured.
2457 10k. Type **700** 2·75 2·20
2458 10k. Swedish flag as map (Alexandros Terzis) 2·75 2·20

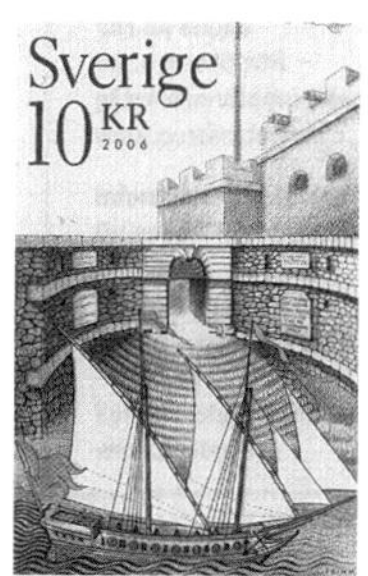

701 Kungsporten and Pojama Class Frigate

2006. Sveaborg Fortress, Suomenlinna—World Heritage Site. Multicoloured.
2459 10k. Type **701** 2·75 2·20
2460 10k. Tenaljen von Fersen and Turkoma class frigate 2·75 2·20
2461 10k. Bastion Hjärne and Udenma class frigate 2·75 2·20
Stamps of the same design were issued by Finland.

702 Musicians (Carl Michael Bellman)

2006. Composers. Coil Stamps. (i) Inscr "FORENINGSBREV".
2462 **702** (4k.80) red, chocolate and blue 1·20 1·00

(ii) Inscr "EKONOMIBREV".
2463 (5k.) blue, chocolate and vermilion 1·30 1·10

(iii) Inscr "BREV".
2464 (5k.50) green, chocolate and vermilion 1·50 1·20
DESIGNS: Type **702**; (5k.) Joseph Martin Kraus; (5k.50) Papageno (character from "The Magic Flute") (Wolfgang Amadeus Mozart).

703 Shipping and Trade

2006. 650th Anniv of Hanseatic League. Multicoloured.
2465 10k. Type **703** 2·75 2·20
2466 10k. Visby 2·75 2·20
2467 10k. Stockholm 2·75 2·20
Stamps of a similar design were issued by Germany.

704

705

706

707

708

709

710

SVERIGE 550
711

2006. Children's Television Programmes. Multicoloured.
2468 **704** 5k.50 multicoloured 1·50 1·20
2469 **705** 5k.50 multicoloured 1·50 1·20
2470 **706** 5k.50 multicoloured 1·50 1·20
2471 **707** 5k.50 multicoloured 1·50 1·20
2472 **708** 5k.50 multicoloured 1·50 1·20
2473 **709** 5k.50 multicoloured 1·50 1·20
2474 **710** 5k.50 multicoloured 1·50 1·20
2475 **711** 5k.50 multicoloured 1·50 1·20

712 Santa and Candles

2006. Christmas. Inscr "Julpost 2006". Multicoloured. (a) Ordinary gum.
2476 (5k.) Type **712** 1·30 1·10

(b) Size 28×26 mm. Self-adhesive.
2477 (5k.) Star 1·30 1·10
2478 (5k.) Spiced orange and heart 1·30 1·10
2479 (5k.) Bullfinch on fat ball and poinsettia 1·30 1·10
2480 (5k.) Candle bridge 1·30 1·10

713 "Bordelle's Heracles in Snow" (Prince Eugen Napolean)

2006. Winter in Art. Multicoloured.

2481	10k. Type **713**	2·75	2·20
2482	10k. "LelleKalle" (Sven Ljungberg)	2·75	2·20
2483	10k. "Modification of Winter Landscape by W. O. Petersen" (Philip von Schantz)	2·75	2·20
2484	10k. "Rime Frost on Ice" (Gustaf Adolf Fjaestad)	2·75	2·20

714 Heart and Two Birds (Fagelhalsning)

2007. Spring. Inscribed "Inrikes Brev". Multicoloured. Self-adhesive.

2485	(5k.50) Type **714**	1·50	1·20
2486	(5k.50) Sun (Ljusare tider)	1·50	1·20
2487	(5k.50) Flowers, heart and dancer (Varyra)	1·50	1·20
2488	(5k.50) Bird in flight (Kvitter)	1·50	1·20

715 *Linnaea borealis* (J. W. Palmstruch)

2007. 300th Birth Anniv of Carl von Linné (Linnaeus) (scientist and plant and animal classification deviser) (1st issue). Multicoloured. (a) Inscribed "Inrikes Brev".

2489	(5k.50) Type **715**	1·50	1·20

(b) With face value.

2490	11k. Linnaeus (Gustaf Lundberg) (43×27 mm)	3·00	2·40

See also No. **MS**2502.

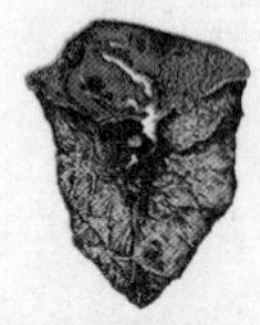

716 "Stenfragment I" (Svenerik Jakobsson)

2007. International Polar Year. Sheet 105×68 mm containing T 716 and similar multicoloured design.

MS2491	10k. Type **716**; 10k. "Arctic Ocean 2001 88° N 145° E" (Johan Petterson) (horiz)	5·25	5·00

717 *Anna Wallenberg* Lifeboat and Modern Rescue Runner

2007. Centenary of Swedish Sea Rescue Society. Multicoloured. (i) Inscr "FORENINGSBREV".

2492	(4k.80) Type **717**	1·20	1·00

(ii) Inscr "EKONOMIBREV".

2493	(5k.) Agusta-Bell AB-206 Jet Ranger (Air sea rescue)	1·30	1·10

(iii) Inscr "BREV".

2494	(5k.50) Victoria class rescue vessel	1·50	1·20

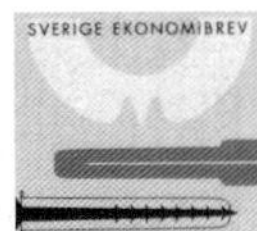

718 Thorsman Plug (Oswald Thorsman) (1957)

2007. Swedish Innovation. Inscr "Ekonomibrev". Multicoloured. Self-adhesive.

2495	(5k.) Type **718**	1·30	1·10
2496	(5k.) "Alogloben" (Elizabeth Gagnemyhr) (2002)	1·30	1·10
2497	(5k.) "Cool globe" (Birgitta Folker-Sundell) (1997)	1·30	1·10
2498	(5k.) Adjustable spanner (Johan Petter Johansson) (1892)	1·30	1·10

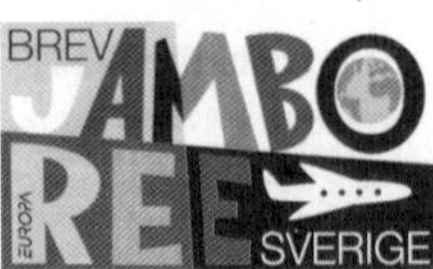

719 "JAMBOREE"

2007. Europa. Centenary of Scouting. Inscr "BREV".

2499	(5k.50) Type **719**	1·50	1·20
2500	(5k.50) Scouts	1·50	1·20

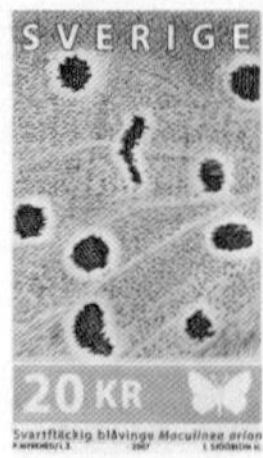

720 Wing (detail)

2007. Large Blue Butterfly (*Myrmica sabuleti*). Self-adhesive.

2501	**720**	20k. multicoloured	5·25	4·75

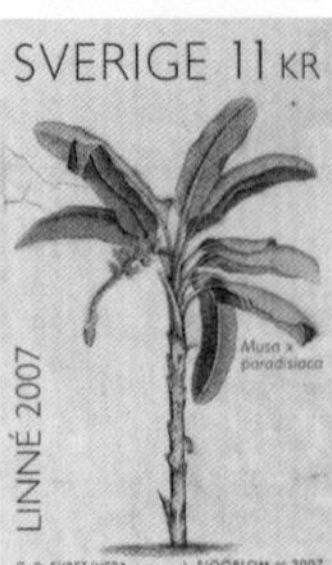

721 *Musa×paradisiaca*

2007. 300th Birth Anniv of Carl von Linne (Linnaeus) (scientist and plant and animal classification deviser) (2nd issue). Drawings by Georg Dionys Ehret. Sheet 125×94 mm containing T 721 and similar vert design.

MS2502	11k.×2, Type **721**; *Podophyllum peltatum*	6·00	5·75

722 Boy fishing in Bucket

2007. Summer Stamps. Fishing. Inscribed 'IRIKES BREV'. Multicoloured. (a) Ordinary gum.

2503	(5k.50) Type **722**	1·50	1·20

(b) Size 38×27 mm. Self-adhesive.

2504	(5k.50) Boy fishing from jetty ('Bryggfiske')	1·50	1·20
2505	(5k.50) Girl kissing fish ('Fiskpuss')	1·50	1·20
2506	(5k.50) Girls each holding fish ('Dubbellycka')	1·50	1·20
2507	(5k.50) Two boys holding rod with fish ('Kompifiske')	1·50	1·20

2007. As T 677.

2508	11k. ultramarine and green	3·00	2·50

DESIGN: Queen Silvia (as No. 2377).

No. 2508 was for use on international mail.

723 Farmhouse and Rape Fields, Skane

2007. Landscapes. Multicoloured.

2509	11k. Type **723**	3·00	2·50
2510	11k. Lake, Muddus National Park, Norrbotten	3·00	2·50
2511	11k. Elk in forest, Sveafallen Nature Reserve, Narke	3·00	2·50
2512	11k. Kallsjon lake, hayfield and huts, Jamtland	3·00	2·50

724 Chocolate Sweets

2007. Chocolate. Inscribed 'IRIKES BREV'. Multicoloured. (a) Ordinary gum.

2513	(5k.50) Type **724**	1·50	1·20

(b) Size 28×28 mm. Self-adhesive.

2514	(5k.50) Chocolate cake	1·50	1·20
2515	(5k.50) Chocolate covered strawberry	1·50	1·20
2516	(5k.50) Cocoa beans	1·50	1·20
2517	(5k.50) Cup of hot chocolate	1·50	1·20

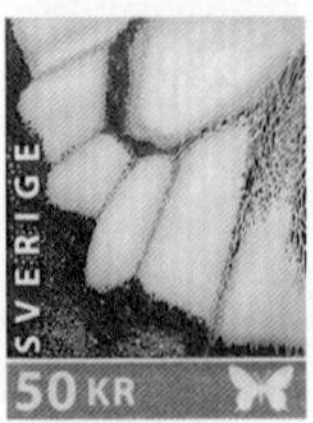

725 Wing (detail)

2007. Swallowtail Butterfly (*Papilio machaon*). Self-adhesive.

2518	**725**	50k. multicoloured	13·00	12·00

726 Evening Dress (Lars Wallin)

2007. Swedish Fashion Design. Multicoloured.

2519	5k.50 Type **726**	1·50	1·20
2520	5k.50 Wrap jacket (Ann-Sofie Back)	1·50	1·20
2521	5k.50 Halter-neck dress (Katja of Sweden)	1·50	1·20
2522	5k.50 Halter-neck dress (Behnaz Aram)	1·50	1·20
2523	5k.50 Ball gown (Gunilla Ponten)	1·50	1·20
2524	5k.50 Dress with tie-neck and bolero (Carin Rodebjer)	1·50	1·20
2525	5k.50 Coat (Rohdi Heintz)	1·50	1·20
2526	5k.50 Jacket (Nakkna)	1·50	1·20

727 Pippi Longstocking making Cakes

2007. Christmas. Inscr 'Julpost 2007'. Multicoloured. (a) Ordinary gum.

2527	(5k) Type **727**	1·30	1·10

(b) Size 28×26 mm. Self-adhesive.

2528	(5k) The Big Red House	1·30	1·10
2529	(5k) Children playing snowballs	1·30	1·10
2530	(5k) Lotta and Christmas tree	1·30	1·10
2531	(5k) Children and sleigh	1·30	1·10

728 Astrid Lindgren and Emil from Lonneberga (character from book)

2007. Birth Centenary of Astrid Lindgren (children's author). Sheet 126×83 mm.

MS2532	**728** 11k. multicoloured	2·75	2·50

A stamp of the same design was issued by Germany.

729 Stylized Reindeer and Sami Flag

2007. Sami Culture. Multicoloured.

2533	11k. Type **729**	2·50	2·30
2534	11k. Silver button (designed by Bertil Ahlin)	2·50	2·30
2535	11k. Glass plate (designed by Monica Edmondson)	2·50	2·30

730 *Bombus hypnorum* (bumble bee)

2008. Insects. Multicoloured. (a) Size 30×24 mm. Inscr 'FORENINGSBREV'.

2536	(4k.80) Type **730**	1·20	1·00

(b) Size 30×26 mm. Inscr 'EKONOMIBREV'.

2537	(5k.) *Formica rufa* (ants)	1·30	1·20

(c) Size 30×31 mm. Inscr 'BREV INRIKES'.

2538	(5k.50) *Cocconella septempunctata* (ladybird)	1·50	1·20

731 Lagatto Romagnola

2008. Dogs. Inscr 'INRIKES BREV'. Multicoloured. Self-adhesive.

2539	(5k.50) Type **731**	1·50	1·20
2540	(5k.50) Saluki	1·50	1·20
2541	(5k.50) Pug	1·50	1·20
2542	(5k.50) Great Dane	1·50	1·20

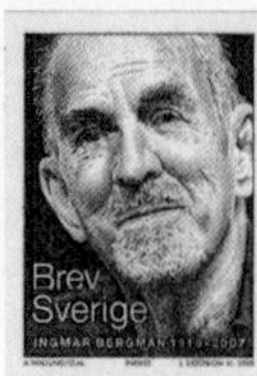

732 Ingmar Bergman

2008. 90th Birth Anniv of Ingmar Bergman (film and theatre director).

2543	**732**	(5k.50) slate	1·50	1·20
MS2544		125×83 mm. 11k. indigo (55×36 mm)	3·00	2·75

DESIGNS: 2543, Ingmar Bergman; **MS**2544, Scene from *Fanny and Alexander*.

No. 2543 was inscribed 'Brev'.

733 'D'

2008. 300th Birth Anniv of Olaf von Dalin (historian and writer). Each black and maroon.

2545	11k. Type **733**	3·00	2·75

2546 11k. Flautist and drover (Title page of *Then Swanska Argus*) 3·00 2·75

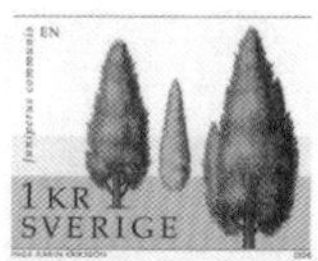

734 *Juniperus communis* (juniper)

2008. Trees. Multicoloured.
2547 1k. Type **734** 30 20
2548 1k. Juniper leaves and berries 30 20
2549 2k. *Betula pendula* (birch) 65 50
2550 2k. Birch leaves and catkins 65 50

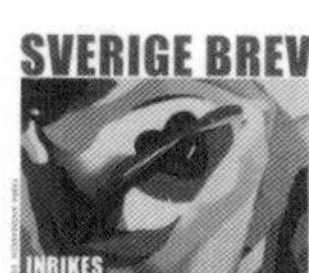

735 Eye

2008. 'Want to see You'. Inscr 'INRIKES BREV'. Multicoloured. Self-adhesive.
2551 (5k.50) Type **735** 1·70 1·50
2552 (5k.50) Eye behind glasses and heart on cheek 1·70 1·50
2553 (5k.50) Eye with heart shaped lashes 1·70 1·50
2554 (5k.50) Eye with heart shaped tears 1·70 1·50

736 Semi-Colon

2008. Europa. The Letter. Each ochre, vermilion and black.
2555 11k. Type **736** 3·00 2·75
2556 11k. Comma 3·00 2·75

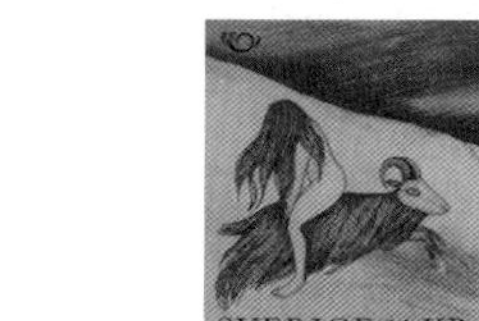

737 Witch riding backwards on Goat

2008. Norse Mythology. Mythical Places. Bakulla (Blue Mountain) (place of witches sabbath). Sheet 105×70 mm containig T 737 and similar vert design. Multicoloured.
MS2557 11k.×2, Type **737**; Bat 6·25 6·00

The stamps and margins of **MS**2557 form a composite design.

Stamps of a similar theme were issued by Aland Islands, Denmark, Faroe Islands, Greenland, Finland, Norway and Iceland.

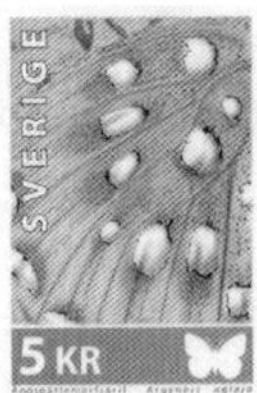

738 Wing (detail), Dark Green Fritillary (*Argynnis aglaja*)

2008. Butterflies. Multicoloured. Self-adhesive.
2558 5k. Type **738** 1·20 1·00
2559 10k. Apollo (*Parnassius apollo*) 3·00 2·75

739 Crawfish

2008. Summer Stamps. Summer Tables. Inscribed 'IRIKES BREV'. Multicoloured. (a) Ordinary gum.
2560 (5k.50) Type **739** 1·50 1·20

(b) Size 37×26 mm. Self-adhesive.
2561 (5k.50) Strawberry gateau 1·50 1·20
2562 (5k.50) Fish on barbeque 1·50 1·20
2563 (5k.50) Coffee and pastries 1·50 1·20
2564 (5k.50) Ham, bread and melon 1·50 1·20

740 *Gunilla*

2008. Sailing Ships. Multicoloured.
2565 11k. Type **740** 3·25 3·00
2566 11k. *Tre Kronor af Stockholm* 3·25 3·00
2567 11k. *Gratitude* 3·25 3·00
2568 11k. *Gladan* and *Falken* 3·25 3·00

741 *Assar* (Ulf Lundkvist)

2008. Comic Strips. Scenes from comic strips. Multicoloured.
2569 5k.50 Type **741** 1·90 1·70
2570 5k.50 *Ensamma mamman* (Cecilia Torudd) 1·90 1·70
2571 5k.50 *Arne Anka* (Charlie Christensen) 1·90 1·70
2572 5k.50 *Rocky* (Martin Kellerman) 1·90 1·70
2573 5k.50 *nameless gloomy girl* (Nina Hemmingsson) 1·90 1·70
2574 5k.50 *Halge* (Lars Mortimer) 1·90 1·70
2575 5k.50 *Socker-Conny* (Joakim Pirinen) 1·90 1·70
2576 5k.50 *Swedish manga* (Asa Ekstrom) 1·90 1·70

742 Beetroot

2008. Autumn Harvest. Organic Growing. Multicoloured. (a) Size 26×31 mm. Inscr 'Brev'. Self-adhesive.
2577 (5k.50) Type **742** 1·60 1·40
2578 (5k.50) Cabbage 1·60 1·40
2579 (5k.50) Pumpkin 1·60 1·40
2580 (5k.50) Potatoes 1·60 1·40

(b) Inscr 'Brev'. (i) Size 31×27 mm
2581 (5k.50) Apples 2·40 2·20

(ii) Size 31×24 mm.
2582 11k. Carrots 2·40 2·20

743 Wreath

2008. Christmas Wreaths. Inscr 'Julpost 2008'. Multicoloured. (a) Ordinary gum.
2583 (5k.) Type **743** 1·50 1·30

(b) Size 28×28 mm. Self-adhesive.
2584 (5k.) Heart shaped wreath 1·50 1·30
2585 (5k.) Mistletoe and wheat stems tied with bow 1·50 1·30
2586 (5k.) Red, white and green wreath 1·50 1·30
2587 (5k.) Star shaped wreath with lights 1·50 1·30

744 Tobogganing

2008. Winter Games. Multicoloured.
2588 11k. Type **744** 3·00 2·75
2589 11k. Snow ball pile and house 3·00 2·75
2590 11k. Making snow man 3·00 2·75

745 Dario Fo

2008. Dario Fo–1997 Nobel Prize for Literature Winner. Sheet 125×83 mm containing T 745 and similar vert design. Multicoloured.
MS2591 11k.×2 Type **745**; Nobel Prize diploma designed by Bo Larsson (34×50 mm) 6·25 6·25

746 Volkswagen Beetle

2009. Classic Cars. Multicoloured. (a) Inscr 'INRIKES BREV'.
2592 (6k.) Type **746** 1·70 1·70
2593 (6k.) Volvo PV 444 1·70 1·70
2594 (6k.) Cadillac Coupe de Ville 1·70 1·70
2595 (6k.) Citroen DS 19 1·70 1·70
2596 (6k.) Ford Mustang convertible 1·70 1·70

(b) Coil stamp.
2597 12k. Volvo Amazon 1·70 1·70

747 Mouth

2009. Greetings Stamps. Inscr 'BREV'. Multicoloured. (a) Ordinary gum.
2598 (6k.) Type **747** 1·70 1·70

(b) Size 32×26 mm. Self-adhesive.
2599 (6k.) Stylized swans 1·70 1·70
2600 (6k.) Stylized skaters 1·70 1·70
2601 (6k.) Heart-shaped clouds 1·70 1·70
2602 (6k.) Heart-shaped flowers 1·70 1·70

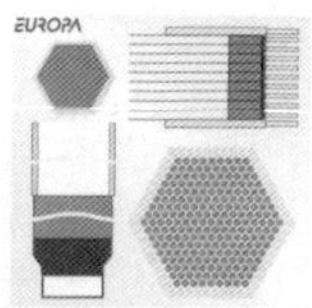

748 Polarimeter

2009. Europa. Astronomy. Multicoloured.
2603 12k. Type **748** 3·00 3·00
2604 12k. Crab Nebula and balloon carrying instruments 3·50 3·50

749 Holding Envelope

2009. Bananas. Inscr 'BREV'. Designs showing banana-shaped clay figures. Multicoloured. Self-adhesive.
2605 (6k.) Type **749** 1·70 1·70
2606 (6k.) Mother and child 1·70 1·70
2607 (6k.) Male figure carrying parcel 1·70 1·70
2608 (6k.) Child offering flower to older male figure 1·70 1·70

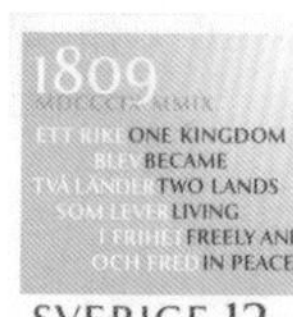

750 'ONE KINGDOM BECAME TWO LANDS...'

2009. Bicentenary of Sweden–Finland Separation (Two Countries–One Future). Multicoloured.
2609 12k. Type **750** 3·50 3·50
2610 12k. Together we are a song... 3·50 3·50

751 Up

2009. 500th Death Anniv of Albertus Pictor (artist). Sheet 105×75 mm containing T 751 and similar vert designs showing part of Wheel of Life (fresco), Harkeberga Church, Stockholm. Multicoloured.
MS2611 12k.×3, Type **751**; Top; Down 10·00 10·00

752 *Pandion haliaetus* (osprey)

2009. Raptors. Multicoloured. (a) Size 25×33 mm. Inscr 'FORENINGSBREV'.
2612 (5k.) Type **752** 1·40 1·40

(b) Size 31×27 mm. Inscr 'EKONOMIBREV'.
2613 (5k.50) *Accipiter nisus* (Eurasian sparrowhawk) 1·50 1·50

(c) Size 30×32 mm. Inscr 'BREV'.
2614 (6k.) *Haliaeetus albicilla* (white-tailed eagle) 1·70 1·70
2615 (6k.) *Asio flammeus* (short-eared owl) 1·70 1·70

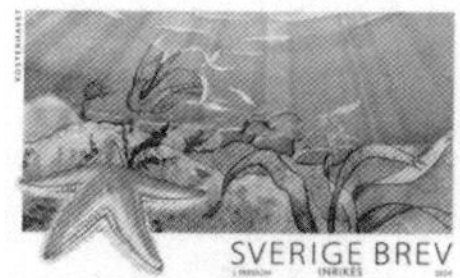

753 Sand Star, Kosterhavet

2009. Nature. Inscr 'INRIKES BREV'. Multicoloured. (a) Ordinary gum.
2616 (6k.) Type **753** 1·70 1·70

(b) Size 38×26 mm. Self-adhesive.
2617 (6k.) Globe flower, Abisko National Park 1·70 1·70
2618 (6k.) Tree frog, Stenshuvud National Park 1·70 1·70
2619 (6k.) Dormouse, Garphyttan National Park 1·70 1·70
2620 (6k.) Cranberries, Store Mosse National Park 1·70 1·70

754 Braille writing (image scaled to 74% of original size)

2009. Through the Eyes of Others. Birth Bicentenary of Louis Braille (inventor of Braille writing for the blind). Sheet 83×125 mm containing T 754 and similar horiz design. Inscr 'INRIKES BREV'. Multicoloured.
MS2621 (6k.)×2, Type **754**; As Type **754** (dull magenta background) 3·50 3·50

755 Kaknäs Tower, Stockholm

2009. Architecture.
2622 12k. slate grey 3·50 3·50
2623 12k. agate 3·50 3·50
2624 12k. agate 3·50 3·50
2625 12k. slate grey 3·50 3·50

DESIGNS: 2622, Type **755**; 2623, Lugnet ski jump, Falun; 2624, Balder roller coaster, Gothenburg; 2625, Turning Torso, Malmo.

2009. Coil Stamp. As T 677.

2626 12k. slate green and agate 3·50 3·50

DESIGN: Queen Silvia (as No. 2377).

No. 2626 was for use on international mail.

756 Christer Fuglesang

2009. Journey into Space. Christer Fuglesang—First Swedish Astronaut. Multicoloured.

[illegible] 6k. Type **756** 1·70 1·70
[illegible] 6k. Space walk 1·70 1·70
[illegible] 6k. Space shuttle *Discovery* 1·70 1·70
[illegible] k. Christer Fuglesang with helmet on lap 1·70 1·70
[illegible] . Christer Fuglesang floating in space (38×38 mm) (rhomboid) 1·70 1·70

757 *Ocimum basilicum* (basil)

2009. Herbs and Spices. (a) Inscr 'INRIKES BREV'. Multicoloured. Self-adhesive.

2632 (6k.) Type **757** 1·70 1·70
2633 (6k.) *Capsicum* (chilli) 1·70 1·70
2634 (6k.) *Rosmarinus officinalis* (rosemary) 1·70 1·70
2635 (6k.) *Allium sativum* (garlic) 1·70 1·70

(b) Ordinary gum.

2636 (6k.) bronze-green and light green (30×22 mm) 1·70 1·70
2637 12k. emerald and deep mauve (42×27 mm) 1·70 1·70

DESGNS: No. 2636, *Anethum graveolens*; No. 2637, *Allium schoenoprasum*.

758 Parcels

2009. Christmas. (a) Inscr 'JUL POST'. Multicoloured. Self-adhesive.

2638 (5k.50.) Type **758** 1·60 1·60
2639 (5k.50.) Parcels including saw and ball 1·60 1·60
2640 (5k.50.) Parcels including teddy bear 1·60 1·60
2641 (5k.50.) Parcels including train engine 1·60 1·60

(b) Ordinary gum.

2642 (5k.50.) Wax seal (31×33 mm) 1·60 1·60

759 *Lagopus muta* (ptarmigan)

2009. Snow-White Animals. Each indigo.

2643 12k. Type **759** 3·50 3·50
2644 12k. *Mustela erminea* (ermine) 3·50 3·50
2645 12k. *Lepus timidus* (alpine hare) 3·50 3·50

760 *Children of the Forest* (written and illustrated by Elsa Beskow)

2010. Europa. Children's Books. Multicoloured.

2646 12k. Type **760** 3·50 3·50
2647 12k. *Maja's Alphabet* (written and illustrated by Lena Anderson) 3·50 3·50

761 Cat

2010. Cats. Inscr 'BREV'. Designs showing cats. Multicoloured. Self-adhesive.

2648 (6k.) Type **761** 1·70 1·70
2649 (6k.) Playing with ball 1·70 1·70
2650 (6k.) Angry with arched back 1·70 1·70
2651 (6k.) Stretching 1·70 1·70

762 Vadstena Castle

2010. Castles and Palaces. Each grey-olive and black.

2652 12k. Type **762** 3·50 3·50
2653 12k. Ulriksdal Palace 3·50 3·50
2654 12k. TjolOholm Castles 3·50 3·50
2655 12k. LAckO Castle (30×38 mm) 3·50 3·50
2656 12k. Sofiero Palace (30×38 mm) 3·50 3·50

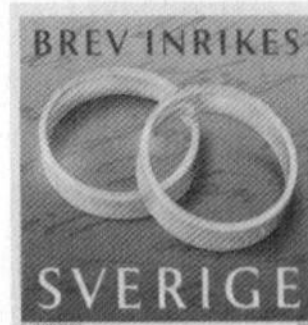

763 Rings

2010. Greeting Stamps. Multicoloured.

(a) Coil stamp

2657 (6k.) Type **763** 1·90 1·90

(b) Booklet stamps

2658 (6k.) Cake 1·90 1·90
2659 (6k.) Two birds holding heart 1·90 1·90
2660 (6k.) Hands and 'TRUE LOVE' 1·90 1·90
2661 (6k.) Champagne glasses 1·90 1·90

764 King Carl XVI Gustav

2010. King Carl XVI Gustav and Queen Silvia

2662 (6k.) blackish olive 1·90 1·90
2663 12k. agate 3·50 3·50

Designs: Type **764**; 2663, Queen Silvia

No. 2662 is inscribed 'BREV' and was originally on sale for 6k.

765 *Mytilus edulis* (blue mussel)

2010. Life at the Coast. Multicoloured.

MS2664 12k.×2, Type **765**; SD 141 *Emelie* 8·00 8·00

Stamps of a similar theme were issued by Denmark, Aland Islands, Faröe Islands, Finland, Iceland, Norway and Greenland.

766 Selenium Crystals

2010. Bicentenary of Karolinska Institutet. Each deep mauve and new blue.

2665 (5k.50) Type **766** 1·60 1·60
2666 (5k.50) Silicon 1·60 1·60

767 Crown Princess Victoria

2010. Wedding of Crown Princess Victoria and Daniel Westling. Each deep blue, grey-blue and silver.

MS2667 6k.×3, Type **767**; Royal monogram; Royal couple (84×126 mm) 5·25 5·25

768 Pansies

2010. Greetings Stamps

(a) Coil stamp

2668 (6k.) Type **768** 1·75 1·75

(b) Size 29×29 mm. Self-adhesive

2669 (6k.) Yellow pansy 1·75 1·75
2670 (6k.) Blue pansy 1·75 1·75
2671 (6k.) Red pansy 1·75 1·75
2672 (6k.) Multicoloured pansy 1·75 1·75

769 *Phocoena phocoena* (harbour porpoise)

2010. Marine Life. Each black, dull ultramarine and turquoise-blue.

2673 12k. Type **769** 1·40 1·40
2674 12k. *Enhydra lutris* (sea otter) 1·40 1·40
2675 12k. *Balaenoptera musculus* (blue whale) 1·40 1·40
2676 12k. *Pusa hispida* (ringed seal) 1·40 1·40

770 Maj Sjöwall and Per Wahlöö (image scaled to 75% of original size)

2010. Crime Writers

2677 6k. Type **770** 1·75 1·75
2678 6k. Henning Mankell 1·75 1·75
2679 6k. Liza Marklund 1·75 1·75
2680 6k. Håkan Nesser (33×30 mm) 1·75 1·75
2681 6k. Steig Larsson (33×30 mm) 1·75 1·75

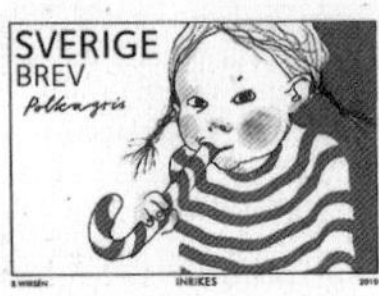

771 Candy Cane

2010. Local Foods. As T **771**

(a) Self-adhesive

2682 (6k.) multicoloured 2·50 2·50
2683 (6k.) multicoloured 2·50
2684 (6k.) multicoloured 2·50 2·50
2685 (6k.) multicoloured 2·50 2·50

(b) Coil stamps.

2686 (6k.) yellow-brown and yellow-orange (31×27 mm) 1·90 1·90
2687 12k. deep brown and buff (44×27 mm) 3·25 3·25

772 Bowl

2010. Art of Engraving

MS2688 12k.×3, Type **772**; Armour; Anneli Alhanko and Per-Arthur Segerström in *Romeo and Juliet* (As No. 850) 10·50 10·50

773 'JUL POST 2010' **774** 'JUL POST 2010'

775 'JUL POST 2010' **776** 'JUL POST 2010'

2010. Christmas. Booklet Stamps

2689 **773** (55c.) multicolured 1·90 1·90
2690 **774** (55c.) multicoloured 1·90 1·90
2691 **775** (55c.) multicoloured 1·90 1·90
2692 **776** (55c.) multicoloured 1·90 1·90

777 Snow Crystals

778 Snow Crystal **779** Snow Crystal

780 Snow Crystal **781** Snow Crystal

2010. Snow Crystals. Booklet Stamps

2693 **777** 12k. multicoloured 4·00 4·00
2694 **778** 12k. multicoloured 4·00 4·00
2695 **779** 12k. multicoloured 4·00 4·00
2696 **780** 12k. multicoloured 4·00 4·00
2697 **781** 12k. multicoloured 4·00 4·00

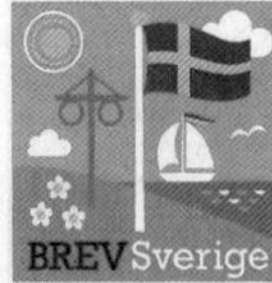

782 National Flag **783** Flag at Lakeside

2011. Blue and Yellow (Swedish colours)

(a) Coil Stamp. Ordinary gum

2698 (60c.) Type **782** 2·00 2·00

(b) Self-adhesive

2699 (60c.) Type **783** 2·00 2·00
2700 (60c.) Arms waving flags 2·00 2·00
2701 (60c.) Child exclaiming 'Heja' (Hurrah) 2·00 2·00
2702 (60c.) Flag from vehicle 2·00 2·00

784 Monark 523 Three-wheeler

2011. Bicycles. Booklet Stamps. Each steel blue, bright mauve and grey.

2703	(60c.) Type **784**	2·00	2·00
2704	(60c.) Crescent's folding bicycle	2·00	2·00
2705	(60c.) Women's tourer	2·00	2·00
2706	(60c.) City bicycle	2·00	2·00
2707	(60c.) Child's tricycle	2·00	2·00

785 Conical Fossil

2011. Fossils. Multicoloured.

2708	30k. Type **785**	10·00	13·00
2709	40k. Ammonite (32×30 mm)		

786 Hand and Web

2011. Networks

2710	FORENINGSBREV(5k.) Type **786**	4·00	4·00
2711	FORENINGSBREV(5k.) Hand, at left, and web (red)	4·00	4·00

Nos. 2710/1 are inscribed 'FORENINGSBREV' and were originally on sale for 5k.

787 Wind Turbine

2011. Renewable Energy

(a) Coil Stamp

2712	BREV(6k.) Type **787**	4·00	4·00

(b) Booklet Stamps. Size 33×22 mm. Self-adhesive

2713	BREV(6k.) Cloud, sun and solar panels	4·00	4·00
2714	BREV(6k.) Grasses and wind turbine	4·00	4·00
2715	BREV(6k.) Bio-energy generator and trees	4·00	4·00
2716	BREV(6k.) Wave power collectors and sea bed	4·00	4·00

788 Girl and Boy with raised Arm

2011. Save the Children. Charity Stamps. Multicoloured.

2717	Brev(6k.+1k.) Type **788**	2·40	2·40
2718	Brev(6k.+1k.) Dark haired girl with slate, boy writing and girl reading	2·40	2·40

789 Section of Birch Tree (Betula)

2011. Europa. Forests. Multicoloured.

2719	12k. Type **789**	4·00	4·00
2720	12k. Section of spruce tree (*Pica abies*)	4·00	4·00

790 Forsvik

2011. Industrial Heritage. Mills

2721	12k. black and reddish brown	4·00	4·00
2722	12k. black and reddish brown (27×35 mm)	4·00	4·00
2723	12k. black and deep brown (27×35 mm)	4·00	4·00
2724	12k. black and reddish brown (27×35 mm)	4·00	4·00
2725	12k. black and reddish brown (27×35 mm)	4·00	4·00

Designs: 2721, Type **790**; 2722, Glass blower, Glasriket; 2723, Chimney and arched windows, Avesta; 2724, Chimney, building and bridge, Jonsered; 2725, Mackmyra Mill

791 Banana Split

2011. Greetings Stamps. Ice Cream

(a) Coil Stamp

2726	Type **791**	2·00	2·00

(b) Booklet Stamps. Size 25×26 mm. Self-adhesive

2727	BREV(6k.) Pink lolly with ice cream filling	2·00	2·00
2728	BREV(6k.) Ice cream cone	2·00	2·00
2729	BREV(6k.) Tub with cherries	2·00	2·00
2730	BREV(6k.) Chocolate topped vanilla cone	2·00	2·00

792 Friedrich Georg Wilhelm von Struve

2011. Struve Geodetic Arc. UNESCO World Heritage Site. Multicoloured.

MS2731	12k.×2, Type **792**; Theodolite	8·00	8·00

793 Red Waterlily

2011. Waterlilies. Multicoloured.

2732	12k. Type **793**	4·00	4·00
2733	12k. Dragonfly and waterlilies	4·00	4·00
2734	12k. Single yellow flower	4·00	4·00
2735	12k. Single white flower	4·00	4·00

OFFICIAL STAMPS

O6

1874

O27	**O6**	2ore orange	1·20	1·40
O28a	**O6**	3ore bistre	1·00	1·60
O29c	**O6**	4ore grey	1·90	40
O30a	**O6**	5ore green	3·25	35
O31a	**O6**	6ore lilac	29·00	42·00
O32	**O6**	6ore grey	£350	£140
O33b	**O6**	10ore red	1·90	35
O34a	**O6**	12ore blue	42·00	15·00
O35a	**O6**	20ore red	£170	1·70
O36	**O6**	20ore blue	3·75	35
O37a	**O6**	24ore yellow	55·00	14·50
O38ca	**O6**	30ore brown	18·00	45
O39a	**O6**	50ore red	£120	18·00
O40	**O6**	50ore grey	14·50	1·40
O41d	**O6**	1k. blue and bistre	7·25	1·60

1889. Surch TJENSTE FRIMARKE, two crowns, and TIO 10 ORE on scroll.

O42	10ore on 12ore blue	10·00	12·00
O43	10ore on 24ore yellow	15·00	22·00

O17

1910

O87	**O17**	1ore black	40	40
O101	**O17**	2ore yellow	20	20
O102	**O17**	3ore brown	30	45
O103	**O17**	4ore lilac	25	25
O104	**O17**	5ore green	20	20
O105	**O17**	7ore green	45	80
O91	**O17**	8ore purple	65	75
O107	**O17**	10ore red	25	20
O108	**O17**	12ore red	25	20
O109	**O17**	15ore brown	40	25
O110	**O17**	20ore blue	40	20
O111	**O17**	25ore orange	1·20	45
O112	**O17**	30ore brown	65	35
O113	**O17**	35ore violet	1·00	55
O114	**O17**	50ore grey	4·25	1·40
O98	**O17**	1k. black on yellow	11·00	6·25
O99	**O17**	5k. purple on yellow	14·00	3·00

POSTAGE DUE STAMPS

D6

1874

D27a	**D 6**	1ore black	2·00	2·40
D28ab	**D 6**	3ore red	4·00	4·50
D29ba	**D 6**	5ore brown	3·00	3·25
D30a	**D 6**	6ore yellow	3·00	3·50
D31	**D 6**	12ore red	4·75	3·25
D32a	**D 6**	20ore blue	3·00	3·00
D33	**D 6**	24ore lilac	39·00	36·00
D34b	**D 6**	24ore grey	14·50	18·00
D35b	**D 6**	30ore green	4·00	3·00
D36a	**D 6**	50ore brown	6·00	3·50
D37a	**D 6**	1k. blue and bistre	30·00	17·00

Pt. 8

SWITZERLAND

A federal republic in central Europe between France, Germany and Italy.

100 rappen = 1 franken.
100 centimes = 1 franc.
100 centesimi = 1 franco.

These are expressions of the same currency in three languages.
For the issues under the Cantonal Administrations of Basel, Geneva and Zurich, see Stanley Gibbons' Part 8 (Italy and Switzerland) Catalogue.

1

1850. Imperf. (a) Inscr "ORTS-POST".

1	1	2½r. black and red	£3000	£1700

(b) Inscr "POSTE LOCALE".

3	2½r. black and red	£2500	£1500

1850. As T 1 but inscr "RAYON I", "II" or "III". Imperf.

6	5r. red, black and blue (I)	£1800	£550
13	5r. red and blue (I)	£600	£150
10	10r. red, black and yellow (II)	£950	£150
24	15rp. red (III)	£2500	£150
21	15 cts. red (III)	£18000	£1100

6

1854. Imperf.

46	6	2r. grey	£250	£550
47a	6	5r. brown	£225	22·00
48	6	10r. blue	£250	22·00
49a	6	15r. pink	£375	65·00
50	6	20r. orange	£500	75·00
51	6	40r. green	£450	85·00
38a	6	1f. lilac	£1500	£950

7

1862. Perf.

52	7	2c. grey	£150	4·25
61	7	2c. brown	2·50	1·80
61a	7	2c. bistre	2·50	1·80
53	7	3c. black	14·50	£150
54b	7	5c. brown	3·75	85
55	7	10c. blue	£750	85
62	7	10c. pink	7·25	1·10
63	7	15c. yellow	7·25	44·00
56a	7	20c. orange	2·50	3·75
64	7	25c. green	1·80	4·25
57	7	30c. red	£1700	44·00
65a	7	30c. blue	£600	14·50
58	7	40c. green	£1600	75·00
66	7	40c. grey	1·80	£160
67	7	50c. purple	55·00	60·00
59	7	60c. bronze	£1500	£200
60a	7	1f. gold	22·00	£120

9

1882

126Bd	9	2c. brown	2·20	1·10
127Bc	9	3c. brown	3·00	14·50
128Bd	9	5c. purple	10·50	85
196a	9	5c. green	9·50	75
130Be	9	10c. red	8·50	85
131Be	9	12c. blue	11·00	1·10
132A	9	15c. yellow	£160	36·00
133Bc	9	15c. violet	75·00	3·75

10

1882

214	10	20c. orange	3·75	5·75
146B	10	25c. green	17·00	2·20
207	10	25c. blue	8·75	2·50
209	10	40c. grey	50·00	22·00
202	10	30c. brown	11·00	3·00
150B	10	50c. blue	65·00	22·00
218	10	50c. green	8·75	29·00
152B	10	1f. purple	60·00	5·75
219	10	1f. red	44·00	14·50
154B	10	3f. brown	£225	36·00

11

1900. 25th Anniv of U.P.U.

191	11	5c. green	3·75	3·00
189	11	10c. red	11·00	3·00
190	11	25c. blue	29·00	44·00

15 Tell's Son

16

1907

225	15	2c. yellow	35	1·50
226	15	3c. brown	35	14·50
227	15	5c. green	4·25	75
228	16	10c. red	2·20	75
229	16	12c. brown	35	5·75
230	16	15c. mauve	4·25	18·00

17

1908

232	17	20c. yellow and red	3·00	1·50
233	17	25c. blue and deep blue	2·50	1·10
234	17	30c. green and brown	2·00	75
235	17	35c. yellow and green	2·50	3·25
236	17	40c. yellow and purple	15·00	1·50
238	17	40c. blue	1·90	65
239a	17	40c. green	37·00	2·10
240a	17	50c. green and deep green	9·50	2·10
241	17	60c. brown	13·00	1·50
242	17	70c. yellow and brown	75·00	25·00
243	17	70c. buff and violet	19·00	5·00
244	17	80c. buff and grey	12·50	2·50
245	17	1f. green and purple	11·00	75
246	17	3f. yellow and bistre	£375	3·75

18 Cord in front of Shaft

19

1908

247	18	2c. bistre	35	2·20
248	18	3c. violet	35	22·00
249	18	5c. green	11·00	35
250	19	10c. red	1·50	75
251	19	12c. brown	75	1·50
252	19	15c. mauve	36·00	1·50

20a Cord behind Shaft

1910

260	20a	2c. brown	10	75
261	20a	2½c. purple	35	1·80
262	20a	2½c. bistre on buff	35	3·75
254	20a	3c. violet	75	35
255	20a	3c. brown	10	35
256a	20a	3c. blue on buff	75	8·00
263	20a	5c. green	1·00	35
264	20a	5c. orange on buff	10	15
265	20a	5c. grey on buff	10	10
266	20a	5c. purple on buff	10	10
267	20a	5c. green on buff	35	30
258	20a	7½c. grey	1·30	35
259	20a	7½c. green on buff	35	5·00

21 William Tell

1914

279	21	10c. red on buff	35	20
280	21	10c. green on buff	10	10
282	21	10c. violet on buff	85	35
283	21	12c. brown on buff	35	6·50
284	21	13c. green on buff	1·70	75
285	21	15c. purple on buff	2·50	75
286	21	15c. red on buff	3·25	6·50
287	21	20c. purple on buff	2·00	20
289	21	20c. red on buff	20	10
291	21	25c. red on buff	75	1·50
292	21	25c. brown on buff	3·75	2·20
293	21	30c. blue on buff	13·00	75

22 The Mythen

1914. Mountain Views.

294	22	3f. green	£850	8·75
295	22	3f. red	£120	2·20
296	-	5f. blue	44·00	3·75
297	-	10f. mauve	£130	3·75
337	-	10f. green	£300	55·00

DESIGNS: 5f. The Rutli; 10f. The Jungfrau and girl holding shield.

1915. Surch.

298	20a	1c. on 2c. brown	10	1·80
307	20a	2½c. on 3c. brown	10	1·50
308	20a	3c. on 2½c. bistre on buff	10	4·25
309	20a	5c. on 2c. brown	10	6·50
310	20a	5c. on 7½c. grey	10	75
312	20a	5c. on 7½c. green on buff	15	75
313	21	10c. on 13c. green on buff	20	3·75
299	19	13c. on 12c. brown	10	16·00
300	21	13c. on 12c. brn on buff	10	1·10
314a	21	20c. on 15c. purple on buff	75	3·75
315	17	20c. on 25c. bl & dp bl	35	75
301	17	80c. on 70c. yell & brn	36·00	28·00

1919. Air. Optd with wings and propeller.

302	30c. green and brown	£150	£1600
303	50c. green and deep green	50·00	£160

31

32

33

1919. Peace Celebrations.

304	31	7½c. green and black	1·00	3·00
305	32	10c. yellow and red	1·50	11·00
306	33	15c. yellow and violet	2·50	3·75

35 Monoplane

36 Pilot

37

38 Biplane

39 Icarus

40

1923. Air.

316	35	15c. green and red	3·25	11·00
317a	35	20c. green and deep green	35	75
318	35	25c. grey and blue	10·00	29·00
319	36	35c. cinnamon and brown	14·50	65·00
320a	37	35c. brown and ochre	8·75	65·00
321	36	40c. lilac and violet	18·00	75·00
322a	37	40c. blue and green	70·00	£120
323	38	45c. red and blue	1·80	12·50
324a	38	50c. grey and red	1·50	2·20
325a	39	65c. blue and deep blue	3·75	11·00
326	39	75c. orange and purple	17·00	95·00
327a	39	1f. lilac and purple	1·80	4·25
328a	40	2f. chestnut, sepia & brn	9·50	14·50

41

1924

329	41	90c. red, dp green & grn	20·00	3·75
330	41	1f.20 red, lake and pink	7·25	7·25
331a	41	1f.50 red, blue & turq	44·00	8·75
332a	41	2f. red, black and grey	40·00	12·50

42 Seat of First U.P.U. Congress

1924. 50th Anniv of U.P.U.

333	-	20c. red	75	2·10
334	**42**	30c. blue	4·25	8·50

DESIGN: 20c. As T **42** but with different frame.

43 The Mythen

1931

335	**43**	3f. brown	60·00	7·25

44 Symbol of Peace

45 "After the Darkness, Light"

46 Peace and the Air Post

1932. International Disarmament Conference.

338	**44**	5c. green (postage)	35	75
339	**44**	10c. orange	35	35
340	**44**	20c. mauve	35	35
341	**44**	30c. blue	2·50	2·20
342	**44**	60c. brown	22·00	13·00
343	**45**	1f. grey and blue	22·00	14·00
344	**46**	15c. lt green & green (air)	75	3·25
345	**46**	20c. pink and red	1·50	4·75
346	**46**	90c. light blue and blue	8·00	55·00

47 Louis Favre (engineer)

1932. 50th Anniv of St. Gotthard Railway.

347	**47**	10c. brown	10	15
348	-	20c. red	35	15
349	-	30c. blue	75	4·25

DESIGNS: 20c. Alfred Escher (President of Railway); 30c. Emil Welti (surveyor).

For redrawn designs, see Nos. 368 etc.

48 Staubbach Falls

1934. Landscapes.

350	**48**	3c. green	35	5·00
351	-	5c. green	20	10
352	-	10c. mauve	50	10
353	-	15c. orange	50	5·00
354	-	20c. red	85	75
355	-	25c. brown	8·75	11·00
356	-	30c. blue	33·00	3·00

DESIGNS: 5c. Mt. Pilatus; 10c. Chillon Castle and Dents du Midi; 15c. Grimsel Pass; 20c. St. Gotthard Railway, Biaschina Gorge; 25c. Viamala Gorge; 30c. Rhine Falls, Schaffhausen.

1934. National Philatelic Exhibition, Zunch ("NABA"). Sheet 62×72 mm.

MS357 Nos 351/4		£500	£850

1935. Air. Surch.

358	**35**	10 on 15c. green and red	5·75	50·00
359	**46**	10 on 15c. light green and green	35	75
360	**46**	10 on 20c. pink and red	40	3·00
361	**46**	30 on 90c. light blue & blue	3·50	24·00
362	**46**	40 on 20c. pink and red	4·50	26·00
363	**46**	40 on 90c. light blue & blue	3·75	26·00
381	**39**	10 on 65c. blue & deep blue	55	1·50

51 Freiburg Cowherd

1936. National Defence Fund.

364	**51**	10c.+5c. violet	75	1·50
365	**51**	20c.+10c. red	1·10	6·00
366	**51**	30c.+10c. blue	5·25	29·00
MS367 109×102 mm. Nos. 364/6			60·00	£300

52 Staubbach Falls

1936. As T 48 but redrawn with figure of value lower down. Various landscapes.

368A	**52**	3c. green	15	15
369A	-	5c. green	15	10
489	-	5c. brown	40	10
370Ad	-	10c. purple	75	10
372A	-	10c. brown	10	10
490	-	10c. green	40	10
373A	-	15c. orange	55	1·50
374Ad	-	20c. red (Railway)	6·75	40
375A	-	20c. red (Lake)	25	10
491	-	20c. brown	40	10
376A	-	25c. brown	75	1·50
492	-	25c. red	2·75	4·25
377A	-	30c. blue	1·10	40
378A	-	35c. green	1·50	3·00
379A	-	40c. grey	6·75	40
494	-	40c. blue	47·00	2·30

DESIGNS: 5c. Mt. Pilatus; 10c. Chillon Castle and Dents du Midi; 15c. Grimsel Pass; 20c. (374d) St. Gotthard Railway, Biaschina Gorge; 20c. (Nos. 375, 491) Lake Lugano and Mt. San Salvatore; 25c. (No. 376) Viamala Gorge; 25c. (No. 492) National Park; 30c. Rhine Falls, Schaffhausen; 35c. Mt. Neufalkenstein and Klus; 40c. Mt. Santis and Lake Seealp.

53 Mobile P.O.

1937. For Mobile P.O. Mail.

380	**53**	10c. yellow and black	40	75

55 International Labour Bureau

1938

382	**55**	20c. red and buff	40	40
383	-	30c. blue and light blue	65	40
384	-	60c. brown and buff	2·50	3·75
385	-	1f. black and buff	9·75	26·00

DESIGNS: 30c. Palace of League of Nations; 60c. Inner courtyard of Palace of League of Nations; 1f. International Labour Bureau (different).

1938. Air. Special Flights. Surch 1938 "PRO AERO" 75 75 and bars.

386	**38**	75c. on 50c. green and red	†	8·25

60 William Tell's Chapel

1938. National Fete. Fund for Swiss Subjects Abroad.

387	**60**	10c.+10c. violet & yellow	40	2·75

1938. National Philatelic Exhibition, Aarau and 25th Anniv of Swiss Air Mail Service. Sheet 74×87 mm.

MS387a Nos. 375 and 381 (sold at 1f.50)		43·00	49·00

61 First Act of Federal Parliament

1938

388A	**61**	3f. brown on blue	13·00	13·50
388C	**61**	3f. brown on buff	4·00	1·50
389A	-	5f. blue on blue	11·00	9·00
389C	-	5f. blue on buff	6·50	1·50
390B	-	10f. green on blue	44·00	3·75
390C	-	10f. green on buff	12·50	5·25

DESIGNS: 5f. "The Assembly at Stans"; 10f. Polling booth.

62 Symbolical of Swiss Culture

1939. National Exhibition, Zurich. Inscr in French (F), German (G) or Italian (I).

391F		10c. violet	40	40
391G		10c.	40	40
391I		10c.	40	40
392F	**62**	20c. carmine	40	40
392G	-	20c.	40	40
392I	-	20c.	7·75	40
393F	-	30c. blue and buff	3·25	13·00
393G	-	30c.	3·50	5·25
393I	-	30c.	2·40	14·50

DESIGNS: 10c. Group symbolic of Swiss Industry and Agriculture; 30c. Piz Rosegg and Tschirva Glacier.

64 Crossbow and Floral Branch

1939. National Exhibition, Zurich. Inscr in French (F), German (G) or Italian (I).

394F		5c. emerald	55	3·75
394G		5c. emerald	55	3·00
394I		5c. emerald	80	6·00
395F	**64**	10c. brown	55	3·75
395G	**64**	10c. brown	55	3·75
395I	**64**	10c. brown	55	5·25
396F	**64**	20c. scarlet	1·25	5·25
396G	**64**	20c. scarlet	1·10	3·00
396I	**64**	20c. scarlet	1·10	7·50
397F	**64**	30c. blue	3·25	14·50
397G	**64**	30c. blue	3·25	12·00
397I	**64**	30c. blue	3·25	15·00

65 Laupen Castle

1939. National Fete. Fund for Destitute Mothers.

398	**65**	10c.+10c. brn, grey & red	40	1·90

66 Geneva

1939. 75th Anniv of Geneva (Red Cross) Convention.

399	**66**	20c. red and buff	40	40
400	**66**	30c. blue, grey and red	40	4·25

67 "Les Rangiers"

1940. National Fete and Red Cross Fund. Memorial designs inscr "FETE NATIONALE 1940" in German (5c., 20c.), Italian (10c.) and French (30c.).

401	-	5c.+5c. black and green	40	1·50
402	-	10c.+5c. black & orange	40	1·10
403	-	20c.+5c. black and red	3·25	1·90
404	**67**	30c.+10c. black and blue	2·00	11·50
MS404a 125×65 mm. Nos. 401/2, 403/4. Imperf (sold at 5f.)			£375	£850

DESIGNS—Battle Memorials: 5c. Sempach; 10c. Giornico; 20c. Calven.

68 "William Tell" (Ferdinand Hodler)

1941. Historical Designs.

405	-	50c. blue on green	6·75	10
406	**68**	60c. brown on cinnamon	12·00	10
407	-	70c. purple on mauve	2·75	2·30
408	-	80c. black on grey	65	10
408a	-	80c. black on mauve	3·25	75
409	-	90c. red on pink	70	10
409a	-	90c. red on buff	4·00	3·75
410	-	1f. green on green	1·10	10
411	-	1f.20 purple on grey	1·10	10
411a	-	1f.20 purple on lilac	4·75	75
412	-	1f.50 blue on buff	2·00	40
413	-	2f. red on pink	2·40	40
413a	-	2f. red on cream	7·00	75

DESIGNS—(Works of art): 50c. "Oath of Union" (James Vibert); 70c. "Kneeling Warrior" (Ferdinand Hodler); 80c. "Dying Ensign" (Hodler); 90c. "Standard Bearer" (Niklaus Deutsch). Portraits: 1f. Col. Louis Pfyffer; 1f.20, George Jenatsch; 1f.50, Lt. Gen. Francois de Reynold; 2f. Col. Joachim Forrer.

69 Ploughing

1941. Agricultural Development Plan.

414	**69**	10c. brown and buff	40	75

70 Douglas DC-2 The Jungfrau

1941. Air. Landscapes.

415	**70**	30c. blue on orange	80	25
415a	-	30c. grey on orange	12·00	20·00
416	-	40c. grey on orange	80	25
416a	-	40c. blue on orange	80·00	3·75
417	-	50c. green on orange	80	25
418	-	60c. brown on orange	1·20	25
419	-	70c. violet on orange	80	75
420	-	1f. green on buff	2·75	75
421	-	2f. red on buff	6·75	5·25
422	-	5f. blue on buff	27·00	23·00

DESIGNS: 40f. Valais; 50c. Lac Leman; 60c. Alpstein; 70c. Ticino; 1f. Lake Lucerne; 2f. Engadin; 5f. Churfirsten.

1941. Air. Special (Buochs–Payerne) Flights. No. 420 with "PRO AERO 28.V.1941" added.

423	1f. green on buff	7·75	28·00

71 Chemin Creux near Kussnacht

1941. National Fete and 650th Anniv of Swiss Confederation.

424	-	10c.+10c. blue, red & yell	40	1·50

425	71	20c.+10c. scarlet, red and buff	40	2·75

DESIGN: 10c. Relief map of Lake Lucerne with Arms of Uri, Schwyz and Unterwalden.

72 Arms of Berne, Masons laying Cornerstone and Knight

1941. 750th Anniv of Berne.

426	72	10c. multicoloured	40	1·50

73 "To survive collect salvage"

1942. Salvage Campaign. Inscr in French (F.), German (G.) or Italian (I.). Value and coat of arms in red, tablets in blue. F.

427F	73	10c. brown	40	1·50

G.

427G	10c. brown	20	20

I.

427I	10c. brown	7·50	2·50

INSCRIPTIONS: (G) "Zum Durchhalten/Alstoffe sammeln"; (I) "PER RESISTERE/RACCOGLIETE/LA ROBA VECCHIA".

74 View of Old Geneva

75 Soldiers' Memorial at Forch, near Zurich

1942. National Fete, National Relief Fund and Bimillenary of Geneva.

428	74	10c.+10c. black, yellow and red	40	1·10
429	75	20c.+10c. red and yellow	40	3·50
MS429a		105×62 mm. Nos. 428/9. Imperf (sold at 2f.)	80·00	£350

76

76a

1943. Cent of Swiss Cantonal Postage Stamps.

430	76	10c.(4+6) black	40	40
MS430a		160×140 mm. No. 430. Imperf (sold at 5f.)	60·00	85·00
MS430b		70×75 mm. T **76a** 4 and 6 (c.) black. Imperf (sold at 3f.)	70·00	85·00

77 Intragna (Ticino)

1943. National Fete and Youth's Vocational Training Fund.

431	77	10c.+10c. black, buff and red	40	1·10
432	-	20c.+10c. red and buff	40	3·50

DESIGN: 20c. Federal Palace, Berne.

1943. Air. Special Flights. 30th Anniv of First Flight across Alps by Oscar Bider. As No. 432, optd PRO AERO 13.VII.1943 and value.

433		1f. red and buff	2·75	15·00

77a "Double Geneva"

1943. National Philatelic Exhibition Geneva ('GEPH') and Centenary of Geneva Cantonal Stamp. Sheet 72×73 mm. Imperf.

MS433a	5c. black and green (sold at 3f.)	65·00	60·00

78 Apollo of Olympia

1944. Olympic Games Jubilee.

434	78	10c. black and orange	40	1·50
435	78	20c. black and red	40	1·50
436	78	30c. black and blue	80	12·00

79 Heiden

1944. National Fete and Red Cross Fund.

437	79	5c.+5c. green, buff & red	40	3·50
438	-	10c.+10c. grey, buff and red	40	75
439	-	20c.+10c. red and buff	40	75
440	-	30c.+10c. blue, buff and red	2·75	26·00

DESIGNS: 10c. St. Jacques on the R. Birs; 20c. Castle Ruins, Mesocco; 30c. Basel.

80 Haefeli DH-3 Biplane

1944. Air. 25th Anniv of National Air Post.

441	80	10c. brown and green	15	75
442	-	20c. red and stone	25	75
443	-	30c. ultramarine and blue	40	2·75
444	-	1f.50 agate, brown and red	7·75	26·00

AIRCRAFT: 20c. Fokker F.VIIb/3m CH-157; 30c. Lockheed 9B Orion; 1f.50, Douglas DC-3 HB-IRI.

81 Symbolical of Faith, Hope and Charity

1945. War Relief Fund.

445	81	10c.+10c. green, black and grey	80	75
446	81	20c.+60c. red, black and grey	3·25	9·00
MS446a		70×110 mm. Imperf. 3f.+7f. blue	£275	£300

81b "Basel Dove"

1945. Centenary of Basel Cantonal Stamp Issue. Sheet 71×63 mm.

MS446b	**81b** 10 (c.) green, red and black (sold at 3f.)	£160	£140

82 Trans "Peace to men of good will"

83 Olive Branch

1945. Peace. Inscr "PAX".

447	82	5c. green and grey	25	75
448	82	10c. brown and grey	40	20
449	82	20c. red and grey	80	20
450	82	30c. blue and grey	1·60	4·50
451	82	40c. orange and grey	4·75	17·00
452	83	50c. red and buff	7·75	34·00
453	-	60c. grey and light grey	12·00	23·00
454	-	80c. green and buff	20·00	£110
455	-	1f. blue and buff	27·00	£130
456	-	2f. brown and buff	80·00	£225
457	-	3f. green on buff	£100	£110
458	-	5f. brown on buff	£160	£400
459	-	10f. violet on buff	£200	£150

DESIGNS—As Type **83**: 60c. Keys; 80c. Horn of plenty; 1f. Dove; 2f. Spade and flowers in ploughed field. 38×21 mm: 3f. Crocuses; 5f. Clasped hands; 10f. Aged couple.

1945. Red Cross. As T 82, but red cross and "5+10" in centre of stamp.

460	5c.+10c. green	80	1·10

85 Silk Weaving

1945. National Fete.

461	85	5c.+5c. green and red	1·30	4·50
462	-	10c.+10c. brown, grey and red	80	1·10
463	-	20c.+10c. red and buff	1·40	1·10
464	-	30c.+10c. blue, grey and red	12·00	19·00

DESIGNS: 10, 20c. Jura and Emmental farmhouses; 30c. Timbered house.

86 J. H. Pestalozzi

1946. Birth Bicentenary of J. H. Pestalozzi (educational reformer).

465	86	10c. purple	40	25

87 Zoglig Instructional Glider

1946. Air. Special (Lausanne, Lucerne, Locarno) Flights.

466	87	1f.50 red and grey	39·00	42·00

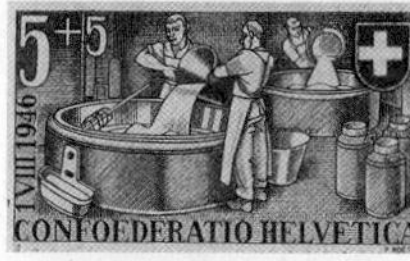

88 Cheese-making

89 Chalet in Appenzell

1946. National Fete and Fund for Swiss Citizens Abroad.

467	88	5c.+5c. green and red	1·30	4·50
468	-	10c.+10c. brown, buff and red	80	1·10
469	89	20c.+10c. red and buff	1·40	1·10
470	-	30c.+10c. blue, grey and red	12·00	19·00

DESIGNS: 10c. Chalet in Vaud; 30c. Chalet in Engadine.

90 Douglas DC-4 Airliner, Statue of Liberty and St. Peter's Cathedral, Geneva

1947. Air. 1st Geneva–New York "Swissair" Flight.

472	90	2f.50 deep blue, blue & red	27·00	30·00

92 Rorschach Station

1947. National Fete. Professional Education of Invalids and Anti-cancer Funds. Inscr "I VIII 1947". Arms in red.

473	-	5c.+5c. green	80	3·75
474	92	10c.+10c. black and buff	1·60	1·10
475	-	20c.+10c. red and buff	1·60	1·50
476	-	30c.+10c. blue and grey	12·00	18·00

DESIGNS: 5c. Platelayers; 20c. Luen-Castiel station; 30c. Fluelen station.

93 "Limmat" (first locomotive in Switzerland)

1947. Centenary of Swiss Federal Railways.

477	93	5c. green, yellow and black	1·60	75
478	-	10c. black and brown	1·60	75
479	-	20c. red, buff and lake	80	75
480	-	30c. blue, grey & light blue	4·00	3·75

DESIGNS: 10c. Class C5/62-10-0 steam locomotive, 1913; 20c. Type Ae8/14 electric locomotive crossing Melide Causeway; 30c. Lorraine Bridge, Berne.

95 Sun of St. Moritz **96** Ice Hockey

1948. 5th Winter Olympic Games.

481	95	5c.+5c. brown, yell & grn	80	2·30
482	-	10c.+10c. blue, light blue and brown	80	1·50
483	96	20c.+10c. yellow, black and purple	1·60	3·00
484	-	30c.+10c. black, light blue and blue	5·50	9·00

DESIGN: 10c. Snow crystals; 30c. Ski-runner.

97 Johann Rudolf Wettstein

1948. Tercentenary of Treaty of Westphalia and Centenaries of the Neuchatel Revolution and Swiss Federation.

485	97	5c. green and deep green	40	75
486	-	10c. black and grey	40	25
487	-	20c. red and pink	80	25
488	-	30c. blue, grey and brown	1·60	2·30

DESIGNS: 10c. Neuchatel Castle; 20c. Symbol of Helvetia; 30c. Symbol of Federal State.

99 Frontier Guard

1948. National Fete and Anti-Tuberculosis Fund. Coat of arms in red.

495	99	5c.+5c. green	1·20	1·90
496	-	10c.+10c. slate and grey	85	1·10
497	-	20c.+10c. red and buff	1·10	1·50

498	-	30c.+10c. blue and grey	6·25	11·50

DESIGNS: 10c., 20c., 30c. Typical houses in Fribourg, Valais and Ticino respectively.

1948. National Philatelic Exhibition, Basel ("IMABA"). Sheet 110×61 mm. T 97.

MS498a 10c. purple and gery; 20c. blue and grey (sold at 3f.)	£120	90·00

101 Glider

1949. Air. Special (La Chaux-de-Fonds–St. Gallen–Lugano) Flights.

499	**101**	1f.50 purple and yellow	60·00	55·00

102 Posthorn

1949. Centenary of Federal Post.

500	**102**	5c. yellow, pink and grey	40	75
501	-	20c. yellow, violet and grey	40	40
502	-	30c. yellow, brown & grey	1·60	13·00

DESIGNS: 20c. Mail coach drawn by five horses; 30c. Postal motor coach and trailer.

103 Main Motif of U.P.U. Monument, Berne

1949. 75th Anniv of U.P.U.

503	**103**	10c. green	40	75
504	-	25c. purple	80	9·00
505	-	40c. blue	1·60	10·50

DESIGNS: 25c. Globe and ribbon; 40c. Globe and pigeons.

104 Postman

1949. National Fete and Youth Fund. T 104 and designs as T 89, but dated "I. VIII. 1949". Arms in red.

506	**104**	5c.+5c. purple	1·20	2·30
507	-	10c.+10c. green & buff	85	1·10
508	-	20c.+10c. brown & buff	1·10	1·20
509	-	40c.+10c. blue & lt blue	8·75	21·00

DESIGNS—Typical houses in: 10c. Basel; 20c. Lucerne; 40c. Prattigau.

106 High-tension Pylons

107 Railway Viaducts over River Sitter, near St. Gall

1949. Landscapes.

510	**106**	3c. black	4·00	3·75
511	**107**	5c. orange	55	10
512	-	10c. green	40	10
513	-	15c. turquoise	80	75
514a	-	20c. purple	80	10
515	-	25c. red	65	10
516	-	30c. green	80	10
517	-	35c. brown	1·60	1·50
518	-	40c. blue	4·00	10
519	-	50c. grey	4·00	10
520	-	60c. green	12·50	1·10
521	-	70c. violet	3·25	75

DESIGNS: 10c. Rack railway, Rochers de Naye; 15c. Rotary snowplough; 20c. Grimsel Reservoir; 25c. Lake Lugano and Melide railway causeway; 30c. Verbois hydro-electric power station; 35c. Alpine road (Val d'Anniviers); 40c. Rhine harbour, Basel; 50c. Suspension railway, Santis; 60c. Railway viaduct, Landwasser; 70c. Survey mark, Finsteraarhorn.

110 First Federal Postage Stamps

111 Putting the Weight

1950. National Fete, Red Cross Fund and Centenary of First Federal Postage Stamps. T 110 and designs, as T 111, inscr "I. VIII. 1950". Coat of arms in red.

522	**110**	5c.+5c. black	80	1·10
523	**111**	10c.+10c. green & grey	2·00	1·10
524	-	20c.+10c. green & grey	2·75	1·90
525	-	30c.+10c. mauve & grey	7·75	34·00
526	-	40c.+10c. blue and grey	12·00	21·00

DESIGNS: 20c. Wrestling; 30c. Sprinting; 40c. Rifle-shooting.

112 Arms of Zurich

113 Valaisan Polka

1951. National Fete, Mothers' Fund and 600th Anniv of Zurich. Coat of arms in red.

527	**112**	5c.+5c. black	80	1·10
528	**113**	10c.+10c. green & grey	80	75
529	-	20c.+10c. green & grey	1·60	1·90
530	-	30c.+10c. mauve & grey	8·75	21·00
531	-	40c.+10c. blue and grey	12·50	26·00

DESIGNS—As Type **113**: 20c. Flag-swinging; 30c. "Hornussen" (game); 40c. Blowing alphorn.

1951. National Philatelic Exhibition, Lucerne ("LUNABA"). Sheet 74×54 mm. As No. 529. Imperf.

MS531a 40c. multicoloured (sold at 3f.)	£275	£250

114 "Telegraph"

1952. Centenary of Swiss Telecommunications.

532	**114**	5c. orange and yellow	40	1·50
533	-	10c. green and pink	40	10
534	-	20c. mauve and lilac	1·60	10
535	-	40c. blue and light blue	4·00	9·75

DESIGNS: 10c. "Telephone"; 20c. "Radio"; 40c. "Television".

115 Arms of Glarus and Zug

116 River Doubs

1952. Pro Patria. Cultural Funds and 600th Anniv of Glarus and Zug joining Confederation.

536	**115**	5c.+5c. red and black	95	1·10
537	**116**	10c.+10c. green and cream	85	75
538	-	20c.+10c. purple & pink	85	1·10
539	-	30c.+10c. brown & buff	5·50	15·00
540	-	40c.+10c. blue & lt blue	7·75	13·50

DESIGNS—As T **116**: 20c. St. Gotthard Lake; 30c. River Moesa; 40c. Marjelen Lake.

1953. Pro Patria. Emigrants' Fund and 600th Anniv of Berne joining Confederation.

541	5c.+5c. red and black	1·20	1·10
542	10c.+10c. green and cream	80	75
543	20c.+10c. purple and pink	1·20	1·10
544	30c.+10c. brown and buff	7·75	15·00
545	40c.+10c. blue & light blue	9·50	13·50

DESIGNS—As T **115**: 5c. Arms of Berne (inscr "BERN 1353"). As T **116** (inscr "PRO PATRIA 1953"): 10c. Rapids, R. Reuss; 20c. Lake Sihl; 30c. Aqueduct, Bisse; 40c. Lac Leman.

119 Zurich Airport

1953. Inauguration of Zurich Airport.

546	**119**	40c. blue, grey and red	7·00	15·00

120 Alpine Postal Coach and Winter Landscape

1953. For Mobile P.O. Mail.

547	**120**	10c. yellow, green and emerald	80	40
548	-	20c. yellow, red and scarlet	80	40

DESIGN: 10c. Alpine postal coach and summer landscape.

121 Ear of Wheat and Flower

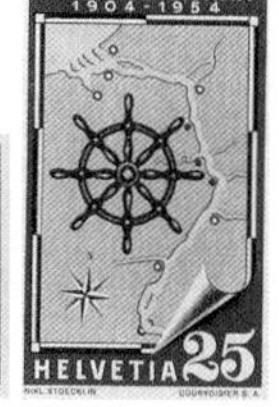

122 Rhine Map and Steering Wheel

1954. Publicity Issue.

549	**121**	10c. multicoloured	40	15
550	-	20c. multicoloured	2·40	15
551	**122**	25c. green, blue and red	1·60	3·75
552	-	40c. blue, yellow and black	5·00	5·25

DESIGNS—HORIZ: 10c. Type **121** (Agricultural Exhibition, Lucerne); 20c. Winged spoon (Cooking Exhibition, Berne); 40c. Football and world map (World Football Championship). VERT: 25c. Type **122** (50th anniv of navigation of River Rhine).

123 Opening Bars of "Swiss Hymn"

1954. Pro Patria. Youth Fund and Death Centenary of Father Zwyssig (composer of "Swiss Hymn").

553	**123**	5c.+5c. green	80	1·50
554	-	10c.+10c. green & turq	80	75
555	-	20c.+10c. purple and cream	1·60	75
556	-	30c.+10c. brown & buff	6·25	13·00
557	-	40c.+10c. deep blue and blue	7·00	15·00

DESIGNS: 10c. Lake Neuchatel; 20c. Maggia River; 30c. Taubenloch Gorge Waterfall; Schuss River; 40c. Lake Sils.

124 Lausanne Cathedral

125 Alphorn Blower

1955. Publicity Issue. Inscr "1955".

558	**124**	5c. multicoloured	80	1·10
559	-	10c. multicoloured	80	75
560	**125**	20c. brown and red	2·00	75
561	-	40c. pink, black and blue	5·00	4·50

DESIGNS—HORIZ: 5c. Type **124** (National Philatelic Exhibition, Lausanne); 10c. Vaud girl's hat (Vevey Winegrowers' Festival); 40c. Car steering-wheel (25th International Motor Show, Geneva). VERT: 20c. Type **125** (Alpine Herdsman and Costume Festival, Interlaken).

1955. National Philatelic Exhibition, Lausanne. Sheet 103×52 mm. T 124. Imperf.

MS561a 10c. and 20c. multicoloured (sold at 2f.)	£130	£120

126 Federal Institute of Technology, Zurich

1955. Pro Patria. Mountain Population Fund and Centenary of Federal Institute of Technology.

562	**126**	5c.+5c. grey	80	1·10
563	-	10c.+10c. green and cream	80	75
564	-	20c.+10c. red and pink	1·60	1·10
565	-	30c.+10c. brown & buff	5·50	9·00
566	-	40c.+10c. blue and light blue	5·50	12·00

DESIGNS: 10c. Grandfey railway viaduct over River Saane, near Fribourg; 20c. Lake Aegeri; 30c. Lake Grappelensee; 40c. Lake Bienne.

127 "Road Safety"

128 Fokker F.VIIb/3m and Douglas DC-6 Aircraft

1956. Publicity Issue. Inscr "1956".

567		5c. yellow, black and green	50	25
568		10c. black, green and red	80	40
569	**127**	20c. multicoloured	2·40	75
570	**128**	40c. blue and red	3·50	3·00

DESIGNS—HORIZ: 5c. First postal motor coach (50th anniv of postal motor coach service); 10c. Electric train emerging from Simplon Tunnel and Stockalper Palace (50th anniv of opening of Simplon Tunnel).

The 40c. commemorates the 25th anniv of Swissair.

129 Rose, Scissors and Tape-measure

1956. Pro Patria. Swiss Women's Fund. T 129 and design as T 116 but inscr "PRO PATRIA 1956".

571	**129**	5c.+5c. green	80	1·90
572	-	10c.+10c. emerald and green	80	75
573	-	20c.+10c. purple & pink	1·60	1·10
574	-	30c.+10c. brown and light brown	4·00	9·00
575	-	40c.+10c. blue and light blue	4·75	12·00

DESIGNS: 10c. R. Rhone at St. Maurice; 20c. Katzensee; 30c. R. Rhine at Trin; 40c. Walensee.

130 Printing Machine's Inking Rollers

1957. Publicity Issue. Inscr "1957".

576	**130**	5c. multicoloured	40	10
577	-	10c. brown, green & turq	4·00	10
578	-	20c. grey and red	40	75
579	-	40c. multicoloured	2·40	1·50

DESIGNS: 10c. Electric train crossing bridge over River Ticino (75th anniv of St. Gotthard Railway); 20c. Civil Defence shield and coat of arms ("Civil Defence"); 40c. Munatius Plancus, Basel and Rhine (2000th anniv of Basel).

The 5c. commemorates "Graphic 57" International Exhibition, Lausanne.

131 Shields of Switzerland and the Red Cross

132 "Charity"

1957. Pro Patria. Swiss Red Cross and National Cancer League Funds. Cross in red.

580	**131**	5c.+5c. red and grey	40	1·10

581 **132** 10c.+10c. purple & grn 80 55
582 **132** 20c.+10c. grey and red 80 60
583 **132** 30c.+10c. blue & brown 4·25 6·75
584 **132** 40c.+10c. brown & blue 5·50 9·00

133 Symbol of Unity

1957. Europa.
585 **133** 25c. red 1·20 1·10
586 **133** 40c. blue 4·25 1·10

134 Nyon Castle (2000th anniv of Nyon)

1958. Publicity Issue. Inscr "1958".
587 **134** 5c. violet, buff and green 40 15
588 - 10c. myrtle, red and green 40 10
589 - 20c. red, lilac and vermilion 80 10
590 - 40c. multicoloured 1·60 1·90
DESIGNS: 10c. Woman's head with ribbons (Saffa Exhibition, Zurich); 20c. Crossbow (25th anniv as symbol of Swiss manufacture); 40c. Salvation Army bonnet (75th anniv of Salvation Army in Switzerland).

135 "Needy Mother" **136** Fluorite

1958. Pro Patria. For Needy Mothers, T 135 and designs showing minerals, rocks and fossils as T 136. Inscr "PRO PATRIA 1958".
591 5c.+5c. purple 45 40
592 10c.+10c. yellow, grn & blk 95 40
593 20c.+10c. bistre, red & blk 95 1·10
594 30c.+10c. purple, brn & blk 3·50 6·75
595 40c.+10c. blue, ultram & blk 3·50 7·50
DESIGNS: 20c. "Lytoceras fimbriatus" ammonite; 30c. Garnet; 40c. Rock crystal.

137 Atomic Symbol

1958. 2nd U.N. Atomic Conference, Geneva.
596 **137** 40c. red, blue and cream 80 75

138 Modern Transport

1959. Publicity Issue. Inscr "1959".
597 5c. multicoloured 40 15
598 10c. yellow, grey and green 40 10
599 20c. multicoloured 80 10
600 50c. blue, violet and light blue 1·60 1·10
DESIGNS: 5c. Type **138** (opening of "The Swiss House of Transport and Communications"); 10c. Lictor's fasces of the Coat of Arms of St. Gall and posthorn (NABAG—National Philatelic Exhibition, St. Gall); 20c. Owl, hare and fish (Protection of Animals); 50c. J. Calvin, Th. de Beze and University building (4th centenary of University of Geneva).

1959. National Philatelic Exhibtion, St. Gallen ("NABAG"). Sheet 94×57 mm. As No. 598. Imperf.
MS600a 10c. and 20c. multicoloured (sold at 2f.) 21·00 19·00

139 "Swiss Citizens Abroad"

1959. Pro Patria. For Swiss Citizens Abroad. T 139 and other designs showing minerals, rocks and fossils as T 136, and inscr "PRO PATRIA 1959".
601 5c.+5c. red and grey 55 75
602 10c.+10c. multicoloured 65 75
603 20c.+10c. multicoloured 80 75
604 30c.+10c. violet, brn & blk 2·40 4·50
605 40c.+10c. blue, turquoise and black 2·75 4·50
DESIGNS: 10c. Agate; 20c. Tourmaline; 30c. Amethyst; 40c. Fossilized giant salamander.

140 "Europa"

1959. Europa.
606 **140** 30c. red 1·60 75
607 **140** 50c. blue 2·40 1·50

1959. European P.T.T. Conference, Montreux. Optd REUNION DES PTT D'EUROPE 1959.
608 30c. red 20·00 12·00
609 50c. blue 20·00 12·00

142 "Campaign against Cancer"

1960. Publicity Issue. Inscr "1460–1960" (20c.) or "1960" (50c., 75c.).
610 10c. red, light green and green 80 15
611 20c. multicoloured 80 15
612 50c. yellow, ultramarine & blue 80 1·50
613 75c. red, black and blue 5·50 5·25
DESIGNS: 10c. Type **142** (50th anniv of Swiss National League for Cancer Control); 20c. Charter and sceptre (500th anniv of Basel University); 50c. "Uprooted tree" (World Refugee Year); 75c. Douglas DC-8 jetliner ("Swissair enters the jet age").

143 15th-century Schwyz Cantonal Messenger **143a** Lausanne Cathedral

1960. Postal History and "Architectural Monuments" (1st series).
614 - 5c. blue 10 10
615 **143** 10c. green 15 10
616 - 15c. red 15 10
617 - 20c. mauve 40 10
618 **143a** 25c. green 85 10
619p - 30c. red 45 10
620 - 35c. red 1·30 1·20
621 - 40c. purple 1·00 10
622 - 50c. blue 1·30 10
623 - 60c. red 1·60 40
624 - 70c. orange 1·70 1·70
625 - 75c. blue 2·40 1·50
626 - 80c. purple 2·20 10
627 - 90c. green 1·70 10
628 - 1f. orange 1·70 10
629 - 1f.20 red 2·20 20
632 - 1f.30 brown on lilac 2·00 15
630 - 1f.50 green 2·50 75
633 - 1f.70 purple on lilac 2·75 15
631 - 2f. blue 4·00 1·50
634 - 2f.20 green on green 3·50 1·50
635 - 2f.80 orange on orange 4·50 1·50
DESIGNS—HORIZ: 5c. 17th-century Fribourg Cantonal messenger; 15c. 17th-century mule-driver; 20c. 19th-century mounted postman; 1f. Fribourg Town Hall; 1f.20, Basel Gate, Solothurn; 1f.50, Ital Reding's house, Schwyz; 1f.70, 2f., 2f.20, Abbey Church, Einsiedeln. VERT: 30c. Grossmunster, Zurich; 35c., 1f.30, Woodcutters Guildhall, Bienne; 40c. St. Peter's Cathedral, Geneva; 50c. Spalentor (gate), Basel; 60c. Clock Tower, Berne; 70c. Collegiate Church of St. Peter and St. Stephen, Bellinzona; 75c. Kapellbrucke (bridge) and Wasserturm, Lucerne; 80c. St. Gall Cathedral; 90c. Munot Fort, Schaffhausen; 2f.80, as 70c. but redrawn without bell-tower.
See also Nos. 698/713 and 1276.

144 Symbols of Occupational Trades

1960. Pro Patria. For Swiss Youth. T 144 and other designs showing minerals, rocks and fossils as T 136 and inscr "PRO PATRIA 1960".
636 5c.+5c. multicoloured 65 1·10
637 10c.+10c. pink, green and black 80 75
638 20c.+10c. yellow, purple and black 95 75
639 30c.+10c. blue, brown and black 4·00 6·50
640 **144** 50c.+10c. gold & blue 4·00 6·00
DESIGNS: 5c. Smoky quartz; 10c. Orthoclase (feldspar); 20c. Devil's toenail (fossil shell); 30c. Azurite; 50c. Type **144** ("50 Years of National Day Collection").

1960. 50th Anniv of Pro Patria Charity Fund. Sheet 85×75 mm. As No. 640. Imperf.
MS641 50c.+10c. gold and blue (block of 4) (sold at 3f.) 55·00 30·00

144a Conference Emblem

1960. Europa.
642 **144a** 30c. red 80 40
643 **144a** 50c. blue 1·20 1·10

145 "Aid for Development"

1961. Publicity Issue.
644 **145** 5c. red, blue and grey 40 25
645 - 10c. yellow and blue 40 15
646 - 20c. multicoloured 95 75
647 - 50c. red, green and blue 1·70 1·50
DESIGNS: 5c. Type **145** ("Aid to countries in process of development"); 10c. Circular emblem ("Hyspa" Exhibition of 20th-century Hygiene, Gymnastics and Sport, Berne); 20c. Hockey stick (World and European Ice Hockey Championships, Geneva and Lausanne); 50c. Map of Switzerland with telephone centres as wiring diagram (inauguration of Swiss fully automatic telephone service).

146 "Cultural Works of Eternity"

1961. Pro Patria. For Swiss Cultural Works, T 146 and other designs showing minerals, rocks and fossils as T 136 and inscr "PRO PATRIA 1961".
648 5c.+5c. blue 60 75
649 10c.+10c. purple, green and black 60 55
650 20c.+10c. red, blue and black 80 60
651 30c.+10c. blue, orange and black 2·00 3·75
652 50c.+10c. bistre, blue and black 2·40 5·25
DESIGNS: 10c. Fluorite; 20c. Glarone rabbitfish; 30c. Lazulite; 50c. Fossilized fern.

147 Doves

1961. Europa.
653 **147** 30c. red 80 40
654 **147** 50c. blue 1·20 1·10

148 St. Matthew

1961. Wood Carvings from St. Oswald's Church, Zug.
655 **148** 3f. red 4·75 35
656 - 5f. blue 7·75 35
657 - 10f. brown 16·00 65
658 - 20f. red 31·00 5·00
DESIGNS: 5f. St. Mark; 10f. St. Luke; 20f. St. John.

149 W.H.O. Emblem and Mosquito

1962. Publicity Issue.
659 5c. multicoloured 80 30
660 10c. bistre, purple and green 80 10
661 20c. multicoloured 3·25 75
662 **149** 50c. green, mauve and blue 1·60 1·50
DESIGNS: 5c. Electric train (introduction of Trans-Europe Express); 10c. Oarsman (World Rowing Championship, Lucerne); 20c. Jungfraujoch and Monch (50th anniv of Jungfraujoch rack railway station); 50c. Type **149** (malaria eradication).

150 Rousseau **151** Schwyz Gold Ducat

1962. Pro Patria. For Swiss Old People's Homes and Cultural Works.
663 **150** 5c.+5c. blue 40 40
664 - 10c.+10c. blue, black and green 55 40
665 **151** 20c.+10c. yellow, black and red 65 75
666 - 30c.+10c. green, blue and red 1·20 2·30
667 - 50c.+10c. violet, black and blue 1·20 2·30
COINS—As Type **151**: 10c. Obwalden silver-half taler; 30c. Uri batzen; 50c. Nidwalden batzen.

152 Europa "Tree"

1962. Europa.
668 **152** 30c. orange, yellow & brn 1·00 95
669 **152** 50c. blue, green and brown 1·60 1·10

153 Campaign Emblem (Freedom from Hunger)

1963. Publicity Issue.
670 - 5c. brown, red and blue 40 20
671 - 10c. red, grey and green 80 10
672 - 20c. lake, red and grey 2·75 15
673 **153** 30c. yellow, brown & green 1·20 1·10
674 - 50c. red, silver and blue 1·70 1·70
675 - 50c. multicoloured 2·20 2·10
DESIGNS: No. 670, Boy scout (50th anniv of Swiss Boy Scout League); 671, Badge (Swiss Alpine Club cent); 672, Luegelkinn Viaduct (50th anniv of Lotschberg Railway); 674, Jubilee Emblem (Red Cross cent); 675, Hotel des Postes, Paris, 1863 (Paris Postal Conference).

1963. International Red Cross Centenary. Sheet 100×80 mm. As No. 674. Imperf.
MS675a 50c. multicoloured (block of 4) (sold at 3f.) 7·75 7·50

154 Dr. Anna Heer (nursing pioneer) **155** Roll of Bandage

1963. Pro Patria. For Swiss Medical and Refugee Aid. T 154 and other designs as T 155 showing Red Cross activities. Inscr "PRO PATRIA 1963".
676 5c.+5c. blue 40 40
677 10c.+10c. red, grey and green 55 40
678 20c.+10c. multicoloured 65 40
679 30c.+10c. multicoloured 1·20 2·30
680 50c.+10c. red, indigo & blue 1·60 2·30

DESIGNS: 20c. Gift parcel; 30c. Blood plasma; 50c. Red Cross brassard.

156 Glider and Jet Aircraft

1963. Air. 25th Anniv of Swiss "Pro Aero" Foundation. Berne–Locarno or Langenbruck–Berne (helicopter feeder) Special Flights.

681	**156**	2f. multicoloured	4·75	4·50

157 "Co-operation"

1963. Europa.

682	**157**	50c. brown and blue	80	75

158 Exhibition Emblem

1963. Swiss National Exhibition, Lausanne.

683	**158**	10c. green and olive	40	10
684	**158**	20c. red and brown	40	10
685	-	50c. blue, grey and red	80	30
686	-	75c. violet, grey and red	1·20	1·50

DESIGNS: 50c. "Outlook" (emblem on globe and smaller globe); 75c. "Insight" (emblem on large globe).

159 Great St. Bernard Tunnel

1964. Publicity Issue.

687	5c. blue, red and green	45	15
688	10c. green and blue	40	15
689	20c. multicoloured	60	15
690	50c. multicoloured	1·80	1·50

DESIGNS: 5c. Type **159** (Opening of Great St. Bernard Road Tunnel); 10c. Ancient "god of the waters" (Protection of water supplies); 20c. Swiss soldiers of 1864 and 1964 (Centenary of Swiss Association of Non-commissioned Officers); 50c. Standards of Geneva and Swiss Confederation (150th anniv of arrival of Swiss in Geneva).

160 Johann Georg Bodmer (inventor)

1964. Pro Patria. For Swiss Mountain Aid and Cultural Funds. T 160 and vert designs of Swiss coins as T 151. Inscr "PRO PATRIA 1964".

691	5c.+5c. blue	40	25
692	10c.+10c. drab, black & grn	40	25
693	20c.+10c. blue, black & mve	55	40
694	30c.+10c. blue, black & orge	80	75
695	50c.+10c. yellow, brn & bl	1·20	1·10

COINS: 10c. Zurich copper; 20c. Basel "doppeldicken"; 30c. Geneva silver thaler; 50c. Berne half gold florin.

161 Europa "Flower"

1964. Europa.

696	**161**	20c. red	80	40
697	**161**	50c. blue	1·60	75

1964. "Architectural monuments" (2nd series). As T 143a.

698	5c. mauve	10	10
699	10c. blue	10	10
700	15c. brown	20	10
701	20c. green	25	10
702	30c. red	45	10
703	50c. blue	80	10
704	70c. brown	1·10	10
705	1f. green	1·60	10
706	1f.20 red	1·90	10
707	1f.30 blue	2·00	1·70
708	1f.50 green	2·40	20
709	1f.70 red	2·75	1·90
710	2f. orange	3·25	20
711	2f.20 green	3·50	1·70
712	2f.50 green	4·00	20
713	3f.50 purple	5·50	30

DESIGNS—HORIZ: 5c. Lenzburg Castle; 10c. Freuler Mansion, Nafels; 15c. Mauritius Church, Appenzell; 20c. Planta House, Samedan; 30c. Town Square, Gais; 50c. Neuchatel Castle and Collegiate Church. VERT: 70c. Lussy "Hochhus", Wolfenschiessen; 1f. Riva San Vitale Church; 1f.20, Payerne Abbey Church; 1f.30, St. Pierre-de Clages Church; 1f.50, Gateway, Porrentruy; 1f.70, Frauenfeld Castle; 2f. Castle Seedorf (Uri); 2f.20, Thomas Tower and Arch, Liestal; 2f.50, St. Oswald's Church, Zug; 3f.50, Benedictine Abbey, Engelberg.

162 Swiss 5r. Stamp of 1854 with "Lozenge" Cancellation

1965. Publicity Issue.

714	-	5c. black, red and blue	10	10
715	**162**	10c. brown, blue and green	10	10
716	-	20c. multicoloured	1·60	10
717	-	50c. red, black and blue	3·25	75

DESIGNS, etc: 5c. Nurse and patient ("Nursing"); 10c. Type **162** ("NABRA 1965" National Stamp Exhibition, Berne); 20c. WAC Officer (25th anniv of Women's Army Corps); 50c. World telecommunications map (centenary of I.T.U.).

1965. National Philatelic Exhibition, Berrie ("NABRA") Sheet 94×61 mm. As T 162. Imperf.

MS718	10c. orange and green (20r.); 20c. blue and red (40r.) (sold at 3f.)	1·60	1·50

163 Father T. Florentini

164 Fish-tailed Goose ("Evil")

1965. Pro Patria. For Swiss Abroad and Art Research. Inscr "PRO PATRIA 1965".

719	**163**	5c.+5c. blue	25	15
720	**164**	10c.+10c. multicoloured	25	15
721	-	20c.+10c. multicoloured	45	15
722	-	30c.+10c. brown & blue	80	75
723	-	50c.+10c. blue & brown	95	75

DESIGNS—As Type **164**: (Ceiling paintings in St. Martin's Church, Zillis (Grisons): 20c. One of the magi journeying to Herod; 30c. Fishermen; 50c. The Temptation of Christ.

165 Swiss Emblem and Arms of Cantons

1965. 150th Anniv of Entry of Valais, Neuchatel and Geneva into Confederation.

724	**165**	20c. multicoloured	40	25

166 Matterhorn

1965. Mobile P.O. Issue.

725	**166**	10c. multicoloured	80	15
726	**166**	30c. multicoloured	1·60	1·10

The 30c. is inscr "CERVIN".

167 Europa "Sprig"

1965. Europa.

727	**167**	50c. green and blue	80	40

168 I.T.U. Emblem and Satellites

1965. I.T.U. Centenary Congress, Montreux. Multicoloured.

728	10c. Type **168**	25	10
729	30c. Symbols of world telecommunications	45	25

169 Figure Skating

1965. World Figure Skating Championships, Davos.

730	**169**	5c. multicoloured	25	15

170 River Kingfisher

1966. Publicity Issue. Multicoloured.

731	10c. Type **170**	25	10
732	20c. Mercury's helmet and laurel twig	30	10
733	50c. Phase in nuclear fission and flags	80	20

PUBLICITY EVENTS: 10c. Preservation of natural beauty; 20c. 50th Swiss Industrial Fair, Basel (MUBA); 50c. International Institute for Nuclear Research (CERN).

171 H. Federer (author)

1966. Pro Patria. For Aid to Mothers. Inscr "PRO PATRIA 1966".

734	**171**	5c.+5c. blue	40	10
735	-	10c.+10c. multicoloured	40	10
736	-	20c.+10c. multicoloured	45	15
737	-	30c.+10c. multicoloured	80	75
738	-	50c.+10c. multicoloured	95	75

DESIGNS—As Type **164**: ("The Flight to Egypt" from ceiling paintings in St. Martin's Church, Zillis (Grisons)): 10c. Joseph's dream; 20c. Joseph on his way; 30c. Virgin and Child; 50c. Angel pointing the way.

172 Society Emblem

1966. 50th Anniv of New Helvetic Society for Swiss Abroad.

739	**172**	20c. red and blue	40	20

173 Europa "Ship"

1966. Europa.

740	**173**	20c. red	40	40
741	**173**	50c. blue	80	40

174 Finsteraarhorn

1966. "Swiss Alps".

742	**174**	10c. multicoloured	20	10

175 White Stick and Motor-car Wheel (Welfare of the Blind)

1967. Publicity Issue.

743	**175**	10c. multicoloured	20	10
744	-	20c. multicoloured	30	10

DESIGN: 20c. Flags of European Free Trade Area countries (abolition of E.F.T.A. tariffs).

176 C.E.P.T. Emblem and Cogwheels

1967. Europa.

745	**176**	30c. blue	85	40

177 Theodor Kocher (surgeon)

1967. Pro Patria. For National Day Collection. Inscr "PRO PATRIA 1967".

746	**177**	5c.+5c. blue	25	10
747	-	10c.+10c. multicoloured	30	10
748	-	20c.+10c. multicoloured	45	10
749	-	30c.+10c. multicoloured	80	75
750	-	50c.+10c. multicoloured	95	75

DESIGNS—As Type **164**: (Ceiling paintings in St. Martin's Church, Zillis (Grisons)): 10c. Annunciation to the Shepherds; 20c. Christ and the woman of Samaria; 30c. Adoration of the Magi; 50c. Joseph seated on throne.

178 Cogwheel and Swiss Emblem

1967. Publicity Issue. Multicoloured.

751	10c. Type **178**	15	10
752	20c. Hour-glass and Sun	30	15
753	30c. San Bernadino highway	40	25
754	50c. "OCTI" emblem	80	60

PUBLICITY EVENTS: 10c. 50th anniv of Swiss Week; 20c. 50th anniv of Aged People Foundation; 30c. Opening of San Bernardino road tunnel; 50c. 75th anniv of Central Office for International Railway Transport (OCTI).

179 "Mountains" and Swiss Emblem

1968. Publicity Issue.

755	10c. multicoloured	10	10
756	20c. yellow, brown and blue	65	40
757	30c. blue, ochre and brown	30	10
758	50c. red, turquoise and blue	40	30

DESIGNS AND EVENTS: 10c. T **179** (50th anniv of Swiss Women's Alpine Club); 20c. Europa "key" (Europa); 30c. Staunton rook and chessboard (18th Chess Olympiad, Lugano); 50c. Dispatch "satellites" and aircraft tail-fin (inauguration of new Geneva Air Terminal).

180 "Maius"

1968. Pro Patria. For National Day Collection. Inscr "PRO PATRIA 1968".

759	**180**	10c.+10c. multicoloured	40	10
760	-	20c.+10c. multicoloured	45	15
761	-	30c.+10c. multicoloured	80	25

762	-	50c.+20c. multicoloured	1·10	75

DESIGNS (Stained-glass panels in the rose window, Lausanne Cathedral): 20c. "Leo"; 30c. "Libra"; 50c. "Pisces" (symbols of the months and signs of the zodiac).

181 Protective helmet

1968. Publicity Issue. Multicoloured.

763	10c. Type **181**	25	10
764	20c. Geneva and Zurich stamps of 1843	40	10
765	30c. Part of Swiss map	40	10
766	50c. "Six Stars" (countries) and anchor	80	40

PUBLICITY EVENTS: 10c. 50th anniv of Swiss Accident Insurance Company; 20c. 125th anniv of Swiss stamps; 30c. 25th anniv of Swiss Territorial Planning Society; 50c. Centenary of Rhine Navigation Act.

182 Guide Camp and Emblem

1969. Publicity Issue. Multicoloured.

767	10c. Type **182**	40	10
768	20c. Pegasus constellation	80	10
769	30c. Emblem of Comptoir Suisse	45	15
770	50c. Emblem of Gymnaestrade	80	60
771	2f. Haefeli DH-3 biplane and Douglas DC-8 jetliner	3·25	2·30

EVENTS: 10c. 50th anniv of Swiss Girl Guides' Federation; 20c. Opening of first Swiss Planeta-rium, Lucerne; 30c. 50th anniv of Comptoir Suisse, Lausanne; 50c. 5th Gymnaestrada, Basel; 2f. 50th anniv of Swiss Airmail Services.

183 Colonnade

1969. Europa.

772	**183**	30c. multicoloured	45	40
773	**183**	50c. multicoloured	80	75

184 "St. Francis of Assisi preaching to the Birds" (Abbey-church, Konigsfelden)

1969. Pro Patria. For National Day Collection. Stained-glass Windows. Multicoloured.

774	10c.+10c. Type **184**	40	10
775	20c.+10c. "The People of Israel drinking" (Berne Cathedral)	45	15
776	30c.+10c. "St. Christopher" (Laufelfingen Church, Basle)	80	40
777	50c.+20c. "Madonna and Child" (St. Jacob's Chapel, Grapplang, Flums)	1·10	75

185 Kreuzberge

1969. Publicity and "Swiss Alps" Issues. Multicoloured.

778	20c. Type **185**	65	10
779	30c. Children crossing road	45	10
780	50c. Hammersmith	80	25

EVENTS: 30c. Road Safety campaign for children; 50c. 50th anniv of I.L.O.

186 Huldrych Zwingli (Protestant reformer)

1969. Swiss Celebrities.

781	**186**	10c. violet	15	10
782	-	20c. green	30	10
783	-	30c. red	40	10
784	-	50c. blue	80	60
785	-	80c. brown	1·20	90

CELEBRITIES: 20c. General Henri Guisan; 30c. Francesco Borromini (architect); 50c. Othmar Schoeck (composer); 80c. Germaine de Stael (writer).

187 Telex Tape

1970. Publicity Issue. Multicoloured.

786	20c. Type **187**	40	10
787	30c. Fireman saving child	65	10
788	30c. "Chained wing" emblem	45	10
789	50c. U.N. emblem	80	75
790	80c. New U.P.U. Headquarters	1·30	1·10

EVENTS: 20c. 75th anniv of Swiss Telegraphic Agency; 30c. (No. 787), Centenary of Swiss Firemen's Assn; 30c. (No. 788), 50th anniv of "Pro Infirmis" Foundation; 50c. 25th anniv of U.N. Organization; 80c. Inauguration of new U.P.U. headquarters, Berne.

188 "Flaming Sun"

1970. Europa.

791	**188**	30c. red	55	40
792	**188**	50c. blue	80	40

1970. Pro Patria. For National Day Collection. Glass paintings by contemporary artists. As T 184 but inscr "1970". Multicoloured.

793	10c.+10c. "Sailor" (G. Casty)	40	40
794	20c.+10c. Architectonic composition (Celestino Piatti)	45	40
795	30c.+10c. "Bull" symbol of Marduk, from "The Four Elements" (Hans Stocker)	80	40
796	50c.+20c. "Man and Woman" (Max Hunziker and Karl Ganz)	1·10	75

189 Footballer (75th Anniv of Swiss Football Association)

1970. Publicity and "Swiss Alps" (30c.) Issue. Multicoloured.

797	10c. Type **189**	80	10
798	20c. Census form and pencil (Federal Census)	40	25
799	30c. Piz Palu, Grisons	80	40
800	50c. Conservation Year Emblem (Nature Conservation Year)	80	75

190 Numeral

1970. Coil Stamps.

801	**190**	10c. red	10	10
802	**190**	20c. green	25	10
803	**190**	50c. blue	80	10

191 Female Gymnasts ("Youth and Sport")

1971. Publicity Issue.

804	**191**	10c. multicoloured	65	40
805	-	10c. multicoloured	65	40
806	-	20c. multicoloured	40	40
807	-	30c. multicoloured	45	40
808	-	50c. brown and blue	80	75
809	-	80c. multicoloured	1·40	1·50

DESIGNS AND EVENTS: 10c. (No. 805), Male athletes ("Youth and Sport" constitutional amendment); 20c. Stylized rose (child welfare); 30c. "Rayon II" stamp of 1850 and basilisk ("NABA" Philatelic Exhibition, Basel); 50c. "Co-operation" symbol (aid for technical development); 80c. "Intelsat 4" (I.T.U. Space Conference).

192 'Rayon I' Stamp of 1850

1971. 'NABA 1971' Stamp Exhibition, Basel. Sheet 61×75 mm. Imperf.

MS810	50c.×4 red, black and blue (sold at 3f.)	3·25	3·25

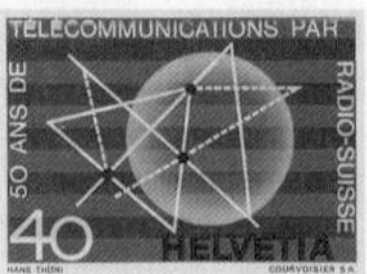

193 Europa Chain

1971. Europa.

811	**193**	30c. yellow and mauve	45	40
812	**193**	50c. yellow and blue	80	75

1971. Pro Patria. For National Day Collection. Contemporary Glass Paintings. As T 184.

813	10c.+10c. "Religious Abstract", (J. F. Comment)	40	40
814	20c.+10c. "Cockerel", (J. Prahin)	45	45
815	30c.+10c. "Fox", (K. Volk)	80	40
816	50c.+20c. "Christ's Passion" (B. Schorderet)	1·10	1·10

194 "Telecommunications Services" (50th anniv of Radio-Suisse)

1971. Publicity and "Swiss Alps" (30c.).

817	-	30c. purple, grey & mauve	80	10
818	**194**	40c. multicoloured	80	75

DESIGN: 30c. Les Diablerets, Vaud.

195 Alexandre Yersin (bacteriologist)

1971. Famous Physicians.

819	**195**	10c. green	10	10
820	-	20c. green	25	10
821	-	30c. red	45	10
822	-	40c. blue	65	75
823	-	80c. purple	1·30	1·10

PHYSICIANS: 20c. Auguste Forel (psychiatrist); 30c. Jules Gonin (ophthalmologist); 40c. Robert Koch (German bacteriologist); 80c. Frederick Banting (Canadian physiologist).

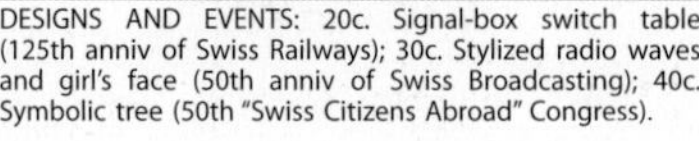

196 Warning Triangle and Wrench (75th Annivs of Motoring Organisations)

1972. Publicity Issue.

824	**196**	10c. multicoloured	25	10
825	-	20c. multicoloured	45	10
826	-	30c. orange, red & carmine	45	10
827	-	40c. violet, green and blue	65	55

DESIGNS AND EVENTS: 20c. Signal-box switch table (125th anniv of Swiss Railways); 30c. Stylized radio waves and girl's face (50th anniv of Swiss Broadcasting); 40c. Symbolic tree (50th "Swiss Citizens Abroad" Congress).

197 Swissair Boeing 747-100 Jetliner

1972. Air. Pro Aero Foundation and 50th Annivs of North Atlantic and Int Airmail Services.

828	**197**	2f.+1f. multicoloured	3·25	3·00

198 "Communications"

1972. Europa.

829	**198**	30c. multicoloured	45	40
830	**198**	40c. multicoloured	70	70

199 Late Stone Age Harpoon Heads

1972. Pro Patria. For National Day Collection. Archaeological Discoveries (1st series). Mult.

831	10c.+10c. Type **199**	40	25
832	20c.+10c. Bronze water-vessel, c. 570 B.C.	65	30
833	30c.+10c. Gold bust of Marcus Aurelius, 2nd cent A.D.	80	40
834	40c.+20c. Alemannic disc. 7th-cent A.D.	2·00	1·90

See also Nos. 869/72, 887/90 and 901/4.

200 Civil Defence Emblem

1972. Publicity and "Swiss Alps" (20c.) Issue. Multicoloured.

835	10c. Type **200**	25	10
836	20c. Spannorter	80	20
837	30c. Sud Aviation SE 3160 Alouette III rescue helicopter	95	10
838	40c. The "Four Elements" (53×31 mm)	65	75

SUBJECTS: 10c. Swiss Civil Defence; 20c. Tourism; 30c. Swiss Air Rescue Service; 40c. Protection of the environment.

201 Alberto Giacometti (painter)

1972. Swiss Celebrities.

839	**201**	10c. black and buff	10	10
840	-	20c. black and bistre	40	10
841	-	30c. black and pink	45	10
842	-	40c. black and blue	65	75
843	-	80c. black and purple	1·30	75

PORTRAITS: 20c. Charles Ramuz (novelist); 30c. Le Corbusier (architect); 40c. Albert Einstein (physicist); 80c. Arthur Honegger (composer).

202 Dish Aerial

1973. Publicity Issue. Multicoloured.

844	15c. Type **202**	40	40
845	30c. Quill pen	45	25
846	40c. Interpol emblem	65	60

EVENTS: 15c. Construction of Satellite Earth Station, Leuk-Brentjong; 30c. Centenary of Swiss Association of Commercial Employees; 40c. 50th anniv of International Criminal Police Organisation (Interpol).

203 Sottoceneri

204 Toggenburg Inn Sign

1973

847	**203**	5c. blue and stone	10	10
848	-	10c. green and purple	10	10
849	-	15c. blue and orange	25	10
850	-	25c. violet and green	30	10
851	-	30c. violet and red	45	10
852	-	35c. violet and orange	55	55
853	-	40c. grey and blue	65	10
854	-	50c. green and orange	80	45
855	-	60c. brown and grey	95	45
856	-	70c. green and purple	1·10	45
857	-	80c. red and green	1·30	75
858	-	1f. purple	1·60	10
859	-	1f.10 blue	1·70	20
860	-	1f.20 red	1·90	40
861	**204**	1f.30 orange	2·00	40
862	-	1f.50 green	2·40	40
863	-	1f.70 grey	2·75	40
864	-	1f.80 red	2·75	40
865	-	2f. blue	3·25	40
866	-	2f.50 brown	4·00	40
866a	-	3f. red	4·75	75
866b	-	3f.50 green	5·50	1·10

DESIGNS—VERT: 10c. Grisons; 15c. Central Switzerland; 25c. Jura; 30c. Simmental; 35c. Houses, Central Switzerland; 40c. Vaud; 50c. Valais; 60c. Engadine; 70c. Sopraceneri; 80c. Eastern Switzerland. HORIZ: 1f. Rose window, Lausanne Cathedral; 1f.10, Gallus portal, Basel Cathedral; 1f.20, Romanesque capital, St.-Jean-Baptiste Church, Grandson; 1f.50, Medallion, St. Georgen Monastery, Stein am Rhein; 1f.70, Roman Capital, St.-Jean-Baptiste Church, Grandson; 1f.80, Gargoyle, Berne Cathedral; 2f. Oriel, Schaffhausen; 2f.50, Weathercock, St. Ursus Cathedral, Solothurn; 3f. Font, St. Maurice Church, Saanen; 3f.50, Astronomical clock, Berne.

205 Europa "Posthorn"

1973. Europa.

867	**205**	25c. yellow and red	65	40
868	**205**	40c. yellow and blue	95	75

1973. Pro Patria. For National Day Collection. Archaeological Discoveries (2nd series). As T 199, but horiz. Multicoloured.

869	15c.+5c. Rauraric jar	40	40
870	30c.+10c. Head of a Gaul (bronze)	80	40
871	40c.+20c. Almannic "Fish" brooches	1·60	1·50
872	60c.+20c. Gold bowl	2·00	1·90

206 Horological Emblem

1973. Publicity Issue. Multicoloured.

873	15c. Type **206**	40	40
874	30c. Skiing emblem	40	25
875	40c. Face of child	70	60

SUBJECTS: 15c. Inaug (1974) of Int Horological Museum, Neuchatel; 30c. World Alpine Skiing Championships, St. Moritz (1974); 40c. "Terre des Hommes" (Child-care organization).

207 Global Hostels

1974. Publicity Issue. Multicoloured.

876	15c. Type **207**	40	10
877	30c. Gymnast and hurdlers	40	10
878	40c. Pistol and target	95	60

SUBJECTS: 15c. "50 Years of Swiss Youth Hostels"; 30c. Centenary of Swiss Workmen's Gymnastics and Sports Assn (S.A.T.U.S.); 40c. World Shooting Championships, 1974.

208 Cantonal Messenger (Basel)

1974. "Internaba 1974" Stamp Exhibition, Basel. Sheet 83×73 mm containing T 208 and similer vert designs, showing Cantonal messengers. Multicoloured.

MS879	30c. Type **208**; 30c. Zug; 60c. Uri; 80c. Schwyz (sold at 30f.)	6·25	6·00

209 "Continuity" (Max Bill)

1974. Europa. Swiss Sculptures.

880	**209**	30c. black and red	80	40
881	-	40c. brown, blue and black	1·00	75

DESIGN: 40c. "Amazone" (Carl Burckhardt).

210 Eugene Borel (first Director of International Bureau, U.P.U.)

1974. Centenary of U.P.U.

882	**210**	30c. black and pink	45	25
883	-	40c. black and grey	65	40
884	-	80c. black and green	1·30	1·10

DESIGNS: 40c. Heinrich von Stephan (founder of U.P.U.); 80c. Montgomery Blair (U.S. Postmaster-General and initiator of 1863 Paris Postal Conference).

211 View of Berne

1974. 17th U.P.U. Congress, Lausanne. Mult.

885	30c. Type **211**	65	40
886	30c. View of Lausanne	65	40

1974. Pro Patria. For National Day Collection. Archaeological Discoveries (3rd series). As T 199 but horiz. Multicoloured.

887	15c.+5c. Glass bowl	40	40
888	30c.+10c. Bull's head (bronze)	80	25
889	40c.+20c. Gold brooch	1·40	1·20
890	60c.+20c. "Bird" vessel (clay)	2·00	1·80

212 "Oath of Allegiance" (sculpture) (W. Witschi)

1974. Publicity Issue.

891	**212**	15c. deep green, green and lilac	40	15
892	-	30c. multicoloured	45	10
893	-	30c. multicoloured	40	10

EVENTS AND COMMEMORATIONS: No. 891, Centenary of Federal Constitution; No. 892, Foundation emblem (Aid for Swiss Sport Foundation); No. 893, Posthorn and "postal transit" arrow (125th anniv of Federal Posts).

213 "Metre" and Krypton Line

1975. Publicity Issue.

894	**213**	15c. orange, blue and green	40	40
895	-	30c. brown, purple & yell	45	30
896	-	60c. red, black and blue	95	40
897	-	90c. multicoloured	1·60	1·30

DESIGNS AND EVENTS: 15c. Centenary of International Metre Convention; 30c. Heads of women (International Women's Year); 60c. Red Cross flag and barbed-wire (Conference on Humanitarian International Law, Geneva); 90c. Astra airship "Ville de Lucerne", 1910 ("Aviation and Space Travel" Exhibition, Transport and Communications Museum, Lucerne).

214 "The Monch" (F. Hodler)

1975. Europa. Paintings. Multicoloured.

898	30c. Type **214**	45	40
899	50c. "Still Life with Guitar" (R. Auberjonois)	80	60
900	60c. "L'effeuilleuse" (M. Barraud)	95	90

1975. Pro Patria. Archaeological Discoveries. (4th series). As T 199. Multicoloured.

901	15c.+10c. Gold brooch, Oron-le-Chatel	65	40
902	30c.+20c. Bronze head of Bacchus, Avenches	95	40
903	50c.+20c. Bronze daggers, Bois-de-Vaux, Lausanne	1·60	1·40
904	60c.+25c. Glass decanter, Maralto	1·70	1·70

215 "Eliminate Obstacles!"

1975. Publicity Issue.

905	**215**	15c. black, green and lilac	40	40
906	-	30c. black, rosine and red	45	30
907	-	50c. brown and bistre	80	75
908	-	60c. multicoloured	95	75

DESIGNS: 30c. Organization emblem (Inter-confessional Pastoral Care by Telephone Organization); 50c. European Architectural Heritage Year emblem; 60c. Beat Fischer von Reichenbach (founder) (300th anniv of Fischer postal service).

216 Forest Scene (Federal Forest Laws Cent)

1976. Publicity Issue.

909	**216**	20c. multicoloured	80	40
910	-	40c. multicoloured	65	40
911	-	40c. black, orange & pur	65	40
912	-	80c. black and blue	1·30	1·10

DESIGNS: No. 910, Fruit and vegetables (campaign to promote nutriments as opposed to alcohol); No. 911, African child (fight against leprosy); No. 912, Early and modern telephones (telephone centenary).

217 Floral Embroidery

1976. Europa. Handicrafts.

913	**217**	40c. yellow, brown & pink	80	40
914	-	80c. blue, red and stone	2·00	1·10

DESIGN: 80c. Decorated pocket watch.

218 Kyburg Castle, Zurich

1976. Pro Patria. Swiss Castles (1st series). Multicoloured.

915	20c.+10c. Type **218**	80	40
916	40c.+20c. Grandson, Vaud	1·20	60
917	40c.+20c. Murten, Fribourg	1·20	60
918	80c.+40c. Bellinzona, Ticino	3·50	3·00

See also Nos. 932/5, 955/8 and 977/80.

219 Roe Deer Fawn, Barn Swallow and Frog (World Fed. for Protection of Animals)

1976. Publicity Issue.

919	**219**	20c. black, brown & green	80	40
920	-	40c. black, yellow and red	65	25
921	-	40c. multicoloured	95	25
922	-	80c. red, violet and blue	1·30	1·20

DESIGNS: No. 920, "Sun" and inscription ("Save Energy" campaign); No. 921, St. Gotthard mountains (Swiss Alps); No. 922, Skater (World Speed Skating Championships, Davos).

220 Oskar Bider and Bleriot XI

1977. Swiss Aviation Pioneers.

923	**220**	40c. black, mauve and red	80	40
924	-	80c. black, purple and blue	2·00	75
925	-	100c. black, green & bistre	1·60	75
926	-	150c. black, brown & grn	2·75	1·10

DESIGNS: 80c. Eduard Spelterini and balloon basket; 100c. Armand Dufaux and Dufaux IV biplane; 150c. Walter Mittelholzer and Dornier Do-B Merkur seaplane "Switzerland".

221 Blue Cross (society for care of alcoholics, cent)

1977. Publicity Issues.

927	**221**	20c. blue and brown	40	25
928	-	40c. multicoloured	65	15
929	-	80c. multicoloured	1·30	1·10

DESIGNS: 40c. Festival emblem (Vevey vintage festival); 80c. Balloons carrying letters ("Juphilex 1977" youth stamp exhibition, Berne).

222 St. Ursanne

1977. Europa. Landscapes. Multicoloured.

930	40c. Type **222**	65	40
931	80c. Sils-Baselgia	1·30	1·10

1977. Pro Patria. Swiss Castles (2nd series). As T 218. Multicoloured.

932	20c.+10c. Aigle, Vaud	45	40
933	40c.+20c. Pratteln, Basel-Landschaft	95	40
934	70c.+30c. Sargans, St. Gallen	2·00	1·90
935	80c.+40c. Hallwil, Aargau	2·50	2·30

223 Factory Worker

1977. Publicity Issue. Multicoloured.

936	20c. Type **223**	40	40
937	40c. Ionic capital	65	25
938	80c. Association emblem and butterfly	1·30	1·10

EVENTS: 20c. Centenary of Federal Factories Act; 40c. Protection of cultural monuments; 80c. Swiss Footpaths Association.

224 Sternsingen, Bergun

1977. Regional Folk Customs.

939	**224**	5c. green	10	10
940	-	10c. red	10	10
941	-	20c. orange	25	10
941b	-	25c. brown	40	40
941c	-	30c. green	55	25
942	-	35c. green	55	25
943	-	40c. purple	65	15
943c	-	45c. blue	80	65
944	-	50c. red	80	10
944b	-	60c. brown	1·00	80
945	-	70c. lilac	1·10	20
946	-	80c. blue	1·30	1·20
947	-	90c. brown	1·60	1·60

DESIGNS: 10c. Sechselauten, Zurich; 20c. Silvesterklause, Herisau; 25c. Chesstete, Solothurn; 30c. Rollelibutzen, Alstatten; 35c. Gansabhauet, Sursee; 40c. Escalade, Geneva; 45c. Klausjagen, Kussnacht; 50c. Archetringele, Laupen; 60c. Schnabelgeissen, Ottenbach; 70c. Processioni storiche, Mendrisio; 80c. Vogel Gryff, Basel; 90c. Roitschaggata, Lotschental.

225 Mailcoach Route Plate, Vaud Canton

1978. Publicity Issue. Multicoloured.

948	20c. Type **225**	40	15
949	40c. View of Lucerne	1·00	25
950	70c. Title page of book "Melusine"	1·10	1·10
951	80c. Stylized camera and lens	1·30	1·30

EVENTS: 20c. "Lemanex '78" National Stamp Exhibition; 40c. 800th anniv of Lucerne; 70c. 500th anniv of Printing at Geneva; 80c. 2nd International Triennial Exhibition of Photography, Fribourg.

226 *La Suisse*, Lake Geneva

1978. "Lemanex 78" National Stamp Exhibtion, Lausanne. Sheet 133×149 mm containg T 226 and similar horiz design, showing steamers, with 4 labels. Multicoloured.

MS952	20c. Type **226**; 20c. *Il Verbano*; 40c. *Gotthard*; 40c. *Ville de Neuchatel*; 40c. *Romanshorn*; 40c. *Le Winkeiried*; 70c. *Loetschberg*; 80c. *Waedenswil* (sold at 5f.)	7·00	7·00

227 Stockalper Palace, Brig

1978. Europa.

953	**227**	40c. multicoloured	80	40
954	-	80c. blue, brown and black	1·60	1·20

DESIGN: 80c. Old Diet Hall, Berne.

1978. Pro Patria. Swiss Castles (3rd series). As T 218.

955	20c.+10c. Hagenwil, Thurgau	45	40
956	40c.+20c. Burgdorf, Berne	95	40
957	70c.+30c. Tarasp, Graubunden	2·00	2·00
958	80c.+40c. Chillon, Vaud	2·50	2·40

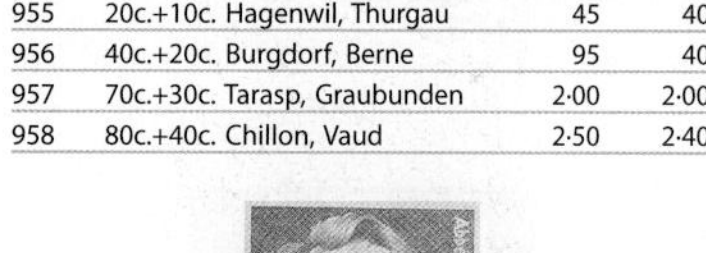

228 Abbe Joseph Bovet (composer)

1978. Celebrities.

959	**228**	20c. green	40	40
960	-	40c. purple	65	40
961	-	70c. grey	1·10	1·10
962	-	80c. blue	1·30	1·30

DESIGNS: 40c. Henri Dunant (founder of Red Cross); 70c. Carl Gustav Jung (psychiatrist); 80c. Auguste Piccard (physicist).

229 Worker wearing Goggles

1978. Safety at Work. Multicoloured.

963	40c. Type **229**	95	65
964	40c. Worker wearing respirator	95	65
965	40c. Worker wearing safety helmet	95	65

230 Arms of Switzerland and Jura

1978. Creation of Canton of Jura.

966	**230**	40c. red, black and stone	65	45

231 Rainer Maria Rilke (writer)

1979. Celebrities.

967	**231**	20c. green	40	30
968	-	40c. red	45	25
969	-	70c. brown	1·10	1·10
970	-	80c. blue	1·30	1·30

DESIGNS: 40c. Paul Klee (artist); 70c. Herman Hesse (novelist and poet); 80c. Thomas Mann (novelist).

232 Othmar H. Ammann and Verrazano Narrows Bridge

1979. Publicity Issue. Multicoloured.

971	20c. Type **232**	40	40
972	40c. Target and marker	65	40
973	70c. Hot-air balloon "Esperanto"	1·10	1·10
974	80c. Aircraft tail fins	1·30	1·30

SUBJECTS: 20c. Birth centenary of O. H. Ammann (engineer); 40c. 50th Federal Riflemen's Festival, Lucerne; 70c. World Esperanto Congress, Lucerne; 80c. Basel-Mulhouse Airport.

233 Old Letter Box, Basel

1979. Europa.

975	**233**	40c. multicoloured	80	45
976	-	80c. blue, lt blue & stone	2·00	1·30

DESIGN: 80c. Alpine relay station on the Jungfraujoch.

1979. Pro Patria. Swiss Castles (4th series). As T 218. Multicoloured.

977	20c.+10c. Oron, Vaud	45	40
978	40c.+20c. Spiez, Berne	95	40
979	70c.+30c. Porrentruy, Jura	2·00	2·00
980	80c.+40c. Rapperswil, St. Gallen	2·50	2·40

234 Gold Stater

1979. Publicity Issue. Multicoloured.

981	20c. Type **234**	40	40
982	40c. Child on dove (horiz)	65	40
983	70c. Morse key and satellite (horiz)	1·10	1·10
984	80c. "Ariane" rocket	1·30	1·30

EVENTS: 20c. Centenary of Swiss Numismatic Society; 40c. International Year of the Child; 70c. 50th anniv of Swiss Radio Amateurs; 80c. European Space Agency.

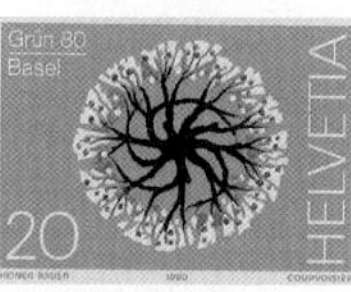

235 Tree in Blossom

1980. Publicity Issue. Multicoloured.

985	20c. Type **235**	40	40
986	40c. Carved milk vessel	65	40
987	70c. Winterthur Town Hall	1·10	1·10
988	80c. Pic-Pic motor car	1·30	1·30

SUBJECTS: 20c. Horticultural and Landscape Gardening Exhibition, Basel; 40c. 50th anniv of Arts and Crafts Centre; 70c. Centenary of Society for Swiss Art History; 80c. 50th International Motor Show, Geneva.

236 Johann Konrad Kern (politician)

1980. Europa.

989	**236**	40c. flesh, black and pink	65	40
990	-	80c. flesh, black and blue	1·30	1·20

DESIGN: 80c. Gustav Adolf Hasler (com- munications pioneer).

237 Mason and Carpenter

1980. Pro Patria. Trade and Craft Signs. Mult.

991	20c.+10c. Type **237**	45	40
992	40c.+20c. Barber	95	40
993	70c.+30c. Hatter	1·70	1·60
994	80c.+40c. Baker	2·40	2·40

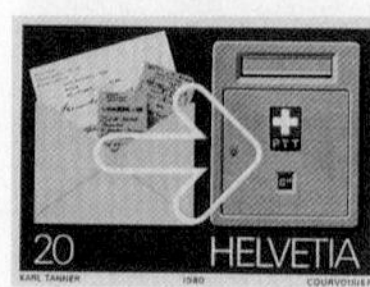

238 Girocheque and Letter Box

1980. Swiss P.T.T. Services.

995	**238**	20c. multicoloured	40	40
996	-	40c. multicoloured	65	40
997	-	70c. brown, black and lilac	1·10	1·10
998	-	80c. multicoloured	1·60	1·30

DESIGNS: 40c. Postbus; 70c. Transfer roller (50th anniv of P.T.T. postage stamp printing office); 80c. Flowers and telephone (centenary of telephone in Switzerland).

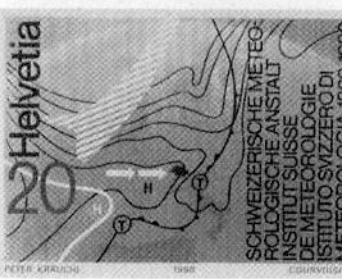

239 Weather Chart

1980. Publicity Issue. Multicoloured.

999	20c. Type **239**	40	30
1000	40c. Figures and cross	65	40
1001	80c. Motorway sign	2·00	1·30

SUBJECTS: 20c. Centenary of Swiss Meteorological Office; 40c. Centenary of Swiss Trades Union Federation; 80c. Opening of St. Gotthard road tunnel.

240 Granary from Kiesen

1981. Publicity Issue. Multicoloured.

1002	20c. Type **240**	40	30
1003	40c. Disabled figures	65	40
1004	70c. "The Parish Clerk" (Albert Anker) (vert)	1·10	1·10
1005	80c. Theodolite and rod	1·30	1·30
1006	110c. Tail of DC9-81	2·40	1·60

SUBJECTS: 20c. Ballenberg Open-air Museum; 40c. International Year of Disabled Persons; 70c. 150th birth anniv of Albert Anker (artist); 80c. 16th International Federation of Surveyors Congress, Montreux; 110c. 50th anniv of Swissair.

241 Figure leaping from Earth

1981. 50th Anniv of Swissair.

1007	**241**	2f.+1f. lilac, violet and yellow	3·25	3·25

242 Dancing Couple

1981. Europa. Multicoloured.

1008	40c. Type **242**	80	40
1009	80c. Stone putter	2·00	1·60

243 Aarburg Post Office Sign, 1685

1981. Pro Patria. Postal Signs. Multicoloured.

1010	20c.+10c. Type **243**	65	40
1011	40c.+20c. Mail coach sign of Fribourg Cantonal Post	95	40
1012	70c.+30c. Gordola Post office sign (Ticino Cantonal Post)	1·60	1·60
1013	80c.+40c. Splugen post office sign	2·40	2·40

244 Seal of Fribourg

1981. 500th Anniv of Covenant of Stans.

1014	**244**	40c. red, black and brown	65	40
1015	-	40c. green, black and purple	65	40
1016	-	80c. brown, black and blue	1·60	1·30

DESIGNS: 40c. (No. 1015) Seal of Solothurn; 80c. Old Town Hall, Stans.

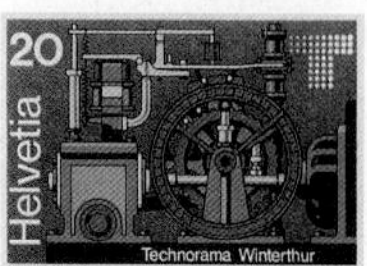

245 Voltage Regulator from Jungfrau Railway's Power Station

1981. Publicity Issue. Multicoloured.

1017	20c. Type **245**	40	25
1018	40c. Crossbow quality seal	65	30
1019	70c. Group of youths	1·10	95
1020	1f.10 Mosaic	1·70	1·60

SUBJECTS: 20c. Opening of Technorama of Switzerland, Winterthur (museum of science and technology); 40c. 50th anniv of Organization for Promotion of Swiss Products and Services; 70c. 50th anniv of Swiss Association of Youth Organizations; 1f.10, Restoration of St. Peter's Cathedral, Geneva.

246 Class C4/5 Steam Locomotive

1982. Centenary of St. Gotthard Railway.

1021 **246** 40c. black and purple 65 40

1022 - 40c. multicoloured 65 40

DESIGN: No. 1022, Class Re 6/6 electric locomotive.

247 Hoteliers Association Emblem

1982. Publicity Issue. Multicoloured.

1023 20c. Type **247** 40 25

1024 40c. Flag formed by four Fs 65 30

1025 70c. Gas flame encircling emblem 1·10 80

1026 80c. Lynx and scientific instruments 1·60 1·60

1027 110c. Retort 1·70 1·60

SUBJECTS: 20c. Centenary of Swiss Hoteliers Association; 40c. 150th anniv of Swiss Gymnastics Association; 70c. 50th anniv of International Gas Union; 80c. 150th anniv of Natural History Museum, Berne; 110c. Centenary of Swiss Society of Chemical Industries.

248 "Swearing Oath of Eternal Fealty, Rutli Meadow" (detail of mural, Heinrich Danioth)

1982. Europa. Multicoloured.

1028 40c. Type **248** 95 40

1029 80c. Treaty of 1291 founding Swiss Confederation 2·00 1·60

249 "The Sun", Willisau

1982. Pro Patria. Inn Signs (1st series). Multicoloured.

1030 20c.+10c. Type **249** 65 40

1031 40c.+20c. "On the Wave", St. Saphorin 95 40

1032 70c.+30c. "The Three Kings", Rheinfelden 1·60 1·60

1033 80c.+40c. "The Crown", Winterhur 2·40 2·40

See also Nos. 1056/9.

250 "Aquarius" and Old Berne

1982. Signs of the Zodiac and Landscapes.

1034 **250** 1f. multicoloured 1·60 10

1035 - 1f.10 brown, blue & vio 1·70 10

1036 - 1f.20 green, blue & brn 1·90 25

1036a - 1f.40 multicoloured 2·20 2·20

1037 - 1f.50 bl, azure & orge 2·40 40

1038 - 1f.60 multicoloured 2·50 1·60

1039 - 1f.70 cobalt, brn & bl 2·75 40

1040 - 1f.80 brn, grn & dp grn 2·75 1·60

1041 - 2f. cobalt, brown & blue 3·50 3·25

1042 - 2f. cobalt, brown & blue 3·25 40

1042a - 2f.50 red, grn & dp grn 4·00 1·20

1043 - 3f. red, green and black 4·75 40

1044 - 4f. green, violet & purple 6·25 80

1045 - 4f.50 ochre, blue & brn 7·00 1·20

DESIGNS: 1f.10, "Pisces" and Nax near Sion; 1f.20, "Aries" and the Graustock, Obwalden; 1f.40, "Gemini" and Bischofszell; 1f.50, "Taurus" and Basel Cathedral; 1f.60, "Gemini" and Schonengrund; 1f.70, "Cancer" and Wetterhorn; 1f.80, "Leo" and Areuse Gorge; 2f. (1041), "Virgo" and Aletsch Glacier; 2f. (1042), "Virgo" and Schwarzsee above Zermatt; 2f.50, "Libra" and Fechy; 3f. "Scorpio" and Corippo; 4f. "Sagittarius" and Glarus; 4f.50, "Capricorn" and Schuls.

251 Articulated Tram

1982. Publicity Issue. Multicoloured.

1046 20c. Type **251** 65 40

1047 40c. Salvation Army singer and guitarist 65 40

1048 70c. Dressage rider 1·10 1·10

1049 80c. Emblem 1·30 1·30

SUBJECTS: 20c. Centenary of Zurich trams; 40c. Centenary of Salvation Army in Switzerland; 70c. World Dressage Championship, Lausanne; 80c. 14th International Water Supply Association Congress, Zurich.

252 Eurasian Perch

1983. Publicity Issue. Multicoloured.

1050 20c. Type **252** 80 25

1051 40c. University of Zurich 65 30

1052 70c. Teleprinter tape forming "JP" 1·10 1·10

1053 80c. Micrometer and cycloidal computer drawing 1·30 1·30

EVENTS: 20c. Centenary of Swiss Fishing and Pisciculture Federation; 40c. 150th anniv of University of Zurich; 70c. Centenary of Swiss Journalists' Federation; 80c. Centenary of Swiss Machine Manufacturers' Association.

253 Jost Burgi's Celestial Globe, 1594

1983. Europa.

1054 **253** 40c. orange, pink and brown 80 40

1055 - 80c. green, blue and black 2·00 1·20

DESIGN: 80c. Niklaus Riggenbach's rack and pinion railway, 1871.

1983. Pro Patria. Inn Signs (2nd series). As T 249. Multicoloured.

1056 20c.+10c. "The Lion", Heimiswil 80 55

1057 40c.+20c. "The Cross", Sachseln 1·00 65

1058 70c.+30c. "The Jug", Lenzburg Castle 1·70 1·60

1059 80c.+40c. "The Cavalier", St. George 2·40 2·40

254 Seal, 1832–48

1983. 150th Anniv of Basel-Land Canton.

1060 **254** 40c. multicoloured 65 40

255 Gallo-Roman Capital, Martigny

1983. Publicity Issue.

1061 **255** 20c. orange and black 40 20

1062 - 40c. multicoloured 1·00 25

1063 - 70c. multicoloured 1·30 1·10

1064 - 80c. multicoloured 1·30 1·30

DESIGNS: 20c. Type **255** (Bimillenary of Octodurus/Martigny); 40c. Bernese shepherd-dog and Schwyz hunting dog (Centenary of Swiss Kennel Club); 70c. Cyclists (Centenary of Swiss Cyclists and Motor Cyclists Federation); 80c. Carrier pigeon and world map (World Communications Year).

256 Pre-stamp Cover, 1839

1984. Publicity Issue. Multicoloured.

1065 25c. Type **256** 80 25

1066 50c. Collegiate Church clock and buildings 80 30

1067 80c. Olympic rings and Lausanne 2·00 1·30

SUBJECTS: 25c. National Stamp Exhibition, Zurich; 50c. 1100th anniv of Saint-Imier; 80c. Permanent headquarters of International Olympic Committee at Lausanne.

257 Bridge

1984. Europa. 25th Anniv of European Posts and Telecommunications Conference.

1068 **257** 50c. purple, red and crimson 1·20 80

1069 **257** 80c. ultramarine, blue and deep blue 2·00 1·30

258 Hexagonal Stove from Rosenburg Mansion, Stans

1984. Pro Patria. Tiled Stoves. Multicoloured.

1070 35c.+15c. Type **258** 80 80

1071 50c.+20c. Winterthur stove (by Hans Heinrich Pfau) Freuler Palace, Nafels 1·20 40

1072 70c.+30c. Box-stove (by Rudolf Stern) from Plaisance, Riaz 2·00 2·00

1073 80c.+40c. Frame-modelled stove (by Leonard Racle) 2·40 2·40

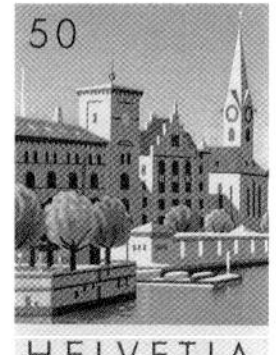

259 Bauschanzli, City Hall and Fraumunster

1984. "Naba Zuri 84" National Stamp Exhibition, Zurich. Sheet 145×70 mm containing T 259 and similar vert designs forming panorama of Zurich. Multicoloured.

MS1074 50c. Type **259**; 50c. St. Peter's; 50c. Town Hall, Helmhaus and Wasser Church; 50c. Cathedral (sold at 3f.) 5·75 5·75

260 Burning Match

1984. Fire Prevention.

1075 **260** 50c. multicoloured 80 40

261 Railway Conductor's Equipment

1985. Publicity Issue. Multicoloured.

1076 35c. Type **261** (cent of Train Staff Association) 80 25

1077 50c. Stone with Latin inscription (2000 years of Rhaeto-Romanic culture) 80 30

1078 70c. Rescue of man (cent of International Lake Geneva Rescue Society) 1·10 1·10

1079 80c. Grande Dixence dam (International Large Dams Congress, Lausanne) 1·60 1·30

262 Ernest Ansermet (orchestral conductor)

1985. Europa. Music Year. Multicoloured.

1080 50c. Type **262** 80 40

1081 80c. Frank Martin (composer) 1·60 1·20

263 Music Box, 1895

1985. Pro Patria. Musical Instruments. Mult.

1082 25c.+10c. Type **263** 80 80

1083 35c.+15c. 18th-century box rattle 95 80

1084 50c.+20c. Emmental necked zither (by Peter Zaugg), 1828 1·20 40

1085 70c.+30c. Drum, 1571 2·00 2·00

1086 80c.+40c. 20th-century diatonic accordion 2·40 2·40

264 Baker

1985. Publicity Issue. Multicoloured.

1087 50c. Type **264** (centenary of Swiss Master Bakers' and Confectioners' Federation) 80 40

1088 70c. Cross on abstract background (50th anniv of Swiss Radio International) 1·10 1·10

1089 80c. Geometric pattern and emblem (Postal, Telegraph and Telephone International World Congress, Interlaken) 1·30 1·30

265 Intertwined Ropes

1986. Publicity Issue.

1090 **265** 35c. multicoloured 55 55

1091 - 50c. deep brown, brown and red 80 40

1092 - 80c. orange, green and black 1·30 1·30

1093 - 90c. multicoloured 1·40 1·40

1094 - 1f.10 multicoloured 1·70 1·70

DESIGNS: 35c. Type **265** (50th anniv of Swiss Workers' Relief Organization); 50c. Battle site on 1698 map (600th anniv of Battle of Sempach); 80c. Statuette of Mercury (2000th anniv of Roman Chur); 90c. Gallic head (2000th anniv of Vindonissa); 1f.10, Roman coin of Augustus (2000th anniv of Zurich).

266 Sportsmen

1986. Pro Sport.

1095 **266** 50c.+20c. mult 1·10 80

267 Woman's Head

1986. Europa. Multicoloured.

1096	50c. Type **267**	1·20	40
1097	90c. Man's head	2·00	2·00

268 "Bridge in the Sun" (Giovanni Giacometti)

1986. Pro Patria. Paintings. Multicoloured.

1098	35c.+15c. Type **268**	95	95
1099	50c.+20c. "The Violet Hat" (Cuno Amiet)	1·30	45
1100	80c.+40c. "After the Funeral" (Max Buri)	2·40	2·40
1101	90c.+40c. "Still Life" (Felix Vallotton)	2·50	2·50

269 Franz Mail Van

1986. The Post Past and Present.

1102	**269**	5c. yellow, purple and red	40	10
1103	-	10c. dp grn, grn & orge	40	10
1104	-	20c. orange, brown & bl	40	15
1105	-	25c. dp blue, bl & yell	65	40
1106	-	30c. grey, black & yellow	45	15
1107	-	35c. lake, red and yellow	80	45
1108	-	45c. blue, black & brown	70	65
1109	-	50c. violet, green & pur	80	15
1110	-	60c. orange, yellow & brn	1·20	80
1111	-	75c. green, dp grn & red	1·20	80
1112	-	80c. indigo, blue & brn	1·60	40
1113	-	90c. olive, brown & green	2·00	1·40

DESIGNS: 10c. Mechanized parcel sorting; 20c. Mule post; 25c. Letter cancelling machine; 30c. Stagecoach; 35c. Post Office counter clerk; 45c. Paddle-steamer "Stadt Luzern", 1830s; 50c. Postman; 60c. Loading mail bags onto Fokker 100 airplane; 75c. 17th-century mounted courier; 80c. Town postman, 1900s; 90c. Interior of railway mail sorting carriage.

270 Stylized Doves (International Peace Year)

1986. Publicity Issue. Multicoloured.

1115	35c. Type **270**	55	55
1116	50c. Sun behind snow-covered tree (50th anniv of Swiss Winter Relief Fund)	80	40
1117	80c. Symbols of literature and art (cent of Berne Convention for protection of literary and artistic copyright)	1·40	1·40
1118	90c. Red Cross, Red Crescent and symbols of aggression (25th Int Red Cross Conference meeting, Geneva)	1·40	1·40

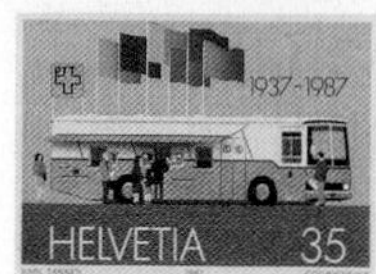

271 Mobile Post Office

1987. Publicity Issue. Multicoloured.

1119	35c. Type **271** (50th anniv of mobile post offices)	80	40
1120	50c. Lecturers of the seven faculties (450th anniv of Lausanne University)	80	30
1121	80c. Profile, maple leaf and logarithmic spiral (150th anniv of Swiss Engineers' and Architects' Association)	1·40	1·20
1122	90c. Boeing 747-300/400 jetliner and electric train (Geneva Airport rail link)	2·00	1·60
1123	1f.10 Symbolic figure and water (2000th anniv of Baden thermal springs)	2·00	2·00

272 "Scarabaeus" (Bernhard Luginbuhl)

1987. Europa. Sculpture. Multicoloured.

1124	50c. Type **272**	1·20	40
1125	90c. "Carnival Fountain", Basel (Jean Tinguely)	2·40	2·00

273 Wall Cabinet, 1764

1987. Pro Patria. Rustic Furniture. Multicoloured.

1126	35c.+15c. Type **273**	95	95
1127	50c.+20c. 16th-century chest	1·30	45
1128	80c.+40c. Cradle, 1782	2·40	2·40
1129	90c.+40c. Wardrobe, 1698	2·50	2·50

274 Butcher cutting Chops

1987. Publicity Issue. Multicoloured.

1130	35c. Type **274** (centenary of Swiss Master Butchers' Federation)	65	65
1131	50c. Profiles on stamps (50th anniv of Stamp Day)	95	40
1132	90c. Cheesemaker breaking up curds (centenary of Swiss Dairying Association)	2·00	2·00

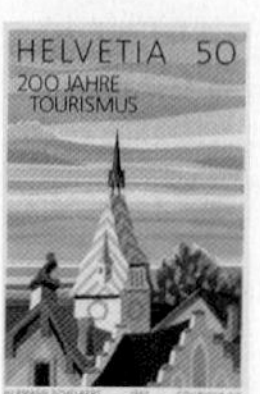

275 Zug Clock Tower

1987. Bicentenary of Tourism. Multicoloured.

1133	50c. Type **275**	80	30
1134	80c. St. Charles's church, Negrentino, Prugiasco/Blenio valley	1·40	1·40
1135	90c. Witches Tower, Sion	2·00	2·00
1136	1f.40 Jorgenberg Castle, Waltensburg/Vuorz, Surselva	2·50	2·50
MS1137	78×102 mm. Nos. 1133/6	6·00	6·00

1987. Flood Victims Relief Fund. No. 1109 surch 7.9.87 +50 and clasped hands.

1138	50c.+50c. violet, grn & pur	1·60	1·20

277 Society Emblem

1988. Publicity Issue. Multicoloured.

1139	25c. Type **277** (cent of Swiss Women's Benevolent Society)	40	40
1140	35c. Brushing woman's hair (centenary of Swiss Master Hairdressers' Association)	55	55
1141	50c. St. Fridolin banner and detail of Aegidius Tschudy's manuscript (600th anniv of Battle of Naefels)	95	40
1142	80c. Map and farming country seen from Beromunster radio tower (European Campaign for Rural Areas)	1·30	1·30
1143	90c. Girl playing shawm (50th anniv of Lucerne Int Music Festival)	1·60	1·60

278 Junkers Ju 52/3m HB-HOT A-702 flying past Matterhorn

1988. 50th Anniv of Pro Aero Foundation.

1144	**278**	140c.+60c. mult	3·25	3·25

279 Rudolf von Neuenburg

1988. Pro Patria. Minnesingers. Multicoloured.

1145	35c.+15c. Type **279**	80	80
1146	50c.+20c. Rudolf von Rotenburg	1·20	40
1147	80c.+40c. Johannes Hadlaub	2·40	2·40
1148	90c.+40c. Hardegger	2·75	3·50

280 Arrows on Map of Europe

1988. Europa. Transport and Communications.

1149	**280**	50c. bistre, emerald and green	1·20	40
1150	-	90c. lilac, green and violet	2·00	2·00

DESIGN: 90c. Computer circuit on map of Europe.

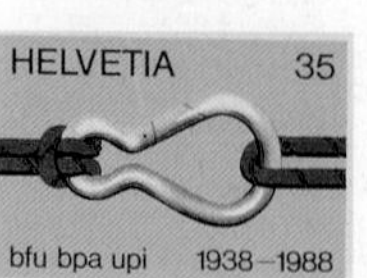

281 Snap Link

1988. Publicity Issue. Multicoloured.

1151	35c. Type **281** (50th anniv of Swiss Accident Prevention Office)	55	55
1152	50c. Drilling letters (cent of Swiss Metalworkers' and Watchmakers' Association)	80	40
1153	80c. Triangulation pyramid, theodolite and map (150th anniv of Swiss Federal Office of Topography)	1·30	1·30
1154	90c. International Red Cross Museum, Geneva (inauguration)	1·70	1·60

282 "Meta" (Jean Tinguely)

1988. Modern Art.

1155	**282**	90c. multicoloured	5·75	5·25

283 Army Postman

1989. Publicity Issue. Multicoloured.

1156	25c. Type **283** (centenary of Swiss Army postal service)	80	40
1157	35c. Fontaine du Sauvage and Porte au Loup, Delemont (700th anniv of granting of town charter)	80	80
1158	50c. Eye and composite wheel (cent of Public Transport Association)	80	40
1159	80c. Class GE 4/4 electric locomotive on viaduct (centenary of Rhaetian Railway)	2·00	2·00
1160	90c. St. Bernard dog and hospice (2000th anniv of Great St. Bernard Pass)	2·00	1·60

284 King Friedrich II presenting Berne Town Charter (Bendicht Tschachtlan Chronicle)

1989. Pro Patria. Medieval Chronicles. Mult.

1161	35c.+15c. Type **284**	95	80
1162	50c.+20c. Adrian von Bubenberg watching troops entering Murten (Diebold Schilling's Berne Chronicle)	1·30	40
1163	80c.+40c. Messenger presenting missive to Council of Zurich (Gerold Edlibach Chronicle)	2·40	2·40
1164	90c.+40c. Schilling presenting Chronicle to Council of Lucerne (Diebold Schilling's Lucerne Chronicle)	2·50	2·75

285 Hopscotch

1989. Europa. Children's Games. Multicoloured.

1165	50c. Type **285**	1·20	40
1166	90c. Blind-man's buff	2·00	2·00

286 Bricklayer

1989. Occupations.

1168	**286**	2f.75 purple, blk & yell	4·25	3·25
1169	-	2f.80 yellow, brn & bl	4·50	3·25
1170	-	3f. blue, dp brown & brn	4·75	80
1171	-	3f.60 orange, brn & pur	5·75	4·00
1173	-	3f.75 deep green, green and light green	6·00	3·25
1174	-	4f. multicoloured	6·25	1·60
1175	-	5f. ultram, stone & bl	7·75	80
1176	-	5f.50 grey, red and mauve	8·75	4·00

DESIGNS: 2f.80, Cook; 3f. Carpenter; 3f.60, Pharmacist; 3f.75, Fisherman; 4f. Vine grower; 5f. Cheesemaker; 5f.50, Dressmaker.

287 Testing Device

1989. Publicity Issue. Multicoloured.

1181	35c. Type **287** (cent of Swiss Electrotechnical Association)	80	80
1182	50c. Family on butterfly (50th anniv of Swiss Travel Fund)	80	40
1183	80c. "Wisdom" and "Science" (bronze statues) (centenary of Fribourg University)	1·30	1·30
1184	90c. Audio tape (1st anniv of National Sound Archives)	1·40	1·40
1185	1f.40 Bands of colour forming bridge (centenary of Inter-parliamentary Union)	2·20	2·20

288 Exercises

1989. Pro Sport.

1186	**288**	50c.+20c. mult	1·10	80

289 1882 5c. and 50c. Stamps and Emblem

1990. Publicity Issue. Multicoloured.

1187	25c. Type **289** (centenary of Union of Swiss Philatelic Societies)	40	40
1188	35c. Electric locomotive and electric double-deck railcar (inauguration of Zurich Rapid Transit System)	1·20	80
1189	50c. Mountain farmer (50th anniv of Assistance for Mountain Communities)	80	40
1190	90c. Ice hockey players (A-series World Ice Hockey Championships, Berne and Fribourg)	2·00	2·00

290 Cats

1990. Animals. Multicoloured.

1192	10c. Cow	10	10
1193	50c. Type **290**	80	15
1194	70c. Rabbit	1·10	25
1195	80c. Barn owls	1·30	30
1196	100c. Horse and foal	1·60	40
1197	110c. Geese	1·70	80
1198	120c. Dog	1·90	80
1199	140c. Sheep	2·20	1·20
1200	150c. Goats	2·40	80
1201	160c. Turkey	2·50	2·40
1202	170c. Donkey	2·75	1·20
1203	200c. Chickens	3·25	80

291 Flyswats and Starch Sprinklers Seller

1990. Pro Patria. Street Criers. Engravings by David Herrliberger. Multicoloured.

1205	35c.+15c. Type **291**	80	80
1206	50c.+20c. Clock seller	1·20	40
1207	80c.+40c. Knife grinder	2·40	2·40
1208	90c.+40c. Couple selling pine-wood sticks	2·75	2·75

292 Lucerne Post Office

1990. Europa. Post Office Buildings. Mult.

1209	50c. Type **292**	1·20	40
1210	90c. Geneva Post Office	2·00	2·00

293 Conrad Ferdinand Meyer (writer)

1990. Celebrities.

1211	**293**	35c. black and green	80	80
1212	-	50c. black and blue	80	40
1213	-	80c. black and yellow	1·60	1·20
1214	-	90c. black and pink	2·00	1·60

DESIGNS: 50c. Angelika Kauffmann (painter); 80c. Blaise Cendrars (writer); 90c. Frank Buchser (painter).

294 Anniversary Emblem and Crosses

1990. 700th Anniv (1991) of Swiss Confederation (1st issue).

1215	50c. Type **294**	80	40
1216	90c. Emblem and crosses (different)	2·40	2·00

See also Nos. 1219/22 and 1224.

295 Geneva Cantonal Post Driver's Brass Badge

1990. "Helvetia Geneve 90" National Stamp Exhibition. Sheet 102×78 mm containing T 295 and similar horiz designs. Multicoloured.

MS1217	50c.+25c. Type **295**; 50c.+25c. Place du Bourg-Four, Geneva; 50c.+25c. Rousseau Island, Geneva; 50c.+25c. Geneva 1843 5+5c. stamp on cover	7·50	7·50

296 Figures on Jigsaw Pieces

1990. Population Census.

1218	**296**	50c. multicoloured	80	40

297 "700 JAHRE"

1991. 700th Anniv of Swiss Confederation (2nd issue). Multicoloured.

1219	50c. Type **297**	1·00	40
1220	50c. "700 ONNS"	1·00	40
1221	50c. "700 ANS"	1·00	40
1222	50c. "700 ANNI"	1·00	40

Nos. 1219/22 were issued together, se-tenant. forming a composite design of the Swiss cross in the centre.

298 Alps and City Skyline

1991. 800th Anniv of Berne.

1223	**298**	80c. multicoloured	1·60	80

299 Federal Palace, Berne, and Capitol, Washington

1991. 700th Anniv of Swiss Confederation (3rd issue). Swiss Emigration to U.S.A.

1224	**299**	160c. multicoloured	3·25	2·20

300 Jettison of "Ariane" Rocket Friction Protection Jacket

1991. Europa. Europe in Space. Multicoloured.

1225	50c. Type **300**	1·20	40
1226	90c. Orbit of Halley's Comet, "Giotto" space probe and its trajectory	2·00	1·60

301 Abstract

1991. Pro Patria. Modern Art. Multicoloured.

1227	50c.+20c. Type **301**	1·20	40
1228	70c.+30c. Artist's monogram	2·00	2·00
1229	80c.+40c. "Labyrinth"	2·40	2·40
1230	90c.+40c. "Man and Beast"	2·75	2·75

302 Stone Bridge, Lavertezzo

1991. Bridges. Multicoloured.

1231	50c. Type **302**	95	40
1232	70c. Wooden Neubrugg, Bremgarten	1·40	95
1233	80c. Koblenz-Felsenau iron truss railway bridge over River Aar	1·60	1·20
1234	90c. Ganter concrete bridge, Simplon Pass	2·00	2·00

303 P.T.T. Employees

1991. Centenary of Swiss Postal, Telephone and Telegraph Officials' Union.

1235	**303**	80c. multicoloured	1·30	1·30

304 Lake Moesola

1991. Mountain Lakes.

1236	**304**	50c. multicoloured	80	25
1237	-	80c. brown, red & purple	1·30	40

DESIGN: 80c. Fishing boat moored at jetty on Melchsee.

See also No. 1257.

305 Mouth of River Rhine and Caspian Tern

1992. Publicity Issue. Multicoloured.

1238	50c. Type **305** (centenary of Treaty for International Regulation of the Rhine)	80	40
1239	80c. Family (50th anniv of Pro Familia)	1·30	1·00
1240	90c. Chemical formula and model of difluorobutane molecule (centenary of International Chemical Nomenclature Conference, Geneva)	1·40	1·40

306 Map of Americas and "Santa Maria"

1992. Europa. 500th Anniv of Discovery of America by Columbus. Multicoloured.

1241	50c. Type **306**	1·60	40
1242	90c. Route map of first voyage and sketch for statue of Columbus (Vincenzo Vela)	2·00	1·60

307 Skier

1992. Sierre Int Comics Festival. Mult.

1243	50c. Type **307**	95	40
1244	80c. Mouse-artist drawing strip	1·60	80
1245	90c. Love-struck man holding bunch of stamp-flowers behind back	1·80	1·60

308 1780s Earthenware Plate, Heimberg

1992. Pro Patria. Folk Art. Multicoloured.

1246	50c.+20c. Type **308**	1·40	80
1247	70c.+30c. Paper cut-out by Johann Jakob Hauswirth	1·70	1·60
1248	80c.+40c. Maplewood cream spoon, Gruyeres	2·40	2·40
1249	90c.+40c. Carnation from 1780 embroidered saddle cloth, Grisons	2·75	2·75

309 Flags and Alps

1992. Alpine Protection Convention.

1250	**309**	90c. multicoloured	1·80	1·40

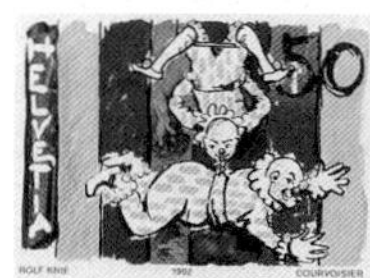

310 Clowns on Trapeze

1992. The Circus. Multicoloured.

1251	50c. Type **310**	95	40
1252	70c. Sealion with Auguste the clown	1·40	80
1253	80c. Chalky the clown and elephant	1·70	1·20
1254	90c. Harlequin and horse	1·80	1·60

311 Sport Pictograms

1992. Pro Sport.

1255	**311**	50c.+20c. black & blue	1·10	80

312 Train and Map

1992. Centenary (1993) of Central Office for International Rail Carriage.

1256	**312**	90c. multicoloured	2·00	1·40

313 "A" (first class) Mail

1993

1257	-	60c. dp blue, yellow & bl	1·60	40

1258 **313** 80c. red, orange and scarlet 1·20 40

DESIGN: 60c. Lake Tanay.

314 Zurich and Geneva 1843 Stamps

1993. 150th Anniv of Swiss Postage Stamps. Multicoloured.

1259	60c. Type **314**	95	40
1260	80c. Postal cancellation (stamps for postage)	1·30	1·00
1261	100c. Magnifying glass (stamp collecting)	1·60	1·60

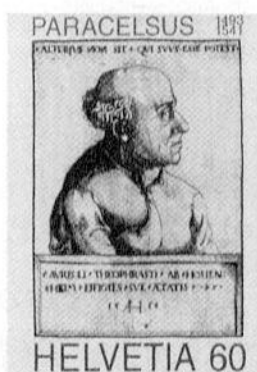

315 Paracelsus (after Augustin Hirschvogel) (500th birth anniv)

1993. Publicity Issue.

1262	**315**	60c. brown, grey and blue	1·20	40
1263	-	80c. multicoloured	1·60	1·20
1264	-	180c. multicoloured	3·50	2·40

DESIGNS—VERT: 80c. Discus thrower (from Greek vase) (inauguration of Olympic Museum, Lausanne). HORIZ: 180c. Worker's head (cent of International Metalworkers' Federation).

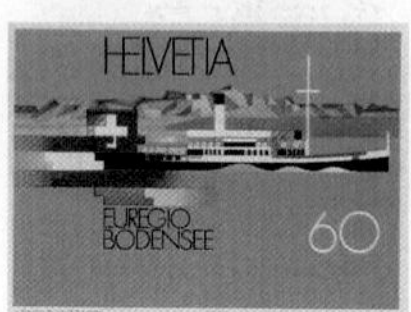

316 "Hohentwiel" (lake steamer) and Flags

1993. Lake Constance European Region.

1265 **316** 60c. multicoloured 1·20 70

317 Interior of Media House, Villeurbanne, France

1993. Europa. Contemporary Architecture.

1266	**317**	60c. ultramarine, blk & bl	1·20	40
1267	-	80c. red, black and grey	2·00	1·60

DESIGN: 80c. House, Breganzona, Ticino.

318 Appenzell Dairyman's Earring

1993. Pro Patria. Folk Art. Multicoloured.

1268	60c.+30c. Type **318**	1·60	1·20
1269	60c.+30c. Fluhli enamelled glass bottle, 1738	1·60	1·20
1270	80c.+40c. Driving cows to summer pasture (detail of mural, Sylvestre Pidoux)	2·40	2·40
1271	100c.+40c. Straw hat ornaments	2·75	2·75

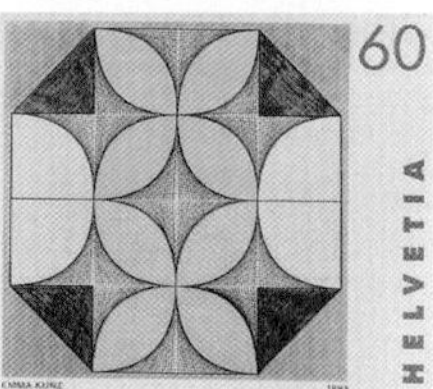

319 "Work No. 095" (Emma Kunz)

1993. Paintings by Swiss Women Artists. Mult.

1272	60c. Type **319**	1·20	40
1273	80c. "Great Singer Lilas Goergens" (Aloise) (33×33 mm)	1·60	80
1274	100c. "Under the Rain Cloud" (Meret Oppenheim) (33×33 mm)	2·00	1·60
1275	120c. "Four Spaces with Horizontal Bands" (Sophi Taeuber-Arp) (33×33 mm)	2·40	2·00

320 Kapell Bridge and Water Tower, Lucerne

1993. Kapell Bridge Restoration Fund.

1276 **320** 80c.+20c. carmine and red 1·60 80

321 Hieroglyphic, Cuneiform and Roman Scripts

1994. "Books and the Press" Exhibition, Geneva. Multicoloured.

1277	60c. Type **321**	1·20	40
1278	80c. Gothic letterpress script	1·30	1·20
1279	100c. Modern electronic fonts	1·60	1·60

322 Athletes

1994. Publicity Issue. Multicoloured.

1280	60c. Type **322** (50th Anniv of National Sports School, Magglingen)	1·20	40
1281	80c. Jakob Bernoulli (mathematician) (after Nicolas Bernoulli) and formula and diagram of the law of large numbers (Int Mathematicians' Congress, Zurich)	1·30	1·10
1282	100c. Heads, Unisource emblem, globe and flags (collaboration of Swiss, Dutch and Swedish telecommunications companies)	1·60	1·60
1283	180c. Radar image, airliner and globe (50th anniv of I.C.A.O.)	3·25	2·75

323 Footballers

1994. World Cup Football Championship, U.S.A., and Cent (1995) of Swiss Football Association.

1284 **323** 80c. multicoloured 2·00 1·20

324 "Trieste" (bathyscaphe)

1994. Europa. Discoveries and Inventions. Vehicles used by Auguste Piccard in Stratospheric and Deep-sea Explorations. Multicoloured.

1285	60c. Type **324**	1·20	40
1286	100c. "F.N.R.S." (stratosphere balloon)	2·40	2·75

325 Neuchatel Weight- driven Clock (Jacques Matthey-Jonais)

1994. Pro Patria. Folk Art. Multicoloured.

1287	60c.+30c. Type **325**	1·60	1·20
1288	60c.+30c. Embroidered pomegranate on linen	1·60	1·20
1289	80c.+40c. Mould for Krafli pastry	2·40	2·40
1290	100c.+40c. Paper-bird cradle mobile	2·75	2·75

326 Symbolic Condom

1994. Anti-AIDS Campaign.

1291 **326** 60c. multicoloured 95 45

327 Simenon and his Home, Echandens Castle, Lausanne

1994. 5th Death Anniv of Georges Simenon (novelist).

1292 **327** 100c. multicoloured 2·00 1·60

328 "Swiss Electricity"

1995. Publicity Issue.

1293	**328**	60c. multicoloured	1·20	40
1294	-	60c. blue and black	95	40
1295	-	80c. multicoloured	1·30	80
1296	-	180c. multicoloured	2·75	2·75

DESIGNS—HORIZ: No. 1293, Type **328** (centenary of Swiss Association of Electricity Producers and Distributors); 1295, "(sda ats)" (centenary of Swiss News Agency); 1296, "ONU UNO" (50th anniv of U.N.O.). VERT: No. 1294, Wrestlers (centenary of Swiss Wrestling Association and National Wrestling and Alpine Herdsmen's Festival, Chur).

329 European Beaver

1995. Endangered Animals. Multicoloured.

1297	60c. Type **329**	1·20	40
1298	80c. Map butterfly	1·60	1·30
1299	100c. Green tree frog	2·00	1·60
1300	120c. Little owl	2·40	1·90

330 Cream Pail, 1776

1995. Pro Patria. Folk Art. Multicoloured.

1301	60c.+30c. Type **330**	1·60	1·20
1302	60c.+30c. Neuchatel straw hat	1·60	1·20
1303	80c.+40c. Detail of chest lock, 1580	2·40	2·40
1304	100c.+40c. Langnau ceramic sugar bowl	2·75	2·75

331 Couple and Dove

1995. Europa. Peace and Freedom.

1305	**331**	60c. blue and cobalt	2·40	40
1306	-	100c. brown and ochre	4·00	2·00

DESIGN: 100c. Europa with Zeus as bull.

332 Basel (right-hand part)

1995. "Basler Taube 1995" Stamp Exhibition, Basel. Sheet 100×131 mm. containing T 332 and similar vert designs.

MS1307 60c.+30c. black, violet and blue; 80c+30c. multicoloured; 100c.+50c. black, violet and blue; 100c+50c. black, violet and blue 8·75 8·75

DESIGNS: 80c.+30c. Basel 2½ Dove stamp (150th Anniv of issue); 60c+30c., 100c.+50c. (2) Panorama of Basel by Matthaus Meriam (composite design).

333 Coloured Ribbons woven through River

1995. Switzerland–Liechtenstein Co-operation.

1308 **333** 60c. multicoloured 95 40

No. 1308 was valid for use in both Switzerland and Liechtenstein (see No. 1106 of Liechtenstein).

334 "The Vocation of Andre Carrel" (1925)

1995. Centenary of Motion Pictures. Multicoloured.

1309	60c. Type **334**	95	40
1310	80c. "Anna Goldin – The Last Witch"	1·30	1·20
1311	150c. "Pipilotti's Mistakes – Absolution"	2·40	2·40

335 Ear, Eye and Mouth

1995. "Telecom 95" International Telecommunications Exhibition, Geneva.

1312 **335** 180c. multicoloured 2·75 2·75

336 "A" (first class) Mail

1995

1313 **336** 90c. blue, red and yellow 1·40 40

See also No. 1480.

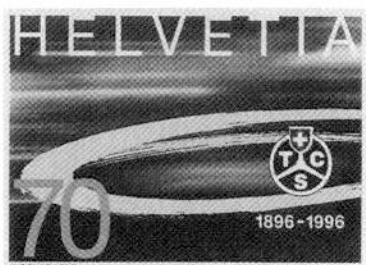

337 Emblem

1996. Publicity Issue. Multicoloured.

1314	70c. Type **337** (centenary of Touring Club of Switzerland)	1·10	55
1315	70c. Heart (50th anniv of charity organizations)	1·10	55
1316	90c. Brass band (30th Federal Music Festival, Interlaken)	1·40	1·40
1317	90c. Young girls (centenary of Pro Filia (girls' aid society))	1·40	1·40
1318	180c. Jean Piaget (child psychologist, birth centenary)	2·75	2·75

338 Coloured Ribbons and "Bern 96" Gymnastic Festival Emblem

1996. Pro Sport.

1319	**338**	70c.+30c. multicoloured	1·60	1·60

339 Corinna Bille (writer)

1996. Europa. Famous Women. Multicoloured.

1320	70c. Type **339**	1·10	40
1321	110c. Iris von Roten-Meyer (feminist writer)	1·70	2·00

340 Magdalena Chapel, Wolfenschiessen, and Cross

1996. Pro Patria. Heritage. Multicoloured.

1322	70c.+35c. Type **340**	2·00	1·20
1323	70c.+35c. Underground sawmill and workshop, Col-des-Roches	2·00	1·20
1324	90c.+40c. Baroque baths, Pfafers	2·75	2·75
1325	110c.+50c. Roman road and milestone, Great St. Bernhard	3·25	3·25

341 Olympic Rings

1996. Centenary of Modern Olympic Games.

1326	**341**	180c. multicoloured	3·50	2·75

342 Representation of 1995 "A" Mail Stamp

1996. Guinness World Record for Largest "Living" Postage Stamp represented by Human Beings (arrangement of people to represent stamp design).

1327	**342**	90c. multicoloured	1·60	1·60

343 Musical Movement and Mechanical Ring (Isaac-Daniel Piguet)

1996. Bicentenary of Antoine Favre-Salomon's Invention of the Metal Teeth System for Music Boxes. Multicoloured.

1328	70c. Type **343**	1·20	55
1329	90c. "Basso-piccolo mandolin" cylinder music box (Eduard Jaccard)	1·60	1·60
1330	110c. Station automaton (Paillard & Co)	2·00	2·00
1331	180c. Kalliope disc music box	3·25	3·25

344 Pattern

1996. Greetings Stamps. Multicoloured. Self-adhesive.

1332	90c. Type **344**	2·00	2·00
1333	90c. Mottled pattern	2·00	2·00
1334	90c. Coil pattern	2·00	2·00
1335	90c. Flower and leaf pattern	2·00	2·00

345 "The Golden Cow" (Daniel Ammann)

1996. Winning Entries in Stamp Design Competition.

1336	**345**	70c. gold and blue	1·10	55
1337	-	90c. multicoloured	2·20	1·40
1338	-	110c. multicoloured	1·70	2·50
1339	-	180c. brown, black and blue	2·75	2·75

DESIGNS: 90c. "Wake with a Smile" (Max Sprick); 110c. "Leaves" (Elena Emma-Pugliese); 180c. "Dove" (Rene Conscience).

346 Globi delivering Mail

1997. Globi (cartoon character by Robert Lips).

1340	**346**	70c. multicoloured	1·10	65

347 Venus of Octodurus

1997. Gallo-Roman Works of Art. Multicoloured.

1341	70c. Type **347** (from Forum Claudii Vallensium (now Martigny))	1·10	80
1342	90c. Bust of Bacchus (from Augusta Raurica (now Augst))	1·40	1·60
1343	110c. Ceramic fragment showing "Victory" (from Iulio Magus (now Schleitheim))	1·70	2·00
1344	180c. Mosaic showing female theatrical mask (from Vallon)	2·75	3·25

Each stamp is inscribed with the name of the Foundation bearing responsibility for the preservation of the respective archaeological sites.

348 Class 460 Series 2000 Electric Locomotive

1997. 150th Anniv of Zurich–Barden Railway. Multicoloured.

1345	70c. Type **348**	1·40	80
1346	90c. Electric "Red Arrow" railcar set, 1935	1·80	1·60
1347	1f.40 Pullman coach, 1930s	2·75	2·40
1348	1f.70 "Limmat", 1847 (first locomotive in Switzerland)	3·25	3·25

349 Douglas DC-4 "Grand Old Lady" over Globe

1997. 50th Anniv of Swissair's North Atlantic Service.

1349	**349**	180c. multicoloured	3·50	2·75

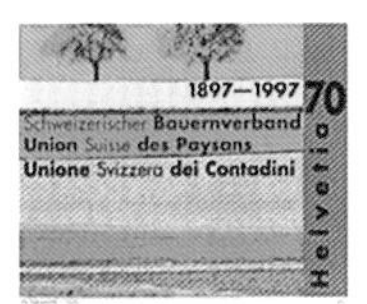

350 Farmland

1997. Publicity Issue. Multicoloured.

1350	70c. Type **350** (centenary of Swiss Farmers' Union)	1·10	45
1351	90c. Street plan (centenary of Swiss Municipalities' Union)	1·40	1·40

351 "Devil and the Goat" (painting by Heinrich Danioth on rock face of Schollenen Gorge)

1997. Europa. Tales and Legends. The Devil's Bridge.

1352	**351**	90c. brown and yellow	1·60	1·60

352 St. Valbert's Church, Soubey (Jura)

1997. Pro Patria. Heritage and Landscapes. Mult.

1353	70c.+35c. Type **352**	2·00	1·20
1354	70c.+35c. Culture mill, Lutzelfluh (Berne)	2·00	1·20
1355	90c.+40c. Ittingen Charterhouse (Thurgau)	2·75	2·75
1356	110c.+50c. Casa Patriziale, Russo (Ticino)	3·25	3·25

353 Clouds (Air)

1997. Energy 2000 (energy efficiency programme). The Elements. Multicoloured.

1357	70c. Type **353**	1·10	65
1358	90c. Burning wood (Fire)	1·40	1·60
1359	110c. Water droplets (Water)	1·70	2·00
1360	180c. Pile of soil (Earth)	2·75	3·25

354 King Rama V and President Adolf Deucher

1997. Centenary of Visit of King Rama V of Siam.

1361	**354**	90c. multicoloured	1·40	1·40

355 Paul Karrer and Molecular Structure of Vitamin A

1997. The Nobel Prize.

1362	**355**	90c. black and grey	1·80	1·40
1363	-	110c. black and purple	2·10	1·70

DESIGNS: 90c. Type **355** (Chemistry Prize, 1937); 110c. Alfred Nobel (founder of Prize Fund).

356 Woman and Boy (German)

1997. "The Post keeps Us in Touch".

1364	**356**	70c. black, red and blue	1·40	45
1365	-	70c. black, yellow and blue	1·40	45
1366	-	70c. black, yellow and green	1·40	45
1367	-	70c. black, green and red	1·40	45

DESIGNS: No. 1365, Boy wearing baseball cap with woman (French); 1366, Young couple (Italian); 1367, Girl and man (Romansch).

357 Postal Service Emblem

1998. Separation of Swiss Post and Swisscom (telecommunications).

1368	**357**	90c. black, yellow and red	1·40	1·40
1369	-	90c. deep blue, blue and red	1·40	1·40

DESIGN: No. 1369, Swisscom emblem.

358 Arrows

1998. Bicentenary of Declaration of Helvetic Republic and 150th Anniv of Swiss Federal State. Multicoloured.

1370	90c. Type **358**	1·60	1·60
1371	90c. Face value at bottom right	1·60	1·60
1372	90c. Face value at top left	1·60	1·60
1373	90c. Face value at top right	1·60	1·60

359 Winter Olympics 2006

1998. Swiss Candidacy for Winter Olympic Games.

1374	**359**	90c. multicoloured	1·60	1·60

360 Elderly Couple

1998. Publicity Issues. Multicoloured.

1375	70c. Type **360** (Old Age and Survivor's Insurance)	1·20	80
1376	70c. National Museum, Prangins Castle (centenary of Swiss National Museum, Zurich, and inauguration of Prangins branch)	1·20	80
1377	90c. Fingerprints (centenary of St. Gallen University)	1·40	80

361 "On Top of the Simplon Pass"

1998. Paintings by Jean-Frederic Schnyder. Multicoloured.

1378	10c. Type **361**	15	15
1379	20c. "Snowdrift near Neuthal"	40	20
1380	50c. "Franches Montagnes"	95	40
1381	70c. "Two Horses"	1·10	40
1382	90c. "En Route"	1·40	40
1383	110c. "Winter Morning by the Alpnachersee"	1·70	80
1385	140c. "Zug"	2·20	80
1386	170c. "Olive Grove"	2·75	95
1387	180c. "Near Reutigen"	2·75	1·40

362 St. Gall, Rhine Valley

1998. Pro Patria. Heritage and Landscapes. Mult.

1390	70c.+35c. Type **362**	2·00	1·60
1391	70c.+35c. Round church, Saas Balen	2·00	1·60
1392	90c.+40c. Forest, Bodmeren	2·50	2·50
1393	90c.+40c. The old Refuge (museum), St. Gotthard	2·50	2·50
1394	110c.+50c. Smithy, Corcelles	3·25	2·30

363 Lanterns

1998. Europa. National Festivals. National Day.

1395	**363**	90c. multicoloured	2·00	1·60

364 In-line Skating

1998. Sports. Multicoloured. Self-adhesive.

1396	70c. Type **364**	1·40	1·40
1397	70c. Snow-boarding	1·40	1·40
1398	70c. Mountain biking	1·40	1·40
1399	70c. Basketball	1·40	1·40
1400	70c. Beach volleyball	1·40	1·40

365 Bridge 24, Slender West Lake, Yangzhou, China

1998. Lakes. Multicoloured.

1401	20c. Type **365**	40	40
1402	70c. Chillon Castle, Lake Geneva	1·10	1·10
MS1403	96×70 mm. 90c. Chillion Castle and Bridge 24 (52×44 mm)	2·40	2·40

366 Emblem and Face

1998. 50th Anniv of Universal Declaration of Human Rights.

1404	**366**	70c. multicoloured	1·10	80

367 Christmas Wrapping

1998. Christmas.

1405	**367**	90c. multicoloured	1·30	1·60

368 Postman with Letter and Posthorn on Globe

1999. 150th Anniv of Swiss Postal Service.

1406	**368**	90c. multicoloured	1·60	1·60

369 Little Pingu carrying Parcel

1999. Youth Stamps. Pingu (cartoon character). Multicoloured.

1407	70c. Type **369**	1·10	80
1408	90c. Papa Pingu driving snowmobile	1·40	1·60

370 Vieux Bois falls in Love at First Sight

1999. Birth Bicentenary of Rodolphe Topffer (cartoonist). Scenes from "The Love of Monsieur Vieux Boris". Multicoloured. Self-adhesive.

1409	90c. Type **370**	1·80	1·80
1410	90c. Vieux Bois declares his love	1·80	1·80
1411	90c. Vieux Bois jumps in air with joy, knocking over furniture	1·80	1·80
1412	90c. Vieux Bois helping his love over wall	1·80	1·80
1413	90c. Wedding of Vieux Bois	1·80	1·80

371 "Breitling Orbiter 3"

1999. 1st World Circumnavigation by Balloon, by Bertrand Piccard and Brian Jones.

1414	**371**	90c. multicoloured	2·00	1·40

372 Envelope Flap

1999. 125th Anniv of Universal Postal Union.

1415	**372**	20c. yellow and black	80	80
1416	-	70c. black, red and yellow	1·60	1·60

DESIGN—55×29 mm: 70c. U.P.U. emblem on card in envelope.

Nos. 1415/16 were printed, *se-tenant*, forming a composite design.

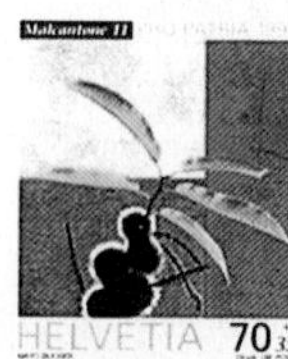

373 Jester and Clown

1999. Publicity Issue.

1417	**373**	70c. multicoloured	1·10	80
1418	-	90c. multicoloured	1·40	1·60
1419	-	90c. multicoloured	1·40	1·60
1420	-	1f.10 red and black	1·70	1·80

DESIGNS: No. 1417, Type **373** (50th anniv of SOS Children's Villages); 1418, Sketch of giant puppets (Winegrowers' Festival, Vevey); 1419, Flags of member countries and emblem (50th anniv of Council of Europe); 1420, Red Cross and emblem (50th anniv of Geneva Conventions).

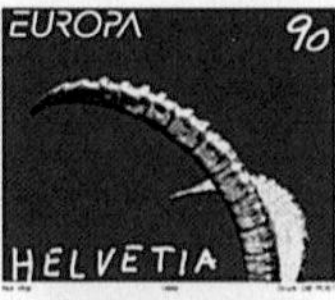

374 Chestnuts from Malcantone

1999. Pro Patria. Heritage and Landscapes. Mult.

1421	70c.+35c. Type **374**	2·00	1·60
1422	70c.+35c. La Sarraz Castle	2·00	1·60
1423	90c.+40c. "Uri" (lake steamer)	2·75	2·50
1424	110c.+50c. St. Christopher carrying Baby Jesus (detail of fresco, St. Paul's Chapel, Rhazuns)	3·25	2·50

375 Ibex Horns (National Park, Engadine)

1999. Europa. Parks and Gardens.

1425	**375**	90c. black and blue	2·00	1·60

376 Roofs of Buildings

1999. "naba 2000" National Stamp Exhibition, St. Gallen (1st issue). Sheet 66×85 mm containing T 376 and similar vert designs. Multicoloured.

MS1426	20c.+10c. Type **376**; 70c.+30c. Spire of St. Laurenzen's Church; 90c.+30c. Oriel window	6·25	6·25

See also No. **MS**1442.

377 Children holding Pictures

1999. Publicity Issue. Multicoloured.

1427	70c. Type **377** (Children's Rights)	1·10	80
1428	90c. Carl Lutz (Swiss diplomat in Budapest during Second World War) (24th death anniv)	1·60	1·60
1429	1f.10 Chemical model of ozone and globe (birth bicentenary of Christian Schönbein (chemist))	1·70	1·70
1430	180c. "Midday in the Alps" (death centenary of Giovanni Segantini (painter))	3·00	3·00

378 Schollenen Gorge Monument, Suvorov and Soldiers

1999. Bicentenary of General Aleksandr Suvorov's Crossing of the Alps. Multicoloured.

1431	70c. Type **378**	1·40	1·10
1432	110c. Suvorov vanguard (after engraving by L. Hess) passing Lake Klontal	2·10	1·70

379 Christmas Bauble

1999. Christmas.

1433	**379**	90c. multicoloured	1·40	1·40

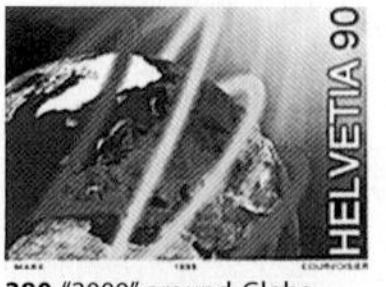

380 "2000" around Globe

1999. Year 2000.

1434	**380**	90c. multicoloured	1·40	1·40

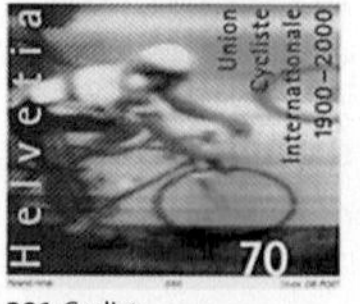

381 Cyclist

2000. Centenary of International Cycling Union.

1435	**381**	70c. multicoloured	1·40	80

382 Alphorn Player

2000. Snow Storms. Multicoloured.

1436	10c. Type **382**	15	10
1437	20c. Fondue	30	25
1438	30c. Jugs and grapes on tray	55	45
1439	50c. Mountain goat	80	80
1440	60c. Clock	95	95
1441	70c. St. Bernards	1·10	40

See also No. 1479.

383 "ON I"

2000. "naba 2000" National Stamp Exhibition, St. Gallen (2nd issue). Sheet 65×85 mm containing T 383 and similar vert designs. Multicoloured.

MS1442	20c.+10c. Type **383** (right-hand corner; 20c.+10c. "5" (bottom left-hand corner); 70c.+35c. "RAY" (top left-hand corner), 90c.+45c. "Rp" (bottom right-hand corner.	7·00	7·00

The four stamps in **MS**1448 were issued together to form a composite design depiting a modern representation of a 1850 5r. Federal Administration stamp.

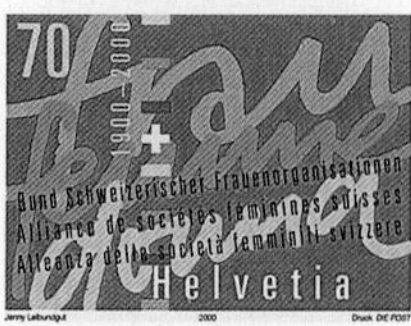

384 "frau" and Emblem

2000. Centenary of National Council of Women.

1443	**384**	70c. multicoloured	1·10	80

385 "Building Europe"

2000. Europa.

1444	**385**	90c. multicoloured	1·60	1·60

386 Town Square, Nafels

2000. Pro Patria. "Townscapes 2000" (rejuvenation projects). Multicoloured.

1445	70c.+35c. Type **386**	2·00	2·00
1446	70c.+35c. Main road, Tengia	2·00	2·00
1447	90c.+40c. Main road, Brugg	2·75	2·75
1448	90c.+40c. Marketplace, Carouge	2·75	2·75

387 Payerne Church and Violin

2000. Tourism. Multicoloured (except 1451, blue, turquoise and red).

1449	90c. Willisan farmhouse and horse	1·80	1·80
1450	100c. *La Suisse* (lake steamer) and woman looking over Lake Geneva	2·00	2·00
1451	110c. Kleine Matterhorn glacier and skier	2·20	2·20
1452	120c. Type **387**	2·00	1·20
1453	130c. St. Saphorin Church and bottle of wine	2·00	1·20
1454	180c. National spring and bather, Vals	2·75	2·40
1455	200c. Landscape and walker	3·25	2·40
1456	220c. Bus and children	4·25	4·25
1457	300c. Stone bridge and mountain bike	4·75	3·25
1459	400c. Airplane fin and man with suitcase	7·75	7·75

388 Embroidery

2000. St. Gallen Embroidery. Self-adhesive

1460	**388**	5f. cobalt and blue	9·50	9·50
MS1461		158×132 mm. No. 1460 ×4	£225	£325

389 Emblem

2000. Population Census.

1462	**389**	70c. multicoloured	1·10	80

390 "Alien from Outer Space" (Yannick Kehrli)

2000. "Stampin' the Future". Winning Entries in Children's International Painting Competition. Multicoloured. Self-adhesive.

1463	70c. Type **390**	2·40	2·40
1464	70c. "Looks below the Sun" (Charlotte Battig)	2·40	2·40
1465	70c. "The Perfect World" (Sandra Dobler)	2·40	2·40
1466	70c. "My Town" (Stephanie Aerschmann)	2·40	2·40

391 Swimming

2000. Olympic Games, Sydney. Multicoloured. Self-adhesive.

1467	90c. Type **391**	2·40	2·40
1468	90c. Cycling	2·40	2·40
1469	90c. Running	2·40	2·40

392 Cathedral and Horsemen

2000. Stamp Day.

1470	**392**	70c. multicoloured	1·40	1·10

393 Dresden-style Tree Decoration

2000. Christmas.

1471	**393**	90c. multicoloured	2·20	1·40

394 Alice Rivaz

2001. Anniversaries.

1472	**394**	70c. multicoloured	1·10	80
1473	-	90c. multicoloured	1·80	1·60
1474	-	110c. red, grey and black	1·70	1·70
1475	-	130c. multicoloured	2·00	2·20

DESIGNS—As Type **394**:70c. Type **394** (writer, birth centenary); 110c. "CARITAS" and jigsaw pieces (centenary of Caritas (Christian charity organization)); 130c. Refugees (50th Anniv of United Nations High Commissioner for Refugees). Size 39×30 mm: 90c. Airplane (centenary of Aero-Club of Switzerland).

395 Flowers and Envelope

2001. Greetings Stamp.

1476	**395**	90c. multicoloured	1·80	1·80

396 Woman's Head

2001. Anniversary and Event. Multicoloured.

1477	70c. Type **396** (re-opening of Vela Museum, Ligornetto)	1·40	1·40
1478	90c. Chocolate segment (centenary of Chocosuisse)	2·40	2·40

No. 1478 is impregnated with the scent of chocolate.

2001. Self-adhesive Stamps.

1479	-	70c. mult (as No. 1441)	1·40	1·40
1480	**336**	90c. blue, orge & lemon	1·80	1·80

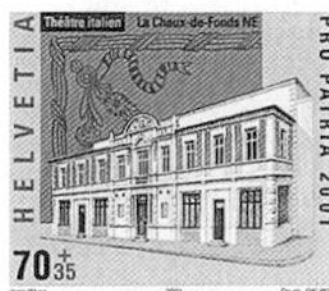
397 Italian Theatre, La Chaux-de-Fonds

2001. Pro Patria. Cultural Heritage.

1481	70c.+35c. black, orange and red	2·00	2·00
1482	70c.+35c. black, brown and green	2·00	2·00
1483	90c.+40c. black, brown and lemon	2·75	2·75
1484	90c.+40c. multicoloured	2·75	2·75

DESIGNS: No. 1482, Hauterive Monastery; 1483, Leuk Castle; 1484, Rorschach Granary.

398 Water

2001. Europa. Water Resources.

1485	**398**	90c. multicoloured	1·80	1·80

399 Blue Rainbow Fish

2001. Illustrations from *Rainbow Fish* (book by Martin Pfister). Multicoloured.

1486	70c. Type **399**	1·40	1·40
1487	90c. Purple rainbow fish	1·80	1·80

400 Straits Rhododendron (*Melastoma malabathricum*)

2001. Switzerland–Singapore Joint Issue. Flowers. Sheet 98×68 mm, containing T 400 and similar horiz designs. Multicoloured.

MS1488 70c. Type **400**; 90c. *Saraca cauliflora*; 110c. Edelweiss (*Leontopodium alpinum*); 130c. Gentian (*Gentiana clusii*) 7·75 7·75

401 "The Birth of Venus"

2001. Death Centenary of Arnold Bocklin (artist).

1489	**401**	180c. multicoloured	3·50	3·50

402 Buildings (Beat Kehrli)

2001. Stamp Day. Winning entry in stamp design competition.

1490	**402**	70c. multicoloured	1·40	1·40

403 Gablonz-style Christmas Tree Ornament

2001. Christmas.

1491	**403**	90c. multicoloured	2·00	1·80

404 Ladder, Wall and Stars

2002. Escalade (festival) (celebrating 400th anniv of defeat of Savoyard attack on the city), Geneva.

1492	**404**	70c. multicoloured	1·40	1·40

405 "E" and Towers, Biel

2002. "Expo '02" National Exhibition, Biel, Murten, Neuchatel and Yverdon-les-Bains (1st issue). Each featuring "Arteplage" (exhibition platform) of each host town. Multicoloured.

1493	70c. Type **405**	1·40	1·40
1494	70c. Reversed "P" and Monolith, Murten	1·40	1·40
1495	70c. "O", pebble-shaped construction over water, Neuchatel	1·40	1·40
1496	70c. "2" and artificial cloud, Yverdon-les-Bains	1·40	1·40

See also No. **MS**1509.

406 RABDe 500 InterCity Tilting Train (ICN)

2002. Centenary of Swiss Federal Railways (SBB) (national railway operator). Multicoloured.

1497	70c. Type **406**	1·60	1·60
1498	90c. InterCity 2000 double-deck train	2·40	2·40
1499	120c. Railcar, Lucerne–Lenzburg Seetal line	2·40	2·40
1500	130c. 119 Re 460 locomotive	3·25	3·25

407 Facade

2002. Centenary of Federal Parliament Building.

1501	**407**	90c. multicoloured	1·80	1·80

408 Augusta A-109-K2 Helicopter and Hawker 800B Air Ambulance

2002. 50th Anniv of Swiss Air Rescue (Rega).

1502	**408**	180c. multicoloured	3·50	3·50

409 Clown

2002. Europa. Circus. Multicoloured.

1503	70c. Type **409**	1·40	1·40
1504	90c. Clown (different)	1·80	1·80

410 Bruzella, Ticino Canton

2002. Pro Patria. Water Mills Preservation. Water mills. Multicoloured.

1505	70c.+35c. Type **410**	2·00	2·00
1506	70c.+35c. Oberdorf, Basel Canton	2·00	2·00
1507	90c.+40c. Lussery-Villars, de Vaud Canton	2·75	2·75
1508	90c.+40c. Buren a. d. Aare, Berne Canton	2·75	2·75

411 "X"

2002. "Expo '02", 6th National Exhibition, Biel, Murten, Neuchatel and Yverdon-les-Bains (2nd issue). Sheet 95×70 mm.

MS1509	**411**	90c. multicoloured	4·00	4·00

412 Two Teddies (Switzerland, c. 1950)

2002. Centenary of the Teddy Bear. Multicoloured. Self-adhesive.

1510	90c. White teddy with pink bow (France, 1925) (26×26 mm, round)	1·80	1·80
1511	90c. Type **412**	1·80	1·80
1512	90c. Teddy with grey-brown bow (Germany, 1904) (22×32 mm, oval)	1·80	1·80
1513	90c. "Philibert", Swiss Post Teddy (Switzerland, 2002) (26×22 mm, rectangle)	1·80	1·80
1514	90c. Teddy with grey paws (England, c. 1920) (26×26 mm, round)	1·80	1·80

413 Emblem

2002. Switzerland's Acccession to the United Nations.

1515	**413**	90c. multicoloured	1·80	1·80

414 Emperor Dragonfly (*Anax imperator*)

2002. Insects. Multicoloured.

1516	10c. Type **414**	25	25
1517	20c. Dark green fritillary (*Mesoacidalia aglaja*)	65	65
1518	50c. Alpine longhorn beetle (*Rosalia alpina*)	95	95
1519	100c. Striped bug (*Graphosoma lineatum*)	2·00	2·00

415 Printing Press (copper engraving, Abraham Bosse)

2002. Swiss Post Stamp Printers, Berne Commemoration.

1520	**415**	70c. multicoloured	1·40	1·40

416 Ladybird on Leaf

2002. Greeting Stamp. Self-adhesive.

1521	**416**	90c. multicoloured	2·00	1·60

417 Quartz

2002. Minerals. Multicoloured.

1522	200c. Type **417**	4·00	4·00
1523	300c. Rutilated quartz	9·75	9·75
1524	400c. Fluorite	1·90	1·60
1525	500c. Titanite	4·50	4·25
1525a	500c. Titanite	9·00	8·50

418 Kingfisher and Jura Water Engineering System (Michele Berri)

2002. Stamp Day. Winning Entry in Stamp Design Competition.

1535	**418**	70c. multicoloured	1·40	1·40

419 Bohemian Cardboard Tree Decoration, c. 1900

2002. Christmas.

1536	**419**	90c. multicoloured	1·80	1·80

420 Skier

2002. World Alpine Skiing Championship, St. Moritz.

1537	**420**	90c. multicoloured	1·80	1·80

421 "70"

2003. Centenary of Swiss National Association of the Blind and Library for the Blind and Visually Impaired.

1538	**421**	70c. orange	1·40	1·40

No. 1538 was embossed with 70 in Braille.

422 Hypericum (*Hypericum perforatum*)

2003. Medicinal Plants. Multicoloured.

1539	70c. Type **422**	1·40	1·40
1540	90c. Periwinkle (*Vinca minor*)	1·80	1·80
1541	110c. Valerian (*Valeriana officinalis*)	2·20	2·20
1542	120c. *Arnica Montana*	2·40	2·40
1543	130c. Centaury (*Centaurium minus*)	2·50	2·50
1544	180c. Mallow (*Malva sylvestris*)	3·50	3·50
1545	220c. Chamomile (*Matricaria chamomilla*)	4·25	4·25

423 Waterfall

2003. International Year of Water.

1546	**423**	90c. multicoloured	1·80	1·80

424 Contour Lines, Compass and Runner

2003. World Orienteering Championships, Rapperswil-Jona.

1547	**424**	90c. multicoloured	1·80	1·80

425 Horse's Head

2003. Centenary of Marche-Concours (horse show and market), Saignelegier.

1548	**425**	90c. multicoloured	1·80	1·80

426 *Alinghi* (yacht)

2003. Switzerland, America's Cup Winners, 2003.

1549	**426**	90c. multicoloured	2·75	2·75

427 Eagle

2003. Ticino 2003 International Stamp Exhibition, Locarno. Sheet 96×70 mm containing T 427 and similar vert design. Multicoloured.

MS1550	20c. Type **427**; 70c. Gentians	2·30	2·30

428 Laura

2003. 20th International Comics Festival, Sierre. Characters created by Tom Tirabosco. Multicoloured.

1551	70c. Type **428**	1·40	1·40
1552	70c. Marco	1·40	1·40
1553	70c. Louis	1·40	1·40
1554	70c. Djema	1·40	1·40
MS1555	96×70 mm. 90c. Heidi	2·30	2·30

429 Innere Wynigen Bridge, Burgdorf, Berne Canton

2003. Historic Bridges and Footbridges. Multicoloured.

1556	70c.+35c. Type **429**	2·30	2·30
1557	70c.+35c. Salginatobel, Schiers, Grisons	2·30	2·30
1558	90c.+40c. Pont St-Jean, Saint Ursanne, Jura Canton	2·75	2·75
1559	90c.+40c. Reuss, Rottenschwil, Aargau Canton	2·75	2·75

430 "Don't Forget the Discount Stamp" (Donald Brun)

2003. Europa. Poster Art.

1560	**430**	90c. multicoloured	1·90	1·70

431 Diddl and Diddlina

2003. Diddl (cartoon character created by Thomas Goletz). Multicoloured.

1561	70c. Type **431**	1·50	1·40
1562	90c. Diddl chasing winged envelopes	2·10	1·80

432 Jungfrau-Aletsch-Bietschhorn Region

2003. UNESCO World Heritage Sites. Multicoloured.

1563	90c. Type **432**	2·10	2·10
1564	90c. Three Castles, Bellinzona	2·10	2·10
1565	90c. Berne Old City	2·10	2·10
1566	90c. St. Gall Abbey Precinct	2·10	2·10
1567	90c. Mustair Convent	2·10	2·10

433 Onion market, Berne

2003. Stamp Day. Winning Entry in Stamp Design Competition.

1568	**433**	70c. multicoloured	1·40	1·20

434 Wooden Horseman (Erzgebirge)

2003. Christmas. Regional Tree Decorations. Multicoloured.

1569	70c. Type **434**	1·50	1·20
1570	90c. Glass Father Christmas (Thuringa)	2·10	1·40

435 Four-leafed Clover

2003. Greetings Stamp.

1571	**435**	1f.30 multicoloured	2·50	2·30

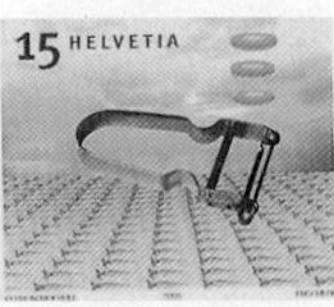

436 Rex Potato Peeler (Alfred Neweczeral, 1947)

2003. Swiss Design Classics. Multicoloured. Self-adhesive gum.

1572	15c. Type **436**	40	35
1573	85c. Station clock (Hans Hilfiker, 1944)	1·40	1·30
1584	100c. Armchair (Heidi Weber (1959) after Le Corbusier (1928)	3·75	3·50
1587	50c. "Riri" (zip fastener)	1·20	1·00
1590	100c. "Landi" (chair) (Hans Coray, 1939)	2·10	1·80
1590a	220c. "Fixpencil" (Caran d'Ache 1929)	4·25	3·75
1591	220c. As No. 1585a	2·00	1·50

437 Titeuf and Nadia

2004. Titeuf (cartoon created by Philippe Chappuis (Zep)). Multicoloured.

1595	85c. Type **437** (Spring)	1·80	1·60
1596	85c. Sitting in refrigerator (Summer)	1·80	1·60
1597	85c. Kicking leaves (Autumn)	1·80	1·60
1598	85c. With snowman (Winter)	1·80	1·60

438 Centenary Emblem

2004. Centenary of FIFA (Federation Internationale de Football Association).

1599	**438**	1f. multicoloured	2·30	2·10

439 Family

2004. Cycling. Sheet 96×70 mm containing T 439 and similar horiz design. Multicoloured.

MS1600 1f. ×2, Type **439**; Two cyclists reading map 4·25 4·25

440 Past and Present Players

2004. 50th Anniv of UEFA (Union of European Football Associations).

1601	**440**	1f.30 multicoloured	2·50	2·30

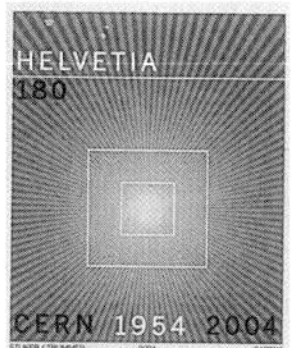

441 Rays

2004. 50th Anniv of CERN (European Organization for Nuclear Research).

1602	**441**	1f.80 gold, light blue and black	3·75	3·50

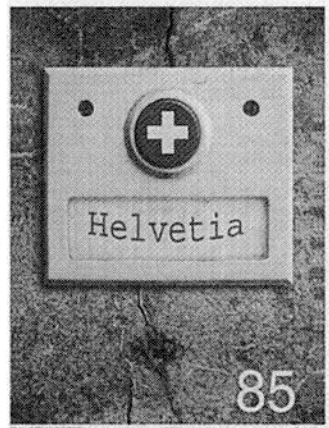

442 Doorbell and "Helvetia" (Emil Steinberger)

2004. Humour.

1603	**442**	85c. multicoloured	2·10	1·80

443 Bathing Pavilion, Gorgier

2004. Pro Patria. Small Buildings Preservation. Multicoloured.

1604	85c.+ 40c. Type **443**	2·50	2·50
1605	85c.+ 40c. Granary, Oberramsern	2·50	2·50
1606	1f.+50c. Seeburg landing stage, Lucerne	3·00	3·00
1607	1f.+50c. Ossuary, Gentilino	3·00	3·00

444 Diddl holding Pimboli

2004. Diddl (cartoon character created by Thomas Goletz) (2nd series). Multicoloured.

1608	85c. Type **444**	1·70	1·50
1609	1f. Diddl holding flower	2·20	2·00

445 Olympic Rings, Stadium and Runner

2004. Olympic Games, Athens.

1610	**445**	1f. multicoloured	2·10	1·80

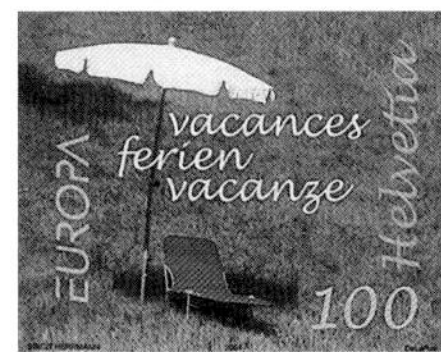

446 Sun Lounger and Parasol

2004. Europa. Holidays.

1611	**446**	1f. multicoloured	2·10	1·80

447 Zeppelin NT Type Z No. 7

2004

1612	**447**	1f.80 multicoloured	3·75	3·50

448 Boy leapfrogging Pumpkin

2004. Suisse Balance (healthy eating campaign).

1613	**448**	85c. multicoloured	1·80	1·60

449 1854 10r. Stamp

2004. 150th Anniv of Strubeli (dishevelled) Stamps (first stamps showing seated Helvetia ("Mother of the Nation")). Sheet 96×70 mm containing T 449 and similar vert design. Multicoloured.

MS1614 85c. ×2, Type **449**; Coin showing Helvetia 3·75 3·75

450 Cat

2004. Swiss Animal Protection (SAP). Mult.

1615	85c. Type **450**	2·10	1·90
1616	1f. Hedgehog	2·30	2·10
1617	1f.30 Pig	2·75	2·50

451 Fossil and Mountains

2004. UNESCO World Heritage Site. Mount San Giorgio.

1618	**451**	1f. mauve and black	2·30	2·10

452 Making Cheese

2004. Traditional Food. Cheese. Multicoloured.

1619	1f. Type **452**	2·30	2·10
1620	1f.30 Cheeses and grapes	2·75	2·50

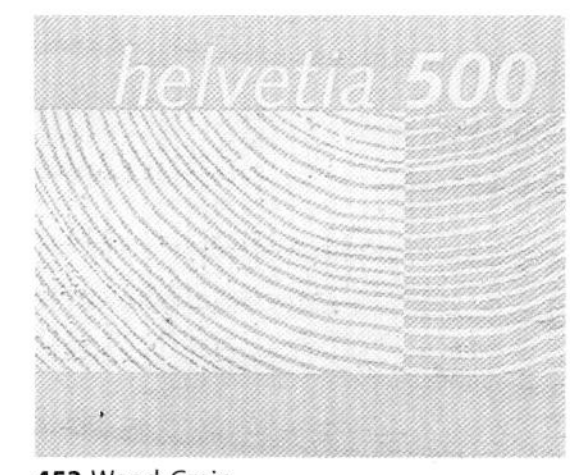

453 Wood Grain

2004. Sustainable Wood Production. Self-adhesive.

1621	**453**	5f. ochre	10·50	9·50

No. 1621 was made from wood veneer which has to be peeled from the backing paper.

454 Hydro Electric Power

2004. Stamp Day. Winning Entry in Stamp Design Competition.

1622	**454**	85c. multicoloured	1·80	1·70

455 Star

2004. Christmas. Tree Decorations. Sheet 160×56 mm containing T 455 and similar vert designs. Multicoloured.

MS1623 85c. Type **455**; 85c. Church; 1f. Angel; 1f. Horse and rider; 1f. Father Christmas 9·75 9·75

457 Children Kissing

2005. Greetings Stamps. Self-adhesive.

1625	**457**	100c. black and vermilion	2·20	2·00
1626	-	100c. multicoloured	2·20	2·00
1627	-	100c. multicoloured	2·20	2·00
1628	-	100c. black and scarlet-vermilion	2·20	2·00

DESIGNS: Type **457**; No. 1626, Couple riding bicycle; 1627, Couple embracing; 1628, Couple in dodgem car.

Nos. 1625/8 were issued with a label inscribed Priority attached at foot.

458 Double Helix, Faces and Building Facade

2005. 150th Anniv of Federal Technology Institute, Zurich.

1629	**458**	85c. multicoloured	1·90	1·70

459 Matterhorn superimposed on Inverted Map of Africa

2005

1630	**459**	85c. multicoloured	1·90	1·70

460 Cheeky Mouse typing Letter

2005. Cheeky Mouse (cartoon character created by Uli Stein). Multicoloured.

1631	85c. Type **460**	1·90	1·70
1632	100c. Playing golf	2·30	2·10

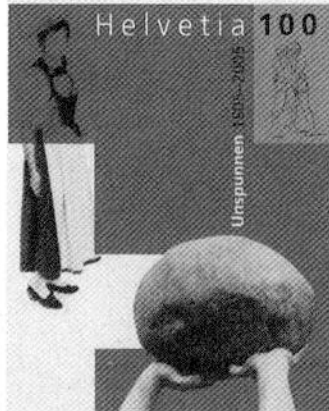

461 Traditional Costume and Unspunnen Stone

2005. Bicentenary of Folklore Festival, Unspunnen.

1633	**461**	100c. multicoloured	2·30	2·10

462 Coach-built Car

2005. Centenary of Motor Show, Geneva. Sheet 96×70 mm containing T 462 and similar horiz design. Multicoloured.

MS1634 100c. Type **462**; 130c. Futuristic car 5·00 5·00

463 Albert Einstein

2005. Centenary of Publication of "Special Theory of Relativity" by Albert Einstein.

1635	**463**	130c. multicoloured	3·00	2·75

464 Felix and Goats

2005. "Letters from Felix" (children's book written by Annette Langen and illustrated by Constanza Droop. Multicoloured.

1636	85c. Type **464**	1·90	1·70

465 Rotach Houses, Wasserwerkstrasse, Zurich

2005. Pro Patria. Multicoloured.

1638	85c.+40c. Type **465**	3·00	3·00
1639	85c.+40c. Monte Carasso Abbey, Bellinzona, Ticino	3·00	3·00
1640	100c.+50c. St. Katherinenthal Abbey, Diessenhofen	3·25	3·25
1641	100c.+50c. Palais Wilson, Geneva	3·25	3·25

466 Butterflies

2005. Greeting Stamp. Self-adhesive.

1642	**466**	100c. multicoloured	2·20	2·00

467 Player

2005. European Football Championship—2008, Switzerland and Austria (1st issue). Football for the Visually Impaired.

1643	**467**	100c. multicoloured	2·20	2·00

See also No. 1681, 1708, 1760 and 1761.

468 "Big-eared Clown" and "Monument in a Fertile Country"

2005. Inauguration of Zentrum Paul Klee Exhibition Centre, Berne.

1644	**468**	100c. multicoloured	2·20	2·00

469 Europe reflected in Dish Cover

2005. Europa. Gastronomy.

1645	**469**	100c. multicoloured	2·20	2·00

470 Subtractive Colours

2005. My Stamp. Colour. Multicoloured. Self-adhesive.

1646	50c. Type **470**	1·50	1·30
1647	100c. Additive colours	2·20	2·00

471 Skiers

2005. Centenary of NaturFreunde Schweiz (conservation organization). Sheet 110×90 mm containing T 471 and similar multicoloured designs.

MS1648 85c. Type **471**; 100c. Chalet (vert); 110c. Hikers; 130c. Rock climber (vert)	9·50	9·50

472 Horse's Head (Brigit Rohrbach)

2005. MMS (multimedia messaging). Multicoloured.

1649	85c. Type **472**	1·90	1·70
1650	100c. Hiker (Peter Schumacher)	2·20	2·00
1651	130c. Sign post (Remy Sager)	3·00	2·75
1652	180c. Footprint (Debora Ronchi)	3·75	3·25

473 Pocket Watch

2005. Watches. Multicoloured.

1653	100c. Type **473**	2·20	2·00
1654	130c. Wristwatch	3·00	2·75

474 Globe and Landscape

2005. Stamp Day. Winning Entry in Stamp Design Competition.

1655	**474**	85c. multicoloured	1·90	1·70

475 Mitre and Crosier

2005. Christmas. Multicoloured.

1656	85c. Type **475**	1·90	1·70
1657	100c. Gingerbread man	2·20	2·00

476 Swiss Papal Guard

2005. 500th Anniv of Swiss Papal Guard. Multicoloured.

1658	85c. Type **476**	1·90	1·70
1659	100c. Three guards facing left	2·20	2·00

Stamps of a similar design were issued by Vatican City.

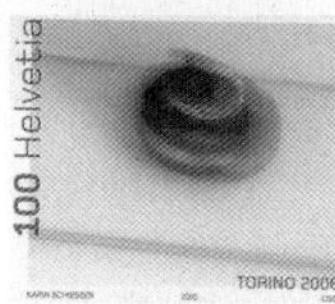

477 Curling

2005. Winter Olympic Games, Turin.

1660	**477**	100c. multicoloured	2·20	2·00

478 Ibex

2006. Centenary of Ibex Re-introduction Programme.

1661	**478**	85c. multicoloured	1·90	1·70

479 Simplon Tunnel between Rhone Valley and Val d'Ossola

2006. Railway Centenaries. Multicoloured.

1662	85c. Type **479**	1·90	1·70
1663	100c. Bern–Lotschberg–Simplon Railway (rapid train service)	2·20	2·00

480 Post Bus

2006. Centenary of the Post Bus Service. Multicoloured. Self-adhesive.

1664	85c. Type **480**	1·90	1·70
1665	100c. Double bus	2·20	2·00
1666	130c. School minibus	2·50	2·40

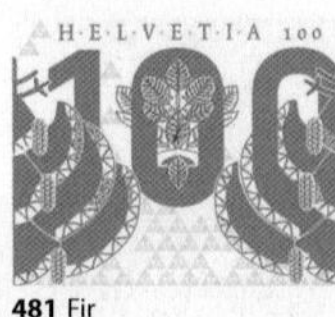

481 Fir

2006. Art Nouveau Exhibition, La Chaux-de-Fonds. Multicoloured.

1667	100c. Type **481**	2·20	2·10
1668	180c. Petals	3·75	3·50

482 Cuckoo

2006. Birds. Multicoloured. Self-adhesive.

1671	85c. Chaffinch (*Fringilla coelebs*)	1·60	1·50
1673	100c. Great tit (*Parus major*)	1·90	1·80
1674	110c. Wall creeper (*Tichodroma muraria*)	2·10	1·90
1674a	120c. Grey-headed wood pecker (*Picus canus*)	2·20	2·10
1674b	130c. Rufus-tailed rockthrush (*Monticola saxatills*)	2·40	2·20
1675	140c. Rock partridge (*Alectoris milivus*) (1.4.09)	2·75	2·20
1676	180c. Tengmalm's owl (*Aegolius funereus*)	3·25	3·00
1676a	180c. Tengmalm's owl (*Aegolius funereus*) (different) (1.7.09)	3·25	3·00
1677	190c. Red kite (*Milivus milivus*) (1.4.09)	3·50	3·25
1679	200c. Great crested grebe (*Podiceps cristatus*)	4·25	3·75
1680	240c. Type **482**	5·75	5·25

No. 1673, 1674b, 1676 and 1679 have a label inscribed "Prioritaire" attached at foot.

483 Player

2006. European Football Championship—2008, Switzerland and Austria (2nd issue). Youth Football.

1681	**483**	85c. multicoloured	1·90	1·80

484 Kasperli

2006. Kasperli (children's character) written by Jorg Schneider and drawn by Heinz Steiger.

1682	**484**	85c. multicoloured	1·90	1·80

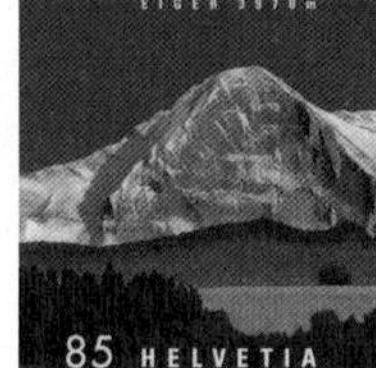

485 Eiger

2006. Mountains. Multicoloured.

1683	85c. Type **485**	1·90	1·80
1684	85c. Monch (30×35 mm)	1·90	1·80
1685	85c. Jungfrau (39×35 mm)	1·90	1·80

Nos. 1683/5 were issued together, se-tenant, forming a composite design of a panorama of the mountain range.

486 Monastery Buildings

2006. NABA National Stamp Exhibition, Baden (1st issue). Wettingen Monastery. Sheet 105×70 mm containing T 486 and similar horiz designs. Multicoloured.

MS1686 85c.+15c. Type **486**; 85c.+15c. Covered bridge; 100c.+50c. Building containing clock tower	7·00	7·00

The stamps and margins of **MS**1686 form a composite design of the monastery.

487 Schloss Heidegg, Gelfingen

2006. Pro Patria. Multicoloured.

1687	85c.+40c. Type **487**	3·00	3·00
1688	85c.+40c. Chateau de Prangins, Prangins	3·00	3·00
1689	100c.+50c. Villa Garbald, Castasegna	3·50	3·50
1690	100c.+50c. Schloss Birseck, Arlesheim	3·50	3·25

488 Cow

2006. Switzerland through the Eyes of Foreign Artists (1st issue). Patrice Killofer (France). Multicoloured.

1691	85c. Type **488**	1·80	1·60
1692	100c. Brown cow in water	2·10	1·90
1693	130c. Seated cow losing its spots	2·75	2·50
1694	180c. Snow covered white cow	4·00	3·50

489 Faces of Many Nations

2006. Europa. Integration.

1695	**489**	100c. multicoloured	2·20	1·90

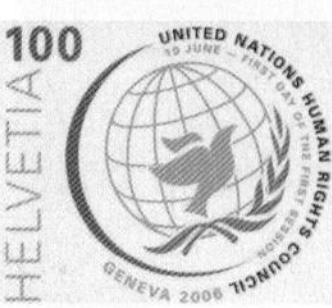

490 Emblem

2006. United Nations Human Rights Council, Geneva.

1696	**490**	100c. multicoloured	2·20	1·90

491 Cocolino

2006. Cocolino (cartoon character created by Oskar Weiss and Oskar Marti). Self-adhesive.

1697 **491** 85c. multicoloured 1·80 1·60

492 Clown juggling Letters

2006. Dimtri the Clown.

1698 **492** 100c. multicoloured 2·20 1·90

493 Clock Face

2006. Baden City Tower. Sheet 105×70 mm containing T 493 and similar vert design. Multicoloured.

MS1699 100c.+50c.×2, Type **493**; Base of tower and fountain 6·75 6·75

The stamps and margins of **MS**1699 form a composite design.

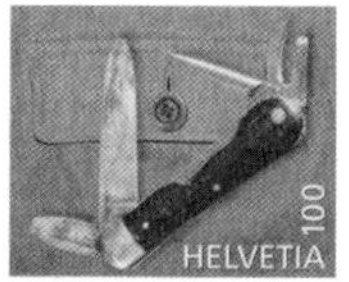

494 First Knife

2006. Victorinox Swiss Officer's Knife. Multicoloured.

1700 100c. Type **494** 2·20 1·90

1701 130c. Modern knife 3·00 2·75

495 Gelterkinder Cherries

2006. ProSpecieRara (rare breeds association) (1st issue). Multicoloured. Self-adhesive.

1702 200c. Type **495** 4·25 4·00

1703 300c. Spatlauber apple 6·50 5·75

See also No. 1707 and 1782.

496 Boy wearing Conductor's Cap

2006. Stamp Day. Winning Entry in Stamp Design Competition. 150th Anniv of Olten, the Railway Town.

1704 **496** 85c. multicoloured 1·80 1·60

497 Star Singers

2006. Christmas Customs. Multicoloured.

1705 85c. Type **497** 1·80 1·60

1706 100c. Candles on Advent wreath 2·20 1·90

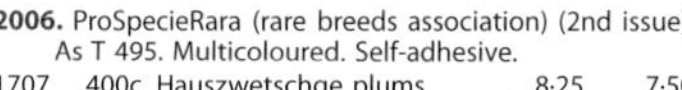

2006. ProSpecieRara (rare breeds association) (2nd issue). As T 495. Multicoloured. Self-adhesive.

1707 400c. Hauszwetschge plums 8·25 7·50

498 Player

2007. European Football Championship—2008, Switzerland and Austria (3rd issue). Women's Football.

1708 **498** 85c. multicoloured 1·80 1·60

499 Bernese Mountain Dog

2007. Centenary of Swiss Club for Bernese Mountain Dogs. Self-adhesive.

1709 **499** 85c. multicoloured 1·80 1·60

500 Town Hall

2007. Stein am Rhein Millenary. Multicoloured.

1710 85c. Type **500** 1·80 1·60

1711 85c. Painted houses (41×36 mm) 1·80 1·60

1712 85c. Municipal (market) fountain and Zur Meise (guildhall) (34×36 mm) 1·80 1·60

Nos. 1710/12 were issued together, se-tenant, forming a composite design.

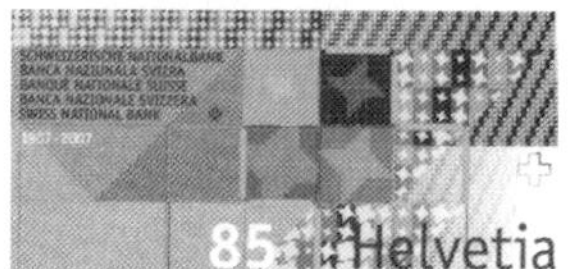

501 Security Features

2007. Centenary of National Bank. Multicoloured. Self-adhesive.

1713 85c. Type **501** 1·80 1·60

1714 100c. Banknote 2·20 1·90

502 Cup, Jewel and Snake ('Legend of Charlemagne and the Snake')

2007. Legends and Stories. Multicoloured.

1715 85c. Type **502** 1·80 1·60

1716 100c. Girl and water lilies ('Fenetta, the Island Maiden') 2·20 1·90

1717 130c. Horse and rider ('The Judge of Bellinzona') 2·75 2·50

1718 180c. Woman flying over lake and mountains ('Margaretha') 4·00 3·50

503 Leonhard Euler

2007. 300th Birth Anniv of Leonhard Euler (mathematician and scientist).

1719 **503** 130c. multicoloured 2·75 2·50

503a Roger Federer and Trophy

2007. Roger Federer—Tennis World Champion.

1720 **503a** 100c. multicoloured 2·20 1·90

504 Coloured Balls

2007. Centenary of Swiss Association of Day Care Centres.

1721 **504** 85c. multicoloured 1·80 1·60

505 Three Adults and Two Children

2007. Centenary of Museum of Communication, Berne. Multicoloured. Self-adhesive.

1722 85c. Type **505** 1·80 1·60

1723 100c. Five adults 2·20 1·90

506 Via Jacobi

2007. Pro Patria. Traditional Routes. Multicoloured.

1724 85c.+40c. Type **506** 2·75 2·75

1725 85c.+40c. Via Jura 2·75 2·75

1726 100c.+50c. Via Cook 4·00 4·00

1727 100c.+50c. Via Gottardo 4·00 4·00

508 Scouts

2007. Europa. Centenary of Scouting.

1728 **508** 100c. multicoloured 2·20 1·90

509 *Skt. Adolf Thron-Fluhe-Blume* (Adolf Wolfli)

2007. Outsider Art. Multicoloured.

1729 100c. Type **509** 2·20 1·90

1730 180c. Untitled (Carlo Zinelli) 3·75 3·25

510 Schellen-Ursli on Bridge

2007. Schellen-Ursli (children's book character created by Selina Chonz and illustrated by Alois Carigiet). Self-adhesive.

1731 **510** 85c. multicoloured 1·80 1·60

511 The Dancer

2007. Nina Corti (flamenco dancer).

1732 **511** 85c. multicoloured 1·80 1·60

512 Family and Hearts

2007. Greetings Stamps. 'Congratulations'. Multicoloured. Self-adhesive.

1733 85c. Type **512** 1·80 1·60

1734 100c. Boy and stars 2·20 1·90

1735 130c. Woman and flowers 2·75 2·50

513 Monch (*Frankenstein* (Mary Shelley))

2007. Switzerland through the Eyes of Foreign Artists. Swiss Landscape and English Literature. Photographs by James Peel (British artist). Multicoloured.

1736 85c. Type **513** 1·80 1·60

1737 100c. Lauterbrunnen (*At Staubbach Falls* (William Wordsworth)) (vert) 2·20 1·90

1738 130c. Lac Leman (*The Prisoner of Chillon* (Lord Byron)) (vert) 2·75 2·50

1739 180c. Reichenbach Fall (*The Final Problem* (Sir Arthur Conan Doyle)) 4·00 3·50

514 Skiers and Bee Tagg

2007. Internet Stamp. Self-adhesive.

1740 **514** 100c. multicoloured 2·20 1·90

No. 1740 contains a Bee Tag (a two dimensional code which, when used with the appropriate software, connects a mobile telephone to the internet). The code gives entry to a competition to win Swiss Tourism prize.

515 Monastery

2007. Einsiedeln. Sheet 105×70 mm.

MS1741 **515** 85c. multicoloured 5·00 5·00

The stamps and margins of **MS**1741 form a composite design.

2007. Christmas. Multicoloured.

1743 100c. Decorated tree 2·20 1·90

1744 130c. Presents 2·75 2·40

No. 1742 and Type **516** have been left for 85c. stamp not yet received.

517 Heart-shaped Silhouette

2007. Silhouettes.

1745	**517**	85c. black and vermilion	2·00	1·80
1746	-	100c. black and emerald	2·30	2·10
1747	-	130c. black and blue	2·75	2·50
1748	-	180c. black and orange	4·00	3·50

DESIGNS: 85c. Type **517**; 100c. Tree shaped in circle; 130c. Tree with family cycling below; 180c. Symetrical tree of peacock feathers with dancers below.

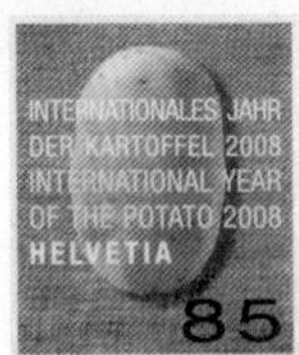

518 Potato

2008. International Year of the Potato.

1749	**518**	85c. multicoloured	2·10	1·90

519 Lars

2008. The Little Polar Bear Lars (created by Hans de Beer). Self-adhesive.

1750	**519**	85c. multicoloured	2·10	1·90

520 Albrecht von Haller

2008. 300th Birth Anniv of Albrecht von Haller (physician, botanist and poet).

1751	**520**	85c. multicoloured	2·10	1·90

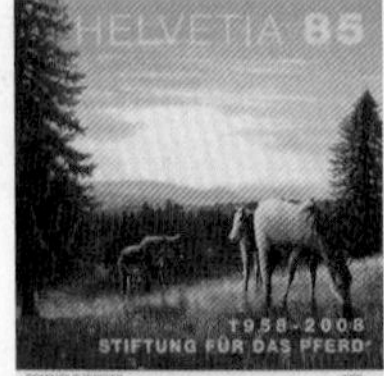

521 Horses

2008. 50th Anniv of Horse Foundation (refuge), Jura. Multicoloured.

1752	85c. Type **521**	2·10	1·90
1753	85c. Track and four horses	2·10	1·90
1754	85c. Two horses and building	2·10	1·90

Nos. 1752/4 were issued together, se-tenant, forming a composite design.

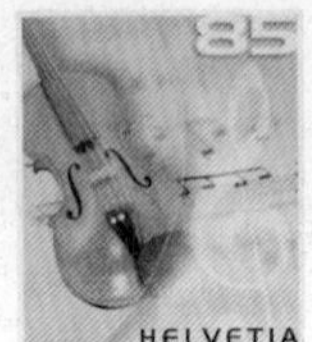

522 Violin

2008. Musical Instruments. Multicoloured.

1755	85c. Type **522**	2·20	2·00
1756	100c. Accordian	2·50	2·40
1757	130c. Electric guitar	3·25	3·00
1758	180c. Saxophone	4·25	4·00

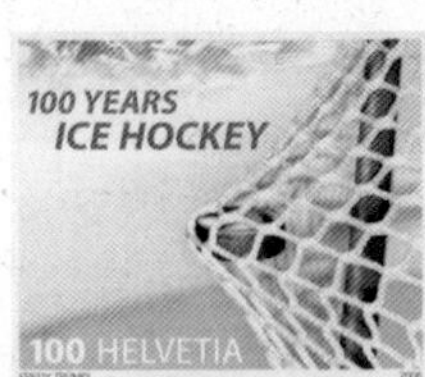

523 Puck in Net

2008. Centenary of Swiss Ice Hockey Association.

1759	**523**	100c. multicoloured	2·50	2·40

524 Player

2008. Euro 2008–European Footbal Championships, Austria and Switzerland (4th issue). Local Football.

1760	**524**	100c. multicoloured	2·50	2·40

Nos. 1643, 1681, 1708 and 1760 together form a composite design of a football enclosing players.

525 Pitch

2008. Euro 2008–European Football Championships, Austria and Switzerland (5th issue). Self-adhesive.

1761	**525**	100c. emerald	2·50	2·40

No. 1762 and Type **526** have been left for 'Euro 2008', issued on 8 May 2008, not yet received.

527 Birds in Flight forming Envelope

2008. Europa. The Letter.

1763	**527**	100c. multicoloured	2·50	2·40

528 '100'

2008. Centenary of Swiss Life Saving Society.

1764	**528**	100c. multicoloured	2·50	2·40

529 Mountain Biking

2008. Olympic Games, Beijing. Multicoloured.

1765	100c. Type **529**	2·50	2·40

No. 1766 is vacant.

530 Via Sbrinz and Schitzturm Tower, Stansstad

2008. Pro Patria. Traditional Routes. Multicoloured.

1767	85c.+40c. Type **530**	3·25	3·00
1768	85c.+40c. East Gate, Avenches and Columns, Nyon	3·25	3·00
1769	100c.+50c. Via Valtellina, Cavaglia and Dürrboden restaurant	3·75	3·50
1770	100c.+50c. Via Stockalper, Engi and Old Hospice	3·75	3·50

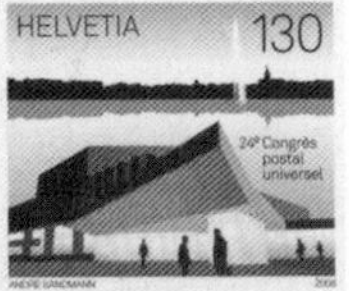

531 Centre International de Conferences Geneve (conference venue)

2008. 24th UPU Congress, Geneva.

1771	**531**	130c. multicoloured	3·25	3·25

532 Wheat

2008. Cereals. Multicoloured. Self-adhesive.

1772	10c. Type **532**	40	35
1773	15c. Barley	50	45
1774	20c. Rye	60	55
1775	50c. Oats	1·40	1·30

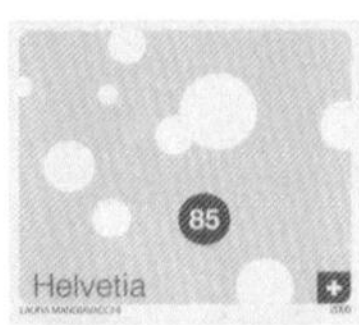

533 Cheese

2008. Switzerland through the Eyes of Foreign Artists. Multicoloured.

1776	85c. Type **533**	2·20	2·00
1777	100c. Chocolate	2·50	2·40
1778	130c. Clock	3·25	3·00
1779	180c. Tools (Swiss army pocket knives)	4·50	4·25

534 Old Bridge, Bad Sackingen—Stein/Aargau

2008. Bridges.

1780	**534**	100c. multicoloured	2·75	2·50

A stamp of a similar design was issued by Germany.

535 Stylized Figures

2008. Fredi Murer (film maker).

1781	**535**	100c. multicoloured	2·75	2·50

2008. ProSpecieRara (rare breeds association) (3rd issue). As T 495. Multicoloured. Self-adhesive.

1782	500c. Catillac pear	12·50	11·50

536 Local Food

2008. Stamp Day, Bellinzona. Sheet 105×70 mm.

MS1783	**536** 85c. multicoloured	2·75	2·50

537 Bauble

2008. Christmas Baubles. Multicoloured.

1784	85c. Type **537**	2·50	2·40
1785	100c. Star shaped bauble	3·00	2·75
1786	130c. Bell shaped bauble	3·75	3·50

538 *Rotes Quadrat* (Max Bill)

2008. Art. Each black and scarlet.

1787	100c. Type **538**	3·00	2·75
1788	130c. *Eier im Spiegel* (eggs in a mirror) (Hans Finsler) (30×42 mm)	4·00	3·75

539 Brown Bear

2009. Centenary of Pro Natura (conservation organization).

1789	**539**	85c. multicoloured	2·75	2·40

540 *Rigi* (steam ship)

2009. 50th Anniv of Verkehrshaus Transport Museum. Multicoloured.

1790	85c. Type **540**	2·75	2·40
1791	100c. Dufaux race car	3·00	3·00
1792	130c. Lockheed Orion 9C Special aircraft	4·00	3·75

541 Boot

2009. International Ice Hockey Federation World Championships, Berne and Zurich–Kloten. Self-adhesive.

1793	**541**	100c. multicoloured	3·00	3·00

542 Vadret da Morteratsch

2009. Glacial Shrinkage.

1794	**542**	100c. multicoloured	3·00	3·00

The printing method allows No. 1794 to show the glacier as it is now, or as it was in 1850 when the stamp is tilted.

543 John Calvin

2009. 500th Birth Anniv of John Calvin (theologian).

1795	**543**	100c. multicoloured	3·00	3·00

544 *The Human Mind*

2009. Birth Centenary of Hans Erni (stamp designer). Multicoloured.

1796	100c. Type **544**	3·00	3·00
1797	130c. *Human Hands*	4·00	3·75

545 Hans Ulrich Grubenmann

2009. 300th Birth Anniv of Hans Ulrich Grubenmann (engineer).
1798 **545** 85c. multicoloured 2·75 2·40

546 Kittens

2009. European Wild Cat (*Felis silvestris*). Self-adhesive.
1799 **546** 85c. multicoloured 2·75 2·40

547 Birch

2009. Ancient Trees. Multicoloured. Self-adhesive.
1800 85c. Type **547** 2·75 2·50
1801 100c. Oak 3·25 3·00
1802 130c. Willow 4·25 3·75

548 Via Francigena and Great St. Bernhard Hospice

2009. Pro Patria. Traditional Routes. Multicoloured.
1803 85c.+40c. Type **548** 4·00 4·00
1804 85c.+40c. Via Salina, track and Berne Gate, Murten 4·00 4·00
1805 100c.+50c. Via Spluga, Viamala, Zillis-Reischen and Albertini House, SplUgen 4·75 4·75
1806 100c.+50c. Via Rhenana, Basel Old Town and salt drilling towers, Rheinfelden 4·75 4·75
MS1807 105×70 mm. 100c.+50c. Illuminated roads (centenary of Pro Patria organization) 5·00 5·00

549 '@' and Type

2009. Graphics–From Guttenberg to the Internet.
1808 **549** 100c. multicoloured 3·25 3·00

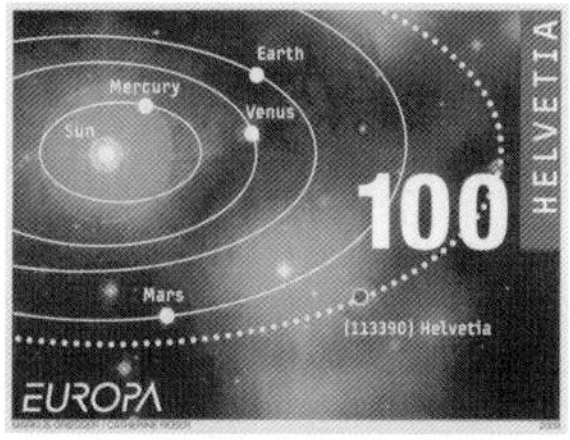

550 Planets and *Helvetia* Asteroid

2009. Europa. Astronomy.
1809 **550** 100c. multicoloured 3·25 3·00

551 Stiva da Morts (Place of Mourning, Vrin)

2009. Architecture. Multicoloured.
1810 100c. Type **551** 3·25 3·00
1811 180c. Pentorama Community Centre, Amriswil 4·50 4·00

552 Princess Lillifee

2009. Princess Lillifee (character created by Monika Finsterbusch). Self-adhesive.
1812 **552** 85c. multicoloured 2·75 2·40

553 Goats and Lead Cows

2009. Alpaufahrt (moving animals to and from alpine pastures), Appenzell. Multicoloured.
1813 85c. Type **553** 2·75 2·40
1814 85c. Cows and calves (32×37 mm) 2·75 2·40
1815 85c. Bull and horse drawn cart (34×37 mm) 2·75 2·40

Nos. 1813/15 were printed, se-tenant, forming a composite design of the procession.

554 'Den Zwang abwrft' (independence)

2009. Switzerland through the Eyes of Foreign Artists. Designs showing red flowers with a central white cross and parts of a poem by Friedrich Schiller describing Swiss virtues. Multicoloured. P 14×13.
1816 85c. Type **554** 2·75 2·40
1817 100c. Sich selbst genug 3·25 3·00
1818 130c. die Menschlichkeit noch ehrt 4·00 3·75
1819 180c. sich bescheidet 4·50 4·00

555 Design as 1903 Stamp (Type **18**)

2009. Centenary of Swiss Stamp Dealers' Association.
1820 **555** 100c. light bright green and bright yellowish green 3·25 3·00

556 Refugees and Red Cross

2009. 60th Anniv of Geneva Conventions.
1821 **556** 100c. multicoloured 3·25 3·00

557 'Wedding'

2009. Greetings Stamps. Multicoloured. Self-adhesive.
1822 100c. Type **557** 3·25 3·00
1823 100c. Birth 3·25 3·00
1824 100c. Anniversary 3·25 3·00

558 Crane (emblem of Gruyères)

2009. Stamp Day. Gruyères. Sheet 70×105 mm.
MS1825 **558** 85c. multicoloured 2·75 2·40

559 Santa Hat

2009. Christmas. Multicoloured.
1826 85c. Type **559** 2·75 2·40
1827 100c. Tree 3·25 3·00
1828 130c. Parcel 4·25 3·75

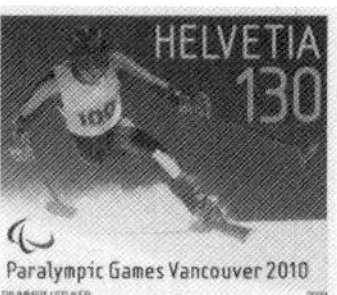

560 Alpine Skier

2009. Paralympic Games, Vancouver.
1829 **560** 130c. multicoloured 4·25 3·75

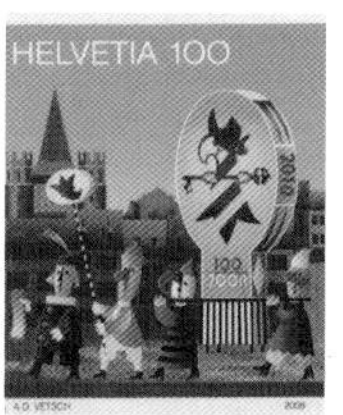

561 Procession

2010. Centenary of Basel Carnival
1830 100c. Type **561** 3·00 3·00
1831 100c. Four figures and float (44×37 mm) 3·00 3·00
1832 100c. Band 3·00 3·00

No 1833 is vacant.

562 Emblem

2010. 550th Anniv of Basel University
1834 **562** 85c. deep turquoise-green, orange-red and black 2·75 2·75

563 Peacock Goats

2010. International Year of Biodiversity
1835 **563** 85c. multicoloured 2·75 2·75

564 Grandjean Monoplane and Ernest Failloubaz

2010. Centenary of Swiss Aviation. Multicoloured.
1836 85c. Type **564** (1st flight of Swiss aircraft by Swiss pilot) 2·75 2·75
1837 100c. Airbus A340 (modern civil aviation) 3·25 3·00

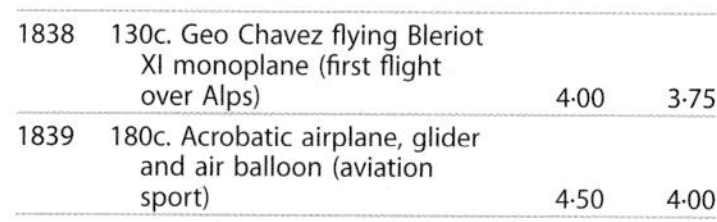
1838 130c. Geo Chavez flying Bleriot XI monoplane (first flight over Alps) 4·00 3·75
1839 180c. Acrobatic airplane, glider and air balloon (aviation sport) 4·50 4·00

565 Script

2010. Centenary of Swiss Cancer League
1840 **565** 100c. multicoloured 3·00 3·00

566 Dancers and Headdress (Federal Costume Festival, Schwyz)

2010. Traditional Swiss Customs. Multicoloured.
1841 100c. Type **566** 3·00 3·00
1842 100c. Alphorn and yodellers (centenary of Swiss Yodelling Association) 3·00 3·00
1843 100c. Drum (Federal Drumming and Piping Festival, Interlaken) 3·00 3·00
1844 100c. Marksman and target (Federal Marksmen's Festival, Aarau) 3·00 3·00

567 Neissen Funicular Railway

2010. Centenary of Bernina Railway
1845 85c. Type **567** 2·50 2·50
1846 100c. Bernina railway line 3·00 3·00

568 School Boy

2010. Death Centenary of Albert Anker (artist)
1847 **568** 85c. multicoloured 2·75 2·75

569 Johann Hebel and Basel

2010. 250th Birth Anniv of Johann Peter Hebel (theologian and writer)
1848 **569** 85c. multicoloured 2·50 2·50

570 Charles the Bold in Flight

2010. Pro Patria. Battle of Murten Panorama by Louis Braun. Multicoloured.
1849 85c.+40c. Type **570** 4·00 4·00
1850 85c.+40c. Archers and Duke of Somerset and mount dead by his tent 4·00 4·00
1851 100c.+50c. Burgundian cavalry under attack 4·75 4·75
1852 100c.+50c. Confederate troops with flags and halberds 4·75 4·75

571 Equilibres (Peter Fischli and David Weiss)

2010. Centenary of Kunsthaus (musuem of fine arts), Zurich

1853	**571**	100c. multicoloured	3·00	3·00

572 Figures

2010. Bicentenary of Public Welfare Society

1854	**572**	100c. new blue and pale grey	3·00	3·00

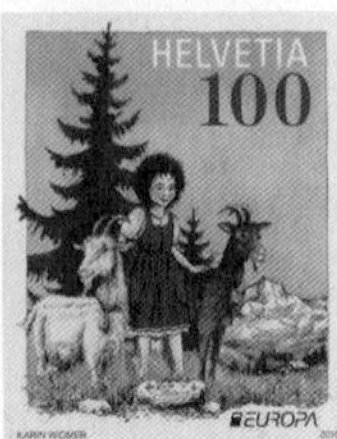

573 Heidi and Goats (*Heidi* by Johanna Spyri)

2010. Europa. Children's Books.

1855	**573**	100c. multticoloured	3·00	3·00

574 Big Top from Below

2010. World Circus 2010, Geneva

1856	**574**	140c. multicoloured	4·25	4·25

FRANK STAMPS

Issued to charity hospitals for free transmission of their mails.

F21

1911. With control figures at top.

F268	**F 21**	2c. red and green	10	10
F269	**F 21**	3c. red and green	3·00	75
F270	**F 21**	5c. red and green	1·40	10
F271	**F 21**	10c. red and green	1·80	10
F272	**F 21**	15c. red and green	25·00	5·00
F273	**F 21**	20c. red and green	4·50	75

F49 Deaconess

1935. With or without control figures.

F358A	**F49**	5c. green	3·75	1·80
F359A	-	10c. violet	3·75	1·80
F360A	-	20c. red	3·75	1·80

DESIGNS: 10c. Sister of the Ingenbohl Order; 20c. Henri Dunant (founder of Red Cross).

OFFICIAL STAMPS

1918. Optd Industrielle Kriegs-wirtschaft.

O308	**18b**	3c. brown	4·25	47·00
O300	**18b**	5c. green	13·00	60·00
O310	**18b**	7½c. grey	4·25	33·00
O303	**21**	10c. red on buff	20·00	70·00
O304	**21**	15c. purple on buff	16·00	80·00
O313	**17**	20c. yellow and red	11·00	75·00
O314	**17**	25c. blue and deep blue	11·00	75·00
O315	**17**	30c. green and brown	17·00	£130

1938. Optd with Geneva Cross.

O381A	**52**	3c. green	15	40
O382A	-	5c. green (No. 369)	15	40
O383A	-	10c. purple (No. 370)	1·20	55
O384A	-	15c. orange (No. 373)	40	2·30
O385A	-	20c. red (No. 375)	60	40
O386A	-	25c. brown (No. 376)	60	1·90
O387A	-	30c. blue (No. 377)	80	1·30
O388A	-	35c. green (No. 378)	80	1·70
O389A	-	40c. grey (No. 379)	80	1·30
O390	**17**	50c. green and deep green	3·25	1·90
O391	**17**	60c. brown	3·25	3·50
O392	**17**	70c. buff and violet	3·25	5·75
O393	**17**	80c. buff and grey	3·25	4·50
O395	**41**	90c. red, dp green & green	4·00	4·50
O394	**17**	1f. green and purple	4·00	4·50
O396	**41**	1f.20 red, lake and pink	4·00	6·00
O397	**41**	1f.50 red, blue & turquoise	4·75	8·25
O398	-	2f. red, black and grey	7·75	9·50

1942. Optd Officiel. (a) Landscape designs of 1936.

O427	**52**	3c. green	40	2·75
O428	-	5c. green	40	40
O430	-	10c. brown	40	55
O431	-	15c. orange	80	2·75
O432	-	20c. red (Lake)	80	55
O433	-	25c. brown	80	3·00
O434	-	30c. blue	1·20	8·75
O435	-	35c. green	1·60	3·75
O436	-	40c. grey	1·60	75

(b) Historical designs of 1941.

O437		50c. blue on green	5·50	6·00
O438	**68**	60c. brown on brown	6·25	6·00
O439	-	70c. purple on mauve	7·00	11·50
O440	-	80c. black on grey	2·00	2·30
O441	-	90c. red on pink	2·40	3·00
O442	-	1f. green on green	2·40	2·30
O443	-	1f.20 purple on grey	3·25	3·75
O444	-	1f.50 blue on buff	3·25	4·50
O445	-	2f. red on pink	4·00	5·25

1950. Landscape designs of 1949 optd Officiel.

O522	**107**	5c. orange	80	1·50
O523	-	10c. green	1·60	1·50
O524	-	15c. turquoise	13·50	23·00
O525	-	20c. purple	4·75	1·50
O526	-	25c. red	7·75	13·50
O527	-	30c. green	5·50	6·00
O528	-	35c. brown	7·75	15·00
O529	-	40c. blue	6·25	6·75
O530	-	50c. grey	9·50	10·50
O531	-	60c. green	12·00	11·50
O532	-	70c. violet	37·00	34·00

For Swiss stamps overprinted for the use of officials of the League of Nations, International Labour Office and other special U.N. Agencies having their headquarters at Geneva, see sub-section INTERNATIONAL ORGANIZATIONS SITUATED IN SWITZERLAND.

POSTAGE DUE STAMPS

D10

1878

D89	**D10**	1c. blue	2·20	1·80
D90	**D10**	2c. blue	2·20	1·80
D98B	**D10**	3c. blue	14·50	12·50
D92	**D10**	5c. blue	20·00	14·50
D99B	**D10**	5c. blue	18·00	8·00
D100B	**D10**	10c. blue	£200	8·00
D101A	**D10**	20c. blue	£250	5·75
D102A	**D10**	50c. blue	£475	25·00
D96	**D10**	100c. blue	£650	18·00
D97	**D10**	500c. blue	£550	29·00

Nos. D89 and D92a have raised backgrounds behind the figure of value.

1883. Numerals in red.

D268	1c. green	45	1·50
D181C	3c. green	6·50	13·00
D269B	5c. green	1·20	1·10
D270A	10c. green	4·00	2·20
D271B	20c. green	14·00	6·50
D204B	50c. green	16·00	5·00
D205B	100c. green	18·00	3·75
D187B	500c. green	£150	16·00

The above were issued in a wide range of shades from pale turquoise to olive between 1883 and 1910. A detailed list of these appears in the Stanley Gibbons Part 8 (Italy and Switzerland) Catalogue.

D21

1910

D274	**D21**	1c. green and red	10	10
D275	**D21**	3c. green and red	10	10
D276	**D21**	5c. green and red	10	10
D277	**D21**	10c. green and red	14·50	10
D278	**D21**	15c. green and red	85	1·50
D279	**D21**	20c. green and red	24·00	10
D280	**D21**	25c. green and red	1·50	75
D281	**D21**	30c. green and red	1·50	75
D282	**D21**	50c. green and red	1·80	1·50

1916. Surch.

D299	**D 21**	5 on 3c. red and green	10	10
D300	**D 21**	10 on 1c. red and green	30	11·00
D301	**D 21**	10 on 3c. red and green	30	1·80
D302	**D 21**	20 on 50c. red & green	1·00	1·80

D41

1924

D329	**D41**	5c. red and green	85	30
D330	**D41**	10c. red and green	3·75	75
D331	**D41**	15c. red and green	3·25	75
D332a	**D41**	20c. red and green	5·75	2·00
D333	**D41**	25c. red and green	3·75	75
D334	**D41**	30c. red and green	3·75	1·00
D335	**D41**	40c. red and green	5·00	90
D336	**D41**	50c. red and green	5·00	90

1937. Surch.

D380	**D 41**	5 on 15c. red and green	1·10	5·00
D381	**D 41**	10 on 30c. red & green	1·10	1·90
D382	**D 41**	20 on 50c. red & green	1·90	6·00
D383	**D 41**	40 on 50c. red & green	3·00	15·00

D54

1938

D384A	**D54**	5c. red	55	10
D385A	**D54**	10c. red	75	10
D386A	**D54**	15c. red	1·50	2·75
D387A	**D54**	20c. red	1·20	10
D388A	**D54**	25c. red	1·80	2·75
D389A	**D54**	30c. red	1·70	1·50
D390A	**D54**	40c. red	2·00	55
D391A	**D54**	50c. red	2·50	2·75

POSTCARD STAMPS

P1 Tourism Emblem

2002. Self-adhesive gum. No value expressed.

P1	**P1**	(1f.30) multicoloured	2·50	2·50
P2	**P1**	(1f.80) multicoloured	3·50	3·50

No. P1 was for use only on postcards sent to countries within Europe and No. P2 to overseas countries. They were not valid for use on other mail or in combination with other stamps.

"PRO JUVENTUTE" CHARITY STAMPS

PREMIUMS. All "Pro Juventute" stamps are sold at an additional premium which goes to Benevolent Societies. Until 1937 these premiums were not shown on the stamps, but were as follows:

2c. for all 3c. franking values; 5c. for all 5, 71/2, 10, 15 and 20c. values and 10c. for all 30 and 40c. values.

From 1937, when the premium first appeared on the designs, we show it in the catalogue listing.

C1 Helvetia and Matterhorn

1913. Children's Fund.

J1	**C1**	5c. green	4·00	11·00

C2 Appenzell

1915. Children's Fund.

J1a	**C2**	5c. green on buff	4·00	14·00
J2	-	10c. red on buff	£140	£120

DESIGN: 10c. Girl from Lucerne.

C 4 Berne

1916. Children's Fund.

J3		3c. violet on buff	7·75	55·00
J4	**C 4**	5c. green on buff	17·00	14·00
J5	-	10c. red on buff	75·00	£100

DESIGNS: 3, 10c. Girls of Freiburg and Vaud.

C 6 Valais

1917. Children's Fund.

J6	**C6**	3c. violet on buff	4·75	75·00
J7	-	5c. green on buff	11·00	7·00
J8	-	10c. red on buff	28·00	35·00

DESIGNS: 5c. Man of Unterwalden; 10c. Girl of Ticino.

C 9 Uri

1918. Children's Fund. Dated "1918".

J9	**C9**	10c. red, yellow and black on buff	12·00	35·00
J10	-	15c. multicoloured on buff	16·00	17·00

ARMS: 15c. Geneva.

1919. Children's Fund. As Type C 9 but dated "1919". Cream paper.

J11	7½c. red, grey and black	4·00	20·00
J12	10c. green, red and black	4·00	20·00
J13	15c. red, violet and black	7·75	9·75

ARMS: 7½c. Nidwalden; 10c. Vaud; 15c. Obwalden.

1920. Children's Fund. As Type C 9 but dated "1920". Cream paper.

J14	7½c. red, grey and black	5·00	21·00
J15	10c. blue, red and black	7·75	22·00
J16	15c. red, blue, violet and black	4·75	10·50

ARMS: 7½c. Schwyz; 10c. Zurich; 15c. Ticino.

1921. Children's Fund. As Type C 9 but dated "1921". Cream paper.

J17	10c. red, black and green	80	4·25
J18	20c. multicoloured	3·25	6·25
J19	40c. red and blue	12·50	75·00

ARMS: 10c. Valais; 20c. Berne; 40c. Switzerland.

1922. Children's Fund. As Type C 9 but dated "1922". Cream paper.

J20	5c. orange, blue and black	80	8·25
J21	10c. green and black	80	3·50
J22	20c. violet, blue and black	1·60	3·50
J23	40c. blue, red and black	14·00	90·00

ARMS: 5c. Zug; 10c. Freiburg; 20c. Lucerne; 40c. Switzerland.

1923. Children's Fund. As Type C 9 but dated "1923". Cream paper.

J24	5c. orange and black	40	7·00
J25	10c. multicoloured	40	3·50
J26	20c. multicoloured	80	3·50
J27	40c. blue, red and black	11·00	70·00

ARMS: 5c. Basel; 10c. Glarus; 20c. Neuchatel; 40c. Switzerland.

1924. Children's Fund. As Type C 9 but dated "1924". Cream paper.

J28	5c. black and lilac	40	2·40
J29	10c. red, green and black	80	1·40
J30	20c. black, yellow and red	80	1·70
J31	30c. red, blue and black	2·40	21·00

ARMS: 5c. Appenzell; 10c. Solothurn; 20c. Schaffhausen; 30c. Switzerland.

1925. Children's Fund. As Type C 9 but dated "1925". Cream paper.

J32		5c. green, black and violet	40	2·10
J33		10c. black and green	40	1·40
J34		20c. multicoloured	55	1·40
J35		30c. red, blue and black	1·40	14·00

ARMS: 5c. St. Gall; 10c. Appenzell-Ausser-Rhoden; 20c. Graubunden; 30c. Switzerland.

1926. Children's Fund. As Type C 9 but dated "1926". Cream paper.

J36		5c. multicoloured	40	1·70
J37		10c. green, black and red	40	1·70
J38		20c. red, black and blue	55	2·10
J39		30c. blue, red and black	1·40	17·00

ARMS: 5c. Thurgau; 10c. Basel; 20c. Aargau; 30c. Switzerland and Lion of Lucerne.

C 40 Forsaken Orphan

C 42 J. H. Pestalozzi

C 43 J. H. Pestalozzi

1927. Children's Fund. Dated "1927".

J40	**C40**	5c. purple & yell on grey	40	3·50
J41	-	10c. green & pink on green	40	70
J42	**C 42**	20c. red	55	70
J43	**C 43**	30c. blue and black	1·40	11·00

DESIGN—As Type C **40**: 40c. Orphan at Pestalozzi School.

C 44 Lausanne

C 47 J. H. Dunant

1928. Children's Fund. Dated "1928".

J44	**C44**	5c. red, purple and black on buff	40	2·75
J45	-	10c. red, green and black on buff	40	1·40
J46	-	20c. black, yellow and red on buff	40	1·40
J47	**C 47**	30c. blue and red	1·60	10·50

DESIGNS—As Type C **44**: 10c. Arms of Winterthur; 20c. Arms of St. Gall.

C 48 Mt. San Salvatore, Lake Lugano

1929. Children's Fund. Dated "1929".

J48	**C 48**	5c. red and violet	25	1·70
J49	-	10c. blue and brown	30	1·70
J50	-	20c. blue and red	40	1·70
J51	-	30c. blue	1·70	17·00

DESIGNS: 10c. Mt. Titlis, Lake Engstlen; 20c. Mt. Lyskamm from Riffelberg; 30c. Nicholas de Flue.

C 50 Freiburg

C 51 A. Bitzius—"Jeremias Gotthelf"

1930. Children's Fund. Dated "1930".

J52	**C 50**	5c. blue, black and green on buff	30	1·70
J53	-	10c. multicoloured on buff	30	1·00
J54	-	20c. multicoloured on buff	40	1·00
J55	**C 51**	30c. blue	1·60	7·75

ARMS—As Type C **51**: 10c. Altdorf; 20c. Schaff-hausen.

C 52 St. Moritz and Silvaplana Lakes

1931. Children's Fund. Dated "1931".

J56	**C 52**	5c. green	65	2·10
J57	-	10c. violet	40	1·00
J58	-	20c. red	95	1·70
J59	-	30c. blue	6·25	25·00

DESIGNS: 10c. The Wetterhorn; 20c. Lac Leman; 30c. Alexandre Vinet.

C 54 Flag swinging

1932. Children's Fund. Dated "1932".

J60	**C 54**	5c. red and green	45	2·40
J61	-	10c. orange	65	2·75
J62	-	20c. red	80	2·40
J63	-	30c. blue	2·75	11·00

DESIGNS: 10c. Putting the weight; 20c. Wrestlers; 30c. Eugen Huber.

C 56 Vaud

1933. Children's Fund. Dated "1933".

J64	**C 56**	5c. green and buff	45	2·10
J65	-	10c. violet and buff	45	2·10
J66	-	20c. scarlet and buff	65	2·75
J67	-	30c. blue	3·25	12·00

DESIGNS: 10c. Swiss girl from Berne; 20c. Swiss girl from Ticino; 30c. Father Gregoire Girard.

C 59 A. von Haller

1934. Children's Fund. Dated "1934".

J68		5c. green and buff	40	2·10
J69		10c. violet and buff	55	1·40
J70		20c. red and buff	65	1·70
J71	**C 59**	30c. blue	3·25	11·00

SWISS GIRL DESIGNS—As Type C **56**: 5c. Appenzell; 10c. Valais; 20c. Graubunden.

C 61 Stefano Franscini

1935. Children's Fund. Dated "1935".

J72	-	5c. green and buff	40	2·40
J73	-	10c. violet and buff	55	1·40
J74	-	20c. red and buff	65	4·25
J75	**C 61**	30c. blue	3·25	14·00

SWISS GIRL DESIGNS—As Type C **56**: 5c. Basel; 10c. Lucerne; 20c. Geneva.

C 62 H. G. Nageli

1936. Children's Fund.

J76	**C62**	5c. green	40	1·10
J77	-	10c. purple and buff	80	1·10
J78	-	20c. red and buff	45	3·00
J79	-	30c. blue and buff	5·00	41·00

SWISS GIRL DESIGNS—As Type C **56**: 10c. Neuchatel; 20c. Schwyz; 30c. Zurich.

C 64 Gen. Henri Dufour

C 66 "Youth"

1937. Children's Fund.

J80	**C 64**	5c.+5c. green	40	75
J81	-	10c.+5c. purple	40	75
J82	**C 66**	20c.+5c. red, buff and silver	65	75
J83	-	30c.+10c. blue, buff and silver	1·70	8·00

DESIGNS: 10c. Nicholas de Flue; 30c. as Type C **66**, but girl's head facing other way.

1937. 25th Anniv of 'Pro Juventute' Stamp Issues. Sheet 105×55 mm. As Nos. J82/3. Imperf.

MSJ83a		20c.+5c. red and silver, 30c.+10c. ultramarine and silver	10·50	75·00

C 67 Salomon Gessner

1938. Children's Fund. Dated "1938".

J84	**C 67**	5c.+5c. green	40	75
J85	-	10c.+5c. violet & buff	40	75
J86	-	20c.+5c. red and buff	55	75
J87	-	30c.+10c. blue & buff	2·20	8·75

SWISS GIRL DESIGNS—As Type C **56**: 10c. St. Gall; 20c. Uri; 30c. Aargau.

C 69 Gen. Herzog

1939. Children's Fund.

J88	**C 69**	5c.+5c. green	40	75
J89	-	10c.+5c. violet & buff	40	75
J90	-	20c.+5c. red and buff	40	2·20
J91	-	30c.+10c. blue & buff	2·00	20·00

SWISS GIRL DESIGNS—As Type C **56**: 10c. Freibourg; 20c. Nidwalden; 30c. Basel.

C 71 Gottfried Keller

1940. Children's Fund. Dated "1940".

J92	**C 71**	5c.+5c. green	40	75
J93	-	10c.+5c. brown & buff	40	75
J94	-	20c.+5c. red and buff	45	75
J95	-	30c.+10c. blue & buff	1·90	12·50

SWISS GIRL DESIGNS—As Type C **56**: 10c. Thurgau; 20c. Solothurn; 30c. Zug.

C 73 Johann Kasper Lavater

1941. Children's Fund. Bicentenary of Birth of Lavater (philosopher) and of Death of Richard (clockmaker). Dated "1941".

J96	**C 73**	5c.+5c. green	40	45
J97	-	10c.+5c. brown & buff	40	50
J98	-	20c.+5c. red and buff	55	50
J99	-	30c.+10c. blue	1·30	9·50
MSJ99a		75×70 mm. Nos J97/8. Imperf	£140	£500

DESIGNS—As Type C **56**: 10c., 20c. Girls in national costumes of Schaffhausen and Obwalden. As Type C **73**: 30c. Daniel Jean Richard.

C 74 Niklaus Riggenbach (rack railway pioneer)

1942. Children's Fund. Dated "1942".

J100	**C 74**	5c.+5c. green	40	75
J101	-	10c.+5c. brn & buff	40	75
J102	-	20c.+5c. red and buff	40	75
J103	-	30c.+10c. blue	2·00	6·50

DESIGNS: 10c. and 20c. Girls in national costumes of Appenzell Ausser-Rhoden and Glarus; 30c. Conrad Escher von der Linth (statesman).

C75 Emanuel von Fellenberg

C76 Silver Thistle

1943. Death Centenary of Philip Emanuel von Fellenberg (economist).

J104	**C 75**	5c.+5c. green	40	75
J105	**C 76**	10c.+5c. green, buff and grey	40	75
J106	-	20c.+5c. red, yellow and pink	40	75
J107	-	30c.+10c. blue, light blue and black	1·60	12·50

FLOWERS: As Type C **76**: 20c. "Ladies slipper"; 30c. Gentian.

C 77 Numa Droz

1944. Birth Centenary of Droz (statesman).

J108	**C77**	5c.+5c. green	40	75
J109	-	10c.+5c. olive, yellow and green	40	75
J110	-	20c.+5c. red, yellow and grey	40	75
J111	-	30c.+10c. blue, grey and blue	1·60	12·50

DESIGNS: 10c. Edelweiss; 20c. Martagon lily; 30c. "Aquilegia alpina".

C 78 Ludwig Forrer

1945. Children's Fund. Centenary of Births of Ludwig Forrer (statesman) and Susanna Orelli (social reformer). Dated "1945".

J112	**C 78**	5c.+5c. green	80	75
J113	-	10c.+10c. brown	80	75
J114	-	20c.+10c. red, pink and yellow	1·20	75
J115	-	30c.+10c. blue, mauve and grey	4·75	13·00

DESIGNS: 10c. Susanna Orelli; 20c. Alpine dog rose; 30c. Spring crocus.

C 79 Rudolf Toepffer

1946. Death Centenary of Rudolf Toepffer (author and painter). Type C 79 and floral designs inscr "PRO JUVENTUTE 1946".

J116	**C79**	5c.+5c. green	80	75
J117	-	10c.+10c. green, grey and orange	80	75
J118	-	20c.+10c. red, grey and yellow	80	1·10
J119	-	30c.+10c. blue, grey and mauve	4·25	11·00

DESIGNS—As Type C **76**: 10c. Narcissus; 20c. Houseleek; 30c. Blue thistle.

C 80 Jacob Burckhardt (historian)

1947. Children's Fund. Type C 80 and floral designs inscr "PRO JUVENTUTE 1947".

J120	**C80**	5c.+5c. green	80	75
J121	-	10c.+10c. black, yellow and grey	80	75
J122	-	20c.+10c. brown, orange and grey	80	75

No.	Type	Description	Unused	Used
J123	-	30c.+10c. blue, pink and grey	3·50	11·50

DESIGNS—As Type C **76**: 10c. Alpine primrose; 20c. Orange lily; 30c. Cyclamen.

C 81 Gen. U. Wille

1948. Children's Fund. Type C 81 and floral designs as Type C 76. Dated "1948".

No.	Type	Description	Unused	Used
J124	**C81**	5c.+5c. purple	80	75
J125	-	10c.+10c. green, yellow and grey	95	75
J126	-	20c.+10c. brown, red and buff	1·20	75
J127	-	40c.+10c. blue, yellow and grey	4·75	11·50

FLOWERS: 10c. Yellow foxglove; 20c. Rust-leaved Alpine rose; 40c. Lily of Paradise.

C 82 Nicholas Wengi

1949. Children's Fund. Type C 82 and floral designs inscr "PRO JUVENTUTE 1949".

No.	Type	Description	Unused	Used
J128	**C82**	5c.+5c. red	80	75
J129	-	10c.+10c. green, grey and yellow	80	75
J130	-	20c.+10c. brown, blue and buff	80	75
J131	-	40c. blue, mauve and yellow	4·75	11·00

DESIGNS—As Type C **76**: 10c. "Pulsatilla alpina"; 20c. Alpine clematis; 40c. Superb pink.

C 83 General Theophil Sprecher von Bernegg

C 84 Red Admiral Butterfly

1950. Children's Fund. Inscr "PRO JUVENTUTE 1950".

No.	Type	Description	Unused	Used
J132	**C83**	5c.+5c. brown	80	35
J133	**C 84**	10c.+10c. mult	80	75
J134	-	20c.+10c. black, blue and orange	1·20	1·10
J135	-	30c.+10c. brown, grey and mauve	6·00	25·00
J136	-	40c.+10c. yellow, brown and blue	6·00	18·00

DESIGNS: 20c. Clifden's nonpareil (moth); 30c. Honey bee; 40c. Moorland clouded yellow (butterfly).

C 85 Johanna Spyri (authoress)

1951. Children's Fund. Type C 85 and various insects as Type C 84. Inscr "PRO JUVENTUTE 1951".

No.	Type	Description	Unused	Used
J137	**C85**	5c.+5c. purple	80	35
J138	-	10c.+10c. blue & grn	80	75
J139	-	20c.+10c. black, cream and mauve	1·20	75
J140	-	30c.+10c. black, orange and green	4·00	11·00
J141	-	40c.+10c. brown, red and blue	5·50	11·00

INSECTS: 10c. Banded agrion (dragonfly); 20c. Scarce swallowtail (butterfly); 30c. Orange-tip (butterfly); 40c. Viennese emperor moth.

C 86 "Portrait of a Boy" (Anker)

1952. Children's Fund. Type C 86 and insects as Type C 84. Inscr "PRO JUVENTUTE 1952".

No.	Type	Description	Unused	Used
J142	**C86**	5c.+5c. red	80	35
J143	-	10c.+10c. orange, black and green	80	75
J144	-	20c.+10c. cream, black and mauve	80	1·10
J145	-	30c.+10c. blue, black and brown	4·00	11·00
J146	-	40c.+10c. buff, brown and blue	4·00	11·00

INSECTS: 10c. Seven-spotted ladybird; 20c. Marbled white (butterfly); 30c. Chalk-hill blue (butterfly); 40c. Oak eggar moth.

1953. Children's Fund. Portraits as Type C 86 and insects as Type C 84. Inscr "PRO JUVENTUTE 1953".

No.	Description	Unused	Used
J147	5c.+5c. red	65	35
J148	10c.+10c. pink, brown and green	80	75
J149	20c.+10c. black, buff and mauve	95	1·10
J150	30c.+10c. black, red & grn	4·00	11·00
J151	40c.+10c. blue	5·50	11·00

DESIGNS: 5c. "Portrait of a girl" (Anker); 10c. Black arches moth; 20c. Camberwell beauty (butterfly); 30c. "Purpureus kaehleri" (longhorn beetle); 40c. F. Hodler (self-portrait).

1954. Children's Fund. Portrait as Type C 85 and insects as Type C 84. Inscr "PRO JUVENTUTE 1954".

No.	Description	Unused	Used
J152	5c.+5c. brown	80	35
J153	10c.+10c. multicoloured	80	75
J154	20c.+10c. multicoloured	1·60	75
J155	30c.+10c. multicoloured	4·75	10·50
J156	40c.+10c. multicoloured	4·75	11·00

DESIGNS: 5c. Jeremias Gotthelf (novelist) (after Albert Bitzius); 10c. Garden tiger moth; 20c. Buff-tailed bumble bee; 30c. "Ascalaphus libelluloides" (owl-fly); 40c. Swallowtail (butterfly).

1955. Children's Fund. Portrait as Type C 85 and insects as Type C 84. Inscr "PRO JUVENTUTE 1955".

No.	Description	Unused	Used
J157	5c.+5c. purple	80	35
J158	10c.+10c. multicoloured	80	75
J159	20c.+10c. multicoloured	1·20	75
J160	30c.+10c. multicoloured	4·75	7·25
J161	40c.+10c. black red & blue	5·50	8·75

DESIGNS: 5c. C. Pictet-de-Rochemont; 10c. Peacock (butterfly); 20c. Great horntail; 30c. Yellow tiger moth; 40c. Apollo (butterfly).

1956. Children's Fund. Portrait as Type C 85 and insects as Type C 84. Inscr "PRO JUVENTUTE 1956".

No.	Description	Unused	Used
J162	5c.+5c. purple	80	35
J163	10c.+10c. deep green, red and green	80	75
J164	20c.+10c. multicoloured	80	75
J165	30c.+10c. blue, indigo and yellow	3·25	6·50
J166	40c.+10c. yellow, brn & bl	3·50	7·25

DESIGNS: 5c. Carlo Maderno (architect); 10c. Common burnet (moth); 20c. Lesser purple emperor (butterfly); 30c. Blue ground beetle; 40c. Large white (butterfly).

1957. Children's Fund. Portrait as Type C 85 and insects as Type C 84. Inscr "PRO JUVENTUTE 1957".

No.	Description	Unused	Used
J167	5c.+5c. purple	80	35
J168	10c.+10c. multicoloured	80	75
J169	20c.+10c. yellow, brown and mauve	80	75
J170	30c.+10c. emerald, green and purple	3·25	6·50
J171	40c.+10c. multicoloured	2·40	5·00

DESIGNS: 5c. L. Euler (mathematician); 10c. Clouded yellow (butterfly); 20c. Magpie moth; 30c. Rose chafer (beetle); 40c. Rosy underwing (moth).

C 92 Albrecht von Haller (naturalist)

C 93 Pansy

1958. Children's Fund. Type C 92 and flowers as Type C 93. Inscr "PRO JUVENTUTE 1958".

No.	Type	Description	Unused	Used
J172	**C92**	5c.+5c. purple	80	35
J173	**C 93**	10c.+10c. yellow, brown and green	80	75
J174	-	20c.+10c. mult	80	75
J175	-	30c.+10c. mult	2·00	4·25
J176	-	40c.+10c. mult	2·00	4·25

FLOWERS: 20c. Chinese aster; 30c. Morning Glory; 40c. Christmas rose.

1959. Children's Fund. Portrait as Type C 92 and flowers as Type C 93. Inscr "PRO JUVENTUTE 1959".

No.	Description	Unused	Used
J177	5c.+5c. purple	40	35
J178	10c.+10c. multicoloured	40	35
J179	20c.+10c. red, green and purple	40	35
J180	30c.+10c. multicoloured	2·40	3·75
J181	50c.+10c. multicoloured	2·40	3·75

DESIGNS: 5c. Karl Hilty (lawyer); 10c. Marsh marigold; 20c. Poppy; 30c. Nasturtium; 50c. Sweet pea.

1960. Children's Fund. Portrait as Type C 92 and flowers as Type C 93. Inscr "PRO JUVENTUTE 1960".

No.	Description	Unused	Used
J182	5c.+5c. blue	40	35
J183	10c.+10c. yellow, drab and green	40	35
J184	20c.+10c. green, brown and mauve	40	35
J185	30c.+10c. green, blue and brown	2·40	5·00
J186	50c.+10c. yellow, grn & bl	2·40	5·75

DESIGNS: 5c. Alexandre Calame (painter); 10c. Dandelion; 20c. Phlox; 30c. Larkspur; 50c. Thorn apple.

1961. Children's Fund. Portrait as Type C 92 and flowers as Type C 93. Inscr "PRO JUVENTUTE 1961".

No.	Description	Unused	Used
J187	5c.+5c. blue	40	35
J188	10c.+10c. multicoloured	40	35
J189	20c.+10c. multicoloured	40	35
J190	30c.+10c. multicoloured	1·60	3·00
J191	50c.+10c. multicoloured	2·00	3·75

DESIGNS: 5c. J. Furrer (first President of Swiss Confederation); 10c. Sunflower; 20c. Lily-of-the-Valley; 30c. Iris; 50c. Silverweed.

C 97 "Child's World"

C 98 Mother and Child

1962. Children's Fund. 50th Anniv of Pro Juventute Foundation. Inscr "1912–1962".

No.	Type	Description	Unused	Used
J192	-	5c.+5c. multicoloured	40	35
J193	**C 97**	10c.+10c. red & green	40	35
J194	**C 98**	20c.+10c. mult	40	75
J195	-	30c.+10c. red, mauve and yellow	1·20	1·50
J196	-	50c.+10c. yellow, brown and blue	1·60	1·50

MSJ196a 82×62 mm. 100c.+20c. multi-coloured (×2) (sold at 3f.) 7·25 5·75

DESIGNS—As Type C **97**: 5c. Apple blossom; 30c. "Child's World" (child in meadow); 50c. Forsythia.

1963. Children's Fund. Portrait as Type C 86 and flowers as Type C 93. Inscr "PRO JUVENTUTE 1963".

No.	Description	Unused	Used
J197	5c.+5c. blue	40	35
J198a	10c.+10c. multicoloured	1·60	1·10
J199a	20c.+10c. red, green and carmine	1·60	1·10
J200	30c.+10c. multicoloured	2·00	2·20
J201	50c.+10c. purple, green and blue	2·00	2·20

DESIGNS: 5c. "Portrait of a Boy" (Anker); 10c. Oxeye daisy; 20c. Geranium; 30c. Cornflower; 50c. Carnation.

1964. Children's Fund. Portrait as Type C 86 and flowers as Type C 93. Inscr "PRO JUVENTUTE 1964".

No.	Description	Unused	Used
J202	5c.+5c. blue	40	35
J203	10c.+10c. orange, yellow and green	40	35
J204	20c.+10c. red, green and carmine	50	35
J205	30c.+10c. purple, green and brown	90	75
J206	50c.+10c. multicoloured	1·20	1·10

DESIGNS: 5c. "Portrait of a Girl" (Anker); 10c. Daffodil; 20c. Rose; 30c. Red clover; 50c. White water-lily.

C 101 Western European Hedgehogs

1965. Children's Fund. Animals. Inscr "PRO JUVENTUTE 1965".

No.	Type	Description	Unused	Used
J207	**C101**	5c.+5c. ochre, brown and red	40	35
J208	-	10c.+10c. mult	40	35
J209	-	20c.+10c. blue, brown and chestnut	50	35
J210	-	30c.+10c. blue, black and yellow	80	75
J211	-	50c.+10c. black, brown and blue	1·00	75

ANIMALS: 10c. Alpine marmots; 20c. Red deer; 30c. Eurasian badgers; 50c. Arctic hares.

1966. Children's Fund. Animals. As Type C 101 but inscr "PRO JUVENTUTE 1966". Mult.

No.	Description	Unused	Used
J212	5c.+5c. Stoat	40	20
J213	10c.+10c. Eurasian red squirrel	40	20
J214	20c.+10c. Red fox	50	20
J215	30c.+10c. Brown hare	80	75
J216	50c.+10c. Chamois	1·00	75

C 102 Roe Deer

1967. Children's Fund. Animals. Inscr "PRO JUVENTUTE 1967". Multicoloured.

No.	Description	Unused	Used
J217	10c.+10c. Type C **102**	40	20
J218	20c.+10c. Pine marten	50	35
J219	30c.+10c. Ibex	80	35
J220	50c.+10c. European otter	1·10	75

1968. Children's Fund. Birds. As Type C 102 but inscr "1968". Multicoloured.

No.	Description	Unused	Used
J221	10c.+10c. Western capercaillie	40	20
J222	20c.+10c. Northern bullfinch	50	35
J223	30c.+10c. Woodchat shrike	80	35
J224	50c.+20c. Firecrest	1·10	75

1969. Children's Fund. Birds. As Type C 102. Inscr "1969". Multicoloured.

No.	Description	Unused	Used
J225	10c.+10c. Eurasian goldfinch	40	20
J226	20c.+10c. Golden oriole	50	35
J227	30c.+10c. Wallcreeper	80	35
J228	50c.+20c. Jay	1·10	75

1970. Children's Fund. Birds. As Type C 102. Inscr "1970". Multicoloured.

No.	Description	Unused	Used
J229	10c.+10c. Blue tits	40	15
J230	20c.+10c. Hoopoe	50	20
J231	30c.+10c. Great spotted woodpecker	80	25
J232	50c.+20c. Great crested grebes	1·10	75

1971. Children's Fund. Birds. As Type C 102. Inscr "1971". Multicoloured.

No.	Description	Unused	Used
J233	10c.+10c. Common redstarts	40	15
J234	20c.+10c. Bluethroats	50	20
J235	30c.+10c. Peregrine falcon	80	30
J236	40c.+20c. Mallards	1·80	1·60

C 104 "McGredy's Sunset" Rose

1972. Children's Fund. Roses. Multicoloured.

No.	Description	Unused	Used
J237	10c.+10c. Type C **104**	40	20
J238	20c.+10c. "Miracle"	50	30
J239	30c.+10c. "Papa Meilland"	1·10	85
J240	40c.+20c. "Madame Dimitriu"	2·00	1·80

See also Nos. J258/61 and J279/82.

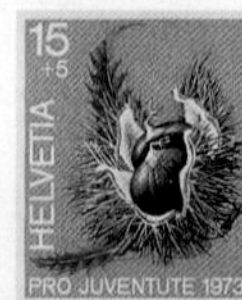
C 105 Chestnut

1973. Children's Fund. "Fruits of the Forest". Multicoloured.

No.	Description	Unused	Used
J241	15c.+5c. Type C **105**	40	20
J242	30c.+10c. Cherries	50	30
J243	40c.+20c. Blackberries	1·10	85
J244	60c.+20c. Bilberries	2·00	1·80

See also Nos. J245/8, J250/3 and J254/7.

1974. Children's Fund. "Fruits of the Forest". Poisonous Plants. As Type C 105. Inscr "1974". Multicoloured.

No.	Description	Unused	Used
J245	15c.+10c. Daphne	40	20
J246	30c.+20c. Belladonna	80	30
J247	50c.+20c. Laburnum	1·20	1·10
J248	60c.+25c. Mistletoe	1·60	1·30

1975. Children's Fund. As Type C 105. Inscr "1975". Multicoloured.

No.	Description	Unused	Used
J249	10c.+5c. "Post-Brent" (postman's hamper)	55	45
J250	15c.+10c. Hepatica	40	30
J251	30c.+20c. Rowan	80	20
J252	50c.+20c. Yellow deadnettle	1·10	1·00
J253	60c.+25c. Sycamore	1·60	1·20

1976. Children's Fund. "Fruits of the Forest". As Type C 105. Inscr "1976". Multicoloured.

No.	Description	Unused	Used
J254	20c.+10c. Barberry	50	20
J255	40c.+20c. Black elder	90	25
J256	40c.+20c. Lime	1·00	35
J257	80c.+40c. Lungwort	2·00	1·80

1977. Children's Fund. Roses. As Type C 104. Inscr "1977". Multicoloured.

No.	Description	Unused	Used
J258	20c.+10c. "Rosa foetida bicolor"	50	20
J259	40c.+20c. "Parfum de l'Hay"	1·00	35
J260	70c.+30c. "R. foetida persiana"	1·60	1·50
J261	80c.+40c. "R. centifolia muscosa"	2·00	1·80

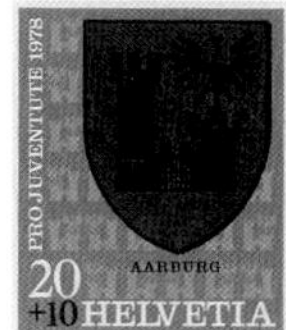

C 106 Arms of Aarburg

1978. Children's Fund. Arms of the Communes (1st series). Multicoloured.

J262	20c.+10c. Type C **106**	50	20
J263	40c.+20c. Gruyeres	1·00	30
J264	70c.+30c. Castasegna	1·60	1·50
J265	80c.+40c. Wangen	2·40	1·80

See also Nos. J266/9, J270/3 and J274/7.

1979. Children's Fund. Arms of the Communes (2nd series). As Type C 106. Multicoloured.

J266	20c.+10c. Cadro	50	20
J267	40c.+20c. Rute	1·00	30
J268	70c.+30c. Schwamendingen	1·60	1·50
J269	80c.+40c. Perroy	2·40	1·80

1980. Children's Fund. Arms of the Communes (3rd series). As Type C 106. Multicoloured.

J270	20c.+10c. Cortaillod	50	20
J271	40c.+20c. Sierre	1·00	30
J272	70c.+30c. Scuol	1·60	1·50
J273	80c.+40c. Wolfenschiessen	2·40	1·80

1981. Children's Fund. Arms of the Communes (4th series). As Type C 106. Multicoloured.

J274	20c.+10c. Uffikon	50	20
J275	40c.+20c. Torre	1·00	30
J276	70c.+30c. Benken	1·60	1·50
J277	80c.+40c. Preverenges	2·40	1·80

C 107 Letter Balance

1982. Children's Fund. Type C 107 and roses as Type C 104. Multicoloured.

J278	10c.+10c. Type C **107**	80	20
J279	20c.+10c. "La Belle Portugaise"	50	20
J280	40c.+20c. "Hugh Dickson"	1·00	20
J281	70c.+30c. "Mermaid"	1·60	1·50
J282	80c.+40c. "Madame Caroline"	2·40	1·80

C 108 Kitchen Stove, c. 1850

1983. Children's Fund. Toys. Multicoloured.

J283	20c.+10c. Type C **108**	80	45
J284	40c.+20c. Rocking horse, 1826	1·20	30
J285	70c.+30c. Doll, c. 1870	1·60	1·50
J286	80c.+40c. Steam locomotive, c. 1900	2·40	1·80

C 109 Heidi and Goat (Johanna Spyri)

1984. Children's Fund. Characters from Children's Books. Multicoloured.

J287	35c.+15c. Type C **109**	80	75
J288	50c.+20c. Pinocchio and kite (Carlo Collodi)	1·10	35
J289	70c.+30c. Pippi Long-stocking (Astrid Lindgren)	2·10	1·80
J290	80c.+40c. Max and Moritz on roof (Wilhelm Busch)	2·40	2·20

1985. Children's Fund. Characters from Children's Books. As Type C 109. Multicoloured.

J291	35c.+15c. Hansel, Gretel and Witch	80	75
J292	50c.+20c. Snow White and the Seven Dwarfs	1·20	35
J293	80c.+40c. Red Riding Hood and Wolf	2·40	1·80
J294	90c.+40c. Cinderella and Prince Charming	2·75	2·20

C 110 Teddy Bear

1986. Children's Fund. Toys. Multicoloured.

J295	35c.+15c. Type C **110**	80	75
J296	50c.+20c. Spinning top	1·20	35
J297	80c.+40c. Steamroller	2·40	2·20
J298	90c.+40c. Doll	2·75	2·50

C 111 Girl carrying Pine Branch and Candle

1987. Children's Fund. Child Development. Pre-school Age. Multicoloured.

J299	25c.+10c. Type C **111**	55	75
J300	35c.+15c. Mother breast-feeding baby	1·10	75
J301	50c.+20c. Toddler playing with bricks	1·20	35
J302	80c.+40c. Children playing in sand	2·00	1·80
J303	90c.+40c. Father with child on his shoulders	2·40	2·20

C 112 Learning to Read

1988. Children's Fund. Child Development. School Age. Multicoloured.

J304	35c.+15c. Type C **112**	80	75
J305	50c.+20c. Playing triangle	1·20	35
J306	80c.+40c. Learning arithmetic	2·40	2·20
J307	90c.+40c. Drawing	2·75	2·50

C 113 Community Work

1989. Children's Fund. Child Development. Adolescence. Multicoloured.

J308	35c.+15c. Type C **113**	80	75
J309	50c.+20c. Young couple (friendship)	1·20	35
J310	80c.+40c. Boy at computer screen (vocational training)	2·40	2·20
J311	90c.+40c. Girl in laboratory (higher education and research)	2·75	2·50

C 114 Building Model Ship (hobbies)

1990. Child Development. Leisure Activities. Mult.

J312	35c.+15c. Type C **114**	1·20	95
J313	50c.+20c. Youth group	1·20	50
J314	80c.+40c. Sport	2·40	2·20
J315	90c.+40c. Music	2·75	2·50

C 115 Ramsons

1991. Woodland Flowers. Multicoloured.

J316	50c.+25c. Type C **115**	1·20	75
J317	70c.+30c. Wood cranesbill	1·60	1·50
J318	80c.+40c. Nettle-leaved bellflower	2·40	2·20
J319	90c.+40c. Few-leaved hawk-weed	2·40	2·20

C 116 Melchior (wood puppet)

1992. Christmas (J320) and Trees (others). Mult.

J320	50c.+25c. Type C **116**	1·50	55
J321	50c.+25c. Beech	1·50	55
J322	70c.+30c. Norway maple	2·30	1·50
J323	80c.+40c. Pedunculate oak	2·40	1·80
J324	90c.+40c. Norway spruce	2·50	2·20

Nos. J321/4 show silhouette of tree and close-up of its leaves and fruit.

C 117 Christmas Wreath

1993. Christmas (J325) and Woodland Plants (others). Multicoloured.

J325	60c.+30c. Type C **117**	1·80	1·00
J326	60c.+30c. Male fern	1·80	1·00
J327	80c.+40c. Guelder rose	2·40	2·00
J328	100c.+50c. "Mnium punctatum"	3·00	2·20

C 118 Candles

1994. Christmas (J329) and Fungi (others). Mult.

J329	60c.+30c. Type C **118**	1·80	1·00
J330	60c.+30c. Wood blewit	1·80	1·00
J331	80c.+40c. Red boletus	2·40	2·00
J332	100c.+50c. Shaggy pholiota	3·00	2·20

C 119 Detail of "The Annunciation" (Bartolome Murillo)

1995. Christmas (J333) and Wildlife (others). Mult.

J333	60c.+30c. Type C **119**	1·80	1·00
J334	60c.+30c. Brown trout	1·80	1·00
J335	80c.+40c. Grey wagtail	2·40	2·00
J336	100c.+50c. Spotted salamander	3·00	2·20

C 120 Shooting Star and Constellations

1996. Christmas (J337) and Wildlife (others). Mult.

J337	70c.+35c. Type C **120**	2·30	1·50
J338	70c.+35c. European graylings (fish)	2·30	1·50
J339	90c.+45c. Crayfish	2·75	2·40
J340	110c.+55c. European otter	3·25	3·00

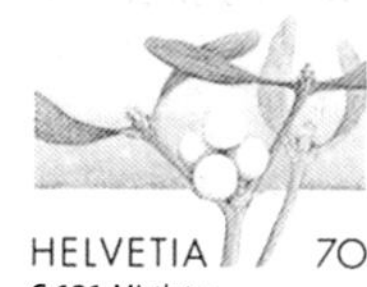

C 121 Mistletoe

1997. Christmas (J341) and Wildlife (others). Mult.

J341	70c.+35c. Type C **121**	2·30	1·50
J342	70c.+35c. Three-spined stickleback	2·30	1·50
J343	90c.+45c. Yellow-bellied toad	4·50	2·40
J344	110c.+55c. Ruff	3·25	3·00

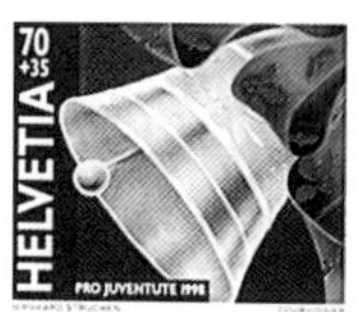

C 122 Christmas Bell

1998. Christmas (J345) and Wildlife (others). Mult.

J345	70c.+35c. Type C **122**	2·30	1·60
J346	70c.+35c. Ramshorn snail	2·30	1·60
J347	90c.+45c. Great crested grebe	2·75	2·50
J348	110c.+55c. Pike	3·25	3·00

C 123 Children and Snowman (Margaret Strub)

1999. Christmas (J349) and Illustrations from "Nicolo the Clown" (picture book by Verena Pavoni) (others). Multicoloured.

J349	70c.+35c. Type C **123**	2·30	1·60
J350	70c.+35c. Nicolo holding guitar	2·30	1·60
J351	90c.+45c. Nicolo with his father	2·75	2·50
J352	110c.+55c. Nicolo with donkey	3·25	3·00

C124 Santa Claus

2000. Christmas. Illustrations from Little Albert (book) by Albert Manser. Multicoloured.

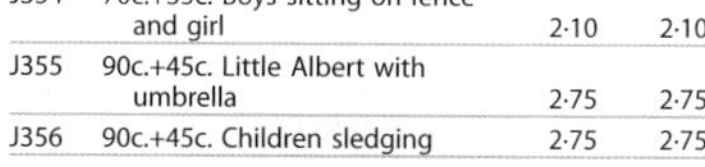

J353	70c.+35c. Type C **124**	2·10	2·10
J354	70c.+35c. Boys sitting on fence and girl	2·10	2·10
J355	90c.+45c. Little Albert with umbrella	2·75	2·75
J356	90c.+45c. Children sledging	2·75	2·75

C125 Santa Claus and Cat

2001. Illustrations from Children's Books. Multicoloured.

J357	70c.+35c. Type C **125** (*What's Santa Claus Doing?* (text by Karin von Oldersausen, illustrations by Gabi Fluck))	2·10	2·10
J358	70c.+35c. Leopold the leopard in tree (*Leopold and the Sun* by Stephan Brülhart)	2·10	2·10
J359	90c.+45c. Bear on scooter (*Honey Bear by S. Brulhart*)	2·75	2·75
J360	90c.+45c. Tom the monkey in tree (*Leopold and the Sun*)	2·75	2·50

C126 "Christmas rose"

2002. Roses. Multicoloured.

J361	70c.+35c. Type C **126**	2·10	2·10

J362	70c.+35c. "Ingrid Bergman"	2·10	2·10
J363	90c.+45c. "Belle Vaudoise"	2·75	2·75
J364	90c.+45c. "Charmian"	2·75	2·75
J365	130c.+65c. "Fruhlingsgold"	4·00	4·00

No. J361 is impregnated with the fragrance of cinnamon and cloves and Nos. J362/5 with the perfume of roses.

C 127 Playing with Christmas Toys

2003. Children's Rights. The Right to Play. Multicoloured. Self-adhesive gum.

J366	70c.+35c. Type C **127**	2·10	2·10
J367	85c.+ 35c. Playing shop	2·50	2·50
J368	90c.+45c. Skateboarding	2·75	2·75
J369	100c.+45c. Playing music	3·00	3·00

C 128 Family and Giraffe

2004. Children's Rights. Right to Education. Multicoloured. Self-adhesive gum.

J370	85c.+40c. Type C **128**	2·75	2·75
J371	85c.+ 40c. Playing cards	2·75	2·75
J372	100c.+50c. Listening to older person read	3·25	3·25
J373	100c.+50c. Teacher and pupils	3·25	3·25

C129 Children enclosed in Lifebuoy

2005. Children's Rights. Right to Leisure and Play. Multicoloured. Self-adhesive.

J374	85c.+40c. Type C **1291**	2·75	2·75
J375	85c.+40c. Boy and girl catching cherries in mouth	2·75	2·75
J376	100c.+50c. Children and laptop computer	3·25	3·25
J377	100c.+50c. Boy wishing	3·25	3·25

C130 Singer (Veronica Jesus Garcia Pinto)

2005. Winning Designs in Children's Painting Competition "My Dream Profession". Multicoloured. Self-adhesive.

J378	85c.+40c. Type C **130**	2·75	2·75
J379	85c.+40c. Workshop (garage owner) (Stephane Arada)	2·75	2·75
J380	100c.+50c. Dog with bandaged leg (vet) (Lea Mayer)	3·25	3·25
J381	100c.+50c. Angel	3·25	3·25

C 131 *Camping* (Christine Fischer)

2007. Winning Designs in Children's Design a Stamp Competition. "Holiday Fun". Multicoloured.

J382	85c.+40c. Type **C 131**	2·75	2·75
J383	85c.+40c. *Mountains* (Jonathon Balest)	2·75	2·75
J384	100c.+50c. *Sunshine* (Morena Rufatti)	3·25	3·25
J385	100c.+50c. Angels carrying heart	3·25	3·25

C 132 *Friendship unites* (Andrea Andreazzi)

2008. Winning Designs in Children's Design a Stamp Competition. "Friendship". Multicoloured.

J386	85c.+40c. Type C **132**	3·75	3·75
J387	85c.+40c. *Friendship provides support* (Manon Peng)	3·75	3·75
J388	100c.+50c. *Friendship is a source of happiness* (Delia Candolo)	4·25	4·25
J389	100+50c. *Friendship is uplifting*	4·25	4·25

C 133 Letters to Parents

2009. Pro Juventute Foundation. Multicoloured. Self-adhesive.

J390	85c.+40c. Type C **133**	3·75	3·75
J391	85c.+40c. Tree branches and children (holiday pass scheme)	3·75	3·75
J392	100c.+50c. Parents back to back (Tel. 147 advice line)	4·25	4·25
J393	100c.+50c. Children and stamps (stamp sales)	4·25	4·25

INTERNATIONAL ORGANIZATIONS SITUATED IN SWITZERLAND

The stamps listed under this heading were issued by the Swiss Post Office primarily for the use of officials of the Organizations named, situated in Geneva.

These stamps could not be legitimately obtained unused before Feburary 1944.

A. LEAGUE OF NATIONS

1922. Optd SOCIETE DES NATIONS.

LN1	**18b**	2½c. bistre on buff		1·10
LN2	**18b**	3c. blue on buff		10·50
LN3	**18b**	5c. orange on buff		7·50
LN4	**18b**	5c. grey on buff		5·25
LN5	**18b**	5c. purple on buff		3·25
LN5a	**18b**	5c. green on buff		32·00
LN6	**18b**	7½c. green on buff		1·10
LN7	**21**	10c. green on buff		1·10
LN8	**21**	10c. violet on buff		2·10
LN9	**21**	15c. red on buff		2·10
LN10	**21**	20c. purple on buff		12·00
LN11	**21**	20c. red on buff		4·25
LN13	**21**	25c. red on buff		2·10
LN14	**21**	25c. brown on buff		27·00
LN15	**17**	30c. green and brown		19·00
LN16	**21**	30c. blue on buff		9·50
LN17	**17**	35c. yellow and green		13·00
LN18	**17**	40c. blue		2·10
LN19	**17**	40c. green and mauve		27·00
LN20a	**17**	50c. green & dp green	†	3·25
LN21	**17**	60c. brown	41·00	2·10
LN22a	**17**	70c. buff and violet	2·10	3·25
LN23a	**17**	80c. buff and grey	3·25	3·25
LN24a	**41**	90c. red, dp green & grn		6·50
LN25a	**17**	1f. green and purple		7·50
LN26b	**41**	1f.20 red, lake and pink	3·25	5·25
LN27a	**41**	1f.50 red, bl & turq	3·25	6·50
LN28a	**41**	2f. red, black and grey	†	7·00
LN29	**22**	3f. red		43·00
LN29a	**43**	3f. brown		£225
LN30	-	5f. blue (No. 296)		95·00
LN32	-	10f. mauve (No. 297)		£180
LN33	-	10f. green (No. 337)		£170

1932. International Disarmament Conference. Optd SOCIETE DES NATIONS.

LN34	**44**	5c. green	24·00
LN35	**44**	10c. orange	2·10
LN36	**44**	20c. mauve	2·10
LN37	**44**	30c. blue	70·00
LN38	**44**	60c. brown	17·00
LN39	**45**	1f. grey and blue	16·00

1934. Landscape designs of 1934 optd SOCIETE DES NATIONS.

LN40	**48**	3c. green	55
LN41	-	5c. green	75
LN42	-	15c. orange	1·80
LN43	-	25c. brown	26·00
LN44	-	30c. blue	2·10

1937. Landscape designs of 1936 optd SOCIETE DES NATIONS.

LN45A	**52**	3c. green	20	55
LN46A	-	5c. green	20	55
LN47Ac	-	10c. purple		1·40
LN49	-	10c. brown	65	1·30
LN50A	-	15c. orange	45	75
LN51A	-	20c. red (railway)		2·75
LN51Ac	-	20c. red (lake)	75	2·10
LN52A	-	25c. brown	65	1·40
LN53A	-	30c. blue	65	1·30
LN54A	-	35c. green	65	1·40
LN55A	-	40c. grey	85	1·50

1938. Nos. 382/5 optd SOCIETE DES NATIONS.

LN56	**55**	20c. red and buff	2·10
LN57	-	30c. blue and light blue	3·75
LN58	-	60c. brown and buff	7·00
LN59	-	1f. black and buff	12·00

1938. Nos. 382/5 optd SERVICE DE LA SOCIETE DES NATIONS in circle.

LN60	**55**	20c. red and buff	2·75
LN61	-	30c. blue and light blue	5·25
LN62	-	60c. brown and buff	9·00
LN63	-	1f. black and buff	15·00

1939. Nos. 388c/90c optd SOCIETE DES NATIONS.

LN64	**61**	3f. brown on buff	4·25	13·00
LN65	-	5f. blue on buff	6·50	19·00
LN66	-	10f. green on buff	14·00	37·00

1944. Optd COURRIER DE LA SOCIETE DES NATIONS. (a) Landscape designs of 1936.

LN67	**52**	3c. green	30	55
LN68	-	5c. green	30	55
LN69	-	10c. brown	95	55
LN70	-	15c. orange	45	65
LN71	-	20c. red (lake)	55	1·10
LN72	-	25c. brown	65	1·40
LN73	-	30c. blue	70	1·40
LN74	-	35c. green	70	1·40
LN75	-	40c. grey	75	1·70
		(b) Historical designs of 1941.		
LN76		50c. blue on green	1·40	2·75
LN77	**68**	60c. brown on brown	1·60	4·25
LN78	-	70c. purple on mauve	1·70	4·25
LN79	-	80c. black on grey	1·50	3·25
LN80	-	90c. red on pink	1·50	3·25
LN81	-	1f. green on green	1·50	3·25
LN82	-	1f.20 purple on grey	2·40	4·75
LN83	-	1f.50 blue on buff	2·75	5·25
LN84	-	2f. red on pink	3·25	7·00
		(c) Parliament designs of 1938.		
LN85	**61**	3f. brown on buff	6·00	14·00
LN86	-	5f. blue on buff	9·50	21·00
LN87	-	10f. green on buff	16·00	43·00

B. INTERNATIONAL LABOUR OFFICE

Optd **S.d.N Bureau international du Travail** (Nos. LB1/47).

1923

LB1	**18b**	2½c. bistre on buff		65
LB2	**18b**	3c. blue on buff		2·10
LB3	**18b**	5c. orange on buff		75
LB4	**18b**	5c. purple on buff		65
LB5	**18b**	7½c. green on buff		65
LB6	**21**	10c. green on buff		75
LB8	**21**	15c. red on buff		2·10
LB9	**21**	20c. purple on buff		21·00
LB10	**21**	20c. red on buff		5·25
LB11	**21**	25c. red on buff		1·40
LB12	**21**	25c. brown on buff		3·75
LB13	**17**	30c. green and brown		85·00
LB14	**21**	30c. blue on buff		3·25
LB15	**17**	35c. yellow and green		14·00
LB16	**17**	40c. blue		1·40
LB17	**17**	40c. green and mauve		28·00
LB18a	**17**	50c. green & deep green	2·10	2·75
LB19	**17**	60c. brown	2·10	2·10
LB20a	**17**	70c. buff and violet	1·90	3·25
LB21	**17**	80c. buff and grey	17·00	2·75
LB22	**41**	90c. red, dp grn & grn		5·25
LB23	**17**	1f. green and purple		3·50
LB24b	**38**	1f.20 red, lake and pink	17·00	4·75
LB25a	**38**	1f.50 red, bl & turq	3·25	3·75
LB26a	**38**	2f. red, black and grey	3·75	7·00
LB27	**22**	3f. red		27·00
LB27a	**43**	3f. brown		£225
LB28	-	5f. blue (No. 296)		43·00
LB30	-	10f. mauve (No. 297)		£190
LB31	-	10f. green (No. 337)		£170

1932. International Disarmament Conference.

LB32	**44**	5c. green	1·60
LB33	**44**	10c. orange	1·60
LB34	**44**	20c. mauve	1·60
LB35	**44**	30c. blue	10·50
LB36	**44**	60c. brown	10·50
LB37	**45**	1f. grey and blue	13·00

1937. Landscape design of 1934.

LB38	**48**	3c. green	7·00

1937. Landscape designs of 1936.

LB39A	**52**	3c. green	30	95
LB40A	-	5c. green	30	95
LB41B	-	10c. purple		2·75
LB41e	-	10c. brown	65	1·10
LB42A	-	15c. orange	45	1·60
LB43A	-	20c. red (railway)		3·25
LB43c	-	20c. red (lake)	75	1·60
LB44A	-	25c. brown	65	2·10
LB45A	-	30c. blue	65	1·90
LB46A	-	35c. green	75	2·40
LB47A	-	40c. grey	1·10	3·25

1938. Nos. 382/5 optd S.d.N. Bureau international du Travail.

LB48	**55**	20c. red and buff	2·10
LB49	-	30c. blue and light blue	4·25
LB50	-	60c. brown and buff	7·00
LB51	-	1f. black and buff	10·50

1938. Nos. 382/5 optd SERVICE DU BUREAU INTERNATIONAL DU TRAVAIL in circle.

LB52	**55**	20c. red and buff	4·25
LB53	-	30c. blue and light blue	4·25
LB54	-	60c. brown and buff	8·50
LB55	-	1f. black and buff	8·50

1939. Nos. 388c/90c optd S.d.N. Bureau international du Travail.

LB56	**61**	3f. brown on buff	5·25	10·50
LB57	-	5f. blue on buff	6·50	21·00
LB58	-	10f. green on buff	10·50	37·00

1944. Optd COURRIER DU BUREAU INTERNATIONAL DU TRAVAIL. (a) Landscape designs of 1936.

LB59	**52**	3c. green	30	45
LB60	-	5c. green	30	45
LB61	-	10c. brown	30	45
LB62	-	15c. orange	55	65
LB63	-	20c. red (lake)	60	75
LB64	-	25c. brown	65	85
LB65	-	30c. blue	85	1·50
LB66	-	35c. green	90	1·60
LB67	-	40c. grey	95	2·10
		(b) Historical designs of 1941.		
LB68		50c. blue on green	2·50	10·50
LB69	**68**	60c. brown on brown	2·50	10·50
LB70	-	70c. purple on mauve	3·00	10·50
LB71	-	80c. black on grey	70	1·70
LB72	-	90c. red on pink	70	1·70
LB73	-	1f. green on green	90	1·70
LB74	-	1f.20 purple on grey	1·10	2·10
LB75	-	1f.50 blue on buff	1·30	3·00
LB76	-	2f. red on pink	1·80	3·75
		(c) Parliament designs of 1938.		
LB77	**61**	3f. brown on buff	4·00	8·00
LB78	-	5f. blue on buff	6·00	14·00
LB79	-	10f. green on buff	13·00	27·00

1950. Landscape designs of 1949 optd BUREAU INTERNATIONAL DU TRAVAIL.

LB80	**107**	5c. orange	9·50	8·50
LB81	-	10c. green	9·50	9·50
LB82	-	15c. turquoise	10·50	10·50
LB83	-	20c. purple	10·50	13·00
LB84	-	25c. red	13·00	10·50
LB85	-	30c. green	13·00	14·00
LB86	-	35c. brown	13·00	14·00
LB87	-	40c. blue	13·00	14·00
LB88	-	50c. grey	21·00	14·00
LB89	-	60c. green	21·00	21·00
LB90	-	70c. violet	26·00	27·00

LB 4 Miners (bas-relief)

1952. Inscr as in Type LB 4.

LB91	**LB4**	5c. purple	20	20
LB92	**LB4**	10c. green	20	20
LB94	-	20c. red	30	30
LB95	-	30c. orange	55	55
LB96	**LB 4**	40c. blue	3·25	3·25
LB97	**LB 4**	50c. blue	75	75
LB98	-	60c. brown	65	65
LB99	-	2f. purple	1·90	1·90

DESIGN—HORIZ: 20, 30, 60c., 2f. Globe, flywheel and factory chimney.

1969. Pope Paul's Visit to Geneva. No. LB95 optd Visite du Pape Paul VI Geneve 10 juin 1969.

LB100	30c. orange	45	45

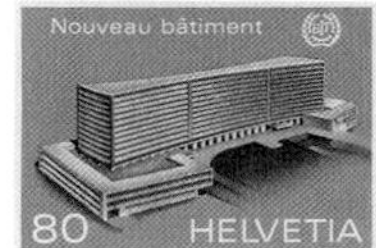

LB 6 New Headquarters Building

1974. Inaug of New I.L.O. Headquarters, Geneva.

LB101	**LB6**	80c. multicoloured	85	85

LB 7 Man at Lathe

1975

LB102	**LB7**	30c. brown	30	30
LB103	-	60c. blue	55	55
LB104	-	90c. brown, red & grn	1·50	1·50
LB105	-	100c. green	85	85
LB106	-	120c. ochre and brown	1·40	1·40

DESIGNS: 60c. Woman at drilling machine; 90c. Welder and laboratory assistant; 100c. Surveyor with theodolite; 120c. Apprentice and instructor with slide rule.

LB 8 Keys

1994. 75th Anniv of I.L.O.

LB107	**LB8**	180c. multicoloured	2·75	2·75

C. INTERNATIONAL EDUCATION OFFICE

1944. Optd COURRIER DU BUREAU INTERNATIONAL D'EDUCATION. (a) Landscape designs of 1936.

LE1	**52**	3c. green	30	1·40
LE2	-	5c. green	60	1·60
LE3	-	10c. brown	65	1·90
LE4	-	15c. orange	65	1·90
LE5	-	20c. red (lake)	65	1·90
LE6	-	25c. brown	65	2·10
LE7	-	30c. blue	1·10	2·75
LE8	-	35c. green	1·10	3·00
LE9	-	40c. grey	1·30	3·25

(b) Historical designs of 1941.

LE10		50c. blue on green	6·50	19·00
LE11	**68**	60c. brown on brown	6·50	19·00
LE12	-	70c. purple on mauve	6·50	19·00
LE13	-	80c. black on grey	65	2·10
LE14	-	90c. red on pink	85	2·75
LE15	-	1f. green on green	1·10	3·00
LE16	-	1f.20 purple on grey	1·20	4·25
LE17	-	1f.50 blue on buff	1·50	4·75
LE18	-	2f. red on pink	2·10	5·25

(c) Parliament designs of 1938.

LE19	**61**	3f. brown on buff	8·00	20·00
LE20	-	5f. blue on buff	12·00	32·00
LE21	-	10f. green on buff	18·00	48·00

1946. Optd BIE vert.

LE22	**86**	10c. purple	75	75

Optd **BUREAU INTERNATIONAL D'EDUCATION** (Nos. LE23/39)

1948. Landscape designs of 1936.

LE23	5c. brown	4·25	4·25
LE24	10c. green	4·25	4·25
LE25	20c. brown	4·25	4·25
LE26	25c. red	4·25	4·25
LE27	30c. blue	4·75	4·75
LE28	40c. blue	4·75	4·75

1950. Landscape designs of 1949.

LE29	**107**	5c. orange	1·80	2·10
LE30	-	10c. green	1·80	2·75
LE31	-	15c. turquoise	1·80	2·75
LE32	-	20c. purple	4·50	10·50
LE33	-	25c. red	12·00	20·00
LE34	-	30c. green	12·00	20·00
LE35	-	35c. brown	8·50	14·00
LE36	-	40c. blue	8·50	14·00
LE37	-	50c. grey	10·50	15·00
LE38	-	60c. green	12·00	18·00
LE39	-	70c. violet	13·00	21·00

LE 3 Globe on Books

1958. Inscr as in Type LE 3.

LE40	**LE3**	5c. purple	10	10
LE41	**LE3**	10c. green	20	20
LE43	-	20c. red	45	45
LE44	-	30c. orange	55	55
LE45	**LE 3**	40c. blue	3·75	3·75
LE46	**LE 3**	50c. blue	65	65
LE47	-	60c. brown	75	75
LE48	-	2f. purple	2·10	2·10

DESIGN—VERT: 20, 30, 60c., 2f. Pestalozzi Monument, Yverdon.

D. WORLD HEALTH ORGANIZATION

1948. Optd ORGANISATION MONDIALE DE LA SANTE. (a) Landscape designs of 1936.

LH1	5c. brown (No. 489)	4·75	4·25
LH2	10c. green (No. 490)	4·75	4·75
LH3	20c. brown (No. 491)	4·75	4·75
LH4	25c. red (No. 492)	5·25	6·00
LH5	40c. blue (No. 494)	5·25	6·00

(b) Landscape designs of 1949.

LH6	**107**	5c. orange	1·30	1·40
LH7	-	10c. green	1·70	2·10
LH8	-	15c. turquoise	2·40	2·75
LH9	-	20c. purple	5·25	8·00
LH10	-	25c. red	5·25	8·00
LH11	-	30c. green	4·25	6·50
LH12	-	35c. brown	4·75	9·50
LH13	-	40c. blue	4·25	4·75
LH14	-	50c. grey	5·25	8·00
LH15	-	60c. green	6·00	13·00
LH16	-	70c. violet	7·00	13·00

(c) Historical designs of 1941 (Nos. 408/13).

LH17	80c. black on grey	5·25	4·75
LH18	90c. red on pink	10·50	13·00
LH19	1f. green on green	7·00	5·25
LH20	1f.20 purple on grey	14·00	18·00
LH21	1f.50 blue on buff	27·00	18·00
LH22	2f. red on pink	10·50	8·50

(d) Parliament designs of 1938.

LH23	**61**	3f. brown on buff	55·00	48·00
LH24	-	5f. blue on buff	21·00	15·00
LH25	-	10f. green on buff	£110	85·00

LH 2 Staff of Aesculapius

1957

LH26	**LH2**	5c. purple	10	10
LH27	**LH2**	10c. green	20	20
LH29	**LH2**	20c. red	45	45
LH30	**LH2**	30c. orange	55	55
LH31	**LH2**	40c. blue	3·75	3·75
LH32	**LH2**	50c. blue	65	65
LH33	**LH2**	60c. brown	75	75
LH34	**LH2**	2f. purple	2·10	2·10

1962. Malaria Eradication. Optd ERADICATION DU PALUDISME.

LH35	50c. blue	95	95

LH 4 Staff of Aesculapius

1975

LH36	**LH4**	30c. green, purple and pink	45	45
LH37	**LH4**	60c. yellow, blue and light blue	75	75
LH38	**LH4**	90c. yellow, violet and light violet	1·10	1·10
LH39	**LH4**	100c. blue, brown and orange	1·30	1·30
LH40	**LH4**	140c. green, turquoise and red	1·60	1·60

LH 5 Staff of Aesculapius

1995

LH41	**LH5**	180c. yellow, brown and red	2·75	2·75

E. INTERNATIONAL REFUGEES ORGANIZATION

Optd **ORGANISATION INTERNATIONALE POUR LES REFUGIES.**

1950. (a) Landscape designs of 1949.

LR1	**107**	5c. orange	37·00	21·00
LR2	-	10c. green	37·00	21·00
LR3	-	20c. purple	37·00	21·00
LR4	-	25c. red	37·00	21·00
LR5	-	40c. blue	37·00	21·00

(b) Historical designs of 1941 (Nos. 408/13).

LR6	80c. black on grey	37·00	48·00
LR7	1f. green on green	37·00	14·00
LR8	2f. red on pink	37·00	14·00

F. WORLD METEOROLOGICAL ORGANIZATION

LM 1 "The Elements"

1956. Inscr as in Type LM 1.

LM1	**LM1**	5c. purple	10	10
LM2	**LM1**	10c. green	20	20
LM4	-	20c. red	45	45
LM5	-	30c. orange	55	55
LM6	**LM 1**	40c. blue	3·75	3·75
LM7	**LM 1**	50c. blue	65	65
LM8	-	60c. brown	75	75
LM9	-	2f. purple	3·25	3·25

DESIGN: 20, 30, 60c., 2f. Weathervane.

LM 2 W.M.O. Emblem

1973. Cent of World Meteorological Organization.

LM10	**LM2**	30c. red	45	45
LM11	**LM2**	40c. blue	55	55
LM12	-	80c. violet and gold	95	95
LM13	**LM2**	1f. brown	1·30	1·30

DESIGN: 80c. Emblem and "OMI OMM 1873 1973".

G. UNIVERSAL POSTAL UNION

LP 1 U.P.U. Monument, Berne

1957. Inscr as in Type LP 1.

LP1	**LP1**	5c. purple	10	10
LP2	-	10c. green	20	20
LP4	-	20c. red	45	45
LP5	-	30c. orange	55	55
LP6	**LP 1**	40c. blue	3·75	3·75
LP7	**LP 1**	50c. blue	65	65
LP8	-	60c. brown	80	80
LP9	**LP 1**	2f. purple	2·20	2·20

DESIGN: 10, 20, 30, 60c. Pegasus (sculpture).

LP 2 "Letter Post"

1976

LP10	**LP2**	40c. purple, blue and claret	55	55
LP11	-	80c. multicoloured	90	90
LP12	-	90c. multicoloured	1·10	1·10
LP13	-	100c. multicoloured	1·20	1·20
LP14	-	120c. multicoloured	1·70	1·70
LP15	-	140c. grey, blue and red	2·20	2·20

DESIGNS: 80c. "Parcel Post"; 90c. "Financial Services"; 100c. Technical co-operation; 120c. Carrier pigeon, international reply coupon and postal money order; 140c. Express Mail Service.

The 120 and 140c. are additionally inscribed "TIMBRE DE SERVICE".

LP 3 Computer, Mail Sacks and Globe

1995

LP16	**LP 3**	180c. multicoloured	2·75	2·75

LP 4 Hand reaching for Rainbow

1999. 125th Anniv of Universal Postal Union. Multicoloured.

LP17	20c. Type LP **4**	35	35
LP18	70c. Hand holding rainbow	1·00	1·00

LP 5 "Q" and Letter

2003

LP19	**LP5**	90c. multicoloured	2·50	2·50

LP 6 Symbols of Communication (Nasir Tahir)

2005

LP20	**LP6**	100c. multicoloured	2·10	2·10

LP 7 Flying Postman and Hands

2007

LP21	**LP7**	180c. multicoloured	3·50	3·50

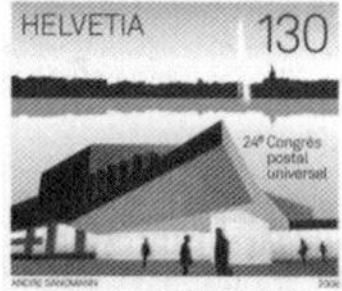

LP 8 Centre International de Conferences Geneve (conference venue)

2008. 24th UPU Congress, Geneva.

LP22	**LP8**	130c. multicoloured	2·75	2·75

LP 9 Rene de Saint-Marceaux (sculptor and creator of statue used as emblem of Universal Postal Union) and UPU Monument

2008. Centenary of UPU Monument. Rene de Saint-Marceaux (sculptor and creator of statue used as emblem of Universal Postal Union) Commemoration.

LP23	180c. multicoloured	3·50	3·50

H. UNITED NATIONS

1950. Optd NATIONS UNIES OFFICE EUROPEEN. (a) Landscape designs of 1949.

LU1	**107**	5c. orange	55	3·25
LU2	-	10c. green	90	3·25
LU3	-	15c. turquoise	1·30	4·50
LU4	-	20c. purple	2·20	6·00
LU5	-	25c. red	3·50	11·00
LU6	-	30c. green	3·50	11·00
LU7	-	35c. brown	3·50	11·00
LU8	-	40c. blue	5·25	12·00
LU9	-	50c. grey	6·75	16·00
LU10	-	60c. green	7·75	17·00
LU11	-	70c. violet	9·00	17·00

(b) Historical designs of 1941 (Nos. 408/13).

LU12	80c. black on grey	13·50	14·50
LU13	90c. red on pink	17·00	17·00
LU14	1f. green on green	17·00	17·00
LU15	1f.20 purple on grey	19·00	19·00
LU16	1f.50 blue on buff	19·00	19·00
LU17	2f. red on pink	19·00	19·00

(c) Parliament designs of 1938.

LU18	**61**	3f. brown on buff	£180	£180
LU19	-	5f. blue on buff	£180	£180
LU20	-	10f. green on buff	£225	£225

LU 2

1955. 10th Anniv of U.N.O.

LU21	**LU2**	40c. blue and yellow	4·50	5·50

LU 4

1955. Nos. LU22/3 and LU27/8 are as Type LU 2 but without dates.

LU22	-	5c. purple	20	20
LU23	-	10c. green	35	35
LU25	**LU 4**	20c. red	45	45
LU26	**LU 4**	30c. orange	55	55
LU27	-	40c. blue	7·25	7·25
LU28	-	50c. blue	65	65
LU29	**LU 4**	60c. brown	80	80
LU30	**LU 4**	2f. purple	3·00	3·00

1960. World Refugee Year. Nos. LU25 and LU28 optd ANNEE MONDIALE DU REFUGIE 1959 1960.

LU31	20c. red	45	45
LU32	50c. blue	65	65

LU 6 Palace of Nations, Geneva

1960. 15th Anniv of U.N.O.

LU33	**LU6**	5f. blue	6·75	6·75

LU 7

1962. Opening of U.N. Philatelic Museum, Geneva.

LU34	**LU7**	10c. green and red	20	20
LU35	-	30c. red and blue	45	45
LU36	**LU 7**	50c. blue and red	65	65
LU37	-	60c. brown and green	90	90

DESIGN—HORIZ: 30, 60c. As Type LU **4** but inscr "ONU MUSEE PHILATELIQUE".

LU 8 UNCSAT Emblem

1963. U.N. Scientific and Technological Conf, Geneva.

LU38	**LU8**	50c. red and blue	65	65
LU39	-	2f. green and purple	2·75	2·75

DESIGN—HORIZ: 2f. As Type LU **4**, but with emblem.

From 1969 stamps for the Geneva Headquarters were issued by the United Nations (q.v.)

I. INTERNATIONAL TELECOMMUNICATION UNION

LT 1 Transmitting Aerial

1958. Inscr as in Type LT 1.

LT1	**LT 1**	5c. purple	10	10
LT2	**LT 1**	10c. green	20	20
LT4	-	20c. red	45	45
LT5	-	30c. orange	55	55
LT6	**LT 1**	40c. blue	4·00	4·00
LT7	**LT 1**	50c. blue	65	65
LT8	-	60c. brown	80	80
LT9	-	2f. purple	2·20	2·20

DESIGN: 20, 30, 60c., 2f. Receiving aerials.

LT 2 New H.Q. Building

1973. Inaug of New I.T.U. Headquarters, Geneva.

LT10	**LT2**	80c. black and blue	1·10	1·10

LT3 Boeing 747 Jetliner and Ocean Liner

1976. World Telecommunications Network.

LT11	-	40c. blue and red	55	55
LT12	**LT 3**	90c. violet, blue & yellow	1·10	1·10
LT13	-	1f. red, green & yellow	1·30	1·30

DESIGNS: 40c. "Sound waves"; 1f. Face and microphone in television screen.

LT4 Optical Fibre Cables

1988

LT14	**LT 4**	1f.40 multicoloured	1·90	1·90

LT5 Emblem emitting Radio Signals

1994. 100 Years of Radio.

LT15	**LT 5**	1f.80 multicoloured	2·75	2·75

LT6 "a b c" and X-ray of Bone Joint ("Teleeducation")

1999. Multicoloured.. Multicoloured..

LT16	10c. Type LT **6**	35	35
LT17	100c. Arrow and X-ray of bone joint ("Telemedicine")	1·40	1·40

LT 7 Stylized Face

2003

LT18	**LT 7**	90c. multicoloured	2·20	2·20

J. WORLD INTELLECTUAL PROPERTY ORGANIZATION

LV 1 WIPO Seal

1989. Multicoloured.. Multicoloured..

LV1	40c. Type LV **1**	55	55
LV2	50c. Face and symbolic representation of intellect	80	80
LV3	80c. WIPO building, Geneva	90	90
LV4	100c. Hand pressing buttons, retort and cogwheel (industrial property)	1·30	1·30
LV5	120c. Head, ballet dancer, cello and book (copyright)	1·70	1·70

K. INTERNATIONAL OLYMPIC COMMITTEE

LW 1 Olympic Rings

2000. Olympic Games, Sydney. Self-adhesive.

LW1	**LW1**	20c. multicoloured	1·10	1·10
LW2	**LW1**	70c. multicoloured	1·70	1·70

LW 2 Olympic Rings, Stadium and Runner

2004. Olympic Games, Athens.

LW3	**LW2**	1f. multicoloured	2·00	2·00

LW 3 Sport

2004. International Year of Sport and Physical Education–2005.

LW4	**LW3**	180c. multicoloured	2·75	2·75

LW 4 Ice Hockey

2005. Winter Olympic Games, Turin.

LW5	**LW4**	130c. multicoloured	2·20	2·20

LW 5 BMX Cyclist

2008. Olympic Games, Beijing.

LW6	**LW5**	180c. multicoloured	2·75	2·75

LW 6 Bobsleigh

2009. Winter Olympic Games, Vancouver.

LW7	**LW6**	100c. multicoloured	1·30	1·30

Pt. 7

THURN AND TAXIS

The Counts of Thurn and Taxis had a postal monopoly in parts of Germany and issued special stamps.

N. District. 30 silbergroschen = 1 thaler.
S. District. 60 kreuzer = 1 gulden.

NORTHERN DISTRICT

1

1852. Imperf.

1	**1**	¼sgr. black on brown	£200	37·00
2	**1**	⅓sgr. black on pink	95·00	£160
4	**1**	½sgr. black on green	£600	32·00
5	**1**	1sgr. black on blue	£1100	95·00
8	**1**	2sgr. black on pink	£700	21·00
11	**1**	3sgr. black on yellow	£700	55·00

1859. Imperf.

12	¼sgr. red	55·00	48·00
20	¼sgr. black	26·00	55·00
21	⅓sgr. green	37·00	£180
13	½sgr. green	£250	70·00
23	½sgr. orange	80·00	32·00
14	1sgr. blue	£250	32·00
25	1sgr. pink	55·00	16·00
15	2sgr. pink	£120	55·00
27	2sgr. blue	48·00	70·00
17	3sgr. red	£120	80·00
29	3sgr. brown	21·00	37·00
18	5sgr. mauve	2·10	£325
19	10sgr. orange	2·10	£650

1865. Rouletted.

31	¼sgr. black	10·50	£550
32	⅓sgr. green	16·00	£325
33	½sgr. yellow	32·00	48·00
34	1sgr. pink	34·00	21·00
35	2sgr. blue	2·10	75·00
36	3sgr. brown	3·75	32·00

SOUTHERN DISTRICT

3

1852. Imperf.

51	**3**	1k. black on green	£190	10·50
53	**3**	3k. black on blue	£750	37·00
57	**3**	6k. black on pink	£950	8·50
58	**3**	9k. black on yellow	£700	12·50

1859. Imperf.

60	1k. green	19·00	7·50
62	3k. blue	£450	16·00
68	3k. pink	10·50	19·00
63	6k. pink	£450	48·00
70	6k. blue	26·00	32·00
65	9k. yellow	£450	65·00
73	9k. brown	12·50	25·00
66	15k. purple	2·10	£130
67	30k. orange	2·10	£350

1865. Roul.

74	1k. green	18·00	16·00
81	3k. pink	2·10	21·00
76	6k. blue	2·10	26·00
77	9k. brown	4·25	37·00

Pt. 8

TRIESTE

The Free Territory of Trieste situated on the Adriatic Coast between the frontiers of Italy and Yugoslavia. In 1954, when the Territory was divided between Italy and Yugoslavia, the overprinted issues were superseded by the ordinary issues of these countries in their respective zones.

For stamps of Italy surcharged **1.V.1945. TRIESTE TRST**, five-pointed star and value, see Venezia Giulia Nos. 20/32.

Allied Military Government.
100 centesimi = 1 lira.
1948. Yugoslav Military Government.
100 centesimi = 1 lira.
1949. 100 paras = 1 dinar.

ZONE A

ALLIED MILITARY GOVERNMENT

Stamps of Italy variously overprinted **A.M.G. F.T.T.** or **AMG-FTT** (Allied Military Government – Free Territory of Trieste) except where otherwise stated.

1947. Postage stamps of 1945, Nos. 647, etc.

1		25c. blue	20	10
2		50c. violet	20	10
3		1l. green	20	10
4		2l. brown	20	10
5		3l. red	20	10
6		4l. red	20	10
7		5l. blue	20	10
8		6l. violet	20	10
9		8l. green	2·10	1·80
10		10l. grey	20	10
11		10l. red	7·75	20
12		15l. blue	50	10
13		20l. violet	2·50	10
14		25l. green	3·75	2·10
15		30l. blue	£190	3·25
16		50l. purple	3·75	2·10
17		100l. red (No. 669)	26·00	14·50

1947. Air stamps of 1945, Nos. 670, etc.

18		1l. grey	30	20
19		2l. blue	30	20
20		5l. green	2·40	1·60
21		10l. red	2·50	1·60
22		25l. brown	8·25	2·50
23		50l. violet	33·00	3·75
24		100l. green	80·00	3·50
25		300l. mauve	11·50	12·50
26		500l. blue	16·00	14·50
27		1000l. brown	£160	£140

1947. Air. 50th Anniv of Radio (Nos. 688/93).

59		6l. violet	1·60	1·80
60		10l. red	1·60	1·80
61		20l. orange	7·75	2·50
62		25l. blue	1·80	2·10
63		35l. blue	2·10	2·50
64		50l. purple	7·75	2·50

1948. Cent of 1848 Revolution (Nos. 706, etc).

65		3l. brown	25	20
66		4l. purple	25	20
67		5l. blue	25	20
68		6l. green	25	20
69		8l. brown	25	20
70		10l. red	35	20
71		12l. green	50	1·00
72		15l. black	20·00	7·25
73		20l. red	21·00	7·25
74		30l. blue	2·50	1·60
75		50l. violet	12·50	16·00
76		100l. blue	42·00	37·00

1948. Trieste Philatelic Congress stamps of 1945 optd A.M.G. F.T.T. 1948 TRIESTE and posthorn.

77		8l. green (postage)	20	20
78		10l. red	20	20
79		30l. blue	2·10	2·10
80		10l. red (air)	30	30
81		25l. brown	75	75
82		50l. violet	75	75

1948. Rebuilding of Bassano Bridge.

84	**209**	15l. green	1·30	1·20

1948. Donizetti.

85	**210**	15l. brown	8·25	1·30

1949. 25th Biennial Art Exhibition, Venice.

86	**212**	5l. red and flesh	1·30	1·00
87	-	15l. green and cream	8·25	9·00
88	-	20l. brown and buff	6·25	1·30
89	-	50l. blue and yellow	12·50	7·25

1949. 27th Milan Fair.

90	**211**	20l. brown	9·50	2·40

1949. 75th Anniv of U.P.U.

91	**213**	50l. blue	4·25	3·75

1949. Centenary of Roman Republic.

92	**214**	100l. brown	80·00	80·00

1949. 1st Trieste Free Election.

93	**218**	20l. red	4·25	2·10

1949. European Recovery Plan.

94	**215**	5l. green	10·50	5·50
95	**215**	15l. violet	10·50	12·50
96	**215**	20l. brown	10·50	8·25

1949. 2nd World Health Congress, Rome.

97	**219**	20l. violet	12·50	4·25

1949. Giuseppe Mazzini.

98	**216**	20l. black	9·50	3·25

1949. Bicentenary of Vittorio Alfieri.

99	**217**	20l. brown	9·50	3·25

1949. 400th Anniv of Palladio's Basilica at Vicenza.

100	**220**	20l. violet	18·00	11·50

1949. 500th Birth Anniv of Lorenzo de Medici.

101	**221**	20l. blue	9·50	3·25

1949. 13th Bari Fair.

102	**222**	20l. red	9·50	3·25

1949. (a) Postage.

103	**195**	1l. green	20	20
104	-	2l. brown (No. 656)	20	20
105	-	3l. red (No. 657)	20	20
106	**193**	5l. blue	20	20
107	**195**	6l. violet	20	20
108	-	8l. green (No. 661)	21·00	7·25
109	**193**	10l. red	20	20
110	**195**	15l. blue	1·70	50
111	-	20l. purple (No. 665)	1·30	50
112	**196**	25l. green	26·00	3·25
113	**196**	50l. purple	37·00	1·60
114	**197**	100l. red	£120	10·50

(b) Air.

115	**198**	10l. red	20	10
116	-	25l. brown (No. 676)	20	10
117	**198**	50l. violet	20	10
118	-	100l. green (No. 911)	1·00	10
119	-	300l. mauve (No. 912)	10·50	6·25
120	-	500l. blue (No. 913)	12·50	9·50
121	-	1000l. purple (No. 914)	27·00	21·00

1949. 150th Anniv of Volta's Discovery of the Electric Cell.

135	**223**	20l. red	3·25	3·25
136	**224**	50l. blue	12·50	12·50

1949. Rebuilding of Holy Trinity Bridge, Florence.

137	**225**	20l. green	4·25	2·10

1949. Death Bimillenary of Catullus (poet).

138	**226**	20l. blue	3·25	2·10

1949. Birth Bicentenary of Domenico Cimarosa (composer).

153	**227**	20l. violet	4·75	2·10

1950. 28th Milan Fair.

154	**228**	20l. brown	4·25	1·80

1950. 32nd Int Automobile Exn, Turin.

155	**229**	20l. violet	1·60	1·40

1950. 5th General UNESCO Conference.

156	-	20l. green	2·50	1·00
157	**230**	55l. blue	10·50	9·50

1950. Holy Year.

158	**231**	20l. violet	3·25	1·00
159	**231**	55l. blue	12·50	10·50

1950. Honouring Gaudenzio Ferrari (painter).

160	**232**	20l. green	2·50	2·10

1950. International Radio Conference.

161	**233**	20l. violet	6·25	4·75
162	**233**	55l. blue	18·00	19·00

1950. Death Bicentenary of Ludovico Murator (historian).

163	**234**	20l. brown	4·75	2·10

1950. 900th Death Anniv of D'Arezzo.

164	**235**	20l. green	4·75	2·10

1950. 14th Levant Fair, Bari.

165	**236**	20l. brown	2·50	2·10

1950. 2nd Trieste Fair. Optd AMG FTT Fiera di Trieste 1950.

166	**195**	15l. blue	2·10	2·30
167	-	20l. purple (No. 665)	2·50	85

1950. Wool Industry Pioneers.

168	**237**	20l. blue	1·60	1·30

1950. European Tobacco Conf (Nos. 755/7).

169		5l. green and mauve	1·00	95
170		20l. green and brown	2·20	2·00
171		55l. brown and blue	23·00	22·00

1950. Bicentenary of Fine Arts Academy.

172	**239**	20l. red and deep brown	3·25	1·60

1950. Birth Centenary of Augusto Righi.

173	**240**	20l. black and buff	4·75	1·60

1950. Provincial Occupations (Nos. 760/78).

176		50c. blue	20	10
177		1l. violet	20	10
178		2l. brown	20	10
179		5l. black	20	10
180		6l. brown	20	10
181		10l. green	50	20
182		12l. green	75	30
183		15l. blue	1·00	20
184		20l. violet	75	10
185		25l. brown	2·10	20
186		30l. purple	65	50
187		35l. red	1·30	1·00
188		40l. brown	1·00	30
189		50l. violet	20	10
190		55l. blue	20	20
191		60l. red	5·25	4·25
192		65l. green	20	20
193		100l. brown	3·75	20
194		200l. brown	2·10	2·50

1951. Centenary of 1st Tuscan Stamp.

195	**249**	20l. red and purple	2·75	2·50
196	**249**	55l. blue and ultramarine	37·00	33·00

1951. 33rd International Motor Show, Turin.

197	**243**	20l. green	1·70	1·80

1951. Consecration of Hall of Peace, Rome.

198	**244**	20l. violet	2·10	1·80

1951. 29th Milan Fair.

199	**245**	20l. brown	2·50	2·30
200	**246**	55l. blue	2·10	2·50

1951. 10th International Textiles Exn, Turin.

201	**247**	20l. violet	2·10	1·80

1951. 500th Birth Anniv of Columbus.

202	**248**	20l. green	2·75	2·75

1951. International Gymnastic Festival, Florence.

203	**249**	5l. red and brown	7·25	12·50
204	**249**	10l. red and green	7·25	12·50
205	**249**	15l. red and blue	7·25	12·50

1951. Restoration of Montecassino Abbey.

206	**250**	20l. violet	85	75
207	-	55l. blue (No. 791)	1·90	1·80

1951. 3rd Trieste Fair. Optd AMG-FTT FIERA di TRIESTE 1951 and shield.

208		6l. brown (No. 764)	50	40
209		20l. violet (No. 768)	75	65
210		55l. blue (No. 774)	1·00	95

1951. 500th Birth Anniv of Perugino.

211	**251**	20l. brown and sepia	1·00	95

1951. Triennial Art Exhibition, Milan.

212	**252**	20l. black and green	1·00	1·20
213	-	55l. pink and blue (No. 794)	2·10	2·30

1951. World Cycling Championship.

214	**253**	25l. black	5·25	1·60

1951. 15th Levant Fair, Bari.

215	**254**	25l. blue	1·20	1·00

1951. Birth Centenary of F. P. Michetti.

216	**255**	25l. brown	1·20	1·00

1951. Sardinian Stamp Centenary.

217	**256**	10l. black and brown	65	75
218	-	25l. green and red (No. 799)	75	50
219	-	60l. red and blue (No. 800)	1·00	1·20

1951. 3rd Industrial and Commercial Census.

220	**257**	10l. green	75	65

1951. 9th National Census.

221	**258**	25l. black	85	75

1951. Forestry Festival.

222	**260**	10l. green and olive	85	75
223	**260**	25l. green (No. 807)	1·00	85

1951. Verdi.

224	-	10l. green and purple (No. 803)	75	65
225	**259**	25l. sepia and brown	85	75
226	-	60l. blue and green (No. 805)	1·50	1·40

1952. Bellini.

227	**261**	25l. black	1·00	75

1952. Caserta Palace.

228	**262**	25l. bistre and green	1·00	75

1952. 1st International Sports Stamps Exn, Rome.

229	**263**	25l. brown and black	90	75

1952. 30th Milan Fair.

230	**264**	60l. blue	1·70	2·30

1952. Leonardo da Vinci.

231	**265**	25l. orange	20	20
232	-	60l. blue (No. 813)	1·30	1·00
233	**265**	80l. red	2·10	1·00

1952. Overseas Fair, Naples.

234	**268**	25l. blue	80	55

1952. Modena and Parma Stamp Centenaries.

235	**267**	25l. black and brown	65	55
236	**267**	60l. indigo and blue	80	65

1952. Art Exhibition, Venice.

237	**269**	25l. black and cream	90	80

1952. 30th Padua Fair.

238	**270**	25l. red and blue	80	55

1952. 4th Trieste Fair.

239	**271**	25l. green, red and brown	80	55

1952. 16th Levant Fair, Bari.

240	**272**	25l. green	80	55

1952. Savonarola.

241	**273**	25l. violet	80	55

1952. 1st Private Aeronautics Conf, Rome.

242	**274**	60l. blue and ultramarine	1·70	2·20

1952. Alpine Troops National Exhibition.

243	**275**	25l. black	1·00	65

1952. Armed Forces Day.

244	**276**	10l. green	20	10
245	**277**	25l. brown & light brown	55	35
246	-	60l. black and blue (No. 827)	80	1·00

1952. Mission to Ethiopia.

247	**278**	25l. deep brown and brown	1·10	55

1952. Birth Centenary of Gemito (sculptor).

248	**279**	25l. brown	1·00	55

1952. Birth Centenary of Mancini (painter).

249	**280**	25l. green	1·00	55

1952. Centenary of Martyrdom of Belfiore.

250	**281**	25l. blue and black	1·00	55

1953. Antonello Exhibition, Messina.

251	**282**	25l. red	90	55

1953. 20th "Mille Miglia" Car Race.

252	**283**	25l. violet	90	55

1953. Labour Orders of Merit.

253	**284**	25l. violet	90	55

1953. 300th Birth Anniv of Corelli.

254	**285**	25l. brown	90	55

1953. Coin type.

255	**286**	5l. grey	20	10
256	**286**	10l. red	20	10
257	**286**	12l. green	20	10
258	**286**	13l. purple	20	10
259	**286**	20l. brown	30	15
260	**286**	25l. violet	35	20
261	**286**	35l. red	45	45
262	**286**	60l. blue	55	55
263	**286**	80l. brown	65	65

1953. 7th Death Centenary of St. Clare.

264	**287**	25l. red and brown	1·10	80

1953. 5th Trieste Fair. Optd V FIERA DI TRIESTE AMG FTT 1953.

265		10l. green (No. 765)	35	45
266		25l. orange (No. 769)	55	45
267		60l. red (No. 775)	55	70

1953. Mountains Festival.

272	**288**	25l. green	1·10	80

1953. International Agricultural Exn, Rome.

273	**289**	25l. brown	55	45
274	**289**	60l. blue	65	65

1953. 4th Anniv of Atlantic Pact.

275	**290**	25l. turquoise and orange	1·10	80
276	**290**	60l. blue and mauve	2·75	3·25

1953. 5th Birth Centenary of Signorelli.

277	**291**	25l. green and brown	1·00	80

1953. 6th Int Microbiological Congress, Rome.

278	**292**	25l. brown and black	1·00	80

1953. Tourist series (Nos. 855/60).

279		10l. brown and sepia	20	20
280		12l. black and blue	25	25
281		20l. brown and orange	30	20
282		25l. green and blue	30	15
283		35l. brown and buff	40	60
284		60l. blue and green	55	70

1954. 25th Anniv of Lateran Treaty.

285	**294**	25l. sepia and brown	45	35
286	**294**	60l. blue and light blue	65	80

1954. Introduction of Television in Italy.

287	**295**	25l. violet	45	35
288	**295**	60l. green	65	80

1954. Encouragement to Taxpayers.

289	**296**	25l. violet	1·10	55

1954. Milan–Turin Helicopter Mail Flight.

290	**297**	25l. green	65	55

1954. 10th Anniv of Resistance Movement.

291	**298**	25l. black and brown	65	55

1954. 6th Trieste Fair. Nos. 282 and 284 of Trieste additionally optd FIERA DI TRIESTE 1954.

292	-	25l. green and blue	65	55
293	**293**	60l. blue and green	80	65

1954. Birth Centenary of Catalani.

294	**299**	25l. green	65	55

1954. 7th Birth Centenary of Marco Polo.

295	**300**	25l. brown	45	35
296	**300**	60l. green	65	80

1954. 60th Anniv of Italian Touring Club.

297	**301**	25l. green and red	80	65

1954. International Police Congress, Rome.

298	**302**	25l. red	45	35
299	**302**	60l. blue	55	45

CONCESSIONAL LETTER POST

1947. Optd A.M.G. F.T.T. in two lines.

CL44	-	1l. brn (No. CL649)	20	10
CL45	**CL201**	8l. red	7·75	1·60
CL46	**CL220**	15l. violet	42·00	4·75

1949. Optd AMG-FTT.

CL122		15l. violet	1·60	20
CL123		20l. violet	7·75	20

CONCESSIONAL PARCEL POST

1953

CP268	**CP288**	40l. orange	8·50	1·70
CP269	**CP288**	50l. blue	8·50	1·70
CP270	**CP288**	75l. brown	8·50	1·70
CP271	**CP288**	110l. pink	8·50	1·70

Unused prices are for the complete stamp, used prices for the left half of the stamp.

EXPRESS LETTER STAMPS

1947. Express Letter stamps optd A.M.G. F.T.T. in two lines.

E28	-	15l. red (No. E681)	20	20
E29	**200**	25l. orange	37·00	5·25
E30	**200**	30l. violet	65	65
E31	-	60l. red (No. E685)	26·00	10·50

1948. Centenary of 1848 Revolution. Express Letter stamp optd A.M.G.-F.T.T.

E83	**E209**	35l. violet	8·25	5·25

1950. Express Letter stamps optd AMG-FTT in one line.

E174		50l. purple	4·75	1·30
E175	-	60l. red (No. E685)	7·75	1·60

PARCEL POST STAMPS

Unused prices are for complete stamps, used prices for half-stamp.

1947. Parcel Post stamps optd A.M.G. F.T.T. in two lines on each half of stamp.

P32	**P201**	1l. brown	50	20
P33	**P201**	2l. blue	65	25
P34	**P201**	3l. orange	75	30
P35	**P201**	4l. grey	1·00	80
P36	**P201**	5l. purple	2·10	1·50
P37	**P201**	10l. violet	4·25	3·00
P38	**P201**	20l. purple	6·25	4·25
P39	**P201**	50l. red	10·50	8·25
P40	**P201**	100l. blue	12·50	10·50
P41	**P201**	200l. green	£425	£450
P42	**P201**	300l. purple	£225	£250
P43	**P201**	500l. brown	£130	£160

1949. Parcel Post stamps optd AMG-FTT in one line on each half of stamp.

P139		1l. brown	1·00	20
P140		2l. blue	30	10
P141		3l. orange	30	10
P142		4l. grey	30	10
P143		5l. purple	30	10
P144		10l. violet	1·30	20
P145		20l. purple	1·30	20
P146		30l. purple	75	20
P147		50l. red	1·00	20
P148		100l. blue	3·25	50
P149		200l. green	26·00	65
P150		300l. purple	80·00	65
P151		500l. brown	49·00	95
P152	**P928**	1000l. blue	£180	6·25

POSTAGE DUE STAMPS

1947. Postage Due stamps optd A.M.G. F.T.T. in two lines.

D44	**D192**	1l. orange	65	40
D48	**D201**	1l. orange	40	75
D49	**D201**	2l. green	40	20
D50	**D201**	3l. red	75	1·30
D51	**D201**	4l. brown	7·25	8·25
D45	**D192**	5l. violet	4·50	30
D52	**D201**	5l. violet	85·00	12·50
D53	**D201**	6l. blue	23·00	22·00
D54	**D201**	8l. mauve	50·00	60·00
D46	**D192**	10l. blue	10·50	1·00
D55	**D201**	10l. blue	£120	12·50
D56	**D201**	12l. brown	18·00	19·00
D47	**D192**	20l. red	23·00	1·60
D57	**D201**	20l. purple	16·00	3·75
D58	**D201**	50l. green	2·10	50

1949. Postage Due stamps optd AMG-FTT in one line.

D122		1l. orange	20	10
D123		2l. green	20	10
D124		3l. red	20	10
D125		5l. violet	75	10
D126		6l. blue	30	10
D127		8l. mauve	30	10
D128		10l. blue	50	10
D129		12l. brown	1·30	10
D130		20l. purple	3·25	20
D131		25l. red	4·00	1·80
D132		50l. green	3·25	1·00
D133		100l. orange	10·50	75
D134		500l. purple and blue	65·00	18·00

ZONE B
YUGOSLAV MILITARY GOVERNMENT

Apart from the definitive issues illustrated below the following are stamps of Yugoslavia (sometimes in new colours), variously overprinted **STT VUJA** or **VUJA-STT** or (Nos. B65 onwards) **STT VUJNA** unless otherwise stated.

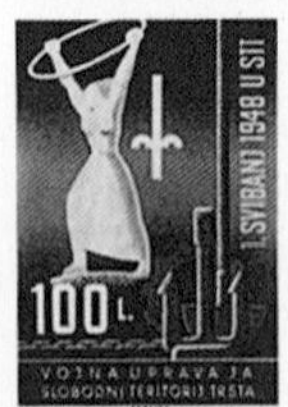

B1

1948. Labour Day.

B1	**B1**	100l. red and stone (A)	5·50	2·75
B2	**B1**	100l. red and stone (B)	5·50	2·75
B3	**B1**	100l. red and stone (C)	5·50	2·75

Inscr in Slovene (A) "I. MAJ 1948 V STO"; Italian (B) "I. MAGGIO 1948 NEL TLT"; or Croat (C) "I. SVIBANJ 1948 U STT".

1948. Red Cross. No. 545 optd and surch.

B3a	**131**	2l. on 50p. brown and red	45·00	45·00

B2

1948. Air. Economic Exhibition, Capodistria.

B4	**B2**	25l. grey	1·10	1·10
B5	**B2**	50l. orange	1·10	1·10

B3 Clasped Hands, Hammer and Sickle

1949. Labour Day.

B6	**B3**	10l. green	1·10	1·10

B4 Fishermen and Flying Boat

B5 Man with Donkey

B6 Mediterranean Gull over Chimneys

1949. Air.

B7	**B4**	1l. turquoise	55	35
B8	**B5**	2l. brown	55	35
B9	**B4**	5l. blue	55	35
B10	**B5**	10l. violet	2·75	2·20
B11	**B4**	25l. brown	7·75	5·50
B12	**B5**	50l. green	7·75	5·50
B13	**B6**	100l. brown	14·50	10·00

1949. Partisans issue.

B14	**119**	50p. grey	55	45
B15	**119**	1d. green	55	45
B16	**120**	2d. red	55	45
B17	-	3d. red (No. 508)	55	45
B18	**120**	4d. blue	1·10	45
B19	-	5d. blue (No. 511)	1·10	45
B20	-	9d. mauve (No. 514)	7·75	1·10
B21	-	12d. blue (No. 515)	7·75	5·50
B22	**119**	16d. blue	11·00	6·75
B23	-	20d. red (No. 517)	22·00	9·00

1949. 75th Anniv of U.P.U.

B24		5d. blue (No. 612)	11·00	11·00
B25	**158**	12d. brown	11·00	11·00

1949. Air. Optd DIN or surch also.

B26	**B4**	1d. turquoise	55	35
B27	**B5**	2d. brown	55	35
B28	**B4**	5d. blue	55	35
B29	**B5**	10d. violet	55	35
B30	**B4**	15d. on 25l. brown	22·00	13·50
B31	**B5**	20d. on 50l. green	6·75	4·50
B32	**B6**	30d. on 100l. purple	7·75	5·50

1950. Centenary of Yugoslav Railways.

B33	**116**	2d. green	4·50	1·10
B34	-	3d. red (No. 632)	4·50	1·10
B35	-	5d. blue (No. 633)	4·50	3·25
B36	-	10d. orange (No. 633a)	20·00	11·00
MSB36Aa		10d. purple. Perf	£275	£225
MSB36Ba		10d. purple. Imperf	£275	£225

B10 Girl on Donkey

1950

B37	**B10**	50p. grey	55	55
B38	-	1d. red (Cockerel)	55	55
B38a	-	1d. brown (Cockerel)	1·70	55
B39	-	2d. blue (Geese)	55	55
B40	-	3d. brown (Bees)	55	55
B40a	-	3d. red (Bees)	2·20	55
B41	-	5d. green (Oxen)	4·50	55
B42	-	10d. brown (Turkey)	4·50	55
B43	-	15d. violet (Kids)	28·00	11·00
B44	-	20d. green (Silkworms)	11·00	5·50

B11 Workers

1950. May Day.

B45	**B11**	3d. violet	80	65
B46	**B11**	10d. red	1·50	1·30

1950. Red Cross.

B47	**160**	50p. brown and red	2·20	1·70

B12 Worker

1951. May Day.

B48	**B12**	3d. red	1·10	55
B49	**B12**	10d. green	1·70	1·10

1951. Red Cross.

B49a	**191**	0d.50 blue and red	£275	£275

B13 P. P. Vergerio Jr.

1951. Festival of Italian Culture.

B50	**B13**	5d. blue	1·10	1·10
B51	**B13**	10d. purple	1·10	1·10
B52	**B13**	20d. brown	1·10	1·10

1951. Cultural Anniversaries.

B53	**189**	10d. orange	1·30	1·10
B54	-	12d. black (As No. 699)	1·30	1·10

B14a Koper Square

1952. Air. 75th Anniv of U.P.U.

B54a	**B14a**	5d. brown	17·00	17·00
B54b	-	15d. blue	11·00	11·00
B54c	-	25d. green	11·00	11·00

DESIGNS—VERT: 15d. Lighthouse, Piran. HORIZ: 25d. Hotel, Portoroz.

B15 Cyclists

1952. Physical Culture Propaganda.

B55	**B15**	5d. brown	95	45
B56	-	10d. green	95	45
B57	-	15d. red	95	45
B58	-	28d. blue	2·20	1·70
B59	-	50d. red	8·00	5·25
B60	-	100d. blue	21·00	12·50

DESIGNS: 10d. Footballers; 15d. Rowing four; 28d. Yachting; 50d. Netball players; 100d. Diver.

1952. Marshal Tito's 60th Birthday. As Nos. 727/9 of Yugoslavia additionally inscr "STT VUJA".

B61	**196**	15d. brown	3·25	1·70
B62	**197**	28d. red	3·25	2·75
B63	-	50d. green (No. 729)	6·75	4·00

1952. Children's Week.

B64	**198**	15d. pink	2·20	1·10

1952. 15th Olympic Games, Helsinki. As Nos. 731/6.

B65	**199**	5d. brown on flesh	2·20	55
B66	-	10d. green on cream	2·20	55
B67	-	15d. violet on mauve	2·20	55
B68	-	28d. brown on buff	2·20	2·20
B69	-	50d. brown on yellow	19·00	13·50
B70	-	100d. blue on pink	45·00	39·00

1952. Navy Day (Nos. 737/9).

B71		15d. purple	2·75	2·20
B72	**200**	28d. brown	3·25	2·20
B73	-	50d. black	5·00	2·75

1952. Red Cross.

B74	**201**	50p. red, grey and black	1·70	1·10

1952. 6th Yugoslav Communist Party Congress.

B75	**202**	15d. brown	1·30	90
B76	**202**	15d. turquoise	1·30	90
B77	**202**	15d. brown	1·30	90
B78	**202**	15d. blue	1·30	90

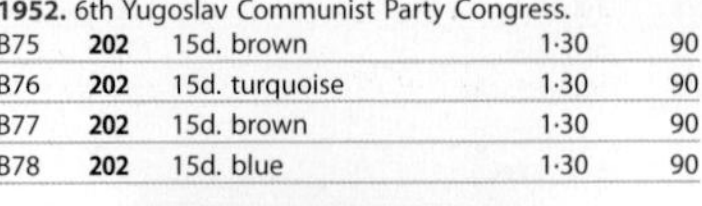

B17 European Anchovy and Starfish

1952. Philatelic Exhibition, Koper.

B78a	**B17**	15d. brown	5·50	5·50
MSB78b		48×70 mm. **B17** 50d. green. Imperf (sold at 85d.)	80·00	80·00

1953. 10th Death Anniv of Tesla (inventor).

B79	**203**	15d. red	55	55
B80	**203**	30d. blue	2·20	2·20

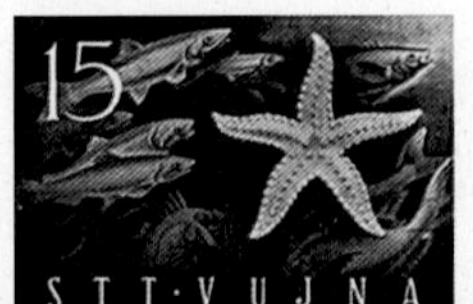

1953. Pictorials of 1950.

B81		1d. grey (No. 705)	13·50	10·00
B86		2d. red (No. 718)	55	45
B82		3d. red (No. 655)	55	45
B87		5d. orange (No. 719)	55	45
B83		10d. green (No. 721)	55	45
B88		15d. red (No. 723)	1·10	1·00
B84		30d. blue (No. 712)	5·50	3·25
B85		50d. turquoise (No. 714)	11·00	5·50

1953. United Nations (Nos. 747/9).

B89	**204**	15d. green	30	20
B90	-	30d. blue	55	35
B91	-	50d. red	1·50	1·30

1953. Adriatic Car Rally. As Nos. 750/3.

B92	**205**	15d. brown and yellow	55	35
B93	-	30d. green and emerald	55	35
B94	-	50d. mauve and orange	55	35
B95	-	70d. deep blue and blue	4·00	2·75

1953. Marshal Tito.

B96	**206**	50d. green	5·50	5·50

1953. 38th Esperanto Congress, Zagreb.

B97	**207**	15d. grn & turq (post-age)	2·75	2·75
B98	**207**	300d. green and violet (air)	£400	£400

1953. 10th Anniv of Liberation of Istria and Slovene Coast.

B99	**209**	15d. blue	5·50	5·50

1953. Death Centenary of Radicevic (poet).

B100	**210**	15d. black	2·20	1·70

1953. Red Cross.

B101	**211**	2d. red and bistre	1·70	1·10

1953. 10th Anniv of 1st Republican Legislative Assembly. As Nos. 762/4.

B102	**212**	15d. violet	1·60	1·10
B103	-	30d. red	1·60	1·10
B104	-	50d. green	1·60	1·10

1954. Air. As Nos. 675 etc.

B108		1d. lilac	1·10	55
B109		2d. green	1·10	55
B110		3d. purple	1·10	55
B111		5d. brown	1·10	55
B112		10d. turquoise	1·10	55
B113		20d. brown	1·10	55
B114		30d. blue	1·10	55
B115		50d. black	1·10	80
B116		100d. red	3·25	2·20
B117		200d. violet	6·75	4·50
B118		500d. orange	39·00	28·00

1954. Animals. As Nos. 765/76.

B119		2d. grey, buff and red	1·10	55
B120		5d. slate, buff and grey	1·10	55
B121		10d. brown and green	1·10	55
B122		15d. brown and blue	1·10	55
B123		17d. sepia and brown	1·10	55
B124		25d. yellow, blue and brown	1·10	55
B125		30d. brown and violet	1·10	55
B126		35d. black and purple	1·10	1·10
B127		50d. brown and green	2·20	1·70
B128		65d. black and brown	6·75	4·50
B129		70d. brown and blue	17·00	9·00
B130		100d. black and blue	45·00	36·00

1954. Serbian Insurrection. As Nos. 778/81.

B131	-	15d. multicoloured	1·10	80
B132	**214**	30d. multicoloured	1·10	80
B133	-	50d. multicoloured	1·10	80
B134	-	70d. multicoloured	2·20	1·70

POSTAGE DUE STAMPS

1948. Red Cross. No. D546 surch VUJA STT and new value.

BD4	**131**	2l. on 50p. green and red	£325	£325

1949. On 1946 issue.

BD26	**D126**	50p. orange	1·10	55
BD27	**D126**	1d. orange	1·10	55
BD74	**D126**	1d. brown	55	35
BD28	**D126**	2d. blue	1·10	55
BD75	**D126**	2d. green	55	35
BD29	**D126**	3d. green	2·20	55
BD30	**D126**	5d. violet	5·50	2·20
BD76	**D126**	5d. blue	55	35
BD77	**D126**	10d. red	55	35
BD78	**D126**	20d. violet	55	35
BD79	**D126**	30d. orange	55	35
BD80	**D126**	50d. blue	55	35
BD81	**D126**	100d. purple	19·00	11·00

Nos. BD26/30 optd **STT VUJA** and the rest **STT VUJNA**.

1950. Red Cross. No. D617 optd VUJA STT.

BD48	**160**	50p. purple and red	2·20	1·70

BD12 European Anchovy

1950. Fishes.

BD49	-	50p. brown	5·50	1·10
BD50	-	1d. green	5·50	2·20
BD51	**BD12**	2d. blue	5·50	2·20
BD52	**BD12**	3d. blue	5·50	2·20
BD53	**BD12**	5d. purple	28·00	9·00

DESIGN: 50p., 1d. Two meagres.

1951. Red Cross. No. D703 optd STT VUJA.

BD54	**191**	0d.50 green and red	£275	£275

1952. Red Cross. No. D741.

BD82	**D202**	50p. red and grey	1·70	1·10

1953. Red Cross. As No. D762.

BD102	**211**	2d. red and purple	1·70	1·10

Pt. 8

TUSCANY

Formerly an independent duchy in C. Italy, now part of Italy.

1851. 60 quattrini = 20 soldi = 12 crazie = 1 Tuscan lira.
1859. 1 Tuscan lira = 1 Italian lira.

1 Arms of Tuscany

1851. Imperf.

1	**1**	1q. black on blue	£15000	£1700
2	**1**	1q. black on grey	£12000	£1800
24	**1**	1q. black	£1600	£950
4	**1**	1s. orange on blue	£20000	£2000
5	**1**	1s. orange on grey	£15000	£1900
25	**1**	1s. buff	£49000	£5500
6	**1**	2s. red on blue	£49000	£7000
7	**1**	1c. red on blue	£9500	£250
9	**1**	1c. red on grey	£8500	£130
26	**1**	1c. red	£11000	£600
10	**1**	2c. blue on blue	£9500	£250
11	**1**	2c. blue on grey	£4750	£150
28	**1**	2c. blue	£3250	£140
13	**1**	4c. green on blue	£11000	£300
14	**1**	4c. green on grey	£8500	£160
30	**1**	4c. green	£8500	£180
16	**1**	6c. blue on blue	£11000	£350
17	**1**	6c. blue on grey	£8500	£250
31	**1**	6c. blue	£11000	£275
20	**1**	9c. purple on blue	£20000	£475
22	**1**	9c. purple on grey	£20000	£225
33	**1**	9c. brown	£46000	£5500
23	**1**	60c. red on blue	£86000	£25000

5 Arms of Savoy

1860. Imperf.

36	**5**	1c. purple	£3000	£950
40	**5**	5c. green	£12000	£250
43	**5**	10c. brown	£3250	60·00
45	**5**	20c. blue	£11000	£180
48	**5**	40c. red	£17000	£300
50	**5**	80c. red	£30000	£1400
51	**5**	3l. buff	£203000	£97000

NEWSPAPER STAMP TAX

N3

1854

N1	**N3**	2s. black	90·00	

Pt. 8; Pt. 2

UNITED NATIONS

B. GENEVA HEADQUARTERS.
100 centimes = 1 Swiss franc.

C. VIENNA HEADQUARTERS.
1979. 100 groschen = 1 schilling.
2002. 100 cents = 1 euro.

B. GENEVA HEADQUARTERS

For use on mail posted at the United Nations Geneva Headquarters. Before 1969 the Swiss PTT issued stamps for use at the Palais des Nations; these are listed at the end of Switzerland.

NOTE: References to numbers and types in this section, other than to those with a "G" prefix are to the United Nations (New York Office) listing. Designs adapted for the Geneva issue are inscribed in French and have face values in francs.

G4 Palais des Nations, Geneva

G5 Palais des Nations, Geneva

1969. Existing United Nations (New York) designs adapted with new colours and values in Swiss francs (F.S.). 30 and 40c. new designs. Multicoloured unless otherwise stated.

G1	-	5c. (As No. 164)	10	10
G2	-	10c. (As No. 94)	15	15
G3	-	20c. (As No. 97)	20	20
G4	**G4**	30c. multicoloured	25	25
G5	**G5**	40c. multicoloured	55	55
G6	-	50c. (As No. 147, but scroll inscr in French)	55	55
G7	-	60c. gold, red and brown (As No. 98)	55	55
G8	-	70c. red, gold and black (As No. 167)	55	55
G9	-	75c. (As No. A125)	60	60
G10	-	80c. (As No. 148)	65	65
G11	**52**	90c. (Inscr in French)	75	75
G12	-	1f. deep green and green (As No. 149)	85	85
G13	**53**	2f. multicoloured	1·80	1·80
G14	**104**	3f. multicoloured	2·50	2·50
G15	**3**	10f. blue	7·50	7·50

1971. Peaceful Uses of the Sea-bed.

G16	**121**	30c. multicoloured	55	55

1971. United Nations Work with Refugees.

G17	**122**	50c. black, orange and red	85	85

1971. World Food Programme.

G18	**123**	50c. multicoloured	85	85

1971. Opening of New Universal Postal Union Headquarters Building, Berne.

G19	**124**	75c. multicoloured	1·10	1·10

1971. Racial Equality Year. Designs as Nos. 220/1, with background colours changed.

G20		30c. Type **125**	45	45
G21		50c. Linked globes (horiz)	65	65

1971. U.N. International Schools.

G22	**130**	1f.10 multicoloured	1·30	1·30

1972. Non-proliferation of Nuclear Weapons.

G23	**131**	40c. multicoloured	85	85

1972. World Health Day.

G24	**132**	80c. multicoloured	1·10	1·10

1972. United Nations Environmental Conservation Conference, Stockholm.

G25	**137**	40c. multicoloured	55	55
G26	**137**	80c. multicoloured	1·10	1·10

1972. Economic Commission for Europe (ECE).

G27	**138**	1f.10 multicoloured	1·80	1·80

1972. United Nations Art.

G28	**139**	40c. multicoloured	55	55
G29	**139**	80c. multicoloured	1·10	1·10

1973. Disarmament Decade.

G30	**140**	60c. multicoloured	65	65
G31	**140**	1f.10 multicoloured	1·20	1·20

1973. "No Drugs" Campaign.

G32	**141**	60c. multicoloured	85	85

1973. U.N. Volunteers Programme.

G33	**142**	80c. multicoloured	1·10	1·10

1973. "Namibia" (South West Africa).

G34	**143**	60c. multicoloured	85	85

1973. 25th Anniv of Declaration of Human Rights.

G35	**144**	40c. multicoloured	45	45
G36	**144**	80c. multicoloured	85	85

1973. Inauguration of New I.L.O. Headquarters, Geneva.

G37	**145**	60c. multicoloured	75	75
G38	**145**	80c. multicoloured	85	85

1973. Centenary of Universal Postal Union.

G39	**146**	30c. multicoloured	45	45
G40	**146**	60c. multicoloured	85	85

1974. Brazilian Peace Mural.

G41	**147**	60c. multicoloured	65	65
G42	**147**	1f. multicoloured	1·10	1·10

1974. World Population Year.

G43	**154**	60c. multicoloured	65	65
G44	**154**	80c. multicoloured	85	85

1974. U.N. Conference on "Law of the Sea".

G45	**155**	1f.30 multicoloured	1·40	1·40

1975. Peaceful Uses of Outer Space.

G46	**156**	60c. multicoloured	65	65
G47	**156**	90c. multicoloured	95	95

1975. International Women's Year.

G48	**157**	60c. multicoloured	65	65
G49	**157**	90c. multicoloured	95	95

1975. 30th Anniv of U.N.O.

G50	**158**	60c. multicoloured	65	65
G51	**158**	90c. multicoloured	95	95
MSG52		92×70 mm. Nos. G50/1. Imperf	1·60	1·60

1975. "Namibia—U.N. Direct Responsibility".

G53	**160**	50c. multicoloured	55	55
G54	**160**	1f.30 multicoloured	1·40	1·40

1975. U.N. Peace Keeping Operations.

G55	**161**	60c. blue	65	65
G56	**161**	70c. violet	75	75

1976. World Federation of U.N. Associations.

G57	**166**	90c. multicoloured	95	95

1976. U.N. Conf on Trade and Development.

G58	**167**	1f.10 multicoloured	1·20	1·20

1976. U.N. Conf on Human Settlements.

G59	**168**	40c. multicoloured	45	45
G60	**168**	1f.50 multicoloured	1·60	1·60

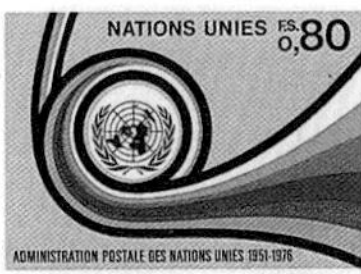

G46 U.N. Emblem within Posthorn

1976. 25th Anniv of U.N. Postal Administration.

G61	**G46**	80c. multicoloured	2·10	2·10
G62	**G46**	1f.10 multicoloured	2·40	2·40

1976. World Food Council Publicity.

G63	**170**	70c. multicoloured	75	75

1977. World Intellectual Property Organization Publicity.

G64	**172**	80c. multicoloured	85	85

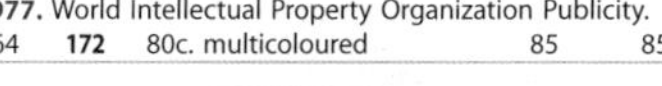

G49 Rain Drop and Globe

1977. U.N. Water Conference.

G65	**G49**	80c. multicoloured	85	85
G66	**G49**	1f.10 multicoloured	1·20	1·20

G50 Protective Hands

1977. Security Council Commemoration.

G67	**G50**	80c. multicoloured	85	85
G68	**G50**	1f.10 multicoloured	1·20	1·20

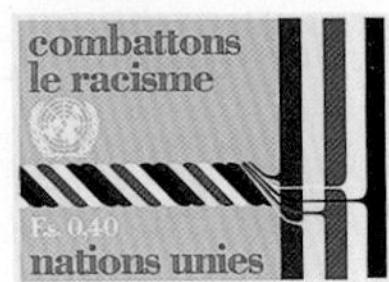

G51 "Intertwining of Races"

1977. "Combat Racism".

G69	**G51**	40c. multicoloured	45	45
G70	**G51**	1f.10 multicoloured	1·20	1·20

G52 Atoms and Laurel Leaf

1977. "Peaceful Uses for Atomic Energy".

G71	**G52**	80c. multicoloured	85	85
G72	**G52**	1f.10 multicoloured	1·20	1·20

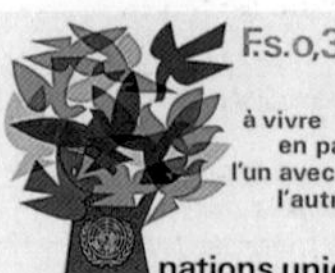

G53 Tree and Birds

1978

G73	**G53**	35c. multicoloured	45	45

G54 Smallpox Bacilli and Globe

1978. Global Eradication of Smallpox.

G74	**G54**	80c. multicoloured	85	85
G75	**G54**	1f.10 multicoloured	1·20	1·20

1978. "Namibia: Liberation, Justice, Co-operation".

G76	**183**	80c. multicoloured	85	85

G56 Aircraft Flightpaths

1978. International Civil Aviation Organization—Safety in the Air.

G77	**G56**	70c. multicoloured	75	75
G78	**G56**	80c. multicoloured	85	85

G57 Globe, Flags and General Assembly Interior

1978. General Assembly.

G79	**G57**	70c. multicoloured	75	75
G80	**G57**	1f.10 multicoloured	1·20	1·20

1978. Technical Co-operation among Developing Countries.

G81	**186**	80c. multicoloured	85	85

G59 "Disaster"

1979. United Nations Disaster Relief Co-ordinator.

G82	**G59**	80c. multicoloured	85	85
G83	**G59**	1f.50 multicoloured	1·60	1·60

G60 Children and Rainbow

1979. International Year of the Child.

G84	**G60**	80c. multicoloured	85	85
G85	**G60**	1f.10 multicoloured	1·20	1·20

1979. "For a Free and Independent Namibia".

G86	**193**	1f.10 multicoloured	1·20	1·20

G62 Int Court of Justice and Scales

1979. International Court of Justice.

G87	**G62**	80c. multicoloured	85	85
G88	**G62**	1f.10 multicoloured	1·20	1·20

G63 Key symbolizing Unity of Action

1980. New International Economic Order.

G89	**G63**	80c. multicoloured	85	85

G64 Emblem

1980. U.N. Decade for Women.

G90	**G64**	40c. multicoloured	45	45
G91	**G64**	70c. multicoloured	75	75

1980. Peace Keeping Operations.

G92	**198**	1f.10 blue and green	1·20	1·20

1980. 35th Anniv of United Nations.

G93	-	40c. black and blue	45	45
G94	**200**	70c. multicoloured	75	75
MSG95 92×73 mm. Nos. G93/4. Imperf			1·30	1·30

DESIGN: 40c. Dove and "35".

1980. Economic and Social Council.

G96	**204**	40c. multicoloured	45	45
G97	-	70c. blue, red and black	75	75

DESIGN: 70c. Human figures ascending graph.

1981. Inalienable Rights of the Palestinian People.

G98	**206**	80c. multicoloured	85	85

G71 Disabled Person

1981. International Year of Disabled Persons.

G99	**G71**	40c. black and blue	45	45
G100	-	1f.50 black and red	1·60	1·60

DESIGN: 1f.50, Knot pattern.

1981. Art.

G101	**209**	80c. multicoloured	85	85

1981. New and Renewable Sources of Energy.

G102	**210**	1f.10 multicoloured	1·20	1·20

1981. 10th Anniv of U.N. Volunteers Programme. Multicoloured.

G103	40c. Type **212**	45	45
G104	70c. Emblems of science, agriculture and industry	75	75

G77 "Anti-apartheid"

1982. Multicoloured.. Multicoloured..

G105	30c. Type G **77**	30	30
G106	1f. Flags	1·10	1·10

1982. Human Environment. Multicoloured.

G107	40c. Leaves	45	45
G108	1f.20 Type **217**	1·30	1·30

1982. Second United Nations Conference on Exploration and Peaceful Uses of Outer Space.

G109	**219**	80c. violet, pink & green	85	85
G110	-	1f. multicoloured	1·10	1·10

DESIGN: 1f. Satellite and emblems.

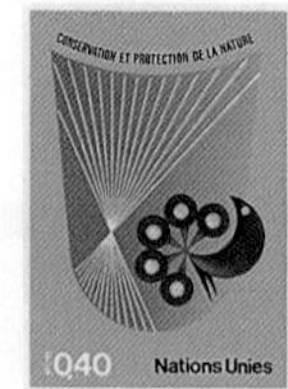

G83 Bird

1982. Conservation and Protection of Nature. Multicoloured.

G111	40c. Type G **83**	45	45
G112	1f.50 Snake (reptiles)	1·60	1·60

G85 Cable Network

1983. World Communications Year.

G113	**G85**	1f.20 multicoloured	1·30	1·30

1983. Safety at Sea: International Maritime Organization. Multicoloured.

G114	40c. Type **224**	45	45
G115	80c. Radar screen within lifebelt	85	85

1983. World Food Programme.

G116	**226**	1f.50 blue	1·60	1·60

1983. Trade and Development. Multicoloured.

G117	80c. Type **227**	85	85
G118	1f.10 Exports	1·20	1·20

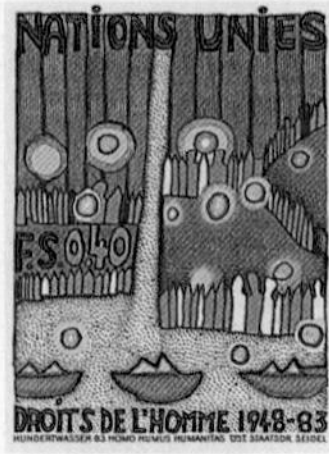

G91 "Homo Humus Humanitas"

1983. 35th Anniv of Universal Declaration of Human Rights. Multicoloured.

G119	40c. Type G **91**	55	55
G120	1f.20 "Droit de Creer"	1·40	1·40

G93 World Housing

1984. International Conference on Population, Mexico City.

G121	**G93**	1f.20 multicoloured	1·30	1·30

G94 Fishing

1984. World Food Day. Multicoloured.

G122	50c. Type G **94**	65	65
G123	80c. Planting saplings	95	95

G96 Fort St. Angelo, Malta (wrongly inscr "Valetta")

1984. World Heritage—UNESCO. Mult.

G124	50c. Type G **96**	65	65
G125	70c. Los Glaciares, Argentina	85	85

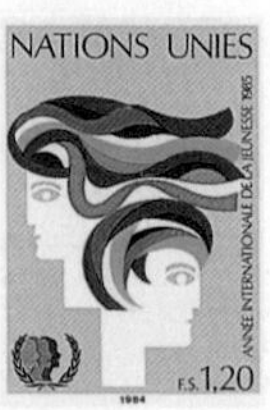

G98 Man and Woman

1984. Future for Refugees.

G126	**G98**	35c. black and green	45	45
G127	-	1f.50 black and brown	1·70	1·70

DESIGN: 1f.50, Head of woman.

G100 Heads

1984. International Youth Year.

G128	**G100**	1f.20 multicoloured	1·50	1·50

1985. 20th Anniv of Turin Centre of International Labour Organization.

G129	**239**	80c. red	95	95
G130	**V43**	1f.20 green	1·40	1·40

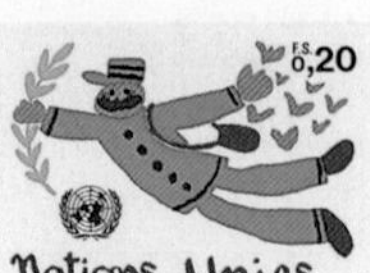

G103 Ploughing and Group of People

1985. 10th Anniv of U.N. University, Tokyo.

G131	**G103**	50c. multicoloured	65	65
G132	**G103**	80c. multicoloured	95	95

G104 Postman

1985

G133	**G104**	20c. multicoloured	25	25
G134	-	1f.20 blue and black	1·30	1·30

DESIGN: 1f.20, Doves.

1985. 40th Anniv of United Nations Organization. Multicoloured.

G135	50c. Type **243**	65	65
G136	70c. "Harvest Scene" (Andrew Wyeth)	85	85
MSG137 76×81 mm. Nos. G135/6. Imperf		2·10	2·10

NATIONS UNIES LA SURVIE DE L'ENFANT F.s.0,50

G108 Children

1985. UNICEF. Child Survival Campaign. Multicoloured.

G138	50c. Type G **108**	55	55
G139	1f.20 Child drinking	1·30	1·30

G110 Children raising Empty Bowls to weeping Mother

1986. Africa in Crisis.

G140	**G110**	1f.40 multicoloured	1·60	1·60

G111 Herring Gulls

1986

G141	**G111**	5c. multicoloured	30	30

G112 Tents in Clearing

1986. Development Programme. Timber Production. Multicoloured.

G142	35c. Type G **112**	2·50	2·50
G143	35c. Felling tree	2·50	2·50
G144	35c. Logs on lorries	2·50	2·50
G145	35c. Girls with sapling	2·50	2·50

Nos. G142/5 were printed together, se-tenant, forming a composite design.

1986. Philately: The International Hobby.

G146	**253**	50c. green and red	65	65
G147	-	80c. black and orange	1·20	1·20

DESIGN: 80c. United Nations stamps (as Type V **56**).

G118 Ribbon forming Dove

1986. International Peace Year. Multicoloured.

G148	45c. Type G **118**	55	55
G149	1f.40 "Paix" and olive branch	1·80	1·80

G120 (image scaled to 40% of original size)

1986. 40th Anniv of World Federation of United Nations associations. Sheet 120×65 mm. Multicoloured.

MSG150 35c. Birds (Benigno Gomez); 45c. Circle and prisms (Alexander Calder); 50c. "Eye" (Joan Miro); 70c. Done and musical instruments (Ole Hamann)	8·50	8·50

1987. 9th Death Anniv of Trygve Lie (first U.N. Secretary-General).

G151	**258**	1f.40 multicoloured	1·60	1·60

G122 Abstract

1987. Multicoloured.. Multicoloured..

G152	90c. Type G **122**	1·10	1·10
G153	1f.40 Armillary Sphere, Geneva Centre (30×30 mm)	1·60	1·60

G124 Mixing Cement and Carrying Bricks

1987. International Year of Shelter for the Homeless.

G154	**G124**	50c. green and black	85	85
G155	-	90c. blue, turquoise and black	1·30	1·30

DESIGN: 90c. Fitting windows and painting.

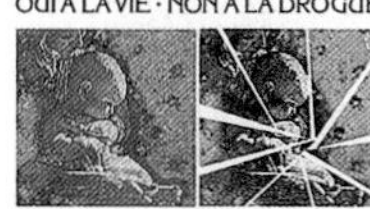

G126 Mother and Baby

1987. Anti-drugs Campaign. Multicoloured.

G156	80c. Type G **126**	1·10	1·10
G157	1f.20 Workers in paddy field	1·60	1·60

G128 People in Boat and Palais des Nations, Geneva

1987. United Nations Day. Multicoloured.

G158	35c. Type G **128**	65	65
G159	50c. Dancers	1·10	1·10

G130 Whooping Cough

1987. "Immunize Every Child". Multicoloured.

G160	90c. Type G **130**	1·30	1·30
G161	1f.70 Tuberculosis	2·10	2·10

G132 Goatherd

1988. International Fund for Agricultural Development "For a World Without Hunger" Campaign. Multicoloured.

G162	35c. Type G **132**	60	60
G163	1f.40 Women and baskets of fruit	1·80	1·80

G134 People

1988

G164	**G134**	50c. multicoloured	75	75

G135 Mountains and Pine Forest

1988. "Survival of the Forests". Multicoloured.

G165	50c. Type G **135**	5·00	5·00
G166	1f.10 Pine forest and lake shore	5·00	5·00

Nos. G165/6 were printed together, se-tenant, forming a composite design.

G137 Instruction in Fruit Growing

1988. International Volunteer Day. Mult.

G167	80c. Type G **137**	1·10	1·10
G168	90c. Teaching animal husbandry (horiz)	1·40	1·40

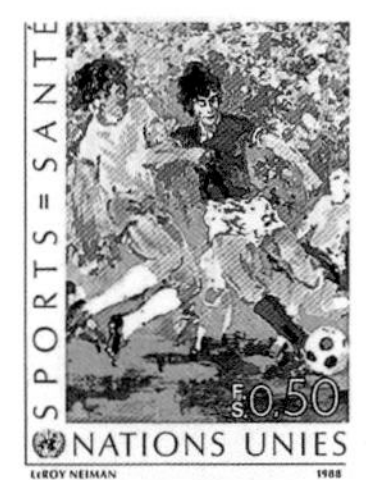

G139 Football

1988. "Health in Sports". Multicoloured.

G169	50f. Type G **139**	65	65
G170	1f.40 Swimming	1·70	1·70

1988. 40th Anniv of Declaration of Human Rights.

G171	**276**	90c. multicoloured	1·10	1·10
MSG172		120×79 mm. 2f. multicoloured	3·25	3·25

G142 Communications

1989. World Bank. Multicoloured.

G173	80c. Type G **142**	1·10	1·10
G174	1f.40 Industry	1·60	1·60

1989. Award of Nobel Peace Prize to United Nations Peace-keeping Forces.

G175	**280**	90c. multicoloured	1·30	1·30

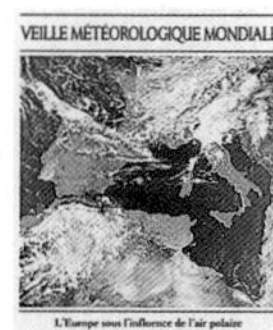

G145 Cold Arctic Air over Europe

1989. 25th Anniv of World Weather Watch.

G176	90c. Type G **145**	1·30	1·30
G177	1f.10 Surface temperatures of Kattegat	1·70	1·70

G147 Tree and Birds

1989. 10th Anniv of United Nations Vienna International Centre.

G178	50c. Type G **147**	75	75
G179	2f. Woman and flower	3·00	3·00

G149 "Young Mother sewing" (Mary Cassatt) (Article 3)

1989. Universal Declaration of Human Rights (1st series). Multicoloured.

G180	35f. Type G **149**	55	55
G181	80f. "Runaway Slave" (Albert Mangones) (Article 4)	95	95

See also Nos. G193/4, G209/10, G224/5 and G234/5.

1990. International Trade Centre.

G182	**288**	1f.50 multicoloured	2·00	2·00

G152 Palais des Nations

1990

G183	**G152**	5f. multicoloured	5·25	5·25

1990. Anti-AIDS Campaign. Multicoloured.

G184	50c. Type **289**	85	85
G185	80c. "Man" (Leonardo da Vinci)	1·30	1·30

G155 Frangipani

1990. Medicinal Plants. Multicoloured.

G186	90c. Type G **155**	1·10	1·10
G187	1f.40 "Cinchona officinalis"	1·60	1·60

G157 Projects forming "45"

1990. 45th Anniv of U.N.O. Multicoloured.

G188	90c. Type G **157**	1·40	1·40
G189	1f.10 Dove and "45"	1·80	1·80
MSG190	100×73 mm. Nos. G188/9	4·75	4·75

G159 Men making Deal over Painting

1990. Crime Prevention. Multicoloured.

G191	50c. Type G **159**	75	75
G192	2f. Man spilling waste from cart	2·75	2·75

1990. Universal Declaration of Human Rights (2nd series). As Type G 149.

G193	35c. multicoloured	55	55
G194	90c. black and flesh	1·30	1·30

DESIGNS: 35c. "Prison Courtyard" (Vincent van Gogh) (Article 9); 90c. "Katho's Son Redeems the Evil Doer from Execution" (Albrecht Durer) (Article 10).

G163/166 Lake (image scaled to 67% of original size)

1991. Economic Commission for Europe. "For a Better Environment".

No.	Type	Description	Unused	Used
G195	**G163**	90c. multicoloured	2·10	2·10
G196	**G164**	90c. multicoloured	2·10	2·10
G197	**G165**	90c. multicoloured	2·10	2·10
G198	**G166**	90c. multicoloured	2·10	2·10

Nos. G195/8 were issued together, se-tenant, forming the composite design illustrated.

G167 Mountains

1991. 1st Anniv of Namibian Independence. Multicoloured.

No.	Type	Description	Unused	Used
G199		70c. Type G **167**	1·10	1·10
G200		90c. Baobab	1·60	1·60

G169 Papers and Ballot Box

1991. Multicoloured.. Multicoloured..

No.	Type	Description	Unused	Used
G201		80c. Type G **169**	1·10	1·10
G202		1f.50 U.N. emblem	1·70	1·70

G171 Baby in Open Hands (Ryuta Nakajima)

1991. 30th Anniv (1989) of U.N. Declaration of the Rights of the Child and 1990 World Summit on Children, New York. Children's Drawings. Multicoloured.

No.	Type	Description	Unused	Used
G203		80c. Type G **171**	1·30	1·30
G204		1f.10 Children playing amongst flowers (David Popper)	1·70	1·70

G173 Bubble of Toxin, City and Drums

1991. Banning of Chemical Weapons. Mult.

No.	Type	Description	Unused	Used
G205		80c. Type G **173**	1·30	1·30
G206		1f.40 Hand pushing back gas mask	2·10	2·10

G175 U.N. (New York) 1951 15c. Stamp

1991. 40th Anniv of United Nations Postal Administration.

No.	Type	Description	Unused	Used
G207	**G175**	50c. blue and lilac on cream	75	75
G208	-	1f.60 blue on cream	2·20	2·20

DESIGN: 1f.60, U.N. (New York) 1951 50c. stamp.

1991. Declaration of Human Rights (3rd series). As Type G 149. Multicoloured.

No.	Type	Description	Unused	Used
G209		50c. "Early Morning in Ro, 1925" (Paul Klee) (Article 15)	65	65
G210		90c. "The Marriage of Arnolfini" (Jan van Eyck) (Article 16)	1·30	1·30

G179 Sagarmatha National Park, Nepal

1992. 20th Anniv of UNESCO World Heritage Convention. Multicoloured.

No.	Type	Description	Unused	Used
G211		50c. Type G **179**	95	95
G212		1f.10 Stonehenge, United Kingdom	2·00	2·00

G181 U.N. Headquarters, New York

1992

No.	Type	Description	Unused	Used
G213	**G181**	3f. multicoloured	3·75	3·75

G182/183 Sea Life

1992. "Clean Oceans".

No.	Type	Description	Unused	Used
G214	**G182**	80c. multicoloured	1·40	1·40
G215	**G183**	80c. multicoloured	1·40	1·40

Nos. G214/15 were issued together, se-tenant, forming the composite design illustrated.

G184/187 Planet Earth (image scaled to 73% of original size)

1992. 2nd U.N. Conference on Environment and Development, Rio de Janeiro.

No.	Type	Description	Unused	Used
G216	**G184**	75c. multicoloured	1·40	1·40
G217	**G185**	75c. multicoloured	1·40	1·40
G218	**G186**	75c. multicoloured	1·40	1·40
G219	**G187**	75c. multicoloured	1·40	1·40

Nos. G216/19 were issued together, se-tenant, forming the composite design illustrated.

G188/189 "Mission Planet Earth" (image scaled to 67% of original size)

1992. International Space Year. Roul.

No.	Type	Description	Unused	Used
G220	**G188**	1f.10 multicoloured	1·60	1·60
G221	**G189**	1f.10 multicoloured	1·60	1·60

Nos. G220/1 were issued together, se-tenant, forming the composite design illustrated.

G190 Women in Science and Technology

1992. Commission on Science and Technology for Development. Multicoloured.

No.	Type	Description	Unused	Used
G222		90c. Type G **190**	1·30	1·30
G223		1f.60 Graduate using V.D.U.	2·50	2·50

1992. Universal Declaration of Human Rights (4th series). As Type G 149. Multicoloured.

No.	Type	Description	Unused	Used
G224		50c. "The Oath of the Tennis Court" (Jacques Louis David) (Article 21)	75	75
G225		90c. "Rocking Chair I" (Henry Moore) (Article 22)	1·40	1·40

G194 Voluntary Work

1993. "Ageing: Dignity and Participation". 10th Anniv (1992) of International Plan of Action on Ageing. Multicoloured.

No.	Type	Description	Unused	Used
G226		50c. Type G **194**	75	75
G227		1f.60 Security of employment	2·50	2·50

G196 Gorilla

1993. Endangered Species (1st series). Multicoloured.

No.	Type	Description	Unused	Used
G228		80c. Type G **196**	1·10	1·10
G229		80c. Peregrine falcon ("Falco peregrinus")	1·10	1·10
G230		80c. Amazon manatee ("Tricheous inunguis")	1·10	1·10
G231		80c. Snow leopard ("Panthera uncia")	1·10	1·10

See also Nos. G246/9, G264/7, G290/3, G308/11, G333/6, G372/5, G389/92, G409/12, G433/6, G460/3, G476/9, G498/501, G520/3 and G544/7.

G200 Neighbourhood and Community Environment

1993. 45th Anniv of W.H.O. Multicoloured.

No.	Type	Description	Unused	Used
G232		60c. Type G **200**	1·10	1·10
G233		1f. Urban environment	1·90	1·90

1993. Declaration of Human Rights (5th series). As Type G 149. Multicoloured.

No.	Type	Description	Unused	Used
G234		50c. "Three Musicians" (Pablo Picasso) (Article 27)	75	75
G235		90c. "Voice of Space" (Rene Magritte) (Article 28)	1·40	1·40

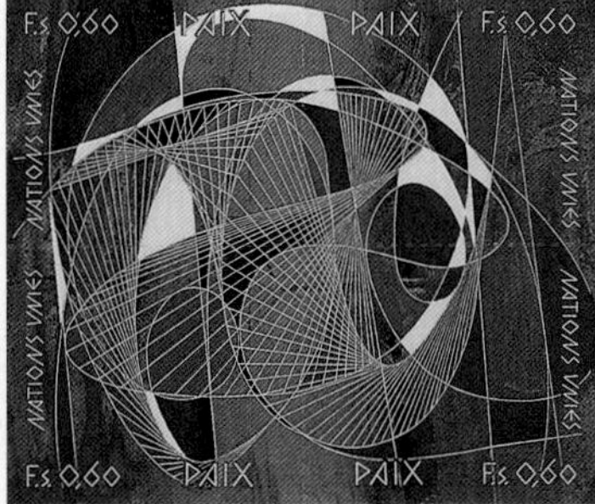

G204/207 Peace (image scaled to 74% of original size)

1993. International Peace Day. Roul.

No.	Type	Description	Unused	Used
G236	**G204**	60c. multicoloured	1·10	1·10
G237	**G205**	60c. multicoloured	1·10	1·10
G238	**G206**	60c. multicoloured	1·10	1·10
G239	**G207**	60c. multicoloured	1·10	1·10

Nos. G236/9 were issued together, se-tenant, forming the composite design illustrated.

G208 Polar Bears

1993. The Environment—Climate. Multicoloured.

No.	Type	Description	Unused	Used
G240		1f.10 Type G **208**	1·80	1·80
G241		1f.10 Whale in melting ice	1·80	1·80
G242		1f.10 Elephant seal	1·80	1·80
G243		1f.10 Adelie penguins	1·80	1·80

Nos. G240/3 were issued together, se-tenant, forming a composite design.

G212 Father calling Child

1994. International Year of the Family. Mult.

No.	Type	Description	Unused	Used
G244		80c. Type G **212**	1·30	1·30
G245		1f. Three generations	1·90	1·90

1994. Endangered Species (2nd series). As Type G 196. Multicoloured.

No.	Type	Description	Unused	Used
G246		80c. Mexican prairie dogs ("Cynomys mexicanus")	1·10	1·10
G247		80c. Jabiru ("Jabiru mycteria")	1·10	1·10
G248		80c. Blue whale ("Balaenoptera musculus")	1·10	1·10
G249		80c. Golden lion tamarin ("Leontopithecus rosalia")	1·10	1·10

G218 Hand delivering Refugee to New Country

1994. U.N. High Commissioner for Refugees.

No.	Type	Description	Unused	Used
G250	**G218**	1f.20 multicoloured	2·40	2·40

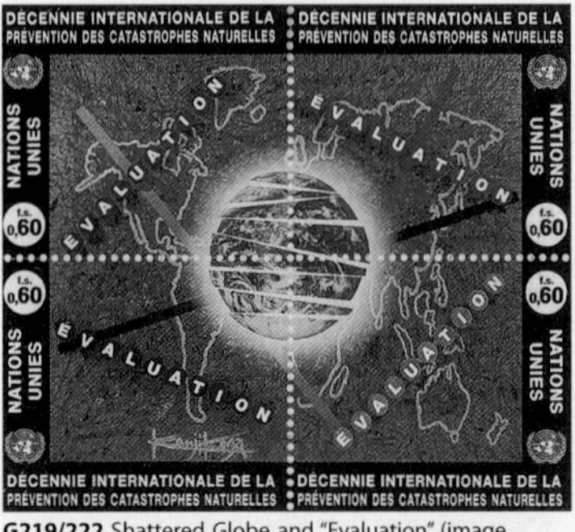

G219/222 Shattered Globe and "Evaluation" (image scaled to 70% of original size)

1994. International Decade for Natural Disaster Reduction.

No.	Type	Description	Unused	Used
G251	**G219**	60c. multicoloured	1·60	1·60
G252	**G220**	60c. multicoloured	1·60	1·60
G253	**G221**	60c. multicoloured	1·60	1·60
G254	**G222**	60c. multicoloured	1·60	1·60

Nos. G251/4 were issued together, se-tenant, forming the composite design illustrated.

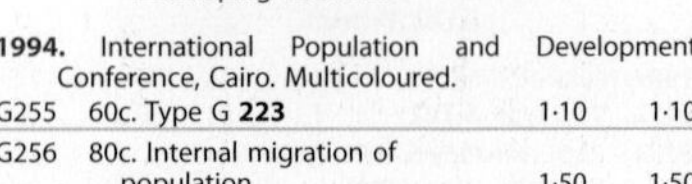

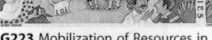

G223 Mobilization of Resources in Developing Countries

1994. International Population and Development Conference, Cairo. Multicoloured.

No.	Type	Description	Unused	Used
G255		60c. Type G **223**	1·10	1·10
G256		80c. Internal migration of population	1·50	1·50

G225 Palais des Nations, Geneva

1994. Multicoloured.. Multicoloured..
G257 60c. Type G **225** 85 85
G258 80c. "Creation of the World" (detail of tapestry, Oili Maki) 1·10 1·10
G259 1f.80 Palais des Nations 2·40 2·40

G228 Map and Linked Ribbons

1994. 30th Anniv of United Nations Conference on Trade and Development.
G260 80c. Type G **228** 1·30 1·30
G261 1f. Map and ribbons 1·70 1·70

1995. 50th Anniv of U.N.O. (1st issue).
G262 **371** 80c. multicoloured 1·30 1·30
See also Nos. G270/1 and G275/86.

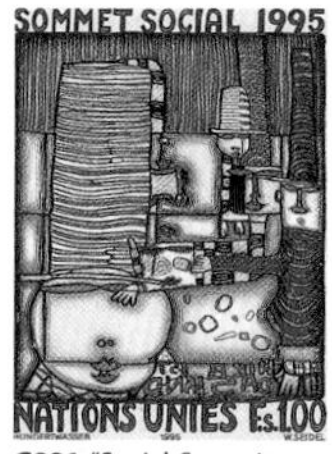

G231 "Social Summit 1995"

1995. World Summit for Social Development, Copenhagen.
G263 **G231** 1f. multicoloured 2·40 2·40

1995. Endangered Species (3rd series). As Type G 196. Multicoloured.
G264 80c. Crowned lemur ("Lemur coronatus") 1·10 1·10
G265 80c. Giant scops owl ("Otus gurneyi") 1·10 1·10
G266 80c. Painted frog ("Atelopus varius zeteki") 1·10 1·10
G267 80c. American wood bison ("Bison bison athabascae") 1·10 1·10

G236 Field in Summer

1995. "Youth: Our Future". 10th Anniv of International Youth Year. Multicoloured.
G268 80c. Type G **236** 1·60 1·60
G269 1f. Field in winter 2·10 2·10

1995. 50th Anniv of U.N.O. (2nd issue).
G270 **379** 60c. purple 1·10 1·10
G271 - 1f.80 green 2·75 2·75
MSG272 92×70 mm. Nos. G270/1. Imperf 3·75 3·75
DESIGN: 1f.80, Veteran's Memorial Hall and Opera House, San Francisco (venue for signing of Charter).

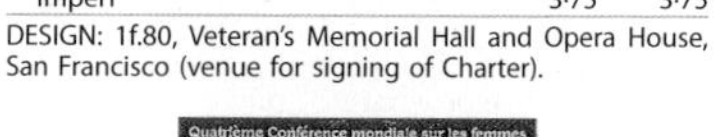

G240 Woman and Cranes

1995. 4th World Conference on Women, Peking. Multicoloured.
G273 60c. Type G **240** 1·10 1·10
G274 1f. Women worshipping (30×49 mm) 1·90 1·90

1995. 50th Anniv of U.N.O. (3rd issue).
G275 **385** 30c. multicoloured 55 55
G276 **386** 30c. multicoloured 55 55
G277 **387** 30c. multicoloured 55 55
G278 **388** 30c. multicoloured 55 55
G279 **389** 30c. multicoloured 55 55
G280 **390** 30c. multicoloured 55 55
G281 **391** 30c. multicoloured 55 55
G282 **392** 30c. multicoloured 55 55
G283 **393** 30c. multicoloured 55 55
G284 **394** 30c. multicoloured 55 55
G285 **395** 30c. multicoloured 55 55
G286 **396** 30c. multicoloured 55 55
Nos. G275/80 and G281/6 respectively were issued together, se-tenant, forming two composite designs.

G254 Catching Fish

1996. 50th Anniv of World Federation of United Nations Associations.
G287 **G254** 80c. multicoloured 1·40 1·40

G255 "Galloping Horse treading on a Flying Swallow" (Chinese bronze sculpture, Han Dynasty)

1996. Multicoloured.. Multicoloured..
G288 40c. Type G **255** 65 65
G289 70c. Palais des Nations, Geneva 1·30 1·30

1996. Endangered Species (4th series). As Type G 196. Multicoloured.
G290 80c. "Paphiopedilum delenatii" 1·10 1·10
G291 80c. "Pachypodium baronii" 1·10 1·10
G292 80c. Yellow amaryllis ("Sternbergia lutea") 1·10 1·10
G293 80c. Cobra plant ("Darlingtonia californica") 1·10 1·10

G261 Family on Verandah of House

1996. "Habitat II" Second United Nations Conference on Human Settlements, Istanbul, Turkey. Multicoloured.
G294 70c. Type G **261** 1·30 1·30
G295 70c. Women in traditional dress in gardens 1·30 1·30
G296 70c. Produce seller and city 1·30 1·30
G297 70c. Boys playing on riverside 1·30 1·30
G298 70c. Elderly couple reading newspaper 1·30 1·30
Nos. G294/8 were issued together, se-tenant, forming a composite design.

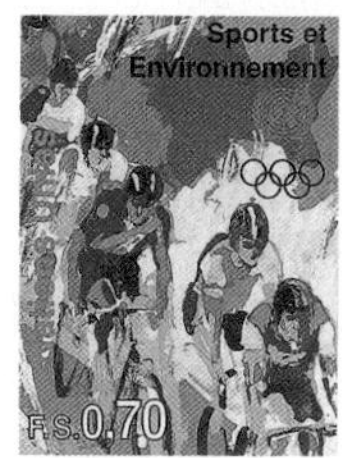

G266 Cycling

1996. Sport and the Environment. Multicoloured.
G299 70c. Type G **266** 1·10 1·10
G300 1f.10 Running (horiz) 1·90 1·90
MSG301 88×78 mm. Nos. G299/300 3·25 3·25

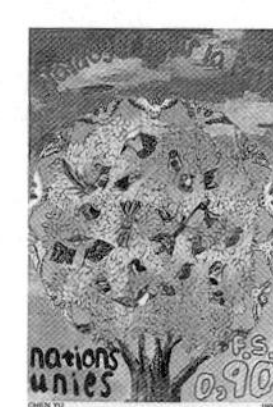

G268 Birds in Treetop

1996. "A Plea for Peace". Winning Entries in China Youth Design Competition. Multicoloured.
G302 90c. Type G **268** 1·50 1·50
G303 1f.10 Flowers growing from bomb 1·90 1·90

G270 "The Sun and the Moon" (South American legend)

1996. 50th Anniv of UNICEF. Multicoloured.
G304 70c. Type G **270** 95 95
G305 1f.80 "Ananse" (African spider tale) 2·50 2·50

G272 U.N. Flag

1997
G306 10c. Type G **272** 20 20
G307 1f.10 "Building Palais des Nations" (detail of fresco, Massimo Campigli) 1·70 1·70

1997. Endangered Species (5th series). As Type G 196. Multicoloured.
G308 80f. Polar bear ("Ursus maritimus") 1·10 1·10
G309 80f. Blue crowned pigeon ("Goura cristata") 1·10 1·10
G310 80f. Marine iguana ("Amblyrhynchus cristatus") 1·10 1·10
G311 80f. Guanaco ("Lama guanicoe") 1·10 1·10

G278/281 Sunrise over Mountains (image scaled to 68% of original size)

1997. "Earth Summit + 5". 5th Anniv of United Nations Conference on Environment and Development.
G312 **G278** 45f. multicoloured 85 85
G313 **G279** 45f. multicoloured 85 85
G314 **G280** 45f. multicoloured 85 85
G315 **G281** 45f. multicoloured 85 85
MSG316 90×75 mm. 1f.10 Motifs as Nos. G312/15. Imperf 2·10 2·10
Nos. G312/15 were issued together, se-tenant, forming the composite design illustrated.

G282 Fokker F.7 Trimotor and Airship

1997. 50th Anniversaries of Economic Commission for Europe and Economic and Social Commission for Asia and the Pacific. Multicoloured.
G317 70f. Type G **282** 1·30 1·30
G318 70f. Lockheed Constellation and Boeing 314 flying boat 1·30 1·30
G319 70f. De Havilland D.H.106 Comet and Boeing 747 jetliners 1·30 1·30
G320 70f. Ilyushin and Boeing 747 jetliners 1·30 1·30
G321 70f. Concorde Supersonic jetliner 1·30 1·30
Nos. 317/21 were issued together, se-tenant, forming a composite design.

1997. "Tribute to Philately". Multicoloured.
G322 70c. Type **G287** 1·10 1·10
G323 1f.10 1986 80c. philately stamp (as Type V **227**) 1·30 1·30

1997. 25th Anniv of World Heritage Convention. Terracotta Warriors from Emperor Qin Shi Huang's Tomb, Xian, China. Multicoloured.
G324 10c. As Type **434** 45 45
G325 10c. As No. 737 45 45
G326 10c. As No. 738 45 45
G327 10c. As No. 739 45 45
G328 10c. As No. 740 45 45
G329 10c. As No. 741 45 45
G330 45c. As No. 738 65 65
G331 70c. As No. 739 1·30 1·30

G295 Palais des Nations, Geneva

1998
G332 **G295** 2f. multicoloured 3·00 3·00

1998. Endangered Species (6th series). As Type G 196. Multicoloured.
G333 80c. Tibetan stump-tailed macaques ("Macaca thibetana") 1·10 1·10
G334 80c. Greater flamingoes ("Phoenicopterus ruber") 1·10 1·10
G335 80c. Queen Alexandra's birdwings ("Ornithoptera alexandrae") 1·10 1·10
G336 80c. Fallow deer ("Cervus dama") 1·10 1·10

G300 Bull Seal

1998. International Year of the Ocean. Multicoloured.
G337 45c. Type G **300** 65 65
G338 45c. Polar bears 65 65
G339 45c. Polar bear, musk oxen, king penguins and seal on ice 65 65
G340 45c. Diver 65 65
G341 45c. Seals 65 65
G342 45c. Narwhal 65 65
G343 45c. Fishes and shark 65 65
G344 45c. Shark's tail, seal and horned puffin 65 65
G345 45c. Fishes and Gentoo penguin's back 65 65
G346 45c. Fish and jellyfishes 65 65
G347 45c. Seal, Gentoo penguin and squid 65 65
G348 45c. Gentoo penguin hunting fishes 65 65

G301 Orang-utan with Young

1998. Rainforest Preservation.
G349 **G301** 70c. multicoloured 1·10 1·10
MSG350 82×70 mm. G **301** 3f. multicoloured 4·50 4·50

G302 Soldier with Children

1998. 50 Years of United Nations Peacekeeping. Multicoloured.
G351 70c. Type G **302** 1·10 1·10
G352 90c. Soldier holding baby 1·30 1·30

G304 Birds

1998. 50th Anniv of Universal Declaration of Human Rights. Multicoloured.

G353		90c. Type G **304**	1·40	1·40
G354		1f.80 Hand releasing birds	2·75	2·75

1998. World Heritage Site. Schonbrunn Palace, Vienna. Multicoloured.

G355		10c. As No. 780	30	30
G356		10c. As No. 781	30	30
G357		10c. As No. 782	30	30
G358		30c. As Type **454**	75	75
G359		30c. As No. 778	75	75
G360		30c. As No. 779	75	75
G361		70c. As No. 781	1·10	1·10
G362		1f.10 As Type **454**	1·60	1·60

G312 Palais Wilson, Geneva

1999. Headquarters of United Nations High Commissioner for Human Rights.

G363	**G312**	1f.70 red	2·40	2·40

1999. World Heritage Sites in Australia. Mult.

G364		10c. As Type **462**	30	30
G365		10c. As No. 796	30	30
G366		10c. As No. 797	30	30
G367		20c. As No. 798	65	65
G368		20c. As No. 799	65	65
G369		20c. As No. 800	65	65
G370		90c. As No. 801	1·30	1·30
G371		1f.10 As No. 802	1·70	1·70

1999. Endangered Species (7th series). As Type G 196. Multicoloured.

G372		90c. Asiatic wild ass ("Equus hemionus")	1·40	1·40
G373		90c. Hyacinth macaw ("Anodorhynchus hyacinthinus")	1·40	1·40
G374		90c. Jamaican boa ("Epicrates subflavus")	1·40	1·40
G375		90c. Bennett's tree kangaroo ("Dendrolagus bennettianus")	1·40	1·40

G323/324 Satellite-aided Agriculture (image scaled to 67% of original size)

1999. 3rd Conference on Exploration and Peaceful Uses of Outer Space, Vienna.

G376	**G323**	45c. multicoloured	65	65
G377	**G324**	45c. multicoloured	65	65
MSG378		90×75 mm. 2f. Combined design as Nos. G376/7 (71×29 mm)	2·75	2·75
MSG379		90×75 mm. 2f. As No. **MS**G378 but additionally inscr "PHILEXFRANCE 99 LE MONDIAL DU TIMBRE PARIS 2 AU 11 JUILLET 1999" in bottom margin	4·25	4·25

Nos. G376/7 were issued together, se-tenant, forming the composite design illustrated.

G325/328 Early 20th-century Mail Transport (image scaled to 68% of original size)

1999. 125th Anniv of Universal Postal Union.

G380	**G325**	70c. multicoloured	1·10	1·10
G381	**G326**	70c. multicoloured	1·10	1·10
G382	**G327**	70c. multicoloured	1·10	1·10
G383	**G328**	70c. multicoloured	1·10	1·10

Nos. G380/3 were issued together, se-tenant, forming the composite design illustrated.

G329 Palais des Nations, Geneva

1999. "In Memoriam: Fallen in the Cause of Peace".

G384	**G329**	1f.10 multicoloured	1·60	1·60
MSG385		90×75 mm. 2f. multicoloured	2·75	2·75

G331 Couple on Globe

1999. Education: Keystone to the 21st Century.

G386		90c. Type G **331**	1·40	1·40
G387		1f.80 "Environment"	2·75	2·75

2000. International Year of Thanksgiving. Mult.

G388		90c. As Type **483**	1·40	1·40

2000. Endangered Species (8th series). As Type G 196. Multicoloured.

G389		90c. Hippopotamus (*Hippopotamus amphibius*)	1·40	1·40
G390		90c. Coscoroba swan (*Coscoroba coscoroba*)	1·40	1·40
G391		90c. Emerald monitor (*Varanus prasinus*)	1·40	1·40
G392		90c. Sea otter (*Enhydra lutris*)	1·40	1·40

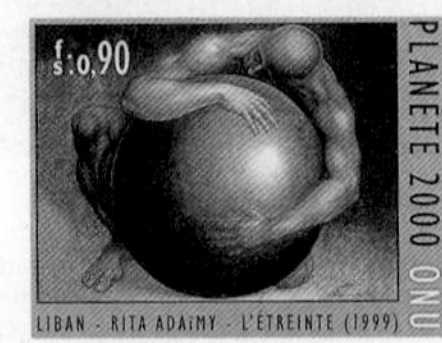

G338 "The Embrace" (Rita Adaimy)

2000. "Our World 2000" International Art Exhibition, New York. Entries in Millennium Painting Competition. Multicoloured.

G393		90c. Type G **338**	1·40	1·40
G394		1f.10 "Living Single" (Richard Kimanthi) (vert)	1·60	1·60

G340 Corner Stone Dedication, 1949

2000. 55th Anniv of the United Nations and 50th Anniv of Opening of U.N. Headquarters, New York.

G395	**G340**	90c. red, blue and ochre	1·40	1·40
G396	-	1f.40 red, blue and ochre	2·00	2·00
MSG397		67×86 mm. Nos. G395/6	3·50	3·50

DESIGN: 1f.40, Window cleaner, Secretariat Building, 1951.

G342 Two Women

G343 (image scaled to 34% of original size)

2000. "The United Nations of the 21st century". Sheet 141×165 mm containing Type G 342 and similar horiz designs, forming the overall design Type G 343. Multicoloured.

MSG398	50c. Type G **342**; 50c. Man carrying bricks on head; 50c. Soldier and villagers; 50c. Dam and doves; 50c. Men digging; 50c. Men damming irrigation channel	5·25	5·25

2000. World Heritage Sites in Spain. Multicoloured.

G399		10c. As Type **496**	25	25
G400		10c. As No. 832	25	25
G401		10c. As No. 833	25	25
G402		20c. As No. 834	55	55
G403		20c. As No. 835	55	55
G404		20c. As No. 836	55	55
G405		1f. As No. 837	1·50	1·50
G406		1f.20 As No. 838	1·90	1·90

G350 Family of Refugees

2000. 50th Anniv of United Nations High Commissioner for Refugees.

G407	**G350**	80c. multicoloured	1·30	1·30
MSG408		121×82 mm. 1f.80 multicoloured	3·25	3·25

2001. Endangered Species (9th series). As Type G 196. Multicoloured.

G409		90c. Lynx (*Felis lynx canadensis*)	1·40	1·40
G410		90c. Green peafowl (*Pavo muticus*)	1·40	1·40
G411		90c. Galapagos tortoise (*Geochelone elephantopus*)	1·40	1·40
G412		90c. Lemur (*Lepilemur sp.*)	1·40	1·40

G356 Hands forming Heart (Ernest Pignon-Ernest)

2001. United Nations International Year of Volunteers. Multicoloured.

G413		90c. Type G **356**	1·40	1·40
G414		1f.30 Women's head and white dove (Paul Siche)	2·10	2·10

2001. World Heritage Sites in Japan. Multicoloured.

G415		10c. As Type **512**	20	20
G416		10c. As No. 858	20	20
G417		10c. As No. 859	20	20
G418		30c. As No. 860	55	55
G419		30c. As No. 861	55	55
G420		30c. As No. 862	55	55
G421		1f.10 As No. 858	1·60	1·60
G422		1f.30 As No. 861	1·80	1·80

2001. 40th Death Anniv of Dag Hammarskjold (United Nations Secretary General, 1953–61).

G423	**518**	2f. red	3·00	3·00

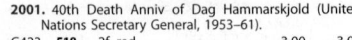

G365 Postman and "Stamps"

2001. 50th Anniv of United Nations Postal Administration.

G424	**G 365**	90c. multicoloured	1·30	1·30
G425	-	1f.30 multicoloured	1·90	1·90
MS426		102×102 mm. 1f.30, 1f.80 cobalt and carmine	4·50	4·50

DESIGNS: G425, Trumpets and "Stamps"; **MS**426, Emblem.

G368 Flowers and Coastline

2001. Climate Change. Multicoloured.

G427		90c. Type G **368**	1·50	1·50
G428		90c. Wind-powered generators and brick making	1·50	1·50
G429		90c. Power station inside glass dome	1·50	1·50
G430		90c. Couple sitting beside lake	1·50	1·50

Nos. G427/30 were issued together, se-tenant, forming a composite design.

2001. Kofi Annan, Winner of Nobel Peace Prize, 2001.

G431	**526**	90c. multicoloured	1·40	1·40

G373 Armillary Sphere, Ariana Park

2002

G432	**G373**	1f.30 multicoloured	1·90	1·90

2002. Endangered Species (10th series). As Type G 196. Multicoloured.

G433		90c. Bald uakari (*Cacajao calvus*)	1·40	1·40
G434		90c. Ratel (*Mellivora capensis*)	1·40	1·40
G435		90c. Pallas's cat (*Otocolobus manul*)	1·40	1·40
G436		90c. Savannah monitor (*Varanus exanthematicus*)	1·40	1·40

2002. East Timor Independence. As T 532. Multicoloured.

G437		90c. Wooden statue	1·40	1·40
G438		1f.30 Carved wooden container	2·00	2·00

2002. International Year of Mountains. As T 534. Multicoloured.

G439		70c. Type Weisshorn, Switzerland	95	95
G440		70c. Mount Fuji, Japan	95	95
G441		1f.20 Vinson Massif, Antarctica	1·70	1·70
G442		1f.20 Kamet, India	1·70	1·70

G384 Sun, Water, Birds and Flowers

2002. World Summit on Sustainable Development, Johannesburg. Multicoloured.

G443		90c. Type G **384**	1·40	1·40
G444		90c. Figure's wearing fashionable dress	1·40	1·40
G445		1f.80 Women's profile	2·75	2·75
G446		1f.80 Yacht	2·75	2·75

2002. World Heritage Sites in Italy. As T 542. Multicoloured.

G447		10c. Duomo di Sant'Andrea, Amalfi Coast	30	30
G448		10c. View across Islands, Aeolian Islands	30	30
G449		10c. Del Moro Fountain, Rome	30	30
G450		20c. Santa Maria del Fiore, Florence	65	65
G451		20c. Leaning Tower, Pisa	65	65
G452		20c. The Forum, Pompeii	65	65

G453 90c. As No. G451 1·40 1·40
G454 1f.30 As No. G448 2·40 2·40

2002. AIDS Awareness Campaign. As T 548.
G455 1f.30 AIDS Symbol on UN Secretariat Building, New York 2·10 2·10
MSG456 80×80 mm. 90c.+30c. AIDS symbol on UN Secretariat Building, New York at night 2·10 2·10
The premium was for AIDS charities.

G396 Doves

2002
G457 **G 396** 3f. multicoloured 4·50 4·50

2003. Indigenous Art (1st series). Sheet 121×97 mm. As T 550. Multicoloured.
MSG458 90c. Inca poncho, Peru; 90c. Bahia statue, Brazil; 90c. Blanket, Ecuador; 90c. Mayan stone sculpture, Xunantunich, Belize; 90c. Embroidered fabric, Guatemala; 90c. Colima terracotta sculpture, Mexico 9·00 9·00
See also Nos. **MS**G480 and **MS**G518.

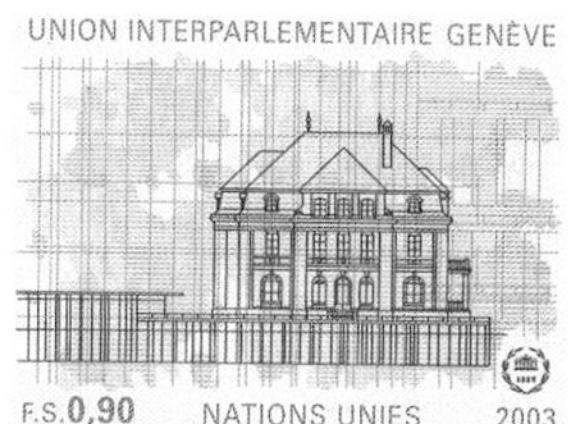

G398 Headquarters Building

2003. Inauguration of New Inter-Parliamentary Union Headquarters, Geneva.
G459 **G398** 90c. multicoloured 1·50 1·50

2003. Endangered Species (11th series). 30th Anniv of Convention on International Trade in Endangered Species (CITES). As Type G 196. Multicoloured.
G460 90c. Red-breasted goose (*Branta ruficollis*) 1·40 1·40
G461 90c. Bald ibis (*Geronticus calvus*) 1·40 1·40
G462 90c. Fulvous whistling duck (*Dendrocygna bicolour*) 1·40 1·40
G463 90c. Channel-billed toucan (*Ramphastos vitellinus*) 1·40 1·40

2003. International Year of Freshwater. As T 559. Multicoloured.
G464 70c. Autumnal trees and stream 1·10 1·10
G465 1f.30 Depleted lake 1·90 1·90
Nos. G464/5 were issued together, se-tenant, forming a composite design.

2003. Ralph Bunche (politician) Commemoration. As T 561. Multicoloured.
G466 1f.80 Ralph Bunche 2·75 2·75

2003. World Heritage Sites in USA. As T 562. Showing USA National Parks. Multicoloured.
G467 10c. Yosemite National Park 20 20
G468 10c. Smoky Mountains 20 20
G469 10c. Olympic National Park 20 20
G470 30c. Hawaii Volcanoes 65 65
G471 30c. Everglades 65 65
G472 30c. Yellowstone National Park 65 65
G473 90c. As G471 1·40 1·40
G474 1f.30 As G472 2·00 2·00
Nos. G467/74 have chestnut bands top and bottom.

2003. In Memoriam. Support for United Nations Staff Killed or Injured in Terrorist Attacks. As T 568. Multicoloured.
G475 85c. Flag at half-mast 1·40 1·40

2004. Endangered Species (12th series). As Type G 196. Multicoloured.
G476 1f. Asiatic Black Bear (*Ursus thibetanus*) 1·40 1·40
G477 1f. Northern Andean Deer (*Hippocamelus antisensis*) 1·40 1·40
G478 1f. Lion-tailed Macaque (*Macaca silenus*) 1·40 1·40
G479 1f. Guar (*Bos Gaurus*) 1·40 1·40

2004. Indigenous Art (2nd series). Sheet 125×96 mm. As T 550. Multicoloured.
MSG480 1f.×6, Cow's decorative headgear, Switzerland; Seated woman (sculpture), Cirna Woda, Romania; Butter pats, France; Herald's embroidered tabard, United Kingdom; Medieval woodcut, Cologne; Mother and child (sculpture), Drenovac, Serbia & Montenegro 9·00 9·00

G418 Hand enclosing Pedestrian (pedestrians awareness campaign)

2004. Road Safety Campaign. Multicoloured.
G481 85c. Type G **418** 1·20 1·20
G482 1f. Seatbelt enclosing Body as Map (seatbelt campaign) (vert) 1·50 1·50

2004. 50th Anniv of Japanese Peace Bell. As Type 567. Multicoloured.
G483 1f.30 Peace Bell, United Nations Headquarters, New York 1·90 1·90

2004. World Heritage Sites in Greece. As T 577. Multicoloured.
G484 20c. Acropolis, Athens 45 45
G485 20c. Ruins, Delphi 45 45
G486 20c. Tunnel, Olympia 45 45
G487 50c. Lions, Delos 95 95
G488 50c. Pythagoreion and Heraion, Samos 95 95
G489 50c. Relief, Mycenae and Tiryns 95 95
G490 1f. As No. G485 1·50 1·50
G491 1f.30 As No. G488 1·90 1·90
Nos. G484/G491 have lake bands at left and bottom edges.

G427 Globe as Face enclosed in Dove and Hands (Anggun Sita Rustinya)

2004. Winning Designs in Children's Painting Competition "My Dream of Peace". Multicoloured.
G492 85c. Type G **427** 1·30 1·30
G493 1f.20 Woman with hair of doves (Amanda Nunez) 1·70 1·70

G429 Woman holding Blue Rose and Musicians

2004. International Decade of Human Rights' Education. Multicoloured.
G494 85c. Type G **429** 1·30 1·30
G495 1f.30 Family and large blue rose 1·90 1·90
The stamps of United Nations Headquarters in New York, Geneva and Vienna form a composite design.

2005. 60th Anniv of United Nations. As T 588.
G496 **588** 1f.30 multicoloured 2·00 2·00
MSG497 100×80 mm. **588** 3f. multicoloured. Imperf 5·25 5·25
Nos. G496/**MS**G497 have lilac borders.

2005. Endangered Species (13th series). As T 589. Multicoloured.
G498 1f. *Laelia milleri* 1·50 1·50
G499 1f. *Psygmorchis pusilla* 1·50 1·50
G500 1f. *Dendrobium cruentum* 1·50 1·50
G501 1f. *Orchis purpurea* 1·50 1·50

G436 Children collecting Water, India

2005. EXPO 2005 World Exhibition, Aichi, Japan. Multicoloured.
G502 **G436** 1f. Type G **436** 1·60 1·60
G503 **G436** 1f.30 *Ophioderma rubicundum*, Bahamas 2·10 2·10

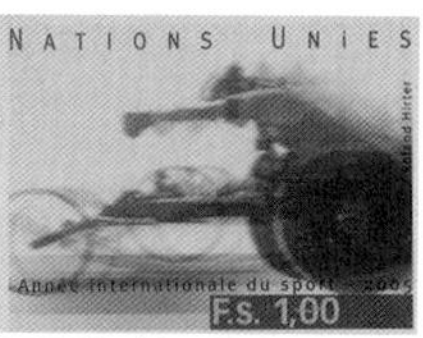

G438 Wheelchair Racer

2005. International Year of Sport. Multicoloured.
G504 1f. Type G **438** 1·60 1·60
G505 1f.30 Cyclists 2·10 2·10

2005. World Heritage. Egypt. As T 577. Multicoloured.
G506 20c. Sphinx, Necropolis, Memphis 35 35
G507 20c. Castle, Philae 35 35
G508 20c. Abu Mena 35 35
G509 50c. Head, Necropolis, Thebes 80 80
G510 50c. Mosque, Cairo 80 80
G511 50c. Saint Catherine Monastery 80 80
G512 1f. Castle, Philae 1·60 1·60
G513 1f.30 Mosque, Cairo 2·10 2·10

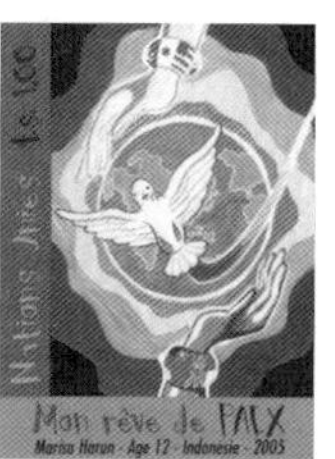

G446 Hands enclosing Globe and Dove (Marisa Harun)

2005. My Dream of Peace One Day. Winning Designs in Children's Painting Competition. Multicoloured.
G514 1f. Type G **446** 1·50 1·50
G515 1f.30 Globe and flags as dream-catcher (Carlos Teixido) 2·00 2·00

G448 Food Aid Delivery by Aircraft and Camels

2005. Food for Life.
G516 **G448** 1f. black, red and blue 1·50 1·50
G517 - 1f.30 black, red and blue 2·00 2·00
DESIGN: Women and lorries carrying food.

2006. Indigenous Art (3rd series). Musical Instruments. Sheet 125×96 mm. As T **550**. Multicoloured
MSG518 1f.20×6, Horse head bell, Benin; Drum, Swaziland; Stringed instrument (Sanza), Congo; Stringed instruments (Cavaquinho and Cimbo), Cape Verde; Gourd Caixixi, Ghana; General De Gaulle shaped bells, Central African Republic 10·50 10·50

G451 Armillary Sphere, Geneva Headquarters

2006
G519 **G451** 1f.30 multicoloured 2·10 2·10

2006. Endangered Species (14th series). As T 589. Multicoloured.
G520 1f. Tomato frog 1·50 1·50
G521 1f. Flap-necked chameleon 1·50 1·50
G522 1f. Emerald tree boa 1·50 1·50
G523 1f. Golfodulcean poison frog 1·50 1·50

G456 Family reading

2006. International Day of Families. Multicoloured.
G524 1f. Type G **456** 1·50 1·50
G525 1f.30 Family riding Motor Scooter 2·00 2·00

2006. World Heritage. France. As T 615.
G526 20c. Banks of the Seine 35 35
G527 20c. Provins 35 35
G528 20c. Carcassonne 35 35
G530 50c. Mont Saint Michel 80 80
G531 50c. Chateau de Chambord 80 80
G532 1f. Provins 1·50 1·50
G533 1f.30 Mont Saint Michel 2·00 2·00
G529 50c. Roman Aqueduct 60 60

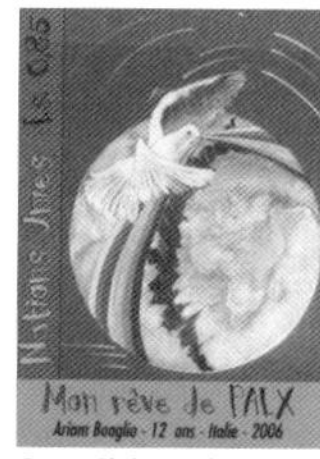

G464 Globe and Dove (Ariam Boaglio)

2006. My Dream of Peace One Day. Winning Designs in Children's Painting Competition. Multicoloured.
G534 85c. Type G **464** 1·40 1·40
G535 1f.20 Dove with Flag covered Chicks (Sierra Spicer) 1·80 1·80

G466 Uganda

2006. Coins and Flags of Member Countries (1st series). Multicoloured.
G536 85c. Type G **466** 1·30 1·30
G537 85c. Luxembourg 1·30 1·30
G538 85c. Italy 1·30 1·30
G539 85c. New Zealand 1·30 1·30
G540 85c. Cape Verde 1·30 1·30
G541 85c. Belgium 1·30 1·30
G542 85c. Switzerland 1·30 1·30
G543 85c. Lebanon 1·30 1·30
See also Nos. G548/55.

2006. Endangered Species (15th series). As T 589. Multicoloured.
G544 1f. Gelada baboon (*Theropithecus gelada*) 1·50 1·50
G545 1f. De Brazza's monkey (*Cercopithecus neglectus*) 1·50 1·50
G546 1f. Ruffed lemur (*Varecia varigata*) 1·50 1·50
G547 1f. Javan gibbon (*Hylobates moloch*) 1·50 1·50

2007. Coins and Flags of Member Countries (2nd series). As Type G 466. Multicoloured.
G548 85c. Burkina Faso 1·30 1·30
G549 85c. France 1·30 1·30
G550 85c. Bolivia 1·30 1·30
G551 85c. Myanmar 1·30 1·30
G552 85c. Moldova 1·30 1·30
G553 85c. Papua New Guinea 1·30 1·30
G554 85c. Mali 1·30 1·30
G555 85c. Tunisia 1·30 1·30

G486 Women with Apples

2007. Peaceful Visions. Multicoloured.

G556	1f.20 Type G **486**	1·70	1·70
G557	1f.80 Women with Doves	2·75	2·75

2007. World Heritage Sites. South America. As T 645. Multicoloured.

G558	20c. Tiwanaku, Bolivia	35	35
G559	20c. Iguacu, Brazil	35	35
G560	20c. Galapagos Islands	35	35
G561	50c. Rapa Nui, Chile	80	80
G562	50c. Cueva de las Manos, Argentina	80	80
G563	50c. Machu Pichu, Peru	80	80
G564	1f. Tiwanaku, Bolivia	1·50	1·50
G565	1f.80 Machu Pichu, Peru	2·50	2·50

2007. Humanitarian Mail. As T 652. Mulricoloured.

G566	1f.80 Flying postman and hands	2·50	2·50

2007. 50th Anniv of Space Exploration. As T 653. Multicoloured.

G567	1f. Astronaut	1·50	1·50
G568	1f.80 Jupiter and spacecraft	2·50	2·50
MSG569	100×80 mm. 3f. Space walk	4·25	4·25

2008. International Holocaust Remembrance Day. As T 656. Multicoloured.

G570	85c. Barbed wire becoming flowers	1·30	1·30

A stamp of a similar design was issued by Israel.

2008. Endangered Species (16th series). As T 589. Multicoloured.

G571	1f. Pacific walrus (*Odobenus rosmarus*)	1·50	1·50
G572	1f. Brain coral (*Platygyra daedalea*)	1·50	1·50
G573	1f. Pygmy seahorse (*Hippocampus bargibanti*)	1·50	1·50
G574	1f. Beluga whale (*Delphinapterus leucas*)	1·50	1·50

2008. Coins and Flags of Member Countries (3rd series). As T G466. Multicoloured.

G575	85c. Madagascar	1·30	1·30
G576	85c. Rwanda	1·30	1·30
G577	85c. Nambia	1·30	1·30
G578	85c. Maldives	1·30	1·30
G579	85c. Benin	1·30	1·30
G580	85c. Iran	1·30	1·30
G581	85c. Albania	1·30	1·30
G582	85c. Turkey	1·30	1·30

2008. Convention on the Rights of People with Disablities. As T 669. Multicoloured.

G583	1f. Rein a Notre Sujet Sans	1·80	1·80
G584	1f.80 Rein a Notre Sujet Sans	3·25	2·25

2008. Olympic Games, Beijing. As T 671. Multicoloured.

G585	1f. Gymnastics	1·80	1·80
G586	1f.80 Tennis	3·25	3·25
MSG587	92×83 mm. As No 1035	5·25	5·25

G 515 Reading and Education (Ranajoy Banerjee)

2008. We Can End Poverty. Winning Designs in Children's Painting Competition. Multicoloured.

G588	1f. Type G **515**	1·80	1·80
G589	1f.80 Children sharing (Elizabeth Elaine Chun Ning Au)	3·25	3·25

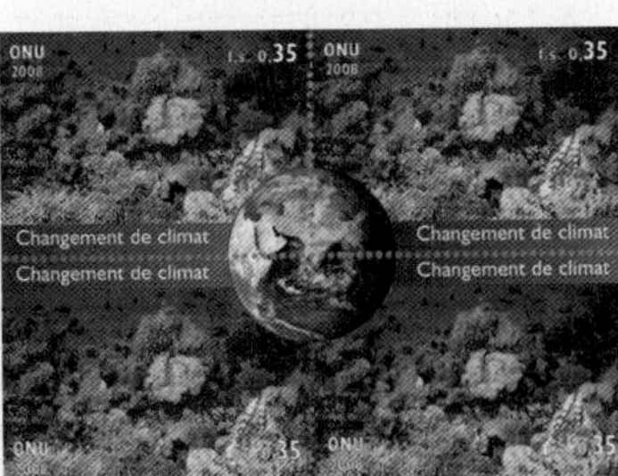

G 517a/d Coral Reef (image scaled to 49% of original size)

G 518a/d (image scaled to 49% of original size)

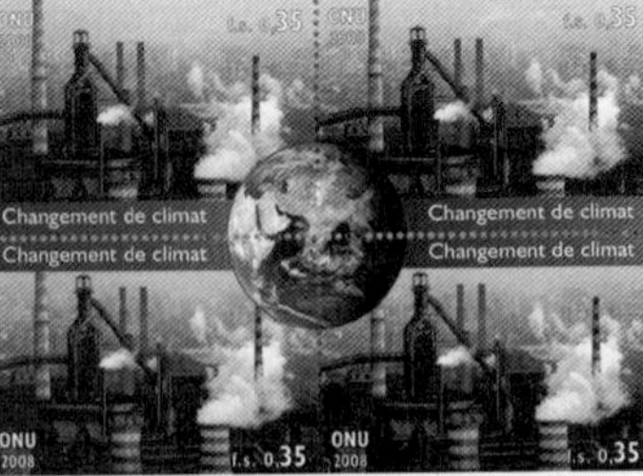

G 519a/d Pollution (image scaled to 49% of original size)

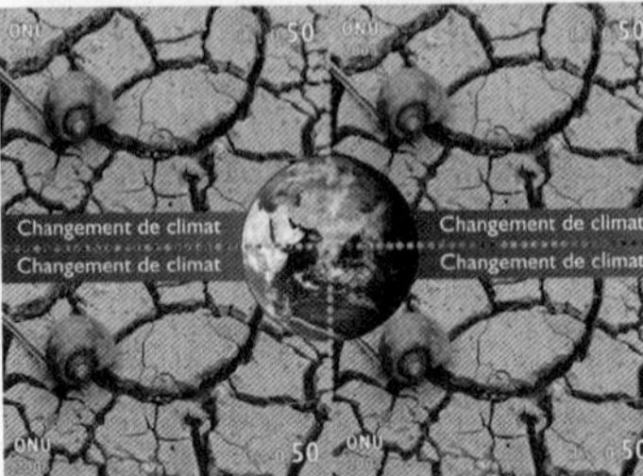

G 520a/d Desert (image scaled to 49% of original size)

G 521a/d Polar Bear (image scaled to 49% of original size)

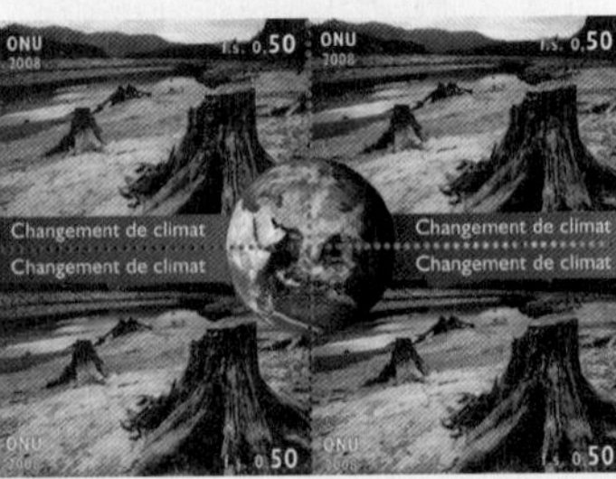

G 522a/d Deforestation (image scaled to 49% of original size)

2008. Action on Climate Change.

G590	**G517a** 35c. multicoloured	70	70
G591	**G517b** 35c. Ice Floes	70	70
G592	**G517c** 35c. multicoloured	70	70
G593	**G517d** 35c. multicoloured	70	70
G594	**G518a** 35c. multicoloured	70	70
G595	**G518b** 35c. multicoloured	70	70
G596	**G518c** 35c. multicoloured	70	70
G597	**G518d** 35c. multicoloured	70	70
G598	**G519a** 35c. multicoloured	70	70
G599	**G519b** 35c. multicoloured	70	70
G600	**G519c** 35c. multicoloured	70	70
G601	**G519d** 35c. multicoloured	70	70
G602	**G520a** 50c. multicoloured	85	85
G603	**G520b** 50c. multicoloured	85	85
G604	**G520c** 50c. multicoloured	85	85
G605	**G520d** 50c. multicoloured	85	85
G606	**G521a** 50c. multicoloured	85	85
G607	**G521b** 50c. multicoloured	85	85
G608	**G521c** 50c. multicoloured	85	85
G609	**G521d** 50c. multicoloured	85	85
G610	**G522a** 50c. multicoloured	85	85
G611	**G522b** 50c. multicoloured	85	85
G612	**G522c** 50c. multicoloured	85	85
G613	**G522d** 50c. multicoloured	85	85
MSG614	120×90 mm. 1f.20×4, As Type **G 521a/d** (Polar bear)	10·00	10·00
MSG615	120×90 mm. 1f.80×4, As Type **G 518a/d** (Ice floes)	14·00	14·00

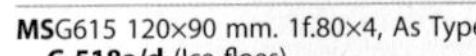

G 523 U Thant

2009. Birth Centenary of U Thant (United Nations Secretary General 1961–1971).

G616	**G 523** 1f.30 multicoloured	3·00	3·00

G 524 *Maculinea arion* (Large blue butterfly)

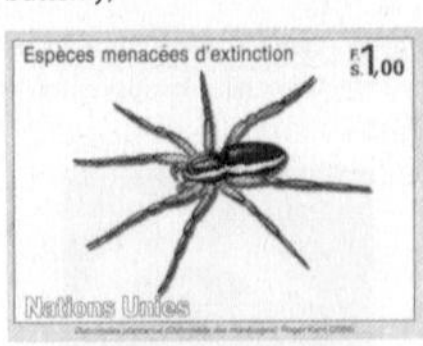

G 525 *Dolomedes plantarius* (Fen raft spider)

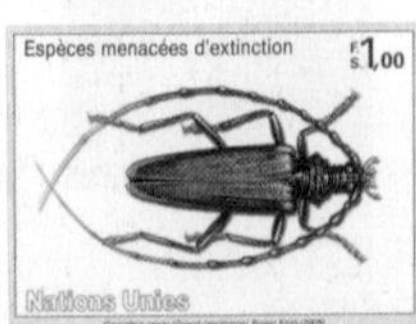

G 526 *Cerambyx cerdo* (Great Capricorn beetle)

G 527 *Coenagrion mercuriale* (Southern damselfly)

2009. Endangered Species (17th series).

G617	**G 524** 1f. multicoloured	1·80	1·80
G618	**G 525** 1f. multicoloured	1·80	1·80
G619	**G 526** 1f. multicoloured	1·80	1·80
G620	**G 527** 1f. multicoloured	1·80	1·80

2009. World Heritage Sites. Germany. As T 689. Multicoloured.

G621	30c. Town Hall and Roland on the Marketplace of Bremen	70	70
G622	30c. Wartburg Castle	70	70
G623	30c. Palaces and Parks of Potsdam and Berlin	70	70
G624	50c. Aachen Cathedral (Cathedrale d'Aix-la-Chapelle)	85	85
G625	50c. Monastic Island of Reichenau	85	85
G626	50c. Luther Memorials in Eisleben and Wittenberg	85	85
G627	1f. As N0. G622	1·80	1·80
G628	1f.30 As No. G625	2·30	2·30

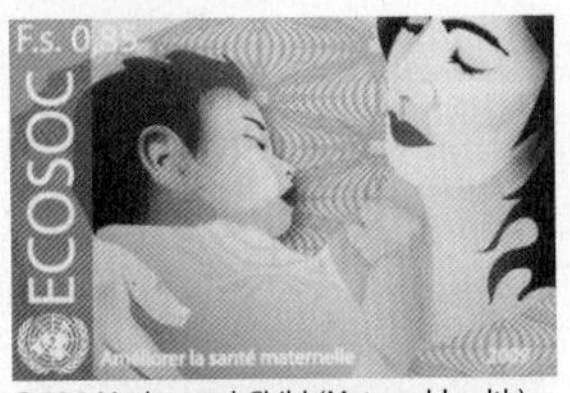

G 534 Mother and Child (Maternal health)

2009. United Nations Economic and Social Council (ECOSOC). Multicoloured.

G629	85c. Type G**534**	1·50	1·50
G630	1f.80 Vaccination (Access to essential medicines)	3·25	3·25

2009. Millennium Development Goals. As Type 697.

G631	1f.30 chrome-yellow, black and red	1·90	1·90
G632	1f.30 bright yellow-green, black and red	1·90	1·90
G633	1f.30 orange-red, black and red	1·90	1·90
G634	1f.30 pale turquoise-blue, black and red	1·90	1·90
G635	1f.30 pale bright rose, black and red	1·90	1·90
G636	1f.30 scarlet-vermilion, black and red	1·90	1·90
G637	1f.30 apple-green, black and red	1·90	1·90
G638	1f.30 blue, black and red	1·90	1·90

DESIGNS: No. G631, Bowl of food (Eradicate extreme poverty and hunger), No. G631, Pencil (Achieve universal primary education), G632, Pencil (Achieve universal primary education); No. G633; Female symbol (Promote gender equality and empower women), No. G634, Teddy bear (Reduce child mortality); No. G635, Female figure enclosing heart (Improve maternal health); No. G636, Medicine jar (Combat HIV/AIDS, malaria and other diseases); No. G637, Stylized Tree (Ensure environmental sustainability); No. G638, Stylized figures (Develop a global partnership for development).

G 544 New Caledonia

2009. Indigenous Peoples. Mmulticoloured.

G639	1f.30 Type G **544**	1·90	1·90
G640	1f.30 Namibia	1·90	1·90
G641	1f.30 Namibia (different)	1·90	1·90
G642	1f.30 United Republic of Tanzania	1·90	1·90
G643	1f.30 Thailand	1·90	1·90
G644	1f.30 French Polynesia	1·90	1·90

G 550 Equatorial Guinea

2010. Coins and Flags of Member Countries (4th series). Multicoloured.

G645	85c. Type G **550**	1·50	1·50
G646	85c. Laos	1·50	1·50
G647	85c. Argentine	1·50	1·50
G648	85c. Morocco	1·50	1·50
G649	85c. Seychelles	1·50	1·50
G650	85c. Mauritania	1·50	1·50
G651	85c. Sudan	1·50	1·50
G652	85c. Brunei Darussalam	1·50	1·50

C. VIENNA HEADQUARTERS.

For use on mail posted at the United Nations Vienna International Centre and by the International Atomic Energy Agency.

NOTE. Reference to numbers and types in this section, other than those with a "V" prefix, are to the United Nations (New York or Geneva) Headquarters listing. Designs adapted for the Vienna issues are inscribed in Austrian and have face values in schillings.

V4 Donaupark Complex

1979. Some designs adapted from issues of New York or Geneva Headquarters. Multicoloured.

V1	50g. Type **G53**	10	10
V2	1s. As No. 94	20	20
V3	2s.50 Type **162**	40	40
V3a	3s. "... for a better world"	45	45
V4	4s. Type **V4**	55	55
V5	5s. Birds in flight	55	55
V6	6s. Aerial view of Donaupark (vert)	65	65
V7	10s. As Type **52**, but without frame	1·10	1·10

1980. New International Economic Order.

V8	**195** 4s. multicoloured	85	85

V9 Dove and World Map

1980. U.N. Decade for Women.
V9 **V9** 4s. multicoloured 55 45
V10 **V9** 6s. multicoloured 75 75

V10 "Peace-keeping"

1980. Peace-keeping Operations.
V11 **V10** 6s. multicoloured 85 85

V11 Dove and "35"

1980. 35th Anniv of U.N.O.
V12 **V11** 4s. black and red 55 55
V13 - 6s. multicoloured 85 85
MSV14 92×73 mm. Nos. V12/13. Imperf 1·40 1·40
DESIGN: 6s. Stylized flower.

V13 Economic and Social Emblems

1980. Economic and Social Council. Multicoloured.
V15 **V13** 4s. multicoloured 55 55
V16 - 6s. green, red and black 85 85
DESIGN: 6s. Figures ascending graph.

1981. "Inalienable Rights of the Palestinian People".
V17 **206** 4s. multicoloured 55 55

1981. International Year of Disabled Persons.
V18 **207** 4s. multicoloured 55 55
V19 - 6s. orange and black 75 75
DESIGN: 6s. Knot pattern.

1981. Art.
V20 **209** 6s. multicoloured 75 75

V19 U.N. Energy Conference Emblem

1981. New and Renewable Sources of Energy.
V21 **V19** 7s.50 gold and mauve 85 85

V20 Symbols of Services

1981. 10th Anniv of U.N. Volunteers Programme. Multicoloured.
V22 5s. Type V **20** 55 55
V23 7s. Emblems of science, agriculture and industry 85 85

V22 Symbols of the Environment

1982. Human Environment. Multicoloured.
V24 5s. Type V **22** 55 55
V25 7s. Leaves 85 85

V24 Satellite and Emblems

1982. Second United Nations Conference on Exploration and Peaceful Uses of Outer Space.
V26 **V24** 5s. multicoloured 75 75

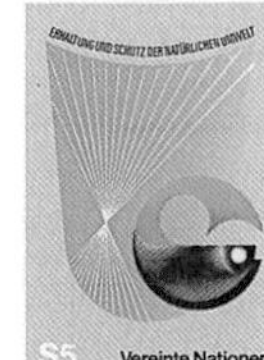

V25 Fish

1982. Conservation and Protection of Nature. Multicoloured.
V27 5s. Type V **25** 55 55
V28 7s. Elephant (mammals) 85 85

1983. World Communications Year.
V29 **222** 4s. multicoloured 55 55

V28 Radar Screen within Lifebelt

1983. Safety at Sea: International Maritime Organization. Multicoloured.
V30 4s. Type V **28** 55 55
V31 6s. Stylized liner 75 75

1983. World Food Programme.
V32 **226** 5s. green 55 55
V33 **226** 7s. brown 85 85

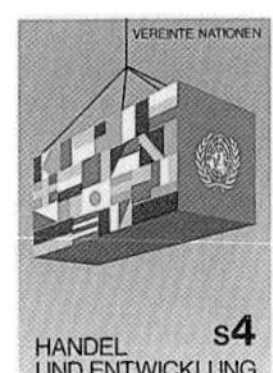

V31 Exports

1983. Trade and Development. Multicoloured.
V34 5s. Type V **31** 55 55
V35 8s.50 Emblems of trade 1·10 1·10

V33 "Die Zweite Haut"

1983. 35th Anniv of Declaration of Human Rights. Multicoloured.
V36 5s. Type V **33** 85 85
V37 7s. "Recht auf Traume" 1·10 1·10

V35 World Agriculture

1984. International Conference on Population, Mexico City.
V38 **V35** 7s. multicoloured 1·10 1·10

V36 Irrigation

1984. World Food Day. Multicoloured.
V39 4s.50 Type V **36** 65 65
V40 6s. Combine harvesters 85 85

V38 Serengeti National Park, Tanzania

1984. World Heritage—UNESCO. Mult.
V41 3s.50 Type V **38** 55 55
V42 15s. Schibam, Yemen 1·70 1·70

V40 Woman with Child

1984. Future for Refugees.
V43 **V40** 4s.50 black and brown 65 65
V44 - 8s.50 black and yellow 1·10 1·10
DESIGN: 8s.50, Woman.

V42 Stylized Figures

1984. International Youth Year.
V45 **V42** 3s.50 multicoloured 45 45
V46 **V42** 6s.50 multicoloured 95 95

V43 U Thant Pavilion

1985. 20th Anniv of Turin Centre of International Labour Organization.
V47 **V43** 7s.50 violet 95 95

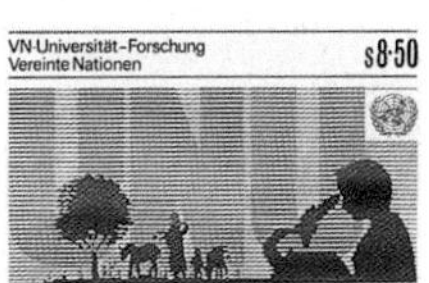

V44 Rural Scene and Researcher with Microscope

1985. 10th Anniv of United Nations University, Tokyo.
V48 **V44** 8s.50 multicoloured 1·10 1·10

V45 "Boat"

1985. Multicoloured.. Multicoloured..
V49 4s.50 Type V **45** 55 55
V50 15s. Sheltering under U.N. umbrella 1·60 1·60

1985. 40th Anniv of United Nations Organization. Multicoloured.
V51 6s.50 Type **243** 85 85
V52 8s.50 "Harvest Scene" (Andrew Wyeth) 1·10 1·10

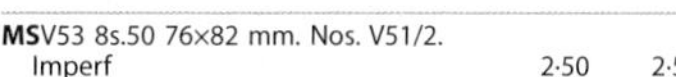
MSV53 8s.50 76×82 mm. Nos. V51/2. Imperf 2·50 2·50

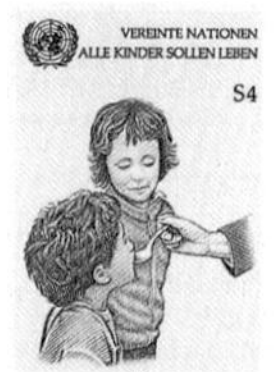

V49 Oral Immunization

1985. UNICEF. Child Survival Campaign. Multicoloured.
V54 4s. Type V **49** 75 75
V55 6s. Mother and baby 95 95

V51 "Africa in Crisis"

1986. "Africa in Crisis".
V56 **V51** 8s. multicoloured 1·10 1·10

V52 Growing Crops

1986. Development Programme. Village Scene. Multicoloured.
V57 4s.50 Type V **52** 1·10 1·10
V58 4s.50 Villagers with livestock 1·10 1·10
V59 4s.50 Woodwork instructor 1·10 1·10
V60 4s.50 Nutrition instructor 1·10 1·10
Nos. V57/60 were issued together, se-tenant, forming a composite design.

V56 United Nations Stamps

1986. Philately: The International Hobby.
V61 **V56** 3s.50 blue and brown 65 65
V62 - 6s.50 blue and red 1·10 1·10
DESIGN: 6s.50, Engraver.

V58 Olive Branch and Rainbow

1986. International Peace Year. Multicoloured.
V63 5s. Type V **58** 75 75
V64 6s. Doves on U.N. emblem 85 85

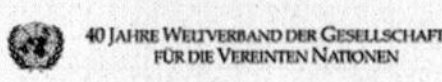

V60 (image scaled to 40% of original size)

1986. 40th Anniv of World Federation of United Nations Associations Sheet 120×65 mm. Multicoloured.
MSV65 V **60** 4s. Horse's head (Elisabeth von Janota-Bzowski; 5s. Horse rider carved from rock face (Ernst Fuchs); 6s. Abstract (Victor Vassrely); 7s. Couple (Wolfgang Hutter) 4·00 4·00

1986. 9th Death Anniv of Trygve Lie (first U.N. Secretary-General).
V66 **259** 8s. multicoloured 1·30 1·30

V62 Family looking at New Houses

1987. International Year of Shelter for the Homeless.

V67	**V62**	4s. orange, blk & yell	65	65
V68	-	9s.50 orange and black	1·50	1·50

DESIGN: 9s.50, Family entering door of new house.

V64 Footballers

1987. Anti-drugs Campaign. Multicoloured.

V69	5s. Type V **64**	85	85
V70	8s. Family	1·30	1·30

V66 U.N. Centre, Vienna

1987. Multicoloured.. Multicoloured..

V71	2s. Type V **66**	30	30
V72	17s. Wreath of olive leaves and doves around globe	1·80	1·80

V68 Dancers and Vienna Headquarters

1987. United Nations Day. Multicoloured.

V73	5s. Type V **68**	75	75
V74	6s. Dancers	85	85

V70 Poliomyelitis

1987. "Immunize Every Child". Multicoloured.

V75	4s. Type V **70**	75	75
V76	9s.50 Diphtheria	1·60	1·60

V72 Woman planting

1987. International Fund for Agricultural Development "For a World without Hunger" Campaign. Multicoloured.

V77	4s. Type V **72**	75	75
V78	6s. Women and foodstuffs	1·10	1·10

V74 Hills and Forest in Autumn

1988. "Survival of the Forests". Multicoloured.

V79	4s. Type V **74**	2·75	2·75
V80	5s. Forest in autumn	3·25	3·25

Nos. V79/80 were issued together, se-tenant, forming a composite design.

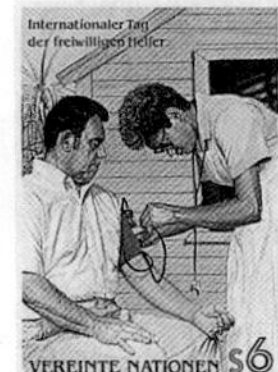

V76 Testing Blood Pressure

1988. International Volunteer Day. Multicoloured.

V81	6s. Type V **76**	85	85
V82	7s.50 Building houses (horiz)	1·30	1·30

V78 Skiing

1988. "Health in Sports". Multicoloured.

V83	6s. Type V **78**	85	85
V84	8s. Tennis (horiz)	1·30	1·30

1988. 40th Anniv of Declaration of Human Rights.

V85	**276**	5s. multicoloured	85	85
MSV86		120×79 mm. 11s. multicoloured	2·20	2·20

V81 Transport

1989. World Bank. Multicoloured.

V87	5s.50 Type V **81**	85	85
V88	8s. Health and education	1·50	1·50

1989. Award of Nobel Peace Prize to United Nations Peace-keeping Forces.

V89	**280**	6s. multicoloured	85	85

V84 Depression over Italy

1989. 25th Anniv of World Weather Watch.

V90		4s. Type V **84**	75	75
V91		9s.50 Short-range rainfall forecast for Tokyo	1·70	1·70

V86 Man in Winter Clothes

1989. 10th Anniv of United Nations Vienna International Centre. Multicoloured.

V92	5s. Type V **86**	85	85
V93	7s.50 Abstract	1·30	1·30

V88 "Prisoners" (Kathe Kollwitz) (Article 5)

1989. Universal Declaration of Human Rights (1st series).

V94	**V88**	4s. black	65	65
V95	-	6s. multicoloured	85	85

DESIGN: 6s. "Jurisprudence" (Raphael) (Article 6).

See also Nos. V107/8, V122/3, V138/9 and V149/150.

1990. International Trade Centre.

V96	**287**	12s. multicoloured	1·70	1·70

V91 "Earth" (painting by Kurt Regschek in I.A.E.A. Building)

1990

V97	**V91**	1s.50 multicoloured	40	40

1990. Anti-AIDS Campaign. Multicoloured.

V98	5s. Type **289**	85	85
V99	11s. Attacking infected blood	1·80	1·80

V94 Annatto

1990. Medicinal Plants. Multicoloured.

V100	4s.50 Type V **94**	85	85
V101	9s.50 Cundeamor	1·70	1·70

V96 "45"

1990. 45th Anniv of U.N.O. Multicoloured.

V102	7s. Type V **96**	1·20	1·20
V103	9s. "45" (different)	1·50	1·50
MSV104	100×73 mm. Nos. V102/3	3·75	3·75

V98 Men fighting

1990. Crime Prevention. Multicoloured.

V105	6s. Type V **98**	1·10	1·10
V106	8s. Masked man damaging painting	1·50	1·50

1990. Universal Declaration of Human Rights (2nd series). As Type V 88. Multicoloured.

V107	4s.50 "Before the Judge" (Sandor Bihari) (Article 11)	75	75
V108	7s. "Young Man greeted by Woman writing Poem" (Suzuki Harunobu) (Article 12)	1·10	1·10

V102/105 Mediterranean Coastline and Wildlife (image scaled to 68% of original size)

1991. Economic Commission for Europe. "For a Better Environment".

V109	**V102**	5s. multicoloured	95	95
V110	**V103**	5s. multicoloured	95	95
V111	**V104**	5s. multicoloured	95	95
V112	**V105**	5s. multicoloured	95	95

Nos. V109/12 were issued together, se-tenant, forming the composite design illustrated.

V106 Scrubland

1991. 1st Anniv of Namibian Independence. Multicoloured.

V113	6s. Type V **106**	1·10	1·10
V114	9s.50 Sand dune	1·70	1·70

V108 Different Races

1991

V115	**V108**	20s. multicoloured	2·75	2·75

V109 Boy and Girl (Anna Harmer)

1991. 30th Anniv (1989) of U.N. Declaration of the Rights of the Child and 1990 World Summit on Children, New York. Children's Drawings. Multicoloured.

V116	7s. Type V **109**	1·20	1·20
V117	9s. Child's world (Emiko Takegawa)	1·60	1·60

V111 City, Bubbles of Toxin and Gas Mask

1991. Banning of Chemical Weapons. Mult.

V118	5s. Type V **111**	85	85
V119	10s. Hand pushing back cloud of toxin sprayed from airplane	1·80	1·80

V113 U.N. (New York) 1951 20c. Stamp

1991. 40th Anniv of United Nations Postal Administration.

V120	**V113**	5s. brown on cream	85	85
V121	-	8s. blue on cream	1·30	1·30

DESIGN: 8s. U.N. (New York) 1951 5c. stamp.

1991. Declaration of Human Rights (3rd series). As Type V 88. Multicoloured.

V122	4s.50 Ancient Mexican pottery (Article 17)	85	85
V123	7s. "Windows, 1912" (Robert Delaunay) (Article 18)	1·30	1·30

V117 Iguacu National Park, Brazil

1992. 20th Anniv of UNESCO. World Heritage Convention. Multicoloured.

V124	5s. Type V **117**	95	95
V125	9s. Abu Simbel, Egypt	1·70	1·70

V119/120 Sea Life

1992. "Clean Oceans".

V126	**V119**	7s. multicoloured	1·20	1·20
V127	**V120**	7s. multicoloured	1·20	1·20

Nos. V126/7 were issued together, se-tenant, forming the composite design illustrated.

V121/124 Planet Earth (image scaled to 73% of original size)

1992. 2nd U.N. Conference on Environment and Development, Rio de Janeiro.

V128	**V121**	5s.50 multicoloured	1·20	1·20
V129	**V122**	5s.50 multicoloured	1·20	1·20
V130	**V123**	5s.50 multicoloured	1·20	1·20
V131	**V124**	5s.50 multicoloured	1·20	1·20

Nos. V128/131 were issued together, se-tenant, forming the composite design illustrated.

V125/126 "Mission Planet Earth" (image scaled to 67% of original size)

1992. International Space Year

V132	**V125**	10s. multicoloured	1·90	1·90
V133	**V126**	10s. multicoloured	1·90	1·90

Nos. V132/3 were printed together, se-tenant, forming the composite design illustrated.

V127 Woman with Book emerging from V.D.U.

1992. Commission on Science and Technology for Development. Multicoloured.

V134	5s.50 Type V **127**	1·10	1·10
V135	7s. Flowers growing from thumb	1·30	1·30

V129 Woman's Profile, Birds, Butterfly and Rose

1992. Painting. Multicoloured.

V136	5s.50 Type V **129**	85	85
V137	7s. Vienna International Centre (horiz)	1·30	1·30

1992. Universal Declaration of Human Rights (4th series). As Type V 88. Multicoloured.

V138	6s. "The Builders" (Fernand Leger) (Article 23)	1·20	1·20
V139	10s. "Sunday Afternoon on the Island of La Grande Jatte" (Georges Seurat) (Article 24)	1·60	1·60

V133 Housing and Environment

1993. "Ageing: Dignity and Participation". 10th Anniv (1992) of International Plan of Action on Ageing. Multicoloured.

V140	5s.50 Type V **133**	1·20	1·20
V141	7s. Education	1·50	1·50

V135 Grevy's Zebra

1993. Endangered Species (1st series). Multicoloured.

V142	7s. Type V **135**	1·20	1·20
V143	7s. Humboldt penguin ("Spheniscus humboldti")	1·20	1·20
V144	7s. Desert monitor ("Varanus griseus")	1·20	1·20
V145	7s. Wolf ("Canis lupus")	1·20	1·20

See also Nos. V161/4, V179/82, V205/8, V223/6, V249/52, V288/91, V304/7, V324/7, V353/6, V398/401 and V442/5.

V139 Globe, Doves and U.N. Emblem

1993

V146	**V139**	13s. multicoloured	2·20	2·20

V140 Regional and National Environment

1993. 45th Anniv of W.H.O. Multicoloured.

V147	6s. Type V **140**	1·10	1·10
V148	10s. Continental and global environment	1·60	1·60

1993. Declaration of Human Rights (5th series). As Type V 88. Multicoloured.

V149	5s. "Lower Austrian Peasants' Wedding" (Ferdinand Waldmuller) (Article 29)	1·10	1·10
V150	6s. "Outback" (Sally Morgan) (Article 30)	1·30	1·30

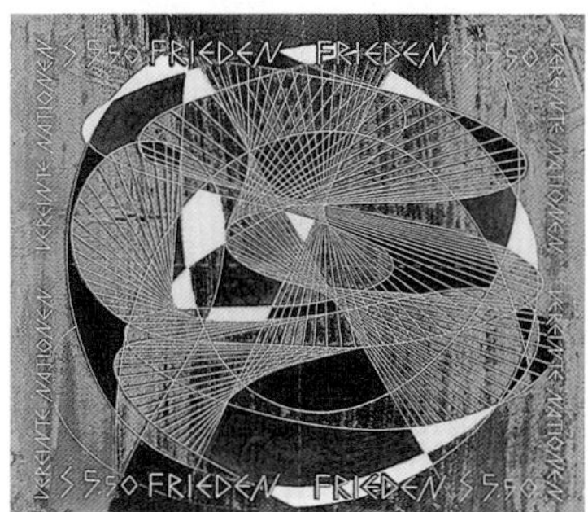

V144/147 Peace (image scaled to 74% of original size)

1993. International Peace Day. Roul.

V151	**V144**	5s.50 multicoloured	95	95
V152	**V145**	5s.50 multicoloured	95	95
V153	**V146**	5s.50 multicoloured	95	95
V154	**V147**	5s.50 multicoloured	95	95

Nos V151/4 were issued together, se-tenant, forming the composite design illustrated.

V148 Monkeys

1993. The Environment—Climate. Multicoloured.

V155	7s. Type V **148**	1·40	1·40
V156	7s. Eastern bluebird and factory chimneys	1·40	1·40
V157	7s. Volcano, smokestacks and tree stumps	1·40	1·40
V158	7s. Great horned owl in desert	1·40	1·40

Nos. V155/8 were issued together, se-tenant, forming a composite design.

V152 Family holding Hands

1994. International Year of the Family. Mult.

V159	5s.50 Type V **152**	1·10	1·10
V160	8s. Family at work	1·60	1·60

1994. Endangered Species (2nd series). As Type V 135. Multicoloured.

V161	7s. Ocelot ("Felis pardalis")	1·20	1·20
V162	7s. White-crested white eye ("Zosterups albogularis")	1·20	1·20
V163	7s. Mediterranean monk seals ("Monachus monachus")	1·20	1·20
V164	7s. Indian elephant ("Elephas maximus")	1·20	1·20

V158 Tree and Doves

1994. Peace. Multicoloured.

V165	50g. Type V **158**	20	20
V166	4s. Herring gulls	75	75
V167	30s. Globe and dove	5·50	5·50

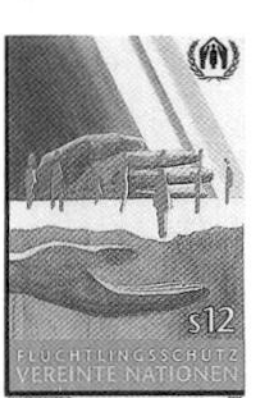

V161 Hands ready to help Refugees

1994. United Nations High Commissioner for Refugees.

V168	**V161**	12s. multicoloured	2·40	2·40

V162/165 Shattered Globe and "Preparation" (image scaled to 70% of original size)

1994. International Decade for Natural Disaster Reduction.

V169	**V162**	6s. multicoloured	1·40	1·40
V170	**V163**	6s. multicoloured	1·40	1·40
V171	**V164**	6s. multicoloured	1·40	1·40
V172	**V165**	6s. multicoloured	1·40	1·40

Nos. V169/72 were issued together, se-tenant, forming the composite design illustrated.

V166 Enhancing Role of Women

1994. International Population and Development Conference, Cairo. Multicoloured.

V173	5s.50 Type V **166**	1·20	1·20
V174	7s. Relationship of population and environment	1·50	1·50

V168 Map and Crossed Ribbons

1994. 30th Anniv of United Nations Conference on Trade and Development. Multicoloured.

V175	6s. Type V **168**	1·30	1·30
V176	7s. Map and ribbons forming star	1·50	1·50

1995. 50th Anniv of U.N.O. (1st issue).

V177	**371**	7s. multicoloured	1·50	1·50

See also Nos. V185/6 and V190/201.

V171 "Social Summit 1995"

1995. World Summit for Social Development, Copenhagen.

V178	**V171**	14s. multicoloured	3·25	3·25

1995. Endangered Species (3rd series). As Type V 135. Multicoloured.

V179	7s. Black rhinoceros ("Diceros bicornis")	1·20	1·20
V180	7s. Golden conure ("Aratinga guarouba")	1·20	1·20
V181	7s. Variegated langur ("Pygathrix nemaeus")	1·20	1·20
V182	7s. Arabian oryx ("Oryx leucoryx")	1·20	1·20

V176 Village in Winter

1995. "Youth: Our Future". 10th Anniv of International Youth Year. Multicoloured.

V183	6s. Type V **176**	1·40	1·40
V184	7s. Wheat stacks in field	1·60	1·60

1995. 50th Anniv of U.N.O. (2nd issue).

V185	**379**	7s. green	1·50	1·50
V186	-	10s. black	1·90	1·90
MSV187 92×70 mm. Nos. V185/6. Imperf			4·25	4·25

DESIGN: 10s. Veterans' Memorial Hall and Opera House, San Francisco (venue for signing of U.N. Charter).

V180 Women in Jungle

1995. 4th World Conference on Women, Peking. Multicoloured.

V188	5s.50 Type V **180**	1·40	1·40

V189	6s. Woman reading book (28×48 mm)	1·50	1·50

1995. 50th Anniv of U.N.O. (3rd issue).

V190	**385** 3s. multicoloured	75	75
V191	**386** 3s. multicoloured	75	75
V192	**387** 3s. multicoloured	75	75
V193	**388** 3s. multicoloured	75	75
V194	**389** 3s. multicoloured	75	75
V195	**390** 3s. multicoloured	75	75
V196	**391** 3s. multicoloured	75	75
V197	**392** 3s. multicoloured	75	75
V198	**393** 3s. multicoloured	75	75
V199	**394** 3s. multicoloured	75	75
V200	**395** 3s. multicoloured	75	75
V201	**396** 3s. multicoloured	75	75

Nos. V190/5 and V196/201 respectively were issued together, se-tenant, forming two composite designs.

V194 Jester holding Dove

1996. 50th Anniv of World Federation of United Nations Associations. Multicoloured.

V202	**V194** 7s. multicoloured	1·30	1·30

V195 U.N. Flag

1996. U.N. Flag. Multicoloured.

V203	1s. Type V **195**	20	20
V204	10s. Abstract painting (Karl Korab)	1·80	1·80

1996. Endangered Species (4th series). As Type V 135. Multicoloured.

V205	7s. Venus slipper orchid ("Cypripedium calceolus")	1·20	1·20
V206	7s. "Aztekium ritteri"	1·20	1·20
V207	7s. "Euphorbia cremersii"	1·20	1·20
V208	7s. "Dracula bella"	1·20	1·20

V201 Family with Agricultural Products

1996. "Habitat II" Second U.N. Conf on Human Settlements, Istanbul, Turkey. Mult.

V209	6s. Type V **201**	1·20	1·20
V210	6s. Women with sacks of grain	1·20	1·20
V211	6s. Woman and city	1·20	1·20
V212	6s. Ploughing with oxen	1·20	1·20
V213	6s. Villlage and elephant	1·20	1·20

Nos. V209/13 were issued together, se-tenant, forming a composite design.

V206 Gymnastics

1996. Sport and the Environment. Multicoloured.

V214	6s. Type V **206**	1·20	1·20
V215	7s. Hurdling	1·60	1·60
MSV216	88×78 mm. Nos. V214/15	3·25	3·25

V208 Dove and Butterflies

1996. "A Plea for Peace". Winners of China Youth Design Competition. Multicoloured.

V217	7s. Type V **208**	1·40	1·40
V218	10s. Children and flowers in dove	2·20	2·20

V210 "Hansel and Gretel" (Brothers Grimm)

1996. 50th Anniv of UNICEF. Children's Stories.

V219	5s.50 Type V **210**	1·10	1·10
V220	8s. "How Maui Stole Fire from the Gods" (Pacific Islands myth)	1·40	1·40

1997. Details of "Phoenixes flying Down" by Sagenji Yoshida. Multicoloured.

V221	5s. Type V **212**	95	95
V222	6s. Green phoenix	1·20	1·20

V212 Red Phoenix

1997. Endangered Species (5th series). As Type V 135. Multicoloured.

V223	7s. Barbary ape ("Macaca sylvanus")	1·30	1·30
V224	7s. Stanley crane ("Anthropoides paradisea")	1·30	1·30
V225	7s. Przewalski's horse ("Equus przewalskii")	1·30	1·30
V226	7s. Giant anteater ("Myrmecophaga tridactyla")	1·30	1·30

V218/221 River Scene (image scaled to 68% of original size)

1997. "Earth Summit + 5". 5th Anniv of United Nations Conference on Environment and Development.

V227	**V218** 3s.50 multicoloured	85	85
V228	**V219** 3s.50 multicoloured	85	85
V229	**V220** 3s.50 multicoloured	85	85
V230	**V221** 3s.50 multicoloured	85	85
MSV231	V **231** 90×75 mm. 11s. Motifs as Nos. V227/30. Imperf	3·50	3·50

Nos. V227/30 were issued together, se-tenant, forming the composite design illustrated.

V222 Stephenson's Locomotive "Rocket" and Darraque Motor Car (1901)

1997. 50th Anniversaries of Economic Commission for Europe and Economic and Social Commission for Asia and the Pacific. Multicoloured.

V232	7s. Type V **222**	1·30	1·30
V233	7s. Russian steam locomotive and American streetcar	1·30	1·30
V234	7s. Diesel train and British double-decker bus	1·30	1·30
V235	7s. Diesel locomotive and articulated trailer lorry	1·30	1·30
V236	7s. High speed electric train and electric-powered car	1·30	1·30

Nos. V232/6 were issued together, se-tenant, forming a composite design.

V227 1986 3s.50 Philately Stamp

1997. "Tribute to Philately". Multicoloured.

V237	6s.50 Type V **227**	1·10	1·10
V238	7s. 1986 6s.50 Philately stamp	1·30	1·30

1997. 25th Anniv of World Heritage Convention. Terracotta Warriors from Emperor Qin Shi Huang's Tomb, Xian, China. Multicoloured.

V239	1s. As Type **434**	45	45
V240	1s. As No. 737	45	45
V241	1s. As No. 738	45	45
V242	1s. As No. 739	45	45
V243	1s. As No. 740	45	45
V244	1s. As No. 741	45	45
V245	3s. As No. 740	85	85
V246	6s. As No. 741	1·50	1·50

V235 Japanese Peace Bell, Vienna

1998. Architecture. Multicoloured.

V247	6s.50 Type V **235**	1·10	1·10
V248	9s. Underground train passing Vienna Centre	1·60	1·60

1998. Endangered Species (6th series). As Type V 135. Multicoloured.

V249	7s. Green turtle ("Chelonia mydas")	1·20	1·20
V250	7s. Burrowing owl ("Speotyto cunicularia")	1·20	1·20
V251	7s. Raja Brooke's birdwing ("Trogonoptera brookiana")	1·20	1·20
V252	7s. Lesser panda ("Ailurus fulgens")	1·20	1·20

V241 Shark

1998. International Year of the Ocean. Multicoloured.

V253	3s.50 Type V **241**	75	75
V254	3s.50 Diver and submersible	75	75
V255	3s.50 Diver and dolphins	75	75
V256	3s.50 School of fishes above diver and submersible	75	75
V257	3s.50 Sealions	75	75
V258	3s.50 Diver and underwater camera	75	75
V259	3s.50 Angelfishes	75	75
V260	3s.50 Fishes and diver	75	75
V261	3s.50 Turtle	75	75
V262	3s.50 Butterflyfishes	75	75
V263	3s.50 Anemonefish, other fishes and starfish	75	75
V264	3s.50 Starfish and butterfly-fishes	75	75

V242 Ocelot

1998. Rainforest Preservation.

V265	**V242** 6s.50 multicoloured	1·40	1·40
MSV266	82×70 mm. 22s. multicoloured	5·50	5·50

V243 Soldier distributing Supplies

1998. 50 Years of United Nations Peacekeeping. Multicoloured.

V267	4s. Type V **243**	85	85
V268	7s.50 Voters	1·50	1·50

V245 Open Head

1998. 50th Anniv of Universal Declaration of Human Rights. Multicoloured.

V269	4s.50 Type V **245**	1·10	1·10
V270	7s. Cogwheels	1·50	1·50

1998. World Heritage Site. Schonbrunn Palace, Vienna. Multicoloured.

V271	1s. As Type **454**	65	65
V272	1s. As No. 778	65	65
V273	1s. As No. 779	65	65
V274	2s. As No. 780	85	85
V275	2s. As No. 781	85	85
V276	2s. As No. 782	85	85
V277	3s.50 As No. 780	1·10	1·10
V278	7s. As No. 779	2·40	2·40

V253 "Volcanic Landscape" (detail, Peter Pongratz)

1999

V279	**V253** 8s. multicoloured	1·40	1·40

1999. World Heritage Sites in Australia. Mult.

V280	1s. As Type **462**	45	45
V281	1s. As No. 796	45	45
V282	1s. As No. 797	45	45
V283	2s. As No. 798	65	65
V284	2s. As No. 799	65	65
V285	2s. As No. 800	65	65
V286	4s.50 As No. 801	95	95
V287	6s.50 As No. 802	1·40	1·40

1999. Endangered Species (7th series). As Type V 135. Multicoloured.

V288	7s. Orang-utan ("Pongo pygmaeus")	1·20	1·20
V289	7s. Dalmatian pelican ("Pelecanus crispus")	1·20	1·20
V290	7s. Yellow anaconda ("Eunectes notaeus")	1·20	1·20
V291	7s. Caracal ("Caracal caracal")	1·20	1·20

V264/265 Global Weather Forecasting (image scaled to 67% of original size)

1999. Third Conference on Exploration and Peaceful Uses of Outer Space, Vienna.

V292	**V264** 3s.50 multicoloured	85	85
V293	**V265** 3s.50 multicoloured	85	85
MSV293	V **294** 90×75 mm. 13s. Combined design as Nos. V292/3 (71×29 mm)	3·00	3·00

Nos. V292/3 were issued together, se-tenant, forming the composite design illustrated.

V266/269 Modern Communications (image scaled to 68% of original size)

1999. 125th Anniv of Universal Postal Union.

V295 **V266** 33c. multicoloured 1·20 1·20
V296 **V267** 33c. multicoloured 1·20 1·20
V297 **V268** 33c. multicoloured 1·20 1·20
V298 **V269** 33c. multicoloured 1·20 1·20

Nos. V295/8 were issued together, se-tenant, forming the composite design illustrated.

V270 U.N. Centre, Vienna

1999. "In Memoriam: Fallen in the Cause of Peace".

V299 **V270** 6s.50 multicoloured 1·40 1·40
MSV300 90×75 mm. 14s. multicoloured 3·00 3·00

V272 Couple leaping over Open Book

1999. Education: Keystone to the 21st Century.

V301 7s. Type V **272** 1·30 1·30
V302 13s. Group of readers 2·40 2·40

DENOMINATION. From Nos. V303 to V346, United Nations Vienna Centre stamps are denominated both in Austrian schillings and in euros. As no cash for the latter was in circulation the catalogue uses the schilling value.

2000. International Year of Thanksgiving.

V303 **483** 7s. multicoloured 1·40 1·40

2000. Endangered Species (8th series). As Type V 135. Multicoloured.

V304 7s. Leopard (*Panthera pardus*) 1·20 1·20
V305 7s. White spoonbill (*Platalea leucorodia*) 1·20 1·20
V306 7s. Chilean guemal (*Hippocamelus bisulcus*) 1·20 1·20
V307 7s. Killer whale (*Orcinus orca*) 1·20 1·20

V279 "Tomorrow's Dream" (Voltaire Perez)

2000. "Our World 2000" International Art Exhibition, New York. Entries in Millennium Painting Competition. Multicoloured.

V308 7s. Type V **279** 1·20 1·20
V309 8s. "Remembrance" (Dimitris Nalbandis) 1·40 1·40

V281 Dome of General Assembly Hall, 1951

2000. 55th Anniv of the United Nations and 50th Anniv of Opening of U.N. Headquarters, New York.

V310 **V281** 7s. green, yellow and ochre 1·30 1·30
V311 - 9s. green, yellow and ochre 1·60 1·60
MSV312 67×86 mm. Nos. V310/11 3·50 3·50

DESIGN: 9s. Ceremony to mark completion of steel framework of Secretariat Building, 1949.

V283 Agriculture

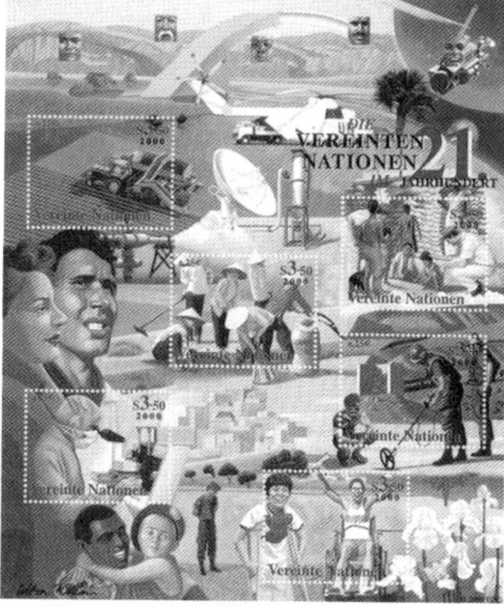
V284 (image scaled to 34% of original size)

2000. "The United Nations in the 21st Century" Sheet 141×165 mm containing Type V 283 and similar horiz designs, forming the overall design Type V 284. Multicoloured.

MSV313 3s.50 Type V **283**; 3s.50 Soldiers with children; 3s.50 Women working; 3s.50 Soldiers using landmine detectors; 3s.50 Detectors; 3s.50 Scientist in laboratory; 3s.50 Disabled athletes 4·75 4·75

2000. World Heritage Sites in Spain. Multicoloured.

V314 1s. As Type **496** 45 45
V315 1s. As No. 832 45 45
V316 1s. As No. 833 45 45
V317 2s. As No. 834 65 65
V318 2s. As No. 835 65 65
V319 2s. As No. 836 65 65
V320 4s.50 As No. 837 95 95
V321 6s.50 As No. 838 1·40 1·40

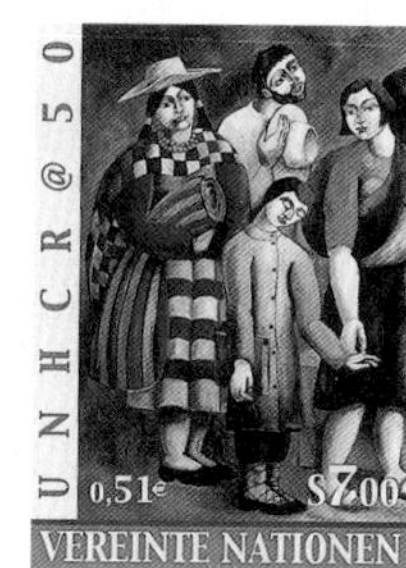

V291 Family of Refugees

2000. 50th Anniv of United Nations Commissioner for Refugees.

V322 **V291** 7s. multicoloured 1·40 1·40
MSV323 121×82 mm. 25s. multicoloured 4·75 4·75

2001. Endangered Species (9th series). As Type V 135. Multicoloured.

V324 7s. Spectacled bear (*Tremarctos ornatus*) 1·20 1·20
V325 7s. Laysan duck (*Anas laysanensis*) 1·20 1·20
V326 7s. Aardwolf (*Proteles cristatus*) 1·20 1·20
V327 7s. Silver langur (*Trachypithecus cristatus*) 1·20 1·20

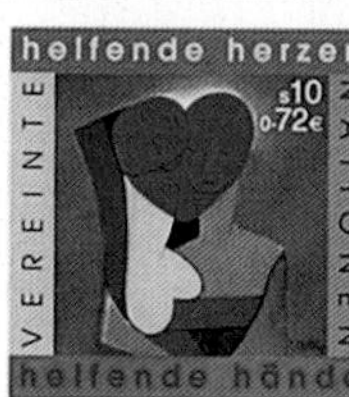

V297 Couple (Nguyen Thanh Chuong)

2001. United Nations International Year of Volunteers. Multicoloured.

V328 10s. Type V **297** 1·60 1·60
V329 12s. Hands and heart (Ikko Tanaka) 2·00 2·00

2001. World Heritage Sites in Japan. Multicoloured.

V330 1s. As Type **512** 30 30
V331 1s. As No. 858 30 30
V332 1s. As No. 859 30 30
V333 2s. As No. 860 65 65
V334 2s. As No. 861 65 65
V335 2s. As No. 862 65 65
V336 7s. As No. 859 1·30 1·30
V337 15s. As No. 862 2·75 2·75

2001. 40th Death Anniv of Dag Hammarskjold (United Nations Secretary General, 1953–61).

V338 **518** 7s. green 1·40 1·40

V306 Balloons

2001. 50th Anniv of United Nations Postal Administration.

V339 **V306** 7s. multicoloured 1·40 1·40
V340 - 8s. multicoloured 1·50 1·50
MSV341 102×102 mm. 21s. ×2 cobalt and green 5·00 5·00

DESIGNS: V340, Cake; **MS**V341, Emblem.

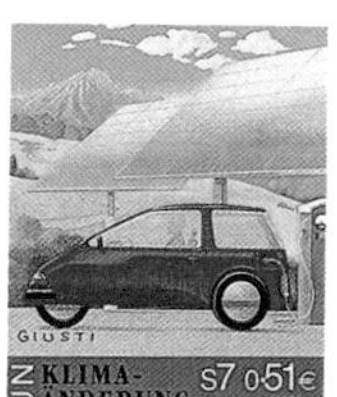

V309 Futuristic Electric Car and Solar Panels

2001. Climate Change. Multicoloured.

V342 7s. Type V **309** 1·50 1·50
V343 7s. Airship, cyclists and horse rider 1·50 1·50
V344 7s. Couple walking, balloon and coastline 1·50 1·50
V345 7s. Train and traffic signs in glass dome 1·50 1·50

Nos. V342/5 were issued together, se-tenant, forming a composite design.

2001. Kofi Annan, Winner of Nobel Peace Prize, 2001.

V346 **526** 7s. multicoloured 1·70 1·70

V314 Semmering Railway

2002. World Heritage Sites in Austria. Multicoloured.

V347 7c. Type V **314** 30 30
V348 51c. Pferdeschwemme, Salzburg 1·30 1·30
V349 58c. Aggstein Ruin 1·40 1·40
V350 73c. Hallstatt 1·70 1·70
V351 87c. Melk Abbey 2·00 2·00
V352 €2.03 Kapitelschwemme, Salzburg 4·50 4·50

2002. Endangered Species (10th series). As Type V 135. Multicoloured.

V353 51c. Siamang gibbon (*Hylobates syndactylus*) 1·20 1·20
V354 51c. Jackass penguin (*Spheniscus demersus*) 1·20 1·20
V355 51c. Banded linsang (*Prionodon linsang*) 1·20 1·20
V356 51c. Sonoran green toad (*Bufo retiformis*) 1·20 1·20

2002. East Timor Independence. As T 532. Multioloured.

V357 51c. Carved deer horn container 1·30 1·30
V358 €1.09 Weaving loom 2·75 2·75

2002. International Year of Mountains. As T 534. Multocoloured.

V359 22c. Mt. Cook, New Zealand 65 65
V360 22c. Mt. Robson, Canada 65 65
V361 51c. Rakaposhi, Pakistan 1·20 1·20
V362 51c. Sagarmatha, Nepal 1·20 1·20

V330 Rainbow

2002. World Summit on Sustainable Development, Johannesburg. Multicoloured.

V363 51c. Type V **330** 1·20 1·20
V364 51c. Women's profiles 1·20 1·20
V365 58c. Figures wearing fashionable dress 1·50 1·50
V366 58c. Wave and doves 1·50 1·50

2002. World Heritage Sites in Italy. As T 542. Multicoloured.

V367 7c. Duomo di Sant'Andrea, Amalfi Coast 30 30
V368 7c. View across Islands, Aeolian Islands 30 30
V369 7c. Del Moro Fountain, Rome 30 30
V370 15c. Santa Maria del Fiore, Florence 65 65
V371 15c. Leaning Tower, Pisa 65 65
V372 15c. The Forum, Pompeii 65 65
V373 51c. As No. 372 1·30 1·30
V374 58c. As No. 369 1·50 1·50

2002. AIDS Awareness Campaign. As T 549. Multicoloured.

V375 €1.53 AIDS Symbol on UN Secretariat Building, New York 4·00 4·00
MSV376 80×80 mm. 51c.+25c. AIDS Symbol on UN Secretariat Building, New York at night 2·40 2·40

The premium was for AIDS charities.

2003. Indigenous Art (1st series). Sheet 121×97 mm. As T 550. Multicoloured.

MSV377 51c. Mola, Panama; 51c. Mochican vessel, Peru; 51c. Tarabuco cloth, Bolivia; 51c. Masks, Cuba; 51c. Aztec headdress, Mexico; 51c. Bird-shaped staff head, Colombia 8·00 8·00

See also No. **MS**V402 and **MS**V441.

V343 Kunsthistorisches Museum, Vienna

2003. Architecture. Multicoloured.

V378 25c. Type V **343** 65 65
V379 €1 Belevedere Palace, Vienna 2·30 2·30

2003. Endangered Species. (11th series). 30th Anniv of Convention on International Trade in Endangered Species (CITES). As Type V 135. Multicoloured.

V380 51c. Baikal teal (*Anas Formosa*) 1·20 1·20
V381 51c. Hagedash ibis (*Bostrychia hagedash*) 1·20 1·20
V382 51c. Toco toucan (*Ramphostos toco*) 1·20 1·20
V383 51c. Egyptian goose (*Alopochen aegyptiacus*) 1·20 1·20

2003. International Year of Freshwater. As T 559. Multicoloured.

V384 55c. Snow scene with bridge 1·20 1·20
V385 75c. Snow scene with horse 1·70 1·70

Nos. V384/5 were issued together, se-tenant, forming a composite design.

V351 Schloss Eggenberg, Graz

2003

V386 **V351** 4c. multicoloured 30 30

2003. Ralph Bunche (politician) Commemoration. As T 561. Multicoloured.

V387 €2.10 Ralph Bunche 5·00 5·00

2003. World Heritage Sites in USA. As T 562. Showing USA National Parks. Multicoloured.

V388 15c. Yosemite National Park 55 55
V389 15c. Smoky Mountains 55 55
V390 15c. Olympic National Park 55 55
V391 20c. Hawaii Volcanoes 65 65
V392 20c. Everglades 65 65
V393 20c. Yellowstone National Park 65 65
V394 55c. As No. V390 1·40 1·40
V395 75c. As No. V392 2·00 2·00

V388/95 have olive bands at top and bottom edges.

2003. In Memoriam. Support for United Nations Staff Killed or Injured in Terrorist Attacks. As T 568. Multicoloured.

V396	€2.10 Flag at half-mast	5·00	5·00

V360 Schonbrunn Schloss, Vienna

2004

V397	**V364** 55c. multicoloured	1·20	1·20

2004. Endangered Species (12th series). As T **V135**. Multicoloured.

V398	55c. Sloth Bear (*Melursus ursinus*)	1·20	1·20
V399	55c. Eld's Deer (*Cervus eldi*)	1·20	1·20
V400	55c. Cherry-crowned Mangabey (*Cercocebus torquatus*)	1·20	1·20
V401	55c. Water Buffalo (*Bubalus arnee*)	1·20	1·20

2004. Indigenous Art (2nd series). Sheet 125×96 mm. As T 550. Multicoloured.

MSV402	55c.×6, Illuminated writing, Book of Kells, United Kingdom; Decorated eggs, Ukraine; Venus of Willendorf (statue), Austria; Carved Flatatunga panel, Iceland; Seated figure (statue), Szegvar-Tuzcoves, Hungary; Illuminated writing enclosing woman, Portugal	8·00	8·00

V366 Car and Bottles (don't drink and drive campaign)

2004. Road Safety Campaign. Multicoloured.

V403	55c. Type V **366**	1·30	1·30
V404	75c. Narrowing Road (speed control campaign) (vert)	1·90	1·90

2004. 50th Anniv of Japanese Peace Bell. As T 576. Multicoloured.

V405	€2.10 Peace Bell, United Nations Headquarters, New York	5·25	5·25

2004. World Heritage Sites in Greece. As T 577. Multicoloured.

V406	25c. Acropolis, Athens	65	65
V407	25c. Lions, Delos	65	65
V408	25c. Ruins, Delphi	65	65
V409	30c. Pythagoreion and Heraion, Samos	75	75
V410	30c. Tunnel, Olympia	75	75
V411	30c. Relief, Mycenae and Tiryns	75	75
V412	55c. As No. V411	1·30	1·30
V413	75c. As No. V410	1·90	1·90

Nos. V406/13 have olive bands at left and bottom edges.

V375 Child sleeping during Battle and in Field (Henry Ulfe Renteria)

2004. Winning Designs in Children's Painting Competition "My Dream of Peace". Multicoloured.

V414	55c. Type V **375**	1·20	1·20
V415	€1 Candle, doves and woman (Michelle Fortaliza)	2·40	2·40

V377 Two Families and Blue Roses

2004. International Decade of Human Rights' Education. Multicoloured.

V416	55c. Type V **377**	1·20	1·20
V417	€1.25 Dove, three couples and blue roses	3·00	3·00

The stamps of United Nations Headquarters in New York, Geneva and Vienna form a composite design.

2005. 60th Anniv of United Nations.

V418	**588** 55c. multicoloured	1·40	1·40
MSV419	100×80 mm. **588** €2.10 multicoloured. Imperf	5·00	5·00

Nos. V418/**MS**V419 have green borders.

V380 United Nations International Centre, Vienna

2005. Greetings from the United Nations.

V420	**V380** 75c. multicoloured	1·90	1·90

2005. Endangered Species (13th series). As T 589. Multicoloured.

V421	55c. *Ansellia Africana*	1·20	1·20
V422	55c. *Phragmipedium kovachi*	1·20	1·20
V423	55c. *Cymbidium ensifolium*	1·20	1·20
V424	55c. *Renanthera imschootiana*	1·20	1·20

V385 Desert, China

2005. EXPO 2005 World Exhibition, Aichi, Japan. Multicoloured.

V425	55c. Type V **385**	1·30	1·30
V426	75c. Cheetahs, Africa	1·80	1·80

V387 Show Jumping

2005. International Year of Sport. Multicoloured.

V427	37c. Type V **387**	1·40	1·40
V428	70c. Football	2·75	2·75

2005. World Heritage. Egypt. As T 577. Multicoloured.

V429	25c. Sphinx, Necropolis, Memphis	70	70
V430	25c. Castle, Philae	70	70
V431	25c. Abu Mena	70	70
V432	30c. Head, Necropolis, Thebes	85	85
V433	30c. Mosque, Cairo	85	85
V434	30c. Saint Catherine Monastery	85	85
V435	55c. Abu Mena	1·40	1·40
V436	75c. Saint Catherine Monastery	2·20	2·20

V395 Globe as Person Holding Umbrella of Flags (Lee Min Gi)

2005. My Dream of Peace One Day. Winning Designs in Children's Painting Competition. Multicoloured.

V437	55c. Type V **395**	1·40	1·40
V438	€1 People of Many Nations holding Flags as Torch (Natalie Chan)	2·40	2·40

V397 Starving Children and School Lesson

2005. Food for Life.

V439	**V397** 55c. black, green and blue	1·30	1·30
V440	- 1f.25 black, green and blue	3·00	3·00

DESIGN: 1f.25 Food aid delivery.

2006. Indigenous Art (3rd series). Musical Instruments. As T 550. Sheet 125×96 mm. Multicoloured.

MSV441	55c.×6, Wooden drum, Republic of Guinea; Carved whistle, Congo; Figure shaped horn, Botswana; Drums, Burundi; Fang harp, Gabon; Double bell, Nigeria	7·50	7·50

2006. Endangered Species (13th series). As Type V 135. Multicoloured.

V442	55c. Red and blue poison frog	1·20	1·20
V443	55c. Carpet chameleon	1·20	1·20
V444	55c. Amazon tree boa	1·20	1·20
V445	55c. Yellow-banded poison frog	1·20	1·20

V404 Children at Waterpipe

2006. International Day of Families. Multicoloured.

V446	55c. Type V **404**	1·30	1·30
V447	1f.25 Pounding Grain	3·00	3·00

2006. World Heritage. France. As T 615. Multicoloured.

V448	25c. Banks of the Seine	70	70
V449	25c. Provins	70	70
V450	25c. Carcassonne	70	70
V451	30c. Roman Aqueduct	85	85
V452	30c. Mont Saint Michel	85	85
V453	30c. Chateau de Chambord	85	85
V454	55c. Carcassonne	1·30	1·30
V455	75c. Chateau de Chambord	1·80	1·80

V412 Dove flying from Cage (Klara Thein)

2006. My Dream of Peace One Day. Winning Designs in Children's Painting Competition. Multicoloured.

V456	55c. Type V **412**	1·30	1·30
V457	€1 Doves and Stylized Figures rising from Globe of Flags (Laurensi Levina)	2·40	2·40

V414 Gambia

2006. Flags and Coins of Member Countries (1st series). Multicoloured.

V458	55c. Type **414**	1·30	1·30
V459	55c. Pakistan	1·30	1·30
V460	55c. Germany	1·30	1·30
V461	55c. Haiti	1·30	1·30
V462	55c. Afghanistan	1·30	1·30
V463	55c. Austria	1·30	1·30
V464	55c. Denmark	1·30	1·30
V465	55c. Netherlands	1·30	1·30

See also Nos. V470/7.

2006. Endangered Species (15h series). As T 589. Multicoloured.

V466	55c. Savanna monkey (*Chlorocebus aethiops*)	1·30	1·30
V467	55c. Long-nosed monkey (*Nasalis larvatus*)	1·30	1·30
V468	55c. Chacma baboon (*Papio hamadryas ursinus*)	1·30	1·30
V469	55c. Patas monkey (*Erythrocebus patas*)	1·30	1·30

2007. Flags and Coins of Member Countries (2nd series). As Type V 414. Multicoloured.

V470	55c. Trinidad and Tobago	1·30	1·30
V471	55c. Sierra Leone	1·30	1·30
V472	55c. Hungary	1·30	1·30
V473	55c. San Marino	1·30	1·30
V474	55c. Croatia	1·30	1·30
V475	55c. Spain	1·30	1·30
V476	55c. Kazakhstan	1·30	1·30
V477	55c. Eire	1·30	1·30

V434 Trees and Figures encircling Globe

2007. Peaceful Visions. Multicoloured.

V478	55c. Type V **434**	1·30	1·30
V479	€1.25 Couple and doves	3·00	3·00

2007. World Heritage Sites. South America. As T 645. Multicoloured.

V480	25c. Rapa Nui, Chile	60	60
V481	25c. Cueva de las Manos, Argentina	60	60
V482	25c. Machu Pichu, Peru	60	60
V483	30c. Tiwanaku, Bolivia	70	70
V484	30c. Iguacu, Brazil	70	70
V485	30c. Galapagos Islands	70	70
V486	55c. Cueva de las Manos, Argentina	1·30	1·30
V487	75c. Iguacu, Brazil	1·80	1·80

2007. Humanitarian Mail. As T 652. Multicoloured.

V488	75c. Flying postman and hands	1·80	1·80

2007. 50th Anniv of Space Exploration. As T 653. Multicoloured.

V489	65c. Satellite	1·50	1·50
V490	€1.15 Satellite (different)	2·50	2·50
MSV491	100×80 mm. $2.10 Jupiter and spacecraft	4·75	4·75

2008. International Holocaust Remembrance Day. As T 656. Multicoloured.

V492	65c. Barbed wire becoming flowers	1·50	1·50

A stamp of a similar design was issued by Israel.

V 447 Johann Straus Memorial, Stadtpark, Vienna

2008. Tourism. Each black.

V493	10c. Type V **447**	45	45
V494	15c. Pallas Athene Fountain, Parliament Square, Vienna (horiz)	55	55
V495	65c. Pegasus Fountain, Mirabelle Palace Gardens, Salzburg (horiz)	1·70	1·70
V496	€1.40 Statue, Belevedere Palace Gardens, Vienna (horiz)	3·75	3·75

2008. Endangered Species (16th series). As T 589. Multicoloured.

V497	65c. Northern elephant seal (*Mirounga angustirostris*)	1·60	1·60
V498	65c. Fire coral (*Millepora alcicornis*)	1·60	1·60
V499	65c. Thorny seahorse (*Hippocampus histrix*)	1·60	1·60
V500	65c. Grey whale (*Eschrichtius robustus*)	1·60	1·60

2008. Flages and Coins of Member Countries (3rd series). As T V414. Multicoloured.

V501	65c. Poland	1·60	1·60
V502	65c. Latvia	1·60	1·60
V503	65c. Sweden	1·60	1·60
V504	65c. Cyprus	1·60	1·60
V505	65c. Portugal	1·60	1·60
V506	65c. Armenia	1·60	1·60
V507	65c. Slovakia	1·60	1·60
V508	65c. Qatar	1·60	1·60

2008. Convention on the Rights of People with Disablities. As T 670. Multicoloured.

V509	55c. Bildung	1·40	1·40
V510	€1.40 Bildung	3·75	3·75

2008. Olympic Games, Beijing. As T 671. Multicoloured.

V511	-	65c. Gymnastics	1·80	1·80
V512	**V 463**	€1.30 Swimming	3·75	3·75
MSV513		92×83 mm. As No. 1035	6·00	6·00

V 464 Fruit picking (Mariam Marukian)

2008. We Can End Poverty. Winning Designs in Children's Painting Competition. Multicoloured.

V514	65c. Type V **464**	2·00	2·00
V515	75c. Shelter, Health, Food and Education (Rufaro Duri)	2·20	2·20

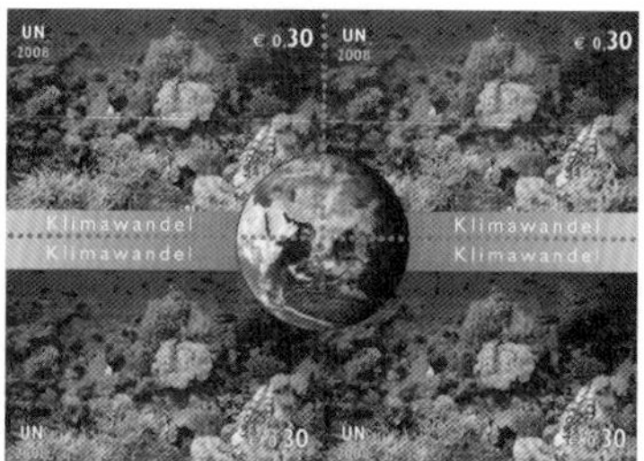

V 466a/d Coral Reef (image scaled to 49% of original size)

V 467a/d Ice Floes (image scaled to 49% of original size)

V 468a/d Pollution (image scaled to 49% of original size)

V 469a/d Desert (image scaled to 49% of original size)

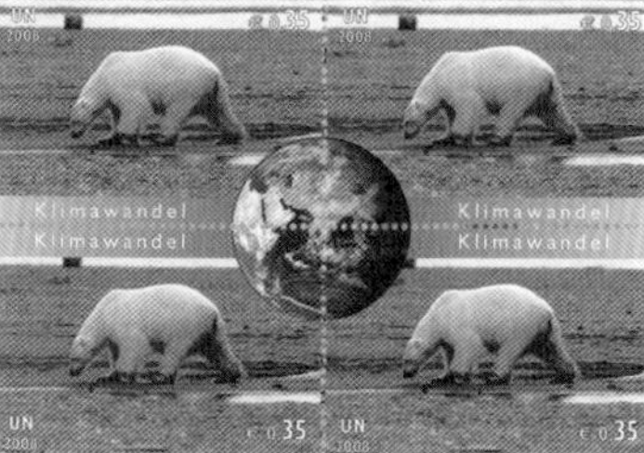

V 470a/d Polar Bear (image scaled to 49% of original size)

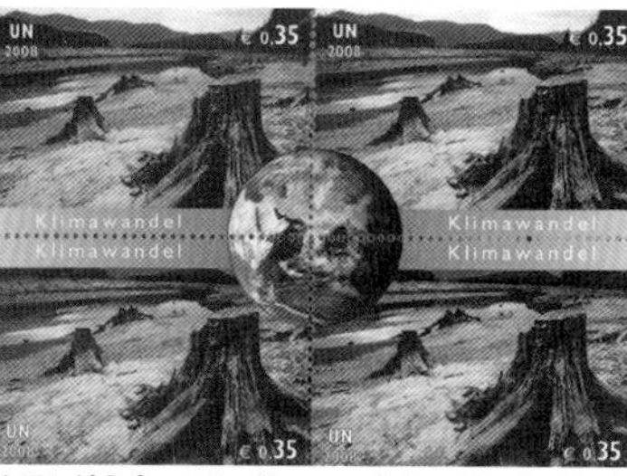

V 471a/d Deforestation (image scaled to 49% of original size)

2008. Action on Climate Change.

V516	30c. Type **V 466a**	95	95
V517	30c. Type **V 466b**	95	95
V518	30c. Type **V 466c**	95	95
V519	30c. Type **V 466d**	95	95
V520	30c. Type **V 467a**	95	95
V521	30c. Type **V 467b**	95	95
V522	30c. Type **V 467c**	95	95
V523	30c. Type **V 467d**	95	95
V524	30c. Type **V 468a**	95	95
V525	30c. Type **V 468b**	95	95
V526	30c. Type **V 468c**	95	95
V527	30c. Type **V 468d**	95	95
V528	35c. Type **V 469a**	95	95
V529	35c. Type **V 469b**	95	95
V530	35c. Type **V 469c**	95	95
V531	35c. Type **V 469d**	95	95
V532	35c. Type **V 470a**	95	95
V533	35c. Type **V 470b**	95	95
V534	35c. Type **V 470c**	95	95
V535	35c. Type **V 470d**	95	95
V536	35c. Type **V 471a**	95	95
V537	35c. Type **V 471b**	95	95
V538	35c. Type **V 471c**	95	95
V539	35c. Type **V 471d**	95	95
MSV540	120×90 mm. 65c.×4, As Type **V 468a/d** (Pollution)	8·50	8·50
MSV541	120×90 mm. €1.15×4, As Type **V 471a/d** (Deforestation)	15·00	15·00

V 472 U Thant

2009. Birth Centenary of U Thant (United Nations Secretary General 1961–1971).

V542	**V 472**	€1.15 multicoloured	3·75	3·75

V 473 *Trogonoptera brookiana* (Rajah Brooke's birdwing)

V 474 *Pandinus imperator* (Emperor scorpion)

V 475 *Carabus intricatus* (Blue ground beetle)

V 476 *Brachypelma smithi* (Mexican red knee tarantula)

2009. Endangered Species (17th series).

V543	**V 473**	65c. multicoloured	1·80	1·80
V544	**V 474**	65c. multicoloured	1·80	1·80
V545	**V 475**	65c. multicoloured	1·80	1·80
V546	**V 476**	65c. multicoloured	1·80	1·80

2009. World Heritage Sites. Germany. As T 689. Multicoloured.

V547	30c. Town Hall and Roland on the Marketplace of Bremen	90	90
V548	30c. Wartburg Castle	90	90
V549	30c. Palaces and Parks of Potsdam and Berlin	90	90
V550	35c. Aachen Cathedral	95	95
V551	35c. Monastic Island of Reichenau	95	95
V552	35c. Luther Memorials in Eisleben and Wittenberg	95	95
V553	65c. As No. V552	1·80	1·80
V554	€1.40 As No. 549	3·75	3·75

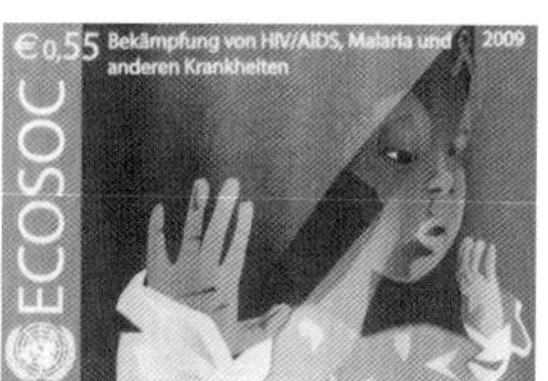

V 483 Child behind Mosquito Netting (prevention of HIV/AIDS, malaria and other diseases)

2009. United Nations Economic and Social Council (ECOSOC). Multicoloured.

V555	55c. Type **V 483**	1·50	1·50
V556	65c. Children (Reduction of child mortality)	1·80	1·80

2009. Millennium Development Goals. As T 697. Multicoloured.

V557	65c. chrome-yellow, black and green	1·80	1·80
V558	65c. bright yellow-green, black and green	1·80	1·80
V559	65c. orange-red, black and green	1·80	1·80
V560	65c. pale turquoise-blue, black and new blue	1·80	1·80
V561	65c. pale bright rose, black and green	1·80	1·80
V562	65c. scarlet-vermilion, black and green	1·80	1·80
V563	65c. apple-green, black and green	1·80	1·80
V564	65c. blue, black and green	1·80	1·80

DESIGNS: No. V557, Bowl of food (Eradicate extreme poverty and hunger); No.V558, Pencil (Achieve universal primary education); No. V559, Female Symbol (Promote gender equality and empower women); No. V560, Teddy bear (Reduce child mortality); No. V561, Female figure enclosing Heart (Improve maternal health); No. V562, Medicine jar (Combat HIV/AIDS, malaria and other diseases); No. V623, Stylized tree (Ensure environmental sustainability); No. V564, Stylized figures (Develop a global partnership for development).

V 493 United Republic of Tanzania

2009. Indigenous Peoples. Multicoloured.

V565	65c. Type V **493**	1·80	1·80
V566	65c. Australia	1·80	1·80
V567	65c. Namibia	1·80	1·80
V568	65c. Indonesia	1·80	1·80
V569	65c. Namibia (different)	1·80	1·80
V570	65c. United Arab Emirates	1·80	1·80

V 499 Romania

2010. Coins and Flags of Member Countries (3rd series). Multicoloured.

V571	65c. Type V **499**	1·80	1·80
V572	65c. Slovenia	1·80	1·80
V573	65c. Belarus	1·80	1·80
V574	65c. Malta	1·80	1·80
V575	65c. Azerbaijan	1·80	1·80
V576	65c. Bangladesh	1·80	1·80
V577	65c. Swaziland	1·80	1·80
V578	65c. Jordan	1·80	1·80

Pt. 8

VATICAN CITY

A small area in Rome under the independent sovereignty of the Pope since 1929.

1929. 100 centesimi = 1 lira.
2002. 100 cents = 1 euro.

1 Papal Tiara and St. Peter's Keys

2 Pope Pius XI

1929

1	**1**	5c. brown on pink	25	30
2	**1**	10c. green on green	55	60
3	**1**	20c. violet on lilac	1·10	85
4	**1**	25c. blue on blue	1·10	1·00
5	**1**	30c. black on yellow	2·10	1·10
6	**1**	50c. black on orange	2·10	1·20
7	**1**	75c. red on grey	3·25	2·20
8	**2**	80c. red	3·25	1·10
9	**2**	1l.25 blue	5·25	2·75
10	**2**	2l. brown	7·50	3·25
11	**2**	2l.50 red	7·50	5·50
12	**2**	5l. green	8·50	16·00
13	**2**	10l. black	18·00	28·00

1931. Surch C. 25 and bars.

14	**1**	25c. on 30c. black on yellow	4·75	2·40

4

1933. "Holy Year" (1933–1934).

15	**4**	25c.+10c. green	7·50	7·00
16	**4**	75c.+15c. red	14·00	24·00
17	**4**	80c.+20c. brown	45·00	32·00
18	**4**	1l.25+25c. blue	14·00	23·00

The 80c. and 1l.25 have inscriptions and frame differently arranged.

6 Arms of Pope Pius XI

9 Pope Pius XI

1933

19	6	5c. red	10	10
20	-	10c. black and brown	10	10
21	-	12½c. black and green	10	10
22	-	20c. black and orange	10	10
23	-	25c. black and green	10	10
24	-	30c. brown and black	10	10
25	-	50c. brown and purple	10	10
26	-	75c. brown and red	10	10
27	-	80c. brown and pink	10	55
28	9	1l. black and violet	5·25	5·00
29	9	1l.25 black and blue	16·00	13·00
30	9	2l. black and brown	55·00	48·00
31	9	2l.75 black and purple	£100	90·00
32	-	5l. green and brown	25	55
33	-	10l. green and blue	25	1·10
34	-	20l. green and black	55	1·10

DESIGNS—As Type **6**: 10c. to 25c. Wing of Vatican Palace; 30c. to 80c. Vatican Gardens and Dome of St. Peter's. As Type **9**: 5l. to 20l. St. Peter's Basilica.

1934. Surch.

35	2	40c. on 80c. red	7·50	5·25
36	2	1l.30 on 1l.25 blue	£130	60·00
37	2	2l.05 on 2l. brown	£350	21·00
38	2	2l.55 on 2l.50 red	£200	£275
39	2	3l.05 on 5l. green	£475	£550
40	2	3l.70 on 10l. black	£550	£650

13 Tribonian presenting Pandects to Justinian

1935. International Juridical Congress, Rome. Frescoes by Raphael.

41	13	5c. orange	1·60	1·90
42	13	10c. violet	2·10	1·90
43	13	25c. green	19·00	12·50
44	-	75c. red	85·00	55·00
45	-	80c. brown	48·00	37·00
46	-	1l.25 blue	80·00	32·00

DESIGN: 75c. to 1l.25, Pope Julius II (wrongly inscribed as representing Pope Gregory IX).

15 Doves and Bell

1936. Catholic Press Exhibition, Rome.

47	15	5c. green	2·10	2·10
48	-	10c. black	2·10	2·10
49	-	25c. green	65·00	16·00
50	15	50c. purple	2·10	2·10
51	-	75c. red	48·00	85·00
52	-	80c. brown	4·25	4·25
53	-	1l.25 blue	4·25	4·25
54	-	5l. brown	5·25	12·00

DESIGNS: 10, 75c. Church and Bible; 25, 80c. St. John Bosco; 1l.25, 5l. St. Francis of Sales.

16 Statue of St. Peter

17 Ascension of Elijah

1938. Air.

55	16	25c. brown	15	25
56	-	50c. green	15	25
57	17	75c. red	15	30
58	-	80c. blue	15	50
59	16	1l. violet	60	70
60	-	2l. blue	70	1·20
61	17	5l. black	1·80	3·00
62	-	10l. purple	2·00	3·25

DESIGNS: 50c., 2l. Dove with olive branch and St. Peter's Square; 80c., 10l. Transportation of the Holy House.

18 Crypt of Basilica of St. Cecilia

1938. International Christian Archaeological Congress. Inscr "CONGRESSVS INTERNAT. ARCHAEOLOGIAE CHRIST".

63	18	5c. brown	35	60
64	18	10c. red	35	60
65	18	25c. green	45	80
66	-	75c. red	9·25	13·50
67	-	80c. violet	36·00	27·00
68	-	1l.25 blue	40·00	40·00

DESIGN: 75, 80c. and 1l.25, Basilica of Saints Nereus and Achilles in the Catacombs of Domitilla.

1939. Death of Pope Pius XI. Optd SEDE VACANTE MCMXXXIX.

69	1	5c. brown on pink	60·00	12·50
70	1	10c. green on green	1·20	30
71	1	20c. violet on lilac	1·20	30
72	1	25c. blue on blue	1·20	8·00
73	1	30c. black on yellow	1·20	60
74	1	50c. black on orange	1·20	60
75	1	75c. red on grey	1·20	60

20 Coronation

1939. Coronation of Pope Pius XII.

76	20	25c. green	1·20	90
77	20	75c. red	45	90
78	20	80c. violet	4·75	5·25
79	20	1l.25 blue	45	1·20

21 Arms of Pope Pius XII

22 Pope Pius XII

1940. 1st Anniv of Coronation of Pope Pius XII.

80	21	5c. red	30	30
81	22	1l. black and violet	30	30
82	-	1l.25 black and blue	30	30
83	22	2l. black and brown	1·20	1·70
84	-	2l.75 black and purple	2·10	3·75
99	21	5c. grey	15	10
100	21	30c. brown	15	10
101	21	50c. green	15	10
102	-	1l. black and brown	15	25
103	-	1l.50 black and red	15	25
104	-	2l.50 black and blue	15	25
105	22	5l. black and lilac	35	30
106	22	20l. black and green	80	50

DESIGN: 1l. (No. 102), 1l.25, 1l.50, 2l.50, and 2l.75, as Type **22** but with portrait of Pope facing left.

23

1942. Prisoners of War Relief Fund (1st series). Inscr "MCMXLII".

85	23	25c. green	10	25
86	23	80c. brown	10	25
87	23	1l.25 blue	10	25

See also Nos. 92/4 and 107/9.

24 Consecration of Archbishop Pacelli

1943. Pope's Episcopal Silver Jubilee.

88	24	25c. turquoise and green	15	25
89	24	80c. chocolate and brown	15	25
90	24	1l.25 blue and ultramarine	15	25
91	24	5l. blue and black	25	60

1944. Prisoners of War Relief Fund (2nd series). Inscr "MCMXLIII".

92	23	25c. green	10	10
93	23	80c. brown	10	10
94	23	1l.25 blue	10	50

25 Raphael

1944. 4th Centenary of Pontifical Academy of the Virtuosi of the Pantheon.

95	25	25c. olive and green	25	25
96	-	80c. violet and lilac	25	60
97	-	1l.25 blue and violet	60	60
98	-	10l. bistre and yellow	1·80	2·75

PORTRAITS: 80c. Antonio da Sangallo (architect); 1l.25, Carlo Maratti (painter) (after Francesco Maratta); 10l. Antonio Canova (sculptor, self-portrait).

1945. Prisoners of War Relief Fund (3rd series). Inscr "MCMXLIV".

107	23	1l. green	15	15
108	23	3l. red	15	15
109	23	5l. blue	30	30

1946. Surch in figures between bars.

110	21	20c. on 5c. grey	10	10
111	21	25c. on 30c. brown	10	10
112	21	1l. on 50c. green	25	25
113	-	1l.50 on 1l. black and brown (No. 102)	45	25
114	-	3l. on 1l.50 black and red (No. 103)	60	25
115	-	5l. on 2l.50 black and blue (No. 104)	60	25
116	22	10l. on 5l. black and lilac	4·00	80
117	22	30l. on 20l. black and green	5·75	3·75

27 St. Ignatius of Loyola

1946. 400th Anniv of Inauguration of Council of Trent.

118	-	5c. brown and bistre	30	30
119	-	25c. brown and violet	30	30
120	-	50c. sepia and brown	30	30
121	27	75c. brown and black	30	30
122	-	1l. brown and purple	30	30
123	-	1l.50 brown and red	30	30
124	-	2l. brown and green	30	30
125	-	2l.50 brown and blue	30	30
126	-	3l. brown and red	30	30
127	-	4l. brown and bistre	35	30
128	-	5l. brown and blue	60	30
129	-	10l. brown and red	1·00	35

DESIGNS: 5c. Trent Cathedral; 25c. St. Angela Merici; 50c. St. Anthony Maria Zaccaria; 1l. St. Cajetan of Thiene; 1l.50, St. John Fisher, Bishop of Rochester; 2l. Cristoforo Madrussi, Bishop of Trent; 2l.50, Reginald Pole, Archbishop of Canterbury; 3l. Marcello Cervini; 4l. Giovanni Maria Del Monte; 5l. Emperor Charles V; 10l. Pope Paul III Farnese.

28 Dove with Olive Branch over St. Peter's Forecourt

29 Barn Swallows circling Spire of St. Peter's Basilica

1947. Air.

130	28	1l. red	30	30
131	-	4l. brown	30	30
132	28	5l. blue	60	30
133	29	15l. violet	1·70	1·50
134	-	25l. green	7·75	3·00
135	29	50l. black	9·25	6·00
136	29	100l. orange	38·00	11·50

DESIGN—As Type **28**: 4l., 25l. Transportation of the Holy House.

30 "Raphael accompanying Tobias" (after Botticelli)

1948. Air.

137	30	250l. black	65·00	5·75
138	30	500l. blue	£950	£650

31 St. Agnes's Basilica

32 Pope Pius XII

1949

139A	31	1l. brown	10	10
140A	-	3l. violet	10	10
141A	-	5l. orange	10	10
142A	-	8l. green	70	30
143A	-	13l. green	7·00	5·25
144A	-	16l. grey	60	60
145A	-	25l. red	18·00	1·50
146A	-	35l. mauve	50·00	25·00
147B	-	40l. blue	85	30
148A	32	100l. black	9·25	6·00

DESIGNS (Basilicas)—VERT: 3l. St. Clement; 5l. St. Praxedes; 8l. St. Mary in Cosmedin. HORIZ: 13l. Holy Cross; 16l. St. Sebastian; 25l. St. Laurence's; 35l. St. Paul's; 40l. Sta. Maria Maggiore.

33 Angels over Globe

1949. Air. 75th Anniv of U.P.U.

149	33	300l. blue	40·00	15·00
150	33	1000l. green	£190	£140

34 "I Will Give You the Keys of the Kingdom"

1949. "Holy Year".

151	**34**	5l. brown and light brown	10	10
152	-	6l. brown and black	10	10
153	-	8l. green and blue	1·40	80
154	-	10l. blue and green	35	25
155	**34**	20l. brown and green	2·30	60
156	-	25l. blue and brown	1·50	60
157	-	30l. purple and green	3·50	2·00
158	-	60l. red and brown	2·20	1·70

DESIGNS: 6, 25l. Four Basilicas; 8, 30l. Pope Boniface VIII; 10, 60l. Pope Pius XII opening the Holy Door.

35 Guards Marching

1950. Centenary of Papal Guard.

159	**35**	25l. brown	8·75	6·25
160	**35**	35l. green	4·50	4·50
161	**35**	55l. brown	3·00	5·25

36 Pope Proclaiming Dogma

1951. Proclamation of Dogma of the Assumption.

162	**36**	25l. purple	16·00	1·70
163	-	55l. blue	8·00	17·00

DESIGN: 55l. Angels over St. Peter's.

37 Pope Pius X

1951. Beatification of Pope Pius X.

164	**37**	6l. gold and violet	60	60
165	**37**	10l. gold and green	2·30	60
166	-	60l. gold and blue	16·00	9·25
167	-	115l. gold and brown	37·00	30·00

DESIGN: 60, 115l. Pope looking left.

38 Final Session of Council (fresco)

1951. 1500th Anniv of Council of Chalcedon.

168	**38**	5l. grey	60	60
169	-	25l. red	5·75	3·50
170	**38**	35l. red	16·00	7·50
171	-	60l. blue	36·00	20·00
172	**38**	100l. brown	80·00	50·00

DESIGN: 25, 60l. "Pope Leo I meeting Attila" (Raphael).

39 Gratian

1951. Air. 800th Anniv of Decree of Gratian.

173	**39**	300l. purple	£450	£275
174	**39**	500l. blue	70·00	35·00

1952. No. 143 surch L. 12 and bars.

175	12l. on 13l. green	3·00	2·10

41 Mail Coach and First Stamp

1952. Centenary of First Papal States' Stamp.

176	**41**	50l. black & blue on cream	6·25	5·75
MS176a		112×121 mm. No. 176 (block of four)	£400	£250

42 St. Maria Goretti

1953. 50th Anniv of Martyrdom of St. Maria Goretti.

177	**42**	15l. violet and brown	6·25	4·00
178	**42**	25l. brown and red	3·50	4·00

43 St. Peter and Inscription

1953. St. Peter's Basilica. Medallions in black.

179	**43**	3l. red	10	10
180	-	5l. grey	10	10
181	-	10l. green	10	10
182	-	12l. brown	10	10
183	-	20l. violet	25	15
184	-	25l. brown	25	15
185	-	35l. red	25	15
186	-	45l. brown	25	30
187	-	60l. blue	25	25
188	-	65l. red	50	30
189	-	100l. purple	40	25

DESIGNS: 5l. Pius XII and Roman sepulchre; 10l. St. Peter's tomb; 12l. St. Sylvester I and Constantine's basilica (previous building); 20l. Julius II and Bramante's design; 25l. Paul III and apse; 35l. Sixtus V and cupola; 45l. Paul V and facade; 60l. Urban VIII and baldaquin; 65l. Alexander VII and colonnade; 100l. Pius VI and sacristy.

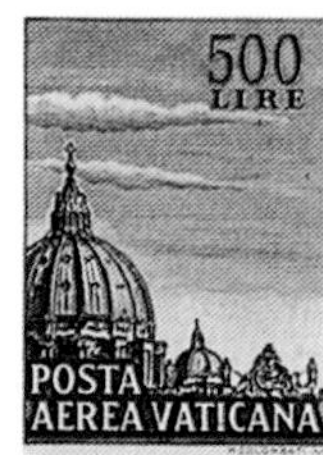

44 Dome of St. Peter's

1953. Air.

190	**44**	500l. brown & deep brown	40·00	12·50
190a	**44**	500l. green and turquoise	10·50	5·75
191	**44**	1000l. blue and deep blue	£140	27·00
191a	**44**	1000l. red and lake	1·20	1·20

45 St. Clare of Assisi (after Giotto)

1953. 700th Death Anniv of St. Clare (founder of Poor Clares Order).

192	**45**	25l. dp brown, brown & bl	4·50	2·30
193	**45**	35l. brown, lt brown & red	25·00	22·00

46 "St. Bernard" (after Lippi)

1953. 800th Death Anniv of St. Bernard of Clairvaux.

194	**46**	20l. purple and green	1·20	1·20
195	**46**	60l. green and blue	11·00	9·25

47 Lombard's Episcopal Seal

1953. 800th Anniv of "Libri Sententiarum" (theological treatise by Peter Lombard, Bishop of Paris).

196	**47**	100l. yellow, blue and red	65·00	46·00

48 Pope Pius XI and Vatican City

1954. 25th Anniv of Lateran Treaty.

197	**48**	25l. red, brown and blue	1·70	1·20
198	**48**	60l. blue, grey and brown	5·25	4·50

49 Pope Pius XII

1954. Marian Year and Centenary of Dogma of the Immaculate Conception.

199	-	3l. violet	10	10
200	**49**	4l. red	10	10
201	-	6l. red	10	10
202	**49**	12l. green	2·00	1·70
203	-	20l. brown	1·30	1·00
204	**49**	35l. blue	2·75	2·50

DESIGN: 3, 6, 20l. Pope Pius IX facing right with different inscr and dates "1854–1954".

50 St. Pius X

1954. Canonization of Pope Pius X.

205	**50**	10l. yellow, red and brown	60	30
206	**50**	25l. yellow, red and violet	3·50	3·00
207	**50**	35l. yellow, red and black	7·00	5·50

51 Basilica of St. Francis of Assisi

1954. Bicentenary of Elevation of Basilica of St. Francis of Assisi to Papal Chapel.

208	**51**	20l. black and cream	2·50	1·50
209	**51**	35l. brown and cream	2·00	2·50

52 "St. Augustine" (after Botticelli)

1954. 1600th Birth Anniv of St. Augustine.

210	**52**	35l. green	1·20	1·00
211	**52**	50l. brown	2·75	2·50

53 Madonna of Ostra Brama, Vilna

1954. Termination of Marian Year.

212	**53**	20l. multicoloured	3·75	1·20
213	**53**	35l. multicoloured	12·50	7·50
214	**53**	60l. multicoloured	25·00	20·00

54 St. Boniface and Fulda Cathedral

1955. 1200th Anniv of Martyrdom of St. Boniface.

215	**54**	10l. green	25	10
216	**54**	35l. violet	75	55
217	**54**	60l. green	1·20	1·10

55 "Pope Sixtus II and St. Lawrence" (fresco, Niccolina Chapel)

1955. 500th Death Anniv of Fra Giovanni da Fiesole, "Fra Angelico" (painter).

218	**55**	50l. red and blue	5·50	3·50
219	**55**	100l. blue and flesh	3·00	3·50

56 Pope Nicholas V

1955. 5th Death Centenary of Pope Nicholas V.

220	**56**	20l. brown and blue	20	20
221	**56**	35l. brown and pink	45	30
222	**56**	60l. brown and green	1·00	75

57 St. Bartholomew

1955. 900th Death Anniv of St. Bartholomew the Young.

223	**57**	10l. black and brown	20	10
224	**57**	25l. black and red	70	45
225	**57**	100l. black and green	2·75	1·90

58 "Annunciation" (Melozzo da Forli)

1956. Air.

226	**58**	5l. black	10	10
227	**A**	10l. green	10	10
228	**B**	15l. orange	25	20
229	**58**	25l. red	25	20
230	**A**	35l. red	75	45
231	**B**	50l. brown	35	25
232	**58**	60l. blue	5·75	3·75
233	**A**	100l. brown	30	25
234	**B**	300l. violet	1·00	80

PAINTINGS: A, "Annunciation" (P. Cavallini); B, "Annunciation" (Leonardo da Vinci).

59 Corporal of the Guard

1956. 450th Anniv of Swiss Guard. Inscr 'GUARDIA SVIZZERA PONTIFICIA'.

235	-	4l. red	20	10
236	**59**	6l. orange	20	10
237	-	10l. blue	20	10
238	-	35l. brown	60	45
239	**59**	50l. violet	1·30	1·00
240	-	60l. green	1·60	1·50

DESIGNS: 4, 35l. Captain Roust; 10, 60l. Two drummers.

60 St. Rita

1956. 5th Death Centenary of St. Rita at Cascia.

241	**60**	10l. grey	10	20
242	**60**	25l. brown	85	75
243	**60**	35l. blue	30	25

61 St. Ignatius presenting Jesuit Constitution to Pope Paul III

1956. 4th Death Centenary of St. Ignatius of Loyola.

244	**61**	35l. brown	60	50
245	**61**	60l. grey	95	75

62 St. John of Capistrano

1956. 5th Death Centenary of St. John of Capistrano.

246	**62**	25l. green and black	2·75	2·40
247	**62**	35l. brown and purple	60	50

63 Madonna and Child

1956. "Black Madonna" of Czestochowa Commemoration.

248	**63**	35l. black and blue	45	30
249	**63**	60l. blue and green	50	45
250	**63**	100l. purple and brown	80	75

64 St. Domenico Savio

1957. Death Centenary of St. Domenico Savio.

251	**64**	4l. brown	20	10
252	-	6l. red	20	10
253	**64**	25l. green	50	35
254	-	60l. blue	1·00	75

DESIGN: 6, 60l. St. Domenico Savio and St. John Bosco.

65 Cardinal D. Capranica (founder) and Capranica College

1957. 5th Centenary of Capranica College.

255	**65**	5l. red	25	20
256	-	10l. brown	25	20
257	**65**	35l. grey	25	20
258	-	100l. blue	75	45

DESIGNS: 10, 100l. Pope Pius XII and plaque.

66 Pontifical Academy of Science

1957. 20th Anniv of the Pontifical Academy of Science.

259	**66**	35l. green and blue	60	60
260	**66**	60l. blue and brown	1·00	1·00

67 Mariazell Basilica

1957. 8th Centenary of Mariazell Basilica.

261	**67**	5l. green	25	25
262	-	15l. black	35	35
263	**67**	60l. blue	1·20	1·20
264	-	100l. violet	1·90	1·90

DESIGN: 15, 100l. Statue of the Virgin of Mariazell within Sanctuary.

68 Apparition of the Virgin Mary

1958. Centenary of Apparition of the Virgin Mary at Lourdes.

265	**68**	5l. blue	10	10
266	-	10l. green	10	10
267	-	15l. brown	10	10
268	**68**	25l. red	10	10
269	-	35l. brown	10	10
270	-	100l. violet	10	10

DESIGNS: 10, 35l. Invalid at Lourdes; 15, 100l. St. Bernadette.

69 "Civitas Dei" ("City of God" at Exhibition)

1958. Brussels International Exhibition.

271		35l. purple	35	25
272	**69**	60l. red	75	60
273	**69**	100l. violet	3·75	2·10
274	-	300l. blue	1·60	1·40
MS274a		91×149 mm. Nos. 271/4	50·00	50·00

DESIGN: 35, 300l. Pope Pius XII.

70 Pope Clement XIII (from sculpture by A. Canova)

1958. Birth Bicentenary of Antonio Canova (sculptor).

275	**70**	5l. brown	20	20
276	-	10l. red	20	20
277	-	35l. green	25	20
278	-	100l. blue	75	70

SCULPTURES: 10l. Pope Clement XIV; 35l. Pope Pius VI; 100l. Pope Pius VII.

71 St. Peter's Keys

1958. "Vacant See".

279	**71**	15l. brown on yellow	2·50	2·20
280	**71**	25l. brown	60	25
281	**71**	60l. brown on lilac	60	25

72 Pope John XXIII

1959. Coronation of Pope John XXIII. Inscr "IV-XI MCMLVIII".

282	**72**	25l. multicoloured	20	20
283	-	35l. multicoloured	20	20
284	**72**	60l. multicoloured	20	20
285	-	100l. multicoloured	25	25

DESIGN: 35, 100l. Arms of Pope John XXIII.

73 St. Lawrence

1959. 1700th Death Annivs (15 to 100l. in 1958) of Martyrs under Valerian.

286	**73**	15l. brown, yellow and red	20	20
287	-	25l. brown, yellow and lilac	20	20
288	-	50l. multicoloured	35	25
289	-	60l. brown, yellow & green	35	30
290	-	100l. brown, yellow & pur	45	35
291	-	300l. sepia and brown	55	55

PORTRAITS: 25l. Pope Sixtus II; 50l. St. Agapitus; 60l. St. Filisissimus; 100l. St. Cyprian; 300l. St. Fructuosus.

74 Pope Pius XI

1959. 30th Anniv of Lateran Treaty.

292	**74**	30l. brown	20	20
293	**74**	100l. blue	30	25

75 Radio Mast

1959. 2nd Anniv of St. Maria di Galeria Radio Station Vatican City.

294	**75**	25l. pink, yellow and black	20	20
295	**75**	60l. yellow, red and blue	30	25

76 Obelisk and St. John Lateran Basilica

1959. Air. Roman Obelisks.

296	**76**	5l. violet	15	15
297	-	10l. green	15	15
298	-	15l. brown	15	15
299	-	25l. green	15	15
300	-	35l. blue	15	15
301	**76**	50l. green	15	15
302	-	60l. red	15	15
303	-	100l. blue	15	15
304	-	200l. brown	25	15
305	-	500l. brown	60	45

DESIGNS: 10, 60l. Obelisk and Church of Sta. Maria Maggiore; 15, 100l. Vatican Obelisk and Apostolic Palace; 25, 200l. Obelisk and Churches of St. Mary in Montesanto and St. Mary of the Miracles, Piazza del Popolo; 35, 500l. Sallustian Obelisk and Trinita dei Monti Church.

77 St. Casimir, Vilna Palace and Cathedral

1959. 500th Birth Anniv of St. Casimir (patron saint of Lithuania).

306	**77**	50l. brown	20	20
307	**77**	100l. green	30	25

78 "Christ Adored by the Magi" (after Raphael)

1959. Christmas.

308	**78**	15l. black	10	10
309	**78**	25l. red	10	10
310	**78**	60l. blue	30	25

79 "St. Antoninus" (after Dupre)

1960. 500th Death Anniv of St. Antoninus of Florence.

311	**79**	15l. blue	10	10
312	-	25l. green	15	20
313	**79**	60l. brown	45	35
314	-	110l. purple	95	80

DESIGN: 25, 110l. "St. Antoninus preaching sermon" (after Portigiani).

80 Transept of St. John Lateran Basilica

1960. Roman Diocesan Synod.

315	**80**	15l. brown	20	20
316	**80**	60l. black	30	25

81 "The Flight into Egypt" (after Beato Angelico)

1960. World Refugee Year.

317	**81**	5l. green	10	10
318	-	10l. brown	15	10
319	-	25l. red	20	15
320	**81**	60l. violet	25	20
321	-	100l. blue	2·75	2·50
322	-	300l. green	1·40	1·20

DESIGNS: 10, 100l. "St. Peter giving Alms" (Masaccio); 25, 300l. "Madonna of Mercy" (Piero della Francesca).

82 Cardinal Sarto (Pius X) leaving Venice for Conclave in Rome

1960. 1st Anniv of Transfer of Relics of Pope Pius X from Rome to Venice.

323	**82**	15l. brown	35	25
324	-	35l. red	4·00	2·50
325	-	60l. green	1·60	1·00

DESIGNS: 35l. Pope John XXIII kneeling before relics of Pope Pius X; 60l. Relics in procession across St. Mark's Square, Venice.

83 "Feeding the Hungry"

1960. "Corporal Works of Mercy". Della Robbia paintings. Centres in brown.

326	**83**	5l. brown	10	10
327	-	10l. green	10	10
328	-	15l. black	10	10
329	-	20l. red	10	10
330	-	30l. violet	10	10
331	-	35l. brown	10	10
332	-	40l. orange	10	10
333	-	70l. stone	10	10

DESIGNS: 10l. "Giving drinks to the thirsty"; 15l. "Clothing the naked"; 20l. "Sheltering the homeless"; 30l. "Visiting the sick"; 35l. "Visiting the imprisoned"; 40l. "Burying the dead"; 70l. Pope John XXIII between "Faith" and "Charity".

84 "The Nativity" after Gerard Honthorst (Gherardo delle Notte)

1960. Christmas.

334	**84**	10l. black and green	20	10
335	**84**	15l. deep brown and brown	20	10
336	**84**	70l. blue and turqoise	30	20

85 St. Vincent de Paul

1960. Death Tercentenaries of St. Vincent de Paul and St. Louise de Marillac.

337	**85**	40l. violet	20	20
338	-	70l. black	45	30
339	-	100l. brown	1·00	85

DESIGNS: 70l. St. Louise de Marillac; 100l. St. Vincent giving child to care of St. Louise.

86 St. Meinrad

1961. 11th Death Centenary of St. Meinrad.

340	**86**	30l. black	55	35
341	-	40l. lilac	2·00	60
342	-	100l. brown	2·00	1·90

DESIGNS—VERT: 40l. The "Black Madonna", Einsiedeln Abbey. HORIZ: 100l. Einsiedeln Abbey, Switzerland.

87 "Pope Leo I meeting Attila" (Algardi)

1961. 15th Death Centenary of Pope Leo I.

343	**87**	15l. red	20	10
344	**87**	70l. green	75	45
345	**87**	300l. brown	2·50	2·20

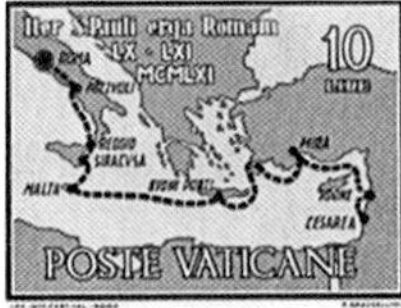

88 Route of St. Paul's Journey to Rome

1961. 1900th Anniv of St. Paul's Arrival in Rome.

346	**88**	10l. green	20	10
347	-	15l. black and brown	20	15
348	-	20l. black and red	20	20
349	**88**	30l. blue	25	25
350	-	75l. black and brown	80	55
351	-	200l. black and blue	2·20	1·90

DESIGNS: 15, 75l. St. Paul's arrival in Rome (after sculpture by Maraini); 20, 200l. Basilica of St. Paul-outside-the-Walls, Rome.

89 "L'Osservatore Romano", 1861 and 1961

1961. Centenary of "L'Osservatore Romano" (Vatican newspaper).

352	**89**	40l. black and brown	20	20
353	-	70l. black and blue	70	55
354	-	250l. black and yellow	2·75	2·40

DESIGNS: 70l. "L'Osservatore Romano" offices; 250l. Printing machine.

90 St. Patrick (ancient sculpture)

1961. 15th Death Centenary of St. Patrick.

355	**90**	10l. green and buff	15	15
356	-	15l. brown and blue	15	15
357	**90**	40l. green and yellow	15	15
358	-	150l. brown and blue	60	50

DESIGN: 15, 150l. St. Patrick's Sanctuary, Lough Derg.

91 Arms of Roncalli Family

1961. Pope John XXIII's 80th Birthday.

359	**91**	10l. brown and black	20	15
360	-	25l. green and brown	25	20
361	-	30l. violet and blue	20	20
362	-	40l. blue and violet	20	20
363	-	70l. brown and grey	25	20
364	-	115l. black and brown	60	50

DESIGNS: 25l. Church of St. Mary, Sotto il Monte; 30l. Church of St. Mary, Monte Santo; 40l. Church of Saints Ambrose and Charles, Rome; 70l. St. Peter's Chair, Vatican Basilica; 115l. Pope John XXIII.

92 "The Nativity"

1961. Christmas. Centres multicoloured.

365	**92**	15l. green	10	10
366	**92**	40l. black	20	20
367	**92**	70l. purple	25	25

93 "Annunciation" (after F. Valle)

1962. Air.

368	**93**	1000l. brown	1·90	1·20
369	**93**	1500l. blue	2·50	1·70

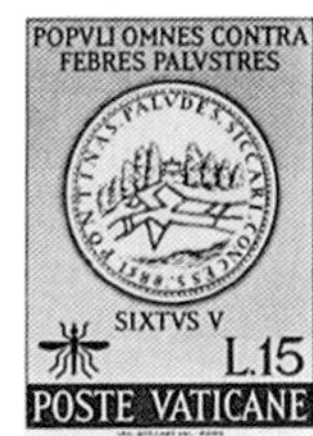

94 "Land Reclamation" Medal of 1588

1962. Malaria Eradication.

370	**94**	15l. violet	10	10
371	-	40l. red	20	20
372	**94**	70l. brown	20	20
373	-	300l. green	60	50

DESIGN: 40, 300l. Map of Pontine Marshes reclamation project (at time of Pope Pius VI).

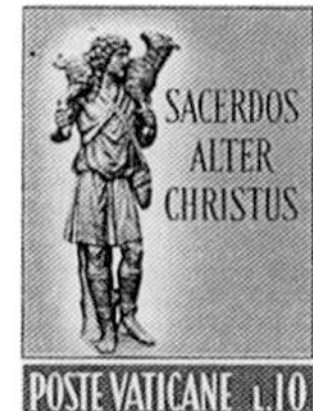

95 "The Good Shepherd" (statue, Lateran Museum)

1962. Religious Vocations.

374	**95**	10l. black and violet	10	10
375	-	15l. brown and blue	10	10
376	**95**	70l. black and green	25	20
377	-	115l. brown and red	2·50	1·40
378	**95**	200l. black and brown	1·40	1·20

DESIGN: 15, 115l. Wheatfield ready for harvest.

96 St. Catherine (after Il Sodoma (Bazzi))

1962. 5th Centenary of St. Catherine of Siena's Canonization.

379	**96**	15l. brown	20	10
380	**96**	60l. violet	30	25
381	**96**	100l. blue	80	75

97 Paulina M. Jaricot

1962. Death Centenary of Paulina M. Jaricot (founder of Society for the Propagation of the Faith). Multicoloured centres.

382	**97**	10l. lilac	10	10
383	**97**	50l. green	25	20
384	**97**	150l. grey	55	50

98 St. Peter and St. Paul (from graffito on child's tomb)

1962. 6th International Christian Archaeology Congress, Ravenna.

385	**98**	20l. brown and violet	10	10
386	-	40l. green and brown	10	10
387	**98**	70l. brown and turquoise	25	25
388	-	100l. green and red	25	25

DESIGN: 40, 100l. "The Passion" (from bas relief on tomb in Domitilla cemetery, near Rome).

99 "Faith" (after Raphael)

1962. Ecumenical Council.

389	**99**	5l. brown and blue	10	10
390	-	10l. brown and green	10	10
391	-	15l. brown and red	10	10
392	-	25l. grey and red	10	10
393	-	30l. black and mauve	10	10
394	-	40l. brown and red	25	10
395	-	60l. brown and green	10	10
396	-	115l. red	25	25

DESIGNS—Divine Virtues: 10l. "Hope"; 15l. "Charity" (both after Raphael); 25l. Arms of Pope John XXIII and symbols of Evangelists (frontispiece of "Humanae Salutis" by Arrigo Bravi); 30l. Central Nave, St. Peter's (council venue); 40l. Pope John XXIII; 60l. "St. Peter" (bronze in Vatican Basilica); 115l. The Holy Ghost in form of dove.

100 "The Nativity"

1962. Christmas. Centres multicoloured.

397	**100**	10l. grey	10	10
398	**100**	15l. drab	10	10
399	**100**	90l. green	20	20

101 "Miracle of the Loaves and Fishes" (after Murillo)

1963. Freedom from Hunger.

400	**101**	15l. sepia and brown	10	10
401	-	40l. green and red	10	10
402	**101**	100l. brown and blue	10	10
403	-	200l. green and turquoise	20	15

DESIGN: 40, 200l. "Miracle of the Fishes" (after Raphael).

102 Pope John XXIII

1963. Award of Balzan Peace Prize to Pope John XXIII.

404	**102**	15l. brown	20	20
405	**102**	160l. black	30	25

103 St. Peter's Keys

1963. "Vacant See".

406	**103**	10l. brown	10	10
407	**103**	40l. brown on yellow	10	10
408	**103**	100l. brown on violet	25	10

104 Pope Paul VI

1963. Coronation of Pope Paul VI.

409	**104**	15l. black	10	10
410	-	40l. red	10	10
411	**104**	115l. brown	15	10
412	-	200l. grey	35	35

DESIGN: 40, 200l. Arms of Pope Paul VI.

105 "The Nativity" (African terracotta statuette)

1963. Christmas.

413	**105**	10l. brown and light brown	10	10
414	**105**	40l. brown and blue	10	10
415	**105**	100l. brown and green	15	10

106 St. Cyril

1963. 1100th Anniv of Conversion of Slavs by Saints Cyril and Methodius.

416	**106**	30l. purple	10	10
417	-	70l. brown	10	10
418	-	150l. purple	15	10

DESIGNS: 70l. Map of Moravia; 150l. St. Methodius.

107 Pope Paul VI

1964. Pope Paul's Visit to the Holy Land.

419	**107**	15l. black	10	10
420	-	25l. red	10	10
421	-	70l. sepia	10	10
422	-	160l. blue	25	15

DESIGNS: 25l. Church of the Nativity, Bethlehem; 70l. Church of the Holy Sepulchre, Jerusalem; 160l. Well of the Virgin Mary, Nazareth.

108 St. Peter, Pharaoh's Tomb, Wadi-es-Sebua

1964. Nubian Monuments Preservation.

423	**108**	10l. brown and blue	10	10
424	-	20l. multicoloured	10	10
425	**108**	70l. brown and light brown	10	10
426	-	200l. multicoloured	25	15

DESIGN: 20, 200l. Philae Temple.

109 Pope Paul VI

1964. Vatican City's Participation in New York World's Fair.

427	**109**	15l. blue	10	10
428	-	50l. brown	10	10
429	**109**	100l. blue	10	10
430	-	250l. brown	25	25

DESIGNS: 50l. Michelangelo's "Pieta"; 250l. Detail of Madonna's head from "Pieta".

110 Michelangelo

1964. 400th Death Anniv of Michelangelo. Paintings in the Sistine Chapel.

431	**110**	10l. black	10	10
432	-	25l. purple	10	10
433	-	30l. green	10	10
434	-	40l. violet	10	10
435	-	150l. green	25	20

PAINTINGS: 25l. Prophet Isaiah; 30l. Delphic Sibyl; 40l. Prophet Jeremiah; 150l. Prophet Joel.

111 "The Good Samaritan" (after Emilio Greco)

1964. Red Cross Centenary (1963). Cross in red.

436	**111**	10l. brown	20	10
437	**111**	30l. blue	20	10
438	**111**	300l. brown	25	25

112 "Christmas Scene" (after Kimiko Koseki)

1964. Christmas.

439	**112**	10l. multicoloured	20	10
440	**112**	15l. multicoloured	20	10
441	**112**	135l. multicoloured	25	20

113 Cues's Birthplace

1964. 500th Death Anniv of Nicholas Cues (Cardinal Cusanus).

442	**113**	40l. green	20	10
443	-	200l. red	25	25

DESIGN: 200l. Cardinal Cusanus's sepulchre, St. Peter's (relief by A. Bregno).

114 Pope Paul at prayer

1964. Pope Paul's Visit to India.

444	**114**	15l. purple	10	10
445	-	25l. green	10	10
446	-	60l. brown	10	10
447	-	200l. purple	25	25

DESIGN—HORIZ: 25l. Public altar, "The Oval", Bombay; 60l. "Gateway to India", Bombay. VERT: 200l. Pope Paul walking across map of India.

115 Sts. Mbaga Tuzinde, Carolus Lwanga and Kizito

1965. Ugandan Martyrs.

448		15l. turquoise	10	10
449	**115**	20l. brown	10	10
450	-	30l. blue	10	10
451	-	75l. black	10	10
452	-	100l. red	10	10
453	-	160l. violet	25	25

DESIGNS: 15l. St. Joseph Mukasa and six other martyrs; 30l. Sts. Matthias Mulumba, Noe Mawagalli and Lucas Banabakintu; 75l. Sts. Gonzaga Gonza, Athanasius Bazzekuketta, Pontianus Ngondwe and Bruno Serunkuma; 100l. Sts. Anatolius Kiriggwajjo, Andreas Kaggwa and Adulphus Mukasa; 160l. Sts. Mukasa Kiriwananvu and Gyavira.

116 Dante (after Raphael)

1965. 700th Anniv of Dante's Birth.

454	**116**	10l. brown and light brown	10	10
455	-	40l. brown and red	10	10
456	-	70l. brown and green	10	10
457	-	200l. brown and blue	25	25

DESIGNS—After drawings by Botticelli: 40l. "Inferno"; 70l. "Purgatory"; 200l. "Paradise".

117 St. Benedict (after Perugino)

1965. Declaration of St. Benedict as Patron Saint of Europe.

458	**117**	40l. brown	10	10
459	-	300l. green	50	50

DESIGN: 300l. Montecassino Abbey.

118 Pope Paul

1965. Pope Paul's Visit to the U.N., New York.

460	**118**	20l. brown	10	10
461	-	30l. blue	10	10
462	-	150l. green	20	20
463	**118**	300l. purple	30	30

DESIGN: 30, 150l. U.N.O. Headquarters, New York.

119 "The Nativity" (Peruvian setting)

1965. Christmas.

464	**119**	20l. red	10	10
465	**119**	40l. brown	10	10
466	**119**	200l. green	25	25

120 Pope Paul

1966

467	**120**	5l. brown	10	10
468	-	10l. violet	10	10
469	-	15l. brown	10	10
470	-	20l. green	10	10
471	-	30l. brown	10	10
472	-	40l. turquoise	10	10
473	-	55l. blue	10	10
474	-	75l. purple	10	10
475	-	90l. mauve	10	10
476	-	130l. green	25	15

DESIGNS (SCULPTURES): 10l. "Music"; 15l. "Science"; 20l. "Painting"; 30l. "Sculpture"; 40l. "Building"; 55l. "Carpentry"; 75l. "Agriculture"; 90l. "Metallurgy"; 130l. "Learning".

121 Queen Dabrowka and King Mieszko I

1966. Poland's Christian Millennium.

477	**121**	15l. black	10	10
478	-	25l. violet	10	10
479	-	40l. red	10	10
480	-	50l. red	10	10
481	-	150l. grey	15	10
482	-	220l. brown	25	25

DESIGNS: 25l. St. Adalbert (Wojciech) and Wroclaw and Gniezno Cathedrals; 40l. St. Stanislas, Skalka Cathedral and Wawel Royal Palace, Cracow; 50l. Queen Jadwiga (Hedwig); Ostra Brama Gate with Mater Misericordiae, Wilno, and Jagellon University Library, Cracow; 150l. "Black Madonna", Jasna Gora Monastery (Czestochowa) and St. John's Cathedral, Warsaw; 220l. Pope Paul VI greeting Poles.

122 Pope John XXIII and St. Peter's, Rome

1966. 4th Anniv of Opening of Ecumenical Council.

483	**122**	10l. black and red	10	10
484	-	15l. green and brown	10	10
485	-	55l. mauve and brown	10	10
486	-	90l. black and green	10	10
487	-	100l. yellow and green	10	10
488	-	130l. sepia and brown	25	25

DESIGNS: 15l. Book of Prayer, St. Peter's; 55l. Mass; 90l. Pope Paul with Patriarch Athenagoras; 100l. Episcopal ring; 130l. Pope Paul at closing ceremony (12.10.65).

123 "The Nativity" (after sculpture by Scorzelli)

1966. Christmas.

489	**123**	20l. purple	10	10
490	**123**	55l. green	10	10
491	**123**	225l. brown	25	25

124 Jetliner over St. Peter's

1967. Air.

492	**124**	20l. violet	10	10
493	-	40l. lilac and pink	10	10
494	-	90l. blue and grey	10	10
495	**124**	100l. black and red	10	10
496	-	200l. lilac and grey	30	25
497	-	500l. brown & light brown	60	35

DESIGNS: 40, 200l. Radio mast and St. Gabriel's statue; 90, 500l. Aerial view of St. Peter's.

125 St. Peter

1967. 1900th Anniv of Martyrdom of Saints Peter and Paul. Multicoloured.

498		15l. Type **125**	10	10
499		20l. St. Paul	10	10
500		55l. The two Saints	10	10
501		90l. Bernini's baldachin, St. Peter's	10	10
502		220l. Arnolfo di Cambio's tabernacle, St. Paul's Basilica	25	25

126 "The Three Shepherd Children" (sculpture)

1967. 50th Anniv of Fatima Apparitions. Multicoloured.

503		30l. Type **126**	10	10
504		50l. Basilica of Fatima	10	10
505		200l. Pope Paul VI praying before Virgin's statue at Fatima	25	25

127 Congress Emblem

1967. 3rd World Apostolic Laity Congress, Rome.

506	**127**	40l. red	20	20
507	**127**	130l. blue	25	20

128 "The Nativity" (Byzantine carving)

1967. Christmas.

508	**128**	25l. multicoloured	10	10
509	**128**	55l. multicoloured	10	10
510	**128**	180l. multicoloured	25	25

129 "Angel Gabriel" (detail from "The Annunciation" by Fra Angelico)

1968. Air.

511	**129**	1000l. red on cream	1·90	1·20
512	**129**	1500l. black on cream	2·30	1·90

130 Pope Paul VI

1968. Pope Paul's Visit to Colombia.

513	**130**	25l. brown and black	10	10
514	-	55l. brown, grey and black	10	10
515	-	220l. brown, blue & black	25	25

DESIGNS: 55l. Monstrance (Raphael's "Disputa"); 220l. Map of South America.

131 "The Holy Child of Prague"

1968. Christmas.

516	**131**	20l. purple and red	10	10
517	**131**	50l. violet and lilac	10	10
518	**131**	250l. blue and light blue	25	75

132 "The Resurrection" (Fra Angelico)

1969. Easter.

519	**132**	20l. red and buff	10	10
520	**132**	90l. green and buff	10	10
521	**132**	180l. blue and buff	20	20

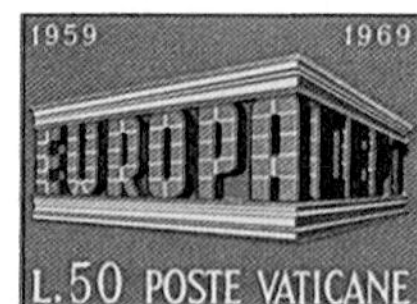

133 Colonnade

1969. Europa.

522	**133**	50l. brown and grey	20	20
523	**133**	90l. brown and red	20	20
524	**133**	130l. brown and green	25	25

134 Pope with Young Africans

1969. Pope Paul's Visit to Uganda.

525	**134**	25l. brown and ochre	10	10
526	-	55l. brown and red	10	10
527	-	250l. multicoloured	25	25

DESIGNS: 55l. Pope with African bishops; 250l. Map of Africa and olive branch.

135 Pope Pius IX

1969. Centenary of St. Peter's Circle Society.

528	**135**	30l. brown	10	10
529	-	50l. grey	10	10
530	-	220l. purple	25	25

DESIGNS: 50l. Monogram of Society; 220l. Pope Paul VI.

136 "Expo 70" Emblem

1970. "Expo 70" World's Fair, Osaka. Mult.

531		25l. Type **136**	10	10
532		40l. Osaka Castle	10	10
533		55l. "Madonna and Child" (Domoto)	10	10
534		90l. Vatican pavilion	10	10
535		110l. Mt. Fuji	20	20

137 Commemorative Medal of Pius IX

1970. Centenary of 1st Vatican Council.

536	**137**	20l. brown and orange	10	10
537	-	50l. multicoloured	10	10
538	-	180l. purple and red	25	25

DESIGNS: 50l. Arms of Pius IX; 180l. Council souvenir medal.

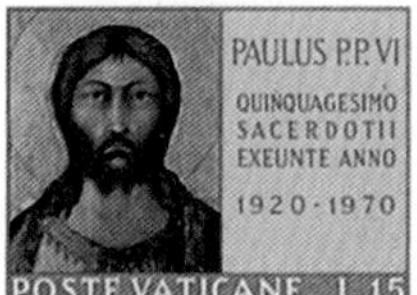

138 "Christ" (Simone Martini)

1970. 50th Anniv of Pope Paul's Ordination as Priest. Multicoloured.

539	15l. Type **138**	10	10
540	25l. "Christ" (R. v. d. Weyden)	10	10
541	50l. "Christ" (Durer)	10	10
542	90l. "Christ" (El Greco)	10	10
543	180l. Pope Paul VI	25	25

139 "Adam" (Michelangelo)

1970. 25th Anniv of United Nations.

544	20l. Type **139**	10	10
545	90l. "Eve" (Michelangelo)	10	10
546	220l. Olive branch	25	25

140 Pope Paul VI

1970. Pope Paul's Visit to Asia and Oceania. Multicoloured.

547	25l. Type **140**	10	10
548	55l. "Holy Child of Cebu" (Philippines)	10	10
549	100l. "Madonna and Child", Darwin Cathedral (G. Hamori)	10	10
550	130l. Manila Cathedral	25	25
551	220l. Sydney Cathedral	30	30

141 "Angel with Lectern"

1971. Racial Equality Year. Multicoloured.

552	20l. Type **141**	10	10
553	40l. "Christ Crucified, and Doves"	10	10
554	50l. Type **141**	10	10
555	130l. As 40l.	10	10

142 "Madonna and Child" (F. Gnissi)

1971. Easter. Religious Paintings. Multicoloured.

556	25l. Type **142**	10	10
557	40l. "Madonna and Child" ("Sassetta", S. di Giovanni)	10	10
558	55l. "Madonna and Child" (C. Crivelli)	10	10
559	90l. "Madonna and Child" (C. Maratta)	10	10
560	180l. "The Holy Family" (G. Ceracchini)	25	25

143 "St. Dominic Guzman" (Sienese School)

1971. 800th Birth Anniv of St. Dominic Guzman (founder of Preaching Friars Order). Mult.

561	25l. Type **143**	10	10
562	55l. Portrait by Fra Angelico	10	10
563	90l. Portrait by Titian	10	10
564	180l. Portrait by El Greco	25	25

144 "St. Matthew"

1971. Air.

565	**144**	200l. black and green	25	25
566	-	300l. black and brown	45	35
567	-	500l. black and pink	80	60
568	-	1000l. black and mauve	1·50	1·20

DESIGNS—"The Four Evangelists" (ceiling frescoes by Fra Angelico in the Niccolina Chapel, Vatican City): 300l. "St. Mark"; 500l. "St. Luke"; 1000l. "St. John".

145 "St. Stephen" (from chasuble, Szekesfehervar Church, Hungary)

1971. Millennium of St. Stephen, King of Hungary.

569	**145**	50l. multicoloured	10	10
570	-	180l. black and yellow	10	10

DESIGN: 180l. "Madonna, Patroness of Hungary", (sculpture, circa 1511).

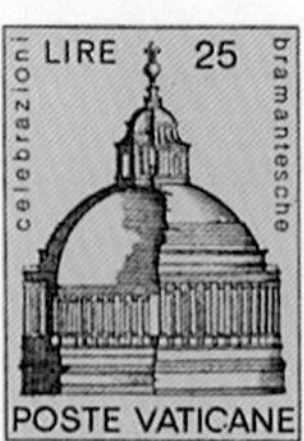

146 Bramante's Design for Cupola, St. Peter's

1972. Bramante Celebrations.

571	**146**	25l. black and yellow	10	10
572	-	90l. black and yellow	10	10
573	-	130l. black and yellow	15	15

DESIGNS: 90l. Donato Bramante (architect) from medal; 130l. Spiral staircase, Innocent VIII's Belvedere, Vatican.

147 "St. Mark at Sea" (mosaic)

1972. UNESCO "Save Venice" Campaign. Multicoloured.

574	25l. Type **147**	30	30
575	50l. Venice (top left-hand section)	20	20
576	50l. Venice (top right-hand section)	20	20
577	50l. Venice (bottom left-hand section)	20	20
578	50l. Venice (bottom right-hand section)	20	20
579	180l. St. Mark's Basilica	80	80
MS580	113×161 mm. Nos. 574/9	3·00	3·00

Nos. 575/8 are smaller 39×28 mm and were issued together, se-tenant, forming a composite design of a 1581 fresco showing a panoramic map of Venice.

148 Gospel of St. Mark (from codex "Biblia dell'Aracoeli")

1972. International Book Year. Illuminated Manuscripts. Multicoloured.

581	30l. Type **148**	10	25
582	50l. Gospel of St. Luke ("Biblia dell'Aracoeli")	10	10
583	90l. 2nd Epistle of St. John (Bologna codex)	10	10
584	100l. Revelation of St. John (Bologna codex)	10	10
585	130l. Epistle of St. Paul to the Romans (Italian codex)	25	25

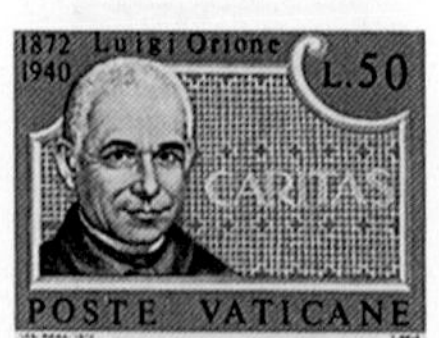

149 Luigi Orione (founder of "Caritas")

1972. Birth Centenaries. Multicoloured.

586	50l. Type **149**	10	10
587	180l. Lorenzo Perosi (composer)	25	25

150 Cardinal Bassarione (Roselli fresco, Sistine Chapel)

1972. 500th Death Anniv of Cardinal Bassarione.

588	-	40l. green	10	10
589	**150**	90l. red	10	10
590	-	130l. black	30	30

DESIGNS: 40l. "Reading of Bull of Union" (relief); 130l. Arms of Cardinal Bassarione.

151 Congress Emblem

1973. Int Eucharistic Congress. Melbourne. Mult.

591	25l. Type **151**	10	10
592	75l. Michelangelo's "Pieta"	10	10
593	300l. Melbourne Cathedral	30	30

152 St. Theresa's Birthplace

1973. Birth Centenary of St. Theresa of Lisieux.

594	**152**	25l. black and red	10	10
595	-	55l. black and yellow	10	10
596	-	220l. black and blue	25	25

DESIGNS: 55l. St. Theresa; 220l. Basilica of Lisieux.

153 Torun (birthplace)

1973. 500th Birth Anniv of Copernicus.

597	**153**	20l. green	10	10
598	-	50l. brown	10	10
599	**153**	100l. purple	20	15
600	-	130l. blue	20	20

DESIGN: 50, 130l. Copernicus.

154 "St. Wenceslas"

1973. Millenary of Prague Diocese. Mult.

601	20l. Type **154**	10	10
602	90l. Arms of Prague Diocese	10	10
603	150l. Tower of Prague Cathedral	20	20
604	220l. "St. Adalbert"	25	25

155 Church of St. Hripsime

1973. 800th Death Anniv of St. Narsete Shnorali (Armenian patriarch).

605	**155**	25l. brown and ochre	10	10
606	-	90l. black and lilac	10	10
607	-	180l. purple and green	15	20

DESIGNS: 90l. Armenian "khatchkar" (stone stele) inscribed "Victory"; 180l. St. Narsete Shnorali.

156 "Angel" (porch of St. Mark's, Venice)

1974. Air.

608	**156**	2500l. multicoloured	3·75	3·00

157 "And there was Light"

1974. International Book Year (1973). "The Bible". Biblical Texts. Multicoloured.

609	15l. Type **157**	10	10
610	25l. "Noah entrusts himself to God" (horiz)	10	10
611	50l. "The Annunciation"	10	10
612	90l. "The Nativity"	10	10
613	180l. "The Lord feeds His People" (horiz)	25	25

158 Noah's Ark and Dove

1974. Centenary of U.P.U. Mosaics. Multicoloured.

614	50l. Type **158**	10	10
615	90l. Sheep in landscape	25	20

159 Pupils

1974. 700th Death Anniv of St. Thomas Aquinas (founder of Fra Angelico School). "The School of St. Thomas" (painting, St. Mark's Convent, Florence). Each brown and gold.

616	50l. Type **159**	10	10
617	90l. St. Thomas and pupils (24×40 mm)	20	20
618	220l. Pupils (different)	25	25

Nos. 616/18 were issued together, se-tenant, forming a composite design.

160 "Civita" (medieval quarter), Bagnoregio

1974. 700th Death Anniv of St. Bonaventura of Bagnoregio. Wood-carvings. Multicoloured.

619	40l. Type **160**	10	10
620	90l. "Tree of Life" (13th-century motif)	10	10
621	220l. "St. Bonaventura (B. Gozzoli)	25	25

161 Christus Victor

1974. Holy Year (1975). Multicoloured.

622	10l. Type **161**	10	10
623	25l. Christ	10	10
624	30l. Christ (different)	10	10
625	40l. Cross and dove	10	10
626	50l. Christ enthroned	10	10
627	55l. St. Peter	10	10
628	90l. St. Paul	10	10
629	100l. St. Peter	10	10
630	130l. St. Paul	10	10
631	220l. Arms of Pope Paul VI	25	25
632	250l. Pope Paul VI giving blessing	30	30

162 Fountain, St. Peter's Square

1975. European Architectural Heritage Year. Fountains.

633	**162**	20l. black and brown	10	10
634	-	40l. black and lilac	10	10
635	-	50l. black and pink	10	10
636	-	90l. black and green	10	10
637	-	100l. black and green	10	10
638	-	200l. black and blue	25	25

FOUNTAINS: 40l. Piazza St. Martha; 50l. Del Forno; 90l. Belvedere courtyard; 100l. Academy of Sciences; 200l. Galley fountain.

163 "Pentecost" (El Greco)

1975. Pentecost.

639	**163**	300l. orange and red	45	45

164 "Miracle of Loaves and Fishes" (gilt glass)

1975. 9th International Christian Archaeological Congress. 4th-century Art. Multicoloured.

640	30l. Type **164**	10	10
641	150l. Christ (painting)	20	15
642	200l. Raising of Lazarus (gilt glass)	30	30

165 Pope Sixtus IV investing Bartolomeo Sacchi as First Librarian (fresco)

1975. 500th Anniv of Apostolic Library.

643	**165**	70l. red and violet	10	10
644	-	100l. green and light green	15	10
645	-	250l. red and blue	30	30

DESIGNS—VERT: 100l. Pope Sixtus IV (codex). HORIZ: 250l. Pope Sixtus IV visiting library (fresco).

166 Passionists' House, Argentario

1975. Death Bicentenary of St. Paul of the Cross (founder of Passionist religious order). Mult.

646	50l. Type **166**	10	10
647	150l. "St. Paul" (D. della Porta) (26×31 mm)	25	25
648	300l. Basilica of Saints John and Paul	35	35

167 Detail from Painting

1975. International Women's Year. Painting by Fra Angelico. Multicoloured.

649	100l. Type **167**	20	20
650	200l. Detail from painting (different)	35	35

168 "The Last Judgement" (detail)

1976. Air.

651	**168**	500l. brown and blue	1·00	1·00
652	-	1000l. brown and blue	1·40	1·20
653	-	2500l. brown and blue	3·25	2·75

DESIGNS: 1000l., 2500l. Different motifs from Michelangelo's "The Last Judgement".

169 "Madonna in Glory with the Child Jesus and Six Saints" (detail)

1976. 400th Death Anniv of Titian. Details from "The Madonna in Glory with the Child Jesus and Six Saints".

654	**169**	100l. red	30	30
655	-	300l. red	50	50

170 Eucharist Ear of Wheat and Globe

1976. 41st Int Eucharist Congress, Philadelphia.

656	**170**	150l. multicoloured	20	20
657	-	200l. gold and blue	30	30
658	-	400l. gold and green	70	70

DESIGNS: 200l. Eucharist within protective hands; 400l. Adoration of the Eucharist.

171 "Transfiguration" (detail)

1976. Details of Raphael's "Transfiguration". Multicoloured.

659	30l. Type **171** ("Moses")	10	10
660	40l. "Christ Transfigured"	10	10
661	50l. "Prophet Elijah"	10	10
662	100l. "Two Apostles"	10	10
663	150l. "The Relatives"	15	10
664	200l. "Landscape"	25	25

172 St. John's Tower and Fountain

1976. Architecture.

665	**172**	50l. brown and lilac	10	10
666	-	100l. sepia and brown	10	10
667	-	120l. black and green	25	25
668	-	180l. black and grey	30	30
669	-	250l. brown and stone	35	35
670	-	300l. purple	50	50

DESIGNS: 100l. Fountain of the Sacrament; 120l. Fountain at entrance to Gardens; 180l. Cupola of St. Peter's and Sacristy Basilica; 250l. Borgia Tower, Sistine Chapel and Via della Fondamenta; 300l. Apostolic Palace, Courtyard of St. Damasius.

173 "Canticles of Brother Sun" (detail)

1977. 750th Death Anniv of St. Francis of Assisi. Details from "Canticles of Brother Sun" by D. Cambellotti. Multicoloured.

671	50l. Type **173** ("The Lord's Creatures")	10	10
672	70l. "Brother Sun"	10	10
673	100l. "Sister Moon and Stars"	10	10
674	130l. "Sister Water"	10	10
675	170l. "Praise in Infirmities and Tribulations"	25	25
676	200l. "Praise for Bodily Death"	30	30

174 Detail from Fresco

1977. 600th Anniv of Return of Pope Gregory from Avignon. Fresco by G. Vasari. Multicoloured.

677	170l. Type **174**	25	30
678	350l. Detail from fresco (different)	50	50

175 "Death of the Virgin"

1977. Festival of Assumption. Miniatures from Apostolic Library. Multicoloured.

679	200l. Type **175**	30	30
680	400l. "Assumption of Virgin into Heaven"	60	60

176 "God of the Nile"

1977. Classical Sculpture in Vatican Museums (1st series). Statues. Multicoloured.

681	50l. Type **176**	10	10
682	120l. "Pericles"	10	10
683	130l. "Husband and Wife with joined Hands"	25	25
684	150l. "Belvedere Apollo"	25	25
685	170l. "Laocoon"	30	30
686	350l. "Belvedere Torso"	50	50

See also Nos. 687/92.

177 "Creation of the Human Race"

1977. Classical Sculpture in Vatican Museums (2nd series). Paleo-Christian Sarcophagi Carvings. Multicoloured.

687	50l. Type **177**	10	10
688	70l. "Three Youths in the Fiery Furnace"	10	10
689	100l. "Adoration of the Magi"	10	10
690	130l. "Christ raising Lazarus from the Dead"	25	25
691	200l. "The Good Shepherd"	25	25
692	400l. "Resurrection"	55	55

178 "Madonna with the Parrot" (detail)

1977. 400th Birth Anniv of Rubens.

693	**178**	350l. multicoloured	60	60

179 "The Face of Christ"

1978. 80th Birthday of Pope Paul VI. Mult.

694	350l. Type **179**	45	50
695	400l. "Pope Paul VI" (drawing by L. B. Barriviera)	60	60

180 Arms of Pope Pius IX

1978. Death Cent of Pope Pius IX. Multicoloured.

696	130l. Type **180**	10	10
697	170l. Seal of Pius IX	25	15
698	200l. Portrait of Pius IX	30	25

181 Microwave Antenna and Radio Vatican Emblem

1978. Air. 10th World Telecommunications Day.

699	**181**	1000l. multicoloured	1·30	1·20
700	**181**	2000l. multicoloured	2·50	2·30
701	**181**	3000l. multicoloured	3·75	3·50

182 St. Peter's Keys

1978. "Vacant See".

702	**182**	120l. blue and violet	20	15
703	**182**	150l. pink and violet	20	15
704	**182**	250l. yellow and violet	30	25

183 St. Peter's Keys

1978. "Vacant See".

705	**183**	120l. yellow, blue & black	20	15
706	**183**	200l. yellow, red and black	20	15
707	**183**	250l. multicoloured	30	25

184 Pope John Paul I on Throne

1978. Pope John Paul I Commem. Mult.

708	70l. Type **184**	10	10
709	120l. The Pope smiling	10	10
710	250l. The Pope in Vatican Gardens	35	35
711	350l. The Pope giving blessing (horiz)	60	50

185 Arms of Pope John Paul II

1979. Inauguration of Pontificate of Pope John Paul II. Multicoloured.

712	170l. Type **185**	25	25
713	250l. The Pope giving his blessing	35	30
714	400l. "Christ handing the keys to St. Peter" (relief, A. Buonvicino)	70	50

186 The Martyrdom (14th-century Latin codex)

1979. 900th Death Anniv of St. Stanislaus. Multicoloured.

715	120l. Type **186**	25	20
716	150l. St. Stanislaus appears to the people (14th century Latin codex)	25	20
717	250l. Gold reliquary	35	30
718	500l. Cracow Cathedral	70	45

187 Meteorograph

1979. Death Centenary of Angelo Secchi (astronomer). Multicoloured.

719	180l. Type **187**	25	25
720	220l. Spectroscope	35	30
721	300l. Telescope	45	35

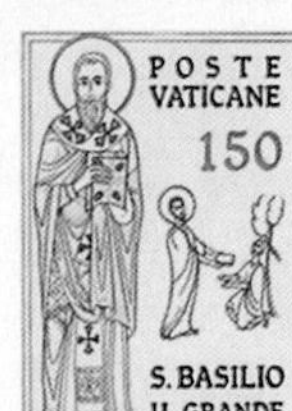

188 St. Basil and Vignette "Handing Monastic Laws to a Hermit"

1979. 160th Death Anniv of St. Basil the Great. Multicoloured.

722	150l. Type **188**	30	30
723	520l. St. Basil and vignette "Caring for the Sick"	70	50

189 Aerial View of Vatican City

1979. 50th Anniv of Vatican City State.

724	**189**	50l. brown, black and pink	10	10
725	-	70l. multicoloured	10	10
726	-	120l. multicoloured	10	10
727	-	150l. multicoloured	25	10
728	-	170l. multicoloured	25	25
729	-	250l. multicoloured	35	30
730	-	450l. multicoloured	75	45

DESIGNS—POPES AND ARMS: 70l. Pius XI; 120l. Pius XII; 150l. John XXIII; 170l. Paul VI; 250l. John Paul I; 450l. John Paul II.

190 Child in Swaddling Clothes (relief, Foundling Hospital, Florence)

1979. International Year of the Child. Sculptures by Della Robbia.

731	**190**	50l. multicoloured	15	15
732	-	120l. multicoloured	25	15
733	-	200l. multicoloured	25	25
734	-	350l. multicoloured	40	35

DESIGNS: 120l. to 350l. Similar sculptures.

191 Abbot Desiderius offering Codices to St. Benedict

1980. 1500th Birth Anniv of St. Benedict of Nursia (founder of Benedictine Order). Multicoloured.

735	80l. Type **191**	10	10
736	100l. St. Benedict composing rules of the Order	10	10
737	150l. Page of St. Benedict's Rules	25	25
738	220l. Death of St. Benedict	30	30
739	450l. Montecassino Abbey (after Paul Bril)	60	35

192 Hands reaching out to Pope and Arms of Santo Domingo

1980. Air. Pope John Paul II's Journeys (1st series). Different coats of arms.

740	**192**	200l. multicoloured	30	25
741	-	300l. multicoloured	40	35
742	-	500l. violet, red and black	70	70
743	-	1000l. multicoloured	1·30	1·00
744	-	1500l. multicoloured	2·00	1·60
745	-	2000l. red, blue and black	3·00	2·30
746	-	3000l. black, red and blue	4·00	3·50

COATS OF ARMS: 300l. Mexico; 500l. Poland; 1000l. Ireland; 1500l. United States; 2000l. United Nations; 3000l. Pope John Paul II, Archbishop Dimitrios and arms of Turkey.

See also Nos. 768/78, 814/25, 862/9, 886/93, 912/16, 940/4, 963/6, 992/6, 1019/22, 1049/51, 1076/80, 1113/14, 1136/41, 1174/9, 1206/11, 1236/40, 1284/8 and 1312/16.

193 Bernini (self-portrait) and Medallion showing Baldacchino, St. Peter's

1980. 300th Death Anniv of Gian Lorenzo Bernini (artist and architect). Multicoloured.

747	80l. Type **193**	10	10
748	170l. Bernini and medallion showing his plan for St. Peter's	25	25
749	250l. Bernini, medallion of bronze chair and group "Doctors of the Church", St. Peter's	35	30
750	350l. Bernini and medallion of Apostolic Palace stairway	50	40

194 St. Albertus on Mission of Peace

1980. 700th Death Anniv of St. Albertus Magnus. Multicoloured.

751	300l. Type **194**	45	35
752	400l. St. Albertus as Bishop	60	45

195 Communion of the Saints

1980. Feast of All Saints. Multicoloured.

753	250l. Type **195**	40	35
754	500l. Christ and saints	75	60

196 Marconi, Pope Pius XI and Radio Emblem

1981. 50th Anniv of Vatican Radio. Mult.

755	100l. Type **196**	15	15
756	150l. Microphone	30	25
757	200l. Antenna of Santa Maria di Galeria Radio Centre and statue of Archangel Gabriel	35	35
758	600l. Pope John Paul II	70	60

197 Virgil and his Writing-desk

1981. Death Bimillenary of Virgil (Roman poet). Multicoloured.

759	350l. Type **197**	45	40
760	600l. As Type **197** but inscr "P. VERGILI MARONIS AENEIDOS LIBRI"	80	75

198 Congress Emblem and Apparition of Virgin to St. Bernadette

1981. 42nd International Eucharistic Congress, Lourdes. Multicoloured.

761	80l. Congress emblem	15	15
762	150l. Type **198**	25	25
763	200l. Emblem and pilgrims going to Lourdes	30	25
764	500l. Emblem and Bishop with faithful venerating Virgin	65	50

199 Jan van Ruusbroec writing Treatise

1981. 600th Death Anniv of Jan van Ruusbroec (Flemish mystic). Multicoloured.

765 200l. Type **199** 30 25
766 300l. Ruusbroec 45 35

200 Turin Shroud and I.Y.D.P. Emblem

1981. International Year of Disabled Persons.

767 **200** 600l. multicoloured 85 70

201 Arms of John Paul II

1981. Pope John Paul II's Journeys (2nd series). Multicoloured.

768 50l. Type **201** 10 10
769 100l. Crucifix and map of Africa 10 10
770 120l. Hands holding crucifix 15 15
771 150l. Pope performing baptism 25 15
772 200l. Pope embracing African bishop 30 25
773 250l. Pope blessing sick man 40 30
774 300l. Notre-Dame Cathedral, Paris 40 35
775 400l. Pope addressing UNESCO, Paris 50 45
776 600l. "Christ of the Andes", Rio de Janeiro 80 70
777 700l. Cologne Cathedral 90 85
778 900l. Pope giving blessing 1·30 1·20

202 Agnes handing Church to Grand Master of the Crosiers of the Red Star

1982. 700th Death Anniv of Blessed Agnes of Prague. Multicoloured.

779 700l. Type **202** 1·00 80
780 900l. Agnes receiving letter from St. Clare 1·30 1·20

203 "Pueri Cantores" (left panel)

1982. 500th Death Anniv of Luca della Robbia (sculptor).

781 **203** 1000l. green and blue 1·20 1·20
782 - 1000l. multicoloured 1·20 1·20
783 - 1000l. green and blue 1·20 1·20

DESIGNS—As T **203**: No. 783, "Pueri Cantores" (right panel). 44×36 mm: No. 782, "Virgin Mary in Prayer".

204 Virgin Mary and St. Joseph clothe St. Theresa

1982. 400th Death Anniv of St. Theresa of Avila.

784 **204** 200l. orange, grey and red 35 35
785 - 600l. grey, orange and blue 80 75
786 - 1000l. grey, orange and mauve 1·30 1·30

DESIGNS: 600l. Ecstasy of St. Theresa; 1000l. St. Theresa writing "The Interior Castle".

205 Examining Globe

1982. 400th Anniv of Gregorian Calendar. Details from Pope Gregory XIII's tomb.

787 **205** 200l. green 30 30
788 - 300l. black 40 35
789 - 700l. mauve 90 80
MS790 159×109 mm. Nos. 787/9 2·30 2·30

DESIGNS: 300l. Presenting proposals to Pope Gregory XIII; 700l. Kneeling figures.

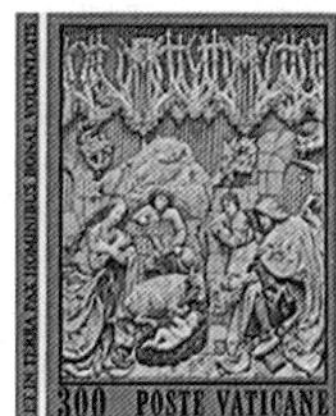

206 "Nativity" (Veit Stoss)

1982. Christmas.

791 **206** 300l. stone, brown & gold 45 40
792 - 450l. lilac, purple and silver 60 50

DESIGN: 450l. "Nativity with Pope John Paul II" (Enrico Manfrini).

207 Crucifixion

1983. Holy Year. Multicoloured.

793 300l. Type **207** 40 35
794 350l. Christ the Redeemer 45 45
795 400l. Pope bringing message of redemption to world 50 50
796 2000l. Dove of the Holy Spirit passing through Holy Door 2·75 2·10

208 Greek Vase

1983. "The Vatican Collections: The Papacy and Art—U.S.A. 1983" Exhibition (1st issue). Sheet 125×170 mm containing T 208 and similar vert designs. Multicoloured.

MS797 100l. Type **208**, 200l. Italiante vase; 250l. Terracotta female bust; 300l. Bust of Emperor Marcus Aurelius; 350l. Bird (fresco fragment); 400l. Sacred vestment of Pope Clement VIII 6·25 5·75

See also Nos. **MS**802 and **MS**803.

209 "Theology"

1983. 500th Birth Anniv of Raphael (artist).

798 **209** 50l. blue and ultramarine 10 10
799 - 400l. purple and mauve 50 40
800 - 500l. brown and chestnut 70 60
801 - 1200l. green and turquoise 1·60 1·20

DESIGNS—Allegories on the Segnatura Room ceiling: 400l. "Poetry"; 500l. "Justice"; 1200l. "Philosophy".

1983. "The Vatican Collections: The Papacy and Art—U.S.A. 1983" Exhibition (2nd issue). Sheet 124×171 mm containing vert designs as T 208. Multicoloured.

MS802 100l. Etruscan terracotta horse's head; 200l. Greek relief of horseman; 300l. Etruscan head of man; 400l. Head of Apollo Belvedere; 500l. Fresco of Moses; 1000l. "Madonna and Child" (Bernardo Daddi) 3·50 3·50

1983. "The Vatican Collections: The Papacy and Art—U.S.A. 1983" Exhibition (3rd issue). Sheet 124×171 mm containing vert designs as T 208. Multicoloured.

MS803 150l. Oedipus and Sphinx (Greek cup); 200l. Votive statue of child (Etruscan bronze); 350l. Statue of Emperor Augustus; 400l. Statue of Good Shepherd; 500l. "St. Nicholas saving ship" (Gentile Fabriano); 1200l. "The Holy Face" (Georges Rouault) 4·00 4·00

210 "Moses explaining the Law to the People" (Luca Signorelli)

1983. Air. World Communications Year. Multicoloured.

804 2000l. Type **210** 2·50 2·30
805 5000l. "St. Paul preaching in Athens" (Raphael) 6·75 5·75

211 Mendel and Hybrid Experiment

1984. Death Centenary of Gregor Johan Mendel (geneticist).

806 **211** 450l. multicoloured 70 60
807 **211** 1500l. multicoloured 2·10 1·50

212 St. Casimir and Vilna Cathedral and Castle

1984. 500th Death Anniv of St. Casimir (patron saint of Lithuania).

808 **212** 550l. multicoloured 75 70
809 **212** 1200l. multicoloured 1·70 1·50

213 Pontifical Academy of Sciences

1984. Cultural and Scientific Institutions.

810 **213** 150l. yellow and brown 25 30
811 - 450l. multicoloured 60 50
812 - 550l. yellow and violet 80 50
813 - 1500l. yellow and blue 2·10 1·80

DESIGNS: 450l. Seals and document from Vatican Secret Archives; 550l. Entrance to Vatican Apostolic Library; 1500l. Vatican Observatory, Castelgandolfo.

214 Pope in Karachi

1984. Pope John Paul II's Journeys (3rd series). Multicoloured.

814 50l. Type **214** 10 10
815 100l. Pope and image of Our Lady of Penafrancia, Philippines 10 10
816 150l. Pope with crucifix (Guam) 25 25
817 250l. Pope and Tokyo Cathedral 35 30
818 300l. Pope at Anchorage, Alaska 40 35
819 400l. Crucifix, crowd and map of Africa 50 40
820 450l. Pope and image of Our Lady of Fatima (Portugal) 65 45
821 550l. Pope, Archbishop of Westminster and Canterbury Cathedral 80 60
822 1000l. Pope and image of Our Lady of Lujan (Argentina) 1·40 80
823 1500l. Pope, Lake Leman and Geneva 2·10 1·40
824 2500l. Pope and Mount Titano (San Marino) 3·50 2·20
825 4000l. Pope and Santiago de Compostela Cathedral (Spain) 5·50 4·50

215 Damascus and Sepulchre of Sts. Marcellinus and Peter

1984. 1600th Death Anniv of Pope St. Damasus. Multicoloured.

826 200l. Type **215** 30 30
827 500l. Damasus and epigraph from St. Januarius's tomb 65 65
828 2000l. Damasus and basilica ruins 2·75 2·20

216 More (after Holbein) and Map

1985. 450th Death Anniv of Saint Thomas More. Multicoloured.

829 250l. Type **216** 35 25
830 400l. St. Thomas More and title page of "Utopia" 60 45
831 2000l. St. Thomas More and title page of "Life of Thomas More" by Domenico Regi 2·75 3·00

217 St. Methodius holding Religious Paintings

1985. 1100th Death Anniv of Saint Methodius. Multicoloured.

832		500l. Type **217**	70	60
833		600l. Saints Cyril and Methodius with Pope Clement I's body	80	80
834		1700l. Saints Benedict, Cyril and Methodius	2·30	1·70

218 Cross on Map of Africa

1985. 43rd International Eucharistic Congress, Nairobi. Multicoloured.

835		100l. Type **218**	15	15
836		400l. Assembly of bishops	50	45
837		600l. Chalice	80	65
838		2300l. Family gazing at cross	3·00	2·00

219 Eagle (from Door, St. Paul's Basilica, Rome)

1985. 900th Death Anniv of Pope Gregory VII. Multicoloured.

839		150l. Type **219**	30	30
840		450l. Pope Gregory VII	65	50
841		2500l. Pope Gregory's former sarcophagus (horiz)	3·50	2·20

220 Mosaic Map of Italy and Symbol of Holy See

1985. Ratification of Modification of 1929 Lateran Concordat.

842	**220**	400l. multicoloured	65	60

221 Carriage

1985. "Italia '85" Int Stamp Exn, Rome.

843	**221**	450l. red and blue	60	50
844	-	1500l. blue and mauve	1·80	1·40
MS845		161×108 mm. Nos. 843/4	3·50	3·50

DESIGN: 1500l. Carriage (different).

222 "Nation shall not Lift up Sword against Nation. . ."

1986. International Peace Year. Multicoloured.

846		50l. Type **222**	10	10
847		350l. Messenger's feet ("How beautiful … are the feet …")	45	35
848		450l. Profiles and olive branch ("Blessed are the peace-makers …")	65	50
849		650l. Dove and sun ("Glory to God in the highest …")	90	80
850		2000l. Pope's hand releasing dove over rainbow ("Peace is a value with no frontiers …")	2·75	1·90

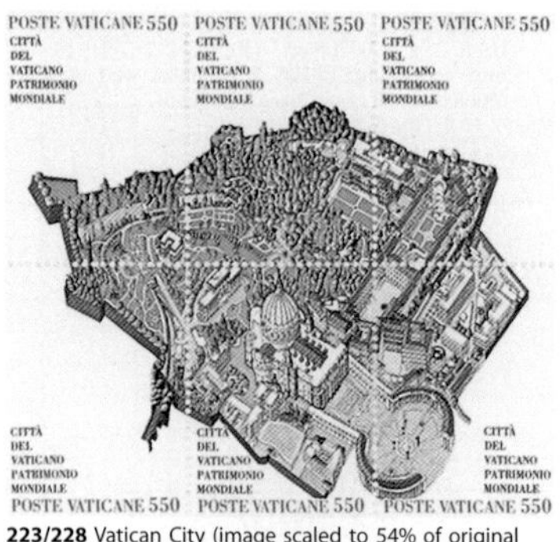

223/228 Vatican City (image scaled to 54% of original size)

1986. World Heritage. Vatican City. Mult.

851	**223**	550l. multicoloured	80	90
852	**224**	550l. multicoloured	80	90
853	**225**	550l. multicoloured	80	90
854	**226**	550l. multicoloured	80	90
855	**227**	550l. multicoloured	80	90
856	**228**	550l. multicoloured	80	90

Nos. 851/6 were printed together, se-tenant, forming the composite design illustrated.

229 St. Camillus saving Invalid from Flood (after Pierre Subleyras)

1986. Centenary of Proclamation of St. Camillus de Lellis and St. John of God as Patron Saints of Hospitals and the Sick.

857	**229**	700l. green, violet and red	90	65
858	-	700l. blue, green and red	90	65
859	-	2000l. multicoloured	2·75	2·20

DESIGNS: No. 858, St. John supporting the sick (after Gomez Moreno); 859, Emblems of Ministers of the Sick and Brothers Hospitallers, and Pope John Paul II talking to patient.

230 "The Philosophers"

1986. 50th Anniv of Pontifical Academy of Sciences. Details from fresco "School of Athens" by Raphael. Multicoloured.

860		1500l. Type **230**	2·00	1·80
861		2500l. "The Scientists"	3·25	3·00

231 Pope and Young People (Central America)

1986. Air. Pope John Paul II's Journeys (4th series). Multicoloured.

862		350l. Type **231**	45	35
863		450l. Pope in prayer, Warsaw Cathedral and Our Lady of Czestochowa (Poland)	60	50
864		700l. Pope kneeling and crowd at Lourdes (France)	90	45
865		1000l. Sanctuary of Mariazell and St. Stephen's Cathedral, Vienna (Austria)	1·40	90
866		1500l. Pope and representatives of nations visited (Alaska, Asia and Pacific Islands)	2·10	1·60
867		2000l. Image of St. Nicholas of Flue, Basilica of Einsiedeln and Pope (Switzerland)	2·75	2·20
868		2500l. Crosses, Notre Dame Cathedral, Quebec, and Pope (Canada)	3·50	2·75
869		5000l. Pope, bishop and young people with cross (Spain, Dominican Republic and Puerto Rico)	7·00	6·25

232 "St. Augustine reading St. Paul's Epistles" (fresco, Benozzo Gozzoli)

1987. 1600th Anniv of Conversion and Baptism of St. Augustine. Multicoloured.

870		300l. Type **232**	40	35
871		400l. "Baptism of St. Augustine" (Bartolomeo di Gentile)	50	50
872		500l. "Ecstasy of St. Augustine" (fresco, Benozzo Gozzoli)	70	60
873		2200l. "Dispute of the Sacrament" (detail of fresco, Raphael)	3·00	2·10

233 Statue of Christ, Lithuanian Chapel, Vatican Crypt

1987. 600th Anniv of Conversion to Christianity of Lithuania. Multicoloured.

874		200l. Type **233**	30	25
875		700l. Statue of Virgin Mary with body of Christ and two angels	85	70
876		3000l. Lithuanian shrine	4·00	3·00

234 Chapter of Riga Church Seal

1987. 800th Anniv of Conversion to Christianity of Latvia. Multicoloured.

877		700l. Type **234**	90	70
878		2400l. Basilica of the Assumption, Aglona	3·25	2·75

235 Judge

1987. "Olymphilex '87" Olympic Stamps Exhibition, Rome. Figures from Caracalla Baths floor mosaic. Multicoloured.

879		400l. Type **235**	50	45
880		500l. Runner	65	60
881		600l. Discus-thrower	80	70
882		2000l. Athlete	2·75	2·00
MS883		151×100 mm. As Nos. 879/82 but with Greek key borders	4·50	4·50

236 Stamp Room and 1929 5c. Stamp

1987. Inauguration of Philatelic and Numismatic Museum. Multicoloured.

884		400l. Type **236**	60	70
885		3500l. Coin room and reverse of 1000l. 1986 coin	4·50	2·75

1987. Pope John Paul II's Journeys (5th series). As T 231. Multicoloured.

886		50l. Youths, Pope and Machu Picchu (Venezuela, Ecuador, Peru, Trinidad and Tobago)	15	15
887		250l. Antwerp Cathedral, smoke stacks and Pope (Netherlands, Luxembourg and Belgium)	35	25
888		400l. People, buildings and Pope (Togo, Ivory Coast, Cameroun, Central African Republic, Zaire, Kenya and Morocco)	60	40
889		500l. Pope holding Cross and youths (Liechtenstein)	70	45
890		600l. Pope, Indians and Delhi Mosque (India)	85	60
891		700l. Pope, people, ceramic and Bogota Cathedral (Colombia and St. Lucia)	1·00	80
892		2500l. Pope, Cure d'Ars and Lyon Cathedral (France)	3·75	3·00
893		4000l. Hands releasing dove and symbols of countries visited (Bangladesh, Singapore, Fiji, New Zealand, Australia and Seychelles)	6·00	4·50

237 Arrival of Relics

1987. 900th Anniv of Transfer of St. Nicholas's Relics from Myra to Bari. Multicoloured.

894		500l. Type **237**	1·60	1·20
895		700l. St. Nicholas giving purses of gold to save from dishonour the three daughters of a poor man	2·40	1·70
896		3000l. St. Nicholas saving a ship	10·50	8·75

238 Children and Sister of Institute of the Daughters of Mary Help of Christians

1988. Death Centenary of St. John Bosco (founder of Salesian Brothers). Multicoloured.

897		500l. Type **238**	70	50
898		1000l. Bosco and children	1·20	1·00
899		2000l. Children and Salesian lay brother	2·30	2·10

Nos. 897/9 were printed together, se-tenant, forming a composite design.

239 The Annunciation

1988. Marian Year. Multicoloured.

900		50l. Type **239**	15	15
901		300l. Nativity	40	35
902		500l. Pentecost	60	50
903		750l. The Assumption	90	80
904		1000l. Mother of the Church	1·40	90
905		2400l. Refuge of Sinners	3·00	2·20

240 Prince Vladimir the Great (15th-century icon)

1988. Millenary of Conversion to Christianity of Rus of Kiev. Multicoloured.

906	450l. Type **240**	60	45
907	650l. St. Sophia's Cathedral, Kiev	80	70
908	2500l. "Mother of God in Prayer" (mosaic, St. Sophia's Cathedral)	3·25	2·50

241 "Marriage at Cana" (detail)

1988. 400th Death Anniv of Paolo Veronese (painter).

909	**241**	550l. blue and red	70	35
910	-	650l. multicoloured	80	70
911	-	3000l. red and brown	3·75	3·25

DESIGNS—HORIZ: 650l. "Self-portrait". VERT: 3000l. "Marriage at Cana" (different detail).

1988. Air. Pope John Paul II's Journeys (6th series). As T 231. Multicoloured.

912	450l. Hands releasing dove, St. Peter's, Rome, Santiago Cathedral and Sanctuary of Our Lady, Lujan (Uruguay, Chile and Argentina)	50	40
913	650l. Pope in act of blessing, Speyer Cathedral and youths (German Federal Republic)	75	70
914	1000l. Hands releasing dove, Gdansk altar and intertwined flowers and thorns (Poland)	60	1·00
915	2500l. Skyscrapers and Pope blessing youths (U.S.A.)	3·00	2·75
916	5000l. Hands releasing dove, tepee at Fort Simpson and American Indians (Canada)	6·00	5·25

242 Angel with Olive Branch

1988. Christmas. Multicoloured.

917	50l. Type **242**	15	15
918	400l. Angel holding olive branch in both hands	50	35
919	500l. Angel with olive branch (flying from right)	70	45
920	550l. Shepherds	75	50
921	850l. Nativity	1·20	85
922	1500l. Wise Men	1·90	1·40
MS923	120×140 mm. As Nos. 917/22 but with gold backgrounds	5·75	5·75

243 Head of Apis

1989. 150th Anniv of Gregorian Egyptian Museum. Sheet 140×100 mm containing T 243 and similar vert designs. Multicoloured.

MS924	400l. Type **243**; 650l. Double-headed statue of Isis and Apis; 750l. Headless statue of physician Ugiahorresne, 2400l. Phoraoh Mentuhotep	5·75	5·75

244 The Annunciation

1989. 600th Anniv of Feast of Visitation of Virgin Mary. Illuminated Initials. Multicoloured.

925	550l. Type **244**	70	45
926	750l. Virgin Mary and St. Elizabeth	90	70
927	2500l. Virgin Mary and St. Elizabeth with Jesus and John the Baptist as babies	3·00	2·50

245 Purple-naped Lory ("Parrot")

1989. Birds featured in "Histoire Naturelle des Oiseaux" by Eleazar Albin. Multicoloured.

928	100l. Type **245**	15	15
929	150l. Green woodpecker	25	30
930	200l. Goldcrest ("Crested wren") and winter ("Common") wren	30	35
931	350l. River kingfisher	45	50
932	500l. Common cardinal ("Red Groas Beak of Virginia")	65	60
933	700l. Northern bullfinch ("Bullfinch")	85	70
934	1500l. Northern lapwing ("Lapwing Plover")	2·00	1·30
935	3000l. Green-winged ("French") teal	4·00	3·00

246 Broken Bread (Congress emblem)

1989. 44th International Eucharistic Congress, Seoul.

936	**246**	550l. red and green	70	65
937	-	850l. multicoloured	1·00	90
938	-	1000l. multicoloured	1·50	1·00
939	-	2500l. green, pink and violet	3·00	2·50

DESIGNS: 850l. Cross; 1000l. Cross and fishes; 2500l. Small cross on wafer.

247 Pope's Arms, Map of South America and Pope

1989. Pope John Paul II's Journeys (7th series). Multicoloured.

940	50l. Type **247**	15	15
941	550l. Austria	75	60
942	800l. Southern Africa	1·20	80
943	1000l. France	1·40	1·00
944	4000l. Italy	5·50	4·50

248 Basilica of the Assumption, Baltimore

1989. Bicentenary of 1st Catholic Diocese in U.S.A. Each agate and brown.

945	450l. Type **248**	60	45
946	1350l. John Carroll (first Archbishop of Baltimore)	1·70	1·50
947	2400l. Cathedral of Mary Our Queen, Baltimore (after Martin Barry)	3·25	2·75

249 Vision of Ursulines on Mystical Stair

1990. 450th Death Anniv of St. Angela Merici (founder of Company of St. Ursula). Mult.

948	700l. Type **249**	1·00	85
949	800l. St. Angela teaching Ursulines	1·10	95
950	2800l. Ursulines	4·00	3·50

250 Ordination and Arrival in Frisia

1990. 1300th Anniv of Beginning of St. Willibrord's Missions. Multicoloured.

951	300l. Type **250**	40	35
952	700l. St. Willibrord in Antwerp, creation as bishop by Pope Sergius I and gift of part of Echternach by Abbess of Euren	90	70
953	3000l. Gift of Echternach by King Pepin and St. Willibrord's death	4·00	3·25

251 Abraham

1990. 40th Anniv of Caritas Internationalis. Details of mosaic from Basilica of Sta. Maria Maggiore, Rome. Multicoloured.

954	450l. Type **251**	80	60
955	650l. Three visitors	1·10	95
956	800l. Sarah making bread	1·30	1·20
957	2000l. Visitors seated at Abraham's table	3·50	3·00
MS958	100×135 mm. As Nos. 954/7 but without gold frame	9·00	9·00

252 Fishermen on Lake Peking

1990. 300th Anniv of Peking–Nanking Diocese. Details of two enamelled bronze vases given by Peking Apostolic Delegate to Pope Pius IX. Multicoloured.

959	500l. Type **252**	60	50
960	750l. Church of the Immaculate Conception (first Peking church, 1650)	95	70
961	1500l. Lake Peking	1·80	1·40
962	2000l. Church of the Redeemer, Peking, 1703	2·75	2·20

253 Pope and African Landscape

1990. Air. Pope John Paul II's Journeys (8th series). Multicoloured.

963	500l. Type **253**	80	60
964	1000l. Northern European landscape (Scandinavia)	1·60	1·30

965	3000l. Cathedral (Santiago de Compostela, Spain)	4·75	3·75
966	5000l. Oriental landscape (Korea, Indonesia and Mauritius)	7·75	6·25

254 Choir of Angels

1990. Christmas. Details of painting by Sebastiano Mainardi. Multicoloured.

967	50l. Type **254**	20	20
968	200l. St. Joseph	40	30
969	650l. Holy Child	1·20	95
970	750l. Virgin Mary	1·40	1·20
971	2500l. "Nativity" (complete picture) (vert)	5·25	4·50

255 "Eleazar" (left half)

1991. Restoration of Sistine Chapel. Details of Lunettes of the Ancestors of Christ by Michelangelo. Multicoloured.

972	50l. Type **255**	20	20
973	100l. "Eleazar" (right half)	20	20
974	150l. "Jacob" (left half)	25	20
975	250l. "Jacob" (right half)	35	25
976	350l. "Josiah" (left half)	50	35
977	400l. "Josiah" (right half)	55	40
978	500l. "Asa" (left half)	60	50
979	650l. "Asa" (right half)	95	70
980	800l. "Zerubbabel" (left half)	1·10	85
981	1000l. "Zerubbabel" (right half)	1·40	1·10
982	2000l. "Azor" (left half)	2·75	2·75
983	3000l. "Azor" (right half)	4·25	3·50

256 Title Page and Pope Leo XIII's Arms

1991. Centenary of "Rerum Novarum" (encyclical on workers' rights).

984	**256**	600l. blue and green	85	60
985	-	750l. green and brown	70	85
986	-	3500l. purple and black	4·75	4·00

DESIGNS: 750l. Allegory of Church, workers and employers (from Leo XIII's 15th Anniv medal, 1892); 3500l. Profile of Pope Leo XIII (from same medal).

257 Astrograph (astronomical camera)

1991. Centenary of Vatican Observatory. Mult.

987	750l. Type **257**	1·10	90
988	1000l. Castelgandolfo observatory (horiz)	1·40	1·20
989	3000l. Vatican Observatory telescope, Mount Graham, Tucson, U.S.A.	4·75	4·00

258 "Apparition of Virgin Mary" (Biagio Puccini)

1991. 600th Anniv of Canonization of St. Bridget (founder of Order of the Holy Saviour). Multicoloured.

990	1500l. Type **258**	2·75	2·30

991	2000l. "Revelation of Christ" (Biagio Puccini)	3·75	3·00

259 Cathedral of the Immaculate Conception, Ouagadougou

1991. Pope John Paul II's Journeys (9th series). Multicoloured.

992	200l. Type **259** (Cape Verde, Guinea-Bissau, Mali, Burkina Faso and Chad)	35	25
993	550l. St. Vitus's Cathedral, Prague (Czechoslovakia)	95	85
994	750l. Basilica of Our Lady of Guadaloupe (Mexico and Curacao)	1·30	1·20
995	1500l. Ta'Pinu Sanctuary, Gozo (Malta)	2·75	2·40
996	3500l. Cathedral of Christ the King, Giteca (Tanzania, Burundi, Rwanda and Ivory Coast)	6·50	5·50

260 Colonnade of St. Peter's Cathedral, Rome

1991. Synod of Bishops' Special Assembly for Europe. Each black and brown.

997	300l. Type **260**	50	35
998	500l. St. Peter's Cathedral and square	85	60
999	4000l. Apostolic Palace and colonnade	6·50	5·50

Nos. 997/9 were issued together, se-tenant, forming a composite design.

261 Christopher Columbus

1992. 500th Anniv of Discovery of America by Columbus. Multicoloured.

1000	500l. Type **261**	70	60
1001	600l. St. Pedro Claver	85	70
1002	850l. "Virgin of the Catholic Kings"	1·20	95
1003	1000l. Bortolome de las Casas	1·40	1·30
1004	2000l. Junipero Serra	3·00	2·40
MS1005	138×95 mm. 1500l. Details of nautical chart from atlas of Battista Agnese	7·75	7·75

262 "Our Lady of Childbirth"

1992. 500th Death Anniv of Piero della Francesca (painter). Multicoloured.

1006	300l. Type **262**	70	65
1007	750l. "Our Lady of Childbirth" (detail)	1·40	1·30
1008	1000l. "The Resurrection"	1·90	1·60
1009	3000l. "The Resurrection" (detail)	5·75	4·75

263 St. Giuseppe comforting the Sick

1992. 150th Death Anniv of St. Giuseppe Benedetto Cottolengo. Multicoloured.

1010	650l. Type **263**	1·30	1·20
1011	850l. St. Giuseppe holding Piccolo Casa della Divina Providenza (infirmary), Turin	1·80	1·60

264 Maize

1992. Plants of the New World. Illustrations from the 18th-century "Phytanthoza Iconographia". Multicoloured.

1012	850l. Type **264**	1·30	1·20
1013	850l. Tomatoes ("Solanum pomiferum")	1·30	1·20
1014	850l. Cactus ("Opuntia")	1·30	1·20
1015	850l. Cacao ("Cacaos, Cacavifera")	1·30	1·20
1016	850l. Peppers ("Solanum tuberosum")	1·30	1·20
1017	850l. Pineapple ("Ananas sagitae")	1·30	1·20

265 Our Lady of Guadalupe, Crucifix and Mitres

1992. 4th Latin American Episcopal Conference, Santo Domingo.

1018	**265**	700l. gold, emerald and green	1·60	1·20

266 Pope, Dove and Map of Europe

1992. Air. Pope John Paul II's Journeys (10th series). Multicoloured.

1019	500l. Type **266** (Portugal)	85	95
1020	1000l. Map of Europe highlighting Poland	1·60	1·60
1021	4000l. Our Lady of Czestochowa and map highlighting Poland and Hungary	6·25	5·00
1022	6000l. Map of South America highlighting Brazil	9·75	9·25

267 "The Annunciation"

1992. Christmas. Mosaics in Church of Sta.Maria Maggiore, Rome. Multicoloured.

1023	600l. Type **267**	1·30	1·20
1024	700l. "Nativity"	1·50	1·40
1025	1000l. "Adoration of the Kings"	2·20	1·90
1026	1500l. "Presentation in the Temple"	3·50	2·75

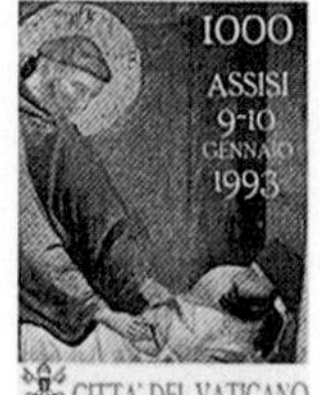

268 "St. Francis healing the Man from Ilerda" (fresco by Giotto in Upper Church, Assisi)

1993. "Peace in Europe" Prayer Meeting, Assisi.

1027	**268**	1000l. multicoloured	1·80	1·60

269 Dome of St. Peter's Cathedral

1993. Architectural Treasures of Rome and the Vatican. Multicoloured.

1028	200l. Type **269**	30	25
1029	300l. St. John Lateran's Basilica	50	35
1030	350l. Basilica of Sta. Maria Maggiore	55	50
1031	500l. St. Paul's Basilica	80	60
1032	600l. Apostolic Palace, Vatican	90	70
1033	700l. Apostolic Palace, Lateran	1·10	95
1034	850l. Papal Palace, Castelgandolfo	1·30	1·10
1035	1000l. Chancery Palace	1·60	1·20
1036	2000l. Palace of Propagation of the Faith	3·25	2·75
1037	3000l. San Calisto Palace	4·75	4·75

270 "The Sacrifice of Isaac"

1993. Ascension Day. Multicoloured.

1038	200l. Type **270**	35	30
1039	750l. Jesus handing New Law to St. Peter	1·30	1·20
1040	3000l. Christ watching servant washing Pilate's hands	3·75	3·50

Nos. 1038/40 were issued together, se-tenant, forming a composite design of the bas-relief "Traditio Legis" from 4th-century sarcophagus.

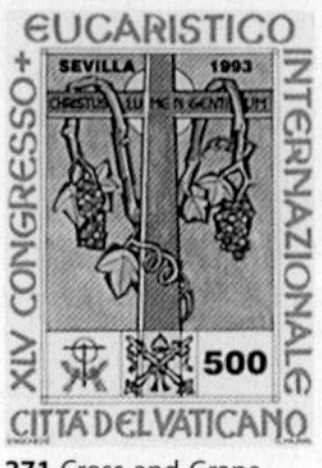

271 Cross and Grape Vines

1993. 45th Int Eucharistic Congress, Seville. Mult.

1041	500l. Type **271**	80	60
1042	700l. Cross and hands offering broken bread	1·10	95
1043	1500l. Hands holding chalice	2·30	2·00
1044	2500l. Cross, banner and ears of wheat	3·75	3·50

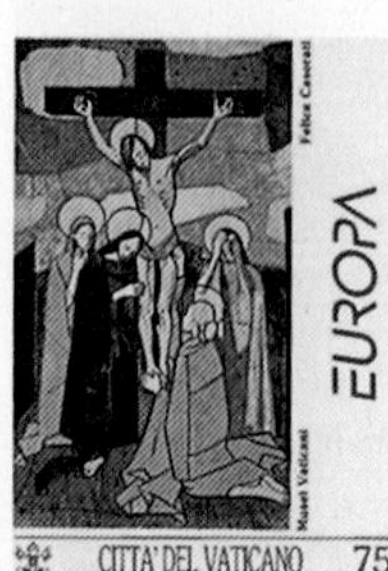

272 "Crucifixion" (Felice Casorati)

1993. Europa. Contemporary Art. Multicoloured.

1045	750l. Type **272**	1·10	95
1046	850l. "Rouen Cathedral" (Maurice Utrillo)	1·30	1·20

273 St. John, Cross, Carp and Moldava River

1993. 600th Death Anniv of St. John of Nepomuk (patron saint of Bohemia). Multicoloured.

1047	1000l. Type **273**	1·10	95
1048	2000l. Charles Bridge, Prague	1·30	1·20

274 Pope praying

1993. Pope John Paul II's Journeys (11th series). Multicoloured.

1049	600l. Type **274** (Senegal, Gambia and Guinea)	1·30	85
1050	1000l. Pope with Pastoral Staff (Angola and St. Thomas and Prince Islands)	2·40	1·60
1051	5000l. Pope with hands clasped in prayer (Dominican Republic)	9·00	7·50

275 "Madonna of Solothurn" (detail)

1993. 450th Death Anniv of Hans Holbein the Younger (artist). Multicoloured.

1052	700l. Type **275**	1·60	95
1053	1000l. "Madonna of Solothurn"	2·30	1·30
1054	1500l. "Self-portrait"	3·25	2·20

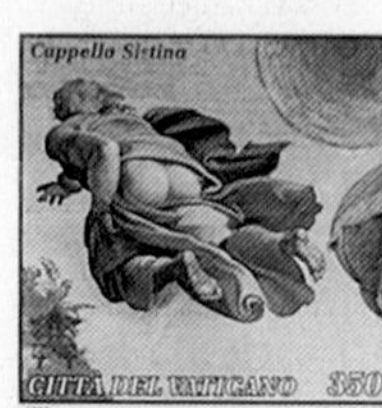

276 "Creation of the Planets" (left detail)

1994. Completion of Restoration of Sistine Chapel. Multicoloured.

1055	350l. Type **276**	85	85
1056	350l. God creating planets (right detail)	85	85
1057	500l. Adam (left detail, "The Creation of Adam")	1·10	1·10
1058	500l. God (right detail)	1·10	1·10
1059	1000l. Adam and Eve taking forbidden fruit (left detail, "The Original Sin")	2·20	2·20
1060	1000l. Angel casting out Adam and Eve from the Garden (right detail)	2·20	2·20
1061	2000l. People climbing from swollen river (left detail, "The Flood")	4·25	4·25
1062	2000l. Floodwaters surrounding temporary shelter (right detail)	4·25	4·25
MS1063	80×110 mm. 4000l. Christ and Virgin Mary (detail, "The Last Judgement")	7·25	7·25

Stamps of the same value were issued together, se-tenant, each pair forming a composite design.

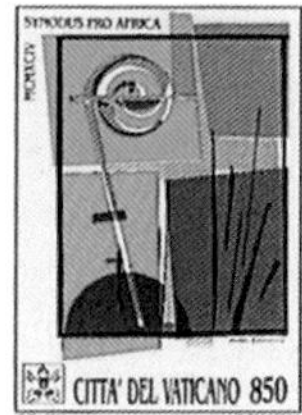

277 Crosier and Dome

1994. Special Assembly for Africa of Synod of Bishops. Multicoloured.

1064	850l. Type **277**	1·30	90
1065	1000l. Crucifix, dome of St. Peter's and African scene (horiz)	1·50	1·10

278 God creating Man and Woman

1994. Int Year of the Family. Mult.

1066	400l. Type **278**	60	55
1067	750l. Family	1·10	95
1068	1000l. Parents teaching son	1·60	1·50
1069	2000l. Youth helping elderly couple	3·25	3·00

279 Timeline of Knowledge from Wheel to Atom

1994. Europa. Discoveries. Multicoloured.

1070	750l. Type **279**	1·40	1·30
1071	850l. Galileo, solar system and scientific apparatus	1·60	1·40

280 Bishop Euphrasius and Archdeacon Claudius

1994. 13th International Congress on Christian Archaeology, Split and Porec, Croatia. Mosaics from Euphrasian Basilica, Porec. Multicoloured.

1072	700l. Type **280**	1·00	95
1073	1500l. Madonna and Child with two angels	2·20	2·00
1074	3000l. Jesus Christ between Apostles St. Peter and St. Paul	4·25	3·50

281 Route Map, Mongolian Village and Giovanni da Montecorvino

1994. 700th Anniv of Evangelization of China.

1075	**281**	1000l. multicoloured	2·30	1·70

282 Houses, Mahdi's Mausoleum, Omdurman, and St. Mary's Basilica, Lodonga (Benin, Uganda and Sudan)

1994. Pope John Paul II's Journeys (12th series).

1076	**282**	600l. brown, green & red	1·20	90
1077	-	700l. violet, brown & grn	1·40	1·10
1078	-	1000l. brown, blue & vio	2·00	1·50
1079	-	2000l. black, blue and red	3·75	2·75
1080	-	3000l. blue, violet & brn	6·00	4·50

DESIGNS: 700l. St. Mary's Church, Apollonia, Mosque and statue of Skanderbeg, Tirana (Albania); 1000l. Church of the Saint, Huelva Region, and The Giralda, Real Maestranza and Golden Tower, Seville (Spain); 2000l. Skyscrapers and St. Thomas's Theological Seminary, Denver, "El Castillo" (pyramid), Kulkulkan, Jamaican girl and Mexican boy (Jamaica, Mexico and United States); 3000l. Tallin, "Hymn to Liberty" (monument), Riga, and Tower, Cathedral Square, Vilnius (Lithuania, Latvia and Estonia).

283 Holy Family

1994. Christmas. Details of "Nativity" by Tintoretto. Multicoloured.

1081	700l. Type **283**	1·80	95
1082	1000l. Upper half of painting (45×28 mm)	2·40	2·20
1083	1000l. Lower half of painting (45×28 mm)	2·40	2·20

Nos. 1082/3 were issued together, se-tenant, forming a composite design of the complete painting.

284 Angel with Chalice (Melozzo da Forli) (St. Mark's)

1995. 700th Anniv of Shrine of the Holy House, Loreto. Details from the vaults of sacristies. Multicoloured.

1084	600l. Type **284**	95	95
1085	700l. Angel with lamb (Melozzo) (Sacristy of St. Mark)	1·20	1·10
1086	1500l. Angel with lute (Luca Signorelli) (St. John's)	2·50	2·20
1087	2500l. Angel (Signorelli) (St. John's)	4·25	3·50
MS1088	75×110 mm. 3000l. Madonna and Child (detail of "Translation of the Holy House" (marble relief) (35×35 mm)	5·00	5·00

285 Hands and Broken Chains

1995. Europa. Peace and Freedom. Multicoloured.

1089	750l. Type **285**	1·20	1·10
1090	850l. Globe, olive wreath, dove and handclasp	1·30	1·30

286 Fountain of the Triton (Bernini), Vatican Gardens

1995. European Nature Conservation Year. Multicoloured.

1091	200l. Type **286**	30	25
1092	300l. Avenue of roses, Castelgandolfo	50	35
1093	400l. Statue of Apollo, Vatican Gardens	60	50
1094	550l. Ruins of Domitian's Villa, Castelgandolfo	85	70
1095	750l. Box elder, Vatican Gardens	1·10	1·10
1096	1500l. Belvedere Gardens, Castelgandolfo	2·30	1·90
1097	2000l. Eagle fountain, Vatican Gardens	3·00	2·75
1098	3000l. Avenue of cypresses, Castelgandolfo	4·75	4·75

287 Guglielmo Marconi and Transmitter

1995. One Hundred Years of Radio. Multicoloured.

1099	850l. Type **287**	1·80	1·80
1100	1000l. Archangel Gabriel, Pope John Paul II with microphone and Vatican broadcasting station	2·40	2·40

288 St. Antony of Padua (statue by Donatello)

1995. Saints' Anniversaries.

1101	**288**	500l. brown and green	1·20	1·20
1102	-	750l. green and violet	1·20	1·20
1103	-	3000l. blue and purple	4·75	4·75

DESIGNS: 500l. Type **288** (800th birth anniv); 750l. St. John of God (founder of Order of Hospitallers, 500th birth anniv) (sculpture, Filippo Valle); 3000l. St. Philip Neri (founder of Friars of the Oratory, 400th death anniv) (sculpture, Giovanni Battista Maini).

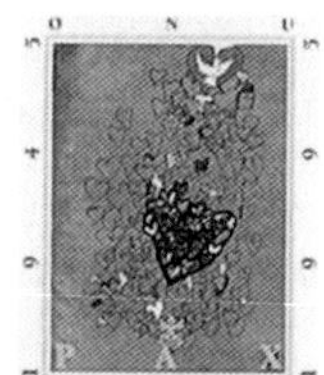

289 Dove and Hearts

1995. 50th Anniv of U.N.O. Multicoloured.

1104	550l. Type **289**	85	85
1105	750l. Human faces	1·10	1·10
1106	850l. Doves	1·20	1·20
1107	1250l. Symbolic lymph system	1·80	1·80
1108	2000l. People gazing at "explosion" of flowers	2·75	2·75

290 "The Annunciation" (Johannes of Ienzenstein)

1995. Holy Year 2000 (1st issue). Illustrations from illuminated manuscripts in Vatican Apostolic Library. Multicoloured.

1109	400l. Type **290**	95	95
1110	850l. "Nativity" (from King Matthias I Corvinus's breviary)	1·40	1·40
1111	1250l. "Flight into Egypt" (from Book of Hours)	2·40	2·40
1112	2000l. "Jesus among the Teachers" (Pietro Lombardo)	3·50	3·50

See also Nos. 1132/5, 1167/70, 1197/1200, 1231/4, 1242/9 and 1265/8.

291 Pope, Statue of Virgin Mary and Zagreb Cathedral

1995. Pope John Paul II's Journeys (13th series). Multicoloured.

1113	1000l. Type **291** (Croatia)	1·90	1·90
1114	2000l. Pope, Genoa Lantern, Orvieto Cathedral and Valley of the Temples, Agrigento (Italy)	4·00	4·00

292 Marco Polo receiving Golden Book from the Great Khan

1996. 700th Anniv of Marco Polo's Return from China. Multicoloured.

1115	350l. Type **292**	60	60
1116	850l. The Great Khan giving alms to poor, Cambaluc	1·40	1·40
1117	1250l. Marco Polo delivering Pope Gregory X's letter to the Great Khan	2·20	2·20
1118	2500l. Marco Polo in Persia listening to Nativity story	4·25	4·25
MS1119	138×100 mm. 2000l. black (Marco Polo) (vert)	3·25	3·25

293 Angel with Crosses

1996. Anniversaries. Multicoloured.

1120	1250l. Type **293** (400th Anniv of Union of Brest-Litovsk)	1·90	1·90
1121	2000l. Latin and Byzantine mitres and Tree of Life (350th Anniv of Union of Uzhorod)	3·00	3·00

294 Gianna Molla (surgeon)

1996. Europa. Famous Women.

1122	**294**	750l. blue	1·10	1·10
1123	-	850l. brown	1·30	1·30

DESIGN: 850l. Edith Stein (Carmelite nun).

295 "Sun and Steel"

1996. Cent of Modern Olympic Games. Mult.

1124	1250l. Type **295**	2·40	2·40
1125	1250l. "Solar Plexus"	2·40	2·40
1126	1250l. Hand and golden beams	2·40	2·40
1127	1250l. "Speculum Aevi" (athlete and shadow)	2·40	2·40
1128	1250l. Hercules	2·40	2·40

296 Wawel Cathedral

1996. 50th Anniv of Ordination of Karol Wojtyla (Pope John Paul II) at Wawel Cathedral, Crakow, Poland. Multicoloured.

1129	500l. Type **296**	1·40	1·40
1130	750l. Pope John Paul II	1·90	3·00
1131	1250l. St. John Lateran's Basilica in Rome (seat of Bishop of Eternal City)	3·25	3·25

297 "Baptism of Jesus"

1996. Holy Year 2000 (2nd issue). Illustrations from 13th-century illuminated New Testament in Vatican Apostolic Library. Multicoloured.

1132	550l. Type **297**	1·20	1·20
1133	850l. "Temptation in the Desert"	1·80	1·80
1134	1500l. "Cure of a Leper"	3·00	3·00
1135	2500l. "Jesus the Teacher"	4·25	4·25

298 Philippines, Papua New Guinea, Australia and Sri Lanka

1996. Pope John Paul II's Journeys (14th series).

1136	**298**	250l. blue and black	35	35
1137	-	500l. green and black	70	70
1138	-	750l. green and black	1·10	1·10
1139	-	1000l. brown and black	1·60	1·60
1140	-	2000l. grey and black	3·00	3·00
1141	-	5000l. pink and black	7·75	7·75

DESIGNS: 500l. Czech Republic and Poland; 750l. Belgium; 1000l. Slovakia; 2000l. Cameroun, South Africa and Kenya; 5000l. United States of America and United Nations Headquarters.

299 "Nativity" (Murillo)

1996. Christmas.

1142	**299**	750l. multicoloured	2·40	2·40

300 Pope St. Celestine V

1996. Saints' Anniversaries. Multicoloured.

1143	1250l. Type **300** (700th death)	2·40	2·40
1144	1250l. St. Alfonso Maria de' Liguori (founder of Redemptorists Order) (300th birth)	2·40	2·40

301 Travelling Carriage

1997. Papal Transport. Multicoloured.

1145	50l. Type **301**	10	10
1146	100l. Graham Paige motor car	25	25
1147	300l. Ceremonial berlin (carriage)	35	35
1148	500l. Citroen Lictoria VI motor car	70	70
1149	750l. Grand ceremonial berlin	95	95
1150	850l. Mercedes Benz motor car	1·10	1·10
1151	1000l. Semi-ceremonial berlin	1·30	1·30
1152	1250l. Mercedes Benz 300 SEL motor car	1·70	1·70
1153	2000l. Travelling carriage (different)	2·75	2·75
1154	4000l. Fiat Campagnola	5·25	5·25

302 Halberdier

1997. Europa. The Swiss Guard. Multicoloured.

1155	750l. Type **302**	95	95
1156	850l. Swordsman	1·20	1·20

303 Aristotle describing the Species ("De Historia Animalium" by Aristotle)

1997. "Looking at The Classics" Exhibition. Illustrations from manuscripts of the Classics. Multicoloured.

1157	500l. Type **303**	70	70
1158	750l. Bacchus riding dragon ("Metamorphoses" by Ovid)	1·10	1·10
1159	1250l. General reviewing his soldiers ("Iliad" by Homer)	1·80	1·80
1160	2000l. Horsemen leaving Canne ("Ab Urbe Condita" by Livy)	3·00	3·00
MS1161	100×135 mm. 1000l. Male and female masks; 1000l. Two female masks; 1000l. Two male masks (Comedies by Terence)	4·75	4·75

304 St. Adalbert

1997. Death Millenary of St. Adalbert (Bishop of Prague).

1162	**304**	850l. lilac	1·80	1·80

305 Eucharist and Arms of Wroclaw

1997. 46th International Eucharistic Congress, Wroclaw, Poland. Multicoloured.

1163	650l. Type **305**	85	85
1164	1000l. Last Supper and Congress emblem	1·30	1·30
1165	1250l. Wroclaw Cathedral and the Holy Dove	1·70	1·70
1166	2500l. Cross, doves and hands around globe	3·25	3·25

306 Jesus healing Paralysed Man

1997. Holy Year 2000 (3rd issue). Illustrations from 14th-century illuminated New Testament in Vatican Apostolic Library. Multicoloured.

1167	400l. Type **306**	1·20	1·20
1168	800l. Calming the tempest	1·80	1·80
1169	1300l. Feeding the five thousand	2·40	2·40
1170	3600l. Peter acclaiming Christ as the Messiah	6·50	6·50

307 St. Ambrose and Ambrosiana Basilica

1997. 1600th Death Anniv of St. Ambrose, Bishop of Milan.

1171	**307**	800l. multicoloured	1·80	1·80

308 Pope Paul VI

1997. Birth Centenary of Pope Paul VI.

1172	**308**	900l. multicoloured	1·70	1·70

1997. Aid for Earthquake Victims. As No. MS958 but additionally inscr "PRO TERREMOTATI 1997" in the margin.

MS1173	100×135 mm. As No. **MS**958 (sold at 8000l.)	34·00	34·00

No. **MS**1173 was issued in an illustrated folder.

309 Guatemala Pyramid and Amerindian Boy

1997. Pope John Paul II's Journeys (15th series). Multicoloured.

1174	400l. Type **309** (Guatemala, Nicaragua, El Salvador, Venezuela)	60	60
1175	900l. St. Francis de Paul and St. Olive's Cathedral and Mosque (Tunisia)	1·20	1·20
1176	1000l. St. Nicholas's Cathedral, Ljubljana, and Blessed Lady's monument, Maribor (Slovenia)	1·80	1·80
1177	1300l. Paderborn Cathedral and Brandenburg Gate, Berlin (Germany)	2·40	2·40
1178	2000l. St. Martin's Abbey, Pannonhalma, and St. Stephen's crown (Hungary)	3·50	3·50
1179	4000l. Reims Cathedral, baptism of Clovis and St. Martin of Tours (France)	7·25	7·25

310 "Madonna of the Belt" (detail of altarpiece, Gozzoli)

1997. Christmas. 500th Death Anniv of Benozzo Gozzoli (artist).

1180	**310**	800l. multicoloured	2·40	2·40

311 Pope Boniface VIII (1300)

1998. Popes and their Holy Years (1st series). Multicoloured.

1181	200l. Type **311**	35	35
1182	400l. Clement VI (1350)	60	60
1183	500l. Boniface IX (1390 and 1400)	70	70
1184	700l. Martinus V (1423)	1·10	1·10
1185	800l. Nicholas V (1450)	1·20	1·20
1186	900l. Sistus IV (1475)	1·40	1·40
1187	1300l. Alexander VI (1500)	2·00	2·00
1188	3000l. Clement VII (1525)	4·50	4·50

See also Nos. 1213/20 and 1255/63.

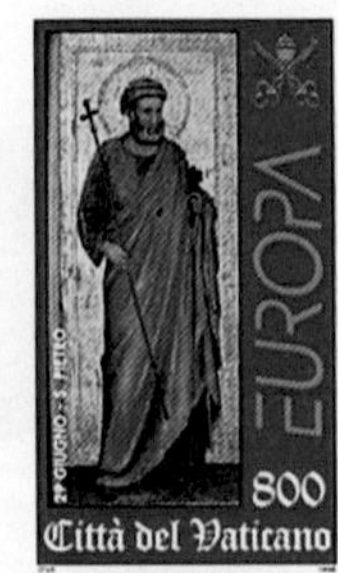

312 St. Peter

1998. Europa. National Festival. The Feast of St. Peter and St. Paul. Multicoloured.

1189	800l. Type **312**	1·20	1·20
1190	900l. St. Paul	1·20	1·20

The designs are details from the Stefaneschi Triptych by Giotto.

313 Angel

1998. Musical Angels from "The Ascension" by Melozzo da Forli in the Basilica of the Apostles, Rome. Multicoloured.

1191	450l. Type **313**	60	60
1192	650l. Angel playing lute	95	95
1193	800l. Angel playing drum	1·20	1·20
1194	1000l. Angel playing viol	1·40	1·40
1195	1300l. Angel playing violin	1·80	1·80
1196	2000l. Angel with tamborine	3·00	3·00

314 Entry into Jerusalem

1998. Holy Year 2000 (4th issue). Illustrations from the illuminated New Testament in Vatican Apostolic Library. Multicoloured.

1197	500l. Type **314**	60	60
1198	800l. Washing of the Apostles' feet	1·20	1·20
1199	1500l. The Last Supper	1·80	1·80
1200	3000l. The Crucifixion	3·50	3·50

315 Turin Shroud

1998. Exhibition of the Holy Shroud, Turin Cathedral.

1201	**315**	900l. white, brown and green	1·40	1·40
1202	-	2500l. black, pink and green	3·75	3·75

DESIGN: 2500l. Turin Cathedral.

316 Pope John Paul II and his Message

1998. "Italia 98" International Stamp Exhibition, Milan (1st issue). Stamp Day.

1203	**316**	800l. multicoloured	7·25	3·00

See also No. 1204.

317 "The Good Shepherd"

1998. "Italia 90" International Stamp Exhibition, Milan (2nd issue). Art Day. T 317 and similar designs showing sculptures from sarcophagi. Multicoloured.

1204	900l. Type **317**	2·40	2·40
MS1205	106×130 mm. 600l. Peter's Denial; 900l. Praying woman; 1000l. Christ with the Cross and two Apostles	6·00	6·00

318 Pope and War Refugees

1998. Pope John Paul II's Journeys (16th series). Multicoloured.

1206	300l. Type **318** (Bosnia and Herzegovina)	50	50
1207	600l. Kneeling in front of statue of Jesus (Czech Republic)	85	85
1208	800l. With girls (Lebanon)	1·10	1·10
1209	900l. Welcome by garlanded girls (Poland)	1·20	1·20
1210	1300l. With young people (France)	1·80	1·80
1211	5000l. With children (Brazil)	6·50	6·50

319 "Nativity" (Giulio Clovio)

1998. Christmas.

1212	**319**	800l. multicoloured	1·80	1·80

1999. Popes and their Holy Years (2nd series). As T 311. Multicoloured.

1213	300l. Julius III (1550)	1·20	1·20
1214	600l. Gregory XIII (1575)	1·80	1·80
1215	800l. Clement VIII (1600)	2·40	2·40
1216	900l. Urban VIII (1625)	2·40	2·40
1217	1000l. Innocent X (1650)	2·40	2·40
1218	1300l. Clement X (1675)	3·00	3·00
1219	1500l. Innocent XII (1700)	3·50	3·50
1220	2000l. Benedict XIII (1725)	4·75	4·75

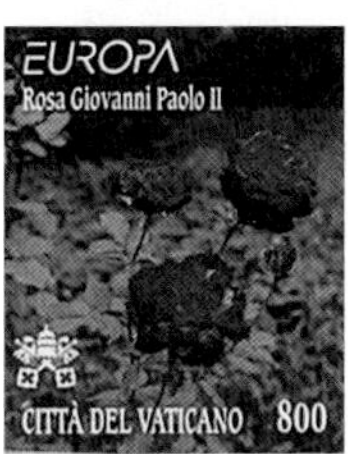

320 Rose "John Paul II"

1999. Europa. Parks and Gardens. Multicoloured.

1221	800l. Type **320**	2·40	2·40
1222	900l. Water lilies (Fountain of the Frogs, Vatican Gardens)	3·00	3·00

321 Father Pio

1999. Beatification of Father Pio da Pietrelcina (Capuchin friar who bore the stigmata). Multicoloured.

1223	800l. Type **321**	95	95
MS1224	86×115 mm. 300l. Monastery Church, San Giovanni Rotondo (29×39 mm); 600l. San Giovanni Rotondo new church (29×39 mm); 900l. Type **321** (59×39 mm)	2·20	2·20

322 Bethlehem

1999. Sacred Places in the Holy Land. Illustrations from "The Holy Land" by I. Messmer. Multicoloured.

1225	200l. Type **322**	10	10
1226	500l. Nazareth	50	50
1227	800l. Lake Tiberius	1·10	1·10
1228	900l. Jerusalem	1·20	1·20
1229	1300l. Mount Tabor	1·70	1·70
MS1230	110×86 mm. 1000l. ×4, composite design of map of the Holy Land (from 17th-century Geographia Blaviana) (each 50×38 mm)	12·00	12·00

323 Deposition from the Cross

1999. Holy Year 2000 (5th issue). Illustrations from illuminated New Testament in Vatican Apostolic Library. Multicoloured.

1231	400l. Type **323**	60	60
1232	700l. The Resurrection	95	95
1233	1300l. Pentecost	1·70	1·70
1234	3000l. The Last Judgement	4·25	4·25

324 Refugees

1999. Kosovo Relief Fund.

1235	**324**	3600l. black	4·75	4·75

325 Visit to Cuba

1999. Pope John Paul II's Journeys (17th series). Multicoloured.

1236	600l. Type **325**	1·20	1·20
1237	800l. Stole over hands and staff (Nigeria)	1·20	1·20
1238	900l. Dove, cathedral and disabled people (Austria)	1·20	1·20
1239	1300l. With crucifix and statue (Croatia)	2·40	2·40
1240	2000l. Quirinal Palace, Rome (Italy)	3·50	3·50

326 Hot Air Balloons, Jigsaw Puzzle of Europe and Magnifying Glass

1999. 50th Anniv of Council of Europe.

1241	**326**	1200l. multicoloured	1·80	1·80

327 "The Cherubim at the Doors of Paradise" and "The Banishment from the Garden of Eden"

1999. Holy Year 2000 (6th issue). Opening of Holy Door, St. Peter's Basilica. Door panels. Mult.

1242	200l. Type **327**	35	35
1243	300l. "The Annunciation" and "Angel"	50	50
1244	400l. "Baptism of Christ" and "Straying Sheep"	60	60
1245	500l. "The Merciful Father" and "Curing Paralysed Man"	70	70
1246	600l. "The Penitent Woman" and "The Obligation to Forgive"	85	85
1247	800l. "Peter's Denial" and "A Thief in Paradise"	1·10	1·10
1248	1000l. "Jesus appears to Thomas" and "Jesus appears to the Eleven"	1·30	1·30
1249	1200l. "Jesus appears to Saul" and "Opening of the Holy Door"	1·80	1·80
MS1250	106×142 mm. As Nos. 1242/9	7·75	7·75

328 St. Joseph (detail)

1999. Christmas. "St. Joseph, the Virgin Mary and the Holy Child" (Giovanni di Petro). Multicoloured.

1251	500l. Type **328**	70	70
1252	800l. Holy Child (detail)	1·20	1·20
1253	900l. Virgin Mary (detail)	1·30	1·30
1254	1200l. Complete painting	1·80	1·80

2000. Popes and their Holy Years (3rd series). As T 311. Multicoloured.

1255	300l. Benedict XIV (1750)	60	60
1256	400l. Pius VI (1775)	1·20	1·20
1257	500l. Leo XII (1825)	1·20	1·20
1258	600l. Pius IX (1875)	1·80	1·80
1259	700l. Leo XIII (1900)	2·40	2·40
1260	800l. Pius XI (1925)	2·40	2·40
1261	1200l. Pius XII (1950)	2·40	2·40
1262	1500l. Paul VI (1975)	4·25	4·25
1263	2000l. John Paul II (2000)	5·50	5·50
MS1264	137×103 mm. 2000l. John Paul II resting face on hand	4·25	3·50

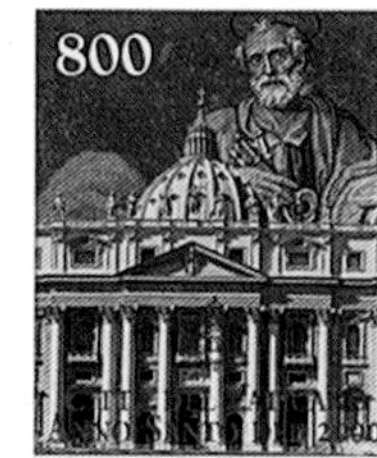

329 St. Peter's Basilica

2000. Holy Year 2000 (7th issue). Multicoloured.

1265	800l. Type **329**	1·20	95
1266	1000l. St. John Lateran Basilica	1·40	1·20
1267	1200l. St. Mary Major Basilica	1·80	1·40
1268	2000l. St. Paul-outside-the-Walls Basilica	2·75	2·40

330 Embroidered Altar Frontal, Holar Cathedral

2000. Millenary of Christianity in Iceland.

1269	**330**	1500l. multicoloured	3·00	3·00

331 "Building Europe"

2000. Europa.

1270	**331**	1200l. multicoloured	2·40	2·40

332 Pope John Paul II

2000. 80th Birthday of Pope John Paul II.

1271	**332**	800l. lilac	1·20	1·20
1272	-	1200l. blue	1·80	1·80
1273	-	2000l. green	3·00	3·00

DESIGNS: 1200l. Black Madonna of Czestochowa; 2000l. Pastoral Staff.

333 "The Calling of St. Peter and St. Andrew" (Domenico Ghirlandaio)

2000. Restoration of the Sistine Chapel (1st series). Multicoloured.

1274	500l. Type **333**	85	85
1275	1000l. "The Trials of Moses" (Sandro Botticelli)	1·60	1·60
1276	1500l. "The Donation of the Keys" (Pietro Perugino)	2·00	2·00
1277	3000l. "The Worship of the Golden Calf" (Cosimo Rosselli)	4·00	4·00

See also Nos. 1294/7 and 1339/42.

334 Congress Emblem

2000. 47th International Eucharistic Congress, Rome.

1278	**334**	1200l. multicoloured	1·80	1·80

335 Pope John Paul II and Youths' Faces

2000. 15th World Youth Day, Rome. Multicoloured. (a) Ordinary gum.

1279	800l. Type **335**	1·20	1·20
1280	1000l. Girl waving flag	1·40	1·40
1281	1200l. Youths' cheering	1·80	1·80
1282	2000l. Youth waving flag	2·20	2·20

(b) Self-adhesive.

1283	1000l. As No. 1280	1·40	1·40

336 Pope and Children

2000. Pope John Paul II's Journeys (18th series). Multicoloured.

1284	1000l. Type **336** (Mexico and United States of America)	1·20	1·20
1285	1000l. Pope praying, building and children waving (Rumania)	1·20	1·20
1286	1000l. Holding Pastoral Staff (Poland)	1·20	1·20
1287	1000l. Pope and Bishop Anton Martin Slomsek (Slovenia)	1·20	1·20
1288	1000l. Pope, churches and crowd (India and Georgia)	1·20	1·20

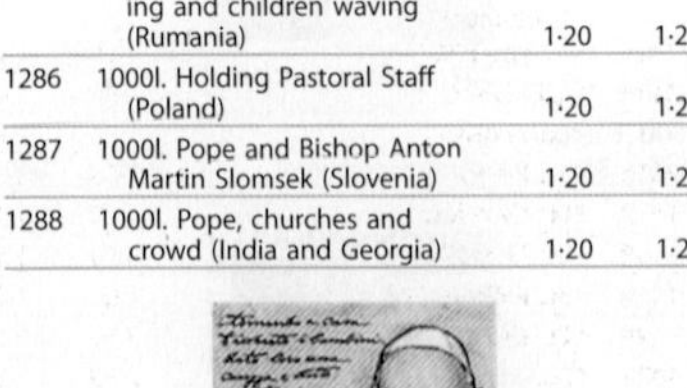

337 Pope John XXIII

2000. Beatification of Pope John XXIII.

1289	**337**	1200l. multicoloured	1·80	1·80

338 Nativity (fresco)

2000. Christmas. Designs showing Fresco by Giotto from St. Francis Basilica. Multicoloured.

1290	800l. Type **338**	1·80	1·80
1291	1200l. Baby Jesus (detail)	2·40	2·40
1292	1500l. Mary (detail)	3·00	3·00
1293	2000l. Joseph (detail)	3·50	3·50

339 Freedom of St. Gregory

2001. Restoration of the Sistine Chapel (2nd series). As T 333. Multicoloured.

1294	800l. "The Baptism of Christ" (Pietro Perugino)	95	95
1295	1200l. "The Passage through the Red Sea" (Biagio d'Antonio)	1·40	1·40
1296	1500l. "The Punishment of Core, Datan and Abiron" (Botticelli)	1·80	1·80
1297	4000l. "The Sermon on the Mount" (Cosimo Rosselli)	4·75	4·75

339 Freedom of St. Gregory

2001. 1700th Anniv of the Adoption of Christianity in Armenia. Multicoloured.

1298	1200l. Type **339**	1·80	1·40
1299	1500l. St. Gregory making Agatangel write	1·80	1·80
1300	2000l. St. Gregory and King Tirade meet Emperor Constantine and Pope Sylvester I	2·40	2·40

340 Hands holding Water and Globe

2001. Europa. Water Resources. Multicoloured.

1301	800l. Type **340**	1·40	1·40
1302	1200l. Hand and catching rain water	2·20	2·20

341 Verdi and Score of *Nabucco*

2001. Death Centenary of Giuseppe Verdi (composer). Multicoloured.

1303	800l. Type **341**	1·20	1·20
1304	1500l. Verdi and character from *Aida*	2·20	2·20
1305	2000l. Verdi and scene from *Otello*	2·75	2·75

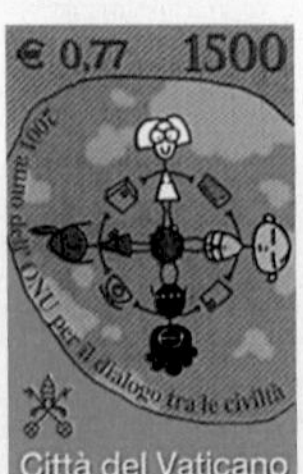

342 Children encircling Globe

2001. U.N. Year of Dialogue between Civilizations.

1306	**342**	1500l. multicoloured	2·40	2·40

343 Couple feeding Poor Man

2001. Cancellation of Foreign Debt of Poor Countries. Showing illustrations from "Works of Corporal Mercy" (15th-century panels by Carlo di Camerino). Multicoloured.

1307	200l. Type **343**	25	25
1308	400l. Giving alms	60	60
1309	800l. Giving clothing	1·10	1·10
1310	1000l. Women caring for sick man	1·30	1·30
1311	1500l. Man visiting prisoner	1·90	1·90

344 Mount Sinai, Monastery of Holy Catherine and Pope

2001. Pope John Paul II's Journeys (19th series). The Holy Land. Multicoloured.

1312	500l. Type **344**	70	70
1313	800l. Pope before Crucifix, Mount Nebo	1·10	1·10
1314	1200l. Pope celebrating Mass	1·60	1·60
1315	1500l. Pope at prayer Holy Sepulchre	1·90	1·90
1316	5000l. Pope praying at Shrine of Fatima	6·25	6·25
MS1317	85×115 mm. 3000l. Pope at Western Wall, Jerusalem (35×27 mm)	3·75	3·75

345 "The Annunciation"

2001. Christmas. Designs showing scenes from "Life of Christ" (enamel, Egino G. Weinert). Multicoloured.

1318	800l. Type **345**	1·20	1·20
1319	1200l. "The Nativity"	1·80	1·80
1320	1500l. "Adoration of the Magi"	2·40	2·40

346 Fibula, 675–650 B.C.

2001. Etruscan Museum Exhibits. Multicoloured.

1321	800l. Type **346**	1·10	1·10
1322	1200l. 6th-century earrings	1·60	1·60
1323	1500l. Embossed Greek stud, 425–400 B.C	1·90	1·90
1324	2000l. 3rd-century Greek head of Medusa	2·75	2·75

347 Emblem

2001. 80th Anniv of Guiseppe Toniolo Institute for Higher Studies and the Catholic University of the Sacred Heart.

1325	**347**	1200l. blue and red	2·20	2·20

348 Our Lady of Women in Labour (14th-century fresco)

2002. Our Lady in the Vatican Basilica. Multicoloured.

1326	8c. Type **348**	25	25
1327	15c. Our Lady with people praying (mosaic)	35	35
1328	23c. Our Lady at the Tomb of Pius XII (15th-century fresco)	60	60
1329	31c. Our Lady of the Fever (13th-century)	70	70
1330	41c. Our Lady of the Slap	95	95
1331	52c. Mary Immaculate (mosaic)	1·30	1·30
1332	62c. Our Lady of Christians	1·60	1·60
1333	77c. The Virgin of the Deesis	1·90	1·90
1334	€1.03 L'Addolorata (painting, Lippo Memmi)	2·50	2·50
1335	€1.55 Presentation of Mary at the Temple (mosaic)	3·75	3·75

349 Pope Clement XI

2002. 300th Anniv of Pontifical Ecclesiastical Academy, Rome.

1336	**349**	77c. purple	1·90	1·90
1337	-	77c. green (46×33 mm)	1·90	1·90
1338	-	77c. purple	1·90	1·90

DESIGNS: No. 1337 Facade of Piazza della Minerva Institute, Rome; 1338 Pope John Paul II.

2002. Restoration of the Sistine Chapel (3rd series). As T 333. Multicoloured.

1339	26c. "The Temptation of Christ" (Botticelli)	95	95
1340	41c. "The Last Supper" (Cosimo Rosselli)	1·40	1·40
1341	77c. "Moses' Journey into Egypt" (Pietro Perugino)	2·20	2·20
1342	€1.55 "The Last Days of Moses" (Luca Signorelli)	3·75	3·75

350 Regina Viarum (Appian Way) and 1852 Papal States Stamp

2002. Centenary of Pontifical Stamps.

1343	**350**	41c. deep brown, purple and brown	1·20	1·20
1344	-	52c. multicoloured	1·40	1·40
1345	-	€1.03 blue, indigo and green	2·75	2·75
MS1346		104×83 mm. €1.55 brown, buff and purple	5·00	4·25

DESIGNS: No. 1344, Cassian Way and 1868 80ch. Papal States stamp; 1345, Porta Angelica, Vatican and 1929 Vatican City State 10ch. stamp. 30×30 mm (circular)—**MS**1346, Courtyard, Palazzo Madama, Rome.

351 "Christ and the Circus" (Aldo Carpi)

2002. Europa. Circus. Multicoloured.

1347	41c. Type **351**	1·20	1·20
1348	62c. Christ with clown (detail of "Christ and the Circus")	1·80	1·80

352 Crucifix, St. Dominic Church, Arezzo

2002. 700th Death Anniv of Cenni di Pepo (Cimabue) (artist). Showing the Crucifix and details thereof. Multicoloured.

1349	41c. Type **352**	85	85
1350	62c. Jesus	1·80	1·80
1351	77c. Mary	1·90	1·90
1352	€1.03 John the Baptist	3·00	3·00

353 Pope Leo IX and Wall Inscription

2002. Birth Millenary of Pope Leo IX. Multicoloured.

1353	41c. Type **353**	1·40	1·40
1354	62c. Arrival in Rome as pilgrim and coronation as Pope	2·00	2·00
1355	€1.29 Leo IX in chains	3·25	3·25

354 "The Nativity" (15th-century painting in style of Di Baldese) (⅔-size illustration)

2002. Christmas.

1356	**354**	41c. multicoloured	3·00	3·00

A stamp of a similar design was issued by New Zealand.

355 Pope John Paul II (Malta)

2002. Journeys of Pope John Paul II in 2001. Multicoloured.

1357	41c. Type **355**	1·40	1·40
1358	62c. Praying (Ukraine)	2·00	2·00
1359	€1.55 Wearing mitre (Kazakhstan)	4·25	4·25

356 Pope John Paul II on Balcony of St. Peter's Basilica, 1978

2003. 25th Anniv of the Pontificate of Pope John Paul II (1st issue). Multicoloured.

1360	41c. Type **356**	1·10	1·10
1361	41c. Celebrating mass, Victory Square, Warsaw, 1979	1·10	1·10
1362	41c. Addressing young people, Parc des Princes Stadium, Paris, 1980	1·10	1·10
1363	41c. Assassination attempt, St. Peter Square, 1981	1·10	1·10
1364	41c. Giving homily surrounded by flowers, Portugal, 1982	1·10	1·10
1365	41c. Kneeling in front of Holy Doors, start of Holy Year of Redemption, 1983	1·10	1·10
1366	41c. Meeting Sandro Pertini, President of Italy, 1984	1·10	1·10
1367	41c. International Youth Day, Rome, 1985	1·10	1·10
1368	41c. First visit of Pope to Synagogue, 1986	1·10	1·10
1369	41c. Inaugurating Year of Mary, 1987	1·10	1·10
1370	41c. Visiting European Parliament, Strasbourg, 1988	1·10	1·10
1371	41c. Meeting President Mikhail Gorbachev, Soviet Union, 1989	1·10	1·10
1372	41c. Visiting lepers in Guinea-Bissau, 1990	1·10	1·10
1373	41c. Addressing Bishop's Synod, 1991	1·10	1·10
1374	41c. Pronouncing the Catechism, 1992	1·10	1·10
1375	41c. Enthroned, Assissi, 1993	1·10	1·10
1376	41c. Celebrating Mass in the Sistine Chapel, 1994	1·10	1·10
1377	41c. Addressing the United Nations, 1995	1·10	1·10
1378	41c. Walking through the Brandenburg Gate with Chancellor Helmut Kohl, 1996	1·10	1·10
1379	41c. Celebrating Mass in Sarajevo, 1997	1·10	1·10
1380	41c. With Fidel Castro, Cuba, 1998	1·10	1·10
1381	41c. Opening door, Christmas, 1999	1·10	1·10
1382	41c. With young people, World Youth Day, Rome, 2000	1·10	1·10
1383	41c. Closing door of St. Peter's Basilica, 2001	1·10	1·10
1384	41c. Visiting the Italian Parliament, 2002	1·10	1·10

Stamps of the same design were issued by Poland.

357 Pope John Paul II

2003. 25th Anniv of the Pontificate of Pope John Paul II (2nd issue). Self-adhesive.

1385	**357**	€2.58 silver	11·00	11·00

A stamp of the same design was issued by Poland.

358 Dove (Holy Year 1975)

2003. Europa. Poster Art. Multicoloured.

1386	41c. Type **358**	1·10	1·10
1387	62c. St. Cyril and St. Methodius	1·60	1·60

359 St. Sixtus ordaining St. Lawrence

2003. Paintings from the Niccolina Chapel by Friar Giovanni da Fiesole (Beato Angelico). Multicoloured.

1388	41c. Type **359**	1·40	1·40
1389	62c. St. Stephen preaching	1·80	1·80
1390	77c. St. Lawrence on trial	2·20	2·20
1391	€1.03 Stoning of St. Stephen	3·00	3·00

360 St. George slaying Dragon

2003. 1700th Anniv of Death of St. George.

1392	**360**	62c. multicoloured	2·50	2·50

361 Dragon

2003. Animal Paintings from the Vatican Basilica. Multicoloured.

1393	21c. Type **361**	70	70
1394	31c. Camel	95	95
1395	77c. Horse	2·30	2·30
1396	€1.03 Leopard	3·00	3·00

362 Mother Teresa

2003. Beatification of Mother Teresa (humanitarian worker).

1397	**362**	41c. multicoloured	1·60	1·60

363 "Blessed are the Pure in Heart" (Paul Gauguin)

2003. Artists' Anniversaries. Multicoloured.

1398	41c. Type **363** (death centenary)	1·40	1·40
1399	62c. "The Pieta" (Vincent van Gogh) (150th birth anniv)	2·10	2·10

364 Josemaria Escriva

2003. Birth Centenary (2002) of Josemaria Escriva De Balaguer (founder of Opus Dei (religious organization)).

1400	**364**	41c. multicoloured	1·40	1·40

365 The Nativity

2003. Christmas. 25th Death Anniv of Pope Paul VI (MS1402).

1401	**365**	41c. multicoloured	1·40	1·40
MS1402		106×83 mm. **365** 41c. multicoloured	2·75	2·75

366 Orthodox Priests and Pope John Paul II (Bulgaria and Azerbaijan)

2003. Journeys of Pope John Paul II in 2002. Multicoloured.

1403	62c. Type **366**	2·20	2·20
1404	77c. Pope John Paul II and World Youth Day emblem (Canada, Guatemala and Mexico City)	2·75	2·75
1405	€2.55 With raised hand (Poland)	7·00	7·00

367 Pope Pius V (detail, altarpiece) (Grazio Cossoli)

2004. 500th Birth Anniv of Pope Pius V. Multicoloured.

1406	4c. Type **367**	15	15
1407	€2 Our Lady of the Rosary (detail, altarpiece) (Grazio Cossoli)	6·50	6·50

368 Pope John Paul II

2004. Pope John Paul II visits to Poland, 1979—2002. Two sheets, each 115×185 mm containing T 368 and similar vert designs. Multicoloured.

MS1408	(a) 45c.×4, Type **368** (1979); At prayer (1983); Holding reliquary (1987); Resting head against staff (1991). (b) 62c.×4, Holding staff (1991); With raised hand (1997); Seated facing right (1999); Seated facing left (2002)	15·00	15·00

Stamps of the same design were issued by Poland.

369 Pope John Paul II (Spain)

2004. Journeys of Pope John Paul II in 2003. Multicoloured.

1409	60c. Type **369**	2·75	2·75
1410	62c. With head in hand (Bosnia and Herzegovina)	2·75	2·75
1411	80c. Holding staff (Croatia)	3·25	3·25
1412	€1.40 Wearing stole and zucchetto (Slovakia)	6·75	6·75

Nos. 1409/10 were issued with a se-tenant label inscribed "Priority Mail".

370 Austrian Flag and Coin

2004. The Euro. Showing country flag and coin. Multicoloured.

1413	4c. Type **370**	25	25
1414	8c. Belgium	40	40
1415	15c. Finland	70	70
1416	25c. France	1·10	1·10
1417	30c. Germany	1·40	1·40
1418	40c. Greece	1·50	1·50
1419	45c. Vatican City	1·60	1·60
1420	60c. Eire	2·10	2·10
1421	62c. Italy	2·10	2·10
1422	70c. Luxembourg	2·50	2·50
1423	80c. Monaco	2·75	2·75
1424	€1 Netherlands	3·00	3·00
1425	€1.40 Portugal	4·00	4·00
1426	€2 San Marino	8·25	8·25
1427	€2.80 Spain	10·50	10·50

371 Children

2004. AIDS Awareness Campaign.

1428	**371**	45c. multicoloured	2·20	2·20

372 Horse Riding

2004. Europa. Holidays. Multicoloured.

1429	45c. Type **372**	2·30	2·30
1430	62c. Walking in French-style garden	3·25	3·25

373 "Still Life with Bottles" (Giorgio Morandi)

2004. Modern Art. Multicoloured.
1431 45c. Type **373** 1·60 1·60
1432 60c. "Falling Angel" (Marino Marini) 2·20 2·20
1433 80c. "Landscape with Houses" (Ezio Pastorio) 3·00 3·00
1434 85c. "Tuscan Dunes" (Giulio Ceasare Vinzio) 3·25 3·25

374 Eucharist

2004. 48th International Eucharist Congress, Guadalajara, Mexico. Multicoloured.
1435 45c. Type **374** 1·80 1·80
1436 65c. Hands 2·75 2·75

375 Petrarch and Script

2004. 700th Birth Anniv of Petrarch (Francesco Petrarca) (poet).
1437 **375** 60c. multicoloured 2·75 2·75

376 Nativity

2004. Christmas.
1438 **376** 80c. brown, green and black 3·50 3·50

377 Emblems, Manuscript and Pen

2005. 20th Anniv of Ratification Italy—Vatican Concordat (abolishing Catholicism as state religion). Multicoloured.
1439 45c. Type **377** 1·60 1·60
1440 €2.80 Emblems and map 10·00 10·00
Stamps of the same design were issued by Italy.

378 Man Sleeping

2005. "Resurrection of Christ" by Pietro Vannucci (Perugino). Details of the painting. Multicoloured.
1441 60c. Type **378** 2·20 2·20
1442 62c. Sleeping soldier 2·30 2·30
1443 80c. With head in hand 2·75 2·75
1444 €1 With raised eyes 3·50 3·50
MS1445 80×120 mm. €2.80 Risen Christ (29×60 mm) 9·75 9·75
Nos. 1441/4, respectively, were each issued with a se-tenant label inscribed "priority mail".

379 Apostolic Camera Arms (Carlo Malli)

2005. "Vacant See".
1446 **379** 60c. multicoloured 1·80 1·80
1447 **379** 62c. multicoloured 2·75 2·75
1448 **379** 80c. multicoloured 3·50 3·50

380 Pope Benedict XVI

2005. Enthronement of Pontificate of Pope Benedict XVI. Multicoloured.
1449 45c. Type **380** 1·80 1·80
1450 62c. With clasped hands 2·75 2·75
1451 80c. With raised hands 3·50 3·50

381 Cross and Globe

2005. World Youth Day.
1452 **381** 62c. multicoloured 2·75 2·75
A stamp of the same design was issued by Germany.

382 Ceramic Plate (Pablo Picasso)

2005. Europa. Gastronomy. Multicoloured.
1453 62c. Type **382** 2·30 2·30
1454 80c. Ceramic plate (Pablo Picasso) (different) 3·00 3·00

383 Pope John Paul II (Bern, Switzerland)

2005. Journeys of Pope John Paul II in 2004. Multicoloured.
1455 45c. Type **383** 1·80 1·80
1456 80c. Facing right (Lourdes) 3·50 3·50
1457 €2 With raised arms (Loreto, Italy) 8·00 8·00

384 "Dinner at Emmaus" (Primo Conti)

2005. Ordinary General Assembly of Bishops' Synod.
1458 **384** 62c. multicoloured 2·30 2·30

385 "The Annunciation"

2005. Art. "The Annunciation" by Raffello Sanzio (Raphael). Multicoloured.
1459 62c. Type **385** 2·30 2·30
1460 €1 "The Annunciation" (different) 3·50 3·50
MS1461 131×86 mm. €1.40×2, As Type **385**; As No. 1460 9·75 9·75
Stamps of a similar design were issued by France.

386 Child with Doves

2005. Christmas. "Adoration of Shepherds" by Francois le Moyne. Showing details from the painting. Multicoloured.
1462 45c. Type **386** 1·60 1·60
1463 62c. Angel 2·30 2·30
1464 80c. Mary and Jesus 2·75 2·75

387 Swiss Papal Guard

2005. 500th Anniv of Swiss Papal Guard. Multicoloured.
1465 62c. Type **387** 2·30 2·30
1466 80c. Three guards facing left 3·00 3·00
Stamps of a similar design were issued by Switzerland.

388 Pierre Favre (500th birth anniv)

2006. Saints' Anniversaries.
1467 **388** 45c. multicoloured 1·60 1·60
1468 - 62c. blue 2·20 2·20
1469 - €2 multicoloured 7·25 7·25
DESIGNS: 45c. Type **388**; 60c. Ignatius Loyola (450th death anniv); €2 Francis Xavier (500th birth anniv).

389 Madonna and Child

2006. 500th Death Centenary of Andrea Mantegna (artist). Designs showing details of San Zeno Polyptych, Verona. Multicoloured.
1470 60c. Type **389** 2·30 2·30
1471 85c. Saint John the Baptist 3·50 3·50
1472 €1 Saints Peter and Paul 3·75 3·75
MS1473 96×116 mm. Size 21×37 mm. €1.40×2, Saints Peter and Paul; Saints John the Baptist and Gregory 9·50 9·50

390 Places of Worship and Hands

2006. Europa. Integration. Multicoloured.
1474 62c. Type **390** 2·40 2·40
1475 80c. Children in classrooms 3·25 3·25

391 Figure and Building

2006. 500th Anniv of Saint Peter's Basilica. Medallions. Multicoloured.
1476 45c. Type **391** 1·50 1·50
1477 45c. Donato Bramante 1·50 1·50
1478 60c. Pope Julius II 2·10 2·10
1479 60c. Basilica 2·10 2·10
Nos. 1476/7 and 1478/9 were issued together, se-tenant, forming a composite design.

392 Pope Benedict XVI (National Eucharistic Congress, Bari)

2006. Apostolic Journeys of Pope Benedict XVI in 2005. Multicoloured.
1480 62c. Type **392** 2·10 2·10
1481 €1.40 World Youth Day, Cologne 4·75 4·75
Nos. 1480/1 each have a label inscribed "Posta Prioritaria" attached at foot.

393 Mozart

2006. 250th Birth Anniv of Wolfgang Amadeus Mozart (composer).
1482 **393** 80c. multicoloured 2·75 2·75

394 Shepherds

2006. Christmas. Multicoloured.
1483 60c. Type **394** 2·10 2·10
1484 65c. Holy Family 2·20 2·20
1485 85c. Three Kings 3·25 3·25

395 Antiphantes

2006. 500th Anniv of Vatican Museums. Multicoloured.
1486 60c. Type **395** 2·10 2·10
1487 65c. Laocoon 2·20 2·20
1488 €1.40 Thymbraeus 5·25 5·25
MS1489 81×95 mm. €2.80 Laocoon (81×30 mm) 9·50 9·50

396 Child and Parched Earth

2006. International Year of Deserts and Desertification. Multicoloured.
1490 62c. Type **396** 2·20 2·20
1491 €1 Child and oxen 3·75 3·75

397 Singapore Merlion and St. Peter's Basilica, Rome

2006. 25th Anniv of Diplomatic Relations between Singapore and Vatican City. Multicoloured.

1492	85c. Type **397**	3·00	3·00
1493	€2 Flags of Singapore and Vatican City	7·25	7·25

398 Francesco di Paola

2007. 500th Death Anniv of Francesco di Paola (St Francis of Paola) (founder of the Order of Minims). Each black and cobalt.

1494	60c. Type **398**	2·10	2·10
1495	€1 Angel	3·50	3·50

399 Pope Benedict XVI

2007. 80th Birth Anniv of Pope Benedict XVI. Multicoloured.

1496	60c. Type **399**	2·30	2·30
1497	65c. Giving blessing	2·40	2·40
1498	85c. Wearing mitre	3·25	3·25

400 Scouts

2007. Europa. Centenary of Scouting. Multicoloured.

1499	60c. Type **400**	2·30	2·30
1500	65c. Campfire	2·40	2·40

401 Carlo Goldoni, Actors and Rialto Bridge, Venice

2007. 300th Birth Anniv of Carlo Goldoni (playwright). Multicoloured.

1501	60c. Type **401**	2·30	2·30
1502	85c. Carlo Goldoni, actors and Notre Dame, France	3·25	3·25
MS1503	285×110 mm. €2.80 Carlo Goldoni	10·00	10·00

No. **MS**1503 was divided into five parts, the whole forming a composite design.

402 Gilded Glass and Silver Vase

2007. 250th Anniv of Christian Museum. Mult.

1504	85c. Type **402**	3·25	3·25
1505	€2 Bronze lamp and silver bottle	7·50	7·50

403 Atomium, Brussels

2007. 50th Anniv of Treaties of Rome. Designs showing original members. Multicoloured.

1506	15c. Type **403**	55	55
1507	30c. Eiffel Tower, Paris	1·10	1·10
1508	60c. Brandenburg Gate, Berlin	2·30	2·30
1509	65c. The Capitol, Rome	2·75	2·75
1510	€1 Vianden Castle, Luxembourg	3·75	3·75
1511	€4 Old Town, Amsterdam	11·50	11·50
MS1512	115×85 mm. €2.80 Mother and child (41×37 mm)	10·50	10·50

The stamp of **MS**1512 is placed in the top right corner and together with the margins forms a composite design.

404 Papal Stamps

2007. Inauguration of Philatelic and Numismatic Museum. Multicoloured.

1513	60c. Type **404**	2·30	2·30
1514	60c. Papal coins	2·30	2·30

405 Poland

2007. Journeys of Benedict XVI. Multicoloured. (a) Ordinary gum.

1515	60c. Type **405**	2·30	2·30
1516	65c. Valencia	2·40	2·40
1517	85c. Germany	3·25	3·25
1518	€1.40 With Bartholomew I (Ecumenical Patriarch of Constantinople), Turkey	5·25	5·25

(b) Self-adhesive.

1519	85c. As No. 1517	3·25	3·25

406 Madonna and Child

2007. Christmas. Designs showing details from painting The Nativity by Giuseppe Cali, St. Andrew's Parish Church, Luqa. Multicoloured.

1520	60c. Type **406**	2·50	2·30
1521	65c. Holy Family, women and child	2·75	2·40
1522	85c. Infant Christ and child	3·50	3·25

Stamps of a similar design were issued by Malta.

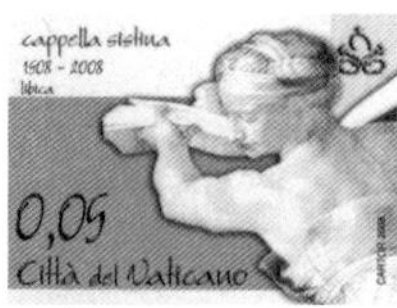

407 St Elizabeth tending the Sick

2007. 800th Birth Anniv of St Elizabeth von Thuringen.

1523	**407**	65c. multicoloured	2·50	2·50

408 'libica' (Libyan Sibyl)

2008. 500th Anniv of Sistine Chapel. Multicoloured.

1524	5c. Type **408**	10	10
1525	10c. 'eritrea' (Eritrean Sibyl)	20	20
1526	25c. 'delfica' (Delphic Sibyl)	80	80
1527	60c. 'cumana' (Cumean Sibyl)	2·30	2·30
1528	65c. 'daniele' (Daniel)	2·50	2·50
1529	85c. 'giona' (Jonah)	3·25	3·25
1530	€2 'ezechiele' (Ezikiel)	6·25	6·25
1531	€5 'zaccaria' (Zacheriah)	18·00	18·00

409 Postmarks

2008. Europa. The Letter. Multicoloured.

1532	60c. Type **409**	2·30	2·30
1533	85c. Pope Benedict XVI writing	3·25	3·25

410 Wedding at Cana, Washing Christ's Feet and The Last Supper

2008. 49th International Eucharistic Congress, Quebec. Multicoloured.

1534	60c. Type **410**	2·50	2·50
1535	85c. Crucifixion, Resurrection and Disciples	3·25	3·25

411 Lourdes

2008. 150th Anniv of Apparition at Lourdes. Multicoloured.

1536	65c. Type **411**	2·75	2·75
1537	85c. Apparition	3·50	3·50

412 Map and Crowd

2008. World Youth Day 2008, Sydney.

1538	**412**	€1 multicoloured	4·00	4·00

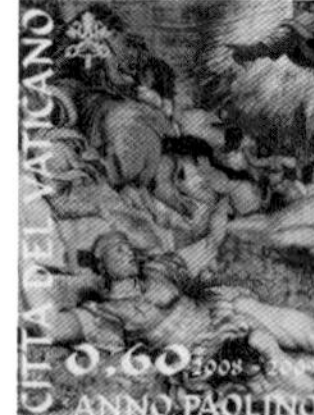

413 UN Emblem and Pope Benedict XVI

2008. Pope Benedict XVI's visit to United Nations to Celebrate 60th Anniv of Universal Declaration of Human Rights.

1539	**413**	€1.40 multicoloured	5·75	5·75

414 Conversion on Road to Damascus

2008. Pauline Year. Designs showing scenes from the life of St. Paul. Multicoloured.

1540	60c. Type **414**	2·50	2·50
1541	65c. Preaching	2·75	2·75
1542	85c. In prison	3·50	3·50

415 Pope Benedict XVI (Brazil)

2008. Apostolic Journeys of Pope Benedict XVI in 2007. Multicoloured.

1543	65c. Type **415**	2·75	2·75
1544	85c. Pope Benedict XVI (Austria)	3·50	3·50

416 *Adoration of the Magi* (Raphael (Raffaello Sanzio))

2008. Christmas. Multicoloured.

(a) Ordinary gum

1545	60c. Type **416**	2·50	2·50
1546	65c. *Birth of Christ* (Albrecht Durer) (vert)	2·50	2·50

(b) Self-adhesive.

1546a	60c. As Type **416**	2·50	2·50

417 Villa Rotonda

2008. 500th Birth Anniv of Andrea Palladio (architect). Multicoloured.

1547	65c. Type **417**	3·25	3·25
1548	85c. San Giorgio Maggiore Church	4·25	4·25
MS1549	88×115 mm. €2.80 Andrea Palladio	14·00	14·00

418 Arms of Vatican and Order of Malta

2008. Vatican City–Order of Malta Postal Convention.

1550	**418**	€2.50 multicoloured	12·50	12·50

419 Pope Pius XI

2009. 80th Anniv of Vatican City State. Multicoloured.

1551	65c. Type **419**	3·00	3·00
1552	65c. Pius XII	3·00	3·00
1553	65c. John XXIII	3·00	3·00
1554	65c. Paul VI	3·00	3·00
1555	65c. John Paul I	3·00	3·00
1556	65c. John Paul II	3·00	3·00
1557	65c. Benedict XVI	3·00	3·00
MS1558	88×115 mm. €2.80 Map of Vatican City (detail) (P. Isola, P. Di Sciuillo and G. Greco)	12·50	12·50

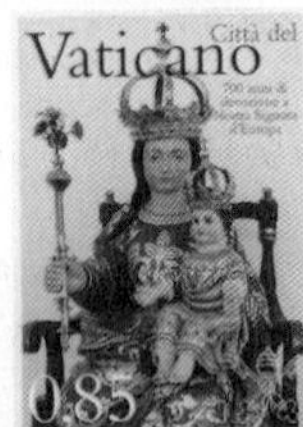
420 Virgin and Child (shrine of Our Lady of Europe at Europa Point, Gibraltar)

2009. 700th Anniv of Our Lady of Europe.

1559	**420**	85c. multicoloured	3·25	3·25

Stamps of a similar design were issued by Gibraltar.

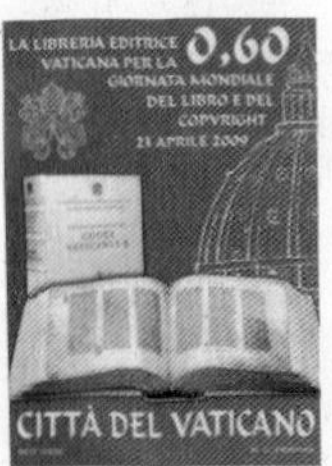
421 Codex Vaticanus

2009. World Book and Copyright Day.

1560	**421**	60c. multicoloured	2·50	2·50

422 *Astronomical Observations–The Sun* (Donato Creti)

2009. Europa. Astronomy. Multicoloured.

1561	60c. Type **422**	2·50	2·50
1562	65c. *Astronomical Observations–Saturn* (Donato Creti)	2·75	2·75

423 Scholar

2009. Centenary of Pontifical Biblical Institute.

1563	**423**	85c. multicoloured	4·25	4·25

424 Healing of Poor Man with Injured Arm

2009. 400th Anniv of Canonization of St. Francisca Romana. Design showing frescoes from Tor de' Specchi Convent. Multicoloured.

1564	85c. Type **424**	4·25	4·25
1565	€1 Miracle of the Grapes	5·25	5·25

425 Vatican Library

2009. International Federation of Library Associations and Institutions General Conference, Milan.

1566	**425**	€1.40 multicoloured	7·00	7·00

426 Cardinal Massaia

2009. Birth Bicentenary of Cardinal Guglielmo Massaia.

1567	**426**	60c. multicoloured	2·50	2·50

427 *Disputation of the Holy Sacrament* (detail)

2009. 500th Anniv of Disputation of the Holy Sacrament (frescoes, Stanza della Segnatura (Raphael)). Designs showing details from the frescoes. Multicoloured.

1568	65c. Type **427**	2·75	2·75
1569	65c. Speaker with arm raised (detail, lower central right)	2·75	2·75
1570	65c. Friar, woman and two men examining book (detail, lower front left)	2·75	2·75
MS1571	110×80 mm. €3.30 Detail, showing upper and lower central	13·00	13·00

428 Pope Benedict XVI praying at Lourdes (France)

2009. Apostolic Journeys of Pope Benedict XVI in 2008. Multicoloured.

1572	65c. Type **428**	2·75	2·75
1573	85c. Pope Benedict XVI (USA)	4·25	4·25
1574	€1 Pope Benedict XVI (Australia)	5·25	5·25

429 Dante and Virgil and Three Wild Beasts (from 15th-century Codex Urbinate Latino 365, Vatican Apostolic Library)

2009. Italia 2009 International Stamp Exhibition, Rome. Italian Language.

1575	**429**	60c. multicoloured	2·50	2·50

A stamp of a similar design was issued by Italy.

430 George Friedrich Handel (250th death anniv)

2009. Composers' Anniversaries. Multicoloured.

1576	65c. Type **430**	2·75	2·75
1577	85c. Franz Joseph Haydn (death bicentenary)	4·25	4·25
1578	€5 Felix Mendelssohn-Bartholdy (birth bicentenary)	26·00	26·00

431 Bronze Panel, Door of Good and Evil, St. Peter's Basilica (Luciano Minguzzi)

2009. 50th Anniv of Convocation of Second Vatican Council.

1579	**431**	60c. multicoloured	2·50	2·75

432 *Madonna and Child enthroned with two Angels and Saints Joachim and Anne* (Francesco Melanzio) (detail)

2009. Christmas. Multicoloured.

1580	60c. Type **432**	2·50	2·50
1581	65c. *Madonna and Child enthroned with two Angels and Saints Joachim and Anne*	2·75	2·75

433 Louis Braille

2009. Birth Bicentenary of Louis Braille (inventor of Braille writing for the blind).

1582	**433**	65c. multicoloured	2·75	2·75

434 Two Women (Three Temptations of Christ)

2010. 500th Death Anniv of Sandro Botticelli (artist). Multicoloured.

1583	60c. Type **434**	2·50	2·50
1584	85c. Woman (*The Life of Moses: Trials and Calling of Moses*)	3·75	3·75
1585	145c. Woman carrying basket (*The Life of Moses: Trials and Calling of Moses*)	4·25	4·25

435 Anàstasis from 4th-century Sarcophagus

2010. Easter

1586	**435**	65c. multicoloured	2·50	2·50

436 Shrine of Our Lady of Mentorella

2010. 1500th Anniv of Shrine of Our Lady of Mentorella

1587	**436**	65c.+20c. multicoloured	3·00	3·00

The premium was for aid to victims of the Haiti earthquake.

437 Father Ricci on and Xu Guangqi (court official)

2010. 400th Death Anniv of Father Matteo Ricci (pioneer of missions to China). Multicoloured.

1588	5c. Type **437**	30	30
1589	€3.30 Father Ricci	15·75	15·75

Nos. 1590/1 and Type **438** are left for Europa. Children's Books issued on 22 June 2010, not yet received.

No. 1592 and Type **439** are left for 400th Death Anniv of Caravaggio, issued on 22 June 2010, not yet received.

440 St. John Vianney

2010. 150th Death Anniv of St Jean-Marie Vianney. Multicoloured.

1593	1.40 Type **440**	4·75	4·75
1594	1.50 As shepherd with sheep	5·25	5·25

441 Pope Leo XIII

2010. Birth Bicentenary of Vincenzo Gioacchino Pecci (Pope Leo XIII)

1595	**441**	65c. multicoloured	5·50	5·50

442 Christ Crucified

2010. Re-opening of Vatican Apostolic Library. Multicoloured.

(a) Ordinary gum

1596	65c. Type **442**	2·00	2·00
1597	85c. St. Cosmas and St. Damian	2·50	2·50

(b) Self-adhesive

1598	€3.90 Pope Sixtus V (vert)	12·00	12·00

443 Fryderyk Franciszek Chopin

2010. Composers' Birth Bicentenaries. Multicoloured.
1599 65c. Type **443** 2·50 2·50
1600 €1 Robert Alexander Schumann 3·00 3·00
MS1601 65×100 mm. €4.40 Score of *Nocturne Opus 9 No. 2*. Imperf 13·50 13·50

444 Parish of Saint Anthony, Luanda

2010. Apostolic Journeys of Pope Benedict XVI in 2008. Multicoloured.
1602 10c. Type **444** 60
1603 65c. Garden of Gethsemane, Israel 2·50 2·50
1604 85c. St. Vitus Cathedral, Prague 3·00 3·00

445 *The Birth of Jesus* (Gheorghe Tattarascu)

2010. Christmas. Multicoloured.

(a) Sheet stamps. Ordinary gum
1605 60c. Type **445** 2·00 2·00
1606 65c. *The Nativity and Adoration of the Shepherds* (school of Murillo) 2·50 2·50

(b) Booklet stamps. Self-adhesive
1607 60c. As Type **445** 2·00 2·50
1608 65c. As No. 1606

446 Chekhov seated on Stage as Spectator viewing *Three Sisters* and *The Cherry Orchard*

2010. Writers' Anniversaries. Multicoloured.
1609 60c. Type **446** (150th birth anniv) 2·00 2·00
1610 65c. Tolstoy as character in *War and Peace*, observed by Anna Karenina (death centenary) 2·50 2·50

447 St. Francis (Giunta Pisano)

2010. 800th Anniv of Papal Approval of Franciscan Rule
1611 **447** 65c. multicoloured 2·75 2·75

448 1852 15c. Stamp (As No. 4) and Modena Cathedral

2011. 150th Anniv of Italian Unification
1612 60c. Type **448** 2·50 2·50
1613 60c. 1852 25 centes Stamp (As No.7) and Parma Cathedral 2·50 2·50
1614 60c. 1859 2g. Stamp (As No. 3) and Sicilian Landscape 2·50 2·50
1615 60c. 1850 45 centes Stamp and Milan Cathedral 2·50 2·50
1616 60c. 1851 20 centes Stamp (As No. 4) and Equestrian Statue of Emanuel Filbert, Piazza San Carlo, Turin 2·50 2·50
1617 60c. 1851 1q. Stamp (As Type **1**) and Palazzo Vecchio, Florence 2·50 2·50
MS1618 96×80 mm. Palazzo Montecitorio, Rome and Palazzo Carignano, Turin, Flaminio Obelisk, Santa Maria dei Miracoli Church and Santa Maria in Montesanto Church, Piazza del Popolo, Rome (48×40 mm) 6·50 6·50

449 The Resurrection (detail of fresco) (Hendrick van den Broeck), Sistine Chapel

2011. Easter
1619 **449** 75c. multicoloured 3·50 3·50

450 Father Kino on Horseback

2011. 300th Death Anniv of Father Eusebio Francisco Kino (missionary and Jesuit explorer)
1620 **450** €1.60 blackish brown and reddish brown 7·00 7·00

451 Pope John Paul II

2011. Beatification of Pope John Paul II
1621 **451** 75c. multicoloured 3·50 3·50

452 Ordination as Priest, 29 June 1951 and Shell of St. Augustine

2011. 60th Anniv of Ordination of Pope Benedict XVI (Joseph Aloisius Ratzinger). Multicoloured.
1622 75c. Type **452** 2·50 2·50
1623 75c. Consecration as Bishop, 28 May 1977 and bear of St. Corbinian, Bishop of Freiseng 2·50 2·50
1624 75c. Created Cardinal, 27 June 1977 and Moor's Head (emblem of Munich and Freising) 2·50 2·50
1625 75c. Elected Pope, 19 April 2005 and complete coat of arms 2·50 2·50

453 *The Journey of Moses into Egypt* (detail) (Perugino)

2011. Europa. Forests. Multicoloured.
1626 60c. Type **453** 2·75 2·75
1627 75c. *The Journey of Moses into Egypt* (detail) (right) 3·25 3·25

Nos. 1626/7 were printed, *se-tenant*, each pair forming a composite design.

454 Emblem

2011. World Youth Day, Madrid
1628 **454** 75c. vermilion, black and yellow 3·25 2·25

455 Leo XII

2011. 150th Anniv of *L'Osservatore Romano* (Vatican daily newspaper)
1629 60c. Type **455** 2·50 2·50
1630 60c. Pius X 2·50 2·50
1631 60c. Benedict XV 2·50 2·50
1632 60c. Pius XI 2·50 2·50
1633 60c. Pius XII 2·50 2·50
1634 60c. John XXIII 2·50 2·50
1635 60c. Paul VI 2·50 2·50
1636 60c. John Paul I 2·50 2·50
1637 60c. John Paul II 2·50 2·50
1638 60c. Benedict XVI 2·50 2·50

EXPRESS LETTER STAMPS

E3

1929
E14 **E3** 2l. red 37·00 34·00
E15 **E3** 2l.50 blue 21·00 30·00

1933
E35 **E12** 2l. brown and red 45 85
E36 **E12** 2l.50 brown and blue 1·20 2·40
E107 **E12** 3l.50 blue and red 60 75
E108 **E12** 5l. green and blue 80 1·10

E12 Vatican City

1945. Surch in figures over bars.
E118 6l. on 3l.50 blue & red 7·00 4·00
E119 12l. on 5l. green & blue 7·50 7·00

E28 Matthew Giberti, Bishop of Verona

1946. 400th Anniv of Council of Trent.
E130 **E28** 6l. brown and green 45 65
E131 - 12l. sepia and brown 80 90

DESIGN: 12l. Cardinal Gaspare Contarini, Bishop of Belluno.

1949. As Nos. 139/48 (Basilicas), but inscr "ESPRESSO".
E149 40l. grey 29·00 9·25
E150 80l. brown 60·00 43·00

DESIGNS—HORIZ: 40l. St. Peter's; 80l. St. John's.

1953. Designs as Nos. 179/89, but inscr "ESPRESSO".
E190 50l. brown and turquoise 40 30
E191 85l. brown and orange 50 50

DESIGNS: 50l. St. Peter and tomb; 85l. Pius XII and sepulchre.

1960. Designs as Nos. 326/33 (Works of Mercy), but inscr "ESPRESSO". Centres in brown.
E334 75l. red 10 10
E335 100l. blue 10 10

DESIGN: 75, 100l. Arms of Pope John XXIII between "Justice" and "Hope".

120 Pope Paul

1966. Designs as Nos. 467/76, but inscr "ESPRESSO".
E477 - 150l. brown 20 15
E478 **120** 180l. brown 25 20

DESIGN: 150l. Arms of Pope Paul VI.

PARCEL POST STAMPS

1931. Optd PER PACCHI.
P15 **1** 5c. brown on pink 45 85
P16 **1** 10c. green on green 45·00 85
P17 **1** 20c. violet on lilac 4·75 5·50
P18 **1** 25c. blue on blue 10·00 11·00
P19 **1** 30c. black on yellow 9·50 8·75
P20 **1** 50c. black on orange 14·00 10·00
P21 **1** 75c. red on grey 2·50 5·00
P22 **2** 80c. red 1·60 5·00
P23 **2** 1l.25 blue 2·75 5·50
P24 **2** 2l. brown 1·70 4·50
P25 **2** 2l.50 red 2·75 7·25
P26 **2** 5l. green 4·00 7·75
P27 **2** 10l. black 2·75 6·50

PARCEL POST EXPRESS STAMPS

1931. Optd PER PACCHI.
PE15 **E3** 2l. red 3·50 7·25
PE16 **E3** 2l.50 blue 6·00 7·75

POSTAGE DUE STAMPS

1931. Optd SEGNATASSE and cross or surch also.
D15 **1** 5c. brown on pink 55 85
D16 **1** 10c. green on green 55 85
D17 **1** 20c. violet on lilac 3·25 4·50
D18 **1** 40c. on 30c. black on yell 3·25 4·50
D19 **2** 60c. on 2l. brown 60·00 41·00
D20 **2** 1l.10 on 2l.50 red 25·00 30·00

D26

1945. Coloured network shown in brackets.
D107 **D26** 5c. black (yellow) 10 10
D108 **D26** 20c. black (violet) 10 10
D109 **D26** 80c. black (red) 10 10
D110 **D26** 1l. black (green) 10 10
D111 **D26** 2l. black (blue) 10 10
D112 **D26** 5l. black (grey) 15 15

D49 State Arms

1954. Coloured network shown in brackets.
D199 **D49** 4l. black (red) 25 15

D200	D49	6l. black (green)	35	30
D201	D49	10l. black (yellow)	25	15
D202	D49	20l. black (blue)	70	65
D203	D49	50l. black (brown)	25	15
D204	D49	70l. black (brown)	25	15

D130

1968

D513	D130	10l. black on grey	10	10
D514	D130	20l. black on blue	10	10
D515	D130	50l. black on pink	10	10
D516	D130	60l. black on green	10	10
D517	D130	100l. black on buff	10	10
D518	D130	180l. black on mauve	10	10

Pt. 3

VENEZIA GIULIA AND ISTRIA

Formerly part of Italy. Stamps issued during the Allied occupation, 1945-7. The Peace Treaty of 1947 established the Free Territory of Trieste (q.v.) and gave the rest of the territory to Yugoslavia.

For stamps of Austria overprinted Venezia Giulia see AUSTRIAN TERRITORIES ACQUIRED BY ITALY, in Volume 1 of Stamps of the World.

100 centesimi = 1 lira.

A. YUGOSLAV OCCUPATION PROVISIONAL ISSUES
Issues for Trieste.

1945. Stamps of Italian Social Republic 1944, surch 1.V.1945 TRIESTE TRST, five-pointed star and value.

4	-	20c.+1l. on 5c. brn (No. 106)	20	80
5	13	+1l. on 25c. green	20	80
6	-	+1l. on 30c. brown (No. 110)	20	80
7	-	+1l. on 50c. violet (No. 111)	20	80
8	-	+1l. on 1l. violet (No. 113)	20	80
9	-	+2l. on 1l.25 blue (No. 114)	20	80
2	12	2+2l. on 25c. green	20	80
10	-	+2l. on 3l. green (No. 115)	20	80
11	-	5+5l. on 1l. violet (No. 113)	55	80
12	-	10+10l. on 30c. brn (No. 110)	20	80
13	-	20+20l. on 5c. brn (No. 106)	9·00	11·00

Issue for Istria

In 1945 various stamps of Italy were overprinted "ISTRA" and further surcharged for use in Istria and Pola but they were not issued. However, four of these were further surcharged and issued later.

1945. Stamps of Italy (No. 14) or Italian Social Republic (others) surch ISTRA with new value and bars obliterating old surch.

14	99	4l. on 2l. on 1l. (No. 249) violet	1·10	1·10
15	-	6l. on 1,50l. on 75c. (No. 112) red	4·50	9·00
16	-	10l. on 0,10l. on 5c. (No. 106) brown	29·00	22·00
17	100	20l. on 1l. on 50c. (No. 247) violet	5·50	9·50

Issues for Fiume

1945. Stamps of Italian Social Republic 1944, surch 3-V-1945 FIUME RIJEKA, five-pointed star over rising sun and new value.

18	12	2l. on 25c. green	1·10	80
20	-	4l. on 1l. violet (No. 113)	1·10	80
21	-	5l. on 10c. brn (No. 107)	1·10	80
22	-	6l. on 10c. brn (No. 107)	1·10	80
23	13	10l. on 25c. green	1·10	80
24	-	16l. on 75c. red (No. 112)	£190	£275
25	E16	20l. on 1l.25c. green	3·25	6·25

B. ALLIED MILITARY GOVERNMENT

1945. Stamps of Italy optd A.M.G. V.G. in two lines. (a) Imperial Series.

26	-	10c. brown (No. 241)	20	55
27	-	10c. brown (No. 633)	20	55
28	99	20c. red (No. 243)	20	35
29	99	20c. red (No. 640)	20	1·10
31	-	60c. red (No. 636)	20	55
32	103	60c. green (No. 641)	20	45
33	99	1l. violet (No. 637)	55	20
34	-	2l. red (No. 638)	55	20
35	98	5l. red (No. 645)	80	45
36	-	10l. violet (No. 646)	90	45
37	99	20l. green (No. 257)	2·20	2·75

(b) Stamps of 1945–48.

[illegible]	-	25c. blue (No. 649)	20	55
[illegible]	-	2l. brown (No. 656)	55	45
40	-	3l. red (No. 657)	55	35
41	-	4l. red (No. 658)	55	35
42	195	6l. violet (No. 660)	1·90	1·30
43	-	20l. purple (No. 665)	55·00	2·20
44	196	25l. green (No. 666)	5·50	5·50
45	196	50l. purple (No. 668)	5·50	8·50
46	197	100l. red (No. 669)	25·00	45·00

1945. Air stamps of Italy, optd as above.

47	110	50c. brown (No. 271)	20	35
48	198	1l. grey (No. 670)	55	1·10
49	-	2l. blue (No. 671)	55	1·10
50	-	5l. green (No. 673)	3·25	2·75
51	198	10l. red (No. 674)	3·25	2·75
52	-	25l. blue (No. 675)	3·25	2·75
53	-	25l. brown (No. 676)	22·00	31·00
54	198	50l. green (No. 677)	5·50	9·00

EXPRESS LETTER STAMPS

1946. Express Letter Stamps of Italy optd A.M.G. V.G. in two lines.

E55	-	10l. blue (No. E680)	5·50	3·25
E56	E200	30l. violet (No. E683)	11·00	17·00

C. YUGOSLAV MILITARY GOVERNMENT

6 Grapes

7 Roman Amphitheatre, Pula, and Istrian Fishing Vessel

8 Blue-finned Tuna

1945. Inscr "ISTRA SLOVENSKO PRIMORJE – ISTRIA LITTORALE SLOVENO".

74	6	0.25l. green	80	55
58	-	0.50l. brown	65	80
59	-	1l. red	35	65
76	-	1l. green	45	55
77	-	1.50l. green	45	55
78	-	2l. green	45	55
100	-	3l. red	4·00	2·50
62	7	4l. blue	35	45
79	7	4l. red	45	55
80	-	5l. black	45	55
101	7	6l. blue	9·00	6·75
81	-	10l. brown	45	55
65	8	20l. purple	10·00	7·25
82	8	20l. blue	4·50	1·10
83	-	30l. mauve	4·00	1·10

DESIGNS—As Type **6**: 0.50l. Donkey and view; 1l. Rebuilding damaged homes; 1.50l. Olive branch; 2, 3l. Duino Castle near Trieste. As Type **7**: 5l. Birthplace of Vladimir Gortan, Piran; 10l. Ploughing. As Type **8**: 30l. Viaduct over River Solkan.

1946. Nos. 82 and 66 surch.

96	8	1 on 20l. blue	1·70	1·70
97	-	2 on 30l. mauve	1·70	1·70

1947. As Nos. 514 and O540 of Yugoslavia with colours changed, surch VOJNA UPRAVA JUGOSLAVENSKE ARMIJE and new value.

102	1l. on 9d. pink	45	55
103	1.50l. on 0.50d. blue	45	55
104	2l. on 9d. pink	45	55
105	3l. on 0.50d. blue	45	55
106	5l. on 9d. pink	55	65
107	6l. on 0.50d. blue	45	55
108	10l. on 9d. pink	55	65
109	15l. on 0.50d. blue	80	90
110	35l. on 9d. pink	80	1·10
111	50l. on 0.50d. blue	1·10	1·20

POSTAGE DUE STAMPS

1945. Stamps of 1945 surch PORTO and value in Lit.

D72	8	0.50 on 20l. purple	1·10	1·50
D67	6	1l. on 0.25l. green	17·00	2·75
D73	-	2l. on 30l. mauve	2·50	3·25
D68	-	4l. on 0.50l. brown	1·90	1·10
D69	-	8l. on 0.50l. brown	1·90	1·10
D70	-	10l. on 0.50l. brown	11·00	3·25
D71	-	20l. on 0.50l. brown	12·50	5·50

1946. Stamps of 1945 surch PORTO and value expressed in Lira.

D90	6	1l. on 0.25l. green	1·10	80
D84		1l. on 1l. green (No. 76)	65	55
D91	6	2l. on 0.25l. green	1·90	1·10
D85		2l. on 1l. green (No. 76)	65	55
D92	6	4l. on 0.25l. green	1·10	80
D86		4l. on 1l. green (No. 76)	90	55
D93	8	10l. on 20l. blue	6·25	2·75
D87		10l. on 30l. mauve (No. 66)	7·25	3·25
D94	8	20l. on 20l. blue	12·50	6·75
D88		20l. on 30l. mauve (No. 66)	11·00	6·25
D95	8	30l. on 20l. blue	14·50	7·75
D89		30l. on 30l. mauve (No. 66)	11·00	6·25

1947. No. D528 of Yugoslavia with colour changed and surch Vojna Uprava Jugoslavenske Armije and value.

D112	1l. on 1d. green	45	65
D113	2l. on 1d. green	45	65
D114	6l. on 1d. green	45	65
D115	10l. on 1d. green	45	65
D116	30l. on 1d. green	65	90

Pt. 7

WURTTEMBERG

Formerly an independent kingdom, Wurttemberg became part of the German Empire in 1902.

1851 60 kreuzer = 1 gulden.
1875. 100 pfennige = 1 mark.

1

1851. Imperf.

1	1	1k. black on buff	£1500	£130
3	1	3k. black on yellow	£400	10·50
5	1	6k. black on green	£1900	42·00
7	1	9k. black on pink	£6500	42·00
9	1	18k. black on lilac	£1900	£950

2

1857. Imperf.

10	2	1k. brown	£1100	£110
24	2	3k. orange	£550	32·00
15	2	6k. green	£1100	85·00
17	2	9k. red	£2500	95·00
19	2	18k. blue	£5500	£2250
85	2	70k. violet	£2250	£5500

1859. Perf.

45	1k. brown	£850	£600
40	3k. yellow	£275	85·00
41	6k. green	£550	£150
42	9k. red	£1700	£400
43	9k. purple	£2000	£475
44	18k. blue	£4000	£3000

1863. Perf or roul.

60	1k. green	60·00	16·00
63	3k. pink	60·00	4·25
54	6k. blue	£200	70·00
66	7k. blue	£1300	£170
57	9k. brown	£350	70·00
59	18k. orange	£1600	£550

3

1869. Roul or perf (1k.); perf (others).

72	3	1k. green	42·00	3·25
74	3	2k. orange	£225	£180
77	3	3k. pink	21·00	2·10
78	3	7k. blue	90·00	23·00
80	3	9k. bistre	£110	55·00
82	3	14k. yellow	£120	65·00

4

1875. New Currency.

123	4	2pf. grey	2·75	1·30
89	4	3pf. green	26·00	2·10
124	4	3pf. brown	1·10	75
91	4	5pf. mauve	12·50	1·10
127	4	5pf. green	2·10	75
93	4	10pf. red	1·60	1·10
95	4	20pf. blue	1·60	1·60
97	4	25pf. brown	£170	12·50
130	4	25pf. orange	3·75	2·10
151	4	30pf. black and orange	4·25	6·25
152	4	40pf. black and red	5·25	7·50
99	4	50pf. grey	£950	55·00
101	4	50pf. green	85·00	8·50
132	4	50pf. brown	3·75	1·30
102	4	2m. yellow	£1100	£350
103	4	2m. red on orange	£3750	£170
121	4	2m. black and orange	10·50	12·50
122	4	5m. black and blue	60·00	£200

For issues of 1947-49 see Germany (French Zone).

MUNICIPAL SERVICE STAMPS

M5

1875

M147	M5	2pf. grey	3·25	2·10
M169	M5	2½pf. grey	1·10	55
M170	M5	3pf. brown	1·30	55
M104	M5	5pf. mauve	60·00	3·25
M171	M5	5pf. green	1·10	55
M172	M5	7½pf. orange	1·10	55
M173	M5	10pf. red	1·10	55
M261	M5	10pf. orange	40	40
M174	M5	15pf. brown	2·75	55
M262	M5	15pf. violet	40	40
M176	M5	20pf. blue	2·10	55
M263	M5	20pf. green	40	40
M177	M5	25pf. orange	1·30	55
M178	M5	25pf. black and brown	1·60	55
M179	M5	35pf. brown	2·10	1·30
M264	M5	40pf. red	40	40
M265	M5	50pf. purple	40	40
M266	M5	60pf. green	65	40
M267	M5	1m.25 green	40	40
M268	M5	2m. grey	40	40
M269	M5	3m. brown	65	40

1906. Centenary of Establishment of Kingdom. Optd 1806–1906 under crown.

M153	2pf. grey	60·00	19·00
M154	3pf. brown	18·00	13·50
M155	5pf. green	6·25	5·50
M156	10pf. pink	6·25	5·00
M157	25pf. orange	65·00	16·00

1916. Surch 25Pf.

M199	25pf. on 25pf. orange	5·25	1·30

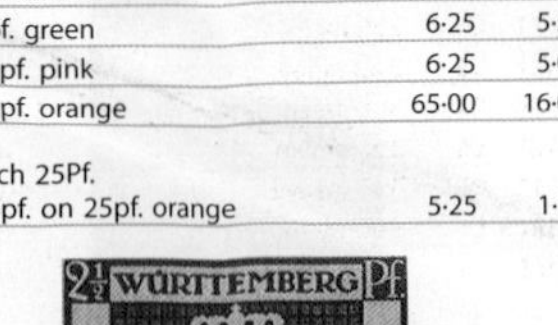

M9

1916. Jubilee of King Wilhelm II.

M202	M9	2½pf. grey	2·10	2·10
M203	M9	7½pf. red	1·70	2·10
M204	M9	10pf. red	1·70	2·10
M205	M9	15pf. bistre	1·70	2·10
M206	M9	20pf. blue	1·70	2·10
M207	M9	25pf. grey	5·25	2·10
M208	M9	50pf. brown	10·50	2·10

1919. Surch 2.

M219	M5	2 on 2½pf. grey	1·10	65

1919. Optd Volksstaat Wurttemberg.

M222	2½pf. grey	55	75
M223	3pf. brown	16·00	75
M224	5pf. green	40	75
M225	7½pf. orange	1·40	75
M226	10pf. pink	40	75
M227	15pf. purple	40	75
M228	20pf. blue	55	75
M229	25pf. black and brown	55	75
M230	35pf. brown	5·25	75
M231	50pf. purple	7·50	75

MUNICIPAL SERVICE STAMPS

M14

1920

M245	**M14**	10pf. purple	1·90	2·10
M246	**M14**	15pf. brown	1·90	2·10
M247	**M14**	20pf. blue	1·90	2·10
M248	**M14**	30pf. green	1·90	2·10
M249	**M14**	50pf. yellow	2·10	2·10
M250	**M14**	75pf. bistre	4·25	2·10

1922. Surch in Marks.

M270	**M5**	5m. on 10pf. orange	30	75
M271	**M5**	10m. on 15pf. violet	30	75
M272	**M5**	12m. on 40pf. red	30	75
M273	**M5**	20m. on 10pf. orange	30	75
M274	**M5**	25m. on 20pf green	30	75
M275	**M5**	40m. on 20pf. green	30	75
M276	**M5**	50m. on 60pf. green	30	75
M277	**M5**	60m. on 1m.25 green	30	75
M278	**M5**	100m. on 40pf. red	30	75
M279	**M5**	200m. on 2m. grey	30	75
M280	**M5**	300m. on 50pf. purple	30	75
M281	**M5**	400m. on 3m. brown	30	75
M282	**M5**	1000m. on 60pf. green	30	75
M283	**M5**	2000m. on 1m.25 grn	30	75

1923. Surch with new value (T=Tausend (thousand); M = Million; Md = Milliard).

M284	5T. on 10pf. orange	30	65
M285	20T. on 40pf. red	30	65
M286	50T. on 15pf. violet	1·10	65
M287	75T. on 2m. grey	2·10	65
M288	100T. on 20pf. green	30	65
M289	250T. on 3m. brown	30	65
M290	1M. on 60pf. green	1·60	65
M291	2M. on 50pf. purple	30	65
M292	5M. on 1m.25 green	30	65
M293	4Md. on 50pf. purple	4·25	65
M294	10Md. on 3m. brown	4·25	65

1923. Surch in figures only, representing gold pfennige.

M295	3pf. on 25pf. orange	60	40
M296	5pf. on 25pf. orange	60	40
M297	10pf. on 25pf. orange	60	40
M298	20pf. on 25pf. orange	60	40
M299	50pf. on 25pf. orange	75	40

OFFICIAL STAMPS

O5

1881

O181	**O5**	2pf. grey	65	40
O182	**O5**	2½pf. grey	[illegible]·50	2·50
O108	**O5**	3pf. green	65	40
O183	**O5**	[illegible]pf. pink	75	65
[illegible]	**O5**	15pf. brown	65	40
O188	**O5**	15pf. purple	75	65
O189	**O5**	20pf. blue	1·60	55
O117	**O5**	25pf. brown	85	40
O191	**O5**	25pf. orange	48·00	8·50
O192	**O5**	25pf. black and brown	65	40
O193	**O5**	30pf. black and orange	55	55
O194	**O5**	35pf. brown	65	40
O195	**O5**	40pf. black and red	2·10	4·25
O119	**O5**	50pf. green	65	40
O141	**O5**	50pf. brown	8·50	11·50
O196	**O5**	50pf. purple	£325	£2250
O120	**O5**	1m. yellow	85	40
O197	**O5**	1m. violet	95·00	£275
O198	**O5**	1m. black and grey	3·25	40
			3·25	1·10

1906. Centenary of Establishment of Kingdom. Optd 1806–1906 under crown.

O158	2pf. grey		
O159	3pf. brown	32·00	26·00
O160	5pf. green	6·75	75
O161	10pf. pink	6·25	75
O162	20pf. blue	5·75	75
O163	25pf. orange	6·25	75
O164	30pf. black and orange	15·00	13·50
O165	40pf. black and red	12·50	12·50
O166	50pf. purple	40·00	18·00
O167	1m. violet	38·00	18·00
		85·00	19·00

1916. Surch.

O200	25pf. on 25pf. orange	3·75	1·10
O201	50pf. on 50pf. purple	2·10	1·50

O10 King Wilhelm II

1916. Jubilee of King Wilhelm II.

O209	**O10**	2½pf. grey	1·10	1·30
O210	**O10**	7½pf. red	1·10	1·30
O211	**O10**	10pf. red	1·10	1·30
O212	**O10**	15pf. bistre	1·10	1·30
O213	**O10**	20pf. blue	1·10	1·30
O214	**O10**	25pf. grey	2·10	1·30
O215	**O10**	30pf. green	2·10	1·30
O216	**O10**	40pf. purple	3·25	1·30
O217	**O10**	50pf. brown	4·25	1·30
O218	**O10**	1m. mauve	4·25	1·30

O5

1919. Surch in figures only.

O220	**O5**	2 on 2½pf. grey	1·90	2·10
O245	**O5**	75 on 3pf. brown (O183)	1·60	1·60

1919. Optd Volksstaat Wurttemberg.

O232	2½pf. grey	75	55
O233	3pf. brown	9·50	1·10
O234	5pf. green	55	55
O235	7½pf. orange	55	55
O236	10pf. pink	55	55
O237	15pf. purple	55	55
O238	20pf. blue	55	55
O239	25pf. black and brown	55	55
O240	30pf. black and orange	1·10	55
O241	35pf. brown	75	55
O242	40pf. black and red	75	55
O243	50pf. purple	1·10	85
O244	1m. black and green	1·10	1·10

O16 Ulm

1920

O251	-	10pf. purple	75	1·60
O252	**O16**	15pf. brown	75	1·60
O253	-	20pf. blue	75	1·60
O254	-	30pf. green	75	1·60
			75	1·60
[illegible]		1m. red	75	1·60
O258	-	1m.25 violet	1·10	1·60
O259	-	2m.50 blue	1·10	1·60
O260	-	3m. green	2·75	1·60
			3·25	1·60

VIEWS: 10, 50pf., 2m.50, 3m. Stuttgart; 20pf., 1m. Tubingen; 30pf., 1m.25, Ellwangen.

Index